Y0-BQN-571

Cruden's
COMPLETE CONCORDANCE

Cruden's

Complete Concordance

to the Old and New Testaments

By ALEXANDER CRUDEN, A.M.

Edited By

A. D. ADAMS, M. A.

C. H. IRWIN, M.A., D.D.

S. A. WATERS

Notes and Biblical Proper Names
Under One
Alphabetical Arrangement
Plus a List of Proper Names with a
Foreword by Dr. Walter L. Wilson

ZONDERVAN PUBLISHING HOUSE

GRAND RAPIDS, MICHIGAN 49506

First Grand Rapids printing	1967
Second printing	February 1968
Third printing	December 1968
Fourth printing	July 1969
Fifth printing	February 1970
Sixth printing	August 1970
Seventh printing	March 1971
Eighth printing	October 1971

Printed in the United States of America

FOREWORD

THE STUDY of the Word of God can best be facilitated by a wise and constant use of this Concordance. Here you will find almost every word of the whole Bible arranged alphabetically, so that at any time the student may find the location of any passage that he may desire. By this means also, the student will discover that many statements are incorrectly quoted from the Bible. Sometimes quotations are made which are not found in the Bible in any form. This may be discovered by consulting your Concordance and looking for any of the prominent words used in that quotation.

By means of this Concordance the student may study any subject desired. For instance, you might wish to study the subject of trees. Find the word "tree" in the Concordance, and then notice every place where the word occurs, and what is the subject under consideration. You will find that the "oak tree" is usually mentioned in connection with death. The "fig tree" is usually connected with political Israel, etc.

If you wish to study the subject of "grace," or "horses," or of the "blood," or of the "coming of Christ," or of the "judgments," or any other subject, just find that word in your Concordance and look up the various Scriptures in which that word occurs. By this means you will become well acquainted with your Bible, and with God's Truth.

If you hear a verse of Scripture quoted, and you do not know where it is found, seek the prominent word in the Concordance, follow down the Scriptures that are listed there, and you will find the verse that you desire to locate.

This Concordance is a library of instruction. It is a lexicon of explanation. It is a source of inspiration and knowledge which is indispensable to the Bible student. Permit me to encourage every student of the Word of God to own a copy of this wonderful and valuable book.

WALTER L. WILSON, M.D., L.H.D.

Kansas City, Missouri

INTRODUCTION

Cruden's Complete Concordance has long been considered the most practical and usable Concordance on the market. This clear-type edition was developed with the average Bible reader and student in mind. The key words in bold face type, easily discernible, and references following have been set up in a type face scientifically analyzed as the most readable.

It is a great pleasure and privilege for the publishers to continue making this edition of *Cruden's Complete Concordance* available to God's people in this and succeeding generations. The additional helps included in this edition are also selected with the Bible student in mind, for they provide information nowhere else available in such concise and usable form.

May your use of this Concordance make your own study of the Bible and related subjects more meaningful and effective.

THE PUBLISHERS

PREFACE

For nearly two hundred years "Cruden's Concordance" has been a household word wherever the English language is spoken and the English Bible read.

Its author, Alexander Cruden, was born in 1701 at Aberdeen, where he was educated at the grammar school and Marischal College. He was intended for the Presbyterian ministry, but ill-health, which for a time affected his mind, led him to take up teaching at the age of twenty-one. After some years spent in private tutorships, he came to London, where in 1732 he opened a bookseller's shop in the Royal Exchange and was appointed bookseller to Queen Caroline. He died at Camden Place, Islington, in 1770, and was buried in Southwark in a burial-ground now said to be included in the premises of a well-known brewery. A bursary provided by him and bearing his name is among the prizes of Aberdeen University.

The first edition of Cruden's Concordance was published in 1737. It won for him special honors at the Universities of Oxford and Cambridge. Two further editions of the Concordance appeared in Cruden's lifetime in 1761 and 1769 respectively. Since that time numerous editions have been published with some claim to revision but have varied slightly from the original text and repeated many inaccuracies which appeared in the early editions.

The present edition may justly claim to be the most accurate and complete Cruden's Concordance to the Old and New Testaments. It contains upwards of 220,000 references. Every quotation and reference in this new Concordance has received careful scrutiny. The esult is that many inaccuracies which appeared in the original editions and others which have from time to time crept in have now een corrected. The explanatory notes, while mainly in the language of Cruden, have embodied the latest Scriptural interpretations and the esults of the most recent discoveries of archeology. The work has he advantage of being edited on both sides of the Atlantic and the ruits of the work of the American revisers of the Bible will be specially found in the explanatory notes.

The text quoted throughout is that of the Authorised Version of 611, known in America as the "King James's Version," and its spelling nd punctuation have generally been followed. Where the Revised

Version of 1881 has altered the sense or made the meaning clearer, this is indicated by an asterisk [*]. Where such alteration has been made by the American Revision, this is indicated by a dagger [†].

The grouping of Proper Names and the general Concordance under one Alphabetical arrangement will greatly facilitate the use of the volume. In the Appendix will be found a list of Proper Names seldom mentioned in Scripture and not included in the body of the Concordance. Every endeavour has been made, in the necessarily shortened quotations, to include the most essential word, and to preserve the true meaning of the text.

The quotation occupies the first position in the column, followed by the main reference, and then by reference to other passages where the principal word is used. The principal word quoted is indicated by its *initial letter in italics.* A colon between the figures (1:6) divides chapter and verse; a semicolon (Isa 9:6; John 3:16, 17) divides the main reference from succeeding references; while a comma divides verses in the same chapter.

Thus, under the heading *Aaron:*

A. shall bear their.	*Ex* 28:12; 29:30
A. shall burn sweet incense.	30:7
A. lighteth the lamps at even.	8
A. shall make an atonement once.	10

In the first line there are two passages quoted with chapter and verse; in the second line one chapter and verse, while the third and fourth lines have the verse only, being a verse of chapter 30 quoted in the preceding lines.

Every modern mechanical facility was employed in the preparation of this edition. The type which was cast expressly for the work combines clearness with compactness. The black face type is restful to the eye. The special type arrangement is an aid to ready reference. Therefore in fulness of contents, clearness of type and logical arrangement, this edition is superior to any other edition of Cruden's Concordance previously published and is especially adapted for school and general use.

And now this new edition is sent forth with the prayer that it may be blessed to the men and women of to-day as it has been blessed in the past, in the fuller, clearer understanding of the Holy Scriptures and the enrichment thereby of Christian character and service.

A COLLECTION OF THE NAMES AND TITLES GIVEN TO JESUS CHRIST

ADAM. *1 Cor* 15:45
Advocate. *1 John* 2:1
Alpha and Omega. *Rev* 1:8, 11; 21:6; 22;13
Amen. *Rev* 3:14
Angel. *Isa* 63:9; *Mal* 3:1
Ancient of Days. *Dan* 7:22
Anointed. *Ps* 2:2; 45:7
Apostle. *Heb* 3:1
Author and Finisher of our faith. *Heb* 12:2
Babe. *Luke* 2:16
Beginning of Creation of God. *Rev* 3:14
Begotten of the Father. *John* 1:14
Beloved. *S of S* 1:13; *Eph* 1:6
Bishop. *1 Pet* 2:25
Blessed. *1 Tim* 6:15
Branch of Righteousness. *Zech* 3:8
Bread of Life. *John* 6:48, 51
Bridegroom. *Mat* 9:15
Bright and Morning Star. *Rev* 22:16
Brightness of the Father's Glory. *Heb.* 1:3
Captain. *Heb* 2:10
Chief Corner stone. *Eph* 2:20; *1 Pet* 2:7
Child. *Isa* 9:6
Chosen. *Mat* 12:18; *Luke* 23:35
Christ. *Mat* 1:16; 2:4
Consolation of Israel. *Luke* 2:25
Covenant. *Isa* 42:6
Counsellor. *Isa* 9:6
Covert. *Isa* 32:2
Creator. *Isa* 43:15
David. *Jer* 30:9; *Ezek* 37:24, 25; *Hos* 3:5
Daysman. *Job* 9:33
Day star. *2 Pet* 1:19
Deliverer. *Rom* 11:26
Desire of all Nations. *Hag* 2:7
Dew. *Hos* 14:5
Diadem. *Isa* 62:3
Door of Sheep. *John* 10:7
Eagle. *Deut* 32:11
Elect. *Isa* 42:1
Emmanuel. *Isa* 7:14; *Mat* 1:23
Everlasting Father. *Isa* 9:6
Express Image. *Heb* 1:3
Faithful Witness. *Rev* 1:5; 3:14; 19:11
Feeder. *Isa* 40:11
First begotten. *Rev* 1:5
Firstfruits. *1 Cor* 15:23
First and Last. *Rev* 2:8
Foundation. *Isa* 28:16
Fountain. *Zech* 13:1
Forerunner. *Heb* 6:20
Friend of Sinners. *Mat* 11:19
Gift of God. *2 Cor* 9:15
God. *John* 1:1; *Rom* 9:5; *1 Tim* 3:16; *1 John* 5:20
Governor. *Mat* 2:6
Gracious. *1 Pet* 2:3
Habitation. *Ps* 91:9
Harmless. *Heb* 7:26
Head of the Church. *Col* 1:18
Heir of all Things. *Heb* 1:2
High Priest. *Heb* 3:1; 7:1
Holy One of God. *Mark* 1:24
Holy Child. *Acts* 4:30
Hope. *Acts* 28:20; *1 Tim* 1:1
Image of God. *Heb* 1:3
Immanuel. *Isa* 7:14; *Mat* 1:23
Immortal. *1 Tim* 1:17
Invisible. *1 Tim* 1:17
Jesus. *Mat* 1:21; *1 Thes* 1:10
Judge. *Acts* 10:42
King. *Mat* 21:5; 25:34
Lamb. *John* 1:29; *Rev* 5:6
Leader. *Isa* 55:4
Light. *John* 1:9; 8:12; 12:46
Life. *John* 14:6
Lion of the Tribe of Judah. *Rev* 5:5
Lord. *Rom* 1:3; *Rev* 17:14
Man. *Acts* 17:31; *1 Tim* 2:5
Master. *Mat* 8:19; 23:8
Mediator. *1 Tim* 2:5
Merciful. *Heb* 2:17
Messiah. *Dan* 9:25; *John* 1:41
Mighty God. *Isa* 9:6
Minister. *Heb* 8:2
Morning star. *Rev* 2:28; 22:16
Nazarene. *Mat* 2:23
Offspring of David. *Rev* 22:16
Only begotten. *John* 1:14
Passover. *1 Cor* 5:7
Potentate. *1 Tim* 6:15
Prince. *Acts* 3:15; 5:31
Prophet. *Luke* 4:19; *Acts* 3:22
Propitiation. *1 John* 2:2; 4:10
Power of God. *1 Cor* 1:24
Purifier. *Mal* 3:3
Physician. *Mat* 9:12
Priest. *Heb* 4:14; 7:26
Prince of Peace. *Isa* 9:6
Ransom. *1 Tim* 2:6
Reaper. *Rev* 14:15
Redeemer. *Isa* 59:20; 60:16
Resurrection. *John* 11:25
Refiner. *Mal* 3:3
Righteousness. *Jer* 23:6
Rock. *1 Cor* 10:4
Rod and Branch. *Isa* 11:1
Root of David. *Rev* 22:16
Ruler in Israel. *Mi* 5:2
Sacrifice. *Eph* 5:2
Sanctification. *1 Cor* 1:30
Saviour Luke 2:11 etc.
Seed of Abraham. *Gal* 3:29
Seed of the Woman. *Gen* 3:15
Seed of David. *2 Tim* 2:8
Second Man. *1 Cor* 15:47
Servant. *Isa* 42:1, 19; 44:21
Shepherd. *John* 10:11; *Heb* 13:20
Shiloh. *Gen* 49:10
Son of God. *Mat* 4:3; 8:29
Son of man. *Mat* 8:20
Sower. *Mat* 13:3
Spirit. *1 Cor* 15:45; *Heb* 9:14
Stone refused. *Mat* 21:42
Sun of Righteousness. *Mal* 4:2
Surety. *Heb* 7:22
Teacher. *John* 3:2
Testator. *Heb* 9:16, 17
Truth. *John* 14:6
Vine. *John* 15:1
Way. *Isa* 35:8; *John* 14:6
Wisdom of God. *1 Cor* 1:24
Witness. *Rev* 1:5; 3:14
Wonderful. *Isa* 9:6; 28:29
Word of God. *Rev* 19:13
Worthy. *Heb* 3:3; *Rev* 5:12

A COLLECTION OF THE TITLES AND DESCRIPTIONS GIVEN TO THE CHURCH OF GOD IN THE SCRIPTURES

ADOPTED Sons. *Gal* 4:5
Angels. *Luke* 20:36
Assembly of Saints. *Heb* 10:25
Believers. *Acts* 5:14
Beloved of God. *Ps* 60:5; 108:6
Blessed. *Ps* 2:12; 32:1
Blameless. *Phil* 2:15
Body of Christ. *Eph* 1:23
Branches of Righteousness. *John* 15:5
Brethren. *Rom* 8:29; 12:1
Bride. *Rev* 21:2, 9 ; 22:17
Building of God. *1 Cor* 3:9
Called. *Isa* 62:12; *Rom* 8:28
Candlestick. *Rev* 1:12; 2:5
Cedars. *Ps* 92:12; *Ezek* 31:8
Children of the Kingdom. *Mat* 13:38
Christians. *Acts* 11:26; *1 Pet* 4:16
Church of the Firstborn. *Heb* 12:23
Church of God. *1 Cor* 1:2
Circumcision. *Phil* 3:3
City of God. *Heb* 12:22; *Rev* 3:12
Citizens. *Eph* 2:19
Complete. *Col* 2:10
Congregation of Saints. *Ps* 149:1
Contrite. *Isa* 57:15; 66:2
Converts. *Isa* 1:27
Daughter of the King. *Ps* 45:13
Dearly Beloved. *Jer* 12:7
Disciples. *Isa* 8:16; *Mat* 5:1
Elect. *Isa* 45:4; *Mat* 24:22
Election. *Rom* 9:11; 11:5, 7
Excellent. *Ps* 16:3; *Pr* 12:26
Faithful. *Eph* 1:1; *Col* 1:2
Family of God. *Eph* 3:15
Fearful. *Isa* 35:4
Firstfruits. *Jas* 1:18
Flock of God. *Acts* 20:28
Firstborn. *Heb* 12:23
Fold of Christ. *John* 10:16
Followers of God. *Eph* 5:1
Friends of God. *Jas* 2:23
Fruitful. *Col* 1:10
Fulness of Christ. *Eph* 1:23
Gathered. *Isa* 56:8
General Assembly. *Heb* 12:23
Generation of the Upright. *Ps* 112:2
Glory of God. *Isa* 46:13
Glorious. *Ps* 45:13
Grapes. *Hos* 9:10
Habitation of God. *Eph* 2:22
Heirs of God. *Rom* 8:17
Heritage of God. *Jer* 12:7
Hidden Ones. *Ps* 83:3
Holy. *1 Cor* 3:17; *Eph* 1:4
House of God. *1 Tim* 3:15
Husbandry of God. *1 Cor* 3:9
Image of God. *Rom* 8:29
Inhabitants of Zion. *Isa* 12:6
Israel of God. *Gal* 6:16
Jacob. *Ps* 14:7; 147:19
Jerusalem above. *Gal* 4:29—heavenly. *Heb* 12:22—holy. *Rev* 21:10
Jewels of the Lord. *Mal* 3:17
Joy of the whole Earth. *Ps* 48:2
Justified. *Acts* 13:39
Kings. *Rev* 1:6; 5:10
Lamb's Wife. *Rev* 21:9
Light of the World. *Mat* 5:14
Lively Stones. *1 Pet* 2:5
Lot of God's Inheritance. *Deut* 32:9
Lowly. *Ps* 138:6; *Pr* 3:34
Members of Christ. *Eph* 5:30
Merciful. *Mat* 5:7
Mighty. *Ps* 112:2; *Acts* 18:24
Mount Sion. *Heb* 12:22
Obedient. *1 Pet* 1:14
Palaces. *Ps* 45:15; 48:3, 13
Palm tree. *Ps* 92:12
Peaceable. *Gen* 34:21
Peculiar People. *1 Pet* 2:9
Perfect. *2 Tim* 3:17; *Heb* 12:23
Pilgrims. *Heb* 11:13
Pillar of Truth. *1 Tim* 3:15
Portion of the Lord. *Deut* 32:9
Precious. *Ps* 116:15; *Isa* 43:4
Pure in Heart. *Mat* 5:8
Ransomed. *Isa* 45:10; 51:11
Redeemed. *Isa* 51:11; 62:12
Sanctified. *1 Cor* 1:2; 6:11
Saved of the Lord. *Deut* 33:29
Sheep. *John* 10:3, 4; 21:16
Sincere. *Phil* 1:10
Stones. *1 Pet* 2:5
Sons of God. *Rom* 8:14
Spiritual. *Gal* 6:1; *1 Pet* 2:5
Strangers. *Ps* 39:12; 119:9
Temple of God. *1 Cor* 3:16
Treasure of God. *Ps* 135:4
Vessels of Mercy. *Rom* 9:23
Vineyard. *Isa* 5:1; 27:2
Wise Men. *1 Cor* 6:5
Woman. *Rev* 12:1
Worshippers. *Heb* 10:2
Worthy to walk with Christ. *Rev* 3:4
Written in Heaven. *Heb* 12:23
Zealous of good works. *Tit* 2:14
Zion. *Ps* 69:35; 76:2; 87:2

CONTENTS

Cruden's
COMPLETE CONCORDANCE

CRUDEN'S COMPLETE CONCORDANCE

NOTE.—*A list of Proper Names is included in this Concordance under one alphabetical arrangement.*

An asterisk [*] following a reference means that the Revised Versions have altered the sense of the verse or have made the meaning clearer.

A dagger [†] following a reference means that the American Revision alone has made this change.

No mark is found where the Revisions are not materially different.

A

Aaron

is not *A.* the Levite thy? *Ex* 4:14
they met Moses and *A.* who. 5:20
A. took Elisheba . . . to wife. 6:23
and *A.* thy brother shall be thy. 7:1
but *A.* rod swallowed up their. 12
A. laid up the pot of manna. 16:34
and *A.* and Hur stayed up. 17:12
shalt come up, thou and *A.* 19:24
and behold *A.* and Hur are. 24:14
A. shall bear their. 28:12; 29:30
A. shall burn sweet incense. 30:7
A. lighteth the lamps at even. 8
A. shall make an atonement once. 10
they made the calf, which *A.* 32:35
Moses and *A.* and his sons. 40:31
he poured oil on *A.* head. *Lev* 8:12
he sprinkled blood on *A.* and. 30
A. blessed them. 9:22
A. held his peace. 10:3
thus shall *A.* come into the holy. 16:3
A. shall cast lots. 8
A. shall lay his hands on the. 21
A. shall order it. 24:3
A. shall number them by. *Num* 1:3
A. shall offer the Levites. 8:11
what is *A.* that ye murmur? 16:11
they, and *A.* to-morrow. 16
Moses and *A.* came before the. 43
write *A.* name upon the rod. 17:3
A. rod again before the testimony. 10
thou and *A.* thy brother speak. 20:8
A. died there in the top of the mount.
28; 33:38; *Deut* 32:50
A. was 123 years old. *Num* 33:39
was very angry with *A.* *Deut* 9:20
I sent Moses and *A.* *Josh* 24:5
1 Sam 12:8; *Mi* 6:4
advanced Moses and *A.* *1 Sam* 12:6
A. and Moses. *1 Chr* 6:3; 23:13
people by Moses and *A.* *Ps* 77:20
Moses and *A.* among his. 99:6
they envied *A.* the saint. 106:16
O house of *A.* trust in the. 115:10
Lord will bless the house of *A.* 12
house of *A.* say, his mercy. 118:3
ran down upon *A.* beard. 133:2
the Lord, O house of *A.* 135:19
was of the daughters of *A.* *Luke* 1:5
saying to *A.* make us gods to.
Acts 7:40
called of God, as was *A.* *Heb* 5:4
called after the order of *A.* 7:11
A. rod that budded and tables. 9:4
Sons of **Aaron**, *see* **Abihu** *and* **Nadab**

Aaronites

was leader of the *A.* *1 Chr* 12:27
Zadok was the ruler of the *A.* 27:17

Abaddon

the bottomless pit is *A.* *Rev* 9:11

Abagtha

A. was chamberlain to. *Esth* 1:10

Abana

(*Revised Version,* Abanah)
are not rivers *A.* and. *2 Ki* 5:12

Abarim

get thee up into this mount *A.*
Num 27:12; *Deut* 32:49
in the mountains of *A.* *Num* 33:47

abase

(*To bring low, usually in spirit; to humble*)
proud, and *a.* him. *Job* 40:11
lion will not *a.* himself. *Isa* 31:4
and *a.* him that is high. *Ezek* 21:26
in pride, is able to *a.* *Dan* 4:37

abased

shall exalt himself shall be *a.*
Mat 23:12; *Luke* 14:11; 18:14
I know how to be *a.* *Phil* 4:12

abasing

an offence in *a.* myself. *2 Cor* 11:7

abated

(*Decreased*)
the waters were *a.* *Gen* 8:3, 11
a. from thy estimation. *Lev* 27:18
Moses' natural force *a.* *Deut* 34:7
anger was *a.* toward him. *Judg* 8:3

abba

a. Father, all things are. *Mark* 14:36
whereby we cry, *a.* Father. *Rom* 8:15
into your hearts crying *a.* *Gal* 4:6

Abda

Adoniram son of A. was. *1 Ki* 4:6
A. was for thanksgiving. *Neh* 11:17

Abdi

Kish the son of *A.* *2 Chr* 29:12
A. of them that married. *Ezra* 10:26

Abdon

A. judged Israel. *Judg* 12:13
A. died. 15
commanded *A.* to inquire. *2 Chr* 34:20

Abed-nego

Azariah the name of *A.* *Dan* 1:7
the king set *A.* over. 2:49; 3:30
A. fell down bound into the. 3:23

Abel, *person, place.*

Lord had respect to A. *Gen* 4:4
stone of *A.* whereon. *1 Sam* 6:18*
ask counsel at *A.* *2 Sam* 20:18
blood of *A.* *Mat* 23:35; *Luke* 11:51
A. offered more excellent. *Heb.* 11:4
things than the blood of *A.* 12:24

Abel-beth-maachah

captains smote *A.* *1 Ki* 15:20
came and took *A.* *2 Ki* 15:29

Abel-maim

Ijon, and Dan, and *A.* *2 Chr* 16:4

Abel-meholah

fled to the border of *A.* *Judg* 7:22
son of Shaphat of *A.* *1 Ki* 19:16

Abel-mizraim

name of it was called *A.* *Gen* 50:11

abhor

[1] *To loath or detest,* Job 42:6. [2] *To despise or neglect,* Ps. 22:24; Amos 6:8. [3] *To reject or cast off,* Ps. 89:38.

my soul shall not *a.* you. *Lev* 26:11
or if your soul *a.* my judgments. 15
destroy, and my soul shall *a.* 30
nor will I *a.* them, to destroy. 44
utterly *a.* it, a cursed. *Deut* 7:26
a. an Edomite, an Egyptian. 23:7
his people to *a.* him. *1 Sam* 27:12
own clothes shall *a.* me. *Job* 9:31
they *a.* me, they flee far. 30:10
I *a.* myself, and repent. 42:6
Lord will *a.* the bloody man. *Ps.* 5:6
I hate and *a.* lying. 119:163
nations shall *a.* him. *Pr* 24:24
do not *a.* us. *Jer* 14:21
a. him that speaketh. *Amos* 5:10
I *a.* the excellency of Jacob. 6:8
hear, ye that *a.* judgment. *Mi* 3:9
a. that which is evil. *Rom* 12:9

abhorred

made our savour to be *a.* *Ex* 5:21
therefore I *a.* them. *Lev.* 20:23
their soul *a.* my statutes. 26:43
Lord saw it, he *a.* *Deut.* 32:19
for men *a.* the offering. *1 Sam* 2:17
art *a.* of thy father. *2 Sam* 16:21
Hadad *a.* Israel. *1 Ki* 11:25
inward friends *a.* me. *Job* 19:19
nor *a.* the affliction of. *Ps* 22:24
and greatly *a.* Israel. 78:59
thou hast cast off and *a.* 89:38*
he *a.* his own inheritance. 106:40
a. of the Lord shall fall. *Pr* 22:14
Lord hath *a.* his sanctuary. *Lam* 2:7
thy beauty to be *a.* *Ezek* 16:25*
and their soul also *a.* me. *Zech* 11:8

abhorrest

the land that thou *a.* *Isa* 7:16
thou that *a.* idols, dost. *Rom* 2:22

abhorreth

life *a.* bread, and his soul. *Job* 33:20
covetous, whom the Lord *a.* *Ps* 10:3*
mischief on his bed, he *a.* not evil.
36:4
soul *a.* all manner of meat. 107:18
nation *a.* to a servant. *Isa* 49:7

abhorring

be an *a.* to all flesh. *Isa* 66:24

Abia, Abiah

Samuel's second son was A. 1 Sam 8:2
A. Hezron's wife. 1 Chr 2:24
Rehoboam was A. 3:10; Mat 1:7
sons of Becher, A. 1 Chr 7:8

Abi-albon

A. was one of David's. 2 Sam 23:31

Abiathar

A. escaped and fled. 1 Sam 22:20
A. son of Ahimelech fled. 23:6
David said to A. bring. 9; 30:7
Ahimelech son of A. 2 Sam 8:17
Zadok and A. were the priests. 20:25; 1 Ki 4:4
kingdom for him and A. 1 Ki 2:22
so Solomon thrust out A. 27
house of G. in days of A. Mark 2:26

Abib

in the month A. Ex 13:4; 34:18
the feast of unleavened bread in the month A. 23:15; 34:18; Deut 16:1

Abidan

A. son of Gideoni. Num 1:11; 2:22
A. of Benjamin offered. 7:60, 65

abide

[1] *To stay*, Gen 22:5. [2] *To dwell or live in a place*, Gen 29:19; Ps 15:1. [3] *To bear or endure*, Jer 10:10; Joel 2:11. [4] *To continue*, Eccl 8:15; John 14:16. [5] *To wait for*, Acts 20:23. [6] *To rest*, Pr 19:23. [7] *To stand firm*, Ps 119:90; 125:1.

a. in the street all night. Gen 19:2
a. you here with the ass, and I. 22:5
damsel a. with us a few days. 24:55
I give her to thee, a. with me. 29:19
a. instead of the lad. 44:33
a. ye every man. Ex 16:29
therefore a. at the door. Lev 8:35
wages of him hired shall not a. 19:13
shall a. to the death. Num 35:25
a. here fast by my maidens. Ruth 2:8
before the Lord, and a. 1 Sam 1:22
ark of God shall not a. 5:7
a. thou with me, fear not. 22:23
made to a. at brook Besor. 30:21
and with him will I a. 2 Sam 16:18
nor a. in the paths of. Job 24:13
and a. in the covert to lie. 38:40
unicorn be willing to a. by. 39:9
shall a. in thy tabernacle? Ps 15:1
I will a. in thy tabernacle. 61:4
he shall a. before God for ever. 7
shall a. under the shadow of. 91:1
feet a. not in her house. Pr 7:11
he that hath it shall a. 19:23
a. with him of his labour. Eccl 8:15
nations not able to a. his. Jer 10:10
if ye a. in this land I. 42:10
no man shall a. 49:18, 33; 50:40
shalt a. for me many days. Hos 3:3
sword shall a. on his cities. 11:6*
is terrible, who can a. it? Joel 2:11
they shall a. for now shall. Mi 5:4
who can a. in the fierceness. Nah 1:6
a. the day of his coming? Mal 3:2
there a. Mat 10:11; Mark 6:10
Luke 9:4
I must a. at thy house. Luke 19:5
a. with us, for it is towards. 24:29
not a. in darkness. John 12:46
Comforter that he may a. 14:16
a. in me and I in you, except ye a. in me. 15:4, 7
if a man a. not in me, he is cast. 6
ye shall a. in my love, and a. 10
it pleased Silas to a. Acts 15:34
come into my house and a. 16:15
bonds and afflictions a. me. 20:23
except these a. in ship. 27:31
if any man's work a. he. 1 Cor 3:14
it is good for them if they a. 7:8
man a. in the same calling. 20
she is happier if she a. after. 40
to a. in the flesh is more Phil 1:24
I know that I shall a. with. 25
I besought thee to a. 1 Tim 1:3
let that a. in you which. 1 John 2:24
ye shall a. in him. 27
children a. in him. 28

abideth

Ziba said, behold he a. 2 Sam 16:3
man being in honour a. Ps 49:12
hear, even he that a. of. 55:19
the earth, and it a. 119:90
mount Zion, which a. for ever. 125:1
heareth reproof, a. Pr 15:31
but the earth a. for ever. Eccl. 1:4
he that a. in this city. Jer 21:9
but the wrath of God a. John 3:36
servant a. not, but the son a. 8:35
corn of wheat die, it a. 12:24
we have heard that Christ a. 34
he that a. in me bringeth. 15:5
a. faith, hope, charity. 1 Cor 13:13
yet he a. faithful. 2 Tim 2:13
Melchizedec a. a priest. Heb 7:3
word of God which a. 1 Pet 1:23
that saith he a. in him. 1 John 2:6
he that loveth his brother a. in. 10
and the word of God a. in you. 14
he that doeth the will of God a. 17
anointing a. in you and teacheth. 27
whosoever a. in him sinneth not. 3:6
loveth not his brother a. in death. 14
we know that he a. in us. 24
whoso a. not in the doctrine of Christ hath not God, he that a. hath the. 2 John 9

abiding

Balaam saw Israel a. Num 24:2
a. in the inheritance. 1 Sam 26:19*
shadow, there is none a. 1 Chr 29:15
shepherds a. in the field. Luke 2:8
not his word a. in you. John 5:38
no murderer hath eternal life a. in him. 1 John 3:15

Abiezer

lot for the children of A. Josh 17:2
A. was gathered after. Judg 6:34
better than the vintage of A. 8:2
A was one of David's. 2 Sam 23:27

Abi-ezrite

pertained to Joash the A. Judg. 6:11

Abigail

of Nabal's wife was A. 1 Sam 25:3
with his two wives, Ahinoam and A. 27:3; 30:5; 2 Sam 2:2
sisters were Zeruiah and A. 1 Chr. 2:16

Abihail

Rehoboam took A. 2 Chr 11:18
Esther the daughter of A. Esth 2:15
9:29

Abihu

Aaron's sons Nadab and A. Ex 6:23; 28:1; Lev 10:1; Num 3:2; 26:60; 1 Chr 6:3; 24:1.

come up, A. Ex 24:1
then A. went up. 9
A. died before. Num 3:4; 26:61

Abijah, Abijam

A. the son of Jeroboam. 1 Ki 14:1
A. the son of Rehoboam. 31; 15:1, 7
eighth lot came forth to A. 1 Chr 24:10
mother's name was A. 2 Chr 29:1
those that sealed were A. Neh 10:7
went up with Zerubbabel A. 12:4
of A. Zichri. 17

ability

his a. that vowed, priest. Lev 27:8
they gave after their a. Ezra 2:69
we after our a. redeemed. Neh 5:8
a. to stand in the king's. Dan 1:4
each according to his a. Mat 25:15
a. determined to send. Acts 11:29
as of the a. God giveth. 1 Pet 4:11*

Abimelech

A. king of Gerar sent. Gen 20:2
A. and Phichol spake to. 21:22
Isaac went unto A. 26:1
A. said, go from us. 16
concubine bare him A. Judg 8:31
A. the son of Jerubbaal went. 9:1
A. son of Jerubbesheth. 2 Sam 11:21
Zadok and A. were. 1 Chr 18:16

Abinadab

ark into the house of A. 1 Sam 7:1
Jesse called A. made him. 16:8
A. followed Saul to the. 17:13
A. son of Saul. 31:2; 1 Chr 10:2
ark on new cart, it out of the house of A. 2 Sam 6:3; 1 Chr 13:7
A. had Solomon's daughter. 1 Ki 4:11

Abinoam, *see* **Barak**

Abiram

Dathan and A. the sons. Num 16:1
26:9
sent to call Dathan and A. 12
he did to Dathan and A. Deut 11:6
laid the foundation in A. 1 Ki 16:34
the company of A. Ps 106:17

Abishag

and A. ministered to. 1 Ki 1:15
and why dost thou ask A. 2:22

Abishai

A. said, I will go. 1 Sam 26:6
sons of Zeruiah there, Joab, A. and Asahel. 2 Sam 2:18; 1 Chr 2:16
fled also before A. 2 Sam 10:14
king charged thee, and A. 18:12
A. succoured him and smote. 21:17
A. was chief. 23:18; 1 Chr 11:20
A. slew of the Edomites. 1 Chr 18:12

Abiud

Zerobabel begat A. and A. Mat 1:13

abjects

the a. gathered together. Ps 35:15

able

provide out of all the people a. men. Ex 18:21, 25
pigeons, such as he is a. Lev 14:22
31
a. to go to war Num 1:3, 20, 22, 24, 26, 28, 30, 32, 34, 36, 38, 40, 42, 45; 26:2.
are well a. to overcome it. 13:30
shall give as he is a. Deut 16:17
no man hath been a. to. Josh 23:9
a. to stand before this. 1 Sam 6:20
a. to judge so great a. 1 Ki 3:9
is a. to build him. 2 Chr 2:6
none is a. to withstand thee. 20:6
is a. to give thee much more. 25:9
who then is a. to stand. Job 41:10
a. to stand before envy. Pr 27:4
offering shall be as he is a. Ezek 46:11
God whom we serve is a. Dan 3:17
thy God is a. to deliver. 6:20
God is a. of these stones to raise up children. Mat 3:9; Luke 3:8
believe ye that I am a. to. Mat 9:28
a. to destroy soul and body. 10:28
he that is a. to receive it, let. 19:12
are ye a. to drink of the cup. 20:22
no man was a. to answer. 22:46
spake he, as they were a. Mark 4:33
no man is a. to pluck. John 10:29
yoke our fathers nor we a. Acts 15:10
his grace, a. to build you. 20:32
among you are a. go down. 25:5*
he was a. to perform. Rom 4:21
for God is a. to graff them in. 11:23
God is a. to make him stand. 14:4
ye are a. also to admonish. 15:14
a. nor yet now are ye a. 1 Cor 3:2
tempted above that ye are a. 10:13
made us a. ministers. 2 Cor 3:6*
God is a. to make all grace. 9:8
a. to do abundantly above. Eph. 3:20
he is a. to subdue all. Phil 3:21
he is a. to keep that I. 2 Tim 1:12
a. to come to the knowledge. 3:7
holy scriptures a. to make wise. 15
he is a. to succour them. Heb 2:18
to him that was a. to save him. 5:7
a. to save to the uttermost. 7:25
God was a. to raise him up. 11:19
the word which is a. to. Jas 1:21
a. also to bridle the whole. 3:2
one lawgiver a. to save. 4:12
to him that is a. to keep. Jude 24
a. to open the book nor. Rev 5:3
a. to make war with the. 13:4
a. to enter into the temple. 15:8

***be* able**

himself be a. to redeem. Lev 25:26
man be a. to stand. Deut 7:24
11:25
be a. to stand before. Josh 1:5

I shall *be a.* to drive. *Josh* 14:12
if he *be a.* to fight with. *1 Sam* 17:9
be a. to offer willingly. *1 Chr* 29:14
God should *be a.* to. *2 Chr* 32:14
thou shalt *be a.* to. *Isa* 47:12
righteous *be a.* to live. *Ezek* 33:12
be a. with 10,000 to. *Luke* 14:31
be a. to separate us from. *Rom* 8:39
ye may *be a.* to bear. *1 Cor* 10:13
be a. to comprehend. *Eph* 3:18*
be a. to stand against the. 6:11
ye shall *be a.* to quench. 16
be a. to teach others. *2 Tim* 2:2
be a. by sound doctrine. *Tit* 1:9
be a. after my decease. *2 Pet* 1:15
who shall *be a.* to stand? *Rev* 6:17

not be **able**

not be a. to deliver. *2 Ki* 18:29
Isa 36:14
shall *not be a.* to rise. *Ps* 36:12
shall he *not be a.* to find. *Eccl* 8:17
not be a. to put it off. *Isa* 47:11
not be a. to escape. *Jer* 11:11
not be a. to hide. 49:10
not be a. to deliver. *Ezek* 7:19
seek, *not be a.* *Luke* 13:24
not be a. to gainsay. 21:15

not **able**

not a. to bring a lamb. *Lev* 5:7
I am *not a.* to bear all. *Num* 11:14
not a. to go up against. 13:31
Lord was *not a.* 14:16; *Deut* 9:28
not a. to go to Tarshish. *2 Chr* 20:37
not a. to stand without. *Ezra* 10:13
not a. to build the wall. *Neh* 4:10
they were *not a.* to rise. *Ps* 18:38
they are *not a.* to perform. 21:11
hold on me, so that I am *not a.* 40:12
land is *not a.* to bear. *Amos* 7:10
not a. to do the thing. *Luke* 12:26
foundation, and is *not a.* to. 14:29
not a. to draw it for the fishes.
John 21:6
not a. to resist the wisdom. *Acts* 6:10

Abner

Ner father of *A.* was. *1 Sam* 14:51
Saul said to *A.* whose son? 17:55
A. and the people lay round. 26:7
cried, answerest thou not, *A.*? 14
A. said, let young men. *2 Sam* 2:14
Jacob said, thou knowest *A.* 3:25
Joab and Abishai his brother slew *A.*
30
buried *A.* in Hebron, king wept. 32
king said, died *A.* as a fool? 33
was not of the king to slay *A.* 37
when Saul's son heard that *A.* 4:1
buried Ish-bosheth's head in *A.* 12
what Joab did to *A.* *1 Ki* 2:5
that *A.* had dedicated. *1 Chr* 26:28
Jaasiel son of *A.* ruler of. 27:21

aboard

ship sailing, we went *a.* *Acts* 21:2

abode, *substantive*

but I know thy *a.* *2 Ki* 19:27*
Isa 37:28*
make our *a.* with him. *John* 14:23

abode, *verb*

Jacob *a.* with him the. *Gen* 29:14
but his bow *a.* in strength. 49:24
glory of the Lord *a.* on Sinai.
Ex 24:16
cloud *a.* Israel. *Num* 9:17, 18, 21
a. in their tents. 20, 22
and *a.* at Hazeroth. 11:35
a. in Kadesh. 20:1; *Judg* 11:17
princes *a.* with Balaam. *Num* 22:8
a. in Kadesh many. *Deut* 1:46
we *a.* in the valley. 3:29
I *a.* in the mount. 9:9
they *a.* in their places. *Josh* 5:8
they *a.* between Bethel and Ai. 8:9
Gilead *a.* beyond Jordan, Asher continued on the sea-shore, and *a.*
Judg 5:17
Levite *a.* with him three. 19:4
a. in the rock Rimmon. 20:47
woman *a.* and gave. *1 Sam* 1:23
ark *a.* in Kirjath-jearim. 7:2
Saul and Jonathan *a.* 13:16
Saul *a.* 22:6*
David *a.* 23:14, 25; 26:3
David *a.* in wood. *1 Sam* 23:18
a. at Ziklag. *2 Sam* 1:1
Uriah *a.* in Jerusalem. 11:12
while I *a.* at Geshur. 15:8
to a loft where he *a.* *1 Ki* 17:19
Jeremiah *a.* in the court. *Jer* 38:28
while they *a.* in Galilee. *Mat* 17:22
Mary *a.* with her. *Luke* 1:56
nor *a.* in any house, but in. 8:27
Spirit, and it *a.* upon. *John* 1:32
they came and *a.* with him. 39
words he *a.* in Galilee. 7:9
murderer, and *a.* 8:44*
a. two days still in the place. 11:6
upper room where *a.* *Acts* 1:13
long time *a.* they speaking. 14:3
Paul *a.* with them and. 18:3
a. with the brethren one day. 21:7
house of Philip and *a.* with him. 8
I went and *a.* with Peter. *Gal.* 1:18

abode *there* or *there* **abode**

days that ye *a. there.* *Deut* 1:46
and *a. there* 3 days. *Josh* 2:22
the people *a. there* till. *Judg* 21:2
there a. we in tents. *Ezra* 8:15
Jerusalem and *a. there* three. 32
Jesus *a. there* two days. *John* 4:40
first baptized, and *there a.* 10:40
Cesarea, and *there a.* *Acts* 12:19*
there they *a.* long time. 14:28
Silas and Timotheus *a. there.* 17:14

abodest

why *a.* thou among the. *Judg* 5:16*

abolish

idols he shall utterly *a.* *Isa.* 2:18*

abolished

righteousness shall not be *a.* *Isa* 51:6
your works may be *a.* *Ezek* 6:6
end of that which is *a.* *2 Cor* 3:13*
a. in his flesh the enmity. *Eph* 2:15
Christ, who hath *a.* death.
2 Tim 1:10

abominable

touch any *a.* unclean. *Lev* 7:21
shall not make yourselves *a.* 11:43
any of these *a.* customs. 18:30
on the third day, it is *a.* 19:7
shall not make your souls *a.* 20:25
not eat any *a.* thing. *Deut* 14:3
king's word was *a.* *1 Chr* 21:6
Asa put away the *a.* idols. *2 Chr* 15:8
much more *a.* and filthy. *Job* 15:16
they have done *a.* works. *Ps* 14:1
and have done *a.* iniquity. 53:1
out like an *a.* branch. *Isa* 14:19
broth of *a.* things is in. 65:4
carcases of their *a.* *Jer* 16:18
O, do not this *a.* thing that. 44:4
nor came *a.* flesh into. *Ezek* 4:14
saw and behold *a.* beasts. 8:10
thy sins committed more *a.* 16:52
scant measure that is *a.* *Mi* 6:10
and I will cast *a.* filth. *Nah* 3:6
works deny him, being *a.* *Tit* 1:16
walked in *a.* idolatries. *1 Pet* 4:3
unbelieving, and the *a.* *Rev* 21:8

abominably

Ahab did very *a.* in. *1 Ki* 21:26

abomination

[1] *A thing hateful and detestable,* Gen 43:32; Pr 29:27. [2] *An idol,* 2 Ki 23:13; Isa 44:19.

an *a.* to the Egyptians. *Gen* 43:32
every shepherd is an *a.* to. 46:34
sacrifice the *a.* of Egyptians. *Ex* 8:26
shall be an *a.* *Lev* 7:18; 11:41, 42
shall be an *a.* to. 11:10, 12, 20, 23
womankind it is *a.* 18:22; 20:13
a. to the Lord. *Deut* 7:25; 17:1
bring an *a.* into thy house. 7:26
every *a.* they have done to. 12:31
such *a.* is wrought. 13:14; 17:4
these things are an *a.* 18:12; 22:5
are an *a.* to the Lord. 23:18
an *a.* before the Lord. 24:4
unrighteously are an *a.* to. 25:16
the man that maketh *a.* 27:15
in *a.* with Philistines. *1 Sam* 13:4
Milcom the *a.* *1 Ki* 11:5, 7
Chemosh the *a.* of Moab. 7
Ashtaroth the *a.* of the. *2 Ki* 23:13
thou hast made me an *a.* *Ps* 88:8
the froward is an *a.* to. *Pr* 3:32
seven things are an *a.* to him. 6:16
wickedness is an *a.* to my lips. 8:7
a false balance is an *a.* to. 11:1
they of a froward heart are an *a.* 20
lying lips are *a.* to. 12:22
a. to fools to depart. 13:19
of the wicked is an *a.* 15:8; 21:27
way of the wicked is an *a.* to. 15:9
thoughts of the wicked are an *a.* 26
is proud in heart is an *a.* 16:5
it is an *a.* to kings to commit. 12
both are an *a.* to the Lord. 17:15
both of them are alike *a.* to. 20:10
divers weights are an *a.* to the. 23
the scorner is an *a.* to men. 24:9
his prayer shall be *a.* 28:9
is an *a.* to the just, and he that is upright in the way, is *a.* 29:27
incense is an *a.* to me. *Isa* 1:13
an *a.* is he that chooseth you. 41:24
the residue thereof an *a*? 44:19
eating swine's flesh, and the *a.* 66:17
ye made my heritage an *a.* *Jer* 2:7
they committed *a.* 6:15; 8:12
do this *a.* to cause Judah. 32:35
and committed *a.* *Ezek* 16:50
eyes to idols and committed *a.* 18:12
a. with his neighbour's wife. 22:11
your sword and ye work *a.* 33:26
a. that maketh desolate. *Dan.* 11:31
a. that maketh desolate set. 12:11
a. is committed in Israel. *Mal* 2:11
ye see *a.* of desolation. *Mat* 24:15
Mark 13:14
men is *a.* with God. *Luke* 16:15
enter that worketh *a.* *Rev* 21:27

abominations

not learn to do after the *a.*
Deut 18:9
with *a.* provoked they him to. 32:16
according to all *a.* *1 Ki* 14:24
through fire according to *a.*
2 Ki 16:3; *2 Chr* 28:3
Manasseh did evil after the *a.* of the heathen. *2 Ki* 21:2; *2 Chr* 33:2
a. spied did Josiah put. *2 Ki* 23:24
2 Chr 34:33
Jehoiakim and his *a.* *2 Chr* 36:8
people transgressed after all *a.* 14
for there are seven *a.* in. *Pr* 26:25
could not bear for the *a.* *Jer* 44:22
for all the evil *a.* of. *Ezek* 6:11
seest thou the great *a.* of Israel, but thou shalt see greater *a.* 8:6
13, 15
behold the wicked *a.* that they do. 9
light thing to commit *a.* here? 17
sigh and cry for all the *a.* 9:4
take away all the *a.* thereof. 11:18
your faces from all your *a.* 14:6
cause Jerusalem to know her *a.* 16:2
righteous doth according to all *a.*
18:24
cause them to know the *a.* 20:4
cast ye away every man the *a.* 7
they did not cast away the *a.* 8
shalt shew her all her *a.* 22:2
loathe yourselves for all your *a.*
36:31
it suffice you of all your *a.* 44:6
broken my covenant for all your *a.* 7
the overspreading of *a.* *Dan* 9:27
a. from between his teeth. *Zech* 9:7
cup in her hand full of *a.* *Rev* 17:4
mother of harlots and *a.* of. 5

their **abominations**

not to do after all *their a.*
Deut 20:18
seen *their a.* and *their.* 29:17
doing according to *their a.* *Ezra* 9:1
their a. which have filled. 11
soul delighteth in *their a.* *Isa* 66:3
their a. in the house.
Jer 7:30; 32:34
committed in all *their a.* *Ezek* 6:9
made the images of *their a.* 7:20
heart walketh after *their a.* 11:21
may declare all *their a.* 12:16
thou not done after *their a.* 16:47
ye whoredom after *their a.* 20:30
yea, declare to them *their a.* 23:36
desolate because of all *their a.* 33:29

defiled my holy name by *their a.* *Ezek* 43:8
bear their shame and *their a.* 44:13
their a. were according. *Hos* 9:10

these **abominations**

commit any of *these a.* *Lev* 18:26
all *these a.* have the men of. 27
shall commit any of *these a.* 29
because of *these a.* the. *Deut* 18:12
Manasseh . . . *these a.* *2 Ki* 21:11
affinity with people of *these a.* *Ezra* 9:14
delivered to do all *these a.* *Jer* 7:10
these a. shall surely die. *Ezek* 18:13

thine or *thy* **abominations**

wilt put away *thine a.* *Jer* 4:1
seen *thine a.* on the hills. 13:27
I have not, because of *thine a.* *Ezek* 5:9
defiled my sanctuary with *thy a.* 11
on thee all *thine a.* 7:3, 4, 8, 9
all *thine a.* thou has not. 16:22
with all the idols of *thine a.* 36
lewdness above all *thine a.* 43
multiplied *thine a.* 51
hast borne *thine a.* saith. 58

abound

the faithful man shall *a.* *Pr* 28:20
because inquity shall *a.* *Mat* 24:12*
that the offence might *a.* *Rom* 5:20
in sin, that grace may *a.* ? 6:1
that ye may *a.* in hope through. 15:13
sufferings *a.* so consolation. *2 Cor* 1:5
a. in every thing, see that ye *a.* 8:7
God is able to make all grace *a.* 9:8
your love may *a.* more. *Phil* 1:9
I know how to *a.* both to *a.* 4:12
but I desire fruit that may *a.* 17*
but I have all and *a.* I am full. 18
Lord make you to *a.* *1 Thes* 3:12
so ye would *a.* more and more. 4:1
things be in you and *a.* *2 Pet* 1:8

abounded, -eth, -ing

fountains *a.* with water. *Pr* 8:24
man *a.* in transgression. 29:22
truth of God hath more *a.* *Rom* 3:7
grace by Jesus Christ hath *a.* 5:15
sin *a.* grace did much more *a.* 20
always *a.* in the work. *1 Cor* 15:58
poverty *a.* to the riches. *2 Cor* 8:2
wherein he hath *a.* toward. *Eph* 1:8
therein with thanksgiving. *Col* 2:7
towards each other *a.* *2 Thes* 1:3

about

a. three months after. *Gen* 38:24
shewed Pharaoh what he is *a.* 41:25
turned himself *a.* from them. 42:24
trade hath been *a.* cattle. 46:34*
a. midnight will I go out. *Ex* 11:4
God led the people *a.* through. 13:18
set bounds *a.* the mount. 19:23
fell that day *a.* 3000 men. 32:28
that *a.* which he hath. *Lev* 6:5
a. the tabernacle of. *Num* 16:24
a. and instructed him. *Deut* 32:10
to go down *a.* a day. *Josh* 10:13
a. which thou cursedst. *Judg* 17:2
and it was *a.* an ephah of. *Ruth* 2:17
was come *a.* Hannah. *1 Sam* 1:20
the ark of God be carried *a.* 5:8
came to pass, *a.* the spring. 9:26
women have been kept from us *a.* 21:5
to fetch *a.* this form. *2 Sam* 14:20*
kingdom is turned *a.* *1 Ki* 2:15
a. going down of sun. 22:36
2 Chr 18:34
a. this season according. *2 Ki* 4:16
which I am *a.* to build *2 Chr* 2:9
employed *a.* this matter. *Ezra* 10:15*
is *a.* to fill his belly. *Job* 20:23
bind them *a.* thy. *Pr* 3:3; 6:21
that goeth *a.* as a tale-bearer. 20:19
heap of wheat set *a.* *S of S* 7:2
compass yourselves *a.* *Isa* 50:11
why gaddest thou *a.* so. *Jer* 2:36
how long wilt thou go *a.* 31:22*
people cast *a.* and returned. 41:14
doings have beset them *a.* *Hos* 7:2
went out *a.* the third. *Mat* 20:3
not so much as *a.* the. *Mark* 2:2
set an hedge *a.* it, and. *Mark* 12:1
a. my Father's business. *Luke* 2:49*
Jesus began to be *a.* thirty. 3:23
loins be girded *a.* and. 12:35
a question *a.* purifying. *John* 3:25
why go ye *a.* to kill me ? 7:19*
of the men was *a.* 5000. *Acts* 4:4
when Paul was *a.* to open. 18:14
a. to flee out of the ship. 27:30*
he was *a.* 100 years old. *Rom* 4:19
going *a.* to establish their own. 10:3*
power to lead *a.* a. *1 Cor* 9:5
bearing *a.* in the body. *2 Cor* 4:10
loins girt *a.* with truth. *Eph* 6:14
wandering *a.* from house. *1 Tim* 5:13
when he was *a.* to make. *Heb* 8:5
silence *a.* the space of half. *Rev.* 8:1
I was *a.* to write, and I. 10:4

see **gone, him, me, thee, them, round, stood, this, time, went.**

above

[1] *Aloft, high,* Gen 6:16; Pr 8:28. [2] *More than,* Gen 3:14; 48:22; 2 Cor 1:8. [3] *Upwards,* Ex 30:14; Lev 27:7. [4] *A higher state or rank,* Num 16:3; Deut 28:13. [5] *Heaven, or the highest place,* Job 3:4; Rom 10:6. [6] *Things that relate to heaven,* Gal 4:26; Col 3:1. [7] *God,* Jas 1:17.

waters *a.* the firmament. *Gen* 1:7
fowl that may fly *a.* the earth. 20
cursed *a.* all cattle, *a.* beast. 3:14
shalt thou finish the ark *a.* 6:16
and the ark was lifted up *a.* 7:17
one portion *a.* thy brethren. 48:22
prevailed *a.* the blessings of. 49:26
I will commune from *a.* *Ex* 25:22
a. the curious girdle of. 28:27, 28
from twenty years old and *a.* 30:14
1 Chr 23:27
which have legs *a.* their. *Lev* 11:21
from sixty years old and *a.* 27:7
a. the congregation. *Num* 16:3
heart be not lifted up *a.* *Deut* 17:20
lest if he should beat him *a.* 25:3
be *a.* only, and not beneath. 28:13
multiply thee *a.* thy fathers. 30:5
come down from *a.* *Josh* 3:13, 16
blessed shall she be *a.* women. *Judg* 5:24
sent from *a.* *2 Sam* 22:17; *Ps* 18:16
covered ark *a.* *1 Ki* 8:7 ; *2 Chr* 5:8
a. the throne of kings. *2 Ki* 25:28
Jer 52:32
Judah prevailed *a.* his. *1 Chr* 5:2
Benaiah was mighty and *a.* 27:6
Hananiah feared God *a.* *Neh* 7:2
up *a.* the house of David. 12:37
not God regard it from *a.* *Job* 3:4
a. shall his branch be cut. 18:16
price of wisdom is *a.* rubies. 28:18
portion of God is there from *a.* ? 31:2
have denied the God that is *a.* 28
thy judgments are *a.* out. *Ps* 10:5
liftest me *a.* those that rise. 18:48
head be lifted up *a.* enemies. 27:6
oil of gladness *a.* 45:7; *Heb* 1:9
the clouds from *a.* *Ps* 78:23
commandments *a.* gold. 119:127
that stretched out the earth *a.* 136:6
if I prefer not Jerusalem *a.* 137:6
send thine hand from *a.* rid. 144:7
his glory is *a.* the earth. 148:13
established the clouds *a.* *Pr* 8:28
way of life is *a.* to the wise. 15:24
for her price is far *a.* rubies. 31:10
man hath no pre-eminence *a.* *Eccl* 3:19
mountain shall be exalted *a.* *Isa* 2:2
a. it stood the seraphims, each. 6:2
the depth or in the height *a.* 7:11
widows increased *a.* sand. *Jer* 15:8
from *a.* hath he sent fire. *Lam* 1:13
appearance of a man *a.* *Ezek* 1:26
God was over them *a.* 10:19 ;11:22
exalt itself any more *a.* the. 29:15
Daniel was preferred *a.* *Dan* 6:3
king magnify himself *a.* 11:36
destroyed his fruit from *a.* *Amos* 2:9
multiplied thy merchants *a.* *Nah* 3:16
disciple not *a.* *Mat* 10:24; *Luke* 6:40
remained over and *a.* *John* 6:13
from *a.* ye are of this world. 8:23
it were given him from *a.* 19:11
man was *a.* forty years. *Acts* 4:22
I saw a light *a.* the brightness. 26:13
bring Christ down from *a.* *Rom* 10:6
esteemeth one day *a.* another. 14:5
not to think of men *a.* *1 Cor* 4:6
you to be tempted *a.* that ye. 10:13
was seen of *a.* 500 brethren. 15:6
out of measure *a.* strength. *2 Cor* 1:8
more, in stripes *a.* measure. 11:23
a. fourteen years ago, whether. 12:2
lest any man should think of me *a.* 6
Jerusalem which is *a.* *Gal* 4:26
given him a name *a.* *Phil* 2:9
seek those things which are *a.* *Col* 3:1
set your affection on things *a.* not. 2
servant, but *a.* a servant. *Philem* 16
a. when he said, sacrifice. *Heb* 10:8
perfect gift is from *a.* *Jas* 1:17
wisdom descendeth not from *a.* 3:15

above *all*

is cursed *a. all* cattle. *Gen* 3:14
very meek *a. all* the men. *Num* 12:3
blessed *a. all* people. *Deut* 7:14
he chose you *a. all* people, as. 10:15
a. all the nations. 14:2; 26:19 ; 28:1
done evil *a. all* that were. *1 Ki* 14:9
provoked *a. all* that their. 22
Ahab did evil *a. all* that. 16:30
done wickedly *a. all* the. *2 Ki* 21:11
over and *a. all* I have. *1 Chr* 29:3
art exalted as head *a. all.* 11
Maachah *a. all* his. *2 Chr* 11:21
for Ezra was *a. all.* *Neh* 8:5
king loved Esther *a. all.* *Esth* 2:17
Lord art high *a. all* the. *Ps* 97:9
is high *a. all* people. 99:2; 113:4
magnified thy word *a. all* thy. 138:2
a. all that were in Jerusalem. *Eccl* 2:7
heart is deceitful *a. all.* *Jer* 17:9
this lewdness *a. all.* *Ezek* 16:43
his height was exalted *a. all.* 31:5
magnify himself *a. all.* *Dan* 11:37
added yet this *a. all.* *Luke* 3:20
sinners *a. all* the Galileans. 13:2, 4
from heaven is *a. all.* *John* 3:31
far *a. all* principality and. *Eph* 1:21
a. all that we ask. 3:20
one God *a. all.* 4:6
a. all taking the shield of faith. 6:16
a. all these things put on. *Col* 3:14
a. all that is called God. *2 Thes* 2:4
a. all things, my brethren. *Jas* 5:12
a. all things have fervent. *1 Pet* 4:8
I wish *a. all* things that. *3 John* 2:1

above *all* **gods,** *see* **gods** ; **above** *heaven, see* **heaven** ; *stood* **above,** *see* **stood** ; **above** *me, him, them, see* **him, me, them.**

Abram, Abraham

Lord said to *A.* get out. *Gen* 12:1
A. went down into Egypt to. 10
A. went up out of Egypt, he. 13:1
A. dwelt in land of Canaan, and. 12
A. came and dwelt in the plain. 18
A. armed his trained servants. 14:14
fear not, *A.* I am thy. 15:1
Lord made a covenant with *A.* 18
thy name shall be *A.* 17:5
1 Chr 1:27; *Neh* 9:7
A. hastened into the tent. *Gen* 18:6
shall I hide from *A.* that thing. 17
but *A.* stood yet before the Lord. 22
A. said of Sarah his wife, she. 20:2
and *A.* planted a grove in. 21:33
God did tempt *A.* and said. 22:1
out of heaven, and said, *A. A.* 11
Sarah died, and *A.* came to. 23:2
A. bought the field of. 17; 49:30
50:13
the Lord had blessed *A.* in all. 24:1
A. said, put thy hand under my. 2
Eliezer said, I am *A.* servant. 34
God of my master *A.* prosper. 42
they sent away Rebekah and *A.* 59
and *A.* gave all that he had. 25:5
the days of the years of *A.* life. 7
Hagar the Egyptian bare to. 12
that was in the days of *A.* 26:1
because *A.* obeyed my voice, kept. 5

multiply thy seed for A. Gen 26:24
give thee the blessing of A. 28:4
except the God of A. had. 31:42
which he sware to A. 50:24
Ex 33:1; Num 32:11; Deut 1:8
6:10; 30:20
I am the God of A. Ex 3:6, 15, 16
4:5; Mat 22:32; Mark 12:26
Luke 20:37; Acts 3:13; 7:32
remember A. Isaac. Ex 32:13
Deut 9:27
people of the God of A. Ps 47:9
covenant he made with A. 105:9
remembered his promise, and A. 42
Lord, who redeemed A. Isa 29:22
art our father, though A. be. 63:16
A. was one, and he. Ezek 33:24
perform the mercy to A. Mi 7:20
son of David, the son of A. Mat 1:1
raise up children unto A. 3:9
Luke 3:8
sit down with A. Mat 8:11
was the son of A. son. Luke 3:34
shall see A. in the kingdom. 13:28
his eyes, and seeth A. 16:23
as he also is the son of A. 19:9
this did not A. John 8:40
A. is dead. 52
hast thou seen A ? 57
before A. was, I am. 58
of the stock of A. Acts 13:26
A. were justified by works. Rom 4:2
A. believed God, and it was counted.
3, 9; Gal 3:6; Jas 2:23
faith are the children of A. Gal 3:7
preached before the gospel to A. 8
faith are blessed with faithful A. 9
God gave the inheritance to A. 18
A. had two sons, the one by a. 4:22
God made promise to A. Heb 6:13
who met A. returning from. 7:1
say, Levi payed tithes in A. 9
A. obeyed. 11:8
by faith A. offered up Isaac. 17

Abraham with *father*

oath to A. thy father. Gen 26:3
God of A. thy father. 24; 28:13
O God of my father A. and. 32:9
I took your father A. Josh 24:3
look to A. your father. Isa 51:2
A. to our father. Mat 3:9; Luke 3:8
he sware to our father A. Luke 1:73
he said, father A. have mercy. 16:24
nay, father A. but if one went. 30
to him A. is our father. John 8:39
greater than our father A. ? 53
your father A. rejoiced to see. 56
appeared to our father A. Acts 7:2
say that A. our father. Rom 4:1
of that faith of our father A. 12
faith of A. who is the father. 16
was not A. our father justified ?
Jas 2:21

Abraham with *seed*

gavest it to seed of A. 2 Chr 20:7
O ye seed of A. his. Ps 105:6
Israel, the seed of A. Isa 41:8
rulers over the seed of A. Jer 33:26
spake to A. and his seed. Luke 1:55
we be A. seed and were. John 8:33
I know ye are A. seed but ye. 37
was not to A. or his seed. Rom 4:13
they are seed of A. 9:7
of the seed of A. 11:1; 2 Cor 11:22
to A. and his seed were Gal 3:16
be Christ's, then are ye A. seed 29
took on him the seed of A. Heb 2:16

abroad

ought of the flesh a. Ex 12:46
a leprosy break out a. Lev 13:12
be born at home or a. 18:9
shall he go a. out of. Deut 23:10
wilt ease thyself a. shalt dig. 13
took daughters from a. Judg 12:9
borrow thee vessels a. 2 Ki 4:3
it to carry it out a. 2 Chr 29:16
the commandment came a. 31:5
queen shall come a. Esth 1:17
wandereth a. for bread. Job 15:23
he goeth a. he telleth it. Ps 41:6
fountains be dispersed a. Pr 5:16
spreadeth a. the earth. Isa 44:24
t out on the children a. Jer 6:11*

a. the sword bereaveth. Lam 1:20
began to blaze a. the. Mark 1:45
but that it should come a. 4:22*
sayings were noised a. Luke 1:65
made known a. the saying. 2:17
this was noised a. the. Acts 2:6*
love of God is shed a. in. Rom 5:5
for your obedience is come a. 16:19
see **cast, spread, stand, scatter, went.**

Absalom

A. the son of. 2 Sam 3:3; 1 Chr 3:2
A. spake to Amnon neither.
2 Sam 13:22
A. had sheep-shearers in. 23
saying, A. hath slain all the. 30
longed to go forth to A. 39
Joab arose and brought A. 14:23
to be so much praised as A. 25
A. said, O that I were made a. 15:4
A. stole the hearts of the men of. 6
among the conspirators with A. 31
A. went in unto his father's 16:22
Ahithophel's counsel pleased A. 17:4
Lord might bring evil upon A. 14
and when A. servants came to. 20
A. passed over Jordan. 24
A. pitched in Gilead. 26
deal gently for my sake with A. 18:5
I saw A. hanged in an oak. 10
darts through the heart of A. 14
it is called unto this day A. 18
is young man A. safe ? 29, 32
O my son A. 33
if A. had lived, and all we had. 19:6
I fled because of A. 1 Ki 2:7
Adonijah, though not after A. 28
Maacah daughter of A. 2 Chr 11:20

absence

to betray him in a. of. Luke 22:6
more in my a. work. Phil 2:12

absent

when we are a. one. Gen 31:49
I verily as a. in body. 1 Cor 5:3
at home in body are a. 2 Cor 5:6
to be a. from the body, present. 8
whether present or a. 9
being a. am bold toward you. 10:1
are by letters when we are a. 11
being a. now I write to. 13:2, 10
I come, or else be a. Phil 1:27
though I be a. in the flesh. Col 2:5

abstain

a. from pollutions of. Acts 15:20
that ye a. from meats offered. 29
that ye should a. from. 1 Thes 4:3
a. from all appearance of evil. 5:22
commanding to a. from. 1 Tim 4:3
a. from fleshly lusts. 1 Pet 2:11

abstinence

after long a. Paul. Acts 27:21*

abundance

God for the a. of all. Deut 28:47
they shall suck of the a. of. 33:19
out of the a. of my. 1 Sam 1:16
no more such a. of spices. 1 Ki 10:10
sycamore-trees for a. 27; 2 Chr 1:15
sound of a. of rain. 1 Ki 18:41
of spices great a. 2 Chr 9:9
a. of waters. Job 22:11; 38:34
shall be a. of peace. Ps 72:7
nor he that loveth a. Eccl 5:10
the a of the rich will not suffer. 12*
a. of milk he shall eat. Isa 7:22
the a. they have gotten. 15:7
great a. of thy enchantments. 47:9
a. of the sea shall be. 60:5
delighted with the a. of her. 66:11
I will reveal to them a. Jer 33:6
a. of idleness was in. Ezek 16:49*
of the a. of his horses. 26:10
silver, and apparel in great a.
Zech 14:14
a. of the heart. Mat 12:34
Luke 6:45
shall have more a. Mat 13:12; 25:29
cast in of their a. Mark 12:44*
Luke 21:4*
receive a. of grace. Rom 5:17
a. of their joy abounded. 2 Cor 8:2
your a. a supply, their a. a. 14
exalted through the a. of the. 12:7*
waxed rich thro' the a. of. Rev 18:3*

***in* abundance**

spoil of the city in a. 2 Sam 12:30
slain oxen in a. 1 Ki 1:19, 25
prepared brass in a. 1 Chr 22:3, 14
trees in a. marble in a. 4; 29:2
workmen with thee in a. 1 Chr 22:15
they offered sacrifices in a. 29:21
me timber in a. 2 Chr 2:9
all these vessels in great a. 4:18
Sheba brought gold in a. 9:1
gave his sons victuals in a. 11:23
sheep and camels in a. 14:15
fell to Asa out of Israel in a. 15:9
to Jehoshaphat, and he had riches
and honour in a. 17:5; 18:1
sheep for Jehoshaphat in a. 18:2
Jehoshaphat found spoil in a. 20:25
they gathered money in a. 24:11
the burnt-offerings were in a. 29:35
Israel brought in a. first-fruits. 31:5
made darts and shields in a. 32:5
cities and possessions in a. 29
and fruit-trees in a. Neh 9:25
them royal wine in a. Esth 1:7
he giveth meat in a. Job 36:31
delight themselves in a. Ps 37:11
trusted in the a. of his riches. 52:7
brought forth frogs in a. 105:30
life consisteth not in a. Luke 12:15
man blame us in this a. 2 Cor 8:20*

abundant

Lord God a. in goodness. Ex 34:6
day, and much more a. Isa 56:12*
Babylon, a. in treasures. Jer 51:13
bestow more a. honour. 1 Cor 12:23
having given more a. honour to. 24
a. grace might redound. 2 Cor 4:15*
his inward affection is more a. 7:15
for the administration is a. 9:12*
in labours more a. in stripes. 11:23
rejoicing may be more a. Phil 1:26
Lord was exceeding a. 1 Tim 1:14
according to his a. mercy. 1 Pet 1:3*

abundantly

waters bring forth a. Gen 1:20, 21
breed a. in the earth. 8:17
bring forth a. in the earth. 9:7
Israel increased a. Ex 1:7
river shall bring forth frogs a. 8:3*
the water came out a. Num 20:11
oil, oxen, and sheep a. 1 Chr 12:40
so David prepared a. before. 22:5
thou hast shed blood a. and made. 8
brought they in a. 2 Chr 31:5
hand God bringeth a. Job 12:6
drop, and distil upon man a. 36:28
they shall be a. satisfied. Ps 36:8
waterest the ridges thereof a. 65:10
I will a. bless her provision. 132:15
shall a. utter the memory. 145:7*
drink a. O beloved. S of S 5:1
shall howl, weeping a. Isa 15:3
it shall blossom a. and rejoice. 35:2
our God, for he will a. pardon. 55:7
have life more a. John 10:10
I laboured more a. 1 Cor 15:10
conversation, and more a. to.
2 Cor 1:12
love I have more a. to you. 2:4
according to our rule a. 10:15
though the more a. I love you. 12:15
that is able to do exceeding a.
Eph 3:20
endeavoured more a. to see.
1 Thes 2:17*
he shed on us a. through Jesus.
Tit 3:6*
God willing more a. to. Heb 6:17
be ministered to you a. 2 Pet 1:11*

abuse, -ed

a. her all the night. Judg 19:25
lest uncircumcised a. me.
1 Sam 31:4; 1 Chr 10:4
I a. not my power in. 1 Cor 9:18*

abusers, -ing

nor a. of themselves. 1 Cor 6:9
use this world as not a. it. 7:31*

accept

[1] *To receive favourably,* Gen 4:7; Job 42:9; Mal 1:10, 13; Acts 10:35. [2] *To show partiality,* Job 13:10; 32:21; Pr 18:5.

[3] *To regard or value,* 2 Cor 8:12.
[4] *To highly esteem,* Luke 4:24.
peradventure he will *a.* *Gen* 32:20
and the owner shall *a.* *Ex* 22:11
a. of the punishment. *Lev* 26:41, 43
bless and *a.* the work. *Deut* 33:11
let him *a.* an offering. *1 Sam* 26:19
the L., thy God *a.* thee. *2 Sam* 24:23
will ye *a.* his person ? *Job* 13:8
if ye do secretly *a.* persons. 10
not *a.* any man's person. 32:21
pray for you, for him will I *a.* 42:8
and *a.* thy burnt-sacrifice. *Ps* 20:3
a. the persons of the wicked. 82:2
a. I beseech thee the free-. 119:108
not good to *a.* the person. *Pr* 18:5
the Lord doth not *a.* them. *Jer* 14:10
I will not *a.* them. 12; *Amos* 5:22
there will I *a.* them. *Ezek* 20:40
a. you with your sweet savour. 41
and I will *a.* you, saith the. 43:27
will he be pleased, or *a.* ? *Mal* 1:8
nor will I *a.* an offering at your. 10
should I *a.* this of your hands ? 13
a. it always, and in all. *Acts* 24:3

acceptable
Often has the stronger meaning of well-pleasing, Rom 14:18; Eph 5:10.
shall not be *a.* for you. *Lev* 22:20
Asher be *a.* to his. *Deut* 33:24
meditation of my heart be *a.* *Ps* 19:14
thee, O Lord, in an *a.* time. 69:13
righteous know what is *a.* *Pr* 10:32
justice and judgment is more *a.* 21:3
preacher sought out *a.* *Eccl* 12:10
in an *a.* time have I heard. *Isa* 49:8
call this an *a.* day to the ? 58:5
to proclaim the *a.* year of. 61:2†
burnt-offerings are not *a.* *Jer* 6:20
O king, let my counsel be *a.* *Dan* 4:27
to preach the *a.* year of. *Luke* 4:19
living sacrifice, holy, *a.* *Rom* 12:1
is that good and *a.* will of God. 2
a. to God and approved of. 14:18
of the Gentiles might be *a.* 15:16
proving what is *a.* unto. *Eph* 5:10
sacrifice *a.* well-pleasing. *Phil* 4:18
this is *a.* in the sight. *1 Tim* 2:3
is good and *a.* before God. 5:4
sacrifices *a.* to God. *1 Pet* 2:5
this is *a.* with God. 20

acceptably
we may serve God *a.* *Heb* 12:28

acceptance
with *a.* on mine altar. *Isa* 60:7

acceptation
saying worthy of all *a.* *1 Tim* 1:15, 4:9

accepted
well, shalt thou not be *a.* *Gen* 4:7
have *a.* thee concerning this. 19:21
they may be *a.* before. *Ex* 28:38
offering shall be *a.* *Lev* 1:4; 22:27
it shall not be *a.* 7:18; 19:7, 22:23, 25
should it have been *a.* in. 10:19*
shall be perfect, to be *a.* 22:21
shall wave the sheaf to be *a.* 23:11
he was *a.* in the sight. *1 Sam* 18:5*
David said, see I have *a.* 25:35
a. of the multitude of. *Esth* 10:3
the Lord also *a.* Job. *Job* 42:9
sacrifice shall be *a.* on. *Isa* 56:7
let my supplication be *a.* *Jer* 37:20
out supplication be *a.* before. 42:2
no prophet is *a.* in his. *Luke* 4:24
worketh righteousness is *a.* *Acts* 10:35
my service may be *a.* of. *Rom* 15:31
present, we may be *a.* *2 Cor* 5:9
time *a.* now is the *a.* time. 6:2
is *a.* according to that a man. 8:12
for indeed he *a.* the exhortation. 17
gospel which ye have not *a.* 11:4
made us *a.* in the beloved. *Eph* 1:6*

acceptest
neither *a.* thou the person. *Luke* 20:21

accepteth
him that *a.* not persons. *Job* 34:19
eat with joy, for God now *a.* *Eccl* 9:7
sacrifice, but the Lord *a.* *Hos* 8:13
God *a.* no man's person. *Gal* 2:6

accepting, *see* **deliverance.**

access
also we *a.* by faith. *Rom* 5:2
through him we both have *a.* to. *Eph* 2:18
have boldness and *a.* by faith. 3:12

Accho
drive out inhabitants of *A.* *Judg* 1:31

accompanied
brethren from Joppa *a.* *Acts* 10:23
these six brethren *a.* me. 11:12
Sopater of Berea *a.* Paul. 20:4
and they *a.* him unto the ship. 38

accompany, *see* **salvation.**

accomplish
(*To perform, finish, or fulfil.*)
sacrifice to *a.* his vow. *Lev* 22:21
a. my desire in giving. *1 Ki* 5:9
a. as an hireling his day. *Job* 14:6
they *a.* a diligent search. *Ps* 64:6
shall *a.* that which I. *Isa* 55:11
surely *a.* your vows. *Jer* 44:25
thus will I *a.* my fury. *Ezek* 6:12
now will I *a.* mine anger upon. 7:8
I *a.* my wrath upon the wall. 13:15
my fury to *a.* my anger. 20:8, 21
would *a.* seventy years. *Dan* 9:2
a. at Jerusalem. *Luke* 9:31

accomplished
by Jeremiah might be *a.* *2 Chr* 36:22
of purification were *a.* *Esth* 2:12, *Luke* 2:22
shall be *a.* before his. *Job* 15:32
the desire *a.* is sweet. *Pr* 13:19
that her warfare is *a.* *Isa* 40:2
when seventy years are *a.* *Jer* 25:12, 29:10
your dispersions are *a.* 25:34*
my words shall be *a.* before. 39:16
the Lord hath *a.* his fury. *Lam* 4:11
punishment of thine iniquity is *a.* 22
when hast *a.* them, lie on. *Ezek* 4:6
thus shall mine anger be *a.* 5:13
till the indignation be *a.* *Dan* 11:36
a. to scatter the power of the. 12:7*
his ministration were *a.* *Luke* 1:23
days were *a.* that she should. 2:6
days were *a.* for circumcising. 21
am I straitened till it be *a.* 12:50
the Son of man, shall be *a.* 18:31
must yet be *a.* in me. 22:37*
all things were now *a.* *John* 19:28*
we had *a.* those days. *Acts* 21:5
same afflictions are *a.* in. *1 Pet* 5:9

accomplishing, *see* **service.**

accomplishment
signify the *a.* of days of. *Acts* 21:26

accord
groweth of its own *a.* *Lev* 25:5
with Israel with one *a.* *Josh* 9:2
all continued with one *a.* *Acts* 1:14
all with one *a.* in one place. 2:1*
daily with one *a.* in temple. 46
their voice to God with one *a.* 4:24
one *a.* in Solomon's porch. 5:12
ran upon Stephen with one *a.* 7:57
people with one *a.* gave heed. 8:6
opened to them of his own *a.* 12:10
they came with one *a.* to him. 20
being assembled with one *a.* 15:25
with one *a.* made insurrection. 18:12
with one *a.* into the theatre. 19:29
forward of his own *a.* *2 Cor* 8:17
being of one *a.* of one. *Phil* 2:2

according
done *a.* as thou badest. *Gen* 27:19
a. as Joseph had said. 41:54
the Lord will give *a.* *Ex* 12:25
be great, *a.* as thou. *Num* 14:17
inheritance *a.* as God. *Deut* 10:9
a. as the Lord thy God. 16:10
a. as he walked before. *1 Ki* 3:6
to find *a.* to his ways. *Job* 34:11
Jer 17:10; 21:14; 32:19
went and did *a.* as the Lord. *Job* 42:9
judge me, O God, *a.* to my. *Ps* 7:8
the Lord *a.* to his righteousness. 17
a. to thy mercy remember thou me. 25:7; 51:1; 106:45; 109:26, 119:124
a. to their deeds, and *a.* 28:4
mercy be on us *a.* as we. 33:22
judge me, O God, *a.* to thy. 35:24
a. to thy name, so is thy. 48:10*
renderest to every man *a.* 62:12, *Pr* 24:12, 29
a. to the greatness of thy. *Ps* 79:11
a. to thy fear, so is thy wrath. 90:11
rewarded us *a.* to our. 103:10
a. to thy word. 119:25, 28, 41, 58, 65, 76, 107, 116, 154, 169, 170
quicken me *a.* to. 119:159; *Isa* 63:7
praise him *a.* to his excellent. *Ps* 150:2
speak not *a.* to this word. *Isa* 8:20
joy *a.* to the joy in harvest. 9:3
a. to all that the Lord has. 63:7
recompense her *a.* to her. *Jer* 50:29
shall rule, and do *a.* *Dan* 11:3
a. to the love of the Lord. *Hos* 3:1
the Lord will punish Jacob *a.* 12:2
a. to the days of thy coming. *Mi* 7:15*
a. to your faith be it. *Mat* 9:29
he will reward every man *a.* to. 16:27; *Rom* 2:6; *2 Tim* 4:14, *Rev* 2:23
nor did *a.* to his will. *Luke* 12:47
judge not *a.* to the. *John* 7:24
made to every man *a.* as. *Acts* 4:35
seed of David *a.* to the flesh. *Rom* 1:3
called *a.* to his purpose. 8:28
gifts differing *a.* to the grace. 12:6
to be like-minded *a.* 15:5
Christ died *a.* to the. *1 Cor* 15:3
man *a.* as he purposeth. *2 Cor* 9:7
end shall be *a.* to their works. 11:15
who gave himself *a.* to. *Gal* 1:4
Abraham's seed, and heirs *a.* 3:29
a. as he hath chosen us in him. *Eph* 1:4
a. to good pleasure. 5
a. to riches of his grace. 7
predestinated *a.* to the purpose. 11
a. to the power that worketh. 3:20
a. to the working. *Phil* 3:21
God shall supply our need *a.* 4:19
not *a.* to our works. *2 Tim* 1:9
a. to his mercy he saved us. *Tit* 3:5
not *a.* to the covenant. *Heb* 8:9
a. to his mercy hath. *1 Pet* 1:3
live *a.* to God in the Spirit. 4:6
a. as his divine power. *2 Pet* 1:3*
we *a.* to his promise look. 3:13
judged *a.* to their works. *Rev* 20:12, 13
I come to give *a.* as his work. 22:12

according *to all, see* **all.**

according *to that*
obey my voice *a. to that.* *Gen* 27:8
do to me *a. to that.* *Judg* 11:36
slew not *a. to that* which. *2 Ki* 14:6
a. to that which was. *2 Chr* 35:26
Tatnai did *a. to that* Darius. *Ezra* 6:13
a. to that which was spoken. *Rom* 4:18
a. to that he hath done. *2 Cor* 5:10
a. to that a man hath, not *a. to that.* 8:12

accordingly, *see* **repay.**

account
your *a.* for the lamb. *Ex* 12:4
that passeth the *a.* *2 Ki* 12:4*
number put in the *a.* *1 Chr* 27:24
number of their *a.* *2 Chr* 26:11*
for he giveth not *a.* *Job* 33:13
man that thou makest *a.* *Ps* 144:3
one to find out the *a.* *Eccl* 7:27
the princes might give *a.* *Dan* 6:2
give *a.* thereof in the day. *Mat* 12:36
take *a.* of his servants. 18:23*
a. of thy stewardship. *Luke* 16:2
we may give an *a.* of. *Acts* 19:40
every one shall give *a.* *Rom* 14:12
may abound to your *a.* *Phil* 4:17
put that on mine *a.* *Philem* 18

they watch as they that must give *a.* *Heb* 13:17
who shall give *a.* to him. *1 Pet* 4:5

account, -ed

which also were *a.* giants. *Deut* 2:11
that also was *a.* a land of giants. 20
Solomon shall be *a.* *1 Ki* 1:21
silver was nothing *a.* of. 10:21
2 Chr 9:20
be *a.* to the Lord for a. *Ps* 22:30*
wherein is he to be *a.* of? *Isa* 2:22
a. to rule over Gentiles. *Mark* 10:42
a. worthy to obtain. *Luke* 20:35
should be *a.* the greatest. 22:24
we are *a.* as sheep for. *Rom* 8:36
let a man so *a.* of us as. *1 Cor* 4:1
a. to him for righteousness. *Gal* 3:6*
a. that the long-suffering *2 Pet* 3:15

accounting

a. that God was able to. *Heb* 11:19

accursed

[1] *Devoted to destruction,* Josh 6:17, *etc.* [2] *Separated from the church,* Rom 9:3; Gal 1:8, 9.
(*Anathema*)

is hanged, is *a.* of God. *Deut* 21:23
city shall be *a.* it and. *Josh* 6:17
any wise keep from the *a.* thing. 18
a. thing; Achan took of *a.* 7:1
even taken of the *a.* thing. 11
because they were *a.* except ye destroy the *a.* 12
there is an *a.* thing in the midst. 13
that is taken with the *a.* thing. 15
commit trespass in *a.* thing. 22:20
in the thing *a.* *1 Chr* 2:7
100 years old shall be *a.* *Isa* 65:20
I could wish myself *a.* *Rom* 9:3
Spirit, calleth Jesus *a.* 1 *Cor* 12:3
gospel, let him be *a.* *Gal* 1:8, 9

accusation

wrote they to him an *a.* *Ezra* 4:6
set over his head his *a.* *Mat* 27:37
Mark 15:26
they might find an *a.* *Luke* 6:7
taken any thing by false *a.* 19:8*
what *a.* bring ye against? *John* 18:29
they brought no *a.* as. *Acts* 25:18
elder receive not an *a.* *1 Tim* 5:19
bring not a railing *a.* *2 Pet* 2:11*
durst not bring a railing *a.* *Jude* 9*

accuse

a. not a servant to his. *Pr* 30:10*
a. him. *Mat* 12:10; *Mark* 3:2
nor *a.* any falsely, and be. *Luke* 3:14
they began to *a.* him, saying. 23:2
those things whereof ye *a.* him. 14
will *a.* you to the Father. *John* 5:45
that they might have to *a.* him. 8:6
Tertullus began to *a.* him. *Acts* 24:2
of all things whereof we *a.* 8
prove things whereof they *a.* me. 13
go down with me, and *a.* 25:5
none of those whereof these *a.* 11
ought to *a.* my nation of. 28:19
falsely *a.* your good. *1 Pet* 3:16*

accused

near, and *a.* the Jews. *Dan* 3:8
them which had *a.* Daniel. 6:24
a. he answered nothing. *Mat* 27:12
priests *a.* him. *Mark* 15:3
Luke 23:10
a. that he had wasted. *Luke* 16:1
certainty wherefore he was *a.*
Acts 22:30
cause whereof they *a.* him. 23:28
be *a.* of questions of their law. 29
is *a.* have the accusers. 25:16
things whereof I am *a.* 26:2
for which hope's sake I am *a.* of 7
faithful children, not *a.* of. *Tit.* 1:6
who *a.* them before our. *Rev* 12:10

accuser, *see* **cast** *down*

accusers

where are those thine *a.*? *John* 8:10*
commandment to his *a.* *Acts* 23:30
hear thee when thine *a.* are. 35
commanding his *a.* to come. 24:8*
before he have the *a.* face. 25:16
against whom, when the *a.* 18
natural affection, false *a.* *2 Tim* 3:3*
a. not given to much wine. *Tit* 2:3*

accuseth, -ing

that *a.* you, even Moses. *John* 5:45
thoughts *a.* or excusing. *Rom* 2:15

accustomed, *see* **do evil.**

aceldama, *see* **field**

Achaia

was the deputy of *A.* *Acts* 18:12
disposed to pass into *A.* 27
it pleased them of *A.* to. *Rom* 15:26
Epenetus, the first-fruits of *A.* 16:5
Stephanus, first-fruits of *A.*
1 Cor 16:15
that *A.* was ready a year. *2 Cor* 9:2
stop me in the regions of *A.* 11:10
ensamples to all in *A.* *1 Thes* 1:7
the word sounded not only in *A.* 8

Achaicus

glad of the coming of *A.* *1 Cor* 16:17

Achan, *or* **Achar**

A. of the tribe of Judah. *Josh* 7:18
did not *A.* son of Zerah commit
22:20
A. the troubler of Israel. *1 Chr* 2:7

Achim

Sadoc begat *A.* and *A.* *Mat* 1:14

Achish

fled and went to *A.* *1 Sam* 21:10
27:2
was afraid of *A.* 21:12
A. gave him Ziklag. 27:6
on in the rereward with *A.* 29:2
A. said, I know thou art good in. 9
Shimei went to Gath to *A.* *1 Ki* 2:40

Achmetha

was found at *A.* a roll. *Ezra* 6:2

Achor

called the valley of *A.* *Josh* 7:26
valley of *A.* a place. *Isa* 65:10
give the valley of *A.* for. *Hos* 2:15

Achsah

will give *A.* to wife. *Josh* 15:16
Judg 1:12

Achshaph

Jabin sent to king of *A.* *Josh* 11:1
king of *A.* one. 12:20
their border *A.* 19:25

Achzib

lot from the coast to *A.* *Josh* 19:29
the houses of *A.* shall be. *Mi* 1:14

acknowledge

[1] *To own, or confess,* Gen 38:26; Ps 32:5. [2] *To esteem and respect,* Isa 61:9; 1 Cor 16:18. [3] *To approve of,* 2 Cor 1:13; Philem 6. [4] *To worship,* Dan 11:39.

a. the son of the hated. *Deut* 21:17
nor did he *a.* his brethren. 33:9
I *a.* my sin. *Ps* 32:5
I *a.* my transgression. 51:3
in all thy ways *a.* him, he. *Pr* 3:6
are near, *a.* my might. *Isa* 33:13
that see them, shall *a.* them. 61:9
father, though Israel *a.* us not. 63:16
only *a.* thine iniquity. *Jer* 3:13
a. O Lord, our wickedness. 14:20
a. them that are carried. 24:5*
god whom he shall *a.* *Dan* 11:39
I will go, till they *a.* *Hos* 5:15
let him *a.* the things. *1 Cor* 14:37*
therefore *a.* ye them that are. 16:18
a. and I trust shall *a.* *2 Cor* 1:13

acknowledged

Judah *a.* them, and said. *Gen* 38:26
also you have *a.* us in. *2 Cor* 1:14

acknowledgeth

a. the Son hath the Father.
1 John 2:23

acknowledging

(*Revised Version,* knowledge)

the *a.* of the truth. *2 Tim* 2:25
a. the truth which is after. *Tit* 1:1
by the *a.* every good thing. *Philem* 6

acknowledgment

a. of the mystery of God. *Col* 2:2*

acquaint, -ed, -ing

a. thyself with him and. *Job* 22:21
thou art *a.* with all my. *Ps* 139:3
a. my heart with wisdom. *Eccl* 2:3
of sorrows, and *a.* with. *Isa* 53:3

acquaintance

let priests take it, every man of his *a.*
2 Ki 12:5
no more money of your *a.* 7
a. are estranged from me. *Job* 19:13
all that had been of his *a.* 42:11
and a fear to mine *a.* *Ps* 31:11
mine equal, and mine *a.* 55:13*
put away mine *a.* far from me. 88:8
lover put from me, and my *a.* 18
sought him among their *a.* *Luke* 2:44
a. stood afar off, beholding. 23:49
forbid none of his *a.* to. *Acts* 24:23*

acquit

not *a.* me from mine iniquity.
Job 10:14
the Lord will not at all *a.* the *Nah.* 1:3

acre, -s

half an *a.* of land. *1 Sam* 14:14
ten *a.* of vineyard shall. *Isa* 5:10

act

pass his *a.* his strange *a.* *Isa* 28:21
the *a.* of violence is in their. 59:6
in adultery, in the very *a.* *John* 8:4

actions

the Lord *a.* are weighed. *1 Sam* 2:3

activity

if knowest any man of *a.* *Gen* 47:6

acts

a. which he did in Egypt. *Deut* 11:3
eyes have seen the great *a.* of. 7
rehearse the righteous *a.* *Judg* 5:11
reason of all righteous *a.* *1 Sam* 12:7
Benaiah the son . . . who had done many *a.* *2 Sam* 23:20; *1 Chr* 11:22
report I heard of thy *a.* *1 Ki* 10:6
a. of Solomon, are they not written in the book of the *a.* 11:41; *2 Chr* 9:5
the *a.* of Jehu, and all. *2 Ki* 10:34
according to all the *a.* he had. 23:19
the *a.* of Josiah and all that he. 28
the *a.* of David, first. *1 Chr* 29:29
behold the *a.* of Asa. *2 Chr* 16:11
the *a.* of Jehoshaphat, first. 20:34
a. of Hezekiah. 32:32; *2 Ki* 20:20
all the *a.* of his power. *Esth* 10:2
a. to the children of Israel. *Ps* 103:7
who can utter the mighty *a.* 106:2
declare thy mighty *a.* 145:4, 6, 12
praise him for his mighty *a.* 150:2

Adam

A. gave names to all cattle. *Gen* 2:20
and called their name *A.* 5:2
separated the sons of *A.* *Deut* 32:8
my transgressions as *A.* *Job* 31:33
death reigned from *A.* to. *Rom* 5:14
for as in *A.* all die. *1 Cor* 15:22
first man *A.* the last *A.* a. 45
for *A.* was first formed. *1 Tim* 2:13
and *A.* was not deceived, but. 14
Enoch the seventh from *A.* *Jude* 14

Adam

the city *A.* that is beside. *Josh* 3:16

adamant

a. have I made thy forehead.
Ezek 3:9
their hearts as an *a.* stone. *Zech* 7:12

Adar

finished on third day of *A.* *Ezra* 6:15
lot till the twelfth month *A.* *Esth* 3:7
13th day of month *A.* 13; 8:12
9:1, 17
gathered on the 14th day of *A.* 9:15
Jews made 14th day of *A.* a day. 19
14th and 15th days of *A.* yearly. 21

add

[1] *To join or put to,* Deut 4:2; Acts 2:41; 2 Pet 1:5. [2] *To increase,* Pr 16:23. [3] *To give, or bestow,* Gen 30:24; Mat 6:33.

a. to me another son. *Gen* 30:24
he shall *a.* a fifth part. *Lev* 5:16
6:5; 27:13, 15, 19, 27, 31; *Num* 5:7
to cities of refuge *a.* forty-two.
Num 35:6
not *a.* to the word. *Deut* 4:2; 12:32
thou shalt *a.* three cities. 19:9
to *a.* drunkenness to thirst. 29:19*
the Lord thy God *a.* to. *2 Sam* 24:3
I will *a.* to your yoke. *1 Ki* 12:11
14; *2 Chr* 10:14

I *a.* to thy days. *2 Ki* 20:6; *Isa* 38:5
mayest *a.* thereto. *1 Chr* 22:14
ye intend to *a.* more to. *2 Chr* 28:13
a. iniquity to their iniquity. *Ps* 69:27
peace shall they *a.* to thee. *Pr* 3:2
a. thou not to his words, lest. 30:6
a. ye year to year, let. *Isa* 29:1
that they may *a.* sin to sin. 30:1
a. one cubit to his. *Mat* 6:27
Luke 12:25
supposing to *a.* affliction. *Phil* 1:16*
this *a.* to your faith. *2 Pet* 1:5
any *a.* God shall *a.* to him. *Rev.* 22:18

added

voice, and he *a.* no more. *Deut* 5:22
a. to all our sins this. *1 Sam* 12:19
were *a.* besides many like words.
Jer 36:32
the Lord hath *a.* grief to my. 45:3
majesty was *a.* to me. *Dan* 4:36
a. to you. *Mat* 6:33; *Luke* 12:31
Herod *a.* yet this above. *Luke* 3:20
they heard, he *a.* and. 19:11
day there were *a.* 3000. *Acts* 2:41
the Lord *a.* to the church daily. 47
believers were the more *a.* to. 5:14
much people were *a.* to the. 11:24
somewhat, *a.* nothing to. *Gal* 2:6
a. because of transgressions. 3:19

adder

Dan shall be an *a.* in. *Gen* 49:17
they are like the deaf *a.* *Ps* 58:4
tread on the lion and *a.* 91:13
a. poison is under their lips. 140:3
last stingeth like an *a.* *Pr* 23:32

addeth

a. rebellion to his sin. *Job* 34:37
and he *a.* no sorrow. *Pr* 10:22
heart of the wise *a.* learning. 16:23
disannulleth or *a.* thereto. *Gal* 3:15

Addi

was the son of *A.* son. *Luke* 3:28

addicted

a. themselves to the. *1 Cor* 16:15*

additions

(*Revised Version,* wreaths)
certain *a.* were made. *1 Ki* 7:29
molten at the side of every *a.* 30
he graved cherubims, and *a.* 36

adjure

[1] *To bind under the penalty of a fearful curse,* Josh 6:26. [2] *To charge earnestly by word or oath,* 1 Ki 22:16; Mat 26:63.

how many times shall I *a.* thee to tell. *1 Ki* 22:16; *2 Chr* 18:15
I *a.* thee by the living. *Mat* 26:63
I *a.* thee by God, thou. *Mark* 5:7
we *a.* you by Jesus. *Acts* 19:13

adjured

Joshua *a.* them at that. *Josh* 6:26
for Saul had *a.* the. *1 Sam* 14:24

Admah

Shinab king of *A.* *Gen* 14:2
like the overthrow of *A.* *Deut* 29:23
shall I make thee as *A*? *Hos* 11:8

administered

(*Revised Version,* ministered)
a. by us to the glory of. *2 Cor* 8:19
in this abundance which is *a.* 20

administration, -s

(*Revised Version,* ministration)
are differences of *a.* *1 Cor* 12:5
for the *a.* of this service. *2 Cor* 9:12

admiration

having men's persons in *a.* *Jude* 16*
I wondered with great *a.* *Rev* 17:6*

admired

to be *a.* in all them. *2 Thes* 1:10*

admonish, -ed

who will no more be *a.* *Eccl* 4:13
by these, my son, be *a.* 12:12
that I have *a.* you. *Jer* 42:19
now past, Paul *a.* them. *Acts* 27:9
also to *a.* one another. *Rom* 15:14
a. one another in psalms. *Col* 3:16
you in Lord, and *a.* you. *1 Thes* 5:12
a. him as a brother. *2 Thes* 3:15
as Moses was *a.* of God. *Heb* 8:5

admonition

are written for our *a.* *1 Cor* 10:11
bring them up in the *a.* of. *Eph* 6:4
the first and second *a.* *Tit* 3:10

ado

why make ye this *a.*? *Mark* 5:39*

Adoni-Bezek

they found *A.* in Bezek. *Judg* 1:5

Adonijah

A. the son of. *2 Sam* 3:4; *1 Chr* 3:2
then *A.* exalted himself. *1 Ki* 1:5
hast thou not heard that *A.*? 11
God save the king *A.* 25
A. feared. 50, 51
let Abishag be given to *A.* 2:21
A. shall be put to death this day. 25
Joab had turned after *A.* though. 28
sent Levites to teach *A.* *2 Chr* 17:8
sealed, *A.* and Adin. *Neh* 10:16

Adonikam

the children of *A.*, 666. *Ezra* 2:13
Neh 7:18

adoption

[1] *A legal action by which a person takes into his family a child not his own, and usually of no kin to him, with the purpose of treating him as, and giving him all the privileges of, an own son. So Moses was adopted by Pharaoh's daughter,* Ex 2:10, *and Esther by Mordecai,* Esth 2:7, 15. *The custom was not common among the Jews, but was so among the Romans, with whom, as with us, an adopted child is legally entitled to all rights and privileges of a natural-born child.*

[2] *The custom, being well-known where Rome held sway, is used in the New Testament to refer:* (a) *to the choice by Jehovah of Israel to be his special people,* Rom 9:4; (b) *the special sense in which all true Christians are the sons of God,* Gal 4:5; Eph 1:4, 5; *and* (c) *the final redemption of the body,* Rom 8:23.

received the spirit of *a.* *Rom* 8:15
for the *a.* the redemption of 23
to whom pertaineth the *a.* 9:4
might receive the *a.* of sons. *Gal* 4:5
us to the *a.* of children. *Eph* 1:5

adorn, -ed, -eth, -ing

as a bride *a.* herself with. *Isa* 61:10
be again *a.* with tabrets. *Jer* 31:4
the temple was *a.* with. *Luke* 21:5
women *a.* in modest. *1 Tim* 2:9
a. the doctrine of God. *Tit* 2:10
whose *a.* let it not be that outward *a.*
1 Pet 3:3
women who trusted in God *a.* 5
a bride *a.* for her husband. *Rev* 21:2

Adrammelech

burnt children to *A.* *2 Ki* 17:31
A. and Sharezer. 19:37; *Isa* 37:38

Adramyttium

entering into a ship of *A.* *Acts* 27:2

Adria

driven up and down in *A.* *Acts* 27:27

Adriel

given unto *A.* to wife. *1 Sam* 18:19
she brought up for *A.* *2 Sam* 21:8

Adullam

the cave *A.* *1 Sam* 22:1; *1 Chr* 11:15
came to David to *A.* *2 Sam* 23:13
come to *A.* the glory of. *Mi* 1:15

adulterer, -s

a. shall surely be put. *Lev* 20:10
the eye of the *a.* waiteth. *Job* 24:15
been partaker with *a.* *Ps* 50:18
seed of *a.* and the whore. *Isa* 57:3
they be all *a.* an assembly. *Jer* 9:2
for the land is full of *a.* for. 23:10
they are all *a.* as an oven. *Hos* 7:4
swift witness against the *a.* *Mal* 3:5
others, extortioners, *a.* *Luke* 18:11
neither *a.* shall inherit. *1 Cor* 6:9
whoremongers and *a.* *Heb* 13:4
ye *a.* know ye not that the. *Jas* 4:4

adulteress, -es

a. shall surely be put. *Lev* 20:10
the *a.* will hunt for the. *Pr* 6:26
shall judge them as *a.* *Ezek* 23:45
love a woman, yet an *a.* *Hos* 3:1
she is no *a.* though she be. *Rom* 7:3

adulterous

way of an *a.* woman. *Pr* 30:20
an *a.* generation. *Mat* 12:39; 16:4
be ashamed in this *a.* *Mark* 8:38

adultery, -ies

[1] *Natural,* Mat 5:28; Mark 10: 11. [2] *Spiritual, which is idolatry,* Jer 3:9; Ezek 23:37.

thou shalt not commit *a.* *Ex* 20:14
Deut 5:18; Mat 5:27; 19:18
Rom 13:9
committeth *a.*, even he that committeth *a.* shall surely be. *Lev* 20:10
commits *a.* lacketh. *Pr* 6:32
Israel committed *a.* *Jer* 3:8
committed *a.* with stones and. 9
then they committed *a.* 5:7
steal, murder, and commit *a.* 7:9
I have seen thine *a.* and. 13:27
they commit *a.* and walk in. 23:14
they have committed *a.* 29:23
wife that committeth *a.* *Ezek* 16:32
have they committed *a.* 23:37
said I to her that was old in *a.* 43
put away her *a.* between. *Hos* 2:2
by lying and committing *a.* 4:2
your spouses shall commit *a.* 13
them when they commit *a.* 14
hath committed *a.* in. *Mat* 5:28
her that is divorced committeth *a.*
32; 19:9; *Luke* 16:18
heart proceed *a.* *Mat* 15:19
Mark 7:21
marry another, committeth *a.*
Mark 10:11; *Luke* 16:18
do not commit *a.* *Mark* 10:19
Luke 18:20; *Jas* 2:11
a woman taken in *a.* *John* 8:3, 4
should not commit *a.* *Rom* 2:22
the flesh are manifest, *a.* *Gal* 5:19
having eyes full of *a.* *2 Pet* 2:14
cast them that commit *a.* *Rev* 2:22

advanced

Lord that *a.* Moses. *1 Sam* 12:6*
Ahasuerus *a.* Haman the. *Esth* 3:1
told him how he had *a.* him. 5:11
whereto the king *a.* 10:2

advantage, -ed, -eth

what *a.* will it be to thee. *Job* 35:3
is a man *a.* if he gain. *Luke* 9:25
what *a.* then hath the Jew. *Rom* 3:1
a. it me if the dead? *1 Cor* 15:32
Satan should get an *a.* *2 Cor* 2:11
in admiration, because of *a.* *Jude* 16

adventure, -ed

not *a.* to set the sole. *Deut* 28:56
father sought and *a.* his. *Judg* 9:17
that he would not *a.* *Acts* 19:31

adversaries

lest their *a.* should. *Deut* 32:27
render vengeance to his *a.* 43
for us, or for our *a.*? *Josh* 5:13
the *a.* of the Lord. *1 Sam* 2:10
this day be *a.* to me. *2 Sam* 19:22
when *a.* of Judah and. *Ezra* 4:1
our *a.* said, they shall not. *Neh* 4:11
evil for good, are my *a.* *Ps* 38:20
mine *a.* are all before thee. 69:19
confounded that are *a.* to. 71:13
my hand against their *a.* 81:14
the right hand of his *a.* 89:42
for my love they are my *a.* 109:4
let this be the reward of my *a.* 20
let my *a.* be clothed with shame. 29
I will ease me of my *a.* *Isa* 1:24
shall set up the *a.* of Rezin. 9:11
the *a.* of Judah shall be. 11:13*
he will repay fury to his *a.* 59:18
our *a.* have trodden down. 63:18
thy name known to thine *a.* 64:2
all thine *a.* shall go into. *Jer* 30:16
he may avenge him of his *a.* 46:10
their *a.* said, we offend not. 50:7
her *a.* are the chief. *Lam* 1:5
the *a.* saw her, and did mock. 7
his *a.* should be round about him. 17
hath set up the horn of thine *a.* 2:17
shall be lifted up upon thy *a.* *Mi* 5:9
take vengeance on his *a.* *Nah* 1:2

all his *a.* were ashamed. *Luke* 13:17
your *a.* shall not be able. 21:15
and there are many *a.* *1 Cor* 16:9
terrified by your *a.* *Phil* 1:28
which shall devour the *a.* *Heb* 10:27

adversary

an *a.* to thine adversaries. *Ex* 23:22
an *a.* against Balaam. *Num* 22:22
her *a.* also provoked her. *1 Sam* 1:6*
in the battle he be an *a.* to us. 29:4
is neither *a.* nor evil. *1 Ki* 5:4
Lord stirred up an *a.* to 11:14, 23
was an *a.* to Israel all the days. 25
the *a.* and enemy is this. *Esth* 7:6
a. had written a book. *Job* 31:35
shall the *a.* reproach? *Ps* 74:10
who is mine *a.* let him. *Isa* 50:8
the *a.* hath spread out. *Lam* 1:10
with his right hand as an *a.* 2:4
the *a.* should have entered. 4:12
an *a.* shall be round. *Amos* 3:11
agree with thine *a.* quickly, lest at any time the *a.* deliver. *Mat* 5:25
goest with thine *a.* *Luke* 12:58
saying, avenge me of mine *a.* 18:3
no occasion to the *a.* *1 Tim* 5:14
a. the devil as a roaring. *1 Pet* 5:8

adversity, -ies

saved you out of all *a.* *1 Sam* 10:19
my soul out of all *a.* *2 Sam* 4:9
did vex them with all *a.* *2 Chr* 15:6
I shall never be in *a.* *Ps* 10:6
thou hast known my soul in *a.* 31:7
but in my *a.* they rejoiced. 35:15
rest from the days of *a.* 94:13
brother is born for *a.* *Pr* 17:17
if thou faint in day of *a.* 24:10
but in the day of *a.* *Eccl* 7:14
give you the bread of *a.* *Isa* 30:20
them which suffer *a.* *Heb* 13:3*

advertise (*To notify, or warn*)

I will *a.* thee, what. *Num* 24:14
I thought to *a.* thee. *Ruth* 4:4*

advice

take *a.* and speak your. *Judg* 19:30
give here your *a.* and counsel. 20:7
blessed be thy *a.* *1 Sam* 25:33*
that our *a.* should. *2 Sam* 19:43
what *a.* give ye, that. *2 Chr* 10:9
after the *a.* of young men. 14
king Amaziah took *a.* and. 25:17
with good *a.* make war. *Pr* 20:18
and herein I give my *a.* *2 Cor* 8:10

advise, -ed

a. and see. *2 Sam* 24:13; *1 Chr* 21:12
how do ye *a.* that. *1 Ki* 12:6
with the well-*a.* is wisdom. *Pr* 13:10
a. to depart thence also. *Acts* 27:12

advisement

the lords upon *a.* sent. *1 Chr* 12:19

advocate

we have an *a.* with. *1 John* 2:1

Æ.—(*For proper names beginning with Æ, see* E)

afar, *usually joined with* **off**

[1] *The distance between place and place,* Gen 37:18. [2] *Estrangement from another,* Ps 38:11

saw the place *a. off.* *Gen* 22:4
brethren saw Joseph *a. off.* 37:18
and worship ye *a. off.* *Ex* 24:1
pitch the tabernacle *a. off.* 33:7
be in a journey *a. off.* *Num* 9:10
man of God saw her *a. off.* *2 Ki* 4:25
noise was heard *a. off.* *Ezra* 3:13
Jerusalem was heard *a. off.* *Neh* 12:43
my knowledge from *a.* *Job* 36:3
a man may behold it *a. off.* 25
and her eyes behold *a. off.* 39:29
them that are *a. off.* *Ps* 65:5
proud he knoweth *a. off.* 138:6
my thoughts *a. off.* 139:2
her food from *a.* *Pr* 31:14
shall carry her *a. off.* *Isa* 23:7
escape to the isles *a. off.* 66:19
and not a God *a. off*? *Jer* 23:23
save thee from *a.* 30:10; 46:27
declare it in the isles *a. off.* 31:10
get you *a. off,* dwell. 49:30
remember the Lord *a. off.* 51:50
rebuke strong nations *a. off.* *Mi* 4:3
Peter followed him *a. off.* *Mat* 26:58
Mark 14:54; *Luke* 22:54
beholding *a. off.* *Mat* 27:55
Mark 15:40
saw Jesus *a. off,* he. *Mark* 5:6
and seeing a fig-tree *a. off.* 11:13
seeth Abraham *a. off.* *Luke* 16:23
to all that are *a. off.* *Acts* 2:39
preached peace to you which were *a. off,* and to them that. *Eph* 2:17
seen the promises *a. off.* *Heb* 11:13
and cannot see *a. off.* *2 Pet* 1:9

see **far, stand, stood**

affairs

to God, and *a.* of the. *1 Chr* 26:32
he will guide his *a.* *Ps* 112:5*
Shadrach over *a.* of the. *Dan* 2:49
Jews whom thou set over *a.* 3:12
ye also may know my *a.* *Eph* 6:21
that ye might know our *a.* 22*
I may hear of your *a.* *Phil* 1:27
himself with the *a.* of life. *2 Tim* 2:4

affect, -ed, -eth

mine eye *a.* my heart. *Lam* 3:51
minds evil *a.* against. *Acts* 14:2
a. you, that ye might *a.* *Gal* 4:17*
good to be zealously *a.* in a. 18*

affection

a. to the house of God. *1 Chr* 29:3
natural *a.* *Rom* 1:31; *2 Tim* 3:3
a. is more abundant. *2 Cor* 7:15
set your *a.* on things. *Col* 3:2*
fornication, inordinate *a.* 5

affectionately

so being *a.* desirous of. *1 Thes* 2:8

affectioned

kindly *a.* one to another. *Rom* 12:10

affections

gave them up to vile *a.* *Rom* 1:26
the flesh with the *a.* *Gal* 5:24

affinity

Solomon made *a.* with. *1 Ki* 3:1
Jehoshaphat joined in *a.* *2 Chr* 18:1
should we join in *a.* *Ezra* 9:14

affirm

To maintain the truth of a thing, Acts 25:19; Tit 3:8.

as some *a.* that we say. *Rom* 3:8
nor whereof they *a.* *1 Tim* 1:7
things I will that thou *a.* *Tit* 3:8

affirmed

an hour after another *a.* *Luke* 22:59
Rhoda constantly *a.* that. *Acts* 12:15
and of Jesus, whom Paul *a.* 25:19

afflict, -est

shall *a.* them 400 years. *Gen* 15:13
if thou shalt *a.* my daughters. 31:50
task-masters to *a.* them. *Ex* 1:11
ye shall not *a.* any widow. 22:22
if thou *a.* them in any wise, and. 23
ye shall *a.* your souls. *Lev* 16:29
31; 23:27, 32; *Num* 29:7
Chittim shall *a.* Ashur. *Num* 24:24
binding oath to *a.* the soul. 30:13
we bind him to *a.* him. *Judg* 16:5
mightest be bound to *a.* thee. 6
to *a.* him, and his strength went. 19
of wickedness *a.* them. *2 Sam* 7:10
will for this *a.* the seed. *1 Ki* 11:39
thou dost *a.* *2 Chr* 6:26; *1 Ki* 8:35
we might *a.* ourselves. *Ezra* 8:21*
Almighty, he will not *a.* *Job* 37:23
how thou didst *a.* the. *Ps* 44:2
God shall hear and *a.* them. 55:19*
son of wickedness *a.* him. 89:22
O Lord, they *a.* thine heritage. 94:5
all them that *a.* my soul. 143:12
did more grievously *a.* her. *Isa* 9:1*
the hand of them that *a.* thee. 51:23
day for a man to *a.* his soul? 58:5
O Lord, wilt thou *a.* us? 64:12
to destroy and to *a.* *Jer* 31:28
the Lord doth not *a.* *Lam* 3:33
they *a.* the just, they. *Amos* 5:12
shall *a.* you from Hemath. 6:14
have afflicted, I will *a.* *Nah* 1:12
will undo all that *a.* thee. *Zeph* 3:19

afflicted

more they *a.* the more. *Ex* 1:12
shall not be *a.* that day. *Lev* 23:29
hast thou *a.* thy? *Num* 11:11*
the Egyptians *a.* us. *Deut* 26:6
the Almighty hath *a.* me. *Ruth* 1:21
and the *a.* people thou. *2 Sam* 22:28
a. in all . . . my father was *a.* *1 Ki* 2:26
rejected Israel and *a.* *2 Ki* 17:20
to him that is *a.* pity. *Job* 6:14*
loosed my cord, and *a.* me. 30:11
heareth the cry of the *a.* 34:28
wilt save the *a.* people. *Ps* 18:27
affliction of the *a.* 22:24
me, for I am desolate and *a.* 25:16
do justice to the *a.* and needy. 82:3
hast *a.* me with all thy waves. 88:7
am *a.* and ready to die from my. 15
days wherein thou hast *a.* us. 90:15
of their iniquities, are *a.* 107:17
I was greatly *a.* 116:10
before I was *a.* 119:67
for me that I have been *a.* 71
thou in faithfulness hast *a.* me. 75
I am *a.* very much, quicken me. 107
they *a.* me from youth. 129:1, 2
maintain the cause of the *a.* 140:12
all the days of the *a.* are. *Pr* 15:15
oppress the *a.* in the gate. 22:22
hateth those that are *a.* 26:28*
pervert the judgment of the *a.* 31:5
when at first he lightly *a.* *Isa* 9:1*
Lord will have mercy on his *a.* 49:13
hear now this, thou *a.* and. 51:21
him smitten of God and *a.* 53:4
he was oppressed, and was *a.* 7
O thou *a.* tossed with. 54:11
have we *a.* our souls? 58:3
if thou satisfy the *a.* soul. 10
sons of them that *a.* thee. 60:14
in all their affliction he was *a.* 63:9
sigh, her virgins are *a.* *Lam* 1:4
prosper, for the Lord hath *a.* her. 5
wherewith the Lord hath *a.* me. 12
gather her that I have *a.* *Mi* 4:6
I have *a.* I will afflict. *Nah* 1:12
leave in thee an *a.* people. *Zeph* 3:12
deliver you up to be *a.* *Mat* 24:9*
whether we be *a.* it is for. *2 Cor* 1:6
she have relieved the *a.* *1 Tim* 5:10
being destitute, *a.* and. *Heb* 11:37
be *a.* and mourn, and. *Jas* 4:9
is any among you *a.*? let. 5:13*

affliction

[1] *Adversity, trouble, or distress,* Job 5:6; Jonah 2:2. [2] *Outward oppression,* Ex 3:7; 14:31; Mark 4:17; Heb 10:32. [3] *Correction from God.*

Lord hath heard thy *a.* *Gen* 16:11
hath looked upon my *a.* 29:32
God hath seen mine *a.* and. 31:42
fruitful in the land of *a.* 41:52
a. of my people. *Ex* 3:7; *Acts* 7:34
bring you out of the *a.* of. *Ex* 3:17
he had looked on their *a.* 4:31
eat even the bread of *a.* *Deut* 16:3
1 Ki 22:27; *2 Chr* 18:26
looked on our *a.* *Deut* 26:7
indeed look on my *a.* *1 Sam* 1:11
Lord will look on my *a.* *2 Sam* 16:12*
the Lord saw the *a.* *2 Ki* 14:26
cry to thee in our *a.* *2 Chr* 20:9
Manasseh was in *a.* and. 33:12*
remnant are in great *a.* *Neh* 1:3
didst see the *a.* of our fathers. 9:9
though *a.* cometh not forth. *Job* 5:6
confusion, see thou mine *a.* 10:15
the days of *a.* have taken. 30:16
the days of *a.* prevented me. 27
they be holden in cords of *a.* 36:8
he delivereth the poor in his *a.* 15
hast thou chosen rather than *a.* 21
my *a.* and pain, forgive. *Ps* 25:18
and forgettest our *a.* and. 44:24
thou laidst *a.* upon our loins. 66:11*
mourneth by reason of *a.* 88:9
he regarded their *a.* 106:44*
being bound in *a.* and iron. 107:10
they are brought low through *a.* 39*
he the poor on high from *a.* 41
this is my comfort in my *a.* 119:50
then have perished in mine *a.* 92
consider mine *a.* and deliver me. 153
give you water of *a.* *Isa* 30:20

thee in the furnace of a. Isa 48:10
in all their a. he was afflicted. 63:9
publisheth a. from mount. Jer 4:15*
thee well in the time of a. 15:11
my refuge in the day of a. 16:19
why criest thou for thine a.? 30:15*
Moab's calamity is near, and a. 48:16
captivity because of a. Lam 1:3
remembered in the days of her a. 7
O Lord, behold mine a. 9
I am the man that hath seen a. 3:1
remembering my a. and my. 19
in their a. they will seek. Hos 5:15
grieved for the a. of. Amos 6:6
have looked on their a. Ob 13
cried by reason of my a. Jonah 2:2
a. shall not rise up the. Nah 1:9
tents of Cushan in a. Hab 3:7
helped forward the a. Zech 1:15
or came in, because of a. 8:10*
pass through the sea with a. 10:11
when a. ariseth for the. Mark 4:17*
for in those days shall be a. 13:19*
a dearth, and great a. Acts 7:11
out of much a. I wrote. 2 Cor 2:4
our light a. which is but for. 4:17
how that in a great trial of a. 8:2
supposing to add a. to. Phil 1:16
with me in my a. 4:14
the word in much a. 1 Thes 1:6
over you in all our a. 3:7
to suffer a. with people. Heb 11:25
the fatherless in their a. Jas 1:27
for an example of suffering a. 5:10*

afflictions

many are the a. of. Ps. 34:19
David, and all his a. 132:1
him out of all his a. Acts 7:10
saying, that bonds and a. 20:23
in much patience, in a. 2 Cor 6:4
behind of the a. of Christ. Col 1:24
be moved by these a. 1 Thes 3:3
be partakers of the a. 2 Tim 1:8*
known the a. which came to. 3:11*
watch in all things, endure a. 4:5*
a great fight of a. Heb 10:32*
were made a gazing-stock by a. 33
same a. accomplished 1 Pet 5:9*

affording

garners full, a. all. Ps 144:13

affright, -ed

shalt not be a. at them. Deut 7:21
with a loud voice to a. 2 Chr 32:18
that went before were a. Job 18:20
at fear, and is not a. 39:22*
panted, fearfulness a. me. Isa 21:4
burnt, and men of war a. Jer 51:32
they were a. Mark 16:5*; Luke 24:37
be not a. ye seek Jesus. Mark 16:6*
the remnant were a. Rev 11:13

afoot

many ran a. thither out. Mark 6:33
minding himself to go a. Acts 20:13*

afore

a. Isaiah was gone out. 2 Ki 20:4
which withereth a. it. Ps 129:6
a. the harvest when the. Isa 18:5
a. he that was escaped. Ezek 33:22
which he had promised a. Rom 1:2
he had a. prepared unto glory. 9:23
mystery, as I wrote a. in. Eph 3:3

aforehand

come a. to anoint my. Mark 14:8

aforetime

and a. I was as a tabret. Job 17:6*
my people went down a. Isa 52:4
also shall be as a. Jer 30:20
his God, as he did a. Dan 6:10
brought him that a. John 9:13
things were written a. Rom 15:4

afraid

money, they were a. Gen 42:35
they were a. to come. Ex 34:30
make you a. Lev 26:6; Job 11:19
why not a. to speak? Num 12:8
people of whom thou art a.
Deut 7:19
whosoever is fearful and a. Judg 7:3
the Philistines were a. 1 Sam 4:7
Saul was yet the more a. of. 18:29
now wast thou not a. to 2 Sam 1:14
people have made me a. 2 Sam 14:15
come on him, and make him a. 17:2
men made me a. 22:5; Ps 18:4
they all made us a. saying. Neh 6:9
I am a. of all my sorrows. Job 9:28
none shall make thee a. 11:19
his excellency make you a.? 13:11
let not thy dread make me a. 21
anguish shall make him a. 15:24
terrors shall make him a. on. 18:11
when I remember, I am a. 21:6*
when I consider, I am a. 23:15
terror shall not make thee a. 33:7
a. as a grasshopper. 39:20*
himself, the mighty are a. 41:25
what time I am a. I will. Ps 56:3
that dwell are a. at thy tokens. 65:8
saw thee, and they were a. 77:16
make them a. with thy storm. 83:15
I am a. of thy judgments. 119:120
none shall make them a. Isa 17:2
Ezek 34:28; Mi 4:4; Zeph 3:13
the sinners in Zion are a. Isa 33:14
ends of the earth were a. 41:5*
of whom hast thou been a. 57:11
none shall make him a. Jer 30:10
yet they were not a. nor. 36:24
Zedekiah said, I am a. of 38:19
men, of whom thou art a. 39:17
made them a. Ezek 39:26; Nah 2:11
dream, which made me a. Dan 4:5
mariners were a. Jonah 1:5, 10
made them a. because of. Hab 2:17
mind, were a. Mark 5:15; Luke 8:35
understood not, and were a.
Mark 9:32
followed, they were a. 10:32
any thing, for they were a. 16:8
they being a. wondered. Luke 8:25
they were all a. of Saul. Acts 9:26
me saw the light, and were a. 22:9*
I am a. of you, lest I. Gal 4:11
not a. of the king's. Heb 11:23
are not a. with any. 1 Pet 3:6
are not a. to speak evil. 2 Pet 2:10*

be **afraid**

neither be a. of. Deut 1:29; 31:6
behold we be a. here in. 1 Sam 23:3
be a. out of close. 2 Sam 22:46*
Ps 18:45*
hired that I should be a. Neh 6:13
thou be a. of destruction. Job 5:21
be ye a. of the sword, for. 19:29
of whom shall I be a.? Ps 27:1
their fear, nor be a. Isa 8:12; 44:8
maketh mention, shall be a. 19:17
that thou shouldest be a. 51:12
which is evil, be a. Rom 13:4

not be **afraid**

not be a. of the face of. Deut 1:17
thou shalt not be a. 7:18; 18:22
I will not be a. of ten. Ps 3:6
I will not be a. what man can. 56:11
thou shalt not be a. for the. 91:5
he shall not be a. of evil. 112:7
is established, he shall not be a. 8
liest down, shalt not be a. Pr 3:24
will trust and not be a. Isa 12:2
will not be a. of their voice. 31:4
and people not be a. Amos 3:6
wilt thou then not be a.? Rom 13:3

be not **afraid**

be not a. of them. Deut 20:1
Josh 11:6; Neh 4:14; Jer 10:5
Ezek 2:6; Luke 12:4
Saul said, be not a. 1 Sam 28:13
go down, be not a. 2 Ki 1:15
be not a. when one is. Ps 49:16
be not a. of sudden fear. Pr 3:25
voice, lift it up, be not a. Isa 40:9
be not a. of their faces. Jer 1:8
son of man be not a. Ezek 2:6
it is I, be not a. Mat 14:27
Mark 6:50; John 6:20
arise, be not a. Mat 17:7
be not a. go tell my brethren. 28:10
saith to the ruler, be not a.
Mark 5:36
be not a. but speak, and. Acts 18:9
be not a. of their terror. 1 Pet 3:14

sore **afraid**

and men were sore a. Gen 20:8
marched, they were sore a. Ex 14:10
Moab was sore a. of. Num 22:3
therefore we were sore a. Josh 9:24
Goliath, and were sore a.
1 Sam 17:24
on the earth, and was sore a. 28:20
was sore a. 31:4; 1 Chr 10:4
sorrow, and was very sore a. Neh 2:2
say, for they were sore a. Mark 9:6
and they were sore a. Luke 2:9

was **afraid**

thy voice, and I was a. Gen 3:10
I laughed not, for she was a. 18:15
then Jacob was greatly a. and 32:7
Moses hid his face, was a. Ex 3:6
I was a. of the anger. Deut 9:19
midnight the man was a. Ruth 3:8
Saul was a. 1 Sam 18:12, 15*
Ahimelech was a. at the. 21:1*
host of Philistines, he was a. 28:5
David was a. 2 Sam 6:9; 1 Chr 13:12
not go, for he was a. 1 Chr 21:30
which I was a. of, is come. Job 3:25
I was a. and durst not shew. 32:6*
Urijah heard it, he was a. Jer 26:21
when he came, was a. Dan 8:17
thy speech, and was a. Hab 3:2
was a. before my name. Mal 2:5*
Joseph was a. to go. Mat 2:22
the wind boisterous, was a. 14:30
I was a. and hid thy talent. 25:25
heard, he was the more a. John 19:8
Cornelius looked, he was a. Acts 10:4

afresh

crucify the Son of God a. Heb 6:6

after

a. I am waxed old. Gen 18:12
three months a. it was told. 38:24
ye seek not a. your. Num 15:39
not go a. other gods. Deut 6:14
that before it, or a. Josh 10:14
turned again a. Saul. 1 Sam 15:31
a. whom is the king come out? a. a
dog. 24:14
and a. make for thee. 1 Ki 17:13
opened till a. the sabbath. Neh 13:19
thou inquirest a. mine. Job 10:6
cried a. them, as a. a thief. 30:5
give them a. the work of. Ps 28:4
that shall come a. Eccl 1:11
judge a. the sight of eyes. Isa 11:3
a. it shall return to the. Ezek 46:17*
shall walk a. the Lord. Hos 11:10
a. I am risen again, I. Mat 26:32
which had seen him a. Mark 16:14
so then a. the Lord had spoken. 19
on the second sabbath a. Luke 6:1*
a. a little while another. 22:58
space of an hour a. another. 59
he might bear it a. Jesus. 23:26
a. the sop Satan entered. John 13:27
space of three hours a. Acts 5:7
which was 430 years a. Gal 3:17
to those that a. should. 2 Pet 2:6*

after *that*

and a. that he will let. Ex 3:20
her a. that she is defiled. Deut 24:4
avenged, and a. that I. Judg 15:7
a. that God was intreated for.
2 Sam 21:14
a. that I have spoken, Job 21:3
and a. that they go to the. Eccl 9:3
a. that I was turned. Jer 31:19
a. that have no more. Luke 12:4
a. that thou shalt cut it. 13:9*
a. that which is lost, until he. 15:4
a. that shall they come. Acts 7:7
a. that he was seen of. 1 Cor 15:6
and a. that he must be. Rev 20:3

after *this*

a. this Abraham buried. Gen 23:19
a. this David enquired. 2 Sam 2:1
a. this I will return. Acts 15:16

afternoon

they tarried till a. and. Judg 19:8*

afterward, -s

a. he will let you go. Ex 11:1
a. shalt thou be gathered. Num 31:2
a. shall thy hands be. Judg 7:11
the sacrifice, a. they eat. 1 Sam 9:13
a. David's heart smote him. 24:5
and a. we will speak. Job 18:2
guide me, and a. receive. Ps 73:24

deceit is sweet, but a. Pr 20:17
prepare thy work, and a. 24:27
a. shall find more favour. 28:23
wise man keepeth it in till a. 29:11*
a. shall the children of. Hos 3:5
a. I will pour out my Spirit. Joel 2:28
a. an hungered. Mat 4:2; Luke 4:2
seen it, repented not a. Mat 21:32
a. Jesus findeth him in. John 5:14
but thou shalt follow me a. 13:36
a. they that are Christ's. 1 Cor 15:23
the faith that should a. Gal 3:23
would not a. have spoken. Heb 4:8
a. it yieldeth the peaceable. 12:11
a. when he would have inherited. 17
a. destroyed them that. Jude 5

Agabus

one of them, named A. Acts 11:28
a prophet named A. 21:10

Agag

shall be higher than A. Num 24:7
the people spared A. 1 Sam 15:9
Samuel hewed A. in pieces. 33

Agagite, *see* Haman

again

I will not a. curse, nor a. Gen 8:21
but they shall come hither a. 15:16
a. feed and keep thy flock. 30:31
Judah knew her a. no more. 38:26
I will see a. thy face no. Ex 10:29
ye shall see them a. no more. 14:13
surely bring it back to him a. 23:4
will yet a. leave them in. Num 32:15
circumcise a. the children. Josh 5:2
and a. whom should. 2 Sam 16:19
child came into him a. 1 Ki 17:22
shall yet a. take root. 2 Ki 19:30
a. break thy commandments. Ezra 9:14
if ye do so a. I will lay. Neh 13:21
man die, shall he live a.? Job 14:14
revive us a. that thy. Ps 85:6
a. they minished and. 107:39
that they rise not up a. 140:10
that go to her return a. Pr 2:19
deliver him, thou must do it a. 19:19
a. there be wicked men. Eccl. 8:14
thou never be found a. Ezek 26:21
will not a. pass by. Amos 7:8; 8:2
shall fall, and never rise up a. 8:14
choose Jerusalem a. Zech 2:12
this water shall thirst a. John 4:13
spirit of bondage a. to. Rom 8:15
rejoice in the Lord, a. I. Phil 4:4
a. I will be to him a. Heb 1:5
and a. I will put my trust in. 2:13
begotten us a. to a lively. 1 Pet 1:3
see **born, bring, brought, come, turn, turned.**

against

hand will be a. every. Gen 16:12
river's brink a. he come. Ex 7:15*
set my face a. Lev 20:3; Deut 29:20
Urijah made it a. king. 2 Ki 16:11
a. whom hast thou exalted. 19:22
have pronounced a. it. Jer 25:13
I am a. your pillows. Ezek 13:20
a. his father. Mat 10:35; Luke 12:53
not with me, is a. me. Mat 12:30
which shall be spoken a. Luke 2:34
a. him with 20,000 to. 14:31
cannot be spoken a. Acts 19:36*
sect is every where spoken a. 28:22
see **another, God, him, Jerusalem, Israel, Lord, me, over, thee, them, us, you.**

Agar

bondage, which is A. Gal 4:24
A. is mount Sinai in Arabia. 25

agate, -s

an a. an amethyst. Ex 28:19; 39:12
make thy windows of a. Isa 54:12
in thy fairs with a. Ezek 27:16*

age

[1] *The whole continuance of a man's life,* Gen 47:28. [2] *Times past, present, or to come,* Eph 2:7; 3:5.

the whole a. of Jacob. Gen 47:28
eyes of Israel were dim for a. 48:10
from the a. of 50 years. Num 8:25
die in the flower of their a. 1 Sam 2:33
were set by reason of a. 1 Ki 14:4
from the a. of 30. 1 Chr 23:3
from the a. of twenty years and. 24
that stooped for a. 2 Chr 36:17*
thy grave in a full a. Job 5:26
I pray thee, of the former a. 8:8
thy a. shall be clearer than. 11:17*
my a. is as nothing before. Ps 39:5
my a. is departed and. Isa 38:12†
man with his staff for a. Zech 8:4
a. of 12 years. Mark 5:42; Luke 8:42
was of a great a. Luke 2:36
to be about 30 years of a. 3:23
he is of a. ask him. John 9:21, 23
pass the flower of her a. 1 Cor 7:36
belongs to them of full a. Heb 5:14*
delivered when she was past a. 11:11
see **old, stricken**

aged

was a very a. man. 2 Sam 19:32
the understanding of a. Job 12:20
grey-headed and very a. men. 15:10
and the a. arose and stood up. 29:8
neither do the a. understand. 32:9
a. with him that is full. Jer 6:11
the a. men be sober, grave. Tit 2:2
the a. women, that they be. 3
such an one as Paul the a. Philem 9

ages

in the a. to come he might. Eph 2:7
in other a. was not made. 3:5*
in the church through all a. 21*
which hath been hid from a. Col 1:26

ago

were lost three days a. 1 Sam 9:20
heard long a. 2 Ki 19:25; Isa 37:26
builded many years a. Ezra 5:11
that fashioned it long a. Isa 22:11
repented long a. Mat 11:21
Luke 10:13
long a. since this came. Mark 9:21
4 days a. I was fasting. Acts 10:30
how that a good while a. 15:17
be forward a year a. 2 Cor 8:10
Achaia was ready a year a. 9:2
a man above fourteen years a. 12:2

agone

(*Revised Version,* ago)
three days a. I fell sick. 1 Sam 30:13

agony

being in an a. he prayed. Luke 22:44

agree, -ed, -eth

[1] *To bargain with,* Mat 20:2, 13. [2] *To approve, or give consent to,* Acts 5:40. [3] *To be like,* Mark 14:70. [4] *To conspire, or resolve,* John 9:22.

together except they be a. Amos 3:3
a. with thine adversary. Mat 5:25
if two of you shall a. on. 18:19
when he had a. with labourers. 20:2
not a. with me for a penny? 13
a. not together. Mark 14:56, 59
art a Galilean, and thy speech a. 70*
out of the new, a. not. Luke 5:36
Jews had a. already. John 9:22
is it that ye have a. to. Acts 5:9
to him they a. and when they. 40
to this a. the words of the. 15:15
Jews have a. to desire. 23:20
when they a. not among. 28:25
blood, these a. in one. 1 John 5:8
a. to give their kingdom. Rev 17:17

agreement

make an a. by a. 2 Ki 18:31
Isa 36:16*
said, with hell are we at a. Isa 28:15
your a. with hell shall not stand. 18
of the north, to make an a. Dan 11:6
what a. hath the temple. 2 Cor 6:16

Agrippa

A. and Bernice came to. Acts 25:13
A. said, I would also hear the. 22
specially before thee, O king A. 26
for which hope's sake, king A. 26:7
A. believest thou the prophets? 27
A. said almost thou persuadest. 28

aground

met, they ran the ship a. Acts 27:41

ague

(*Revised Version,* fever)
terror and the burning a. Lev 26:16

Agur

the words of A. the son of. Pr 30:1

ah

nor say, a. so would. Ps 35:25*
a. sinful nation, a people. Isa. 1:4
a. I will ease me of mine. 24
said I, a. Lord God, I. Jer 1:6
a. Lord God, thou hast. 4:10
a. Lord God, the prophets. 14:13
a. brother, a. sister, a. Lord, a. 22:18
a. Lord, thou hast made the. 32:17
lament thee, saying, a. Lord. 34:5
a. Lord, my soul hath not. Ezek 4:14
a. Lord, wilt thou destroy the. 9:8
a. Lord, wilt thou make a full. 11:13
a. Lord, they say of me, doth. 20:49
a. the sword is made bright, it. 21:15
a. thou that destroyest. Mark 15:29*

aha

they said, a. our eye. Ps 35:21
desolate, that say unto me a. 40.15
turned back that say a. a. 70:3
a. I am warm, I have. Isa 44:16
a. against my sanctuary. Ezek. 25:3
because Tyrus hath said, a. 26:2
a. the ancient places are ours. 36:2

Ahab

A. did evil above all. 1 Ki 16:30
A. did more to provoke Lord. 33
Elijah, go shew thyself to A. 18:1
A. went one way, and Obadiah. 6
deliver me into the hand of A. 9
so A. went up to eat and to drink. 42
Elijah ran before A. to the. 46
there came a prophet to A. 20:13
A. came to his house heavy. 21:4
I will cut off from A. him that. 21
there was none like A. who did. 25
seest thou how A. humbleth. 29
persuade A. that he may go up and fall at? 22:20; 2 Chr 18:19
so A. slept with his fathers. 1 Ki 22:40
after death of A. 2 Ki 1:1; 3:5
Jeroboam walked as did the house of A. for the daughter of A. 8:18, 27
thou shalt smite the house of A. 9:7
for the whole house of A. shall. 8
when I and thou rode after A. 25
slew all that remained of A. 10:11
Manasseh did as A. king of. 21:3
the plummet of house of A. 13
of the house of A. 2 Chr. 21:13
saith the Lord of A. son. Jer 29:21
the Lord make thee like A. 22
works of the house of A. Mi 6:16

Ahasuerus

in the reign of A. wrote. Ezra 4:6
this is A. which reigned. Esth 1:1
Esther was taken unto king A. 2:16
to lay hand on the king A. 21; 6:2
in the name of A. was it. 3:12; 8:10
A. gave to Esther the house. 8:1
the Jew was next to king A. 10:3
first year of Darius son of A. Dan 9:1

Ahava

the river that runneth to A. Ezra 8:15
a fast at A. 21
then we departed from A. 31

Ahaz

A. was twenty years old when he began to. 2 Ki 16:2; 2 Chr 28:1
made an altar against A. 2 Ki 16:11
in the dial of A. 20:11; Isa 38:8
the altars of A. did Josiah. 2 Ki 23:12
Micah, Pithon, A. 1 Chr 8:35; 9:41
Judah low, because of A. 2 Chr 28:19
this is that king, A. 22
A. gathered vessels. 24
the vision in days of A. Isa 1:1
Hos 1:1; Mi 1:1
go forth to meet A. Isa 7:3
the Lord spake to A. 10

Ahaziah

A. reigned in. 1 Ki 22:40; 2 Ki 8:24
A. fell through a lattice. 2 Ki 1:2
A. king of Judah went down. 8:29
A. there is treachery, O A. 9:23

A. fled, and Jehu followed. *2 Ki* 9:27
we are the brethren of *A.* 10:13
did join with *A.* *2 Chr* 20:35
destruction of *A.* was of God. 22:7
house of *A.* had no power to keep. 9

Ahiah

A. son of Ahitub, the. *1 Sam* 14:3
Saul said to *A.* bring hither the. 18
Elihoreph and *A.* were. *1 Ki* 4:3

Ahijah

the prophet *A.* found. *1 Ki* 11:29
his saying, which the Lord spake by *A.* 12:15; *2 Chr* 10:15
there is *A.* which told me I. *1 Ki* 14:2
wife came to the house of *A.* 4
it was so, when *A.* heard the. 6
Baasha son of *A.* conspired 15:27
Jerahmeel, Hezron, *A.* *1 Chr* 2:25
David's valiant men, *A.* the. 11:36
over treasury of Levites *A.* 26:20
Solomon in prophecy of *A.* *2 Chr* 9:29
sealed the covenant, *A.* *Neh* 10:26

Ahikam

commanded *A.* the son of Shaphan. *2 Ki* 22:12; *2 Chr* 34:20
Gedaliah the son of *A.* *2 Ki* 25:22
the hand of *A.* was with. *Jer* 26:24
to Gedaliah the son of *A.* 40:6

see **Gedaliah**

Ahimaaz

was the daughter of *A.* *1 Sam* 14:50
Jonathan and *A.* staid. *2 Sam* 17:17
is like the running of *A.* son. 18:27
A. was in Naphtali, he. *1 Ki* 4:15
begat Zadok, and Zadok *A.* *1 Chr* 6:8

Ahiman

A. was of the children. *Num* 13:22
Judah slew *A.* *Judg* 1:10
porters, *A.* *1 Chr* 9:17

Ahimelech

A. was afraid at the. *1 Sam* 21:1
the son of Jesse coming to *A.* 22:9
thou shalt surely die, *A.* 16
David said to *A.* who will go? 26:6
Zadok and *A.* priests. *2 Sam* 8:17; *1 Chr* 18:16
A. of the sons of Ithamar. *1 Chr* 24:3
scribe wrote them before *A.* 6
in the presence of David and *A.* 31

Ahinoam

Saul's wife was *A.* *1 Sam* 14:50
David also took *A.* of Jezreel. 25:43

see **Abigail**

Ahio

A. drave the cart. *2 Sam* 6:3; *1 Chr* 13:7

Ahisamach

both he and the son of *A.* *Ex* 35:34

Ahithophel

Absalom sent for *A.* *2 Sam* 15:12
Lord, turn the counsel of *A.* into. 31
thou defeat the counsel of *A.* 34
to Jerusal, and *A.* with him. 16:15
counsel of *A.* was as if a man. 23
the counsel of *A.* is not good. 17:7
thus did *A.* counsel Absalom. 15
A. saw that his counsel was not. 23
A. was the king's. 1 *Chr* 27:33

Ahitub

hear now, thou son of *A.* *1 Sam* 22:12
son of *A.* *2 Sam* 8:17; *1 Chr* 18:16

Aholah, Aholibah

is *A.* Jerusalem Aholibah. *Ezek* 23:4
judge *A.* and Aholibah? 36

Aholiab

wrought Bezaleel and *A.* *Exod* 36:1

Aholibamah

Esau took to wife *A.* *Gen* 36:2
A. bare Jeush. 5

Ai, *or* Hai

between Beth-el and *A.* *Gen* 13:3
fled before the men of *A.* *Josh* 7:4
go up to *A.* 8:1
Gibeon was greater than *A.* 10:2
men of Beth-el and *A.* *Ezra* 2:28; *Neh* 7:32
howl, O Heshbon, for *A.* *Jer* 49:3

Aiath

he is come to *A.* he is. *Isa* 10:28

aided

a. him in the killing of. *Judg* 9:24

ailed, -eth

what *a.* thee, Hagar? *Gen* 21:17
to Micah, what *a.* thee? *Judg* 18:23
a. the people to weep? *1 Sam* 11:5
said, what *a.* *2 Sam* 14:5; *2 Ki* 6:28
what *a.* thee, O sea, that? *Ps* 114:5
what *a.* thee now, that. *Isa* 22:1

air

nor birds of the *a.* to. *2 Sam* 21:10
no *a.* can come between. *Job* 41:16
way of an eagle in the *a.* *Pr* 30:19
bird of the *a.* shall carry. *Eccl* 10:20
the birds of the *a.* have. *Mat.* 8:20*
the birds of the *a.* come and lodge in. 13:32*; *Mark* 4:32*; *Luke* 9:58*
they threw dust into the *a.* *Acts* 22:23
I, not as one that beateth the *a.* *1 Cor* 9:26
for ye shall speak into the *a.* 14:9
prince of the power of the *a.* *Eph* 2:2
meet the Lord in the *a.* *1 Thes* 4:17
the sun and the *a.* were. *Rev* 9:2
poured out his vial into the *a.* 16:17

see **fowls**

Ajalon

moon, in the valley of *A.* *Josh* 10:12

alabaster

having an *a.* box. *Mat* 26:7; *Mark* 14:3

alarm

blow an *a.* then the. *Num* 10:5, 6
blow, but shall not sound an *a.* 7
go to war, then ye shall blow an *a.* 9
trumpets to cry an *a.* *2 Chr* 13:12
O my soul, the *a.* of war. *Jer* 4:19
day is come, I will cause an *a.* 49:2
sound an *a.* in my holy. *Joel* 2:1
a day of *a.* against the. *Zeph* 1:16

alas

Aaron said to Moses, *a.* *Num* 12:11
a. who shall live when God? 24:23
Joshua said, *a.* O Lord, *Josh* 7:7
a. because I have seen an. *Judg* 6:22
a. daughter, thou hast brought. 11:35
mourned over him, *a.* *1 Ki* 13:30
a. that the Lord hath. *2 Ki* 3:10
he cried *a.* master, for it was. 6:5
servant said, *a.* my master, how. 15
a. for that day is great. *Jer* 30:7
with thy foot, and say *a.* *Ezek* 6:11
a. for the day, for the. *Joel* 1:15
say in the highways, *a.* *Amos* 5:16
a. *a.* that great city, Babylon *Rev.* 18:10*, 16, 19*

albeit

the Lord saith, *a.* I have. *Ezek* 13:7
a. I say not, how thou. *Philem* 19

Alexander

Simon the father of *A.* *Mark* 15:21
Annas, Caiaphas, *A.* were. *Acts* 4:6
they drew *A.* out of the. 19:33
is Hymeneus and *A.* *1 Tim* 1:20
A. the copper smith did. *2 Tim* 4:14

Alexandria, -ans

of the Libertines and *A.* *Acts* 6:9
named Apollos, born at *A.* 18:24
centurion found a ship of *A.* 27:6

alien, -s

an *a.* in a strange land. *Ex* 18:3
mayest sell it to an *a.* *Deut* 14:21
I am an *a.* in their sight. *Job* 19:15
a. to my mother's children. *Ps* 69:8
sons of the *a.* shall be. *Isa* 61:5
houses are turned to *a.* *Lam* 5:2
a. from the commonwealth. *Eph* 2:12
flight the armies of *a.* *Heb* 11:34

alienate, -ed

her mind was *a.* from. *Ezek* 23:17
mind was *a.* from her as from. 18
from whom thy mind is *a.* 22, 28
they shall not *a.* the first fruits. 48:14
a. from the life of God. *Eph* 4:18
sometimes *a.* enemies. *Col* 1:21

alike

and clean eat *a.* *Deut* 12:22; 15:22
they shall part *a.* *1 Sam* 30:24
they shall lie down *a.* in. *Job* 21:26
fashioneth their hearts *a.* *Ps.* 33:15*
and light are both *a.* *Ps* 139:12
both are *a.* abomination to. *Pr* 20:10
a contentious woman are *a.* 27:15
all things come *a.* to all. *Eccl* 9:2
they both shall be *a.* good. 11:6
esteemeth every day *a.* *Rom* 14:5

alive

[1] *Naturally,* Gen 43:27. [2] *Supernaturally, being raised from the dead,* Luke 24:23. [3] *Spiritually,* Rom 6:11.

Noah only remained *a.* *Gen* 7:23
kill me, and save thee *a.* 12:12
day, to save much people *a.* 50:20
the men children *a.* *Ex* 1:17, 18
every daughter ye shall save *a.* 22
theft be found in his hand *a.* 22:4
Aaron's sons left *a.* *Lev* 10:16
command to take two birds *a.* 14:4
scapegoat shall be presented *a.* 16:10
are left *a.* of you, I will send. 26:36
they went down *a.* into. *Num* 16:33
Og, till there was none left *a.* 21:35
slain thee, and saved her *a.* 22:33
ye saved all the women *a.*? 31:15
are *a.* every one of you. *Deut* 4:4
who are all of us *a.* here this. 5:3
he might preserve us *a.* at. 6:24
a. nothing that breatheth. 20:16
and I make *a.* 32:39; *1 Sam* 2:6
will save *a.* my father. *Josh* 2:13
saved Rahab the harlot *a.* 6:25
the king of Ai they took *a.* 8:23
Lord hath kept me *a.* as he. 14:10
if ye had saved them *a.* I. *Judg* 8:19
which they had saved *a.* 21:14
Agag the king of Amalek *a.* *1 Sam* 15:8
left neither man nor woman *a.* 27:9
horses and mules *a.* *1 Ki* 18:5
peace or war take them *a.* 20:18
Naboth is not *a.* but dead. 21:15
God, to kill and make *a.*? *2 Ki* 5:7
if they save us *a.* we shall live. 7:4
out we shall catch them *a.* 12
a. and they took them *a.* 10:14
ten thousand left *a.* *2 Chr* 25:12
thou hast kept me *a.* *Ps* 30:3
let us swallow them up *a.* *Pr* 1:12
fatherless I will preserve *a.* *Jer* 49:11
will ye save the souls *a.*? *Ezek* 13:18
save the souls *a.* that should. 19
right, he shall save his soul *a.* 18:27
whom he would, he kept *a.* *Dan* 5:19
heard that he was *a.* *Mark* 16:11
was dead and is *a.* *Luke* 15:24, 32
angels who said he was *a.* 24:23
shewed himself *a.* after his. *Acts* 1:3
the widows, presented her *a.* 9:41
they brought the young man *a.* 20:12
whom Paul affirmed to be *a.* 25:19
a. to God through Christ. *Rom* 6:11
God, as those that are *a.* from. 13
for I was *a.* without the law. 7:9
so in Christ shall all be made *a.* *1 Cor* 15:22
are *a.* and remain. *1 Thes* 4:15, 17
and behold I am *a.* for. *Rev* 1:18
last, which was dead, and is *a.* 2:8
both cast *a.* into a lake of fire. 19:20

***keep* alive, *see* keep**

***yet* alive**

is your father *yet a.*? *Gen* 43:7
is he *yet a.*? 27
he is well, he is *yet a.* 28
saying, Joseph is *yet a.* 45:26, 28
die, because thou art *yet a.* 46:30
see whether they be *yet a.* *Ex* 4:18
I am *yet a.* with you. *Deut* 31:27
child was *yet a.* *2 Sam* 12:18; 21, 22
while he was *yet a.* in the. 18:14
is he *yet a.*? he is my. *1 Ki* 20:32
living which are *yet a.* *Eccl* 4:2
although they were *yet a.* *Ezek* 7:13
said, while he was yet *a.* *Mat* 27:63

all

surely die, thou and *a.* *Gen* 20:7
to him hath he given *a.* that. 24:36
Laban said, *a.* that thou. 31:43
Jacob loved Joseph more than *a.* 37:3

Lord made *a.* he did to. *Gen* 39:3
we are *a.* one man's sons, we. 42:11
lest thou and *a.* thou hast. 45:11
the God which fed me *a.* my. 48:15
earth, sea, and *a.* in them. *Ex* 20:11
I will make *a.* my goodness. 33:19
a. that come into the tent. *Num* 19:14
and shalt not see them *a.* 23:13
are *a.* of us here alive. *Deut* 5:3
days shalt thou labour and do *a.* 13
ye stand *a.* of you before the? 29:10
a. came to pass. *Josh* 21:45; 23:14
plague was on you *a.* *1 Sam* 6:4
I will tell thee *a.* that is in. 9:19
Samuel said, are here *a.* thy? 16:11
and without fail recover *a.* 30:8
are *a.* that pertained to. *2 Sam* 16:4
away dung till it be *a.* *1 Ki* 14:10
Omri did worse than *a.* before. 16:25
lord, I am thine, and *a.* that. 20:4
the son of Uzzi, *a.* of. *1 Chr* 7:3
is against *a.* that forsake. *Ezra* 8:22
thou preservest them *a.* and. *Neh* 9:6
comforters are ye *a.* *Job* 16:2
for they *a.* are the work of. 34:19
a. gone aside, *a.* become. *Ps* 14:3
a. my bones, they stare upon. 22:17
delivereth him out of them *a.* 34:19
Lord, *a.* my desire is before. 38:9
a. this is come upon us, yet. 44:17
mine adversaries are *a.* 69:19
these wait *a.* on thee, that. 104:27
they continue, for *a.* are thy. 119:91
cast in thy lot, let us *a* have. *Pr* 1:14
Lord is the maker of them *a.* 22:2
a. are of dust, *a.* turn to. *Eccl* 3:20
behold, see, we are *a.* thy. *Isa* 64:9
a. adulterers. *Jer* 9:2; *Hos* 7:4
a. of them mourning. *Ezek* 7:16
a. of them in the land shall. 20:40
king shall be king to them *a.* 37:22
son of man, declare *a.* that. 40:4
shew them *a.* the forms, *a.* the. 43:11
among them *a.* none. *Dan* 1:19
been a rebuker of them *a.* *Hos* 5:2
cut them in the head *a.* *Amos* 9:1
city, it is *a.* full of lies. *Nah* 3:1
have we not *a.* one Father. *Mal* 2:10
bring *a.* the tithes into the. 3:10*
pass from the law till *a.* *Mat* 5:18
sisters, are they not *a.* 13:56
she be, for they *a.* had her. 22:28
than *a.* burnt-offerings. *Mark* 12:33
cast in *a.* even *a.* 44; *Luke* 21:4
thou worship me, *a.* shall. *Luke* 4:7
looking round about on them *a.* 6:10
they were *a.* waiting for him. 8:40
except ye repent, ye shall *a.* 13:3
he said, son *a.* that I have is. 15:31
ye, when ye have done *a.* say. 17:10
sell *a.* that thou hast, and. 18:22
of his fulness have *a.* we. *John* 1:16
woman said, he told me *a.* 4:39
saith, ye are clean, but not *a.* 13:10
that they *a.* may be one, as. 17:21
grace was upon them *a.* *Acts* 4:33
we are *a.* here present before 10:33
he exhorted them *a.* to cleave. 11:23
do thyself no harm, we are *a.* 16:28
zealous towards God, as ye *a.* 22:3
but also *a.* that hear me this. 26:29
thanks in presence of them *a.* 27:35
through Jesus Christ for you *a.* *Rom* 1:8
delivered him up for us *a.* 8:32
a. are yours, and ye. *1 Cor* 3:22
more abundantly than they *a.* 15:10
concluded *a.* under sin. *Gal* 3:22
but I have *a.* and abound. *Phil* 4:18
that they *a.* might be. *2 Thes* 2:12
out of them *a.* the Lord. *2 Tim* 3:11
they not *a.* ministering. *Heb* 1:14
chastisement, whereof *a.* are. 12:8
be ye *a.* of one mind. *1 Pet* 3:8
that *a.* should come to. *2 Pet* 3:9
that they were not *a.* of. *1 John* 2:19

above **all**, *see* **above**

according to **all**

Noah did *ac. to a.* *Gen* 6:22; 7:5
according to a. the Lord. *Ex* 31:11
36:1; 39:32, 42; 40:16; *Num* 2:34
8:20; 9:5; 29:40; *Deut* 1:3, 41
took the land *ac. to a.* *Josh* 11:23
given rest *ac. to a.* that. *1 Ki* 8:56
shalt reign *ac. to a.* that thy. 11:37
ac. to a. his father had done. 22:53
2 Ki 23:32, 37; 24:9, 19
2 Chr 26:4; 27:2
done *ac. to a.* that was. *2 Ki* 10:30
ac to a. David. 18:3; *2 Chr* 29:2
ac. to a. these words, *ac. to a.* this. *1 Chr* 17:15
think . . . for good, *ac. to a. Neh* 5:19
ac. to a. his wondrous. *Jer* 21:2
ac. to a. that the Lord shall. 42:20
ac. to a. that Babylon hath. 50:29
ac. to a. that he hath. *Ezek* 24:24
ac. to a. thy righteousness. *Dan* 9:16

after **all**

not to do *after a.* their. *Deut* 20:18
the word to do *after a.* 2 Chr 34:21
after a. that is come on. *Ezra* 9:13
after a. thy wickedness. *Ezek* 16:23
after a. these things do. *Mat* 6:32
for he longed *after* you *a.* *Phil* 2:26

at **all**

delivered thy people *at a.* *Ex* 5:23
afflict, and they cry *at a.* to. 22:23
if he will *at a.* redeem. *Lev* 27:13*
I now any power *at a.* *Num* 22:38
if thou do *at a.* forget. *Deut* 8:19*
if thy father *at a.* miss. *1 Sam* 20:6
if ye shall *at a.* turn. *1 Ki* 9:6*
not save them *at a.* *Jer* 11:12
mind shall not be *at a.* *Ezek* 20:32
most High, none *at a.* *Hos* 11:7
weep ye not *at a.* roll. *Mi* 1:10
Lord will not *at a.* acquit. *Nah* 1:3
have no power *at a.* *John* 19:11
his will was not *at a.* *1 Cor* 16:12
him is no darkness *at a.* *1 John* 1:5
be found no more *at a.* *Rev* 18:21
shall be heard no more *at a.* 22

before **all**

before a. that went in at. *Gen* 23:18
before a. the people I will. *Lev* 10:3
I have chosen *before a.* *2 Chr* 33:7
an honour *before a.* *Jer* 33:9
denied *before* them *a.* *Mat* 26:70
to Peter *before* them *a.* *Gal* 2:14
sin rebuke *before a.* that. *1 Tim* 5:20

for **all**

Levites *for a.* first-born. *Num* 8:18
for a. that do so. *Deut* 22:5; 25:16
hide my face in that day *for a.* 31:18
for a. his enemies, he. *Ps* 10:5
for a. this they sinned still. 78:32
what render to the Lord *for a.* 116:12
profit of the earth is *for a.* *Eccl* 5:9
for a. these God will bring thee. 11:9
hath received double *for a.* *Isa* 40:2
alas *for a.* the evil. *Ezek* 6:11
loathe yourselves *for a.* 20:43
and in it was meat *for a.* *Dan* 4:21
for a. the evils Herod. *Luke* 3:19
God of the living, *for a.* live. 20:38
for a. have sinned and. *Rom* 3:23
if one died *for a.* then. *2 Cor* 5:14
for a. seek their own, not. *Phil* 2:21
himself a ransom *for a.* *1 Tim* 2:6
for a. shall know me. *Heb* 8:11
the body of Christ once *for a.* 10:10

from **all**

redeemed me *from a.* *Gen* 48:16
be clean *from a.* your. *Lev* 16:30
and delivered me *from a.* *Ps* 34:4
from a lands whither he. *Jer* 16:15
diverse *from a.* the beasts. *Dan* 7:7
seventh day *from a.* works. *Heb* 4:4

in **all**

in a. that Sarah hath said. *Gen* 21:12
God is with thee *in a.* that thou. 22
ye may prosper *in a.* *Deut* 29:9
obeyed my voice *in a.* *Josh* 22:2
thirty and seven *in a.* *2 Sam* 23:39
thou mayest prosper *in a.* *1 Ki* 2:3
afflicted *in a.* my father was. 26
Zerah, five of them *in a.* *1 Chr* 2:6
just *in a.* that is brought. *Neh* 9:33
God is not *in a.* his. *Ps* 10:4
in a. thy ways acknowledge. *Pr* 3:6
nothing *in a.* his dominion. *Isa* 39:2
in a. their afflictions he was. 63:9
have done evil *in a.* they. *Jer* 38:9
in a. your doings your. *Ezek* 21:24
in a. my labours shall find. *Hos* 12:8
in a. in the ship 276 souls. *Acts* 27:37
in a. these more than. *Rom* 8:37
God worketh all *in a.* *1 Cor* 12:6
that God may be all *in a.* 15:28
him that filleth all *in a.* *Eph* 1:23
but Christ is all and *in a.* *Col* 3:11
to be admired *in a.* *2 Thes* 1:10
is honourable *in a.* *Heb* 13:4
as also *in a.* his epistles. *2 Pet* 3:16

all *night, see* **night**

of **all**

took them wives *of a.* *Gen* 6:2
him tithes *of a.* 14:20; *Heb* 7:2
of a. that thou shalt give. *Gen* 28:22
nothing die *of a.* that is. *Ex* 9:4
not a word *of a.* which *Josh* 8:35
of a. I said to the. *Judg* 13:13
shall hands *of a.* with. *2 Sam* 16:21
Jehu said, to which *of a.* *2 Ki* 9:5
let nothing fail *of a.* thou. *Esth* 6:10
so are the paths *of a.* that. *Job* 8:13
he wanteth nothing *of a.* *Eccl.* 6:2
if they be ashamed *of a.* *Ezek* 43:11
you only have I known *of a.* *Amos* 3:2
be servant *of a.* *Mark* 9:35; 10:44
of a. which hath given. *John* 6:39
Christ, he is Lord *of a.* *Acts* 10:36
of a. judged *of a.* *1 Cor* 14:24
heir, though he be lord *of a.* *Gal* 4:1
God who is Father *of a.* *Eph.* 4:6
to God the Judge *of a.* *Heb* 12:23
one point, he is guilty *of a.* *Jas* 2:10

on or upon **all**

of the Lord was *upon a.* *Gen* 39:5
for *upon a.* the glory shall. *Isa* 4:5
set thy heart *upon a.* that. *Ezek* 40:4
unto all, and *upon a.* them. *Rom* 3:22
might have mercy *upon a.* 11:32
execute judgment *upon a.* *Jude* 15
temptation shall come *upon a.* *Rev* 3:10

over **all**

mayest reign *over a.* *2 Sam* 3:21
and thou reignest *over a.* *1 Chr* 29:12
kingdom ruleth *over a.* *Ps* 103:19
ruler *over a.* *Mat* 24:47; *Luke* 12:44
given him power *over a.* *John* 17:2
who is *over a.* God blessed. *Rom* 9:5
the same Lord *over a.* is rich. 10:12

all, *that he had*

him and *a. that he had.* *Gen* 12:20
of Egypt, and *a. that he had.* 13:1
Abraham gave *a. that he had.* 25:5
Jacob fled with *a. that he had.* 31:21
a. that he had he put into. 39:4
Lord was on *a. that he had.* 5
sold, *a. that he had.* *Mat* 18:25
spent *a. that she had.* *Mark* 5:26
cast in *a. that she had.* 12:44
Luke 21:4

all *these*

he took to him *a. these.* *Gen* 15:10
Jacob said, *a. these* things. 42:36
a. these are the twelve tribes. 49:28
God spake *a. these* words. *Ex.* 20:1
not that in *a. these.* *Job* 12:9
for *a. these* nations are. *Jer* 9:26
shall not *a. these* take. *Hab* 2:6
a. these shall. *Mat* 6:33; *Luke* 12:31
a. these are the beginning. *Mat* 24:8
a. these evil things. *Mark* 7:23
are not *a. these* which. *Acts* 2:7
a. these worketh that. *1 Cor* 12:11
now you put off *a. these.* *Col* 3:8
a. these died in faith, not. *Heb* 11:13

all *the while*

a. the while David. *1 Sam* 22:4
nothing missing *a. the while.* 25:7
manner *a the while* he. 27:11
a. the while my breath is. *Job* 27:3*

all *this*

hath shewed thee *a. this.* *Gen* 41:39
Lord hath not done *a. this.* *Deut* 32:27
is *a. this* befallen us? *Judg* 6:13
knew nothing of *a. this.* *1 Sam* 22:15
hand of Joab in *a. this*? *2 Sam* 14:19
a. this the Lord made. *1 Chr* 28:19
after *a. this* the Lord. *2 Chr* 21:18
a. this continued till the. 29:28
a. this was a burnt-. *Ezra* 8:35

because of a. this we. Neh 9:38
yet a. this availeth me. Esth 5:13
a. this Job sinned. Job 1:22; 2:10
lo, mine eye hath seen a. this. 13:1
a. this is come upon us, yet. Ps 44:17
for a. this they sinned still. 78:32
a. this have I proved by. Eccl 7:23
a. this have I seen, and applied. 8:9
a. this I considered in my heart, to declare a. this. 9:1
for a. this his anger is not. Isa 5:25
9:12, 17, 21; 10:4
thou hast heard, see a. this. 48:6
a. this came upon. Dan 4:28
though thou knewest a. this. 5:22
asked him the truth of a. this. 7:16
nor seek him for a. this. Hos 7:10
of Jacob is a. this. Mi 1:5
a. this was done that the prophets might be. Mat 1:22; 21:4; 26:56
a. this there is a gulf. Luke 16:26
besides a. this to-day is. 24:21

to or *unto* **all**

the Lord is good to a. and. Ps 145:9
event happeneth to a. Eccl 2:14
9:3, 11
things come alike to a. one. 9:2
so is Pharaoh to a. that. Isa 36:6
I say unto a. watch. Mark 13:37
to us, or even to a.? Luke 12:41
the promise is to a. that. Acts 2:39
manifest to a. that dwell in. 4:16
Lord is rich unto a. that. Rom 10:12
render therefore to a. their. 13:7
myself a servant unto a. 1 Cor 9:19
profiting may appear to a. 1 Tim 4:15

with **all**

with a. that appertain. Num 16:30
Lord with a. thy heart, with a. thy.
Deut 6:5; 11:13; Mat 22:37
with a. the children of. 2 Chr 25:7
with a. thy getting, get. Pr 4:7
feared God with a. Acts 10:2; 16:34
with a. that in every place. 1 Cor 1:2
and continue with you a. Phil 1:25
I joy and rejoice with you a. 2:17

all *ye*

a. ye assemble yourselves. Isa 48:14
behold a. ye that kindle a. 50:11
be glad with her, a. ye that. 66:10
hear the word, a. ye of. Jer 29:20
it nothing to you, a. ye? Lam 1:12
come to me, a. ye that. Mat 11:28
one is your master; and a. ye. 23:8
a. ye shall be. 26:31; Mark 14:27
a. ye that dwell at. Acts 2:14
see further other usual substantives: **congregation, day, earth, Israel, men, people, things,** *etc.*

alleging

a. Christ must needs. Acts 17:3

allegory

which things are an a. for. Gal 4:24

alleluiah

(*Revised Version*, hallelujah)
I heard a great voice, saying, a.
Rev 19:1, 3, 4, 6

allied

Eliashib the priest was a. Neh 13:4

allow

that ye a. the deeds. Luke 11:48*
they themselves also a. Acts 24:15*
that which I do, I a. not. Rom 7:15*

allowance

his a. was a continual a. 2 Ki 25:30

allowed, -eth

(*Revised Version*, approved, -eth)
that thing which he a. Rom 14:22
but as we were a. of. 1 Thes 2:4

allure

I will a. and bring her into. Hos 2:14
they a. through the lusts. 2 Pet 2:18

almighty

I am the a. God, walk. Gen 17:1
God a. bless thee, and make. 28:3
I am God a. be fruitful and. 35:11
God a give you mercy before. 43:14
God a. appeared to me at Luz. 48:3
by the a. who shall bless thee. 49:25
Abram by the name God a. Ex 6:3
the vision of the a. Num 24:4, 16
for the a. hath dealt. Ruth 1:20
seeing the a. hath afflicted me. 21
the chastening of the a. Job 5:17
for the arrows of the a. are. 6:4
he forsaketh the fear of the a. 14
or doth the a. pervert justice? 8:3
make thy supplication to the a. 5
canst thou find out the a.? 11:7
surely I would speak to the a. 13:3
himself against the a. 15:25
what is the a. that we? 21:15
drink of the wrath of the a. 20
is it any pleasure to the a.? 22:3
which said, what can the a. do? 17
if thou return to the a. thou shalt. 23
yea, the a. shall be thy defence. 25
thou have thy delight in the a. 26
my heart soft, and the a. 23:16
times are not hid from the a. 24:1
and the a. who hath vexed my. 27:2
will he delight himself in the a.? 10
with the a. will I not conceal. 11
which they shall receive of the a. 13
when the a. was yet with me. 29:5
what inheritance of the a.? 31:2
my desire is, that the a. would. 35
inspiration of the a. giveth. 32:8
and the breath of the a. hath. 33:4
far be it from the a. to. 34:10
neither will the a. pervert. 12
the a. will not regard vanity. 35:13
touching the a. we cannot. 37:23
contendeth with the a. instruct. 40:2
when the a. scattered. Ps 68:14
under the shadow of the a. 91:1
as destruction from the a. Isa 13:6
the voice of the a. Ezek 1:24; 10:5
as destruction from the a. Joel 1:15
sons, saith the Lord a. 2 Cor 6:18
was, and is to come, the a. Rev 1:8
Lord God a. which was. 4:8; 11:17
Lord a. just and true are. 15:3; 16:7
of that great day of God a. 16:14
wine-press of wrath of the a. 19:15
God a. and the Lamb are. 21:22

almond, -s

spices, myrrh, nuts, and a. Gen 43:11
made like to a. Ex 25:33*, 34*
37:19, 20*
Aaron for Levi yielded a. Num 17:8
when the a. tree shall. Eccl 12:5
I see a rod of an a. tree. Jer 1:11

almost

they be a. ready to stone. Ex 17:4
me, my feet were a. gone. Ps 73:2
soul had a. dwelt in silence. 94:17*
they had a. consumed me. 119:87
I was a. in all evil in the. Pr 5:14*
came a. the whole city. Acts 13:44
only at Ephesus, but a. 19:26
seven days were a. ended. 21:27
a. thou persuadest me to. 26:28*
were both a. and altogether. 29*
a. all things by the law. Heb 9:22

alms

that ye do not your a. Mat 6:1*
therefore when thou doest thine a. 2*
that thine a. may be in secret, and. 4
give a. of such things. Luke 11:41
sell that ye have, and give a. 12:33
they laid, to ask a. of. Acts 3:2
seeing Peter and John, asked an a. 3
that it was he which sat for a. 10
Cornelius gave much a. to the. 10:2
a. are come up for a memorial. 4, 31
I came to bring a. to my. 24:17

almsdeeds

Dorcas full of a. which. Acts 9:36

almug-trees

Ophir plenty of a.-trees. 1 Ki 10:11
a.-tree pillars, there came no such a.-trees. 12

aloes

thy garments smell of a. Ps 45:8
perfumed my bed with a. Pr 7:17
myrrh, a. with all the. S of S 4:14
brought a mixture of a. John 19:39

alone

that man should be a. Gen 2:18
perform it thyself a. Ex 18:18
Moses a. shall come near. Ex 24:2
leper dwell a. without. Lev 13:46
to bear all this people a. Num 11:14
Deut 1:9, 12
thou bear it not thyself a. Num 11:17
the people shall dwell a. not. 23:9
so the Lord a. did lead. Deut 32:12
then shall dwell in safety a. 33:28*
Achan perished not a. Josh 22:20
a man running a. 2 Sam 18:24, 26
if he be a. there is tidings in his. 25
they two were a. in. 1 Ki 11:29
art the God a. 2 Ki 19:15; Isa 37:16
Ps 86:10
Solomon, whom a. God. 1 Chr 29:1
lay hands on Mordecai a. Esth 3:6
escaped a. to tell. Job 1:15, 16, 17, 19
God who a. spreadeth out the. 9:8
to whom a. the earth was. 15:19
eaten my morsel myself a.? 31:17
thou whose name a. is. Ps 83:18
watch and am as a sparrow a. 102:7
who a. doth great wonders. 136:4
for his name a. is excellent. 148:13
is one a. and there is not. Eccl 4:8
but woe to him that is a. when he. 10
Lord a. shall be exalted. Isa 2:11, 17
none shall be a. in his. 14:31*
I called him a. and blessed. 51:2*
have trodden the wine-press a. 63:3
he sitteth a. and keepeth. Lam 3:28
I Daniel a. saw the vision. Dan 10:7
to Assyria, a wild ass a. Hos 8:9
live by bread a. Mat 4:4; Luke 4:4
come, he was a. Mat 14:23
Luke 9:18
between thee and him a. Mat 18:15
when they were a. he. Mark 4:34
was in midst of sea, and he a. 6:47
forgive sins but God a.? Luke 5:21
to eat, but for the priests a. 6:4
came to pass, as Jesus was a. 9:18
voice was past, Jesus was found a. 36
sister hath left me to serve a. 10:40
into a mountain a. John 6:15
disciples were gone away a. 22
for I am not a. but I. 8:16; 16:32
neither pray I for these a. 17:20
and hear that not a. Acts 19:26
written for his sake a. Rom 4:23
have rejoicing in himself a. Gal 6:4
went the high-priest a. Heb 9:7
not works is dead, being a. Jas 2:17*

left **alone**

Jacob left a. and there. Gen 32:24
dead, and he is left a. 42:38*; 44:20
I was left a. these where. Isa 49:21
I was left a. and saw this. Dan 10:8
and Jesus was left a. John 8:9
the Father hath not left me a. for. 29
I am left a. and they. Rom 11:3

let **alone**

let us a. that we may serve. Ex 14:12
let me a. that my wrath may. 32:10
let me a. that I may. Deut 9:14
let me a. two months. Judg 11:37
let him a. let him curse. 2 Sam 16:11
let her a. her soul is. 2 Ki 4:27
let the work of this . . . a. Ezra 6:7
let me a. that I may. Job 10:20
hold your peace let me a. that. 13:13
joined to idols, let him a. Hos 4:17
let them a. they be blind. Mat 15:14
let us a. what have we to do with thee? Mark 1:24*; Luke 4:34*
Jesus said, let her a. why? Mark 14:6
let a. let us see whether. 15:36*
Lord, let it a. this year. Luke 13:8
if we let him a. all men. John 11:48
let her a. against the day of my. 12:7*
from these men, let them a. Acts 5:38

along

will go a. by the king's. Num 21:22
kine went a. the highway. 1 Sam 6:12
then Saul fell all a. on the. 28:20*
went with her a. 2 Sam 3:16*
Shimei went a. cursing, and. 16:13
went, weeping all a. Jer 41:6

aloof

my friends stand a. from. Ps 38:11

aloud, *see* **cry, cried, sing**

Alpha
A. and Omega. Rev 1:8; 21:6; 22:13

Alpheus
James the son of A. Mat 10:3
Mark 3:18; Luke 6:15; Acts 1:13
he saw Levi the son of A. Mark 2:14

already
Joseph was in Egypt a. Ex 1:5
it hath been a. of old. Eccl 1:10
I have cursed them a. Mal 2:2
unto you, Elias is come a. Mat 17:12
not is condemned a. John 3:18
in spirit, have judged a. 1 Cor 5:3
whereto we have a. Phil 3:16
are a. turned aside . 1 Tim 5:15
but that which ye have a. Rev 2:25

also
man, for that he a. is flesh. Gen 6:3
ye the priesthood a.? Num 16:10
Saul answered, God do so and more a. 1 Sam 14:44; 2 Sam 3:35; 19:13
if we sit still here, we die a. 2 Ki 7:4
yea, for the rebellious a. Ps 68:18
ye weary my God a.? Isa 7:13
of hosts I will go a. Zech 8:21
heart be a. Mat 6:21; Luke 12:34
surely thou art a. one of. Mat 26:73
I may preach there a. Mark 1:38
Son of man is Lord a. 2:28*
Luke 6:5*
thou reproachest us a. Luke 11:45
what he doth, these a. John 5:19
where I am, there shall a. 12:26
where I am, there ye may be a. 14:3
proceeded to take Peter a. Acts 12:3
many, and of myself a. Rom 16:2*
not the law the same a. 1 Cor 9:8
last of all, he was seen of me a. 15:8
persuaded that in thee a. 2 Tim 1:5
without works is dead, a. Jas 2:26
God, love his brother a. 1 John 4:21

altar
Literally, any structure on which sacrifices were offered. In speaking of spiritual worship the word is used figuratively as a symbol easily understood by both Jew and Gentile.
Noah builded an a. to. Gen 8:20
Abraham built an a. to. 12:7; 22:9
Beth-el, and make there an a. 35:1
Beth-el, I will make there an a. 3
built an a. Jehovah-nissi. Ex 17:15
an a. of earth shalt thou make. 20:24
shalt take him from mine a. 21:14
sanctify it, it shall be an a. 29:37
sanctify the tabernacle and a. 44
a. of incense. 30:27
a. of burnt-offering. 40:10
the fire of the a. shall. Lev 6:9
the dedication of the a. Num 7:84
they shall not come nigh the a. 18:3
of Gad called the a. Ed. Josh 22:34
throw down the a. of Baal. Judg 6:25
because one hath cast down his a. 31
not cut off mine a. 1 Sam 2:33
go up, rear an a. to the. 2 Sam 24:18
against the a. O. a. 1 Ki 13:2
Elijah repaired the a. of the. 18:30
and the water ran about the a. 35
before this a. 2 Ki 18:22; Isa 36:7
so will I compass thine a. Ps 26:6
will I go to the a. of God, to. 43:4
a. to the Lord in the. Isa 19:19
stones of the a. as chalk-stones. 27:9
sacrifices be accepted on mine a. 56:7
Lord hath cast off his a. Lam 2:7
the porch and a. 25 men. Ezek 8:16
howl, ye ministers of the a. Joel 1:13
weep between the porch and a. 2:17
to pledge by every a. Amos 2:8
polluted bread on mine a. Mal 1:7
nor do kindle fire on mine a. 10
covering the a. of the Lord. 2:13
thou bring thy gift to the a. Mat 5:23
whoso shall swear by the a. 23:18
the temple and a. 35; Luke 11:51
I found an a. with this. Acts 17:23
the a. partakers with a. 1 Cor 9:13
10:18
gave attendance at the a. Heb 7:13
we have an a. whereof they. 13:10
I saw under the a. the. Rev 6:9
it with prayers on the golden a. 8:3
voice from horns of the golden a. 9:13
see **built**

altars
shall destroy their a. Ex 34:13
Deut 7:5; 12:3
build here seven a. Num 23:1
thrown down thine a. 1 Ki 19:10, 14
bones of priests on the a. 2 Chr 34:5
thine a. O Lord of hosts. Ps 84:3
he shall not look to the a. Isa 17:8
graven on horns of the a. Jer 17:1
their children remember their a. 2
your a. shall be desolate. Ezek 6:4
made a. to sin, a. shall be. Hos 8:11
thistle shall come on their a. 10:8
a. are as heaps in the furrows. 12:11
I will also visit the a. of. Amos 3:14
digged down thine a. Rom 11:3

alter
he shall not a. it, a good. Lev 27:10
that whosoever shall a. Ezra 6:11
all that put their hand to a. this. 12
nor a. the thing gone out. Ps 89:34

altered
be not a. that Vashti. Esth 1:19
his countenance was a. Luke 9:29

altereth
the law which a. not. Dan 6:8, 12

although
a. that was near, for God. Ex 13:17
a. my house be not so. 2 Sam 23:5*
a. thou movedst me. Job 2:3
a. I was an husband unto. Jer 31:32
a. I have cast them far. Ezek 11:16*
a. the fig-tree shall not. Hab 3:17
a. all shall be offended. Mark 14:29

altogether
make thyself a. a. Num 16:13*
which is a. just shalt. Deut 16:20
are a. become filthy. Ps 14:3; 53:3
of the Lord are righteous a. 19:9
man at his best state is a. 39:5
that I was a. such a one as. 50:21
O Lord, thou knowest it a. 139:4
sweet, yea, he is a. S of S 5:16
thou wast a. born in. John 9:34
almost and a. such as. Acts 26:29*
a. with the fornicators. 1 Cor 5:10†
or saith he it a. for our sakes? 9:10

alway, always
keep my commands a. Deut 5:29
keep his commandments a. 11:1
learn to fear the Lord a. 14:23
it, I would not live a. Job 7:16
will he a. call upon God? 27:10*
I have set the Lord a. Ps 16:8
he will not a. chide, nor keep. 103:9
to perform thy statutes a. 119:112*
I was by him, rejoicing a. Pr 8:30
neither will I be a. wroth. Isa 57:16
I am with you a. to the. Mat 28:20
ye have not a. Mark 14:7; John 12:8
I do a. those things. John 8:29
I know that thou hearest me a. 11:42
Cornelius prayed to God a. Acts 10:2
God, who a. causeth us. 2 Cor 2:14
a. in every prayer of. Phil 1:4
as a. so now also, Christ shall. 20
as ye have a. obeyed, not. 2:12
rejoice in the Lord a. and. 4:4
to fill up their sins a. 1 Thes 2:16
a. in remembrance. 2 Pet 1:15*

am I
am I my brother's keeper? Gen 4:9
am I in God's stead, who? 30:2
am I God, to kill and? 2 Ki 5:7
am I come up. 18:25; Isa 36:10
am I a God at hand. Jer 23:23
there *am I* in the midst. Mat 18:20
yet a little while *am I*. John 7:33
am I not an apostle? *am I* not free? 1 Cor 9:1
weak, then *am I* strong. 2 Cor 12:10

***I* am**
amongst whom *I am*. Num 11:21
there that being as *I am*. Neh 6:11
he is not a man as *I am*. Job 9:32
say to my soul, *I am* thy. Ps 35:3
I may know how frail *I am*. 39:4
O Israel, *I am* God, even. Ps 50:7
destroy them, for *I am* thy. 143:12
I am the first, *I am* the. Isa 44:6
48:12
I am, and none. 47:8; Zeph 2:15
and he shall say, here *I am*. Isa 58:9
men say that *I* the Son of man *am*? Mat 16:13; Mark 8:27; Luke 9:18
God, ye say that *I am*. Luke 22:70
Jesus said, *I am* the bread. John 6:35
I am the light of the world. 8:12
before Abraham was, *I am*. 58
where *I am* there shall my. 12:26
may be with me where *I am*. 17:24
altogether such as *I am*. Acts 26:29
angel of God, whose *I am*, and. 27:23
I am what *I am*. 1 Cor 15:10
as *I am*, for *I am*. Gal 4:12
learned in what state *I am*. Phil 4:11
I am he that liveth, *I am*. Rev 1:18
see thou do it not, *I am* thy. 19:10

***I* am *that I* am**
I am that I am hath sent. Ex 3:14
here **am** *I*, or *here I* **am**, *see* **here**

Amalek
to Eliphas Esau's son A. Gen 36:12
then came A. and fought. Ex 17:8
out the remembrance of A. 14
sworn he will have war with A. 16
when he looked on A. ... parable and said, A. was. Num 24:20
what A. did. Deut 25:17; 1 Sam 15:2
the remembrance of A. Deut 25:19
was a root against A. Judg 5:14
smite A. 1 Sam 15:3
Saul came to the city of A. 5
not execute his wrath on A. 28:18
Gebal, Ammon, A. are. Ps 83:7

Amalekite, -s
the A. came down and. Num 14:45
Israel had sown the A. Judg 6:3
Midianites and A. lay like. 7:12
the A. did oppress you, and. 10:12
Saul smote the A. 1 Sam 14:48; 15:7
get you from among A. 15:6
I have utterly destroyed the A. 20
and his men invaded the A. 27:8
the A. had invaded the south. 30:1
from the slaughter of A. 2 Sam 1:1
answered him, I am an A. 8, 13
smote the rest of the A. 1 Chr 4:43

Amana
look from the top of A. S of S 4:8

Amasa
Absalom made A. captain of the host, which A. was the. 2 Sam 17:25
Joab took A. by the beard to. 20:9
A. wallowed in blood in the. 12
what Joab did to A. 1 Ki 2:5, 32
Abigail bare A. the. 1 Chr 2:17
A. son of Hadlai stood. 2 Chr 28:12

amazed
of Benjamin were a. Judg 20:41*
were a. they answered. Job 32:15
be a. one at another. Isa 13:8
many people a. at thee. Ezek 32:10
were exceedingly a. Mat 19:25
all a. and glorified God. Mark 2:12
Luke 5:26
began to be sore a. and. Mark 14:33
all a. and spake among. Luke 4:36
were all a. at the mighty. 9:43
that heard Saul were a. Acts 9:21

amazement
filled with a. at what had. Acts 3:10
are not afraid with any a. 1 Pet 3:6*

Amaziah
A. his son reigned. 2 Ki 12:21
2 Chr 24:27
fought against A. 2 Ki 13:12; 14:15
A. would not hear, therefore. 14:11
father A. had done. 15:3; 2 Chr 26:4
of Merari. A. the son. 1 Chr 6:45
after A. did turn from. 2 Chr 25:27
A. priest of Beth-el sent. Amos 7:10

ambassador
but a faithful a. is health. Pr 13:17
an a. sent to the heathen. Jer 49:14
Ob 1
which I am an a. in bonds. Eph 6:20

ambassadors
as if they had been *a.* *Josh* 9:4
the business of the *a.* *2 Chr* 32:31
he sent *a.* what have I to. 35:21
that sendeth *a.* by the sea. *Isa* 18:2
princes at Zoan, his *a.* came. 30:4
a. of peace shall weep bitterly 33:7
rebelled in sending *a.* *Ezek* 17:15
then we are *a.* for Christ. *2 Cor* 5:20

ambassage
sendeth an *a.* and. *Luke* 14:32

amber, *see* **colour**

ambush, -es
lay thee an *a.* for the. *Josh* 8:2
watchmen, prepare the *a.* *Jer* 51:12

ambushment, -s
caused an *a.* the *a.* was. *2 Chr* 13:13
Lord set *a.* against Ammon. 20:22

amen
The Hebrew means true, faithful, certain. It is used in the end of prayer as an earnest wish to be heard; amen, so be it, so shall it be. *The word* amen *is used in many languages.*
woman shall say *a. a.* *Num* 5:22
the people shall say *a.* *Deut* 27:15
Benaiah answered *a.* the. *1 Ki* 1:36
people said *a.* and. *1 Chr* 16:36
to everlasting: *a.* and *a.* *Ps* 41:13
with his glory; *a.* and *a.* 72:19
Lord for evermore *a.* and *a.* 89:52
and let all the people say *a.* 106:48
prophet Jeremiah said *a.* *Jer* 28:6
the glory for ever, *a.* *Mat* 6:13
of the unlearned, say *a.* *1 Cor* 14:16
in him are yea and *a.* *2 Cor* 1:20
am alive for evermore, *a.* *Rev* 1:18
write these things, saith the *a.* 3:14
four beasts said *a.* 5:14; 19:4
come quickly, *a.* even so, 22:20

amend
a. ways, and doings. *Jer* 7:3, 5
26:13; 35:15
hour when he began to *a.* *John* 4:52

amends
(*Revised Version,* restitution)
make *a.* for the harm. *Lev* 5:16

amerce
(*Punish by fine*)
a. him in an 100 shekels. *Deut* 22:19

amethyst, *see* **agate** *and* **jacinth**

amiable
how *a.* are thy tabernacles. *Ps* 84:1

amiss
sinned, we have done *a.* *2 Chr* 6:37*
speak any thing *a.* against. *Dan* 3:29
man hath done nothing *a.* *Luke* 23:41
not, because ye ask *a.* *Jas* 4:3

Ammah
were come to the hill *A.* *2 Sam* 2:24

Ammi
unto your brethren, *A.* *Hos* 2:1

Amminadab
Elisheba daughter of *A.* *Ex* 6:23
A. begat. *Ruth* 4:20; *Mat* 1:4

Ammi-nadib
me like the chariots of *A.* *S of S* 6:12

Ammon
father of children of *A.* *Gen* 19:38
I deliver you from *A.*? *Judg* 10:11
the children of *A.* made war. 11:4
the land of the children of *A.* 15
thus the children of *A.* were. 33
if the children of *A.* be too strong for thee. *2 Sam* 10:11; *1 Chr* 19:12
children of *A.* saw that. *2 Sam* 10:14
with sword of children of *A.* 12:9
all children of *A.* 31; *1 Chr* 20:3
the abomination of the children of *A.* *1 Ki* 11:7; *2 Ki* 23:13
god of the children of *A.* *1 Ki* 11:33
had married wives of *A.* *Neh* 13:23
Gebal and *A.* confederate. *Ps* 83:7
the children of *A.* shall. *Isa* 11:14
punish the children of *A.* *Jer* 9:26
made children of *A.* to drink. 25:21
bring again the captivity of *A.* 49:6
escape, the chief of *A.* *Dan* 11:41
children of *A.* shall be as. *Zeph* 2:9

Ammonite, -s
A. not enter. *Deut* 23:3; *Neh* 13:1
slew the *A.* till the. *1 Sam* 11:11
loved women of the *A.* *1 Ki* 11:1
and the *A.* gave gifts. *2 Chr* 26:8
to the abomination of *A.* *Ezra* 9:1
send to the king of *A.* *Jer* 27:3
to be heard in Rabbah of *A.* 49:2
make *A.* a couchingplace. *Ezek* 25:5
A. may not be remembered. 10

Amnon
David's first-born was *A.* *2 Sam* 3:2; *1 Chr* 3:12
A. vexed, fell sick for. *2 Sam* 13:2
I pray thee, let my brother *A.* 26
when I say, smite *A.* then kill. 28
Shimon, *A.* Rinnah. *1 Chr* 4:20

Amon
back to *A.* *1 Ki* 22:26; *2 Chr* 18:25
A. reigned. *2 Ki* 21:18
his servants slew *A.* 23
A. sacrificed to carved. *2 Chr* 33:22
captivity children of *A.* *Neh* 7:59
Manasses begat *A.* and *A.* *Mat* 1:10

among
thou, Lord, art *a.* them. *Num* 14:14
a. the sons of the priests. *Ezra* 10:18
yet *a.* many nations. *Neh* 13:26
an interpreter, one *a.* *Job* 33:23
their life is *a.* the unclean. 36:14
evil common *a.* men. *Eccl* 6:1
one *a.* 1,000, but a woman *a.* 7:28
chiefest *a.* ten thousand. *S of S* 5:10
a. my people are found. *Jer* 5:26
there is none upright *a.* *Mi* 7:2
blessed art thou *a.* *Luke* 1:28*
I send you forth as lambs *a.* 10:3
what are they *a.* so many? *John* 6:9

Amorite, -s
iniquity of the *A.* is not. *Gen* 15:16
which I took from *A.* with. 48:22
utterly destroy the *A.* *Deut* 20:17
fail drive out the *A.* *Josh* 3:10
the Lord delivered up *A.* 10:12
or gods of *A.* in whose land. 24:15
not the gods of the *A.* *Judg* 6:10
God hath dispossessed the *A.* 11:23
between Israel and the *A.* *1 Sam* 7:14
Gibeonites were of the *A.* *2 Sam* 21:2
abominably as did the *A.* *1 Ki* 21:26
above all the *A.* did. *2 Ki* 21:11
father an *A.* mother. *Ezek* 16:3, 45
yet destroyed I the *A.* *Amos* 2:9

Amos, *or,* **Amoz**
Isaiah the son of *A.* *2 Ki* 19:2, 20
20:1; *2 Chr* 26:22; 32:20, 32
Isa. 1:1; 2:1; 13:1; 20:2; 37:2
21; 38:1
then *A.* said, I was no. *Amos* 7:14
which was the son of *A.* *Luke* 3:25

Amphipolis
had passed through *A.* *Acts* 17:1

Amplias
greet *A.* my beloved in. *Rom* 16:8

Amram
of Kohath, *A.* *Ex* 6:18; *Num* 3:19
Dishon, *A.* and Eshban. *1 Chr* 1:41
the children of *A.* Aaron. 6:3
sons of Bani, Maadai, *A.* *Ezra* 10:34

Anah
this was that *A.* that. *Gen* 36:24

Anak
saw the children of *A.* *Num* 13:28, 33
before the children of *A.* *Deut* 9:2
Caleb drove thence the three sons of *A.* *Josh* 15:14; *Judg* 1:20

Anakims
and tall as the *A.* *Deut* 2:10; 9:2
none of the *A.* were left. *Josh* 11:22
was a great man among the *A.* 14:15

Anammelech
Adrammelech, *A.* gods. *2 Ki* 17:31

Ananias
A. hearing these words. *Acts* 5:5
seen in a vision *A.* 9:12; 22:12
high-priest *A.* commanded. 23:2
A. the priest descended with. 24:1

Anathema
him be *a.* maran-atha. *1 Cor* 16:22

Anathoth
of Benjamin, *A.* with her suburbs, Almon. *Josh* 21:18; *1 Chr* 6:60
get thee to *A.* to. *1 Ki* 2:26
the sons of Becher *A.* *1 Chr* 7:8
A. and Nebai sealed. *Neh* 10:19
up thy voice, O poor *A.* *Isa* 10:30
evil on the men of *A.* *Jer* 11:23
not reproved Jeremiah of *A.* 29:27
my field that is in *A.* 32:7, 8

ancestors
the covenant of their *a.* *Lev* 26:45

anchor
they would have cast *a.* *Acts* 27:30
hope we have as an *a.* *Heb* 6:19

ancient
[1] *Old, of former time,* 1 Chr 4:22. [2] *Very old men,* Job 12:12. [3] *Men of former times,* 1 Sam 24:13 [4] *Elders of the people* Jer 19:1.
the chief things of the *a.* *Deut* 33:15
a. river, the river Kishon. *Judg* 5:21
of *a.* times. *2 Ki* 19:25; *Isa* 37:26
and these are *a.* things. *1 Chr* 4:22
were *a.* men, and had. *Ezra* 3:12*
with the *a.* is wisdom. *Job* 12:12*
remove not the *a.* land-. *Pr* 22:28
prudent and *a.* the Lord. *Isa* 3:2*
the *a.* and honourable, he. 9:15*
say ye, I am the son of *a.*? 19:11
whose antiquity is of *a.* days. 23:7
since I appointed the *a.* people. 44:7
upon the *a.* hast thou laid thy. 47:6*
of the Lord, as in the *a.* days. 51:9*
to stumble from *a.* paths. *Jer* 18:15
then they began at the *a.* *Ezek* 9:6
the *a.* of days did sit. *Dan* 7:9
the Son of man came to *a.* of. 13
till the *a.* of days came, and. 22

ancients
(*Revised Version, usually,* elders)
the proverb of the *a.* *1 Sam* 24:13
more than the *a.* *Ps* 119:100
into judgment with the *a.* *Isa* 3:14
Lord shall reign before his *a.* 24:23
a. of the people and *a.* of. *Jer* 19:1
shall perish from the *a.* *Ezek* 7:26
hast thou seen what the *a.* do? 8:12
the *a.* of Gebal were in thee. 27:9

ancle bones
a. bones received strength. *Acts* 3:7

ancles
the waters were to the *a.* *Ezek* 47:3

Andrew
into the house of *A.* *Mark* 1:29
James, John, and *A.* asked. 13:3
which heard was *A.* *John* 1:40
of Bethsaida the city of *A.* 44
Philip telleth *A.* and *A.* told. 12:22
Peter, John, James, and *A.* *Acts* 1:13

Andronicus
salute *A.* and Junia my. *Rom* 16:7

Aner
A. Eshcol, let them take. *Gen* 14:24
half tribe of Manasseh, *A.* *1 Chr* 6:70

angel
Literally 'messenger': [1] *A celestial being, a messenger of God,* Gen 24:7; Dan 3:28; Acts 12:8. [2] *A minister or pastor of a church,* Rev 2:1. [3] *An evil, or fallen angel,* Mat 25:41.
a. of the Lord said. *Gen* 22:11
send his *a.* before thee. 24:7, 40
the *a.* who redeemed me. 48:16
send *a.* before thee. *Ex* 23:20, 23
32:34; 33:2
sent an *a.* and brought. *Num* 20:16
the *a.* did wondrously. *Judg* 13:19
the *a.* stretched out his hand, the *a.* that. *2 Sam* 24:16; *1 Chr* 21:15
spake . . . saw the *a.* *2 Sam* 24:17
a. spake to me by the. *1 Ki* 13:18
an *a.* touched Elijah and said. 19:5
God sent an *a.* to. *1 Chr* 21:15
turned back, and saw the *a.* 20
the Lord commanded the *a.* and. 27
the Lord sent an *a.* *2 Chr* 32:21
nor say before the *a.* *Eccl* 5:6
the *a.* of his presence. *Isa* 63:9
God who hath sent *a.* and. *Dan* 3:28

God hath sent his *a.* and. *Dan* 6:22
he had power over the *a.* *Hos* 12:4
a. talked with me said. *Zech* 1:9; 4:5
Lord answered the *a.* that. 1:13
a. that communed with me said. 14
a. that talked. 19; 4:4; 5:10; 6:4
a. that talked . . . and another *a.* 2:3
and stood before the *a.* 3:3
a. that talked with me, went. 5:5
a. answered, these are the four. 6:5
a. answered the woman. *Mat* 28:5
the *a.* said, fear not. *Luke* 1:13
the *a.* answered and said, I am. 19
in the sixth month the *a.* Gabriel. 26
a. said to her, fear not, Mary. 30
a. answered, Holy Ghost shall. 35
a. said to the shepherds, fear. 2:10
suddenly there was with the *a.* a. 13
so named of the *a.* before he was. 21
an *a.* strengthening him. 22:43
an *a.* went down at a. *John* 5:4*
others said, an *a.* spake to. 12:29
been the face of an *a.* *Acts* 6:15
hands of the *a.* that appeared. 7:35
in the wilderness with the *a.* 38
a. which spake to Cornelius. 10:7
from God by an holy *a.* to send. 22
how he had seen an *a.* in his. 11:13
the *a.* said to Peter, bind on. 12:8
true which was done by the *a.* 9
forthwith the *a.* departed from. 10
the Lord hath sent his *a.* and. 11
then said they, it is his *a.* 15
Sadducees say, neither *a.* 23:8
if a spirit or an *a.* hath spoken to. 9
into an *a.* of light. *2 Cor* 11:14
an *a.* from heaven preach. *Gal* 1:8
he signified it by his *a.* *Rev* 1:1
a. of the church. 2:1, 8, 12, 18
3:1, 7, 14
I saw a strong *a.* proclaiming. 5:2
I saw another *a.* ascending. 7:2
another *a.* came and stood. 8:3
ascended before God out of the *a.* 4
the *a.* took the censer, and filled. 5
the first *a.* sounded. 7
second *a.* sounded. 8
third *a.* sounded. 10
fourth *a.* sounded. 12
I heard an *a.* flying through. 13*
fifth *a.* sounded. 9:1
the *a.* of the bottomless pit. 11
sixth *a.* sounded. 13
to the sixth *a.* loose the four *a.* 14
I saw another *a.* 10:1; 18:1; 20:1
the *a.* which I saw stand on. 10:5
days of the voice of the seventh *a.* 7
the book in the hand of the *a.* 8
I took the book. 10
and the *a.* stood, saying. 11:1*
seventh *a.* sounded, and there. 15
I saw another *a.* fly in. 14:6
another *a.* followed saying. 8
third *a.* followed. 9
another *a.* came. 15, 17, 18
and the *a.* thrust in his sickle in. 19
a. poured out. 16:2, 3, 4, 8, 10, 12, 17
and I heard the *a.* of the waters. 5
a. said, wherefore didst thou. 17:7
mighty *a.* took up a stone. 18:21
and I saw an *a.* standing in. 19:17
of a man, that is of the *a.* 21:17
to worship before the feet of *a.* 22:8
I Jesus have sent mine *a.* to. 16

angel *of God*

a. of God who went. *Ex* 14:19
countenance of an *a. of God.*
Judg 13:6
sight, as an *a. of God.* *1 Sam* 29:9
as an *a. of God.* *2 Sam* 14:17; 19:27
the wisdom of an *a. of God.* 14:20
this night the *a. of God.* *Acts* 27:23
me as an *a. of God.* *Gal* 4:14

angel *of the Lord*

a. of the L. found Hagar. *Gen* 16:7
the *a. of the L.* said. 9, 10, 11; 22:11
Num 22:32, 35; *Judg* 13:18
2 Ki 1:3, 15
a. of the L. called. *Gen* 22:11, 15
ass saw the *a. of the L.* *Num* 22:23
25:27
a. of the L. stood in a path. 22:24, 26
Balaam saw *a. of the L.* standing. 31
Balaam said to *a. of the L.* *Num* 22:34
a. of the L. said to Balaam, go. 35
a. of the L. came up. *Judg* 2:1
1 Ki 19:7; *Acts* 12:7
when *a. of the L.* spake. *Judg* 2:4
Meroz, said the *a. of the L.* 5:23
came an *a. of the L.* and sat. 6:11
a. of the L. appeared to Gideon. 12
the *a. of the L.* put forth the. 21
perceived he was an *a. of the L.* 22
a. of the L. appeared to the. 13:3
knew not he was an *a. of the L.* 16
a. of the L. ascended in the flame. 20
a. of the L. was by threshing.
2 Sam 24:16; *1 Chr* 21:15
a. of the L. smote. *2 Ki* 19:35
Isa 37:36
a. of the L. destroying. *1 Chr* 21:12
a. of the L. commanded Gad to. 18
the sword of *a. of the L.* 30
a. of the L. encampeth. *Ps* 34:7
let *a. of the L.* chase them. 35:5
let *a. of the L.* persecute them. 6
answered the *a. of the L.* *Zech* 1:11
a. of the L. answered, wilt thou. 12
a. of the L. stood by Joshua. 3:5
a. of the L. protested. 6
of David as the *a. of the L.* 12:8
a. of the L. *Mat* 1:20; 2:13, 19
Joseph did as the *a. of the L.* 1:24
for the *a. of the L.* descended. 28:2
Zacharias an *a. of the L.* *Luke* 1:11
a. of the L. came upon them. 2:9
a. of the L. by night. *Acts* 5:19
a. of the L. spake to Philip. 8:26
a. of the L. smote Herod. 12:23

angels

there came two *a.* to. *Gen* 19:1
when the morning arose, the *a.* 15
lower than the *a.* *Ps* 8:5*; *Heb* 2:7, 9
of God are thousands of *a.* *Ps* 68:17*
man did eat *a.* food, he sent. 78:25*
and trouble, by sending evil *a.* 49
a. came and. *Mat* 4:11; *Mark* 1:13
the reapers are the *a.* *Mat* 13:39
the *a.* shall come forth and sever. 49
their *a.* always behold the. 18:10
a. in heaven. 24:36; *Mark* 13:32
Son of man, and all the holy *a.* with.
Mat 25:31
more than twelve legions of *a.* 26:53
Son of man . . . of his Father with
the holy *a.* *Mark* 8:38; *Luke* 9:26
marry, but are as the *a.* *Mark* 12:25
as the *a.* were gone. *Luke* 2:15
and was carried by the *a.* 16:22
they are equal unto the *a.* 20:36
had also seen a vision of *a.* 24:23
seeth two *a.* in white. *John* 20:12
law by disposition of *a.* *Acts* 7:53
a. able to separate us. *Rom* 8:38
to the world, to *a.* and. *1 Cor* 4:9
not that we shall judge *a.*? 6:3
on her head, because of the *a.* 11:10
with tongues of men and *a.* 13:1
it was ordained by *a.* in. *Gal* 3:19
you in worshipping of *a.* *Col* 2:18
heaven with mighty *a.* *2 Thes* 1:7
seen of *a.* preached to. *1 Tim* 3:16
before God and the elect *a.* 5:21
so much better than the *a.* *Heb* 1:4
the *a.* said he at any time. 5, 13
a. he saith, who maketh his *a.* 1:7
if the word spoken by *a.* was. 2:2
a. hath he not put in subjection. 5
him the nature of *a.* but seed. 16
innumerable company of *a.* 12:22
for some have entertained *a.* 13:2
which things the *a.* *1 Pet* 1:12
a. and powers being made. 3:22
if God spared not the *a.* *2 Pet* 2:4
whereas *a.* greater in power and. 11
a. who kept not their first. *Jude* 6
seven stars, *a.* of the. *Rev* 1:20
the voice of many *a.* about. 5:11
I saw four *a.* standing on the. 7:1
with a loud voice to the four *a.* 2
all the *a.* stood round about the. 11
trumpet of the three *a.* which. 8:13
loose the four *a.* which are. 9:14
the *a.* were loosed, which were. 15
in presence of the holy *a.* 14:10
and at the gates twelve *a.* 21:12

angels *of God*

a. of God ascend and descend.
Gen 28:12; *John* 1:51
and *a. of God* met him. *Gen* 32:1
as *a. of God.* *Mat* 22:30; *Mark* 12:25
confess before *a. of God.* *Luke* 12:8
be denied before the *a. of God.* 9
the presence of the *a. of God.* 15:10
all the *a. of God* worship. *Heb* 1:6

his **angels**

and *his a.* he charged with. *Job* 4:18
give *his a.* charge. *Ps* 91:11
Mat 4:6; *Luke* 4:10
ye *his a.* which excel in. *Ps* 103:20
his a. spirits. 104:4*; *Heb* 1:7
all *his a.* praise. *Ps* 148:2
man shall send forth *his a.* *Mat* 13:41
glory of his Father with *his a.* 16:27
send *his a.* with a great sound. 24:31
Mark 13:27
for the devil and *his a.* *Mat* 25:41
before my Father and *his a.* *Rev* 3:5
his a. the dragon, and *his a.* 12:7
dragon was cast out, and *his a.* 9

anger, *verb*

foolish nation I will *a.* *Rom* 10:19

anger

till thy brother's *a.* turn. *Gen* 27:45
and let not thine *a.* burn. 44:18
cursed be their *a.* for it was. 49:7
dancing, Moses' *a.* waxed. *Ex* 32:19
Aaron said, let not the *a.* of my. 22
I was afraid of the *a.* and. *Deut* 9:19
from the fierceness of his *a.* 13:17
Josh 7:26
heat of this great *a.*? *Deut* 29:24
then their *a.* was abated. *Judg* 8:3
Ahasuerus his *a.* burned. *Esth* 1:12
will not withdraw his *a.* *Job* 9:13
oven in the time of thine *a.* *Ps* 21:9
a. endureth but a moment. 30:5
cease from *a.* and forsake. 37:8
my flesh because of thine *a.* 38:3
let thy wrathful *a.* take hold. 69:24
why doth thy *a.* smoke. 74:1
and *a.* also came up against. 78:21
many a time turned he his *a.* 38
on them the fierceness of his *a.* 49
he made a way to his *a.* he. 50
the fierceness of thine *a.* 85:3
and cause thine *a.* towards us to. 4
wilt thou draw out thine *a.* to? 5
we are consumed by thine *a.* 90:7
knoweth the power of thine *a.* 11
nor will he keep his *a.* for. 103:9
Jer 3:5
grievous words stir up *a.* *Pr* 15:1
of a man deferreth his *a.* 19:11
a gift in secret pacifieth *a.* 21:14
the rod of his *a.* shall fail. 22:8
wrath is cruel, and *a.* is. 27:4
a. resteth in the bosom of. *Eccl* 7:9
for all this his *a.* is not turned away.
Isa 5:25; 9:12, 17, 21; 10:4
fear not, for the *a.* of Rezin. 7:4
O Assyrian, the rod of mine *a.* 10:5
shall cease, and my *a.* in their. 25
thou wast angry, thine *a.* 12:1
the Lord cometh with fierce *a.* 13:9
day of his fierce *a.* 13; *Lam* 1:12
Lord cometh burning with *a.* *Isa* 30:27
shew the indignation of his *a.* 30
poured on him the fury of *a.* 42:25
sake will I defer mine *a.* 48:9
will come to render his *a.* 66:15
surely his *a.* shall turn. *Jer* 2:35
mine *a.* to fall on you, I am merciful,
and I will not keep mine *a.* 3:12
were broken down by his *a.* 4:26
mine *a.* shall be poured on. 7:20
them in the time of thine *a.* 18:23
desolate because of his *a.* 25:38
as a provocation of mine *a.* 32:31
great is the *a.* the Lord hath. 36:7
as mine *a.* hath been poured. 42:18
wherefore mine *a.* was poured. 44:6
on them, my fierce *a.* 49:37
his footstool in the day *a.* *Lam* 2:1
in the indignation of his *a.* 6
them in the day of thine *a.* 21
in the day of the Lord's *a.* none. 22
thou hast covered with *a.* and. 3:43
he hath poured out his fierce *a.* 4:11

mine *a.* be accomplished. *Ezek* 5:13
I will send mine *a.* upon thee. 7:3
accomplish mine *a.* on. 8; 20:8, 21
Edom, according to mine *a.* 25:14
even do according to thine *a.* 35:11
thine *a.* be turned away. *Dan* 9:16
the fierceness of mine *a.* *Hos* 11:9
for mine *a.* is turned away. 14:4
a. did tear perpetually. *Amos* 1:11
turn from his fierce *a.* *Jonah* 3:9
he retained not his *a.* for. *Mi* 7:18
abide ... fierceness of his *a.*? *Nah* 1:6
a. against the rivers? *Hab* 3:8
them all my fierce *a.* *Zeph* 3:8
looked on them with *a.* *Mark* 3:5
all *a.* be put. *Eph* 4:31; *Col* 3:8

anger *of the Lord*

fierce *a. of the Lord* may. *Num* 25:4
augment the *a. of the Lord.* 32:14
a. of the Lord shall. *Deut* 29:20
a. of the Lord against Israel.
Judg 2:14, 20; 3:8; 10:7
through the *a. of the Lord* it came to pass. *2 Ki* 24:20; *Jer* 52:3
fierce *a. of the Lord* is not. *Jer* 4:8
fierce *a. of the Lord.* 12:13; 25:37
a. of the Lord shall not. 23:20; 30:24
from the fierce *a. of the Lord.* 51:45
a. of the Lord hath. *Lam* 4:16
before the fierce *a. of the Lord.*
Zeph 2:2
be hid in the day of *a. of the Lord.* 3

in **anger**

for *in* their *a.* they slew. *Gen* 49:6
out from Pharaoh *in a.* *Ex* 11:8
Lord overthrew *in a.* *Deut* 29:23
them out of the land *in a.* 28
rose from the table *in a.* *1 Sam* 20:34
home *in* great *a.* *2 Chr* 25:10
overturneth them *in* his *a.* *Job* 9:5
he teareth himself *in* his *a.* 18:4
distributeth sorrows *in* his *a.* 21:17
not so, he hath visited *in* his *a.* 35:15
me not *in* thy *a.* *Ps* 6:1; *Jer* 10:24
arise, O Lord, *in* thine *a.* lift. *Ps* 7:6
put not thy servant away *in a.* 27:9
in thine *a.* cast down the. 56:7
hath he *in a.* shut up his? 77:9
called my mighty ones *in a.* *Isa* 13:3
he that ruled the nations *in a.* 14:6
tread them *in* mine *a.* 63:3, 6
against you, even *in a.* *Jer* 21:5
have driven them *in* mine *a.* 32:37
whom I have slain *in* mine *a.* 33:5
Zion with a cloud *in* his *a.* *Lam* 2:1
he hath cut off *in a.* all the horn. 3
and destroy them *in a.* 3:66
judgments in thee *in a.* *Ezek* 5:15
overflowing shower *in* mine *a.* 13:13
gather you *in* mine *a.* and. 22:20
have consumed them in mine *a.* 43:8
destroyed, neither *in a.* *Dan* 11:20
thee a king *in* mine *a.* *Hos* 13:11
execute vengeance *in a.* *Mi* 5:15
thresh the heathen *in a.* *Hab* 3:12

anger *kindled*

a. of Jacob was *k.* against. *Gen* 30:2
a. of the Lord was *k.* against Moses.
Ex 4:14
a. of the Lord was *k.* *Num* 11:1, 10
12:9; 22:22
Balaam's *a.* was *k.* and he. 22:27
Balak's *a.* was *k.* against. 24:10
the *a.* of the Lord was *k.* against Israel. 25:3; 32:13; *Josh* 7:1
2 Sam 24:1; *2 Ki* 13:3
Lord's *a.* was *k.* the same. *Num* 32:10
lest the *a.* of the Lord be *k.* against thee. *Deut* 6:15
so will the *a.* of the Lord be *k.* 7:4
the *a.* of the Lord was *k.* against this land. 29:27
mine *a.* shall be *k.* 31:17; *Josh* 23:16
fire is *k.* in *a.* *Deut* 32:22; *Jer* 15:14
Zebul's *a.* was *k.* *Judg* 9:30
Samson's *a. k.* and he went. 14:19
Saul heard, his *a.* was *k.* *1 Sam* 11:6
Eliab's *a.* was *k.* against. 17:28
Saul's *a.* was *k.* against. 20:30
a. of Lord *k.* against Uzzah.
2 Sam 6:7; *1 Chr* 13:10
David's *a.* was *k.* against the.
2 Sam 12:5

wherewith his *a.* was *k.* *2 Ki* 23:26
their *a.* was *k.* against. *2 Chr* 25:10
a. of the Lord was *k.* against Amaziah. 15
the *a.* of the Lord *k.* against his people. *Isa* 5:25
have *k.* a fire in mine *a.* *Jer* 17:4
mine *a.* is *k.* against them. *Hos* 8:5
mine *a.* was *k.* against the shepherds.
Zech 10:3

provoke or *provoked to* **anger**

to *pr.* him *to a.* *Deut* 4:25; 9:18
31:29; *2 Ki* 17:17; 21:6; 23:19
2 Chr 33:6
abominations *pr. to a.* *Deut* 32:16
pr. me *to a.* I will *pr.* them *to a.* 21
and *pr.* the Lord *to a.* *Judg* 2:12
images to *pr. to a.* *1 Ki* 14:9; 15:30
groves *pr.* Lord *to a.* 14:15; 16:7, 13
to *pr.* me *to a.* with their sins. 16:2
2 Ki 17:11; *Jer* 11:17; 32:29, 32
Ezek 16:26
Ahab did *pr.* the Lord *to a.* *1 Ki* 16:33
thou hast *pr.* me *to a.* 21:22
Ahaz *pr. to a.* the Lord God. 22:53
pr. me *to a.* since the day. *2 Ki* 21:15
that they might *pr.* me *to a.* 22:17
2 Chr 34:25; *Jer* 25:7
pr. to a. the Lord God. *2 Chr* 28:25
have *pr.* thee *to a.* before. *Neh* 4:5
pr. him *to a.* with. *Ps* 78:58; 106:29
whoso *pr.* him *to a.* sinneth. *Pr* 20:2
pr. the Holy One . . . *to a.* *Isa* 1:4*
a people that *pr.* me *to a.* 65:3*
may *pr.* me *to a.* *Jer* 7:18
do they *pr.* me *to a.* 19
why have they *pr. to a.* 8:19
pr. me not *to a.* 25:6
Israel have *pr.* me *to a.* 32:30
their wickedness to *pr.* me *to a.* 44:3
Ezek 8:17
Ephraim *pr.* him *to a.* *Hos* 12:14
pr. not your children *to a.* *Col* 3:21*

slow to **anger**

ready to pardon, *slow to a.* *Neh* 9:17
slow to a. plenteous. *Ps* 103:8; 145:8
he that is *slow to a.* *Pr* 15:18
he that is *slow to a.* better. 16:32
slow to a. of great. *Joel* 2:13
Jonah 4:2
the Lord is *slow to a.* great. *Nah* 1:3

angered

they *a.* him at the waters. *Ps* 106:32

angle

they that cast *a.* shall. *Isa* 19:8
up all of them with the *a.* *Hab* 1:15

angry

let not the Lord be *a.* *Gen* 18:30, 32
be not *a.* with yourselves that. 45:5
and Moses was *a.* with. *Lev* 10:16
a. with me for you. *Deut* 1:37; 4:21
Lord was *a.* with you to have. 9:8
the Lord was very *a.* with Aaron. 20
lest *a.* fellows run upon. *Judg* 18:25
wherefore be ye *a.* for. *2 Sam* 19:42
be *a.* with them. *1 Ki* 8:46; *2 Ch* 6:36
Lord was *a.* with Solomon. *1 Ki* 11:9
therefore the Lord was *a.* *2 Ki* 17:18
wouldst thou not be *a.* *Ezra* 9:14
I was very *a.* when I. *Neh* 5:6
kiss the Son, lest he be *a.* *Ps* 2:12
God is *a.* with the wicked. 7:11
stand when once thou art *a.*? 76:7
wilt thou be *a.*? 79:5; 80:4; 85:5
he that is soon *a.* dealeth. *Pr* 14:17
wilderness, than with an *a.* 21:19*
friendship with an *a.* man. 22:24
a. countenance, a backbiting. 25:23
a. man stirreth up strife, and. 29:22
wherefore should God be *a.*? *Eccl* 5:6
be not hasty in thy spirit to be *a.* 7:9
mother's children were *a.* *S of S* 1:6
though thou wast *a.* with. *Isa* 12:1
and will be no more *a.* *Ezek* 16:42
this cause the king was *a.* *Dan* 2:12
and he was very *a.* *Jonah* 4:1
Doest thou well to be *a.*? 4:4, 9
he said, I do well to be *a.* even. 9
whosoever is *a.* with his. *Mat* 5:22
of the house being *a.* *Luke* 14:21
he was *a.* and would not. 15:28
are ye *a.* at me because. *John* 7:23

be *a.* and sin not, let not. *Eph* 4:26
be blameless, not soon *a.* *Tit* 1:7
the nations were *a.* thy. *Rev* 11:18

anguish

in that we saw the *a.* *Gen* 42:21*
hearkened not to Moses for *a.* *Ex* 6:9
tremble, and be in *a.* *Deut* 2:25
slay me, for *a.* is come. *2 Sam* 1:9
I will speak in the *a.* of my. *Job* 7:11
trouble and *a.* shall make him. 15:24
trouble and *a.* have. *Ps* 119:143
when distress and *a.* come. *Pr* 1:27
and behold dimness of *a.* *Isa* 8:22
into the land of trouble and *a.* 30:6
a. as of her that bringeth. *Jer* 4:31
a. hath taken. 6:24; 49:24; 50:43
no more her *a.* for joy. *John* 16:21
tribulation and *a.* upon. *Rom* 2:9
for out of much *a.* of heart. *2 Cor* 2:4

anise

ye pay tithe of mint, *a.* *Mat* 23:23

Anna

A. a prophetess daughter. *Luke* 2:36

Annas

A. and Caiaphas being. *Luke* 3:2
A. was father in law to. *John* 18:13
A. had sent Jesus bound to. 24

anoint

[1] *To pour oil upon with the idea of consecrating the person or thing to God, or to set him apart for an office,* Gen 31:13; Ex 28:41. *Since kings and priests were the persons most frequently anointed on taking office, they were frequently spoken of as God's anointed,* 2 Sam 23:1; Isa 45:1. *In like manner Jesus Christ as King and Priest, was so termed,* Acts 10:38. [2] *Anointing with various preparations was one of the principal methods of healing in the small knowledge of medicine in Palestine in Bible times,* Jas 5:14. *The word is so used of Jesus in healing the eyes of the blind,* John 9:6, 11.

a. and consecrate. *Ex* 28:41; 30:30
40:15
oil and *a.* him. 29:7; 40:13
thou shalt *a.* the altar. 29:36; 40:10
a. the tabernacle. 30:26; 40:9
thou shalt *a.* the laver and. 40:11
priest whom he shall *a.* *Lev* 16:32
but thou shalt not *a.* *Deut* 28:40
the trees went to *a.* a king. *Judg* 9:8
if in truth ye *a.* me king over. 15
thyself therefore and *a.* *Ruth* 3:3
a. him to be captain. *1 Sam* 9:16
Lord sent me to *a.* thee king. 15:1
thou shalt *a.* him whom I name. 16:3
the Lord said, arise, *a.* him, this. 12
a. not thyself with oil. *2 Sam* 14:2
let Zadok *a.* him king. *1 Ki* 1:34
a. Hazael king. 19:15
a. Jehu, *a.* Elisha. 16
arise ye princes, and *a.* *Isa* 21:5
seal up the vision, and *a.* *Dan* 9:24
neither did I *a.* myself at all. 10:3
a. themselves with the. *Amos* 6:6
the olives, but not *a.* *Mi* 6:15
when thou fastest *a.* thine. *Mat* 6:17
is come to *a.* my body. *Mark* 14:8
spices that they might *a.* him. 16:1
with oil thou didst not *a.* *Luke* 7:46
a. thine eyes with eye-. *Rev* 3:18

anointed

sons after him, to be *a.* *Ex* 29:29
if the priest that is *a.* do sin. *Lev* 4:3
of Aaron, when he is *a.* 6:20
in the day that he *a.* them. 7:36
a. the tabernacle. 8:10
a. the altar. 11; *Num* 7:1
oil on Aaron's head, and *a.* *Lev* 8:12
sons of Aaron *a.* *Num* 3:3
offered after it was *a.* 7:10, 84, 88
Lord *a.* thee captain. *1 Sam* 10:1
a. Saul. 15:17
a. David. 16:13; *2 Sam* 2:4, 7
5:3, 17; 12:7; *2 Ki* 9:3, 6, 12
1 Chr 11:3; 14:8
house of Judah have *a.* *2 Sam* 2:7
day weak, though *a.* king. 3:39

from the earth, and *a.* *2 Sam* 12:20
David the *a.* of the God of. 23:1
the Lord hath *a.* *Isa* 61:1; *Luke* 4:18
thou art the *a.* cherub. *Ezek* 28:14
kissed his feet and *a.* *Luke* 7:38
but this woman hath *a.* my feet. 46
he *a.* the eyes of the blind. *John* 9:6
Jesus made clay, and *a.* mine. 11
it was that Mary which *a.* the. 11:2
took Mary ointment and *a.* 12:3
Jesus, whom thou hast *a.* *Acts* 4:27
how God *a.* Jesus of Nazareth. 10:38
which hath *a.* us is God. *2 Cor* 1:21

anointed *ones*

are the two *a. ones.* *Zech* 4:14

his **anointed**

and exalt horn of *his a.* *1 Sam* 2:10
me before the Lord and *his a.* 12:3
the Lord and *his a.* is witness. 5
sheweth mercy to his *a.* *2 Sam* 22:51
Ps 18:50
the Lord, and against *his a.* *Ps* 2:2
that the Lord saveth *his a.* 20:6
the saving strength of *his a.* 28:8
thus saith the Lord to *his a.* *Isa* 45:1

Lord's **anointed**

surely the *Lord's a.* is. *1 Sam* 16:6
to my master, the *Lord's a.* 24:6
my lord, for he is the *Lord's a.* 10
his hand against the *Lord's a.* 26:9
ye have not kept the *Lord's a.* 16
not afraid to destroy the *Lord's a.*? *2 Sam* 1:14
because he cursed the *Lord's a.* 19:21
the *a. of Lord* was taken. *Lam* 4:20

mine **anointed**

walk before *mine a.* *1 Sam* 2:35
not *mine a.* *1 Chr* 16:22; *Ps* 105:15
a lamp for *mine a.* *Ps* 132:17

anointed *with oil*

priest *a.* with holy *oil.* *Num* 35:25
had not been *a. with oil.* *2 Sam* 1:21
God *a.* thee *with oil* of. *Ps* 45:7
Heb 1:9
with my holy *oil* have I *a.* *Ps* 89:20
I shall be *a. with* fresh *oil.* 92:10

thine **anointed**

O Lord God, turn not away the face of *thine a.* *2 Chr* 6:42; *Ps* 132:10
look on face of *thine a.* *Ps* 84:9
been wroth with *thine a.* 89:38
the footsteps of *thine a.* 51
for salvation with *thine a.* *Hab* 3:13

anointedst

of Beth-el where thou *a.* *Gen* 31:13
a. my head with oil, my. *Ps* 23:5

anointing

their *a.* be an everlasting. *Ex* 40:15
destroyed because of the *a.* *Isa* 10:27
but the *a.* which ye have received of him as the same *a.* *1 John* 2:27

anointing *oil*

he made the holy *a. oil.* *Ex* 37:29
he poured of the *a. oil.* *Lev* 8:12
for the *a. oil* of the Lord is. 10:7
on whose head the *a. oil* was 21:10
Eleazar pertaineth *a. oil.* *Num* 4:16
a. him with *oil* in the. *Jas* 5:14

anon

(*Revised Version*, straightway)
heareth, and *a.* with joy. *Mat* 13:20
mother lay sick, and *a.* *Mark* 1:30

another

appointed me *a.* seed. *Gen* 4:25
Lord shall add to me *a.* son. 30:24
asked us, have ye *a.* brother ? 43:7
thing, which *a.* challengeth. *Ex* 22:9*
Caleb, because he had *a.* *Num* 14:24
a. generation that knew. *Judg* 2:10
be weak, and be as *a.* man. 16:7
shalt be turned into *a.* *1 Sam* 10:6
was so, that God gave him *a.* 9
give her royal estate to *a.* *Esth* 1:19
shall behold and not *a.* *Job* 19:27†
let *a.* take his. *Ps* 109:8; *Acts* 1:20
not a secret to *a.* *Pr* 25:9
let *a.* praise thee, and not thy. 27:2
will I not give to *a.* *Isa* 42:8; 48:11
a. shall call himself by the. 44:5
hast discovered thyself to *a.* 57:8
call his servants by *a.* name. 65:15
shalt not be for *a.* man. *Hos* 3:3*
man strive nor reprove *a.* *Hos* 4:4*
or do we look for *a.* ? *Mat* 11:3
is it I ? *a.* said, is it I ? *Mark* 14:19
said he to *a.* how much. *Luke* 16:7
faithful in that which is *a.* man's. 12
a. Jesus, *a.* Spirit, or *a.* *2 Cor* 11:4*
which is not *a.* but there be. *Gal* 1:7
rejoicing in himself and not in *a.* 6:4*
exhort one *a.* while. *Heb* 3:13; 10:25
not have spoken of *a.* day. 4:8

one **another**, *see* **love**

one against **another**

one man sin *against a.* *1 Sam* 2:25
dash them *one against a.* *Jer* 13:14
puffed up *one against a.* *1 Cor* 4:6
grudge not *one against a.* *Jas* 5:9

one for **another**

to eat, tarry *one for a.* *1 Cor* 11:33
have same care *one for a.* 12:25
pray *one for a.* that ye may. *Jas* 5:16

answer

[1] *To reply,* Pr 26:4. [2] *To begin to speak, when no question is asked,* Dan 2:26; Acts 5:8. [3] *To witness,* Gen 30:33. [4] *To grant what one desires in prayer,* Ps 27:7; 86:7; Isa 65:24.

Pharaoh an *a.* of peace. *Gen* 41:16
the city make thee an *a.* *Deut* 20:11
see what *a.* I shall. *2 Sam* 24:13
return Mordecai this *a.* *Esth* 4:15
and he gave me no *a.* *Job* 19:16
because they found no *a.* 32:3
cry, but none giveth *a.* 35:12
a soft *a.* turneth away. *Pr* 15:1
a man hath joy by the *a.* of his. 23
the *a.* of the tongue is from. 16:1
his lips that giveth a right *a.* 24:26
him, but he gave me no *a.* *S of S* 5:6
the lips, for there is no *a.* *Mi* 3:7
they marvelled at his *a.* *Luke* 20:26
that we may give *a.* to. *John* 1:22
thou ? Jesus gave him no *a.* 19:9
what saith the *a.* of God ? *Rom* 11:4
mine *a.* to them that do. *1 Cor* 9:3
my first *a.* none stood. *2 Tim* 4:16*
be ready to give an *a.* *1 Pet* 3:15
a. of a good conscience towards. 21

answers

in your *a.* remaineth. *Job* 21:34
because of his *a.* for wicked. 34:36
were astonished at his *a.* *Luke* 2:47

answer, *verb*

my righteousness *a.* for. *Gen* 30:33
all the people shall *a.* *Deut* 27:15
voice, nor any to *a.* *1 Ki* 18:29
thou, and I will *a.* and *a.* *Job* 13:22
the words that he would *a.* me. 23:5
visiteth, what shall I *a.* him ? 31:14
a. thee, God is greater. 33:12; 35:4
that reproveth God, let him *a.* 40:2
mercy also on me, and *a.* *Ps* 27:7
things in right, wilt thou *a.* us. 65:5
thee, for thou wilt *a.* me. 86:7
the day when I call, *a.* me. 102:2
thy right hand, and *a.* me. 108:6
O Lord, in thy faithfulness *a.* 143:1
the righteous studieth to *a.* *Pr* 15:28
thou mightest *a.* the words. 22:21*
a. a fool according to his folly. 26:5
what shall one then *a.* *Isa* 14:32
was there none to *a.* ? 50:2; 66:4
thou call, and the Lord will *a.* 58:9
are not careful to *a.* thee. *Dan* 3:16
yea the Lord will *a.* and. *Joel* 2:19
what I shall *a.* when I. *Hab* 2:1
no man was able to *a.* *Mat* 22:46
heaven or of men ? *a.* *Mark* 11:30
wist they what to *a.* him. 14:40
he from within shall *a.* *Luke* 11:7
how or what thing ye shall *a.* 12:11
he shall *a.* I know you not. 13:25
before what ye shall *a.* 21:14
more cheerfully *a.* for myself. *Acts* 24:10*; 25:16*; 26:2*
have somewhat to *a.* *2 Cor* 5:12
know how ye ought to *a.* *Col* 4:6

I will **answer**

call, *I will a.* *Job* 13:22; 14:15
Ps 91:15; *Jer* 33:3
before they call *I will a.* *Isa* 65:24
I the Lord *will a.* him. *Ezek* 14:4

not **answer**

brethren could *not a.* him. *Gen* 45:3
he could *not a.* Abner. *2 Sam* 3:11
was, *a. not.* *2 Ki* 18:36; *Isa* 36:21
a. him one of a thousand. *Job* 9:3
but I will *not a.* *Pr* 1:28
a. not a fool according to his. 26:4
understand, he will *not a.* 29:19*
I called, ye did *not a.* *Isa* 65:12
but they will *not a.* thee. *Jer* 7:27
they could *not a.* him. *Luke* 14:6
if I ask, you will *not a.* nor. 22:68

answerable

a. to the hangings of the. *Ex* 38:18

answered

(*Revised Version, frequently,* said)
Penuel *a.* as ... of Succoth *a.* *Judg* 8:8
and he *a.* here am I. *1 Sam* 3:4, 16
the women *a.* one another as. 18:7*
men of Judah *a.* the. *2 Sam* 19:42
and thus he *a.* me. *1 Ki* 2:30
king *a.* people. 12:13; *2 Chr* 10:13
no voice, nor any that *a.* *1 Ki* 18:26
the man of God *a.* the. *2 Chr* 25:9
multitude of words be *a.* ? *Job* 11:2
I *a.* O Lord God, thou. *Ezek* 37:3
Daniel *a.* with counsel. *Dan* 2:14
Balaam the son of Beor *a.* *Mi* 6:5
accused he *a.* nothing. *Mat* 27:12
14; *Mark* 14:61; 15:5; *Luke* 23:9
perceiving that he had *a.* *Mark* 12:28
when Jesus saw that he *a.* 34
held their peace, James *a.* *Acts* 15:13
I *a.* who art thou, Lord ? and. 22:8
he *a.* for himself. 25:8*; 26:1*

answered, *referring to God*

who *a.* me in the day of. *Gen* 35:3
Moses spake, and God *a.* *Ex* 19:19
and the Lord *a.* it is. *2 Sam* 21:1
he *a.* him from heaven. *1 Chr* 21:26
that the Lord had *a.* him. 28
a. thee in the secret place. *Ps* 81:7
the Lord, and he *a.* them. 99:6
the Lord *a.* me, and set me. 118:5
a. till the cities be wasted. *Isa* 6:11
what hath the Lord *a.* *Jer* 23:35, 37
the Lord *a.* me, write the. *Hab* 2:2
the Lord *a.* the angel. *Zech* 1:13
he *a.* one of them and. *Mat* 20:13
his lord *a.* and said, thou. 25:26

answered *not*

she *a.* not, nor did she. *1 Sam* 4:20
he *a.* him *not* that day. 14:37; 28:6
a. them *not.* *2 Sam* 22:42; *Ps* 18:41
people *a.* him *not* a word. *1 Ki* 18:21
2 Ki 18:36; *Isa* 36:21
you, but ye *a. not.* *Jer* 7:13; 35:17
but he *a.* her *not* a word. *Mat* 15:23

answered *and said*

Moses *a. and said,* will not. *Ex* 4:1
servants *a. and said,* let. *2 Ki* 7:13
then *a.* I them *and said.* *Neh* 2:20
Job *a. and said.* *Job* 6:1; 9:1
12:1; 16:1; 19:1
a. and said, Babylon is. *Isa* 21:9
then *a.* I *and said,* so be it. *Jer* 11:5

answeredst

thou *a.* them, O Lord our. *Ps* 99:8
day when I cried thou *a.* me. 138:3

answerest

David cried, *a.* thou ? *1 Sam* 26:14
thee, that thou *a.* ? *Job* 16:3
a. thou nothing ? *Mat* 26:62
Mark 14:60; 15:4
a. thou the high-priest ? *John* 18:22

answereth

God is departed and *a.* *1 Sam* 28:15
let the God that *a.* by. *1 Ki* 18:24
on God, and he *a.* him. *Job* 12:4
that *a.* a matter before. *Pr* 18:13
the poor intreat, but the rich *a.* 23
as face *a.* to face, so the. 27:19
God *a.* him in the joy of. *Eccl* 5:20
maketh merry, but money *a.* 10:19
and *a.* to Jerusalem that. *Gal* 4:25

answering

the other *a.* rebuked. *Luke* 23:40
be obedient, not *a.* again. *Tit* 2:9

ant, -s

go to the *a.* thou sluggard . *Pr* 6:6
the *a.* are a people not strong. 30:25

Antichrist, -s
A. will come, now there are many *A.* *1 John* 2:18
he is *A.* that denieth the Father. 22
this is that spirit of *A.* whereof. 4:3
this is a deceiver and an *A.* *2 John* 7

Antioch
travelled as far as *A.* *Acts* 11:19, 22
when they were come to *A.* spake. 20
were called Christians first in *A.* 26
they came to *A.* in Pisidia. 13:14
from Attalia they sailed to *A.* 14:26
of their own company to *A.* 15:22
Barnabas continued in *A.* 35
when Peter was come to *A.* *Gal* 2:11
which came to me at *A.* *2 Tim* 3:11

Antipas, *see* **Martyr**

Antipatris
Paul by night to *A.* *Acts* 23:31

antiquity
joyous city, whose *a.* is of. *Isa* 23:7

anvil
him that smote the *a.* *Isa* 41:7

any
against *a.* of the children. *Ex* 11:7
sin against *a.* of the commandments. *Lev* 4:2, 13, 22, 27; 5:17
lieth, in *a.* of all these that a. 6:3
nor *a.* that can deliver. *Deut* 32:39
word with *a.* *2 Sam* 7:7; *1 Chr* 17:6
yet *a.* left of the house? *2 Sam* 9:1
was no voice, nor *a.* *1 Ki* 18:26
he looketh, and if *a.* say. *Job* 33:27*
who will shew us *a.* good? *Ps* 4:6
turneth not away for *a.* *Pr* 30:30
no God, I know not *a.* *Isa* 44:8
shall say, is there yet *a.* *Amos* 6:10
nor go nor tell it to *a.* in. *Mark* 8:26*
if ye have ought against *a.* 11:25
nor could be healed of *a.* *Luke* 8:43
if he found *a.* of this way. *Acts* 9:2
brought under power of *a.* *1 Cor* 6:12
if *a.* lack wisdom, let him. *Jas* 1:5
not willing that *a.* should. *2 Pet* 3:9
if there come *a.* and bring. *2 John* 10
see **further, God, man, more, thing, time, while, wise.**

apace, *see* **flee, fled**

apart
shalt set *a.* all that open. *Ex* 13:12
shall be put *a.* seven. *Lev* 15:19*
approach, as long as she is *a.* 18:19*
the Lord hath set *a.* him. *Ps* 4:3
a. their wives *a.* *Zech* 12:12, 14
into a desert place *a.* *Mat* 14:13
into a mountain *a.* 23; 17:1
the disciples to Jesus *a.* 17:19
come ye yourselves *a.* *Mark* 6:31
lay *a.* all filthiness. *Jas* 1:21

Apelles
salute *A.* approved in. *Rom* 16:10

Aphek
pitched in *A.* *1 Sam* 4:1; 29:1
the rest fled to *A.* there. *1 Ki* 20:30
smite the Syrians in *A.* *2 Ki* 13:17

apes, *see* **peacocks**

apiece
five shekels *a.* by poll. *Num* 3:47
spoons weighing ten shekels *a.* 7:86
their princes gave him a rod *a.* 17:6
eighteen cubits high *a.* *1 Ki* 7:15
nor have two coats *a.* *Luke* 9:3
two or three firkins *a.* *John* 2:6

Apollonia
had passed through *A.* *Acts* 17:1

Apollos
certain Jew named *A.* *Acts* 18:24
I am of *A.* *1 Cor* 1:12; 3:4
who is *A.*? 3:5
I have planted, *A.* watered, God. 3:6
in a figure transferred to *A.* 4:6
bring Zenas and *A.* on. *Tit* 3:13

Apollyon
tongue, his name is *A.* *Rev* 9:11

apostle
Literally, one sent forth. *Used as referring* [1] *chiefly to one of the 12 disciples of Christ,* Matt. 10:2; or [2] *to any of various other followers of Christ who did evangelistic work,* Rom 1:1.
called to be an *a.* *Rom* 1:1; *1 Cor* 1:1
inasmuch as I am the *a.* *Rom* 11:13
am I not an *a.*? *1 Cor* 9:1, 2
meet to be called an *a.* 15:9
an *a.* of Jesus. *2 Cor* 1:1; *Eph* 1:1 *Col* 1:1; *1 Tim* 1:1; *2 Tim* 1:1 *Gal* 1:1
signs of an *a.* were. *2 Cor* 12:12
ordained an *a.* *1 Tim* 2:7; *2 Tim* 1:11
Paul a servant of God, and *a.* *Tit* 1:1
the *a.* and high-priest. *Heb* 3:1

apostles
names of the 12 *a.* *Mat* 10:2
a. gathered themselves. *Mark* 6:30
whom he named *a.* *Luke* 6:13
a. when they were returned. 9:10
send them prophets and *a.* 11:49
a. said to the Lord, increase. 17:5
and the twelve *a.* with him. 22:14
told these things to the *a.* 24:10
with the eleven *a.* *Acts* 1:26
were done by the *a.* 2:43; 5:12
down at the *a.* feet. 4:35, 37; 5:2
laid their hands on the *a.* and. 5:18
scattered abroad, except the *a.* 8:1
of note among the *a.* *Rom* 16:7
set forth us the *a.* last. *1 Cor* 4:9
God hath set first *a.* 12:28
are all *a.*? 29
for I am the least of the *a.* 15:9
behind the chiefest *a.* *2 Cor* 11:5 12:11
false *a.* deceitful workers. 11:13
them that were *a.* before. *Gal* 1:17
but other of the *a.* saw I none. 19
now revealed to his holy *a.* *Eph* 3:5
some *a* and some prophets. 4:11
burdensome as the *a.* *1 Thes* 2:6
commandment of us the *a.* *2 Pet* 3:2
words spoken before of the *a.* *Jude* 17
them which say they are *a.* *Rev* 2:2
rejoice over her, ye holy *a.* 18:20

apostleship
(*The office of the apostles*)
he may take part of this *a.* *Acts* 1:25
have received grace and *a.* *Rom* 1:5
the seal of mine *a.* are ye. *1 Cor* 9:2
effectually in Peter to the *a.* *Gal* 2:8

apothecary
(*Revised Version,* perfumer)
compounded after art of *a.* *Ex* 30:25
after the art of the *a.* 35; 37:29
the ointment of the *a.* *Eccl* 10:1

apparel
arose and changed his *a.* *2 Sam* 12:20
the attendance of his ministers, and their *a.* *1 Ki* 10:5; *2 Chr* 9:4
the changeable suits of *a.* *Isa* 3:22*
and wear our own *a.* 4:1
that is glorious in his *a.* 63:1
are clothed in strange *a.* *Zeph* 1:8
stood by them in white *a.* *Acts* 1:10
coveted no man's silver or *a.* 20:33
themselves in modest *a.* *1 Tim* 2:9
if a man come in goodly *a.* *Jas* 2:2
gold, or putting on *a.* *1 Pet* 3:3
see **royal**

apparelled
virgins, were *a.* *2 Sam* 13:18
which are gorgeously *a.* *Luke* 7:25

apparently
(*Revised Version,* manifestly)
I speak even *a.* and not. *Num* 12:8

appeal, -ed
I *a.* unto Caesar. *Acts* 25:11, 21
liberty, if he had not *a.* to. 26:32
I was constrained to *a.* to. 28:19

appear
God said, let the dry land *a.* *Gen* 1:9
and none shall *a.* before me empty. *Ex* 23:15; 34:20; *Deut* 16:16
the year all males shall *a.* *Ex* 23:17
when thou shalt go to *a.* 34:24
Israel is come to *a.* *Deut* 31:11
when shall I come and *a.*? *Ps* 42:2
thy work *a.* to thy servants. 90:16
flowers *a.* on the earth. *S of S* 2:12*
a flock of goats that *a.* 4:1*; 6:5
when ye come to *a.* *Isa* 1:12
that thy shame may *a.* *Jer* 13:26
doings your sins do *a.* *Ezek* 21:24
that they may *a.* to men. *Mat* 6:16
so ye outwardly *a.* righteous. 23:28
then shall *a.* the sign of the. 24:30
as graves which *a.* not. *Luke* 11:44
kingdom of God should *a.* 19:11
in which I will *a.* to thee. *Acts* 26:16
but sin, that it might *a.* *Rom* 7:13
we must all *a.* before. *2 Cor* 5:10*
who is our life shall *a.* then. *Col* 3:4
that thy profiting may *a.* *1 Tim* 4:15
now to *a.* in the presence. *Heb* 9:24
to them shall he *a.* the second. 28
not made of things which do *a.* 11:3
ungodly and sinner *a.*? *1 Pet* 4:18
when the chief Shepherd shall *a.* 5:4
when he shall *a.* we may. *1 John* 2:28
it doth not yet *a.* what we shall . . . know that when he shall *a.* we. 3:2
thy nakedness do not *a.* *Rev* 3:18

appear, *referred to God*
to-day the Lord will *a.* to. *Lev* 9:4, 6
I will *a.* in the cloud on the. 16:2
did I plainly *a.* to the. *1 Sam* 2:27
that night did God *a.* *2 Chr* 1:7
build up Zion, he shall *a.* *Ps* 102:16
he shall *a.* to your joy. *Isa* 66:5*
in the which I will *a.* *Acts* 26:16

appearance
as the *a.* of fire. *Num* 9:15, 16
looketh on the outward *a.* *1 Sam* 16:7
as the *a.* of a man. *Dan* 8:15; 10:18
his face as the *a.* of lightning. 10:6
not according to the *a.* *John* 7:24
which glory in *a.* and. *2 Cor* 5:12
things after the outward *a.*? 10:7*
abstain from all *a.* of. *1 Thes* 5:22*

appeared
a. to Abram. *Gen* 12:7; 17:1; 18:1
Lord *a.* to Isaac, and said. 26:2, 24
Jacob said, God Almighty *a.* to. 48:3
angel of the Lord *a.* in. *Ex* 3:2
the Lord hath not *a.* to thee. 4:1
I *a.* to Abraham by name of. 6:3
returned when the morning *a.* 14:27
channels of the sea *a.* *2 Sam* 22:16
which had *a.* to Solomon. *1 Ki* 11:9
there *a.* a chariot of fire. *2 Ki* 2:11
the work till the stars *a.* *Neh* 4:21
the Lord hath *a.* of old to. *Jer* 31:3
what time the star *a.* *Mat* 2:7
the blade sprung, then *a.* the. 13:26
a. to them Moses. 17:3; *Mark* 9:4
holy city, and *a.* to many. *Mat* 27:53
Jesus *a.* first to Mary. *Mark* 16:9
after that he *a.* in another form to. 12
after he *a.* to the eleven as they. 14
there *a.* to him an angel. *Luke* 1:11
who *a.* in glory, and spake. 9:31
there *a.* an angel to him. 22:43
Lord is risen indeed, and *a.* 24:34
there *a.* to them cloven. *Acts* 2:3
the God of glory *a.* to our. 7:2
even Jesus, that *a.* to thee. 9:17
I have *a.* to thee for this. 26:16
neither sun nor stars *a.* 27:20
the grace of God hath *a.* *Tit* 2:11
love of God toward man *a.* 3:4
in the end hath he *a.* to. *Heb* 9:26
there *a.* a great wonder. *Rev* 12:1, 3

appeareth
as the leprosy *a.* in the. *Lev* 13:43
deliver him, as *a.* this. *Deut* 2:30*
every one of them in Zion *a.* *Ps* 84:7
the hay *a.* and the tender. *Pr* 27:25*
for evil *a.* out of the north. *Jer* 6:1
shall stand when he *a.*? *Mal* 3:2
is even as a vapour that *a.* *Jas* 4:14

appearing
commandment till *a.* *1 Tim* 6:14
made manifest by the *a.* *2 Tim* 1:10
the quick and dead at his *a.* 4:1
all them also that love his *a.* 8
looking for glorious *a.* of. *Tit* 2:13
found to praise at the *a.* *1 Pet* 1:7

appease
I will *a.* him with the. *Gen* 32:20

appeased, -eth
Ahasuerus *a.* he. *Esth* 2:1
slow to anger *a.* strife. *Pr* 15:18
town-clerk had *a.* the. *Acts* 19:35

appertain
them, with all that *a.* *Num* 16:30
fear, for to thee doth it a. *Jer* 10:7
see **pertain**

appertained
men that *a.* to Korah. *Num* 16:32, 33

appertaineth, -ing
give it to him to whom it *a.* *Lev* 6:5
Abraham, our father, as *a.* *Rom* 4:1

appetite
wilt thou fill the *a.* of the. *Job* 38:39
if thou be a man given to *a.* *Pr* 23:2
all labour for mouth, yet *a.* *Eccl* 6:7
awaketh, and his soul hath *a.* *Isa* 29:8

Appii-forum
meet us as far as *A.* *Acts* 28:15

apple *of the eye*
(*The eyeball*)
as the *a.* *of his eye.* *Deut* 32:10
keep me as the *a. of the eye.* *Ps* 17:8
law as the *a. of thine eye.* *Pr* 7:2
let not the *a. of thine eye.* *Lam* 2:18
toucheth the *a. of his eye.* *Zech* 2:8

apples
like *a.* of gold in pictures. *Pr* 25:11
comfort me with *a.* for I. *S of S* 2:5
and smell of thy nose like *a.* 7:8

apple-tree
as the *a.-tree* among. *S of S* 2:3
raised thee up under the *a.-tree.* 8:5
palm-tree and *a.-tree.* *Joel* 1:12

applied
I *a.* my heart to know. *Eccl* 7:25*
I *a.* my heart to every work. 8:9
when I *a.* mine heart to know. 16

apply
we may *a.* our hearts. *Ps* 90:12*
and *a.* thine heart to. *Pr* 2:2
hear words, *a.* thine heart to. 22:17
a. thine heart to instruction. 23:12

appoint
(*To establish, to set apart for an office, or to decree*)
a. me thy wages, and I. *Gen* 30:28
let Pharaoh *a.* officers over. 41:34
I will *a.* over you terror. *Lev* 26:16
Aaron and his sons *a.* *Num* 4:19
to *a.* me ruler over the. *2 Sam* 6:21
I will *a.* a place for my people. 7:10
that thou wouldest *a.* me. *Job* 14:13
salvation will God *a.* for. *Isa* 26:1
a. them that mourn in Zion. 61:3
a. over them four kinds. *Jer* 15:3
chosen man that I may *a.* over her? who will *a.* me? 49:19; 50:44
he kingdoms *a.* a captain. 51:27
. these two ways. *Ezek* 21:19
. a way that. 20
hey shall *a.* themselves. *Hos* 1:11
. him his portion with the. *Mat* 24:51
. him his portion with. *Luke* 12:46
a. you a kingdom, as my. 22:29
even men whom we *a.* *Acts* 6:3

appointed
he that thou hast *a.* for. *Gen* 24:14
assover in *a.* seasons. *Num* 9:2, 3
n offering, but at an *a.* season. 7
rought not offering in *a.* season. 13
ese were the cities *a.* *Josh* 20:9
as an *a.* sign between. *Judg* 20:38
ot within the days *a.* *1 Sam* 13:11
amuel standing as *a.* over. 19:20*
ord had *a.* to defeat. *2 Sam* 17:14
have *a.* him to be ruler. *1 Ki* 1:35
t go a man whom I had *a.* 20:42*
ou hast *a.* prophets to. *Neh* 6:7
eir rebellion *a.* a captain to. 9:17
earisome nights are *a.* to. *Job* 7:3
ou hast *a.* his bounds, that. 14:5
d the heritage *a.* to him. 20:29
death, and to the house *a.* 30:23
st given us like sheep *a.* *Ps* 44:11
a law in Israel, which he. 78:5
ose that are *a.* to die. 79:11
loose those that are *a.* to. 102:20
me home at the day *a.* *Pr* 7:20*
en he *a.* the foundations of. 8:29
use of all such as are *a.* to. 31:8*
w-moons and your *a.* *Isa* 1:14
who, since I *a.* the ancient. *Isa* 44:7†
he reserveth the *a.* weeks. *Jer* 5:24
sea-shore, there hath he *a.* 47:7
I have *a.* thee each day. *Ezek* 4:6
the rod, and who hath *a.* it. *Mi* 6:9
field, as the Lord *a.* *Mat* 27:10
more than what is *a.* you. *Luke* 3:13
after these the Lord *a.* other. 10:1
kingdom, as my Father hath *a.* 22:29
they *a.* two, Joseph and. *Acts* 1:23*
he hath *a.* a day in which. 17:31
apostles last, *a.* to death. *1 Cor* 4:9*
you know that we are *a.* *1 Thes* 3:3
God hath not *a.* us to wrath. 5:9
whereunto I am *a.* a. *2 Tim* 1:11
elders in every city, as I *a.* *Tit* 1:5
faithful to him that *a.* *Heb* 3:2
as it is *a.* to men once to die. 9:27
also they were *a.* *1 Pet* 2:8

appointed *time* and *times*
at the *time a.* will I. *Gen* 18:14
Lord *a.* a set *time*, saying. *Ex* 9:5
unleavened bread in *time a.* 23:15
the set *time* Samuel *a.* *1 Sam* 13:8
into the field at the *time a.* 20:35
the set *time a.* him. *2 Sam* 20:5
to their *a. time* every. *Esth* 9:27
is there not an *a. time* to? *Job* 7:1*
the days of my *a. time* will. 14:14*
trumpet in the *time a.* *Ps* 81:3*
be alone in his *a. times.* *Isa* 14:31
heaven knoweth her *a. times.* *Jer* 8:7
he hath passed the *time a.* 46:17
for at the *time a.* the end. *Dan* 8:19
thing was true, but the *time a.* 10:1*
end shall be at the *time a.* 11:27
time a. shall return, and come. 29
because it is yet for a *time a.* 35
vision is yet for an *a. time.* *Hab* 2:3
times before *a.* *Acts* 17:26
under tutors, until the *time a.* *Gal* 4:2

appointeth
he *a.* over it whomsoever. *Dan* 5:21*

appointment
at the *a.* of Aaron and. *Num* 4:27*
by the *a.* of Absalom. *2 Sam* 13:32
wheat, salt according to *a.* *Ezra* 6:9*
had made an *a.* together. *Job* 2:11

apprehend
(*To seize or take prisoner*)
garrison desirous to *a.* *2 Cor* 11:32*
I may *a.* that for which. *Phil* 3:12

apprehended
when he *a.* Peter, he put. *Acts* 12:4
I am *a.* of Christ Jesus. *Phil* 3:12
not myself to have *a.* but. 13

approach
[1] *To draw nigh, or come near,* 2 Sam 11:20; Ps 65:4; Isa 58:2. [2] *To contract marriage with,* Lev 18:6.
none of you shall *a.* to. *Lev* 18:6
not *a.* to offer the bread. 21:17, 18
ye *a.* this day to battle. *Deut* 20:3
behold, thy days *a.* that thou. 31:14
make his sword to *a.* *Job* 40:19†
man whom thou causeth to *a.* *Ps* 65:4
a. to me, for who is this that engaged his heart to *a.* to me? *Jer* 30:21
light no man can *a.* unto. *1 Tim* 6:16

approached
wherefore *a.* ye so? *2 Sam* 11:20
the king *a.* to the altar. *2 Ki* 16:12

approacheth, -ing
they take delight in *a.* to. *Isa* 58:2
where no thief *a.* nor. *Luke* 12:33
more as ye see the day *a.* *Heb* 10:25

approve
(*To like or commend*)
yet their posterity *a.* *Ps* 49:13
whom you shall *a.* by. *1 Cor* 16:3
that ye may *a.* things. *Phil* 1:10

approved
Jesus, a man *a.* of God. *Acts* 2:22
acceptable to God, and *a.* *Rom* 14:18
salute Apelles *a.* in Christ. 16:10
are *a.* may be made. *1 Cor* 11:19
in all things you have *a.* *2 Cor* 7:11
commendeth himself is *a.* 10:18
not that we should appear *a.* but. 13:7
study to shew thyself *a.* *2 Tim* 2:15

approvest, -eth
a man, the Lord *a.* not. *Lam* 3:36
a. the things that are. *Rom* 2:18

approving
but in all things *a.* *2 Cor* 6:4

apron, -s
fig-leaves together, and made *a.* *Gen* 3:7
brought to the sick *a.* *Acts* 19:12

apt
a. for war, king of. *2 Ki* 24:16
be *a.* to teach. *1 Tim* 3:2; *2 Tim* 2:24

Aquila
a certain Jew named *A.* *Acts* 18:2
when *A.* and Priscilla heard. 26
greet *A.* and Priscilla. *Rom* 16:3
2 Tim 4:19
A. and Priscilla salute. *1 Cor* 16:19

Ar
consumed *A.* of Moab. *Num* 21:28
I have given *A.* to the. *Deut* 2:9
in the night *A.* of Moab is. *Isa* 15:1

Arabia
kings of *A.* *1 Ki* 10:15; *2 Chr* 9:14
A. shall lodge in *A.* *Isa* 21:13
all the kings of *A.* *Jer* 25:24
I went into *A.* and. *Gal* 1:17
Agar is mount Sinai in *A.* 4:25

Arabian, -s
the *A.* brought. *2 Chr* 17:11
helped Uzziah against the *A.* 26:7
nor shall the *A.* pitch tent. *Isa* 13:20
thou sattest for them as *A.* *Jer* 3:2
Cretes and *A.* we do hear. *Acts* 2:11

Aram
sons of Shem, Lud, *A.* *Gen* 10:22
1 Chr 1:17
Moab brought me from *A.* *Num* 23:7
Esrom begat *A.* *Mat* 1:3
A. begat Aminadab. 4:4
which was the son of *A.* *Luke* 3:33
see **Padan**

Ararat
on the mountains of *A.* *Gen* 8:4
her the kingdoms of *A.* *Jer* 51:27

Araunah
the threshing-place of *A.* *2 Sam* 24:16
all these did *A.* as a king give. 23

Arba
A. was a great man. *Josh* 14:15

Arba
gave them *A.* which city. *Josh* 21:11

archangel
with the voice of the *a.* *1 Thes* 4:16
Michael the *a.* when. *Jude* 9

archer, -s
grew and became an *a.* *Gen* 21:20
the *a.* have sorely grieved. 49:23
a. hit him. *1 Sam* 31:3; *1 Chr* 10:3
his *a.* compass me round. *Job* 16:13
they are bound by the *a.* *Isa* 22:3
bendeth let *a.* bend bow. *Jer* 51:3

arches
narrow windows to the *a.* *Ezek* 40:16

Archelaus
heard that *A.* did reign. *Mat* 2:22

Archippus
say to *A.* take heed to. *Col* 4:17
Paul to *A.* fellow-soldier. *Philem* 2

Arcturus
which maketh *A.* Orion and. *Job* 9:9
or canst thou guide *A.* with? 38:32

Areopagite
was Dionysius the *A.* *Acts* 17:34

Areopagus
and brought him to *A.* *Acts* 17:19

Aretas
the governor under *A.* *2 Cor* 11:32

Argob
region of *A.* *Deut* 3:4; 13:14
1 Ki 4:13

arguing
doth your *a.* reprove? *Job* 6:25*

arguments
would fill my mouth with *a.* *Job* 23:4

Ariel

sent for Eliezer and *A.* *Ezra* 8:16
woe to *A.* the city where. *Isa* 29:1
A. it shall be to me as *A.* 2
nations that fight against *A.* 7

aright

his conversation *a.* *Ps* 50:23
that set not their heart *a.* 78:8
the wise useth knowledge *a.* *Pr* 15:2
wine, when it moveth itself *a.* 23:31
but they spake not *a.* *Jer* 8:6

Arimathea

Joseph of *A.* who was. *Mat* 27:57
Mark 15:43; *Luke* 23:51
John 19:38

Arioch

in the days of *A.* king of. *Gen* 14:1
then *A.* brought in Daniel. *Dan* 2:25

arise

[1] *To proceed from,* Acts 20:30. [2] *To be raised and comforted,* Amos 7:2.

now *a.* get thee out of. *Gen* 31:13
a. go up to Beth-el, and. 35:1
if there *a.* among you a. *Deut* 13:1
then shalt thou *a.* and get. 17:8
now therefore *a.* go over. *Josh* 1:2
a. Barak, lead thy. *Judg* 5:12
let the young men *a.* *2 Sam* 2:14
I will *a* and gather all Israel. 3:21
so be that the king's wrath *a.* 11:20
after thee shall any *a.* *1 Ki* 3:12
make Jehu *a.* from. *2 Ki* 9:2
a. be doing, the Lord. *1 Chr* 22:16
we his servants will *a.* *Neh* 2:20
a. too much contempt. *Esth* 1:18
then shall enlargement *a.* to. 4:14
when shall I *a.* and night? *Job* 7:4
whom doth not his light *a.*? 25:3
a. O Lord, save me, O my. *Ps* 3:7
a. O Lord, in thine anger lift. 7:6
now will I *a.* saith the Lord, I. 12:5
a. for our help, and redeem. 44:26
let God *a.* let his enemies be. 68:1
shall the dead *a.* and praise? 88:10
when the waves of sea *a.* thou. 89:9
thou shalt *a.* and have mercy. 102:13
when wilt thou *a.* out of. *Pr* 6:9
a. my love, my fair one. *S of S* 2:13
a. ye princes, and anoint. *Isa* 21:5
my dead body shall they *a.* 26:19
kings shall *a.* princes shall. 49:7
a. shine, for thy light is come. 60:1
but the Lord shall *a.* upon thee. 2
in trouble they will say. *a.* *Jer* 2:27
shall they fall and not *a.*? 8:4
a. ye, let us go up to Zion to. 31:6
a. cry out in the night. *Lam* 2:19
after thee shall *a.* *Dan* 2:39
whom shall Jacob *a.* *Amos* 7:2*, 5
a. ye and depart. *Mi* 2:10
a. and thresh, O daughter of. 4:13
enemy, when I fall I shall *a.* 7:8
saith to the dumb stone *a.* *Hab* 2:19
Sun of righteousness *a.* *Mal* 4:2
say *a.* and walk? *Mat* 9:5; *Mark* 2:9
there shall *a.* false Christs. *Mat* 24:24
say to thee *a.* *Mark* 5:41; *Luke* 8:54
man, I say to thee *a.* *Luke* 7:14
I will *a.* and go to my father. 15:18
and why do thoughts *a.* in? 24:38
even so I do, *a.* let us. *John* 14:31
body said, Tabitha, *a.* *Acts* 9:40
selves shall men *a.* speaking. 20:30
why tarriest thou? *a.* and be. 22:16
a. from the dead, and. *Eph* 5:14
till the day-star *a.* in. *2 Pet* 1:19

see **rise**

ariseth

behold, there *a.* a little. *1 Ki* 18:44
to the upright *a.* light in. *Ps* 112:4
a. to shake terribly the. *Isa* 2:19, 21
when persecution *a.* *Mat* 13:21
Mark 4:17
for out of Galilee *a.* *John* 7:52
the similitude of Melchizedec *a.*
Heb 7:15

see **sun**

Aristarchus

caught Gaius and *A.* *Acts* 19:29
A. accompanied Paul into. 20:4
one *A.* a Macedonian being. 27:2
A. fellow-prisoner. *Col* 4:10
Philem 24

Aristobulus

that are of *A.* household. *Rom* 16:10

ark

[1] *A chest or coffer to keep things sure or secret,* Ex 2:3. [2] *The great vessel in which Noah and his family were preserved during the flood,* Gen 6:14, 15; Heb 11:7. [3] *That chest wherein the two tables of the law, Aaron's rod, and the pot of manna were kept,* Ex 37:1; Heb 9:4.

an *a.* of gopher-wood. *Gen* 6:14
and the *a.* went on the face of. 7:18
she took for him an *a.* of. *Ex* 2:3
put into the *a.* the testimony which I
shall give thee. 25:16, 21; 40:3, 20
made the *a.* of shittim-wood. 37:1
charge shall be the *a.* *Num* 3:31
a. of the Lord. *Josh* 4:11; 6:12
1 Sam 4:6; 6:1; *2 Sam* 6:9
they looked into *a.* *1 Sam* 6:19
the *a.* and Israel abide. *2 Sam* 11:11
thou barest the *a.* of. *1 Ki* 2:26
was nothing in the *a.* save the. 8:9
after that the *a.* had. *1 Chr* 6:31
let us bring again the *a.* of. 13:3
put forth his hand to hold the *a.* 9
prepared a place for the *a.* 15:1
and *a.* of thy strength. *2 Chr* 6:41
Ps 132:8
whereunto the *a.* hath. *2 Chr* 8:11
Noah entered the *a.* *Mat* 24:38
Luke 17:27
of God prepared an *a.* *Heb* 11:7
waited while the *a* was. *1 Pet* 3:20
seen in his temple the *a.* *Rev* 11:19

before the **ark**

altar of gold *before the a.* *Ex* 40:5
were cut off *before the a.* *Josh* 4:7
earth on his face *before the a.* 7:6
his face *before the a.* *1 Sam* 5:3
left *before the a.* Asaph. *1 Chr* 16:37
assembled *before the a.* *2 Chr* 5:6

ark *of the covenant*

a. of covenant of Lord. *Num* 10:33
inside of *a. of covenant.* *Deut.* 31:26
off before *a. of covenant.* *Josh* 4:7
a. of covenant of God. *Judg* 20:27
the *a. of the covenant* of. *1 Sam* 4:3
bearing *a. of covenant.* *2 Sam* 15:24
a. of covenant remained. *1 Chr* 17:1
more, the *a. of covenant.* *Jer* 3:16
had the *a. of the covenant.* *Heb* 9:4

ark *of God*

where the *a. of God* was. *1 Sam* 3:3
the *a. of God* was taken. 4:11; 17:22
if ye send away the *a. of God.* 6:3
died before the *a. of God.* *2 Sam* 6:7
but the *a. of God* dwelleth. 7:2
carry back the *a. of God* into. 15:25
I bring the *a. of God.* *1 Chr* 13:12
ought to carry the *a. of God.* 15:2

arm

Literally, for the part of the body so called, 2 Sam 1:10. [2] *Figuratively for power or strength,* Ps 10:15; Jer 27:5; Isa 53:1; John 12:38.

by greatness of thine *a.* *Ex* 15:16
he teareth the *a.* with. *Deut* 33:20
I will cut off thine *a.* *1 Sam* 2:31
that was on his *a.* *2 Sam* 1:10
with him is an *a.* of. *2 Chr* 32:8
savest thou the *a.* that. *Job* 26:2
a. fall from my shoulder. 31:22*
cry out by reason of the *a.* of. 35:9
the high *a.* shall be broken. 38:15
hast thou an *a.* like God? 40:9
break thou the *a.* of the. *Ps* 10:15
own *a.* save them, but thy *a.* 44:3
hast with thy *a.* redeemed. 77:15
thou hast a mighty *a.* strong. 89:13
mine *a.* also shall strengthen him. 21
his holy *a.* hath gotten him. 98:1
set me as a seal on thine *a.* *S of S* 8:6
man the flesh of his *a.* *Isa* 9:20
thou their *a.* every morning. 33:2
God will come, and his *a.* shall. 40:10
gather the lambs with his *a.* 11
a. shall judge the people, the isles ...
me, and on my *a.* *Isa* 51:5
put on strength, O *a.* of the Lord. 9
hath made bare his holy *a.* 52:10
believed our report? and to whom is
the *a.* of the? 53:1; *John* 12:38
a. brought salvation. *Isa* 59:16; 63:5
Lord hath sworn by the *a.* of. 62:8
led them with his glorious *a.* 63:12
that maketh flesh his *a.* *Jer* 17:5
fight against you with a strong *a.* 21:5
and thine *a.* shall be. *Ezek* 4:7
I have broken *a.* of Pharaoh. 30:21
into hell that where his *a.* 31:17
retain the power of the *a.* *Dan* 11:6
sword be on his *a.* his *a.* *Zech* 11:17
strength with his *a.* *Luke* 1:51
with an high *a.* brought. *Acts* 13:17

arm, *verb*

a. some of yourselves to. *Num* 31:3
a. yourselves with the. *1 Pet* 4:1

stretched-out **arm**

you with a *stretched-out a.* *Ex* 6:6
nation with *stretched-out a.*
Deut 4:34
thee out thence with a *stretched-out*
a. 5:15; 7:19; 26:8; *Jer* 32:21
not seen *stretched-out a.* *Deut* 11:2
come for thy *stretched-out a.*
2 Chr 6:32
with a *stretched-out a.* *Ps* 136:12
my *stretched-out a.* *Jer* 27:5; 32:17
with a *stretched-out a.* *Ezek* 20:33
with a *stretched-out a.* and fury. 34

Armageddon

them together to *A.* *Rev* 16:16

armed

Abram *a.* his trained. *Gen* 14:14
tribe, twelve thousand *a.* *Num* 31:5
ourselves will go ready *a.* 32:17, 32
pass over *a.* *Deut* 3:18; *Josh* 1:14
let him that is *a.* pass on. *Josh* 6:7
so the *a.* men left the. *2 Chr* 28:14
he goeth on to meet the *a.* *Job* 39:21
of Ephraim being *a.* *Ps* 78:9
want as an *a.* man. *Pr* 6:11; 24:34
when a strong man *a.* *Luke* 11:21

Armenia

into land of *A.* *2 Ki* 19:37; *Isa* 37:38

arm-holes

rags under thy *a.-holes.* *Jer* 38:12
sew pillows to *a.-holes.* *Ezek* 13:18

armies

(*Used frequently in the sense of hosts, great numbers*)

and bring forth my *a.* *Ex* 7:4
same day I brought your *a.* 12:17
went forth with their *a.* *Num* 33:
captains of the *a.* to lead. *Deut* 20:
I defy the *a.* of Israel. *1 Sam* 17:1
that he should defy the *a.* of the. 2
name of the God of the *a.* of. 4
there any number of his *a.*? *Job* 25:
not forth with our *a.* *Ps* 44:
kings of *a.* did flee apace, she. 68:1
the company of two *a.* *S of S* 6:1
his fury upon all their *a.* *Isa* 34:
he sent forth his *a.* and. *Mat* 22:
compassed with *a.* *Luke* 21:2
who turned to flight the *a.* *Heb* 11:3
and the *a.* in heaven. *Rev* 19:1
kings of the earth and their *a.*

armour

[1] *Weapons or instruments of wa*[r,] 1 Sam 17:54. [2] *Those things which one trusts for protectio*[n,] Luke 11:22; Rom 13:12; Eph 6:1

David put Goliath's *a.* *1 Sam* 17:
and take thee his *a.* *2 Sam* 2:
they washed his *a.* *1 Ki* 22:3
all able to put on *a.* *2 Ki* 3:
have a fenced city also and *a.* 10
silver and gold, the house of his *a*
20:13; *Isa* 39
look in that day to *a.* of. *Isa* 22
taketh his *a.* wherein he. *Luke* 11:
and let us put on the *a.* *Rom* 13:
approving by the *a.* of. *2 Cor* 6
put on the *a.* of God to. *Eph* 6:
take to you the whole *a.* of God.

armour-bearer
called his *a.-b.*, saying. *Jud*: 9:54
a.-b. said, do all that is. *1 Sam* 14:7
David, and he became his *a.-b.* 16:21
his three sons, and his *a.-b.* 31:6

armoury
of David builded for an *a.* *S of S* 4:4
the Lord hath opened his *a.* *Jer* 50:25

arms
the *a.* of his hands were. *Gen* 49:24
are the everlasting *a.* *Deut* 33:27
brake them from his *a.* *Judg* 16:12
steel is broken by mine *a.*
2 Sam 22:35; *Ps* 18:34
Jehoram between his *a.* *2 Ki* 9:24
the *a.* of the fatherless. *Job* 22:9
the *a.* of the wicked shall. *Ps* 37:17
strengtheneth her *a.* *Pr* 31:17
with strength of his *a.* *Isa* 44:12
bring thy sons in their *a.* 49:22
and my *a.* shall judge the. 51:5
tear them from your *a.* *Ezek* 13:20
will break Pharaoh's *a.* 30:22, 24
will strengthen the *a.* of king. 24, 25
breast and his *a.* of silver. *Dan* 2:32
a. and feet like to polished. 10:6
the *a.* of the south shall not. 11:15
with the *a.* of a flood shall they. 22
and *a.* shall stand on this part. 31
and strengthened their *a.* *Hos* 7:15
to go, taking them by their *a.* 11:3
taken him in his *a.* he. *Mark* 9:36
them up in his *a.* put his hands. 10:16
took Christ in his *a.* *Luke* 2:28

army
what he did to the *a.* of. *Deut* 11:4
give bread to thine *a.* *Judg* 8:6
he said, increase thine *a.* 9:29
of Benjamin out of *a.* *1 Sam* 4:12
Philistines had put *a.* against *a.* 17:21
thee an *a.* like the *a.* *1 Ki* 20:25
praise before the *a.* *2 Chr* 20:21
O king, let not the *a.* of Israel. 25:7
his brethren, and the *a.* *Neh* 4:2
I dwelt as a king in the *a.* *Job* 29:25
as an *a.* with banners. *S of S* 6:4, 10
up for fear of Pharaoh's *a.* *Jer* 37:11
caused his *a.* to serve. *Ezek* 29:18
up an exceeding great *a.* 37:10
to his will in the *a.* of. *Dan* 4:35
his voice before his *a.* *Joel* 2:11
locust, my great *a.* which I sent. 25
house, because of the *a.* *Zech* 9:8
then came I with an *a.* *Acts* 23:27
the number of the *a.* of. *Rev* 9:16
that sat on horse and his *a.* 19:19
see **Chaldeans**

Arnon
he did in the brooks of *A.* *Num* 21:14
met Balaam in the border of *A.* 22:36
and pass over the river *A.* *Deut* 2:24
dwelt by the coasts of *A.* *Judg* 11:26
Moab shall be at fords of *A.* *Isa* 16:2
tell ye it in *A.* that Moab is. *Jer* 48:20

Aroer
children of Gad built *A.* *Num* 32:34
a present to them in *A.* *1 Sam* 30:28
Jordan and pitched in *A.* *2 Sam* 24:5
Bela, who dwelt in *A.* *1 Chr* 5:8
cities of *A.* are forsaken. *Isa* 17:2
O inhabitant of *A.* stand. *Jer* 48:19

arose
perceived not when she *a.* *Gen* 19:33
o my sheaf *a.* and. 37:7
. up a new king. *Ex* 1:8; *Acts* 7:18
. a generation that knew. *Judg* 2:10
ill I Deborah *a.* till I *a.* a. 5:7
ll the people *a.* as one man. 20:8
hey *a.* early. *1 Sam* 9:26; *Isa* 37:36
when he *a.* against me. *1 Sam* 17:35
either after him *a.* *2 Ki* 23:25
he wrath of the Lord *a.* *2 Chr* 36:16
oung men hid, aged *a.* *Job* 29:8
hen God *a.* to judgement. *Ps* 76:9
his place where he *a.* *Eccl* 1:5
ing *a.* early and went. *Dan* 6:19
and took the young. *Mat* 2:14, 21
and ministered. 8:15; *Luke* 4:39
e *a.* and rebuked the winds and the
Mat 8:26; *Mark* 4:39; *Luke* 8:24
and followed. *Mat* 9:9, 19
Mark 2:14
the hand, and the maid *a.* *Mat* 9:25
bodies of saints which slept *a.* 27:52
lifted him up, and he *a.* *Mark* 9:27
flood *a.* the stream beat. *Luke* 6:48
he *a.* and came to his father. 15:20
persecution which *a.* *Acts* 11:19
there *a.* no small stir about. 19:23
said there *a.* dissension. 23:7, 10
see **rose**

arose *and went*
Samuel *a. and went* to. *1 Sam* 3:6
Jonathan *a. and went* to David. 23:16
David *a. and went* to the. 25:1
Elisha *a. and went* after. *1 Ki* 19:21
Jonah *a. and went* to. *Jonah* 3:3
then Peter *a. and went.* *Acts* 9:39

Arpad, Arphad
gods of *A.* *2 Ki* 18:34; *Isa* 36:19
where is the king of *A.*? *2 Ki* 19:13
Isa 37:13
is not Hamath as *A.*? *Isa* 10:9
is confounded and *A.* *Jer* 49:23

Arphaxad
the son of Shem *A.* *Gen* 10:22
11:10; *1 Chr* 1:17
who was the son of *A.* *Luke* 3:36

array
[1] *To put on apparel,* Esth 6:9; Rev. 7:13. [2] *To put an army in a fit posture to fight.* 2 Sam 10:9.
that they may *a.* the man. *Esth* 6:9
a. thyself with glory. *Job* 40:10
shall *a.* himself with the. *Jer* 43:12
adorn, not with costly *a.* *1 Tim* 2:9

array
Joab put the choice in *a.* *2 Sam* 10:9
God set themselves in *a.* *Job* 6:4
yourselves in *a.* against. *Jer* 50:14
see **battle**

arrayed
Pharaoh *a.* Joseph in fine. *Gen* 41:42
captives, with spoil *a.* *2 Chr* 28:15
not *a.* like. *Mat* 6:29; *Luke* 12:27
his men of war *a.* Christ. *Luke* 23:11
Herod *a.* in royal apparel. *Acts* 12:21
are these that are *a.* in? *Rev* 7:13
the woman was *a.* in purple. 17:4
her was granted to be *a.* in fine. 19:8

arrived
they *a.* at the country of. *Luke* 8:26
and the next day we *a.* *Acts* 20:15

arrogancy
not *a.* come out of your. *1 Sam* 2:3
pride and *a.* and the evil. *Pr* 8:13
cause the *a.* of the proud. *Isa* 13:11
Moab, his loftiness, his *a.* *Jer* 48:29

arrow
[1] *Literally, a dart used for pleasure or in war,* 1 Sam 20:20; Jer 51:11. [2] *Figuratively, any word or judgement which pierces the mind or the soul as does an arrow the flesh,* Job 6:4; Ps 64:3; 2 Sam 22:15.
Jonathan shot an *a.* *1 Sam* 20:36
and the *a.* went out at. *2 Ki* 9:24
a. of Lord's deliverance from. 13:17
shoot an *a.* there. 19:32; *Isa* 37:33
a. cannot make him flee. *Job* 41:28
they make ready their *a.* *Ps* 11:2
with an *a.* suddenly shall. 64:7
afraid for the *a.* that flieth. 91:5
false witness is a sharp *a.* *Pr* 25:18
their tongue is as an *a.* shot. *Jer* 9:8
set me as a mark for the *a.* *Lam* 3:12
his *a.* shall go forth as. *Zech* 9:14

arrows
them through with his *a.* *Num* 24:8
I will spend mine *a.* *Deut* 32:23
I will make mine *a.* drunk with. 42
I will shoot three *a.* on. *1 Sam* 20:20
he sent out *a.* and scattered them.
2 Sam 22:15; *Ps* 18:14
a. took to him bow and *a.* *2 Ki* 13:15
take the *a.* and smite upon the. 18
the *a.* of the Almighty are. *Job* 6:4
he ordaineth *a.* against the. *Ps* 7:13
shalt make ready thine *a.* 21:12
for thine *a.* stick fast in me. 38:2
thine *a.* are sharp in the heart. 45:5
whose teeth are spears and *a.* 57:4
bendeth his bow to shoot his *a.* *Ps* 58:7
bows to shoot their *a.* even. 64:3
brake he the *a.* of the bow, the. 76:3
clouds poured, thine *a.* also. 77:17
sharp *a.* of the mighty, with. 120:4
as *a.* are in the hand of a. 127:4
shoot out thine *a.* and destroy. 144:6
mad man who casteth *a.* *Pr* 26:18
whose *a.* are sharp and. *Isa* 5:28
with *a.* and bows shall men. 7:24
their *a.* shall be as of an. *Jer* 50:9
shoot at Babylon, spare no *a.* 14
make bright the *a.* gather the. 51:11
hath caused the *a.* of his. *Lam* 3:13
I shall send the evil *a.* *Ezek* 5:16
he made his *a.* bright, he. 21:21
I will cause thy *a.* to fall out. 39:3
go forth, and burn bows and *a.* 9
at the light of thine *a.* *Hab* 3:11

art, *verb*
to Adam, where *a.* thou? *Gen* 3:9
from the place where thou *a.* 13:14
whose daughter *a.* thou? 24:23, 47
and he said *a.* thou my very? 27:24
whose *a.* thou? whither goest? 32:17
thee, because thou *a.* his wife. 39:9
discreet and wise as thou *a.* 41:39
die because thou *a.* yet alive. 46:30
a bloody husband thou *a.* *Ex* 4:26
a. thou for us, or our? *Josh* 5:13
they answered, as thou *a.* *Judg* 8:18
the men said to him, *a.* thou? 12:5
a. thou the man that spakest? 13:11
stand by where thou *a.* *1 Sam* 19:3
a prophet also as thou *a.* *1 Ki* 13:18
said, I am as thou *a.* 22:4; *2 Ki* 3:7
a. not thou our God. *2 Chr* 20:7
hurt a man as thou *a.* *Job* 35:8
a. thou also become ... ? *a.* *Isa* 14:10
a. not thou he, O Lord our? *Jer* 14:22
a. thou he that should? *Luke* 7:19
Rabbi, thou *a.* the Son of. *John* 1:49
a. not thou that Egyptian? *Acts* 21:38
the captain said, tell me, *a*? 22:27
a. and wast, and *a.* *Rev* 11:17; 16:5

art, -s, *substantive*
ointment after the *a.* of. *Ex* 30:25
spices prepared by *a.* *2 Chr* 16:14
like stones graven by *a.* *Acts* 17:29
of them which used curious *a.* 19:19

Artaxerxes
in the days of *A.* wrote. *Ezra* 4:7
to the commandment of *A.* 6:14
in the reign of *A.* Ezra. 7:1; 8:1
the copy of a letter that *A.* gave. 7:11
I, even I *A.* the king do make a. 21
in 20th year of *A.* wine was. *Neh* 2:1
from 20th to 32nd year of *A.* 5:14

Artemas
when I shall send *A.* to. *Tit* 3:12

artificer
an instructor of every *a.* *Gen* 4:22
captain and the cunning *a.* *Isa* 3:3

artificers
of works made by *a.* *1 Chr* 29:5
to *a.* and builders gave. *2 Chr* 34:11

artillery
Jonathan gave his *a.* *1 Sam* 20:40

as
ye shall be *a.* gods. *Gen* 3:5
behold the man is become *a.* 22
the Lord seeth not *a.* *1 Sam* 16:7
he did evil *a.* did the. *2 Ki* 8:27
had made in the temple, *a.* 24:13
a. thou hast said, so. *Ezra* 10:12
a. for such *a.* turn aside. *Ps* 125:5
say not, I will do to him *a.* *Pr* 24:29
a. with the people, *a.* *Isa* 24:2
a. his master, servant *a.* *Mat* 10:25
love thy neighbour *a.* thyself. 19:19
Rom 13:9
the glory *a.* of the only-. *John* 1:14
ye resist Holy Ghost, *a.* *Acts* 7:51
but *a.* of sincerity, but *a.* *2 Cor* 2:17
be *a.* I am, for I am *a.* ye. *Gal* 4:12
a. ye have received Christ. *Col* 2:6

even **as**
even as the Lord gave to. *1 Cor* 3:5
so love his wife *even a.* *Eph* 5:33
even a. Christ forgave you. *Col* 3:13
even a. I received of my. *Rev* 2:27

Asa
A. did what. *1 Ki* 15:11; *2 Chr* 14:2
A. heart. *1 Ki* 15:14; *2 Chr* 15:17
A. took the silver. *1 Ki* 15:18
2 Chr 16:2
Berechiah the son of A. *1 Chr* 9:16
A. cried to the Lord. *2 Chr* 14:11
Azariah went out to meet A. 15:2
no war to the 35th year of A. 19
A. was wroth . . . A. oppressed. 16:10
the pit was it which A. had. *Jer* 41:9
Abia begat A. *Mat* 1:7
A. begat Josaphat. 8

Asahel
sons of Zeruiah, Joab, A. *2 Sam* 2:18
1 Chr 2:16
A. would not turn aside. *2 Sam* 2:21
they took up A. and buried him. 32
Abner died for the blood of A. 3:27
A. was one of the thirty. 23:24
1 Chr 11:26
Levites, Zebadiah, A. *2 Chr* 17:8
Jehiel, Nahath and A. were. 31:13
son of A. was employed. *Ezra* 10:15

Asaiah
Jeshohaiah and A. *1 Chr* 4:36
sons of Merari, Haggiah, A. 6:30
Shilonites, A. the first-born. 9:5
king Josiah sent A. to. *2 Chr* 34:20

Asaph
Joah the son of A. the recorder.
2 Ki 18:18, 37; *Isa* 36:3, 22
A. son of Berechiah. *1 Chr* 6:39
9:15; 15:17
delivered first this psalm to A. 16:7
of the sons of A. 25:1, 2; 26:1
2 Chr 5:12; 20:14; 29:13; 35:15
Ezra 2:41; 3:10; *Neh* 7:44; 11:17
22, 12:35.
first lot came forth for A. *1 Chr* 25:9
to sing with words of A. *2 Chr* 29:30
to the commandment of A. 35:15
a letter to A. keeper of the. *Neh* 2:8
in the days of A. were songs. 12:46

ascend
[1] *To climb up,* Josh 6:5. [2] *To go up to heaven,* Eph 4:9, 10.

the people shall a. up. *Josh* 6:5
a. into the hill of the Lord, and shall stand in? *Ps* 24:3; *Rom* 10:6
he causeth vapours to a. *Ps* 135:7
Jer 10:13; 51:16
if I a. up into heaven, thou. *Ps* 139:8
hast said, I will a. *Isa* 14:13, 14
thou shalt a. and come. *Ezek* 38:9
see the Son of man a. up. *John* 6:62
a. to my Father, and your. 20:17
beast shall a. out of the. *Rev* 17:8

ascended
the angel of the Lord a. *Judg* 13:20
thou hast a. up on high. *Ps* 68:18
who hath a. up into heaven. *Pr* 30:4
no man hath a. to heaven. *John* 3:13
touch me not, I am not yet a. 20:17
David is not yet a. into. *Acts* 2:34
when he a. up on high, he. *Eph* 4:8
now that he a. 9
is the same also that a. 10
the smoke of the incense a. *Rev* 8:4
they a. up to heaven in a cloud. 11:12

ascendeth
the beast that a. out of. *Rev* 11:7
the smoke of their torment a. 14:11

ascending
the angels of God a. and. *Gen* 28:12
said, I saw gods a. out. *1 Sam* 28:13
he went before, a. up to. *Luke* 19:28
of God a. and descending. *John* 1:51
I saw another angel a. from. *Rev* 7:2

ascent
up by the a. of Olivet. *2 Sam* 15:30
and his a. by. *1 Ki* 10:5; *2 Chr* 9:4

ascribe
a. ye greatness to our. *Deut* 32:3
I will a. righteousness to. *Job* 36:3
a. ye strength to God, his. *Ps* 68:34

ascribed
a. to David 10,000, to me a. but.
1 Sam 18:8

Asenath
A. daughter of. *Gen* 41:45, 50; 46:20

ash
he planteth an a. the rain. *Isa* 44:14*

ashamed
(*The American Revision frequently changes this word to* confounded *or* put to shame)
and his wife were not a. *Gen* 2:25
tarried till they were a. *Judg* 3:25
the men were greatly a. *2 Sam* 10:5
1 Chr 19:5
being a. steal away. *2 Sam* 19:3
urged him till he was a. *2 Ki* 2:17
his countenance till he was a. 8:11
the Levites were a. *2 Chr* 30:15
a. to require of the king. *Ezra* 8:22
a. and blush to lift up my face. 9:6
came thither, and were a. *Job* 6:20
shall no man make a.? 11:3
are not a. to make yourselves. 19:3
their faces were not a. *Ps* 34:5
not the oppressed return a. 74:21
she that maketh a. is as. *Pr* 12:4
shall be a. of Ethiopia. *Isa* 20:5
the sun shall be a. when the. 24:23
all a. of a people that could. 30:5
earth mourneth, Lebanon is a. 33:9
as the thief is a. when he. *Jer* 2:26
a.? they were not at all a. 6:15; 8:12
the wise men are a. they are. 8:9
plowmen were a. they covered. 14:4
a. of Chemosh, as Israel was a. 48:13
of the Philistines are a. *Ezek* 16:27
with terror they are a. of. 32:30
his adversaries were a. *Luke* 13:17
I cannot dig, to beg I am a. 16:3
I am not a. of the gospel. *Rom* 1:16
hope maketh not a. because the. 5:5
things whereof ye are now a. 6:21
anything, I am not a. *2 Cor* 7:14
nevertheless I am not a. *2 Tim* 1:12
Onesiphorus was not a. of my. 16
he is not a. to call them. *Heb* 2:11
God is not a. to be called. 11:16
ashamed *and confounded, see* **confounded**

be **ashamed**
it to her, lest we be a. *Gen* 38:23
let all my enemies be a. and. *Ps* 6:10
wait on thee be a. let them be a. who transgress without cause. 25:3
put my trust, let me never be a. 31:1
be a. let the wicked be a. 17; 35:26
let not them that wait be a. 69:6
hate me, may see it and be a. 86:17
they arise, let them be a. 109:28
let proud be a. for they. 119:78
for they shall be a. of the. *Isa* 1:29
be thou a. O Zidon, the sea. 23:4
they shall see and be a. for. 26:11
they shall be greatly a. that. 42:17
know, that they may be a. 44:9
fellows shall be a. shall be a. 11
incensed against him shall be a. 45:24
rejoice, but ye shall be a. 65:13
your joy, and they shall be a. 66:5
shalt be a. of Egypt, as a. *Jer* 2:36
forehead, refusedst to be a. 3:3
they shall be a. of your. 12:13
all that forsake thee shall be a. 17:13
shall stumble and be a. 20:11
Moab shall be a. of Chemosh. 48:13
that bare you shall be a. 50:12
thy ways, and be a. *Ezek* 16:61
shew Israel, they may be a. 43:10
and if they be a. of all that. 11
they shall be a. because. *Hos* 4:19
and Israel shall be a. of his. 10:6
be ye a. O ye husbandmen. *Joel* 1:11
people shall never be a. 2:26, 27
her expectation shall be a. *Zech* 9:5
the prophets every one be a. 13:4
shall be a. of me and. *Mark* 8:38
Luke 9:26
should be a. in this same. *2 Cor* 9:4
in nothing I shall be a. *Phil* 1:20
him, that he may be a. *2 Thes* 3:14
on the contrary part may be a. *Tit* 2:8
be a. that falsely accuse. *1 Pet* 3:16

not be, or be not, **ashamed**
should she not be a.? *Num* 12:14
in thee, let me not be a. *Ps* 25:2
me not be a. O Lord. 31:17; 119:116
shall not be a. in the evil time. 37:19
then shall I not be a. when. *Ps* 119:6
of thy testimonies, and not be a. 46
heart be sound, that I be not a. 80
they shall not be a. but shall. 127:5
Lord, Jacob shall not be a. *Isa* 29:22
ye shall not be a. world. 45:17
they shall not be a. that wait. 49:23
flint, I know I shall not be a. 50:7
fear not, for thou shalt not be a. 54:4
shalt thou not be a. *Zeph* 3:11
him shall not be a. *Rom* 9:33; 10:11
boast, I should not be a. *2 Cor* 10:8
be not therefore a. of. *2 Tim* 1:8
workman that needeth not be a. 2:15
Christian, let him not be a. *1 Pet* 4:16
not be a. before him. *1 John* 2:28

Ashdod
brought the ark to A. *1 Sam* 5:1
Lord was heavy on them of A. 6
wall of A. and built cities about A.
2 Chr 26:6
had married wives of A. *Neh* 13:23
spake half in the speech of A. 24
came and fought against A. *Isa* 20:1
I made remnant of A. *Jer* 25:20
the inhabitant from A. *Amos* 1:8
publish in the palaces at A. and 3:9
they shall drive out A. *Zeph* 2:4
a bastard shall dwell in A. *Zech* 9:6

Asher
Leah called his name A. *Gen* 30:13
Zilpah, Leah's maid, Gad, A. 35:26
the children of A. 46:17; *Num* 1:40
26:44; *1 Chr* 7:30, 40; 12:36
out of A. his bread shall. *Gen* 49:20
A. was Pagiel. *Num* 1:13; 2:27; 7:72
the name of the daughter of A. 26:46
to curse; Gad and A. *Deut* 27:13
A. he said, let A. be blessed. 33:24
A. continued on the sea. *Judg* 5:17
Gideon sent messengers to A. 6:35
men out of A. pursued the. 7:23
son of Hushai was in A. *1 Ki* 4:16
A. expert in war 40,000. *1 Chr* 12:36
divers of A. humbled. *2 Chr* 30:11
a portion for A. *Ezek* 48:2
one gate of A. 34

tribe of **Asher**
the tribe of A. 41,500. *Num* 1:41
the tribe of A. shall encamp. 2:27
over the host of tribe of A. 10:26
of the tribe of A. to spy the. 13:13
prince of the tribe of A. to. 34:27
lot for the tribe of A. *Josh* 19:24
inheritance of the tribe of A. 31
had cities out of the tribe of A. 21:6
30; *1 Chr* 6:62, 74
of Phanuel of tribe of A. *Luke* 2:36
the tribe of A. were sealed. *Rev* 7:6

ashes
The remains of fuel after it has been burned, 2 Pet 2:6. *They were used in mourning to show that joy had perished,* Esth 4:1; Isa 61:3

which am but dust and a. *Gen* 18:2
priest shall take up the a. *Lev* 6:1
and carry forth the a. without. 1
clean shall gather the a. *Num* 19:
Tamar put a. on her. *2 Sam* 13:1
altar shall be rent, and a. *1 Ki* 13:
disguised himself with a. 20:38
put on sackcloth with a. *Esth* 4:
and many lay in sackcloth and a.
Job sat down among the a. *Job* 2:
remembrances are like to a. 13:1
I am become like dust and a. 30:1
and repent in dust and a. 42:
have eaten a. like bread. *Ps* 102:
the hoar-frost like a. 147:1
he feedeth on a. a. *Isa* 44:2
to spread sackcloth and a. 58:
to give them beauty for a. the. 61
wallow thyself in a. *Jer* 6:2
hath covered me with a. *Lam* 3:1
I will bring thee to a. on. *Ezek* 28:
to seek in sackcloth and a. *Dan* 9
sackcloth, and sat in a. *Jonah* 3
wicked shall be a. under. *Mal* 4
have repented long ago in sackclo
and a. *Mat* 11:21; *Luke* 10:
a. of an heifer sanctifieth. *Heb* 9:
cities of Sodom into a. *2 Pet* 2

Ashtaroth
Og, who dwelt at *A*. *Deut* 1:4
Josh 9:10; 12:4
Israel served *A*. *Judg* 2:13; 10:6
strange gods and *A*. *1 Sam* 7:3, 4
because we have served *A*. 12:10
armour in the house of *A*. 31:10
have worshipped *A*. *1 Ki* 11:33
Gershom was given *A*. *1 Chr* 6:71

Ashur, *or* **Assur**
A. went forth and built. *Gen* 10:11
Shem, Elam and *A*. 22; *1 Chr* 1:17
till *A*. shall carry thee. *Num* 24:22
from Chittim and afflict *A*. 24
Hezron's wife bare him *A*. *1 Chr* 2:24
A. had two wives, Helah and. 4:5
Esar-haddon king of *A*. *Ezra* 4:2
A. also is joined with them. *Ps* 83:8
A. and Chilmad were. *Ezek* 27:23
A. is there, and all her. 32:22
A. shall not save us, we. *Hos* 14:3

Asia
A. disputing with Stephen. *Acts* 6:9
to preach the word in *A*. 16:6
all they that dwelt in *A*. heard. 19:10
A. and the world worshippeth. 27
certain of the chief of *A*. sent. 31
he would not spend time in *A*. 20:16
first day that I came into *A*. 18
meaning to sail by coasts of *A*. 27:2
churches of *A*. salute. *1 Cor* 16:19
which came to us in *A*. *2 Cor* 1:8
they which are in *A*. *2 Tim* 1:15
strangers scattered in *A*. *1 Pet* 1:1
see **churches**

aside
said, thou shalt set *a*. *2 Ki* 4:4
he took him *a*. from the. *Mark* 7:33
he riseth and laid *a*. his. *John* 13:4
let us lay *a*. every weight. *Heb* 12:1
see **go, gone, turn, went, lay**

ask
[1] *To enquire*, Gen 32:29; Mark 9:32. [2] *To require, or demand*, Gen 34:12; Dan 2:10. [3] *To seek counsel*, Isa 30:2; Hag 2:11. [4] *To pray*, John 15:7; *Jas* 1:6. [5] *To expect*, Luke 12:48.

wherefore dost thou *a*.? *Gen* 32:29
a. me never so much dowry. 34:12
for *a*. now of the days. *Deut* 4:32
shall *a*. diligently, and if it be. 13:14
a. thy father, and he will shew. 32:7
children *a*. their fathers. *Josh* 4:6, 21
a. counsel, we pray thee. *Judg* 18:5
added this evil to *a*. *1 Sam* 12:19
why dost thou *a*. of me? 28:16
from me the thing I *a*. *2 Sam* 14:18
a. what I shall. *1 Ki* 3:5; *2 Chr* 1:7
Jeroboam cometh to *a*. *1 Ki* 14:5
Elijah said *a*. what I shall. *2 Ki* 2:9
Judah gathered to *a*. *2 Chr* 20:4
a the beasts, and they. *Job* 12:7
a. of me, and I will give. *Ps* 2:8
a. thee a sign of Lord, *a*. it. *Isa* 7:11
I will not *a*. nor will I tempt. 12
the Lord, *a*. me of things. 45:11
they *a*. of me the ordinances of. 58:2
a. for the old paths, and. *Jer* 6:16
who shall go aside, to *a*. what. 15:5
a. ye now among the heathen. 18:13
a. and see whether a man doth. 30:6
will *a*. thee a thing, hide. 38:14
a. him that fleeth, and her. 48:19
hey shall *a*. the way to Zion. 50:5
he young children *a*. bread. *Lam* 4:4
. a petition of any. *Dan* 6:7, 12
y people *a*. counsel at. *Hos* 4:12
now the priests. *Hag* 2:11
ye of the Lord rain. *Zech* 10:1
eed of, before ye *a*. him. *Mat* 6:8
and it shall be. 7:7; *Luke* 11:9
is son *a*. bread. *Mat* 7:9; *Luke* 11:11
ood things to them that *a*. *Mat* 7:11
er whatsoever she would *a*. 14:7
uching any thing they shall *a*. 18:19
hat ye *a*. 20:22; *Mark* 10:38
hatsoever ye *a*. in prayer. *Mat* 21:22
r durst any man *a*. him more.
22:46; *Mark* 12:34; *Luke* 20:40
what thou wilt. *Mark* 6:22, 23
raid to *a*. him. 9:32; *Luke* 9:45
taketh thy goods, *a*. them. *Luke* 6:30
Holy Spirit to them that *a*. 11:13
of him they will *a*. more. 12:48
Jews sent priests to *a*. *John* 1:19
he is of age, *a*. him. 9:21, 23
thou wilt *a*. of God, he will. 11:22
to him that he should *a*. 13:24*
whatsoever ye *a*. in. 14:13; 15:16
if ye *a*. any thing in my name I. 14:14
if ye abide in me, *a*. what ye. 15:7
that they were desirous to *a*. 16:19
and in that day ye shall *a*. me. 23
a. and ye shall receive, that your. 24
that any man should *a*. thee. 30
a. them which heard me what. 18:21
I *a*. therefore for what. *Acts* 10:29
them *a*. their husbands. *1 Cor* 14:35
above all that we can *a*. *Eph* 3:20
lack wisdom, let him *a*. *Jas* 1:5
but let him *a*. in faith, nothing. 6
yet ye have not, because ye *a*. 4:2
a. and receive not, because ye *a*. 3
whatsoever we *a*. we. *1 John* 3:22
if we *a*. any thing according to. 5:14
he heareth us, whatsoever we *a*. 15
is not unto death, he shall *a* 16
see **counsel**

asked
Jacob *a*. him and said. *Gen* 32:29
the man *a*. us straitly of our. 43:7
him the city which he *a*. *Josh* 19:50
he *a*. water, she gave. *Judg* 5:25
I *a*. him not whence he was. 13:6
petition thou hast *a*. *1 Sam* 1:17
hath given me my petition I *a*. 27
a. this thing and not *a*. *1 Ki* 3:11
thou hast *a*. a hard thing. *2 Ki* 2:10
a. their names to certify. *Ezra* 5:10
have ye not *a*. them that. *Job* 21:29
he *a*. life of thee, thou. *Ps* 21:4
the people *a*. and he. 105:40
and have not *a*. at my. *Isa* 30:2
when I *a*. of them, could. 41:28
I am sought of them that *a*. 65:1
there is no king that *a*. *Dan* 2:10
I came and *a*. him the truth of. 7:16
he *a*. his disciples. *Mat* 16:13
Mark 8:27; *Luke* 9:18
Sadducees *a*. him. *Mat* 22:23, 35
Mark 9:11; 10:2; 12:18
when come near he *a*. *Luke* 18:40
thou wouldest have *a*. *John* 4:10
hitherto have ye *a*. nothing. 16:24
to them that *a*. not. *Rom* 10:20

Askelon, *or* **Ashkelon**
Judah took Gaza and *A*. *Judg* 1:18
Samson went down to *A*. and. 14:19
for *A*. one, for Gath one. *1 Sam* 6:17
not in the streets of *A*. *2 Sam* 1:20
I made *A*. and Azzah to. *Jer* 25:20
A. is cut off with remnant of. 47:5
hath given it a charge against *A*. 7
that holds sceptre from *A*. *Amos* 1:8
Gaza shall be forsaken, *A*. *Zeph* 2:4
in the houses of *A*. shall they lie. 7
A. shall see it, and fear; king shall perish from Gaza, and *A*. *Zech* 9:5

askest
why *a*. thou thus after. *Judg* 13:18
a. drink of me, a woman. *John* 4:9
why *a*. thou me, ask them. 18:21

asketh
thy son *a*. thee. *Ex* 13:14; *Deut* 6:20
prince *a*. and the judge *a*. *Mi* 7:3
give to him that *a*. thee. *Mat* 5:42
Luke 6:30
that *a*. receiveth. *Mat* 7:8; *Luke* 11:10
of you *a*. me, whither? *John* 16:5
to every one that *a*. you. *1 Pet* 3:15

asking
wickedness in *a*. a king. *1 Sam* 12:17
Saul died for *a*. counsel. *1 Chr* 10:13
tempted God by *a*. meat. *Ps* 78:18
hearing them, and *a*. *Luke* 2:46
they continued *a*. he lifted. *John* 8:7
a. no question for. *1 Cor* 10:25, 27

asleep
[1] *To take rest in sleep*, Jonah 1:5; Mat 26:40. [2] *To die*, Acts 7:60; 2 Pet 3:4.

for Sisera was fast *a*. *Judg* 4:21
lips of those that are *a*. *S of S* 7:9
Jonah lay, and was fast *a*. *Jonah* 1:5
but he was *a*. *Mat* 8:24; *Mark* 4:38
disciples *a*. *Mat* 26:40; *Mark* 14:40
had said this, he fell *a*. *Acts* 7:60
but some are fallen *a*. *1 Cor* 15:6
which are fallen *a*. in Christ. 18
them that are *a*. *1 Thes* 4:13
shall not prevent them that are *a*. 15
since the fathers fell *a*. *2 Pet* 3:4

Asnappar
whom the noble *A*. brought. *Ezra* 4:10

asp, -s
is the cruel venom of *a*. *Deut* 32:33
his meat is the gall of *a*. *Job* 20:14
suck the poison of *a*. the viper's. 16
play on the hole of the *a*. *Isa* 11:8
the poison of *a*. is under. *Rom* 3:13

ass
up early, and saddled his *a*. *Gen* 22:3
abide you here with the *a*. and I. 5
Issachar is a strong *a*. 49:14
every firstling of an *a*. *Ex* 13:13
if thou meet thine enemy's *a*. 23:4
that thine ox and thine *a*. may. 12
taken one *a*. from them. *Num* 16:15
the *a*. saw the angel. 22:23; 25:27
opened the mouth of the *a*. 22:28
a. said to Balaam, am not I thine *a*.? 30
plow with an ox and *a*. *Deut* 22:10
lighted off her *a*. Caleb. *Josh* 15:18
Judg 1:14; *1 Sam* 25:23
the jaw-bone of an *a*. *Judg* 15:16
had not torn the *a*. *1 Ki* 13:28
until an *a*. head sold for. *2 Ki* 6:25
they drive away the *a*. of. *Job* 24:3
a bridle for the *a*. and a. *Pr* 26:3
ox his owner, and the *a*. his. *Isa* 1:3
forth the feet of the ox and *a*. 32:20
with the burial of an *a*. *Jer* 22:19
riding on an *a*. and on a colt the foal of an *a*. *Zech* 9:9; *Mat* 21:5
be the plague of the *a*. *Zech* 14:15
ye shall find an *a*. tied. *Mat* 21:2
not each loose his *a*. on. *Luke* 13:15
which of you shall have an *a*. 14:5
he found a young *a*. sat. *John* 12:14
the dumb *a*. speaking. *2 Pet* 2:16
see **saddle**

wild **ass**
doth the *wild a*. bray when? *Job* 6:5
sent out the *wild a*. free? 39:5
a *wild a*. used to the. *Jer* 2:24
they are gone, a *wild a*. alone. *Hos* 8:9

assault, -ed
perish all that would *a*. *Esth* 8:11
when there was an *a*. *Acts* 14:5
they *a*. the house of Jason, and. 17:5

assay, -ed, -ing
hath God *a*. to go and. *Deut* 4:34
David *a*. to go, for he. *1 Sam* 17:39
if we *a*. to commune with. *Job* 4:2
Saul *a*. to join himself to. *Acts* 9:26
they *a*. to go to Bithynia, but. 16:7
the Egyptians *a*. to do. *Heb* 11:29

assemble
the assembly shall *a*. *Num* 10:3
a. me the men of Judah. *2 Sam* 20:4
he shall *a*. the outcasts. *Isa* 11:12
a. yourselves, and come, draw. 45:20
all ye *a*. yourselves and hear. 48:14
a. yourselves, and let us go. *Jer* 4:5
why do we sit still? *a*. 8:14
I will *a*. you out of the. *Ezek* 11:17
a. yourselves, gather to my. 39:17
they *a*. themselves for corn. *Hos* 7:14
a. the elders, gather the. *Joel* 2:16
a. yourselves and come, all. 3:11
a. yourselves on the. *Amos* 3:9
I will surely *a*. O Jacob. *Mi* 2:12
saith the Lord I will *a*. her. 4:6
I will *a*. the kingdoms to. *Zeph* 3:8

assembled
women which *a*. at the. *Ex* 38:8*
with the women that *a*. *1 Sam* 2:22*
David *a*. the children of. *1 Chr* 15:4
a. much people to keep. *2 Chr* 30:13
then *a*. to me every one. *Ezra* 9:4
had prayed, there *a*. to him. 10:1
the children of Israel *a*. *Neh* 9:1
lo the kings were *a*. they. *Ps* 48:4

let the people be *a.* who. *Isa* 43:9
a. themselves by troops in. *Jer* 5:7
these men *a.* and found. *Dan* 6:11
when they *a.* they gave. *Mat* 28:12
the disciples *a.* for fear. *John* 20:19
being *a.* commanded them. *Acts* 1:4
shaken where they were *a.* 4:31
a whole year they *a.* with. 11:26
it seemed good to us *a.* with. 15:25

assemblies

the *a.* of violent men. *Ps* 86:14*
by the masters of *a.* *Eccl* 12:11
the calling of *a.* I cannot. *Isa* 1:13
God will create on her *a.* a. 4:5
my laws in all mine *a.* *Ezek* 44:24*
smell in your solemn *a.* *Amos* 5:21

assembling

forsake not the *a.* *Heb* 10:25

assembly

to their *a.* mine honour be. *Gen* 49:6
the whole *a.* shall kill it. *Ex* 12:6
to kill this whole *a.* with. 16:3
hid from the eyes of the *a.* *Lev* 4:13
trumpets for calling the *a.* *Num* 10:2
Aaron went from presence of *a.* 20:6
of the midst of the fire, in the day of your *a.* *Deut* 9:10; 10:4; 18:16
Jabesh-Gilead to the *a.* *Judg* 21:8
all this *a.* shall know. *1 Sam* 17:47
whole *a.* took counsel. *2 Chr* 30:23
I set a great *a.* against. *Neh* 5:7
the *a.* of the wicked have. *Ps* 22:16
God is to be feared in the *a.* 89:7*
praise him in the *a.* of the. 107:32
I will praise him in the *a.* of. 111:1
evil in the midst of the *a.* *Pr* 5:14
I will pour it on the *a.* of. *Jer* 6:11
for they be an *a.* of treacherous. 9:2
in the *a.* of the mockers. 15:17
the places of the *a.* *Lam* 2:6
shall not be in the *a.* of. *Ezek* 13:9*
against Aholibah with an *a.* 23:24
the *a.* was confused, and. *Acts* 19:32
determined in a lawful *a.* 39
thus spoken, he dismissed the *a.* 41
to the general *a.* of the. *Heb* 12:23
if there come to your *a.* *Jas* 2:2

solemn **assembly**

on the eighth day it is a *solemn a.* *Lev* 23:36; *Num* 29:35; *Neh* 8:18
seventh day a *solemn a.* *Deut* 16:8
proclaim a *solemn a.* *2 Ki* 10:20
eighth day . . . a *solemn a.* *2 Chr* 7:9
call a *solemn a.* *Joel* 1:14; 2:15
are sorrowful for the *solemn a.* *Zeph* 3:18

assent, -ed

to the king with one *a.* *2 Chr* 18:12
Jews also *a.* that these. *Acts* 24:9

asses

had he-*a.* and she-*a.* *Gen* 12:16
much cattle, camels, and *a.* 30:43
as he fed the *a.* of Zibeon. 36:24
bread in exchange for *a.* 47:17
ye that ride on white *a.* *Judg* 5:10
he will take your *a.* to. *1 Sam* 8:16
the *a.* of Kish, Saul's. 9:3
thy *a.* that were lost, they. 20; 10:2
the *a.* be for the king's. *2 Sam* 16:2
and over the *a.* was. *1 Chr* 27:30
feeble of them upon *a.* *2 Chr* 28:15
a. that went up. *Ezra* 2:67; *Neh* 7:69
and a thousand she-*a.* *Job* 42:12
he saw a chariot of *a.* and. *Isa* 21:7
flesh is as the flesh of *a.* *Ezek* 23:20

wild **asses**

as *wild a.* in the desert. *Job* 24:5
the *wild a.* quench their. *Ps* 104:11
shall be a joy of *wild a.* *Isa* 32:14
wild a. snuffed up the wind. *Jer* 14:6
dwelling, was with *w. a.* *Dan* 5:21

young **asses**

their riches on *young a.* *Isa* 30:6
young a. that ear the ground shall. 24

assigned

priests had a portion *a.* *Gen* 47:22
they *a.* Bezer a city of. *Josh* 20:8
he *a.* Uriah to a place. *2 Sam* 11:16

assist

that ye *a.* her in. *Rom* 16:2

associate

a. yourselves and ye shall. *Isa* 8:9*

as soon

a. as I am gone out of the. *Ex* 9:29
a. as the commandment. *2 Chr* 31:5
a. as they hear of me. *Ps* 18:44
a. as Zion travailed, she. *Isa* 66:8
a. as the voice of thy. *Luke* 1:44
a. as it was sprung up, it. 8:6
a. as he said, I am he. *John* 18:6
came I *a.* as I was. *Acts* 10:29
a. as it was day there was no. 12:18
a. as I had eaten it, my. *Rev* 10:10
for to devour the child *a.* as it. 12:4

ass's colt

binding his *a. colt* to the. *Gen* 49:11
born like a wild *a. colt.* *Job* 11:12
sitting on an *a. colt.* *John* 12:15

assurance

have none *a.* of thy life. *Deut* 28:66
effect of righteousness, *a.* *Isa* 32:17*
whereof he hath given *a.* *Acts* 17:31
to all riches of the full *a.* of. *Col* 2:2
gospel came in much *a.* *1 Thes* 1:5
to the full *a.* of hope to. *Heb* 6:11*
let us draw near in full *a.* 10:22*

assure

shall *a.* our hearts. *1 John* 3:19

assured

fifth, and it shall be *a.* *Lev* 27:19
I will give you *a.* peace in. *Jer* 14:13
things thou hast been *a.* *2 Tim* 3:14

assuredly

know *a.* thou shalt go. *1 Sam* 28:1
a. Solomon thy son. *1 Ki* 1:13, 17, 30
plant them in this land *a.* *Jer* 32:41
if thou *a.* go forth to the. 38:17
they have *a.* drunken, and. 49:12
house of Israel know *a.* *Acts* 2:36
a. gathering that the Lord. 16:10

asswage, -ed

(*Old spelling of* assuage)

and the waters were *a.* *Gen* 8:1
of my lips should *a.* your. *Job* 16:5
I speak, yet my grief is not *a.* 6

Assyria

goeth toward the east of *A.* *Gen* 2:14
sons dwelt as thou goest to *A.* 25:18
carried captive to *A.* *2 Ki* 15:29; 17:6; 18:11
bee that is in the land of *A.* *Isa* 7:18
remnant of his people from *A.* 11:11
for his people left from *A.* 16
an highway out of Egypt to *A.* 19:23
be the third with Egypt and *A.* 24
blessed be *A.* the work of my. 25
who were ready to perish in *A.* 27:13
to do in the way of *A.*? *Jer* 2:18
Egypt, as wast ashamed of *A.* 36
whoredoms with men of *A.* *Ezek* 23:7
they go to *A.* *Hos* 7:11
they are gone up to *A.* 8:9
shall eat unclean things in *A.* 9:3
it shall be carried to *A.* for a. 10:6
as a dove out of land of *A.* 11:11
shall waste the land of *A.* *Mi* 5:6
he shall come to thee from *A.* 7:12
and he will destroy *A.* *Zeph* 2:13
gather them out of *A.* *Zech* 10:10
the pride of *A.* shall be brought. 11

see **king, kings**

Assyrian

O *A.* the rod of mine anger. *Isa* 10:5
people, be not afraid of the *A.* 24
that I will break the *A.* in my. 14:25
this people was not till the *A.* 23:13
the *A.* shall be beaten down. 30:31
then shall the *A.* fall with the. 31:8
the *A.* oppressed them without. 52:4
the *A.* was a cedar in. *Ezek* 31:3
went Ephraim to the *A.* *Hos* 5:13
but the *A.* shall be his king. 11:5
be the peace when *A.* come. *Mi* 5:5
shall he deliver us from the *A.* 6

Assyrians

smote in the camp of *A.* 185,000 men. *2 Ki* 19:35; *Isa* 37:36
given the hand to the *A.* *Lam* 5:6
the whore with the *A.* *Ezek* 16:28
she doted on the *A.* her. 23:5, 12
delivered her into the hand of the *A.* 9
I will bring all the *A.* against. 23
a covenant with the *A.* *Hos* 12:1

astonied

(*Old form of* astonished)

the hair, and sat down *a.* *Ezra* 9:3
upright men shall be *a.* at. *Job* 17:8
come after him shall be *a.* 18:20
that they may be *a.* one. *Ezek* 4:17
Nebuchadnezzar was *a.* *Dan* 3:24
Daniel was *a.* for one hour. 4:19
was changed, his lords *a.* 5:9*

astonished

your enemies shall be *a.* *Lev* 26:32
passeth by shall be *a.* *1 Ki* 9:8; *Jer* 18:16; 19:8; 49:17; 50:13
heaven tremble and are *a.* *Job* 26:11
as many were *a.* at thee. *Isa* 52:14
be *a.* O ye heavens, at this. *Jer* 2:12
heart of the priests shall be *a.* 4:9
shouldest thou be as a man *a.* 14:9
I remained *a.* among them. *Ezek* 3:15
at every moment, and be *a.* 26:16
know thee shall be *a.* at thee. 28:19
Daniel was *a.* at the vision. *Dan* 8:27
the people were *a.* *Mat* 7:28; 22:33; *Mark* 1:22; 6:2; 11:18; *Luke* 4:32
they were *a.* with great. *Mark* 5:42
beyond measure *a.* 7:37; 10:26
the disciples were *a.* at his. 10:24
a. at his understanding. *Luke* 2:47
a. at the draught of fishes. 5:9
her parents were *a.* but he. 8:56
certain women also made us *a.* 24:22
Saul trembling and *a.* said. *Acts* 9:6*
which believed, were *a.* 10:45
and saw Peter, they were *a.* 12:16
he saw, believed, being *a.* 13:12

astonishment

shall smite thee with *a.* *Deut* 28:28
thou shalt become an *a.* and a. 37
this house shall be an *a.* *2 Chr* 7:21
he hath delivered them to *a.* 29:8
to drink the wine of *a.* *Ps* 60:3*
I am black, *a.* hath taken. *Jer* 8:21
I will make them an *a.* 25:9, 18
land shall be a desolation and *a.* 11
them to be a curse and an *a.* 29:18
an execration and an *a.* 42:18; 44:12
therefore is your land an *a.* 44:22
shall become heaps and an *a.* 51:37
they shall drink water by measure, and with *a.* *Ezek* 4:16; 12:19
it shall be an *a.* to the nations. 5:15
filled with the cup of *a.* 23:33
smite every horse with *a.* *Zech* 12:4

astray, *see* **went, go, gone**

astrologers

[1] *Those we now call astrologers.*
[2] *Enchanters of any sort.*

a. the star-gazers, stand. *Isa* 47:13
ten times better than *a.* *Dan* 1:20
secret cannot the *a.* shew to. 2:27
in the magicians and the *a.* 4:7
cried aloud, to bring in the *a.* 5:7

asunder, *see* **cleave, cut, divide, put**

as well

as well the stranger, as. *Lev* 24:1
one law, *as well* for the stranger. 2
heart faint, *as well* as. *Deut* 20:
devours one *as well* as. *2 Sam* 11:2
they cast lots, *as well.* *1 Chr* 25:
to give *as well* to the. *2 Chr* 31:1
understanding *as well* as. *Job* 12:
as well the singers as the. *Ps* 87:
the Holy Ghost *as well.* *Acts* 10:4
about a sister *as well* as. *1 Cor* 9:
gospel preached *as well* as. *Heb* 4:

Asyncritus

salute *A.* Phlegon. *Rom* 16:1

Atad

to the threshing-floor of *A.* *Gen* 50:1
saw mourning in floor of *A.*

ate

a. the sacrifices of the. *Ps* 106:
I *a.* no pleasant bread. *Dan* 10
took the little book, and *a.* *Rev* 10:

Athaliah

mother was *A.* *2 Ki* 8:26; *2 Chr* 22
A. arose. *2 Ki* 11:1; *2 Chr* 22:
hid from *A.* *2 Ki* 11:2; *2 Chr* 22:
they slew *A.* *2 Ki* 11:20; *2 Chr* 23:
Shehariah and *A.* *1 Chr* 8:

sons of *A.* that wicked. *2 Chr* 24:7
Jeshaiah son of *A.* with. *Ezra* 8:7

Athenians

A. spent their time in. *Acts* 17:21

Athens

and brought Paul to *A.* *Acts* 17:15
while Paul waited for them at *A.* 16
ye men of *A.* I perceive ye are. 22
Paul departed from *A.* and. 18:1
good to be left at *A.* *1 Thes* 3:1

athirst

Samson was sore *a.* and. *Judg* 15:18
when *a.* go to the vessels. *Ruth* 2:9
when saw we thee *a.*? *Mat* 25:44
give to him that is *a.* of. *Rev* 21:6
bride say, let him that is *a.* 22:17

atonement

Reconciliation, at-one-ment; chiefly used of Christ's atoning death, Rom 5:11.

eat things wherewith *a.* *Ex* 29:33
offer a bullock every day for *a.* 36
seven days thou shalt make *a.* for. 37
once in year shall make *a.* 30:10
to make an *a.* for your. 15; *Lev* 17:11
thou shalt take the *a.* money. *Ex* 30:16
I shall make an *a.* for sin. 32:30
accepted for him to make *a.* *Lev* 1:4
priest shall make an *a.* for them. 4:20
26, 31, 35; 5:6; 6:7; 12:8; 14:18
Num 15:25
hath commanded to make *a.* *Lev* 8:34
make *a.* for thyself and. 9:7; 16:24
given it you to make *a.* for. 10:17
make an *a.* for her, and she. 12:7
make an *a.* for the house. it. 14:53
shall be presented to make *a.* 16:10
Aaron shall make an *a.* for. 11
he shall make an *a.* for the holy. 16
no man there, when he maketh *a.* 17
he shall go and make *a.* for the. 18
was brought in to make *a.* 27
he shall make *a.* for the holy. 33
everlasting statute to make *a.* 34
there shall be a day of *a.* 23:27
it is a day of *a.* to make *a.* 28
in the day of *a.* make the. 25:9
given Levites to make *a.* *Num* 8:19
made *a.* for the Levites. 21
go quickly, make *a.* for wrath. 16:46
because he made an *a.* 25:13
sin-offering to make *a.* 28:22, 30
goats to make an *a.* for you. 29:5
ear-rings to make an *a.* for. 31:50
shall I make the *a.*? *2 Sam* 21:3
sons appointed to make *a.* *1 Chr* 6:49
killed them to make *a.* *2 Chr* 29:24
for offering to make an *a.* *Neh* 10:33
we have now received *a.* *Rom* 5:11

attain

(*To reach by growth, or by continued effort*)

it is high, I cannot *a.* unto. *Ps* 139:6
of understanding shall *a.* *Pr* 1:5
as his hand shall *a.* to it. *Ezek* 46:7*
ere they *a.* to innocency? *Hos* 8:5
they might *a.* to Phenice. *Acts* 27:12
a. to the resurrection. *Phil* 3:11

attained

have not *a.* to the days of. *Gen* 47:9
he *a.* not to the first. *2 Sam* 23:19
23; *1 Chr* 11:21, 25
the Gentiles have *a.* to. *Rom* 9:30
Israel hath not *a.* to the law of. 31
though I had already *a.* *Phil* 3:12
whereto we have already *a.* let. 16
whereto thou hast *a.* *1 Tim* 4:6

Attalia

they went down into *A.* *Acts* 14:25

attend

ne appointed to *a.* her. *Esth* 4:5
a. to my cry. *Ps* 17:1; 61:1; 142:6
a. to me, hear me, I mourn. 55:2
nd *a.* to the voice of. 86:6
ear and *a.* to know. *Pr* 4:1
ny son, *a.* to my words. 20; 7:24
ny son, *a.* to my wisdom, and 5:1
nay *a.* on the Lord. *1 Cor* 7:35

attendance

he *a.* of his ministers. *1 Ki* 10:5
2 Chr 9:4

till I come, give *a.* to. *1 Tim* 4:13*
which no man gave *a.* at. *Heb* 7:13

attended

I *a.* to you, none of you. *Job* 32:12
he hath *a.* to the voice of. *Ps* 66:19
she *a.* to the things. *Acts* 16:14*

attending

ministers *a.* continually. *Rom* 13:6

attent

(*Old form of* attentive)

let thine ears be *a.* to. *2 Chr* 6:40
mine ears shall be *a.* at the. 7:15

attentive

ear now be *a.* *Neh* 1:6, 11; *Ps* 130:2
the people were *a.* 8:3; *Luke* 19:48

attentively

hear *a.* the noise of his. *Job* 37:2*

attire, -ed

mitre shall Aaron be *a.* *Lev* 16:4
him a woman with *a.* of an. *Pr* 7:10
can a bride forget her *a.*? *Jer* 2:32
exceeding in dyed *a.* on. *Ezek* 23:15

audience

(*Used as* hearing, *not* a company of hearers)

spake to Ephron in *a.* of. *Gen* 23:13
covenant, and read in *a.* *Ex* 24:7
maid speak in thy *a.* *1 Sam* 25:24
in the *a.* of our God. *1 Chr* 28:8
the book of Moses in the *a.* *Neh* 13:1
all his sayings in the *a.* *Luke* 7:1
in *a.* of the people he said to. 20:45
ye that fear God, give *a.* *Acts* 13:16
then all the multitude gave *a.* 15:12
they gave him *a.* to this. 22:22

augment

ye are risen to *a.* the. *Num* 32:14

Augustus

a decree from Caesar *A.* *Luke* 2:1
had appealed to *A.* *Acts* 25:21, 25
Julius, a centurion of *A.* band. 27:1

aunt

to his wife, she is thy *a.* *Lev* 18:14

austere

because thou art an *a.* *Luke* 19:21

author

God is not the *a.* of. *1 Cor* 14:33*
became the *a.* of eternal. *Heb* 5:9
Jesus, the *a.* and finisher of. 12:2

authority

[1] *Power, rule, or dignity,* Mat 7:29; 20:25; Luke 19:17. [2] *A warrant or order,* Mat 21:23; Acts 9:14.

Mordecai wrote with *a.* *Esth* 9:29
when righteous are in *a.* *Pr* 29:2*
taught them as one having *a.*
Mat 7:29; *Mark* 1:22
a man under *a.* *Mat* 8:9; *Luke* 7:8
exercise *a.* *Mat* 20:25; *Mark* 10:42
by what *a.* doest thou these things?
Mat 21:23; *Mark* 11:28
with *a.* commandeth he even the unclean. *Mark* 1:27; *Luke* 4:36
his house, and gave *a.* to. *Mark* 13:34
gave them power and *a.* *Luke* 9:1
been faithful, have thou *a.* 19:17
might deliver him to *a.* of. 20:20
that exercise *a.* are called. 22:25
hath given him *a.* to. *John* 5:27
eunuch of great *a.* under. *Acts* 8:27
hath *a.* to bind. 9:14; 26:10, 12
have put down all *a.* *1 Cor* 15:24
somewhat more of our *a.* *2 Cor* 10:8
for kings and all in *a.* *1 Tim* 2:2
I suffer not a woman to usurp *a.* 12
and rebuke with all *a.* *Tit* 2:15
angels and *a.* made. *1 Pet* 3:22
him power and great *a.* *Rev* 13:2

availeth

yet all this *a.* me nothing. *Esth* 5:13
circumcision *a.* not. *Gal* 5:6*; 6:15
a righteous man *a.* much. *Jas* 5:16

Aven

the young men of *A.* *Ezek* 30:17
the high places of *A.* the. *Hos* 10:8
cut off the inhabitant of *A.* *Amos* 1:5

avenge

thou shalt not *a.* nor. *Lev* 19:18*
that shall *a.* the quarrel of. 26:25*

a. Israel of the Midianites. *Num* 31:2
he will *a.* the blood of. *Deut* 32:43
the Lord judge and *a.* *1 Sam* 24:12
of Ahab, that I may *a.* *2 Ki* 9:7
Jews *a.* themselves on. *Esth* 8:13
a. me of mine enemies. *Isa* 1:24
vengeance that he may *a.* *Jer* 46:10
a. the blood of Jezreel. *Hos* 1:4
saying, *a.* me of mine. *Luke* 18:3
shall not God *a.* his own elect. 7
I tell you that he will *a.* them. 8
a. not yourselves, but. *Rom* 12:19
how long dost thou not *a.*? *Rev* 6:10

avenged

should be *a.* seven-fold. *Gen* 4:24
stayed till people had *a.* *Josh* 10:13
done this, yet I will be *a.* *Judg* 15:7
may be *a.* on Philistines for. 16:28
food, that I may be *a.* *1 Sam* 14:24
hundred foreskins, to be *a.* 18:25
or that my Lord hath *a.* 25:31
the Lord hath *a.* my. *2 Sam* 4:8
how the Lord hath *a.* him of. 18:19
the Lord hath *a.* thee this day. 31
my soul be *a.* on such a nation.
Jer 5:9, 29; 9:9
Moses *a.* him that was. *Acts* 7:24
rejoice, for God hath *a.* *Rev* 18:20*
hath *a.* blood of his servants. 19:2

avenger

cities for refuge from the *a.*
Num 35:12; *Josh* 20:3
lest the *a.* of blood pursue. *Deut* 19:6
him into the hand of the *a.* 12
if the *a.* of blood pursue. *Josh* 20:5
not die by the hand of the *a.* till. 9
still the enemy and *a.* *Ps* 8:2
by reason of the enemy and *a.* 44:16
the Lord is the *a.* *1 Thes* 4:6

avengeth

God that *a.* *2 Sam* 22:48; *Ps* 18:47

avenging

praise the Lord for the *a.* *Judg* 5:2*
withholden thee from *a.* *1 Sam* 25:26
thou who kept me from *a.* 33

averse

by securely, as men *a.* *Mi* 2:8

avoid

(*To shun, turn away from, escape from*)

a. it, pass not by it. *Pr* 4:15
cause divisions, and *a.* *Rom* 16:17
to *a.* fornication, let. *1 Cor* 7:2
unlearned questions *a.* *2 Tim* 2:23
a. foolish questions and. *Tit* 3:9

avoided, -ing

David *a.* out of his. *1 Sam* 18:11
a. this, that no man. *2 Cor* 8:20
a. profane and vain. *1 Tim* 6:20

avouched

(*Acknowledged deliberately and openly*)

this day *a.* the Lord to. *Deut* 26:17
the Lord hath *a.* thee to be his. 18

awake

[1] *To come out of natural sleep,* Luke 9:32. [2] *To rouse out of spiritual sleep,* Rom 13:11; Eph 5:14. [3] *To raise from the dead,* Job 14:12; John 11:11.

a. a. Deborah *a. a.* utter. *Judg* 5:12
surely now he would *a.* *Job* 8:6
no more, they shall not *a.* 14:12
a. for me to the. *Ps* 7:6; 35:23
be satisfied when I *a.* with. 17:15
a. why sleepest thou, O Lord? 44:23
a. my glory, I myself will *a.* 57:8
108:2
they prepare, *a.* to help me. 59:4
O Lord God, *a.* to visit all the. 5
when shall I *a.* I will seek. *Pr* 23:35
a. my love. *S of S* 2:7; 3:5; 8:4
a. O north wind, and come. 4:16
a. and sing ye that dwell. *Isa* 26:19
a a. put on strength, O arm of the Lord, *a.* as in the. 51:9; 52:1
a. a. stand up, O Jerusalem. 51:17
perpetual sleep, and not *a.* *Jer* 51:57
sleep in the dust shall *a.* *Dan* 12:2
a. ye drunkards, weep. *Joel* 1:5
shall they not *a.* that. *Hab* 2:7

him that saith to the wood *a.* *Hab* 2:19
a. O sword, against my. *Zech* 13:7
asleep, and they *a.* him. *Mark* 4:38
when they were *a.* they. *Luke* 9:32
I go that I may *a.* him. *John* 11:11
it is high time to *a.* out. *Rom* 13:11
a. to righteousness, and. *1 Cor* 15:34
a. thou that sleepest, and. *Eph* 5:14

awaked

Jacob *a.* out of his sleep. *Gen* 28:16
Samson *a.* and went. *Judg* 16:14
nor knew it, neither *a.* *1 Sam* 26:12
and must be *a.* *1 Ki* 18:27
him, the child is not *a.* *2 Ki* 4:31
I *a.* for the Lord sustained. *Ps* 3:5
then the Lord *a.* as one out. 78:65
upon this I *a.* and beheld. *Jer* 31:26

awakest

when thou *a.* shalt despise. *Ps* 73:20
when thou *a.* it shall talk. *Pr* 6:22

awaketh, -ing

as a dream when one *a.* so. *Ps* 73:20
a. and his soul is empty, *a.* *Isa* 29:8
keeper of the prison *a.* *Acts* 16:27

aware

I was *a.* my soul made. *S of S* 6:12
Babylon, and thou art not *a.* *Jer* 50:24
over them, are not *a.* *Luke* 11:44

away

Abraham drove them *a.* *Gen* 15:11
not go very far *a.* *Ex* 8:28
the Lord said to him, *a.* get. 19:24*
have me *a.* for I am. *2 Chr* 35:23
assemblies I cannot, *a.* *Isa* 1:13
a. with this man, release. *Luke* 23:18
a. with him, *a.* with him. *John* 19:15
Acts 21:36
a. with such a fellow. *Acts* 22:22

awe

stand in *a.* and sin not. *Ps* 4:4
of the world stand in *a.* of him. 33:8
my heart standeth in *a.* of. 119:161

awl

bore his ear with an *a.* *Ex* 21:6
thou shalt take an *a.* *Deut* 15:17

awoke

Noah *a.* from his wine. *Gen* 9:24
fat kine, so Pharaoh *a.* 41:4, 7, 21
Samson *a.* out of his. *Judg* 16:20
Solomon *a.* and behold it. *1 Ki* 3:15
disciples came and *a.* him. *Mat* 8:25
Luke 8:24

ax

[1] *Literally, the ax similar to that in modern use.* [2] *Figuratively, any instrument used in inflicting judgement,* Isa 10:15; Mat 3:10.

a stroke with the *ax.* *Deut* 19:5
the trees by forcing an *ax.* 20:19
Abimelech took an *ax* in. *Judg* 9:48
down to sharpen his *ax.* *1 Sam* 13:20
neither hammer nor *ax.* *1 Ki* 6:7
the *ax*-head fell into. *2 Ki* 6:5
shall the *ax* boast itself. *Isa* 10:15
cuts a tree with the *ax.* *Jer* 10:3
thou art my battle-*ax* and. 51:20
ax is laid to root of trees. *Mat* 3:10
Luke 3:9

axes

had a file for the *a.* *1 Sam* 13:21
under saws and *a.* of iron, and made them. *2 Sam* 12:31; *1 Chr* 20:3
famous as he lifted up *a.* *Ps* 74:5
down the carved work with *a.* 6
come against her with *a.* *Jer* 46:22
with *a.* he shall break. *Ezek* 26:9

axle-trees

the *a.-t.* of the wheel join. *1 Ki* 7:32
a.-t. naves, and felloes, were. 33

Azariah

A. was one of Solomon's. *1 Ki* 4:2
A. the son of Nathan was over. 5
Judah made *A.* king. *2 Ki* 14:21
A. son of Ethan. *1 Chr* 2:8
Jehu begat *A.* 38
Amaziah his son, *A.* his son. 3:12
Ahimaaz begat *A.* 6:9
Johanan begat *A.* 10
Hilkiah begat *A.* 13
Zephaniah begat *A.* 36
of God came on *A.* *2 Chr* 15:1
A. son of Jehoshaphat. *2 Chr* 21:2
A. son of Jehoram. 22:6
A. son of Jehoram, and *A.* 23:1
A. the priest went in. 26:17, 20
the son of *A.* the son. *Ezra* 7:1, 3
A. the son of Maaseiah. *Neh* 3:23
Nehemiah *A.* came up with. 7:7
A. caused the people to. 8:7
those that sealed were *A.* 10:2
A. and all the proud men. *Jer* 43:2
of Judah was Daniel, *A.* *Dan* 1:6
A. the name of Abed-nego. 7
made the thing known to *A.* 2:17

Azekah

stones on them to *A.* *Josh* 10:11
Babylon fought against *A.* *Jer* 34:7

B

Baal

to high places of *B.* *Num* 22:41
Israel served *B.* and. *Judg* 2:13
throw down the altar of *B.* 6:25
will ye plead for *B.*? will ye? 31
Ahab served *B.* and. *1 Ki* 16:31
but if *B.* be God, then follow. 18:21
name of *B.* saying, O *B.* hear. 26
take the prophets of *B.* let none. 40
seven thousand in Israel . . . not bowed to *B.* 19:18; *Rom* 11:4
sacrifice to do to *B.* *2 Ki* 10:19
a solemn assembly for *B.* 20
thus Jehu destroyed *B.* out of. 28
brake down the house of *B.* 11:18
host of heaven, served *B.* 17:16
reared up altars for *B.* 21:3
all the vessels made for *B.* 23:4
them that burnt incense to *B.* 5
prophets prophesied by *B.* *Jer* 2:8
burn incense to *B.*? 7:9; 11:13, 17
32:29
my people to swear by *B.* 12:16
built the high places of *B.* . . fire for burnt-offerings to *B.* 19:5
they prophesied in *B.* and. 23:13
have forgotten my name for *B.* 27
which they prepared for *B.* *Hos* 2:8
when Ephraim offended in *B.* 13:1
cut off the remnant of *B.* *Zeph* 1:4

Baal-berith

of Israel made *B.* *Judg* 8:33

Baal-hamon

had a vineyard at *B.* *S of S* 8:11

Baali

shalt call me no more *B.* *Hos* 2:16

Baalim

Israel served *B.* *Judg* 2:11; 3:7
10:6, 10
Israel went a whoring after *B.* 8:33
of Israel put away *B.* *1 Sam* 7:4
thou hast followed *B.* *1 Ki* 18:18
sought not unto *B.* *2 Chr* 17:3
things did they bestow on *B.* 24:7
also molten images for *B.* 28:2
reared up altars for *B.* 33:3
brake down the altars of *B.* 34:4
I have not gone after *B.* *Jer* 2:23
have walked after *B.* which. 9:14
visit on her the days of *B.* *Hos* 2:13
take away the names of *B.* 17

Baalis

B. king of Ammonites hath. *Jer* 40:14

Baal-meon

Beth-jeshimoth, *B.* *Ezek* 25:9

Baal-peor

Israel joined himself to *B.* and the. *Num* 25:3; *Ps* 106:28; *Hos* 9:10
men that were joined unto *B.*
Num 25:5
Lord did because of *B.* *Deut* 4:3

Baal-perazim

that place *B.* *2 Sam* 5:20; *1 Chr* 14:11

Baal-shalisha

came a man from *B.* *2 Ki* 4:42

Baal-tamar

themselves in array at *B.* *Judg* 20:33

Baal-zebub

enquire of *B.* the God. *2 Ki* 1:2, 16

Baal-zephon

over against *B.* *Ex* 14:2; *Num* 33:7

Baanah

Rechab and *B.* his. *2 Sam* 4:6
Heleb the son of *B.* one of. 23:29
B. the son of Hushai. *1 Ki* 4:16
B. came to. *Ezra* 2:2; *Neh* 7:7
Harim, *B.* sealed the. *Neh* 10:27

Baasha

war between Asa and *B.* *1 Ki* 15:16, 32
thy league with *B.* 19; *2 Chr* 16:3
B. son of Ahijah conspired. *1 Ki* 15:27
Lord came to Jehu against *B.* 16:1
B. slept with his fathers and was. 6
slew all the house of *B.* 11, 12
like the house of *B.* 21:22; *2 Ki* 9:9
Asa made for fear of *B.* *Jer* 41:9

babbler

will bite, and a *b.* is. *Eccl* 10:11*
what will this *b.* say? *Acts* 17:18

babbling, -s

contentions? who hath *b.*? *Pr* 23:29*
profane and vain *b.* *1 Tim* 6:20
shun profane and vain *b.* *2 Tim* 2:16

babe

[1] *An infant or child,* Ex 2:6; Luke 2:12. [2] *Such as are weak in faith and knowledge,* 1 Cor 3:1; Heb 5:13.

child, and behold the *b.* *Ex* 2:6
heard Mary, the *b.* *Luke* 1:41
the *b.* leaped in my womb for joy. 44
find *b.* wrapped in swaddling. 2:12
came and found the *b.* lying in. 16
the word, for he is a *b.* *Heb* 5:13

Babel

of his kingdom was *B.* *Gen* 10:10
is the name of it called *B.* 11:9

babes

the mouth of *b.* *Ps* 8:2; *Mat* 21:16
of their substance to their *b.* *Ps* 17:14
their princes and *b.* shall. *Isa* 3:4
hast revealed them to *b.* *Mat* 11:25
Luke 10:21
foolish, a teacher of *b.* *Rom* 2:20
carnal, even as unto *b.* *1 Cor* 3:1
as new-born *b.* desire the. *1 Pet* 2:2

Babylon

the men of *B.* made. *2 Ki* 17:30
that were in *B.* 25:28; *Jer* 52:32
of the princes of *B.* *2 Chr* 32:31
vessels in his temple at *B.* 36:7
take out of temple of *B.* *Ezra* 5:14
treasures were laid up in *B.* 6:1
mention of Rahab and *B.* *Ps* 87:4
by the rivers of *B.* there we. 137:1
burden of *B.* which Isaiah. *Isa* 13:1
B. shall be as when God. 19
B. is fallen. 21:9; *Jer* 51:8
Rev 14:8; 18:2
will do his pleasure on *B.* *Isa* 48:14
go ye forth of *B.* flee from the. 20
carry them captive into *B.* *Jer* 20:4
of Judah that went into *B.* 28:4
be accomplished at *B.* 29:10
raised us up prophets in *B.* 15
to come with me into *B.* 40:4
the Lord spake against *B.* 50:1
remove out of the midst of *B.* 8
one that goeth by *B.* shall hiss. 13
how is *B.* become a desolation? 23
together the archers against *B.* 29
disquiet the inhabitants of *B.* 34
counsel of the Lord against *B.* 45
flee out of the midst of *B.* 51:6
violence done to me be upon *B.* 35
the sea is come up upon *B.* she is. 42
and earth shall sing for *B.* 48
at *B.* shall fall the slain of all. 49
though *B.* should mount up. 53
because the Lord hath spoiled *B.* 55
broad walls of *B.* shall be. 58
the evil that shall come on *B.* 6
thus shall *B.* sink, and shall not. 6
him in the midst of *B.* *Ezek* 17:1
is not this great *B.* that I? *Dan* 4:3
till the carrying into *B.* *Mat* 1:1
carry you away beyond *B.* *Acts* 7:4
the church at *B.* saluteth. *1 Pet* 5:1
great *B.* came in. *Rev* 16:1
B. the great, the mother of. 17:
alas, alas, that great city *B.* 18:1
thus shall that great city *B.* be. 2
see **daughter, province,** *wise* **me**

from **Babylon**
country *from B. 2 Ki* 20:14; *Isa* 39:3
began he to go up *from B. Ezra* 7:9
went up with me *from B.* 8:1
I will cut off *from B.* the. *Isa* 14:22
off the sower *from B. Jer* 50:16
sound of a cry cometh *from B.* 51:54
which are come *from B. Zech* 6:10

king of **Babylon**
serve the *king of B. 2 Ki* 25:24
Jer 27:17; 40:9
the hand of the *king of B.* the.
Ezra 5:12; *Jer* 21:7; 22:25
proverb against *king of B. Isa* 14:4
fight against the *king of B. Jer* 21:4
serve the *king of B.* 70 years. 25:11
I will punish the *king of B.* 12
will not serve *king of B.* 27:8, 13
the yoke of the *king of B.* 28:11
whom the *king of B.* roasted. 29:22
behold the eyes of *king of B.* 34:3
king of B. shall certainly come. 36:29
king of B. gave charge. 39:11
be not afraid of the *king of B.* 42:11
king of B. hath taken counsel. 49:30
the *king of B.* hath broken. 50:17
sword of the *king of B. Ezek* 21:19
king of B. caused his army. 29:18
give Egypt unto the *king of B.* 19
the arms of *king of B.* 30:24, 25
sword of the *king of B.* shall. 32:11

to or *unto* **Babylon**
shall be carried *to B. 2 Ki* 20:17
24:15; 25:7, 13; *1 Chr* 9:1
2 Chr 36:6, 7, 20; *Ezra* 5:12; *Isa*
39:6; *Jer* 27:20; 28:3; 29:1, 4
40:1, 7
and carried him *to B. 2 Chr* 33:11
all these he brought *to B.* 36:18
sake I have sent *to B. Isa* 43:14
thou shalt come *to B. Jer* 20:6
thou shalt go *to B.* 34:3
I will render *unto B.* 51:24
when comest *to B.* 61
I will bring him *to B. Ezek* 17:20
of Zion shall go *to B. Mi* 4:10
they were carried *to B. Mat* 1:11

Babylonians
manner of the *B.* of. *Ezek* 23:15
the *B.* came to her into the bed. 17

Babylonish
saw a goodly *B.* garment. *Josh* 7:21

Baca
through the valley of *B. Ps* 84:6

back
after he had sent her *b. Ex* 18:2
astray, thou shalt bring it *b.* 23:4
I will get me *b. Num* 22:34
Lord hath kept thee *b.* 24:11
drew not his hand *b.* till. *Josh* 8:26
damsel that came *b. Ruth* 2:6
return, and take *b.* thy. *2 Sam* 15:20
not of bringing the king *b.*? 19:10
but camest *b.* and hast. *1 Ki* 13:22
and carry him *b.* to Amon. 22:26
when Judah looked *b. 2 Chr* 13:14
soldiers that Amaziah sent *b.* 25:13
he holdeth *b.* the face of. *Job* 26:9
fled apace, and look not *b. Jer* 46:5
slideth *b.* as a backsliding. *Hos* 4:16
they cry, none shall look *b. Nah* 2:8
that is in field return *b. Mat* 24:18
angel rolled *b.* the stone from. 28:2
the ship, and returned *b. Luke* 8:37
to plough, and looking *b.* 9:62
let him likewise not return *b.* 17:31
see **draw, go, bring, keep, kept, turn, went**

back, *substantive*
he turned his *b.* to go. *1 Sam* 10:9
behind thy *b. 1 Ki* 14:9; *Ezek* 23:35
make them turn their *b. Ps* 21:12
the plowers plowed on my *b.* 129:3
b. of him. *Pr* 10:13; 19:29; 26:3
cast my sins behind thy *b. Isa* 38:17
I gave my *b.* to the smiters. 50:6
they have turned their *b. Jer* 2:27
I will shew them the *b.* and. 18:17
have turned to me the *b.* 32:33
how hath Moab turned the *b.* 48:39
which had on the *b.* of it. *Dan* 7:6
bow down their *b.* alway. *Rom* 11:10

backbiters
b. haters of God. *Rom* 1:30

backbiteth
he that *b.* not with his. *Ps* 15:3*

backbiting
countenance, a *b.* tongue. *Pr* 25:23
be debates, strifes, *b. 2 Cor* 12:20

back-bone
take off hard by the *b.-b. Lev* 3:9

back-parts
thou shalt see my *b.-p. Ex* 33:23

backs
thy law behind their *b. Neh* 9:26
with their *b.* towards. *Ezek* 8:16
their whole body and *b.* full. 10:12
see **turned**

backside
Moses led the flock to the *b. Ex* 3:1
shall hang over the *b.* 26:12
on the *b.* sealed with seven. *Rev* 5:1

backslider
b. in heart be filled. *Pr* 14:14

backsliding, -s
and thy *b.* shall reprove. *Jer* 2:19
hast thou seen what *b.* Israel? 3:6
whereby *b.* Israel committed. 8
the *b.* Israel hath justified. 11
return thou *b.* Israel, saith the. 12
b. children, saith the Lord. 14, 22
their transgressions and *b.* 5:6
slidden back by a perpetual *b.* 8:5
for our *b.* are many, we sinned. 14:7
about, O *b.* daughter. 31:22; 49:4
slideth back, as a *b. Hos* 4:16*
my people are bent to *b.* 11:7
I will heal their *b.* I will love. 14:4

backward
b. and their faces were *b. Gen* 9:23
that his rider shall fall *b.* 49:17
fell from off the seat *b. 1 Sam* 4:18
let the shadow return *b. 2 Ki* 20:10
Isa 38:8
b. but I cannot perceive. *Job* 23:8
let them be driven *b.* that. *Ps* 40:14
them be turned *b.* that desire. 70:2
and are gone away *b. Isa* 1:4
that they might go and fall *b.* 28:13
that turneth wise men *b.* and. 44:25
judgement is turned away *b.* 59:14
but they went *b.* and not. *Jer* 7:24
thou art gone *b.* therefore I. 15:6
sigheth and turneth *b. Lam* 1:8
they went *b.* and fell to. *John* 18:6

bad
speak to thee *b.* or good. *Gen* 24:50
to Jacob good or *b.* 31:24, 29
good for a *b.* or a *b.* for. *Lev* 27:10
value it, whether it be good or *b.* 12
house, whether it be good or *b.* 14
search whether it be good or *b.* 33
dwell in, if good or *b. Num* 13:19
to do either good or *b.* of my. 24:13
neither good nor *b. 2 Sam* 13:22
lord the king to discern good or *b.*
14:17
may discern good and *b. 1 Ki* 3:9*
the rebellious and *b.* city. *Ezra* 4:12
be eaten, they were so *b. Jer* 24:2
good but cast the *b.* away. *Mat* 13:48
good and *b.* and the wedding was.
22:10
done, whether good or *b. 2 Cor* 5:10

bade, -est
according as thou *b.* me. *Gen* 27:19
the man did as Joseph *b.* 43:17
till morning, as Moses *b. Ex* 16:24
all the congregation *b. Num* 14:10
to them as the Lord *b. Josh* 11:9
that her mother-in-law *b. Ruth* 3:6
some *b.* me kill thee. *1 Sam* 24:10
David *b.* them teach. *2 Sam* 1:18
for thy servant Joab he *b.* me. 14:19
third day as the king *b. 2 Chr* 10:12
Esther *b.* them return. *Esth* 4:15
how he *b.* them not. *Mat* 16:12
b. thee and him. *Luke* 14:9, 10
man made a supper and *b.* 16
and the Spirit *b.* me go. *Acts* 11:12
but *b.* them farewell, saying. 18:21
b. that he should be. 22:24

badgers'-skins
(*Revised Version*, seal-skins)
take of them. *b.-skins. Ex* 25:5
for the tent above of *b.-skins.* 26:14
rams' skins dyed red, *b.-skins.* 35:7
found skins of rams, and *b.-skins.* 23
made a covering of *b.-skins.* 36:19
a covering of *b.-skins. Num* 4:10
shod thee with *b.-skins. Ezek* 16:10

badness
the land of Egypt for *b. Gen* 41:19

bag
thy *b.* divers weights. *Deut* 25:13
and put them in a *b. 1 Sam* 17:40
is sealed up in a *b. Job* 14:17
he hath taken a *b.* of. *Pr* 7:20
all the weights of the *b.* 16:11
lavish gold out of the *b. Isa* 46:6
the *b.* of deceitful weights. *Mi* 6:11
to put in a *b.* with holes. *Hag* 1:6
a thief, and had the *b. John* 12:6
because Judas had the *b.* 13:29

bags
two talents in two *b. 2 Ki* 5:23
they put up in *b.* and told. 12:10
provide yourselves *b. Luke* 12:33*

Bahurim
weeping behind her to *B. 2 Sam* 3:16
when David came to *B.* Shimei. 16:5
came to a man's house in *B.* 17:18
a Benjamite of *B.* 19:16; *1 Ki* 2:8

Bajith
up to *B.* and to Dibon to. *Isa* 15:2

bake
Lot did *b.* unleavened. *Gen* 19:3
b. that which you will *b. Ex* 16:23
take flour and *b.* twelve. *Lev* 24:5
ten women shall *b.* your. 26:26
woman at Endor did *b. 1 Sam* 28:24
took flour and did *b. 2 Sam* 13:8
shalt *b.* it with man's. *Ezek* 4:12
the place where they shall *b.* 46:20

baked
they *b.* unleavened cakes. *Ex* 12:39
and *b.* it in pans, and. *Num* 11:8*
and for that which is *b. 1 Chr* 23:29

bake-meats
manner of *b.-meats* for. *Gen* 40:17

baken
meat-offering *b.* in. *Lev* 2:4; 7:9
it shall not be *b.* with leaven. 6:17
two wave-loaves shall be *b.* 23:17
behold, a cake was *b. 1 Ki* 19:6

baker
the butler and *b.* had. *Gen* 40:1
head of the chief butler and *b.* 20
he hanged the *b.* as Joseph. 22
ward both me and the chief *b.* 41:10
as an oven heated by the *b. Hos* 7:4
their *b.* sleepeth all the night. 6

bakers
against the chief of the *b. Gen* 40:2
your daughters to be *b. 1 Sam* 8:13
Jeremiah bread out of *b. Jer* 37:21

baketh
he *b.* bread, yea, he. *Isa* 44:15

Balaam
sent messengers to *B. Num* 22:5
God came to *B.* and said, what. 9
they said, *B.* refuseth to come. 14
the ass crushed *B.* foot against. 25
Lord opened the eyes of *B.* 31
B. went with the princes of Balak. 35
God met *B.* and said. 23:4, 16
Balak did as *B.* had said, and. 30
B. lifted up his eyes and saw. 24:2
B. the son of Beor hath said. 3, 15
B. rose up and returned to his. 25
B. the son of Beor. 31:8; *Josh* 13:22
the counsel of *B.* to. *Num* 31:16
they hired *B. Deut* 23:4; *Neh* 13:2
would not hearken to *B. Deut* 23:5
Balak sent and called *B. Josh* 24:9
remember what *B. Mi* 6:5
way of B. the son of Bosor. *2 Pet* 2:15
after the error of *B. Jude* 11
hold the doctrine of *B. Rev* 2:14

Balak
B. was king of the. *Num* 22:4
saith *B.* let nothing hinder thee. 16

B. did as Balaam had. *Num* 23:2, 30
B. king of Moab hath brought me. 7
rise up *B.* and hear. 18
B. anger kindled. 24:10
if *B.* would give me his house. 13
then *B.* arose and warred. *Josh* 24:9
any thing better than *B.*? *Judg* 11:25
remember what *B.* king of. *Mi* 6:5
B. to cast a stumbling. *Rev* 2:14

balance

be weighed in an even *b.* *Job* 31:6
laid in the *b.* are altogether. *Ps* 62:9
a false *b.* is. *Pr* 11:1; 20:23
a just weight and *b.* are the. 16:11
weighed the hills in a *b.*? *Isa* 40:12
as the small dust of the *b.* 15
gold, and weigh silver in the *b.* 46:6

balances

just *b.* a just. *Lev* 19:36; *Ezek* 45:10
calamity laid in the *b.* *Job* 6:2
him the money in the *b.* *Jer* 32:10
b. to weigh, and divide. *Ezek* 5:1
thou art weighed in the *b.* *Dan* 5:27
the *b.* of deceit are in. *Hos* 12:7
and falsifying the *b.* by. *Amos* 8:5
them pure with wicked *b.*? *Mi* 6:11
on him had a pair of *b.* *Rev* 6:5

balancings

dost thou know the *b.*? *Job* 37:16

bald

is *b.* yet is he clean. *Lev* 13:40, 41
b. head, go up thou *b.* *2 Ki* 2:23
nor make themselves *b.* *Jer* 16:6
every head shall be *b.* and. 48:37
themselves utterly *b.* *Ezek* 27:31
every head was made *b.* and. 29:18
make thee *b.* and poll thee. *Mi* 1:16

bald-locust

ye may eat the *b.-locust.* *Lev* 11:22

baldness

Frequently a sign of mourning, Isa. 15:2; Jer 47:5.

they shall not make *b.* *Lev* 21:5
nor make any *b.* between. *Deut* 14:1
of well set hair, *b.* *Isa* 3:24
on all their heads shall be *b.* 15:2
did call to mourning and to *b.* 22:12
b. is come upon Gaza. *Jer* 47:5
and *b.* upon all. *Ezek* 7:18; *Amos* 8:10
enlarge thy *b.* as the eagle. *Mi* 1:16

ball

turn and toss thee like a *b.* *Isa* 22:18

balm

Ishmaelites bearing *b.* *Gen* 37:25
take in your vessels a little *b.* 43:11
is there no *b.* in Gilead? *Jer* 8:22
go up to Gilead, and take *b.* 46:11
howl for her, take *b.* for her. 51:8
honey, and oil, and *b.*. *Ezek* 27:17

Bamah

thereof is called *B.* *Ezek* 20:29

band, -s

[1] *Material chains,* Luke 8:29; Acts 16:26. [2] *Moral or spiritual bonds, as government and laws,* Ps 2:3; *or faith and love,* Col 2:19.

a *b.* round that it should. *Ex* 39:23
I have broken the *b.* of. *Lev* 26:13
his *b.* loosed from off. *Judg* 15:14
put Jehoahaz in *b.* *2 Ki* 23:33
darkness a swaddling *b.* *Job* 38:9
Pleiades, or loose the *b.* of? 31
or who hath loosed the *b.* of? 39:5
bind the unicorn with his *b.*? 10
let us break their *b.* asunder. *Ps* 2:3
for there are no *b.* in their. 73:4
he brake their *b.* in sunder. 107:14
heart snares, hands as *b.* *Eccl* 7:26
be not mockers, lest *b.* *Isa* 28:22
loose thyself from the *b.* of thy. 52:2
this the fast, to loose the *b.* 58:6
thy yoke, burst thy *b.* *Jer* 2:20
they shall put *b.* on thee. *Ezek* 3:25
and behold I will lay *b.* upon. 4:8
when I have broken the *b.* 34:27
a *b.* of iron and brass. *Dan* 4:15, 23
drew them with *b.* of love. *Hos* 11:4
two staves, beauty and *b.* *Zech* 11:7
asunder mine other staff, even *b.* 14
he brake *b.* and was. *Luke* 8:29
and every one's *b.* were. *Acts* 16:26
loosed Paul from his *b.* 22:30
which all the body by *b.* *Col* 2:19

see **bonds**

band, -s

(*Company of soldiers*)

the camels into two *b.* *Gen* 32:7
and now I am become two *b.* 10
went with him a *b.* *1 Sam* 10:26*
two men, captains of *b.* *2 Sam* 4:2
so the *b.* of Syria came. *2 Ki* 6:23
b. of the Moabites invaded. 13:20
burying a man, they spied a *b.* 21
against him *b.* of Chaldeans, *b.* 24:2
them were *b.* of soldiers. *1 Chr* 7:4
made them captains of the *b.* 12:18
helped David against the *b.* of. 21
require of the king a *b.* *Ezra* 8:22
made out three *b.* and fell. *Job* 1:17
the *b.* of the wicked. *Ps* 119:61
go forth all of them by *b.* *Pr* 30:27
I will scatter all his *b.* *Ezek* 12:14
all his *b.* Togarmah his *b.* 38:6
rain upon him and upon his *b.* 22
of Israel thou and thy *b.* 39:4
him whole *b.* *Mat* 27:27; *Mark* 15:16
having received a *b.* *John* 18:3
the *b.* and captain and officers. 12
the *b.* called the Italian *b.* *Acts* 10:1
to the chief captain of the *b.* 21:31
a centurion of Augustus' *b.* 27:1

banded

certain of the Jews *b.* *Acts* 23:12

banished

not fetch home his *b.* *2 Sam* 14:13
doth devise means that his *b.* 14

banishment

it be to death or to *b.* *Ezra* 7:26
burdens and causes of *b.* *Lam* 2:14

bank

[1] *The side, or brink of a river,* Gen 41:17. [2] *A mound, or heap of earth raised to cover besiegers, while they batter the walls of a city, or shoot at those who defend them,* 2 Sam 20:15. [3] *A place where there is a great sum of money taken in, and let out to use,* Luke 19:23.

behold I stood on the *b.* *Gen* 41:17
by the *b.* of the river Arnon.
Deut 4:48; *Josh* 12:2*; 13:9, 16*
cast up a *b.* against. *2 Sam* 20:15
Elisha stood by the *b.* *2 Ki* 2:13
shall not cast a *b.* 19:32; *Isa* 37:33
at the *b.* of the river. *Ezek* 47:7
the *b.* of the river, the other on that side of the *b.* *Dan* 12:5
my money into the *b.*? *Luke* 19:23

banks

overfloweth all his *b.* *Josh* 3:15; 4:18
had overflowed his *b.* *1 Chr* 12:15
shall go over all his *b.* *Isa* 8:7
man's voice between the *b.* *Dan* 8:16

banner

hast given a *b.* to them. *Ps* 60:4
to banquet, and his *b.* *S of S* 2:4
lift ye up a *b.* on the high. *Isa* 13:2

banners

our God we set up our *b.* *Ps* 20:5
terrible as an army with *b.* *S of S* 6:4

banquet

Haman come to the *b.* *Esth* 5:4, 5, 8
to Esther at the *b.* of wine. 6; 7:2
companions make a *b* of? *Job* 41:6*
the *b.* of them that. *Amos* 6:7

banquet-house

came into the *b.*-house. *Dan* 5:10

banqueting, -s

me into the *b.*-house. *S of S* 2:4
in lusts, revellings, *b.* *1 Pet* 4:3

baptism

[1] *The outward ordinance, or sacrament, wherein the washing with water represents the cleansing of the souls,* Luke 7:29; Acts 18:25; 1 Pet 3:21. [2] *Inward spiritual washing, signified by the outward sign,* Mat 3:11. [3] *The sufferings of Christ,* Mat 20:22; Luke 12:50.

Pharisees come to his *b.* *Mat* 3:7
be baptized with the *b.* 20:22*
Mark 10:38
the *b.* of John, whence was it, from?
Mat 21:25; *Mark* 11:30; *Luke* 20:4
and preach the *b.* *Mark* 1:4; *Luke* 3:3
baptized with the *b.* of. *Luke* 7:29
I have a *b.* to be baptized. 12:50
beginning from the *b.* of. *Acts* 1:22
word, after the *b.* which John. 10:37
preached the *b.* of repentance. 13:24
Apollos knowing only the *b* 18:25
they said unto John's *b.* 19:3
John baptized with the *b.* of. 4
buried with him by *b.* *Rom* 6:4
one Lord, one faith, one *b.* *Eph* 4:5
buried with him in *b.* ye. *Col* 2:12
of doctrine of *b.* and laying. *Heb* 6:2
figure whereunto, even *b.* *1 Pet* 3:21

Baptist

in those days came John *B.* *Mat* 3:1
there hath not risen a greater than John the *B.* 11:11; *Luke* 7:28
the days of John the *B.* *Mat* 11:12
this is John the *B.* he is risen. 14:2
said, give me John the *B.* head. *Mat* 14:8
art John the *B.* 16:14; *Mark* 8:28
he spake of John the *B.* *Mat* 17:13
John the *B.* was risen. *Mark* 6:14
charger the head of John the *B.* 25
John the *B.* hath sent us. *Luke* 7:20
John the *B.* came neither eating. 33
answering said, John the *B.* 9:19

baptize

I *b.* you with water, he shall *b.*
Mat 3:11; *Mark* 1:8; *Luke* 3:16
John 1:26
John did *b.* in the. *Mark* 1:4
that sent me to *b.* said. *John* 1:33
Christ sent me not to *b.* *1 Cor* 1:17

baptized

b. of him in. *Mat* 3:6; *Mark* 1:5
cometh Jesus to John to be *b.*
Mat 3:13
I have need to be *b.* of thee. 14
Jesus, when he was *b.* went up. 16
Jesus was *b.* of John. *Mark* 1:9
I am *b.* withal, shall ye be *b.* 10:39
he that believeth and is *b.* 16:16
that came to be *b.* *Luke* 3:7
publicans to be *b.* 12; 7:29
Jesus being *b.* and praying. 3:21
lawyers, being not *b.* of him. 7:30
tarried with them and *b.* *John* 3:22
and they came and were *b.* 23
Jesus made and *b.* more. 4:1
though Jesus himself *b.* not, but. 2
place where John at first *b.* 10:40
b. with water, but ye shall be *b.* with.
Acts 1:5; 11:16
repent, be *b.* every one of you. 2:38
gladly received his word were *b.* 41
they were *b.* both men and. 8:12
believed also, and when he was *b.* 13
only they were *b.* in the name of. 16
what doth hinder me to be *b.*? 36
Philip and eunuch, and he *b.* him. 38
sight, and arose and was *b.* 9:18
that these should not be *b.* 10:47
Peter commanded them to be *b.* 48
Lydia when she was *b.* and. 16:15
jailer was *b.* and all his. 33
Corinth. believed, and were *b.* 18:8
to what then were ye *b.*? 19:3
when they heard this they were *b.* 5
arise, and be *b.* and wash. 22:16
b. into Jesus, were *b.* *Rom* 6:3
were ye *b.* in the name? *1 Cor* 1:13
thank God that I *b.* none of you. 14
b. household of Stephanas, not *b.* 16
and were all *b.* to Moses in. 10:2
by one Spirit are we all *b.* 12:13
what shall they do who are *b.* for the dead, why are they *b.*? 15:29
have been *b.* into Christ. *Gal* 3:27

baptizest

why *b.* thou, if thou be? *John* 1:25

baptizeth

the same is he who *b.* *John* 1:33
behold, the same *b.* all men. 3:26

baptizing

teach all nations, *b.* them. *Mat* 28:19

Jordan, where John was *b.* *John* 1:28
am I come *b.* with water. 31
and John was also *b.* in Enon. 3:23

bar

them shut the doors, and *b.* *Neh* 7:3

bar, *substantive*

the middle *b.* in midst of. *Ex* 26:28
made the middle *b.* to shoot. 36:33
shall put it upon a *b.* *Num* 4:10*, 12*
of the city, posts, *b.* *Judg* 16:3
I will break also the *b.* *Amos* 1:5

Barabbas

release *B.* *Mat* 27:17, 21
Mark 15:11; *Luke* 23:18
not this man but *B.* now *B.* was a.
John 18:40

Barachias

of Zacharias, son of *B.* *Mat* 23:35

Barak

Deborah called *B.* the son. *Judg* 4:6
Deborah went with *B.* 9
B. pursued after. 16
then sang Deborah and *B.* son. 5:1
arise *B.* and lead thy captivity. 12
would fail me to tell of *B.* *Heb* 11:32

barbarian

a *b.* and he a *b.* to me. *1 Cor* 14:11
neither Greek nor Jew, *b.* *Col* 3:11

barbarians

the *b.* saw the venomous. *Acts* 28:4
both to the Greeks and *b.* *Rom* 1:14

barbarous

b. people shewed no. *Acts* 28:2

barbed

fill his skin with *b.* irons ? *Job* 41:7

barber

son of man, take thee a *b.* *Ezek* 5:1

bare

b. the ark. *Gen* 7:17; *Deut* 31:9, 25
Josh 3:15; 4:10; 8:33; *2 Sam* 6:13
1 Chr 15:15, 26, 27
torn of beasts, I *b.* the. *Gen* 31:39
how I *b.* you on eagles'. *Ex* 19:4
thy God *b.* thee as a. *Deut* 1:31
sent the people that *b.* *Judg* 3:18
the young man that *b.* his armour.
1 Sam 14:1, 6; *2 Sam* 18:15
that *b.* burdens. *1 Ki* 5:15; *Neh* 4:17
of Judah that *b.* shield. *1 Chr* 12:24
2 Chr 14:8
he *b.* the sin of many. *Isa* 53:12
he *b.* them all the days of old. 63:9
the stuff I *b.* upon my. *Ezek* 12:7
saying, himself *b.* our. *Mat* 8:17
and they that *b.* him. *Luke* 7:14
made wine, and they *b.* it. *John* 2:8
had the bag, and *b.* what was. 12:6
his own self *b.* our sins. *1 Pet* 2:24

bare

was 60 years, when she *b.* *Gen* 25:26
then all the cattle *b.* speckled. 31:8
at Chezib, when she *b.* him. 38:5
ye know that my wife *b.* me. 44:27
Jochebed *b.* to Amram. *Ex* 6:20
wife was barren, and *b.* *Judg* 13:2
child Uriah's wife *b.* *2 Sam* 12:15
his mother *b.* him after. *1 Ki* 1:6
Jabez, because I *b.* him. *1 Chr* 4:9
bitterness to her that *b.* *Pr* 17:25
she that *b.* thee shall rejoice. 23:25
choice one of her that *b.* *S of S* 6:9
brought thee forth that *b.* thee. 8:5
look unto Sarah that *b.* you. *Isa* 51:2
their mother that *b.* them. *Jer* 16:3
wherein my mother *b.* me. 20:14
and thy mother that *b.* thee. 22:26
b. you shall be ashamed. 50:12
the womb that *b.* thee. *Luke* 11:27
are the wombs that never *b.* 23:29

bare *fruit*

sprang up, and *b.* *fruit.* an *Luke* 8:8
b. twelve manner of *fruits.* *Rev* 22:2

bare *rule*

officers that *b.* *rule* over the people.
1 Ki 9:23; *2 Chr* 8:10
their servants *b.* *rule.* *Neh* 5:15

bare *witness, and record*

b. false *witness.* *Mark* 14:56, 57
all *b.* him *witness,* and. *Luke* 4:22
b. *witness* of him. *John* 1:15, 32, 34
John *b.* *witness* to truth. *John* 5:33
that was with him *b.* *record.* 12:17
he that saw it *b.* *record,* and. 19:35
hearts, *b.* them *witness.* *Acts* 15:8
who *b.* *record* of the word. *Rev* 1:2

bare, *adjective*

be rent and his head *b.* *Lev* 13:45*
whether it be *b.* within or without. 55
strip ye, make ye *b.* and. *Isa* 32:11
b. the leg, uncover the thigh. 47:2
the Lord hath made *b.* his. 52:10
are thy heels made *b.* *Jer* 13:22
I have made Esau *b.* I have. 49:10
thou wast naked and *b.* *Ezek* 16:7
when thou wast naked, and *b.* 22
leave thee naked and *b.* 39; 23:29
hath made it clean and *b.* *Joel* 1:7
shall be, but *b.* grain. *1 Cor* 15:37

barefoot

he went *b.* and the. *2 Sam* 15:30
so, walking naked and *b.* *Isa* 20:2, 3
Egyptians prisoners, naked and *b.* 4

barest

because thou *b.* the ark. *1 Ki* 2:26
never *b.* rule over them. *Isa* 63:19
he to whom thou *b.* *John* 3:26

Bar-jesus

whose name was *B.* *Acts* 13:6

Bar-jona

blessed art thou, Simon *B.* *Mat* 16:17

bark

dumb dogs, they cannot *b.* *Isa* 56:10

barked

laid my vine waste, and *b.* *Joel* 1:7

barley

b. was smitten, for *b.* *Ex* 9:31
an homer of *b.* seed. *Lev* 27:16
part of an ephah of *b.* *Num* 5:15
a land of wheat, and *b.* *Deut* 8:8
cake of *b.* bread tumbled. *Judg* 7:13
beginning of *b.* harvest. *Ruth* 1:22
gleaned about an ephah of *b.* 2:17
she kept fast to the end of *b.* 23
Boaz winnoweth *b.* to-night. 3:2
he measured six measures of *b.* 15
is near, he hath *b.* *2 Sam* 14:30
Barzillai brought beds, *b.* and. 17:28
Saul's sons were hanged in *b.* 21:9
b. also and straw for the. *1 Ki* 4:28
of God 20 loaves of *b.* *2 Ki* 4:42
of *b.* for a shekel. 7:1, 16, 18
of ground full of *b.* *1 Chr* 11:13
20,000 measures of *b.* *2 Chr* 2:10
wheat, and *b.* the oil, and wine. 15
gave 10,000 measures of *b.* 27:5
cockle grow instead of *b.* *Job* 31:40
wheat, and appointed *b.* *Isa* 28:25
treasures of wheat and *b.* *Jer* 41:8
take to thee wheat, and *b.* *Ezek* 4:9
thou shalt eat it as *b.* cakes, and. 12
pollute me for handfuls of *b.* 13:19
an ephah of an homer of *b.* 45:13
an homer of *b.* and half. *Hos* 3:2
howl for wheat and *b.* *Joel* 1:11
which hath five *b.* loaves. *John* 6:9
fragments of the five *b.* loaves. 13
voice say, 3 measures of *b.* *Rev* 6:6

barn

(A storehouse for grain)

thee out of the *b.* floor ? *2 Ki* 6:27
thy seed into the *b.* *Job* 39:12*
is seed yet in *b.* vine. *Hag* 2:19
the wheat into my *b.* *Mat* 13:30
no store-house nor *b.* *Luke* 12:24

Barnabas

apostles was surnamed *B.* *Acts* 4:36
B. should go as far as. 11:22
departed *B.* to Tarsus to seek. 25
by the hands of *B.* and Saul. 30
B. and Saul returned from. 12:25
at Antioch were teachers, as *B.* 13:1
Holy Ghost said, separate me *B.* 2
persecution, against Paul and *B.* 50
they called *B.* Jupiter; Paul. 14:12
Paul and *B.* had no small. 15:2
the multitude gave audience to *B.* 12
B. determined to take with. 37
or I only and *B.* have. *1 Cor* 9:6
again to Jerusalem with *B.* *Gal* 2:1
gave to me and *B.* the right hands. 9
B. carried away with their. *Gal* 2:13
Marcus, sister's son to *B.* *Col* 4:10

see **Saul, Paul**

barns

so shall thy *b.* be filled. *Pr* 3:10
the *b.* are broken down. *Joel* 1:17
not, nor gather into *b.* *Mat* 6:26
I will pull down my *b.* *Luke* 12:18

barrel, -s

(American Revision, jar, jars)

handful of meal in a *b.* *1 Ki* 17:12
the *b.* of meal shall not waste. 14
fill four *b.* with water, and. 18:33

barren

but Sarai was *b.* she had. *Gen* 11:30
Rebekah was *b.* 25:21
Rachel was *b.* 29:31
cast young nor be *b.* *Ex* 23:26
not be male or female *b.* *Deut* 7:14
was *b.* and bare not. *Judg* 13:2, 3
so that the *b.* hath born. *1 Sam* 2:5
naught, and the ground *b.* *2 Ki* 2:19
from thence death, or *b.* land. 21
he evil entreateth the *b.* *Job* 24:21
I have made the *b.* land his. 39:6
he maketh the *b.* woman. *Ps* 113:9
the grave and *b.* womb. *Pr* 30:16
b. among them. *S of S* 4:2*; 6:6*
sing, O *b.* thou that didst. *Isa* 54:1
drive him into a land *b.* *Joel* 2:20
because Elisabeth was *b.* *Luke* 1:7
with her, who was called *b.* 36
shall say, blessed are the *b.* 23:29
is written, rejoice thou *b.* *Gal* 4:27
that ye be neither *b.* nor. *2 Pet* 1:8*

barrenness

a fruitful land into *b.* *Ps* 107:34*

bars

b. of shittim-wood for the boards.
Ex 26:26; 36:31
of the sons of Merari, shall be the
boards and *b.* *Num* 3:36; 4:31
fenced with gates and *b.* *Deut* 3:5
1 Ki 4:13; *2 Chr* 8:5; 14:7
a town that hath *b.* *1 Sam* 23:7
set up locks thereof and *b.* *Neh* 3:3
6, 13, 14, 15
shall go down to the *b.* *Job* 17:16
set *b.* and doors for the sea. 38:10
his bones are like *b.* of iron. 40:18
cut *b.* of iron. *Ps* 107:16; *Isa* 45:2
hath strengthened the *b.* *Ps* 147:13
contentions are like the *b.* *Pr* 18:19
have neither gates nor *b.* *Jer* 49:31
they have Babylon, her *b.* 51:30
and broken her *b.* *Lam* 2:9
neither gates nor *b.* *Ezek* 38:11
the earth with her *b.* was. *Jonah* 2:6
fire shall devour thy *b.* *Nah* 3:13

Barsabas

Joseph called *B.* *Acts* 1:23
Judas *B.* 15:22

Bartholomew

Mat 10:3; *Mark* 3:18; *Luke* 6:14
Acts 1:13

Bartimaeus

B. sat by the way-side. *Mark* 10:46

Baruch

B. son of Zabbai earnestly. *Neh* 3:20
B. sealed the covenant. 10:6
Maaseiah son of *B.* dwelt at. 11:5
the evidence to *B.* *Jer* 32:12, 16
Jeremiah called *B.* and *B.* 36:4
read *B.* in the book in the house. 10
B. took the roll in his hand and. 14
king commanded to take *B.* the. 26
B. setteth thee on against us. 43:3
Johanan took Jeremiah and *B.* 6
word that Jeremiah spake to *B.* 45:1

Barzillai

B. of Rogelim brought. *2 Sam* 17:27
B. was a very aged man. 19:32
the king kissed *B.* and blessed. 39
brought up for Adriel son of *B.* 21:8
kindness to the sons of *B.* *1 Ki* 2:7
of *B.* which took a wife of the daughters of *B.* *Ezra* 2:61; *Neh* 7:63

base, -s

b. four cubits the length of one *b.*
1 Ki 7:27
the *b.* Solomon made. *2 Ki* 25:13, 16

set the altar upon his *b.* *Ezra* 3:3
set there upon her own *b.* *Zech* 5:11

base, *adjective*

(*Used mainly in the obsolete sense of humble, lowly*)

and will be *b.* in mine. *2 Sam* 6:22
they were children of *b.* *Job* 30:8
and the *b.* against the. *Isa* 3:5
kingdom might be *b.* *Ezek* 17:14
and they shall be there a *b.* 29:14
I have made you *b.* *Mal* 2:9
b. things of this world. *1 Cor* 1:28
who in presence am *b.* *2 Cor* 10:1

baser

lewd fellows of the *b.* *Acts* 17:5*

basest

Pathros shall be the *b.* *Ezek* 29:15
up over it the *b.* of men. *Dan* 4:17*

Bashan

up by the way of *B.* *Num* 21:33
Deut 3:1
Og king of *B.* *Num* 32:33; *Deut* 1:4
3:1, 3, 11; 4:47; 29:7; *Josh* 9:10
12:4; 13:30; *1 Ki* 4:19; *Neh* 9:22
Ps 135:11; 136:20
kingdom of Og in *B.* *Deut* 3:4, 10
Josh 13:12, 30, 31
Golan in *B.* *Deut* 4:43; *Josh* 20:8
21:27
rams of the breed of *B.* *Deut* 32:14
Dan shall leap from *B.* 33:22
he had Gilead and *B.* *Josh* 17:1
even Gilead and *B.* *2 Ki* 10:33
of Gershon, Golan in *B.* *1 Chr* 6:71
strong bulls of *B.* have. *Ps* 22:12
hill of God is as the hill of *B.* 68:15
I will bring again from *B.* 22
B. and Carmel shake off. *Isa* 33:9
lift up thy voice in *B.* *Jer* 22:20
shall feed on Carmel and *B.* 50:19
all of them fatlings of *B.* *Ezek* 39:18
this word, ye kine of *B.* *Amos* 4:1
let them feed in *B.* as in. *Mi* 7:14
B. languished, Carmel. *Nah* 1:4

see **oaks**

Bashemath

Esau took to wife *B.* the. *Gen* 26:34
B. Ishmael's daughter, sister of. 36:3

basket

These were of different sizes, shapes, and construction, and had different names. [1] Sal, *made of twigs, specially for bread,* Gen 40:17. [2] Salsillôth, *a similar basket used for gathering grapes,* Jer 6:9. [3] Tene, *in which the first-fruits were offered,* Deut 26:4. [4] Dud, *to carry fruit,* Jer 24:1; *and clay to the brickyard,* Ps 81:6 (pote, *in Authorized Version*), *or for holding bulky articles,* 2 Ki 10:6. *In the New Testament there were three names used. One meant the small wallet carried by travellers and another the large sort in which Saul escaped from Damascus,* Acts 9:25.

in the *b.* all manner of. *Gen* 40:17
b. of the unleavened. *Ex* 29:23
Lev 8:2, 26; *Num* 6:15, 17
the bread in the *b.* of. *Lev* 8:31
priest shall take the *b.* *Deut* 26:4
blessed shall be thy *b.* and thy. 28:5
cursed shall be thy *b.* and thy. 17
put the flesh in a *b.* *Judg* 6:19
b. had very good figs, the other *b.*
Jer 24:2
a *b.* of summer fruit. *Amos* 8:1, 2
wall in a *b.* *Acts* 9:25; *2 Cor* 11:33

baskets

I had three white *b.* *Gen* 40:16
Joseph said, the three *b.* are. 18
put their heads in *b.* *2 Ki* 10:7
grape-gatherer into the *b.* *Jer* 6:9
behold, two *b.* of figs were set. 24:1
took up twelve *b.* full. *Mat* 14:20
Mark 6:43; *Luke* 9:17; *John* 6:13
seven *b.* full. *Mat* 15:37; *Mark* 8:8
five loaves, and how many *b.* ye took
up ? *Mat* 16:9, 10; *Mark* 8:19, 20

bason

(*Revised Version,* basin)

blood that is in the *b.* *Ex* 12:22
by weight for every *b.* *1 Chr* 28:17
he poureth water into a *b.* *John* 13:5

basons

(*Revised Version,* basins)

put half of the blood in *b.* *Ex* 24:6
brought beds and *b.* *2 Sam* 17:28
lavers and the shovels and the *b.*
1 Ki 7:40, 45; *2 Chr* 4:8, 11
b. and fire-pans the. *Jer* 52:19

bastard, -s

a *b.* shall not enter into. *Deut* 23:2
b. shall dwell in Ashdod. *Zech* 9:6
chastisement, then are *b.* *Heb* 12:8

bat, -s

lapwing and *b.* are. *Lev* 11:19
Deut 14:18
his idols to the moles and *b.* *Isa* 2:20

bath

(*A measure used among the Hebrews which contained about nine gallons. It was equal to the* Ephah)

vineyard shall yield one *b.* *Isa* 5:10
just ephah, a just *b.* *Ezek* 45:10
the ephah and *b.* shall be of one. 11
offer the tenth part of a *b.* 14

bathe

shall *b.* himself in water. *Lev* 15:5
8, 11, 13, 21, 22, 27; 16:26, 28
17:15; *Num* 19:7, 8, 19
them not, nor *b.* his flesh. *Lev* 17:16

bathed

my sword shall be *b.* in. *Isa* 34:5*

baths

sea contained 2000 *b.* *1 Ki* 7:26
one laver containing 40 *b.* every. 38
servants 20,000 *b.* of. *2 Chr* 2:10
sea received and held 3000 *b.* 4:5
b. of wine, 100 *b.* of oil. *Ezra* 7:22
homer of ten *b.* for ten *b.* *Ezek* 45:14

Bath-sheba

is not this *B.* daughter. *2 Sam* 11:3
David comforted *B.* his wife. 12:24
B. went to the king into. *1 Ki* 1:15
then the king said, call me *B.* 28
B. bowed. 31
Adonijah came to *B.* the. 2:13

battered

people with Joab *b.* *2 Sam* 20:15

battering

set *b.* rams against it. *Ezek* 4:2
to appoint *b.* rams against. 21:22

battle

[1] *A general fight,* Deut 20:3. [2] *Victory,* Eccl 9:11.

they joined *b.* *Gen* 14:8; *1 Sam* 4:2
1 Ki 20:29
before the Lord to *b.* *Num* 32:27
contend with Sihon in *b.* *Deut* 2:24
approach this day to *b.* 20:3
return, lest he die in the *b.* 5, 6, 7
all other they took in *b.* *Josh* 11:19
yet again go out to *b.* ? *Judg* 20:28
they turned, but the *b.* overtook. 42
after Philistines in *b.* *1 Sam* 14:22
the host shouted for the *b.* 17:20
art come down to see the *b.* 28
b. is the Lord's. 47; *2 Chr* 20:15
shall descend into the *b.* *1 Sam* 26:10
thou shalt go out with me to *b.* 28:1
in the *b.* he be an adversary. 29:4
go forth to *b.* *2 Sam* 11:1; *1 Chr* 20:1
front of the hottest *b.* *2 Sam* 11:15
we anointed is dead in *b.* 19:10
if thy people go out to *b.* *1 Ki* 8:44
went out into midst of the *b.* 20:39
go with me to *b.* ? 22:4; *2 Ki* 3:7
they cried to God in the *b.* *1 Chr* 5:20
men of war fit for the *b.* 12:8
David came upon them, and set *b.* in.
19:17; *2 Chr* 13:3; 14:10
do it, be strong for *b.* *2 Chr* 25:8
as a king ready to the *b.* *Job* 15:24
he smelleth the *b.* afar off. 39:25
remember the *b.* do no more. 41:8
me with strength to *b.* *Ps* 18:39
glory, the Lord mighty in *b.* 24:8
delivered my soul from the *b.* 55:18
shield, the sword, and the *b.* 76:3
made him to stand in the *b.* *Ps* 89:43
not to the swift, nor *b.* *Eccl* 9:11
every *b.* of the warrior. *Isa* 9:5*
mustereth the host of the *b.* 13:4
thy slain men are not dead in *b.* 22:2
and thorns against me in *b.* 27:4
that turn the *b.* to the gate. 28:6
on him the strength of the *b.* 42:25
horse rusheth into the *b.* *Jer* 8:6
men be slain by sword in *b.* 18:21
and shield, draw near to *b.* 46:3
her, and rise up to the *b.* 49:14
a sound of *b.* is in the land. 50:22
in array, like a man to *b.* against. 42
but none goeth to the *b.* *Ezek* 7:14
to stand in the *b.* in the day. 13:5
save them by bow nor by *b.* *Hos* 1:7
I will break the bow and *b.* 2:18
b. in Gibeah; did not overtake. 10:9
a strong people set in *b.* *Joel* 2:5
rise up against Edom in *b.* *Ob* 1
his goodly horse in the *b.* *Zech* 10:3
down their enemies in the *b.* 5
nations against Jerusalem to *b.* 14:2
prepare himself to the *b.*? *1 Cor* 14:8
like horses prepared to *b.* *Rev* 9:7
of many horses running to *b.* 9
the *b.* of the great day. 16:14; 20:8

day of **battle**

pass in the *day of b.* *1 Sam* 13:22
against the *day of b.* *Job* 38:23
back in the *day of b.* *Ps* 78:9
my head in the *day of b.* 140:7
prepared against the *day of b.*
Pr 21:31
Beth-arbel in *day of b.* *Hos* 10:14
shouting in the *day of b.* *Amos* 1:14
fought in the *day of b.* *Zech* 14:3

battle-ax, *see* **ax**

battle-bow

and the *b.-bow* shall be. *Zech* 9:10
of him came forth the *b.-bow.* 10:4

battlement, -s

thou shalt make a *b.* for. *Deut* 22:8
take away her *b.* they. *Jer* 5:10*

battles

before us and fight our *b.* *1 Sam* 8:20
valiant, and fight the Lord's *b.* 18:17
my lord fighteth the *b.* of the. 25:28
spoils won in *b.* dedicate. *1 Chr* 26:27
God, to fight our *b.* *2 Chr* 32:8
and in *b.* of shakings. *Isa* 30:32

bay

grizzled and *b.* horses. *Zech* 6:3
and the *b.* went forth and sought. 7

bay-tree

like a green *b.-tree.* *Ps* 37:35*

bdellium

in Havilah there is *b.* *Gen* 2:12
manna as the colour of *b.* *Num* 11:7

be

that man should *be* alone. *Gen* 2:18
whether thou *be* my very son. 27:21
there they *be* as the. *Deut* 10:5
if the Lord *be* with us. *Judg* 6:13
thine enemies *be* as. *2 Sam* 18:32
they that *be* with us are more than
they that *be.* *2 Ki* 6:16
God *be* with. *2 Chr* 36:23; *Ezra* 1:3
be ye far from thence. *Ezra* 6:6
if I *be* wicked, woe to me; if I *be.*
Job 10:15
and *be* it indeed that I have. 19:4
see if there *be* any. *Ps* 139:24
be a wall, if she *be* a. *S of S* 8:9
be your fear, let him *be.* *Isa* 8:13
former things what they *be.* 41:22
none know where you *be.* *Jer* 36:19
it *be* ere thou *be* quiet ? 47:6
thy way till the end *be.* *Dan* 12:13
how long will it *be* ere ? *Hos* 8:5
if thou *be* the Son of God. *Mat* 4:3, 6
27:40
and many there *be* that go. 7:13
the things that *be* of God, but those
that *be.* 16:23; *Mark* 8:33
be to thee as an heathen. *Mat* 18:17
put away, except it *be.* 19:9
if the son of peace *be.* *Luke* 10:6
how can these things *be* ? *John* 3:9
there *be* any Holy Ghost. *Acts* 19:2

except it be for this one Acts 24:21
those things which be not. Rom 4:17
if God be for us, who can be? 8:31
that he might be Lord of the. 14:9
that God may be all in. 1 Cor 15:28
him be anathema maran-atha. 16:22
if there be first a willing. 2 Cor 8:12
they which be of faith are. Gal 3:9
I beseech you, be as I am, for. 4:12
judgement, whosoever he be. 5:10
let this mind be in you. Phil 2:5
but if ye be without. Heb 12:8
if so be ye have tasted. 1 Pet 2:3
if the will of God be so. 3:17
whatsoever craft he be. Rev 18:22
let him be unjust still; he which is filthy, let him be filthy. 22:11

if it **be**

if it be your mind that I. Gen 23:8
she said, if it be so, why? 25:22
if it be a son kill him, if it be a. Ex 1:16
if it be, give me thy. 2 Ki 10:15
if it be marvellous in the. Zech 8:6
if it be thou, bid me. Mat 14:28
if it be of God, ye. Acts 5:39
but if it be a question of. 18:15
in vain? if it be in vain. Gal 3:4

may **be,** *see* **may;** *peace* **be,** *see* **peace**

not **be.** **be** *not*

let it not be grievous in. Gen 21:12
if the woman will not be. 24:5
the seed should not be his. 38:9
my father, and the lad be not. 44:30
ye should not be their. Lev 26:13
let her not be as one. Num 12:12
that he be not as Korah and. 16:40
neither will I be with. Josh 7:12
man will not be in rest. Ruth 3:18
be not like your fathers. 2 Chr 30:7
Zech 1:4
be not thou far away. Ps 22:19
35:22; 38:21; 71:12
be ye not mockers, lest. Isa 28:22
I will not be to the. Zech 8:11
for it cannot be that a. Luke 13:33
he cannot be my disciple. 14:26, 33
if thou be not that Christ. John 1:25
be not wise in your own. Rom 12:16
if I be not an apostle. 1 Cor 9:2
be not children in. 14:20
be not unequally yoked. 2 Cor 6:14
should not be the servant. Gal 1:10
be not therefore partakers. Eph 5:7
be ye not unwise, but. 17
works, that they be not. Tit 3:14
thy benefit should not be. Philem 14
on earth, should not be a. Heb 8:4
not be that outward. 1 Pet 3:3

let there **be**

let there be light. Gen 1:3
let there be a firmament. 6
let there be no strife between. 13:8
let there be now an oath. 26:28
let there be more work laid. Ex 5:9
let there be search made. Ezra 5:17

shall **be,** *or shalt* **be**

they shall be one flesh. Gen 2:24
to thee shall be his desire. 4:7
a servant shall he be to his. 9:25
Shem, and Canaan shall be. 26
and thou shalt be a blessing. 12:2
so shall thy seed be. 15:5; Rom 4:18
Sarah shall be a mother. Gen 17:16
and he shall be blessed. 27:33
then shall Lord be my God. 28:21
Israel shall be. 35:10; 1 Ki 18:31
God shall be with you. Gen 48:21
shall the gathering of the people be. 49:10
shalt be to him instead. Ex 4:16
ye shall be a peculiar. 19:5
the dead shall be his own. 21:36
shall his habitation be. Lev 13:46
shall be holy to me, ye shall be. 20:26
shall be head, and thou shalt be. Deut 28:44
see what their end shall be. 32:20
Philistine shall be as. 1 Sam 17:36
shall thy judgement be. 1 Ki 20:40
the Lord shall be. 2 Chr 19:11

in fulness he shall be in. Job 20:22
yea, the Almighty shall be. 22:25
happy shalt thou be, it shall be. Ps 128:2
my prayer also shall be in. 141:5
is that which shall be. Eccl 1:9
man cannot tell what shall be. 10:14
falleth, there it shall be. 11:3
the holy seed shall be. Isa 6:13
the glory of the Lord shall be. 58:8
when shall it once be. Jer 13:27
thou shalt be as my mouth. 15:19
and there shall he be till I. 32:5
it shall be to me a name of. 33:9
neither shall be so. Ezek 16:16
wicked shall be on him. 18:20
shalt be a terror, and never shalt be. 27:36
what shall be in the latter. Dan 2:28
the end shall be. 8:19; 11:27
known that which shall be. Hos 5:9
God of hosts shall be. Amos 5:14
save you, and shall be a. Zech 8:13
shall be as David, house of David shall be as. 12:8
shall be a delightsome. Mal 3:12
no, nor ever shall be. Mat 24:21
Mark 13:19
shall I be with you. Mark 9:19
Luke 9:41
with you, and shall be in. John 14:17
lots for it, whose it shall be. 19:24
that it shall be even as. Acts 27:25
that body that shall be. 1 Cor 15:37
appear what we shall be. 1 John 3:2
and wast, and shall be. Rev 16:5
man as his work shall be. 22:12

shall not, or shalt not **be**

saying, this shall not be. Gen 15:4
thou shalt not be to him. Ex 22:25
shalt not be beneath. Deut 28:13
see me not, it shall not be so. 2 Ki 2:10
morning, but I shall not be. Job 7:21
it shall not be. Ps 37:10; Jer 48:30
Dan 11:29; Amos 7:3, 6
thou shalt not be for. Hos 3:3
this shall not be to thee. Mat 16:22
shall not be so among you. 20:26
Mark 10:43; Luke 22:26

to **be**

to be a God to thee and. Gen 17:7
hearkened not to her to be. 39:10
out to be your God. Lev 22:33; 25:38
desire to be with them. Pr 24:1
that which is to be hath. Eccl 3:15
spent all, he began to be. Luke 15:14
good for a man so to be. 1 Cor 7:26
which he seeth me to be. 2 Cor 12:6
having a desire to be. Phil 1:23
things ought not so to be. Jas 3:10
persons ought ye to be. 2 Pet 3:11

will **be**

will be a wild man, his hand will be against every man. Gen 16:12
I will be their God. 17:8; Ex 29:45
Jer 24:7; 32:38; 2 Cor 6:16
I will be with thee. Gen 26:3; 31:3
Ex 3:12; Judg 6:16; 1 Ki 11:38
if God will be with me. Gen 28:20
if ye will be as we be. 34:15
all places they will be. Neh 4:12
he will be our guide. Ps 48:14
I will be your God. Jer 7:23; 30:22
I will be to them as a. Ezek 11:16
that ye say, we will be as. 20:32
O death, I will be thy plagues, O grave, I will be thy. Hos 13:14
I will be as the dew unto Israel. 14:5
the Lord will be the hope. Joel 3:16
will be to her a wall of fire round about, I will be the. Zech 2:5
there will your heart be. Mat 6:21
I will be a Father to you. 2 Cor 6:18
such will we be also indeed. 10:11
they that will be rich fall. 1 Tim 6:9
I will be to him a Father. Heb 1:5
I will be to them a God, they. 8:10
whosoever will be a friend. Jas 4:4
I will be his God, and. Rev 21:7

beacon

be left as a b. on the. Isa 30:17

beam

with the pin of the b. Judg 16:14
his spear was like a weaver's b.
1 Sam 17:7; 1 Chr 11:23; 20:5
and take thence a b. 2 Ki 6:2
as one was felling a b. ax-head. 5
the b. out of the timber. Hab 2:11
not the b. Mat 7:3; Luke 6:41, 42
behold, a b. is in thine own. Mat 7:4
first cast out the b. 5; Luke 6:42

beams

overlaid the b. the posts. 2 Chr 3:7
give timber to make b. Neh 2:8
who layeth the b. in the. Ps 104:3
b. of our house are cedar. S of S 1:17

beans

Barzillai brought b. 2 Sam 17:28
take unto thee wheat, b. Ezek 4:9

bear

[1] *To carry*, Jer 17:21; Mat 27:32. [2] *To bring forth, produce, or yield*, Gen 18:13; Jas 3:12. [3] *To uphold, or support*, Ps 91:12.

is greater than I can b. Gen 4:13
land not able to b. them. 13:6; 36:7
let me b. the blame. 43:9; 44:32
Issachar bowed to b. 49:15
they shall b. the burden. Ex 18:22
b. the ark. 25:27; 27:7, 30:4; 37:5
Deut 10:8; Josh 3:8, 13, 14; 4:16
2 Sam 15:24
Aaron shall b. their names. Ex 28:12
shalt not b. any grudge. Lev 19:18
not able to b. all this people.
Num 11:14; Deut 1:9
how long shall I b. with? Num 14:27
children shall b. 33; Ezek 23:35
God bare as a man b. Deut 1:31
let me b. the king. 2 Sam 18:19
puttest on me, I will b. 2 Ki 18:14
b. up pillars of the earth. Ps 75:3*
how I do b. in my bosom the. 89:50
they shall b. thee up. 91:12
Mat 4:6; Luke 4:11
scornest, thou shalt b. it. Pr 9:12
a wounded spirit who can b.? 18:14
for four which it cannot b. 30:21
feasts, I am weary to b. Isa 1:14
I have made and I will b. you. 46:4
b. him upon the shoulder. 7
be clean that b. vessels of. 52:11
truly this grief, I must b. Jer 10:19
b. no burden sabbath-day. 17:21, 27
I did b. the reproach of my. 31:19
so the Lord could no longer b. 44:22
good to b. yoke in youth. Lam 3:27
their sight shalt thou b. Ezek 12:6
the prince shall b. upon his. 12
b. punishment of iniquity. 14:10
b. thine own shame for. 16:52, 54
b. shame with. 32:30; 36:7; 44:13
nor b. shame of the heathen.
Ezek 34:29; 36:15
land is not able to b. Amos 7:10
b. reproach of my people. Mi 6:16
I will b. indignation of the. 7:9
one b. holy flesh in skirt. Hag 2:12
do these b. ephah? Zech 5:10
he shall b. glory. 6:13
shoes I am not worthy to b. Mat 3:11
found Simon, compelled him to b. 27:32; Mark 15:21; Luke 23:26
doth not b. his cross. Luke 14:27
avenge elect, though he b. 18:7
ye cannot b. them now. John 16:12
is chosen to b. my name. Acts 9:15
a yoke, we were able to b. 15:10
reason I should b. with you. 18:14
b. infirmities of the weak. Rom 15:1
were not able to b. it. 1 Cor 3:2
to escape, that ye may b. 10:13
shall b. the image of heavenly. 15:49
ye could b. with me. 2 Cor 11:1
ye might well b. with him. 4
b. one another's burdens. Gal 6:2
for every man shall b. his own. 5
b. in my body marks of Lord. 17
fig-tree b. olive-berries? Jas 3:12
not b. them that are evil. Rev 2:2

bear *fruit, see* **fruit**

bear *iniquity*

Aaron may b. iniq. Ex 28:38
and his sons, b. not iniq. 43

he shall *b.* his *iniq.* *Lev* 5:1, 17
7:18; 17:16; 19:8; 20:17
hath given to you to *b. iniq.* 10:17
the goat *b.* upon him all *iniq.* 16:22
they shall *b.* their *iniq.* 20:19
Num 18:23; *Ezek* 44:10, 12
or suffer them to *b. iniq.* *Lev* 22:16
this woman *b.* her *iniq.* *Num* 5:31
ye shall *b.* your *iniq.* 14:34
Aaron and his sons *b. iniq.* 18:1
he heard, he shall *b.* her *iniq.* 30:15
my servant shall *b. iniq.* *Isa* 53:11
number of days, thou shalt *b. iniq.*
Ezek 4:4; 5:6
not son *b. iniq.* of father ? 18:19
the son not *b.* the *iniq.* of. 20

bear *judgement*

Aaron shall *b. judg.* of. *Ex* 28:30
that troubleth *b.* his *judg.* *Gal* 5:10

bear *record, see* **record**

bear *rule*

man *b. rule* in his house. *Esth* 1:22
hand of diligent *b. rule.* *Pr* 12:24
the priests *b. rule* by. *Jer* 5:31
strong rods for them that *b. rule.*
Ezek 19:11
of brass shall *b. rule.* *Dan* 2:39

bear *sin*

they shall *b.* their *sin.* *Lev* 20:20
lest they *b. sin* for it, and die. 22:9
curseth his God, shall *b. sin.* 24:15
that man shall *b.* his *sin.* *Num* 9:13
come nigh, lest they *b. sin.* 18:22
shall *b.* no *sin* when ye heaved. 32
ye *b. sin* of your idols. *Ezek* 23:49
Christ was once offered to *b. sin.*
Heb 9:28

bear *witness*

shalt not *b.* false *wit.* *Ex* 20:16
Deut 5:20; *Mat* 19:18; *Rom* 13:9
set two men to *b. wit.* *1 Ki* 21:10
do not *b.* false *wit.* *Mark* 10:19
Luke 18:20
ye *b. wit.* that ye allow. *Luke* 11:48*
same came to *b. wit.* *John* 1:7
was sent to *b. wit.* of that light. 8
yourselves *b.* me *wit.* that. 3:28
if I *b. wit.* of myself. 5:31
works I do *b. wit.* of me. 36; 10:25
b. wit. of myself, and the. 8:18
ye shall also *b. wit.* 15:27
if I have spoken evil, *b. wit.* 18:23
that I should *b. wit.* 37
priest doth *b.* me *wit.* *Acts* 22:5
thou must *b. wit.* at Rome. 23:11
have seen and *b. wit.* *1 John* 1:2
three that *b. wit.* in earth. 5:8

bear

Sarah that is old *b* ? *Gen* 17:17
shall I of a surety *b.* a child. 18:13
but if she *b.* a maid child. *Lev* 12:5
her children she shall *b.* *Deut* 28:57
conceive and *b.* a son. *Judg* 13:3
not my son that I did *b.* *1 Ki* 3:21
every one *b.* twins. *S of S* 4:2, 6:6
a virgin shall *b.* a son, and. *Isa* 7:14
sing, O barren, that didst not *b.* 54:1
b. sons and daughters. *Jer* 29:6
Elisabeth shall *b.* a son. *Luke* 1:13
women marry,*b.* children. *1 Tim* 5:14

bear, -s

came a lion and a *b.* *1 Sam* 17:34
servant slew the lion and the *b.* 36
chafed, as a *b.* robbed. *2 Sam* 17:8
came forth two she-*b.* *2 Ki* 2:24
b. robbed of her whelps. *Pr* 17:12
a roaring lion, and ranging *b.* 28:15
cow and *b.* feed their. *Isa* 11:7
we roar like *b.* mourn like. 59:11
to me as a *b.* in wait. *Lam* 3:10
beast, a second like to a *b.* *Dan* 7:5
them as a *b.* bereaved. *Hos* 13:8
as a man did flee from *b.* *Amos* 5:19
his feet as the feet of a *b.* *Rev* 13:2

beard, -s

a man hath plague on *b.* *Lev* 13:29
shall shave hair off head and *b.* 14:9
mar the corners of *b.* 19:27; 21:5
I caught him by his *b.* *1 Sam* 17:35
David let spittle fall on his *b.* 21:13
tarry at Jericho till *b.* grow, then.
2 Sam 10:5; *1 Chr* 19:5
Mephibosheth trimmed not *b.*
2 Sam 19:24
Joab took Amasa by the *b.* 20:9
plucked off hair of my *b.* *Ezra* 9:3
down on *b,* Aaron's *b.* *Ps* 133:2
shall also consume the *b.* *Isa* 7:20
on heads baldness, every *b.* cut. 15:2
fourscore men their *b.* *Jer* 41:5
head bald, every *b.* clipt. 48:37
a razor to pass on *b.* *Ezek* 5:1

bearers

set 70,000 to be *b.* of. *2 Chr* 2:18
also they were over the *b.* 34:13
strength of the *b.* is. *Neh* 4:10

bearest

art barren, and *b* not. *Judg* 13:3
favour thou *b.* thy people. *Ps* 106:4
b. record of thyself, thy. *John* 8:13
b. not the root. *Rom* 11:18
rejoice thou that *b.* not. *Gal* 4:27

beareth

he that *b.* the carcase. *Lev* 11:28
and he that *b.* these things. 15:10
as a father *b.* child. *Num* 11:12
first-born she *b.* succeed. *Deut* 25:6
there be a root that *b.* gall. 29:18
it is not sown, nor *b.* 23
as an eagle *b.* her young. 32:11
evil entreateth that *b.* not. *Job* 24:21
every one *b.* twins. *S of S* 6:6
not afraid, the tree *b.* fruit. *Joel* 2:22
which also *b.* fruit. *Mat* 13:23
every branch that *b.* not. *John* 15:2
b. not the sword in vain. *Rom* 13:4
charity *b.* all things. *1 Cor* 13:7
which *b.* thorns is rejected. *Heb* 6:8

beareth *rule*

when the wicked *b. rule.* *Pr* 29:2

beareth *witness*

b. wit. to my face. *Job* 16:8
b. false *wit.* is a maul. *Pr* 25:18
another that *b. wit.* of me. *John* 5:32
and the Father *b. wit.* of me. 8:18
the Spirit *b. wit.* with. *Rom* 8:16
the Spirit that *b. wit.* *1 John* 5:6

bearing

every herb *b.* seed. *Gen* 1:29
the Lord restrained me from *b.* 16:2
called his name Judah, left *b.* 29:35
Ishmaelites *b.* spicery. 37:25
forward, *b.* tabernacle. *Num* 10:17
Kohathites set forward, *b.* 21
the priest *b.* the ark. *Josh* 3:3, 14
2 Sam 15:24
one *b.* a shield went. *1 Sam* 17:7
goeth *b.* precious seed. *Ps* 126:6
meet you a man *b.* a pitcher of water.
Mark 14:13; *Luke* 22:10
he *b.* his cross, went. *John* 19:17
conscience *b.* witness. *Rom* 2:15
my conscience *b.* me witness. 9:1
b. in the body dying of. *2 Cor* 4:10
God also *b.* them witness. *Heb* 2:4
let us go forth *b.* his reproach. 13:13
be saved in child-*b.* *1 Tim* 2:15

beast

(*Used for cattle, wild beasts or any living thing apart from man*)

let earth bring forth *b.* *Gen* 1:24
God made *b.* of the earth. 25
serpent more subtil than any *b.* 3:1
evil *b.* hath devoured him. 37:20, 33
every firstling of a *b.* *Ex* 13:12
put his *b.* in another's field. 22:5
deliver to his neighbour any *b.* 10
whoso lieth with *b.* be put to. 19
Lev 18:23; 20:15, 16; *Deut* 27:21
the *b.* of the field multiply. *Ex* 23:29
b. that may be eaten, and *b.* that
may not. *Lev* 11:47
if it be *b.* men bring offering. 27:9
the likeness of any *b.* *Deut* 4:17
smote as well men as *b.* *Judg* 20:48
nor any *b.* save *b.* I rode. *Neh* 2:12
so ignorant, I was as a *b.* *Ps* 73:22
he giveth to the *b.* his food. 147:9
man regards life of *b.* *Pr* 12:10
no pre-eminence above *b.* *Eccl* 3:19
the *b.* shall honour me. *Isa* 43:20
as a *b.* that goeth into valley. 63:14
dead or torn, fowl or *b.* *Ezek* 44:31
let a *b.* heart be given. *Dan* 4:16
I beheld till the *b.* was. *Dan* 7:11
the truth of the fourth *b.* 19
set him on his own *b.* *Luke* 10:34
Paul shook off the *b.* *Acts* 28:5
a *b.* touch the mountain. *Heb* 12:20
first *b.* like a lion, second *b.* *Rev* 4:7
I heard the second *b.* say. 6:3
b. that ascendeth out of the pit. 11:7
I saw a *b.* rise up out of. 13:1
I beheld a *b.* out of earth. 11
got the victory over the *b.* 15:2
spirits out of mouth of *b.* 16:13
thou sawest the *b.* that. 17:8, 11
I saw *b.* and kings of the. 19:19
where *b.* and false prophet. 20:10

every **beast**

to *every b.* green herb. *Gen* 1:30
God formed *every b.* 2:19
gave names to *every b.* 20
art cursed above *every b.* 3:14
of *every* clean *b.* take to. 7:2, 8
and *every b.* after his kind. 14
every b. went out of the ark. 8:19
of *every* clean *b.* he offered. 20
of you shall be on *every b.* 9:2
your blood I require of *every b.* 5
to *every b.* of the earth. 10
shall not *every b.* be ours ? 34:23
the carcases of *every b.* which
divideth. *Lev* 11:26; *Deut* 14:6
every b. of the forest is. *Ps* 50:10
they give drink to *every b.* 104:11
my flock meat to *every b.* *Ezek* 34:8
son of man, speak to *every b.* 39:17

beast, joined with *man*

will destroy both *man* and *b.* *Gen* 6:7
became lice in *man* and *b.* *Ex* 8:17
with blains on *man* and *b.* 9:9, 10
hail on *man* and *b.* 19, 22, 25
a dog move against *man* or *b.* 11:7
smite first-born in Egypt. *man* and *b.*
12:12; 13:15; *Ps* 135:8
first-born of *man* and *b.* is mine.
Ex 13:2; *Num* 8:17
man or *b.* it shall not live. *Ex* 19:13
thing of *man* or *b.* *Lev* 27:28
first-born of *man* and *b.* *Num* 3:13
prey taken, both of *man* and *b.* 31:26
thou preservest *man* and *b.* *Ps.* 36:6
fury on *man* and *b.* *Jer* 7:20; 21:6
36:29; *Ezek* 14:13, 17, 19, 21
25:13; 29:8; *Zeph* 1:3
I have made *man* and *b.* *Jer* 27:5
sow with seed of *man* and *b.* 31:27
it is desolate without *man* or *b.*
32:43, 33:10, 12 ; 36:29; 51:62
they shall depart *man* and *b.* 50:3
will multiply *man* and *b.* *Ezek* 36:11
let not *man* nor *b.* taste. *Jonah* 3:7

unclean **beast**

soul touch *unclean b.* *Lev* 5:2; 7:21
if it be *unclean b.* 27:11, 27

wild **beast**

there passed by a *wild b.* and trod
down. *2 Ki* 14:9; *2 Chr* 25:1
wild b. may break them. *Job* 39:1
the *wild b.* of the field. *Ps* 80:1
wild b. shall tear them. *Hos* 13:

beasts

that which was torn of *b.* *Gen* 31:3
Ex. 22:31; *Lev* 7:24; 17:15; 22:
Esau took all his *b.* *Gen* 36:
lade your *b.* and go. 45:1
the first-born of *b.* shall die. *Ex* 11:
b. ye shall eat. *Lev* 11:2; *Deut* 14:
chew cud among *b.* *Lev* 11:
Deut 14:
for *b.* increase be meat. *Lev* 25:
I will rid evil *b.* out of land. 26:
congregation and *b.* drink. *Num* 20:
of all *b.* give to the Levites. 31:
I will send *b.* on them. *Deut* 32:
Solomon spake of *b.* *1 Ki* 4:
find grass, that we lose not *b.* 18
drink ye, cattle and *b.* *2 Ki* 3:
help him with *b.* *Ezra* 1
ask the *b.* and they shall. *Job* 12
wherefore are we counted as *b.* 18
then the *b.* go into dens. 37
man is like the *b.* that. *Ps* 49:12,
wherein the *b.* of forest. 104:
the sea, both small and great *b.*

b. and all cattle, praise. Ps 148:10
wisdom hath killed her b. Pr 9:2
a lion strongest among b. 30:30
themselves are b. Eccl 3:18
befalleth men, befalleth b. 19
burden of b. of the south. Isa 30:6
b. thereof for a burnt-offering. 40:16
their idols were on b. and. 46:1
swift b. to my holy mountain. 66:20
the b. are fled. Jer 9:10
the b. are consumed. 12:4
I send famine and evil b. pestilence.
Ezek. 5:17; 14:15
I will fill the b. of whole. 32:4
I will destroy all the b. 13; 34:25, 28
let the b. get away. Dan 4:14
let his portion be with the b. 15
four great b. are four kings. 7:17
that no b. might stand before. 8:4
how do the b. groan ! Joel 1:18
peace-offerings of fat b. Amos 5:22
spoil of b. Hab 2:17
place for b. to lie down. Zeph 2:15
the plague of all the b. Zech 14:15
have ye offered slain b. ? Acts 7:42
provide b. to set Paul on. 23:24
an image made like to b. Rom 1:23
if I have fought with b. 1 Cor 15:32
for every kind of b. is tamed. Jas 3:7
these as natural brute b. 2 Pet 2:12
what they know as brute b. Jude 10
four b. full of eyes. Rev 4:6
the four b. had each six wings. 8
when b. give glory and honour. 9
midst of throne and four b. a. 5:6
the four b. said Amen. 14
one of four b. saying. 6:1; 15:7
angels about throne and four b. 7:11
song before throne and four b. 14:3
the elders and b. fell down to. 19:4

beasts *of the earth*

meat to all b. of earth. Deut 28:26
of Philistines to b. of earth.
1 Sam 17:46
afraid of the b. of earth. Job 5:22
teacheth more than b. of earth. 35:11
saints to the b. of earth. Ps 79:2
be left to the b. of earth. Isa 18:6
the people meat for b. of the earth.
Jer 7:33; 16:4; 19:7; 34:20
appoint b. of earth to devour. 15:3
all four-footed b. of the earth.
Acts 10:12; 11:6
kill with the b. of earth. Rev 6:8

beasts *of the field*

poor leave, b. of field eat. Ex 23:11
lest b. of field increase. Deut 7:22
thy flesh to b. of field. 1 Sam 17:44
b. of the field by night. 2 Sam 21:10
b. of the field at peace. Job 5:23
where b. of the field play. 40:20
b. of field under his feet. Ps 8:7
b. of field come to devour. Isa 56:9
assemble all b. of field. Jer 12:9
b. of the field have I given him
27:6; 28:14; Dan 2:38
I have given thee for meat to b. of
the field. Ezek 29:5; 34:5; 39:4
his branches b of the field. 31:6
b. of field on his branches. 13
b. of the field shall shake. 38:20
b. of field had shadow. Dan 4:12
dwelling with b. of field. 25, 32
covenant for with b. of field. Hos 2:18
and shall mourn with b. of field. 4:3
b. of field cry also to. Joel 1:20
be not afraid, ye b. of field. 2:22

wild **beasts**

I will also send wild b. Lev 26:22
Philistines to wild b. 1 Sam 17:46
wild b. of the field are. Ps 50:11
wild b. of the desert lie. Isa 13:21
wild b. of the islands cry. 22
wild b. of desert shall meet with wild
b. of the island. 34:14; Jer 50:39
Christ was with wild b. Mark 1:13
sheet, with wild b. Acts 10:12; 11:6

beat

[1] *To strike, pound, or bruise,* Num 11:8; 2 Ki 3:25; Mat 21:35.
[2] *To get the better of, or overcome,* 2 Ki 13:25.

shalt b. spices very small. Ex 30:36
they b. the gold into thin. 39:3
people b. manna in a. Num 11:8
lest he exceed and b. him. Deut 25:3
b. down tower of Penuel. Judg 8:17
Abimelech b. down the city. 9:45
sons of Belial b. at the door. 19:22
b. that she had gleaned. Ruth 2:17
I b. them small. 2 Sam 22:43
Ps 18:42
Israelites b. down the. 2 Ki 3:25
Joash did b. Ben-hadad. 13:25
altars did the king b. down. 23:12
I will b. down his foes. Ps 89:23
b. him with the rod. Pr 23:14
b. their swords. Isa 2:4; Mi 4:3
what mean ye, to b. my people ?
Isa 3:15*
Lord shall b. off from channel. 27:12
thresh mountains, b. small. 41:15
b. plowshares into swords. Joel 3:10
sun b. on head of Jonah. Jonah 4:8
b. in pieces many people. Mi 4:13
and b. on that house. Mat 7:25, 27
Luke 6:48, 49
his servants, and b. one. Mat 21:35
Mark 12:3; Luke 20:10, 11
waves b. into the ship. Mark 4:37
b. the men-servants. Luke 12:45
commanded to beat them. Acts 16:22
Greeks took Sosthenes and b. 18:17
imprisoned and b. in every. 22:19

beaten

officers of Israel were b. Ex 5:14, 16
cherubims of b. work. 25:18; 37:17
22; Num 8:4
two cherubims b. out of one. Ex 37:7
offer corn b. out of full. Lev 2:14
man be worthy to be b. Deut 25:2
made as if were b. Josh 8:15
Abner was b. and men. 2 Sam 2:17
b. images to powder. 2 Chr 34:7
they have b. me. Pr 23:35
fitches are b. with staff. Isa 28:27
the Assyrian shall be b. 30:31*
their mighty ones are b. Jer 46:5
graven images b. to pieces. Mi 1:7
synagogue ye shall be b. Mark 13:9
and did not shall be b. Luke 12:47
called the apostles and b. Acts 5:40
b. us openly uncondemned. 16:37
thrice, was I b. with. 2 Cor 11:25

beaten *gold*

candlestick was b. gold. Num 8:4
targets of b. gold. 1 Ki 10:16
shields of b. gold. 17; 2 Chr 9:16
shekels of b. gold. 2 Chr 9:15

beaten *oil*

pure oil b. for the light. Ex 27:20
Lev 24:2
an hin of b. oil. Ex 29:40; Num 28:5

beatest

when thou b. olive tree. Deut 24:20
b. him with rod, shall not. Pr 23:13

beateth

as one that b. the air. 1 Cor 9:26

beating

b. down one another. 1 Sam 14:16*
b. some, and killing. Mark 12:5

beauties

in b. of holiness, from. Ps 110:3*

beautiful

Rachel was b. Gen 29:17
the captives a b. woman. Deut 21:11
of a b. countenance. 1 Sam 16:12
Abigail of a b. countenance. 25:3
Bath-sheba was very b. 2 Sam 11:2
Esther was fair and b. Esth 2:7
b. for situation is mount. Ps 48:2
hath made every thing b. Eccl 3:11
thou art b. O my love. S of S 6:4
how b. thy feet, O princess. 7:1
the branch of Lord be b. Isa 4:2
Zion, put on thy b. garments. 52:1
b. feet of them that. 7; Rom 10:15
our holy and b. house is. Isa 64:11
where is thy b. flock ? Jer 13:20
how is staff broken, and b. 48:17
a b. crown upon thine. Ezek 16:12
thou wast exceeding b. 13
the Sabeans put on b. crowns. 23:42

sepulchres, appear b. Mat 23:27
at the gate called b. Acts 3:2, 10

beautify

king's heart to b. Lord's. Ezra 7:27
he will b. the meek with. Ps 149:4
b. place of my sanctuary. Isa 60:13

beauty

[1] *Literally, outward comeliness, or handsomeness,* 2 Sam 14:25.
[2] *Figuratively, for* (a) *a chief person, or city,* 2 Sam 1:19; Isa 13:19; Lam 2:1; (b) *Splendour, glory, or dignity,* Lam 1:6; (c) *Joy and gladness,* Isa 61:3.

for Aaron, for glory and b. Ex 28:2
the b. of Israel is slain. 2 Sam 1:19*
so praised as Absalom for b. 14:25
worship the Lord in b. of holiness.
1 Chr 16:29; Ps 29:2; 96:9
praise b. of holiness. 2 Chr 20:21
to shew her b. Esth 1:11
array with glory and b. Job 40:10*
to behold the b. of the. Ps 27:4
makest his b. to consume. 39:11
shall greatly desire thy b. 45:11
their b. shall consume in. 49:14
perfection of b. God shined. 50:2
let the b. of the Lord be on. 90:17*
strength and b. in his sanctuary. 96:6
lust not after b. in thy. Pr 6:25
b. of old men is grey head. 20:29
favour is deceitful, b. is vain. 31:30
burning instead of b. Isa 3:24
Babylon the b. of the. 13:19
glorious b. is a fading. 28:1, 4
Lord will be for a diadem of b. 5
shalt see the King in his b. 33:17
according to the b. of a man. 44:13
no b. that we should desire. 53:2
them that mourn b. for ashes. 61:3*
Zion all b. is departed. Lam 1:6*
cast down from heaven b. of. 2:1
city men call the perfection of b. 15
the b. of his ornament. Ezek 7:20
went among heathen for b. 16:14
thou didst trust in thine own b. 15
thou hast made thy b. abhorred. 25
said, I am of perfect b. 27:3; 28:12
builders have perfected thy b.
27:4, 11
swords against b. of thy. 28:7
heart lifted up because of thy b. 17
no tree was like Assyrian in b. 31:8
whom dost thou pass in b ? 32:19
b. shall be as the olive-. Hos 14:6
great his goodness and b. Zech 9:17
two staves, one I called b. 11:7, 10

became

man b. a living soul. Gen 2:7
Lot's wife b. a pillar of salt. 19:26
Issachar b. a servant. 49:15
it b. a serpent. Ex 4:3
b. a rod in his hand. 4
coupled it, it b. one tabernacle. 36:13
Nabal's heart b. as a. 1 Sam 25:37
thing b. a sin. 1 Ki 12:30; 13:34
the stone b. a great. Dan 2:35
to the Jews I b. a Jew. 1 Cor 9:20
such an High Priest b. us. Heb 7:26
whilst ye b. companions of. 10:33
the sea b. as blood of. Rev 16:3

becamest

thou, Lord, b. their God. 1 Chr 17:22
thou b. mine. Ezek 16:8

because

b. thou hast done this. Gen 3:14
b. even b. they despised. Lev 26:43
b. he did this, b. he had. 2 Sam 12:6
b. I called, and ye refused. Pr 1:24
b. even b. they seduced. Ezek 13:10
shall be offended b. of. Mat 26:31*
water, b. ye belong to. Mark 9:41
ye seek me, not b. ye saw, but b. ye
did eat and were filled. John 6:26
even b. ye cannot hear my. 8:43
fleeth, b. he is an hireling. 10:13
b. I live, ye shall live also. 14:19
life b. of righteousness. Rom 8:10
b. of these cometh wrath. Eph 5:6
b. he could swear by no. Heb 6:13
b. we love brethren. 1 John 3:14
we love him b. he first loved. 4:19

beckoned

Zacharias *b.* speechless. *Luke* 1:22*
b. to their partners in other. 5:7
Peter *b.* that he should. *John* 13:24
Alexander *b.* with his. *Acts* 19:33
Paul stood on stairs, and *b.* 21:40
Paul, after the governor had *b.* 24:10

beckoning

Peter *b.* unto them. *Acts* 12:17
Paul stood up, *b.* with his. 13:16

become

man is *b.* as one of us. *Gen* 3:22
what will *b.* of his dreams. 37:20
the Lord my strength, is *b.* my.
Ex 15:2; *Ps* 118:14; *Isa* 12:2
this Moses that brought us up, what is *b.* *Ex* 32:1, 23; *Acts* 7:40
thou art *b.* the people. *Deut* 27:9
Lord is *b.* thine enemy. *1 Sam* 28:16
what would *b.* of the city. *Jonah* 4:5
is *b.* head of corner. *Mat* 21:42*
Mark 12:10*; *Luke* 20:17*
Acts 4:11*
power to *b.* the sons of. *John* 1:12
all things are *b.* new. *2 Cor* 5:17
b. the kingdoms of Lord. *Rev* 11:15

becometh

(*Sometimes used as meaning worthy of, or worthily*)
holiness *b.* thy house. *Ps* 93:5
he *b.* poor that dealeth. *Pr* 10:4
excellent speech *b.* not a fool. 17:7
man void of understanding *b.* 18
born in his kingdom *b.* *Eccl* 4:14*
thus it *b.* us to fulfil all. *Mat* 3:15
deceitfulness of riches choketh word, he *b.* 13:22; *Mark* 4:19
b. a tree. *Mat* 13:32; *Mark* 4:32
our sister as *b.* saints. *Rom* 16:2
not be named, as *b.* saints. *Eph* 5:3
be as *b.* the gospel. *Phil* 1:27
b. women professing. *1 Tim* 2:10
behaviour as *b.* holiness. *Tit* 2:3*

bed

(*Usually only a thick quilt or thin mattrass. Sometimes the rich had couches made of valuable materials. Bedsteads such as we use were rare*)
bowed on *b.* *Gen* 47:31; *1 Ki* 1:47
thy father's *b.* *Gen* 49:4; *1 Chr* 5:1
he die not, keepeth his *b.* *Ex* 21:18
b. whereon he lieth. *Lev* 15:4, 24
took image laid it in *b.* *1 Sam* 19:13
who lay on a *b.* at noon. *2 Sam* 4:5
David arose from his *b.* 11:2
not come from that *b.* *2 Ki* 1:4; 6:16
let us set there for him a *b.* 4:10
my *b.* shall comfort me. *Job* 7:13
made my *b.* in the darkness. 17:13
in slumberings upon the *b.* 33:15
your heart on your *b.* *Ps* 4:4
he deviseth mischief on his *b.* 36:4
all his *b.* in his sickness. 41:3
I remember thee upon my *b.* 63:6
nor go up into my *b.* till. 132:3
if I make my *b.* in hell, thou. 139:8
my *b.* with tapestry. *Pr* 7:16, 17
why should he take thy *b.* ? 22:27
the slothful on his *b.* 26:14
also our *b.* is green. *S of S* 1:16
by night on my *b.* I sought. 3:1
behold, his *b.* which is Solomon's. 7*
the *b.* is shorter than. *Isa* 28:20
mountain hast thou set thy *b.* 57:7
out in the corner of a *b.* *Amos* 3:12
take up thy *b.* and walk. *Mat* 9:6
Mark 2:9, 11; *John* 5:11, 12
a candle under a *b.* *Mark* 4:21
Luke 8:16
children with me in *b.* *Luke* 11:7
two men in one *b.* one taken. 17:34
I will cast her into a *b.* *Rev* 2:22

bed *of love*

Babylonians in *b. of love.* *Ezek* 23:17

bed *of spices*

are as a *b. of spices.* *S of S* 5:13
is gone to the *b. of spices.* 6:2

bed *undefiled*

honourable and *b. unde.* *Heb* 13:4

Bedan

the Lord sent *B.* and. *1 Sam* 12:11
the sons of Ulam, *B.* *1 Chr* 7:17

bed-chamber

frogs came into thy *b.-c.* *Ex* 8:3
lay in his *b.-c.* they. *2 Sam* 4:7
telleth the words in *b.-c.* *2 Ki* 6:12
hid him in *b.-c.* 11:2; *2 Chr* 22:11
curse not . . . in thy *b.-c.* *Eccl* 10:20

beds

sing aloud on their *b.* *Ps* 149:5
they shall rest in their *b.* *Isa* 57:2
they howled upon their *b.* *Hos* 7:14
lie on *b.* of ivory. *Amos* 6:4
them that work evil on *b.* *Mi* 2:1

bedstead

(*Rarely used, and only here named in the Bible*)
his *b.* was a *b.* of iron. *Deut* 3:11

bee, bees

chased you as *b.* in Seir. *Deut* 1:44
a swarm of *b.* in carcase. *Judg* 14:8
compassed me like *b.* *Ps* 118:12
hiss for the *b.* in Assyria. *Isa* 7:18

Beelzebub

have called the master *B.* *Mat* 10:25
cast out devils, but by *B.* prince of.
12:24; *Mark* 3:22; *Luke* 11:15
if I by *B.* cast. *Mat* 12:27
Luke 11:18, 19

been

pleasant hast thou *b.* *2 Sam* 1:26
if that had *b.* too little. 12:8
then had I *b.* at rest. *Job* 3:13
thou hast *b.* my help. *Ps* 27:9; 63:7
unless the Lord had *b.* my. 94:17
thy peace *b.* as a river. *Isa* 48:18
these, where had they *b.* ? 49:21
we had *b.* in days of our. *Mat* 23:30
we trusted it had *b.* he. *Luke* 24:21
they had *b.* with Jesus. *Acts* 4:13
we had *b.* as Sodom. *Rom* 9:29
widow, having *b.* wife of. *1 Tim* 5:9
it had *b.* better not to. *2 Pet* 2:21
if they hath *b.* of us. *1 John* 2:19

hath **been**

God of my father *hath b.* *Gen* 31:5
thy God *hath b.* with. *Deut* 2:7
wherein this sin *hath b.* *1 Sam* 14:38
Israel *hath b.* without. *2 Chr* 15:3
which *hath b.* is now, that which is to be *hath* already *b.* *Eccl* 3:15
this *hath b.* thy manner. *Jer* 22:21
hath this *b.* in your days? *Joel* 1:2
hath b. dead four days. *John* 11:39
hath b. his counsellor ? *Rom* 11:34

have **been**

servants as they *have b.* *1 Sam* 4:9
have b. with thee. *1 Chr* 17:8
our fathers *have* we *b.* *Ezra* 9:7
have b. as if I had not *b.* *Job* 10:19
thy tender mercies *have b.* *Ps* 25:6
have b. young, and now old. 37:25
my tears *have b.* my meat. 42:3
have b. as Sodom, *have b.* *Isa* 1:9
so *have* we *b.* in thy sight, O. 26:17
have b. with child, *have b.* in. 18
all those things *have b.* saith. 66:2*
have I *b.* a wilderness ? *Jer* 2:31
the prophets that *have b.* 28:8
I *have b.* a rebuker of. *Hos* 5:2*
have b. partial in the law. *Mal* 2:9*
they *have b.* with me. *Mark* 8:2
have b. since the world. *Luke* 1:70
have I *b.* so long time? *John* 14:9
because ye *have b.* with me. 15:27
what manner I *have b.* *Acts* 20:18
have I *b.* in the deep. *2 Cor* 11:25
righteousness should *have b.* by.
Gal 3:21

not **been**

as hath *not b.* in Egypt. *Ex* 9:18
hast *not b.* as my servant. *1 Ki* 14:8
untimely birth I had *not b.* *Job* 3:16
b. as though I had *not b.* 10:19
if it had *not b.* the Lord. *Ps* 124:1, 2
better is he that hath *not b.* *Eccl* 4:3
as though they had *not b.* *Ob* 16
good he had *not b.* born. *Mat* 26:24
have *not b.* faithful. *Luke* 16:11, 12

Beer-sheba

in wilderness of *B.* *Gen* 21:14
Abraham planted a grove in *B.* 33
to *B.* Abraham dwelt at *B.* 22:19
the name of the city is *B.* *Gen* 26:33
Jacob went out from *B.* 28:10
his journey and came to *B.* 46:1
in their inheritance *B.* *Josh* 19:2
for his life and came to *B.* *1 Ki* 19:3
Beth-el, and pass not to *B.* *Amos* 5:5
the manner of *B.* liveth. 8:14

beetle

(*Revised Version,* cricket)
ye may eat, the *b.* *Lev* 11:22

beeves

(*The plural of* beef, *used as a generic term for bulls, cows, or oxen*)
offer of the *b.* *Lev* 22:19
offers a freewill offering in *b.* 21
tribute to the Lord of *b.* *Num* 31:28
Lord's tribute of *b.* threescore and. 38

befall

(*To happen or occur to, to come upon*)
lest mischief *b.* him. *Gen* 42:4
if mischief *b.* him then. 38; 44:29
that I may tell you what shall *b.*
49:1; *Deut* 31:29; *Dan* 10:14
troubles shall *b.* them. *Deut* 31:17
shall no evil *b.* thee. *Ps* 91:10
things that shall *b.* me. *Acts* 20:22

befallen

such things have *b.* me. *Lev* 10:17
travail that hath *b.* us. *Num* 20:14
many troubles are *b.* *Deut* 31:21
why is all this *b.* us ? *Judg* 6:13
something had *b.* him. *1 Sam* 20:26
every thing that had *b.* *Esth* 6:13
was *b.* to the possessed. *Mat* 8:33

befalleth

which *b.* sons of men, *b.* beasts, even one thing *b.* them. *Eccl* 3:19

befell

worse than all that *b.* *2 Sam* 19:7
told how it *b.* to him. *Mark* 5:16
b. me by the lying in. *Acts* 20:19

before

[1] *In sight of,* Gen. 43:14. [2] *Rather than,* 2 Sam 6:21. [3] *Free to one's view and choice,* Gen 20:15. [4] *First,* (a) *In order of time,* Isa 43:13 (*Revised Version frequently changes to* beforehand); (b) *In order of place,* Josh 8:10; Luke 22:47.
behold my land is *b.* *Gen* 20:15
b. I had done speaking. 24:45
countenance was not as *b.* 31:2
Lord give you mercy *b.* the. 43:14
he set Ephraim *b.* Manasseh. 48:20
Aaron laid it up *b.* the. *Ex* 16:34
days that were *b.* shall be. *Num* 6:12
flowed over banks as *b.* *Josh* 4:18
was no day like that *b.* it. 10:14
such as *b.* knew nothing. *Judg* 3:2
said, I will go as *b.* 16:20
chose me *b.* thy father, and *b.* his.
2 Sam 6:21
saw battle was against him *b.* 10:9
1 Chr 19:10
hand became as it was *b.* *1 Ki* 13:6
the battle was *b.* and. *2 Chr* 13:14
Manasseh his trespass *b.* 33:19
my sighing cometh *b.* I eat. *Job* 3:24
b. I go, whence I shall not. 10:21
Job twice as much as he had *b.* 42:10
I am cut off from *b.* *Ps* 31:22
spare me *b.* I go hence. 39:13
thou preparedst room *b.* it. 80:9
b. I was afflicted I went. 119:67
hast beset me behind and *b.* 139:5
thou die *b.* thy time ? *Eccl* 7:17
Syrians *b.* and Philistines. *Isa* 9:12
and behold, *b.* the morning. 17:14
b. the day was, I am he. 43:13*
that *b.* they call I will. 65:24
b. I formed thee I knew. *Jer* 1:5
ministered *b.* their idols. *Ezek* 44:12
a widow that had a priest *b.* 22
doings, are *b.* my face. *Hos* 7:2
every cow at that *b.* her *Amos* 4:3
me, and was afraid *b.* *Mal* 2:5
send Elijah *b.* the coming. 4:5
b. they came together. *Mat* 1:18
knoweth what things ye need *b.* 6:8

come to torment us *b.*? *Mat* 8:29
behold, I have told you *b.* 24:25
not see death *b.* he had. *Luke* 2:26
for *b.* they were at enmity. 23:12
of man where he was *b.* *John* 6:62
law judge man *b.* it hear? 7:51
I tell you *b.* it come. 13:19; 14:29
he seeing this *b.* spake. *Acts* 2:31
do thy counsel determined *b.* 4:28
to witnesses chosen *b.* of God. 10:41
who have begun *b.* to. *2 Cor* 8:10*
of which I tell you *b.* *Gal* 5:21*
to things that are *b.* *Phil* 3:13
whereof ye heard *b.* in. *Col* 1:5
that we had suffered *b.* *1 Thes* 2:2
with you, we told you *b.* 3:4
was *b.* a blasphemer. *1 Tim* 1:13
the command going *b.* *Heb* 7:18*
after that he had said *b.* 10:15*
of words spoken *b.* *2 Pet* 3:2
seeing ye know these things *b.* 17
to worship *b.* thy feet. *Rev* 3:9
full of eyes *b.* and behind. 4:6

come **before**

shall *come b.* the judges. *Ex* 22:9
come b. his presence. *Ps* 100:2
shall I *come b.* the Lord? *Mi* 6:6
come b. winter. *2 Tim* 4:21

before *the people*

bowed *b. the people.* *Gen* 23:12
of fire from *b. the people.* *Ex* 13:22
said, go on *b. the people.* 17:5
b. thy people I will do marvels. 34:10
went *b. the people* to Ai. *Josh* 8:10
came in *b. the people.* *1 Sam* 18:13
set them *b. the people.* *Mark* 8:6
his words, *b. the people.* *Luke* 20:26
b. many *peoples.* *Rev* 10:11*

before *whom*

Lord *b. whom* I walk. *Gen* 24:40
God *b. whom* my fathers. 48:15
As the Lord liveth, *b. whom* I stand.
1 Ki 17:1; 18:15; *2 Ki* 3:14; 5:16
b. whom thou hast begun. *Esth* 6:13
b. whom were three horns. *Dan* 7:8
and *b. whom* three fell. 20
the king *b. whom* I. *Acts* 26:26

see further, **all, ark, God, him, Lord, me, mount, stand, stood, thee, them, as, went, you.**

beforehand

take no thought *b.* *Mark* 13:11
make up *b.* your bounty. *2 Cor* 9:5
some men's sins open *b.* *1 Tim* 5:24*
works of some are manifest *b.* 25*
testified *b.* sufferings of. *1 Pet* 1:11

beforetime

he hated him not *b.* *Josh* 20:5
b. in Israel, when a man went to enquire; he now called a prophet was *b.* called a seer. *1 Sam* 9:9
nor afflict them as *b.* *2 Sam* 7:10*
Israel dwelt in tents as *b.* *2 Ki* 13:5
I had not been *b.* sad. *Neh* 2:1
who hath declared *b.* *Isa* 41:26
Simon which *b.* used. *Acts* 8:9

beg

be vagabonds and *b.* *Ps* 109:10
shall the sluggard *b.* *Pr* 20:4
I cannot dig, to *b.* I am. *Luke* 16:3

began

b. men to call on the. *Gen* 4:26
b. to commit whoredom. *Num* 25:1
they *b.* to smite Israel. *Judg* 20:31
Lord *b.* to cut Israel. *2 Ki* 10:32
when they *b.* to sing. *2 Chr* 20:22
in the third month they *b.* 31:7
young Josiah *b.* to seek God. 34:3
then they *b.* at the ancient. *Ezek* 9:6
then Jesus *b.* to preach. *Mat* 4:17
been since the world *b.* *Luke* 1:70
this man *b.* to build. 14:30
the hour when he *b.* to. *John* 4:52
since the world *b.* 9:32; *Acts* 3:21
Rom 16:25*
in Christ before the world *b.*
2 Tim 1:9*; *Tit* 1:2*
salvation at first *b.* to be. *Heb* 2:3*

begat

hearken to him that *b.* *Pr* 23:22
concerning fathers that *b.* *Jer* 16:3
and he that *b.* her. *Dan* 11:6
and mother that *b.* him. *Zech* 13:3
of his own will *b.* he us. *Jas* 1:18
that loveth him that *b.* *1 John* 5:1

beget

twelve princes shall he *b.* *Gen* 17:20
thou shalt *b.* children. *Deut* 4:25
thou shalt *b.* sons, but shalt. 28:41
sons which thou shalt *b.* shall they.
2 Ki 20:18; *Isa* 39:7
if a man *b.* 100 children. *Eccl* 6:3
take wives, and *b.* sons. *Jer* 29:6
if he *b.* a son that is. *Ezek* 18:10
he *b.* a son that seeth all. 14

begettest

issue which thou *b.* thine. *Gen* 48:6
his father, what *b.* thou? *Isa* 45:10

begetteth

he that *b.* a fool, doeth it. *Pr* 17:21
that *b.* a wise child shall. 23:24
he *b.* a son, and nothing. *Eccl* 5:14

beggar

he lifteth the *b.* from. *1 Sam* 2:8*
a *b.* named Lazarus. *Luke* 16:20
b. died, and was carried by. 22

beggarly

turn ye again to *b.* elements. *Gal* 4:9

begged

b. the body of Jesus. *Mat* 27:58
Luke 23:52
is not this he that *b.*? *John* 9:8

begging

have not seen his seed *b.* *Ps* 37:25
Bartimaeus sat *b.* *Mark* 10:46
Luke 18:35

begin

this they *b.* to do, and. *Gen* 11:6
day I *b.* to put dread. *Deut* 2:25
day will I *b.* to magnify. *Josh* 3:7
when I *b.* I will also. *1 Sam* 3:12
did I then *b.* to inquire of? 22:15
Mattaniah to *b.* *Neh* 11:17
I *b.* to bring evil on the. *Jer* 25:29
and *b.* at my sanctuary. *Ezek* 9:6
and *b.* not to say. *Luke* 3:8
then shall he *b.* to say. 13:26
all that behold it, *b.* to mock. 14:29
these things *b.* to come to. 21:28
do we *b.* again to? *2 Cor* 3:1
that judgement *b.* at the house of God, and if it first *b.* at us. *1 Pet* 4:17

beginnest

thou *b.* to put sickle. *Deut* 16:9

beginning, *noun*

[1] *That which is the first,* Ex 12:2.
[2] *The creation,* Gen 1:1.

Reuben, thou art the *b.* of. *Gen* 49:3
this month shall be the *b.* *Ex* 12:2
is the *b.* of his strength. *Deut* 21:17
though thy *b.* was small. *Job* 8:7
the latter more than *b.* 42:12
fear of Lord *b.* *Ps* 111:10; *Pr* 9:10
fear of the Lord is the *b.* of. *Pr* 1:7
b. of strife, as when one. 17:14
is the end than the *b.* *Eccl* 7:8
b. of words of his mouth is. 10:13
since *b.* of the world. *Isa* 64:4*
is the *b.* of sin to the. *Mi* 1:13
these are *b.* of sorrows. *Mat* 24:8
Mark 13:8
tribulation, not since the *b.*
Mat 24:21
the *b.* of the gospel. *Mark* 1:1
this *b.* of miracles did. *John* 2:11
who is the *b.* the first born. *Col* 1:18
if we hold the *b.* of our. *Heb* 3:14
having neither *b.* of days. nor. 7:3
end is worse than the *b.* *2 Pet* 2:20
I am the *b.* *Rev* 1:8*; 21:6; 22:13
these things saith the *b.* of. 3:14

at the **beginning**

kindness than *at the b.* *Ruth* 3:10
waste as *at b.* *1 Chr* 17:9*
an inheritance *at the b.* *Pr* 20:21
counsellors as *at the b.* *Isa* 1:26
at the b. of supplications. *Dan* 9:23
made them, *at b.* made. *Mat* 19:4
things I said not *at the b.* *John* 16:4
them as on us *at the b.* *Acts* 11:15

from the **beginning**

from the b. of year. *Deut* 11:12
from the b. of revenges. 32:42
is true *from the b.* *Ps* 119:160*
I was set up *from the b.* *Pr* 8:23
work God maketh *from b.* *Eccl* 3:11
a people terrible *from b.* *Isa* 18:2, 7
not been told *from the b.*? 40:21
who hath declared *from b.*? 41:26
declaring the end *from the b.* 46:10
not spoken in secret *from b.* 48:16
high throne *from the b.* *Jer* 17:12
from the b. it was not so. *Mat* 19:8
us, which *from b.* were. *Luke* 1:2
Jesus knew *from the b.* *John* 6:64
saith, I said to you *from b.* 8:25
was a murderer *from b.* and. 44
been with me *from the b.* 15:27
which *from b.* of the world. *Eph* 3:9*
hath *from b.* chosen. *2 Thes* 2:13
continue as *from the b.* *2 Pet* 3:4
which ye have heard *from b.*
1 John 2:7; 3:11
have known him that is *from b.* 2:13
for the devil sinneth *from the b.* 3:8
which we had *from the b.* *2 John* 5

in the **beginning**

in the b. God created. *Gen* 1:1
possessed me in *the b.* of. *Pr* 8:22
in b. was the Word. *John* 1:1
the same was *in the b.* with God. 2
ye know that *in the b.* *Phil* 4:15
thou Lord *in the b.* hast. *Heb* 1:10

beginning, *verb*

b. to sink he cried, Lord. *Mat* 14:30
give their hire, *b.* from the. 20:8
among all nations, *b.* at. *Luke* 24:47
went out, *b.* at the eldest. *John* 8:9
b. from baptism of John. *Acts* 1:22

beginnings

in *b.* of months. *Num* 10:10; 28:11
I will do better than at *b.* *Ezek* 36:11

begotten

have I *b.* them? *Num* 11:12
children *b.* of them. *Deut* 23:8
Gideon had 70 sons, *b.* *Judg* 8:30
or who hath *b.* drops of? *Job* 38:28
Son, this day have I *b.* thee. *Ps* 2:7
Acts 13:33; *Heb* 1:5; 5:5
say, who hath *b.* these? *Isa* 49:21
have *b.* strange children. *Hos* 5:7
glory as of the only *b.* of. *John* 1:14
only *b.* Son, he hath declared. 18
loved, that he gave his only *b.* 3:16
not believed in the only *b.* Son. 18
I have *b.* you through. *1 Cor* 4:15
Onesimus, I have *b.* *Philem* 10
bringeth in first *b.* *Heb* 1:6
by faith offered up only *b.* 11:17
who hath *b.* us again to. *1 Pet* 1:3
sent his only *b.* Son. *1 John* 4:9
that begat, loveth him that is *b.* 5:1
he that is *b.* of God keepeth. 18
Jesus who is the first *b.* *Rev* 1:5

beguile

lest any *b.* you with words. *Col* 2:4*
let no man *b.* you of your. 18*

beguiled, -ing

said, serpent *b.* me. *Gen* 3:13
wherefore hast thou *b.* me? 29:25
b. you in the matter. *Num* 25:18
wherefore have ye *b.* us? *Josh* 9:22
fear lest as the serpent *b.* *2 Cor* 11:3
cease from sin, *b.* *2 Pet* 2:14*

begun

the plague is *b.* *Num* 16:46
the plague was *b.* 47
b. to shew greatness. *Deut* 3:24
thou hast *b.* to fall. *Esth* 6:13
undertook to do as they had *b.* 9:23
he had *b.* to reckon. *Mat* 18:24
as he had *b.* so he would. *2 Cor* 8:6
expedient for you who have *b.* 10
are ye so foolish, having *b.*? *Gal* 3:3
which hath *b.* a good work. *Phil* 1:6
have *b.* to wax wanton. *1 Tim* 5:11

behalf

a statute on *b.* of Israel. *Ex* 27:21
Abner sent David on *b.* *2 Sam* 3:12
strong in *b.* of them. *2 Chr* 16:9

yet to speak on God's *b*. *Job* 36:2
a prince for his own *b*. *Dan* 11:18*
glad on your *b*. *Rom* 16:19*
thank my God on your *b*. *1 Cor* 1:4*
thanks given on your *b*. *2 Cor* 1:11
occasion to glory on our *b*. 5:12
it is given in *b*. of Christ. *Phil* 1:29
glorify God on this *b*. *1 Pet* 4:16

behave

lest adversaries *b*. *Deut* 32:27*
let us *b*. ourselves. *1 Chr* 19:13*
I will *b*. wisely in perfect. *Ps* 101:2
the child shall *b*. himself. *Isa* 3:5
charity doth not *b*. itself. *1 Cor* 13:5
how thou oughtest to *b*. *1 Tim* 3:15

behaved

David *b*. wisely. *1 Sam* 18:5
14, 15, 30
b. as though he had been. *Ps* 35:14
I have *b*. myself as a child. 131:2*
b. themselves ill in doings. *Mi* 3:4*
how unblameably we *b*. *1 Thes* 2:10
b. not ourselves disorderly.
2 Thes 3:7

behaveth

think he *b*. uncomely to. *1 Cor* 7:36

behaviour

David changed his *b*. *1 Sam* 21:13
bishop must be of good *b*. *1 Tim* 3:2*
women in *b*. becometh. *Tit* 2:3*

beheaded

hands over the heifer *b*. *Deut* 21:6*
smote Ish-bosheth, and *b*. him.
2 Sam 4:7
b. John. *Mat* 14:10; *Mark* 6:16, 27
Luke 9:9
souls of them that were *b*. *Rev* 20:4

beheld

he *b*. serpent of brass. *Num* 21:9
hath not *b*. iniquity in Jacob. 23:21
destroying, the Lord *b*. *1 Chr* 21:15
if I *b*. the sun when it. *Job* 31:26
I *b*. transgressors. *Ps* 119:158
I *b*. but there was no man. 142:4*
b. among the simple ones. *Pr* 7:7
then I *b*. the work of God. *Eccl* 8:17
I *b*. and there was no man. *Isa* 41:28
Jer 4:25
I *b*. the earth without form. *Jer* 4:23
Mary Magdalene and Mary *b*.
Mark 15:47; *Luke* 23:55
I *b*. Satan as lightning. *Luke* 10:18
he *b*. the city, and wept over. 19:41
and we *b*. his glory. *John* 1:14
while they *b*. Jesus was. *Acts* 1:9*
I passed by and *b*. your. 17:23
I *b*. and in midst of the. *Rev* 5:6
and their enemies *b*. them. 11:12

behemoth

(*Probably the hippopotamus*)
behold now *b*. which I. *Job* 40:15

behind

[1] *Backwards*, Judg 20:40. [2] *After*, 2 Sam 3:16. [3] *Remaining*, Lev 25:51. [4] *Past*, Phil. 3:13.

shall not an hoof be left *b*. *Ex* 10:26
be yet many years *b*. *Lev* 25:51*
Benjamites looked *b*. *Judg* 20:40
those left *b*. stayed. *1 Sam* 30:9
husband went weeping *b*. *2 Sam* 3:16
cast me *b*. thy back. *1 Ki* 14:9
Ezek 23:35
rulers were *b*. Judah. *Neh* 4:16
cast thy law *b*. their backs. 9:26
he standeth *b*. our wall. *S of S* 2:9
cast all my sins *b*. thy. *Isa* 38:17
she came in the press *b*. *Mark* 5:27
the child Jesus tarried *b*. *Luke* 2:43
so that ye come *b*. in. *1 Cor* 1:7
I was not *b*. *2 Cor* 11:5; 12:11
forgetting those things *b*. *Phil* 3:13
what is *b*. of afflictions. *Col* 1:24*

see further, **before, him, we, thee, them, us**

behold

(*An interjection, calling attention to what is to follow. Literally*, lo, look)

b. I am with thee, and. *Gen* 28:15
looked, and *b*. they were sad. 40:6
b. thy father is sick. 48:1
Israel said, *b*. I die. *Gen* 48:21
b. the bush burned with. *Ex* 3:2
b. I will rain bread from. 16:4
b. I send an angel before. 23:20
b. we are in Kadesh. *Num* 20:16
b. king ye have chosen. *1 Sam* 12:13
answered, *b*. thy servant. *2 Sam* 9:6
b. child shall be born to. *1 Ki* 13:2
b. they spied band of. *2 Ki* 13:21
b. I will bring evil upon this. 22:16
2 Chr 34:24
b. I say, how they. *2 Chr* 20:11
b. all that he hath is in. *Job* 1:12
b. the fear of the Lord. 28:28
b. in this thou art not just. 33:12
b. God is mighty, despiseth. 36:5, 26
b. I am vile, what shall I ? 40:4
b. eye of the Lord is on. *Ps* 33:18
b. I was shapen in iniquity. 51:5
b. these are the ungodly. 73:12
b. he smote the rock, waters. 78:20
if I make my bed in hell, *b*. 139:8
b. thou art fair, my love *b*.
S of S 1:15, 16; 4:1
b. a virgin. *Isa* 7:14; *Mat* 1:23
b. I and the children. *Isa* 8:18
Heb 2:13
look to the earth, and *b*. *Isa* 8:22
b. God is my salvation, I will. 12:2
hungry man dreameth, and *b*. 29:8
say to Judah, *b*. your God. 40:9
first shall say to Zion, *b*. *b*. 41:27
b. my servant whom I uphold. 42:1
b. I will do a new thing. 43:19
lest thou shouldest say *b*. I. 48:7
looked for peace *b*. *Jer* 8:15; 14:19
b. I am in your hands. 26:14
b. I am for you, and. *Ezek* 36:9
b. I will bring my servant. *Zech* 3:8
b. the man whose name is. 6:12
b. thy King cometh. 9:9; *Mat* 21:5
John 12:15
b. I will send my messenger. *Mal* 3:1
4:5; *Mat* 11:10; *Mark* 1:2
and *b*. beam in thine own. *Mat* 7:4
b. he is in the desert, *b*. he. 24:26
is risen *b*. the place. *Mark* 16:6
b. I send the promise. *Luke* 24:49
b. the Lamb of God. *John* 1:29, 36
b. an Israelite indeed. 47
Pilate saith *b*. the man. 19:5
Saul of Tarsus, for *b*. he. *Acts* 9:11
as dying, and *b*. we live. *2 Cor* 6:9
b. what manner of love. *1 John* 3:1
b. I stand at the door. *Rev* 3:20
b. I come as a thief, blessed. 16:15
b. I come quickly. 22:7, 12

behold *it is*

b. *it is* between Kadesh. *Gen* 16:14
the land, *b*. *it is* large enough. 34:21
b. *it is* a stiff-necked. *Ex* 32:9
but now *b*. *it is* dry. *Josh* 9:12
seen the land, *b*. *it is*. *Judg* 18:9
that doth speak, *b*. *it is* I. *Isa* 52:6
b. the day, *b*. *it is* come. *Ezek* 7:10
b. *it is* come, and it is done. 39:8

now **behold**, or **behold** *now*

now b. the king walketh. *1 Sam* 12:2
now b. thou trustest on. *2 Ki* 18:21
also *now b*. my witness. *Job* 16:19
now b. I loose thee this. *Jer* 40:4
now b. ye have heard. *Mat* 26:65
now b. the hand of the. *Acts* 13:11
now b. I go bound in the. 20:22
b. *now* is the time, *b*. *now*. *2 Cor* 6:2

behold *it was*, **behold** *there was*, *see* **was**

behold, *verb*

[1] *To look on a thing with our eyes*, Num 24:17. [2] *To think over a thing in our minds*, Lam 1:12; Rom 11:22.

b. this heap, *b*. this. *Gen* 31:51
Moses said, *b*. the blood. *Ex* 24:8
of the Lord shall he *b*. *Num* 12:8
see him, from the hills I *b*. 23:9
but not now, shall *b*. him. 24:17
b. it with thine eyes. *Deut* 3:27
b. the king whom ye. *1 Sam* 12:13
mine eyes shall *b*. and. *Job* 19:27
nor shall his place any more *b*. 20:9
but I cannot *b*. him. 23:9
hideth his face, who can *b*.? 34:29
his work, which men *b*. *Job* 36:24*
his eyes *b*. his eye-lids. *Ps* 11:4
countenance doth *b*. the upright. 7
let thine eyes *b*. the things. 17:2
will *b*. thy face in righteousness. 15
b. the beauty of the Lord. 27:4
mark the perfect man, *b*. 37:37
come, *b*. the works of the Lord. 46:8
awake to help me, and *b*. 59:4
ruleth for ever, his eyes *b*. 66:7
look down from heaven, *b*. 80:14
with thine eyes shalt thou *b*. 91:8
from heaven did the Lord *b*. 102:19
he humbleth himself to *b*. 113:6
open mine eyes, that I may *b*. 119:18
thine eyes shall *b*. *Pr* 23:33
pleasant thing it is to *b*. *Eccl* 11:7
he will not *b*. majesty of. *Isa* 26:10
I said, I shall *b*. man no more. 38:11
or evil, that we may *b*. it. 41:23
b. from thy habitation. 63:15
I said, *b*. me, *b*. me, to a. 65:1
thine eyes shall *b*. thy. *Jer* 20:4
neither *b*. the good I will do. 29:32
his eyes shall *b*. his. 32:4; 34:3
but a few, as thine eyes do *b*. 42:2
b. and see if any sorrow. *Lam* 1:12
hear all people, and *b*. my. 18
the Lord look down and *b*. 3:50
O Lord, consider and *b*. 5:1
b. the wicked. *Ezek* 8:9
kings that they may *b*. 28:17
ashes in sight of all that *b*. 18
man, *b*. with thine eyes. 40:4; 44:5
open thine eyes, and *b*. *Dan* 9:18
light, and I shall *b*. *Mi* 7:9
enemy, mine eyes shall *b*. her. 10
cause me to *b*. grievances? *Hab* 1:3
art of purer eyes than to *b*. evil. 13
their angels alway *b*. *Mat* 18:10
all that *b*. it mock him. *Luke* 14:29
for these things which ye *b*. 21:6
b. my hands and my feet. 24:39
with me, to *b*. my glory. *John* 17:24
as he drew near to *b*. it. *Acts* 7:31
Moses trembled, and durst not *b*. 32
Israel could not *b*. face. *2 Cor* 3:7
your good works they *b*. *1 Pet* 2:12
they *b*. your chaste conversation. 3:2
they *b*. the beast that. *Rev* 17:8

beholdest

thou *b*. all mischief to. *Ps* 10:14
why *b*. thou the mote ? *Mat* 7:3
Luke 6:41
b. not the beam that is. *Luke* 6:42

beholdeth

b. not way of vineyards. *Job* 24:18*
the Lord *b*. all the sons. *Ps* 33:13
he *b*. himself and goeth. *Jas* 1:24

beholding

turn mine eyes from *b*. *Ps* 119:37
Lord in every place, *b*. evil. *Pr* 15:3*
saving the *b*. of them. *Eccl* 5:11
women *b*. *Mat* 27:55; *Luke* 23:49
Jesus *b*. him, loved him. *Mark* 10:21
people stood *b*. and. *Luke* 23:35
b. things done, smote their. 48
b. man which was healed. *Acts* 4:14
Paul earnestly *b*. the council. 23:1*
with open face *b*. as in. *2 Cor* 3:18
in spirit, joying, and *b*. *Col* 2:5
a man *b*. his natural face. *Jas* 1:23

behoved

(*Was necessary or proper for*)
it *b*. Christ to suffer. *Luke* 24:46
b. him to be made like. *Heb* 2:17

being

I *b*. in the way, the. *Gen* 24:27*
the owner thereof not *b*. *Ex* 22:14
shall not defile himself, *b*. *Lev* 21:4
vow *b*. in her father's. *Num* 30:3, 16
our enemies *b*. judges. *Deut* 32:31
freed from *b*. bondmen. *Josh* 9:23
rejected thee from *b*. king.
1 Sam 15:23, 26
Maachah his mother, he removed from *b*. *1 Ki* 15:13; *2 Chr* 15:16
in *b*. like the house. *1 Ki* 16:7
who is there that *b*. as? *Neh* 6:11
man *b*. in honour, abideth. *Ps* 49:12
cut them off from *b*. a nation. 83:4
b. an Hebrew or. *Jer* 34:9
her husband *b*. a just. *Mat* 1:19

woman *b.* a daughter. *Luke* 13:16
in hell he lift up his eyes *b.* 16:23
b. children of the resurrection. 20:36
b. in agony, he prayed. 22:44
conveyed—multitude *b.* *John* 5:13
that thou, *b.* a man, makest. 10:33
all the members *b.* *1 Cor* 12:12
Jesus Christ *b.* the chief. *Eph* 2:20
who *b.* in the form of God. *Phil* 2:6
as *b.* yourselves also. *Heb* 13:3
she *b.* with child, cried. *Rev* 12:2

being

praise my God while I have my *b.*
Ps 104:33; 146:2
in him move, and have *b.* *Acts* 17:28

bekah

a *b.* for each, that is half a. *Ex* 38:26

Bel

B. boweth down, Nebo. *Isa* 46:1
Babylon is taken, *B.* is. *Jer* 50:2
I will punish *B.* in Babylon. 51:44

belch

behold, they *b.* out. *Ps* 59:7

Belial

certain children of *B.* *Deut* 13:13
certain sons of *B.* beset. *Judg* 19:22
the man, the children of *B.* 20:13
a daughter of *B.* *1 Sam* 1:16
sons of Eli were sons of *B.* 2:12
children of *B.* said, how shall? 10:27
he is such a son of *B.* 25:17
lord regard this man of *B.* 25
then answered the men of *B.* 30:22
out, thou man of *B.* *2 Sam* 16:7
to be there a man of *B.* Sheba. 20:1
the sons of *B.* shall be as. 23:6
set two sons of *B.* *1 Ki* 21:10, 13
Jeroboam children of *B.* *2 Chr* 13:7
hath Christ with *B.*? *2 Cor* 6:15

belied

they have *b.* the Lord. *Jer* 5:12

belief

sanctification of Spirit, and *b.* of.
2 Thes 2:13

believe

[1] *To give credit to any thing*, Gen 45:26, Acts 8:13. [2] *To be fully* persuaded, John 1:12; 3:15, 16; 6:69; Rom 9:33; 10:4. [3] *To put confidence in*, 2 Chr 20:20.

that they may *b.* Lord hath. *Ex* 4:5
that they may hear and *b.* 19:9
how long ere they *b.*? *Num* 14:11
b. in the Lord God, *b.* *2 Chr* 20:20
ye may know and *b.* me. *Isa* 43:10
b. ye that I am able? *Mat* 9:28
whoso offend one of these little ones which *b.* in me. 18:6; *Mark* 9:42
repented not that ye might *b.*
Mat 21:32
let him come down, we will *b.* 27:42
repent and *b.* the gospel. *Mark* 1:15
be not afraid, *b.* 5:36; *Luke* 8:50
thou canst *b.* all things. *Mark* 9:23*
Lord, I *b.* help mine. 24; *John* 9:38
shall *b.* those things. *Mark* 11:23
b. ye receive, and ye shall. 24
descend, that we may *b.* 15:32
shall follow them which *b.* 16:17
taketh word, lest they *b.* *Luke* 8:12
no root, which for a while *b.* 13
slow of heart to *b.* 24:25
men through him might *b.* *John* 1:7
of God, even to them that *b.* 12
how shall ye *b.* if I tell you? 3:12
woman, *b.* me, hour cometh. 4:21
now we *b.* not because of. 42
ye *b.* which receive honour? 5:44
if not writings, how shall ye *b.*? 47
work of God, that ye *b.* on. 6:29
we *b.* and are sure that thou art. 69
neither did his brethren *b.* in. 7:5
Spirit, which they that *b.* 39
dost thou *b.* on Son of God? 9:35
who is he, Lord, that I might *b.*? 36
b. works, that ye may *b.* 10:38*
not there, to intent ye may *b.* 11:15
I *b.* that thou art the Christ. 27
said I not, if thou wouldst *b.* 40
they may *b.* that thou hast sent. 42
let him alone, all men will *b.* 48
while ye have light, *b.* in. *John* 12:36
it come to pass, ye may *b.* 13:19
not troubled, ye *b.* in God, *b.* 14:1
b. I am in the Father, or *b.* 11
when it come to pass ye might *b.* 29
by this we *b.* thou camest. 16:30
Jesus answered, do ye now *b.*? 31
I pray for them which shall *b.* 17:20
that world may *b.* thou hast. 21
he saith true, that ye might *b.* 19:35
written that ye might *b.* 20:31
b. Jesus Christ is Son. *Acts* 8:37*
by him all that *b.* are. 13:39
a work you shall in no wise *b.* 41
by me should hear and *b.* 15:7
b. through grace we shall be. 11
b. on the Lord Jesus, and. 16:31
b. on him that should come. 19:4
many Jews there are which *b.* 21:20
touching the Gentiles which *b.* 25
I *b.* God that it shall be as. 27:25
righteousness on all that *b.*
Rom 3:22
father of all them that *b.* 4:11
it shall be imputed, if we *b.* 24
if dead, we *b.* that we shall live. 6:8
b. in thy heart that God raised. 10:9
how shall they *b.* in him? 14
save them that *b.* *1 Cor* 1:21
be divisions, and I partly *b.* it. 11:18
that *b.* but prophesying serveth them which *b.* 14:22
we also *b.* and therefore. *2 Cor* 4:13
promise given to them that *b.*
Gal 3:22
of power to us who *b.* *Eph* 1:19
it is given not only to *b.* *Phil* 1:29
ensamples to all that *b.* *1 Thes* 1:7
we behaved among you that *b.* 2:10
which worketh in you that *b.* 13
if we *b.* that Jesus died and. 4:14
admired in all those that *b.*
2 Thes 1:10
delusion that they should *b.* 2:11
pattern to them that *b.* *1 Tim* 1:16
thanksgiving of them that *b.* 4:3
Saviour, especially those that *b.* 10
them that *b.* to saving. *Heb* 10:39*
that cometh to God must *b.* 11:6
the devils also *b.* and. *Jas* 2:19
who by him do *b.* in. *1 Pet* 1:21
to you which *b.* he is precious. 2:7
commandment that we should *b.*
1 John 3:23
to you that *b.* that ye may *b.* 5:13*

believe *not*, or *not* **believe**

behold, they will *not b.* me. *Ex* 4:1
come to pass, if they will *not b.* 8, 9
yet in this ye did *not b.* *Deut* 1:32
their fathers did *not b.* *2 Ki* 17:14
yet would I *not b.* that he. *Job* 9:16
speaketh fair, *b.* him *not.* *Pr* 26:25
if ye will *not b.* ye shall not. *Isa* 7:9
b. not them. *Jer* 12:6
which ye will *not b.* *Hab* 1:5
why did ye *not b.* him? *Mat* 21:25
Mark 11:31
b. it *not*. *Mat* 24:23, 26; *Mark* 13:21
if I tell you will *not b.* *Luke* 22:67
earthly things, ye *b. not.* *John* 3:12
except ye see ye will *not b.* 4:48
whom he hath sent, ye *b. not.* 5:38
b. not his writings how shall ye *b.* my words? 47
also have seen me and *b. not.* 6:36
there some of you which *b. not.* 64
ye *b. not* I am he, ye shall die. 8:24
I tell you truth, ye *b.* me *not.* 45
why do ye *not b.* me? 46
ye *b. not,* because ye are not. 10:26
do not the works, *b.* me *not.* 37
though ye *b. not* me, believe. 38
they could *not b.* because. 12:39
if any hear words, and *b. not.* 47
reprove of sin, they *b. not.* 16:9
into his side, I will *not b.* 20:25
what if some did *not b.*? *Rom* 3:3*
from them that do *not b.* 15:31*
if any that *b. not* bid. *1 Cor* 10:27
a sign to them that *b. not.* 14:22
blinded minds that *b. not.* *2 Cor* 4:4
if we *b. not,* he abideth. *2 Tim* 2:13*
b. not every spirit. *1 John* 4:1

believed

b. in the Lord. *Gen* 15:6; *Rom* 4:3
Gal 3:6; *Jas* 2:23
Aaron spake, people *b.* *Ex* 4:31
b. the Lord and Moses. 14:31
and Achish *b.* David. *1 Sam* 27:12
had fainted, unless I had *b.* *Ps* 27:13
then *b.* they his words, they. 106:12
I *b.*, therefore have I spoken. 116:10
2 Cor 4:13
teach me, for I have *b.* *Ps* 119:66
who hath *b.* our report? *Isa* 53:1
John 12:38; *Rom* 10:16
hurt on him, because he *b.* *Dan* 6:23*
people of Nineveh *b.* God. *Jonah* 3:5
as thou hast *b.* so be it. *Mat* 8:13
publicans and harlots *b.* him. 21:32
and told it, neither *b.* *Mark* 16:13
which are most surely *b.* *Luke* 1:1
blessed is she that *b.* for there. 45
his glory, and disciples *b.* *John* 2:11
they *b.* the scripture. 22
the man *b.* the word. 4:50
the father himself *b.* and. 53
ye *b.* Moses, ye would have *b.* 5:46
have any rulers or Pharisees *b.*? 7:48
said Jesus to Jews that *b.* 8:31
had seen things Jesus did, *b.* 11:45
the Jews went away and *b.* 12:11
loveth you, because you *b.* 16:27
they have *b.* thou didst send. 17:8
that other disciple saw and *b.* 20:8
hast *b.* have not seen and *b.* 29
all that *b.* were together. *Acts* 2:44
many of them which heard *b.* 4:4
multitude of them that *b.* were. 32
but when they *b.* Philip. 8:12
then Simon himself *b.* also. 13
they of circumcision who *b.* 10:45
gave them gift as us who *b.* 11:17
great number *b.* and turned. 21
deputy *b.* being astonished. 13:12
were ordained to eternal life *b.* 48
of both Jews and Greeks *b.* 14:1
commended them to Lord they *b.* 23
some of them *b.* and. 17:4*
certain men clave to him and *b.* 34
Crispus chief ruler *b.* on Lord. 18:8
helped them which had *b.* 27
the Holy Ghost since ye *b.*? 19:2
beat in synagogue them that *b.* 22:19
the centurion *b.* the master. 27:11*
some *b.*, and some *b.* not. 28:24
against hope *b.* in hope. *Rom* 4:18
salvation nearer than when we *b.*
13:11
ministers by whom ye *b.* *1 Cor* 3:5
unless ye have *b.* in vain. 15:2
so we preach, and so ye *b.* 11
even we have *b.* in Jesus. *Gal* 2:16
in whom after ye *b.* *Eph* 1:13
our testimony was *b.* *2 Thes* 1:10
b. on in the world. *1 Tim* 3:16
I know whom I have *b.* *2 Tim* 1:12
they which have *b.* in God. *Tit* 3:8
which have *b.* do enter. *Heb* 4:3
have *b.* the love of God. *1 John* 4:16

many **believed**

at the passover *many b.* *John* 2:23
many of the Samaritans *b.* on. 4:39
many of the Jews *b.* 11:45
the chief rulers also *many b.* 12:42
many of Corinthians *b.* *Acts* 18:8
many that *b.* came and. 19:18

believed *not*, or *not* **believed**

heart fainted, he *b. not.* *Gen* 45:26
because he *b.* me *not.* *Num* 20:12
rebelled, and *b.* him *not.* *Deut* 9:23
I *b. not* words. *1 Ki* 10:7; *2 Chr* 9:6
I laughed, they *b.* it *not.* *Job* 29:24
because they *b. not* in God. *Ps* 78:22
sinned, and *b. not* for his. 32
despised the land, *b. not.* 106:24
but Gedaliah *b.* them *not.* *Jer* 40:14
world would *not* have *b.* *Lam* 4:12
came, and ye *b.* him *not.* *Mat* 21:32
they heard he was alive *b. not.*
Mark 16:11
because they *b. not.* 14
why then *b.* him *not*? *Luke* 20:5
while they *b. not* for joy. 24:41
because he hath *not b.* *John* 3:18
Jesus knew who *b. not.* 6:64

I told you and ye b. not. John 10:25
many miracles, yet they b. not. 12:37
afraid, and b. not that. Acts 9:26
Jews which b. not moved. 17:5
were hardened and b. not. 19:9*
in whom they have not b. Rom 10:14
times past have not b. God. 11:30*
even so have these not b. 31
damned who b. not. 2 Thes 2:12
into rest, that b. not. Heb 3:18*
not with them that b. not. 11:31*
destroyed them that b. not. Jude 5

believers

b. were the more added. Acts 5:14
be thou an example of b. 1 Tim 4:12

believest

dumb because thou b. not. Luke 1:20
I saw thee, b. thou ? John 1:50
in me shall never die, b. ? 11:26
b. thou not ? 14:10
thou b. with thine heart. Acts 8:37*
b. thou ? I know thou b. 26:27
b. that there is one God. Jas 2:19

believeth

he b. not that he shall. Job 15:22
simple b. every word. Pr 14:15
that b. not make haste. Isa 28:16
possible to him that b. Mark 9:23
he that b. and is baptized...he that b. not shall be damned. 16:16
b. in him not perish. John 3:15, 16
he that b. on him is not condemned, that b. not is condemned. 18
that b. hath everlasting. 36; 6:47
b. on him that sent me hath. 5:24
he that b. shall never thirst. 6:35
he that seeth the Son and b. 40
he that b. on me, out of his. 7:38
he that b. though he were. 11:25
whosoever liveth and b. in me. 26
he that b. on me, b. not on. 12:44
whoso b. on me, should not. 46
he that b. on me, the works. 14:12
whoso b. in him receive. Acts 10:43
God to every one that b. Rom 1:16
the justifier of him that b. 3:26*
him that worketh not, but b. 4:5
whoso b. shall not be. 9:33; 10:11
end of law to every one that b. 10:4
for with the heart man b. 10
for one b. that he may eat. 14:2*
hath a wife that b. not. 1 Cor 7:12
love b. all things, hopeth all. 13:7
come in one that b. not. 14:24
part hath he that b. ? 2 Cor 6:15
if any man that b. have. 1 Tim 5:16
he that b. shall not be. 1 Pet 2:6
whoso b. Jesus is Christ. 1 John 5:1
overcometh, but he that b. 5
that b. on the Son; he that b. not God, because he b. not the record. 10

believing

ask in prayer, b. receive. Mat 21:22
be not faithless but b. John 20:27
that b. ye might have life. 31
rejoiced, b. in God. Acts 16:34
b. all things which are written. 24:14
all joy and peace in b. Rom 15:13
they that have b. masters. 1 Tim 6:2
yet b. ye rejoice with. 1 Pet 1:8

bell, -s

b. of gold. Ex 28:33; 39:25
a golden b. and pomegranate. 28:34
39, 26
upon b. of horses. Zech 14:20

bellow, *see* **bulls**

bellies

are alway liars, slow b. Tit 1:12

bellows

b. are burnt, lead. Jer 6:29

belly

[1] *The part of the body which contains the bowels,* Mat 15:17. [2] *The womb,* Jer 1:5.

b. shalt thou go, and. Gen 3:14
goeth upon the b. Lev 11:42
thigh to rot, thy b. Num 5:21†
and woman through the b. 25:8†
and thrust it in his b. Judg 3:21†
over against the b. 1 Ki 7:20
give up ghost out of the b. Job 3:11†
fill his b. with the east wind. Job 15:2
vanity, and their b. prepareth. 35
shall cast out of his b. 20:15
not feel quietness in his b. 20*
about to fill his b. God shall. 23
behold my b. is as wine. 32:19†
whose b. thou fillest. Ps 17:14
my God from my mother's b. 22:10
soul bowed down, b. 44:25†
the b. of the wicked. Pr 13:25
innermost parts of the b. 18:8†
26:22†
a man's b. shall be satisfied. 18:20
inward parts of the b. 20:27†
stripes inward parts of b. 30†
his b. is as bright ivory. S of S 5:14*
b. is like an heap of wheat. 7:2†
borne by me from the b. Isa 46:3
I formed thee in the b. I. Jer 1:5
he hath filled his b. with. 51:34*
man, cause thy b. to eat. Ezek 3:3
this image's b. of brass. Dan 2:32
Jonah was in b. of the fish. Jonah 1:17; Mat 12:40
out of the b. of hell cried. Jonah 2:2
I heard, my b. trembled. Hab 3:16†
entereth mouth goeth into the b. Mat 15:17; Mark 7:19
fain have filled his b. Luke 15:16
out of his b. shall flow. John 7:38†
our Lord but their own b. Rom 16:18
meats for the b. and b. 1 Cor 6:13
whose God is their b. Phil 3:19
shall make thy b. bitter. Rev 10:9
as soon as I had eaten it, my b. 10

belong

interpretations b. to God. Gen 40:8
return to whom it did b. Lev 27:24
secret things b. to God, revealed b. Deut 29:29
shields of earth b. to God. Ps 47:9
to our God b. the issues. 68:20
these things b. to wise. Pr 24:23
to the Lord b. mercies. Dan 9:9
my name, because ye b. Mark 9:41
the things which b. to. Luke 19:42
careth for things that b. 1 Cor 7:32

belonged, -est

to whom b. thou ? 1 Sam 30:13
mighty men, which b. to. 1 Ki 1:8
as he knew he b. to. Luke 23:7

belongeth

to me b. vengeance. Deut 32:35
Ps 94:1; Heb 10:30
b. to Benjamin Judg 19:14; 20:4
arise, for this matter b. Ezra 10:4
salvation b. unto the Lord. Ps 3:8
have I heard, power b. 62:11
also unto thee, b. mercy. 12
righteousness b. to thee. Dan 9:7
to us b. confusion of face. 8
strong meat b. to them. Heb 5:14

belonging

of sanctuary b. to them. Num 7:9
part of a field b. to Boaz. Ruth 2:3
meddleth with strife b. Pr 26:17
he went into a desert b. Luke 9:10

beloved

two wives, the one b. Deut 21:15
b. of the Lord shall dwell. 33:12
Solomon, b. of his God. Neh 13:26
that thy b. may. Ps 60:5; 108:6
for so he giveth his b. sleep. 127:2
and only b. in the sight of. Pr 4:3
drink abundantly, O b. S of S 5:1
is thy b. more than another b. ? 9
whither is thy b. gone ? 6:1
who cometh leaning on her b. ? 8:5
art greatly b. Dan 9:23; 10:11, 19
go yet, love a woman b. Hos 3:1
I will slay the b. 9:16
men with b. Barnabas. Acts 15:25
to all that are in Rome, b. Rom 1:7
I will call b. which was not b. 9:25
they are b. for Father's sake. 11:28
salute b. Persis who. 16:12
accepted in the b. Eph 1:6
a b. brother and. 6:21; Col 4:7
elect of God, holy and b. Col 3:12
Onesimus, a faithful and b. 4:9
Luke the b. physician and. 14
knowing b. your election. 1 Thes 1:4
because they are b. 1 Tim 6:2
a servant, a brother b. Philem 16
b. we are persuaded. Heb 6:9
b. be not ignorant of this. 2 Pet 3:8
even as our b. brother Paul. 15
b. now are we sons of. 1 John 3:2
b. condemn us not. 21
b. believe not every spirit, but. 4:1
b. let us love one another. 7
b. if God so loved us, we. 11
b. follow not evil, but. 3 John 11
but ye b. building up. Jude 20
compassed the b. city. Rev 20:9

dearly **beloved,** *see* **dearly**

my **beloved**

my b. is a cluster of. S of S 1:14
behold thou art fair, my b. 16
as the apple-tree, so is my b. 2:3
it is the voice of my b. 2:8; 5:2
my b. is like a roe or a. 2:9
my b. is mine, I am his. 16; 6:3
turn my b. and be thou like. 2:17
let my b. come into his garden. 4:16
I rose up to open to my b. 5:5
I opened to my b. 6
my b. is white and ruddy. 10
this is my b. 16
my b. is gone. 6:2
I am my b. and my b. mine. 3; 7:10
I have laid up for thee, my b. 7:13
a song of my b. touching. Isa 5:1
what hath my b. to do ? Jer 11:15
my b. Son. Mat 3:17; 17:5
Mark 1:11; 9:7; Luke 3:22
9:35*; 2 Pet 1:17
behold my b. in whom my. Mat 12:18
I will send my b. son. Luke 20:13
greet Amplias my b. Rom 16:8
as my b. sons I warn. 1 Cor 4:14
Timothy my b. son. 17; 2 Tim 1:2
do not err, my b. brethren. Jas 1:16

Belshazzar

O B. hast not humbled. Dan 5:22
in the first year of B. 7:1
in third year of B. 8:1

Belteshazzar

to Daniel the name of B. Dan 1:7
name was B. 2:26; 4:8, 9, 19
5:12; 10:1

bemoan, -ed, -ing

they b. Job, comforted. Job 42:11
who shall b. thee ? Jer 15:5
neither go to lament, nor b. 16:5
weep not for the dead, nor b. 22:10
I have heard Ephraim b. 31:18
all ye that are about him b. 48:17
is laid waste, who will b. ? Nah 3:7

Benaiah

did B. 2 Sam 23:22; 1 Chr 11:24
call me Zadok and B. 1 Ki 1:32
the king put B. in Joab's room. 2:35
B. the son of Jehoiada was. 4:4
Jesimiel and B. sons. 1 Chr 4:36
B. the Pirathonite, a mighty. 11:31
second degree B. 15:18,20; 16:5, 6
captain for third month, B. 27:5
for the eleventh month, B. 14
Mahath and B. were. 2 Chr 31:13
B. son of Parosh. Ezra 10:25
B. son of Pahath-moab. 30
B. the son of Bani. 35
B. son of Nebo. 43
I saw Pelatiah son of B. Ezek 11:1
when I prophesied, the son of B. 13

Ben-ammi

called his name B. Gen 19:38

benches

thy b. of ivory. Ezek 27:6

bend

the wicked b. their bow. Ps 11:2
who b. their bows to shoot. 64:3*
b. their tongue like a bow. Jer 9:3
Lydians, handle and b. bow. 46:9
all ye that b. the bow. 50:14, 29
against him, let the archer b. 51:3
this vine did b. roots. Ezek 17:7

bendeth, -ing

when he b. his bow. Ps 58:7*
that afflicted thee shall b. Isa 60:14
against him that b. let. Jer 51:3*

beneath
in the earth *b*. *Ex* 20:4; *Deut* 5:8
he brake the tables *b*. mount. *Ex* 32:19
on the earth *b*. there. *Deut* 4:39
be above only, and not be *b*. 28:13
the deep that coucheth *b*. 33:13
roots shall be dried up *b*. *Job* 18:16
that ye depart from hell *b*. *Pr* 15:24
hell from *b*. is moved. *Isa* 14:9
your eyes, look on the earth *b*. 51:6
foundations can be searched *b*. *Jer* 31:37
ye are from *b*. I am. *John* 8:23

benefactors
that exercise authority are called *b*. *Luke* 22:25

benefit
good wherewith I *b*. them. *Jer* 18:10

benefit, -s
[1] *The gifts and favours of God to men*, 2 Chr 32:25; Ps 68:19; 103:2.
not according to *b*. *2 Chr* 32:25
Lord loadeth us with *b*. *Ps* 68:19*
the Lord, forget not all his *b*. 103:2
shall I render for his *b*.? 116:12
might have second *b*. *2 Cor* 1:15
partakers of the *b*. *1 Tim* 6:2
b. should not be of. *Philem* 14*

benevolence
husband render due *b*. *1 Cor* 7:3*

Ben-hadad
to *B*. *1 Ki* 15:18; *2 Chr* 16:2
thus saith *B*. thy silver. *1 Ki* 20:2
B. was drinking himself drunk. 16
B. escaped on an horse, with. 20
thy servant *B*. saith, I pray thee. 32
B. went up and besieged. *2 Ki* 6:24
B. was sick. 8:7
thy son *B*. hath sent me. 9
Israel into the hand of *B*. 13:3
took again out of the hand of *B*. 25
palaces of *B*. *Jer* 49:27; *Amos* 1:4

Benjamin
his father called him *B*. *Gen* 35:18
Rachel, Joseph and *B*. 24; 46:19
not, and ye will take *B*. 42:36
away your brother and *B*. 43:14
and when Joseph saw *B*. 16, 29
B. mess was five times so. 34
cup was found in *B*. sack. 44:12
he fell on his brother *B*. neck. 45:14
sons of *B*. 46:21; *Num* 26:38, 41
1 Chr 7:6; 8:1, 40; 9:7; *Neh* 11:7
B. shall ravin as a wolf. *Gen* 49:27
prince of *B*. was Abidan. *Num* 1:11
stand to bless, Joseph, *B*. *Deut* 27:12
of *B*. Moses said, the. 33:12
after thee, *B*. among thy. *Judg* 5:14
Gibeah, which belongs to *B*. 19:14
out to battle against *B*. 20:20
the Lord smote *B*. before Israel. 35
all day of *B*. were 25,000 men. 46
give his daughter to *B*. 21:1, 18
women are destroyed out of *B*. 16
there ran a man of *B*. *1 Sam* 4:12
there was a man of *B*. whose. 9:1
sepulchre, in the border of *B*. 10:2
in Gibeah of *B*. 13:2; 14:16; 15:16
by number twelve of *B*. *2 Sam* 2:15
also spake in the ears of *B*. 3:19
were a thousand men of B. 19:17
Saul buried they in *B*. 21:14
son of Elah officer in *B*. *1 Ki* 4:18
Bilhan, Jeush and *B*. *1 Chr* 7:10
Levi and *B*. counted he not. 21:6
over *B*. was Jaasiel the son. 27:21
of *B*. Eliada a mighty. *2 Chr* 17:17
all in Jerusalem and *B*. 34:32
after him repaired *B*. and. *Neh* 3:23
there is little *B*. with. *Ps* 68:27
before *B*. and Manasseh, stir. 80:2
was in the gate of *B*. *Jer* 37:13
sitting in the gate of *B*. 38:7
B. shall have a portion. *Ezek* 48:23
one gate of *B*. 32
Beth-aven, after thee, O *B*. *Hos* 5:8
possess Ephraim, *B*. shall. *Ob* 19
inhabited from *B*. gate. *Zech* 14:10
see **children**

Benjamin with *Judah*
to fight *Judah* and *B*. *Judg* 10:9
speak to house of *Judah* and *B*. *1 Ki* 12:23; *2 Chr* 11:3
came of *B*. and *Judah*. *1 Chr* 12:16
having *Judah* and *B*. *2 Chr* 11:12
Asa, and all *Judah* and *B*. 15:2
idols out of *Judah* and *B*. 8
captains through *Judah* and *B*. 25:5
altars out of *Judah* and *B*. 31:1
was gathered of *Judah* and *B*. 34:9
fathers of *Judah* and *B*. *Ezra* 1:5
the adversaries of *Judah* and *B*. 4:1
children of *Judah* and *B*. *Neh* 11:4
after them went *Judah*, *B*. 12:34
border of *Judah* and *B*. *Ezek* 48:22

land of **Benjamin**
go into the *land of B*. *Judg* 21:21
man out of the land *of B*. *1 Sam* 9:16
idols out of *land of* B. *2 Chr* 15:8
from *land of B*. bringing. *Jer* 17:26
witnesses in the *land of B*. 32:44
in the *land of B*. shall flocks. 33:13
went to go into the *land of B*. 37:12

tribe of **Benjamin**
tribe of B. numbered. *Num* 1:37
captain of the *tribe of B*. 2:22; 10:24
of the *tribe of B*. to spy the. 13:9
of the *tribe of B*. to divide. 34:21
the lot of the *tribe of B*. *Josh* 18:11
the cities of the *tribe of B*. 21
of the tribe of Judah and the *tribe of B*. 21:4, 17; *1 Chr* 6:60, 65
men through all the *tribe of B*. *Judg* 20:12
families of the *tribe of B*. *1 Sam* 9:21
come near, the *tribe of B*. 10:20
man of the *tribe of B*. *Acts* 13:21
the *tribe of B*. *Rom* 11:1; *Phil* 3:5
of the *tribe of B*. were. *Rev* 7:8

Benjamite
Ehud a *B*. *Judg* 3:15
Kish a *B*. *1 Sam* 9:1
and said, am not I a *B*.? 21
Shimei a *B*. *2 Sam* 16:11; 19:16 *1 Ki* 2:8
Sheba a *B*. *2 Sam* 20:1
Mordecai a *B*. *Esth* 2:5

Benjamites
men of the place were *B*. *Judg* 19:16
destroyed of the *B*. 25,100. 20:35
thus they inclosed the *B*. round. 43
Saul, hear now, ye *B*. *1 Sam* 22:7
was Abiezer of *B*. *1 Chr* 27:12

Benoni
she called his name *B*. *Gen* 35:18

bent
b. his bow. *Ps* 7:12; *Lam* 2:4; 3:12
have *b*. their bow to cast. *Ps* 37:14
sharp, and their bows *b*. *Isa* 5:28
fled from the swords and *b*. 21:15
people *b*. to backsliding. *Hos* 11:7
when I have *b*. Judah. *Zech* 9:13

Beor
son of *B*. reigned. *Gen* 36:32 *1 Chr* 1:43
Balaam the son of *B*. *Num* 22:5
24:3, 15; 31:8; *Deut* 23:4
Josh 13:22; 24:9; *Mi* 6:5

Berachah
B. came to David. *1 Chr* 12:3
called the valley of *B*. *2 Chr* 20:26

Berea
and Silas by night to *B*. *Acts* 17:10
heard that Paul preached at *B*. 13
Sopater of *B*. accompanied. 20:4

bereave
I labour and *b*. my soul. *Eccl* 4:8*
I will *b*. them. *Jer* 15:7; 18:21
evil beasts shall *b*. thee. *Ezek* 5:17
no more *b*. them of men. 36:12, 14
bring up children, will I *b*. *Hos* 9:12

bereaved
have *b*. of my children. *Gen* 42:36
b. of my children, I am *b*. 43:14
land hast *b*. thy nations. *Ezek* 36:13
meet them as a bear *b*. *Hos* 13:8

bereaveth
abroad the sword *b*. *Lam* 1:20

Berith
the house of their God *B*. *Judg* 9:46

Bernice
B. came unto. *Acts* 25:13, 23
the governor and *B*. 26:30

berries
two or three *b*. in bough. *Isa* 17:6
fig-tree bear olive *b*.? *Jas* 3:12*

beryl
his body was like the *b*. *Dan* 10:6
eighth foundation was *b*. *Rev* 21:20

beseech
(*Beg, pray, intreat*)
I *b*. thee shew me thy. *Ex* 33:18
heal, O Lord, I *b*. thee. *Num* 12:13
return, we *b*. thee. *Ps* 80:14
Lord, I *b*. thee deliver me. 116:4
save I *b*. O Lord, I *b*. thee. 118:25
accept, I *b*. thee, offerings. 119:108
obey, I *b*. thee, voice of. *Jer* 38:20
O Lord God, forgive I *b*. *Amos* 7:2
we *b*. thee, O Lord, we *b*. *Jonah* 1:14
O Lord, take, I *b*. thee my. 4:3
b. God, that he will be. *Mal* 1:9
I *b*. thee, torment me. *Luke* 8:28
saying, master, I *b*. thee look. 9:38
wherefore I *b*. thee to hear. *Acts* 26:3
I *b*. you by the mercies. *Rom* 12:1
I *b*. you, be followers. *1 Cor* 4:16
I *b*. you, confirm your. *2 Cor* 2:8
as though God did *b*. you by. 5:20
we *b*. you receive not. 6:1
I Paul *b*. you by the meekness. 10:1
I *b*. you, be as I am. *Gal* 4:12
prisoner of the Lord *b*. *Eph* 4:1
yet for love's sake I *b*. *Philem* 9
I *b*. thee for my son Onesimus. 10
but I *b*. you the rather. *Heb* 13:19
I *b*. you as strangers. *1 Pet* 2:11
now I *b*. thee, lady, not. *2 John* 5
see **brethren**

beseeching
came a centurion *b*. him. *Mat* 8:5 *Luke* 7:3
there came a leper *b*. *Mark* 1:40

beset
sons of Belial *b*. *Judg* 19:22; 20:5
bulls of Bashan have *b*. *Ps* 22:12
thou hast *b*. me behind and. 139:5
their own doings have *b*. *Hos* 7:2
sin which doth so easily *b*. *Heb* 12:1

beside, besides
hast thou here any *b*. *Gen* 19:12
a famine *b*. the first famine. 26:1
b. the other in her life. *Lev* 18:18
b. sabbaths, *b*. gifts, *b*. vows *b*. your offerings, which ye give. 23:38
man has lain with thee *b*. *Num* 5:20
law of Nazarite, *b*. that his. 6:21
there is nothing *b*. manna. 11:6
offer *b*. burnt-offering. 28:23; 29:6
b. the covenant he made. *Deut* 29:1
in building an altar, *b*. *Josh* 22:19, 29
if it be dry on earth *b*. *Judg* 6:37
b. her Jephthah had no. 11:34
I will go out and stand *b*. *1 Sam* 19:3
b. that which Solomon. *1 Ki* 10:13
not a prophet *b*. 22:7; *2 Chr* 18:6
b. his sin, wherewith he. *2 Ki* 21:16
he leadeth me *b*. still. *Ps* 23:2
feed thy kids *b*. the tents. *S of S* 1:8
blessed ye that sow *b*. all. *Isa* 32:20
I will gather others to him *b*. 56:8
b. this, between us and. *Luke* 16:26
b. all this, to-day is the third. 24:21
to me thine ownself *b*. *Philem* 19

beside
friends said, he is *b*. *Mark* 3:21
Paul, thou art *b*. thyself. *Acts* 26:24
we be *b*. ourselves. *2 Cor* 5:13

besiege
he shall *b*. thee in gates. *Deut* 28:52
if enemies *b*. *1 Ki* 8:37; *2 Chr* 6:28
go, O Elam, *b*. O Media. *Isa* 21:2

besieged
dried up all rivers of *b*. places. *2 Ki* 19:24*; *Isa* 37:25*
great king and *b*. it. *Eccl* 9:14
daughter of Zion is as a *b*. *Isa* 1:8
he that is *b*. shall die by. *Ezek* 6:12

besom
(A broom)
it with b. of destruction. Isa 14:23

Besor
men came to the brook B. 1 Sam 30:9

besought
(Begged, prayed, intreated)
when he b. we would not. Gen 42:21
b. the Lord. Ex 32:11; Deut 3:23
David b. God for. 2 Sam 12:16
and the man of God b. 1 Ki 13:6
fell on his knees and b. 2 Ki 1:13
Jehoahaz b. the Lord. 13:4
Manasseh b. the Lord. 2 Chr 33:12
we fasted and b. our God. Ezra 8:23
b. him with tears to put. Esth 8:3
not Hezekiah fear, and b. Jer 26:19
so the devils b. him. Mat 8:31
Mark 5:10, 12; Luke 8:31, 32
b. him to depart. Mat 8:34
Luke 8:37
Jairus b. him greatly. Mark 5:23
Luke 8:41
Samaritans b. that he. John 4:40
nobleman of Capernaum b. 47
b. Pilate that he might take. 19:38
Gentiles b. that these. Acts 13:42
Lydia b. us, saying, if ye. 16:15
magistrates b. them, and. 39
b. him not to go to Jerusalem. 21:12
for this thing I b. Lord. 2 Cor 12:8

best
take of the b. fruits in. Gen 43:11
in b. of land make father. 47:6, 11
of b. of his own field. Ex 22:5
heave-offering of the b. Num 18:29
marry to whom they think b. 36:6
dwell where it likes him b. Deut 23:16
he will take the b. of. 1 Sam 8:14
Saul spared the b. of sheep. 15:9, 15
seemeth you b. I will. 2 Sam 18:4
look out the b. of your. 2 Ki 10:3
every man at b. state is. Ps 39:5
of thy mouth like b. wine. S of S 7:9
b. of them is as a brier. Mi 7:4
bring forth the b. robe. Luke 15:22
covet earnestly the b. 1 Cor 12:31

bestead
pass through it hardly b. Isa 8:21†

bestir
hearest the sound b. 2 Sam 5:24

bestow
that he may b. a blessing. Ex 32:29
b. money for what. Deut 14:26
they did b. on Baalim. 2 Chr 24:7
thou shalt have occasion to b. out of the king's treasure. Ezra 7:20
no room where to b. my. Luke 12:17
and there will I b. all my fruits. 18
on these we b. more. 1 Cor 12:23
though I b. all my goods to. 13:3

bestowed
Gehazi b. them in house. 2 Ki 5:24
Lord b. on Solomon. 1 Chr 29:25
all the Lord hath b. on us. Isa 63:7
reap that whereon ye b. John 4:38
greet Mary, who b. much. Rom 16:6
his grace b. on me not. 1 Cor 15:10
for the gift b. on us. 2 Cor 1:11
do you to wit of the grace b. 8:1
lest I have b. on you. Gal 4:11
love Father b. on us. 1 John 3:1

Bethabara
these things done in B. John 1:28

Bethany
Jesus went into B. Mat 21:17; 26:6
Mark 11:1, 11; 14:3; Luke 19:29
John 12:1
when come from B. Mark 11:12
out as far as to B. Luke 24:50
sick, named Lazarus of B. John 11:1

Beth-aven
Ai, which is beside B. Josh 7:2
battle passed over to B. 1 Sam 14:23
Gilgal, nor go ye up to B. Hos 4:15
cry aloud at B. after thee. 5:8
because of the calves of B. 10:5

Beth-diblathaim
judgement is come upon B. Jer 48:22

Beth-el
the place B. Gen 28:19; 35:15
I am God of B. where thou. 31:13
go up to B. 35:1, 3
so Jacob came to B. 6
Joseph goeth from B. Josh 16:2
Joseph went up against B. Judg 1:22
between Ramah and B. 4:5
is on the north side of B. 21:19
from year to year to B. 1 Sam 7:16
men going up to God to B. 10:3
were with Saul in mount B. 13:2
them which were in B. 30:27
the one calf in B. 1 Ki 12:29, 33
a man of God to B. 13:1
against the altar in B. 4, 32
dwelt an old prophet in B. 13:11
Lord hath sent me to B. 2 Ki 2:2
went up from thence unto B. 23
not from the calves in B. 10:29
priests came and dwelt in B. 17:28
and carried the ashes to B. 23:4
the altar at B. Josiah brake. 15
against the altar of B. 17
all that he had done in B. 19
men of B. Ezra 2:28; Neh 7:32
Israel was ashamed of B. Jer 48:13
so shall B. do to you. Hos 10:15
he found him in B. there he. 12:4
visit the altars of B. Amos 3:14
come to B. and transgress. 4:4
seek not B. for B. shall come. 5:5
be none to quench it in B. 6
not again any more at B. 7:13

Beth-elite
Hiel the B. did build. 1 Ki 16:34

Bether
on the mountains of B. S of S 2:17

Bethesda
pool called in Hebrew B. John 5:2

Beth-ezel
in the mourning of B. Mi 1:11

Beth-gamul
judgement is come upon B. Jer 48:23

Beth-haccerem
set up a sign of fire in B. Jer 6:1

Beth-horon
going down to B. the. Josh 10:11
gave Levites B. 21:22; 1 Chr 6:68
company turned to B. 1 Sam 13:18
Solomon built B. 1 Ki 9:17
2 Chr 8:5
daughter Sherah built B. 1 Chr 7:24

bethink
if they shall b. in the land whither were. 1 Ki 8:47; 2 Chr 6:37

Bethlehem
Rachel died in way to B. Gen 35:19; 48:7
Idalah and B. cities of. Josh 19:15
after him Ibzan of B. Judg 12:8
went till they came to B. Ruth 1:19
Boaz came from B. 2:4
be famous in B. 4:11
Samuel came to B. 1 Sam 16:4
asked leave to run to B. 20:6, 28
would give me water of the well of B. 2 Sam 23:15; 1 Chr 11:17
Salma father of B. 1 Chr 2:51, 54
first-born of Ephratah, of B. 4:4
Rehoboam built B. 2 Chr 11:6
children of B. Ezra 2:21; Neh 7:26
dwelt in habitation by B. Jer 41:17
Jesus was born in B. Mat 2:1, 5
B. in land of Judah, art not. 6
slew children in B. 16
went up from Galilee to B. Luke 2:4
let us now go to B. and see. 15
Christ cometh out of B. John 7:42

Beth-lehem-ephratah
thou B.-Ephratah, though. Mi 5:2

Beth-lehemite
Jesse the B. 1 Sam 16:1, 18; 17:58
Elhanan the B. slew. 2 Sam 21:19

Beth-lehem-judah
a Levite of B. went. Judg 17:7, 8, 9
Levite took concubine out of B. 19:1
passing from B. I went to B. 18
Elimelech of B. went. Ruth 1:1
son of Ephrathite of B. 1 Sam 17:12

Beth-peor
in valley over-against B. Deut 3:29
Moses spake over-against B. 4:46
buried Moses over-against B. 34:6

Bethphage
come to B. Mat 21:1; Mark 11:1
Luke 19:29

Bethsaida
woe unto B. Mat 11:21; Luke 10:13
disciples to go to B. Mark 6:45
cometh to B. they bring blind. 8:22
he went into a desert place belonging to B. Luke 9:10
Philip was of B. John 1:44; 12:21

Beth-shan
fastened body to wall of B. 1 Sam 31:10

Beth-shemesh
border of Judah went to B. Josh 15:10
Issachar's coast reacheth B. 19:22
Beth-anath and B. cities of. 38
Judah gave to Levites B. 21:16
inhabitants of B. Judg 1:33
goeth up by way of B. 1 Sam 6:9
kine took straight way to B. 12
he smote the men of B. 19
son of Dekar was in B. 1 Ki 4:9
looked one another in the face at B. 2 Ki 14:11; 2 Chr 25:21
Philistines had taken B. 2 Chr 28:18
break the images of B. Jer 43:13

Bethuel
Milcah bare to Nahor, B. Gen 22:22
B. begat Rebekah. 23; 24:15; 25:20
I am the daughter of B. 24:24, 47
go to the house of B. 28:2

betimes
[1] Early, Gen 26:31. [2] Seasonably, in due and proper time, Pr 13:24. [3] Diligently, Job 8:5.
rose up b. and. Gen 26:31
God sent by messengers rising b. 2 Chr 36:15
thou wouldest seek God b. Job 8:5
as wild asses go they, rising b. 24:5
loveth, chasteneth him b. Pr 13:24

betray
if ye be come to b. me. 1 Chr 12:17
and shall b. one another. Mat 24:10
he sought opportunity to b. him. 26:16; Mark 14:11; Luke 22:
one of you shall b. me. Mat 26:2
Mark 14:18; John 13:2
he is at hand and doth b. Mat 26:4
brother shall b. brother. Mark 13:1
Jesus knew who should b. him. John 6:64; 13:1
put into heart of Judas to b. 13:

betrayed
Judas who b. him. Mat 10:
Mark 3:1
Son of man b. into hands of men. Mat 17:22; 20:18; 26:2, 4
Mark 14:4
woe to man by whom Son of man b. Mat 26:24; Mark 14:2
Luke 22:2
he that b. Mat 26:48; Mark 14:4
I have sinned, in that I b. Mat 27:
and ye shall be b. Luke 21:1
Judas which b. him. John 18
night he was b. he took. 1 Cor 11:

betrayers
of whom ye have been b. Acts 7:

betrayest, -eth
let us go, lo, he that b. Mark 14:
the hand of him that b. Luke 22:
b. thou the Son of man with?
which is he that b.? John 21:

betroth
(In Bible times a betrothal u considered as binding as a marria and there were formal ceremon to celebrate it)
shall b. a wife, another Deut 28:
I will b. thee to me for. Hos 2
b. thee to me in faithfulness.

betrothed
please not master who *b.* *Ex* 21:8*
man entice a maid not *b.* 22:16
Deut 22:28
lieth with a woman *b.* *Lev* 19:20
who hath *b.* a wife, and. *Deut* 20:7
if a man find a virgin *b.* and. 22:23
b. damsel cried there was none. 27

better
[1] *More valuable, or preferable,* Eccl. 9:4, 16, 18. [2] *More acceptable,* 1 Sam 15:22. [3] *More able,* Dan 1:20. [4] *More advantageous,* Phil 1:23. [5] *More holy,* *1 Cor* 8:8. [6] *More safe,* Ps 118:8. [7] *More comfortable,* Pr 15:16, 17. [8] *More precious,* Pr 8:11.
b. I give her to thee. *Gen* 29:19
b. for us to have served. *Ex* 14:12
were it not *b.* for us to ? *Num* 14:3
gleanings of Ephraim *b.* *Judg* 8:2
nor art thou any thing *b.* 11:25
am not I *b.* to thee ? *1 Sam* 1:8
nothing *b.* than to go to. 27:1
name of king Solomon *b.* *1 Ki* 1:47
fell upon two men *b.* than he. 2:32
Elijah said, I am not *b.* than. 19:4
I will give thee for it a *b.* 21:2
rivers of Damascus *b.* *2 Ki* 5:12
hast slain brethren *b.* *2 Chr* 21:13
shall please the Lord *b.* *Ps* 69:31
nothing *b.* for a man than. *Eccl* 2:24
nothing *b.* than to rejoice in. 3:22
b. is he than both they, which. 4:3
two are *b.* than one. 9
what is man the *b.* ? 6:11
that the former days were *b.* 7:10
bite, and a babbler is no *b.* 10:11*
give a name *b.* than of. *Isa* 56:5
they that be slain are *b.* *Lam* 4:9
will settle you, and do *b.* *Ezek* 36:11
n all matters he found *b.* *Dan* 1:20
hen was it *b.* than now. *Hos* 2:7
e they *b.* than these ? *Amos* 6:2
rt thou *b.* than populous ? *Nah* 3:8
he fowls of the air, are you not much *b.* ? *Mat* 6:26; *Luke* 12:24
ow much is a man *b.* ? *Mat* 12:12
were *b.* that a millstone were about. *Mat* 18:6; *Mark* 9:42; *Luke* 17:2
re we *b.* than they ? no. *Rom* 3:9
iveth her not, doth *b.* *1 Cor* 7:38
or neither if we eat are we *b.* 8:8
. for me to die, than to. 9:15
ou come together not for *b.* 11:17
et each esteem other *b.* *Phil* 2:3
eing made so much *b.* *Heb* 1:4
eloved, we are persuaded *b.* 6:9
ontradiction less is blessed of *b.* 7:7
ringing in of a *b.* hope did. 19
esus was made a surety of a *b.* 22
e is the Mediator of a *b.* covenant, established on *b.* promises. 8:6
eavenly things with *b.* 9:23
heaven a *b.* and enduring. 10:34
ey desire a *b.* country, an. 11:16
ey might obtain a *b.* 35
od having provided *b.* thing. 40
eaketh *b.* things than Abel. 12:24
for them not to have. *2 Pet* 2:21

better *is*
is little with fear of. *Pr* 15:16
is a dinner of herbs where. 17
is a little with righteousness. 16:8
w much *b.* *is* it to get wisdom. 16
is a dry morsel and. 17:1
is the poor. 19:1; 28:6
is a neighbour that is near. 27:10
is an handful with. *Eccl* 4:6
is a poor wise child than. 13
is the sight of the eyes than. 6:9
is the end of a thing than. 7:8
is thy love than wine. *S of S* 4:10

is **better,** or *is it* **better**
ether *is* *b.* for you. *Judg* 9:2
it *b.* to be a priest to one ? 18:19
daughter *is* *b.* to. *Ruth* 4:15
ey *is* *b.* than sacrifice. *1 Sam* 15:22
en to a neighbour that *is* *b.* 28
unsel of Hushai *is* *b.* *2 Sam* 17:14
ate to another that *is* *b.* *Esth* 1:19
hteous man hath *is* *b.* *Ps* 37:16

loving-kindness *is* *b.* than. *Ps* 63:3
a day in thy courts *is* *b.* than. 84:10
the law of thy mouth *is* *b.* 119:72
merchandise of wisdom *is* *b.* *Pr* 3:14
wisdom is *b.* than rubies. 8:11
my fruit *is* *b.* than gold. 19
is *b.* than he that honoureth. 12:9
slow to anger *is* *b.* than. 16:32
and a poor man *is* *b.* than a. 19:22
open rebuke *is* *b.* than secret. 27:5
untimely birth *is* *b.* than. *Eccl* 6:3
a good name *is* *b.* than precious. 7:1
sorrow *is* *b.* than laughter, by sadness of countenance heart *is* *b.* 3
patient in spirit *is* *b.* than proud. 8
living dog *is* *b.* than a dead lion. 9:4
wisdom *is* *b.* than strength. 16
wisdom *is* *b.* than weapons. 18
thy love *is* *b.* than wine. *S of S* 1:2
he saith, the old *is* *b.* *Luke* 5:39
to be with Christ, *is* far *b.* *Phil* 1:23

it is **better,** or **better** *it is*
it is *b.* I give her to thee. *Gen* 29:19
it is *b.* thou succour us. *2 Sam* 18:3
it is *b.* to trust in the Lord than. *Ps* 118:8, 9
b. *it is* to be of humble. *Pr* 16:19
it is *b.* to dwell in a. 21:9; 25:24
it is *b.* to dwell in wilderness. 21:19
b. *it is* that it be said to thee. 25:7
b. *it is* that thou shouldest. *Eccl* 5:5
it is *b.* to go to house of. 7:2
it is *b.* to hear rebuke of wise. 5
it is *b.* for me to die. *Jonah* 4:3, 8
it is *b.* to enter into life halt or. *Mat* 18:8, 9; *Mark* 9:43, 45, 47
for *it is* *b.* to marry than. *1 Cor* 7:9
it is *b.* that ye suffer for. *1 Pet* 3:17

bettered
was nothing *b.* but. *Mark* 5:26

between
I will put enmity *b.* thy. *Gen* 3:15
the covenant *b.* God and. 9:16
a burning lamp passeth *b.* 15:17
nor a lawgiver from *b.* his. 49:10
a division *b.* my people. *Ex* 8:23
and a memorial *b.* thine eyes. 13:9, 16; *Deut* 6:8; 11:18
they come, and I judge *b.* *Ex* 18:16
vail shall divide *b.* holy. 26:33
while flesh was *b.* *Num* 11:33
b. blood and blood, *b.* plea, *b.* *Deut* 17:8
he shall dwell *b.* his shoulders. 33:12
Deborah dwelt *b.* Ramah. *Judg* 4:5
there was peace *b.* *1 Sam* 7:14
b. good and evil. *2 Sam* 19:35
1 Ki 3:9
how long halt ye *b.* two ? *1 Ki* 18:21
the lot parteth *b.* *Pr* 18:18
passed *b.* parts of. *Jer* 34:18, 19
b. cattle and cattle, *b.* rams. *Ezek* 34:17
her adulteries from *b.* *Hos* 2:2
the priests weep *b.* *Joel* 2:17
break brotherhood *b.* *Zech* 11:14
slew *b.* the temple and. *Mat* 23:35
b. John's disciples and. *John* 3:25
no difference *b.* Jew and. *Rom* 10:12
difference *b.* wife and a. *1 Cor* 7:34
one Mediator *b.* God. *1 Tim* 2:5

betwixt
the cloud that cometh *b.* *Job* 36:32*
lie all night *b.* my. *S of S* 1:13
I am in a strait *b.* two. *Phil* 1:23

Beulah
call thy land *B.* for Lord. *Isa* 62:4

bewail
b. the burning the Lord. *Lev* 10:6
and *b.* her father and. *Deut* 21:13
I may go and *b.* *Judg* 11:37, 38
I will *b.* with weeping of. *Isa* 16:9
that I shall *b.* many. *2 Cor* 12:21
shall *b.* her. *Rev* 18:9

bewailed, -eth
daughter of Zion that *b.* *Jer* 4:31*
and all wept and *b.* her. *Luke* 8:52
of women also who *b.* 23:27

beware
(*To take care: to be on one's guard*)
b. that thou bring not my. *Gen* 24:6
b. of him and obey. *Ex* 23:21
b. lest thou forget. *Deut* 6:12; 8:11
b. there be not a wicked. 15:9
b. I pray thee. *Judg* 13:4, 13
b. that none touch. *2 Sam* 18:12
b. that thou pass not. *2 Ki* 6:9
b. lest he take thee away. *Job* 36:18
scorner, and simple *b.* *Pr* 19:25*
b. lest Hezekiah persuade. *Isa* 36:18
b. of false prophets. *Mat* 7:15
b. of men. 10:17
b. of the leaven of the. 16:6, 11
Mark 8:15; *Luke* 12:1
b. of the scribes. *Mark* 12:38
Luke 20:46
take heed and *b.* *Luke* 12:15*
b. lest that come which. *Acts* 13:40
b. of dogs, *b.* of evil workers, *b.* of. *Phil* 3:2
b. lest any man spoil. *Col* 2:8
b. lest ye also. *2 Pet* 3:17

bewitched
Simon *b.* the people. *Acts* 8:9*, 11
Galatians, who hath *b.* ? *Gal* 3:1

bewray
(*American Revision,* betray)
hide the outcasts, *b.* not. *Isa* 16:3

bewrayeth
of his right hand *b.* *Pr* 27:16*
heareth cursing, and *b.* it. 29:24*
of them, speech *b.* thee. *Mat* 26:73*

beyond
Balaam said, I cannot go *b.* word. *Num* 22:18; 24:13
nor is it *b.* the sea. *Deut* 30:13
arrows *b.* thee. *1 Sam* 20:22; 36:37
b. the river. *2 Sam* 10:16; *1 Ki* 14:15
1 Chr 19:16; *Ezra* 4:17, 20
6:6, 8; 7:21, 25; *Neh* 2:7, 9
Isa 7:20; 18:1; *Zeph* 3:10
b. the sea. *2 Chr* 20:2; *Jer* 25:22
amazed *b.* measure. *Mark* 6:51
7:37
and *b.* their power. *2 Cor* 8:3
for we stretch not *b.* 10:14
b. measure I persecuted. *Gal* 1:13
that no man go *b.* and. *1 Thes* 4:6

beyond *Jordan, see* **Jordan**

Bezaleel
I have called by name *B.* of tribe of. *Ex* 31:2; 35:30; *1 Chr* 2:20
then wrought *B.* *Ex* 36:1
B. made the ark. 37:1
B. made all Lord commanded. 38:22
the brazen altar *B.* had. *2 Chr* 1:5
sons of Pahath-moab, *B.* *Ezra* 10:30

Bezek
slew in *B.* 10,000 men. *Judg* 1:4, 5
numbered Israel in *B.* *1 Sam* 11:8

Bichri
Sheba the son of *B.* *2 Sam* 20:1
man followed Sheba son of *B.* 2
now shall the son of *B.* do. 6
cut off head of Sheba son of *B.* 22

bid
[1] *To invite,* Mat 22:9; Luke 14:12. [2] *To command,* Mat 14:28. [3] *To wish,* 2 John 10.
the day I *b.* you shout. *Josh* 6:10
b. the servant pass on. *1 Sam* 9:27
how long ere *b.* people. *2 Sam* 2:26
not riding except I *b.* *2 Ki* 4:24
if the prophet had *b.* thee do. 5:13
all that thou shalt *b.* us. 10:5
the preaching that I *b.* *Jonah* 3:2
for the Lord hath *b.* *Zeph* 1:7
b. me come to thee. *Mat* 14:28
as many as ye shall find *b.* 22:9
what they *b.* you observe. 23:3
let me first *b.* them. *Luke* 9:61
b. her therefore that she. 10:40
lest they also *b.* thee again. 14:12
if any that believe not *b.* *1 Cor* 10:27
receive him not, nor *b.* *2 John* 10*

bidden
they eat that be *b.* *1 Sam* 9:13
curse, for Lord hath *b.* *2 Sam* 16:11
Joseph did as angel had *b.* *Mat* 1:24
sent to call them that were *b.* 22:3
tell them *b.* I have prepared my. 4
they who were *b.* were not. 8

the Pharisee who had *b*. *Luke* 7:39
a parable to those who were *b*. 14:7
when thou art *b*. lest a more honourable man be *b*. 8
when thou art *b*. go and sit in. 10
none of those *b*. shall taste. 24

biddeth, bidding

goeth at thy *b*. *1 Sam* 22:14
he that *b*. him God. *2 John* 11*

bide

if they *b*. not in unbelief. *Rom* 11:23

Bidkar

Jehu said to *B*. his. *2 Ki* 9:25

bier

David followed the *b*. *2 Sam* 3:31
came and touched the *b*. *Luke* 7:14

Bigthan

B. sought to lay hand on. *Esth* 2:21
that Mordecai had told *B*. 6:2

Bildad

B. the Shuhite. *Job* 2:11; 8:1; 18:1; 25:1; 42:9

Bilhah

Laban gave to Rachel *B*. *Gen* 29:29
behold my maid *B*. go in. 30:3, 4
B. conceived. 5, 7
Reuben lay with *B*. 35:22
sons of *B*. 35:25; 37:2; 46:25; *1 Chr* 7:13
his sons dwelt at *B*. *1 Chr* 4:29

bill

take thy *b*. and write 50. *Luke* 16:6*
take thy *b*. 7*
see **divorce**

billows

thy *b*. gone over me. *Ps* 42:7; *Jonah* 2:3

bind

[1] *To tie up, or fasten together*, Gen 37:7; Deut 14:25. [2] *To keep fast, or sure*, Pr 3:3; 6:21. [3] *To engage by vow, or promise*, Num 30:2. [4] *To restrain*, Job 28:11.

they shall *b*. the breast-. *Ex* 28:28
swear an oath to *b*. his. *Num*. 30:2
shalt *b*. them for a sign. *Deut* 6:8
shalt *b*. up the money. 14:25
thou shalt *b*. this line. *Josh* 2:18
to *b*. Samson are we. *Judg* 15:10
we are come down to *b*. thee. 12
no, but we will *b*. thee fast. 13
that we may *b*. Samson. 16:5
I will *b*. it as a crown. *Job* 31:36
canst *b*. sweet influences? 38:31
canst thou *b*. the unicorn? 39:10
hide them, and *b*. their. 40:13
wilt thou *b*. Leviathan? 41:5
to *b*. his princes at his. *Ps* 105:22
b. the sacrifice with cords. 118:27
to *b*. their kings with. 149:8
b. them about thy neck. *Pr* 3:3
b. them continually. 6:21
b. them on thy fingers, write. 7:3
b. up the testimony. *Isa* 8:16
and *b*. them on thee as a. 49:18
he hath sent me to *b*. up the. 61:7
I will *b*. up what was. *Ezek* 34:16
commanded most mighty men to *b*. *Dan* 3:20
smitten us, and will *b*. us. *Hos* 6:1
when they *b*. themselves. 10:10
b. the chariot to the swift. *Mi* 1:13
first *b*. the strong man, then will. *Mat* 12:29; *Mark* 3:27
b. the tares in bundles. *Mat* 13:30
whatsoever thou shalt *b*. 16:19; 18:18
b. him hand and foot. 22:13
b. heavy burdens. 23:4
no man could *b*. him. *Mark* 5:3
authority to *b*. all that. *Acts* 9:14
gird thyself, *b*. on thy sandals. 12:8
so shall the Jews *b*. 21:11

bindeth

maketh sore and *b*. up. *Job* 5:18
b. up the waters in his. 26:8
he *b*. the floods. 28:11
it *b*. me about as the collar. 30:18
they cry not when he *b*. them. 36:13
nor he that *b*. sheaves. *Ps* 129:7
the broken in heart, *b*. up. *Ps* 147:3
as he that *b*. a stone. *Pr* 26:8
the Lord *b*. up the breach. *Isa* 30:26

binding

we were *b*. sheaves in. *Gen* 37:7
b. his foal to the vine. 49:11
every *b*. oath. *Num* 30:13
b. and delivering into. *Acts* 22:4

bird

(*A fowl, small or large*)

every *b*. of every sort. *Gen* 7:14
cleanse the house with living *b*. *Lev* 14:52
play with him as with a *b*.? *Job* 41:5
flee as a *b*. to your. *Ps* 11:1
our soul is escaped as a *b*. 124:7
net spread in sight of *b*. *Pr* 1:17
and as a *b*. from the hand. 6:5
as a *b*. hasteth to the snare. 7:23
as the *b*. by wandering. 26:2*
as a *b*. that wandereth from. 27:8
b. of the air shall tell. *Eccl* 10:20
rise up at the voice of the *b*. 12:4
as a wandering *b*. *Isa* 16:2
calling a ravenous *b*. 46:11
heritage is as speckled *b*. *Jer* 12:9
chased me like a *b*. *Lam* 3:52
shall fly away like a *b*. *Hos* 9:11
they shall tremble as a *b*. 11:11
can a *b*. fall where no gin? *Amos* 3:5
of unclean and hateful *b*. *Rev* 18:2

birds

the *b*. divided he not. *Gen* 15:10
the *b*. did eat them. 40:17
the *b*. shall eat thy flesh. 19
command to take two *b*. *Lev* 14:4
of all clean *b*. eat. *Deut* 14:11
suffered not *b*. to rest. *2 Sam* 21:10
where *b*. make their nests. *Ps* 104:17
as *b*. that are caught. *Eccl* 9:12
time of singing of *b*. is. *S of S* 2:12
as *b*. flying, so will Lord. *Isa* 31:5
all the *b*. of the heaven. *Jer* 4:25
as a cage full of *b*. so are. 5:27
beasts are consumed and *b*. 12:4
the *b*. round about are against. 9
give thee to ravenous *b*. *Ezek* 39:4
nails were grown like *b*. *Dan* 4:33
b. of the air. *Mat* 8:20; *Luke* 9:58
b. lodge in the branches. *Mat* 13:32
into an image like to *b*. *Rom* 1:23
of fishes, another of *b*. *1 Cor* 15:39
every kind of beasts and *b*. *Jas* 3:7

birth

Is [1] *Natural*, Ex 28:10. [2] *Supernatural, as was the birth of Christ*, Mat 1:18; Luke 1:14. [3] *Figurative*, 2 Ki 19:3; Tit 3:5; Gal 4:19.

children come to *b*. *2 Ki* 19:3; *Isa* 37:3
as an hidden untimely *b*. *Job* 3:16
pass like the untimely *b*. *Ps* 58:8
an untimely *b*. is better. *Eccl* 6:3
day of death better than day of *b*. 7:1
shall I bring to the *b*.? *Isa* 66:9
thy *b*. and nativity. *Ezek* 16:3
glory of Ephraim fly from *b*. *Hos* 9:11
the *b*. of Jesus Christ. *Mat* 1:18
shall rejoice at his *b*. *Luke* 1:14
a man blind from his *b*. *John* 9:1
of whom I travail in *b*. *Gal* 4:19
cried, travailing in *b*. *Rev* 12:2

birthday

third day, Pharaoh's *b*. *Gen* 40:20
Herod's *b*. *Mat* 14:6; *Mark* 6:21

birthright

sell me this day thy *b*. *Gen* 25:31
he sware, and sold his *b*. 33
thus Esau despised *b*. 34
took my *b*., now my blessing. 27:36
first-born according to *b*. 43:33
Reuben's *b*. given to sons. *1 Chr* 5:1
for one morsel sold *b*. *Heb* 12:16

bishop, -s

saints at Philippi, with *b*. *Phil*. 1:1
if man desire office of *b*. *1 Tim* 3:1
a *b*. must be blameless. 2; *Tit* 1:7
returned to *b*. of your souls. *1 Pet* 2:25

bishopric

his *b*. let another take. *Acts* 1:20*

bit, -s

mouth must be held in with *b*. *Ps* 32:9
put *b*. in horses' mouths. *Jas* 3:3

bit

fiery serpents, *b*. people. *Num* 21:6
and a serpent *b*. him. *Amos* 5:19

bite

serpent shall *b*. him. *Eccl* 10:8
the serpent will *b*. without. 11
serpents, they shall *b*. you. *Jer* 8:17
command serpent, and he shall *b*. *Amos* 9:3
prophets that *b*. with teeth. *Mi* 3:5
they rise up that shall *b*.? *Hab* 2:7
if ye *b*. and devour one. *Gal* 5:15

biteth

Dan an adder, that *b*. *Gen* 49:17
at the last it *b*. like. *Pr* 23:32

Bithynia

assayed to go into *B*. *Acts* 16:7
scattered throughout *B*. *1 Pet* 1:1

bitten

every one that is *b*. *Num* 21:8
if a serpent had *b*. any man. 9

bitter

Esau cried with a *b*. cry. *Gen* 27:34
made their lives *b*. *Ex* 1:14
with *b*. herbs eat it. 12:8; *Num* 9:11
waters of Marah were *b*. *Ex* 15:23
devoured with *b*. destruction. *Deut* 32:24
grapes of gall, their clusters are *b*. 32
saw affliction of Israel it was *b*. *2 Ki* 14:26
cried with a *b*. cry. *Esth* 4:1
is life given to *b*. in soul? *Job* 3:20
thou writest *b*. things against. 13:26
even to-day is my complaint *b*. 23:2*
their arrows, *b*. words. *Ps* 64:3
end is *b*. as wormwood. *Pr* 5:4
hungry soul *b*. thing is sweet. 27:7
I find more *b*. than death. *Eccl* 7:26
that put *b*. for sweet, sweet for *b*. *Isa* 5:20
strong drink shall be *b*. to. 24:9
it is an evil thing and *b*. *Jer* 2:19
thy wickedness, because it is *b*. 4:18
most *b*. lamentation as for a. 6:26
voice heard in Ramah, *b*. 31:15
weep with *b*. wailing. *Ezek* 27:31
end thereof, as a *b*. day. *Amos* 8:10
Chaldeans, that *b*. and. *Hab* 1:6
love your wives, be not *b*. *Col* 3:19
if ye have *b*. envying. *Jas* 3:14
of waters because made *b*. *Rev* 8:11
eat it, it shall make thy belly *b*. 10:9
soon as I had eaten, belly was *b*. 10

bitter *water*

the *b*. *water* that causeth. *Num* 5:18
send sweet *water* and *b*.? *Jas* 3:11

bitterly

curse *b*. the inhabitants. *Judg* 5:23
Almighty hath dealt *b*. *Ruth* 1:20
look from me, I will weep *b*. *Isa* 22:4
of peace shall weep *b*. 33:7
pilots of Tyre shall cry *b*. *Ezek* 27:30
Ephraim provoked him *b*. *Hos* 12:14
mighty man shall cry *b*. *Zeph* 1:14
Peter wept *b*. *Mat* 26:75; *Luke* 22:62

bittern

(*Revised Version*, porcupine)

a possession for the *b*. *Isa* 14:23; 34:11
the *b*. shall lodge in the. *Zeph* 2:14

bitterness

Hannah was in *b*. of. *1 Sam* 1:10
surely the *b*. of death is past. 15:32
the sword will be *b*. *2 Sam* 2:2[illegible]
I will complain in *b*. *Job* 7:1[illegible]
but filleth me with *b*. 9:1[illegible]
I will speak in *b*. of my soul. 10:[illegible]
another dieth in the *b*. of. 21:2[illegible]
heart knoweth his own *b*. *Pr* 14:1[illegible]
a foolish son is *b*. 17:2[illegible]
go softly all my years in *b*. *Isa* 38:1[illegible]
behold, for peace I had great *b*. 1[illegible]
are afflicted, she is in *b*. *Lam* 1:[illegible]

he hath filled me with *b*. *Lam* 3:15
took me, I went in *b*. *Ezek* 3:14
with *b*. sigh before their eyes. 21:6
shall weep for thee with *b*. 27:31
be in *b*. as one that is in *b*. *Zech* 12:10
thou art in the gall of *b*. *Acts* 8:23
whose mouth is full of *b*. *Rom* 3:14
let all *b*. be put away. *Eph* 4:31
any root of *b*. springing. *Heb* 12:15

black

there is no *b*. hair in it. *Lev* 13:31
and there is *b*. hair grown. 37
the heaven was *b*. *1 Ki* 18:45
my skin is *b*. upon me. *Job* 30:30
in the evening, in the *b*. *Pr* 7:9*
I am *b*. but comely, O. *S of S* 1:5*
look not upon me, I am *b*. 6*
his locks are bushy and *b*. 5:11
the heavens shall be *b*. *Jer* 4:28
my people am I hurt, I am *b*. 8:21
gates thereof languish, are *b*. 14:2
skin was *b*. like an oven. *Lam* 5:10
in second chariot *b*. *Zech* 6:2
b. horses go forth into north. 6
make one hair white or *b*. *Mat* 5:36
I beheld, lo a *b*. horse. *Rev* 6:5
sun became *b*. as sackcloth. 12

blacker

visage is *b*. than a coal. *Lam* 4:8

blackish

b. by reason of the ice. *Job* 6:16

blackness

let *b*. of the day terrify it. *Job* 3:5
I clothe heavens with *b*. *Isa* 50:3
all faces gather *b*. *Joel* 2:6* *Nah* 2:10
are not come to *b*. *Heb* 12:18
to whom is reserved *b*. of. *Jude* 13

blade

also went in after the *b*. *Judg* 3:22
arm fall from shoulder-*b*. *Job* 31:22
b. was sprung up. *Mat* 13:26 *Mark* 4:28

blains

a boil breaking forth with *b*. *Ex* 9:9, 10

blame

let me bear *b*. *Gen* 43:9; 44:32
no man should *b*. us. *2 Cor* 8:20
holy and without *b*. *Eph* 1:4*

blamed

the ministry be not *b*. *2 Cor* 6:3
because he was to be *b*. *Gal* 2:11*

blameless

ye shall be *b*. *Gen* 44:10
we will be *b*. of this. *Josh* 2:17
now shall I be more *b*. *Judg* 15:3
profane sabbath, are *b*. *Mat* 12:5
ordinances of the Lord *b*. *Luke* 1:6
ye may be *b*. in the day. *1 Cor* 1:8
b. and harmless. *Phil* 2:15
touching righteousness of law *b*. 3:6
spirit, soul, and body, *b*. *1 Thes* 5:23
bishop must be *b*. *1 Tim* 3:2 *Tit* 1:7
office of a deacon, found *b*. *1 Tim* 3:10
in charge, that they may be *b*. 5:7
if any be *b*. the husband of. *Tit* 1:6
without spot and *b*. *2 Pet* 3:14

blaspheme

(*In old Jewish law, to revile or curse God, or the king, who was God's representative. It means intentional indignity offered to God or sacred things*)

enemies of Lord to *b*. *2 Sam* 12:14
b. God and the king. *1 Ki* 21:10, 13
shall the enemy *b*. thy? *Ps* 74:10
wherewith they shall *b*. *Mark* 3:28
that shall *b*. against Holy Ghost. 29
I compelled them to *b*. *Acts* 26:11
may learn not to *b*. *1 Tim* 1:20
do not they *b*. that worthy? *Jas* 2:7
to *b*. his name and. *Rev* 13:6

blasphemed

Israelitish woman's son *b*. *Lev* 24:11
servants of king of Assyria have *b*. me. *2 Ki* 19:6, 22; *Isa* 37:6, 23
foolish have *b*. thy name. *Ps* 74:18
my name continually is *b*. *Isa* 52:5
have burnt incense, and *b*. 65:7
your fathers have *b*. me. *Ezek* 20:27
opposed themselves and *b*. *Acts* 18:6
the name of God is *b*. *Rom* 2:24
God and doctrine be not *b*. *1 Tim* 6:1
that word of God be not *b*. *Tit* 2:5
scorched with heat, and *b*. *Rev* 16:9
b. the God of heaven because. 11
men *b*. God because of plague. 21

blasphemer, -s

nor *b*. of your goddess. *Acts* 19:37
who was before a *b*. *1 Tim* 1:13
last days men shall be *b*. *2 Tim* 3:2

blasphemest, -eth

whoso *b*. the Lord, be. *Lev* 24:16
the voice of him that *b*. *Ps* 44:16
scribes said, this man *b*. *Mat* 9:3
Father sanctified, thou *b*. *John* 10:36

blasphemies

I have heard all thy *b*. *Ezek* 35:12
out of heart proceed *b*. *Mat* 15:19
doth this man speak *b*.? *Mark* 2:7
and *b*. wherewith they shall. 3:28
who speaketh *b*.? *Luke* 5:21
given him speaking *b*. *Rev* 13:5

blaspheming

contradicting and *b*. *Acts* 13:45

blasphemous

heard him speak *b*. words. *Acts* 6:11
ceaseth not to speak *b*. words. 13

blasphemously

many things *b*. spake. *Luke* 22:65

blasphemy

this day of *b*. *2 Ki* 19:3; *Isa* 37:3
all manner of *b*. forgiven, *b*. against Holy Ghost not be. *Mat* 12:31
he hath spoken *b*., now ye have heard his *b*. 26:65; *Mark* 14:64
out of heart proceed *b*. *Mark* 7:22
stone thee not, but for *b*. *John* 10:33
ye also put off malice, *b*. *Col* 3:8
I know the *b*. of them that. *Rev* 2:9
upon his heads the name of *b*. 13:1
and he opened his mouth in *b*. 6

blast

[1] *A violent gust of wind*, Job 4:9. [2] *To wither or blight*, Gen 41:6.

with *b*. of thy nostrils. *Ex* 15:8
when they make a long *b*. *Josh* 6:5
at rebuke of Lord, at *b*. of breath of. *2 Sam* 22:16; *Ps* 18:15
a *b*. on Sennacherib. *2 Ki* 19:7* *Isa* 37:7*
by *b*. of God they perish. *Job* 4:9*
when the *b*. of the terrible. *Isa* 25:4

blasted

seven thin ears *b*. with the east wind. *Gen* 41:6, 23, 27
as corn *b*. *2 Ki* 19:26; *Isa* 37:27

blasting

Lord shall smite with *b*. *Deut* 28:22
if there be *b*. *1 Ki* 8:37; *2 Chr* 6:28
have smitten you with *b*. *Amos* 4:9
smote you with *b*. *Hag* 2:17

Blastus

having made *B*. friend. *Acts* 12:20

blaze

he began to *b*. abroad. *Mark* 1:45*

bleating, -s

abodest to hear *b*. of. *Judg* 5:16
what meaneth this *b*.? *1 Sam* 15:14

blemish

lamb without *b*. *Ex* 12:5; *Lev* 9:3 14:10; 23:12; *Num* 6:14
two rams without *b*. *Ex* 29:1; *Lev* 5:15, 18 6:6; 9:2; *Ezek* 46:4
male without *b*. *Lev* 1:3, 10; 4:23 22:19
male or female without *b*. 3:1, 6
bullock without *b*. 4:3; *Deut* 17:1 *Ezek* 45:18
bring kid, a female without *b*. *Lev* 4:28
hath *b*. not approach. 21:17, 18, 21, 23
but whatsoever hath a *b*. shall not be acceptable. 22:20; *Deut* 15:21
in offering no *b*. *Lev* 22:21
if a man cause *b*. in neighbour 24:19
as he hath caused a *b*. in a man. 20
a red heifer without *b*. *Num* 19:2
bullock, ram, lambs without *b*. 29:2
no *b*. in Absalom. *2 Sam* 14:25
in whom was no *b*. *Dan* 1:4
holy and without *b*. *Eph* 5:27
as of a lamb without *b*. *1 Pet* 1:19

blemishes

b. in them, they shall. *Lev* 22:25
spots they are and *b*. *2 Pet* 2:13

bless

I. *God blesses*. [1] *By giving riches and prosperity*, Gen 30:27; 39:5. [2] *By giving spiritual and temporal good things*, Ps 29:11; Eph 1:3. [3] *By consecrating or hallowing*, Gen 2:3; Ex 20:11. II. *Men bless God*. [1] *When they praise him for his goodness*, Ps 104:1. [2] *When they thank him for his benefits to them*, Ps 103:1. III. *Men bless other men*. [1] *When they utter a solemn benediction, as a father praying for his son, and naming him heir and successor*, Gen 27:23. [2] *When they pray to God for his blessing on other men*, Num 6:23, 24; 2 Sam 6:18.

bless, *God being agent*

I will *b*. thee. *Gen* 12:2; 26:3, 24
I will *b*. them that bless thee. 12:3
I will *b*. her and give. 17:16
blessing I will *b*. thee. 22:17 *Heb* 6:14
God Almighty *b*. thee, and. *Gen* 28:3
let thee go, except thou *b*. 32:26
b. the lads, and let my name. 48:16
the Almighty who shall *b*. 49:25
come to thee, and *b*. thee. *Ex* 20:24
he shall *b*. thy bread and. 23:25
the Lord *b*. thee. *Num* 6:24
name on Israel, I will *b*. them. 27
saw it pleased the Lord to *b*. 24:1
b. you as he hath. *Deut* 1:11
he will *b*. thee, *b*. the fruit. 7:13
the Lord *b*. thee. 14:29; 23:20 24:19
no poor, for Lord shall *b*. thee. 15:4
the Lord thy God shall *b*. 10
Lord thy God shall *b*. thee. 18; 30:16
the Lord shall *b*. thee. 16:15
look down and *b*. thy people. 26:15
he shall *b*. thee in the land. 28:8
b. all the work of thine hand. 12
b. Lord, his substance. 33:11
the Lord *b*. thee. *Ruth* 2:4 *Jer* 31:23
let it please thee to *b*. the house of thy. *2 Sam* 7:29; *1 Chr* 17:27
O that thou wouldest *b*. *1 Chr* 4:10
thou, Lord, wilt *b*. righteous. *Ps* 5:12
save thy people, *b*. thine. 28:9
the Lord will *b*. his people. 29:11
God, our God, shall *b*. us. 67:1, 6, 7
the Lord will *b*. us, *b*. the house of Israel, *b*. the house of. 115:12
b. them that fear the Lord. 13
Lord shall *b*. thee out of Zion. 128:5
abundantly *b*. her provision. 132:15
Lord *b*. thee out of Zion. 134:3
the Lord of hosts shall *b*. *Isa* 19:25
this day will I *b*. you. *Hag* 2:19
sent him to *b*. you. *Acts* 3:26

bless, *God being the object*

then thou shalt *b*. the. *Deut* 8:10
b. ye the Lord. *Judg* 5:9; *Ps* 103:21 134:1
David said, now *b*. Lord. *1 Chr* 29:20
stand up and *b*. the Lord. *Neh* 9:5
I will *b*. the Lord. *Ps* 16:7
in congregations will I *b*. Lord. 26:12
I will *b*. the Lord at all times. 34:1
thus will I *b*. thee while I live. 63:4
O *b*. our God. 66:8
b. ye God in congregations. 68:26
sing to the Lord, *b*. his name. 96:2
be thankful, *b*. his name. 100:4 103:1
b. the Lord. 103:1, 2, 22; 104:1, 35
b. the Lord, ye his angels. 103:20

b. the Lord, ye his hosts. *Ps* 103:21
b. the Lord all his works. 22
we will *b.* the Lord. 115:18
lift your hands, *b.* the Lord. 134:2
b. the Lord, O Israel, *b.* the Lord, O house of Aaron. 135:19
O, ye that fear the Lord, *b.* the. 20
I will *b.* thy name for ever. 145:1
every day will I *b.* thee. 2
O Lord, thy saints shall *b.* thee. 10
let all flesh *b.* his holy name. 21
therewith *b.* we God. *Jas* 3:9

bless, *man agent* and *object*

my soul may *b.* thee. *Gen* 27:4, 25
b. me, even me my father. 34, 38
them to me, and I will *b.* 48:9
in thee shall Israel *b.* saying. 20
take flocks and begone, *b.* *Ex* 12:32
on this wise *b.* Israel. *Num* 6:23
received commandment to *b.* 23:20
neither curse them, nor *b.* 25
Lord separated Levi to *b.* *Deut* 10:8; 21:5
in his own raiment, and *b.* 24:13
shall stand on Gerizim to *b.* 27:12
heareth words of curse, he *b.* 29:19
commanded they should *b.* *Josh* 8:33
he doth *b.* the sacrifice. *1 Sam* 9:13
David returned to *b.* his household. *2 Sam* 6:20; *1 Chr* 16:43
sent Joram to *b.* David. *2 Sam* 8:10
that ye may *b.* the inheritance. 21:3
came to *b.* David. *1 Ki* 1:47
and to *b.* in his name. *1 Chr* 23:13
they *b.* with their mouths. *Ps* 62:4
let them curse, but *b.* thou. 109:28
we *b.* you in name of the. 129:8
generation that curseth father, and doth not *b.* mother. *Pr* 30:11
shall *b.* himself in God. *Isa* 65:16
nations shall *b.* themselves. *Jer* 4:2
b. them that curse you. *Mat* 5:44 *Luke* 6:28
b. them which persecute you, *b.* and curse not. *Rom* 12:14
being reviled we *b.* *1 Cor* 4:12
else when shalt thou *b.* 14:16

bless

cup of blessing we *b.* *1 Cor* 10:16

blessed, *man agent* and *object*

Melchisedek *b.* Abram, and said *b.* *Gen* 14:19
they *b.* Rebekah, and said. 24:60
Isaac *b.* Jacob and said. 27:23, 27
and *b.* be he that blesseth thee. 29
I have *b.* him, and he shall be *b.* 33
blessing wherewith his father *b.* 41
Isaac called Jacob, *b.* him. 28:1
as he *b.* him he gave. 6; *Heb* 11:20
daughters will call me *b.* *Gen* 30:13*
sons and daughters, and *b.* 31:55
Jacob *b.* Pharaoh. 47:7, 10
he *b.* Joseph. 48:15
Jacob *b.* Manasseh and. 48:20 *Heb* 11:21
Jacob *b.* his sons, every one he *b.* *Gen* 49:28
Moses *b.* them. *Ex* 39:43 *Deut* 33:1
Aaron lifted up hand and *b.* *Lev* 9:22
Moses and Aaron *b.* people. 23
whom thou blessest is *b.* *Num* 22:6
thou hast *b.* them. 23:11; 24:10
b. he that enlargeth Gad. *Deut* 33:20
let Asher be *b.* with children. 24
Joshua *b.* Caleb, and. *Josh* 14:13
Joshua *b.* them. 22:6, 7
therefore Balaam *b.* you still. 24:10
b. above women Jael. *Judg* 5:24
b. be he that did take. *Ruth* 2:19
Eli *b.* Elkanah and. *1 Sam* 2:20
b. be thy advice, and *b.* be. 25:33
Saul said, *b.* be thou my son. 26:25
David *b.* the people. *2 Sam* 6:18 *1 Chr* 16:2
he would not go, but *b.* him. *2 Sam* 13:25
king kissed Barzillai, and *b.* 19:39
king Solomon shall be *b.* *1 Ki* 2:45
Solomon *b.* congregation. 8:14, 55
congregation *b.* Solomon. 66 *2 Chr* 6:3
and Levites *b.* people. *2 Chr* 30:27
people *b.* all that offered. *Neh* 11:2
the ear heard me, it *b.* *Job* 29:11
if his loins have not *b.* me. 31:20
while he lived *b.* his soul. *Ps* 49:18
men *b.* in him, nations call him *b.* 72:17*
b. he that cometh in name of the Lord, we have *b.* you. 118:26
her children call her *b.* *Pr* 31:28
b., O land, when thy king. *Eccl* 10:17*
daughters saw her, and *b.* *S of S* 6:9
incense, as if he *b.* idol. *Isa* 66:3
my mother bare me be *b.* *Jer* 20:14
all nations shall call you *b.* *Mal* 3:12*
b. be the kingdom of. *Mark* 11:10
all generations call me *b.* *Luke* 1:48
Simeon *b.* them, and said. 2:34
more *b.* to give than to. *Acts* 20:35
looking for that *b.* hope. *Tit* 2:13
met Abraham and *b.* him. *Heb* 7:1, 6
the less is *b.* of the better. 7

blessed, *God the agent*

God *b.* them. *Gen* 1:22, 28; 5:2
b. the seventh day. 2:3; *Ex* 20:11
b. Noah and his sons. *Gen* 9:1
in thee all families be *b.* 12:3; 18:18 22:18; 26:4; 28:14; *Acts* 3:25 *Gal* 3:8
I have *b.* Ishmael. *Gen* 17:20
Lord *b.* Abraham. 24:1
he said, come in, *b.* of the. 31
God *b.* Isaac. 25:11; 26:12
thou art the *b.* of the Lord. 26:29
smell of a field Lord hath *b.* 27:27
that the Lord hath *b.* me. 30:27
the Lord hath *b.* thee since. 30
b. Jacob there. 32:29; 35:9; 48:3
that the Lord *b.* Egyptian's. 39:5
for the people are *b.* *Num* 22:12
he hath *b.* and I cannot. 23:20
thy God hath *b.* thee. *Deut* 2:7 12:7; 15:14; 16:10
shalt be *b.* above all people. 7:14
when the Lord hath *b.* 14:24
b. shalt thou be in the city, *b.* 28:3
b. shall be fruit of thy body. 4
b. thy basket. 5
of Joseph he said, *b.* of Lord. 33:13
as the Lord hath *b.* me. *Josh* 17:14
Samson grew, the Lord *b.* *Judg* 13:24
b. be thou of Lord. 17:2; *Ruth* 3:10 *1 Sam* 15:13
b. be he of the Lord. *Ruth* 2:20
b. be thou of the Lord. 3:10
b. be ye. *1 Sam* 23:21; *2 Sam* 2:5
the Lord *b.* Obed-edom. *2 Sam* 6:11 12; *1 Chr* 13:14; 26:5
house of thy servant be *b.* *2 Sam* 7:29
O Lord, and it shall be *b.* *1 Chr* 17:27
the Lord hath *b.* *2 Chr* 31:10
thou hast *b.* the work. *Job* 1:10
Lord *b.* latter end of Job. 42:12
hast made him most *b.* *Ps* 21:6
b. is the nation whose God is. 33:12
such as be *b.* of him. 37:22
lendeth, and his seed is *b.* 26
and he shall be *b.* 41:2
therefore God hath *b.* thee. 45:2
b. is the people that know. 89:15
the upright shall be *b.* 112:2
you are *b.* of the Lord. 115:15
b. are the undefiled. 119:1
b. is every one that feareth. 128:1
thus the man be *b.* that feareth. 4
he hath *b.* thy children. 147:13
let thy fountain be *b.* *Pr* 5:18
the memory of the just is *b.* 10:7
just man's children are *b.* 20:7
end thereof shall not be *b.* 21
he that hath bountiful eye be *b.* 22:9
b. be Egypt my people. *Isa* 19:25
for I called him and *b.* him. 51:2
seed the Lord hath *b.* 61:9; 65:23
b. are the poor in spirit. *Mat* 5:3
b. are the meek. 5
b. are the merciful. 7
b. are the pure in heart. 8
b. are the peace-makers. 9
b. are they which are persecuted. 10
b. are your eyes. 13:16; *Luke* 10:23
he *b.* and brake. *Mat* 14:19; 26:26 *Mark* 6:41; 14:22; *Luke* 9:16 24:30
Jesus said, *b.* art thou. *Mat* 16:17
b. that servant. 24:46; *Luke* 12:43
come ye *b.* of my Father. *Mat* 25:34
them up in his arms, *b.* *Mark* 10:16
art thou Christ, Son of the *b.*? 14:61
b. among women. *Luke* 1:28, 42
b. is she that believed. 45
b. be ye poor. 6:20
b. is the womb that bare. 11:27
b. are those servants whom Lord shall find watching. 12:37, 38
thou shalt be *b.* 14:14
b. be the King that cometh. 19:38
b. are the barren that never. 23:29
he *b.* them. 24:50
while he *b.* them. 51
b. with faithful Abraham. *Gal* 3:9
b. us with spiritual. *Eph* 1:3
this man shall be *b.* *Jas* 1:25
b. are the dead. *Rev* 14:13

blessed, *God the object*

he said, *b.* be the Lord. *Gen* 9:26 24:27; *Ex* 18:10; *Ruth* 4:14 *1 Sam* 25:32, 39; *2 Sam* 18:28 *1 Ki* 1:48; 5:7; 8:15, 56; 10:9 *1 Chr* 16:36; *2 Chr* 2:12; 6:4; 9:8 *Ezra* 7:27; *Ps* 28:6; 31:21; 41:13 68:19; 72:18; 89:52; 106:48; 124:6; 135:21; 144:1; *Zech* 11:5 *Luke* 1:68
b. be most high God. *Gen* 14:20
children of Israel *b.* God. *Josh* 22:33
and *b.* be my rock. *2 Sam* 22:47 *Ps* 18:46
David *b.* the Lord, *b.* *1 Chr* 29:10
all the congregation *b.* Lord. 20
there they *b.* Lord. *2 Chr* 20:26
they saw the heaps, they *b.* 31:8
and Ezra *b.* the Lord. *Neh* 8:6
b. be thy glorious. 9:5; *Ps* 72:19
b. be the name of Lord. *Job* 1:21 *Ps* 113:2
b. be God. *Ps* 66:20; 68:35 *2 Cor* 1:3
b. art thou, O Lord, teach. *Ps* 119:12
b. be the glory of. *Ezek* 3:12
Daniel *b.* God of. *Dan* 2:19, 20
Nebuchadnezzar *b.* most High. 4:34
him in his arms and *b.* *Luke* 2:28
b. is the King of Israel. *John* 12:13
than Creator, who is *b.* *Rom* 1:25
Christ, who is over all, God *b* 9:5
is *b.* for evermore. *2 Cor* 11:31
b. be the Father. *Eph* 1:3; *1 Pet* 1:3
Gospel of the *b.* God. *1 Tim* 1:11
the *b.* and only Potentate. 6:15

blessed *are they*

b. are they that put trust. *Ps* 2:12
b. are they that dwell. 84:4
b. are they that keep judgement. 106:3
b. are they that keep. 119:2
for *b. are they* that keep. *Pr* 8:32
b. are they that wait. *Isa* 30:18
b. are they that mourn. *Mat* 5:4
b. are they who hunger. 6
b. are they who are persecuted. 10
b. are they that hear. *Luke* 11:28
b. are they that believed. *John* 20:29
b. are they whose iniquities. *Rom* 4:7
b. are they who are called. *Rev* 19:9
b. are they that do his. 22:14

blessed *are ye*

b. are ye that sow. *Isa* 32:20
b. are ye when men. *Mat* 5:11
b. are ye that hunger, be filled; *b. are ye* that weep. *Luke* 6:21
b. are ye when men hate you. 22

blessed *is he*

b. is he that blesseth. *Num* 24:9
b. is he whose sin is. *Ps* 32:1
b. is he that considereth poor. 41:1
b. is he that waiteth. *Dan* 12:12
and *b. is he* whosoever shall not be. *Mat* 11:6; *Luke* 7:23
b. is he that cometh in name. *Mat* 21:9; 23:39; *Mark* 11:9 *Luke* 13:35
b. is he that shall eat. *Luke* 14:15
b. is he that readeth. *Rev* 1:3
b. is he that watcheth. 16:15
b. is he that hath part in. 20:6
b. is he that keepeth sayings. 22:7

blessed *is the man*
b. is the man that walketh not in. *Ps* 1:1
b. is the man to whom Lord imputeth not iniquity. 32:2; *Rom* 4:8
b. is the man that trusteth in him. *Ps* 34:8; 84:12; *Jer* 17:7
b. is the man that maketh the Lord. *Ps* 40:4
b. is the man whom thou choosest. 65:4
b. is the man whose strength. 84:5
b. is the man thou chastenest. 94:12
b. is the man that feareth Lord. 112:1
b. is the man that heareth. *Pr* 8:34
b. is the man that doth this. *Isa* 56:2
b. is the man that endureth. *Jas* 1:12

blessedness
as David describeth *b.* *Rom* 4:6
cometh this *b.* on the? 9
where is then the *b.*? *Gal* 4:15*

blessest
I wot that he thou *b.* *Num* 22:6
thou *b.* O Lord, and it. *1 Chr* 17:27
thou *b.* the springing. *Ps.* 65:10

blesseth
blessed is he that *b.* thee. *Gen* 27:29
Num 24:9
thy God *b.* thee as he. *Deut* 15:6
b. covetous whom the. *Ps* 10:3*
he *b.* them so that they are. 107:38
but he *b.* the habitation. *Pr* 3:33
he that *b.* his friend. 27:14
he *b.* himself in the earth. *Isa* 65:16

blessing
[1] *The favour, kindness, and goodness of God, making what his people do succeed and prosper,* Ps 3:8. [2] *All good things which God bestows upon his people, whether spiritual or temporal,* Deut 28:2; Ps 24:5; Isa 44:3; Eph 1:3. [3] *The means of conveying a blessing to others,* Isa 19:24. [4] *Wishing, praying for, and endeavouring the good of our enemies,* 1 Pet 3:9. [5] *A gift, or present,* Gen 33:11; 1 Ki 5:15.

bless thee, thou shalt be a *b.* *Gen* 12:2
in *b.* I will bless. 22:17; *Heb* 6:14
a curse on me, not a *b.* *Gen* 27:12
brother hath taken thy *b.* 35
hast thou but one *b.*? 38
God give thee *b.* of Abraham. 28:4
take, I pray thee, my *b.* 33:11*
the *b.* of the Lord was on all. 39:5
every one according to his *b.* 49:28
bestow on you a *b.* *Ex* 32:29
command my *b.* on you. *Lev* 25:21
set before you *b.* *Deut* 11:26; 30:19
a *b.* if ye obey the. 11:27
put the *b.* on Gerizim. 29
to the *b.* of the Lord. 12:15; 16:17
Lord turned curse into *b.* 23:5
command a *b.* on store-houses. 28:8
is the *b.* wherewith Moses. 33:1, 7
let the *b.* come upon. 33:16
Naphtali full with the *b.* 23
give me a *b.* *Josh* 15:19; *Judg* 1:15
b. thy handmaid hath. *1 Sam* 25:27*
with thy *b.* let my house. *2 Sam* 7:29
I pray thee take a *b.* *2 Ki* 5:15*
exalted above all *b.* and. *Neh* 9:5
God turned the curse into a *b.* 13:2
b. of him that was ready. *Job* 29:13
thy *b.* is upon thy people. *Ps* 3:8
he shall receive the *b.* 24:5
as he delighted not in *b.* 109:17
b. of the Lord be upon you. 129:8
Lord commanded the *b.* 133:3
b. of Lord maketh rich. *Pr* 10:22
by the *b.* of the upright the. 11:11
a *b.* on the head of him. 26
a good *b.* shall come on. 24:25
a *b.* in midst of land. *Isa* 19:24
and I will pour my *b.* on thy. 44:3
destroy it not, a *b.* is in it. 65:8
I will make them a *b.* there shall be showers of *b.* *Ezek* 34:26
may cause the *b.* to rest. 44:30
if he will leave a *b.* *Joel* 2:14
I will save, ye shall be a *b.* *Zech* 8:13
and pour you out a *b.* *Mal* 3:10
in the temple *b.* God. *Luke* 24:53
in the fulness of the *b.* *Rom* 15:29
the cup of *b.* which. *1 Cor* 10:16
the *b.* of Abraham. *Gal* 3:14
for the earth receiveth *b.* *Heb* 6:7
he would have inherited the *b.* 12:17
of same mouth proceed *b.* *Jas* 3:10
but contrariwise *b.*, that ye should inherit a *b.* *1 Pet* 3:9
to receive honour glory, *b.* *Rev* 5:12
b. to him that sitteth on the. 13
b. and glory to our God. 7:12

blessings
Almighty bless thee with *b.* of heaven, *b.* of deep, *b.* *Gen* 49:25
b. of father prevailed above *b.* of. 26
all these *b.* shall come. *Deut* 28:2
afterwards he read the *b.* *Josh* 8:34
thou preventest him with *b.* *Ps* 21:3
b. are upon head of just. *Pr* 10:6
faithful man abound with *b.* 28:20
and will curse your *b.* *Mal* 2:2
blessed us with spiritual *b.* *Eph* 1:3

blew, *verb*
priests passed on and *b.* *Josh* 6:8
Ehud *b.* a trumpet. *Judg* 3:27
Spirit come on Gideon, he *b.* 6:34
they *b.* the trumpets. 7:19, 20, 22
Saul *b.* saying, let. *1 Sam* 13:3
Joab *b.* a trumpet. *2 Sam* 2:28
18:16; 20:22
Sheba *b.* a trumpet and said. 20:1
b. the trumpet, people said, God. *1 Ki* 1:39; *2 Ki* 9:13; 11:14
winds *b.*, beat on house. *Mat* 7:25, 27
a great wind that *b.* *John* 6:18
when the south-wind *b.* *Acts* 27:13
28:13*

blind
[1] *Those deprived of natural sight,* John 9:1; Acts 13:11. [2] *The morally blind, whose judgement is so corrupted by taking of bribes that they cannot, or will not discern between right and wrong,* Ex 23:8; Deut. 16:19. [3] *The spiritually blind, whether through ignorance or self-will,* Mat 15:14; Deut 27:18.

who maketh the seeing *b.* *Ex* 4:11
stumbling-block before *b.* *Lev* 19:14
a *b.* or lame man not offer. 21:18
not offer the *b.* to the Lord. 22:22
Deut 15:21
that maketh the *b.* to. *Deut* 27:18
grope at noon-day, as *b.* 28:29
take away the *b.* and. *2 Sam* 5:6
the lame and *b.*, the *b.* and the lame shall not come into house. 8
I was eyes to the *b.* *Job* 29:15
Lord openeth eyes of *b.* *Ps* 146:8
eyes of *b.* shall see. *Isa* 29:18; 35:5
a light to open the *b.* eyes. 42:7
bring *b.* by a way they knew not. 16
hear ye deaf, look, ye *b.* 18
who is *b.* but my servant? *b.* as he that is perfect, and *b.*? 19
bring forth the *b.* people. 43:8
his watchmen are *b.* 56:10
grope for the wall like the *b.* 59:10
gather with them the *b.* *Jer* 31:8
they wandered as *b.* *Lam* 4:14
shall walk like *b.* men. *Zeph* 1:17
offer the *b.* for sacrifice. *Mal* 1:8
two *b.* men followed him. *Mat* 9:27
20:30
b. receive their sight. 11:5; 12:22
Luke 7:22
b. leaders of the *b.* if the *b.* lead the *b.* both. *Mat* 15:14; *Luke* 6:39
woe to you, ye *b.* guides. *Mat* 23:16
ye fools and *b.* 17, 19
b. Pharisee, cleanse first within. 26
he took the *b.* by hand. *Mark* 8:23
b. Bartimaeus sat by the way. 10:46
recovery of sight to *b.* *Luke* 4:18
to many that were *b.* he gave. 7:21
thou makest a feast, call *b.* 14:13
lay a great multitude of *b.* *John* 5:3
he saw a man *b.* from his birth. 9:1
they which see might be made *b.* 39
are we *b.* also? *John* 9:40
if ye were *b.* 41
can a devil open eyes of *b.*? 10:21
thou shalt be *b.* not. *Acts* 13:11
thou art a guide to the *b.* *Rom* 2:19
he that lacketh these is *b.* *2 Pet* 1:9
not that thou art *b.* *Rev* 3:17

blind, *verb*
a gift doth *b.* the eyes. *Deut* 16:19
received I a bribe to *b.* *1 Sam* 12:3

blinded, -eth
take no gift, a gift *b.* *Ex* 23:8
he hath *b.* their eyes. *John* 12:40
obtained, the rest are *b.* *Rom* 11:7
their minds were *b.* *2 Cor* 3:14
god of this world hath *b.* the. 4:4
because darkness hath *b.* his eyes. *1 John* 2:11

blindfolded
when they had *b.* him. *Luke* 22:64

blindness
smote the men with *b.* *Gen* 19:11
shall smite thee with *b.* *Deut* 28:28
Elisha prayed, smite this people with *b.*, smote them with *b.* *2 Ki* 6:18
smite every horse with *b.* *Zech* 12:4
b. in part has happened. *Rom* 11:25
because of *b.* of heart. *Eph* 4:18

block, *see* **stumbling**

blood
The word is used [1] *literally as in* Ex 29:12; Acts 17:26. [2] *Figuratively, for murder,* Hab 2:12; Mat 27:24; *and for the blood of Christ, the blood of the covenant, where the idea is the death of Christ on the cross,* Rom 3:25; 5:9; Eph 1:7.

thy brother's *b.* crieth. *Gen* 4:10
the life which is the *b.* 9:4
your *b.* of your lives, I will require. 5
killed kid and dipped coat in *b.* 37:31
water shall become *b.* on. *Ex* 4:9
waters shall be turned into *b.* 7:17
b. shall be for a token, when I see *b.* 12:13
shalt not offer the *b.* with leaven. 23:18; 34:25
thou shalt take of the *b.* 29:21
b. of it was not brought. *Lev* 10:18
and if issue in flesh shall be *b.* 15:19
b. imputed unto that man. 17:4
for it is the *b.* that maketh. 11
not stand against the *b.* of thy. 19:16
and drink the *b.* of. *Num* 23:24
not cleansed but by the *b.* 35:33
matter between *b.* and *b.* *Deut* 17:8; *2 Chr* 19:10
the *b.* shall be forgiven. *Deut* 21:8
battlement, that bring not *b.* 22:8
avenge the *b.* of his servants. 32:43
and their *b.* be laid upon. *Judg* 9:24
let not my *b.* fall. *1 Sam* 26:20
David said, thy *b.* be. *2 Sam* 1:16
from the *b.* of the slain, from. 22
I and kingdom guiltless the *b.* 3:28
hath returned upon thee the *b.* 16:8
Amasa wallowed in *b.* 20:12
b. of the men? 23:17; *1 Chr* 11:19
the *b.* of war on his girdle. *1 Ki* 2:5
b. on thy head. 37; *Ezek* 33:4
the *b.* gushed out upon. *1 Ki* 18:28
saw the waters red as *b.* *2 Ki* 3:22
said, this is *b.* the kings are. 23
I have seen *b.* of Naboth, *b.* of. 9:26
O earth, cover not my *b.* *Job* 16:18
the eagles' young suck up *b.* 39:30
what profit is in my *b.*? *Ps* 30:9
or will I drink *b.* of goats? 50:13
righteous wash his feet in *b.* 58:10
foot may be dipped in the *b.* 68:23
precious shall their *b.* be in. 72:14
doth violence to *b.* of any. *Pr* 28:17
hands are full of *b.* *Isa* 1:15
the Lord shall purge the *b.* of. 4:4
noise, and garments rolled in *b.* 9:5
the waters of Dimon full of *b.* 15:9
his ear from hearing of *b.* 33:15
shall be melted with their *b.* 34:3
is found the *b.* of the poor. *Jer* 2:34
pour out their *b.* by the. 18:21*
he that keepeth sword from *b.* 48:10

b. be on the inhabitants. *Jer* 51:35
polluted themselves with *b.* *Lam* 4:14
pestilence and *b.* pass. *Ezek* 5:17
the land is full of *b.* 9:9
pour out my fury upon it in *b.* 14:19
to thee when thou wast in thy *b.* 16:6
I will give thee *b.* in fury and. 38
beget son that is shedder of *b.* 18:10
he shall die, his *b.* shall be upon. 13
mother is like a vine in thy *b.* 19:10
thy *b.* in midst of land. 21:32; 22:12
the city sheddeth *b.* in the. 22:3
and *b.* is in their hands. 23:37, 45
I have set her *b.* on the rock. 24:8
I will send *b.* into her streets. 28:23
I water with thy *b.* the land. 32:6
I will prepare thee to *b.* thou hast not hated *b.* even *b.* shall. 35:6
offer my bread, fat and *b.* 44:7, 15
I will avenge the *b.* *Hos* 1:4
b. fire, and pillars of smoke. *Joel* 2:30; *Acts* 2:19
moon turned into *b.* *Joel* 2:31 *Acts* 2:20
I will cleanse their *b.* *Joel* 3:21
their *b.* shall be poured. *Zeph* 1:17
issue of *b.* twelve years. *Mat* 9:20 *Mark* 5:25; *Luke* 8:43
b. hath not revealed. *Mat* 16:17
not partakers in the *b.* of. 23:30
b. of righteous Abel. 35; *Luke* 11:51
b. of the new testament. *Mat* 26:28 *Mark* 14:24
because it is price of *b.* *Mat* 27:6
called the field of *b.* 8; *Acts* 1:19
innocent of the *b.* of this. *Mat* 27:24
whose *b.* Pilate had. *Luke* 13:1
the new testament in my *b.* 22:20 *1 Cor* 11:25
sweat was as great drops of *b.* *Luke* 22:44
which were born not of *b.* *John* 1:13
my flesh drinketh my *b.* 6:54, 56
my flesh is meat, my *b.* is drink. 55
forthwith came thereout *b.* 19:34
ye bring this man's *b.* *Acts* 5:28
they abstain from *b.* 15:20, 29; 21:25
and hath made of one *b.* all. 17:26
your *b.* be on your own heads. 18:6
I am pure from the *b.* of all. 20:26
guilty of body and *b.* of. *1 Cor* 11:27
flesh and *b.* cannot inherit. 15:50
not against flesh and *b.* *Eph* 6:12
peace through *b.* of cross. *Col* 1:20
partakers of flesh and *b.* *Heb* 2:14
not without *b.* which he offered. 9:7
by *b.* of goats, but by his own *b.* 12
b. of bulls and goats sanctifieth. 13
this is the *b.* of the testament. 20
without shedding of *b.* there is. 22
into holiest by *b.* of Jesus. 10:19
passover, and sprinkling of *b.* 11:28
ye have not yet resisted unto *b.* 12:4
b. of sprinkling that speaketh. 24
whose *b.* is brought into. 13:11
sprinkling of *b.* of Jesus. *1 Pet* 1:2
b. of Jesus Christ cleanseth us. *1 John* 1:7
he that came by water and *b.* 5:6
three in earth, Spirit, water, *b.* 8
hast redeemed us by thy *b.* *Rev* 5:9
dost thou not avenge our *b.*? 6:10
and the moon became as *b.* 12
white in the *b.* of the Lamb. 7:14
third part of sea became *b.* 8:8; 16:3
power to turn the waters into *b.* 11:6
overcame him by *b.* of Lamb. 12:11
b. came out of the wine-press. 14:20
thou hast given them *b.* to drink. 16:6
in her was found the *b.* of. 18:24
avenged the *b.* of his servants. 19:2
clothed with vesture dipped in *b.* 13

see **avenger, revenger**

blood *be upon*

curseth his father, his *b.* *be upon.* *Lev* 20:9
sodomy, their *b.* *be upon* them. 13
wizard, their *b.* *be upon* them. 27
b. shed, and *be upon.* *Deut* 19:10
abominations, his *b.* *be upon.* *Ezek* 18:13
warning, his *b.* shall *be upon.* 33:5*

blood with *bullock*

take *b.* of *bullock.* *Ex* 29:12 *Lev* 4:5; 16:14, 18
pour *b.* of *bullock* at. *Lev* 4:7
he did with *b.* of the *bullock.* 16:15
delight not in *b.* of *bullocks.* *Isa* 1:11

blood *of Christ*

communion of the *b. of Christ*? *1 Cor* 10:16
made nigh by *b.* of *Christ.* *Eph* 2:13
shall *b. of Christ* purge? *Heb* 9:14
b. of Christ as of a lamb. *1 Pet* 1:19
b. of Christ cleanseth us. *1 John* 1:7

blood *of the covenant*

behold the *b. of the covenant.* *Ex* 24:8
by the *b. of* thy *covenant.* *Zech* 9:11
hath counted *b. of covenant* unholy. *Heb* 10:29
b. of the everlasting *covenant.* 13:20

blood, with *eat*

eat neither fat nor *b.* *Lev* 3:17
ye shall *eat* no manner of *b.* 7:26
27; 17:14; *Deut* 12:16, 23; 15:23
eateth b. that soul be cut off. *Lev* 7:27, 17:10
people did *eat* with *b.* *1 Sam* 14:32
ye eat with *b.* and. *Ezek* 33:25

for **blood**

not pollute land, *for b.* *Num* 35:33
died *for* the *b.* of Asahel. *2 Sam* 3:27
for the *b.* of the sons. *2 Chr* 24:25
he maketh inquisition *for b.* *Ps* 9:12
let us lay wait *for b.* *Pr* 1:11, 18
wicked are to lie in wait *for b.* 12:6
they all lie in wait *for b.* *Mi* 7:2

his **blood**

if we conceal *his b.* *Gen* 37:26
behold *his b.* is required. 42:22
his b. shall be upon his. *Josh* 2:19
I not require *his b.*? *2 Sam* 4:11
Lord shall return *his b.* *1 Ki* 2:32
die in his iniquity, but *his b.* will I require. *Ezek* 3:18, 20; 33:4, 6, 8
shall he leave *his b.* on. *Hos* 12:14
take away *his b.* *Zech* 9:7
his b. be on us. *Mat* 27:25
purchased with *his b.* *Acts* 20:28
through faith in *his b.* *Rom* 3:25
being now justified by *his b.* 5:9
redemption through *his b.* *Eph* 1:7 *Col* 1:14
by *his* own *b.* he entered. *Heb* 9:12
he might sanctify with *his b.* 13:12
from our sins in *his b.* *Rev* 1:5

innocent **blood**

innoc. b. be not shed. *Deut* 19:10
put away guilt of *innoc. b.* 13; 21:9
lay not *innoc. b.* to people's 21:8
sin against *innocent b.* *1 Sam* 19:5
take away *innoc. b.* *1 Ki* 2:31
shed *innoc. b.* *2 Ki* 21:16; 24:4
they condemn *innoc. b.* *Ps* 94:21
shed *innoc b.*, *b.* of sons and. 106:38
hands that shed *innoc. b.* *Pr* 6:17
haste to shed *innoc. b.* *Isa* 59:7
shed not *innoc. b.* *Jer* 7:6; 22:3
eyes and heart shed *innoc. b.* 22:17
ye shall surely bring *innoc. b.* 26:15
they have shed *innoc. b.* *Joel* 3:19
lay not on us *innoc. b.* *Jonah* 1:14
I have betrayed *innoc. b.* *Mat* 27:4

shed **blood**

sheddeth man's *b.* his *b.* be *shed.* *Gen* 9:6
Reuben said, *shed* no *b.* 37:22
there shall no *b.* be *shed.* *Ex.* 22:2
be risen upon him, *b.* be *shed.* 3*
hath *shed b.* that man. *Lev* 17:4
cleansed of *b. shed* but by *b.* *Num* 35:33
have not *shed* this *b.* *Deut* 21:7
coming to *shed b.* *1 Sam* 25:26*
slew and *shed b.* of war. *1 Ki* 2:5
thou hast *shed b.* much *b.* *1 Chr* 22:8; 28:3
their *b. shed* like water. *Ps* 79:3
revenging *b.* of thy servants *shed.* 10
make haste to *shed b.* *Pr* 1:16 *Rom* 3:15
prophets have *shed* the *b.* *Lam* 4:13
as women that *shed b.* *Ezek* 16:38 23:45
guilty in thy *b.* thou hast *shed.* 22:4
to their power to *shed b.* 6
women that *shed b.* 23:45
ye *shed b.* shall ye possess? 33:25
thou hast *shed b.* of children. 35:5*
fury on them for *b.* they *shed.* 36:18
all the righteous *b. shed.* *Mat* 23:25
my *b.* which is *shed.* *Mark* 14:24 *Luke* 22:20
b. of the prophets *shed.* *Luke* 11:50
b. of Stephen was *shed.* *Acts* 22:20
they have *shed* the *b.* *Rev* 16:6

sprinkle **blood**

ram's *b.* and *sprinkle* it. *Ex* 29:16
sprinkle b. on altar. 20; *Lev* 1:5
11; 3:2, 8, 13; 7:2; 17:6 *Num* 18:17
sprinkle b. seven times. *Lev* 4:6, 17 16:14, 19
sprinkle b. of sin-offering on. 5:9
the priests that *sprinkle* the *b.* 7:14
sprinkle of the *b.* before. *Num* 19:4
sprinkle on it the *b.* *2 Ki* 16:15
an altar to *sprinkle b.* *Ezek* 43:18

blood *sprinkled*

half of *b.* Moses *sprinkled* on. *Ex* 24:6; *Lev* 8:19, 24
Moses took *b.* and *sprinkled* on. *Ex* 24:8
when there is *sprinkled b.* *Lev* 6:27
took *b.* and *sprinkled* on Aaron. 8:30
Aaron's sons *b. he sprinkled.* 9:12, 18
Athaliah's *b. sprinkled* on. *2 Ki* 9:33
Ahaz *sprinkled* the *b.* of his. 16:13
sprinkled b. of bullocks. *2 Chr* 29:22 30:16
the priests *sprinkled* the *b.* 35:11
their *b.* shall be *sprinkled.* *Isa* 63:3
he *sprinkled* with *b.* the. *Heb* 9:21

with **blood**

make atonement *with b.* *Ex* 30:10
cleanse the house *with b.* *Lev* 14:52
ye not eat any thing *with b.* 19:26
head bring down *with b.* *1 Ki* 2:9
land was polluted *with b.* *Ps* 106:38
filled *with b.* made fat *with b.* *Isa* 34:6
their land shall be soaked *with b.* 7
be drunken *with* their own *b.* 49:26
your hands are defiled *with b.* 59:3
filled this place *with b.* *Jer* 19:4
be made drunk *with* their *b.* 46:10
polluted themselves *with b.* *Lam* 4:14
plead against him *with b.* *Ezek* 38:22
a city polluted *with b.* *Hos* 6:8
they build up Zion *with b.* *Mi* 3:10
buildeth a town *with b.* *Hab* 2:12
I conferred not *with b.* *Gal* 1:16
all things purged *with b.* *Heb* 9:22
and fire, mingled *with b.* *Rev* 8:7
saw woman drunken *with b.* 17:6

bloodguiltiness

deliver me from *b.* *Ps* 51:14

bloodthirsty

the *b.* hate the upright. *Pr* 29:10

bloody

a *b.* husband art thou. *Ex* 4:25, 26
come out, thou *b.* man. *2 Sam* 16:7
famine is for Saul, and his *b.* 21:1
Lord will abhor *b.* man. *Ps* 5:6
gather not my life with *b.* men. 26:9
b. men not live out half their. 55:23
deliver me, save me from *b.* 59:2
depart from me ye *b.* men. 139:19
land is full of *b.* crimes. *Ezek* 7:23
wilt thou judge the *b.* city? 22:2
woe to the *b.* city. 24:6, 9; *Nah* 3:1
lay sick of a *b.* flux. *Acts* 28:8*

bloomed

Aaron's rod *b.* blossoms. *Num* 17:8

blossom

her *b.* shot forth. *Gen* 40:10
their *b.* shall go as dust. *Isa* 5:24

blossom, -ed

[1] *To put forth flowers,* Num 17:5 Hab 3:17. [2] *To increase and prosper,* Isa 27:6.

the man's rod shall *b.* *Num* 17:5

Israel shall *b.* and bud. *Isa* 27:6
desert shall rejoice and *b.* 35:1
b. abundantly and rejoice. 2
the rod hath *b.* pride. *Ezek* 7:10
fig-tree shall not *b.* nor. *Hab* 3:17

blot
(*Spot, stain, disgrace*)
if any *b.* hath cleaved. *Job* 31:7
the wicked, getteth a *b.* *Pr* 9:7

blot *out*
(*Cancel, expunge, efface*)
not, *b.* me *out* of thy book. *Ex* 32:32
whosoever sinned, will I *b. out.* 33
shall *b.* them *out* with. *Num* 5:23
me alone that I *b. out.* *Deut* 9:14
b. out the remembrance of. 25:19
Lord shall *b. out* his name. 29:20
he would *b. out* Israel. *2 Ki* 14:27
have mercy, O God, *b. out.* *Ps* 51:1
hide my sins and *b. out* all. 9
nor *b. out* their sin from. *Jer* 18:23
I will not *b.* his name *out.* *Rev* 3:5

blotted
let not their sin be *b.* out. *Neh* 4:5
let them be *b.* out of. *Ps* 69:28
let their name be *b.* out. 109:13
not the sin of his mother be *b.* 14
b. out as a thick cloud. *Isa* 44:22
your sins may be *b.* out. *Acts* 3:19

blotteth, -ing
I am he that *b.* out thy. *Isa* 43:25
b. out the hand-writing. *Col* 2:14

blow
consumed by the *b.* of thy. *Ps* 39:10
broken with grievous *b.* *Jer* 14:17*

blow, *verb*
didst *b.* with thy wind. *Ex* 15:10
when ye *b.* an alarm. *Num* 10:5, 6
then ye shall *b.* an alarm. 9*
when I *b.*, then *b.* ye. *Judg* 7:18
caused an east-wind to *b.* *Ps* 78:26
caused his wind to *b.* 147:18
come, thou south, *b.* *S of S* 4:16
he shall also *b.* upon them. *Isa* 40:24
I *b.* against thee. *Ezek* 21:31; 22:21
b. ye the cornet in Gibeah. *Hos* 5:8
b. the trumpet in Zion. *Joel* 2:15
ye brought it, I did *b.* *Hag* 1:9
ye see south-wind *b.* *Luke* 12:55
that wind should not *b.* *Rev* 7:1
see **trumpet**

bloweth
Spirit of the Lord *b.* on it. *Isa* 40:7
I have created smith that *b.* 54:16
wind *b.* where it listeth. *John* 3:8

blown
fire not *b.* shall consume. *Job* 20:26

blue
b. purple. *Ex* 25:4; 26:1, 31, 36
27:16
robe of the ephod of *b.* 28:31; 39:22
cut gold to work it in the *b.* 39:3
the fringes ribband of *b.* *Num* 15:38
cunning to work in *b.* *2 Chr* 2:7, 14
b. hangings, pavement of *b.* *Esth* 1:6*
Mordecai went in apparel of *b.* 8:15
b. and purple is their. *Jer* 10:9
Assyrians clothed with *b.* *Ezek* 23:6
b. and purple from the isles. 27:7
in *b.* clothes and broidered. 24
see **purple, cloth, lace, loops**

blueness
b. of a wound cleanseth. *Pr* 20:30*

blunt
if iron be *b.* and he do. *Eccl* 10:10

blush
I *b.* to lift my face to thee. *Ezra* 9:6
neither could they *b.* *Jer* 6:15; 8:12

Boanerges
surnamed them *B.* *Mark* 3:17

boar
b. out of the wood. *Ps* 80:13

board, -s
overlay *b.* with gold. *Ex* 26:29; 36:34
hollow with *b.* make. 27:8
under every *b.* were two. 36:30
under Merari shall be *b.* *Num* 3:36
will enclose her with *b.* *S of S* 8:9
the rest, some on *b.* *Acts* 27:44*

boast, *substantive*
my soul shall make her *b.* *Ps* 34:2
Jew, and makest thy *b.* *Rom* 2:17*
thou that makest thy *b.* 23*

boast, *verb*
not *b.* as he that putteth. *1 Ki* 20:11
heart lifteth thee to *b.* *2 Chr* 25:19
in God we *b.* all the day. *Ps* 44:8
b. themselves in their riches. 49:6
the workers of iniquity *b.* 94:4
confounded be they that *b.* of. 97:7
b. not thyself of. *Pr* 27:1
shall the ax *b.* itself. *Isa* 10:15
in their glory shall you *b.* 61:6
b. not against branches, if thou *b.*
Rom 11:18*
for which I *b.* to them. *2 Cor* 9:2*
for though I should *b.* 10:8*
we will not *b.* of things. 13*
to *b.* in another man's line. 16*
receive me that I may *b.* 11:16*
not of works lest any *b.* *Eph* 2:9*

boasted
with mouth ye have *b.* *Ezek* 35:13*
if I have *b.* any thing. *2 Cor* 7:14*

boasters
proud, *b.* inventors of. *Rom* 1:30
covetous, *b.* proud. *2 Tim* 3:2

boastest, -eth
the wicked *b.* of his. *Ps* 10:3
why *b.* thou in mischief ? 52:1
gone his way, then he *b.* *Pr* 20:14
whoso *b.* of a false gift. 25:14
a little member, and *b.* *Jas* 3:5

boasting, *participle*
rose Theudas, *b.* himself. *Acts* 5:36*
not *b.* of things without. *2 Cor* 10:15*

boasting, *substantive*
where is *b.* then ? *Rom* 3:27*
b. before Titus is. *2 Cor* 7:14*
shew ye the proof of our *b.* 8:24*
lest our *b.* of you should be. 9:3*
should be ashamed in confident *b.* 4*
shall stop me of this *b.* 11:10*
were foolishly in confidence of *b.* 17*
but now ye rejoice in *b.* *Jas* 4:16

boat, -s
people saw there was no *b.*, and that
Jesus went not into *b.* *John* 6:22
came other *b.* from Tiberias. 23
work to come by the *b.* *Acts* 27:16
when they had let down the *b.* 30
soldiers cut off the ropes of *b.* 32

Boaz
left pillar called *B.* *1 Ki* 7:21
2 Chr 3:17

Boaz
kinsman, his name was *B.* *Ruth* 2:1
with whom I wrought, is *B.* 19
is not *B.* of our kindred ? 3:2
when *B.* had eaten. 7
then went *B.* up to the gate. 4:1
so *B.* took Ruth. 13
B. begat Obed. 21; *1 Chr* 2:12
Mat 1:5
Obed the son of *B.* *Luke* 3:32

Bochim
came from Gilgal to *B.* *Judg* 2:1
called the name of place *B.* 5

bodies
ought left, but our *b.* *Gen* 47:18
took *b.* of Saul's sons. *1 Sam* 31:12
1 Chr 10:12
dominion over our *b.* *Neh* 9:37
b. are like unto *b.* of. *Job* 13:12*
two wings covered *b.* *Ezek* 1:11 23
on whose *b.* fire had. *Dan* 3:27
yielded their *b.* that they might. 28
many *b.* of saints which. *Mat* 27:52
b. should not remain on. *John* 19:31
to dishonour their own *b.* *Rom* 1:24
shall quicken your mortal *b.* 8:11
that ye present your *b.* a. 12:1
b. are members of. *1 Cor* 6:15
are celestial *b.* and *b.* 15:40
their wives as their own *b.* *Eph* 5:28
b. washed with pure. *Heb* 10:22
the *b.* of beasts, whose. 13:11

dead **bodies**
were *dead b.* fallen. *2 Chr* 20:24
they found with *dead b.* 25
dead b. of thy servants. *Ps* 79:2
fill the places with the *dead b.* 110:6
valley of *dead b.* shall be. *Jer* 31:40
fill them with *dead b.* of men. 33:5
dead b. shall be for meat. 34:20
wherein Ishmael cast *dead b.* 41:9
shall be many *dead b.* *Amos* 8:3
dead b. shall lie in. *Rev* 11:8
nations see their *dead b.*, nor suffer
their *dead b.* to be put in. 9

bodily
descended in *b.* shape. *Luke* 3:22
his *b.* presence is weak. *2 Cor* 10:10
fulness of the Godhead *b.* *Col* 2:9
b. exercise profiteth little. *1 Tim* 4:8

body
[1] *The physical part of man as distinct from the spiritual,* 1 Sam 31:4; Mat 6:22. [2] *Used figuratively for the Church,* 1 Cor 12:27; Eph 3:6.
as the *b.* of heaven in. *Ex* 24:10*
took the *b.* of Saul. *1 Sam* 31:12
1 Chr 10:12
sake of my own *b.* *Job* 19:17†
my skin worms destroy this *b.* 26
drawn and cometh out of *b.* 20:25
when thy flesh and *b.* *Pr* 5:11
consume both soul and *b.* *Isa* 10:18
and thou hast laid thy *b.* 51:23*
their whole *b.* full. *Ezek* 10:12
in spirit in midst of *b.* *Dan* 7:15
whole *b.* be cast into. *Mat* 5:29, 30
light of *b.* is eye. 6:22; *Luke* 11:34
b. full of light. *Mat* 6:22
Luke 11:34, 36
b. shall be full of darkness. *Mat* 6:23
no thought for *b.* 25; *Luke* 12:22
b. more than raiment. *Mat* 6:25
Luke 12:23
them which kill *b.* *Mat* 10:28
Luke 12:4
disciples came and took *b.* *Mat* 14:12
poured this ointment on my *b.* 26:12
Jesus said, take, eat, this is my *b.*
26:26; *Mark* 14:22; *Luke* 22:19
1 Cor 11:24
Joseph begged the *b.* of Jesus. *Mat*
27:58; *Mark* 15:43; *Luke* 23:52
in *b.* that she was healed. *Mark* 5:29
is come to anoint my *b.* 14:8
a linen cloth cast about his *b.* 51
gave *b.* to Joseph. 15:45; *Mat* 27:58
where the *b.* is, thither. *Luke* 17:37
found not *b.* of Lord Jesus. 24:3
the *b.* of Jesus had lain. *John* 20:12
the *b.* of sin destroyed. *Rom* 6:6
dead to the law by *b.* of Christ. 7:4
deliver me from *b.* of this ? 24
Christ in you, the *b.* is dead. 8:10
the Spirit mortify deeds of *b.* 13
adoption, redemption of *b.* 23
b. is not for fornication, but the Lord,
and the Lord for *b.* *1 Cor* 6:13
every sin is without the *b.* 18
b. is the temple of Holy Ghost. 19
hath no power of her own *b.* 7:4
I keep under my *b.* 9:27
communion of the *b.* of Christ. 10:16
guilty of the *b.* and blood of. 11:27
not discerning the Lord's *b.* 29
for the *b.* is not one member. 12:14
is it therefore not of *b.* ? 15, 16
whole *b.* were an eye where. 12:17
where were the *b.* ? 19
yet but one *b.* 20
now ye are the *b.* of Christ. 27
though I give my *b.* to be. 13:3
with what *b.* do dead come ? 15:35
thou sowest not that *b.* that. 37
but God giveth it a *b.* as. 38
natural *b.* raised spiritual *b.* 44
to be absent from *b.* *2 Cor* 5:8
fellow-heirs of the same *b.* *Eph* 3:6
for edifying of *b.* of Christ. 4:12
from whom whole *b.* fitly joined. 16
he is the Saviour of the *b.* 5:23
shall change our vile *b.* *Phil* 3:21
he is the head of the *b.* *Col* 1:18
in putting off the *b.* of the sins. 2:11
a shadow, but the *b.* is of Christ. 17
from which the *b.* by joints. 19
shew of wisdom in neglecting *b.* 23

pray your soul and *b.* *1 Thes* 5:23
b. hast thou prepared me. *Heb* 10:5
through offering of the *b.* of Jesus. 10
not things needful to *b.* *Jas* 2:16
as *b.* without the Spirit is dead. 26
and is able to bridle the whole *b.* 3:2
we turn about their whole *b.* 3
the tongue defileth the whole *b.* 6
disputed about *b.* of Moses *Jude* 9

dead **body**
not go into any *dead b.* *Lev* 21:11
Num 6:6
defiled by a *dead b.* *Num* 9:6, 7
unclean by *dead b.* 10; *Hag* 2:13
toucheth *dead b.* *Num* 19:11, 16
restored a *dead b.* to life. *2 Ki* 8:5*
with my *dead b.* shall. *Isa* 26:19*
cast his *dead b.* into. *Jer* 26:23
nis *dead b.* shall be cast out. 36:30

fruit of the **body**
blessed the *fruit of thy b.* *Deut* 28:4
plenteous in *fruit of thy b.* 11; 30:9
cursed shall be *fruit of thy b.* 28:18
shalt eat the *fruit of thy b.* 53
fruit of thy b. will I set. *Ps* 132:11
fruit of my b. for sin of my. *Mi* 6:7

his **body**
his b. not remain. *Deut* 21:23
had 70 sons of *his b.* *Judg* 8:30
fastened *his b.* to wall. *1 Sam* 31:10
his b. wet with dew. *Dan* 4:33; 5:21
till beast was slain, and *his b.* 7:11
his b. also was like the beryl. 10:6
how *his b.* was laid. *Luke* 23:55
when they found not *his b.* 24:23
the temple of *his b.* *John* 2:21
his b. were brought. *Acts* 19:12
he considered not *his b.* *Rom* 4:19
sinneth against *his b.* *1 Cor* 6:18
the power of *his* own *b.* 7:4
the things done in *his b.* *2 Cor* 5:10
which is *his b.* fulness. *Eph* 1:23
like to *his* glorious *b.* *Phil* 3:21
for *his b.* sake. *Col* 1:24
bare our sins in *his b.* *1 Pet* 2:24

in **body**
ruddy *in b.* than rubies. *Lam* 4:7
let not sin reign *in b.* *Rom* 6:12
I verily as absent *in b.* *1 Cor* 5:3
glorify God *in* your *b.* 6:20
that she may be holy *in b.* 7:34
members every one *in* the *b.* 12:18
be no schism *in* the *b.* 25
bearing *in* the *b.* the dying of our Lord that life *in* our *b.* *2 Cor* 4:10
whilst we are at home *in b.* 5:6
in b. or out of the *b.* 12:2
I bear *in b.* marks of Lord. *Gal* 6:17
Christ magnified *in* my *b.* *Phil* 1:20
reconciled *in b.* of his. *Col* 1:22
yourselves also *in* the *b.* *Heb* 13:3

one **body**
many members in *one b.* *Rom* 12:4
are *one b.* in Christ. 5; *1 Cor* 10:17
joined to harlot, is *one b.* *1 Cor* 6:16
as the *b.* is *one.* 12:12
baptized into *one b.* whether. 13
many members, yet but *one b.* 20
both to God in *one b* *Eph* 2:16
there is *one b.* and one Spirit. 4:4
ye are called in *one b.* *Col* 3:15

boil
it shall be a *b.* with blains. *Ex* 9:9
it became a *b.* breaking forth. 10
could not stand because of the *b.* 11
b. the flesh at the door. *Lev* 8:31
flesh also in which was a *b.* 13:18
took figs and laid on the *b.* *2 Ki* 20:7
Isa 38:21
smote Job with sore *b.* *Job* 2:7
he maketh the deep to *b.* 41:31
fire causeth waters to *b.* *Isa* 64:2
and make it *b.* well. *Ezek* 24:5
place where priests shall *b.* 46:20, 24

boiled
yoke of oxen and *b.* them. *1 Ki* 19:21
so we *b.* my son. *2 Ki* 6:29
my bowels *b.*, rested not. *Job* 30:27

boiling
made with *b.* places. *Ezek* 46:23

boisterous
when he saw wind *b.* *Mat* 14:30*

bold
righteous are *b.* as a lion. *Pr* 28:1
and Barnabas waxed *b.* *Acts* 13:46
Esaias is very *b.* and. *Rom* 10:20
being absent, am *b.* *2 Cor* 10:1*
b. wherewith I think to be *b.* 2*
wherein any is *b.* I am *b.* 11:21
much more *b.* to speak. *Phil* 1:14
we were *b.* in our God. *1 Thes* 2:2
though I might be much *b.* *Philem* 8

boldly
Levi came on the city *b.* *Gen* 34:25*
came, and went in *b.* *Mark* 15:43
he speaketh *b.* and. *John* 7:26*
how he preached *b.* *Acts* 9:27
he spake *b.* in name of the Lord. 29
time abode they, speaking *b.* 14:3
Apollos began to speak *b.* 18:26
spake *b.* for the space of. 19:8
have written the more *b.* *Rom* 15:15
I may open my mouth *b.* *Eph* 6:19
that I may speak *b.* as I ought. 20
let us come *b.* to. *Heb* 4:16
that we may *b.* say. 13:6*

boldness
the *b.* of his face shall. *Eccl* 8:1*
when they saw the *b.* of. *Acts* 4:13
that with all *b.* they may speak. 29
spake the word of God with *b.* 31
great is my *b.* of speech. *2 Cor* 7:4
in whom we have *b.* *Eph* 3:12
but that with all *b.* *Phil* 1:20
they purchase great *b.* *1 Tim* 3:13
having *b.* to enter. *Heb* 10:19
that we may have *b.* *1 John* 4:17

bolled
(*Gone to seed*)
barley in the ear, and flax *b.* *Ex* 9:31

bolster
goats' hair for his *b.* *1 Sam* 19:13, 16
spear at *b.* 26:7, 11, 12
water at *b.* 16

bolt, -ed
b. the door. *2 Sam* 13:17
he *b.* the door. 18

bond
bind his soul with a *b.* *Num* 30:2
vow and bind herself by a *b.* 3
father hear her vow and her *b.* 4
I will bring you into *b.* *Ezek* 20:37
be loosed from his *b.* *Luke* 13:16
in the *b.* of inquity. *Acts* 8:23
baptized into one body, *b.* or free.
1 Cor 12:13
unity of the Spirit, in *b.* *Eph* 4:3
put on charity, the *b.* of. *Col* 3:14
see **free**

bondage
[1] *Slavery,* Ex 2:23; Ezra 9:8, 9. [2] *Subjection to sin,* Gal 4:3. [3] *Subjection to the ceremonial law,* Gal 2:4.
lives bitter with hard *b.* *Ex* 1:14
Israel sighed by reason of the *b.* cried to God by reason of *b.* 2:23
I will rid you out of their *b.* 6:6
not to Moses for cruel *b.* 9
ye came out of the house of *b.* 13:3
Lord brought us out of *b.* 14; 20:2
Deut 5:6; 6:12; 8:14; 13:5, 10
Josh 24:17; *Judg* 6:8
laid upon us hard *b.* *Deut* 26:6
bring into *b.* our sons and daughters, some are brought into *b.* *Neh* 5:5
because the *b.* was heavy. 18
a captain to return to *b.* 9:17
rest from thy hard *b.* *Isa* 14:3
not received spirit of *b.* *Rom* 8:15
delivered from *b.* of. 21
Sinai, which gendereth to *b.* *Gal* 4:24
be not entangled with yoke of *b.* 5:1
all their life subject to *b.* *Heb* 2:15

in, into, or *under* **bondage**
the Egyptians keep *in b.* *Ex* 6:5
a little reviving *in* our *b.* *Ezra* 9:8
God hath not forsaken us *in b.* 9
we were never *in b.* to. *John* 8:33
should bring them *into b.* *Acts* 7:6
nation to whom they be *in b.* 7
or sister not *under b.* 1 *Cor* 7:15
a man bring you *into b.* *2 Cor* 11:20
bring us *into b.* *Gal* 2:4
were *in b.* under the elements. 4:3
ye desire again to be *in b.* 9
to Jerusalem, which is *in b.* 25
is he brought *into b.* *2 Pet* 2:19

bondmaid, -s
whoso lieth with a *b.* *Lev* 19:20
b. shall be heathen, buy ye *b.* 25:44
one by a *b.* the other by. *Gal* 4:22*

bondman
abide instead of lad a *b.* *Gen* 44:33
thou wast a *b.* the Lord redeemed.
Deut 15:15; 16:12; 24:18, 22
every *b.* hid themselves. *Rev* 6:15

bondmen
he may take us for *b.* *Gen* 43:18
we will be my lord's *b.* 44:9
shall not be sold as *b.* *Lev* 25:42
b. of the heathen, of them buy *b.* 44
they shall be your *b.* for ever. 46
that ye should not be their *b.* 26:13
we were Pharaoh's *b.* *Deut* 6:21
you out of house of *b.* 7:8*
there ye shall be sold for *b.* 28:68
of you freed from *b.* *Josh* 9:23
Solomon made no *b.* *1 Ki* 9:22
to take my two sons to be *b.* *2 Ki* 4:1
children of Judah for *b.* *2 Chr* 28:10
we were *b.* yet God hath. *Ezra* 9:9
if we had been sold for *b.* *Esth* 7:4
out of the house of *b.* *Jer* 34:13*

bonds
not any of her vows or *b.* *Num* 30:5
b. wherewith she bound her. 7
he established all her *b.* 14
he looseth *b.* of kings. *Job* 12:18
thou hast loosed my *b.* *Ps* 116:16
the yoke, and burst the *b.* *Jer* 5:5*
make thee *b.* and yokes. 27:2*
his yoke, and burst thy *b.* 30:8*
I will burst *b.* in sunder. *Nah* 1:13
b. with afflictions abide. *Acts* 20:23
worthy of death or *b.* 23:29; 26:31
a certain man left in *b.* by. 25:14*
such as I am, except these *b.* 26:29
I am an ambassador in *b.* *Eph* 6:20*
in *b.* ye are partakers of. *Phil* 1:7
b. in Christ are manifest. 13
waxing confident by my *b.* 14
supposing to add affliction to *b.* 16
for which I am in *b.* *Col* 4:3
remember my *b.* 18
I suffer trouble, even to *b.* *2 Tim* 2:9
I have begotten in my *b.* *Philem* 10
ministered to me in the *b.* 13
had compassion in my *b.* *Heb* 10:34
of *b.* and imprisonment. 11:36
remember them that are in *b.* 13:3

bondservant
him to serve as a *b.* *Lev* 25:39

bondservice
levy a tribute of *b.* *1 Ki* 9:21

bondwoman
cast out this *b.* and her son, son of *b.* shall not. *Gen* 21:10; *Gal* 4:30
not grievous because of *b.* *Gen* 21:12
son of the *b.* will I make. 13
son of the *b.* was born. *Gal* 4:23*
we are not children of the *b.* 31*

bondwomen, *see* **bondmen**

bone
this is *b.* of my bones. *Gen* 2:23
surely thou art my *b.* 29:14
break a *b.* *Ex* 12:46; *Num* 9:12
toucheth a *b.* of a man. *Num* 19:16
that I am your *b.* *Judg* 9:2
are thy *b.* *2 Sam* 5:1; *1 Chr* 11:1
art thou not of my *b.*? *2 Sam* 19:13
touch his *b.* and flesh. *Job* 2:5
my *b.* cleaveth to my skin. 19:20
arm be broken from the *b.* 31:22
soft tongue breaketh *b.* *Pr* 25:15
bones came together, *b.* to his *b.*
Ezek 37:7
when any seeth a man's *b.* 39:15
a *b.* shall not be broken. *John* 19:36

bones
(*Sometimes used as meaning the whole body*)
Moses took the *b.* of. *Ex* 13:19
the *b.* of Joseph. *Josh* 24:32

divided his concubine with her *b.* *Judg* 19:29*
took the *b.* of Saul, *b.* *2 Sam* 21:12
b. of Saul and Jonathan buried. 14
men's *b.* shall be burnt. *1 Ki* 13:2
touched the *b.* of Elisha. *2 Ki* 13:21
filled the places with *b.* of. 23:14
and took the *b.* out of the. 16
he burnt men's *b.* upon altars. 20
he burnt the *b.* of the. *2 Chr* 34:5
hast fenced me with *b.* *Job* 10:11
b. thou hast broken may. *Ps* 51:8
God scattereth the *b.* of him. 53:5
our *b.* are scattered at grave's. 141:7
It shall be marrow to thy *b.* *Pr* 3:8
envy the rottenness of *b.* 14:30
a good report maketh the *b.* 15:30
pleasant words health to *b.* 16:24
a broken spirit drieth the *b.* 17:22
nor how the *b.* do grow. *Eccl* 11:5
Lord shall make fat thy *b.* *Isa* 58:11
your *b.* shall flourish. 66:14
bring the *b.* of the kings, *b.* of priests, *b.* of prophets, and *b.* *Jer* 8:1
I will scatter your *b.* *Ezek* 6:5
fill it with the choice *b.* 24:4
burn *b.* 5, 10
valley full of *b.* 37:1
can these *b.* live? 3
prophesy upon these *b*, O ye dry *b.* 4
these *b.* are house of Israel, our *b.* 11
because he burnt *b.* of. *Amos* 2:1
burneth him, to bring out *b.* 6:10
they gnaw not the *b.* till. *Zeph* 3:3*
full of dead men's *b.* *Mat* 23:27
spirit hath not flesh and *b.* *Luke* 24:39

his **bones**

lay my *b.* beside *his b.* *1 Ki* 13:31
man move *his b.* so they let *his b.* *2 Ki* 23:18
his b. are full of sin of. *Job* 20:11
his b. are moistened with. 21:24
the multitude of *his b.* 33:19
and *his b.* that were not seen. 21
his b. as brass, *his b.* as iron. 40:18*
he keepeth all *his b.* *Ps* 34:20
let it come like oil into *his b.* 109:18
as rottenness in *his b.* *Pr* 12:4
hath broken *his b.* *Jer* 50:17
of his flesh and of *his b.* *Eph* 5:30
gave command concerning *his b.* *Heb* 11:22

my **bones**

carry up *my b.* *Gen* 50:25; *Ex* 13:19
ye are *my b.* and my. *2 Sam* 19:12
my b. beside his *b.* *1 Ki* 13:31
made all *my b.* to shake. *Job* 4:14
my b. are pierced in me. 30:17
my skin is black, *my b.* burnt. 30
O Lord, heal me, *my b.* are. *Ps* 6:2
all *my b.* are out of joint. 22:14
I may tell *my b.* 17
my b. are consumed. 31:10
my b. waxed old. 32:3
my b. shall say. Lord who? 35:10
neither there rest in *my b.* 38:3
as with a sword in *my b.* 42:10
days consumed, *my b.* are. 102:3
by reason of groaning *my b.* 5
so will he break all *my b.* *Isa* 38:13
as a fire shut up in *my b.* *Jer* 20:9
is broken, all *my b.* shake. 23:9
he sent fire into *my b.* *Lam* 1:13
he hath broken *my b.* 3:4
rottenness entered *my b.* *Hab* 3:16

their **bones**

Israel shall break *their b.* *Num* 24:8
their b. and buried. *1 Sam* 31:13
buried *their b.* under. *1 Chr* 10:12
skin cleaveth to *their b.* *Lam* 4:8
shall be on *their b.* *Ezek* 32:27
lions brake all *their b.* *Dan* 6:24
skin and flesh from *their b.* *Mi* 3:2
they break *their b.* and chop. 3

bonnets

(*Revised Version*, headtires)
thou shalt make *b.* *Ex* 28:40
put the *b.* on them. 29:9; *Lev* 8:13
they made goodly *b.* *Ex* 39:28
Lord will take away *b.* *Isa* 3:20
they shall have linen *b.* *Ezek* 44:18

book

(A record written in some permanent form. Ancient books were written on clay tablets, as in Assyria; on sheets of papyrus fastened together and (usually) rolled on one or two sticks; or of parchment in like form. Rarely sheets were fastened together somewhat like our books. The word book is sometimes used merely meaning record of any sort)

a memorial in a *b.* *Ex* 17:14
blot me out of thy *b.* 32:32
sinned, will I blot out of my *b.* 33
write these curses in a *b.* *Num* 5:23
it is said in the *b.* of the wars. 21:14
a copy of his law in a *b.* *Deut* 17:18
made end of writing law in *b.* 31:24
in the book of Jasher. *Josh* 10:13 *2 Sam* 1:18
seven parts in a *b.* *Josh* 18:9
Samuel wrote it in a *b.* *1 Sam* 10:25
written in the *b.* of acts. *1 Ki* 11:41
Hilkiah gave the *b.* to. *2 Ki* 22:8
Hilkiah delivered me a *b.* 10 *2 Chr* 34:15, 18
all the words of the *b.* *2 Ki* 22:16
the words written in *b.* 23:24
written in *b.* of kings. *1 Chr* 9:1
written in the *b.* of Samuel. 29:29*
acts of Solomon in *b.* *2 Chr* 9:29*
acts of Rehoboam in *b.* 12:15*
acts of Jehoshaphat in *b.* 20:34*
Shaphan carried *b.* to king. 34:16
words of the *b.* that is found. 21
curses that are written in the *b.* 24
search may be made in *b.* *Ezra* 4:15
Ezra opened the *b.* *Neh* 8:5
commanded to bring the *b.* *Esth* 6:1
Purim, and it was written in *b.* 9:32
they were printed in *b.* *Job* 19:23
adversary had written a *b.* 31:35*
in thy *b.* *Ps* 40:7; *Heb* 10:7
tears, are they not in thy *b.*? *Ps* 56:8
let them be blotted out of *b.* 69:28
in thy *b.* all my members. 139:16
as the words of a *b.* *Isa* 29:11
b. is delivered to him that. 12
deaf shall hear words of the *b.* 18
now go and note it in a *b.* 30:8
seek ye out of *b.* of the Lord. 34:16
write the words in a *b.* *Jer* 30:2
that subscribed the *b.* of. 32:12*
take a roll of a *b.* 36:2
read in the *b.* 10
written the words in a *b.* 45:1
so Jeremiah wrote in a *b.* all. 51:60
and lo, a roll of a *b.* *Ezek* 2:9
one found written in *b.* *Dan* 12:1
O Daniel, seal the *b.* 4
b. of the vision of Nahum. *Nah* 1:1
a *b.* of remembrance. *Mal* 3:16
the *b.* of the generation. *Mat* 1:1
as it is written in the *b.* *Luke* 3:4
delivered to Jesus the *b.* of prophet Esaias, and he opened the *b.* 4:17
he closed the *b.* and gave it to. 20
in *b.* of Psalms. 20:42; *Acts* 1:20
it is written in the *b.* *Acts* 7:42
he sprinkled the *b.* *Heb* 9:19
what thou seest, write in *b.* *Rev* 1:11
a *b.* written within. 5:1
who is worthy to open the *b.*? 2
no man was able to open the *b.* 3
he had in his hand a little *b.* 10:2
go and take the little *b.* 8
give me the little *b.* 9
I took the little *b.* 10
another *b.* was opened, the *b.* 20:12
if any take away from words of *b.* 22:19*

see **covenant**

book *of the law*

plague not in *b. of law.* *Deut* 28:61
curses in this *b. of the law.* 29:21
statutes in this *b. of the law.* 30:10
take this *b. of the law.* 31:26
this *b. of the law.* *Josh* 1:8
in *b. of the law.* 8:31; *2 Ki* 14:6
have found *b. of the law.* *2 Ki* 22:8
read in the *b. of the law.* *Neh* 8:8
are written in *b. of the law.* *Gal* 3:10

book *of life*

are written in *b. of life.* *Phil* 4:3
his name out of *b. of life.* *Rev* 3:5
not written in *b. of life.* 13:8; 17:8
b. opened, which is *b. of life.* 20:12
was not found in the *b. of life.* 15
written in Lamb's *b. of life.* 21:27
his part out of the *b. of life.* 22:19

book *of Moses*

is written in *b. of Moses.* *2 Chr* 25:4
as it is written in *b. of Moses.* 35:12
priests, as written in *b. of Moses.* *Ezra* 6:18
day they read in the *b. of Moses.* *Neh* 13:1
ye not read in the *b. of Moses*? *Mark* 12:26

this **book**

this is the *b.* of generation. *Gen* 5:1
do all written in *this b.* *Deut* 28:58 *2 Chr* 34:21
curses written in *this b.* *Deut* 29:20, 27
words of *this b.*, not hearkened to the words of *this b.* *2 Ki* 22:13
perform words written in *this b.* 23:3
all that is written in *this b.* *Jer* 25:13
an end of reading *this b.* 51:63
are not written in *this b.* *John* 20:30
the prophecy of *this b.* *Rev* 22:7
keep the sayings of *this b.* 9
seal not prophecy of *this b.* 10
prophecy of *this b.* if any add, add to him plagues written in *this b.* 18
his part from things in *this b.* 19

books

of making many *b.* *Eccl* 12:12
the *b.* were opened. *Dan* 7:10 *Rev* 20:12
I understood by *b.* the. *Dan* 9:2
could not contain the *b.* *John* 21:25
many brought their *b.* *Acts* 19:19
bring the *b.* especially. *2 Tim* 4:13
dead judged out of *b.* *Rev* 20:12

booth

as *b.* the keeper maketh. *Job* 27:18
Jonah made him a *b.* *Jonah* 4:5

booths

and Jacob made *b.* for. *Gen* 33:17
ye shall dwell in *b.* *Lev* 23:42
children of Israel dwell in *b.* 43
Israel should dwell in *b.* *Neh* 8:14
made *b.* 16

booty, -ies

b. the rest of the prey. *Num* 31:32
their camels shall be a *b.* *Jer* 49:32
thou shalt be for *b.* *Hab* 2:7
goods shall become a *b.* *Zeph* 1:13

border

Zebulun his *b.* shall. *Gen* 49:13
or touch the *b.* of the. *Ex* 19:12
it a *b.* of a handbreath, make a golden crown to the *b.* 25:25
Israel through his *b.* *Num* 21:23
ye shall point out your *b.* 34:8
slayer shall come without *b.* 35:26
Lord shall enlarge thy *b.* *Deut* 12:20
Lord made Jordan a *b.* *Josh* 22:25
buried Joshua in the *b.* of his inheritance in. 24:30; *Judg* 2:9
he went to recover his *b.* *2 Sam* 8:3*
Solomon reigned over kingdoms unto *b.* of. *1 Ki* 4:21; *2 Chr* 9:26
were able stood in *b.* *2 Ki* 3:21
brought them to the *b.* of. *Ps* 78:54
he will establish the *b.* *Pr* 15:25
into the height of his *b.* *Isa* 37:24
children come again to *b.* *Jer* 31:17
judge you in *b.* of. *Ezek* 11:10, 11
this shall be the *b.* whereby. 47:13
remove them from their *b.* *Joel* 3:6
might enlarge their *b.* *Amos* 1:13
their *b.* greater than your *b.* 6:2
have brought thee even to *b.* *Ob* 7
themselves against their *b.* *Zeph* 2:8
shall call them the *b.* of. *Mal* 1:4
Lord will be magnified from *b.* of. 5
if it were but the *b.* *Mark* 6:56
behind, and touched *b.* *Luke* 8:44

see **east, south**

border, *verb*

Hamath shall *b.* thereby. *Zech* 9:2

borders
the trees in all the b. Gen 23:17
till they come to the b. Ex 16:35
out nations, and enlarge b. 34:24
fringes in b. on fringe of b. a ribband. Num 15:38
until we passed b. 20:17; 21:22
they had b. and b. were. 1 Ki 7:28†
Ahaz cut off the b. of. 2 Ki 16:17
I will enter lodgings of his b. 19:23*
thou hast set the b. of the. Ps 74:17
he maketh peace in thy b. 147:14
we will make the b. of. S of S 1:11*
I will make thy b. of. Isa 54:12
for all thy sins, in thy b. Jer 15:13
shall be holy in the b. Ezek 45:1
he treadeth within our b. Mi 5:6
in the b. of Zabulon. Mat 4:13
enlarge the b. of their garments. 23:5

bore, -ed
master shall b. his ear. Ex 21:6
Jehoiada took chest b. 2 Ki 12:9
canst thou b. his jaw? Job 41:2*

born *again*
except a man be b. a. John 3:3, 5
ye must be b. a. 7
being b. a. not of. 1 Pet 1:23

see **first-born**

born, for *brought forth*
a child b. to him. Gen 17:17; 21:5
I have b. him a son. 21:7
Rebekah came, who was b. 24:15
because I have b. him three. 29:34
because I have b. him six. 30:20
children which they have b.? 31:43
every son b. ye shall cast. Ex 1:22
law of her that hath b. Lev 12:7
stranger shall be as one b. 19:34*
Israelites b. shall dwell in. 23:42
law for him that is b. Num 15:29
b. in the wilderness. Josh 5:5
as well stranger, as he b. 8:33*
the child that shall be b. Judg 13:8
city after name of Dan b. to. 18:29
daughter-in-law hath b. Ruth 4:15
so that the barren hath b. 1 Sam 2:5
fear not, thou hast b. a son. 4:20
child b. to thee shall. 2 Sam 12:14
a child shall be b. to. 1 Ki 13:2
the men of Gath b. in. 1 Chr 7:21
behold a son shall be b. 22:9
day perish wherein I was b. Job 3:3
yet man is b. to trouble as. 5:7
though man be b. like a wild. 11:12
thou the first man b.? 15:7
because thou wast then b.? 38:21
to people that shall be b. Ps 22:31
go astray as soon as they be b. 58:3
even children that should be b. 78:6
this man was b. there. 87:4, 6
that man b. 5
a brother is b. for. Pr 17:17
a time to be b. Eccl 3:2
b. in his kingdom. 4:14
for unto us a child is b. Isa 9:6
shall a nation be b. at once? 66:8
she that hath b. seven. Jer 15:9
woe is me, that thou hast b. 10
sons and daughters b. in this. 16:3
cursed be day wherein I was b. 20:14
where ye were not b. there. 22:26
in day thou wast b. Ezek 16:4
thy person in day thou wast b. 5
sons whom thou hast b. to me. 20
in the day that she was b. Hos 2:3
where is he that is b. king? Mat 2:2
where Christ should be b. 4
eunuchs which were so b. 19:12
had not been b. 26:24; Mark 14:21
holy thing that shall be b. Luke 1:35
to you is b. this day in city. 2:11
can a man be b. when? John 3:4
except a man be b. of water. 5
that b. of flesh is flesh, that b. of. 6
so is every one that is b. of. 8
they said to him, we be not b. 8:41
did sin, that he was b. blind? 9:2
wast altogether b. in sins, and? 34
for joy that a man is b. 16:21
to this end was I b. 18:37
tongue wherein we were b. Acts 2:8
in which time Moses was b. 7:20
Jew named Aquila b. in. Acts 18:2*
a Jew named Apollos b. at. 24*
I am a Jew b. in Tarsus. 22:3
I was free b. 28
children being not yet b. Rom 9:11
seen of me, as of one b. 1 Cor 15:8
of bond-woman, b. Gal 4:23, 29
by faith Moses when b. Heb 11:23
as new b. babes desire. 1 Pet 2:2
righteousness, is b. of. 1 John 2:29*
the child as soon as b. Rev 12:4

born *of God*
b. not of blood, but of God. John 1:13
b. of God doth not commit sin, because b. of God. 1 John 3:9
one that loveth is b. of God. 4:7
Jesus is Christ is b. of God. 5:1
is b. of God overcometh. 4
is b. of God sinneth not. 18

born *in the house*
servants b. in his house. Gen 14:14
one b. in my house is my heir. 15:3
b. in the house circumcised. 17:12
13, 23, 27
b. in the priest's house. Lev 22:11
servants b. in my house. Eccl 2:7

born *in the land*
stranger or b. in the land. Ex 12:19
the stranger as b. in the land. 48
b. in the land that blasphemeth. Lev 24:16*
stranger and b. in land. Num 9:14
whether b. in land. 15:30*

born *of a woman,* or *women*
man that is b. of a woman. Job 14:1
that is b. of a woman that he? 15:14
he be clean b. of a woman? 25:4
them that are b. of a woman. Mat 11:11; Luke 7:28

borne
ark may be b. with them. Ex 25:14
that the table may be b. with. 28
which the house was b. Judg 16:29
I have b. chastisement. Job 34:31
enemy, then I could have b. Ps 55:12
for thy sake I have b. 69:7
surely he hath b. griefs. Isa 53:4
ye shall be b. upon her sides. 66:12
they must be b. because. Jer 10:5
because he hath b. it. Lam 3:28*
fathers sinned, and we have b. 5:7
hast b. thy lewdness. Ezek 16:58
b. their shame. 32:24; 36:6; 39:26
have b. the tabernacle of. Amos 5:26
which have b. burden. Mat 20:12
burdens, grievous to be b. 23:4
Luke 11:46
sick of palsy, was b. of. Mark 2:3
hast b. him hence tell. John 20:15
he was b. of the soldiers. Acts 21:35
as we have b. image of. 1 Cor 15:49
has b. and hast patience. Rev 2:3

see **witness**

borrow
every woman shall b. of. Ex 3:22*
11:2*
if a man b. ought. 22:14
thou shalt not b. Deut 15:6; 28:12
go b. vessels abroad, b. 2 Ki 4:3
him that would b. of thee. Mat 5:42

borrowed
they b. of Egyptians. Ex 12:35*
alas, master, for it was b. 2 Ki 6:5
we have b. money for. Neh 5:4

borrower
and the b. is servant to. Pr 22:7
with the lender, so with b. Isa 24:2

borroweth
wicked b. and payeth not. Ps 37:21

bosom
given my maid into thy b. Gen 16:5
put now thy hand into thy b. Ex 4:6
carry them in thy b. Num 11:12
the wife of thy b. entice. Deut 13:6
evil toward the wife of his b. 28:54
evil toward husband of her b. 56
child and laid it in her b. Ruth 4:16
lay in his b. 2 Sam 12:3
thy master's wives into thy b. 8
let her lie in thy b. 1 Ki 1:2
took my son, and laid it in her b. and laid dead child in my b. 1 Ki 3:20
Elijah took him out of her b. 17:19
hiding iniquity in my b. Job 31:33
prayer returned into my b. Ps 35:13
right hand out of thy b. 74:11
render seven-fold into their b. 79:12
bear in my b. the reproach. 89:50
he that bindeth sheaves, his b. 129:7
wilt thou embrace the b.? Pr 5:20
can a man take fire in his b.? 6:27
man taketh gift out of the b. 17:23
hideth his hand in b. 19:24*; 26:15*
a reward in the b. pacifieth. 21:14
anger resteth in the b. of. Eccl 7:9
carry the lambs in his b. Isa 40:11
even recompense into their b. 65:6
measure former work into their b. 7
iniquity of fathers into b. Jer 32:18
poured into mother's b. Lam 2:12
from her that lieth in thy b. Mi 7:5
good measure into your b. Luke 6:38
angels into Abraham's b. 16:22
Abraham, and Lazarus in his b. 23
in the b. of the Father. John 1:18
leaning on Jesus' b. a disciple. 13:23

Bosor, *see* **Balaam**

bosses
thick b. of his bucklers. Job 15:26

botch
(*Revised Version,* boil)
the Lord will smite thee with the b. Deut 28:27, 35

both
were b. naked. Gen 2:25
the eyes of b. opened. 3:7
b. the daughters of Lot with. 19:36
b. of them made a covenant. 21:27
so they went b. of them. 22:8
deprived of you b. in one day? 27:45
they may judge betwixt us b. 31:37
cause of b. shall come. Ex 22:9
oath of the Lord be between b. 11
b. of them surely be put to death. Lev 20:11, 12; Deut 22:22
and Miriam, b. came. Num 12:5
Phinehas thrust b. through. 25:8
shall stand before Lord. Deut 19:17
they shall die b. of them. 1 Sam 2:34
went out b. of them. 9:26
as we have sworn b. of us. 20:42
that might lay hand on b. Job 9:33
b. are abomination. Pr 17:15; 20:10
the Lord hath made even b. 20:12
knoweth the ruin of them b.? 24:22
better than b. is he that. Eccl 4:3
they shall b. burn together. Isa 1:31
land shall be forsaken of b. 7:16
and they are fallen b. Jer 46:12
b. twain shall come forth. Ezek 21:19
then I saw that they b. 23:13
do evil with b. hands. Mi 7:3
of peace between b. Zech 6:13
b. shall fall. Mat 15:14; Luke 6:39
frankly forgave them b. Luke 7:42
but Pharisees confess b. Acts 23:8
peace, who hath made b. Eph 2:14
he might reconcile b. unto God. 16
in b. I stir up your 2 Pet 3:1
b. were cast alive into. Rev 19:20

bottle
(*Ancient Eastern bottles were generally the skins of the smaller animals. Clay bottles made by the potters were less common, but are meant in some verses, as* Jer 19:1. *Glass bottles were known in Egypt and so probably to the Hebrews, but were largely tear-bottles, in which mourners collected their tears, afterwards putting them into the tombs. This custom is referred to in* Ps 56:8)
took a b. of water. Gen 21:14
water was spent in the b. 15
she filled the b. 19
she opened a b. of milk. Judg 4:19
Hannah took a b. of. 1 Sam 1:24
meet another carrying a b. 10:3
Jesse took a b. of wine. 16:20
fruits, a b. of wine. 2 Sam 16:1
thou my tears into thy b. Ps 56:8

I am become like a *b.* *Ps* 119:83
every *b.* shall be filled. *Jer* 13:12
get a potter's earthen *b.* 19:1
break the *b.* 10
puttest thy *b.* to him. *Hab* 2:15*

bottles
(*Revised Version,* wine-skins, *except where marked* *)
Gibeonites took wine *b.* *Josh* 9:4
b. of wine which we filled. 13
Abigail took two *b.* of. *1 Sam* 25:18
ready to burst like new *b.* *Job* 32:19
or who can stay the *b.* of ? 38:37
empty his vessels, break *b.* *Jer* 48:12
sick with *b.* of wine. *Hos* 7:5*
into old *b.* else *b.* break. *Mat* 9:17
Mark 2:22; *Luke* 5:37, 38

bottom
they sank into the *b.* as. *Ex* 15:5
pour blood beside *b.* of altar. 29:12
Lev 4:7, 18, 25, 30; 5:9; 8:15; 9:9
covereth the *b.* of the sea. *Job* 36:30
the *b.* thereof of gold. *S of S* 3:10
they came at the *b.* of. *Dan* 6:24
hid from my sight in *b.* *Amos* 9:3
I went down to the *b.* of. *Jonah* 2:6
myrtle-trees in the *b.* *Zech* 1:8
top to *b.* *Mat* 27:51; *Mark* 15:38

bottomless *pit*
(*Revised Version,* abyss)
given the key of the *b. pit.* *Rev* 9:1
he opened the *b. pit.* 2
a king, the angel of the *b. pit.* 11
that ascendeth out of *b. pit.* 11:7
beast shall ascend out of *b. pit.* 17:8
angel having key of the *b. pit.* 20:1
and cast him into the *b. pit.* 3

bough
Joseph is a fruitful *b.* even a *b.* by a well. *Gen* 49:22
Abimelech cut down a *b.* *Judg* 9:48
cut down every man his *b.* 49
the Lord shall lop the *b.* *Isa* 10:33
berries in top of uttermost *b.* 17:6
strong cities be as a forsaken *b.* 9*

boughs
b. of goodly trees, *b.* *Lev* 23:40*
shalt not go over *b.* *Deut* 24:20
mule went under the *b.* *2 Sam* 18:9
and brought forth *b.* like. *Job* 14:9
b. were like cedar-trees. *Ps* 80:10
she sent out her *b.* 11
I will take hold of the *b.* *S of S* 7:8
when the *b.* thereof are. *Isa* 27:11
it shall bring forth *b.* *Ezek* 17:23
was among the thick *b.* 31:3, 14
made their nests in *b.* 6; *Dan* 4:12

bought
man-child born in house *b.* with his. *Gen* 17:12, 13, 23, 27; *Ex* 12:44
Jacob *b.* a field. *Gen* 33:19
Josh 24:32
Potiphar *b.* Joseph of the. *Gen* 39:1
money for the corn they *b.* 47:14
Joseph *b.* all land of Egypt. 20, 23
Abraham *b.* 49:30; 50:13; *Acts* 7:16
n hand of him that *b.* it. *Lev* 25:28
established for ever to him that *b.* 30
reckon with him that *b.* him. 50
he money that he was *b.* for. 51
sanctify a field which he *b.* 27:22
return to him of whom it was *b.* 24
father that *b.* thee ? *Deut* 32:6
have *b.* all that was. *Ruth* 4:9
little ewe-lamb he had *b.* *2 Sam* 12:3
David *b.* threshing-floor and. 24:24
Omri *b.* the hill Samaria. *1 Ki* 16:24
continued in work, nor *b.* *Neh* 5:16
b. the field of Hanameel. *Jer* 32:9
fields shall be *b.* in this land. 43
b. her to me for 15 pieces. *Hos* 3:2
all that he had, and *b.* *Mat* 13:46
cast out them that sold and *b.* in. 21:12; *Mark* 11:15; *Luke* 19:45
took counsel, and *b.* field. *Mat* 27:7
Joseph *b.* fine linen. *Mark* 15:46
had *b.* sweet spices to come. 16:1
have *b.* a piece of. *Luke* 14:18
have *b.* five yoke of oxen. 19
did eat, they drank, they *b.* 17:28
are *b.* with a price, *1 Cor* 6:20; 7:23
denying the Lord that *b.* *2 Pet* 2:1

bound, *actively*
b. Isaac his son, and laid. *Gen* 22:9
the midwife *b.* on his hand. 38:28
took Simeon and *b.* him. 42:24
he *b.* the ephod with. *Lev* 8:7
she had *b.* her soul. *Num* 30:4, 5
6, 7, 8, 9, 10, 11
she *b.* a scarlet line in. *Josh* 2:21
they *b.* Samson with. *Judg* 15:13
b. with withs. 16:8
b. with ropes. 12
b. with fetters. 21
he *b.* two talents of silver. *2 Ki* 5:23
he shut up Hoshea and *b.* 17:4
they *b.* Zedekiah with. 25:7
b. Manasseh. *2 Chr* 33:11
b. Jehoiakim. 36:6
who hath *b.* the waters in. *Pr* 30:4
have *b.* and strengthened. *Hos* 7:15
Herod *b.* John. *Mat* 14:3
Mark 6:17
b. Jesus. *Mat* 27:2; *Mark* 15:1
John 18:12
daughter whom Satan *b.* *Luke* 13:16
Agabus *b.* his own. *Acts* 21:11
as they *b.* Paul he said. 22:25*, 29
b. themselves under curse. 23:12
14, 21
b. Satan a thousand years. *Rev* 20:2

bound, *passively*
king's prisoners are *b.* *Gen* 39:20
prison where Joseph was *b.* 40:3
butler and baker which were *b.* 5
one of your brethren be *b.* 42:19
no cover *b.* on it. *Num* 19:15
mightest be *b.* *Judg* 16:6, 10, 13
soul of my lord *b.* *1 Sam* 25:29
thy hands were not *b.* *2 Sam* 3:34
if they be *b.* in fetters. *Job* 36:8
being *b.* in affliction. *Ps* 107:10
foolishness is *b.* in heart. *Pr* 22:15
b. by the archers, all are *b.* *Isa* 22:3
of prison to them that are *b.* 61:1
of my transgressions is *b.* *Lam* 1:14
b. in their coats. *Dan* 3:21
fell down *b.* 23
did not we cast three men *b.*? 24
be *b.* in heaven. *Mat* 16:19; 18:18
lay *b.* with them that. *Mark* 15:7
b. hand and foot, face *b.* *John* 11:44
b. to Caiaphas. 18:24
bring them *b.* *Acts* 9:2, 21; 22:5
Peter *b.* with chains. 12:6
behold I go *b.* in the Spirit. 20:22
I am ready not to be *b.* only. 21:13
left Paul *b.* 24:27
b. by law of husband. *Rom* 7:2
1 Cor 7:39
art thou *b.* unto a wife? *1 Cor* 7:27
b. to thank God. *2 Thes* 1:3; 2:13
the word of God is not *b.* *2 Tim* 2:9
that are in bonds, as *b.* *Heb* 13:3
loose the angels *b.* *Rev* 9:14

bound *with chains*
which are *b. with chains.* *Ps* 68:6*
Zedekiah *b. with chains.*
Jer 39:7; 52:11
Jeremiah *b. with chains.* 40:1
great men *b. with chains.* *Nah* 3:10
been often *b. with chains.* *Mark* 5:4
was kept *b. with chains.* *Luke* 8:29
Paul to be *b. with* two *chains.*
Acts 21:33
I am *b. with* this *chain.* 28:20

bound *up*
his life is *b. up* in the. *Gen* 44:30
not been closed neither *b. up.* *Isa* 1:6
plead, that thou be *b. up.* *Jer* 30:13
it shall not be *b. up.* *Ezek* 30:21
nor have ye *b. up* that. 34:4
the wind hath *b.* her *up.* *Hos* 4:19*
iniquity of Ephraim is *b. up.* 13:12
he *b. up* his wounds. *Luke* 10:34

bound, *substantive*
to utmost *b.* of the. *Gen* 49:26
take it to the *b.* thereof. *Job* 38:20
to waters set a *b.* *Ps* 104:9
sand for the *b.* of the sea. *Jer* 5:22
them that remove the *b.* *Hos* 5:10*

bounds
thou shalt set *b.* to the. *Ex* 19:12
set *b.* about the mount. 23
I will set thy *b.* from the. 23:31
he set the *b.* of the. *Deut* 32:8
hast appointed his *b.* *Job* 14:5
compassed the waters with *b.* 26:10*
I have removed the *b.* *Isa* 10:13
hast determined the *b.* *Acts* 17:26

bountiful
he that hath a *b.* eye. *Pr* 22:9
churl be said to be *b.* *Isa* 32:5

bountifully
he hath dealt *b.* with me. *Ps* 13:6
the Lord hath dealt *b.* 116:7
deal *b.* with thy servant. 119:17
thou shalt deal *b.* with me. 142:7
soweth *b.* shall reap *b.* *2 Cor* 9:6

bountifulness
enriched to all *b.* *2 Cor* 9:11*

bounty
gave of his royal *b.* *1 Ki* 10:13
and make up your *b.* that the same might be ready as *b.* *2 Cor.* 9:5

bow, *noun*
[1] *An instrument for shooting arrows,* Gen 27:3; 2 Ki 9:24. [2] *The rainbow,* Gen 9:13, 14. [3] *Faith and patience,* Gen 49:24.
set my *b.* in the cloud. *Gen* 9:13
the *b.* shall be seen. 14, 16
take, thy quiver and thy *b.* 27:3
I took of the Amorite with *b.* 48:22
his *b.* abode in strength. 49:24
with thy sword nor *b.* *Josh* 24:12
gave David his sword, *b.* *1 Sam* 18:4
Judah use of the *b.* *2 Sam* 1:18
the *b.* of Jonathan turned not. 22
a certain man drew a *b.* and smote the king. *1 Ki* 22:34; *2 Chr* 18:33
smite those taken with *b.* *2 Ki* 6:22
Jehu drew a *b.* with his full. 9:24
take *b.* and arrows, he took *b.* 13:15
put thy hand upon the *b.* 16
able to shoot with *b.* *1 Chr* 5:18
armed with *b.* and shooting *b.* 12:2
my *b.* was renewed. *Job* 29:20
I will not trust in my *b.* *Ps* 44:6
he breaketh the *b.* and. 46:9
there brake arrows of the *b.* 76:3
aside like a deceitful *b.* 78:57
gave them as stubble to *b.* *Isa* 41:2
escape to nations that draw *b.* 66:19
they shall lay hold on *b.* *Jer* 6:23
behold, I will break the *b.* 49:35
they shall hold the *b.* 50:42
he hath bent his *b.* *Lam* 2:4
as appearance of the *b.* *Ezek* 1:28
I will smite thy *b.* 39:3
I will break *b.* of Israel. *Hos* 1:5
I will not save them by *b.* 7
I will break the *b.* 2:18
they are like a deceitful *b.* 7:16
he that handleth *b.* *Amos* 2:15
thy *b.* was made naked. *Hab* 3:9
when I filled the *b.* *Zech* 9:13
sat on the horse had a *b.* *Rev* 6:2
see **bend, bent, battle-bow**

bow, *verb*
nor serve, nor *b.* yourselves to their gods. *Josh* 23:7; *2 Ki* 17:35
I *b.* myself in house of. *2 Ki* 5:18
they *b.* themselves. *Job* 39:3
go down to dust, shall *b.* *Ps* 22:29
dwell in wilderness shall *b.* 72:9
b. thy heavens, O Lord. 144:5
and *b.* thine ear, to my. *Pr* 5:1*
evil *b.* before the good. 14:19
the strong men shall *b.* *Eccl* 12:3
and *b.* myself before? *Mi* 6:6
the perpetual hills did *b.* *Hab* 3:6

bow *down*
b. down, mother's sons *b. down.* *Gen* 27:29
shall thy brethren *b. down*? 37:10
father's children shall *b. down.* 49:8
servants shall *b. down* to. *Ex* 11:8
shalt not *b. down.* 20:5; *Deut* 5:9
thou shalt not *b. down* to. *Ex* 23:24
up image to *b. down* to it. *Lev* 26:1
other gods to *b. down.* *Judg* 2:19
I *b. down* in house of. *2 Ki* 5:18
b. down thine ear. 19:16*; *Ps* 86:1
and let others *b. down.* *Job* 31:10
b. down thine ear. *Ps* 31:2; *Pr* 22:17

let us worship and *b. down. Ps* 95:6
without me they *b. down. Isa* 10:4
they stoop, they *b. down.* 46:2
and queens shall *b. down.* 49:23
have said, *b. down.* 51:23
is it to *b. down* his head ? 58:5
despised thee shall *b. down.* 60:14
ye shall all *b. down* to. 65:12
eyes darkened, *b. down. Rom* 11:10

bow *knee*

before him *b.* the *knee. Gen* 41:43
every *knee* shall *b. Isa* 45:23
Rom 14:11
I *b.* my *knees* unto Father. *Eph* 3:14
every *knee* shall *b. Phil* 2:10

bowed

and their children *b. Gen* 33:6
Leah with children *b.*, Rachel *b.* 7
Joseph's brethren *b.* 43:26
Issachar *b.* his shoulder. 49:15
served other gods, and *b.* to them.
Josh 23:16; *Judg* 2:12, 17
he *b.* where he *b.* he fell. *Judg* 5:27
fell on her face and *b. Ruth* 2:10
Phinehas' wife *b. 1 Sam* 4:19
David *b.* himself. 20:41
Abigail *b.* 25:23, 41
David *b.* the heart of. *2 Sam* 19:14
he *b.* heavens. 22:10; *Ps* 18:9
Bath-sheba *b. 1 Ki* 1:16, 31
not *b.* to Baal. 19:18; *Rom* 11:4
sons of the prophets *b. 2 Ki* 2:15
b. herself to ground. 4:37
b. themselves upon the. *2 Chr* 7:3
the king and all present *b.* 29:29
b. to Haman. *Esth* 3:2
Mordecai *b.* not. 5
b. the knee before him. *Mat* 27:29*
spirit of infirmity, was *b. Luke* 13:11

bowed *down*

Abraham *b. down. Gen* 23:12
Joseph's brethren *b. down.* 42:6
43:28
did eat, and *b. down* to. *Num* 25:2
of the people *b. down* on. *Judg* 7:6
be his gods, and *b. down. 2 Chr* 25:14
I *b. down* heavily. *Ps* 35:14
I am *b. down* greatly. 38:6
our soul is *b. down.* 44:25
my soul is *b. down.* 57:6
raiseth those *b. down.* 145:14
146:8
haughtiness of men shall be *b. down.*
Isa 2:11
loftiness of man be *b. down.* 17
I was *b. down* at the hearing. 21:3*
were afraid and *b. down. Luke* 24:5

bowed *head*

man *b.* his *head. Gen* 24:26, 48
they *b.* their *heads.* 43:28
then they *b.* their *heads* and.
Ex 4:31; 12:27; *Neh* 8:6
Moses *b.* his head to earth. *Ex* 34:8
Balaam *b.* his *head. Num* 22:31
b. down their *heads. 1 Chr* 29:20
Jehoshaphat *b.* his *head. 2 Chr* 20:18
sang praises and *b. heads.* 29:30
Jesus *b.* his *head* and. *John* 19:30

bowed *himself*

Abraham *b. himself. Gen* 18:2; 23:7,
12
Lot *b. himself.* 19:1
Jacob *b. himself.* 33:3; 47:31
Joseph *b. himself.* 48:12
Samson *b. himself. Judg* 16:30
David stooped and *b. himself.*
1 Sam 24:8*
Saul *b. himself.* 28:14*
Mephibosheth *b. himself.*
2 Sam 9:8*
Joab *b. himself.* 14:22*
Absalom *b. himself.* 33
Cushi *b. himself* to Joab. 18:21
Araunah *b. himself* before king.
24:20; *1 Chr* 21:21
Nathan *b. himself. 1 Ki* 1:23
the king *b. himself* on bed. 47
Adonijah came and *b. himself.* 53*
Solomon rose and *b. himself.* 2:19

bowels

(Used often in Scripture for the seat of pity or kindness)

out of thine own *b.* shall. *Gen* 15:4
people shall be from thy *b.* 25:23
for his *b.* did yearn. 43:30
water shall go into thy *b. Num* 5:22
which proceed of thy *b. 2 Sam* 7:12
son which came forth of my *b.* 16:11
Joab shed out Amasa's *b.* 20:10
for her *b.* yearned. *1 Ki* 3:26
by disease of thy *b. 2 Chr* 21:15
the Lord smote him in his *b.* 18
his *b.* fell out. 19
that came of his own *b.* slew. 32:21
meat in his *b.* is turned. *Job* 20:14
my *b.* boiled, and rested not. 30:27
in the midst of my *b. Ps* 22:14
took me out of my mother's *b.* 71:6
let it come into his *b.* 109:18*
my *b.* were moved. *S of S* 5:4
my *b.* shall sound. *Isa* 16:11
the offspring of thy *b.* 48:19
from the *b.* of my mother. 49:1
is the sounding of thy *b.* ? 63:15
my *b.* my *b.* I am pained. *Jer* 4:19
therefore my *b.* are troubled. 31:20
O Lord, my *b.* are. *Lam* 1:20; 2:11
fill thy *b.* with this roll. *Ezek* 3:3
satisfy their souls, nor fill *b.* 7:19
Judas burst, and all his *b. Acts* 1:18
straitened in your *b. 2 Cor* 6:12*
long after you in *b.* of. *Phil* 1:8*
in Christ if there be any *b.* 2:1*
put on *b.* of mercies. *Col* 3:12*
the *b.* of the saints are. *Philem* 7*
receive him that is my own *b.* 12
yea, brother, refresh my *b.* 20*
and shutteth up his *b. 1 John* 3:17*

boweth

b. on his knees to drink. *Judg* 7:5
the mean man *b. Isa* 2:9

bowing

Eliezer *b.* himself to. *Gen* 24:52
set their eyes, *b.* down. *Ps* 17:11*
as a *b.* wall shall ye be. 62:3*
did spit upon him, *b. Mark* 15:19

bowl

each *b.* weighing seventy. *Num* 7:85
wringed the dew, a *b. Judg* 6:38
the golden *b.* be broken. *Eccl* 12:6
candlestick of gold with *b. Zech* 4:2
olive trees one on right side of *b.* 3

bowls

make *b.* to cover. *Ex* 25:29; 37:16
dishes and *b. Num* 4:7
b. and snuffers of pure. *1 Ki* 7:50
1 Chr 28:17
that drink wine in *b. Amos* 6:6
shall be filled like *b. Zech* 9:15
pots in Lord's house like *b.* 14:20

bowmen

from the noise of the *b. Jer* 4:29

bows

b. are broken. *1 Sam* 2:4
were armed with *b. 1 Chr* 12:2
army that drew *b. 2 Chr* 14:8
Uzziah prepared for them *b.* 26:14
I set the people with *b. Neh* 4:13
the other half held spears and *b.* 16
their *b.* shall be broken. *Ps* 37:15
with arrows and *b. Isa* 7:24
their *b.* shall dash young men. 13:18
every one of their *b. Jer* 51:56
they shall burn the *b. Ezek* 39:9

bowshot

him as it were a *b. Gen* 21:16

box

(*Revised Version,* vial *or* cruse)
take this *b.* of oil. *2 Ki* 9:1, 3
alabaster *b. Mat* 26:7; *Mark* 14:3
brake *b.* and poured. *Mark* 14:3
Luke 7:37

box-tree

the desert the pine and *b. Isa* 41:19
of Lebanon shall come, the *b.* 60:13

boy, -s

the *b.* grew, and Esau. *Gen* 25:27
they have given a *b. Joel* 3:3
streets shall be full of *b. Zech* 8:5

Bozrah

Jobab of *B.* reigned. *Gen* 36:33
Lord hath a sacrifice in *B. Isa* 34:6
with dyed garments from *B. Isa* 63:1
judgement is come from *B. Jer* 48:24
B. shall become desolation. 49:13
shall spread his wings over *B.* 22
shall devour palaces of *B. Amos* 1:12
together as sheep of *B. Mi* 2:12

bracelet, -s

when he saw *b. Gen* 24:30
thy signet, thy *b.* 38:18*, 25
were willing, brought *b. Ex* 35:22*
Num 31:50
the *b.* on his arm. *2 Sam* 1:10
take away the chains, *b. Isa* 3:19
and I put *b. Ezek* 16:11

brake

the hail *b.* every tree. *Ex* 9:25
the people *b.* off the ear-rings. 32:3
cast tables and *b.* 19; *Deut* 9:17
they *b.* pitchers. *Judg* 7:19, 20
a piece of a millstone to *b.* 9:53
b. the withs as a thread. 16:9
b. new ropes. 12
Eli fell and his neck *b. 1 Sam* 4:18
mighty men *b.* through. *2 Sam* 23:16
1 Chr 11:18
strong wind *b.* in pieces. *1 Ki* 19:11
Baal's images *b.* they. *2 Ki* 11:18
b. images, *b.* brazen serpent. 18:4
Josiah *b.* the images. 23:14
2 Chr 34:4
Arabians came and *b. 2 Chr* 21:17
shut up the sea when it *b.* ? 38:8
and *b.* up for it my decreed. 10*
there *b.* he the arrows. *Ps* 76:3
moreover, he *b.* the whole. 105:16
smote their vines, *b.* trees. 33
and the plague *b.* in. 106:29
out of darkness he *b.* their. 107:14
took the yoke and *b.* it. *Jer* 28:10
my covenant they *b.* through. 31:32
whose covenant he *b. Ezek* 17:16
spirit troubled and sleep *b. Dan* 2:1
smote the image and *b.* feet. 34, 45
the lions *b.* all their bones. 6:24
fourth beast devoured and *b.* 7:7
goat smote ram, and *b.* his. 8:7
blessed and *b. Mat* 14:19; 15:36
26:26; *Mark* 6:41; 8:6; 14:22
Luke 9:16; 22:19; 24:30
1 Cor 11:24
I *b.* the five loaves. *Mark* 8:19
she *b.* the box and poured. 14:3
their net *b. Luke* 5:6
he *b.* the bands. 8:29
soldiers *b.* the legs. of. *John* 19:32
saw that he was dead, *b.* not legs. 33

brake *down*

b. down image of Baal. *2 Ki* 10:27
2 Chr 23:17
people went and *b. down. 2 Ki* 11:18
king of Israel *b. down* wall. 14:13
2 Chr 25:23; 36:19; *Jer* 39:8
52:14
he *b. down* the houses of. *2 Ki* 23:7
he *b. down* high places. 8
b. down altars. 12, 15
Asa *b. down* images. *2 Chr* 14:3
Uzziah *b. down* the wall of. 26:6
they *b. down* the altars. 34:4

brakest

the first table thou *b. Ex* 34:1
Deut 10:2
thou *b.* heads of. *Ps* 74:13, 14
leaned on thee, thou *b. Ezek* 29:

bramble, -s

said all the trees to *b. Judg* 9:14
b. said, let fire come out of *b.* 1
nettles and *b.* shall come. *Isa* 34:13
nor of a *b.*-bush gather. *Luke* 6:4

branch

knop and flower in one *b. Ex* 25:3
37:1
cut down a *b.* with. *Num* 13:2
his *b.* shooteth forth. *Job* 8:16
and the tender *b.* thereof. 14:
and his *b.* shall not be green. 15:3
above shall his *b.* be cut off. 18:1
dew lay all night upon my *b.* 29:1
the *b.* thou madest strong. *Ps* 80:1
righteous flourish as a *b. Pr* 11:28
in that day shall *b.* of the. *Isa* 4:
the Lord will cut off *b.* and. 9:1

and a b. shall grow out. Isa 11:1
cast out like an abominable b. 14:19
cities be as an uppermost b. 17:9*
nor any work which b. or. 19:15*
the b. of terrible ones shall. 25:5*
the b. of my planting. 60:21
to David a righteous b. Jer 23:5
b. of righteousness grow. 33:15
they put the b. to their. Ezek 8:17
the vine tree more than b.? 15:2
eagle took the highest b. 17:3*, 22*
out of a b. of her roots. Dan 11:7*
forth my servant the b. Zech 3:8
the man whose name is the b. 6:12
them neither root nor b. Mal 4:1
when b. is yet tender. Mat 24:32
Mark 13:28
every b. that beareth not, and every b. that beareth. John 15:2
as the b. cannot bear fruit itself. 4
he is cast forth as a b. 6

branches

in vine were three b. Gen 40:10
the three b. are three days. 12
a bough, whose b. run over. 49:22
six b. come out of candlestick, three b. Ex 25:32; 37:18, 21
take b. of palm trees. Lev 23:40
Neh 8:15
flame shall dry up his b. Job 15:30
she sent out her b. to. Ps 80:11*
fowls which sing among b. 104:12
Moab's b. are stretched. Isa 16:8
in the utmost fruitful b. 17:6
take away and cut down b. 18:5*
there shall he consume the b. 27:10
and the b. are broken. Jer 11:16
spreading vine whose b. Ezek 17:6
she was fruitful and full of b. 19:10
fire is gone out of a rod of her b. 14
not like the Assyrian's b. 31:8
of Israel, ye shall shoot b. 36:8
hew down tree, cut off b. Dan 4:14
consume Ephraim's b. Hos 11:6*
his b. shall spread. 14:6
my vine waste, b. Joel 1:7
have marred their vine b. Nah 2:2
be these two olive b.? Zech 4:12
birds lodge in the b. Mat 13:32
Luke 13:19
others cut down b. Mat 21:8
Mark 11:8; John 12:13
shooteth out b. Mark 4:32
am the vine, ye are b. John 15:5
oot be holy, so the b. Rom 11:16
f the b. be broken off. 17, 19
oast not against the b. 18
God spared not the natural b. 21

brand, -s

e had set b. on fire. Judg 15:5
s not this a b. plucked.? Zech 3:2

brandish

hall I b. my sword? Ezek 32:10

brasen

(American Revision, brazen)
ake b. rings. Ex 27:4
grate. 35:16; 38:4
eir b. sockets twenty. 38:10
dden in a b. pot. Lev 6:28
censers. Num 16:39
bars. 1 Ki 4:13
wheels. 7:30
ade b. shields. 14:27
oxen. 2 Ki 16:17
ake the b. serpent. 18:4
sea Chaldees. 25:13; Jer 52:17
ade a b. scaffold. 2 Chr 6:13
ade thee this day b. Jer 1:18
ake thee a fenced b. wall. 15:20
b. bulls. 52:20
vessels. Mark 7:4

brass

Modern brass, the alloy of copper d zinc, is not meant by the name the Bible, as zinc was not then own. The word is generally used a simple metal, and means cop-r. In other places it is properly onze, the alloy of copper and tin. e word is very often used uratively to represent great ength, or great hardness)

take gold, silver, b. Ex 25:3; 35:5
taches of b. 26:11; 36:18
cast five sockets of b. 26:37; 27:10
17, 18; 36:38; 38:11, 17, 19
overlay altar with b. 27:2, 6; 38:2
net work of b. 27:4
pins of the court of b. 19
laver of b., foot of b. 30:18
work in gold, silver, b. 31:4; 35:32
rings of b. 38:5
overlaid the staves with b. 6
the b. of the offering was. 29
brasen altar, and grate of b. 39:39
made a serpent of b.... a pole, when he beheld serpent of b. Num 21:9
hills thou mayest dig b. Deut 8:9
heaven over thy head be b. 28:23
bound with fetters of b. Judg 16:21
Goliath had an helmet of b.
1 Sam 17:5, 38
and he had greaves of b. 6
David took much b. 2 Sam 8:8
1 Chr 18:8
Hiram was worker in b. 1 Ki 7:14
cast pillars of b. 7:15; 2 Ki 25:13
chapiters of b. 1 Ki 7:16; 2 Ki 25:17
Jer 52:22
bases of b. 1 Ki 7:27
plates of b. 30
lavers of b. 38; 2 Chr 4:16
pots and shovels of bright b.
1 Ki 7:45
weight of the b. was not found.
47; 2 Chr 4:18
Zedekiah with fetters of b. 2 Ki 25:7
carried b. to Babylon. 13; Jer 52:17
sound with cymbals of b. 1 Chr 15:19.
b. in abundance. 22:3; 29:7
prepared the b. for things of b. 29:2
Rehoboam made shields of b.
2 Chr 12:10
is my flesh b.? Job 6:12
bones are as strong pieces of b. 40:18
Leviathan esteemeth b. as. 41:27
hath broken gates of b. Ps 107:16
in pieces the gates of b. Isa 45:2
for wood I bring b. for b. 60:17
that the b. of it may. Ezek 24:11
belly and thighs were of b. Dan 2:32
another third kingdom of b. 39
whose nails were of b. 7:19
his feet in colour polished b. 10:6
horn iron, and hoofs b. Mi 4:13
were mountains of b. Zech 6:1
provide neither gold nor b. Mat 10:9
sounding b. or cymbal. 1 Cor 13:1
feet like to fine b. Rev 1:15; 2:18
should not worship idols of b. 9:20

iron and **brass**

instructor in b. and iron. Gen 4:22
your heaven iron, your earth b.
Lev 26:19
b. and iron which may. Num 31:22
shoes be iron and b. as. Deut 33:25
return with b. and iron. Josh 22:8
prepared b. and iron. 1 Chr 22:14, 16
to work in b. and iron. 2 Chr 2:7, 14
wrought in iron and b. to. 24:12
iron out of the earth, and b. Job 28:2
an iron sinew, and brow b. Isa 48:4
for b. gold, for iron silver. 60:17
they are b. and iron. Jer 6:28
Ezek 22:18
they gather iron and b. Ezek 22:20
was iron, clay, b. Dan 2:35, 45
a band of iron and b. in. 4:15, 23
gods of silver, b. and iron. 5:4

vessels of **brass**

make all vessels of b. Ex 27:3
made vessels of b. 38:3
all vessels of b. Josh 6:19
vessels of b. and iron they put. 24
brought vessels of b. 2 Sam 8:10
1 Chr 18:10
vessels of b. took they. 2 Ki 25:14
Jer 52:18
the b. of all these vessels was without weight. 2 Ki 25:16; Jer 52:20
traded in vessels of b. Ezek 27:13
Rev 18:12

bravery

will take away their b. Isa 3:18†

brawler, -s

(Revised Version, contentious)
a bishop must be no b. 1 Tim 3:3
to be no b. Tit 3:2

brawling

with b. woman in. Pr 25:24

bray, -ed

doth the wild ass b. Job 6:5
among the bushes they b. 30:7
though thou shouldest b. Prov. 27:22

breach

(*A gap; a rupture; a breaking. Used literally and figuratively*)
the midwife said, this b. Gen 38:29
b. for b. eye for eye. Lev 24:20
ye shall know my b. Num 14:34*
the Lord hath made a b. Judg 21:15
broken forth as the b. 2 Sam 5:20
Lord made a b. on Uzzah. 6:8*
1 Chr 13:11*
any b. shall be found. 2 Ki 12:5
Lord our God made a b. 1 Chr 15:13
and there was no b. Neh 6:1
he breaketh me with b. upon b.
Job 16:14
Moses stood in the b. Ps 106:23
but perverseness is a b. Pr 15:4
us make a b. therein. Isa 7:6
iniquity shall be to you as b. 30:13
the day the Lord bindeth up b. 26*
called repairer of the b. 58:12
people broken with a b. Jer 14:17
thy b. is great like sea. Lam 2:13
a city wherein is a b. Ezek 26:10

breaches

Asher abode in his b. Judg 5:17*
repaired b. of the city. 1 Ki 11:27
let them repair the b. 2 Ki 12:5
priests had not repaired the b. 6
masons to repair b. of. 12; 22:5
b. began to be stopped. Neh 4:7
heal the b. thereof. Ps 60:2
ye have seen the b. Isa 22:9
shall go out at the b. Amos 4:3
smite the great house with b. 6:11
I will close up the b. thereof. 9:11

bread

[1] *The eatable made of grain,* Gen 3:19; 49:20. [2] *All things necessary for this life,* Mat 6:11. [3] *Manna wherewith God fed the children of Israel in the wilderness,* Neh 9:15; John 6:31.

(*The word is used figuratively in many ways. The best known is its use for Christ in the term* bread of life)

king of Salem brought b. Gen 14:18
I will fetch a morsel of b. 18:5
Abraham took b. and gave to. 21:14
then Jacob gave Esau b. 25:34
savoury meat and b. to. 27:17
in land of Egypt was b. 41:54
people cried to Pharaoh for b. 55
set on b. 43:31
b. for his father. 45:23
his father's house with b. 47:12
give us b. 15
gave them b. for horses. 17
buy us and our land for b. 19
out of Asher his b. shall. 49:20
I will rain b. from heaven. Ex 16:4
in the morning b. to the full. 8, 12
giveth on the sixth day the b. 29
they may see the b. 32
he shall bless thy b. and. 23:25
and the b. in the basket. 29:32
if ought of the b. remain unto. 34
he set the b. in order. 40:23
he took a cake of oiled b. Lev 8:26
what remaineth of b. ye shall. 32
b. of their God. 21:6, 8, 17, 21, 22
nor from stranger offer b. 22:25
ye shall offer with the b. 23:18
women shall bake your b. 26:26
the continual b. shall be. Num 4:7
the people of the land are b. 14:9
b. nor water, our soul ... b. 21:5
my b. for my sacrifices. 28:2
man doth not live by b. only.
Deut 8:3; Mat 4:4; Luke 4:4
met you not with b. and. Deut 23:4

ye have not eaten b. nor. Deut 29:6
all b. of their provision. Josh 9:5
this our b. we took hot for. 12
a cake of barley b. Judg 7:13
give b. to thy army. 8:6, 15
comfort thy heart with b. 19:5
and there is b. and wine. 19
visited his people giving b. Ruth 1:6
hired themselves for b. 1 Sam 2:5
crouch to him for a morsel of b. 36
for the b. is spent in our. 9:7
took an ass laden with b. 16:20
but there is hallowed b. 21:4
b. is common. 5*
hallowed b. to put hot b. in day. 6
thou hast given him b. 22:13
shall I take my b. and my. 25:11
let me set a morsel of b. 28:22
Egyptian and gave him b. 30:11
fail one that lacketh b. 2 Sam 3:29
if I taste b. or ought else till. 35
to every one a cake of b. 6:19
back and hast eaten b. 1 Ki 13:22
after he had eaten b. and. 23
ravens brought b. and. 17:6
bring me, a morsel of b. 11
fed them with b. and. 18:4, 13
brought the man of God b. 2 Ki 4:42
take you to a land of b. 18:32
Isa 36:17
Zabulon brought b. 1 Chr 12:40
have not eaten the b. Neh 5:14
and gavest them b. from. 9:15
they met not Israel with b. 13:2
wandereth abroad for b. Job 15:23
thou hast withholden b. from. 22:7
offspring shall not be satisfied with b. 27:14
the earth, out of it cometh b. 28:5
his life abhorreth b. and. 33:20
nor his seed begging b. Ps 37:25
can he give b.? 78:20
feedest them with b. of tears. 80:5
eaten ashes like b. 102:9
and b. which strengtheneth. 104:15
satisfied them with the b. 105:40
let them seek their b. 109:10
will satisfy her poor with b. 132:15
b. eaten secret is pleasant. Pr 9:17
better than he that honoureth himself and lacketh b. 12:9
land be satisfied with b. 11; 28:19
thou shalt be satisfied with b. 20:13
b. of deceit is sweet to a man. 17
he giveth of his b. to the poor. 22:9
eateth not the b. of idleness. 31:27
is not to swift, nor b. to. Eccl 9:11
cast thy b. upon the waters. 11:1
away the whole stay of b. Isa 3:1
for in my house is neither b. nor. 7
they prevented with their b. 21:14
the b. of adversity. 30:20
his b. shall be given him. 33:16
he baketh b. on coals. 44:15, 19
should not die, nor his b. fail. 51:14
money for that which is not b.? 55:2
seed to the sower, b. to eater. 10
is it not to deal thy b. to? 58:7
nor have hunger of b. Jer 42:14
people sigh, they seek b. Lam 1:11
young children ask b. no man. 4:4
to be satisfied with b. 5:6
we gat our b. with peril of our. 9
thou shalt prepare thy b. Ezek 4:15
that they may want b. and water. 17
pride, fulness of b. 16:49
given his b. to the hungry. 18:7, 16
strangers when ye offer my b. 44:7
lovers that give me b. Hos 2:5
sacrifices shall be as the b. of. 9:4
given you want of b. Amos 4:6
not a famine of b. but of. 8:11
if one do touch b. or. Hag 2:12
ye offer polluted b. Mal 1:7
these stones be made b. Mat 4:3
Luke 4:3
our daily b. Mat 6:11; Luke 11:11
if son ask b. will he give? Mat 7:9
take children's b. 15:26; Mark 7:27
whence have so much b.? Mat 15:33
Mark 8:4
had forgotten to take b. Mat 16:5
Mark 8:14
I spake not concerning b. Mat 16:11
not beware of leaven of b. Mat 16:12
Jesus took b. and blessed it. 26:26
Mark 14:22
came neither eating b. Luke 7:33
nothing for journey, neither b. 9:3
servants of my father's have b. 15:17
took b. gave thanks. 22:19; 24:30
known of them in breaking b. 24:35
two hundred penny-worth of b.
John 6:5
Moses gave you not that b. . . Father giveth you the true b. John 6:32
the b. of God is he. 33
Lord, give us this b. 34
I am the b. of life. 35, 48
I am b. which came down. 41, 50, 58
he that eateth of this b. shall. 58
he that eateth b. with me. 13:18
fire and fish laid thereon and b. 21:9
Jesus then taketh b. and giveth. 13
continued in breaking of b. Acts 2:42
and breaking b. from house. 46
the disciples came to break b. 20:7
when he had broken b. and eaten. 11
he took b. and gave thanks. 27:35
b. we break, is it not? 1 Cor 10:16
we being many are one b. 17
Lord Jesus, the same night in which he was betrayed, took b. 11:23
minister b. to your food. 2 Cor 9:10

see **affliction**

bread corn

b. corn is bruised. Isa 28:28

bread, with eat

sweat of thy face eat b. Gen 3:19
Lord will give me b. to eat. 28:20
called his brethren to eat b. 31:54
brethren sat down to eat b. 37:25
he had, save b. he did eat. 39:6
heard they should eat b. there. 43:25
Egyptians might not eat b. with. 32
him that he may eat b. Ex 2:20
and when we did eat b. 16:3
b. Lord hath given you to eat. 15
came to eat b. with. 18:12
did not eat b. forty days. 34:28
Deut 9:9, 18
there eat it, with the b. Lev 8:31
he shall eat the b. of his God. 21:22
ye shall neither eat b. nor. 23:14
ye shall eat your b. to the full. 26:5
when ye eat the b. of. Num 15:19
thou shalt eat b. without. Deut 8:9
I will not eat thy b. Judg 13:16
come thou, and eat b. Ruth 2:14
eat b. at my table. 2 Sam 9:7, 10
neither did he eat b. with. 12:17
set b. and he did eat. 20
didst rise and eat b. 21
b. and summer fruit to eat. 16:2
nor will I eat b. 1 Ki 13:8, 16
charged me, saying, eat no b. 9
come home with me and eat b. 15
arise, eat b. let thy heart. 21:7
constrained Elisha to eat b. 2 Ki 4:8
b. and water, they may eat. 6:22
did eat of the unleavened b. 23:9
did eat b. before. 25:29; Jer 52:33
and did eat b. with Job. Job 42:11
eat up my people, as they eat b.
Ps 14:4; 53:4
who did eat of my b. hath. 41:9
that I forget to eat my b. 102:4
vain to sit up late, to eat the b. 127:2
they eat b. of wickedness. Pr 4:17
come, eat of my b. and drink of. 9:5
eat not the b. of him that hath. 23:6
if enemy hunger, give b. to eat. 25:21
go thy way, eat thy b. with. Eccl 9:7
we will eat our b. and wear. Isa 4:1
eat up thy harvest and thy b.
Jer 5:17
there they did eat b. together. 41:1
they eat their defiled b. Ezek 4:13
they shall eat b. by weight and. 16
eat b. with quaking. 12:18
eat b. with care. 19
and eat not b. of men. 24:17, 22
prince sit in it to eat b. before. 44:3
into Judah, there eat b. Amos 7:12
they that eat thy b. have. Ob 7
wash not when they eat b. Mat 15:2
not so much as eat b. Mark 3:20
b. they have nothing to eat. Mark 6:36
saw disciples eat b. with. 7:2, 5
Pharisee's house to eat b. Luke 14:1
is he that shall eat b. 15
b. that these may eat? John 6:5
place where they did eat b. 23
gave them b. from heaven to eat. 31
if any man eat of this b. he shall. 51
as often as ye eat this b. 1 Cor 11:26
whosoever shall eat this b. and. 27
we eat any man's b.? 2 Thes 3:8
quietness they work and eat b. 12

leavened **bread**
(Bread leavened with yeast)

who eateth leav. b. that. Ex 12:15
no leav. b. be eaten. 13:3
no leav. b. be seen. 7; Deut 16:3, 4
not offer blood with leav. b. Ex 23:18
shall offer leav. b. Lev 7:13

loaf, or loaves of **bread**
(In the East, flat cakes like the large, thin, American pilot bread)

one loaf of b. with ram. Ex 29:23
give loaf of b. to people. Judg 8:5
three loaves of b. 1 Sam 10:3
and give thee two loaves of b. 4
give me five loaves of b. 21:3
two hundred loaves of b. 2 Sam 16:1
one of Israel a loaf of b. 1 Chr 16:3

no **bread**

there was no b. in the. Gen 47:13
there is no b. and our. Num 21:5
there is no common b. 1 Sam 21:4
for there was no b. there, but. 6
Saul had eaten no b. all the. 28:20
the Egyptian had eaten no b. 30:12
eat no b. nor. 1 Ki 13:9; 17:22
away, and would eat no b. 21:4
that thou eatest no b.? 5
there was no b. for the. 2 Ki 25:3
Jer 52:6
came, he did eat no b. Ezra 10:6
there is no more b. in. Jer 38:9
I ate no pleasant b. nor. Dan 10:3
it is because we have taken no b.
Mat 16:7, 8; Mark 8:16, 17
take no scrip, no b. no. Mark 6:8

piece, or pieces of **bread**

I may eat a piece of b. 1 Sam 2:36
brought to a piece of b. Pr 6:26
for a piece of b. that man. 28:21
Jeremiah daily piece of b. Jer 37:21
ye pollute me for pieces of b.?
Ezek 13:19

shewbread, see **shew**

staff of **bread**

broken staff of your b. Lev 26:26
brake whole staff of b. Ps 105:16
I will break staff of b. Ezek 4:16
5:16; 14:13

unleavened **bread**
(Bread without yeast, used figuratively for purity)

Lot did bake unleav. b. Gen 19:3
eat passover with unleav. b.
Ex 12:18; Num 9:11
seven days eat unleav. b. Ex 12:15
13:6, 7; 23:15; 34:18; Lev 23:
Num 28:17; Deut 16:
on fourteenth day eat unleav. b.
Ex 12:1
your habitations eat unleav. b. 2
take unleav. b. to hallow. 29:
shall eat with unleav. b. Lev 6:1
wafers of unleav. b. Num 6:1
six days eat unleav. b. Deut 16:
did bake unleav. b. 1 Sam 28:2
did eat unleav. b. 2 Ki 23:
passover of unleav. b. Ezek 45:2
first day of unleav. b. Mark 14:1
came days of unleav. b. Luke 22:
Acts 12:
after days of unleav. b. Acts 20:
with the unleav. b. 1 Cor 5:

see **basket, feast**

breadth

ark, and b. fifty cubits. Gen 6:
through the land in the b. of. 13:
b. of the court fifty cubits. Ex 27:
a span the b. thereof. 28:6; 39
five cubits the b. thereof. 38

so much as a foot *b.* *Deut* 2:5*
stones at an hair's *b.* *Judg* 20:16
the *b.* of the Lord's house. *1 Ki* 6:2
2 Chr 3:3
b. of the porch was thirty. *1 Ki* 7:6
the *b.* of the altar was. *2 Chr* 4:1
b. of the Lord's house. *Ezra* 6:3
and the *b.* of the waters. *Job* 37:10
hast thou perceived the *b.*? 38:18
wings shall fill the *b.* *Isa* 8:8
the *b.* of the building. *Ezek* 40:5
b. of the entry. 11
the *b.* of the gate. 13, 20, 48
b. of the porch. 49
the *b.* of the tabernacle. 41:1
b. of the door. 2, 3
b. of side chambers. 5
b. of house was upward. 7
the *b.* of place left. 11
b. of face of the house. 14
the *b.* of the holy portion. 45:1
the *b.* of the image. *Dan* 3:1
march through *b.* of land. *Hab* 1:6
Jerusalem, to see the *b.* *Zech* 2:2
I see a flying roll, the *b.* 5:2
what is the *b.* and length. *Eph* 3:18
they went up on the *b.* *Rev* 20:9
length is as large as the *b.* 21:16

break

to Hebron at *b.* of day. *2 Sam* 2:32
he talked till *b.* of day. *Acts* 20:11

break

they came near to *b.* *Gen* 19:9
thou shalt *b.* his yoke from. 27:40*
nor *b.* a bone. *Ex* 12:46; *Num* 9:12
shalt *b.* his neck. *Ex* 13:13; 34:20
but ye shall *b.* their images. 34:13
vessel unclean ye shall *b.* *Lev* 11:33
I will *b.* the pride of your. 26:19
shall *b.* their bones. *Num* 24:8
if a man vow, he shall not *b.* 30:2
ye shall *b.* their pillars. *Deut* 12:3
b. away every man. *1 Sam* 25:10
b. thy league with. *1 Ki* 15:19
2 Chr 16:3
should we again *b.* thy. *Ezra* 9:14
wilt thou *b.* a leaf? *Job* 13:25*
forgetteth wild beast may *b.* 39:15*
let us *b.* their bands. *Ps* 2:3
shalt *b.* them with a rod of iron. 9
b. thou the arm of wicked. 10:15
b. their teeth, O God. 58:6
if they *b.* my statutes. 89:31
an oil which shall not *b.* 141:5*
day *b.* and shadows flee away.
S of S 2:17*; 4:6*
will *b.* the Assyrians. *Isa* 14:25
. the clods. 28:24
ot *b.* it with a wheel. 28
. it as a potter's vessel. 30:14
s a lion so will he *b.* all. 38:13
eed will he not *b.* 42:3; *Mat* 12:20
s not this the fast, ye *b.*? *Isa* 58:6
hall iron *b.* the northern? *Jer* 15:12
. bottle, so will I *b.* 19:10, 11
ill *b.* yoke of king. 28:4, 11; 30:8
e shall *b.* the images. 43:13
will send wanderers and *b.* 48:12
aith Lord, I will *b.* bow of. 49:35
the staff of bread. *Ezek* 4:16
5:16; 14:13
s women that *b.* wedlock. 16:38
ou shalt *b.* sherds thereof. 23:34*
ey took hold thou didst *b.* 29:7
shall *b.* the yokes of Egypt. 30:18
will *b.* Pharaoh's arms. 22, 24
will *b.* the bow of Israel. *Hos* 1:5
will *b.* the bow. 2:18
all plow, Jacob shall *b.* 10:11
rch and not *b.* *Joel* 2:7
the bar of Damascus. *Amos* 1:5
y their skin, and *b.* *Mi* 3:3
w will I *b.* his yoke. *Nah* 1:13
at I might *b.* the. *Zech* 11:14
one of these least. *Mat* 5:19
e the bottles *b.* and the. 9:17*
me together to *b.* *Acts* 20:7
ean ye to weep and to *b.*? 21:13
ead we *b.* is it? *1 Cor* 10:16

break *covenant*

that ye *b.* my *cov.* *Lev* 26:15
ill not *b.* my *cov.* 44
ople will *b.* *cov.* *Deut* 31:16, 20
I will never *b.* my *cov.* *Judg* 2:1
my *cov.* will I not *b.* *Ps* 89:34
remember, *b.* not thy *cov.* *Jer* 14:21
if you can *b.* my *cov.* 33:20
shall he *b.* *cov.*? *Ezek* 17:15
that I might *b.* my *cov.* *Zech* 11:10

break *down*

b. down their images. *Ex* 23:24
Deut 7:5
shall *b. down* house. *Lev* 14:45
I will *b. down* tower. *Judg* 8:9
if a fox go up, *b. down.* *Neh* 4:3
now they *b. down* the. *Ps* 74:6
a time to *b. down* and. *Eccl* 3:3
I will *b. down* the wall. *Isa* 5:5
over them to *b. down.* *Jer* 31:28
I have built will I *b. down.* 45:4
so will I *b. down* wall. *Ezek* 13:14
b. down thy high places. 16:39
b. down the towers of Tyrus. 26:4
they shall *b. down* thy walls. 12
he shall *b. down* their. *Hos* 10:2

break *forth*

lest Lord *b. forth.* *Ex* 19:22, 24
they *b. forth* into singing. *Isa* 14:7
44:23; 49:13; 54:1
b. forth into joy. 52:9
for thou shalt *b. forth* on the. 54:3
hills shall *b. forth* before. 55:12
then shall thy light *b. forth.* 58:8
north an evil shall *b. forth.* *Jer* 1:14
b. forth and cry. *Gal* 4:27

break *off*

thou shalt *b.* his yoke *off.* *Gen* 27:40
b. off golden ear-rings. *Ex* 32:2, 24
O king, *b. off* thy sins by. *Dan* 4:27

break *out*

if fire *b. out.* *Ex* 22:6
if leprosy *b. out.* *Lev* 13:12
if the plague again *b. out.* 14:43
b. out the great teeth of. *Ps* 58:6
wilderness waters *b. out.* *Isa* 35:6
b. out, and blood. *Hos* 4:2
lest he *b. out* like fire. *Amos* 5:6

break *in pieces*

Chaldeans *b. in pieces.* *2 Ki* 25:13
will ye *b.* me *in pieces*? *Job* 19:2
shall *b. in pieces* mighty. 34:24
he shall *b. in pieces* the. *Ps* 72:4
they *b. in pieces* thy people. 94:5
I will *b. in pieces* the gates. *Isa* 45:2
thee will I *b. in pieces.* *Jer* 51:20
b. in pieces horse and rider. 21
with thee *b. in pieces* man. 22
b. in pieces and bruise. *Dan* 2:40, 44
fourth beast shall *b. in pieces.* 7:23

break *through*

lest they *b. through* to. *Ex* 19:21
not priests and people *b. through.* 24
to *b. through* to the king. *2 Ki* 3:26
thieves *b. through.* *Mat* 6:19
thieves *b.* not *through.* 20

break *up*

b. up fallow ground. *Jer* 4:3
Hos 10:12

breaker

b. is come up. *Mi* 2:13
if a *b.* of law. *Rom* 2:25

breakers

covenant *b.* *Rom* 1:31

breakest

thou *b.* ships of Tarshish. *Ps* 48:7

breaketh

let me go, for the day *b.* *Gen* 32:26
for he *b.* me with tempest. *Job* 9:17
he *b.* down, and it cannot. 12:14
he *b.* me with breach upon. 16:14
the blood *b.* out from. 28:4
b. the cedars. *Ps* 29:5
he *b.* the bow. 46:9
my soul *b.* for the longing. 119:20
a soft tongue *b.* the bone. *Pr* 25:15
whoso *b.* an hedge, a. *Eccl* 10:8
which is crushed *b.* out. *Isa* 59:5
as one *b.* a potter's vessel. *Jer* 19:11
my word like hammer that *b.*? 23:29
ask bread, no man *b.* *Lam* 4:4
forasmuch as iron *b.* in. *Dan* 2:40*

breaking

wrestled a man till *b.* of. *Gen* 32:24
shall be a boil *b.* forth. *Ex.* 9:9, 10
if a thief be found *b.* up. *Ex* 22:2
on enemies, like *b.* *1 Chr* 14:11
upon me as a wide *b.* *Job* 30:14
by reason of *b.* they. 41:25
that there be no *b.* *Ps* 144:14
b. down walls, and of. *Isa* 22:5
whose *b.* cometh suddenly. 30:13
shall break it as the *b.* of. 14
despised the oath in *b.* *Ezek* 16:59
17:18
sigh, son of man, with *b.* 21:6
long in place of *b.* *Hos* 13:13
known of them in *b.* of. *Luke* 24:35
continued in *b.* of bread. *Acts* 2:42
in the temple, *b.* bread from. 46
through *b.* the law. *Rom* 2:23*

breast

take the *b.* of the ram. *Ex* 29:26
shall sanctify *b.* of wave. 27
fat with *b.*, *b.* be waved. *Lev* 7:30
but the *b.* shall be Aaron's. 31
the wave-*b.* and heave-shoulder. 34
Moses took the *b.* and waved. 8:29
the wave-*b.* shall ye eat. 10:14
to the priest, with wave-*b.* *Num* 6:20
as wave-*b.* and right. 18:18
pluck fatherless from *b.* *Job* 24:9
thou shalt suck the *b.* of. *Isa* 60:16
sea monsters draw out *b.* *Lam* 4:3
head of gold, his *b.* *Dan* 2:32
publican smote upon *b.* *Luke* 18:13
on Jesus' *b.* saith. *John* 13:25; 21:20

breastplate

[1] *A piece of embroidery about ten inches square, of very rich work, which the high-priest wore upon his breast, and which was set with four rows of precious stones, upon every one of which was engraven the name of one of the tribes of Israel. It was double, or made of two pieces folded one upon the other, like a kind of bag, in which were put the* Urim *and* Thummim, Lev 8:8. [2] *A piece of defensive armour,* Rev 9:9. *In which sense, faith and love are called* breastplates, 1 Thes 5:8.

stones to be set in *b.* *Ex* 25:7; 35:9
make a *b.* and. 28:4, 15; 39:8
make upon the *b.* chains. 28:22
rings on ends of *b.* 28:23, 26; 39:16
bind *b.* by the rings. 28:28; 39:21
bear the names of Israel in *b.* 28:29
b. of judgement Urim. 30; *Lev* 8:8
put on righteousness as *b.* *Isa* 59:17
having on the *b.* of. *Eph* 6:14
putting on the *b.* of. *1 Thes* 5:8
b. as it were *b.* of iron. *Rev.* 9:9
having *b.* of fire, of jacinth. 17

breasts

bless with blessings of *b.* *Gen* 49:25
put fat on the *b.* *Lev* 9:20
b. Aaron waved. 21
the *b.* that I should suck. *Job* 3:12
his *b.* full of milk, and. 21:24
I was on mother's *b.* *Ps* 22:9
let her *b.* satisfy thee. *Pr* 5:19
all night betwixt my *b.* *S of S* 1:13
two *b.* like two young roes. 4:5; 7:3
thy *b.* are like two clusters. 7:7
thy *b.* shall be as clusters. 8
my brother that sucked the *b.* 8:1
a little sister, and she hath no *b.* 8
I am a wall and my *b.* like towers. 10
weaned from the *b.* *Isa* 28:9
be satisfied with the *b.* of her. 66:11
thy *b.* are fashioned. *Ezek* 16:7
there were their *b.* pressed. 23:3
and they bruised the *b.* 8
thou shalt pluck off thine own *b.* 34
away adulteries from her *b.* *Hos* 2:2
miscarrying womb and dry *b.* 9:14
those that suck the *b.* *Joel* 2:16
doves tabering on their *b.* *Nah* 2:7
the people smote their *b.* *Luke* 23:48
having their *b.* girded. *Rev* 15:6

breath

(Used figuratively many times for the life of man, or the anger of God)

his nostrils the *b.* of life. *Gen* 2:7
flesh wherein is the *b.* of life. 6:17

and two wherein is *b.* of. *Gen* 7:15
all in whose nostrils was *b.* of. 22
foundations discovered, at blast of *b.* of his. *2 Sam* 22:16; *Ps* 18:15
and there was no *b.* *1 Ki* 17:17
by the *b.* of his nostrils. *Job* 4:9*
not suffer to take my *b.* 9:18
in whose hand is the *b.* of. 12:10
by the *b.* of his mouth. 15:30
my *b.* is corrupt, my days. 17:1*
my *b.* is strange to my wife. 19:17
all the while my *b.* is in me. 27:3
the *b.* of the Almighty hath. 33:4
gather to himself Spirit and *b.* 34:14
by *b.* of God frost is given. 37:10
his *b.* kindleth coals. 41:21
all of them made by *b.* of. *Ps* 33:6
takest away their *b.* they. 104:29
nor is there any *b.* in their. 135:17
his *b.* goeth forth. 146:4
every thing that hath *b.* praise. 150:6
they have all one *b.* *Eccl* 3:19
cease from man, whose *b.* *Isa* 2:22
with *b.* of his lips will he slay. 11:4
his *b.* as an overflowing. 30:28
b. of the Lord like a stream. 33
your *b.* as fire shall devour. 33:11
giveth *b.* to the people upon it. 42:5
no *b.* in them. *Jer* 10:14; 51:17
the *b.* of our nostrils. *Lam* 4:20
I will cause *b.* to enter. *Ezek* 37:5
cover you with skin and put *b.* 6
there was no *b.* in them. 8
and say, come, O *b.* 9
and the *b.* came into them. 10
God in whose hand *b.* is. *Dan* 5:23
no strength, neither is there *b.* 10:17
there is no *b.* at all in. *Hab* 2:19
giveth to all life and *b.* *Acts* 17:25

breathe

was not any left to *b.* *Josh* 11:11, 14
such as *b.* out cruelty. *Ps* 27:12
come, O breath, and *b.* *Ezek* 37:9

breathed

b. into man's nostrils the breath of life. *Gen* 2:7
destroyed all that *b.* *Josh* 10:40
to Jeroboam any that *b.* *1 Ki* 15:29
he *b.* on them and saith. *John* 20:22

breatheth, -ing

save alive nothing that *b.* *Deut* 20:16
not thine ear at my *b.* *Lam* 3:56
Saul yet *b.* out. *Acts* 9:1

bred

some left, and it *b.* *Ex* 16:20

breeches

make them linen *b.* *Ex* 28:42; 39:28
priest shall put on linen *b.* *Lev* 6:10
he shall have the linen *b.* 16:4
they shall have linen *b.* *Ezek* 44:18

breed

they may *b.* abundantly. *Gen* 8:17
rams of *b.* of Bashan. *Deut* 32:14

breeding

as Sodom, even *b.* of. *Zeph* 2:9*

brethren

[1] *The sons of one father and mother, or of either of them,* Gen 42:13. [2] *Those neighbours or kinsmen who are closely banded together,* Gen 13:8; 19:7. [3] *Those who have made profession of the same faith and religion,* Acts 6:3, *etc.*

be no strife, we be *b.* *Gen* 13:8
Lot said, I pray you *b.* do not. 19:7
led me to my master's *b.* 24:27
said to her father and to her *b.* 34:11
Dinah's *b.* took each man his. 25
Joseph's ten *b.* went down. 42:3
b. came and bowed. 6
we are twelve *b.* 13, 32
Joseph's *b.* are come. 45:16
are *b.* of cruelty. 49:5
Joseph's *b.* saw their father. 50:15
possession among the *b.* *Num* 27:4
possession among our father's *b.* 7
no *b.* give it to his father's *b.* 10
if his father have no *b.* ye shall. 11
if *b.* dwell together. *Deut* 25:5
brought out father and *b.* *Josh* 6:23
an inheritance among the *b.* *Josh* 17:4
went to his mother's *b.* *Judg* 9:1
his mother's *b.* spake of him to. 3
answered, we are *b.* *2 Ki* 10:13
there came of Saul's *b.* *1 Chr* 12:2
sons of Shemaiah, whose *b.* 26:7
Elihu, one of the *b.* of David. 27:18
he had *b.* the sons. *2 Chr* 21:2
when Jehu found the *b.* 22:8
pleasant for *b.* to dwell. *Ps* 133:1
soweth discord among *b.* *Pr* 6:19
part of the inheritance among *b.* 17:2
all the *b.* of the poor do hate. 19:7
Jesus saw two *b.* *Mat* 4:18
saw other two *b.* 21
hath forsaken houses, *b.* 19:29
indignation against two *b.* 20:24
with us seven *b.* 22:25; *Mark* 12:20
your Master, all ye are *b.* *Mat* 23:8
no man hath left *b.* for my sake. *Mark* 10:29; *Luke* 18:29
receive hundred-fold, *b.* *Mark* 10:30
and hate not children, *b.* *Luke* 14:26
for I have five *b.* that he. 16:28
betrayed by parents and *b.* 21:16
went abroad among *b.* *John* 21:23
b. I wot that through. *Acts* 3:17
wherefore *b.* look among. 6:3
sirs, ye are *b.* 7:26
which when the *b.* knew. 9:30
certain *b.* from Joppa. 10:23
moreover these six *b.* 11:12
determined to send relief to *b.* 29
these things to James and to *b.* 12:17
minds evil-affected against *b.* 14:2
men from Judea taught the *b.* 15:1
caused great joy to all the *b.* 3
and Silas chief among the *b.* 22
apostles and elders and *b.* send greeting to *b.* of the Gentiles. 23
exhorted the *b.* 15:32; *1 Thes* 5:14
let go in peace from the *b.* *Acts* 15:33
being recommended by the *b.* 40
well reported of by the *b.* 16:2
when they had seen the *b.* 40
drew Jason and certain *b.* 17:6
b. immediately sent Paul. 10, 14
Paul took his leave of the *b.* 18:18
the *b.* wrote exhorting to. 27
now *b.* I commend you to. 20:32
to Ptolemais and saluted *b.* 21:7
come to Jerusalem, *b.* received. 17
also I received letters to the *b.* 22:5
I wist not *b.* that he was. 23:5
where we found *b.* and were. 28:14
when the *b.* heard of us. 15
nor any of the *b.* that came. 21
you ignorant *b.* *Rom* 1:13; 11:25
1 Cor 10:1; 12:1; *1 Thes* 4:13
know ye not *b.* that the law. *Rom* 7:1
b. we are debtors, not to. 8:12
first-born among many *b.* 29
b. my prayer to God for Israel. 10:1
I beseech you therefore *b.* 12:1
15:30; 16:17; *1 Cor* 1:10; 16:15
Gal 4:12; *Heb* 13:22
salute the *b.* *Rom* 16:14; *Col* 4:15
ye see your calling *b.* *1 Cor* 1:26
and I *b.* when I came to you. 2:1
I *b.* could not speak to you. 3:1
these things *b.* I have in a. 4:6
but this I say *b.* 7:29; 15:50
when ye sin so against the *b.* 8:12
and as the *b.* of the Lord. 9:5
now I praise you *b.* 11:2
how is it *b.* when ye? 14:26
seen of above 500 *b.* at once. 15:6
beloved *b.* be steadfast. 58; *Jas* 2:5
I look for him with the *b.* *1 Cor* 16:11
I desired him to come with *b.* 12
the *b.* greet you. 20; *Phil* 4:21
yet have I sent the *b.* *2 Cor* 9:3
I thought it necessary to exhort *b.* 5
the *b.* which came from. 11:9
in perils among false *b.* 26
finally *b.* farewell. 13:11
all *b.* that are with me. *Gal* 1:2
because of false *b.* 2:4
peace to the *b.* *Eph.* 6:23
many of the *b.* *Phil* 1:14
to saints and faithful *b.* *Col* 1:2
we beseech you *b.* *1 Thes* 4:1, 10
5:12; *2 Thes* 2:1
ye do it toward all *b.* *1 Thes* 4:10
b. pray for us. *1 Thes* 5:25; *2 Thes* 3:1
greet *b.* with holy kiss. *1 Thes* 5:26
this epistle be read to the holy *b.* 27
put *b.* in remembrance. *1 Tim* 4:6
intreat younger men as *b.* 5:1
despise them because they are *b.* 6:2
ashamed to call them *b.* *Heb* 2:11
holy *b.* partakers, consider. 3:1
unfeigned love of *b.* *1 Pet* 1:22
be of one mind, love as *b.* 3:8
because we love *b.* *1 John* 3:14
lay down our lives for the *b.* 16
rejoiced greatly when *b.* *3 John* 3
whatsoever thou dost to the *b.* 5
neither doth he receive the *b.* 10

his **brethren**

Ham told *his* two *b.* *Gen* 9:22
a servant of servants to *his b.* 25
in presence of *his b.* 16:12; 25:18
his b. have I given to him. 27:37
feeding the flock with *his b.* 37:2
dreamed a dream and told *his b.* 5
his b. envied him. 11
Reuben returned to *his b.* 30
lest he die also as *his b.* did. 38:11
let the lad go up with *his b.* 44:33
nourished his father and *his b.* 47:12
separate from *his b.* 49:26
Deut 33:16
Joseph died, *his b.* and. *Ex* 1:6
Moses went out to *his b.*... spied an Egyptian smiting one of *his b.* 2:11
high-priest among *his b.* *Lev* 21:10
one of *his b.* may redeem. 25:48
brought to *his b.* *Num* 25:6
give his inheritance to *his b.* 27:9
no part with *his b.* *Deut* 10:9
be not lifted up above *his b.* 17:20
he shall minister as all *his b.* 18:7
lest *his b.* heart faint as. 20:8
stealing any of *his b.* 24:7
nor did he acknowledge *his b.* 33:9
blessed and acceptable to *his b.* 24
Abimelech slew *his b.* *Judg* 9:5
Gaal came with *his b.* 26
which he did in slaying *his* 70 *b.* 56
Jephthah fled from *his b.* 11:3
be not cut off from *his b.* *Ruth* 4:10
anointed him in midst of *his b.*
1 Sam 16:13
when *his b.* and father's. 22:1
rise up from among *his b.* *2 Ki* 9:2
honourable than *his b.* *1 Chr* 4:9
Judah prevailed above *his b.* 5:2
Ephraim mourned, *his b.* came. 7:22
with *his b.* and sons were. 25:9
Jehoram slew all *his b.* *2 Chr* 21:4
was accepted of *his b.* *Esth* 10:3
fruitful among *his b.* *Hos* 13:15
remnant of *his b.* shall. *Mi* 5:3
his mother and *his b.* *Mat* 12:46
Mark 3:31; *Luke* 8:19
neither did *his b.* believe. *John* 7:5
was known to *his b.* *Acts* 7:13
into Moses' heart to visit *his b.* 23
for he supposed *his b.* would. 25
to judge between *his b.* *1 Cor* 6:5
made like to *his b.* *Heb* 2:17

men and **brethren**

men and b. this scripture. *Acts* 1:1
men and b. let me freely. 2:2
to Peter and rest, *men and b.* 3
he said, *men, b.* and fathers. 7:
men and b. if ye have any. 13:1
men and b. children of stock of. 2
be it known to you, *men and b.* 3
men and b. ye know God. 15:
answered, *men and b.* hearken. 1
men, b. and fathers, hear my. 22:
men and b. I have lived in all. 23:
men and b. I am a Pharisee.
men and b. I have committed. 28:1

my **brethren**

my b. whence be ye? *Gen* 29:
set it here before *my b.* and. 31:3
I seek *my b.* tell me where. 37:1
my b. and father's. 46:31; 47:
return to *my b.* in Egypt. *Ex* 4:1
alive father and *my b.* *Josh* 2:1
my b. made the heart of. 14
they were *my b.* *Judg* 8:1
my b. I pray you, do not. 19:
away, and see *my b.* *1 Sam* 20:

ye shall not do so, my b. 1 Sam 30:23
ye are my b. my bones. 2 Sam 19:12
said, hear me, my b. 1 Chr 28:2
Hanani, one of my b. Neh 1:2
I nor my b. nor guard put off. 4:23
I and my b. might exact. 5:10
and my b. have not eaten bread. 14
my b. dealt deceitfully. Job 6:15
he hath put my b. far from. 19:13
thy name unto my b. Ps 22:22
Heb 2:12
I am a stranger unto my b. Ps 69:8
for my b. and companions. 122:8
who are my b.? Mat 12:48
Mark 3:33
mother and my b. Mat 12:49
Mark 3:34
the least of these my b. Mat 25:40
go tell my b. that they go. 28:10
my b. are these which. Luke 8:21
go to my b. and say. John 20:17
from Christ for my b. Rom 9:3
take my b. the prophets. Jas 5:10
above all things, my b. swear not. 12

our brethren

before our b. discern. Gen 31:32
when our b. died before. Num 20:3
our b. have discouraged. Deut 1:28
have our b. stolen? 2 Sam 19:41
send abroad to our b. 1 Chr. 13:2
flesh is as flesh of our b. Neh 5:5
ability have redeemed our b. 8
us go again visit our b. Acts 15:36
or our b. be inquired of. 2 Cor 8:23
the accuser of our b. Rev 12:10

their brethren

minister with their b. Num 8:26
no inheritance among their b.
Deut 18:2
a prophet from among their b. 18
to the voice of their b. Judg 20:13
when their b. come to us. 21:22
from following their b. 2 Sam 2:26
bread among their b. 2 Ki 23:9
dwelt with their b. 1 Chr 8:32; 9:38
all their b. were at their. 12:32
drinking, for their b. had. 39
brought them to their b. 2 Chr. 28:15
cry against their b. the. Neh 5:1
to distribute to their b. 13:13
inheritance among their b. Job 42:15
slew them not among their b.
Jer 41:8
tithes of people, of their b. Heb 7:5
their b. should be killed. Rev 6:11

thy brethren

be lord over thy b. Gen 27:29
set it before thy b. 31:37
and thy b. come to bow? 37:10
to not thy b. feed the flock? 13
whether it be well with thy b. 14
one portion above thy b. 48:22
e whom thy b. shall. 49:8
a poor man of thy b. Deut 15:7
rom among thy b. shalt thou. 17:15
will raise a prophet of thy b. 18:15
ot oppress the poor of thy b. 24:14
hou shalt bring thy b. Josh 2:18
mong daughters of thy b. Judg 14:3
hy b. run to camp to thy b.
1 Sam 17:17
ok how thy b. fare. 18
eturn, take thy b. 2 Sam 15:20
ast slain thy b. 2 Chr 21:13
hy b. dealt treacherously. Jer 12:6
y b. even thy b. Ezek 11:15
other and thy b. stand. Mat 12:47
Mark 3:32; Luke 8:20
ll not thy b. Luke 14:12
rengthen thy b. 22:32
t, I am of thy b. Rev 19:10; 22:9

your brethren

e of your b. be. Gen 42:19
ave one of your b. here. 33
rry your b. from before. Lev 10:4
your b. bewail the burning. 6
er your b. ye shall not. 25:46
ave taken your b. the. Num 18:6
all your b go to war and? 32:6
uses between your b. Deut 1:16
er armed before your b. 3:18
Josh 1:14
st to your b. Deut 3:20; Josh 1:15
ye have not left your b. Josh 22:3
hath given rest to your b. 4
divide the spoil with your b. 8
fight against your b. 1 Ki 12:24
2 Chr 11:4
come to you of your b. and wrath come upon your b. 2 Chr 19:10
captives of your b. 28:11
be ye not like your b. which. 30:7
if ye turn, your b. shall. 9
and fight for your b. Neh 4:14
will you even sell your b.? 5:8
your b. that hated you. Isa 66:5
bring your b. for an. 20
I have cast out all your b. Jer 7:15
say to your b. Ammi. Hos 2:1
if ye salute your b. only. Mat 5:47
a prophet of your b. Acts 3:22; 7:37
defraud and that your b. 1 Cor 6:8
accomplished in your b. 1 Pet 5:9

bribe, -s

Samuel's sons took b. 1 Sam 8:3
whose hand received any b.? 12:3*
right hand is full of b. Ps 26:10
shaketh his hands from b. Isa 33:15
they take a b. and turn. Amos 5:12

bribery

consume tabernacles of b. Job 15:34

brick

us make b. they had b. Gen 11:3
made their lives bitter in b. Ex 1:14
more give straw to make b. 5:7, 16
incense on altars of b. Isa 65:3

brickkiln

them pass through b. 2 Sam 12:31
stones in the clay in b. Jer 43:9*
make strong the b. Nah 3:14

bricks

the tale of b. you shall lay. Ex 5:8
yet shall ye deliver tale of b. 18, 19
the b. are fallen down. Isa 9:10

bride

them on thee, as b. doth. Isa 49:18
as a b. adorneth herself. 61:10
as bridegroom rejoiceth over b. 62:5
a b. forget her attire? Jer 2:32
cease the voice of b. 7:34; 16:9
25:10
in this place voice of the b. 33:11
and let the b. go out. Joel 2:16
he that hath the b. is the. John 3:29
voice of the b. heard. Rev 18:23
prepared as a b. adorned. 21:2
I will shew thee the b. the. 9
the Spirit and the b. say. 22:17

bridechamber

children of the b. mourn? Mat 9:15
children of b. fast? Mark 2:19
Luke 5:34

bridegroom

as a b. coming out of. Ps 19:5
as a b. decketh himself. Isa 61:10
as b. rejoiceth over bride. 62:5
children mourn while b.? Mat 9:15
Mark 2:19; Luke 5:34
went forth to meet b. Mat 25:1
while the b. tarried. 5
cry made, b. cometh. 6, 10
governor of feast called b. John 2:9
hath the bride is the b. but friend of b. rejoiceth because of b. 3:29

see **bride**

bridle

(*Used both literally; and figuratively for restraint*)

put my b. in thy lips. 2 Ki 19:28
Isa 37:29
have let loose the b. Job 30:11
to him with his double b.? 41:13
mouth must be held with a b. Ps 32:9
keep my mouth with a b. 39:1
a b. for the ass, a rod. Pr 26:3
there shall be a b. Isa 30:28
any seem religious and b. Jas 1:26
able also to b. the whole body. 3:2
blood came out of wine-press even unto horse b. Rev 14:20

briefly

it is b. comprehended. Rom 13:9*
Sylvanus I have written b. 1 Pet 5:12

brier

instead of the b. come up. Isa 55:13
no more a pricking b. Ezek 28:24
best of them is as a b. Mi 7:4

briers

will tear your flesh with b. Judg 8:7
took the elders of the city and b. 16
there shall come up b. and. Isa 5:6
it shall even be for b. 7:23
land shall become b. and thorns. 24
not come thither the fear of b. 25
wickedness shall devour b. 9:18
devour his b. and thorns. 10:17
would set b. and thorns. 27:4
on the land shall come up b. 32:13
though b. and thorns be. Ezek 2:6
that which beareth b. and. Heb 6:8*

brigandine

(*Revised Version*, coat of mail)

put on the b. Jer 46:4
that lifteth up himself in his b. 51:3

bright

have a b. spot. Lev 13:2, 24, 38
if the b. spot be white in the skin. 4
if b. spot stay in his place. 23, 28*
law for a scab and for a b. spot. 14:56
vessels Hiram made were of b.
1 Ki 7:45*; 2 Chr 4:16
scattered his b. cloud. Job 37:11*
now men see not the b. light. 21
belly is as b. ivory. S of S 5:14*
make b. the arrows. Jer 51:11*
the fire was b. Ezek 1:13
the sword is made b. 21:15*
king of Babylon made arrows b. 21*
b. iron and cassia were in. 27:19
b. lights I will make dark. 32:8
horseman lifteth up b. Nah 3:3*
Lord make b. clouds. Zech 10:1*
behold a b. cloud. Mat 17:5
as when the b. shining. Luke 11:36
man stood before me in b. Acts 10:30
the b. and morning star. Rev 22:16

brightness

through b. before him were coals of fire. 2 Sam 22:13; Ps 18:12
the moon walking in b. Job 31:26
we wait for b. but walk. Isa 59:9
kings shall come to the b. 60:3
nor for b. shall the moon give. 19
righteousness go forth as b. 62:1
a fire and a b. about it. Ezek 1:4, 27
so was the appearance of b. 28
as the appearance of b. as. 8:2
the court was full of b. 10:4
strangers shall defile thy b. 28:7
corrupted by reason of thy b. 17
great image, whose b. Dan 2:31
my honour and b. returned. 4:36
wise shall shine as the b. 12:3
be very dark and no b. Amos 5:20
his b. was as the light. Hab 3:4
from heaven above b. Acts 26:13
destroy with the b. 2 Thes 2:8*
being the brightness of his. Heb 1:3

brim

feet of priest dipped in b. Josh 3:15*
b. like b. of a cup. 1 Ki 7:26
2 Chr 4:5
a molten sea from b. to b. 2 Chr 4:2
filled them up to the b. John 2:7

brimstone

(*Sulphur*)

rained b. Gen 19:24; Luke 17:29
the whole land is b. Deut 29:23
b. shall be scattered on. Job 18:15
upon wicked he shall rain fire and b.
Ps 11:6; Ezek 38:22
like a stream of b. Isa 30:33
and the dust turned into b. 34:9
issued fire and b. Rev 9:17
third part of men killed by b. 18
tormented with fire and b. 14:10
of fire, burning with b. 19:20; 20:10
shall have their part in lake which burneth with fire and b. 21:8

bring

I do b. a flood of waters. Gen 6:17
two of every sort shalt thou b. 19
when I b. a cloud over earth. 9:14
Abraham did b. them. 18:16
the Lord may b. on Abraham. 19

b. to me that I may eat. *Gen* 27:4, 25
b. me venison. 5
I shall *b.* a curse on me. 12
b. your youngest brother. 42:20, 34
if I *b.* him not. 37; 43:9; 44:32
b. these men home. 43:16
take wagons and *b.* your. 45:19
b. them I pray to me. 48:9
else to-morrow I will *b.* *Ex* 10:4
yet will I *b.* one plague more. 11:1
the Lord shall *b.* thee. 13:5, 11
that thou mayest *b.* causes. 18:19
his master shall *b.* him to. 21:6
if it be torn in pieces, *b.* it. 22:13
thou shalt surely *b.* it back. 23:4
first of first-fruits shalt *b.* 19; 34:26
I will send an Angel to *b.* thee. 23:20
of a willing heart, let him *b.* 35:5
the people *b.* much more. 36:5
not able to *b.* a lamb. *Lev* 5:7, 11
12:8
he shall *b.* them to the priest. 5:8, 12
shall *b.* fire and incense. 16:12
that Israel may *b.* their. 17:5
shalt *b.* the Levites. *Num* 8:9, 10
Lord delight in us, he will *b.* 14:8
Lord was not able to *b.* 16
Deut 9:28
Caleb, him will I *b.* *Num* 14:24
b. before the Lord every man. 16:17
shall not *b.* this congregation. 20:12
give this land, and *b.* us not. 32:5
too hard for you, *b.* it to. *Deut* 1:17
when the Lord shall *b.* thee. 7:1
then thou shalt *b.* her home. 21:12
then thou shalt *b.* it unto. 22:2
b. it to us. 30:12, 13
hear, Lord, and *b.* Judah. 33:7
child be weaned, then I will *b.* him.
1 Sam 1:22
Saul, what shall we *b.* the man ? 9:7
b. the portion I gave thee. 23
b. the men, that we may. 11:12
why shouldest thou *b.* me ? 20:8
hand with thee, to *b.* *2 Sam* 3:12
except thou *b.* Michal. 13
saith aught to thee, *b.* him. 14:10
are ye last to *b.* the king ? 19:11
and the king said, *b.* me. *1 Ki* 3:24
the wicked, to *b.* his way. 8:32
b. him back with thee. 13:18
b. me a morsel of bread. 17:11
he said, go ye *b.* him. 20:33
b. me a new cruse. *2 Ki* 2:20
b. yet a vessel. 4:6
b. meal and cast it. 41
I will *b.* you to the man. 6:19
b. an offering and come. *1 Chr* 16:29
of them to me, that I may *b.* 21:2
since people began to *b.* *2 Chr* 31:10
did not our God *b.* ? *Neh* 13:18
did I say *b.* unto me. *Job* 6:22
wilt thou *b.* me into ? 10:9
who can *b.* a clean thing ? 14:4
b. him to the king of terrors. 18:14
I know thou wilt *b.* me to. 30:23
to *b.* back his soul. 33:30
b. me to thy holy hill. *Ps* 43:3
b. me into strong city ? 60:9; 108:10
the mountains shall *b.* peace. 72:3
he shall *b.* on them. 94:23
scornful men *b.* *Pr* 29:8
who shall *b.* him ? *Eccl* 3:22
know that God will *b.* 11:9
God shall *b.* every work. 12:14
I would *b.* thee into my. *S of S* 8:2
Lord shall *b.* on thee. *Isa* 7:17
the people shall *b.* them. 14:2
for I will *b.* more upon Dimon. 15:9
shall he *b.* to the ground. 25:12
tell ye and *b.* them near. 45:21
I *b.* near my righteousness. 46:13
them will I *b.* to my holy. 56:7
that thou *b.* the poor to thy. 58:7
for brass *b.* gold, for iron *b.* 60:17
b. their fear upon them. 66:4
I will take you and *b.* *Jer* 3:14
not in anger, lest thou *b.* 10:24
I will *b.* on them all the. 11:8
b. upon them, day of evil. 17:18
I will *b.* them from north. 31:8
I will *b.* on them all the good. 32:42
I will *b.* it health and. 33:6
them that shall *b.* sacrifice of. 11

behold, I will *b.* a fear upon. *Jer* 49:5
I, even I, will *b.* a sword. *Ezek* 6:3
I will *b.* you out of. 11:9
that I would not *b.* them. 20:15
I will *b.* on the necks of. 21:29
I will *b.* them against thee. 23:22
b. them to land. 34:13; 36:24; 37:21
that I would *b.* thee against. 38:17
I will allure and *b.* her. *Hos* 2:14
b. and let us drink. *Amos* 4:1
b. your sacrifices. 4
yet will I *b.* an heir to. *Mi* 1:15
I will *b.* them, and. *Zech* 8:8
b. all the tithes into the. *Mal* 3:10
be thou there till I *b.* *Mat* 2:13
therefore if thou *b.* thy. 5:23
b. him hither to. 17:17; *Mark* 9:19
ass and a colt, loose them and *b.*
Mat 21:2; *Mark* 11:2; *Luke* 19:30
and they *b.* to him. *Mark* 7:32
for I *b.* you good tidings. *Luke* 2:10
choked with tares, *b.* no fruit. 8:14
when they *b.* you into the. 12:11
them also I must *b.* *John* 10:16
and *b.* all things to your. 14:26
what accusation *b.* you ? 18:29
b. of the fish which ye have. 21:10
ye intend to *b.* this. *Acts* 5:28
that they should *b.* them. 7:6
b. them bound to Jerusalem. 9:2, 21
went to Damascus to *b.* them. 22:5
commanded to *b.* Paul into. 23:10
b. this young man to the chief. 17
I will *b.* to nothing. *1 Cor* 1:19
b. to nought things that are. 28
shall *b.* you into remembrance. 4:17
keep under my body, *b.* it. 9:27
that ye may *b.* me on my. 16:6
ye suffer, if a man *b.* *2 Cor* 11:20
schoolmaster to *b.* us. *Gal* 3:24
will God *b.* with him. *1 Thes* 4:14
take Mark and *b.* him. *2 Tim* 4:11
he might *b.* us to God. *1 Pet* 3:18
if any come and *b.* not. *2 John* 10
whom if thou *b.* forward. *3 John* 6
kings do *b.* their glory. *Rev* 21:24
b. the glory of nations into it. 26

see **home, hither**

bring *again*

I *b.* thy son *again* ? *Gen* 24:5
thou *b.* not my son *again*. 6, 8
I will *b.* thee *again*. 28:15; 48:21
and *b.* word *again*. 37:14
I will *b.* him to thee *again*. 42:37
b. it back to him *again*. *Ex* 23:4
b. Aaron's rod *again*. *Num* 17:10
lodge this night, *b.* word *again*. 22:8
b. us word *again* what. *Deut* 1:22
in any case *b.* them *again*. 22:1
b. thee into Egypt *again*. 28:68
if ye *b.* me home *again*. *Judg* 11:9
and went to *b.* her *again*. 19:3
can I *b.* him *again* ? *2 Sam* 12:23
b. young man Absalom *again*. 14:21
the Lord shall *b.* me *again*. 15:8
he will *b.* me *again* and shew me. 25
forgive and *b.* *again*. *1 Ki* 8:34
2 Chr 6:25
b. kingdom *again* to Rehoboam.
1 Ki 12:21; *2 Chr* 11:1
let us *b.* *again* the ark. *1 Chr* 13:3
what word I shall *b.* *again*. 21:2
sent prophets to *b.* them *again*.
2 Chr 24:19
mightest *b.* them *again*. *Neh* 9:29
Lord said, I will *b.* *again*, I will *b.*
again my people. *Ps* 68:22
not *b.* it to his mouth *again*. *Pr* 19:24
grieveth him to *b.* it *again*. 26:15
I will *b.* *again* the shadow. *Isa* 38:8
b. it *again* to mind. 46:8
to *b.* Jacob *again* to him. 49:5
when the Lord shall *b.* *again*. 52:8
will *b.* them *again*. *Jer* 12:15; 50:19
then will I *b.* thee *again*. *Jer* 15:19
I will *b.* them *again* to their land.
16:15; 24:6; 32:37
I will *b.* them *again* into their. 23:3
in two years I will *b.* *again* the. 28:3
b. *again* to this place Jeconiah. 4, 6
I will *b.* *again* captivity. 30:3, 18
31:23; *Ezek* 39:25; *Amos* 9:14
b. *again* captivity of Moab. *Jer* 48:47

b. *again* captivity of Ammon. *Jer* 49:6
when I *b.* *again* their captivity, I will
b. *again*. *Ezek* 16:53
b. *again* the captivity of Egypt. 29:14
I will *b.* *again* that. *Ezek* 34:16
that time I *b.* you *again*. *Zeph* 3:20
I will *b.* them *again*. *Zech.* 10:6
I will *b.* them again out of. 10
b. me word *again*. *Mat* 2:8

see **captivity**

bring *down*

b. *down* my grey hairs. *Gen* 42:38
44:29, 31
b. your brother *down*. 43:7; 44:21
haste and *b.* *down* my father. 45:13
he shall *b.* them *down*. *Deut* 9:3
b. them *down* to the water. *Judg* 7:4
b. me *down*, I will *b.* thee *down*.
1 Sam 30:15
haughty, to *b.* *down*. *2 Sam* 22:28
Solomon *b.* him *down*. *1 Ki* 1:33
his hoary head *b.* thou *down*. 2:9
b. *down* high looks. *Ps* 18:27
shalt *b.* them *down* to pit. 55:23
b. *down* noise of strangers. *Isa* 25:5
he shall *b.* *down* their pride. 11
the high fort shall he *b.* *down*. 12
I will *b.* *down* their strength. 63:6
I *b.* *down* from thence. *Jer* 49:16
Ob 4
I will *b.* them *down* like. *Jer* 51:40
I shall *b.* thee *down*. *Ezek* 26:20
they shall *b.* thee *down* to pit. 28:8
I will *b.* them *down*. *Hos* 7:12
b. them *down* to valley. *Joel* 3:2
b. *down* thy strength. *Amos* 3:11
thence will *b.* them *down*. 9:2
who shall *b.* me *down* ? *Ob* 3
that he *b.* him *down*. *Acts* 23:15
desire thou wouldst *b.* *down*. 20
that is to *b.* Christ *down*. *Rom* 10:6

see **evil**

bring *forth*

let earth *b.* *forth*. *Gen* 1:11, 24
waters *b.* *forth*. 20
in sorrow thou shalt *b.* *forth*. 3:16
and thistles shall it *b.* *forth*. 18
b. *forth* every living thing. 8:17
b. *forth* abundantly in the. 9:7
Judah said *b.* her *forth*. 38:24
thou mayest *b.* *forth*. *Ex* 3:10
that I should *b.* *forth* Israel ? 11
may *b.* *forth* my armies. 7:4
the river shall *b.* *forth* frogs. 8:3
magicians did so to *b.* *forth* lice. 18
b. *forth* him that hath cursed.
Lev 24:14, 23
it shall *b.* *forth* fruit for. 25:21
ye shall eat and *b.* *forth*. 26:10
shalt *b.* *forth* water. *Num* 20:8
b. *forth* all tithe of. *Deut* 14:28
b. *forth* that man or woman. 17:5
b. *forth* the tokens of. 22:15
b. *forth* the men. *Josh* 2:3
till I come and *b.* *forth*. *Judg* 6:18
b. *forth* the man that came. 19:2
b. *forth* vestments for. *2 Ki* 10:2
is no strength to *b.* *forth*. 19:
Isa 37:
b. *forth* all the vessels. *2 Ki* 23:
those did Cyrus *b.* *forth*. *Ezra* 1:
it will bud and *b.* *forth*. *Job* 14:
mischief, and *b.* *forth* vanity. 15:3
thou *b.* *forth* Mazzaroth ? 38:3
wild goats *b.* *forth* ? 39:1, 2,
surely the mountains *b.* *forth*. 40:2
b. *forth* thy righteousness. *Ps* 37:
they shall still *b.* *forth* *fruit*. 92:1
that he may *b.* *forth* food. 104:1
that our sheep may *b.* *forth*. 144:1
what a day *may* *b.* *forth* ? *Pr* 27:
that it *b.* *forth* grapes. *Isa* 5:2,
I travail not, nor *b.* *forth*. 23
conceive chaff, and *b.* *forth*. 33:
b. *forth* your strong reasons. 41:
let them *b.* *forth* and shew.
he shall *b.* *forth* judgement. 42
b. *forth* judgement unto truth.
b. *forth* blind people. 43
let them *b.* *forth* witnesses.
open, and *b.* *forth* salvation. 45
earth, and maketh it *b.* *forth*. 55:
mischief, and *b.* *forth* iniquity. 59

and I will *b. forth* a seed. *Isa* 65:9
not labour in vain, nor *b. forth.* 23
earth be made to *b. forth* in? 66:8
and not cause *to b. forth*? 9
grow, they *b. forth* fruit. *Jer* 12:2
b. forth out of mouth what. 51:44
b. forth thy stuff. *Ezek* 12:4
and it shall *b. forth* boughs. 17:23
to *b.* them *forth* of the land. 20:6
I will *b.* them *forth* out of. 38
therefore will I *b. forth* a fire. 28:18
I will *b.* thee *forth* thine army. 38:4
shall *b. forth* new fruit. 47:12
Ephraim shall *b. forth.* *Hos* 9:13
though thy *b. forth,* yet will I. 16
labour to *b. forth,* O Zion. *Mi* 4:10
he will *b.* me *forth* to the light. 7:9
before the decree *b. forth.* *Zeph* 2:2
I will *b. forth* my servant. *Zech* 3:8
shall *b. forth* the head-stone. 4:7
b. forth a curse, and it shall. 5:4
virgin shall *b. forth* a son.
Mat 1:21, 23
b. forth fruit meet. 3:8; *Luke* 3:8
cannot *b. forth* evil fruit. *Mat* 7:18
Luke 6:43
b. forth fruit, some 30. *Mark* 4:20
b. forth a son, and shalt. *Luke* 1:31
word, keep it, and *b. forth* fruit. 8:15
b. forth the best robe. 15:22
may *b. forth* more fruit. *John* 15:2
that you should *b. forth* fruit. 16
I *b.* him *forth* to you. 19:4
Easter to *b.* him *forth.* *Acts* 12:4
that we should *b. forth.* *Rom* 7:4
the motions of sin to *b. forth.* 5

bring *in*

I will *b.* you *into* the land. *Ex* 6:8
shall *b. in* and plant them. 15:17
prepare that they *b. in.* 16:5
Angel shall *b.* thee *in.* 23:23
them will I *b. in.* *Num* 14:31
proclamation to *b. in* to the Lord the
collection Moses laid. *2 Chr* 24:9
ye shall not *b. in* the captives. 28:13
b. in no burden on the. *Jer* 17:24
b. me *in* before the king. *Dan* 2:24
king cried to *b. in* astrologers. 5:7
b. in everlasting righteousness. 9:24
sown much and *b. in* little. *Hag* 1:6
means to *b.* him *in.* *Luke* 5:18
b. in hither the poor, the. 14:21
b. in damnable heresies. *2 Pet* 2:1

bring *out*

b. them *out* to us. *Gen* 19:5, 8, 12
make mention, and *b.* me *out.* 40:14
God will visit and *b.* you *out.* 50:24
I will *b.* you *out* from. *Ex* 6:6
charge to *b.* Israel *out* of. 13, 26, 27
7:5; 12:51; *Jer* 31:32
mishief did he *b.* them *out.* *Ex* 32:12
lay hold and *b.* him *out.* *Deut* 21:19
b. out the damsel. 22:21
b. both *out* to the gate. 24
shall *b. out* the pledge. 24:11
b. out thence Rahab. *Josh* 6:22
b. out those five kings. 10:22
b. out thy son that. *Judg* 6:30
them I will *b. out.* 19:24
O *b.* thou me *out* of. *Ps* 25:17
b. my soul out of prison. 142:7
O Lord, *b.* my soul *out.* 143:11
to *b. out* the prisoners. *Isa* 42:7
shall *b. out* the bones. *Jer* 8:1
b. out all thy wives and. 38:23
I will *b.* you forth *out.* *Ezek* 11:7
b. you *out* from people. 20:34; 34:13
accept you, when I *b.* you *out.* 20:41
b. it *out* piece by piece. 24:6
burneth him to *b. out.* *Amos* 6:10
sought to *b.* them *out.* *Acts* 17:5

bring *to pass*

will shortly *b.* it *to pass.* *Gen* 41:32
to *b. to pass* as at this day. 50:20
he shall *b.* it *to pass.* *Ps* 37:5
and *b. to pass* his act. *Isa* 28:21
I will also *b.* it *to pass.* 46:11

bring *up*

will also *b.* thee *up* again. *Gen* 46:4
and to *b.* them *up* out. *Ex* 3:8
I have said, I will *b.* you *up* out. 17
see, thou sayest to me, *b. up.* 33:12
men that *b. up* evil. *Num* 14:37
b. up Aaron and his son. 20:25
b. up an evil name. *Deut* 22:14
did not the Lord *b.* us *up*? *Judg* 6:13
b. him *up* in the bed. *1 Sam* 19:15
whom shall I *b. up, b. up*? 28:11
men did David *b. up.* *2 Sam* 2:3
to *b. up* from thence the ark. 6:2
1 Ki 8:1, 4; *1 Chr* 13:6; 15:3, 12
14, 25; *2 Chr* 5:2, 5
since I did *b. up* Israel. *1 Chr* 17:5
did Sheshbazzar *b. up.* *Ezra* 1:11
shall *b. up* tithes. *Neh* 10:38
b. not forth children, nor nourish *up*
young men, nor *b. up.* *Isa* 23:4
then will I *b.* them *up.* *Jer* 27:22
shall *b. up* a company. *Ezek* 16:40
I will *b. up* a company. 23:46
when I shall *b. up* the. 26:19
will *b.* thee *up* out of the midst. 29:4
a company shall *b.* thee *up.* 32:3
I will *b.* up flesh on you. 37:6
though they *b. up* children. *Hos* 9:12
I will *b. up* sackcloth. *Amos* 8:10
to *b. up* Christ. *Rom* 10:7
b. them *up* in nurture of. *Eph* 6:4

bringers

the *b.* up of children. *2 Ki* 10:5

bringest

and *b.* me into judgement. *Job* 14:3
O Jerusalem that *b.* good. *Isa* 40:9
thou *b.* strange things. *Acts* 17:20

bringeth

who *b.* you out from. *Ex* 6:7
I am the Lord that *b.* you. *Lev* 11:45
b. it not to door of tabernacle. 17:4, 9
the Lord *b.* thee into. *Deut* 8:7
b. down to the grave, and *b.* up.
1 Sam 2:6
Lord maketh poor, he *b.* low. 7
that *b.* down the people. *2 Sam* 22:48
and that *b.* me forth from. 49
into whose hand God *b.* *Job* 12:6
he *b.* to light the shadow. 22
wrath *b.* the punishments. 19:29
the thing that is hid *b.* he. 28:11
that *b.* forth his fruit. *Ps* 1:3
b. back the captivity. 14:7; 53:6
Lord *b.* the counsel of the. 33:10
the man who *b.* wicked. 37:7
he *b.* out them that are bound. 68:6
and *b.* them out. 107:28
he *b.* them to their desired. 30
b. wind out of treasures. 135:7
Jer 10:13; 51:16
the mouth of the just *b.* *Pr* 10:31
moving his lips he *b.* evil. 16:30
a man's gift *b.* him. 18:16
son that causeth shame, and *b.* 19:26
a wise king *b.* the wheel. 20:26
much more when he *b.* it. 21:27
a child left, *b.* his mother. 29:15
he that delicately *b.* up servant. 21
the fear of man *b.* a snare. 25
b. forth butter, *b.* blood, *b.* 30:33
like ships, she *b.* her food. 31:14
water the wood that *b.* *Eccl* 2:6*
Lord *b.* on them waters. *Isa* 8:7
b. down them that dwell on high, *b.*
to dust. 26:5
b. the princes to nothing. 40:23
that *b.* out their host. 26
which *b.* forth the chariot. 43:17
the smith that *b.* forth. 54:16
for as the earth *b.* forth. 61:11
anguish of her that *b.* *Jer* 4:31
which *b.* iniquity. *Ezek* 29:16
Israel *b.* forth fruit. *Hos* 10:1
which ground *b.* forth. *Hag* 1:11
that *b.* not forth good fruit is hewn
down. *Mat* 3:10; 7:19; *Luke* 3:9
every good tree *b.* forth. *Mat* 7:17
good man *b.* forth good things, evil
man *b.* forth. 12:35; *Luke* 6:45
b. forth some an hundred. *Mat* 13:23
who *b.* out of his treasures. 52
Jesus *b.* them up into. 17:1
the earth *b.* forth fruit. *Mark* 4:28
good tree *b.* not forth. *Luke* 6:43
if it die, *b.* forth. *John* 12:24; 15:5
gospel *b.* forth fruit. *Col* 1:6
grace of God *b.* salvation. *Tit* 2:11
b. in the first-begotten. *Heb* 1:6
the earth *b.* forth herbs. *Heb* 6:7
lust *b.* forth sin, sin *b.* *Jas* 1:15

see **tidings**

bringing

much observed for *b.* *Ex* 12:42
people were restrained from *b.* 36:6
an offering *b.* iniquity. *Num* 5:15
by *b.* up a slander upon. 14:36
of *b.* the king back. *2 Sam* 19:10, 43
navy *b.* gold and silver. *1 Ki* 10:22
2 Chr 9:21
I am *b.* such evil on. *2 Ki* 21:12
on the sabbath *b.* in. *Neh* 13:15
rejoicing, *b.* his sheaves. *Ps* 126:6
b. burnt-offerings, *b.* *Jer* 17:26
made myself known in *b.* *Ezek* 20:9
his word by *b.* upon us. *Dan* 9:12
to a nation *b.* forth. *Mat* 21:43
b. one sick of the palsy. *Mark* 2:3
b. the spices which. *Luke* 24:1
multitude *b.* sick folks. *Acts* 5:16
b. me into captivity to. *Rom* 7:23
and *b.* into captivity. *2 Cor* 10:5
b. many sons unto glory. *Heb* 2:10
the *b.* in of a better hope. 7:19
b. in the flood on the. *2 Pet* 2:5

brink

by the kine on the *b.* *Gen* 41:3
ark in flags by river's *b.* *Ex* 2:3
shalt stand by the river's *b.* 7:15
from Aroer by the *b.* of. *Deut* 2:36
when ye are come to *b.* of. *Josh* 3:8
caused me return to the *b.* *Ezek* 47:6

broad

make censers, *b.* plates. *Num* 16:38
make *b.* plates for the. 39*
repaired, and they fortified Jerusalem to the *b.* wall. *Neh* 3:8; 12:38
out of strait into *b.* place. *Job* 36:16
thy commandment is exceeding *b.*
Ps 119:96
in the *b.* ways I will seek. *S of S* 3:2
Lord will be place of *b.* *Isa* 33:21
know and seek in the *b.* *Jer* 5:1
the *b.* walls of Babylon. 51:58
chariots shall justle in *b.* *Nah* 2:4
b. is the way that leadeth. *Mat* 7:13
make *b.* their phylacteries. 23:5

broader

the measure is *b.* than. *Job* 11:9

broidered

make a robe, a *b.* coat. *Ex* 28:4*
clothed thee with *b.* *Ezek* 16:10
raiment was of silk and *b.* 13
tookest thy *b.* garments and. 18
princes put off *b.* garments. 26:16
linen with *b.* work from. 27:7
occupied in thy fairs with *b.* 16
merchants in blue clothes and *b.* 24
women adorn, not with *b.* *1 Tim* 2:9

broiled

gave him a piece of *b.* *Luke* 24:42

broken

b. my covenant. *Gen* 17:14; *Ps* 55:20
Isa 24:5; 33:8; *Jer* 11:10
vessel wherein sodden, shall be *b.*
Lev 6:28
vessel that he touched be *b.* 15:12
man that is *b.* footed, or *b.* 21:19
that hath his stones *b.* let. 20
blind, *b.* or maimed. 22:22, 24
and I have *b.* the bands. 26:13
when I have *b.* the staff of. 26
because he hath *b.* *Num* 15:31
were the horse-hoofs *b.* *Judg* 5:22
the withs, as a thread is *b.* 16:9
bows of the mighty are *b.* *1 Sam* 2:4
a bow of steel is *b.* *2 Sam* 22:35
Ps 18:34
the ships were *b.* *1 Ki* 22:48
God hath *b.* in upon. *1 Chr* 14:11
b. thy works, ships *b.* *2 Chr* 20:37
also he built wall that was *b.* 32:5
teeth of young lions are *b.* *Job* 4:10
my skin is *b.* and become. 7:5
I was at ease, but he hath *b.* 16:12
arms of fatherless have been *b.* 22:9
and wickedness shall be *b.* 24:20
and let mine arm be *b.* from. 31:22
the high arm shall be *b.* 38:15

thou hast *b.* the teeth of. *Ps* 3:7
forgotten, I am like *b.* vessel. 31:12
Lord is nigh them of *b.* 34:18; 51:17
keepeth his bones, not one is *b.* 34:20
their bows shall be *b.* 37:15
arms shall be *b.* 17
I am feeble and sore *b.* 38:8
though thou hast *b.* us in the. 44:19
that the bones thou hast *b.* 51:8
sacrifices of God are a *b.* spirit. 17
the earth to tremble, hast *b.* 60:2
reproach hath *b.* my heart. 69:20
he hath *b.* the gates of brass. 107:16
he might even slay the *b.* 109:16
the snare is *b.* and we are. 124:7
he healeth the *b.* in heart. 147:3
suddenly shall he be *b.* *Pr* 6:15
sorrow of heart spirit is *b.* 15:13
a *b.* spirit drieth the bones. 17:22
is like a *b.* tooth and a foot. 25:19
cord is not quickly *b.* *Eccl* 4:12
golden bowl be *b.* or pitcher *b.* 12:6
nor latchet of shoes be *b.* *Isa* 5:27
sixty-five years Ephraim be *b.* 7:8
many shall fall and be *b.* 8:15
for thou hast *b.* the yoke. 9:4
the Lord hath *b.* the staff. 14:5
rod of him that smote thee is *b.* 29
shall be *b.* in the purposes. 19:10
all graven images he hath *b.* 21:9
might fall backward and be *b.* 28:13
he hath *b.* the covenant. 33:8
nor the cords thereof be *b.* 20
trustest in staff of this *b.* reed. 36:6
hewed out *b.* cisterns that. *Jer* 2:13
the children have *b.* crown. 16
of old I have *b.* thy yoke. 20
these have *b.* thy yoke. 5:5
all my cords are *b.* 10:20
the branches of it are *b.* 11:16
daughter of my people is *b.* 14:17
Coniah a despised *b.* idol? 22:28
mine heart is *b.* because. 23:9
I have *b.* the yoke of the. 28:2
Hananiah, thou hast *b.* 13
may also my covenant be *b.* 33:21
how is the strong staff *b.*? 48:17
the arm of Moab is *b.* 25
I have *b.* Moab like a vessel. 38
this Nebuchadnezzar hath *b.* 50:17
hammer of whole earth cut and *b.* 23
every one of their bows is *b.* 51:56
walls of Babylon be utterly *b.* 58
he hath destroyed and *b.* *Lam* 2:9
he hath *b.* my bones. 3:4
he hath *b.* my teeth. 16
altars, and images be *b.* *Ezek* 6:4, 6
because I am *b.* with their. 9
my covenant that he hath *b.* 17:19
her strong rods were *b.* 19:12
aha, she is *b.* that was the. 26:2
the east-wind hath *b.* 27:26
time when thou shalt be *b.* 34
I have *b.* the arm of Pharaoh. 30:21
strong and that which was *b.* 22
his boughs are *b.* by all. 31:12
be *b.* in the midst of the. 32:28
nor bound up that which was *b.* 34:4
bind up that which was *b.* 16
when I have *b.* the bands. 27
and they have *b.* my covenant. 44:7
kingdom partly strong, and partly *b.* *Dan* 2:42
the great horn was *b.* 8:8
now that being *b.* whereas four. 22
shall be *b.* without hand. 25
his kingdom shall be *b.* 11:4
with flood be overthrown and *b.* 22
Ephraim is oppressed and *b.* *Hos* 5:11
ship was like to be *b.* *Jonah* 1:4
and it was *b.* in that day. *Zech* 11:11
shall not heal that which is *b.* 16
took up of the *b.* meat. *Mat* 15:37; *Mark* 8:8
on this stone, shall be *b.* *Mat* 21:44; *Luke* 20:18
suffered house to be *b.* *Luke* 12:39
not only *b.* the sabbath. *John* 5:18
that law of Moses not be *b.* 7:23
and scripture cannot be *b.* 10:35
besought Pilate their legs be *b.* 19:31
a bone of him shall not be *b.* 36
so many, yet was not net *b.* 21:11
had *b.* bread and talked. *Acts* 20:11
gave thanks, when he had *b.* 27:35
but the hinder part was *b.* 41*
my body *b.* for you. *1 Cor* 11:24
as vessels shall they be *b.* *Rev* 2:27

broken *down*

oven or ranges *b. d.* *Lev* 11:35
altar that was *b. d.* *1 Ki* 18:30
watch, that it be not *b. d.* *2 Ki* 11:6*
Hezekiah had *b. d.* *2 Chr* 33:3
Josiah had *b. d.* the altars. 34:7
wall of Jerusalem is *b. d.* *Neh* 1:3
viewed walls which were *b. d.* 2:13
why hast thou *b. d.*? *Ps* 80:12
thou hast *b. d.* all his hedges. 89:40
the stone wall was *b. d.* *Pr* 24:31
like a city *b. d.* 25:28
b. d. the principal plants. *Isa* 16:8
the houses have ye *b. d.* 22:10
city of confusion is *b. d.* 24:10
the earth is utterly *b. d.* 19
cities were *b. d.* *Jer* 4:26
Moab *b. d.* 48:20, 39
foundations shall be *b. d.* *Ezek* 30:4
the barns are *b. d.* *Joel* 1:17
Christ hath *b. d.* middle. *Eph* 2:14

broken *forth*

how hast thou *b. forth*? *Gen* 38:29
the Lord hath *b. forth.* *2 Sam* 5:20

broken *in*

God hath *b. in.* *1 Chr* 14:11

broken *off*

my purposes are *b. off.* *Job* 17:11
boughs are withered, they shall be *b. off.* *Isa* 27:11
branches be *b. off.* *Rom* 11:17, 19
unbelief they were *b. off.* 20

broken *out*

leprosy *b. out* of the. *Lev* 13:20, 25

broken *in,* or *to pieces*

adversaries *b. in pieces.* *2 Sam* 2:10
rock, were *b. in pieces.* *2 Chr* 25:12
hast *b.* Rahab *in pieces.* *Ps* 89:10
ye shall be *b. in pieces.* *Isa* 8:9
potter's vessel *b. in pieces.* 30:14
Merodach is *b. in pieces.* *Jer* 50:2*
silver, gold, *b. to pieces.* *Dan* 2:35
of Samaria *b. in pieces.* *Hos* 8:6
and fetters been *b. in p.* *Mark* 5:4

broken *up*

the great deep *b. up.* *Gen* 7:11
city Jerusalem was *b. up.* *2 Ki* 25:4; *Jer* 39:2; 52:7
sons of Athaliah *b. up.* *2 Chr.* 24:7
the depths are *b. up.* *Pr* 3:20
of Chaldeans was *b. up.* *Jer* 37:11
they have *b. up* and. *Mi* 2:13
suffered house be *b. up* *Mat* 24:43
they had *b.* roof *up.* *Mark* 2:4
congregation was *b. up.* *Acts* 13:43

brokenhearted

to bind up the *b.* *Isa* 61:1
to heal *b.*, to preach. *Luke* 4:18

brood

as a hen gathers her *b.* *Luke* 13:34

brook

sent them over the *b.* *Gen* 32:23*
take willows of the *b.* *Lev* 23:40
came to *b.* Eshcol and. *Num* 13:23*
called, *b.* Eshcol because of. 24*
b. Zered, went over *b.* *Deut* 2:13, 14
and cast the dust thereof into *b.* 9:21
smooth stones out of *b.* *1 Sam* 17:40
David came to the *b.* Besor. 30:9
king passed over the *b.* *2 Sam* 15:23
they be gone over the *b.* 17:20
day thou passest over *b.* *1 Ki* 2:37
idol burnt by the *b.* Kidron. 15:13; *2 Chr* 15:16
hide thyself by *b.* Cherith. *1 Ki* 17:3, 5
he drank of the *b.* 6
brought them to the *b.* Kishon. 18:40
burnt the grove at the *b.* *2 Ki* 23:6
dust into *b.* Kidron. 12; *2 Chr* 30:14
find them at end of the *b.* *2 Chr* 20:16
Levites carried it to the *b.* 29:16
people stopped the *b.* 32:4
went up by the *b.* and. *Neh* 2:15
dealt deceitfully as a *b.* *Job* 6:15
the willows of the *b.* compass. 40:22
as to Jabin at *b.* Kison. *Ps* 83:9*
he shall drink of the *b.* in. 110:7
wisdom as a flowing *b.* *Pr* 18:4
carry away to the *b.* *Isa* 15:7
fields to *b.* Kidron be holy. *Jer* 31:40
with his disciples over *b.* *John* 18:1

brooks

in Red sea and *b.* of. *Num* 21:14
at the stream of the *b.* that. 15*
to a land of *b.* of water. *Deut* 8:7
of the *b.* of Gaash. *2 Sam* 23:30; *1 Chr* 11:32
go unto all *b.* of water. *1 Ki* 18:5
and as the stream of *b.* *Job* 6:15
he shall not see the *b.* of. 20:17*
gold as stones of the *b.* 22:24
hart panteth after water *b.* *Ps* 42:1
b. of defence shall be. *Isa* 19:6*
paper reeds by the *b.*, by the *b.*, every thing sown by the *b.* 7*
they that cast angle into the *b.* 8

broth

Gideon put the *b.* in a. *Judg* 6:19
angel said, pour out the *b.* 20
b. of abominable things. *Isa* 65:4

brother

(*For uses see* **brethren**)

hand of every man's *b.* *Gen* 9:5
Rebekah had a *b.* 24:29
gave also to her *b.* and mother. 53
told Rachel he was father's *b.* 29:12
to tell ye had yet a *b.*, have ye another *b.*? 43:6, 7; 44:19
her husband's *b.* shall. *Deut* 25:5
blood laid on their *b.* *Judg* 9:24
repented them for their *b.* 21:6
eating in their elder *b.* *Job* 1:13, 18
I am a *b.* to dragons. 30:29
and a *b.* is born for. *Pr* 17:17
he that is slothful is *b.* to him. 18:9
a *b.* offended is harder to be. 19
friend that sticketh closer than *b.* 24
better neighbour near than *b.* 27:10
he hath neither child nor *b.* *Eccl* 4:8
trust not in any *b.* for *b.* will. *Jer* 9:4
for *b.* they may. *Ezek* 44:25
not Esau Jacob's *b.*? *Mal* 1:2
b. shall deliver up the *b.* *Mat* 10:21; *Mark* 13:12
if a man's *b.* die and. *Mark* 12:19; *Luke* 20:28
Mary, whose *b.* Lazarus. *John* 11:2
comfort them concerning their *b.* 19
b. Saul, receive. *Acts* 9:17; 22:13
he killed James the *b.* of. 12:2
thou seest, *b.* how many. 21:20
and Quartus a *b.* *Rom* 16:23
if any man called a *b.* *1 Cor* 5:11
b. goeth to law with *b.* 6:6
if any *b.* hath a wife. 7:12
a *b.* or sister is not under. 15
thy knowledge shall weak *b.* 8:11
have sent with him the *b.* *2 Cor* 8:18
withdraw from every *b.* *2 Thes* 3:6
but admonish him as a *b.* 15
are refreshed by thee, *b.* *Philem* 7
but above a servant, a *b.* 16

his **brother**

and after that came *his b.* *Gen* 25:26
should give seed to *his b.* 38:9
his b. is dead. 42:38; 44:20
slay every man *his b.* *Ex* 32:27
for his father or *his b.* *Lev* 21:2
not make unclean for *his b.* *Num* 6:7
not exact of neighbour or *his b.* *Deut* 15:2
thought to have done to *his b.* 19:19
succeed in name of *his b.* 25:6
shall be evil towards *his b.* 28:54
fear of Abimelech *his b.* *Judg* 9:21
for blood of Asahel *his b.* *2 Sam* 3:27
but Solomon *his b.* *1 Ki* 1:1
usury every one of his *b.* *Neh* 5:
none can redeem *his b.* *Ps* 49:
shall take hold of *his b.* *Isa* 3:
no man shall spare *his b.* 9:1
fight every one against *his b.* 19:
every one said to *his b.* 41:
no more every man *his b.* *Jer* 31:3; *Heb* 8:1
none serve of a Jew *his b.* *Jer* 34:
let ye go every man *his b.* 1
liberty every one to *his b.* 1

because he spoiled *his b.* *Ezek* 18:18
speak every one to *his b.* 33:30
Jacob took *his b.* *Hos* 12:3
he did pursue *his b.* *Amos* 1:11
hunt every man *his b.* *Mi* 7:2
by the sword of *his b.* *Hag* 2:22
mercy every man to *his b.* *Zech* 7:9
none imagine evil against *his b.* 10
treacherously against *his b.*? *Mal* 2:10
shall say to *his b.*, Raca! *Mat* 5:22
also to you, if ye from your hearts forgive not every one *his b.* 18:35
raise seed to *his b.* 22:24
Mark 12:19; *Luke* 20:28
left his wife unto *his b.* *Mat* 22:25
he findeth his *b.* *John* 1:41
occasion to fall in *his b.* way. *Rom* 14:13
no man defraud *his b.* *1 Thes* 4:6
evil of *his b.* and judgeth *his b.* *Jas* 4:11
and hateth *his b.* *1 John* 2:9, 11
he that loveth *his b.* 10
he that loveth not *his b.* 3:10, 14
who was of that wicked one, and slew *his b.* because *his b.* 3:12
hatheth *his b.* is a. 3:15; 4:20
loveth God, love *his b.* 4:21
if any see *his b.* sin a. 5:16

my **brother**

am I *my b.* keeper? *Gen* 4:9
said, he is *my b.* 20:5, 13; *1 Ki* 20:32
then I slay *my b.* Jacob. *Gen* 27:41
because thou art *my b.* 29:15
battle against Benjamin *my b.* *Judg* 20:23, 28
for thee, *my b.* *2 Sam* 1:26
nay *my b.* do not force me. 13:12
saying, alas *my b.* *1 Ki* 13:30
as he had been *my b.* *Ps* 35:14
thou wert as *my b.* *S of S* 8:1
lament, saying, ah *my b.* *Jer* 22:18
is *my b.* and sister. *Mat* 12:50
Mark 3:35
how oft shall *my b.* sin? *Mat* 18:21
speak to *my b.* *Luke* 12:13
if hadst been here, *my b.* *John* 11:21
if meat make *my b.* to. *1 Cor* 8:13
I found not Titus *my b.* *2 Cor* 2:13

our **brother**

profit if we slay *our b.*? *Gen* 37:26
for he is *our b.* 27; *Judg* 9:3
guilty concerning *our b.* *Gen* 42:21
if thou wilt send *our b.* 43:4
sent with them *our b.* *2 Cor* 8:22
and Timothy *our b.* *Philem* 1

thy **brother**

where is Abel *thy b.*? *Gen* 4:9
voice of *thy b.* blood. 10
and shalt serve *thy b.* 27:40
thy b. wife raise up seed to *thy b.* 38:8
is not Aaron *thy b.*? *Ex* 4:14
take to thee Aaron *thy b.* 28:1
shalt not hate *thy b.* *Lev* 19:17
fear thy God that *thy b.* 25:36
Aaron *thy b.* *Num* 27:13; *Deut* 32:50
if *thy b.* entice thee. *Deut* 13:6
open thy hand wide to *thy b.* 15:11
if *thy b.* an Hebrew be sold. 12
bring them again to *thy b.* 22:1
with all lost things of *thy b.* 3
not abhor Edomite, he is *thy b.* 23:7
not lend upon usury to *thy b.* 19
up my face to *thy b.* *2 Sam* 2:22
hold thy peace, he is *thy b.* 13:20
said, *thy b.* Benhadad. *1 Ki* 20:33
a pledge from *thy b.* *Job* 22:6
speakest against *thy b.* *Ps* 50:20
nor go into *thy b.* house. *Pr* 27:10
thy violence against *thy b.* *Ob* 10
looked on the day of *thy b.* 12
rememberest that *thy b.* *Mat* 5:23
first be reconciled to *thy b.* 24
mote in *thy b.* eye. 7:3, 5
Luke 6:41, 42
if *thy b.* trespass, hast gained *thy b.* *Mat* 18:15; *Luke* 17:3
thy b. shall rise again. *John* 11:23
judge *thy b.*? why dost thou set at nought *thy b.*? *Rom* 14:10

your **brother**

bring *your b.* so will I deliver you *your b.* *Gen* 42:34
not see my face, except *your b.* 43:3
take *your b.* arise, and go. 13
I am Joseph *your b.* 45:4
king, because he is your *b.* *Judg* 9:18
John, who also am *your b.* *Rev* 1:9

brotherhood

might break *b.* between. *Zech* 11:14
love the *b.* fear God. *1 Pet* 2:17

brotherly

remembered not the *b.* *Amos* 1:9
affectioned, with *b.* love. *Rom* 12:10
as touching *b.* love. *1 Thes* 4:9
let *b.* love continue. *Heb* 13:1
to godliness *b.* kindness, and to *b.* kindness charity. *2 Pet* 1:7

brought

hast *b.* on me and my. *Gen* 20:9
the Lord thy God *b.* it to. 27:20
that torn of beasts I *b.* not. 31:39
they *b.* him the present. 43:26
beast in field not *b.* *Ex* 9:19
b. east-wind, east-wind *b.* 10:13
hard causes they *b.* to Moses. 18:26
how I bare you and *b.* you. 19:4
man that *b.* us out of Egypt. 32:1, 23
that thou hast *b.* so great a sin. 21
had purple and scarlet *b.* 35:23
b. to Aaron the priest. *Lev* 13:2, 9
till he have *b.* an offering. 23:14
they *b.* the blasphemer. 24:11
he shall be *b.* to door. *Num* 6:13
because *b.* not the offering. 9:13
wherefore hath the Lord *b.*? 14:3
and he hath *b.* thee near. 16:10
Moses *b.* their cause. 27:5
have therefore *b.* an oblation. 31:50
till we have *b.* them. 32:17
the Lord thy God *b.* *Deut* 5:15
I have *b.* the first-fruits. 26:10
I have *b.* away the hallowed. 13
in morning ye shall be *b.* *Josh* 7:14
they took and *b.* them. 23
they *b.* them to the valley. 24
Lord *b.* the sea upon them. 24:7
I have *b.* you unto land. *Judg* 2:1
the Philistines *b.* money. 16:18
who *b.* thee hither? 18:3
she *b.* Samuel to the. *1 Sam* 1:24
they slew a bullock and *b.* 25
despised him, and *b.* him no. 10:27
wherefore then have ye *b.*? 21:14
what Abigail had *b.* him. 25:35
found and *b.* an Egyptian to. 30:11
crown and bracelet, *b.* *2 Sam* 1:10
who am I? what is my house, that thou hast *b.*? 7:18; *1 Chr* 17:16
Lord *b.* evil. *1 Ki* 9:9; *2 Chr* 7:22
they *b.* every man his present. *1 Ki* 10:25; *2 Chr* 9:24
hast thou also *b.* evil? *1 Ki* 17:20
the king died, and was *b.* to. 22:37
not receiving what he *b.* *2 Ki* 5:20
Hoshea *b.* no presents to. 17:4
carry thither the priest ye *b.* 27
he *b.* the shadow ten degrees. 20:11
craftsmen the king *b.* captive. 24:16
with jeopardy of lives *b.* *1 Chr* 11:19
the Lord *b.* fear of him. 14:17
children of Israel *b.* *2 Chr* 13:18
b. to Jehoshaphat presents. 17:5
b. Ahaziah to Jehu, and. 22:9
the king of Syria *b.* Israel. 28:5
b. captives to Jericho to. 15
many *b.* gifts to the Lord. 32:23
they *b.* us a man of. *Ezra* 8:18
God had *b.* counsel. *Neh* 4:15
people *b.* them and made. 8:16
thou art just in all that is *b.* 9:33
Judah *b.* tithe of corn and. 13:12
the royal apparel be *b.* *Esth* 6:8
of slain in Shushan *b.* 9:11
a thing was secretly *b.* *Job* 4:12
yet shall he be *b.* to the. 21:32
be *b.* to confusion. *Ps* 35:4, 26
with joy shall they be *b.* 45:15
they are *b.* to shame. 71:24
a man is *b.* to a piece. *Pr* 6:26
b. me to banqueting-. *S of S* 2:4
Ar is *b.* to silence, Kir of Moab *b.* to silence. *Isa* 15:1
b. Chaldeans to ruin. *Isa* 23:13
terrible one is *b.* to nought. 29:20
hast not *b.* small cattle. 43:23, 24
have called him, I have *b.* 48:15
b. as a lamb to the slaughter. 53:7
arm *b.* salvation. 59:16; 63:5
that their kings may be *b.* 60:11
they that *b.* it shall drink. 62:9
as an ox that is *b.* *Jer* 11:19
I have *b.* on them a spoiler. 15:8
as I have *b.* all this evil. 32:42
now Lord hath *b.* it and done. 40:3
concerning the evil I *b.* *Ezek* 14:22
left she her whoredoms *b.* 23:8
thou shalt not be *b.* together. 29:5
might shew them, art thou *b.* 40:4
b. me through the waters to. 47:3, 4
nor instruments of music *b.* *Dan* 6:18
b. him near before ancient of. 7:13
Lord watched evil, and *b.* it. 9:14
given up, and they that *b.* her. 11:6
when ye *b.* it home. *Hag* 1:9
ye *b.* what was torn. *Mal* 1:13
shall be *b.* before kings. *Mat* 10:18
Mark 13:9; *Luke* 21:12
kingdom *b.* to desolation. *Mat* 12:25
Luke 11:17
b. John Baptist's head. *Mat* 14:11
I *b.* him to thy disciples. 17:16
one was *b.* that owed him. 18:24
b. to him little children. 19:13
Mark 10:13
a candle *b.* to be put. *Mark* 4:21
king commanded head to be *b.* 6:27
disciples rebuked those that *b.* 10:13
b. him to Jerusalem. *Luke* 2:22
a woman *b.* an alabaster box. 7:37
b. him to an inn and. 10:34
why have ye not *b.* him? *John* 7:45
prison to have them *b.* *Acts* 5:21
Barnabas *b.* him to the. 9:27
and being *b.* on their way. 15:3
who *b.* her masters gain. 16:16
b. them to the magistrates. 20
from his body were *b.* 19:12
b. their books, and burned them. 19
Demetrius *b.* no small gain. 24
ye *b.* hither these men, no robbers. 37
and they *b.* the young man. 20:12
they all *b.* us on our way. 21:5
commanded Paul to be *b.* 25:6
thou must be *b.* before Caesar. 27:24
to be *b.* on my way. *Rom* 15:24
I will not be *b.* under. *1 Cor* 6:12
of you to be *b.* on. *2 Cor* 1:16
b. life and immortality. *2 Tim* 1:10
grace that is to be *b.* to. *1 Pet* 1:13
of the same is he *b.* in. *2 Pet* 2:19

brought *again*

Abram *b. again* his. *Gen* 14:16
the money that was *b. again.* 43:12
Moses and Aaron *b. again.* *Ex* 10:8
the Lord *b. again* the waters. 15:19
b. us word *again* and. *Deut* 1:25
b. him word *again.* *Josh* 14:7
hath *b.* me home *again.* *Ruth* 1:21
Philistines *b. again* ark. *1 Sam* 6:21
b. again Abner. *2 Sam* 3:26
came and *b.* the king word *again.*
2 Ki 22:9, 20; *1 Ki* 20:9; *2 Chr* 34:28
b. Manasseh *again.* *2 Chr* 33:13
b. I *again* the vessels of. *Neh* 13:9
vessels shall be *b. again.* *Jer* 27:16
ye have not *b. again.* *Ezek* 34:4
when I have *b. again.* 39:27
repented and *b. again.* *Mat* 27:3
of peace that *b. again.* *Heb* 13:20

brought *back*

Abram *b. back* all. *Gen* 14:16
b. back word to them. *Num* 13:26
prophet whom he had *b. back.* *1 Ki* 13:23
Jehoshaphat *b.* them *back.* *2 Chr* 19:4
hast *b. back* captivity of. *Ps* 85:1
come into land *b. back.* *Ezek* 38:8

brought *down*

Joseph was *b. down* into. *Gen* 39:1
he *b. down* the people. *Judg* 7:5
Philistines *b. down* Samson. 16:21
he had *b.* him *down.* *1 Sam* 30:16
they *b.* Adonijah *down.* *1 Ki* 1:53
Elijah *b.* the child *down.* 17:23

b. them down to brook. 1 Ki 18:40
are b. down and fallen. Ps 20:8
he b. down their heart. 107:12
mean man shall be b. down. Isa 5:15
thy pomp is b. down to. 14:11
thou shalt be b. down to hell. 15
shalt be b. down and speak. 29:4
your sake I have b. down. 43:14
he hath b. them down. Lam 2:2
the Lord have b. down. Ezek 17:24
shall be b. down with. 31:18
of Assyria be b. down. Zech 10:11
Capernaum be b. down. Mat 11:23
brethren b. him down. Acts 9:30

brought *forth*

earth b. forth grass and. Gen 1:12
waters b. forth abundantly. 21
king of Salem b. forth. 14:18
Lord b. forth Abram abroad. 15:5
angels b. Lot forth, and. 19:16
the servant b. forth jewels. 24:53
when b. forth, she sent to. 38:25
earth b. forth by handfuls. 41:47
when thou hast b. forth. Ex 3:12
for ye have b. us forth. 16:3
Lord who b. them forth out of Egypt.
29:46; Lev 25:38; 26:13, 45
Aaron's rod b. forth. Num 17:8
sent an angel, and b. us forth. 20:16
God b. him forth out of. 24:8
who b. thee forth. Deut 6:12; 8:14
who b. forth water out of. 8:15
people b. forth have corrupted. 9:12
the Lord b. us forth with a. 26:8
made when he b. them forth. 29:25
for precious fruits b. forth. 33:14
b. forth those five kings. Josh 10:23
she b. forth butter in. Judg 5:25
b. you forth out of house of. 6:8
Moses, who b. forth. 1 Sam 12:8
b. me forth into large. 2 Sam 22:20
Ps 18:19
forsook the Lord who b. forth their
fathers. 1 Ki 9:9; 2 Chr 7:22
b. forth vestments. 2 Ki 10:22
b. forth the king's son. 11:12
hast b. me forth out. Job 10:18
wicked shall be b. forth. 21:30
mischief, and b. forth. Ps 7:14
before mountains were b. forth. 90:2
their land b. forth frogs. 105:30
he b. forth his people with. 43
I was b. forth. Pr 8:24
before the hills was I b. forth. 25
mother b. thee forth, she b. forth.
S of S 8:5
for grapes, and it b. forth. Isa 5:2
b. forth wind. 26:18
what hast thou b. forth. 45:10
among sons, she hath b. forth. 51:18
she travailed, she b. forth. 66:7
as Zion travailed, she b. forth. 8
thou hast b. me forth. Jer 2:27
commanded in day I b. forth. 11:4
34:13
Pashur b. forth Jeremiah. 20:3
hast b. forth thy people. 32:21
Lord b. forth the weapons. 50:25
the Lord hath b. forth our. 51:10
I b. forth my stuff by. Ezek 12:7
a remnant shall be b. forth. 14:22
in whose sight b. them forth. 20:22
travaileth hath b. forth. Mi 5:3
olive-tree hath not b. forth. Hag 2:19
till she had b. forth her. Mat 1:25
good ground, and b. forth fruit.
13:8; Mark 4:8
Elisabeth's time came, she b. forth.
Luke 1:57
she b. forth her first-born son. 2:7
ground of a rich man b. forth. 12:16
that, he b. forth Jesus. John 19:13
prison doors, b. them forth. Acts 5:19
Herod would have b. him forth. 12:6
the man to be b. forth. 25:17
and the earth b. forth. Jas 5:18
she b. forth a man-child. Rev 12:5
persecuted woman which b. forth. 13

brought *in*

hath b. in an Hebrew. Gen 39:14
Joseph b. in Jacob his father. 47:7
blood was not b. in. Lev 10:18
goat, whose blood was b. in. 16:27
not till Miriam was b. in. Num 12:15
for righteousness Lord b. me in.
Deut 9:4
when the Lord hath b. thee in. 11:29
Joab b. in a great spoil. 2 Sam 3:22
b. in the ark of the Lord. 6:17
1 Ki 8:6
no burden b. in on the. Neh 13:19
by his power he b. in. Ps 78:26
then was Daniel b. in. Dan 5:13
John's head was b. in. Mat 14:11
b. in with Jesus into. Acts 7:45
false brethren b. in to. Gal 2:4

brought *into*

not b. us into a land. Num 16:14
Lord hath b. thee into. Deut 6:10
31:20
b. ark into Dagon's. 1 Sam 5:2
b. them into the parlour. 9:22
b. thy servant into a. 20:8
sin-money not b. into. 2 Ki 12:16
hast b. me into. Ps 22:15
king hath b. me into his. S of S 1:4
I b. you into a plentiful. Jer 2:7
hath b. me into darkness. Lam 3:2
have b. thee into waters. Ezek 27:26
b. into my sanctuary. 44:7
led him and b. him into. Acts 9:8
b. Greeks into the temple. 21:28
we b. nothing into. 1 Tim 6:7
whose blood is b. into. Heb 13:11

brought *low*

hast b. me very low. Judg 11:35
Lord b. Judah low. 2 Chr 28:19
they are b. low. Job 14:21
wicked are gone and b. low. 24:24
prevent us, we are b. low. Ps 79:8
and were b. low for. 106:43
are b. low, through. 107:39
I was b. low, and he helped. 116:6
for I am b. very low. 142:6
of music shall be b. low. Eccl 12:4
lifted up, shall be b. low. Isa 2:12
of terrible ones be b. low. 25:5
mountain and hill b. low. Luke 3:5
Isa 40:4

brought *out*

that b. thee out of Ur. Gen 15:7
they b. him hastily out. 41:14
and he b. Simeon out. 43:23
by strength of hand Lord b. you out.
Ex 13:3, 9, 14, 16; Deut 6:21
which b. out. Ex 20:2; Lev 19:36
Num 15:41; Deut 5:6; Ps 81:10
b. them out of Egypt. Lev 23:43
1 Ki 8:21
Lord b. thee out thence. Deut 5:15
b. them out to slay them. 9:28
young men b. out Rahab. Josh 6:23
afterward I b. you out. 24:5
servant b. her out. 2 Sam 13:18
he b. out the grove. 2 Ki 23:6
he b. out the people. 1 Chr 20:3
b. out the king's son. 2 Chr 23:11
priests b. out all uncleanness. 29:16
he b. streams also out. Ps 78:16
b. a vine out of Egypt. 80:8
he b. them out of darkness. 107:14
and b. out Israel from. 136:11
in the day I b. them out. Jer 7:22
father b. out of Jewry. Dan 5:13
the Lord b. Israel out. Hos 12:13
Moses, which b. us out. Acts 7:40
how the Lord b. him out. 12:17
with an high arm b. them out. 13:17
b. out, and said, what must? 16:30
besought them, and b. them out. 39

brought *to pass*

I have b. it to pass. 2 Ki 19:25
Isa 37:26
and shall be b. to pass. Ezek 21:7
shall be b. to pass. 1 Cor 15:54

brought *up*

hast thou b. us up? Ex 17:3
Num 21:5
Moses that b. us up. Ex 32:1, 23
gods which b. thee up. 4, 8
1 Ki 12:28
and people thou hast b. up. Ex 33:1
b. up an evil report. Num 13:32
thing that thou hast b. us up? 16:13
have ye b. up congregation of? 20:4
with thee, which b. up. Deut 20:1
because he b. up an evil. 22:19
he it is that b. us up. Josh 24:17
bones of Joseph b. up. 32
I b. you up from Egypt. Judg 6:8
1 Sam 10:18
b. Samson up. Judg 15:13
the lords b. up to her. 16:8
b. him up and buried. 31
all flesh-hook b. up the. 1 Sam 2:14
day I b. them up. 8:8; 2 Sam 7:6
1 Chr 17:5
that b. your fathers up. 1 Sam 12:6
David went and b. up. 2 Sam 6:12
15; 1 Ki 8:4; 1 Chr 15:28; 2 Chr 1:4
b. up for Adriel. 2 Sam 21:8
b. up the bones of Saul. 13
that b. up Ahab's. 2 Ki 10:1, 6
against Lord who b. them up. 17:7
the Lord who b. you up. 36
b. up Zedekiah to king. 25:6
Jer 39:5
Solomon b. up daughter. 2 Chr 8:11
with young men b. up. 10:8, 10
all these vessels b. up. Ezra 1:11
king of Assur b. us up hither. 4:2
God that b. thee up. Neh 9:18
Mordecai b. up Esther. Esth 2:7
like as when she was b. up. 20
from youth he was b. up. Job 31:18
thou hast b. up my soul. Ps 30:3
b. me up out of an horrible pit. 40:2
as one b. up with him. Pr 8:30
I nourished and b. up. Isa 1:2
who hath b. up these? 49:21
to guide of sons she b. up. 51:18
he that b. them up? 63:11; Jer 2:6
in the day I b. them up. Jer 11:7
Lord that b. up Israel. 16:14; 23:7
b. up Israel from the north. 15; 23:8
those I b. up hath my. Lam 2:22
that were b. up in scarlet. 4:5
b. up one of her whelps. Ezek 19:3
when I have b. you up out. 37:13
I b. you up. Amos 2:10; 3:1; 9:7
Mi 6:4
yet hast b. up my. Jonah 2:6
she shall be b. up. Nah 2:7
where she had been b. up. Luke 4:16
been b. up with Herod. Acts 13:1
yet b. up in this city at feet. 22:3
widow, if she have b. up. 1 Tim 5:10

broughtest

thy people thou b. out. Ex 32:7
thou b. up this people. Num 14:13
lest land whence thou b. Deut 9:28
thine inheritance thou b. out. 29
1 Ki 8:51
he that b. in Israel. 2 Sam 5:2
1 Chr 11:2
b. our fathers out of. 1 Ki 8:53
b. him forth out of Ur. Neh 9:7
thou b. forth water for them. 15
b. them into the land. 23
thou b. us into the net. Ps 66:11
but thou b. us out into a. 12

brow

iron sinew, thy b. brass. Isa 48:4
led him to the b. of hill. Luke 4:29

brown

(Revised Version, black)
b. cattle among the sheep. Gen 30:32
35:40
every one that is not b. shall be. 30:33

bruise, *noun*

saith the Lord, thy b. is. Jer 30:12*
is no healing of thy b Nah 3:19*

bruise

b. thy head, thou shalt b. Gen 3:15
nor will he b. it with. Isa 28:28*
it pleased the Lord to b. him. 53:10
iron shall it break and b. Dan 2:40*
of peace shall b. Satan. Rom 16:20

bruised

not offer to Lord what is b. Lev 22:2[illegible]
trusteth on staff of this b. 2 Ki 18:2[illegible]
b. reed shall he not break. Isa 42:[illegible]
Mat 12:2[illegible]
he was b. for our iniquities. Isa 53:[illegible]
there they b. the teats. Ezek 23:[illegible]
b. the breasts of her virginity.
liberty them that are b. Luke 4:1[illegible]

bruises
soundness, but wounds, *b.* *Isa* 1:6
bruising
b. thy teats by Egyptians. *Ezek* 23:21
the spirit *b.* him, hardly. *Luke* 9:39
bruit
behold, the noise of the *b.* *Jer* 10:22*
all that hear *b.* of thee. *Nah* 3:19†
brute, *see* **beasts**
brutish
fool and the *b.* person. *Ps* 49:10
a *b.* man knoweth not. 92:6
understand, ye *b.* among. 94:8
he that hateth reproof is *b.* *Pr* 12:1
I am more *b.* than any man. 30:2
counsel of the wise counsellors of Pharaoh is become *b.* *Isa* 19:11
they are altogether *b.* *Jer* 10:8
every man is *b.* 14; 51:17
pastors are become *b.* 10:21
deliver into hand of *b.* *Ezek* 21:31
bucket, -s
pour water out of his *b.* *Num* 24:7
nations are as a drop of a *b.* *Isa* 40:15
buckler
A shield, 1 Chr 5:18. *God is often called the buckler, or shield of his people,* Ps 18:2; Pr 2:7. *Faith is called the Christian's shield,* Eph 6:16.
b. to all that trust in. *2 Sam* 22:31 *Ps* 18:30
men able to bear *b.* *1 Chr* 5:18
Gadites that could handle *b.* 12:8*
Lord is my God, my *b.* *Ps* 18:2
take hold of shield and *b.* 35:2
truth shall be thy shield and *b.* 91:4
he is a *b.* to them that. *Pr* 2:7
order ye the *b.* and shield. *Jer* 46:3
set against the *b.* shield. *Ezek* 23:24
shall lift up the *b.* against. 26:8
bucklers
Jehoiada delivered spears, *b.* *2 Chr* 23:9
upon thick bosses of *b.* *Job* 15:26
hang a thousand *b.* *S of S* 4:4
great company with *b.* *Ezek* 38:4
set on fire shields, *b.* and. 39:9
bud, *noun*
cause *b.* of the tender. *Job* 38:27
afore harvest, when *b.* is. *Isa* 18:5*
as earth bringeth forth her *b.* 61:11
thee to multiply as *b.* *Ezek* 16:7
b. shall yield no meal. *Hos* 8:7*
bud, *verb*
scent of water it will *b.* *Job* 14:9
horn of David to *b.* *Ps* 132:17
f pomegranates *b.* forth. *S of S* 7:12
Israel shall blossom and *b.* *Isa* 27:6
earth to bring forth and *b.* 55:10
ause horn of Israel to *b.* *Ezek* 29:21
budded
ine was as though it *b.* *Gen* 40:10
he house of Levi *b.* *Num* 17:8
whether pomegranates *b.* *S of S* 6:11
blossomed, pride hath *b.* *Ezek* 7:10
was Aaron's rod that *b.* *Heb* 9:4
buds
od brought forth *b.* *Num* 17:8
buffet
messenger of Satan to *b.* *2 Cor* 12:7
buffeted
nd *b.* him. *Mat* 26:67; *Mark* 14:65
present hour we are *b.* *1 Cor* 4:11
when ye be *b.* for. *1 Pet* 2:20
build referred to *God*
a priest, and will *b.* *1 Sam* 2:35 *2 Sam* 7:27; *1 Ki* 11:38
at the Lord will *b.* *1 Chr* 17:10
st told that thou wilt *b.* him. 25
all destroy, and not *b.* *Ps* 28:5
good to Zion, *b.* the walls. 51:18
r God will *b.* the cities. 69:35
d *b.* up thy throne to. 89:4
hen Lord shall *b.* up Zion. 102:16
cept Lord *b.* house. 127:1
ord doth *b.* up Jerusalem. 147:2
ncerning a nation to *b.* *Jer* 18:9
and not pull down. 24:6; 31:28

again I will *b.* thee. *Jer* 31:4
I will *b.* Judah and Israel. 33:7
abide in this land I will *b.* 42:10
I the Lord *b.* ruined. *Ezek* 36:36
I *b.* it as in days of old. *Amos* 9:11
on this rock will I *b.* *Mat* 16:18
able to *b.* it in three days. 26:61 *Mark* 14:58
I will *b.* again tabernacle. *Acts* 15:16
build *altars*
shalt not *b.* an *altar* of. *Ex* 20:25
b. me here seven *altars.* *Num* 23:1, 29
thou shalt *b.* an *altar.* *Deut* 27:5
thou shalt *b.* *altar* of Lord of. 6
we rebel and *b.* an *altar.* *Josh* 22:29
see **began**
build joined with *house*
not *b.* his brother's *house.* *Deut* 25:9
shalt *b.* an *house,* not dwell. 28:30 *Zeph* 1:13
two did *b.* the *house* of. *Ruth* 4:11
shalt *b.* me an *house* ? *2 Sam* 7:5
spake I, why *b.* ye not me an *h.* ? 7
he shall *b.* an *house.* 7:13; *1 Ki* 5:5
8:19; *1 Chr* 17:12; 22:10
b. thee an *h.* in Jerusalem. *1 Ki* 2:36
David could not *b.* an *house.* 5:3
I purpose to *b.* an *house* to Lord. 5 *2 Chr* 2:1
no city to *b.* an *house.* *1 Ki* 8:16 *2 Chr* 6:5
heart of David my father to *b. house.* *1 Ki* 8:17; *1 Chr* 28:2; *2 Chr* 6:7
shall *b.* me an *house.* *1 Chr* 17:12 *2 Chr* 6:9
shalt not *b.* an *house* because. *1 Chr* 22:8
my son, *b.* the *house* of Lord. 11
Solomon shall *b.* my *house.* 28:6
behold, I *b.* an *house.* *2 Chr* 2:4
the *house* I *b.* is great. 5
who is able to *b.* him an *house* ? that I should *b.* an *house.* 6
charged me to *b.* an *house.* 36:23 *Ezra* 1:2
go to *b.* the *house of* Lord. *Ezra* 1:3
commanded you to *b. house* ? 5:3, 9
let the governor *b.* this *house.* 6:7
except the Lord *b. house.* *Ps* 127:1
afterwards *b.* thy *house.* *Pr* 24:27
they shall *b. houses* and. *Isa* 65:21
where is the *house* that ye *b.* ? 66:1
I will *b.* me a wide *house.* *Jer* 22:14
b. houses and dwell in. 29:5, 28
neither shall ye *b. house* nor. 35:7
not near, let us *b. houses.* *Ezek* 11:3
safely, and shall *b. houses.* 28:26
bring wood, *b.* house. *Hag* 1:8
to *b.* it an *house* in the. *Zech* 5:11
what *house* will ye *b.* ? *Acts* 7:49
build
let us *b.* us a city and a. *Gen* 11:4
and they left off to *b.* the city. 8
we will *b.* sheep-folds. *Num* 32:16
b. cities for your little ones. 24
thou shalt *b.* bulwarks. *Deut* 20:20
Solomon desired to *b.* in Jerusalem. *1 Ki* 9:19; *2 Chr* 8:6
then did *b.* Millo. *1 Ki* 9:24
Solomon did *b.* an high place. 11:7
Hiel the Bethelite *b.* Jericho. 16:34
b. ye the sanctuary. *1 Chr* 22:19
an heart to *b.* the palace. 29:19
let us *b.* these cities. *2 Chr* 14:7
let us *b.* with you. *Ezra* 4:2
let us *b.* the wall. *Neh* 2:17
let us rise and *b.* 18
we his servants will rise and *b.* 20
which they *b.* if a fox go up. 4:3
so that we are not able to *b.* 10
and a time to *b.* up. *Eccl* 3:3
we will *b.* upon her. *S of S* 8:9
are fallen, but we will *b.* *Isa* 9:10
he shall *b.* my city 45:13
b. the old waste places. 58:12; 61:4
sons of strangers shall *b.* up. 60:10
they shall not *b.* and another. 65:22
set thee over nations to *b.* *Jer* 1:10
b. a fort against it. *Ezek* 4:2; 21:22
restore and *b.* Jerusalem. *Dan* 9:25
b. it as in the days of old. *Amos* 9:11
Israel shall *b.* the waste cities. 14

they *b.* up Zion with blood. *Mi* 3:10
he shall *b.* the temple. *Zech* 6:12, 13
that are far off shall *b.* 15
Tyrus did *b.* herself a strong. 9:3
they shall *b.* but I. *Mal* 1:4
ye *b.* tombs of prophets. *Mat* 23:29 *Luke* 11:47, 48
down my barns and *b.* *Luke* 12:18
which of you intending to *b.* ? 14:28
this man began to *b.* and not. 30
able to *b.* you up. *Acts* 20:32
I *b.* on another man's *Rom* 15:20
b. on this foundation. *1 Cor* 3:12
if I *b.* again the things. *Gal* 2:18
builded
Cain *b.* a city. *Gen* 4:17
Noah *b.* an altar to the Lord. 8:20
Asher *b.* Nineveh, Rehoboth. 10:11
the tower children of men *b.* 11:5
Abram *b.* an altar. 12:7; 13:18
Isaac *b.* an altar. 26:25
Moses *b.* an altar under. *Ex* 24:4
ye have *b.* an altar. *Josh* 22:16
less this house I have *b.* *1 Ki* 8:27, 43
wherewith Baasha had *b.* 15:22
Solomon had *b.* for. *2 Ki* 23:13
house to be *b.* must be. *1 Chr* 22:5
adversaries heard that they *b.* *Ezra* 4:1
that if this city be *b.* 13, 16
that this city be not *b.* 4:21
house of great God which is *b.* 5:8
we build the house that was *b.* 11
let the house of God be *b.* 15; 6:3
elders of the Jews *b.* 6:14
his sword girded, and so *b.* *Neh* 4:18
away an house he *b.* not. *Job* 20:19
Jerusalem is *b.* a city. *Ps* 122:3
Wisdom hath *b.* her house. *Pr* 9:1
through wisdom is house *b.* 24:3
I *b.* me houses, I. *Eccl* 2:4
like tower of David *b.* *S of S* 4:4
the city shall be *b.* *Jer* 30:18
he hath *b.* against me. *Lam* 3:5
waste shall be *b.* *Ezek* 36:10, 33
sold, they plant, they *b.* *Luke* 17:28
in whom ye are *b.* together. *Eph* 2:22
he who *b.* the house hath. *Heb* 3:3
for every house is *b.* by some. 4
builder, -s
Solomon's and Hiram's *b.* *1 Ki* 5:18
laid money out to the *b.* *2 Ki* 12:11
carpenters and *b.* 22:6; *2 Chr* 34:11
when *b.* laid foundation. *Ezra* 3:10
to anger before the *b.* *Neh* 4:5
stone which *b.* refused. *Ps* 118:22 *Mat* 21:42; *Mark* 12:10 *Luke* 20:17; *Acts* 4:11
thy *b.* have perfected. *Ezek* 27:4
as a wise master-*b.* I. *1 Cor* 3:10
city whose *b.* and maker. *Heb* 11:10
the stone which the *b.* *1 Pet* 2:7
buildest
goodly cities thou *b.* not. *Deut* 6:10
thou *b.* a new house. 22:8
for which cause thou *b.* *Neh* 6:6
in that thou *b.* thine. *Ezek* 16:31
thou that destroyest the temple and *b.* it in. *Mat* 27:40; *Mark* 15:29
buildeth
cursed be the man that *b.* *Josh* 6:26
b. his house as a moth. *Job* 27:18
every wise woman *b.* her. *Pr* 14:1
woe to him that *b.* by. *Jer* 22:13
Israel *b.* temples. *Hos* 8:14
it is he that *b.* his stories. *Amos* 9:6
woe to him that *b.* a. *Hab* 2:12
foundation, another *b.* *1 Cor* 3:10
building
not against Lord in *b.* *Josh* 22:19
till he made an end of *b.* *1 Ki* 3:1
no tool of iron heard while *b.* 6:7
so was Solomon seven years in *b.* 38
Solomon was *b.* his own house. 7:1
wherewith Baasha was *b.* *2 Chr* 16:6
b. rebellious and bad city. *Ezra* 4:12
by *b.* forts to cut off. *Ezek* 17:17
temple was forty-six years in *b.* *John* 2:20
b. up yourselves on holy. *Jude* 20
building, *substantive*
Solomon finished *b.* house. *1 Ki* 9:1

he left off *b.* of Ramah. *1 Ki* 15:21
2 Chr 16:5
made ready for the *b.* *1 Chr* 28:2
instructed for the *b.* *2 Chr* 3:3
of men that made this *b.* *Ezra* 5:4
what ye shall do for the *b.* of. 6:8
by slothfulness the *b.* *Eccl* 10:18*
measured the breadth of the *b.*
Ezek 40:5; 41:15
there was a row of *b.* round. 46:23
God's husbandry, God's *b.* *1 Cor* 3:9
we have a *b.* of God. *2 Cor* 5:1
in whom all the *b.* *Eph* 2:21
tabernacle not of this *b.* *Heb* 9:11*
b. of wall was of jasper. *Rev* 21:18

buildings

to shew him *b.* of temple. *Mat* 24:1
see what *b.* are here. *Mark* 13:1, 2

built

it shall not be *b.* again. *Deut* 13:16
the cities that Ahab *b.* *1 Ki* 22:39
every side, so they *b.* *2 Chr* 14:7
have *b.* thee a sanctuary. 20:8
Uzziah *b.* towers in. 26:9, 10
Jotham *b.* in the forests. 27:4
who *b.* desolate places. *Job* 3:14
breaketh down, cannot be *b.* 12:14
to Almighty, shalt be *b.* up. 22:23
he *b.* his sanctuary. *Ps* 78:69
I have said, mercy shall be *b.* 89:2
b. a tower in the midst. *Isa* 5:2
saith to Judah, ye shall be *b.* 44:26
Jerusalem, thou shalt be *b.* 28
shall they be *b.* in midst. *Jer* 12:16
be *b.* O virgin of Israel. 31:4
provocation from day they *b.* 32:31
which I have *b.* will I break. 45:4
thou hast *b.* to thee. *Ezek* 16:24
hast *b.* thy high place at. 25
thou shalt be *b.* no more. 26:14
great Babylon I have *b.*? *Dan* 4:30
the street shall be *b.* again. 9:25
that temple be *b.* *Zech* 8:9
b. a tower. *Mat* 21:33; *Mark* 12:1
the centurion hath *b.* us. *Luke* 7:5
abide which he hath *b.* *1 Cor* 3:14
b. on the foundation of. *Eph* 2:20
rooted and *b.* up in him. *Col* 2:7
he that *b.* all things is God. *Heb* 3:4

built *altar*

Moses *b.* an *altar.* *Ex* 17:15; 24:4
Aaron *b.* an *altar.* 32:5
Joshua *b.* an *altar.* *Josh* 8:30
half tribe *b.* an *altar.* 22:10
Gideon *b.* an *altar.* *Judg* 6:24
people *b.* an *altar.* 21:4
Samuel *b.* an *altar.* *1 Sam* 7:17
Saul *b.* an *altar.* 14:35
David *b.* an *altar.* *2 Sam* 24:25
offered on the *altar* he *b.* *1 Ki* 9:25
with stones Elisha *b.* *altar* in. 18:32
Urijah *b.* an *altar.* *2 Ki* 16:11

built *altars*

Balak *b.* seven *altars.* *Num* 23:14
he *b.* *altars* in house of. *2 Ki* 21:4
b. *altars* for all the host. 5; *2 Chr* 33:5
away *altars* he had *b.* *2 Chr* 33:15

built *city*

let city of Sihon be *b.* *Num* 21:27
Joshua *b.* the *city.* *Josh* 19:50
Danites *b.* *city.* *Judg* 18:28
Omri *b.* *city.* *1 Ki* 16:24
David *b.* *city* round. *1 Chr* 11:8
no *city* it shall never be *b.* *Isa* 25:2
city shall be *b.* to Lord. *Jer* 31:38
hill whereon *city* was *b.* *Luke* 4:29

built *cities*

b. for Pharaoh treasure-*cities.*
Ex 1:11
cities which ye *b.* not. *Josh* 24:13
cities which Asa *b.* *1 Ki* 15:23
cities Huram restored, Solomon *b.*
2 Chr 8:2
Rehoboam *b.* *cities* for defence. 11:5
Asa *b.* fenced *cities* in Judah. 14:6
Jehoshaphat *b.* castles and *c.* 17:12
Uzziah *b.* *cities* about. 26:6
Jotham *b.* *cities* in mountains. 27:4
saith to *cities* of Judah, ye shall be *b.*
Isa 44:26

built *high places*

Judah *b.* *high p.* images. *1 Ki* 14:23
Israel *b.* *high p.* in cities. *2 Ki* 17:9
Manasseh *b.* up again *high p.* 21:3
2 Chr 33:3
b. *high p.* of Tophet. *Jer* 7:31
b. *high p.* of Baal. 19:5; 32:35

built *house,* or *houses*

hast *b.* goodly *houses.* *Deut* 8:12
man hath *b.* a new *house*? 20:5
there was no *house* *b.* to. *1 Ki* 3:2
Solomon *b.* *houses.* 6:9, 14
I have *b.* thee an *house.* 8:13
and have *b.* an *house* for the. 20
toward *house* I have *b.* 8:44, 48
2 Chr 6:34, 38
sure *house,* as I *b.* for David.
1 Ki 11:38
ye not *b.* me an *house*? *1 Chr* 17:6
less this *house* I have *b.*? *2 Chr* 6:18
ye have *b.* *houses* of. *Amos* 5:11
Lord's *house* should be *b.* *Hag* 1:2
my *house* shall he *b.* in. *Zech* 1:16
b. his *house* on a rock. *Mat* 7:24
Luke 6:48
b. his house on sand. *Mat* 7:26
Luke 6:49
Solomon *b.* him an *house.* *Acts* 7:47
are *b.* up a spiritual *h.* *1 Pet* 2:5

built *wall,* or *walls*

Solomon *b.* *walls* of. *1 Ki* 6:15
on *walls* of Ophel he *b.* *2 Chr* 27:3
Hezekiah *b.* up the *wall.* 32:5
Manasseh *b.* a *wall* without. 33:14
so *b.* we the *wall.* *Neh* 4:6
when *wall* was *b.* 7:1
one *b.* up the *wall.* *Ezek* 13:10
street be *b.* again and *wall.* *Dan* 9:25
day thy *walls* are to be *b.* *Mi* 7:11

Bul

in month *B.* house was. *1 Ki* 6:38

bull

[1] *The beast so called, or representations of it,* Job 21:10; Jer 52:20. [2] *Wicked, violent, and furious enemies,* Ps 22:12.

their *b.* gendereth and. *Job* 21:10
thy sons lie as wild *b.* *Isa* 51:20*

bullock

(*Generally used for a young bull*)
in the basket with *b.* *Ex* 29:3
kill *b.* before Lord. 11; *Lev* 1:5
9:18*
bring the *b.* to the door. *Lev* 4:4
b. a meat-offering. *Num* 15:9; 29:37
sacrifice to Lord any *b.* *Deut* 17:1*
glory is like firstling of a *b.* 33:17
young *b.* the second *b.* *Judg* 6:25, 26
choose one *b.* *1 Ki* 18:23, 25
Elijah cut *b.* in pieces. 33
I will take no *b.* out. *Ps* 50:9
better than a *b.* that hath. 69:31
lion eat straw like *b.* *Isa* 65:25*
as *b.* unaccustomed to. *Jer* 31:18*

bullock with *sin-offering*

a *b.* for a *sin-offering.* *Ex* 29:36
offer *b.* of the *sin-offering.* *Lev* 16:6
prepare a *b.* for a *sin-offering.*
Ezek 45:22

see **blood**

young **bullock**

bring a *young b.* *Lev* 4:3
Ezek 43:19
shall offer a *young b.* *Lev* 4:14
Num 15:24
holy place with a *young b.* *Lev* 16:3
one *young b.* one. *Num* 7:15, 21, 27
33, 39, 45, 51, 57, 63, 69, 75, 81
himself with *young b.* *2 Chr* 13:9
take a *young b.* and. *Ezek* 45:18
day of new moon a *young b.* 46:6

bullocks

fourth day ten *b.* two. *Num* 29:23
offered thousand *b.* for. *1 Chr* 29:21
the dedication 100 *b.* *Ezra* 6:17
shall they offer *b.* on thy. *Ps* 51:19
I will offer unto thee *b.* 66:15
delight not in the blood of *b.* *Isa* 1:11
the *b.* with the bulls shall. 34:7
hired men like fatted *b.* *Jer* 46:21*
slay all her *b.* let them go. 50:27
the blood of goats, of *b.* *Ezek* 39:18
they sacrifice *b.* in Gilgal. *Hos* 12:11

see **seven**

bulls

Jacob took ten *b.* as. *Gen* 32:15
b. have compassed me, strong *b.*
Ps 22:12
will I eat flesh of *b.* or drink. 50:13
rebuke multitude of the *b.* 68:30
bullocks with the *b.* *Isa* 34:7
ye bellow as *b.* *Jer* 50:11*
twelve brasen *b.* under the. 52:20
if the blood of *b.* and. *Heb* 9:13
not possible blood of *b.* take. 10:4

bulrush, -es

took for him an ark of *b.* *Ex* 2:3
ambassadors in vessels of *b.*
Isa 18:2*
bow down his head like a *b.*? 58:5*

bulwarks

thou shalt build *b.* *Deut* 20:20
engines on the *b.* *2 Chr* 26:15
mark well her *b.* consider. *Ps* 48:13
king came and built *b.* *Eccl* 9:14
appoint for walls and *b.* *Isa* 26:1

bunch, -es

take a *b.* of hyssop and. *Ex* 12:22
with 100 *b.* of raisins. *2 Sam* 16:1
Zebulun brought *b.* of. *1 Chr* 12:40
treasures upon *b.* of. *Isa* 30:6†

bundle, -s

every man's *b.* of money. *Gen* 42:35
bound in *b.* of life. *1 Sam* 25:29
a *b.* of myrrh my well-. *S of S* 1:13
bind the tares in *b.* *Mat* 13:30
Paul had gathered a *b.* of. *Acts* 28:3

burden

A weight or load of the capacity of the bearer to carry, 2 Ki 5:17; Jer 17:27. *This may be used literally or figuratively of taxes, grief or illness,* Ps 55:22; Hos 8:10; Gal 6:2.

bear the *b.* with thee. *Ex* 18:22
Num 11:17
the ass lying under *b.* *Ex* 23:5
appoint each to his *b.* *Num* 4:19
layest the *b.* of all this people. 11:11
I myself bear your *b.*? *Deut* 1:12
then thou shalt be a *b.* *2 Sam* 15:33
should thy servant be a *b.*? 19:35
servant two mules' *b.* of. *2 Ki* 5:17
forty camels' *b.* to Elisha. 8:9
it shall not be a *b.* *2 Chr* 35:3
no *b.* be brought in. *Neh* 13:19
I am a *b.* to myself. *Job* 7:20
iniquities as a *b.* they are. *Ps* 38:4
cast thy *b.* on the Lord. 55:22
removed his shoulder from *b.* 81:6
grasshopper shall be a *b.* *Eccl* 12:5
broken the yoke of his *b.* *Isa* 9:4
his *b.* shall be taken from. 10:27
b. depart from off their. 14:25
name of the Lord, the *b.* 30:27*
your carriages are a *b.* to. 46:1
no *b.* on sabbath. *Jer* 17:21, 22, 27
reproach of it was a *b.* *Zeph* 3:18
and my *b.* is light. *Mat* 11:30
which have borne the *b.* and. 20:12
lay on you no greater *b.* *Acts* 15:28
the ship was to unlade *b.* 21:3
put upon you none other *b.* *Rev* 2:24

burden

(*Meaning here a prophecy of doom*

Lord laid this *b.* upon. *2 Ki* 9:2
the *b.* of Babylon. *Isa* 13:
king Ahaz died, was this *b.* 14:2
the *b.* of Moab. 15:
the *b.* of Damascus. 17:
the *b.* of Egypt. 19:
the *b.* of the desert of the sea. 21:
the *b.* of Dumah.
the *b.* upon Arabia.
the *b.* of the valley of vision. 22:
the *b.* that was upon it shall.
the *b.* of Tyre. 23:
b. of the beasts of south. 30:
what is *b.* of the Lord? what *b.*?
Jer 23:
the *b.* of the Lord shall ye.
but since ye say, the *b.* of.
this *b.* concerneth the. *Ezek* 12:
sorrow a little for the *b.* *Hos* 8:

the *b.* of Nineveh. *Nah* 1:1
b. which Habakkuk the. *Hab* 1:1
b. of the word of the Lord. *Zech* 9:1
b. of the word of the Lord for. 12:1
b. of the word of the Lord to. *Mal* 1:1
every man bear his own *b.* *Gal* 6:5

burden, -ed

all that *b.* themselves. *Zech* 12:3
we groan being *b.* *2 Cor* 5:4
not that others be eased, you *b.* 8:13
but be it so, I did not *b.* you. 12:16

burdens

couching between two *b.* *Gen* 49:14
to afflict them with their *b.* *Ex* 1:11
Moses looked on their *b.* 2:11
get you to your *b.* 5:4
you make them rest from *b.* 5
bring you from the *b.* of. 6:6, 7
appoint to them all their *b.* *Num* 4:27
strength of bearers of *b.* *Neh* 4:10
they that bare *b.* with other. 17
all manner of *b.* brought in. 13:15
the fast, to undo heavy *b.* *Isa* 58:6*
prophets have seen for thee false *b.* *Lam* 2:14
ye take from the poor *b.* *Amos* 5:11*
bind heavy *b.* *Mat* 23:4; *Luke* 11:46
bear ye one another's *b.* *Gal* 6:2

burdensome

Jerusalem a *b.* stone. *Zech* 12:3
kept myself from being *b.* *2 Cor* 11:9
it be that I was not *b.* 12:13
third time I come, I will not be *b.* 14
we might have been *b.* *1 Thes* 2:6†

burial

also that he have no *b.* *Eccl* 6:3
joined with them in *b.* *Isa* 14:20
buried with the *b.* of an. *Jer* 22:19
she did it for my *b.* *Mat* 26:12
carried Stephen to his *b.* *Acts* 8:2

buried

there was Abraham *b.* *Gen* 25:10
b. Abraham and Sarah, Isaac and Rebekah, there I *b.* Leah. 49:31
there they *b.* people. *Num* 11:34
Miriam died, and was *b.* there. 20:1
Egyptians *b.* all first-born. 33:4
died, and there he was *b.* *Deut* 10:6
the bones of Joseph *b.* *Josh* 24:32
die, and there will be *b.* *Ruth* 1:17
took head and *b.* it. *2 Sam* 4:12
Saul and Jonathan they *b.* 21:14
where man of God is *b.* *1 Ki* 13:31
and so I saw the wicked *b.* *Eccl* 8:10
not be gathered nor *b.* *Jer* 8:2
16:6; 20:6; 25:33
shall not be lamented nor *b.* 16:4
be *b.* with the burial of an ass. 22:19
sign, till buriers have *b.* *Ezek* 39:15
took the body and *b.* it. *Mat* 14:12
rich man died and was *b.* *Luke* 16:22
David is dead and *b.* *Acts* 2:29
feet of them which *b.* thy. 5:9
carrying her forth, *b.* her by. 10
b. with him by baptism. *Rom* 6:4
that he was *b.* and rose. *1 Cor* 15:4
b. with him in baptism. *Col* 2:12

buried *him*

e *b. him* in a valley. *Deut* 34:6
lessed be ye that *b.* Saul. *2 Sam* 2:5
hey *b. him,* all Israel. *1 Ki* 14:18
hey *b.* Jehoram in. *2 Chr* 21:20
. Jehoiada in city of David. 24:16
hey *b. him* not in the sepulchres. 25
en carried and *b. him.* *Acts* 5:6

buried *in*

nd thou shalt be *b. in* a. *Gen* 15:15
avid was *b. in* the city. *1 Ki* 2:10
oab *b. in* his own house. 34
Ianasseh was *b. in.* *2 Ki* 21:18
mon was *b. in* sepulchre, in. 26
at remain be *b. in.* *Job* 27:15

buried *with his fathers*

ehoboam *b. with his f.* *1 Ki* 14:31
sa *b. with his f.* 15:24
hoshaphat *b. with his f.* 22:50
ram *b. with his f.* *2 Ki* 8:24
ash *b. with his f.* 12:21
naziah *b. with his f.* 14:20
zariah *b. with his f.* 15:7
tham *b. with his f.* 38
az *b. with his f.* 16:20

buriers

set up a sign till *b.* have. *Ezek* 39:15

burn

(*To consume, or destroy with fire,* Josh 11:13. *Used also figuratively for intense indignation, passion, or zeal*)

let not thine anger *b.* *Gen* 44:18
bring pure olive-oil to cause the lamp to *b.* alway. *Ex* 27:20; *Lev* 24:2
take caul, kidneys and fat and *b.* *Ex* 29:13, 18, 25; *Lev* 1:9, 15
2:2, 9, 16; 3:5, 11, 16; 5:12; 6:15
9:17; *Num* 5:26
fat and *b.* upon. *Lev* 4:19, 26, 31
7:31; 16:25; 17:6; *Num* 18:17
one shall *b.* the heifer. *Num* 19:5
Hazor did, Joshua *b.* *Josh* 11:13
let them not fail to *b.* *1 Sam* 2:16
save only to *b.* sacrifice. *2 Chr* 2:6
and they *b.* to the Lord. 13:11
they shall both *b.* together. *Isa* 1:31
it shall *b.* and devour. 10:17
go through them, and *b.* 27:4
Lebanon is not sufficient to *b.* 40:16
shall it be for a man to *b.* 44:15
my fury shall *b.* and not. *Jer* 7:20
so shall they *b.* odours for. 34:5
that the king would not *b.* 36:25
b. also the bones under it. *Ezek* 24:5
of it may be hot and may *b.* 11
they shall set on fire and *b.* 39:9
he shall *b.* bullock in the. 43:21
I will *b.* her chariots. *Nah* 2:13
day cometh that shall *b.* *Mal* 4:1
tares in bundles to *b.* *Mat* 13:30
but chaff he will *b.* with. *Luke* 3:17
did not heart *b.* within us ? 24:32
better to marry than to *b.* *1 Cor* 7:9
offended, and I *b.* not? *2 Cor* 11:29

burn, joined with *fire*

remaineth till morning *b.* with *fire.* *Ex* 12:10; 29:34; *Lev* 8:32
b. that wherein the plague is with *fire.* *Lev* 13:57
b. with *fire* their skins, flesh. 16:27
mountain did *b.* with *fire.* *Deut* 5:23
b. their images with *fire.* 7:5, 25
b. groves with *fire.* 12:3
fire shall *b.* to lowest hell. 32:22
Jer 17:4
b. their chariots with *fire.* *Josh* 11:6
tower to *b.* it with *fire.* *Judg* 9:52
we will *b.* thine house with *fire.* 12:1
b. thee with *fire.* 14:15
thy jealousy *b.* like *fire* ? *Ps* 79:5
thy wrath *b.* like *fire* ? 89:46
the *fire* shall *b.* them. *Isa* 47:14
forth like *fire* and *b.* *Jer* 4:4; 21:12
b. sons and daughters in *fire.* 7:31
19:5
shall *b.* city with *fire.* 21:10; 32:29
34:2, 22; 37:8, 10; 38:18
b. with *fire* a third part. *Ezek* 5:2
they *b.* thine houses with *fire.* 16:41
23:47
b. up the chaff with unquenchable *fire.* *Mat* 3:12; *Luke* 3:17
flesh and *b.* her with *fire.* *Rev* 17:16

burn *incense*

an altar to *b. inc.* on. *Ex* 30:1
b. thereon sweet *inc.* 7, 8
by the altar to *b. inc.* *1 Ki* 13:1
Israel did *b. inc.* to it. *2 Ki* 18:4
and his sons to *b. inc.* *1 Chr* 23:13
house to *b.* sweet *inc.* *2 Chr* 2:4
b. every morning sweet *inc.* 13:11
into temple to *b. inc.* 26:16, 19
made high places to *b. inc.* 28:25
Lord hath chosen you to *b. inc.* 29:11
and *b. inc.* on it. 32:12
steal and *b. inc.* to Baal ? *Jer* 7:9
11:13
b. inc. to the queen of heaven. 44:17
they *b. inc.* upon the hills. *Hos* 4:13
therefore they *b. inc.* *Hab* 1:16
his lot was to *b. inc.* *Luke* 1:9

burned

bush *b.* with fire. *Ex* 3:2
the mountain *b.* with fire. *Deut* 4:11
I came down, and mount *b.* 9:15
b. them with fire. *Josh* 7:25
b. Ziklag with fire. *1 Sam* 30:1
men *b.* their images. *2 Sam* 5:21*
shall be utterly *b.* with fire. 23:7
b. the grove at the brook. *2 Ki* 23:6
b. the chariots with fire. 11
she *b.* the high place. 15
bones out of sepulchres and *b.* 16
gods were *b.* with fire. *1 Chr* 14:12
Amaziah *b.* incense to. *2 Chr* 25:14
forsaken me, and *b.* incense. 34:25
gates thereof *b.* with. *Neh* 1:3; 2:17
wroth, anger *b.* in him. *Esth* 1:12
God hath *b.* up the sheep. *Job* 1:16
and my bones are *b.* with heat. 30:30
I was musing, fire *b.* *Ps* 39:3*
b. up all the synagogues. 74:8
it is *b.* with fire, it is cut. 80:16
my skin black, bones are *b.* 102:3
flame *b.* up the wicked. 106:18
his clothes not be *b.* *Pr* 6:27
on coals and his feet not be *b.*? 28*
your cities are *b.* with fire. *Isa* 1:7
inhabitants of the earth are *b.* 24:6
it *b.* him, yet he laid it not. 42:25
walkest through fire not be *b.* 43:2
and beautiful house *b.* with. 64:11
which have *b.* incense on the. 65:7
his cities are *b.* *Jer* 2:15
the bellows are *b.* 6:29
b. up that none can pass. 9:10, 12
my people have *b.* incense to. 18:15
in roll Jehoiakim hath *b.* 36:28
city shall not be *b.* with fire. 38:17
cause this city to be *b.* with fire. 23
that their wives had *b.* incense. 44:15
daughters be *b.* with fire. 49:2
reeds they have *b.* with fire. 51:32
high gates shall be *b.* with fire. 58
he *b.* against Jacob like. *Lam* 2:3
and all faces shall be *b.* *Ezek* 20:47
and let the bones be *b.* 24:10
wherein she *b.* incense. *Hos* 2:13
they sacrificed and *b.* incense. 11:2
the flame hath *b.* all the. *Joel* 1:19
because he *b.* the bones. *Amos* 2:1
hires thereof be *b.* with. *Mi* 1:7
and the earth is *b.* at. *Nah* 1:5
king sent and *b.* up their. *Mat* 22:7
are gathered and *b.* *John* 15:6
their books and *b.* *Acts* 19:19
b. in their lust one. *Rom* 1:27
if any man's work be *b.* *1 Cor* 3:15
I give my body to be *b.* 13:3
whose end is to be *b.* *Heb* 6:8
not come to the mount that *b.* 12:18
those beasts are *b.* 13:11
works therein be *b.* up. *2 Pet* 3:10
his feet like brass, as if *b.* *Rev* 1:15
she be utterly *b.* with fire. 18:8

burneth

he that *b.* them shall wash clothes. *Lev* 16:28; *Num* 19:8
breaketh the bow and *b.* *Ps* 46:9
as the fire *b.* wood, and as. 83:14
a fire *b.* up his enemies. 97:3
for wickedness *b.* as fire. *Isa* 9:18
he *b.* part thereof in fire. 44:16
thereof as a lamp that *b.* 62:1
as when the melting fire *b.* 64:2
are a smoke and fire that *b.* 65:5
he that *b.* incense, as if he. 66:3
cause to cease that *b.* *Jer* 48:35
behind them a flame *b.* *Joel* 2:3
part in lake which *b.* with. *Rev* 21:8

burning

b. lamp passed between. *Gen* 15:17
fire of altar shall be *b.* in it. *Lev* 6:9*
12, 13
appoint over you the *b.* ague. 26:16*
be devoured with *b.* heat. 32:24
of his mouth go *b.* lamps. *Job* 41:19
let *b.* coals fall upon. *Ps* 140:10
there is as a *b.* fire. *Pr* 16:27
as coals are to *b.* coals. 26:21*
b. lips and a wicked heart are. 23
of Lord cometh far, *b.* *Isa* 30:27
land shall become *b.* pitch. 34:9
was in my heart as *b.* fire. *Jer* 20:9
was like *b.* coals. *Ezek* 1:13
into midst of *b.* furnace. *Dan* 3:6, 11
able to deliver us from *b.* furnace. 17
and to cast them into the *b.* fiery furnace. 3:20; 21, 23

Nebuchadnezzar came near the b. Dan 3:26
his wheels were as b. fire. 7:9
and b. coals went forth at. Hab 3:5*
be girded, and lights b. Luke 12:35
he was a b. and shining. John 5:35
were seven lamps b. before. Rev 4:5
as it were a great mountain b. 8:8
there fell a great star b. 10
were cast alive into a lake b. 19:20

burning, *substantive*

b. for b. wound for. Ex 21:25
bewail the b. which Lord. Lev 10:6
if spot stay, it is rising of b. 13:28
the Lord shall smite thee with an extreme b. Deut 28:22*
is brimstone, salt, and b. 29:23
made a very great b. 2 Chr 16:14
people made no b. like the b. 21:19
there shall be b. instead. Isa 3:24*
purged Jerusalem by spirit of b. 4:4
but this shall be with b. and. 9:5
kindle b. like b. of fire. 10:16
people shall be as the b. of. 33:12
plucked out of the b. Amos 4:11
they see the smoke of b. Rev 18:9

burnings

dwell with everlasting b.? Isa 33:14
with b. of thy fathers. Jer 34:5

burnished

they sparkled like b. brass. Ezek 1:7

burnt

her forth, let her be b. Gen 38:24
see why bush is not b. Ex 3:3
for they shall not be b. Lev 2:12
meat-offering be wholly b. 6:22, 23
8:21
sought goat, and it was b. 10:16
took the brazen censers, wherewith they that were b. Num 16:39
shall be b. with hunger. Deut 32:24
before they b. fat. 1 Sam 2:15
men's bones shall be b. 1 Ki 13:2
Asa b. her idol. 15:13; 2 Chr 15:16
b. the house of Lord. 2 Ki 25:9
2 Chr 36:19
I will make thee a b. Jer 51:25

burnt, joined with *fire*

he b. the calf in the fire. Ex 32:20
Deut 9:21
sin-offering be b. in the fire.
Lev 6:30
of flesh of sacrifice on third day be b. with fire. 7:17; 19:6
man take a wife and her mother they shall be b. with fire. 20:14
daughter of priest profane by playing whore... be burnt with fire. 21:9
fire of the Lord b. Num 11:1, 3
daughters b. in the fire. Deut 12:31
b. Jericho with fire. Josh 6:24
he that is taken with the accursed thing shall be b. with fire. 7:15
b. their chariots with fire. 11:9
took Hazor and b. it with fire. 11
b. her and father with fire. Judg 15:6
as flax that was b. with fire. 14
Laish and b. it with fire. 18:27
had b. Gezer with fire. 1 Ki 9:16
Zimri b. king's house with fire. 16:18
fire from heaven b. 2 Ki 1:14
b. their children with fire. 17:31
man's house b. he with fire. 25:9
b. his children in the fire. 2 Chr 28:3

burnt *incense*

b. sweet inc. thereon. Ex 40:27
only Solomon b. inc. 1 Ki 3:3
Solomon b. inc. upon the. 9:25
Jeroboam offered and b. inc. 12:33
people b. inc. 22:43; 2 Ki 12:3
14:4; 15:4, 35
Ahaz b. inc. in high. 2 Ki 16:4
2 Chr 28:3, 4
and have not b. inc. 2 Chr 29:7

burnt-offering

is lamb for a b.-off.? Gen 22:7
God will provide a lamb for b.-off. 8
he offered him for a b.-off. 13
Jethro took a b.-off. Ex 18:12
the ram is a b.-off. 29:18
hand on head of b.-off. Lev 1:4
slay sin-offering in place of b.-off.
Lev 4:29, 33; 6:25; 7:2; 14:13
this is law of the b.-off. 6:9; 7:37
priest have skin of b.-off. 7:8
ram for a b.-off. 9:2; 16:3, 5; 23:18
calf and a lamb for a b.-off. 9:3; 12:6
23:12
one lamb of first year for a b.-off.
Num 7:15, 21, 27, 33, 39, 51, 57
63, 69, 75, 81; Ezek 45:15
stand by thy b.-off. Num 23:3, 15
this is the b.-off. 28:10
for a b.-off. of a sweet savour. 13
this is the b.-off. of every month. 14
meat-offering and daily b.-off. 29:6
altar not for a b.-off. Josh 22:26
a b.-off. at our hands. Judg 13:23
was offering up a b.-off. 1 Sam 7:10
offered a b.-off. 13:12
offered him for a b.-off. 2 Ki 3:27
fire consumed the b.-off. 2 Chr 7:1
the b.-off. should be made. 29:24
b.-off. hast thou not. Ps 40:6
delightest not in b.-off. 51:16
with b.-off. and whole b.-off. 19
nor beasts for a b.-off. Isa 40:16
for I hate robbery for b.-off. 61:8*
shall slay the b.-off. Ezek 44:11
prepare the b.-off. for Israel. 45:17
priest prepare prince's b.-off. 46:2
thou shalt daily prepare a b.-off. 13

continual **burnt-offering**

a continual b.-off. Ex 29:42
Num 28:3, 6, 10, 15, 24, 31; 29:11
16, 19, 22; Ezra 3:5; Neh 10:33
Ezek 46:15

offer **burnt-offering**

offer him there for a b.-off. Gen 22:2
and offer thy b.-off. Lev 9:7
of months offer b.-off. Num 28:11
offer these besides b.-off. 23
offer it up for a b.-off. Judg 11:31
if thou offer a b.-off. offer. 13:16
offered kine for b.-off. 1 Sam 6:14
Samuel offered a sucking lamb for a b.-off. 7:9
offer neither b.-off. 2 Ki 5:17
commanded to offer b.-off.
2 Chr 29:27
offer up a b.-off. Job 42:8
b.-off. prince shall offer. Ezek 46:4

burnt-offerings

Noah offered b.-off. Gen 8:20
give sacrifices and b.-off. Ex 10:25
sacrifice thereon thy b.-off. 20:24
trumpets over b.-off. Num 10:10
bring your b.-off. Deut 12:6, 11
14, 27
of the Lord with b.-off. Josh 22:27
great delight in b.-off. 1 Sam 15:22
Solomon offered b.-off. 1 Ki 3:15
of the court, he offered b.-off. 8:64
they offered b.-off. to. 1 Chr 29:21
I build house for b.-off. 2 Chr 2:4
altar not able to receive b.-off. 7:7
have not offered b.-off. in. 29:7
could not slay all the b.-off. 34
Levites brought b.-off. 30:15
busied in offering b.-off. 35:14
offered daily b.-off. Ezra 3:4
they have need for b.-off. 6:9
offered b.-off. according. Job 1:5
not reprove thee for b.-off. Ps 50:8
into thy house with b.-off. 66:13
full of the b.-off. of. Isa 1:11
small cattle of thy b.-off. 43:23
their b.-off. shall be accepted. 56:7
your b.-off. are not. Jer 6:20
put your b.-off. to your. 7:21
spake not concerning b.-off. 22
from south, bringing b.-off. 17:26
burn their sons for b.-off. 19:5
part to give b.-off. Ezek 45:17
knowledge more than b.-off. Hos 6:6
before him with b.-off.? Mi 6:6
is more than b.-off. Mark 12:33
in b.-off. for sin thou. Heb 10:6

offer **burnt-offerings**

down to offer b.-off. 1 Sam 10:8
nor offer b.-off. of that which cost me. 2 Sam 24:24; 1 Chr 21:24
b.-off. did Solomon offer. 1 Ki 3:4
year did Solomon offer b.-off.
1 Ki 9:25
builded altar to offer b.-off. Ezra 3:2
want man to offer b.-off. Jer 33:18
make it to offer b.-off. Ezek 43:18
ye offer me b.-off. Amos 5:22

burnt-sacrifice

strange incense, nor b.-s. Ex 30:9
burn all to be a b.-s. Lev 1:9; 3:5
lo, he stood by his b.-s. Num 23:6
put whole b.-s. on. Deut 33:10
here be oxen for b.-s. 2 Sam 24:22
fire consumed the b.-s. 1 Ki 18:38
altar burn king's b.-s. 2 Ki 16:15
accept thy b.-s. Ps. 20:3

burnt-sacrifices

b.-s. in the sabbaths. 1 Chr 23:31
and evening b.-s. 2 Chr 13:11
I will offer to thee b.-s. Ps 66:15

burnt *up*

the foxes b. up shocks. Judg 15:5
fire came down, and b. up. 2 Ki 1:14
third part of trees was b. up, and all green grass was b. up. Rev 8:7

burst

to b. like new bottles. Job 32:19
presses shall b. with new. Pr 3:10
I have b. thy bands. Jer 2:20; 5:5
30:8; Nah 1:13
new wine b. bottles. Mark 2:22
Luke 5:37
he b. asunder in midst. Acts 1:18

bursting

not be found in the b. Isa 30:14*

bury

that I may b. my dead. Gen 23:4
choice of our sepulchres b. 6, 11, 15
b. me not in Egypt. 47:29; 49:29
let me go and b. my father. 50:5
go up and b. thy father. 6
shalt in any wise b. Deut 21:23
fall upon Joab and b. 1 Ki 2:31
Joab was gone up to b. the. 11:15
came to mourn and b. 13:29
when I am dead, b. me in the. 31
Israel shall mourn and b. him. 14:13
be none to b. Jezebel. 2 Ki 9:10
see now this cursed woman, b. 34
they went to b. her, but. 35
there was none to b. them. Ps 79:3
shall b. in Tophet. Jer 7:32; 19:11
they shall have none to b. 14:16
there shall they b. Gog. Ezek 39:11
people of the land shall b. them. 13
Memphis shall b. them. Hos 9:6
me to go b. my father. Mat 8:21
Luke 9:59
let dead b. their dead. Mat 8:22
Luke 9:60
potter's field to b. Mat 27:7
manner of Jews is to b. John 19:40

burying

a possession of a b. place. Gen 23:4
9; 49:30; 50:13
buried Samson in b. Judg 16:31
as they were b. a man. 2 Ki 13:21
months shall Israel be b. Ezek 39:12
anoint my body to b. Mark 14:[illegible]
against day of my b. John 12:[illegible]

bush, -es

in fire in the b. Ex 3:2; Acts 7:3[illegible]
out of the midst of the b. Ex 3:[illegible]
of him that dwelt in b. Deut 33:1[illegible]
cut up mallows by the b. Job 30:[illegible]
among the b. they brayed.
come and rest upon all b. Isa 7:19
how in b. God spake. Mark 12:26
nor of a bramble b. Luke 6:4[illegible]
dead are raised, Moses shewed [illegible] the b. 20:3[illegible]
angel which appeared in b. Acts 7:3[illegible]

bushel

put it under a b. but on. Mat 5:1[illegible]
Mark 4:21; Luke 11:3[illegible]

bushy

his locks are b. and. S of S 5:[illegible]

business

into house to do his b. Gen 39:[illegible]
nor charged with any b. Deut 24[illegible]
if ye utter not our b. Josh 2:[illegible]
if thou utter this our b. we will.

no *b.* with any man. *Judg* 18:7*, 28*
hide thyself when *b.* *1 Sam* 20:19
let no man know of the *b.* 21:2
because king's *b.* required haste. 8
Levites wait on their *b.* *2 Chr* 13:10*
in the *b.* of the ambassadors. 32:31
every man in his *b.* *Neh* 13:30*
that have charge of *b.* *Esth* 3:9*
do *b.* in great waters. *Ps* 107:23
man diligent in his *b.*? *Pr* 22:29
through multitude of *b.* *Eccl* 5:3
and did the king's *b.* *Dan* 8:27
about my Father's *b.*? *Luke* 2:49*
we may appoint over *b.* *Acts* 6:3
not slothful in *b.* *Rom* 12:11*
assist her in what *b.* 16:2*
study to do your own *b.* *1 Thes* 4:11

busy, -ied

servant was *b.* here and. *1 Ki* 20:40
the sons of Aaron *b.* in. *2 Chr* 35:14

busybody, -ies

but some of you are *b.* *2 Thes* 3:11
1 Tim 5:13
none of you suffer as a *b.* *1 Pet* 4:15

but

b. a step between me. *1 Sam* 20:3
kill us, we shall *b.* die. *2 Ki* 7:4
b. speak not; eyes *b.* *Ps* 115:5
ears *b.* hear not; noses *b.* 6
have hands *b.* handle not; feet *b.* 7
b. of that day and hour. *Mat* 24:36
b. as the days of Noe were. 37
said, if I may touch *b.* *Mark* 5:28
know not the speech, *b.* *1 Cor* 4:19
b. ye are washed. 6:11
yet not I, *b.* the Lord. 7:10
b. the same Spirit. 12:4
b. the same Lord. 5
b. it is the same God which. 6
hath not grieved me *b.* *2 Cor* 2:5
our light affliction, which is *b.* 4:17

butler

b. of the king of Egypt. *Gen* 40:1
chief *b.* told dream to Joseph. 9
he restored his chief *b.* to his. 21
the chief *b.* said, I remember. 41:9

butter

(*While butter was not unknown the word usually means curdled milk*)
Abraham took *b.* and. *Gen* 18:8
b. of kine, milk of. *Deut* 32:14
she brought forth *b.* *Judg* 5:25
Barzillai brought *b.* *2 Sam* 17:29
brooks of honey and *b.* *Job* 20:17
I washed my steps with *b.* 29:6
words smoother than *b.* *Ps* 55:21
of milk bringeth forth *b.* *Pr* 30:33
b. and honey shall he. *Isa* 7:15, 22

buttocks

cut to *b.* *2 Sam* 10:4; *1 Chr* 19:4
with *b.* uncovered to the. *Isa* 20:4

buy

you down to Egypt and *b.* *Gen* 42:2
land of Canaan to *b.* food. 7; 43:20
b. us and our land for bread. 47:19
if thou *b.* an Hebrew. *Ex* 21:2
if priests *b.* any soul. *Lev* 22:11
after the jubilee *b.* of thy. 25:15
of them shall ye *b.* bondmen. 44, 45
ye shall *b.* meat of them. *Deut* 2:6
be sold, and no man shall *b.* 28:68
b. it before inhabitants. *Ruth* 4:4
thou must *b.* it also of Ruth. 5
b. the threshing-floor. *2 Sam* 24:21
24; *1 Chr* 21:24
masons *b.* timber. *2 Ki* 12:12; 22:6
we would not *b.* it on. *Neh* 10:31
come, *b.* and eat, *b.* wine. *Isa* 55:1
b. thee my field that is in. *Jer* 32:7
men shall *b.* fields for money. 44
b. victuals. *Mat* 14:15; *Mark* 6:36
go to them that sell, and *b.* *Mat* 25:9
while they went to *b.* the. 10
shall we go and *b.*? *Mark* 6:37
except we *b.* meat for. *Luke* 9:13
sell his garment and *b.* one. 22:36
disciples were gone to *b.* *John* 4:8
whence shall we *b.* bread? 6:5
b. those things that we have. 13:29
they that *b.* as though. *1 Cor* 7:30
and we will *b.* and sell. *Jas* 4:13
I counsel thee to *b.* of me. *Rev* 3:18
no man *b.* or sell, save he. 13:17

buy *corn*

came to Joseph to *b. corn.* *Gen* 41:57
brethren went to *b. corn.* 42:3
our lands to *b. corn.* *Neh* 5:3

buy *poor*

that we may *b.* the *poor.* *Amos* 8:6

buy *truth*

b. the *truth* and sell it not. *Pr* 23:23

buyer

it is naught, saith the *b.* *Pr* 20:14
as with the *b.* so with. *Isa* 24:2
let not the *b.* rejoice. *Ezek* 7:12

buyest

if thou sell ought, or *b.* *Lev* 25:14
day thou *b.* field of. *Ruth* 4:5

buyeth

considereth a field, *b.* it. *Pr* 31:16
selleth all he hath, and *b.* *Mat* 13:44
man *b.* her merchandise. *Rev* 18:11

Buz

Milcah bare to Nahor *B.* *Gen* 22:21
Jahdo, the son of *B.* *1 Chr* 5:14
made Dedan and *B.* to. *Jer* 25:23

Buzi

Ezekiel the priest, son of *B.* *Ezek* 1:3

Buzite

Elihu son of the *B.* *Job* 32:2, 6

by *and* **by**

b. and b. he is offended. *Mat* 13:21
give me *b. and b.* in a. *Mark* 6:25
say to him *b. and b.* *Luke* 17:7
but the end is not *b. and b.* 21:9

by-ways

walked through *b.* *Judg* 5:6

by-word

thou shalt become a *b.* *Deut* 28:37
Israel shall be a *b.* *1 Ki* 9:7
house a proverb and a *b.* *2 Chr* 7:20
he hath made me a *b.* *Job* 17:6
I their song, yea, their *b.* 30:9
thou makest us a *b.* *Ps* 44:14

C

cab

(*A measure of about 2 quarts*)
fourth part of a *c.* of. *2 Ki* 6:25

cabins

(*Revised Version,* cells)
Jeremiah entered the *c.* *Jer* 37:16

Cabul

called them land of *C.* *1 Ki* 9:13

Caesar (Cesar)

to give tribute to *C.*? *Mat* 22:17
Mark 12:14; *Luke* 20:22
to *C.* the things that are *Cesar's.* to. *Mat* 22:21; *Mark* 12:17
decree from *C.* Augustus. *Luke* 2:1
the fifteenth year of Tiberius *C.* 3:1
forbidding to give tribute to *C.* 23:2
thou art not *Cesar's* friend speaketh against *C.* *John* 19:12
we have no king but *C.* 15
in days of Claudius *C.* *Acts* 11:28
do contrary to decrees of *C.* 17:7
nor against *C.* have I offended. 25:8
I appeal unto *C.* 11
till I send him to *C.* 21
if he had not appealed to *C.* 26:32
must be brought before *C.* 27:24
constrained to appeal to *C.* 28:19
they that are of *C.'s* *Phil* 4:22

cage

as a *c.* is full of birds. *Jer* 5:27
Babylon is *c.* of unclean. *Rev* 18:2*

Caiaphas

high-priest who was *C.* *Mat* 26:3
they led Jesus away to *C.* 57
C. said, ye know nothing. *John* 11:49
C. was he that gave counsel. 18:14
led Jesus from *C.* to the hall. 28

see **Annas**

Cain

C. and Gibeah cities. *Josh* 15:57

Cain

but *C.* was a tiller of. *Gen* 4:2
to *C.* and his offering he. 5
the Lord set a mark on *C.* *Gen* 4:15
seed instead of Abel whom *C.* 25
excellent sacrifice than *C.* *Heb* 11:4
not as *C.* who was of. *1 John* 3:12
gone in the way of *C.* *Jude* 11

Cainan

was the son of *C.* *Luke* 3:36, 37

cake, -s

they baked unleavened *c.* *Ex* 12:39
thanksgiving, unleavened *c.* *Lev* 7:12
take fine flour, bake twelve *c.* 24:5
offer up a *c.* of the first. *Num* 15:20
and lo, a *c.* tumbled. *Judg* 7:13
dealt to every one *c.* *2 Sam* 6:19
make me a couple of *c.* 13:6
I have not a *c.* *1 Ki* 17:12
make me a little *c.* first. 13
there was a *c.* baken on coals. 19:6
to make *c.* to the. *Jer* 7:18; 44:19
shalt eat it as barley *c.* *Ezek* 4:12
Ephraim is a *c.* not turned. *Hos* 7:8

see **figs, unleavened**

calamity, -ies

the day of their *c.* *Deut* 32:35
in day of *c.* *2 Sam* 22:19; *Ps* 18:18
and my *c.* laid in. *Job* 6:2
they set forward my *c.* 30:13
my refuge until these *c.* *Ps* 57:1
prayer also be in their *c.* 141:5*
I will laugh at your *c.* *Pr* 1:26
therefore his *c.* shall come. 6:15
he that is glad at *c.* shall. 17:5
a foolish son is the *c.* 19:13
their *c.* shall rise suddenly. 24:22
brother's house in day of *c.* 27:10
shew the back in day of *c.* *Jer* 18:17
the day of their *c.* was come. 46:21
the *c.* of Moab is near to. 48:16
for I will bring the *c.* 49:8
I will bring their *c.* from all. 32
blood of Israel in their *c.* *Ezek* 35:5
in the day of their *c.* *Ob* 13

calamus

of sweet *c.* 250 shekels. *Ex* 30:23
spikenard, saffron, *c.* *S of S* 4:14
c. was in the market of. *Ezek* 27:19

caldron

struck it into the pan, *c.* *1 Sam* 2:14
as out of a seething *c.* *Job* 41:20*
this city is the *c.* *Ezek* 11:3, 7
this city shall not be your *c.* 11
chop them as flesh within *c.* *Mi* 3:3

caldrons

sold they in pots and *c.* *2 Chr* 35:13
c. also and spoons. *Jer* 52:18, 19

Caleb

the tribe of Judah, *C.* *Num* 13:6
and *C.* stilled the people. 30
my servant *C.* having another spirit. 14:24, 30; 32:12; *Deut* 1:36
and *C.* lived. *Num* 14:38; 26:65
of the tribe of Judah, *C.* 34:19
Joshua gave *C.* Hebron. *Josh* 14:13
C. drove thence three sons of. 15:14
C. said, he that smiteth. 16
C. gave her the springs. *Judg* 1:15
Nabal was of house of *C.* *1 Sam* 25:3
C. begat children. *1 Chr* 2:18, 42, 50
4:15

Caleb

on the south of *C.* we. *1 Sam* 30:14

Caleb-ephratah

Hezron was dead in *C.* *1 Chr* 2:24

calf

Abraham fetched a *c.* *Gen* 18:7
he made it a molten *c.* *Ex* 32:4
Moses burnt *c.* and strawed. 20
take thee a young *c.* *Lev* 9:2
take a *c.* and a lamb for. 3
and made a molten *c.* *Deut* 9:16
Neh 9:18; *Ps* 106:19
and casteth not her *c.* *Job* 21:10
them to skip like a *c.* *Ps* 29:6
the *c.* and the young lion. *Isa* 11:6
there shall the *c.* feed. 27:10
when they cut the *c.* *Jer* 34:18
were like the sole of a *c.* *Ezek* 1:7
thy *c.* O Samaria, hath. *Hos* 8:5
c. of Samaria shall be broken. 6
hither the fatted *c.* *Luke* 15:23

hath killed fatted *c.* *Luke* 15:27, 30
and they made a *c.* in. *Acts* 7:41
second beast was like a *c.* *Rev* 4:7

calkers

of Gebal were thy *c.* *Ezek* 27:9
c. shall fall into midst. 27

call

to see what he would *c.* *Gen* 2:19
c. to thee a nurse of the. *Ex* 2:7
where is he ? *c.* him that he. 20
Moses sent to *c.* Dathan. *Num* 16:12
if the men *c.* thee, rise up. 22:20
God is in all things we *c.* *Deut* 4:7
I *c.* to witness. 26; 30:19; 31:28
c. for Samson that he. *Judg* 16:25
they sent to *c.* peaceably. 21:13
thou didst *c.* me. *1 Sam* 3:6, 8
c. Jesse to the sacrifice, and. 16:3
king sent to *c.* Ahimelech. 22:11
then said Absalom, *c.* *2 Sam* 17:5
c. Bath-sheba. *1 Ki* 1:28
c. Zadok and Nathan. 32
hearken to them in all they *c.* 8:52
art come to me to *c.* my sin ? 17:18
c. ye on name of your. 18:24, 25
Elisha said, *c.* this. *2 Ki* 4:12
c. unto me all the prophets. 10:19
c. now if there be any. *Job* 5:1
c. thou, I will answer. 13:22; 14:15
hear when I *c.* O God of. *Ps* 4:1
the Lord will hear when I *c.* 3
who eat up my people, and *c.* 14:4
let king hear us when we *c.* 20:9
they *c.* their lands after their. 49:11
I *c.* to remembrance my song. 77:6
plenteous in mercy to all that *c.* 86:5
Samuel among them that *c.* 99:6
in the day when I *c.* answer. 102:2
Lord is nigh all them that *c.* 145:18
unto you, O men, I *c.* *Pr* 8:4
to *c.* passengers who go right. 9:15
children arise, *c.* her blessed. 31:28
to them that *c.* evil good. *Isa* 5:20
in that day did the Lord *c.* 22:12
I the Lord which *c.* thee. 45:3
they *c.* themselves of holy. 48:2
when I *c.* to them they stand. 13
c. ye upon him while he is. 55:6
wilt thou *c.* this a fast ? 58:5
c. the sabbath a delight, holy. 13
c. his servants by another. 65:15
it shall come, that before they *c.* 24
consider and *c.* for the. *Jer* 9:17
c. unto me, and I will. 33:3
is this city that men *c.* ? *Lam* 2:15
the Lord said, *c.* his. *Hos* 1:4
God said unto him, *c.* her name. 6
c. his name Lo-ammi, for ye are. 9
they *c.* to Egypt, they go. 7:11
sanctify a fast, *c.* *Joel* 1:14; 2:15
O sleeper, arise, *c.* *Jonah* 1:6
ye shall *c.* every man. *Zech* 3:10
now we *c.* proud happy. *Mal* 3:15
not come to *c.* righteous. *Mat* 9:13
Mark 2:17; *Luke* 5:32
c. the labourers and give. *Mat* 20:8
sent his servants to *c.* them. 22:3
how then doth David in spirit *c.* ? 43
c. no man your father upon. 23:9
why *c.* ye me Lord and ? *Luke* 6:46
when thou makest a feast *c.* 14:13
go *c.* thy husband and. *John* 4:16
ye *c.* me Master and Lord. 13:13
to bind all that *c.* on. *Acts* 9:14
to *c.* over them which had. 19:13
after the way they *c.* heresy. 24:14
Lord is rich to all that *c.* *Rom* 10:12
I *c.* God for a record. *2 Cor* 1:23
when I *c.* to remembrance. *2 Tim* 1:5
follow peace with them that *c.* 2:22
not ashamed to *c.* them. *Heb* 2:11
but *c.* to remembrance. 10:32
let him *c.* the elders of. *Jas* 5:14
if ye *c.* on the Father. *1 Pet* 1:17

call *on the name of the Lord*

c. upon *name of the L.* *Gen* 4:26
I will *c.* *on the name of the L.*
1 Ki 18:24; *Ps* 116:17
he will *c.* *on name of L.* *2 Ki* 5:11
c. upon his *name.* *1 Chr* 16:8
Ps 105:1; *Isa* 12:4
whosoever shall *c.* *on name of L.*
Joel 2:32; *Acts* 2:21; *Rom* 10:13

all *c.* upon *name of L.* *Zeph* 3:9
c. on the name of the L. *1 Cor* 1:2

not **call**

not c. her name Sarai. *Gen* 17:15
didst *not c.* us to go. *Judg* 12:1
c. me *not* Naomi, *c.* me. *Ruth* 1:20
and they *c. not* upon. *Ps* 14:4
yet he will *not c.* back. *Isa* 31:2
upon families that *c. not.* *Jer* 10:25
c. not thy friends. *Luke* 14:12
I *c.* you *not* servants. *John* 15:15
c. not thou common. *Acts* 10:15; 11:9
God hath shewed me *not* to *c.* 10:28

shall or *shalt* **call**

and thou *shalt c.* his. *Gen* 17:19
elders of this city *shall c.* *Deut* 25:8
thou *shalt c.* them to mind. 30:1
they *shall c.* the people. 33:19
thou *shalt c.* and I will. *Job* 14:15
he *shall c.* to the heavens. *Ps* 50:4
all nations *shall c.* him. 72:17
shall c. his name Immanuel (or Emmanuel). *Isa* 7:14; *Mat* 1:23
they *shall c.* the nobles to. *Isa* 34:12
from rising of sun *shall* he *c.* 41:25
another *shall c.* himself by. 44:5
and who, as I, *shall c.* and. 7
thou *shalt c.* a nation that. 55:5
then *shalt* thou *c.* and Lord. 58:9
they *shall c.* thee the city of. 60:14
shalt c. thy walls salvation. 18
men *shall c.* you ministers of. 61:6
shalt c. them the holy people. 62:12
they *shall c.* Jerusalem. *Jer* 3:17
shalt c. me, my father. 19
reprobate silver *shall* men *c.* 6:30
shalt c. to them, but they will. 7:27
thou *shalt c.* me no more. *Hos* 2:16
whom the Lord *shall c.* *Joel* 2:32
shall c. the husbandmen. *Amos* 5:16
shall c. on my name. *Zech* 13:9
they *shall c.* them the. *Mal* 1:4
all nations *shall c.* you blessed. 3:12
shalt c. his name Jesus. *Mat* 1:21
how much more *shall c.* them ? 10:25
shalt c. his name John. *Luke* 1:13
all generations *shall c.* me. 48
many as the Lord *shall c.* *Acts* 2:39
how then *shall* they *c.* on. *Rom* 10:14

will **call**

we *will c.* the damsel. *Gen* 24:57
daughters *will c.* me blessed. 30:13
I *will c.* unto Lord. *1 Sam* 12:17
will c. on the. *2 Sam* 22:4; *Ps* 18:3
will hypocrite *c.* on God ? *Job* 27:10
I will *c.* upon God. *Ps* 55:16; 86:7
quicken us, and we *will c.* 80:18
therefore *will* I *c.* on him. 116:2
that I *will c.* my servant. *Isa* 22:20
I *will c.* all families of. *Jer* 1:15
I will *c.* for sword. 25:29; *Ezek* 38:21
will c. to remembrance. *Ezek* 21:23
I *will c.* for the corn. 36:29
season I *will c.* for. *Acts* 24:25
I *will c.* them my people. *Rom* 9:25

call *upon me*

c. upon me in day of. *Ps* 50:15
he shall *c. upon me,* and. 91:15
shall *c. upon me,* but. *Pr* 1:28
shall ye *c. upon me* and. *Jer* 29:12

called

the name of it *c.* Babel. *Gen* 11:9
angel of God *c.* to Hagar. 21:17
angel *c.* to Abraham out. 22:11
name shall not be *c.* Jacob. 35:10
c. him Ben-oni, but his father *c.* 18
she *c.* to the men of her. 39:14
King of Egypt *c.* for the. *Ex* 1:18
Pharaoh *c.* for Moses. 8:8, 25
9:27; 10:16, 24; 12:31
Moses *c.* Oshea son of. *Num* 13:16
Moses *c.* all Israel. *Deut* 5:1; 29:2
not exact it, because it is *c.* 15:2
shall see thou art *c.* by. 28:10
have ye *c.* us to take ? *Judg* 14:15
cast away the jaw-bone, and *c.* 15:17
Samson was sore athirst, and *c.* 18
Samson *c.* to the Lord. 16:28
c. a prophet, *c.* a seer. *1 Sam* 9:9
whose name is *c.* by. *2 Sam* 6:2
take the city, and it be *c.* 12:28

watchman *c.* to porter. *2 Sam* 18:26
the king *c.* the Gibeonites. 21:2
Adonijah *c.* all. *1 Ki* 1:9; 19:25
Ahab *c.* Obadiah. 18:3
c. on the name of Baal. 26
c. to her husband and. *2 Ki* 4:22
they came and *c.* to porter. 7:10
and Jabez *c.* on the. *1 Chr* 4:10
ark of God, whose name is *c.* 13:6
David *c.* on the Lord. 21:26
except she were *c.* *Esth* 2:14
who is not *c.* I have not been *c.* 4:11
people have not *c.* upon G. *Ps* 53:4
the kingdoms that have not *c.* 79:6
of shepherds is *c.* forth. *Isa* 31:4
but thou hast not *c.* on me. 43:22
O Jacob, ye that are *c.* by. 48:1
hearken, O Jacob, and Israel my *c.* 12
that they might be *c.* trees of. 61:3
shall no more be *c.* *Jer* 7:32
wilt bring day thou hast *c.* *Lam* 1:21
thou hast *c.* as a solemn day. 2:22
thereof is *c.* Bamah. *Ezek* 20:29
now let Daniel be *c.* and. *Dan* 5:12
Jesus, who is *c.* Christ. *Mat* 1:16
first Simon, who is *c.* Peter. 10:2
is not his mother *c.* Mary ? 13:55
Jesus *c.* a little child unto. 18:2
many be *c.* few chosen. 20:16; 22:14
and Jesus stood still, and *c.* 20:32
be not ye *c.* Rabbi. 23:8, 10
one of the twelve *c.* Judas. 26:14
release Jesus, *c.* Christ ? 27:17, 22
commanded him to be *c.* *Mark* 10:49
Peter *c.* to mind the word. 14:72
of thy kindred is *c.* *Luke* 1:61
signs how he would have him *c.* 62
no more worthy to be *c.* thy. 15:19, 21
commanded servants to be *c.* 19:15
to the place that is *c.* Calvary. 23:33
before that Philip *c.* thee. *John* 1:48
Messiah cometh, who is *c.* 4:25
a man *c.* Jesus made clay. 9:11
into the street *c.* Straight. *Acts* 9:11
disciples were *c.* Christians. 11:26
who *c.* for Barnabas and Saul. 13:7
then Saul, *c.* Paul, filled with. 9
on whom my name is *c.* 15:17
to be *c.* in question for. 19:40
I am *c.* in question. 23:6; 24:21
Paul the prisoner *c.* and. 23:18
Paul *c.* to be an. *Rom* 1:1; *1 Cor* 1:1
among whom are ye also *c.* *Rom* 1:6
c. to be saints. 7; *1 Cor* 1:2
thou art *c.* a Jew. *Rom* 2:17
who are the *c.* 8:28
by whom ye were *c.* *1 Cor* 1:9
to them which are *c.* 24
not many mighty are *c.* 26
if any man *c.* a brother be. 5:11
is any man *c.* being circumcised ? is any *c.* in uncircumcision ? 7:18
art thou *c.* being a servant ? 21
let every man wherein he is *c.* 24
removed from him that *c.* *Gal* 1:6
brethren, ye have been *c.* 5:13
c. uncircumcision by that *c.* *Eph* 2:11
vocation wherewith ye are *c.* 4:1
even as ye are *c.* in one hope. 4
to the which ye are *c.* *Col* 3:15
Jesus, which is *c.* Justus. 4:11
above all that is *c.* God. *2 Thes* 2:4
whereto thou art *c.* *1 Tim* 6:12
of science, falsely so *c.* 20
exhort daily while it is *c.* *Heb* 3:13
the tabernacle which is *c.* the. 9:2
they that are *c.* might receive. 15
God is not ashamed to be *c.* 11:16
Moses refused to be *c.* son of. 24
name by which ye are *c.* *Jas* 2:7
of him who hath *c.* you. *1 Pet* 2:9
for hereunto were ye *c.* 21
knowing ye are thereunto *c.* 3:9
that hath *c.* us to glory. *2 Pet* 1:3
that we should be *c.* the. *1 John* 3:1
in Jesus Christ, and *c.* *Jude* 1
name of the star is *c.* *Rev* 8:11
spiritually is *c.* Sodom and. 11:8
that old serpent *c.* the Devil. 12:9
that are with him, are *c.* 17:14
blessed that are *c.* to the. 19:9

called, joined with *God* or *Lord*

c. light day, darkness he *c.* *Gen* 1:5

God *c.* firmament, Heaven. *Gen* 1:8
c. dry-land Earth, waters *c.* Seas. 10
and *c.* their name Adam. 5:2
God *c.* to him out of the. *Ex* 3:4
the Lord *c.* to him out of the. 19:3
the Lord *c.* Moses up to the top. 20
see, the Lord hath *c.* my. 35:30
Lord *c.* Aaron and. *Num* 12:5
Lord *c.* Samuel. *1 Sam* 3:4, 6, 8, 10
c. these three kings. *2 Ki* 3:10, 13
the Lord hath *c.* for a famine. 8:1
Lord hath *c.* the earth. *Ps* 50:1
Lord raised, and *c.* him. *Isa* 41:2
the Lord have *c.* thee. 42:6
the Lord hath *c.* me. 49:1
the Lord hath *c.* thee as a. 54:6
Lord *c.* thy name a green. *Jer* 11:16
hath not *c.* thy name Pashur. 20:3
Lord God *c.* to contend. *Amos* 7:4
that the Lord had *c.* us. *Acts* 16:10
but God hath *c.* us. *1 Cor* 7:15
as the Lord hath *c.* every one. 17
it pleased God, who *c.* *Gal* 1:15
c. you to his kingdom. *1 Thes* 2:12
for God hath not *c.* us to. 4:7
whereunto God *c.* you. *2 Thes* 2:14
who hath *c.* us. *2 Tim* 1:9
but he that is *c.* of God. *Heb* 5:4
c. of God an high-priest after. 10
God of all grace, who *c.* *1 Pet* 5:10

he **called**

he c. that place Beer-sheba. *Gen* 21:31
he c. their names as his. 26:18
thy name is Jacob, *he c.* his. 35:10
the Lord *c.* to Moses. *Ex* 24:16
he c. him Jerubbaal. *Judg* 6:32
he saw me and *c.* to me. *2 Sam* 1:7
then *he c.* his servant that. 13:17
Solomon his brother *he c.* not. *1 Ki* 1:10; 19:26
he c. them land of Cabul. 9:13
he c. to Gehazi, so *he c.* *2 Ki* 4:36
brake brazen serpent, *he c.* 18:4
he c. for a famine. *Ps* 105:16
then *c. he* Johanan and. *Jer* 42:8
he hath *c.* an assembly. *Lam* 1:15
he c. to the man. *Ezek* 9:3
he c. the twelve. *Mat* 10:1
he c. the multitude. 15:10
straightway *he c.* them. *Mark* 1:20
Jesus saw her, *he c.* *Luke* 13:12
if *he c.* them gods. *John* 10:35
he had *c.* the saints. *Acts* 9:41
then *c. he* them in. 10:23
then *he c.* for a light. 16:29
whom *he c.* together. 19:25
he c. unto him two centurions. 23:23
he also c. whom *he c.* *Rom* 8:30
even us whom *he* hath *c.* not. 9:24
as *he* which hath *c.* you. *1 Pet* 1:15
see **called** *the name*

I called, or, *I have* **called**

I c. thee to curse. *Num* 24:10
when *I c.* you, ye. *Judg* 12:2
Eli said, *I c.* not. *1 Sam* 3:5, 6
I have c. thee. 28:15
in my distress *I c.* *2 Sam* 22:7
Ps 18:6; 118:5
I c. the priests. *Neh* 5:12
if *I* had *c.* and he had. *Job* 9:16
I c. my servant, and he gave. 19:16
I have c. on thee, for. *Ps* 17:6
not be ashamed, for *I have c.* 31:17
Lord, *I have c.* daily upon. 88:9
then *c. I* upon the Lord. 116:4
because *I have c.* *Pr* 1:24
I c. him, but he gave. *S of S* 5:6
I have c. my mighty ones. *Isa* 13:3
I have c. thee from the. 41:9
I c. thee by thy name. 43:1; 45:4
yea, *I have c.* him. 48:15
when *I c.* was there none? 50:2
for *I c.* him alone. 51:2
I c. ye did not answer. 65:12
Jer 7:13
because when *I c.* none did. *Isa* 66:4
because *I have c.* to them. *Jer* 35:17
I c. for my lovers. *Lam* 1:19
I c. on thy name out of. 3:55
drewest near in the day *I c.* 57
I c. my Son out of Egypt. *Hos* 11:1
Mat 2:15
I c. for a drought upon. *Hag* 1:11
one *I c.* Beauty, the other *I c.* *Zech* 11:7
not servants, *I have c.* *John* 15:15
work whereto *I have c.* *Acts* 13:2
for this cause *have I c.* for. 28:20

called *by my name*

people who are *c. by my n.* *2 Chr* 7:14
one that is *c. by my n.* *Isa* 43:7
nation that was not *c. by my n.* 65:1
house *c. by my n.* *Jer* 7:10, 11, 14
30; 32:34; 34:15
evil on the city *c. by my n.* 25:29
heathen which are *c. by my n.* *Amos* 9:12

called *by thy name*

house is *c. by thy n.* *1 Ki* 8:43
2 Chr 6:33
let us be *c. by thy n.* to. *Isa* 4:1
c. thee *by thy n.* 43:1; 45:4
they were not *c. by thy n.* 63:19
Lord, we are *c. by thy n.* *Jer* 14:9
for I am *c. by thy n.* 15:16
city which is *c. by thy n.* *Dan* 9:18
city and people are *c. by thy n.* 19

called *his name*

he *c. his n.* Israel. *Gen* 35:10
she *c. his n.* Benoni. 18
mother *c. his n.* Jabez. *1 Chr* 4:9
she *c. his n.* Peresh. 7:16
and he *c. his n.* Beriah. 23
and he *c. his n.* Jesus. *Mat* 1:25
and *his name is c.* the. *Rev* 19:13

called *the name*

c. the n. of place. *Gen.* 28:19; 35:15
Israel *c. the n.* manna. *Ex* 16:31
c. the n. of the place Massah. 17:7
Moses *c. the n.* of the altar. 15
Samson *c. the n.* *Judg* 15:19
c. the n. of that place. *2 Sam* 5:20
c. the n. thereof Jachin. *1 Ki* 7:21
2 Chr 3:17
he *c. the n.* of the first. *Job* 42:12

sent and **called**

she *sent and c.* Jacob. *Gen* 27:42
Jacob *sent and c.* Rachel. 31:4
then Pharaoh *sent and c.* 41:14
Balak *sent and c.* Balaam. *Josh* 24:9
she *sent and c.* Barak. *Judg* 4:6
she *sent and c.* the lords. 16:18
he *sent and c.* his name. *2 Sam* 12:25
king *sent and c.* for. *1 Ki* 2:36, 42
sent and c. Jeroboam. 12:3
2 Chr 10:3
Haman *sent and c.* for. *Esth* 5:10
sent to Ephesus, *and c.* *Acts* 20:17

shall be **called**

shall be c. woman. *Gen* 2:23
thy name *shall be c.* Abraham. 17:5
in Isaac *shall* thy seed *be c.* 21:12
Rom 9:7; *Heb* 11:18
shall be c. no more Jacob. *Gen* 32:28
thy issue *shall be c.* after. 48:6
his name *shall be c.* in. *Deut* 25:10
wise in heart *shall be c.* *Pr* 16:21
deviseth evil, *shall be c.* a. 24:8
Jerusalem *shall be c.* *Isa* 4:3
name *shall be c.* Wonderful. 9:6
one *shall be c.* the city of. 19:18
vile person *shall* no more *be c.* 32:5
shall be c. way of holiness. 35:8
the whole earth *shall* he *be c.* 54:5
shall be c. house of prayer. 56:7
Mat 21:13
shall no more *be c.* Tophet.
Jer 7:32; 19:6
shall be c. Lord our. 23:6; 33:16
Jerusalem *shall be c.* a. *Zech* 8:3
be fulfilled, *shall be c.* a. *Mat* 2:23
peace-makers *shall be c.* 5:9
he *shall be c.* the least in. 19
and he *shall be c.* the. *Luke* 1:32
that holy thing *shall be c.* the. 35
mother said he *shall be c.* John. 60
every male *shall be c.* holy. 2:23
she be married, *shall be c.* *Rom* 7:3
they *shall be c.* the children. 9:26

shalt be **called**

thou *shalt be c.* the city of. *Isa* 1:26
thou *shalt be c.* no more tender. 47:1
thou *shalt* no more *be c.* lady of. 5
thou *shalt be c.* the repairer. 58:12
shalt be c. by a new name. *Isa* 62:2
thou *shalt be c.* Hephzi-bah. 4
thou *shalt be c.* sought for. 12
thou *shalt be c.* Prophet. *Luke* 1:76
thou *shalt be c.* Cephas. *John* 1:42

they **called**

they c. Lot, and said. *Gen* 19:5
they c. the people to. *Num* 25:2
they c. for Samson. *Judg* 16:25
they c. these days Purim. *Esth* 9:26
they c. upon the Lord. *Ps* 99:6
they have *c.* a multitude. *Jer* 12:6
because *they c.* thee an. 30:17
as *they c.* to them, so. *Hos* 11:2
they c. them to the most High. 7
if *they* have *c.* master. *Mat* 10:25
they c. him Zacharias. *Luke* 1:59
they c. parents of him. *John* 9:18
then again *they c.* the man. 24
they c. them, and. *Acts* 4:18
when *they* had *c.* the apostles. 5:40
they c. Barnabas, Jupiter. 14:12

was **called**

which *was c.* the land of. *Deut* 3:13
place *was c.* the valley. *2 Chr* 20:26
was c. after their name. *Ezra* 2:61
Neh 7:63
wast c. a transgressor. *Isa* 48:8
whose name *was c.* *Dan* 10:1
priest, who *was c.* Caiaphas. *Mat* 26:3
was c. the field of blood. 27:8
her who *was c.* barren. *Luke* 1:36
his name *was c.* Jesus. 2:21
Jesus *was c.* and his. *John* 2:2
Simeon, that *was c.* Niger. *Acts* 13:1
and when he *was c.* forth. 24:2
knew the island *was c.* Melita. 28:1
calling wherein he *was c.* *1 Cor* 7:20
Abraham when he *was c.* *Heb* 11:8
was c. the friend of God. *Jas* 2:23
that set on him *was c.* *Rev* 19:11

calledst, callest

that thou *c.* us not when. *Judg* 8:1
here am I, for thou *c.* *1 Sam* 3:5
thou *c.* in trouble, and I. *Ps* 81:7
c. to remembrance. *Ezek* 23:21
why *c.* thou me good? *Mat* 19:7
Mark 10:18; *Luke* 18:19

calleth

do according to all that the stranger *c.* to. *1 Ki* 8:43; *2 Chr* 6:33
who *c.* on God, and he. *Job* 12:4
deep *c.* unto deep at. *Ps* 42:7
c. them all by their names. 147:4
Isa 40:26
fool's mouth *c.* for strokes. *Pr* 18:6
he *c.* to me out of Seir. *Isa* 21:11
none *c.* for justice. 59:4
there is none that *c.* on thy. 64:7
there is none that *c.* to. *Hos* 7:7
c. for waters of the sea. *Amos* 5:8
9:6
c. for Elias. *Mat* 27:47; *Mark* 15:35
c. to him whom he would. *Mark* 3:13
c. to him the twelve. 6:7
Jesus *c.* his disciples. 8:1
arise, he *c.* thee. 10:49
if David therefore *c.* him Lord. 12:37
Luke 20:44
he *c.* together his friends. *Luke* 15:6
she *c.* her friends and her. 9
when he *c.* the Lord. 20:37
and he *c.* his own sheep. *John* 10:3
master is come and *c.* for. 11:28
c. things which be not, as. *Rom* 4:17
might stand, of him that *c.* 9:11
no man by the Spirit *c.* *1 Cor* 12:3
cometh not of him that *c.* *Gal* 5:8
faithful is he that *c.* *1 Thes* 5:24
Jezebel, that *c.* herself a. *Rev* 2:20

calling

[1] *Any lawful employment, or way of living,* 1 Cor 7:20. [2] *The calling of the gospel of Christ,* Phil 3:14; Heb 3:1.

use trumpets for *c.* of. *Num* 10:2
the *c.* of assemblies. *Isa* 1:13
in *c.* to remembrance. *Ezek* 23:19
the *c.* of God without. *Rom* 11:29
see your *c.* brethren. *1 Cor* 1:26
let every man abide in same *c.* 7:20
what is the hope of his *c.* *Eph* 1:18

called in one hope of your c. Eph 4:4
for the prize of the high c. Phil 3:14
you worthy of this c. 2 Thes 1:11
called us with an holy c. 2 Tim 1:9
partakers of the heavenly c. Heb 3:1
your c. and election sure. 2 Pet 1:10

calling, *participle*

c. the generations from. Isa 41:4
c. a ravenous bird from the. 46:11
c. to their fellows. Mat 11:16
Luke 7:32
Peter, c. to remembrance.
Mark 11:21
stoned Stephen c. upon. Acts 7:59
wash away thy sins, c. on. 22:16
obeyed Abraham, c. 1 Pet 3:6

calm

maketh the storm a c. Ps 107:29
that the sea may be c. Jonah 1:11
so shall the sea be c. to you. 12
there was a great c. Mat 8:26
Mark 4:39; Luke 8:24

Calneh

Babel and C. in land of. Gen 10:10
pass ye unto C. from. Amos 6:2

Calno

not C. as Carchemish? Isa 10:9

Calvary

come to place called C. Luke 23:33

calve, -ed, -eth

their cow c. and casteth. Job 21:10
mark when the hinds do c.? 39:1
Lord maketh hinds to c. Ps 29:9
the hind c. in the field. Jer 14:5

calves

and bring their c. home. 1 Sam 6:7
king made two c. of gold. 1 Ki 12:28
sacrificing to the c. that he. 32
not from the golden c. 2 Ki 10:29
ordained priests, for c. 2 Chr 11:15
there are with you golden c. 13:8
rebuke bulls with the c. Ps 68:30
fear, because of the c. of. Hos 10:5
men that sacrifice kiss the c. 13:2
so will we render the c. of. 14:2
and eat c. out of the midst. Amos 6:4
shall I come with c.? Mi 6:6
grow up as c. of the stall. Mal 4:2
by blood of goats and c. Heb 9:12
took blood of c. and sprinkled. 19

came

of whom c. Gen 10:14; 1 Chr 1:12
c. two angels to Sodom. Gen 19:1
God c. to Abimelech. 20:3
brother c. with subtilty. 27:35
God c. to Laban the Syrian. 31:24
c. to thy brother Esau, he. 32:6
laid up garment until his lord c. 39:16
c. to the land whither. Num 13:27
red heifer, upon which never c. 19:2
God c. to Balaam at. 22:9, 20
Spirit of God c. on him. 24:2
Judg 3:10; 1 Sam 10:10
we c. to Kadesh-barnea. Deut 1:19
the Lord c. from Sinai. 33:2
as she c. to him she moved.
Josh 15:18; Judg 1:14
kings c. and fought. Judg 5:19
cake of bread c. to a tent. 7:13
they robbed all that c. along. 9:25
upon them c. curse of Jotham. 57
c. not within border of Moab. 11:18
the man that c. to me. 13:10
Manoah arose and c. to the. 11
bring forth the man that c. 19:22
all that c. to hand. 20:48
Moabitish damsel that c. Ruth 2:6
priest's servant, c. 1 Sam 2:13, 15
to all Israelites that c. thither. 14
there c. a man of God to Eli. 27
and the word of Samuel c. 4:1
they c. no more into coast. 7:13
told Samuel before Saul c. 9:15
saw asses no where, c. to. 10:14
but Samuel c. not to Gilgal. 13:8
there c. a lion and a bear. 17:34
men of Judah c. and. 2 Sam 2:4
thou knowest Abner, that c. 3:25
the way tidings c. to David. 13:30
behold, king's sons c. and wept. 36
when any c. to king. 15:2
Absalom and Ahithophel c.
2 Sam 16:15
saw every one that c. by him. 20:12
Jonathan son of Abiathar c. 1 Ki 1:42
c. of all people to hear wisdom. 4:34
there c. no more such spices. 10:10
there c. no such almug-trees. 12
Jeroboam and all the people c.
12:12; 2 Chr 10:12
not by way he c. to. 1 Ki 13:10
he c. thither to a cave. 19:9
king of Israel c. heavy to. 20:43
it fell on a day that he c. 2 Ki 4:11
when she c. to the man of God. 27
Naaman c. and stood before. 5:15
the bands of Syria c. 6:23
but ere messenger c. to him. 32
Hazael departed from Elisha, c. 8:14
wherefore c. this mad fellow? 9:11
Jehu arose, departed, and c. 10:12
all worshippers of Baal c. 21
of the priests c. and dwelt. 17:28
by the way that he c. shall. 19:33
command of the Lord c. this. 24:3
these c. in the days of. 1 Chr 4:41
Judah prevailed, of him c. 5:2
Ephraim's brethren c. to. 7:22
are they that c. to David. 12:1
there c. to David to help him. 22
Levites left all and c. 2 Chr 11:14
guard c. and fetched the. 12:11
fear of Lord c. upon them. 14:14
the band of men that c. with. 22:1
wrath c. on Judah and. 24:18
not hear, for it c. of God. 25:20
humbled themselves and c. 30:11
as soon as commandment c. 31:5
which c. with Zerubbabel. Ezra 2:2
cease till matter c. to Darius. 5:5
when seventh month c. Neh 7:73
Vashti brought in, she c. Esth 1:17
then thus c. every maiden to. 2:13
Mordecai c. even before. 4:2
whither the king's decree c. 8:17
rest, yet trouble c. Job 3:26
of him ready to perish c. 29:13
evil c. darkness c. 30:26
my cry c. before me. Ps 18:6
when my foes c. upon me. 27:2
wrath of God c. upon them. 78:31
until time that his word c. 105:19
spake, and there c. divers sorts. 31
he spake, and locusts c. and. 34
to go as he c. Eccl 5:15, 16
year that Tartan c. Isa 20:1
and his ambassadors c. to. 30:4
ends of earth, drew near and c. 41:5
nor c. it into my mind. Jer 7:31
19:5; 32:35
looked for peace, no good c. 8:15
incense you burnt, c. it not? 44:21
nor c. abominable flesh. Ezek 4:14
c. to Lebanon, and took the. 17:3
afore he that escaped c. 33:22
the bones c. together. 37:7
breath c. into them, they lived. 10
glory of God of Israel c. 43:2
all this c. on the king. Dan 4:28
one like Son of Man c. 7:13
till the ancient of days c. 22
to whom house of Israel c. Amos 6:1
for word c. to the king. Jonah 3:6
God c. from Teman, and. Hab 3:3
and lo it c. to little. Hag 1:9
when one c. to the press-fat. 2:16
c. a great wrath from. Zech 7:12
of all the nations that c. 14:16
c. wise men from the east. Mat 2:1
till it c. and stood over where. 9
those days c. John the Baptist. 3:1
descended, and floods c. 7:25, 27
he passed over and c. into. 9:1
a woman c. behind, touched. 20
the blind men c. to Jesus. 28
Son of Man c. not to be. 20:28
c. to the first and said. 21:28
he c. to the second, and said. 30
John c. to you in the way of. 32
went to buy, bridegroom c. 25:10
in prison, and ye c. to me. 36
forthwith he c. to Jesus. 26:49
though false witnesses c. yet. 60
his disciples c. by night. 28:13
what he did, c. to him. Mark 3:8
how long is it since this c.? Mark 9:21
one of the scribes c. 12:28
c. a certain poor widow. 42
there c. a cloud and. Luke 9:34
there c. a voice out of the cloud. 35
when he c. to himself. 15:17
he arose and c. to his father. 20
same c. to bear witness. John 1:7
he c. to his own, and his own. 11
but grace and truth c. by Jesus. 17
same c. to Jesus by night. 3:2
7:50; 19:39
and they c. and were baptized. 3:23
upon this c. his disciples. 4:27
gods to whom word of God c. 10:35
the voice c. not because. 12:30
at even c. Jesus, and stood. 20:19
preached, till he c. to. Acts 8:40
c. hither for that intent. 9:21
as many as c. with Peter. 10:45
the vessel descended, and it c. 11:5
when he c. and had seen. 23
and many that believed c. 19:18
nor brethren that c. spake. 28:21
judgement c. free gift c. Rom 5:18
when the commandment c. sin. 7:9
concerning the flesh, Christ c. 9:5
man c. death, by man c. 1 Cor 15:21
for before that certain c. Gal 2:12
before faith c. we were kept. 3:23
and c. and preached peace. Eph 2:17
our gospel c. not in word. 1 Thes 1:5
that Christ c. to save. 1 Tim 1:15
persecutions which c. 2 Tim 3:11
there c. such a voice. 2 Pet 1:17
this voice which c. from heaven. 18
prophecy c. not in old time. 21
this is he that c. by. 1 John 5:6
when brethren c. and. 3 John 3
and great Babylon c. Rev 16:19
see Spirit of the **Lord**

came *again*

angel c. again to the. Judg 13:9
spirit c. again. 15:19; 1 Sam 30:12
and Benjamin c. again. Judg 21:14
soul of the child c. again. 1 Ki 17:22
angel of the Lord c. again. 19:7
his flesh c. again like. 2 Ki 5:14
lepers c. again, and entered. 7:8
these c. again to. Ezra 2:1; Neh 7:6
Mordecai c. again. Esth 6:12
c. again and touched. Dan 10:18
the angel c. again. Zech 4:1
her spirit c. again. Luke 8:55
and early he c. again. John 8:2

came *down*

Lord c. down to see. Gen 11:5
when the fowls c. down. 15:11
O sir, we c. down at first. 43:20
the Lord c. down upon. Ex 19:20
when Moses c. down. 34:29
and Aaron c. down. Lev 9:22
Lord c. down in a cloud. Num 11:25
12:5
then Amalekites c. down. 14:45
out of Machir c. down. Judg. 5:14
and c. down. 2 Sam 22:10; Ps 18:9
c. down fire from heaven. 2 Ki 1:10
12, 14
men of Gath c. down. 1 Chr 7:21
of praying, fire c. down. 2 Chr 7:1, 3
therefore she c. down. Lam 1:9
an holy one c. down. Dan 4:13
evil c. down from Lord. Mi 1:12
c. down from mountain. Mat 17:9
Mark 9:9
c. down a certain priest. Luke 10:31
he made haste and c. down. 19:6
he that c. down from. John 3:13
I c. down from heaven, not. 6:38
bread which c. down. 41, 51, 58
men which c. down. Acts 15:1
c. down from Judea a. 21:10
fire c. down from God. Rev 20:9

came *forth*

to me when I c. forth. Ex 13:8
why c. we forth out of Egypt?
Num 11:20
Aaron and Miriam, c. forth. 12:5
water when ye c. forth. Deut 23:4
hot on day we c. forth. Josh 9:12
out of eater c. forth meat, and out of
strong c. forth. Judg 14:14

Shimei *c. forth* and. *2 Sam* 16:5
son which *c. forth* of my bowels. 11
c. forth a spirit, and. *1 Ki* 22:21
c. forth little children. *2 Ki* 2:23
c. forth two she-bears and tare. 24
fathers *c. forth.* 21:15; *Jer* 7:25
c. forth of his bowels. *2 Chr* 32:21
therefore *c.* I *forth* to. *Pr* 7:15
as he *c. forth* naked. *Eccl* 5:15
wherefore *c.* I *forth.* *Jer* 20:18
they *c. forth* of the. *Dan* 3:26
c. forth fingers and wrote. 5:5
a fiery stream *c. forth.* 7:10
out of one of them *c. forth.* 8:9
the command *c. forth* and I. 9:23
out of him *c. forth* corner. *Zech* 10:4
for therefore *c.* I *forth.* *Mark* 1:38
that was dead *c. forth.* *John* 11:44
I *c. forth* from the Father. 16:28
Jesus *c. forth* wearing the. 19:5

***I* came**

I c. this day to the well. *Gen* 24:42
little thou hadst before *I c.* 30:30
which were born before *I c.* 48:5
when *I c.* from Padan, Rachel. 7
I c. to speak to Pharaoh *Ex* 5:23
when *I c.* to her found. *Deut* 22:14
I c. into Gibeah. *Judg* 20:4
believed not till *I c.* *1 Ki* 10:7
2 Chr 9:6
afterwards *I c.* to the. *Neh* 6:10
I c. to the king and. 13:6
I c. to Jerusalem and understood. 7
wherefore, when *I c.* *Isa* 50:2
then *I c.* to them of the. *Ezek* 3:15
when *I c.* to destroy the city. 43:3
I c. not to send peace. *Mat* 10:34
I c. not to call the righteous.
Mark 2:17; *Luke* 5:32
I know whence *I c.* *John* 8:14
I c. from God, nor *c. I* of. 42
but for this cause *I c.* 12:27
for *I c.* not to judge the world. 47
for this cause *c. I* into the. 18:37
therefore *c. I* as soon as. *Acts* 10:29
the first day *I c.* into Asia. 20:18
being led by the hand, *I c.* 22:11
then *c. I* with an army. 23:27
I c. to bring alms to my. 24:17
when *I c.* to you *I c.* not. *1 Cor* 2:1
to spare you *I c.* not. *2 Cor* 1:23
lest when *I c.* I should have. 2:3
when *I c.* to Troas to preach. 12
afterwards *I c.* into. *Gal* 1:21

came *in*

sons of God, *c. in* to. *Gen* 6:4
where are the men that *c. in.* 19:5
Judah *c. in* unto her. 38:18
he *c. in* to lie with me. 39:14
if he *c. in* by himself. *Ex* 21:3
went out, and none *c. in.* *Josh* 6:1
went out and *c. in.* *1 Sam* 18:13, 16
she *c. in* to him. *2 Sam* 11:4
as she *c. in* at the door. *1 Ki* 14:6
no peace to him that *c. in.* *2 Chr* 15:5
Zech 8:10
c. in unto the king no more. *Esth* 2:14
and they *c. in* and. *Jer* 32:23
now Jeremiah *c. in* and went. 37:4
way of the gate he *c. in.* *Ezek* 46:9
c. in the magicians. *Dan* 4:7; 5:8
but at the last Daniel *c. in.* 4:8
my prayer *c. in.* *Jonah* 2:7
when the king *c. in* to. *Mat* 22:11
the angel *c. in* to Mary. *Luke* 1:28
this woman since I *c. in.* 7:45
wife not knowing *c. in.* *Acts* 5:7
the young men *c. in* and found. 10
who *c. in* privily to spy. *Gal* 2:4

came *near*

they pressed, and *c. near.* *Gen* 19:9
the one *c.* not *near* the. *Ex* 14:20
when they *c. near* to the altar. 40:32
captains *c. near* to Moses.
Num 31:48
the chief of Joseph *c. near.* 36:1
ye *c. near* to me. *Deut* 1:22; 5:23
c. near and put feet on. *Josh* 10:24
c. near before Eleazar. 17:4; 21:1
Elijah *c. near* and said. *1 Ki* 18:36
Gehazi *c. near* to thrust. *2 Ki* 4:27
Zedekiah *c. near* and. *2 Chr* 18:23
even to greatest *c. near.* *Jer* 42:1
Chaldeans *c. near* and. *Dan* 3:8
Nebuchadnezzar *c. near* to. 26
he *c. near* to Damascus. *Acts* 9:3

came *nigh*

as soon as he *c. nigh.* *Ex* 32:19
the children of Israel *c. nigh.* 34:32
when any *c. nigh* to do. *2 Sam* 15:5
Jesus *c. nigh* to the sea. *Mat* 15:29
when they *c. nigh* to. *Mark* 11:1
when he *c. nigh* to gate. *Luke* 7:12

came *over*

Israel *c. over* this Jordan. *Josh* 4:22
the Levite *c. over.* *Judg* 19:10
they *c. over* to the other. *Mark* 5:1

came *out*

behold Rebekah *c. out.* *Gen* 24:15
first *c. out* red, all over like. 25:25
midwife said, this *c. out* first. 38:28
all the souls which *c. out* of. 46:26
day in which ye *c. out.* *Ex* 13:3, 4
a fire *c. out.* *Lev* 9:24; *Num* 16:35
they three *c. out.* *Num* 12:4
Dathan and Abiram *c. out.* 16:27
smote rock, and water *c. out.* 20:11
Egypt whence ye *c. out.* *Deut* 11:10
all that *c. out* were. *Josh* 5:4, 5
all that *c. out* of Egypt. 6
Jael *c. out* to meet him. *Judg* 4:22
I am he that *c. out.* *1 Sam* 4:16
three days since I *c. out.* 21:5
spear *c. out* behind. *2 Sam* 2:23
Michal *c. out* to meet David. 6:20
men prevailed and *c. out.* 11:23
and all the people *c. out.* 18:4
covenant with Israel when they *c.*
out of. *1 Ki* 8:9; *2 Chr* 5:10
princes of provinces *c. out.* *1 Ki* 20:19
when they *c. out.* *2 Chr* 20:10
naked *c.* I *out* of my. *Job* 1:21
why did I not give up the ghost,
when I *c. out* of the belly? 3:11
that which *c. out* of my. *Jer* 17:16
whirlwind *c. out* of the. *Ezek* 1:4
c. out as a whirlwind. *Hab* 3:14
c. out two women. *Zech* 5:9
the whole city *c. out* to. *Mat* 8:34
return to house whence I *c. out.*
12:44; *Luke* 11:24
as they *c. out* they found. *Mat* 27:32
and *c. out* of the graves after. 53
unclean spirit *c. out.* *Mark* 1:26
9:26
c. out he saw much people. 6:34
a voice *c. out* of the cloud. 9:7
when he *c. out* he could. *Luke* 1:22
and he *c. out* of him. 4:35
therefore *c. out* his father. 15:28
believed I *c. out* from. *John* 16:27
have known that I *c. out.* 17:8
forthwith *c. out* blood and. 19:34
unclean spirits *c. out.* *Acts* 8:7
and the spirit *c. out.* 16:18
c. word of God *out.* *1 Cor* 14:36
not all that *c. out* of. *Heb* 3:16
c. out of great tribulation. *Rev* 7:14
angel *c. out* of the temple. 14:15, 17
angel *c. out* from the altar. 18
seven angels *c. out* of temple. 15:6
a voice *c. out* of the throne. 19:5

came *to pass*

it *c. to pass,* even the self-same day
it *c. to pass.* *Ex* 12:41, 51
it *c. to pass.* *Deut* 2:16; *1 Sam* 13:22
2 Ki 15:12; *Esth* 2:8; *Acts* 27:44
it *c. to pass* when Israel. *Josh* 17:13
all *c. to pass.* 21:45
for it *c. to pass.* *Judg* 13:20
1 Ki 11:4, 15
but it *c. to pass.* *Judg* 15:1; *2 Ki* 3:5
Neh 2:1; 4:1, 7; 6:1; 7:1
Jer 35:11
it *c. to pass* when the. *1 Sam* 1:20
and all those signs *c. to pass.* 10:9
it *c. to pass* when the evil. 16:23
it *c. to pass* after. *2 Sam* 2:1; 8:1
10:1; *2 Ki* 6:24; *2 Chr* 20:1
it *c. to pass* on morrow. *2 Ki* 8:15
1 Chr 10:8; *Jer* 20:3; *Acts* 4:5
and they *c. to pass.* *Isa* 48:3
before it *c. to pass* I shewed. 5
even as it *c. to pass.* *1 Thes* 3:4

then **came**

then c. Amalek and. *Ex* 17:8
then c. the daughters. *Num* 27:1
then c. David to. *1 Sam* 21:1
then c. all the tribes. *2 Sam* 5:1
then they *c.* to Gilead. 24:6
then c. Eliakim. *2 Ki* 18:37
Isa 36:22
then c. Solomon. *2 Chr* 1:13
then c. Shemaiah the prophet. 12:5
then c. Sheshbazzar. *Ezra* 5:16
then Hanani *c.* *Neh* 1:2
then I *c.* to the governors. 2:9
for good, *then* evil *c.* *Job* 30:26
then c. Jeremiah from. *Jer* 19:14
then c. all the princes. 38:27
then c. certain of elders. *Ezek* 14:1
then they *c.* the same day. 23:39
then c. to him the. *Mat* 9:14
then c. to Jesus scribes and. 15:1
then c. his disciples. 12; 17:19
then c. she, and worshipped. 15:25
Mark 7:25
then c. Peter to him. *Mat* 18:21
then c. mother of Zebedee's. 20:20
then c. they, and laid hands. 26:50
then c. also publicans. *Luke* 3:12
then c. day of unleavened. 22:7
then c. the officers to. *John* 7:45
then c. a voice from heaven. 12:28
then c. Jesus, the doors. 20:26

they **came,** or *came* **they**

they c. to Haran and. *Gen* 11:31
into the land of Canaan, *they c.* 12:5
they c. to the place which God. 22:9
till *they c.* to a land. *Ex* 16:35
same day *c. they* into the 19:1
they c. he lay on bed. *2 Sam* 4:7
and Nathan, *they c.* *1 Ki* 1:32
so *they c.* to me, when I fled. 2:7
they c. and told it in city. 13:25
I will not leave, so *they c.* *2 Ki* 2:4
when *they c.* to Jordan. 6:4
whence *c. they*? 20:14; *Isa* 39:3
out of all Judah *they c.* *2 Chr* 20:4
on eighth day *c. they* to. 29:17
some when *they c.* offered. *Ezra* 2:68
from that time *c. they.* *Neh* 13:21
they c. thither and were. *Job* 6:20
they c. upon me as a wide. 30:14
they c. round about me. *Ps* 88:17
they c. to the pits. *Jer* 14:3
c. they even to Tahpanhes. 43:7
messenger was sent, lo *they c.*
Ezek 23:40
they c. and stood before. *Dan* 2:2
or ever *they c.* at the bottom. 6:24
before *they c.* together. *Mat* 1:18
they c. into the land of. 14:34
they c. and told their Lord all.
18:31; *Luke* 14:21
after a while *c. they.* *Mat* 26:73
they c. to him from. *Mark* 1:45
whom he would, and *they c.* 3:13
they c. with haste. *Luke* 2:16
they c. saying, that they. 24:23
and *they c.* not for Jesus'. *John* 12:9
they c. unto a certain. *Acts* 8:36
they c. to the iron gate. 12:10
they c. with one accord and. 20
they c. thither also and stirred. 17:13
they c. to the chief priests. 23:14
who when *they c.* to Caesarea. 33
and whence *c. they*? *Rev* 7:13

word of the Lord **came**

word of Lord c. to Abram.
Gen 15:1, 4
word of Lord c. to Samuel.
1 Sam 15:10
c. the *word of Lord* to Gad.
2 Sam 24:11
word of Lord c. to Solomon. *1 Ki* 6:11
word of Lord c. to Jehu. 16:1, 7
the *word of Lord c.* unto Elijah.
17:2, 8; 18:1; 19:9; 21:17, 28
whom *word of Lord c.* saying. 18:31
word of Lord c. to Isaiah.
2 Ki 20:4; *Isa* 38:4
word of Lord c. to Nathan.
1 Chr 17:3
word of Lord c. to David. 22:8
word of Lord c. to Shemaiah.
2 Chr 11:2; 12:7; *1 Ki* 12:22

word of Lord c. to Jeremiah. *Jer* 1:2
4; 2:1; 14:1; 29:30; 33:1, 19
Dan 9:2
word of Lord c. expressly to Ezekiel.
Ezek 1:3; 3:16
word of Lord c. to Hosea. *Hos* 1:1
word of Lord c. to Joel. *Joel* 1:1
word of Lord c. to Jonah. *Jonah* 1:1
3:1
word of Lord c. to Micah. *Mi* 1:1
word of Lord c. to Zephaniah.
Zeph 1:1
word of Lord c. by Haggai. *Hag* 1:1
word of Lord c. to Zechariah.
Zech 1:1
c. *word of Lord* of hosts. 7:4; 8:1

camel

(*Camels were the usual riding animals in the East, as they were stronger than horses, and had much more endurance. As so much of the Bible world was either desert, or dry at certain seasons of the year, the peculiar adaptation of the camel to deserts was of unusual importance. Very frequently a man's wealth was estimated in camels. They were bred for work or for swift riding, and their hair was used for clothing*)

saw Isaac, lighted off *c.* *Gen* 24:64
shall not eat, the *c.* *Lev* 11:14
Deut 14:7
slay infant, ox, and *c.* *1 Sam* 15:3
the plague of the *c.* and. *Zech* 14:15
easier for a *c.* to go. *Mat* 19:24
Mark 10:25; *Luke* 18:25
at a gnat and swallow a *c.* *Mat* 23:24

camels

Abram had sheep, oxen, *c.* *Gen* 12:16
will draw water for thy *c.* 24:19, 44
had much cattle, asses, *c.* 30:43
Rachel put them in the *c.* 31:34
Ishmaelites came with their *c.* 37:25
hand of Lord on *c.* and. *Ex* 9:3
they and their *c.* *Judg* 6:5; 7:12
ornaments on *c.* necks. 8:21, 26
David took away *c.* and. *1 Sam* 27:9
men who rode on *c.* and fled. 30:17
to Jerusalem with *c.* *1 Ki* 10:2
2 Chr 9:1
Hazael took forty *c.* *2 Ki* 8:9
took away of *c.* 50,000. *1 Chr* 5:21
Zebulun brought bread on *c.* 11:40
over the *c.* also was Obil. 27:30
c. were 435. *Ezra* 2:67; *Neh* 7:69
by post on mules, *c.* *Esth* 8:10*, 14*
also was three thousand *c.* *Job* 1:3
the Chaldeans fell on the *c.* 17
chariot of asses and of *c.* *Isa* 21:7
carry treasures on bunches of *c.* 30:6
multitude of *c.* cover thee. 60:6
take to themselves their *c.* *Jer* 49:29
their *c.* shall be a booty. 32
Rabbah a stable for *c.* *Ezek* 25:5
raiment of *c.* hair. *Mat* 3:4
Mark 1:6

camest

Hagar, whence *c.* thou? *Gen* 16:8
the land from whence thou *c.* 24:5
eaten of all before thou *c.* 27:33
in it thou *c.* from Egypt. *Ex* 23:15
34:18
wherefore *c.* thou not? *Num* 22:37
to land of Ammon *c.* not. *Deut* 2:37
day thou *c.* thou *c.* in haste. 16:3
thou *c.* not within the. *1 Sam* 13:11
why *c.* thou down hither? 17:28
c. thou not from thy? *2 Sam* 11:10
whereas thou *c.* but yesterday. 15:20
by the way thou *c.* *1 Ki* 13:9, 17
art thou the man of God that *c.*? 14
turn thee back by the way by which thou *c.* *2 Ki* 19:28; *Isa* 37:29
thou *c.* down also on. *Neh* 9:13
c. down the mountains. *Isa* 64:3
before thou *c.* forth, I. *Jer* 1:5
and thou *c.* forth with. *Ezek* 32:2*
friend, how *c.* thou in? *Mat* 22:12
said, Rabbi, when *c.*? *John* 6:25
we believe that thou *c.* forth. 16:30
to thee in way, as thou *c.* *Acts* 9:17

Camon

Jair died, was buried in *C.* *Judg* 10:5

camp

of Lord went before *c.* *Ex* 14:19
quails came up and covered *c.* 16:13
there is a noise of war in *c.* 32:17
go through *c.* and slay every. 27
proclaimed through the *c.* 36:6
man killeth goat in *c.*? *Lev* 17:3
strove together in the *c.* 24:10
every one by his own *c.* *Num* 1:52
on the east-side shall the *c.* of. 2:3
when *c.* setteth forward. 4:5
as the *c.* is to set forward. 15
them in utmost parts of the *c.* 11:1
and Medad prophesied in the *c.* 26
shall not come within *c.* *Deut* 23:10
Lord walked in midst of thy *c.* 14
make *c.* of Israel a curse. *Josh* 6:18
to the outside of the *c.* *Judg* 7:17
began to move him in the *c.* 13:25
there came none to the *c.* 21:8
they brought them to the *c.* 12
this great shout in the *c.*? *1 Sam* 4:6
and run to the *c.* to thy. 17:17
made Omri king in *c.* *1 Ki* 16:16
such a place shall be my *c.* *2 Ki* 6:8
they left the *c.* as it was. 7:7
when these lepers came to *c.* 8
angel of Lord smote *c.* of Assyrians.
19:35; *Isa* 37:36
came with Arabians to *c.* *2 Chr* 22:1
fall in the midst of their *c.* *Ps* 78:28
envied Moses also in the *c.* 106:16
lay siege, set the *c.* also. *Ezek* 4:2
for his *c.* is very great. *Joel* 2:11
compassed *c.* of saints. *Rev* 20:9

into the **camp**

he shall come *into c.* *Lev* 14:8
16:26, 28
Moses gat him *into c.* *Num* 11:30
he shall come *into c.* *Deut* 23:11
God is come *into c.* *1 Sam* 4:7

out of the **camp**

forth people *out of the c.* *Ex* 19:17
your brethren *out of c.* *Lev* 10:4
priest shall go forth *out of the c.* 14:3
killeth a goat *out of the c.* 17:3
him that had cursed *out of c.* 24:23
put every leper *out of c.* *Num* 5:2
Miriam be shut *out of the c.* 12:14
Moses departed not *out of c.* 14:44
shall go abroad *out of c.* *Deut* 23:10
spoilers came *out of c.* *1 Sam* 13:17
out of c. from Saul. *2 Sam* 1:2
out of c. of Israel am I escaped. 3

round about the **camp**

quails fell, spread them *round about c.* *Num* 11:31, 32
stood every man in place *round about c.* *Judg* 7:21

without the **camp**

burn *without the c.* *Ex* 29:14
Lev 8:17; 9:11; 16:27
sought Lord, went *without c.* *Ex* 33:7
ashes *without the c.* *Lev* 6:11
plague shall dwell *without c.* 13:46
leper be *without the c.* *Num* 5:3
stoned *without the c.* 15:35
bring red heifer *without c.* 19:3
do ye abide *without the c.* 31:19
place also *without c.* *Deut* 23:12
left kindred *without the c.* *Josh* 6:23
beasts burnt *without c.* *Heb* 13:11
let us go forth to him *without c.* 13

camp

I will *c.* against thee. *Isa* 29:3
bend the bow *c.* against. *Jer* 50:29
which *c.* in the hedges in. *Nah* 3:17

camped

there Israel *c.* before the. *Ex* 19:2

camphire

beloved is as cluster of *c.* *S of S* 1:14
plants are an orchard of *c.* 4:13

camps

that they defile not their *c* *Num* 5:3
trumpets for journeying of *c.* 10:2
made stink of your *c.* *Amos* 4:10

can

c. we find such a one as? *Gen* 41:38
I *c.* no more go out. *Deut* 31:2
he is dead, *c.* I bring? *2 Sam* 12:23
c. I discern, *c.* I hear voice? 19:35
c. that which is unsavoury? *Job* 6:6
c. rush grow without mire? *c.* 8:11
c. a man be profitable to God? 22:2
c. he judge through dark cloud? 13
c. any understand spreading? 36:29
c. God furnish a table? *Ps* 78:19
c. he give bread also? *c.* he? 20
who *c.* be compared? *c.* be? 89:6
c. a man take fire in his? *Pr* 6:27
c. one go on hot coals and? 28
yet *c.* he not answer. *Isa* 46:7
c. a woman forget her? 49:15
c. a maid forget her? *Jer* 2:32
c. any hide himself in secret? 23:24
c. two walk together? *Amos* 3:3
c. a bird fall in a snare where? 5
who *c.* but prophesy? 8
who *c.* be saved? *Mat* 19:25
Mark 10:26; *Luke* 18:26
make it as sure as you *c.* *Mat* 27:65
c. children of bridechamber fast?
Mark 2:19
this kind *c.* come forth but. 9:29
c. ye drink of the cup? 10:38
c. the blind lead blind? *Luke* 6:39
c. any good come out? *John* 1:46
hard saying, who *c.* hear it? 6:60
c. a devil open the eyes of? 10:21
no more *c.* ye except ye. 15:4
c. any man forbid water? *Acts* 10:47
to law, nor indeed *c.* *Rom* 8:7
not works, *c.* faith save? *Jas* 2:14
c. the fig-tree bear olive-? 3:12

how **can**

how c. I alone bear? *Deut* 1:12
how c. I go, if Saul? *1 Sam* 16:2
how c. I endure to see? *Esth* 8:6
how c. a man be justified? *Job* 25:4
how c. man understand? *Pr* 20:24
how c. one be warm? *Eccl* 4:11
how c. it be quiet seeing? *Jer* 47:7
how c. ye being evil? *Mat* 12:34
how c. a man be born? *John* 3:4
how c. these things be? 9
how c. this man give us? 6:52
how c. we know the way? 14:5
how c. I except some? *Acts* 8:31

Cana

was a marriage in *C.* *John* 2:1
beginning of miracles in *C.* 11
so Jesus came again into *C.* 4:46
Thomas and Nathanael of *C.* 21:2

Canaan

Ham is the father of *C.* *Gen* 9:18
Ham the father of *C.* saw the. 22
cursed be *C.* 25
C. shall be his servant. 26, 27
C. begat Sidon. 10:15; 1 *Chr* 1:13
wife of daughters of *C.* *Gen* 28:1

Canaan

the inhabitants of *C.* *Ex* 15:15
not known all wars of *C.* *Judg* 3:1
sold them to Jabin king of *C.* 4:2
God subdued Jabin king of *C.* 23, 2
then fought the kings of *C.* 5:1
sacrificed to the idols of *C.* *Ps* 106:3
smote the kingdoms of *C.* 135:1
Egypt speak language of *C.* *Isa* 19:1
O *C.* I will even destroy. *Zeph* 2:
a woman of *C.* cried. *Mat* 15:2

land of **Canaan**

go into the *land of C.* *Gen* 12:
dwelt ten years in *land of C.* 16:
give thee *land of C.* 17:8; *Lev* 25:3
Num 34:2; *Deut* 32:4
1 Chr 16:18; *Ps* 105:1
Jacob dwelt in *land of C.* *Gen* 37:
famine was in the *land of C.* 42:
they said, from *land of C.*
sons of one man in *land of C.*
get ye up unto *land of C.* 45:
carried him into *land of C.* 50:
come into the *land of C.* *Lev* 14:
Num 34
after doings of *land of C.* *Lev* 18
sent to spy *land of C.* *Num* 13:
over armed into *land of C.* 32:
fruit of *land of C.* *Josh* 5:
altar over against *land of C.* 22:
led him through the *land of C.* 24

nativity is of *land of C.* *Ezek* 16:3
dearth over all *land of C.* *Acts* 7:11
seven nations in *land of C.* 13:19

Canaanite, -s

C. was then in land. *Gen* 12:6; 13:7
the Amorites, *C.*, Girgashites. 15:21
Ex. 3:8, 17; 23:23; *Deut* 7:1
20:17; *Josh* 3:10; 12:8; *Judg* 3:5
Neh 9:8
shalt not take a wife of *C.* *Gen* 24:3
make me to stink amongst *C.* 34:30
daughter of a certain *C.* 38:2
drive out the *C.* *Ex* 23:28; 33:2
34:11
Lord delivered up the *C.* *Num* 21:3
Neh 9:24
C. would dwell in land. *Josh* 17:12
Judg 1:27
shalt drive out the *C.* *Josh* 17:18
up against the *C.* first ? *Judg* 1:1
to fight against the *C.* 9, 10
did Ephraim drive out *C.* 29
Naphtali dwelt among the *C.* 33
Pharaoh had slain the *C.* *1 Ki* 9:16
to abominations of *C.* *Ezra* 9:1
shall possess that of *C.* *Ob* 20
no more *C.* in house of. *Zech* 14:21
Simon the *C.* *Mat* 10:4; *Mark* 3:18

Canaanitess

to Judah of Shua the *C.* *1 Chr* 2:3

Candace

eunuch of great authority under *C.*
Acts 8:27

candle

(*Revised Version,* lamp *in every case. The candle, as we know it, was not used in the East, the reference being to small earthen lamps in which a wick floating in the oil gave a feeble light. They were of different sizes and shapes. The word* candlestick, *however, remains in the Revisions in nearly every instance, a few being translated* lampstand, Mat 5:15)

his *c.* shall be put out. *Job* 18:6
how oft is *c.* of wicked put ? 21:17
his *c.* shined upon my head. 29:3
thou wilt light my *c.* God. *Ps* 18:28
spirit of man is *c.* of. *Pr* 20:27
c. of wicked shall be put out. 24:20
her *c.* goeth not out by night. 31:18
from them light of *c.* *Jer* 25:10
light a *c.* and put it under. *Mat* 5:15
Mark 4:21; *Luke* 8:16; 11:33
bright shining of a *c.* *Luke* 11:36
doth not she light a *c.* and. 15:8
light of a *c.* shine no. *Rev* 18:23
and they need no *c.* nor light. 22:5

candles

search Jerusalem with *c.* *Zeph* 1:12

candlestick

c. of pure gold. *Ex* 25:31; 37:17
Num 8:4
six branches out of the *c.* *Ex* 25:33
37:19
in *c.* four bowls. 25:34; 37:20
thou shalt set the *c.* over. 26:35
put the *c.* in the tent. 40:24
order the lamps on the *c.* *Lev* 24:4
charge shall be ark and *c.* *Num* 3:31
take a cloth and cover the *c.* 4:9
light over against the *c.* 8:2
bed, a table, a *c.* *2 Ki* 4:10
by weight for every *c.* *1 Chr* 28:15
set they in order the *c.* *2 Chr* 13:11
wrote over against the *c.* *Dan* 5:5
looked, and behold a *c.* *Zech* 4:2
two olive-trees on right side of *c.* 11
c. and it giveth light. *Mat* 5:15*
Luke 8:16; 11:33
a candle brought not to be set on a *c.* ? *Mark* 4:21*
first, wherein was the *c.* *Heb* 9:2
come and remove thy *c.* *Rev* 2:5

candlesticks

made *c.* of pure gold. *1 Ki* 7:49
2 Chr 4:7
weight for the *c.* of gold. *1 Chr* 28:15
took away the *c.* *Jer* 52:19
two *c.* standing before the. *Rev* 11:4

see **seven**

cane

brought me no sweet *c.* *Isa* 43:24
sweet *c.* from a far. *Jer* 6:20

canker, -ed

will eat as doth a *c.* *2 Tim* 2:17*
your gold and silver is *c.* *Jas* 5:3*

cankerworm

c. eaten, and what *c.* left. *Joel* 1:4
2:25
like *c.* make thyself as *c.* *Nah* 3:15
the *c.* spoileth, and fleeth away. 16

cannot

calling of assemblies I *c.* *Isa* 1:13
read this, he saith, I *c.* for. 29:11
waves *c.* prevail, *c.* pass. *Jer* 5:22
c. I do with you as this potter ? 18:6
secret king demanded, *c.* *Dan* 2:27
c. ye discern the signs ? *Mat* 16:3
c. be that a prophet. *Luke* 13:33
pass from hence to you *c.* 16:26
of which we *c.* now speak. *Heb* 9:5

canst

c. not see my face and. *Ex* 33:20
itch, whereof thou *c.* *Deut* 28:27
if thou *c.* answer me, set. *Job* 33:5
Lord, if thou wilt, thou *c.* *Mat* 8:2
if thou *c.* do any thing. *Mark* 9:22
chief captain said, *c.* ? *Acts* 21:37

Capernaum

Nazareth, dwelt in *C.* *Mat* 4:13
Jesus was entered into *C.* 8:5
thou *C.* which art exalted. 11:23
Luke 10:15
they were come to *C.* *Mat* 17:24
they went into *C.* *Mark* 1:21; 2:1
have heard done in *C.* *Luke* 4:23
not many days in *C.* *John* 2:12
whose son was sick at *C.* 4:46
over the sea towards *C.* 6:17
people came to *C.* seeking. 24
things said he, as he taught in *C.* 59

Caphtor

remnant of country of *C.* *Jer* 47:4
the Philistines from *C.* *Amos* 9:7

Cappadocia

the dwellers in *C.* we hear. *Acts* 2:9
strangers scattered throughout *C.*
1 Pet 1:1

captain

A name applied, [1] *To the king, or prince of a people,* 1 Sam 9:16. [2] *To a general, or commander in an army,* Gen 26:26; 2 Sam 5:8. [3] *To the head of a family, or tribe,* Num 2:3. [4] *To such as have the command of a company,* Deut 1:15. [5] *Christ Jesus is called the Captain of salvation,* Heb 2:10.

Joseph to Potiphar, *c.* *Gen* 37:36
c. of the guard charged Joseph. 40:4
Nahshon, *c.* of children of. *Num* 2:3
Nethaneel, *c.* of the children of. 5
make a *c.* and return. 14:4
Neh 9:17
as *c.* of the host of the. *Josh* 5:14
the *c.* of the Lord's host. 15
c. of Jabin's host. *Judg* 4:2, 7
1 Sam 12:9
come and be our *c.* *Judg* 11:6
him head and *c.* over them. 11
anoint him *c.* over. *1 Sam* 9:16; 10:1
commanded him to be *c.* 13:14
these ten cheeses to the *c.* 17:18
and David became a *c.* 22:2
shalt feed, and be a *c.* *2 Sam* 5:2
be chief and *c.* 8; *1 Chr* 11:6
if thou be not *c.* of host. *2 Sam* 19:13
Abishai was therefore their *c.* 23:19
Israel made Omri, *c.* *1 Ki* 16:16
the king sent a *c.* with. *2 Ki* 1:9
sent to him another *c.* 11, 13
thou be spoken for to *c.* ? 4:13
Naaman, *c.* of the host of. 5:1
I have an errand to thee, O *c.* 9:5
Pekah, a *c.* of his, conspired. 15:25
turn away face of one *c.* 18:24
Isa 36:9
tell Hezekiah *c.* of my. *2 Ki* 20:5
Nebuzar-adan, *c.* of guard. 25:8
Jer 52:12
for he was their *c.* *1 Chr* 11:21
killed Shophach *c.* of. 19:18
2 Sam 10:18
the third *c.* Benaiah. *1 Chr* 27:5
fourth *c.* Asahel. 7
the fifth *c.* Shamhuth. 8
the sixth *c.* Ira. 9
God himself is our *c.* *2 Chr* 13:12
Lord doth take away *c.* *Isa* 3:3
a *c.* of the ward Irijah. *Jer* 37:13
c. of the guard took Jeremiah. 40:2
c. gave victuals and a reward. 5
call together, appoint a *c.* 51:27
band and the *c.* took. *John* 18:12
the *c.* with officers went. *Acts* 5:26
c. of their salvation. *Heb* 2:10

captains

chosen *c.* also are drowned. *Ex* 15:4
Moses was wroth with *c.* *Num* 31:14
I made wise men *c.* over. *Deut* 1:15
shall make *c.* of the army. 20:9
he will appoint him *c.* *1 Sam* 8:12
son of Jesse make you all *c.* 22:7
king gave all *c.* charge. *2 Sam* 18:5
sat in the seat chief among *c.* 23:8
what Joab did to the *c.* *1 Ki* 2:5
they were his princes, and *c.* 9:22
take kings away, and put *c.* 20:24
when *c.* perceived that he was not king of Israel. 22:23; *2 Chr* 18:32
Jehoiada commanded *c.* *2 Ki* 11:15
having for *c.* Pelatiah. *1 Chr* 4:42
now three of the 30 *c.* went. 11:15
of Naphtali a thousand *c.* 12:34
smote Edomites and *c.* *2 Chr* 21:9
Lord brought on them the *c.* 33:11
the king had sent *c.* of. *Neh* 2:9
the thunder of the *c.* *Job* 39:25
hast taught them to be *c.* *Jer* 13:21*
will I break in pieces *c.* 51:23
I will make drunk her *c.* 57
c. to open the mouth in. *Ezek* 21:22
c. and rulers all. 23:6, 12, 23
the *c.* saw these men. *Dan* 3:27
the *c.* have consulted to. 6:7
thy *c.* as the great. *Nah* 3:17
made supper to his *c.* *Mark* 6:21
communed with the *c.* *Luke* 22:4
may eat the flesh of *c.* *Rev* 19:18

captive

his brother was taken *c.* *Gen* 14:14
their wives took they *c.* 34:29
unto first-born of the *c.* *Ex* 12:29
hast taken them *c.* *Deut* 21:10
away *c.* a little maid. *2 Ki* 5:2
smite those thou hast taken *c.* 6:22
I am desolate, a *c.* and. *Isa* 49:21
or shall the lawful *c.* be ? 24
the *c.* exile hasteneth, that. 51:14
loose thyself, O *c.* daughter. 52:2
go *c.* with first that go *c.* *Amos* 6:7
who are taken *c.* by will. *2 Tim* 2:26

carry or *carried* **captive,** or **captives**

carried away daughters as *c.*
Gen 31:26
shall *carry* thee away *c.* *Num* 24:22
they *carry* them away *c.* *1 Ki* 8:46
2 Chr 6:36
if bethink in land whither they were *carried c.* *1 Ki* 8:47; *2 Chr* 6:37
carried them *c.* to. *2 Ki* 15:29
carried people of Damascus *c.* 16:9
king of Assyria *carried c.* *1 Chr* 5:6
other 10,000 did Judah *carry c.*
2 Chr 25:12
carried a great multitude *c.* 28:5
carried c. of their brethren. 8
that *carried* them *c.* *Ps* 106:46
that *carried* us *c.* required. 137:3
Lord's flock is *carried c.* *Jer* 13:17
Judah shall be *carried* away *c.* 19
carry them *c.* to Babylon. 20:4
them that are *carried c.* 24:5
took not when he *carried c.* 27:20
to all that are *carried c.* 29:4
bring you into place whence I caused you to be *carried* away *c.* 14
which were *carried c.* 40:1; 52:27
that were not *carried c.* 40:7
Ishmael *carried* away *c.* 41:10
shall *carry* the Egyptians *c.* 43:12
Nebuchadnezzar *carried c.* 52:29

carried away *c.* of the Jews. *Jer* 52:30
whither they be *carried c.* *Ezek* 6:9
and shall also *carry c.* *Dan* 11:8
because they *carried c.* *Amos* 1:6
that strangers *carried c.* *Ob* 11

carrying **captive**

carrying away of Jerusalem *c.* *Jer* 1:3

lead, or *led* **captive**

lead thy captivity *c.* thou. *Judg* 5:12
enemies who *led* them *c.* *1 Ki* 8:48
before them that *lead c.* *2 Chr* 30:9
hast *led* captivity *c.* *Ps* 68:18
Eph 4:8
whither they *led* him *c.* *Jer* 22:12
Israel shall be *led c.* out. *Amos* 7:11
led c. her maids shall *lead.* *Nah* 2:7
shall be *led* away *c.* *Luke* 21:24
lead c. silly women. *2 Tim* 3:6

captives

all women of Midian *c.* *Num* 31:9
they brought the *c.* 12
purify your *c.* 19
seest among the *c.* a. *Deut* 21:11
arrows drunk with blood of *c.* 32:42
two wives were taken *c.* *1 Sam* 30:5
from Jerusalem 10,000 *c.* *2 Ki* 24:14
me, and deliver the *c.* *2 Chr* 28:11
ye shall not bring in the *c.* hither. 13
take them *c.* whose *c.* *Isa* 14:2
lead away the Ethiopians *c.* 20:4
he shall let go my *c.* not for. 45:13
c. of the mighty shall be. 49:25
proclaim liberty to the *c.* 61:1
Luke 4:18
daughters are taken *c.* *Jer* 48:46
all that took them *c.* held. 50:33
I was among the *c.* by. *Ezek* 1:1
bring again captivity of thy *c.* 16:53
found a man of the *c.* *Dan* 2:25

captivity

(*The servitudes spoken of in Judges, and those under the Greeks and the Romans, are sometimes spoken of as* Captivities. *More exactly, however, the word is used of the carrying away of the people of Israel and of Judah into Babylonia and Assyria, when the kingdom of Israel was finally destroyed, and the kingdom of Judah lost its independence, Jerusalem and the Temple being destroyed.*
The word is also frequently used in the Bible in its ordinary sense of bondage or servitude without reference to any historical event)

his daughters into *c.* *Num* 21:29
put raiment of *c.* from. *Deut* 21:13
Lord will turn thy *c.* and have. 30:3
till the day of the *c.* *Judg* 18:30
carried into c. to Babylon. *2 Ki* 24:15
thirty-seventh year of the *c.* 25:27
Jer 52:31
in their steads until *c.* *1 Chr* 5:22
Jehozadak went into *c.* when. 6:15
pray to thee in land of *c.* *2 Chr* 6:37
return to thee in land of their *c.* 38
sons and our wives are in *c.* 29:9
have been delivered to *c.* *Ezra* 9:7
Jews which were left of *c.* *Neh* 1:2
them for a prey in land of *c.* 4:4
carried away with the *c.* *Esth* 2:6
Lord turned the *c.* of Job. *Job* 42:10
bringeth back the *c.* *Ps* 14:7; 85:1
delivereth his strength into *c.* 78:61
when Lord turned again *c.* 126:1
turn again our *c.* O Lord. 4
my people are gone into *c.* *Isa* 5:13
thee away with a mighty *c.* 22:17
themselves are gone into *c.* 46:2
for the *c.* to the *c.* *Jer* 15:2; 43:11
I will turn away your *c.* 29:14
30:3; 32:44; 33:7, 11, 26
hear ye, all ye of *c.* 29:20
a curse by all the *c.* of Judah. 22
this *c.* is long. 28
send to all them of the *c.* saying. 31
from the land of *c.* 30:10; 46:27
nor hath he gone into *c.* 48:11
Judah is gone into *c.* *Lam* 1:3
her children are gone into *c.* 5
to turn away thy *c.* *Lam* 2:14
no more carry thee into *c.* 4:22
fifth year of Jehoiachin's *c.* *Ezek* 1:2
get to them of the *c.* 3:11
I came to them of the *c.* 15; 11:24
I spake to them of the *c.* 11:25
as stuff for *c.* 12:7
bring again their *c.* the *c.* of Sodom, *c.* of Samaria. 16:53
when thou went into *c.* 25:3
in the twelfth year of the *c.* 33:21
house of Israel went into *c.* 39:23
five and twentieth year of *c.* 40:1
Daniel which is of the *c.* *Dan* 6:13
shall fall by *c.* and by spoil. 11:33
when I return the *c.* of. *Hos* 6:11
the *c.* of this host, the *c.* *Ob* 20
they are gone into *c.* *Mi* 1:16
she [No] went into *c.* *Nah* 3:10
shall gather *c.* as sand. *Hab* 1:9
shall turn away *c.* *Zeph* 2:7; 3:20
take of them of the *c.* *Zech* 6:10
and bringing me into *c.* *Rom* 7:23
bringing into *c.* every. *2 Cor* 10:5

see **captive**

bring **captivity**

bring up with them of *c.* *Ezra* 1:11
God *bringeth* back *c.* *Ps* 53:6
I will *bring* again the *c.* *Jer* 30:18
I shall *bring* again their *c.* 31:23
yet will I *bring* again the *c.* 48:47
I will *bring* again the *c.* of Ammon. 49:6
I will *bring* again the *c.* of Elam. 39
I will *bring* again the *c.* of Egypt. *Ezek* 29:14
now will I *bring* again the *c.* 39:25
when I *bring* again the *c.* *Joel* 3:1
I will *bring* again the *c.* of my people. *Amos* 9:14

children of **captivity**

heard that *children of c.* *Ezra* 4:1
the rest of *children of c.* 6:16
the *children of c.* kept passover. 19
killed passover for *children of c.* 20
proclamation to *children of c.* 10:7
the *children of c.* did so. 16
of *children of c.* of Judah. *Dan* 5:13

go into **captivity**

daughters shall *go into c.* *Deut* 28:41
thine house shall *go into c.* *Jer* 20:6
thy lovers shall *go into c.* 22:22
one of them shall *go into c.* 30:16
furnish thyself to *go into c.* 46:19
Chemosh shall *go into c.* 48:7
their kings *go into c.* 49:3
as they that *go into c.* *Ezek* 12:4
these cities shall *go into c.* 30:17
her daughters shall *go into c.* 18
Syria shall *go into c.* unto. *Amos* 1:5
their king shall *go into c.* 15
Gilgal shall surely *go into c.* 5:5
will I cause you to *go into c.* 27
Israel shall surely *go into c.* 7:17
and though they *go into c.* 9:4
half of city shall *go into c.* *Zech* 14:2
leadeth into *c. go into c.* *Rev* 13:10

out of **captivity**

these went up *out of c.* *Ezra* 2:1
Neh 7:6
up *out of c.* *Ezra* 3:8; *Neh* 8:17
children of Israel which were come again *out of c.* did eat. *Ezra* 6:21
were come *out of c.* offered. 8:35

carbuncle, -s

(*A precious stone of a red colour. Probably the red garnet*)

first row shall be a . *Ex* 28:17
39:10
I will make thy gates of *c.* *Isa* 54:12
topaz and *c.* were thy. *Ezek* 28:13

carcase

touch *c.* of unclean thing. *Lev* 5:2
c. ye shall not touch. 11:8
Deut 14:8
c. shall be meat unto. *Deut* 28:26
should take his *c.* down. *Josh* 8:29
see the *c.* of the lion, honey in *c.* *Judg* 14:8
thy *c.* shall not come to. *1 Ki* 13:22
c. cast in way, a lion stood by *c.* 24
the *c.* of Jezebel. *2 Ki* 9:37
cast out as a *c.* trodden. *Isa* 14:19
where the *c.* is, there. *Mat* 24:28

carcases

fowls came down on *c.* *Gen* 15:11
c. in abomination. *Lev* 11:11, 26
cast your *c.* on *c.* of your idols. 26:30
your *c.* shall fall in. *Num* 14:29
I will give the *c.* of. *1 Sam* 17:46
their *c.* were torn in midst. *Isa* 5:25
stink shall come up out of *c.* 34:3
look on *c.* of them that have. 66:24
c. of this people shall be meat for the. *Jer* 7:33; 16:4; 19:7
filled mine inheritance with *c.* 16:18
I will lay the *c.* of Israel. *Ezek* 6:5
my name no more defile by *c.* 43:7
put *c.* of their kings far from me. 9
there is a great number of *c.* *Nah* 3:3
grieved with them whose *c.* *Heb* 3:17

Carchemish

up to fight against *C.* *2 Chr* 35:20
is not Calno as *C.* ? *Isa* 10:9
river Euphrates in *C.* *Jer* 46:2

care

(*Formerly used in the sense of anxiety, especially the wearing, painful sense of anxiety. This is a common meaning of the word in the Bible, and in almost all such cases the Revised Version replaces it by a more modern term*)

father hath left the *c.* *1 Sam* 10:2
careful for us with all this *c.* *2 Ki* 4:13
nation that dwelleth without *c.* *Jer* 49:31
bread by weight with *c.* *Ezek* 4:16*
c. of this world chokes. *Mat* 13:22
he took *c.* of him. *Luke* 10:34
take *c.* of him. 35
doth God *c.* for oxen ? *1 Cor* 9:9*
should have the same *c.* one. 12:25
but that our *c.* for you. *2 Cor* 7:12
put the same earnest *c.* in. 8:16
besides *c.* of all churches. 11:28*
shall he take *c.* of church. *1 Tim* 3:5
casting your *c.* on him. *1 Pet* 5:7*

care, -ed

we flee, they will not *c.* *2 Sam* 18:3
no man *c.* for my soul. *Ps* 142:4
dost thou not *c.* that my? *Luke* 10:40
he said, not that he *c.* *John* 12:6
and Gallio *c.* for none. *Acts* 18:17
being a servant, *c.* not. *1 Cor* 7:21
who will naturally *c.* for. *Phil* 2:20

careful

behold thou hast been *c.* *2 Ki* 4:13
shall not be *c.* in year. *Jer* 17:8
O Nebuchadnezzar, we are not *c.* *Dan* 3:16*
Martha, thou art *c.* *Luke* 10:41
c. for nothing, but by. *Phil* 4:6
wherein ye were *c.* but lacked. 10*
c. to maintain good works. *Tit* 3:8

carefully

(*Revised Version,* diligently)

thou *c.* hearken unto. *Deut* 15:5
of Maroth waiteth *c.* *Mi* 1:12
I sent him the more *c.* *Phil* 2:28
though he sought it *c.* *Heb* 12:17

carefulness

drink water with trembling and *c.* *Ezek* 12:18
they shall eat their bread with *c.* 19
have you without *c.* *1 Cor* 7:32
c. it wrought in you. *2 Cor* 7:11

careless

saw how they dwelt *c.* *Judg* 18:7
hear my voice, ye *c.* *Isa* 32:9
shall be troubled ye *c.* women. 10
ye *c.* ones : strip you, and. 11
make *c.* Ethiopians afraid. *Ezek* 30:9

carelessly

now thou that dwellest *c.* *Isa* 47:8
among them that dwell *c.* *Ezek* 39:6
rejoicing city that dwelt *c.* *Zeph* 2:15

cares

c. of this world choke. *Mark* 4:19
they are choked with *c.* *Luke* 8:14
be overcharged with the *c.* 21:34

carest, -eth, -ing
which the Lord *c.* for. *Deut* 11:12
lest thy father leave *c.* *1 Sam* 9:5
thou art true, nor *c.* *Mat* 22:16
c. thou not that we perish? *Mark* 4:38
art true, and *c.* for no man. 12:14
because an hireling *c.* *John* 10:13
unmarried *c.* for things. *1 Cor* 7:32
married *c.* for things of. 33, 34
on him, for he *c.* for you. *1 Pet* 5:7

Carmel
C. and Ziph in the. *Josh* 15:55
Saul came to *C.* *1 Sam* 15:12
Nabal's possessions were in *C.* 25:2
all the while they were in *C.* 7
were come to Abigail to *C.* 40
all Israel to mount *C.* *1 Ki* 18:19
Elijah went up to top of *C.* 42
Elisha went to mount *C.* *2 Ki* 2:25
of Shunem came to mount *C.* 4:25
into forest of his *C.* 19:23; *Isa* 37:24
vine-dressers in *C.* *2 Chr* 26:10
thine head is like *C.* *S of S* 7:5
the excellency of *C.* *Isa* 35:2
and as *C.* by the sea. *Jer* 46:18
the top of *C.* shall wither. *Amos* 1:2
they hide in the top of *C.* 9:3
solitarily in the midst of *C.* *Mi* 7:14
see **Bashan**

Carmelite
wife of Nabal the *C.* *1 Sam* 30:5
2 Sam 2:2; 3:3
Hezrai the *C.* *2 Sam* 23:35

Carmi
C. son of Reuben. *Gen* 46:9
Achan the son of *C.* *Josh* 7:1, 18
1 Chr 2:7
sons of Judah, Hezron, *C.* *1 Chr* 4:1

carnal
(*Belonging to the flesh in distinction from the spirit. It does not necessarily infer sin, although when definitely contrasted with spirit it sometimes is so intended. It comes from the Latin* carnis, *flesh*)
spiritual, but I am *c.* *Rom* 7:14
the *c.* mind is enmity against. 8:7*
duty to minister to them in *c.* 15:27
as unto *c.* even to babes. *1 Cor* 3:1
for ye are yet *c.* 3
are ye not *c.*? 4*
thing if we reap *c.* things? 9:11
of our warfare not *c.* *2 Cor* 10:4*
not after the law of a *c.* *Heb* 7:16
which stood in *c.* ordinances. 9:10

carnally
shalt not lie *c.* with thy. *Lev* 18:20
lieth *c.* with a bond-maid. 19:20
a man lie with her *c.* *Num* 5:13
for to be *c.* minded is. *Rom* 8:6*

carpenter, -s
sent *c.* to David. *2 Sam* 5:11
1 Chr 14:1
they laid it out to *c.* *2 Ki* 12:11
hired *c.* to repair. *2 Chr* 24:12
Ezra 3:7
c. encouraged goldsmith. *Isa* 41:7
c. stretcheth out his rule. 44:13
c. and smiths he carried away. *Jer* 24:1*; 29:2*
Lord shewed me four *c.* *Zech* 1:20*
s not this the *c.* son? *Mat* 13:55
s not this the *c.* the son? *Mark* 6:3

Carpus
loke that I left with *C.* *2 Tim* 4:13

carriage, -s
(*This word means things carried, r burdens, not vehicles, and is o put in Revisions*)
he Danites, and the *c.* *Judg* 18:21*
eft *c.* with keeper of *c.* *1 Sam* 17:22
e hath laid up his *c.* at. *Isa* 10:28
our *c.* were heavy laden. 46:1
e took up our *c.* went. *Acts* 21:15

carried
ons of Israel *c.* Jacob. *Gen* 46:5
50:13
c. them in their coats. *Lev* 10:5
they *c.* the stones over. *Josh* 4:8
he *c.* them up to top of. *Judg* 16:3
let ark of God be *c.* *1 Sam* 5:8
David *c.* the ark aside. *2 Sam* 6:10
1 Chr 13:13
Abiathar *c.* ark of God. *2 Sam* 15:29
he *c.* him into a loft. *1 Ki* 17:19
they *c.* Naboth forth and. 21:13
and *c.* thence silver and. *2 Ki* 7:8
c. him in a chariot. 9:28; 23:30
laid up in store shall be *c.* to Babylon. 20:17; *Isa* 39:6
c. the ashes of the vessels. *2 Ki* 23:4
he *c.* out thence all the. 24:13
bound Zedekiah and *c.* him. 25:7
c. the chest to his. *2 Chr* 24:11
and *c.* all the feeble of them. 28:15
who took and *c.* Manasseh. 33:11
Shaphan *c.* the book to. 34:16
Necho took and *c.* Jehoahaz. 36:4
of the froward is *c.* *Job* 5:13
I should have been *c.* from. 10:19
the mountains be *c.* into. *Ps* 46:2
remnant which are *c.* from. *Isa* 46:3
thy daughters shall be *c.* on. 49:22
borne our griefs, *c.* our. 53:4
he bare and *c.* them all. 63:9
c. into Babylon. *Jer* 27:22; 28:3
52:11, 17
he *c.* twigs into a. *Ezek* 17:4
and *c.* me out in the Spirit. 37:1
which he *c.* into land. *Dan* 1:2
be also *c.* into Assyria. *Hos* 10:6
make a covenant, and oil is *c.* 12:1
and ye have *c.* into your. *Joel* 3:5
was a dead man *c.* out. *Luke* 7:12
and beggar was *c.* by angels. 16:22
parted from them, and *c.* up. 24:51
lame from his mother's womb was *c.* *Acts* 3:2
young men *c.* Ananias out. 5:6
our fathers were *c.* over into. 7:16
devout men *c.* Stephen to. 8:2
commanded him to be *c.* 21:34
c. about with every wind. *Eph* 4:14
be not *c.* about with. *Heb* 13:9
clouds that are *c.* with. *2 Pet* 2:17
clouds without water, *c.* *Jude* 12
see **captive**

carried *away*
Jacob *c.* *away* all his. *Gen* 31:18
hath *c.* *away* my daughters. 26
but *c.* them *away*. *1 Sam* 30:2, 18
c. Israel *away*. *2 Ki* 17:6, 23
heathen whom Lord *c.* *away*. 11
one whom they had *c.* *away*. 28
c. *away* all Jerusalem. 24:14
c. *away* Jehoiachin to Babylon. 15
so Judah was *c.* *away*. 25:21
Tilgath-pilneser *c.* *away*. *1 Chr* 5:26
when the Lord *c.* *away* Judah. 6:15
who were *c.* *away* for their. 9:1
Shishak *c.* *away* the. *2 Chr* 12:9
c. *away* much spoil. 14:13
21:17
they *c.* *away* sheep and camels. 14:15
these that had been *c.* *away*. *Ezra* 2:1
Neh 7:6
that had been *c.* *away*. *Ezra* 9:4; 10:6
congregation of those *c.* *away*. 10:8
upon camels, *c.* them *away*. *Job* 1:17
to be *c.* *away* captive. *Jer* 29:4
and winds *c.* them *away*. *Dan* 2:35
No was *c.* *away* into. *Nah* 3:10
time they were *c.* *away*. *Mat* 1:11
c. Jesus *away* and. *Mark* 15:1
were Gentiles *c.* *away*. *1 Cor* 12:2
Barnabas was *c.* *away*. *Gal* 2:13
cause her to be *c.* *away*. *Rev* 12:15
c. me *away* in Spirit. 17:3; 21:10

carriest, -eth, -ing
one *c.* three kids, *c.* *1 Sam* 10:3
chaff that storm *c.* away. *Job* 21:18
east-wind *c.* rich man away. 27:21
Ephraim *c.* bows. *Ps* 78:9
thou *c.* them away as with. 90:5
c. into Babylon, from the *c.* *Mat* 1:17
they *c.* her and buried. *Acts* 5:10
mystery of beast that *c.* *Rev* 17:7

carry
Ishmaelites going to *c.* *Gen* 37:25
go ye, *c.* corn for the famine. 42:19
c. the man a present. 43:11
the money brought, *c.* 12
as much as they can *c.* 44:1
wagons Joseph sent to *c.* him. 45:27
46:5
c. up my bones. 50:25; *Ex* 13:19
presence go not, *c.* us not. *Ex* 33:15
c. your brethren out of. *Lev* 10:4
c. them in thy bosom. *Num* 11:12
thou art not able to *c.* it. *Deut* 14:24
c. the twelve stones over. *Josh* 4:3
c. these ten cheeses. *1 Sam* 17:18
Jonathan said, go *c.* them. 20:40
a ferry-boat to *c.* over. *2 Sam* 19:18
Spirit of the Lord shall *c.* *1 Ki* 18:12
his father said, *c.* him. *2 Ki* 4:19
c. Jehu to an inner chamber. 9:2
c. thither one of the priests. 17:27
sent to Philistines to *c.* *1 Chr* 10:9
none ought to *c.* the ark but. 15:2
the Levites shall no more *c.* 23:26
thou shalt *c.* the wood. *2 Chr* 2:16
c. him to Babylon. 36:6; *Jer* 39:7
c. vessels into temple. *Ezra* 5:15
c. the silver and gold freely. 7:15
bird of the air shall *c.* *Eccl* 10:20
her own feet shall *c.* her. *Isa* 23:7
they will *c.* their riches on. 30:6
c. the lambs in his bosom. 40:11
even to hoary hairs will I *c.* you. 46:4
they *c.* him and set him in. 7
will I take them and *c.* *Jer* 20:5
should *c.* Jeremiah home. 39:14
in thee are men *c.* tales. *Ezek* 22:9
and began to *c.* about. *Mark* 6:55
not suffer any to *c.* a vessel. 11:16
c. neither purse, nor. *Luke* 10:4
not lawful for thee to *c.* *John* 5:10
and *c.* thee whither thou. 21:18

carry *away*
Assyria did *c.* *away*. *2 Ki* 18:11
did Nebuzar-adan *c.* *away*. 25:11
than they could *c.* *away*. *2 Chr* 20:25
heart *c.* thee *away*? *Job* 15:12
dieth he shall *c.* nothing *away*. *Ps* 49:17
which he may *c.* *away*. *Eccl* 5:15
c. the prey *away* safe. *Isa* 5:29
laid up, shall they *c.* *away*. 15:7
the Lord will *c.* thee *away*. 22:17
wind *c.* them *away*. 41:16; 57:13
no more *c.* thee *away*. *Lam* 4:22
come to *c.* *away* silver? *Ezek* 38:13
and I will *c.* you *away*. *Acts* 7:43
see **captive**

carry *back*
c. *back* the ark of God. *2 Sam* 15:25
c. Micaiah *back*. *1 Ki* 22:26
2 Chr 18:25

carry *forth*
shalt not *c.* *forth* aught. *Ex* 12:46
thus with us to *c.* us *forth*. 14:11
bullock shall he *c.* *forth*. *Lev* 4:12, 21
c. *forth* ashes without camp. 6:11
14:45; 16:27
c. *forth* filthiness out. *2 Chr* 29:5
nor *c.* *forth* a burden on. *Jer* 17:22
c. it *forth* in twilight. *Ezek* 12:6

carry *out*
shalt *c.* me *out* of Egypt. *Gen* 47:30
shall *c.* much seed *out*. *Deut* 28:38
then *c.* him *out* and. *1 Ki* 21:10
c. me *out* of the host. 22:34
2 Chr 18:33
c. it *out* abroad into. *2 Chr* 29:16
and *c.* *out* thereby. *Ezek* 12:5
and shall *c.* thee *out*. *Acts* 5:9
we can *c.* nothing *out*. *1 Tim* 6:7

cart
new *c.* and tie kine to *c.* *1 Sam* 6:7
set ark on a new *c.* *2 Sam* 6:3
and Ahio drave the *c.* *1 Chr* 13:7
corn with wheel of *c.* *Isa* 28:28
as a *c.* is pressed that is. *Amos* 2:13

cart rope
draw sin as with a *c.* *rope*. *Isa* 5:18

cart wheel
nor is *c.* *wheel* turned. *Isa* 28:27

carved, -ing, -ings
c. of timber. *Ex* 31:5; 35:33
fetched the c. image. *Judg* 18:18*
of house within was c. *1 Ki* 6:18
he c. all the walls of house. 29, 32
he set a c. image in. *2 Chr* 33:7*
Amon sacrificed to c. images. 22*
purged Judah from c. images. 34:3*
he cut down the c. images. 4
they break down the c. *Ps* 74:6
decked bed with c. work. *Pr* 7:16*

case, -s
that they were in evil c. *Ex* 5:19
is the c. of the slayer. *Deut* 19:4
thou shalt in any c. bring. 22:1
in any c. thou shalt deliver. 24:13
happy people in such a c. *Ps* 144:15
ye shall in no c. enter. *Mat* 5:20*
if the c. of the man be so. 19:10
been long time in that c. *John* 5:6
under bondage in such c. *1 Cor* 7:15

casement
I looked through my c. *Pr* 7:6*

Casiphia
chief at the place C. *Ezra* 8:17

cassia
(*A sweet spice, called in Hebrew* Kiddah, Ex 30:21. *This aromatic is said to be the bark of a tree very like cinnamon, and grows in the* Indies *without cultivation*)
take of c. 500 shekels. *Ex* 30:24
smell of aloes and c. *Ps* 45:8
c. and calamus were. *Ezek* 27:19

cast
about a stone's c. *Luke* 22:41

cast
[1] *To fling, or throw,* Dan 3:6. [2] *To miscarry,* Gen 31:38, Ex 23:26. [3] *To melt, make, or frame,* Ex 25:12.
c. the child under a. *Gen* 21:15
she-goats have not c. their. 31:38
let us slay him, and c. him. 37:20
his master's wife c. her eyes. 39:7
every son ye shall c. *Ex* 1:22
said, c. it, and he c. the rod. 4:3
Zipporah c. the foreskin at. 25
took locusts and c. them. 10:19
Pharaoh's chariots he c. 15:4
c. the tree into the waters. 25
not eat flesh torn of beasts, c. 22:31
shall nothing c. their young. 23:26
c. four rings of. 25:12; 37:3, 13; 38:5
Moses c. tables out of his. 32:19
I c. into the fire, there came. 24
talents of the silver were c. 38:27
priest c. cedar wood. *Num* 19:6
c. any thing on him without. 35:22
seeing him not, and c. it. 23
the Lord c. them into. *Deut* 29:28
c. king of Ai at the gate. *Josh* 8:29
c. them into the cave wherein. 10:27
c. every one ear-rings. *Judg* 8:25
c. piece of millstone. 9:53; *2 Sam* 11:21
c. the javelin. *1 Sam* 18:11; 20:33
Shimei c. stones at. *2 Sam* 16:6
threw stones and c. dust. 13
c. Absalom into a great pit. 18:17
Joab's man c. a cloth upon. 20:12
in plain of Jordan c. *1 Ki* 7:46; *2 Chr* 4:17
thou hast c. me behind. *1 Ki* 14:9
Elijah c. mantle upon Elisha. 19:19
lest the Spirit c. him. *2 Ki* 2:16
went to spring and c. salt in. 21
every good piece of land c. 3:25
then bring meal, and he c. it. 4:41
he c. in the stick. 6:6
c. him in portion of field. 9:25, 26
c. the man into the. 13:21
neither c. he them from. 23
c. their gods into. 19:18; *Isa* 37:19
nor c. a bank. *2 Ki* 19:32; *Isa* 37:33
c. thy law behind their. *Neh* 9:26
they c. Pur, that is. *Esth* 3:7
Haman had c. Pur, that is. 9:24
for he is c. into a net. *Job* 18:8
God shall c. the fury of his. 20:23
God shall c. upon him, and. 27:22
hath c. me into the mire. *Job* 30:19
c. abroad the rage of thy. 40:11
I was c. upon thee from. *Ps* 22:10
they c. iniquity on me. 55:3
c. thy burden on the Lord. 22
they have c. fire into sanctuary. 74:7
chariot and horse are c. into. 76:6
he c. on them the fierceness. 78:49
let him be c. into the fire. 140:10
c. in thy lot among us. *Pr* 1:14
the lot is c. into the lap. 16:33
c. thy bread on the. *Eccl* 11:1
a man shall c. his idols. *Isa* 2:20
the face of the covering c. 25:7
thou hast c. all my sins. 38:17
are c. into a land which. *Jer* 22:28
c. Urijah's body into the. 26:23
c. it into the fire that was. 36:23
c. Jeremiah into dungeon. 38:6, 9
took thence old c. clouts and. 11
put now these old c. clouts under. 12
Ishmael slew, and c. them. 41:7
cut off my life, and c. *Lam* 3:53
they shall c. their silver. *Ezek* 7:19
although I have c. them far. 11:16
the vine-tree is c. into the. 15:4
because thou hast c. me. 23:35
I will c. thee to the ground. 28:17
be c. into the midst of a. *Dan* 3:6
to c. them into the fiery furnace. 20
these were c. into the midst of. 21
did not we c. three men bound? 24
be c. into the den of lions. 6:7, 16
c. them into the den of lions. 24
for thou hadst c. me. *Jonah* 2:3
then I said, I am c. out of. 4
I will make her c. off. *Mi* 4:7
wilt c. all their sins into. 7:19
will c. abominable filth on. *Nah* 3:6
c. it into the ephah, c. the. *Zech* 5:8
c. it to the potter, c. them. 11:13
nor vine c. her fruit. *Mal* 3:11
down, c. into the fire. *Mat* 3:10; 7:19; *Luke* 3:9
John was c. into prison. *Mat* 4:12
deliver thee to judge, be c. 5:25
and c. it from thee. 29, 30; 18:8, 9
to-morrow is c. into oven. 6:30; *Luke* 12:28
nor c. your pearls before. *Mat* 7:6
children's bread, and c. it to. 15:26; *Mark* 7:27
c. an hook, and take up. *Mat* 17:27
c. him into prison, till he pay. 18:30
be thou c. into the sea. 21:21
c. him into outer. 22:13; 25:30
the thieves c. the same in. 27:44
oft-times it hath c. him. *Mark* 9:22
he were c. into sea. 42; *Luke* 17:2
two eyes, feet, c. *Mark* 9:45, 47
c. their garments on him. 11:7; *Luke* 19:35
at him they c. stones. *Mark* 12:4
c. money into the. 41; *Luke* 21:4
widow hath c. more. *Mark* 12:43, 44
power to c. into hell. *Luke* 12:5
thy enemies shall c. a trench. 19:43
for murder c. into prison. 23:19, 25
for John was not yet c. *John* 3:24
let him first c. a stone at her. 8:7
Peter did c. himself into sea. 21:7
c. thy garment about. *Acts* 12:8
c. Paul and Silas into prison. 16:23
we must be c. on a certain. 27:26
who could swim c. themselves. 43
not that I may c. snare. *1 Cor* 7:35
devil should c. some of. *Rev* 2:10
who taught Balak to c. 14
I will c. her into a bed, and. 22
the elders c. their crowns. 4:10
hail and fire were c. on the. 8:7
a mountain burning was c. into. 8
dragon saw that he was c. 12:13
like a mill-stone and c. it. 18:21
these both were c. alive into. 19:20
the devil was c. into lake. 20:10
death and hell were c. into. 14
not found in the book of life, c. 15

cast *away*
I will not c. them *away*. *Lev* 26:44*
c. *away* the jaw-bone. *Judg* 15:17
of the mighty is c. *away*. *2 Sam* 1:21
Syrians had c. *away* in. *2 Ki* 7:15
Ahaz did c. *away*. *2 Chr* 29:19
have c. them *away* for. *Job* 8:4*
behold God will not c. *away* a. 20
let us c. *away* their cords. *Ps* 2:3
c. me not *away* from thy. 51:11
time to c. *away* stones. *Eccl* 3:5, 6
have c. *away* the law. *Isa* 5:24*
shall c. them *away* as a. 30:22
every man shall c. *away* his. 31:7
thee, and not c. thee *away*. 41:9
cut off hair, and c. it *away*. *Jer* 7:29
I c. *away* the seed of Jacob. 33:26
c. *away* from you all. *Ezek* 18:31
c. *away* abominations of his. 20:7
they did not c. *away* the. 8
my God will c. them *away*. *Hos* 9:17
but c. the bad *away*. *Mat* 13:48
or be c. *away*. *Luke* 9:25
hath God c. *away* his. *Rom* 11:1
God hath not c. *away* his people. 2
c. not *away* your confidence. *Heb* 10:35

cast *down*
Aaron c. *down* his rod. *Ex* 7:10
they c. *down*. 12
c. *down* great stones. *Josh* 10:11
altar of Baal was c. *down*. *Judg* 6:28
Elijah c. himself *down*. *1 Ki* 18:42
to help and c. *down*. *2 Chr* 25:8
and c. them *down* from the top. 12
they were c. *down* in. *Neh* 6:16
own counsel c. him *down*. *Job* 18:7
when men are c. *down*. 22:29
countenance c. not *down*. 29:24
shall not one be c. *down*? 41:9
disappoint him, c. him *down*. *Ps* 17:13
they are c. *down* and shall. 36:12
bent their bow to c. *down*. 37:14
shall not be utterly c. *down*. 24
art thou c. *down*? 42:5, 11; 43:5
O my God, my soul is c. *down*. 42:6
in anger c. *down* the people. 56:7
consult to c. him *down* from. 62:4
thou hast c. his throne *down*. 89:44
me up, and c. me *down*. 102:10
for she hath c. *down*. *Pr* 7:26
the Lord shall c. *down*. *Isa* 28:2
they shall be c. *down*. *Jer* 6:15; 8:12
c. *down* to the earth the. *Lam* 2:1
I will c. *down* your slain. *Ezek* 6:4
thy mother was c. *down* to. 19:12
c. the Assyrian *down* to hell. 31:16
for Egypt, and c. her *down*. 32:18
the thrones were c. *down*. *Dan* 7:9*
the he-goat c. *down* the ram. 8:7
c. *down* some of the host. 10
sanctuary was c. *down*. 11
c. *down* truth to the ground. 12
he shall c. *down* many. 11:12
c. thyself *down*. *Mat* 4:6; *Luke* 4:9
c. them *down* at Jesus' feet. *Mat* 15:30
he c. *down* the pieces of silver. 27:5
might c. Jesus *down*. *Luke* 4:29
we are c. *down*. *2 Cor* 4:9
comforteth those are c. *down*. 7:6
but c. the angels *down*. *2 Pet* 2:4
of brethren is c. *down*. *Rev* 12:10

cast *forth*
c. *forth* household stuff. *Neh* 13:8
c. *forth* lightning. *Ps* 144:6
Jehoiakim c. *forth*. *Jer* 22:19
I will c. thee *forth*. *Ezek* 32:4
shall c. *forth* his roots. *Hos* 14:5
mariners c. *forth* the. *Jonah* 1:5
c. me *forth* into the sea. 12
took Jonah and c. him *forth*. 15
would c. *forth* devil. *Mark* 7:26
c. *forth* as a branch. *John* 15:6

cast *lots*
Aaron shall c. *lots*. *Lev* 16:8
Joshua c. *lots*. *Josh* 18:10
c. *lots* between me. *1 Sam* 14:42
c. *lots* as well small as. *1 Chr* 26:13
they c. *lots* upon my vesture. *Ps* 22:18; *Mat* 27:35; *John* 19:24
hath c. the *lot* for them. *Isa* 34:1
c. *lots* for my people. *Joel* 3:
c. *lots* upon Jerusalem. *Ob* 1
come and let us c. *lots*. *Jonah* 1:
and they c. *lots* for her. *Nah* 3:1

cast *off*
I will c. off this city. 2 Ki 23:27
he will c. thee off for. 1 Chr 28:9
Jeroboam had c. them off.
2 Chr 11:14
shall c. off his flower. Job 15:33
dost thou c. me off ? Ps 43:2
thou hast c. off. 44:9; 60:1, 10
89:38; 108:11
O Lord, c. us not off for ever. 44:23
c. me not off in the time of. 71:9
hast thou c. us off for ever ? 74:1
will the Lord c. off for ever ? 77:7
not c. off his people. 94:14
Lam 3:31
I will c. Hananiah off. Jer 28:16
c. off seed of Israel. 31:37; 33:24
hath c. off his altar. Lam 2:7
Israel hath c. off the thing. Hos 8:3
calf, O Samaria, hath c. thee off. 5
Edom did c. off all pity. Amos 1:11
I had not c. them off. Zech 10:6
they cried and c. off. Acts 22:23
let us c. off works of. Rom 13:12
c. off their first faith. 1 Tim 5:12*

cast *out*
c. out this bondwoman. Gen 21:10
I will c. out the nations. Ex 34:24
nations are defiled which I c. out.
Lev 18:24; 20:23; Deut 7:1
I c. the two tables out. Deut 9:17
Moses smite, and c. out. Josh 13:12
c. out Sheba's head to. 2 Sam 20:22
house will I c. out. 1 Ki 9:7
2 Chr 7:20
Amorites, whom the Lord c. out.
1 Ki 21:26; 2 Ki 16:3
the captains c. them out. 2 Ki 10:25
till he had c. them out. 17:20; 24:20
have ye not c. out priests ? 2 Chr 13:9
to come to c. us out of. 20:11
they were of you c. out. Neh 1:9
God shall c. them out of. Job 20:15
bow themselves, they c. out. 39:3
c. them out in their. Ps 5:10
I did c. them out as dirt. 18:42
afflict people and c. them out. 44:2
over Edom will I c. out. 60:8; 108:9
c. out the heathen. 78:55; 80:8
c. out scorner, contention go out.
Pr 22:10
art c. out of thy grave. Isa 14:19
as a wandering bird c. out of. 16:2
earth shall c. out the dead. 26:19
their slain also be c. out. 34:3
bring poor that are c. out. 58:7
brethren that c. you out for. 66:5
c. you out of my sight, as I have c.
out. Jer 7:15
our dwellings have c. us out. 9:19
c. them out of my sight. 15:1
23:39; 52:3
will I c. you out of this land. 16:13
I will c. thee out, and thy. 22:26
his dead body shall be c. out. 36:30
Nebuchadnezzar hath c. me out.
51:34
but thou wast c. out in. Ezek 16:5
will c. thee as profane out. 28:16
and shall be c. out. Amos 8:8
ny people have ye c. out. Mi 2:9
Lord hath c. out thine. Zeph 3:15
o c. out the horns of. Zech 1:21
he Lord will c. her out. 9:4
ınsavoury to be c. out. Mat 5:13
Luke 14:35
ırst c. out the beam. Mat 7:5
Luke 6:42
n thy name c. out devils ? Mat 7:22
f the kingdom be c. out. 8:12
nd he c. out the spirits with. 16
thou c. us out, suffer us to. 31
hen the devil was c. out. 9:33
gainst spirits to c. them out. 10:1
aise the dead, c. out devils. 8
ot c. out devils. 12:24; Luke 11:18
Satan c. out Satan. Mat 12:26
ıe Spirit of God c. out devils. 28
ıto belly, and is c. out. 15:17
ould not we c. him out ? 17:19
Mark 9:28
out all that sold. Mat 21:12
Mark 11:15; Luke 19:45

c. him out of vineyard. Mat 21:39
Mark 12:8; Luke 20:15
and c. out many devils. Mark 1:34
39; 6:13
power to heal and c. out devils. 3:15
how can Satan c. out Satan ? 23
out of whom he had c. seven. 16:9
in my name shall they c. out. 17
c. out your name as evil. Luke 6:22
if I with finger of God c. out. 11:20
I c. out devils, and do cures. 13:32
wounded him also and c. him out.
20:12
I will in no wise c. out. John 6:37
and they c. him out. 9:34
prince of this world be c. out. 12:31
c. out their young. Acts 7:19
Moses was c. out Pharaoh's. 21
they c. Stephen out of the city. 58
third day we c. out the. 27:19
c. four anchors out. 29
c. out wheat into the sea. 38
c. out the bondwoman. Gal 4:30
great dragon was c. out. Rev 12:9
serpent c. out of his mouth. 15, 16

Lord **cast** *out*
which the Lord c. out. 1 Ki 14:24
2 Ki 16:3; 2 Chr 28:3; 33:2
Lord c. out before. 2 Ki 17:8; 21:2
the Lord will c. her out. Zech 9:4

cast *up*
they c. up a bank. 2 Sam 20:15
c. ye up, prepare. Isa 57:14; 62:10
sea, whose waters c. up. 57:20
in a way not c. up. Jer 18:15
c. her up as heaps. 50:26
c. up dust. Lam 2:10; Ezek 27:30
king of north shall c. up. Dan 11:15

castaway
I myself should be a c. 1 Cor 9:27*

castest, -eth
yea, thou c. off fear and. Job 15:14
thy cow calveth and c. not. 21:10
seeing thou c. my words. Ps 50:17
thou c. them down into. 73:18
why c. thou off my soul ? 88:14
the Lord c. the wicked down. 147:6
he c. forth his ice like morsels. 17
he c. away the substance. Pr 10:3
slothfulness c. into a deep. 19:15
c. down the strength of the. 21:22
as a madman c. fire-brands. 26:18
as a fountain so she c. Jer 6:7
c. out devils. Mat 9:34; Mark 3:22
Luke 11:15
but perfect love c. fear. 1 John 4:18
c. them out of church. 3 John 10
fig-tree c. untimely figs. Rev 6:13

casting
he smote Moab, c. 2 Sam 8:2
all of them had one c. 1 Ki 7:37
weeping and c. himself. Ezra 10:1
ye see my c. down and. Job 6:21
by c. down dwelling place. Ps 74:7
profaned his crown by c. it. 89:39
thy c. down shall be in. Mi 6:14
c. a net into the sea. Mat 4:18
parted his garments, c. lots. 27:35
Mark 15:24
saw one c. out devils. Mark 9:38
Luke 9:49
he saw the rich men c. Luke 21:1
also a poor widow c. in two mites. 2
if c. away of them be. Rom 11:15
c. down imaginations. 2 Cor 10:5
c. all your care upon him. 1 Pet 5:7

castle
David took c. of Zion. 1 Chr 11:5*
David dwelt in c. the city of. 7*
are like bars of a c. Pr 18:19
Paul to be carried into c. Acts 21:34
37; 22:24; 23:10
into the c. and told Paul. 23:16

castles
of Ishmael's sons by their c.
Gen 25:16*
burnt their goodly c. Num 31:10
these the priests' c. in. 1 Chr 6:54*
over treasures, and in c. 27:25
Jehoshaphat built c. in. 2 Chr 17:12
Jotham in the forest built c. 27:4

castor, *see* **sign**

catch
fire break out and c. Ex 22:6
c. you every man his. Judg 21:21
men did hastily c. it. 1 Ki 20:33
we shall c. them alive. 2 Ki 7:12
wait to c. poor, he doth c. Ps 10:9
let his net that he hath hid c. 35:8
let the extortioner c. all. 109:11
set a trap, they c. men. Jer 5:26
learned to c. the prey. Ezek 19:3, 6
c. them in their net and. Hab 1:15
send Herodians to c. Mark 12:13
thou shalt c. men. Luke 5:10
seeking to c. something. 11:54

catcheth, -ing
who c. any beast or. Lev 17:13
the devil c. away. Mat 13:19
wolf c. and scattereth. John 10:12

caterpiller, -s
if there be any c. 1 Ki 8:37
2 Chr 6:28
gave their increase to c. Ps 78:46
he spake, and c. came. 105:34
spoil like gathering of c. Isa 33:4
thee with men as with c. Jer 51:14
horses come up as the rough c. 27
worm left, hath c. eaten. Joel 1:4
restore the years the c. hath. 2:25

cattle
(*This word is sometimes used for sheep, etc., and is then translated in the Revised Version by* flock *or* flocks)
God made the c. after. Gen 1:25
thou art cursed above all c. 3:14
died, both of fowl and c. 7:21
God remembered Noah, and c. 8:1
establish covenant with fowls, c. 9:10
Abram was very rich in c. 13:2
put them not to Laban's c. 30:40
God hath taken away the c. 31:9
these c. are my c. all. 43
his sons were with the c. 34:5
trade hath been to feed c. 46:32
make them rulers over my c. 47:6
gave bread in exchange for c. 17
sever between c. of Israel and c.
Ex 9:4
made his servants and c. flee. 20
smote all first-born of c. 12:29
bring your offering of c. Lev 1:2
take c. of the Levites. Num 3:41
if I and my c. drink, I will. 20:19
land for c. thy servants have c. 32:4
c. we took for a. Deut 2:35; 3:7
c. shall ye take for a prey. Josh 8:2
only c. Israel took. 27; 11:14
slew oxen and c. 1 Ki 1:9, 19, 25
the c. also concerning the. Job 36:33
c. upon a thousand hills. Ps 50:10
causeth grass to grow for c. 104:14
beasts and all c. praise. 148:10
of great and small c. Eccl 2:7
for treading of lesser c. Isa 7:25
hast not brought small c. 43:23
idols were upon beasts and c. 46:1
hear the voice of the c. Jer 9:10
between c. and c. Ezek 34:17, 20, 22
drought upon land and c. Hag 1:11
multitude of men and c. Zech 2:4
men taught me to keep c. 13:5
servant feeding c. will. Luke 17:7
children drank, and his c. John 4:12

much **cattle**
and had much c. Gen 30:43
of Egypt with much c. Ex 12:38
I know ye have much c. Deut 3:19
return with very much c. Josh 22:8
Uzziah had much c. 2 Chr 26:10
wherein is much c. Jonah 4:11

our **cattle**
our c. also shall go. Ex 10:26
our children, and our c. 17:3
that we and our c. Num 20:4
build sheepfolds for our c. 32:16
all our c. shall be there. 26
with suburbs for our c. Josh 21:2
over our bodies and our c. Neh 9:37
first-born of our sons and our c.
10:36

their **cattle**
shall not their c. and. Gen 34:23

took spoil of *their c.* *Num* 31:9
for *their c.* 35:3; *Josh* 14:4
Midianites came up with *their c.* *Judg* 6:5
brought away *their c.* *1 Sam* 23:5
because *their c.* were. *1 Chr* 5:9
down to take away *their c.* 7:21
he gave up *their c.* also. *Ps* 78:48
he suffered not *their c.* to. 107:38
camels a booty, *their c.* *Jer* 49:32

thy cattle

knowest how *thy c.* was. *Gen* 30:29
thee six years for *thy c.* 31:41
of the Lord is on *thy c.* *Ex* 9:3
send now and gather *thy c.* 19
servant nor *thy c.* do any. 20:10
Deut 5:14
firstling among *thy c.* is. *Ex* 34:19
let not *thy c.* gender. *Lev* 19:19
the land meat for *thy c.* 25:7
grass in fields for *thy c.* *Deut* 11:15
be the fruit of *thy c.* 28:4, 11; 30:9
shall eat the fruit of *thy c.* 28:51
day shall *thy c.* feed. *Isa* 30:23

your cattle

give *your c.*; and I will give you for *your c.* *Gen* 47:16
will destroy *your c.* *Lev* 26:22
your c. shall abide in. *Deut* 3:19
Josh 1:14
be barren among *your c.* *Deut* 7:14
drink, both ye and *your c.* *2 Ki* 3:17

caught

behind him a ram *c.* by. *Gen* 22:13
she *c.* him by garment. 39:12
put forth his hand, and *c.* *Ex* 4:4
the men of war had *c.* *Num* 31:32
c. Adoni-bezek, and cut. *Judg* 1:6
c. a young man of the men. 8:14
Samson went and *c.* 300. 15:4
took wives whom they *c.* 21:23
I *c.* him by his beard. *1 Sam* 17:35
and they *c.* every one. *2 Sam* 2:16
Absalom's head *c.* hold of. 18:9
and Adonijah *c.* hold. *1 Ki* 1:50
Joab *c.* hold on the horns of. 2:28
Ahijah *c.* the new garment. 11:30
the Shunammite *c.* Elisha. *2 Ki* 4:27
they *c.* Ahaziah and. *2 Chr* 22:9
so she *c.* him, and kissed. *Pr* 7:13
thou art found and also *c.* *Jer* 50:24
Jesus *c.* Peter, and said. *Mat* 14:31
the husbandmen *c.* him. 21:39
they *c.* the servant and. *Mark* 12:3
oftentimes it *c.* him. *Luke* 8:29
that night *c.* nothing. *John* 21:3
came upon Stephen and *c.* *Acts* 6:12
Spirit of the Lord *c.* away. 8:39
they *c.* Paul and Silas. 16:19
for these causes the Jews *c.* 26:21
when the ship was *c.* we let. 27:15
I know a man *c.* up to. *2 Cor* 12:2
how he was *c.* up into paradise. 4
being crafty, I *c.* you with guile. 16
we shall be *c.* up. *1 Thes* 4:17
her child was *c.* up to God. *Rev* 12:5

caul, -s

the *c.* above liver. *Ex* 29:13, 22
Lev 3:4, 10, 15; 4:9; 7:4; 8:16, 25; 9:10, 19
will take away their *c.* *Isa* 3:18
will rend the *c.* of their. *Hos* 13:8

cause

[1] *A ground, reason, or motive*, 1 Sam 17:29. [2] *A suit, action, or controversy*, Ex 22:9; Isa 1:23. [3] *Sake, or account*, 2 Cor 7:12.

c. of both shall come. *Ex* 22:9
nor speak in a *c.* to decline. 23:2
countenance a poor man in his *c.* 3
wrest judgement of poor in his *c.* 6
for which *c.* thou and all. *Num* 16:11
Moses brought their *c.* before. 27:5
the *c.* that is too hard. *Deut* 1:17
manslayer shall declare his *c.* *Josh* 20:4
said, is there not a *c.*? *1 Sam* 17:29
Lord hath pleaded the *c.* of. 25:39
there is no *c.* this evil. *2 Sam* 13:16
that hath any suit or *c.* 15:4
maintain their *c.* *1 Ki* 8:45, 49, 59
2 Chr 6:35, 39
was the *c.* that he lift. *1 Ki* 11:27
for the *c.* was from the Lord. 12:15
2 Chr 10:15
he be a *c.* of trespass. *1 Chr* 21:3
what *c.* shall come. *2 Chr* 19:10
for which *c.* this city. *Ezra* 4:15
for which *c.* thou buildest. *Neh* 6:6
God will I commit my *c.* *Job* 5:8
I have ordered my *c.* 13:18
I would order my *c.* before. 23:4
the *c.* which I knew not. 29:16
if I did despise the *c.* of my. 31:13
hast maintained my *c.* *Ps* 9:4
awake to my *c.* my God. 35:23
that favour my righteous *c.* 27
Lord will maintain the *c.* 140:12
first in his own *c.* *Pr* 18:17
debate thy *c.* with thy. 25:9
righteous considereth the *c.* 29:7
for the dumb in the *c.* 31:8
what is the *c.* that. *Eccl* 7:10
nor doth *c.* of the widow. *Isa* 1:23
produce your *c.* saith the. 41:21
God that pleadeth the *c.* of. 51:22
judge not the *c.* of the. *Jer* 5:28
thee have I revealed my *c.* 11:20
unto thee have I opened my *c.* 20:12
he judged the *c.* of the. 22:16
to subvert in a *c.* the. *Lam* 3:36
Lord, judge my *c.* 59
know for whose *c.* *Jonah* 1:7, 8
wife, saving for the *c.* *Mat* 5:32
put away his wife for every *c.* 19:3
declared for what *c.* *Luke* 8:47
found no *c.* of death in him. 23:22
what the *c.* wherefore? *Acts* 10:21
though they found no *c.* of. 13:28
Festus declared Paul's *c.* to. 25:14
was no *c.* of death in me. 28:18
which *c.* we faint not. *2 Cor* 4:16
it is for your *c.* 5:13
I did it not for his *c.* that had. 7:12
for the same *c.* also do. *Phil* 2:18
for which *c.* I suffer. *2 Tim* 1:12
for which *c.* he is not. *Heb* 2:11

plead cause

the Lord *plead* my *c.* *1 Sam* 24:15
Ps 35:1; 43:1; 119:154
plead thine own *c.* *Ps* 74:22
Lord will *plead* their *c.* *Pr* 22:23
he shall *plead* their *c.* 23:11
open thy mouth, *plead* the *c.* 31:9
none to *plead* thy *c.* *Jer* 30:13
thoroughly *plead* their *c.* 50:34
behold, I will *plead* thy *c.* 51:36
until he *plead* my *c.* *Mi* 7:9

for this cause

for this c. have I raised. *Ex* 9:16
for this c. Hezekiah. *2 Chr* 32:20
for this c. the king. *Dan* 2:12
for this c. shall a man. *Mat* 19:5
Mark 10:7; *Eph* 5:31
but *for this c.* came I. *John* 12:27
and *for this c.* came I. 18:37
for this c. God gave. *Rom* 1:26
for this c. pay ye tribute. 13:6
for this c. I will confess to. 15:9
for this c. many are. *1 Cor* 11:30
for this c. I bow my knees. *Eph* 3:14
for this c. thank God. *1 Thes* 2:13
for this c. God shall. *2 Thes* 2:11
howbeit, *for this c.* I. *1 Tim* 1:16
for this c. he is the. *Heb* 9:15
for this c. was the gospel. *1 Pet* 4:6

without cause

slay David *without* a *c.*? *1 Sam* 19:5
destroy him *without* a *c.* *Job* 2:3
my wounds *without c.* 9:17
I delivered him that *without c.* is. *Ps* 7:4
that transgress *without c.* 25:3
without c. they hid for me a net, digged a pit *without c.* 35:7
that hate me *without c.* 19; 69:4
John 15:25
against me *without c.* *Ps* 109:3
perversely with me *without c.* 119:78
persecuted me *without c.* 161
for the innocent *without c.* *Pr* 1:11
strive not with a man *without c.* 3:30
who hath wounds *without c.*? 23:29
against neighbour *without c.* 24:28
oppressed them *without c.* *Isa* 52:4
me sore *without c.* *Lam* 3:52
have not done *without c.* *Ezek* 14:23
with his brother *without c.* *Mat* 5:22

cause

I will *c.* it to rain upon the. *Gen* 7:4
he cried, *c.* every man to go. 45:1
c. frogs to come up on land. *Ex* 8:5
and shall *c.* him to be. 21:19
thy daughter, to *c.* her. *Lev* 19:29
and *c.* sorrow of heart. 26:16
is holy, the Lord will *c.* *Num* 16:5
he shall *c.* Israel to inherit it. *Deut* 1:38; 3:28; 31:7
choose to *c.* his name to. 12:11
thou shalt not *c.* the land. 24:4
whither shall I *c.* my? *2 Sam* 13:13
oath laid on him to *c.* *1 Ki* 8:31
c. him to fall by sword. *2 Ki* 19:7
Isa 37:7
outlandish women *c.* to. *Neh* 13:26
c. to perish all the Jews. *Esth* 3:13
8:11
c. Haman make haste to do. 5:5
c. me to understand. *Job* 6:24
c. every man to find. 34:11
wilt *c.* thine ear to hear. *Ps* 10:17
c. his face to shine. 67:1; 80:3, 7, 19
thou didst *c.* judgement to. 76:8
c. me to hear, *c.* me to. 143:8
unless they *c.* some to fall. *Pr* 4:16
suffer not thy mouth to *c.* *Eccl* 5:6
hearken to thy voice, *c.* *S of S* 8:13
who lead thee *c.* *Isa* 3:12; 9:16
he shall *c.* them of Jacob. 27:6
this is the rest ye may *c.* 28:12
the Lord *c.* his glorious voice. 30:30
nor *c.* his voice to be heard. 42:2
I will *c.* thee to ride upon. 58:14
Lord will *c.* righteousness. 61:11
bring to birth, and not *c.*? 66:9
not *c.* mine anger to fall. *Jer* 3:12
I will *c.* you to dwell in this. 7:3, 7
Lord before he *c.* darkness. 13:16
I will *c.* the enemy to. 15:11
think to *c.* my people. 23:27
Israel, when I went to *c.* 31:2
I will *c.* them to walk by rivers. 9
c. their captivity to. 32:44; 33:26
though he *c.* grief. *Lam* 3:32
I will *c.* you to pass. *Ezek* 20:37
that it might *c.* fury to come. 24:8
I will *c.* them to lie down. 34:15
I will *c.* men to walk on you. 36:12
he shall *c.* craft to prosper. *Dan* 8:25
c. thy face to shine on. 9:17
thither *c.* thy mighty. *Joel* 3:11
c. the seat of violence to. *Amos* 6:3
I will *c.* sun to go down at. 8:9
c. me to behold grievance? *Hab* 1:3
c. them to be put to death. *Mat* 10:21
Mark 13:12; *Luke* 21:16
mark them who *c.* *Rom* 16:17
c. that it be read in. *Col* 4:16

cause *to cease, see* cease

caused

God *c.* a deep sleep to. *Gen* 2:21
God *c.* me to wander from. 20:13
Lord *c.* the sea to go. *Ex* 14:21
c. Israel to commit. *Num* 31:16
is the land, I have *c.* *Deut* 34:4
c. thee to rest from. *2 Sam* 7:11
c. a seat to be set for. *1 Ki* 2:19
he *c.* all present in. *2 Chr* 34:32
God hath *c.* his name. *Ezra* 6:12
Levites *c.* people to. *Neh* 8:7, 8
Haman *c.* gallows to be. *Esth* 5:14
if I have *c.* eyes of. *Job* 31:16
hast *c.* men to ride. *Ps* 66:12
and *c.* them to pass through. 78:13
he *c.* an east-wind to blow in. 26
word on which thou hast *c.* 119:49
with fair speech she *c.* *Pr* 7:21
they have *c.* Egypt to err. *Isa* 19:1[illegible]
I have not *c.* thee to serve. 43:2[illegible]
Spirit of the Lord *c.* him. 63:1[illegible]
I have *c.* my people Israel. *Jer* 12:1[illegible]
I have *c.* to cleave to me. 13:1[illegible]
Shemaiah *c.* you to trust in. 29:3[illegible]
therefore thou hast *c.* all this. 32:2[illegible]
c. the servants to return. 34:11, [illegible]
her little ones have *c.* a cry. 48:[illegible]
I have *c.* thee to multiply. *Ezek* 16:[illegible]

till I have *c.* my fury to. *Ezek* 24:13
Nebuchadnezzar *c.* his army. 29:18
c. terror in land. 32:23, 24, 25, 26
Gabriel being *c.* to fly. *Dan* 9:21
spirit of whoredoms *c.* *Hos* 4:12
their lies *c.* them to err. *Amos* 2:4
I *c.* rain on one city, I *c.* not. 4:7
I have *c.* thine iniquity. *Zech* 3:4
ye have *c.* many to. *Mal* 2:8
have *c.* this man should. *John* 11:37
they *c.* great joy to all. *Acts* 15:3
but if any have *c.* grief. *2 Cor* 2:5
c. all to receive a mark. *Rev* 13:16

causeless

thou hast shed blood *c.* *1 Sam* 25:31
curse *c.* shall not come. *Pr* 26:2

causes

that thou mayest bring *c.* *Ex* 18:19
hard *c.* they brought to Moses. 26
hear the *c.* between. *Deut* 1:16
c. whereby backsliding. *Jer* 3:8
but have seen for thee *c.* *Lam* 2:14
thou hast pleaded the *c.* of. 3:58
for these *c.* the Jews. *Acts* 26:21

causest

thou *c.* me to ride. *Job* 30:22
blessed is man thou *c.* *Ps* 65:4

causeth

water that *c.* curse. *Num* 5:18, 19
22, 24, 27
c. them to wander in. *Job* 12:24
Ps 107:40
spirit of understanding *c.* *Job* 20:3
he *c.* it to come hither. 37:13
c. the grass to grow. *Ps* 104:14
c. vapours to ascend. 135:7
Jer 10:13; 51:16
c. his wind to blow. *Ps* 147:18
son that *c.* shame. *Pr* 10:5; 17:2
19:26
servant shall rule over a son *c.* 17:2
instruction that *c.* to err. 19:27
whoso *c.* righteous to go. 28:10
fire *c.* the waters to boil. *Isa* 64:2
any thing that *c.* sweat. *Ezek* 44:18
put away wife *c.* her to. *Mat* 5:32
thanks be to God, who *c.* *2 Cor* 2:14*
c. through us thanksgiving. 9:11
c. the earth to worship. *Rev* 13:12

causeway

lot came forth by *c.* of. *1 Chr* 26:16
at Parbar westward, four at *c.* 18

causing

c. the lips of those. *S of S* 7:9*
a bridle in the jaws *c.* *Isa* 30:28
in *c.* you to return to. *Jer* 29:10
shepherds *c.* their flocks. 33:12

cave, -s

Lot dwelt in a *c.* he and. *Gen* 19:30
field and *c.* made sure. 23:17, 20
buried Sarah in the *c.* 19
me with my father in *c.* 49:29
kings fled and hid in *c.* *Josh* 10:16
17
Midianites Israel made *c.* *Judg* 6:2
hide in *c.* in rocks. *1 Sam* 13:6
David escaped to the *c.* of. 22:1
into my hand in the *c.* 24:10
came to David to *c.* *2 Sam* 23:13
hid by fifty in a *c.* *1 Ki* 18:4, 13
Elijah came to a *c.* and. 19:9
they shall go into *c.* *Isa* 2:19
die that be in the *c.* *Ezek* 33:27
grave, it was a *c.* a. *John* 11:38
wandered in dens and *c.* *Heb* 11:38*

cease

day and night shall not *c.* *Gen* 8:22
the thunder shall *c.* *Ex* 9:29
from age of fifty shall *c.* *Num* 8:25
elders prophesied, did not *c.* 11:25
I will make to *c.* murmurings. 17:5
the poor shall never *c.* *Deut* 15:11
remembrance of them to *c.* 32:26
so make our children *c.* *Josh* 22:25
be avenged, after I will *c.* *Judg* 15:7
go to battle, or shall I *c.*? 20:28
not to cry to Lord. *1 Sam* 7:8
Baasha heard it, let his work *c.*
2 Chr 16:5
made them to *c.* by force. *Ezra* 4:23
why should the work *c.*? *Neh* 6:3
there the wicked *c.* from. *Job* 3:17
my days few, *c.* then. 10:20
branch thereof will not *c.* 14:7
c. from anger, forsake. *Ps* 37:8
he maketh wars to *c.* to the. 46:9
hast made his glory to *c.* 89:44
c. to hear instruction. *Pr* 19:27
honour for a man to *c.* from. 20:3*
yea strife and reproach shall *c.* 22:10
labour to be rich, *c.* from. 23:4
the grinders *c.* because. *Eccl* 12:3
c. to do evil. *Isa* 1:16
c. ye from man. 2:22
and indignation shall *c.* 10:25*
their vintage shouting to *c.* 16:10
the fortress also shall *c.* from. 17:3
thereof have I made to *c.* 21:2
when thou shalt *c.* to spoil. 33:1
and let them not *c.* *Jer* 14:17
leaf green, nor shall *c.* from. 17:8
then seed of Israel shall *c.* 31:36
not apple of thine eye *c.* *Lam* 2:18
idols may be broken and *c.* *Ezek* 6:6
pomp of the strong to *c.* 7:24
I will make this proverb *c.* 12:23
I make thy lewdness to *c.* 23:27
the multitude of Egypt to *c.* 30:10
of her strength shall *c.* 18; 33:28
c. by whom shall Jacob. *Amos* 7:5
will not *c.* to pervert. *Acts* 13:10
be tongues, they shall *c.* *1 Cor* 13:8
I *c.* not to give thanks. *Eph* 1:16
we do not *c.* to pray for. *Col* 1:9
eyes that cannot *c.* from. *2 Pet* 2:14

cause to **cease**

cause these men *to c.* *Ezra* 4:21
they could not *cause* them *to c.* 5:5
slay and *cause* work *to c.* *Neh* 4:11
cause thine anger *to c.* *Ps* 85:4
lot *causeth* contentions *to c.* *Pr* 18:18
cause arrogancy of proud *to c.*
Isa 13:11
cause holy One of Israel *to c.* 30:11
cause mirth *to c.* from. *Jer* 7:34
cause to c. man. 36:29; *Hos* 2:11
I will *cause to c.* in. *Jer* 48:35
cause thee *to c.* from. *Ezek* 16:41
will I *cause* lewdness *to c.* 23:48
cause noise of thy songs *to c.* 26:13
I will *cause* their images *to c.* 30:13
cause them *to c.* from. 34:10
I will *cause to c.* evil beasts. 25
cause the oblation *to c.* *Dan* 9:27
cause reproach offered by him *to c.*
11:18
will *cause to c.* kingdom. *Hos* 1:4

ceased

it *c.* to be with Sarai. *Gen* 18:11
thunders and hail *c.* *Ex* 9:33
saw that the thunders *c.* 34
the manna *c.* on the. *Josh* 5:12
they *c.* not from their. *Judg* 2:19
inhabitants of villages *c.* they *c.* 5:7
they that were hungry *c.* *1 Sam* 2:5
in the name of David and *c.* 25:9
then *c.* the work of. *Ezra* 4:24
so these three men *c.* to. *Job* 32:1
did tear me and *c.* not. *Ps* 35:15
sore ran in the night and *c.* 77:2*
oppressor *c.* golden city *c.* *Isa* 14:4
the elders have *c.* from. *Lam* 5:14
the joy of our heart is *c.* 15
took up Jonah, sea *c.* *Jonah* 1:15
the wind *c.* *Mat* 14:32; *Mark* 4:39
6:51
woman hath not *c.* to. *Luke* 7:45
praying in a place, when he *c.* 11:1
they *c.* not to teach and. *Acts* 5:42
after the uproar was *c.* Paul. 20:1
by space of three years I *c.* not. 31
would not be persuaded we *c.* 21:14
then is offence of cross *c.* *Gal* 5:11*
he also hath *c.* from his. *Heb* 4:10*
then they would not have *c.* 10:2
suffered in flesh, hath *c.* *1 Pet* 4:1

ceaseth

help, Lord, for godly man *c.* *Ps* 12:1
precious, and it *c.* for ever. 49:8*
is no tale-bearer strife *c.* *Pr* 26:20
the spoiler *c.* *Isa* 16:4
of tabrets *c.* joy of harp *c.* 24:8
the way-faring man *c.* 33:8
eye trickleth down *c.* not. *Lam* 3:49
c. from raising after he. *Hos* 7:4
this man *c.* not to speak. *Acts* 6:13

ceasing

I should sin in *c.* to. *1 Sam* 12:23
was made without *c.* *Acts* 12:5*
without *c.* I make. *Rom* 1:9
1 Thes 1:3
we thank God without *c.* *1 Thes* 2:13
pray without *c.* in every. 5:17
without *c.* I have. *2 Tim* 1:3

cedar

(*An evergreen tree of great value to building in Bible times. It was much used in building the Temple. The cedars of Lebanon are the most famous; of them only a few remain*)

I dwell in an house of *c.* *2 Sam* 7:2
build ye not me an house of *c.*? 7
he spake from the *c.* to. *1 Ki* 4:33
all thy desire concerning *c.* 5:8
thistle sent to the *c.* *2 Ki* 14:9
2 Chr 25:18
moveth his tail like a *c.* *Job* 40:17
shall grow like a *c.* *Ps* 92:12
beams of house are *c.* *S of S* 1:17
inclose her with boards of *c.* 8:9
in the wilderness the *c.* *Isa* 41:19
it is cieled with *c.* *Jer* 22:14
thou closest thyself in *c.* 15
eagle took highest branch of *c.*
Ezek 17:3
of the highest branch of the *c.* 22
bear fruit and be a goodly *c.* 23
chests made of *c.* among. 27:24
the Assyrian was a *c.* in. 31:3
he shall uncover the *c.* *Zeph* 2:14
howl, fir-tree, for the *c.* *Zech* 11:2

cedar trees

Israel's tabernacles are *c.* *Num* 24:6
Hiram sent *c.* to David. *2 Sam* 5:11
they hew me *c.* out of. *1 Ki* 5:6
so Hiram gave Solomon *c.* 10; 9:11
cut down the tall *c.* *2 Ki* 19:23
David prepared *c.* in. *1 Chr* 22:4
c. made he as sycomore. *2 Chr* 1:15
9:27
send me *c.* and fir-trees. 2:8
gave money to bring *c.* *Ezra* 3:7

cedar wood

c. and hyssop. *Lev* 14:4, 6, 49, 51, 52
priest shall take *c.* and. *Num* 19:6
they brought much *c.* *1 Chr* 22:4

cedars

c. made he to be as. *1 Ki* 10:27
I dwell in an house of *c.* *1 Chr* 17:1
didst send David *c.* to. *2 Chr* 2:3
voice of Lord breaketh *c.* *Ps* 29:5
boughs were like goodly *c.* 80:10
praise him also *c.* and. 148:9
excellent as the *c.* *S of S* 5:15
the sycomores into *c.* *Isa* 9:10
I will cut down the tall *c.* 37:24
he heweth him down *c.* 44:14
cut down thy choice *c.* *Jer* 22:7
Lebanon, that makest nest in *c.* 23
c. in garden of God. *Ezek* 31:8
height as height of *c.* *Amos* 2:9
fire may devour thy *c.* *Zech* 11:1

cedars *of Lebanon*

fire devour *c. of Leb.* *Judg* 9:15
the *c. of Leb.* which. *Ps* 104:16
upon all the *c. of Leb.* *Isa* 2:13
c. of Leb. rejoice at thee. 14:8
c. from *Leb.* to make. *Ezek* 27:5

Cedron

disciples over brook *C.* *John* 18:1*

celebrate

from even to even shall *c.* *Lev* 23:32
a statute, ye shall *c.* it in. 41
death cannot *c.* the. *Isa* 38:18

celestial

c. bodies, glory of *c.* is. *1 Cor* 15:40

cellars

over the *c.* of oil was. *1 Chr* 27:28

Cenchrea

shorn his head in *C.* *Acts* 18:18
a servant of church at *C.* *Rom* 16:1

censer, -s
took either of them *c.* *Lev* 10:1
he shall take a *c.* full of. 16:12
upon it vessels, even *c.* *Num* 4:14*
this do, take ye *c.* 16:6
every man his *c.* 17
Eleazar took the brasen *c.* 39
made *c.* of pure gold. *1 Ki* 7:50* *2 Chr* 4:22*
Uzziah had a *c.* in his. *2 Chr* 26:19
with every man his *c.* *Ezek* 8:11
had the golden *c.* and the ark of the covenant. *Heb* 9:4
came, having a golden *c.* *Rev* 8:3
the angel took the *c.* and filled. 5

centurion, -s
(*Officer in the Roman army over a century, or 100 men*)
there came unto him a *c.* *Mat* 8:5
c. said, Lord, I am not worthy. 8
when the *c.* saw earthquake. 27:54
certain *c.'s* servant, who was dear unto him. *Luke* 7:2
now when the *c.* saw what. 23:47
Cornelius was a *c.* of. *Acts* 10:1
Cornelius the *c.* a just man. 22
who immediately took soldiers and *c.* and ran down. 21:32
when the *c.* heard that. 22:26
Paul called one of the *c.* to. 23:17
called to him two *c.* saying. 23
and he commanded a *c.* to. 24:23
delivered Paul to Julius a *c.* 27:1
c. believed the master more. 11
c. willing to save Paul, kept. 43
c. delivered the prisoners to. 28:16

Cephas
thou shalt be called *C.* *John* 1:42
I am of *C.* *1 Cor* 1:12
whether Paul, or Apollos, or *C.* 3:22
brethren of the Lord, and *C.* 9:5
that he was seen of *C.* 15:5
James, *C.* and John, who seemed to be pillars. *Gal* 2:9

ceremonies
passover according to all the *c.* thereof. *Num* 9:3*

certain
gather a *c.* rate every day. *Ex* 16:4
Korah rose with *c.* of. *Num* 16:2
c. men the children of Belial. *Deut* 13:13
wicked man be beaten by a *c.* 25:2
after a *c.* rate every day, offering according. *2 Chr* 8:13
Hanani came, he and *c.* *Neh* 1:2
I mourned *c.* days, and fasted. 4
a *c.* portion should be for the singers. 11:23
I smote *c.* of them, and. 13:25
came *c.* from Shechem. *Jer* 41:5
captain carried away *c.* of. 52:15
fainted and was sick *c.* *Dan* 8:27
king of north shall come after *c.* years. 11:13
likened to *c.* king. *Mat* 18:28; 22:2
and her sons desiring a *c.* 20:20
came a *c.* poor widow. *Mark* 12:42 *Luke* 21:2
arose *c.* and bare false witness against him. *Mark* 14:57
when he was in a *c.* *Luke* 5:12
told him by *c.* thy mother. 8:20
went into a *c.* village. 10:38; 17:12
a *c.* woman lifted up voice. 11:27
a *c.* Pharisee besought him to. 37
this parable to *c.* who trusted. 18:9
who for a *c.* sedition and. 23:19
c. women also made us. 24:22
c. of them with us went to the. 24
angel went down at a *c.* *John* 5:4
Saul was *c.* days with. *Acts* 9:19
prayed Peter to tarry *c.* days. 10:48
Herod the king to vex *c.* 12:1
c. which went from us have. 15:24
as *c.* of your own poets. 17:28
contribution for *c.* saints. *Rom* 15:26
for before that *c.* came. *Gal* 2:12
one in a *c.* place testified. *Heb* 2:6
he spake in a *c.* place of the seventh day. 4:4
he limiteth a *c.* day, saying. 7
a *c.* fearful looking for. *Heb* 10:27
there are *c.* men crept in. *Jude* 4

certain
it be truth and thing *c.* *Deut* 13:14 17:4
for *c.* thou shalt die. *1 Ki* 2:37, 42
know for *c.* if ye put. *Jer* 26:15
the dream is *c.* and. *Dan* 2:45
I have no *c.* thing to write unto my lord. *Acts* 25:26
no *c.* dwelling-place. *1 Cor* 4:11
c. we can carry nothing. *1 Tim* 6:7

certainly
I will *c.* return to thee. *Gen* 18:10
we saw *c.* that the Lord was with thee. 26:28
could we *c.* know he would. 43:7*
such a man as I can *c.*? 44:15
will *c.* requite us all the. 50:15*
c. I will be with thee. *Ex* 3:12
if theft be *c.* found in his. 22:4
he hath *c.* trespassed. *Lev* 5:19
congregation shall *c.* stone. 24:16
because it was *c.* told. *Josh* 9:24
if ye can *c.* declare the. *Judg* 14:12
thy father *c.* knoweth. *1 Sam* 20:3
if I knew *c.* evil were. 9*
c. heard that Saul will. 23:10
Lord will *c.* make my lord. 25:28
even so will I *c.* do. *1 Ki* 1:30
thou mayest *c.* recover. *2 Ki* 8:10
thou *c.* return in peace. *2 Chr* 18:27
for riches *c.* make. *Pr* 23:5
lo, *c.* in vain made he it. *Jer* 8:8
do we not *c.* know every. 13:12
ye shall *c.* drink. 25:28
king of Babylon shall *c.* 36:29
dost thou *c.* know that Baal? 40:14
know *c.* I have admonished. 42:19
c. ye shall die by sword and. 22
c. do what thing goeth out. 44:17
c. this is the day that. *Lam* 2:16
one shall *c.* come. *Dan* 11:10*, 13*
saying, *c.* this was a righteous man. *Luke* 23:47

certainty
know for *c.* Lord will. *Josh* 23:13
come ye again with *c.* *1 Sam* 23:23
make known the *c.* of. *Pr* 22:21
I know of *c.* ye would. *Dan* 2:8
thou mightest know the *c.* *Luke* 1:4
could not know the *c.* *Acts* 21:34
would have known the *c.* 22:30

certify, -ied
word from you to *c.* *2 Sam* 15:28
we sent and *c.* the king. *Ezra* 4:14
we *c.* the king, that if this city. 16
their names also to *c.* thee. 5:10
we *c.* you not to impose toll. 7:24
Esther *c.* king thereof. *Esth* 2:22*
I *c.* you gospel I preached. *Gal* 1:11*

Cesar, *see* **Caesar**

Cesarea (Caesarea)
came into coasts of *C.* *Mat* 16:13
into the towns of *C.* *Mark* 8:27
till he came to *C.* *Acts* 8:40
brought Paul down to *C.* 9:30
morrow after entered into *C.* 10:24
sent three men from *C.* 11:11
Herod went from Judea to *C.* 12:19
when he had landed at *C.* 18:22
with us also certain of the disciples of *C.* 21:16
200 soldiers to go to *C.* 23:23
3 days he ascended from *C.* 25:1
Paul should be kept at *C.* 4

chafed
they be *c.* in their minds. *2 Sam* 17:8

chaff
(*The refuse of winnowed grain*)
as *c.* that the storm carrieth away. *Job* 21:18
like the *c.* which the wind. *Ps* 1:4
let them be as *c.* before wind. 35:5
as flame consumeth the *c.* *Isa* 5:24*
nations shall be chased as *c.* 17:13
terrible ones shall be as *c.* 29:5
ye shall conceive *c.* and. 33:11
and make the hills as *c.* 41:15
is the *c.* to the wheat? *Jer* 23:28*
became like the *c.* of. *Dan* 2:35
as the *c.* which is driven. *Hos* 13:3
before day pass as *c.* *Zeph* 2:2
burn up the *c.* with fire. *Mat* 3:12 *Luke* 3:17

chain
gold *c.* about his neck. *Gen* 41:42 *Dan* 5:7, 16, 29
them about as a *c.* *Ps* 73:6
ravished my heart with one *c.* of thy neck. *S of S* 4:9
hath made my *c.* heavy. *Lam* 3:7
make a *c.* for land is full of crimes. *Ezek* 7:23
bracelets, and a *c.* on thy. 16:11
I am bound with this *c.* *Acts* 28:20
not ashamed of my *c.* *2 Tim* 1:16
an angel and a great *c.* *Rev* 20:1

chains
fasten the wreathen *c.* *Ex* 28:14, 24
made on breast-plate *c.* 39:15
for atonement, *c.* and. *Num* 31:50*
besides the *c.* about. *Judg* 8:26
by the *c.* of gold before. *1 Ki* 6:21
bind their kings with *c.* *Ps* 149:8
instruction shall be *c.* *Pr* 1:9
thy neck comely with *c.* *S of S* 1:10*
Lord will take away *c.* *Isa* 3:19*
and casteth silver *c.* 40:19
shall come after thee in *c.* 45:14
loose thee this day from *c.* *Jer* 40:4
brought him with *c.* into. *Ezek* 19:4*
they put in ward in *c.* 9
bind him, no not with *c.* *Mark* 5:3
the *c.* had been oft plucked by him. 4
Peter's *c.* fell off. *Acts* 12:7
delivered them into *c.* of. *2 Pet* 2:4
reserved in everlasting *c.* *Jude* 6*
see **bound**

chainwork
wreaths of *c.* for. *1 Ki* 7:17

chalcedony
third foundation was a *c.* *Rev* 21:19

Chalcol
Solomon was wiser than *C.* *1 Ki* 4:31
of Zerah, Heman, *C.* *1 Chr* 2:6

Chaldea
C. shall be a spoil. *Jer* 50:10
render to inhabitants of *C.* 51:24
blood be upon inhabitants of *C.* 35
thy fornication to *C.* *Ezek* 16:29
messengers to them into *C.* 23:16

Chaldean
hand of Nebuchadnezzar the *C.* *Ezra* 5:12
asked such things at any *C.* *Dan* 2:10

Chaldeans
C. made out three bands. *Job* 1:17
land of *C.* the Assyrian. *Isa* 23:13
I have brought down the *C.* 43:14
throne, O daughter of the *C.* 47:1
darkness, O daughter of the *C.* 5
his arm shall be on the *C.* 48:14
flee from the *C.* 20
ye fight against the *C.* *Jer* 21:4
he that falleth to the *C.* 9; 38:2
punish land of *C.* 25:12; 50:1, 45
though ye fight with the *C.* 32:5
is given into hand of the *C.* 24, 43
the *C.* shall come and set fire. 29
come to fight with the *C.* 33:5
the *C.* shall come again and. 37:8
surely the *C.* shall depart. 9
though ye had smitten army of *C.* 10
I fall not away to the *C.* 14
of Jews that are fallen to *C.* 38:19
bring out thy children to the *C.* 2
C. burnt king's house, and. 39:
fear not to serve the *C.* 40:
at Mizpah, to serve the *C.* 1
Ishmael slew the *C.* that were. 41:
thee on to deliver us to *C.* 43:
a sword is upon the *C.* 50:3
Lord hath purposed against *C.* 4
shall fall in the land of *C.* 51:
army of *C.* pursued Zedekiah. 52:
to the land of the *C.* *Ezek* 12:1
she saw the images of the *C.* 23:1
teach tongue of the *C.* *Dan* 1:
king commanded to call the *C.* 2:
at that time certain *C.* accused. 3:

then came in the *C.* and the. *Dan* 4:7
king cried aloud to bring in *C.* 5:7
thy father made master of *C.* 11
Darius made king over the *C.* 9:1
lo, I raise up the *C.* that. *Hab* 1:6
came out of land of *C.* *Acts* 7:4

Chaldees

him bands of the *C.* *2 Ki* 24:2
the *C.* were against the city. 25:4
the army of the *C.* brake. 10
for they were afraid of the *C.* 26
brought king of *C.* *2 Chr* 36:17
Babylon the beauty of *C.* *Isa* 13:19
see **Ur**

chalk-stones

stones of the altar *c.* *Isa* 27:9

challengeth

any lost thing another *c.* *Ex* 22:9

chamber

(*An apartment, or room in a house, not confined, as now generally understood, to bed-chamber,* 2 Sam 13:10; Ps 104:3; Ezek 42:13)

Joseph entered into his *c.* *Gen* 43:30
in to my wife into the *c.* *Judg* 15:1
in wait abiding in the *c.* 16:9, 12
bring meat into the *c.* *2 Sam* 13:10
Elisha turned into the *c.* *2 Ki* 4:11
for Tobiah a great *c.* *Neh* 13:5
cast household stuff out of the *c.* 8
bridegroom cometh out of his *c.* *Ps* 19:5
into the *c.* of her that. *S of S* 3:4
read the book in the *c.* *Jer* 36:10
laid up the roll in *c.* of. 20
c. whose prospect. *Ezek* 40:45, 46
being open in his *c.* to. *Dan* 6:10
bridegroom go forth of *c.* *Joel* 2:16

bed-chamber, *see* **bed ; guard-chamber,** *see* **guard**

guest-**chamber**

where is the *guest-c.*? *Mark* 14:14
Luke 22:11

inner **chamber**

and came into *inner c.* *1 Ki* 20:30
into *inner c.* to hide. 22:25
2 Chr 18:24
carry Jehu into *inner c.* *2 Ki* 9:2

little **chamber**

let us make a *little c.* *2 Ki* 4:10
little *c.* was one reed. *Ezek* 40:7*
gate from roof of one *little c.* 13*

side **chamber, -s**

breadth of every *side-c.* *Ezek* 41:5
the *side-c.* were three, one. 6
thickness of wall for *side-c.* 9

upper **chamber**

lattice in his *upper-c.* *2 Ki* 1:2
altars in top of the *upper-c.* 23:12
laid Dorcas in an *upper-c.* *Acts* 9:37
Peter, when come into *upper-c.* 39
many lights in *upper-c.* where. 20:8

chambering

walk not in *c.* and. *Rom* 13:13

chamberlain, -s

chamber of the *c.* *2 Ki* 23:11
seven *c.* that served. *Esth* 1:10
but what Hegai the king's *c.* 2:15
two of king's *c.* were wroth. 21
Blastus the king's *c.* *Acts* 12:20
Erastus, *c.* of the city. *Rom* 16:23

chambers

wall of house he built *c.* *1 Ki* 6:5
chief porters over the *c.* *1 Chr* 9:26
23:28
prepare *c.* *2 Chr* 31:11
weigh them in the *c.* *Ezra* 8:29
and they cleansed the *c.* *Neh* 13:9
which maketh the *c.* of. *Job* 9:9
layeth beams of his *c.* *Ps* 104:3
watereth the hills from his *c.* 13
brought forth frogs in *c.* 105:30
hell going down to *c.* *Pr* 7:27
knowledge *c.* shall be. 24:4
hath brought me into *c.* *S of S* 1:4
enter thou into thy *c.* *Isa* 26:20
woe to him that buildeth *c.* *Jer* 22:13
wide house, and large *c.* 14
Rechabites into one of *c.* 35:2
every man in the *c.* *Ezek* 8:12

entereth into their privy *c.* *Ezek* 21:14
they be holy *c.* where priests. 42:13
he is in the secret *c.* *Mat* 24:26

upper-**chambers**

overlaid the *upper-c.* *2 Chr* 3:9
the *upper-c.* were shorter. *Ezek* 42:5

chameleon

ferret, and the *c.* and. *Lev* 11:30

chamois

eat, wild ox and the *c.* *Deut* 14:5

champaign

who dwell in the *c.* *Deut* 11:30*

champion

there went out a *c.* *1 Sam* 17:4
when Philistines saw *c.* was dead. 51

chance

if a bird's nest *c.* to. *Deut* 22:6
it may *c.* of wheat. *1 Cor* 15:37

chance

it was a *c.* that. *1 Sam* 6:9
as I happened by *c.* *2 Sam* 1:6
time and *c.* happeneth. *Eccl* 9:11
by *c.* a priest came. *Luke* 10:31

chancellor

Rehum *c.* wrote letter. *Ezra* 4:8, 9
king sent answer to Rehum the *c.* 17

chanceth

uncleanness that *c.* him. *Deut* 23:10

change, -s

both it and the *c.* *Lev* 27:33
will give you thirty *c.* *Judg* 14:12
shall give me thirty *c.* of. 13
days will I wait till my *c.* *Job* 14:14
with them given to *c.* *Pr* 24:21
clothe thee with *c.* of. *Zech* 3:4*
necessity a *c.* of the law. *Heb* 7:12

change, *verb*

be clean and *c.* your. *Gen* 35:2
he shall not *c.* it. *Lev* 27:10
nor *c.* it, if he *c.* 33
they *c.* the night into day. *Job* 17:12
as a vesture shalt thou *c.* *Ps* 102:26
but we will *c.* them. *Isa* 9:10
gaddest thou to *c.* thy way ? *Jer* 2:36
can Ethiopian *c.* his skin ? 13:23
think to *c.* times and laws. *Dan* 7:25
I will *c.* their glory into. *Hos* 4:7
then shall his mind *c.* *Hab* 1:11
I am the Lord, I *c.* not. *Mal* 3:6
shall *c.* the customs. *Acts* 6:14
their women did *c.* the. *Rom* 1:26
present, and *c.* my voice. *Gal* 4:20
who shall *c.* our vile body. *Phil* 3:21

changeable

Lord take away the *c.* *Isa* 3:22*

changed, -eth

father *c.* my wages. *Gen* 31:7, 41
Joseph *c.* his raiment, and. 41:14
raw flesh turn and be *c.* *Lev* 13:16
if plague have not *c.* his colour. 55
he *c.* his behaviour. *1 Sam* 21:13
David *c.* his apparel. *2 Sam* 12:20
king of Babylon *c.* his. *2 Ki* 24:17
c. prison-garments. 25:29; *Jer* 52:33
disease is my garment *c.* *Job* 30:18*
sweareth to his hurt, *c.* not. *Ps* 15:4
as vesture shall be *c.* 102:26
Heb 1:12
thus they *c.* their glory. *Ps* 106:20
boldness of face shall be *c.* *Eccl* 8:1
c. the ordinance, broken. *Isa* 24:5
c. their gods, people have *c.* *Jer* 2:11
and his scent is not *c.* 48:11
is the most fine gold *c.*! *Lam* 4:1
hath *c.* my judgements. *Ezek* 5:6*
till the time be *c.* *Dan* 2:9
he *c.* the times and seasons. 21
form of his visage was *c.* 3:19
nor were their coats *c.* nor. 27
let his heart be *c.* from man's. 4:16
sign writing that it be not *c.* 6:8
no decree may be *c.* 15
purpose might not be *c.* 17
he hath *c.* the portion of. *Mi* 2:4
the barbarians *c.* their. *Acts* 28:6
c. the glory of the. *Rom* 1:23
c. the truth of God into a lie. 25
we shall all be *c.* *1 Cor* 15:51, 52
c. into same image from. *2 Cor* 3:18
for priesthood being *c.* a. *Heb* 7:12

changers

tables of money-*c.* *Mat* 21:12
Mark 11:15; *John* 2:14, 15

changes

he gave *c.* to Benjamin five *c.* *Gen* 45:22
took with him ten *c.* *2 Ki* 5:5
give them, I pray thee, two *c.* 22
bound two *c.* of garments. 23
c. and war are against. *Job* 10:17
because they have no *c.* *Ps* 55:19

changest, -ed, *countenance*

thou *c.* his *countenance.* *Job* 14:20
king's *countenance* was *c.* *Dan* 5:6, 9
nor let thy *countenance* be *c.* 10
my *countenance c.* in me. 7:28

changing

in Israel concerning *c.* *Ruth* 4:7

channel, -s

c. of the sea appeared. *2 Sam* 22:16
Ps 18:15
come up over all his *c.* *Isa* 8:7
Lord shall beat off from *c.* 27:12*

chant

they *c.* to the sound of. *Amos* 6:5*

chapel

it is the king's *c.* *Amos* 7:13*

chapiter, -s

(*American Revision,* capital)

overlaid their *c.* with gold. *Ex* 36:38; 38:28
overlaying of their *c.* 38:17, 19
made two *c.* of brass. *1 Ki* 7:16
2 Chr 4:12, 13
c. upon it was brass. *2 Ki* 25:17
Jer 52:22

chapmen

besides what *c.* and. *2 Chr* 9:14*

chapt

because ground is *c.* *Jer* 14:4

Charashim

father of the valley of *C.* *1 Chr* 4:14

charge

[1] *To command,* Ex 1:22. [2] *To adjure, or bind by a solemn oath,* 1 Sam 14:27. [3] *To load, or burden,* Deut 24:5; *1 Tim* 5:16. [4] *An office, or duty,* Num 8:26.

Abraham kept my *c.* *Gen* 26:5
Isaac gave Jacob a *c.* saying. 28:6
Moses and Aaron a *c.* *Ex* 6:13
this is the *c.* of their. *Num* 4:31
the Levites, touching their *c.* 8:26
Israel kept *c.* of the Lord. 9:19, 23
gave Joshua a *c.* 27:23; *Deut* 31:23
blood to people's *c.* *Deut* 21:8
Reubenites have kept *c.* *Josh* 22:3
the king gave *c.* *2 Sam* 18:5
ruler over all the *c.* *1 Ki* 11:28
the lord to have the *c.* *2 Ki* 7:17
because the *c.* was. *1 Chr* 9:27
Levites had the *c.* of. *2 Chr* 30:17
I gave Hanani *c.* over. *Neh* 7:2
of those that had *c.* of. *Esth* 3:9
who hath given him a *c.* *Job* 34:13
laid to my *c.* things I. *Ps* 35:11
king of Babylon gave *c.* *Jer* 39:11
Lord hath given it a *c.* 47:7
cause them that have *c.* *Ezek* 9:1
ye have not kept the *c.* of. 44:8
priests that kept the *c.* of. 15
priests kept my *c.* who. 48:11
lay not this sin to their *c.* *Acts* 7:60
an eunuch, who had *c.* of. 8:27
received such a *c.* thrust. 16:24
nothing laid to his *c.* worthy. 23:29
shall lay any thing to *c.* *Rom* 8:33
gospel of Christ without *c.* *1 Cor* 9:18
c. I commit to thee. *1 Tim* 1:18
not be laid to their *c.* *2 Tim* 4:16
see **keep**

give **charge**

and *give* Joshua a *c.* *Num* 27:19
I may *give* him a *c.* *Deut* 31:14
go, and I will *give c.* *2 Sam* 14:8
give thee wisdom and *c.* *1 Chr* 22:12
give his angels *c.* *Ps* 91:11
Mat 4:6; *Luke* 4:10

will I *give* him a *c*. *Isa* 10:6
these things *give* in *c*. *1 Tim* 5:7
I *give* thee *c*. in sight of God. 6:13

charge

go down, *c*. the people. *Ex* 19:21
priest shall *c*. her. *Num* 5:19
but *c*. Joshua and. *Deut* 3:28
to *c*. ourselves yearly. *Neh* 10:32
c. Esther that she go in. *Esth* 4:8
I *c*. you, O ye daughters. *S of S* 2:7
3:5; 5:8; 8:4
that thou dost so *c*. us ? 5:9
I *c*. thee come out and. *Mark* 9:25
I *c*. you that this. *1 Thes* 5:27
c. that they teach no. *1 Tim* 1:3
I *c*. thee before God and. 5:21
2 Tim 4:1
c. them that are rich in. *1 Tim* 6:17

chargeable

lest we be *c*. to thee. *2 Sam* 13:25*
governors were *c*. to. *Neh* 5:15
with you, I was *c*. *2 Cor* 11:9*
we would not be *c*. *1 Thes* 2:9*
we might not be *c*. to. *2 Thes* 3:8*

charged

Abimelech *c*. his people. *Gen* 26:11
Isaac called Jacob, and *c*. 28:1
captain of the guard *c*. 40:4
Jacob *c*. his sons, and. 49:29
Pharaoh *c*. all his people. *Ex* 1:22
I *c*. your judges. *Deut* 1:16
nor shall he be *c*. with. 24:5
Moses *c*. the people the. 27:11
when Saul *c*. people. *1 Sam* 14:27
the king *c*. thee. *2 Sam* 18:12
David *c*. Solomon his son. *1 Ki* 2:1
the commandment that I have *c*. 43
so was it *c*. me by. 13:9
Lord *c*. me to build. *2 Chr* 36:23
Ezra 1:2
c. they not be opened. *Neh* 13:19
as Mordecai *c*. her. *Esth* 2:10, 20
Job sinned not, nor *c*. *Job* 1:22
and his angels he *c*. with folly. 4:18
c. Baruch before them. *Jer* 32:13
Jonadab in all that he *c*. us. 35:8
Jesus straitly *c*. them. *Mat* 9:30
Mark 5:43; *Luke* 9:21
Jesus *c*. them not make him known.
Mat 12:16 *Mark* 3:12
c. not to tell. *Mark* 7:36; 8:30
9:9; *Luke* 5:14; 8:56
many *c*. him that he. *Mark* 10:48
we *c*. every one of. *1 Thes* 2:11
let not church be *c*. *1 Tim* 5:16

chargedst

thou *c*. us, saying. *Ex* 19:23

charger, -s

(*A sort of dish or platter*)

offering was one silver *c*. *Num* 7:13
19, 25, 31, 37, 43, 49, 61, 67, 73, 79
dedication of altar, twelve *c*. 7:84
each *c*. of silver weighing 130. 85
number one thousand *c*. *Ezra* 1:9
John Baptist's head in a *c*. *Mat* 14:8
Mark 6:25

charges

the Levites to their *c*. *2 Chr* 8:14
from 20 years old in their *c*. 31:17
he set priests in their *c*. 35:2
them take, and be at *c*. *Acts* 21:24
warfare at his own *c*.? *1 Cor* 9:7

chargest

thou *c*. me to day. *2 Sam* 3:8

charging

c. the jailor to keep. *Acts* 16:23
c. that they strive. *2 Tim* 2:14

chariot

(*Among the ancients a two-wheeled vehicle for war, racing, or pleasure*)

to ride in the second *c*. *Gen* 41:43
Lord took off *c*. wheels. *Ex* 14:25
like work of a *c*. wheel. *1 Ki* 7:33
prepare thy *c*. and get. 18:44
number thee *c*. for *c*. and. 20:25
caused him to come into the *c*. 33
blood ran into the midst of *c*. 22:35
washed the *c*. in pool of. 38
appeared a *c*. of fire and. *2 Ki* 2:11
father, the *c*. of Israel. 12; 13:14
lighted from the *c*. to meet. 5:21
Jehu rode in a *c*. *2 Ki* 9:16
smite him in the *c*. 27
carried him in a *c*. to. 28; 23:30
gold for pattern of *c*. *1 Chr* 28:18
took him out of the *c*. *2 Chr* 35:24
he burneth the *c*. in. *Ps* 46:9
c. and horse are cast into. 76:6
made a *c*. of the wood. *S of S* 3:9*
a *c*. with horsemen, a *c*. *Isa* 21:7*
here cometh a *c*. of men. 9*
who bringeth forth the *c*. 43:17
break in pieces the *c*. *Jer* 51:21
bind the *c*. to the swift. *Mi* 1:13
first *c*. red horses, second *c*.
Zech 6:2
I will cut off the *c*. from. 9:10
go join thyself to his *c*. *Acts* 8:29
commanded *c*. to stand still. 38

his **chariot**

Joseph made ready *his c*. *Gen* 46:29
Pharaoh made ready *his c*. *Ex* 14:6
Sisera lighted off *his c*. *Judg* 4:15
why is *his c*. so long in ? 5:28
made speed to *his c*. *1 Ki* 12:18
2 Chr 10:18
said to the driver of *his c*. *1 Ki* 22:34
Ahab was stayed up in *his c*. 35
Naaman came with *his c*. *2 Ki* 5:9
turned again from *his c*. 26
his c. was made ready, went out each in *his c*. 9:21
and he sunk down in *his c*. 24
made him to ride in *his c*. 10:16
who maketh clouds *his c*. *Ps* 104:3
his c. shall be as a. *Jer* 4:13
sitting in *his c*. read. *Acts* 8:28

chariot-cities

horsemen placed in *c.-cities*.
2 Chr 1:14
all the *c.-cities*. 8:6
bestowed in the *c.-cities* and. 9:25

chariot-horses

houghed all *c.-horses*. *2 Sam* 8:4
1 Chr 18:4
therefore two *c.-horses*. *2 Ki* 7:14

chariot-man

he said to the *c.-man*. *2 Chr* 18:33

chariots

went up with Joseph *c*. *Gen* 50:9
took 600 *c*. and all the *c*. *Ex* 14:7
I will get honour upon his *c*. 17
the waters covered all the *c*. 28
Pharaoh's *c*. and host. 15:4
horse of Pharaoh went in with *c*. 19
have *c*. of iron. *Josh* 17:16, 18
Judg 1:19; 4:3
Sisera and all his *c*. *Judg* 4:15
why tarry the wheels of his *c*.? 5:28
appoint them for his *c*. *1 Sam* 8:11
fight against Israel, 30,000 *c*. 13:5
c. and horsemen followed. *2 Sam* 1:6
David slew the men of 700 *c*. 10:18
Solomon had 1400 *c*. *1 Ki* 10:26
Zimri captain of half his *c*. 16:9
when the captains of the *c*. 22:32
left but ten *c*. and. *2 Ki* 13:7
thy trust on Egypt for *c*. 18:24
Isa 36:9
the *c*. of God are 20,000. *Ps* 68:17
my soul like the *c*. of. *S of S* 6:12
nor is any end of their *c*. *Isa* 2:7
c. of thy glory be the shame. 22:18
woe to them that trust in *c*. 31:1
by the multitude of my *c*. 37:24
Lord will come with fire and *c*. 66:15
Jer 4:13; *Dan* 11:40
at rushing of his *c*. *Jer* 47:3
come against thee with *c*. *Ezek* 23:24
shake at the noise of the *c*. 26:10
like the noise of the *c*. *Joel* 2:5
off horses, and destroy *c*. *Mi* 5:10
c. shall be with flaming. *Nah* 2:3
c. shall rage in streets and. 4
I am against, and will burn her *c*. 13
I will overthrow the *c*. *Hag* 2:22
as the sound of *c*. *Rev* 9:9

chariots with *horses*

the *horses* and *c*. of. *Ex* 14:9, 23
did to their *horses* and *c*. *Deut* 11:4
when thou seest *horses* and *c*. 20:1
hough their *horses*, burn *c*. *Josh* 11:6
houghed *horses*, burnt their *c*. 9
prepared *horses* and *c*. *2 Sam* 15:1
Samaria with *c*. and *horses*.
1 Ki 20:1
was full of *c*. and *horses*. *2 Ki* 6:17
to hear a noise of *horses* and *c*. 7:6
are with you *c*. and *horses*. 10:2
in *c*. and some in *horses*. *Ps* 20:7
to *horses* in Pharaoh's *c*. *S of S* 1:9
on *horses* and in *c*. *Isa* 66:20
enter princes riding in *c*. and on *horses*. *Jer* 17:25; 22:4
ye *horses*, and rage, ye *c*. 46:9
upon their *horses* and their *c*. 50:37
with *horses* and with *c*. *Ezek* 26:7
my table with *horses* and *c*. 39:20
prancing *horses* and jumping *c*.
Nah 3:2
ride on thy *horses* and *c*. *Hab* 3:8
buys their *horses* and *c*. *Rev* 18:13

charitably

now walkest not *c*. *Rom* 14:15*

charity

[1] *Christian love or benevolence.* [2] *More generally, love, good will.* [3] *Good will to the poor, hence almsgiving. The word is used in the New Testament only, and in the Revised Version is always translated* love, *since the word* charity *has now come to have to most readers only the third meaning given above.*

but *c*. edifieth. *1 Cor* 8:1
and have not *c*. 13:1, 2, 3
c. suffereth long, and is kind, *c*. 4
c., but the greatest of these is *c*. 13
follow after *c*. and desire. 14:1
all things be done with *c*. 16:14
above all put on *c*. *Col* 3:14
of your faith and *c*. *1 Thes* 3:6
c. towards each other. *2 Thes* 1:3
end of commandment is *c*. *1 Tim* 1:5
continue in faith and *c*. 2:15
be an example in *c*. in spirit. 4:12
follow faith, *c*. peace. *2 Tim* 2:22
my doctrine, life, faith, *c*. 3:10
sound in faith, in *c*. *Tit* 2:2
fervent *c*. for *c*. shall. *1 Pet* 4:8
one another with a kiss of *c*. 5:14
to brotherly-kindness, *c*. *2 Pet* 1:7
borne witness of thy *c*. *3 John* 6
spots in your feasts of *c*. *Jude* 12
I know thy works, and *c*. *Rev* 2:19

charmed

serpents which will not be *c*. *Jer* 8:17

charmer, -s

found among you a *c*. *Deut* 18:11
not hearken to voice of *c*. *Ps* 58:5

Charran

Abraham dwelt in *C*. *Acts* 7:2, 4

chase

shall *c*. your enemies. *Lev* 26:
five of you shall *c*. an.
sound of a shaking leaf shall *c*. 3
should one *c*. 1000. *Deut* 32:3
Josh 23:1
let angel of Lord *c*. *Ps* 35:5

chased, -eth, -ing

the Amorites *c*. you as. *Deut* 1:4
Abimelech *c*. him. *Judg* 9:4
inclosed Benjamites and *c*. 20:4
Israel returned from *c*. *1 Sam* 17:5
therefore I *c*. him. *Neh* 13:2
he shall be *c*. out of. *Job* 18:1
he shall be *c*. away as a vision. 20:
and he that *c*. away. *Pr* 19:2
it shall be as the *c*. roe. *Isa* 13:1
they shall be *c*. as the chaff. 17:1
mine enemies *c*. me sore. *Lam* 3:5

chaste

you as a *c*. virgin. *2 Cor* 11
young women be *c*. obedient. *Tit* 2
your *c*. conversation. *1 Pet* 3

chasten

(*To correct or punish*)

I will *c*. him with rod. *2 Sam* 7:
nor *c*. me in displeasure. *Ps* 6
38
c. thy son while there is. *Pr* 19:
thou didst *c*. thyself. *Dan* 10:1
as I love I rebuke and *c*. *Rev* 3:

chastened
they have *c.* him. *Deut* 21:18
he is *c.* also with pain. *Job* 33:19
I wept, and *c.* my soul. *Ps* 69:10
all day been plagued, and *c.* 73:14
Lord hath *c.* me sore. 118:18
we are *c.* that we be. *1 Cor* 11:32
dying, yet live, as *c.* and. *2 Cor* 6:9
they for a few days *c.* *Heb* 12:10

chastenest, -eth, -ing
c. his son, so Lord *c.* *Deut* 8:5
despise not thou the *c.* of Almighty. *Job* 5:17; *Pr* 3:11; *Heb* 12:5
is the man whom thou *c.* *Ps* 94:12
he that loveth him *c.* *Pr* 13:24
a prayer when thy *c.* *Isa* 26:16
whom Lord loveth he *c.* *Heb* 12:6
endure *c.* what son father *c.* not? 7
no *c.* for present seems to be. 11

chastise
I will *c.* you seven. *Lev* 26:28
take the man and *c.* *Deut* 22:18
I will *c.* you with. *1 Ki* 12:11, 14; *2 Chr* 10:11, 14
I will *c.* them as their. *Hos* 7:12
my desire that I should *c.* 10:10
I will *c.* him, and. *Luke* 23:16, 22

chastised, -eth
c. you with whips. *1 Ki* 12:11, 14; *2 Chr* 10:11, 14
he that *c.* heathen. *Ps* 94:10
hast *c.* me, and I was *c.* *Jer* 31:18

chastisement
who have not seen the *c.* *Deut* 11:2
I have borne *c.* I will not. *Job* 34:31
c. of our peace was. *Isa* 53:5
have wounded with the *c.* *Jer* 30:14
if without *c.* then are. *Heb* 12:8

chatter
so did I *c.* *Isa* 38:14

Chebar
by river of *C.* *Ezek* 1:1, 3; 3:15, 23; 10:15, 20

check
I have heard the *c.* of. *Job* 20:3*

checker work
Hiram made nets of *c.-w* *1 Ki* 7:17

cheek
smote Micaiah on the *c.* *1 Ki* 22:24; *2 Chr* 18:23
smitten me on the *c.* *Job* 16:10
he giveth his *c.* to him. *Lam* 3:30
Judge with a rod on the *c.* *Mi* 5:1
smiteth one *c.* offer also. *Luke* 6:29

right **cheek**
smite thee on thy *right c.* *Mat* 5:39

cheek-bone
all mine enemies on *c.-bone.* *Ps* 3:7

cheeks
o priest the two *c.* *Deut* 18:3
hy *c.* are comely with. *S of S* 1:10
is *c.* are as a bed of spices. 5:13
gave my *c.* to them. *Isa* 50:6
nd her tears are on her *c.* *Lam* 1:2

cheek-teeth
ome up, hath *c.-teeth.* *Joel* 1:6

cheer
hall *c.* up his wife he. *Deut* 24:5
et thy heart *c.* thee in. *Eccl* 11:9
on, be of good *c.* thy. *Mat* 9:2
e of good *c.* it is I. 14:27; *Mark* 6:50
e of good *c.* *John* 16:33
e of good *c.* Paul. *Acts* 23:11
exhort you to be of good *c.* 27:22
herefore, sirs, be of good *c.* 25
en were they all of good *c.* 36

cheereth
ave my wine, which *c.* *Judg* 9:13

cheerful
erry heart maketh a *c.* *Pr* 15:13
ouse of Judah joy and *c.* *Zech* 8:19
rn shall make young men *c.* 9:17*
r God loveth a *c.* *2 Cor* 9:7

cheerfully
do the more *c.* answer. *Acts* 24:10

cheerfulness
eweth mercy with *c.* *Rom* 12:8

cheese, -s
carry these ten *c.* to. *1 Sam* 17:18
sheep and *c.* to David. *2 Sam* 17:29
curdled me like *c.*? *Job* 10:10

Chemarims
cut off the name of *C.* *Zeph* 1:4

Chemosh
undone, O people of *C.* *Num* 21:29
possess what *C.* giveth? *Judg* 11:24
an high place for *C.* *1 Ki* 11:7, 33
and *C.* shall go forth. *Jer* 48:7
Moab shall be ashamed of *C.* 13
woe to thee, O Moab, people of *C.* 46

Chenaniah
C. chief of Levites. *1 Cor* 15:22, 27

Cherethims
behold, I will cut off *C.* *Ezek* 25:16

Cherethites
invasion on south of *C.* *1 Sam* 30:14
Benaiah was over *C.* *2 Sam* 8:18; 20:23; *1 Chr* 18:17
unto the nation of the *C.* *Zeph* 2:5

cherish
let her *c.* him, and lie. *1 Ki* 1:2

cherished
damsel was fair, and *c.* *1 Ki* 1:4

cherisheth
c. his own flesh, as the. *Eph* 5:29
gentle, even as a nurse *c.* *1 Thes* 2:7

Cherith
hide thyself by brook *C.* *1 Ki* 17:3

cherub
[1] *One of an order of angels, usually below the seraphim. Plural properly* cherubim, *in Authorized Version* cherubims. [2] *A winged figure used in connection with the mercy seat of the Jewish ark of the covenant,* Ex 25:18–22; 37:7–9. [3] *A mysterious composite figure described in* Ezek 1 and 10.
one *c.* on one end, and the other *c.* *Ex* 25:19; 37:8
he rode upon a *c.* *2 Sam* 22:11; *Ps* 18:10
other *c.* was ten cubits. *1 Ki* 6:25
the height of one *c.* ten cubits. 26
glory of God was gone from the *c.* to. *Ezek* 9:3; 10:4
and one *c.* stretched forth his. 10:7
first face was the face of a *c.* 14
thou art the anointed *c.* 28:14
will destroy thee, O covering *c.* 16
between a *c.* and a *c.* every *c.* 41:18

cherubims
at the east of the garden *c.* *Gen* 3:24
thou shalt make two *c.* *Ex* 25:18
tabernacle of *c.* of cunning. 26:1, 31
he made two *c.* of beaten. 37:7
within oracle two *c.* *1 Ki* 6:23
both the *c.* were of one measure. 25
overlaid the *c.* with gold. 28
c. covered the ark. 8:7; *2 Chr* 5:8; *Heb* 9:5
most holy place two *c.* *2 Chr* 3:10
sound of the *c.* wings. *Ezek* 10:5
when *c.* went, the wheels went. 16
c. lift up their wings and. 19; 11:22

between the **cherubims**
thee from *between the c.* *Ex* 25:22
from *between the* two *c.* *Num* 7:89
dwelleth *between the c.* *1 Sam* 4:4; *2 Sam* 6:2; *2 Ki* 19:15; *Isa* 37:16
dwelleth *between the c.* shine. *Ps* 80:1
he sitteth *between the c.* 99:1
of fire from *between c.* *Ezek* 10:2
between c. to fire was *between c.* 7

chesnut-tree, -s
took him rods of *c.-tree.* *Gen* 30:37*
the *c.-trees* were not. *Ezek* 31:8*

chest, -s
Jehoiada took *c.* and. *2 Ki* 12:9
they made *c.* *2 Chr* 24:8
and emptied the *c.* 11
in *c.* of rich apparel. *Ezek* 27:24

chew
of them that *c.* cud. *Lev* 11:4; *Deut* 14:7

chewed
ere the flesh was *c.* *Num* 11:33

cheweth
because he *c.* cud. *Lev* 11:4, 5, 6; *Deut* 14:6
swine *c.* not cud. *Lev* 11:7; *Deut* 14:8

chickens
a hen gathereth her *c.* *Mat* 23:37

chide
people did *c.*, why *c.* ye? *Ex* 17:2*
men of Ephraim did *c.* *Judg* 8:1
he will not always *c.* *Ps* 103:9

chiding
Meribah, because of *c.* *Ex* 17:7*

chief
[1] *The head of a family, tribe, army, etc.,* Num 3:30; Deut 1:15; 1 Sam 14:38; 2 Sam 5:8. *In such cases the Revised Version commonly changes the word to* princes, *or* captains, *or* heads. [2] *The best, or most valuable,* 1 Sam 15:21. [3] *The dearest, or most familiar,* Pr 16:28.
the *c.* butler told his. *Gen* 40:9
he restored the *c.* butler to. 21
but hanged the *c.* baker as. 22
c. over *c.* of Levites. *Num* 3:32
the *c.* of your tribes. *Deut* 1:15
the people took the *c.* *1 Sam* 15:21
brother of Joab *c.* *2 Sam* 23:18
these were the *c.* of. *1 Ki* 9:23
of Judah came the *c.* *1 Chr* 5:2
first shall be *c.* and captain, Joab went first and was *c.* 11:6
sons of David were *c.* about. 18:17
his father made him *c.* 26:10
the rulers have been *c.* *Ezra* 9:2
c. of the province that. *Neh* 11:3
taketh away heart of *c.* *Job* 12:24
chose out their way, and sat *c.* 29:25
behemoth is the *c.* of the. 40:19
smote *c.* of their strength. *Ps* 78:51; 105:36
Jerusalem above my *c.* joy. 137:6
Wisdom crieth in *c.* place. *Pr* 1:21
a whisperer separateth *c.* friends. 16:28
orchard with all the *c.* *S of S* 4:14
stirreth up the *c.* ones. *Isa* 14:9
hast taught them as *c.* *Jer* 13:21
sing and shout among the *c.* 31:7
her adversaries are the *c.* *Lam* 1:5
c. of children of Ammon. *Dan* 11:41
which are named *c.* *Amos* 6:1
anoint themselves with *c.* 6
whosoever will be *c.* *Mat* 20:27
c. seats in the synagogues. 23:6; *Mark* 12:39
supper to his *c.* estates. *Mark* 6:21
out devils through *c.* *Luke* 11:15
house of one of *c.* Pharisees. 14:1
they chose *c.* rooms. 7; 20:46
and he that is *c.* as he that. 22:26
among *c.* rulers many. *John* 12:42
Paul was the *c.* speaker. *Acts* 14:12
and of *c.* women not a few. 17:4
c. of Asia. 19:31*
the *c.* corner-stone. *Eph* 2:20; *1 Pet* 2:6
sinners, of whom I *c.* *1 Tim* 1:15
when *c.* Shepherd shall. *1 Pet* 5:4

chief *captain*
shall be *c.* and *captain.* *2 Sam* 5:8
came to the *c. captain.* *Acts* 21:31
when they saw the *c. captain.* 32
this young man to *c. captain.* 23:17
c. captain Lysias came upon. 24:7
c. captain shall come. 22

chief *captains*
Tachmonite sat *c.* among *captains.* *2 Sam* 23:8
c. of all the *captains.* *1 Chr* 27:3
c. of Solomon's *captains.* *2 Chr* 8:9
Agrippa entered with *c. captains.* *Acts* 25:23
rich men and *c. captains.* *Rev* 6:15

chief *fathers*
thou and *c. fathers* of. *Num* 31:26
c. fathers of Levites. *1 Chr* 9:34
the *c. fathers* of priests and. 24:31
2700 *c. fathers* made rulers. 26:32

of *c. fathers* of mighty. *2 Chr* 26:12
c. of the *fathers* of Judah. *Ezra* 1:5
c. of the *fathers* gave. *Neh* 7:70, 71

chief *house*
c. of *house* of Gershonites. *Num* 3:24
c. of *house* of Kohathites. 30
c. of the *house* of the Merarites. 35
Zimri was of a *c. house.* 25:14
Cozbi, of a *c. house* in Midian. 15
out of each *c. house* a. *Josh* 22:14

chief *man,* or *men*
being a *c. man* *Lev* 21:4
all of them *c. men.* *1 Chr* 7:3
more *c. men* of Eleazar than. 24:4
names of *men* that were *c. Ezra* 5:10
I gathered together *c. men.* 7:28
thee from the *c. men.* *Isa* 41:9
Jews stirred up *c. men.* *Acts* 13:50
Judas and Silas, *c. men.* 15:22
possessions of the *c. man.* 28:7

chief *priest*
Seraiah the *c. priest.* *2 Ki* 25:18
Benaiah a *c. priest.* *1 Chr* 27:5
anointed Zadok to be *c. priest.* 29:22
Amariah *c. priest* is. *2 Chr* 19:11
and Azariah the *c. priest.* 26:20

chief *priests*
twelve of *c.* of *priests.* *Ezra* 8:24
made the *c. priests* and all. 10:5
these were *c. priests* in. *Neh* 12:7
many things of *c. priests. Mat* 16:21
multitude from the *c. priests.* 26:47
c. priests sought to. 59
Mark 14:1, 55; *Luke* 9:22; 22:2
was accused of *c. priests. Mat* 27:12
Mark 15:3
c. priests mocking. *Mat* 27:41
Mark 15:31
voices of them and *c. priests.* *Luke* 23:23
c. priests sent officers to. *John* 7:32
18:3
c. priests answered, we have. 19:15
authority from *c. priests.* *Acts* 9:14
26:10
commanded the *c. priests.* 22:30

chief *prince,* or *princes*
of Asher, *c.* of *princes.* *1 Chr* 7:40
Gog *c. prince* of. *Ezek* 38:2, 3; 39:1
Michael one of *c. princes. Dan* 10:13

chief *singer,* or *singers*
were *c.* of the *singers.* *Neh* 12:46
to the *c. singer* on my. *Hab* 3:19

chiefest
fat with *c.* offerings. *1 Sam* 2:29
made them sit in *c.* place. 9:22
Doeg an Edomite, *c.* of herd-. 21:7
Hezekiah buried in *c.* *2 Chr* 32:33
my beloved is the *c.* *S of S* 5:10
who will be *c.* shall. *Mark* 10:44
not a whit behind *c.* *2 Cor* 11:5
12:11

chiefly
c. because to them were. *Rom* 3:2
c. of they that are of. *Phil* 4:22
c. them that walk after. *2 Pet* 2:10

child
[1] *One young in years,* 1 Sam 1:22. [2] *One weak in knowledge,* Isa 10:19; 1 Cor 13:11. [3] *Such as are humble and docile,* Mat 18:3, 4.

(*The words child, children are frequently used for any descendant or descendants however remote, as the children of Israel. Such expressions as children of light, children of darkness, mean those who follow the light, or try to hide in the darkness. "Children of God" in the Old Testament is used sometimes for angels, sometimes for good men. In the New Testament the term is more often used of those who have believed and accepted Christ*)

see **son, sons**
Hagar cast the *c.* under. *Gen* 21:15
let me not see the death of *c.* 16
the *c.* is not, and I, whither? 37:30
do not sin against the *c.*? *Gen* 42:22
called the *c.* mother. *Ex* 2:8
not afflict any fatherless *c.* 22:22
was his only *c.* *Judg* 11:34
teach us what we shall do to *c.* 13:8
brought the *c.* to Eli. *1 Sam* 1:25
the Lord had called the *c.* 3:8
c. that is born to thee. *2 Sam* 12:14
Lord struck the *c.* that Uriah's. 15
David besought God for the *c.* 16
David perceived that *c.* was dead. 19
divide the living *c.* in. *1 Ki* 3:25
what shall become of the *c.* 14:3
the soul of the *c.* came into. 17:22
he told him, the *c.* is. *2 Ki* 4:31
the *c.* sneezed, and *c.* opened. 35
correction from the *c.* *Pr* 23:13
he hath neither *c.* nor. *Eccl* 4:8
with second *c.* that shall stand. 15
c. shall behave himself. *Isa* 3:5
for before the *c.* shall know. 7:16
the *c.* shall know to cry, my. 8:4
weaned *c.* shall put his hand. 11:8
the *c.* shall die an hundred. 65:20
bringeth forth her first *c.* *Jer* 4:31
is he a pleasant *c.*? 31:20
cut off man, woman, and *c.* 44:7
father shall deliver *c.* to. *Mat* 10:21
the *c.* was cured from. 17:18
twofold more the *c.* of hell. 23:15
came to circumcise *c.* *Luke* 1:59
what manner of *c.* shall this? 66
thou *c.* shalt be called Prophet. 76
the *c.* grew, and waxed. 80; 2:40
parents brought in *c.* Jesus. 2:27
my son, he is my only *c.* 9:38
Jesus healed *c.* and delivered. 42
come down ere my *c.* die. *John* 4:49
as she is delivered of *c.* 16:21
against thy holy *c.* Jesus. *Acts* 4:27*
signs may be done by name of *c.* 30*
Saul said, thou *c.* of the devil. 13:10
to devour her *c.* as soon. *Rev* 12:4
her *c.* was caught up to God. 5

a **child**
bear *a c.* who am old? *Gen* 18:13
father, and *a c.* of his old age. 44:20
saw he was *a* goodly *c.* *Ex* 2:2
Heb 11:23
Samuel, *a c.* girded. *1 Sam* 2:18
wast delivered of *a c.* *1 Ki* 3:17
a c. shall be born to house of. 13:2
shall be fresher than *a c.* *Job* 33:25
as *a c.* as *a* weaned *c.* *Ps* 131:2
even *a c.* is known. *Pr* 20:11
train up *a c.* in the way he. 22:6
bound in the heart of *a c.* 15
a c. left to himself bringeth. 29:15
bringeth up his servant from *a c.* 21
better is *a* wise *c.* than. *Eccl* 4:13
to thee, when thy king is *a c.* 10:16
for unto us *a c.* is born. *Isa* 9:6
trees shall be few, that *a c.* 10:19
cannot speak, I am *a c.* *Jer* 1:6, 7
tidings, saying, *a* man *c.* is. 20:15
when Israel was *a c.* *Hos* 11:1
he said of *a c.* *Mark* 9:21
took *a c.* and set. 36; *Luke* 9:47
a c. I spake as *a c.* understood as *a c.* I thought as *a c.* *1 Cor* 13:11
heir as long as he is *a c.* *Gal* 4:1
from *a c.* hast known. *2 Tim* 3:15
Sarah delivered of *a c.* *Heb* 11:11
brought forth *a* man *c.* *Rev* 12:5

little **child**
am a *little c.* I know not. *1 Ki* 3:7
fled into Egypt, being a *little c.* 11:17
the flesh of a *little c.* *2 Ki* 5:14
a *little c.* shall lead them. *Isa* 11:6
Jesus called a *little c.* to. *Mat* 18:2
shall receive one such *little c.* 5
not receive the kingdom of God as a *little c.* *Mark* 10:15; *Luke* 18:17

no **child**
but Sarai had *no c.* *Gen* 11:30
priest's daughter have *no c.* *Lev* 22:13
die, and have *no c.* *Deut* 25:5
Michal had *no c.* unto. *2 Sam* 6:23
verily she hath *no c.* *2 Ki* 4:14
they had *no c.* because. *Luke* 1:7
promised when he had *no c. Acts* 7:5

sucking **child**
father beareth *sucking c. Num* 11:12
sucking c. shall play on. *Isa* 11:8
woman forget her *sucking c.*? 49:15
tongue of *sucking c.* *Lam* 4:4

this **child**
take *this c.* and nurse. *Ex* 2:9
told concerning *this c.* *Luke* 2:17
this c. is set for fall and rising. 34
whoso shall receive *this c.* 9:48

with **child**
Hagar, thou art *with c.* *Gen* 16:11
daughters of Lot were *with c.* 19:36
Tamar thy daughter is *with c.* 38:24
whose these are, am I *with c.* 25
hurt a woman *with c.* *Ex* 21:22
Phinehas' wife was *with c.* *1 Sam* 4:19
Bath-sheba said, I am *with c.* *2 Sam* 11:5
rip up women *with c.* *2 Ki* 8:12
15:16
of her that is *with c.* *Eccl* 11:5
like a woman *with c.* *Isa* 26:17
we have been *with c.* we have. 18
that didst not travail *with c.* 54:1
man doth travail *with c.* *Jer* 30:6
from north woman *with c.* 31:8
their women *with c.* *Hos* 13:16
ripped up the women *with c.* *Amos* 1:13
she was found *with c.* of. *Mat* 1:18
a virgin shall be *with c.* 23
woe to them that are *with c.* 24:19
Mark 13:17; *Luke* 21:23
Mary, being great *with c. Luke* 2:5
upon a woman *with c.* *1 Thes* 5:3
she being *with c.* cried. *Rev* 12:2

young **child**
and the *c.* was *young.* *1 Sam* 1:24
search diligently for the *young c.* *Mat* 2:8
take *young c.* and his mother. 13
took the *young c.* and his mother. 14

childbearing
she shall be saved in *c.* *1 Tim* 2:15

childhood
before you from my *c.* *1 Sam* 12:2
c. and youth are vanity. *Eccl* 11:10

childish
I put away *c.* things. *1 Cor* 13:11

childless
give me, seeing I go *c.*? *Gen* 15:2
their sin, shall die *c.* *Lev* 20:20
thy sword hath made women *c.* so shall thy mother be *c. 1 Sam* 15:33
write you this man *c.* *Jer* 22:30
her to wife, and died *c. Luke* 20:30

children
(*Revised Version frequently changes this word to sons*)
in sorrow bring forth *c.* *Gen* 3:1
it may be I may obtain *c.* 16:
the *c.* struggled together. 25:2
give me *c.* or I die. 30:
the *c.* which God hath given. 33:
thy father's *c.* shall bow down. 49:
600,000 men, besides *c.* *Ex* 12:3
iniquity of the fathers upon *c.* 20:
34:7; *Num* 14:18; *Deut* 5:
the wife and her *c.* shall. *Ex* 21:
saw the *c.* of Anak. *Num* 13:2
the *c.* of Korah died not. 26:1
Ar to the *c.* of Lot. *Deut* 2:9, 1
can stand before the *c.* of Anak? 9:
the *c.* of Belial are gone. 13:1
ye are the *c.* of the Lord. 14:
have born him *c.* both beloved. 21:1
the *c.* begotten of them shall. 23:
fathers shall not be put to death f c. nor *c.* for. 24:16; *2 Chr* 25:
c. in whom there is no faith. *Deut* 32:
let Asher be blessed with *c.* 33:
c. of Reuben, Gad and Manasse built there an. *Josh* 22:9, 10,
take 10,000 men of *c.* of. *Judg* 4
each one resembled the *c.* of. 8:
a riddle to *c.* of people. 14:
deliver us the *c.* of Belial. 20:1

she that hath many c. 1 Sam 2:5
c. of Belial said, how shall ? 10:27†
neither shall c. of wickedness afflict them. 2 Sam 7:10; 1 Chr 17:9
two men, c. of Belial. 1 Ki 21:13*
bears came and tare 42 c. 2 Ki 2:24
Elisha called one of the c. 9:1
salute the c. of the king, c. 10:13
but the c. of murderers he slew not. 14:6; 2 Chr 25:4
do as Lord commanded c. 2 Ki 17:34
c. are come to birth. 19:3; Isa 37:3
Seled died without c. 1 Chr 2:30
and Jether died without c. 32
Shimei's brethren had not many c. 4:27
c. of Jacob his. 16:13; Ps 105:6
gathered to Jeroboam c. 2 Chr 13:7*
Lord is not with the c. of. 25:7
smote of c. of Seir 10,000. 11
are c. of the province. Ezra 2:1
Neh 7:6
by whom they had c. Ezra 10:44
c. multipliedst thou as. Neh 9:23
I intreated for the c. sake. Job 19:17
were c. of fools, yea c. 30:8
he is a king over all the c. 41:34
they are full of c. and. Ps 17:14
come, ye c. hearken to me. 34:11
an alien to my mother's c. 69:8
he shall save the c. of needy. 72:4
the c. which should be born. 78:6
and all of you are c. of the 82:6
have holpen the c. of Lot. 83:8
the c. of thy servants shall. 102:28
to be a joyful mother of c. 113:9
lo c. are an heritage of Lord. 127:3
as arrows in the hand, so are c. 4
remember, O Lord, c. of. 137:7
let old men and c. praise. 148:12
let the c. of Zion be joyful. 149:2
hear, ye c. instruction. Pr 4:1
5:7; 7:24; 8:32
and the glory of c. are. 17:6
her c. arise up and call her. 31:28
if a man beget 100 c. Eccl 6:3
mother's c. were angry. S of S 1:6
I have brought up c. Isa 1:2
ah sinful nation, c. that are. 4
they please themselves in c. 2:6
I will give c. to be their princes. 3:4
as for my people, c. are their. 12
. whom Lord hath. 8:18; Heb 2:13
their eye not spare c. Isa 13:18
mighty men of c. of Kedar. 21:17
travail not, nor bring forth c. 23:4
woe to the rebellious c. saith. 30:1
ying c. c. that will not hear Lord. 9
ather to the c. make known. 38:19
neither know the loss of c. 47:8
ome in one day the loss of c. 9
he c. which thou shalt have. 49:20
or more are c. of the desolate than c. 54:1; Gal 4:27
re ye not c. of transgression? Isa 57:4
laying the c. in the valleys. 5
hey are my people, c. that. 63:8
he brought forth c. 66:8
urn, O backsliding c. Jer 3:14, 22
ow shall I put thee among c.? 19
ey are sottish c. 4:22
will pour it out upon the c. 6:11
e c. gather wood. 7:18
r death entered to cut off c. 9:21
will bereave them of c. 15:7
eeping for her c. 31:15; Mat 2:18
teeth are set on edge. Jer 31:29
Ezek 18:2
all the women eat c.? Lam 2:20
ung men to grind, c. fell. 5:13
they are impudent c. Ezek 2:4
e c. rebelled against me. 20:21
e c. still are talking. 33:30
rangers shall beget c. 47:22
in whom was no blemish. Dan 1:4
rer and fatter than all c. 15
for these four c. God gave. 17
ichael shall stand for the c. 12:1
e unto thee c. of. Hos 1:2
have mercy on her c. they be c. 2:4
battle against the c. of. 10:9
shed in pieces upon her c. 14

then the c. shall tremble. Hos 11:10
in place of breaking forth of c. 13:13
gather c. and those that. Joel 2:16
be glad then ye c. of Zion. 23
are ye not as c. of the ? Amos 9:7
poll thee for delicate c. Mi 1:16
I will punish the king's c. Zeph 1:8
turn the heart of fathers to the c. and heart of c. Mal 4:6; Luke 1:17
Herod slew all the c. in. Mat 2:16
of these stones to raise up c. 3:9
Luke 3:8
that ye may be c. of your. Mat 5:45
but the c. of the kingdom. 8:12
can c. of bride-chamber mourn ? 9:15; Mark 2:19; Luke 5:34
c. shall rise against. Mat 10:21
Mark 13:12
wisdom justified of her c. Mat 11:19*
Luke 7:35
good seed are the c. of kingdom, tares are the c. of. Mat 13:38
not meet to take c. bread. 15:26
Mark 7:27
then are the c. free. Mat 17:26
forsaken wife or c. for my. 19:29
Mark 10:29
mother of Zebedee's c. Mat 20:20
priests and scribes saw c. 21:15
c. of them that killed. 23:31
let the c. first be filled. Mark 7:27
dogs eat of the c. crumbs. 28
receive one of such c. 9:37, 41
be the c. of the Highest. Luke 6:35
c. of this world wiser than c. 16:8
a wife, and died without c. 20:29
the c. of this world marry. 34
if ye were Abraham's c. John 8:39
c. have ye any meat ? 21:5
ye are c. of the prophets. Acts 3:25
if c. then heirs, heirs of. Rom 8:17
seed of Abraham are they all c. 9:7
for c. being not yet born, nor. 11
be not c. in understanding; howbeit in malice be ye c. 1 Cor 14:20
c. ought not to lay up for the parents, but parents for c. 2 Cor 12:14
of faith, the same are c. Gal 3:7
so we, when we were c. were. 4:3
in bondage with her c. 25
are not c. of bond-woman. 31
us to adoption of c. Eph 1:5
the spirit that worketh in c. 2:2
were by nature c. of wrath. 3
no more c., tossed to and fro. 4:14
followers of God as dear c. 5:1
wrath cometh on c. of. 6; Col 3:6
c. obey your parents. Eph 6:1
Col 3:20
if any widow have c. 1 Tim 5:4
if she hath brought up c. 10
younger women marry, bear c. 14
the c. are partakers of. Heb 2:14
speaketh to you as to c. 12:5
as obedient c. not. 1 Pet 1:14
of adultery, cursed c. 2 Pet 2:14
c. of God manifest, c. of. 1 John 3:10
to the elect lady and her c. 2 John 1
c. of thy elect sister greet thee. 13
I will kill her c. with. Rev 2:23

see **Ammon, captivity**

children *of Benjamin*

of the c. of B. by their. Num 1:36
c. of B. did not drive. Judg 1:21
c. of B. would not hearken. 20:13
c. of B. gathered. 2 Sam 2:25
dwelt of c. of B. 1 Chr 9:3
Neh 11:4
there came of c. of B. 1 Chr 12:16
O ye c. of Benjamin. Jer 6:1

children's **children**

thou and thy ch. c. Gen 45:10
iniquity of fathers on ch. c. Ex 34:7
beget c. and ch. c. Deut 4:25
both their c. and ch. c. 2 Ki 17:41
righteousness unto ch. c. Ps 103:17
shalt see thy ch. c. and. 128:6
inheritance to his ch. c. Pr 13:22
ch. c. are crown of old men, glory of c. 17:6
with your ch. c. will I plead. Jer 2:9
their ch. c. for ever. Ezek 37:25

fatherless **children**

any to favour father. c. Ps 109:12
leave thy father. c. I. Jer 49:11

children *of God*

be called the c. of G. Mat 5:9
the c. of G. being c. of. Luke 20:36
together in one c. of G. John 11:52
that we are the c. of G. Rom 8:16
glorious liberty of c. of G. 21
c. of the flesh, not c. of G. 9:8
be called c. of living G. 26
ye are all c. of G. by. Gal 3:26
c. of G. manifest, c. of. 1 John 3:10
know that we love c. of G. 5:2

his **children**

Abraham will command his c. Gen 18:19
loved Joseph more than his c. 37:3
his days, he and his c. Deut 17:20
their spot is not spot of his c. 32:5
nor knew his own c. 33:9
his wife and his c. 1 Sam 30:22
it grew up with his c. 2 Sam 12:3
give him a light, and his c. 2 Ki 8:19
burnt his c. in fire after. 2 Chr 28:3
caused his c. to pass through. 33:6
his c. are far from safety. Job 5:4
even the eyes of his c. 17:5
his c. shall seek to please. 20:10
layeth up his iniquity for his c. 21:19
if his c. be multiplied, it is. 27:14
if his c. forsake my law. Ps 89:30
as a father pitieth his c. 103:13
let his c. be fatherless. 109:9
let his c. be vagabonds. 10
his c. shall have a place. Pr 14:26
the just man, his c. are. 20:7
slaughter for his c. for. Isa 14:21
when he seeth his c. in. 29:23
Ephraim bring forth his c. Hos 9:13
his c. and cattle drank. John 4:12
charged you as father doth his c. 1 Thes 2:11
having his c. in subjection. 1 Tim 3:4

children *of Israel*

an oath of the c. of Isr. Gen 50:25
c. of Isr. were fruitful. Ex 1:7
grieved because of c. of Isr. 12
c. of Isr. sighed. 2:23
God looked on c. of Isr. 25
Lord had visited c. of Isr. 4:31
heard groaning of the c. of Isr. 6:5
bring c. of Isr. out. 13, 26, 27; 12:51
nothing die of all that is c. of Isr. 9:4
c. of Isr. journeyed about. 12:37
there I will meet with c. of Isr. 29:43
sign between me and c. of Isr. 31:17
whosoever he be, c. of Isr. Lev 17:13
for to me the c. of Isr. 25:55
Lord appeared before c. of Isr. Num 14:10
c. of Isr. could not stand. Josh 7:12
numbered c. of Isr. 1 Sam 11:8
were not of c. of Isr. 2 Sam 21:2
them instead of c. of Isr. 2 Ki 17:24
had not the c. of Isr. done. Neh 8:17
his acts to c. of Isr. Ps 103:7
even of the c. of Isr., a. 148:14
one by one, O ye c. of Isr. Isa 27:12
when c. of Isr. went. Ezek 44:15
48:11
thus, O ye c. of Isr.? Amos 2:11
liketh you, O ye c. of Isr. 4:5
many of the c. of Isr. Luke 1:16
visit brethren c. of Isr. Acts 7:23
Moses which said to the c. of Isr. 37
bear my name before c. of Isr. 9:15
word God sent to c. of Isr. 10:36
number of c. of Isr. be. Rom 9:27
c. of Isr. could not behold face of. 2 Cor 3:7
of departing of c. of Isr. Heb 11:22
block before c. of Isr. Rev 2:14
of all tribes of the c. of Isr. 7:4
of twelve tribes of c. of Isr. 21:12

children *of Judah*

of the c. of Judah by. Num 1:26
c. of Judah came to. Josh 14:6
bade teach c. of Judah. 2 Sam 1:18
c. of Judah prevailed. 2 Chr 13:18
other 10,000 did c. of Judah. 25:12
to keep under c. of Judah. 28:10

the evil of *c. of Judah.* *Jer* 32:32
they and the *c. of Judah* going. 50:4
Israel and *c. of Judah* were. 33
against the *c. of Judah.* *Joel* 3:19

children *of light*

c. of this world wiser than *c. of light.* *Luke* 16:8
may be the *c. of light.* *John* 12:36
walk as *c. of light.* *Eph* 5:8
ye are all *c. of light.* *1 Thes* 5:5

little **children**

little c. stood in door. *Num* 16:27
came forth *little c.* and. *2 Ki* 2:23
one day to destroy *little c.* *Esth* 3:13
slay utterly maids, *little c.* *Ezek* 9:6
and become as *little c.* *Mat* 18:3
were brought to him *little c.* 19:13
suffer *little c.* to come. 14
Mark 10:14; *Luke* 18:16
little c. yet a little while. *John* 13:33
my *little c.* of whom. *Gal* 4:19
my *little c.* I write. *1 John* 2:1, 12, 13
are of God, *little c.* and have. 4:4
little c. keep from idols. 5:21

children *of men*

tower which *c. of men.* *Gen* 11:5
if they be *c. of men.* *1 Sam* 26:19
with stripes of *c. of men.* *2 Sam* 7:14
hearts of *c. of men.* *1 Ki* 8:39
2 Chr 6:30
eye-lids try the *c. of men.* *Ps* 11:4
fail from among *c. of men.* 12:1
down upon *c. of men.* 14:2; 53:2
c. of men put their trust. 36:7
thou art fairer than *c. of men.* 45:2
sayest, return ye *c. of men.* 90:3
works to *c. of men.* 107:8, 15, 21, 31
earth given to *c. of men.* 115:16
then hearts of *c. of men.* *Pr* 15:11
nor grieve *c. of men.* *Lam* 3:33
wherever *c. of men* dwell. *Dan* 2:38

men-**children**

saved *men-c.* alive. *Ex* 1:17, 18
all the *men-c.* shall appear. 34:23
the *male c.* of Manasseh. *Josh* 17:2

men, women, and **children**

destroyed *m. w. and c.* *Deut* 3:6
gather *m. w. and c.* to hear. 31:12
smote Nob, *m. w. and c.* and. *1 Sam* 22:19
congregation of *m. w. and c.* *Ezra* 10:1
to Gedaliah *m. w. and c.* *Jer* 40:7
about 5000 *m.* beside *w. and c.* *Mat* 14:21; 15:38

my **children**

my wives and *my c.* for. *Gen* 30:26
these *c.* are *my c.* these cattle. 31:43
me ye have bereaved of *my c.* 42:36
if I be bereaved of *my c.* I. 43:14
the first-born of *my c.* *Ex* 13:15
love my master, wife, and *my c.* 21:5
for my wives and *my c.* *1 Ki* 20:7
that I were as when *my c.* *Job* 29:5
seeing I have lost my *c.* *Isa* 49:21
my c. are gone forth of. *Jer* 10:20
my c. are desolate. *Lam* 1:16
thou hast slain *my c.*? *Ezek* 16:21
trouble me not, *my c.* *Luke* 11:7
I speak as to *my c.* *2 Cor* 6:13
joy to hear that *my c.* walk. *3 John* 4

no **children**

Abram's wife bare him *no c.* *Gen* 16:1
Rachel saw that she bare *no c.* 30:1
died, and had *no c.* *Num* 3:4
but Hannah had *no c.* *1 Sam* 1:2
man die having *no c.* *Mat* 22:24
Mark 12:19
seven left *no c.* *Luke* 20:31

our **children**

riches are ours and *our c.* *Gen* 31:16
to kill us, and *our c.* *Ex* 17:3
our wives and *our c.* be. *Num* 14:3
belong to us and to *our c.* *Deut* 29:29
your *c.* speak to *our c.* *Josh* 22:24
your *c.* make *our c.* cease from. 25
brethren, *our c.* as their *c.* *Neh* 5:5
blood be on us and our *c.* *Mat* 27:25

children *of promise*

c. of prom. are counted. *Rom* 9:8
Isaac was, are *c. of prom.* *Gal* 4:28

strange **children**

deliver me from *strange c.* *Ps* 144:7† 11†
have begotten *strange c.* *Hos* 5:7

their **children**

to daughters or *their c.* *Gen* 31:43
they may teach *their c.* *Deut* 4:10
might be well with *their c.* 5:29
that *their c.* may learn to. 31:13
and *their c.* them Joshua. *Josh* 5:7
of *their c.* did Solomon. *1 Ki* 9:21
wilt dash *their c.* and. *2 Ki* 8:12
burnt *their c.* in the fire to. 17:31
their c. served images as did. 41
with wives and *their c.* *2 Chr* 20:13
he slew not *their c.* but did. 25:4
their c. thou multipliedst. *Neh* 9:23
their c. spake half in the. 13:24
their c. dance. *Job* 21:11
yieldeth food for *their c.* 24:5
not hide them from *their c.* *Ps* 78:4
and declare them to *their c.* 6
let thy glory appear to *their c.* 90:16
their c. shall sit on thy. 132:12
their c. shall be dashed. *Isa* 13:16
whilst *their c.* remember. *Jer* 17:2
therefore deliver up *their c.* 18:21
their c. also shall be as. 30:20
iniquity into bosom of *their c.* 32:18
for good of them and of *their c.* 39
shall not look back to *their c.* 47:3
have sodden *their c.* *Lam* 4:10
I said to *their c.* in. *Ezek* 20:18
when they had slain *their c.* 23:39
they and *their c.* shall. 37:25
cast them and *their c.* *Dan* 6:24
though bring up *their c.* *Hos* 9:12
c. tell *their c.* and *their c.* *Joel* 1:3
from *their c.* have ye taken. *Mi* 2:9
yea, *their c.* shall see it. *Zech* 10:7
they shall live with *their c.* 9
fulfilled to us *their c.* *Acts* 13:33
deacons rule *their c.* *1 Tim* 3:12
to love husbands and their *c.* *Tit* 2:4

thy **children**

first-born among *thy c.* *Ex* 13:13
well with *thy c.* *Deut* 4:40; 12:25, 28
teach them diligently to *thy c.* 6:7
thou and *thy c.* shall obey. 30:2
be thine and *thy c.* for. *Josh* 14:9
are here all *thy c.*? *1 Sam* 16:11
if *thy c.* take heed to. *1 Ki* 2:4
that *thy c.* heed. 8:25; *2 Chr* 6:16
wives also and *thy c.* *1 Ki* 20:3
live thou and *thy c.* *2 Ki* 4:7
thy c. of fourth generation. 10:30
smite *thy* people and *c.* *2 Chr* 21:14
if *thy c.* have sinned. *Job* 8:4
instead of fathers shall be *thy c.* *Ps* 45:16
against generation of *thy c.* 73:15
thy c. like olive-plants. 128:3
if *thy c.* will keep my. 132:12
he hath blessed *thy c.* 147:13
thy c. shall make haste. *Isa* 49:17
and I will save *thy c.* 25
thy c. shall be taught of Lord, great shall be peace of *thy c.* 54:13
thy c. have forsaken me. *Jer* 5:7
there is hope that *thy c.* shall. 31:17
they shall bring out *thy c.* to. 38:23
by blood of *thy c.* thou. *Ezek* 16:36
I will also forget *thy c.* *Hos* 4:6
would I have gathered *thy c.* *Mat* 23:37; *Luke* 13:34
shall lay *thy c.* within. *Luke* 19:44
found of *thy c.* walking. *2 John* 4

your **children**

when *your c.* shall say. *Ex* 12:26
wives be widows, and *your c.* 22:24
as inheritance for *your c.* *Lev* 25:46
beasts shall rob you of *your c.* 26:22
your c. shall wander. *Num* 14:33
your c. shall go in thither. *Deut* 1:39
I speak not with *your c.* who. 11:2
ye shall teach them *your c.* 19
days of *your c.* be multiplied. 21
generation to come of *your c.* 29:22
ye shall command *your c.* 32:46
when *your c.* ask. *Josh* 4:6, 21
then ye shall let *your c.* know. 22
if *your c.* turn from. *1 Ki* 9:6
an inheritance to *your c.* *1 Chr* 28:8
Ezra 9:12
your c. shall find. *2 Chr* 30:9
increase you and *your c.* *Ps* 115:14
have I smitten *your c.* *Jer* 2:30
good gifts to *your c.* *Mat* 7:11
Luke 11:13
by whom do *your c.* cast? *Mat* 12:27
weep for yourselves and *your c.* *Luke* 23:28
for the promise is unto you and to *your c.* *Acts* 2:39
else were *your c.* unclean. *1 Cor* 7:14
provoke not *your c.* to. *Eph* 6:4
Col 3:21

young **children**

young c. despised me. *Job* 19:18
the *young c.* ask bread. *Lam* 4:4
her *young c.* were dashed. *Nah* 3:10
brought *young c.* to him. *Mark* 10:13
cast out their *young c.* *Acts* 7:19

Chilion, *see* **Mahlon**

Chilmad

Ashur and *C.* were. *Ezek* 27:23

Chimham

thy servant *C.* *2 Sam* 19:37, 38, 40
dwelt in habitation of *C.* *Jer* 41:17

chimney

be as smoke out of the *c.* *Hos* 13:3

Chios

next day over-against *C.* *Acts* 20:15

Chisleu

in the month *C.* *Neh* 1:1
ninth month *C.* *Zech* 7:1

Chittim

ships shall come from *C.* *Num* 24:24
from the land of *C.* *Isa* 23:1
pass over to *C.* 12
pass over the isles of *C.* *Jer* 2:10
ivory brought out of isles *C.* *Ezek* 27:6
ships of *C.* shall come. *Dan* 11:30

Chiun

have born Moloch and *C.* *Amos* 5:26

Chloe

which are of house of *C.* *1 Cor* 1:11

chode

Jacob was wroth, and *c.* *Gen* 31:36
people *c.* with Moses. *Num* 20:3*

choice

in *c.* of our sepulchres. *Gen* 23:6
ass's colt to the *c.* vine. 49:11
bring all your *c.* vows. *Deut* 12:11
Saul a *c.* young man. *1 Sam* 9:2
c. of Israel. *2 Sam* 10:9; *1 Chr* 19:10
cut down *c.* fir-trees. *2 Ki* 19:23
Isa 37:24
found 300,000 *c.* men. *2 Chr* 25:5
for me daily six *c.* sheep. *Neh* 5:1
knowledge rather than *c.* gold. *Pr* 8:1
revenue is better than *c.* silver. 1
tongue of just is as *c.* silver. 10:2
she is the *c.* one of her. *S of S* 6:
they shall cut down thy *c.* *Jer* 22:
set on a pot, fill it with *c.* *Ezek* 24:
take the *c.* of the flock and burn.
God made *c.* among us. *Acts* 15:

choicest

vineyard with the *c.* vine. *Isa* 5:
thy *c.* valley shall be full of. 22:

choke

deceitfulness of riches *c.* the word. *Mat* 13:22; *Mark* 4:1

choked

thorns *c.* them. *Mat* 13:
Mark 4:7; *Luke* 8:
were *c.* in the sea. *Mark* 5:
Luke 8:3
go forth and are *c.* with. *Luke* 8:

choler

an he-goat moved with *c.* *Dan* 8
south shall be moved with *c.* 11:

choose, *as an act of God*

Lord doth *c.* shall be holy. *Num* 16
man's rod whom I shall *c.* 17

Lord did not *c.* you. *Deut* 7:7
place Lord shall *c.* 12:5, 11, 14, 18
26; 14:23, 24, 25; 15:20; 16:2, 6
7, 15, 16; 17:8, 10; 18:6; 26:2
31:11; *Josh* 9:27
king, whom Lord shall *c. Deut* 17:15
did I *c.* him out of. *1 Sam* 2:28
Lord and his people *c. 2 Sam* 16:18
in Gibeah whom Lord did *c.* 21:6
city which Lord did *c.* *1 Ki* 14:21
God who didst *c.* Abram. *Neh* 9:7
teach in way he shall *c.* *Ps* 25:12
he shall *c.* our inheritance. 47:4
the Lord will yet *c.* Israel. *Isa* 14:1
he shall *c.* thee. 49:7
I also will *c.* their delusions. 66:4
yet *c.* Jerusalem. *Zech* 1:17; 2:12

choose

c. us out men, and go. *Ex* 17:9
dwell in place he shall *c. Deut* 23:16
therefore *c.* life, that thou. 30:19
c. this day whom you. *Josh* 24:15
c. you a man for you. *1 Sam* 17:8
let me *c.* 12,000 men. *2 Sam* 17:1
c. one of them. 24:12; *1 Chr* 21:10
c. one bullock. *1 Ki* 18:23, 25
c. out my words to reason. *Job* 9:14
let us *c.* to us judgement. 34:4
thou refuse, or whether thou *c.* 33
and did not *c.* the fear. *Pr* 1:29
the oppressor, and *c.* none. 3:31
refuse evil, and *c.* good. *Isa* 7:15, 16
to the eunuchs that *c.* things. 56:4
and did *c.* that wherein I. 65:12
c. a place, *c.* it at the. *Ezek* 21:19*
yet what I shall *c.* *Phil* 1:22

choosest, -eth, -ing

so that my soul *c.* *Job* 7:15
and thou *c.* the tongue of. 15:5
blessed is the man whom thou *c.*
Ps 65:4
he *c.* a tree that will not. *Isa* 40:20
abomination is he that *c.* you. 41:24
c. rather to suffer. *Heb* 11:25

chop

break bones and *c.* them. *Mi* 3:3

Chorazin

woe unto thee, *C.* *Mat* 11:21
Luke 10:13

chose

wives of all which they *c.* *Gen* 6:2
then Lot *c.* him all the plain. 13:11
Moses *c.* able men, and. *Ex* 18:25
he *c.* their seed. *Deut* 4:37; 10:15
c. 30,000 mighty men. *Josh* 8:3
they *c.* new gods. *Judg* 5:8
the Lord who *c.* me. *2 Sam* 6:21
I *c.* no city out of all Israel to build.
1 Ki 8:16; *2 Chr* 6:5
the Lord *c.* me before. *1 Chr* 28:4
I *c.* out their way. *Job* 29:25
and *c.* not the tribe of. *Ps* 78:67
but *c.* the tribe of Judah. 68
he *c.* David also his servant. 70
and *c.* that in which I. *Isa* 66:4
day when I *c.* Israel. *Ezek* 20:5
of his disciples he *c.* *Luke* 6:13
when he marked how they *c.* 14:7
c. Stephen a man full of. *Acts* 6:5
God of this people Israel *c.* 13:17
Paul *c.* Silas and departed. 15:40

chosen

his *c.* captains are drowned. *Ex* 15:4
him whom he hath *c.* *Num* 16:5
ye have *c.* you the Lord. *Josh* 24:22
cry to gods ye have *c.* *Judg* 10:14
king ye have *c.* *1 Sam* 8:18; 12:13
I know that thou hast *c.* the. 20:30
hast *c.* a great people. *1 Ki* 3:8
the city thou hast *c.* 8:44, 48
2 Chr 6:34, 38
children of Jacob his *c. 1 Chr* 16:13
this hast thou *c.* *Job* 36:21
people he hath *c.* for. *Ps* 33:12
made a covenant with my *c.* 89:3
I have exalted one *c.* 19
the children of Jacob his *c.* 105:6
forth his *c.* with gladness. 43
see the good of thy *c.* 106:5
had not Moses his *c.* stood. 23
understanding to be *c.* *Pr* 16:16
good name rather to be *c.* 22:1
drink to my people, my *c. Isa* 43:20
your name a curse to my *c.* 65:15
they have *c.* their own ways. 66:3
death shall be *c.* rather. *Jer* 8:3
who is a *c.* man. 49:19; 50:44
called, but few *c. Mat* 20:16; 22:14
elect's sake whom he hath *c.*
Mark 13:20
and Mary hath *c.* the. *Luke* 10:42
of these two thou hast *c.* *Acts* 1:24
for he is a *c.* vessel to me. 9:15
salute Rufus, *c.* in the. *Rom* 16:13
c. of the churches to. *2 Cor* 8:19
please him who hath *c.* *2 Tim* 2:4
ye are a *c.* generation. *1 Pet* 2:9
they are called, *c.* *Rev* 17:14

chosen *of God*

Christ, the *c. of God.* *Luke* 23:35
witnesses *c.* before *of God.*
Acts 10:41
living stone, *c. of God.* *1 Pet* 2:4

God hath **chosen**

God hath c. to put. *Deut* 12:21
16:11
God hath c. to minister unto. 21:5
Solomon whom *God hath c.*
1 Chr 29:1
God of our fathers *hath c. Acts* 22:14
God hath c. foolish things, *God hath*
c. weak things. *1 Cor* 1:27
things despised *God hath c.* and. 28
God from the beginning *hath c.*
2 Thes 2:13
hath not *God c.* the poor? *Jas* 2:5

I have **chosen**

David's sake and Jerusalem's sake
I have c. *1 Ki* 11:13; *2 Ki* 21:7
23:27; *2 Chr* 6:6
the city which *I have c.* *1 Ki* 11:32
them to place *I have c.* *Neh* 1:9
I have c. way of. *Ps* 119:30, 173
Jacob whom *I have c.* *Isa* 41:8
I have c. thee, and not cast. 9
servant whom *I have c.* 43:10
Mat 12:18
Israel whom *I have c.* *Isa* 44:1
Jesurun whom *I have c.* 2
I have c. thee in the furnace. 48:10
this the fast *I have c.*? 58:5, 6
I have c. thee, saith. *Hag* 2:23
I know whom *I have c.* *John* 13:18
not *c.* me, but *I have c.* 15:16
I have c. you out of the world. 19

Lord hath **chosen**

Lord hath c. thee. *Deut* 7:6; 14:2
the *Lord hath c.* him out of. 18:5
whom *Lord hath c.* like. *1 Sam* 10:24
neither *hath* the *Lord c.* this. 16:8
the *Lord hath* not *c.* these. 10
them the *Lord hath c.* *1 Chr* 15:2
Lord hath c. Judah ruler. 28:4
Lord hath c. Solomon to sit. 5, 10
Lord hath c. you to. *2 Chr* 29:11
Aaron whom *he had c.* *Ps* 105:26
Lord hath c. Zion. 132:13
Lord hath c. Jacob. 135:4
families *Lord hath c.* *Jer* 33:24
Lord that *hath c.* Jerusalem.
Zech 3:2
according as *he hath c.* *Eph* 1:4

chosen *men*

seven hundred *c. men.* *Judg* 20:16
Judah 180,000 *c. men.* *1 Ki* 12:21
2 Chr 11:1
array with 400,000 *c. men,* Jeroboam
with 800,000 *c. men.* *2 Chr* 13:3
smote down the *c. men* of Israel.
Ps 78:31*
to send *c.* men of. *Acts* 15:22*, 25

Christ

The anointed one. The Greek name Christos *from the word anointed. The Hebrew word was* Messiah. *The expected king and deliverer of the Jews, who expected a strong and glorious earthly king, to deliver them from oppressors and form again a great independent kingdom of the Jews. He was to be a descendant of David, and bring the whole world under his sway. There are many passages in the Old Testament which refer to this great deliverer under various names. Among these references are verses in* Ps 22, 45, 55; Isa 9, 11, 53; Dan 2, 9; etc.

The Jews were looking for this deliverer down the ages from the time of the Captivity, and more definitely at about the time of the coming of Jesus. When he was announced as being the Christ, *or the* Messiah, *the rulers among the Jews refused to accept him largely because he and the method of his coming were so utterly different from their ideas of what the Messiah was to be. There are, however, very many verses in the Old Testament which were believed by the Jews themselves to refer to the Messiah and his coming which speak of his suffering and lowliness, etc. But their minds were shut against such ideas as these.*

In modern usage the name is used as a synonym for Jesus, *or added to that name to refer to* Jesus, *the* Christ *of the Jews,* and *the Saviour of mankind.*

see **Messiah, Jesus**

demanded where *C.* *Mat* 2:4
thou art *C.* the Son of the. 16:16
is your Master, even *C.* 23:8, 10
I am *C.* and shall deceive. 24:5
Mark 13:6; *Luke* 21:8
thou *C.* who smote thee. *Mat* 26:68
because ye belong to *C.* *Mark* 9:41
let *C.* descend now from. 15:32
not die, before he had seen *C.*
Luke 2:26
they knew that he was *C.* 4:41
if he be *C.* the chosen of God. 23:35
saying, if thou be *C.* save. 39
ought not *C.* have suffered? 24:26
thus it behoved *C.* to suffer. 46
which is called *C.* *John* 4:25
when *C.* cometh no man. 7:27, 28
when *C.* cometh, will he do? 31
shall *C.* come out of Galilee? 41
C. cometh of seed of David. 42
any did confess that he was *C.* 9:22
we have heard that *C.* abideth. 12:34
he would raise up *C.* to. *Acts* 2:30*
made that Jesus both Lord and *C.* 36
God had before shewed that *C.* 3:18
Philip went and preached *C.* to. 8:5
straightway he preached *C.* 9:20*
alleging that *C.* must needs. 17:3
that *C.* should suffer. 26:23
in due time *C.* died for. *Rom* 5:6
we were yet sinners *C.* died. 8
like as *C.* was raised up from. 6:4
knowing that *C.* being raised. 9
dead to law by the body of *C.* 7:4
if any have not the Spirit of *C.* 8:9
if *C.* be in you, the body is dead. 10
he that raised up *C.* from dead. 11
wish myself accursed from *C.* 9:3
of whom *C.* came, who is over. 5
C. is the end of the law for. 10:4
that is, to bring *C.* down. 6
that is, to bring up *C.* 7
for to this end *C.* died. 14:9
destroy not him for whom *C.* died. 15
that in these things serveth *C.* 18
for even *C.* pleased not himself. 15:3
as *C.* also received us. 7
of things which *C.* hath not. 18
I strived to preach, not where *C.* 20
the first-fruits of Achaia to *C.* 16:5
we preach *C.* crucified. *1 Cor* 1:23
C. the power of God. 24
ye are *C.* and *C.* is God's. 3:23
C. our passover is sacrificed. 5:7
brother perish, for whom *C.* 8:11
but under the law to *C.* 9:21
and that rock was *C.* 10:4
nor let us tempt *C.* as some. 9*
how *C.* died for our sins. 15:3
if *C.* be preached that he rose. 12
dead rise not, then is not *C.* 16

and if *C.* be not raised. *1 Cor* 15:17
every man in his own order, *C.* 23
trust have we through *C.* *2 Cor* 3:4
though we have known *C.* 5:16
what concord hath *C.* with? 6:15
you as a chaste virgin to *C.* 11:2
I live, yet not I, but *C.* *Gal* 2:20
then *C.* died in vain. 21
C. hath redeemed us from. 3:13
our schoolmaster, to bring us to *C.* 24
if ye be *C.* then are Abraham's. 29
heir of God through *C.* 4:7*
of whom I travail, till *C.* be. 19
the liberty wherewith *C.* hath. 5:1
if ye be circumcised, *C.* shall. 2
C. is become of no effect unto. 4
that are *C.* have crucified flesh. 24
ye were without *C.* *Eph* 2:12
C. may dwell in your hearts. 3:17
which is the head, even *C.* 4:15
ye have not so learned *C.* 20
as *C.* also loved us, and hath. 5:2
arise from the dead, and *C.* shall. 14
head of the wife, as *C.* is the head. 23
as the church is subject to *C.* 24
love your wives, as *C.* also. 25
but I speak concerning *C.* and. 32
in singleness of heart as to *C.* 6:5
some indeed preach *C.* *Phil* 1:15
the one preach *C.* of contention. 16
C. is preached, and I therein. 18
so now *C.* shall be magnified in. 20
but dung, that I may win *C.* 3:8
I can do all through *C.* who. 4:13*
world, and not after *C.* *Col* 2:8
where *C.* sitteth on the right. 3:1
when *C.* who is our life shall. 4
bond nor free, but *C.* is all. 11
even as *C.* forgave you, 13*
for ye serve the Lord *C.* 24
but *C.* as a son. *Heb* 3:6
so also *C.* glorified not himself. 5:5
C. being come an high-priest. 9:11
C. not entered into holy place. 24
C. was once offered to bear the. 28
because *C.* also suffered. *1 Pet* 2:21
C. hath once suffered for sins. 3:18
C. suffered for us in the flesh. 4:1
of our Lord and his *C.* *Rev* 11:15
now is come power of his *C.* 12:10

against **Christ**

gathered *against* his *C.* *Acts* 4:26*
sin against brethren ye sin *against C.* *1 Cor* 8:12
wax wanton *against C.* *1 Tim* 5:11

by **Christ**

consolation aboundeth *by C.* *2 Cor* 1:5
seek to be justified *by C.* *Gal* 2:17
glory in church *by C.* Jesus. *Eph* 3:21

for **Christ**

for C. sent me not to. *1 Cor* 1:17
fools *for C.* sake, ye are wise in *C.* 4:10
are ambassadors *for C.* *2 Cor* 5:20
pleasure in distresses *for C.* 12:10
as God *for C.* sake hath. *Eph* 4:32
those I counted loss *for C.* *Phil* 3:7
patient waiting *for C.* *2 Thes* 3:5

Jesus with **Christ**

Jesus, who is called *C.* *Mat* 1:16
27:17, 22
truth came by *Jesus C.* *John* 1:17
know thee, and *Jesus C.* 17:3
baptized in name of *Jesus C.* *Acts* 2:38
in the name of *Jesus C.* rise up. 3:6
shall send *Jesus C.* who was. 20
by the name of *Jesus C.* doth. 4:10
ceased not to preach *Jesus C.* 5:42
Philip preaching things concerning *Jesus C.* they were baptized. 8:12
I believe that *Jesus C.* is the. 37*
Jesus C. maketh thee whole. 9:34
preaching peace by *Jesus C.* 10:36
in name of *Jesus C.* come out. 16:18
Jesus I preach to you is *C.* 17:3
to the Jews that *Jesus* was *C.* 18:5
the scriptures that *Jesus* was *C.* 28
should believe on *C. Jesus.* 19:4*
Paul a servant of *Jesus C.* *Rom* 1:1
Phil 1:1

concerning Son *Jesus C.* *Rom* 1:3*
the called of *Jesus C.* 6
through *Jesus C.* for you all. 8
secrets of men by *Jesus C.* 2:16
which is by faith of *Jesus C.* 3:22
through redemption in *Jesus C.* 24
which is by one man *Jesus C.* 5:15
reign in life by one *Jesus C.* 17
were baptized into *Jesus C.* 6:3
to them that are in *C. Jesus.* 8:1
Spirit of life in *C. Jesus* hath. 2
my helpers in *C. Jesus.* 16:3
Paul apostle of *Jesus C.* *1 Cor* 1:1
2 Cor 1:1; *Eph* 1:1
call on the name of *Jesus C.* *1 Cor* 1:2
grace given you by *Jesus C.* 4
but of him are ye in *C. Jesus.* 30
save *Jesus C.* crucified. 2:2
for in *C. Jesus* have I begotten. 4:15
knowledge of God in *Jesus C.* *2 Cor* 4:6
us to himself by *Jesus C.* 5:18
how that *Jesus C.* is in you. 13:5
by the faith of *Jesus C.* *Gal* 2:16
the Gentiles through *Jesus C.* 3:14
for ye are all one in *C. Jesus.* 28
an angel, even as *C. Jesus.* 4:14
heavenly places in *C. Jesus.* *Eph* 2:6
Jesus C. the chief corner stone. 20
I long after you in *Jesus C.* *Phil* 1:8
which was also in *C. Jesus.* 2:5
Jesus C. is Lord, to glory of. 2:11
all the things which are *Jesus C.* 21
loss for excellency of *C. Jesus.* 3:8
I am apprehended of *C. Jesus.* 12
riches in glory by *C. Jesus.* 4:19
have received *C. Jesus* so. *Col* 2:6
C. Jesus came to save. *1 Tim* 1:15
one mediator, man *C. Jesus.* 2:5
before *C. Jesus* who witnessed. 6:13
grace given us in *C. Jesus.* *2 Tim* 1:9
love, which is in *C. Jesus.* 13
prisoner of *Jesus C.* *Philem* 1, 9, 23
Jesus C. same yesterday. *Heb* 13:8
blood of *Jesus C.* *1 John* 1:7*
an advocate, *Jesus C.* the. 2:1
by water and blood, *Jesus C.* 5:6
even in his Son *Jesus C.* 20

Lord Jesus **Christ**

believed on the *L. J. C.* *Acts* 11:17
through the grace of *L. J. C.* 15:11
believe on the *L. J. C.* 16:31*
faith toward our *L. J. C.* 20:21
peace with God through *L. J. C.* *Rom* 5:1
joy in God, through our *L. J. C.* 11
eternal life through our *L. J. C.* 6:23
love of God in *C. J.* our *L.* 8:39
put ye on *L. J. C.* and make. 13:14
grace of *L. J. C.* be with. 16:20, 24*
2 Cor 13:14; *Gal* 6:18
2 Thes 3:18; *Rev* 22:21
for coming of *L. J. C.* *1 Cor* 1:7
but to us one *L. J. C.* by whom. 8:6
victory through our *L. J. C.* 15:57
any man love not the *L. J. C.* 16:22
and peace from *L. J. C.* *2 Cor* 1:2
Gal 1:3; *Eph* 1:2; *Col* 1:2*
know grace of our *L. J. C.* *2 Cor* 8:9
in cross of our *L. J. C.* *Gal* 6:14
Father of our *L. J. C.* *Eph* 1:3
God of our *L. J. C.* give you. 17
of hope in our *L. J. C.* *1 Thes* 1:3
joy in presence of our *L. J. C.* 2:19
at coming of our *L. J. C.* 3:13
unto coming of our *L. J. C.* 5:23
by coming of *L. J. C.* *2 Thes* 2:1
now our *L. J. C.* hath given us. 16
charge before *L. J. C.* *1 Tim* 5:21
2 Tim 4:1
the *L. J. C.* be with thy. *2 Tim* 4:22
into kingdom of *L. J. C.* *2 Pet* 1:11
in knowledge of *L. J. C.* 3:18

in **Christ**

concerning the faith *in C.* *Acts* 24:24
I say the truth *in C.* *Rom* 9:1
many are one body *in C.* 12:5
of note, who also were *in C.* 16:7
salute Urbane, our helper *in C.* 9
salute Apelles approved *in C.* 10
even as unto babes *in C.* *1 Cor* 3:1
fools, but ye are wise *in C.* 4:10
10,000 instructors *in C.* not. 15

fallen asleep *in C.* *1 Cor* 15:18
in this life only hope *in C.* 19
even so *in C.* shall all be made. 22
stablisheth us *in C.* *2 Cor* 1:21
causeth us to triumph *in C.* 2:14
speak we *in C.* 17
vail is done away *in C.* 3:14
if any man be *in C.* he is. 5:17
that God was *in C.* reconciling. 19
we pray you *in C.* stead. 20
I knew a man *in C.* above. 12:2
we speak before God, *in C.* 19
to churches of Judea *in C.* *Gal* 1:22
confirmed before of God *in C.* 3:17*
as have been baptized *into C.* 27
spiritual blessings *in C.* *Eph* 1:3
gather in one all things *in C.* 10
his glory, who first trusted *in C.* 12
which he wrought *in C.* 20
partakers of his promise *in C.* 3:6
bonds *in C.* are manifest. *Phil* 1:13
if there be any consolation *in C.* 2:1
stedfastness of faith *in C.* *Col* 2:5
dead *in C.* shall rise. *1 Thes* 4:16
I speak the truth *in C.* *1 Tim* 2:7
good conversation *in C.* *1 Pet* 3:16

is **Christ**

say, lo, here *is C.* *Mat* 24:23
Mark 13:21
C. is the son of David. *Mark* 12:35
Luke 20:41
Saviour who *is C.* the. *Luke* 2:11
he himself *is C.* a king. 23:2
others said, this *is* the *C.* *John* 7:41
proving this *is* very *C.* *Acts* 9:22
Jesus whom I preach you *is C.* 17:3
it *is C.* that died, yea. *Rom* 8:34
is C. divided? *1 Cor* 1:13
being free, *is C.'s* servant. 7:22
the head of every man *is C.* 11:3
many are one body, so *is C.* 12:12
dead rise not, then *is C.* 15:13, 16
but now is *C.* risen from dead. 20
trust that he *is C.* *2 Cor* 10:7
is therefore *C.* the? *Gal* 2:17
to thy seed, which *is C.* 3:16
for me to live *is C.* *Phil* 1:21
which *is C.* in you the hope. *Col* 1:27

of **Christ**

in prison works *of C.* *Mat* 11:2
what think you *of C.*? 22:42
have not the Spirit *of C.* *Rom* 8:9
separate us from love *of C.*? 35
before judgement seat *of C.* 14:10*
lest cross *of C.* be made. *1 Cor* 1:17
we have the mind *of C.* 2:16
bodies are members *of C.* 6:15
cup, communion of blood *of C.* bread, communion of body *of C.* 10:16
followers of me, as I am *of C.* 11:1
the head *of C.* is God. 3
now ye are the body *of C.* 12:27
as the sufferings *of C.* *2 Cor* 1:5
forgave it in the person *of C.* 2:10
a sweet savour *of C.* 15
ye are the epistles *of C.* 3:3
light of glorious gospel *of C.* 4:4
love *of C.* constraineth us. 5:14
they are the glory *of C.* 8:23
meekness and gentleness *of C.* 10:1
thought to the obedience *of C.* 5
as the truth *of C.* is in me. 11:10
power of *C.* may rest on me. 12:9
Rev 12:10
ye seek a proof *of C.* *2 Cor* 13:3
not be servant *of C.* *Gal* 1:10
be justified by the faith *of C.* 2:16
persecution for the cross *of C.* 6:12
nigh by the blood *of C.* *Eph* 2:13
knowledge in mystery *of C.* 3:4
preach unsearchable riches *of C.* 8
know the love *of C.* which. 1
the measure of the gift *of C.* 4:7
inheritance in the kingdom *of C.* 5:5
as servants *of C.* doing. 6:
offence till day *of C.* *Phil* 1:1
it is given in behalf *of C.* 2
rejoice in the day *of C.* 2:1
for work *of C.* he was nigh to. 3
enemies of the cross *of C.* 3:1
fill up afflictions *of C.* *Col* 1:2
mystery of Father, and *of C.* 2:
shadow, but the body is *of C.* 1

let the word *of C.* dwell in. *Col* 3:16
to speak the mystery *of C.* 4:3
nameth the name *of C.* *2 Tim* 2:19*
we are partakers *of C.* if. *Heb* 3:14
how much more blood *of C.* 9:14
reproach *of C.* greater. 11:26
what time Spirit *of C.* *1 Pet* 1:11
redeemed with blood *of C.* 19
partakers *of C.* sufferings. 4:13
reproached for name *of C.* 14
priests of God and *of C.* *Rev* 20:6

that **Christ**

if be not *that C.* nor Elias. *John* 1:25
we are sure thou art *that C.* 6:69*

the **Christ**

tell no man he was *the C.* *Mat* 16:20
tell whether thou be *the C.* 26:63
thou art *the C.* *Mark* 8:29
art thou *the C.* the Son of ? 14:61
whether he were *the C.* *Luke* 3:15
thou art *the C.* of God. 9:20
art thou *the C.*? tell us. 22:67
confessed, I am not *the C.* *John* 1:20
the Messias, which is *the C.* 41
I said, I am not *the C.* but. 3:28
is not this *the C.*? 4:29
this is indeed *the C.* 42; 7:26
others said, this is *the C.* but. 7:41
if thou be the *C.* tell us. 10:24
I believe thou art *the C.* 11:27
believe that Jesus is *the C.* 20:31
denieth that Jesus is *the C.*
1 John 2:22
whoso believeth Jesus is *the C.* 5:1

with **Christ**

if we be dead *with C.* *Rom* 6:8
then joint-heirs *with C.* 8:17
crucified *with C.* I live, *C.* *Gal* 2:20
quickened us together *with C.*
Eph 2:5
to depart and be *with C.* *Phil* 1:23
if ye be dead *with C.* *Col* 2:20
if ye be risen *with C.* seek. 3:1
and your life is hid *with C.* 3
and they reigned *with C.* *Rev* 20:4

christian, -s

disciples first called *c.* *Acts* 11:26
almost persuadest me to be *c.* 26:28
any man suffer as a *c.* not. *1 Pet* 4:16

christs

there shall arise false *c.* *Mat* 24:24
Mark 13:22

chronicles

acts of Jeroboam are in *c.* *1 Ki* 14:19
put in the account of *c.* *1 Chr* 27:24
book of the records of *c.* *Esth* 6:1

see **book**

chrysolite

(*A semi-precious stone of a yellow or green colour*)
seventh foundation *c.* *Rev* 21:20

chrysoprasus

(*A light green chalcedony*)
tenth foundation of city was a *c.*
Rev 21:20

church

[1] *The body of Christians in general.* [2] *A body of Christians with the same general creed and under the same ecclesiastical authority.* [3] *Any body of worshippers of God, as the* Jewish church, Acts 7:38.

rock I will build my *c.* *Mat* 16:18
tell it to *c.* if he neglect to hear *c.*
18:17
Lord added to *c.* daily. *Acts* 2:47
fear came on all the *c.* and as. 5:11
great persecution against *c.* 8:1
assembled themselves with *c.* 11:26
ordained elders in every *c.* 14:23
gathered the *c.* together. 27
brought on way by the *c.* 15:3
pleased elders with whole *c.* 22
gone up and saluted the *c.* 18:22
greet the *c.* that is in. *Rom* 16:5
every where, in every *c.* *1 Cor* 4:17
prophesieth edifieth the *c.* 14:4
except interpret that the *c.* may. 5
the *c.* be come together. 23
salute you, with *c.* that is. 16:19

head over all to the *c.* *Eph* 1:22
might be known by the *c.* the. 3:10
as the *c.* is subject to Christ. 5:24
Christ loved the *c.* and gave. 25
present to himself a glorious *c.* 27
even as the Lord the *c.* 29
speak concerning Christ and *c.* 32
persecuting the *c.* *Phil* 3:6
no *c.* communicated with me. 4:15
head of the body the *c.* *Col* 1:18
body's sake, which is the *c.* 24
salute the *c.* which is in. 4:15
let not the *c.* be charged. *1 Tim* 5:16
Paul a prisoner, to *c.* in. *Philem* 2
to *c.* of the first-born in. *Heb* 12:23
the *c.* at Babylon. *1 Pet* 5:13
witness of thy charity before *c.*
3 John 6
I wrote unto *c.* but Diotrephes. 9

in the **church**

is he that was *in the c.* *Acts* 7:38
prophets *in the c.* at Antioch. 13:1
least esteemed *in the c.* *1 Cor* 6:4
ye come together *in the c.* 11:18
God hath set some *in the c.* 12:28
yet *in the c.* I had rather. 14:19
let him keep silence *in the c.* 28
for women to speak *in the c.* 35
to him be glory *in the c.* *Eph* 3:21
it to be read *in the c.* *Col* 4:16

of the **church**

made havock *of the c.* *Acts* 8:3
tidings came to ears *of the c.* 11:22
Herod vexed certain *of the c.* 12:1
prayer was made *of the c.* unto. 5
they were received *of the c.* 15:4
called the elders *of the c.* 20:17
a servant *of the c.* *Rom* 16:1
mine host and *of the* whole *c.* 23
excel to edifying *of the c.* *1 Cor* 14:12
Christ is head *of the c.* *Eph* 5:23
in midst *of the c.* I will. *Heb* 2:12
call for elders *of the c.* *Jas* 5:14
casteth them out *of the c.* *3 John* 10
angel *of the c.* of Ephesus. *Rev* 2:1
of the c. in Smyrna. 8
of the c. in Pergamos. 12
of the c. in Thyatira. 18
of the c. of Sardis. 3:1
of the c. in Philadelphia. 7
of the c. of the Laodiceans. 14

church *of God*

feed the *c. of God.* *Acts* 20:28
to the *c. of God* which. *1 Cor* 1:2
none offence to *c. of God.* 10:32
or despise ye the *c. of God.* 11:22
I persecuted *c. of God.* 15:9
Gal 1:13
care of the *c. of God* ? *1 Tim* 3:5

churches

then had the *c.* rest. *Acts* 9:31
through Syria confirming the *c.* 15:41
so were the *c.* established. 16:5
who are neither robbers of *c.* 19:37*
to whom all *c.* of. *Rom* 16:4
salute one another, the *c.* of. 16
so ordain I in all *c.* *1 Cor* 7:17
neither *c.* of Christ. 11:16
author of peace as in all *c.* 14:33
women keep silence in the *c.* 34
as I have given order to *c.* 16:1
c. of Asia salute you. 19
the grace bestowed on *c.* *2 Cor* 8:1
who was chosen of the *c.* to. 19
are the messengers of the *c.* 23
I robbed other *c.* taking. 11:8
upon me daily care of all *c.* 28
wherein ye were inferior to *c.*? 12:13
unknown by face to *c.* of. *Gal* 1:22
followers of *c.* of God. *1 Thes* 2:14
glory in you in the *c.* *2 Thes* 1:4
John to the seven *c.* in. *Rev* 1:4
send it to the seven *c.* which. 11
angels of the seven *c.* and seven candlesticks are the seven *c.* 20
hear what Spirit saith unto *c.* 2:7
11, 17, 29; 3:6, 13, 22
c. know I am he which. 2:23
testify these things in the *c.* 22:16

churl

nor shall the *c.* be said. *Isa* 32:5
instruments also of the *c.* are. 7

churlish

man Nabal was *c.* and. *1 Sam* 25:3

churning

surely the *c.* of milk. *Pr* 30:33

Chushan-rishathaim

Israel into the hand of *C.* *Judg* 3:8

Chuza

Joanna wife of *C.* *Luke* 8:3

cieled (ceiled)

he *c* the greater house. *2 Chr* 3:5
it is *c.* with cedar and. *Jer* 22:14
to dwell in your *c.* houses. *Hag* 1:4

cieling (ceiling)

built walls of house with *c.* *1 Ki* 6:15

Cilicia

they of *C.* disputed with. *Acts* 6:9
which are of Gentiles in *C.* 15:23
through *C.* confirming the. 41
of Tarsus, a city in *C.* 21:39; 22:3
23:34
sailed over the sea of *C.* 27:5
into the regions of *C.* *Gal* 1:21

cinnamon

take of sweet *c.* half so. *Ex* 30:23
my bed with aloes and *c.* *Pr* 7:17
an orchard of calamus and *c.*
S of S 4:14
her merchandise of *c.* *Rev* 18:13

circle

he that sitteth on the *c.* *Isa* 40:22

circuit, -s

from year to year in *c.* *1 Sam* 7:16
he walked in the *c.* of. *Job* 22:14†
c. and his *c.* from ends. *Ps* 19:6
again according to his *c.* *Eccl* 1:6

circumcise

ye shall *c.* the flesh of. *Gen* 17:11
c. therefore fore-skin. *Deut* 10:16
the Lord thy God will *c.* 30:6
c. again children of Israel. *Josh* 5:2
this is cause why Joshua did *c.* 4
c. yourselves to the Lord. *Jer* 4:4
day they came to *c.* *Luke* 1:59
ye on the sabbath-day *c.* *John* 7:22
it was needful to *c.* them. *Acts* 15:5
that they ought not to *c.* 21:21

circumcised

every man-child be *c.* *Gen* 17:10
whose flesh is not *c.* that soul. 14
and Abraham *c.* the flesh of their. 23
in that day Abraham was *c.* 26
that every male of you be *c.* 34:15
every male was *c.* 24; *Ex* 12:48
Joshua *c.* children of. *Josh* 5:3
because they had not *c.* them. 7
will punish all *c.* with. *Jer* 9:25
except ye be *c.* ye. *Acts* 15:1, 24
Paul *c.* Timothy because. 16:3
that believe, though not *c.* *Rom* 4:11
c. let him not become uncircumcised, in uncircumcision not be *c.*
1 Cor 7:18
neither Titus be *c.* *Gal* 2:3
if *c.* Christ profit you nothing. 5:2
constrain you to be *c.* lest. 6:12
they that are *c.* kept not the law. 13
c. the eighth day. *Phil* 3:5
in whom also ye are *c.* *Col* 2:11

circumcising

when they had done *c.* *Josh* 5:8
accomplished for *c.* child. *Luke* 2:21

circumcision

(*Literally, the cutting off of the prepuce, a religious rite of the Jews. Metaphorically, the purifying spiritually. Since all male Jews must by law be circumcised, the word is often used to mean the Jews in distinction from Gentiles. In this case also it is used metaphorically*)

Moses gave unto you *c.* *John* 7:22
if man on sabbath-day receive *c.* 23
c. profiteth, if thou keep law; if break law, *c.* is made. *Rom* 2:25
nor is that *c.* which is outward. 28
and *c.* is that of the heart. 29
who shall justify the *c.* 3:30
blessedness then on *c.* only ? 4:9
when he was in *c.*? not in *c.* 10

c. is the keeping of the. 1 Cor 7:19
they should go unto the c. Gal 2:9
in Jesus Christ neither c. 5:6; 6:15
brethren, if I yet preach c. 5:11
that which is called c. Eph 2:11
we are the c. which. Phil 3:3
c. without hands, by c. of. Col 2:11
neither c. nor uncircumcision. 3:11

of circumcision

bloody husband, because of c. Ex 4:26
Abraham covenant of c. Acts 7:8
they of c. which believed. 10:45
they of the c. contended with. 11:2
what profit is there of c.? Rom 3:1
he received the sign of c. a. 4:11
father of c. to them not of c. 12
Jesus Christ a minister of c. 15:8
as the gospel of c. was. Gal 2:7
Peter to apostleship of the c. 8
who are of c. salute you. Col 4:11
especially they of the c. Tit 1:10

circumspect

I have said to you, be c. Ex 23:13*

circumspectly

see that ye walk c. not as. Eph 5:15*

cistern

(An artificial reservoir, built of rock or brick, excavated in the rock to hold rain water. Many of the houses had their own private cisterns, provided with a bucket and windlass (Eccl. 12:6) *and filled as are ours by water conducted to them from the roof)*

drink ye waters of his c. 2 Ki 18:31
waters out of thine own c. Pr 5:15
wheel broken at the c. Eccl 12:6
drink waters of own c. Isa 36:16

cisterns

hewed out c. broken c. Jer 2:13

cities

destroyed the c. of the. Gen 19:29
terror of God upon the c. 35:5
laid up food in the c. 41:48
people removed to the c. 47:21
the c. of the Levites. Lev 25:32
what c. they be that. Num 13:19
every one shall give of his c. 35:8
nor camest thou to c. Deut 2:37
c. thereof gave I to Reubenites. 3:12
abide in your c. which I have. 19
to give thee great and goodly c. 6:10
flee to one of these c. 19:5
Israel came to their c. Josh 9:17
not to enter into their c. 10:19
as for the c. that stood still in. 11:13
described it by c. into seven. 18:9
buried in one of the c. Judg 12:7
set fire on all the c. they. 20:48
they repaired the c. 21:23
Israelites forsook the c. 1 Sam 31:7
for the c. of our God. 2 Sam 10:12
1 Chr 19:13
from Tyre to see the c. 1 Ki 9:12
what c. are these that thou? 13
the c. my father took I will. 20:34
Jair had 23 c. in the. 1 Chr 2:22
these were their c. to the. 4:31
so did he in the c. of. 2 Chr 34:6
Israelites were in their c. Ezra 3:1
Neh 7:73
nine parts dwell in other c. Neh 11:1
dwelleth in desolate c. Job 15:28
thou hast destroyed c. Ps 9:6
answered, till c. be wasted. Isa 6:11
nor fill face of world with c. 14:21
in that day shall five c. in. 19:18
he hath despised the c. he. 33:8
thy holy c. are a wilderness. 64:10
his c. are burnt. Jer 2:15
according to thy c. 28; 11:13
c. of south be shut up. 13:19
that man be as the c. which. 20:16
turn again to these thy c. 31:21
all the c. thereof shall be. 49:13
I will kindle fire in his c. 50:32
like the c. that are not. Ezek 26:19
and these c. shall go into. 30:17
thy c. shall not return. 35:9
I will send fire upon his c. Hos 8:14
sword shall abide on his c. 11:6
two or three c. wandered. Amos 4:8
I will cut off the c. of. Mi 5:11
so will I destroy thy c. 14
their c. are destroyed. Zeph 3:6
my c. by prosperity shall. Zech 1:17
not have gone over c. Mat 10:23
teach and preach in their c. 11:1
persecuted them even to strange c. Acts 26:11
turning c. of Sodom and. 2 Pet 2:6
and c. about them in like. Jude 7
the c. of the nations. Rev 16:19

all cities

took all these c. and dwelt in c.
Num 21:25; Deut 2:34; 3:4
Josh 10:39
they burnt all their c. Num 31:10
Judg 20:48
all c. of Levites 48 c. Num 35:7
thus do to all c. Deut 20:15
all the c. of the kings. Josh 11:12
all c. of Aaron were 13 c. 21:19
all c. of Gershonites were 13 c. 33
all c. of Merari by lot 12 c. 40
all c. of Levites were 48 c. 41
women came out of all c. 1 Sam 18:6
thus did he to all c. 2 Sam 12:31
they came to all the c. of. 24:7
all c. Ahab built are. 1 Ki 22:39
Asa smote all the c. 2 Chr 14:14
tithes in all the c. of. Neh 10:37
all the c. thereof were. Jer 4:26
in all c. thereof an habitation. 33:12
save thee in all thy c. Hos 13:10
preached in all c. till he. Acts 8:40

defenced cities

against the defenced c. Isa 36:1
lay waste the defenced c. 37:26
let us go into defenced c. Jer 4:5
8:14
these defenced c. remained. 34:7

fenced cities

dwell in the fenced c. Num 32:17
all these c. were fenced. Deut 3:5
c. fenced to heaven. 9:1; Josh 14:12
entered into fenced c. Josh 10:20
lest he get him fenced c. 2 Sam 20:6
Shishak took fenced c. 2 Chr 12:4
Asa built fenced c. in Judah. 14:6
forces in the fenced c. 17:2
through all fenced c. of. 19:5
gave his sons fenced c. in. 21:3
impoverish thy fenced c. Jer 5:17
take the most fenced c. Dan 11:15
Judah multiplied fenced c. Hos 8:14
alarm against fenced c. Zeph 1:16

cities of Judah

to any of c. of Judah. 2 Sam 2:1
incense in c. of Judah. 2 Ki 23:5
gave the c. of Judah. 1 Chr 6:57
to teach in c. of Judah. 2 Chr 17:7
business in c. of Judah. 13
set judges in c. of Judah. 19:5
Levites out of all c. of Judah. 23:2
Israel in the c. of Judah. 31:6
of war in c. of Judah. 33:14
in c. of Judah each dwelt. Neh 11:3
Zion, build c. of Judah. Ps 69:35
say to the c. of Judah. Isa 40:9
and that saith to c. of Judah. 44:26
north against c. of Judah. Jer 1:15
against the c. of Judah. 4:16
do in the c. of Judah. 7:17
c. of Judah desolate. 9:11; 10:22
34:22
shall c. of Judah go and cry. 11:12
witness in the c. of Judah. 32:44
even in the c. of Judah. 33:10
in c. of Judah shall flocks pass. 13
anger kindled in c. of Judah. 44:6
incense burnt in c. of Judah. 21
maids in the c. of Judah. Lam 5:11
mercy on the c. of Judah. Zech 1:12

cities of refuge

six c. for refuge. Num 35:6, 13, 14
appoint c. of refuge. 11; Josh 20:2
of Kohath of c. of refuge. 1 Chr 6:67

six cities

six c. for refuge. Num 35:6, 13, 15
mountains of Judah six c. Josh 15:59

cities with suburbs

the suburbs of their c. Lev 25:34
to Levites suburbs for c. Num 35:2
Levites c. and suburbs. Josh 21:3
c. of Levites 48 with suburbs. 41

cities with villages

c. and country villages. 1 Sam 6:18
houses in c. and villages. 1 Chr 27:25
all the c. and villages teaching and preaching. Mat 9:35; Luke 13:22
entered into villages or c. Mark 6:56

cities with waste

make your c. waste. Lev 26:31, 33
waste c. desolations. Isa 61:4
c. shall be laid waste. Jer 4:7
dwellings your c. shall be waste. Ezek 6:6
laid waste their c. 19:7
I will lay thy c. waste. 35:4
waste c. are become fenced. 36:35
so shall waste c. be filled. 38
shall build thy waste c. Amos 9:14

your cities

your c. are burnt with fire. Isa 1:7
and dwell in your c. Jer 40:10
cleanness of teeth in your c. Amos 4:6

citizen, -s

joined himself to a c. Luke 15:15
his c. hated him, and sent. 19:14
I am of Tarsus, a c. of. Acts 21:39
but fellow-c. with saints. Eph 2:19

city

(In Hebrew usage, a collection of permanent human habitations, whether many or few, especially if surrounded by a wall. The word was also used, as now, metaphorically for the people of the city)

Cain builded a c. and. Gen 4:17
let us build us a c. and a. 11:4
Lord came down to see c. and. 5
and they left off to build c. 8
fifty righteous within the c. 18:26
destroy all c. for lack of five? 28
daughters of the c. come to. 24:13
all that went out of gate of c. 34:24
came upon the c. boldly. 25
flame is gone out from c. Num 21:28
there was not one c. Deut 2:36
not one c. we took not from. 3:4
smite inhabitants of that c. 13:15
c. next to slain man take. 21:3, 6
very far from c. Adam. Josh 3:16
ye shall compass c. and go. 6:3, 7
burnt the c. with fire. 24; Deut 13:16
Josh 8:8, 19; Judg 1:8; 18:27
an ambush for c. behind it. Josh 8:2
they left the c. open, and. 17
smoke of the c. ascended up. 20
was not a c. made peace. 11:19
c. of Arba, which c. is. 15:13
they gave Joshua the c. which. 19:50
at the entry of the gate of c. 20:4
feared men of the c. Judg 6:27
Gideon slew men of the c. 8:17
and beat down the c. and. 9:45
all they of the c. fled, and. 51
flame of the c. ascended. 20:40
all the c. was moved. Ruth 1:19
for all the c. of my people. 3:11
this man went out of c. 1 Sam 1:3
when man told it, all c. cried. 4:13
deadly destruction through c. 5:11
go ye every man to his c. 8:22
1 Ki 22:36; Ezra 2:1; Neh 7:
buried him in Ramah, his c. 1 Sam 28:3
two men in one c. one. 2 Sam 12:1
of what c. art thou? 15:2
I may die in mine own c. 19:3
seekest to destroy a c. and. 20:1
so that the c. rang again. 1 Ki 1:4
for Jerusalem's sake, c. 11:32, 3
neither is this the c. 2 Ki 6:1
and the c. was in quiet. 11:2
c. Jerusalem was. 24:10; 25:
was destroyed of c. for. 2 Chr 15:
judges in the land c. by c. 19:
posts passed from c. to c. 30:1
that they might take the c. 32:1
building the rebellious c. Ezra 4:1
sad, when c. lieth waste. Neh 2:3,

Judah was second over c. Neh 11:9
but the c. Shushan. Esth 3:15
c. of Shushan rejoiced. 8:15
c. of the great King. Ps 48:2
Mat 5:35
go round about the c. Ps 59:6, 14
they of c. shall flourish. 72:16
they found no c. to dwell in. 107:4
Jerusalem is builded as a c. 122:3
except Lord keep the c. 127:1
Wisdom crieth at entry of c. Pr 8:3
wealth is his strong c. 10:15; 18:11
c. rejoiceth, shouting when. 11:10
by blessing of upright the c. 11
than he that taketh a c. 16:32
is like a c. broken down. 25:28
scornful men bring a c. into. 29:8
there was a little c. Eccl 9:14
poor wise man delivered the c. 15
c. of righteousness, faithful c.
Isa 1:26, 21
cry, O c. whole Palestina. 14:31
taken away from being a c. 17:1
shall fight, c. against c. 19:2
the c. of confusion is. 24:10
of a c. an heap, to be no c. 25:2
Zion, c. of our solemnities. 33:20
they shall call thee the c. of. 60:14
thou shalt be called a c. 62:12
I will take you one of a c. Jer 3:14
whole c. shall flee from noise. 4:29
even make this c. as Tophet. 19:12
to bring evil on the c. called. 25:29
come to the c. and the c. is. 32:24
the c. was broken up. 39:2; 52:7
I will destroy the c. and the. 46:8
c. of praise not left, c. of joy. 49:25
how doth c. sit solitary! Lam 1:1
c. that men called perfection? 2:15
pourtray on it the c. even. Ezek 4:1
make a chain, for the c. is. 7:23
them that have charge over c. 9:1
go through midst of c. Jerusalem. 4
land full of blood, the c. is full. 9
scatter coals of fire over c. 10:2
what c. is like Tyrus? 27:32
the c. is smitten. 33:21
name of the c. shall be. 48:35
the c. called by thy. Dan 9:18, 19
Gilead a c. of them. Hos 6:8
I caused to rain on one c. Amos 4:7
c. that went out by thousand. 5:3
Lord's voice crieth to c. Mi 6:9
him that stablisheth c. by. Hab 2:12
to polluted, oppressing c. Zeph 3:1
Jerusalem called a c. of. Zech 8:3
streets of the c. shall be full. 5
c. shall be taken, residue of people
shall not be cut off from c. 14:2
a c. that is set on a hill. Mat 5:14
Jerusalem, is c. of great King. 35
the whole c. came out to. 8:34
into whatsoever c. ye shall. 10:11
than for that c. 15; Mark 6:11
Luke 10:12
all the c. was moved. Mat 21:10
sent and burnt up their c. 22:7
persecute them from c. to c. 23:34
all c. was gathered. Mark 1:33
told it in c. 5:14; Luke 8:34
every one to his own c. Luke 2:3
much people of the c. was. 7:12
he beheld the c. and wept. 19:41
of Arimathaea, a c. of the. 23:51
many of that c. believed. John 4:39
great joy in that c. Acts 8:8
almost the whole c. to hear. 13:44
we were abiding in that c. 16:12
set all the c. in an uproar. 17:5
the whole c. was filled. 19:29
all the c. was moved, and. 21:30
he looked for a c. that. Heb 11:10
hath prepared for them a c. 16
ye are come to the c. of the. 12:22
we have no continuing c. 13:14
into such a c. buy and. Jas 4:13
compassed the beloved c. Rev 20:9
wall of the c. had twelve. 21:14
c. was pure gold, like to. 18
c. had no need of the sun nor. 23

bloody **city**

thou judge the bloody c.? Ezek 22:2
woe to bloody c. 24:6, 9; Nah 3:1

defenced **city**

of a defenced c. a ruin. Isa 25:2
the defenced c. shall be. 27:10
thee this day a defenced c. Jer 1:18

city *of David*

the c. of D. 2 Sam 5:9; 1 Chr 11:7
the ark into the c. of D. 2 Sam 6:10
ark into the c. of D. 12, 16
David buried in c. of D. 1 Ki 2:10
brought her into the c. of D. 3:1
ark out of c. of D. 8:1; 2 Chr 5:2
Solomon buried in c. of D.
1 Ki 11:43; 2 Chr 9:31
Rehoboam buried in c. of D.
1 Ki 14:31; 2 Chr 12:16
buried Abijam in c. of D. 1 Ki 15:8
2 Chr 14:1
Jehoshaphat buried in c. of D.
1 Ki 22:50; 2 Chr 21:1
Joram buried in c. of D. 2 Ki 8:24
2 Chr 21:20
Ahaziah buried in c. of D. 2 Ki 9:28
Jehoash buried in c. of D. 12:21
2 Chr 24:25
Amaziah buried in c. of D. 2 Ki 14:20
Azariah buried in c. of D. 15:7
Jothan buried in c. of D. 38
2 Chr 27:9
Ahaz buried in c. of D. 2 Ki 16:20
buried Jehoiada in c. of D. 2 Chr 24:16
breaches of the c. of D. Isa 22:9
the c. where D. dwelt. 29:1
Joseph went into c. of D. Luke 2:4
to you is born in c. of D. a. 11

elders with **city**

elders of his c. shall. Deut 19:12
the elders of that c. next to. 21:6
say to the elders of his c. our. 20
spread cloth before elders of c. 22:17
elders of his c. shall call him. 25:8
cause to elders of c. Josh 20:4
Gideon took elders of c. Judg 8:16
ten men of elders of c. Ruth 4:2
them elders of every c. Ezra 10:14

every **city**

smote men of every c. Judg 20:48
smite every fenced c. 2 Ki 3:19
in every c. Rehoboam. 2 Chr 11:12
in every c. of Judah he. 28:25
of sons of Aaron in every c. 31:19
every c. shall be forsaken. Jer 4:29
spoiler come upon every c. 48:8
every c. divided against. Mat 12:25
two and two into every c. Luke 10:1
hath in every c. them. Acts 15:21
visit our brethren in every c. 36
witnesseth in every c. that. 20:23
ordain elders in every c. Tit 1:5

fenced **city**

with you a fenced c. 2 Ki 10:2
watchmen to the fenced c. 17:9
dispersed of all his children unto
every fenced c. 2 Chr 11:23

city *of God*

make glad the c. of G. Ps 46:4
to be praised in c. of our G. 48:1
c. of G. God will establish it. 8
spoken of thee, O c. of G. 87:3
to the c. of the living G. Heb 12:22
the name of c. of my G. Rev 3:12

great **city**

Resen, same is a great c. Gen 10:12
Gibeon was a great c. Josh 10:2
c. was large and great. Neh 7:4
done thus to this great c.? Jer 22:8
Nineveh, that great c. Jonah 1:2; 3:2
was an exceeding great c. 3:3
spare Nineveh that great c.? 4:11
bodies in streets of great c. Rev 11:8
that great c. 14:8; 18:10, 16, 19, 21
the great c. was divided. 16:19
the woman is that great c. 17:18
he shewed me that great c. 21:10

holy **city**

in Jerusalem the holy c. Neh 11:1
the Levites of the holy c. were. 18
themselves of the holy c. Isa 48:2
beautiful garments, O holy c. 52:1
determined on thy holy c. Dan 9:24
taketh him up into holy c. Mat 4:5
went into the holy c. and. 27:53
holy c. shall they tread. Rev 11:2
I John saw the holy c. coming. 21:2
his part out of the holy c. 22:19

in, or into the **city**

hast in the c. bring. Gen 19:12
all that is in the c. Deut 20:14
blessed shalt thou be in the c. 28:3
cursed shalt thou be in the c. 16
people went into the c. Josh 6:20
destroyed all that was in the c. 21
they entered into the c. and. 8:19
the entrance into the c. Judg 1:24
Gideon put the ephod in his c. 8:27
man came into the c. 1 Sam 4:13
carry ark into the c. 2 Sam 15:25
return into the c. and your. 27
and told it in the c. 1 Ki 13:25
dieth of Jeroboam in the c. 14:11
when thy feet enter into the c. 12
that dieth of Baasha in the c. 16:4
came into the c. into an. 20:30
in the c. dogs eat. 21:24
we will enter into the c. 2 Ki 7:4
catch them, get into the c. 12
brought water into the c. 20:20
famine prevailed in the c. 25:3
he hath shewed me marvellous
kindness in a strong c. Ps 31:21
violence and strife in the c. 55:9
in the c. Wisdom. Pr 1:21
mighty men in the c. Eccl 7:19
wicked were forgotten in c. 8:10
in the c. is left desolation. Isa 24:12
if I enter into the c. Jer 14:18
is no more bread in the c. 38:9
famine was sore in the c. 52:6
gave up the ghost in the c. Lam 1:19
in the c. famine shall. Ezek 7:15
went forth and slew in the c. 9:7
I will not enter into the c. Hos 11:9
run to and fro in the c. Joel 2:9
trumpet be blown in the c. shall
there be evil in a c. Amos 3:6
an harlot in the c. thy sons. 7:17
began to enter into the c. Jonah 3:4
and came into his own c. Mat 9:1
into any c. of the Samaritans. 10:5
and into whatsoever c. ye. 11
go into the c. to such a man. 26:18
some of watch came into the c. 28:11
saith, go into the c. Mark 14:13
Acts 9:6
taxed, every one into his c. Luke 2:3
a woman in the c. which. 7:37
there was in a c. a judge. 18:2
there was a widow in that c. 3
when ye are entered into the c. 22:10
tarry ye in the c. of. 24:49
were gone into the c. John 4:8
I was in the c. of Joppa. Acts 11:5
rose up and came into the c. 14:20
Trophimus with him in the c. 21:29
in synagogues nor in the c. 24:12
perils in the c. in sea. 2 Cor 11:26
through gates into the c. Rev 22:14

city *of the Lord*

wicked doers from c. of L. Ps 101:8
call thee c. of the L. Isa 60:14

out of the **city**

were gone out of the c. Gen 44:4
as I am gone out of the c. Ex 9:29
Moses went out of the c. 33
them forth out of the c. Lev 14:45
side issued out of the c. Josh 8:22
man come out of the c. Judg 1:24
succour us out of the c. 2 Sam 18:3
a wise woman out of the c. 20:16
Naboth out of the c. 1 Ki 21:13
come out of the c. 2 Ki 7:12
let none escape out of the c. 9:15
much spoil out of the c. 1 Chr 20:2
cast idols out of the c. 2 Chr 33:15
groan from out of the c. Job 24:12
went out of the c. Jer 39:4; 52:7
the goings out of the c. Ezek 48:30
go forth out of the c. Mi 4:10
left them, and went out of the c.
Mat 21:17
even was come, went out of the c.
Mark 11:19
thrust him out of the c. Luke 4:29
when ye go out of that c. 9:5

went *out of c.* and came. *John* 4:30
cast Stephen *out of the c. Acts* 7:58
Paul, drew him *out of the c.* 14:19
sabbath we went *out of the c.* 16:13
till we were *out of the c.* 21:5

city *of refuge*

restore him to *c. of refuge.* *Num* 35:25
without border of *c. of refuge.* 26, 27
remained in the *c. of refuge.* 28
fled to the *c. of refuge.* 32
Hebron to be a *c. of refuge.* *Josh* 21:13, 21, 27, 32, 38
of Aaron, Hebron a *c. of refuge.* *1 Chr* 6:57

this **city**

Lord will destroy *this c. Gen* 19:14
behold now, *this c.* is near to. 20
I will not overthrow *this c.* 21
he that buildeth *this c.* *Josh* 6:26
us turn in unto *this c.* *Judg* 19:11
there is in *this c.* a. *1 Sam* 9:6
the situation of *this c.* *2 Ki* 2:19
this c. shall not. 18:30; *Isa* 36:15
not come into *this c. 2 Ki* 19:32, 33 *Isa* 37:34
I will defend *this c.* *2 Ki* 19:34 20:6; *Isa* 37:35; 38:6
cast off *this c.* Jerusalem. *2 Ki* 23:27
pray to thee toward *this c. 2 Chr* 6:34
if *this c.* be builded. *Ezra* 4:13, 16
this c. is a rebellious city. 15
bring evil up on *this c.?* *Neh* 13:18
this is the *c.* to be visited. *Jer* 6:6
Jerusalem, and *this c.* shall. 17:25
I will make *this c.* desolate. 19:8
break this people and *this c.* 11
I will bring upon *this c.* and. 15
the strength of *this c.* 20:5
he that abideth in *this c.* shall. 21:9
I set my face against *this c.* 10
Lord done thus unto *this c.?* 22:8
I will make *this c.* a curse. 26:6
innocent blood on *this c.* 15
should *this c.* be laid waste? 27:17
this c. to Chaldeans. 32:3, 28; 34:2
this c. hath been to me as a. 32:31
have hid my face from *this c.* 33:5
cause them to return to *this c.* 34:22
this c. shall not be burnt. 38:17
thou shalt cause *this c.* to be. 23
my words on *this c.* for evil. 39:16
wicked counsel in *this c. Ezek* 11:2
this c. is the caldron, and we. 3, 7
this c. shall not be your caldron. 11
persecute you in *this c.* *Mat* 10:23
much people in *this c.* *Acts* 18:10
I was brought up in *this c.* 22:3

without the **city**

men set him *without the c. Gen* 19:16
unclean place *without the c.* *Lev* 14:40, 41
measure from *without c. Num* 35:5
fountains *without the c. 2 Chr* 32:3
trodden *without the c.* *Rev* 14:20

clad

Jeroboam *c.* himself with. *1 Ki* 11:29
for clothing was *c.* with. *Isa* 59:17

clamorous

a foolish woman is *c.* *Pr* 9:13

clamour

all anger and *c.* be put. *Eph* 4:31

clap

men shall *c.* hands at. *Job* 27:23
c. your hands, all ye. *Ps* 47:1
let floods *c.* their hands, let. 98:8
trees of the field shall *c. Isa* 55:12
all that pass by *c.* their. *Lam* 2:15
fruit of thee shall *c.* *Nah* 3:19

clapped

c. their hands, and said. *2 Ki* 11:12
thou hast *c.* thine hands. *Ezek* 25:6

clappeth

he *c.* his hands among us. *Job* 34:37

clave
(*Cut, split*)

Abraham *c.* the wood. *Gen* 22:3
the ground *c.* asunder. *Num* 16:31
God *c.* an hollow place. *Judg* 15:19
they *c.* wood of cart. *1 Sam* 6:14
c. the rocks in. *Ps* 78:15; *Isa* 48:21

clave
(*Held to, clung to*)

his soul *c.* to Dinah. *Gen* 34:3
but Ruth *c.* to her. *Ruth* 1:14
men of Judah *c.* to. *2 Sam* 20:2
he smote till his hand *c.* to. 23:10
Solomon *c.* to these in. *1 Ki* 11:2
for Hezekiah *c.* to Lord. *2 Ki* 18:6
they *c.* to their brethren. *Neh* 10:29
certain men *c.* to Paul. *Acts* 17:34

claws

cleaveth cleft in two *c.* *Deut* 14:6*
nails grown like birds' *c.* *Dan* 4:33
he shall tear their *c.* *Zech* 11:16*

clay

dwell in houses of *c.* *Job* 4:19
thou hast made me as the *c.* 10:9
bodies are like to bodies of *c.* 13:12
prepare raiment as the *c.* 27:16
am formed out of the *c.* 33:6
it is turned as *c.* to the seal. 38:14
brought me out of miry *c.* *Ps* 40:2
esteemed as potter's *c.* *Isa* 29:16
as the potter treadeth the *c.* 41:25
shall the *c.* say to him? 45:9
we are *c.* thou our potter 64:8
vessel that he made of *c. Jer* 18:4
as *c.* is in the potter's hand. 6
stones, hide them in the *c.* 43:9*
part of iron, part *c. Dan* 2:33, 34, 42
c. broken in pieces. 35, 45
feet and toes part of potter's *c.* 41
go into *c.* and tread the. *Nah* 3:14
ladeth himself with *c.* *Hab* 2:6*
made *c* of spittle, anointed eyes of blind man with *c.* *John* 9:6
he put *c.* on mine eyes, I see. 15
potter power over the *c.?* *Rom* 9:21

clean

not make *c.* riddance in. *Lev* 23:22
passed *c.* over Jordan. *Josh* 3:17 4:1, 11
is his mercy *c.* gone for? *Ps* 77:8
earth is *c.* dissolved, is. *Isa* 24:19
he hath made it *c.* bare. *Joel* 1:7
arm shall be *c.* dried up. *Zech* 11:17
c. escaped from them. *2 Pet* 2:18

clean, *adjective*

[1] *Free from filth or dirt.* [2] *Ceremonially pure,* Lev 10:10; Acts 10:15. [3] *Metaphorically, innocent, delivered from the power of sin,* Acts 18:6; Ps 51:10; 1 John 1:9.

of every *c.* beast thou. *Gen* 7:2
of every *c.* beast and *c.* fowl. 8:20
Jacob said, be *c.* and change. 35:2
bullock unto *c.* place. *Lev* 4:12; 6:11
the flesh, all that be *c.* shall. 7:19
put difference between *c.* 10:10 11:47; 20:25; *Ezek* 22:26; 44:23
eat in *c.* place. *Lev* 10:14; *Num* 19:9
that ye may be *c.* from. *Lev* 16:30
not eat of holy things till he be *c.* 22:4
on seventh day be *c.* *Num* 19:12
a *c.* person shall take hyssop. 18
unclean and *c.* may eat. *Deut* 12:15 15:22
not *c.* surely he is not *c. 1 Sam* 20:26
again, and thou be *c.* *2 Ki* 5:10, 14
I wash in them and be *c.?* 12
wash and be *c.* 13
I am *c.* in thine eyes. *Job* 11:4
who can bring a *c.* thing out? 14:4
man that he should be *c.?* 15:14
heavens are not *c.* in his sight. 15
how can he be *c.* that is? 25:4
I am *c.* without transgression. 33:9
the ways of a man are *c.* *Pr* 16:2
things come alike to the *c. Eccl* 9:2
wash ye, make you *c.* *Isa* 1:16
so that there is no place *c.* 28:8
and young asses shall eat *c.* 30:24*
be ye *c.* that bear the vessels. 52:11
bring an offering in a *c.* vessel. 66:20
wilt thou not be made *c.?* *Jer* 13:27
then will I sprinkle *c.* *Ezek* 36:25
thou canst make me *c.* *Mat* 8:2 *Mark* 1:40; *Luke* 5:12
I will, be thou *c.* *Mat* 8:3 *Mark* 1:41; *Luke* 5:13

make *c.* the outside. *Mat* 23:25 *Luke* 11:39
all things are *c.* unto you. *Luke* 11:41
ye are not all *c.* *John* 13:11
now ye are *c.* through word I. 15:3
own heads, I am *c.* *Acts* 18:6
in fine linen, *c.* *Rev* 19:8*, 14*

clean *hands*

make my *hands* ever so *c. Job* 9:30
he that hath *c. hands* shall. 17:9
he that hath *c. hands* and a pure heart. *Ps* 24:4

clean *heart*

create in me a *c. heart.* *Ps* 51:10
and such as are of a *c. heart.* 73:1*
I have made my *heart c.?* *Pr* 20:9

is **clean**

he *is c.* *Lev* 13:13, 17, 37, 39
yet *is* he *c.* 40, 41
spit on him that is *c.* 15:8
man that *is c.* *Num* 9:13; 19:9
fear of the Lord *is c.* *Ps* 19:9
no oxen are, the crib *is c.* *Pr* 14:4
wash his feet, but *is c.* *John* 13:10

pronounce **clean**

pronounce him *c.* *Lev* 13:6; 14:7

shall be **clean**

is water *shall be c.* *Lev* 11:36
she *shall be c.* 12:8; 15:28
it *shall be c.* 13:58; 14:53 *Num* 31:23
in water, he *shall be c. Lev* 14:9, 20 15:13; 17:15; 22:7; *Num* 19:12, 19
and ye *shall* be *c.* *Num* 31:24 *Ezek* 36:25
hyssop, and I *shall* be *c.* *Ps* 51:7

cleanness

to *c.* of my hands hath Lord. *2 Sam* 22:21; *Ps* 18:20
to my *c.* in his sight. *2 Sam* 22:25 *Ps* 18:24
I have also given you *c.* *Amos* 4:6

cleanse

shalt *c.* altar. *Ex* 29:36; *Lev* 16:19
to *c.* house, two birds. *Lev* 14:49, 52
take the Levites and *c.* *Num* 8:6
c. house of Lord. *2 Chr* 29:15, 16
Levites should *c.* themselves. *Neh* 13:22
c. thou me from secret. *Ps* 19:12*
wash me throughly, and *c.* 51:2
a young man *c.* his way? 119:9
wind not to fan nor to *c.* *Jer* 4:11
c. them from iniquity. 33:8 *Ezek* 37:23
from idols will I *c.* you. *Ezek* 36:25
they may *c.* the land. 39:12, 16
thus shalt thou *c.* and purge it. 43:20
a young bullock, and *c.* the. 45:18
I will *c.* their blood. *Joel* 3:21
heal the sick, *c.* lepers. *Mat* 10:8
c. first that which is within. 23:26
let us *c.* ourselves from. *2 Cor* 7:1
might *c.* it with washing. *Eph* 5:26
c. your hands, ye sinners. *Jas* 4:8
to *c.* us from all. *1 John* 1:9

cleansed

so shall it be *c.* *Lev* 11:32
she shall be *c.* from the issue. 12:7
him that is to be *c.* 14:4, 14, 17 18, 19, 25, 28, 31
the land cannot be *c.* *Num* 35:33
from which we are not *c. Josh* 22:17
we have *c.* all house of. *2 Chr* 29:18
many had not *c.* themselves. 30:18
though he be not *c.* 19
Josiah *c.* Judah and Jerusalem. 34:5
they *c.* the chambers. *Neh* 13:9
thus I *c.* them from strangers. 30
what profit, if I be *c.?* *Job* 35:3
I have *c.* my heart in vain. *Ps* 73:1
the land that is not *c.* *Ezek* 22:2
after he is *c.* reckon to him. 44:2
then shall sanctuary be *c. Dan* 8:1
c. their blood I have not *c. Joel* 3:2
his leprosy was *c.* *Mat* 8:
the lepers are *c.* 11:5; *Luke* 7:2
leprosy departed, and he was *c.* *Mark* 1:4
was *c.* save Naaman. *Luke* 4:2
the lepers *c.*, the deaf hear. 7:2
as lepers went they were *c.* 17:1

were there not ten c.? *Luke* 17:17
what God hath c. *Acts* 10:15; 11:9

cleanseth

wind passeth and c. them. *Job* 37:21
blueness of a wound c. *Pr* 20:30
blood of Jesus Christ c. *1 John* 1:7

cleansing

of the priest for his c. *Lev* 13:7
shave head in day of his c. *Num* 6:9
go and offer for thy c. *Mark* 1:44
Luke 5:14

clear

thou shalt be c. from. *Gen* 24:8, 41
how shall we c. ourselves? 44:16
no means c. the guilty. *Ex* 34:7
as tender grass, by c. *2 Sam* 23:4
mightest be c. when. *Ps* 51:4
c. as the sun, terrible as. *S of S* 6:10
dwelling-place like a c. *Isa* 18:4
darken earth in a c. day. *Amos* 8:9
light shall not be c. nor. *Zech* 14:6*
approved yourselves to be c.
2 Cor 7:11*
c. as crystal. *Rev* 21:11; 22:1*
city was pure gold, like to c. 21:18*

clearer

thine age shall be c. *Job* 11:17

clearing

and by no means c. *Num* 14:18
what c. of yourselves. *2 Cor* 7:11

clearly

my lips shall utter knowledge c.
Job 33:3
see c. to pull out the. *Mat* 7:5
Luke 6:42
and saw every man c. *Mark* 8:25
things from creation c. *Rom* 1:20

clearness

body of heaven in his c. *Ex* 24:10

cleave

man shall c. to his wife. *Gen* 2:24
Mat 19:5; *Mark* 10:7
he shall c. it with the. *Lev* 1:17
ye that did c. to Lord. *Deut* 4:4
to him shalt thou c. 10:20; 11:22
13:4; 30:20; *Josh* 22:5
shall c. nought of cursed. *Deut* 13:17
but c. to Lord your God. *Josh* 23:8
leprosy of Naaman shall c. *2 Ki* 5:27
and the clods c. fast. *Job* 38:38
thou didst c. the fountain. *Ps* 74:15
hate the work, it shall not c. 101:3
my bones c. to my skin. 102:5
let my tongue c. to roof of. 137:6
they shall c. to house of. *Isa* 14:1
so have I caused to c. *Jer* 13:11
I make thy tongue c. to. *Ezek* 3:26
but they shall not c. one. *Dan* 2:43
many shall c. to them with. 11:34
thou didst c. the earth. *Hab* 3:9
the mount shall c. in. *Zech* 14:4
with purpose of heart c. *Acts* 11:23
abhor evil, c. to that. *Rom* 12:9

cleaved

Jehoram c. to Jeroboam's. *2 Ki* 3:3
their tongue c. to roof of. *Job* 29:10
and if any blot have c. to my. 31:7

cleaveth

ny bone c. to my skin. *Job* 19:20
ny tongue c. to jaws. *Ps* 22:15
n evil disease, say they, c. 41:8
ur belly c. to earth. 44:25
ny soul c. to the dust. 119:25
s the girdle c. to loins of. *Jer* 13:11
ongue of sucking child c. *Lam* 4:4
heir skin c. to their bones. 8
ust of your city which c. *Luke* 10:11

cleaveth

east that c. the cleft. *Deut* 14:6*
e c. my reins asunder. *Job* 16:13
hen one cutteth and c. *Ps* 141:7
hat c. wood shall be. *Eccl* 10:9

cleft

hat cleaveth the c. *Deut* 14:6*
e valleys shall be c. as. *Mi* 1:4

clefts

ou art in c. of the. *S of S* 2:14
to the c. of the rocks. *Isa* 2:21*
ou that dwellest in c. *Jer* 49:16
Ob 3
mite little house with c. *Amos* 6:11

clemency

hear us of thy c. a few. *Acts* 24:4

Cleopas

whose name was C. *Luke* 24:18
Mary the wife of C. *John* 19:25

clerk

when town c. had. *Acts* 19:35

cliff, -s

come up by the c. of. *2 Chr* 20:16*
to dwell in the c. of the. *Job* 30:6*

clift, -s

will put thee in the c. *Ex* 33:22*
in valleys under c. of. *Isa* 57:5*

climb, -ed, -eth

Jonathan c. up upon. *1 Sam* 14:13
they shall c. up upon. *Jer* 4:29
they shall c. the wall. *Joel* 2:7
they shall c. up upon the houses. 9
they c. up to heaven. *Amos* 9:2
Zaccheus c. up into a. *Luke* 19:4
c. up some other way. *John* 10:1

clipped

head be bald, beard be c. *Jer* 48:37

clods

flesh is clothed with c. *Job* 7:5
the c. of the valley shall. 21:33
and the c. cleave fast. 38:38
doth plowman break c.? *Isa* 28:24
Jacob shall break his c. *Hos* 10:11
seed is rotten under c. *Joel* 1:17

cloke

clad with zeal as a c. *Isa* 59:17†
let him have thy c. also. *Mat* 5:40
him that taketh thy c. *Luke* 6:29
now they have no c. *John* 15:22*
nor used we a c. of. *1 Thes* 2:5
the c. I left at Troas. *2 Tim* 4:13
not using liberty for a c. *1 Pet* 2:16

close

and it be kept c. from. *Num* 5:13
afraid out of c. places. *2 Sam* 22:46
Ps 18:45
David yet kept himself c. *1 Chr* 12:1
and kept c. from fowls. *Job* 28:21
shut up together as with a c. 41:15
famine follow c. after you. *Jer* 42:16
and I saw him come c. *Dan* 8:7
and c. up the breaches. *Amos* 9:11
kept it c. and told no man. *Luke* 9:36
they sailed c. by Crete. *Acts* 27:13

closed

Lord c. up the flesh. *Gen* 2:21
the Lord had fast c. up all. 20:18
earth c. upon them. *Num* 16:33
fat c. upon the blade. *Judg* 3:22
they have not been c. *Isa* 1:6
Lord hath c. your eyes. 29:10
for the words are c. up. *Dan* 12:9
the depth c. me round. *Jonah* 2:5
eyes have c. *Mat* 13:15; *Acts* 28:27
he c. book, and gave it. *Luke* 4:20

closer

friend that sticketh c. *Pr* 18:24

closest

thou reign, because c. *Jer* 22:15*

closet, -s

bride go out of her c. *Joel* 2:16
enter into thy c. *Mat* 6:6*
ye have spoken in c. *Luke* 12:3*

cloth

spread on them a c. *Num* 4:8
put them in a c. of blue. 12
shall spread the c. *Deut* 22:17*
covered image with a c. *1 Sam* 19:13
sword of Goliath, wrapt in a c. 21:9
and cast a c. on him. *2 Sam* 20:12*
Hazael took a thick c. *2 Ki* 8:15*
away as a menstruous c. *Isa* 30:22*
putteth a piece of new c. *Mat* 9:16
Mark 2:21
he wrapped it in a linen c. *Mat* 27:59
having a linen c. *Mark* 14:51

clothe

bring his sons and c. *Ex* 40:14
raiment to c. Mordecai. *Esth* 4:4
I will c. her priests. *Ps* 132:16
his enemies will I c. with. 18
drowsiness shall c. a. *Pr* 23:21
I will c. him with thy robe. *Isa* 22:21
thou shalt surely c. thee. *Isa* 49:18
I c. the heavens with blackness. 50:3
shall c. themselves with. *Ezek* 26:16
ye eat the fat, and c. you. 34:3
ye c. you, but there is. *Hag* 1:6
I will c. thee with. *Zech* 3:4
if God so c. grass of field, much more
c. you? *Mat* 6:30; *Luke* 12:28

clothed

coats of skins and c. *Gen* 3:21
Moses c. Aaron with robe. *Lev* 8:7
weep over Saul who c. *2 Sam* 1:24
David and Israel c. with. *1 Chr* 21:16
priests be c. with. *2 Chr* 6:41
king of Israel and Judah c. 18:9
spoil c. all that were naked. 28:15
none enter king's gate c. *Esth* 4:2
flesh is c. with worms. *Job* 7:5
c. me with skin and flesh. 10:11
put on righteousness and it c. 29:14
hast thou c. his neck. 39:19
be c. with shame. *Ps* 35:26; 109:29
the pastures are c. with. 65:13
c. with majesty, Lord is c. 93:1
thou art c. with honour and. 104:1
as he c. himself with cursing. 109:18
let thy priests be c. with. 132:9
her household are c. with. *Pr* 31:21
c. me with garments of. *Isa* 61:10
I c. thee also with. *Ezek* 16:10
c. Daniel with scarlet. *Dan* 5:29
all such as are c. with. *Zeph* 1:8
Joshua was c. with filthy. *Zech* 3:3
man c. in soft raiment. *Mat* 11:8
Luke 7:25
naked and ye c. me. *Mat* 25:36
naked and ye c. me not. 43
John was c. with camel's. *Mark* 1:6
sitting and c. 5:15; *Luke* 8:35
c. Jesus with purple. *Mark* 15:17
certain rich man c. in. *Luke* 16:19
desiring to be c. upon. *2 Cor* 5:2
if so be that being c. we shall not. 3
and be c. with humility. *1 Pet* 5:5*
that thou mayest be c. *Rev* 3:18
I saw another mighty angel c. 10:1
two witnesses shall prophesy c. 11:3
appeared a woman c. with. 12:1
he was c. with a vesture 19:13

clothed with *linen*

one man c. with *linen*. *Ezek* 9:2
be c. with *linen* garments. 44:17
certain man c. with *linen*. *Dan* 10:5
said to man c. in *linen*. 12:6
c. in pure and white *linen*. *Rev* 15:6
18:16; 19:14

shall be **clothed**

that hate thee *shall be* c. *Job* 8:22
the prince *shall be* c. *Ezek* 7:27
read this writing, *shall be* c. *Dan* 5:7
wherewithal *shall we be* c.?
Mat 6:31
overcometh *shall be* c. *Rev* 3:5; 4:4

clothes

he washed his c. in the. *Gen* 49:11
troughs bound up in their c. *Ex* 12:34
the c. of service. 35:19; 39:1, 41
nor rend your c. *Lev* 10:6; 21:10
c. are not waxen old. *Deut* 29:5
Neh 9:21
Saul stript off his c. *1 Sam* 19:24
covered David with c. *1 Ki* 1:1
took hold of his own c. *2 Ki* 2:12
thou didst rend thy c. *2 Chr* 34:27
none of us put off our c. *Neh* 4:23
and my own c. shall abhor. *Job* 9:31
take fire, and his c. not? *Pr* 6:27
strip thee also of c. *Ezek* 16:39
23:26
return back to take his c. *Mat* 24:18
if I touch but his c. *Mark* 5:28
put his own c. on him. 15:20
him in swaddling c. *Luke* 2:7, 12
a man that ware no c. neither. 8:27
went they spread their c. 19:36
the linen c. laid. 24:12; *John* 20:5
bound with grave c. *John* 11:44
and wound it in linen c. 19:40
napkin not lying with linen c. 20:7*
laid down their c. *Acts* 7:58
cried out and cast off their c. 22:23

rent **clothes**

Reuben *rent* his *c*. *Gen* 37:29
Jacob *rent* his *c*. 34
Joseph's brethren *rent* their *c*. 44:13
and Caleb *rent* their *c*. *Num* 14:6
Joshua *rent* his *c*. *Josh* 7:6
Jephthah *rent* his *c*. *Judg* 11:35
rend your *c*. gird you. *2 Sam* 3:31
Ahab *rent* his *c*. *1 Ki* 21:27
king of Israel *rent c*. *2 Ki* 5:8; 6:30
Athaliah *rent* her *c*. 11:14
2 Chr 23:13
Hezekiah heard he *rent* his *c*.
2 Ki 19:1; *Isa* 37:1
Mordecai perceived, he *rent* his *c*.
Esth 4:1
high priest *rent* his *c*. *Mat* 26:65
Mark 14:63
and Paul *rent* their *c*. *Acts* 14:14
magistrates *rent* off their *c*. 16:22

clothes *rent*

leper's *c*. shall be *rent*. *Lev* 13:45
to Shiloh with *c*. *rent*. *1 Sam* 4:12
from Saul with *c*. *rent*. *2 Sam* 1:2
servants stood with *c*. *rent*. 13:31
to Hezekiah with *c*. *rent*. *2 Ki* 18:37
Isa 36:22
men having their *c*. *rent*. *Jer* 41:5

wash **clothes**

wash their *c*. *Ex* 19:10; *Num* 8:7
wash his *c*. *Lev* 11:25, 40; 13:6
14:8, 9, 47; 15:5, 8, 11, 22; 16:26
28; *Num* 19:10, 19
priest shall *wash c*. *Num* 19:7, 8, 19
ye shall *wash* your *c*. on. 31:24

washed **clothes**

people *washed* their *c*. *Ex* 19:14
Levites *washed* their *c*. *Num* 8:21
washed not his *c*. *2 Sam* 19:24

clothest

though thou *c*. thyself. *Jer* 4:30

clothing

stripped naked of their *c*. *Job* 22:6
naked to lodge without *c*. 24:7
to go naked without *c*. 10
any perish for want of *c*. 31:19
as for me, my *c*. was. *Ps* 35:13
king's daughter, her *c*. is. 45:13
lambs are for thy *c*. *Pr* 27:26
virtuous woman's *c*. is silk. 31:22
strength and honour are her *c*. 25
thou hast *c*. be thou our. *Isa* 3:6
house is neither bread nor *c*. 7
shall be for durable *c*. 23:18
garments of vengeance for *c*. 59:17
and purple is their *c*. *Jer* 10:9
in sheep's *c*. *Mat* 7:15
that wear soft *c*. 11:8
scribes that go in long *c*. *Mark* 12:38
man stood before me in bright *c*.
Acts 10:30
him that weareth gay *c*. *Jas* 2:3

cloud

In addition to the common meaning this word is used frequently of, [1] *A great number,* Heb 12:1. [2] *A fog, or mist,* Hos 6:4. [3] *The sky,* Ps 36:5; 68:34; Pr 8:28.
(*At the Exodus God gave the Israelites a pillar of cloud to direct them in their march. This attended them through the wilderness. It was clear and bright during the night, in order to give them light when it grew dark; and in the day time it was thick and gloomy, the better to defend them from the excessive heats of the Arabian deserts. It also gave the signal for marching and for halting*)

set my bow in the *c*. for. *Gen* 9:13
bow shall be seen in *c*. 14, 16
it was *c*. and darkness. *Ex* 14:20
glory of Lord appeared in *c*. 16:10
I come unto thee in a thick *c*. 19:9
Moses went up, and a *c*. 24:15
c. covered it six days, seventh day
God called out of *c*. 16
Moses went into midst of *c*. 18
Lord descended in the *c*. 34:5
Num 11:25
c. covered the tent of the. *Ex* 40:34
the *c*. of Lord was on the. 38
I will appear in the *c*. *Lev* 16:2
when the *c*. tarried long. *Num* 9:19
the *c*. of the Lord was upon. 10:34
the *c*. filled house of Lord. *1 Ki* 8:10
2 Chr 5:13; *Ezek* 10:4
ariseth a little *c*. like. *1 Ki* 18:44
day be darkness, let a *c*. *Job* 3:5
he judge through dark *c*.? 22:13
welfare passeth away as a *c*. 30:15
when I made the *c*. the. 38:9
day-time led them with *c*. *Ps* 78:14
spread a *c*. for a covering. 105:39
his favour is as a *c*. *Pr* 16:15
create on her assemblies *c*. *Isa* 4:5
like a *c*. of dew in heat of. 18:4
Lord rideth upon a swift *c*. 19:1
blotted out as a thick *c*. transgressions, and as *c*. thy sins. 44:22
are these that flee as a *c*.? 60:8
daughter of Zion with *c*. *Lam* 2:1
covered thyself with a *c*. 3:44
a great *c*. and a fire. *Ezek* 1:4
appearance of bow in the *c*. 28
a thick *c*. of incense. 8:11
the house was filled with the *c*. 10:4
as for her, a *c*. shall cover. 30:18
I will cover sun with a *c*. 32:7
shalt be like a *c*. to. 38:9, 16
a bright *c*. overshadowed them and a voice out of *c*. said. *Mat.* 17:5
Mark 9:7; *Luke* 9:34, 35
when ye see a *c*. rise. *Luke* 12:54
Son of Man coming in a *c*. 21:27
a *c*. received him out of. *Acts* 1:9
fathers were under the *c*. *1 Cor* 10:1
all baptized to Moses in the *c*. 2
angel clothed with a *c*. *Rev* 10:1
ascended to heaven in a *c*. 11:12
c. and upon *c*. one sat. 14:14, 15, 16

cloud *abode*

because the *c*. *abode*. *Ex* 40:35
where *c*. *abode* there. *Num* 9:17
as long as *c*. *abode* they. 18

morning **cloud**

is as a *morning c*. *Hos* 6:4
shall be as the *morning c*. 11:3

pillar of **cloud**

by day in a *p*. *of c*. *Ex* 13:21
took not away the *p*. *of c*. 22
on Egyptians through *p*. *of c*. 14:24
down in *p*. *of c*. and. *Num* 12:5
in *p*. *of c*. and *p*. *of c*. *Deut* 31:15
p. *of c*. departed not. *Neh* 9:19

cloud *taken up*

the *c*. was *taken up*. *Ex* 40:36
Num 9:17
if the *c*. were not *taken up*. *Ex* 40:37
c. was *taken up* from tabernacle.
Num 9:17; 10:11

white **cloud**

a *white c*. and on *c*. one. *Rev* 14:14

cloud *of witnesses*

with so great a *c*. of *w*. *Heb* 12:1

clouds

with darkness, *c*. and. *Deut* 4:11
heavens dropped, *c*. also. *Judg* 5:4
about him thick *c*. of. *2 Sam* 22:12
as a morning without *c*. 23:4
heaven was black with *c*. *1 Ki* 18:45
though head reach to *c*. *Job* 20:6
thick *c*. are a covering that. 22:14
bindeth up waters in thick *c*. 26:8
understand spreadings of *c*.? 36:29
the balancings of the *c*.? 37:16
who can number the *c*. in ? 38:37
faithfulness reacheth to *c*. *Ps* 36:5
thy truth reacheth to the *c*. 57:10
108:4
and his strength is in the *c*. 68:34
c. poured out water. 77:17
commanded the *c*. from. 78:23
c. and darkness are round. 97:2
maketh the *c*. his chariot. 104:3
covers heaven with *c*. 147:8
c. dropped down the dew. *Pr* 3:20
when he established the *c*. 8:28
is like *c*. and wind without. 25:14
regardeth the *c*. shall not. *Eccl* 11:4
nor *c*. return after the rain. 12:2
I will command the *c*. *Isa* 5:6
ascend above height of the *c*. 14:14
shall come up as *c*. and. *Jer* 4:13
with the *c*. of heaven. *Dan* 7:13
c. and darkness. *Joel* 2:2; *Zeph* 1:15
c. are the dust of his feet. *Nah* 1:3
Lord shall make bright *c*. *Zech* 10:1
Son of Man coming in *c*. *Mat* 24:30
26:64; *Mark* 13:26; 14:62
up with them in *c*. *1 Thes* 4:17
they are *c*. carried. *2 Pet* 2:17
c. they are without water. *Jude* 12
behold he cometh with *c*. *Rev* 1:7

cloudy

the *c*. pillar descended. *Ex* 33:9
people saw the *c*. pillar. 10
in day by *c*. pillar. *Neh* 9:12
spake in the *c*. pillar. *Ps* 99:7
day of the Lord, a *c*. day. *Ezek* 30:3
been scattered in the *c*. day. 34:12

clouted

old shoes and *c*. on. *Josh* 9:5†

clouts

took old cast *c*. and rags. *Jer* 38:11
put these old cast *c*. under. 12

cloven

whatsoever is *c*.-footed. *Lev* 11:3
though the swine be *c*.-footed. 7
not *c*.-footed are unclean to you. 26
Deut 14:7
to them *c*. tongues. *Acts* 2:3*

cluster

a branch with one *c*. *Num* 13:23
my beloved is as a *c*. *S of S* 1:14
wine found in the *c*. so. *Isa* 65:8
woe is me, there is no *c*. *Mi* 7:1

clusters

the *c*. thereof brought. *Gen* 40:10
grapes their *c*. bitter. *Deut* 32:32
Abigail brought 100 *c*. *1 Sam* 25:18
gave the Egyptian two *c*. 30:12
breasts like two *c*. of. *S of S* 7:7, 8
gather the *c*. of the vine. *Rev* 14:18

coal

so shall quench my *c*. *2 Sam* 14:7
seraphim having a live *c*. *Isa* 6:6
there shall not be a *c*. to. 47:14
visage is blacker than *c*. *Lam* 4:8

coals

censer full of burning *c*. *Lev* 16:12
a cake baken on the *c*. *1 Ki* 19:6
his breath kindleth *c*. *Job* 41:21
there went fire, *c*. were. *Ps* 18:8
hail-stones and *c*. of fire. 12
arrows of mighty with *c*. 120:4
let burning *c*. fall on them. 140:10
can one go on hot *c*.? *Pr* 6:28
heap *c*. of fire. 25:22; *Rom* 12:20
as *c*. are to burning *c*. and. *Pr* 26:21
c. thereof are *c*. of fire. *S of S* 8:6
the smith worketh in *c*. *Isa* 44:12
have baked bread upon the *c*. 19
smith that bloweth the *c*. 54:16
appearance like burning *c*. *Ezek* 1:13
fill thine hand with *c*. of fire. 10:2
set it empty on the *c*. 24:11
burning *c*. went forth at. *Hab* 3:5
had made a fire of *c*. *John* 18:18
they saw a fire of *c*. and fish. 21:9

coast

(*Not as now* sea-coast *but border, whether by the sea or not. It is usually rendered in the Revisions by border, or side*)

the locusts into thy *c*. *Ex* 10:4
ships shall come from *c*. *Num* 24:2
uttermost sea shall *c*. be. *Deut* 11:2
if the Lord enlarge thy *c*. 19:
going down of sun your *c*. *Josh* 1:
Judah shall abide in their *c*. 18:
not Israel to pass his *c*. *Judg* 11:2
up by way of his own *c*. *1 Sam* 6:
no more into the *c*. of Israel. 7:1
to seek any more in any *c*. 27:
made an invasion on the *c*. 30:1
Jeroboam restored *c*. of. *2 Ki* 14:2
me, and enlarge my *c*. *1 Chr* 4:1
the *c*. shall be for the. *Zeph* 2:

sea **coast**
remnant of the sea c. Ezek 25:16
woe to inhabitants of sea c. Zeph 2:5
the sea c. shall be dwellings for. 6
in Capernaum upon sea c. Mat 4:13
multitude from sea c. Luke 6:17

south **coast**
uttermost part of south c. Josh 15:1
this shall be your south c. 4
this was the south c. 18:19

coasts
locusts rested in all the c. Ex 10:14
not one locust in all the c. of. 19
to pass through c. of. Deut 2:4
no leavened bread seen in thy c. 16:4
thou shalt divide the c. 19:3
shall abide in their c. on. Josh 18:5
five men from their c. Judg 18:2*
sent concubine into all the c. 19:29
the c. thereof did Israel. 1 Sam 7:14
send messengers into all c. 11:3, 7
destroyed from c. of. 2 Sam 21:5
destroyed through all c. 1 Chr 21:12
to him out of all c. 2 Chr 11:13
lice in all their c. Ps 105:31
and brake trees of their c. 33
whirlwind raised from c. Jer 25:32
take a man of their c. Ezek 33:2
to do with me, all c. Joel 3:4*
slew children in all c. Mat 2:16
depart out of their c. 8:34; Mark 5:17
Jesus departed into c. of Tyre. Mat 15:21*
departing from c. of. Mark 7:31
and Barnabas out of c. Acts 13:50

coat
Jacob made Joseph a c. Gen 37:3
sent c. of many colours, and said, know whether it be thy son's c. 32
Aaron a robe and a broidered c. Ex 28:4
shalt put upon Aaron the c. 29:5
he put upon him the c. Lev 8:7
put on the holy linen c. 16:4
made Samuel a little c. 1 Sam 2:19*
armed with a c. of mail. 17:5, 38
met David with c. rent. 2 Sam 15:32
as collar of my c. Job 30:18
I have put off my c. S of S 5:3
and take away thy c. Mat 5:40
forbid not to take thy c. Luke 6:29
c. was without seam. John 19:23
Peter girt his fisher's c. unto. 21:7

coats
God made c. of skins. Gen 3:21
for Aaron's sons make c. Ex 28:40
and put c. on them. 29:8; 40:14
Moses put c. upon. Lev 8:13
they carried them in their c. 10:5
were bound in their c. Dan 3:21*
nor were their c. changed, nor. 27*
neither provide two c. Mat 10:10
and put not on two c. Mark 6:9
he that hath two c. Luke 3:11
shewing the c. which. Acts 9:39

cock
night before c. crow. Mat 26:34, 75
Mark 14:30, 72; Luke 22:34, 61
c. crew. Mat 26:74; Luke 22:60
John 18:27
master cometh at c. crow. Mark 13:35
porch, and the c. crew. 14:68, 72
the c. shall not crow till thou hast denied me thrice. John 13:38

cockatrice, -s
(*A basilisk, or adder*)
his hand on the c. den. Isa 11:8
root shall come forth a c. 14:29
they hatch c. eggs. 59:5
will send serpents, c. Jer 8:17

cockle
and let c. grow instead. Job 31:40

coffer
jewels of gold in a c. 1 Sam 6:8
they laid ark and c. with mice. 11
Levites took down the c. with. 15

coffin
Joseph was put in c. in. Gen 50:26

cogitations
my c. much troubled me. Dan 7:28*

cold
c. and heat, day and. Gen 8:22
no covering in the c. Job 24:7
and c. cometh out of north. 37:9
stand before his c.? Ps 147:17
not plow by reason of c. Pr 20:4*
as the c. of snow in time. 25:13
taketh away a garment in c. 20
as c. waters to a thirsty soul. 25
shall c. flowing waters? Jer 18:14
camp in hedges in c. day. Nah 3:17
a cup of c. water. Mat 10:42
love of many shall wax c. 24:12
a fire, for it was c. John 18:18
received us, because of c. Acts 28:2
in fastings often, in c. 2 Cor 11:27
neither c. nor hot. Rev 3:15, 16

collar, -s
from Midian, beside c. Judg 8:26*
disease bindeth me as c. Job 30:18

collection
bring out of Judah c. 2 Chr 24:6*, 9*
concerning the c. for. 1 Cor 16:1

college
dwelt in c. 2 Ki 22:14*; 2 Chr 34:22*

collops
because he maketh c. of. Job 15:27†

colony
city of Macedonia, and c. Acts 16:12

Colosse
saints and brethren at C. Col 1:2

colour
have not changed his c. Lev 13:55
the c. as the c. of. Num 11:7*
when wine giveth his c. Pr 23:31
as the c. of amber. Ezek 1:4†
sparkled like c. of. 7†; Dan 10:6
wheels like unto c. of a. Ezek 1:16† 10:9
firmament was as the c. of. 1:22†
under c. as though they. Acts 27:30
in purple and scarlet c. Rev 17:4*

coloured
woman sit on scarlet c. Rev 17:3

colours
coat of many c. for. Gen 37:3
Sisera a prey of divers c. Judg 5:30
a garment of divers c. 2 Sam 13:18
stones of divers c. 1 Chr 29:2
lay thy stones with fair c. Isa 54:11
deckedst high places with c. Ezek 16:16
an eagle with divers c. came. 17:3

colt, -s
camels with their c. forty. Gen 32:15
binding his ass' c. to the. 49:11
sons that rode on 30 ass c. Judg 10:4
nephews rode on 70 ass c. 12:14
born like a wild ass's c. Job 11:12
riding upon a c. Zech 9:9; Mat 21:5
John 12:15
find ass tied, c. with her. Mat 21:2
Mark 11:2; Luke 19:30
brought ass and c. and. Mat 21:7
Mark 11:7
what do ye, loosing the c.? Mark 11:5; Luke 19:33
cast garments on c. Luke 19:35

come
[1] *To draw nigh, or approach,* Ex 34:3. [2] *To proceed from,* 1 Chr 29:14. [3] *To attain to,* Acts 26:7. [4] *To touch,* Ezek 44:25. [5] *To arise,* Num 24:7.
two of every sort shall c. Gen 6:20
c. thou, and all thy house. 7:1
c. let us make our father. 19:32
wherefore c. ye to me? 26:27
c. let us make a covenant. 31:44
c. let us slay him, and cast. 37:10
whence c. ye? 42:7; Josh 9:8
bring your father and c. Gen 45:19
from Judah till Shiloh c. 49:10
lo, I c. to thee in a. Ex 19:9
I record name I will c. and. 20:24
people to whom thou shalt c. 23:27
c. thou with us, we will. Num 10:29
c. I pray thee, curse this. 22:6, 11
out of Jacob shall c. he. 24:19
if a Levite c. and c. Deut 18:6
all these blessings shall c. Deut 28:2
all these curses c. on thee. 15, 45
no razor c. on his head. Judg 13:5
1 Sam 1:11
shall c. on thy two sons. 1 Sam 2:34
people will not eat till he c. 9:13
tarry, till I c. to thee. 10:8
but I c. to thee in the name. 17:45
then c. thou, for there is. 20:21
shall ark of Lord c. to? 2 Sam 6:9
I will c. on him while he is. 17:2
c. thou over with me and I. 19:33
and the oath c. before. 1 Ki 8:31
if any thing would c. from. 20:33
feed this fellow until I c. in. 22:27
let him c. now to me. 2 Ki 5:8
till I c. and take. 18:32; Isa 36:17
riches and honour c. 1 Chr 29:12
all things c. of thee, and of. 14
ark of Lord hath c. 2 Chr 8:11
Vashti refused to c. at. Esth 1:12
how endure to see evil c. to? 8:6
let no joyful voice c. Job 3:7
that I may speak, let c. on. 13:13
will I wait till my change c. 14:14
his sons c. to honour, and he. 21
caused it to c. for correction. 37:13
hitherto shalt thou c. but. 38:11
lo, I c. Ps 40:7; Heb 10:7, 9
when shall I c. and appear? Ps 42:2
our God shall c. and not. 50:3
unto thee shall all flesh c. 65:2
stir up thy strength, and c. 80:2
all nations shall c. and. 86:9
when wilt thou c. unto me? 101:2
loved cursing, so let it c. 109:17
mercies c. unto me. 119:41, 77
shall thy poverty c. Pr 6:11; 24:34
fear of the wicked shall c. 10:24
curse causeless shall not c. 26:2
all things c. alike to all. Eccl 9:2
up, my love, and c. S of S 2:10, 13
c. with me from Lebanon. 4:8
and c. thou south, blow upon. 16
of Holy One of Israel c. Isa 5:19
c. from a far country. 13:5
the day of the Lord, it shall c. 6
inquire ye; return, c. 21:12
c. my people, enter into. 26:20
cause them that c. of Jacob. 27:6
c. with vengeance, he will c. 35:4
the Lord will c. with a. 40:10
raised up one, and he shall c. 41:25
things coming, and shall c. 44:7
assemble yourselves, and c. 45:20
even to him shall men c. 24
the redeemed shall c. with. 51:11
c. ye to the waters, c. ye, buy, c. 55:1
c. unto me, hear, and your. 3
and the Redeemer shall c. 59:20
Gentiles shall c. to thy light. 60:3, 5
behold, Lord will c. with fire. 66:15
say they, we will c. Jer 2:31
behold, we c. to thee, for thou. 3:22
mourning women, that they c. 9:17
wherefore c. these things? 13:22
word of the Lord? let it c. 17:15
him till time of his land c. 27:7
they shall c. with weeping. 31:9
princes hear, and c. to thee. 38:25
good to c. if ill to c. forbear. 40:4
as Carmel, so shall he c. 46:18
trusted, saying, who shall c.? 49:4
none c. to solemn feasts. Lam 1:4
let all their wickedness c. 22
abominations whither they c. Ezek 12:16
save souls alive that c.? 13:18
that sword may c. 21:19, 20; 32:11
shall be no more, till he c. 21:27
he seeth the sword c. on. 33:3, 6
they c. to thee as the people. 31
lo it will c. then shall know. 33
they are at hand to c. 36:8
c. let us return to Lord. Hos 6:1
and he shall c. to us, as the. 3
to seek the Lord till he c. 10:12
as a destruction shall it c. Joel 1:15
before terrible day of Lord c. 2:31
c. let us cast lots. Jonah 1:7
to thee shall it c. kingdom c. Mi 4:8
because it will surely c. Hab 2:3
anger of Lord c. on you. Zeph 2:2
what c. these to do? Zech 1:21

God shall *c.* and all the. *Zech* 14:5
Lord ye seek shall *c.* *Mal* 3:1
lest I *c.* and smite the earth. 4:6
for out of thee shall *c.* *Mat* 2:6
first be reconciled, then *c.* 5:24
thy kingdom *c.* thy. 6:10; *Luke* 11:2
false prophets *c.* to you in. *Mat* 7:15
Jesus saith to him, I will *c.* 8:7
not worthy thou shouldest *c.* 8
and to another, *c.* and. 9; *Luke* 7:8
many shall *c.* from east. *Mat* 8:11
he that should *c.*? 11:3; *Luke* 7:19, 20
c. all ye that labour and. *Mat* 11:28
if any man will *c.* after me. 16:24
Elias must first *c.*? 17:10, 11
sell, and *c.* 19:21; *Luke* 18:22
all things are ready, *c.* *Mat* 22:4
preached, then shall end *c.* 24:14
what hour your Lord doth *c.* 42
c. ye blessed of my Father. 25:34
art thou *c.* to destroy us? *Mark* 1:24 *Luke* 4:34
whosoever will *c.* after me let him deny. *Mark* 8:34; *Luke* 9:23; 14:27
suffer the little children to *c.* unto me. *Mark* 10:14; *Luke* 18:16
c. take up the cross. *Mark* 10:21
this is the heir, *c.* let us kill. 12:7; *Luke* 20:14
he himself would *c.* *Luke* 10:1
three years I *c.* seeking fruit. 13:7
there are six days, in them *c.* 14
kingdom of God should *c.* 17:20
occupy till I *c.* 19:13
he shall *c.* and destroy. 20:16
till kingdom of God shall *c.* 22:18
c. and see. *John* 1:39
baptizeth, and all men *c.* to him. 3:26
lest a worse thing *c.* to thee. 5:14
ye will not *c.* to me, that ye. 40
Father giveth me shall *c.* 6:37
c. to me, except Father. 44, 65
thither ye cannot *c.* 7:34
let him *c.* to me and drink. 37
ye cannot tell whence I *c.* and. 8:14
you before it *c.* that when it *c.* 13:19
comfortless, I will *c.* 14:18
and we will *c.* unto him. 23
these are in the world, I *c.* 17:11, 13
if I will he tarry till I *c.*? 21:22, 23
this Jesus shall so *c.* *Acts* 1:11
and notable day of Lord *c.* 2:20
when times of refreshing *c.* 3:19
c. down and now *c.* I will send. 7:34
pray that none of these *c.* 8:24
that he would not delay to *c.* 9:38
lest that *c.* on you that is. 13:40
c. over into Macedonia. 16:9
believe on him that should *c.* 19:4
forbid no acquaintance to *c.* 24:23
our twelve tribes hope to *c.* 26:7*
and Moses did say should *c.* 22
let us do evil, that good *c.* *Rom* 3:8
at this time, will I *c.* 9:9
judge nothing till Lord *c.* *1 Cor* 4:5
the Lord's death till he *c.* 11:26
rest will I set in order when I *c.* 34
with what body do they *c.*? 15:35
no gatherings when I *c.* 16:2
if Timothy *c.* see he be with you. 10
I desired him to *c.* to you. 12
I was minded to *c.* to. *2 Cor* 1:15
for I fear, lest when I *c.* I. 12:20
if righteousness *c.* by law. *Gal* 2:21
blessing of Abraham *c.* on. 3:14
till the seed should *c.* to whom. 19
when he shall *c.* to be. *2 Thes* 1:10
day shall not *c.* except there *c.* 2:3*
and of that to *c.* *1 Tim* 4:8
till I *c.* give attendance to. 13
perilous times shall *c.* *2 Tim* 3:1
time will *c.* they will not endure. 4:3
be diligent to *c.* to me. *Tit* 3:12
let us *c.* boldly to the. *Heb* 4:16
he is able to save them that *c.* 7:25
he that shall *c.* will *c.* and. 10:37
whence *c.* wars, *c.* they? *Jas* 4:1
weep for miseries that shall *c.* 5:1
but that all should *c.* *2 Pet* 3:9
day of Lord will *c.* as a thief in the night. 10; *Rev* 3:3; 16:15
antichrist shall *c.* *1 John* 2:18
if I *c.* I will remember. *3 John* 10
repent, or else I will *c.* *Rev* 2:5
hold fast till I *c.* 25
I *c.* quickly, hold. 3:11; 22:7, 20
four beasts, saying, *c.* 6:1, 3, 5, 7
in one hour is judgement *c.* 18:10
and let him that is athirst *c.* 22:17

come *again*

so that I *c. again* to my. *Gen* 28:21
that waters may *c. again.* *Ex* 14:26
if the plague *c. again.* *Lev* 14:43
when I *c. again* in peace. *Judg* 8:9
let man of God *c. again* to us. 13:8
to Gath, and was *c. again.* *1 Ki* 2:41
and then *c. again.* 12:5; *2 Chr* 10:5
this child's soul *c. again.* *1 Ki* 17:21
Israel *c. again.* *Ezra* 6:21; *Neh* 8:17
he shall *c. again.* *Ps* 126:6
say not go and *c. again.* *Pr* 3:28
Chaldeans shall *c. again.* *Jer* 37:8
when I *c. again* I will. *Luke* 10:35
I will *c. again* and. *John* 14:3
I go away and *c. again.* 28
that I would not *c. again.* *2 Cor* 2:1
lest, when I *c. again,* God. 12:21
I write, that if I *c. again.* I. 13:2

come *down*

c. down to me, tarry not. *Gen* 45:9
I am *c. down* to deliver. *Ex* 3:8
the Lord will *c. down* on. 19:11
I will *c. down* and talk. *Num* 11:17
from heaven it *c. down.* *Deut* 28:24
saying, *c. down* against. *Judg* 7:24
they said, we are *c. down.* 15:12
c. down and fetch ark. *1 Sam* 6:21
will Saul *c. down*? he will *c. down.* 23:11
c. down, according to the. 20
thou shalt not *c. down.* *2 Ki* 1:4; 6:16
thou man of God, *c. down.* 1:9
let fire *c. down.* 10, 11, 12
work, I cannot *c. down.* *Neh* 6:3
his dealing shall *c. down.* *Ps* 7:16
he shall *c. down* like rain. 72:6
the heavens, and *c. down.* 144:5
my sword, it shall *c. down.* *Isa* 34:5
c. down, sit in the dust. 47
that thou wouldest *c. down.* 64:1
your principalities shall *c. down.* *Jer* 13:18
who shall *c. down* against us? 21:13
c. down from thy glory. 48:18
of the sea shall *c. down.* *Ezek* 26:16
all pilots shall *c. down* from. 27:29
of her power shall *c. down.* 30:6
cause mighty to *c. down.* *Joel* 3:11
not *c. down* to take. *Mat* 24:17
c. down from cross. 27:40, 42; *Mark* 15:30
fire to *c. down*? *Luke* 9:54
Zacchaeus, haste and *c. down.* 19:5
Sir, *c. down* ere child. *John* 4:49
the gods are *c. down.* *Acts* 14:11
devil is *c. down* to you. *Rev* 12:12
maketh fire *c. down* from. 13:13
angel *c. down* having key. 20:1

come *forth*

he that shall *c. forth* out. *Gen* 15:4
Hebrews *c. forth* out. *1 Sam* 14:11
thus saith king, *c. forth.* *1 Ki* 2:30
slay them, let none *c. forth.* *2 Ki* 10:25
I shall *c. forth* as gold. *Job* 23:10
let my sentence *c. forth.* *Ps* 17:2
and I cannot *c. forth.* 88:8
feareth God shall *c. forth.* *Eccl* 7:18
shall *c. forth* a rod out of. *Isa* 11:1
art *c. forth* out of waters. 48:1
my fury *c. forth* like fire. *Jer* 4:4*
Pharaoh's army was *c. forth.* 37:5, 7
let mighty men *c. forth.* 46:9*
a fire shall *c. forth* out of. 48:45
twain shall *c. forth* out. *Ezek* 21:19
servants of most high God, *c. forth.* *Dan* 3:26
O Daniel, I am *c. forth* to. 9:22
a fountain shall *c. forth.* *Joel* 3:18
out of thee shall *c. forth.* *Mi* 5:2
c. forth and flee from land. *Zech* 2:6
angels shall *c. forth.* *Mat* 13:49
c. forth from the heart. 15:18
this kind *c. forth* by. *Mark* 9:29
and will *c. forth* and. *Luke* 12:37
shall *c. forth,* they that. *John* 5:29
cried, Lazarus, *c. forth.* 11:43
shall *c. forth* and serve. *Acts* 7:7

come *hither*

fourth generation *c. hither.* *Gen* 15:16
Samson is *c. hither.* *Judg* 16:2
c. thou *hither* and eat. *Ruth* 2:14
inquired if the man should *c. hither.* *1 Sam* 10:22
not sit down till he *c. hither.* 16:11
c. hither that I may. *2 Sam* 14:32
say to Joab, *c. hither* that I. 20:16
man of God is *c. hither.* *2 Ki* 8:7
said to thee, *c.* up *hither.* *Pr* 25:7
c. forth and *c. hither.* *Dan* 3:26
thou *c. hither* to torment? *Mat* 8:29
neither *c. hither* to draw. *John* 4:15
call thy husband and *c. hither.* 16
turned world are *c. hither.* *Acts* 17:6
c. up *h.* *Rev* 4:1; 11:12; 17:1; 21:9

I am **come**, or *am I* **come**

I thy father-in-law *am c.* *Ex* 18:6
lo *I am c.* to thee. *Num* 22:38
I am c. into country. *Deut* 26:3
I am c. to sacrifice. *1 Sam* 16:2, 5
now that *I am c.* to. *2 Sam* 14:15
wherefore *am I c.* from? 32
I am c. first to meet my. 19:20
I am c. into deep waters. *Ps* 69:2
I communed, lo, *I am c.* *Eccl* 1:16
I am c. into my garden. *S of S* 5:1
I am c. to shew. *Dan* 9:23; 10:14
I am c. for thy words. 10:12
think not *I am c.* to. *Mat* 5:17
I am not *c.* to call righteous. 9:13
think not that *I am c.* to. 10:34
I am c. to set a man at. 35
suppose ye that *I am c.* *Luke* 12:51
am I c. baptizing with. *John* 1:31
I am c. in my Father's name. 5:43
I am not *c.* of myself. 7:28
for judgement *I am c.* into. 9:39
I am c. that they might have. 10:10
I am c. a light into world. 12:46
I am c. into the world. 16:28

come *in,* or *into.*

shalt *c. into* the ark, and. *Gen* 6:18
not a man in earth to *c. in.* 19:31
said, *c. in* thou blessed of. 24:31
destroyer to *c. in.* *Ex* 12:23
when they *c. in* unto the. 28:43*
afterward shall *c. into* the camp. *Lev* 16:26, 28; *Num* 19:7; 31:24
at his word shall *c. in.* *Num* 27:21
no more go out and *c. in.* *Deut* 31:2
to go out and *c. in.* *Josh* 14:11
I will *c. in* after thee. *1 Ki* 1:14
not how to go out or *c. in.* 3:7
he said, *c. in* thou wife of. 14:6
suffer any to go out or *c. in.* 15:17
when *c. in* shut door. *2 Ki* 4:4
took each his men to *c. in.* 11:9
go out and *c. in* before. *2 Chr* 1:10
let none go out or *c. in* to Asa. 16:1
none *c. into* the house of Lord. 23:6
till I *c. into* Judah. *Neh* 2:7
Esther let no man *c. in.* *Esth* 5:12
king said, let Haman *c. in.* 6:5
King of glory shall *c. in.* *Ps* 24:7, 9
for the waters are *c. in.* 69:1
offering and *c. into* his courts. 96:8
so let it *c. into* his bowels. 109:18
let my beloved *c. into.* *S of S* 4:16
Lord shall *c. into* Egypt. *Isa* 19:
the Assyrian shall *c. into.* 2
shut up, that no man *c. in.* 24:1
when the enemy shall *c. in.* 59:1
the kings of Judah *c. in.* *Jer* 17:1
and let Jerusalem *c. into.* 51:5
strangers are *c. into* the. 5
things that *c. into* mind. *Ezek* 11:
shall things *c. into* thy mind. 38:1
Assyrian shall *c. into* land. *Mi* 5:
ye *c. into* an house. *Mat* 10:1
Son of man shall *c. in* glory. 16:2
many shall *c. in* my name. 24: *Mark* 13:6; *Luke* 21
Son of man *c. in* his glory. *Mat* 25:
which *c. in* may see. *Luke* 11:3
c. in second watch, or *c. in.* 12:

will c. in a day when he. Luke 12:46
and compel them to c. in. 14:23
lest they c. into this place. 16:28
c. in my Father's name, if another c. in his own name. John 5:43
should c. into world. 6:14; 11:27
Lydia, saying, c. into. Acts 16:15
of Gentiles be c. in. Rom 11:25
there c. in those that. 1 Cor 14:23
if there c. in one that. 24
there c. in also a poor man. Jas 2:2
I will c. in to him, and. Rev 3:20

come, *passive*

the end of all flesh is c. Gen 6:13
for therefore are ye c. to. 18:5
the cry which is c. to me. 21
therefore is this distress c. 42:21
cry of children of Israel is c. Ex 3:9
fear not, for God is c. to. 20:20
there is a people c. out. Num 22:11
when all Israel is c. to. Deut 31:11
host of Lord am I c. Josh 5:14
Samson is c. hither. Judg 16:2
said, God is c. into. 1 Sam 4:7
because their cry is c. to me. 9:16
anguish is c. upon me. 2 Sam 1:9
speech of all Israel is c. to. 19:11
the creditor is c. to. 2 Ki 4:1
when this letter is c. to thee. 5:6
man of God is c. hither. 8:7
and after all that is c. Ezra 9:13
thing I feared is c. Job 3:25; 4:5
all this is c. upon us. Ps 44:17
salvation of Israel were c. 53:6
and trembling are c. 55:5
I am c. into deep waters. 69:2
yea the set time is c. 102:13
he is c. to Aiath. Isa 10:28
my salvation is near to c. 56:1
light is c. and glory of Lord. 60:1
year of my redeemed is c. 63:4
sinned, therefore this is c. Jer 40:3
baldness is c. on Gaza. 47:5
woe to them, their day is c. 50:27
thy day is c. the time that. 31
on many waters, thy end is c. 51:13
our end is c. Lam 4:18
remember, O Lord, what is c. 5:1
end, the end is c. Ezek 7:2, 6
an only evil, behold, is c. 5
the morning is c. upon thee. 7
the day, behold, it is c. 10; 39:8
king of Babylon is c. to. 17:12
prince whose day is c. 21:25, 29
all this evil is c. on us. Dan 9:13
the end is c. on my. Amos 8:2
he is c. to gate of my. Mi 1:9
to flee from wrath to c.? Mat 3:7
the kingdom of God is c. 12:28
when he is c. he findeth it. 44
Son of man is c. to save lost. 18:11
because the harvest is c. Mark 4:29
she is c. aforehand to anoint. 14:8
it is enough, the hour is c. 41
the Son of man is c. Luke 7:34
thy brother is c. father hath. 15:27
this day is salvation c. to this. 19:9
the Son of man is c. to seek. 10
that light is c. into the. John 3:19
when he is c. he will tell. 4:25
he Master is c. and calleth. 11:28
hour is c. Son of man. 12:23; 17:1
when the Comforter is c. 15:26
when he is c. he will reprove. 16:8
when the Spirit of truth is c. 13
sorrow because hour is c. 21
salvation is c. unto the. Rom 11:11
or your obedience is c. 16:19
s perfect is c. then. 1 Cor 13:10
ut after that faith is c. Gal 3:25
which gospel is c. to you. Col 1:6
esus Christ is c. in. 1 John 4:2
onfesseth not that Jesus Christ is c. in flesh is not of God. 3; 2 John 7
now Son of God is c. 1 John 5:20
reat day of wrath is c. Rev 6:17
nd thy wrath is c. and. 11:18
c. salvation and strength. 12:10
our of his judgement is c. 14:7
reat riches is c. to nought. 18:17
r marriage of Lamb is c. 19:7

come *near*

bram was c. near to. Gen 12:11
Abimelech had not c. near. Gen 20:4
let him c. near and keep. Ex 12:48
c. near before the Lord. 16:9
c. near to the altar. 28:43; 30:20
cause him to c. near. Num 16:5
that no stranger c. near to. 40
c. near, put feet on. Josh 10:24
caused tribes to c. near. 1 Sam 10:20
lest they c. near unto thee. Ps 32:9*
let my cry c. near before. 119:169
let us c. near together. Isa 41:1
c. ye near unto me, hear ye. 48:16
adversary ? let him c. near me. 50:8
nor hath c. near to a. Ezek 18:6
which c. near to the Lord to. 40:46
they shall c. near to me. 44:15
they shall c. near to my table. 16
of violence to c. near. Amos 6:3
and I will c. near to you. Mal 3:5
when he was c. near. Luke 19:41
we, or he c. near, are. Acts 23:15

come *nigh*

afraid to c. nigh him. Ex 34:30
sanctified in all that c. nigh me. Lev 10:3
hath blemish c. nigh. 21:21, 23
a stranger not c. nigh. Num 18:4
you are c. nigh to battle. Deut 20:2
kingdom of God c. nigh unto you. Luke 10:9, 11

come *not*

be ready, c. not at your. Ex 19:15
but they shall not c. nigh. 24:2
ye shall not c. into land. Num 14:30
we will not c. up. 16:12, 14
unclean shall not c. Deut 23:10
c. not near unto the ark. Josh 3:4
that ye c. not among. 23:7
hath not c. a razor on. Judg 16:17
would not c. he sent the second time, he would not c. 2 Sam 14:29
carcase not c. to. 1 Ki 13:22
king of Assyria shall not c. into. 2 Ki 19:32, 33; Isa 37:33, 34
I c. not against thee. 2 Chr 35:21
whosoever would not c. Ezra 10:8
Moabite not c. into. Neh 13:1*
not c. into the number. Job 3:6
an hypocrite shall not c. 13:16
floods they shall not c. Ps 32:6
let them not c. into thy. 69:27
it shall not c. nigh thee. 91:7
I will not c. into tabernacle. 132:3
c. not nigh the door. Pr 5:8
days that have not c. Isa 7:17
there shall not c. the fear of. 25
scourge shall not c. to me. 28:15
the gathering shall not c. 32:10
terror, it shall not c. near thee. 54:14
by thyself, c. not near me. 65:5
king of Babylon shall not c. Jer 37:19
like things shall not c. Ezek 16:16
they shall not c. near to me. 44:13
c. not ye unto Gilgal. Hos 4:15
their soul shall not c. into. 9:4
family of Egypt c. not. Zech 14:18*
and they would not c. Mat 22:3
could not c. nigh for. Mark 2:4
Luke 8:19
married a wife, I cannot c. Luke 14:20
and shall not c. into. John 5:24
ye will not c. to me that ye. 40
thither ye cannot c. 7:34, 36
think ye that he will not c.? 11:56
if I had not c. they had. 15:22
not away, Comforter will not c. 16:7
as though I would not c. 1 Cor 4:18

come *out*

afterwards shall c. out. Gen 15:14
kings c. out of thee. 17:6; 35:11
daughters of city c. out. 24:13
till he c. out and have. Lev 16:17
shall eat till it c. out. Num 11:20
c. out ye three unto. 12:4
lest I c. out against thee. 20:18
people c. out of Egypt. 22:5, 11
year after Israel were c. out. 33:38
c. out one way, and. Deut 28:7
let fire c. out of the. Judg 9:15
increase army and c. out. 29
let not arrogancy c. out. 1 Sam 2:3
to-morrow we will c. out. 11:3, 10
king of Israel c. out ? 1 Sam 24:14
c. out, c. out, thou. 2 Sam 16:7*
480th year after Israel were c. out. 1 Ki 6:1
there are men c. out. 20:17
he will c. out to me. 2 Ki 5:11
agreement and c. out. 18:31
Isa 36:16
behold, he is c. out to fight. 2 Ki 19:9
salvation were c. out. Ps 14:7
princes shall c. out of. 68:31
the just shall c. out. Pr 12:13
their stink shall c. out. Isa 34:3
there is one c. out. Nah 1:11*
by no means c. out till. Mat 5:26
are ye c. out as against a thief? 26:55
Mark 14:48; Luke 22:52
hold thy peace, and c. out of him. Mark 1:25; Luke 4:35
c. out, unclean spirit. Mark 5:8
Luke 8:29
any good thing c. out of? John 1:46
Christ c. out of Galilee? 7:41
name of Jesus to c. out. Acts 16:18
there shall c. out of. Rom 11:26
wherefore c. out from. 2 Cor 6:17
though they c. out of loins. Heb 7:5
saw spirits c. out of. Rev 16:13
c. out of her, my people. 18:4

come *to pass*

it shall c. to pass if they. Ex 4:8, 9
word shall c. to pass or. Num 11:23
c. to pass the man's rod I. 17:5
c. to pass if ye hearken. Deut 7:12
11:13; 28:1
sign or wonder c. to pass. 13:2
all are c. to pass, no. Josh 23:14
let thy words c. to pass. Judg 13:12
when thy sayings c. to pass. 17
why is this c. to pass in? 21:3
shall surely c. to pass. 1 Ki 13:32
nor shall it c. to pass. Isa 7:7
so shall it c. to pass. 14:24
former things are c. to pass. 42:9
it shall c. to pass if ye. Jer 17:24
hast spoken is c. to pass. 32:24
I speak shall c. to pass. Ezek 12:25
it shall c. to pass, I will do it. 24:14
to thee what shall c. to p. Dan 2:29
c. to pass that I will break. Hos 1:5
c. to pass that whosoever. Joel 2:32
c. to pass I will cause sun. Amos 8:9
this shall c. to pass. Zech 6:15
therefore it is c. to pass, that. 7:13
things must c. to pass. Mat 24:6
saith shall c. to pass. Mark 11:23
ye shall see these c. to pass. 13:29
Luke 21:31
thing which is c. to pass. Luke 2:15
sign when things shall c. to pass. 21:7, 28
wondering at what was c. to pass. 24:12
not known things which c. to pass. 18
when it is c. to pass. John 13:19
14:29
c. to pass that every. Acts 3:23
must shortly c. to pass. Rev 1:1
22:6

come *short*

sinned and c. short of. Rom 3:23
seem to c. short of it. Heb 4:1

come joined with *time*

answer in time to c. Gen 30:33
son asketh thee in time to c. Ex 13:14; Deut 6:20; Josh 4:6, 21
in time to c. your. Josh 22:24, 28
time was c. after. 1 Sam 1:20
time to favour Zion, set time is c. Ps 102:13
rejoice in time to c. Pr 31:25
time of singing of birds is c. S of S 2:12
her time is near to c. Isa 13:22
that it may be for time to c. 30:8
hearken and hear for time to c. 42:23
time is c. the day of. Ezek 7:7
time is not c. the Lord's. Hag 1:2
time was c. he should. Luke 9:51
fulness of time was c. Gal 4:4
foundation against time to c. 1 Tim 6:19
time is c. that judgement. 1 Pet 4:17

come *together*

we should c. *together*. *Job* 9:32
his troops c. *together* against. 19:12
shall c. *together* out of. *Jer* 3:18
and Judah shall c. *together*. 50:4
were c. *together*. *Acts* 1:6; 28:17
many that were c. *together*. 10:27
wherefore they were c. *together*. 19:32
multitude must c. *together*. 21:22
c. *together* again, that. *1 Cor* 7:5*
c. *together*, not for better. 11:17
c. *together* in church. 18, 20, 33
14:26
c. not *together* to condemnation. 11:34
if church be c. *together*. 14:23

come *up*

trumpet sound shall c. *up*. *Ex* 19:13
thou shalt c. *up*, thou and. 24
c. *up* to me into the mount. 24:12
I will c. *up* into midst of. 33:5
and c. *up* in the morning to. 34:2
no man shall c. *up* with thee. 3
us c. *up* out of Egypt? *Num* 20:5
c. *up* out of Jordan. *Josh* 4:16, 17, 18
c. *up* to me, and help me to. 10:4
c. *up* to us quickly, save us. 6
c. *up* with me into my lot. *Judg* 1:3
why are ye c. *up* against? 15:10
saying, c. *up* this once. 16:18
if they say, c. *up* to us. *1 Sam* 14:10
this man that is c. *up*? 17:25
then ye shall c. *up*. *1 Ki* 1:35
king of Syria will c. *up*. 20:22
c. *up* and save me. *2 Ki* 16:7
am I now c. *up* without Lord. 18:25
Isa 36:10
they c. *up* by the cliff. *2 Chr* 20:16
shall c. up no more. *Job* 7:9
be said, c. *up* hither. *Pr* 25:7
there shall c. *up* briers. *Isa* 5:6
and he shall c. *up* over all his. 8:7
laid down no fellow is c. *up*. 14:8
they shall c. *up* with. 60:7
death is c. *up* into our. *Jer* 9:21
c. *up* like a lion. 49:19; 50:44
behold, he shall c. *up* and fly. 49:22
cause the horses to c. *up* as. 51:27
sea is c. *up* upon Babylon. 42
and c. *up* upon my neck. *Lam* 1:14
cause fury to c. *up* to. *Ezek* 24:8
and cause you to c. *up* out. 37:12
thou shalt c. *up* against my. 38:16
c. *up* out of the land. *Hos* 1:11*
the thistle shall c. *up* on. 10:8
wind of Lord shall c. *up*. 13:15
and ill savour shall c. *up*. *Joel* 2:20
draw near, let them c *up*. 3:9
let heathen c. *up* to valley of. 12
of your camps to c. *up*. *Amos* 4:10
saviours shall c. *up* on. *Obad* 21
wickedness is c. *up* before me. *Jonah* 1:2
made a gourd to c. *up* over. 4:6
the breaker c. *up* before. *Mi* 2:13
dasheth in pieces is c. *up*. *Nah* 2:1
whoso will not c. *up*. *Zech* 14:17
desired Philip to c. *up*. *Acts* 8:31
were c. *up* out of the water. 39
Cornelius, thy alms are c. *up*. 10:4*
c. *up* hither, and I. *Rev* 4:1; 11:12

yet **come**

ye are not as *yet* c. *Deut* 12:9
my hour is not *yet* c. *John* 2:4
my time is not *yet* c. 7:6, 8
his hour was not *yet* c. 30; 8:20
Jesus was not *yet* c. 11:30
the other is not *yet* c. *Rev* 17:10

comeliness

he hath no form nor c. nor. *Isa* 53:2
perfect through my c. *Ezek* 16:14*
Persia and Lud set forth thy c. 27:10
my c. was turned in me. *Dan* 10:8
have more abundant c. *1 Cor* 12:23

comely

David, a c. person. *1 Sam* 16:18
not conceal c. proportion. *Job* 41:12†
praise is c. for the. *Ps* 33:1; 147:1
yea, four are c. in going. *Pr* 30:29*
it is c. for one to eat. *Eccl.* 5:18
I am black but c. *S of S* 1:5
thy cheeks are c. with rows. 10
and thy countenance is c. *S of S* 2:14
thy speech is c. 4:3
thou art c. O my love, as. 6:4
shall be excellent and c. *Isa* 4:2
daughter of Zion to a c. *Jer* 6:2
speak for that which is c. *1 Cor* 7:35*
is it c. that a woman pray? 11:13*
our c. parts have no need. 12:24

comers

can never make the c. *Heb* 10:1*

comest

from Sidon as thou c. *Gen* 10:19*
Egypt, as thou c. unto Zoar. 13:10*
when thou c. to my kindred. 24:41
thou c. nigh children of. *Deut* 2:19
when thou c. nigh to city. 20:10*
blessed when thou c. in. 28:6
cursed when thou c. in. 19
Micah ... whence c. thou? *Judg* 17:9
old man ... whence c. thou? 19:17
c. thou peaceably? *1 Sam* 16:4
1 Ki 2:13
I a dog, that thou c. to. *1 Sam* 17:43
thou c. to me with a sword. 45
bring Michal when c. *2 Sam* 3:13
when thou c. anoint. *1 Ki* 19:15
whence c. thou, Gehazi? *2 Ki* 5:25
whence c. thou? Satan. *Job* 1:7; 2:2
when thou c. to Babylon. *Jer* 51:61
occupation? whence c.? *Jonah* 1:8
and c. thou to me? *Mat* 3:14
remember me when c. *Luke* 23:42

cometh

behold this dreamer c. *Gen* 37:19
on which such water c. is. *Lev* 11:34
beside what c. of sale. *Deut* 18:8
cover that which c. from. 23:13
when ark c. among us. *1 Sam* 4:3
all that man of God saith c. 9:6
wherefore c. not the son of? 20:27
he c. not to the king's table. 29
for when she c. in will. *1 Ki* 14:5
but he c. not again. *2 Ki* 9:18, 20
king as he c. in. 11:8; *2 Chr* 23:7
for death, and it c. not. *Job* 3:21
whence c. wisdom? 28:20
but joy c. in the morning. *Ps* 30:5
from him cometh my salvation. 62:1
promotion c. not from the east. 75:6
before Lord, for he c. to. 96:13
blessed is he that c. in name. 118:26
from whence c. my help. 121:1
my help c. from the Lord. 2
will mock when your fear c. *Pr* 1:26
when your destruction c. 27
when pride c. then c. shame. 11:2
when the wicked c. then c. 18:3
he c. in with vanity. *Eccl* 6:4
all that c. is vanity. 11:8
he c. leaping upon. *S of S* 2:8
the day of the Lord c. *Isa* 13:9
whose breaking c. suddenly. 30:13
the name of the Lord c. from. 27
behold, thy salvation c. 62:11
is this that c. from Edom? 63:1
shall not see when good c. *Jer* 17:6
and shall not see when heat c. 8
when he c. he shall smite. 43:11
saith, and it c. to pass. *Lam* 3:37
c. to a prophet to. *Ezek* 14:4, 7
that which c. in your mind. 20:32
because it c. behold it c. 21:7
when this c. ye shall know I. 24:24
come to thee as people c. 33:31
when this c. to pass, then shall. 33
thing live whither rivers c. 47:9
that c. against him. *Dan* 11:16
blessed is he that c. to. 12:12
the thief c. in, and the. *Hos* 7:1*
day of the Lord c. *Joel* 2:1
Zech 14:1; *1 Thes* 5:2
from Assyrians when he c. *Mi* 5:6
the day c. that shall burn as an oven; the day that c. *Mal* 4:1
he that c. after me is. *Mat* 3:11
Mark 1:7; *Luke* 3:16
more than these c. of evil. *Mat* 5:37
come, and he c. 8:9; *Luke* 7:8
then c. the wicked one. *Mat* 13:19
king c. unto thee. 21:5; *John* 12:15
he that c. in name of Lord. *Mat* 21:9
Mark 11:9; *Luke* 13:35; 19:38
lord of those servants c. *Mat* 25:19
he c. to them walking. *Mark* 6:48
be ashamed when he c. in. 8:38
Elias c. first, and restoreth. 9:12
while he yet spake, c. Judas. 14:43
whoso c. to me. *Luke* 6:47
the Lord when he c. 12:37
Son of man c. at an hour. 40
his lord, when he c. shall find. 43
there will be heat, and it c. 55
kingdom of God c. not. 17:20
Son of man c. shall he find? 18:8
canst not tell whence it c. *John* 3:8
nor c. to the light. 20
he that doth the truth, c. to the. 21
the hour c. 4:21, 23; 16:32
he that c. to me shall. 6:35, 37
learned of the Father c. to me. 45
when Christ c. no man. 7:27, 31
Christ c. of the seed of. 42
the night c. when no man can. 9:4
c. unto the Father but by me. 14:6
the time c. that whosoever. 16:2
time c. I shall no more speak. 25
the hour c. that ye shall be. 32
who when he c. shall. *Acts* 10:32
c. this blessedness upon? *Rom* 4:9*
so then, faith c. by hearing. 10:17
then c. the end, when. *1 Cor* 15:24
besides that which c. *2 Cor* 11:28*
c. wrath of God. *Eph* 5:6; *Col* 3:6
day of Lord so c. as a *1 Thes* 5:2
he that c. to God must. *Heb* 11:6
the Lord c. with 10,000 of. *Jude* 14
he c. with clouds. *Rev* 1:7
when he c. he must continue a. 17:10

cometh *down*

as the rain c. *down*. *Isa* 55:10
is he which c. *down*. *John* 6:33, 50
and perfect gift c. *down*. *Jas* 1:17
Jerusalem which c. *down*. *Rev* 3:12

cometh *forth*

when virgin c. *forth*. *Gen* 24:43
also behold he c. *forth*. *Ex* 4:14
Pharaoh, lo, he c. *forth* to. 8:20
c. *forth* of the doors. *Judg* 11:31
whosoever c. not *forth*. *1 Sam* 11:7
affliction c. not *forth*. *Job* 5:6
he c. *forth* like a flower. 14:2
this also c. *forth* from. *Isa* 28:29
words c. *forth* from. *Ezek* 33:30
behold, the Lord c. *forth*. *Mi* 1:3

cometh *nigh*

the stranger that c. *nigh* shall be. *Num* 1:51; 3:10, 38; 18:7

cometh *out*

be heard when he c. *out*. *Ex* 28:35
when he c. *out*. *Num* 12:12
toward young that c. *out*. *Deut* 28:57
a stranger that c. *out* of. *1 Ki* 8:41
drawn, and c. *out* of. *Job* 20:25
fair weather c. *out* of the. 37:22
who is this that c. *out*? *S of S* 3:6
the Lord c. *out* of his. *Isa* 26:21
and that which c. *out* of it. 42:5
it c. *out* of the north. *Jer* 46:20
it with dung that c. *out*. *Ezek* 4:12
that which c. *out* of the mouth. *Mat* 15:11*; *Mark* 7:20
for as lightning c. *out* of. 24:27

cometh *up*

old man c. *up* covered. *1 Sam* 28:14
who is this that c. *up*? *S of S* 8:5
and he that c. *up* out. *Isa* 24:18
who is this that c. *up*? *Jer* 46:7*
out of north there c. *up* a. 50:3
when he c. *up* to people. *Hab* 3:16
up the fish first c. *up*. *Mat* 17:27

comfort, *substantive*

then should I yet have c. *Job* 6:10
that I may take c. a little. 10:2
this is my c. in my. *Ps* 119:5
kindness be for my c. 7
should I receive c.? *Isa* 57:6
thou art a c. to them. *Ezek* 16:5
daughter, be of good c. *Mat* 9:22
Luke 8:4
be of good c. rise. *Mark* 10:49
walking in the c. of the. *Acts* 9:3
through patience and c. *Rom* 15:
to exhortation and c. *1 Cor* 14:3
even the God of all c. *2 Cor* 1:
by the c. wherewith we are.

I am filled with *c*. *2 Cor* 7:4
comforted in your *c*. 13
be perfect, be of good *c*. 13:11
if there be any *c*. of love. *Phil* 2:1*
that I may also be of good *c*. 19
have been a *c*. to me. *Col* 4:11

comfort, *verb*

this same shall *c*. us. *Gen* 5:29
c. ye your hearts. 18:5
as touching thee doth *c*. 27:42
and daughters rose up to *c*. 37:35
c. thy heart with a. *Judg* 19:5, 8
David sent to *c*. him. *2 Sam* 10:2
1 Chr 19:2
brethren came to *c*. him. *1 Chr* 7:22
came to Hanun to *c*. him. 19:2
to mourn with and *c*. *Job* 2:11
I say, my bed shall *c*. me. 7:13
I will forget, I will *c*. myself. 9:27*
how then *c*. ye me in vain. 21:34
rod and thy staff, they *c*. *Ps* 23:4
thou shalt increase and *c*. 71:21
when wilt thou *c*. me? 119:82
c. me with apples. *S of S* 2:5
labour not to *c*. me. *Isa* 22:4
c. ye, *c*. ye my people. 40:1
Lord shall *c*. Zion, he will *c*. 51:3
by whom shall I *c*. thee? 19
he hath sent me to *c*. 61:2
so will I *c*. you. 66:13
when I would *c*. myself. *Jer* 8:18
neither shall men tear to *c*. 16:7
for I will *c*. them. 31:13
hath none to *c*. her. *Lam* 1:2, 17
there is none to *c*. me. 21
that I may *c*. thee? 2:13
they shall *c*. you when. *Ezek* 14:23
Lord shall yet *c*. Zion. *Zech* 1:17
told false dreams, they *c*. in. 10:2
to *c*. them concerning. *John* 11:19*
we may be able to *c*. *2 Cor* 1:4
rather to forgive and *c*. him. 2:7
and that he might *c*. *Eph* 6:22
know your estate, *c*. *Col* 4:8
to *c*. you concerning. *1 Thes* 3:2
wherefore *c*. one another. 4:18
wherefore *c*. yourselves. 5:11*
c. the feeble-minded. 14*
our Lord Jesus *c*. *2 Thes* 2:17

comfortable

word of my Lord be *c*. *2 Sam* 14:17
the angel with *c*. words. *Zech* 1:13

comfortably

go forth and speak *c*. *2 Sam* 19:7
he spake *c*. to all. *2 Chr* 30:22
over people, and spake *c*. 32:6
speak *c*. to Jerusalem. *Isa* 40:2
allure her, and speak *c*. *Hos* 2:14

comforted

Isaac was *c*. after his. *Gen* 24:67
Jacob refused to be *c*. 37:35
Judah was *c*. and went. 38:12
Joseph *c*. his brethren. 50:21
that thou hast *c*. me. *Ruth* 2:13
David *c*. Bath-sheba. *2 Sam* 12:24
c. concerning Ammon. 13:39
all his brethren *c*. him. *Job* 42:11
my soul refused to be *c*. *Ps* 77:2
Lord, hast holpen and *c*. 86:17
judgements, have *c*. myself. 119:52
hath *c*. his people. *Isa* 49:13; 52:9
afflicted, tossed, and not *c*. 54:11
ye shall be *c*. in Jerusalem. 66:13
refused to be *c*. for child. *Jer* 31:15
to rest, I will be *c*. *Ezek* 5:13
ye shall be *c*. concerning. 14:22
all that drink water be *c*. 31:16
see them, and shall be *c*. 32:31
would not be *c*. because. *Mat* 2:18
for they shall be *c*. 5:4
now he is *c*. and thou. *Luke* 16:25
the Jews which *c*. her. *John* 11:31
seen brethren, *c*. them. *Acts* 16:40
were not a little *c*. 20:12
that I may be *c*. with. *Rom* 1:12
and all may be *c*. *1 Cor* 14:31
wherewith we are *c*. of. *2 Cor* 1:4
God *c*. us by coming of Titus. 7:6
wherewith he was *c*. in you. 7
therefore we were *c*. in your. 13
their hearts might be *c*. *Col* 2:2
how he exhorted and *c*. *1 Thes* 2:11*
we were *c*. over you in all. 3:7

comfortedst

is turned away, thou *c*. *Isa* 12:1*

comforter, -s

hath sent *c*. *2 Sam* 10:3; *1 Chr* 19:3
miserable *c*. are ye all. *Job* 16:2
I looked for *c*. but. *Ps* 69:20
and they had no *c*. *Eccl* 4:1
she had no *c*. *Lam* 1:9
c. that should relieve is far. 16
whence shall I seek *c*.? *Nah* 3:7
another *C*. to abide. *John* 14:16
the *C*. which is Holy Ghost. 26
when the *C*. is come. 15:26
if I go not *C*. will not come. 16:7

comforteth

I dwelt, as one that *c*. *Job* 29:25
I, even I, am he that *c*. *Isa* 51:12
as one whom his mother *c*. 66:13
who *c*. us in all our. *2 Cor* 1:4
God that *c*. those that are cast. 7:6

comfortless

I will not leave you *c*. *John* 14:18*

comforts

thy *c*. delight my soul. *Ps* 94:19
and restore *c*. to him. *Isa* 57:18

coming

blessed thee since my *c*. *Gen* 30:30*
nothing hinder from *c*. *Num* 22:16
chariot so long in *c*.? *Judg* 5:28
tremble at his *c*. *1 Sam* 16:4*
c. in with me, since day of *c*. 29:6
going out and thy *c*. in. *2 Sam* 3:25
invaded the land at *c*. *2 Ki* 13:20
going out and *c*. in. 19:27; *Isa* 37:28
he seeth that his day is *c*. *Ps* 37:13
preserve going out and *c*. in. 121:8
to meet thee at *c*. *Isa* 14:9
the things that are *c*. let. 44:7
observe time of their *c*. *Jer* 8:7
saw an holy one *c*. down. *Dan* 4:23
days of *c*. out of Egypt. *Mi* 7:15
may abide day of his *c*.? *Mal* 3:2
before the *c*. of the great day. 4:5
they see Son of man *c*. *Mat* 16:28
shall be the sign of thy *c*.? 24:3
so shall the *c*. of the Son. 27, 37, 39
see the Son of man *c*. 30; 26:64
Mark 13:26; 14:62; *Luke* 21:27
my Lord delayeth *c*. *Mat* 24:48
Luke 12:45
at my *c*. received own. *Mat* 25:27
Luke 19:23
for there were many *c*. *Mark* 6:31
as he was yet *c*. the. *Luke* 9:42
lest by her continual *c*. she. 18:5
while I am *c*. another *John* 5:7
the hour is *c*. 25, 28
seeth the wolf *c*. 10:12
shewed before of the *c*. *Acts* 7:52
with them *c*. in and going. 9:28*
as Peter was *c*. in Cornelius. 10:25
had preached before his *c*. 13:24
waiting for the *c*. of. *1 Cor* 1:7*
they that are Christ's at his *c*. 15:23
glad of *c*. of Stephanas and. 16:17
comforted us by the *c*. *2 Cor* 7:6
not by his *c*. only, but by. 7
more abundant by my *c*. *Phil* 1:26*
rejoicing at our Lord's *c*. *1 Thes* 2:19
hearts unblameable at the *c*. 3:13
we who remain to the *c*. 4:15
preserved blameless to the *c*. 5:23
beseech you by *c*. of. *2 Thes* 2:1
destroy with brightness of his *c*. 8
even him whose *c*. is after the. 9
patient, brethren, to the *c*. *Jas* 5:7
for the *c*. of the Lord. 8
to whom *c*. as unto a. *1 Pet* 2:4
make known power and *c*. *2 Pet* 1:16
where is promise of his *c*.? 3:4
looking and hasting to the *c*. of. 12
not be ashamed before him at his *c*.
1 John 2:28
beheld another beast *c*. *Rev* 13:11
Jerusalem *c*. down from God. 21:2

comings

goings out and *c*. in. *Ezek* 43:11

command

Abraham will *c*. his. *Gen* 18:19
sacrifice as God shall *c*. *Ex* 8:27
and God *c*. thee so. 18:23
hear what Lord will *c*. *Num* 9:8
thing which the Lord doth *c*. 36:6
the Lord shall *c*. the. *Deut* 28:8
ye shall *c*. your children. 32:46
so did Moses *c*. Joshua. *Josh* 11:15
eagle mount up at thy *c*.? *Job* 39:27
the Lord will *c*. his. *Ps* 42:8
art my king, O God, *c*. 44:4
work of my hands, *c*. me. *Isa* 45:11
c. them to say to their. *Jer* 27:4
heathen didst *c*. they. *Lam* 1:10
c. these stones be made. *Mat* 4:3
Luke 4:3
why did Moses *c*. to? *Mat* 19:7
c. therefore that sepulchre. 27:64
what did Moses *c*. you? *Mark* 10:3
he would not *c*. them. *Luke* 8:31
wilt thou we *c*. fire to come? 9:54
did not we straitly *c*. you? *Acts* 5:28
and to *c*. them to keep. 15:5
and will do things we *c*. *2 Thes* 3:4
we *c*. you, brethren, in name. 6
that are such we *c*. and exhort. 12
these *c*. and teach. *1 Tim* 4:11

***I* command**

speak all that *I c*. thee. *Ex* 7:2
Jer 1:7, 17
observe what *I c*. thee. *Ex* 34:11
Deut 12:28
I will *c*. my blessing. *Lev* 25:21
not add to the word *I c*. *Deut* 4:2
I c. thee this day. 7:11; 8:11; 10:13
11:8, 27; 13:18; 30:8
I c. thee to do this. 24:18, 22
I c. thee this day to love. 30:16
I will *c*. the clouds. *Isa* 5:6
do all which *I c*. you. *Jer* 11:4
I will *c*. saith the Lord. 34:22
thence will *I c*. serpent. *Amos* 9:3
thence *I c*. the sword. 4
I will *c*. and I will sift the. 9
friends, if ye do what *I c*. *John* 15:14
these things *I c*. you, that ye. 17
I c. thee in the name. *Acts* 16:18
I c. yet not I, but Lord. *1 Cor* 7:10

commanded

now thou art *c*. this do. *Gen* 45:19
to him as he *c*. them. 50:12
not as king of Egypt *c*. *Ex* 1:17
for so I am *c*. *Lev* 10:13
I c. you all things. *Deut* 1:18
3:18, 21
Israel did as Joshua *c*. *Josh* 4:8
see I have *c*. you. 8:8
obeyed my voice in all I *c*. 22:2
all that I *c*. her. *Judg* 13:14
hath *c*. me to be there. *1 Sam* 20:29
the king *c*. me a business. 21:2
have not I *c*. you? *2 Sam* 13:28
performed all the king *c*. 21:14
that Jehoiada priest *c*. *2 Ki* 11:9
to all that king Ahaz *c*. 16:16
is it not I *c*. people to? *1 Chr* 21:17
David man of God *c*. *2 Chr* 8:14
Asa *c*. Judah to seek Lord. 14:4
Manasseh *c*. Judah. 33:16
I *c*. that the gates. *Neh* 13:19
I *c*. Levites to cleanse. 22
for the king had so *c*. *Esth* 3:2
according to all that Haman *c*. 12
according as Esther *c*. him. 4:17
according to all Mordecai *c* 8:9
hast thou *c*. morning? *Job* 38:12
my molten image hath *c*. *Isa* 48:5
our father *c*. us. *Jer* 35:6, 10, 14, 16
18
so as I was *c*. *Ezek* 12:7; 37:7
to you it is *c*. O people. *Dan* 3:4
he *c*. that they should heat. 19
king *c*. and they brought Daniel. 6:16
king *c*. and they brought those. 24
c. the prophets, saying. *Amos* 2:12
c. it to be given her. *Mat* 14:9
Mark 6:27
c. multitude to sit down. *Mat* 14:19
15:35; *Mark* 6:39
his lord *c*. him to be sold. *Mat* 18:25
and did as Jesus *c*. them. 21:6*
observe all things I have *c*. 28:20
he *c*. them to tell no. *Luke* 9:21
c. them to be baptized. *Acts* 10:48
Festus *c*. Paul to be brought. 25:6
c. to be under. *1 Cor* 14:34*

with hands as we c. 1 Thes 4:11
we c. you that if any. 2 Thes 3:10
endure that which was c. Heb 12:20
it was c. them not to. Rev 9:4

***God* commanded**

God c. man to eat. Gen 2:16
according to all that God c. 6:22
into ark as God had c. 7:9, 16
21:4; Deut 20:17; Josh 10:40
God c. thee to keep. Deut 5:15
do as the Lord your God c. 32
in ways the Lord your God c. 33
God c. to teach you. 6:1, 20; 13:5
this day Lord thy God c. 26:16
hath not Lord God c. to go? Judg 4:6
did as God c. him. 1 Chr 14:16
God c. me, make haste. 2 Chr 35:21
c. by the God of heaven. Ezra 7:23
God hath c. thy strength. Ps 68:28
for God c. saying. Mat 15:4
things that are c. of God. Acts 10:33
God who c. light to. 2 Cor 4:6

***Lord* or *God* commanded**

tree I c. not to eat. Gen 3:11, 17
according to all Lord c. 7:5
did as the Lord c. them. Ex 7:6
10:20; 12:28, 50; Num 17:11
this is the thing Lord c. Ex 16:16
32; 35:4; Num 30:1
Lord c. Moses. Ex 16:34; 34:4
39:1, 5, 7, etc.; 40:19, etc.
Lev 8:9; 9:10
as I c. in the time. Ex 23:15
in the day he c. the. Lev 7:38
did as Lord c. him. 8:4
Num 20:27; 27:11
strange fire which he c. not.
Lev 10:1
Lord c. my lord to. Num 36:2
the Lord c. us to do all. Deut 6:24
aside out of the way Lord c. 9:16
there they be as Lord c. 10:5
gods, which I have not c. 17:3
18:20; Jer 19:5; 23:32; 29:23
have not I c. thee? Josh 1:9
my covenant I c. 7:11; Judg 2:20
lot, as I have c. thee. Josh 13:6
Lord c. him to be. 1 Sam 13:14
c. to feed my people. 2 Sam 7:7
1 Chr 17:6
since I c. judges. 2 Sam 7:11
1 Chr 17:10
went up, as Lord c. 2 Sam 24:19
c. him concerning this. 1 Ki 11:10
I have c. the ravens to feed. 17:4
I have c. a widow woman. 9
the word which he c. to. 1 Chr 16:15
Ps 105:8
in the law, which he c. 1 Chr 16:40
Lord c. the angel. 21:27
Lord God of Israel c. him. 24:19
to judgement thou has c. Ps 7:6
he c. and it stood fast. 33:9
whom the Lord c. them. 106:34
c. his covenant for ever. 111:9
thou hast c. us to keep thy. 119:4
testimonies thou hast c. are. 138
there the Lord c. the blessing. 133:3
for the Lord c. and they. 148:5
I have c. my sanctified. Isa 13:3
for my mouth it hath c. 34:16
heavens and their host I c. 45:12
but this thing c. I them. Jer 7:23
c. them not. 31; 19:5; 32:35
words of covenant which I c. 11:8
by Euphrates, as Lord c. 13:5
hallow the sabbath, as I c. 17:22
all that I have c. thee. 50:21
Lord hath c. concerning. Lam 1:17
his word he had c. in days. 2:17
I have done as thou hast c. me.
Ezek 9:11
in morning as I was c. 24:18; 37:10
my words which I c. Zech 1:6
law which I c. in Horeb. Mal 4:4
is done as thou hast c. Luke 14:22
he c. us to preach to. Acts 10:42
so hath the Lord c. 13:46, 47

***Moses* commanded**

took as Moses had c. Num 16:47
aside from way I c. Deut 31:29
Moses c. us a law. 33:4
according to all Moses c. Josh 1:7
kept all that Moses c. you. 22:2
Moses c. according to. 1 Chr 15:15
offer the gift that Moses c. Mat 8:4
offer those things which Moses c.
Mark 1:44; Luke 5:14
Moses in law c. that. John 8:5

commandedst

which thou c. thy. Neh 1:7, 8
thou c. them precepts. 9:14
done nothing that thou c. Jer 32:23

commander

him for a leader and c. Isa 55:4

commandest

all that thou c. us we. Josh 1:16
hearken in all that thou c. 18
nothing of all thou c. Jer 32:23
c. me to be smitten? Acts 23:3

commandeth

will do as my lord c. Num 32:25
God, who c. the sun. Job 9:7
he c. that they return from. 36:10
and c. it not to shine. 32
they may do whatever he c. 37:12
he c. and raiseth the. Ps 107:25
when Lord c. it not? Lam 3:37
Lord c. and he will. Amos 6:11
he c. the unclean spirits. Mark 1:27
Luke 4:36
he c. the winds. Luke 8:25
c. all men to repent. Acts 17:30

commanding

Jacob made an end of c. Gen 49:33
Jesus made an end of c. Mat 11:1
c. his accusers to come. Acts 24:8
c. to abstain from meats. 1 Tim 4:3

commandment

he gave them in c. all. Ex 34:32
broken his c. that soul. Num 15:31
I have received c. to bless. 23:20
ye rebelled against my c. 27:14
this c. I command. Deut 30:11
thou not kept the c. I? 1 Ki 2:43
king's c. was, answer him not.
2 Ki 18:36; Isa 36:21
brethren were at their c. 1 Chr 12:32
people will be wholly at thy c. 28:31
according to the c. of. 2 Chr 8:13
shall come between law and c. 19:10
one heart to do the c. of. 30:12
and as soon as the c. came. 31:5
I sent them with c. to. Ezra 8:17
those that tremble at the c. 10:3
it was the king's c. Neh 11:23
to come at king's c. Esth 1:12
Esther did the c. of Mordecai. 2:20
transgressest thou king's c.? 3:3
when king's c. drew nigh to be. 9:1
nor gone back from c. Job 23:12
thy c. is exceeding broad. Ps 119:96
he sendeth forth his c. 147:15
the c. is a lamp. Pr 6:23
waters should not pass his c. 8:29
he that feareth the c. shall. 13:13
he that keepeth the c. 19:16
whoso keepeth c. shall. Eccl 8:5
their father Jonadab's c. Jer 35:14
because the king's c. Dan 3:22
the c. came forth, and I am. 9:23
willingly walked after c. Hos 5:11
O ye priests, this c. is for. Mal 2:1
that I have sent this c. to. 4
why transgress the c. of? Mat 15:3
thus have ye made the c. of. 6
which is the great c. in law? 22:36
first and great c. 38; Mark 12:30
aside the c. of God. Mark 7:8
full well ye reject the c. of. 9
is no other c. greater than. 12:31
transgressed I thy c. Luke 15:29
rested according to the c. 23:56
this c. have I received. John 10:18
he gave me a c. what. 12:49
I know that his c. is life. 50
as the Father gave me c. 14:31
my c. that ye love one. 15:12
1 John 3:23
we gave no such c. Acts 15:24
receiving a c to Silas. 17:15
and gave c. to his accusers. 23:30
at Festus' c. Paul was. 25:23
sin taking occasion by c. Rom 7:8, 11
when the c. came, sin revived. 9
c. which was ordained to life. 10
and the c. is holy, and just. 12
that sin by c. might become. 13
if there be any other c. it is. 13:9
according to the c. of the. 16:26
by permission, not of c. 1 Cor 7:6
I speak not by c. but by. 2 Cor 8:8
the first c. with promise. Eph 6:2
by the c. of God our. 1 Tim 1:1
Tit 1:3
the end of the c. is charity. 1 Tim 1:5
not after law of a carnal c. Heb 7:16
there is a disannulling of c. 18
Joseph gave c. concerning. 11:22
not afraid of the king's c. 23
to turn from holy c. 2 Pet 2:21
mindful of c. of us the apostles. 3:2
but an old c. 1 John 2:7
this is his c. that we should. 3:23
this c. have we from him. 4:21
we have received a c. 2 John 4
this is the c. that as ye have. 6

***give* or *given* commandment**

which I will give thee in c. Ex 25:22
Lord had given him in c. Deut 1:3
give c. to cease till c. Ezra 4:21
hast given c. to save me. Ps 71:3
hath given c. against. Isa 23:11
hath given c. concerning. Nah 1:14
given c. if any knew. John 11:57

***keep* commandment, *see* keep**

commandment *of the Lord*

journeyed according to the c. of Lord.
Ex 17:1; Num 9:18, 20; 10:13
numbered at c. of Lord. Num 3:39
go beyond c. of Lord to. 24:13
went up to Hor at c. of Lord. 33:38
charge of c. of Lord your. Josh 22:3
not rebel against the c. of Lord.
1 Sam 12:14
but rebel against c. of Lord. 15
hast not kept the c. of Lord. 13:13
I have performed the c of Lord. 15:13
have transgressed the c. of Lord. 24
despised c. of Lord. 2 Sam 12:9
at the c. of Lord came. 2 Ki 24:3
for so was c. of Lord. 2 Chr 29:25
the c. of Lord is pure. Ps 19:8
I have no c. of Lord. 1 Cor 7:25

***new* commandment**

a new c. I give unto. John 13:34
I write no new c. unto. 1 John 2:7
a new c. I write unto you. 8
though I wrote a new c. 2 John 5

***rebelled against the* commandment**

ye rebelled ag. my c. Num 27:14
ye rebelled ag. c. of the Lord your God. Deut 1:26, 43
rebelled ag. c. of Lord and. 9:23
I have rebelled ag. his c. Lam 1:18

commandments

Abraham kept my c. Gen 26:5
thou wilt give ear to his c. Ex 15:26
wrote on tables the ten c. 34:28
Deut 4:13; 10:4
somewhat against any of the c.
Lev 4:13, 27
commit sin forbidden by c. 5:17
these are the c. the Lord. 27:34
remember all the c. of. Num 15:39
in not keeping c. Deut 8:11
shall hearken to c. 11:13; 28:13
Judg 3:4
if ye obey the c. of. Deut 11:27
if ye will not obey the c. of. 28
hath not performed c. 1 Sam 15:11
because he kept my c. 1 Ki 11:34
David who kept my c. 14:8
in that ye have forsaken c. 18:18
and they left all c. of. 2 Ki 17:16
Judah kept not the c. of. 19
but kept his c. which he. 18:6
if ye forsake my c. 2 Chr 7:19
why transgress ye the c. of? 24:20
we have forsaken thy c. Ezra 9:10
should we again break thy c. 14
if they keep not my c. Ps 89:31
all his c. are sure. 111:7
delighteth greatly in his c. 112:1

me not wander from thy c. Ps 119:10
I am a stranger, hide not thy c. 19
make me to go in path of thy c. 35
I will delight in thy c. 47
I have believed thy c. 66
that I may learn thy c. 73
all thy c. are faithful. 86
thou through thy c. hast made. 98
I love thy c. 127
I longed for thy c. 131
thy c. are my delights. 143
all thy c. are truth. 151
I have done thy c. 166
all thy c. are righteousness. 172
not forget thy c. 176
if thou wilt hide my c. Pr 2:1
keep my words and lay up c. 7:1
wise in heart will receive c. 10:8
hadst hearkened to my c. Isa 48:18
break one of these least c. Mat 5:19
for doctrines the c. of men. 15:9*
Mark 7:7*
on these two c. hang all. Mat 22:40
thou knowest the c. Mark 10:19
Luke 18:20
the first of all the c. is. Mark 12:29
walking in all the c. of. Luke 1:6
he that hath my c. and. John 14:21
c. as I have kept Father's c. 15:10
keeping the c. of God. 1 Cor 7:19
things I write you, are the c. 14:37
after the c. and. Col 2:22*
for ye know what c. 1 Thes 4:2*
that keepeth not his c. 1 John 2:4
he that keepeth his c. dwelleth. 3:24
that we walk after his c. 2 John 6

do **commandments**

do all my c. and be. Num 15:40
observe to do all c. Deut 6:25
15:5; 28:1, 15; 30:8
constant to do my c. 1 Chr 28:7
remember his c. to do. Ps 103:18*
they that do his c. 111:10†
blessed that do his c. Rev 22:14*

not do **commandments**

ye will not do these c. Lev 26:14
so that ye will not do all my c. 15

keep **commandments**, *see* **keep**

commend

[1] *To praise*, 2 Cor 3:1; 5:12. [2] *To commit, or give in charge*, Luke 23:46. [3] *To make one more acceptable*, 1 Cor 8:8.

into thy hands I c. my. Luke 23:46
brethren, I c. you to God. Acts 20:32
our unrighteousness c. Rom 3:5
I c. unto you Phebe our sister. 16:1
do we begin again to c.? 2 Cor 3:1
for we c. not ourselves. 5:12
ourselves with some that c. 10:12

commendation

need we, epistles of c.? 2 Cor 3:1

commended

the princes c. Sarai. Gen 12:15*
a man shall be c. Pr 12:8
then I c. mirth. Eccl 8:15
Lord c. the unjust. Luke 16:8
c. them to the Lord. Acts 14:23
I ought to have been c. 2 Cor 12:11

commendeth

but God c. his love. Rom 5:8
but meat c. us not to. 1 Cor 8:8
not he that c. himself is approved. 2 Cor 10:18

commending

c. ourselves to every. 2 Cor 4:2

commission, -s

delivered the king's c. Ezra 8:36
as I went with c. from. Acts 26:12

commit

thou shalt not c. adultery. Ex 20:14
Deut 5:18; Mat 5:27; 19:18
Rom 13:9
if sin, and c. any of. Lev 5:17
not c. any of these. 18:26, 30
who shall c. any of these. 29
if man or woman c. any. Num 5:6
c. no more any such. Deut 19:20
caused Jerusalem to c. 2 Chr 21:11
unto God would I c. my. Job 5:8
into thine hand I c. my. Ps 31:5
c. thy way unto the Lord. Ps 37:5
c. thy works unto the. Pr 16:3
an abomination to kings to c. 12
I will c. thy government. Isa 22:21
c. Jeremiah to court of. Jer 37:21
why c. ye this great evil? 44:7
c. abominations they c. Ezek 8:17
and thou shalt not c. this. 16:43
in the midst of thee they c. 22:9
priests murder, they c. Hos 6:9
for they c. falsehood, and. 7:1
and did c. things worthy. Luke 12:48
who will c. to your trust? 16:11
Jesus did not c. himself. John 2:24
they which c. such things. Rom 1:32
against them which c. such. 2:2
abhorrest idols, dost thou c.? 22
neither c. fornication. 1 Cor 10:8
this charge I c. to thee. 1 Tim 1:18
the same c. thou to. 2 Tim 2:2
respect to persons ye c. Jas 2:9
c. the keeping of souls. 1 Pet 4:19
born of God doth not c. 1 John 3:9
Israel to c. fornication. Rev 2:14
my servants to c. fornication. 20

see **adultery**

commit *iniquity*

if he c. iniquity I will. 2 Sam 7:14
he should c. iniquity. Job 34:10
themselves to c. iniquity. Jer 9:5
and c. iniquity. Ezek 3:20; 33:13

commit *trespass*

if a soul c. a trespass. Lev 5:15
go aside and c. trespass. Num 5:12
caused Israel to c. trespass. 31:16
Achan c. a trespass. Josh 22:20

commit *whoredom* or *whoredoms*

will cut off that c. whor. Lev 20:5
to c. whor. with the. Num 25:1
and thou didst c. whor. Ezek 16:17
none followeth to c. whor. 34
c. ye whor. after their? 20:30
will they c. whor. with her. 23:43
they shall c. whor. and. Hos 4:10
daughters shall c. whor. 13, 14

committed

c. all that he hath to. Gen 39:8
the keeper c. to Joseph all. 22
for sin he hath c. Lev 4:35
customs which were c. 18:30
they c. these things, and. 20:23
if aught be c. by. Num 15:24*
man or woman that c. Deut 17:5
if a man have c. a sin worthy. 21:22
they have c. folly and. Judg 20:6
sinned, we have c. 1 Ki 8:47
provoked him with sins, they c. 14:22
brasen shields c. he. 27; 2 Chr 12:10
died for his transgression he c. 1 Chr 10:13
people have c. two evils. Jer 2:13
and horrible thing is c. in. 5:30
our sin that we have c. 16:10
which they have c. to 44:3, 9
hast c. fornication with. Ezek 16:26
nor hath Samaria c. half. 51
from all sins he hath c. 18:21, 22, 28
for evils ye have c. 20:43
they c. whoredoms in Egypt. 23:3
thus she c. whoredoms with. 7
none of the sins he c. shall. 33:16
for the land hath c. great. Hos 1:2
they have c. whoredom. 4:18
who had c. murder in. Mark 15:7
to whom men have c. Luke 12:48
Father hath c. judgement. John 5:22
c. them to prison. Acts 8:3
if I have c. any thing. 25:11
had found he had c. nothing. 25
they c. themselves to sea. 27:40*
though I have c. nothing. 28:17
to them were c. oracles. Rom 3:2
gospel is c. to me. 1 Cor 9:17
Tit 1:3
fornication as some of them c. 10:8
hath c. to us the word. 2 Cor 5:19
lasciviousness which they c. 12:21
gospel of uncircumcision c. Gal 2:7
1 Tim 1:11
keep what is c. to thee. 1 Tim 6:20
to keep that which I c. 2 Tim 1:12
if he have c. sins, they. Jas 5:15
c. himself to him that. 1 Pet 2:23
deeds which they have c. Jude 15
kings c. fornication. Rev 17:2
18:3, 9

see **abominations**

committed *iniquity*

we have c. iniq. we. Ps 106:6
for iniq. he hath c. Ezek 33:13, 18
we have c. iniq. and. Dan 9:5

committed *trespass*

for his tres. he c. two. Lev 5:7
Israel c. a tres. in the. Josh 7:1
what tres. is this ye have c.? 22:16
not c. this tres. against Lord. 31
they have c. tres., I will. Ezek 15:8
in that they c. a tres. 20:27

committest, -eth, -ing

poor c. himself to thee. Ps 10:14
abomination that Israel c. Ezek 8:6
in statutes of life without c. 33:15
killing, stealing, and c. Hos 4:2
O Ephraim, thou c. whoredom. 5:3
whosoever c. sin is the. John 8:34
he that c. fornication. 1 Cor 6:18
c. sin transgresseth. 1 John 3:4
he that c. sin is of the devil. 8

commodious

the haven was not c. to. Acts 27:12

common

[1] *That which is ordinary, or usual; as* a common death, Num 16:29. [2] *That which is ceremonially unclean*, Acts 11:9. [3] *Had in common; to use together as belonging to all*, Acts 2:44.

if these men die the c. Num 16:29
there is no c. bread. 1 Sam 21:4
bread is in a manner c. 5
an evil, and it is c. Eccl 6:1*
shall eat them as c. things. Jer 31:5*
men of c. sort were. Ezek 23:42
took Jesus into the c. Mat 27:27*
had all things c. Acts 2:44; 4:32
put apostles in the c. prison. 5:18*
never eaten anything c. 10:14; 11:8
God cleansed call not c. 10:15; 11:9
should not call any thing c. 10:28
no temptation but c. 1 Cor 10:13*
my own son, after c. faith. Tit 1:4
to write to you of the c. Jude 3

common *people*

if any of c. people sin. Lev 4:27
body into graves of c. people. Jer 26:23
and the c. people heard. Mark 12:37

commonwealth

being aliens from c. of. Eph 2:12

commonly, *see* **reported**

commotion, -s

a great c. out of north. Jer 10:22
when ye hear of c. be. Luke 21:9*

commune

I will meet and c. with. Ex 25:22
c. with David secretly. 1 Sam 18:22
and I will c. with my father. 19:3
if we essay to c. with thee? Job 4:2
c. with your own heart on. Ps 4:4
they c. of laying snares. 64:5
in the night I c. with mine. 77:6

communed

Abraham c. with them. Gen 23:8
Hamor c. with Jacob. 34:6, 8
Joseph c. with them. 42:24
Abimelech c. with them. Judg 9:1
Samuel c. with Saul. 1 Sam 9:25
David c. with Abigail. 25:39
queen of Sheba c. with Solomon of. 1 Ki 10:2; 2 Chr 9:1
they c. with Huldah. 2 Ki 22:14
I c. with mine own heart. Eccl 1:16
and king c. with them. Dan 1:19
the angel that c. with. Zech 1:14
they c. what they might. Luke 6:11
Judas c. to betray Jesus. 22:4
while they c. Jesus himself. 24:15
Felix sent and c. Acts 24:26

communicate

let him that is taught c. to. Gal 6:6
that ye did c. with my. Phil 4:14*

do good, be willing to c. 1 Tim 6:18
to do good and to c. Heb 13:16

communicated

I c. to them that gospel. Gal 2:2*
no church c. with me. Phil 4:15

communication, -s

Abner had c. with. 2 Sam 3:17
the man and his c. 2 Ki 9:11*
let your c. be yea. Mat 5:37
what manner of c. are? Luke 24:17
evil c. corrupt good. 1 Cor 15:33*
no corrupt c. proceed. Eph 4:29
Col 3:8
that c. of thy faith may. Philem 6*

communing

Lord left c. with. Gen 18:33
had made an end of c. on. Ex 31:18

communion

This word signifies fellowship, concord, or agreement, 2 Cor 6:14. *Communion is likewise taken for a sacrament, or sacred sign of our spiritual fellowship with Christ,* 1 Cor 10:16.

blood of Christ, c. of body of Christ. 1 Cor 10:16
what c. hath light with? 2 Cor 6:14
c. of the Holy Ghost be. 13:14

compact

Jerusalem is a city c. Ps 122:3

compacted

body fitly joined and c. Eph 4:16*

companied

these men which have c. Acts 1:21

companies

men into three c. Judg 7:16
three c. blew the trumpets. 20
against Shechem in four c. 9:34
divided them into three c. 43
put people in three c. 1 Sam 11:11
spoilers came out in three c. 13:17
Syrians had gone out by c. 2 Ki 5:2*
two great c. of them. Neh 12:31, 40
the c. of Sheba waited. Job 6:19
O ye travelling c. of. Isa 21:13†
when thou criest, let thy c. 57:13*
make all sit down by c. Mark 6:39

companion

slay every man his c. Ex 32:27
wife given to c. Judg 14:20; 15:6
Hushai was king's c. 1 Chr 27:33*
brother to dragons, a c. Job 30:29
I am a c. to all them. Ps 119:63
but a c. of fools shall. Pr 13:20
but a c. of riotous men. 28:7
the same is the c. of a destroyer. 24
yet she is thy c. wife. Mal 2:14
and c. in labour. Phil 2:25*
I John, your brother and c. Rev 1:9*

companions

with her c. and bewailed. Judg 11:38
they brought thirty c. to. 14:11
answer thee and thy c. Job 35:4
shall the c. make a banquet. 41:6*
her c. shall be brought. Ps 45:14
for my c. sake, I will say. 122:8
aside by flocks of thy c. S of S 1:7
c. hearken to thy voice. 8:13
princes are rebellious and c. Isa 1:23
Judah and Israel his c. Ezek 37:16
the thing known to his c. Dan 2:17
having caught Paul's c. Acts 19:29
ye became c. of them. Heb 10:33*

company

if Esau come to the one c. Gen 32:8
lodged that night in the c. 21
a c. of nations shall be of. 35:11
Korah and his c. Num 16:6
be thou and all thy c. 16*
he be not as Korah and c. 40
now shall this c. lick up. 22:4*
strove in c. of Korah. 26:9; 27:3
another c. come along. Judg 9:37
thou comest with such a c.? 18:23
thou shalt meet a c. of. 1 Sam 10:5*
they saw the c. of prophets. 19:20
bring me down to this c.? 30:15*
he and all his c. came. 2 Ki 5:15
c. of Jehu, said, I see a c. 9:17
came with a small c. 2 Chr 24:24
made desolate all my c. Job 16:7
goeth in c. with workers of. 34:8
to house of God in c. Ps 55:14*
rebuke the c. of spearmen, 68:30*
earth covered c. of Abiram. 106:17
fire was kindled in their c. 18
that keepeth c. with. Pr 29:3
to a c. of horses in. S of S 1:9*
as it were the c. of two. 6:13*
bring up a c. against. Ezek 16:40*
I will bring up a c. on them. 23:46*
Ashur is there and all her c. 32:22
thou and all thy c. 38:7
c. of priests murder in. Hos 6:9
supposing him in the c. Luke 2:44
he came down the c. of. 6:17
separate you from their c. 22
sit down by fifties in a c. 9:14*
a man of the c. cried out. 38
a woman of our c. made. 24:22
they went to their own c. Acts 4:23
unlawful for Jew to keep c. 10:28*
to send chosen men of their c. 15:22
Jews gathered a c. and set. 17:5*
we of Paul's c. departed. 21:8
filled with your c. Rom 15:24
not to keep c. with a. 1 Cor 5:11
and have no c. with. 2 Thes 3:14
to an innumerable c. of. Heb 12:22*
c. in ships and sailors. Rev 18:17*

***great* company**

with Joseph a *great* c. Gen 50:9
Sheba came with *great* c. 2 Chr 9:1*
no might against this great c. 20:12
great was the c. of those. Ps 68:11*
a *great* c. shall return. Jer 31:8
Pharaoh with *great* c. Ezek 17:17
saw a *great* c. come to. John 6:5
great c. of priests. Acts 6:7

comparable

precious sons of Zion c. to. Lam 4:2

compare, -ed, -ing

who in heaven can be c.? Ps 89:6
all the things thou canst desire are not to be c. unto her. Pr 3:15; 8:11
I have c. thee, O my. S of S 1:9
what likeness will ye c.? Isa 40:18
to whom will ye c. me? 46:5
are not worthy to be c. Rom 8:18
c. spiritual things. 1 Cor 2:13†
c. ourselves with some, c. themselves amongst. 2 Cor 10:12

comparison

have I done in c. of? Judg 8:2, 3
it not in your eyes in c.? Hag 2:3
or with what c. shall it? Mark 4:30*

compass, *substantive*

put the net under the c. Ex 27:5*
a grate of net-work under c. 38:4*
but fetch a c. behind. 2 Sam 5:23*
they fetched a c. of. 2 Ki 3:9*
when he set a c. on the. Pr 8:27*
marketh image out with c. Isa 44:13
thence we fetched a c. Acts 28:13*

compass, *verb*

they journeyed to c. the. Num 21:4
ye shall c. the city. Josh 6:3
the seventh day c. the city. 4
c. the king round about. 2 Ki 11:8
2 Chr 23:7
his archers c. me round. Job 16:13
willows of the brook c. 40:22
with favour wilt thou c. Ps 5:12
congregation of the people c. 7:7
deadly enemies who c. me. 17:9
so will I c. thine altar, O Lord. 26:6
shalt c. me about with songs. 32:7
trusteth in Lord, mercy shall c. 10
iniquity of my heels shall c. 49:5
the head of those that c. 140:9
the righteous shall c. me. 142:7
that c. yourselves about. Isa 50:11*
a woman shall c. a man. Jer 31:22
the wicked doth c. about. Hab 1:4
woe to you, ye c. sea. Mat 23:15
thine enemies shall c. Luke 19:43

compassed

the men of Sodom c. Gen 19:4
and we c. mount Seir. Deut 2:1
ark of the Lord c. city. Josh 6:11
then they c. land of. Judg 11:18
they c. Samson, and laid. 16:2
Saul and his men c. 1 Sam 23:26
waves of death c. me. 2 Sam 22:5
Ps 18:4; 116:3
host c. city with horses. 2 Ki 6:15*
smote Edomites which c. 2 Chr 21:9
God hath c. me with his. Job 19:6
he hath c. the waters. 26:10*
they have now c. us in. Ps 17:11
many bulls c. me. 22:12
for dogs have c. me. 16
he hath c. me with. Lam 3:5
ye see Jerusalem c. Luke 21:20
that he himself also is c. Heb 5:2

compassed *about*

men c. Absalom *about.* 2 Sam 18:15
sorrows of hell c. me *about.* 22:6
Ps 18:5
night and c. city *about.* 2 Ki 6:14
Edomites which c. him *about.* 8:21
c. *about* Jehoshaphat. 2 Chr 18:31
evils have c. me *about.* Ps 40:12
they c. me *about* together. 88:17
109:3; 118:11, 12
all nations c. me *about.* 118:10
floods c. me *about* thy. Jonah 2:3
Jericho fell, c. *about* 7. Heb 11:30
c. *about* with such a cloud of. 12:1
c. camp of saints *about.* Rev 20:9

compassest, -eth

c. Havilah. Gen 2:11
c. the land of Ethiopia. 13
c. them about as a chain. Ps 73:6
thou c. my path and my. 139:3*
Ephraim c. me about. Hos 11:12

compassion

(*Literally, suffering with another; hence having pity or sympathy for another*)

give them c. before. 1 Ki 8:50
children shall find c. 2 Chr 30:9
Jesus moved with c. Mat 9:36
14:14; Mark 6:34
lord of servant moved with c. Mat 18:27
Jesus moved with c. Mark 1:41
be of one mind, having c. 1 Pet 3:8
shutteth up bowels of c. 1 John 3:17

***full of* compassion**

(*Revised Version,* merciful)

being *full of* c. forgave. Ps 78:38
thou art a God *full of* c. 86:15
111:4; 112:4; 145:8

***have* or *had* compassion**

and she *had* c. on him. Ex 2:6
Lord may *have* c. on. Deut 13:17
Lord thy God will *have* c. on. 30:3
be ye, for ye *have* c. 1 Sam 23:21
that they may *have* c. 1 Ki 8:50
was gracious and *had* c. 2 Ki 13:23
because he *had* c. on. 2 Chr 36:15
Chaldees *had* no c. on young. 17
she should not *have* c. Isa 49:15
return and *have* c. on. Jer 12:15
will he *have* c. Lam 3:32; Mi 7:19
I *have* c. Mat 15:32; Mark 8:2
also have *had* c. on thy. Mat 18:33*
so Jesus *had* c. on them. 20:34
Lord hath *had* c. on. Mark 5:19*
if thou canst, *have* c. on us. 9:22
saw her, he *had* c. on. Luke 7:13
Samaritan saw him, *had* c. 10:33
father *had* c. and ran and. 15:20
have c. on whom I *have* c. Rom 9:15
can *have* c. on ignorant. Heb 5:2*
had c. of me in my bonds. 10:34
of some *have* c. making. Jude 22*

compassions

not consumed, because his c. Lam 3:22
shew mercy and c. every. Zech 7:9

compel

not c. him to serve as a. Lev 25:39
c. thee to go a mile. Mat 5:41
they c. one Simon to. Mark 15:21
go into highways, c. Luke 14:23

compelled, -est

servants with woman c. 1 Sam 28:23
Jehoram c. Judah. 2 Chr 21:11
Simon, him they c. to. Mat 27:32
I c. them to blaspheme. Acts 26:11
glorying, ye have c. me. 2 Cor 12:11

nor Titus a Greek was *c.* *Gal* 2:3
why *c.* thou the Gentiles to ? 14

complain, -ed, -ing

people *c.* it displeased. *Num* 11:1
brethren came to us to *c. Judg* 21:22
I will *c.* in bitterness of. *Job* 7:11
furrows likewise thereof *c.* 31:38*
I *c.* and my spirit was. *Ps* 77:3
that there be no *c.* in. 144:14
doth a living man *c.*? *Lam* 3:39

complainers

these are murmurers, *c.* *Jude* 16

complaint, -s

of abundance of my *c.* *1 Sam* 1:16
couch shall ease my *c.* *Job* 7:13
if I say, I will forget my *c.* 9:27
I will leave my *c.* on myself. 10:1
as for me, is my *c.* to man ? 21:4
even to-day is my *c.* bitter. 23:2
I mourn in my *c.* *Ps* 55:2
I poured out my *c.* before. 142:2
laid *c.* against Paul. *Acts* 25:7

complete

seven sabbaths shall be *c. Lev* 23:15
ye are *c.* in him who is. *Col* 2:10
that ye may stand *c.* in all. 4:12

composition

nor make any after *c.* *Ex* 30:32, 37

compound, -eth

an ointment *c.* after art. *Ex* 30:25
whosoever *c.* any thing like it. 33

comprehend

things which we cannot *c.* *Job* 37:5
able to *c.* with saints. *Eph* 3:18*

comprehended

hath *c.* the dust of the. *Isa* 40:12
the darkness *c.* it not. *John* 1:5*
is briefly *c.* in this saying. *Rom* 13:9*

conceal, -ed, -eth

if we slay brother and *c.* *Gen* 37:26
neither shalt thou *c.* him. *Deut* 13:8
I have not *c.* the words. *Job* 6:10*
the Almighty will I not *c.* 27:11
I will not *c.* his parts nor. 41:12*
not *c.* thy loving-kindness. *Ps* 40:10
of a faithful spirit *c.* the. *Pr* 11:13
a prudent man *c.* knowledge. 12:23
it is the glory of God to *c.* 25:2
publish and *c.* not. *Jer* 50:2

conceit, -s

as an high wall in *c.* *Pr* 18:11*
lest he be wise in his own *c.* 26:5
seest a man wise in his own *c.*? 12
sluggard is wiser in his own *c.* 16
rich man is wise in his own *c.* 28:11
ye be wise in own *c.* *Rom* 11:25
be not wise in your own *c.* 12:16

conceive, -ing

they should *c.* when. *Gen* 30:38
shall be free, and *c.* seed. *Num* 5:28
c. and bear a son. *Judg* 13:3, 5, 7
Luke 1:31
hey *c.* mischief. *Job* 15:35; *Isa* 59:4
n sin did my mother *c.* me. *Ps* 51:5
virgin shall *c.* and bear. *Isa* 7:14
hall *c.* chaff. 33:11
. words of falsehood. 59:13
eceived strength to *c.* *Heb* 11:11

conceived

Eve *c.* and bare Cain. *Gen* 4:1
Cain's wife *c.* and bare Enoch. 17
Hagar *c.* 16:4
Sarah *c.* and bare Isaac. 21:2
Rebekah his wife *c.* 25:21
eah *c.* 29:32, 33
Bilhah *c.* 30:5
Rachel *c.* and bare a son. 23
he flocks *c.* 39; 31:10
huah *c.* 38:3, 4, 5
amar *c.* 18
ochebed *c.* and bare. *Ex* 2:2
ave *c.* seed, and born. *Lev* 12:2
ave I *c.* all this people ? *Num* 11:12
and bare son, Samuel. *1 Sam* 1:20
2:21
ath-sheba *c.* and sent. *2 Sam* 11:5
hunammite *c.* *2 Ki* 4:17
ophetess *c.* *Isa* 8:3
ere is a man child *c.* *Job* 3:3
mischief, brought forth. *Ps* 7:14

chamber of her that *c.* *S of S* 3:4
and hath *c.* a purpose. *Jer* 49:30
Gomer which *c.* and. *Hos* 1:3
she that *c.* them hath done. 2:5
that which is *c.* in her is of the Holy Ghost. *Mat* 1:20
Elisabeth hath *c.* a son. *Luke* 1:36
named before he was *c.* 2:21
hast thou *c.* this thing ? *Acts* 5:4
when Rebekah had *c.* *Rom* 9:10
when lust hath *c.* it. *Jas* 1:15

conception

multiply sorrow and *c.* *Gen* 3:16
the Lord gave her *c.* *Ruth* 4:13
shall flee from birth and *c. Hos* 9:11

concern, -eth

perfect that which *c.* me *Ps* 138:8
this burden *c.* the prince. *Ezek* 12:10
things which *c.* Lord Jesus Christ. *Acts* 28:31
glory in things which *c.* *2 Cor* 11:30

concerning

accepted thee *c.* this. *Gen* 19:21
c. which I did swear to. *Ex* 6:8
Num 14:30
atonement for him *c. Lev* 4:26; 5:6
found what was lost, lieth *c.* it. 6:3
hath spoken good *c.* *Num* 10:29
commanded him *c.* this. *1 Ki* 11:10
I asked them *c.* the Jews. *Neh* 1:2
repent thee *c.* servants. *Ps* 90:13
135:14
dost not inquire wisely *c.* *Eccl* 7:10
therefore have I cried *c.* this. 30:7
ask me *c.* my sons, and *c.* 45:11
saith Lord *c.* sons, *c.* daughters, *c.* mothers, *c.* fathers. *Jer* 16:3
c. pillars, *c.* sea, *c.* bases, *c.* vessels. 27:19
comforted *c.* the evil, even *c.* all that I have brought. *Ezek* 14:22
the Lord *c.* Ammonites. 21:28
c. which I have lifted up. 47:14
desire mercies of God *c.* *Dan* 2:18
might not be changed *c.* Daniel. 6:17
I speak it not to you *c.* *Mat* 16:11
saw, told also *c.* swine. *Mark* 5:16
expounded the things *c.* *Luke* 24:27
as *c.* that he raised. *Acts* 13:34
as *c.* this sect, we know. 28:22
as *c.* flesh Christ came. *Rom* 9:5
as *c.* the gospel, are enemies. 11:28
and simple *c.* evil. 16:19
I speak as *c.* reproach. *2 Cor* 11:21
but I speak *c.* Christ. *Eph* 5:32
c. giving and receiving. *Phil* 4:15
professing have erred *c.* *1 Tim* 6:21
who *c.* the truth have. *2 Tim* 2:18
reprobates *c.* the faith. 3:8
think it not strange *c.* *1 Pet* 4:12
see **him, me, thee, them, us, you**

concision

(*A cutting off, hence,* a faction)
beware of the *c.* *Phil* 3:2

conclude

we *c.* a man is justified. *Rom* 3:28*

concluded

the Gentiles, we have *c. Acts* 21:25*
for God hath *c.* them. *Rom* 11:32*
the scripture hath *c.* *Gal* 3:22*

conclusion

let us hear the *c.* of. *Eccl* 12:13

concord

what *c.* hath Christ ? *2 Cor* 6:15

concourse

crieth in chief place of *c.* *Pr* 1:21
give account of this *c.* *Acts* 19:40

concubine

(*A secondary wife under the system of polygamy practised by the Jews and named in the Bible. Concubines were frequently purchased slaves. They were more easily put away than a wife, but their rights were carefully guarded under Jewish law*)

his *c.* played the whore. *Judg* 19:2
he laid hold on his *c.* and. 29
Gibeah, I and my *c.* to. 20:4
in to my father's *c.*? *2 Sam* 3:7
Rizpah the *c.* of Saul had. 21:11

concubines

to sons of *c.* Abraham. *Gen* 25:6
David took more *c.* *2 Sam* 5:13
Absalom went in to father's *c.* 16:22
thy life, and lives of thy *c.* 19:5
king put his *c.* in ward and. 20:3
had three hundred *c.* *1 Ki* 11:3
Rehoboam took threescore *c.* *2 Chr* 11:21
Shaashgaz who kept *c.* *Esth* 2:14
60 queens and 80 *c.* and. *S of S* 6:8
yea, the queens and the *c.* 9
king and his *c.* drank. *Dan* 5:3, 23

concupiscence

wrought all manner of *c.* *Rom* 7:8*
mortify members, evil *c.* *Col* 3:5*
not in the lust of *c.* *1 Thes* 4:5*

condemn

whom the judges shall *c.* *Ex* 22:9
judge them, and *c.* the. *Deut* 25:1
my mouth shall *c.* me. *Job* 9:20
I will say to God do not *c.* 10:2
and wilt thou *c.* him ? 34:17
wilt thou *c.* me, that thou ? 40:8
not leave him, nor *c.* *Ps* 37:33
they *c.* the innocent blood. 94:21
save him from those that *c.* 109:31
wicked devices will he *c.* *Pr* 12:2
is he that shall *c.* me ? *Isa* 50:9
shall rise against thee shall *c.* 54:17
shall *c.* it. *Mat* 12:41; *Luke* 11:32
rise up in judgement and *c.* it. *Mat* 12:42; *Luke* 11:31
c. him to death. *Mat* 20:18
Mark 10:33
c. not, and ye shall not. *Luke* 6:37
God sent not Son to *c.* *John* 3:17
neither do I *c.* thee, go and. 8:11
I speak not this to *c.* *2 Cor* 7:3
if our heart *c.* us, God. *1 John* 3:20
if our heart *c.* us not, then. 21

condemnation

[1] *Declaring guilty, or pronouncing the sentence,* John 8:10. [2] *Censuring other men's persons, purposes, words, or actions, either rashly, unjustly, or uncharitably,* Luke 6:37.

thou art in the same *c.* *Luke* 23:40
this is the *c.* that light. *John* 3:19*
believeth not come into *c.* 5:24*
judgement was by one to *c. Rom* 5:16
judgement came on all men to *c.* 18
there is no *c.* to them who are. 8:1
come not together to *c. 1 Cor* 11:34*
if the ministration of *c.* *2 Cor* 3:9
lest he fall into the *c.* *1 Tim* 3:6
shall receive greater *c.* *Jas* 3:1*
lest ye fall into *c.* 5:12
of old ordained to this *c.* *Jude* 4

condemned

and *c.* the land in. *2 Chr* 36:3*
answer, yet had *c.* Job. *Job* 32:3
judged, let him be *c.* *Ps* 109:7
drink the wine of *c.* in. *Amos* 2:8*
would not have *c.* the. *Mat* 12:7
by thy words thou shalt be *c.* 37
when he saw that he was *c.* 27:3
they all *c.* him to be. *Mark* 14:64
delivered him to be *c.* *Luke* 24:20
believeth on him is not *c.* but he that believeth not is *c.* *John* 3:18*
hath no man *c.* thee ? 8:10
c. sin in the flesh. *Rom* 8:3
we should not be *c.* *1 Cor* 11:32
speech that cannot be *c.* *Tit* 2:8
sinneth, being *c.* of himself. 3:11
by which he *c.* the world. *Heb* 11:7
ye have *c.* and killed just. *Jas* 5:6
not one another, lest ye be *c.* 9*
God *c.* them with. *2 Pet* 2:6

condemnest, eth, -ing

judge thy servants *c.* *1 Ki* 8:32
thine own mouth *c.* thee. *Job* 15:6
he that *c.* the just, is. *Pr* 17:15
fulfilled them in *c.* him. *Acts* 13:27
judgest another thou *c.* *Rom* 2:1
who is he that *c.*? 8:34
that *c.* not himself in that. 14:22

condescend

not high things, but *c.* *Rom* 12:16

condition, -s
on this *c.* I will make. *1 Sam* 11:2
sendeth and desireth *c.* *Luke* 14:32

conduct, -ed
came to *c.* king. *2 Sam* 19:15, 31
all the people of Judah *c.* 40*
they that *c.* Paul. *Acts* 17:15
c. him forth in peace. *1 Cor* 16:11*

conduit
came and stood by *c.* *2 Ki* 18:17
Isa 36:2
he made a pool and a *c.* *2 Ki* 20:20
meet Ahaz at end of the *c.* *Isa* 7:3

coney, -ies
(*A variety of rabbit*)
and the *c.* because he is unclean to.
Lev 11:5; *Deut* 14:7
rocks are a refuge for *c.* *Ps* 104:18
c. are but a feeble folk. *Pr* 30:26

confection
shalt make a *c.* after. *Ex* 30:35*

confectionaries
your daughters to be *c.* *1 Sam* 8:13†

confederacy
a *c.* to whom people say a *c.*
Isa 8:12*
all men of thy *c.* brought. *Ob* 7

confederate
and these were *c.* *Gen* 14:13
they are *c.* against thee. *Ps* 83:5*
it was told, Syria is *c.* *Isa* 7:2

conference
for they in *c.* added. *Gal* 2:6*

conferred
Adonijah *c.* with Joab. *1 Ki* 1:7
they *c.* among themselves. *Acts* 4:15
Festus, when he had *c.* 25:12
immediately I *c.* not with. *Gal* 1:16

confess
[1] *Publicly to own and acknowledge as his own,* Luke 12:8. [2] *To profess Christ, and to obey his commandments,* Mat 10:32. [3] *To own our sins and offences, either in private or public,* Josh 7:19; Ps 32:5; Mat 3:6; Jas 5:16; 1 John 1:9.

he shall *c.* that he hath. *Lev* 5:5
Aaron shall *c.* over live goat. 16:21
if they shall *c.* their iniquity. 26:40
they shall *c.* their sins. *Num* 5:7
Israel *c.* thy name and. *1 Ki* 8:33
2 Chr 6:24
c. thy name and turn. *1 Ki* 8:35
2 Chr 6:26
and *c.* the sins of the. *Neh* 1:6
I will *c.* that thy hand. *Job* 40:14
I will *c.* my transgressions. *Ps* 32:5
shall *c.* me before men, him will I *c.* before. *Mat* 10:32; *Luke* 12:8
if any man did *c.* that. *John* 9:22
rulers did not *c.* him. 12:42
but Pharisees *c.* both. *Acts* 23:8
this I *c.* that after the way. 24:14
shalt *c.* with thy mouth. *Rom* 10:9
every tongue shall *c.* to God. 14:11
I will *c.* to thee among the. 15:9*
every tongue shall *c.* *Phil* 2:11
c. your faults one to. *Jas* 5:16
if we *c.* our sins. *1 John* 1:9
whoso shall *c.* that Jesus. 4:15
who *c.* not that Jesus. *2 John* 7
but I will *c.* his name. *Rev* 3:5

confessed, -eth, -ing
when Ezra had *c.* *Ezra* 10:1
c. their sins, a fourth part *c.* *Neh* 9:2
but whoso *c.* and forsaketh. *Pr* 28:13
while *c.* my sin and the. *Dan* 9:20
baptized *c.* their sins. *Mat* 3:6
John *c.* I am not Christ. *John* 1:20
many came and *c.* and. *Acts* 19:18
these *c.* that they were. *Heb* 11:13
every spirit that *c.* Christ. *1 John* 4:2
every spirit that *c.* not that. 3

confession
and make *c.* to him. *Josh* 7:19
offerings and making *c.* *2 Chr* 30:22
now therefore make *c.* *Ezra* 10:11
to my God and made *c.* *Dan* 9:4

with the mouth *c.* is. *Rom* 10:10
Pilate witnessed good *c.* *1 Tim* 6:13

confidence
[1] *Boldness,* Acts 28:31. [2] *Trust,* Job 4:6. [3] *That wherein one trusts,* Jer 48:13.

put their *c.* in Gaal. *Judg* 9:26
great king of Assyria, what *c.* is this wherein? *2 Ki* 18:19; *Isa* 36:4
is not this thy fear, thy *c.*? *Job* 4:6
his *c.* shall be rooted out. 18:14
thou art my *c.* 31:24
who art the *c.* of all. *Ps* 65:5
trust in Lord than to put *c.* 118:8
to trust in Lord than to put *c.* in. 9
for Lord shall be thy *c.* *Pr* 3:26
in fear of Lord is strong *c.* 14:26
the strength of the *c.* thereof. 21:22
c. in an unfaithful man is. 25:19
in quietness and *c.* shall. *Isa* 30:15
ashamed of Beth-el their *c.* *Jer* 48:13
they shall dwell with *c.* *Ezek* 28:26
no more the *c.* of house of. 29:16
put ye not *c.* in a guide. *Mi* 7:5
of God with all *c.* *Acts* 28:31
in this *c.* I was minded. *2 Cor* 1:15
having *c.* in you all. 2:3
I rejoice that I have *c.* 7:16
the great *c.* I have in you. 8:22
that *c.* wherewith I think to. 10:2
foolishly in this *c.* of boast. 11:17
I have *c.* in you through. *Gal* 5:10
in whom access with *c.* *Eph* 3:12
having this *c.* I shall. *Phil* 1:25
and have no *c.* in flesh. 3:3
though I might have *c.* in flesh. 4
we have *c.* in Lord. *2 Thes* 3:4
c. in thy obedience. *Philem* 21
if we hold fast the *c.* *Heb* 3:6
hold beginning of our *c.* stedfast. 14
cast not away your *c.* 10:35
appear, we may have *c.* *1 John* 2:28
then have *c.* toward God. 3:21
and this is the *c.* that we. 5:14

confidences
Lord hath rejected thy *c.* *Jer* 2:37

confident
in this will I be *c.* *Ps* 27:3
the fool rageth and is *c.* *Pr* 14:16
art *c.* thou thyself art a. *Rom* 2:19
we are always *c.* *2 Cor* 5:6
we are *c.* willing rather to be. 8
ashamed in this same *c.* 9:4
c. of this very thing. *Phil* 1:6
many of the brethren waxing *c.* 14

confidently
another *c.* affirmed. *Luke* 22:59

confirm
[1] *To strengthen, settle, or establish,* 1 Chr 14:2; Acts 14:22. [2] *To give new assurance of the truth and certainty of any thing,* 1 Ki 1:14; 2 Cor 2:8. [3] *To ratify, or make sure,* Ruth 4:7.

the manner for to *c.* all. *Ruth* 4:7
come in after and *c.* thy. *1 Ki* 1:14
to *c.* the kingdom. *2 Ki* 15:19
wrote to *c.* second letter. *Esth* 9:29
to *c.* these days of Purim in. 31
didst *c.* thine inheritance. *Ps* 68:9
weak hands and *c.* feeble. *Isa* 35:3
hope that they would *c.* *Ezek* 13:6
he shall *c.* the covenant. *Dan* 9:27
even I stood to *c.* and to. 11:1
to *c.* the promises made. *Rom* 15:8
who shall also *c.* you. *1 Cor* 1:8
ye would *c.* your love. *2 Cor* 2:8

confirmation
in defence and *c.* of the. *Phil* 1:7
an oath of *c.* is to them. *Heb* 6:16

confirmed
c. to thyself thy people. *2 Sam* 7:24
soon as kingdom was *c.* *2 Ki* 14:5
Lord had *c.* him king. *1 Chr* 14:2
hath *c.* the same. 16:17; *Ps* 105:10
Esther *c.* these matters. *Esth* 9:32
hath *c.* his words which. *Dan* 9:12
exhorted brethren and *c.* *Acts* 15:32
testimony of Christ was *c.* *1 Cor* 1:6
yet if it be *c.* no man. *Gal* 3:15
the covenant that was *c.* 17

was *c.* to us by them. *Heb* 2:3
immutability of counsel, he *c.* 6:17

confirmeth, -ing
bonds on her, he *c.* *Num* 30:14
cursed be he that *c.* not. *Deut* 27:26
that *c.* the word of. *Isa* 44:26
preached, *c.* word with. *Mark* 16:20
c. souls of the disciples. *Acts* 14:22
through Syria and Cilicia *c.* 15:41

confiscation
let judgement be executed to *c.*
Ezra 7:26

conflict
having the same *c.* *Phil* 1:30
ye knew what great *c.* *Col* 2:1*

conformable
him, being made *c.* *Phil* 3:10*

conformed
predestinate to be *c.* *Rom* 8:29
be not *c.* to this world. 12:2*

confound
[1] *To throw into confusion,* Gen 11:7. [2] *To confute,* Acts 9:22. [3] *To discomfit,* Job 6:20. [4] *To be amazed, astonished,* Acts 2:6.

let us go down and *c.* *Gen* 11:7, 9
be not dismayed, lest I *c.* *Jer* 1:17*
c. the wise, to *c.* things. *1 Cor* 1:27*

confounded
the inhabitants were *c.* *2 Ki* 19:26
Isa 37:27
they were *c.* because. *Job* 6:20
let them be *c.* that seek. *Ps* 35:4*
not those that seek thee be *c.* 69:6*
let them be *c.* that are. 71:13*
for they are *c.* that seek. 24
let them be *c.* and troubled. 83:17*
c. be all they that serve. 97:7*
let them all be *c.* turned. 129:5*
shall be *c.* for gardens. *Isa* 1:29
weave net-works shall be *c.* 19:9*
were dismayed and *c.* 37:27
greatly *c.* because we have. *Jer* 9:19
is *c.* by graven image. 10:14*; 51:17
let them be *c.* that persecute. 17:18*
daughter of Egypt *c.* 46:24*
Moab is *c.* 48:20*
Hamath is *c.* 49:23
Babylon taken, Bel *c.* 50:2*
mother shall be sore *c.* 12*
her whole land shall be *c.* 51:47*
we are *c.* because we have. 51*
be thou *c.* and. *Ezek* 16:52*, 54, 63
nations shall see and be *c.* *Mi* 7:16*
riders on horses be *c.* *Zech* 10:5
came together and were *c.* *Acts* 2:6
Saul *c.* the Jews who dwelt. 9:22

ashamed and **confounded**
asha. and c. that seek. *Ps* 40:14
70:2
moon be *c. and* sun *asha.* *Isa* 24:23
thee shall be *asha. and c.* 41:11
idol-makers be *asha. and c.* 45:16
not be *asha.*, neither be thou *c.* 54:4
little ones *asha. and c.* *Jer* 14:3
hath been *asha. and c.* 15:9
shalt thou be *asha. and c.* 22:2
I was *asha.* yea, even *c.* 31:1
be *asha. and c.* for your. *Ezek* 36:3
seers be *asha. and* diviners *c.* *Mi* 3:

not **confounded**
trusted, and were *not c.* *Ps* 22:5
not ashamed nor *c.* *Isa* 45:1
therefore shall I *not* be *c.* 50:
believeth on him *not* be *c.* *1 Pet* 2:6

confused
battle of warrior with *c.* *Isa* 9:
for the assembly was *c.* *Acts* 19:3

confusion
lie down thereto, it is *c.* *Lev* 18:2
put to death, have wrought *c.* 20:1
chosen David to thine own *c.* an unto the *c.* *1 Sam* 20:30
been delivered to *c.* of. *Ezra* 9:
I am full of *c.* therefore. *Job* 10:15
let them be brought to *c.* *Ps* 35:4
c. is continually before me. 44:15
let them be put to *c.* that. 70:
let me never be put to *c.* 71:
cover themselves with own *c.* 109:2

the city of *c.* is broken. *Isa* 24:10
in the shadow of Egypt your *c.* 30:3
stretch out upon it line of *c.* 34:11
images are wind and *c.* 41:29
makers of idols go to *c.* 45:16
for *c.* they shall rejoice in. 61:7*
lie in shame and our *c.* *Jer* 3:25
provoke themselves to *c.* 7:19
their everlasting *c.* shall. 20:11*
us belongeth *c.* of face. *Dan* 9:7, 8
city was filled with *c.* *Acts* 19:29
God is not author of *c.* *1 Cor* 14:33
and strife is, there is *c.* *Jas* 3:16

congealed
the depths were *c.* in. *Ex* 15:8

congratulate
of his welfare and *c.* *1 Chr* 18:10*

congregation
(*Generally this means assembly or meeting*)
a sin-offering for the *c.* *Lev* 4:21
you to bear iniquity of *c.* 10:17
make an atonement for the *c.* 16:33
the renowned of the *c.* *Num* 1:16
but when *c.* is to be gathered. 10:7
shall I bear with this evil *c.*? 14:27
one ordinance shall be for *c.* 15:15
separate yourselves from *c.* 16:21
get you from among this *c.* 45
Aaron ran into the midst of *c.* 47
that soul cut off from the *c.* 19:20
Lord set a man over the *c.* 27:16
manslayer die not, till he stand before *c.* 35:12; *Josh* 20:6
drawers of water for *c.* *Josh* 9:27
the *c.* was gathered as. *Judg* 20:1
came not up with the *c.* 21:5
called Jeroboam to *c.* *1 Ki* 12:20
Hezekiah did give to *c.* *2 Chr* 30:24
separated from the *c.* *Ezra* 10:8
should not come into the *c.* *Neh* 13:1
for the *c.* of hypocrites. *Job* 15:34
I stood up and cried in the *c.* 30:28
nor sinners in the *c.* of. *Ps* 1:5
in the midst of the *c.* will I. 22:22
I have hated the *c.* of evil. 26:5
speak righteousness, O *c.*? 58:1
remember thy *c.* thou hast. 74:2
forget not the *c.* of thy poor. 19*
when I receive the *c.* I will. 75:2*
God standeth in the *c.* of the. 82:1
thy faithfulness also in *c.* 89:5
let them exalt him also in *c.* 107:32
Lord in the assembly and *c.* 111:1
in all evil in midst of *c.* *Pr* 5:14
men shall remain in the *c.* 21:16
sit upon the mount of *c.* *Isa* 14:13
and know, O *c.* what is. *Jer* 6:18
their *c.* shall be established. 30:20
not enter into thy *c.* *Lam* 1:10
chastise them as their *c.* *Hos* 7:12
sanctify the *c.* *Joel* 2:16
now when the *c.* was. *Acts* 13:43*

all the **congregation**
gather *all the c.* together. *Lev* 8:3
atonement for *all the c.* 16:17
all the c. stone him. 24:14, 16 *Num* 15:35
all the c. bade stone. *Num* 14:10
seeing *all the c.* are holy. 16:3
wilt thou be wroth with *all c.?* 22
in sight of *all the c.* 20:27; 25:6
Eleazar and *all the c.* 27:19, 22
read not before *all the c.* *Josh* 8:35
all the c. murmured. 9:18
wrath fell on *all the c.* 22:20
king blessed *all the c.* *1 Ki* 8:14, 55
all the c. blessed. *1 Chr* 29:20
all the c. made a. *2 Chr* 23:3
all the c. worshipped and. 29:28
all the c. said, amen. *Neh* 5:13
all the c. that were come. 8:17

elders of the **congregation**
elders of the c. shall. *Lev* 4:15
elders of c. said, how? *Judg* 21:16

great **congregation**
feast, all Israel with him, a *great c.* *1 Ki* 8:65; *2 Chr* 7:8; 30:13
out of Israel a *great c.* *Ezra* 10:1
of thee in the *great c.* *Ps* 22:25
thanks in the great *c.* 35:18

righteousness in the *great c.* *Ps* 40:9
not concealed truth from *great c.* 10

congregation *of Israel*
c. of Israel shall kill it. *Ex* 12:6
cut off from the *c. of Israel.* 19
all the *c. of Israel* shall keep. 47
if whole *c. of Israel* sin. *Lev* 4:13
separated you from *c. of Israel.* *Num* 16:9
Solomon and *c. of Israel.* *2 Chr* 5:6
commandment of *c. of Israel.* 24:6

congregation *of the Lord*
why lift yourselves above the *c. of the Lord?* *Num* 16:3
c. of Lord not as sheep that. 27:17
plague among *c. of the Lord.* 31:16 *Josh* 22:17
not enter into the *c. of the Lord.* *Deut* 23:1, 2, 3
in sight of *c. of Lord.* *1 Chr* 28:8
a cord by lot in *c. of Lord.* *Mi* 2:5

tabernacle of the **congregation**
brought before *tab. of c.* *Ex* 29:10
I will sanctify *tab. of c.* 44
anoint *tab. of c.* 30:26
called it the *tab. of c.* went out to the *tab. of c.* 33:7
kill it before *tab. of c.* *Lev* 3:8, 13
bring it to *tab. of c.* 4:5
not go out from door of *tab. of c.* 10:7
no wine when ye go into *tab. of c.* 9
so do for *tab. of c.* 16:16
atonement for *tab. of c.* 33
work of *tab. of c.* *Num* 4:3, 23, 25 30, 35, 39, 43
bring Levites before *tab. of c.* 8:9
come out ye three to *tab. of c.* 12:4
appeared in the *tab. of c.* 14:10
lay up in *tab. of c.* 17:4
keep charge of *tab. of c.* 18:4
weeping before door of *tab. of c.* 25:6
yourselves in *tab. of c.* *Deut* 31:14
set up *tab of c.* there. *Josh* 18:1
brought up *tab. of c.* *1 Ki* 8:4 *2 Chr* 5:5
was *tab. of c.* of God. *2 Chr* 1:3
see **door**

tent of the **congregation**
tent of the c. finished. *Ex* 39:32
set up *tent of the c.* 40:2
table in *tent of the c.* 22
candlestick in *tent of the c.* 24
golden altar in the *tent of the c.* 26
cloud covered the *tent of the c.* 34
not able to enter into *tent of the c.* 35

whole **congregation**
the *whole c.* of Israel. *Ex* 16:2
the charge of *whole c.* *Num* 3:7
be wroth with *whole c.* *Josh* 22:18
whole c. sent to speak. *Judg* 21:13
king blessed the *whole c.* *2 Chr* 6:3
the *whole c.* *Ezra* 2:64; *Neh* 7:66
shewed before *whole c.* *Pr* 26:26

congregations
in the *c.* will I bless. *Ps* 26:12
bless ye God in the *c.* even. 68:26
enemies roar in midst of thy *c.* 74:4

Coniah
though *C.* were the signet. *Jer* 22:24
man *C.* despised, broken idol? 28
Zedekiah reigned instead of *C.* 37:1

conquer
conquering and to *c.* *Rev* 6:2

conquerors
we are more than *c.* *Rom* 8:37

conscience
(*That faculty within us which decides as to the moral quality of our thoughts, words, and acts. It gives consciousness of the good of one's conduct or motives, or causes feelings of remorse at evil-doing. A conscience can be educated, or trained to recognize good and evil, but its action is involuntary. A good conscience is one which has no feeling of reproach against oneself, does not accuse oneself of wilful wrong,* Acts 24:16)
convicted by their own *c.* *John* 8:9
I have lived in all good *c.* *Acts* 23:1
to have a *c.* void of offence. 24:16
their *c.* also bearing. *Rom* 2:15
my *c.* bearing me witness in. 9:1
subject also for *c.* sake. 13:5
with *c.* of the idol to this hour eat it, and their *c.* being weak. *1 Cor* 8:7
shall not *c.* of him which is weak? 10
when ye wound their weak *c.* 12
no question for *c.* sake. 10:25, 27
eat not, for *c.* sake. 28
c. I say, not thine own, but. 29
testimony of our *c.* *2 Cor* 1:12
commending to every man's *c.* 4:2
pure heart, and a good *c.* *1 Tim* 1:5
holding faith and a good *c.* 19
mystery of faith in a pure *c.* 3:9
having their *c.* seared. 4:2
God, whom I serve with *c.* *2 Tim* 1:3
even their mind and *c.* is. *Tit* 1:15
as pertaining to the *c.* *Heb* 9:9
purge *c.* from dead works to. 14
should have had no more *c.* of. 10:2
hearts sprinkled from an evil *c.* 22
we trust we have a good *c.* 13:18
if a man for *c.* toward. *1 Pet* 2:19
having a good *c.* as they. 3:16
but the answer of a good *c.* 21

consciences
made manifest in your *c.* *2 Cor* 5:11

consecrate
To devote any thing to God's worship and service; to hallow, or sanctify whether persons, Ex 13:2, 12, 15; 19:6; Num 1:49; 3:12 1 Sam 1:11, 22; *or things,* Lev 27:28.
c. Aaron. *Ex* 28:3*
anoint and *c.* Aaron's sons. 41
c. Aaron and sons. 29:9; 30:30*
seven days shalt thou *c.* 35; *Lev* 8:33
Moses said, *c.* yourselves. *Ex* 32:29
shall *c.* to Lord the days. *Num* 6:12*
to *c.* his service this. *1 Chr* 29:5
to *c.* himself with a. *2 Chr* 13:9
they shall *c.* themselves. *Ezek* 43:26*
I will *c.* their gain to. *Mi* 4:13*

consecrated
sons of Aaron, whom he *c.* *Num* 3:3
vessels are *c.* to the. *Josh* 6:19
Micah *c.* one of sons. *Judg* 17:5, 12
Jeroboam *c.* him. *1 Ki* 13:33
ye have *c.* yourselves. *2 Chr* 29:31
c. things were 600 oxen. 33
holy things which were *c.* 31:6
feasts of Lord that were *c.* *Ezra* 3:5
the Son, *c.* for evermore. *Heb* 7:28*
living way which he hath *c.* 10:20*

consecration, -s
of ram, for it is ram of *c.* *Ex* 29:22
if aught of the flesh of the *c.* 34
this is the law of the *c.* *Lev* 7:37
c. for a sweet savour to the. 8:28
with bread that is in basket of *c.* 31
till the days of your *c.* be. 33
because the *c.* of his God. *Num* 6:7*
hath defiled the head of his *c.* 9

consent, -ed, -ing
but in this will we *c.* *Gen* 34:15
only let us *c.* to them. 23
shalt not *c.* to him. *Deut* 13:8
but would not *c.* *Judg* 11:17
hearken not to him, nor *c.* *1 Ki* 20:8
the priests *c.* to receive. *2 Ki* 12:8
sawest a thief, thou *c.* *Ps* 50:18
if sinners entice thee, *c.* not. *Pr* 1:10
so he *c.* to them, and. *Dan* 1:14*
the same had not *c.* *Luke* 23:51
and Saul was *c.* to. *Acts* 8:1; 22:20
tarry longer with them, *c.* not. 18:20
if I do that which I would not, I *c.* unto the law. *Rom* 7:16
if any man *c.* not to. *1 Tim* 6:3

consent, *substantive*
came out with one *c.* *1 Sam* 11:7*
together with one *c.* *Ps* 83:5
of the priests murder by *c.* *Hos* 6:9
to serve him with one *c.* *Zeph* 3:9
all with one *c.* began to. *Luke* 14:18
except it be with *c.* for. *1 Cor* 7:5

consider
[1] *To meditate upon,* 2 Tim 2:7.
[2] *To view, or observe,* Lev 13:13.

[3] *To determine,* Judg 18:14. [4] *To pity, comfort, or relieve,* Ps 41:1. [5] *To remember,* 1 Sam 12:24.

then the priest shall *c.* *Lev* 13:13
know this day and *c.* *Deut* 4:39
that they were wise to *c.* 32:29
now therefore *c.* what. *Judg* 18:14
c. how great things. *1 Sam* 12:24
therefore know and *c.* what. 25:17
will he not then *c.* it ? *Job* 11:11
when I *c.* I am afraid of him. 23:15
and would not *c.* of his ways. 34:27
stand still and *c.* the works. 37:14
c. my meditation. *Ps.* 5:1
when I *c.* the heavens. 8:3
c. my trouble. 9:13
c. and hear. 13:3; 45:10
c. my enemies. 25:19
shalt diligently *c.* his place. 37:10
c. her palaces, that ye may. 48:13
now *c.* this, ye that forget. 50:22
for they shall wisely *c.* 64:9
I will *c.* thy testimonies. 119:95
c. mine affliction, and deliver. 153
c. how I love thy precepts. 159
go to the ant, *c.* her ways. *Pr* 6:6
with a ruler, *c.* diligently. 23:1
pondereth the heart *c.* it ? 24:12
for they *c.* not that they. *Eccl* 5:1
c. the work of God, who. 7:13
but in day of adversity *c.* 14
my people doth not *c.* *Isa* 1:3
neither *c.* the operation of. 5:12
narrowly look upon thee and *c.* 14:16
and I will *c.* in my dwelling-. 18:4
may see, and know, and *c.* 41:20
remember ye not, nor *c.* 43:18
had not heard shall they *c.* 52:15
c. and see if there be. *Jer* 2:10
latter days ye shall *c.* 23:20; 30:24
O Lord, *c.* to whom. *Lam* 2:20
O Lord, *c.* and behold our. 5:1
it may be they will *c.* *Ezek* 12:3
understand, and *c.* the vision. *Dan* 9:23
they *c.* not in their hearts. *Hos* 7:2
c. your ways. *Hag* 1:5, 7
pray you, *c.* from this day. 2:15, 18
c. the lilies. *Mat* 6:28; *Luke* 12:27
c. the ravens, for they. *Luke* 12:24
nor *c.* it is expedient. *John* 11:50
the elders came to *c.* *Acts* 15:6
c. and the Lord give. *2 Tim* 2:7
brethren, *c.* the Apostle. *Heb* 3:1
now *c.* how great this man. 7:4
c. one another to provoke. 10:24
c. him that endured. 12:3

considered, -est

when I *c.* in morning. *1 Ki* 3:21
I have *c.* things which thou. 5:8
c. my servant Job ? *Job* 1:8; 2:3
glad, for thou hast *c.* my. *Ps* 31:7
then I saw and *c.* it well. *Pr* 24:32
I *c.* all the oppressions. *Eccl* 4:1
again I *c.* all travail. 4
for all this I *c.* in my heart. 9:1
c. not what this people. *Jer* 33:24
c. the horns, and behold. *Dan* 7:8
c. not the beam that is. *Mat* 7:3
they *c.* not the miracle. *Mark* 6:52
when Peter had *c.* the. *Acts* 12:12
he *c.* not his own body. *Rom* 4:19

considereth, -ing

hearts alike, he *c.* all. *Ps* 33:15
blessed is he that *c.* the poor. 41:1
righteous man *c.* house. *Pr* 21:12
and *c.* not that poverty shall. 28:22
the righteous *c.* the cause of. 29:7
c. a field, and buyeth it. 31:16
none *c.* in his heart to say. *Isa* 44:19
none *c.* that the righteous is. 57:1
c. and doth not. *Ezek* 18:14, 28
as I was *c.* behold. *Dan* 8:5
c. thyself, lest thou. *Gal* 6:1
c. the end of their. *Heb* 13:7

consist, -eth

a man's life *c.* not in. *Luke* 12:15
by him all things *c.* *Col* 1:17

consolation

(*Comfort or relief in distress or depression*)

men give them cup of *c.* *Jer* 16:7
waiting for the *c.* of. *Luke* 2:25
for ye have received your *c.* 6:24
interpreted, the son of *c.* *Acts* 4:36*
they rejoiced for the *c.* 15:31
God of *c.* grant you to. *Rom* 15:5
so our *c.* also aboundeth. *2 Cor* 1:5
we be afflicted, it is for your *c.* 6
so shall ye be partakers of the *c.* 7
but by the *c.* wherewith he was. 7:7
if there be any *c.* in Christ. *Phil* 2:1*
given us everlasting *c.* *2 Thes* 2:16
have great joy and *c.* *Philem* 7
might have a strong *c.* *Heb* 6:18*

consolations

are the *c.* of God small ? *Job* 15:11
and let this be your *c.* 21:2
with the breasts of her *c.* *Isa* 66:11

consorted

(*Companied with*)

some of them *c.* with. *Acts* 17:4

conspiracy

and Absalom's *c.* was. *2 Sam* 15:12
his servants made a *c.* *2 Ki* 12:20
made a *c.* against Amaziah. 14:19
2 Chr 25:27
Shallum and his *c.* *2 Ki* 15:15
Hoshea made a *c.* against. 30
the king of Assyria found *c.* 17:4
a *c.* is found among the. *Jer* 11:9
is a *c.* of her prophets. *Ezek* 22:25
forty who had made this *c.* *Acts* 23:13

conspirators

Ahithophel is among *c.* *2 Sam* 15:31

conspired

they *c.* against Joseph. *Gen* 37:18
that all of you have *c.* *1 Sam* 22:8
why have ye *c.* against me ? 13
Baasha son of Ahijah *c.* *1 Ki* 15:27
Zimri *c.* against Elah. 16:9, 16
Jehu son of Nimshi *c.* *2 Ki* 9:14
I *c.* against my master. 10:9
Shallum *c.* against Zachariah. 15:10
Pekah *c.* against Pekahiah. 25
servants of Amon *c.* 21:23
slew all that *c.* 24; *2 Chr* 33:25
they *c.* against Jehoiada. *2 Chr* 24:21
the servants of Joash *c.* 25, 26
c. all of them together. *Neh* 4:8
Amos hath *c.* against. *Amos* 7:10

constant, -ly

if he be *c.* to do my. *1 Chr* 28:7
that heareth, speaketh *c.* *Pr* 21:28*
Rhoda *c.* affirmed that. *Acts* 12:15*
these things thou affirm *c.* *Tit* 3:8*

constellations

the *c.* thereof shall not. *Isa* 13:10

constrain

c. you to be circumcised. *Gal* 6:12*

constrained, -eth

woman of Shunem *c.* *2 Ki* 4:8
spirit within me *c.* me. *Job* 32:18
Jesus *c.* his disciples. *Mat* 14:22
Mark 6:45
they *c.* him, saying. *Luke* 24:29
Lydia *c.* us to come. *Acts* 16:15
I was *c.* to appeal to Caesar. 28:19
for love of Christ *c.* us. *2 Cor* 5:14

constraint

oversight, not by *c.* but. *1 Pet* 5:2

consult

only *c.* to cast him down. *Ps* 62:4

consultation

chief priests held a *c.* *Mark* 15:1

consulted

Rehoboam *c.* with. *1 Ki* 12:6, 8
David *c.* with captains. *1 Chr* 13:1
Jehoshaphat *c.* with. *2 Chr* 20:21
I *c.* with myself, and. *Neh* 5:7
they have *c.* against thy. *Ps* 83:3
for they have *c.* together with. 5
king of Babylon *c.* with. *Ezek* 21:21
presidents and captains *c.* *Dan* 6:7
Balak king of Moab *c.* *Mi* 6:5
hast *c.* shame to thy. *Hab* 2:10
c. that they might take. *Mat* 26:4
chief priests *c.* to put. *John* 12:10

consulter

not found among you a *c.* *Deut* 18:11

consulteth

c. whether he be able. *Luke* 14:31

consume

[1] *To destroy,* Ex 32:10. [2] *To spend, or squander away,* Jas 4:3. [3] *To burn up,* Luke 9:54.

famine shall *c.* the land. *Gen* 41:30
lest I *c.* thee in the way. *Ex* 33:3, 5
that shall *c.* the eyes. *Lev* 26:16
this great fire will *c.* us. *Deut* 5:25
thou shalt *c.* all people. 7:16
for locust shall *c.* it. 28:38, 42*
kindled in mine anger shall *c.* 32:22*
will *c.* you after he hath. *Josh* 24:20
shall be to *c.* thine eyes. *1 Sam* 2:33
let fire *c.* thee and. *2 Ki* 1:10, 12
fire shall *c.* the tabernacles. *Job* 15:34
a fire not blown shall *c.* him. 20:26*
drought and heat *c.* the. 24:19
c. into smoke shall they *c.* *Ps* 37:20
makest his beauty to *c.* 39:11
their beauty shall *c.* in. 49:14
their days did he *c.* in. 78:33
it shall also *c.* the beard. *Isa* 7:20
and shall *c.* the glory of his. 10:18
there shall the calf *c.* the. 27:10
fire shall *c.* the palaces. *Jer* 49:27*
and *c.* away for their. *Ezek* 4:17*
hail-stones in my fury to *c.* it. 13:13
is drawn, it is furbished to *c.* 21:28*
I will *c.* thy filthiness out. 22:15
kindle the fire, *c.* the flesh. 24:10*
desolate, are given us to *c.* 35:12*
c. all these kingdoms. *Dan* 2:44
and the sword shall *c.* *Hos* 11:6
I will *c.* all things from. *Zeph* 1:2
c. man and beast, I will *c.* fowls. 3
remain in his house and *c.* *Zech* 5:4
their flesh, eyes, shall *c.* away. 14:12
whom the Lord shall *c.* *2 Thes* 2:8*
ye ask that ye may *c.* *Jas* 4:3*

consume *them*

that I may *c. them.* *Ex* 32:10, 12
c. them in moment. *Num* 16:21, 45
thou mayest not *c. them.* *Deut* 7:22
didst not utterly *c. them.* *Neh* 9:31
c. them in wrath, *c. them.* *Ps* 59:13
I will surely *c. them.* *Jer* 8:13
but I will *c. them* by the. 14:12
fury on them to *c. them.* *Ezek* 20:13
and *c. them,* as Elias did. *Luke* 9:54

consumed

lest thou be *c.* in the. *Gen* 19:15
mountain, lest thou be *c.* 17
in day the drought *c.* me. 31:40
bush burned, was not *c.* *Ex* 3:2
sentest thy wrath, which *c.* 15:7
if the corn or the field be *c.* 22:6
and *c.* upon the altar. *Lev* 9:24
c. them in uttermost. *Num* 11:1*
one of whom flesh is half *c.* 12:12
depart lest ye be *c.* in all. 16:26
there came out fire and *c.* the. 35*
a fire is gone out, it hath *c.* 21:28*
I *c.* not the children of Israel. 25:11
generation . . . done evil was *c.* 32:13
men of war were *c.* *Deut* 2:16
rose fire out of rock and *c.* *Judg* 6:21
the man that *c.* us. *2 Sam* 21:5
fire of Lord fell and *c.* *1 Ki* 18:38
2 Chr 7:1
fire *c.* him and fifty. *2 Ki* 1:10, 12
children of Israel *c.* not. *2 Chr* 8:8
gates are *c.* with fire. *Neh* 2:3, 1
fire of God hath *c.* sheep. *Job* 1:16
by breath of his nostrils *c.* 4:9
snow and ice are *c.* out. 6:1
as the cloud is *c.* and. 7:
though my reins be *c.* 19:2
his flesh is *c.* away. 33:2
mine eyes *c.* *Ps* 6:7; 31:
my bones *c.* 31:10*; 102:
I am *c.* by the blow of. 39:
be confounded and *c.* that. 71:
are utterly *c.* with terrors. 73:
fire *c.* their young men. 78:6
for we are *c.* by thine anger. 90:
let the sinners be *c.* out of. 104:
they had almost *c.* me upon. 119:
my zeal hath *c.* me. 1
flesh and thy body are *c.* *Pr* 5:
the oppressors are *c.* *Isa* 16
scorner is *c.* and all that. 29:
thou hast *c.* us. 64
hast *c.* them, but they. *Jer* 5

the lead is c. Jer 6:29
the beasts are c. 12:4
that my days should be c. 20:18
till all the roll was c. 36:23
we have been c. by sword. 44:18
hath mine enemy c. Lam 2:22
Lord's mercies we are not c. 3:22
her rods broken, fire c. Ezek 19:12
22:31
that the scum of it may be c. 24:11
wherefore I have c. them. 43:8
sons of Jacob are not c. Mal 3:6
take heed ye be not c. Gal 5:15

shall be **consumed**

in wilderness shall be c. Num 14:35
shall die, shall we be c.? 17:13*
ye shall be c. both you. 1 Sam 12:25
forsake Lord shall be c. Isa 1:28
shall be c. together: they that eat swine's flesh shall be c. 66:17
famine shall prophets be c. Jer 14:15
shall be c. by sword. 16:4; 44:12, 27
famine shall they be c. Ezek 5:12
it shall fall, ye shall be c. in. 13:14
they shall be no more c. 34:29
nor shall the fruit be c. 47:12*
by his hand shall be c. Dan 11:16*

consumed with till, or until

to destroy, until they were c. Deut 2:15; Josh 5:6
until he have c. thee. Deut 28:21
slaying them till they were c. Josh 10:20
fight until they be c. 1 Sam 15:18
I turned not again until I had c. them. 2 Sam 22:38; Ps 18:37
Syrians until thou have c. 1 Ki 22:11
2 Ki 13:17, 19; 2 Chr 18:10
angry till thou hadst c. us. Ezra 9:14
a sword after them till I have c. Jer 9:16; 24:10; 27:8; 49:37

consumeth, -ing

thy God is a c. fire. Deut 4:24*
Heb 12:29
before thee as a c. fire. Deut 9:3*
he c. as a garment. Job 13:28
remnant of them the fire c. 22:20
for it is a fire that c. to. 31:12
as the flame c. chaff. Isa 5:24*

consummation

desolate, even until c. Dan 9:27

consumption
(Wasting)

appoint over you terror, c. Lev 26:16
Lord smite thee with a c. Deut 28:22
he c. decreed shall. Isa 10:22
Lord God of hosts make a c. 23*
have heard from Lord God of hosts a c. 28:22*

contain

of heavens cannot c. thee. 1 Ki 8:27
2 Chr 2:6; 6:18
ath may c. tenth part. Ezek 45:11
he world could not c. John 21:25
ut if they cannot c. 1 Cor 7:9*

contained, -eth, -ing

rink of sister's cup, it c. Ezek 23:32
x water-pots c. 2 or 3. John 2:6
o by nature things c. Rom 2:14
aving abolished law c. Eph 2:15
is c. in scripture. 1 Pet 2:6

contemn, -ed, -eth
(To scorn or despise)

o the wicked c. God? Ps 10:13
vile person is c. 15:4
ey c. the counsel of the. 107:11
r love, it would be c. S of S 8:7
ory of Moab shall be c. Isa 16:14
c. the rod of my son. Ezek 21:10
d what if the sword c. even? 13

contempt

us shall arise much c. Esth 1:18
poureth c. on princes. Job 12:21
Ps 107:40
d c. of families terrify? Job 31:34
move reproach and c. Ps 119:22
e exceedingly filled with c. 123:3
r soul is filled with the c. 4
en cometh c. Pr 18:3
bring into c. all the. Isa 23:9
ake to everlasting c. Dan 12:2

contemptible

ye say, table of Lord is c. Mal 1:7
even his meat is c. 12
I also made you c. 2:9
is weak, his speech c. 2 Cor 10:10

contemptuously

which speak c. against. Ps 31:18

contend

To strive, either bodily or in debate or discussion, to dispute, Job 9:3; 40:2; Jer 18:19; Acts 11:2.

c. with Moabites. Deut 2:9, 24
if c. he cannot answer. Job 9:3
accept his person, and c. 13:8
such as keep the law c. Pr 28:4
nor may he c. with him. Eccl 6:10
c. with them that c. with. Isa 49:25
that justifieth me, who will c.? 50:8
I will not c. for ever. 57:16
then how canst thou c.? Jer 12:5
to voice of them that c. with. 18:19
Lord God called to c. Amos 7:4
hear ye, arise, c. thou. Mi 6:1
should earnestly c. for faith. Jude 3

contended

then c. I with rulers. Neh 13:11, 17
I c. with them, and cursed. 25
servants when they c. Job 31:13
not find them that c. Isa 41:12
they of circumcision c. Acts 11:2

contendest

shew me wherefore thou c. Job 10:2

contendeth

shall he that c. with? Job 40:2
if a wise man c. with. Pr 29:9

contending

c. with devil, he disputed. Jude 9

content

his brethren were c. Gen 37:27
Moses was c. to dwell. Ex 2:21
heard that, he was c. Lev 10:20
to God we had been c. Josh 7:7
Levite was c. to dwell. Judg 17:11
be c. I pray thee, and. 19:6
Naaman said, be c. 2 Ki 5:23
one said, be c. and go with. 6:3
now therefore be c. Job 6:28
nor will he rest c. though. Pr 6:35
Pilate willing to c. Mark 15:15
nor accuse falsely, be c. Luke 3:14
in every state to be c. Phil 4:11
and raiment, let us be c. 1 Tim 6:8
be c. with such things. Heb 13:5
and not c. with prating. 3 John 10

contention

only by pride cometh c. Pr 13:10
leave off c. before it be. 17:14
a fool's lips enter into c. 18:6
cast out the scorner, and c. 22:10
hast borne me a man of c. Jer 15:10
that raise up strife and c. Hab 1:3
the c. was so sharp. Acts 15:39
preach Christ of c. Phil 1:16*
gospel of God with much c. 1 Thes 2:2

contentions

lot causeth c. to cease. Pr 18:18
and their c. are like the bars. 19
c. of a wife are a. 19:13; 27:15
who hath woe? who hath c.? 23:29
that there are c. among. 1 Cor 1:11
avoid c. and strivings. Tit 3:9

contentious

than with a c. and angry. Pr 21:19
as wood to fire, so is a c. 26:21
a continual dropping and a c. 27:15
but to them that are c. Rom 2:8*
if any man seem to be c. 1 Cor 11:16

contentment

but godliness with c. 1 Tim 6:6

continual

this shall be a c. burnt-. Ex 29:42
and the c. bread shall. Num 4:7
house for c. shew-bread. 2 Chr 2:4
merry heart hath a c. feast. Pr 15:15
smote the people with c. Isa 14:6
for in going up c. weeping. Jer 48:5
there was a c. diet given him. 52:34
2 Ki 25:30
sever out men of c. Ezek 39:14

lest by her c. coming she. Luke 18:5
that I have c. sorrow. Rom 9:2*

continually

imagination of heart evil c. Gen 6:5
before the Lord c. Ex 28:30
lambs of first year, day by day c. 29:38
to cause lamps to burn c. Lev 24:2
David's enemy c. 1 Sam 18:29
eat bread at my table c. 2 Sam 9:7
Jehoiakim eat bread c. 2 Ki 25:29
Jer 52:33
seek his face c. 1 Chr 16:11
between Jeroboam and Rehoboam c. 2 Chr 12:15
his sons, thus did Job c. Job 1:5
his praise shall be c. Ps 34:1; 71:6
say c. the Lord be magnified. 35:27
40:16; 70:4
and my sorrow is c. before. 38:17
loving-kindness and truth c. 40:11
they c. say, Where is thy God? 42:3
my confusion is c. before me. 44:15
burnt-offerings to have been c. 50:8
goodness of God endureth c. 52:1
whereunto I c. resort. 71:3
my praise shall be c. 6
I will hope c. and praise thee. 14
I am c. with thee. 73:23
tumult increaseth c. 74:23
be before the Lord c. 109:15
so shall I keep thy law c. 119:44
my soul is c. in my hand. 109
have respect to thy statutes c. 117
c. are they gathered for war. 140:2
he deviseth mischief c. Pr 6:14
bind them c. on thy heart. 21
I stand c. upon watch-. Isa 21:8
walls are c. before me. 49:16
and hast feared c. every day. 51:13
my name c. every day is. 52:5
Lord shall guide thee c. 58:11
thy gates shall be open c. 60:11
provoketh me to anger c. 65:3
before me c. is grief and. Jer 6:7
a meat-offering c. to. Ezek 46:14
God whom thou servest c. Dan 6:16, 20
committed whoredom c. Hos 4:18
and wait on thy God c. 12:6
so shall the heathen drink c. Ob 16
thy wickedness passed c.? Nah 3:19
shall they not spare c.? Hab 1:17
were c. in the temple. Luke 24:53
we will give ourselves c. Acts 6:4*
that waited on Cornelius c. 10:7
attending c. upon this. Rom 13:6
abideth a priest c. Heb 7:3
sacrifices offered year by year c. 10:1
offer the sacrifice of praise c. 13:15

continuance

great plagues of long c. Deut 28:59
my members which in c. Ps 139:16*
in those is c. and we. Isa 64:5*
by patient c. in well doing. Rom 2:7*

continue

if he c. a day or two. Ex 21:21
c. in blood of purifying. Lev 12:4, 5
c. following the Lord. 1 Sam 12:14
thy kingdom shall not c. 13:14
that it may c. for ever. 2 Sam 7:29
Lord may c. his word. 1 Ki 2:4*
nor shall his substance c. Job 15:29
doth not mine eye c. in their? 17:2
O c. thy loving-kindness. Ps 36:10
that their houses shall c. 49:11
children of thy servants c. 102:28
they c. according to thine. 119:91
that c. till night, till wine. Isa 5:11
that the evidences may c. Jer 32:14
c. more years than the. Dan 11:8*
because they c. with me. Mat 15:32
if ye c. in my word. John 8:31
so have I loved you, c. 15:9
persuaded to c. in. Acts 13:43
and exhorting them to c. 14:22
obtained help of God, I c. 26:22
shall we c. in sin that? Rom 6:1
goodness, if thou c. in. 11:22
truth of gospel might c. Gal 2:5
I know that I shall c. Phil 1:25

if ye *c.* in the faith. *Col* 1:23
c. in prayer, and watch. 4:2
if they *c.* in faith. *1 Tim* 2:15
take heed to thy doctrine, *c.* 4:16
c. in the things which. *2 Tim* 3:14
priests not suffered to *c.* *Heb* 7:23
let brotherly love *c.* 13:1
and *c.* there a year. *Jas* 4:13
the fathers, all things *c.* *2 Pet* 3:4
ye shall *c.* in the Son. *1 John* 2:24
power was given him to *c.* *Rev* 13:5
when he cometh, he must *c.* 17:10

continued

served them, and *c.* a. *Gen* 40:4
as she *c.* praying. *1 Sam* 1:12
c. till burnt-offering was. *2 Chr* 29:28
also I *c.* in the work of. *Neh* 5:16
his name shall be *c.* as. *Ps* 72:17
Daniel *c.* to first year. *Dan* 1:21
c. all night in prayer. *Luke* 6:12
ye are they that *c.* with me. 22:28
all *c.* with one accord. *Acts* 1:14
they *c.* stedfastly in the. 2:42
Simon himself *c.* with Philip. 8:13
but Peter *c.* knocking. 12:16
Paul preached and *c.* his. 20:7
because they *c.* not in. *Heb* 8:9
would no doubt have *c.* *1 John* 2:19

continueth, -ing

as a shadow, and *c.* *Job* 14:2
a *c.* whirlwind, it shall. *Jer* 30:23
c. daily with one accord. *Acts* 2:46
rejoicing in hope, *c.* *Rom* 12:12
cursed that *c.* not in all. *Gal* 3:10
she that is a widow *c.* *1 Tim* 5:5
this man, because he *c.* *Heb* 7:24*
here we have no *c.* city. 13:14*
into perfect law, and *c.* *Jas* 1:25

contradicting

filled with envy, *c.* and. *Acts* 13:45

contradiction

without *c.* the less is. *Heb* 7:7
him that endured such *c.* 12:3*

contrariwise

c. ye ought rather to. *2 Cor* 2:7
c. when they saw the gospel. *Gal* 2:7
not rendering railing, *c.* *1 Pet* 3:9

contrary

if ye walk *c.* *Lev* 26:21, 23, 27, 40
then will I walk *c.* to you. 24, 28, 41
it was turned to the *c.* *Esth* 9:1
the *c.* is in thee, therefore thou art *c.* *Ezek* 16:34
for the wind was *c.* *Mat* 14:24
these all do *c.* to the. *Acts* 17:7
men to worship *c.* to the law. 18:13
me to be smitten *c.* to the law. 23:3
to do many things *c.* to the. 26:9
grafted *c.* to nature into. *Rom* 11:24
c. to the doctrine ye have. 16:17
and these are *c.* the one. *Gal* 5:17
hand-writing which was *c.* *Col* 2:14
not God, and are *c.* to. *1 Thes* 2:15
if any thing that is *c.* *1 Tim* 1:10
that he of the *c.* part. *Tit* 2:8

contribution

to make *c.* for the poor. *Rom* 15:26

contrite

saveth such as be of *c.* *Ps* 34:18
a *c.* heart, O God, thou. 51:17
c. and humble spirit, to revive heart of *c.* ones. *Isa* 57:15
that is of a *c.* spirit and. 66:2

controversy

being matters of *c.* *Deut* 17:8
men between whom the *c.* 19:17
shall every *c.* be tried. 21:5
if there be a *c.* between men. 25:1
any that had a *c.* came. *2 Sam* 15:2
set the Levites for *c.* *2 Chr* 19:8
recompences for the *c.* of. *Isa* 34:8
the Lord hath a *c.* *Jer* 25:31
in *c.* they shall stand. *Ezek* 44:24
the Lord hath a *c.* with. *Hos* 4:1
Lord hath a *c.* with Judah. 12:2
Lord hath *c.* with his people. *Mi* 6:2
without *c.* great is the. *1 Tim* 3:16

convenient

[1] *Needful*, Pr 30:8. [2] *Fitting*, Rom 1:28. [3] *Befitting*, Eph 5:4; *Philem* 8.

feed me with food *c.* *Pr* 30:8*
seemeth good and *c.* *Jer* 40:4, 5
when a *c.* day was. *Mark* 6:21
when I have a *c.* season. *Acts* 24:25
things which are not *c.* *Rom* 1:28*
he shall have *c.* time. *1 Cor* 16:12*
jesting, which are not *c.* *Eph* 5:4*
to enjoin that which is *c.* *Philem* 8*

conveniently

how he might *c.* betray. *Mark* 14:11

conversant

and strangers were *c.* *Josh* 8:35
as long as we were *c.* *1 Sam* 25:15

conversation

(*Behaviour, or manner of life. It does not in the Bible mean discourse with another. The Revised Versions change the word in all cases*)

slay such as be of upright *c.* *Ps* 37:14
to him that ordereth his *c.* 50:23
we have had our *c.* *2 Cor* 1:12
ye have heard of my *c.* *Gal* 1:13
whom also we all had our *c.* *Eph* 2:3
put off concerning former *c.* 4:22
only let your *c.* be as. *Phil* 1:27
for our *c.* is in heaven. 3:20
example of believers in *c.* *1 Tim* 4:12
let your *c.* be without. *Heb* 13:5
considering the end of their *c.* 7
shew out of a good *c.* *Jas* 3:13
holy in all manner of *c.* *1 Pet* 1:15
corruptible things from vain *c.* 18
having your *c.* honest among. 2:12
they also may be won by the *c.* 3:1
behold your chaste *c.* 2
falsely accuse your good *c.* 16
Lot vexed with filthy *c.* *2 Pet* 2:7
ought ye to be, in all holy *c.* 3:11

conversion

(*Literally, a turning, the word is used to mean, theologically, the spiritual or moral change which accompanies the turning of a sinner from his sins to God*, Ps 51:13)

the *c.* of the Gentiles. *Acts* 15:3

convert, -ed

(*The Revised Versions usually use the literal form,* turn again)

and sinners shall be *c.* *Ps* 51:13
they understand, and *c.* *Isa* 6:10
abundance of sea shall be *c.* 60:5*
should be *c.* and I should heal them. *Mat* 13:15; *Mark* 4:12
ye be *c.* and become as. *Mat* 18:3
when *c.* strengthen thy. *Luke* 22:32
be *c.* and I heal them. *John* 12:40
Acts 28:27
repent and be *c.* that sins. *Acts* 3:19
err from truth, and one *c.* *Jas* 5:19

converteth, -ing

law of Lord is perfect, *c.* *Ps* 19:7*
that he who *c.* a sinner. *Jas* 5:20

converts

her *c.* shall be redeemed. *Isa* 1:27

convey, -ed

I will *c.* them by sea. *1 Ki* 5:9*
that they may *c.* me over. *Neh* 2:7
Jesus had *c.* himself. *John* 5:13

convicted

c. by their own conscience. *John* 8:9

convince, -ed, -eth

none of you *c.* Job. *Job* 32:12
which of you *c.* me of? *John* 8:46*
for he mightily *c.* the. *Acts* 18:28*
he is *c.* of all, he is. *1 Cor* 14:24*
that he may be able to *c.* *Tit* 1:9*
and are *c.* of the law. *Jas* 2:9*
to *c.* all that are ungodly. *Jude* 15*

convocation, -s

(*An assembly of persons called together for a purpose*)

shall be an holy *c.* *Ex* 12:16
Lev 23:7, 24, 35; *Num* 28:18; 29:1
proclaim to be holy *c.* *Lev* 23:2
4, 21, 37
seventh day as an holy *c.* 23:3, 8
Num 28:25
tenth day an holy *c.* *Lev* 23:27
Num 29:7

eighth day shall be holy *c.* *Lev* 23:36
first-fruits have holy *c.* *Num* 28:26
day seventh month holy *c.* 29:12

cook, -s

take daughters to be *c.* *1 Sam* 8:13
Samuel said to *c.* bring portion. 9:23
c. took up the shoulder and set. 24

cool

walking in garden in the *c.* *Gen* 3:8
dip tip of finger and *c.* *Luke* 16:24

copied

men of Hezekiah *c.* out. *Pr* 25:1

coping

stones from foundation to *c.* *1 Ki* 7:9

copper

two vessels of fine *c.* *Ezra* 8:27

coppersmith

Alexander the *c.* did. *2 Tim* 4:14

copulation

if any man's seed of *c.* *Lev* 15:16
skin whereon is seed of *c.* shall. 17
shall lie with seed of *c.* 18

copy

write him a *c.* of law. *Deut* 17:18
he wrote on stones a *c.* *Josh* 8:32
c. of a letter sent. *Ezra* 4:11; 5:6
c. of Artaxerxes' letter was. 4:23
c. of the letter Artaxerxes gave. 7:11
c. of a writing for. *Esth* 3:14; 8:13
Mordecai gave Hatach a *c.* 4:8

cor

(*A measure, either dry or liquid. About* 11 *bushels or* 90 *gallons*)

part of a bath out of *c.* *Ezek* 45:14

coral

no mention made of *c.* *Job* 28:18
was thy merchant in *c.* *Ezek* 27:16

corban

it is *c.* that is to say. *Mark* 7:11

cord

let spies down by a *c.* *Josh* 2:15
he hath loosed my *c.* *Job* 30:11
out leviathan's tongue with *c.*? 41:1
a threefold *c.* is not. *Eccl* 4:12
or ever the silver *c.* be loosed. 12:6
spare not, lengthen *c.* *Isa* 54:2
a *c.* by lot in congregation. *Mi* 2:5

cords

of the court and their *c.* *Ex* 35:18
Samson with new *c.* *Judg* 15:13*
if they be holden in *c.* *Job* 36:8
cast away their *c.* from us. *Ps* 2:3
bind the sacrifice with *c.* 118:27
he hath cut asunder the *c.* 129:4
have hid a snare and *c.* 140:5
shall be holden with *c.* *Pr* 5:22
that draw iniquity with *c.* *Isa* 5:18
nor shall any of the *c.* thereof. 33:20
all my *c.* broken. *Jer* 10:2
let down Jeremiah with *c.* 38:
drew up Jeremiah with *c.* 1
in chests bound with *c.* *Ezek* 27:2
I drew them with the *c.* *Hos* 11:
a scourge of small *c.* *John* 2:1

coriander

manna was like *c.* seed. *Ex* 16:3
Num 11:

Corinth

things, Paul came to *C.* *Acts* 18:
while Apollos was at *C.* 19:
unto church of God at *C.* to them. *1 Cor* 1:2; *2 Cor* 1:
I came not as yet to *C.* *2 Cor* 1:2
Erastus abode at *C.* *2 Tim* 4:2

Corinthians

many of the *C.* hearing. *Acts* 18
O ye *C.* our mouth is. *2 Cor* 6:1

cormorant

have in abomination *c.* and great. *Lev* 11:7; *Deut* 14:
but the *c.* shall possess. *Isa* 34:1
Zeph 2:1

corn

(*Always, in the Bible, grain various sorts, not Indian corn would be understood in the Unit States by the term. The Americ Revision changes the word in* t *Old Testament to* grain)

came to Joseph to buy *c. Gen* 41:57
there was *c.* in Egypt. 42:2
Acts 7:12
carry *c.* for the famine. *Gen* 42:19
so that the stacks of *c. Ex* 22:6
burn part of beaten *c. Lev* 2:16
neither bread nor parched *c.* 23:14
as though it were the *c. Num* 18:27
to put the sickle to *c. Deut* 16:9
not muzzle ox when he treadeth out
c. 25:4; *1 Cor* 9:9; *1 Tim* 5:18
did eat of the old *c. Josh* 5:11, 12
he reached her parched *c. Ruth* 2:14
lie down at end of heap of *c.* 3:7
an ephah of parched *c. 1 Sam* 17:17
five measures of parched *c.* 25:18
brought parched *c. 2 Sam* 17:28
as blasted *c. 2 Ki* 19:26; *Isa* 37:27
we take up *c.* for them. *Neh* 5:2
as a shock of *c.* cometh. *Job* 5:26
they reap every one his *c.* 24:6
young ones grow up with *c.* 39:4
preparest them *c. Ps* 65:9
valleys are covered with *c.* 13
there shall be a handful of *c.* 72:16
had given them of the *c.* 78:24
that withholdeth *c. Pr* 11:26
harvest-man gathereth *c. Isa* 17:5
I will no more give thy *c.* 62:8
I will call for the *c. Ezek* 36:29
I will take away my *c. Hos* 2:9
loveth to tread out the *c.* 10:11
they shall revive as the *c.* 14:7
for the *c.* is wasted. *Joel* 1:10
barns are broken down, for *c.* 17
that we may sell *c. Amos* 8:5
I will sift Israel like as *c.* 9:9
after that the full *c. Mark* 4:28
except a *c.* of wheat. *John* 12:24*

ears of **corn**

seven *ears of c.* came up. *Gen* 41:5
offer green *ears of c. Lev* 2:14
let me glean *ears of c. Ruth* 2:2
brought full *ears of c. 2 Ki* 4:42
off as tops of the *ears of c. Job* 24:24
to pluck *ears of c. Mat* 12:1
Mark 2:23; *Luke* 6:1

corn *fields*

c. fields on the sabbath. *Mark* 2:23
Mat 12:1; *Luke* 6:1

corn *floor*

and the *c.* of my *floor. Isa* 21:10
reward on every *c. floor. Hos* 9:1

standing **corn**

that the *standing c.* be. *Ex* 22:6
come into *standing c. Deut* 23:25
foxes go into *standing c.* burn up
standing c. Judg 15:5

corn *and wine*

plenty of *c. and wine. Gen* 27:28
with *c. and wine* have I. 37
bless thy *c. and wine. Deut* 7:13
gather in thy *c. and wine.* 11:14
not eat tithe of *c. and wine.* 12:17
14:23
hast gathered in *c. and wine.* 16:13
first-fruit of *c. and wine* and. 18:4
not leave thee *c. and wine* or. 28:51
upon a land of *c. and wine.* 33:28
a land of *c. and wine. 2 Ki* 18:32
Isa 36:17
brought first-fruits of *c. and wine.*
2 Chr 31:5
increase of *c. and wine.* 32:28
restore part of *c. wine. Neh* 5:11
c. of new *wine.* 10:39; 13:5, 12
time their *c. and wine. Ps* 4:7
where is *c. and wine* ? *Lam* 2:12
gave her *c. wine,* and oil. *Hos* 2:8
earth shall hear *c. and wine.* 22
assemble for *c. and wine.* 7:14
I will send you *c. and wine. Joel* 2:19
brought on *c. and* new *wine.*
Hag 1:11
shall make young men cheerful,
and new *wine* maids. *Zech* 9:17

Cornelius

man in Cesarea, called *C. Acts* 10:1
angel which spake to *C.* 7
met Peter, and fell down. 25
thy prayer is heard. 31

corner

shave off the *c.* of their. *Lev* 21:5
altars in every *c.* of. *2 Chr* 28:24
through street near *c. Pr* 7:8
lieth in wait at every *c.* 12
better to dwell in *c.* of. 21:9; 25:24
not be removed into a *c. Isa* 30:20
flame shall devour the *c. Jer* 48:45
take of thee a stone for a *c.* 51:26
in every *c.* of court. *Ezek* 46:21
in Samaria in the *c.* of. *Amos* 3:12
came forth the *c.* and. *Zech* 10:4*
stone builders rejected is become
head of *c. Mat* 21:42; *Ps* 118:22
Mark 12:10; *Luke* 20:17
Acts 4:11; *1 Pet* 2:7
was not done in a *c. Acts* 26:26

corner-gate

Ephraim to the *c.-gate. 2 Ki* 14:13
towers at *c.-gate. 2 Chr* 26:9
built from tower to *gate* of *c.*
Jer 31:38
inhabited to the *c.-gate. Zech* 14:10

corner-stone

or who laid the *c.-stone* ? *Job* 38:6
head-*stone* of the *c. Ps* 118:22
daughters be as *c.-stones.* 144:12
a precious *c.-stone. Isa* 28:16
1 Pet 2:6
Christ chief *c.-stone. Eph* 2:20

corners

rings in four *c.* of ark. *Ex* 25:12*
26; 27:4; 37:13
horns upon the four *c.* 27:2; 38:2
not reap the *c.* of field. *Lev* 19:9
23:22
ye shall not round *c.* of heads. 27
shall smite *c.* of Moab. *Num* 24:17
will scatter them into *c. Deut* 32:26*
thou didst divide into *c. Neh* 9:22*
wind smote the four *c. Job* 1:19
dispersed of Judah from *c. Isa* 11:12
punish circumcised with ... in uttermost *c. Jer* 9:25, 26; 25:23; 49:32
end is come upon four *c. Ezek* 7:2
put blood upon four *c.* 45:19
pray in *c.* of the streets. *Mat* 6:5
sheet knit at *c. Acts* 10:11; 11:5
angels standing on four *c. Rev* 7:1

cornet

ark with sound of *c. 1 Chr* 15:28
with sound of the *c.* make. *Ps* 98:6
hear the sound of *c. Dan* 3:5, 15
every man shall hear sound of *c.* 10
blow ye the *c.* in Gibeah. *Hos* 5:8

cornets

played before Lord on *c. 2 Sam* 6:5*
shouting with *c. 2 Chr* 15:14

corpse, -s

they were all dead *c. 2 Ki* 19:35
Isa 37:36
no end of *c.* stumble on *c. Nah* 3:3
disciples took John's *c. Mark* 6:29

correct

when thou dost *c.* man. *Ps* 39:11
heathen, shall not he *c.*? 94:10
c. thy son, and he shall. *Pr* 29:17
own wickedness shall *c. Jer* 2:19
c. me, but with judgement. 10:24
c. thee in measure. 30:11; 46:28

corrected, -eth

is man whom God *c. Job* 5:17
whom Lord loveth, he *c. Pr* 3:12*
a servant will not be *c.* 29:19
of our flesh which *c. Heb* 12:9*

correction

whether for *c.* or mercy. *Job* 37:13
neither be weary of his *c. Pr* 3:11*
he goeth as a fool to the *c.* 7:22
c. is grievous to him that. 15:10
but the rod of *c.* shall. 22:15
withhold not *c.* from child. 23:13
children received no *c. Jer* 2:30
have refused to receive *c.* 5:3
a nation that receiveth not *c.* 7:28*
hast established them for *c. Hab* 1:12
obeyed not, received not *c. Zeph* 3:2
scripture is profitable for *c.*
2 Tim 3:16

corrupt

[1] *To consume,* Mat 6:19. [2] *To defile, or pollute,* Ex 32:7. [3] *To mar, or spoil,* 1 Cor 15:33. [4] *To pervert or lead astray,* 2 Cor 11:3. [5] *To break, or make void,* Mal 2:8. [6] *Vicious and unsound,* 1 Tim 6:5; 2 Tim 3:8.

earth also was *c. Gen* 6:11, 12
my breath is *c.* my days. *Job* 17:1*
they are *c. Ps* 14:1; 53:1; 73:8
my wounds stink and are *c.* 38:5
troubled fountain and *c. Pr* 25:26
not according to your *c. Ezek* 20:44
she was more *c.* in her. 23:11
lying and *c.* words. *Dan* 2:9
that sacrificeth a *c.* thing. *Mal* 1:14*
a *c.* tree bringeth forth. *Mat* 7:17
nor can a *c.* tree. 18; *Luke* 6:43
tree *c.* and his fruit *c. Mat* 12:33
the old man which is *c. Eph* 4:22
let no *c.* communication proceed. 29
disputings of men of *c. 1 Tim* 6:5
men of *c.* minds. *2 Tim* 3:8

corrupt, *verb*

lest ye *c.* yourselves. *Deut* 4:16, 25
after my death ye will *c.* 31:29
do wickedly shall he *c. Dan* 11:32*
behold I will *c.* your. *Mal* 2:3*
moth and rust doth *c. Mat* 6:19*
neither moth nor rust doth *c.* 20*
evil communications *c. 1 Cor* 15:33
which *c.* the word of God. *2 Cor* 2:17
in those things they *c. Jude* 10*
great whore did *c.* earth. *Rev* 19:2

corrupted, -eth

for all flesh had *c.* his way. *Gen* 6:12
the land was *c.* by. *Ex* 8:24
for thy people have *c.* themselves.
32:7; *Deut* 9:12; 32:5
c. themselves more. *Judg* 2:19
thou wast *c.* more. *Ezek* 16:47
thou hast *c.* thy wisdom. 28:17
have deeply *c.* themselves. *Hos* 9:9
rose early and *c.* all. *Zeph* 3:7
ye have *c.* covenant of. *Mal* 2:8
nor moth *c. Luke* 12:33
have *c.* no man. *2 Cor* 7:2
lest your minds be *c.* from. 11:3
your riches are *c. Jas* 5:1, 2

corrupters

children that are *c. Isa* 1:4
brass and iron, all *c. Jer* 6:28

corruptible

image made like to *c. Rom* 1:23
they do it to obtain *c. 1 Cor* 9:25
for this *c.* must put on. 15:53
not redeemed with *c. 1 Pet* 1:18
born again, not of *c.* seed. 23
let it be in that which is not *c.* 3:4

corrupting

daughter of women *c. Dan* 11:17

corruption

(*Frequently used as a synonym of death; laying stress on the decay of the body after it is in the grave*)

their *c.* is in them. *Lev* 22:25
right hand of mount of *c. 2 Ki* 23:13
I have said to *c.* thou. *Job* 17:14
nor wilt thou suffer thine holy One to
see *c. Ps* 16:10; *Acts* 2:27; 13:35
live for ever, and not see *c. Ps* 49:9
delivered it from pit of *c. Isa* 38:17
was turned in me to *c. Dan* 10:8
up my life from *c. Jonah* 2:6*
nor his flesh did see *c. Acts* 2:31
no more to return to *c.* 13:34
laid to his fathers and saw *c.* 36
raised again saw no *c.* 37
from the bondage of *c. Rom* 8:21
it is sown in *c.*; raised. *1 Cor* 15:42
neither doth *c.* inherit. 50
shall of flesh reap *c. Gal* 6:8
escaped the *c.* that. *2 Pet* 1:4
utterly perish in own *c.* 2:12*
themselves are servants of *c.* 19

corruptly

people did yet *c. 2 Chr* 27:2
we have dealt very *c. Neh* 1:7

cost

eaten at all of king's *c.*? *2 Sam* 19:42

of that which *c.* nothing. *2 Sam* 24:24
offerings without *c.* *1 Chr* 21:24
and counteth *c.* *Luke* 14:28

costliness

ships made rich by her *c.* *Rev* 18:19

costly

they brought *c.* stones. *1 Ki* 5:17
all these were of *c.* stones. 7:9
foundation was of *c.* stones. 10
and above were *c.* stones. 11
of spikenard, very *c.* *John* 12:3*
not with *c.* array. *1 Tim* 2:9

cotes

Hezekiah made *c.* *2 Chr* 32:28*

cottage, -s

of Zion is left as a *c.* *Isa* 1:8*
earth shall be removed like *c.* 24:20*
sea-coast shall be *c.* *Zeph* 2:6

couch, -es

and went up to my *c.* *Gen* 49:4
I say, my *c.* shall ease. *Job* 7:13
all night I water my *c.* *Ps* 6:6
in Damascus in a *c.* *Amos* 3:12
stretch themselves upon *c.* 6:4
through tiling with his *c.* *Luke* 5:19
arise, take up thy *c.* 24
laid sick folk on *c.* *Acts* 5:15

couch

when they *c.* in dens. *Job* 38:40

couched

Judah *c.* as a lion. *Gen* 49:9
he *c.* he lay down as. *Num* 24:9

coucheth

and for deep that *c.* *Deut* 33:13

couching

Issachar *c.* down. *Gen* 49:14
make Ammonites a *c.* *Ezek* 25:5

could

old, so that he *c.* not see. *Gen* 27:1
forth lice, but *c.* not. *Ex* 8:18
he *c.* not see. *1 Sam* 3:2
Ahijah *c.* not see. *1 Ki* 14:4
to king of Edom, *c.* not. *2 Ki* 3:26
but David *c.* not go. *1 Chr* 21:30
c. not withstand them. *2 Chr* 13:7
but he *c.* not be found. *Ps* 37:36
what *c.* have been done? *Isa* 5:4
my mind *c.* not be. *Jer* 15:1
bring it to land, *c.* not. *Jonah* 1:13
Herodias would have killed him, but she *c.* not. *Mark* 6:19
cast him out, *c.* not. 9:18; *Luke* 9:40
she hath done what she *c.* *Mark* 14:8
the world *c.* not contain. *John* 21:25
from which ye *c.* not be. *Acts* 13:39

couldest

evil things as thou *c.* *Jer* 3:5*
yet *c.* not be satisfied. *Ezek* 16:28

coulter -s

to sharpen each his *c.* *1 Sam* 13:20
they had a file for their *c.* 21

council, -s

shall be in danger of *c.* *Mat* 5:22
deliver you to *c.* 10:17; *Mark* 13:9
c. sought false witness. *Mat* 26:59
Mark 14:55
elders, scribes and whole *c.* *Mark* 15:1
elders led Jesus into *c.* *Luke* 22:66
chief priests gathered *c.* *John* 11:47
Acts 5:21
them to go out of the *c.* *Acts* 4:15
and set them before the *c.* 5:27
then stood up one in the *c.* 34
departed from the *c.* rejoicing. 41
and brought him to the *c.* 6:12
all in the *c.* looking on him. 15
commanded all their *c.* to. 22:30
ye with the *c.* signify to the. 23:15
while I stood before the *c.* 24:20

counsel

[1] *Advice,* Pr 20:18; Dan 4:27. [2] *God's purpose,* Acts 4:28. [3] *The most secret resolutions,* 1 Cor 4:5.

I will give thee *c.* *Ex* 18:19
Eleazar, who shall ask *c.* for. *Num* 27:21*
caused Israel through *c.* of Balaam, to commit trespass. 31:16
are a nation void of *c.* *Deut* 32:28
asked not *c.* at mouth. *Josh* 9:14
give here advice and *c.* *Judg* 20:7
turn *c.* of Ahithophel. *2 Sam* 15:31
all the *c.* of Ahithophel. 16:23
Lord defeated the good *c.* of. 17:14
shall surely ask *c.* at Abel. 20:18
let me give thee *c.* *1 Ki* 1:12
forsook *c.* of old men. 12:8, 13
2 Chr 10:8, 13
king of Syria took *c.* *2 Ki* 6:8
c. and strength for war. 18:20
Isa 36:5
Saul died for asking *c.* *1 Chr* 10:13
Ahaziah walked after *c.* *2 Chr* 22:5
art thou made of king's *c.*? 25:16
the king had taken *c.* to. 30:2
the assembly took *c.* to keep. 23
according to *c.* of my. *Ezra* 10:3
according to the *c.* of the princes. 8
God brought their *c.* to. *Neh* 4:15
the *c.* of the froward. *Job* 5:13
should shine upon the *c.* of. 10:3
and strength he hath *c.* and. 12:13
the *c.* of the wicked is. 21:16; 22:18
who is this that darkeneth *c.*? 38:2
who is he that hideth *c.*? 42:3
walketh not in the *c.* *Ps* 1:1
you have shamed the *c.* of. 14:6
who hath given me *c.* 16:7
and fulfil all thy *c.* 20:4
while they took *c.* together. 31:13
Lord brings the *c.* of the. 33:10
we took sweet *c.* together. 55:14
hide me from the secret *c.* 64:2
princes of Judah and their *c.* 68:27
shalt guide me with thy *c.* 73:24
they have taken crafty *c.* 83:3
they waited not for his *c.* 106:13
provoked him with their *c.* 43
the *c.* of the Most High. 107:11
c. is mine, sound wisdom. *Pr* 8:14
where no *c.* is, the people. 11:14*
he that hearkeneth unto *c.* 12:15
without *c.* purposes are. 15:22
hear *c.* and receive. 19:20
c. in the heart of man is. 20:5
every purpose established by *c.* 18
there is no wisdom nor *c.* 21:30
for by wise *c.* thou shalt. 24:6*
of a friend by hearty *c.* 27:9
let *c.* of the Holy One. *Isa* 5:19
they have taken evil *c.* 7:5
spirit of *c.* and might shall. 11:2
I will destroy the *c.* of Egypt. 19:3
c. of counsellors of Pharaoh. 11
taken this *c.* against Tyre? 23:8*
Lord, who is wonderful in *c.* 28:29
that seek deep to hide *c.* 29:15
with whom took he *c.*? 14
and performeth the *c.* 44:26
nor shall *c.* perish. *Jer* 18:18
thou knowest all their *c.* 23
I will make void *c.* of Judah. 19:7
mighty God, great in *c.* 32:19
if I give thee *c.* wilt not. 38:15
is *c.* perished from prudent? 49:7
king of Babylon hath taken *c.* 30
and *c.* shall perish. *Ezek* 7:26
and that give wicked *c.* 11:2
Daniel answered with *c.* *Dan* 2:14
my people ask *c.* at their. *Hos* 4:12
neither understand his *c.* *Mi* 4:12
the *c.* of peace shall be. *Zech* 6:13
the Pharisees held a *c.* *Mat* 12:14
they took *c.* and bought. 27:7
when they had taken *c.* 28:12
took *c.* against Jesus. *Mark* 3:6
John 11:53
not consented to the *c.* *Luke* 23:51
Caiaphas gave *c.* *John* 18:14
what thy *c.* determined. *Acts* 4:28
when they heard, they took *c.* 5:33*
if this *c.* be of men, it will. 38
the Jews took *c.* to kill him. 9:23*
soldiers' *c.* was to kill the. 27:42
worketh after the *c.* of. *Eph* 1:11
the immutability of his *c.* *Heb* 6:17

counsel *of God or Lord*

ask *c.* we pray *of God.* *Judg* 18:5
Israel asked *c. of God.* 20:18
Saul asked *c. of God.* *1 Sam* 14:37
c. of the *Lord* standeth. *Ps* 33:11
c. of the *Lord* of hosts. *Isa* 19:17*
stood in *c. of the Lord*? *Jer* 23:18*
hear *c. of* the *Lord.* 49:20; 50:45
rejected the *c. of God.* *Luke* 7:30
by determinate *c. of God.* *Acts* 2:23
declare to you all *c. of God.* 20:27

my **counsel**

not hearkened to *my c.* *2 Chr* 25:16
kept silence at *my c.* *Job* 29:21
set at nought all *my c.* *Pr* 1:25
they would none of *my c.* 30
my c. shall stand and. *Isa* 46:10
man that executeth *my c.* 11
they had stood in *my c.* *Jer* 23:22
my c. be acceptable to. *Dan* 4:27

own **counsel**

his *own c.* shall cast him. *Job* 18:7
ashamed of his *own c.* *Hos* 10:6

take **counsel**

let us *take c.* together. *Neh* 6:7
rulers *take c.* against. *Ps* 2:2
how long shall I *take c.*? 13:2
take c. together. 71:10
take c. and it shall. *Isa* 8:10
take c. execute judgement. 16:3
woe to children that *take c.* 30:1
let them *take c.* together. 45:21

counsel, -ed

which Ahithophel *c.* *2 Sam* 16:23
c. that all Israel be gathered. 17:11
thus Ahithophel *c.* thus I *c.* 15, 21
how hast thou *c.* him? *Job* 26:3
c. thee to keep the king's. *Eccl* 8:2
I *c.* thee to buy of me. *Rev* 3:18

counsellor

David's *c.* *2 Sam* 15:12; *1 Chr* 27:33
Zechariah his son, a wise *c.* *1 Chr* 26:14
David's uncle, was a *c.* 27:32
Athaliah was his *c.* *2 Chr* 22:3
Lord taketh away the *c.* *Isa* 3:3
shall be called Wonderful, *C.* 9:6
or being his *c.* hath taught? 40:13
there was no man, no *c.* 41:28
is thy *c.* perished? *Mi* 4:9
out of thee a wicked *c.* *Nah* 1:11*
Joseph an honourable *c.* *Mark* 15:43
Luke 23:50
who hath been his *c.*? *Rom* 11:34

counsellors

they were his *c.* after. *2 Chr* 22:4
they hired *c.* against them. *Ezra* 4:5
sent of king, and his seven *c.* 7:14
mercy to me before king and *c.* 28
gold, which king and *c.* had. 8:25
rest with kings and *c.* *Job* 3:14
leadeth *c.* away spoiled. 12:17
thy testimonies my *c.* *Ps* 119:24
in multitude of *c.* *Pr* 11:14; 24:
deceit in heart, but to the *c.* 12:2
in the multitude of *c.* they. 15:2
I will restore thy *c.* *Isa* 1:2
counsel of wise *c.* of Pharaoh. 19:1
said to his *c.* did not we? *Dan* 3:2
king's *c.* being gathered, saw. 2
my *c.* and my lords sought. 4:3
all the *c.* and the captains. 6:

counsels

turned round by his *c.* *Job* 37:12
them fall by their own *c.* *Ps* 5:1
walked in their own *c.* 81:1
shall attain to wise *c.* *Pr* 1:
c. of the wicked are deceit. 12:
written excellent things in *c.*? 22:2
thy *c.* of old are. *Isa* 25:
wearied in multitude of *c.* 47:1
walked in the *c.* of their. *Jer* 7:2
because of their own *c.* *Hos* 11:
walk in *c.* of house of. *Mi* 6:1
will make manifest *c.* of. *1 Cor* 4:

count

shall make your *c.* *Ex* 12
c. from the morrow after. *Lev* 23:
let him *c.* the years. 25:27,
who can *c.* the dust? *Num* 23:
c. not me daughter of. *1 Sam* 1:
and my maids *c.* me. *Job* 19:
doth not he see my ways, *c.*? 31:
the Lord shall *c.* when. *Ps* 87
if I *c.* them, they are more. 139:
I *c.* them mine enemies. 2

shall I *c.* them pure. *Mi* 6:11*
neither *c.* I my life dear. *Acts* 20:24*
I *c.* all things loss, and do *c.* them. *Phil* 3:8
I *c.* not myself to have. 13
God would *c.* you. *2 Thes* 1:11
c. him not as an enemy. 3:15
c. their masters worthy. *1 Tim* 6:1
if thou *c.* me a partner. *Philem* 17
c. it joy when ye fall. *Jas* 1:2
behold, we *c.* them happy. 5:11*
as they that *c.* it pleasure. *2 Pet* 2:13
as some men *c.* slackness. 3:9
let him *c.* the number. *Rev* 13:18

counted

believed, and he *c.* it for. *Gen* 15:6
Ps 106:31; *Rom* 4:3; *Gal* 3:6
the sheep that shall be *c.* *Gen* 30:33
are we not *c.* strangers? 31:15
cannot be numbered or *c.* *1 Ki* 3:8
Levi and Benjamin *c.* *1 Chr* 21:6
for they were *c.* faithful. *Neh* 13:13
wherefore we are *c.* as. *Job* 18:3
darts are *c.* as stubble. 41:29
we are *c.* as sheep for. *Ps* 44:22
I am *c.* with them that go. 88:4
a fool, when he holdeth his peace is *c.* wise. *Pr* 17:28
rising early, it shall be *c.* 27:14
horses' hoofs shall be *c.* *Isa* 5:28
and the fruitful field be *c.* 32:15
where is he that *c.* towers? 33:18*
the nations are *c.* as. 40:15
all nations are *c.* to him. 17
but they were *c.* as a. *Hos* 8:12
c. him as a prophet. *Mat* 14:5
Mark 11:32
be *c.* worthy to escape. *Luke* 21:36
that they were *c.* worthy. *Acts* 5:41
burned their books, and *c.* 19:19
uncircumcision be *c.* for. *Rom* 2:26
him that believeth, his faith is *c.* 4:5
children of promise are *c.* 9:8
gain, those I *c.* loss for. *Phil* 3:7
c. worthy of kingdom of. *2 Thes* 1:5
for that he *c.* me faithful. *1 Tim* 1:12
let elders be *c.* worthy of. 5:17
this man was *c.* worthy. *Heb* 3:3
he whose descent is not *c.* 7:6
hath *c.* blood of the covenant. 10:29

see **accounted**

countenance

wroth, and his *c.* fell. *Gen* 4:5
Jacob beheld the *c.* of Laban. 31:2
I see your father's *c.* that it. 5
nor shalt thou *c.* a poor. *Ex* 23:3*
the Lord lift up his *c.* *Num* 6:26
bring a nation of fierce *c.* *Deut* 28:50
c. was like *c.* of an angel. *Judg* 13:6
Hannah, her *c.* was no. *1 Sam* 1:18
look not on his *c.* or the. 16:7
David was of beautiful *c.* 12; 17:42
Abigail of beautiful *c.* 25:3
Tamar of a fair *c.* *2 Sam* 14:27
settled his *c.* stedfastly. *2 Ki* 8:11
why is thy *c.* sad? *Neh* 2:2
why should not my *c.* be sad? 3
hou changest his *c.* and. *Job* 14:20
nd the light of my *c.* 29:24
ift thou up the light of thy *c.* *Ps* 4:6
vicked, through pride of *c.* 10:4
is *c.* doth behold upright. 11:7
nade him glad with thy *c.* 21:6*
raise him for help of his *c.* 42:5
vho is the health of my *c.* 11; 43:5
ght of thy *c.* did save them. 44:3
erish at rebuke of thy *c.* 80:16
the light of thy *c.* 89:15
ur secret sins in light of thy *c.* 90:8
eart maketh cheerful *c.* *Pr* 15:13
the light of the king's *c.* 16:15
o doth the angry *c.* a. 25:23
a man sharpeneth the *c.* 27:17
sadness of *c.* the. *Eccl* 7:3
ee thy *c.* thy *c.* is. *S of S* 2:14
s *c.* is as Lebanon. 5:15*
e shew of their *c.* doth. *Isa* 3:9
oubled in their *c.* *Ezek* 27:35
ng's *c.* was changed. *Dan* 5:6
ng of fierce *c.* shall stand. 8:23
pocrites, of a sad *c.* *Mat* 6:16
like lightning. 28:3*; *Luke* 9:29
l of joy with thy *c.* *Acts* 2:28

Moses for glory of his *c.* *2 Cor* 3:7
and his *c.* was as. *Rev* 1:16

see **changed**

countenances

let our *c.* be looked. *Dan* 1:13
their *c.* appeared fairer and. 15

countervail

enemy could not *c.* king's. *Esth* 7:4*

counteth, -ing

c. me as one of his enemies. *Job* 19:11; 33:10
c. one by one, to find. *Eccl* 7:27*
down first, *c.* the cost. *Luke* 14:28

countries

will I give these *c.* *Gen* 26:3, 4
all *c.* came into Egypt to. 41:57
who among all *c.* *2 Ki* 18:35
and glory throughout *c.* *1 Chr* 22:5
fear of God on all those *c.* *2 Chr* 20:29
because of people of *c.* *Ezra* 3:3
who have ruled over all *c.* 4:20
wound heads over many *c.* *Ps* 110:6
give ear all ye of far *c.* *Isa* 8:9
gather remnant of my flock out of all *c.* and. *Jer* 23:3, 8; 32:37
prophesied against many *c.* 28:8
Jerusalem in midst of *c.* *Ezek* 5:5
changed my statutes more than *c.* 6
be scattered through the *c.* 6:8
scattered among the *c.* yet I will be as a little sanctuary in *c.* 11:16
assemble you out of *c.* 17; 20:34, 41
thee a mocking to all *c.* 22:4
cause thee to perish out of *c.* 25:7
disperse them through *c.* 29:12
36:19
these two *c.* shall be mine. 35:10
he shall enter into *c.* *Dan* 11:40
many *c.* shall be overthrown. 41
stretch forth his hand upon *c.* 42
remember me in far *c.* *Zech* 10:9
not them that are in *c.* *Luke* 21:21

country

smoke of the *c.* went up. *Gen* 19:28
but thou shalt go to my *c.* 24:4
must not be so done in our *c.* 29:26
that I may go to my *c.* 30:25
Shechem the prince of the *c.* 34:2
the lord of the *c.* said unto us. 42:33
all born in the *c.* shall. *Num* 15:13*
the *c.* which the Lord smote. 32:4
I am come into the *c.* *Deut* 26:3
men to search out the *c.* *Josh* 2:2, 3
go up and view the *c.* 7:2
possessed that *c.* *Judg* 11:21
and the destroyer of our *c.* 16:24
came into the *c.* of Moab. *Ruth* 1:2
returned out of *c.* of Moab. 22
cities and *c.* villages. *1 Sam* 6:18
all thy *c.* wept with. *2 Sam* 15:23
bones of Saul buried they in *c.* 21:14
Syrians filled the *c.* *1 Ki* 20:27
and the *c.* was filled. *2 Ki* 3:20
your *c.* is desolate, your. *Isa* 1:7
toss thee like a ball in large *c.* 22:18
nor see his native *c.* *Jer* 22:10
bring them from the north *c.* 31:8
is come upon the plain *c.* 48:21
to come from the north *c.* 50:9
them forth out of the *c.* *Ezek* 20:38
glory of *c.* Beth-jeshimoth. 25:9
be to you as born in the *c.* 47:22*
when I was yet in my *c.* *Jonah* 4:2
abroad his fame in *c.* *Mat* 9:31
not send them out of *c.* *Mark* 5:10
told it in city, and *c.* 14; *Luke* 8:34
to a citizen of that *c.* *Luke* 15:15
c. was nourished by king's *c.* *Acts* 12:20
they drew near to some *c.* 27:27
promise as in strange *c.* *Heb* 11:9*
that they seek a *c.* 14
had been mindful of that *c.* 15
now they desire a better *c.* 16

far **country**

be come from *far c.* *Josh* 9:6, 9
out of *far c.* *1 Ki* 8:41; *2 Chr* 6:32
they are come from a *far c.* *2 Ki* 20:14; *Isa* 39:3
good news from a *far c.* *Pr* 25:25
from a *far c.* to destroy. *Isa* 13:5

my counsel from *far c.* *Isa* 46:11
watchers come from *far c.* *Jer* 4:16
them that dwell in a *far c.* 8:19*
went into a *far c.* *Mat* 21:33
Mark 12:1
man travelling into *far c.* *Mat* 25:14
his journey into *far c.* *Luke* 15:13

own **country**

one of your *own c.* *Lev* 16:29*
17:15*; 24:22*
went to her *own c.* *1 Ki* 10:13
that I may go to my *own c.* 11:21
every man to his *own c.* 22:36
go every one to his *own c.* *Jer* 51:9
departed into their *own c.* *Mat* 2:12
save in his *own c.* 13:57
Mark 6:4; *Luke* 4:24
and came into his *own c.* *Mark* 6:1
prophet hath no honour in *own c.* *John* 4:44

thy **country**

get thee out of *thy c.* *Gen* 12:1
Acts 7:3
return unto *thy c.* and. *Gen* 32:9
us pass through *thy c.* *Num* 20:17
what is *thy c.*? *Jonah* 1:8
do here in *thy c.* *Luke* 4:23

countrymen

in perils by mine own *c.* *2 Cor* 11:26
like things of your *c.* *1 Thes* 2:14

couple

make me a *c.* of cakes. *2 Sam* 13:6
Ziba met David with a *c.* 16:1
chariot with a *c.* of. *Isa* 21:7, 9

couple, *verb*

c. curtains with taches. *Ex* 26:6, 9
make taches to *c.* tent. 11; 36:18
made shoulder-pieces to *c.* 39:4*

coupled, -eth

curtains be *c.* *Ex* 26:3; 36:10, 13, 16
in edge of the curtain which *c.* 26:10
two boards shall be *c.* 24; 36:29
by the two edges was it *c.* 39:4*
chaste conversation *c.* *1 Pet* 3:2

coupling, -s

loops from selvedge in *c.* *Ex* 26:4
36:11
in *c.* of second. 26:4; 36:11, 12
that is outmost in *c.* 26:10; 36:17
over-against other *c.* 28:27; 39:20
stone and timber for *c.* *2 Chr* 34:11

courage

remain any more *c.* *Josh* 2:11*
he took *c.* and put. *2 Chr* 15:8
shall stir up his *c.* *Dan* 11:25
Paul thanked God, took *c.* *Acts* 28:15

good **courage**

be ye of *good c.* and. *Num* 13:20
strong, and of *good c.* *Deut* 31:6
7, 23; *Josh* 1:6, 9, 18; 10:25
1 Chr 22:13; 28:20
be of *good c.* let us. *2 Sam* 10:12
1 Chr 19:13; *Ezra* 10:4; *Isa* 41:6
be of *good c.* and he shall strengthen thine heart. *Ps* 27:14; 31:24

courageous

be thou strong and very *c.* *Josh* 1:7
23:6; *2 Chr* 32:7
fear not, be *c.* and be. *2 Sam* 13:28
that is *c.* among mighty. *Amos* 2:16

courageously

deal *c.* and Lord shall. *2 Chr* 19:11

course

[1] *A prescribed track for a race. Used figuratively for the work given one to do in life,* Acts 13:25; 2 Tim 4:7. [2] *Order or turn,* 2 Chr 5:11. [3] *Progress and success,* 2 Thes 3:1. [4] *A voyage,* Acts 21:7.

chief fathers of every *c.* *1 Chr* 27:1
priests did not wait by *c.* *2 Chr* 5:11
they sung together by *c.* *Ezra* 3:11
of earth are out of *c.* *Ps* 82:5*
every one turned to his *c.* *Jer* 8:6
their *c.* is evil, and their. 23:10
Zacharias was of the *c.* *Luke* 1:5
executed in the order of his *c.* 8
as John fulfilled his *c.* *Acts* 13:25
came with straight *c.* 16:11; 21:1

might finish my *c.* with joy. *Acts* 20:24
we had finished our *c.* 21:7*
three, and that by *c.* *1 Cor* 14:27
the Lord have free *c.* *2 Thes* 3:1*
I have finished my *c.* *2 Tim* 4:7
tongue setteth on fire *c.* of. *Jas* 3:6*

water-course, *see* **water**

courses

stars in their *c.* fought. *Judg* 5:20
divided Levites into *c.* *1 Chr* 23:6
Solomon appointed *c.* *2 Chr* 8:14
Jehoiada dismissed not the *c.* 23:8
Hezekiah appointed the *c.* 31:2
Levites stood in their *c.* 35:10
set the Levites in their *c.* *Ezra* 6:18

court

In the Bible, [1] *Usually the uncovered area enclosed within the walls of the tabernacle or temple ; or* [2] *a similar area surrounded by the rooms of the house, that being the general way of building in the East,* 2 Sam 17:18; Esth 6:4, 5.
(*The great* courts *belonging to the temple were three ; the first called the* court *of the Gentiles, because the Gentiles were allowed to enter so far, and no farther. The second called the* court *of Israel, because all the Israelites, if purified, had the right of admission. The third* court *was that of the Priests, where the altar of burnt-offerings stood, and where the Priests and Levites exercised their ministry*)

c. of tabernacle: shall be hangings for *c.* *Ex* 27:9; 35:17; 38:9; 39:40
breadth of the *c.* 27:12, 13
length of the *c.* 18
pins of the *c.* 19; 35:18; 38:20, 31
thou shalt set up the *c.* 40:8
in *c.* of tabernacle eat. *Lev* 6:16, 26
had a well in his *c.* *2 Sam* 17:18
Isaiah gone into middle *c.* *2 Ki* 20:4*
stood before the new *c.* *2 Chr* 20:5
stoned Zechariah in *c.* of. 24:21
out the uncleanness into *c.* 29:16
Esther stood in inner *c.* *Esth* 5:1
king said, who is in the *c.*? 6:4
behold Haman standeth in *c.* 5
and a *c.* for owls. *Isa* 34:13
Jeremiah stood in the *c.* *Jer* 19:14
stand in the *c.* of the Lord's. 26:2
prophet was shut in *c.* of. 32:2
33:1; 39:15
into the dungeon in the *c.* 38:6
me to the door of *c.* *Ezek* 8:7, 16
the cloud filled the inner *c.* 10:3
into outward *c.* 40:17; 42:1; 46:21
he brought me to the inner *c.* 40:28
Spirit brought me into inner *c.* 43:5
blood upon gate of inner *c.* 45:19
in every corner of *c.* was a *c.* 46:21
and it is the king's *c.* *Amos* 7:13*
c. without the temple. *Rev* 11:2

courteous

love, be pitiful, be *c.* *1 Pet* 3:8*

courteously

Julius *c.* entreated Paul. *Acts* 27:3*
and lodged us 3 days *c.* 28:7

courts

altars for all host of heaven in two *c.* *2 Ki* 21:5; *2 Chr* 33:5
altars in the two *c.* *2 Ki* 23:12
office was to wait in *c.* *1 Chr* 23:28
Solomon shall build my *c.* 28:6
David gave Solomon pattern of *c.* 12
people shall be in the *c.* *2 Chr* 23:5
that he dwell in thy *c.* *Ps* 65:4
my soul fainteth for the *c.* 84:2
shall flourish in the *c.* of. 92:13
offering and come into *c.* 96:8
enter into his *c.* with praise. 100:4
pay my vows in the *c.* 116:19
ye that stand in the *c.* of. 135:2
this to tread my *c.*? *Isa* 1:12
they shall drink in the *c.* 62:9
fill the *c.* with slain. *Ezek* 9:7
my house, and keep my *c.* *Zech* 3:7
live delicately in king's *c.* *Luke* 7:25

cousin

thy *c.* Elisabeth hath. *Luke* 1:36*

cousins

her neighbours and *c.* *Luke* 1:58*

covenant

The most common uses of the word in the Bible are for the covenant between God and his people. [1] *The covenant between God and man, of continued life and favour on condition of obedience,* Gen 2:16. [2] *That between God and Noah, that there should not be another flood,* Gen 9:12-16. [3] *With Abraham and his descendants as individuals and as a nation, frequently mentioned throughout the history. This was the Old Covenant, the Old Dispensation. The New Covenant is the spiritual covenant of God in Christ with his followers, frequently mentioned in the New Testament.*

token of *c.* *Gen* 9:12; 13:17; 17:11
behold, my *c.* is with thee. 17:4
c. be in your flesh for everlasting *c.* 13
he hath broken my *c.* 14
sabbath for a perpetual *c.* *Ex* 31:16
he wrote the words of the *c.* 34:28
but ye break my *c.* *Lev* 26:15
I give to him my *c.* *Num* 25:12
c. of everlasting priesthood 13
declared unto you his *c.* *Deut* 4:13
lest ye forget the *c.* of the. 23
Lord will not forget the *c.* 31
gone to receive tables of *c.* 9:9
Lord gave me tables of the *c.* 11
the two tables of the *c.* were. 15
these are the words of the *c.* 29:1
thou shouldest enter into *c.* 12
according to curses of the *c.* 21
because ye have forsaken the *c.* 25
provoke me, and break *c.* 31:20
I will never break my *c.* *Judg* 2:1
thy servant into *c.* of. *1 Sam* 20:8
Israel have forsaken *c.* *1 Ki* 19:10
14
I will send thee away with *c.* 20:34
because of his *c.* with. *2 Ki* 13:23
to perform words of *c.* and people stood to *c.* 23:3; *2 Chr* 34:31
be always of *c.* *1 Chr* 16:15
they entered into *c.* *2 Chr* 15:12
they have defiled the *c.* *Neh* 13:29
he will shew them his *c.* *Ps* 25:14
neither dealt falsely in *c.* 44:17
that thou shouldest take my *c.* 50:16
he hath broken *c.* 55:20
have respect to the *c.* 74:20
nor were they stedfast in *c.* 78:37
mercy keep and *c.* shall. 89:28
my *c.* will I not break. 34
thou hast made void the *c.* 39
will ever be mindful of his *c.* 111:5
commanded his *c.* for ever. 9
and forgetteth the *c.* of. *Pr* 2:17
your *c.* with death shall. *Isa* 28:18
he hath broken the *c.* he. 33:8
and give thee for a *c.* 42:6; 49:8
nor the *c.* of my peace be. 54:10
eunuchs that take hold of *c.* 56:4, 6
as for me, this is my *c.* 59:21
hear words of this *c.* *Jer* 11:2, 6
man that obeyeth not words of *c.* 3
break not thy *c.* with us. 14:21
they have forsaken the *c.* of. 22:9
which my *c.* they brake. 31:32
break my *c.* of day and *c.* 33:20
then may *c.* be broken with. 21
if my *c.* be not with day. 25
had entered into *c.* heard. 34:10
not performed words of this *c.* 18
join to Lord in perpetual *c.* 50:5
and entered into a *c.* with. *Ezek* 16:8
in breaking the *c.* 59; 17:18
for daughters, not by thy *c.* 16:61
or shall he break the *c.*? 17:15
oath he despised, whose *c.* 16
my *c.* he hath broken, it. 19
bring you into bond of *c.* 20:37
they have broken my *c.* 44:7
confirm *c.* with many. *Dan* 9:27
yea also the prince of the *c.* 11:22
shall be against the holy *c.* 28
indignation against holy *c.* *Dan* 11:30
such as do wickedly against *c.* 32
falsely in making *c.* *Hos* 10:4
I might break my *c.* *Zech* 11:10
my *c.* might be with. *Mal* 2:4, 5
ye have corrupted *c.* of Levi. 8
by profaning the *c.* of our. 10
and the wife of thy *c.* 14
even messenger of the *c.* 3:1
ye are children of *c.* *Acts* 3:25
and he gave him the *c.* of. 7:8
c. breakers. *Rom* 1:31
this is my *c.* when I take. 11:27
though it be a man's *c.* *Gal* 3:15
that the *c.* was confirmed. 17
Mediator of a better *c.* *Heb* 8:6
if first *c.* had been faultless. 7
they continued in my *c.* 9
then verily the first *c.* 9:1
and tables of the *c.* 4

see **ark, blood, break**

book of the **covenant**

took the *book of the c.* *Ex* 24:7
Josiah read all the words of the *book of the c.* *2 Ki* 23:2; *2 Chr* 34:30
it is written in *book of c.* *2 Ki* 23:21

establish **covenant**

will I *establish* my *c.* *Gen* 6:18; 9:9
I will *establish* my *c.* between. 17:7
establish c. with Isaac and. 19, 21
I have *established* my *c.* *Ex* 6:4
establish my *c.* with you. *Lev* 26:9
he may *establish* his *c.* *Deut* 8:18
establish to thee an everlasting *c.* *Ezek* 16:60
I will *establish* my *c.* with thee. 62

everlasting **covenant**

remember *everlast. c.* *Gen* 9:16
in your flesh for an *everlast. c.* 17:13
c. with Isaac for an *everlast. c.* 19
Israel by an *everlast. c.* *Lev* 24:8
with me an *everlast. c.* *2 Sam* 23:5
confirmed the same to Israel for *everlast. c.* *1 Chr* 16:17; *Ps* 105:10
broken the *everlast. c.* *Isa* 24:5
make *everlast. c.* with you. 55:3
61:8; *Jer* 32:40
an *everlast. c.* with them. *Ezek* 37:26
blood of the *everlast. c.* *Heb* 13:20

keep, keeping, keepeth, or *kept* **covenant**

thou shalt *keep* my *c.* *Gen* 17:9
my *c.* which ye shall *keep.* 10
my voice and *keep* my *c.* *Ex* 19:5
who *keepeth c.* *Deut* 7:9, 12
1 Ki 8:23; *2 Chr* 6:14; *Neh* 1:5
9:32
keep the words of this *c.* *Deut* 29:9
observed thy word, *kept c.* 33:9
not *kept* my *c.* *1 Ki* 11:11; *Ps* 78:10
to such as *keep c.* *Ps* 25:10; 103:18
children will *keep* my *c.* and. 132:12
by *keeping* of his *c.* *Ezek* 17:14
keeping c. and mercy to. *Dan* 9:4

made **covenant**

day the Lord *made a c.* *Gen* 15:18
and Abimelech *made* a *c.* 21:27, 32
I have *made* a *c.* with. *Ex* 34:27
Lord our God *made* a *c.* *Deut* 5:2
made not this *c.* with. 3; *Heb* 8:
besides the *c.* he *made.* *Deut* 29:
break my *c.* I have *made.* 31:1
Joshua *made* a *c.* with. *Josh* 24:2
David *made c.* *1 Sam* 18:3; 23:1
Jonathan *made* a *c.* with. 20:1
Lord *made* a *c.* with. *1 Ki* 8:
2 Chr 6:1
c. of Lord which he *made.* *1 Ki* 8:2
made a *c.* with Ben-hadad. 20:3
Jehoiada *made* a *c.* *2 Ki* 11:
made c. between the Lord and. 1
Israel rejected his *c.* he *made.* 17:1
whom the Lord had *made* a *c.* 3
the *c.* *made* with you ye shall. 3
Josiah *made* a *c.* 23:3; *2 Chr* 34:3
David *made* a *c.* with. *1 Chr* 11:
mindful even of the *c.* *made* with. 16:16; *Neh* 9:8; *Ps* 105:
of *c.* he had *made* with David. *2 Chr* 21:
all congregation *made* a *c.* 23
I *made* a *c.* with mine. *Job* 31

that have *made* a c. with. *Ps* 50:5
have *made* a c. with my. 89:3
ye have *made* a c. with. *Isa* 28:15
enlarged thy bed, and *made* c. 57:8
broke the c. I *made*. *Jer* 11:10
not according to c. I *made*. 31:32
Zedekiah had *made* a c. 34:8, 15
saith the Lord, I *made* a c. 13
ye had *made* a c. before me. 15
words of the c. ye had *made*. 18
and *made* a c. with him. *Ezek* 17:13

make **covenant**

I will *make* my c. *Gen* 17:2
let us *make* a c. 26:28; 31:44
Ezra 10:3
shalt *make* no c. *Ex* 23:32; *Deut* 7:2
I *make a* c. before all thy. *Ex* 34:10
lest thou *make* a c. with. 12, 15
do I *make* this c. *Deut* 29:14
make a c. with us. *1 Sam* 11:1
on this condition will I *make* c. 2
my heart to *make* a c. *2 Chr* 29:10
and we *make* a sure c. *Neh* 9:38
will he *make* a c.? *Job* 41:4
this shall be the c. that I will *make*.
Jer 31:33; *Heb* 8:10; 10:16
make with them a c. of peace.
Ezek 34:25; 37:26
I will *make* a c. for them. *Hos* 2:18
and they do *make* a c. with. 12:1

new **covenant**

new c. with Israel. *Jer* 31:31
Heb 8:8
a *new* c. he hath made. *Heb* 8:13
Jesus the Mediator of *new* c. 12:24

remember **covenant**

I will *remember* my c. *Gen* 9:15
Lev 26:42; *Ezek* 16:60
I have *rem*. my c. *Ex* 6:5, 6
for their sakes *rem*. c. *Lev* 26:45
hath *rem*. c. for ever. *Ps* 105:8
106:45
rem. not brotherly c. *Amos* 1:9
and to *rem*. his holy c. *Luke* 1:72

covenant *of salt*

the *salt of* c. of thy God. *Lev* 2:13
it is a c. *of salt* for. *Num* 18:19
to David and sons by c. *of salt*.
2 Chr 13:5

transgressed **covenant**

.ath wrought wickedness in *trans*. his c. *Deut* 17:2
.ave also *trans*. my c. *Josh* 7:11
.e *trans*. c. of Lord. 15; *Judg* 2:20
2 Ki 18:12
'e *trans*. c. of the Lord. *Josh* 23:16
nen that *trans*. my c. *Jer* 34:18
nen have *trans*. the c. *Hos* 6:7
ecause they have *trans*. my c. 8:1

covenanted

ccording as I have c. *2 Chr* 7:18
ne word that I c. with. *Hag* 2:5
ney c. with him for. *Mat* 26:15*
'ere glad, and c. to. *Luke* 22:5

covenants

ertaineth the glory and c. *Rom* 9:4
ese are the two c. *Gal* 4:24
rangers from the c. of. *Eph* 2:12

cover

1] *To hide*, Pr 12:16. [2] *To* *othe*, 1 Sam 28:14. [3] *To pro-* *ct and defend*, Ps 91:4. [4] *To* *rdon, or forgive*, Ps. 32:1; Rom 7. [5] *To vail*, 1 Cor 11:6.

e locusts shall c. the. *Ex* 10:5
all dig a pit and not c. it. 21:33
ien breeches to c. 28:42
will c. thee with my hand. 33:22
ou shalt c. the ark with. 40:3*
oud of incense may c. *Lev* 16:13
ur out the blood, and c. 17:13
hold they c. the face. *Num* 22:5
d c. that which. *Deut* 23:13
Lord shall c. him all day. 33:12
ul went in to c. his. *1 Sam* 24:3
not their iniquity. *Neh* 4:5
not thou my blood. *Job* 16:18
wn in dust, worms shall c. 21:26
undance of waters c. thee. 22:11
38:34
shady trees c. him with. 40:22
he shall c. thee with his. *Ps* 91:4
they turn not again to c. 104:9
c. themselves with their. 109:29
surely darkness shall c. me. 139:11*
mischief of their lips c. them. 140:9
as the waters c. the sea. *Isa* 11:9
Hab 2:14
the worms c. thee. *Isa* 14:11
the Lord will surely c. thee. 22:17*
the earth shall no more c. 26:21
that c. with a covering. 30:1†
that thou c. him. 58:7
neither c. themselves. 59:6
darkness shall c. the earth. 60:2
multitude of camels shall c. 6
and will c. the earth. *Jer* 46:8
horror shall c. them. *Ezek* 7:18
thou shalt c. thy face. 12:6
he shall c. his face that. 12
poured it not on ground to c. 24:7
c. not thy lips, and eat not. 17
ye shall not c. your lips. 22
their dust shall c. thee. 26:10
great waters shall c. thee. 19
a cloud shall c. her and. 30:18
I will c. the heaven, I will c. 32:7
I will c. you with skin. 37:6
like a cloud to c. land. 38:9, 16
recover my flax given to c. *Hos* 2:9
say to the mountains, c. us. 10:8
Luke 23:30
shame shall c. thee. *Ob* 10
yea, they shall all c. their. *Mi* 3:7
and shame shall c. her that. 7:10
violence of Lebanon c. *Hab* 2:17
to spit on him and c. *Mark* 14:65
a man ought not to c. *1 Cor* 11:7*
for charity shall c. the. *1 Pet* 4:8

covered

mountains were c. *Gen* 7:19, 20
they c. the nakedness of. 9:23
took a vail and c. herself. 24:65
Tamar c. her with a vail. 38:14
frogs came up and c. land. *Ex* 8:6
the waters c. the chariots. 14:28
the depths c. them, they. 15:5
the sea c. them. 10; *Josh* 24:7
came and c. the camp. *Ex* 16:13
a cloud c. the mount. 24:15, 16
c. with their wings over. 37:9
the vail c. the ark of the. 40:21*
a cloud c. the tent of the. 34
if the leprosy have c. *Lev* 13:13
when holy things are c. *Num* 4:20*
cloud c. the tabernacle. 9:15, 16
16:42
waxen fat, thou art c. *Deut* 32:15*
Jael c. him with a. *Judg* 4:18, 19
Michal c. the pillow. *1 Sam* 19:13
an old man cometh up c. 28:14
c. king David with clothes. *1 Ki* 1:1
cherubims c. ark. 8:7; *1 Chr* 28:18
2 Chr 5:8
rent his clothes and c. *2 Ki* 19:1
Isa 37:1
nor c. he the darkness. *Job* 23:17
if I c. my transgressions. 31:33
shame of face hath c. me. *Ps* 44:15
though thou hast c. us with. 19
the valleys also are c. over. 65:13
as the wings of a dove c. 68:13
let them be c. with reproach. 71:13
glory to cease, thou hast c. 89:45
the earth c. the company of. 106:17
thou hast c. me in my. 139:13
like a potsherd c. with. *Pr* 26:23*
whose hatred is c. by deceit. 26
his name shall be c. with. *Eccl* 6:4
he c. his face, he c. his feet. *Isa* 6:2
and the seers hath he c. 29:10
I have c. thee in the shadow. 51:16
he c. me with the robe of. 61:10
she is c. with multitude. *Jer* 51:42
c. the daughter of Zion. *Lam* 2:1
he hath me with ashes. 3:16
thou hast c. with anger. 43
thou hast c. thyself with a cloud. 44
two wings c. bodies. *Ezek* 1:11, 23
I spread my skirt, and c. thy. 16:8
girded thee with linen, I c. thee. 10
and hath c. the naked. 18:7, 16
that her blood should not be c. 24:8
blue and purple c. thee. 27:7*
I c. the deep for him. *Ezek* 31:15
flesh came up, and skin c. 37:8
the king of Nineveh c. *Jonah* 3:6
let man and beast be c. 8
God came, his glory c. *Hab* 3:3
the ship was c. with. *Mat* 8:24
there is nothing c. that shall not be revealed. 10:26; *Luke* 12:2
if the woman be not c. *1 Cor* 11:6

covered *face*

Tamar had c. her *face*. *Gen* 38:15
the locusts c. the *face* of. *Ex* 10:15
David c. his *face* and. *2 Sam* 19:4
they c. Haman's *face*. *Esth* 7:8
shame hath c. my *face*. *Ps* 69:7
nettles had c. the *face*. *Pr* 24:31
with twain he c. his *face*. *Isa* 6:2
shame hath c. our *face*. *Jer* 51:51

head **covered**

man had his *head* c. *2 Sam* 15:30
mourning, his *head* c. *Esth* 6:12
hast c. my *head* in the. *Ps* 140:7
confounded, and c. their *heads*.
Jer 14:3, 4
praying, having his *head* c. *1 Cor* 11:4

covered *sin*, or *sins*

whose *sin* is c. *Ps* 32:1; *Rom* 4:7
thou hast c. all their *sins*. *Ps* 85:2

coveredst

thou c. it with the deep. *Ps* 104:6
garments and c. them. *Ezek* 16:18

coverest

wherewith thou c. thyself.
Deut 22:12
who c. thyself with light. *Ps* 104:2

covereth

take all the fat that c. *Ex* 29:13, 22
Lev 3:3, 9, 14; 4:8; 7:3; 9:19
a people which c. the. *Num* 22:11
surely he c. his feet in. *Judg* 3:24
c. the faces of the judges. *Job* 9:24
because he c. his face. 15:27
he c. the bottom of the sea. 36:30
with clouds he c. light. 32
violence c. them as a. *Ps* 73:6
as the garment which c. him. 109:19
c. the heavens with clouds. 147:8
violence c. the mouth. *Pr* 10:6, 11
love c. all sins. 12
a prudent man c. shame. 12:16
he that c. a transgression. 17:9
he that c. his sins shall not. 28:13
our confusion c. us. *Jer* 3:25
anointed cherub that c. *Ezek* 28:14
one c. violence with his. *Mal* 2:16
he lighted candle c. it. *Luke* 8:16

covering

Noah removed the c. *Gen* 8:13
behold, he is to thee a c. 20:16
that is his c. raiment. *Ex* 22:27
leper shall put a c. on. *Lev* 13:45
vessel which hath no c. *Num* 19:15
woman spread a c. *2 Sam* 17:19
thick clouds are a c. *Job* 22:14
that the naked have no c. 24:7
destruction hath no c. 26:6
seen any poor without c. 31:19
a cloud for c. and fire. *Ps* 105:39
the c. of it of purple. *S of S* 3:10
he discovered c. of Judah. *Isa* 22:8
destroy the face of the c. 25:7
the c. narrower than he can. 28:20
that cover with a c. but not. 30:1
ye shall defile the c. of thy. 22
and make sackcloth their c. 50:3
stones was thy c. *Ezek* 28:13
hair is given her for a c. *1 Cor* 11:15

see **badgers'** *skins*

covering

c. the mercy seat with. *Ex* 25:20
take down the c. vail. *Num* 4:5*
thee, O c. cherub. *Ezek* 28:16
c. the altar with tears. *Mal* 2:13

coverings

decked my bed with c. *Pr* 7:16*
she maketh herself c. of. 31:22*

covers

and make c. thereof. *Ex* 25:29*
he made his c. 37:16
put thereon c. to cover. *Num* 4:7*

covert

[1] *A covered, protected place,* 1 Sam 25:20. [2] *A thicket for wild beasts,* Job 38:40.

Abigail came down by *c.* *1 Sam* 25:20
the *c.* for the sabbath. *2 Ki* 16:18*
lions abide in the *c.* *Job* 38:40
behemoth lieth in the *c.* 40:21
will trust in the *c.* of. *Ps* 61:4
a tabernacle for a *c.* *Isa* 4:6
be thou a *c.* to them from. 16:4
a man shall be a *c.* from. 32:2
he hath forsaken his *c.* *Jer* 25:38

covet

(*To wish for with eagerness; usually used in the sense of a fault, though not always*)

thou shalt not *c.* thy. *Ex* 20:17
Deut 5:21; *Rom* 7:7; 13:9
they *c.* fields and take. *Mi* 2:2
but *c.* earnestly the. *1 Cor* 12:31*
c. to prophesy, and forbid. 14:39*

coveted

then I *c.* them, took. *Josh* 7:21
c. no man's silver or. *Acts* 20:33
which while some *c.* *1 Tim* 6:10*

coveteth

he *c.* greedily all the. *Pr* 21:26
woe to him that *c.* an. *Hab* 2:9*

covetous

the wicked blesseth *c.* *Ps* 10:3
Pharisees who were *c.* *Luke* 16:14*
not altogether with *c.* *1 Cor* 5:10
if any brother be *c.* with such. 11
nor *c.* shall inherit. 6:10; *Eph* 5:5
a bishop must not be *c.* *1 Tim* 3:3*
men shall be *c.* boasters. *2 Tim* 3:2*
with *c.* practices. *2 Pet* 2:14*

covetousness

able men, men hating *c.* *Ex* 18:21*
incline not my heart to *c.* *Ps* 119:36
he that hateth *c.* shall. *Pr* 28:16
for the iniquity of his *c.* *Isa* 57:17
is given to *c.* *Jer* 6:13; 8:10
but for thy *c.* 22:17
and the measure of thy *c.* 51:13
their heart goeth after their *c.*
Ezek 33:31*
him that coveteth an evil *c.* *Hab* 2:9*
of heart proceedeth *c.* *Mark* 7:22
heed, and beware of *c.* *Luke* 12:15
being filled with all *c.* *Rom* 1:29
of bounty, and not of *c.* *2 Cor* 9:5*
but *c.* let it not be named. *Eph* 5:3
mortify your members and *c.* *Col* 3:5
nor used we a cloke of *c.* *1 Thes* 2:5
let your conversation be without *c.*
Heb 13:5*
through *c.* shall they make. *2 Pet* 2:3

cow

whether *c.* or ewe. *Lev* 22:28
firstling of a *c.* thou. *Num* 18:17*
their *c.* calveth, and. *Job* 21:10
nourisheth a young *c.* *Isa* 7:21
and the *c.* and the bear shall. 11:7
I have given thee *c.* *Ezek* 4:15
every *c.* at that which. *Amos* 4:3*

Cozbi

name of woman was *C.* *Num* 25:15
beguiled you in matter of *C.* 18

crackling

as *c.* of thorns under a pot. *Eccl* 7:6

cracknels

thee ten loaves and *c.* *1 Ki* 14:3†

craft

policy shall cause *c.* to. *Dan* 8:25
take him by *c.* and put. *Mark* 14:1
he was of the same *c.* *Acts* 18:3*
ye know that by this *c.* 19:25*
so that not only this our *c.* 27*
of whatsoever *c.* he be. *Rev* 18:22

craftiness

the wise in their *c.* *Job* 5:13
1 Cor 3:19
he perceived their *c.* *Luke* 20:23
not walking in *c.* nor. *2 Cor* 4:2
no more carried by *c.* *Eph* 4:14

craftsman

the work of the *c.* *Deut* 27:15
no *c.* shall be found any. *Rev* 18:22

craftsmen

carried away all *c.* *2 Ki* 24:14, 16
for they were *c.* *1 Chr* 4:14
the valley of *c.* *Neh* 11:35
all of it the work of *c.* *Hos* 13:2
no small gain to *c.* *Acts* 19:24
if the *c.* have a matter. 38

crafty

disappointed devices of *c.* *Job* 5:12
choosest the tongue of the *c.* 15:5
have taken *c.* counsel. *Ps* 83:3
being *c.* I caught. *2 Cor* 12:16

crag

the eagle abideth on *c.* *Job* 39:28†

crane

like a *c.* or swallow. *Isa* 38:14
c. and swallow observe time. *Jer* 8:7

crashing

there shall be a great *c.* *Zeph* 1:10

craved

Joseph went, and *c.* *Mark* 15:43*

craveth

his mouth *c.* it. *Pr* 16:26

create

To bring into being, usually understood as meaning to make out of nothing, Gen 1:1.

c. in me a clean heart. *Ps* 51:10
c. on every dwelling-place. *Isa* 4:5
and *c.* darkness, I *c.* evil. 45:7
I *c.* the fruit of the lips. 57:19
behold, I *c.* new heavens. 65:17
rejoice for ever in that which I *c.* 18

created

in the beginning God *c.* *Gen* 1:1
God *c.* great whales and. 21
c. man in his own image, male and female *c.* he them. 27; 5:2
he had rested from all he *c.* 2:3
I will destroy man whom I *c.* 6:7
since day God *c.* man. *Deut* 4:32
and south thou hast *c.* *Ps* 89:12
people which shall be *c.* 102:18
forth thy Spirit, they are *c.* 104:30
commanded, and they were *c.* 148:5
behold who hath *c.* *Isa* 40:26
holy One of Israel hath *c.* it. 41:20
he that *c.* the heavens. 42:5
Lord that *c.* thee, O Jacob. 43:1
have *c.* him for my glory. 7
I the Lord have *c.* it. 45:8
I have made the earth, and *c.* 12
he hath established it, *c.* it. 18
they are *c.* now, and not. 48:7
I have *c.* the smith, I have *c.* 54:16
for the Lord hath *c.* a. *Jer* 31:22
judge thee where thou wast *c.*
Ezek 21:30
in the day that thou wast *c.* 28:13
perfect from day that thou wast *c.* 15
hath not one God *c.* us? *Mal* 2:10
creation which God *c.* *Mark* 13:19
neither was the man *c.* *1 Cor* 11:9
we are his workmanship, *c.* *Eph* 2:10
hid in God, who *c.* all things. 3:9
the new man, after God is *c.* 4:24
by him were all things *c.*, all things were *c.* by him. *Col* 1:16
after image of him that *c.* him. 3:10
from meats which God *c.* *1 Tim* 4:3
thou hast *c.* all things, and for thy pleasure they were *c.* *Rev* 4:11
who *c.* heaven and the things. 10:6

createth

he that *c.* the wind. *Amos* 4:13

creation

from the *c.* God made. *Mark* 10:6
was not from beginning of *c.* 13:19
things of him from *c.* *Rom* 1:20
we know that the whole *c.* 8:22
continue as from the *c.* *2 Pet* 3:4
beginning of the *c.* of God. *Rev* 3:14

creator

remember thy *c.* in the. *Eccl* 12:1
the Lord, the *c.* of the. *Isa* 40:28
Lord, the *c.* of Israel. 43:15
creature more than the *c.* *Rom* 1:25
in well-doing as to a faithful *c.*
1 Pet 4:19

creature

bring forth moving *c.* *Gen* 1:20
is the law of every *c.* *Lev* 11:46
the gospel to every *c.* *Mark* 16:15*
Col 1:23
expectation of *c.* waiteth. *Rom* 8:19
for *c.* was made subject to. 20*
the *c.* shall be delivered. 21*
nor any *c.* shall be able to. 39
in Christ, he is a new *c.* *2 Cor* 5:17
but a new *c.* *Gal* 6:15
first-born of every *c.* *Col* 1:15*
for every *c.* of God. *1 Tim* 4:4
nor is there any *c.* that. *Heb* 4:13
every *c.* in heaven heard. *Rev* 5:13*

living **creature**

created every *living c.* *Gen* 1:21
earth bring forth the *living c.* 24
Adam called every *living c.* 2:19
covenant with every *living c.* 9:10
between me and *living c.* 12, 15
law of every *living c.* *Lev* 11:46
spirit of *living c.* *Ezek* 1:20, 21
10:17
the *living c.* that I saw. 10:15, 20

creatures

houses full of doleful *c.* *Isa* 13:21
a kind of first-fruits of *c.* *Jas* 1:18
a third part of the *c.* in. *Rev* 8:9

living **creatures**

likeness of four *living c.* *Ezek* 1:5
up and down among the *living c.* 13
living c. ran, and returned. 14
living c., one wheel by *living c.* 15
when the *living c.* went, the. 19
noise of wings of *living c.* 3:13

creditor

every *c.* that lendeth. *Deut* 15:2
c. is come to take my. *2 Ki* 4:1
there was a certain *c.* *Luke* 7:41*

creditors

which of my *c.* is it? *Isa* 50:1

creek

discovered a certain *c.* *Acts* 27:39*

creep

unclean among all that *c.* *Lev* 11:31
beasts of the forest do *c.* *Ps* 104:20
this sort are they who *c.* *2 Tim* 3:6

creepeth

every thing that *c.* *Gen* 1:25, 26
to every thing that *c.* upon. 30
every thing that *c.* went. 7:8, 14
died of every thing that *c.* 21
bring forth every thing that *c.* 8:17
whatsoever *c.* on the earth. 19*
c. on the earth shall be an abomination. *Lev* 11:41*, 43, 44; 20:25*
likeness of any thing that *c.* on.
Deut 4:1[illegible]

creeping

dominion over every *c.* *Gen* 1:2[illegible]
every *c.* thing after his kind. 7:1[illegible]
touch carcase of *c.* things. *Lev* 5:[illegible]
these may ye eat, of *c.* thing. 11:2[illegible]
whosoever toucheth *c.* thing. 22:[illegible]
every *c.* thing that. *Deut* 14:1[illegible]
spake of beasts, *c.* things. *1 Ki* 4:3[illegible]
in the sea are *c.* things. *Ps* 104:2[illegible]
all cattle, *c.* things praise. 148:1[illegible]
form of *c.* things. *Ezek* 8:1[illegible]
all *c.* things shall shake. 38:2[illegible]
a covenant with the *c.* *Hos* 2:1[illegible]
maketh men as *c.* things. *Hab* 1:1[illegible]
Peter saw *c.* things. *Acts* 10:1[illegible]
11:[illegible]
an image like *c.* things. *Rom* 1:2[illegible]

crept

for there are certain men *c.* *Jude* [illegible]

Crescens

C. is departed to Galatia. *2 Tim* 4:1[illegible]

Crete

we sailed under *C.* *Acts* 27[illegible]
Phenice, an haven of *C.*
close by *C.*
and not have loosed from *C.*
cause left I thee in *C.* *Tit* 1[illegible]

Cretes

C., we do hear them speak. *Acts* 2:[illegible]

Cretians

the *C.* are always liars. *Tit* 1:[illegible]

crew
immediately the cock c. Mat 26:74
Mark 14:68; Luke 22:60
second time cock c. Mark 14:72
John 18:27

crib
will unicorn abide by c.? Job 39:9
where no oxen are, the c. is. Pr 14:4
ass knoweth his master's c. Isa 1:3

cried
Esau c. with a great. Gen 27:34
lifted up my voice and c. 39:15
and they c. before him. 41:43
people c. to Pharaoh for. 55
he c. cause every man to go. 45:1
the officers came and c. Ex 5:15
the people c. to Moses. Num 11:2
damsel, because she c. Deut 22:24
the damsel c. and there was. 27
Sisera's mother c. Judg 5:28
and all the host ran and c. 7:21
and ye c. to me, and I. 10:12
he stood and c. unto the. 1 Sam 17:8
Jonathan c. after the lad. 20:37, 38
then c. a wise woman. 2 Sam 20:16
I c. to my God, and he did. 22:7
he c. against the altar. 1 Ki 13:2, 4
and they c. aloud. 18:28
Elisha saw it, and c. 2 Ki 2:12
he c. alas, master, for it was. 6:5
the woman c. to the king. 8:5
and Athaliah c., Treason. 11:14
they c. to God in battle. 1 Chr 5:20
Isaiah prayed and c. 2 Chr 32:20
when they c. to thee. Neh 9:27, 28
delivered the poor that c. Job 29:12
they c. after them. 30:5
in my distress I c. unto. Ps 18:6
they c. but there was none. 41
they c. to thee and. 22:5
but when he c. unto him. 24
O Lord my God, I c. to thee. 30:2
I c. to thee, O Lord, and. 8
my supplications when I c. 31:22
this poor man c. and the. 34:6
I c. unto him with. 66:17; 77:1
O Lord, I have c. day and. 88:1
unto thee have I c. O Lord. 13
I c. with my whole heart. 119:145
out of the depths have I c. 130:1
in the day when I c. thou. 138:3
moved at voice of him that c. Isa 6:4
therefore I c. concerning this. 30:7
upon destruction is c. Jer 4:20
fell on my face and c. Ezek 9:8
it was c. to them in my. 10:13
c. with a lamentable voice. Dan 6:20
they have not c. to me. Hos 7:14
the mariners c. every. Jonah 1:5
c. by reason of mine affliction; out of the belly of hell c. I. 2:2
as he c. and they would not hear, so they c. and I would. Zech 7:13
Peter c. saying, Lord. Mat 14:30
they c. the more, saying. 20:31
Mark 10:48; Luke 18:39
the spirit c. and rent. Mark 9:26
Jesus c. if any man thirst. John 7:37
some c. one thing. Acts 19:32; 21:34
might know wherefore they c. 22:24
when he c. seven thunders. Rev 10:3
and she being with child, c. 12:2
c. with a loud cry to him. 14:18
he c. mightily with a strong. 18:2
c. when they saw the smoke. 18
they c. weeping and wailing. 19

cried *to the Lord*
Moses c. *to Lord.* Ex 8:12; 15:25
17:4; Num 12:13
srael c. *to the Lord.* Ex 14:10
Judg 3:9, 15; 4:3; 6:7; 10:10
when we c. *to the Lord.* Num 20:16
Deut 26:7
when they c. *to the Lord.* Josh 24:7
amuel c. *to Lord.* 1 Sam 7:9; 15:11
lijah c. *to the Lord.* 1 Ki 17:20, 21
saiah c. *to the Lord.* 2 Ki 20:11
ney c. *to the Lord.* 2 Chr 13:14
Ps 107:6, 13; Jonah 1:14
sa c. *to the Lord.* 2 Chr 14:11
c. *to Lord.* Ps 3:4; 120:1; 142:1
eir heart c. *to the Lord.* Lam 2:18

cried *with a loud voice*
woman c. *with a loud voice.*
1 Sam 28:12
David c. *with loud voice.* 2 Sam 19:4
Rabshakeh c. *with a loud voice.*
2 Ki 18:28; Isa 36:13
Levites c. *with loud voice.* Neh 9:4
Ezekiel c. *with a loud voice.*
Ezek 11:13
Jesus c. *with loud voice.* Mat 27:46
50; Mark 15:34, 37; Luke 23:46
John 11:43
evil spirit c. *with a loud voice.*
Mark 1:26
Stephen's enemies c. *with a loud voice.* Acts 7:57
Stephen c. *with a loud voice.* 60
Paul c. *with a loud voice.* 16:28
they c. *with loud voice.* Rev 6:10
angel c. *with a loud voice.* 7:2; 10:3
19:17
before Lamb c. *with a loud voice.*
7:10

cried *out*
all the city c. *out.* 1 Sam 4:13
Ekronites c. *out.* 5:10
Jehoshaphat c. *out.* 1 Ki 22:32
2 Chr 18:31
c. *out,* there is death. 2 Ki 4:40
I c. *out,* I cried violence. Jer 20:8
the spirits c. *out.* Mat 8:29
Luke 4:33
disciples c. *out* for fear. Mat 14:26
Mark 6:49
blind men c. *out,* have. Mat 20:30
they c. out the more. 27:23
Mark 15:13; Luke 23:18
John 19:6
with unclean spirit c. *out.* Mark 1:23
father of the child c. *out.* 9:24
Luke 9:38
they c. *out,* saying. Acts 19:28, 34
as they c. *out,* and threw. 22:23
Paul c. *out* in the council. 23:6

cries
the c. of them that reaped. Jas 5:4

criest, -eth
of thy brother's blood c. Gen 4:10
wherefore c. thou to me? Ex 14:15
when he c. unto me. 22:27
who art thou that c. to? 1 Sam 26:14
soul of wounded c. out. Job 24:12
deliver needy when he c. Ps 72:12
my heart and flesh c. out for. 84:2
wisdom c. Pr 1:20; 8:3; 9:3
yea, if thou c. after. 2:3
like as a woman that c. Isa 26:17
the voice of him that c. in. 40:3
when thou c. let companies. 57:13
my heritage c. out. Jer 12:8
c. thou for thine affliction? 30:15
Lord's voice c. to city. Mi 6:9
send her away, she c. Mat 15:23
he suddenly c. out. Luke 9:39
Esaias also c. concerning. Rom 9:27
hire of the labourers c. Jas 5:4

crime, -s
this is an heinous c. Job 31:11
land is full of bloody c. Ezek 7:23
to answer concerning c. Acts 25:16*
and not to signify the c. 27

crimson
(*A deep red colour tinged with blue, derived from kermes, the dried bodies of certain insects allied to the cochineal insects. Three Hebrew words are used, the most frequent being* cochineal)
a man cunning to work in c.
2 Chr 2:7, 14
the vail of blue, c. and. 3:14
your sins be red like c. Isa 1:18
clothest thyself with c. Jer 4:30*

cripple
being a c. from his. Acts 14:8

crisping-pins
take away mantles and c. Isa 3:22*

Crispus
C. chief ruler of the. Acts 18:8
that I baptized none of you, but C.
1 Cor 1:14

crookbackt
a man that is c. shall. Lev 21:20

crooked
and c. generation. Deut 32:5
hand formed c. serpent. Job 26:13*
turn aside to their c. ways. Ps 125:5
whose ways are c. and. Pr 2:15
what is c. cannot. Eccl 1:15; 7:13
punish Leviathan, that c. Isa 27:1
c. be made straight. 40:4; 42:16
Luke 3:5
make c. places straight. Isa 45:2*
they have made them c. paths. 59:8
he hath made my paths c. Lam 3:9
in midst of a c. nation. Phil 2:15

crop
shall pluck away his c. Lev 1:16
I will c. off from top. Ezek 17:22

cropped
he c. off the top of his. Ezek 17:4

cross
[1] *An instrument of punishment used by the Romans generally for the punishment of slaves. Specifically, the cross on which our Lord died, as recorded in the Gospels.* [2] *Trials or misfortunes, especially when considered as tests of Christian patience or virtue,* Mat 16:24.
he that taketh not his c. Mat 10:38
Luke 14:27
take up his c. and follow. Mat 16:24
Mark 8:34; 10:21; Luke 9:23
compelled to bear his c. Mat 27:32
Mark 15:21; Luke 23:26
be Son of God, come down from c.
Mat 27:40, 42; Mark 15:30, 32
he bearing his c. went. John 19:17
a title, and put it on the c. 19
there stood by the c. of Jesus. 25
should not remain on the c. on. 31
lest c. of Christ be. 1 Cor 1:17
preaching of the c. is to them. 18
then is offence of the c. Gal 5:11
persecution for the c. of Christ. 6:12
glory, save in the c. 14
reconcile both by the c. Eph 2:16
obedient unto death of the c.
Phil 2:8
enemies of the c. of Christ. 3:18
peace through blood of c. Col 1:20
nailing it to his c. 2:14
before him, endured the c. Heb 12:2

crossway
thou have stood in c. Ob 14

crouch
shall come and c. to. 1 Sam 2:36*

croucheth
he c. humbleth himself. Ps 10:10

crow, crowing, *see* **cock**

crown
A garland or fillet for the head, used as a mark of distinction. Hence [1] *the special head-dress of a sovereign,* 2 Ki 11:12. [2] *The wreath given to a victor in a Greek game,* 1 Cor 9:25. [3] *Any honour or dignity,* Lam 5:16; Phil 4:1; Rev 4:4.
shalt make a golden c. Ex 25:25
put the holy c. upon the mitre. 29:6
rings to it under the c. 30:4; 37:27
the plate of the c. of gold. 39:30
he put the holy c. Lev 8:9
c. of the anointing oil is. 21:12
put the c. upon Joash. 2 Ki 11:12
2 Chr 23:11
bring Vashti with the c. Esth 1:11
I would bind it as a c. Job 31:36
thou hast profaned his c. Ps 89:39
upon himself shall his c. 132:18
a c. of glory shall she. Pr 4:9
a virtuous woman is a c. 12:4
the c. of the wise is their. 14:24
hoary head is a c. of glory. 16:31
children's children are c. of. 17:6
doth the c. endure to every? 27:24
king Solomon with c. S of S 3:11
woe to the c. of pride. Isa 28:1

Lord of hosts shall be for a *c.* *Isa* 28:5
thou shalt also be a *c.* of glory. 62:3
the *c.* of your glory shall. *Jer* 13:18
take off the *c.* *Ezek* 21:26
as stones of a *c.* lifted. *Zech* 9:16
Jesus wearing a *c.* of. *John* 19:5
to obtain a corruptible *c.* *1 Cor* 9:25
my joy and *c.* *Phil* 4:1
what is our hope, or *c.* *1 Thes* 2:19
is laid up for me a *c.* *2 Tim* 4:8
shall receive the *c.* of life. *Jas* 1:12
receive a *c.* of glory. *1 Pet* 5:4
I will give a *c.* of life. *Rev* 2:10
that no man take thy *c.* 3:11
a *c.* given to him, went forth. 6:2

crown *of gold*

make upon it a *c.* *of gold.* *Ex* 25:11
24; 30:3; 37:2, 11, 12, 26
out with great *c.* *of gold.* *Esth* 8:15
c. *of* pure *gold* on his head. *Ps* 21:3

crown with *head*

on *c.* of Joseph's *head.* *Gen* 49:26
arm with *c.* of *head.* *Deut* 33:20
took *c.* upon his *head.* *2 Sam* 1:10
took king's *c.* from his *head.* 12:30
1 Chr 20:2
even to *c.* of his *head.* *2 Sam* 14:25
Job 2:7
set royal *c.* on her *head.* *Esth* 2:17
the *c.* royal upon his *head.* 6:8
taken *c.* from my *head.* *Job* 19:9
smite with scab *c.* of *head.* *Isa* 3:17
broken the *c.* of thy *head.* *Jer* 2:16
the *c.* of the *head* of the. 48:45
c. is fallen from our *head.* *Lam* 5:16
c. on thine *head.* *Ezek* 16:12
c. of thorns, and put it on his *head.*
Mat 27:29; *Mark* 15:17; *John* 19:2
upon her *head* a *c.* of. *Rev* 12:1
having on his *head* a golden *c.* 14:14

crowned

thou hast *c.* him with glory. *Ps* 8:5
the prudent are *c.* with. *Pr* 14:18
wherewith his mother *c.* *S of S* 3:11
thy *c.* are as the locusts. *Nah* 3:17
he is not *c.* except he. *2 Tim* 2:5
we see Jesus *c.* with. *Heb* 2:9

crownedst

thou *c.* him with glory. *Heb* 2:7

crownest

c. year with thy goodness. *Ps* 65:11

crowneth

who *c.* thee with loving-. *Ps* 103:4

crowning

against Tyre the *c.* city. *Isa* 23:8

crowns

c. on their heads. *Ezek* 23:42
take gold, and make *c.* *Zech* 6:11
the *c.* shall be to Helem. 14
elders had *c.* of gold. *Rev* 4:4
and they cast their *c.* before. 10
on locusts' heads were *c.* 9:7
red dragon having seven *c.* 12:3*
upon his horns ten *c.* 13:1*
on his head were many *c.* 19:12*

crucified

is betrayed to be *c.* *Mat* 26:2
Luke 24:7
said, let him be *c.* *Mat* 27:22, 23
delivered him to be *c.* 26; *John* 19:16
c. him and parted his garments.
Mat 27:35; *John* 19:23
two thieves *c.* with. *Mat* 27:38, 44
Mark 15:32; *Luke* 23:33
John 19:18
I know ye seek Jesus which was *c.*
Mat 28:5; *Mark* 16:6
where Jesus was *c.* *John* 19:20, 41
by wicked hands have *c.* *Acts* 2:23
Jesus, whom ye *c.* Lord. 36; 4:10
our old man is *c.* with. *Rom* 6:6
was Paul *c.* for you ? *1 Cor* 1:13
we preach Christ *c.* unto the. 23
save Jesus Christ and him *c.* 2:2
would not have *c.* Lord of glory. 8
for though he was *c.* *2 Cor* 13:4
I am *c.* with Christ. *Gal* 2:20
Christ hath been set forth, *c.* 3:1
they that are Christ's have *c.* 5:24
by whom the world is *c.* to me. 6:14
also our Lord was *c.* *Rev* 11:8

crucify

To put to death on a cross (*Latin crux, gen. crucis, a cross*)

him to Gentiles to *c.* *Mat* 20:19
of them ye shall kill, and *c.* 23:34
led him away to *c.* him. 27:31
Mark 15:20
cried out again, *c.* *Mark* 15:13, 14
with him they *c.* two thieves. 27
cried, *c.* him, *c.* him. *Luke* 23:21
John 19:6, 15
they *c.* to themselves. *Heb* 6:6

cruel

their wrath, for it was *c.* *Gen* 49:7
hearkened not for *c* bondage. *Ex* 6:9
wine as the *c.* venom. *Deut* 32:33
thou art become *c.* to me. *Job* 30:21
hate me with *c.* hatred. *Ps* 25:19
deliver me out of hand of *c.* 71:4
thou give thy years to *c.* *Pr* 5:9
but he that is *c.* troubleth. 11:17
mercies of wicked are *c.* 12:10
a *c.* messenger shall be sent. 17:11
wrath is *c.* 27:4
jealousy is *c.* *S of S* 8:6
day of Lord cometh, *c.* *Isa* 13:9
Egyptians will I give over to *c.* 19:4
they are *c.* and. *Jer* 6:23; 50:42
with chastisement of a *c.* 30:14
of my people is become *c.* *Lam* 4:3
trial of *c.* mockings. *Heb* 11:36

cruelly

because he *c.* oppressed. *Ezek* 18:18

cruelty

instruments of *c.* are. *Gen* 49:5*
c. done to the sons of. *Judg* 9:24*
such as breathe out *c.* *Ps* 27:12
full of habitations of *c.* 74:20*
force and *c.* have ye. *Ezek* 34:4*

crumbs

dogs eat of the *c.* which fall from.
Mat 15:27; *Mark* 7:28
to be fed with *c.* which. *Luke* 16:21

cruse

take spear and *c.* of. *1 Sam* 26:11
took the spear and *c.* 12, 16
take with thee a *c.* *1 Ki* 14:3
I have but a little oil in a *c.* 17:12
nor *c.* of oil fail, till the Lord. 14, 16
Elijah had a *c.* of water. 19:6
bring me a new *c.* *2 Ki* 2:20

crush

forgetteth her foot may *c.* *Job* 39:15
assembly against me to *c.* *Lam* 1:15
to *c.* under his feet the. 3:34
kine of Bashan which *c.* *Amos* 4:1

crushed

not offer that which is *c.* *Lev* 22:24
the ass *c.* Balaam's. *Num* 22:25
oppressed and *c.* alway. *Deut* 28:33
in dust, which are *c.* *Job* 4:19
children far from safety, are *c.* 5:4
that which is *c.* breaketh. *Isa* 59:5
Nebuchadnezzar hath *c.* *Jer* 51:34

cry

according to the *c.* *Gen* 18:21
their *c.* came up. *Ex* 2:23; 3:9
I have heard their *c.* 3:7
Israel fled at the *c.* of. *Num* 16:34
c. of the city went up. *1 Sam* 5:12
because their *c.* is come up. 9:16
and my *c.* did enter. *2 Sam* 22:7
hearken unto the *c.* and to the prayer. *1 Ki* 8:28; *2 Chr* 6:19
angry when I heard their *c.* *Neh* 5:6
thou heardest their *c.* by the. 9:9
with loud and bitter *c.* *Esth* 4:1
of their fastings and their *c.* 9:31
O earth, let my *c.* have. *Job* 16:18
cause the *c.* of the poor to come, he heareth the *c.* of the. 34:28
hearken to voice of my *c.* *Ps* 5:2
forgetteth not the *c.* of. 9:12
O Lord, attend unto my *c.* 17:1
my *c.* came before him. 18:6
his ears are open to their *c.* 34:15
O Lord, give ear to my *c.* 39:12
unto me, and heard my *c.* 40:1
incline thine ear unto my *c.* 88:2
O Lord, and let my *c.* come. 102:1
when he heard their *c.* 106:44
let my *c.* come near. *Ps* 119:169
attend to my *c.* 142:6
stoppeth his ears at *c.* of. *Pr* 21:13
more than the *c.* of him. *Eccl* 9:17
righteousness, behold a *c.* *Isa* 5:7
they shall raise up a *c.* of. 15:5
the *c.* is gone round about the. 8
gracious at voice of thy *c.* 30:19
Chaldeans, whose *c.* is in. 43:14
nor lift up *c.* nor. *Jer* 7:16; 11:14
voice of the *c.* of my people. 8:19
the *c.* of Jerusalem is gone up. 14:2
let a *c.* be heard from. 18:22
c. of the shepherds shall be. 25:36
thy *c.* hath filled the land. 46:12
her little ones have caused a *c.* 48:4
the enemies have heard a *c.* of. 5
the earth is moved at the *c.* 49:21
the *c.* is heard at taking of. 50:46
a sound of a *c.* cometh. 51:54
not thine ear at my *c.* *Lam* 3:56
suburbs shake at *c.* of. *Ezek* 27:28
there shall be a *c.* from. *Zeph* 1:10
at midnight a *c.* made. *Mat* 25:6

great **cry**

c. of Sodom is *great.* *Gen* 18:20
19:13
with a *great* and bitter *c.* 27:34
a *great* *c.* through Egypt. *Ex* 11:6
was a *great* *c.* in Egypt. 12:30
was *great* *c.* of the people. *Neh* 5:1
there arose a *great* *c.* *Acts* 23:9

hear **cry**

will surely *hear* their *c.* *Ex* 22:23
will God *hear* his *c.*? *Job* 27:9
hear my *c.* O God. *Ps* 61:1
he also will *hear* their *c.* 145:19
let them *hear* the *c.* *Jer* 20:16

not hear **cry**

I will *not hear* their *c.* *Jer* 14:12

cry, *verb*

idle, therefore they *c.* *Ex* 5:8
and they *c.* unto me. 22:23
is it voice of them that *c.* 32:18
cover his upper lip, and *c.* *Lev* 13:45
go *c.* to the gods ye. *Judg* 10:14
right have I yet to *c.* *2 Sam* 19:28
she went to *c.* for her. *2 Ki* 8:3
and *c.* in our affliction. *2 Chr* 20:9
I *c.* unto thee. *Job* 30:20
c. in his destruction. 24
make oppressed to *c.* they *c.* 35:9
they *c.* but none giveth answer. 12
they *c.* not when he. 36:13
when his young ones *c.* to. 38:41
I *c.* in the day time. *Ps* 22:2
hear, O Lord, when I *c.* 27:7; 28:2
to thee will I *c.* O Lord. 28:1, 2
the righteous *c.* and the. 34:17
when I *c.* then shall mine. 56:9
I will *c.* to God most high. 57:2
from end of earth will I *c.* 61:2
O Lord, for I *c.* to thee. 86:3
he shall *c.* unto me. 89:26
Lord, I *c.* unto thee. 141:1
food to young ravens which *c.* 147:9
doth not wisdom *c.* and. *Pr* 8:1
he also shall *c.* but shall. 21:13
child have knowledge to *c.* *Isa* 8:4
wild beasts of island shall *c.* 13:22
c. O city, thou Palestina. 14:31
Heshbon shall *c.* and Elealeh. 15:4
their valiant ones shall *c.* 33:7
and the satyr shall *c.* to. 34:14
c. to Jerusalem, her warfare. 40:2
c. and he said, what shall I *c.*?
he shall not *c.* nor cause. 42:
he shall *c.* yea, prevail. 1
now will I *c.* like a travailing. 1
one shall *c.* to him, yet can. 46:
thou shalt *c.* and he shall say. 58:
ye shall *c.* for sorrow of. 65:1
c. in ears of Jerusalem. *Jer* 2:
wilt thou not from this time *c.*? 3:
blow trumpet in land, *c.* gather. 4:
though they *c.* to me. 11:1
c. to the gods to whom they. 1
not hear when they *c.* 14; *Ezek* 8:1
go up to Lebanon, and *c.* *Jer* 22:2
howl, ye shepherds, and *c.* 25:3
48:20; *Ezek* 21:1

watchmen on Ephraim shall c. Jer 31:6
when I c. and shout he. Lam 3:8
c. for all abominations. Ezek 9:4
forbear to c. make no. 24:17*
shake, when the wounded c. 26:15
they shall c. bitterly for. 27:30
Israel shall c. unto me. Hos 8:2
O Lord, to thee will I c. Joel 1:19
the beasts of the field c. 20
let man and beast c. Jonah 3:8
bite with their teeth, and c. Mi 3:5
stand, stand, shall they c. Nah 2:8
mighty men shall c. Zeph 1:14
angel said unto me, c. Zech 1:14
shall not strive, nor c. Mat 12:19
God avenge elect, who c. Luke 18:7
the Spirit, whereby we c. Rom 8:15
break forth and c. thou. Gal 4:27

cry *against*

c. to the Lord *against*. Deut 15:9; 24:15
to c. alarm *against* you. 2 Chr 13:12
if my land c. *against* me. Job 31:38
to Nineveh, c. *against* it. Jonah 1:2

cry *aloud*

Elijah said, c. *aloud*. 1 Ki 18:27
I c. *aloud*, but there is no. Job 19:7
will I pray and c. *aloud*. Ps 55:17
they shall c. *aloud* from. Isa 24:14
into singing, and c. *aloud*. 54:1
c. *aloud*, spare not. 58:1
in Ramah, c. *aloud* at. Hos 5:8
why dost thou c. *aloud*? Mi 4:9

cry *to the Lord*

c. unto *the Lord* for us. 1 Sam 7:8
they c. *to the Lord* in. Ps 107:19, 28
they shall c. *to the Lord*. Isa 19:20
fast, and c. *to the Lord*. Joel 1:14
shall c. *to the Lord*, but. Mi 3:4

cry *out*

ye shall c. *out* that day. 1 Sam 8:18
I c. *out* of wrong, but. Job 19:7
they c. *out* by reason of. 35:9
c. *out* and shout. Isa 12:6
soldiers of Moab shall c. *out*. 15:4
my heart shall c. *out* for Moab. 5
wonder, c. *out* and cry. 29:9*
I will howl, and c. *out* for. Jer 48:31
arise, c. *out* in the night. Lam 2:19
will a young lion c. *out*? Amos 3:4
I c. *out* to thee, but. Hab 1:2
for the stone shall c. *out* of. 2:11
he began to c. *out* and. Mark 10:47
stones would c. *out*. Luke 19:40

crying

Eli heard noise of the c. 1 Sam 4:14
ashes, and went on c. 2 Sam 13:19
nor regardeth he the c. Job 39:7
thy soul spare for his c. Pr 19:18
leech hath two daughters c. 30:15
it is day of trouble and c. Isa 22:5
there is a c. for wine. 24:11
voice of c. shall be no more. 65:19
a voice of c. shall be. Jer 48:3
forth head-stone with c. Zech 4:7
altar of the Lord with c. Mal 2:13
voice of one c. in wilderness. Mat 3:3; Mark 1:3; Luke 3:4; John 1:23
and saw children c. in. Mat 21:15
devils c. thou art Christ. Luke 4:41
or unclean spirits c. Acts 8:7
ran in among the people, c. 14:14
laid hands on him, c. out. 21:28
the multitude followed, c. away. 36
Spirit into your hearts, c. Gal 4:6
prayers with strong c. Heb 5:7
no more death nor c. Rev 21:4

crystal

the gold and the c. Job 28:17*
is colour of terrible c. Ezek 1:22
sea of glass like unto c. Rev 4:6
light of city was clear as c. 21:11
river of water of life, clear as c. 22:1

cubit

(The distance from the elbow bending inwards to the extremity of the middle finger, or about 18 inches. Standards varied, however, in different places, and no measures can be defined with exactness. Different periods also had different standards)

in a c. shalt thou finish. Gen 6:16
breadth of it, after c. Deut 3:11
compassing it, ten in a c. 1 Ki 7:24
ten in a c. compassing. 2 Chr 4:3
the c. is a c. and an. Ezek 43:13
add one c. to stature. Mat 6:27; Luke 12:25

cubits

of ark 300 c. breadth 50 c. Gen 6:15
fifteen c. upward did the. 7:20
two c. and a half the. Ex 25:10
Goliath's height six c. 1 Sam 17:4
length of the house 60 c. 1 Ki 6:2
each of cherubims ten c. 23
and every laver was four c. 7:38
brake down the walls of Jerusalem, 400 c. 2 Ki 14:13; 2 Chr 25:23
height 60 c. breadth 60 c. Ezra 6:3
gallows be fifty c. high. Esth 5:14; 7:9
from gate to gate 100 c. Ezek 40:23
the court 100 c. 47
breadth of the door was ten c. 41:2
thickness of the wall five c. 9
and the altar twelve c. long. 43:16
the settle 14 c. 17
height of image 60 c. Dan 3:1
length of flying roll 20 c. Zech 5:2
land as it were 200 c. John 21:8
the wall of the city 144 c. Rev 21:17

cuckow

c. have in abomination. Lev 11:16*; Deut 14:15*

cucumbers

we remember the c. and. Num 11:5
a lodge in a garden of c. Isa 1:8

cud, *see* chew and cheweth

cumbered

Martha was c. about. Luke 10:40

cumbereth

cut it down, why c. it? Luke 13:7

cumbrance

can I alone bear your c.? Deut 1:12

cummin

doth he not scatter c. Isa 28:25
cart-wheel turned upon the c. but the c. is beaten out with a. 27
ye pay tithes of c. Mat 23:23

cunning

(American Revision changes to skilful *or* expert*)*

Esau was a c. hunter. Gen 25:27
cherubims of c. work. Ex 26:1; 36:8
make breast-plate of c. work. 28:15
to devise c. works in gold. 31:4
Aholiab a c. workman and. 38:23
made breast-plate of c. work. 39:8
man who is a c. player. 1 Sam 16:16
seen a son of Jesse that is c. 18
all that were c. in songs. 1 Chr 25:7
man c. to work in gold. 2 Chr 2:7
I have sent a c. man of Huram. 13
let right hand forget her c. Ps 137:5
work of a c. workman. S of S 7:1
take away the c. artificer. Isa 3:3
seeketh to him a c. workman. 40:20
send for c. women that. Jer 9:17
they are all the work of c. 10:9
well favoured, c. in. Dan 1:4
about by c. craftiness. Eph 4:14

cunningly

not followed c. devised. 2 Pet 1:16

cup

This word is used, [1] *literally, for a material cup from which one drinks; and* [2] *figuratively, for the contents of a cup,* 1 Cor 11:27; *or* [3] *for sufferings which one undergoes as one drinks a cup of nauseous medicine to the dregs,* Isa 51:17; Mat 26:39; *or* [4] *for the blessings which God gives to us, as a pleasant and refreshing drink,* Ps 23:5.

and Pharaoh's c. was in. Gen 40:11
put my c. my silver c. in the. 42:2
it drank of its own c. 2 Sam 12:3
wrought like brim of a c. 1 Ki 7:26; 2 Chr 4:5
be the portion of their c. Ps 11:6
Lord is the portion of my c. 16:5
my c. runneth over. 23:5
waters of a full c. are wrung. 73:10
in the hand of Lord there is a c. 75:8
I will take the c. of salvation. 116:13
giveth his colour in the c. Pr 23:31
drunk at the hand of the Lord the c. the dregs of the c. of. Isa 51:17
taken out of thy hand c. of. 22
nor shall men give them c. Jer 16:7
take the wine-c. of his fury. 25:15
then took I the c. at the Lord's. 17
if they refuse to take the c. 28
judgement was not to drink c. 49:12
Babylon hath been a golden c. 51:7
c. also shall pass through. Lam 4:21
I will give her c. into. Ezek 23:31
thou shalt drink of thy sister's c. 32
c. of Lord's right hand. Hab 2:16
Jerusalem c. of trembling. Zech 12:2
c. of cold water only. Mat 10:42; Mark 9:41
are ye able to drink of the c.? Mat 20:22; Mark 10:38
ye shall drink indeed of my c. Mat 20:23; Mark 10:39
make clean outside of c. Mat 23:25
cleanse first what is within c. 26
took the c. and gave thanks. 26:27; Mark 14:23; Luke 22:17, 20; 1 Cor 11:25
let this c. pass from. Mat 26:39; Mark 14:36; Luke 22:42
this c. may not pass away. Mat 26:42
c. is the new testament. Luke 22:20; 1 Cor 11:25
c. which my Father hath. John 18:11
the c. of blessing we. 1 Cor 10:16
the c. of Lord and c. of devils. 21
as often as ye drink of this c. 11:26
and drink this c. of the Lord. 27
without mixture into c. Rev 14:10
to give unto her the c. 16:19
the woman having a golden c. 17:4
in the c. she filled, fill to her. 18:6

cup-bearer, -s

queen of Sheba saw *cup-bearers*. 1 Ki 10:5; 2 Chr 9:4
was the king's *cup-bearer*. Neh 1:11

cups

pure gold for the c. 1 Chr 28:17
on Eliakim vessels of c. Isa 22:24
sets pots full of wine and c. Jer 35:5
took away spoons and c. 52:19
washing of c. and pots. Mark 7:4, 8

curdled

hast not thou c. me? Job 10:10

cure, -ed

I will c. them, and will. Jer 33:6
of Egypt, shalt not be c. 46:11
yet could he not c. you. Hos 5:13
they could not c. him. Mat 17:16
the child was c. from that. 18
in that hour he c. many. Luke 7:21
gave them power to c. diseases. 9:1
said to him that was c. John 5:10

cures

cast out devils, do c. Luke 13:32

curious

c. girdle. Ex 28:8*, 27*, 28*; 29:5*; 39:5*; Lev 8:7*
and to devise c. works. Ex 35:32*
used c. arts brought. Acts 19:19

curiously

and c. wrought in the. Ps 139:15

current

c. money with the. Gen 23:16

curse

[1] *To call on divine power to send some injury upon the one cursed. This was often pronounced as by a mouthpiece of God to man, and sometimes as a statement of what would happen, uttered without ill-feeling,* Gen 9:25; 49:7; Josh 6:26. [2] *Profanity or blasphemy,* Ex 22:28; Ps 11:26; Mat 26:74.

I shall bring a c. on me. Gen 27:12
upon me be thy c. my son. 13

the bitter water that causeth the *c.* *Num* 5:18, 19, 22, 24, 27
the woman shall be a *c.* 27
I set before you a blessing and *c.* *Deut* 11:26; 30:1
a *c.* if you will not obey the. 11:28
and shalt put the *c.* upon. 29
c. into a blessing. 23:5; *Neh* 13:2
heareth words of this *c.* *Deut* 29:29
make camp of Israel a *c.* *Josh* 6:18
on them came the *c.* of. *Judg* 9:57
me with a grievous *c.* *1 Ki* 2:8
they should become a *c.* *2 Ki* 22:19
they entered into a *c.* *Neh* 10:29
to sin by wishing a *c.* *Job* 31:30
the *c.* of Lord is in the. *Pr* 3:33
so the *c.* causeless shall not. 26:2
it shall be counted a *c.* to. 27:14
eyes shall have many a *c.* 28:27
hath the *c.* devoured. *Isa* 24:6
come down on people of my *c.* 34:5
I have given Jacob to the *c.* 43:28
shall leave your name for a *c.* 65:15
them to be a taunt and *c.* *Jer* 24:9
25:18; 29:18*; 42:18; 44:8, 12
I will make this city a *c.* 26:6
therefore is your land a *c.* 44:22
that Bozrah shall become a *c.* 49:13
give them sorrow, thy *c.* *Lam* 3:65
therefore the *c.* is poured. *Dan* 9:11
this is the *c.* that goeth. *Zech* 5:3
that as we were a *c.* among. 8:13
I will send a *c.* upon you. *Mal* 2:2
ye are cursed with a *c.* 3:9
and smite the earth with a *c.* 4:6
themselves under *c.* *Acts* 23:12, 14
of law, are under the *c.* *Gal* 3:10
from the *c.* being made a *c.* 13
shall be no more *c.* but. *Rev* 22:3

curse, *verb*

Lord said, I will not *c.* *Gen* 8:21
and I will *c.* him that curseth. 12:3
thou shalt not *c.* ruler. *Ex* 22:28
thou shalt not *c.* the deaf. *Lev* 19:14
I pray thee, *c.* me this. *Num* 22:6, 17
now, *c.* me them. 11; 23:7, 13
thou shalt not *c.* the people. 22:12
how shall I *c.* whom God ? 23:8
to *c.* mine enemies. 11; 24:10
neither *c.* them at all. 23:25
hired Balaam to *c.* thee. *Deut* 23:4
Neh 13:2
stand on mount Ebal to *c.* *Deut* 27:13
called Balaam to *c.* *Josh* 24:9
c. ye Meroz, said the angel, *c.* ye bitterly. *Judg* 5:23
should this dead dog *c.*? *2 Sam* 16:9
let him *c.* because Lord hath said unto him, *c.* David. 10, 11
and he will *c.* thee. *Job* 1:11*; 2:5*
said his wife to him, *c.* God. 2:9*
let them *c.* it that *c.* the day. 3:8
bless with mouth but *c.* *Ps* 62:4
let them *c.* but bless thou. 109:28
people shall *c.* him. *Pr* 11:26
him shall the people *c.* 24:24
servant to master, lest he *c.* 30:10
hear thy servant *c.* thee. *Eccl* 7:21
c. not the king in thought, *c.* 10:20
c. their king and God. *Isa* 8:21
every one of them doth *c.* *Jer* 15:10
I will *c.* your blessings, I. *Mal* 2:2
bless them that *c.* you. *Mat* 5:44
Luke 6:28
he began to *c.* and to. *Mat* 26:74
Mark 14:71
bless and *c.* not. *Rom* 12:14
therewith *c.* we men. *Jas* 3:9

cursed

the serpent *c.* *Gen* 3:14
c. is the ground. 17
now art thou [Cain] *c.* 4:11
ground which Lord hath *c.* 5:29
Noah said, *c.* be Canaan. 9:25
c. be every one. 27:29; *Num* 24:9
c. be their anger, for it. *Gen* 49:7
he hath *c.* his father or. *Lev* 20:9
name of the Lord and *c.* 24:11
bring forth him that *c.* 14, 23
whom thou cursest is *c.* *Num* 22:6
c. be he. *Deut* 27:15, 16, 17, 18
19, 20, 21, 22, 23, 24, 25, 26
c. shalt thou be in the city, *c.* 28:16
c. shall be thy basket. *Deut* 28:17
c. shall be the fruit of thy body. 18
c. when thou comest in, when. 19
c. be man that buildeth. *Josh* 6:26
ye Gibeonites are *c.* none of. 9:23
eat and drink, and *c.* *Judg* 9:27
c. be he that giveth a wife to. 21:18
c. that eateth food. *1 Sam* 14:24, 28
and the Philistine *c.* David. 17:43
but if men, *c.* be they before. 26:19
came forth, and *c.* still. *2 Sam* 16:5
7, 13
for this, because he *c.* the. 19:21
Shimei who *c.* me with. *1 Ki* 2:8
and *c.* them in the name. *2 Ki* 2:24
go see now this *c.* woman. 9:34
I contended with them, and *c.* *Neh* 13:25
my sons have sinned and *c.* *Job* 1:5
Job opened his mouth and *c.* 3:1
taking root, suddenly I *c.* 5:3
their portion is *c.* in earth. 24:18
they that be *c.* of him. *Ps* 37:22
rebuked the proud that are *c.* 119:21
likewise hast *c.* others. *Eccl* 7:22
c. be the man obeyeth not. *Jer* 11:3
c. be the man that trusteth. 17:5
c. be the day wherein I was. 20:14
c. be the man who brought. 15
c. be he that doeth Lord's work deceitfully, *c.* that keepeth. 48:10
but *c.* be the deceiver. *Mal* 1:14
yea, I have *c.* your blessings. 2:2
ye are *c.* with a curse, for. 3:9
depart from me, ye *c.* *Mat* 25:41
knoweth not law, are *c.* *John* 7:49
c. is every one that. *Gal* 3:10
c. is every one that hangeth. 13
c. children, who have. *2 Pet* 2:14*

cursed *thing*

be a *c. thing,* for it is a *c. thing.* *Deut* 7:26*
cleave nought of the *c. thing.* 13:17*

cursedst

from thee, which thou *c.* *Judg* 17:2
the fig-tree thou *c.* is. *Mark* 11:21

curses

shall write these *c.* in. *Num* 5:23
all these *c.* shall. *Deut* 28:15, 45
all the *c.* that are written. 29:20, 27
2 Chr 34:24
all *c.* of the covenant in. *Deut* 29:21
thy God will put these *c.* on. 30:7

curseth

c. his father or mother shall be put. *Ex* 21:17; *Lev* 20:9; *Pr* 20:20
whosoever *c.* his God. *Lev* 24:15
generation that *c.* father. *Pr* 30:11
he that *c.* father or mother, let. *Mat* 15:4*; *Mark* 7:10*

cursing

woman with oath of *c.* *Num* 5:21
shall send upon thee *c.* *Deut* 28:20
set before you blessing and *c.* 30:19
me good for his *c.* *2 Sam* 16:12
his mouth is full of *c.* *Ps* 10:7
Rom 3:14
and for *c.* and lying. 59:12
as he loved *c.* so let it. 109:17
as he clothed himself with *c.* 18
he heareth *c.* and. *Pr* 29:24*
beareth thorns is nigh to *c.* *Heb* 6:8
same mouth blessing and *c.* *Jas* 3:10

cursings

read the blessings and *c.* *Josh* 8:34

curtain, -s

tabernacle with ten *c.* *Ex* 26:1, 2
36:9
bear the *c.* of tabernacle. *Num* 4:25
ark dwelleth within *c.* *2 Sam* 7:2
1 Chr 17:1
stretchest out the heavens like a *c.* *Ps* 104:2; *Isa* 40:22
but I am comely as the *c.* *S of S* 1:5
let them stretch forth *c.* *Isa* 54:2
tents spoiled, and my *c.* *Jer* 4:20
and set up my *c.* 10:20
take to themselves their *c.* 49:29
c. of the land of Midian. *Hab* 3:7

Cush

sons of Ham, *C.* *Gen* 10:6; *1 Chr* 1:8
the sons of *C.* Seba, and. *Gen* 10:7
1 Chr 1:9
remnant left from *C.* *Isa* 11:11

Cushan

I saw the tents of *C.* in. *Hab* 3:7

Cushi

C. tell the king what. *2 Sam* 18:21
Ahimaaz ran, and overran *C.* 23
all princes sent son of *C.* *Jer* 36:14
to Zephaniah son of *C.* *Zeph* 1:1

custody

c. of sons of Merari. *Num* 3:36*
fair virgins to the *c.* *Esth* 2:3, 8
to the *c.* of Shaashgaz the king's. 14

custom

[1] *Manner, or way,* Luke 4:16. [2] *A duty paid to the king or prince upon the importation or exportation of goods,* Rom 13:7.

for the *c.* of women is. *Gen* 31:35
and it was a *c.* in Israel. *Judg* 11:39
the priests' *c.* with. *1 Sam* 2:13
according to the *c.* *Ezra* 3:4*
Jer 32:11
not pay toll, tribute, and *c.* *Ezra* 4:13
been mighty kings, and *c.* was. 20
not be lawful to impose *c.* on. 7:24
sitting at the receipt of *c.* *Mat* 9:9*
Mark 2:14*; *Luke* 5:27*
kings of earth take *c.*? *Mat* 17:25*
according to the *c.* of. *Luke* 1:9
to do for him after *c.* of law. 2:27
went to Jerusalem after the *c.* 42
as Jesus' *c.* was, he went. 4:16
ye have a *c.* that I should. *John* 18:39
render *c.* to whom *c.* is. *Rom* 13:7
we have no such *c.* nor. *1 Cor* 11:16

customs

commit none of these *c.* *Lev* 18:30
c. of the people are vain. *Jer* 10:3
shall change the *c.* Moses. *Acts* 6:14
teach *c.* which are not lawful. 16:21
ought not to walk after *c.* 21:21
thee to be expert in all *c.* 26:3
committed nothing against *c.* 28:17

cut

and *c.* it in wires to work. *Ex* 39:3
shall *c.* the burnt-. *Lev* 1:6, 12
c. ram into pieces. 8:20; *Ex* 29:17
not offer to Lord what is *c.* *Lev* 22:24
ye shall not *c.* yourselves. *Deut* 14:1
my concubine and *c.* *Judg* 20:6
c. bullock in pieces. *1 Ki* 18:23, 33
c. themselves after their manner. 28
he *c.* in pieces all the vessels of. *2 Ki* 24:13; *2 Chr* 28:24
people, he *c.* them with. *1 Chr* 20:3
servants can skill to *c.* *2 Chr* 2:8, 10
let them be as *c.* in pieces. *Ps* 58:7
c. bars of iron. 107:16; *Isa* 25:4
art thou not it that hath *c.*? *Isa* 51:9
nor lament, nor *c.* *Jer* 16:6
when they *c.* the calf in. 34:18
he *c.* the roll with the. 36:23
clothes rent, and having *c.* 41:5
how long wilt thou *c.* thyself ? 47:5
born thy navel was not *c.* *Ezek* 16:4
ye will not, ye shall be *c.* *Dan* 2:5
speak against God shall be *c.* 3:29
and *c.* them in the head. *Amos* 9:1*
all that burden themselves with it shall be *c.* *Zech* 12:3*
when they heard that, they were *c.* to the heart. *Acts* 5:33; 7:54

cut *asunder*

he hath *c. asunder* cords. *Ps* 129:4
hammer of earth *c. asunder.* *Jer* 50:23
staff Beauty, and *c.* it *asunder.* *Zech* 11:1
then I *c. asunder* my other staff. 1
shall *c.* him *asunder.* *Mat* 24:5
Luke 12:4

cut *down*

but ye shall *c. down.* *Ex* 34:1
will *c. down* your images. *Lev* 26:3
c. down from thence. *Num* 13:23, 2
and *c. down* groves. *Deut* 7:5
2 Ki 18:4; 23:1
thou shalt not *c.* them *down.* *Deut* 20:1

not for meat c. down. Deut 20:20
and c. down the grove. Judg 6:25
I will c. down cedars. 2 Ki 19:23
Isa 37:24
Asa c. down her idol. 2 Chr 15:16
Josiah c. down all the idols. 34:7*
greenness, not c. down. Job 8:12
cometh like a flower, is c. down. 14:2
hope of a tree if it be c. down. 7
the wicked were c. down. 22:16*
our substance is not c. down. 20
shall soon be c. down. Ps 37:2
is burnt, and is c. down. 80:16
in the evening it is c. down. 90:6
sycamores are c. down. Isa 9:10
how art thou c. down! 14:12
nail be removed and c. down. 22:25*
shall c. down thy choice. Jer 22:7
peaceable habitation c. down. 25:37*
also thou shalt be c. down. 48:2*
your images be c. down. Ezek 6:6*
yet shall they be c. down. Nah 1:12
merchant-people are c. down.
Zeph 1:11*
others c. down branches. Mat 21:8
Mark 11:8
c. it down; why cumbereth it the ground? Luke 13:7
after that thou shalt c. it down. 9

cut *off*

neither all flesh be c. off. Gen 9:11
uncircumcised child be c. off. 17:14
and c. off fore-skin of son. Ex 4:25
soul shall be c. off from. 12:15, 19
31:14; Num 15:30, 31; 19:13
and I will c. them off. Ex 23:23
be c. off from people. 30:33, 38
Lev 7:20, 21, 25, 27; 17:4, 9
19:8; 23:29; Num 9:13
will c. him off from his people.
Lev 17:10; 18:29; 20:3, 6, 18
Num 19:20
whosoever eateth blood be c. off.
Lev 17:14
shall be c. off in sight of. 20:17
that soul shall be c. off from. 22:3
c. ye not off the tribe. Num 4:18
that soul shall utterly be c. off. 15:31
when God shall c. off. Deut 12:29
hath c. off nations. 19:1; Josh 23:4
hath privy member c. off. Deut 23:1
thou shalt c. off her hand. 25:12
waters of Jordan shall be c. off.
Josh 3:13, 16; 4:7
and shall c. off our name. 7:9
at that time Joshua c. off. 11:21
and c. off his thumbs. Judg 1:6
there is one tribe c. off from. 21:6
name of dead be not c. off. Ruth 4:10
days come that I will c. off.
1 Sam 2:31
man whom I shall not c. off. 33
palms of Dagon's hands c. off. 5:4
David ran and c. off. 17:51
not c. off kindness from my. 20:15
David c. off the skirt of. 24:4, 5
for in that I c. off the. 11
thou wilt not c. off my seed. 21
knowest how Saul hath c. off. 28:9
and they c. off Saul's head. 31:9
slew them and c. off. 2 Sam 4:12
and c. off their garments in the.
10:4; 1 Chr 19:4
c. off head of Sheba. 2 Sam 20:22
then will I c. off Israel. 1 Ki 9:7
till he had c. off every male. 11:16
to c. off Jeroboam's. 13:34; 14:14
will c. off from Jeroboam. 14:10
when Jezebel c. off prophets. 18:4
will c. off from Ahab him. 21:21
2 Ki 9:8
Ahaz c. off borders. 2 Ki 16:17
Hezekiah c. off the gold from. 18:16
have c. off all thine. 1 Chr 17:8
Lord anointed to c. off. 2 Chr 22:7
angel to c. off all mighty men. 32:21
were the righteous c. off? Job 4:7
loose his hand, and c. me off. 6:9
whose hope shall be c. off. 8:14*
if he c. off, then who can? 11:10*
shall his branch be c. off. 18:16
of his months is c. off. 21:21
because I was not c. off. 23:17
they are c. off as tops of. Job 24:24
when people are c. off in their. 36:20
the Lord shall c. off all. Ps 12:3
I am c. off from before. 31:22
to c. off remembrance of. 34:16
for evil doers shall be c. off. 37:9
cursed of him, shall be c. off. 22
seed of wicked shall be c. off. 28
when the wicked are c. off. 34
end of wicked shall be c. off. 38
he shall reward, c. them off. 54:5
horns of wicked will I c. off. 75:10
he shall c. off the spirit. 76:12
come, and let us c. them off. 83:4
and they are c. off from thy. 88:5
terrors have c. me off. 16
he shall c. them off in their. 94:23
neighbour will I c. off. 101:5*
that I may c. off all wicked doers. 8
let his posterity be c. off. 109:13
that the Lord may c. off the. 15
and of thy mercy c. off. 143:12
wicked shall be c. off from. Pr 2:22
expectation not be c. off. 23:18
24:14
Lord will c. off from Israel. Isa 9:14
to destroy and c. off nations. 10:7
adversaries of Judah be c. off. 11:13
I will c. off from Babylon. 14:22
and every beard c. off. 15:2
burden upon it shall be c. off. 22:25
watch for iniquity are c. off. 29:20*
he will c. me off with. 38:12*
refrain, that I c. thee not off. 48:9
name should not have been c. off. 19
he was c. off out of the land. 53:8
a sign that shall not be c. off. 55:13
as if he c. off a dog's neck. 66:3*
truth is perished and c. off. Jer 7:28
c. off thine hair, O Jerusalem. 29
to c. off the children without. 9:21
let us c. him off from land. 11:19
to c. off from you man and. 44:7
that ye might c. yourselves off. 8
and to c. off all Judah. 11
to c. off from Tyrus. 47:4
Ashkelon is c. off. 5*
come, let us c. it off from. 48:2
horn of Moab is c. off, his arm. 25
men of war be c. off. 49:26*; 50:30*
c. off the sower from. 50:16
flee out, and be not c. off. 51:6
against this place to c. it off. 62
c. off in his anger the. Lam 2:3
they have c. off my life in. 3:53
and I will c. him off. Ezek 14:8
c. off man and beast. 13, 17, 19, 21
25:13; 29:8
shall he not c. off fruit? 17:9
building forts to c. off many. 17
c. off the righteous and. 21:3, 4
behold, I will c. thee off. 25:7
I will c. off the Cherethims. 16
and I will c. off the multitude. 30:15
terrible nations c. him off. 31:12
I will c. off from Seir him. 35:7
hope is lost, we are c. off. 37:11
hew down the tree, c. off. Dan 4:14
Messiah shall be c. off. 9:26
made idols, that they be c. off.
Hos 8:4
her king is c. off as the. 10:7, 15
the new wine is c. off. Joel 1:5, 9
is not the meat c. off? 16
I will c. off the inhabitant. Amos 1:5
I will c. off the inhabitant from Ashdod. 8
I will c. off the judge from. 2:3
horns of altar shall be c. off. 3:14
by night, art thou c. off. Ob 5
every one of Esau may be c. off. 9
and thou shalt be c. off for ever. 10
nor stand to c. off those of his. 14
thine enemies shall be c. off. Mi 5:9
witchcrafts be c. off. 12
graven images I c. off. 13; Nah 1:14
wicked is utterly c. off. Nah 1:15
and I will c. off thy prey. 2:13
the sword shall c. thee off. 3:15
the flock shall be c. off. Hab 3:17
I will c. off man from. Zeph 1:3
c. off remnant of Baal. 4
that bear silver c. off. 11
I have c. off the nations. 3:6
should not be c. off. Zeph 3:7
stealeth, and every one that sweareth, shall be c. off. Zech 5:3
I will c. off pride of Philistines. 9:6
I will c. off chariot from. 10
three shepherds also I c. off. 11:8
is to be c. off, let it be c. off. 9
I will c. off the names of. 13:2
two parts in land shall be c. off. 8
of people shall not be c. of. 14:2
Lord will c. off the. Mal 2:12
right hand offend thee, c. it off.
Mat 5:30; 18:8; Mark 9:43, 45
and c. off his ear. Mark 14:47*
Luke 22:50*; John 18:10, 26
soldiers c. off the ropes. Acts 27:32
thou shalt also be c. off. Rom 11:22
I may c. off occasion. 2 Cor 11:12
I would they were c. off. Gal 5:12

cut *out*

froward tongue be c. out. Pr 10:31
stone c. out without. Dan 2:34, 45
for if thou wert c. out. Rom 11:24

cut *short*

began to c. Israel short. 2 Ki 10:32
will finish and c. it short. Rom 9:28

cut *up*

who c. up mallows by. Job 30:4*
as thorns c. up shall. Isa 33:12

cuttest, -eth

when thou c. down. Deut 24:19*
he c. out rivers among. Job 28:10
he breaketh bow, and c. Ps 46:9
as when one c. and cleaveth. 141:7
message by fool, c. off. Pr 26:6
one c. a tree out of the. Jer 10:3
build chambers and c. him. 22:14

cutting

c. of stones to set. Ex 31:5; 35:33
I said in the c. off of my. Isa 38:10*
consulted shame by c. Hab 2:10
crying and c. himself. Mark 5:5

cuttings

not any c. for dead. Lev 19:28; 21:5
all hands shall be c. and. Jer 48:37

cymbal

brass, or a tinkling c. 1 Cor 13:1

cymbals

played on cornets and c. 2 Sam 6:5
1 Chr 13:8
harps and c. 1 Chr 15:16; 16:42
Asaph made a sound with c. 16:5
in the house of Lord with c. 25:6
lift up their voice with c. 2 Chr 5:13
Levites in house of Lord with c. 29:25
sons of Asaph with c. Ezra 3:10
Neh 12:27
upon loud-sounding c. Ps 150:5

cypress

he taketh the c. and oak. Isa 44:14*

Cyprus

Joses was of country of C. Acts 4:36
as far as Phenice and C. 11:19
some of them were men of C. 20
from Seleucia they sailed to C. 13:4
Barnabas sailed to C. 15:39
when we had discovered C. 21:3
with him Mnason of C. 16
launched, sailed under C. 27:4

Cyrene

found a man of C. Mat 27:32
parts of Lybia about C. Acts 2:10
were men of Cyprus and C. 11:20
Lucius of C. was in church. 13:1

Cyrenian

compel Simon a C. to. Mark 15:21

Cyrenians

the synagogue of the C. Acts 6:9

Cyrenius

made when C. was. Luke 2:2

Cyrus

first year of C. the Lord stirred up spirit of C. 2 Chr 36:22; Ezra 1:1
saith C. king of Persia. 2 Chr 36:23
Ezra 1:2
C. brought forth. Ezra 1:7, 8; 5:14
grant they had of C. 3:7
will build as C. the king hath. 4:3
C. made a decree to build. 5:13, 17
that saith of C. he is. Isa 44:28

saith Lord to anointed, to *C. Isa* 45:1
to the first year of *C. Dan* 1:21
Daniel prospered in reign of *C.* 6:28
third year of *C.* a thing was. 10:1

D

Dabbasheth
toward sea reached to *D. Josh* 19:11

Daberath
and then goeth out to *D. Josh* 19:12
out of Issachar, *D. 1 Chr* 6:72

dagger
Ehud made him a *d. Judg* 3:16*
took the *d.* from right thigh. 21*
that he could not draw the *d.* 22*

Dagon
to offer a sacrifice to *D. Judg* 16:23
ark into the house of *D. 1 Sam* 5:2
D. was fallen. 3
the head of *D.* was cut off. 4
is sore on us, and on *D.* our. 7
head in temple of *D. 1 Chr* 10:10

daily
as much as gathered *d. Ex* 16:5
d. meat-offering. *Num* 4:16* *Ezek* 46:13
after this manner offer *d. Num* 28:24
beside the *d.* burnt-offering. 29:6* *Ezra* 3:4
when she pressed him *d. Judg* 16:16
allowance was a *d.* rate. *2 Ki* 25:30
was prepared for me *d. Neh* 5:18*
spake *d.* hearkened not. *Esth* 3:4
sorrow in my heart *d. Ps* 13:2*
while they say *d.* to me. 42:10*
be merciful, he fighting *d.* 56:1*
mine enemies would *d.* swallow. 2*
I will sing, that I may *d.* 61:8
the Lord who *d.* loadeth us. 68:19
he shall live and *d.* shall be. 72:15*
man reproacheth thee *d.* 74:22*
I cry to thee *d.* 86:3*
I called *d.* upon thee. 88:9
came round about me *d.* 17*
I was *d.* his delight. *Pr* 8:30
that heareth me, watching *d.* 34
yet they seek me *d.* and. *Isa* 58:2
d. rising up early and. *Jer* 7:25
I am in derision *d.* 20:7*, 8*
Noph have distresses *d. Ezek* 30:16*
king appointed them a *d. Dan* 1:5
and by him the *d.* sacrifice was. 8:11*; 11:31*; 12:11*
Ephraim *d.* increaseth. *Hos* 12:1*
give us this day our *d.* bread. *Mat* 6:11; *Luke* 11:3
sat *d.* with you teaching. *Mat* 26:55 *Mark* 14:49; *Luke* 19:47; 22:53
take up his cross *d. Luke* 9:23
continuing *d.* with one. *Acts* 2:46
Lord added to the church *d.* 47
widows were neglected in *d.* 6:1
churches increased in number *d.* 16:5
searched the scriptures *d.* 17:11
I die *d. 1 Cor* 15:31
but exhort *d. Heb* 3:13
who needeth not *d.* to. 7:27
and destitute of *d.* food. *Jas* 2:15

dainty, -ies
shall yield royal *d. Gen* 49:20
soul abhorreth *d.* meat. *Job* 33:20
let me not eat of their *d. Ps* 141:4
be not desirous of his *d. Pr* 23:3
neither desire thou his *d.* meats. 6
all things which were *d. Rev* 18:14

dale
which is the king's *d. Gen* 14:17*
a pillar in the king's *d. 2 Sam* 18:18

Dalmatia
Titus is departed to *D. 2 Tim* 4:10

dam
seven days with his *d.* on eighth give it me. *Ex* 22:30; *Lev* 22:27
shalt not take the *d. Deut* 22:6
in any wise let the *d.* go. 7

damage
d. grow to the hurt of. *Ezra* 4:22
not countervail king's *d. Esth* 7:4

and drinketh *d. Pr* 26:6
king should have no *d. Dan* 6:2
with hurt and much *d. Acts* 27:10*
that ye might receive *d. 2 Cor* 7:9*

Damaris
and a woman named *D. Acts* 17:34

Damascus
steward is Eliezer of *D. Gen* 15:2
David put garrisons in Syria of *D.* *2 Sam* 8:6; *1 Chr* 18:6
Rezon went to *D.* reigned in *D.* *1 Ki* 11:24
on way to wilderness of *D.* 19:15
make streets for thee in *D.* 20:34
Pharpar, rivers of *D.*? *2 Ki* 5:12
Elisha came to *D.* 8:7
Jeroboam recovered *D.* 14:28
king of Assyria went against *D.* 16:9
Ahaz saw an altar at *D.* 10
Syrians of *D.* came to. *1 Chr* 18:5
the spoil to king of *D. 2 Chr* 24:23
multitude of captives to *D.* 28:5
Ahaz sacrificed to gods of *D.* 23
Lebanon, looketh toward *D.* *S of S* 7:4
of Syria is *D.* head of *D. Isa* 7:8
riches of *D.* shall be taken. 8:4
is not Samaria as *D.*? 10:9
the burden of *D.* 17:1; *Jer* 49:23
kingdom cease from *D. Isa* 17:3
D. is waxed feeble. *Jer* 49:24
I will kindle a fire in wall of *D.* 27
D. thy merchant in. *Ezek* 27:18
three transgressions of *D. Amos* 1:3
I will break also the bar of *D.* 5
that dwell in *D.* in a couch. 3:12
go into captivity beyond *D.* 5:27
and *D.* shall be the rest. *Zech* 9:1
desired letters to *D. Acts* 9:2
there was a disciple at *D.* 10
was Saul with the disciples at *D.* 19
confounded Jews who dwelt at *D.* 22
how he preached boldly at *D.* 27
come nigh to *D.* 22:6; 26:12
arise, and go into *D.* 22:10
in *D.* governor desirous. *2 Cor* 11:32
I returned again unto *D. Gal* 1:17

damnable
shall bring in *d.* heresies. *2 Pet* 2:1*

damnation
(*In Revised Versions this word is rendered* judgement *or* condemnation *in every case except those starred. A similar change also in the other forms of the word*)
receive the greater *d. Mat* 23:14* *Mark* 12:40; *Luke* 20:47
can ye escape *d.* of hell ? *Mat* 23:33
is in danger of eternal *d. Mark* 3:29*
to the resurrection of *d. John* 5:29
good may come, whose *d. Rom* 3:8
shall receive to themselves *d.* 13:2
eateth and drinketh *d. 1 Cor* 11:29
having *d.* because they. *1 Tim* 5:12
not, and their *d. 2 Pet* 2:3*

damned
believeth not shall be *d. Mark* 16:16
he that doubteth is *d. Rom* 14:23
all might be *d.* who. *2 Thes* 2:12

damsel
the *d.* abide few days. *Gen* 24:55
loved *d.* and spake kindly to *d.* 34:3
but give me the *d.* to wife. 12
forth tokens of the *d. Deut* 22:15
tokens be not found for the *d.* 20
they shall bring out the *d.* and. 21
the *d.* because she cried not. 24
there is in the *d.* no sin worthy. 26
shall give the *d.'s* father fifty. 29
to every man a *d. Judg* 5:30
the *d.'s* father retained him. 19:4
Boaz said, whose *d.* is ? *Ruth* 2:5
it is Moabitish *d.* that came back. 6
and the *d.* was very fair. *1 Ki* 1:4
brought in a charger, and given to *d.* *Mat* 14:11; *Mark* 6:28
a *d.* came to Peter. *Mat* 26:69* *John* 18:17*
the *d.* is not dead. *Mark* 5:39
father and mother of the *d.* and entereth in where *d.* was lying. 40

a *d.* came to hearken. *Acts* 12:13*
a certain *d.* possessed with. 16:16*

damsels
Rebekah arose and her *d. Gen* 24:61
Abigail rode with five *d. 1 Sam* 25:42
amongst them were the *d. Ps* 68:25

Dan, *a person*
called she his name *D. Gen* 30:6
son of Bilhah, *D.* 35:25
sons of *D.* 46:23; *Num* 26:42
D. shall judge his people. *Gen* 49:16
D. shall be a serpent by. 17
of *D.* Ahiezer the son. *Num* 1:12
standard of the camp of *D.* 2:25
all numbered in the camp of *D.* 31
of *D.* he said, *D.* is. *Deut* 33:22
after the name of *D. Josh* 19:47 *Judg* 18:29
and why did *D.* remain ? *Judg* 5:17
moved him in camp of *D.* 13:25
a portion for *D. Ezek* 48:1
one gate of *D.* 32
see **children**

tribe of **Dan**
Aholiab of the *tribe of D. Ex* 31:6 35:34; 38:23
Dibri, of *tribe of D. Lev* 24:11
of *tribe of D.* 62,700. *Num* 1:39
of *tribe of D.* to spy the land. 13:12
of *tribe of D.* to divide the. 34:22
for the *tribe of D. Josh* 19:40, 48
out of the *tribe of D.* 21:5, 23
priests to *tribe of D. Judg* 18:30

Dan, *a place*
pursued them unto *D. Gen* 14:14
Moses all Gilead unto *D. Deut* 34:1
they called Leshem, *D. Josh* 19:47 *Judg* 18:29
from *D.* to Beer-sheba. *Judg* 20:1 *1 Sam* 3:20; *2 Sam* 3:10; 17:11 24:2, 15; *1 Ki* 4:25; *1 Chr* 21:2 *2 Chr* 30:5
other calf put he in *D. 1 Ki* 12:29 *2 Ki* 10:29
smote *D. 1 Ki* 15:20; *2 Chr* 16:4
voice declareth from *D. Jer* 4:15
of horses heard from *D.* 8:16
D. and Javan occupied. *Ezek* 27:19
thy God, O *D.* liveth. *Amos* 8:14

dance
praise in the *d. Ps* 149:3; 150:4
virgins shall rejoice in *d. Jer* 31:13
d. is turned into mourning. *Lam* 5:15

dance, *verb*
of Shiloh come to *d. Judg* 21:21
their children *d. Job* 21:11
mourn, a time to *d. Eccl* 3:4
satyrs shall *d.* there. *Isa* 13:21

danced
to their number that *d. Judg* 21:23
and David *d.* before. *2 Sam* 6:14
and ye have not *d. Mat* 11:17 *Luke* 7:32
daughter of Herodias *d. Mat* 14:6 *Mark* 6:22

dances
went after her with *d. Ex* 15:20
to meet him with *d. Judg* 11:34
not sing of him in *d. 1 Sam* 21:11 29:5
shalt go forth in the *d. Jer* 31:4

dancing
he saw the calf and *d. Ex* 32:19
came out singing and *d. 1 Sam* 18:6
on all earth, eating and *d.* 30:16
she saw king David *d. 2 Sam* 6:1[illegible] *1 Chr* 15:2[illegible]
my mourning into *d. Ps* 30:1[illegible]
he heard music and *d. Luke* 15:2[illegible]

dandled
and ye shall be *d.* upon. *Isa* 66:1[illegible]

danger
shall be in *d.* of. *Mat* 5:21, 2[illegible]
be in *d.* of the council, in *d.* 2[illegible]
but is in *d.* of eternal. *Mark* 3:29
this our craft is in *d. Acts* 19:2[illegible]
in *d.* to be called in question. 4[illegible]

dangerous
when sailing was now *d. Acts* 27:[illegible]

Daniel
David had *D.* of. *1 Chr* 3:[illegible]

of Ithamar, *D.* *Ezra* 8:2
D. sealed. *Neh* 10:6
though Noah, *D.* *Ezek* 14:14, 20
thou art wiser than *D.* 28:3
D. of Judah. *Dan* 1:6
to *D.* the name of Belteshazzar. 7
D. had understanding in. 17
none was found like *D.* 19
sought *D.* to be slain. 2:13
then *D.* went in. 16
the secret was revealed to *D.* 19
Nebuchadnezzar worshipped *D.* 46
then king made *D.* a great man. 48
D. sat in the gate. 49
at last *D.* came in. 4:8
then *D.* was astonied for. 19
of doubts found in *D.* 5:12
they clothed *D.* with scarlet and. 29
of whom *D.* was first. 6:2
not find occasion against *D.* 5
these men found *D.* praying. 11
D. regardeth not thee, O king, 13
king set his heart on *D.* 14
that they should take up *D.* 23
men tremble before God of *D.* 26
who hath delivered *D.* from. 27
so this *D.* prospered in reign. 28
D. had a dream, and visions. 7:1
as for me *D.* 28
a vision, even unto me *D.* 8:1
he said, fear not, *D.* 10:12
he said, go thy way, *D.* 12:9
of desolation, spoken of by *D.*
Mat 24:15; *Mark* 13:14

I Daniel

I D. was grieved. *Dan* 7:15
when *I*, even *I D.* had seen. 8:15
I D. fainted. 27
I D. understood by books. 9:2
I D. was mourning three. 10:2
I D. alone saw the vision. 7
I D. looked. 12:5

O Daniel

O D. servant of the. *Dan* 6:20
O D. I am now come to. 9:22
O D. a man greatly beloved. 10:11
O D. shut up the words and. 12:4

dare

none is so fierce that *d.* *Job* 41:10
good man some would *d.* *Rom* 5:7
for I will not *d.* to speak of. 15:18
d. any of you go to law ? *1 Cor* 6:1
d. not make ourselves. *2 Cor* 10:12*

Darius

till the reign of *D.* *Ezra* 4:5, 24
till the matter came to *D.* 5:5
D. the king made a decree. 6:1, 12
finished in sixth year of *D.* 15
priests to the reign of *D.* *Neh* 12:22
D. the Median took. *Dan* 5:31
king *D.* signed the writing. 6:9
king *D.* wrote to all people. 25
in the first year of *D.* 9:1; 11:1
in second year of *D.* *Hag* 1:1, 15
2:10; *Zech* 1:7
in fourth year of *D.* *Zech* 7:1

dark

went down, and it was *d.* *Gen* 15:17
if plague be *d.* *Lev* 13:6, 21, 26
28, 56
and not in *d.* speeches. *Num* 12:8
when it was *d.* the men. *Josh* 2:5
d. waters. *2 Sam* 22:12; *Ps* 18:11
Jerusalem began to be *d.* *Neh* 13:19
stars of the twilight be *d.* *Job* 3:9
they grope in the *d.* 12:25
the light shall be *d.* in his. 18:6
judge through the *d.* cloud ? 22:13
in the *d.* they dig through. 24:16
let their way be *d.* and. *Ps* 35:6
I will open my *d.* saying. 49:4
d. places of the earth are. 74:20
I will utter *d.* sayings of old. 78:2
thy wonders be known in *d.*? 88:12
sent darkness and made it *d.* 105:28
words of wise and their *d.* *Pr* 1:6
in the black and *d.* night. 7:9
their works are in the *d.* *Isa* 29:15
not spoken in a *d.* place. 45:19
feet stumble upon the *d.* *Jer* 13:16
he hath set me in *d.* places. *Lam* 3:6
house of Israel do in the *d.* *Ezek* 8:12
make the stars thereof *d.* *Ezek* 32:7
bright lights of heaven I make *d.* 8
in the cloudy and *d.* day. 34:12
king understanding *d.* *Dan* 8:23
sun and moon shall be *d.* *Joel* 2:10
that maketh day *d.* *Amos* 5:8, 20
it shall be *d.* unto you, the day shall
be *d.* *Mi* 3:6*
light not be clear, nor *d.* *Zech* 14:6*
light, having now part *d.* *Luke* 11:36
and it was now *d.* *John* 6:17
early, when it was yet *d.* 20:1
light that shineth in a *d.* *2 Pet* 1:19

darken

I will *d.* the earth. *Amos* 8:9

darkened

so that the land was *d.* *Ex* 10:15
let eyes be *d.* *Ps* 69:23; *Rom* 11:10
or the stars be not *d.* *Eccl* 12:2
look out of the windows be *d.* 3
the light is *d.* in the. *Isa* 5:30
the land is *d.* 9:19*
the sun *d.* 13:10; *Joel* 3:15
all joy is *d.* the mirth of. *Isa* 24:11
Tehaphnehes day be *d.* *Ezek* 30:18*
eye shall be utterly *d.* *Zech* 11:17
then shall the sun be *d.* *Mat* 24:29
Mark 13:24
and the sun was *d.* *Luke* 23:45*
their foolish heart was *d.* *Rom* 1:21
the understanding *d.* *Eph* 4:18
third part of them was *d.* *Rev* 8:12
the sun and the air were *d.* 9:2

darkeneth

who is this that *d.*? *Job* 38:2

darkish

bright spots in skin be *d.* *Lev* 13:39

darkly

see through a glass *d.* *1 Cor* 13:12

darkness

Literally, the absence of natural light, Mat 27:45.

Figuratively, [1] *The place of misery,* Mat 22:13. [2] *Ignorance,* John 3:19. [3] *Secret,* Mat 10:27. [4] *The land of darkness is the grave,* Job 10:21, 22. [5] *The children of darkness are the wicked, in opposition to the good who are called children of light,* 2 Cor 6:14.

d. was upon face of deep. *Gen* 1:2
the light day, and the *d.* night. 5
to divide the light from the *d.* 18
an horror of great *d.* fell upon. 15:12
there be *d.* over Egypt. *Ex* 10:21
there was a thick *d.* in all. 22
it was a cloud and *d.* to. 14:20
Moses drew near to thick *d.* 20:21
burnt with thick *d.* *Deut* 4:11
Lord spake out of thick *d.* 5:22
d. between you and the. *Josh* 24:7
d. was under his feet. *2 Sam* 22:10
Ps 18:9
made *d.* pavilions. *2 Sam* 22:12
will enlighten my *d.* 29; *Ps* 18:28
d. and the shadow of. *Job* 3:5
as for that night, let *d.* seize. 6
meet with *d.* in the day time. 5:14
a land of *d.* as *d.* itself. 10:22†
and he hath set *d.* in my. 19:8
all *d.* shall be hid in his. 20:26
or *d.* that thou canst not see. 22:11
not cut off before *d.* neither hath he
covered the *d.* 23:17
an end to *d.* the stones of *d.* 28:3
no *d.* where workers of. 34:22
our speech by reason of *d.* 37:19
when I made thick *d.* a. 38:9
and as for *d.* where is the ? 19
d. his secret place. *Ps* 18:11
mine acquaintance into *d.* 88:18
clouds and *d.* round about. 97:2
makest *d.* and it is night. 104:20
he sent *d.* and made it dark. 105:28
if I say, surely the *d.* shall. 139:11
yea, *d.* hideth not from thee. 12
to walk in ways of *d.* *Pr* 2:13
the way of wicked is as *d.* 4:19
name be covered with *d.* *Eccl* 6:4
look to the land, behold *d.* *Isa* 5:30
and behold trouble and *d.* 8:22
give thee treasures of *d.* *Isa* 45:3
get thee into *d.* O daughter of. 47:5
d. shall cover the earth, and gross *d.*
the people, but. 60:2
d. and make gross *d.* *Jer* 13:16
I will set *d.* upon thy. *Ezek* 32:8
d. of clouds and of thick *d.* *Joel* 2:2
sun shall be turned into *d.* 31
Acts 2:20
maketh the morning *d.* *Amos* 4:13
d. shall pursue his enemies. *Nah* 1:8
whole body full of *d.* *Mat* 6:23
Luke 11:34
cast out into outer *d.* *Mat* 8:12
22:13; 25:30
from sixth hour was *d.* 27:45
Mark 15:33
hour and power of *d.* *Luke* 22:53
there was *d.* over all earth. 23:44
on him a mist and a *d.* *Acts* 13:11
fellowship with works of *d.* *Eph* 5:11
against the rulers of the *d.* 6:12
us from power of *d.* *Col* 1:13
not of night nor of *d.* *1 Thes* 5:5
to blackness and *d.* *Heb* 12:18
delivered them into *d.* *2 Pet* 2:4
to whom the mist of *d.* is. 17
because that *d.* hath. *1 John* 2:11
in chains under *d.* *Jude* 6
is reserved blackness of *d.* 13
kingdom was full of *d.* *Rev* 16:10

darkness with *day*

let that *day* be *d.* let not. *Job* 3:4
he knoweth that *day* of *d.* 15:23
remember the *days* of *d.* *Eccl* 11:8
thy *d.* be as noon-*day*. *Isa* 58:10
a *day* of *d.* and gloominess.
Joel 2:2; *Zeph* 1:15
day of the Lord be *d.*? *Amos* 5:20

in **darkness**

grope as the blind *in d.* *Deut* 28:29
wicked be silent *in d.* *1 Sam* 2:9
Lord said that he would dwell *in*
thick *d.* *1 Ki* 8:12; *2 Chr* 6:1
made my bed *in* the *d.* *Job* 17:13
they walk on *in d.* *Ps* 82:5
thou hast laid me *in d.* 88:6
pestilence that walketh *in d.* 91:6
such as sit *in d.* and shadow. 107:10
made me to dwell *in d.* 143:3
lamp be put out *in d.* *Pr* 20:20
the fool walketh *in d.* *Eccl* 2:14
he eateth *in d.* 5:17
he departeth *in d.* 6:4
bring them that sit *in d.* *Isa* 42:7
to them that are *in d.* 49:9
wait for light, we walk *in d.* 59:9
as slippery ways *in d.* *Jer* 23:12
knoweth what is *in* the *d.* *Dan* 2:22
me shall not walk *in d.* *John* 8:12
that walketh *in d.* knoweth not. 12:35
should not abide *in d.* 46
brethren, are not *in d.* *1 Thes* 5:4
and walk *in d.* we lie. *1 John* 1:6
hateth his brother, is *in d.* 2:9
he that hateth his brother, is *in d.*
and walketh *in d.* 11

land of **darkness**

even to the *land of d.* *Job* 10:21
a *land of d.* as *d.* itself. 22
have I been a *land of d.*? *Jer* 2:31

darkness with *light*

divided *light* from the *d.* *Gen* 1:4
lights to divide *light* from *d.* 18
a land where *light* is as *d.* *Job* 10:22
light is short because of *d.* 17:12
driven from *light* into *d.* 18:18
his *light* I walked through *d.* 29:3
for *light*, there came *d.* 30:26
there ariseth *light* in *d.* *Ps* 112:4
d. and *light* are both alike. 139:12
far as *light* excelleth *d.* *Eccl* 2:13
d. for light, and *light* for *d.* *Isa* 5:20
walked in *d.* have seen great *light*,
upon them *light*. 9:2; *Mat* 4:16
make *d. light* before. *Isa* 42:16
I form *light* and create *d.* 45:7
walketh in *d.* and hath no *light*. 50:10
light, he make gross *d.* *Jer* 13:16
d. but not into *light*. *Lam* 3:2
Lord is *d.* and not *light*. *Amos* 5:18
in *d.* Lord shall be a *light*. *Mi* 7:8

light in thee be d. how great is that d.! Mat 6:23
tell in d. speak in light. 10:27
Luke 12:3
light to them that sit in d.
Luke 1:79; Rom 2:19
light which is in thee be not d.
Luke 11:35
light shineth in d. d. John 1:5
men loved d. rather than light. 3:19
while ye have light, lest d. 12:35
them from d. to light. Acts 26:18
works of d. put on light. Rom 13:12
to light hidden things of d. 1 Cor 4:5
light to shine out of d. 2 Cor 4:6
communion hath light with d.? 6:14
d. into marvellous light. 1 Pet 2:9
God is light, and in him is no d.
1 John 1:5
d. is past, and true light now. 2:8

out of **darkness**

the voice out of the d. Deut 5:22
deep things out of d. Job 12:22
he shall return out of d. 15:22
he shall not depart out of d. 30
brought them out of d. Ps 107:14
of blind shall see out of d. Isa 29:18

darling

deliver my d. from power. Ps 22:20
rescue my d. from the lions. 35:17

dart, -s

Joab took three d. in. 2 Sam 18:14
Hezekiah made d. and. 2 Chr 32:5*
the spear nor the d. Job 41:26
d. are counted as stubble. 29*
till a d. strike through. Pr 7:23*
to quench the fiery d. Eph 6:16
thrust through with a d. Heb 12:20*

dash

thou wilt d. their children. 2 Ki 8:12
lest d. them in pieces like. Ps 2:9
bear thee up, lest thou d. thy foot.
91:12; Mat 4:6; Luke 4:11
their bows shall d. the. Isa 13:18
I will d. them one. Jer 13:14

dashed

hand, hath d. in pieces. Ex 15:6
children also shall be d. Isa 13:16
Hos 13:16; Nah 3:10
the mother was d. upon. Hos 10:14

dasheth

that d. thy little ones. Ps 137:9

Dathan, see **Abiram**

daub, -ed, -ing

she d. the ark with slime. Ex 2:3
others d. it with. Ezek 13:10
say to them which d. it. 11
where is d. wherewith ye d. it ? 12
break down wall ye have d. 14
her prophets have d. them. 22:28

daughter

[1] *A female child, without particular meaning as to exact relationship,* Gen 34:1; Ex 2:21; Ruth 3:18. [2] *The inhabitants of a city or country,* Isa 16:2; Mat 21:5. [3] *In a figurative use, as daughters of music, or singing birds, which may mean the power of making music,* Eccl 12:4.

d. of my father, not d. Gen 20:12
whose d. art thou ? 24:23, 47
take my master's brother's d. 48
Dinah, the d. of Leah. 34:1
folly in lying with Jacob's d. 7
Shechem longeth for your d. 8
then will we take our d. and. 17
he had delight in Jacob's d. 19
but if it be a d. then. Ex 1:16
whether he gored a son or a d. 21:31
days are fulfilled for a d. Lev 12:6
nor take her daughter's d. 18:17
the d. of any priest, if she. 21:9
if the priest's d. be married. 22:12
if the priest's d. be a widow. 13
if he have no d. give. Num 27:9
every d. that possesseth an. 36:8
lieth with sister, d. of his father or d. of his mother. Deut 27:22
eye be evil towards her d. 28:56
Jephthah's d. came out. Judg 11:34
to lament Jephthah's d. Judg 11:40
not thine handmaid a d. 1 Sam 1:16†
when Saul's d. should have. 18:19
lamb was unto him as d. 2 Sam 12:3
Solomon took Pharaoh's d. 1 Ki 3:1
with the d. of Pharaoh. 11:1
the d. of Ahab was. 2 Ki 8:18
Jezebel, for she is a king's d. 9:34
and the d. of Caleb. 1 Chr 2:49
uncle's d. for his own d. Esth 2:7
O d. and consider, and. Ps 45:10
king's d. is all glorious within. 13
with shoes, O prince's d. S of S 7:1
about, backsliding d. Jer 31:22; 49:4
O d. dwelling in Egypt. 46:19
d. that dost inhabit Dibon. 48:18
deliver son nor d. Ezek 14:16; 18:20
is the mother, so is her d. 16:44
thou art thy mother's d. that. 45
for son or d. they may defile. 44:25
king's d. of the south. Dan 11:6
shall give him the d. of women. 17
again, and bare a d. Hos 1:6
O d. of troops. Mi 5:1
d. riseth up against her mother. 7:6
Mat 10:35; Luke 12:53
d. of my dispersed shall. Zeph 3:10
hath married the d. of. Mal 2:11
d. be of good comfort. Mat 9:22
Mark 5:34; Luke 8:48
he that loveth son or d. Mat 10:37
the d. of Herodias danced. 14:6
her d. was made whole from. 15:28
forth devil out of her d. Mark 7:26
he had one only d. Luke 8:42
not this woman, being d. 13:16
Pharaoh's d. took him. Acts 7:21
to be son of Pharaoh's d. Heb 11:24

daughter of Babylon

O d. of Babylon, who art. Ps 137:8
O d. of Babylon, sit on. Isa 47:1
against thee d. of Babylon. Jer 50:42
d. of Babylon is like a. 51:33
O Zion, that dwellest with the d. of Babylon. Zech 2:7

daughter of the Chaldeans

throne, O d. of Chaldeans. Isa 47:1
darkness, O d. of Chaldeans. 5

daughter of Edom

be glad, O d. of Edom. Lam 4:21
visit thine iniquity, O d. of Edom. 22

daughter of Egypt

O virgin, d. of Egypt. Jer 46:11
d. of Egypt shall be confounded. 24

daughter of Gallim

voice, O d. of Gallim. Isa 10:30

his **daughter**

Rachel his d. cometh. Gen 29:6
if a man sell his d. Ex 21:7
for his son or his d. Lev 21:2
to pass to his d. Num 27:8
between the father and his d. 30:16
nor his d. shalt thou. Deut 7:3
that maketh his d. to pass through fire. 18:10; 2 Ki 23:10
not any of us give his d. Judg 21:1
and give him his d. 1 Sam 17:25

daughter of Jerusalem

the d. of Jerusalem hath shaken.
2 Ki 19:21; Isa 37:22
I liken to thee, O d. of Jerusalem.
Lam 2:13
wag head at d. of Jerusalem. 15
come to d. of Jerusalem. Mi 4:8
rejoice, O d. of Jerusalem.
Zeph 3:14
shout, O d. of Jerusalem. Zech 9:9

daughter of Judah

trodden d. of Judah. Lam 1:15
strong holds of d. of Judah. 2:2
increased in d. of Judah mourning. 5

daughter-in-law

she was his d.-in-law. Gen 38:16
Tamar thy d.-in-law hath. 24
uncover thy d.-in-law. Lev 18:15
a man lie with his d.-in-law. 20:12
and Ruth her d.-in-law. Ruth 1:22
d.-in-law which loveth thee. 4:15
d.-in-law Phinehas' wife. 1 Sam 4:19
defileth his d.-in-law. Ezek 22:11
d.-in-law riseth up against the.
Mi 7:6; Mat 10:35; Luke 12:53

my **daughter**

gave my d. to this man. Deut 22:16
the tokens of my d.'s virginity. 17
him will I give my d. Josh 15:16
Judg 1:12
alas, my d. thou hast. Judg 11:35
behold, here is my d. a. 19:24
said unto her, go, my d. Ruth 2:2
blessed be thou of Lord, my d. 3:10
who art thou, my d.? 16
sit still, my d. till thou know. 18
a ruler, saying, my d. Mat 9:18
my d. is grievously vexed. 15:22
my little d. lieth at death. Mark 5:23

daughter of my people

spoiling of d. of my p. Isa 22:4
wind toward d. of my p. Jer 4:11
healed hurt of d. of my p. 6:14; 8:11
O, d. of my people, gird thee. 6:26
voice of cry of d. of my p. 8:19
for hurt of d. of my p. am I. 21
why is not health of d. of my p.? 22
weep for slain of d. of my p. 9:1
how shall I do for d. of my p.? 7
virgin d. of my p. is broken. 14:17
destruction of d. of my p. Lam 2:11
3:48
d. of my p. is become cruel. 4:3
the iniquity of the d. of my p. 6
meat in destruction of d. of my p. 10

daughter of Tarshish

a river, O d. of Tarshish. Isa 23:10

thy **daughter**

7 years for thy younger d. Gen 29:18
nor thy son, nor thy d. Ex 20:10
Deut 5:14
nakedness of thy daughter's d.
Lev 18:10
do not prostitute thy d. to. 19:29
thy d. shalt thou not. Deut 7:3
rejoice and thy d. 12:18; 16:11, 14
if thy son or thy d. entice. 13:6
I found not thy d. a maid. 22:17
give thy d. to my son. 2 Ki 14:9
2 Chr 25:18
said, thy d. is dead. Mark 5:35
Luke 8:49
devil is gone out of thy d. Mark 7:29

daughter of Tyre

d. of Tyre shall be there. Ps 45:12

daughter of Zidon

virgin, d. of Zidon. Isa 23:12

daughter of Zion

d. of Z. hath despised thee.
2 Ki 19:21; Isa 37:22
the gates of the d. of Z. Ps 9:14
d. of Z. left as a cottage. Isa 1:8
washed away filth of d. of Z. 4:4
against mount of d. of Z. 10:32; 16:1
loose thyself, d. of Z. 52:2
say to the d. of Z. thy. 62:11
voice of the d. of Z. Jer 4:31
I have likened d. of Z. to a. 6:2
of war against thee, O d. of Z. 23
from the d. of Z. beauty. Lam 1:6
Lord covereth the d. of Z. 2:1
slew in tabernacle of d. of Z. 4
to destroy wall of d. of Z. 8
the elders of d. of Z. sit on the. 10
shall I equal to thee, d. of Z.? 13
O wall of the d. of Z. let tears. 18
accomplished, O d. of Z. 4:22
beginning of sin to d. of Z. Mi 1:13
strong hold of the d. of Z. 4:8
labour to bring forth, O d. of Z. 10
arise and thresh, O d. of Z. 13
sing, O d. of Z. shout. Zeph 3:14
rejoice, O d. of Z. Zech 2:10; 9:9
tell ye the d. of Z. thy. Mat 21:5
fear not, d. of Z. thy. John 12:15

daughter of Zur

Cozbi the d. of Zur. Num 25:15

daughters

and when d. were born. Gen 6:1
sons of God saw the d. of men. 2
sons of God came in unto d. 4
to them which married his d. 19:14
both d. of Lot with child by. 36

a wife of *d.* of Canaan. *Gen* 24:3, 37
28:1, 6
the *d.* of the city came. 24:13
because of the *d.* of Heth. 27:46
happy am I, for the *d.* will. 30:13
thou hast carried away my *d.* 31:26
these *d.* are my *d.* 43
if thou afflict my *d.* 50
Dinah went out to see *d.* 34:1
give your *d.* to us, and take our *d.* 9
we give our *d.* to you, take *d.* 16
priest of Midian had seven *d. Ex* 2:16
deal with her after manner of *d.* 21:9
their *d.* go a whoring after. 34:16
the flesh of your *d.* shall. *Lev* 26:29
d. of Zelophehad. *Num* 26:33; 27:1
Josh 17:3
d. of Zelophehad speak. *Num* 27:7
so did the *d.* of Zelophehad. 36:10
no whore of the *d.* of. *Deut* 23:17
they took their *d.* to be. *Judg* 3:6
we will not give them of our *d.* 21:7
not give them wives of our *d.* 18
turn again, my *d.* *Ruth* 1:11, 12
nay, my *d.* it grieveth me. 13
take your *d.* to be. *1 Sam* 8:13
were king's *d.* virgins. *2 Sam* 13:18
Shallum, he and his *d.* *Neh* 3:12
d. are brought into bondage. 5:5
one of *d.* of Barzillai to wife. 7:63
Ezra 2:61
not give our *d.* to people. *Neh* 10:30
women so fair as *d.* of. *Job* 42:15
king's *d.* among thy. *Ps* 45:9
that our *d.* may be as. 144:12
d. have done virtuously. *Pr* 31:29
so is my love among *d.* *S of S* 2:2
the *d.* saw her and blessed. 6:9
ye careless *d.* give ear. *Isa* 32:9
thy *d.* shall be nursed at. 60:4
teach your *d.* wailing. *Jer* 9:20
give your *d.* to husbands, that. 29:6
her *d.* shall be burnt with. 49:2
cry, ye *d.* of Rabbah, gird ye. 3
because of all the *d.* of. *Lam* 3:51
set thy face against *d.* *Ezek* 13:17
and her *d.* Sodom, and her *d.* 16:46
idleness was in her and in her *d.* 49
bring back the captivity of her *d.* 53
when thy sister Sodom and *d.* 55
I will give them unto thee for *d.* 61
two women, the *d.* of one. 23:2
her *d.* shall be slain. 26:6, 8
d. shall go into captivity. 30:18
the *d.* of the nations shall. 32:16
your *d.* shall commit. *Hos* 4:13
I will not punish your *d.* when. 14
his wife was of the *d.* of. *Luke* 1:5
the same man had four *d. Acts* 21:9
whose *d.* ye are as long. *1 Pet* 3:6*

daughters *of Israel*

be no whore of *d. of Isr. Deut* 23:17
d. of Isr. went yearly. *Judg* 11:40
ye d. of Isr. weep. *2 Sam* 1:24

daughters *of Jerusalem*

comely, O *d. of Jerus.* *S of S* 1:5
charge you, O *d. of Jerus.* 2:7
3:5; 5:8; 8:4
love for the *d. of Jerus.* 3:10
my beloved, O *d. of Jerus.* 5:16
d. of Jerus. weep not. *Luke* 23:28

daughters *of Judah*

let *d. of Judah* be glad. *Ps* 48:11
the *d. of Judah* rejoiced. 97:8

daughters-in-law

arose with her *d.-in-law. Ruth* 1:6, 7
Naomi said to her two *d.-in-law.* 8

daughters *of Moab*

whoredom with *d. of M. Num* 25:1
so the *d. of M.* shall be at. *Isa* 16:2

daughters *of music*

he *d. of music* shall be. *Eccl* 12:4

daughters *of the Philistines*

woman of *d. of Phil.* *Judg* 14:1
een a woman of *d. of Phil.* 2
est *d. of Phil.* rejoice. *2 Sam* 1:20
delivered thee to *d. of Phil.*
Ezek 16:27
he *d. of Phil.* which despise. 57

daughters *of Shiloh*

. *of Shiloh* come out, catch a wife
of *d. of Shiloh.* *Judg* 21:21

daughters joined with *sons*

he begat *sons* and *d.* *Gen* 5:4
7:10, 13, 16; 11:11
thy *sons* and *d.* bring out. 19:12
to kiss my *sons* and *d.* 31:28
he kissed his *sons* and *d.* and. 55
all his *sons* and *d.* rose to. 37:35
them on your *sons* and *d.* *Ex* 3:22
with our *sons* and with our *d.* 10:9
she have born him *sons* or *d.* 21:4
ear-rings of your *sons* and *d.* 32:2
take of their *d.* to thy *sons.* 34:16
thou, thy *sons* and *d.* shall eat in the.
Lev 10:14; *Num* 18:11, 19
given his *sons* and *d.* *Num* 21:29
Zelophehad had no *sons,* but *d.*
26:33; *Josh* 17:3
ye and your *sons* and *d.* rejoice.
Deut 12:12
sons and *d.* they have burnt in fire.
31; *2 Ki* 17:17; *Jer* 7:31; 32:35
thy *sons* and *d.* given to. *Deut* 28:32
beget *sons* and *d.* but shalt not. 41
the flesh of thy *sons* and *d.* 53
provoking of his *sons* and *d.* 32:19
Achan, his *sons* and *d.* *Josh* 7:24
d. of Manasseh had inheritance
among *sons.* 17:6
gave their *d.* to their *sons.* *Judg* 3:6
took in thirty *d.* for his *sons.* 12:9
Peninnah, her *sons* and *d.* portions.
1 Sam 1:4
Hannah bare three *sons* and two *d.*
2:21
their *sons* and *d.* were taken. 30:3
grieved, every man for *sons* and *d.* 6
lacking, neither *sons* nor *d.* 19
were yet *sons* and *d.* born to David.
2 Sam 5:13; *1 Chr* 14:3
saved lives of thy *sons* and *d.*
2 Sam 19:5
Sheshan had no *sons* but *d.*
1 Chr 2:34
Shimei had sixteen *sons* six *d.* 4:27
died, and had no *sons* but *d.* 23:22
Heman fourteen *sons* and three *d.*
25:5
had 28 *sons* and 60 *d.* *2 Chr* 11:21
Abijah begat 22 *sons* and *d.* 13:21
wives and begat *sons* and *d.* 24:3
200,000 women, *sons* and *d.* 28:8
our *sons, d.* and wives are in. 29:9
genealogy of their *sons* and *d.* 31:18
of their *d.* for their *sons.* *Ezra* 9:2
give not your *d.* to their *sons.* 12
Neh 13:25
fight for your *sons* and *d.* *Neh* 4:14
our *sons* and our *d.* are many 5:2
bondage our *sons* and our *d.* 5
their *sons* and *d.* clave to. 10:28
born to Job 7 *sons* and 3 *d.* *Job* 1:2
42:13
a day when *sons* and *d.* 1:13, 18
their *sons* and *d.* to devils. *Ps* 106:37
shed blood of their *sons* and *d.* 38
my *sons* from far, and my *d.* from.
Isa 43:6
sons in their arms, and thy *d.* 49:22
a name better than of *s.* and *d.* 56:5
devoured *sons* and *d.* *Jer* 3:24
eat that which thy *sons* and *d.* 5:17
sons and their *d.* shall die. 11:22
none to bury their *sons* and *d.* 14:16
have *sons* and *d.* in this place. 16:2
concerning the *sons* and *d.* 3
eat the flesh of *sons* and *d.* 19:9
wives and beget *sons* and *d.* 29:6
we, our *sons* and our *d.* drink. 35:8
sons and thy *d.* taken captives. 48:46
deliver neither *sons* nor *d.*
Ezek 14:16, 18
brought forth, *sons* and *d.* 22
sons and *d.* and sacrificed. 16:20
mine, and bare *sons* and *d.* 23:4
her *sons* and *d.* and slew her. 10, 25
they shall slay their *sons* and *d.* 47
your *sons* and *d.* fall by sword.
24:21; *Amos* 7:17
take from them their *sons* and *d.*
Ezek 24:25
sons and *d.* prophesy. *Joel* 2:28
Acts 2:17
will sell your *sons* and *d.* *Joel* 3:8
shall be my *sons* and *d.* *2 Cor* 6:18

daughters *of Syria*

reproach of *d. of Syria. Ezek* 16:57

two **daughters**

I have *two d.* let me. *Gen* 19:8
take thy wife and thy *two d.* 15
in a cave, he and his *two d.* 30
Laban had *two d.* Leah and. 29:16
fourteen years for thy *two d.* 31:41
went out with her *two d.* *Ruth* 1:7
Hannah conceived and bare *two d.*
1 Sam 2:21
two *d.* were Merab and Michal. 14:49
the horseleech hath *two d.* *Pr* 30:15

daughters *of the uncircumcised*

lest *d. of the uncirc.* *2 Sam* 1:20

daughters *of Zion*

go forth, O ye *d. of Z.* *S of S* 3:11
because the *d.* of *Z.* *Isa* 3:16
smite head of the *d.* of *Z.* 17
washed away filth of *d. of Z.* 4:4

David

Jesse begat *D.* *Ruth* 4:22; *Mat* 1:6
Luke 3:31
Spirit of Lord came upon *D.*
1 Sam 16:13
send me *D.* thy son. 19
D. came to Saul. 21
D. played. 23; 18:10; 19:9
D. was youngest. 17:14
D. returned from Saul. 15
D. heard the words of Goliath. 23
Eliab's anger kindled against *D.* 28
Saul armed *D.* 38
when Goliath saw *D.* 42
the Philistines cursed *D.* 43
D. prevailed over Philistine. 50
as *D.* returned from slaughter. 57
soul of Jonathan knit to *D.* 18:1
Jonathan and *D.* made a covenant. 3
D. went out whithersoever Saul. 5
D. hath slain ten thousands. 7; 29:5
Saul eyed *D.* from that day. 18:9
D. behaved himself wisely in all. 14
all Israel and Judah loved *D.* 16
on this manner spake *D.* 24
knew the Lord was with *D.* 28
and Saul became *D.*'s enemy. 29
spake to his servants to kill *D.* 19:1
against innocent blood to slay *D.*? 5
sought to smite *D.* but *D.* 10, 18
D. is at Naioth. 19
where are Samuel and *D.*? 22
D. asked leave of me to. 20:6, 28
and Jonathan caused *D.* to. 17
D. hid himself. 24
D.'s place was empty. 25, 27
for he was grieved for *D.* 34
wept one with another till *D.* 41
afraid at the meeting of *D.* 21:1
D. arose, and fled to Achish. 10
is not this *D.* the king ? 11; 29:3
D. departed and escaped to. 22:1
and *D.* went thence to Mizpeh. 3
D. departed and came into forest. 5
who is so faithful as *D.*? 14
their hand also is with *D.* 17
D. inquired of the Lord. 23:2, 4
30:8; *2 Sam* 2:1; 3:19, 22; 21:1
D. and his men went to. *1 Sam* 23:5
D. knew that Saul practised. 9
D. was in the wilderness of Ziph. 15
D. and his men were in. 24
Saul returned from pursuing *D.* 28
D. is in wilderness of En-gedi. 24:1
D.'s heart smote him. 5
D. stayed his servants. 7
this thy voice, my son *D.*? 16; 26:17
D. sware unto Saul. 24:22
D. went to Paran. 25:1
D. sent out ten young men. 5
do God to the enemies of *D.* 22
doth not *D.* hide himself in ? 26:1
and *D.* beheld the place where. 5
D. took the spear and the cruse. 12
Saul knew *D.*'s voice. 17
return, my son *D.* 21
D. said, I shall perish by the. 27:1
D. was fled to Gath. 4
D. invaded Geshurites. 8
so did *D.* and so will be. 11
it to thy neighbour, to *D.* 28:17
is not this *D.*? 29:3

then Achish called D. 1 Sam 29:6
when D. and his men were. 30:1
and D.'s two wives were taken. 5
D. pursued. 10
D. smote them from the twilight. 17
D. recovered all. 18, 19
D. took the flocks. 20
D. took hold on clothes. 2 Sam 1:11
D. called one of the young men. 15
D. lamented over Saul. 17
D. sent messengers to men. 2:5
house of Judah followed D. 10
house of D. waxed stronger. 3:1
unto D. were sons born in Hebron. 2
except as Lord hath sworn to D. 9
ye sought for D. in times past. 17
D. said, I and my kingdom are. 28
came all tribes of Israel to D. 5:1
thinking, D. cannot come in. 6
D. took the strong-hold of Zion. 7
D. grew great. 10
D. perceived the Lord had. 12
D. heard of it, and went down. 17
D. burnt their images. 21
D. went to bring up the ark. 6:2
D. all Israel played before the. 5
and D. was afraid of the Lord. 9
D. danced. 14
so D. brought up the ark. 15
what can D. say more to thee?
7:20; 1 Chr 17:18
D. smote the Philistines. 2 Sam 8:1
D. smote Hadadezer. 3
Lord preserved D. 6, 14
D. took shields of gold. 7; 1 Chr 18:7
D. gat him a name. 2 Sam 8:13
D. reigned over. 15; 1 Chr 18:14
D. reigned; executed. 2 Sam 8:15
D. sent to comfort. 10:2; 1 Chr 19:2
thinkest thou D. doth honour thy?
2 Sam 10:3; 1 Chr 19:3
D. slew men of 700. 2 Sam 10:18
D. sent and enquired after. 11:3
D. sent for Uriah. 6
D. wrote a letter to Joab. 14
the thing D. had done displeased. 27
D.'s anger was kindled. 12:5
D. said, I have sinned against. 13
D. besought God for child, D. 16
D. perceived child was dead. 19
and D. comforted Bath-sheba. 24
D. fought against Rabbah and. 29
king's crown was set on D. 30
D. sent to Tamar. 13:7
tidings came to D. 30
D. went up by the ascent of. 15:30
Shimei cast stones at D. 16:6
said unto him, curse D. 10
I will arise and pursue after D. 17:1
send quickly and tell D. 16
then D. arose. 22
D. was come to Mahanaim. 27
honey for D. 29
D. numbered the people that. 18:1
D. sat between the two gates. 24
we have also more right in D. 19:43
we have no part in D. 20:1
and D. came to his house. 3
he that is for D. let him go. 11
Ishbi-benob thought to have slain D.
21:16
mercy unto D. 22:51; Ps 18:50
the last words of D. 2 Sam 23:1
mighty men D. had. 8; 1 Chr 11:10
D. longed and said. 2 Sam 23:15
D.'s heart smote him. 24:10
D. built there an altar unto. 25
and D. our Lord. 1 Ki 1:11
D. slept with his fathers. 2:10
slew them, my father D. not. 32
knowest what thou didst to D. 44
thou wilt walk as thy father D. 3:14
who hath given D. a wise son. 5:7
D. to be over my people. 8:16
I am risen up in the room of D. 20
as I promised to D. 9:5
as I built for D. 11:38
for this afflict the seed of D. 39
portion have we in D.? see to thine
own house, D. 12:16; 2 Chr 10:16
turned kingdom to D. 1 Chr 10:14
D. made a covenant with them. 11:3
thine are we, D. then D. 12:18
they helped D. against the. 21

the fame of D. went out. 1 Chr 14:17
D. was clothed with a robe. 15:27
set the ark in tent D. had. 16:1
and D. returned to bless his. 43
Ornan saw D. bowed to D. 21:21
so when D. was old and full. 23:1
D. blessed Lord before the. 29:10
great mercy unto D. 2 Chr 1:8
began to seek after God of D. 34:3
of sons of D. Hattush. Ezra 8:2
against sepulchres of D. Neh 3:16
with musical instruments of D. 12:36
prayers of D. the son of. Ps 72:20
I will not lie unto D. 89:35
swarest to D. 49
Lord, remember D. 132:1
hath sworn to D. 11
there will I make horn of D. to 17
is like the tower of D. S of S 4:4
on the throne of D. and. Isa 9:7
woe to Ariel, city where D. 29:1
the sure mercies of D. 55:3
Acts 13:34
sitting on throne of D. Jer 17:25
I will raise to D. a righteous. 23:5
branch to grow up unto D. 33:15
D. shall never want a man to. 17
none to sit on throne of D. 36:30
of music like D. Amos 6:5
will I raise up the tabernacle of D.
9:11; Acts 15:16
feeble be as D. and D. Zech 12:8
son of D. have mercy. Mat 9:27
15:22; 20:30, 31; Mark 10:47, 48
Luke 18:38, 39
D. did when he was an hungered?
Mat 12:3; Mark 2:25; Luke 6:3
is not this the son of D.? Mat 12:23
Hosanna to the son of D. 21:9, 15
Christ is the son of D. 22:42
Mark 12:35
if D. then call him Lord. Mat 22:45
Mark 12:37; Luke 20:41, 44
the kingdom of our father D.
Mark 11:10
Christ cometh of the seed of D.
John 7:42
speak of patriarch D. Acts 2:29
for D. is not ascended into the. 34
he raised up to them D. to. 13:22
for D. fell on sleep. 36
made of the seed of D. Rom 1:3
2 Tim 2:8
even as D. also describeth. Rom 4:6
certain day, saying, in D. Heb 4:7
time would fail me to tell of D. 11:32
hath the key of D. Rev 3:7
root of D. 5:5; 22:16

see **city, father**

days of **David**

famine in the days of D. 2 Sam 21:1
days of D. drew nigh. 1 Ki 2:1
number was in days of D. 1 Chr 7:2
in the days of D. were. Neh 12:46
drave out unto days of D. Acts 7:45

hand of **David**

require it at h. of D. 1 Sam 20:16
thee into h. of D. 2 Sam 3:8
by h. of my servant D. I will. 18
fell by h. of D. 21:22; 1 Chr 20:8

house of **David**

covenant with h. of D. 1 Sam 20:16
the h. of Saul and D. 2 Sam 3:1, 6
let h. of thy servant D. 7:26
Israel rebelled against the h. of D.
1 Ki 12:19; 2 Chr 10:19
none followed h. of D. 1 Ki 12:20
shall kingdom return to h. of D. 26
a child be born to the h. of D. 13:2
rent kingdom from h. of D. 14:8
2 Ki 17:21
not destroy the h. of D. 2 Chr 21:7
thrones of the h. of D. Ps 122:5
it was told the h. of D. Isa 7:2
hear, O h. of D. 13; Jer 21:12
key of h. of D. I will lay. Isa 22:22
that the glory of h. of D. Zech 12:7
feeble as D. and the h. of D. 8
I will pour on h. of D. the spirit. 10
the family of the h. of D. shall. 12
a fountain opened to h. of D. 13:1
was Joseph, of h. of D. Luke 1:27

horn of salvation in h. of D. Luke 1:69
was of h. and lineage of D. 2:4

David *joined with* *king*

is not this D. the king? 1 Sam 21:11
they anointed D. king. 2 Sam 2:4
time that D. was king in Hebron. 11
and king D. himself followed. 3:31
king D. made a league ... anointed
D. king. 5:3; 1 Chr 11:3; 12:31, 38
which king D. did dedicate to Lord.
2 Sam 8:11; 1 Chr 26:26
against king, even D. 2 Sam 20:21
than throne of king D. 1 Ki 1:37
servants came to bless king D. 47
D. the king rejoiced. 1 Chr 29:9
to D. the king a wise son. 2 Chr 2:12
ordained by D. king of. 29:27
Ezra 3:10
serve Lord and D. their king. Jer 30:9
seek Lord and D. their king. Hos 3:5
D. the king and D. the king. Mat 1:6
raised up D. to be king. Acts 13:22

servant **David**

by hand of my servant D. 2 Sam 3:18
go and tell my servant D. 7:5, 8
let the house of thy servant D. be
established. 26; 1 Chr 17:24
shewed thy servant D. 1 Ki 3:6
kept with thy servant D. that. 8:24
keep with thy servant D. 25, 26
2 Chr 6:16
done for D. his servant. 1 Ki 8:66
D. my servant's sake, and for Jerusalem's. 11:13, 32, 34; Ps 132:10
Isa 37:35
D. my servant may have a light.
1 Ki 11:36
keep my statutes, as my servant D.
38; 14:8
mercies of D. thy servant. 2 Chr 6:42
chose D. also his servant. Ps 78:70
sworn unto D. my servant. 89:3
I have found D. my servant. 20
who delivered D. his servant. 144:10
broken with D. my servant. Jer 33:21
multiply seed of D. my servant. 22
away the seed of D. my servant. 26
my servant D. shall feed them.
Ezek 34:23
my servant D. shall be a prince. 24
D. my servant shall be king. 37:24
servant D. shall be their prince. 25
house of his servant D. Luke 1:69
mouth of thy servant D. Acts 4:25

dawn, -ing

they rose about the d. Josh 6:15
woman in the d. of day. Judg 19:26
neither let it see the d. of. Job 3:9
full of tossings to the d. of. 7:4
I prevented the d. of. Ps 119:147
as it began to d. towards. Mat 28:1
till day d. and day-star. 2 Pet 1:19

day

The word day is used of [1] *one period of the earth's revolution, or twenty-four hours,* Gen 7:24; Job 3:6. *This period the Hebrews reckoned as beginning at sunset,* Lev 23:32. [2] *The period between dawn and dark, variable in different latitudes and at different seasons,* Gen 8:22, Ps 19:2; 2 Pet 1:19. [3] *Any period of action or state of being, without definite reference to time,* Job 19:25; Zech 4:10; Hos 1:11; Eccl. 7:14; Ezek 30:9. *In the day that usually has merely the meaning of when, and is sometimes so translated,* 1 Ki 2:8; Isa 30:26. "*In thy days*" *means* "*in thy lifetime,*" 1 Ki 11:12.

God called the light d. Gen 1:
let me go, for d. breaketh. 32:2
if he continue a d. or two. Ex 21:2
journeyed not, till the d. it. 40:3
every thing upon his d. Lev 23:3
the d. I smote first-born. Num 3:1
offer his offering on his d. 7:1
each d. for a year shall bear. 14:3
husband disallow her on d. 30:8, 1
d. thou stoodest before. Deut 4:1
no manner of similitude on d.

from *d.* thou didst depart. *Deut* 9:7
have been rebellious from *d.* 24
at his *d.* thou shalt give him. 24:15
till *d.* I bid you shout. *Josh* 6:10
on *d.* we came forth to go to. 9:12
sun hasted not down about a *d.* 10:13
was no *d.* like that before or. 14
when it is *d.* we shall kill. *Judg* 16:2*
from the *d.* that Israel came out. 30
what *d.* thou buyest the. *Ruth* 4:5
Lord told Samuel a *d.* *1 Sam* 9:15
behold the *d.* of which the. 24:4
smite him, or his *d.* shall. 26:10
while it was yet *d.* *2 Sam* 3:35
Jer 15:9
d. he forced his sister. *2 Sam* 13:32
from *d.* king departed, till *d.* 19:24
on *d.* thou goest out. *1 Ki* 2:37, 42
till *d.* the Lord sendeth rain. 17:14
it fell on a *d.* that Elisha passed.
2 Ki 4:8, 11, 18
they make an end in a *d.*? *Neh* 4:2
and labour in the *d.* 22
d. of feasting. *Esth* 9:17, 18, 19
feasted, every one his *d.* *Job* 1:4
a *d.* when sons of God. 6, 13; 2:1
let *d.* perish wherein I was. 3:3
till he accomplish his *d.* 14:6
be astonied at his *d.* 18:20
he shall stand at latter *d.* 19:25
the wicked is reserved to *d.* 21:30
d. unto *d.* uttereth speech. *Ps* 19:2
seeth that his *d.* is coming. 37:13
nor remembered *d.* when he. 78:42
a *d.* in thy courts is better. 84:10
seven times a *d.* do I. 119:164
and more to perfect *d.* *Pr* 4:18
he will come home at the *d.* 7:20*
knowest not what a *d.* may. 27:1
till *d.* break, and. *S of S* 2:17; 4:6
from *d.* that Ephraim. *Isa* 7:17
before the *d.* was, I am he. 43:13
a *d.* for a man to afflict his soul ? this
a fast, an acceptable *d.* to ? 58:5
d. of vengeance of God. 61:2; 63:4
prepare them for the *d.* *Jer* 12:3
there shall they be till *d.* 27:22
d. they built it, even to this *d.* 32:31
d. I spake, even to this *d.* 36:2
till *d.* Jerusalem was taken. 38:28
because of the *d.* that cometh. 47:4
woe, for their *d.* is come. 50:27
appointed thee each *d.* *Ezek* 4:6
behold the *d.* behold it is. 7:10
wicked prince, whose *d.* 21:25, 29
from *d.* thou wast created. 28:15
howl ye, woe worth the *d.*! 30:2
for the *d.* is near. 3
at Tehaphnehes the *d.* shall. 18
petition three times a *d.* *Dan* 6:10
13
will ye do in solemn *d.*? *Hos* 9:5
a *d.* of darkness and. *Joel* 2:2
him that maketh *d.* dark. *Amos* 5:8
the end thereof as a bitter *d.* 8:10
and *d.* shall be dark. *Mi* 3:6
the *d.* of thy watchmen. 7:4
before decree, the *d.* pass. *Zeph* 2:2
till the *d.* that I rise up to. 3:8
who hath despised *d.*? *Zech* 4:10
who may abide the *d.*? *Mal* 3:2
d. cometh that shall burn. 4:1
till the *d.* Noe entered. *Mat* 24:38
Luke 17:27
come in a *d.* when he looketh not.
Mat 24:50; *Luke* 12:46
neither know the *d.* nor. *Mat* 25:13
great while before *d.* *Mark* 1:35
dumb till *d.* these things. *Luke* 1:20
child grew till *d.* of his shewing. 80
trespass seven times in a *d.* 17:4
Son of man be in his *d.* 24
raise it again at last *d.* *John* 6:39
raise him up at last *d.* 40, 44, 54
Abraham rejoiced to see my *d.* 8:56
work of him while it is *d.* 9:4
until the *d.* in which he. *Acts* 1:2
on a set *d.* Herod sat upon. 12:21
when it was *d.* 16:35; 23:12; 27:39
he hath appointed a *d.* 17:31
anchors, and wished for *d.* 27:29
wrath against the *d.* of. *Rom* 2:5
. is at hand, let us therefore. 13:12
regardeth a *d.* regardeth it. 14:6
for the *d.* shall declare it. *1 Cor* 3:13
behold, now is the *d.* of. *2 Cor* 6:2
ye are sealed to the *d.* *Eph* 4:30
will perform it until *d.* *Phil* 1:6
ye are all children of *d.* *1 Thes* 5:5
let us who are of *d.* be sober. 8
he limiteth a certain *d.* *Heb* 4:7
afterward spoken of another *d.*? 8
the more as ye see the *d.* 10:25
till the *d.* dawn, and the. *2 Pet* 1:19
hasting to coming of the *d.* 3:12
in the Spirit on the Lord's *d.* *Rev.* 1:10
for an hour and a *d.* 9:15

see **atonement, battle, calamity, darkness, evil, holy, last**

all the **day**

on thee do I wait *all the d.* *Ps* 25:5
forth thy salvation *all the d.* 71:15
shall they rejoice *all the d.* 89:16
reproach me *all the d.* 102:8
law is my meditation *all the d.* 119:97
plowman plow *all d.* *Isa* 28:24*
spread out hands *all the d.* 65:2
a fire that burneth *all the d.* 5
and faint *all the d.* *Lam* 1:13
turneth hand against me *all d.* 3:3
derision to my people *all the d.* 14
their device against me *all the d.* 62
here *all the d.* idle ? *Mat* 20:6

all the **day** *long*

longing for them *all the d. long.*
Deut 28:32
shall cover him *all the d. long.* 33:12
roaring *all the d. long.* *Ps* 32:3
thy praise *all the d. long.* 35:28
I go mourning *all the d. long.* 38:6
imagine deceits *all the d. long.* 12
God we boast *all the d. long.* 44:8
thy sake are killed *all the d. long.* 22
righteousness *all the d. long.* 71:24
for *all the d. long* have I. 73:14
greedily *all the d. long.* *Pr* 21:26
in fear of Lord *all the d. long.* 23:17
all d. long I stretched. *Rom* 10:21

by **day**, *and day by day*

spake to Joseph *d. by d.* *Gen* 39:10
went before them *by d.* *Ex* 13:21
not away pillar of cloud *by d.* 22
two lambs of the first year *d. by d.*
29:38; *Num* 28:3
cloud was upon the tabernacle *by d.*
fire by. *Ex* 40:38; *Num* 9:16*
cloud was on them *by d.* *Num* 10:34
14:14; *Deut* 1:23; *Neh* 9:19
he could not do it *by d.* *Judg* 6:27
nor birds rest *by d.* *2 Sam* 21:10
d. by d. there came to. *1 Chr* 12:22
of the sickness *d. by d.* *2 Chr* 21:15
thus they did *d. by d.* and. 24:11
priests praised Lord *d. by d.* 30:21
let it be given *d. by d.* *Ezra* 6:9
d. by d. he read in law. *Neh* 8:18
nor arrow that flieth *by d.* *Ps* 91:5
sun shall not smite thee *by d.* 121:6
sun to rule *by d.* for his. 136:8
no more thy light *by d.* *Isa* 60:19
the sun for a light *by d.* *Jer* 31:35
and remove *by d.* in. *Ezek* 12:3
I brought forth my stuff *by d.* 7
give us *d. by d.* our. *Luke* 11:3
man renewed *d. by d.* *2 Cor* 4:16
gates not be shut *by d.* *Rev* 21:25

day *of death*

I know not *d. of* my *death.* *Gen* 27:2
be a Nazarite to *d. of* his *death.*
Judg 13:7
see Saul till *d. of death.* *1 Sam* 15:35
no child till *d. of death.* *2 Sam* 6:23
shut up to *d. of* their *death.* 20:3
Uzziah was a leper to the *d. of* his
death. *2 Ki* 15:5; *2 Chr* 26:21
d. of death better than *d.* *Eccl* 7:1
power in the *d. of death.* 8:8
prison till *d. of* his *death.* *Jer* 52:11
portion, till *d. of* his *death.* 34

every **day**

a certain rate *every d.* *Ex* 16:4
offer a bullock *every d.* 29:36
sought David *every d.* *1 Sam* 23:14
David mourned for his son *every d.*
2 Sam 13:37
daily rate for *every d.* *2 Ki* 25:30
minister, as *every d.* *1 Chr* 16:37
a certain rate *every d.* *2 Chr* 8:13
duty *every d.* required. 14; *Ezra* 3:4
singers, due for *every d.* *Neh* 11:23
and the porters *every d.* his. 12:47
Mordecai walked *every d.* *Esth* 2:11
angry with wicked *every d.* *Ps* 7:11
every d. they wrest my words. 56:5
every d. will I bless thee. 145:2
feared continually *every d.* *Isa* 51:13
and my name *every d.* is. 52:5
prepare *every d.* a goat. *Ezek* 43:25
sumptuously *every d.* *Luke* 16:19
esteemeth *every d.* alike. *Rom* 14:5

feast **day**

trumpet on solemn *feast-d.* *Ps* 81:3
they said, not on the *feast-d.*
Mat 26:5*; *Mark* 14:2*
feast-d. many believed. *John* 2:23*

first **day**

and morning were *first d.* *Gen* 1:5
on *first d.* of the month mountains.
8:5, 13; *Ex* 40:2, 17; *Lev* 23:24
the *first d.* put away leaven, whoso
eateth from *first d.* *Ex* 12:15
in the *first d.* an holy convocation. 16
Lev 23:7, 35; *Num* 28:18; 29:1
first d. shall be sabbath. *Lev* 23:39
shall take on *first d.* boughs of. 40
spake to Moses on *first d.* *Num* 1:1
assembled congregation on *first d.* 18
on the *first d.* Aaron went. 33:38
flesh sacrificed *first d.* not. *Deut* 16:4
on *first d.* to sanctify. *2 Chr* 29:17
from the *first d.* began. *Ezra* 3:6
on the *first d.* began he to go up . . . on
first d. came he to Jerusalem. 7:9
sat down on *first d.* of the. 10:16
by *first d.* of first month they. 17
brought law on *first d.* of. *Neh* 8:2
from *first* unto last *d.* he read. 18
in *first d.* word of Lord. *Ezek* 26:1
29:17; 31:1; 32:1; *Hag* 1:1
in *first d.* of the month. *Ezek* 45:18
from *first d.* thou didst. *Dan* 10:12
first d. of unleavened bread.
Mat 26:17; *Mark* 14:12
first d. I came into Asia. *Acts* 20:18
fellowship from *first d.* *Phil* 1:5

see **week**

second **day**

and morning *second d.* *Gen* 1:8
went out the *second d.* *Ex* 2:13
on *second d.* Nethaneel. *Num* 7:18
on *second d.* offer twelve. 29:17
second d. they compassed. *Josh* 6:14
took Lachish on *second d.* 10:32
Benjamin *second d.* *Judg* 20:24
eat no meat *second d.* *1 Sam* 20:34
began to build *second d.* *2 Chr* 3:2
on the *second d.* were. *Neh* 8:13
to Esther the *second d.* *Esth* 7:2
second d. after he had. *Jer* 41:4
second d. thou shalt offer a kid.
Ezek 43:22

third **day**

and morning *third d.* *Gen* 1:13
on *third d.* Abraham saw. 22:4
it was told Laban on *third d.* 31:22
on *third d.* when they were. 34:25
ready against the *third d.* for the
third d. Lord will. *Ex* 19:11, 15
remainder of flesh of sacrifice on
third d. shall be. *Lev* 7:17; 19:6
purify himself on *third d.*
Num 19:12; 31:19
sprinkle unclean on *third d.* 19:19
on *third d.* eleven bullocks. 29:20
to cities on *third d.* *Josh* 9:17
Benjamin the *third d.* *Judg* 20:30
to Rehoboam *third d.* *1 Ki* 12:12
2 Chr 10:12
on the *third d.* go up. *2 Ki* 20:5, 8
house finished on *third d.* *Ezra* 6:15
on *third d.* Esther put on. *Esth* 5:1
in *third d.* he will raise. *Hos* 6:2
and be raised again the *third d.*
Mat 16:21; 17:23; *Luke* 9:22
the *third d.* rise again. *Mat* 20:19
Mark 9:31; 10:34; *Luke* 18:33
24:7, 46
sepulchre be made sure till the *third*
d. *Mat* 27:64

the *third d.* I shall be. *Luke* 13:32
to-day is the *third d.* since. 24:21
on *third d.* there was a. *John* 2:1
the *third d.* we cast out. *Acts* 27:19
he rose again the *third d.* *1 Cor* 15:4

fourth **day**

and morning *fourth d.* *Gen* 1:19
fourth d. ten bullocks. *Num* 29:23
on the *fourth d.* they assembled. *2 Chr* 20:26
on *fourth d.* was silver. *Ezra* 8:33
Zechariah on *fourth d.* *Zech* 7:1

fifth **day**

and morning *fifth d.* *Gen* 1:23
fifth d. nine bullocks. *Num* 29:26
in the *fifth d.* of. *Ezek* 1:1, 2; 8:1
in the *fifth d.* one came. 33:21

sixth **day**

and morning *sixth d.* *Gen* 1:31
on *sixth d.* gather twice. *Ex* 16:5, 22
giveth you on the *sixth d.* bread. 29
on the *sixth d.* Eliasaph. *Num* 7:42
on *sixth d.* eight bullocks. 29:29

seventh **day**

seventh d. God ended his. *Gen* 2:2
God blessed *seventh d.* 3; *Ex* 20:11
leaven from first *d.* to *seventh d.* *Ex* 12:15
on *seventh d.* an holy convocation. 16; *Lev* 23:8; *Num* 28:25
in the *seventh d.* shall be. *Ex* 13:6
but the *seventh d.* is the sabbath. 16:26; 20:10; *Lev* 23:3; *Deut* 5:14
went some on *seventh d.* *Ex* 16:27
out of his place on *seventh d.* 29
seventh d. he called Moses. 24:16
seventh d. God rested. 31:17 *Heb* 4:4
seventh d. thou shalt rest. *Ex* 34:21
seventh d. there shall be holy *d.* 35:2
priest shall look on him *seventh d.* *Lev* 13:5, 6, 27, 32, 34, 51; 14:39
the *seventh d.* he shall shave. 14:9 *Num* 6:9
seventh d. he shall be clean. *Num* 19:12
on the *seventh d.* purify. 19; 31:19
wash your clothes on *seventh d.* 31:24
on *seventh d.* a solemn. *Deut* 16:8
seventh d. compass. *Josh* 6:4, 15
seventh d. they said to. *Judg* 14:15
on the *seventh d.* he told her. 17
seventh d. child died. *2 Sam* 12:18
in *seventh d.* battle was. *1 Ki* 20:29
seventh d. came Nebuzar-adan. *2 Ki* 25:8
seventh d. when Ahasuerus was. *Esth* 1:10
seventh d. word came. *Ezek* 30:20
and so do the *seventh d.* 45:20
spake of *seventh d.* on this wise, God did rest *seventh d.* *Heb* 4:4

eighth **day**

on the *eighth d.* thou. *Ex* 22:30
on the *eighth d.* Moses. *Lev* 9:1
on *eighth d.* flesh of fore-skin. 12:3
eighth d. take two he-lambs. 14:10
two turtles *on eighth d.* 23; 15:14 *Num* 6:10
the *eighth d.* it shall be. *Lev* 22:27
on the *eighth d.* shall be an. 23:36
on the *eighth d.* a sabbath. 39
eighth d. a solemn assembly. *Num* 29:35; *2 Chr* 7:9; *Neh* 8:18
on *eighth d.* priests. *Ezek* 43:27
eighth d. came to circumcise child. *Luke* 1:59; *Acts* 7:8; *Phil* 3:5

ninth **day**

your souls in *ninth d.* *Lev* 23:32
on *ninth d.* famine was. *2 Ki* 25:3 *Jer* 52:6
the *ninth d.* the city. *Jer* 39:2

tenth **day**

tenth d. of this month. *Ex* 12:3
tenth d. of month ye shall afflict. *Lev* 16:29; 23:27; *Num* 29:7
on *tenth d.* the trumpet of. *Lev* 25:9
of Jordan on *tenth d.* *Josh* 4:19
tenth d. Nebuchadnezzar came. *2 Ki* 25:1; *Jer* 52:4; *Ezek* 24:1
tenth d. burnt house of. *Jer* 52:12
on *tenth d.* elders came. *Ezek* 20:1
on *tenth d.* hand of Lord was. 40:1

eleventh **day**

eleventh d. Pagiel offered. *Num* 7:72

twelfth **day**

on *twelfth d.* Ahira. *Num* 7:78
departed on *twelfth d.* to. *Ezra* 8:31
on *twelfth d.* word came. *Ezek* 29:1

thirteenth **day**

scribes were called on *thirteenth d.* *Esth* 3:12
destroy all Jews on *thirteenth d.* 13; 8:12; 9:1
thirteenth d. of Adar they. 9:17
Jews assembled on *thirteenth d.* 18

fourteenth **day**

lamb till *fourteenth d.* *Ex* 12:6
on *fourteenth d.* ye shall eat. 18
fourteenth d. is the Lord's. *Lev* 23:5 *Num* 9:3, 5; 28:16; *Josh* 5:10 *2 Chr* 30:15; 35:1; *Ezra* 6:19 *Ezek* 45:21
on *fourteenth d.* at even. *Num* 9:11
gathered on *fourteenth d.* *Esth* 9:15
fourteenth d. of same rested. 17
this is *fourteenth d.* ye. *Acts* 27:33

fifteenth **day**

of Sinai on *fifteenth d.* *Ex* 16:1
on *fifteenth d.* is feast. *Lev* 23:6 *Num* 28:17
fifteenth d. of seventh month. *Lev* 23:34, 39; *Num* 29:12 *Ezek* 45:25
Ramases on *fifteenth d.* *Num* 33:3
feast on *fifteenth d.* *1 Ki* 12:32, 33
fifteenth d. rested. *Esth* 9:18, 21
on *fifteenth d.* word. *Ezek* 32:17

sixteenth **day**

in *sixteenth d.* they. *2 Chr* 29:17

seventeenth **day**

on *seventeenth d.* were. *Gen* 7:11
ark rested on *seventeenth d.* 8:4

twentieth **day**

on *twentieth d.* cloud. *Num* 10:11
on *twentieth d.* people. *Ezra* 10:9

twenty-first **day**

bread till *twenty-first d.* *Ex* 12:18
twenty-first d. came word. *Hag* 2:1

twenty-third **day**

twenty-third day Solomon sent. *2 Chr* 7:10
on *twenty-third d.* written. *Esth* 8:9

twenty-fourth **day**

twenty-fourth d. Israel. *Neh* 9:1
twenty-fourth d. I was by. *Dan* 10:4
in *twenty-fourth d.* Lord. *Hag* 1:15
in *twenty-fourth d.* word. 2:10, 20
consider from *twenty-fourth d.* 18
on *twenty-fourth d.* came word to Zechariah. *Zech* 1:7

twenty-fifth **day**

finished in *twenty-fifth d.* *Neh* 6:15
on *twenty-fifth d.* Evil-merodach. *Jer* 52:31

twenty-seventh **day**

on *twenty-seventh d.* was. *Gen* 8:14
on *twenty-seventh d.* Evil-merodach. *2 Ki* 25:27

good **day**

we come in a *good d.* *1 Sam* 25:8
gladness and a *good d.* *Esth* 8:17 9:19
from mourning into a *good d.* 9:22

great **day**

alas, that *d.* is *great.* *Jer* 30:7
for *great* shall be the *d.* *Hos* 1:11
d. of the Lord is *great.* *Joel* 2:11
before the *great* and terrible *d.* of the Lord come. 31; *Acts* 2:20
the *great d.* of the Lord. *Zeph* 1:14
before coming of *great d.* *Mal* 4:5
that *great d.* of the feast. *John* 7:37
the judgement of *great d.* *Jude* 6
great d. of his wrath is. *Rev* 6:17
gather to battle of the *great d.* 16:14

in the **day**

in the d. the Lord made. *Gen* 2:4
in the d. thou eatest thereof. 17
in the d. ye eat, your eyes. 3:5
in the d. drought consumed. 31:40
answered me *in the d.* of. 35:3
in the d. when I visit. *Ex* 32:34
in the d. of his trespass. *Lev* 6:5
offer *in the d.* when he is. 20; 7:36
in the d. he presented. 7:35
law of leper *in the d.* 14:2; *Num* 6:9
in the d. of first-fruits. *Num* 28:26
if her father disallow *in the d.* 30:5
husband held his peace *in the d.* 7
in the d. Lord delivered. *Josh* 10:12
as strong as I was *in the d.* 14:11
put hot bread *in the d.* *1 Sam* 21:6
in the d. the Lord had. *2 Sam* 22:1
cursed me *in the d.* that. *1 Ki* 2:8
in the day wherein they. *Neh* 13:15
in the d. the enemies. *Esth* 9:1
goods flow away *in the d.* *Job* 20:28
as *in the d.* of temptation. *Ps* 95:8 *Heb* 3:8
hide not thy face *in the d.* of trouble, *in the d.* when I call. *Ps* 102:2
people be willing *in the d.* 110:3
strike through kings *in the d.* 5
remember Edom *in the d.* of. 137:7
in the d. when I cried, thou. 138:3
not spare *in the d.* of. *Pr* 6:34
riches profit not *in the d.* of. 11:4
faint *in the d.* of adversity. 24:10
in the d. of prosperity be joyful, *in the d.* of adversity. *Eccl* 7:14
power *in the d.* of death. 8:8
in the d. when the keepers. 12:3
crowned him *in the d.* of his espousals, and *in the d.* *S of S* 3:11
in the d. when she shall be. 8:8
broken yoke as *in the d.* *Isa* 9:4
what will ye do *in the d.* of? 10:3
in the d. he came out of Egypt. 11:16 *Hos* 2:15
remove *in the d.* of his. *Isa* 13:13
in the d. shalt thou make thy plant grow, *in the d.* of grief. 17:11
in the d. of great slaughter. 30:25
in the d. that the Lord bindeth. 26
in the d. of your fast you. 58:3
my refuge *in the d.* of. *Jer* 16:19
my hope *in the d.* of evil. 17:17
back and not face *in the d.* 18:17
dead body be cast out *in the d.* 36:30
afflicted me *in the d.* of. *Lam* 1:12
not his footstool *in the d.* of. 2:1
thou drewest near *in the d.* 3:57
not deliver them *in the d.* *Ezek* 7:19
thy nativity *in the d.* thou. 16:4, 5
Sodom not mentioned *in the d.* 56
fall *in the d.* of thy ruin. 27:27
great pain came as *in the d.* of. 30:9
every man for life *in the d.* 32:10
in the d. he turneth from wickedness, not able to live *in the d.* 33:12
lest I set her as *in the d.* *Hos* 2:3
shalt thou fall *in the d.* 4:5
with a tempest *in the d.* *Amos* 1:14
darken earth *in the* clear *d.* 8:9
in the d. thou stoodest. *Ob* 11
nor rejoiced *in the d.* of their. 12
did remain *in the d.* of distress. 14
in the d. that I shall do. *Mal* 4:3
in the d. when Son is. *Luke* 17:30
if any walk *in the d.* he. *John* 11:9
in d. when God shall. *Rom* 2:16
walk honestly as *in the d.* 13:13
be blameless *in the d.* *1 Cor* 1:8
in the d. of salvation I. *2 Cor* 6:2
rejoice *in the d.* of Christ. *Phil* 2:16
in the d. when I took them. *Heb* 8:9
glorify God *in the d.* of. *1 Pet* 2:12

day *of judgement*

tolerable for Sodom in *d. of judg.* *Mat* 10:15; 11:24; *Mark* 6:11*
and Sidon in *d. of judg.* *Mat* 11:22
give account in *d. of judg.* 12:36
the unjust to *d. of judg.* *2 Pet* 2:9
reserved against *d. of judg.* 3:7
boldness in *d. of judg.* *1 John* 4:17

day *of the Lord*

d. of the L. shall be on. *Isa* 2:12
d. of the L. is at hand. 13:6 *Joel* 1:15; *Zeph* 1:7
d. of the L. cometh. *Isa* 13:9 *Joel* 2:1; *Zech* 14:1
d. of the L.'s vengeance. *Isa* 34:8
this is the *d. of the L.* *Jer* 46:10
in *d. of the L.'s* anger. *Lam* 2:22

in battle in *d. of the L.* *Ezek* 13:5
the *d. of the L.* is near. 30:3
Joel 3:14; *Ob* 15
desire the *d. of the L.* *Amos* 5:18
in *d. of the L.'s* sacrifice. *Zeph* 1:8
deliver them in *d. of L.'s* wrath. 18
before the *d. of the L.'s* anger. 2:2
hid in *d. of the L.'s* anger. 3
coming of the *d. of the L.* *Mal* 4:5
saved in *d. of the L.* *1 Cor* 5:5
ours in the *d. of the L.* *2 Cor* 1:14
d. of the L. cometh as a thief.
1 Thes 5:2; *2 Pet* 3:10

one **day**

of you both in *one d.?* *Gen* 27:45
not kill it and her young both in *one d.* *Lev* 22:28
ye shall not eat *one d.* *Num* 11:19
in *one d.* they shall die. *1 Sam* 2:34
I shall *one d.* perish by the. 27:1
provision for *one d.* was. *1 Ki* 4:22
of Syrians 100,000 in *one d.* 20:29
in Judah 120,000 in *one d.* *2 Chr* 28:6
is this work of *one d.* *Ezra* 10:13
kill in *one d.* *Esth* 3:13; 8:12
branch and rush in *one d.* *Isa* 9:14
his thorns and briers in *one d.* 10:17
two things shall come in *one d.* 47:9
earth bring forth in *one d.?* 66:8
iniquity of land in *one d.* *Zech* 3:9
it shall be *one d.* which. 14:7
abode with brethren *one d.* *Acts* 21:7
after *one d.* the south wind. 28:13
one esteemeth *one d.* *Rom* 14:5
fell in *one d.* 23,000. *1 Cor* 10:8
one d. is with the Lord as. *2 Pet* 3:8
her plagues come in *one d.* *Rev* 18:8

day joined with *night*

to divide *d.* from *night*. *Gen* 1:14
rule over *d.* and over the *night*. 18
cold and heat, *d.* and *night*. 8:22
whether stolen by *d.* or *night*. 31:39
east-wind *d.* and *night*. *Ex* 10:13
light to go by *d.* and *night*. 13:21
abide at door *d.* and *night*. *Lev* 8:35
that *d.* and all *night*. *Num* 11:32
shalt fear *d.* and *night*. *Deut* 28:66
thou shalt meditate therein *d.* and *night*. *Josh* 1:8; *Ps* 1:2
that *d.* and that *night*. *1 Sam* 19:24
toward this house *night* and *d.*
1 Ki 8:29; *2 Chr* 6:20
I pray before thee *d.* and *night*.
Neh 1:6
watch against them *d.* and *night*. 4:9
eat nor drink *night* or *d.* *Esth* 4:16
they change *night* into *d.* *Job* 17:12
till the *d.* and *night* come. 26:10*
d. and *night* thy hand was. *Ps* 32:4
tears my meat *d.* and *night*. 42:3
d. and *night* they go about it. 55:10
the *d.* is thine, the *night* also. 74:16
I have cried *d.* and *night*. 88:1
the *night* shineth as the *d.* 139:12
neither *d.* nor *night* seeth. *Eccl* 8:16
smoke by *d.*, fire by *night*. *Isa* 4:5
Lord will keep it *d.* and *night*. 27:3
not be quenched *d.* nor *night*. 34:10
sickness from *d.* to *night*. 38:12
from *d.* to *night* wilt thou make. 13
not be shut *d.* nor *night*. 60:11
hold their peace *d.* nor *night*. 62:6
might weep *d.* and *night*. *Jer* 9:1
eyes run down tears *d.* and *night*.
14:17; *Lam* 2:18
other gods *d.* and *night*. *Jer* 16:13
should not be *d.* nor *night*. 33:20
not *d.* nor *night*. *Zech* 14:7
and rise *night* and *d.* *Mark* 4:27
d. and *night* he was in. 5:5
this *d.* even this *night*, before. 14:30
and prayers *night* and *d.* *Luke* 2:37
elect, which cry *d.* and *night*. 18:7
watched gates *night* and *d.* *Acts* 9:24
warn every one *night* and *d.* 20:31
serving God *d.* and *night*. 26:7
suffered shipwreck, a *night* and a *d.* I have been. *2 Cor* 11:25
abouring *d.* and *night*. *1 Thes* 2:9
ight and *d.* praying. 3:10; *1 Tim* 5:5
vith labour *night* and *d.* *2 Thes* 3:8
emembrance of thee in my prayers *night* and *d.* *2 Tim* 1:3

rest not *d.* and *night*. *Rev* 4:8
and serve him *d.* and *night*. 7:15
d. shone not for a third part of it and the *night*. 8:12
accused them *d.* and *night*. 12:10
have no rest *d.* nor *night*. 14:11
tormented *d.* and *night* for ever.
20:10

sabbath-**day**

seventh *d.* is the *sabbath*. *Ex* 16:26
20:10
remember the *sabbath-d.* to. 20:8
Deut 5:12
Lord blessed the *sabbath-d.* *Ex* 20:11
doth any work on *sabbath-d.* 31:15
kindle no fire on *sabbath-d.* 35:3
sticks on *sabbath-d.* *Num* 15:32
offer on *sabbath-d.* two lambs. 28:9
to keep the *sabbath-d.* *Deut* 5:15
sell victuals on *sabbath-d.* *Neh* 10:31
burdens brought on *sabbath-d.* 13:15
and profane the *sabbath-d.* 17
no burden brought in *sabbath-d.* 19
keep gates to sanctify *sabbath-d.* 22
no burden on *sabbath-d.* *Jer* 17:21
nor carry burden on *sabbath-d.* 22
shall offer in *sabbath-d.* *Ezek* 46:4
the *sabbath-d.* through the corn.
Mat 12:1; *Mark* 2:23
Son of man is Lord of *sabbath-d.*
Mat 12:8
a pit on *sabbath-d.* 11; *Luke* 14:5
flight be not on *sabbath-d.* *Mat* 24:20
why do they on *sabbath-d.* that ?
Mark 2:24
would heal on *sabbath-d.* 3:2
Luke 6:7
into synagogue on the *sabbath-d.*
Mark 6:2; *Luke* 4:16; *Acts* 13:14
from bond on *sabbath-d.* *Luke* 13:16
to eat bread on *sabbath-d.* 14:1
and rested the *sabbath-d.* 23:56
it is *sabbath-d.* it is not. *John* 5:10
done these things on *sabbath-d.* 16
ye on *sabbath-d.* circumcise. 7:22
it was the *sabbath-d.* when. 9:14
remain on cross on *sabbath-d.* 19:31
read every *sabbath-d.* *Acts* 13:27
15:21
next *sabbath-d.* came almost. 13:44

same **day**

the *same d.* were the. *Gen* 7:11
the self-*same d.* entered Noah. 13
in that *same d.* the Lord. 15:18
same d. I brought. *Ex* 12:17, 51
flesh eaten *same d.* *Lev* 7:15, 16
19:6; 22:30
no parched corn till *same d.* 23:14
do no work in that *same d.* 28
not be afflicted in that *same d.* 29
his head that *same d.* *Num* 6:11
to Moses that *same d.* *Deut* 32:48
same d. king hallowed. *1 Ki* 8:64
a sign the *same d.* saying. 13:3
defiled my sanctuary, *same d.*
Ezek 23:38, 39
same d. king of Babylon set himself against Jerusalem *same d.* 24:2
same d. will I punish. *Zeph* 1:9
and come the *same d.* *Zech* 6:10
the *same d.* Lot went. *Luke* 17:29
same d. Pilate and Herod. 23:12
and on the *same d.* was. *John* 5:9
same d. at evening, Jesus. 20:19
unto the *same d.* that he. *Acts* 1:22
same d. were added to church. 2:41

since the **day**

since the d. they were. *Ex* 10:6
since the d. that God. *Deut* 4:32
since the d. that I brought them.
1 Sam 8:8; *1 Ki* 8:16; *1 Chr* 17:5
since the day that she left. *2 Ki* 8:6
since the d. your fathers. *Jer* 7:25
as in you, *since the d.* *Col* 1:6
since the d. we heard it, do not. 9

that **day**

I will sever in *that d.* land. *Ex* 8:22
east-wind on land all *that d.* 10:13
that d. thou seest my face, thou. 28
shalt shew thy son in *that d.* 13:8
Lord saved Israel *that d.* 14:30
fell of the people *that d.* 32:28
that d. shall the priest. *Lev* 16:30

not keep passover *that d.* *Num* 9:6
held his peace in *that d.* 30:14
your children in *that d.* *Deut* 1:39
in any wise bury him *that d.* 21:23
hide my face in *that d.* 31:18
that d. they compassed. *Josh* 6:15
heardest in *that d.* how. 14:12
fasted *that d.* *Judg* 20:26; *1 Sam* 7:6
cry out in *that d.* and Lord will not hear you in *that d.* *1 Sam* 8:18
did eat with Samuel *that d.* 9:24
signs came to pass *that d.* 10:9
sent thunder and rain *that d.* 12:18
Lord saved Israel *that d.* 14:23
he answered him not *that d.* 37
of Lord on David from *that d.* 16:13
Saul eyed David from *that d.* 18:9
afraid of Lord *that d.* *2 Sam* 6:9
abode in Jerusalem *that d.* 11:12
cut off Jeroboam *that d.* *1 Ki* 14:14
thou shalt see on *that d.* *2 Chr* 18:24
to *that d.* Israel had not. *Neh* 8:17
ready against *that d.* *Esth* 3:14; 8:13
let *that d.* be darkness. *Job* 3:4
in *that* very *d.* his. *Ps* 146:4
shall be exalted *that d.* *Isa* 2:11, 17
he remain at Nob *that d.* 10:32
Egyptians know Lord *that d.* 19:21
in *that d.* the Lord shall. 24:21
in *that d.* shall this song be. 26:1
in *that d.* shall the deaf hear. 29:18
they shall know in *that d.* 52:6
accomplished in *that d.* *Jer* 39:16
I will deliver thee in *that d.* 17
in *that d.* Israel shall be. *Ezek* 29:21
in *that d.* there shall be a. 38:19
know I am Lord from *that d.* 39:22
name of city from *that d.* 48:35
in *that d.* will I make. *Hos* 2:18
in *that d.* mountains shall. *Joel* 3:18
flee away naked in *that d.* *Amos* 2:16
songs be howlings in *that d.* 8:3
shall I not in *that d.* destroy ? *Ob* 8
that d. is a day of wrath. *Zeph* 1:15
joined to Lord in *that d.* *Zech* 2:11
God shall save them in *that d.* 9:16
my covenant broken in *that d.* 11:11
the feeble at *that d.* shall be. 12:8
that d. shall be great mourning. 11
that d. shall there be a fountain. 13:1
his feet shall stand *that d.* 14:4
in *that d.* shall there be one Lord. 9
that d. when I make up. *Mal* 3:17
many will say in *that d.* *Mat* 7:22
of *that d.* knoweth no man. 24:36
Mark 13:32
that d. I drink it new. *Mat* 26:29
Mark 14:25
rejoice ye in *that d.* *Luke* 6:23
more tolerable in *that d.* 10:12
and so *that d.* come on you. 21:34
that d. was the preparation. 23:54
abode with him *that d.* *John* 1:39
from *that d.* they took. 11:53
at *that d.* ye shall know I. 14:20
in *that d.* ye shall ask me. 16:23
that d. ye shall ask in my name. 26
that d. should overtake. *1 Thes* 5:4
testimony was believed in *that d.*
2 Thes 1:10
that d. shall not come, except. 2:3
to him against *that d.* *2 Tim* 1:12
find mercy of Lord in *that d.* 18
Lord shall give me at *that d.* 4:8

this **day**

driven me out *this d.* *Gen* 4:14
send me good speed *this d.* 24:12
sell me *this d.* thy birthright. 25:31
swear *this d.* and he sware. 33
I remember my faults *this d.* 41:9
fed me all my life to *this d.* 48:15
this d. shall be for a. *Ex* 12:14
therefore observe *this d.* in. 17
remember *this d.* in which. 13:3, 4
this d. as the stars of. *Deut* 1:10
this d. will I begin to put dread. 2:25
alive every one *this d.* 4:4; 5:3
I command thee *this d.* 4:40; 6:6
7:11; 8:1, 11; 10:13; 30:2, 8
this d. that God doth talk. 5:24
it is at *this d.* 6:24; 8:18; *Ezra* 9:7
testify against you *this d.* *Deut* 8:19
I command you *this d.* 11:8, 13, 27
28; 13:18; 15:5; 19:9; 27:1, 4

set before you *this d.* *Deut* 11:32
all things ye do here *this d.* 12:8
avouched *this d.* the Lord. 26:17
this d. thou art become people. 27:9
you ears to hear to *this d.* 29:4
ye stand *this d.* all of you. 10
whose heart turneth away *this d.* 18
before thee *this d.* life. 30:15, 19
I commanded thee *this d.* to. 16
yet alive with you *this d.* 31:27
knoweth his sepulchre to *this d.* 34:6
this d. will I begin to. *Josh* 3:7
twelve stones there unto *this d.* 4:9
Lord shall trouble thee *this d.* 7:25
now I am *this d.* eighty-five. 14:10
I am as strong *this d.* as when. 11
to turn away *this d.* from. 22:16
not cleansed till *this d.* 17
save us not *this d.* 22
cleave to Lord as unto *this d.* 23:8
choose you *this d.* whom ye. 24:15
Luz is name unto *this d.* *Judg* 1:26
us only, we pray thee, *this d.* 10:15
Israel came up out of Egypt to *this d.*
19:30; *1 Sam* 8:8; *2 Sam* 7:6
2 Ki 21:15; *1 Chr* 17:5; *Jer* 7:25
are witnesses *this d.* *Ruth* 4:9, 10
have *this d.* rejected. *1 Sam* 10:19
man be put to death *this d.* 11:13
hath wrought with God *this d.* 14:45
rent kingdom from thee *this d.* 15:28
I defy armies of Israel *this d.* 17:10
thou shalt *this d.* be my. 18:21
it were sanctified *this d.* in. 21:5
lie in wait as at *this d.* 22:8, 13
Lord which sent thee *this d.* 25:32
who kept me *this d.* from. 33
precious in thine eyes *this d.* 26:21
thy life was much set by *this d.* 24
ordinance for Israel to *this d.* 30:25
I am *this d.* weak. *2 Sam* 3:39
sojourners unto *this d.* 4:3
his commands as at *this d.* *1 Ki* 8:61
this d. is a day of good. *2 Ki* 7:9
this d. do after former. 17:34, 41
there it is unto *this d.* *2 Chr* 5:9
come not against thee *this d.* 35:21
we are servants *this d.* *Neh* 9:36
thou art my Son, *this d.* have I.
Ps 2:7; *Acts* 13:33; *Heb* 1:5
this is the *d.* which the Lord. 118:24
they continue *this d.* 119:91
this d. have I paid vows. *Pr* 7:14
made known to thee *this d.* 22:19
praise thee, as I do *this d.* *Isa* 38:19
to-morrow shall be as *this d.* 56:12
a curse, as at *this d.* *Jer* 25:18
44:22
for to *this d.* they drink none. 35:14
days of Josiah even to this *d.* 36:2
not humbled even unto *this d.* 44:10
certainly *this* is the *d.* *Lam* 2:16
this is the *d.* whereof. *Ezek* 39:8
of faces, as at *this d.* *Dan* 9:7
consider from *this d.* *Hag* 2:15, 18
from *this d.* will I bless you. 19
this d. our daily bread. *Mat* 6:11
have remained to *this d.* 11:23
field of blood to *this d.* 27:8
suffered many things *this d.* 19
reported among Jews to *this d.* 28:15
to you is born *this d.* *Luke* 2:11
this d. is this scripture. 4:21
this d. is salvation come to. 19:9
hadst known, in *this* thy *d.* 42
cock not crow *this d.* before. 22:34
his sepulchre is with us to *this d.*
Acts 2:29
as ye are all *this d.* 22:3
before God till *this d.* 23:1
in question by you *this d.* 24:21
unto *this d.* witnessing to. 26:22
I would all that hear me *this d.* 29
not hear unto *this d.* *Rom* 11:8
till *this d.* remaineth. *2 Cor* 3:14, 15

*to-***day**

heard I of it but *to-d.* *Gen* 21:26
pass through all thy flock *to-d.* 30:32
look ye so sadly *to-d.*? 40:7
are come so soon *to-d.*? *Ex* 2:18
salvation he will shew *to-d.* 14:13
bake that which you will *to-d.* 16:23*
consecrate yourselves *to-d.* 32:29
for *to-d.* the Lord will. *Lev* 9:4
command thee this *to-d.* *Deut* 15:15
he may establish thee *to-d.* 29:13
Lord smitten us *to-d.*? *1 Sam* 4:3
to-d. Lord wrought salvation. 11:13
the Lord had delivered thee *to-d.*
into mine hand. 24:10; 26:23
glorious was king *to-d.*! *2 Sam* 6:20
to-d. shall house of Israel. 16:3
shew myself to him *to-d.* *1 Ki* 18:15
enquire at word of Lord *to-d.* 22:5
2 Chr 18:4
thou go to him *to-d.*? *2 Ki* 4:23
son that we may eat him *to-d.* 6:28
to-d. is my complaint. *Job* 23:2
to-d. if ye will hear his voice.
Ps 95:7; *Heb* 3:7, 15; 4:7
to-d. do I declare. *Zech* 9:12
grass of field, which *to-d.* is, and.
Mat 6:30; *Luke* 12:28
son, go work *to-d.* in. *Mat* 21:28
seen strange things *to-d.* *Luke* 5:26
behold, I do cures *to-d.* and. 13:32
I must walk *to-d.* and the day. 33
for *to-d.* I must abide at thy. 19:5
to-d. shalt thou be with me. 23:43
besides all this, *to-d.* is the. 24:21
while it is called *to-d.* *Heb* 3:13
thou art my Son, *to-d.* have I. 5:5
Christ, same yesterday, *to-d.* 13:8
ye that say, *to-d.* or. *Jas* 4:13

day *to* **day**

why art thou lean from *day to d.*?
2 Sam 13:4
shew from *day to d.* his salvation.
1 Chr 16:23; *Ps* 96:2
cast the lot from *day to d.* *Esth* 3:7
vexed righteous soul from *day to d.*
2 Pet 2:8

day *of trouble*

is a *d. of trouble.* *2 Ki* 19:3
Isa 37:3
hear thee in *d. of trouble.* *Ps* 20:1
call upon me in *d. of trouble.* 50:15
my refuge in *d. of trouble.* 59:16
in the *d. of trouble* I sought. 77:2
in *d. of trouble* I will call on. 86:7
it is a *d. of trouble,* and. *Isa* 22:5
in the *d. of trouble* they. *Jer* 51:2
time is come, *d. of trouble.* *Ezek* 7:7
strong hold in *d. of trouble.* *Nah* 1:7
might rest in *d. of trouble.* *Hab* 3:16
that day is a *d. of trouble.* *Zeph* 1:15

days

after 150 *d.* waters were. *Gen* 8:3
d. of mourning for my father. 27:41
the *d.* of my pilgrimage are. 47:9
when the *d.* of his mourning. 50:4
after the number of *d.* ye. *Num* 14:34
ask now of the *d.* past. *Deut* 4:32
I stayed in the mount forty *d.* 10:10
camest not within *d.* *1 Sam* 13:11
and the *d.* were not expired. 18:26
been with me these *d.* 29:3
the *d.* David reigned. *1 Ki* 2:11
house built to Lord till those *d.* 3:2
d. that Jeroboam reigned. 14:20
war all their *d.* 30
between Asa and Baasha all their *d.*
15:16, 32
into the hand of Ben-hadad all their
d. *2 Ki* 13:3
to those *d.* Israel did burn. 18:4
from *d.* of the judges. 23:22
David old and full of *d.* *1 Chr* 23:1
d. are on earth as. 29:15; *Job* 8:9
died full of *d.* riches. *1 Chr* 29:28
Jehoiada was old and full of *d.*
2 Chr 24:15
d. Esar-haddon brought us. *Ezra* 4:2
since *d.* of our fathers have we. 9:7
and mourned certain *d.* *Neh* 1:4
since *d.* of Jeshua, son of. 8:17
as the *d.* whereon the. *Esth* 9:22
they called these *d.* Purim. 26
these *d.* should be remembered. 28
let it not be joined to the *d.* *Job* 3:6
are not his *d.* also like the *d.*? 7:1
in length of *d.* understanding. 12:12
they spend their *d.* in wealth. 21:13
the *d.* of affliction have taken. 30:16
the *d.* of affliction prevented me. 27
I said, *d.* should speak, and. 32:7
he shall return to the *d.* of. *Job* 33:25
they shall spend their *d.* in. 36:11
Job died, old and full of *d.* 42:17
gavest him length of *d.* *Ps* 21:4
the Lord knoweth the *d.* of. 37:18
work thou didst in their *d.* 44:1
not live out half their *d.* 55:23
I have considered the *d.* of old. 77:5
d. did he consume in vanity. 78:33
his throne as *d.* of heaven. 89:29
the *d.* of his youth hast thou. 45
all our *d.* are passed away in. 90:9
d. of our years threescore and. 10
so teach us to number our *d.* 12
and be glad all our *d.* 14
give him rest from the *d.* 94:13
how many are the *d.* of thy? 119:84
I remember the *d.* of old. 143:5
length of *d.* shall they add. *Pr* 3:2
length of *d.* is in her right hand. 16
not much remember *d.* of. *Eccl* 5:20
the cause that the former *d.* 7:10
shall abide with him the *d.* 8:15
him remember *d.* of darkness. 11:8
while the evil *d.* come not. 12:1
antiquity is of ancient *d.* *Isa* 23:7
according to *d.* of one king. 15
the *d.* of thy mourning shall. 60:20
no more thence an infant of *d.* 65:20
as the *d.* of a tree are the *d.* 22
forgotten me *d.* without. *Jer* 2:32
with him that is full of *d.* 6:11
after those *d.* I will put my. 31:33
from the *d.* of Josiah even to. 36:2
our *d.* are fulfilled, our. *Lam* 4:18
to number of the *d.* *Ezek* 4:4; 5:9
d. are at hand, and effect. 12:23
not remembered *d.* of youth. 16:22
43
unto 2300 *d.* sanctuary. *Dan* 8:14*
abomination set up, 1290 *d.* 12:11
blessed that waiteth to 1335 *d.* 12
I will visit on her the *d.* *Hos* 2:13
d. of visitation, *d.* of recompence. 9:7
sinned from *d.* of Gibeah. 10:9
according to *d.* of thy coming. 7:15
since those *d.* were. *Hag* 2:16*
ye that hear in these *d.* *Zech* 8:9
before these *d.* there was no. 10
I will not be as in former *d.* 11
so have I thought in these *d.* 15
from *d.* of our fathers ye. *Mal* 3:7
from *d.* of John the. *Mat* 11:12
except those *d.* should be shortened.
24:22; *Mark* 13:20
as *d.* of Noe, so shall the coming.
Mat 24:37
after those *d.* Elisabeth. *Luke* 1:24
these be the *d.* of vengeance. 21:22
likewise foretold of these *d.*
Acts 3:24
for before these *d.* rose up. 5:36
in these *d.* came prophets. 11:27
the *d.* of unleavened bread. 12:3
sailed after *d.* of unleavened. 20:6
which before these *d.* madest. 21:38
ye observed *d.* and. *Gal* 4:10
because the *d.* are evil. *Eph* 5:16
neither beginning of *d.* nor. *Heb* 7:3
to remembrance former *d.* 10:32
would see good *d.* let. *1 Pet* 3:10
shall prophesy 1260 *d.* in. *Rev* 11:3
should feed her there 1260 *d.* 12:6

see **David, last, old, journey**

all the **days**

dust shalt thou eat *all the d.*
Gen 3:14
all the d. Adam lived 930 years. 5:5
all the d. of Seth 912 years. 8
all the d. of Enos 905 years. 11
all the d. of Cainan 910 years. 14
all the d. of Enoch 365 years. 23
all the d. of Methuselah 969. 27
all the d. of Noah 950 years. 9:29
all the d. wherein plague. *Lev* 13:46
all the d. of her issue. 15:25, 26
all the d. of his separation. *Num* 6:4
5, 6, 8
from thy heart *all the d.* *Deut* 4:9
to fear me *all the d.* 10; *1 Ki* 8:40
to possess it *all the d.* ye. 12:1
served Lord *all the d.* of Joshua and
all the d. *Josh* 24:31; *Judg* 2:7

delivered them *all the d.* *Judg* 2:18
him to Lord *all d.* of. *1 Sam* 1:11
against Philistines *all* the *d.* 7:13
Samuel judged Israel *all the d.* 15
dwelt safely *all the d.* *1 Ki* 4:25
Rezon was adversary *all the d.* 11:25
oppressed Israel *all the d.* *2 Ki* 13:22
nor in *all the d.* of kings of. 23:22
all the d. of Jehoiada. *2 Chr* 24:2, 14
their purposes *all the d.* *Ezra* 4:5
all the d. of my appointed. *Job* 14:14
mercy shall follow me *all the d.* *Ps* 23:6
in the house of Lord *all the d.* 27:4
all the d. of afflicted are. *Pr* 15:15
not evil, *all the d.* of her life. 31:12
in holiness *all the d.* *Luke* 1:75

see his **life**, *thy* **life**

days *come*

bring *d.* that have not *come.* *Isa* 7:17
behold the *d. come.* *Jer* 23:5, 7
30:3; 31:27, 31, 38
d. come that he will. *Amos* 4:2
d. shall *come* when bridegroom.
Mat 9:15; *Mark* 2:20; *Luke* 5:35
d. come when ye shall. *Luke* 17:22
d. come thy enemies shall. 19:43
d. come in which there shall. 21:6
d. come when I will make. *Heb* 8:8

few **days**

abide with us a *few d.* *Gen* 24:55
tarry a *few d.* till thy. 27:44
seemed to him but a *few d.* 29:20
few and evil are the *d.* of. 47:9
cloud was a *few d.* on. *Num* 9:20
born of woman is of *few d.* *Job* 14:1
let his *d.* be *few.* *Ps* 109:8
within *few d.* he shall be. *Dan* 11:20
for a *few d.* chastened. *Heb* 12:10

his **days**

his d. shall be 120 years. *Gen* 6:3
in *his d.* was earth divided. 10:25
1 Chr 1:19
her away all *his d.* *Deut* 22:19, 29
Asa was perfect all *his d.*
1 Ki 15:14; *2 Chr* 15:17
in *his d.* did Hiel build. *1 Ki* 16:34
not bring the evil in *his d.* 21:29
in *his d.* Edom revolted. *2 Ki* 8:20
2 Chr 21:8
Jehoash did right all *his d.* *2 Ki* 12:2
he departed not all *his d.* 15:18
quietness to Israel in *his d.*
1 Chr 22:9
all *his d.* departed. *2 Chr* 34:33
his d. are determined. *Job* 14:5
travaileth with pain all *his d.* 15:20
know him not see *his d.*? 24:1
in *his d.* shall righteous. *Ps* 72:7
as for man, *his d.* are as. 103:15
his d. are as a shadow. 144:4
covetousness prolong *his d.* *Pr* 28:16
all *his d.* are sorrows. *Eccl* 2:23
all *his d.* also he eateth in. 5:17
though *his d.* be prolonged. 8:12
wicked shall not prolong *his d.* 13
that hath not filled *his d.* *Isa* 65:20
leave them in midst of *his d.*
Jer 17:11
that shall not prosper in *his d.* 22:30
in *his d.* Judah shall be saved. 23:6

in the **days**

Reuben went *in the d.* *Gen* 30:14
in the d. of Shamgar, *in the d.*
Judg 5:6
quietness 40 years *in the d.* 8:28
old man *in the d.* of. *1 Sam* 17:12
famine *in the d.* of. *2 Sam* 21:1
put to death *in the d.* of harvest, *in the* first *d.* in beginning of. 9
silver was nothing accounted of *in the d.* of. *1 Ki* 10:21; *2 Chr* 9:20
remained *in the d.* of Asa.
1 Ki 22:46
in the d. of Hezekiah. *1 Chr* 4:41
enquired not at it *in the d.* of. 13:3
sought God *in the d.* of. *2 Chr* 26:5
came not on them *in the d.* 32:26
in the d. when God. *Job* 29:2
as I was *in the d.* of my youth. 4
in the d. of famine. *Ps* 37:19
should I fear *in the d.* of evil? 49:5
in the d. to come shall. *Eccl* 2:16
thy heart cheer thee *in the d.* 11:9
remember thy Creator *in the d.* 12:1
Micah prophesied *in the d.* *Jer* 26:18
Jerusalem remembered *in the d.*
Lam 1:7
my covenant *in the d.* *Ezek* 16:60
or hands be strong *in the d.* 22:14
in the d. of these kings. *Dan* 2:44
in the d. of thy father, light. 5:11
shall sing as *in the d.* *Hos* 2:15
deeply corrupted as *in the d.* 9:9
to dwell, as *in the d.* of the. 12:9
hath this been *in the d.*? *Joel* 1:2
Jesus was born *in the d.* *Mat* 2:1
if we had been *in the d.* of. 23:30
for as *in the d.* that were. 24:38
the house of God *in d.* *Mark* 2:26*
dealt with me *in the d.* *Luke* 1:25
many widows were *in the d.* 4:25
as *in the d.* of Noe. 17:26
in the d. of Lot. 28
rose up Judas *in the d.* *Acts* 5:37
came to pass *in the d.* of. 11:28
who *in the d.* of his flesh. *Heb* 5:7
waited *in the d.* of Noah. *1 Pet* 3:20
in the d. of the voice. *Rev* 10:7
that it rain not *in the d.* of. 11:6

in those **days**

giants in earth *in those d.* *Gen* 6:4
judge *in those d.* *Deut* 17:9; 19:17
priest that shall be *in those d.* 26:3
in those d. there was no king in.
Judg 17:6; 18:1; 21:25
ark of God there *in those d.* 20:27
word precious *in those d.* *1 Sam* 3:1
counselled *in those d.* *2 Sam* 16:23
in those d. was Hezekiah sick unto.
2 Ki 20:1; *2 Chr* 32:24; *Isa* 38:1
in those d. shall *Judah.* *Jer* 33:16
in those d. Israel shall go up. 50:4
in those d. iniquity shall be. 20
in those d. will I pour out my Spirit.
Joel 2:29; *Acts* 2:18
give suck *in those d.* *Mat* 24:19
Mark 13:17; *Luke* 21:23
Mary arose *in those d.* *Luke* 1:39
one of *those d.* as he taught. 20:1
made a calf *in those d.* *Acts* 7:41
not denied faith *in those d.* *Rev* 2:13
in those d. shall men seek. 9:6

latter **days**

to thy people in *latter d.* *Num* 24:14
latter d. if thou turn. *Deut* 4:30
evil befall you in *latter d.* 31:29
latter d. consider. *Jer* 23:20; 30:24
captivity of Moab in *latter d.* 48:47
captivity of Elam in *latter d.* 49:39
people in the *latter d.* *Ezek* 38:16
what shall be in *latter d.* *Dan* 2:28
befall thy people in *latter d.* 10:14
fear Lord in *latter d.* *Hos* 3:5

many **days**

mourned for son *many d.* *Gen* 37:34
brethren these *many d.* *Josh* 22:3
at Jerusalem *many d.* *1 Ki* 2:38
her house, did eat *many d.* 17:15
Ephraim mourned *many d.* *1 Chr* 7:22
what man loveth *many d.*? *Ps* 34:12
how *many* are the *d.* of? 119:84
d. of his years be *many.* *Eccl* 6:3
shalt find it after *many d.* 11:1
after *many d.* shall they be visited.
Isa 24:22; *Ezek* 38:8
many d. and years shall ye. *Isa* 32:10
continue *many d.* *Jer* 32:14; 35:7
remained there *many d.* 37:16
the vision is for *many d.* *Ezek* 12:27
Dan 8:26; 10:14
captivity spoil *many d.* *Dan* 11:33
abide for me *many d.* *Hos* 3:3
Israel shall abide *many d.* 4
not *many d.* after. *Luke* 15:13
continued not *many d.* *John* 2:12
Holy Ghost, not *many d.* *Acts* 1:5
he was seen *many d.* of. 13:31
this did she *many d.* 16:18
nor sun nor stars in *many d.* 27:20

my **days**

me my wife, for *my d.* *Gen* 29:21
and truth be in *my d.* *2 Ki* 20:19
my d. are swifter than a. *Job* 7:6
for *my d.* are vanity. 16
now *my d.* are swifter than. *Job* 9:25
are not *my d.* few? cease then. 10:20
my d. are extinct, graves are. 17:1
my d. are past, my purposes. 11
shall multiply *my d.* as sand. 29:18
and measure of *my d.* *Ps* 39:4
hast made *my d.* as an hand-breadth. 5
for *my d.* are consumed like. 102:3
my d. are like a shadow that. 11
he shortened *my d.* 23
take not away in midst of *my d.* 24
in cutting off of *my d.* *Isa* 38:10
peace and truth in *my d.* 39:8
my d. shall be consumed. *Jer* 20:18

now-a-**days**

many servants *now-a-d.* break.
1 Sam 25:10

prolong, -ed, -eth, **days**

ye shall not *prolong* your *d.*
Deut 4:26; 30:18
thou mayest *prolong d.* 4:40; 22:7
that thy *d.* be *prolonged.* 5:16; 6:2
prolong your *d.* in land. 5:33; 11:9
end that he may *prolong d.* 17:20
ye shall *prolong* your *d.* in. 32:47
fear of Lord *prolongeth d.* *Pr* 10:27
covetousness, *prolong* his *d.* 28:16
sinner's *d.* be *prolonged.* *Eccl* 8:12
neither wicked *prolong* his *d.* 13
d. shall not be *prolonged.* *Isa* 13:22
seed, he shall *prolong* his *d.* 53:10
d. are *prolonged,* vision. *Ezek* 12:22

sabbath-**days**

how on the *sabbath-d.* *Mat* 12:5
is it lawful to heal on *sabbath-d.*? 10
to do well on the *sabbath-d.* 12
do good on *sabbath-d.* *Mark* 3:4
Luke 6:9
taught them on *sabbath-d.* *Luke* 4:31
not lawful to do on *sabbath-d.* 6:2
three *sabbath-d.* reasoned. *Acts* 17:2
in respect of *sabbath-d.* *Col* 2:16

thy **days**

honour thy father and thy mother, that *thy d.* may be. *Ex* 20:12
the number of *thy d.* I will. 23:26
prosperity all *thy d.* *Deut* 23:6
thy d. may be lengthened. 25:15
and the length of thy *d.* 30:20
thy d. approach that thou. 31:14
and as *thy d.* so shall thy. 33:25
evil not found all *thy d.* *1 Sam* 25:28
and when *thy d.* be. *2 Sam* 7:12
any like thee all *thy d.* *1 Ki* 3:13
then I will lengthen *thy d.* 14
in *thy d.* I will not do it. 11:12
I will add to *thy d.* 15 years.
2 Ki 20:6; *Isa* 38:5
when *thy d.* be expired. *1 Chr* 17:11
thy d. as the days of man. *Job* 10:5
morning since *thy d.*? 38:12
the number of *thy d.* is great. 21
for by me *thy d.* shall be. *Pr* 9:11
thou hast caused *thy d.* *Ezek* 22:4

two **days**

sixth day bread of *two d.* *Ex* 16:29
whether it were *two d.* *Num* 9:22
not eat one, nor *two d.* nor. 11:19
David had abode *two d.* *2 Sam* 1:1
work of one day or *two d.* *Ezra* 10:13
would keep these *two d.* *Esth* 9:27
after *two d.* will he revive. *Hos* 6:2
after *two d.* is the feast. *Mat* 26:2
Mark 14:1
he abode there *two d.* *John* 4:40
now after *two d.* he departed. 43
he abode *two d.* still in the. 11:6

three **days**

branches are *three d.* *Gen* 40:12
within *three d.* shall Pharaoh. 13, 19
three baskets are *three d.* 18
into ward *three d.* 42:17
let us go *three d.* journey to sacrifice. *Ex* 3:18; 5:3; 8:27; 15:22
darkness in Egypt *three d.* 10:22
rose any from place for *three d.* 23
three d. ye shall pass. *Josh* 1:11
hide yourselves *three d.* 2:16, 22
abode with him *three d.* *Judg* 19:4
asses lost *three d.* ago. *1 Sam* 9:20
kept from us these *three d.* 21:5

had eaten no bread *three d.* *1 Sam* 30:12
master left me, because *three d.* 13
assembled men of Judah in *three d.* *2 Sam* 20:4
there be *three d.*' pestilence. 24:13
1 Chr 21:12
depart for *three d.* *1 Ki* 12:5
2 Chr 10:5
sought him *three d.* *2 Ki* 2:17
were *three d.* gathering. *2 Chr* 20:25
abode in tents *three d.* *Ezra* 8:15
would not come in *three d.* 10:8, 9
eat nor drink *three d.* *Esth* 4:16
Jonah was in belly of fish *three d.* *Jonah* 1:17; *Mat* 12:40
they continue with me now *three d.* *Mat* 15:32; *Mark* 8:2
build it in *three d. Mat* 26:61; 27:40 *Mark* 14:58; 15:29; *John* 2:19
after *three d.* I will rise again. *Mat* 27:63; *Mark* 8:31
after *three d.* found him. *Luke* 2:46
three d. without sight. *Acts* 9:9
Publius lodged us *three d.* 28:7
their dead bodies *three d. Rev* 11:9
after *three d.* and an half. 11

four **days**
lament *four d.* *Judg* 11:40
lain in grave *four d.* *John* 11:17
he hath been dead *four d.* 39
four d. ago I was fasting. *Acts* 10:30

five **days**
nor *five d.* nor ten *d.* *Num* 11:19
came to Troas *in five d.* *Acts* 20:6
after *five d.* Ananias the high. 24:1

six **days**
six d. ye shall gather it. *Ex* 16:26
six d. shalt thou labour and do all. 20:9; 23:12; 34:21; *Deut* 5:13
six d. Lord made heaven. *Ex* 20:11; 31:17
cloud covered Sinai *six d.* 24:16
six d. may work be done. 31:15
35:2; *Lev* 23:3
six d. shalt thou eat. *Deut* 16:8
thus shalt thou do *six d.* *Josh* 6:3
so they did *six d.* 14
gate shut *six* working *d.* *Ezek* 46:1
six d. in which men. *Luke* 13:14
Jesus *six d.* before. *John* 12:1

seven **days**
yet *seven d.* I will cause. *Gen* 7:4
stayed yet other *seven d.* 8:10, 12
Joseph mourned *seven d.* 50:10
seven d. eat unleavened. *Ex* 12:15
13:6, 7; 23:15; 34:18; *Lev* 23:6 *Num* 28:17; *Deut* 16:3
seven d. no leaven be found. *Ex* 12:19; *Deut* 16:4
seven d. with the dam. *Ex* 22:30
Lev 22:27
priest shall put them on *seven d.* *Ex* 29:30
seven d. shalt thou consecrate. 35
Lev 8:33
seven d. shalt make an atonement. *Ex* 29:37
shall be unclean *seven d.* *Lev* 12:2
then priest shall shut him up *seven d.* 13:5, 21, 26, 33, 50, 54
abroad out of tent *seven d.* 14:8
shall be put apart *seven d.* 15:19
offering by fire to Lord *seven d.* 23:8
keep a feast to the Lord *seven d.* 23:39, 40, 41; *Num* 29:12
be ashamed *seven d.*? *Num* 12:14
shall be unclean *seven d.* 19:14
of tabernacles *seven d.* *Deut* 16:13
it to me within *seven d.* *Judg* 14:12
wept before him *seven d.* 17
seven d. shalt thou tarry till I come. *1 Sam* 10:8
give us *seven d.*' respite. 11:3
he tarried *seven d.* according. 13:8
fasted *seven d.* 31:13; *1 Chr* 10:12
feast before Lord *seven d. 1 Ki* 8:65
Zimri did reign *seven d.* in. 16:15
of altar *seven d.* *2 Chr* 7:9
kept the feast of unleavened bread *seven d.* 30:21; 35:17; *Ezra* 6:22
to keep other *seven d.* *2 Chr* 30:23
a feast *seven d.* *Esth* 1:5
as the light of *seven d.* *Isa* 30:26
astonished *seven d.* *Ezek* 3:15
seven d. shall they purge. 43:26
were compassed *seven d. Heb* 11:30

eight **days**
he that is *eight d.* old shall be circumcised. *Gen* 17:12; 21:4
sanctify house in *eight d. 2 Chr* 29:17
when *eight d.* were accomplished. *Luke* 2:21
after *eight d.* Jesus. *John* 20:26

ten **days**
not eat *ten d.* nor. *Num* 11:19
ten d. after Lord smote. *1 Sam* 25:38
once in *ten d.* store of. *Neh* 5:18
after *ten d.* word of Lord. *Jer* 42:7
prove thy servants *ten d.* *Dan* 1:12
at the end of *ten d.* their. 15
tarried more than *ten d.* *Acts* 25:6
have tribulation *ten d.* *Rev* 2:10

eleven **days**
eleven d.' journey. *Deut* 1:2

twelve **days**
there are but *twelve d.* *Acts* 24:11

fourteen **days**
held a feast *fourteen d.* *1 Ki* 8:65

fifteen **days**
abode with Peter *fifteen d. Gal* 1:18

twenty **days**
not eat flesh *twenty d.* *Num* 11:19

twenty-one **days**
withstood me *twenty-one d.* *Dan* 10:13

thirty **days**
for Aaron *thirty d.* *Num* 20:29
wept for Moses *thirty d.* *Deut* 34:8
to king these *thirty d.* *Esth* 4:11
petition for *thirty d.* *Dan* 6:7, 12

thirty-three **days**
purifying *thirty-three d.* *Lev* 12:4

forty **days**
to rain on earth *forty d.* *Gen* 7:4
forty d. were fulfilled for. 50:3
in mount *forty d.* and *forty* nights. *Ex* 24:18; 34:28; *Deut* 9:9; 10:10
returned after *forty d.* *Num* 13:25
14:34
before the Lord *forty d.* *Deut* 9:25
strength of meat *forty d.* *1 Ki* 19:8
iniquity of Judah *forty d.* *Ezek* 4:6
forty d. and Nineveh be. *Jonah* 3:4
fasted *forty d.* and forty. *Mat* 4:2
Jesus was *forty d.* in the wilderness. *Mark* 1:13; *Luke* 4:2
seen of them *forty d.* *Acts* 1:3

fifty-two **days**
wall was finished in *fifty-two d.* *Neh* 6:15

your **days**
that *your d.* may be. *Deut* 11:21
to cease in *your d.* mirth. *Jer* 16:9
all *your d.* ye shall dwell in. 35:7
your d. will I say word. *Ezek* 12:25
hath this been in *your d.*? *Joel* 1:2
work a work in *your d.* *Hab* 1:5
Acts 13:41

daysman
neither is there any *d.* *Job* 9:33

dayspring
caused the *d.* to know. *Job* 38:12
d. from on high visited. *Luke* 1:78

daystar
and the *d.* arise in. *2 Pet* 1:19

daytime
meet with darkness in *d.* *Job* 5:14
through houses marked in *d.* 24:16
I cry in the *d.* but thou. *Ps* 22:2
command loving-kindness in *d.* 42:8
in *d.* also he led them. 78:14
tabernacle for shadow in *d.* *Isa* 4:6
I stand on watch-tower in *d.* 21:8
in *d.* he was teaching in. *Luke* 21:37
it pleasure to riot in *d.* *2 Pet* 2:13

deacon, -s
saints with bishops and *d.* *Phil* 1:1
the *d.* must be grave. *1 Tim* 3:8
let them use the office of a *d.* 10, 13
d. be the husband of one wife. 12

dead

[1] *Deprived of natural life,* Ruth 1:8; Job 1:19. [2] *Without warmth or fervour, or energy in the spiritual life,* Eph 2:1; 1 Tim 5:6. [3] *Entirely without life,* Isa 8:19; Mat 22:32.

thou art but a *d.* man. *Gen* 20:3
Abraham stood up from his *d.* 23:3
the men are *d.* which. *Ex* 4:19
not one of Israelites' cattle *d.* 9:7
house where was not one *d.* 12:30
Egyptians said, we be all *d.* men. 33
Israel saw Egyptians *d.* on. 14:30
the *d.* beast shall be his. 21:34, 36
and the *d.* ox also they shall. 35
thing unclean by the *d.* *Lev* 22:4
whosoever is defiled by *d. Num* 5:2
let her not be as one *d.* 12:12
he stood between the *d.* and. 16:48
wife of the *d.* not marry. *Deut* 25:5
lord was fallen down *d.* *Judg* 3:25
he came in, Sisera lay *d.* 4:22
the *d.* which Samson slew. 16:30
as ye have dealt with *d.* *Ruth* 1:8
to raise up name of the *d.* 4:5
and Phinehas are *d.* *1 Sam* 4:17
father-in-law and husband were *d.* 19
thou pursue ? after a *d.* dog. 24:14
Saul and his sons were *d.* 31:7
1 Chr 10:7
on such a *d.* dog as I. *2 Sam* 9:8
all the king's sons are *d.* 13:33
why should this *d.* dog curse. 16:9
my father's house were but *d.* 19:28
the living is my son, and the *d.* is thy son. *1 Ki* 3:22, 23
when I am *d.* bury me in. 13:31
Naboth is not alive but *d.* 21:15
on young men, they are *d.* *Job* 1:19
d. things are formed from. 26:5
forgotten as a *d.* man. *Ps* 31:12
and horse are cast into *d.* 76:6
free among the *d.* like slain. 88:5
wilt thou shew wonders to *d.*? 10
ate the sacrifices of the *d.* 106:28
the *d.* praise not the Lord. 115:17
those that have been long *d.* 143:3
and her paths unto the *d.* *Pr* 2:18
he knoweth not that the *d.* 9:18
remain in congregation of *d.* 21:16
the *d.* which are already *d. Eccl* 4:2
and after that they go to the *d.* 9:3
living dog is better than *d.* lion. 4
the *d.* know not any thing. 5
d. flies cause the ointment. 10:1
for the living to the *d.* *Isa* 8:19
it stirreth up the *d.* for thee. 14:9
not slain with sword, nor *d.* 22:2
they are *d.*, they shall not live. 26:14
d. men shall live, with my *d.* 19
desolate places as *d.* men. 59:10
they that be *d.* of old. *Lam* 3:6
come at no *d.* person. *Ezek* 44:25
are *d.* that sought the. *Mat* 2:20
and let the *d.* bury their *d.* 8:22
give place, for the maid is not *d.* 9:24; *Mark* 5:39; *Luke* 8:52
heal sick, raise the *d.* *Mat* 10:8
deaf hear, *d.* are raised. 11:5
Luke 7:22
touching resurrection of the *d.* *Mat* 22:31; *Mark* 12:26
not the God of the *d.* but. *Mat* 22:32
Mark 12:27; *Luke* 20:38
full of *d.* men's bones. *Mat* 23:27
the keepers became as *d.* 28:4
one *d.* many said, he is *d. Mark* 9:26
if he were already *d.* 15:44
a *d.* man carried out. *Luke* 7:12
departed, leaving him half *d.* 10:30
why seek ye living among *d.*? 24:5
the Father raiseth up *d.* *John* 5:21
when the *d.* shall hear voice of. 25
did eat manna, and are *d.* 6:49, 58
believeth, though he were *d.* 11:25
patriarch David is both *d. Acts* 2:29
came in and found her *d.* 5:10
ordained of God to be the Judge of quick and *d.* 10:42; *2 Tim* 4:1
supposing he had been *d. Acts* 14:19
down, and was taken up *d.* 20:9
that God should raise the *d.* 26:8

swollen, or fallen down *d.* *Acts* 28:6
God who quickeneth *d.* *Rom* 4:17
considered not his body now *d.* 19
thro' offence of one many be *d.* 5:15
we that are *d.* to sin, live. 6:2
if we be *d.* with Christ. 8
reckon ye yourselves to be *d.* to. 11
if husband be *d.* 7:2, 3; *1 Cor* 7:39
are become *d.* to the law. *Rom* 7:4
Gal 2:19
lord both of *d.* and living. *Rom* 14:9
if so be that *d.* rise not. *1 Cor* 15:15
how are the *d.* raised? 35
and the *d.* shall be raised. 52
trust in God who raiseth *d.* *2 Cor* 1:9
one died for all, then all *d.* 5:14
were *d.* in trespasses and sins.
Eph 2:1, 5; *Col* 2:13
if ye be *d.* with Christ. *Col* 2:20
2 Tim 2:11
ye are *d.* and your life hid. *Col* 3:3
and the *d.* in Christ. *1 Thes* 4:16
repentance from *d.* works. *Heb* 6:1
conscience from *d.* works. 9:14
is of force after men are *d.* 17
and by it he being *d.* yet. 11:4
of one, and him as good as *d.* 12
women received their *d.* raised. 35
we being *d.* to sin should. *1 Pet* 2:24
ready to judge the quick and *d.* 4:5
gospel preached to them that are *d.* 6
twice *d.* plucked up by the. *Jude* 12
first-begotten of the *d.* *Rev* 1:5
saw him, fell at his feet as *d.* 17
name that thou livest, and art *d.* 3:1
blessed are the *d.* who die. 14:13
sea became as blood of a *d.* 16:3
rest of the *d.* lived not again. 20:5
saw the *d.* stand before God. 12
sea gave up *d.* which were in it. 13
see **body, bury, carcase, resurrection**

for the **dead**
not make cuttings *for d.* *Lev* 19:28
none be defiled *for the d.* 21:1
not make baldness *for d.* *Deut* 14:1
not given ought thereof *for d.* 26:14
that mourned *for the d.* *2 Sam* 14:2
to comfort them *for the d.* *Jer* 16:7
weep ye not *for the d.* nor. 22:10
no mourning *for the d.* *Ezek* 24:17
baptized *for the d.* why baptized *for the d.*? *1 Cor* 15:29

from the **dead**
he is risen *from the d.* *Mat* 14:2
rising *from the d.* mean? *Mark* 9:10
if one went *from the d.* *Luke* 16:30
though one rose *from the d.* 31
rise *from the d.* third day. 24:46
John 20:9
after he rose *from d.* *Acts* 10:41
first that should rise *from d.* 26:23
that are alive *from the d.* *Rom* 6:13
bring Christ again *from the d.* 10:7
be, but life *from the d.*? 11:15
be preached that rose *from the d.*
1 Cor 15:12
arise *from the d.* Christ. *Eph* 5:14
first-born *from the d.* *Col* 1:18
able to raise him *from d.* *Heb* 11:19
brought again *from the d.* 13:20
see **raised, risen**

is **dead**
his brother *is d.* *Gen* 42:38; 44:20
name of brother that *is d.* *Deut* 25:6
Moses my servant *is d.* *Josh* 1:2
they forced, that she *is d.* *Judg* 20:5
Saul *is d.* *2 Sam* 2:7; 4:10
Uriah *is d.* 11:21, 24
the child *is d.* 12:18, 19
Amnon only *is d.* 13:32
a widow, my husband *is d.* 14:5
2 Ki 4:1
because king's son *is d.* *2 Sam* 18:20
Absalom *is d.* 19:10
Naboth *is d.* *1 Ki* 21:14
priests not eat that *is d.* *Ezek* 44:31
my daughter *is d.* *Mat* 9:18
Mark 5:35; *Luke* 8:49
that many said, he *is d.* *Mark* 9:26
Abraham *is d.* and. *John* 8:52, 53
Lazarus *is d.* 11:14

he that *is d.* is freed. *Rom* 6:7
if Christ be in you, body *is d.* 8:10
law, Christ *is d.* in vain. *Gal* 2:21
liveth in pleasure, *is d.* *1 Tim* 5:6
hath not works *is d.* *Jas* 2:17, 20*
body without spirit *is d.* so. 26

was **dead**
when the judge *was d.* *Judg* 2:19
men saw Abimelech *was d.* 9:55
their champion *was d.* *1 Sam* 17:51
David heard Nabal *was d.* 25:39
saw Saul *was d.* 31:5; *1 Chr* 10:5
son heard Abner *was d.* *2 Sam* 4:1
Bath-sheba heard husband *was d.*
11:26
David perceived child *was d.* 12:19
Amnon, seeing he *was d.* 13:39
my child suck, it *was d.* *1 Ki* 3:21
Hadad heard that Joab *was d.* 11:21
Jezebel heard Naboth *was d.* 21:15
when Ahab *was d.* Moab. *2 Ki* 3:5
child *was d.* and laid on his. 4:32
Athaliah saw her son *was d.* 11:1
2 Chr 22:10
but when Herod *was d.* *Mat* 2:19
he that *was d.* sat up. *Luke* 7:15
to scorn, knowing she *was d.* 8:53
my son *was d.* and is alive. 15:24
for this thy brother *was d.* and is. 32
sister of him that *was d.* *John* 11:39
and he that *was d.* came forth. 44
saw that Jesus *was d.* brake. 19:33
Jesus which *was d.* *Acts* 25:19
without the law sin *was d.* *Rom* 7:8
he that liveth, and *was d.* *Rev* 1:18

deadly
was a *d.* destruction. *1 Sam* 5:11
deliver me from *d.* enemies. *Ps* 17:9
groanings of a *d.* wounded man.
Ezek 30:24
drink *d.* thing, it shall. *Mark* 16:18
unruly evil, full of *d.* *Jas* 3:8
d. wound was healed. *Rev* 13:3, 12

deadness
neither yet the *d.* of. *Rom* 4:19

deaf
or who maketh the *d.*? *Ex* 4:11
shalt not curse the *d.* *Lev* 19:14
but I as a *d.* man heard. *Ps* 38:13
they are like the *d.* adder. 58:4
in that day shall *d.* hear. *Isa* 29:18
the ears of the *d.* shall be. 35:5
hear, ye *d.* look, ye blind. 42:18
who is *d.* as my messenger? 19
bring forth blind, and the *d.* 43:8
their ears shall be *d.* *Mi* 7:16
the *d.* hear. *Mat* 11:5; *Luke* 7:22
brought one that was *d.* *Mark* 7:32
he maketh the *d.* to hear. 37
thou dumb and *d.* spirit. 9:25

deal, *verb*
now will we *d.* worse. *Gen* 19:9
now if you will *d.* truly. 24:49
return, and I will *d.* well with. 32:9
should he *d.* with our sister? 34:31
come on, let us *d.* wisely. *Ex* 1:10
d. with her after the manner. 21:9
in like manner *d.* with thy. 23:11
not steal, nor *d.* falsely. *Lev* 19:11
if thou *d.* thus with me. *Num* 11:15
thus shall ye *d.* with. *Deut* 7:5
as thou didst *d.* with David my father, even so *d.* *2 Chr* 2:3
lest I *d.* with you after. *Job* 42:8
I said to fools, *d.* not. *Ps* 75:4
d. subtilly with his. 105:25
d. bountifully with. 119:17; 142:7
d. with thy servant. 119:124
but they that *d.* truly. *Pr* 12:22
he will *d.* unjustly. *Isa* 26:10
my servant shall *d.* prudently. 52:13
is it not to *d.* thy bread to? 58:7
d. thus with them in. *Jer* 18:23
if so be that the Lord *d.* with. 21:2
will I also *d.* in fury. *Ezek* 8:18
I will *d.* with thee as thou. 16:59
hands be strong in days I *d.* 22:14
and they shall *d.* furiously. 23:25
he shall surely *d.* with him. 31:11
and as thou seest *d.* *Dan* 1:13
and shall *d.* against them and. 11:7
see **treacherously**

deal
a tenth *d.* of flour. *Ex* 29:40*
Lev 14:21*; *Num* 15:4*; 29:4*
a several tenth *d.* *Num* 28:13*
29:15*
so much more a great *d.* *Mark* 7:36
cried a great *d.* Son of David. 10:48

dealer
the treacherous *d.* dealeth. *Isa* 21:2

dealers
treacherous *d.* have dealt. *Isa* 24:16

dealest
wherefore *d.* thou thus? *Ex* 5:15
thee that spoilest and *d.* *Isa* 33:1

dealeth
thus and thus *d.* Micah. *Judg* 18:4
told me he *d.* subtilly. *1 Sam* 23:22
he becometh poor that *d.* *Pr* 10:4
every prudent man *d.* 13:16*
that is soon angry *d.* foolishly. 14:17
scorner is his name, who *d.* 21:24*
treacherous dealer *d.* *Isa* 21:2
from the prophet even to the priest every one *d.* *Jer* 6:13; 8:10
God *d.* with you as sons. *Heb* 12:7

dealing, -s
I hear of your evil *d.* *1 Sam* 2:23
his violent *d.* shall come. *Ps* 7:16
the Jews have no *d.* with. *John* 4:9

deals
(*Revised Version*, parts of an ephah)
take three tenth *d.* of fine flour.
Lev 14:10; *Num* 15:9
two tenth *d.* for a meat. *Lev* 23:13
Num 28:9
two wave-loaves of two tenth *d.*
Lev 23:17
two tenth *d.* in one cake. 24:5
for a ram two tenth *d.* of flour.
Num 15:6; 28:20, 28; 29:3, 9, 14
three tenth *d.* 28:20, 28; 29:3, 9, 14

dealt
when Sarai *d.* hardly. *Gen* 16:6
God hath *d.* graciously with. 33:11
wherefore *d.* ye so ill with me? 43:6
therefore God *d.* well. *Ex* 1:20
wherefore hast thou *d.* thus? 14:11
wherein they *d.* proudly. 18:11
seeing he hath *d.* deceitfully. 21:8
if ye have *d.* well with Jerubbaal.
Judg 9:16
if ye have *d.* truly, rejoice in. 19
have *d.* with the dead. *Ruth* 1:8
the Almighty hath *d.* bitterly. 20
hast *d.* well with me. *1 Sam* 24:18
Lord shall have *d.* well. 25:31
d. among the people. *2 Sam* 6:19
1 Chr 16:3
they *d.* faithfully. *2 Ki* 12:15; 22:7
Manasseh *d.* with familiar. 21:6
2 Chr 33:6
so *d.* David with cities. *1 Chr* 20:3
amiss, and *d.* wickedly. *2 Chr* 6:37
Rehoboam *d.* wisely. 11:23
have *d.* very corruptly. *Neh* 1:7
knewest they *d.* proudly. 9:10; 16:29
have *d.* deceitfully. *Job* 6:15
Lord hath *d.* bountifully. *Ps* 13:6
116:7
nor have we *d.* falsely in. 44:17
and *d.* unfaithfully like. 78:57
he hath not *d.* with us. 103:10
hast *d.* well with servant. 119:65
they *d.* perversely with me. 78*
he hath not *d.* so with. 147:20
dealers have *d.* very. *Isa* 24:16
Jer 3:20; 5:11; 12:6; *Lam* 1:2
they *d.* by oppression. *Ezek* 22:7
Edom hath *d.* against Judah. 25:12
because Philistines have *d.* 15
have *d.* treacherously. *Hos* 5:7
d. treacherously against me. 6:7
of your God that hath *d.* *Joel* 2:26
Lord thought, so hath he *d.* *Zech* 1:6
Judah hath *d.* treacherously and.
Mal 2:11
thou hast *d.* treacherously. 14
thus hath Lord *d.* with. *Luke* 1:25*
hast thou thus *d.* with us? 2:48
the same *d.* subtilly with. *Acts* 7:19
multitude of Jews have *d.* 25:24*
according as God hath *d.* *Rom* 12:3

dear
Ephraim my *d.* son, is he? *Jer* 31:20
servant, who was *d.* to. *Luke* 7:2
neither count I my life *d.* *Acts* 20:24
followers of God as *d.* *Eph* 5:1*
of Epaphras our *d.* fellow. *Col* 1:7*
into kingdom of his *d.* Son. 13*
because ye were *d.* unto. *1 Thes* 2:8*

dearly *beloved*
(*In the Revised Versions the word* dearly *is omitted in all but the first of these references*)
given *d. beloved* of my soul to. *Jer* 12:7
d. beloved, avenge not. *Rom* 12:19
my *d. beloved.* *1 Cor* 10:14
Phil 4:1; *2 Tim* 1:2
d. beloved. *2 Cor* 7:1; 12:19
1 Pet 2:11
Philemon our *d. beloved.* *Philem* 1

dearth
d. began to come, *d.* *Gen* 41:54*
there was a *d.* in land. *2 Ki* 4:38
if there be a *d.* in land. *2 Chr* 6:28*
buy corn because of the *d.* *Neh* 5:3
to Jeremiah concerning *d.* *Jer* 14:1*
there came a *d.* over. *Acts* 7:11*
there should be a great *d.* 11:28*

death
[1] *Total and final cessation of all vital functions,* Gen 25:11. [2] *Cessation of spiritual life, spoken of as spiritual death,* Rom 7:24; 1 John 3:14. [3] *Used figuratively for what would cause death,* 2 Ki 4:40. [4] *Gates of death, the brink of the grave,* Ps 9:13.
let me not see the *d.* of. *Gen* 21:16
comforted after mother's *d.* 24:67
after the *d.* of Abraham, God. 25:11
and bless thee before my *d.* 27:7
bless thee before his *d.* 10
take from me this *d.* only. *Ex* 10:17
men die common *d.* of. *Num* 16:29
let me die *d.* of righteous. 23:10
slayer shall abide in it unto *d.* of. 35:25, 28, 32; *Josh* 20:6
life of murderer guilty *d.* *Num* 35:31
set before you life and good, *d.* and evil. *Deut* 30:15; *Jer* 21:8
rebel after my *d.*! *Deut* 31:27
I know after my *d.* ye will. 29
blessed Israel before his *d.* 33:1
jeoparded lives to the *d.* *Judg* 5:18
that his soul was vexed unto *d.* 16:16
dead which he slew at his *d.* 30
if ought but *d.* part thee. *Ruth* 1:17
all thou hast done since *d.* of. 2:11
about time of her *d.* *1 Sam* 4:20
surely the bitterness of *d.* 15:32
but a step between me and *d.* 20:3
I have occasioned *d.* of thy. 22:22
in their *d.* were not. *2 Sam* 1:23
in *d.* or life, there will thy. 15:21
when waves of *d.* compassed me. 22:5; *Ps* 18:4; 116:3
the snares of *d.* prevented me. *2 Sam* 22:6; *Ps* 18:5
Egypt till *d.* of Solomon. *1 Ki* 11:40
shall not be any more *d.* *2 Ki* 2:21
man of God, there is *d.* in pot. 4:40
so David prepared before his *d.* *1 Chr* 22:5
counsellors after *d.* of. *2 Chr* 22:4
did Hezekiah honour at his *d.* 32:33
whether it be unto *d.* or to. *Ezra* 7:26
which long for *d.* but it. *Job* 3:21
so that my soul chooseth *d.* 7:15
first-born of *d.* shall devour. 18:13
remain of him be buried in *d.* 27:15
destruction and *d.* say, we. 28:22
thou wilt bring me to *d.* 30:23
in *d.* is no remembrance. *Ps* 6:5
prepared instruments of *d.* 7:13
lest I sleep the sleep of *d.* 13:3
brought me into dust of *d.* 22:15
be our guide, even unto *d.* 48:14
grave, *d.* shall feed on them. 49:14
terrors of *d.* are fallen upon me. 55:4
let *d.* seize on them, and let. 15
there are no bands in their *d.* 73:4
man liveth, shall not see *d.*? 89:48
loose those appointed to *d.* *Ps* 102:20
precious in sight of Lord is *d.* 116:15
not given me over unto *d.* 118:18
her house inclineth to *d.* *Pr* 2:18
her feet go down to *d.*; her steps. 5:5
going down to chambers of *d.* 7:27
all they that hate me love *d.* 8:36
evil, pursueth it to his own *d.* 11:19
ways thereof there is no *d.* 12:28
to depart from the snares of *d.* 13:14; 14:27
righteous hath hope in his *d.* 14:32
as messengers of *d.* 16:14
d. and life are in the power. 18:21
of them that seek *d.* 21:6
them that are drawn to *d.* 24:11
who casteth arrows and *d.* 26:18
I find more bitter than *d.* *Eccl* 7:26
for love is strong as *d.* *S of S* 8:6
he will swallow up *d.* in. *Isa* 25:8
for *d.* cannot celebrate thee. 38:18
and with the rich in his *d.* 53:9
he poured out his soul unto *d.* 12
d. shall be chosen rather. *Jer* 8:3
d. is come up to our windows. 9:21
such as are for *d.* to *d.* 15:2; 43:11
at home there is as *d.* *Lam* 1:20
no pleasure in the *d.* of the wicked. *Ezek* 18:32; 33:11
are all delivered unto *d.* 31:14
O *d.* I will be thy plagues. *Hos* 13:14
to be angry even unto *d.* *Jonah* 4:9
who is as *d.* and cannot. *Hab* 2:5
there till *d.* of Herod. *Mat* 2:15
brother deliver brother to *d.* 10:21
Mark 13:12
curseth father or mother, let him die the *d.* *Mat* 15:4; *Mark* 7:10
shall not taste of *d.* till. *Mat* 16:28
Mark 9:1; *Luke* 9:27
shall condemn him to *d.* *Mat* 20:18
Mark 10:33
soul is sorrowful to *d.* *Mat* 26:38
Mark 14:34
said, he is guilty of *d.* *Mat* 26:66
Mark 14:64
lieth at the point of *d.* *Mark* 5:23
should not see *d.* before. *Luke* 2:26
with thee both to prison and *d.* 22:33
I have found no cause of *d.* 23:22
heal his son, at point of *d.* *John* 4:47
if a man keep my saying, he shall never see *d.* 8:51, 52
this sickness is not unto *d.* 11:4
howbeit, Jesus spake of his *d.* 13
signifying what *d.* 12:33; 18:32
by what *d.* he should glorify. 21:19
having loosed pains of *d.* *Acts* 2:24
Saul consenting to his *d.* 8:1; 22:20
found no cause of *d.* in him. 13:28
persecuted this way unto *d.* 22:4
was no cause of *d.* in me. 28:18
we were reconciled to God by the *d.* of his Son. *Rom* 5:10; *Col* 1:22
and *d.* by sin, and so *d.* *Rom* 5:12
d. reigned from Adam to. 14, 17
as sin hath reigned to *d.* even. 21
so many of us as were baptized into Christ, baptized into his *d.*? 6:3
buried with him by baptism into *d.* 4
planted in likeness of his *d.* 5
dieth no more, *d.* hath no more. 9
servants, whether of sin unto *d.* 16
for end of those things is *d.* 21
for the wages of sin is *d.* but. 23
sins did work to bring *d.* 7:5
commandment of life to be to *d.* 10
which is good made *d.* to me? 13
me from the body of this *d.*? 24
free from law of sin and *d.* 8:2
to be carnally minded is *d.* but. 6
nor *d.* nor life shall separate us. 38
world, life, or *d.* all are. *1 Cor* 3:22
as it were appointed to *d.* 4:9
ye do shew the Lord's *d.* 11:26
for since by man came *d.* by. 15:21
last enemy be destroyed is *d.* 26
d. is swallowed up in victory. 54
O *d.*, where is thy sting? 55
sting of *d.* is sin. 56
we had the sentence of *d.* *2 Cor* 1:9
delivered us from so great a *d.* 10
we are the savour of *d.* unto *d.* 2:16
if the ministration of *d.* was. 3:7
always delivered to *d.* *2 Cor* 4:11
so then *d.* worketh in us. 12
sorrow of world worketh *d.* 7:10
whether by life or by *d.* *Phil* 1:20
obedient unto *d.* even *d.* of. 2:8
Epaphroditus was nigh to *d.* 27
work of Christ was nigh to *d.* 30
made conformable unto his *d.* 3:10
who hath abolished *d.* *2 Tim* 1:10
Jesus, for suffering of *d.* crowned, that he should taste *d.* *Heb* 2:9
through *d.* might destroy him that had power of *d.* 14
them who through fear of *d.* 15
to continue, by reason of *d.* 7:23
that by means of *d.* for the. 9:15
there must of necessity be *d.* 16
that he should not see *d.* 11:5
finished bringeth forth *d.* *Jas* 1:15
his brother abideth in *d.* *1 John* 3:14
there is a sin unto *d.* 5:16
a sin not unto *d.* 17
keys of hell and of *d.* *Rev* 1:18
be faithful unto *d.* I will give. 2:10
shall not be hurt of second *d.* 11
name that sat on him was *d.* 6:8
men shall seek *d.* and *d.* shall. 9:6
loved not their lives to *d.* 12:11
as it were wounded to *d.* 13:3
plagues come in one day, *d.* 18:8
on such the second *d.* hath no. 20:6
and *d.* and hell delivered up. 13
d. and hell cast into lake, this is the second *d.* 14
and there shall be no more *d.* 21:4
see **day**

from **death**
deliver our lives *from d.* *Josh* 2:13
shall redeem thee *from d.* *Job* 5:20
deliver their soul *from d.* *Ps* 33:19
delivered my soul *from d.* 56:13
116:8
to God belong issues *from d.* 68:20
spared not their soul *from d.* 78:50
delivereth *from d.* *Pr* 10:2; 11:4
will redeem thee *from d.* *Hos* 13:14
is passed *from d.* to life. *John* 5:24
1 John 3:14
able to save him *from d.* *Heb* 5:7
shall save a soul *from d.* *Jas* 5:20

gates of **death**
have *gates of d.* been? *Job* 38:17
me up from *gates of d.*? *Ps* 9:13
draw near to the *gates of d.* 107:18

put to **death**
man, shall be *put to d.* *Gen* 26:11
his owner also be *put to d.* *Ex* 21:29
on sabbath, shall be *put to d.* 35:2
shall not be *put to d.* *Lev* 19:20
both of them shall be *put to d.* 20:11
killeth *put to d.* 24:21; *Num* 35:30
stranger that cometh nigh be *put to d.* *Num* 1:51; 3:10, 38; 18:7
dreamer be *put to d.* *Deut* 13:5
first upon him to *put to d.* 9; 17:7
of one witness not be *put to d.* 17:6
be *put to d.* and thou hang. 21:22
not be *put to d.* for children, nor children *put to d.* 24:16; *2 Ki* 14:6
rebel be *put to d.* *Josh* 1:18
for Baal be *put to d.* *Judg* 6:31
we may *put* them *to d.* 20:13
1 Sam 11:12
not a man be *put to d.* *1 Sam* 11:13
2 Sam 19:22
measured he to *put to d.* *2 Sam* 8:2
shall not Shimei be *put to d.*? 19:21
were *put to d.* in the days. 21:9
I will not *put* thee *to d.* *1 Ki* 2:8
Adonijah shall be *put to d.* 2[illegible]
not at this time *put* thee *to d.* 2[illegible]
seek Lord be *put to d.* *2 Chr* 15:1[illegible]
into house, shall be *put to d.* 23:[illegible]
law of his to *put* him *to d.* *Esth* 4:1[illegible]
their men be *put to d.* *Jer* 18:2[illegible]
that if ye *put* me *to d.* 26:1[illegible]
all Judah *put* him at all *to d.*? [illegible]
sought to *put* Urijah *to d.* 2[illegible]
let this man be *put to d.* 38:[illegible]
thou not surely *put* me *to d.*? [illegible]
I will not *put* thee *to d.* 16, 2[illegible]
that they might *put* us *to d.* 43:[illegible]
and *put* them *to d.* in Riblah 52:[illegible]

cause them to be *put to d. Mat* 10:21
Mark 13:12; *Luke* 21:16
would *put* him *to d.* he. *Mat* 14:5
sought false witness to *put* him *to d.*
26:59; 27:1; *Mark* 14:55
by craft and *put to d. Mark* 14:1
scourge and *put to d. Luke* 18:33
malefactors led to be *put to d.* 23:32
counsel to *put* him *to d. John* 11:53
put Lazarus also *to d.* 12:10
for us to *put* any man *to d.* 18:31
keepers to be *put to d. Acts* 12:19
when they were *put to d.* I. 26:10
put to d. in flesh, but. *1 Pet* 3:18

see **surely**

shadow of **death**

let the *shad. of d.* stain it. *Job* 3:5
darkness and *shad. of d.* 10:21, 22
bringeth to light *shad. of d.* 12:22
on eyelids is *shad. of d.* 16:16
morning is even as *shad. of d.* 24:17
out darkness and *shad. of d.* 28:3
is no *shad. of d.* where. 34:22
seen doors of the *shad. of d.*? 38:17
valley of *shad. of d. Ps* 23:4
covered us with *shad. of d.* 44:19
in darkness, and *shad. of d.* 107:10
of darkness and *shad. of d.* 14
in land of the *shad. of d. Isa* 9:2
land of *shad. of d. Jer* 2:6
light, he turn it into *shad. of d.* 13:16
turneth *shad. of d.* into. *Amos* 5:8
in region and *shad. of d. Mat* 4:16
light to them in *shad. of d. Luke* 1:79

ways of **death**

the end *ways of d. Pr* 14:12; 16:25

with **death**

made a covenant *with d. Isa* 28:15
your covenant *with d.* shall. 18
kill her children *with d. Rev* 2:23
power was given to kill *with d.* 6:8

worthy of **death**

that is *worthy of d. Deut* 17:6*
he was not *worthy of d.* 19:6
committed a sin *worthy of d.* 21:22
in damsel no sin *worthy of d.* 22:26
thou art *worthy of d. 1 Ki* 2:26
lo, nothing *worthy of d. Luke* 23:15
his charge *worthy of d. Acts* 23:29
any thing *worthy of d.* 25:11
committed nothing *worthy of d.* 25
doth nothing *worthy of d.* 26:31
such things *worthy of d. Rom* 1:32

deaths

shall die of grevious *d. Jer* 16:4
shalt die *d.* of them that. *Ezek* 28:8
thou shalt die the *d.* of the. 10
in prisons frequent, in *d. 2 Cor* 11:23

debase

and didst *d.* thyself. *Isa* 57:9

debate, *verb*

d. thy cause with thy. *Pr* 25:9
in measure, thou wilt *d. Isa* 27:8*

debate, -s

ye fast for strife and *d. Isa* 58:4*
full of envy, murder, *d. Rom* 1:29*
I fear lest there be *d.* wrath.
2 Cor 12:20*

Deborah

out *D.* Rebekah's nurse. *Gen* 35:8
D. a prophetess judged. *Judg* 4:4
D. arose a mother in Israel. 5:7
awake *D.* 12
he princes were with *D.* 15

debt

That which is due by one man to
nother, Neh 10:31. *Sins are by*
esemblance called debts, Mat 6:12.

very one that was in *d. 1 Sam* 22:2
ell the oil, pay thy *d. 2 Ki* 4:7
he exaction of every *d. Neh* 10:31
nd forgave him the *d. Mat* 18:27
ast into prison till he pay *d.* 30
forgave thee all that *d.* 32
eckoned of grace but *d. Rom* 4:4

debtor

estored to the *d.* his. *Ezek* 18:7
gold of temple is a *d. Mat* 23:16
am *d.* to the Greeks. *Rom* 1:14
e is a *d.* to do the whole. *Gal* 5:3

debtors

as we forgive our *d. Mat* 6:12
creditor had two *d. Luke* 7:41
called every one of his lord's *d.* 16:5
we are *d.* not to flesh. *Rom* 8:12
and their *d.* they are 15:27

debts

that are sureties for *d. Pr* 22:26
forgive us our *d.* as we. *Mat* 6:12

Decapolis

followed him from *D. Mat* 4:25
he began to publish in *D. Mark* 5:20
through midst of coasts of *D.* 7:31

decay

be poor and fallen in *d. Lev* 25:35*

decayed

of bearers of burdens *d. Neh* 4:10
I will raise up the *d. Isa* 44:26*

decayeth

and as the flood *d.* and. *Jer* 14:11†
slothfulness building *d. Eccl* 10:18*
that which *d.* is ready to. *Heb* 8:13*

decease

and spake of his *d.* at. *Luke* 9:31
after my *d.* to have in. *2 Pet* 1:15

deceased

they are *d.* they shall. *Isa* 26:14
when he had married, *d. Mat* 22:25

deceit

their belly prepareth *d. Job* 15:35
nor my tongue utter *d.* 27:4
if my foot hath hasted to *d.* 31:5
full of cursing, *d.* and. *Ps* 10:7
words are iniquity and *d.* 36:3
thy tongue frameth *d.* 50:19
d. and guile depart not. 55:11*
redeem their soul from *d.* 72:14*
he that worketh *d.* shall not. 101:7
them that err, their *d.* is. 119:118
counsels of the wicked are *d. Pr* 12:5
a false witness sheweth forth *d.* 17
d. is in the heart of them that. 20
but the folly of fools is *d.* 14:8
bread of *d.* is sweet to a. 20:17
he that hateth, layeth up *d.* 26:24
whose hatred is covered by *d.* 26
neither was any *d.* in his. *Isa* 53:9
so are houses full of *d. Jer* 5:27
hold fast *d.* they refuse to. 8:5
through *d.* they refuse to know. 9:6
tongue, it speaketh *d.* 8
they prophesy the *d.* of their. 14:14
they are prophets of *d.* 23:26
compasseth me with *d. Hos* 11:12
the balances of *d.* are in. 12:7
falsifying balances by *d. Amos* 8:5
fill masters' houses with *d. Zeph* 1:9
heart of men proceed *d. Mark* 7:22
of murder, debate, *d. Rom* 1:29
tongues they have used *d.* 3:13
through philosophy and vain *d.*
Col 2:8
exhortation was not of *d. 1 Thes* 2:3*

deceitful

abhor bloody and *d.* man. *Ps* 5:6
they devise *d.* matters. 35:20
deliver me from the *d.* and. 43:1
O thou *d.* tongue. 52:4
bloody and *d.* men shall not. 55:23
turned aside like a *d.* bow. 78:57
the mouth of the *d.* are. 109:2
deliver my soul from a *d.* 120:2
wicked worketh a *d.* work. *Pr* 11:18
but a *d.* witness speaketh. 14:25
for they are *d.* meat. 23:3
kisses of an enemy are *d.* 27:6*
the poor and the *d.* man. 29:13*
favour is *d.* and beauty is. 31:30
heart is *d.* above all. *Jer* 17:9
are like a *d.* bow. *Hos* 7:16
and with bag of *d.* weights. *Mi* 6:11
and their tongue is *d.* in. 12
nor shall a *d.* tongue be. *Zeph* 3:13
apostles, *d.* workers. *2 Cor* 11:13
corrupt according to *d. Eph* 4:22

deceitfully

Hamor and Shechem *d. Gen* 34:13
let not Pharaoh deal *d. Ex* 8:29
seeing he hath dealt *d.* with. 21:8
which he hath *d.* gotten. *Lev* 6:4
brethren have dealt *d. Job* 6:15
will ye talk *d.* for him? *Job* 13:7
up his soul nor sworn *d. Ps* 24:4
a sharp razor, working *d.* 52:2
doeth the work of Lord *d. Jer* 48:10
made, he shall work *d. Dan* 11:23
handling word of God *d. 2 Cor* 4:2

deceitfulness

and the *d.* of riches choke the word.
Mat 13:22; *Mark* 4:19
hardened through *d.* of sin. *Heb* 3:13

deceits

and imagine *d.* all day. *Ps* 38:12
smooth things, prophesy *d. Isa* 30:10

deceive

Abner came to *d.* thee. *2 Sam* 3:25
I say, do not *d.* me? *2 Ki* 4:28
let not Hezekiah *d.* you. 18:29
2 Chr 32:15; *Isa* 36:14
let not thy God *d.* thee. *2 Ki* 19:10
Isa 37:10
be not a witness, and *d. Pr* 24:28
they will *d.* every one. *Jer* 9:5
that be in midst of you *d.* 29:8
saith the Lord *d.* not yourselves. 37:9
neither wear garment to *d. Zech* 13:4
take heed that no man *d.* you.
Mat 24:4; *Mark* 13:5
I am Christ; and shall *d.* many.
Mat 24:5, 11; *Mark* 13:6
if possible they shall *d. Mat* 24:24
by fair speech *d.* the. *Rom* 16:18
let no man *d.* himself. *1 Cor* 3:18
they lie in wait to *d. Eph* 4:14
let no man *d.* you. 5:6; *2 Thes* 2:3
1 John 3:7
we have no sin, we *d. 1 John* 1:8
that he should *d.* the. *Rev* 20:3
go to *d.* nations in four quarters. 8

deceivableness

and with all *d.* of. *2 Thes* 2:10

deceived

father hath *d.* me and. *Gen* 31:7
or if a soul sin, or hath *d. Lev* 6:2*
your heart be not *d. Deut* 11:16
why hast thou *d.* me? *1 Sam* 19:17
28:12
O king, my servant *d. 2 Sam* 19:26
the *d.* and the deceiver. *Job* 12:16
let not him that is *d.* trust. 15:31
if mine heart have been *d.* 31:9
princes of Noph are *d. Isa* 19:13
a *d.* heart hath turned him. 44:20
thou hast greatly *d. Jer* 4:10
thou hast *d.* me, and I was *d.* 20:7
thy terribleness hath *d.* thee. 49:16
my lovers, but they *d. Lam* 1:19
if prophet be *d.* I have *d. Ezek* 14:9
of thine heart hath *d. Ob* 3
men at peace with thee have *d.* 7
heed that ye be not *d. Luke* 21:8
answered, are ye also *d.*? *John* 7:47
by commandment *d.* me. *Rom* 7:11
be not *d. 1 Cor* 6:9; 15:33; *Gal* 6:7
d. but woman being *d. 1 Tim* 2:14
deceiving and being *d. 2 Tim* 3:13
we were foolish, *d. Tit* 3:3
all nations were *d. Rev* 18:23
he *d.* them that had received. 19:20
devil that *d.* them was cast. 20:10

deceiver

seem to my father as a *d. Gen* 27:12
the deceived and the *d. Job* 12:16
cursed be *d.* who hath. *Mal* 1:14
remember that that *d. Mat* 27:63
not Jesus this is a *d. 2 John* 7

deceivers

and good report, as *d. 2 Cor* 6:8
many *d.* especially of. *Tit* 1:10
for many *d.* are entered. *2 John* 7

deceiveth

so is the man that *d.* his. *Pr* 26:19
nay, but he *d.* the people. *John* 7:12
when nothing, *d.* himself. *Gal* 6:3
d. his own heart. *Jas* 1:26
called the devil, which *d. Rev* 12:9
and *d.* them that dwell on. 13:14

deceiving

men wax worse, *d. 2 Tim* 3:13
not hearers only, *d.* your. *Jas* 1:22

deceivings
sporting with their own *d.* *2 Pet* 2:13

decently
let all things be done *d.* *1 Cor* 14:40

decided
thyself hast *d.* it. *1 Ki* 20:40

decision
in valley of *d.* for day. *Joel* 3:14

deck
d. thyself now with. *Job* 40:10
they *d.* it with silver. *Jer* 10:4

decked
d. my bed with covering. *Pr* 7:16*
I *d.* thee also with. *Ezek* 16:11
thou wast thus *d.* with gold. 13
and she *d.* herself with. *Hos* 2:13
was arrayed and *d.* with. *Rev* 17:4
that great city that was *d.* 18:16

deckedst
didst take garments and *d.*
Ezek 16:16*
didst wash and *d.* thyself. 23:40

deckest, -eth
as a bridegroom *d.* *Isa* 61:10
though thou *d.* thee with. *Jer* 4:30

declaration
d. of the greatness of. *Esth* 10:2*
and hear my *d.* with. *Job* 13:17
to set forth in order a *d.* *Luke* 1:1*
and to the *d.* of your. *2 Cor* 8:19*

declare
none that could *d.* it. *Gen* 41:24
Moab began Moses to *d.* *Deut* 1:5
d. his cause in ears of. *Josh* 20:4
if ye can *d.* it me within. *Judg* 14:12
words of the prophets *d.* good.
1 Ki 22:13; *2 Chr* 18:12
d. his glory among the heathen.
1 Chr 16:24; *Ps* 96:3
to shew copy and *d.* it. *Esth* 4:8
fishes of the sea shall *d.* *Job* 12:8
d. his way to his face? 21:31
then did he see it, and *d.* it. 28:27
I would *d.* to him the. 31:37
foundations of earth, *d.* if thou. 38:4
breadth of earth, *d.* if thou. 18
will demand of thee, *d.* 40:7; 42:4
d. among the people his. *Ps* 9:11
the heavens *d.* the glory. 19:1
come and *d.* righteousness. 22:31
50:6; 97:6
shall it *d.* thy truth? 30:9
if I would *d.* and speak of. 40:5
what hast thou to do to *d.*? 50:16
all men shall fear and *d.* 64:9
trust in Lord that I may *d.* 73:28*
is near, wondrous works *d.* 75:1*
should arise and *d.* them. 78:6*
to *d.* the name of the Lord. 102:21
and *d.* his works with. 107:22
but live and *d.* the works. 118:17
one generation shall *d.* thy. 145:4
in my heart even to *d.* *Eccl* 9:1*
d. their sin as Sodom. *Isa* 3:9
d. his doings among people. 12:4
set a watchman, let him *d.* 21:6
or let them *d.* to us things. 41:22
and new things do I *d.* 42:9
and let them *d.* his praise. 12
who among them can *d.* this? 43:9
d. thou that thou mayest be. 26*
I shall call, and shall *d.* it? 44:7
I the Lord *d.* things that are. 45:19
all this, and will not ye *d.* 48:6
who shall *d.* his generation? 53:8*
Acts 8:33
they shall *d.* my glory. *Isa* 66:19
d. this in house of Jacob. *Jer* 5:20
hath spoken, that he may *d.* 9:12
d. it in isles afar off, and say. 31:10
if I *d.* it to thee, wilt thou? 38:15
d. unto us what thou hast said. 25
what God shall say, *d.* to us. 42:20
d. in Zion the vengeance of. 50:28
let us *d.* in Zion work of. 51:10
may *d.* all their. *Ezek* 12:16; 23:36
d. all that thou seest to the. 40:4
O Belteshazzar, *d.* the. *Dan* 4:18
to *d.* to Jacob his. *Mi* 3:8
even to-day do I *d.* that. *Zech* 9:12
d. unto us this parable. *Mat* 13:36*
d. unto us this parable. 15:15
d. unto you glad. *Acts* 13:32*
though a man *d.* it to you. 41
ignorantly worship, him *d.* 17:23*
not shunned to *d.* to you the. 20:27
set forth to *d.* his righteousness.
Rom 3:25*, 26*
the day shall *d.* it. *1 Cor* 3:13
in this that I *d.* to you. 11:17*
I *d.* unto you the gospel. 15:1*
state shall Tychicus *d.* *Col* 4:7*
that say such things *d.* *Heb* 11:14*
which we have seen *d.* *1 John* 1:3
then is message which we *d.* 5*

I will **declare**
I have seen *I will d.* *Job* 15:17
I will d. the decree. *Ps* 2:7*
I will d. thy name to brethren.
22:22; *Heb* 2:12
I will d. mine iniquity. *Ps* 38:18
I will d. what he hath done. 66:16
but *I will d.* for ever, I will. 75:9
I will d. thy greatness. 145:6
I will d. thy righteousness. *Isa* 57:12
I will d. it, I will keep. *Jer* 42:4
thy name, *will d.* it. *John* 17:26*

declare *ye*
a voice of singing *d. ye.* *Isa* 48:20
d. ye in Judah, and. *Jer* 4:5
d. ye in Egypt, and publish. 46:14
d. ye among the nations. 50:2
d. ye it not at Gath. *Mi* 1:10*

declared
that my name may be *d.* *Ex* 9:16
Moses *d.* to children of. *Lev* 23:44
they *d.* their pedigrees. *Num* 1:18
because it was not *d.* 15:34
and he *d.* to you his. *Deut* 4:13
for thou hast *d.* this. *2 Sam* 19:6
words that were *d.* to. *Neh* 8:12
plentifully *d.* thing as it. *Job* 26:3
I have *d.* thy faithfulness. *Ps* 40:10
hitherto have I *d.* thy works. 71:17
hast *d.* thy strength among. 77:14*
loving-kindness be *d.* in the. 88:11
with my lips have I *d.* all. 119:13
I have *d.* my ways, and thou. 26
a grievous vision is *d.* *Isa* 21:2
heard of God have I *d.* unto you. 10
who hath *d.* from. 41:26; 45:21*
I have *d.* and have saved. 43:12
44:8; 48:5
I have *d.* former things from. 48:3
them hath *d.* these things? 14
Micaiah *d.* all the words. *Jer* 36:13
I have this day *d.* it to you. 42:21
she *d.* to him before all. *Luke* 8:47
he hath *d.* him. *John* 1:18
I have *d.* to them thy name. 17:26*
he *d.* to them how he had. *Acts* 9:27
when he had *d.* all these. 10:8*
d. how Lord had brought him. 12:17
d. all things that God had. 15:4*
Simeon had *d.* how God at. 14*
Festus *d.* Paul's cause to. 25:14
d. to be the Son of God. *Rom* 1:4
that my name might be *d.* 9:17*
for it hath been *d.* to. *1 Cor* 1:11*
d. to be the epistle of. *2 Cor* 3:3*
who also *d.* to us your. *Col* 1:8
of God be finished as he *d.* *Rev* 10:7

declareth, -ing
there is none that *d.* *Isa* 41:26
d. the end from beginning. 46:10
a voice *d.* from Dan. *Jer* 4:15
my people, their staff *d.* *Hos* 4:12
he that *d.* to man what. *Amos* 4:13
d. the conversion of the. *Acts* 15:3
d. what miracles God hath. 12*
d. to you the testimony. *1 Cor* 2:1*

decline
(*To turn aside, deviate, or stray*)
speak in a cause, to *d.* *Ex* 23:2
not *d.* from sentence. *Deut* 17:11
d. from thy testimonies. *Ps* 119:157
neither *d.* from words of. *Pr* 4:5
heart *d.* to her ways, go not. 7:25

declined, -eth
d. neither to right hand. *2 Chr* 34:2
way have I kept and not *d.* *Job* 23:11
nor have our steps *d.* *Ps* 44:18
days are like shadow that *d.* 102:11
like the shadow when it *d.* *Ps* 109:23
yet have I not *d.* from thy. 119:51

decrease
and suffer not cattle to *d.* *Ps* 107:38
increase, but I must *d.* *John* 3:30

decreased
waters *d.* continually until. *Gen* 8:5

decree, *substantive*
[1] *An authoritative order,* 2 Chr 30:5; Ezra 6:1. [2] *An eternal purpose of God,* Ps 2:7; Dan 4:24.
so they established a *d.* *2 Chr* 30:5
king Cyrus made a *d.* *Ezra* 5:13, 17
Darius made a *d.* 6:1, 12
Artaxerxes do make a *d.* 7:21
the *d.* was given to Shushan.
Esth 3:15; 9:14
d. of Esther confirmed. 9:32
made a *d.* for the rain. *Job* 28:26
I will declare the *d.* the. *Ps* 2:7
he hath made a *d.* which. 148:6
he gave to sea his *d.* *Pr* 8:29
sea by a perpetual *d.* *Jer* 5:22
there is but one *d.* for. *Dan* 2:9
this matter is by the *d.* of the. 4:17
this is the *d.* of the most High. 24
now, O king, establish the *d.* 6:8
regardeth not thee, nor *d.* 13
I make a *d.* that in every. 26
proclaimed by the *d.* of. *Jonah* 3:7
in that day shall the *d.* be. *Mi* 7:11
before the *d.* bring forth. *Zeph* 2:2
there went out a *d.* *Luke* 2:1

decree, *verb*
thou shalt also *d.* a. *Job* 22:28
kings reign, and princes *d.* *Pr* 8:15
woe to them that *d.* *Isa* 10:1

decreed
remembered what was *d.* *Esth* 2:1
as they had *d.* for themselves. 9:31
brake up for it my *d.* *Job* 38:10
consumption *d.* overflow. *Isa* 10:22
hath so *d.* in his heart. *1 Cor* 7:37

decrees
that decree unrighteous *d.* *Isa* 10:1
they delivered them the *d.* *Acts* 16:4
do contrary to the *d.* of Caesar. 17:7

Dedan
Sheba, *D.* *Gen* 10:7; *1 Chr* 1:9
Jokshan, Sheba, and *D.* *1 Chr* 1:32
made *D.* and Tema, and. *Jer* 25:23
deep, O inhabitants of *D.* 49:8
they of *D.* shall fall by. *Ezek* 25:13
D. was thy merchant in. 27:20

Dedanim
travelling companies of *D.* *Isa* 21:13

dedicate
die and another man *d.* *Deut* 20:5
which also David did *d.* *2 Sam* 8:11
out of spoils did they *d.* to. 27
I build an house to *d.* *2 Chr* 2:4

dedicated
a new house and not *d.* *Deut* 20:5
I had wholly *d.* the silver. *Judg* 17:3
things which David had *d.* *1 Ki* 7:51
1 Chr 18:11; *2 Chr* 5:1
the king and Israel *d.* *1 Ki* 8:63
2 Chr 7:5
had *d.* and things himself had *d.*
1 Ki 15:15; *2 Chr* 15:18
all the money of the *d.* *2 Ki* 12:4*
hallowed things that kings of Judah had *d.* 12:18
over treasures of *d.* *1 Chr* 26:20, 26
captains of hosts had *d.* 26
that Samuel, Saul, and Joab *d.* 28
pattern of the treasuries of the *d* things 28:12
the *d.* things did they bestow.
2 Chr 24:
and brought in the *d.* things. 31:1
every *d.* thing in Israel. *Ezek* 44:29
nor first testament *d.* *Heb* 9:18

dedicating
princes offered for *d.* *Num* 7:1
each prince on his day for *d.* 1

dedication
this was the *d.* of. *Num* 7:84, 8
for they kept the *d.* of. *2 Chr* 7:

kept the d. with joy. Ezra 6:16
offered at d. of house of God. 17
at the d. of the wall. Neh 12:27
come to d. of image. Dan 3:2, 3
at Jerusalem feast of d. John 10:22

deed

what d. is this ye have? Gen 44:15
in very d. for this cause. Ex 9:16
was no such d. done. Judg 19:30
in very d. except thou. 1 Sam 25:34
Saul was come in very d. 26:4*
by this d. given great. 2 Sam 12:14
for this d. of queen shall. Esth 1:17
had not consented to d. Luke 23:51
a prophet mighty in d. 24:19
be examined of the good d. Acts 4:9
obedient by word and d. Rom 15:18
that hath done this d. 1 Cor 5:2
him that hath done this d. 3
ye do in word or d. do. Col 3:17
shall be blessed in his d. Jas 1:25
love in d. and in truth. 1 John 3:18

deeds

hast done d. that ought not. Gen 20:9
make known his d. 1 Chr 16:8
Ps 105:1
his d. first and last. 2 Chr 35:27
come upon us for evil d. Ezra 9:13
also reported his good d. Neh 6:19
wipe not out my good d. 13:14
them according to their d. Ps 28:4
according to their d. Isa 59:18
they overpass the d. of. Jer 5:28
them according to their d. 25:14
that ye allow the d. of. Luke 11:48
the due reward of our d. 23:41
because their d. were. John 3:19
to the light, lest his d. should. 20
that his d. may be made. 21
ye do the d. of your father. 8:41
mighty in word and in d. Acts 7:22
Dorcas was full of alms-d. 9:36
confessed, and shewed their d. 19:18
very worthy d. are done. 24:2*
man according to his d. Rom 2:6
by the d. of the law shall no. 3:20
is justified by faith without d. 28*
if ye mortify the d. of the. 8:13
in signs and mighty d. 2 Cor 12:12
put off old man with his d. Col 3:9
soul with their unlawful d. 2 Pet 2:8
is partaker of his evil d. 2 John 11
I will remember his d. 3 John 10
them of their ungodly d. Jude 15
thou hatest the d. of the. Rev 2:6
except they repent of their d. 22
repented not of their d. 16:11

deemed

the shipmen d. that. Acts 27:27

deep

[1] *Extending a great way below the surface*, Ezek 32:24. [2] *The sea*, Job 41:31. [3] *Used for any great danger or profound or incomprehensible matter*, Ps 69:15; Isa 33:19; Dan 2:22.

darkness was upon the face of the d. Gen 1:2
the fountains of the d. were. 7:11
fountains also of the d. were. 8:2
thee with blessings of the d. 49:25
the d. that coucheth. Deut 33:13
face of the d. is frozen. Job 38:30
the d. to boil like a pot. 41:31
would think the d. to be hoary. 32
judgements are a great d. Ps 36:6
d. calleth unto d. at noise of. 42:7
neither let the d. swallow. 69:15
coveredst it with the d. as. 104:6
these see wonders in the d. 107:24
strengthens fountains of d. Pr 8:28
saith to the d. be dry. Isa 44:27
dried waters of great d.? 51:10
led them through the d. 63:13
when I bring up the d. Ezek 26:19
the d. set him on high with. 31:4
covered the d. for him. 15
devoured great d. and. Amos 7:4
hast cast me into the d. Jonah 2:3
the d. uttered his voice. Hab 3:10
launch out into the d. and. Luke 5:4
command them to go into d. 8:31*
shall descend into d.? Rom 10:7*
night and day in the d. 2 Cor 11:25

deep, *adjective*

he discovereth d. things. Job 12:22
thought and heart is d. Ps 64:6
I sink in d. mire, I am come into d. waters. 69:2
delivered out of the d. waters. 14
didst cause it to take d. root. 80:9
thy thoughts are very d. 92:5
in his hand are the d. places. 95:4
in the seas and all d. places. 135:6
them be cast into d. pits. 140:10
mouth are as d. waters. Pr 18:4
counsel is like d. waters. 20:5
of strange women is a d. pit. 22:14
for a whore is a d. ditch. 23:27
exceeding d. who can? Eccl 7:24
woe to them that seek d. Isa 29:15
made Tophet d. and large. 30:33
turn back, dwell d. Jer 49:8
drink thy sister's cup d. Ezek 23:32
will I make their waters d. 32:14*
and to have drunk d. waters. 34:18*
he revealeth the d. and. Dan 2:22
digged d. laid foundation. Luke 6:48
to draw, and well is d. John 4:11
Spirit searcheth d. 1 Cor 2:10
d. poverty abounded to. 2 Cor 8:2

deep *sleep*

God caused a d. sleep. Gen 2:21
a d. sleep fell on Abram. 15:12
a d. sleep was fallen. 1 Sam 26:12
d. sleep falleth. Job 4:13; 33:15
casteth into d. sleep. Pr 19:15
on you spirit of d. sleep. Isa 29:10
I was in a d. sleep. Dan 8:18; 10:9
fallen into d. sleep. Acts 20:9

deeper

plague in sight be d. than skin. Lev 13:3; 25:30
bright spot in sight be not d. 13:4
31, 32, 34
it is d. than hell. Job 11:8
a people of d. speech. Isa 33:19

deeply

of Israel d. revolted. Isa 31:6
they have d. corrupted. Hos 9:9
Jesus sighed d. in his. Mark 8:12

deepness

they had no d. of earth. Mat 13:5

deeps

thou threwest into d. Neh 9:11
hast laid me in the d. Ps 88:6
praise Lord, dragons and all d. 148:7
all the d. of the river. Zech 10:11

deer

shall eat the fallow d. Deut 14:5*
Solomon had fallow d. 1 Ki 4:23

defamed

being d. we intreat. 1 Cor 4:13

defaming

for I heard d. of many. Jer 20:10

defeat

d. the counsel of Ahithophel. 2 Sam 15:34; 17:14

defence

their d. is departed. Num 14:9
Rehoboam built cities for d. 2 Chr 11:5
Almighty shall be thy d. Job 22:25*
my d. is of God who. Ps 7:10*
be thou an house of d. to. 31:2
for God is my d. 59:9*, 17*
thou hast been my d. and. 16*
God is my d. I shall not. 62:2*, 6*
for the Lord is our d. 89:18*
Lord is my d. and God. 94:22*
is a d. money is a d. Eccl 7:12
all glory shall be a d. Isa 4:5*
the brooks of d. shall be. 19:6*
his place of d. shall be the. 33:16
the d. shall be prepared. Nah 2:5*
would have made his d. Acts 19:33
hear my d. which I make. 22:1
in my bonds and in d. Phil 1:7
I am set for the d. of the gospel. 17

defenced

(*Fortified by a wall*)

of a d. city a ruin. Isa 25:2
against all d. cities of Judah. Isa 36:1
to lay waste d. cities into. 37:26
let us go into the d. cities. Jer 4:5
for these d. cities remained. 34:7

see **city, cities**

defend

Tolah arose to d. Israel. Judg 10:1*
I will d. city. 2 Ki 19:34; 20:6
Isa 37:35; 38:6
name of God of Jacob d. Ps 20:1*
d. me from them that rise up. 59:1*
d. the poor and fatherless. 82:3*
so will Lord of hosts d. Isa 31:5*
Lord of hosts shall d. Zech 9:15
d. inhabitants of Jerusalem. 12:8

defended

Shammah stood and d. 2 Sam 23:12
he d. them and. Acts 7:24

defendest

for joy, because thou d. Ps 5:11

defending

d. Jerusalem he will. Isa 31:5

defer

thou vowest a vow, d. Eccl 5:4
name's sake will I d. Isa 48:9
d. not for thine own sake. Dan 9:19

deferred

the young man d. not. Gen 34:19
hope d. maketh heart sick. Pr 13:12
when Felix heard he d. Acts 24:22

deferreth

discretion of a man d. Pr 19:11*

defied

whom Lord hath not d.? Num 23:8
he hath d. the armies. 1 Sam 17:36
the God whom thou hast d. 45
when he d. Israel, Jonathan slew him. 2 Sam 21:21; 1 Chr 20:7
d. the Philistines. 2 Sam 23:9

defile

[1] *To make foul*, 1 Cor 8:7; Tit 1:15. [2] *To make ceremonially unclean*, Lev 11:44; Mark 7:2.

nor d. yourselves. Lev 11:44; 18:24
when they d. my tabernacle. 15:31
to d. thyself with thy. 18:20
neither lie with any beast to d. 23
spue not you out when ye d. 28
to d. my sanctuary. 20:3
he shall not d. himself. 21:4
nor d. himself for his father or. 11
he shall not eat to d. himself. 22:8
they d. not their camps. Num 5:3
d. not the land which ye. 35:34
high places did king d. 2 Ki 23:13
how shall I d. them? S of S 5:3
shall d. the covering of. Isa 30:22
called by my name to d. Jer 32:34
robbers enter into it and d. it. Ezek 7:22*
d. the house, fill courts with. 9:7
d. not yourselves with idols. 20:7, 18
idols against herself to d. 22:3
they shall d. thy brightness. 28:7
ye d. every one his. 33:26
nor shall they d. themselves. 37:23
name shall Israel no more d. 43:7
at no dead person to d. 44:25
would not d. himself. Dan 1:8
and they d. the man. Mat 15:18
Mark 7:15, 23
if any man d. temple. 1 Cor 3:17*
law is for them that d. 1 Tim 1:10*
these filthy dreamers d. Jude 8

defiled

with Dinah, and d. her. Gen 34:2*
Jacob heard that he had d. Dinah. 5
because he had d. Dinah. 13, 27
a man shall be d. with. Lev 5:3
that he should be d. thereby. 11:43
plague is in him be d. 13:46*
the law of him that is d. 15:32*
all these things nations are d. 18:24
the land is d. I visit. 25, 27
seek after wizards to be d. 19:31
shall none be d. for the dead. 21:1
a virgin, for her may he be d. 3
put out whosoever is d. Num 5:2*
and if she be d. 13, 27
if she be not d. 14, 28

and he hath *d.* the head of. *Num* 6:9
because his separation was *d.* 12
men who were *d.* by dead. 9:6*, 7*
d. the sanctuary of Lord. 19:20
that thy land be not *d.* *Deut* 21:23
fruit of thy vineyard be *d.* 22:9*
may not take her after *d.* 24:4
Josiah *d.* high places. *2 Ki* 23:8
d. Topheth. 10
forasmuch as he *d.* his. *1 Chr* 5:1
because they have *d.* *Neh* 13:29
I have *d.* my horn. *Job* 16:15*
d. dwelling-place of. *Ps* 74:7*; 79:1
thus were they *d.* with. 106:39
the earth is *d.* under. *Isa* 24:5*
your hands are *d.* with blood. 59:3
but when ye entered, ye *d.* *Jer* 2:7
lightness of whoredom she *d.* 3:9*
because they have *d.* land. 16:18*
of the kings of Judah be *d.* 19:13
Israel eat *d.* bread. *Ezek* 4:13*
surely because thou hast *d.* 5:11
their holy places shall be *d.* 7:24*
neither *d.* neighbour's wife. 18:6, 15
hath even *d.* his neighbour's. 11
wherein ye have been *d.* 20:43*
and hast *d.* thyself. 22:4; 23:7
another hath lewdly *d.* his. 22:11
I saw that she was *d.* 23:13
the Babylonians *d.* her. 17
they have *d.* my sanctuary. 38
thou hast *d.* thy sanctuaries. 28:18*
they *d.* it by their own way. 36:17
they have *d.* my holy name. 43:8
and Israel is *d.* *Hos* 5:3; 6:10
nations say, let her be *d.* *Mi* 4:11
disciples eat bread with *d.* *Mark* 7:2
not in, lest they be *d.* *John* 18:28
conscience being weak is *d.* *1 Cor* 8:7
to *d.* is nothing pure, mind and conscience *d.* *Tit* 1:15
and therefore many be *d.* *Heb* 12:15
a few who have not *d.* *Rev* 3:4
these are they who are not *d.* 14:4

defiledst

to father's bed, then *d.* it. *Gen* 49:4

defileth

that *d.* sabbath. *Ex* 31:14*
d. the tabernacle. *Num* 19:13
not pollute land, blood *d.* 35:33
goeth into the mouth *d.* *Mat* 15:11
eat with unwashen hands *d.* not. 20
out of man that *d.* *Mark* 7:20
so is tongue, that it *d.* the. *Jas* 3:6
enter any thing that *d.* *Rev* 21:27*

defraud

not *d.* thy neighbour. *Lev* 19:13*
do not bear false witness, *d.* not. *Mark* 10:19
nay you do wrong, and *d.* *1 Cor* 6:8
d. not, except it be with. 7:5
no man *d.* his brother. *1 Thes* 4:6*

defrauded

whom have I *d.*? *1 Sam* 12:3
thou hast not *d.* nor oppressed. 4
rather suffer yourselves to be *d.* *1 Cor* 6:7
wronged no man, have *d.* *2 Cor* 7:2*

defy

curse me Jacob, *d.* *Num* 23:7
how shall I *d.* whom Lord hath? 8
I *d.* the armies of. *1 Sam* 17:10
is come up, surely to *d.* Israel. 25
that he should *d.* the armies. 26

degenerate

turned into the *d.* plant. *Jer* 2:21

degree, -s

Songs of degrees: *This title is given to fifteen Psalms, from* 120 *to* 134, *inclusive. The* Hebrew *text calls each, A song of ascents. There is a great diversity of views as to the meaning of this title, but the most probable is that they were pilgrim songs, sung by the people as they went up to Jerusalem.*
or backward ten *d.* *2 Ki* 20:9*, 10* 11*; *Isa* 38:8*
brethren of second *d.* *1 Chr* 15:18
state of a man of high *d.* 17:17
low *d.* vanity, high *d.* a lie. *Ps* 62:9
exalted them of low *d.* *Luke* 1:52
to themselves a good *d.* *1 Tim* 3:13*
let brother of low *d.* *Jas* 1:9

delay, -ed, -eth

thou shalt not *d.* to offer. *Ex* 22:29
the people saw that Moses *d.* 32:1
d. not to keep thy. *Ps* 119:60
my lord *d.* his coming. *Mat* 24:48* *Luke* 12:45
that he would not *d.* *Acts* 9:38
without any *d.* I sat on. 25:17

delectable

their *d.* things not profit. *Isa* 44:9

delicacies

merchants rich through *d.* *Rev* 18:3*

delicate

the *d.* man or. *Deut* 28:54, 56
more called tender and *d.* *Isa* 47:1
Zion to comely *d.* woman. *Jer* 6:2
bald for thy *d.* children. *Mi* 1:16*

delicately

Agag came to him *d.* *1 Sam* 15:32†
he that *d.* bringeth up his. *Pr* 29:21
they that did feed *d.* are. *Lam* 4:5
they that live *d.* are in. *Luke* 7:25

delicateness

foot on ground for *d.* *Deut* 28:56

delicates

filled his belly with *d.* *Jer* 51:34†

deliciously

glorified herself and lived *d.* *Rev* 18:7*, 9*

delight, *substantive*

Shechem had *d.* in. *Gen* 34:19
Lord had a *d.* in thy. *Deut* 10:15
if thou have no *d.* in her. 21:14
great *d.* in offerings? *1 Sam* 15:22
behold, the king hath *d.* in. 18:22
I have no *d.* in thee. *2 Sam* 15:26
shalt thou have *d.* in. *Job* 22:26
but his *d.* is in the law. *Ps* 1:2
excellent, in whom is my *d.* 16:3
testimonies also are my *d.* 119:24
for thy law is my *d.* 77, 174
I was daily his *d.* *Pr* 8:30
a just weight is the Lord's *d.* 11:1
upright in their way are his *d.* 20
they that deal truly are his *d.* 12:22
prayer of the upright is his *d.* 15:8
righteous lips are *d.* of kings. 16:13
fool hath no *d.* in understanding. 18:2
d. is not seemly for a fool. 19:10*
that rebuke him shall be *d.* 24:25
he shall give *d.* unto thy soul. 29:17
under his shadow with *d.* *S of S* 2:3
take *d.* in approaching to. *Isa* 58:2
if thou call the sabbath a *d.* 13
they have no *d.* in word. *Jer* 6:10

delight, *verb*

if the Lord *d.* in us, then. *Num* 14:8
why should the king *d.*? *2 Sam* 24:3
will he *d.* himself in? *Job* 27:10
that he *d.* himself with God. 34:9
d. thyself also in the Lord. *Ps* 37:4
meek shall *d.* in abundance of. 11
I *d.* to do thy will, O my God. 40:8
they *d.* in lies. 62:4
the people that *d.* in war. 68:30
thy comforts *d.* my soul. 94:19
d. myself in thy statutes. 119:16, 35
d. in thy commandments. 47
I *d.* in thy law 70
how long will scorners *d.*? *Pr* 1:22
and *d.* in frowardness of. 2:14
I *d.* not in the blood of. *Isa* 1:11
they shall not *d.* in it. 13:17
and let your soul *d.* itself 55:2
they seek me, and *d.* to know. 58:2
then shalt thou *d.* thyself in. 14
in these things I *d.* *Jer* 9:24
covenant whom ye *d.* in. *Mal* 3:1
I *d.* in the law of God. *Rom* 7:22

delighted

Jonathan *d.* much in. *1 Sam* 19:2
because he *d.* in me. *2 Sam* 22:20 *Ps* 18:19
the Lord who *d.* in thee. *1 Ki* 10:9 *2 Chr* 9:8
and *d.* themselves in thy. *Neh* 9:25
no more, except king *d.* *Esth* 2:14
deliver him, seeing he *d.* *Ps* 22:8
as he *d.* not in blessing. 109:17
choose that wherein I *d.* not. *Isa* 65:12; 66:4
be *d.* with the abundance of. 66:11

delightest

not sacrifice, thou *d.* not. *Ps* 51:16

delighteth

king *d.* to honour. *Esth* 6:6, 7, 9, 11
ordered by Lord, and he *d.* *Ps* 37:23
that *d.* greatly in his. 112:1
he *d.* not in the strength. 147:10
as father son in whom he *d.* *Pr* 3:12
in whom my soul *d.* *Isa* 42:1
Hephzi-bah, for the Lord *d.* 62:4
and their soul *d.* in their. 66:3
not anger, *d.* in mercy. *Mi* 7:18
when ye say, God *d.* in. *Mal* 2:17

delights

in scarlet with other *d.* *2 Sam* 1:24*
unless law had been my *d.* *Ps* 119:92
thy commandments are my *d.* 143
my *d.* with the sons of. *Pr* 8:31
men-singers, and *d.* of. *Eccl* 2:8
art thou, O love, for *d.* *S of S* 7:6

delightsome

ye shall be a *d.* land. *Mal* 3:12

Delilah

in valley of Sorek, *D.* *Judg* 16:4
D. therefore took new ropes. 12

deliver

[1] *Restore, or give,* Gen 37:22; 40:13. [2] *Save, rescue,* Ps 7:2; 2 Cor 1:10.

thou shalt *d.* Pharaoh's. *Gen* 40:13*
yet shall ye *d.* the tale. *Ex* 5:18
if a man shall *d.* unto. 22:7, 10
d. it by that the sun goes down. 26*
I will *d.* the inhabitants of. 23:31
if thou wilt indeed *d.* *Num* 21:2
the congregation shall *d.* the. 35:25
he shall *d.* their kings. *Deut* 7:24
thou shalt not *d.* to his. 23:15
to *d.* her husband out of the. 25:11
any that can *d.* out. 32:39; *Isa* 43:13
that ye will *d.* our lives. *Josh* 2:13
for your God will *d.* it into. 8:7
they shall not *d.* the slayer. 20:5
and *d.* the Midianites. *Judg* 7:7
if thou shalt without fail *d.* 11:30
Samson shall begin to *d.* 13:5*
the coasts did Israel *d.* *1 Sam* 7:14
which cannot profit nor *d.* 12:21
I will *d.* the Philistines. 23:4 *2 Sam* 5:19
I will *d.* thine enemy. *1 Sam* 24:4
the Lord will *d.* Israel to. 28:19
king will hear to *d.* his. *2 Sam* 14:16
d. thy servant to Ahab. *1 Ki* 18:9
I will *d.* this multitude. 20:13, 28
go up, for the Lord shall *d.* it. 22:6, 12, 15; *2 Chr* 18:5, 11
he will *d.* the Moabites. *2 Ki* 3:18
d. it for breaches of house. 12:7
Lord *d.* Jerusalem. 18:35; *Isa* 36:20
let them *d.* it into hand. *2 Ki* 22:5
who could not *d.* their. *2 Chr* 25:15
now hear me and *d.* the. 28:11*
gods of nations able to *d.*? 32:13
that your God be able to *d.* 14, 17
those *d.* thou before the. *Ezra* 7:19
there is none can *d.* out. *Job* 10:7
he shall *d.* the island of. 22:30
he will *d.* his soul from. 33:28*
d. my soul. *Ps* 6:4; 17:13; 22:20 116:4; 120:2
while there is none to *d.* 7:2; 50:22
nor shall he *d.* any by his. 33:17
to *d.* their soul from death. 19
not *d.* my feet from falling? 56:13
for he shall *d.* the needy. 72:12
d. not soul of thy turtle-dove. 74:19
d. poor and needy out of. 82:4
shall he *d.* his soul from? 89:48
crown of glory shall she *d.* to. *Pr* 4:9
do this now, and *d.* thyself. 6:3
thou shalt *d.* his soul from. 23:14
wickedness *d.* those. *Eccl* 8:
safe, and none shall *d.* it. *Isa* 5:2
which men *d.* to one. 29:1
defending also he will *d.* it. 31:
he cannot *d.* his soul. 44:2
they stoop, they could not *d.* 46:
they shall not *d.* themselves. 47:1

have I no power to *d.*? *Isa* 50:2
residue of them will I *d.* *Jer* 15:9
therefore *d.* up their children. 18:21
I will *d.* all strength of city. 20:5*
afterwards I will *d.* Zedekiah. 21:7
d. the spoiled out of the hand. 22:3
d. such as are for death. 43:11
d. every man his soul. 51:6*, 45*
I will *d.* my people. *Ezek* 13:21, 23
should *d.* but own souls. 14:14, 20
shall *d.* neither sons nor. 16, 18, 20
taketh warning shall *d.* soul. 33:5
I will *d.* my flock from. 34:10
no other god can *d.* *Dan* 3:29
nor was there any that could *d.* 8:4
none that could *d.* the ram. 7
none shall *d.* her out of. *Hos* 2:10
neither shall mighty *d.* *Amos* 2:14
swift of foot shall not *d.* himself. 15
I will *d.* the city. 6:8
in pieces and none *d.* *Mi* 5:8
take hold, but shalt not *d.* 6:14*
d. thyself, O Zion, that. *Zech* 2:7*
I will *d.* every one into his. 11:6
brother shall *d.* brother. *Mat* 10:21
manner of Romans to *d.* *Acts* 25:16*
d. such one to Satan. *1 Cor* 5:5
from death, and doth *d.* *2 Cor* 1:10
Lord knoweth how to *d.* *2 Pet* 2:9

deliver *him*

rid him, to *d. him* to. *Gen* 37:22*
d. him into my hand. 42:37
but God will *d. him.* *Ex* 21:13
that he might *d. him.* *Deut* 2:30
I will *d.* him and his people. 3:2
d. him into the hand of. 19:12
in any case shalt *d. him.* 24:13*
draw Sisera and *d. him.* *Judg* 4:7
our part be to *d. him.* *1 Sam* 23:20
d. him that smote his. *2 Sam* 14:7
d. him and I will depart. 20:21
d. him from going down. *Job* 33:24
d. him, let him *d. him.* *Ps* 22:8*
Lord will *d. him* in time of. 41:1
thou wilt not *d. him* to will of. 2
for there is none to *d. him.* 71:11
therefore will I *d. him.* 91:14
I will be with him, will *d. him.* 15
if thou *d.* him, thou must. *Pr* 19:19
d. him that is spoiled. *Jer* 21:12
righteousness of righteous shall not *d. him.* *Ezek* 33:12
on Daniel to *d. him.* *Dan* 6:14*
a shadow to *d. him* from. *Jonah* 4:6
d. him to Gentiles to crucify.
Mat 20:19; *Mark* 10:33
Luke 20:20; *Acts* 21:11
give, and I will *d. him.* *Mat* 26:15
let him *d. him* now. 27:43

deliver *me*

d. me, I pray thee, from. *Gen* 32:11
he will *d. me* out of. *1 Sam* 17:37
will men of Keilah *d. me* ? 23:11, 12
and *d. me* out of thy hand. 24:15
let him *d. me* out of all. 26:24
nor *d. me* into the hands. 30:15
d. me my wife Michal. *2 Sam* 3:14
d. me silver and gold. *1 Ki* 20:5
d. me from enemies. *Job* 6:23
Ps 31:15; 59:1
me from them and *d. me.* *Ps* 7:1
keep my soul, and *d. me.* 25:20
d. me not over to the will. 27:12
d. me in thy righteousness. 31:1
71:2
d. me speedily. 31:2
d. me from my transgressions. 39:8
be pleased to *d. me.* 40:13
d. me from the deceitful and. 43:1
d. me from blood-guiltiness. 51:14
d. me from workers of. 59:2
d. me out of the mire. 69:14
and redeem it, *d. me.* 18*
make haste to *d. me.* 70:1
d. me, O my God, out of. 71:4*
mercy is good *d.* thou *me.* 109:21
d. me from oppression. 119:134*
mine affliction, and *d. me.* 153
plead my cause, and *d. me.* 154*
d. me according to thy word. 170
d. me, O Lord, from the evil. 140:1
d. me from my persecutors. 142:6
d. me from mine enemies. 143:9

d. me out of great waters. *Ps* 144:7
d. me from the hand of strange. 11
d. me, for thou art my. *Isa* 44:17
the Jews, lest they *d. me.* *Jer* 38:19
no man may *d. me.* *Acts* 25:11*
who shall *d. me* from? *Rom* 7:24
the Lord shall *d. me.* *2 Tim* 4:18

deliver *thee*

people which Lord *d. thee.* *Deut* 7:16
midst of thy camp to *d. thee.* 23:14
that we may *d. thee.* *Judg* 15:12, 13
the Lord will *d. thee.* *1 Sam* 17:46
they will *d. thee* up. 23:12
I will *d. thee* two. *2 Ki* 18:23*
will *d. thee* and city. 20:6; *Isa* 38:6
d. thee in six troubles. *Job* 5:19
great ransom cannot *d. thee.* 36:18*
I will *d. thee,* and thou. *Ps* 50:15
he shall *d. thee* from snare. 91:3
to *d. thee* from the way. *Pr* 2:12
to *d. thee* from the strange. 16
let thy companies *d. thee.* *Isa* 57:13
to *d. thee.* *Jer* 1:8, 19; 15:20, 21
they shall not *d. thee.* 38:20
I will *d. thee* in that day. 39:17
I will surely *d. thee.* 18
d. thee into the hand. *Ezek* 21:31
I will *d. thee* to them. 23:28
I will *d. thee* to men of east. 25:4
I will *d. thee* for a spoil. 7
thou servest will *d. thee.* *Dan* 6:16
is thy God able to *d. thee* ? 20
how shall I *d. thee,* Israel ?
Hos 11:8
judge *d. thee* to the. *Mat* 5:25
Luke 12:58

deliver *them*

come down to *d. them.* *Ex* 3:8
Acts 7:34
thy God shall *d. them.* *Deut* 7:2, 23
to-morrow will I *d. them.* *Josh* 11:6
and if the Lord *d. them.* *Judg* 11:9
to-morrow I will *d. them.* 20:28
wilt thou *d. them.* *1 Sam* 14:37
2 Sam 5:19; *1 Chr* 14:10
d. them to the enemy. *1 Ki* 8:46
2 Ki 21:14
d. them into hand of. *2 Ki* 3:10, 13
will *d. them* into thy. *1 Chr* 14:10
and *d. them* over. *2 Chr* 6:36
that he might *d. them.* 25:20
times didst *d. them.* *Neh* 9:28
neither any to *d. them.* *Job* 5:4
trusted, thou didst *d. them.* *Ps* 22:4
the Lord shall *d. them.* 37:40*
many times did he *d. them.* 106:43
of upright shall *d. them.* *Pr* 11:6
mouth of upright shall *d. them.* 12:6
forbear to *d. them* that. 24:11
a Saviour and *d. them.* *Isa* 19:20
I will *d. them* to. *Jer* 24:9*; 29:18
d. them into hand of. 29:21; 46:26
gold shall not *d. them.* *Ezek* 7:19
Zeph 1:18
will I seek and *d. them.* *Ezek* 34:12
carried away to *d. them.* *Amos* 1:6
I will not *d. them.* *Zech* 11:6
God would *d. them.* *Acts* 7:25
d. them who through fear. *Heb* 2:15

deliver *us*

to *d. us* into hand of. *Deut* 1:27
Josh 7:7
d. us only, we pray. *Judg* 10:15
d. us the men, the children. 20:13
who shall *d. us* out of? *1 Sam* 4:8
d. us out of hand of enemies. 12:10
the Lord will *d. us.* *2 Ki* 18:30, 32
Isa 36:15, 18
d. us from the heathen. *1 Chr* 16:35
our God shall *d. us.* *2 Chr* 32:11
d. us, and purge away. *Ps* 79:9
to *d. us* into the hand. *Jer* 43:3
none that doth *d. us* out. *Lam* 5:8
to *d. us,* and will *d. us.* *Dan* 3:17
thus shall he *d. us* from. *Mi* 5:6
but *d. us* from evil. *Mat* 6:13
Luke 11:4
that he will yet *d. us.* *2 Cor* 1:10
that he might *d. us* from. *Gal* 1:4

deliver *you*

I *d. you* your brother. *Gen* 42:34
they shall *d. you* your. *Lev* 26:26

did not I *d. you* from? *Judg* 10:11*
forsaken me, I will *d. you* no. 13*
let them *d. you* in the time of. 14*
he will *d. you* from. *1 Sam* 7:3
he shall *d. you* from. *2 Ki* 17:39
shall not be able to *d. you.* 18:29
Isa 36:14
be able to *d. you* out. *2 Chr* 32:14
I will carry, and will *d. you.* *Isa* 46:4
I will *d. you* into hands. *Ezek* 11:9
God that shall *d. you* ? *Dan* 3:15
for they will *d. you* up. *Mat* 10:17
Mark 13:9
but when they *d. you* up. *Mat* 10:19
24:9; *Mark* 13:11

deliverance

your lives by a great *d.* *Gen* 45:7
hast given this great *d.* *Judg* 15:18
Lord had given *d.* to. *2 Ki* 5:1*
arrow of the Lord's *d.* of *d.* 13:17*
saved them by great *d.* *1 Chr* 11:14*
grant them some *d.* *2 Chr* 12:7
given us such a *d.* as. *Ezra* 9:13*
d. arise to the Jews. *Esth* 4:14
great *d.* giveth he to. *Ps* 18:50
with songs of *d.* 32:7
wrought any *d.* in earth. *Isa* 26:18
in Jerusalem shall be *d.* *Joel* 2:32*
upon mount Zion shall be *d.* *Ob* 17*
sent me to preach *d.* to. *Luke* 4:18*
tortured, not accepting *d.* *Heb* 11:35

deliverances

my King, command *d.* *Ps* 44:4

delivered

into your hand are they *d.* *Gen* 9:2
God who *d.* thine enemies. 14:20
when her days to be *d.* 25:24
d. ere the midwives come. *Ex* 1:19
neither hast thou *d.* thy. 5:23
smote the Egyptians, and *d.* 12:27
who hath *d.* people from. 18:10
the Lord our God *d.* all. *Deut* 2:36
God *d.* into our hands the. 3:3
Lord *d.* unto me two tables. 9:10
and Moses *d.* the law unto. 31:9
Lord *d.* their enemies. *Josh* 21:44
he *d.* the Canaanites into. *Judg* 1:4
after him Shamgar *d.* Israel. 3:31*
they that are *d.* from the. 5:11*
when Lord hath *d.* Zebah and. 8:7
Lord *d.* Sihon into hand. 11:21
our god hath *d.* Samson. 16:23, 24
was near to be *d.* *1 Sam* 4:19
I smote him and *d.* it. 17:35
who *d.* the company that. 30:23
of Saul's sons be *d.* *2 Sam* 21:6
and I was *d.* of child. *1 Ki* 3:17
I was *d.* this woman was *d.* 18
and shalt thou be *d.*? *2 Ki* 19:11
Isa 37:11
d. that parcel and slew. *1 Chr* 11:14*
on that day David *d.* 16:7*
Jehoiada *d.* to the. *2 Chr* 23:9
d. money that was brought. 34:9
Hilkiah *d.* book to Shaphan. 15
the vessels were *d.* to. *Ezra* 5:14
d. the king's commissions. 8:36
it is *d.* by the pureness. *Job* 22:30
so should I be *d.* for ever. 23:7
I *d.* the poor that cried. 29:12
cried to thee, and were *d.* *Ps* 22:5
a mighty man is not *d.* by. 33:16
he hath *d.* my soul in peace. 55:18*
d. my soul from death. 56:13; 86:13
116:8
beloved may be *d.* 60:5; 108:6
let me be *d.* from them. 69:14
and *d.* his strength into. 78:61
the righteous is *d.* out of. *Pr* 11:8
knowledge shall the just be *d.* 9
seed of righteous shall be *d.* 21
whoso walketh wisely be *d.* 28:26
by wisdom he *d.* city. *Eccl* 9:15
to be *d.* from the king. *Isa* 20:6
the book is *d.* to him that is. 29:12
and have they *d.* Samaria ? 36:19
thou hast *d.* it from the pit of. 38:17
shall the lawful captive be *d.*? 49:24
prey of the terrible shall be *d.* 25
before pain came, she was *d.* 66:7
we are *d.* to do all. *Jer* 7:10
d. the soul of the poor. 20:13
when I had *d.* the evidence. 32:16

but thou hast *d.* thy soul.
Ezek 3:19, 21; 33:9
they only shall be *d.* 14:16, 18
break covenant and be *d.*? 17:15*
for they are all *d.* unto. 31:14
she is *d.* to the sword. 32:20
and *d.* his servants. *Dan* 3:28
who *d.* Daniel from the power. 6:27
thy people shall be *d.* 12:1
name of Lord shall be *d.* *Joel* 2:32
that escapeth not be *d.* *Amos* 9:1*
there shalt thou be *d.* *Mi* 4:10*
that he may be *d.* from. *Hab* 2:9
they that tempt God *d.* *Mal* 3:15†
all things are *d.* unto me of my.
Mat 11:27; *Luke* 10:22
commanded body be *d.* *Mat* 27:58*
tradition which ye have *d.* *Mark* 7:13
Son of man shall be *d.* to. 10:33
Barabbas, and *d.* Jesus. 15:15
Luke 23:25
time that she be *d.* *Luke* 1:57; 2:6
that is *d.* unto me, and to. 4:6
there was *d.* unto him the book. 17
Son of man shall be *d.* into. 9:44
diligence that thou be *d.* 12:58*
for he shall be *d.* unto. 18:32
as soon as she is *d.* of. *John* 16:21
that I should not be *d.* 18:36
being *d.* by the counsel. *Acts* 2:23
came to Antioch and *d.* 15:30
and they *d.* the epistle to. 23:33
they *d.* Paul to one Julius. 27:1
yet was I *d.* prisoner. 28:17
was *d.* for our offences. *Rom* 4:25
now we are *d.* from the law. 7:6*
creature itself shall be *d.* 8:21
I may be *d.* from them. 15:31
are alway *d.* to death. *2 Cor* 4:11
we may be *d.* from. *2 Thes* 3:2
I have *d.* to Satan. *1 Tim* 1:20
d. out of mouth of lion. *2 Tim* 4:17
by faith Sarah was *d.* *Heb* 11:11
and *d.* just Lot. *2 Pet* 2:7
from the commandment *d.* 21
the faith which was once *d.* *Jude* 3
and pained to be *d.* *Rev* 12:2
before woman ready to be *d.* 4

see **hand, hands**

delivered *him*
Reuben *d. him.* *Gen* 37:21
was *d. him* to keep. *Lev* 6:2*, 4
Lord our God *d. him.* *Deut* 2:33
Lord *d. him* to the lion. *1 Ki* 13:26
Elijah *d. him* unto his mother. 17:23
d. him that is mine. *Ps* 7:4
the Lord *d. him* to the. *Mat* 18:34
d. him to Pilate. 27:2; *Mark* 15:1
for envy they had *d. him.* *Mat* 27:18
Mark 15:10
d. him to be crucified. *Mat* 27:26
John 19:16
and Jesus *d. him* to. *Luke* 7:15*
healed child and *d. him.* 9:42
d. him to be condemned. 24:20
not have *d. him* to thee. *John* 18:30
God *d. him* out of his. *Acts* 7:10
d. him to four quaternions. 12:4

delivered *me*
God *d. me* from sword. *Ex* 18:4
I saw ye *d. me* not. *Judg* 12:3*
the Lord that *d. me.* *1 Sam* 17:37
d. me from strong. *2 Sam* 22:18
he *d. me* because. 20; *Ps* 18:19
hast *d. me* from violent man.
2 Sam 22:49; *Ps* 18:48
Hilkiah *d. me* a book. *2 Ki* 22:10
God hath *d. me* to the. *Job* 16:11
d. me from strong enemies. *Ps* 18:17
hast *d. me* from the strivings. 43
the Lord heard and *d. me.* 34:4
d. me out of all trouble. 54:7
he that *d. me* to thee. *John* 19:11
of them all Lord *d. me.* *2 Tim* 3:11

delivered *thee*
Lord *d. thee* to-day. *1 Sam* 24:10
I *d. thee* out of hand of. *2 Sam* 12:7
in trouble, and I *d. thee.* *Ps* 81:7
I *d. thee* to will of them. *Ezek* 16:27
chief priests *d. thee.* *John* 18:35

delivered *them*
how the Lord *d. them.* *Ex* 18:8
tables of stone, *d. them.* *Deut* 5:22*
deliverer, who *d. them.* *Judg* 3:9*
gods of nations *d. them.* *2 Ki* 19:12
Isa 37:12
hath *d. them* to trouble. *2 Chr* 29:8
when he *d. them.* *Ps* 78:42*
d. them out of their. 107:6
d. them from destructions. 20
d. them to the slaughter. *Isa* 34:2
d. them to cause them. *Ezek* 16:21
and *d.* to *them* his goods. *Mat* 25:14
even as they *d. them* to. *Luke* 1:2
he *d. them* ten pounds, and. 19:13*
they *d. them* the decrees. *Acts* 16:4
as I *d. them* to you. *1 Cor* 11:2
and *d. them* into chains. *2 Pet* 2:4*

delivered *up*
Lord *d. up* Canaanites. *Num* 21:3
Lord *d. up* Amorites. *Josh* 10:12
d. up the men that. *2 Sam* 18:28
because they *d. up* the. *Amos* 1:9
nor shouldest have *d. up.* *Ob* 14
his Son whom ye *d. up.* *Acts* 3:13
but *d.* him *up* for us. *Rom* 8:32
have *d. up* kingdom. *1 Cor* 15:24
death and hell *d. up.* *Rev* 20:13*

delivered *us*
an Egyptian *d. us* from. *Ex* 2:19
customs Moses *d. us.* *Acts* 6:14
d. us from so great a. *2 Cor* 1:10
hath *d. us* from power of. *Col* 1:13
Jesus, who *d. us* from. *1 Thes* 1:10

delivered *you*
doctrine which was *d. you.* *Rom* 6:17
I received of the Lord that which also
I *d.* unto *you.* *1 Cor* 11:23; 15:3

deliveredst, -est
thou *d.* them to enemies. *Neh* 9:27
who *d.* poor from him. *Ps* 35:10
what thou *d.* will I give. *Mi* 6:14*
Lord, thou *d.* unto me. *Mat* 25:20
thou *d.* unto me two talents. 22

deliverer
a *d.* to Israel. *Judg* 3:9*, 15*
there was no *d.* 18:28
Lord is my rock and *d.* *2 Sam* 22:2
Ps 18:2
my help and my *d.* *Ps* 40:17; 70:5
my high tower, and my *d.* 144:2
did God send to be a *d.* *Acts* 7:35
out of Sion the *d.* *Rom* 11:26

delivereth
he *d.* the poor in his. *Job* 36:15
he *d.* me from mine. *Ps* 18:48*
and *d.* them. 34:7
the Lord *d.* them out of. 17*, 19
he *d.* them out of the hand. 97:10
who *d.* David from. 144:10*
righteousness *d.* *Pr* 10:2; 11:4
a true witness *d.* souls. 14:25
and she *d.* girdles. 31:24
for a prey, and none *d.* *Isa* 42:22
God *d.* and rescueth. *Dan* 6:27

delivering
d. you up to synagogues. *Luke* 21:12
d. into prisons both. *Acts* 22:4
d. thee from the people. 26:17

delivery
near the time of her *d.* *Isa* 26:17

delusion
send them strong *d.* *2 Thes* 2:11*

delusions
I also will choose their *d.* *Isa* 66:4

demand
the *d.* by the word of. *Dan* 4:17

demand, -ed, *verb*
d. why have ye not? *Ex* 5:14
David *d.* of Uriah. *2 Sam* 11:7*
I will *d.* of thee, answer. *Job* 38:3
40:7; 42:4
secret which the king *d.* *Dan* 2:27
d. where Christ should. *Mat* 2:4*
the soldiers *d.* of him. *Luke* 3:14*
and when he was *d.* of the. 17:20*
the chief captain *d.* *Acts* 21:33*

Demas
Luke and *D.* greet you. *Col* 4:14
Philem 24
D. hath forsaken me. *2 Tim* 4:10

Demetrius
D. a silversmith, who. *Acts* 19:24
if *D.* have a matter against. 38
D. hath good report of. *3 John* 12

demonstration
but in *d.* of the Spirit. *1 Cor* 2:4

den, -s
of Israel made them *d.* *Judg* 6:2
then beasts go into *d.* *Job* 37:8*
they couch in their *d.* 38:40
in wait as a lion in his *d.* *Ps* 10:9
lay themselves down in *d.* 104:22
from the lion's *d.* *S of S* 4:8
hand on cockatrice' *d.* *Isa* 11:8*
the towers shall be for *d.* 32:14
house become a *d.* of? *Jer* 7:11
Jerusalem a *d.* of dragons. 9:11*
cities of Judah a *d.* of. 10:22*
cast into *d.* of lions. *Dan* 6:7, 12
they cast him into the *d.* 16
king arose went in haste to the *d.* 19
take Daniel up out of the *d.* 23
cast them into the *d.* of lions. 24
lion cry out of his *d.*? *Amos* 3:4
the lion filled his *d.* with. *Nah* 2:12
house of prayer, but ye have made
it a *d.* *Mat* 21:13; *Mark* 11:17
in deserts and in *d.* *Heb* 11:38*
and freeman hid in *d.* *Rev* 6:15*

denied
Sarah *d.* saying, I. *Gen* 18:15
and I *d.* him not. *1 Ki* 20:7
I should have *d.* God. *Job* 31:28*
Peter *d.* before them all, saying, I.
Mat 26:70, 72; *Mark* 14:70
Luke 22:57; *John* 18:25, 27
when all *d.* that they. *Luke* 8:45
who denies shall be *d.* before. 12:9
and *d.* not, I am not. *John* 1:20
till thou hast *d.* me thrice. 13:38
d. in presence of Pilate. *Acts* 3:13
but ye *d.* the holy One and the. 14
he hath *d.* the faith. *1 Tim* 5:8
and not *d.* my faith. *Rev* 2:13
and hast not *d.* my name. 3:8

denieth, -ing
he that *d.* me before. *Luke* 12:9
form of godliness, but *d.* *2 Tim* 3:5
that *d.* ungodliness and. *Tit* 2:12
even *d.* the Lord that. *2 Pet* 2:1
is a liar, that *d.* Jesus. *1 John* 2:22
who *d.* the Son. 23
d. the only Lord God. *Jude* 4

denounce
I *d.* this day. *Deut* 30:18

deny
lest ye *d.* your God. *Josh* 24:27
d. me not. *1 Ki* 2:16; *Pr* 30:7
then it shall *d.* him. *Job* 8:18
lest I be full and *d.* thee. *Pr* 30:9
d. me, him will I *d.* *Mat* 10:33
let him *d.* himself. 16:24
Mark 8:34; *Luke* 9:23
cock crow thou shalt *d.* me thrice.
Mat 26:34, 75; *Mark* 14:30, 72
yet will I not *d.* thee. *Mat* 26:35
Mark 14:31
d. there is any resurrection.
Luke 20:27
d. him, he will *d.* us. *2 Tim* 2:12
abideth faithful, cannot *d.* 13
but in works they *d.* him. *Tit* 1:16

depart
if thou *d.* to the right. *Gen* 13:9
Moses let father-in-law *d.* *Ex* 18:27
d. thou and the people thou. 33:1
I will *d.* to mine own. *Num* 10:30
from day thou didst *d.* *Deut* 9:7
Joshua let people *d.* to. *Josh* 24:28
Levite rose up to *d.* *Judg* 19:5, 7, 8, 9
abide not in hold, *d.* *1 Sam* 22:5
be up and have light, *d.* 29:10
and his men rose up to *d.* 1
lead them away and *d.* 30:2
I will let thee *d.* *2 Sam* 11:1
make speed to *d.* lest. 15:1
d. for three days. *1 Ki* 12:
increase of house shall *d.* *Job* 20:2
envy of Ephraim shall *d.* *Isa* 11:1
d. ye, *d.* ye, out. 52:11; *Lam* 4:1
for the mountains shall *d.* *Isa* 54:1
they shall *d.* man and. *Jer* 50:

arise ye, and d. this is. Mi 2:10
sceptre of Egypt shall d. Zech 10:11
besought him that he d. out of their coasts. Mat 8:34; Mark 5:17
when ye d. out of that house or city. Mat 10:14; Mark 6:11; Luke 9:4
thy servant d. in peace. Luke 2:29
d. hence, Herod will kill thee. 13:31
which are in midst d. out. 21:21
they said, d. hence and. John 7:3
when Jesus knew he should d. 13:1
but if I d. I will send him. 16:7
d. and go in peace. Acts 16:36
desired them to d. out of city. 39
them ready to d. on morrow. 20:7
d. for I will send thee to the. 22:21
that he himself would d. 25:4
more part advised to d. 27:12
if she d. let her remain. 1 Cor 7:11
if the unbelieving d. let him d. 15
a desire to d. and to be. Phil 1:23
say to them, d. in peace. Jas 2:16

depart *from*

frogs shall d. from thee. Ex 8:11
swarms of flies may d. from. 29
so that her fruit d. from. 21:22
then shall he d. from. Lev 25:41
d. from the tents of. Num 16:26
lest they d. from thy. Deut 4:9
fearful, let him d. from. Judg 7:3
d. from the Amalekites. 1 Sam 15:6
sword never d. from. 2 Sam 12:10
and I will d. from the city. 20:21
d. from me. 1 Ki 15:19; 2 Chr 16:3
moved them to d. from. 2 Chr 18:31
to God, d. from us. Job 21:14; 22:17
and to d. from evil is. 28:28
d. from me, ye workers. Ps 6:8
Mat 7:23; Luke 13:27
d. from evil, and do good. Ps 34:14
37:27
froward heart shall d. from. 101:4
d. from me, ye evil doers. 119:115
d. from me therefore. 139:19
and d. from evil. Pr 3:7
to d. from the snares. 13:14; 14:27
to fools to d. from evil. 13:19
that he may d. from hell. 15:24
fear of Lord men d. from evil. 16:6
of upright is to d. from evil. 17
his burden d. from off. Isa 14:25
lest my soul d. from thee. Jer 6:8*
that d. from me shall be. 17:13
f those ordinances d. from. 31:36
Chaldeans shall surely d. from. 37:9
ealousy shall d. from. Ezek 16:42
o them when I d. from. Hos 9:12
. from me, ye cursed. Mat 25:41
bide, till ye d. from. Mark 6:10
. from me, I am a sinful. Luke 5:8
esought him to d. from. 8:37
ot d. from Jerusalem. Acts 1:4
l the Jews to d. from Rome. 18:2
t not wife d. from her. 1 Cor 7:10
at it might d. from. 2 Cor 12:8
all d. from the faith. 1 Tim 4:1*
from iniquity. 2 Tim 2:19

not **depart**

eptre shall not d. Gen 49:10
ok of law shall not d. Josh 1:8
not hence, till I come. Judg 6:18
y mercy shall not d. 2 Sam 7:15
s statutes, I did not d. from. 22:23
ey might not d. 2 Chr 35:15
w long wilt thou not d.? Job 7:19*
all not d. out of darkness. 15:30
ceit and guile d. not. Ps 55:11
them not d. Pr 3:21; 4:21
ar me, and d. not from. 5:7
l shall not d. from his. 17:13
en old he will not d. from it. 22:6
l not his foolishness d. 27:22
dness shall not d. Isa 54:10
irit, and words, shall not d. 59:21
y shall not d. from. Jer 32:40
they shall not d. 37:9
y need not d. give. Mat 14:16
t should not d. from. Luke 4:42
u shalt not d. thence, till. 12:59

departed

Abraham d. as. Gen 12:4
y took Lot and d. 14:12
gar d. 21:14
Eliezer d. Gen 24:10
Isaac d. 26:17
Laban d. 31:55
they are d. hence, to Dothan. 37:17
laded their asses and d. 42:26
brethren away, and they d. 45:24
was kindled, and he d. Num 12:9
elders of Moab and Midian d. 22:7
spies away, and they d. Josh 2:21
d. every man to his. Judg 9:55
2 Sam 6:19
then the five men d. Judg 18:7, 21
the Levite d. 19:10
Israel d. thence. 21:24
Israel go, and they d.? 1 Sam 6:6
David d. 20:42; 22:1, 5
so Nathan d. 2 Sam 12:15
from day the king d. 19:24
and the people d. 1 Ki 12:5
2 Chr 10:5
wife arose and d. to. 1 Ki 14:17
Elijah d. and. 19:19; 2 Ki 1:4
the messengers d. and. 1 Ki 20:9
prophet d. and waited for. 38
Naaman d. 2 Ki 5:5
Jehu arose and d. 10:12, 15
so Sennacherib d. 19:36; Isa 37:37
all people d. every. 1 Chr 16:43
wherefore Joab d. and. 21:4
Jehoram d. without. 2 Chr 21:20
Egypt glad when they d. Ps 105:38
mine age is d. and. Isa 38:12
Ishmael d. to go over. Jer 41:10
all her beauty is d. Lam 1:6
king, wise men d. Mat 2:9, 12
arose, and d. into Egypt. 14
Jesus d. 4:12; 9:27; 11:1; 12:9
13:53; 14:13; 15:21, 29; 16:4
19:15; Mark 1:35; 6:46
8:13; Luke 4:42; John 4:3, 43
6:15; 12:36
Judas d. Mat 27:5
Zacharias d. to his house. Luke 1:23
he d. to his own house. 5:25
messengers of John were d. 7:24
out of whom the devils were d. 8:35
thieves wounded him and d. 10:30
when the Samaritan d. 35
the man d. and told. John 5:15
when the angel d. Acts 10:7
Barnabas d. 11:25
Peter d. 12:17
they d. to Seleucia. 13:4
Paul d. 14:20; 18:7, 23
20:1, 11
Paul and Barnabas d. asunder. 15:39
Paul and Silas d. 16:40
d. and went. 21:5, 8; 28:10, 11
these words, the Jews d. 28:29
forsaken me, is d. to. 2 Tim 4:10
perhaps he therefore d. Philem 15*
and the heaven d. as. Rev 6:14

departed *from*

arose and d. from. Gen 26:31
my sleep d. from mine. 31:40*
were d. from. Ex 19:2; Num 33:15
all Israel d. from presence. Ex 35:20
plague be d. from them. Lev 13:58
they d. from the mount. Num 10:33*
the cloud d. from off. 12:10
defence is d. from them. 14:9
they d. from Rameses. 33:3
d. from Succoth. 6
d. from Pi-hahiroth. 8
d. from Dophkah. 13
All their departures set down to verse 49
we d. from Horeb. Deut 1:19
not that Lord d. from. Judg 16:20
glory is d. from. 1 Sam 4:21, 22
when thou art d. from me. 10:2
Kenites d. from among the. 15:6
Spirit d. from Saul. 16:14; 18:12
the evil spirit d. from him. 23
God is d. from me. 28:15
seeing the Lord is d. from thee. 16
as thou art d. from me. 1 Ki 20:36
they d. from him to. 2 Ki 3:27
so he d. from Elisha. 5:19; 8:14
Sennacherib d. from. 19:8; Isa 37:8
they were d. from him. 2 Chr 24:25
then we d. from the river. Ezra 8:31
wickedly d. from my God. Ps 18:21
Ephraim d. from Judah. Isa 7:17
smiths were d. from. Jer 29:2
Chaldeans heard they d. from. 37:5*
which hath d. from us. Ezek 6:9
glory of the Lord d. from. 10:18
the kingdom is d. from. Dan 4:31
glory of Samaria d. from. Hos 10:5
Jesus d. from thence. Mat 15:29
he d. from Galilee. 19:1
as they d. from Jericho. 20:29
Jesus d. from the temple. 24:1
they d. quickly from the. 28:8
leprosy d. from him. Mark 1:42
Luke 5:13
angel d. from Mary. Luke 1:38
the devil d. from him for. 4:13
as they d. from him. 9:33
d. from the presence. Acts 5:41
forthwith angel d. from him. 12:10
they had d. from Perga. 13:14*
John d. from them from. 15:38
Paul d. from them. 17:33; 18:1
19:9; Phil 4:15
diseases d. from them. Acts 19:12
after are d. from thee, and all things dainty are d. from. Rev 18:14*

departed *not from*

not d. from my God. 2 Sam 22:22
Ps 18:21
he d. not therefrom. 2 Ki 3:3; 13:2
Jehu d. not from sins of. 10:29, 31
13:6, 11; 14:24; 15:9, 18; 17:22
Hezekiah d. not from. 18:6
d. not from commandment of.
2 Chr 8:15
Jehoshaphat d. not from the. 20:32*
d. not from following Lord. 34:33
cloud d. not from them. Neh 9:19
I have not d. from thy. Ps 119:102
Anna d. not from temple. Luke 2:37

departed *out*

old when he d. out of. Gen 12:4
when she is d. out of. Deut 24:2
angel of the Lord d. out. Judg 6:21
Levite d. out of Beth-lehem. 17:8
David and men d. out. 1 Sam 23:13
Uriah d. out of king's. 2 Sam 11:8
ye are d. out of the way. Mal 2:8*
devil, and he d. out of. Mat 17:18

departed *not out*

Joshua d. not out of. Ex 33:11
and Moses d. not out. Num 14:44

departeth

him away, and he d. Job 27:21
a wise man feareth, and d. 14:16
in with vanity, and d. Eccl 6:4
he that d. from evil. Isa 59:15
wife treacherously d. Jer 3:20
cursed be man whose heart d. 17:5
bloody city, prey d. not. Nah 3:1
hardly d. from him. Luke 9:39

departing

as her soul was in d. Gen 35:18
after their d. out of land. Ex 16:1
in lying and d. away. Isa 59:13
we have sinned, by d. Dan 9:5*, 11
committed whoredom d. Hos 1:2
the people saw them d. Mark 6:33
d. from coast of Tyre and. 7:31
John d. from them. Acts 13:13
after my d. shall wolves. 20:29
an evil heart, in d. Heb 3:12
Joseph made mention of d. 11:22

departure

isles shall be troubled at thy d.
Ezek 26:18
time of my d. is at hand. 2 Tim 4:6

deposed

was d. from kingly. Dan 5:20

deprived

why should I be d.? Gen 27:45*
because God hath d. her. Job 39:17
I am d. of the residue of. Isa 38:10

depth

d. saith it is not in me. Job 28:14*
walked in search of the d.? 38:16*
he layeth up the d. Ps 33:7*
compass on face of the d. Pr 8:27*
and the earth for d. 25:3
ask it either in the d. Isa 7:11

the *d.* closed me round. *Jonah* 2:5
drowned in the *d.* of the. *Mat* 18:6
because it had no *d.* of. *Mark* 4:5
nor *d.* separate us from. *Rom* 8:39
O the *d.* of the riches both. 11:33
what is breadth and *d.* *Eph* 3:18

depths

the *d.* have covered them. *Ex* 15:5
the *d.* were congealed in the. 8*
the *d.* that spring out of. *Deut* 8:7
my people from the *d.* *Ps* 68:22
shall bring me up from the *d.* 71:20
waters were afraid, the *d.* 77:16
drink as out of great *d.* 78:15
he led them through *d.* as. 106:9
they go down again to *d.* 107:26
out of the *d.* have I cried. 130:1
by his knowledge the *d.* *Pr* 3:20
when there no *d.* I was. 8:24
guests are in *d.* of hell. 9:18
that hath made the *d.* of. *Isa* 51:10
broken in *d.* of waters. *Ezek* 27:34
cast their sins into *d.* of. *Mi* 7:19
have not known the *d.* *Rev* 2:24

deputed

there is no man *d.* of. *2 Sam* 15:3

deputies

written to *d.* and rulers. *Esth* 8:9*
and the *d.* and officers. 9:3*
there are *d.* let them. *Acts* 19:38*

deputy

no king in Edom, a *d.* *1 Ki* 22:47
Bar-jesus which was with the *d.* *Acts* 13:7*
seeking to turn away the *d.* 8*
and when Gallio was the *d.* 18:12*

deride

shall *d.* every strong hold. *Hab* 1:10

derided

these things, and *d.* *Luke* 16:14
rulers also with people *d.* 23:35

derision

than I, have me in *d.* *Job* 30:1
Lord shall have them in *d.* *Ps* 2:4
a *d.* to them that are. 44:13; 79:4
all the heathen in *d.* 59:8
proud had me greatly in *d.* 119:51
I am in *d.* daily. *Jer* 20:7
was made a *d.* daily. 8
Moab also shall be in *d.* 48:26, 39
for was not Israel a *d.*? 27
I was a *d.* to my people. *Lam* 3:14
drink and be glad in *d.* *Ezek* 23:32
to cities which became a *d.* 36:4
this shall be their *d.* *Hos* 7:16

descend

the border shall *d.* *Num* 34:11
he shall *d.* into battle. *1 Sam* 26:10
his glory shall not *d.* *Ps* 49:17
with them that *d.* *Ezek* 26:20; 31:16
let Christ *d.* now. *Mark* 15:32
vessel *d.* as a great sheet. *Acts* 11:5
or who shall *d.* into? *Rom* 10:7
Lord shall *d.* from. *1 Thes* 4:16

descended

because the Lord *d.* on. *Ex* 19:18
the cloudy pillar *d.* 33:9
d. in a cloud. 34:5
brook that *d.* out of. *Deut* 9:21
so the two men *d.* *Josh* 2:23
as dew that *d.* on. *Ps* 133:3
up to heaven, or *d.*? *Pr* 30:4
the rain *d.* and. *Mat* 7:25, 27
for angel of the Lord *d.* 28:2
the Holy Ghost *d.* in a. *Luke* 3:22
Ananias high-priest *d.* *Acts* 24:1
he that *d.* is the same. *Eph* 4:10

descendeth

this wisdom *d.* not from. *Jas* 3:15

descending

and angels ascending and *d.* *Gen* 28:12; *John* 1:51
saw the Spirit of God *d.* *Mat* 3:16; *Mark* 1:10
I saw the Spirit *d.* from. *John* 1:32
whom thou shalt see the Spirit *d.* 33
a vessel *d.* as it had. *Acts* 10:11
that great city *d.* out of. *Rev* 21:10

descent

when come nigh at *d.* *Luke* 19:37
father, mother, and *d.* *Heb* 7:3*
but he whose *d.* is not counted. 6*

describe, -ed, -eth

go through land *d.* it. *Josh* 18:4, 6, 8
charged them that went to *d.* 8
and they *d.* it by cities into seven. 9
he *d.* to him the princes. *Judg* 8:14
even as David also *d.* *Rom* 4:6
for Moses *d.* righteousness. 10:5*

description

and ye shall bring the *d.* *Josh* 18:6

descry

of Joseph sent to *d.* *Judg* 1:23*

desert

(*In the Bible this word means a deserted place, wilderness, not desert in the modern usage of the term. Revised Versions frequently translate by* wilderness)

flock to backside of the *d.* *Ex* 3:1
three days' journey into *d.* 5:3
they were come to the *d.* 19:2
I will set thy bounds from *d.* 23:31
Israel came into *d.* of Zin. *Num* 20:1
against me in the *d.* of Zin. 27:14
removed from the *d.* of Sinai. 33:16
built towers in the *d.* *2 Chr* 26:10
as wild asses in the *d.* go. *Job* 24:5
grieve him in the *d.*? *Ps* 78:40
like pelican, an owl of *d.* 102:6
and tempted God in the *d.* 106:14
wild beasts of *d.* shall lie. *Isa* 13:21; 34:14; *Jer* 50:39
so it cometh from the *d.* *Isa* 21:1
the *d.* shall rejoice. 35:1
streams in the *d.* 6
make straight in *d.* a high. 40:3
I will set in *d.* the fir-tree. 41:19
make rivers in the *d.* 43:19, 20
will make her *d.* like garden. 51:3
be like heath in the *d.* *Jer* 17:6
people that dwell in *d.* shall. 25:24
be a dry land and a *d.* 50:12
waters go down into *d.* *Ezek* 47:8*
behold, he is in the *d.* *Mat* 24:26
did eat manna in the *d.* *John* 6:31
to Gaza, which is *d.* *Acts* 8:26

desert

render them their *d.* *Ps* 28:4

desert *land*

found him in a *d. land.* *Deut* 32:10

desert *place*

departed into a *d. place.* *Mat* 14:13; *Mark* 6:32; *Luke* 4:42
this is a *d. place.* *Mat* 14:15; *Mark* 6:35; *Luke* 9:12
come ye into a *d. place.* *Mark* 6:31
aside into a *d. place.* *Luke* 9:10

deserts

he led them through *d.* *Isa* 48:21
that led us through *d.* *Jer* 2:6
prophets like foxes in *d.* *Ezek* 13:4
John was in the *d.* till. *Luke* 1:80
they wandered in *d.* *Heb* 11:38

deserts

according to their *d.* *Ezek* 7:27

deserve

less than our iniquities *d.* *Ezra* 9:13

deserveth

less than thy iniquity *d.* *Job* 11:6

deserving

done according to *d.* of. *Judg* 9:16

desirable

all of them *d.* young men. *Ezek* 23:6, 12, 23

desire

[1] *Longing, coveting,* 2 Sam 23:5; Pr 11:23; 2 Cor 7:7. [2] *An expressed wish, or petition,* Ps 10:17; 1 Ki 2:20.

thy *d.* shall be to thy. *Gen* 3:16
to thee shall be his *d.* 4:7
and come with all the *d.* *Deut* 18:6
and hast a *d.* to her. 21:11
on whom is the *d.* of Israel? *1 Sam* 9:20*
according to all the *d.* of. 23:20
my salvation, all my *d.* *2 Sam* 23:5
I will do all thy *d.* *1 Ki* 5:8
thou shalt accomplish my *d.* 9
to all Solomon's *d.* *1 Ki* 5:10; 9:11
and all his *d.* 9:1
gave to the queen of Sheba all her *d.* 10:13; *2 Chr* 9:12
sought him with their whole *d.* *2 Chr* 15:15
thou wilt have a *d.* to work. *Job* 14:15
withheld poor from their *d.* 31:16
my *d.* is that Almighty would. 35*
d. is that Job may be tried. 34:36*
boasteth of his heart's *d.* *Ps* 10:3
thou hast heard the *d.* of. 17
hast given his heart's *d.* 21:2
Lord, all my *d.* is before. 38:9
eye hath seen his *d.* 54:7; 92:11
God shall let me see my *d.* 59:10
he gave them their own *d.* 78:29*
mine ears shall hear my *d.* of. 92:11
till he see his *d.* on his. 112:8
d. of the wicked shall perish. 10
therefore shall I see my *d.* 118:7
thou satisfiest the *d.* of. 145:16
he will fulfil the *d.* of them. 19
the *d.* of righteous shall. *Pr* 10:24
the *d.* of the righteous is. 11:23
but when *d.* cometh. 13:12
the *d.* accomplished is sweet. 19
d. of a man is his kindness. 19:22*
the *d.* of the slothful. 21:25
than wandering of *d.* *Eccl* 6:9
d. shall fail, because man. 12:5*
my beloved's, his *d.* is. *S of S* 7:10
d. of our soul is to thy. *Isa* 26:8
snuffeth up wind at *d.* *Jer* 2:24
land to which you have a *d.* 44:14
I will take from thee *d.* *Ezek* 24:16
profane *d.* of your eyes. 21, 25
neither shall he regard *d.* *Dan* 11:37
it is my *d.* I should. *Hos* 10:10
uttereth his mischievous *d.* *Mi* 7:3
enlargeth his *d.* as hell. *Hab* 2:5
the *d.* of all nations. *Hag* 2:7*
with *d.* have I desired. *Luke* 22:15
my heart's *d.* to God. *Rom* 10:1
having a great *d.* to come. 15:23
told us your earnest *d.* *2 Cor* 7:7
what fear, what vehement *d.* 11
in a strait, having a *d.* to. *Phil* 1:23
your face with great *d.* *1 Thes* 2:17

desire, *verb*

for that ye did *d.* *Ex* 10:11
neither shall any man *d.* 34:24
nor shalt thou *d.* thy. *Deut* 5:21
thou shalt not *d.* the silver. 7:25*
I would *d.* a request of. *Judg* 8:24
I *d.* one small petition. *1 Ki* 2:20
did I *d.* a son of my lord? *2 Ki* 4:28
thy servants who *d.* to. *Neh* 1:11*
surely I *d.* to reason. *Job* 13:3
for we *d.* not knowledge of. 21:14
speak, for I *d.* to justify thee. 33:32
d. not the night when. 36:20
offering thou didst not *d.* *Ps* 40:
so shall the king greatly *d.* 45:1
put to confusion that *d.* my. 70:
there is none on earth I *d.* 73:2
all thou canst *d.* are not. *Pr* 3:1
neither *d.* thou his dainty. 23:
against evil men, nor *d.* to be. 24:
no beauty that we should *d.* *Isa* 53:
land whereunto they *d.* *Jer* 22:2
die in the place whither ye *d.* 42:2
I would *d.* mercies of the. *Dan* 2:1
woe to you that *d.* day. *Amos* 5:1
if any man *d.* to be first. *Mark* 9:3
for us whatsoever we shall *d.* 10:
what things soever ye *d.* 11:2
began to *d.* him to do as. 15:
when ye shall *d.* to see. *Luke* 17:
the scribes which *d.* to walk. 20:
Jews have agreed to *d.* *Acts* 23:
we *d.* to hear of thee. 28:
follow after charity, *d.* *1 Cor* 14
from them which *d.* *2 Cor* 11:
though I would *d.* to glory. 12
whereunto ye *d.* again to. *Gal* 4
I *d.* to be present with you now.
tell me, ye that *d.* to be under?
as many as *d.* to make fair. 6:
but *d.* to have you circumcised.
wherefore I *d.* that ye. *Eph* 3:
d. a gift, but I *d.* fruit. *Phil* 4:
to *d.* that ye might be filled. *Col* 1

if a man d. the office of a. 1 Tim 3:1
we d. every one of you. Heb 6:11
they d. a better country. 11:16
ye kill, ye d. to have. Jas 4:2*
which things angels d. to. 1 Pet 1:12
as new-born babes d. sincere. 2:2
men shall d. to die, and. Rev 9:6

desired

and a tree to be d. to. Gen 3:6
the king whom ye d. 1 Sam 12:13
desire which Solomon d. 1 Ki 9:19
2 Chr 8:6
and Rehoboam d. many. 2 Chr 11:23
whatsoever she d. was. Esth 2:13
save of that which he d. Job 20:20*
more to be d. are they. Ps 19:10
one thing I d. of the Lord. 27:4
bringeth them to d. haven. 107:30
he hath d. Zion for his. 132:13
will I dwell, for I have d. 14
all that may be d. not. Pr 8:11
there is a treasure to be d. 21:20*
what my eyes d. I kept. Eccl 2:10
of the oaks ye have d. Isa 1:29
with my soul have I d. 26:9
nor have I d. woeful day. Jer 17:16
Daniel went and d. of. Dan 2:16
known unto me what we d. 23
for I d. mercy and not. Hos 6:6
no cluster, my soul d. fruit. Mi 7:1
O nation not d. Zeph 2:1*
righteous men have d. to. Mat 13:17
the Pharisees d. he would. 16:1
prisoner whom they d. Mark 15:6
Luke 23:25
one of the Pharisees d. Luke 7:36
Herod d. to see him. 9:9*
many kings have d. to. 10:24
I have d. to eat passover. 22:15
Satan hath d. to have you to. 31
released him whom they d. 23:25
d. a murderer to be. Acts 3:14
and d. to find a tabernacle. 7:46
the eunuch d. Philip to come. 8:31
Paul d. of the high priest. 9:2
Tyre and Sidon d. peace. 12:20
Sergius Paulus d. to hear. 13:7*
afterward they d. a king. 21
yet d. they Pilate that he. 28
and d. them to depart out of. 16:39
d. favour against Paul that. 25:3
I greatly d. him to. 1 Cor 16:12
we d. Titus to finish in. 2 Cor 8:6*
I d. Titus, and with him. 12:18*
we have petitions we d. 1 John 5:15

desiredst

according to all thou d. Deut 18:16
thee, because thou d. Mat 18:32

desires

he shall give thee the d. Ps 37:4
grant not, O Lord, the d. 140:8
fulfilling the d. of the. Eph 2:3

desirest

thou d. truth in the. Ps 51:6
thou d. not sacrifice. 16*

desireth

whatsoever thy soul d. Deut 14:26
take as much as soul d. 1 Sam 2:16
king d. not any dowry. 18:25
what thy soul d. 20:4; 1 Ki 11:37
over all that thy heart d. 2 Sam 3:21
as a servant earnestly d. Job 7:2
what his soul d. even that. 23:13
what man is he that d. life. Ps 34:12
the hill which God d. to. 68:16
the wicked d. the net. Pr 12:12
the soul of the sluggard d. 13:4
soul of the wicked d. evil. 21:10
nothing of all that he d. Eccl 6:2
old wine straightway d. Luke 5:39
he sendeth and d. conditions. 14:32
office of a bishop, he d. 1 Tim 3:1

desiring

his brethren d. to. Mat 12:46*, 47*
worshipping and d. a. 20:20
brethren stand without d. Luke 8:20
d. to be fed with the crumbs. 16:21
d. to have judgement. Acts 25:15*
d. to be clothed upon. 2 Cor 5:2
d. greatly to see us. 1 Thes 3:6
d. to be teachers. 1 Tim 1:7
greatly d. to see thee. 2 Tim 1:4

desirous

be not d. of his dainties. Pr 23:3
Herod was d. to see him. Luke 23:8
Jesus knew they were d. John 16:19
with a garrison d. to. 2 Cor 11:32*
let us not be d. of vain. Gal 5:26*
so being affectionately d. 1 Thes 2:8

desolate

[1] Deserted, hence gloomy, Jer 6:8; 12:10. [2] Laid waste, Isa 1:7. [3] Left alone; forsaken, Ps 34:22.

Tamar remained d. 2 Sam 13:20
he dwelleth in d. cities. Job 15:28
made d. all my company. 16:7
wilderness in former time d. 30:3
to satisfy the d. and waste. 38:27
mercy on me, for I am d. Ps 25:16
let them be d. for a reward. 40:15
let their habitation be d. 69:25
my heart within me is d. 143:4
your country is d. your. Isa 1:7
she being d. shall sit upon. 3:26
shall rest all of them in d. 7:19
beast shall cry in their d. 13:22*
they that dwell therein are d. 24:6*
to inherit the d. heritages. 49:8
have lost my children, am d. 21*
more are the children of the d. 54:1
Gal 4:27
make the d. cities to be. Isa 54:3
be ye very d. saith. Jer 2:12
lest I make thee d. a land not. 6:8
make cities of Judah d. 9:11; 10:22
33:10; 44:6
have made his habitation d. 10:25
made it d. and being d. it. 12:11
I will make this city d. 19:8*
it is d. without. 32:43; 33:12
their habitations d. 49:20; 50:45
all her gates are d. Lam 1:4
he hath made me d. 13; 3:11
my children are d. the. 1:16
did feed delicately are d. 4:5
mountain of Zion which is d. 5:18
altars may be made d. Ezek 6:6
he knew their d. palaces. 19:7
that I might make them d. 20:26
I will make Edom d. from. 25:13
when I make thee a d. city. 26:19
midst of countries that are d. 29:12
I will make Pathros d. and. 30:14
I will make thee most d. 35:3, 7
they are d. they are given us. 12
I will make thee d. 14
rejoice, because it was d. 15
because they have made you d. 36:3
saith Lord to hills and d. wastes. 4
the d. cities are become fenced. 35
I plant that that was d. 36
on sanctuary that is d. Dan 9:17
for abominations shall make it d. 27
that maketh d. 11:31; 12:11
Samaria shall become d. Hos 13:16*
the garners are laid d. Joel 1:17
flocks of sheep are made d. 18
the idols thereof will I lay d. Mi 1:7
in making thee d. because of. 6:13
their towers are d. Zeph 3:6
house is left to you d. Mat 23:38
Luke 13:35
let his habitation be d. Acts 1:20
a widow indeed and d. 1 Tim 5:5
hate whore, and make d. Rev 17:16
in one hour is she made d. 18:19

land desolate

seed that land be not d. Gen 47:19
lest land become d. Ex 23:29
land enjoy her sabbaths lieth d.
Lev 26:34, 35, 43; 2 Chr 36:21
until the land be utterly d. Isa 6:11
cometh to lay the land d. 13:9
land any more be termed d. 62:4
gone forth to make land d. Jer 4:7
the whole land shall be d. 27
for the land shall be d. 7:34
d. the whole land is made d. 12:11
to make their land d. and. 18:16*
for their land is d. because. 25:38
land whereof ye say it is d. 32:43
nation which shall make land d. 50:3
the land d. yea more d. Ezek 6:14
her land may be d. from. 12:19
cities laid waste, land be d. 20
land shall be d. Ezek 14:16; Mi 7:13
I will make the land d. Ezek 15:8
land was d. and the fulness. 19:7
the land of Egypt shall be d. 29:9
10, 12; 30:7; 32:15
I will lay the land most d. 33:28
when I have laid the land most d. 29
d. land tilled, whereas it lay d. 36:34
the land that was d. is like. 35
to a land barren and d. Joel 2:20
land was d. for they laid pleasant land d. Zech 7:14

desolate places

which built d. places for. Job 3:14*
bread out of d. places. Ps 109:10
thy waste and d. places. Isa 49:19
we are in d. places as dead. 59:10*
high places shall be d. Ezek 6:6
set thee in places d. of old. 26:20
thine hand upon the d. places. 38:12
high places of Isaac be d. Amos 7:9
return, and build d. places. Mal 1:4

shall be, or shalt be desolate

your highways shall be d. Lev 26:22
your land shall be d. 33
hypocrites shall be d. Job 15:34*
hate righteous shall be d. Ps 34:21*
none that trust in him shall be d. 22*
many houses shall be d. Isa 5:9
waters of Nimrim shall be d. 15:6
Jer 48:34
defenced city shall be d. Isa 27:10*
this city shall be d. Jer 26:9
place which ye say shall be d. 33:10
Noph shall be d. without. 46:19*
cities thereof shall be d. 48:9
Rabbah shall be a d. heap. 49:2
Babylon shall be wholly d. 50:13
thou shalt be d. for ever. 51:26
your altars shall be d. Ezek 6:4
cities of Egypt shall be d. 29:12
mountains of Israel shall be d. 33:28
mount Seir, thou shalt be d. 35:4, 15
Ephraim shall be d. in day. Hos 5:9

desolate wilderness

portion a d. wilderness. Jer 12:10
behind it is a d. wilderness. Joel 2:3
and Edom a d. wilderness. 3:19

desolation

your sanctuaries to d. Lev 26:31
and I will bring the land into d. 32
made Ai a d. unto this day. Josh 8:28
that they become a d. 2 Ki 22:19
who gave them to d. 2 Chr 30:7
in d. they rolled. Job 30:14*
to d. in a moment. Ps 73:19
your fear cometh as d. Pr 1:27*
be not afraid of d. of wicked. 3:25
in that day shall be d. Isa 17:9
in the city is left d. the gate. 24:12
and d. shall come upon thee. 47:11
two things come unto thee, d. 51:19
a wilderness, Jerusalem a d. 64:10
house shall become a d. Jer 22:5
this whole land shall be a d. 25:11
make Jerusalem and Judah a d. 18
I will make cities of Judah a d. 34:22
this day they are a d. 44:2
is your land a d. and a curse. 22
Bozrah a d. 49:13*
Edom a d. 17*
Hazor a d. 33
how is Babylon become a d.! 50:23
to make Babylon a d. 51:29
her cities are a d. a dry land. 43*
snare is come on us, d. Lam 3:47*
prince be clothed with d. Ezek 7:27
filled with the cup of d. 23:33
the transgression of d. Dan 8:13
increaseth lies and d. Hos 12:1
and Edom shall be a d. Joel 3:19
I should make thee a d. Mi 6:16
houses shall become a d. Zeph 1:13
day of wrath, wasteness, and d. 15
Ashkelon shall be a d. 2:4
Moab a perpetual d. 9
he will make Nineveh a d. 13
d. shall be in thresholds. 14
how is Nineveh become a d.! 15
every kingdom divided against itself is brought to d. Mat 12:25
Luke 11:17

see abomination of d. Mat 24:15
Mark 13:14
then know that the d. Luke 21:20

desolations

and to repair d. thereof. Ezra 9:9*
what d. he hath made. Ps 46:8
lift up thy feet to perpetual d. 74:3*
shall raise up the former d. the d. of many generations. Isa 61:4
these nations perpetual d. Jer 25:9
land of Chaldeans perpetual d. 12
mount Seir perpetual d. Ezek 35:9
seventy years in d. of. Dan 9:2
thine eyes, and behold our d. 18
to the end of the war d. 26

despair

and Saul shall d. of me. 1 Sam 27:1
cause my heart to d. Eccl 2:20
perplexed, but not in d. 2 Cor 4:8

despaired

insomuch that we d. 2 Cor 1:8

desperate

reprove speeches of one d. Job 6:26
of grief and of d. sorrow. Isa 17:11

desperately

deceitful, and d. wicked. Jer 17:9

despise

if ye shall d. my statutes. Lev 26:15*
that d. me shall be. 1 Sam 2:30
why then did ye d. us? 2 Sam 19:43
they d. their husbands. Esth 1:17*
d. not thou the chastening of the. Job 5:17; Pr 3:11; Heb 12:5
I were perfect, I would d. Job 9:21
thou shouldest d. the work of. 10:3
if I did d. the cause of my. 31:13
heart, thou wilt not d. Ps 51:17
thou shalt d. their image. 73:20
he will not d. their prayer. 102:17
but fools d. wisdom. Pr 1:7
d. not chastening of Lord. 3:11
Heb 12:5
men do not d. a thief, if. Pr 6:30
a fool will d. the wisdom of. 23:9
and d. not thy mother when. 22
because ye d. this word. Isa 30:12
thy lovers will d. thee. Jer 4:30
say still to them that d. me. 23:17
all that honoured her, d. Lam 1:8
Philistines which d. thee. Ezek 16:57*
judgement on all that d. 28:26*
I hate, I d. your feast. Amos 5:21
O priests, that d. my. Mal 1:6
one, and d. the other. Mat 6:24
Luke 16:13
that ye d. not one of these. Mat 18:10
not him that eateth, d. Rom 14:3*
or d. ye the church of. 1 Cor 11:22
let no man therefore d. him. 16:11
d. not prophesyings. 1 Thes 5:20
let none d. thy youth. 1 Tim 4:12
let them not d. them. 6:2
let no man d. thee. Tit 2:15
them that d. government. 2 Pet 2:10
d. dominion, and speak evil. Jude 8*

despised

Hagar's mistress was d. Gen 16:4
she had conceived, I was d. 5
thus Esau d. his birthright. 25:34
they d. my judgements. Lev 26:43*
ye have d. the Lord. Num 11:20*
know the land ye have d. 14:31*
because ye d. word of Lord. 15:31
the people thou hast d.? Judg 9:38
d. him and brought. 1 Sam 10:27
she d. him in her heart. 2 Sam 6:16
1 Chr 15:29
why hast thou d. commandment? 2 Sam 12:9
because thou hast d. me. 10
daughter of Zion hath d. thee. 2 Ki 19:21; Isa 37:22
but they mocked and d. 2 Chr 36:16
laughed us to scorn and d. Neh 2:19
hear, for we are d. and turn. 4:4
he is a lamp d. of him. Job 12:5*
yea, young children d. me. 19:18
I am d. of the people. Ps 22:6
Isa 53:3
he hath not d. the affliction. Ps 22:24
because God hath d. them. 53:5*
yea, they d. the pleasant. 106:24
I am small and d. yet do. Ps 119:141
they d. all my reproof. Pr 1:30
hath my heart d. reproof? 5:12
of a perverse heart shall be d. 12:8
he that is d. and hath a servant. 9*
poor man's wisdom is d. Eccl 9:16
yea I should not be d. S of S 8:1
d. the word of holy One. Isa 5:24
he hath d. the cities, he. 33:8
he is d. and rejected of men, he was d. and we esteemed him not. 53:3
all they that d. thee shall bow. 60:14
Coniah a d. broken idol. Jer 22:28
thus they have d. my people. 33:24
I will make thee small and d. 49:15
he hath d. in indignation. Lam 2:6
hast d. oath. Ezek 16:59; 17:16
18, 19
they d. my judgements. 20:13*
because they d. my judgements. 16*
but had d. my statutes. 24*
thou hast d. mine holy things. 22:8
because they d. the law. Amos 2:4*
thou art greatly d. Ob 2
who hath d. day of? Zech 4:10
have we d. thy name? Mal 1:6
righteous, and d. others. Luke 18:9*
of Diana should be d. Acts 19:27*
things which are d. hath. 1 Cor 1:28
ye are honourable, we are d. 4:10*
my temptation ye d. not. Gal 4:14
d. Moses' law, died. Heb 10:28*
but ye have d. the poor. Jas 2:6*

despisers

behold, ye d. and. Acts 13:41
incontinent, fierce, d. of. 2 Tim 3:3*

despisest

or d. thou the riches of? Rom 2:4

despiseth

God is mighty, and d. not. Job 36:5
for the Lord d. not. Ps 69:33
void of wisdom d. Pr 11:12
whoso d. the word shall be. 13:13
perverse in his ways d. him. 14:2
that d. his neighbour sinneth. 21
fool d. his father's instruction. 15:5
but a foolish man d. his mother. 20
he that refuseth instruction d. 32
he that d. his ways shall. 19:16*
eye that d. to obey his mother. 30:17
he that d. the gain of. Isa 33:15
saith Lord to him whom man d. 49:7
d. you, d. me; d. me, d. him that. Luke 10:16*
d. d. not man but God. 1 Thes 4:8*

despising

the cross, d. the shame. Heb 12:2

despite

thy d. against the land. Ezek 25:6
hath done d. to the Spirit. Heb 10:29

despiteful

vengeance with a d. Ezek 25:15
with d. minds to cast it out. 36:5
haters of God, d. proud. Rom 1:30*

despitefully

pray for them that d. Mat 5:44
Luke 6:28
assault was made to use them d. Acts 14:5*

destitute

who hath not left d. my. Gen 24:27
regard prayer of the d. Ps 102:17
leave not my soul d. 141:8
folly is joy to him that is d. Pr 15:21*
be d. of that whereof. Ezek 32:15
of corrupt minds, d. of. 1 Tim 6:5*
being d. afflicted. Heb 11:37
or sister be naked and d. Jas 2:15*

destroy

This is used [1] *of demolishing buildings or cities,* Gen 18:28; Jer 6:5; [2] *of putting an end to anything,* 1 Ki 16:12; Jer 51:20; [3] *of killing a person or persons,* Deut 9:14, 25; [4] *of nullifying,* Isa 19:3.

wilt thou d. righteous? Gen 18:23
wilt thou d. and not spare? 24
wilt thou d. all city for? 28
we will d. this place. 19:13
d. this city. 14
my hand shall d. them. Ex 15:9
ye shall d. their altars. 34:13
Deut 7:5
I will send beasts to d. Lev 26:22
d. the children of Sheth. Num 24:17
and ye shall d. all this people. 32:15
shall d. their pictures and. 33:52
lest anger of Lord d. thee. Deut 6:15
Lord shall d. them with a. 7:23*
thou shalt d. their name. 24
he shall d. them, and. 9:3
let me alone, that I may d. 14
Lord had said he would d. 25
trees that are not for meat d. 20:20
the Lord thy God he will d. 31:3
d. the young man and virgin. 32:25
thrust out enemy, and say, d. 33:27
except ye d. accursed. Josh 7:12
depart, lest I d. you. 1 Sam 15:6
we will d. the heir also. 2 Sam 14:7
not suffer revengers to d. any more, lest they d. my son. 11
that would d. me and my son. 16
I should swallow or d. 20:20
I might d. them that hate me. 22:41
Ps 18:40
thus did Zimri d. the. 1 Ki 16:12
he might d. worshippers. 2 Ki 10:19
against this land, and d. it. 18:25
Isa 36:10
d. kings that shall put to. Ezra 6:12
if he d. him from his place. Job 8:18
yet thou dost d. me. 10:8
after my skin worms d. this. 19:26
thou shalt d. them. Ps 5:6
d. them, O God, let them fall. 10*
their fruit shalt thou d. 21:10
he shall d. them, and not. 28:5
God shall likewise d. thee. 52:5
d. O Lord, and divide their. 55:9
that would d. me are mighty. 69:4
let us d. them together. 74:8
and d. all them that afflict. 143:12
shoot out thine arrows and d. 144:6*
all the wicked will he d. 145:20
prosperity of fools shall d. Pr 1:32
of transgressors shall d. 11:3
Lord will d. house of proud. 15:25
robberies of wicked shall d. 21:7
why should God d. work? Eccl 5:6
why shouldest thou d. thyself? 7:16
and they d. the way of. Isa 3:12
nor d. in holy mountain. 11:9; 65:25
he shall d. the sinners thereof. 13:9
he will d. in this mountain. 25:7
go ye upon her walls and d. Jer 5:10
let us go by night and d. her. 6:5
let us d. the tree with the. 11:19
I will pluck up and d. that. 12:17
spare nor have mercy, but d. 13:14
my hand against thee and d. 15:6
and d. them with double. 17:18
woe to pastors that d. sheep. 23:1
king of Babylon shall d. 36:29
he shall d. thy strong holds. 48:18
thieves by night will d. 49:
spare ye not, d. ye utterly all. 51:
persecute and d. them. Lam 3:6
thou d. all the residue? Ezek 9:
d. the remnant of sea-coast. 25:1
and they shall d. the walls. 26:
shall d. thy pleasant houses. 1
hew tree down and d. it. Dan 4:2
d. wonderfully, and d. mighty. 8:2
by peace shall he d. many. 2
people shall d. the city and. 9:2
that feed on his meat shall d. 11:2
shall I not d. the wise men? Ob
it is polluted, it shall d. Mi 2:1
north, and d. Assyria. Zeph 2:1
they might d. him. Mat 12:1
Mark 3:6; 11:
d. those wicked men. Mat 21:
should ask Barabbas, and d. 27:
will d. the husbandmen. Mark 12
Luke 20:
d. this temple. John 2:
Jesus of Nazareth shall d. Acts 6:
God shall d. both it and. 1 Cor 6:
shall d. with brightness. 2 Thes 2
d. him that had power of. Heb 2:
that he might d. works. 1 John 3
d. them which d. earth. Rev 11:

I will, or will I **destroy**
I will d. man whom I. Gen 6:7
I will d. them with the earth. 13
every living substance will I d. 7:4
and I will d. all people. Ex 23:27*
the same soul will I d. Lev 23:30
I will d. your high places. 26:30
Ezek 6:3
I will early d. all wicked. Ps 101:8
name of Lord will I d. 118:10, 11, 12
and I will d. the counsel. Isa 19:3
I will cry, I will d. and. 42:14*
I will d. my people. Jer 15:7
I will d. the city, and the. 46:8
I will d. from thence the king. 49:38
battle-ax, with thee will I d. 51:20
I the Lord will d. that. Ezek 14:9
I will d. thee, and thou shalt know.
25:7; 28:16; Zeph 2:5
I will d. the idols. Ezek 30:13
I will d. also all the beasts. 32:13
but I will d. the fat and. 34:16
I will d. her vines and. Hos 2:12
and I will d. thy mother. 4:5
I will d. sinful kingdom. Amos 9:8
I will d. thy chariots. Mi 5:10
so will I d. thy cities. 14
I will d. the strength of. Hag 2:22
I will d. this temple. Mark 14:58
I will d. the wisdom of. 1 Cor 1:19

not **destroy**
find forty-five I will not d. Gen 18:28
will not d. it for twenty's sake. 31
not d. Sodom for ten's sake. 32
not forsake thee, nor d. Deut 4:31
d. not thy people and. 9:26
the Lord would not d. thee. 10:10
thou shalt not d. the trees. 20:19
wilt not d. my name. 1 Sam 24:21
David said to Abishai, d. not. 26:9
would not d. Judah for. 2 Ki 8:19
would not d. them, nor cast. 13:23
therefore I will not d. 2 Chr 12:7
that the Lord would not d. him. 12
Lord would not d. the house. 21:7
forbear that he d. thee not. 35:21
they did not d. nations. Ps 106:34
d. it not, for a blessing is in it: that I
may not d. them all. Isa 65:8
that I should not d. it. Ezek 22:30
d. not the wise men of. Dan 2:24
he shall not d. fruits of. Mal 3:11
d. not him with thy meat. Rom 14:15
for meat d. not the work of God. 20

to **destroy**
flood of waters to d. all. Gen 6:17
any more a flood to d. 9:11, 15
the Lord hath sent us to d. it. 19:13
intreat for thee to d. frogs. Ex 8:9
plague shall not be on you to d. 12:13
to deliver us into hand of Amorites
to d. us. Deut 1:27; Josh 7:7
hand of Lord to d. them. Deut 2:15
them that hate him to d. them. 7:10
was wroth against you to d. 9:19
Lord will rejoice over you to d. 28:63
to d. all the inhabitants. Josh 9:24
to d. land where Reubenites. 22:33
Midianites entered to d. Judg. 6:5
Saul seeketh to d. city. 1 Sam 23:10
came in one of people to d. 26:15
not afraid to d. Lord's. 2 Sam 1:14
suffer revengers of blood to d. 14:11
thou seekest to d. a. 20:19
his hand on Jerusalem to d. 24:16
house of Jeroboam to d. 1 Ki 13:34
them against Judah to d. 2 Ki 24:2
angel to Jerusalem to d. 1 Chr 21:15
determined to d. thee. 2 Chr 25:16
Haman sought to d. Jews. Esth 3:6
13; 4:7, 8; 9:24
thou movedst me to d. Job 2:3
would please God to d. me. 6:9
seek after my soul to d. it.
Ps 40:14; 63:9
wicked have waited to d. me. 119:95
is in his heart to d. and. Isa 10:7
they come from far to d. 13:5
hath given commandment to d. 23:11
deviseth wicked devices to d. 32:7
oppressor were ready to d. 51:13
have created waster to d. 54:16

I have set thee to d. Jer 1:10
18:7; 31:28
appoint beasts of earth to d. 15:3
device against Babylon to d. it. 51:11
Lord hath purposed to d. Lam 2:8
I will send to d. you. Ezek 5:16
and to d. souls, to get gain. 22:27
a despiteful heart to d. it. 25:15
nations shall be brought to d. 30:11
vision I saw when I came to d. 43:3
to d. all wise men of. Dan 2:12, 24
and to d. his dominion. 7:26
go forth with great fury to d. 11:44
not return to d. Ephraim. Hos 11:9
that I will seek to d. all. Zech 12:9
seek young child to d. Mat 2:13
think not that I am come to d. law, I
am not come to d. but to. 5:17
fear him who is able to d. 10:28
I am able to d. the temple. 26:61
art thou come to d. us? Mark 1:24
Luke 4:34
sabbath to save life or to d. Luke 6:9
Son of man is not come to d. 9:56
chief of people sought to d. 19:47
thief cometh not but to d. John 10:10
able to save and to d. Jas 4:12

destroyed
before Lord d. Sodom. Gen 13:10
when God d. the cities of. 19:29
knowest not Egypt is d.? Ex 10:7
the Lord d. them. Deut 2:21; 4:3
11:4; 2 Ki 21:9; 2 Chr 33:9
destruction, till they be d. Deut 7:23
able to stand till thou have d. 24
was angry with you to have d. 9:8
after that they be d. from. 12:30
until thou be d. 28:20, 24, 45, 51, 61
yoke on thy neck till he have d. 48
and I d. them from. Josh 24:8
Benjamin d. of Israel. Judg 20:21, 25
children of Israel d. 35, 42
that we should be d. 2 Sam 21:5
the angel that d. 24:16; 1 Chr 21:15
Asa d. her idol and. 1 Ki 15:13
thus Jehu d. Baal. 2 Ki 10:28
Athaliah arose and d. all the. 11:1
they have d. them. 19:18; Isa 37:19
people whom God d. 1 Chr 5:25
were d. before Lord. 2 Chr 14:13
nation was d. of nation. 15:6
which kings of Judah had d. 34:11
for which cause was city d. Ezra 4:15
written, that they may be d. Esth 3:9
he hath d. me on every. Job 19:10
thou hast d. the wicked. Ps 9:5
thou hast d. cities. 6
d. all them that go a whoring. 73:27
frogs among them, which d. 78:45
he d. their vines with hail, and. 47
Babylon, who art to be d. 137:8
there is that is d. for. Pr 13:23
because thou hast d. land. Isa 14:20
hast thou visited and d. 26:14
many pastors have d. Jer 12:10
Moab is d. 48:4
Babylon is suddenly d. 51:8
hath d. out of Babylon. 55
Lord hath d. his strong. Lam 2:5
he hath d. his places of the. 6
he hath d. and broken her bars. 9
Tyrus, like the d. in the. Ezek 27:32
beast was slain, his body d. Dan 7:11
O Israel, thou hast d. Hos 13:9
yet d. I the Amorite, I d. Amos 2:9
sent his armies and d. Mat 22:7
the flood came, and d. Luke 17:27
it rained fire from heaven and d. 29
is not this he that d.? Acts 9:21
when he had d. seven nations. 13:19
magnificence should be d. 19:27*
body of sin might be d. Rom 6:6
d. of serpents. 1 Cor 10:9
d. of the destroyer. 10
preacheth faith which he d. Gal 1:23
build again things which I d. 2:18
lest he that d. first-born. Heb 11:28
as brute beasts made to be d.
2 Pet 2:12
the Lord afterward d. them. Jude 5
third part of ships were d. Rev 8:9

are **destroyed**
the women are d. out. Judg 21:16
they are d. from morning. Job 4:20
overturneth them so they are d. 34:25
are led of them are d. Isa 9:16
for all thy lovers are d. Jer 22:20
my people are d. for lack. Hos 4:6
their cities are d. Zeph 3:6

not **destroyed**
but they d. them not. 2 Chr 20:10
Ps 78:38
kingdom which shall not be d.
Dan 7:14
cast down, but not d. 2 Cor 4:9

shall be **destroyed**
and I shall be d. I and. Gen 34:30
father's house shall be d. Esth 4:14
transgressors shall be d. Ps 37:38
it is that they shall be d. 92:7
despiseth word shall be d. Pr 13:13
companion of fools shall be d. 20*
hardeneth his neck shall be d. 29:1
the yoke shall be d. Isa 10:27
the plain shall be d. Jer 48:8
all her helpers shall be d. Ezek 30:8
a kingdom which shall never be d.
Dan 2:44; 6:26
within few days he shall be d. 11:20
sin of Israel shall be d. Hos 10:8
will not hear shall be d. Acts 3:23
last enemy that shall be d. is death.
1 Cor 15:26

utterly **destroyed**
sacrificeth to any god, save unto the
Lord, shall be utterly d. Ex 22:20
utterly d. the Canaanites. Num 21:3
we utterly d. Sihon. Deut 2:34
we utterly d. cities of Og. 3:6
Josh 2:10
if ye corrupt yourselves ye shall be
utterly d. Deut 4:26
Jericho utterly d. Josh 6:21
Ai utterly d. 8:26; 10:1
Hebron utterly d. 10:37
he utterly d. all that breathed. 40
Joshua utterly d. them. 11:12, 21
and Simeon utterly d. Judg 1:17
Saul utterly d. people. 1 Sam 15:8
he would not utterly d. the best. 9
and rest we have utterly d. 15
I have utterly d. Amalekites. 20
should have been utterly d. 21*
[of Gedor] utterly d. 1 Chr 4:41
Hezekiah utterly d. the images.
2 Chr 31:1
nations my father utterly d. 32:14
hath utterly d. all nations. Isa 34:2

destroyer
will not suffer d. to come. Ex 12:23
hath delivered the d. of. Judg 16:24
in prosperity d. shall. Job 15:21
kept me from paths of d. Ps 17:4
is the companion of a d. Pr 28:24
the d. of the Gentiles. Jer 4:7
were destroyed of the d. 1 Cor 10:10

destroyers
life draweth near to d. Job 33:22
thy d. shall go forth. Isa 49:17
and I will prepare d. Jer 22:7
ye rejoiced, O d. of my. 50:11*

destroyest, -eth
as nations the Lord d. Deut 8:20
he d. the perfect and the. Job 9:22
increaseth the nations, and d. 12:23
and thou d. the hope of man. 14:19
he that doth it, d. his. Pr 6:32
hypocrite with his mouth d. 11:9
thy ways to that which d. kings. 31:3
and a gift d. heart. Eccl 7:7
sinner d. much good. 9:18
which d. all the earth. Jer 51:25
thou that d. the temple. Mat 27:40
Mark 15:29

destroying
angel of the Lord d. 1 Chr 21:12
as he was d. the Lord repented. 15
a strong one, as a d. Isa 28:2
sword devoured like a d. Jer 2:30
against Babylon a d. wind. 51:1
against thee, O d. mountain. 25
withdrawn his hand from d. Lam 2:8
every man with d. weapon. Ezek 9:1
mine eye spared them from d. 20:17

see **utterly**

destruction

destroy them with a mighty *d*. *Deut* 7:23*
devoured with bitter *d*. 32:24
Lord was against the city with a great *d*. *1 Sam* 5:9*
for there was a deadly *d*. 11*
I appointed to utter *d*. *1 Ki* 20:42
his counsellors to his *d*. *2 Chr* 22:4
d. of Ahaziah was of God, by. 7
heart was lifted up to his *d*. 26:16*
how endure to see the *d*.? *Esth* 8:6
smote their enemies with *d*. 9:5
neither be afraid of *d*. *Job* 5:21
at *d*. and famine thou shalt laugh. 22
and *d*. shall be ready. 18:12*
how oft cometh their *d*.? 21:17*
his eyes shall see his *d*. and. 20
wicked is reserved to day of *d*. 30*
hell is naked before him, *d*. 26:6*
d. and death say, we have. 28:22
against me ways of their *d*. 30:12
though they cry in his *d*. 24*
is not *d*. to the wicked? 31:3
a fire that consumeth to *d*. 12
for *d*. from God was a terror. 23*
if I rejoiced at the *d*. of him. 29
let *d*. come upon him, his net catch himself, into that very *d*. *Ps* 35:8
them down to the pit of *d*. 55:23
castedst them down into *d*. 73:18
faithfulness be declared in *d*.? 88:11
thou turnest man to *d*. and. 90:3
nor for the *d*. that wasteth. 91:6
redeemeth thy life from *d*. 103:4
when your *d*. cometh. *Pr* 1:27*
mouth of foolish is near *d*. 10:14
the *d*. of poor is their poverty. 15
d. shall be to workers of. 29; 21:15
openeth his lips shall have *d*. 13:3
want of people is the *d*. of. 14:28
hell and *d*. are before Lord. 15:11*
pride goeth before *d*. 16:18
that exalteth gate seeketh *d*. 17:19
a fool's mouth is his *d*. 18:7
before *d*. the heart of man is. 12
for their heart studieth *d*. 24:2*
hell and *d*. are never full. 27:20*
as are appointed to *d*. 31:8
d. of transgressors and. *Isa* 1:28
anger shall cease in their *d*. 10:25
it shall come as a *d*. from. 13:6
Babylon with the besom of *d*. 14:23
shall raise up a cry of *d*. 15:5
shall be called city of *d*. 19:18
the gate is smitten with *d*. 24:12
the land of thy *d*. shall be. 49:19
desolation and *d*. are come. 51:19
wasting and *d*. are in their. 59:7
d. shall no more be heard. 60:18
from north a great *d*. *Jer* 4:6; 6:1
d. upon *d*. is cried, for the land. 4:20
destroy them with double *d*. 17:18
d. cometh, it cometh out. 46:20
Horonaim, spoiling and *d*. 48:3
enemies have heard a cry of *d*. 5
a sound of great *d*. is in. 50:22
great *d*. from land of. 51:54
d. of the daughter. *Lam* 2:11; 3:48
desolation and *d*. is come. 3:47
in the *d*. of the daughter of. 4:10
send famine for their *d*. *Ezek* 5:16
d. cometh, and they shall. 7:25
when I bring thy *d*. among. 32:9
d. to them, because they. *Hos* 7:13
they are gone, because of *d*. 9:6
I will be thy *d*. repentance hid. 13:14
as a *d*. from Almighty. *Joel* 1:15
rejoiced in day of their *d*. *Ob* 12
destroy you with a sore *d*. *Mi* 2:10
be no more utter *d*. *Zech* 14:11*
is way that leadeth to *d*. *Mat* 7:13
d. and misery are in. *Rom* 3:16
vessels of wrath fitted to *d*. 9:22
deliver to Satan for *d*. *1 Cor* 5:5
given us not for your *d*. *2 Cor* 10:8
13:10
walk whose end is *d*. *Phil* 3:19*
then sudden *d*. cometh. *1 Thes* 5:3
punished with everlasting *d*. *2 Thes* 1:9
which drown men in *d*. *1 Tim* 6:9
upon themselves swift *d*. *2 Pet* 2:1
unstable wrest to their own *d*. 3:16

destructions

O enemy, *d*. are come. *Ps* 9:6*
rescue my soul from their *d*. 35:17
delivereth them from their *d*. 107:20

detain, -ed

let us *d*. thee till we. *Judg* 13:15
though thou *d*. me, I will not. 16
Doeg was that day *d*. *1 Sam* 21:7

determinate

delivered by *d*. counsel. *Acts* 2:23

determination

d. is to gather nations. *Zeph* 3:8

determine

shall pay as the judges *d*. *Ex* 21:22

determined

sure that evil is *d*. by. *1 Sam* 20:7
if I knew that evil were *d*. 9
Jonathan knew that it was *d*. 33
for evil is *d*. against our. 25:17
Absalom hath been *d*. *2 Sam* 13:32
Solomon *d*. to build a. *2 Chr* 2:1
I know that God hath *d*. 25:16
that there was evil *d*. *Esth* 7:7
seeing his days are *d*. *Job* 14:5
a consumption *d*. *Isa* 10:23; 28:22
of Lord which hath *d*. 19:17*
seventy weeks are *d*. *Dan* 9:24*
to end of war desolations are *d*. 26
and that *d*. shall be poured upon. 27
that is *d*. shall be done. 11:36
of man goeth as was *d*. *Luke* 22:22
when Pilate was *d*. to. *Acts* 3:13
to do what thy counsel *d*. 4:28*
the disciples *d*. to send. 11:29
d. that Paul and Barnabas. 15:2*
and Barnabas *d*. to take with. 37*
and hath *d*. the times before. 17:26
be *d*. in a lawful assembly. 19:39
for Paul had *d*. to sail by. 20:16
I have *d*. to send Paul. 25:25
it was *d*. that we should sail. 27:1
I *d*. not to know any thing. *1 Cor* 2:2
but I *d*. this with myself. *2 Cor* 2:1
Nicopolis, for I have *d*. *Tit* 3:12

detest

but thou shalt utterly *d*. *Deut* 7:26

detestable

defiled my land with *d*. *Jer* 16:18
defiled sanctuary with *d*. *Ezek* 5:11
made images of their *d*. things. 7:20
shall take away all *d*. things. 11:18
heart walketh after their *d*. things. 21
any more defile with their *d*. 37:23

device

to find out every *d*. *2 Chr* 2:14
to put away his *d*. that. *Esth* 8:3
his wicked *d*. should return. 9:25
imagined a mischievous *d*. *Ps* 21:11
further not his wicked *d*. 140:8
there is no work nor *d*. *Eccl* 9:10
I devise a *d*. against you. *Jer* 18:11
for his *d*. is against Babylon. 51:11
and their *d*. against me. *Lam* 3:62*
stone graven by man's *d*. *Acts* 17:29

devices

he disappointeth the *d*. *Job* 5:12
d. which ye wrongfully. 21:27
let them be taken in *d*. *Ps* 10:2
he maketh the *d*. of people. 33:10*
man who bringeth wicked *d*. 37:7
filled with their own *d*. *Pr* 1:31
but a man of wicked *d*. will. 12:2
there are many *d*. in a man's. 19:21
he deviseth wicked *d*. to. *Isa* 32:7
they had devised *d*. *Jer* 11:19
we will walk after our own *d*. 18:12
come and let us devise *d*. 18
he shall forecast his *d*. *Dan* 11:24
for they shall forecast *d*. 25
are not ignorant of his *d*. *2 Cor* 2:11

devil

[1] *Satan, (i.e. adversary), the supreme evil spirit, referred to in the N.T. under the name of devil,* Mat 4:1; Luke 8:12; John 8:44; Rev 12:9. *The word devil is not used of Satan in the Old Testament. Abaddon in Hebrew, Apollyon in Greek, that is, destroyer,* Rev 9:11.—*Angel of the bottomless pit,* Rev. 9:11.—*Prince of this world,* John 12:31.—*Prince of darkness,* Eph 6:12.—*A roaring Lion, and an Adversary,* 1 Pet 5:8. —*Beelzebub,* Mat 12:24.—*Accuser,* Rev 12:10.—*Dragon,* Rev 12:7.—*Lucifer,* Isa 14:12.—*Serpent,* Rev 20:2.—*Satan,* Job 2:6.—*The god of this world,* 2 Cor 4:4.

[2] *Inferior evil spirits. In this sense the American Revision translates the word* demon.

led to be tempted of the *d*. *Mat* 4:1
d. taketh him up to holy city. 5
the *d*. taketh him up to an high. 8
d. leaveth him. 11
man possessed with *d*. 9:32; 12:22
say he hath a *d*. 11:18; *Luke* 7:33
that sowed them is *d*. *Mat* 13:39
daughter is vexed with a *d*. 15:22
Jesus rebuked the *d*. 17:18
fire, prepared for the *d*. 25:41
possessed with the *d*. *Mark* 5:15
16, 18
the *d*. is gone out of. 7:29, 30
forty days tempted of *d*. *Luke* 4:2
the *d*. said to him, all this power. 3, 6
the *d*. taking him up. 5
when the *d*. had ended all the. 13
had a spirit of an unclean *d*. 33
and when the *d*. had thrown him. 35
then cometh the *d*. and taketh. 8:12
was driven of the *d*. into the. 29
as he was coming the *d*. 9:42
casting out a *d*. when the *d*. 11:14
and one of you is a *d*. *John* 6:70
said, thou hast a *d*. 7:20; 8:48
ye are of your father the *d*. 8:44
I have not a *d*. 49
we know that thou hast a *d*. 52
many said, he hath a *d*. 10:20
not words of him that hath a *d*. 21
the *d*. having put into heart. 13:2
that were oppressed of *d*. *Acts* 10:38
thou child of the *d*. 13:10
neither give place to *d*. *Eph* 4:27
to stand against wiles of *d*. 6:11
into condemnation of *d*. *1 Tim* 3:6
into reproach, and snare of *d*. 7
out of the snare of the *d*. *2 Tim* 2:26
power of death, that is *d*. *Heb* 2:14
resist the *d*. and he will. *Jas* 4:7
your adversary the *d*. *1 Pet* 5:8
sin is of the *d*. that he might destroy the works of the *d*. *1 John* 3:8
in this the children of the *d*. are 10
when contending with the *d*. *Jude* 9
the *d*. shall cast some. *Rev* 2:10
the old serpent called the *d*. 12:9
for the *d*. is come down to you. 12
that old serpent, which is *d*. 20:2
d. that deceived them was cast. 10

devilish

this wisdom is earthy, *d*. *Jas* 3:15

devils

more offer sacrifices to *d*. *Lev* 17:7
they sacrificed to *d*. *Deut* 32:17
he ordained him priests for the *d*. *2 Chr* 11:15
sons and daughters to *d*. *Ps* 106:37
those possessed with *d*. *Mat* 4:2
8:16, 28, 33; *Mark* 1:32; *Luke* 8:3
the *d*. besought him. *Mat* 8:3
Mark 5:1
saw one casting out *d*. in thy name *Mark* 9:38; *Luke* 9:4
my name shall cast out *d*. *Mark* 16:1
and *d*. also came out of. *Luke* 4:4
out of whom went seven *d*. 8
he that was possessed of *d*.
and authority over all *d*. 9
even the *d*. are subject to us. 10:
that fox, behold, I cast out *d*. 13:
sacrifice to *d*. . . . ye should ha fellowship with *d*. *1 Cor* 10:
cup of Lord and cup of *d*; of Lord table and of table of *d*.
heed to doctrines of *d*. *1 Tim* 4
the *d*. also believe and. *Jas* 2:
should not worship *d*. *Rev* 9:
spirits of *d*. working miracles. 16:
is become habitation of *d*. 18

see **cast**

devise
d. cunning works in gold. *Ex* 31:4
35:35
to *d.* curious works in gold. 35:32
yet doth he *d.* means. *2 Sam* 14:14
to confusion, that *d.* my. *Ps* 35:4
but they *d.* deceitful matters. 20
against me do they *d.* my hurt. 41:7
d. not evil against. *Pr* 3:29
they not err that *d.* evil? mercy and truth to them that *d.* good. 14:22
shutteth his eyes to *d.* 16:30
behold, I *d.* a device. *Jer* 18:11
come and let us *d.* devices. 18
men that *d.* mischief. *Ezek* 11:2
woe to them that *d.* *Mi* 2:1
against this family do I *d.* an evil. 3

devised
that consumed us *d.* *2 Sam* 21:5
month which he had *d.* of. *1 Ki* 12:33
devise that he had *d.* *Esth* 8:3
be written to reverse letters *d.* 5
d. to take away my life. *Ps* 31:13
not that they had *d.* *Jer* 11:19
in Heshbon they have *d.* evil. 48:2
Lord hath both *d.* and done. 51:12
Lam 2:17
not followed cunningly *d.* *2 Pet* 1:16

deviseth
he *d.* mischief on his bed. *Ps* 36:4
thy tongue *d.* mischief like. 52:2
d. mischief continually. *Pr* 6:14
an heart that *d.* wicked. 18
man's heart *d.* his way. 16:9
d. to do evil shall be called. 24:8
he *d.* wicked devices to. *Isa* 32:7
but the liberal *d.* liberal things. 8

devote
thing that a man shall *d.* *Lev* 27:28

devoted
to Lord, as a field *d.* *Lev* 27:21
no *d.* thing sold, every *d.* thing. 28
every thing *d.* in Israel. *Num* 18:14
thy servant, who is *d.* *Ps* 119:38*

devotions
by and beheld your *d.* *Acts* 17:23*

devour
[1] *To eat up, or swallow greedily, either literally or figuratively,* Gen 37:20; Mat 23:14. [2] *To waste, or spend riotously,* Luke 15:30.

in morning he shall *d.* *Gen* 49:27
and sword *d.* flesh. *Deut* 32:42
shall sword *d.* for ever? *2 Sam* 2:26
command locusts to *d.* *2 Chr* 7:13
firstborn of death shall *d.* *Job* 18:13
wild beasts of field doth *d.* *Ps* 80:13
jaw-teeth as knives to *d.* *Pr* 30:14
your land strangers *d.* it. *Isa* 1:7
they shall *d.* Israel with. 9:12
for wickedness shall *d.* briers. 18
not of a mean man, shall *d.* 31:8
will destroy and *d.* at. 42:14*
all ye beasts of the field come to *d.*
56:9; *Jer* 12:9; 15:3
that *d.* Israel shall offend. *Jer* 2:3
word of the Lord shall *d.* 12:12
46:10, 14
and all that *d.* thee shall. 30:16
flame shall *d.* corner of Moab. 48:45
and pestilence shall *d.* *Ezek* 7:15
neither shall beasts of land *d.* 34:28
therefore shalt thou *d.* men. 36:14
arise, *d.* much flesh. *Dan* 7:5
whole earth. 23
now shall a month *d.* them. *Hos* 5:7
sword shall *d.* his branches. 11:6
there will I *d.* them like a lion. 13:8
fire shall *d.* the palaces. *Amos* 1:4
7, 10, 12
kindle in them, and *d.* them. *Ob* 18
sword shall *d.* young. *Nah* 2:13
rejoicing was as to *d.* *Hab* 3:14
they shall *d.* and subdue. *Zech* 9:15
they shall *d.* all the people. 12:6
you, hypocrites, for ye *d.* *Mat* 23:14
Mark 12:40; *Luke* 20:47
suffer, if a man *d.* you. *2 Cor* 11:20
but if ye bite and *d.* one. *Gal* 5:15
shall *d.* adversaries. *Heb* 10:27
seeking whom he may *d.* *1 Pet* 5:8
to *d.* her child as soon. *Rev* 12:4

fire **devour**
let *fire d.* the cedars. *Judg* 9:15
let *fire d.* the men of Shechem. 20
and *fire* shall *d.* them. *Ps* 21:9
shall come, a *fire* shall *d.* 50:3
fire of thine enemies shall *d.*
Isa 26:11
your breath as *fire* shall *d.* 33:11
another *fire* shall *d.* *Ezek* 15:7
for them through *fire* to *d.* 23:37
break out like *fire* and *d.* *Amos* 5:6
the *fire* shall *d.* thy bars. *Nah* 3:13
there shall the *fire d.* thee. 15
fire may *d.* thy cedars. *Zech* 11:1

it shall **devour**
it shall d. the strength. *Job* 18:13
it shall burn and *d.* his. *Isa* 10:17
my words fire, *it shall d.* *Jer* 5:14
a fire and *it shall d.* the palaces of Jerusalem. 17:27; *Amos* 2:5
it shall d. all things. *Jer* 21:14
50:32
it shall d. every tree. *Ezek* 20:47
it shall d. and I will bring. 28:18
it shall d. palaces of Judah. *Hos* 8:14
it shall d. palaces of Rabbah.
Amos 1:14
it shall d. palaces of Kirioth. 2:2

devoured
and quite *d.* our money. *Gen* 31:15
some evil beast hath *d.* 37:20, 33
seven thin ears *d.* seven. 41:7, 24
fire from Lord and *d.* *Lev* 10:2
time the fire *d.* 250 men. *Num* 26:10
my face, they shall be *d.* *Deut* 31:17
they shall be *d.* with burning. 32:24
d. more than sword *d.* *2 Sam* 18:8
and fire out of his mouth *d.* 22:9
Ps 18:8
sorts of flies which *d.* *Ps* 78:45
for they have *d.* Jacob. 79:7
the locusts *d.* the fruit of. 105:35
if ye rebel, ye shall be *d.* *Isa* 1:20
therefore hath the curse *d.* 24:6
sword hath *d.* prophets. *Jer* 2:30
for shame hath *d.* the labour. 3:24
they are come, and have *d.* 8:16
have eaten up Jacob, and *d.* 10:25
that devour thee shall be *d.* 30:16
all that found them have *d.* 50:7
king of Assyria hath *d.* him. 17
Nebuchadrezzar hath *d.* me. 51:34
it hath *d.* foundations. *Lam* 4:11
when the fire hath *d.* it. *Ezek* 15:5
sacrificed thy sons to be *d.* 16:20
to catch prey, *d.* men. 19:3, 6
fire is gone out, which hath *d.* 14
a roaring lion, they have *d.* 22:25
and thy residue shall be *d.* 23:25
give to the beasts to be *d.* 33:27
39:4
d. and brake in pieces. *Dan* 7:7, 19
and have *d.* their judges. *Hos* 7:7
strangers have *d.* his strength. 9
fire hath *d.* pastures. *Joel* 1:19, 20
palmer-worm *d.* them. *Amos* 4:9
and it *d.* the great deep. 7:4
they shall be *d.* as stubble. *Nah* 1:10
land shall be *d.* by fire. *Zeph* 1:18
all the earth shall be *d.* with. 3:8
Tyrus shall be *d.* with fire. *Zech* 9:4
fowls came and *d.* them. *Mat* 13:4
Mark 4:4; *Luke* 8:5
thy son who hath *d.* *Luke* 15:30
fire came down and *d.* *Rev* 20:9

devourer
I will rebuke the *d.* for. *Mal* 3:11

devourest
thou land *d.* up men. *Ezek* 36:13

devoureth
sword *d.* one as well. *2 Sam* 11:25
mouth of the wicked *d.* *Pr* 19:28
a snare to the man who *d.* 20:25
as fire *d.* stubble, and. *Isa* 5:24
Joel 2:5
a flaming fire which *d.* *Lam* 2:3
the fire *d.* both the ends. *Ezek* 15:4
a fire *d.* before them. *Joel* 2:3
wicked *d.* man that is. *Hab* 1:13
fire *d.* their enemies. *Rev* 11:5

devouring
appearance like *d.* fire. *Ex* 24:17
thou lovest all *d.* words. *Ps* 52:4
visited with *d.* fire. *Isa* 29:6; 30:30
his tongue is as a *d.* fire. 30:27
shall dwell with the *d.* fire? 33:14

devout
Simeon was just and *d.* *Luke* 2:25
at Jerusalem Jews, *d.* *Acts* 2:5
d. men carried Stephen to his. 8:2
Cornelius was a *d.* man. 10:2
a *d.* soldier. 7
Jews stirred up *d.* women. 13:50
of the *d.* Greeks a multitude. 17:4
Paul disputed with Jews and *d.* 17
Ananias a *d.* man. 22:12

dew
This was formerly thought to fall like a light rain during the night, and the references to it in the Bible are usually worded according to this idea, as are many of our customary phrases with reference to it as the falling of the dew. In warm countries, and in places where it rains but seldom, the night-dews supply in some sort the want of rain. And therefore the bestowing of it is a blessing from God, Deut 33:13; *and the withholding of it a curse,* 2 Sam 1:21.

God give thee of *d.* of. *Gen* 27:28, 39
in the morning *d.* lay. *Ex* 16:13
and when the *d.* that lay was. 14
when *d.* fell on camp. *Num* 11:9
speech shall distil as *d.* *Deut* 32:2
blessed is Joseph's land for *d.* 33:13
his heaven shall drop down *d.* 28
if *d.* be on fleece only. *Judg* 6:37
on ground let there be *d.* 39
there was *d.* 40
let there be no *d.* nor. *2 Sam* 1:21
we will light on him as *d.* 17:12
there shall not be *d.* nor. *1 Ki* 17:1
the *d.* lay all night on. *Job* 29:19
hath begotten drops of *d.*? 38:28
hast the *d.* of thy youth. *Ps* 110:3
as *d.* of Hermon, and as *d.* 133:3
clouds drop down the *d.* *Pr* 3:20
but his favour is as *d.* 19:12
my head is filled with *d.* *S of S* 5:2
like a cloud of *d.* in heat. *Isa* 18:4
for thy *d.* is as the *d.* of. 26:19
wet with *d.* of heaven. *Dan* 4:15, 23
shall wet thee with *d.* of heaven. 25
his body was wet with *d.* 33; 5:21
goodness is as early *d.* *Hos* 6:4
13:3
I will be as *d.* to Israel. 14:5
Jacob shall be as the *d.* *Mi* 5:7
over you stayed from *d.* *Hag* 1:10
heavens shall give their *d.* *Zech* 8:12

diadem
was as a robe and a *d.* *Job* 29:14
and for a *d.* of beauty. *Isa* 28:5
and a royal *d.* in the hand. 62:3
remove the *d.* take off. *Ezek* 21:26*

dial
gone down in *d.* of Ahaz. *2 Ki* 20:11
Isa 38:8

diamond
second row a *d.* *Ex* 28:18; 39:11
is written with point of *d.* *Jer* 17:1
the *d.* the beryl. *Ezek* 28:13

Diana
silver shrines for *D.* *Acts* 19:24
temple of great goddess *D.* 27
great is *D.* of Ephesians. 28, 34
worshipper of the goddess *D.* 35

Dibon
perished even to *D.* *Num* 21:30
children of Gad built *D.* 32:34
Moses gave *D.* to Reuben. *Josh* 13:17
Judah dwelt at *D.* *Neh* 11:25
gone up to *D.* the high. *Isa* 15:2
that dost inhabit *D.* *Jer* 48:18
judgement is come upon *D.* 22

Dibon-gad
pitched in *D.* *Num* 33:45
removed from *D.* 46

did
mischief that Hadad *d.* *1 Ki* 11:25
d. right according to all David *d.* *2 Ki* 18:3
I knew not what I *d.* *Neh* 2:16
to know how Esther *d.* *Esth* 2:11
not read what David *d.*? *Mat* 12:3
saw wonderful things he *d.* 21:15
what great things he *d.* *Mark* 3:8
saw miracles which he *d.* *John* 2:23
6:2, 14
me all things that ever I *d.* 4:29, 39
what *d.* he to thee ? 9:26
works which none other man *d.* 15:24
through ignorance ye *d.* it, as *d.* *Acts* 3:17
I also *d.* in Jerusalem. 26:10
and this they *d.* not as. *2 Cor* 8:5
who *d.* no sin, nor was. *1 Pet* 2:22

did joined with *as*
Lord *d.* to Sarah *as* he. *Gen* 21:1
the man *d.* *as* Joseph bade. 43:17
his sons *d.* to him *as* he. 50:12
d. *as* Lord commanded. *Ex* 7:6
10, 20; 12:28, 50; 39:32; *Lev* 8:4
16:34; 24:23; *Num* 1:54; 2:34
20:7; 27:22; 31:31
as he *d.* with the bullock. *Lev* 4:20
16:15
Balak *d.* *as* Balaam. *Num* 23:2, 30
as Israel *d.* to the land. *Deut* 2:12
as he *d.* to children of Esau. 22
as we *d.* unto Sihon. 3:6
flowed, *as* they *d.* before. *Josh* 4:18
as the Lord your God *d.* to. 23
d. to king of Makkedah, *as* he *d.* 10:28
Joshua *d.* to them *as* Lord. 11:9
Gideon *d.* *as* Lord had. *Judg* 6:27
as they *d.* to me, so I have. 15:11
as what the king *d.* *2 Sam* 3:36
and David *d.* so *as* the Lord. 5:25
elders *d.* *as* Jezebel had. *1 Ki* 21:11
Ahab *d.* according *as* *d.* the. 26
Jehoram, *as* *d.* the. *2 Ki* 8:18
as *d.* the heathen which. 17:11
as *d.* their fathers, so do they. 41
David *d.* *as* God. *1 Chr* 14:16
d. *as* it is written in law. *2 Chr* 25:4
seek me *as* a nation that *d.* *Isa* 58:2
gave thanks *as* he *d.* *Dan* 6:10
Joseph *d.* *as* the angel. *Mat* 1:24
d. *as* Jesus commanded. 21:6; 26:19
so watch *d.* *as* they were. 28:15
them, even *as* Elias *d.* *Luke* 9:54
ignorance ye did it, *as* *d.* *Acts* 3:17
Holy Ghost, *as* your fathers *d.* 7:51
gave them like gift, *as* he *d.* 11:17
from works, *as* God *d.* *Heb* 4:10

did joined with *evil*
requite us the *evil* we *d.* *Gen* 50:15
for they *d.* to thee *evil.* 17
d. *evil* in sight of Lord. *Judg* 2:11
3:7, 12; 4:1; 6:1; 10:6; 13:1
1 Ki 14:22; 15:26, 34; 16:7, 30
2 Ki 8:27; 13:2, 11; 14:24; 15:9
18, 24, 28; 17:2; *2 Chr* 22:4
Solomon *d.* *evil* in sight. *1 Ki* 11:6
Manasseh *d.* *evil.* *2 Ki* 21:2
2 Chr 33:2
Jehoahaz *d.* *evil.* *2 Ki* 23:32
Jehoiakim *d.* *evil.* 37
Jehoiachim *d.* *evil* 24:9
Zedekiah *d.* *evil.* 19
Rehoboam *d.* *evil.* *2 Chr* 12:14
Amon *d.* *evil.* 33:22
they had rest, they *d.* *evil.* *Neh* 9:28
the *evil* that Eliashib *d.* 13:7
but *d.* *evil* before mine eyes. *Isa* 65:12; 66:4
Alexander *d.* me much *evil.* *2 Tim* 4:14

did *not*
midwives *d.* *not* as king. *Ex* 1:17
Ahaz *d.* *not* what was right. *2 Ki* 16:2; *2 Chr* 28:1
d. *not* your fathers thus, and *d.* *not* our God bring this ? *Neh* 13:18
but they *d.* them *not.* *Jer* 11:8
of the evil, and *d.* it *not.* *Jonah* 3:10
d. *not* many mighty. *Mat* 13:58
d. it *not* to these, *d.* it *not* to. 25:45
me, this *d.* *not* Abraham. *John* 8:40
I *d.* it *not* for his cause. *2 Cor* 7:12*

did *so*
as God commanded *so* *d.* he. *Gen* 6:22
Jacob *d.* *so* and fulfilled. 29:28
youngest brother, they *d.* *so.* 42:20
Lord commanded *so* *d.* *Ex* 7:6, 10
12:28, 50; 39:32; 40:16; *Num* 1:54
magicians *d.* *so.* *Ex* 7:22; 8:7, 18
Lord *d.* *so.* 8:24
Moses *d.* *so.* 17:6
Joshua *d.* *so.* 10
Aaron *d.* *so.* *Num* 8:3
so *d.* the daughters of. 36:10
city, *so* they *d.* six days. *Josh* 6:14
so *d.* Moses command, and *so* *d.* 11:15
they *d.* not *so.* *Judg* 2:17
God *d.* *so* that night. 6:40
as he *d.* *so* year by year. *1 Sam* 1:7
so they *d.* in Shiloh to all. 2:14
so *d.* David, and so will be. 27:11
so *d.* he in Beth-el. *1 Ki* 12:32
Jeroboam's wife *d.* *so,* and. 14:4
so they *d.* *Ezra* 6:13
but *so* *d.* not I. *Neh* 5:15
Isaiah *d.* *so,* walking naked. *Isa* 20:2
Jeremiah *d.* *so.* *Jer* 38:12
and I *d.* *so.* *Ezek* 12:7
Jesus arose, and *so* *d.* *Mat* 9:19
his hand, and he *d.* *so.* *Luke* 6:10
so *d.* their fathers to false. 26
followed Jesus and *so* *d.* *John* 18:15
sons of Sceva who *d.* *so.* *Acts* 19:14

thus **did**
fill their sacks, *thus* *d.* *Gen* 42:25
thus *d.* he to both of. *Ex* 36:29
thus *d.* Moses, according as. 40:16
thus *d.* your fathers. *Num* 32:8
thus *d.* he to all cities. *2 Sam* 12:31
thus *d.* Urijah the priest. *2 Ki* 16:16
thus they *d.* day by day. *2 Chr* 24:11
thus *d.* Hezekiah throughout. 31:20
d. not your fathers *thus.* *Neh* 13:18
sanctified them, *thus* *d.* *Job* 1:5

didst
d. this in integrity of. *Gen* 20:6
do as thou *d.* to Sihon. *Num* 21:34
Deut 3:2
as thou *d.* to Jericho. *Josh* 8:2
thou *d.* it secretly. *2 Sam* 12:12
than other that thou *d.* to. 13:16
that thou *d.* to David. *1 Ki* 2:44
d. well that it was in thy. 8:18
2 Chr 6:8
thy wonders that thou *d.* *Neh* 9:17
dumb, because thou *d.* it. *Ps* 39:9
told us what work thou *d.* 44:1
when *d.* terrible things. *Isa* 64:3
thou kill me as thou *d.*? *Acts* 7:28*

Didymus
Thomas, who is called *D.* *John* 11:16
20:24; 21:2

die
see **dead** and **death**
every thing in earth shall *d.* *Gen* 6:17
overdrive them, flock will *d.* 33:13
let him *d.* 44:9
his father would *d.* 22
now let me *d.* 46:30
that Israel must *d.* 47:29
fish in the river shall *d.* *Ex* 7:18
nothing shall *d.* that is the. 9:4
thou seest my face shalt *d.* 10:28
firstborn in land of Egypt shall *d.* 11:5
that they bear not iniquity and *d.* 28:43; *Lev* 22:9
beast which ye may eat *d.* *Lev* 11:39
sin, they shall *d.* childless. 20:20
holy thing, lest they *d.* *Num* 4:15
things covered, lest they *d.* 20
if any man *d.* very suddenly. 6:9
and there they shall *d.* 14:35
if these *d.* the common death. 16:29
near tabernacle *d.* 17:13; 18:22
neither they, nor you also *d.* 18:3*
Aaron, shall *d.* on mount Hor. 20:26
let me *d.* death of righteous. 23:10
speak, saying, if a man *d.* 27:8
shalt stone them that they *d.* *Deut* 17:5; 22:21, 24
that men shall *d.* 17:12
prophet shall *d.* 18:20
both shall *d.* 22:22
the man only shall *d.* 25
if the latter husband *d.* 24:3
that thief shall *d.* 7
one *d.* and have no children. 25:5
Mark 12:19
to Moses, thy days approach that thou *d.* *Deut* 31:14
land of Canaan, and *d.* 32:50
me *d.* with Philistines. *Judg* 16:30
increase of house shall *d.* *1 Sam* 2:33
in one day they shall *d.* both. 34
said, shall Jonathan *d.*? 14:45
nor if half of us *d.* *2 Sam* 18:3
enter city, child shall *d.* *1 Ki* 14:12
shalt *d.* and not live. *2 Ki* 20:1
Isa 38:1
fathers not *d.* for children, man shall *d.* *2 Chr* 25:4; *Jer* 31:30
wife said, curse God and *d.* *Job* 2:9
excellency goeth away, they *d.* 4:21
wisdom shall *d.* with you. 12:2
though the stock thereof *d.* 14:8
if a man *d.* shall he live again ? 14
in a moment shall they *d.* 34:20
if obey not, they shall *d.* 36:12
they *d.* in youth, their life is. 14
seeth that wise men *d.* *Ps* 49:10
away their breath, they *d.* 104:29
fools *d.* for want of. *Pr* 10:21
shouldest thou *d.* before ? *Eccl* 7:17
living know they shall *d.* but. 9:5
country, there thou shalt *d.* *Isa* 22:18
that dwell therein shall *d.* 51:6
be afraid of a man that shall *d.* 12
for child shall *d.* a hundred. 65:20
young men shall *d.* by sword, their sons and daughters *d.* *Jer* 11:22
shall *d.* of grievous deaths. 16:4
both great and small shall *d.* 6
this year thou shalt *d.* 28:16
but thou shalt *d.* in peace. 34:5
the soul that sinneth, it shall *d.* *Ezek* 18:4, 20
thou shalt *d.* deaths of them. 28:8
thou shalt *d.* the deaths of the. 10
that wicked man shall *d.* in. 33:8
they in the caves shall *d.* 27
Moab shall *d.* with. *Amos* 2:2
men in one house they shall *d.* 6:9
Jeroboam shall *d.* by sword. 7:11
shalt *d.* in a polluted land. 17
sinners of my people shall *d.* 9:10
that that dieth, let it *d.* *Zech* 11:9
two parts shall be cut off and *d.* 13:8
he that curseth father or mother, le[t] him *d.* *Mat* 15:4; *Mark* 7:1
man *d.* having no seed. *Mat* 22:2
Luke 20:2
nor can they *d.* any. *Luke* 20:3
down ere my child *d.* *John* 4:4
one man *d.* for people. 11:50; 18:1
prophesied that Jesus should *d.* 11:5
corn of wheat *d.* but if it *d.* it. 12:2
righteous man will one *d.* *Rom* 5:
for as in Adam all *d.* *1 Cor* 15:2
sowest not quickened except it *d.* 3
here men that *d.* receive. *Heb* 7:
blessed are dead that *d.* *Rev* 14:1

he **die**
for he said, lest *he* *d.* as. *Gen* 38:1
lad is not with us, *he* will *d.* 44:3
a man, so that *he* *d.* *Ex* 21:1
take him from altar, that *he* *d.*
smite his servant, and *he* *d.*
found and smitten that *he* *d.* 22
smite him so that *he* *d.* *Num* 35:
20, 21, 23; *Deut* 13:10; 19:5,
21:
wherewith *he* may *d.* *Num* 35:
18:23; *Deut* 19:
return, lest *he* *d.* in battle. *Deut* 20:5, 6
bring thy son that *he* *d.* *Judg* 6:
from him that *he* *d.* *2 Sam* 11:
if wickedness be in him, *he* shall
1 Ki 1:
of David drew nigh that *he* *d.*
Elijah requested that *he* might *d.* 1

stone him that *he* may *d.* *1 Ki* 21:10
when shall *he d.* and? *Ps* 41:5
he shall *d.* without instruction. *Pr* 5:23
he that hateth reproof *d.* 15:10
he that despiseth ways shall *d.* 19:16
he shall *d.* whither they. *Jer* 22:12
out of dungeon before he *d.* 38:10
wicked, *he* shall *d.* in his. *Ezek* 3:19
20; 18:18, 24, 26; 33:9, 13, 18
not see it, though *he* shall *d.* 12:13
in Babylon *he* shall *d.* 17:16
what death *he* should *d.* *John* 12:33
18:32

I **die**

evil take me, and *I d.* *Gen* 19:19
I said, lest *I d.* for her. 26:9
soul may bless thee before *I d.* 27:4
give me children, or else *I d.* 30:1
go and see him before *I d.* 45:28
said to Joseph, behold, *I d.* 48:21
lo, *I d.* there bury me. 50:5
Joseph said to his brethren, *I d.* 24
I must *d.* in this land. *Deut* 4:22
now shall *I d.* for thirst. *Judg* 15:18
where thou diest will *I d.* *Ruth* 1:17
but taste, and *I* must *d.* *1 Sam* 14:43
that *I* may *d.* in mine. *2 Sam* 19:37
nay, but *I* will *d.* here. *1 Ki* 2:30
till *I d.* I will not remove. *Job* 27:5
then I said, *I* shall *d.* in my. 29:18
deny me them not before *I d.* *Pr* 30:7
to return, lest *I d.* there. *Jer* 37:20
though *I* should *d.* with. *Mat* 26:35
Mark 14:31
by your rejoicing, *I d.* *1 Cor* 15:31

not **die**

may live and *not d.* *Gen* 42:2; 43:8
47:19
be verified, ye shall *not d.* 42:20
and he *d. not,* but. *Ex* 21:18
sound heard, that he *d. not.* 28:35
that they *d. not.* 30:20, 21
charge of the Lord that ye *d. not.* *Lev* 8:35
they *d. not.* 15:31; *Num* 4:19; 17:10
at all times, that he *d. not.* *Lev* 16:2
cloud cover mercy-seat, he *d. not.* 13
the manslayer *d. not.* *Num* 35:12
Josh 20:9
this fire, that I *d. not.* *Deut* 18:16
let Reuben live and *not d.* 33:6
fear not, thou shalt *not d.* *Judg* 6:23
1 Sam 20:2; *2 Sam* 12:13; 19:23
Jer 38:24
for us, that we *d. not.* *1 Sam* 12:19
kindness of Lord that I *d. not.* 20:14
ye may live and *not d.* *2 Ki* 18:32
fathers shall *not d.* for. *2 Chr* 25:4
I shall *not d.* but live. *Ps* 118:17
with rod, he shall *not d.* *Pr* 23:13
Ezek 18:17, 21, 28; 33:15
John 21:23
that he should *not d.* *Isa* 51:14
their worm shall *not d.* nor. 66:24
d. not by our hand. *Jer* 11:21
Zedekiah, thou shalt *not d.* by. 34:4
souls that should *not d.* *Ezek* 13:19
we shall *not d.* Lord. *Hab* 1:12
eat thereof, and *not d.* *John* 6:50
hat disciple should *not d.* 21:23

surely **die**

halt *surely d.* *Gen* 2:17; 20:7
1 Sam 14:44; 22:16; *1 Ki* 2:37, 42
Jer 26:8; *Ezek* 3:18; 33:8, 14
e shall not *surely d.* *Gen* 3:4
hey shall *surely d.* *Num* 26:65
ve shall *surely d.* *Judg* 13:22
ny son, he shall *surely d.*
1 Sam 14:39; 20:31; *2 Sam* 12:5
2 Ki 8:10; *Ezek* 18:13
hild born to thee shall *surely d.*
2 Sam 12:14
halt not come down, but shalt *surely d.* *2 Ki* 1:4, 6, 16

to **die**

am at the point *to d.* *Gen* 25:32
d. in the wilderness. *Ex* 14:11
Num 21:5
ny, to cause him *to d.* *Num* 35:30
s day shall come *to d.* *1 Sam* 26:10
are worthy *to d.* because. 16
y life, to cause me *to d.* 28:9
to give yourselves *to d.* *2 Chr* 32:11
that are appointed *to d.* *Ps* 79:11
afflicted and ready *to d.* 88:15
to be born, a time *to d.* *Eccl* 3:2
is worthy *to d.* *Jer* 26:11
not worthy *to d.* 16
he is like to *d.* for hunger. 38:9
return to Jonathan's house *to d.* 26
better for me *to d.* *Jonah* 4:3, 8
wished in himself *to d.* 8
servant ready *to d.* *Luke* 7:2
by our law he ought *to d.* *John* 19:7
I am ready also *to d.* *Acts* 21:13
I refuse not *to d.*: but if. 25:11
Romans to deliver any *to d.* 16
would even dare *to d.* *Rom* 5:7
better for me *to d.* than. *1 Cor* 9:15
are in our hearts *to d.* *2 Cor* 7:3
live is Christ, and *to d.* is. *Phil* 1:21
to men once *to d.* *Heb* 9:27
that are ready *to d.* *Rev* 3:2
desire *to d.* and death shall. 9:6

we **die**

why should *we d.*? *Gen* 47:15
than that *we* should *d.* *Ex* 14:12
let not God speak, lest *we d.* 20:19
Deut 5:25
we d. we perish, we all. *Num* 17:12
we and out cattle should *d.* 20:4
pray, that *we d.* not. *1 Sam* 12:19
for *we* must needs *d.* *2 Sam* 14:14
we may eat it and *d.* *1 Ki* 17:12
sit we here till *we d.*? *2 Ki* 7:3, 4
if they kill us, *we* shall but *d.* 4
to-morrow *we* shall *d.* *Isa* 22:13
1 Cor 15:32
let us go that *we* may *d.* *John* 11:16
whether *we d. we d.* *Rom* 14:8

ye **die**

neither touch it, lest *ye d.* *Gen* 3:3
rend clothes, lest *ye d.* *Lev* 10:6*
go out from door, lest *ye d.* 7
nor pollute, lest *ye d.* *Num* 18:32
but *ye* shall *d.* like men. *Ps* 82:7
not be purged till *ye d.* *Isa* 22:14
there shall *ye d.* *Jer* 22:26; 42:16
for why will *ye d.*? 27:13
Ezek 18:31; 33:11
know that *ye* shall *d.* *Jer* 42:22
ye shall *d.* in sins. *John* 8:21, 24
after the flesh *ye* shall *d.* *Rom* 8:13

died

all flesh *d.* *Gen* 7:21, 22
and Haran *d.* 11:28
Terah *d.* 32
Sarah *d.* 23:2
Abraham *d.* 25:8
Ishmael d. 17
Deborah the nurse *d.* 35:8
Rachel *d.* 18, 19; 48:7
Isaac *d.* 35:29
Belah *d.* 36:33
Jobab *d.* 34
Husham *d.* 35
Hadad *d.* 36; *1 Chr* 1:51
Samlah *d.* *Gen* 36:37
Saul *d.* 38
Baal-hanan son of Achbor *d.* 39
Judah's wife *d.* 38:12
Er and Onan *d.* in Canaan. 46:12
Jacob *d.* 50:16
Joseph *d.* 26; *Ex* 1:6
the king of Egypt *d.* *Ex* 2:23
the fish *d.* 7:21
the frogs *d.* 8:13
the cattle of Egypt *d.* 9:6
would to God we had *d.* in Egypt. 16:3
Num 14:2; 20:3; 26:10
Nadab and Abihu *d.* *Lev* 10:2; 16:1
Num 3:4; 26:61; *1 Chr* 24:2
searchers of the land *d.* *Num* 14:37
Aaron *d.* 20:28; 33:38, 39
Deut 10:6; 32:50
they that *d.* beside them that *d.* about matter of Korah. *Num* 16:49
Miriam *d.* 20:1
much people of Israel *d.* 21:6
those that *d.* in plague were. 25:9
the children of Korah *d.* not. 26:11
Zelophehad our father, *d.* in the wilderness, but *d.* in his own sin. 27:3
Moses *d.* *Deut* 34:5
he was 120 years when he *d.* 7
even all men of war *d.* *Josh* 5:4
which *d.* with hailstones. 10:11
Joshua the son of Nun *d.* 24:29
Judg 2:8
Eleazar the son of Aaron *d.*
Josh 24:33; *1 Chr* 23:22
Adonibezek *d.* *Judg* 1:7
Othniel *d.* 3:11
Gibeon *d.* 8:32
men of tower of Shechem *d.* 9:49
Tola *d.* 10:2
Jair *d.* 5
judged Israel six years, then *d.* 12:7
Ibzan *d.* 10
Elon *d.* 12
Abdon *d.* 15
Elimelech *d.* *Ruth* 1:3
Mahlon, Chilion *d.* 5
that *d.* not were smitten. *1 Sam* 5:12
Samuel *d.* 25:1
Nabal's heart *d.* within him. 37
Saul was dead, armour-bearer . . . and *d.* 31:5, 6; *1 Chr* 10:5, 13
Asahel *d.* *2 Sam* 2:23
d. Abner as a fool. 3:33
he *d.* before Lord. 6:7; *1 Chr* 13:10
king of Ammon *d.* *2 Sam* 10:1
1 Chr 19:1
Shobach *d.* *2 Sam* 10:18
Uriah the Hittite *d.* 11:17
on seventh day child *d.* 12:18
Ahithophel hanged himself *d.* 17:23
would God I had *d.* for thee. 18:33
and all we had *d.* this day. 19:6
d. of people, even from Dan. 24:15
this woman's child *d.* *1 Ki* 3:19
came to threshold child *d.* 14:17
Zimri *d.* 16:18
Tibni *d.* 22
Ahab *d.* 22:35, 37
till noon and then *d.* *2 Ki* 4:20
fled to Megiddo and *d.* there. 9:27
Elisha *d.* 13:14, 20
Hazael king of Syria *d.* 24
came to Egypt and *d.* there. 23:34
but Seled *d.* without. *1 Chr* 2:30
and Jether *d.* 32
Asa *d.* *2 Chr* 16:13
Jehoiada full of days *d.* 24:15
when he *d.* he said. 22
why *d.* I not from womb? *Job* 3:11
so Job *d.* being old and. 42:17
year that king Uzziah *d.* *Isa* 6:1
year that king Ahaz *d.* 14:28
Hananiah *d.* *Jer* 28:17
Pelatiah *d.* *Ezek* 11:13
at even my wife *d.* 24:18
he offended in Baal, he *d.* *Hos* 13:1
last of all the woman *d.* *Mat* 22:27
Mark 12:22; *Luke* 20:32
d. rich man also *d.* *Luke* 16:22
my brother not *d.* *John* 11:21, 32
this man should not have *d.* 37
Dorcas was sick and *d.* *Acts* 9:37
in due time Christ *d.* *Rom* 5:6, 8
sin revived and I *d.* 7:9
it is Christ that *d.* 8:34
to this end Christ both *d.* rose. 14:9
destroy not him with thy meat for whom Christ *d.* 15; *1 Cor* 8:11
how that Christ *d.* *1 Cor* 15:3
if one *d.* for all, then. *2 Cor* 5:14
should live to him who *d.* for. 15
we believe that Jesus *d.* *1 Thes* 4:14
who *d.* for us that we should. 5:10
despised Moses' law *d.* *Heb* 10:28
these *d.* in faith, not having. 11:13
by faith Joseph when he *d.* 22
third part of creatures *d.* *Rev* 8:9
many men *d.* of waters that. 11
every living soul *d.* in the sea. 16:3

and he, so he, that he **died**

Adam 930 years *and he d.* *Gen* 5:5
Noah's days 950 years, *and he d.* 9:29
into his temple, *so he d.* *Judg* 4:21
Eli's neck brake *and he d.* for he. *1 Sam* 4:18
Jonathan *that he d.* not. 14:45
Lord smote Nabal *that he d.* 25:38
Abimelech *that he d.* *2 Sam* 11:21
stoned Adoram *that he d.*
1 Ki 12:18; *2 Chr* 10:18

so he d. according to the. *2 Ki* 1:17
him in the gate *and he d.* 7:17, 20
cloth on his face, *so that he d.* 8:15
Jeroboam *and he d.* *2 Chr* 13:20
bowels fell out, *so he d.* 21:19
and he d. without. *Luke* 20:29, 30
Jacob *d.* in Egypt, *he and. Acts* 7:15
in *that he d. he d.* unto. *Rom* 6:10
that he d. for all. *2 Cor* 5:15

diest

where thou *d.* will I die. *Ruth* 1:17

diet

for his *d.* there was a continual *d.* given him. *Jer* 52:34*

dieth

fat of beast that *d.* of. *Lev* 7:24
d. of itself not eat. 22:8; *Deut* 14:21
when a man *d.* in a tent. *Num* 19:14
died Abner as a fool *d.*? *2 Sam* 3:33
him that *d.* in the city. *1 Ki* 14:11
d. in field fowls of air. 16:4; 21:24
man *d.* and wasteth. *Job* 14:10
one *d.* in his full strength. 21:23
another *d.* in the bitterness. 25
when he *d.* he shall carry. *Ps* 49:17
when a wicked man *d.* *Pr* 11:7
how *d.* the wise man? *Eccl* 2:16
as the one *d.* so *d.* the other. 3:19
their fish stinketh and *d.* *Isa* 50:2
he that eateth of their eggs *d.* 59:5
nor eaten that which *d.* *Ezek* 4:14
committeth iniquity, and *d.* 18:26
in the death of him that *d.* 32
that that *d.* let it die. *Zech* 11:9
worm *d.* not. *Mark* 9:44, 46, 48
raised from dead *d.* no. *Rom* 6:9
and no man *d.* to himself. 14:7

differ

who maketh thee *to d.*? *1 Cor* 4:7

difference

Lord put a *d.* between. *Ex* 11:7
put a *d.* between holy. *Lev* 10:10
to make a *d.* between unclean. 11:47
d. between clean beasts and. 20:25*
no *d.* they shewed no *d. Ezek* 22:26*
shall teach my people the *d.* 44:23
and put no *d.* between. *Acts* 15:9*
for there is no *d.* *Rom* 3:22*
is no *d.* between Jew and. 10:12*
is *d.* between a wife and. *1 Cor* 7:34
compassion making a *d.* *Jude* 22*

differences

d. of administration. *1 Cor* 12:5*

differeth

star *d.* from another in. *1 Cor* 15:41
heir when a child *d.* *Gal* 4:1

differing

gifts *d.* according to the grace. *Rom* 12:6

dig

if a man *d.* a pit, and not. *Ex* 21:33
of whose hills mayest *d.* *Deut* 8:9
shalt have a paddle, and *d.* 23:13
d. for it more than for. *Job* 3:21
ye *d.* a pit for your friend. 6:27*
thou shalt *d.* about thee. 11:18*
in the dark they *d.* 24:16
son of man, *d.* now in. *Ezek* 8:8
d. thou through the wall. 12:5, 12
though they *d.* in hell. *Amos* 9:2
let it alone, till I shall *d. Luke* 13:8
cannot *d.* to beg I am ashamed. 16:3

digged

a witness that I have *d.* *Gen* 21:30
wells his father's servants had *d.* 26:15, 18
Isaac's servants *d.* in. 19, 21, 22, 25
told Isaac of well they had *d.* 32
in their self-will they *d.* 49:6*
my grave which I had *d.* 50:5
Egyptians *d.* for water to. *Ex* 7:24
princes *d.* the well, nobles *d.* it. *Num* 21:18*
wells *d.* thou. *Deut* 6:11*; *Neh* 9:25*
I have *d.* and drunk strange waters, and dried. *2 Ki* 19:24; *Isa* 37:25
Uzziah *d.* many wells. *2 Chr* 26:10*
made a pit and *d.* it. *Ps* 7:15; 57:6
without cause they *d.* a pit. 35:7
till pit be *d.* for the wicked. 94:13
proud have *d.* pits for me. 119:85
shall not be pruned nor *d.* *Isa* 5:6*
all hills be *d.* with the mattock. 7:25
to the pit whence ye are *d.* 51:1
I went to Euphrates and *d. Jer* 13:7
have *d.* a pit for my soul. 18:20, 22
when I had *d.* in the wall. *Ezek* 8:8
hedged it, and *d.* a. *Mat* 21:33
d. in the earth, and hid. 25:18
who *d.* and laid the. *Luke* 6:48
Lord, they have *d.* down. *Rom* 11:3

diggedst

wells digged which thou *d.* not. *Deut* 6:11*

diggeth

an ungodly man *d.* up. *Pr* 16:27*
whoso *d.* pit fall. 26:27; *Eccl* 10:8

dignity

thou art excellency of *d.* *Gen* 49:3
what *d.* hath been done? *Esth* 6:3
folly is set in great *d.* *Eccl* 10:6
d. shall proceed of. *Hab* 1:7

dignities

speak evil of *d.* *2 Pet* 2:10; *Jude* 8

diligence

keep thy heart with all *d.* *Pr* 4:23
give *d.* that thou mayest. *Luke* 12:58
that ruleth with *d.* *Rom* 12:8
abound in faith and *d.* *2 Cor* 8:7*
do thy *d.* to come. *2 Tim* 4:9, 21
one of you shew same *d.* *Heb* 6:11
giving all *d.* to add to. *2 Pet* 1:5
brethren, give *d.* to make your. 10
when I gave all *d.* to write. *Jude* 3

diligent

judges shall make *d.* *Deut* 19:18
take *d.* heed to do the. *Josh* 22:5
accomplish a *d.* search. *Ps* 64:6
and spirit made *d.* search. 77:6
but the hand of the *d.* *Pr* 10:4
the hand of the *d.* bear rule. 12:24
but the substance of a *d.* man. 27
but the soul of the *d.* shall. 13:4
the thoughts of *d.* tend. 21:5
seest thou a man *d.* in his? 22:29
be thou *d.* to know state of. 27:23
proved *d.* but now much more *d.* *2 Cor* 8:22*
be *d.* to come unto me. *Tit* 3:12
be *d.* that ye be found. *2 Pet* 3:14

diligently

if thou wilt *d.* hearken to. *Ex* 15:26
Deut 11:13; 28:1; *Jer* 17:24
Moses *d.* sought the goat. *Lev* 10:16
heed and keep soul *d.* *Deut* 4:9
thou shalt teach them *d.* to. 6:7
d. keep commandments. 17; 11:22
make search, and ask *d.* 13:14
heed that thou observe *d.* 24:8
now the men did *d.* *1 Ki* 20:33
let it be *d.* done for. *Ezra* 7:23*
hear *d.* my speech. *Job* 13:17; 21:2
shalt *d.* consider his place. *Ps* 37:10
us to keep thy precepts *d.* 119:4
I came forth *d.* to. *Pr* 7:15
he that *d.* seeketh good. 11:27
consider *d.* what is before thee. 23:1
he hearkened *d.* with. *Isa* 21:7
hearken *d.* to me, and eat. 55:2
consider *d.* see if there. *Jer* 2:10
if they will *d.* learn the ways. 12:16
if ye will *d.* obey the. *Zech* 6:15
he inquired *d.* when. *Mat* 2:7*
Herod said, go and search *d.* 8
which he had *d.* inquired. 16*
sweep house and seek *d. Luke* 15:8
taught *d.* the things of. *Acts* 18:25
if she have *d.* followed. *1 Tim* 5:10
in Rome he sought me *d. 2 Tim* 1:17
bring Zenas and Apollos on their journey *d.* *Tit* 3:13
rewarder of them that *d.* *Heb* 11:6
looking *d.* lest any man fail. 12:15*
the prophets searched *d. 1 Pet* 1:10

dim

Isaac was old, his eyes *d. Gen* 27:1
the eyes of Israel were *d.* 48:10
Moses' eye was not *d.* *Deut* 34:7
Eli's eyes began to wax *d.* *1 Sam* 3:2; 4:15*
mine eye also is *d.* by. *Job* 17:7
eyes of them that see not be *d.* *Isa* 32:3
how is gold become *d.*! *Lam* 4:1
for these things our eyes are *d.* 5:17

diminish, -ed

you shall not *d.* ought. *Ex* 5:8
not ought of your work be *d.* 11, 19
duty of marriage not *d.* 21:10
to the years thou *d.* *Lev* 25:16
nor shall you *d.* *Deut* 4:2; 12:32
gotten by vanity be *d.* *Pr* 13:11
men of Kedar shall be *d. Isa* 21:17*
speak, *d.* not a word. *Jer* 26:2
may be increased and not *d.* 29:6
will I also *d.* thee. *Ezek* 5:11
behold, I have *d.* thine. 16:27
I will *d.* them, they shall. 29:15

diminishing

d. of them be riches. *Rom* 11:12*

dimness

behold trouble darkness *d. Isa* 8:22*
d. shall not be such as was. 9:1*

Dimon

waters of *D.* shall be full of blood, for I will bring more upon *D. Isa* 15:9

Dinah

bare daughter called *D.* *Gen* 30:21
Jacob heard he had defiled *D.* 34:5

dine, -d

these men shall *d.* *Gen* 43:16
Pharisee besought him to *d.* *Luke* 11:37
come and *d.* *John* 21:12*
so when they had *d.* Jesus. 15*

dinner

better is a *d.* of herbs. *Pr* 15:7
I have prepared my *d.* *Mat* 22:4
first washed before *d.* *Luke* 11:38
when makest a *d.* or supper. 14:12

Dionysius

among which was *D.* *Acts* 17:34

Diotrephes

D. who loveth to have pre-eminence. *3 John* 9

dip

d. it in the blood that is. *Ex* 12:22
priest shall *d.* finger. *Lev* 4:6; 17:14 16
d. the cedar wood and. 14:6, 51
clean person should *d.* *Num* 19:18
let Asher *d.* his foot in. *Deut* 33:24
Boaz said to Ruth, *d.* *Ruth* 2:14
Lazarus that he may *d.* *Luke* 16:24

dipped, -eth

d. the coat in blood. *Gen* 37:31
Aaron *d.* his finger in the. *Lev* 9:9
the priests' feet were *d. Josh* 3:15
he *d.* end of rod in an. *1 Sam* 14:27
Naaman *d.* in Jordan. *2 Ki* 5:14
Hazael took a cloth and *d.* it. 8:15
that thy foot be *d.* in. *Ps* 68:23
he that *d.* his hand with me in the. *Mat* 26:23; *Mark* 14:20
I give a sop, when I have *d.*; *d.* the sop, gave it to Judas. *John* 13:26
with a vesture *d.* in blood. *Rev* 19:13

direct

he sent Judah to *d.* his. *Gen* 46:28*
in the morning will I *d.* *Ps* 5:3*
he shall *d.* thy paths. *Pr* 3:6
righteousness of perfect shall *d.* 11:5
wisdom is profitable to *d. Eccl* 10:10
raised him up, I will *d.* *Isa* 45:13*
I will *d.* their way in truth. 61:8*
man that walketh to *d.* *Jer* 10:23
Lord Jesus Christ *d.* *1 Thes* 3:11
Lord *d.* your hearts into. *2 Thes* 3:5

directed

he hath not *d.* his words. *Job* 32:14
that my ways were *d.* to. *Ps* 119:5*
who hath *d.* the Spirit? *Isa* 40:13

directeth

he *d.* it under the heaven. *Job* 37:3*
ways, but the Lord *d.* his. *Pr* 16:9
as for upright he *d.* his way. 21:29*

direction

princes judged it by *d.* *Num* 21:18*

directly

sprinkle blood *d.* before. *Num* 19:4*
even the way *d.* before. *Ezek* 42:12

dirt
fat closed, and *d.* came. *Judg* 3:22
cast them out as *d.* in. *Ps* 18:42*
waters cast up mire and *d. Isa* 57:20

disallow, -ed
because her father *d.* *Num* 30:5
but if her husband *d.* her. 8
he *d.* her not. 11
d. indeed of men, but. *1 Pet* 2:4*
stone which the builders *d.* is. 7*

disannul
wilt thou also *d.* my? *Job* 40:8†
purposed who shall *d.* it? *Isa* 14:27†
covenant law cannot *d.* *Gal* 3:17

disannulled
with death shall be *d.* *Isa* 28:18†

disannulleth
covenant no man *d.* or. *Gal* 3:15*

disannulling
there is a *d.* of the. *Heb* 7:18

disappoint
arise, O Lord, *d.* him. *Ps* 17:13*

disappointed
without counsel purposes *d. Pr* 15:22

disappointeth
he *d.* devices of crafty. *Job* 5:12*

discern
[1] *To see and identify by noting differences,* Gen 31:32. [2] *To see by the eye or the understanding,* 2 Sam 14:17; Heb 5:14.
d. thou what is thine. *Gen* 31:32
d. I pray thee, whose are. 38:25
so is my lord to *d.* *2 Sam* 14:17
can I *d.* between good and? 19:35
I may *d.* between good. *1 Ki* 3:9
hast asked understanding to *d.* 11
people could not *d.* the. *Ezra* 3:13
but I could not *d.* the. *Job* 4:16
my taste *d.* perverse things? 6:30
d. between unclean and. *Ezek* 44:23
d. between right hand. *Jonah* 4:11
d. between the righteous. *Mal* 3:18
d. the face of the sky. *Mat* 16:3
Luke 12:56
senses exercised to *d.* *Heb* 5:14

discerned, -eth
d. him not, his hands. *Gen* 27:23
king of Israel *d.* him. *1 Ki* 20:41
I *d.* among the youth a. *Pr* 7:7
a wise man *d.* time and. *Eccl* 8:5
they are spiritually *d.* *1 Cor* 2:14

discerner
word is a *d.* of thoughts. *Heb* 4:12

discerning
unworthily, not *d.* *1 Cor* 11:29
another is given *d.* of spirits. 12:10

discharge, -d
will cause them to be *d.* *1 Ki* 5:9*
there is no *d.* in that war. *Eccl* 8:8

disciple
Literally, a scholar, a learner; especially one who believes in the doctrine of his teacher and follows him. In the New Testament the followers of John the Baptist were called his disciples, Mark 2:18; John 3:25. *Also the followers of Moses, in distinction from the followers of John or Jesus,* Mark 2:18; John 9:28. *But most often the word is used with reference to the believers in Christ, both those who believed during his life, and those who later joined the early Church,* Matt 27:57; John 19:38; Acts 9:36. *The twelve Apostles, also, are frequently called by this name,* Mat. 10:1; John 20:2.
d. not above master. *Mat* 10:24
Luke 6:40
it is enough for the *d.* *Mat* 10:25
give a cup of cold water to a *d.* 42
of Arimathaea was Jesus' *d.* 27:57
thou art his *d.* we are. *John* 9:28
so did another *d.* that *d.* was. 18:15
then went out that other *d.* that. 16
the *d.* standing by, whom. 19:26
to that *d.* behold thy mother, and from that hour that *d.* took. *John* 19:27
being a *d.* but secretly, for fear. 38
other *d.* Jesus loved. 20:2; 21:7, 20
went forth, and that other *d.* 20:3
the other *d.* did outrun Peter. 4
went in also that other *d.* and. 8
saying, that that *d.* should. 21:23
this is the *d.* that testifieth these. 24
there was a certain *d.* at. *Acts* 9:10
believed not that he was a *d.* 26
at Joppa a *d.* named Tabitha. 36
a certain *d.* was there. 16:1
an old *d.* with whom we. 21:16

my **disciple**
not life, cannot be *my d. Luke* 14:26
bear his cross, cannot be *my d.* 27
forsaketh not all, cannot be my *d.* 33

disciples
then came the *d.* of John. *Mat* 9:14
unto him his twelve *d.* 10:1
an end of commanding his *d.* 11:1
when the *d.* saw him walking. 14:26
when the *d.* heard it they. 17:6
the *d.* rebuked them. 19:13
Mark 10:13
Jesus took the twelve *d. Mat* 20:17
Jesus sent two *d.* saying, go. 21:1
sent unto him their *d.* 22:16
bread, and gave it to the *d.* 26:26
not deny thee, likewise said the *d.* 35
then all the *d.* forsook him. 56
do *d.* of John and of Pharisees fast, thy *d.*? *Mark* 2:18; *Luke* 5:33
now *d.* had forgotten to. *Mark* 8:14
the *d.* began to rejoice. *Luke* 19:37
between John's *d.* and. *John* 3:25
that Jesus baptized more *d.* 4:1
but we are Moses' *d.* 9:28
he began to wash the *d'.* feet. 13:5
also one of this man's *d.*? 18:17
Mary told *d.* that she had. 20:18
out slaughter against *d.* *Acts* 9:1
Saul essayed to join himself to *d.* 26
the *d.* were called Christians. 11:26
and finding certain *d.* 19:1
Paul would have entered, *d.* 30
first day of week *d.* came. 20:7
to draw away *d.* after them. 30

his **disciples**
his d. came and awoke. *Mat* 8:25
and followed, and so did *his d.* 9:19
and tell *his d.* he is risen. 28:7
say ye, *his d.* came by night and. 13
in house *his d.* asked. *Mark* 10:10
murmured against *his d. Luke* 5:30
he lifted up his eyes on *his d.* 6:20
teach us, as John taught *his d.* 11:1
his glory, and *his d.* *John* 2:11
Jesus baptized not, but *his d.* 4:2
upon this came *his d.* and. 27
and there he sat with *his d.* 6:3
but *his d.* were gone away alone. 22
will ye be *his d.* 9:27
said *his d.* Lord if he sleep. 11:12
he went with *his d.* over brook. 18:1
often resorted thither with *his d.* 2
again, *his d.* were within. 20:26

of his **disciples**
John sent two *of his d.* *Mat* 11:2
Mark 11:1; 14:13; *Luke* 19:29
some *of his d.* eat with. *Mark* 7:2
time many *of his d.* *John* 6:66
priest asked Jesus *of his d.* 18:19
art not thou also one *of his d.*? 25
none *of his d.* durst ask him. 21:12

to his **disciples**
gave the loaves *to his d. Mat* 14:19
all things *to his d.* *Mark* 4:34
turned *to his d.* and. *Luke* 10:23
shewed himself *to his d. John* 21:14

my **disciples**
seal law among *my d.* *Isa* 8:16
keep the passover at thy house with *my d.* *Mat* 26:18
Mark 14:14; *Luke* 22:11
then are ye *my d. John* 8:31; 13:35
so shall ye be *my d.* 15:8

thy **disciples**
we fast, *thy d.* fast not. *Mat* 9:14
Mark 2:18
thy d. do that which is not. *Mat* 12:2
why do *thy d.* trangress the? 15:2
I brought him to *thy d.* they. 17:16
why walk not *thy d.*? *Mark* 7:5
to *thy d.* to cast him out. 9:18
Luke 9:40
Master, rebuke *thy d.* *Luke* 19:39
thy d. may see works. *John* 7:3

discipline
also their ears to *d.* *Job* 36:10*

disclose
earth also shall *d.* her. *Isa* 26:21

discomfited
Joshua *d.* Amalek and. *Ex* 17:13
smote and *d.* them. *Num* 14:45
d. them before Israel. *Josh* 10:10
the Lord *d.* Sisera and. *Judg* 4:15
Gideon pursued them, and *d.* 8:12
Philistines, and *d.* them. *1 Sam* 7:10
and *d.* them. *2 Sam* 22:15; *Ps* 18:14
young men shall be *d.* *Isa* 31:8*

discomfiture
was a very great *d.* *1 Sam* 14:20

discontented
every one that was *d.* *1 Sam* 22:2

discontinue
and thou shalt *d.* from. *Jer* 17:4

discord
mischief, he soweth *d.* *Pr* 6:14
and him that soweth *d.* 19

discover
[1] *An old meaning, reveal, uncover.* [2] *To manifest, especially unintentionally,* Pr 18:2. [3] *To detect for the first time,* Acts 27:39.
a man shall not *d.* his. *Deut* 22:30
we will *d.* ourselves. *1 Sam* 14:8
who can *d.* the face? *Job* 41:13
that his heart may *d.* *Pr* 18:2
and *d.* not a secret to another. 25:9
the Lord will *d.* their. *Isa* 3:17
I will *d.* thy skirts. *Jer* 13:26
Nah 3:5
of Edom, he will *d.* thy. *Lam* 4:22
I will *d.* thy nakedness. *Ezek* 16:37
I will *d.* her lewdness. *Hos* 2:10
I will *d.* the foundations. *Mi* 1:6

discovered
thy nakedness be not *d.* *Ex* 20:26
he hath *d.* her fountain. *Lev* 20:18
both *d.* themselves. *1 Sam* 14:11
Saul heard David was *d.* 22:6
foundations of world were *d.* at the rebuking. *2 Sam* 22:16; *Ps* 18:15
he *d.* covering of Judah. *Isa* 22:8
for thou hast *d.* thyself to. 57:8
iniquity are thy skirts *d.* *Jer* 13:22
have not *d.* thine iniquity. *Lam* 2:14
foundation thereof be *d. Ezek* 13:14
thy nakedness *d.* through. 16:36
before thy wickedness was *d.* 57
your transgressions are *d.* 21:24
in thee have they *d.* their. 22:10
these *d.* nakedness, they. 23:10
she *d.* her whoredoms, *d.* her. 18
of whoredoms shall be *d.* 29
iniquity of Ephraim was *d. Hos* 7:1
when we had *d.* Cyprus. *Acts* 21:3*
but they *d.* a certain creek. 27:39*

discovereth
he *d.* deep things out of. *Job* 12:22
voice of Lord *d.* forest. *Ps* 29:9

discovering
by *d.* the foundation to. *Hab* 3:13

discourage
why *d.* ye hearts of people?
Num 32:7

discouraged
soul of people much *d.* *Num* 21:4
they *d.* the heart of children. 32:9
it, fear not, nor be *d.* *Deut* 1:21
our brethren have *d.* our heart. 28
shall not fail nor be *d.* *Isa* 42:4
children, lest they be *d.* *Col* 3:21

discreet
look out a man *d.* and. *Gen* 41:33
there is none so *d.* and wise as. 39
teach young women to be *d. Tit* 2:5*

discreetly
saw that he answered *d. Mark* 12:34

discretion
guide his affairs with d. Ps 112:5*
young man knowledge and d. Pr 1:4
d. shall preserve thee. 2:11
keep sound wisdom and d. 3:21
thou mayest regard d. and keep. 5:2
fair woman who is without d. 11:22
d. of a man deferreth his. 19:11
doth instruct him to d. Isa 28:26*
out heavens by his d. Jer 10:12*

disdained
Goliath saw David, he d. him. 1 Sam 17:42
would d. to set with dogs. Job 30:1

disease
The ancient Hebrews, who were very little versed in the study of natural philosophy, and not much accustomed to consult physicians when they were sick, imputed their diseases generally to evil spirits, or to the hand of God, generally in punishment for some sin; and king Asa is blamed for placing his confidence in physicians, when he had a very painful fit of the gout in his feet, instead of to God, 2 Chr. 16:12.

In the New Testament, the cause of many diseases is attributed to the devil, Luke 13:16. *And the various forms of insanity and allied troubles were spoken of as being possessed of a devil. There seems to have been also something beyond ordinary insanity included among these, but there is no means of telling either what it was, or what proportion of the cases might be considered as coming under it.*

The diseases of *Egypt, from which God promised to defend his people,* Ex 15:26; *and which he threatens, in case of their disobedience, to inflict upon them,* Deut 28:60; *are either the plagues with which God afflicted Egypt before the departure of the Israelites, or the diseases which were most common in the country, such as blindness, ulcers in the legs, consumptions, and the leprosy, called* Elephantiasis, *which was peculiar to this country* (Pliny).

if I shall recover of d. 2 Ki 1:2
shall I recover of this d.? 8:8, 9
Asa diseased till his d. was exceeding great, yet in his d. 2 Chr 16:12
great sickness by d. of thy. 21:15
smote him with an incurable d. 18
my d. is my garment. Job 30:18
filled with a loathsome d. Ps 38:7*
an evil d. say they, cleaveth. 41:8
vanity, and it is an evil d. Eccl. 6:2
healing all manner of d. Mat 4:23
9:35; 10:1
whole of whatsoever d. John 5:4

diseased
Asa was d. in his feet. 1 Ki 15:23
2 Chr 16:12
d. have not strengthened. Ezek 34:4
pushed the d. with your horns. 21
d. with an issue of blood. Mat 9:20
they brought all that were d. 14:35
Mark 1:32
did on them that were d. John 6:2

diseases
put none of these d. on you.
Ex 15:26; Deut 7:15
thee all the d. of Egypt. Deut 28:60
out, he died of sore d. 2 Chr 21:19
him in great d. his servants. 24:25
Lord, who healeth all thy d. Ps 103:3
people that were taken with divers d.
Mat 4:24; Mark 1:34; Luke 4:40
over devils, and cure d. Luke 9:1
d. departed from them. Acts 19:12
others which had d. in island. 28:9

disfigure
hypocrites, for they d. Mat 6:16

disgrace
do not d. the throne. Jer 14:21

disguise, -d
and Saul d. himself. 1 Sam 28:8
Jeroboam said, arise, and d.
1 Ki 14:2
sons of the prophets d. 20:38
Ahab king of Israel said, I will d. myself, and he d. 22:30; 2 Chr 18:29
Josiah d. himself to. 2 Chr 35:22

disguiseth
waiteth and d. his face. Job 24:15

dish, -es
make d. thereof. Ex 25:29; 37:16
thereon d. and spoons. Num 4:7
forth butter in a lordly d. Judg 5:25
as a man wipeth a d. 2 Ki 21:13
dippeth with me in the d. Mat 26:23
Mark 14:20

dishonest, *see* **gain**

dishonesty
hidden things of d. 2 Cor 4:2

dishonour
for us to see king's d. Ezra 4:14
clothed with shame and d. Ps 35:26
71:13
known my shame and my d. 69:19
wound and d. shall he get. Pr 6:33
to honour, another to d. Rom 9:21
sown in d. it is raised. 1 Cor 15:43
by honour and d. by. 2 Cor 6:8
to honour, some to d. 2 Tim 2:20

dishonour, -est, -eth, *verb*
for the son d. father. Mi 7:6
my Father, and ye d. me. John 8:49
to d. their own bodies. Rom 1:24
of the law, d. thou God? 2:23
man d. his head. 1 Cor 11:4
woman d. her head. 5

disinherit
will d. them, and make. Num 14:12

dismayed
nor forsake thee, fear not, nor be d.
Deut 31:8; Josh 1:9; 8:1; 10:25
1 Chr 22:13; 28:20; 2 Chr 20:15
17; 32:7
they were d. 1 Sam 17:11
2 Ki 19:26; Isa 37:27
I was bowed down, d. at. Isa 21:3
fear not, be not d. 41:10; Jer 1:17
10:2; 23:4; 30:10; 46:27
Ezek 2:6; 3:9
may be d. and behold it. Isa 41:23
wise men are d. Jer 8:9; 10:2
be d. but let not me be d. 17:18
seen them d. turned back? 46:5
Misgab is d. 48:1*
cause Elam to be d. 49:37
men of Babylon shall be d. 50:36
O Teman, shall be d. Ob 9

dismaying
Moab shall be a d. to. Jer 48:39†

dismissed
Jehoiada the priest d. not. 2 Chr 23:8
d. they came to Antioch. Acts 15:30
spoken, he d. assembly. 19:41

disobedience
by one man's d. many. Rom 5:19
to revenge all d. 2 Cor 10:6
worketh in children of d. Eph 2:2
wrath of God on children of d. 5:6
Col 3:6
d. received a just. Heb 2:2

disobedient
who was d. to the word. 1 Ki 13:26
were d. and rebelled. Neh 9:26
turn d. to the wisdom of. Luke 1:17
not d. to the heavenly. Acts 26:19
boasters d. to parents. Rom 1:30
2 Tim 3:2
forth my hands to a d. Rom 10:21
made for lawless and d. 1 Tim 1:9*
being abominable and d. Tit 1:16
we also were sometimes d. 3:3
which be d. stone which. 1 Pet 2:7*
who stumble at word, being d. 8
spirits in prison, which sometime were d. 3:20

disobeyed
hast d. mouth of Lord. 1 Ki 13:21

disorderly
warn them that are d. 1 Thes 5:14
brother who walks d. 2 Thes 3:6
we behaved not ourselves d. 7
some who walk among you d. 11

dispatch
d. them with swords. Ezek 23:47

dispensation
a d. of the gospel is. 1 Cor 9:17*
in d. of fulness of times. Eph 1:10
ye have heard of the d. of grace. 3:2
a minister according to d. Col 1:25

disperse
Saul said, d. 1 Sam 14:34
lips of wise d. knowledge. Pr 15:7
scatter them and d. Ezek 12:15
20:23; 29:12; 30:23, 26
and I will d. thee in countries. 22:15

dispersed
Rehoboam d. of all his. 2 Chr 11:23
certain people d. among. Esth 3:8
he hath d. he hath given. Ps 112:9
2 Cor 9:9
let thy fountains be d. Pr 5:16
together d. of Judah. Isa 11:12
d. through countries. Ezek 36:19
daughter of my d. shall. Zeph 3:10
to d. among Gentiles? John 7:35*
as obeyed him were d. Acts 5:37*

dispersions
days of your d. are. Jer 25:34*

displayed
banner that it may be d. Ps 60:4

displease
let it not d. my lord. Gen 31:35*
if it d. thee, I will get. Num 22:34
that thou d. not lords. 1 Sam 29:7
to Joab, let not this d. 2 Sam 11:25
Lord see it, and it d. him. Pr 24:18

displeased
he did d. the Lord. Gen 38:10*
on head of Ephraim, it d. 48:17
complained, it d. Lord. Num 11:1*
was kindled, Moses also was d. 10
but the thing d. Samuel. 1 Sam 8:6
very wroth, and the saying d. 18:8
David was d. because the Lord had.
2 Sam 6:8; 1 Chr 13:11
David had done d. Lord. 2 Sam 11:27
his father had not d. him. 1 Ki 1:6
king of Israel went to his house d.
20:43; 21:4
God was d. with this. 1 Chr 21:7
been d. O turn thyself to. Ps 60:1
d. him that there was. Isa 59:15
the king was sore d. Dan 6:14
it d. Jonah exceedingly. Jonah 4:1
was the Lord d. against? Hab 3:8
Lord hath been sore d. Zech 1:2
I am very sore d. with heathen; for I was but a little d. they helped. 15
scribes saw, were d. Mat 21:15*
Jesus saw it, he was much d.
Mark 10:14*
began to be much d. with James. 41*
d. was highly d. with. Acts 12:20

displeasure
afraid of the hot d. of. Deut 9:19
though I do them a d. Judg 15:3*
vex them in his sore d. Ps 2:5
neither chasten me in hot d. 6:1
38:1

disposed
who hath d. whole world? Job 34:13
thou know when God d.? 37:15*
when he was d. to pass. Acts 18:27*
and ye be d. to go. 1 Cor 10:27

disposing
the whole d. thereof is. Pr 16:33

disposition
received law by d. of. Acts 7:53*

dispossess, -ed
children of Machir d. Num 32:3
ye shall d. the inhabitants of. 33:5
how can I d. them? Deut 7:1
Lord God hath d. the. Judg 11:2

disputation
had no small d. Acts 15:2

disputations
but not to doubtful d. Rom 14:

dispute
there righteous might d. Job 23:7

disputed
was it that ye *d.*? *Mark* 9:33*
for they had *d.* who should be. 34
Saul *d.* against Grecians. *Acts* 9:29
Paul *d.* in synagogue with. 17:17*
Michael *d.* about body of. *Jude* 9

disputer
where is *d.* of world ? *1 Cor* 1:20

disputing
them of Asia *d.* with. *Acts* 6:9
had been much *d.* Peter rose. 15:7
d. and persuading things. 19:8*, 9*
they neither found me *d.* 24:12

disputings
things without murmurings and *d.* *Phil* 2:14†
perverse *d.* of men of. *1 Tim* 6:5*

disquiet
and *d.* inhabitants of. *Jer* 50:34

disquieted
why hast thou *d.* me ? *1 Sam* 28:15
surely they are *d.* in vain. *Ps* 39:6
O my soul, why art thou *d.* within ? 42:5, 11; 43:5
three things earth is *d.* *Pr* 30:21*

disquietness
roared by reason of *d.* *Ps* 38:8

dissembled
also stolen and *d.* also. *Josh* 7:11
for ye *d.* in your hearts. *Jer* 42:20*
other Jews *d.* likewise. *Gal* 2:13

dissemblers
nor will I go in with *d.* *Ps* 26:4

dissembleth
he that hateth *d.* with. *Pr* 26:24

dissension
Barnabas had no small *d.* *Acts* 15:2
arose a *d.* between Pharisees. 23:7
when there arose a great *d.* 10

dissimulation
let love be without *d.* *Rom* 12:9*
Barnabas carried away with their *d.* *Gal* 2:13

dissolve
that thou canst *d.* doubts. *Dan* 5:16

dissolved
and all inhabitants are *d.* *Ps* 75:3
whole Palestina are *d.* *Isa* 14:31*
earth is clean *d.* the earth. 24:19
the host of heaven be *d.* 34:4
and the palace shall be *d.* *Nah* 2:6
this tabernacle were *d.* *2 Cor* 5:1
all these things shall be *d.* *2 Pet* 3:11
heavens being on fire shall be *d.* 12

dissolvest
and thou *d.* my substance. *Job* 30:22

dissolving
d. of doubts found in. *Dan* 5:12

distaff
her hands hold the *d.* *Pr* 31:19

distant
had two tenons equally *d.* *Ex* 36:22*

distil
speech shall *d.* as dew. *Deut* 32:2
the clouds *d.* on man. *Job* 36:28*

distinction
except they give a *d.* *1 Cor* 14:7

distinctly
book of the law of God *d.* *Neh* 8:8

distracted
suffer thy terrors, I am *d.* *Ps* 88:15

distraction
attend on Lord without *d.* *1 Cor* 7:35

distress
me in day of my *d.* *Gen* 35:3
therefore is this *d.* come. 42:21
me now, when in *d.* *Judg* 11:7
me in *d.* came to David. *1 Sam* 22:2
my *d.* I called on the. *2 Sam* 22:7
Ps 18:6; 118:5; 120:1
my soul out of all *d.* *1 Ki* 1:29*
his *d.* Ahaz trespassed. *2 Chr* 28:22
said, ye see the *d.* *Neh* 2:17*
and we are in great *d.* 9:37
enlarged me when I was in *d.* *Ps* 4:1
will mock when *d.* *Pr* 1:27
strength to the needy in *d.* *Isa* 25:4
O Lord, for I am in *d.* *Lam* 1:20
proudly in day of *d.* *Ob* 12
delivered up those in day of *d.* 14
a day of trouble and *d.* *Zeph* 1:15
I will bring *d.* upon men. 17
there shall be great *d.* *Luke* 21:23
on the earth *d.* of nations. 25
d. separate us from love. *Rom* 8:35*
good for the present *d.* *1 Cor* 7:26
over you in your *d.* *1 Thes* 3:7

distress, -ed, *verb*
was greatly afraid and *d.* *Gen* 32:7
Moab was *d.* *Num* 22:3
d. not the Moabites. *Deut* 2:9*
Ammonites, *d.* them not. 19*
enemies shall *d.* 28:53†, 55†, 57†
Israel *d.* *Judg* 2:15; 10:9
for people were *d.* did. *1 Sam* 13:6
men of Israel were *d.* 14:24
Saul was *d.* 28:15
David was greatly *d.* for. 30:6
I am *d.* for thee. *2 Sam* 1:26
king of Assyria *d.* Ahaz. *2 Chr* 28:20
yet I will *d.* Ariel. *Isa* 29:2
that *d.* her shall be as a dream. 7
I will *d.* the inhabitants. *Jer* 10:18
on every side, yet not *d.* *2 Cor* 4:8*

distresses
bring thou me out of my *d.* *Ps* 25:17
delivered them out of their *d.* 107:6
saved them out of their *d.* 13, 19
bringeth them out of their *d.* 28
Noph shall have *d.* *Ezek* 30:16*
approving ourselves in *d.* *2 Cor* 6:4
I take pleasure in *d.* for. 12:10

distribute
which Moses did *d.* for. *Josh* 13:32
Kore to *d.* oblations. *2 Chr* 31:14
office was to *d.* to. *Neh* 13:13
sell all thou hast, and *d.* *Luke* 18:22
rich to be ready to *d.* *1 Tim* 6:18

distributed
Eleazar and Joshua *d.* for. *Josh* 14:1
David *d.* them, according to their. *1 Chr* 24:3*; *2 Chr* 23:18
Jesus gave thanks and *d.* *John* 6:11
but as God hath *d.* *1 Cor* 7:17
the rule God hath *d.* to. *2 Cor* 10:13

distributeth, -ing
God *d.* sorrows in his. *Job* 21:17
d. to the necessities of. *Rom* 12:13*

distribution
d. was made to every one. *Acts* 4:35
for your liberal *d.* to. *2 Cor* 9:13

ditch
shalt thou plunge me in *d.* *Job* 9:31
he is fallen into the *d.* *Ps* 7:15
a whore is a deep *d.* *Pr* 23:27
ye made a *d.* between. *Isa* 22:11*
both shall fall into *d.* *Mat* 15:14*
Luke 6:39*

ditches
this valley full of *d.* *2 Ki* 3:16*

divers, diverse
cattle gender with *d.* *Lev* 19:19
not sow vineyard with *d.* *Deut* 22:9*
not wear garment of *d.* sorts. 11*
not have in thy bag *d.* 25:13
in thy house *d.* measures. 14
of *d.* colours, a prey of *d.* *Judg* 5:30
Tamar had a garment of *d.* colours. *2 Sam* 13:18, 19
glistering stones of *d.* *1 Chr* 29:2
they laid Asa in the bed filled with odours and *d.* kinds. *2 Chr* 16:14
Jehoram slew *d.* of the princes. 21:4
d. of Asher humbled. 30:11
the vessels being *d.* one. *Esth* 1:7
their laws are *d.* from all. 3:8
he sent *d.* sorts of flies. *Ps* 78:45*
there came *d.* sorts of flies. 105:31*
d. weights and *d.* measures. *Pr* 20:10
d. weights are an abomination to. 23
there are also *d.* vanities. *Eccl* 5:7
deckest high places with *d.* colours. *Ezek* 16:16
great eagle had *d.* colours. 17:3
beasts came up, *d.* one. *Dan* 7:3
a fourth beast *d.* from all. 7, 19
d. from all kingdoms. 23
d. from the first. 24
brought to Jesus sick people with *d.*
Mat 4:24; *Mark* 1:34; *Luke* 4:40
pestilences, and earthquakes in *d.*
Mat 24:7; *Mark* 13:8; *Luke* 21:11
for *d.* of them came. *Mark* 8:3*
when *d.* were hardened. *Acts* 19:9*
to another *d.* kinds. *1 Cor* 12:10
women led away with *d.* *2 Tim* 3:6
deceived, serving *d.* lusts. *Tit* 3:3
who in *d.* manners spake. *Heb* 1:1
witness with signs and *d.* 2:4*
stood in *d.* washings. 9:10
d. and strange doctrines. 13:9
fall into *d.* temptations. *Jas* 1:2*

diversities
d. of gifts. *1 Cor* 12:4
d. of operations. 6
God hath set in church *d.* 28*

divide
and let the firmament *d.* *Gen* 1:6
be lights, to *d.* day from. 14, 18
and at night he shall *d.* 49:27
hand over sea and *d.* it. *Ex* 14:16
d. the money, *d.* the dead ox. 21:35
veil shall *d.* between holy. 26:33
but not *d.* it asunder. *Lev* 1:17; 5:8
not eat of them that *d.* hoof. 11:4, 7
Deut 14:7
and *d.* the prey into. *Num* 31:27
d. land by lot. 33:54*; 34:17, 18, 29
d. the coasts of thy land. *Deut* 19:3
d. for an inheritance. *Josh* 1:6*
13:6*, 7; 18:5
d. the spoil of your enemies. 22:8
thou and Ziba *d.* land. *2 Sam* 19:29
d. living child in two. *1 Ki* 3:25, 26
thou didst *d.* the sea. *Neh* 9:11
Ps 74:13
and thou didst *d.* them into. *Neh* 9:22*
innocent shall *d.* silver. *Job* 27:17
and *d.* their tongues. *Ps* 55:9
than to *d.* the spoil. *Pr* 16:19
as men rejoice when they *d.* *Isa* 9:3
he shall *d.* the spoil with. 53:12
take the balances and *d.* *Ezek* 5:1
d. land by lot. 45:1; 47:21, 22
the land which ye shall *d.* 48:29
he shall *d.* the land. *Dan* 11:39
that he *d.* inheritance. *Luke* 12:13
take this, and *d.* it among. 22:17

I will **divide**
I will d. them in Jacob. *Gen* 49:7
enemy said, *I will d.* *Ex* 15:9
I will d. Shechem. *Ps* 60:6; 108:7
will I d. him a portion. *Isa* 53:12

divided
God *d.* the light. *Gen* 1:4
God *d.* the waters. 7
these the isles of Gentiles *d.* 10:5
in his days was the earth *d.* 25
1 Chr 1:19
by these were nations *d.* *Gen* 10:32
Abram *d.* himself against. 14:15
Abram *d.* them, the birds *d.* 15:10
Jacob *d.* the people that was. 32:7
d. children to Leah and. 33:1
and waters were *d.* *Ex* 14:21
to these land shall be *d.* *Num* 26:53
lot shall possession of land be *d.* 56
which Moses *d.* from men. 31:42
which Lord hath *d.* *Deut* 4:19
when the most High *d.* to. 32:8*
they *d.* the land. *Josh* 14:5; 18:10
19:51*; 23:4
have they not *d.* the prey. *Judg* 5:30
d. the 300 men into three. 7:16
Abimelech *d.* them into three. 9:43
Levite *d.* her with her bones. 19:29
death they were not *d.* *2 Sam* 1:23
were people of Israel *d.* *1 Ki* 16:21
Ahab and Obadiah *d.* the land. 18:6
waters were *d.* hither. *2 Ki* 2:8
David *d.* them into. *1 Chr* 23:6
chief men, thus were they *d.* 24:4, 5
they *d.* other offerings. *2 Chr* 35:13*
hath *d.* a water-course ? *Job* 38:25*
that tarried at home *d.* *Ps* 68:12
he *d.* the sea and caused. 78:13*
d. them an inheritance by line. 55*
Acts 13:19
which *d.* the Red Sea. *Ps* 136:13
is prey of great spoil *d.* *Isa* 33:23
his hand hath *d.* it to them. 34:17

the Lord that *d.* the sea. *Isa* 51:15*
anger of the Lord hath *d.* *Lam* 4:16
nor shall they be *d.* into. *Ezek* 37:22
kingdom shall be *d.* but. *Dan* 2:41
thy kingdom is *d.* and given. 5:28
his kingdom shall be *d.* toward. 11:4
their heart is *d.* now. *Hos* 10:2
thy land shall be *d.* by line. *Amos* 7:17
he hath *d.* our fields. *Mi* 2:4
thy spoil shall be *d.* in. *Zech* 14:1
kingdom or house *d.* *Mat* 12:25
Mark 3:24, 25; *Luke* 11:17
he is *d.* against himself. *Mat* 12:26
Mark 3:26; *Luke* 11:18
the two fishes *d.* he. *Mark* 6:41
five in one house *d.* *Luke* 12:52
the father shall be *d.* against. 53
he *d.* unto them his living. 15:12
multitude of the city was *d.*
Acts 14:4; 23:7
is Christ *d.*? *1 Cor* 1:13
the great city was *d.* *Rev* 16:19

divider

who made me a *d.* over ? *Luke* 12:14

divideth

cheweth cud, but *d.* *Lev* 11:4, 5, 6
carcases of every beast which *d.* 26
swine, because it *d.* *Deut* 14:8
d. the sea with his. *Job* 26:12*
voice of the Lord *d.* *Ps* 29:7
which *d.* the sea when. *Jer* 31:35*
as a shepherd *d.* his. *Mat* 25:32
his armour, and *d.* *Luke* 11:22

dividing

an end of *d.* the land. *Josh* 19:49*
so they made an end of *d.* the. 51
led them, *d.* the water. *Isa* 63:12
times, and a *d.* of time. *Dan* 7:25
d. to every man. *1 Cor* 12:11
a workman rightly *d.* *2 Tim* 2:15
piercing to *d.* asunder. *Heb* 4:12

divination

A foreseeing or foretelling of future events or discovery of hidden knowledge. In eastern nations, and especially in Bible times, this was done by interpreting dreams or other signs, or by some peculiarities in the sacrifices, whether offered to God or to an idol. There were several sorts of divinations, *namely, by water, fire, earth, air; by the flight of birds, and their singing; by lots, by dreams, by the staff, or wand, by the entrails of victims, and by cups. The custom has been universal in all ages and all nations, civilized or savage. In the Bible the word is used of false systems of ascertaining the Divine will.*

with the rewards of *d.* *Num* 22:7
neither is there any *d.* 23:23
or that useth *d.* *Deut* 18:10
2 Ki 17:17
prophesy visions and *d.* *Jer* 14:14
nor flattering *d.* in. *Ezek* 12:24
seen vanity, and lying *d.* 13:6
have ye not spoken a lying *d.*? 7
of Babylon stood to use *d.* 21:21
at his right hand was the *d.* of. 22
as a false *d.* in their sight. 23
possessed with spirit of *d.* *Acts* 16:16

divinations

see no more divine *d.* *Ezek* 13:23

divine

such a man as I can *d.* *Gen* 44:15
d. to me by familiar. *1 Sam* 28:8
on prophets that *d.* lies. *Ezek* 13:9
no more vanity, or *d.* divinations. 23
whiles they *d.* a lie unto thee. 21:29
you, that ye shall not *d.* *Mi* 3:6
and the prophets thereof *d.* 11

divine, *adjective*

a *d.* sentence is in the. *Pr* 16:10
had ordinances of *d.* *Heb* 9:1
as his *d.* power hath. *2 Pet* 1:3
be partakers of the *d.* nature. 4

diviner, -s

nations hearkened to *d.* *Deut* 18:14
Philistines called for *d.* *1 Sam* 6:2
turneth, that maketh *d.* *Isa* 44:25
hearken not to your *d.* *Jer* 27:9
let not your prophets and *d.* 29:8
and the *d.* confounded. *Mi* 3:7
the *d.* have seen a lie. *Zech* 10:2

divineth

it whereby indeed he *d.*? *Gen* 44:5

divining

and *d.* lies to them. *Ezek* 28:28

division

will put a *d.* between. *Ex* 8:23
according to the *d.* of. *2 Chr* 35:5*
nay, but rather *d.* *Luke* 12:51
a *d.* among the people, because of.
John 7:43; 9:16; 10:19

divisions

gave the land to Israel, according to their *d.* *Josh* 11:23; 12:7; 18:10
2 Chr 35:5, 12
for *d.* of Reuben, there were great thoughts of heart. *Judg* 5:15*, 16*
these are *d.* of the sons of. 24:1*
the *d.* of porters. 26:1*, 12*, 19*
the priests in their *d.* *Ezra* 6:18
Neh 11:36*
them which cause *d.* *Rom* 16:17
that there be no *d.* *1 Cor* 1:10
is among you strife and *d.* 3:3
I hear there be *d.* among you 11:18

divorce

The legal dissolution of marriage. Moses tolerated divorces, Deut 24:1-4.

The school of Shammah, who lived a little before our Saviour, taught, that a man could not lawfully be divorced from his wife, unless he had found her guilty of some action which was really infamous, and contrary to the rules of virtue. But the school of Hillel, who was Shammah's disciple, taught, on the contrary, that the least reasons were sufficient to authorize a man to put away his wife; for example, if she did not cook his food well, or if he found any woman whom he liked better.

The Pharisees attempted to trap our Lord into some statement with which they could take issue, but he declined to interpret Moses' words, though he declared that he regarded all lesser causes than fornication as standing on too weak ground.

and given a bill of *d.* *Jer* 3:8

divorced

high priest not take a *d.* woman.
Lev 21:14
daughter be a widow or *d.* 22:13
vow of her that is *d.* *Num* 30:9
marry her that is *d.* *Mat* 5:32

divorcement

write her a bill of *d.* *Deut* 24:1, 3
is bill of your mother's *d.*? *Isa* 50:1
suffered to write bill of *d.* *Mark* 10:4
see **writing**

do

do to her as it pleaseth. *Gen* 16:6
Judge of all earth *do* right ? 18:25
God hath said to thee, *do.* 31:16
I will surely *do* thee good. 32:12
what he is about to *do.* 41:25, 28
teach you what ye shall *do.* *Ex* 4:15
if thou wilt *do* that which is. 15:26
Deut 6:18; 12:25; 13:18; 21:9
the work that they must *do.*
Ex 18:20
Lord hath spoken we will *do.* 19:8
six days *do* all thy work. 20:9; 23:12
Deut 5:13
shalt thou *do* to Aaron. *Ex* 29:35
ye shall *do* my judgements. *Lev* 18:4
19:37; 20:22; *Ezek* 36:27
which if a man *do.* *Lev* 18:5
Neh 9:29; *Ezek* 20:11, 13, 21
ye shall *do* my statutes. *Lev* 25:18
20:8; 22:31; *Deut* 17:19; 26:16
that shalt thou *do.* *Num* 22:20
what this people shall *do* to. 24:14
servants will *do* as my lord. 32:25
keep commandments to *do* them.
Deut 7:11; 11:22
do according to sentence. 17:10, 11
do to him as he thought to *do.* 19:19
shalt thou *do* to all the cities. 20:15
all the words of this law to *do.* 27:26
may hear it and *do* it. 30:12, 13
the Lord shall *do* to them as. 31:4
do ye thus requite the Lord. 32:6
thus shalt thou *do* six days. *Josh* 6:3
what wilt thou *do* to thy ? 7:9
thus shall the Lord *do* to. 10:25
what have ye to *do* with God ? 22:24
d. all that is written in book of law of.
23:6; *1 Chr* 16:40; *2 Chr* 34:21
as I *do* so shall ye *do.* *Judg* 7:17
what was I able to *do* in ? 8:3
do to us whatsoever seemeth. 10:15
what ye have to *do.* 18:14
then said the priest, what *do* ye ? 18
tell thee what thou shalt *do.* *Ruth* 3:4
shew thee what thou shalt *do.*
1 Sam 16:3
till I know what God will *do.* 22:3
thou shalt *do* great things. 26:25
now then *do* it. *2 Sam* 3:18
I were judge, I would *do.* 15:4
here I am, let him *do* to me. 26
do it to thee. 24:12; *1 Chr* 21:10
do therefore according. *1 Ki* 2:6
do as he hath said. 31
then hear, and *do,* and judge. 8:32
forgive, and *do.* 39; *2 Chr* 6:23
do that is right. *1 Ki* 11:33, 38; 14:8
do it the second time, *do* it. 18:34
what hast thou to *do* ? *2 Ki* 9:18, 19
to this day they *do* after the. 17:34
the Lord will *do* as he. 20:9
Nathan said, *do* all that. *1 Chr* 17:2
and *do* as thou hast said. 23
do away the iniquity of. 21:8
king, to *do* judgement. *2 Chr* 9:8
take heed what ye *do.* 19:6
now take heed and *do* it. 7
thus shall ye *do* in the fear of. 9
nor know we what to *do.* 20:12
if thou wilt go, *do* it, be strong. 25:8
seek your God, as ye *do.* *Ezra* 4:2
to seek law of Lord, and *do.* 7:10
that *do* after the will of your. 18
hath put in my heart to *do.* *Neh* 2:12
they should *do* according to. 5:12
that they might *do* with them. 9:24
what shall I *do* to thee ? *Job* 7:20
as heaven, what canst thou *do* ? 11:8
only *do* not two things unto. 13:20
I delight to *do* thy will. *Ps* 40:8
what hast thou to *do* to ? 50:16
do unto them as unto the. 83:9
but *do* thou for me. 109:21*
as thou usest to *do* to those. 119:132
teach me to *do* thy will. 143:10
power of thy hand to *do.* *Pr* 3:27
do it with thy might. *Eccl* 9:10
what will ye *do* in day of ? *Isa* 10:3
that he may *do* his work. 28:21
I the Lord *do* all these things. 45:7
hast thou to *do* in way of Egypt
what hast thou to *do* in ? *Jer* 2:1
what wilt thou *do* ? 4:3
and what will ye *do* in the end ? 5:31
seest thou not what they *do* ? 7:17
obey my voice, and *do* them. 11:
what hath my beloved to *do* in ? 1
how wilt thou *do* in swelling ? 12:
do thou it for thy name's sake. 14:
do to him, even as he shall. 39:1
shew thing that we may *do.* 42:
as she hath done, *do.* 50:15, 2
do unto them as thou. *Lam* 1:2
seest thou what they *do* ? *Ezek* 8:
no eye pitied thee, to *do* any. 16:
man be just, and *do* that which is.
18:5, 21; 33:14,
shall *do* as I have done. 24:22,
I will be enquired of to *do* it. 36:3
hearken and *do,* defer. *Dan* 9:
do according to will. 11:3, 16,
thus shall he *do* in the most.
what will ye *do* in solemn ? *Hos* 9
what then should a king *do* ? 10
what have ye to *do* with ? *Joel* 3
the Lord will *do* nothing. *Amos* 3
I *do* well to be angry. *Jonah* 4

but to *do* justly, and to. *Mi* 6:8
what come these to *do* ? *Zech* 1:21
are the things that ye shall *do*. 8:16
but whosover shall *do*. *Mat* 5:19
brethren only, what *do* ye more ? 47
what have we to *do* with thee ?
8:29; *Mark* 1:24; *Luke* 4:34
whosoever shall *do* the will of my Father. *Mat* 12:50; *Mark* 3:35
lawful to *do* what I will. *Mat* 20:15
do to you ? 20:32; *Mark* 10:36
by what authority I *do* these things. *Mat* 21:24; *Mark* 11:29
neither tell by what authority I *do*. *Mat* 21:27; *Mark* 11:33; *Luke* 20:8
what will he *do* to those ? *Mat* 21:40
Mark 12:9; *Luke* 20:15
all their works they *do*. *Mat* 23:5
have nothing to *do* with. 27:19
such like things, ye *do*. *Mark* 7:8, 13
ye suffer him no more to *do*. 12
gave thee authority to *do* ? 11:28
have heard done, *do* in. *Luke* 4:23
do that which is not lawful to *do* ? 6:2
communed what they might *do*. 11
as ye would that men *do*, *do* ye. 31
hear the word of God and *do* it. 8:21
I am resolved what to *do*. 16:4
that which was duty to *do*. 17:10
not find what they might *do*. 19:48
if they *do* these things in a. 23:31
they know not what they *do*. 34
whatsoever he saith, *do* it. *John* 2:5
my meat is to *do* the will of. 4:34
of mine own self *do* nothing. 5:30
the works that I *do* bear. 36
himself knew what he would *do*. 6:6
what shall we *do* ? 28; *Acts* 2:37
16:30
if thou *do* these things, shew. *John* 7:4
if any man will *do* his will. 17
I *do* always those things. 8:29
ye would *do* the works of. 39
if not of God, he could *do*. 9:33
the works that I *do* in my. 10:25
Pharisees said, what *do* we ? 11:47
what I *do* thou knowest not. 13:7
that ye should *do* as I have done. 15
happy are ye if ye *do* them. 17
works that I *do* shall he *do*. 14:12
any thing in my name, I will *do* it. 14
my friends, if ye *do*. 15:14
these things will they *do*. 21; 16:3
the work thou gavest me to *do*. 17:4
what shall this man *do* ? 21:21
all that Jesus began to *do*. *Acts* 1:1
to *do* whatsoever thy counsel. 4:28
what wilt thou have me to *do* ? 9:6
thee what thou oughtest to *do*. 10:6
sirs, why *do* ye these things ? 14:15
brethren, see how they *do*. 15:36
do thyself no harm, for we. 16:28
these *do* contrary to decrees of. 17:7
not only *do* the same. *Rom* 1:32
do by nature things contained. 2:14
do I allow not, what I would that *do* I not, what I hate *do* I. 7:15
f I *do* that which I would not. 16
is no more I that *do* it. 17, 20
et him *do* it with simplicity. 12:8
et him *do* what he will. *1 Cor* 7:36
whatsoever ye do, *do* all to. 10:31
work of Lord as I also *do*. 16:10
ot only to *do*, but also. *2 Cor* 8:10
hat ye should *do* that. 13:7
which I was forward to *do*. *Gal* 2:10
s *do* the Jews, to live as *do*. 14
ritten in book of the law to *do*. 3:10
ey which *do* such things. 5:21
asters, *do* the same. *Eph* 6:9
now my affairs, and how I *do*. 21
oth to will and to *do*. *Phil* 2:13
e have heard and seen, *do*. 4:9
hatsoever ye *do* in word or deed, *do* all in the name of. *Col* 3:17
hatsoever ye *do*, *do* it heartily. 23
love, even as we *do*. *1 Thes* 3:12
deed ye *do* it towards. 4:10
t us not sleep as *do* others. 5:6
lify one another, as also ye *do*. 11
ho also will *do* it. 24
both *do* and will *do*. *2 Thes* 3:4
the work of an evangelist.
2 Tim 4:5
do thy diligence to come.
2 Tim 4:9, 21
thou wilt *do* more than. *Philem* 21
with whom we have to *do*. *Heb* 4:13
lo, I come to *do* thy will. 10:7, 9
not fear what man shall *do*. 13:6
in every work, to *do*. 21
him *do* it as of ability. *1 Pet* 4:11*
if ye *do* these. *2 Pet* 1:10
wrest, as they *do* also other. 3:16
we lie, *do* not the truth. *1 John* 1:6
do those things that are. 3:22
and repent, and *do* the. *Rev* 2:5

can or *canst* **do**

what *can* I do to these ? *Gen* 31:43
none *can do* according. *Deut* 3:24
what thy servant *can do*. *1 Sam* 28:2
speeches wherewith he *can do* no.
Job 15:3
what *can* the Almighty *do* ? 22:17
I know that thou *canst do*. 42:2
what *can* the righteous *do* ? *Ps* 11:3
not fear what flesh *can do*. 56:4, 11
not fear what man *can do* to. 118:6
what *can* man *do* that ? *Eccl* 2:12
that *can do* any thing. *Jer* 38:5
if thou *canst do*. *Mark* 9:22
no more they *can do*. *Luke* 12:4
for no man *can do* these. *John* 3:2
the Son *can do* nothing. 5:19, 30
without me ye *can do* nothing. 15:5
we *can do* nothing. *2 Cor* 13:8
I *can do* all things through. *Phil* 4:13

do with *evil*

a multitude to *do evil*. *Ex* 23:2
if a soul swear to *do evil*. *Lev* 5:4
shall *do evil* in sight. *Deut* 4:25
because ye will *do evil* in. 31:29
please my father to *do* thee *evil*.
1 Sam 20:13
despised Lord to *do evil*. *2 Sam* 12:9
know the *evil* thou wilt *do*. *2 Ki* 8:12
sold themselves to *do evil* in. 17:17
seduced them to *do* more *evil*. 21:9
against them that *do evil*. *Ps* 34:16
in any wise to *do evil*. 37:8
who rejoice to *do evil*. *Pr* 2:14
he that deviseth to *do evil*. 24:8
not that they *do evil*. *Eccl* 5:1
of men fully set to *do evil*. 8:11
though a sinner *do evil* an. 12
you clean, cease to *do evil*. *Isa* 1:16
do good or *evil*, that we may. 41:23
people are wise to *do evil*. *Jer* 4:22
for they cannot *do evil*. 10:5
accustomed to *do evil*. 13:23
if it *do evil* in my sight. 18:10
that I would *do* this *evil*. *Ezek* 6:10
that they may *do evil*. *Mi* 7:3
not do good, nor *do evil*. *Zeph* 1:12
to do good or *do evil* ? *Mark* 3:4
Luke 6:9
let us *do evil* that good. *Rom* 3:8
but if thou *do* that which is *evil*. 13:4
God that ye *do* no *evil*. *2 Cor* 13:7
against them that *do evil*. *1 Pet* 3:12

do joined with *good*

do ye to them as is *good*. *Gen* 19:8
what *good* shall my life *do* ? 27:46
pronouncing to *do good*. *Lev* 5:4
we will *do* thee *good*. *Num* 10:29
to *do* either *good* or bad of. 24:13
is *good* for us to *do*. *Deut* 1:14
prove thee, to *do* thee *good*. 8:16
rejoiced over you to *do good*. 28:63
and he will *do* thee *good*, and. 30:5
Lord will *do* me *good*. *Judg* 17:13
do with them what seemeth *good* to.
19:24
do what seemeth thee *good*.
1 Sam 1:23; 14:36, 40
2 Sam 19:27, 37
Lord, let him *do* what seemeth him *good*. *1 Sam* 3:18; *2 Sam* 10:12
do that which is *good*. *2 Ki* 10:5
Lord *do* what is *good*. *1 Chr* 19:13
king *do* that which is *good*. 21:23
is not *good* that ye *do*. *Neh* 5:9
do good. *Ps* 34:14; 37:3, 27; 51:18
125:4; *Mat* 5:44; *Luke* 6:9, 35
to be wise and to *do good*. *Ps* 36:3
she will *do* him *good*. *Pr* 31:12
for a man to *do good*. *Eccl* 3:12
yea *do good* or do evil. *Isa* 41:23
but to *do good* they have. *Jer* 4:22
nor is it in them to *do good*. 10:5
then may ye *do good* that. 13:23
do with me as seemeth *good*. 26:14
behold the *good* I will *do*. 29:32
from them to *do* them *good*. 32:40
over them to *do* them *good*. 41
shall hear all the *good* I *do*. 33:9
not my words *do good* to. *Mi* 2:7
Lord will not *do good*. *Zeph* 1:12
is it lawful to *do good* on sabbath-days, or ? *Mark* 3:4; *Luke* 6:9
ye may *do* them *good*. *Mark* 14:7
do good to them that *do good* to you.
Luke 6:33
good that I would, I *do*. *Rom* 7:19
when I would *do good* evil is. 21
do what is *good*, and thou. 13:3
let us *do good* to all. *Gal* 6:10
rich, that they *do good*. *1 Tim* 6:18
to *do good* and communicate.
Heb 13:16
that knoweth to *do good*. *Jas* 4:17
eschew evil, and *do good*. *1 Pet* 3:11

have I to **do**

what *have I to do* ? *2 Sam* 16:10
19:22
have I to do with thee ? *1 Ki* 17:18
2 Ki 3:13; *2 Chr* 35:21; *Mark* 5:7
Luke 8:28; *John* 2:4
what *have I to do* any ? *Hos* 14:8
have I to do to judge ? *1 Cor* 5:12

I shall, or *I will* **do**; or *will I*, *shall I* **do**

what *shall I do* now to ? *Gen* 27:37
I will do as thou hast said. 47:30
I will do in the midst. *Ex* 3:20
shalt see what *I will do*. 6:1
shall I do to this people ? 17:4
I will do marvels, for it is a terrible thing that *I will do*. 34:10
I will surely *do* it to. *Num* 14:35
I will do whatsoever thou. 22:17
I shall do to you as I thought. 33:56
sayest to me *I will do*. *Ruth* 3:5
I will do to thee all that thou. 11
then *will I do* the part of a. 13
behold, *I will do* a. *1 Sam* 3:11
saying, what *shall I do* for ? 10:2
thy soul desireth, *I will do* it. 20:4
known to me what *I shall do*. 28:15
but *I will do* this thing. *2 Sam* 12:12
seemeth best *I will do*. 18:4; 19:38
what *shall I do* for you ? 21:3
that *will I do* for you. 4
I will do all thy desire for. *1 Ki* 5:8
didst send for *I will do*. 20:9
what *I shall do* for thee. *2 Ki* 2:9
Elisha said, what *shall I do* ? 4:2
I will do to-morrow as. *Esth* 5:8
what *shall I do* to thee ? *Job* 7:20
what then *shall I do* when ? 31:14
I will do no more. 34:32
I will do so to him as he. *Pr* 24:29
I will tell what *I will do*. *Isa* 5:5
these things *will I do*. 42:16
I will do a new thing. 43:19
I will do all my pleasure. 46:10
purposed it, *I will* also *do* it. 11
for mine own sake *will I do* it. 48:11
therefore *will I do* unto. *Jer* 7:14
how *shall I do* for daughter ? 9:7
thus *will I do* to this place. 19:12
provoke me not, and I *will do*. 25:6
the good that *I will do* for. 29:32
I will do judgement on. 51:47
I will do in thee what I. *Ezek* 5:9
I will do unto them after. 7:27
I have spoken, and *will do* it. 22:14
24:14; 36:36
I will even *do* according to. 35:11
I will do better to you than. 36:11
what *shall I do* unto thee ? *Hos* 6:4
thus *will I do* unto thee. *Amos* 4:12
good *thing shall I do* ? *Mat* 19:16
what *shall I do* with Jesus ? 27:22
what *shall I do*, because. *Luke* 12:17
what *shall I do* ? 16:3; 20:13
Acts 22:10
ask, that *will I do*. *John* 14:13
ask in my name *I will do* it. 14
what I do, that *I will do*. *2 Cor* 11:12

without thy mind *would I do* nothing. *Philem* 14
see **judgement**

must **do**

work that they *must do*. *Ex* 18:20
all the Lord speaketh, that I *must do*. *Num* 23:26
thou *must do* it again. *Pr* 19:19
must I *do* to be saved ? *Acts* 16:30

do joined with *no*, or *not*

not do it for forty's sake. *Gen* 18:29
I will *not do* it if I find thirty. 30
I *cannot do* any thing till. 19:22
deferred *not* to *do* the thing. 34:19
shalt *not do* any work. *Ex* 20:10
Lev 23:31
if he *do not* these three. *Ex* 21:11
shalt *not do* after their works. 23:24
afflict your souls and *do no* work. *Lev* 16:29; 23:3, 28; *Deut* 15:19
Jer 17:24
doings ye shall *not do*. *Lev* 18:3
do no unrighteousness. 19:15, 35
do no servile work. 23:7, 8, 21
25, 35, 36; *Num* 28:18, 25, 26
will *not do* my commandments. *Lev* 26:14, 15
fifty years shall *do no*. *Num* 8:26
said, and shall he *not do* it ? 23:19
ye shall *not do* any work. 29:7
Deut 5:14; 16:8
shall *not do* after all the. *Deut* 12:8
do no more such wickedness. 13:11
fear and *do no* more. 17:13
could *not do* it by day. *Judg* 6:27
I pray you, *do not* this folly. 19:23
to this man *do not* so vile a. 24
will *not do* the part of a. *Ruth* 3:13
no more *do* thee harm. *1 Sam* 26:21
days I will *not do* it. *1 Ki* 11:12
lepers said we *do not*. *2 Ki* 7:9
charged they should *not do*. 17:15
not hear them, *nor do* them. 18:12
whoso will *not do* law. *Ezra* 7:26
only *do not* two things. *Job* 13:20
God will *not do* wickedly. 34:12
remember the battle, *do no*. 41:8
they *do no* iniquity. *Ps* 119:3
cannot I *do* with you as this potter ? *Jer* 18:6
do no wrong, *do no* violence. 22:3
be a true witness, if we *do not*. 42:5
I will *not do* any more. *Ezek* 5:9
may be taught *not* to *do* after. 23:48
but they will *not do* them. 33:31
but they *do* them *not*. 32
Lord, will *not do* iniquity. *Zeph* 3:5
remnant of Israel shall *not do*. 13
do not even publicans ? *Mat* 5:46, 47
take heed ye *do not* your. 6:1
doest alms *do not* sound a trumpet. 2
which is *not* lawful to *do* on. 12:2
thou shalt *do no* murder. 19:18
friend, I *do* thee *no* wrong. 20:13
do not after their works, they say and *do not*. 23:3
could there *do no* mighty. *Mark* 6:5
and *do not* the things. *Luke* 6:46
I came down *not* to *do*. *John* 6:38
if I *do not* the works of. 10:37
would, that *do* I *not*. *Rom* 7:15, 19
for what law could *not do*. 8:3
ye *cannot do* the things. *Gal* 5:17
lie, and *do not* the truth. *1 John* 1:6
see thou *do* it *not*. *Rev* 19:10; 22:9

observe with **do**

ye shall *observe* to *do* as. *Deut* 5:32
8:1; 11:32; 12:1; 24:8; *2 Ki* 17:37
observe to *do*. *Deut* 6:3; 12:32
28:13, 15, 58; 31:12; 32:46
if *we observe* to *do* these. 6:25
to *observe* to *do* all these. 15:5
thou shalt *observe* and *do*. 16:12
shalt *observe* to *do* as they. 17:10
mayest *observe* to *do*. *Josh* 1:7
if they will *observe* to *do*. *2 Ki* 21:8
oath to *observe* and *do*. *Neh* 10:29
observe and *do* them. *Ezek* 37:24
bid, that *observe* and *do*. *Mat* 23:3

will we **do**, *we will* **do**

said *we will do*. *Ex* 19:8; 24:3, 7
goodness *will we do* to. *Num* 10:32
we will hear it and *do* it. *Deut* 5:27
thou commandest us *we will do*. *Josh* 1:16
thing which *we will do*. *Judg* 20:9
we will do all that thou. *2 Ki* 10:5
we will every one *do*. *Jer* 18:12
declare unto us, *we will do* it. 42:20
we will certainly *do*. 44:17

shall we **do**, *we shall* **do**

teach us what *we shall do*. *Judg* 13:8
how *shall we do* unto him ? 12
how *shall we do* for wives ? 21:7, 16
shall we do with ark ? *1 Sam* 5:8
what *shall we do* to the ark ? 6:2
counsel what *shall do*. *2 Sam* 16:20
shall we do after this saying ? 17:6
master, how *shall we do* ? *2 Ki* 6:15
shall we do for the 100 ? *2 Chr* 25:9
shall we do to the queen ? *Esth* 1:15
through God *we shall do*. *Ps* 60:12
108:13
what *shall we do* for our ? *S of S* 8:8
what *shall we do* to thee ? *Jonah* 1:11
what *shall we do* ? *Luke* 3:10, 12, 14
shall we do that we ? *John* 6:28
brethren, what *shall we do* ? *Acts* 2:37
shall we do to these men ? 4:16

do joined with *so*

so do as thou hast said. *Gen* 18:5
do not *so* wickedly. 19:7; *Judg* 19:23
forbid that I should *do so*. *Gen* 44:17
it is not meet *so* to *do*. *Ex* 8:26
so shall he *do*. *Lev* 4:20; 16:16
Num 9:14; 15:14
so Lord hath commanded to *do*. *Lev* 8:34
so will I *do*. *Num* 14:28; 32:31
Isa 65:8; *Ezek* 35:15
so shall he *do* to every one. *Num* 15:12
was I ever wont to *do so* ? 22:30
if ye will not *do so* ye have. 32:23
so shall the Lord *do* to. *Deut* 3:21
shall not *do so* to the Lord. 12:4, 31
nations serve gods ? *so* I *do*. 30
hath not suffered thee *so* to *do*. 18:14
and *so* shalt thou *do* with. 22:3
all that *do so* are abomination. 5
as I *do*, *so* shall ye *do*. *Judg* 7:17
if we *do* not *so* according. 11:10
so used the young men to *do*. 14:10
this man *do* not *so* vile a. 19:24
Lord *do so* to me. *Ruth* 1:17
1 Sam 14:44
God *do so* to thee. *1 Sam* 3:17
so do they also to thee. 8:8
Lord *do so* and much more. 20:13
so and more also *do* God. 25:22
shall not *do so*, my brethren. 30:23
so do God to Abner, even *so* I *do* to. *2 Sam* 3:9
do so to me, and more. 3:35; 19:13
1 Ki 2:23; 20:10; *2 Ki* 6:31
so shall thy servant *do*. *2 Sam* 9:11
so will I certainly *do*. *1 Ki* 1:30
so will thy servant *do*. 2:38
so let the gods *do* to me. 19:2
forth and *do so*. 22:22; *2 Chr* 18:21
did their fathers, *so do*. *2 Ki* 17:41
said they would *do so*. *1 Chr* 13:4
hast said, *so* must we *do*. *Ezra* 10:12
said, *so* will we *do* as. *Neh* 5:12
I should be afraid, and *do so*. 6:13
if ye *do so* again I will. 13:21
do even *so* to Mordecai. *Esth* 6:10
is he durst presume to *do so* ? 7:5
man mocketh, *do* ye *so* ? *Job* 13:9
so do stripes the inward. *Pr* 20:30*
say not, I will *do so* to him as. 24:29
I *so do* to Jerusalem. *Isa* 10:11
the Lord *do so*, the Lord. *Jer* 28:6
so thou shalt *do* seventh. *Ezek* 45:20
so shall he *do*, he shall. *Dan* 11:30
so shall Beth-el *do* to. *Hos* 10:15
do not even publicans *so* ? *Mat* 5:47
do to you, *do* ye even *so* to. 7:12
so shall my heavenly Father *do*. 18:35
commandment, *so* I *do*. *John* 14:31
as fathers did, *so do* ye. *Acts* 7:51
order, even *so do* ye. *1 Cor* 16:1
Christ forgave you, *so do*. *Col* 3:13
which is in faith, *so do*. *1 Tim* 1:4
so do ye, as they that. *Jas* 2:12

do joined with *this*

and *this* they begin to *do*. *Gen* 11:6
I *do this* great wickedness. 39:9
let Pharaoh *do this*, let him. 41:34
Joseph said, *this do* and. 42:18
it must be, *do this*. 43:11; 45:17, 19
I will *do this* to you. *Lev* 26:16
this do, take you censers. *Num* 16:6
this we will *do* to the. *Josh* 9:20
I pray, *do* not *this* folly. *Judg* 19:23
do not thou *this* folly. *2 Sam* 13:12
far from me that I *do this*. 23:17
zeal of Lord shall *do this*. *2 Ki* 19:31
Isa 37:32
this do and ye shall. *2 Chr* 19:10
fail not to *do this*. *Ezra* 4:22
do this now, my son. *Pr* 6:3
praise thee, as I *do this*. *Isa* 38:19
they should *do this*. *Jer* 32:35
I would *do this* evil. *Ezek* 6:10
I *do* not *this* for your. 36:22, 32
because I will *do this*. *Amos* 4:12
in day that I shall *do this*. *Mal* 4:3
to my servant, *do this*, and he doeth it. *Mat* 8:9; *Luke* 7:8
I am able to *do this* ? *Mat* 9:28
ye shall not only *do this*. 21:21
why *do* ye *this* ? *Mark* 11:3
whom he should *do this*. *Luke* 7:4
he said to him, *this do*, and. 10:28
he said, *this* will I *do*. 12:18
this do in remembrance. 22:19
1 Cor 11:24, 25
do therefore *this*. *Acts* 21:23
if I *do this* thing. *1 Cor* 9:17
and *this* I *do* for the gospel's. 23
and *this* will we *do*. *Heb* 6:3
I beseech you rather to *do this*. 13:19
we will *do this* or that. *Jas* 4:15
see **this, thing**

do *well*

learn to *do well*. *Isa* 1:17
I *do well* to be angry. *Jonah* 4:9
do well to Jerusalem. *Zech* 8:15
is lawful to *do well* on. *Mat* 12:12
sleep, he shall *do well*. *John* 11:12
yourselves, ye *do well*. *Acts* 15:29
royal law, ye *do well*. *Jas* 2:8
praise of them that *do well*. *1 Pet* 2:14
but if when ye *do well* and. 20
daughters as long as ye *do well*. 3:6
whereto ye *do well*. *2 Pet* 1:19
thou bring, shalt *do well*. *3 John* 6

doctor

(*Used in its old meaning of teacher, or learned man. Latin, doctor from* docere, *to teach*)

stood up Gamaliel, a *d*. *Acts* 5:34

doctors

Jesus sitting in midst of the *d*. *Luke* 2:46
there were Pharisees and *d*. 5:17

doctrine

(*Used in old meaning of teaching, instruction (see* **doctor**). *In the New Testament the Revised Version almost universally translates it* teaching)

make to understand *d*. *Isa* 28:9*
murmured shall learn *d*. 29:24†
the stock is a *d*. of vanities. *Jer* 10:8
people astonished at his *d*. *Mat* 7:28
22:33; *Mark* 1:22; 11:18
Luke 4:32
beware of the *d*. of the. *Mat* 16:12
saying, what new *d*.? *Mark* 1:27
and said to them in *d*. 4:2; 12:38
he shall know of the *d*. *John* 7:17
priest then asked Jesus of *d*. 18:19
continued in apostles' *d*. *Acts* 2:42
filled Jerusalem with your *d*. 5:28
astonished at *d*. of Lord. 13:12
know what this new *d*. is ? 17:19
obeyed that form of *d*. *Rom* 6:17
contrary to the *d*. which ye. 16:17
except I speak by *d*. *1 Cor* 14:6
every one of you hath a *d*. 26
with every wind of *d*. *Eph* 4:14
they teach no other *d*. *1 Tim* 1:3
attendance to reading, to *d*. 4:13

heed to thyself, and to thy *d.* *1 Tim* 4:16
labour in the word and *d.* 5:17
the name of God and his *d.* be. 6:1
and to *d.* which is according to. 3
is profitable for *d.* *2 Tim* 3:16
with all long suffering and *d.* 4:2
in *d.* shewing incorruptness. *Tit* 2:7
that they may adorn the *d.* of. 10
leaving principles of *d.* *Heb* 6:1*
of the *d.* of baptisms, and of. 2
whoso abideth not in the *d.*; he that abideth in *d.* of Christ. *2 John* 9
hast them that hold *d.* of. *Rev* 2:14
that hold *d.* of the Nicolaitans. 15

good **doctrine**

I give you *good d* *Pr* 4:2
in the words of *good d.* *1 Tim* 4:6

my **doctrine**

my d. shall drop as rain. *Deut* 32:2
my d. is pure, and I am. *Job* 11:4
my d. is not mine. *John* 7:16
hast fully known *my d.* *2 Tim* 3:10

sound **doctrine**

is contrary to *sound d.* *1 Tim* 1:10
will not endure *sound d.* *2 Tim* 4:3
by *sound d.* to exhort. *Tit* 1:9
things which become *sound d.* 2:1

this **doctrine**

and bring not *this d.* *2 John* 10
many as have not *this d.* *Rev* 2:24

doctrines

for *d.* the commandments of men. *Mat* 15:9; *Mark* 7:7
after commandments and *d.* *Col* 2:22
heed to *d.* of devils. *1 Tim* 4:1
about with strange *d.* *Heb* 13:9

Doeg

and his name was *D.* *1 Sam* 21:7
D. turned and slew priests. 22:18
I knew it that day *D.* was there. 22

doer

he was the *d.* of it. *Gen* 39:22
Lord reward *d.* of evil. *2 Sam* 3:39
rewardeth the proud *d.* *Ps* 31:23
a wicked *d.* giveth heed. *Pr* 17:4
an hypocrite and evil *d.* *Isa* 9:17
suffer trouble as an evil *d.* *2 Tim* 2:9
a hearer, not a *d.* of word. *Jas* 1:23
not a forgetful hearer, but a *d.* 25
thou art not a *d.* of the law. 4:11
none suffer as an evil *d.* *1 Pet* 4:15

doers

et them give it to the *d.* *2 Ki* 22:5*
ut off all wicked *d.* *Ps* 101:8*
ut the *d.* of the law. *Rom* 2:13
e ye *d.* of the word. *Jas* 1:22

see **evil**

doest

d. well, and if thou *d.* not. *Gen* 4:7
ith thee in all that thou *d.* 21:22
at thou *d.* is not good. *Ex* 18:17
hen thou *d.* that which. *Deut* 12:28
less thee in all that thou *d.* 15:18
know all that thou *d.* *2 Sam* 3:25
rosper in all thou *d.* *1 Ki* 2:3
hat *d.* thou here, Elijah ? 19:9, 13
nd see what thou *d.* 20:22
y, what *d.* thou ? *Job* 9:12
Eccl 8:4; *Dan* 4:35
thou sinnest, what *d.*? *Job* 35:6
hen thou *d.* well to. *Ps* 49:18
e God that *d.* wonders. 77:14
ou art great, and *d.* 86:10
ou art good, and *d.* good. 119:68
hen thou *d.* evil. *Jer* 11:15
ide to ask how thou *d.*? 15:5*
use said, what *d.* thou ? *Ezek* 12:9
ak heart, seeing thou *d.* 16:30
ese are to us, that thou *d.* 24:19
thou well to be angry ? *Jonah* 4:4, 9
u *d.* thine alms. *Mat* 6:2, 3
at authority *d.* thou these things ? 21:23; *Mark* 11:28; *Luke* 20:2
n seeing that thou *d.*? *John* 2:18
se miracles that thou *d.* 3:2
ciples may see works thou *d.* 7:3
t thou *d.* do quickly. 13:27
e heed what thou *d.* *Acts* 22:26

thou that judgest, *d.* *Rom* 2:1, 3
believest on God, thou *d.* *Jas* 2:19
d. faithfully what thou *d.* *3 John* 5

doeth

seen all that Laban *d.* to. *Gen* 31:12
whosoever *d.* work therein shall be cut off. *Ex* 31:14, 15; *Lev* 23:30
these that a man *d.* *Lev* 6:3
shall live when God *d.*! *Num* 24:23
to God who *d.* great. *Job* 5:9
9:10; 37:5; *Ps* 72:18; 136:4
soul desireth, that he *d.* *Job* 23:13
whatsoever he *d.* prosper. *Ps* 1:3
there is none that *d.* good. 14:1, 3
53:1, 3; *Rom* 3:12
he that *d.* these things shall. *Ps* 15:5
blessed is he that *d.* 106:3
right hand of Lord *d.* 118:15, 16
he that *d.* it, destroyeth. *Pr* 6:32
merciful man *d.* good to. 11:17
a merry heart *d.* good like. 17:22
I said of mirth, what *d.* it ? *Eccl* 2:2
God *d.* shall be for ever, and God *d.* it that men should fear. 3:14
there is not a man *d.* good. 7:20
he *d.* whatsoever pleaseth him. 8:3
blessed is the man that *d.* *Isa* 56:2
shall he escape that *d.*? *Ezek* 17:15
that *d.* the like to any one of. 18:10
that *d.* not any of those duties. 11
d. that which is lawful and. 27
d. according to will in. *Dan* 4:35
God is righteous in all he *d.* 9:14
saith Lord that *d.* this. *Amos* 9:12
cut off man that *d.* this. *Mal* 2:12
know what thy right *d.* *Mat* 6:3
he that *d.* will of my Father. 7:21
whoso heareth sayings, and *d.* 24
heareth and *d.* not. 26; *Luke* 6:49
and he *d.* it. *Mat* 8:9; *Luke* 7:8
every one that *d.* evil. *John* 3:20
but he that *d.* truth cometh. 21
things soever he *d.* these *d.* 5:19
hear him and know what he *d.* 7:51
but if any man *d.* his will. 9:31
knoweth not what his lord *d.* 15:15
will think he *d.* God service. 16:2
every soul that *d.* evil. *Rom* 2:9
the man that *d.* these things shall live by them. 10:5; *Gal* 3:12
wrath upon him that *d.* *Rom* 13:4
every sin a man *d.* is. *1 Cor* 6:18
that he keep his virgin, *d.* well. 7:37
giveth her in marriage *d.* well. 38
d. he it by works of law ? *Gal* 3:5
good thing any man *d.* *Eph* 6:8
forth fruit, as it *d.* also. *Col* 1:6
but he that *d.* wrong, shall. 3:25
exhorted as a father *d.* *1 Thes* 2:11
to do good, and *d.* it not. *Jas* 4:17
he that *d.* will of God. *1 John* 2:17
that *d.* righteousness is born. 29; 3:7
remember his deeds which he *d.* *3 John* 10
but he that *d.* evil hath not. 11
and he *d.* great wonders. *Rev* 13:13

dog

Frequently mentioned in the Scripture. It was used by the Hebrews as a watch for their houses, Isa 56:10, *and for guarding their flocks,* Job 30:1. *There were numerous troops of wild, masterless dogs which devoured dead bodies and other offal,* 1 Ki 14:11, *and became so fierce and such objects of dislike that fierce and cruel enemies were poetically called dogs,* Ps 22:16, etc. *The dog being an unclean animal the name was used as a term of reproach, or of humility of speaking of oneself,* 1 Sam 24:14; 2 Sam 16:9.

against Israel shall not a *d.* *Ex* 11:7
not bring price of a *d.* *Deut* 23:18
that lappeth as a *d.* *Judg* 7:5
Philistine said to David, am I a *d.*? *1 Sam* 17:43
thou pursue ? after a *d.*? 24:14
Abner said, am I a *dog's* ? *2 Sam* 3:8
look upon such dead *d.* as I am. 9:8
this dead *d.* curse my lord ? 16:9
is thy servant a *d.*? *2 Ki* 8:13

darling from power of *d.* *Ps* 22:20
they make a noise like a *d.* 59:6, 14
as *d.* returneth to his vomit, so a fool. *Pr* 26:11; *2 Pet* 2:22
like one that taketh a *d.* *Pr* 26:17
a living *d.* is better than. *Eccl* 9:4
as if he cut off a *dog's.* *Isa* 66:3

dogs

torn of beasts, ye shall cast it to *d.* *Ex* 22:31; *Mat* 15:26; *Mark* 7:27
shall the *d.* eat. *1 Ki* 14:11; 16:4
21:24
place where *d.* licked the blood of Naboth, shall *d.* lick thy. 21:19
d. eat Jezebel. 23; *2 Ki* 9:10, 36
d. licked up Ahab's. *1 Ki* 22:38
to have set with *d.* of. *Job* 30:1
for *d.* have compassed me. *Ps* 22:16
and the tongue of thy *d.* in. 68:23
they are all dumb *d.* *Isa* 56:10
greedy *d.* 11
to slay, the *d.* to tear. *Jer* 15:3
give not holy unto *d.* *Mat* 7:6
d. eat of crumbs. 15:27; *Mark* 7:28
d. came and licked. *Luke* 16:21
beware of *d.* beware of. *Phil* 3:2
for without are *d.* and. *Rev* 22:15

doing

done foolishly in so *d.* *Gen* 31:28
ye have done evil in so *d.* 44:5
in praises, *d.* wonders. *Ex* 15:11
without *d.* any thing. *Num* 20:19
ye sinned in *d.* wickedly. *Deut* 9:18
he sinned in *d.* evil. *1 Ki* 16:19
2 Ki 21:16
d. that which was right. *1 Ki* 22:43
2 Chr 20:32
arise, and be *d.* *1 Chr* 22:16
I am *d.* a great work. *Neh* 6:3
in so *d.* my Maker. *Job* 32:22
wisely consider of his *d.* *Ps* 64:9
he is terrible in *d.* toward. 66:5
the Lord's *d.* marvellous in our. 118:23; *Mat* 21:42; *Mark* 12:11
keepeth his hand from *d.* *Isa* 56:2
from *d.* thy pleasure on my. 58:13
his Lord shall find so *d.* *Mat* 24:46
Luke 12:43
who went about *d.* good. *Acts* 10:38
they have found any evil *d.* in. 24:20
for in so *d.* thou shalt. *Rom* 12:20
therefore perform the *d.* *2 Cor* 8:11
servants of Christ, *d.* will. *Eph* 6:6
in *d.* this shalt save. *1 Tim* 4:16
d. nothing by partiality. 5:21

well-**doing**

patient continuance in *well-d.* *Rom* 2:7
not be weary in *well-d.* *Gal* 6:9
2 Thes 3:13
with *well-d.* ye may. *1 Pet* 2:15
better that ye suffer for *well-d.* 3:17
their souls to him in *well-d.* 4:19

doings

after *d.* of Egypt, and after *d.* of Canaan, shall ye not. *Lev* 18:3
of wickedness of thy *d.* *Deut* 28:20
not from their own *d.* *Judg* 2:19
and evil in his *d.* *1 Sam* 25:3
walked not after the *d.* *2 Chr* 17:4
among the people his *d.* *Ps* 9:11
Isa 12:4
I will talk of thy *d.* *Ps* 77:12
child is known by his *d.* *Pr* 20:11
put away evil of your *d.* *Isa* 1:16
because their tongue and *d.* 3:8
shall eat the fruit of their *d.* 10
because of the evil of your *d.* *Jer* 4:4; 21:12; 26:3; 44:22
thy *d.* have procured these. 4:18
amend your *d.* 7:3, 5; 26:13; 35:15
thou shewedst me their *d.* 11:18
according to fruit of *d.* 17:10; 21:14
make your ways and *d.* good. 18:11
upon you evil of your *d.* 23:2
from evil of their *d.* 22; 25:5
Zech 1:4
according to fruit of his *d.* *Jer* 32:19
see their way and *d.* *Ezek* 14:22
shall ye remember your *d.* 20:43
nor according to your corrupt *d.* 44
in all your *d.* your sins do. 21:24
according to thy *d.* shall. 24:14

defiled it by their own way and *d.* *Ezek* 36:17
and according to their *d.* I. 19
remember your *d.* that were. 31
and reward their *d.* *Hos* 4:9
they will not frame their *d.* to. 5:4
now their own *d.* have set. 7:2
for the wickedness of their *d.* 9:15
according to his *d.* will he. 12:2
Jacob, are these his *d.*? *Mi* 2:7
themselves ill in their *d.* 3:4
desolate for fruit of their *d.* 7:13
corrupted all their *d.* *Zeph* 3:7
not be ashamed for all thy *d.*? 11
according to our *d.* so. *Zech* 1:6

doleful

houses full of *d.* creatures. *Isa* 13:21
day shall lament with a *d.* *Mi* 2:4

dominion

[1] *Supreme power or sovereignty,* Neh 9:28; Rom 6:9. [2] *Persons or territory ruled over,* Ps 114:2.

have *d.* over fish. *Gen* 1:26, 28
when thou shalt have *d.* 27:40*
shalt thou indeed have *d.*? 37:8
he that shall have *d.* *Num* 24:19
he made him have *d.* *Judg* 5:13*
time Philistines had *d.* over. 14:4*
Solomon had *d.* over all. *1 Ki* 4:24
build in land of his *d.* 9:19; *2 Chr* 8:6
nothing in his house or in all his *d.* *2 Ki* 20:13; *Isa* 39:2
men of Chozeba had *d.* *1 Chr* 4:22
as he went to stablish his *d.* 18:3
Edomites from under Judah's *d.* *2 Chr* 21:8*
so that they had the *d.* *Neh* 9:28
also they have *d.* over our. 37*
d. and fear are with him. *Job* 25:2
canst thou set *d.* thereof? 38:33
to have *d.* over the works. *Ps* 8:6
let them not have *d.* over. 19:13
the upright shall have *d.* 49:14
he shall have *d.* also from. 72:8
bless Lord in places of his *d.* 103:22
his sanctuary, Israel his *d.* 114:2
let not iniquity have *d.* 119:133
thy *d.* endureth through. 145:13
other lords had *d.* over. *Isa* 26:13
his *d.* is from generation. *Dan* 4:3
thy *d.* reacheth to the end. 22
whose *d.* is an everlasting *d.* 34; 7:14
d. of my kingdom men tremble before God of Daniel, his *d.* 6:26
beast had four heads, and *d.* 7:6
the rest of the beasts had their *d.* 12
there was given him *d.* and. 14
they shall take away his *d.* 26
d. shall be given to saints of. 27
mighty king rule with great *d.* 11:3, 5
not according to his *d.* which he. 4
shall come even first *d.* *Mi* 4:8
d. shall be from sea to. *Zech* 9:10
of Gentiles exercise *d.* *Mat* 20:25*
death hath no more *d.* *Rom* 6:9
sin shall not have *d.* over you. 14
law hath *d.* over a man as long. 7:1
not that we have *d.* *2 Cor* 1:24*
all power, might, and *d.* *Eph* 1:21
to whom be praise and *d.* *1 Pet* 4:11 5:11; *Rev* 1:6
to the only wise God be *d.* *Jude* 25

dominions

and all *d.* shall serve. *Dan* 7:27
they be thrones, or *d.* or. *Col* 1:16

done

what younger son had *d.* *Gen* 9:24
they have *d.* according to the. 18:21
told Isaac all that he had *d.* 24:66
have *d.* to thee nothing but. 26:29
not be *d.* in our country. 29:26
folly, which ought not to be *d.* 34:7
ye have *d.* evil in so doing. 44:5
what deed is this ye have *d.*? 15
have ye *d.* this thing? *Ex* 1:18
stood to wit what would be *d.* 2:4
no manner of work shall be *d.*, save that which man must eat. 12:16
this is *d.* because of that the. 13:8
Jethro heard all that God had *d.* 18:1
goodness which Lord had *d.* 9
this judgement shall it be *d.* 21:31
six days work be *d.* *Ex* 31:15; 35:2 *Lev* 23:3
they had *d.* it as Lord commanded, even so had they *d.* it. *Ex* 39:43
things forbidden to be *d.* *Lev* 5:17
commanded to be *d.* 8:5; *Deut* 26:14
wherein any work is *d.* *Lev* 11:32
have the men of land *d.* 18:27
eye for eye, so shall it be *d.* 24:20
confess sin they have *d.* *Num* 5:7
wherein we have *d.* foolishly. 12:11
not declared what should be *d.* 15:34
Balak saw all that Israel had *d.* 22:2
name of father be *d.* away? 27:4*
all that had *d.* evil in sight. 32:13
is thy God that hath *d.* *Deut* 10:21
so shall it be *d.* to that man. 25:9
wherefore hath the Lord *d.* thus to? 29:24; *1 Ki* 9:8; *2 Chr* 7:21
as he had *d.* also to. *Josh* 10:32, 39
he had *d.* to Lachish. 35
he had *d.* to Eglon. 37
if we had not rather *d.* it. 22:24
had known all that he had *d.* 24:31
not works he had *d.* *Judg* 2:10
because they had *d.* evil in. 3:12
d. truly and sincerely, and have *d.* to Jerubbaal according to. 9:16
cruelty *d.* to the seventy sons of. 24
there was no such deed *d.* 19:30
her all the man had *d.* *Ruth* 3:16
what is there *d.* my son? *1 Sam* 4:16*
so shall it be *d.* to his oxen. 11:7
what shall be *d.* to the man? 17:26
so shall it be *d.* to the man that. 27
when Lord shall have *d.* 25:30
Lord hath *d.* as he spake. 28:17 *Ezek* 12:28
thing David had *d.* *2 Sam* 11:27
no such thing ought to be *d.* in. 13:12
have they *d.*? 24:17; *1 Chr* 21:17
goodness Lord hath *d.* *1 Ki* 8:66
above all their fathers had *d.* 14:22
told Jezebel all Elijah had *d.* 19:1
according to all his father had *d.* 22:53; *2 Ki* 15:3, 9, 34; 23:32
what is to be *d.* for thee? *2 Ki* 4:13
great things Elisha hath *d.* 8:4
d. that which he spake by servant. 10:10; *Isa* 38:15; *Jer* 40:3
heard what kings of Assyria have *d.* *2 Ki* 19:11; *2 Chr* 32:13; *Isa* 37:11
they have *d.* evil. *2 Ki* 21:15 *2 Chr* 29:6
all acts that he had *d.* in. *2 Ki* 23:19
because he had *d.* good. *2 Chr* 24:16
rejoiced, for the thing was *d.* 29:36
not according to benefit *d.* to. 32:25
to inquire of wonder that was *d.* 31
a decree, let it be *d.* *Ezra* 6:12
when these things were *d.* the. 9:1
are no such things *d.* *Neh* 6:8
we have *d.* wickedly. 9:33; *Ps* 106:6 *Dan* 9:5, 15
Vashti, and what she had *d.* *Esth* 2:1
Mordecai perceived all was *d.* 4:1
what shall be *d.* to the man? 6:6
thus shall it be *d.* to the man. 9
him what he hath *d.*? *Job* 21:31
whether it be *d.* against a. 34:29
he spake and it was *d.* *Ps* 33:9
he hath *d.* great things. 71:19 106:21; 126:2, 3
what shall be *d.* to thee? 120:3
strive not if he have *d.* *Pr* 3:30
sleep not, except they have *d.* 4:16
d. is that which shall be *d.* *Eccl* 1:9
have seen the works are *d.* 14; 4:1, 3
that which hath been already *d.* 2:12
who hath wrought and *d.* it? *Isa* 41:4
sing, for the Lord hath *d.* 44:23
lest my idol hath *d.* them. 48:5
backsliding Israel hath *d.* *Jer* 3:6
thus shall it be *d.* unto them. 5:13
ye have *d.* all these works. 7:13
children of Judah have *d.* evil. 30
had *d.* right in my sight. 34:15
have *d.* all that Jonadab. 35:10, 18
these men have *d.* evil to. 38:9
have *d.* we and our fathers. 44:17
and say, what is *d.* 48:19
vengeance as she hath *d.* 50:15, 29
the violence *d.* to me. 51:35
Lord hath *d.* that which. *Lam* 2:17
thus have they *d.* in. *Ezek* 23:39
it is come, it is *d.* saith. 39:8
of all that they have *d.* 43:11
and for all that shall be *d.* 44:14
is determined shall be *d.* *Dan* 11:36
priests have *d.* violence. *Zeph* 3:4
thy will be *d.* *Mat* 6:10; 26:42 *Luke* 11:2; 22:42
believed, so be it *d.* *Mat* 8:13
mighty works *d.* in you had been *d.* 11:21; *Luke* 10:13
they ask, it shall be *d.* for. *Mat* 18:19
fellow-servants saw what was *d.* 31
cast into sea, it shall be *d.* 21:21
these ought ye to have *d.* 23:23 *Luke* 11:42
well *d.* good and. *Mat* 25:21, 23
as ye have *d.* it to one of least of these my brethren, ye have *d.* 40
things that were *d.* 27:54; 28:11
out to see what was *d.* *Mark* 5:14 *Luke* 8:35
tell what great things the Lord hath *d.* for. *Mark* 5:19, 20; *Luke* 8:39
what was *d.* in her. *Mark* 5:33
told him what they had *d.* 6:30
have *d.* to him whatsoever. 9:13
not pass till these things be *d.* 13:30
him to do, as he had ever *d.* 15:8
he that is mighty hath *d.* *Luke* 1:49
for the evils Herod had *d.* 3:19
to tell no man what was *d.* 8:56
told him all that they had *d.* 9:10
Lord, it is *d.* as thou. 14:22
ye, when ye shall have *d.* all, we have *d.* that which was our duty. 17:10
what shall be *d.* in the dry? 23:31
centurion saw what was *d.* 47
third day since these were *d.* 24:21
d. good to resurrection of life; have *d.* evil, to damnation. *John* 5:29
what ye will, and it shall be *d.* 15:7
these things were *d.* that the. 19:36
many signs were *d.* by. *Acts* 2:43
of the good deed *d.* to the. 4:9
a notable miracle hath been *d.* 16
God for that which was *d.* 21
determined before to be *d.* 28
wife, not knowing what was *d.* 5:7
not it was true which was *d.* 12:9
all that God had *d.* 14:27; 15:4
the will of the Lord be *d.* 21:14
captain demanded what he had *d.* 33
neither having *d.* good. *Rom* 9:11
nor that it should be *d.* *1 Cor* 9:15
in part shall be *d.* away. 13:10
all things be *d.* to edifying. 14:26
be *d.* decently. 40
be *d.* with charity. 16:14
glory was to be *d.* away. *2 Cor* 3:7
which veil is *d.* away in Christ. 14
receive the things *d.* in his body, according to that he hath *d.* 5:10
things which are *d.* of. *Eph* 5:12
and having *d.* all to stand. 6:13
nothing be *d.* through. *Phil* 2:3
ye have well *d.* that ye did. 4:14
known all things that are *d.* *Col* 4:9
righteousness we have *d.* *Tit* 3:5
d. despite to the Spirit. *Heb* 10:29
saying, it is *d.* *Rev* 16:17; 21:6
which must shortly be *d.* 22:6

have I **done**

in innocency *have I d.* *Gen* 20:
and here also *have I d.* 40:1
what *have I d.*? *Num* 22:2 *1 Ki* 19:20; *Mi* 6:
thus and thus *have I d.* *Josh* 7:2
what *have I* now *d.*? *Judg* 8: *1 Sam* 17:2
what *have I d.*? *1 Sam* 20:1; 26:1 29:8; *Jer* 8:
transgressions *have I d.* *Ezek* 39:2
Jews *have I d.* no wrong. *Acts* 25:1

he hath **done**, or, *hath he* **done**

he hath d. evil to this. *Ex* 5:2
for harm *he hath d.* *Lev* 5:1
as *he hath d.* so Lord. 8:3
atonement for sin *he hath d.* 19:2
as *he hath d.* so shall it be. 24:1
you, after *he hath d.* *Josh* 24:2
to him as *he hath d.* to. *Judg* 15:1
then *he hath d.* us this. *1 Sam* 6:

how great things *he hath d.* *1 Sam* 12:24
what *hath he d.*? 20:32
marvellous works that *he hath d.*
1 Chr 16:12; *Ps* 78:4; 98:1; 105:5
declare what *he hath d.* *Ps* 66:16
God *hath d.* whatsoever *he.* 115:3
to him as *he hath d.* to me. *Pr* 24:29
to Lord for *he hath d.* *Isa* 12:5
righteousness *he hath d.* *Ezek* 3:20
18:24
he hath d. these things. 17:18
he hath d. all these abominations.
18:13
father's sins which *he hath d.* 14
righteousness that *he hath d.* 22
to all that *he hath d.* 24:24
he hath d. that which is. 33:16
because *he hath d.* great. *Joel* 2:20
what evil *hath he d.*? *Mat* 27:23
Mark 15:14; *Luke* 23:22
he hath d. all things. *Mark* 7:37
much evil *hath he d.* to. *Acts* 9:13
receive according to that *he hath d.*
2 Cor 5:10
for wrong *he hath d.* *Col* 3:25

I have **done**

nor smite every thing as *I have d.*
Gen 8:21
kindness *I have d.* thee. 21:23
I have d. as thou badest me. 27:19
till *I have d.* that which I. 28:15
my service *I have d.* thee. 30:26
signs which *I have d.* *Ex* 10:2
have seen what *I have d.* *Josh* 24:7
as *I have d.* so God hath. *Judg* 1:7
they did to me, so *have I d.* 15:11
behold now *I have d.* *2 Sam* 14:21
I have sinned in that *I have d.*, *I have*
d. very. 24:10; *1 Chr* 21:8
and *I have d.* wickedly. *2 Sam* 24:17
I have d. according to. *1 Ki* 3:12
heard, how *I have d.* it ? *2 Ki* 19:25
that *I have d.* for house. *Neh* 13:14
if *I have d.* iniquity. *Job* 34:32
O Lord, if *I have d.* this. *Ps* 7:3
I have d. judgement and. 119:121
I have d. no wickedness. *Pr* 30:20
as *I have d.* to Samaria. *Isa* 10:11
strength of my hand *I have d.* 13
ye far off what *I have d.* 33:13
not heard how *I have d.* it ? 37:26
repent of evil *I have d.* to. *Jer* 42:10
have d. as thou hast. *Ezek* 9:11
as *I have d.* so shall it be. 12:11
know that *I have* not *d.* without
cause, all that *I have d.* in. 14:23
ye shall do as *I have d.* 24:22
thee, *have I d.* no hurt. *Dan* 6:22
weep, as *I have d.* these. *Zech* 7:3
have d. one work. *John* 7:21
he had washed their feet, he said,
know ye what *I have d.* to ? 13:12
should do as *I have d.* to you. 15

hast thou **done**

said, what *hast thou d.*? *Gen* 4:10
31:26; *Num* 23:11; *1 Sam* 13:11
2 Sam 3:24; *John* 18:35
what *hast thou d.* to us ? *Gen* 20:9
Judg 15:11
heart *hast thou d.* *2 Sam* 7:21
wherefore *hast thou d.* so ? 16:10
why *hast thou d.* so ? *1 Ki* 1:6
Lord, *hast thou d.* *1 Chr* 17:19
these things *hast thou d.* *Ps* 50:21
why *hast thou d.* this ? *Jonah* 1:10

thou hast **done**

this that *thou hast d.*? *Gen* 3:13
12:18; 26:10; 29:25; *Judg* 15:11
2 Sam 12:21
because *thou hast d.* this. *Gen* 3:14
22:16; *2 Chr* 25:16
thou *hast d.* deeds which. *Gen* 20:9
that which *thou hast d.* to. 27:45
thou *hast* now *d.* foolishly. 31:28
1 Sam 13:13; *2 Chr* 16:9
tell me what *thou hast d.* *Josh* 7:19
1 Sam 14:43
all *thou hast d.* *Ruth* 2:11
thou *hast d.* to me this. *1 Sam* 24:19
good that *thou hast d.* 26:16
thou hast d. evil. *1 Ki* 14:9
thou *hast d.* well in. *2 Ki* 10:30
thou hast d. against altar. *2 Ki* 23:17
for *thou hast d.* right. *Neh* 9:33
works which *thou hast d.* *Ps* 40:5
thee, because *thou hast d.* it. 52:9
know that *thou hast d.* it. 109:27
if *thou hast d.* foolishly. *Pr* 30:32
exalt thee, for *thou hast d.* *Isa* 25:1
know what *thou hast d.* *Jer* 2:23
thou hast spoken and *d.* evil. 3:5
glad that *thou hast d.* it. *Lam* 1:21
do unto them as *thou hast d.* 22
consider to whom *thou hast d.* 2:20
Sodom hath not done as *thou hast d.*
Ezek 16:48
abominations which *thou hast d.* 51
deal with thee as *thou hast d.* 59
pacified for all that *thou hast d.* 63
as *thou hast d.* it shall be. *Ob* 15
O Lord, *thou hast d.* as. *Jonah* 1:14
thou hast d. well that. *Acts* 10:33

not **done**

that ought *not* to be *d.* *Gen* 20:9
which thing ought *not* to be *d.* 34:7
such as have *not* been *d.* *Ex* 34:10
things which ought *not* to be *d.*
Lev 4:2, 13
I have *not d.* them of. *Num* 16:28
Lord hath *not d.* all. *Deut* 32:27
wouldest thou *not* have *d.*? *2 Ki* 5:13
they had *not d.* it of. *2 Chr* 30:5
from work, that it be *not d.* *Neh* 6:9
Israel had *not d.* so. 8:17
Vashti had *not d.* wrong. *Esth* 1:16
that I have *not d.* *Isa* 5:4
things that are *not* yet *d.* 46:10
neither shall that be *d.* *Jer* 3:16
in thee that I have *not d.* *Ezek* 5:9
for under heaven hath *not* been *d.* as
hath been done upon. *Dan* 9:12
that which fathers have *not d.* 11:24
and Lord hath *not d.* it. *Amos* 3:6
if I had *not d.* among. *John* 15:24
scarce restrained they had *not d.*
Acts 14:18
this thing *not d.* in a corner. 26:26

done with *this*

wot not who hath *d. this.* *Gen* 21:26
what is *this* that God hath *d.*? 42:28
deed is *this* that ye have *d.*? 44:15
have ye *d. this* thing. *Ex* 1:18
this is *d.* because of that which. 13:8
why have we *d. this* ? 14:5
afraid, and have *d. this* ? *Josh* 9:24
as ye have *d.* to *this* day. 23:8
why have ye *d.* this ? *Judg* 2:2
who hath *d. this* thing ? 6:29; 15:6
she said, let *this* thing be *d.* 11:37
ye have *d. this*, yet will. 15:7
wickedness is *this* that is *d.* 20:12
d. all *this* wickedness. *1 Sam* 12:20
hath the Lord *d. this* thing. 28:18
ye have *d. this* thing. *2 Sam* 2:6
man that hath *d. this* thing. 12:5
hath Joab *d. this* thing ? 14:20
now, I have *d. this* thing. 21
is *this d.* by my lord ? *1 Ki* 1:27
forasmuch as *this* is *d.* of. 11:11
return, for *this* thing is *d.* *2 Chr* 11:4
O Lord, if I have *d. this.* *Ps* 7:3
declare that he hath *d. this.* 22:31
I have sinned, and *d. this* evil. 51:4
hand of Lord hath *d. this.* *Isa* 41:20
this they have *d.* unto. *Ezek* 23:38
this have ye *d.* again. *Mal* 2:13
now all *this* was *d.* *Mat* 1:22; 21:4
26:56
an enemy hath *d. this.* 13:28
this which is *d.* to fig-tree. 21:21
this that this woman hath *d.* 26:13
Mark 14:9
that had *d. this* thing. *Mark* 5:32
when they had *d. this.* *Luke* 5:6
but *this* man hath *d.* nothing. 23:41
miracles than these *this* man hath *d.*?
John 7:31
heard he had *d. this* miracle. 12:18
what power have ye *d. this* ? *Acts* 4:7
this was *d.* thrice. 10:16; 11:10
so when *this* was *d.* others. 28:9
not mourned that he hath *d. this.*
1 Cor 5:2

door

Besides its common uses as the entrance to a house or building, this word is used metaphorically as the entrance to any thing: as our Saviour says, I am the door, *the entrance into the kingdom,* John 10:1. *The door of faith is the opportunity of belief offered to the Gentiles,* Acts 14:27. *Elsewhere also it means opportunity,* 2 Cor 2:12; Rev 3:8.

sin lieth at the *d.* *Gen* 4:7
came near to break the *d.* 19:9
Lord will pass over *d.* *Ex* 12:23
master shall bring him to *d.* 21:6
it through his ear to *d.* *Deut* 15:17
put her from me, bolt *d.* *2 Sam* 13:17
and he bolted the *d.* after her. 18
called, she stood in *d.* *2 Ki* 4:15
then open the *d.* and flee. 9:3
those who kept *d.* *Esth* 2:21* 6:2*
laid wait at neighbour's *d.* *Job* 31:9
that I went not out of the *d.*? 34
keep *d.* of my lips. *Ps* 141:3
as *d.* turneth upon. *Pr* 26:14
hand by hole of *d.* *S of S* 5:4
if she be a *d.* we will inclose. 8:9
brought me to the *d.* *Ezek* 8:3, 7
digged in the wall, behold a *d.* 8
every one stood at the *d.* 10:19
behold, at the *d.* of the gate. 11:1
the breadth of the *d.* was. 41:2*
people shall worship at the *d.* 46:3
valley of Achor for a *d.* of. *Hos* 2:15
smite the lintel of the *d.* *Amos* 9:1*
he rolled a great stone to the *d.* of.
Mat 27:60; *Mark* 15:46
angel rolled stone from *d.* *Mat* 28:2*
city was gathered at *d.* *Mark* 1:33
not so much as about the *d.* 2:2
shall roll the stone from *d.*? 16:3
entereth not by the *d.* *John* 10:1
that entereth in by the *d.* 2
I am the *d.* 7, 9
but Peter stood at the *d.* 18:16
damsel that kept the *d.* to Peter. 17
feet of them are at the *d.* *Acts* 5:9
as Peter knocked at the *d.* 12:13
when they had opened the *d.* 16
opened the *d.* of faith to. 14:27
a great *d.* and effectual. *1 Cor* 16:9
a *d.* was opened to me. *2 Cor* 2:12
God would open a *d.* of. *Col* 4:3
judge standeth before *d.* *Jas* 5:9
set before thee an open *d.* *Rev* 3:8
at *d.* and knock, if any open *d.* 20
I looked, and a *d.* was open. 4:1

door with *house*

smote them at *d.* of the *house.*
Gen 19:11
communed at *d.* of the *house.* 43:19
out at *d.* of his *house.* *Ex* 12:22
shall go to *d.* of *house.* *Lev* 14:38
d. of her father's *house.* *Deut* 22:21
fell down at *d.* of the man's *house.*
Judg 19:26, 27
slept at *d.* of king's *house.*
2 Sam 11:9
Naaman stood at *d.* of *house.*
2 Ki 5:9
unto the *d.* of the *house.* *Neh* 3:20
repaired from *d.* of the *house.* 21
not nigh *d.* of her *house.* *Pr* 5:8
sitteth at the *d.* of her *house.* 9:14
to *d.* of Lord's *h.* *Ezek* 8:14; 47:1

door with *shut*

Lot *shut* the *d.* *Gen* 19:6
angels *shut* the *d.* 10
when come in shalt *shut d.* *2 Ki* 4:4
she *shut d.* upon her. 5
she *shut d.* on him. 21
he went in and *shut* the *d.* 33
shut the *d.* and hold him at *d.* 6:32
when thou hast *shut* thy *d.* *Mat* 6:6
the *d.* was *shut.* 25:10
the *d.* is now *shut.* *Luke* 11:7
and hath *shut* to the *d.* 13:25
open *d.* no man can *shut.* *Rev* 3:8

door with *tabernacle*

bring to *d.* of *tabernacle.* *Ex* 29:4
40:12; *Lev* 4:4; 8:3, 4; 12:6
Num 6:10

kill bullock by *d.* of *tabernacle.*
Ex 29:11, 32; 40:29; *Lev* 1:5
Num 27:2
burnt offering at *d.* of *tabernacle.*
Ex 29:42; 33:9, 10; 38:8; 40:28
Lev 1:3; 3:2; 4:7, 18
before the *d.* of the *tabernacle.*
Ex 40:6; *Num* 25:6
at the *d.* of the *tabernacle. Lev* 8:31
35; 14:11; 16:7; 17:6; *Num* 6:18
10:3; *Josh* 19:51
not go out of *d.* of the *tabernacle.*
Lev 8:33
go out from *d.* of *tabernacle.* 10:7
unto *d.* of *tabernacle.* 14:23; 15:14
29; 19:21; *Num* 16:18, 19, 50; 20:6
not to *d.* of *tabernacle. Lev* 17:4, 9
stood in the *d.* of the *tabernacle.*
Num 12:5; 16:18
pillar of cloud over *d.* of *tabernacle.*
Deut 31:15
porter of *d.* of *tabernacle. 1 Chr* 9:21

door joined with *tent*

Abraham sat in *tent d.* *Gen* 18:1
he ran to meet them from *tent d.* 2
Sarah heard it in the *tent d.* 10
every man at *tent d.* *Ex* 33:8
worshipped, every man in *tent d.* 10
weeping, every man in the *d.* of his *tent.* *Num* 11:10
Abiram in *d.* of their *tents.* 16:27
stand in *d.* of the *tent.* *Judg* 4:20

doorkeeper

be a *d.* in house of God. *Ps* 84:10
of Maaseiah *keeper* of *d.* *Jer* 35:4

doorkeepers

which *keepers* of the *d.* *2 Ki* 22:4
the *keepers* of the *d.* to bring. 23:4
of guard took chief priest and three *keepers* of *d.* 25:18; *Jer* 52:24
Berechiah, Elkanah, *d.* *1 Chr* 15:23
Obed-edom and Jehiah *d.* 24
keepers of the *d.* sought. *Esth* 6:2*

door-post

bring him to the *d.-post.* *Ex* 21:6
measured *post* of the *d.* *Ezek* 41:3*

door-posts

blood on upper *d.-posts.* *Ex* 12:7*
write them on *d.-posts. Deut* 11:20
the *posts* of the *d.* moved. *Isa* 6:4
he measured the *d.-posts.*
Ezek 41:16*

doors

shall go out of the *d.* *Josh* 2:19
the *d.* of the parlour. *Judg* 3:24
opened not *d.* of the parlour. 25
what cometh forth of the *d.* 11:31
Samson took the *d.* of the gate. 16:3
her lord rose up, opened the *d.* 19:27
Samuel opened the *d.* *1 Sam* 3:15
David scrabbled on the *d.* of. 21:13
cut off gold from the *d.* *2 Ki* 18:16
Levites be porters of *d.* *2 Chr* 23:4
Hezekiah opened the *d.* of. 29:3
set up the *d.* of it. *Neh* 3:1, 3; 7:1
but I opened my *d.* to. *Job* 31:32
when I set bars and *d.* 38:10
hast thou seen the *d.* of the ? 17*
who can open the *d.* of his ? 41:14
up, ye everlasting *d.* *Ps* 24:7, 9
though he had opened *d.* of. 78:23
crieth at coming in at *d.* *Pr* 8:3
waiting at the posts of my *d.* 34
behind *d.* hast thou set up. *Isa* 57:8
still talking in the *d.* *Ezek* 33:30
keep the *d.* of thy mouth. *Mi* 7:5
open thy *d.* O Lebanon. *Zech* 11:1
know it is near, at the *d. Mat* 24:33
Mark 13:29
angel opened prison *d.* *Acts* 5:19
keepers standing before the *d.* 23
immediately all the *d.* were. 16:26
awaking and seeing prison *d.* 27

shut **doors**

Ehud *shut* the *d.* of. *Judg* 3:23
Ahaz *shut* up the *d.* of. *2 Chr* 28:24
our fathers have *shut* the *d.* 29:7
and let us *shut* the *d.* of. *Neh* 6:10
shut the *d.* and bar them. 7:3
because *shut* not up *d.* of. *Job* 3:10
or who *shut* up sea with *d.*? 38:8
the *d.* shall be *shut* in. *Eccl* 12:4
enter, and *shut* thy *d.* *Isa* 26:20
that would *shut* the *d.*? *Mal* 1:10
when *d.* were *shut.* *John* 20:19, 26
forthwith *d.* were shut. *Acts* 21:30

Dor

drive out inhabitants of *D. Judg* 1:27
Abinadab in region of *D.* *1 Ki* 4:11

Dorcas

by interpretation is *D.* *Acts* 9:36
shewing coats and garments *D.* 39

dote

and they shall *d.* *Jer* 50:36

doted

Aholah *d.* on her lovers. *Ezek* 23:5
whoredoms with all on whom she *d.* 7
Assyrians, on whom she *d.* 9, 12
as soon as she saw them, she *d.* 16
for she *d.* upon their paramours. 20

Dothan

to *D.* he found them in *D. Gen* 37:17
behold Elisha is in *D.* *2 Ki* 6:13

doting

d. about questions and. *1 Tim* 6:4

double

and take *d.* money in. *Gen* 43:12
and they took *d.* money. 15
theft be found, restore *d.* *Ex* 22:4
if found, let him pay *d.* 7
he shall pay *d.* 9
made breast-plate *d.* a span. 39:9
been worth a *d.* hired. *Deut* 15:18
by giving him a *d.* portion. 21:17
let a *d.* portion of thy. *2 Ki* 2:9
they were not of a *d.* *1 Chr* 12:33
that they are *d.* to that. *Job* 11:6*
to him with his *d.* bridle ? 41:13
with a *d.* heart do speak. *Ps* 12:2
she hath received *d.* for. *Isa* 40:2
for shame ye shall have *d.* in their land they shall possess the *d.* 61:7
recompense their sin *d.* *Jer* 16:18
destroy them with *d.* 17:18
I will render *d.* to thee. *Zech* 9:12
deacons grave, not *d.* *1 Tim* 3:8
counted worthy of *d.* honour. 5:17
d. unto her, *d.* according to works, cup fill to her *d.* *Rev* 18:6

double, *verb*

shalt *d.* sixth curtain. *Ex* 26:9
and *d.* unto her *d.* *Rev* 18:6

double-minded

d.-minded man is unstable. *Jas* 1:8
your hearts, ye *d.-minded.* 4:8

doubled

the dream was *d.* to. *Gen* 41:32
four-square, being *d.* *Ex* 28:16
was breadth thereof, being *d.* 39:9
let the sword be *d.* the. *Ezek* 21:14

doubt

Joseph is without *d.* *Gen* 37:33
life shall hang in *d.* *Deut* 28:66
no *d.* but ye are the people. *Job* 12:2
no *d.* kingdom of God. *Luke* 11:20
were in *d.* saying. *Acts* 2:12*
no *d.* this man is a murderer. 28:4
for our sakes, no *d.* *1 Cor* 9:10
voice I stand in *d.* of you. *Gal* 4:20*
no *d.* have continued. *1 John* 2:19

doubt, *verb*

wherefore didst thou *d.*? *Mat* 14:31
if ye have faith, and *d.* not. 21:21
not *d.* in his heart, but. *Mark* 11:23
thou make us to *d.*? *John* 10:24

doubted

worshipped him, some *d. Mat* 28:17
they *d.* whereunto. *Acts* 5:24*
now while Peter *d.* in. 10:17*
because I *d.* of such manner. 25:20*

doubteth

d. is damned if he eat. *Rom* 14:23

doubtful

neither be of *d.* mind. *Luke* 12:29
not to *d.* disputations. *Rom* 14:1

doubting

looked, *d.* of whom he. *John* 13:22
with them, nothing *d.* *Acts* 10:20
11:12*
pray without wrath and *d. 1 Tim* 2:8*

doubtless

d. ye shall not come. *Num* 14:30
I will *d.* deliver the. *2 Sam* 5:19
he shall *d.* come again. *Ps* 126:6
d. thou art our Father. *Isa* 63:16
if not to others, yet *d.* *1 Cor* 9:2
is not expedient for me *d. 2 Cor* 12:1
yea *d.* I count all things. *Phil* 3:8

doubts

dissolving of *d.* was. *Dan* 5:12
heard that thou canst dissolve *d.* 16

dough

people took their *d.* before it was leavened. *Ex* 12:34
unleavened cakes of the *d.* 39
offer a cake of the first of your *d.*
Num 15:20, 21
bring firstfruits of our *d. Neh* 10:37
women knead their *d.* to. *Jer* 7:18
priests first of your *d.* *Ezek* 44:30
he hath kneaded the *d.* *Hos* 7:4

dove

[1] *Any one of numerous birds of the pigeon family, although commonly the name is applied to the smaller varieties. This bird is very common in Palestine. It was considered clean and was used in sacrifices. Because of this they were sold in the temple courts,* Lev 12:6, 8; Luke 2:24; Mark 11:15. [2] *The dove is the symbol of gentleness and innocence,* Mat 10:16. *It is defenceless, faithful to its mate and home-loving. This last is the secret of the success of the training of carrier-pigeons.* [3] *The dove is used as a symbol of the Holy Spirit,* Mat 3:16.

The expression dove's dung, in 2 Ki 6:25, *may mean what it apparently does ; or it may mean a common plant which had some nutritive quality, and which rose to famine prices at the siege of Jerusalem.*

Noah sent forth a *d. Gen* 8:8, 10, 12
the *d.* found no rest for the. 8:9
the *d.* came in to him in the. 11
take a turtle-*d.* 15:9; *Lev* 12:6
oh that I had wings like a *d. Ps* 55:6
ye shall be as wings of a *d.* 68:13
not the soul of thy turtle-*d.* 74:19
thou hast *d.* eyes. *S of S* 1:15; 4:1
O my *d.* let me see thy. 2:14
open to me, my sister, my *d.* 5:2
my *d.* my undefiled is but one. 6:9
I did mourn as a *d.* *Isa* 38:14
dwell in rock, be like *d.* *Jer* 48:28
Ephraim is like a silly *d.* *Hos* 7:11
shall tremble as a *d.* out. 11:11
God descending like a *d.* *Mat* 3:16
Mark 1:10; *Luke* 3:22; *John* 1:32

doves

fourth part of a cab of *d.* *2 Ki* 6:2
eyes are as eyes of *d.* *S of S* 5:1
we mourn sore like *d.* *Isa* 59:1
that flee as the *d.* to their. 60:
shall be like the *d.* of. *Ezek* 7:1
lead her as with voice of *d. Nah* 2:
serpents, harmless as *d.* *Mat* 10:1
of them that sold *d.* 21:1
Mark 11:1
temple those that sold *d.* *John* 2:1
said unto them that sold *d.* 1

turtle-**doves**

shall take two *turtle-d.* *Lev* 14:2
sacrifice of two *turtle-d.* *Luke* 2:2

down

when the sun is *d.* *Lev* 22:
Deut 23:1
sun was *d.* commanded to take ki of Ai's carcase *d.* *Josh* 8:
taste aught till sun be *d. 2 Sam* 3:
walking up and *d.* *Job* 1:7; 2
let them wander up and *d. Ps* 59:
I am tossed up and *d.* as. 109:
hast walked up and *d.* *Ezek* 28:
shall walk up and *d.* *Zech* 10:
we were driven up and *d. Acts* 27:
clothed with a garment *d.* *Rev* 1:

down-sitting
thou knowest my *d.-s.* *Ps* 139:2

downward
again take root *d.* *2 Ki* 19:30
Isa 37:31
of beast that goeth *d.* *Eccl* 3:21
appearance of his loins *d.* *Ezek* 1:27
8:2

dowry
(*The money or estate a woman brings to her husband on marriage*)
endued me with good *d.* *Gen* 30:20
ask me never so much *d.* and. 34:12
pay according to the *d.* *Ex* 22:17
king desireth not any *d.* *1 Sam* 18:25

drag
gather them in their *d.* *Hab* 1:15
they burn incense to their *d.* 16

dragging
in little ship, *d.* the net. *John* 21:8

dragon
[1] *The Hebrew word* tan, *translated in Authorized Version* dragon, *is always used in the plural, and is applied to some creatures inhabiting the desert. It probably refers to wild beasts and not to any of the serpent family to which a dragon belongs. The Revised Version translates it in every case by the word* jackals. [2] *The Hebrew word* tannin *seems to refer to any great monster of land or sea, usually some kind of serpent or reptile, but not invariably. In the New Testament it is found only in the Revelation, applied metaphorically to* Satan, Rev 12:3, etc. *Either word is frequently used metaphorically.*
d. shalt thou trample. *Ps* 91:13*
he shall slay the *d.* that. *Isa* 27:1†
Rahab, and wounded the *d.* 51:9†
hath swallowed me up like a *d.*
Jer 51:34†
Pharaoh, the great *d.* *Ezek* 29:3
behold, a great red *d.* *Rev* 12:3
the *d.* stood. 4
d. fought. 7
d. was cast out. 9, 13
flood which the *d.* cast out. 16
the *d.* was wroth with the woman. 17
the *d.* gave him his power. 13:2
they worshipped the *d.* 4
he spake as a *d.* 11
frogs came out of mouth of *d.* 16:13
he laid hold on the *d.* 20:2

dragons
wine is the poison of *d.* *Deut* 32:33
I am a brother to *d.* *Job* 30:29*
broken us in place of *d.* *Ps* 44:19*
thou breakest the heads of *d.* 74:13
praise Lord from earth, ye *d.* 148:7
d. in pleasant palaces. *Isa* 13:22*
an habitation for *d.* 34:13*; 35:7*
the *d.* and owls shall honour. 43:20*
Jerusalem a den of *d.* *Jer* 9:11*
cities of Judah a den of *d.* 10:22*
snuffed up the wind like *d.* 14:6*
Hazor a dwelling for *d.* 49:33*
Babylon a dwelling for *d.* 51:37*
make a wailing like the *d.* *Mi* 1:8*
his heritage waste for *d.* *Mal* 1:3*

dragon well
even before the *d.-well.* *Neh* 2:13

drams
(*The Persian* daric *worth about five dollars, or a little more than an English pound.* Daric *always in Revisions*)
gold ten thousand *d.* *1 Chr* 29:7
gave 61,000 *d.* of gold. *Ezra* 2:69
of gold, of a thousand *d.* 8:27
thousand *d.* of gold. *Neh* 7:70
twenty thousand *d.* of gold. 71, 72

drank
Noah *d.* of the wine. *Gen* 9:21
d. and she made camels drink.
24:46
brought him wine, and he *d.* 27:25
the congregation *d.* *Num* 20:11
and *d.* wine of their. *Deut* 32:28
nor *d.* water three days. *1 Sam* 30:12
his own meat, and *d.* *2 Sam* 12:3
his house, and *d.* water. *1 Ki* 13:19
flesh, and he *d.* of the brook. 17:6
of the wine which he *d.* *Dan* 1:5
not defile himself with wine he *d.* 8
Belshazzar *d.* wine before the. 5:1
wives and his concubines *d.* in. 3
d. wine, and praised the gods. 4
and they all *d.* of it. *Mark* 14:23
they eat, they *d.* *Luke* 17:27, 28
our father Jacob who *d.* *John* 4:12
d. of that spiritual rock. *1 Cor* 10:4

draught
is cast out in the *d.* *Mat* 15:17
Mark 7:19
let down your nets for a *d.* *Luke* 5:4
for he was astonished at the *d.* 9

draught house
made Baal's house a *d.-h.* *2 Ki* 10:27

drave
(*The old form of* drove. *The American Revision replaces it with the modern form*)
chariot wheels, they *d.* *Ex* 14:25
they *d.* not out the. *Josh* 16:10
and *d.* them out. 24:12; *Judg* 6:9
Lord *d.* out before us all. *Josh* 24:18
Judah *d.* out inhabitants. *Judg* 1:19
which they *d.* before. *1 Sam* 30:20
Uzzah and Ahio *d.* the new cart.
2 Sam 6:3; *1 Chr* 13:7
that time Rezin *d.* Jews. *2 Ki* 16:6
Jeroboam *d.* Israel from. 18:21
whom God *d.* out. *Acts* 7:45*
Gallio *d.* them from. 18:16
see **drove**

draw
and I will also *d.* for. *Gen* 24:44
said, I will *d.* my sword. *Ex* 15:9
d. toward mount Tabor. *Judg* 4:6
will *d.* to thee Sisera. 7
Abimelech said, *d.* thy sword. 9:54
1 Sam 31:4; *1 Chr* 10:4
d. them from the city. *Judg* 20:32
d. that city into river. *2 Sam* 17:13
every man shall *d.* after. *Job* 21:33
d. me not away with the. *Ps* 28:3
d. me, we will run after. *S of S* 1:4
woe to those who *d.* iniquity. *Isa* 5:18
to the nations that *d.* the bow. 66:19
I will *d.* my sword out. *Ezek* 21:3
strangers shall *d.* their swords. 28:7
they shall *d.* their swords. 30:11
d. her, and all her multitudes. 32:20
hast nothing to *d.* with. *John* 4:11
thirst not, nor come hither to *d.* 15
except Father which sent me *d.* 6:44
I be lifted up from earth, *d.* all. 12:32
now they were not able to *d.* 21:6
to *d.* away disciples. *Acts* 20:30
d. you before judgement seats.
Jas 2:6*

draw *back*
faith, but if any *d. back.* *Heb* 10:38*
are not of them who *d. back* to. 39*

draw *near*
let us *d. near* to one. *Judg* 19:13
let us *d. near* to God. *1 Sam* 14:36
Saul said, *d.* ye *near* hither. 38
good for me to *d. near.* *Ps* 73:28
they *d. near* to the gates. 107:18
this people *d. near* with their lips.
Isa 29:13
d. near, ye that are escaped. 45:20
d. near hither, ye sons of. 57:3
will cause him to *d. near.* *Jer* 30:21
order buckler, and *d. near* to. 46:3
charge over city to *d. near.* *Ezek* 9:1
hast caused thy days to *d. near.* 22:4
let all men of war *d. near.* *Joel* 3:9
d. near with a true heart. *Heb* 10:22

draw *nigh*
d. not *nigh* hither, put off. *Ex* 3:5
d. nigh to my soul. *Ps* 69:18
d. nigh that follow mischief. 119:150
nor years *d. nigh.* *Eccl* 12:1
counsel of Holy One *d. nigh.* *Isa* 5:19
by the which we *d. nigh.* *Heb* 7:19
d. nigh to God, will *d. nigh.* *Jas* 4:8

draw *out*
d. out and take you a. *Ex* 12:21
I will *d. out* a sword. *Lev* 26:33
could not *d.* dagger *out.* *Judg* 3:22
thou *d. out* leviathan ? *Job* 41:1
d. out also the spear. *Ps* 35:3
wilt thou *d. out* thine anger ? 85:5
of understanding will *d. out.* *Pr* 20:5
against whom do ye *d. out* ? *Isa* 57:4
if thou *d. out* thy soul to the. 58:10
least of the flock *d.* them *out.*
Jer 49:20*; 50:45*
even sea monsters *d. out.* *Lam* 4:3
I will *d. out* a sword after them.
Ezek 5:2, 12; 12:14
one came to *d. out* fifty. *Hag* 2:16
d. out now, and bear to. *John* 2:8

draw *up*
trusteth that he can *d. up.* *Job* 40:23*

draw joined with *water.*
women go out to *d. water.*
Gen 24:11, 43
daughters come out to *d. water.* 13
ran again to well to *d. water.* 20
maidens going to *d. water.*
1 Sam 9:11
with joy shall ye *d. water.* *Isa* 12:3
d. thee *waters* for siege. *Nah* 3:14
of Samaria to *d. water.* *John* 4:7

drawer
from hewer of wood to *d.* *Deut* 29:11

drawers
be *d.* of water to. *Josh* 9:21, 27
d. of water for house of my God. 23

draweth
wife of the one *d.* near. *Deut* 25:11
now the day *d.* towards. *Judg* 19:9
he *d.* also the mighty. *Job* 24:22
yea his soul *d.* near to grave. 33:22
catch the poor when he *d.* *Ps* 10:9
my life *d.* nigh unto the grave. 88:3
that *d.* near the time of. *Isa* 26:17
time is come, day *d.* *Ezek* 7:12
this people *d.* nigh with. *Mat* 15:8
I am Christ, the time *d.* *Luke* 21:8
for your redemption *d.* nigh. 28
the coming of Lord *d.* nigh. *Jas* 5:8

drawing
delivered in places of *d.* *Judg* 5:11
they see Jesus *d.* nigh. *John* 6:19

drawn
angel, and his sword *d.* *Num* 22:23
31; *Josh* 5:13; *1 Chr* 21:16
heifer, which hath not *d.* *Deut* 21:3
but shalt be *d.* away, and. 30:17
till we have *d.* them. *Josh* 8:6
they were *d.* away. 16; *Judg* 20:31
which young men have *d.* *Ruth* 2:9
it is *d.* and cometh out. *Job* 20:25
wicked have *d.* out sword. *Ps* 37:14
softer than oil, yet *d.* swords. 55:21
deliver them that are *d.* *Pr* 24:11*
fled from the *d.* swords. *Isa* 21:15
that are *d.* from the breasts. 28:9
d. and cast forth beyond. *Jer* 22:19
with lovingkindness have I *d.* 31:3
d. back his right hand. *Lam* 2:3
I Lord have *d.* sword. *Ezek* 21:5, 28
all were *d.* up again to. *Acts* 11:10
when he is *d.* away of. *Jas* 1:14

dread
the *d.* of you shall be on. *Gen* 9:2
fear and *d.* shall fall upon. *Ex* 15:16
this day will I begin to put the *d.*
Deut 2:25; 11:25
shall not his *d.* fall ? *Job* 13:11
let not thy *d.* make me afraid. 21*
let him be your *d.* *Isa* 8:13

dread, *verb*
I said to you, *d.* not. *Deut* 1:29
be strong, *d.* not. *1 Chr* 22:13*

dreadful
how *d.* is this place ! *Gen* 28:17
a *d.* sound in his ears. *Job* 15:21
their rings, they were *d.* *Ezek* 1:18
fourth beast, *d.* and. *Dan* 7:7*, 19*
O Lord, the great and *d.* God. 9:4
the Chaldeans are terrible and *d.*
Hab 1:7
my name is *d.* among. *Mal* 1:14*
coming of great and *d.* day. 4:5*

dream

The Eastern people, and in particular the Jews, had a very great regard for dreams; they observed them, and applied to those who professed to explain them. We see the antiquity of this custom among the Egyptians, in the history of Pharaoh's butler and baker, and in Pharaoh himself, Gen 40:5, 8; 41:15. *Nebuchadnezzar is an instance of the same among the Chaldeans,* Dan 2:1, 2, 3, etc.

As the belief in dreams was generally connected with consultation of idol-priests, or those pretending to deal in magic, the Israelites were warned against dealing with these. But God revealed his will frequently in dreams, and there were those who could explain them, Gen 20:3; 28:12; 37:4; Num 12:6; Deut 13:1.

to Abimelech in a *d.* *Gen* 20:3, 6
Jacob saw in a *d.* the rams. 31:10
angel of God spake to Jacob in *d.* 11
God came to Laban in a *d.* 24
Joseph dreamed a *d.* 37:5, 9, 10
butler and baker dreamed a *d.* 40:5
and behold, it was a *d.* 41:7
1 Ki 3:15
to each according to *d.* *Gen* 41:12
the *d.* of Pharaoh is one. 25, 26
for that the *d.* was doubled. 32
will speak to him in a *d.* *Num* 12:6
a man that told a *d.* to. *Judg* 7:13
Gideon heard telling of the *d.* 15
Lord appeared in a *d.* *1 Ki* 3:5
shall fly away as a *d.* *Job* 20:8
in a *d.* he openeth the ears. 33:15
as a *d.* when one awaketh. *Ps* 73:20
for a *d.* cometh through. *Eccl* 5:3
against Ariel be as a *d.* *Isa* 29:7
hath a *d.* let him tell a *d.* *Jer* 23:28
was troubled to know *d.* *Dan* 2:3
tell thy servants the *d.* 4
if ye shew the *d.* 6
this is the *d.* and we will tell. 36
my lord, the *d.* be to them. 4:19
Daniel had a *d.* he wrote the *d.* 7:1
the angel appeared to Joseph in a *d.*
Mat 1:20; 2:13, 19
being warned of God in a *d.* 2:12, 22
suffered many things in a *d.* 27:19

dream, *verb*

we were like them that *d.* *Ps* 126:1
your old men *d.* dreams. *Joel* 2:28
Acts 2:17

dreamed

Jacob *d.* *Gen* 28:12
Joseph *d.* a dream. 37:5
the officers *d.* 40:5
Pharaoh *d.* 41:1, 15
Joseph remembered the dreams which he *d.* 42:9
I have *d.* I have *d.* *Jer* 23:25
dreams which you cause to be *d.* 29:8
Nebuchadnezzar *d.* dreams. *Dan* 2:1
the king said, I have *d.* a dream. 5

dreamer

behold, this *d.* cometh. *Gen* 37:19
if a *d.* of dreams arise. *Deut* 13:1
thou shalt not hearken to that *d.* 3
that prophet or *d.* of dreams. 5

dreamers

not to diviners nor *d.* *Jer* 27:9
those filthy *d.* defile flesh. *Jude* 8

dreameth

man *d.* a thirsty man *d.* *Isa* 29:8

dreams

hated Joseph for his *d.* *Gen* 37:8
see what will become of his *d.* 20
and he interpreted our *d.* 41:12
Joseph remembered the *d.* he. 42:9
Lord answered him not by *d.*
1 Sam 28:6, 15
thou scarest me with *d.* *Job* 7:14
in multitude of *d.* are. *Eccl* 5:7
forget my name with *d.* *Jer* 23:27
them that prophesy false *d.* 32
Daniel had understanding in *d.*
Dan 1:17; 5:12
diviners have told false *d.* *Zech* 10:2

dregs

d. thereof the wicked. *Ps* 75:8
hast drunken the *d.* *Isa* 51:17*, 22*

dress

[1] *To till or prune, as land, trees, etc.,* Gen 2:15. [2] *To prepare for food,* Gen 18:7.

man into the garden to *d.* *Gen* 2:15
a young man, he hasted to *d.* 18:7
plant vineyards, and *d.* *Deut* 28:39
to *d.* of his own for the. *2 Sam* 12:4
let Tamar *d.* the meat in. 13:5
go to Amnon's house, *d.* him meat. 7
that I may *d.* it for me. *1 Ki* 17:12
I will *d.* the other bullock. 18:23
d. it first, for ye are many. 25

dressed

took calf which he had *d.* *Gen* 18:8
d. in the fryingpan be. *Lev* 7:9
took five sheep ready *d.* *1 Sam* 25:18
poor man's lamb and *d.* *2 Sam* 12:4
Mephibosheth had not *d.* his. 19:24
they *d.* it, and called on. *1 Ki* 18:26
herbs for them by whom it is *d.*
Heb 6:7*

dresser

then said he to the *d.* *Luke* 13:7

dresseth

when he *d.* the lamps. *Ex* 30:7

drew

Rebekah *d.* water. *Gen* 24:20, 45
they *d.* and lifted up Joseph. 37:28
Zarah *d.* back his hand. 38:29
because I *d.* him out of. *Ex* 2:10
Jethro's daughters came and *d.* 16
an Egyptian *d.* water enough. 19
for Joshua *d.* not his hand. *Josh* 8:26
fell 120,000 men that *d.* *Judg* 8:10
but the youth *d.* not his sword. 20
chief of Israel 400,000 that *d.* 20:2
numbered 26,000 that *d.* sword. 15
all these *d.* the sword. 25, 35
liers in wait *d.* themselves along. 37
of Benjamin 25,000 that *d.* sword. 46
buy it for thee, so he *d.* *Ruth* 4:8
to Mizpeh, and *d.* water. *1 Sam* 7:6
David *d.* Goliath's sword. 17:51
he took me, he *d.* me out of many waters *2 Sam* 22:17; *Ps* 18:16
three mighty men *d.* water out of well of. *2 Sam* 23:16; *1 Chr* 11:18
in Israel 800,000 that *d.* *2 Sam* 24:9
certain man *d.* a bow. *1 Ki* 22:34
2 Chr 18:33
Moab took 700 that *d.* *2 Ki* 3:26
Jehu *d.* a bow with his full. 9:24
they sent and *d.* forth. *1 Chr* 19:16
eleven hundred thousand men that *d.* sword, Judah 470,000 that *d.* 21:5
d. out staves of the ark. *2 Chr* 5:9
1 Ki 8:8
of Benjamin that *d.* bows. *2 Chr* 14:8
they *d.* up Jeremiah. *Jer* 38:13
I *d.* them with cords. *Hos* 11:4
full, they *d.* to shore. *Mat* 13:48
Mark 6:53*
Peter *d.* his sword. *Mat* 26:51
Mark 14:47; *John* 18:10
and the sabbath *d.* on. *Luke* 23:54
servants which *d.* water. *John* 2:9
and *d.* the net to land full. 21:11
and *d.* away much people. *Acts* 5:37
stoned Paul and *d.* him out. 14:19
and *d.* Paul and Silas into. 16:19
the jailor *d.* his sword, and. 27
they *d.* Jason and certain. 17:6
d. Alexander out of the. 19:33
they took Paul and *d.* him out. 21:30
his tail *d.* the third part. *Rev* 12:4

drew *near,* or *nigh*

Abraham *d.* *near* and. *Gen* 18:23
time *d.* *nigh* that Israel. 47:29
when Pharaoh *d.* *nigh.* *Ex* 14:10
Moses *d.* *near* to thick. 20:21
the congregation *d.* *near.* *Lev* 9:5
people *d.* *nigh* before Ai. *Josh* 8:11
the Philistines *d.* *near.* *1 Sam* 7:10
Saul *d.* *near* to Samuel. 9:18
Goliath *d.* *near* morning and. 17:16
41, 48
David *d.* *near* to Goliath the. 40
Joab *d.* *nigh* against. *2 Sam* 10:13
Ahimaaz came and *d.* *near.* 18:25
Esther *d.* *near* and. *Esth* 5:2
the king's decree *d.* *near* to be. 9:1
she *d.* not *near* to God. *Zeph* 3:2
and when they *d.* *nigh.* *Mat* 21:1
when the time of fruit *d.* *near.* 34
d. *near* the publicans. *Luke* 15:1
elder son came, as he *d.* *nigh.* 25
feast of unleavened bread *d.* nigh.
22:1
and Judas *d.* *near* to Jesus. 47
Jesus himself *d.* *near.* 24:15
they *d.* *nigh* to the village where. 28
time of promise *d.* *nigh.* *Acts* 7:17
as he *d.* *near* to behold it. 31
as they *d.* *nigh* to the city. 10:9
deemed that they *d.* *near.* 27:27

drewest

thou *d.* near in the day. *Lam* 3:57

dried

until waters were *d.* up. *Gen* 8:7, 13
twenty-seventh day was earth *d.* 14
green ears of corn *d.* by. *Lev* 2:14
nor eat moist grapes or *d.* *Num* 6:3
our soul is *d.* away. 11:6
heard how Lord *d.* up. *Josh* 2:10
your God *d.* up Jordan, as Lord did Red sea, which he *d.* up. 4:23
heard Lord had *d.* up Jordan. 5:1
bind with withs never *d.* *Judg* 16:7
Jeroboam's hand *d.* up. *1 Ki* 13:4
brook *d.* because there had. 17:7
with the sole of my feet have I *d.* all the rivers. *2 Ki* 19:24; *Isa* 37:25
his roots shall be *d.* up. *Job* 18:16
they are *d.* up, they are. 28:4
my strength is *d.* up. *Ps* 22:15
my throat is *d.* mine eyes. 69:3
the Red sea, and it was *d.* 106:9
and their multitude *d.* up. *Isa* 5:13
river shall be wasted and *d.* up. 19:5
of defence be emptied and *d.* up. 6
art thou not it which hath *d.*? 51:10
places of wilderness *d.* up. *Jer* 23:10
and they shall be *d.* up. 50:38
know that I have *d.* up. *Ezek* 17:24
the east wind *d.* up her fruit. 19:12
our bones are *d.* and hope is. 37:11
their root is *d.* up. *Hos* 9:16
his fountain shall be *d.* up. 13:15
the new wine is *d.* up. *Joel* 1:10
the vine is *d.* up. 12
rivers of water are *d.* up. 20
arm shall be clean *d.* up. *Zech* 11:17
fountain of blood was *d.* *Mark* 5:29
they saw the fig tree *d.* up. 11:20
water of Euphrates was *d.* up.
Rev 16:12

driedst

the flood, thou *d.* up. *Ps* 74:15

drieth

flood decayeth and *d.* up. *Job* 14:11
but a broken spirit *d.* *Pr* 17:22
makes sea dry, and *d.* *Nah* 1:4

drink, *noun*

bottle, and gave lad *d.* *Gen* 21:19
I will give thy camels *d.* 24:14, 46
all *d.* that may be drunk. *Lev* 11:34
give the congregation *d.* *Num* 20:8
she gave Sisera *d.* and. *Judg* 4:19
gave meat and *d.* to. *Ezra* 3:7
them *d.* in vessels of gold. *Esth* 1:7
he gave them *d.* as out. *Ps* 78:15
I have mingled my *d.* with. 102:9
gave *d.* to every beast of. 104:11
he will cause the *d.* of. *Isa* 32:6
to give *d.* to my people. 43:20
my lovers that give me *d.* *Hos* 2:5
their *d.* is sour, they have. 4:18
giveth his neighbour *d.* *Hab* 2:15
ye are not filled with *d.* *Hag* 1:6
I was thirsty, and ye gave me *d.*
Mat 25:35
when gave thee *d.*? 37
thirsty, and ye gave me no *d.* 42
a Jew, askest *d.* of me. *John* 4:9
my blood is *d.* indeed. 6:55
enemy thirst, give him *d.* *Rom* 12:20
of God not meat and *d.* 14:17
drink same spiritual *d.* *1 Cor* 10:4
man judge in meat or in *d.* *Col* 2:16

drink, *verb*

The word drink is frequently used of taking in through the senses, or through the mind, the pleasures or the sorrows sent upon man. To eat and drink meant to enjoy themselves in any manner, Eccl 5:18. To drink blood *was to be satiated with slaughter,* Ezek 39:18. *As cup is used figuratively for the blessings and punishments of God, so to drink of the cup was to receive these,* Ps 75:8.

let me *d.* *Gen* 24:14, 17, 45
d. my lord. 18, 46
rods when flocks came to *d.* 30:38
what shall we *d.*? *Ex* 15:24
Moses made Israel *d.* of it. 32:20
not *d.* wine nor strong *d.* *Lev* 10:9
neither shall he *d.* *Num* 6:3
down on knees to *d.* *Judg* 7:5
go to the vessels and *d.* *Ruth* 2:9
drew water, but David would not *d.* *2 Sam* 23:16, 17; *1 Chr* 11:18, 19
that thou shalt *d.* of. *1 Ki* 17:4
and Haman sat down to *d.* *Esth* 3:15
he shall *d.* the wrath of. *Job* 21:20
make them *d.* of the river. *Ps* 36:8
made us to *d.* the wine of. 60:3
they gave me vinegar to *d.* 69:21
wicked of earth shall *d.* 75:8
they could not *d.* 78:44
thou gavest them tears to *d.* 80:5
he shall *d.* of the brook. 110:7
for they *d.* the wine of. *Pr* 4:17
lest they *d.* and forget law. 31:5
let him *d.* and forget his poverty. 7
d. yea *d.* abundantly. *S of S* 5:1
bitter to them that *d.* it. *Isa* 24:9
thou shalt no more *d.* it. 51:22
shall *d.* it in the courts. 62:9
my servants shall *d.* but ye. 65:13
cup of consolation to *d.* *Jer* 16:7
make them *d.* water of gall. 23:15
nations, to whom I send thee, to *d.* 25:15
and they shall *d.* and be moved. 16
cup and made all nations to *d.* 17
d. ye, and be drunken, and spue. 27
saith Lord, ye shall certainly *d.* 28
to this day they *d.* none. 35:14
they whose judgement was not to *d.* cup, shalt surely *d.* of it. 49:12
d. by measure, from time to time shalt thou *d.* *Ezek* 4:11
shalt *d.* of sister's cup deep. 23:32
they *d.* that which ye have. 34:19
that concubines might *d.* *Dan* 5:2
bring, and let us *d.* *Amos* 4:1
so shall all the heathen *d.*, yea, they shall *d.* and shall. *Ob* 16
d. thou, let thy foreskin. *Hab* 2:16
ye *d.* but ye are not filled. *Hag* 1:6
and they shall *d.* and. *Zech* 9:15
whoso shall give to *d.* *Mat* 10:42
able to *d.* of cup that I shall *d.* of and be baptized? 20:22; *Mark* 10:38
d. indeed of my cup. *Mat* 20:23
Mark 10:39
gave the cup, saying *d.* *Mat* 26:27
not *d.* henceforth till that day when I *d.* 29; *Mark* 14:25; *Luke* 22:18
if cup may not pass except I *d.* *Mat* 26:42
gave him vinegar to *d.* 27:34
filled a sponge with vinegar, and gave him to *d.* 48; *Mark* 15:36
d. any deadly thing. *Mark* 16:18
to thee, give me to *d.* *John* 4:10
let him come to me and *d.* 7:37
cup given me, shall I not *d.*? 18:11
all *d.* same spiritual drink. *1 Cor* 10:4
cannot *d.* the cup of the Lord. 21
oft as ye *d.* in remembrance. 11:25
have been all made to *d.* into. 12:13

strong **drink**

do not drink *strong d.* *Lev* 10:9
himself from *strong d.* *Num* 6:3
money for *strong d.* *Deut* 14:26
nor have ye drunk *strong d.* 29:6
not drink *strong d.* *Judg* 13:4, 7, 14
wine nor *strong d.* *1 Sam* 1:15
wine is a mocker, *strong d.* *Pr* 20:1
for princes to drink *strong d.* *Pr* 31:4
give *strong d.* to him that is. 6
may follow *strong d.* woe. *Isa* 5:11
of strength to mingle *strong d.* 22
strong d. shall be bitter to. 24:9
erred through *strong d.* and are out of way through *strong d.* 28:7
stagger, but not with *strong d.* 29:9
fill ourselves with *strong d.* 56:12
of wine and *strong d.* *Mi* 2:11
drink wine nor *strong d.* *Luke* 1:15

drink *water*, or *waters*

water of thy pitcher to *d.* *Gen* 24:43
shall lothe to *d.* *water*. *Ex* 7:18, 21
digged about river for *water* to *d.* 24
could not *d.* of the *waters*. 15:23
no *water* for the people to *d.* 17:1
water out of it, that they may *d.* 6
cause to *d.* bitter *water*. *Num* 5:24
26:27
neither any *water* to *d.* 20:5; 33:14
nor will we *d.* of *water*. 20:17; 21:22
buy *water* for money, that ye may *d.* *Deut* 2:6, 28
give me a little *water* to *d.* *Judg* 4:19
bowed upon knees to *d.* *water*. 7:6
the Egyptian *d.* *water*. *1 Sam* 30:11
to *d.* of the *water* of well of Bethlehem. *2 Sam* 23:15; *1 Chr* 11:17
eat bread, nor *d.* *water*. *1 Ki* 13:8, 9
water in a vessel that I may *d.* 17:10
filled with *water* that ye may *d.* *2 Ki* 3:17
d. every one *waters* of his. 18:31
Isa 36:16
given *water* to weary to *d.* *Job* 22:7
d. *waters* out of thine own. *Pr* 5:15
if enemy be thirsty, give *water* to *d.* 25:21
to *d.* the *waters* of Sihor. *Jer* 2:18
water of gall to *d.* 8:14; 9:15
d. *water* by measure. *Ezek* 4:11, 16
d. thy *water* with trembling. 12:18
they shall *d.* their *water* with. 19
all trees that *d.* *water*. 31:14, 16
pulse to eat, *water* to *d.* *Dan* 1:12
wandered to *d.* *water* but. *Amos* 4:8
not feed nor *d.* *water*. *Jonah* 3:7
a cup of *water* to *d.* *Mark* 9:41
give me *water* to *d.* *John* 4:7
d. no longer *water*, but. *1 Tim* 5:23

drink with *wine*

our father *d.* *wine*. *Gen* 19:32, 34
made their father *d.* *wine*. 33, 35
nor *d.* *wine* when ye go. *Lev* 10:9
Nazarite *d.* no vinegar of *wine*. *Num* 6:3
after that Nazarite may *d.* *wine*. 20
plant vineyards, but shalt not *d.* of *wine*. *Deut* 28:39; *Amos* 5:11
Manoah's wife might *d.* no *wine*. *Judg* 13:4, 7, 14
wine, that such as be faint may *d.* *2 Sam* 16:2
hast made us *d.* *wine* of. *Ps* 60:3
for they *d.* the *wine* of. *Pr* 4:17
and *d.* of the *wine* which I. 9:5
not for kings, to *d.* *wine*. 31:4
go and *d.* thy *wine* *Eccl* 9:7
thee to *d.* spiced *wine*. *S of S* 8:2
are mighty to *d.* *wine*. *Isa* 5:22
shall not *d.* *wine* with a song. 24:9
of stranger not *d.* thy *wine*. 62:8
give Rechabites *wine* to *d.* *Jer* 35:2
will *d.* no *wine*, ye shall *d.* no *wine*. 6
shall any priest *d.* *wine*. *Ezek* 44:21
took away *wine* that they should *d.* *Dan* 1:16
sold a girl for *wine* to *d.* *Joel* 3:3
they *d.* the *wine* of the. *Amos* 2:8
gave the Nazarites *wine* to *d.* 12
that *d.* *wine* in bowls. 6:6
plant vineyards, and *d.* *wine*. 9:14
but shall not *d.* *wine*. *Mi* 6:15
Zeph 1:13
gave him to *d.* *wine*. *Mark* 15:23
John shall *d.* neither *wine*. *Luke* 1:15
to eat flesh or *d.* *wine*. *Rom* 14:21
all nations *d.* of the *wine*. *Rev* 14:8
same shall *d.* of the *wine* of the. 10

drinkers

and howl, all ye *d.* of *wine*. *Joel* 1:5

drinketh

in which my lord *d.*? *Gen* 44:5
land *d.* water of rain. *Deut* 11:11
the poison whereof *d.* up. *Job* 6:4
who *d.* iniquity like water! 15:16
like Job who *d.* up scorning. 34:7
behold, he *d.* up a river. 40:23*
sendeth by a fool, *d.* *Pr* 26:6
he *d.* but he awaketh. *Isa* 29:8
the smith, he *d.* no water. 44:12
he *d.* with publicans? *Mark* 2:16
whosoever *d.* of this water shall. *John* 4:13
whosoever *d.* of water that I. 14
whoso *d.* of my blood. 6:54
that *d.* my blood dwelleth in me. 56
he that *d.* unworthily *d.* *1 Cor* 11:29
earth which *d.* in rain. *Heb* 6:7

drinking

camels till they have done *d.* *Gen* 24:19
as camels had done *d.* man took. 22
till Boaz have done eating and *d.* *Ruth* 3:3
eating and *d.* and. *1 Sam* 30:16
multitude, eating and *d.* *1 Ki* 4:20
d. vessels of gold. 10:21; *2 Chr* 9:20
Elah was *d.* *1 Ki* 16:9
Ben-hadad was *d.* 20:12, 16
three days eating and *d.* *1 Chr* 12:39
d. was according to the law. *Esth* 1:8
and daughters were *d.* *Job* 1:13, 18
eating flesh, and *d.* wine. *Isa* 22:13
John came neither eating nor *d.* *Mat* 11:18; *Luke* 7:33
Son of man came eating and *d.* *Mat* 11:19; *Luke* 7:34
were eating and *d.* till. *Mat* 24:38
eating and *d.* such things. *Luke* 10:7

drink offering

Jacob poured a *d.-off.* *Gen* 35:14
and fourth part of an hin of wine for *d.-off.* *Ex* 29:40; *Num* 15:5
do according to the *d.-off.* *Ex* 29:41
nor shall ye pour *d.-off.* 30:9
d.-off. shall be of wine. *Lev* 23:13
priest shall offer also his *d.-off.* *Num* 6:17
for a *d.-off.* a third part. 15:7
bring for a *d.-off.* half an hin. 10
his *d.-off.* according to the. 24
besides the continual *d.-off.* 28:10
15, 24; 29:16
hast thou poured a *d.-off.* *Isa* 57:6
that furnish the *d.-off.* 65:11*
the *d.-off.* is cut off from. *Joel* 1:9
the *d.-off.* is withholden. 13
return and leave a *d.-off.* 2:14

drink offerings

for a burnt-offering with *d.-off.* *Lev* 23:18, 37; *Num* 6:15; 28:31
29:11, 18, 19, 21, 24, 30, 33, 37, 39
their *d.-off.* shall be. *Num* 28:14
drank the wine of their *d.-off.* *Deut* 32:38
offered with their *d.-off.* *1 Chr* 29:21
2 Chr 29:35
buy meat-offerings and *d.-off.* *Ezra* 7:17
their *d.-off.* of blood. *Ps* 16:4
pour out *d.-off.* to other gods. *Jer* 7:18; 19:13; 32:29
pour out *d.-off.* 44:17, 18, 19, 25
poured out their *d.-off.* *Ezek* 20:28
princes part to give *d.-off.* 45:17

drinks

only in meats, and *d.* *Heb* 9:10

drive

strong hand shall he *d.* *Ex* 6:1
send hornets, which shall *d.* 23:28
I will not *d.* them out before thee. 29
by little and little I will *d.* them. 30
and thou shalt *d.* them out. 31
I will *d.* out the Canaanite. 33:2
behold I *d.* out before thee. 34:11
I may *d.* them out of the. *Num* 22:6
I may be able to overcome and *d.* 11
then shall ye *d.* out all. 33:52
but if ye will not *d.* out the. 55
to *d.* out nations greater and. *Deut* 4:38; 9:4, 5; *Josh* 3:10
so shalt thou *d.* them out. *Deut* 9:3

then will the Lord *d.* out. *Deut* 11:23
Lord thy God doth *d.* them. 18:12
them will I *d.* out from. *Josh* 13:6
then I shall be able to *d.* them. 14:12
children of Judah could not *d.* 15:63
of Manasseh could not *d.* out. 17:12
did not utterly *d.* them out. 13
Judg 1:28
shalt *d.* out Canaanites. *Josh* 17:18
Lord shall *d.* them out of. 23:5
the Lord will no more *d.* out. 13
Judg 2:3, 21
not *d.* inhabitants of. *Judg* 1:19
did not *d.* out Jebusites. 21
other tribes, 27, 29, 30, 31, 33
whom Lord our God shall *d.* 11:24*
d. go forward, slack not. *2 Ki* 4:24
who didst *d.* out the. *2 Chr* 20:7
make afraid, and *d.* *Job* 18:11*
they *d.* away the ass of. 24:3
how thou didst *d.* out. *Ps* 44:2
smoke is driven away, so *d.* 68:2
rod of correction shall *d.* it. *Pr* 22:15
and I will *d.* thee from. *Isa* 22:19*
be a curse, whither I shall *d.* *Jer* 24:9
that I should *d.* you out. 27:10, 15
because Lord did *d.* them. 46:15
Gentiles, whither I will *d.* *Ezek* 4:13
and they shall *d.* thee. *Dan* 4:25, 32
I will *d.* them out of my. *Hos* 9:15
I will *d.* the northern. *Joel* 2:20
shall *d.* out Ashdod. *Zeph* 2:4
ship was caught, we let her *d.*
Acts 27:15

driven

thou hast *d.* me out this. *Gen* 4:14
were *d.* from Pharaoh's. *Ex* 10:11
the beast be *d.* away. 22:10
have *d.* out enemies. *Num* 32:21
thou shouldest be *d.* to. *Deut* 4:19*
whither Lord hath *d.* thee. 30:1
if any of them be *d.* out to. 4*
the Lord hath *d.* out. *Josh* 23:9
they have *d.* me out. *1 Sam* 26:19
wisdom *d.* quite from me? *Job* 6:13
wilt thou break a leaf *d.* to? 13:25
he shall be *d.* from light into. 18:18
d. forth from among men. 30:5
let them be *d.* backward. *Ps* 40:14
as smoke is *d.* away, so drive. 68:2
Jordan was *d.* back. 114:3, 5*
wicked is *d.* away in his. *Pr* 14:32*
shall be *d.* to darkness. *Isa* 8:22
sown by brooks be *d.* away. 19:7
he gave them as *d.* stubble. 41:2
places whither I have *d.* *Jer* 8:3
23:3, 8; 29:14, 18; 32:37
from lands whither he had *d.* 16:15
ye have *d.* them away. 23:2
shall be *d.* on and fall therein. 12
out of all places whither they were *d.*
40:12; 43:5
of nations whither I have *d.* 46:28
ye shall be *d.* out every man. 49:5
the lions have *d.* him away. 50:17
I have *d.* him out for his. *Ezek* 31:11
again which was *d.* away. 34:4, 16
and he was *d.* from men. *Dan* 4:33
5:21
countries whither thou hast *d.* 9:7
as the chaff that is *d.* *Hos* 13:3
I will gather her that was *d.* *Mi* 4:6
Zeph 3:19
he was *d.* of the devil. *Luke* 8:29
strake sail, and were *d.* *Acts* 27:17
we were *d.* up and down in. 27
is like a wave of the sea *d.* *Jas* 1:6
ships though great are *d.* of. 3:4

driver

Ahab said to *d.* of his. *1 Ki* 22:34
nor regardeth crying of *d.* *Job* 39:7

driveth

is like Jehu, for he *d.* *2 Ki* 9:20
like chaff which wind *d.* *Ps* 1:4
the north wind *d.* away. *Pr* 25:23*
the spirit *d.* him into. *Mark* 1:12

driving

those nations without *d.* *Judg* 2:23
d. is like the *d.* of Jehu. *2 Ki* 9:20
by *d.* out nations before. *1 Chr* 17:21

dromedaries

(Originally this word was applied to any fleet camel bred especially for riding. See **camel***)*
barley and straw for *d.* *1 Ki* 4:28*
letters by riders on *d.* *Esth* 8:10*
d. of Midian and Ephah. *Isa* 60:6

dromedary

thou art a swift *d.* *Jer* 2:23

drop

nations are as the *d.* of. *Isa* 40:15

drop, *verb*

my doctrine shall *d.* as. *Deut* 32:2
heavens shall *d.* down dew. 33:28
Pr 3:20
which clouds do *d.* and. *Job* 36:28*
and thy paths *d.* fatness. *Ps* 65:11
they *d.* on the pastures of the. 12
lips of a strange woman *d.* *Pr* 5:3
thy lips, my spouse, *d.* *S of S* 4:11
d. down, ye heavens. *Isa* 45:8
d. thy word toward. *Ezek* 20:46
d. thy word toward holy places. 21:2
mountains shall *d.* down new wine.
Joel 3:18; *Amos* 9:13
d. not thy word against. *Amos* 7:16

dropped

d. the clouds also *d.* water. *Judg* 5:4
into wood, honey *d.* *1 Sam* 14:26
till water *d.* on them. *2 Sam* 21:10
and my speech *d.* upon. *Job* 29:22
the heavens also *d.* at. *Ps* 68:8
my hands *d.* with myrrh. *S of S* 5:5

droppeth

idleness the house *d.* *Eccl* 10:18*

dropping

contentions of a wife are a continual *d.* *Pr* 19:13; 27:15
d. sweet smelling myrrh. *S of S* 5:13

drops

he maketh small the *d.* *Job* 36:27
who hath begotten the *d.*? 38:28
my locks with the *d.* *S of S* 5:2
sweat was as great *d.* *Luke* 22:44

dropsy

a man before him, who had *d.*
Luke 14:2

dross

take away the *d.* from. *Pr* 25:4
potsherd covered with silver *d.* 26:23
silver is become *d.* wine. *Isa* 1:22
I will purely purge away thy *d.* 25
house of Israel is to me become *d.*
Ezek 22:18, 19

drought

in the day *d.* consumed. *Gen* 31:40
fiery serpents and *d.* *Deut* 8:15*
d. and heat consume. *Job* 24:19
moisture is turned into *d.* *Ps* 32:4
Lord satisfy thy soul in *d.* *Isa* 58:11*
us through a land of *d.* *Jer* 2:6
not be careful in year of *d.* 17:8
a *d.* is upon her waters. 50:38
thee in land of great *d.* *Hos* 13:5
and I called for a *d.* *Hag* 1:11

drove, -s

every *d.* by themselves, and put a space betwixt *d.* and *d.* *Gen* 32:16
commanded all that followed *d.* 19
meanest thou by all this *d.*? 33:8*

drove, *verb*

so God *d.* out the man. *Gen* 3:24
fowls came, Abram *d.* them. 15:11
shepherds came and *d.* *Ex* 2:17
they *d.* out the Amorites. *Num* 21:32
Caleb *d.* thence the. *Josh* 15:14
who *d.* away the. *1 Chr* 8:13*
and *d.* asunder the nations. *Hab* 3:6
he *d.* them all out of. *John* 2:15*

drown

love, nor can floods *d.* it. *S of S* 8:7
foolish lusts, that *d.* *1 Tim* 6:9

drowned

chosen captains are *d.* *Ex* 15:4*
it shall be *d.* as by flood. *Amos* 8:8*
9:5*
better he were *d.* in. *Mat* 18:6*
Egyptians assaying to do, were *d.*
Heb 11:29*

drowsiness

d. shall clothe a man. *Pr* 23:21

drunk

all drink that may be *d.* *Lev* 11:34
not eaten bread, nor *d.* *Deut* 29:6
I will make mine arrows *d.* 32:42
when Samson had *d.* *Judg* 15:19
Boaz had eaten and *d.* *Ruth* 3:7
Hannah rose up after they *d.*
1 Sam 1:9
I have *d.* neither wine nor. 15
David made Uriah *d.* *2 Sam* 11:13
hast eaten bread and *d.* *1 Ki* 13:22
Elah was in Tirzah, drinking himself *d.* 16:9
Ben-hadad drinking himself *d.* 20:16
they had eaten and *d.* *2 Ki* 6:23
digged and *d.* strange waters. 19:24
Isa 37:25
I have *d.* my wine with. *S of S* 5:1
which hast *d.* the cup of. *Isa* 51:17
will make them *d.* in my fury. 63:6
sword shall be made *d.* *Jer* 46:10
I will make *d.* her princes. 51:57
and to have *d.* of the. *Ezek* 34:18
they *d.* wine, and praised. *Dan* 5:4
and thy concubines have *d.* 23
as ye have *d.* upon my. *Ob* 16
man having *d.* old wine. *Luke* 5:39
we have eaten and *d.* in. 13:26
when men have well *d.* *John* 2:10
be not *d.* with wine. *Eph* 5:18
made *d.* with the wine of. *Rev* 17:2
for all nations have *d.* of wine. 18:3

drunkard

son is a glutton and *d.* *Deut* 21:20
for *d.* and glutton shall. *Pr* 23:21
thorn goeth up into hand of *d.* 26:9
reel to and fro like a *d.* *Isa* 24:20
with a fornicator or *d.* eat. *1 Cor* 5:11

drunkards

I was the song of the *d.* *Ps* 69:12
woe to pride, to the *d.* *Isa* 28:1, 3
awake, ye *d.* and weep. *Joel* 1:5
they are drunken as *d.* *Nah* 1:10
nor *d.* shall inherit the. *1 Cor* 6:10

drunken

Noah was *d.* and he. *Gen* 9:21
Hannah had been *d.* *1 Sam* 1:13
how long wilt thou be *d.*? 14
merry, for he was very *d.* 25:36
to stagger like a *d.* man. *Job* 12:25
Ps 107:27
as a *d.* man staggereth. *Isa* 19:14
they are *d.* but not. 29:9; 51:21
be *d.* with their own blood. 49:26
thou hast *d.* the dregs of cup. 51:17
I am like a *d.* man. *Jer* 23:9
be *d.* and spue, and fall. 25:27
make ye him *d.* for he. 48:26
they have assuredly *d.* and. 49:12
cup that made all earth *d.* 51:7
I will make them *d.* that they. 39
he hath made me *d.* *Lam* 3:15*
O Edom, thou shalt be *d.* 4:21
Nah 3:11
have *d.* water for money. *Lam* 5:4
drink blood till ye be *d.* *Ezek* 39:19
and while they are *d.* *Nah* 1:10
and makest him *d.* also. *Hab* 2:15
fellow-servants, to eat and drink with *d.* *Mat* 24:49; *Luke* 12:45
till I have eaten and *d.* *Luke* 17:8
for these are not *d.* as. *Acts* 2:15
and another is *d.* *1 Cor* 11:21
they that be *d.* are *d.* *1 Thes* 5:7
I saw the woman *d.* with. *Rev* 17:6

drunkenness

to add *d.* to thirst. *Deut* 29:19*
strength, and not for *d.* *Eccl* 10:17
of Jerusalem with *d.* *Jer* 13:13
shalt be filled with *d.* *Ezek* 23:33
be overcharged with *d.* *Luke* 21:34
not in rioting and *d.* *Rom* 13:13
of flesh are murders, *d.* *Gal* 5:21

Drusilla

came with his wife *D.* *Acts* 24:24

dry

mingled with oil and *d.* *Lev* 7:1
it is a *d.* scald, a leprosy. 13:3
was *d.* and mouldy. *Josh* 9:5, 1
it be *d.* on all earth. *Judg* 6:3
it now be *d.* only on the fleece. 3

wilt thou pursue the d.? Job 13:25
they ran in d. places. Ps 105:41
better is a d. morsel and. Pr 17:1
as the heat in a d. place. Isa 25:5
as rivers of water in a d. 32:2
that saith to the deep, be d. 44:27
neither let eunuch say, I am a d. 56:3
a d. wind, not to fan, nor. Jer 4:11*
dry up, and make springs d. 51:36
made the d. tree flourish. Ezek 17:24
it shall devour every d. tree. 20:47
I will make the rivers d. 30:12
the bones were very d. 37:2
O ye d. bones. 4
Lord give them d. breasts. Hos 9:14
spring shall become d. 13:15
the sea, and maketh it d. Nah 1:4
devoured as stubble fully d. 10
will make Nineveh d. Zeph 2:13
he walketh through d. places.
Mat 12:43; Luke 11:24
green tree what shall be done in d.?
Luke 23:31

dry *ground*

face of the ground was d. Gen 8:13
shall go on d. ground. Ex 14:16, 22
ark stood on d. ground, Israel passed
on d. ground. Josh 3:17
Elijah and Elisha went on d. ground.
2 Ki 2:8
springs into d. ground. Ps 107:33*
turneth d. ground into water. 35
floods upon the d. ground. Isa 44:3
root out of a d. ground. 53:2
a d. and thirsty ground. Ezek 19:13
see **land**

dry, *verb*

waters and they d. up. Job 12:15
the flame shall d. up his. 15:30
d. up herbs, I will d. up. Isa 42:15
I will d. up thy rivers. 44:27
I d. up the sea. 50:2
Lord, I will d. up her sea. Jer 51:36
deeps of river shall d. up. Zech 10:11

dryshod

river, and men go d.-shod. Isa 11:15

due

thy d. and thy son's d. Lev 10:13, 14
this shall be priest's d. Deut 18:3
sought him not after d. 1 Chr 15:13*
the glory d. to his name. 16:29
Ps 29:2; 96:8
portion for singers, d. for. Neh 11:23
withhold not to whom it is d. Pr 3:27
he pay all that was d. Mat 18:34
receive the d. reward. Luke 23:41
to whom tribute is d. Rom 13:7

due *benevolence*

render to wife d. ben. 1 Cor 7:3

due *season*

you rain in d. season. Lev 26:4
Deut 11:14
to me in their d. season. Num 28:2
give them their meat in d. season.
Ps 104:27; 145:15
word spoken in d. season. Pr 15:23
princes eat in d. season. Eccl 10:17
to give them meat in d. season.
Mat 24:45; Luke 12:42
in d. season we shall reap. Gal 6:9

due *time*

foot shall slide in d. time. Deut 32:35
in d. time Christ died. Rom 5:6
one born out of d. time. 1 Cor 15:8
ransom, testified in d. time. 1 Tim 2:6
in d. time manifested. Tit 1:3
exalt you in d. time. 1 Pet 5:6

dues

to all their d. tribute. Rom 13:7

duke

d. Alvah, d. Jetheth. Gen 36:40†
1 Chr 1:51†

dukes

d. of sons of Esau. Gen 36:15†, 19†
the d. of the Horites. 21†, 29†
then the d. of Edom. Ex 15:15†
which were d. of Sihon. Josh 13:21*

dulcimer

lute, d. all kinds. Dan 3:5, 10, 15

dull

heart is waxed gross, and ears are d.
Mat 13:15; Acts 28:27
utter, seeing ye are d. Heb 5:11

Dumah

sons of Ishmael, D. Massa.
Gen 25:14; 1 Chr 1:30

Dumah

D. was in Judah's. Josh 15:52
the burden of D. he. Isa 21:11

dumb

[1] Unable to speak for want of physical power, Ex 4:11. *[2] Unable to speak to, and teach others, for lack of grace and knowledge,* Isa 56:10. *[3] Unable to speak for oneself, either through ignorance or fear of those in whose presence one is,* Ps 39:9; Pr 31:8; Dan 10:15.

who maketh the d. or deaf ? Ex 4:11
I was as a d. man. Ps 38:13
I was d. with silence. 39:2, 9
open thy mouth for d. Pr 31:8
and the tongue of the d. Isa 35:6
a sheep before shearers is d. 53:7
are blind, all d. dogs. 56:10
be d. and shalt not be. Ezek 3:26
speak, and be no more d. 24:27
and I was no more d. 33:22
face to ground, became d. Dan 10:15
to make him d. idols. Hab 2:18
woe to him that saith to d. stone. 19
brought to him a d. man. Mat 9:32
devil was cast out, the d. spake. 33
Luke 11:14
one blind and d. and he. Mat 12:22
those that were blind, d. 15:30
wondered, when they saw the d.
speak, the blind. 31; Mark 7:37
son who hath a d. spirit. Mark 9:17
thou d. spirit, I charge thee. 25
be d. until the day that. Luke 1:20
like a lamb d. before. Acts 8:32
carried away to d. idols. 1 Cor 12:2
the d. ass speaking with. 2 Pet 2:16

dung

By dung is represented any thing that is nauseous or loathsome, Jer 8:2; 9:22; Job 20:7; Phil 3:8.

flesh, skin, and d. burn. Ex 29:14
Lev 4:11; 8:17; 16:27; Num 19:5
a man taketh away d. 1 Ki 14:10
of a cab of doves' d. 2 Ki 6:25
of Jezebel shall be as d. 9:37
eat their own d. 18:27; Isa 36:12
for ever like his own d. Job 20:7
they became as d. Ps 83:10
they shall be for d. on. Jer 8:2
they shall be as d. 16:4
they shall be d. 25:33
bake it with d. that. Ezek 4:12
given thee cow's d. for man's d. 15
flesh shall be as the d. Zeph 1:17
spread d. on your faces, even the d.
of your solemn feasts. Mal 2:3
count all things but d. Phil 3:8†
dove's dung, *see on* **dove**

dung, *verb*

I dig about it, and d. it. Luke 13:8

dungeon

should put me into d. Gen 40:15
Joseph hastily out of d. 41:14
firstborn of captive in d. Ex 12:29
was entered into the d. Jer 37:16
cast him into d. no water in d. 38:6, 9
take up Jeremiah out of the d. 10
down by cords into the d. to. 11
drew up Jeremiah out of d. 13
cut off my life in the d. Lam 3:53
I called on thy name, out of d. 55

dung gate

valley gate to d.-gate. Neh 3:13
the d.-gate repaired Malchiah. 14
company went toward d.-gate. 12:31

dunghill

lifteth up beggar from d. 1 Sam 2:8
Ps 113:7
his house be made a d. Ezra 6:11
straw is trodden for d. Isa 25:10
your houses be made a d. Dan 2:5
their houses shall be made a d. 3:29

unsavoury salt not fit for land or d.
Luke 14:35

dunghills

up in scarlet, embrace d. Lam 4:5

Dura

set image up in plain of D. Dan 3:1

durable

yea, d. riches and. Pr 8:18
merchandise shall be for d. Isa 23:18

dureth

not root in himself, d. Mat 13:21

durst

he that d. presume in. Esth 7:5
afraid, I d. not shew. Job 32:6
nor d. ask any more. Mat 22:46
Mark 12:34; Luke 20:40
none of disciples d. ask. John 21:12
and of the rest d. no man. Acts 5:13
Moses trembled and d. not. 7:32
he d. not bring a railing. Jude 9

dust

The Hebrews, when they mourned, put dust *or* ashes *upon their heads,* Josh 7:6; Isa 47:1; Lam 3:29. *The dust denotes likewise the grave and death,* Gen 3:19; Job 7:21; Ps 22:15. *The dust represents also a multitude,* Gen 13:16; Num 23:10; Ps 78:27.

d. shalt thou eat all days. Gen 3:14
thou art, and unto d. shalt. 19
if a man can number the d. 13:16
speak to Lord, who am but d. 18:27
say to Aaron, smite the d. Ex 8:16
Aaron smote d. of the earth. 17
become small d. in all the land. 9:9
shall pour out the d. Lev 14:41*
pour out blood, cover it with d. 17:13
can count the d. of Jacob ? 23:10
I cast the d. into brook. Deut 9:21
2 Ki 23:12
make rain of thy land d. Deut 28:24
and the elders put d. on. Josh 7:6
Shimei cursed David, and cast d.
2 Sam 16:13
fire of Lord consumed d. 1 Ki 18:38
if the d. of Samaria shall. 20:10
Josiah made d. of the. 2 Chr 34:4
they sprinkled d. upon. Job 2:12
with worms and clods of d. 7:5
wilt bring me into d. again ? 10:9
as for the earth, it hath d. of. 28:6
man shall turn again to d. 34:15
d. groweth into hardness. 38:38
repent in d. and ashes. 42:6
brought me into the d. Ps 22:15
shall d. praise thee, shall it ? 30:9
his enemies shall lick the d. 72:9
flesh also upon them as d. 78:27
thy servants favour the d. 102:14
remembereth that we are d. 103:14
then shall d. return. Eccl 12:7
their d. shall be made fat. Isa 34:7
the d. thereof shall be turned. 9
who hath comprehended d.? 40:12
lick up the d. of thy feet. 49:23
shake thyself from the d. 52:2
d. shall be the serpent's meat. 65:25
cast d. on their heads. Lam 2:10
Ezek 27:30
to cover it with d. Ezek 24:7
I will also scrape her d. from. 26:4
their d. shall cover thee. 10
that pant after the d. of. Amos 2:7
shall lick the d. like. Mi 7:17
and the clouds are the d. Nah 1:3
for they shall heap d. Hab 1:10
shake off the d. of your. Mat 10:14
Mark 6:11; Luke 9:5
d. of your city we do. Luke 10:11
they shook off the d. Acts 13:51
as they threw d. into the air. 22:23
cast d. on their heads. Rev 18:19

as the **dust**

and make thy seed as the d. of the.
Gen 13:16; 28:14; 2 Chr 1:9
calf small as the d. Deut 9:21
I beat them as small as d.
2 Sam 22:43; Ps 18:42
lay up gold as the d. Job 22:24
heap up silver as the d. 27:16
blossom shall go up as d. Isa 5:24

nations *as the* small *d.* of. *Isa* 40:15
he gave them *as the d.* to his. 41:2
blood be poured out *as d. Zeph* 1:17
Tyrus heaped up silver *as the d.* *Zech* 9:3

in the **dust**

foundation is *in the d.* *Job* 4:19
now shall I sleep *in the d.* 7:21
defiled my horn *in the d.* 16:15
rest together is *in the d.* 17:16
lie down with him *in the d.* 20:11
shall lie down alike *in the d.* 21:16
warmeth them *in the d.* 39:14
hide them *in the d.* together. 40:13
lay mine honour *in the d.* *Ps* 7:5
hide thee *in the d.* for fear. *Isa* 2:10
sing, ye that dwell *in the d.* 26:19
come down and sit *in the d.* 47:1
putteth his mouth *in the d. Lam* 3:29
many that sleep *in the d. Dan* 12:2
roll thyself *in the d.* *Mi* 1:10
nobles shall dwell *in the d. Nah* 3:18

like the **dust**

make them *like the d.* *2 Ki* 13:7
thy strangers be *like d.* *Isa* 29:5

of the **dust**

Lord formed man *of the d. Gen* 2:7
priest take *of the d.* *Num* 5:17
of serpents *of the d.* *Deut* 32:24
raiseth poor out *of the d. 1 Sam* 2:8 *Ps* 113:7
exalted thee out *of the d. 1 Ki* 16:2
affliction cometh not *of the d. Job* 5:6
things that grow out *of the d.* 14:19
nor highest part *of the d.* *Pr* 8:26
all are *of the d.* *Eccl* 3:20
speech shall be out *of the d. Isa* 29:4

to the **dust**

all that go down *to the d.* *Ps* 22:29
soul is bowed down *to the d.* 44:25
die and return *to* their *d.* 104:29
my soul cleaveth *to the d.* 119:25
d. and all turn *to d.* again. *Eccl* 3:20
bring fortress *to the d.* *Isa* 25:12
the lofty city *to the d.* 26:5

duties

son that doth not those *d. Ezek* 18:11

duty

her *d.* of marriage shall. *Ex* 21:10
perform *d.* of husband's. *Deut* 25:5
will not perform the *d.* of my. 7
d. of every day required. *2 Chr* 8:14 *Ezra* 3:4
this is whole *d.* of man. *Eccl* 12:13
which was our *d.* to do. *Luke* 17:10
their *d.* is to minister. *Rom* 15:27*

dwarf

a *d.* shall not come nigh. *Lev* 21:20

dwell

(*To abide as a resident ; live ; reside. To continue a long time*)

Japhet shall *d.* in tents. *Gen* 9:27
he shall *d.* in the presence 16:12
for he feared to *d.* in Zoar. 19:30
d. where it pleaseth thee. 20:15
Canaanites, amongst whom I *d.* 24:3
land before you, *d.* and trade. 34:10
we will *d.* with you, and. 16
go up to Beth-el, and *d.* there. 35:1
Moses was content to *d.* *Ex* 2:21
d. amongst them. 25:8; 29:46
I will *d.* amongst children of. 29:45
unclean shall *d.* alone. *Lev* 13:46
d. in booths. 23:42, 43; *Neh* 8:14
camps, in the midst whereof I *d.* *Num* 5:3
lo, the people shall *d.* alone. 23:9
our little ones shall *d.* in. 32:17
give to the Levites, cities to *d.* in. 35:2, 3; *Josh* 14:4; 21:2
Lord *d.* among children. *Num* 35:34
to cause his name to *d.* there. *Deut* 12:11; *Ezra* 6:12
servant escaped shall *d. Deut* 23:16
he shall *d.* between his. 33:12
ye *d.* among us. *Josh* 9:7, 22
he shall *d.* in that city. 20:6
cities ye built not, and ye *d.* 24:13
Gaal should not *d.* in. *Judg* 9:41
Micah said to Levite, *d.* with. 17:10
that I may *d.* there, why should thy servant *d.* in the ? *1 Sam* 27:5
d. among children of. *1 Ki* 6:13
would *d.* in thick darkness. 8:12 *2 Chr* 6:1
to Zarephath, and *d.* there. *1 Ki* 17:9
I *d.* among own people. *2 Ki* 4:13
let them go and *d.* there. 17:27
let a cloud *d.* upon it. *Job* 3:5
let not wickedness *d.* in thy. 11:14
shall *d.* in his tabernacle. 18:15
to *d.* in the clifts of the. 30:6
neither evil *d.* with thee. *Ps* 5:4*
who shall *d.* in thy holy hill ? 15:1
his soul shall *d.* at ease. 25:13
depart from evil, and *d.* 37:27
that he may *d.* in thy courts. 65:4
they that *d.* in uttermost parts. 8
hill which God desireth to *d.* in, yea the Lord will *d.* in it. 68:16
Lord might *d.* among them. 18
build Judah that they may *d.* 69:35
they that *d.* in the wilderness. 72:9
and made Israel to *d.* in. 78:55
d. in tents of wickedness. 84:10
faithful, that they may *d.* with. 101:6
they found no city to *d.* in. 107:4
he maketh the hungry to *d.* 36
that I *d.* in tents of Kedar. 120:5
will I *d.* for I have desired it. 132:14
if I *d.* in uttermost parts of. 139:9
upright shall *d.* in thy. 140:13
made me to *d.* in darkness. 143:3
hearkeneth to me shall *d.* *Pr* 1:33
I wisdom *d.* with prudence. 8:12
it is better to *d.* in wilderness. 21:19
I *d.* in midst of a people. *Isa* 6:5
the wolf shall *d.* with the. 11:6
owls shall *d.* there, satyrs. 13:21
let mine outcasts *d.* with thee. 16:4
merchandise for them that *d.* 23:18
that *d.* therein are desolate. 24:6
bringeth down them that *d.* on. 26:5
awake and sing, ye that *d.* 19
people *d.* in Zion at Jerusalem. 30:19
then judgement shall *d.* in. 32:16
people *d.* in peaceful habitation. 18
who shall *d.* with devouring fire? who shall *d.* with everlasting ? 33:14
he shall *d.* on high. 16
the people that *d.* therein. 24
owl and the raven shall *d.* 34:11
them out as a tent to *d.* in. 40:22
give place that I may *d.* 49:20
restorer of paths to *d.* in. 58:12
and my servants shall *d.* there. 65:9
Shemaiah shall not have a man to *d.* *Jer* 29:32
shall *d.* in Judah husbandmen. 31:24
all your days ye shall *d.* in. 35:7
and *d.* with him among. 40:5
d. at Mizpah to serve Chaldeans. 10
into Egypt, and there *d.* 42:14
a desire to return to *d.* there. 44:14
flee ye, *d.* deep, O inhabitants. 49:8
nor a son of man *d.* 18*, 33*; 50:40*
which *d.* alone. 49:31
that *d.* in midst of them. 51:1
dost *d.* among scorpions. *Ezek* 2:6
and her daughters *d.* at left. 16:46
where I will *d.* in midst of Israel for. 43:7, 9; *Zech* 2:10, 11
I will make thee to *d.* in. *Hos* 12:9
they that *d.* under his shadow. 14:7
but Judah shall *d.* for ever. *Joel* 3:20
be taken out that *d.* in. *Amos* 3:12*
thou shalt *d.* in the field. *Mi* 4:10
the flock which *d.* solitarily. 7:14
thy nobles *d.* in dust. *Nah* 3:18*
to *d.* in cieled houses ? *Hag* 1:4
old men and women shall *d.* in. *Zech* 8:4
a bastard shall *d.* in Ashdod. 9:6
and men shall *d.* in it. 14:11
enter in and *d.* there. *Mat* 12:45 *Luke* 11:26
as a snare shall it come on all that *d.* *Luke* 21:35; *Acts* 17:26
into land wherein ye *d.* *Acts* 7:4
Paul was suffered to *d.* by. 28:16
Spirit of God *d.* in you. *Rom* 8:9, 11
and she be pleased to *d. 1 Cor* 7:12
God hath said, I will *d.* *2 Cor* 6:16
Christ may *d.* in your. *Eph* 3:17
in him should all fulness *d. Col* 1:19
word of Christ *d.* in you richly. 3:16
likewise, ye husbands, *d.* *1 Pet* 3:7
know we that we *d.* in. *1 John* 4:13
on the throne shall *d.* *Rev* 7:15*
heavens, and ye that *d.* in. 12:12
against them that *d.* in heaven. 13:6
men, and he will *d.* with them. 21:3

dwell with *earth*

will God *d.* on *earth* ? *1 Ki* 8:27 *2 Chr* 6:18
languages, that *d.* in all the *earth.* *Dan* 4:1; 6:25
try them that *d.* on *earth. Rev* 3:10
avenge on them that *d.* on *earth.* 6:10
they that *d.* on the *earth.* 11:10
all that *d.* on the *earth* shall. 13:8
deceiveth them that *d.* on *earth.* 14
preach to them that *d.* on *earth.* 14:6
they that *d.* on the *earth.* 17:8

dwell with *house*

build an *house,* and not *d.* therein. *Deut* 28:30; *Amos* 5:11
I *d.* in a *house* of cedar. *2 Sam* 7:2 *1 Chr* 17:1
shall build me an *house* to *d.* in. *2 Sam* 7:5; *1 Chr* 17:1
build *house* in Jerusalem and *d.* *1 Ki* 2:36
this woman *d.* in one *house.* 3:17
surely built thee *house* to *d.* in. 8:13
not *d.* in *house* of David. *2 Chr* 8:11
that *d.* in *houses* of clay. *Job* 4:19
they that *d.* in my *house.* 19:15
will *d.* in the *house* of the. *Ps* 23:6
that I may *d.* in the *house* of. 27:4
blessed that *d.* in thy *house.* 84:4
worketh deceit, shall not *d.* in my *house.* 101:7
better *d.* in the corner of a *house.* *Pr* 21:9; 25:24
d. in thy *house* go to. *Jer* 20:6
build ye *houses, d.* in them. 29:5, 28
not to build *houses* for us to *d.* 35:9

dwell with *Jerusalem*

d. in *Jerusalem* for ever. *1 Chr* 23:25
of ten to *d.* in *Jerusalem. Neh* 11:1
offered to *d.* at *Jerusalem.* 2
Jerusalem shall *d.* safely. *Jer* 33:16
for fear we *d.* at *Jerusalem.* 35:11
d. in midst of *Jerusalem.* *Zech* 8:3
d. in the midst of *Jerusalem.* 8
all ye that *d.* at *Jerusalem. Acts* 2:14
all them that *d.* in *Jerusalem.* 4:16
they that *d.* at *Jerusalem.* 13:27

dwell with *land*

Canaanites in whose *land* I *d.* *Gen* 24:37
d. in the *land* which I shall. 26:2
let them *d.* in the *land.* 34:21
and thou shalt *d.* in *land.* 45:10
may *d.* in the *land* of Goshen. 46:34
in *land* of Goshen let them *d.* 47:6
land of Goshen, in which my people *d.* *Ex* 8:22
they shall not *d.* in thy *land.* 23:33
ye shall *d.* in the *land.* *Lev* 25:18
shall eat and *d.* in your *land.* 26:5
what the *land* is they *d. Num* 13:19
defile not *land* wherein I *d.* 35:34
d. in the *land* which the Lord giveth. *Deut* 12:10
d. in the *land* Lord sware. 30:20
but the Canaanites would *d.* in that *land.* *Josh* 17:12; *Judg* 1:27
the gods in whose *land* ye *d.* *Josh* 24:15; *Judg* 6:10
fear not, *d.* in *land.* *2 Ki* 25:24 *Jer* 25:5; 40:9
so shalt thou *d.* in the *land. Ps* 37:3
rebellious *d.* in a dry *land.* 68:6
glory may *d.* in our *land.* 85:9
upright shall *d.* in *land.* *Pr* 2:21
d. in *land* of shadow. *Isa* 9:2
d. in their own *land. Jer* 23:8; 27:11
that *d.* in the *land* of Egypt. 24:8 44:1, 8, 13, 26
ye shall *d.* in the *land.* 35:15 *Ezek* 36:28; 37:25
we will not *d.* in this *land. Jer* 42:13
to *d.* in the *land* of Judah. 43:4, 5
land desolate, none shall *d.* 50:
then *d.* in their *land.* *Ezek* 28:25
people that *d.* in midst of *land.* 38:1
not *d.* in Lord's *land.* *Hos* 9:

violence of land, and all that d. Hab 2:8, 17
riddance of all that d. in the land. Zeph 1:18

dwell with *place*

place thou hast made to d. Ex 15:17
made them to d. in this place. 1 Sam 12:8
may d. in a place of. 2 Sam 7:10
place where we d. is. 2 Ki 6:1
make us a place where we may d. 2
shall d. in their place. 1 Chr 17:9
d. in high and holy place. Isa 57:15
I will cause you to d. in this place. Jer 7:3, 7

dwell *safely*

hearkeneth to me shall d. safely. Pr 1:33
Israel shall d. safely. Jer 23:6
Ezek 28:26; 34:25, 28; 38:8
cause them to d. safely. Jer 32:37
at rest that d. safely. Ezek 38:11

dwell *in safety*

and ye shall d. in the land in safety. Lev 25:18, 19; Deut 12:10
of Lord d. in safety. Deut 33:12
Israel shall d. in safety alone. 28
makest me to d. in safety. Ps 4:8

dwell *therein*

enemies which d. therein. Lev 27:32
land I sware to make you d. therein. Num 14:30
shall d. therein. 33:53; Deut 11:31
world and they that d. therein. Ps 24:1
righteous shall d. therein. 37:29
love his name shall d. therein. 69:36
for wickedness of them that d. therein. 107:34; Jer 12:4
that d. therein are desolate. Isa 24:6; Amos 9:5
people that d. therein are. Isa 33:24
to generation shall d. therein. 34:17
they that d. therein shall die. 51:6
not a man d. therein. Jer 4:29
the city, all that d. therein. 8:16
wickedness of them that d. therein. 12:4
land and them that d. therein. 47:2
desolate without any to d. therein. 48:9
and the owls shall d. therein. 50:39
violence of them that d. therein. Ezek 12:19
smite them that d. therein. 32:15
they and children d. therein. 37:25
desolate, because of them that d. therein. Mi 7:13
world is burnt, and all that d. therein. Nah 1:5
his habitation, let no man d. therein. Acts 1:20

dwell *together*

d. together, their substance . . . they could not d. together. Gen 13:6
more than might d. together. 36:7
if brethren d. together. Deut 25:5
for brethren to d. together. Ps 133:1

dwelled

the Perizzite d. then in. Gen 13:7
Abram d. in the land of Canaan, Lot d. in the cities of the plain. 12
Abraham d. between Kadesh. 20:1
d. there about ten years. Ruth 1:4
delivered you, ye d. 1 Sam 12:11

dwellers

ye d. on earth, see ye. Isa 18:3
it was known to the d. Acts 1:19
the d. in Mesopotamia. 2:9

dwellest

succeedest them and d. Deut 12:29
God of Israel, which d. between. 2 Ki 19:15*; Ps 80:1*; Isa 37:16*
O thou that d. in the. Ps 123:1*
thou that d. in gardens. S of S 8:13
O my people that d. in. Isa 10:24
hear now this, thou that d. 47:8
thou that d. in the clefts. Jer 49:16
Ob 3
that d. upon many waters. Jer 51:13
of Edom, that d. in land. Lam 4:21

thou that d. in the land. Ezek 7:7
d. in the midst of rebellious. 12:2
that d. with the daughter. Zech 2:7
Master, where d. thou? John 1:38
works, and where thou d. Rev 2:13

dwelleth

stranger that d. with you. Lev 19:34*
brother that d. by thee be. 25:39, 47
God d. as a lion. Deut 33:20
Rahab d. in Israel. Josh 6:25
wherein Lord's tabernacle d. 22:19
covenant of Lord, who d. 1 Sam 4:4*
2 Sam 6:2*; 1 Chr 13:6*
ark d. within curtains. 2 Sam 7:2
he d. in desolate cities. Job 15:28
where is way where light d.? 38:19
she d. and abideth on rock. 39:28
to the Lord who d. in Zion. Ps 9:11
place where thine honour d. 26:8
d. in secret place of most High. 91:1
Lord our God who d. on high? 113:5
blessed be the Lord who d. 135:21
seeing he d. securely. Pr 3:29
Lord, who d. in mount. Isa 8:18
Lord is exalted, for he d. on. 33:5
desolation, and no man d. Jer 44:2
wealthy nation that d. without. 49:31
she d. among the heathen. Lam 1:3
younger sister d. at right. Ezek 16:46
where king d. that made him. 17:16
and the light d. with him. Dan 2:22
land shall mourn, every one that d. therein. Hos 4:3; Amos 8:8
the Lord d. in Zion. Joel 3:21
sweareth by it and him that d. Mat 23:21
drinketh my blood, d. in. John 6:56
the Father that d. in me. 14:10
the Spirit, for he d. in you. 17
d. not in temples made with hands. Acts 7:48; 17:24
more I, but sin that d. Rom 7:17, 20
I know that in my flesh d. no. 18
by his Spirit that d. in you. 8:11
that Spirit of God d. in. 1 Cor 3:16
d. fulness of Godhead. Col 2:9
Holy Ghost which d. in. 2 Tim 1:14
spirit that d. in us lusteth. Jas 4:5
a new earth wherein d. 2 Pet 3:13
how d. the love of God? 1 John 3:17
keepeth his commandments, d. 24
love one another, God d. in. 4:12
Jesus is Son of God, God d. in. 15
he that d. in love, d. in God. 16
truth's sake which d. in us. 2 John 2
among you, where Satan d. Rev 2:13

dwelling, *substantive*

d. shall be the fatness. Gen 27:39
at beginning of their d. 2 Ki 17:25
built a place for thy d. 2 Chr 6:2
in grave from their d. Ps 49:14
any plague come nigh thy d. 91:10
there is oil in the d. of. Pr 21:20
lay not wait against the d. 24:15
Hazor shall be a d. for. Jer 49:33
gods, whose d. is not. Dan 2:11
thy d. be with beasts. 4:25, 32; 5:21
where is the d. of lions? Nah 2:11
his d. among the tombs. Mark 5:3

dwelling

Jacob a plain man, d. in. Gen 25:27
any man sell a d. house. Lev 25:29
strong is thy d. place. Num 24:21
hear in heaven thy d. place. 1 Ki 8:30
39, 43, 49; 2 Chr 6:21, 30, 39
their prayer came up to his holy d. 2 Chr 30:27
Lord hath compassion on d. 36:15
the d. place of the wicked. Job 8:22
are d. places of wicked? 21:28
d. places to all generations. Ps 49:11
pluck thee out of thy d. 52:5
by casting down the d. place. 74:7
Salem his tabernacle, his d. 76:2
have laid waste his d. place. 79:7
Lord, thou hast been our d. 90:1
Lord will create on every d. Isa 4:5
I will consider in my d. place. 18:4
I will have mercy on his d. Jer 30:18
O thou daughter d. in Egypt. 46:19
have burnt their d. places. 51:30
Babylon shall become a d. place. 37
all your d. places the cities. Ezek 6:6

save them out of all d. Ezek 37:23
all of them d. without walls. 38:11
Lord your God d. in Zion. Joel 3:17
to possess the d. places. Hab 1:6
their d. should not be cut. Zeph 3:7
were d. at Jerusalem. Acts 2:5
known to the Greeks, d. at. 19:17
have no certain d. place. 1 Cor 4:11
d. in the light no man. 1 Tim 6:16
d. in tabernacles with. Heb 11:9
Lot, that righteous man, d. 2 Pet 2:8

dwellings

of Israel had light in d. Ex 10:23
perpetual statute throughout your d. Lev 3:17; 23:14; Num 35:29
no blood in any of your d. Lev 7:26
do no work in all your d. 23:3, 31
have any remaining in d. Job 18:19*
surely such are the d. of the. 21
made the barren land his d. 39:6
wickedness is in their d. Ps 55:15
more than all the d. of Jacob. 87:2
people dwell in sure d. Isa 32:18
our d. have cast us out. Jer 9:19
men of east make their d. Ezek 25:4
sea coast shall be d. Zeph 2:6*

dwelt

and they d. there. Gen 11:2, 31
26:17; 2 Ki 16:6; 1 Chr 4:43
2 Chr 28:18
d. among children of. Gen 23:10*
of Egypt wherein ye d. Lev 18:3
wherein they d. Num 31:10
2 Ki 17:29
d. an old prophet. 1 Ki 13:11, 25
and I d. as a king in. Job 29:25
Zion wherein thou hast d. Ps 74:2
Ariel, city where David d. Isa 29:1*
a land where no man d. Jer 2:6
Jeremiah d. among people. 39:14
d. by the river of Chebar. Ezek 3:15
under shadow d. great. 31:6, 17
lands wherein your fathers d. 37:25
which beasts of field d. Dan 4:21
rejoicing city that d. Zeph 2:15
fear came on all that d. Luke 1:65
Word was made flesh and d. John 1:14
came and saw where he d. 39
they d. as strangers. Acts 13:17*
good report of all that d. 22:12
Paul d. two years in his own. 28:30
tormented them that d. Rev 11:10

dwelt *at*

and Abraham d. at Beer-sheba. Gen 22:19
Amorites which d. at Heshbon. Num 21:34; Deut 3:2
Abimelech d. at Arumah. Judg 9:41
Ben-hadad d. at Damascus. 1 Ki 15:18; 2 Chr 16:2
Sennacherib d. at Nineveh. 2 Ki 19:36; Isa 37:37
of the scribes which d. at. 1 Chr 2:55
of Levites d. at Jerusalem. 9:34
Saul confounded Jews that d. at. Acts 9:22
Peter came to saints who d. at. 32

dwelt *in*

we have d. in Egypt. Num 20:15
Israel d. in the land of the. 21:31
d. in their stead. Deut 2:12, 21, 22
23; 1 Chr 5:22
good will of him that d. in. Deut 33:16
way of them that d. in. Judg 8:11
Jerubbaal went and d. in his. 29
and Samuel d. in. 1 Sam 19:18
Philistines came and d. in them. 31:7; 1 Chr 10:7
I have not d. in any house since I brought. 2 Sam 7:6; 1 Chr 17:5
that d. in house of Ziba. 2 Sam 9:12
Absalom d. two full years in. 14:28
Shimei d. in Jerusalem. 1 Ki 2:28
Jeroboam fled from Solomon, d. in Egypt. 12:2
Israel d. in their tents. 2 Ki 13:5
Ahaziah d. in a. 15:5; 2 Chr 26:21
Huldah the prophetess d. in Jerusalem. 2 Ki 22:14; 2 Chr 34:22
and d. in their rooms. 1 Chr 4:41
Hagarites fell, and they d. in. 5:10
chief men d. in Jerusalem. 8:28

and David d. in the castle. 1 Chr 11:7
2 Sam 5:9
priests, Levites, and Nethinims, d. in. Ezra 2:70; Neh 3:26; 11:21
Nethinims and all Israel d. in their. Neh 7:73
honourable men d. in it. Job 22:8
my soul had almost d. in. Ps 94:17
nor shall it be d. in from generation. Isa 13:20; Jer 50:39
but we have d. in tents. Jer 35:10
they d. in the habitation. 41:17
Israel d. in their own. Ezek 36:17
when d. safely in their land. 39:26
fowls of the heaven d. in. Dan 4:12
Joseph d. in a city called. Mat 2:23
Jesus d. in Capernaum. 4:13
sinners above all d. in. Luke 13:4
Abraham d. in Charran. Acts 7:2, 4
all they who d. in Asia heard. 19:10
faith which d. first in thy grandmother Lois. 2 Tim 1:5

dwelt *therein*

gave Gilead to Machir, he d. therein. Num 32:40
Enims d. therein. Deut 2:10
giants d. therein in old time. 20
Damascus and d. therein. 1 Ki 11:24
built Shechem, and d. therein. 12:25
there d. men of Tyre also therein. Neh 13:16
thy congregation hath d. therein. Ps 68:10

dwelt *with*

and Ruth d. with her. Ruth 2:23
and mother d. with. 1 Sam 22:4
there they d. with king. 1 Chr 4:23
d. with their brethren. 8:32; 9:38
my soul hath long d. with. Ps 120:6
Jeremiah d. with him. Jer 40:6

dyed

rams' skins d. red. Ex 25:5; 26:14
35:7; 36:19; 39:34
cometh with d. garments. Isa 63:1
exceeding in d. attire. Ezek 23:15

dying

be consumed with d.? Num 17:13*
the first, d. left no seed. Mark 12:20
Jairus' daughter lay a d. Luke 8:42
bearing in body the d. of. 2 Cor 4:10
as d. and behold we live. 6:9
by faith, Jacob when d. Heb 11:21

E

each

Abram laid e. piece. Gen 15:10
Simeon and Levi took e. 34:25
e. man his dream. 40:5
e. changes of raiment. 45:22
asked e. other of their. Ex 18:7
of e. there be a like weight. 30:34
e. one was for house of. Num 1:44
they brought for e. one an ox. 7:3
thou also and Aaron e. of you. 16:17
of e. chief house a prince, e. one. Josh 22:14
e. one resembled children. Judg 8:18
we reserved not to e. man. 21:22
they may find rest e. of you. Ruth 1:9
e. man his month in year. 1 Ki 4:7
and the kings e. sat on. 22:10
exacted of e. man fifty. 2 Ki 15:20
and peace kissed e. other. Ps 85:10
they made e. one for. Isa 2:20
stood the seraphims, e. one. 6:2
where e. lay, shall be grass. 35:7
e. one walking in uprightness. 57:2
appointed thee e. day for. Ezek 4:6
doth not e. on sabbath. Luke 13:15
cloven tongues sat upon e. Acts 2:3
let e. esteem other better. Phil 2:3
charity toward e. other. 2 Thes 1:3
four beasts had e. of them. Rev 4:8

eagle

At least eight distinct kinds of eagles and vultures have been observed in Palestine. The Hebrew word nesher *is used almost entirely in the Bible for* eagle, *and it is impossible to determine exactly which is intended. Most probably it is the general term for any eagle, as it merely means a tearer with the beak.*

Most frequently in the Bible the reference is to some characteristic of the eagle, and is made as a vivid expression of some quality in that which is compared to it. Among these are its swiftness of flight, Deut 28:49; Pr 23:5; *its strength of wing,* Pr 30:19; Ezek 17:3; *its eating of carrion,* Mat 24:28 (*this is true only of the vultures*) ; *the building of its nest high on the mountain cliff,* Jer 49:16; *the baldness of one variety,* Mi 1:16. *There is also reference to the ancient belief that at the end of a certain period the eagle moults and by some unknown means renews its youth,* Ps 103:5; *probably derived from the extreme length of the eagle's vigorous life. The custom of carrying its young from the inaccessible cliffs on its broad wings is also made a symbol for the deliverance of the Israelites,* Ex 19:4.

have e. in abomination. Lev 11:13
Deut 14:12
a nation as swift as e. Deut 28:49
as an e. stirreth up her nest. 32:11
as the e. that hasteth. Job 9:26
doth the e. mount up at thy? 39:27
riches fly away as an e. Pr 23:5
the way of an e. in the air. 30:19
fly as an e. over Moab. Jer 48:40
make thy nest high as e. 49:16
four also had the face of an e. Ezek 1:10; 10:14
a great e. with great wings. 17:3, 7
grown like e. feathers. Dan 4:33
like a lion, and had e. wings. 7:4
as an e. against the house. Hos 8:1
though thou exalt thyself as e. Ob 4
enlarge thy baldness as e. Mi 1:16
Chaldeans shall fly as e. Hab 1:8
beast was like a flying e. Rev 4:7
were given wings of great e. 12:14

eagles

I bare you on e'. wings. Ex 19:4
were swifter than e. 2 Sam 1:23
thy youth is renewed like e. Ps 103:5
and the young e. shall. Pr 30:17
mount up with wings as e. Isa 40:31
horses are swifter than e. Jer 4:13
persecutors swifter than e. Lam 4:19
there will e. be gathered. Mat 24:28
Luke 17:37

ear

(*The use of the word* ear *in the Bible is used most often as attention, hearing, etc., rather than of the actual physical ear. To have the ears heavy is to pay no attention; to open the ear is to pay attention; uncircumcised ears are those which are deaf to the word of God. To tell something in the ear, is to speak in secret*)

master shall bore his e. Ex 21:6
Deut 15:17
hath told Samuel in e. 1 Sam 9:15*
bow down thine e. 2 Ki 19:16
Ps 31:2; 86:1
let thine e. be attentive. Neh 1:6, 11
mine e. received a little. Job 4:12
doth not the e. try? 12:11; 34:3
mine e. hath heard and. 13:1
when the e. heard me. 29:11
to me men gave e. waited. 21
behold, I gave e. to. 32:11*
he openeth also their e. 36:10
of thee by hearing of the e. 42:5
wilt cause thine e. to hear. Ps 10:17
bow down thine e. to me. 31:2
deaf adder, that stoppeth her e. 58:4
unto God, and he gave e. 77:1
he that planted the e. 94:9
because he hath inclined e. 116:2
and bow thine e. to my. Pr 5:1
nor inclined my e. to them. 13
the e. that heareth the. 15:31
and a liar giveth e. to a. 17:4
e. of the wise seeketh. 18:15
hearing e. the seeing eye. Pr 20:12
bow thine e. hear the words. 22:17
a wise reprover on obedient e. 25:12
that turneth away his e. from. 28:9
nor is the e. filled. Eccl 1:8
thine e. was not opened. Isa 48:8
he wakeneth my e. to hear. 50:4
Lord hath opened mine e. 5
nor is his e. heavy that it. 59:1
not heard, nor perceived by e. 64:4
behold, their e. is. Jer 6:10
not, nor inclined e. 7:24, 26; 11:8
17:23; 25:4; 34:14; 44:5
let your e. receive the word. 9:20
ye have not inclined your e. 35:15
hide not thine e. at my. Lam 3:56
from lion a piece of an e. Amos 3:12
what ye hear in the e. Mat 10:27
smote off his e. 26:51; Mark 14:47
ye have spoken in e. Luke 12:3
and he touched his e. 22:51
servant, whose e. Peter. John 18:26
not seen, nor e. heard. 1 Cor 2:9
if e. shall say, because I am. 12:16
he that hath an e. let. Rev 2:7, 11
17, 29; 3:6, 13, 22; 13:9

give **ear**

if wilt give e. to his. Ex 15:26
Lord would not hearken nor give e. Deut 1:45; 2 Chr 24:19; Neh 9:30
give e. O heavens. Deut 32:1
O ye kings, give e. O. Judg 5:3
give e. to me, ye that. Job 34:2
give e. to my words. Ps 5:1; 54:2
give e. unto my prayer. 17:1; 55:1
86:6
give e. to my cry. 39:12; 141:1
give e. all ye inhabitants. 49:1
give e. O my people. 78:1
give e. shepherd. 80:1
hear my prayer, give e. 84:8
give e. to my supplications. 143:1
give e. O earth, for the. Isa 1:2
give e. to law of our God. 10
give e. all ye of far countries. 8:9
give ye e. and hear my voice. 28:23
careless daughters, give e. to. 32:9
who among you will give e.? 42:23
hearken and give e. to me. 51:4
give e. be not proud. Jer 13:15
and give ye e. O house of. Hos 5:1
give e. all ye inhabitants. Joel 1:2

incline **ear**

incline thine e. to me. Ps 17:6
71:2; 88:2; Isa 37:17; Dan 9:18
consider, and incline thine e. Ps 45:10
I will incline mine e. to a. 49:4
thou incline thine e. to. Pr 2:2
my son, incline thine e. 4:20
incline your e. and come. Isa 55:3

right **ear**

upon tip of right e. of. Ex 29:20
Lev 8:23, 24; 14:14, 17, 25, 28
one cut off his right e. Luke 22:50
John 18:10

ear, *grain*

for barley was in the e. Ex 9:31
e. the full corn in the e. Mark 4:28

ear, *verb*

(*An old word for* plow *or* till)
king will set them to e. 1 Sam 8:12*
oxen that e. the ground. Isa 30:24*

eared

rough valley neither e. Deut 21:4*

earing

neither e. nor harvest. Gen 45:6*
in e. time and harvest. Ex 34:21*

early

ye shall rise e. and go. Gen 19:2
fearful, let him depart e. Judg 7:3
to-morrow get you e. on your. 19:9
man of God was risen e. 2 Ki 6:15
help her, and that right e. Ps 46:5
myself will awake e. 57:8; 108:2
my God, e. will I seek thee. 63:1†
and enquired e. after God. 78:34
O satisfy us e. with thy. 90:14
I will e. destroy all the. 101:8
they shall seek me e. Pr 1:28
those that seek me e. shall. 8:17
let us get up e. to the. S of S 7:1
will I seek thee e. Isa 26:9

in affliction seek me *e.* *Hos* 5:15*
and as the *e.* dew it. 6:4; 13:3
women who were *e.* at. *Luke* 24:22
Jesus to hall, it was *e.* *John* 18:28
cometh Mary Magdalene *e.* 20:1
receive the *e.* and latter. *Jas* 5:7
see **arose, rise, risen, rising, rose, morning**

earnest

(*The word used as a noun means a pledge; as an adjective or adverb, eager, sincere, serious, etc.*)

e. expectation of the. *Rom* 8:19
hath given the *e.* of the Spirit. *2 Cor* 1:22; 5:5
he told us your *e.* desire. 7:7*
put same *e.* care into Titus. 8:16
the *e.* of our inheritance. *Eph* 1:14
e. expectation and hope. *Phil* 1:20
ought to give the more *e.* *Heb* 2:1

earnestly

did I not *e.* send to? *Num* 22:37
David *e.* asked leave of me. *1 Sam* 20:6, 28
Baruch *e.* repaired the. *Neh* 3:20
as a servant *e.* desireth. *Job* 7:2
for I *e.* protested to. *Jer* 11:7
I do *e.* remember him still. 31:20
do evil with both hands *e.* *Mi* 7:3*
agony prayed more *e.* *Luke* 22:44
but a certain maid *e.* looked. 56*
why look ye so *e.* on us? *Acts* 3:12*
Paul *e.* beholding council. 23:1*
but covet *e.* best gifts. *1 Cor* 12:31
in this we groan, *e.* *2 Cor* 5:2*
Elias prayed *e.* that. *Jas* 5:17*
that ye should *e.* contend. *Jude* 3

earneth

he that *e.* wages, *e.* to. *Hag* 1:6

earring

the man took a golden *e.* *Gen* 24:22*
when Laban saw *e.* and. 30
I put the *e.* upon her face. 47*
gave Job an *e.* of gold. *Job* 42:11*
as an *e.* of gold. *Pr* 25:12

earrings

gave to Jacob all their *e.* *Gen* 35:4*
break off the golden *e.* *Ex* 32:2*
brought *e.* for their offerings. 35:22
we have brought *e.* to. *Num* 31:50
give every man the *e.* *Judg* 8:24
Lord will take away *e.* *Isa* 3:20*
I put *e.* in thine ears. *Ezek* 16:12
decked herself with her *e.* *Hos* 2:13

ears

a word in my lord's *e.* *Gen* 44:18
in the *e.* of Pharaoh. 50:4
tell it in *e.* of thy son. *Ex* 10:2
rehearse it in *e.* of Joshua. 17:14
for ye have wept in *e.* *Num* 11:18
Moses spake in the *e.* *Deut* 31:30
declare cause in the *e.* of. *Josh* 20:4
in the *e.* of the men of. *Judg* 9:2, 3
the *e.* of every one that heareth shall. *1 Sam* 3:11; *2 Ki* 21:12; *Jer* 19:3
rehearseth them in *e.* of. *1 Sam* 8:21
according to all we have heard with our *e.* *2 Sam* 7:22; *1 Chr* 17:20
cry did enter into his *e.* *2 Sam* 22:7
sound is in his *e.* in. *Job* 15:21
the fame thereof with our *e.* 28:22
he openeth the *e.* of men. 33:16
cry came even into his *e.* *Ps* 18:6
and his *e.* are opened to. 34:15
we have heard with our *e.* 44:1
e. but hear not. 115:6; 135:17
whoso stoppeth his *e.* at. *Pr* 21:13
speak not in the *e.* of a fool. 23:9
that taketh a dog by *e.* 26:17
after the hearing of his *e.* *Isa* 11:3
the *e.* of them that hear. 32:3
that stoppeth his *e.* from. 33:15
e. of deaf shall be unstopped. 35:5
opening the *e.* but he heareth not. 42:20
blind and deaf that have *e.* 43:8
go, and cry in the *e.* of. *Jer* 2:2
people, which have *e.* and. 5:21
Zephaniah read in the *e.* of. 29:29
sit down and read it in our *e.* 36:15
Jehudi read it in the *e.* of. 21

come to governor's *e.* *Mat* 28:14
put his fingers into his *e.* *Mark* 7:33
straightway his *e.* were opened. 35
having *e.* hear ye not? 8:18
in heart and *e.* resist. *Acts* 7:51
tidings came to the *e.* of. 11:22
strange things to our *e.* 17:20
hath given *e.* that they. *Rom* 11:8
having itching *e.* *2 Tim* 4:3
are entered into *e.* of Lord. *Jas* 5:4
and his *e.* are open to. *1 Pet* 3:12

ears *to hear*

not given you *e. to hear.* *Deut* 29:4
they have *e. to hear.* *Ezek* 12:2
he that hath *e. to hear.* *Mat* 11:15
13:9, 43; *Mark* 4:9, 23; 7:16
Luke 8:8; 14:35

mine **ears**

spoken in *mine e.* I will. *Num* 14:28
thou spakest of in *mine e.* *Judg* 17:2
of sheep in mine *e.*? *1 Sam* 15:14
tumult come into *mine e.* *2 Ki* 19:28; *Isa* 37:29
and *mine e.* attent to. *2 Chr* 7:15
mine e. hast thou opened. *Ps* 40:6
mine e. hear my desire of. 92:11
in *mine e.* said the Lord. *Isa* 5:9
it was revealed in *mine e.* 22:14
cry in *mine e.* with loud. *Ezek* 8:18
cried also in *mine e.* with loud. 9:1
thy salutation sounded in *mine e.* *Luke* 1:44

ears *of the people*

speak now in *e. of the people.* *Ex* 11:2
spake in *e. of the people.* *Deut* 32:44
proclaim in the *e. of the people.* *Judg* 7:3
tidings in the *e. of the people.* *1 Sam* 11:4
talk not in the *e. of the people.* *2 Ki* 18:26; *Isa* 36:11
e. of the people were attentive. *Neh* 8:3
read in *e. of the people.* *Jer* 28:7
36:6, 10, 13, 14

their **ears**

these things in *their e.* *Gen* 20:8
earrings which were in *their e.* 35:4
brake off earrings in *their e.* *Ex* 32:3
these words in *their e.* *Deut* 31:28
read in *their e.* *2 Ki* 23:2
2 Chr 34:30; *Jer* 36:15
he openeth *their e.* in. *Job* 36:15
make heart fat, *their e.* heavy, lest they hear with *their e.* *Isa* 6:10
Mat 13:15; *Acts* 28:27
their e. shall be deaf. *Mi* 7:16
but they stopped *their e.* *Zech* 7:11
Acts 7:57
away *their e.* from truth. *2 Tim* 4:4

thine **ears**

let *thine e.* be attent. *2 Chr* 6:40
wilt cause *thine e.* to. *Ps* 10:17
let *thine e.* be attentive to. 130:2
apply *thine e.* to words. *Pr* 23:12
thine e. hear a word. *Isa* 30:21
children say again in *thine e.* 49:20
that I speak in *thine e.* *Jer* 28:7
and hear with *thine e.* *Ezek* 3:10
40:4; 44:5
earrings in *thine e.* and. 16:12
away thy nose and *thine e.* 23:25
thee to hear with *thine e.* 24:26

your **ears**

which I speak in *your e.* *Deut* 5:1
declaration with *your e.* *Job* 13:17
incline *your e.* to words. *Ps* 78:1
have heard with *your e.* *Jer* 26:11
sent me to speak in *your e.* 15
but blessed are *your e.* *Mat* 13:16
scripture is fulfilled in *your e.* *Luke* 4:21
sayings sink down in *your e.* 9:44

ears

e. of corn came up. *Gen* 41:5, 22
a meat offering green *e.* *Lev* 2:14
not eat green *e.* till ye bring. 23:14
mayest pluck the *e.* *Deut* 23:25
go and glean *e.* of corn. *Ruth* 2:2
man of God full *e.* of. *2 Ki* 4:42

wicked cut off as tops of *e.* *Job* 24:24
as when one reapeth *e.* *Isa* 17:5
an hungered, and began to pluck *e.* *Mat* 12:1; *Mark* 2:23; *Luke* 6:1
see **seven**

earth

[1] *The globe or planet which we inhabit,* Gen 1:10; Ps 24:1. [2] *The world in distinction from heaven or hell,* John 3:31; Col 3:1, 2. [3] *The people on the globe,* Gen 11:1, Ps 96:1. [4] *Certain parts of the earth—countries,* Ezra 1:2; Rom 9:28. [5] *The ground, in distinction from the water of the globe,* Gen 4:11; Num 6:30. *A man of the earth is taken as meaning a mortal, earthly-minded man,* Ps 10:18.

e. was without form. *Gen* 1:2
and God called the dry land *e.* 10
let *e.* bring forth grass. 11, 24
e. brought forth grass and herb. 12
be fruitful, replenish *e.* and. 28; 9:1
the *e.* also was corrupt before. 6:11
ark was lifted up above *e.* 7:17
in second month was the *e.* 8:14
while *e.* remaineth, seedtime. 22
covenant between me and *e.* 9:13
in his days was the *e.* divided. 10:25; *1 Chr* 1:19
nations of *e.* shall be blessed in. *Gen* 18:18; 22:18; 26:4; 28:14
give thee of fatness of the *e.* 27:28
in plenteous years *e.* brought. 41:47
the Lord in midst of the *e.* *Ex* 8:22
know that *e.* is the Lord's. 9:29
Deut 10:14; *Ps* 24:1; *1 Cor* 10:26
one cannot be able to see *e.* *Ex* 10:5
e. swallowed them. 15:12
an altar of *e.* thou shalt. 20:24
if *e.* open her mouth. *Num* 16:30*
the *e.* opened. 32; 26:10; *Ps* 106:17
lest the *e.* swallow us up. *Num* 16:34
above all nations of *e.* *Deut* 28:1
e. under thee shall be iron. 23
O *e.* the words of my mouth. 32:1
ride on high places of *e.* 13
a fire shall consume the *e.* 22
for the pillars of the *e.* *1 Sam* 2:8
so that the *e.* rang again. 4:5
trembled, and the *e.* quaked. 14:15
a man came out with *e.* upon his head. *2 Sam* 1:2; 15:32
then *e.* shook and. 22:8; *Ps* 18:7
so that the *e.* rent. *1 Ki* 1:40
two mules' burden of *e.* *2 Ki* 5:17
and let the *e.* rejoice. *1 Chr* 16:31
Ps 96:11
because God cometh to judge the *e.* *1 Chr* 16:33; *Ps* 96:13; 98:9
of God of heaven and *e.* *Ezra* 5:11
thou hast made the *e.* *Neh* 9:6
Isa 45:12
offspring as grass of *e.* *Job* 5:25
which shaketh the *e.* 9:6
the *e.* is given into the hand of. 24
thereof is longer than the *e.* 11:9
waters and they overturn *e.* 12:15
to whom alone the *e.* was. 15:19*
O *e.* cover not thou my. 16:18
shall the *e.* be forsaken? 18:4
and the *e.* shall rise up. 20:27
as for mighty man, he had *e.* 22:8
the poor of the *e.* hide. 24:4
he hangeth the *e.* upon nothing. 26:7
to dwell in caves of the *e.* 30:6
they were viler than the *e.* 8*
him a charge over the *e.*? 34:13
when he quieteth the *e.* by. 37:17
I laid the foundations of *e.* 38:4
perceived breadth of the *e.*? 18
uttermost parts of the *e.* *Ps* 2:8
be instructed, ye judges of *e.* 10
that the man of the *e.* may. 10:18
silver tried in a furnace of *e.* 12:6
his seed shall inherit the *e.* 25:13
e. is full of the goodness of. 33:5
looketh on all inhabitants of *e.* 14
those that wait upon the Lord shall inherit the *e.* 37:9*, 11*, 22*
not fear though *e.* be removed. 46:2
uttered his voice, *e.* melted. 6

for the shields of the e. Ps 47:9
the joy of the whole e. is. 48:2
hast made e. to tremble. 60:2*
into lower parts of the e. 63:9
in uttermost parts of the e. 65:8
thou visitest the e. and waterest. 9
then shall e. yield her increase. 67:6
Ezek 34:27
the e. shook, the heavens. Ps 68:8
sing unto God, ye kingdoms of e. 32
up from depths of the e. 71:20
as showers that water the e. 72:6
tongue walketh through e. 73:9
the e. and all the inhabitants are dissolved. 75:3; Isa 24:19
wicked of e. shall wring. Ps 75:8
the e. feared. 76:8
God arose to save meek of e. 9
the e. trembled. 77:18; 97:4
like e. which he hath. 78:69
O God, judge the e. thou. 82:8
ever thou hadst formed the e. 90:2
Lord reigneth, let e. rejoice. 97:1
Lord reigneth, let the e. be. 99:1
thou laid foundation of the e. 102:25
104:5; Pr 8:29; Isa 48:13
e. is satisfied with fruit. Ps 104:13
the e. is full of thy riches. 24
tremble, O e. at presence. 114:7
e. hath he given to the. 115:16
the e. O Lord, is full of. 119:64
thou hast established the e. 90
prepareth rain for the e. 147:8
his glory is above the e. 148:13
Lord hath founded the e. Pr 3:19
Isa 24:1
from everlasting, or ever e. Pr 8:23
had not made the e. nor fields. 26
e. for depth and heart of. 25:3
the e. that is not filled. 30:16
for three things the e. is. 21
the e. abideth for ever. Eccl 1:4
the profit of the e. is for all. 5:9
the fruit of the e. shall be. Isa 4:2*
that smiteth the e. with rod. 11:4
e. shall be full of the knowledge. 9
the e. shall remove out of. 13:13
man that made the e. to? 14:16
the e. mourneth and. 24:4; 33:9
the e. is defiled under the. 24:5
e. is utterly broken down, e. 19
e. shall reel. 20
e. shall cast out the dead. 26:19
the e. also shall disclose. 21
let the e. hear, and all. 34:1
sitteth on circle of the e. 40:22
the Creator of ends of the e. 28
that spread abroad the e. 44:24
let the e. open. 45:8
I have made the e. 12
be ye saved, all the ends of the e. 22
and be joyful, O e. 49:13
look on the e. the e. shall. 51:6
saith the Lord, the e. is my. 66:1
shall the e. be made to bring? 8*
I beheld the e. it was. Jer 4:23
for this shall the e. mourn. 28
hear, O e. I will bring evil. 6:19
at his wrath the e. shall. 10:10
O e. e. e. hear word of Lord, write. 22:29; Mi 1:2
go up and cover the e. Jer 46:8
the e. is moved at. 49:21; 50:46
made the e. by his power. 51:15
give it to wicked of the e. Ezek 7:21
the Lord hath forsaken the e. 9:9
and the e. shined with his. 43:2
the e. shall hear the corn. Hos 2:22
e. shall quake before. Joel 2:10
darken e. in clear day. Amos 8:9
the e. with her bars. Jonah 2:6
strong foundations of e. Mi 6:2
move out like worms of e. 7:17
the e. is burnt up at. Nah 1:5
e. filled with knowledge. Hab 2:14
the e. was full of his praise. 3:3
didst cleave the e. with rivers. 9
the e. is stayed from. Hag 1:10
sent to walk to and fro through the e. Zech 1:10; 6:7
eyes of Lord run through e. 4:10
smite the e. with a curse. Mal 4:6
for they shall inherit e. Mat 5:5
swear not by the e. it is God's. 35
had not much e. Mat 13:5
Mark 4:5
for the e. bringeth forth. Mark 4:28
he that is of the e. is earthly, and speaketh of the e. John 3:31
first man is of the e. 1 Cor 15:47
vessels of wood and of e. 2 Tim 2:20
the e. which drinketh in. Heb 6:7*
voice then shook the e. but. 12:26
for precious fruit of e. Jas 5:7
the e. brought forth her fruit. 18
the e. and works therein. 2 Pet 3:10
hurt not the e. nor sea. Rev 7:3
trees before the God of the e. 11:4
have power to smite the e. with. 6
the e. opened and swallowed. 12:16
causeth the e. to worship. 13:12
and the e. was lightened. 18:1
whore, which did corrupt e. 19:2
from whose face e. fled away. 20:11
see **beasts, dust, ends, face, heaven, kings, people, whole**

all the **earth**

dominion over all the e. Gen 1:26
seed alive on face of all the e. 7:3
confound language of all the e. 11:9
not Judge of all the e. do? 18:25
us after manner of all the e. 19:31
none like me in all the e. Ex 9:14
my name declared through all the e. 16; Rom 9:17
treasure; for all the e. is. Ex 19:5
not been done in all the e. 34:10
all the e. shall be filled. Num 14:21
the Lord of all the e. Josh 3:11
Zech 6:5
going way of all the e. Josh 23:14
1 Ki 2:2
be dry on all the e. Judg 6:37*
all the e. may know. 1 Sam 17:46
all the e. sought to. 1 Ki 10:24
no God in all the e. but. 2 Ki 5:15
judgements are in all the e. 1 Chr 16:14; Ps 105:7
sing to the Lord, all the e. 1 Chr 16:23; Ps 96:1
fear before him, all the e. 1 Chr 16:30
Ps 33:8; 96:9
thy name in all the e. Ps 8:1, 9
make princes in all the e. 45:16
great king over all the e. 47:2
Zech 14:9
let thy glory be above all the e. Ps 57:5, 11; 108:5
all the e. shall worship thee. 66:4
most high over all the e. 83:18; 97:9
make a joyful noise, all the e. 98:4
I gathered all the e. Isa 10:14
excellent things, known in all e. 12:5
of his people, from all the e. 25:8
city a curse to all the e. Jer 26:6
an honour before all the e. 33:9
golden cup that made all the e. 51:7
O mountain, destroyest all the e. 25
shall fall the slain of all the e. 49*
bear rule over all the e. Dan 2:39
let all the e. keep silence. Hab 2:20
all the e. be devoured. Zeph 3:8
all the e. sitteth still. Zech 1:11
darkness over all the e. Luke 23:44*
sound went into all the e. Rom 10:18
of God sent into all the e. Rev 5:6

from the **earth**

up a mist from the e. Gen 2:6
cursed from the e. 4:11*
were destroyed from the e. 7:23
waters were abated from the e. 8:11
thou shalt be cut off from the e. Ex 9:15; Josh 7:9; Ps 109:15
Pr 2:22; Nah 2:13
Saul arose from the e. 1 Sam 28:23
shall I not take you away from the e.? 2 Sam 4:11
to raise him from the e. 12:17
David arose from the e. 20
shall perish from the e. Job 18:17
their fruit from the e. Ps 21:10
remembrance of them from the e. 34:16
praise Lord from the e. 148:7
to devour poor from the e. Pr 30:14
shall perish from the e. Jer 10:11
were lifted up from e. Ezek 1:19, 21
it was lifted up from the e. Dan 7:4
up a snare from the e. Amos 3:5*
I be lifted up from the e. John 12:32
life is taken from the e. Acts 8:33
Saul arose from the e. 9:8
with such a fellow from the e. 22:22
to take peace from the e. Rev 6:4
were redeemed from the e. 14:3

in the **earth**

let fowl multiply in the e. Gen 1:22
a vagabond in the e. 4:12, 14
of man was great in the e. 6:5
Nimrod a mighty one in the e. 10:8
not a man in the e. to come. 19:31
you a posterity in the e. 45:7
that is in the e. beneath. Ex 20:4
they are hid in the e. Josh 7:21
any thing that is in the e. Judg 18:10
like to name of the great men in the e. 2 Sam 7:9; 1 Chr 17:8
what nation in e. like Israel? 2 Sam 7:23; 1 Chr 17:21
all things that are in the e. 2 Sam 14:20
all that is in the e. is. 1 Chr 29:11
no God like thee in the e. 2 Chr 6:14
to and fro in the e. Job 1:7; 2:2
none like him in the e. 1:8; 2:3
root thereof wax old in the e. 14:8
portion is cursed in the e. 24:18
leaveth her eggs in the e. 39:14
saints that are in the e. Ps 16:3
what desolations in the e. 46:8
I will be exalted in the e. 10
God that judgeth in the e. 58:11
handful of corn in the e. 72:16
I am a stranger in the e. 119:19
speaker be established in e. 140:11
be recompensed in the e. Pr 11:31
judgements are in the e. Isa 26:9
not wrought deliverance in the e. 18
not take root in the e. 40:24
have set judgement in the e. 42:4
Jerusalem a praise in the e. 62:7
who blesseth himself in the e. and he that sweareth in the e. 65:16
thee, be written in the e. Jer 17:13
created a new thing in the e. 31:22
sow her unto me in the e. Hos 2:23
shew wonders in the e. Joel 2:30
off righteousness in the e. Amos 5:7
digged in the e. and hid. Mat 25:18
and hid thy talent in the e. 25
when it is sown in the e. less than all seeds in the e. Mark 4:31
three that bear witness in the e. 1 John 5:8

on, or, upon the **earth**

had made man on the e. Gen 6:6
God looked upon the e. behold. 12
cause it to rain upon the e. 7:4
rain was upon the e. forty. 12, 17
and multiply upon the e. 8:17
sun was risen upon the e. 19:23
a ladder set upon the e. 28:12
day they were upon the e. Ex 10:6
things that creep upon the e. Lev 11:29, 42, 44
live upon the e. Deut 4:10; 12:1, 19
upon the e. he shewed thee his. 4:36
shall pour it upon the e. 12:16, 24
David lay upon the e. 2 Sam 12:16
nor remainder upon the e. 14:7
but will God indeed dwell on the e.? 1 Ki 8:27; 2 Chr 6:18
sends rain upon the e. 1 Ki 17:14
our days on e. as a. 1 Chr 29:15
Job 8:9
time to man upon e.? Job 7:1
stand at latter day upon the e. 19:25
since man was placed on the e. 20:4
the snow, be thou on the e. 37:6
on e. there is not his like. 41:33
tread down my life on the e. Ps 7:5
he shall be blessed upon the e. 41:2
way may be known upon the e. 67:2
there is none upon e. I. 73:25
seed be mighty upon the e. 112:2
four things little upon the e. Pr 30:24
not a just man upon the e. Eccl 7:20
princes walking upon the e. 10:7
evil shall be done upon e. 11:2
empty themselves upon the e. 3
flowers appear on the e. S of S 2:12

determined upon the e. Isa 28:22
lift your eyes, look upon the e. 51:6
for truth upon the e. Jer 9:3*
liver is poured upon the e. Lam 2:11
not a man on the e. can. Dan 2:10
fall in snare upon the e. Amos 3:5
least grain fall upon the e. 9:9
not up treasures upon e. Mat 6:19
Son of man hath power on e. to. 9:6
Mark 2:10; Luke 5:24
come to send peace on e.
Mat. 10:34
thou shalt bind on e. 16:19; 18:18
two of you shall agree on e. 18:19
no man your father upon the e. 23:9
blood shed upon the e. 35
so as no fuller on e. can. Mark 9:3
glory to God, on e. Luke 2:14
that built a house upon the e. 6:49
come to send fire on the e. 12:49
come to give peace on e.? 51
shall he find faith on e.? 18:8
for things coming on the e. 21:26*
glorified thee on the e. John 17:4
short work will Lord make on the e.
Rom 9:28
not on things on the e. Col 3:2
mortify members upon the e. 5
if he were on e. he. Heb 8:4
they were strangers on the e. 11:13
refused him that spake on e. 12:25
lived in pleasure on the e. Jas 5:5
it rained not on the e. for. 17
that dwell upon the e. Rev 3:10
priests, we shall reign on e. 5:10
on them that dwell on the e. 6:10
wind should not blow on the e. 7:1
hail, and fire, cast upon the e. 8:7
which standeth upon the e. 10:8
dwell on the e. 11:10; 13:8, 14
14:6; 17:8
thrust in his sickle on the e. 14:16
first poured out vial upon the e. 16:2
blood of all slain upon the e. 18:24

out of the **earth**

ascending out of the e. 1 Sam 28:13
springing out of the e. 2 Sam 23:4
and out of the e. shall. Job 8:19
iron is taken out of the e. 28:2
as for the e. out of it cometh. 5
shall spring out of the e. Ps 85:11
bring food out of the e. 104:14
be consumed out of the e. 35
kings, arise out of the e. Dan 7:17
break battle out of the e. Hos 2:18
man perished out of the e. Mi 7:2
coming up out of the e. Rev 13:11

to, or, *unto the* **earth**

bowing himself to the e. Gen 24:52
bow down to thee, to the e. 37:10
bowed to the e. 42:6; 43:26
bowed with his face to the e. 48:12
Joshua fell on his face to the e.
Josh 5:14; 7:6
Dagon fallen on his face to the e.
1 Sam 5:3*
Goliath fell on face to the e. 17:49
David stooped face to the e. 24:8
she bowed herself to the e. 25:41
1 Ki 1:31
me smite him, to the e. 1 Sam 26:8
not my blood fall to the e. 20
to David he fell to the e. 2 Sam 1:2
not one hair shall fall to the e.
14:11; 1 Ki 1:52
fall to the e. nothing. 2 Ki 10:10
bodies fallen to the e. 2 Chr 20:24
or speak to the e. Job 12:8
bowing down to the e. Ps 17:11
belly cleaveth unto the e. 44:25
he shall call to the e. that. 50:4
he returneth to the e. 146:4
beast that goeth to the e. Eccl 3:21
then shall dust return to the e. 12:7
they shall look unto the e. Isa 8:22
bring down strength to the e. 63:6
of contention to the e. Jer 15:10
and former rain to the e. Hos 6:3
their faces to the e. Luke 24:5
Saul fell to the e. and. Acts 9:4
great sheet, let down to the e. 10:11
we were all fallen to the e. 26:14
of heaven fell to the e. Rev 6:13
did not cast them to the e. Rev 12:4
saw he was cast unto the e. 13

earthen

the e. vessel wherein it. Lev 6:28
the e. vessel whereinto. 11:33
of birds killed in e. vessel. 14:5, 50
holy water in e. vessel. Num 5:17
brought beds, and e. 2 Sam 17:28
and get a potter's e. bottle. Jer 19:1
put evidences in an e. vessel. 32:14
esteemed as e. pitchers. Lam 4:2
treasure in e. vessels. 2 Cor 4:7

earthly

if I have told you e. John 3:12
he that is of the earth is e. 31
if our e. house of. 2 Cor 5:1
walk, who mind e. things. Phil 3:19
this wisdom is e., sensual. Jas 3:15

earthquake

The scripture speaks of several earthquakes. *One of the most remarkable occurred in the twenty-seventh year of Uzziah, king of Judah,* Zech 14:5.

Another very memorable earthquake, was that at the time of our Saviour's crucifixion, Mat 27:51.

Great alterations and changes are expressed in scripture by a shaking of the earth, Heb 12:26. *The delivering of the Israelites out of Egypt is called a moving, or shaking, of the earth,* Ps 68:8. *And an extraordinary and unexpected alteration in the state of affairs, civil or ecclesiastical, is represented by a great* earthquake, Rev 6:12 and 16:18.

an e. Lord was not in e. 1 Ki 19:11
after the e. a fire, Lord was not. 12
visited of the Lord with e. Isa 29:6
saw two years before e. Amos 1:1
ye fled from before the e. Zech 14:5
when centurion saw the e. Mat 27:54
there was a great e., the angel. 28:2
Acts 16:26; Rev 6:12; 11:13
thunderings and an e. Rev 8:5; 11:19
a great e. so mighty an e. 16:18

earthquakes

and e. in divers places. Mat 24:7
Mark 13:8; Luke 21:11

earthy

first man is of earth, e. 1 Cor 15:47
e. such are they also that are e. 48
have borne the image of the e. 49

ease

nations shalt find no e. Deut 28:65
trod the Benjamites down with e.
Judg 20:43*
in thought of him at e. Job 12:5
I was at e. 16:12
dieth, being wholly at e. 21:23
his soul shall dwell at e. Ps 25:13
with scorning of those at e. 123:4
ye women that are at e. Isa 32:9
tremble, ye women that are at e. 11
Jacob shall return, be in rest, at e.
Jer 46:27
Moab hath been at e. from. 48:11
of a multitude being at e. Ezek 23:42
woe to them that are at e. Amos 6:1
with heathen at e. Zech 1:15
take thine e. eat, drink. Luke 12:19

ease, *verb*

when thou e. thyself. Deut 23:13*
e. thou somewhat the. 2 Chr 10:4, 9
my couch e. my complaint. Job 7:13
ah, I will e. me of mine. Isa 1:24

eased

I forbear, what am I e.? Job 16:6
that other men be e. and. 2 Cor 8:13

easier

so shall it be e. for. Ex 18:22
e. to say, thy sins be forgiven, or to.
Mat 9:5; Mark 2:9; Luke 5:23
e. for a camel to go. Mat 19:24
Mark 10:25; Luke 18:25
it is e. for heaven and. Luke 16:17

easily

charity is not e. provoked. 1 Cor 13:5
sin which doth so e. beset. Heb 12:1

east

(*The Hebrews express the east, west, north, and south, by words which signify,* before, behind, left, *and* right, *according to the position of a man with his face turned towards the* east. *The term* Kedem (*before or east*), *as generally used, refers to the lands directly east of Palestine : Arabia, Mesopotamia, and Babylon. Another term,* Mizrach, *used of* far east, *has no definite signification*)

God placed at the e. of. Gen 3:24
removed to a mountain on e. 12:8
Lot chose plain, journeyed e. 13:11
abroad to the west and e. 28:14
into land of people of the e. 29:1
that encamp toward e. Num 3:38
Balak hath brought me out of e. 23:7
the children of the e. came. Judg 6:3
33; 7:12; 8:10; 1 Ki 4:30
three looking toward e. 1 Ki 7:25
2 Chr 4:4
porters towards the e. 1 Chr 9:24
to flight them toward the e. 12:15
greatest of all men of e. Job 1:3
cometh not from e. nor. Ps 75:6
as far as e. is from west. 103:12
gathered them from the e. 107:3
be replenished from e. Isa 2:6
spoil them of e. 11:14; Jer 49:28
righteous man from the e. Isa 41:2
thy seed from the e. 43:5; Zech 8:7
ravenous bird from the e. Isa 46:11
their faces towards e. Ezek 8:16
deliver thee to men of e. 25:4, 10
to gate which looketh toward e.
40:6, 22; 43:1; 44:1; 46:1, 12
of God came from way of e. 43:2
waters issue out toward the e. 47:8
toward the e. ten thousand. 48:10
suburbs of city toward the e. 17
waxed great toward e. Dan 8:9
tidings out of the e. shall. 11:44
drive him toward e. sea. Joel 2:20
wander from north to e. Amos 8:12
mount cleave toward e. Zech 14:4
came wise men from e. Mat 2:1
we have seen star in the e. 2, 9
come from e. and. 8:11; Luke 13:29
lightning cometh out of e. Mat 24:27
angel ascending from e. Rev 7:2*
the way of kings of e. 16:12*
on the e. three gates, on the. 21:13

east border

point out e. border. Num 34:10
in e. border of Jericho. Josh 4:19
e. border was the salt sea. 15:5
west border to e. border. Ezek 45:7
oblation toward e. border. 48:21

Easter

(*The Passover. The name Easter was given later to the Christian celebration of this season*)

intending after E. to. Acts 12:4

east gate

the keeper of the e. gate. Neh 3:29
by entry of the e. gate. Jer 19:2*
stood at door of e. gate. Ezek 10:19
Spirit brought me unto e. gate. 11:1

east side

of court on the e.-side. Ex 27:13
and on the e.-side shall. Num 2:3
Ai, on e.-side of Beth-el. Josh 7:2
of inheritance on the e.-side. 16:5
came by e.-side of land. Judg 11:18
mountain on the e.-side. Ezek 11:23
he measured the e.-side with. 42:16
from the e.-side even unto the. 48:2
3, 4, 5, 6, 7, 8, 23, 24, 25, 26, 27
Jonah sat on the e.-side. Jonah 4:5

eastward

lift up thine eyes e. and. Gen 13:14
Deut 3:27
open the window e. and. 2 Ki 13:17
e. were six Levites. 1 Chr 26:17
with line went forth e. Ezek 47:3

east wind

blasted with the e. wind. Gen 41:6
23, 27

Lord brought an *e.-wind.* *Ex* 10:13
14:21
fill his belly with *e.-wind.* *Job* 15:2
e.-wind carrieth him away. 27:21
which scattereth *e.-wind.* 38:24
ships with an *e.-wind.* *Ps* 48:7
caused an *e.-wind* to blow. 78:26
wind in day of *e.-wind.* *Isa* 27:8
scatter them as with an *e.-wind.*
Jer 18:17
wither when the *e.-wind.* *Ezek* 17:10
and the *e.-wind* drieth up. 19:12
the *e.-wind* hath broken. 27:26
followeth after *e.-wind.* *Hos* 12:1
he be fruitful, an *e.-wind.* 13:15
a vehement *e.-wind.* *Jonah* 4:8
faces sup up as the *e.-wind.* *Hab* 1:9

easy

knowledge is *e.* to him. *Pr* 14:6
my yoke is *e.* my burden. *Mat* 11:30
except ye utter words *e.* *1 Cor* 14:9
wisdom from above is *e.* *Jas* 3:17

eat

The word is used in Scripture as we use it and its synonyms devour, consume, etc., both literally and figuratively. [1] *To chew and swallow food,* Gen 27:4. [2] *To waste, consume,* Eccl 5:11. [3] *To oppress and destroy,* Ps 14:4. [4] *To have close union with Christ, symbolized by eating his flesh,* John 6:56. [5] *To read closely and attentively, as we say devour a book,* Jer 15:16.

Eating with a person, in the East, is regarded almost as making a covenant of friendship which must not be broken ; hence the scandal to the Jews of Jesus' eating with publicans and sinners, Mat 9:11; *and the special sin of the betrayal by Judas, who had so often eaten with his Master.*

of every tree freely *e.* *Gen* 2:16
in the day ye *e.* your eyes. 3:5
Eve took and did *e.* 6
and I did *e.* 12, 13
dust shalt thou *e.* all days. 14
in sorrow shalt thou *e.* of it all. 17
by angels, they did *e.* 18:8; 19:3
bring it to me, that I may *e.* 27:4
and they did *e.* there upon. 31:46
the birds did *e.* them out. 40:17
Egyptians did *e.* by themselves.
43:32
locusts shall *e.* every. *Ex* 10:5
the locusts may *e.* every herb. 12
with bitter herbs they shall *e.* it. 12:8
save that which every man *e.* 16
shall no stranger *e.* 43, 48; *Lev* 22:13
circumcised, then shall he *e.*
Ex 12:44
e. that to-day, for to-day is. 16:25
children of Israel did *e.* manna forty.
35; *John* 6:31, 49, 58
poor of thy people may *e.* *Ex* 23:11
Aaron and sons shall *e.* 29:32
Lev 6:16; 8:31
thou *e.* of his sacrifice. *Ex* 34:15
males shall *e.* it. *Lev* 6:18, 29; 7:6
Num 18:10
priest that offereth it *e.* it. *Lev* 6:26
all that be clean *e.* 7:19; *Num* 18:11
shall in no wise *e.* of it. *Lev* 7:24
e. of it without leaven. 10:12
yet these ye may *e.* 11:21, 22
Deut 14:20
Aaron and his sons shall *e.* *Lev* 24:9
what shall we *e.* the seventh. 25:20
your enemies shall *e.* it. 26:16
remember fish we did *e.* *Num* 11:5
give us flesh, that we may *e.* 13
shall not lie down till he *e.* 23:24
the people did *e.* of their. 25:2
buy meat of them that ye may *e.*
Deut 2:6
e. in gates. 12:15, 21; 15:22; 26:12
unclean and clean may *e.* 12:15, 22
15:22
e. before Lord. 12:18; 14:26; 15:20
I will *e.* flesh, thou mayest *e.* 12:20
give it to stranger that he *e.* 14:21

and another man *e.* of it. *Deut* 20:6*
then thou mayest *e.* grapes. 23:24
gather grapes, worms shall *e.* 28:39
e. fruit of own body. 53; *Lam* 2:20
which did *e.* the fat of. *Deut* 32:38
did *e.* of the old corn. *Josh* 5:11
vineyards ye planted not ye *e.* 24:13
they tarried, and did *e.* *Judg* 19:8
Hannah did *e.* and was. *1 Sam* 1:18
and afterwards they *e.* 9:13
and *e.* and sin not against. 14:34
Jonathan did *e.* no meat. 20:34
and *e.* that thou mayest have. 28:22
he shall *e.* at my table. *2 Sam* 9:11
1 Ki 2:7
of Jeroboam shall dogs *e.* *1 Ki* 14:11
16:4; 21:23; *2 Ki* 9:10, 36
that we may *e.* and die. *1 Ki* 17:12
angel said, arise and *e.* 19:5
Acts 10:13; 11:7
they shall *e.* and leave. *2 Ki* 4:43
they did *e.* and left thereof. 44
give thy son that we may *e.* him to-day, and we will *e.* my son. 6:28
we boiled my son, and did *e.* 29
ye *e.* every man of. 18:31; *Isa* 36:16
yet did they *e.* passover. *2 Chr* 30:18
children of Israel did *e.* *Ezra* 6:21
take corn, that we may *e.* *Neh* 5:2
so they did *e.* and. 9:25; *Ps* 78:29
sighing cometh before I *e.* *Job* 3:24
let me sow, and let another *e.* 31:8
the meek shall *e.* and. *Ps* 22:26
they that be fat on earth shall *e.* 29
will I *e.* the flesh of bulls. 50:13
man did *e.* angels' food. 78:25
shalt *e.* the labour of thine. 128:2
e. the fruit of own way. *Pr* 1:31
Isa 3:10
soul of transgressors shall *e.* *Pr* 13:2
they that love it shall *e.* 18:21
my son, *e.* thou honey. 24:13
whoso keepeth fig-tree shall *e.* 27:18
and young eagles shall *e.* it. 30:17
for who can *e.* or hasten ? *Eccl* 2:25
they are increased that *e.* 5:11
sleep is sweet, whether he *e.* 12
princes *e.* in the morning. 10:16
blessed, when thy princes *e.* in. 17
his garden and *e.* his. *S of S* 4:16
we will *e.* our own bread. *Isa* 4:1
butter and honey shall he *e.* 7:15
and honey shall every one *e.* 22
e. on the left hand. 9:20
lion shall *e.* straw. 11:7; 65:25
oxen and asses shall *e.* 30:24
plant vineyards, and *e.* fruit thereof.
37:30; 65:21; *Jer* 29:5, 28
the worm shall *e.* them. *Isa* 51:8
come ye, buy and *e.* yea, 55:1
hearken to me, and *e.* that which. 2
they that gathered it shall *e.* 62:9
a people which *e.* swine's. 65:4
my servants shall *e.* but ye shall. 13
shall not plant and another *e.* 22
words were found, and I did *e.* them.
Jer 15:16
shall *e.* every one the flesh of. 19:9
open thy mouth and *e.* *Ezek* 2:8
e. that thou findest, *e.* this roll. 3:1
e. by weight. 4:10
fathers shall *e.* sons. 5:10
thou didst *e.* fine flour, and. 16:13
and in thee they *e.* upon the. 22:9
ye *e.* the fat, and clothe you. 34:3
Nebuchadnezzar did *e.* *Dan* 4:33
for they shall *e.* and not. *Hos* 4:10
Mi 6:14; *Hag* 1:6
shall *e.* unclean things. *Hos* 9:3
all that *e.* thereof shall be. 4
that *e.* the lambs out of. *Amos* 6:4
who also *e.* the flesh. *Mi* 3:3
let the rest *e.* every one. *Zech* 11:9
but he shall *e.* the flesh of the. 16
how David did *e.* the. *Mat* 12:4
did all *e.* and were filled. 14:20
15:37; *Mark* 6:42; 8:8; *Luke* 9:17
yet the dogs *e.* of the. *Mat* 15:27
Mark 7:28
that did *e.* were 4,000. *Mat* 15:38
as they did *e.* he said. 26:21
Mark 14:18, 22
brake it, and said, take *e.* *Mat* 26:26
Mark 14:22; *1 Cor* 11:24

when they saw him *e.* *Mark* 2:16
they that did *e.* were above. 6:44
no man *e.* fruit of thee. 11:14
that thou mayest *e.* passover ? 14:12
14; *Luke* 22:8, 11; *John* 18:28
and did *e.* rubbing them. *Luke* 6:1
him that he would *e.* with. 7:36
e. such things as are set. 10:8
let us *e.* and be merry. 15:23
took it, and did *e.* before. 24:43
prayed him, Master, *e.* *John* 4:31
because ye did *e.* of loaves. 6:26
that a man may *e.* thereof. 50
except ye *e.* the flesh of Son. 53
they did *e.* their meat. *Acts* 2:46
wentest in and didst *e.* with. 11:3
we will *e.* nothing till we. 23:14*
one believeth he may *e.* *Rom* 14:2
doubteth is damned if he *e.* 23
some *e.* it as a thing. *1 Cor* 8:7
we *e.* are we better; if we *e.* not. 8
I will eat no flesh while the. 13
all *e.* the same spiritual meat. 10:3
who *e.* of the sacrifices. 18
whatsoever is sold, that *e.* 25
e. asking no question for. 27
if any man hunger, let him *e.* 11:34
not, neither should he *e.* *2 Thes* 3:10
their word will *e.* as. *2 Tim* 2:17
and shall *e.* your flesh. *Jas* 5:3
shall *e.* her flesh, and. *Rev* 17:16
that ye may *e.* flesh of kings. 19:18

see **blood, bread**

eat with *drink*

they did *e.* and *drink.* *Gen* 24:54
26:30; *Ex* 24:11; *Judg* 9:27; 19:4
sat down to *e.* and *drink.* *Ex* 32:6
1 Cor 10:7
nor *e.* bread, nor *drink.* *Ex* 34:28
Deut 9:9, 18
did *e.* bread and *drink.* *1 Sam* 30:11
house to *e.* and *drink* ? *2 Sam* 11:11
did *e.* of his meat and *drink.* 12:3
taste what I *e.* or *drink* ? 19:35
they *e.* and *drink* before. *1 Ki* 1:25
neither will I *e.* bread nor *drink* water. 13:8, 9, 17, 22
will I *e.* bread nor *drink.* 16
get thee up, *e.* and *drink.* 18:41
they may *e.* and *drink.* *2 Ki* 6:22
one tent did *e.* and *drink.* 7:8
e. own dung, *drink.* 18:27; *Isa* 36:12
and did *e.* and *drink* before Lord.
1 Chr 29:22
them to *e.* and *drink.* *2 Chr* 28:15
e. no bread nor *drink.* *Ezra* 10:6
e. the fat and *drink.* *Neh* 8:10
nor *e.* nor *drink* three. *Esth* 4:16
sisters to *e.* and *drink.* *Job* 1:4
so is he, *e.* and *drink.* *Pr* 23:7
better than that he *e.* and *drink.*
Eccl 2:24; 3:13; 5:18; 8:15
e., yea, *drink* abundantly. *S of S* 5:1
e. *drink,* ye princes. *Isa* 21:5
let us *e.* and *drink,* to-morrow we shall die. 22:13; *1 Cor* 15:32
not father *e.* and *drink* ? *Jer* 22:15
e. thy fruit and *drink.* *Ezek* 25:4
may *e.* flesh and *drink* blood. 39:17
pulse to *e.* and water to *drink.*
Dan 1:12
e. and when ye did *drink.* *Zech* 7:6
what shall *e.* or *drink.* *Mat* 6:25, 31
Luke 12:29
to *e.* and *drink* with drunken.
Mat 24:49; *Luke* 12:45
why do ye *e.* and *d.*? *Luke* 5:30
but thy disciples *e.* and *d.* 33
take thine ease, *e.* *drink.* 12:19
afterward thou shalt *e.* and *drink.*
17:8
they did *e.* they *drank,* they. 27, 28
e. and *drink* at my table. 22:30
Saul three days did neither *e.* nor *drink.* *Acts* 9:9
e. nor *drink* till they. 23:12, 21
e. flesh nor *drink* wine. *Rom* 14:21
power to *e.* and to *drink* ? *1 Cor* 9:4
ye *e.* or *drink,* or whatever. 10:31
not houses to *e.* and *drink* in ? 11:22
as ye *e.* this bread and *drink.* 26
shall *e.* and *drink* unworthily. 27
and so let him *e.* and *drink.* 28

he did **eat**
Eve gave, and *he did e.* *Gen* 3:6
loved Esau, because *he did e.* 25:28
near to Isaac, and *he did e.* 27:25
not aught, save bread *he did e.* 39:6
Egyptian bread, and *he did e.*
1 Sam 30:11
he did e. continually. *2 Sam* 9:13
bread before him, *he did e.* 12:20
John *did e.* locusts and. *Mark* 1:6
those days *he did e.* *Luke* 4:2
for before *he did e.* *Gal* 2:12

eat *not*
tree of knowledge of good and evil,
shalt *not e.* *Gen* 2:17; 3:1, 3
commanded thee *not* to *e.* 3:11, 17
blood thereof shall ye *not e.* 9:4
Lev 19:26; *Deut* 12:16, 23, 24, 25
15:23
I will *not e.* till I have. *Gen* 24:33
children of Israel *e. not.* 32:32
Egyptians might *not e.* with. 43:32
e. not of it raw, nor. *Ex* 12:9
a foreigner shall *not e.* 45; 29:33
these shall ye *not e.* *Lev* 11:4
Deut 14:3, 7
a leper *not e.* of. *Lev* 22:4, 6, 10, 12
that torn he shall *not e.* to. 8
ye shall *not e.* one day. *Num* 11:19
ye shall *not e.* of any thing that.
Deut 14:21; *Ezek* 44:31
ox slain, thou shalt *not e.* *Deut* 28:31
and *e. not* any unclean. *Judg* 13:4
7, 14
she wept and did *not e.* *1 Sam* 1:7
for the people will *not e.* till. 9:13
and said, I will *not e.* 28:23
and they could *not e.* *2 Ki* 4:40
with thy eyes, but *not e.* 7:2, 19
not e. of most holy things. *Ezra* 2:63
Neh 7:65
and let me *not e.* of. *Ps* 141:4
e not bread of him that. *Pr* 23:6
e. not bread of men. *Ezek* 24:17
except they wash, *e. not.* *Mark* 7:3, 4
I will not *e.* thereof. *Luke* 22:16
such an one *not* to *e.* *1 Cor* 5:11
neither if we *e. not* are we. 8:8
e. not, for his sake that. 10:28

shall ye **eat**
thus *shall ye e.* it. *Ex* 12:11
seven days *shall ye e.* 15, 20
nor *shall ye e.* flesh torn. 22:31
wave-breast *shall ye e.* *Lev* 10:14
cheweth the cud, that *shall ye e.*
11:3; *Deut* 14:4, 6
these *shall ye e.* of all that. *Lev* 11:9
in fifth year *shall ye e.* of. 19:25
flesh of daughters *shall ye e.* 26:29
fins and scales *shall ye e.* *Deut* 14:9

ye shall **eat**
and *ye shall e.* the fat. *Gen* 45:18
ye shall e. it in haste. *Ex* 12:11
first month at even *ye shall e.* 18
at even *ye shall e.* flesh. 16:12
ye shall e. no fat. *Lev* 7:23, 24
ye shall e. no blood. 26; 17:14
ye shall e. it in holy place. 10:13
ye shall e. neither bread nor. 23:14
ye shall e. the increase. 25:12
ye shall e. your fill. 19
ye shall e. of old store. 22; 26:10
ye shall e. and not be. 26:26
ye shall e. flesh of your sons. 29
Lord will give flesh, and *ye shall e.*
Num 11:18
and *ye shall e.* in every place. 18:31
ye shall e. before Lord. *Deut* 12:7
of all clean birds *ye shall e.* 14:11
go up, for *ye shall e.* *1 Sam* 9:19
a sign, *ye shall e.* this year such.
2 Ki 19:29; *Isa* 37:30
obedient *ye shall e.* good. *Isa* 1:19
ye shall e. the riches of the. 61:6
and *ye shall e.* fat till. *Ezek* 39:19
ye shall e. in plenty. *Joel* 2:26
thought what *ye shall e.* *Luke* 12:22

to **eat**
n evening flesh *to e.* *Ex* 16:8
who shall give us flesh *to e.*?
Num 11:4, 18
soul longeth *to e.* flesh. *Deut* 12:20
have like portions *to e.* 18:8
to the high place *to e.* *1 Sam* 9:13
king sat him down *to e.* meat. 20:24
to cause David *to e.* *2 Sam* 3:35
master's son have food *to e.* 9:10
but he refused *to e.* 13:9
fruit for the young men *to e.* 16:2
for people with him *to e.* 17:29
poured out for men *to e.* *2 Ki* 4:40
have had enough *to e.* *2 Chr* 31:10
land thou gavest, *to e.* the. *Neh* 9:36
manna on them *to e.* *Ps* 78:24
when thou sittest *to e.* *Pr* 23:1
not good *to e.* much honey. 25:27
given him power *to e.* *Eccl* 5:19
God giveth him not power *to e.* 6:2
shall be for them *to e.* *Isa* 23:18
cause them *to e.* flesh. *Jer* 19:9
he caused me *to e.* roll. *Ezek* 3:2
son of man, cause thy belly *to e.* 3
make thee *to e.* grass. *Dan* 4:25, 32
there is no cluster *to e.* *Mi* 7:1
as eagle that hasteth *to e.* *Hab* 1:8*
pluck ears of corn and *to e.* *Mat* 12:1
not lawful for him *to e.* 4
Mark 2:26; *Luke* 6:4
give ye them *to e.* *Mat* 14:16
Mark 6:37; *Luke* 9:13
to e. with unwashen. *Mat* 15:20
multitude have nothing *to e.* 32
Mark 8:1, 2
prepare *to e.* passover. *Mat* 26:17
should be given her *to e.* *Mark* 5:43
no leisure so much as *to e.* 6:31
to e. this passover. *Luke* 22:15
I have meat *to e.* that ye. *John* 4:32
any brought him aught *to e.*? 33
this man give us his flesh *to e.*? 6:52
broken it, he began *to e.* *Acts* 27:35
emboldened *to e.* things. *1 Cor* 8:10
ye come, this is not *to e.* 11:20
when ye come together *to e.* 33
have no right *to e.* *Heb* 13:10
will I give *to e.* of tree of. *Rev* 2:7
to e. things sacrificed unto. 14, 20
I will give *to e.* of hidden manna. 17

eat *up*
lean did *e. up* the. *Gen* 41:4, 20
land of enemies *e.* you *up.* *Lev* 26:38
he shall *e. up* nations. *Num* 24:8
nation thou knowest not shall *e. up.*
Deut 28:33
on me to *e. up* my flesh. *Ps* 27:2
did *e. up* all the herbs. 105:35
moth *e.* them *up.* *Isa* 50:9; 51:8
shall *e. up* thine harvest, *e. up* thy
flocks, *e. up* thy vines. *Jer* 5:17
wind shall *e. up* thy pastures. 22:22*
e. up the sin of my people. *Hos* 4:8*
and did *e. up* a part. *Amos* 7:4
it shall *e.* thee *up* like. *Nah* 3:15*
said, take it, and *e.* it *up.* *Rev* 10:9

eaten
hast thou *e.* of tree? *Gen* 3:11
that which young men have *e.* 14:24
rams of thy flock have I not *e.* 31:38
had *e.* them up, it could not be known
that they had *e.* them. 41:21
in one house shall it be *e.* *Ex* 12:46
no leavened bread be *e.* 13:3, 7
his flesh shall not be *e.* 21:28
a field or vineyard to be *e.* 22:5
it shall not be *e.* because. 29:34
be *e.* in the holy place. *Lev* 6:16
26; 7:6
burnt, it shall not be *e.* 6:23; 7:19
no sin-offering shall be *e.* 6:30
be *e.* the same day it. 7:15, 16
if sacrifice of peace-offering be *e.* 18
ye not *e.* the sin offering? 10:17
ye should indeed have *e.* it in. 18
if I had *e.* the sin-offering. 19
shall not be *e.* 11:13, 41; *Deut* 14:19
be *e.* the same day. *Lev* 19:6; 22:30
be *e.* at all on the third day. 19:7
unleavened bread be *e.* *Num* 28:17
Ezek 45:21
when thou shalt have *e.* and be full.
Deut 6:11; 8:10, 12
roe-buck and the hart is *e.* 12:22
vineyard, hath not *e.* of it. 20:6*
I have not *e.* thereof. 26:14
ye have not *e.* bread nor. 29:6
when they shall have *e.* and. 31:20
had *e.* of the old corn. *Josh* 5:12
when Boaz had *e.* and. *Ruth* 3:7
if people had *e.* freely. *1 Sam* 14:30
for he had *e.* no bread all. 28:20
had *e.* his spirit came again. 30:12
have we *e.* at all of? *2 Sam* 19:42
camest back, and hast *e.* *1 Ki* 13:22
the lion had not *e.* the carcase. 28
have not *e.* the bread. *Neh* 5:14
unsavoury be *e.* without salt. *Job* 6:6
have *e.* my morsel alone. 31:17
if I have *e.* the fruits thereof. 39
zeal of thine house hath *e.* me up.
Ps 69:9; *John* 2:17
I have *e.* ashes like bread. *Ps* 102:9
and bread *e.* in secret. *Pr* 9:17
morsel that thou hast *e.* shalt. 23:8
I have *e.* my honey-comb. *S of S* 5:1
have *e.* up the vineyard. *Isa* 3:14
they have *e.* up Jacob. *Jer* 10:25
figs could not be *e.* 24:2, 3, 8; 29:17
e. sour grapes. 31:29; *Ezek* 18:2
I have not *e.* that. *Ezek* 4:14
not *e.* upon mountains. 18:6, 15
even hath *e.* upon mountains. 11
ye have *e.* fruit of lies. *Hos* 10:13
locust hath left, canker-worm *e.*
Joel 1:4; 2:25
and they that had *e.* *Mat* 14:21
Mark 8:9
we have *e.* and drunk. *Luke* 13:26
e. afterward thou shalt *e.* 17:8
to them that had *e.* *John* 6:13
became hungry, and would have *e.*
Acts 10:10
Lord, I have never *e.* any. 14
he was *e.* of worms, and. 12:23
broken bread and *e.* departed. 20:11
when they had *e.* enough. 27:38
as soon as I had *e.* it. *Rev* 10:10

eater
out of the *e.* came meat. *Judg* 14:14
may give bread to the *e.* *Isa* 55:10
fall into mouth of the *e.* *Nah* 3:12

eaters
be not among riotious *e.* *Pr* 23:20

eatest
in the day thou *e.* thou. *Gen* 2:17
said Elkanah, why *e.*? *1 Sam* 1:8
spirit so sad that thou *e.*? *1 Ki* 21:5

eateth
e. leavened bread be. *Ex* 12:15, 19
the soul that *e.* *Lev* 7:18, 20, 25, 27
17:10, 15
every one that *e.* shall bear. 19:8
a land that *e.* up the. *Num* 13:32
cursed be the man that *e.*
1 Sam 14:24, 28
harvest the hungry *e.* up. *Job* 5:5
and another never *e.* with. 21:25*
behemoth which I made, he *e.* 40:15
similitude of ox that *e.* *Ps* 106:20
righteous *e.* to satisfying. *Pr* 13:25
she *e.* and wipeth her mouth. 30:20
and she *e.* not the bread. 31:27
fool foldeth hands and *e.* *Eccl* 4:5
all his days also he *e.* in. 5:17
but a stranger *e.* it, this is. 6:2
yet in his hand he *e.* it up. *Isa* 28:4
behold, he *e.* but awaketh. 29:8
with part thereof he *e.* flesh. 44:16
he that *e.* of their eggs dieth. 59:5
man that *e.* sour grape. *Jer* 31:30
why *e.* your master with publicans?
Mat 9:11; *Mark* 2:16; *Luke* 15:2
one of you who *e.* with me, shall betray me. *Mark* 14:18; *John* 13:18
whoso *e.* my flesh hath. *John* 6:54
he that *e.* my flesh dwelleth in. 56
so he that *e.* me, even he. 57
he that *e.* of this bread, shall. 58
another who is weak *e.* *Rom* 14:2
that *e.* despise him that *e.* not. 3
he that *e.*, *e.* to Lord; he that *e.* not,
to Lord he *e.* not. 6
evil for that man who *e.* with. 20
because he *e.* not of faith. 23
planteth vineyard, and *e.* not of fruit
thereof? and *e.* not of. *1 Cor* 9:7
e. unworthily, *e.* damnation. 11:29

eating
a lamb according to number of souls
to *e.* *Ex* 12:4; 16:16, 18, 21

Samson took thereof, and went on e. Judg 14:9
not against Lord in e. 1 Sam 14:34
spread abroad on all earth e. 30:16
guests made an end of e. 1 Ki 1:41
they were e. of pottage. 2 Ki 4:40
upon him while he is e. Job 20:23
e. swine's flesh, and the. Isa 66:17
they made an end of e. Amos 7:2
were e. Jesus took bread. Mat 26:26
concerning e. of things. 1 Cor 8:4
in e. every one taketh his. 11:21
see **drinking**

Ebal

put curse upon mount E. Deut 11:29
these stones in mount E. 27:4
stand upon mount E. to curse. 13
built an altar in mount E. Josh 8:30
half of them over-against E. 33

Ebed

words of Gaal son of E. Judg 9:30
E. the son of Jonathan. Ezra 8:6

Ebed-melech

E. spake to the king. Jer 38:8
speak to E. the Ethiopian. 39:16

Eben-ezer

Israel pitched beside E. 1 Sam 4:1
Philistines brought ark from E. 5:1
Samuel called name of stone E. 7:12

Eber

Shem father of the children of E. Gen 10:21
unto E. were born two sons. 25
1 Chr 1:19
ships shall afflict E. Num 24:24

Ed

called the altar E. Josh 22:34

Eden

put man into garden of E. Gen 2:15
forth from the garden of E. 3:23
make her wilderness like E. Isa 51:3; Ezek 36:35
been in E. the garden. Ezek 28:13
so that all the trees of E. 31:9
the trees of E. be comforted. 16
brought down with trees of E. 18
land is as the garden of E. Joel 2:3
holds sceptre from E. Amos 1:5

edge

Etham in e. of wilderness. Ex 13:20
Num 33:6
make fifty loops in the e. Ex 26:10
and he do not whet the e. Eccl 10:10
see **teeth**

edge *of the sword*

slew Hamor with the e. of sword. Gen 34:26
Amalek with e. of sword. Ex 17:13
Sihon with e. of sword. Num 21:24
all with e. of sword. Josh 6:21
smote Ai with e. of sword. 8:24
Sisera with e. of sword. Judg 4:15
Jabesh-gilead with e. of sword. 21:10
servants slain with e. of sword. Job 1:15, 17
turned the e. of the sword. Ps 89:43
them with e. of sword. Jer 21:7
fall by the e. of sword. Luke 21:24
escaped the e. of sword. Heb 11:34

edged

and a two-e. sword in. Ps 149:6
sharp as a two-e. sword. Pr 5:4
sharper than two-e. Heb 4:12
out of mouth went two-e. Rev 1:16

edges

joined at the two e. Ex 28:7*; 39:4*
dagger had two e. Judg 3:16
sharp sword with two e. Rev 2:12

edification

(*Literally, a building up, constructing; hence edify meant to organize, establish: also to instruct and improve, especially morally*)

his neighbour to e. Rom 15:2
prohesieth speaketh to e. 1 Cor 14:3
Lord hath given us for e. 2 Cor 10:8*
which Lord hath given to e. 13:10*

edified

churches had rest, were e. Acts 9:31
but the other is not e. 1 Cor 14:17

edifieth

but charity e. 1 Cor 8:1
speaks in an unknown tongue e. himself; he that prophesieth e. 14:4

edify

wherewith one may e. Rom 14:19
things lawful, but e. not. 1 Cor 10:23
e. one another, even. 1 Thes 5:11*

edifying

that church may receive e. 1 Cor 14:5
that ye may excel to the e. 12
let all things be done to e. 26
do all things for your e. 2 Cor 12:19
for the e. of the body. Eph 4:12*
increase of the body to the e. 16*
which is good to use of e. 29
questions rather than e. 1 Tim 1:4*

Edom

his name called E. Gen 25:30
Esau is E. 36:1
dukes of E. amazed. Ex 15:15
Moses sent messengers to the king of E. Num 20:14; Judg 11:17
E. refused to give Israel. Num 20:21
E. shall be a possession. 24:18
out of the field of E. Judg 5:4
against Moab and E. 1 Sam 14:47
David put garrisons in E. 2 Sam 8:14; 1 Chr 18:13
Hadad of king's seed in E. 1 Ki 11:14
he had cut off every male in E. 16
there was then no king in E. 22:47
water by the way of E. 2 Ki 3:20
in his days E. revolted from. 8:20
thou hast indeed smitten E. 14:10
sought after gods of E. 2 Chr 25:20
over E. will I cast out my shoe. Ps 60:8; 108:9
lead me into E.? 60:9; 108:10
the tabernacles of E. are. 83:6
remember the children of E. 137:7
shall lay their hand on E. Isa 11:14
who cometh from E.? 63:1
E. I will punish. Jer 9:26; 25:21
and yokes to king of E. 27:3
concerning E. saith Lord. 49:7; Ob 1
E. shall be a desolation. Jer 49:17
counsel he hath taken against E. 20
because E. hath dealt. Ezek 25:12
lay my vengeance upon E. 14
there is E. her kings and. 32:29
E. shall escape out of. Dan 11:41
E. shall be a wilderness. Joel 3:19
deliver them up to E. Amos 1:6, 9
burnt bones of the king of E. 2:1
possess the remnant of E. 9:12
destroy wise men out of E. Ob 8
whereas E. saith, we are. Mal 1:4
see **daughter**

Edomite, -s

Esau father of E. Gen 36:9, 43
shalt not abhor an E. Deut 23:7
stirred up Hadad the E. 1 Ki 11:14
Joram smote the E. 2 Ki 8:21
2 Chr 21:9
E. became David's. 1 Chr 18:13
the E. revolted from. 2 Chr 21:10
lo, thou hast smitten the E. 25:19
the E. had come and smitten. 28:17
see **Doeg**

effect

make her vow of no e. Num 30:8
spake to her to that e. 2 Chr 34:22
of people of none e. Ps 33:10
the e. of righteousness. Isa 32:17
his lies shall not so e. it. Jer 48:30*
days are at hand, and e. Ezek 12:23
commandment of none e. Mat 15:6*
word of God of none e. Mark 7:13*
faith of God without e.? Rom 3:3
promise of none e. 4:14; Gal 3:17
word hath taken none e. Rom 9:6*
of Christ be of none e. 1 Cor 1:17*
Christ become of no e. to. Gal 5:4*

effected

Solomon prosperously e. 2 Chr 7:11

effectual

for a great door and e. 1 Cor 16:9
e. in enduring the same. 2 Cor 1:6*
e. working of his power. Eph 3:7
according to the e. working. 4:16*
thy faith may become e. Philem 6
the e. prayer of righteous. Jas 5:16*

effectually

that wrought e. in Peter. Gal 2:8
the word e. worketh in. 1 Thes 2:13

effeminate

nor e. shall inherit the. 1 Cor 6:9

egg

any taste in white of an e.? Job 6:6
if he ask an e. will offer. Luke 11:12

eggs

young ones or e. the dam sitting on the young or e. shall. Deut 22:6
ostrich leaveth her e. Job 39:14
one gathereth e. that are. Isa 10:14
cockatrice' e. he that eateth e. 59:5
as partridge sitteth on e. Jer 17:11

Eglah

Ithream, by E. David's wife. 2 Sam 3:5

Eglaim

howling is gone unto E. Isa 15:8

Eglon

Israel served E. the king. Judg 3:14
brought presents to E. and E. 17

Egypt

from the river of E. to. Gen 15:18
God hath made me lord of all E. 45:9
I will smite E. Ex 3:20; Jer 9:26
46:25
I may lay my hand on E. Ex 7:4
stretched hand over waters of E. 8:6
between cattle of Israel and E. 9:4
knowest thou not that E. is? 10:7
thou camest out of E. 23:15; 34:18
thou hast forgiven this people from E. Num 14:19
is a people come out of E. 22:5
shewed great signs upon E. Deut 6:22
none of the diseases of E. on. 7:15
what he did unto army of E. 11:4
smite thee with botch of E. 28:27
on thee all diseases of E. 60
rolled away reproach of E. Josh 5:9
and I plagued E. 24:5
I am a young man of E. 1 Sam 30:13
excelled wisdom of Egypt. 1 Ki 4:30
thou trustest on E. 2 Ki 18:21, 24
Isa 36:6, 9
E. was glad when. Ps 105:38
who smote firstborn of E. 135:8
wonders into midst of thee, O E. 9
to him that smote E. in. 136:10
bed with fine linen of E. Pr 7:16
after the manner of E. Isa 10:24
Amos 4:10
recover remnant from E. Isa 11:11
burden of E. the idols of E. 19:1
the spirit of E. shall fail in. 3
in that day shall E. be like. 16
shall Israel be third with E. 24
blessed be ye E. my people. 25
be ashamed of E. their glory. 20:5
as at report concerning E. so. 23:5
beat off from stream of E. 27:12
trust in the shadow of E. your. 30:3
I gave E. for thy ransom. 43:3
the labour of E. shall come. 45:14
what to do in way of E.? Jer 2:18
shalt be ashamed of E. as. 36
of Lord which came against E. 46:2
E. is like a fair heifer, but. 20
defile not yourselves with the idols of E. Ezek 20:7
nor left she her idols from E. 23:8
thou shalt not remember E. 27
with broidered work from E. 27:
prophesy against him and all E. 29:
bring again the captivity of E. 1
they also that uphold E. shall. 30:
pain come as in day of E.
fury on Sin, strength of E. 1
shall spoil the pomp of E. 32:1
lament for ever, even for E. 1
wail for the multitude of E. 1
precious things of E. Dan 11:4
gone, E. shall gather them. Hos 9:
E. shall be a desolation. Joel 3:1
as by the flood of E. Amos 8:8; 9:
Ethiopia and E. were her. Nah 3:
the sceptre of E. shall. Zech 10:1

if family of *E.* go not up. *Zech* 14:18
him governor over *E.* *Acts* 7:10
by faith he forsook *E.* *Heb* 11:27
is called Sodom and *E.* *Rev* 11:8
see **daughter**

in **Egypt**
tell of all my glory *in E.* *Gen* 45:13
me not, I pray thee *in E.* 47:29
affliction of my people *in E.* *Ex* 3:7
which is done to you *in E.* 16
hail, such as hath not been *in E.* 9:18
I wrought *in E.* 10:2; *Josh* 24:7
a great cry *in E.* *Ex* 12:30
no graves *in E.* 14:11
it was well with us *in E.* *Num* 11:18
and we have dwelt *in E.* a. 20:15
all that he did for you *in E.*
Deut 1:30; 4:34
all that he did *in E.* *Josh* 9:9
wrought his signs *in E.* *Ps* 78:43
smote all the firstborn *in E.* 51
not thy wonders *in E.* 106:7
had done great things *in E.* 21
famine shall follow after you *in E.*
Jer 42:16
declare ye *in E.* and publish. 46:14
whoredoms *in E.* *Ezek* 23:3
I have set a fire *in E.* 30:8, 16
will I execute judgements *in E.* 19
an angel appeared *in E.* *Mat* 2:19
dwellers *in E.* we do hear. *Acts* 2:10
than the treasures *in E.* *Heb* 11:26

into **Egypt**
countries came *into E.* *Gen* 41:57
I will go down with thee *into E.* 46:4
that came with Jacob *into E.* 26
better to return *into E.* *Num* 14:3, 4
Lord shall come *into E.* *Isa* 19:1
walk to go down *into E.* 30:2
fled and went *into E.* *Jer* 26:21
faces to go *into E.* 41:17; 42:15
go ye not *into E.* 42:19; 43:2
ambassadors *into E.* *Ezek* 17:15
carry captives *into E.* *Dan* 11:8
and oil is carried *into E.* *Hos* 12:1
flee *into E.* *Mat* 2:13
he departed *into E.* 14
sold Joseph *into E.* *Acts* 7:9
come, I will send thee *into E.* 34
hearts turned back again *into E.* 39
see **king**

land of **Egypt**
Sodom like *land of E.* *Gen* 13:10
Ishmael's wife out of *land of E.*
21:21
never saw in all the *land of E.* 41:19
plenty through *land of E.* 29, 30, 53
set over *land of E.* 41; 45:8, 26
in the *land of E.* was bread. 41:54
good of the *land of E.* 45:18, 20
the *land of E.* is before thee. 47:6
money failed in the *land of E.* 15
Joseph bought all the *land of E.* 20
made it a law over *land of E.* 26
all elders of the *land of E.* 50:7
blood in all *land of E.* *Ex* 7:19
frogs, lice, flies covered *land of E.*
8:6, 16, 24
blains, hail, locusts in *land of E.*
9:9, 22; 10:14
darkness over *land of E.* 10:21, 22
Moses was great in *land of E.* 11:3
Lord smote firstborn in *land of E.*
12:29; 13:15
would God we had died in *land of E.*
16:3; *Num* 14:2
you out of *land of E.* *Ex* 16:6
20:2; 29:46
strangers in *land of E.* 22:21; 23:9
Lev 19:34; *Deut* 10:19; *Acts* 13:17
gods which brought thee out of *land of E.* *Ex* 32:4; *1 Ki* 12:28; *Neh* 9:18
after doings of *land of E.* *Lev* 18:3
Lord thy God, who brought you out
of *land of E.* 19:36; 26:13
Num 15:41; *Deut* 5:6; 13:5, 10
20:1; *Judg* 2:12; *1 Sam* 12:6
from day thou didst depart out of
land of E. *Deut* 9:7; *Judg* 19:30
Isa 11:16; *Jer* 7:22; 11:7; 34:13
Mi 7:15
goest is not *land of E.* *Deut* 11:10
camest out of the *land of E.* in. 16:3
things in the *land of E.* *Ps* 78:12
out through the *land of E.* 81:5
shall in *land of E.* speak. *Isa* 19:18
altar for witness in *land of E.* 19, 20
outcasts in the *land of E.* 27:13
will go into *land of E.* *Jer* 42:14
sword overtake you in *land of E.* 16
they came into the *land of E.* 43:7
array himself with *land of E.* 12
return out of the *land of E.* 44:28
to them in *land of E.* *Ezek* 20:5
the harlot in the *land of E.* 23:19
whoredom from the *land of E.* 27
the *land of E.* desolate. 29:9, 12
land of E. utterly waste. 10
given him the *land of E.* for. 20
no more prince of *land of E.* 30:13
land of E. not escape. *Dan* 11:42
derision in *land of E.* *Hos* 7:16
thy God from *land of E.* 12:9; 13:4
them out of *land of E.* *Zech* 10:10
lead them out of *land of E.* *Heb* 8:9
people out of *land of E.* *Jude* 5

out of **Egypt**
Abraham *out of E.* *Gen* 13:1
carry me *out of E.* 47:30
bring Israel *out of E.* *Ex* 3:11
they were thrust *out of E.* 12:39
with a strong hand hath the Lord
brought thee *out of E.* 13:9, 16
came we forth *out of E.*? *Num* 11:20
is a people come *out of E.* 22:11
of men that came *out of E.* 32:11
thou camest *out of E.* *Deut* 16:6
when ye came *out of E.* *Josh* 2:10
till all that came *out of E.* 5:6
I made you go *out of E.* *Judg* 2:1
1 Sam 10:18
Israel came *out of E.* *1 Sam* 15:6
hast redeemed *out of E.* *1 Chr* 17:21
came with him *out of E.* *2 Chr* 12:3
princes come *out of E.* *Ps* 68:31
brought a vine *out of E.* 80:8
when Israel went *out of E.* 114:1
a highway *out of E.* *Isa* 19:23
set forth Urijah *out of E.* *Jer* 26:23
army was come *out of E.* 37:5
called my son *out of E.* *Hos* 11:1
Mat 2:15
tremble as a bird *out of E.* *Hos* 11:11
Lord brought Israel *out of E.* 12:13
when ye came *out of E.* *Hag* 2:5
not all that came *out of E.* *Heb* 3:16

to **Egypt**
the Edomites came *to E.* *1 Ki* 11:18
Jehoahaz came *to E.* *2 Ki* 23:34
2 Chr 36:4
Judah be a terror *to E.* *Isa* 19:17
Lord shall be known *to E.* 21
woe to them that go *to E.* for. 31:1
they call *to E.* they go. *Hos* 7:11
see **return**

Egyptian
handmaid an *E.* *Gen* 16:1, 3; 21:9
an *E.* bought Joseph of. 39:1
Lord blessed the *E.* house for. 5
Hebrews are not as *E.* *Ex* 1:19
Moses spied an *E.* smiting. 2:11
slew *E.* and hid him. 12; *Acts* 7:24
an *E.* delivered us out of the. *Ex* 2:19
whose father was an *E.* *Lev* 24:10
shalt not abhor an *E.* *Deut* 23:7
they found an *E.* in. *1 Sam* 30:11
Benaiah slew an *E.*, and the *E.* had a.
2 Sam 23:21; *1 Chr* 11:23
had servant an *E.* Jarha. *1 Chr* 2:34
Lord destroy tongue of *E.* *Isa* 11:15
and the *E.* shall come into. 19:23
art not thou that *E.* who? *Acts* 21:38

Egyptians
Pharaoh said to the *E.* *Gen* 41:55
abomination to *E.* 43:32; 46:34
the *E.* mourned for Jacob. 50:3
ye shall spoil the *E.* *Ex* 3:22; 12:36
sacrifice abomination of *E.*? 8:26
difference between *E.* and. 11:7
they borrowed of the *E.* 12:35
but the *E.* pursued them. 14:9, 10
E. whom ye have seen to-day. 13
E. said, let us flee from Israel...
fighteth for them against *E.* 25
the Lord overthrew *E.* in the. 27
seen what I did to the *E.* *Ex* 19:4
should the *E.* speak and say? 32:12
then the *E.* shall hear it. *Num* 14:13
E. vexed us and our fathers. 20:15
E. evil entreated and. *Deut* 26:6
darkness between you and the *E.*
Josh 24:7
deliver you from the *E.*? *Judg* 10:11
gods that smote the *E.* *1 Sam* 4:8
why harden your hearts, as *E.*? 6:6
to abominations of *E.* *Ezra* 9:1
set the *E.* against the *E.* *Isa* 19:2
the *E.* will I give into hand of a. 4
the *E.* shall know the Lord in. 21
the *E.* shall serve with the. 23
king of Assyria lead away *E.* 20:4
the *E.* shall help in vain and. 30:7
now *E.* are men and not God. 31:3
houses of gods of the *E.* *Jer* 43:13
given the hand to the *E.* *Lam* 5:6
fornication with *E.* *Ezek* 16:26
in bruising thy teats by *E.* 23:21
and I will scatter the *E.* 29:12
30:23, 26
I will gather the *E.* from. 29:13
learned in wisdom of *E.* *Acts* 7:22
which *E.* assaying to do. *Heb* 11:29

Ehud
raised up E. the son of. *Judg* 3:15
E. made him a dagger. 16
E. went forth. 23
and *E.* escaped while they. 26
Israel again did evil, when *E.* 4:1
sons of Bilham, *E.* *1 Chr* 7:10
the sons of *E.* 8:6

eight
is *e.* days old shall be circumcised.
Gen 17:12; 21:4; *Luke* 2:21
these *e.* Milcah did bear. *Gen* 22:23
they shall be *e.* boards. *Ex* 26:25
Moses gave *e.* oxen to. *Num* 7:8
on the sixth day *e.* bullocks. 29:29
Israel served Chushan-rishathaim
e. years. *Judg* 3:8
Abdon judged Israel *e.* years. 12:14
the Ephrathite had *e.* *1 Sam* 17:12
was of stones of *e.* cubits. *1 Ki* 7:10
Jehoram reigned *e.* *2 Ki* 8:17
Josiah was *e.* years old when he.
22:1; *2 Chr* 34:1
e. among sons of Ithamar.
1 Chr 24:4
sanctified house of Lord in *e.* days.
2 Chr 29:17
to seven, and also to *e.* *Eccl* 11:2
Ishmael escaped with *e.* *Jer* 41:15
going up had *e.* steps. *Ezek* 40:31
34, 37
e. tables, whereon slew sacrifices. 41
e. principal men. *Mi* 5:5
about an *e.* days after. *Luke* 9:28
after *e.* days disciples. *John* 20:26
had kept his bed *e.* years. *Acts* 9:33
wherein *e.* souls were. *1 Pet* 3:20

eight *hundred*
begat Seth *e. hun.* years. *Gen* 5:4
he begat Enoch *e. hun.* years. 19
Adino slew *e. hun.* *2 Sam* 23:8
array *e. hun.* thousand. *2 Chr* 13:3

eighteen
served Eglon *e.* years. *Judg* 3:14
oppressed Israel *e.* years. 10:8
two pillars of brass *e.* *1 Ki* 7:15
2 Ki 25:17; *Jer* 52:21
sons and brethren *e.* *1 Chr* 26:9
Rehoboam took *e.* *2 Chr* 11:21
those *e.* on whom tower. *Luke* 13:4
Satan hath bound these *e.* years. 16

eighteen *thousand*
of Israel *e. thous.* *Judg* 20:25
there fell of Benjamin *e. thous.* 44
of Manasseh, *e. thous.* *1 Chr* 12:31
slew of Edomites *e. thous.* 18:12
princes gave of brass *e. thous.* 29:7
city round was *e. thous.* *Ezek* 48:35

eighteenth
in *e.* year of Jeroboam. *1 Ki* 15:1
2 Chr 13:1
Jehoram reigned the *e.* *2 Ki* 3:1
in the *e.* year of king Josiah. 22:3
23:23; *2 Chr* 34:8; 35:19
the *e.* lot came forth. *1 Chr* 24:15

the e. to Hanani, he. 1 Chr 25:25
e. year of Nebuchadnezzar. Jer 32:1; 52:29

eighth

and ye shall sow the e. Lev 25:22
in Bul, which is e. 1 Ki 6:38
ordained a feast in the e. 12:32
the e. lot came forth to. 1 Chr 24:10
the e. to Jeshaiah. 25:15
Peulthaia the e. 26:5
the e. captain for the e. 27:11
in e. month word came. Zech 1:1
but saved Noah the e. 2 Pet 2:5*
is not, even he is the e. Rev 17:11
the e. foundation was a beryl. 21:20
see **day, days**

either

Jacob e. good or bad. Gen 31:24, 29
Nadab and Abihu took e. his censer. Lev 10:1
other gods, e. sun or. Deut 17:3
nation shall not leave thee e. 28:51
e. he is talking, or. 1 Ki 18:27
prosper, e. this or that. Eccl 11:6
ask a sign e. in depth or. Isa 7:11
for e. he will hate the one, and. Mat 6:24; Luke 16:13
e. make the tree good. Mat 12:33
e. how canst thou say to. Luke 6:42
e. what woman having ten. 15:8
crucified, on e. side one. John 19:18
except I speak to you e. 1 Cor 14:6
e. can a vine bear figs? Jas 3:12
of e. side the river there. Rev 22:2

Ekron

as the ark came to E. 1 Sam 5:10
restored to Israel from E. 7:14
Baal-zebub the god of E. 2 Ki 1:2
3, 6, 16
mine hand against the E. Amos 1:8
E. shall be rooted up. Zeph 2:4
E. very sorrowful. Zech 9:5
E. a Jebusite. 7

Ekronites

the land of the E. not. Josh 13:3
ark came to Ekron, E. 1 Sam 5:10

Elah

duke E. Gen 36:41
Shimei son of E. 1 Ki 4:18
E. son of Baasha began. 16:8
Hoshea son of E. 2 Ki 15:30; 17:1
18:1, 9
Caleb, E. the sons of E. 1 Chr 4:15
E. the son of Uzzi, the son of. 9:8

Elah

pitched by valley of E. 1 Sam 17:2
slew Goliath in valley of E. 21:9

Elam

of Shem, E. and Ashur. Gen 10:22
of Chedorlaomer king of E. 14:1
Hananiah and E. of. 1 Chr 8:24
E. fifth son of Meshelemiah. 26:3
the children of E. Ezra 2:7, 31
8:7; Neh 7:12, 34
one of sons of E. answered. Ezra 10:2
chief of the people, E. Neh 10:14
Jehohanan and E. and Ezer. 12:42
recover people from E. Isa 11:11
go up, O E. 21:2
and E. bare the quiver. 22:6
made the kings of E. to. Jer 25:25
of Lord that came against E. 49:34
upon E. will I bring the four. 36
bring again the captivity of E. 39
there is E. and all her. Ezek 32:24
Shushan in province of E. Dan 8:2

Elamites

the E. wrote a letter to. Ezra 4:9
Parthians, E. we hear them. Acts 2:9

Elath

Azariah built E. 2 Ki 14:22
that time Rezin recovered E. 16:6

El-bethel

altar, and called it E. Gen 35:7

Eldad

name of the one was E. Num 11:26
E. and Medad do prophesy. 27

elder

The original government of the Hebrews was patriarchal, where the head of the family exercised the supreme rule over all of his descendants; his married sons doing the same with their children and other descendants, but still remaining subordinate to the supreme head. At the father's death his firstborn succeeded him in supreme headship. Naturally only men of mature age came into these positions, hence the designation elder. In that way Jacob was the head of all who went to Egypt with him, although his sons had families of their own. From this came [1] the great influence of the older people of the nation; [2] the division of the Israelites into tribes, with a head, chief, or prince over each as a whole; [3] the general use, in other nations as well as the Hebrews, of the term elder as an official title for those who as representatives of the people made all their decisions.

The earliest mention of elders *as a political body is at the time of the Exodus. The seventy elders mentioned in Exodus and Numbers were a sort of governing body, a parliament, and the origin of the tribunal of seventy elders called the* Sanhedrin *or* Council. *There were also, after the founding of towns and cities, those who were put at the head of affairs who could not always derive their authority from their position in the tribe. These were also called elders, and they served as judges, to decide both civil and criminal causes.*

The Sanhedrin was a supreme council, serving as a court of appeal, and having a general oversight over the inferior courts, and the general affairs of the nation. In the New Testament Church the elders or presbyters were the same as the bishops. It was an office derived from the Jewish usage of elders or rulers of synagogues.

Shem the brother of Japhet the e. Gen 10:21*
e. serve younger. 25:23; Rom 9:12
my e. daughter Merab. 1 Sam 18:17
kingdom, he is mine e. 1 Ki 2:22
aged men, much e. than. Job 15:10
Elihu waited, they were e. 32:4
thy e. sister is Samaria. Ezek 16:46
names were Aholah the e. 23:4
his e. son was in field. Luke 15:25
intreat the e. women. 1 Tim 5:2
younger, submit to the e. 1 Pet 5:5

elder for *ruler*

rebuke not an e. but. 1 Tim 5:1
against an e. receive not. 19
exhort, who am also an e. 1 Pet 5:1
the e. to the elect lady. 2 John 1
e. unto well-beloved. 3 John 1

elders

e. of his house went. Gen 50:7
the e. of congregation. Lev 4:15
of Spirit to seventy e. Num 11:25
go to the gate to the e. Deut 25:7
stand before the Lord your e. 29:10
gather to me all e. of your. 31:28
ask thy father and e. and. 32:7
Israel served Lord all days of Joshua and e. Josh 24:31; Judg 2:7
described to him the e. Judg 8:14
e. of the town trembled. 1 Sam 16:4
sent of the spoil to the e. of. 30:26
all the e. said to him. 1 Ki 20:8
the e. did as Jezebel had. 21:11
Elisha sat in house, e. 2 Ki 6:32
Jehu wrote letters and sent to e. 10:1
Hezekiah sent e. of priests to Isaiah the prophet. 19:2; Isa 37:2
eye of God upon the e. Ezra 5:5
the e. of the Jews builded. 6:14
counsel of the princes and e. 10:8
him in assembly of e. Ps 107:32
husband known among e. Pr 31:23
my priests and e. gave. Lam 1:19
e. of Zion sit upon the ground. 2:10
favoured not e. 4:16; 5:12
e. have ceased from gate. 5:14
and the e. of Judah. Ezek 8:1
sanctify a fast, gather e. Joel 1:14
2:16
the tradition of the e.? Mat 15:2
suffer many things of the e. 16:21
27:12
the e. sought false witness. 26:59
priests and e. persuaded the. 27:20
chief priests mocking with e. 41
they were assembled with e. 28:12
the tradition of the e. Mark 7:3
be rejected of e. 8:31; Luke 9:22
great multitude from e. Mark 14:43
priests held consultation with e. 15:1
unto the captains and e. Luke 22:52
their rulers and e. were. Acts 4:5
they reported all that e. had. 23
stirred up the people and e. 6:12
sent it to e. by Barnabas. 11:30
when they ordained e. in. 14:23
of the church and of the e. 15:4
apostles and e. came together. 6
the apostles, e. and brethren. 23
decrees ordained of the e. 16:4
he sent and called the e. of. 20:17
all the estate of the e. bear. 22:5
Ananias descended with e. 24:1
about whom the e. of Jews. 25:15
let e. that rule well be. 1 Tim 5:17
thou shouldest ordain e. Tit 1:5
by faith the e. obtained. Heb 11:2
let him call for the e. Jas 5:14
e. which are among you. 1 Pet 5:1
upon seats I saw 24 e. Rev 4:4
the 24 e. fall before him. 10
5:8, 14; 11:16; 19:4
one of e. saith unto me, weep. 5:5
in midst of the e. a Lamb. 6
voice of many angels about e. 11
all angels stood about e. 7:11
one of e. answered saying to me. 13
new song before throne and e. 14:3

elders with *city*

e. of his city shall fetch. Deut 19:1[illegible]
e. of that city shall take and. 21:[illegible]
e. of that city wash their hands.
their son to e. of his city. 1[illegible]
of virginity to e. of the city. 22:1[illegible]
the e. of his city shall call. 25:[illegible]
declare his cause to e. Josh 20:[illegible]
took the e. of the city. Judg 8:1[illegible]
ten men of e. of city. Ruth 4:[illegible]
them e. of every city. Ezra 10:1[illegible]

elders of *Israel*

gather e. of Israel together. Ex 3:1[illegible]
called for all the e. of Israel. 12:2[illegible]
take with thee of e. of Israel. 17:[illegible]
e. of Israel came to eat with. 18:1[illegible]
seventy of the e. of Israel. 24:1, Num 11:1[illegible]
e. of Israel commanded. Deut 27:[illegible]
this law to the e. of Israel. 31:[illegible]
e. of Israel put dust on. Josh 7:[illegible]
so all the e. of Israel came to king 2 Sam 5:3; 1 Ki 8:3; 2 Chr 5:[illegible]
pleased all e. of Israel. 2 Sam 17:[illegible]
Ahithophel counsel e. of Israel. 1[illegible]
e. of Israel came to king. 1 Chr 11:[illegible]
David and e. of Israel fell. 21:1[illegible]
came the e. of Israel. Ezek 14:[illegible]
e. of Israel came to inquire. 20:[illegible]
rulers of people, e. of Israel. Acts 4:[illegible]

elders with *people*

called for e. of the people. Ex 19:[illegible]
to be e. of the people. Num 11:1[illegible]
70 men of the e. of the people. 2[illegible]
buy it before e. of people. Ruth 4:[illegible]
before e. of my people. 1 Sam 15:3[illegible]
the e. of the people came. Mat 21:23; Luke 22:[illegible]
a multitude from e. of the people. Mat 26:4[illegible]
e. of the people took counsel. 27:[illegible]
stirred up people and e. Acts 6:1[illegible]

eldest

Abraham said to his e. Gen 24:[illegible]
Isaac called Esau his e. son. 27:[illegible]
searched, and began at the e. 44:1[illegible]
Israel's e. son. Num 1:20; 26:[illegible]

three *e*. sons of Jesse followed. *1 Sam* 17:13, 14
Eliab his *e*. brother heard. 28
he took his *e*. son and. *2 Ki* 3:27
of men had slain the *e*. *2 Chr* 22:1
drinking in their *e*. *Job* 1:13, 18
one by one, beginning at *e*. *John* 8:9

Elealeh

of Reuben built *E*. *Num* 32:37
Heshbon shall cry, and *E*. *Isa* 15:4
water thee with my tears, O *E*. 16:9
cry of Hesbon even to *E*. *Jer* 48:34

Eleazar

Aaron's son *E*. *Ex* 6:25; 28:1
Num 3:2; 26:60; *1 Chr* 6:3; 24:1
Ezra 8:33
Moses was angry with *E*. *Lev* 10:16
E. ministered in priest's. *Num* 3:4
E. son of Aaron shall be chief. 32
to the office of *E*. pertaineth. 4:16
E. the priest took the. 16:39
put his garments upon *E*. 20:26
Moses and *E*. came down. 28
numbered by Moses and *E*. 26:63
he set Joshua before *E*. 27:22
brought spoil to Moses and *E*. 31:12
take sum of prey thou and *E*. 26
Moses gave tribute unto *E*. 41
E. and Joshua divide land. 34:17
came near before *E*. *Josh* 17:4
E. died. 24:33
sanctified *E*. to keep. *1 Sam* 7:1
after him *E*. son of Dodo.
2 Sam 23:9; *1 Chr* 11:12
son of *E*. was ruler. *1 Chr* 9:20
sons of Mahli, *E*. 23:21; 24:28
E. died, and had no sons. 23:22
more chief men of sons of *E*. 24:4
governors were of sons of *E*. 5
Shemaiah and *E*. were. *Neh* 12:42
Eliud begat *E*. and *E*. *Mat* 1:15

elect

Or Chosen, is used, [1] *Of Christ,* Isa 42:1. [2] *Of good angels,* 1 Tim 5:21. [3] *Of the Israelites, who were God's chosen and peculiar people,* Isa 65:9, 22. [4] *Of those in whom Divine grace has achieved its supreme triumph, and who have passed from death unto life, and from the power of sin to the glad and eager service of God and our Lord Jesus Christ.*

behold mine *e*. in whom. *Isa* 42:1*
Israel mine *e*. I have called. 45:4*
mine elect shall inherit it. 65:9*
mine *e*. shall long enjoy work. 22*
but for the *e*.'s sake those days shall.
Mat 24:22; *Mark* 13:20
possible deceive very *e*. *Mat* 24:24
Mark 13:22
and they shall gather his *e*. from.
Mat 24:31; *Mark* 13:27
not God avenge his *e*.? *Luke* 18:7
any thing to charge of God's *e*.?
Rom 8:33
put on as the *e*. of God. *Col* 3:12
charge thee before the *e*. *1 Tim* 5:21
endure all things for *e*.'s. *2 Tim* 2:10
according to faith of God's *e*. *Tit* 1:1
according to foreknowledge.
1 Pet 1:2
ion a chief corner-stone, *e*. 2:6
e elder to the *e*. lady. *2 John* 1
e children of thy *e*. sister. 13

elected

urch at Babylon *e*. *1 Pet* 5:13

election

e. might stand. *Rom* 9:11
remnant according to *e*. of 11:5
e *e*. hath obtained it, the rest. 7
t as touching the *e*. they. 28
ethren, your *e*. of God. *1 Thes* 1:4
ur calling and *e*. sure. *2 Pet* 1:10

El-elohe-Israel

led altar *E.-Israel*. *Gen* 33:20

elements

bondage under *e*. of. *Gal* 4:3*
ain to weak and beggarly *e*. 9*
e. shall melt. *2 Pet* 3:10, 12

elephant, *see* **ivory**

eleven

Jacob took his *e*. sons. *Gen* 32:22
sun, moon, and *e*. stars made. 37:9
curtains of goats' hair, *e*. *Ex* 26:7
the *e*. curtains shall be all of. 8
e. curtains he made. 36:14
e. of one size. 15
on third day *e*. bullocks. *Num* 29:20
are *e*. days' journey. *Deut* 1:2
e. cities with villages. *Josh* 15:51
give thee *e*. hundred pieces of silver.
Judg 16:5
I took the *e*. hundred shekels. 17:2
restored *e*. hundred shekels to. 3
Jehoiakim reigned *e*. years in.
2 Ki 23:36; *2 Chr* 36:5
Zedekiah *e*. years. *2 Ki* 24:18
2 Chr 36:11; *Jer* 52:1
then the *e*. disciples. *Mat* 28:16
he appeared to the *e*. *Mark* 16:14
all these things to the *e*. *Luke* 24:9
found the *e*. gathered together. 33
was numbered with the *e*. *Acts* 1:26
Peter standing up with *e*. 2:14

eleventh

in the *e*. year was house. *1 Ki* 6:38
in *e*. year of Joram. *2 Ki* 9:29
Jerusalem was besieged to the *e*.
2 Ki 25:2; *Jer* 52:5
the *e*. lot came forth. *1 Chr* 24:12
the *e*. to Azareel, he, his. 25:18
e. captain for the *e*. month. 27:14
Jeremiah prophesied in *e*. *Jer* 1:3
in the *e*. year the city was. 39:2
word of the Lord came to Ezekiel in
e. year. *Ezek* 26:1; 30:20; 31:1
and about the *e*. hour. *Mat* 20:6
that were hired about the *e*. hour. 9
e. foundation of city was. *Rev* 21:20

Elhanan

E. slew brother of Goliath.
2 Sam 21:19; *1 Chr* 20:5
E. the son of Dodo. *2 Sam* 23:24
1 Chr 11:26

Eli

brought the child to *E*. *1 Sam* 1:25
minister to Lord before *E*. 2:11; 3:1
now the sons of *E*. were sons. 2:12
came a man of God to *E*. and. 27
Samuel ran to *E*. and. 3:5; 6:8
in that day perform against *E*. 3:12
iniquity of *E*.'s house shall. 14
came in hastily and told *E*. 4:14
he spake concerning *E*. *1 Ki* 2:27

Eli, Eli, *lama sabachthani*

E. E. lama sab. *Mat* 27:46
Eloi, Eloi, lama sab. *Mark* 15:34

Eliab

of tribe of Zebulon, *E*. *Num* 1:9
2:7; 7:24, 29; 10:16
Abiram sons of *E*. 16:1, 12; 26:9
sons of Pallu, *E*. 26:8
he did to sons of *E*. *Deut* 11:6
looked on *E*. *1 Sam* 16:6
E. heard, and his anger. 17:28
begat his firstborn *E*. *1 Chr* 2:13
E. the son of Nahath, the. 6:27
E. captain of the Gadites. 12:9
E. porter. 15:18, 20
E. with a psaltery. 16:5
took the daughter of *E*. *2 Chr* 11:18

Eliada

E. a son of David. *2 Sam* 5:16
1 Chr 3:8
of Benjamin, *E*. *2 Chr* 17:17

Eliakim

came out *E*. the son of Hilkiah.
2 Ki 18:18; *Isa* 36:3
Hezekiah sent *E*. to Isaiah.
2 Ki 19:2; *Isa* 37:2
made *E*. son of Josiah king.
2 Ki 23:34; *2 Chr* 36:4
E. and Maaseiah the. *Neh* 12:41
will call my servant *E*. *Isa* 22:20
Abiud begat *E*. and *E*. *Mat* 1:13
Jonan, the son of *E*. *Luke* 3:30

Eliam

the daughter of *E*. *2 Sam* 11:3
E. the son of Ahithophel the. 23:34

Elias, *see* **Elijah**

Eliashib

E. and Pelaiah sons of. *1 Chr* 3:24
eleventh lot came forth to *E*.
1 Chr 24:12
Johanan the son of *E*. *Ezra* 10:6
Neh 12:23
E. a singer. *Ezra* 10:24
E. the son of Zattu. 27
E. son of Bani. 36
E. the high priest. *Neh* 3:1
Joiakim begat *E*. and *E*. 12:10
E. was allied to Tobiah. 13:4
the evil *E*. did. 7
of sons of Joiada, son of *E*. 28

Eliezer

steward of my house is *E*. *Gen* 15:2
name of Moses' son was *E*.
Ex 18:4; *1 Chr* 23:15
sons of Becher, *E*. and. *1 Chr* 7:8
Benaiah and *E*. the priests. 15:24
son of *E*. was Rehabiah the. 23:17
ruler of Reubenites was *E*. 27:16
E. prophesied against. *2 Chr* 20:37
then sent I for *E*. and. *Ezra* 8:16
E. had taken strange. 10:18, 23, 31
Jose, the son of *E*. *Luke* 3:29

Elihoreph

E. and Ahiah, sons of. *1 Ki* 4:3

Elihu

of Jeroham, son of *E*. *1 Sam* 1:1
E. fell to David out. *1 Chr* 12:20
E. and Semachiah strong men. 26:7
of Judah, *E*. one of the. 27:18
wrath of *E*. the Buzite. *Job* 32:2
E. had waited. 4
E. answered. 6; 34:1; 35:1

Elijah, or **Elias**

E. the Tishbite said to. *1 Ki* 17:1
did according to saying of *E*. 15
Lord heard the voice of *E*. 22
E. took the child, and brought. 23
E. went to shew himself. 18:2
art thou that my lord *E*.? 7
E. is here. 8
Ahab went to meet *E*. 16
E. mocked them. 27
E. slew all the prophets of Baal. 40
hand of the Lord was on *E*. 46
Ahab told Jezebel all that *E*. 19:1
what doest thou here, *E*.? 9, 13
and ran after *E*. 20, 21
Ahab said to *E*. hast thou ? 21:20
it is *E*. the Tishbite. *2 Ki* 1:8
third captain fell before *E*. 13
according to the word *E*. had. 17
when Lord would take up *E*. 2:1
E. took his mantle, and wrapt it. 8
E. went up by a whirlwind. 11
where is Lord God of *E*.? 14
spirit of *E*. doth rest on Elisha. 15
poured water on the hands of *E*. 3:11
which he spake by *E*. 9:36; 10:10, 17
a writing from *E*. *2 Chr* 21:12
Maaseiah and *E*. sons of. *Ezra* 10:21
behold, I will send you *E*. *Mal* 4:5
this is *Elias* which was. *Mat* 11:14
some say, *Elias*. 16:14; *Mark* 6:15
Luke 9:8, 19
there appeared *Elias*. *Mat* 17:3
Mark 9:4; *Luke* 9:30
three tabernacles, one for *Elias*.
Mat 17:4; *Mark* 9:5; *Luke* 9:33
that *Elias* must first come.
Mat 17:10; *Mark* 9:11
Elias shall come and restore things.
Mat 17:11; *Mark* 9:12
Elias is come already. *Mat* 17:12
Mark 9:13
this man calleth for *Elias*.
Mat 27:47; *Mark* 15:35
let us see whether *Elias* will.
Mat 27:49; *Mark* 15:36
in the power of *Elias*. *Luke* 1:17
widows in the days of *Elias*. 4:25
fire to consume them as *Elias*. 9:54
art thou *Elias* ? art thou ? *John* 1:21
if thou be not *Elias*, why ? 25
scripture saith of *Elias*. *Rom* 11:2
Elias was a man subject. *Jas* 5:17

Elim

came to *E*. *Ex* 15:27; *Num* 33:9
took their journey from *E*.
Ex 16:1; *Num* 33:10

Elimelech
name of man was *E.* *Ruth* 1:2
E. died. 3
Boaz a kinsman of family of *E.* 2:1
I have bought all that was *E.'s* 4:9

Eliphalet
Eliada and *E.* David's son. *2 Sam* 5:16; *1 Chr* 3:6, 8

Eliphaz
Adah bare to Esau, *E.* *Gen* 36:4, 10
1 Chr 1:35
the sons of *E.* *Gen* 36:11, 12, 15
1 Chr 1:36
E. came from his place. *Job* 2:11
E. the Temanite. 4:1; 15:1; 22:1
E. did as Lord commanded. 42:9

Elisabeth
Zacharias' wife *E.* *Luke* 1:5
E. was barren. 7
E. conceived. 24, 36
Mary saluted *E.* 40
E.'s full time came that she. 57

Elisha, Eliseus
thou shalt anoint *E.* *1 Ki* 19:16
escaped from Jehu, shall *E.* slay. 17
Elijah departed, and found *E.* 19
at Jericho came to *E.* *2 Ki* 2:5
E. saw it, and cried, my father. 12
spirit of Elijah doth rest on *E.* 15
is *E.* the son of Shaphat. 3:11
cried a certain woman unto *E.* 4:1
E. passed to Shunem, where was. 8
bare a son at that season that *E.* 17
when *E.* was come, behold. 32
came and stood at door of *E.* 5:9
E. telleth the words that. 6:12
E. prayed to the Lord . . . according to the word of *E.* 18
E. said, Lord, open eyes of. 20
if the head of *E.* stand on him. 31
the great things that *E.* hath. 8:4
the woman whose son *E.* restored. 5
what said *E.* to thee ? 14
E. was fallen sick. 13:14
E. put his hands upon king's. 16
E. said, shoot. 17
cast man into sepulchre of *E.* 21
lepers in Israel in days of *Eliseus.* *Luke* 4:27

Elishah
blue and purple from *E.* *Ezek* 27:7

Elishama
E. the son of Ammihud. *Num* 1:10
2:18; 7:48, 53; 10:22; *1 Chr* 7:26
E. David's son. *2 Sam* 5:16
1 Chr 3:6, 8; 14:7
and Jekamiah begat *E.* *1 Chr* 2:41
he sent with them *E.* *2 Chr* 17:8
E. scribe. *Jer* 36:12
E. of the seed royal. 41:1

Elisheba
Aaron took him *E.* *Ex.* 6:23

Elishua
E. David's. *2 Sam* 5:15; *1 Chr* 14:5

Eliud
Achim begat *E.* *Mat* 1:14
E. begat Eleazar. 15

Elkanah
sons of Korah; Assir, and *E.* *Ex* 6:24
his name was *E.* *1 Sam* 1:1
E. went up to offer sacrifice. 21
E. went to his house. 2:11
Eli blessed *E.* 20
the son of *E.* *1 Chr* 6:23, 27, 34
35; 9:16
the sons of *E.* 6:25, 26
E. the Korhite. 12:6
E. was doorkeeper for ark. 15:23
E. that was next to king. *2 Chr* 28:7

Elmodam
Cosam, the son of *E.* *Luke* 3:28

Elnathan
Nehushta daughter of *E.* *2 Ki* 24:8
I sent for *E.* and Jarib, *Ezra* 8:16
Jehoiakim sent *E.* into. *Jer* 26:22
E. the son of Achbor. 36:12
E. had made intercession to. 25

Elon
Bashemath daughter of *E.* *Gen* 26:34
Esau took Adah daughter of *E.* *Gen* 36:2
sons of Zebulun, Sered and *E.* 46:14
E. judged Israel. *Judg* 12:11
E. died. 12

eloquent
O my Lord, I am not *e.* *Ex* 4:10
doth take away *e.* orator. *Isa* 3:3*
named Apollos, an *e.* *Acts* 18:24*

else
give me children or *e.* I. *Gen* 30:1
doing any thing *e.* go. *Num* 20:19
the Lord he is God, there is none *e.*
Deut 4:35, 39; *1 Ki* 8:60; *Isa* 45:5
6, 14, 18, 21, 22; 46:9; *Joel* 2:27
e. if ye in any wise go. *Josh* 23:12
nothing *e.* save sword. *Judg* 7:14
if I taste aught *e.* till. *2 Sam* 3:35
or *e.* three days sword. *1 Chr* 21:12
whoso *e.* cometh in. *2 Chr* 23:7
nothing *e.* but sorrow of. *Neh* 2:2
not sacrifice, *e.* would I. *Ps* 51:16
who *e.* can hasten here ? *Eccl* 2:25
I am, none *e.* besides. *Isa* 47:8, 10
or *e.* believe me for. *John* 14:11
time in nothing *e.* but. *Acts* 17:21
accusing, or *e.* excusing. *Rom* 2:15
e. were your children. *1 Cor* 7:14
e. when thou shalt bless. 14:16
repent, or *e.* I will. *Rev* 2:5, 16

Elul
25th day of the month *E.* *Neh* 6:15

Elymas
but *E.* the sorcerer. *Acts* 13:8

embalm
physicians to *e.* his. *Gen* 50:2

embalmed
the physicians *e.* Israel. *Gen* 50:2
days of those that are *e.* 3
they *e.* Joseph, put him in a. 26

emboldened
conscience of weak be *e.* *1 Cor* 8:10

emboldeneth
what *e.* thee that thou ? *Job* 16:3*

embrace
about this season thou shalt *e.* *2 Ki* 4:16
they *e.* the rock for want. *Job* 24:8
when thou dost *e.* her. *Pr* 4:8
why wilt thou *e.* bosom of ? 5:20
a time to *e.* and refrain. *Eccl* 3:5
right hand doth *e.* *S of S* 2:6; 8:3
brought up in scarlet *e.* *Lam* 4:5

embraced
Laban *e.* Jacob. *Gen* 29:13
Esau ran and *e.* Jacob. 33:4
Jacob kissed and *e.* Joseph's. 48:10
Paul *e.* disciples and. *Acts* 20:1*
having seen and *e.* *Heb* 11:13*

embracing
and a time to refrain *e.* *Eccl* 3:5
Paul *e.* Eutychus said. *Acts* 20:10

embroider
thou shalt *e.* the coat. *Ex* 28:39*

embroiderer
manner of work of *e.* *Ex* 35:35
with him Aholiab, an *e.* in. 38:23

emerald, -s
second row an *e.* *Ex* 28:18; 39:11
in thy fairs with *e.* *Ezek* 27:16
precious stone thy covering, *e.* 28:13
in sight like unto *e.* *Rev* 4:3
fourth foundation was an *e.* 21:19

emerods
Lord will smite with *e.* *Deut* 28:27
smote Ashdod with *e.* *1 Sam* 5:6*
men of the city had *e.* 9*
that died not were smitten with *e.* 12*
five golden *e.* and five. 6:4*, 17*
make images of your *e.* 5*, 11*

Emims
came and smote the *E.* *Gen* 14:5
the *E.* dwelt therein in. *Deut* 2:10

eminent
built to thee an *e.* *Ezek* 16:24, 31
shall throw down thine *e.* place. 39
an high mountain and *e.* 17:22

Emmanuel
Or Immanuel, *is a* Hebrew *word, meaning* God with us. *A child whose birth is prophesied in* Isa 7:14 *as a sign from God. In its final fulfilment it has always been held to refer to the Messiah,* Mat 1:23, *and the name is applied to Christ by early Christian writers, and by modern writers down to our own day.*
shall call his name *Em.* *Isa* 7:14
Mat 1:23
fill breadth of thy land, O *Em.* *Isa* 8:8

Emmaus
that same day to *E.* *Luke* 24:13

Emmor
bought of sons of *E.* *Acts* 7:16

empire
published throughout all his *e.* *Esth* 1:20*

employ
tree is man's life, to *e.* *Deut* 20:19*

employed
these singers *e.* day and. *1 Chr* 9:33
and Jahaziah *e.* about. *Ezra* 10:15*

employment
out men of continual *e.* *Ezek* 39:14

emptied
hasted and *e.* her. *Gen* 24:20
came to pass as they *e.* sacks. 42:35
high priest's officer *e.* *2 Chr* 24:11
be he shaken out and *e.* *Neh* 5:13
brooks of defence shall be *e.* *Isa* 19:6*
land shall be utterly *e.* and. 24:3
Moab not been *e.* from. *Jer* 48:11
emptiers have *e.* them. *Nah* 2:2

emptiers
e. have emptied them out. *Nah* 2:2

emptiness
upon it the stones of *e.* *Isa* 34:11

empty
hadst sent me away *e.* *Gen* 31:42
the pit was *e.* there was no. 37:24
the seven *e.* ears blasted. 41:27
go, ye shall not go *e.* *Ex* 3:21
Egypt, none shall appear before me *e.* 23:15; 34:20; *Deut* 16:16
not let him go away *e.* *Deut* 15:13
in every man's hand *e.* *Judg* 7:16
brought me home *e.* *Ruth* 1:21
not *e.* to thy mother-in-law. 3:17
send not ark away *e.* *1 Sam* 6:3
thy seat will be *e.* 20:18, 25, 27
sword of Saul returned not *e.* *2 Sam* 1:22
borrow thee *e.* vessels. *2 Ki* 4:3
hast sent widows away *e.* *Job* 22:9
stretcheth north over *e.* place. 26:7
Lord maketh earth *e.* *Isa* 24:1
awaketh, and his soul is *e.* 29:8
make *e.* soul of the hungry. 32:6
returned with their vessels *e.* *Jer* 14:3
king of Babylon made me *e.* 51:3
then set it *e.* upon the. *Ezek* 24:1
Israel is an *e.* vine. *Hos* 10:1
Nineveh is *e.* and void. *Nah* 2:1
is come, he findeth it *e.* *Mat* 12:4
and sent him away *e.* *Mark* 12:
Luke 20:10, 1
rich he hath sent *e.* away. *Luke* 1:5

empty, *verb*
command that they *e.* *Lev* 14:3
clouds *e.* themselves. *Eccl* 11:
wanderers shall *e.* his. *Jer* 48:1
fanners fan her and *e.* her. 51:
they therefore *e.* their net. *Hab* 1:1
which *e.* the golden oil. *Zech* 4:1

emulation
if I may provoke to *e.* *Rom* 11:1

emulations
works of the flesh are *e.* *Gal* 5:2

enabled
Christ Jesus who hath *e.* *1 Tim* 1:

encamp
e. before Pi-hahiroth. Ex 14:2
the Levites shall e. Num 1:50
as they e. so set forward. 2:17
but those that e. before the. 3:38
knowest how we are to e. 10:31
e. against Rabbah. 2 Sam 12:28
his troops come and e. Job 19:12
host should e. against me. Ps 27:3
I will e. about mine house. Zech 9:8

encamped
e. in Etham. Ex 13:20
e. by the waters. 15:27
where Moses e. at mount. 18:5
from Elim they e. by. Num 33:10
from Red Sea, and e. in the. 11
people came up and e. in Gilgal. Josh 4:19; 5:10
kings of the Amorites e. 10:5
Midianites e. against. Judg 6:4
Abimelech e. against Thebez. 9:50
children of Ammon e. in Gilead, Israel e. at Mizpeh. 10:17
Nahash e. against. 1 Sam 11:1
Philistines e. in Michmash. 13:16
the servants are e. in. 2 Sam 11:11
e. against Gibbethon. 1 Ki 16:15, 16
the Philistines e. in. 1 Chr 11:15
Sennacherib e. against. 2 Chr 32:1

encampeth
angel of the Lord e. Ps 34:7
scattered bones of him that e. 53:5

encamping
Egyptians overtook them e. Ex 14:9

enchanter
shall not be found an e. Deut 18:10

enchanters
not to dreamers nor e. Jer 27:9*

enchantments
magicians did so with e. Ex 7:11, 22; 8:7, 18
nor shall ye use e. nor. Lev 19:26
there is no e. against. Num 23:23
Balaam went not to seek for e. 24:1
used divination and e. 2 Ki 17:17
Manasseh used e. 21:6; 2 Chr 33:6
serpent will bite without e. Eccl 10:11*
for abundance of thine e. Isa 47:9
stand now with thine e. and. 12

encline, enclose, *see* **incline, inclose**

encountered
certain philosophers e. Acts 17:18

encourage
e. him, he shall cause to inherit it. Deut 1:38; 3:28
say to Joab, and e. 2 Sam 11:25
they e. themselves in an. Ps 64:5

encouraged
David e. himself in. 1 Sam 30:6*
priests and Levites be e. 2 Chr 31:4*
Josiah e. them to the service. 35:2
the carpenter e. goldsmith. Isa 41:7

end
[1] *A limit or boundary*, Job 37:3; 38:18. [2] *Termination, issue, or result*, 1 Sam 14:27. [3] *Death or destruction*, Gen 6:13; Amos 8:2; Mat 24:6. [4] *Purpose, aim*, Rom 10:4; 1 Tim 1:5.
the e. of all flesh is. Gen 6:13
of Egypt to the other e. 47:21
feast of in-gathering in the e. of year. Ex 23:16; 34:22
one cherub on the one e. the other cherub on other e. of. 25:19
scatter from one e. of. Deut 28:64
will see what their e. shall. 32:20
angel put forth the e. Judg 6:21
the day groweth to an e. 19:9
Jonathan put forth e. of. 1 Sam 14:27
Baal was full from one e. 2 Ki 10:21
with blood from one e. 21:16
after the e. of two years. 2 Chr 21:19
uncleanness from one e. to. Ezra 9:11
what is my e. that I? Job 6:11
shall vain words have e.? 16:3
day and night come to an e. 26:10
he setteth an e. to darkness. 28:3
wicked come to an e. Ps 7:9
destructions come to perpetual e. Ps 9:6
going forth is from the e. of. 19:6
for the e. of that man is. 37:37
the e. of the wicked shall be. 38†
make me to know mine e. 39:4
from the e. of the earth will. 61:2
I understood their e. 73:17*
and thy years have no e. 102:27
seen an e. of all perfection. 119:96
her e. is bitter. Pr 5:4*
but the e. thereof are. 14:12
there is an e. 23:18
not what to do in the e. 25:8
yet there is no e. of all. Eccl 4:8
there is no e. of all people. 16
the e. of all men. 7:2
better the e. of a thing. 8
e. of his talk is mischievous. 10:13
many books there is no e. 12:12
nor is there any e. of their treasures, nor any e. of their. Isa 2:7
his government shall be no e. 9:7
come from the e. of heaven. 13:5*
the extortioner is at an e. 16:4
after e. of 70 years Tyre. 23:15, 17
sing praise from e. of earth. 42:10
confounded world without e. 45:17
declaring the e. from the. 46:10
will you do in the e.? Jer 5:31
sword of Lord shall devour from one e. to the other e. 12:12; 25:33
at his e. he shall be a fool. 17:11
to give you an expected e. 29:11
there is hope in thine e. 31:17
till there be an e. of them. 44:27
his city is taken at one e. 51:31
our e. is near, our e. is. Lam 4:18
an e. the e. is come. Ezek 7:2, 3, 6
iniquity have an e. 21:25, 29; 35:5
hitherto is the e. of. Dan 7:28
time of e. shall be vision. 8:17
time appointed the e. 19*; 11:27
e. with a flood, and to e. 9:26
in the e. of years they shall. 11:6
purge them even to time of e. 35
at time of the e. king of south. 40
yet he shall come to his e. 45
seal book to time of the e. 12:4
shall be the e. of these things? 8*
words are closed, till time of the e. 9
go thou thy way till the e. be. 13
great houses have an e. Amos 3:15
to what e. is it for you? 5:18
the e. is come upon my people. 8:2
I will make the e. thereof. 10
for there is none e. of. Nah 2:9
there is none e. of their corpses. 3:3
the harvest is the e. of. Mat 13:39
shall be the sign of the e.? 24:3
gospel be preached, then shall e. 14
gather from one e. of heaven to. 31
went in and sat to see the e. 26:58
in the e. of the sabbath came. 28:1
cannot stand, hath an e. Mark 3:26
kingdom shall be no e. Luke 1:33
a parable to them, to this e. 18:1
things concerning me have e. 22:37
a king, to this e. was. John 18:37
for the e. of those. Rom 6:21
fruit to holiness, e. everlasting. 22
Christ is the e. of the law. 10:4
to this e. Christ both died. 14:9
for to this e. also. 2 Cor 2:9
e. shall be according to their. 11:15
glory world without e. Eph 3:21
many walk, whose e. is. Phil 3:19
e. of commandment is. 1 Tim 1:5
whose e. is to be burned. Heb 6:8
oath is to them an e. of all. 16
having neither beginning nor e. 7:3
but now once in the e. hath. 9:26
considering the e. of their. 13:7*
and ye have seen e. of. Jas 5:11
receiving e. of your faith. 1 Pet 1:9
what shall be the e. of them? 4:17
I am Alpha and Omega, the beginning and the e. Rev 21:6; 22:13

at the **end**
at the e. of forty days. Gen 8:6
at the e. of two years Pharaoh. 41:1
at the e. of 430 years. Ex 12:41
of consecration at an e. Lev 8:33
at the e. of 40 days. Deut 9:11
at the e. of three years. 14:28
at the e. of every seventh year a release. 15:1
at the e. of every seventh year read this law. 31:10
at the e. of three days. Josh 9:16
at the e. of two months. Judg 11:39
Boaz lay down at e. of. Ruth 3:7
at the e. of every year. 2 Sam 14:26
came to Jerusalem at the e. 24:8
at the e. of 3 years two. 1 Ki 2:39
at the e. of 7 years the. 2 Ki 8:3
at the e. of three years they. 18:10
find them at the e. of brook. 2 Chr 20:16
at the e. of year host of Syria. 24:23
stagger, and are at wits' e. Ps 107:27
go to meet Ahaz at the e. Isa 7:3
at the e. of seven years let go. Jer 34:14
at the e. of seven days. Ezek 3:16
at the e. they might stand. Dan 1:5
at the e. of 12 months he. 4:29
stand in the lot at the e. of. 12:13
at the e. it shall speak. Hab 2:3
in the e. of this world. Mat 13:40

but the **end**
seems right to a man, but the e. are ways of death. Pr 14:12; 16:25
but the e. thereof shall not. 20:21
but the e. is not yet. Mat 24:6
Mark 13:7; Luke 21:9
but the e. of all things. 1 Pet 4:7

last **end**
let my last e. be like. Num 23:10
shall not see our last e. Jer 12:4
remembereth not her last e. Lam 1:9
what shall be in last e. Dan 8:19

latter **end**
his latter e. shall be. Num 24:20
good at thy latter e. Deut 8:16
would consider their latter e. 32:29
kindness in the latter e. Ruth 3:10
bitterness in latter e. 2 Sam 2:26
yet thy latter e. should. Job 8:7
Lord blessed the latter e. of. 42:12
be wise in thy latter e. Pr 19:20
and know the latter e. Isa 41:22
remember the latter e. of it. 47:7
the latter e. is worse. 2 Pet 2:20

made an **end**
as Isaac had made an e. Gen 27:30
Jacob made an e. of. 49:33
made an e. of reconciling. Lev 16:20
made an e. of covering. Num 4:15
had made an e. of speaking. 16:31
Deut 20:9
made an e. of tithing. Deut 26:12
Moses had made an e. 31:24
made an e. of speaking. 32:45
Judg 15:17; 1 Sam 18:1; 24:16
2 Sam 13:36; 1 Ki 1:41; 3:1
Jer 26:8; 43:1; 51:63
made an e. of slaying. Josh 8:24
10:20
made an e. of dividing. 19:49, 51
had made an e. to offer. Judg 3:18
1 Sam 13:10
he had made an e. of. 1 Sam 10:13
made an e. of telling. 2 Sam 11:19
Hiram made an e. of. 1 Ki 7:40
Solomon made an e. of praying. 8:54; 2 Chr 7:1
made an e. of offering. 2 Ki 10:25
1 Chr 16:2; 2 Chr 29:29
made an e. of the. 2 Chr 20:23
till they had made an e. 24:10
made an e. with all that. Ezra 10:17
he had made an e. of measuring inner house. Ezek 42:15
thou hast made an e. of. 43:23
made an e. of eating. Amos 7:2
made an e. of commanding. Mat 11:1

make an **end**
I will also make an e. 1 Sam 3:12
will they make an e. in a? Neh 4:2
long ere you make an e.? Job 18:2
thou shalt make an e. to. Isa 33:1
thou make an e. of me. 38:12, 13
nor did I make an e. of. Ezek 20:17
to make an e. of sins. Dan 9:24
he will make an utter e. Nah 1:8, 9

make a full **end**
desolate, yet will I not *make a full e.* *Jer* 4:27; 5:18; 30:11; 46:28
destroy, but *make* not *a full e.* 5:10
thou *make a full e.*? *Ezek* 11:13

to the **end**
to the e. thou mayest know that I. *Ex* 8:22; *Ezek* 20:26
to the e. Israel may. *Lev* 17:5
to the e. that he should. *Deut* 17:16
to the e. that he may prolong. 20
their words *to the e.* of. *Ps* 19:4
to the e. my glory may sing. 30:12
thy statutes even *to the e.* 119:112
from beginning *to the e.* *Eccl* 3:11
to the e. man should find. 7:14
utter it even *to the e.* *Isa* 48:20
be my salvation *to the e.* 49:6
will he keep it *to the e.*? *Jer* 3:5
to the e. that none of. *Ezek* 31:14
sight thereof *to the e.* *Dan* 4:11
dominion reacheth *to the e.* of. 22
how long shall be *to the e.*? 12:6
to the e. that every one. *Ob* 9
endureth *to the e.* shall be saved. *Mat* 10:22; 24:13; *Mark* 13:13
cast out, *to the e.* they. *Acts* 7:19
to the e. you may be. *Rom* 1:11
to the e. the promise might. 4:16
acknowledge *to the e.* *2 Cor* 1:13
look *to the e.* of that. 3:13
to the e. he may establish. *1 Thes* 3:13
sober, and hope *to the e.* *1 Pet* 1:13

unto the **end**
beginning *unto the e.* *Deut* 11:12
the east border was *unto the e.* *Josh* 15:5
to glean *unto the e.* of. *Ruth* 2:23
may be tried *unto the e.* *Job* 34:36
wars to cease *unto the e.* *Ps* 46:9
I shall keep it *unto the e.* 119:33
proclaimed *unto the e.* of. *Isa* 62:11
it came *unto the e.* of. *Jer* 1:3
dominion even *unto the e.* *Dan* 6:26
destroy his dominion *unto the e.* 7:26
and *unto the e.* of the war. 9:26
alway, even *unto the e.* *Mat* 28:20
loved them *unto the e.* *John* 13:1
confirm you *unto the e.* *1 Cor* 1:8
fast confidence *unto the e.* *Heb* 3:6
beginning stedfast *unto the e.* 14
assurance of hope *unto the e.* 6:11
my works *unto the e.* *Rev* 2:26

endamage
so thou shalt *e.* the. *Ezra* 4:13†

endanger
make me *e.* my head to. *Dan* 1:10

endangered
cleaveth wood shall be *e.* *Eccl* 10:9

endeavour
I will *e.* that you may. *2 Pet* 1:15*

endeavoured
we *e.* to go into Macedonia. *Acts* 16:10*
we *e.* to see your face. *1 Thes* 2:17

endeavouring
e. to keep the unity of. *Eph* 4:3*

endeavours
to wickedness of their *e.* *Ps* 28:4*

ended
seventh day God *e.* work. *Gen* 2:2
years of plenteousness *e.* 41:53
words till they were *e.* *Deut* 31:30
mourning for Moses were *e.* 34:8
so they *e.* the matter. *2 Sam* 20:18
the words of Job are *e.* *Job* 31:40
prayers of David are *e.* *Ps* 72:20
days of thy mourning *e.* *Isa* 60:20
is past, summer is *e.* *Jer* 8:20
when Jesus had *e.* these. *Mat* 7:28
when forty days were *e.* *Luke* 4:2
when the devil had *e.* all. 13
supper being *e.* the devil. *John* 13:2

endeth
noise of them that rejoice *e.* *Isa* 24:8

ending
I am the beginning and *e.* *Rev* 1:8

endless
heed to *e.* genealogies. *1 Tim* 1:4
after power of an *e.* life. *Heb* 7:16

En-dor
Manasseh had *E.* *Josh* 17:11
a woman at *E.* hath a. *1 Sam* 28:7
Jabin, which perished at *E.* *Ps* 83:10

endow
he shall surely *e.* her. *Ex* 22:16*

ends
push the people to *e.* *Deut* 33:17
shall judge the *e.* of the. *1 Sam* 2:10
the *e.* of staves were seen. *1 Ki* 8:8 *2 Chr* 5:9
for he looketh to the *e.* *Job* 28:24
directeth his lightning to *e.* 37:3
it might take hold of the *e.* 38:13
and his circuit to the *e.* *Ps* 19:6
all the *e.* of the world shall. 22:27
thy praise to *e.* of the earth. 48:10
God ruleth in Jacob to the *e.* 59:13
confidence of all the *e.* of. 65:5
all the *e.* of the earth shall fear. 67:7
the *e.* of earth have seen the. 98:3
vapours to ascend from the *e.* of the earth. 135:7; *Jer* 10:13; 51:16
eyes of a fool are in *e.* *Pr* 17:24
established all *e.* of the earth? 30:4
creator of the *e.* of earth. *Isa* 40:28
e. of the earth were afraid. 41:5
taken from *e.* of the earth. 9
daughters from *e.* of the earth. 43:6
to me and be saved, all the *e.* 45:22
all *e.* shall see the salvation. 52:10
Gentiles come from *e.* *Jer* 16:19
a noise shall come to the *e.* 25:31
fire devoureth both the *e.* *Ezek* 15:4
shall he be great to *e.* *Mi* 5:4
dominion to *e.* of earth. *Zech* 9:10
salvation to *e.* of the earth. *Acts* 13:47*
words to *e.* of the world. *Rom* 10:18
on whom *e.* of the world. *1 Cor* 10:11

endued
God hath *e.* me with. *Gen* 30:20*
a wise son, *e.* with. *2 Chr* 2:12
have sent a cunning man, *e.* with. 13
till ye be *e.* with. *Luke* 24:49*
and *e.* with knowledge ? *Jas* 3:13*

endure
[1] *To last,* Ps 72:12; 1 Pet 1:25. [2] *To suffer patiently,* Mat 24:13. [3] *To sustain or bear up under,* Gen 33:14. [4] *To tolerate,* Esth 8:6.

as children be able to *e.* *Gen* 33:14*
thou shalt be able to *e.* *Ex* 18:23
for how can I *e.* to see evil. *Esth* 8:6
fast, but it shall not *e.* *Job* 8:15
I could not *e.* 31:23*
the Lord shall *e.* for ever. *Ps* 9:7* 102:12, 26; 104:31
weeping may *e.* for a night. 30:5
as long as sun and moon *e.* 72:5
his name shall *e.* for ever. 17
seed will I make to *e.* 89:29, 36
doth the crown *e.* to ? *Pr* 27:24
can thy heart *e.* or ? *Ezek* 22:14
that shall *e.* to the end. *Mat* 24:13 *Mark* 13:13
no root, and so *e.* but. *Mark* 4:17
tribulations that ye *e.* *2 Thes* 1:4
therefore *e.* hardness. *2 Tim* 2:3*
therefore I *e.* all things for. 10
will not *e.* sound doctrine. 4:3
watch in all things, *e.* afflictions. 5
if ye *e.* chastening. *Heb* 12:7
they could not *e.* what was. 20
count them happy who *e.* *Jas* 5:11
for conscience *e.* grief. *1 Pet* 2:19

endured
time should have *e.* for. *Ps* 81:15
if God *e.* with much. *Rom* 9:22
persecutions I *e.* *2 Tim* 3:11
after he had patiently *e.* *Heb* 6:15
ye *e.* a great fight of afflictions. 10:32
for Moses *e.* as seeing him. 11:27
he *e.* the cross. 12:2
he *e.* such contradiction. 3

endureth
for his anger *e.* but a. *Ps* 30:5
goodness of God *e.* continually. 52:1
peace so long as moon *e.* 72:7
truth *e.* to all generations. 100:5
dominion *e.* throughout all. 145:13
he that *e.* to the end. *Mat* 10:22
meat which *e.* unto life. *John* 6:27
hopeth all things, *e.* all. *1 Cor* 13:7
blessed is man that *e.* *Jas* 1:12

endureth *for ever*
his mercy *e. for ever.* *1 Chr* 16:34, 41 *2 Chr* 5:13; 7:3, 6; 20:21 *Ezra* 3:11; *Ps* 106:1; 107:1 118:1, 2, 3, 4; 136:1, 2, 3, etc. 138:8; *Jer* 33:11
his righteousness *e. for ever.* *Ps* 111:3; 112:3, 9
his praise *e. for ever.* 111:10
his truth *e. for ever* 117:2
thy judgements *e. for ever.* 119:160
name, O Lord, *e. for ever.* 135:13
word of Lord *e. for ever.* *1 Pet* 1:25

enduring
fear of Lord is clean, *e.* *Ps* 19:9
is effectual in *e.* the. *2 Cor* 1:6
in heaven a better and *e.* *Heb* 10:34

Eneas, Aeneas
E. had kept his bed eight. *Acts* 9:33
E. Jesus maketh thee whole. 34

En-eglaim
from En-gedi to *E.* *Ezek* 47:10

enemies
(*The Revised Version frequently substitutes the words* adversaries, adversary, *which have slightly different meanings, but not so different as to make it worth while to star each reference so changed*)

avenged of the king's *e.* *1 Sam* 18:25
when Lord hath cut off *e.* 20:15
Lord require it of David's *e.* 16
so and more do God to *e.* 25:22
a present of the spoil of *e.* of. 30:26
to *e.* to blaspheme. *2 Sam* 12:14
the *e.* of my lord be as. 18:32
Lord fought against *e.* *2 Chr* 20:29
e. of the Jews hoped to. *Esth* 9:1
me from my deadly *e.* *Ps* 17:9
the *e.* of the Lord shall be. 37:20
sharp in heart of king's *e.* 45:5
speak with the *e.* in gate. 127:5
beloved into hands of *e.* *Jer* 12:7
the *e.* have heard a cry of. 48:5
her friends become her *e.* *Lam* 1:2
her *e.* prosper. 5
a man's *e.* are the men of. *Mi* 7:6
if when we were *e.* *Rom* 5:10
concerning gospel, they are *e.* 11:28
till he hath put all *e.* *1 Cor* 15:25
are the *e.* of the cross. *Phil* 3:18
were *e.* in your mind. *Col* 1:21

his **enemies**
possess the gate of *his e.* *Gen* 22:17
eat up nations *his e.* *Num* 24:8*
he hath driven out *his e.* 32:21
help to him from *his e.* *Deut* 33:7
him rest from *his e.* *2 Sam* 7:1
hath avenged him of *his e.* 18:19
him out of hand of *his e.* 22:1
him rest from all *his e.* *1 Chr* 22:
counteth me as one of *his e.* *Job* 19:11
as for all *his e.* he. *Ps* 10:
not deliver him to will of *his e.* 41:
let *his e.* be scattered. 68:1
God shall wound head of *his e.* 21
his e. shall lick the dust. 72:
he smote *his e.* in the hinder. 78:66
made all *his e.* to rejoice. 89:4
a fire burneth up *his e.* 97:
see his desire upon *his e.* 112:
his e. will I clothe with. 132:1
he maketh *his e.* to be at. *Pr* 16:
Lord shall join *his e.* *Isa* 9:1
shall prevail against *his e.* 42:1
repay, recompence to *his e.* 59:1
rendereth recompence to *his e.* 66:
indignation known towards *his e.* 1
Pharaoh into hand of *his e.* *Jer* 44:3
reserveth wrath for *his e.* *Nah* 1:
darkness shall pursue *his e.*
till *his e.* be made his footstool. *Heb* 10:1

mine **enemies**
curse *mine e.* *Num* 23:11; 24:
vengeance to *mine e.* *Deut* 32:
enlarged over *mine e.* *1 Sam* 2

I be avenged on mine e. 1 Sam 14:24
Lord hath broken forth upon mine e. 2 Sam 5:20; 1 Chr 14:11
be saved from mine e. 2 Sam 22:4
Ps 18:3
have pursued mine e. 2 Sam 22:38
Ps 18:3
hast given me the necks of mine e. 2 Sam 22:41; Ps 18:40
me forth from mine e. 2 Sam 22:49
to betray to mine e. 1 Chr 12:17*
hast smitten all mine e. Ps 3:7
lead me, because of mine e. 5:8
eye waxeth old because of mine e. 6:7
let all mine e. be ashamed. 10
because of rage of mine e. 7:6
when mine e. are turned. 9:3
delivereth me from mine e. 18:48
table in presence of mine e. 23:5
let not mine e. triumph. 25:2; 35:19
consider mine e. for they. 25:19
mine e. came upon me. 27:2
head be lifted up above mine e. 6
plain path, because of mine e. 11
deliver me not to will of mine e. 12
a reproach among all mine e. 31:11
deliver me from mine e. 15
but mine e. are lively. 38:19
mine e. speak evil of me. 41:5
mine e. reproach. 42:10; 102:8
shall reward evil to mine e. 54:5
mine eye hath seen his desire upon mine e. 7; 59:10
mine e. would swallow me up. 56:2
then shall mine e. turn back. 9
deliver me from mine e. 59:1; 143:9
they being mine e. wrongfully. 69:4
deliver me because of mine e. 18
mine e. speak against me. 71:10
see my desire on mine e. 92:11
made me wiser than mine e. 119:98
because mine e. have forgotten. 139
many are mine e. yet do I not. 157
forth thy hand against mine e. 138:7
I count them mine e. 139:22
of thy mercy cut off mine e. 143:12
avenge me of mine e. Isa 1:24
all mine e. have heard. Lam 1:21
mine e. chased me sore like. 3:52
mine e. bring hither. Luke 19:27

our **enemies**

they join also to our e. Ex 1:10
our e. themselves being. Deut 32:31
out of hand of our e. 1 Sam 4:3
deliver us out of hand of our e. 12:10
2 Sam 19:9; Ps 44:7
of the reproach of our e. Neh 5:9
when rest of our e. heard. 6:1, 16
will we push down our e. Ps 44:5
tread down our e. 60:12; 108:13
and our e. laugh among. 80:6
redeemed us from our e. 136:24
our e. have opened their. Lam 3:46
be saved from our e. Luke 1:71
delivered out of hands of our e. 74

their **enemies**

naked amongst their e. Ex 32:25
faintness in land of their e. Lev 26:36
when they be in land of their e. 44
backs before their e. Josh 7:8, 12
stood not a man of all their e; Lord delivered their e. into. 21:44
rest from their e. 23:1; Esth 9:16
sold into hand of their e. Judg 2:14
out of hand of their e. 18; 8:34
into the hand of their e. 2 Ki 21:14
2 Chr 6:36; 25:20; Neh 9:27
sea overwhelmed their e. Ps 78:53
soon have subdued their e. 81:14
stronger than their e. 105:24
the waters covered their e. 106:11
their e. oppressed them. 42
sword before their e. Jer 15:9
sword before their e. 19:7; 20:4
their e. shall straiten them. 9
Judah give into hands of their e.
20:5; 21:7; 34:20, 21; Ezek 39:23
out of their e. lands. Ezek 39:27
captivity before their e. Amos 9:4
which tread down their e. Zech 10:5
he devoureth their e. Rev 11:5
ascended, and their e. beheld. 12

thine **enemies**

who delivered thine e. Gen 14:20
hand be in neck of thine e. 49:8
be an enemy to thine e. Ex 23:22
I will make thine e. to turn. 27
rise, Lord, let thine e. Num 10:35
cast out all thine e. Deut 6:19
goest against thine e. 20:1; 21:10
thine e. distress thee. 28:53, 55, 57
thine e. be found liars to. 33:29
not stand before thine e. Josh 7:13
so let all thine e. perish. Judg 5:31
vengeance for thee of thine e. 11:36
thine e. be as Nabal. 1 Sam 25:26
the souls of thine e. shall. 29
cut off all thine e. 2 Sam 7:9
1 Chr 17:8
in that lovest thine e. 2 Sam 19:6
three months before thine e. 24:13
nor hast asked life of thine e.
1 Ki 3:11; 2 Chr 1:11
while sword of thine e. 1 Chr 21:12
strength because of thine e. Ps 8:2
hand find out all thine e. 21:8
power shall thine e. submit. 66:3
foot dipped in blood of thine e. 68:23
thine e. roar. 74:4
forget not the voice of thine e. 23
thine e. make a tumult. 83:2
thou hast scattered thine e. 89:10
wherewith thine e. have. 51
lo, thine e. O Lord, thine e. 92:9
make thine e. thy footstool. 110:1
Mat 22:44; Mark 12:36
Luke 20:43; Heb 1:13
rule in midst of thine e. Ps 110:2
thine e. take thy name in. 139:20
the fire of thine e. shall. Isa 26:11
corn to be meat for thine e. 62:8
thee pass with thine e. Jer 15:14
thine e. have opened. Lam 2:16
interpretation to thine e. Dan 4:19
redeem thee from thine e. Mi 4:10
all thine e. shall be cut off. 5:9
gate be set open to thine e. Nah 3:13
thine e. cast a trench. Luke 19:43

your **enemies**

ye shall chase your e. Lev 26:7
your e. shall fall before you. 8
sow in vain, for your e. shall. 16
ye shall be slain before your e. 17
no power to stand before your e. 37
be saved from your e. Num 10:9
be not smitten before your e. 14:42
Deut 1:42
rest from all your e. Deut 12:10
to battle against your e. 20:3
goeth to fight against your e. 4
ye shall be sold to your e. 28:68
Lord do to all your e. Josh 10:25
divide the spoil of your e. 22:8
delivered you out of hand of your e.
1 Sam 12:11; 2 Ki 17:39
but I say, love your e. Mat 5:44
Luke 6:27, 35

enemy

hand dashed in pieces e. Ex 15:6
the e. said, I will pursue. 9
then I will be an e. to. 23:22
go to war against the e. Num 10:9
and was not his e. nor. 35:23
I feared wrath of the e. Deut 32:27
the beginning of revenges upon e. 42
he shall thrust out the e. 33:27
hath delivered our e. Judg 16:23, 24
thou shalt see an e. 1 Sam 2:32*
Saul became David's e. 18:29
if a man find his e. will he? 24:19
thy people be smitten down before e.
1 Ki 8:33; 2 Chr 6:24
thou deliver them to e. 1 Ki 8:46
make thee fall before e. 2 Chr 25:8
e. could not countervail. Esth 7:4
the e. is this wicked Haman. 6
deliver me from e.'s hand? Job 6:23
he counteth me for his e. 33:10
let the e. persecute my. Ps 7:5
thou mightest still the e. 8:2
e. destructions are come to. 9:6
mourning because of e.? 42:9; 43:2
us turn back from the e. 44:10
because of voice of the e. 55:3
not an e. that reproached me. 12
a strong tower from the e. Ps 61:3
my life from fear of e. 64:1
even all that the e. hath. 74:3
shall e. blaspheme thy name? 10
e. hath reproached, O Lord. 18
when he delivered from e. 78:42
his glory into the e.'s hand. 61
e. shall not exact upon him. 89:22
for the e. hath persecuted. 143:3
kisses of an e. are. Pr 27:6
when the e. shall come in. Isa 59:19
he was turned to be their e. 63:10
the sword of the e. is. Jer 6:25
I will cause the e. to entreat. 15:11
them with east wind before e. 18:17
thee with wound of an e. 30:14
into captivity before e. Lam 1:5
for e. hath magnified himself. 9
children are desolate, because e. 16
drawn back his hand before e. 2:3
he hath bent his bow like an e. 4
the Lord was an e. he hath. 5
that e. should have entered. 4:12
because the e. had said. Ezek 36:2
the e. shall pursue him. Hos 8:3
people is risen up as an e. Mi 2:8
seek strength because of e. Nah 3:11
his e. came, sowed tares. Mat 13:25
said, an e. hath done this. 28
the e. that sowed them is. 39
tread over power of e. Luke 10:19
child of devil, thou e. of. Acts 13:10
last e. to be destroyed. 1 Cor 15:26
am I become your e.? Gal 4:16
count him not as an e. 2 Thes 3:15
a friend of world is the e. Jas 4:4

hand of the **enemy**

into the hand of the e. Lev 26:25
Neh 9:27
delivered us from the hand of the e.
Ezra 8:31
not shut me up into hand of the e.
Ps 31:8
his glory into the hand of e. 78:61
redeemed from the hand of the e.
106:10; 107:2
fell into hand of the e. Lam 1:7
given into the hand of the e. 2:7

mine **enemy**

sent away mine e.? 1 Sam 19:17
delivered me from my e.
2 Sam 22:18; Ps 18:17
found me, O mine e.? 1 Ki 21:20
mine e. sharpeneth his. Job 16:9
let mine e. be as wicked. 27:7
delivered him that is mine e. Ps 7:4
how long shall mine e. be? 13:2
lest mine e. say, I have prevailed. 4
because mine e. doth not. 41:11
I swaddled hath mine e. Lam 2:22
rejoice not, O mine e. Mi 7:8
then she that is mine e. shall. 10

thine **enemy**

if thou meet thine e. Ex 23:4
thine e. shall distress. Deut 28:57
deliver thine e. 1 Sam 24:4; 26:8
Lord is become thine e. 28:16
of Ish-bosheth thine e. 2 Sam 4:8
thou me for thine e.? Job 13:24
rejoice not when thine e. Pr 24:17
if thine e. hunger. 25:21; Rom 12:20
hath caused thine e. to. Lam 2:17
Lord hath cast out thine e. Zeph 3:15
thou shalt hate thine e. Mat 5:43

enflame, *see* **inflame**

engaged

who is this that e. his? Jer 30:21*

En-gedi

wilderness of Judah, E. Josh 15:62
David dwelt in the holds at E.
1 Sam 23:29; 24:1
Hazazon-tamar, is E. 2 Chr 20:2
in the vineyards of E. S of S 1:14
fishers stand from E. Ezek 47:10

engine, -s

Uzziah made e. 2 Chr 26:15
set e. of war against. Ezek 26:9

engrafted

with meekness e. word. Jas 1:21*

engrave

like a signet shalt e. Ex 28:11
I will e. the graving. Zech 3:9

engraven
ministration of death e. 2 Cor 3:7

engraver
with the work of an e. Ex 28:11
all manner of work of the e. 35:35
Aholiab, of tribe of Dan, an e. 38:23

engravings
like e. of a signet. Ex 28:11, 21, 36
39:14, 30

enjoin
to e. thee that which is. Philem 8

enjoined
Purim as Esther had e. Esth 9:31
who hath e. him his ways ? Job 36:23
blood of testament God e. Heb 9:20*

enjoy
land e. her sabbaths. Lev 26:34, 43
that Israel may e. Num 36:8*
beget sons, not e. them. Deut 28:41
return to land and e. it. Josh 1:15*
e. pleasure, behold this. Eccl 2:1
make soul e. good. 24; 3:13; 5:18
elect shall long e. work. Isa 65:22
thee we e. great quietness. Acts 24:2
giveth us all things to e. 1 Tim 6:17
than e. the pleasures of. Heb 11:25

enjoyed
till the land e. her. 2 Chr 36:21

enlarge
God shall e. Japhet. Gen 9:27
cast out nations and e. Ex 34:24
when Lord shall e. thy. Deut 12:20
if the Lord e. thy coast as. 19:8
bless me, and e. coast. 1 Chr 4:10
thou shalt e. my heart. Ps 119:32
e. the place of thy tent. Isa 54:2
might e. their border. Amos 1:13
make bald, e. thy. Mi 1:16
and e. the borders of. Mat 23:5

enlarged
my mouth is e. over. 1 Sam 2:1
thou hast e. my steps. 2 Sam 22:37
Ps 18:36
thou hast e. me when I. Ps 4:1*
troubles of my heart are e. 25:17
hell hath e. herself. Isa 5:14
thou hast e. thy bed, and. 57:8
thine heart shall fear and be e. 60:5
our heart is e. 2 Cor 6:11
recompence in same, be ye also e. 13
we shall be e. by you. 10:15*

enlargement
then e. shall arise from. Esth 4:14*

enlargeth
blessed be he that e. Deut 33:20
he e. the nations, and. Job 12:23*
who e. his desire as hell. Hab 2:5

enlarging
and there was an e. Ezek 41:7*

enlighten
Lord will e. my darkness. Ps 18:28*

enlightened
Jonathan's eyes were e. 1 Sam 14:27
29
to be e. with the light of. Job 33:30
his lightnings e. the world. Ps 97:4*
understanding being e. Eph 1:18
for those who were e. Heb 6:4

enlightening
Lord is pure, e. the eyes. Ps 19:8

enmity
I will put e. between thee. Gen 3:15
or in e. smite him. Num 35:21
thrust him suddenly without e. 22
before they were at e. Luke 23:12
carnal mind is e. against. Rom 8:7
abolished in his flesh e. Eph 2:15
cross, having slain the e. 16
friendship of world is e. Jas 4:4

Enoch
Cain's wife bare E. Gen 4:17
Jared begat E. 5:18
E. walked with God. 22, 24
which was the son of E. Luke 3:37
by faith E. was translated. Heb 11:5
E. also prophesied of these. Jude 14

Enon
John was baptizing in E. John 3:23

Enos
Seth called son's name E. Gen 4:26
which was son of E. Luke 3:38

enough
straw and provender e. Gen 24:25
I have e. my brother. 33:9
my blessing, because I have e. 11
it is large e. for them. 34:21
it is e. Joseph is yet alive. 45:28
entreat Lord, for it is e. Ex 9:28
bring much more than e. for. 36:5
dwelt long e. in this mount. Deut 1:6
compassed this mountain long e. 2:3
the hill is not e. for us. Josh 17:16
it is e.: stay now thine hand.
2 Sam 24:16; 1 Ki 19:4; 1 Chr 21:15
Mark 14:41; Luke 22:38
we have had e. to eat. 2 Chr 31:10
have goats' milk e. for. Pr 27:27
he that followeth after vain persons
shall have poverty e. 28:19
four things say not, it is e. 30:15
the fire that saith not, it is e. 16
which can never have e. Isa 56:11
destroy till they have e. Jer 49:9
eat, and not have e. Hos 4:10
not have stolen till they had e. Ob 5
the lion did tear e. for. Nah 2:12
but ye have not e. ye. Hag 1:6
not be room e. to receive it. Mal 3:10
it is e. for the disciple. Mat 10:25
lest there be not e. for us. 25:9
servants have bread e. Luke 15:17
they had eaten e. Acts 27:38

enquire
call damsel, and e. at her. Gen 24:57
Rebekah went to e. of Lord. 25:22
the people come to e. of. Ex 18:15
and that thou e. not. Deut 12:30
then shalt thou e. and. 13:14
come unto the judge and e. 17:9
man doth come and e. of. Judg 4:20
when a man went to e of. 1 Sam 9:9
did I then begin to e. of God ? 22:15
woman, that I may e. of her. 28:7
Jehoshaphat said, e. I pray thee, at.
1 Ki 22:5; 2 Chr 18:4
we may e. of. 1 Ki 22:7; 2 Chr 18:6
go, e. of Baal-zebub. 2 Ki 1:2
not here a prophet to e.? 3:11
meet the man, and e. of the. 8:8
altar shall be for me to e. 16:15
go ye, e. of Lord. 22:13; 2 Chr 34:21
which sent you to e. 2 Ki 22:18
2 Chr 34:26
a familiar spirit, to e. 1 Chr 10:13
Tou sent to David to e. of. 18:10*
David could not go to e. of. 21:30
to e. concerning Judah. Ezra 7:14
for e. I pray thee of the. Job 8:8
beauty of Lord and to e. in. Ps 27:4
thou dost not e. wisely. Eccl 7:10
if ye will e. e. ye. Isa 21:12
e. I pray thee, of Lord. Jer 21:2
of Judah that sent you to e. 37:7
cometh to prophet to e. Ezek 14:7
elders of Israel came to e. 20:1
saith Lord, are ye come to e.? 3
e. who in it is worthy. Mat 10:11*
to e. among themselves.
Luke 22:23*; John 16:19
e. for Saul. Acts 9:11
if ye e. concerning other. 19:39*
as though ye would e. 23:15*, 20
any do e. of Titus my. 2 Cor 8:23

enquired
heard of it, and e. Deut 17:4
children of Israel e. of. Judg 20:27
they e. of the Lord. 1 Sam 10:22
and he e. of the Lord. 22:10, 13
David e. of Lord. 23:2, 4; 30:8
2 Sam 2:1; 5:19, 23; 21:1*
1 Chr 14:10, 14
Saul e. Lord answered. 1 Sam 28:6
David sent and e. 2 Sam 11:3
as if a man had e. at the. 16:23
Saul e. not of the Lord. 1 Chr 10:14
for we e. not at the ark in. 13:3*
they returned and e. Ps 78:34*
should I be e. of at all ? Ezek 14:3
saith the Lord, I will not be e. 20:3
shall I be e. of by you ? as I live, saith
Lord God, I will not be e. of. 31
I will yet for this be e. of. Ezek 36:37
matters the king e. of. Dan 1:20
those that have not e. for. Zeph 1:6
Herod e. of wise men. Mat 2:7*, 16*
then e. he the hour he. John 4:52
or our brethren be e. of. 2 Cor 8:23
of salvation prophets e. 1 Pet 1:10*

enquirest
e. after mine iniquity and. Job 10:6

enquiry
after vows to make e. Pr 20:25
the men had made e. Acts 10:17

enrich
the king will e. him. 1 Sam 17:25
thou didst e. the kings. Ezek 27:33

enriched
in every thing ye are e. 1 Cor 1:5
being e. in every thing. 2 Cor 9:11

enrichest
thou greatly e. it with. Ps 65:9

En-rogel
Ahimaaz stayed by E. 2 Sam 17:17
slew sheep and oxen by E. 1 Ki 1:9

enrolled
This word is used in the Revisions in two places ; in place of taxed *in* Luke 2:1; *and in place of* written *in* Heb 12:23. *The word was also put into the margin of the old version, previous to the revision.*
all the world should be e. Luke 2:1
church of firstborn e. in. Heb 12:23

ensample
as ye have us for an e. Phil 3:17
to make ourselves an e. 2 Thes 3:9
an e. to those that. 2 Pet 2:6*

ensamples
happened to them for e. 1 Cor 10:11*
so that ye were e. to all. 1 Thes 1:7
but being e. to the flock. 1 Pet 5:3

ensign
he will lift up an e. to. Isa 5:26
which shall stand for an e. 11:10
shall set up an e. for nations. 12
when he lifteth up an e. 18:3
left as an e. on an hill. 30:17
princes shall be afraid of e. 31:9
of a crown lifted as e. Zech 9:16

ensigns
they set up their e. for. Ps 74:4

ensnared
reign not, lest people be e. Job 34:30

ensue
seek peace, and e. it. 1 Pet 3:11*

entangle
(Frequently used as meaning perplex, bewilder, or insnare)
how they might e. him. Mat 22:15*

entangled
Pharaoh will say, they are e. Ex 14:3
be not e. again with yoke. Gal 5:1
are again e. therein and. 2 Pet 2:20

entangleth
e. himself with affairs of. 2 Tim 2:4

enter
not slothful to e. to. Judg 18:9
prince shall e. by the porch.
Ezek 44:3; 46:2, 8
also set his face to e. Dan 11:17
he shall e. peaceably on fattest. 24
some must e. therein. Heb 4:6

enter *in* or *into*
near to e. into Egypt. Gen 12:11
Moses not able to e. into. Ex 40:35
all that e. in to perform. Num 4:23
water that causeth curse shall e.
into the woman, and. 5:24, 27
children shall e. into. Deut 23:
shouldest e. into covenant. 29:1
not to e. into their cities. Josh 10:1
cry did e. into his ears. 2 Sam 22:
thy feet e. into city. 1 Ki 14:1
disguise myself and e into. 22:3
if we e. into the city. 2 Ki 7:
third part of you that e. in. 11:
will e. into lodgings of borders, and
19:23; Isa 37:2
unclean should e. in. 2 Chr 23:1
e. into his sanctuary. 30:

house that I shall *e. into.* *Neh* 2:8
none might *e. into* king's. *Esth* 4:2
will he *e.* with thee *into* ? *Job* 22:4
he should *e. into* judgement. 34:23
sword *e. into* their heart. *Ps* 37:15
e. into the king's palace. 45:15
e. into his gates with. 100:4
gate *into* which righteous shall *e.* 118:20
a fool's lips *e. into.* *Pr* 18:6
e. into the rock, and. *Isa* 2:10
Lord will *e. into* judgement. 3:14
righteous nation may *e. in.* 26:2
my people, *e.* thou *into* thy. 20
he shall *e. into* peace. 57:2
that *e. in* at these gates. *Jer* 7:2
17:20; 22:2
e. into defenced cities. 8:14
if I *e. into* the city, behold. 14:18
e. into gates kings. 17:25; 22:4
who shall *e. into* habitations ? 21:13
departed to go to *e. into.* 41:17
set your faces to *e. into.* 42:15
caused arrows to *e. into.* *Lam* 3:13
robbers shall *e. into* it. *Ezek* 7:22
nor shall they *e. into* land of. 13:9
shall *e. into* thy gates, as men *e. into* a city wherein is. 26:10
cause breath to *e. into* you. 37:5
the priests *e. therein,* then. 42:14
gate be shut, no man *e. in* by. 44:2
they shall *e. into* my sanctuary. 16
when they *e. in* at the gates of. 17
shall *e. into* the fortress. *Dan* 11:7
he shall *e. into* the countries. 40
shall *e.* also *into* glorious land. 41
like a thief they shall *e. in.* *Joel* 2:9
nor *e. into* Gilgal. *Amos* 5:5
Jonah began to *e. into.* *Jonah* 3:4
flying roll shall *e. into.* *Zech* 5:4
in no case *e. into* kingdom. *Mat* 5:20
prayest, *e. into* thy closet. 6:6
e. in at strait gate. 7:13; *Luke* 13:24
not every one shall *e. in.* *Mat* 7:21
into what city ye shall *e.* 10:11
Luke 10:8, 10
e. into a strong man's house.
Mat 12:29; *Mark* 3:27
e. in and dwell there. *Mat* 12:45
Luke 11:26
better for thee to *e. into* life halt.
Mat 18:8; *Mark* 9:43, 45, 47
wilt *e. into* life, keep. *Mat* 19:17
a rich man shall hardly *e. into.* 23
than for rich man to *e. into* kingdom.
24; *Mark* 10:25; *Luke* 18:25
e. into joy of thy Lord. *Mat* 25:21
no more openly *e. into.* *Mark* 1:45
may *e. into* the swine. 5:12
Luke 8:32
what house ye *e. into.* *Mark* 6:10
Luke 9:4; 10:5
and *e.* no more *into.* *Mark* 9:25
lest ye *e. into* temptation. 14:38
Luke 22:46
they which *e. in* may see. *Luke* 8:16
many will seek to *e. in* and. 13:24
and to *e. into* his glory ? 24:26
can he *e. into* his ? *John* 3:4
cannot *e. into* kingdom of God. 5
by me, if any man *e. in* he. 10:9
tribulation *e. into* the. *Acts* 14:22
grievous wolves shall *e. in.* 20:29
do *e. into* rest, if they *e. into* rest.
Heb 4:3, 5
labour therefore to *e. into* rest. 11
boldness to *e. into* holiest by. 10:19
man was able to *e. into.* *Rev* 15:8
in no wise *e. into* it any. 21:27
may *e. in* through the gates. 22:14

enter *not*

e. not into judgement. *Ps* 143:2
e. not into the path. *Pr* 4:14
e. not into the fields of the. 23:10
e. not into house of. *Jer* 16:5
city of Samaritans *e. not.* *Mat* 10:5
that ye *e. not* into temptation. 26:41
Luke 22:40

not **enter**

Aaron shall *not e.* into. *Num* 20:24
not *e.* into congregation. *Deut* 23:1
2, 3
priests could *not e.* into. *2 Chr* 7:2
not e. into my rest. *Ps* 95:11
and equity *cannot e.* *Isa* 59:14
they should *not e.* into. *Lam* 1:10
shall *not e.* into the land. *Ezek* 20:38
nor uncircumcised *e.* into. 44:9
I will *not e.* into city. *Hos* 11:9
not e. into kingdom of. *Mat* 18:3
he shall *not e.* therein. *Mark* 10:15
Luke 18:17
shall *not e.* into rest. *Heb* 3:11, 18
we see they could *not e.* 19
see **kingdom of God**

entered

self-same day *e.* Noah. *Gen* 7:13
the angels turned in, and *e.* 19:3
sun was risen when Lot *e.* into. 23
Joseph *e.* into his chamber. 43:30
as Moses *e.* into the. *Ex* 33:9
bring men that are *e.* into. *Josh* 2:3
and they *e.* into the land. *Judg* 6:5
e. into an hold of god Berith. 9:46
e. into another tent. *2 Ki* 7:8
as Jehu *e.* in at the gate. 9:31
when king *e.* into the. *2 Chr* 12:11
e. into a covenant to seek. 15:12
Jotham *e.* not into the temple. 27:2
they *e.* into a curse. *Neh* 10:29
hast thou *e.* into springs ? *Job* 38:16
hast thou *e.* into treasures of ? 22
but when ye *e.* ye defiled. *Jer* 2:7
death is *e.* into our windows. 9:21
the people which had *e.* into. 34:10
when Jeremiah was *e.* into. 37:16
heathen *e.* her sanctuary. *Lam* 1:10
enemy should have *e.* gates. 4:12
spirit *e.* into me. *Ezek* 2:2; 3:24
I sware and *e.* into a covenant. 16:8
they *e.* unto the heathen. 36:20
the God of Israel hath *e.* 44:2
in day that foreigners *e.* *Ob* 11
shouldest not have *e.* into gate. 13
e. into my bones, I. *Hab* 3:16
when Jesus was *e.* into. *Mat* 8:5
he *e.* into a ship and passed. 9:1
how he *e.* into house of God. 12:4
day Noah *e.* into the ark. 24:38
Luke 17:27
the unclean spirits went out and *e.*
Mark 5:13; *Luke* 8:33
whithersoever he *e.* *Mark* 6:56
Mary *e.* into house. *Luke* 1:40
I *e.* thine house, thou gavest. 7:44
feared as they *e.* into cloud. 9:34
woe to lawyers, ye *e.* not in. 11:52
then *e.* Satan into Judas. 22:3
John 13:27
when ye are *e.* the city. *Luke* 22:10
are *e.* into their labours. *John* 4:38
a garden, into the which he *e.* 18:1
Pilate *e.* into the judgement-hall. 33
Ananias *e.* and putting. *Acts* 9:17
nothing unclean hath *e.* into. 11:8
e. into castle and told Paul. 23:16
Agrippa was *e.* into place of. 25:23
to whom Paul *e.* in, and. 28:8
sin *e.* into the world. *Rom* 5:12
the law *e.* 20
neither have *e.* into heart. *1 Cor* 2:9
e. not in because of. *Heb* 4:6
for he that is *e.* into his rest. 10
forerunner is for us *e.* even. 6:20
e. in once into holy place. 9:12, 24
are *e.* into the ears of. *Jas* 5:4
many deceivers are *e.* *2 John* 7
Spirit of life from God *e.* *Rev* 11:11

entereth

number every one that *e.* into the.
Num 4:30, 35, 39, 43
to every one that *e.* *2 Chr* 31:16
when wisdom *e.* into. *Pr* 2:10
reproof *e.* more into a wise. 17:10
sword *e.* into their. *Ezek* 21:14
he that *e.* in by the way of. 46:9
whatsoever *e.* in at the mouth.
Mat 15:17*; *Mark* 7:18
and *e.* in where the. *Mark* 5:40
follow him where he *e.* *Luke* 22:10
e. not by the door into. *John* 10:1
he that *e.* in by the door. 2
which *e.* into that within. *Heb* 6:19
as the high priest *e.* every. 9:25

entering

cast it at the *e.* of gate. *Josh* 8:29
shall stand at the *e.* of gate.
Josh 20:4
Gaal stood in the *e.* *Judg* 9:35
Abimelech stood in the *e.* 44
men of Dan stood by the *e.* 18:16
the priest stood in the *e.* of gate. 17
by *e.* into a town that. *1 Sam* 23:7
battle in array at *e.* in. *2 Sam* 10:8
for the *e.* of the oracle. *1 Ki* 6:31
Elijah stood in the *e.* in. 19:13
four leprous men at *e.* *2 Ki* 7:3
lay heads in two heaps at *e.* 10:8
that were in the *e.* of the gate. 23:8
kings sat at *e.* of gate. *2 Chr* 18:9*
there is no house, no *e.* *Isa* 23:1
thrones at the *e.* of. *Jer* 1:15; 17:27
mark well the *e.* in of. *Ezek* 44:5
nor suffer ye them that are *e.* to.
Mat 23:13; *Luke* 11:52
lusts of other things *e.* *Mark* 4:19
nothing without *e.* into him. 7:15*
e. into the sepulchre they saw. 16:5
at your *e.* ye shall. *Luke* 19:30
Saul *e.* into every house. *Acts* 8:3
what manner of *e.* in. *1 Thes* 1:9
a promise left us of *e.* *Heb* 4:1

enterprise

hands cannot perform *e.* *Job* 5:12

entertain

be not forgetful to *e.* *Heb* 13:2*

entertained

some have *e.* angels. *Heb* 13:2

entice

To persuade, or allure, Judg 14:15; 16:5; 2 Chr 18:19. *In the Bible usually in the bad sense.*

if a man *e.* a maid not. *Ex* 22:16
if wife *e.* thee secretly. *Deut* 13:6
e. husband, that he may. *Judg* 14:15
lords said to Delilah, *e.* him. 16:5
who shall *e.* Ahab ? *2 Chr* 18:19
I will *e.* him. 20
thou shalt *e.* him and prevail. 21
if sinners *e.* thee. *Pr* 1:10

enticed

if heart been secretly *e.* *Job* 31:27
peradventure he will be *e.* *Jer* 20:10†
when drawn away and *e.* *Jas* 1:14

enticeth

a violent man *e.* his. *Pr* 16:29

enticing

was not with *e.* words. *1 Cor* 2:4*
man beguile you with *e.* *Col* 2:4*

entire

that ye be perfect and *e.* *Jas* 1:4

entrance

us the *e.* into the city. *Judg* 1:24
shewed them the *e.* they smote it. 25
ran before Ahab to *e.* of. *1 Ki* 18:46
the two kings sat in the *e.* 22:10
kept the *e.* of king's. *2 Chr* 12:10*
the *e.* of thy words. *Ps* 119:130*
yourselves know our *e.* *1 Thes* 2:1
so an *e.* shall be. *2 Pet* 1:11

entreat

In the Bible, frequently, to treat, deal with, use (obsolete elsewhere), Jer 15:11.

cause the enemy to *e.* *Jer* 15:11*
e. them evil 400 years. *Acts* 7:6
see **intreat**

entreated

he *e.* Abraham well for. *Gen* 12:16†
so evil *e.* this people ? *Ex* 5:22†
and Egyptians evil *e.* us. *Deut* 26:6†
and *e.* them spitefully. *Mat* 22:6
Luke 18:32
e. him shamefully. *Luke* 20:11*
same evil *e.* our fathers. *Acts* 7:19
Julius courteously *e.* Paul. 27:3*
we were shamefully *e.* *1 Thes* 2:2

entreateth

he evil *e.* the barren. *Job* 24:21*

entries

the chambers and *e.* *Ezek* 40:38*

entry

king's *e.* without turned. *2 Ki* 16:18
fathers were keepers of *e.* *1 Chr* 9:19

doors of *e.* of house. *2 Chr* 4:22
crieth at the gates, at *e.* *Pr* 8:3
Jeremiah into third *e.* *Jer* 38:14
hide the stones at the *e.* of. 43:9
image of jealousy in the *e. Ezek* 8:5

envied

the Philistines *e.* Isaac. *Gen* 26:14
Rachel *e.* her sister, and. 30:1
Joseph's brethren *e.* him. 37:11
they *e.* Moses also in. *Ps* 106:16
for this man is *e.* of. *Eccl* 4:4
trees in garden of God *e. Ezek* 31:9

envies

aside all malice, guile, *e. 1 Pet* 2:1

enviest

Moses said, *e.* thou ? *Num* 11:29*

envieth

charity suffereth, and *e. 1 Cor* 13:4

envious

nor be *e.* against workers. *Ps* 37:1
for I was *e.* at the foolish. 73:3
be not thou *e.* against. *Pr* 24:1
fret not, neither be thou *e.* 19

environ

Canaanites hear and *e.* *Josh* 7:9*

envy

(Discontent at the excellence or good fortune of another. Frequently in the Bible with the distinct idea of malice or spite. The Revisions often replace it by jealousy)

wrath killeth, and *e.* *Job* 5:2
e. is rottenness of bones. *Pr* 14:30
who is able to stand before *e.*? 27:4
love, hatred, and *e.* is. *Eccl* 9:6
the *e.* also of Ephraim. *Isa* 11:13
and be ashamed for their *e.* 26:11
do according to thine *e. Ezek* 35:11
for *e.* they delivered him. *Mat* 27:18
Mark 15:10
patriarchs moved with *e.* *Acts* 7:9
Jews filled with *e.* spake. 13:45
believed not, moved with *e.* 17:5
full of *e.* murder, debate. *Rom* 1:29
preach Christ, even of *e.* *Phil* 1:15
whereof cometh *e.* strife. *1 Tim* 6:4
living in malice and *e.* *Tit* 3:3
dwelleth in us lusteth to *e. Jas* 4:5

envy, *verb*

e. thou not oppressor. *Pr* 3:31
let not thine heart *e.* sinners. 23:17
Ephraim not *e.* Judah. *Isa* 11:13

envying

not in strife and *e.* *Rom* 13:13*
there is among you *e.* *1 Cor* 3:3*
provoking one another, *e.* *Gal* 5:26
but if ye have bitter *e.* *Jas* 3:14*
where *e.* is, there is confusion. 16*

envyings

there be debates, *e.* *2 Cor* 12:20*
works of the flesh are *e.* *Gal* 5:21

Epaphras

as ye learned of *E.* our. *Col* 1:7
E. saluteth you. 4:12; *Philem* 23

Epaphroditus

to send to you *E.* *Phil* 2:25
received of *E.* 4:18

Epenetus

salute my well-beloved *E. Rom* 16:5

ephah

(A Hebrew measure of the same capacity as the bath, *containing ten* homers. *About a bushel, dry measure, or nine gallons liquid measure)*

see **bath**, *and* **homer**

homer is tenth part of *e.* *Ex* 16:36
tenth part of an *e.* *Lev* 5:11; 6:20
have a just *e.* 19:36; *Ezek* 45:10
tenth part of an *e.* of. *Num* 5:15
unleavened cakes of an *e. Judg* 6:19
and it was about an *e.* *Ruth* 2:17
take now an *e.* of this. *1 Sam* 17:17
seed of an homer shall yield an *e.*
Isa 5:10
the *e.* and baths shall. *Ezek* 45:11
an hin of oil to an *e.* 46:5, 7, 11
making the *e.* small. *Amos* 8:5

he said, this is an *e.* *Zech* 5:6
cast it into midst of the *e.* 8

Ephah

E. the son of Midian. *Gen* 25:4
1 Chr 1:33
E. Caleb's concubine. *1 Chr* 2:46
sons of Jahdai, Pelet, *E.* 47
the dromedaries of *E.* *Isa* 60:6

Ephes-dammim

Philistines pitched in *E. 1 Sam* 17:1

Ephesians

great is Diana of *E.* *Acts* 19:28, 34
the city of the *E.* is a worshipper. 35

Ephesus

Paul came to *E.* *Acts* 18:19
sailed from *E.* 21
Jew named Apollos came to *E.* 24
to Jews and Greeks at *E.* 19:17
not alone at *E.* but through Asia. 26
ye men of *E.* 35
Paul determined to sail by *E.* 20:16
fought with beasts at *E. 1 Cor* 15:32
I will tarry at *E.* 16:8
thee to abide still at *E.* *1 Tim* 1:3
ministered to me at *E.* *2 Tim* 1:18
Tychicus have I sent to *E.* 4:12
send it to *E.* *Rev* 1:11
to the angel at *E.* 2:1

ephod

The upper garment worn by the Jewish priests. There were two sorts of ephods, one of plain linen for the priests, and another embroidered for the high priest. That for the high priest was of gold, blue, purple, crimson, and twisted linen. The shoulder pieces were held together by two onyx stones, each engraved with the names of six tribes of Israel, Ex 28:4, 5, 6, *etc.*

The Ephod worn by ordinary priests was of linen only, neither so rich, nor so much adorned.

to be set in. *e.* *Ex* 25:7; 35:9, 27
they shall make an *e.* and. 28:4, 6
curious girdle of *e.* 8*, 27, 28
39:5*, 20; *Lev* 8:7
on shoulders of *e.* *Ex* 28:12, 25
after the work of the *e.* 15; 39:8
robe of the *e.* of blue. 28:31; 39:22
he made the *e.* of gold, blue. 39:2
he put the *e.* upon him. *Lev* 8:7
and Gideon made an *e.* *Judg* 8:27
man Micah made an *e.* and. 17:5
there is in these houses an *e.* 18:14
girded with a linen *e.* *1 Sam* 2:18
choose him to wear an *e.* 28
the Lord's priest wearing an *e.* 14:3
sword is wrapt in cloth behind *e.* 21:9
85 persons that did wear *e.* 22:18
Abimelech fled with an *e.* in. 23:6
bring hither the *e.* 9; 30:7
danced before Lord, girded with linen *e. 2 Sam* 6:14; *1 Chr* 15:27
shall abide without an *e.* *Hos* 3:4

Ephphatha

he saith to him, *E.* that. *Mark* 7:34

Ephraim, *a place*

had sheep-shearers beside *E.*
2 Sam 13:23
Abijah took *E.* and. *2 Chr* 13:19
into a city called *E.* *John* 11:54

mount **Ephraim**

if *mount E.* be too. *Josh* 17:15
Shechem in *mount E.* 20:7; 21:21
Joshua in *mount* of *E.* *Judg* 2:9
messengers through *mount E.* 7:24
Micah of *mount E.* 17:1
Levite came *to mount E.* 8
Danites passed unto *mount E.* 18:13
sojourning on side of *mount E.* 19:1
Elkanah of *mount E.* *1 Sam* 1:1
Saul passed through *mount E.* 9:4
Sheba of *mount E.* *2 Sam* 20:21
two men be come from *mount E.*
2 Ki 5:22
affliction from *mount E.* *Jer* 4:15
watchman upon *mount E.* 31:6
Israel be satisfied on *mount E.* 50:19

Ephraim, *a person*, or *people*

of Joseph's second son *E. Gen* 41:52
Israel laid right hand on *E. Gen* 48:14
saying, God make thee as *E.* and he set *E.* before Manasseh. 20
prince of *E.* was. *Num* 1:10; 7:48
on west side standard of *E.* 2:18
standard of the camp of *E.* 10:22
the sons of *E.* 26:35; *1 Chr* 7:20
the ten thousands of *E. Deut* 33:17
cities for the children of *E.*
Josh 16:9; 17:9
nor did *E.* drive out the. *Judg* 1:29
out of *E.* was there a root. 5:14
gleaning of the grapes of *E.* 8:2
fought with *E.* smote *E.* 12:4
Ish-bosheth king over *E. 2 Sam* 2:9
E. their father mourned. *1 Chr* 7:22
dwelt of the children of *E.* 9:3
strangers out of *E.* fell. *2 Chr* 15:9
set garrisons in cities of *E.* 17:2
separated the army out of *E.* 25:10
Zichri a mighty man of *E.* 28:7
of *E.* had not cleansed. 30:18
all Israel brake images in *E.* 31:1
children of *E.* being armed. *Ps* 78:9
before *E.* stir up thy strength. 80:2
Syria is confederate with *E. Isa* 7:2
E. hath taken evil counsel. 5
sixty-five years shall *E.* 8
the head of *E.* is Samaria. 9
from the day that *E.* departed. 17
E. that say in the pride and. 9:9
Manasseh shall eat *E.* and *E.* 21
E. shall depart; *E.* not envy Judah, Judah not vex *E.* 11:13
fortress also shall cease from *E.* 17:3
woe to the drunkards of *E.* 28:1
drunkards of *E.* be trodden under. 3
cast out whole seed of *E. Jer* 7:15
I have heard *E.* bemoaning. 31:18
the stick of *E.* *Ezek* 37:16
stick of Joseph in hand of *E.* 19
a portion for *E.* 48:5
E. O *E.* thou committest. *Hos* 5:3
Israel and *E.* shall fall in iniquity. 5
E. shall be desolate. 9
I will be unto *E.* as a moth. 12
when *E.* saw his sickness, *E.* 13
E. as a lion. 14
O. *E.* what shall I do to thee ? 6:4
there is the whoredom of *E.* 10
the iniquity of *E.* 7:1
E. hath mixed himself among. 8
E. hired lovers. 8:9
E. made altars to sin. 11
E. shall eat unclean things. 9:3
watchmen of *E.* was with my God. 8
E. their glory shall fly away. 11
E. shall bring forth children to. 13
E. shall receive shame. 10:6
I will make *E.* to ride. 11
I taught *E.* to go. 11:3
how shall I give thee up, *E.*? 8
I will not return to destroy *E.* 9
E. compasseth me about with. 12
E. feedeth on wind. 12:1
E. said, I am rich. 8
E. provoked him to anger. 14
when *E.* spake trembling, he. 13:1
iniquity of *E.* is bound up. 12
E. say, what have I to do ? 14:8
shall possess the fields of *E. Ob* 19
cut off chariot from *E.* *Zech* 9:10
have filled the bow with *E.* 13
they of *E.* be like a mighty. 10:7

see **gate**

Ephraim *is*

E. is the strength. *Ps* 60:7; 108:8
E. is my firstborn. *Jer* 31:9
is E. my dear son ? 20
E. is joined to idols. *Hos* 4:17
E. is oppressed. 5:11
E. is a cake not turned. 7:8
E. is like a silly dove. 11
E. is smitten. 9:16
E. is as an heifer that is. 10:11

Ephraim with *tribe*

of the *tribe* of *E.* 40,500. *Num* 1:33
of the *tribe* of *E.* to spy. 13:8
of *tribe* of *E.* to divide. 34:24
inheritance of *tribe* of *E.* *Josh* 16:8
Kohathites had cities out of the *tribe* of *E.* 21:5, 20; *1 Chr* 6:66
chose not the *tribe* of *E.* *Ps* 78:67

Ephraimite, -s
art thou an *E.*? *Judg* 12:5
fell at that time of *E.* 42,000. 6

Ephratah
do thou worthily in *E.* *Ruth* 4:11
Hur, firstborn of *E.* *1 Chr* 2:50; 4:4
lo, we heard of it at *E.* *Ps* 132:6
thou, Beth-lehem *E.* *Mi* 5:2

Ephrath
little way to come to *E.* *Gen* 35:16
Rachel buried in way to *E.* 19; 48:7
Caleb took to him *E.* *1 Chr* 2:19

Ephrathite, -s
Mahlon, Chilion, *E.* of. *Ruth* 1:2
Elkanah was an *E.* *1 Sam* 1:1
Jesse an *E.* 17:12
Jeroboam *E.* of Zereda. *1 Ki* 11:26

Ephron
intreat for me to *E.* the. *Gen* 23:8
to *E.* weighed silver to *E.* 16
buried in the field of *E.* 25:9
bought with field of *E.* 49:30; 50:13

Epicureans
certain of *E.* encountered. *Acts* 17:18

epistle
(*A letter. In the New Testament, usually, a letter of an Apostle to a church or an individual*)
delivered the *e.* *Acts* 15:30; 23:33
Tertius who wrote this *e.* *Rom* 16:22
I wrote to you in an *e.* *1 Cor* 5:9
e. written in our hearts. *2 Cor* 3:2
declared to be the *e.* of Christ. 3
I perceive the same *e.* made. 7:8
when this *e.* is read, likewise read the *e.* from. *Col* 4:16
this *e.* be read to all. *1 Thes* 5:27
by word or our *e.* *2 Thes* 2:15
any obey not our word by this *e.* 3:14
which is the token in every *e.* 17
this second *e.* I now. *2 Pet* 3:1

epistles
we *e.* of commendation. *2 Cor* 3:1
as also in all his *e.* *2 Pet* 3:16

equal
behold things that are *e.* *Ps* 17:2*
t was thou, a man, mine *e.* 55:13
egs of the lame are not *e.* *Pr* 26:7*
whom shall I be *e.*? *Isa* 40:25; 46:5
what shall I *e.* to thee. *Lam* 2:13
way of Lord not *e.* hear, is not my way *e.*? *Ezek* 18:25, 29; 33:17, 20
srael, are not my ways *e.*? 18:29
or them, their way is not *e.* 33:17
ast made them *e.* to us. *Mat* 20:12
or they are *e.* to angels. *Luke* 20:36
imself *e.* with God. *John* 5:18
ot robbery to be *e.* *Phil* 2:6*
our servants what is *e.* *Col* 4:1
nd height of city are *e.* *Rev* 21:16

equal, *verb*
old and crystal cannot *e.* *Job* 28:17
e topaz of Ethiopia not *e.* it. 19

equality
e. that there be an *e.* *2 Cor* 8:14

equally
o tenons *e.* distant. *Ex* 36:22

equals
ove many my *e.* *Gal* 1:14*

equity
dge the people with *e.* *Ps* 98:9
ou dost establish *e.* 99:4
truction of wisdom and *e.* *Pr* 1:3
derstand judgement and *e.* 2:9
to strike princes for *e.* 17:26*
n whose labour is in *e.* *Eccl* 2:21*
h *e.* for meek of the. *Isa* 11:4
th is fallen in street, and *e.* 59:14*
r this, ye that pervert *e.* *Mi* 3:9
h me in peace and *e.* *Mal* 2:6*

Er
ed his name *E.* *Gen* 38:3
k a wife for *E.* 6
was wicked. 7; *1 Chr* 2:3
father of Lecah. *1 Chr* 4:21
nodam, the son of *E.* *Luke* 3:28

Erastus
sent Timotheus and *E.* *Acts* 19:22
E. abode at Corinth. *2 Tim* 4:20

ere
delivered *e.* midwives. *Ex* 1:19
long *e.* they believe me ? *Num* 14:11
how long *e.* you make ? *Job* 18:2
long *e.* thou be quiet ? *Jer* 47:6
how long *e.* they attain ? *Hos* 8:5
come down *e.* my child. *John* 4:49

erected
Jacob *e.* there an altar. *Gen* 33:20

err
(*To go astray ; to fall into error*)
made Judah to *e.* *2 Chr* 33:9
a people that do *e.* in. *Ps* 95:10
which do *e.* from thy. 119:21*
hast trodden them that *e.* 118
not *e.* that devise evil ? *Pr* 14:22
instruction that causeth to *e.* 19:27
they which lead thee cause thee to *e.* *Isa* 3:12; 9:16
have caused Egypt to *e.* 19:14*
they *e.* in vision, they. 28:7
a bridle causing them to *e.* 30:28
the wayfaring men shall not *e.* 35:8
why hast thou made us to *e.*? 63:17
prophets in Baal, and caused people Israel to *e.* *Jer* 23:13; *Mi* 3:5
of whoredom caused them to *e.* *Hos* 4:12
lies caused them to *e.* *Amos* 2:4
ye do *e.* not knowing the scriptures. *Mat* 22:29; *Mark* 12:24, 27
always *e.* in their hearts. *Heb* 3:10
do not *e.* my brethren. *Jas* 1:16*
if any of you do *e.* from truth. 5:19

errand
eat till I have told *e.* *Gen* 24:33
I have a secret *e.* unto. *Judg* 3:19
I have an *e.* to thee, O. *2 Ki* 9:5

erred
ignorance wherein he *e.* *Lev* 5:18
ye have *e.* and not. *Num* 15:22
I have *e.* exceedingly. *1 Sam* 26:21
understand wherein I have *e.* *Job* 6:24
be it indeed that I have *e.* 19:4
yet I *e.* not from. *Ps* 119:110*
e. through wine and ... priest and the prophet have *e.* *Isa* 28:7*
they also that *e.* in spirit. 29:24
coveted they have *e.* *1 Tim* 6:10*
some professing have *e.* 21
concerning truth have *e.* *2 Tim* 2:18

erreth
he that refuseth reproof *e.* *Pr* 10:17
do for every one that *e.* *Ezek* 45:20

error
[1] *A mistake or oversight,* Eccl 5:6. [2] *False doctrine, which is not agreeable to the word of God,* 1 John 4:6. [3] *Sins of all sorts,* Ps 19:12; Heb 9:7.
smote Uzzah for his *e.* *2 Sam* 6:7
if erred mine *e.* remaineth. *Job* 19:4
neither say that it was an *e.* *Eccl* 5:6
evil which I have seen as an *e.* 10:5
and to utter *e.* against. *Isa* 32:6
neither was there any *e.* found. *Dan* 6:4
last *e.* shall be worse. *Mat* 27:64
recompence of their *e.* *Rom* 1:27
converteth sinner from *e.* *Jas* 5:20
from them who live in *e.* *2 Pet* 2:18
ye being led away with the *e.* 3:17
know we the spirit of *e.* *1 John* 4:6
have ran greedily after *e.* *Jude* 11

errors
who can understand his *e.*? *Ps* 19:12
vanity, the work of *e.* *Jer* 10:15*; 51:18*
he offered for *e.* of people. *Heb* 9:7

Esaias, *see* **Isaiah**

Esarhaddon
E. reigned in his stead. *2 Ki* 19:37; *Isa* 37:38
since the days of *E.* king. *Ezra* 4:2

Esau
they called his name *E.* *Gen* 25:25
E. was a hunter. *Gen* 25:27
E. came from field. 29
thus *E.* dispised his birthright. 34
E. my brother is a hairy man. 27:11
whether thou be my son *E.* 21, 24
E. hated Jacob because of the. 41
these words of *E.* were told to. 42
then went *E.* to Ishmael. 28:9
Jacob sent messengers to *E.* 32:3
deliver me from hand of *E.* 11
a present sent unto my lord *E.* 18
E. ran to meet him. 33:4
E. said, I have enough, my. 9
thou fleddest from *E.* thy. 35:1
these are generations of *E.* 36:1
E. the father of the Edomites. 43
given mount Seir to *E.* *Deut* 2:5, 12; *Josh* 24:4
did to the children of *E.* *Deut* 2:22
unto Isaac, Jacob, and *E.* *Josh* 24:4; *1 Chr* 1:34
calamity of *E.* on him. *Jer* 49:8
I have made *E.* bare. 10
are things of *E.* searched out! *Ob* 6
house of *E.* shall be for stubble. 18
to judge the mount of *E.* 21
was not *E.* Jacob's ? *Mal* 1:2
and I hated *E.* 3; *Rom* 9:13
blessed Jacob and *E.* *Heb* 11:20
be any profane person, as *E.* 12:16

escape
e. for thy life, *e.* to. *Gen* 19:17
O let me *e.* 20
haste thee, *e.* thither. 22
company which is left shall *e.* 32:8
none of them remain or *e.* *Josh* 8:22
e. into the land of the. *1 Sam* 27:1
for we shall not else *e.* *2 Sam* 15:14
get him fenced cities and *e.* 20:6
let none of them *e.* *1 Ki* 18:40; *2 Ki* 9:15
if any I have brought *e.* *2 Ki* 10:24
that *e.* out of Zion. 19:31; *Isa* 37:32
leave us a remnant to *e.* *Ezra* 9:8
think not thou shalt *e.* *Esth* 4:13
wicked shall not *e.* *Job* 11:20
shall they *e.* by iniquity ? *Ps* 56:7
me, and cause me to *e.* 71:2*
wicked fall, whilst I *e.* 141:10
speaketh lies shall not *e.* *Pr* 19:5
pleaseth God shall *e.* *Eccl* 7:26
help, how shall we *e.*? *Isa* 20:6
I will send those that *e.* to. 66:19
shall not be able to *e.* *Jer* 11:11
nor principal of flock to *e.* 25:35
Zedekiah shall not *e.* 32:4; 34:3; 38:18, 23
that go into Egypt *e.* 42:17; 44:14
return but such as shall *e.* 44:14
yet a small number that *e.* 28
swift flee, nor mighty man *e.* 46:6
spoiler shall come, no city *e.* 48:8
of them that flee and *e.* 50:28
let none thereof *e.* recompense. 29
some that shall *e.* the. *Ezek* 6:8
and they that *e.* of you shall. 9
they that *e.* shall *e.* and be. 7:16
e. that doth such things ? 17:15
all these things, shall not *e.* 18
but these shall *e.* out. *Dan* 11:41*
land of Egypt shall not *e.* 42
and nothing shall *e.* them. *Joel* 2:3
off those of his that did *e.* *Ob* 14
can ye *e.* damnation of ? *Mat* 23:33
accounted worthy to *e.* *Luke* 21:36
kill prisoners, lest any *e.* *Acts* 27:42
that thou shalt *e.* the ? *Rom* 2:3
also make a way to *e.* *1 Cor* 10:13
and they shall not *e.* *1 Thes* 5:3
shall we *e.* if we neglect ? *Heb* 2:3
much more shall not we *e.* 12:25

escape
I would hasten my *e.* *Ps* 55:8*

escaped
came one that had *e.* *Gen* 14:13
the locust eat what is *e.* *Ex* 10:5
given his sons that *e.* *Num* 21:29*
not deliver servant *e.* *Deut* 23:15
and Ehud *e.* while. *Judg* 3:26
there *e.* not a man. 29; *1 Sam* 30:17
for them that be *e.* *Judg* 21:17
Jonathan taken, but people *e.* *1 Sam* 14:41

David fled and *e.* *1 Sam* 19:10, 12, 18
of camp of Israel I *e.* *2 Sam* 1:3
and Baanah his brother *e.* 4:6
Ben-hadad the king *e.* *1 Ki* 20:20
remnant that is *e.* of Judah take root. *2 Ki* 19:30; *Isa* 37:31
smote rest that were *e.* *1 Chr* 4:43
is the host of Syria *e.* *2 Chr* 16:7
will return to you that are *e.* 30:6
for we remain yet *e.* *Ezra* 9:15
concerning Jews that had *e.* *Neh* 1:2
I only am *e.* *Job* 1:15, 16, 17, 19
am *e.* skin of my teeth. 19:20
is *e.* as a bird, the snare is broken and we are *e.* *Ps* 124:7
comely for them that are *e.* *Isa* 4:2
remnant and such as are *e.* 10:20
draw near, ye that are *e.* 45:20
son of Nethaniah *e.* *Jer* 41:15
ye that have *e.* remember. 51:50
that none in that day *e.* *Lam* 2:22
opened to him that is *e.* *Ezek* 24:27
one that had *e.* came. 33:21, 22
he *e.* out of their hands. *John* 10:39
to pass, they all *e.* safe. *Acts* 27:44
though he *e.* the sea, yet. 28:4
I was let down and *e.* *2 Cor* 11:33
through faith *e.* edge of. *Heb* 11:34
if they *e.* not who refused. 12:25
e. the corruption that. *2 Pet* 1:4
those that were clean *e.* 2:18*
after they have *e.* the pollutions. 20

escapeth

him that *e.* the sword of Hazael shall Jehu slay; him that *e.* *1 Ki* 19:17
lions upon him that *e.* of. *Isa* 15:9
ask her that *e.* and ? *Jer* 48:19
he that *e.* in that day. *Ezek* 24:26
he that *e.* of them shall. *Amos* 9:1

escaping

be no remnant nor *e.* *Ezra* 9:14

eschew

e. evil and do good. *1 Pet* 3:11*

eschewed

feared God and *e.* *Job* 1:1†, 8†; 2:3†

Esek

called name of well *E.* *Gen* 26:20

Eshcol

Amorite, brother of *E.* *Gen* 14:13
E. let them take their portion. 24
was called the brook *E.* *Num* 13:24
up unto the valley of *E.* 32:9

Esli

Naum, the son of *E.* *Luke* 3:25

especially *and* **specially**

s. the day thou stoodest. *Deut* 4:10
a reproach *e.* among. *Ps* 31:11*
and *s.* before thee. *Acts* 25:26
e. because I know thee expert. 26:3
e. to them of household. *Gal* 6:10
the Saviour, *s.* of those. *1 Tim* 4:10
provide, *s.* for them of his. 5:8
e. they who labour in word. 17
the cloke bring, but *e.* *2 Tim* 4:13
deceivers, *s.* they of the. *Tit* 1:10
brother beloved, *s.* to. *Philem* 16

espied

he *e.* his money in his. *Gen* 42:27
a land that I had *e.* for. *Ezek* 20:6

see **spy, spied**

espousals

him in day of his *e.* *S of S* 3:11
the love of thine *e.* *Jer* 2:2

espoused

Espousing, or betrothing, was done either by a formal contract in presence of witnesses; or without writing, by the man's giving a piece of silver to the bride before witnesses, and saying to her, Receive this piece of silver as a pledge that at such a time you shall become my spouse. *After the marriage was thus contracted, the young people had the liberty of seeing each other, which was not allowed them before. The union of believers with Christ is expressed under the figure of a marriage,* Isa 54:5; 2 Cor 11:2.

wife Michal whom I *e.* *2 Sam* 3:14
his mother Mary was *e.* *Mat* 1:18
to a virgin *e.* to a man. *Luke* 1:27
to be taxed with Mary his *e.* 2:5
for I have *e.* you to one. *2 Cor* 11:2

espy

Moses sent me to *e.* *Josh* 14:7*
stand by way, and *e.* *Jer* 48:19

Esrom

E. begat Aram. *Mat* 1:3; *Luke* 3:33

establish *and* **stablish**

Stablish is an obsolete form of establish, *which word is most frequently substituted for it in the Revisions. Such passages are not here marked.* [1] *To settle,* 1 Ki 9:5. [2] *To confirm,* Num 30:13. [3] *To perform, or make good,* Ps 119:38. [4] *To ordain, or appoint,* Hab 1:12.

thee will I *e.* my covenant. *Gen* 6:18
9:9; 17:7; *Lev* 26:9; *Ezek* 16:62
e. my covenant with. *Gen* 17:19, 21
her husband may *e.* it. *Num* 30:13
may *e.* his covenant he. *Deut* 8:18
the Lord shall *e.* thee an. 28:9
that he may *e.* thee to-day. 29:13
only Lord *e.* his word. *1 Sam* 1:23
2 Sam 7:25*
I will *e.* his kingdom. *2 Sam* 7:12
13; *1 Chr* 17:11; 22:10; 28:7
I will *e.* throne of thy. *1 Ki* 9:5
to set up his son, and to *e.* 15:4
and I will *s.* his throne. *1 Chr* 17:12
as he went to *s.* his dominion. 18:3
then will I *s.* throne. *2 Chr* 7:18
God loved Israel to *e.* them. 9:8
to *s.* among them days. *Esth* 9:21
yea he doth *e.* them for. *Job* 36:7*
but *e.* the just. *Ps* 7:9*
God will *e.* it. 48:8
the Highest himself shall *e.* 87:5
thy faithfulness shalt thou *e.* 89:2
thy seed will I *e.* for ever. 4
e. thou work of our hands, *e.* 90:17
thou dost *e.* equity, thou. 99:4
s. thy word to thy servant. 119:38
he will *e.* the border of. *Pr* 15:25
to *e.* it with judgement. *Isa* 9:7
give thee for a covenant to *e.* 49:8*
till he *e.* and make Jerusalem. 62:7
Lord that formed it, to *e.* it. *Jer* 33:2
I will *e.* an everlasting. *Ezek* 16:60
consulted to *e.* a royal. *Dan* 6:7
O king, *e.* the decree, and sign. 8
shall exalt themselves to *e.* 11:14
love the good, and *e.* *Amos* 5:15
yea, we *e.* the law. *Rom* 3:31
going about to *e.* their own. 10:3
to him that is of power to *s.* 16:25
Timothy our brother to *e.* *1 Thes* 3:2
to the end he may *s.* your hearts. 13
s. you in every good. *2 Thes* 2:17
the Lord shall *s.* you, and keep. 3:3
first, that he may *e.* *Heb* 10:9
also patient, *s.* your hearts. *Jas* 5:8
God of all grace *s.* *1 Pet* 5:10

established, stablished

covenant which I have *e.* *Gen* 9:17
because the thing is *e.* by 41:32
have also *e.* my covenant. *Ex* 6:4
in sanctuary thy hands have *e.* 15:17
made thee, and *e.* thee ? *Deut* 32:6
Samuel was *e.* prophet. *1 Sam* 3:20
now would Lord have *e.* thy. 13:13
not be *e.* nor thy kingdom. 20:31
perceived Lord had *e.* *2 Sam* 5:12
let house of thy servant David be *e.* for ever. 7:26; *1 Chr* 17:24
his kingdom was *e.* *1 Ki* 2:12
Lord liveth, which hath *e.* me. 24
kingdom was *e.* in the hand. 46
let the thing be *e.* *1 Chr* 17:23, 24
let thy promise be *e.* *2 Chr* 1:9
when Rehoboam had *e.* the. 12:1
the Lord *s.* the kingdom in his. 17:5
when the kingdom was *e.* to. 25:3
so they *e.* a decree to keep. 30:5
their seed is *e.* in their. *Job* 21:8
he hath *e.* it upon floods. *Ps* 24:2
set my feet on a rock, and *e.* 40:2
he *e.* a testimony in Jacob. 78:5
earth he hath *e.* for. 69; 119:90
the world is *e.* 93:1
thy throne is *e.* of old. *Ps* 93:2
his heart is *e.* he shall not. 112:8
let not an evil speaker be *e.* 140:11
he hath *s.* the waters for. 148:6
by understanding, hath *e.* *Pr* 3:19
and let all thy ways be *e.* 4:26
when he *e.* the clouds above. 8:28*
man shall not be *e.* by. 12:3
of counsellors they are *e.* 15:22
for the throne is *e.* 16:12
purpose is *e.* by counsel. 20:18
by understanding is an house *e.* 24:3
e. all the ends of the earth. 30:4
believe, ye shall not be *e.* *Isa* 7:9
in mercy shall the throne be *e.* 16:5
God made earth, he hath *e.* it. 45:18
he *e.* the world. *Jer* 10:12; 51:15
I was *e.* in my kingdom. *Dan* 4:36
O mighty God, thou *e.* *Hab* 1:12
in the mouth of two witnesses every word be *e.* *Mat* 18:16
so were the churches *e.* *Acts* 16:5
to end you may be *e.* *Rom* 1:11
built up in him, and *s.* *Col* 2:7
which was *e.* upon better. *Heb* 8:6*
it is good that the heart be *e.* 13:9
though ye be *e.* in the. *2 Pet* 1:12

shall be **established**

house *shall be e.* for. *Lev* 25:30*
2 Sam 7:16
of two or three witnesses *shall* matter *be e.* *Deut* 19:15; *2 Cor* 13:1
kingdom *shall be e.* *1 Sam* 24:20
thy kingdom, and thy throne, *shall be e.* for. *2 Sam* 7:16*; *1 Ki* 2:45
and his throne *shall be e.* for evermore. *1 Chr* 17:14; *Ps* 89:37
believe in God, so *shall* ye *be e.*
2 Chr 20:20
decree, and it *shall be e.* *Job* 22:28
my hand *shall be e.* *Ps* 89:21
world *shall be e.* before thee. 96:10
and their seed *shall be e.* 102:28
of truth *shall be e.* for. *Pr* 12:19
thy thoughts *shall be e.* 16:3
his throne *shall be e.* 25:5; 29:14
of Lord's house *shall be e.* *Isa* 2:2
in mercy *shall* throne *be e.* 16:5
in righteousness *shalt be e.* 54:14
congregation *shall be e.* *Jer* 30:20
house of Lord *shall be e.* *Mi* 4:1
house, and it *shall be e.* *Zech* 5:11*

establisheth

he *e.* all her vows. *Num* 30:14
the king by judgement, *e.* *Pr* 29:4
no decree the king *e.* *Dan* 6:15
woe to him that *e.* city. *Hab* 2:12
he which *e.* us with you. *2 Cor* 1:21

establishment

after *e.* Sennacherib. *2 Chr* 32:1*

estate, state

[1] *Condition of life,* Gen 43:7. [2] *Social standing,* 1 Chr. 17:17. [3] *Pomp,* Esth 1:19.

man asked us of our *s.* *Gen* 43:7
to the *e.* of a man of. *1 Chr* 17:17
set house of God in his *s.* *2 Chr* 24:1
according to the *s.* of. *Esth* 1:7
let the king give her royal *e.* to. 1
gifts according to the *s.* of. 2:1
every man at best *s.* *Ps* 39:
remembered us in our low *e.* 136:2
diligent to know *s.* of thy. *Pr* 27:2
by a man of knowledge *s.* 28:
lo, I am come to great *e.* *Eccl* 1:
concerning the *e.* of sons of. 3:1
from thy *s.* shall he pull. *Isa* 22:
return to her former *e.* *Ezek* 16:
stand up in his *e.* *Dan* 11:7*, 2
then shall stand up in his *e.* 2
but in his *e.* shall he honour. 3
other spirits enter, the last *s.* of th man. *Mat* 12:45; *Luke* 11:
hath regarded low *e.* of. *Luke* 1:
all the *e.* of the elders. *Acts* 22
condescend to men of low *e.*
Rom 12:1
when I know your *s.* *Phil* 2:
will naturally care for your *s.*
in whatsoever *s.* I am to be. 4:
all my *s.* shall Tychicus. *Col* 4
sent, that he might know your *e.*
angels which kept not first *e.* *Jude*

estates
you after your old e. Ezek 36:11
supper to his chief e. Mark 6:21*

esteem
will he e. thy riches? Job 36:19*
I e. all thy precepts to. Ps 119:128
we did e. him smitten of. Isa 53:4
each e. other better than. Phil 2:3
to e. them highly for. 1 Thes 5:13

esteemed
e. rock of his salvation. Deut 32:15
me shall be lightly e. 1 Sam 2:30
a poor man and lightly e. 18:23
I have e. the words of. Job 23:12*
e. a man of understanding. Pr 17:28
turning shall be e. as the. Isa 29:16*
fruitful field shall be e. as a. 17*
despised, and we e. him not. 53:3
how are they e. as! Lam 4:2
highly e. among men. Luke 16:15*
to judge who are least e. 1 Cor 6:4*

esteemeth
he e. iron as straw. Job 41:27*
one e. one day above another; another e. every day. Rom 14:5
to him that e. any thing to. 14*

esteeming
e. reproach of Christ. Heb 11:26*

Esther
brought up Hadassah, E. Esth 2:7
the king loved E. 17
king made feast, even E.'s feast. 18
told it to E. 22
E.'s maids came, she sent. 4:4
told to Mordecai E.'s words. 12
Mordecai did all that E. had. 17
king held out to E. golden. 5:2; 8:4
what wilt thou, queen E.? 5:3
E. let no man come in with. 12
what is thy petition, queen E.? 7:2
to make request for life to E. 7
and E. spake yet again. 8:3
I have given E. the house. 7
E. the queen wrote with. 9:29
decree of E. confirmed these. 32

estimate
priest shall e. it good or bad, as the priest shall e. it. Lev 27:14

estimation
bring a ram with thy e. Lev 5:15
shall be for Lord, by thy e. 27:2
thy e. shall be of the male from. 3, 5
This word frequently occurs in this chapter
old, according to thy e. Num 18:16

estimations
all thy e. according to. Lev 27:25

estranged
mine acquaintance are e. Job 19:13
the wicked are e. from. Ps 58:3
were not e. from their lust. 78:30
because they have e. this. Jer 19:4
they are all e. from me. Ezek 14:5

Etam
Samson dwelt in top of E. Judg 15:8
men went to top of the rock E. 11

eternal
. God is thy refuge. Deut 33:27
hee an e. excellency. Isa 60:15
s in danger of e. Mark 3:29
ven his e. power and. Rom 1:20*
vorketh an e. weight of. 2 Cor 4:17
hings which are not seen are e. 18
n house e. in the heavens. 5:1
ccording to e. purpose. Eph 3:11
nto the King e. be. 1 Tim 1:17
alvation with e. glory. 2 Tim 2:10
e author of e. salvation. Heb 5:9
octrine of baptisms, and e. 6:2
aving obtained e. redemption. 9:12
ho through the e. Spirit offered. 14
e promise of e. inheritance. 15
s unto his e. glory. 1 Pet 5:10
uffering the vengeance of e. Jude 7

eternal ***life***
at I may have e. life? Mat 19:16
ghteous shall go into life e. 25:46
all I do, that I may inherit e. life? Mark 10:17; Luke 10:25; 18:18
world to come e. life. Mark 10:30
in him should have e. life. John 3:15
gathereth fruit unto life e. 4:36
in them ye have e. life. 5:39
drinketh my blood hath e. life. 6:54
hast words of e. life. 68
give unto my sheep e. life. 10:28
his life, keep it to e. life. 12:25
he should give e. life to as. 17:2
this is life e. that they might. 3
were ordained to e. life. Acts 13:48
who seek glory, e. life. Rom 2:7
might grace reign to e. life. 5:21
but the gift of God is e. life. 6:23
lay hold on e. life. 1 Tim 6:12, 19*
in hope of e. life. Tit 1:2
according to hope of e. life. 3:7
e. life which was with. 1 John 1:2
promise he promised, e. life. 2:25
no murderer hath e. life. 3:15
God hath given to us e. life. 5:11
may know that ye have e. life. 13
is the true God, and e. life. 20
mercy of Lord unto e. life. Jude 21

eternity
One that inhabiteth e. Isa 57:15

Etham
encamped in E. Ex 13:20; Num 33:6
three days' journey in E. Num 33:8

Ethan
Solomon was wiser than E. 1 Ki 4:31
Zerah, Zimri, and E. 1 Chr 2:6

Ethanim
Israel assembled in the month E. 1 Ki 8:2

Ethiopia
heard say of Tirhakah king of E. 2 Ki 19:9; Isa 37:9
Ahasuerus reigned from India to E. Esth 1:1; 8:9
the topaz of E. not equal. Job 28:9
E. stretch out hands to. Ps 68:31
Philistia and Tyre with E. 87:4
is beyond the rivers of E. Isa 18:1
Zeph 3:10
bare-foot for sign on E. Isa 20:3
they shall be ashamed of E. 5
gave Egypt for thy ransom, E. 43:3
the merchandise of E. shall. 45:14
great pain in E. Ezek 30:4
E. shall fall. 5; 38:5
E. and Egypt were the. Nah 3:9
a man of E. eunuch of. Acts 8:27

Ethiopian
because of E. woman. Num 12:1
Zerah the E. came out. 2 Chr 14:9
can E. change his skin? Jer 13:23
Ebed-melech the E. 38:7, 10, 12
39:16

Ethiopians
Lord smote E. the E. 2 Chr 14:12
the E. and Lubims a huge? 16:8
stirred Arabians near E. 21:16
shall lead the E. captives. Isa 20:4
E. that handle the shield. Jer 46:9
make careless E. afraid. Ezek 30:9
the Lybians and E. shall. Dan 11:43
ye not as children of E.? Amos 9:7
ye E. shall be slain. Zeph 2:12
under Candace of E. Acts 8:27

Eubulus
E. greeteth thee. 2 Tim 4:21

Eunice
faith which dwelt in E. 2 Tim 1:5

eunuch
Originally an impotent man. Since those put in charge of the harems of Eastern monarchs were as a general rule of this class, the name became practically synonymous with chamberlain, with no indication of his condition, although probably its use in scripture was strict. Eunuchs were not allowed by Jewish law to enter the house of God, Deut 23:1; *but they were present at the court,* 1 Chr 28:1, marg. *A eunuch was over the treasure of queen Candace of Ethiopia, and he was admitted to baptism,* Acts 8:27, 37.
neither let the e. say. Isa 56:3
an e. had come to. Acts 8:27
e. said, of whom speaks? 34
e. said, what doth hinder me? 36
Spirit caught Philip, e. saw. 39

eunuchs
looked out two or three e. 2 Ki 9:32
and they shall be e. in palace. 20:18
Isa 39:7
Ahab called for one of e. 2 Chr 18:8
saith the Lord to the e. Isa 56:4
after that the e. were. Jer 29:2
e. which passed between the. 34:19
when Ebed-melech one of e. 38:7
e. whom he had brought. 41:16
spake to master of his e. Dan 1:3
to whom the prince of the e. 7
Daniel requested of prince of e. 8
into favour with prince of e. 9
then prince of the e. brought. 18
e. who were so born, made e. of men. Mat 19:12

Euodias
I beseech E. and. Phil 4:2

Euphrates
the fourth river is E. Gen 2:14
unto great river, the river E. 15:18
go to great river E. Deut 1:7
Josh 1:4
yours from the river E. Deut 11:24
smote Hadadezer at the river E. 2 Sam 8:3; 1 Chr 18:3
Necho went up to E. 2 Ki 23:29
2 Chr 35:20
took from Egypt to E. 2 Ki 24:7
inhabited from river E. 1 Chr 5:9
arise, go to E. Jer 13:4
so I hid it by E. 5
I went to E. 7
came against Pharaoh by E. 46:2
stumble and fall by river E. 6
hath a sacrifice by E. 10
cast it into midst of E. 51:63
bound in the river E. Rev 9:14
angel poured out vial on E. 16:12

euroclydon
(A tempestuous north-east wind of the Mediterranean, very dangerous to the sort of shipping used in the time of the Apostles. In the Revisions the name is given as Euraquilo)
arose tempestuous wind, called e. Acts 27:14

Eutychus
a young man named E. Acts 20:9

evangelist
house of Philip the e. Acts 21:8
do the work of an e. 2 Tim 4:5

evangelists
some apostles, some e. Eph 4:11

Eve
called his wife's name E. Gen 3:20
Adam knew E. his wife. 4:1
as serpent beguiled E. 2 Cor 11:3
first formed, then E. 1 Tim 2:13

even
(The close of the day)
two angels to Sodom at e. Gen 19:1
fourteenth day of month at e. Ex 12:18
Moses said, at e. then shall. 16:6
at e. eat flesh. 12
at e. the quails came. 13
stand from morning to e. 18:14
Aaron lighteth lamps at e. 30:8
unclean until e. Lev 11:24, 25, 27, 28, 31, 39, 40; 14:46; 15:5, 6, 7, etc. 17:15; 22:6; Num 19:7, 8, 10, 21, 22
fourteenth day of first month, at e. Lev 23:5; Num 9:3; Deut 16:6
day of second month at e. Num 9:11
when cloud abode from e. to. 21
shall be clean at e. 19:19
would God it were e. Deut 28:67
wept before Lord till e. Judg 20:23
and fasted till e. 26; 2 Sam 1:12
the people abode till e. 21:2
gleaned in field until e. Ruth 2:17
unto third day at e. 1 Sam 20:5
Ahab died at e. 1 Ki 22:35
2 Chr 18:34

praise Lord every morning and *e*. *1 Chr* 23:30
shalt go forth at *e*. in. *Ezek* 12:4
in the *e*. I digged through the wall. 7
and at *e*. my wife died. 24:18
when the *e*. was come. *Mat* 8:16
20:8; 26:20; 27:57; *Mark* 4:35
6:47; 11:19; 15:42
at *e*. they brought to. *Mark* 1:32
at *e*. at midnight, or cockcrow. 13:35
when *e*. was come. *John* 6:16

even

mine eyes *e*. seeing it. *1 Ki* 1:48
known to thee, *e*. to. *Pr* 22:19
flock of sheep that are *e*. *S of S* 4:2
e. saying to Jerusalem. *Isa* 44:28
e. to them will I give a name. 56:5
if a man do, he shall *e*. *Ezek* 20:11
if sword contemn *e*. the rod. 21:13
e. we ourselves groan. *Rom* 8:23
not *e*. nature itself? *1 Cor* 11:14
kingdom to God, *e*. the. 15:24
e. the Father of our Lord. *2 Cor* 1:3
a measure to reach *e*. to you. 10:13
obedient to death, *e*. *Phil* 2:8

even, *adjective*

that net may be *e*. to. *Ex* 27:5
weighed in an *e*. balance. *Job* 31:6
my foot standeth in *e*. *Ps* 26:12
shall lay thee *e*. with. *Luke* 19:44

evening

came in to him in the *e*. *Gen* 8:11
came out of field in *e*. 30:16
of Israel kill it in *e*. *Ex* 12:6
but when *e*. cometh. *Deut* 23:11
hanging on trees until *e*. *Josh* 10:26
day draweth towards *e*. *Judg* 19:9
cursed that eateth till *e*. *1 Sam* 14:24
David smote them to the *e*. 30:17
in the *e*. she went. *Esth* 2:14
they return at *e*. they. *Ps* 59:6
at *e*. let them return and. 14
in the *e*. it is cut down. 90:6
forth to his labour until *e*. 104:23
went way to her house in *e*. *Pr* 7:9
in the *e*. withhold not. *Eccl* 11:6
the shadows of the *e*. *Jer* 6:4
of Lord was on me in *e*. *Ezek* 33:22
gate shall not be shut till *e*. 46:2
in Ashkelon lie down in *e*. *Zeph* 2:7
when *e*. was come. *Mat* 14:23
when it is *e*. ye say, it. 16:2
in the *e*. he cometh. *Mark* 14:17
abide with us, for it is *e*. *Luke* 24:29
same day at *e*. came. *John* 20:19

evening with *morning*

the *e*. and *morning* were first day.
Gen 1:5, 8, 13, 19, 23, 31
Moses from *morning* to *e*. *Ex* 18:13
shall order it from *e*. to *morning*.
27:21; *Lev* 24:3
Philistine drew near *morning* and *e*.
1 Sam 17:16
bread *morning* and *e*. *1 Ki* 17:6
offerings *morning and e*. *1 Chr* 16:40
2 Chr 2:4; 13:11; 31:3; *Ezra* 3:3
are destroyed from *morning* to *e*.
Job 4:20
e. and *morning*, and at. *Ps* 55:17
outgoings of *morning* and *e*. 65:8
vision of *e*. and *morning* is. *Dan* 8:26
persuading them from *morning* to *e*.
Acts 28:23

evening, *adjective*

prophesied till *e*. *1 Ki* 18:29
at time of offering of the *e*. 36
on great altar burn *e*. *2 Ki* 16:15
astonished until the *e*. *Ezra* 9:4
at *e*. sacrifice I arose from my. 5
let my prayer be as the *e*. *Ps* 141:2
the time of *e*. oblation. *Dan* 9:21
more fierce than the *e*. *Hab* 1:8
her judges are *e*. wolves. *Zeph* 3:3
at *e*. time shall be light. *Zech* 14:7

evenings

a wolf of the *e*. shall. *Jer* 5:6

event

one *e*. happeneth to. *Eccl* 2:14; 9:3
one *e*. to the righteous and. 9:2

eventide, *or* **eveningtide**

went out to meditate at *e*. *Gen* 24:63
Joshua fell on his face till *e*. *Josh* 7:6
of Ai he hanged on tree till *e*. 8:29
in an *e*. David walked. *2 Sam* 11:2
behold, at *e*. trouble. *Isa* 17:14
now the *e*. was come. *Mark* 11:11
him in hold, for it was *e*. *Acts* 4:3

ever

fire shall *e*. be burning. *Lev* 6:13
hast ridden on, *e*. since. *Num* 22:30
did *e*. people hear voice? *Deut* 4:33
to love God, and to walk *e*. 19:9
e. fight against Israel? *Judg* 11:25
Hiram was *e*. a lover. *1 Ki* 5:1
who *e*. perished, being? *Job* 4:7
that trust, let them *e*. *Ps* 5:11
tender mercies have been *e*. 25:6
mine eyes are *e*. towards Lord. 15
he is *e*. merciful, and. 37:26*
and my sin is *e*. before me. 51:3
or *e*. thou hadst formed earth. 90:2
Pr 8:23
will *e*. be mindful of his. *Ps* 111:5
commandments are *e*. with. 119:98
or *e*. I was aware, my. *S of S* 6:12†
because he will not *e*. be. *Isa* 28:28
not one of the stakes shall *e*. 33:20
e. they came at bottom. *Dan* 6:24†
hath not been *e*. the like. *Joel* 2:2
was not, no, nor *e*. shall. *Mat* 24:21
him to do as he had *e*. *Mark* 15:8*
son, thou art *e*. with. *Luke* 15:31
told me all things *e*. I. *John* 4:29, 39
but the Son abideth *e*. 8:35
all that *e*. came before me. 10:8
I *e*. taught in the synagogue. 18:20
we, or *e*. he come, are. *Acts* 23:15
for no man *e*. yet hated. *Eph* 5:29
so shall we *e*. be with. *1 Thes* 4:17
but *e*. follow that which is. 5:15
e. learning, and never. *2 Tim* 3:7
because he continueth *e*. *Heb* 7:24
e. liveth to make intercession. 25
be glory, now and *e*. *Jude* 25

see **endureth**

for **ever**

(*Many believe that the words* for ever *or* everlasting *are not to be taken as synonymous with eternal, as being without end, but to be understood merely as meaning a very long time, to be left indeterminate. There seems to be a considerable amount of argument in favour of this in many cases, but it is not safe to conclude that it always should be so limited*)

give it and thy seed *for e*. *Gen* 13:15
me bear blame *for e*. 43:9; 44:32
this is my name *for e*. *Ex* 3:15
feast by an ordinance *for e*. 12:14, 17
to thee, and to thy sons *for e*. 24
see them again no more *for e*. 14:13
people may believe thee *for e*. 19:9
and he shall serve him *for e*. 21:6
between me and Israel *for e*. 31:17
and they shall inherit it *for e*. 32:13
land not be sold *for e*. *Lev* 25:23*
the house be established *for e*. 30*
shall be your bondmen *for e*. 46
for an ordinance *for e*. *Num* 10:8
15:15; 18:8
covenant of salt *for e*. 18:19
Amalek shall perish *for e*. 24:20
afflict Eber, he shall perish *for e*. 24
earth which God giveth thee *for e*.
Deut 4:40
be well with them *for e*. 5:29; 12:28
it shall be an heap *for e*. 13:16
shall be thy servant *for e*. 15:17
him and his sons *for e*. 18:5
not seek their peace *for e*. 23:6
upon thee for a sign *for e*. 28:46
revealed belong to us *for e*. 29:29
stones be a memorial *for e*. *Josh* 4:7
fear the Lord your God *for e*. 24
Ai, made it an heap *for e*. 8:28
land be thine inheritance *for e*. 14:9
before the Lord and abide *for e*.
1 Sam 1:22
house walk before me *for e*. 2:30
not be an old man in house *for e*. 32
walk before mine Anointed *for e*. 35
I will judge his house *for e*.
1 Sam 3:13
of Eli's house not purged *for e*. 14
not cut off thy kindness *for e*. 20:15
between thee and me *for e*. 23, 42
shall be my servant *for e*. 27:12
keeper of mine head *for e*. 28:2
sword devour *for e*.? *2 Sam* 2:26
and my kingdom guiltless *for e*. 3:28
confirmed Israel to thee *for e*. 7:24
let thy name be magnified *for e*. 26
his house may continue *for e*. 29
for thee to abide in *for e*. *1 Ki* 8:13
to put my name there *for e*. 9:3
the Lord loved Israel *for e*. 10:9
David's seed, but not *for e*. 11:39
will be thy servants *for e*. 12:7
2 Chr 10:7
leprosy cleave to thee *for e*.
2 Ki 5:27
make thine own *for e*. *1 Chr* 17:22
he and sons *for e*. to burn. 23:13
he will cast thee off *for e*. 28:9
God of Israel, keep this *for e*. 29:18
name may be there *for e*. *2 Chr* 7:16
to give a light to sons *for e*. 21:7
which he hath sanctified *for e*. 30:8
Jerusalem my name be *for e*. 33:4
congregation of God *for e*. *Neh* 13:1
they perish *for e*. without. *Job* 4:20
prevailest *for e*. against. 14:20
iron pen in the rock *for e*. 19:24
yet he shall perish *for e*. 20:7
should I be delivered *for e*. 23:7
he doth establish them *for e*. 36:7
Lord shall endure *for e*. *Ps* 9:7
of poor shall not perish *for e*. 18
thou shalt preserve them *for e*. 12:7
thou forget me, O Lord, *for e*.? 13:1
fear of Lord enduring *for e*. 19:9
made him most blessed *for e*. 21:6
in house of the Lord *for e*. 23:6
and lift them up *for e*. 28:9
the Lord sitteth king *for e*. 29:10
thanks to thee *for e*. 30:12; 79:13
counsel of Lord standeth *for e*. 33:11
their inheritance shall be *for e*. 37:18
his saints are preserved *for e*. 28
righteous shall dwell in land *for e*. 29
me before thy face *for e*. 41:12
and we praise thy name *for e*. 44:8
O Lord, cast us not off *for e*. 23
God hath blessed thee *for e*. 45:2
redemption of their soul ceaseth *for e*. 49:8
their houses continue *for e*. 11
God shall destroy thee *for e*. 52:5
I will praise thee *for e*. 9
abide in thy tabernacle *for e*. 61:4
he shall abide before God *for e*. 7
sing praise unto thy name *for e*. 8
he ruleth by his power *for e*. 66:7
Lord will dwell in it *for e*. 68:16
his name shall endure *for e*. 72:17
blessed be his glorious name *for e*. 19
my strength and portion *for e*. 73:26
hast thou cast us off *for e*.? 74:1
enemy blaspheme name *for e*.? 10
forget not thy poor *for e*. 19
I will declare *for e*. I will. 75:9
will Lord cast off *for e*.? 77:7
is mercy clean gone *for e*.? 8
wilt thou be angry *for e*.? 79:5
should have endured *for e*. 81:15
confounded and troubled *for e*. 83:17
thou be angry with us *for e*.? 85:5
sing of mercies of Lord *for e*. 89:1
mercy shall be built up *for e*. 2
his seed will I make to endure *for e*
29, 3
wilt thou hide thyself *for e*.? 4
they should be destroyed *for e*. 92:
holiness becometh house *for e*. 93:
neither keep his anger *for e*. 103:
remembered his covenant *for e*.
105:
thou art a priest *for e*. after. 110:
Heb 5:6; 6:20; 7:17, 2
commanded his covenant *for e*.
Ps 111:
he shall not be moved *for e*. 112:
for e. O Lord, thy word is. 119:8
from henceforth even *for e*. 125:
131:3; *Isa* 9:

this is my rest for e. Ps 132:14
Lord who keepeth truth for e. 146:6
the Lord shall reign for e. 10
for riches are not for e. Pr 27:24
wise more than fool for e. Eccl 2:16
God doth, it shall be for e. 3:14
have they more a portion for e. 9:6
trust ye in Lord for e. Isa 26:4
and assurance for e. 32:17
smoke shall go up for e. 34:10
shall possess it for e. from. 17
word of our God stand for e. 40:8
I shall be a lady for e. 47:7
my salvation shall be for e. 51:6
my righteousness shall be for e. 8
will not contend for e. nor. 57:16
words shall not depart for e. 59:21
people shall inherit land for e. 60:21
nor remember iniquity for e. 64:9
be glad and rejoice for e. 65:18
he reserve anger for e.? Jer 3:5
I will not keep anger for e. 12
a fire which shall burn for e. 17:4
and this city shall remain for e. 25
not be plucked up for e. 31:40
heart that they may fear for e. 32:39
ye shall drink no wine for e. 35:6
Jonadab shall not want a man to stand before me for e. 19
dragons and a desolation for e. 49:33
more inhabited for e. 50:39; 51:26 62
will not cast off for e. Lam 3:31
thou remainest for e. thy. 5:19
dost thou forget us for e.? 20
their children dwell for e. and David be their prince for e. Ezek 37:25
in midst of Israel for e. 43:7, 9
kingdom shall stand for e. Dan 2:44
honoured him that liveth for e. 4:34
living God and stedfast for e. 6:26
saints possess kingdom for e. 7:18
sware by him that liveth for e. 12:7
betroth thee unto me for e. Hos 2:19
Judah shall dwell for e. Joel 3:20
off pity kept wrath for e. Amos 1:11
Edom, shalt be cut off for e. Ob 10
with bars about me for e. Jonah 2:6
taken away my glory for e. Mi 2:9
Lord shall reign over them for e. 4:7
retaineth not anger for e. 7:18
Lord hath indignation for e. Mal 1:4
is power and glory for e. Mat 6:13
no fruit grow on thee for e. 21:19 Mark 11:14
reign over Jacob for e. Luke 1:33
to Abraham and seed for e. 55
abideth not in house for e. John 8:35
that Christ abideth for e. 12:34
may abide with you for e. 14:16
Creator, who is blessed for e. Rom 1:25
is over all, God blessed for e. 9:5
to whom be glory for e. 11:36; 16:27
righteousness remaineth for e. 2 Cor 9:9
receive him for e. Philem 15
for e. sat down on the. Heb 10:12
perfected for e. them that are. 14
the same to-day and for e. 13:8
word of God, liveth for e. 1 Pet 1:23
word of Lord endureth for e. 25
to whom mist of darkness is reserved for e. 2 Pet 2:17; Jude 13
shall be with us for e. 2 John 2
see **establish, established**

live for **ever**

tree of life, and live for e. Gen 3:22
hand and say, I live for e. Deut 32:40
king David live for e. 1 Ki 1:31
let the king live for e. Neh 2:3
hearts shall live for e. Ps 22:26
that he should still live for e. 49:9
O king, live for e. Dan 2:4; 3:9 5:10; 6:6, 21
do they live for e.? Zech 1:5
if any man eat of this bread he shall live for e. John 6:51, 58

for **ever** *and* **ever**

Lord reign for e. and e. Ex 15:18
blessed be God for e. and e. people. 1 Chr 16:36*; 29:10; Dan 2:20
bless your God for e. and e. Neh 9:5
out their name for e and e. Ps 9:5
Lord is King for e. and e. 10:16
him length of days for e. and e. 21:4
thy throne is for e. and e. 45:6
people praise thee for e. and e. 17
God is our God for e. and e. 48:14
in mercy of God for e. and e. 52:8
they stand fast for e. and e. 111:8
I keep thy law for e. and e. 119:44
bless thy name for e. and e. 145:1
praise thy name for e. and e. 2, 21
stablished them for e. and e. 148:6
time to come, for e. and e. Isa 30:8
pass through it for e. and e. 34:10
land I gave for e. and e. Jer 7:7*
you and fathers for e. and e. 25:5*
the kingdom for e. and e. Dan 7:18
shine as stars for e. and e. 12:3
walk in the name of God for e and e. Mi 4:5
whom be glory for e. and e. Gal 1:5 Phil 4:20; 1 Tim 1:17 2 Tim 4:18; Heb 13:21
throne, O God, is for e. and e. Heb 1:8
to him who liveth for e. and e. Rev 4:9, 10; 5:14; 10:6; 15:7
be to the Lamb for e. and e. 5:13
power be unto God for e. and e. 7:12
Christ shall reign for e. and e. 11:15
ascendeth for e. and e. 14:11; 19:3
tormented day and night for e. and e. 20:10
shall reign for e. and e. 22:5

statute for **ever**

be a statute for e. Ex 27:21; 28:43 30:21; Lev 6:18; 10:9; 17:7 23:14, 21, 31, 41; 24:3 Num 18:23
a statute for e. Ex 29:28; Lev 7:34 36; 10:15; 16:31; Num 18:11, 19
a statute for e. unto Lord. Lev 6:22
stranger for statute for e. Num 19:10

everlasting

(*See note on* **for ever**. *The Revisions very frequently substitute the word* eternal *for everlasting*)

land of Canaan for an e. possession. Gen 17:8; 48:4
the e. God. 21:33; Isa 40:28 Rom 16:26
utmost bound of e. hills. Gen 49:26
an e. priesthood. Ex 40:15 Num 25:13
be an e. statute. Lev 16:34
e. arms. Deut 33:27
lift up, ye e. doors. Ps 24:7, 9
mercy e. 100:5
righteous in e. remembrance. 112:6
is an e. righteousness. 119:142, 144
and lead me in way e. 139:24
kingdom is an e. kingdom. 145:13 Dan 4:3; 7:27; 2 Pet 1:11
righteous is an e. foundation. Pr 10:25
be called, the e. Father. Isa 9:6
Jehovah is e. strength. 26:4
dwell with e. burnings ? 33:14
they shall come with e. joy. 35:10 51:11; 61:7
with an e. salvation. 45:17
with e. kindness. 54:8
for an e. sign. 55:13
an e. name. 56:5; 63:12
unto thee an e. light. 60:19, 20
God is an e. King. Jer 10:10
e. confusion. 20:11
an e. reproach upon you. 23:40
I have loved thee with e. love. 31:3
dominion is an e. dominion. Dan 4:34 7:14
e. mountains were. Hab 3:6
cast into e. fire. Mat 18:8, 25, 41
go away into e. punishment. 25:46
you into e. habitations. Luke 16:9
with e. destruction. 2 Thes 1:9
hath given us e. consolation. 2:16
be honour and power e. 1 Tim 6:16
angels reserved in e. chains. Jude 6
having the e. gospel to. Rev 14:6
see **covenant**

from **everlasting**

blessed be God from e. Ps 41:13 106:48
even from e. to everlasting. 90:2
thou art from e. 93:2
mercy of Lord is from e. 103:17
I was set up from e. Pr 8:23
thy name is from e. Isa 63:16
forth have been from e. Mi 5:2
art thou not from e.? Hab 1:12

everlasting *life*

awake, some to e. life. Dan 12:2
shall inherit e. life. Mat 19:29
world to come e. life. Luke 18:30
believeth have e. life. John 3:16, 36
a well springing up to e. life. 4:14
heareth my words hath e. life. 5:24
meat which endureth to e. life. 6:27
who seeth Son may have e. life. 40
believeth on me hath e. life. 47
his commandment is life e. 12:50
unworthy of e. life. Acts 13:46
ye have the end e. life. Rom 6:22
of Spirit reap life e. Gal 6:8
believe on him to life e. 1 Tim 1:16

evermore

oppressed and spoiled e. Deut 28:29
mercy unto David e. 2 Sam 22:51
observe to do for e. 2 Ki 17:37
throne shall be established for e. 1 Chr 17:14
right hand pleasures for e. Ps 16:11
mercy to David and seed for e. 18:50
do good, and dwell for e. 37:27
doth his promise fail for e.? 77:8
and glorify thy name for e. 86:12
mercy I keep for him for e. 89:28
blessed be the Lord for e. 52
thou, Lord, most high for e. 92:8
seek his face e. 105:4
him for righteousness for e. 106:31
blessed be name of Lord for e. 113:2
we will bless the Lord for e. 115:18
going out and coming in e. 121:8
shall sit upon throne for e. 132:12
the blessing, life for e. 133:3
will set my sanctuary in the midst of them for e. Ezek 37:26, 28
e. give us this bread. John 6:34
of Lord blessed for e. 2 Cor 11:31
rejoice e. pray. 1 Thes 5:16
who is consecrated for e. Heb 7:28
was dead, I am alive for e. Rev 1:18

every

e. imagination of his heart. Gen 6:5
e. man-child be circumcised. 17:10
nor shalt gather e. Lev 19:10
put out of camp e. leper. Num 5:2
Samuel told him e. whit. 1 Sam 3:18
refrained from e. evil. Ps 119:101
I hate e. false way. 104, 128
understand e. good path. Pr 2:9
she lieth in wait at e. corner. 7:12
the simple believeth e. word. 14:15
eyes of Lord in e. place. 15:3
but e. fool will be meddling. 20:3
e. word of God is pure. 30:5
e. knee shall bow, e. Isa 45:23 Rom 14:11
e. purpose of Lord shall. Jer 51:29
and effect of e. vision. Ezek 12:23
magnify himself above e. Dan 11:36
land mourn, e. family. Zech 12:12
e. place incense offered. Mal 1:11
by e. word that. Mat 4:4
put away his wife for e. 19:3
came to him from e. Mark 1:45
fame of him went into e. Luke 4:37
for e. tree is known by his. 6:44
and fear came upon e. Acts 2:43
Moses hath in e. city them. 15:21
teach e. where in e. 1 Cor 4:17
bringing into captivity e. 2 Cor 10:5
far above e. name named. Eph 1:21 Phil 2:9
e. joint supplieth, in measure of e. Eph 4:16
salute e. saint in Christ. Phil 4:21
e. creature of God is. 1 Tim 4:4
prepared unto e. good. 2 Tim 2:21
let us lay aside e. weight. Heb 12:1
e. good and perfect gift. Jas 1:17
submit to e. ordinance. 1 Pet 2:13

believe not *e.* spirit, but. *1 John* 4:1
see **beast, city, day, man, morning, side, thing, way**

every *one*

that *e. one* that findeth. *Gen* 4:14
cursed be *e. one* that curseth. 27:29
are holy, *e. one* of them. *Num* 16:3
ye are alive *e. one* of you. *Deut* 4:4
hearken, *e. one* of you. *1 Ki* 22:28
eat ye *e. one* of his fig. *2 Ki* 18:31
Lord pardon *e. one.* *2 Chr* 30:18
of *e. one* that willingly. *Ezra* 3:5
were assembled to me *e. one.* 9:4
e. one that is proud. *Job* 40:11
look on *e. one* that is proud. 12
in temple *e. one* doth. *Ps* 29:9
for this shall *e. one* that is. 32:6
e. one that sweareth by him. 63:11
till *e. one* submit himself. 68:30
thy power to *e. one* that is. 71:18
is *e. one* that trusteth. 115:8; 135:18
e. one of thy judgements 119:160
blessed is *e. one* that feareth. 128:1
he saith to *e. one* that. *Eccl* 10:3
e. one beareth twins. *S of S* 4:2; 6:6
honey shall *e. one* eat. *Isa* 7:22
for *e. one* is an hypocrite. 9:17
vultures be gathered, *e. one.* 34:15
even *e. one* that is called by. 43:7
ho, *e. one* that thirsteth. 55:1
e. one that goeth out. *Jer* 5:6
e. one neighed after neighbour's. 8
e. one is given to covetousness. 6:13
derision daily, *e. one* mocketh. 20:7
turn ye now *e. one* from. 25:5
mourning, *e. one* for. *Ezek* 7:16
opened thy feet to *e. one.* 16:25
behold *e. one* were in thee to. 22:6
e. one that be found. *Dan* 12:1
they shall march *e. one.* *Joel* 2:7
e. one that stealeth shall. *Zech* 5:3
e. one that asketh. *Mat* 7:8
Luke 11:10
to me, *e. one* of you. *Mark* 7:14
to *e. one* which hath. *Luke* 19:26
so is *e. one* that is born of. *John* 3:8
e. one that is of truth. 18:37
and be baptized, *e. one* of. *Acts* 2:38
not far from *e. one* of us. 17:27
I ceased not to warn *e. one.* 20:31
e. one give account of. *Rom* 14:12
Lord hath called *e. one.* *1 Cor* 7:17
cursed is *e. one* that. *Gal* 3:10
e. one that nameth the. *2 Tim* 2:19
e. one that loveth is. *1 John* 4:7
white robes given to *e. one.* *Rev* 6:11

every *where*

to our brethren *e. where.* *1 Chr* 13:2
and preached *e. where.* *Mark* 16:20
preaching gospel *e. where.* *Luke* 9:6
Acts 8:4
all men *e. where* to. 17:30
it is *e. where* spoken against. 28:22
as I teach *e. where* in. *1 Cor* 4:17
e. where, and in all. *Phil* 4:12
that men pray *e. where.* *1 Tim* 2:8

evidence

I subscribed the *e.* *Jer* 32:10*
so I took the *e.* 11*
I gave the *e.* to Baruch. 12*
e. both which is sealed, *e.* open. 14*
when I delivered the *e.* of the. 16*
faith is the *e.* of things. *Heb* 11:1*

evidences

take these *e.* *Jer* 32:14*
fields for money subscribe *e.* 44*

evident

it is *e.* to you if I lie. *Job* 6:28*
no man justified by law is *e.* *Gal* 3:11
an *e.* token of perdition. *Phil* 1:28
it is *e.* our Lord sprang. *Heb* 7:14
and it is yet far more *e.* for. 15

evidently

saw in a vision *e.* an. *Acts* 10:3*
Christ hath been *e.* set. *Gal* 3:1*

evil

[1] *Sin, moral evil,* 1 Ki 16:25; Eccl 9:3. [2] *Injurious or mischievous beasts or men,* Gen 37:20. [3] *Calamity,* Pr 22:3; Job 2:10.

The evil eye, according to ancient superstition, was one which could harm by merely looking at a person or his possessions. In the Bible, however, it more generally means the eye of envy, or of grudging benevolence, Pr 23:6; Mat 20:15.

lest some *e.* take me. *Gen* 19:19
ye have done *e.* in so doing. 44:5
lest I see the *e.* that shall come. 34
ye thought *e.* against me. 50:20
he hath done *e.* to people. *Ex* 5:23
look to it, for *e.* is before you. 10:10
the Lord repented of the *e.* 32:14
2 Sam 24:16; *1 Chr* 21:15
commit no more such *e.* *Deut* 19:20
shall separate him to *e.* out. 29:21
set before thee death and *e.* 30:15
and *e.* will befall you in. 31:29
if it seem *e.* to you to. *Josh* 24:15
hand of Lord against them for *e.*
Judg 2:15
e. of the men of Shechem. 9:57
but they knew not that *e.* was. 20:34
that *e.* is determined. *1 Sam* 20:7
if I knew certainly that *e.* were. 9
e. nor transgression in. 24:11
whereas I have rewarded thee *e.* 17
for *e.* is determined against. 25:17
they that seek *e.* to my lord. 26
e. hath not been found in thee. 28
what *e.* is in my hand? 26:18
I have not found *e.* in thee. 29:6
shall reward doer of *e.* *2 Sam* 3:39
I will raise up *e.* against thee. 12:11
will be worse than all the *e.* 19:7
but hast done *e.* above. *1 Ki* 14:9
Omri wrought *e.* in eyes of. 16:25
and the Lord hath spoken *e.* concerning thee. 22:23; *2 Chr* 18:22
I am bringing such *e.* on. *2 Ki* 21:2
eyes shall not see all *e.* on. 22:20
have sinned and done *e.* *1 Chr* 21:17
if when *e.* cometh on us. *2 Chr* 20:9
there was *e.* determined. *Esth* 7:7
how can I endure to see *e.*? 8:6
feared God, eschewed *e.* *Job* 1:1, 8
2:3
in seven there shall no *e.* 5:19
lift up myself when *e.* found. 31:29
comforted him over all the *e.* 42:11
neither *e.* dwell with thee. *Ps* 5:4
if I have rewarded *e.* to him. 7:4
nor doth *e.* to his neighbour. 15:3
they intended *e.* against thee. 21:11
I will fear no *e.* thou art with. 23:4
e. shall slay wicked. 34:21
mischief, he abhorreth not *e.* 36:4
to shame that wish me *e.* 40:14
mine enemies speak *e.* of me. 41:5
should I fear in days of *e.*? 49:5
thou givest thy mouth to *e.* 50:19
reward *e.* unto mine enemies. 54:5
thoughts are against me for *e.* 56:5
years wherein we have seen *e.* 90:15
no *e.* befall thee. 91:10; *Jer* 23:17
that love the Lord, hate *e.* *Ps* 97:10
and of them that speak *e.* 109:20
e. shall hunt violent man to. 140:11
for their feet run to *e.* *Pr* 1:16
Isa 59:7
be quiet from fear of *e.* *Pr* 1:33
devise not *e.* against neighbour. 3:29
I was almost in all *e.* in midst. 5:14
he that pursueth *e.* pursueth. 11:19
heart of them that imagine *e.* 12:20
no *e.* happen to the just. 21
e. pursueth sinners. 13:21
the *e.* bow before the good. 14:19
that devise *e.* 22
even wicked for day of *e.* 16:4
ungodly man diggeth up *e.* fire. 27
moving his lips he bringeth *e.* 30
shall not be visited with *e.* 19:23
king scattereth away all *e.* 20:8
say not thou, I will recompense *e.* 22
soul of wicked desireth *e.* 21:10
prudent man foreseeth *e.* 22:3
27:12
if thou hast thought *e.* lay. 30:32
is vanity, and a great *e.* *Eccl* 2:21
there is a sore *e.* which I. 5:13, 16
an *e.* which I have seen. 6:1; 10:5
this is an *e.* among things...the heart of sons of men is full of *e.* 9:3
knowest not what *e.* shall be. 11:2

for they have rewarded *e.* *Isa* 3:9
punish world for their *e.* 13:11
shutteth eyes from seeing *e.* 33:15
I make peace and create *e.* 45:7
shall *e.* come upon thee. 47:11
keepeth his hand from any *e.* 56:2
is taken away from the *e.* 57:1
out of north *e.* break. *Jer* 1:14; 6:1
e. shall come upon them. 2:3
forth like fire, because of *e.* of.
4:4; 23:2; 26:3; 44:22
neither shall *e.* come upon us. 5:12
children of Judah have done *e.* 7:30
when thou dost *e.* then thou. 11:15
pronounced *e.* against thee for *e.* 17
thee well in time of *e.* 15:11
my hope in the day of *e.* 17:17
bring on them the day of *e.* 18
nation turn from *e.* I will repent of *e.*
18:8; 26:3, 13, 19; 42:10
I frame *e.* against you. 18:11
I will bring all *e.* that I. 19:15
my face against city for *e.* 21:10
e. shall go forth from. 25:32
prophesied of war and of *e.* 28:8
of peace and not of *e.* 29:11
children of Judah have done *e.* 32:20
because of all the *e.* of the. 32
on Judah and Jerusalem all the *e.* I have. 35:17; 36:31
these men have done *e.* in. 38:9
against you for *e.* and cut off. 44:11
and were well, and saw no *e.* 17
I will watch over them for *e.* and. 27
words stand against you for *e.* 29
Heshbon they have devised *e.* 48:2
will render to Babylon all *e.* 51:24
wrote all *e.* that should come. 60
an *e.* an only *e.* behold. *Ezek* 7:5
comforted concerning the *e.* 14:22
hath watched upon *e.* *Dan* 9:14
repenteth him of the *e.* *Joel* 2:13
there be *e.* in a city? *Amos* 3:6
who say, *e.* shall not overtake. 9:10
God repented of *e.* *Jonah* 3:10; 4:2
but *e.* came down from. *Mi* 1:12
woe to them that work *e.* 2:1
this family do I devise *e.* 3
no *e.* can come. 3:11
that imagineth *e.* against. *Nah* 1:11
purer eyes than to behold *e.* *Hab* 1:13
delivered from the power of *e.* 2:9
not see *e.* any more. *Zeph* 3:15
none imagine *e.* *Zech* 7:10; 8:17
and sick, is it not *e.*? *Mal* 1:8
every one that doeth *e.* is. 2:17
shall say all manner of *e.* *Mat* 5:11
more than these, cometh of *e.* 37*
that ye resist not *e.* 39*
sufficient for day is *e.* thereof. 6:34
wherefore think ye *e.* in your? 9:4
what *e.* hath he done? 27:23
Mark 15:14; *Luke* 23:22
lightly speak *e.* of me. *Mark* 9:39
evil man bringeth forth *e.* *Luke* 6:45
every one that doeth *e.* *John* 3:20
they that have done *e.* to. 5:29
e. bear witness of the *e.* 18:23
how much *e.* he hath. *Acts* 9:13
we find no *e.* in this man. 23:9
soul of man that doeth *e.* *Rom* 2:9
the *e.* which I would not. 7:19
abhor that which is *e.* 12:9
recompense to no man *e.* for *e.* 17
not overcome of *e.* overcome *e.* 21
wrath on him doeth *e.* 13:4
is *e.* for that man who eateth. 14:20
simple concerning *e.* 16:19
charity thinketh no *e.* *1 Cor* 13:5
none render *e.* for *e.* to. *1 Thes* 5:1
abstain from all appearance of *e.* 2
money is root of all *e.* *1 Tim* 6:10
in mind to speak *e.* of no. *Tit* 3:
tongue is an unruly *e.* *Jas* 3:
not rendering *e.* for *e.* or. *1 Pet* 3:
he that doeth *e.* hath not. *3 John* 1

evil, *adjective*

thoughts were only *e.* *Gen* 6:5; 8:2
e. beast devoured him. 37:20, 3
did see they were in *e.* case. *Ex* 5:1
people heard these *e.* tidings. 33:
bear this *e.* congregation. *Num* 14:2
bring us in unto this *e.* place. 20:

not one of e. generation. Deut 1:35
bring up an e. name. 22:14, 19
his eye shall be e. toward. 28:54
eye shall be e. toward her. 56
hear of your e. dealings. 1 Sam 2:23
neither adversary nor e. 1 Ki 5:4
that is come on us for e. Ezra 9:13
an e. disease cleaveth. Ps 41:8
encourage themselves in an e. 64:5
trouble by sending e. angels. 78:49
shall not be afraid of e. tidings. 112:7
let not an e. speaker be. 140:11
to keep thee from e. Pr 6:24
riches perish by e. travel. Eccl 5:14
vanity, and it is an e. disease. 6:2
as fishes taken in an e. net. 9:12
have taken e. counsel. Isa 7:5
instruments of churl are e. 32:7
remain of this e. family. Jer 8:3
against all mine e. neighbours. 12:14
this e. people refuse to hear. 13:10
their course is e. their force. 23:10
e. figs, very e. so e. 24:3, 8; 29:17
they have heard e. tidings. 49:23
send on them e. arrows. Ezek 5:16
send on you famine and e. beasts. 17
alas, for e. abominations of. 6:11
I will cause the e. beasts to. 34:25
shalt think an e. thought. 38:10
that coveteth an e. Hab 2:9
his sun to rise on e. Mat 5:45
if ye being e. 7:11; Luke 11:13
not bring forth e. fruit. Mat 7:18
how can ye being e. speak? 12:34
an e. generation seeketh a sign. 39
Luke 11:29
out of heart proceed e. thoughts,
murders. Mat 15:19; Mark 7:21
if that e. servant shall say. Mat 24:48
cast out your name as e. Luke 6:22
kind to unthankful and to the e. 35
for their deeds were e. John 3:19
have found any e. doing. Acts 24:20
e. communications. 1 Cor 15:33
might deliver us from e. Gal 1:4
let e. speaking be put. Eph 4:31
beware of e. workers. Phil 3:2
mortify e. concupiscence. Col 3:5
whereof cometh e. 1 Tim 6:4
the Cretians are e. beasts. Tit 1:12
hearts sprinkled from e. Heb 10:22
become judges of e. Jas 2:4
all such rejoicing is e. 4:16
all malice and e. 1 Pet 2:1
not bear them who are e. Rev 2:2

evil, *adverb*

why so e. entreated? Ex 5:22†
Egyptians e. entreated. Deut 26:6†
because it went e. 1 Chr 7:23
he e. entreateth barren. Job 24:21*
if I have spoken e. John 18:23
entreat them e. 400 years. Acts 7:6
same e. entreated our fathers. 19
their minds e. affected. 14:2
but spake e. of that way. 19:9
shall not speak e. of ruler. 23:5
good be e. spoken of. Rom 14:16
why am I e. spoken of? 1 Cor 10:30
e. one of another, he that speaks e. of
brother, speaks e. of. Jas 4:11
whereas they speak e. 1 Pet 3:16
for well-doing than for e. 17
think it strange, speaking e. 4:4
their part he is e. spoken of. 14
way of truth be e. 2 Pet 2:2
are not afraid to speak e. 10; Jude 8
as natural brute beasts, speak e.
2 Pet 2:12; Jude 10

bring, brought **evil**

shall bring on you all e. Josh 23:15
overtake and bring e. 2 Sam 15:14
that Lord might bring e. 17:14
I will bring e. on house. 1 Ki 14:10
hast thou also brought e. on? 17:20
I will bring e. upon thee. 21:21
not bring e. in his days, but. 29
behold, I will bring e. upon this.
2 Ki 22:16; 2 Chr 34:24
all the e. I will bring. 2 Chr 34:28
I will bring e. and not. Isa 31:2
I will bring e. from north. Jer 4:6
will bring e. upon this people. 6:19
I will bring e. upon them. 11:11
I will bring e. upon men of. Jer 11:23
will bring e. on this place. 19:3, 15
I will bring e. even year of. 23:12
I begin to bring e. on city. 25:29
will bring on Judah e. 35:17; 36:31
bring my words on city for e. 39:16
will bring e. upon all flesh. 45:5
see **did, do**

evil *joined with good*

tree of knowledge of good and e.
Gen 2:9, 17
gods knowing good and e. 3:5, 22
ye rewarded e. for good? 44:4
no knowledge between good and e.
Deut 1:39
requited me e. for good. 1 Sam 25:21
between good and e.? 2 Sam 19:35
not prophesy good concerning me,
but e. 1 Ki 22:8, 18
never good to me, but e. 2 Chr 18:7
not prophesy good to me, but e. 17
receive good, and not e.? Job 2:10
looked for good, then e. came. 30:26
rewarded me e. for good. Ps 35:12
109:5
that render e. for good are. 38:20
lovest e. more than good. 52:3
beholding e. and the good. Pr 15:3
whoso rewardeth e. for good. 17:13
will do him good and not e. 31:12
call e. good, and good e. Isa 5:20
to refuse e. choose good. 7:15, 16
e. be recompensed for good?
Jer 18:20
whether it be good or e. we. 42:6
proceedeth not e. and good.
Lam 3:38
seek good and not e. Amos 5:14
eyes on them for e. not for good. 9:4
who hate good, and love e. Mi 3:2
when I would do good, e. present.
Rom 7:21
neither having done good or e. 9:11
to discern good and e. Heb 5:14
is e. but what is good. 3 John 11
see **great**

from **evil**

redeemed me from all e. Gen 48:16
kept his servant from e. 1 Sam 25:39
wouldest keep me from e. 1 Chr 4:10
and to depart from e. is. Job 28:28
keep thy tongue from e. Ps 34:13
depart from e. 14; 37:27; Pr 3:7
preserve thee from all e. 121:7
remove thy foot from e. Pr 4:27
to fools to depart from e. 13:19
and departeth from e. 14:16
of Lord men depart from e. 16:6
of upright is to depart from e. 17
that departeth from e. Isa 59:15
they proceed from e. to evil. Jer 9:3
have turned them from their e. way,
and from the e. of. 23:22
Babylon not rise from e. 51:64
deliver us from e. Mat 6:13*
Luke 11:14
keep them from e. John 17:15*
stablish you, keep you from e.
2 Thes 3:3*
refrain his tongue from e. 1 Pet 3:10

put away **evil**

put the e. away from. Deut 13:5
so thou shalt put the e. away. 17:7
19:19; 21:21; 22:21, 24; 24:7
put ye away e. from Israel. 17:12
22:21; Judg 20:13
put away e. from flesh. Eccl 11:10
put away e. of your doings. Isa 1:16

evil *in the sight of the Lord*

had done e. in the sight of the Lord.
Num 32:13; Judg 3:12
Israel did e. in the sight of the Lord.
Judg 2:11; 3:7, 12; 4:1; 6:1
10:6; 13:1; 1 Ki 11:6; 14:22
15:26, 34; 16:7, 30; 22:52
2 Ki 8:18, 27; 13:2, 11; 14:24
15:9, 18, 24, 28; 17:2; 21:2, 20
2 Chr 22:4; 33:2, 22; 36:5, 9, 12
thou didst e. in the sight of the Lord.
1 Sam 15:19
in doing e. in the sight of the Lord.
1 Ki 16:19
sold to work e. in the sight of the
Lord. 1 Ki 21:20
he wrought e. in the sight of the
Lord. 2 Ki 3:2
sold themselves to do e. in the sight
of the Lord. 17:17
to sin, doing e. in the sight of the
Lord. 21:16; 23:32, 37; 24:9, 19
Er was e. in the sight of the Lord.
1 Chr 2:3
wrought much e. in the sight of Lord.
2 Chr 33:6

this **evil**

and repent of this e. Ex 32:12
done us this great e. 1 Sam 6:9
we have added this e. to. 12:19
this e. in sending. 2 Sam 13:16*
brought on them all this e. 1 Ki 9:9
this e. is of the Lord. 2 Ki 6:33
therefore he brought this e. on them.
2 Chr 7:22
God bring all this e. on? Neh 13:18
to you to do all this great e.? 27
friends heard of this e. Job 2:11
done this e. in thy sight. Ps 51:4
pronounced all this e. Jer 16:10
hast caused all this e. on. 32:23
like as I have brought all this e. 42
God hath pronounced this e. 40:2
why commit ye this great e.? 44:7
therefore this e. is happened. 23
it is written, all this e. is. Dan 9:13
for whose cause this e. Jonah 1:7, 8

evil *day* or *days*

few and e. have the days. Gen 47:9
days of the afflicted are e. Pr 15:15
while the e. days come not. Eccl 12:1
put far away the e. day. Amos 6:3
because days are e. Eph 5:16
be able to withstand in e. day. 6:13
day of **evil**, *see* **evil**, *substantive*

evil *doer*, or *doers*

neither help the e. doers. Job 8:20
hated the congregation of e. doers.
Ps 26:5
fret not because of e. doers. 37:1
e. doers shall be cut off. 9
up for me against e. doers? 94:16
depart from me, ye e. doers. 119:115
nation, a seed of e. doers. Isa 1:4
an hypocrite, an e. doer. 9:17
the seed of e. doers shall. 14:20
arise against house of e. doers. 31:2
soul of poor from e. doers. Jer 20:13
strengthen hands of e. doers. 23:14
trouble as an e. doer. 2 Tim 2:9*
against you as e. doers. 1 Pet 2:12
for the punishment of e. doers. 14
evil of you as of e. doers. 3:16
suffer as thief or an e. doer. 4:15
see **doings, eye**

evil *heart*

of man's heart is e. Gen 8:21
the imagination of e. heart. Jer 3:17
walked in imagination of e. heart.
7:24
every one in imagination of his e.
heart. 11:8
every one after his e. heart. 16:12
do imagination of his e. heart. 18:12
be in any an e. heart. Heb 3:12

evil *man* or *men*

of pride of e. men. Job 35:12
arm of the e. man. Ps 10:15
deliver me from the e. man. 140:1
from way of the e. man. Pr 2:12
go not in the way of e. men. 4:14
wicked desireth net of e. men. 12:12
e. man seeketh only rebellion. 17:11
not envious against e. men. 24:1
fret not because of e. men. 19
be no reward to the e. man. 20
e. men understand not. 28:5
in transgression of an e. man. 29:6
e. man out of the evil treasure.
Mat 12:35; Luke 6:45
e. men shall wax worse. 2 Tim 3:13
see **report**

evil *spirit* or *spirits*

e. sp. between Abimelech. Judg 9:23
an e. sp. from Lord. 1 Sam 16:14, 15
when e. sp. from God is upon. 16

and the *e. sp.* departed from. *1 Sam* 16:23
e. sp. from God came. 18:10; 19:9
cured many of *e. sp.* *Luke* 7:21
a woman healed of *e. sp.* 8:2
and the *e. sp.* went out. *Acts* 19:12
over them which had *e. sp.* 13
e. sp. said, Jesus I know. 15
man in whom the *e. sp.* was. 16

evil *thing*
what *e. thing* is this ? *Neh* 13:17
not heart to any *e. thing.* *Ps* 141:4
stand not in an *e. thing.* *Eccl* 8:3
shall feel no *e. thing.* 5
thing, whether good or *e.* 12:14
know that it is an *e. thing.* *Jer* 2:19
having no *e. thing* to say. *Tit* 2:8

evil *things*
bring on you *e. things.* *Josh* 23:15
poureth out *e. things.* *Pr* 15:28
hast done *e. things.* *Jer* 3:5
man bringeth *e. things.* *Mat* 12:35
all these *e. things* come. *Mark* 7:23
Lazarus *e. things.* *Luke* 16:25
inventors of *e. things.* *Rom* 1:30
not lust after *e. things.* *1 Cor* 10:6

evil *time*
be ashamed in *e. time.* *Ps* 37:19
men snared in an *e. time.* *Eccl* 9:12
for it is an *e. time.* *Amos* 5:13
haughtily, for *time* is *e.* *Mi* 2:3

evil *way*
returned not from *e. way.* *1 Ki* 13:33
feet from every *e. way.* *Ps* 119:101
fear of Lord to hate *e. way.* *Pr* 8:13
to go astray in *e. way.* 28:10
every one from his *e. way.* *Jer* 18:11
25:5; 26:3; 35:15; 36:3, 7
turned them from *e. way.* 23:22
every one from *e. way.* *Jonah* 3:8
they turned from *e. way.* 10

evil *ways*
turn from your *e. ways.* *2 Ki* 17:13
Ezek 33:11
your own *e. ways.* *Ezek* 36:31
now from your *e. ways.* *Zech* 1:4

evil *work* or *works*
not seen *e. work* that is. *Eccl* 4:3
sentence against an *e. work* is. 8:11
the *works* thereof are *e.* *John* 7:7
terror to good *works* but *e.* *Rom* 13:3
me from every *e. work.* *2 Tim* 4:18
and every *e. work.* *Jas* 3:16
his own *works* were *e.* *1 John* 3:12

Evil-merodach
E. king of Babylon did lift up the.
2 Ki 25:27; *Jer* 52:31

evils
e. and troubles befall them, they say, are not these *e.*? *Deut* 31:17
for all the *e.* which they have. 18
when many *e.* and troubles are. 21
innumerable *e.* compassed. *Ps* 40:12
people committed two *e.* *Jer* 2:13
lothe themselves for *e.* *Ezek* 6:9
lothe yourselves for all your *e.* 20:43
all the *e.* which Herod. *Luke* 3:19

ewe *or* **ewes**
Abraham set seven *e.* *Gen* 21:28
mean these seven *e.* lambs ? 29
e. and she goats have not. 31:38
two hundred *e.* and twenty. 32:14
take one *e.* lamb of. *Lev* 14:10
whether cow or *e.* ye. 22:28
save one *e.* lamb. *2 Sam* 12:3
him from following the *e.* *Ps* 78:71

exact
not *e.* it of neighbour. *Deut* 15:2
of a foreigner thou mayest *e.* 3
you *e.* usury every one of. *Neh* 5:7
I likewise might *e.* of them. 10*
hundredth part of money ye *e.* 11
enemy shall not *e.* upon. *Ps* 89:22
in your fasts ye *e.* all. *Isa* 58:3
e. no more than what. *Luke* 3:13*

exacted
Menahem *e.* the money. *2 Ki* 15:20
Jehoiakim *e.* the silver and. 23:35

exacteth
e. of thee less than. *Job* 11:6

exaction
we should leave the *e.* *Neh* 10:31

exactions
take away your *e.* *Ezek* 45:9

exactors
will also make thine *e.* *Isa* 60:17

exalt
my father's God, I will *e.* *Ex* 15:2
he shall *e.* the horn of. *1 Sam* 2:10
shalt thou not *e.* them. *Job* 17:4
and let us *e.* his name. *Ps* 34:3
he shall *e.* thee to inherit. 37:34
let not rebellious *e.* themselves. 66:7
but my horn shalt thou *e.* 92:10
e. ye the Lord our God. 99:5, 9
let them *e.* him in the. 107:32
my God, I will *e.* thee. 118:28
lest wicked *e.* themselves. 140:8
e. her, and she shall. *Pr* 4:8
e. the voice unto them. *Isa* 13:2
I will *e.* my throne above. 14:13
thou art my God, I will *e.* 25:1
e. him that is low. *Ezek* 21:26
nor shall it *e.* itself any. 29:15
that none of the trees *e.* 31:14
robbers of people shall *e.* *Dan* 11:14
the king shall *e.* himself. 36
none at all would *e.* him. *Hos* 11:7
though thou *e.* thyself as. *Ob* 4*
whoso shall *e.* himself. *Mat* 23:12
if a man *e.* himself. *2 Cor* 11:20
that he may *e.* in due. *1 Pet* 5:6

exalted
his kingdom shall be *e.* *Num* 24:7
mine horn is *e.* in Lord. *1 Sam* 2:1
Lord had *e.* his kingdom. *2 Sam* 5:12
e. be the God of the rock of my.
22:47; *Ps* 18:46
then Adonijah *e.* himself. *1 Ki* 1:5
I *e.* thee from people. 14:7; 16:2
against whom hast thou *e.* thy voice ?
2 Ki 19:22; *Isa* 37:23
and thou art *e.* as. *1 Chr* 29:11
is *e.* above all blessings. *Neh* 9:5
who mourn may be *e.* *Job* 5:11
they are *e.* for a little while. 24:24
them for ever, they are *e.* 36:7
walk when vilest men are *e.* *Ps* 12:8
long shall my enemy be *e.*? 13:2
be thou *e.* Lord, in thine. 21:13
I will be *e.* among the heathen, I will be *e.* in the earth. 46:10
he is greatly *e.* 47:9
be thou *e.* O God, above. 57:5, 11
horns of righteous shall be *e.* 75:10
righteousness shall they be *e.* 89:16
in thy favour our horn shall be *e.* 17
I have *e.* one chosen out. 19
in my name shall his horn be *e.* 24
thou, Lord, art *e.* far above. 97:9
be thou *e.* O God, above. 108:5
horn shall be *e.* with honour. 112:9
right hand of the Lord is *e.* 118:16
of the upright city is *e.* *Pr* 11:11
mountain of Lord's house shall be *e.*
Isa 2:2; *Mi* 4:1
be *e.* in that day. *Isa* 2:11, 17; 5:16
mention that his name is *e.* 12:4
will be *e.* that he may have. 30:18
the Lord is *e.* 33:5
now will I be *e.* 10
every valley shall be *e.* 40:4
my highways shall be *e.* 49:11
behold my servant shall be *e.* 52:13
Lord have *e.* the low. *Ezek* 17:24
and her stature was *e.* 19:11; 31:5
he *e.* himself in Israel. *Hos* 13:1
and their heart was *e.* 6
Capernaum *e.* to heaven. *Mat* 11:23
Luke 10:15
e. himself abased, humble himself *e.*
Mat 23:12; *Luke* 14:11; 18:14
e. them of low degree. *Luke* 1:52
right hand of God *e.* *Acts* 2:33
hath God *e.* with his right. 5:31
God of Israel *e.* people. 13:17
that you might be *e.* *2 Cor* 11:7
lest I should be *e.* 12:7
God hath highly *e.* him. *Phil* 2:9
brother rejoice that he is *e.* *Jas* 1:9

exaltest
as yet *e.* thou thyself. *Ex* 9:17

exalteth
God *e.* by his power. *Job* 36:22*
he *e.* horn of his people. *Ps* 148:14
hasty of spirit *e.* folly. *Pr* 14:29
righteousness *e.* a nation. 34
he that *e.* his gate seeketh. 17:19
he that *e.* himself shall. *Luke* 14:11
18:14
every thing that *e.* itself. *2 Cor* 10:5
who *e.* himself above all. *2 Thes* 2:4

examination
that, after *e.* had, I. *Acts* 25:26

examine
sat down to *e.* matter. *Ezra* 10:16
e. me, O Lord, prove me. *Ps* 26:2
answer to them that *e.* *1 Cor* 9:3
let a man *e.* himself. 11:28
e. yourselves, prove. *2 Cor* 13:5

examined
I have *e.* him before you. *Luke* 23:14
if we this day be *e.* of. *Acts* 4:9
Herod *e.* keepers. 12:19
brought, that he should be *e.* 22:24
who should have *e.* him. 29
when they had *e.* me would. 28:18

examining
by *e.* of whom thou. *Acts* 24:8

example
not make her a publick *e.* *Mat* 1:19
have given you an *e.* *John* 13:15
but be thou an *e.* of. *1 Tim* 4:12
man fall after same *e.* *Heb* 4:11
serve unto the *e.* of heavenly. 8:5
take prophets for an *e.* *Jas* 5:10
for us, leaving us an *e.* *1 Pet* 2:21
set forth for an *e.*, suffering. *Jude* 7

examples
these things were our *e.* *1 Cor* 10:6
see **ensample, -s**

exceed
not *e.*: lest, if he should *e.*, thy brother seem vile to thee. *Deut* 25:3
except righteousness *e.* *Mat* 5:20
of righteousness doth *e.* *2 Cor* 3:9

exceeded
wept, till David *e.* *1 Sam* 20:41
Solomon *e.* all kings of. *1 Ki* 10:23
transgressions that they *e.* *Job* 36:9*

exceedest
thou *e.* the fame that I. *2 Chr* 9:6

exceedeth
thy wisdom *e.* the fame. *1 Ki* 10:7

exceeding
and thy *e.* great reward. *Gen* 15:1
I will make thee *e.* fruitful. 17:6
Esau cried with an *e.* bitter. 27:34
Israel waxed *e.* mighty. *Ex* 1:7
voice of trumpet *e.* loud. 19:16
land we passed through *e.* *Num* 14:7
talk no more so *e.* *1 Sam* 2:3
David took *e.* much brass.
2 Sam 8:8
rich man had *e.* many flocks. 12:2
gave Solomon wisdom *e.* *1 Ki* 4:29
vessels unweighed, were *e.* 7:47
he brought *e.* much spoil. *1 Chr* 20:2
house must be *e.* magnifical. 22:5
made cities *e.* strong. *2 Chr* 11:12
there was *e.* much spoil. 14:14
until his disease waxed *e.* 16:12
Hezekiah had *e.* much riches. 32:27
thou hast made him *e.* *Ps* 21:6
I go unto God, my *e.* joy. 43:4
thy commandment is *e.* 119:96
four things which are *e.* *Pr* 30:24
that which is *e.* deep. *Eccl* 7:24
pride of Moab, he is *e.* *Jer* 48:29
iniquity of Israel *e.* great. *Ezek* 9:9
didst eat oil, and wast *e.* 16:13
e. in dyed attire upon heads. 23:15
upon feet an *e.* great army. 37:1
fish of the great sea, *e.* many. 47:1
the furnace was *e.* hot. *Dan* 3:2
then was the king *e.* glad. 6:2
fourth beast *e.* dreadful. 7:1
a little horn, which waxed *e.* 8:
Nineveh was an *e.* great. *Jonah* 3:
so Jonah was *e.* glad of 4:
they rejoiced with *e.* great. *Mat* 2:1
Herod was *e.* wroth.
taketh him up into *e.* high. 4:

rejoice and be *e.* glad. *Mat* 5:12
two possessed with devils, *e.* 8:28
kill him; they were *e.* sorry. 17:23
they were *e.* sorrowful. 26:22
soul *e.* sorrowful. 38; *Mark* 14:34
the king was *e.* sorry. *Mark* 6:26
raiment became *e.* white as. 9:3
Herod saw Jesus, was *e.* *Luke* 23:8
Moses born, and was *e.* *Acts* 7:20
that sin become *e.* sinful. *Rom* 7:13
worketh for us an *e.* *2 Cor* 4:17
I am *e.* joyful in all our. 7:4
who long after you, for *e.* 9:14
what is the *e.* greatness. *Eph* 1:19
might shew the *e.* riches of. 2:7
able to do *e.* abundantly. 3:20
grace of our Lord *e.* *1 Tim* 1:14
be glad also with *e.* joy. *1 Pet* 4:13
given to us *e.* great and *2 Pet* 1:4
faultless with *e.* joy. *Jude* 24
plague thereof was *e.* *Rev* 16:21

exceedingly

the waters prevailed *e.* *Gen* 7:19
men of Sodom were sinners *e.* 13:13
I will multiply thy seed *e.* 16:10
covenant and multiply thee *e.* 17:2
I will multiply Ishmael *e.* 20
Isaac trembled very *e.* and. 27:33
Jacob increased *e.* 30:43; 47:27
the fool and erred *e.* *1 Sam* 26:21
Amnon hated her *e.* *2 Sam* 13:15
the elders were *e.* afraid. *2 Ki* 10:4
magnified Solomon *e.* *1 Chr* 29:25
2 Chr 1:1
Jehoshaphat great *e.* *2 Chr* 17:12
Uzziah strengthened himself *e.* 26:8
heard, it grieved them *e.* *Neh* 2:10
queen was *e.* grieved. *Esth* 4:4
rejoice *e.* when they can. *Job* 3:22
let the righteous *e.* rejoice. *Ps* 68:3
lusted *e.* in the wilderness. 106:14
testimonies, I love them *e.* 119:167
for we are *e.* filled with. 123:3, 4
earth is moved *e.* *Isa* 24:19
a fourth beast strong *e.* *Dan* 7:7
men were *e.* afraid. *Jonah* 1:10
then men feared the Lord *e.* 16
but it displeased Jonah *e.* 4:1
they were *e.* amazed. *Mat* 19:25
they feared *e.* and. *Mark* 4:41
cried out the more *e.* crucify. 15:14
these men do *e.* trouble. *Acts* 16:20
being *e.* mad against them. 26:11
and we being *e.* tossed. 27:18
and *e.* the more joyed. *2 Cor* 7:13
being more *e.* zealous of. *Gal* 1:14
night and day praying *e.* *1 Thes* 3:10
your faith groweth *e.* *2 Thes* 1:3
I *e.* fear and quake. *Heb* 12:21

excel

thou shalt not *e.* *Gen* 49:4*
on the Sheminith to *e.* *1 Chr* 15:21*
angels, that *e.* in. *Ps* 103:20*
graven images did *e.* *Isa* 10:10
seek that ye may *e.* *1 Cor* 14:12*

excelled

Solomon's wisdom *e.* *1 Ki* 4:30

excellency

the *e.* of dignity, and *e.* *Gen* 49:3†
in the greatness of thine *e.* *Ex* 15:7
who rideth in his *e.* *Deut* 33:26
who is the sword of thy *e.* 29
doth not their *e.* go? *Job* 4:21*
his *e.* make you afraid? 13:11
though his *e.* mount up. 20:6
thundereth with voice of his *e.* 37:4
thyself with majesty and *e.* 40:10
the *e.* of Jacob. *Ps* 47:4†
to cast him down from his *e.* 62:4†
his *e.* is over Israel. 68:34
the *e.* of knowledge is. *Eccl* 7:12
beauty of Chaldees' *e.* *Isa* 13:19*
e. of Carmel, Sharon; the *e.* 35:2
make thee an eternal *e.* 60:15
my sanctuary, the *e.* *Ezek* 24:21*
abhor the *e.* of Jacob. *Amos* 6:8
Lord hath sworn by *e.* of Jacob. 8:7
Lord hath turned away *e.* of Jacob, as the *e.* of Israel. *Nah* 2:2
not with *e.* of speech. *1 Cor* 2:1
e. of the power be of. *2 Cor* 4:7*
all things loss for the *e.* *Phil* 3:8

excellent

Ahasuerus shewed *e.* *Esth* 1:4
Almighty is *e.* in power. *Job* 37:23
how *e.* is thy name in! *Ps* 8:1, 9
and to the *e.* in whom is all. 16:3
e. is thy lovingkindness! 36:7*
thou art more *e.* than the. 76:4
me, it shall be an *e.* oil. 141:5*
his name alone is *e.* 148:13*
according to *e.* greatness. 150:2
for I will speak of *e.* things. *Pr* 8:6
righteous is more *e.* than. 12:26*
e. speech becometh not a fool. 17:7
man of understanding is of an *e.* 27*
written to thee *e.* things? 22:20
his countenance *e.* as. *S of S* 5:15
fruit of earth shall be *e.* *Isa* 4:2
sing to Lord, he hath done *e.* 12:5
the Lord of hosts is *e.* in. 28:29
come to *e.* ornaments. *Ezek* 16:7
whose brightness was *e.* *Dan* 2:31
an *e.* majesty was added. 4:36
e. spirit found in Daniel. 5:12; 6:3
I heard that *e.* wisdom is. 5:14
to thee, *e.* Theophilus. *Luke* 1:3
to *e.* governor Felix. *Acts* 23:26
approvest things more *e.* *Rom* 2:18
Phil 1:10
shew you a more *e.* way. *1 Cor* 12:31
obtained a more *e.* name. *Heb* 1:4
he obtained a more *e.* ministry. 8:6
Abel offered more *e.* sacrifice. 11:4
a voice from the *e.* *2 Pet* 1:17†

excellest

virtuously, but thou *e.* all. *Pr* 21:29

excelleth

wisdom *e.* folly, as light *e.* *Eccl* 2:13
by reason of glory that *e.* *2 Cor* 3:10

except

e. the God of my father. *Gen* 31:42
not let thee go, *e.* thou bless. 32:26
e. youngest brother. 42:15; 43:3, 5
e. we had lingered, we. 43:10
e. the land of the priests only. 47:26
e. thou make thyself a. *Num* 16:13
e. their Rock had. *Deut* 32:30
e. you destroy accursed. *Josh* 7:12
e. thou hadst hasted. *1 Sam* 25:34
e. as the Lord hath. *2 Sam* 3:9
e. thou first bring Michal. 13
e. thou take away the blind. 5:6
slack not thy riding, *e.* I. *2 Ki* 4:24
e. the king delighted in. *Esth* 2:14
e. king hold out golden. 4:11
e. Lord build the house, *e.* Lord keep the city, the watchman. *Ps* 127:1
sleep not, *e.* they have. *Pr* 4:16
e. the Lord had left a. *Isa* 1:9
Rom 9:29
none other can shew it, *e.* *Dan* 2:11
nor worship any god, *e.* their. 3:28
e. we find it concerning the law. 6:5
two walk together, *e.*? *Amos* 3:3
e. your righteousness. *Mat* 5:20
e. he first bind the strong man. 12:29; *Mark* 3:27
e. ye be converted. *Mat* 18:3
put away his wife, *e.* for. 19:9
e. those days be shortened should no flesh be saved. 24:22; *Mark* 13:20
cup may not pass, *e.* I drink. *Mat* 26:42
Pharisees, *e.* they wash. *Mark* 7:3
e. we go and buy meat. *Luke* 9:13
e. ye repent, ye shall all. 13:3, 5
these miracles, *e.* God. *John* 3:2
e. a man be born again, he cannot. 3
e. a man be born of water and. 5
nothing, *e.* it be given from. 27
e. ye see signs and wonders. 4:48
e. the Father who hath sent. 6:44
e. ye eat the flesh of the Son. 53
e. it were given unto him of. 65
e. a corn of wheat fall. 12:24
cannot bear fruit, *e.* ye abide. 15:4
no power, *e.* it were given. 19:11
e. I shall see the prints of. 20:25
all scattered, *e.* apostles. *Acts* 8:1
how can I, *e.* some man? 31
e. ye be circumcised, ye. 15:1
e. it be for this one voice. 24:21
such as I am, *e.* these bonds. 26:29
e. these abide in ship, ye. 27:31
not known lust, *e.* the law. *Rom* 7:7
preach, *e.* they be sent? 10:15
not one another *e.* it. *1 Cor* 7:5
speaketh with tongues, *e.* he. 14:5
e. I shall speak to you either. 6
e. they give a distinction in the. 7
e. ye utter words easy to be. 9
sowest is not quickened, *e.* 15:36
e. it be that I was not. *2 Cor* 12:13
Christ is in you, *e.* ye be? 13:5
e. there come a falling. *2 Thes* 2:3
he is not crowned, *e.* *2 Tim* 2:5
remove thy candlestick, *e.* *Rev* 2:5
e. they repent their deeds. 22

excepted

he is *e.* who did put all. *1 Cor* 15:27

excess

full of extortion and *e.* *Mat* 23:25
with wine, wherein is *e.* *Eph* 5:18*
walked in lusts, *e.* of. *1 Pet* 4:3
run not with them to same *e.* 4

exchange

bread in *e.* for horses. *Gen* 47:17
then it and the *e.* thereof. *Lev* 27:10
and the *e.* of it shall not. *Job* 28:17
what shall a man give in *e.* for his soul? *Mat* 16:26; *Mark* 8:37

exchange

not sell of it, nor *e.* *Ezek* 48:14

exchangers

to put my money to *e.* *Mat* 25:27

exclude

they would *e.* you, that. *Gal* 4:17

excluded

is boasting? it is *e.* *Rom* 3:27

excommunicated

Excommunication is an ecclesiastical censure, whereby the person against whom it is pronounced is, for the time, cast out of the communion of the church.

The word is not used in the Bible, but the act is referred to in various ways, all easily recognizable. An example in the Jewish church is in John 9:34.

excuse

began to make *e.* *Luke* 14:18
that they are without *e.* *Rom* 1:20

excuse

that we *e.* ourselves? *2 Cor* 12:19

excused

pray thee have me *e.* *Luke* 14:18, 19

excusing

thoughts accusing or else *e.* *Rom* 2:15

execration

and ye shall be an *e.* *Jer* 42:18
they shall be an *e.* and a. 44:12

execute

e. judgement on gods of. *Ex* 12:12
the priest shall *e.* upon. *Num* 5:30
that they may *e.* the service. 8:11
doth *e.* the judgement of. *Deut* 10:18
if thou *e.* my judgements. *1 Ki* 6:12
when wilt thou *e.*? *Ps* 119:84
to *e.* vengeance upon. 149:7
to *e.* upon them the judgement. 9
take counsel, *e.* judgement. *Isa* 16:3
e. judgement between man. *Jer* 7:5
e. judgement in the morning. 21:12
e. judgement and. 22:3
branch *e.* judgement. 23:5; 33:15
I will *e.* judgements. *Ezek* 5:8, 10
when I shall *e.* judgements in. 15
will *e.* judgements among you. 11:9
they shall *e.* judgements. 16:41
and I will *e.* judgements. 25:11
and I will *e.* great vengeance. 17
fire in Zoan, *e.* judgements. 30:14
thus *e.* judgements in Egypt. 19
remove violence, *e.* judgement. 45:9
not *e.* fierceness of mine. *Hos* 11:9
and I will *e.* vengeance. *Mi* 5:15
plead my cause, *e.* judgement. 7:9
e. true judgement and. *Zech* 7:9
e. the judgement of truth and. 8:16
authority to *e.* judgement. *John* 5:27
minister of God to *e.* *Rom* 13:4
to *e.* judgement on all. *Jude* 15

executed
on their gods Lord e. Num 33:4
he e. justice of Lord. Deut 33:21
David e. judgement. 2 Sam 8:15
1 Chr 18:14
that e. priest's office. 1 Chr 6:10
Eleazar and Ithamar e. the. 24:2
they e. judgement. 2 Chr 24:24
judgement be e. speedily. Ezra 7:26
Phinehas, e. judgement. Ps 106:30
sentence is not e. Eccl 8:11
not return till he have e. Jer 23:20
neither e. judgements. Ezek 11:12
20:24
hath e. true judgement. 18:8, 17
for they had e. judgement. 23:10
shall have e. judgements. 28:22, 26
heathen see judgement I have e.
39:21
Zacharias e. priest's office. Luke 1:8

executedst
nor e. his fierce wrath. 1 Sam 28:18

executest
thou e. judgement and. Ps 99:4

executeth
known by judgement he e. Ps 9:16
the Lord e. righteousness. 103:6
the Lord e. judgement for. 146:7
man that e. my counsel. Isa 46:11
if any e. judgement. Jer 5:1
is strong that e. his word. Joel 2:11

executing
thou hast done well in e. 2 Ki 10:30
cast them off from e. 2 Chr 11:14
when Jehu was e. judgement. 22:8

execution
drew near to be put in e. Esth 9:1

executioner
king sent an e. and. Mark 6:27*

exempted
proclamation, none was e. 1 Ki 15:22

exercise
bodily e. profiteth little. 1 Tim 4:8

exercise
nor do I e. myself. Ps 131:1
Lord which e. loving. Jer 9:24
Gentiles e. dominion over them, and
they that are great e. Mat 20:25*
Mark 10:42*; Luke 22:25*
herein do I e. myself. Acts 24:16
and e. thyself rather. 1 Tim 4:7

exercised
be e. therewith. Eccl 1:13; 3:10
of land have e. robbery. Ezek 22:29
senses e. to discern. Heb 5:14
to them which are e. thereby. 12:11
an heart e. with. 2 Pet 2:14

exerciseth
he e. all the power of. Rev 13:12

exhort
did he testify and e. Acts 2:40
and now I e. you to be of. 27:22
it necessary to e. 2 Cor 9:5*
beseech you and e. you. 1 Thes 4:1
now we e. you, warn them. 5:14
we command and e. 2 Thes 3:12
I e. that first of all. 1 Tim 2:1
these things teach and e. 6:2
e. with all long suffering. 2 Tim 4:2
may be able to e. and. Tit 1:9
young men likewise e. to be. 2:6
e. servants to be obedient to. 9
speak, e. rebuke with authority. 15
e. one another daily. Heb 3:13
elders among you, I e. 1 Pet 5:1
for me to write and e. Jude 3

exhortation
other things in his e. Luke 3:18
have any word of e. say. Acts 13:15
when Paul had given them e. 20:2
let him wait on e. Rom 12:8
speaketh unto men to e. 1 Cor 14:3*
he accepted the e. 2 Cor 8:17
for our e. was not of. 1 Thes 2:3
give attendance to e. 1 Tim 4:13
ye have forgotten the e. Heb 12:5
suffer the word of e. 13:22

exhorted
Barnabas e. them to. Acts 11:23
they e. the brethren with. Acts 15:32
as you know how we e. 1 Thes 2:11

exhorting
e. them to continue in. Acts 14:22
wrote, e. disciples to. 18:27*
but e. one another, and. Heb 10:25
I have written briefly, e. 1 Pet 5:12

exile
stranger and also an e. 2 Sam 15:19
the captive e. hasteneth. Isa 51:14

exorcists
(This word comes from the Greek exorkizein, and means one who drives off an evil spirit by adjuration)
of vagabond Jews, e. Acts 19:13

expectation
the e. of the poor shall. Ps 9:18
wait thou on God, for my e. 62:5
e. of wicked shall. Pr 10:28; 11:7
but the e. of the wicked is. 11:23
e. not be cut off. 23:18*; 24:14*
be ashamed of their e. Isa 20:5
behold, such is our e. 6
Ekron; for her e. shall. Zech 9:5
people were in e., John. Luke 3:15
delivered me from e. of. Acts 12:11
for the e. of creature. Rom 8:19
to my earnest e. and. Phil 1:20

expected
to give you an e. end. Jer 29:11*

expecting
e. to receive something. Acts 3:5
e. till his enemies be. Heb 10:13

expedient
that it is e. for us. John 11:50
I tell you, it is e. for you that. 16:7
it was e. that one man die. 18:14
all things not e. 1 Cor 6:12; 10:23
this is e. for you who. 2 Cor 8:10
not e. for me doubtless to. 12:1

expel
God shall e. them. Josh 23:5*
did not ye hate me, e.? Judg 11:7*

expelled
Israel e. not Geshurites. Josh 13:13*
e. thence sons of Anak. Judg 1:20*
his banished be not e. 2 Sam 14:14*
they e. them out of. Acts 13:50*

expences
e. be given out of king's. Ezra 6:4
decree that e. forthwith be given. 8

experience
by e. the Lord hath. Gen 30:27*
my heart had great e. Eccl 1:16
worketh e. and e. hope. Rom 5:4*

experiment
whiles by the e. of. 2 Cor 9:13

expert
of Zebulun fifty thousand e. in war.
1 Chr 12:33*
of Danites 28,600. e. 35*
of Asher 40,000 e. 36*
swords, being e. in war. S of S 3:8
arrows as of an e. man. Jer 50:9
I know thee to be e. in. Acts 26:3

expired
the days were not e. 1 Sam 18:26
after the year was e. 2 Sam 11:1*
1 Chr 20:1*
come to pass days be e. 1 Chr 17:11*
when year e. Nebuchadnezzar sent.
2 Chr 36:10*
when these days were e. Esth 1:5*
when these days are e. Ezek 43:27*
when forty years were e. Acts 7:30*
when 1000 years are e. Rev 20:7*

exploits
his land he shall do e. Dan 11:28*
people shall be strong and do e. 32

expound
not in three days e. Judg 14:14*

expounded
garments to them who e. the riddle.
Judg 14:19*
alone, he e. all things. Mark 4:34
he e. to them in all. Luke 24:27*
but Peter e. it by order. Acts 11:4
Aquila and Priscilla e. Acts 18:26
Paul e. and testified the. 28:23

express
being the e. image of. Heb 1:3*

expressed
men which are e. by. Num 1:17
of Manasseh 18,000, e. 1 Chr 12:31
who were e. by name. 16:41
men e. took captives. 2 Chr 28:15
men e. to give portions to. 31:19
Nethinims were e. by. Ezra 8:20

expressly
if I e. say to the lad. 1 Sam 20:21
the word came e. to. Ezek 1:3
the Spirit speaketh e. 1 Tim 4:1

extend
none to e. mercy to him. Ps 109:12
behold, I will e. peace. Isa 66:12

extended
e. mercy to me. Ezra 7:28
e. mercy to us. 9:9

extendeth
my goodness e. not to. Ps 16:2*

extinct
my days are e. the graves. Job 17:1
they are e. are quenched. Isa 43:17

extol
I will e. thee, O Lord. Ps 30:1
e. him that rideth upon. 68:4*
I will e. thee, my God. 145:1
Nebuchadnezzar e. King. Dan 4:37

extolled
and he was e. with. Ps 66:17
my servant shall be e. Isa 52:13*

extortion
greedily gained by e. Ezek 22:12*
they are full of e. Mat 23:25

extortioner
let the e. catch all. Ps 109:11
the e. is at an end. Isa 16:4
any man be drunkard, e. 1 Cor 5:11

extortioners
not as other men are, e. Luke 18:11
not altogether with e. 1 Cor 5:10
nor e. inherit kingdom of God. 6:10

extreme
shall smite thee with e. Deut 28:22*

extremity
knoweth it not in great e. Job 35:15*

eye
This is used [1] *literally, in man places.* [2] *Figuratively, for discernment, judgement, that b which the mind apprehends.*
e. for e. Ex 21:24; Lev 24:2
Deut 19:21; Mat 5:3
man smite e. of servant, or e.
Ex 21:2
hath a blemish in his e. Lev 21:2
his e. shall be evil. Deut 28:54
her e. shall be evil towards. 5
he kept him as apple of his e. 32:1
his e. was not dim, nor. 34:7
the e. of their God was. Ezra 5:5
e. that hath seen me. Job 7:8
given up ghost, and no e. had. 10:18
the e. which saw him, see. 20:9
e. of adulterer waiteth for twilight
saying, no e. shall see me. 24:15
a path which vulture's e. 28:7
and his e. seeth every precious. 10
when the e. saw me. 29:11
e. of the Lord is on them. Ps 33:18
neither wink with the e. 35:19
aha, aha, our e. hath seen it. 21
he that formed the e. shall? 94:9
that winketh with the e. Pr 10:10
the seeing e. hearing ear. 20:12
he that hath a bountiful e. shall. 22:9
the e. that mocketh at. 30:17
the e. is not satisfied. Eccl 1:8
neither is his e. satisfied. 4:8
their e. shall not spare. Isa 13:18
for they shall see e. to e. 52:8
neither hath the e. seen what he hath
prepared. 64:4; 1 Cor 2:
that were pleasant to the e. Lam 2:
let not your e. spare. Ezek 9:
none e. pitied, to do any of. 16:

defiled, and let our *e.* *Mi* 4:11
light of the body is the *e.* *Mat* 6:22
Luke 11:34
mote in thy brother's *e.* and not beam in own *e.* *Mat* 7:3; *Luke* 6:41, 42
e. offend thee, pluck it out. *Mat* 18:9
easier for camel to go through *e.* of. 19:24; *Mark* 10:25; *Luke* 18:25
because I am not the *e.* *1 Cor* 12:16
if the whole body were an *e.* 17
e. cannot say. 21
in twinkling of an *e.* at last. 15:52
he cometh, and every *e.* *Rev* 1:7

evil **eye**

bread of him that hath an *evil e.* *Pr* 23:6
to be rich hath an *evil e.* 28:22
but if thine *e.* be *evil.* *Mat* 6:23
Luke 11:34
is thine *e.* *evil* because ? *Mat* 20:15
heart proceedeth *evil e.* *Mark* 7:22

mine **eye**

kill thee, but *mine e.* *1 Sam* 24:10
mine e. no more see good. *Job* 7:7
mine e. hath seen all this. 13:1
mine e. poureth out tears. 16:20
doth *mine e.* continue in ? 17:2
mine e. also is dim by. 7
but now *mine e.* seeth thee. 42:5
mine e. consumed. *Ps* 6:7; 31:9
I will guide thee with *mine e.* 32:8
mine e. hath seen his desire. 54:7
mine e. mourneth by reason. 88:9
mine e. shall see my desire. 92:11
mine e. *mine e.* runneth down. *Lam* 1:16; 3:48
mine e. trickleth down and. 3:49
mine e. affecteth my heart. 51
shall *mine e.* spare. *Ezek* 5:11
7:4, 9; 8:18; 9:10
mine e. spared them. 20:17

right **eye**

sword shall be on arm, and his *right e.*: his *right e.* utterly. *Zech* 11:17
if *right e.* offend thee. *Mat* 5:29

thine **eye**

thine e. shall not pity. *Deut* 7:16
13:8; 19:13, 21; 25:12
and *thine e.* be evil against. 15:9
apple of *thine e.* cease. *Lam* 2:18
if *thine e.* be single. *Mat* 6:22
Luke 11:34
beam in *thine* own *e.* *Mat* 7:3
Luke 6:41
if *thine e.* offend thee. *Mat* 18:9
Mark 9:47

see **apple**

eyebrows

shave all his hair off *e.* *Lev* 14:9

eyed

and Saul *e.* David. *1 Sam* 18:9

tender **eyed**

Leah was *tender e.* *Gen* 29:17

eyelids

on mine *e.* is shadow of. *Job* 16:16
eyes are like *e.* of morning. 41:18
e. try the children of men. *Ps* 11:4
or slumber to mine *e.* 132:4
let thine *e.* look straight. *Pr* 4:25
to thine eyes, slumber to *e.* 6:4
let her take thee with her *e.* 25
their *e.* are lifted up. 30:13
that our *e.* may gush out. *Jer* 9:18

eyes

for food pleasant to *e.* *Gen* 3:6
e. of them both were opened. 7
mistress was despised in her *e.* 16:4
conceived, I was despised in her *e.* 5
is to thee a covering of *e.* 20:16
God opened Hagar's *e.* 21:19
Jacob laid rods before *e.* of. 30:41
master's wife cast her *e.* on. 39:7
good in the *e.* of Pharaoh. 41:37
the *e.* of Israel were dim. 48:10
to be abhorred in the *e.* of. *Ex* 5:21
glory of Lord like fire in *e.* 24:17
and the thing be hid from the *e.* of. *Lev* 4:13
burning ague consume the *e.* 26:16
be hid from the *e.* of her. *Num* 5:13
thou mayest be to us *e.* 10:31
wilt thou put out the *e.* of ? 16:14
sanctify me in *e.* of Israel. *Num* 20:12
Lord opened *e.* of Balaam. 22:31
man whose *e.* are open. 24:3, 15
a gift doth blind the *e.* *Deut* 16:19
Lord give thee failing of *e.* 28:65
Lord hath not given you *e.* to. 29:4
be avenged for my two *e.* *Judg* 16:28
uncovered himself in *e.* *2 Sam* 6:20
that the *e.* of my lord the king. 24:3
e. of all Israel upon thee. *1 Ki* 1:20
Lord opened the *e.* of the. *2 Ki* 6:17
Lord, open the *e.* of these men. 20
put out *e.* of Zedekiah. 25:7
Jer 39:7; 52:11
was right in the *e.* of. *1 Chr* 13:4
hast thou *e.* of flesh ? *Job* 10:4
the *e.* of the wicked shall fail. 11:20
even the *e.* of his children. 17:5
seeing it is hid from the *e.* 28:21
I was *e.* to the blind. 29:15
caused *e.* of the widow to fail. 31:16
and her *e.* behold afar off. 39:29
in whose *e.* a vile person. *Ps* 15:4
pure, enlightening *e.* 19:8
e. have they, but. 115:5; 135:16
as the *e.* of servants, the. 123:2
the *e.* of all wait upon thee. 145:15
Lord openeth the *e.* of blind. 146:8
as smoke to the *e.* so is. *Pr* 10:26
light of the *e.* rejoiceth. 15:30
as a precious stone in *e.* of. 17:8
the *e.* of a fool are in ends. 24
who hath redness of *e.*? 23:29
e. of man are never satisfied. 27:20
the wise man's *e.* are. *Eccl* 2:14
better the sight of *e.* than. 6:9
pleasant for the *e.* to behold. 11:7
thou hast dove's *e.* *S of S* 1:15; 4:1
to provoke the *e.* of his. *Isa* 3:8
daughters walk with wanton *e.* 16
e. of the lofty be humbled. 5:15
the *e.* of the blind shall see. 29:18
the *e.* of them that see. 32:3
the *e.* of the blind shall be. 35:5
to open the blind *e.* to bring. 42:7
bring forth blind that have *e.* 43:8
Lord made bare his arm in *e.* 52:10
we grope as if we had no *e.* 59:10
which have *e.* and see not. *Jer* 5:21
Ezek 12:2
their rings were full of *e.* *Ezek* 1:18
the wheels were full of *e.* 10:12
as she saw them with her *e.* 23:16
known in *e.* of many nations. 38:23
in horn were *e.* like the *e.* *Dan* 7:8
even of that horn that had *e.* 20
of purer *e.* than to behold. *Hab* 1:13
upon one stone seven *e.* *Zech* 3:9
if it be marvellous in the *e.* 8:6
when the *e.* of man shall be. 9:1
rather than having two *e.* to be cast. *Mat* 18:9; *Mark* 9:47
having *e.* see ye not ? *Mark* 8:18
e. of all were fastened. *Luke* 4:20
blessed are the *e.* which see. 10:23
anointed the *e.* of blind. *John* 9:6
any opened *e.* of one born blind. 32
can a devil open *e.* of blind ? 10:21
this man, which opened *e.*? 11:37
Dorcas opened her *e.* *Acts* 9:40
hath given them *e.* they. *Rom* 11:8
before whose *e.* Christ. *Gal* 3:1
e. of your understanding. *Eph* 1:18
things are open to *e.* of. *Heb* 4:13
having *e.* full of adultery. *2 Pet* 2:14
the lust of the *e.* and. *1 John* 2:16
of throne beasts full of *e.* *Rev* 4:6
each six wings, full of *e.* within. 8
a Lamb having seven *e.* 5:6

his **eyes**

old, and *his e.* were dim. *Gen* 27:1
his e. red with wine. 49:12
having *his e.* open. *Num* 24:4, 16
find no favour in *his e.* *Deut* 24:1
Philistines put out *his e.* *Judg* 16:21
Eli, *his e.* began to. *1 Sam* 3:2; 4:15
he tasted, and *his e.* were. 14:27
Ahijah not see, *his e.* were. *1 Ki* 14:4
put *his e.* on *his e.* *2 Ki* 4:34
the child opened *his e.* 35
I pray thee, open *his e.* 6:17
slew sons of Zedekiah before *his e.* 25:7; *Jer* 39:6; 52:10
king do what is good in *his e.* *1 Chr* 21:23
and I be pleasing in *his e.* *Esth* 8:5
enemy sharpeneth *his e.* *Job* 16:9
his e. shall see his destruction. 21:20
resteth, yet *his e.* are on. 24:23
the rich man openeth *his e.* 27:19
his e. are on the ways of. 34:21
he withdraweth not *his e.* 36:7
he taketh it with *his e.* 40:24*
his *e.* are like the eyelids. 41:18
his e. are privily set. *Ps* 10:8
his e. behold children of men. 11:4
no fear of God before *his e.* 36:1
ruleth by power, *his e.* behold. 66:7
he winketh with *his e.* *Pr* 6:13
he shutteth *his e.* to. 16:30
scattereth away evil with *his e.* 20:8
findeth no favour in *his e.* 21:10
he that hideth *his e.* shall. 28:27
sleepeth with *his e.* *Eccl* 8:16
his e. are as eyes of. *S of S* 5:12
in *his e.* as one that found. 8:10
after the sight of *his e.* *Isa* 11:3
his e. shall have respect to. 17:7
and shutteth *his e.* from. 33:15
his e. shall behold *his e.* *Jer* 32:4
see not the ground with *his e.* *Ezek* 12:12
away abomination of *his e.* 20:7
horn between *his e.* *Dan* 8:5, 21
his e. were as lamps of fire. 10:6
he had spit on *his e.* *Mark* 8:23
he put his hands again on *his e.* 25
made clay, opened *his e.* *John* 9:14
or who hath opened *his e.* 21
Peter fastening *his e.* *Acts* 3:4
and when *his e.* were opened. 9:8
there fell from *his e.* as it had. 18
then Saul set *his e.* on him. 13:9
because darkness hath blinded *his e.* *1 John* 2:11
his e. as a flame of fire. *Rev* 1:14
2:18; 19:12

lift or *lifted up* **eyes**

Lot *lifted up* his *e.* and. *Gen* 13:10
lift up now thine *e.* and. 14; 31:12
Deut 3:27; *2 Ki* 19:22; *Isa* 49:18
60:4; *Jer* 3:2; *Ezek* 8:5; *Zech* 5:5
Abraham *lift up* his *e.* *Gen* 18:2; 22:4, 13
Isaac *lifted up his e.* 24:63
Rebekah *lifted up* her *e.* 64
Jacob *lifted up* his *e.* 31:10; 33:1
Joseph *lifted up* his *e.* 43:29
lifted up their *e.* the Egyptians. *Ex* 14:10
Balaam *lifted up* his *e.* *Num* 24:2
lest thou *lift up* thine *e.* *Deut* 4:19
Joshua *lifted up* his *e.* *Josh* 5:13
old man *lifted up* his *e.* *Judg* 19:17
lifted up their *e.* and. *1 Sam* 6:13
young man that kept the watch *lifted up e.* *2 Sam* 13:34; 18:24
David *lifted up* his *e.* and. *1 Chr* 21:16
they *lifted up* their *e.* and. *Job* 2:12
lift up mine *e.* to hills. *Ps* 121:1
unto thee *lift* I *up* mine *e.* 123:1
hast thou *lifted up* thy *e.*? *Isa* 37:23
lift up your *e.* 51:6; *Ezek* 33:25
John 4:35
lifted up e. to idols. *Ezek* 18:6, 15
hath *lifted up* his *e.* to idols. 12
thou shalt not *lift up* thine *e.* 23:27
Nebuchadnezzar *lift. up e.* *Dan* 4:34
then I *lifted up* mine *e.* 8:3; 10:5
Zech 1:18; 2:1; 5:1, 5, 9; 6:1
had *lifted up* their *e.* they. *Mat* 17:8
Jesus *lifted up* his *e.* *Luke* 6:20
John 6:5; 11:41; 17:1
in hell he *lift up* his *e.* *Luke* 16:23
not *lift up* so much as his *e.* 18:13

eyes *of the Lord*

grace in *e. of the Lord.* *Gen* 6:8
the *e. of the Lord* are. *Deut* 11:12
right in the *e. of the Lord.* 13:18
set by in *e. of the Lord.* *1 Sam* 26:24
favour in *e. of the Lord.* *2 Sam* 15:25
David did right in the *e. of the Lord.* *1 Ki* 15:5, 11; 22:43; *2 Chr* 14:2
e. of the Lord run to and fro through. *2 Chr* 16:9; *Zech* 4:10

Artaxerxes king to *E.* *Ezra* 7:12
thou, *E.* after the wisdom of. 25
when *E.* had prayed and. 10:1
E. brought the law. *Neh* 8:2
and *E.* blessed the Lord. 6
priests, Seraiah, Jeremiah, *E.* 12:1
of *E.* Meshullam was priest. 13
were in days of *E.* the priest. 26
and *E.* the scribe before them. 36

F

fables

nor give heed to *f.* and. *1 Tim* 1:4
refuse profane and old wives' *f.* 4:7
shall be turned unto *f.* *2 Tim* 4:4
not giving heed to Jewish *f.* *Tit* 1:14
cunningly devised *f.* *2 Pet* 1:16

face

[1] *The literal meaning, the face, the front part of the head,* Gen 3:19. [2] *Presence,* Lev 19:32. [3] Before the face of *means in the sight of,* Ps 41:12.

in sweat of thy *f.* shalt. *Gen* 3:19
I flee from the *f.* of mistress. 16:8
put the earring upon her *f.* 24:47*
fleddest from the *f.* of Esau. 35:1, 7
Esau went from *f.* of his. 36:6
sent to Joseph to direct his *f.* 46:28*
bowed with his *f.* to the earth. 48:12
Moses fled from the *f.* *Ex* 2:15
let us flee from the *f.* of. 14:25
the skin of *f.* shone. 34:29, 30, 35
he put a vail on his *f.* 33
hair fallen towards his *f.* *Lev* 13:41
honour the *f.* of old man. 19:32
father had spit in her *f.* *Num* 12:14
slay red heifer before his *f.* 19:3
shall not be afraid of *f.* *Deut* 1:17
them that hate him to *f.* 7:10
Lord destroyeth before your *f.* 8:20
wicked man be beaten before *f.* 25:2
and spit in his *f.* and say. 9
ass taken before thy *f.* 28:31
give them up before your *f.* 31:5
liest thou upon thy *f.*? *Josh* 7:10
Dagon was fallen on his *f.* *1 Sam* 5:3, 4
David stooped with his *f.* to. 24:8
Abigail bowed on her *f.* and. 25:41
Saul stooped with his *f.* to. 28:14
should I hold up my *f.*? *2 Sam* 2:22
Absalom bowed on his *f.* to. 14:33
bowed himself before the king on his *f.* 24:20; *1 Chr* 21:21
Nathan bowed with his *f.* *1 Ki* 1:23
Bath-sheba bowed with her *f.* 31
king turned *f.* about. 8:14; *2 Chr* 6:3
put *f.* between knees. *1 Ki* 18:42
wrapped his *f.* in his mantle. 19:13
himself with ashes on his *f.* 20:38*
Ahab turned away his *f.* and. 21:4
lay my staff upon *f.* of. *2 Ki* 4:29
Gehazi laid staff on the *f.* of. 31
Hazael spread it on his *f.* so. 8:15
Jezebel painted her *f.* and. 9:30*
Jehu lifted his *f.* to the window. 32
Joash wept over his *f.* and. 13:14
wilt thou turn away *f.* of one. 18:24
Isa 36:9
Hezekiah turned *f.* to wall. *2 Ki* 20:2
Isa 38:2
turn not away the *f.* of thine.
2 Chr 6:42; *Ps* 132:10
Lord will not turn away his *f.* from.
2 Chr 30:9
he returned with shame of *f.* 32:21
Josiah would not turn his *f.* 35:22
I blush to lift up my *f.* *Ezra* 9:6
to confusion of *f.* 7; *Dan* 9:8
will curse thee to thy *f.* *Job* 1:11; 2:5
a spirit passed before my *f.* 4:15
then shalt thou lift up thy *f.* 11:15
leanness beareth witness to *f.* 16:8
my *f.* is foul with weeping. 16
declare his way to his *f.*? 21:31
and thou shalt lift up thy *f.* 22:26
and disguiseth his *f.* 24:15
he holdeth back the *f.* of. 26:9
spare not to spit in my *f.* 30:10
who can discover the *f.* of? *Job* 41:13
who can open doors of his *f.*? 14
way straight before my *f.* *Ps* 5:8
behold thy *f.* in righteousness. 17:15
arrows against the *f.* of them. 21:12
thou settest me before thy *f.* 41:12
look upon the *f.* of thine. 84:9
and truth go before thy *f.* 89:14
beat down his foes before his *f.* 23
with an impudent *f.* said. *Pr* 7:13
wicked man hardeneth his *f.* 21:29
the boldness of his *f.* *Eccl* 8:1
covert from *f.* of the spoiler. *Isa* 16:4
destroy the *f.* of the covering. 25:7
he hath made plain the *f.* 28:25
neither his *f.* now wax pale. 29:22
bow down to thee with their *f.* 49:23
me continually to my *f.* 65:3
back, and not *f.* *Jer* 2:27; 32:33
though thou rentest thy *f.* 4:30*
I discover thy skirts upon thy *f.* that.
13:26; *Nah* 3:5
the back, and not the *f.* *Jer* 18:17
from hand of them whose *f.* 22:25
remove it from before my *f.* 32:31
the right of man before *f.* *Lam* 3:35
the *f.* of a man, the *f.* of a lion, *f.* of an ox, the *f.* of an eagle. *Ezek* 1:10
I made thy *f.* strong against. 3:8
my *f.* will I also turn from. 7:22
f. of a man, *f.* of a lion, *f.* of an eagle.
10:14; 41:19
stumblingblock before their *f.* 14:3
fury shall come up in my *f.* 38:18*
a deep sleep on *f.* *Dan* 8:18; 10:9
f. as appearance of lightning. 10:6
turn his *f.* unto the isles. 11:18
pride of Israel testifieth to his *f.*
Hos 5:5; 7:10
they are before my *f.* 7:2
before their *f.* people be. *Joel* 2:6*
drive him with his *f.* toward. 20*
come before thy *f.* *Nah* 2:1
anoint head, wash thy *f.* *Mat* 6:17
I send my messenger before thy *f.*
11:10; *Mark* 1:2; *Luke* 7:27
angels behold *f.* of my. *Mat* 18:10
then did they spit in his *f.* 26:67
hast prepared before *f.* *Luke* 2:31
messengers before his *f.* 9:52; 10:1
his *f.* was as though he would. 9:53
they struck him on the *f.* 22:64
his *f.* was bound about. *John* 11:44
foresaw Lord always before my *f.*
Acts 2:25
God drave out before the *f.* 7:45
so falling down on his *f.* *1 Cor* 14:25
not stedfastly behold *f.* *2 Cor* 3:7
as Moses, who put vail over *f.* 13
but we all with open *f.* beholding. 18
glory of God, in *f.* of Jesus. 4:6
if a man smite you on the *f.* 11:20
I was unknown by *f.* to. *Gal* 1:22
I withstood him to the *f.* 2:11
natural *f.* in a glass. *Jas* 1:23
third beast had a *f.* as a. *Rev* 4:7
his *f.* was as it were the sun. 10:1
were nourished from the *f.* 12:14
from whose *f.* the earth and. 20:11
see **seek, set, shine, sky, waters, wilderness, world**

face with *cover,* or *covered*

she *covered* her *f.* *Gen* 38:15
locusts *cover f.* of the earth.
Ex 10:5, 15
they *cover f.* of the earth. *Num* 22:5
the king *covered* his *f.* *2 Sam* 19:4
they *covered* Haman's *f.* *Esth* 7:8
covereth his *f.* with. *Job* 15:27
neither hath he *covered* darkness from my *f.* 23:17
shame of my *f.* hath *covered* me.
Ps 44:15
sake shame hath *covered* my *f.* 69:7
nettles had *covered f.* *Pr* 24:31
with twain he *covered* his *f.* *Isa* 6:2
thou shalt *cover* thy *f.* *Ezek* 12:6
the prince shall *cover* his *f.* 12
spit on him, and *cover* his *f.*
Mark 14:65

face *of the country*

scattered over *f. of the country.*
2 Sam 18:8

face *of the deep*

darkness upon *f. of the deep.*
Gen 1:2
f. of the deep is frozen. *Job* 38:30
compass on *f. of the depth.* *Pr* 8:27

face *of the earth*

herb upon *f. of the earth.* *Gen* 1:29
driven me from *f. of the earth.* 4:14
to multiply on *f. of the earth.* 6:1
seed alive on *f. of* all *the earth.* 7:3
destroy from off *f. of the earth.* 4
Deut 6:15; *1 Ki* 13:34; *Amos* 9:8
waters on *f. of the* whole *earth.*
Gen 8:9
scattered on *f. of the earth.* 11:4
famine over *f. of the earth.* 41:56
consume them from *f. of the earth.*
Ex 32:12
all people unto *f. of the earth.* 33:16
meek above all men on *f. of the earth.* *Num* 12:3
above all people on *f. of the earth.*
Deut 7:6
cut off every one from *f. of the earth.*
1 Sam 20:15
renewest the *f. of the earth.*
Ps 104:30
kingdoms on the *f. of the earth.*
Isa 23:17
dung on the *f. of the earth.*
Jer 8:2; 16:4
cast thee from *f. of the earth.* 28:16
men on the *f. of the earth* shake.
Ezek 38:20
he goat came on the *f. of the earth.*
Dan 8:5
poureth them on *f. of the earth.*
Amos 5:8; 9:6
curse goeth over the *f. of the earth.*
Zech 5:3
discern *f. of the earth.* *Luke* 12:56
dwell on *f. of the* whole *earth.* 21:35
dwell on *f. of the earth.* *Acts* 17:26

face *to* **face**

I have seen God *f. to f.* *Gen* 32:30
Lord spake to Moses *f. to f.*
Ex 33:11
Lord, art seen *f. to f.* *Num* 14:14
talked with you *f. to f.* *Deut* 5:4
whom Lord knew *f. to f.* 34:10
seen an angel *f. to f.* *Judg* 6:22
in water *f.* answereth *to f.* *Pr* 27:19
plead with you *f. to f.* *Ezek* 20:35
have accusers *f. to f.* *Acts* 25:16
a glass, then *f. to f.* *1 Cor* 13:12
to you, speak *f. to f.* *2 John* 12
see thee and speak *f. to f.* *3 John* 14

fell on **face** or **faces**

Joseph *fell on* father's *f.* *Gen* 50:1
brethren *fell down* before his *f.* 18
people saw, *fell on* their *f.* *Lev* 9:24
Moses and Aaron *fell on f.* *Num* 14:5
16:22, 45
Moses *fell on f.* 16:4
Balaam *fell* flat *on* his *f.* 22:31
Joshua *fell on f.* *Josh* 5:14; 7:6
and his wife *fell on f.* *Judg* 13:20
then she *fell on* her *f.* *Ruth* 2:10
Goliath *fell on f.* *1 Sam* 17:49
David *fell on* his *f.* 20:41
Abigail *fell on f.* 25:23
Mephibosheth *fell on f.* *2 Sam* 9:6
woman of Tekoah *fell on f.* 14:4
Joab *fell on f.* 22
Ahimaaz *fell on* his *f.* 18:28
Obadiah *fell on f.* *1 Ki* 18:7
people *fell on* their *f.* 39
and elders *fell on f.* *1 Chr* 21:16
I saw it I *fell upon f.* *Ezek* 1:28
3:23; 9:8; 11:13; 43:3; 44:4
Dan 8:17
Nebuchadnezzar *fell upon* his *f.*
Dan 2:46
disciples *fell on f.* *Mat* 17:6
Jesus *fell on* his *f.* 26:39
leper *fell on f.* *Luke* 5:12
Samaritan *fell on* his *f.* 17:16
four and twenty elders *fell on* their *f.* *Rev* 11:16

face *of the field*

dung on *f. of the field.* *2 Ki* 9:37

face *of the gate*
from f. of the gate. Ezek 40:15
face *of the ground*
mist watered the f. of the ground.
Gen 2:6
was on the f. of the ground. 7:23
abated from f. of the ground. 8:8
the f. of the ground was dry. 13
hide, hideth, or *hid* **face**
from thy f. shall I be hid. Gen 4:14
and Moses hid his f. Ex 3:6
hide my f. from them. Deut 31:17
18; 32:20
wherefore hidest thou thy f. and?
Job 13:24; Ps 44:24; 88:14
when he hideth his f. Job 34:29
he hideth his f. he will. Ps 10:11
how long wilt thou hide thy f.? 13:1
neither hath he hid his f. 22:24
hide not thy f. 27:9; 69:17; 102:2
143:7
thou didst hide thy f. 30:7; 104:29
hide thy f. from my sins. 51:9
hideth his f. from the. Isa 8:17
I hid not my f. from shame. 50:6
a little wrath I hid my f. 54:8
your sins have hid his f. 59:2
thou hast hid thy f. from us. 64:7
ways not hid from my f. Jer 16:17
hid my f. from this city. 33:5
therefore hid I my f. Ezek 39:23, 24
nor will I hide my f. any more. 29
will even hide his f. Mi 3:4
hide us from the f. of. Rev 6:16
face *of the house*
breadth of f. of the house.
Ezek 41:14
face *of the Lord*
cry great before f. of the Lord.
Gen 19:13
blood fall before f. of Lord.
1 Sam 26:20
entreat f. of the Lord. 1 Ki 13:6*
f. of the Lord is against them.
Ps 34:16; 1 Pet 3:12
heart before f. of the Lord. Lam 2:19
go before f. of the Lord. Luke 1:76
face *of the porch*
f. of the porch were. Ezek 40:15*
thick planks on f. of the p. 41:25
face joined with *see, saw, seen*
afterward will see his f. Gen 32:20
therefore have I seen thy f. 33:10
not see f. except. 43:3, 5; 44:23
may not see man's f. 44:26
me die, I have seen thy f. 46:30
not thought to see thy f. 48:11
Pharaoh said, see my f. Ex 10:28
I will see thy f. again no more. 29
thou canst not see my f. 33:20
my f. shall not be seen. 23
children of Israel saw f. of. 34:35
not see my f. except. 2 Sam 3:13
let him not see my f. 14:24
dwelt and saw not king's f. 28
now let me see the king's f. 32
let us look one another in the f.
2 Ki 14:8; 2 Chr 25:17
looked one another in f. 2 Ki 14:11
princes who saw king's f. Esth 1:14
he shall see his f. with. Job 33:26
saw his f. as it had been f. Acts 6:15
shall see my f. no more. 20:25, 38
as have not seen my f. Col 2:1
endeavoured to see your f.
1 Thes 2:17
that we might see your f. 3:10
and they shall see his f. Rev 22:4
seek **face**
seek his f. continually. 1 Chr 16:11
Ps 105:4
people pray and seek my f.
2 Chr 7:14
generation that seek thy f. Ps 24:6
seek ye my f. my heart said, thy f.
Lord will I seek. 27:8
diligently to seek thy f. Pr 7:15
return, till they seek my f. Hos 5:15
set **face**
Jacob set his f. toward. Gen 31:21
I will set my f. against that soul.
Lev 17:10; 20:6

set my f. against that man.
Lev 20:3, 5; Ezek 14:8
set my f. against you. Lev 26:17
Jer 44:11
Balaam set his f. toward. Num 24:1
Hazael set his f. to. 2 Ki 12:17
I have set my f. like a. Isa 50:7
set my f. against this city. Jer 21:10
set thy f. against it. Ezek 4:3
thou shalt set thy f. towards. 7
set thy f. towards mountains. 6:2
set thy f. against daughters. 13:17
I will set my f. against them. 15:7
set thy f. toward south. 20:46
set thy f. toward Jerusalem. 21:2
go whithersoever thy f. is set. 16
set thy f. against Ammonites. 25:2
set thy f. against Zidon. 28:21
set thy f. against Pharaoh. 29:2
set thy f. against mount Seir. 35:2
set thy f. against Gog. 38:2
I set my f. unto Lord. Dan 9:3
I set my f. toward ground and. 10:15
he shall set his f. to enter. 11:17
stedfastly set his f. to. Luke 9:51
face *shine*
his f. to shine upon thee. Num 6:25
make thy f. to shine on thy.
Ps 31:16; 119:135
cause his f. to shine on us. 67:1
cause thy f. shine. 80:3, 7, 19
oil to make his f. to shine. 104:15
wisdom maketh f. to shine. Eccl 8:1
cause thy f. to shine on. Dan 9:17
his f. did shine as sun. Mat 17:2
face *of the sky*
ye can discern the f. of the sky.
Mat 16:3; Luke 12:56
face *of the waters*
moved on f. of the waters. Gen 1:2
ark went upon f. of the waters. 7:18
face *of the wilderness*
on f. of the wilderness. Ex 16:14
face *of the world*
commandeth on f. of world.
Job 37:12
nor fill f. of the world. Isa 14:21
Israel shall fill f. of the world. 27:6
faces
their f. were backward. Gen 9:23
set f. of the flocks toward. 30:40
bowed with f. to the earth. 42:6
Moses laid before their f. Ex 19:7
fear may be before your f. 20:20
and their f. shall look one. 25:20
mercy seatward were f. of. 37:9
turned their f. and said. Judg 18:23
thou hast shamed the f. 2 Sam 19:5
all Israel set their f. on. 1 Ki 2:15
whose f. were like the f. 1 Chr 12:8
their f. were inward. 2 Chr 3:13
fathers have turned away f. 29:6
worshipped with their f. Neh 8:6
covereth f. of the judges. Job 9:24
and bind their f. in secret. 40:13
and f. were not ashamed. Ps 34:5
fill their f. with shame. 83:16
ye grind the f. of the poor. Isa 3:15
amazed, their f. shall be as. 13:8
wipe away tears from off all f. 25:8
hid as it were our f. from him. 53:3
be not afraid of their f. Jer 1:8
be not dismayed at their f. 17
their f. harder than a rock. 5:3
to confusion of their own f. 7:19
all f. are turned into paleness. 30:6
set their f. to enter Egypt. 42:15
17; 44:12
with their f. thitherward. 50:5
shame hath covered our f. 51:51
the f. of elders were not. Lam 5:12
every one four f. Ezek 1:6, 10, 11, 15
face strong against their f. 3:8
shame shall be on their f. 7:18
men, with f. toward the east. 8:16
turn away your f. from. 14:6
all f. shall be burnt therein. 20:47
every cherub had two f. 41:18
he see your f. worse. Dan 1:10
but unto us confusion of f. as. 9:7
be much pained, all f. Joel 2:6
f. of them all gather. Nah 2:10

their f. shall sup up as. Hab 1:9
spread dung on your f. Mal 2:3
hypocrites disfigure their f. Mat 6:16
bowed down their f. to. Luke 24:5
before throne on their f. Rev 7:11
f. of the locusts were as f. 9:7
fade
strangers f. away. 2 Sam 22:46
Ps 18:45
we all f. as a leaf. Isa 64:6
them, and leaf shall f. Jer 8:13
whose leaf shall not f. Ezek 47:12
rich man shall f. away. Jas 1:11
fadeth
an oak, whose leaf f. Isa 1:30
mourneth and f., the world f. 24:4
grass withereth, the flower f. 40:7, 8
inheritance that f. not. 1 Pet 1:4
a crown of glory that f. not. 5:4
fading
glorious beauty a f. flower. Isa 28:1
beauty shall be a f. flower. 4
fail
will without f. drive out. Josh 3:10
f. deliver Ammon. Judg 11:30*
shalt without f. recover. 1 Sam 30:8
day by day without f. Ezra 6:9
fail, *verb*
your cattle, if money f. Gen 47:16
eyes shall f. with longing. Deut 28:32
he will not f. thee nor forsake thee.
31:6, 8; Josh 1:5; 1 Chr 28:20
not f. to burn fat. 1 Sam 2:16*
let no man's heart f. him. 17:32
I should not f. to sit with. 20:5
not f. from house of. 2 Sam 3:29
not f. thee a man on. 1 Ki 2:4
8:25; 9:5; 2 Chr 6:16
neither cruse of oil f. 1 Ki 17:14, 16
take heed that ye f. not. Ezra 4:22*
let nothing f. of all. Esth 6:10
not f. to keep these days. 9:27, 28
eyes of the wicked f. Job 11:20
as waters f. from the sea. 14:11
even eyes of children shall f. 17:5
caused eyes of widow to f. 31:16
for the faithful f. from. Ps 12:1
mine eyes f. while I wait. 69:3
doth his promise f. for? 77:8
nor my faithfulness to f. 89:33
mine eyes f. for thy word. 119:82
mine eyes f. for thy salvation. 123
rod of his anger shall f. Pr 22:8
desire f. because man. Eccl 12:5
spirit of Egypt shall f. Isa 19:3*
waters shall f. 5
glory of Kedar f. 21:16
and they all shall f. together. 31:3
cause drink of the thirsty to f. 32:6
troubled, for vintage shall f. 10
no one of these shall f. nor. 34:16*
mine eyes f. with. 38:14
he shall not f. nor be. 42:4
that his bread should not f. 51:14
for the spirit should f. 57:16
spring whose waters f. not. 58:11
their eyes did f. because. Jer 14:6
unto me as waters that f.? 15:18
I caused wine to f. from. 48:33*
Hos 9:2
eyes do f. with tears. Lam 2:11
his compassions f. not. 3:22
poor of the land to f. Amos 8:4
labour of olive shall f. Hab 3:17
that when ye f. they. Luke 16:9
than one tittle of the law to f. 17*
prayed that thy faith f. not. 22:32
prophecies, they shall f. 1 Cor 13:8*
thy years shall not f. Heb 1:12
the time would f. me to tell. 11:32
looking lest any man f. of. 12:15*
failed
their heart f. them. Gen 42:28
and when money f. in the. 47:15*
waters f. were cut off. Josh 3:16*
f. not any good thing which Lord.
21:45; 23:14; 1 Ki 8:56
my kinsfolk have f. and. Job 19:14
refuge f. me, no man. Ps 142:4
my soul f. when he. S of S 5:6
their might f. they. Jer 51:30
our eyes as yet f. for. Lam 4:17

faileth
should we die ? money *f.* *Gen* 47:15
bull gendereth and *f.* not. *Job* 21:10
my strength *f.* me. *Ps* 31:10; 38:10
my heart *f.* me. 40:12; 73:26
forsake me not when strength *f.* 71:9
knees are weak, my flesh *f.* 109:24
O Lord, my spirit *f.* 143:7
his wisdom *f.* him. *Eccl* 10:3
the grass *f.* there is. *Isa* 15:6
strong in power, not one *f.* 40:26*
seek water, their tongue *f.* 41:17
hungry and his strength *f.* 44:12
truth *f.* and he that. 59:15*
and every vision *f.* *Ezek* 12:22
judgement to light, *f.* not. *Zeph* 3:5
treasure in the heavens that *f.* not. *Luk:* 12:33
charity never *f.* but. *1 Cor* 13:8

failing
Lord shall give thee *f.* *Deut* 28:65
men's hearts *f.* them. *Luke* 21:26

fain
he would *f.* flee. *Job* 27:22
f. have filled his belly. *Luke* 15:16

faint
field, and he was *f.* *Gen* 25:29, 30
smote thee when thou wast *f.* *Deut* 25:18
f. yet pursuing. *Judg* 8:4
bread to people, for they be *f.* 5
people were very *f.* *1 Sam* 14:28, 31
so *f.* they could not go. 30:10, 21
wine, that such as be *f.* *2 Sam* 16:2
David fought and waxed *f.* 21:15
the whole heart is *f.* *Isa* 1:5
therefore shall all hands be *f.* 13:7*
awaketh, and behold he is *f.* 29:8
he giveth power to the *f.* 40:29
he drinketh no water, and is *f.* 44:12
my heart is *f.* *Jer* 8:18
are many, my heart is *f.* *Lam* 1:22
for this our heart is *f.* our. 5:17

faint, *verb*
let not your hearts *f.* *Deut* 20:3
lest his brethren's heart *f.* 8*
inhabitants of land *f.* *Josh* 2:9*
all the inhabitants of country *f.* 24*
if thou *f.* in the day of. *Pr* 24:10
even the youths shall *f.* *Isa* 40:30 *Amos* 8:13
not be weary, walk, not *f.* *Isa* 40:31
lest your hearts *f.* *Jer* 51:46
he hath made me *f.* all. *Lam* 1:13
young children *f.* 2:19
every spirit shall *f.* *Ezek* 21:7
their heart may *f.* and. 15*
send fasting, lest they *f.* *Mat* 15:32
them fasting, they will *f.* *Mark* 8:3
ought to pray, not to *f.* *Luke* 18:1
received mercy we *f.* not. *2 Cor* 4:1
for which cause we *f.* not. 16
shall reap, if we *f.* not. *Gal* 6:9
that ye *f.* not at my. *Eph* 3:13
lest ye be wearied and *f.* *Heb* 12:3
nor *f.* when thou art rebuked. 5

fainted
Jacob's heart *f.* for he. *Gen* 45:26
all the land of Canaan *f.* by. 47:13
I had *f.* unless I had. *Ps* 27:13
hungry and thirsty, soul *f.* 107:5
thy sons *f.* they lie at. *Isa* 51:20
I *f.* in my sighing. *Jer* 45:3*
trees of the field *f.* for. *Ezek* 31:15
I Daniel *f.* and was sick. *Dan* 8:27
soul *f.* I remembered. *Jonah* 2:7
that he *f.* and wished in. 4:8
compassion on them, because they *f.* *Mat* 9:36*
laboured and hast not *f.* *Rev* 2:3*

faintest
come upon thee, and thou *f.* *Job* 4:5

fainteth
my soul *f.* for courts. *Ps* 84:2
my soul *f.* for thy salvation. 119:81
a standardbearer *f.* *Isa* 10:18
Creator of ends of earth *f.* not. 40:28

fainthearted
who is fearful and *f.* let. *Deut* 20:8
fear not, nor be *f.* for. *Isa* 7:4
Hamath and Arpad *f.* *Jer* 49:23*

faintness
I will send a *f.* into. *Lev* 26:36

fair
daughters of men were *f.* *Gen* 6:2
Sarah was *f.* 12:11, 14
Rebekah was *f.* 24:16; 26:7
David was of *f.* countenance. *1 Sam* 17:42
Tamar was *f.* *2 Sam* 13:1; 14:27
Abishag a *f.* damsel. *1 Ki* 1:4
Vashti the queen was *f.* *Esth* 1:11
let *f.* virgins be sought for. 2:2
gather the *f.* young virgins. 3
Esther was *f.* and beautiful. 7
f. weather cometh out. *Job* 37:22*
no women found so *f.* as. 42:15
with *f.* speech she. *Pr* 7:21
so is a *f.* woman without. 11:22
when he speaketh *f.* believe. 26:25
thou art *f.* *S of S* 1:15, 16; 4:1, 7
rise up, my love, my *f.* one. 2:10, 13
how *f.* is thy love, my sister ! 4:10
f. as the moon. 6:10
how *f.* art thou, O love. 7:6
many houses great and *f.* *Isa* 5:9
thy stones with *f.* colours. 54:11
in vain make thyself *f.* *Jer* 4:30
and olive tree *f.* and of fruit. 11:16
though they speak *f.* words. 12:6
Egypt is like a very *f.* heifer. 46:20
also taken thy *f.* jewels. *Ezek* 16:17
shall take thy *f.* jewels. 39; 23:26
a cedar in Lebanon with *f.* 31:3
thus was he *f.* in his greatness. 7
I have made him *f.* by multitude. 9
leaves were *f.* fruit. *Dan* 4:12, 21
passed over her *f.* neck. *Hos* 10:11
f. virgins shall faint for. *Amos* 8:13
set a *f.* mitre upon his. *Zech* 3:5†
it will be *f.* weather, for. *Mat* 16:2
Moses was born, exceeding *f.* *Acts* 7:20
by *f.* speeches deceive. *Rom* 16:18
a desire to make a *f.* shew. *Gal* 6:12

fair *havens*
place called *f. havens.* *Acts* 27:8

fairer
is not younger sister *f.*? *Judg* 15:2
thou art *f.* than the. *Ps* 45:2
countenances appeared *f.* *Dan* 1:15

fairest
f. among women. *S of S* 1:8; 5:9 6:1

fairs
(*Revisions*, wares)
traded in *f.* *Ezek* 27:12, 14, 16, 19, 22
thy riches and thy *f.* shall. 27

faith
Faith is a dependence on the veracity of another; firm belief or trust in a person, thing, doctrine, or statement. And one is said to keep faith when he performs a promise made to another.
I. *Historical faith is a belief in the truthfulness and accuracy of the Scriptural narrative and teachings,* Jas 2:17, 24.
II. *Saving faith is the acceptance by the intellect, affection, and will of God's favour extended to man through Christ. This faith produces a sincere obedience in the life and conversation. The firm foundation of faith is the essential supreme perfection of God; his unerring knowledge, immutable truth, infinite goodness, and almighty power.*
By this faith, we are said to be justified, Rom 5:1. *Not formally, as if it were our righteousness before God. It is called the faith through which we are saved,* Eph 2:8. *Faith is, as it were, a condition on our part whereby we come to be partakers of the blessings of the new covenant. It is a faith which worketh by love,* Gal 5:6. *It is not an idle, inactive grace, but shews itself by producing in us love to God and our neighbour.*
Faith, in scripture, is also taken for the truth and faithfulness of God, Rom 3:3. Faith *is also used for the doctrine of the gospel, which is the object of faith,* Acts 24:24; Gal 1:23.
children in whom is no *f.* *Deut* 32:20
O ye of little *f.* *Mat* 6:30; 8:26 14:31; 16:8; *Luke* 12:28
so great *f.* no, not in Israel. *Mat* 8:10; *Luke* 7:9
f. as a grain of mustard seed. *Mat* 17:20
if ye have *f.* ye shall not. 21:21
judgement, mercy, and *f.* 23:23
how is it ye have no *f.*? *Mark* 4:40
have *f.* in God. 11:22
Lord, increase our *f.* *Luke* 17:5
if ye had *f.* ye might say to. 6
shall he find *f.*? 18:8
f. which is by him. *Acts* 3:16
Stephen, a man full of *f.* 6:5, 8
of priests obedient to the *f.* 7
Barnabas a good man, full of *f.* 11:24
to turn the deputy from the *f.* 13:8
perceiving that he had *f.* 14:9
them to continue in the *f.* 22
he had opened door of *f.* 27
churches established in the *f.* 16:5
f. toward our Lord Jesus. 20:21
Felix heard Paul concerning the *f.* 24:24
grace for obedience to *f.* *Rom* 1:5
revealed from *f.* to *f.* 17
unbelief make *f.* without effect. 3:3*
is excluded by law of *f.* 27
f. counted for righteousness. 4:5, 9
a seal of righteousness of *f.* 11
also walk in steps of that *f.* 12
through the righteousness of *f.* 13
if they of law be heirs, *f.* is. 14
it is of *f.* . . . which is of the *f.* of. 16
righteousness, which is of *f.* 9:30 10:6
that is the word of *f.* which. 10:8
f. cometh by hearing, hearing. 17*
God hath dealt measure of *f.* 12:3
according to proportion of *f.* 6
hast thou *f.*? have it to. 14:22
of *f.* what is not of *f.* is sin. 23
to nations for obedience of *f.* 16:26
to another *f.* by the. *1 Cor* 12:9
though I have all *f.* and have. 13:2
now abideth *f.* hope, charity. 13
having same Spirit of *f.* *2 Cor* 4:13
now preached *f.* which. *Gal* 1:23
or by the hearing of *f.* 3:2, 5
that they which are of *f.* 7, 9
law is not of *f.* but the man. 12
before *f.* came. 23
after that *f.* is come. 25
but *f.* which worketh by love. 5:6
fruit of Spirit is love, joy, *f.* 22*
who are of household of *f.* 6:10
one Lord, one *f.* one. *Eph* 4:5
all come in the unity of the *f.* 13
taking the shield of *f.* 6:16
peace to brethren, with *f.* from. 23
furtherance and joy of *f.* *Phil* 1:25
striving together for the *f.* of the. 27
remembering work of *f.* *1 Thes* 1:3
putting on breastplate of *f.* 5:8
glory for patience and *f.* *2 Thes* 1:4
would fulfil the work of *f.* 11
for all men have not *f.* 3:2
f. unfeigned. *1 Tim* 1:5
grace of Lord abundant with *f.* 14
f. and a good conscience; some put away, concerning *f.* have. 19
holding the mystery of *f.* in a. 3:9
some shall depart from the *f.* 4:1
nourished up in words of *f.* 6
he hath denied the *f.* 5:8
they have cast off their first *f.* 12†
erred from the *f.* 6:10, 21
and follow after *f.* 11
fight the good fight of *f.* 12
the unfeigned *f.* that is. *2 Tim* 1:5
overthrow the *f.* of some. 2:18
follow *f.* 22
reprobate concerning the *f.* 3:8
hast fully known my *f.*, charity. 3:10
finished my course, kept *f.* 4:7
according to the *f.* of. *Tit* 1:1
mine own son, after common *f.* 4

hearing of thy f. toward. Philem 5
not being mixed with f. Heb 4:2
not laying again foundation of f. 6:1
heart in full assurance of f. 10:22
hold fast profession of our f. 23*
f. is substance of things hoped. 11:1
without f. it is impossible to. 6
the author and finisher of our f. 12:2
whose f. follow, considering 13:7
have not f. with respect. Jas 2:1
a man say he hath f. can f. save ? 14
f. without works is dead. 17, 20, 26
a man say, thou hast f. and. 2:18
how f. wrought with his works, and
by works was f. made. 22
the prayer of f. shall save. 5:15
obtained like precious f. 2 Pet 1:1
the world, even our f. 1 John 5:4
earnestly contend for f. Jude 3
building up on your most holy f. 20
and hast not denied my f. Rev 2:13
I know thy works, and f. and. 19
the patience and the f. of. 13:10
they that keep f. of Jesus. 14:12

by faith

just shall live by his f. Hab 2:4
Rom 1:17; Gal 3:11; Heb 10:38
purifying hearts by f. Acts 15:9
who are sanctified by f. 26:18
comforted by mutual f. Rom 1:12
the righteousness of God by f. 3:22
justified by f. 28; 5:1; Gal 2:16
3:24
justify circumcision by f. Rom 3:30
by whom we have access by f. 5:2
they sought it not by f. 9:32
standest by f. 11:20; 2 Cor 1:24
for we walk by f. not. 2 Cor 5:7
I live by the f. of the Son. Gal 2:20
the promise by f. 3:22
ye are children of God by f. 26
for hope of righteousness by f. 5:5
whom have access by f. Eph 3:12
Christ dwell in your hearts by f. 17
righteousness of God by f. Phil 3:9
by f. Abel. Heb 11:4
by f. Enoch. 5
by f. Noah. 7
by f. Abraham. 8, 9, 17
by f. Isaac blessed Jacob. 20
by f. Jacob. 21
by f. Joseph made mention. 22
by f. Moses. 23, 24, 27
by f. passed through Red sea. 29
by f. walls of Jericho fell down. 30
by f. Rahab. 31
by works a man is justified, not by f.
only. Jas 2:24

in faith

being not weak in f. Rom 4:19
staggered not, was strong in f. 20
him that is weak in the f. 14:1
stand fast in the f. 1 Cor 16:13
as ye abound in f. 2 Cor 8:7
examine whether ye be in the f. 13:5
if ye continue in the f. Col 1:23
and stablished in the f. 2:7
Timothy my own son in f. 1 Tim 1:2
godly edifying which is in f. 4
a teacher of the Gentiles in f. 2:7
saved, if they continue in f. 15
purchase great boldness in f. 3:13
an example of believers in f. 4:12
hold fast form in f. 2 Tim 1:13
be found in the f. Tit 1:13; 2:2
greet them that love us in f. 3:15
these all died in f. Heb 11:13
but let him ask in f. Jas 1:6
poor of this world, rich in f. 2:5
resist, stedfast in the f. 1 Pet 5:9

their faith

Jesus seeing their f. Mat 9:2
Mark 2:5; Luke 5:20

through faith

through f. in his name. Acts 3:16
a propitiation through f. Rom 3:25
uncircumcision through f. 30
make void law through f.? 31
justify heathen through f. Gal 3:8
promise of Spirit through f. 14
grace saved through f. Eph 2:8
righteousness which is through f.
Phil 3:9
risen through the f. of. Col 2:12
to salvation through f. 2 Tim 3:15
who through f. inherit. Heb 6:12
through f. we understand. 11:3
through f. Sara received. 11
through f. he kept passover. 28
through f. subdued kingdoms. 33
a good report through f. 39
power of God through f. 1 Pet 1:5

thy faith

thy f. made thee whole. Mat 9:22
Mark 5:34; 10:52; Luke 8:48
17:19
O woman, great is thy f. Mat 15:28
thy f. hath saved. Luke 7:50; 18:42
prayed that thy f. fail not. 22:32
communication of thy f. Philem 6
shew me thy f. without. Jas 2:18

your faith

according to your f. be. Mat 9:29
where is your f.? Luke 8:25
your f. is spoken of. Rom 1:8
your f. should not stand. 1 Cor 2:5
your f. is also vain. 15:14, 17
dominion over your f. 2 Cor 1:24
having hope when your f. is. 10:15
after I heard of your f. Eph 1:15
on service of your f. Phil 2:17
since we heard of your f. Col 1:4
stedfastness of your f. in Christ. 2:5
your f. toward God. 1 Thes 1:8
comfort you concerning your f. 3:2
I sent to know your f. 5
Timothy brought tidings of your f. 6
comforted over you by your f. 7
perfect what is lacking in your f. 10
that your f. groweth. 2 Thes 1:3
trying of your f. worketh. Jas 1:3
the trial of your f. being. 1 Pet 1:7
end of your f. even salvation. 9
that your f. and hope might be. 21
add to your f. virtue, to. 2 Pet 1:5

faithful

Moses is f. in mine house.
Num 12:7; Heb 3:2, 5
the f. God who keepeth. Deut 7:9
raise me up a f. priest. 1 Sam 2:35
who is so f. as David ? 22:14
one of them f. in Israel. 2 Sam 20:19
Hananiah was a f. man. Neh 7:2
foundest his heart f. before. 9:8
for they were counted f. 13:13
for the f. fail from among. Ps 12:1
for Lord preserveth the f. 31:23
as a f. witness in heaven. 89:37
eyes shall be on the f. of. 101:6
all thy commandments are f. 119:86
testimonies righteous and very f. 138
a f. spirit concealeth. Pr 11:13
a f. ambassador is health. 13:17
a f. witness will not lie, but. 14:5
a f. man who can find ? 20:6
as snow in harvest, so is a f. 25:13
f. are the wounds of a friend. 27:6
a f. man shall abound with. 28:20
how is the f. city become ! Isa 1:21
afterwards be called f. city. 26
I took unto me f. witnesses. 8:2
because of the Lord that is f. 49:7
Lord be a f. witness. Jer 42:5
forasmuch as he was f. Dan 6:4
but Judah is f. with. Hos 11:12
who then is a f. and ? Mat 24:45
well done, thou good and f. 25:21
f. in a few things. 23; Luke 19:17
who then is that f. and ? Luke 12:42
is f. in the least is f. also. 16:10
not been f. in unrighteous. 11
have not been f. in what is. 12
judged me f. to Lord. Acts 16:15
God is f. by whom. 1 Cor 1:9; 10:13
in stewards, that a man be f. 4:2
sent you Timothy f. in Lord. 17
mercy of Lord to be f. 7:25†
blessed with f. Abraham. Gal 3:9
to the saints and f. in. Eph 1:1
Tychicus a f. minister. 6:21
saints and f. brethren. Col 1:2
Epaphras, for you f. minister. 7; 4:7
Onesimus, a f. brother. 4:9
f. is he that calleth you. 1 Thes 5:24
the Lord is f. who shall. 2 Thes 3:3
that he counted me f. 1 Tim 1:12
is a f. saying. 1 Tim 1:15; 4:9; Tit 3:8
must be sober, and f. 1 Tim 3:11
service because they are f. 6:2*
same commit to f. men. 2 Tim 2:2
it is a f. saying. 11
yet he abideth f. 13
blameless, having f. Tit 1:6*
holding fast the f. word. 9
might be a f. high priest. Heb 2:17
f. to him that appointed him. 3:2
is f. that promised. 10:23; 11:11
souls, as unto a f. 1 Pet 4:19
by Silvanus a f. brother. 5:12
he is f. to forgive us. 1 John 1:9
Christ the f. witness. Rev 1:5; 3:14
be f. unto death, I will give. 2:10
wherein Antipas was f. martyr. 13
with him, are called, and f. 17:14
that sat upon him was called F. 19:11
words are true and f. 21:5; 22:6

faithfully

for they dealt f. 2 Ki 12:15; 22:7
do in fear of Lord f. 2 Chr 19:9
they brought in offerings f. 31:12
the men did the work f. 34:12
the king that f. judgeth. Pr 29:14
him speak my word f. Jer 23:28
doest f. whatsoever thou. 3 John 5

faithfulness

render to every man f. 1 Sam 26:23
there is no f. in their mouth. Ps 5:9
thy f. reacheth unto clouds. 36:5
I have declared thy f. and. 40:10
or shall thy f. be declared ? 88:11
I will make known thy f. 89:1
thy f. shalt thou establish. 2
thy f. also in the congregation. 5
who is like to thee, or to thy f.? 8
but my f. and my mercy shall. 24
nor will I suffer my f. to fail. 33
good to shew forth thy f. 92:2
thou in f. hast afflicted me. 119:75
thy f. is unto all generations. 90
in thy f. answer me. 143:1
and f. the girdle of his. Isa 11:5
thy counsels of old are f. 25:1
great is thy f. Lam 3:23
betroth thee unto me in f. Hos 2:20

faithless

O f. generation. Mat 17:17
Mark 9:19; Luke 9:41
be not f. but believing. John 20:27

fall, *substantive*

haughty spirit before a f. Pr 16:18
righteous shall see their f. 29:16
moved at noise of their f. Jer 49:21
isles shake at sound of their f.
Ezek 26:15
isles tremble in day of thy f. 18
to shake at sound of his f. 31:16
for his life in day of thy f. 32:10
and great was the f. of it. Mat 7:27
child is set for the f. Luke 2:34
through their f. salvation. Rom 11:11
if the f. of them be riches of. 12

fall, *verb*

a deep sleep to f. upon. Gen 2:21
occasion against us, and f. 43:18
see that ye f. not out by way. 45:24
so that rider f. backward. 49:17
fear and dread shall f. Ex 15:16
dig a pit, ox or ass f. therein. 21:33
on whatsoever any f. Lev 11:32
if their carcase f. on any. 37, 38
lest land f. to whoredom. 19:29
they shall f. before you. 26:7, 8
shall f. when none pursueth. 36
shall f. one upon another. 37*
let them f. by the camp. Num 11:31
your carcases shall f. in. 14:29, 32
is the land that shall f. to. 34:2
if any man f. from. Deut 22:8
rise thou, and f. upon us. Judg 8:21
swear ye will not f. upon me. 15:12
and f. into the hand of the. 18
let f. some handfuls of. Ruth 2:16*
know how matter will f. 3:18
none of his words f. 1 Sam 3:19
not one hair of his head f. to. 14:45
2 Sam 14:11; 1 Ki 1:52; Acts 27:34
to make David f. 1 Sam 18:25
would not f. on the priests. 22:17

turn thou, and *f.* on priests. *1 Sam* 22:18
therefore let not my blood *f.* 26:20
near and *f.* on him. *2 Sam* 1:15
1 Ki 2:29, 31
let us *f.* into the hand of God, not *f.*
2 Sam 24:14; *1 Chr* 21:13
shall persuade Ahab to go up and *f.*
1 Ki 22:20; *2 Chr* 18:19
let us *f.* unto the host. *2 Ki* 7:4
shall *f.* nothing of word of. 10:10
meddle, that thou shouldst *f.*? 14:10
f. to his master Saul. *1 Chr* 12:19
till thy bowels *f.* out. *2 Chr* 21:15
God shall make thee *f.* 25:8*
that thou shouldest *f.* and Judah. 19
thou hast begun to *f.* shall not prevail, but shalt surely *f.* *Esth* 6:13
not his dread *f.* upon you? *Job* 13:11
let thine arm *f.* from my. 31:22
let them *f.* by their own. *Ps* 5:10
mine enemies shall *f.* and. 9:3*
that the poor may *f.* by. 10:10
into that destruction let him *f.* 35:8
f. shall not be utterly cast. 37:24
arrows, whereby people *f.* 45:5
make their tongue to *f.* 64:8*
and he let it *f.* in midst of. 78:28
but ye shall *f.* like one of the. 82:7
a thousand shall *f.* at thy side. 91:7
thrust at me that I might *f.* 118:13
burning coals *f.* upon them. 140:10
let wicked *f.* into their own. 141:10
Lord upholdeth all that *f.* 145:14
unless they cause some to *f.* *Pr* 4:16
a prating fool shall *f.* 10:8, 10
the wicked shall *f.* by his. 11:5
where no counsel is people *f.* 14
trusteth in his riches shall *f.* 28
of the Lord shall *f.* therein. 22:14
wicked shall *f.* into mischief. 24:16*
whoso diggeth a pit shall *f.* therein.
26:27; *Eccl* 10:8
causeth to go astray shall *f.* *Pr* 28:10
that hardeneth his heart shall *f.* 14
he that is perverse shall *f.* at. 18
if they *f.* one will lift. *Eccl* 4:10
if the tree *f.* toward the south. 11:3
shall stumble and *f.* *Isa* 8:15
they shall *f.* under the slain. 10:4
and Lebanon shall *f.* by a. 34
nail fastened in sure place *f.* 22:25
fleeth from fear *f.* into pit. 24:18
the earth shall *f.* and not rise. 20
that they might go and *f.* 28:13
as a breach ready to *f.* 30:13
of slaughter, when towers *f.* 25
young men shall utterly *f.* 40:30
therefore mischiefs shall *f.* 47:11
whoso gather against shall *f.* 54:15
anger to *f.* on you. *Jer* 3:12*
f. amongst them that *f.* 6:15; 8:12
the fathers and sons shall *f.* 6:21*
shall they *f.* and not arise? 8:4
the carcases of men shall *f.* 9:22
I have caused him to *f.* 15:8
shall be driven out and *f.* 23:12
a whirlwind *f.* on head. 19*; 30:23*
be drunken, and spue, and *f.* 25:27
ye shall *f.* like a pleasant vessel. 34
it is false; I *f.* not away to. 37:14
shall all *f.* in the land of. 44:12*
they shall stumble and *f.* 46:6
made many to *f.* yea one. 16*
fleeth shall *f.* into the pit. 48:44
her young men *f.* in. 49:26; 50:30
most proud stumble and *f.* 50:32
the slain shall *f.* in land. 51:4, 47, 49
wall of Babylon shall *f.* 51:44
Babylon caused slain of Israel to *f.* 49
made my strength to *f.* *Lam* 1:14*
the slain shall *f.* in the. *Ezek* 6:7
that it shall *f.* and ye, O great hailstones, shall *f.* and a. 13:11
foundation discovered, it shall *f.* 14
let no lot *f.* on it. 24:6
all thy company shall *f.* 27:27, 34
thou shalt *f.* upon. 29:5; 39:5
when slain shall *f.* in Egypt. 30:4
they that uphold Egypt shall *f.* 6
I will cause the sword to *f.* out. 22
I cause multitude to *f.* 32:12
not *f.* thereby in the day. 33:12
in all thy rivers shall they *f.* 35:8
steep places shall *f.*, every wall shall *f.* *Ezek* 38:20
arrows to *f.* 39:3
shalt *f.* on the mountains. 4
they caused Israel to *f.* 44:12
this land shall *f.* to you for. 47:14
robbers of thy people shall *f.*
Dan 11:14
but he shall stumble and *f.* 19
when they shall *f.* 34
some *f.* to try them. 35
shalt thou *f.* in the day, the prophet also shall *f.* with thee. *Hos* 4:5*
that doth not understand shall *f.* 14*
and Ephraim *f.* Judah shall *f.* 5:5*
shall say to the hills, *f.* on us. 10:8
transgressors shall *f.* therein. 14:9
can a bird *f.* in a snare? *Amos* 3:5
the horns of the altar shall *f.* 14
even they shall *f.* and never. 8:14
shall not the least grain *f.* to. 9:9
rejoice not, when I *f.* *Mi* 7:8
they shall *f.* into mouth. *Nah* 3:12
not one sparrow *f.* to. *Mat* 10:29
if it *f.* into a pit on sabbath. 12:11
both shall *f.* into the ditch. 15:14
Luke 6:39
crumbs which *f.* from. *Mat* 15:27
whoso *f.* on this stone be broken, on whom it *f.* it. 21:44; *Luke* 20:18
and the stars shall *f.* from heaven.
Mat 24:29; *Mark* 13:25
Satan as lightning *f.* *Luke* 10:18
to say to mountains, *f.* on us. 23:30
except a corn *f.* into. *John* 12:24
fearing lest they should *f.* into.
Acts 27:17*
soldiers cut ropes and let her *f.* 32
shall not an hair *f.* from head. 34*
stumbled that they should *f.*
Rom 11:11
put an occasion to *f.* in his. 14:13
take heed lest he *f.* *1 Cor* 10:12
he *f.* into condemnation. *1 Tim* 3:6
a good report, lest he *f.* into. 7
they that be rich *f.* 6:9
lest any *f.* after the. *Heb* 4:11
fearful to *f.* into hands of. 10:31
when ye *f.* into temptation. *Jas* 1:2
lest ye *f.* into condemnation. 5:12
things ye shall never *f.* *2 Pet* 1:10*
beware lest ye *f.* from your. 3:17
mountains and rocks, *f.* on. *Rev* 6:16
I saw a star *f.* from heaven. 9:1

fall *away*

of temptation *f. away.* *Luke* 8:13
if they *f. away* to renew. *Heb* 6:6

fall *down*

brother's ass *f. down.* *Deut* 22:4
of city shall *f. down* flat. *Josh* 6:5
David let his spittle *f. down.*
1 Sam 21:13
all kings shall *f. down.* *Ps* 72:11
that is holpen shall *f. down.* *Isa* 31:3
their host shall *f. down* as. 34:4
f. down to stock of a tree? 44:19
Sabeans shall *f. down* unto. 45:14
they *f.* down, they worship. 46:6
of Pharaoh *f. down.* *Ezek* 30:25
ye *f. down* and worship. *Dan* 3:5, 10
if ye *f. down* and worship image. 15
many shall *f. down* slain. 11:26
these things will I give thee, if thou wilt *f. down.* *Mat* 4:9; *Luke* 4:7
twenty-four elders *f. down.* *Rev* 4:10

fall, joined with *sword*

f. on us with pestilence or *sword.*
Ex 5:3
this land to *f.* by *sword.* *Num* 14:3
ye shall *f.* by the *sword.* 43
Sennacherib *f.* by *sword.* *2 Ki* 19:7
they shall *f.* by the *sword.*
Ps 63:10*; *Ezek* 6:11
thy men shall *f.* by *sword.* *Isa* 3:25
every one shall *f.* by *sword.* 13:15
Assyrian *f.* with the *sword.* 31:8
I will cause him to *f.* by the *sword* in.
37:7; *Jer* 19:7
friends *f.* by *sword.* *Jer* 20:4
thou shalt not *f.* by the *sword.* 39:18
third part *f.* by *sword.* *Ezek* 5:12
that is near *f.* by the *sword.* 6:12
ye shall *f.* by the *sword.* 11:10
fugitives shall *f.* by *sword.*
Ezek 17:21
remnant shall *f.* by the *sword.* 23:25
and daughters *f.* by *sword.* 24:21
of Dedan shall *f.* by *sword.* 25:13
men in league *f.* by the *sword.* 30:5
tower of Syene, *f.* by the *sword.* 6
young men shall *f.* by the *sword.* 17
I will cause the *sword* to *f.* 22
in wastes shall *f.* by *sword.* 33:27
understand *f.* by *sword.* *Dan* 11:33
princes *f.* by the *sword.* *Hos* 7:16
Samaria shall *f.* by the *sword.* 13:16
when they *f.* on *sword.* *Joel* 2:8
sons and daughters *f.* by *sword.*
Amos 7:17
f. by edge of the *sword.* *Luke* 21:24

fallen

why is thy countenance *f.*? *Gen* 4:6
that hath his hair *f.* off. *Lev* 13:41
if thy brother be *f.* in decay. 25:35*
all Ai were *f.* on edge of. *Josh* 8:24
lord was *f.* down dead. *Judg* 3:25
inheritance had not *f.* unto. 18:1
the woman was *f.* at the. 19:27
Dagon was *f.* *1 Sam* 5:3
a deep sleep *f.* 26:12
found Saul and his sons *f.* 31:8
1 Chr 10:8
not live after he was *f.* *2 Sam* 1:10
mourned, because they were *f.* 12
there is a great man *f.* this. 3:38
now Elisha was *f.* sick. *2 Ki* 13:14
dead bodies *f.* to earth. *2 Chr* 20:24
our fathers have *f.* by sword. 29:9
Haman was *f.* on bed. *Esth* 7:4
brought down and *f.* *Ps* 20:8
there are workers of iniquity *f.* 36:12
how art thou *f.* from! *Isa* 14:12
nor inhabitants of world *f.* 26:18
f. by the sword. *Ezek* 32:22, 23, 24
hast *f.* by thine iniquity. *Hos* 14:1
of you have an ox *f.*? *Luke* 14:5
the Holy Ghost was *f.* *Acts* 8:16
Eutychus being *f.* into a. 20:9*
when we were all *f.* I heard. 26:14
lest they should have *f.* 27:29*
when Paul should have *f.* 28:6
f. out to the furtherance. *Phil* 1:12
from whence thou art *f.* *Rev* 2:5

are **fallen**

are f. and dead. *2 Sam* 1:4
how are the mighty *f.*! 19, 25, 27
are f. under feet. 22:39; *Ps* 18:38
the lines *are f.* to me. *Ps* 16:6
terrors of death *are f.* upon. 55:4
midst whereof they *are f.* 57:6
reproaches of them *are f.* 69:9
the bricks *are f.* down. *Isa* 9:10
the Jews that *are f.* to. *Jer* 38:19
mighty men, they *are f.* 46:12
Babylon's foundations *are f.* 50:15
my virgins *are f.* by. *Lam* 2:21
his branches *are f.* his. *Ezek* 31:12
not lie with mighty that are *f.* 32:27
all their kings *are f.* *Hos* 7:7
some *are f.* asleep. *1 Cor* 15:6, 18
ye *are f.* from grace. *Gal* 5:4
seven kings, five *are f.* *Rev* 17:10

is **fallen**

man whose hair *is f.* *Lev* 13:40
our lot *is f.* on this. *Num* 32:19
your terror *is f.* upon us. *Josh* 2:9
fire of God *is f.* from. *Job* 1:16
and *is f.* into the ditch. *Ps* 7:15
and Judah *is f.* *Isa* 3:8
for thy harvest *is f.* 16:9
Babylon *is f. is f.* 21:9
Rev 14:8; 18:2
truth *is f.* in the streets. *Isa* 59:14
the spoiler *is f.* on thy. *Jer* 48:32
Babylon *is* suddenly *f.* 51:8
crown *is f.* from our. *Lam* 5:16
lo, when the wall is *f.* *Ezek* 13:12
virgin of Israel *is f.* *Amos* 5:2
raise up tabernacle that *is f.* 9:11
for the cedar *is f.* *Zech* 11:2
tabernacle of David which *is f.*
Acts 15:16

fallest

f. away to Chaldeans. *Jer* 37:13

falleth

when there *f.* out any. *Ex* 1:10

vessel whereinto any *f.* *Lev* 11:33
whereupon their carcase *f.* 35
inheritance where lot *f.* *Num* 33:54
not fail one that *f.* on. *2 Sam* 3:29
as a man *f.* before wicked men. 34
will light on him as dew *f.* 17:12
when deep sleep *f.* on men. *Job* 4:13
33:15
wicked messenger *f.* *Pr* 13:17
perverse tongue *f.* into. 17:20
a just man *f.* seven times. 24:16
rejoice not when thine enemy *f.* 17
to him alone when he *f.* *Eccl* 4:10
of men are snared when it *f.* 9:12
where tree *f.* there shall it be. 11:3
leaf *f.* off from vine. *Isa* 34:4*
and *f.* down thereto. 44:15, 17
he that *f.* to Chaldeans. *Jer* 21:9
whoso *f.* not down. *Dan* 3:6, 11
oft-times he *f.* into fire. *Mat* 17:15
a house divided *f.* *Luke* 11:17
give me the portion that *f.* 15:12
own master standeth or *f.* *Rom* 14:4
the flower thereof *f.* *Jas* 1:11
1 Pet 1:24

falling

f. into a trance. *Num* 24:4, 16
upholden him that was *f.* *Job* 4:4
the mountain *f.* cometh to. 14:18
deliver feet from *f.* *Ps* 56:13; 116:8
a righteous man *f.* *Pr* 25:26*
and as a *f.* fig from. *Isa* 34:4*
came trembling and *f.* *Luke* 8:47
great drops of blood *f.* down. 22:44
and Judas *f.* headlong. *Acts* 1:18
and *f.* into a place where. 27:41*
and so *f.* down, he. *1 Cor* 14:25
except there come a *f.* *2 Thes* 2:3
able to keep you from *f.* *Jude* 24*

fallow

break up your *f.* ground. *Jer* 4:3
Hos 10:12

see **deer**

false

shalt not raise a *f.* report. *Ex* 23:1
keep thee far from a *f.* matter. 7
it is *f.* tell us now. *2 Ki* 9:12
my words shall not be *f.* *Job* 36:4
hate every *f.* way. *Ps* 119:104, 128
done to thee, thou *f.* tongue ? 120:3*
a *f.* balance is an. *Pr* 11:1
wicked doer giveth heed to *f.* 17:4*
and *f.* balance is not good. 20:23
whoso boasteth of a *f.* gift. 25:14
they prophesy a *f.* vision. *Jer* 14:14*
them that prophesy *f.* 23:32*
it is *f.* I fall not away. 37:14
have seen *f.* burdens. *Lam* 2:14*
them as a *f.* divination. *Ezek* 21:23*
love no *f.* oath. *Zech* 8:17
diviners have told *f.* dreams. 10:2
swift witness against *f.* *Mal* 3:5
there arise *f.* Christs and *f.* prophets.
Mat 24:24; *Mark* 13:22
taken by *f.* accusation. *Luke* 19:8*
for such are *f.* apostles. *2 Cor* 11:13
in perils among *f.* brethren. 26
because of *f.* brethren. *Gal* 2:4
without affection, *f.* *2 Tim* 3:3
they be not *f.* accusers. *Tit* 2:3*
f. teachers among you. *2 Pet* 2:1

see **prophet**

false *prophets*

beware of *f.* prophets. *Mat* 7:15
many *f. prophets* rise. 24:11, 24
f. prophets shall rise. *Mark* 13:22
fathers to *f. prophets.* *Luke* 6:26
f. prophets among people. *2 Pet* 2:1
f. prophets are gone out. *1 John* 4:1

false *witness*

shalt not bear *f. witness* against thy.
Ex 20:16; *Deut* 5:20; *Mat* 19:18
if a *f. witness* rise up. *Deut* 19:16*
if witness be a *f. witness.* 18
a *f. witness* that speaketh. *Pr* 6:19
f. witness sheweth forth. 12:17; 14:5
f. witness not be unpunished. 19:5, 9
a *f. witness* shall perish. 21:28
man that beareth *f. witness.* 25:18
heart proceed *f. witness.* *Mat* 15:19
elders sought *f. witness.* 26:59
bare *f. witness* against him.
Mark 14:56, 57

false *witnesses*

f. witnesses are risen up. *Ps* 27:12
f. witnesses did rise. 35:11*
f. witnesses came, at last came two
f. witnesses. *Mat* 26:60
set up *f. witnesses.* *Acts* 6:13
f. witnesses of God. *1 Cor* 15:15

falsehood

wrought *f.* against my. *2 Sam* 18:13*
in answers remaineth *f.* *Job* 21:34
he hath brought forth *f.* *Ps* 7:14
them down, deceit is *f.* 119:118
is a right hand of *f.* 144:8, 11
under *f.* have we hid. *Isa* 28:15
are ye not a seed of *f.*? 57:4
words of *f.* 59:13
his molten image is *f.*
Jer 10:14; 51:17
forgotten me, and trusted in *f.* 13:25
they commit *f.* and thief. *Hos* 7:1
walking in spirit and *f.* *Mi* 2:11

falsely

thou wilt not deal *f.* *Gen* 21:23
was lost, sweareth *f.* *Lev* 6:3
which he hath sworn *f.* 5
neither deal *f.* nor lie. 19:11
shall not swear by my name *f.* 12
witness have testified *f.* *Deut* 19:18
nor have we dealt *f.* *Ps* 44:17
they swear *f.* *Jer* 5:2
prophets prophesy *f.* 31; 29:9
every one dealeth *f.* 6:13; 8:10
steal, murder, and swear *f.*? 7:9
thou speakest *f.* of Ishmael. 40:16
speakest *f.* the Lord hath. 43:2
swearing *f.* in making. *Hos* 10:4
house that sweareth *f.* *Zech* 5:4
say evil against you *f.* *Mat* 5:11
nor accuse any *f.* *Luke* 3:14*
oppositions of science, *f.* *1 Tim* 6:20
f. accuse conversation. *1 Pet* 3:16

falsifying

and *f.* the balances. *Amos* 8:5*

fame

f. heard in Pharaoh's. *Gen* 45:16
nations heard *f.* of thee. *Num* 14:15
Joshua's *f.* was noised. *Josh* 6:27
we heard the *f.* of God. 9:9
his *f.* was in all nations. *1 Ki* 4:31
queen heard *f.* of. 10:1; *2 Chr* 9:1
wisdom exceedeth *f.* *1 Ki* 10:7
2 Chr 9:6
the *f.* of David went to. *1 Chr* 14:17
house must be of *f.* and of. 22:5
Mordecai's *f.* went. *Esth* 9:4
heard *f.* with our ears. *Job* 28:22*
isles that have not heard my *f.*
Isa 66:19
have heard the *f.* our hands. *Jer* 6:24
and I will get them *f.* *Zeph* 3:19*
the *f.* of Jesus went. *Mat* 4:24*
Mark 1:28*; *Luke* 4:14, 37*; 5:15*
f. thereof went abroad. *Mat* 9:26
departed, spread abroad his *f.* 31
Herod heard of *f.* of Jesus. 14:1*

familiar

f. friends have forgotten. *Job* 19:14
my *f.* friend hath lifted up. *Ps* 41:9

familiar *spirit*

woman of a *f. spirit.* *Lev* 20:27
a *f. spirit* to enquire of her; a *f. spirit*
at Endor. *1 Sam* 28:7
divine to me by the *f. spirit.* 8
of one that had *f. spirit.* *1 Chr* 10:13
Manasseh dealt with a *f. spirit.*
2 Chr 33:6
of one that hath a *f. spirit.* *Isa* 29:4

familiar *spirits*

that have *f. spirits.* *Lev* 19:31
that turneth after *f. spirits.* 20:6
consulter with *f. spirits.* *Deut* 18:11
put away those that had *f. spirits.*
1 Sam 28:3
cut off those that have *f. spirits.* 9
Manasseh dealt with *f. spirits.*
2 Ki 21:6
workers with *f. spirits* Josiah. 23:24
say, seek *f. spirits.* *Isa* 8:19
to them that have *f. spirits.* 19:3

familiars

all my *f.* watched for. *Jer* 20:10*

families

isles of Gentiles divided after *f.*
Gen 10:5
were the *f.* of the Canaanites. 18
the sons of Ham after their *f.* 20
f. of Shem. 31
all *f.* of earth blessed. 12:3; 28:14
dukes of Esau according to *f.* 36:40
nourished brethren with *f.* 47:12
these be *f.* of Reuben. *Ex* 6:14
Num 26:7; *Josh* 13:15, 23
these are the *f.* of Simeon. *Ex* 6:15
Num 26:12, 14; *Josh* 19:1, 8
f. of Gershon. *Ex* 6:17; *Num* 3:18
21; 4:22, 24, 38, 40, 41; *Josh* 21:33
f. of Levi. *Ex* 6:19, 25; *Num* 4:46
26:57, 58; *Josh* 21:27; *1 Chr* 6:19
lamb according to your *f.* *Ex* 12:21
of the *f.* of strangers. *Lev* 25:45
of Israel after their *f.* *Num* 1:2
sons of Kohath by their *f.* 3:19
27, 29, 30; 4:37; *Josh* 21:4, 10
sons of Merari, by *f.* *Num* 3:20, 33, 35
4:33, 42, 44, 45; *Josh* 21:34, 40
1 Chr 6:63
cut not off tribe of *f.* of. *Num* 4:18
heard them weep through *f.* 11:10
the *f.* of Gad. 26:15, 18
Josh 13:24, 28
the *f.* of Judah. *Num* 26:20, 22
Josh 15:1, 12, 20
sons of Issachar after *f.* *Num* 26:23
25; *Josh* 19:17, 23; 21:6
1 Chr 6:62; 7:5
f. of Zebulun. *Num* 26:26, 27
Josh 19:10, 16
Joseph after *f.* *Num* 26:28; 36:1
the *f.* of Manasseh. 26:34; 36:12
Josh 13:29; 17:2
Ephraim after *f.* *Num* 26:35, 37
Josh 16:5, 8; 21:5, 20; *1 Chr* 6:66
of Benjamin after *f.* *Num* 26:38, 41
Josh 18:11, 20, 21; *1 Sam* 10:21
sons of Dan after their *f.* *Num* 26:42
Josh 19:40, 48
sons of Asher after *f.* *Num* 26:44
Josh 19:24, 31
sons of Naphtali after *f.* *Num* 26:48
50; *Josh* 19:32
of Zelophehad of Manasseh's *f.*
Num 27:1
divide land by lot among *f.* 33:54
chief fathers of *f.* of Gilead. 36:1
come according to *f.* *Josh* 7:14
half children of Machir, by *f.* 13:31
tribe of Dan according to *f.* 19:40, 48
least of *f.* of Benjamin. *1 Sam* 9:21
f. of Kirjath-jearim. *1 Chr* 2:53
f. of scribes which dwelt at Jabez. 55
these are *f.* of Zorathites. 4:2
f. of them that wrought fine. 21
mentioned princes in their *f.* 38
according to divisions of the *f.*
2 Chr 35:5*, 12*
set people after their *f.* *Neh* 4:13
contempt of *f.* terrify me ? *Job* 31:34
God setteth solitary in *f.* *Ps* 68:6
maketh him *f.* like a flock. 107:41
I will call all the *f.* of. *Jer* 1:15
hear, all ye *f.* of the house. 2:4
fury on the *f.* that call not on. 10:25
I will take all *f.* of the north. 25:9
I will be God of all the *f.* of. 31:1
the two *f.* which Lord hath. 33:24
we will be as the *f.* of. *Ezek* 20:32
you have I known of all *f.* *Amos* 3:2
that selleth *f.* through. *Nah* 3:4
all the *f.* that remain. *Zech* 12:14
will not come up of the *f.* 14:17

family

my face against his *f.* *Lev* 20:5
return every man to his *f.* 25:10, 41
himself to stock of stranger's *f.* 47
his uncle or any of his *f.* may. 49
of Gershon was the *f.* *Num* 3:21
of Kohath was the *f.* of. 27
f. of Hanochites, *f.* of Palluites. 26:5
family *mentioned often to the 59th verse*
name done away from *f.*? 27:4
inheritance to next of his *f.* 11
marry to *f.* of father's. 36:6, 8, 12
lest a *f.* turn away. *Deut* 29:18

the *f.* which the Lord. *Josh* 7:14
took the *f.* of the Zarhites. 17
go man and all his *f.* *Judg* 1:25
my *f.* is poor in Manasseh. 6:15
communed with the *f.* of his. 9:1
Manoah a man of *f.* of the. 13:2
a Levite of the *f.* of Judah. 17:7
Danites sent of their *f.* five. 18:2
be a priest to a *f.* in Israel. 19
departed every man to his *f.* 21:24
a kinsman of the *f.* of. *Ruth* 2:1
f. least of Benjamin. *1 Sam* 9:21
f. of Matri was taken. 10:21
my life, or my father's *f.* 18:18
yearly sacrifice for all *f.* 20:6, 29
whole *f.* is risen against. *2 Sam* 14:7
a man of the *f.* of Saul. 16:5
neither did *f.* multiply. *1 Chr* 4:27
to *f.* of Kohath cities. 6:61, 70
ark remained with *f.* of. 13:14
of Purim kept by every *f.* *Esth* 9:28
a city, and two of a *f.* *Jer* 3:14
chosen by residue of this evil *f.* 8:3
against *f.* I brought out. *Amos* 3:1
every *f.* mourn. *Zech* 12:12, 13, 14
if the *f.* of Egypt go not up. 14:18
whole *f.* in heaven and. *Eph* 3:15

famine

Famines of more or less intensity frequently occurred in Palestine because of its dependence upon the rain, and in Egypt because of its dependence on a proper overflow of the Nile. Not until modern times has it been possible to store rain, or to regulate the flow of rivers, to any appreciable extent. Famine also came naturally when locusts or other insects destroyed the crops. The worst famine named in the Bible is that in Egypt and the surrounding countries in the time of Joseph, Gen 41.

for the *f.* was grievous. *Gen* 12:10
a *f.* in land, besides first *f.* 26:1
empty ears seven years of *f.* 41:27
the *f.* shall consume the land. 30
not be known by reason of *f.* 31
to Joseph two sons before the *f.* 50
the *f.* was over all the face of. 56
land fainted by reason of *f.* 47:13
there was a *f.* *Ruth* 1:1
a *f.* in days of David. *2 Sam* 21:1
shall seven years of *f.* come? 24:13
if there be in land *f.* *1 Ki* 8:37
2 Chr 20:9
a sore *f.* in Samaria. *1 Ki* 18:2
2 Ki 6:25
then *f.* is in the city. *2 Ki* 7:4
the Lord hath called for a *f.* 8:1
the *f.* prevailed in Jerusalem. 25:3
you to die by *f.* *2 Chr* 32:11
in *f.* he shall redeem thee. *Job* 5:20
at destruction and *f.* thou. 22
for want and *f.* were solitary. 30:3
keep them alive in *f.* *Ps* 33:19
in the days of *f.* they shall be. 37:19
he called for a *f.* on land. 105:16
I will kill thy root with *f.* *Isa* 14:30
destruction, *f.* and sword. 51:19
see sword, nor *f.* *Jer* 5:12; 14:13, 15
sword and *f.* shall prophets. 14:15
people cast out, because of *f.* 16
behold them that are sick with *f.* 18
as are for the *f.* to the *f.* 15:2
deliver up their children to *f.* 18:21
from *f.* to Nebuchadnezzar. 21:7
send the *f.* among. 24:10; 29:17
nation will I punish with the *f.* 27:8
persecute with sword and *f.* 29:18
to Chaldeans because of *f.* 32:24
a liberty for you to the *f.* 34:17
f. shall follow close after. 42:16
the *f.* was sore in the city. 52:6
was black, because of *f.* *Lam* 5:10
part consumed with *f.* *Ezek* 5:12
send on them evil arrows of *f.* 16
so will I send on you *f.* 17; 14:13
f. within, *f.* and pestilence. 7:15
leave a few men from *f.* 12:16
and I will lay no *f.* upon you. 36:29
receive no more reproach of *f.* 30
a *f.* not of bread, but of. *Amos* 8:11
great *f.* was through the. *Luke* 4:25
there arose a mighty *f.* 15:14
shall *f.* separate us from? *Rom* 8:35
in one day, death, *f.* *Rev* 18:8

by the **famine**

sons and daughters die *by the f.*
Jer 11:22
consume them *by the f.* 14:12, 15
shall be consumed *by f.* 16:4
44:12, 18, 27
abideth in city die *by the f.* 21:9
why will ye die *by the f.*? 27:13
to king of Babylon *by the f.* 32:36
remaineth in city die *by f.* 38:2
Ezek 6:12
die *by f.* and pestilence. *Jer* 42:17
know that ye shall die *by the f.* 22
punished Jerusalem *by the f.* 44:13
they shall fall *by the f.* *Ezek* 6:11

famines

there shall be *f.* pestilences, and.
Mat. 24:7; *Mark* 13:8; *Luke* 21:11

famish *and* **famished**

all land of Egypt was *f.* *Gen* 41:55
suffer righteous to *f.* *Pr* 10:3
honourable men are *f.* *Isa* 5:13
he will *f.* all gods of the. *Zeph* 2:11

famous

princes *f.* in. *Num* 16:2*; 26:9*
thou *f.* in Beth-lehem. *Ruth* 4:11
his name may be *f.* in Israel. 14
were *f.* men. *1 Chr* 5:24; 12:30
a man was *f.* as he had. *Ps* 74:5*
thanks to him who slew *f.* 136:18
and she became *f.* *Ezek* 23:10*
daughters of the *f.* nations. 32:18

fan, *substantive*

winnowed with the *f.* *Isa* 30:24
I will fan them with a *f.* *Jer* 15:7
whose *f.* is in his hand. *Mat* 3:12
Luke 3:17

fan, *verb*

shalt *f.* them, wind shall. *Isa* 41:16†
a dry wind not to *f.* nor. *Jer* 4:11†
I will *f.* them with a fan. 15:7
fanners that shall *f.* her. 51:2†

far

that be *f.* from thee to. *Gen* 18:25
you shall not go very *f.* *Ex* 8:28
keep thee *f.* from false matter. 23:7
if the place be too *f.* *Deut* 12:21
14:24
stranger come from a *f.* land. 29:22
waters stood very *f.* *Josh* 3:16
go not very *f.* from the city. 8:4
we are *f.* from you, when ye. 9:22
father adventured life *f.* *Judg* 9:17
f. from the Zidonians. 18:7, 28
by Jebus, day was *f.* spent. 19:11
f. be it from thee. *1 Sam* 20:9
they carry them away *f.* *1 Ki* 8:46
his name spread *f.* *2 Chr* 26:15
now therefore be ye *f.* *Ezra* 6:6
separated one *f.* from. *Neh* 4:19
all Jews both nigh and *f.* *Esth* 9:20
children are *f.* from safety. *Job* 5:4
put iniquity *f.* away. 11:14; 22:23
f. be it from God to do. 34:10
judgements are *f.* out of. *Ps* 10:5
why art thou so *f.* from? 22:1
they that are *f.* from thee. 73:27
thou art exalted *f.* above all. 97:9
as *f.* as the east is from the west, so
f. hath he removed. 103:12
let blessing be *f.* from him. 109:17
that follow mischief are *f.* 119:150
salvation is *f.* from wicked. 155
perverse lips put *f.* from. *Pr* 4:24
remove thy way *f.* from her. 5:8
Lord is *f.* from wicked. 15:29
his friends go *f.* from him. 19:7
his soul shall be *f.* from them. 22:5
rod of correction shall drive it *f.* 15
price is *f.* above rubies. 31:10
as *f.* as light excelleth. *Eccl* 2:13
Lord have removed men *f.* *Isa* 6:12
shall turn the rivers *f.* away. 19:6
removed the nations *f.* 26:15
hear ye that are *f.* from. 46:12
swallowed thee be *f.* away. 49:19
shalt be *f.* from oppression. 54:14
therefore is judgement *f.* from. 59:9
thou art *f.* from their. *Jer* 12:2
all the kings of the north *f.* 25:26
to remove you *f.* from land. 27:10
upon all cities of Moab *f.* or. 48:24
thus *f.* is judgement of Moab. 47
thus *f.* are words of Jeremiah. 51:64
my soul *f.* from peace. *Lam* 3:17
have I set it *f.* from. *Ezek* 7:20
said, get ye *f.* from Lord. 11:15
the fourth king *f.* richer. *Dan* 11:2
ye might remove them *f.* *Joel* 3:6
that put *f.* away evil day. *Amos* 6:3
in that day decree be *f.* *Mi* 7:11
be it *f.* from thee, Lord. *Mat* 16:22
when day was now *f.* *Mark* 6:35
not *f.* from the kingdom of. 12:34
is as a man taking *f.* journey. 13:34
was not *f.* from house. *Luke* 7:6
Jesus said, suffer ye thus *f.* 22:51
abide with us, for day is *f.* 24:29
led them out as *f.* as to. 50
were not *f.* from land. *John* 21:8
travelled as *f.* as Phenice. *Acts* 11:19
Barnabas go as *f.* as Antioch. 22
he be not *f.* from every one. 17:27
I will send thee *f.* hence to. 22:21
came to meet us as *f.* as. 28:15
the night is *f.* spent, the. *Rom* 13:12
a *f.* more exceeding. *2 Cor* 4:17
we are come as *f.* as to you. 10:14
f. above all principality. *Eph* 1:21
that ascended up *f.* above all. 4:10
Christ, which is *f.* better. *Phil* 1:23
it is yet *f.* more evident. *Heb* 7:15*
see **country, countries**

far *from me*

saith, be it *f. from me.* *1 Sam* 2:30
22:15; *2 Sam* 20:20; 23:17
withdraw hand *f. from me.* *Job* 13:21
my brethren *f. from me.* 19:13
of wicked *f. from me.* 21:16; 22:18
they flee *f. from me.* 30:10
not *f. from me,* for trouble. *Ps* 22:11
19; 35:22; 38:21; 71:12
hide not thy face *f. from me.* 27:9
mine acquaintance *f. from me.* 88:8
lover and friend *f. from me.* 18
remove *f. from me* vanity. *Pr* 30:8
but it was *f. from me.* *Eccl* 7:23
their heart *f. from me.* *Isa* 29:13
they are gone *f. from me.* *Jer* 2:5
comforter is *f. from me.* *Lam* 1:16
of kings *f. from me.* *Ezek* 43:9
Levites gone *f. from me.* 44:10
heart is *f. from me.* *Mat* 15:8
Mark 7:6

from **far**

against thee *from f.* *Deut* 28:49
Jer 5:15
fetch my knowledge *from f.* *Job* 36:3
up an ensign *from f.* *Isa* 5:26
which shall come *from f.* 10:3
bound which are fled *from f.* 22:3
name of Lord cometh *from f.* 30:27
bring my sons *from f.* 43:6; 60:9
hearken, ye people, *from f.* 49:1
these shall come *from f.* 12
thy sons shall come *from f.* 60:4
I will save thee *from f.* *Jer* 30:10
for men to come *from f.* *Ezek* 23:40
horsemen shall come *from f.*
Hab 1:8
divers of them came *from f.*
Mark 8:3

far *off*

gone, and not yet *f. off.* *Gen* 44:4
shall pitch *f. off* about. *Num* 2:2
gods of people *f. off.* *Deut* 13:7
do to all the cities *f. off.* 20:15
neither is commandment *f. off.* 30:11
king tarried in a place *f. off.*
2 Sam 15:17
captives to a land *f. off.* *2 Chr* 6:36
lo, I would wander *f. off.* *Ps* 55:7
than a brother *f. off.* *Pr* 27:10
f. off who can find out? *Eccl* 7:24
they shall flee *f. off.* *Isa* 17:13
hear, ye that are *f. off.* 33:13
shall behold land that is *f. off.* 17
righteousness not be *f. off.* 46:13
send thy messengers *f. off.* 57:9
peace to him that is *f. off.* 19
look for salvation, it is *f. off.* 59:11

he that is f. off shall die. Ezek 6:12
that I should go f. off. 8:6
although I cast them f. off. 11:16
prophesieth of times f. off. 12:27
those that be f. off from thee. 22:5
to Israel near and f. off. Dan 9:7
I will remove f. off the. Joel 2:20
sell them to Sabeans f. off. 3:8
her that was cast f. off. Mi 4:7
f. off shall come and. Zech 6:15
ye who were f. off made. Eph 2:13

fare

look how thy brethren f. 1 Sam 17:18

fare

so he paid the f. thereof. Jonah 1:3

fared

the rich man f. Luke 16:19

farewell

first go bid them f. at. Luke 9:61
yourselves, ye do well, f. Acts 15:29
Paul bade them f. saying. 18:21
they had to say against him, f. 23:30
finally, brethren, f. be. 2 Cor 13:11

farm

their ways, one to his f. Mat 22:5

farther

f. though a wise man. Eccl 8:17
f. and fell on his face. Mat 26:39
had gone a little f. thence. Mark 1:19
see **further**

farthing, -s

paid the uttermost f. Mat 5:26
two sparrows sold for a f.? 10:29†
in two mites, a f. Mark 12:42
sparrows sold for two f.? Luke 12:6†

fashion

this is the f. thou shalt. Gen 6:15*
f. of the tabernacle. Ex 26:30
bowls made he after the f. 37:19*
according to all the f. 1 Ki 6:38
Ahaz sent the f. of. 2 Ki 16:10
shew them form and f. Ezek 43:11
never saw it on this f. Mark 2:12
f. of his countenance. Luke 9:29
tabernacle according to f. Acts 7:44*
f. of this world passeth. 1 Cor 7:31
found in f. as a man. Phil 2:8
grace of f. of it perisheth. Jas 1:11

fashion

one f. us in the womb? Job 31:15

fashioned

Aaron f. the calf. Ex 32:4
thine hands have f. me. Job 10:8
Ps 119:73
in continuance were f. Ps 139:16
respect to him that f. it. Isa 22:11
thy breasts are f., thine. Ezek 16:7
that it may be f. like. Phil 3:21*

fashioneth

he f. their hearts alike. Ps 33:15
the smith f. it with the. Isa 44:12
clay say to him that f. it? 45:9

fashioning

not f. yourselves to. 1 Pet 1:14

fashions

were according to f. Ezek 42:11

fast, *adverb*

the Lord had f. closed. Gen 20:18
Sisera was f. asleep and. Judg 4:21
but we will bind thee f. 15:13
if they bind me f. with. 16:11*
here f. by my maidens. Ruth 2:8
Boaz said to me, keep f. by. 21
this work goeth f. on. Ezra 5:8*
clods cleave f. together. Job 38:38
he commanded, it stood f. Ps 33:9
his strength setteth f. 65:6
f. hold of instruction. Pr 4:13
of Moab hasteth f. Jer 48:16
took captives held them f. 50:33
in ship, and was f. asleep. Jonah 1:5
who made their feet f. Acts 16:24
forepart stuck f. remained. 27:41*

fast

Fasting has, in all ages, and among all nations, been much in use in times of mourning, sorrow, and afflictions. It is in some sort inspired by nature, which, in these circumstances, denies itself nourishment, and takes off the edge of hunger. There is no example of fasting, properly so called, to be seen before Moses; yet it is presumable that the patriarchs fasted, since we see that there were very great mournings among them, such as that of Abraham for Sarah, Gen 23:2; *and that of Jacob for his son Joseph,* Gen 37:34.

Moses enjoins no particular fast, excepting that upon the day of atonement, which was generally and strictly observed, Lev 23:27, 29. *Since the time of Moses, examples of fasting have been very common among the Jews. Joshua and the elders of Israel remained prostrate before the ark from morning until evening, without eating, after the Israelites were defeated by the men of Ai,* Josh 7:6. *The eleven tribes which had taken arms against that of Benjamin, seeing they could not hold out against the inhabitants of Gibeah, fell down before the ark upon their faces, and so continued till the evening without eating,* Judg 20:26. *The Israelites perceiving themselves to be pressed by the Philistines, assembled before the Lord at Mizpeh, and fasted in his presence till the evening,* 1 Sam 7:6. *And David fasted while the first child he had by Bath-sheba, the wife of Uriah, was sick,* 2 Sam 12:16.

Moses fasted forty days on mount Horeb, Ex 34:28. *Elijah passed as many days without eating any thing,* 1 Ki 19:8. *And our Saviour fasted in the wilderness forty days and forty nights,* Mat 4:2. *These fasts were out of the common rules of nature.*

It does not appear by our Saviour's own practice, or any commands that he gave to his disciples, that he instituted any particular fasts, or enjoined any to be kept out of pure devotion. It is however inferred from such statements as those in Luke 5:33–35, *that he expected his followers would do so. The one condition he made was that it be sincere,* Mat. 6:16.

proclaim a f., set Naboth. 1 Ki 21:9
they proclaimed a f. and set. 12
Jehoshaphat proclaimed a f.
2 Chr 20:3
Ezra proclaimed a f. at. Ezra 8:21
in the day of your f. you. Isa 58:3
such f. I have chosen? call this f.? 5
is not this f. that I have chosen? 6
they proclaimed a f. Jer 36:9
sanctify a f. Joel 1:14; 2:15
Nineveh proclaimed a f. Jonah 3:5
f. of the fourth month, of. Zech 8:19
f. was now already past. Acts 27:9

fast, *verb*

thou didst f. and weep. 2 Sam 12:21
is dead, wherefore should I f.? 23
I and my maidens f. Esth 4:16
ye f. for strife, not f. as. Isa 58:4
when they f. I will not. Jer 14:12
did ye at all f. unto me? Zech 7:5
f. be not as hypocrites of a sad . . .
appear to men to f. Mat 6:16
thou appear not to men to f. 18
why do we f. disciples f. not? 9:14
Mark 2:18
then shall they f. Mat 9:15
Mark 2:20; Luke 5:35
disciples of John used to f.
Mark 2:18
f. while bridegroom with them? they cannot f. 19; Luke 5:35
of John f. often? Luke 5:33
I f. twice in the week. 18:12

fasted

the people f. that day. Judg 20:26
drew water, and f. 1 Sam 7:6
buried them, and f. seven days. 31:13
1 Chr 10:12
and f. for Saul. 2 Sam 1:12
David f. 12:16
while the child was alive I f. 22
Ahab f. 1 Ki 21:27
so we f. Ezra 8:23
Nehemiah f. and prayed. Neh 1:4
why have we f. say they? Isa 58:3
when ye f. in fifth and. Zech 7:5
Jesus f. forty days and. Mat 4:2
ministered to Lord and f. Acts 13:2
when they had f. they laid hands. 3

fasten

shalt f. the chains. Ex 28:14*, 25*
to f. the plate on high. 39:31
I will f. him as a nail. Isa 22:23
they f. it with nails. Jer 10:4

fastened

ends of chains they f. Ex 39:18*
Moses f. his sockets, set up. 40:18*
Jael f. the nail into. Judg 4:21*
Delilah f. it with a pin, and. 16:14
f. Saul's body to wall. 1 Sam 31:10
with a sword f. upon. 2 Sam 20:8
beams should not be f. 1 Ki 6:6*
f. his head in temple. 1 Chr 10:10
six steps were f. to. 2 Chr 9:18
hangings f. with cords of. Esth 1:6
are the foundations f. Job 38:6
as nails f. by masters. Eccl 12:11
nail f. in the sure place. Isa 22:25
f. it with nails that it should. 41:7
within were hooks f. Ezek 40:43
the eyes of all were f. on. Luke 4:20
when I had f. mine eyes. Acts 11:6
a viper out of heat and f. on. 28:3

fastening

Peter f. his eyes upon him. Acts 3:4

fastest

thou f. anoint thy head. Mat 6:17

fasting

were assembled with f. Neh 9:1
decree came, was f. Esth 4:3
humbled my soul with f. Ps 35:13
and chastened soul with f. 69:10
knees are weak through f. 109:24
words of Lord on the f. Jer 36:6
king passed the night f. Dan 6:18
himself to seek by prayer and f. 9:3
turn ye with f. weeping. Joel 2:12
not send them away f. Mat 15:32
goeth not out but by f. 17:21
Mark 9:29
if I send them away f. Mark 8:3
four days ago I was f. Acts 10:30
ordained elders, and prayed f. 14:23
fourteenth day ye continued f. 27:33
may give yourselves to f. 1 Cor 7:5

fastings

the matters of the f. Esth 9:31
Anna served God with f. Luke 2:37
approving ourselves in f. 2 Cor 6:5
in f. often, in cold and. 11:27

fat

The Mosaic law declared that to the Lord belongs all the fat of sacrificial animals, Lev 3:16, 17. *Neither it nor the blood was eaten, but was burned as an offering to God,* Ex 29:13, 22; Lev 4:8, 9. *The ground of this law was that the fat was the richest part of the animal, and therefore belonged to God.*

The word is used figuratively to mean the best part of a thing, or the richest productions, Neh 9:25; Ps 63:5; Isa 25:6; Rom 11:17.

Abel also brought of f. Gen 4:4
the f. of sacrifice remain. Ex 23:18
take f. that covereth the inwards, and f. upon kidneys. 29:13, 22
Lev 3:3, 4, 9, 10, 14, 15; 4:8; 7:3, 4
head and f. in order. Lev 1:8, 12
sweet savour, the f. is Lord's. 3:16
he shall take off the f. of. 4:8, 31, 35
burn his f. 26; 6:12; 7:3, 31; 17:6
Num 18:17
f. of beast dieth of itself. Lev 7:24
the f. with breast, it shall he. 30

he that offereth *f.* shall have. *Lev* 7:33
Moses burnt head and *f.* of. 8:20
one wafer and put them on *f.* 26
but the *f.* he burnt. 9:10, 20
fire from Lord consumed *f.* 24
the *f.* of sin offering shall. 16:25
f. of lambs with *f.* of *Deut* 32:14
and the *f.* closed upon. *Judg* 3:22
before they burnt *f.* *1 Sam* 2:15
let them not fail to burn the *f.* 16
to hearken is better than *f.* of. 15:22
from *f.* of mighty. *2 Sam* 1:22
altar too little to receive *f.* *1 Ki* 8:64
offered *f.* of. *2 Chr* 7:7; 29:35
priests busied in offering *f.* 35:14
he maketh collops of *f.* *Job* 15:27
inclosed in their own *f.* *Ps* 17:10
enemies of Lord as the *f.* of. 37:20
full of *f.* of fed beasts. *Isa* 1:11
made *f.* with the *f.* of kidneys. 34:6
nor hast filled me with *f.* of. 43:24
when ye offer the *f.* and. *Ezek* 44:7
stand to offer to me the *f.* 15

fat, *adjective*

came seven kine *f.* *Gen* 41:2
did eat up seven *f.* kine. 4, 20
out of Asher bread shall be *f.* 49:20
land is, whether *f.* or. *Num* 13:20
waxen *f.* then they turn. *Deut* 31:20
f. and kicked, thou waxen *f.* 32:15
Eglon was a very *f.* man. *Judg* 3:17
to make yourselves *f.* *1 Sam* 2:29
the woman had a *f.* calf. 28:24
Adonijah slew *f.* cattle. *1 Ki* 1:9
19, 25
provision for one day ten *f.* 4:23
they found *f.* pasture. *1 Chr* 4:40
a *f.* land became *f.* *Neh* 9:25
not served thee in large and *f.* 35
that be *f.* on earth shall. *Ps* 22:29
shall be *f.* and flourishing. 92:14*
their heart as *f.* as grease. 119:70
soul shall be made *f.* *Pr* 11:25
soul of diligent be made *f.* 13:4
a good report maketh bones *f.* 15:30
in Lord shall be made *f.* 28:25
waste places of *f.* ones. *Isa* 5:17
make heart of this people *f.* 6:10
Lord shall send among his *f.* 10:16
make a feast of *f.* things. 25:6
on the head of *f.* valleys. 28:1
on the head of the *f.* valley. 4
and bread shall be *f.* and. 30:23
sword of Lord is made *f.* 34:6
and their dust shall be made *f.* 7
Lord shall make *f.* thy. 58:11*
they are waxen *f.* they. *Jer* 5:28
grown *f.* as the heifer at. 50:11*
in a *f.* pasture shall feed. *Ezek* 34:14
but I will destroy the *f.* and. 16
I will judge between the *f.* 20
one lamb out of *f.* pastures. 45:15†
offering of *f.* beasts. *Amos* 5:22
by them their portion is *f.* *Hab* 1:16

eat **fat**

and ye shall *eat* the *f.* *Gen* 45:18
a statute that ye *eat* no *f.*
Lev 3:17; 7:23
whoso *eateth* *f.* of the beast. 7:25
which did *eat* the *f.* *Deut* 32:38
eat the *f.* and drink sweet. *Neh* 8:10
ye *eat* *f.* and clothe you. *Ezek* 34:3
eat *f.* till ye be full and. 39:19
eat the flesh of the *f.* *Zech* 11:16

father

In addition to its common use, this word is also used [1] *in the sense of seniors,* Acts 7:2; 22:1; *and of parents in general, or ancestors,* Dan 5:2; Jer 27:7; Mat 23:30, 32. [2] *The founder of a trade or profession, and the head of the inhabitants of a town,* Gen 4:20–22; 1 Chr 2:51; 4:14, 18. [3] *God, either as the Creator of the human race or as the loving guardian of his spiritual children, or in his relation to Jesus Christ,* Mal 2:10; Rom 8:15; Mark 14:36.

Jabal was *f.* of such as. *Gen* 4:20
Jubal was the *f.* of all such as. 21
and Ham is the *f.* of. 9:18
f. of nations. 17:4, 5; *Rom* 4:17, 18
have ye a *f.*? *Gen* 44:19
and we said, we have a *f.* 20
God made me *f.* to Pharaoh. 45:8
whose *f.* was an Egyptian. *Lev* 24:10
as a nursing *f.* beareth. *Num* 11:12
statutes between *f.* and. 30:16
f. shall bring forth. *Deut* 22:15
man give damsel's *f.* fifty. 29
of house of mother's *f.* *Judg* 9:1
with me, and be to me a *f.* 17:10
go with us, and be to us a *f.* 18:19
the *f.* of the damsel saw him. 19:3
damsel's *f.* retained him, he. 4
Kish was the *f.* of Saul. *1 Sam* 9:3
14:51
Salem the *f.* of. *1 Chr* 2:51
of Hemath the *f.* of house of. 55
Joab the *f.* of the valley of. 4:14
at Gibeon dwelt *f.* of. 8:29; 9:35
Esther had neither *f.* nor. *Esth* 2:7
I was a *f.* to the poor. *Job* 29:16
up with me, as with a *f.* 31:18
hath the rain a *f.*? 38:28
f. of fatherless, and judge. *Ps* 68:5
as a *f.* pitieth his children. 103:13
correcteth, even as a *f.* *Pr* 3:12
hear the instruction of a *f.* 4:1
son maketh a glad *f.* 10:1; 15:20
f. of a fool hath no joy. 17:21
f. of the righteous rejoice. 23:24
called, the everlasting *F.* *Isa* 9:6
Eliakim shall be a *f.* to. 22:21
the *f.* to child shall make. 38:19
for I am a *f.* to Israel. *Jer* 31:9
as the soul of the *f.* so. *Ezek* 18:4
son bear the iniquity of *f.*? 19
son shall not bear iniquity of *f.* 20
in thee they set light by *f.* 22:7
for *f.* or mother they may. 44:25
the son dishonoureth *f.* *Mi* 7:6
if I then be a *f.* where? *Mal* 1:6
have we not all one *f.*? 2:10
f. deliver up the child. *Mat* 10:21
Mark 13:12
he that loveth *f.* or. *Mat* 10:37
I thank thee, O *F.* Lord of. 11:25
so *F.* it seemed good. 26; *Luke* 10:21
John 11:41
knoweth Son, but the *F.* *Mat* 11:27
that curseth *f.* let him die. 15:4
Mark 7:10
leave *f.* and mother, and. *Mat* 19:5
that hath forsaken *f.* mother, or.
29; *Mark* 10:29
baptizing in name of *F.* *Mat* 28:19
taketh *f.* of damsel. *Mark* 5:40
Luke 8:51
the *f.* of the child cried. *Mark* 9:24
knoweth no man, but the *F.* 13:32
Abba, *F.*, all things are. 14:36
Simon *f.* of Alexander. 15:21
no man knows who *F.* is. *Luke* 10:22
ask bread of any that is a *f.* 11:11
f. shall be divided against the son, the son against the *f.* 12:53
f. I have sinned against. 15:21
f. said, bring forth best robe. 22
I pray thee, *f.* send to my. 16:27
F. if thou be willing, remove. 22:42
F. forgive them, they know. 23:34
F. into thy hands I commend. 46
of the only begotten of *F.* *John* 1:14
Son which is in bosom of the *F.* 18
the *F.* loveth the Son. 3:35; 5:20
nor at Jerusalem worship *F.* 4:21
shall worship the *F.* in spirit. 23
the *f.* knew that it was at the. 53
but what he seeth *F.* do. 5:19
for as the *F.* raiseth up dead. 21
F. judgeth no man, but hath. 22
they honour the *F.*: he that honoureth not Son, honoureth not *F.* 23
for as the *F.* hath life in himself. 26
seek not mine own, but will of *F.* 30
works which *F.* hath given me bear witness that the *F.* hath sent. 36
F. which sent me, hath borne. 37
8:16; 12:49; 14:24; *1 John* 4:14
think not that I accuse you to the *F.*
John 5:45
him hath God the *F.* sealed. 6:27
all that the *F.* giveth me shall. 37
and this is the *F.'s* will, that. 39
is not this Jesus, whose *f.* and? 42
no man can come, except *F.*
John 6:44
that hath learned of the *F.* 45
any hath seen *F.* he hath seen *F.* 46
F. hath sent me, and I live by *F.* 57
not alone, but I and the *F.* 8:16
the *F.* that sent me beareth. 18
understood not he spake of *F.* 27
F. hath not left me alone. 29
we have one *F.* even God. 41
devil is a liar, and the *f.* of it. 44
F. knoweth me, so know I *F.* 10:15
say ye of him whom the *F.* 36
believe that the *F.* is in me. 38
F. save me from this hour. 12:27
F. glorify thy name; then came. 28
even as the *F.* said unto me. 50
he should depart unto *F.* 13:1
knowing that the *F.* had given all. 3
I am the way, truth, and life, no man cometh to the *F.* but by me. 14:6
Lord, shew us the *F.* and. 8
hath seen me, hath seen the *F.* 9
I am in the *F.* and *F.* in. 11; 17:21
that the *F.* may be glorified. 14:13
I will pray the *F.* for you. 16; 16:26
Comforter whom the *F.* will. 14:26
I love the *F.*: as the *F.* gave me. 31
as the *F.* hath loved me, so. 15:9
whatsoever ye shall ask of the *F.* in my name, he may. 16; 16:23
from the *F.* the Spirit who proceedeth from the *F.* 15:26
they have not known the *F.* 16:3
all things that the *F.* hath are. 15
because I go the the *F.* 16, 17
shew you plainly of the *F.* 25
the *F.* loveth you, because ye. 27
forth from the *F.* and go to the *F.* 28
not alone, because the *F.* is. 32
F. the hour is come. 17:1
O *F.* glorify thou me with. 5
Holy *F.* keep those whom thou. 11
F. I will that they also, whom. 24
O righteous *F.* the world hath. 25
for promise of the *F.* *Acts* 1:4
the *F.* hath put in his own power. 7
received of the *F.* the promise. 2:33
he might be *f.* of all. *Rom* 4:11
and the *f.* of circumcision to them. 12
faith of Abraham, the *f.* of. 16
raised from the dead by the *F.* 6:4
whereby we cry, Abba, *F.* 8:15
are beloved for *F.'s* sake. 11:28
glorify God the *F.* of our. 15:6
2 Cor 1:3; 11:31; *Eph* 1:3
1 Pet 1:3
but one God, the *F.* *1 Cor* 8:6
up kingdom to God the *F.* 15:24
F. of mercies, the God. *2 Cor* 1:3
I will be a *F.* unto you. 6:18
Paul an apostle by Jesus Christ and God the *F.* *Gal* 1:1
peace from God the *F.* 3; *2 Tim* 1:2
Tit 1:4
will of God and our *F.* *Gal* 1:4
until time appointed of the *F.* 4:2
Spirit into your hearts, crying, *F.* 6
our Lord Jesus, the *F.* *Eph* 1:17
access by one Spirit to the *F.* 2:18
for this cause I bow unto *F.* 3:14
one God and *F.* of all. 4:6
giving thanks to the *F.* 5:20
Col 1:3, 12; 3:17
faith from God the *F.* *Eph* 6:23
to the glory of the *F.* *Phil* 2:11
as a son with the *f.* he hath. 22
it pleased *F.* that in him. *Col* 1:19
of the mystery of the *F.* 2:2
church which is in God *F.* *1 Thes* 1:1
we charged you, as a *f.* doth. 2:11
entreat him as a *f.* *1 Tim* 5:1
will be to him a *F.* *Heb* 1:5
Melchisedec without *f.* 7:3
whom the *F.* chasteneth not? 12:7
be in subjection to *F.* of spirits. 9
good gift cometh from *F.* *Jas* 1:17
religion before God and *F.* 27
therewith bless God, even *F.* 3:9
foreknowledge of God *F.* *1 Pet* 1:2
if ye call on the *F.* who. 17
received from God the *F.* *2 Pet* 1:17
life, which was with *F.* *1 John* 1:2
our fellowship is with the *F.* 3

have an Advocate with the *F*. *1 John* 2:1
because ye have known the *F*. 13
the love of *F*. is not in him. 15
pride of life is not of the *F*. 16
he is antichrist that denieth *F*. 22
denieth the Son, hath not *F*.: he that acknowledgeth Son hath *F*. 23
continue in Son and in the *F*. 24
what manner of love *F*. hath. 3:1
three bear record, *F*. the Word. 5:7
the *F*. and from Lord Jesus Christ the Son of the *F*. *2 John* 3
a commandment from the *F*. 4
he that abideth in Christ hath *F*. 9
sanctified by God the *F*. *Jude* 1
see **Abraham**

her father

in and lay with her *f*. *Gen* 19:33
Rachel came with *her f.'s*. 29:9
her f.'s brother, told *her f*. 12
images that were *her f.'s*. 31:19
Tamar dwelt in *her f.'s*. 38:11
if *her f*. utterly refuse. *Ex* 22:17
she profaneth *her f*. *Lev* 21:9
returned to *her f.'s* house as in youth, shall eat of *her f.'s* meat. 22:13
her f. had but spit in. *Num* 12:14
woman vow a vow in *her f.'s*. 30:3
and *her f*. hear her, and shall hold. 4
if *her f*. disallow her in the day. 5
her youth, in *her f.'s* house. 16
wife to one of tribe of *her f*. 36:8
bewail *her f*. and mother a month. *Deut* 21:13
to door *of her f.'s* house, to play whore in *her f.'s* house. 22:21
brought Rahab and *her f*. *Josh*. 6:23
he saved *her f.'s* household. 25
to ask of *her f*. a field. 15:18
Judg 1:14
months returned to *her f*. *Judg* 11:39
but *her f*. would not suffer. 15:1
Philistines burnt her and *her f*. 6
brought him into *her f.'s*. 19:3
when *her f*. and *mother*. *Esth* 2:7

his father

shall a man leave *his f*. and mother. *Gen* 2:24; *Mark* 10:7; *Eph* 5:31
saw nakedness of *his f*. *Gen* 9:22
Haran died before *his f*. 11:28
blessing wherewith *his f*. 27:41
Jacob obeyed *his f*. and. 28:7
Jacob sware by fear of *his f*. 31:53
in the land wherein *his f*. 37:1
Joseph brought to *his f*. their. 2
told the dream to *his f*. *his f*. 10
brethren envied, but *his f*. 11
rid him, to deliver him to *his f*. 22
the lad cannot leave *his f*. 44:22
sacrifices to the God of *his f*. 46:1
went up to meet Israel *his f*. 29
Joseph nourished *his f*. and. 47:12
made a mourning for *his f*. 50:10
Amram took *his f.'s* sister. *Ex* 6:20
he that smiteth *his f*. shall. 21:15
curseth *his f*. shall die. 17; *Lev* 20:9
fear every man his mother and *his f*. *Lev* 19:3
man that lieth with *his f.'s*. 20:11
if a man take *his f.'s* daughter. 17
of Aaron be defiled for *his f*. 21:2
priest not defile himself for *his f*. 11
Nazarite not unclean for *his f*. *Num* 6:7
inheritance to *his f.'s*. 27:10
if *his f*. have no brethren. 11
will not obey *his f*. *Deut* 21:18
his f. bring him to the elders. 19
man shall not take *his f.'s*. 22:30
he that setteth light by *his f*. 27:16
lieth with daughter of *his f*. 22
said to *his f*. I have not seen. 33:9
Gideon feared *his f.'s*. *Judg* 6:27
buried in sepulchre of *his f*. 8:32
wickedness he did to *his f*. 9:56
his f. knew not that it was of. 14:4
Jonathan told not *his f*. *1 Sam* 14:1
heard not when *his f*. charged. 27
spake good of David to *his f*. 19:4
it was determined of *his f*. 20:33
because *his f*. had done shame. 34
in sepulchre of *his f*. *2 Sam* 2:32
I will be *his f*. and he. *2 Sam* 7:14
as *his f*. shewed kindness. 10:2
1 Chr 19:2
Absalom went in unto *his f.'s*. *2 Sam* 16:22
Ahithophel buried in sepulchre of *his f*. 17:23
Saul buried in sepulchre of *his f*. 21:14
his f. was a man of Tyre. *1 Ki* 7:14
2 Chr 2:14
his f. had dedicated. *1 Ki* 7:51
15:15; *2 Chr* 15:18
as heart of David *his f*. *1 Ki* 11:4
Solomon went not fully after Lord, as did David *his f*. 6; 15:11
2 Ki 18:3; *2 Chr* 28:1; 29:2
not as did David *his f*. *1 Ki* 11:33
2 Ki 14:3; 16:2
walked in all sins of *his f*. *1 Ki* 15:3
Nadab did evil and walked in way of *his f*. 26; 22:43, 52; *2 Ki* 21:21
did evil, not like *his f*. *2 Ki* 3:2
together after Ahab *his f*. 9:25
cities taken out of hand of *his f*. 13:25
son of Joash, slew servants who had slain *his f*. 14:5; *2 Chr* 25:3
king instead of *his f*. *2 Ki* 14:21
23:30, 34
Reuben defiled *his f.'s*. *1 Chr* 5:1
I will be *his f*. he shall. 17:13; 28:6
not firstborn, yet *his f*. 26:10
appeared to David *his f*. *2 Chr* 3:1
to order of David *his f*. 8:14
walked in first ways of *his f*. 17:3
Jehoshaphat sought God of *his f*. 4
walked in way of Asa *his f*. 20:32
counsellors after death of *his f*. 22:4
in ways of David *his f*. 34:2, 3
heareth instruction of *his f*. *Pr* 13:1
fool despiseth *his f.'s* instruction. 15:5
foolish son is a grief to *his f*. 17:25
foolish son calamity of *his f*. 19:13
he that wasteth *his f*., is a son. 26
whoso curseth *his f*. his lamp. 20:20
of riotous men shameth *his f*. 28:7
whoso robbeth *his f*. or mother. 24
wisdom, rejoiceth *his f*. 29:3
ravens pick out eye that mocketh *his f*. 30:17
to him that saith to *his f*. *Isa* 45:10
a son that seeth *his f.'s*. *Ezek* 18:14
not die for iniquity of *his f*. 17
as for *his f*. because he cruelly. 18
bring golden vessels *his f*. *Dan* 5:2
a man and *his f*. go in to. *Amos* 2:7
his f. and mother shall. *Zech* 13:3
a son honours *his f*. a. *Mal* 1:6
at variance against his *f*. *Mat* 10:35
whoso shall say to *his f*. it. 15:5
Mark 7:11
and honour not *his f*. or. *Mat* 15:6
of man come in glory of *his F*. 16:27
Mark 8:38; *Luke* 9:26
did the will of *his f*.? *Mat* 21:31
he asked *his f*. how ? *Mark* 9:21
him the throne of *his f*. *Luke* 1:32
called him after name of *his f*. 59
they made signs unto *his f*. 62
his f. Zacharias was filled with. 67
Jesus delivered him to *his f*. 9:42
to me, and hate not *his f*. 14:26
younger of them said to *his f*. 15:12
arose and came to *his f*. *his f*. saw. 20
therefore came *his f*. and. 28
said, God was *his F*. *John* 5:18
but *his f*. was a Greek. *Acts* 16:1
have *his f.'s* wife. *1 Cor* 5:1
was yet in loins of *his f*. *Heb* 7:10
priests to God and his *F*. *Rev* 1:6
his F.'s name written in. 14:1
see **house**

my father

yesternight with my *f*. *Gen* 19:34
she is daughter of *my f*. not. 20:12
my f. peradventure will feel. 27:12
bless me, even me also, O *my f*. 34
the God of *my f*. 31:5, 42; 32:9
Ex 18:4
came to thy servant *my f*. *Gen* 44:24, 27, 30
surety for the lad to *my f*. *Gen* 44:32
doth *my f*. yet live ? 45:3
haste to go up to *my f*. 9
tell *my f*. 13
my f. and brethren are come. 47:1
not so, *my f*. for this is. 48:18
ready to perish *my f*. *Deut* 26:5
will save alive *my f*. *Josh* 2:13
my f. fought for you. *Judg* 9:17
my f. if thou hast opened. 11:36
not told it *my f*. nor my. 14:16
lest *my f*. leave caring. *1 Sam* 9:5
my f. troubled the land. 14:29
and what is *my f.'s* family ? 18:18
Saul *my f*. seeketh to kill. 19:2
I will commune with *my f*. of thee. 3
my f. will do nothing, but he. 20:2
as he hath been with *my f*. 13
let my *f*. and my mother be. 22:3
hand of Saul *my f*. shall not. 28:17
the kingdom of *my f*. *2 Sam* 16:3
buried by grave of *my f*. 19:37
ark of Lord before David *my f*. in all wherein *my f*. was. *1 Ki* 2:26
my f. David not knowing. 32
that thou didst to David *my f*. 44
thou hast shewed to David *my f*. 3:6
thy servant king instead of *my f*. 7
David *my f*. could not build. 5:3
Lord spake to David *my f*. saying. 5
in the heart of David *my f*. to. 8:17
kept with thy servant David *my f*. 24
let my word be verified to *my f*. 26
2 Chr 6:16
shall be thicker than my *f.'s*. loins. *1 Ki* 12:10; *2 Chr* 10:10
my f. did lade you with. *1 Ki* 12:11
2 Chr 10:11
my f. chastised you. *1 Ki* 12:14
2 Chr 10:14
league between *my f*. *1 Ki* 15:19
2 Chr 16:3
kiss *my f*. and mother. *1 Ki* 19:20
cities *my f*. took I will. 20:34
saw it, cried, *my f*. *my f*. *2 Ki* 2:12
my f. shall I smite them ? 6:21
my f. *my f*. the chariot of. 13:14
chose me before house of *my f*. and among sons of *my f*. *1 Chr* 28:4
didst deal with *my f*. *2 Chr* 2:3
of *my f.'s* sepulchres. *Neh* 2:3
send me to city of *my f.s'*. 5
corruption, thou art *my f*. *Job* 17:14
my f. and my mother. *Ps* 27:10
cry unto me, thou art *my F*. 89:26
for I was *my f.'s* son. *Pr* 4:3
knowledge to cry, *my f*. *Isa* 8:4
stock, thou art *my f*. *Jer* 2:27
not cry unto me, *my f*.? 3:4, 19
who brought tidings to *my f*. 20:15
whom *my f*. brought out. *Dan* 5:13
doeth the will of *my F*. *Mat* 7:21
12:50
go and bury *my f*. 8:21; *Luke* 9:59
I confess before *my F*. *Mat* 10:32
him will I deny before *my F*. 33
are delivered to me of *my F*. 11:27
Luke 10:22
plant *my* heavenly *F*. *Mat* 15:13
my F. who is in heaven. 16:17
angels behold face of *my F*. 18:10
it shall be done of *my F*. 19
so shall *my* heavenly *F*. also. 35
whom prepared of *my F*. 20:23
no man but *my F*. only. 24:36
come ye blessed of *my F*. 25:34
new with you in *my F.'s*. 26:29
O *my F*. if it be possible, let. 39
my F. if this cup may not pass. 42
thinkest I cannot pray to *my F*.? 53
must be about *my F.'s*. *Luke* 2:49
many hired servants of *my f*. 15:17
arise, and go to *my f*. and say, *f*. 18
send him to *my f.'s* house. 16:27
as *my F*. hath appointed. 22:29
I send the promise of *my F*. 24:49
my F. worketh hitherto. *John* 5:17
but the will of *my F*. 30
I am come in *my F.'s* name. 43
my F. giveth you true bread. 6:32
except it be given of *my F*. 65
neither know me, nor *my F*. 8:19
my F. hath taught me, I speak. 28
which I have seen with *my F*. 38

but I honour *my F.* and ye. *John* 8:49
it is *my F.* that honoureth me. 54
therefore doth *my F.* love. 10:17
commandment received of *my F.* 18
works I do in *my F.'s* name bear. 25
my F. who gave them, none is able to pluck them out of *my F.'s.* 29
I and *my F.* are one. 30
works I shewed from *my F.* 32
if I do not works of *my F.* 37
me, him will *my F.* honour. 12:26
should have known *my F.* 14:7
because I go to *my F.* 12; 16:10
know that I am in *my F.* 14:20
loveth me, be loved of *my F.* 21, 23
my F. is greater than I. 28
I am the vine, *my F* is the. 15:1
herein is *my F.* glorified. 8
kept *my F.'s* commandments. 10
all that I heard of *my F.* I have. 15
hateth me, hateth *my F.* 23, 24
the cup *my F.* hath given. 18:11
for I am not yet ascended to *my F.* I ascend to *my F.* and. 20:17
as *my F.* hath sent me. 21
as I received of *my F.* *Rev* 2:27
confess his name before *my F.* 3:5

our **father**

our f. is old. *Gen* 19:31
make *our f.* drink wine. 32
away all that was *our f.'s.* 31:1, 16
youngest is this day with *our f.* 42:13, 32
thy servant *our f.* is in. 43:28
bring *our f.* with sorrow. 44:31
our f. died in wilderness. *Num* 27:3
why should the name of *our f.*? 4
God of Israel *our F.* *1 Chr* 29:10
thou art *our F.*, Abraham. *Isa* 63:16
O Lord, thou art *our F.* 64:8
our f. commanded us. *Jer* 35:6
obeyed the voice of *our f.* 8, 10
our F. which art in heaven. *Mat* 6:9; *Luke* 11:2
kingdom of *our f.* David. *Mark* 11:10
sware to *our f.* Abraham. *Luke* 1:73
we have Abraham to *our f.* 3:8
art thou greater than *our f.*? *John* 4:12; 8:53
of glory appeared to *our f.* *Acts* 7:2
and peace from God *our F.* *Rom* 1:7
1 Cor 1:3; *2 Cor* 1:2; *2 Thes* 1:2
1 Tim 1:2; *Philem* 3
even by *our f.* Isaac. *Rom* 9:10
will of God, and *our F.* *Gal* 1:4
peace from God *our F.* *Eph* 1:2
Phil 1:2; *Col* 1:2; *1 Thes* 1:1
unto God *our F.* be. *Phil* 4:20
sight of God and our *F.* *1 Thes* 1:3
now God *our F.* direct our. 3:11
you in holiness before *our F.* 13
Paul unto church in God *our F.* *2 Thes* 1:1
now God, even *our F.* comfort. 2:16

their **father**

nakedness of *their f.* and saw not nakedness of *their f.* *Gen* 9:23
made *their f.* drink wine. 19:33
daughters with child by *their f.* 36
went to feed *their f.'s* flock. 37:12
to water *their f.'s* flock. *Ex* 2:16
anoint them as thou didst *their f.* 40:15
to the tribe of *their f.* *Num* 36:6
after Dan *their f.* *Josh* 19:47
Judg 18:29
to voice of *their f.* *1 Sam* 2:25
one said, who is *their f.*? 10:12
prophet's sons told *their f.* *1 Ki* 13:11
Ephraim *their f.* *1 Chr* 7:22
died before *their f.* 24:2
under hands of *their f.* 25:3, 6
their f. gave them gifts. *2 Chr* 21:3
their f. gave inheritance. *Job* 42:15
a generation that curseth *their f.* *Pr* 30:11
consolation for *their f.* *Jer* 16:7
Jonadab's sons obeyed *their f.'s.* 35:14, 16
their f.'s nakedness. *Ezek* 22:10
ship with Zebedee *their f.* *Mat* 4:21
they left ship and *their f.* and. 22

shine in kingdom of *their f.* *Mat* 13:43

thy **father**

thee from *thy f.'s* house. *Gen* 12:1
I heard *thy f.* speak to Esau. 27:6
thou shalt bring it to *thy f.* 10
remain a widow at *thy f.'s.* 38:11
I am the God of *thy f.*, fear. 46:3
by the God of *thy f.* 49:25
the blessings of *thy f.* have. 26
thy f. commanded before he. 50:16
forgive servants of God of *thy f.* 17
honour *thy f.* and mother. *Ex* 20:12
Deut 5:16; *Mat* 15:4; 19:19
brethren of tribe of *thy f.* *Num* 18:2
God of *thy f.* promised. *Deut* 6:3
is not he *thy f.*? 32:6
ask *thy f.* and he will shew thee. 7
hast left *thy f.* and. *Ruth* 2:11
is my sin before *thy f.*? *1 Sam* 20:1
if *thy f.* miss me, then say. 6
chose me before *thy f.* *2 Sam* 6:21
David doth honour *thy f.* that he sent comforters to ? 10:3; *1 Chr* 19:3
served in *thy f.'s* presence. *2 Sam* 16:19
do it for David *thy f.'s.* *1 Ki* 11:12
thy f. made yoke grievous. 12:4, 10
2 Chr 10:4
a league between my father and *thy f.* *1 Ki* 15:19
cities my father took from *thy f.* 20:34
thee to prophets of *thy f.* *2 Ki* 3:13
Lord, the God of David *thy f.* 20:5
2 Chr 21:12; *Isa* 38:5
know thou the God of *thy f.* *1 Chr* 28:9
walk before me as *thy f.* *2 Chr* 7:17
aged men elder than *thy f.* *Job* 15:10
instruction of *thy f.* *Pr* 1:8; 23:22
keep *thy f.'s* commandment. 6:20
thy f. and mother be glad. 23:25
thine own and *thy f.'s.* friend. 27:10
thy first *f.* hath sinned. *Isa* 43:27
thee with heritage of *thy f.* 58:14
house of *thy f.* dealt. *Jer* 12:6
did not *thy f.* eat, drink, and? 22:15
thy f. was an Amorite. *Ezek* 16:3
of *thy f.* the king, *thy f.* *Dan* 5:11
God gave *thy f.* a kingdom. 18
thy F. which seeth. *Mat* 6:4, 6, 18
shut thy door, pray to *thy F.* 6
honour *thy f.* and mother. *Mark* 7:10
10:19; *Luke* 18:20; *Eph* 6:2
thy f. and I sought. *Luke* 2:48
thy f. hath killed the fatted. 15:27
said they, where is *thy f.*? *John* 8:19

your **father**

power I served *your f.* *Gen* 31:6
your f. hath deceived me. 7
is *your f.* alive ? 43:7
you up in peace to *your f.* 44:17
you wagons, bring *your f.* 45:19
hearken unto Israel *your f.* 49:2
obeyed Jonadab *your f.* *Jer* 35:18
your f. an Amorite. *Ezek* 16:45
may glorify *your F.* who. *Mat* 5:16
may be children of *your F.* 45
be ye perfect, as *your F.* in. 48
have no reward of *your F.* 6:1
your F. knoweth what things ye. 8, 32; *Luke* 12:30
forgive, *your* heavenly *F.* *Mat* 6:14
if ye forgive not, neither will *your F.* 15; *Mark* 11:25, 26
sparrow fall without *your F.* *Mat* 10:29
it is not the will of *your F.* 18:14
call no man *your f.* upon earth, one is *your F.* which is in heaven. 23:9
your F. also is merciful. *Luke* 6:36
it is *your F.'s* pleasure to. 12:32
have seen with *your f.* *John* 8:38
ye do the deeds of *your f.* then. 41
if God were *your F.* ye would. 42
ye are of *your f.* the devil, the lusts of *your f.* ye will do. 44
I ascend to my Father and *your F.* 20:17

father-in-law

thy *f.-in-law* goeth to Timnath. *Gen* 38:13

she went to her *f.-in-law.* *Gen* 38:25
flock of Jethro his *f.-in-law.* *Ex* 3:1; 4:18
Moses' *f.-in-law.* 18:1, 8, 14, 17
Judg 1:16*; 4:11*
let his *f.-in-law* depart. *Ex* 18:27
Raguel, Moses' *f.-in-law.* *Num* 10:29
f.-in-law retained him. *Judg* 19:4
rose to depart, his *f.-in-law* urged. 7
f.-in-law was dead. *1 Sam* 4:19, 21
Annas was *f.-in-law* to. *John* 18:13

fatherless

not afflict any *f.* child. *Ex* 22:22
be widows, and children *f.* 24
execute the judgement of the *f.* and. *Deut* 10:18; *Ps* 82:3; *Isa* 1:17
ye overwhelm the *f.* and *Job* 6:27
the arms of the *f.* have been. 22:9
they drive away the ass of *f.* 24:3
pluck the *f.* from the breast. 9
delivered the poor and the *f.* 29:12
eaten alone, and *f.* have not. 31:17
lifted up my hand against the *f.* 21
art the helper of the *f.* *Ps* 10:14
to judge the *f.* and the oppressed. 18
a father of the *f.* a judge of. 68:5
let his children be *f.* 109:9
nor any favour his *f.* children. 12
not into fields of the *f.* *Pr* 23:10
judge not the *f.* *Isa* 1:23; *Jer* 5:28
not have mercy on their *f.* *Isa* 9:17
that they may rob the *f.* 10:2
leave thy *f.* children. *Jer* 49:11
we are orphans and *f.* *Lam* 5:3
have they vexed the *f.* *Ezek* 22:7
in thee *f.* findeth mercy. *Hos* 14:3
those that oppress the *f.* *Mal* 3:5
pure religion to visit *f.* and. *Jas* 1:27

fatherless with *stranger*

the *stranger*, the *f.*, the widow come. *Deut* 14:29; 24:19, 20, 21; 26:12, 13
stranger and *f.* rejoice. 16:11, 14
judgement of *stranger* nor *f.* 24:17
judgement of *stranger* and *f.* 27:19
they slay *stranger*, murder the *f.* *Ps* 94:6
preserveth *strangers* and *f.* 146:9
oppressed not *stranger*, *f.* and. *Jer* 7:6; 22:3; *Zech* 7:10

fathers

heads of their *f.*' houses. *Ex* 6:14, 25
Josh 14:1; 19:51; 21:1
1 Chr 8:10, 13, 28
thy father, nor thy *f.* *Ex* 10:6
iniquity of the *f.* upon the. 20:5
34:7; *Num* 14:18; *Deut* 5:9
f. shall not be put to death . . . for *f.* *Deut* 24:16; *2 Ki* 14:6
whose *f.* I would have. *Job* 30:1
and riches inheritance of *f.* *Pr* 19:14
kings be thy nursing *f.* *Isa* 49:23
f. and sons shall fall. *Jer* 6:21; 13:14
children gather wood, *f.* 7:18
f. eaten sour grapes. 31:29
Ezek 18:2
iniquity of the *f.* on. *Jer* 32:18
the *f.* shall not look back to. 47:3
f. shall eat the sons in. *Ezek* 5:10
the *f.* to children, and children to *f.* *Mal* 4:6; *Luke* 1:17
not of Moses, but of the *f.* *John* 7:22
and *f.* hearken. *Acts* 7:2; 22:1
promise made unto the *f.* 13:32
of the law of the *f.* 22:3
whose are the *f.* of whom. *Rom* 9:5
yet have not many *f.* *1 Cor* 4:15
f. provoke not children. *Eph* 6:4
Col 3:21
in times past to the *f.* *Heb* 1:1
we had *f.* of our flesh who. 12:9
since the *f.* fell asleep. *2 Pet* 3:4
I write unto you *f.* *1 John* 2:13, 14
see **buried, chief**

his **fathers**

removed the idols *his f.* *1 Ki* 15:12
the things *his f.* had. *2 Ki* 12:18
did what was evil as *his f.* 15:9
forsook Lord God of *his f.* 21:22
2 Chr 21:10
according to all *his f.* had done. *2 Ki* 23:32, 37; 24:9

like burning of his f. 2 Chr 21:19
Ahaz provoked God of his f. 28:25
heart to seek God of his f. 30:19
himself before God of his f. 33:12
to generation of his f. Ps 49:19
let the iniquity of his f. be. 109:14
do what his f. have not. Dan 11:24
regard the God of his f. 37
and a god whom his f. knew not. 38
David was laid to his f. Acts 13:36

my fathers

to the years of my f. Gen 47:9
I will lie with my f. 30
the name of my f. be named. 48:16
bury me with my f. in the. 49:29
he is my f.' God, I will. Ex 15:2
no better than my f. 1 Ki 19:4
inheritance of my f. to thee. 21:3, 4
have gods delivered them my f.? 2 Ki 19:12; 2 Chr 32:14; Isa 37:12
not what I and my f. 2 Chr 32:13
sojourner as all my f. Ps 39:12
praise thee, O God of my f. Dan 2:23
worship I God of my f. Acts 24:14
of traditions of my f. Gal 1:14

our fathers

now both we and also our f. Gen 46:34; 47:3
how our f. went down. Num 20:15
not covenant with our f. Deut 5:3
land which he sware to our f. 6:23; 26:3, 15
cried to the God of our f. 26:7
pattern of altar our f. Josh 22:28
brought our f. out of Egypt. 24:17
miracles which our f. told of? Judg 6:13
with us, as with our f. 1 Ki 8:57
which he commanded our f. 58
because our f. have not. 2 Ki 22:13
the God of our f. look. 1 Chr 12:17
sojourners, as were all our f. 29:15
Lord God of our f. keep in thoughts of thy people. 18; 2 Chr 20:6
thou gavest our f. 2 Chr 6:31; Neh 9:36
for our f. have trespassed. 2 Chr 29:6
our f. have fallen by the sword. 9
our f. have not kept word of. 34:21
our f. provoked God. Ezra 5:12
blessed be the God of our f. 7:27
since the days of our f. in a. 9:7
affliction of our f. in Egypt. Neh 9:9
our f. dealt proudly, and. 16
our f. trusted in thee. Ps 22:4
our f. have told us. 41:1; 78:3
we have sinned with our f. 106:6
our f. understood not thy wonders. 7
where our f. praised thee. Isa 64:11
devoured labour of our f. Jer 3:24
we and our f. have not obeyed. 25
our f. have inherited lies. 16:19
have done, we and our f. 44:17
our f. have sinned, and. Lam 5:7
confusion of face to our f. Dan 9:8
our sins and iniquities of our f. 16
sworn to our f. from. Mi 7:20
the covenant of our f. Mal 2:10
had been in days of our f. Mat 23:30
as he spake to our f. Luke 1:55
mercy promised to our f. 72
our f. worshipped in. John 4:20
our f. did eat manna in the. 6:31
God of our f. hath glorified his Son. Acts 3:13
covenant God made with our f. 25
God of our f. raised up Jesus. 5:30
our f. found no sustenance. 7:11
Jacob died, and our f. 15
and evil entreated our f. and. 19
spake in Sinai and with our f. 38
to whom our f. would not obey. 39
our f. had the tabernacle of. 44
God of Israel chose our f. 13:17
a yoke which our f. nor we. 15:10
promise made to our f. 26:6
spake Holy Ghost to our f. 28:25
our f. were under cloud. 1 Cor 10:1

slept with fathers

David slept with his f. 1 Ki 2:10; 11:21
Solomon slept with his f. 2:43; 2 Chr 9:31
Jeroboam slept with f. 1 Ki 14:20; 2 Ki 14:29
Rehoboam slept with f. 1 Ki 14:31; 2 Chr 12:16
Abijam slept with his f. 1 Ki 15:8; 2 Chr 14:1
Asa slept with his f. 1 Ki 15:24; 2 Chr 16:13
so Baasha slept with f. 1 Ki 16:6
Omri slept with f. 28
Ahab slept with f. 22:40
Jehoshaphat slept with f. 50; 2 Chr 21:1
Joram slept with his f. 2 Ki 8:24
Jehu slept with his f. 10:35
Jehoahaz slept with his f. 13:9
Joash slept with his f. 13; 14:16
that the king slept with his f. 14:22; 2 Chr 26:2
Azariah slept with his f. 2 Ki 15:7
Menahem slept with his f. 22
Jotham slept with f. 38; 2 Chr 27:9
Ahaz slept with his f. 2 Ki 16:20; 2 Chr 28:27
Hezekiah slept with f. 2 Ki 20:21; 2 Chr 32:33
Manasseh slept with f. 2 Ki 21:18; 2 Chr 33:20
Jehoiakim slept with f. 2 Ki 24:6
Uzziah slept with his f. 2 Chr 26:23

their fathers

God of their f. hath. Ex 4:5
heads of their f. 6:14, 25; Josh 14:1; 19:51; 21:1; 1 Chr 5:24; 7:2, 7; 8:6; 9:9, 13
in iniquity of their f. Lev 26:39
confess iniquity of their f. 40
land thou swarest to give to their f. Num 11:12; 14:23; Deut 10:11; 31:20; Josh 1:6; 5:6; 21:43, 44; Jer 32:22
the covenant of their f. Deut 29:25
children ask their f. Josh 4:6, 21
head of house of their f. 22:14
were gathered to their f. Judg 2:10
forsook the Lord God of their f. 12
turned out of way their f. walked. 17
corrupted more than their f. 19
covenant I commanded their f. 20
keep way of Lord, as their f. 22
which he commanded their f. 3:4
again to land thou gavest to their f. 1 Ki 8:34, 48; 2 Chr 6:25, 38
their f. out of Egypt. 1 Ki 9:9
of land he gave to their f. 14:15; 2 Ki 21:8; Jer 16:15; 24:10
above all that their f. 1 Ki 14:22
since day their f. came. 2 Ki 21:15
house of their f. increased greatly. 1 Chr 4:38
against God of their f. 5:25
blessed the God of their f. 29:20
forsook God of their f. 2 Chr 7:22; 24:24; 28:6
sacrifice to God of their f. 11:16
relied on Lord God of their f. 13:18
to seek God of their f. 14:4; 15:12
them to the God of their f. 19:4
hearts to God of their f. 20:33
trespassed against God of their f. 30:7
confession to God of their f. 22
covenant of God of their f. 34:32
following the God of their f. 33
God of their f. sent by his. 36:15
confessed sins of their f. Neh 9:2
into land promisedst to their f. 23
to the search of their f. Job 8:8
men have told from their f. 15:18
as their f. a stubborn. Ps 78:8
things did he in sight of their f. 12
dealt unfaithfully like their f. 57
of children are their f. Pr 17:6
for iniquity of their f. Isa 14:21
did worse than their f. Jer 7:26
after Baalim, which their f. 9:14
whom they nor their f. have. 16; 19:4
covenant I made with their f. 11:10; 31:32; Heb 8:9
as their f. have forgotten. 23:27
against Lord, hope of their f. Jer 50:7
they and their f. have. Ezek 2:3
eat sons, and sons eat their f. 5:10
know abominations of their f. Ezek 20:4
eyes were after their f.' idols. 24
which their f. walked. Amos 2:4
heart of children to their f. Mal 4:6
like manner did their f. Luke 6:23
for so did their f. to the false. 26

thy fathers

go to thy f. in peace. Gen 15:15
thy f.' children shall bow. 49:8
land which he sware to thy f. Ex 13:5, 11; Deut 6:10, 18; 7:12, 13; 8:18; 9:5; 13:17; 19:8; 28:11; 29:13; 30:20
it, as God of thy f. said. Deut 1:21
nor forget covenant of thy f. 4:31
because he loved thy f. 37; 10:15
with manna which thou knewest not, neither did thy f. 8:3, 16
thy f. went into Egypt. 10:22
the God of thy f. giveth thee. 12:1
gods thou nor thy f. 13:6; 28:64
land he promised thy f. 19:8; 27:3
nation thou nor thy f. have. 28:36
multiply thee above thy f. 30:5
rejoice over thee, as over thy f. 9
sleep with thy f. 31:16; 2 Sam 7:12
to sepulchre of thy f. 1 Ki 13:22
what thy f. laid up. 2 Ki 20:17
I will gather thee to thy f. 22:20; 2 Chr 34:28
go to be with thy f. 1 Chr 17:11
book of records of thy f. Ezra 4:15
instead of thy f. shall be. Ps 45:16
not land-mark thy f. set. Pr 22:28
with burnings of thy f. Jer 34:5
I am God of thy f. the. Acts 7:32

your fathers

you to land of your f. Gen 48:21
God of your f. sent me. Ex 3:13; Deut 1:11; 4:1; Josh 18:3; 2 Chr 28:9; 29:5
did your f. Num 32:8; Neh 13:18
risen up in your f.' stead. Num 32:14
land Lord sware to your f. Deut 1:8, 35; 7:8; 8:1; 11:9, 21; Judg 2:1
sacrificed to gods whom your f. Deut 32:17
your f. dwelt on other. Josh 24:2
I brought your f. out of Egypt. 6
put away gods your f. served. 14
the gods which your f. served. 15
did to you and your f. 1 Sam 12:7
your f. cried, Lord brought your f. 8
Lord against you as against your f. 15
I commanded your f. 2 Ki 17:13
fight not against God of your f. 2 Chr 13:12
not like your f. and brethren. 30:7, 8; Zech 1:4
of land appointed for your f. 2 Chr 33:8
offering to God of your f. Ezra 8:28
confession to God of your f. 10:11
when your f. tempted me. Ps 95:9; Heb 3:9
and iniquities of your f. Isa 65:7
what iniquity have your f.? Jer 2:5
to land I have given to your f. 3:18
dwell in land I gave to your f. 7:7; 14; 23:39; 25:5; 35:15; Ezek 20:42; 36:28; 47:14
I spake not to your f. in. Jer 7:22
since the day your f. came. 25
I commanded your f. 11:4; 17:22
earnestly protested unto your f. 11:7
your f. have forsaken me. 16:11
done worse than your f. 12
ye nor your f. 13
made covenant with your f. 34:13
but your f. hearkened not unto. 14
not, neither they nor your f. 44:3
forgotten wickedness of your f.? 9
I set before you and your f. 10
the incense ye, your f. and. 21
not in statutes of your f. Ezek 20:18
in this your f. have blasphemed. 27
polluted after manner of your f.? 30
like as I pleaded with your f. 36
in land wherein your f. dwelt. 37:25
I saw your f. as the first. Hos 9:10
been in days of your f.? Joel 1:2
displeased with your f. Zech 1:2

be not as your f. Zech 1:4
your f. where are they? 5
my words take hold of your f.? 6
when your f. provoked me to. 8:14
from days of your f. Mal 3:7
the measure of your f. Mat 23:32
prophets, and your f. Luke 11:47
ye allow the deeds of your f. 48
your f. did eat manna. John 6:49
not as your f. did eat manna. 58
ye resist Holy Ghost as your f. did. Acts 7:51
who of prophets have not your f.? 52
by tradition from your f. 1 Pet 1:18

fathoms

twenty f. again fifteen f. Acts 27:28

fatling

calf, young lion, and f. Isa 11:6

fatlings

Agag and best of the f. 1 Sam 15:9
sacrificed oxen and f. 2 Sam 6:13
offer burnt sacrifices of f. Ps 66:15
all of them f. of Bashan. Ezek 39:18
my oxen and my f. are. Mat 22:4

fatness

God give thee of f. of. Gen 27:28
thy dwelling shall be the f. of. 39
thick and covered with f. Deut 32:15
should I leave my f.? Judg 9:9
his face with his f. Job 15:27
thy table should be full of f. 36:16
be satisfied with the f. Ps 36:8
as with marrow and f. 63:5
all thy paths drop f. 65:11
eyes stand out with f. 73:7
my flesh faileth of f. 109:24
f. of his flesh wax lean. Isa 17:4
sword of Lord is made fat with f. 34:6
dust shall be made fat with f. 7
let your soul delight itself in f. 55:2
the soul of priests with f. Jer 31:14
with them partakest of f. Rom 11:17

fats

(*Revisions*, vats)
the f. shall overflow with. Joel 2:24
press is full, the f. overflow. 3:13

fatted

oxen, harts, f. fowl. 1 Ki 4:23
hired men are like f. Jer 46:21*

see **calf**

fatter, *see* **countenances**

fattest

wrath of God slew the f. Ps 78:31
shall enter on f. places. Dan 11:24

fault, -s

remember my f. this. Gen 41:9
. is in thine own people. Ex 5:16
e beaten according to f. Deut 25:2*
have found no f. in. 1 Sam 29:3
ne this day with f. 2 Sam 3:8
leanse me from secret f. Ps 19:12
nd prepare without my f. 59:4
nd no occasion or f. Dan 6:4
thy brother trespass, tell him his f. Mat 18:15
ney found f. Mark 7:2
find no f. in this man. Luke 23:4
14; John 18:38*; 19:4, 6*
hy doth he yet find f.? Rom 9:19
ow there is utterly a f. 1 Cor 6:7*
an be overtaken in a f. Gal 6:1*
nding f. with them, he. Heb 8:8
onfess your f. one to. Jas 5:16*
buffeted for your f. 1 Pet 2:20*
ithout f. before throne. Rev 14:5*

faultless

st covenant had been f. Heb 8:7
able to present you f. Jude 24

faulty

th speak as one which is f. 2 Sam 14:13*
all they be found f. Hos 10:2*

favour

ve Joseph f. in sight of. Gen 39:21
n sight of the Egyptians, not go empty. Ex 3:21; 11:3; 12:36
ich shall not shew f. Deut 28:50
Naphtali, satisfied with f. 33:23
t they might have no f. Josh 11:20
Samuel was in f. with. 1 Sam 2:26
granted me life and f. Job 10:12†
with f. wilt compass him. Ps 5:12
his f. is life, weeping may. 30:5
thy f. thou hast made mountain to. 7
thou hadst a f. unto them. 44:3
even rich shall entreat thy f. 45:12
in thy f. horn shall be exalted. 89:17
remember me with the f. Ps 106:4
a good man sheweth f. and. 112:5*
I entreated thy f. with my. 119:58
seeketh good procureth f. Pr 11:27
good understanding giveth f. 13:15
among the righteous there is f. 14:9*
king's f. is toward a wise. 35
his f. is as a cloud of the. 16:15
many will entreat the f. of. 19:6
the king's f. is as dew upon. 12
his neighbour findeth no f. 21:10
loving f. rather to be chosen. 22:1
may seek the ruler's f. 29:26
f. is deceitful, beauty is vain. 31:30†
race not to swift, nor f. Eccl 9:11
f. be shewed to wicked. Isa 26:10
them will shew them no f. 27:11
but in my f. have I had. 60:10
I will not shew you f. Jer 16:13
had brought Daniel into f. Dan 1:9†
Jesus increased in f. Luke 2:52
having f. with all people. Acts 2:47
God gave Moses f. in sight of. 7:10
high priest desired f. against. 25:3

find, or *found* **favour**

have found f. in thy sight. Gen 18:3
30:27; Num 11:15; 1 Sam 20:29
Neh 2:5; Esth 5:8; 7:3; 8:5
have I not found f.? Num 11:11
to pass she find no f. Deut 24:1
let me find f. in thy sight. Ruth 2:13
David hath found f. in. 1 Sam 16:22
let the young men find f. in. 25:8
shall find f. in eyes of. 2 Sam 15:25
Hadad found f. in sight. 1 Ki 11:19
so shalt thou find f. in. Pr 3:4
shall find more f. than he. 28:23
as one that found f. S of S 8:10*
hast found f. with God. Luke 1:30
David found f. before. Acts 7:46

obtain, or *obtained* **favour**

Esther obtained f. Esth 2:15, 17† 5:2
findeth me, shall obtain f. Pr 8:35
a good man obtaineth f. of. 12:2
findeth a wife, obtaineth f. 18:22

favour, *verb*

the lords f. thee not. 1 Sam 29:6
glad, that f. my righteous. Ps 35:27
the set time to f. her is. 102:13*
thy servants f. dust thereof. 14*
let any to f. his fatherless. 109:12*

favourable

be f. unto them for our. Judg 21:22*
and God will be f. unto. Job 33:26
cast off, be f. no more? Ps 77:7
thou hast been f. to thy land. 85:1

favoured

beautiful and well f. Gen 29:17
Joseph was well f. 39:6
well f. kine. 41:2, 4, 18
of river ill f. kine. 3, 4, 19, 21, 27
they f. not the elders. Lam 4:16
children well f. and. Dan 1:4
whoredoms of well f. harlot. Nah 3:4
thou art highly f. Lord. Luke 1:28

evil **favouredness**

bullock wherein any evil f. Deut 17:1

favourest

I know that thou f. me. Ps 41:11*

favoureth

he that f. Joab, let him. 2 Sam 20:11

fear

(*The fear of God means that reverence for God which leads to obedience because of one's realization of his power, as well as of his love to man*)
the f. of you shall be. Gen 9:2
except the f. of Isaac had. 31:42
Jacob sware by the f. of his. 53
f. and dread fall upon. Ex 15:16*
I will send my f. before thee. 23:27*
I will put the f. of thee. Deut 2:25
Lord shall lay the f. of you. 11:25
Lord brought f. of him. 1 Chr 14:17
f. was on them because. Ezra 3:3
them that put me in f. Neh 6:14, 19
the f. of the Jews. Esth 8:17; 9:2
the f. of Mordecai fell on. 9:3
this thy f. thy confidence? Job 4:6
f. came upon me and trembling. 14
forsaketh f. of the Almighty. 6:14
let not his f. terrify me. 9:34*
yea, thou castest off f. and. 15:4
houses safe from f. nor. 21:9
snares round about, sudden f. 22:10
dominion and f. are with him. 25:2
he mocketh at f. and is not. 39:22
in thy f. will I worship. Ps 5:7
put them in f. O Lord. 9:20
there were they in great f. 14:5
a f. to mine acquaintance. 31:11
f. was on every side. 13*
f. took hold upon them. 48:6*
in f. where no f. was. 53:5
preserve my life from f. of. 64:1
to thy f. so is thy wrath. 90:11
f. of them fell upon them. 105:38
who is devoted to thy f. 119:38
mock when your f. cometh. Pr 1:26
your f. cometh as desolation. 27
shall be quiet from f. of evil. 33
be not afraid of sudden f. nor. 3:25
the f. of the wicked shall. 10:24
the f. of a king is as roaring. 20:2*
f. of man bringeth a snare. 29:25
his sword because of f. S of S 3:8
not come the f. of briers. Isa 7:25
neither f. ye their f. nor. 8:12
the Lord, let him be your f. and. 13
give thee rest from thy f. 14:3*
of pleasure turned unto f. 21:4*
f. and the pit, and the snare. 24:17
that fleeth from f. 18; Jer 48:44
f. toward me is taught. Isa 29:13
our heart from thy f. 63:17
evil thing, that my f. is not. Jer 2:19
sword and f. on every. 6:25*; 20:10
have heard a voice of f. not. 30:5
will put my f. in their hearts. 32:40
f. and the pit shall be upon. 48:43
I will bring a f. upon thee. 49:5
hath seized on Damascus. 24*
cry to them, f. is on every side. 29*
f. and a snare is come. Lam 3:47
a f. in land of Egypt. Ezek 30:13
if master, where is my f.? Mal 1:6
Zacharias saw him, f. Luke 1:12
f. came on all. 65; 7:16; Acts 2:43
5:5, 11; 19:17; Rev 11:11
f. to whom f. is due. Rom 13:7
in weakness and in f. 1 Cor 2:3
what f.! what desire! 2 Cor 7:11
not given us spirit of f. 2 Tim 1:7
them who through f. of. Heb 2:15
God with reverence, godly f. 12:28*
your sojourning here in f. 1 Pet 1:17
answer with meekness and f. 3:15
no f. in love, love casteth out f. 1 John 4:18

for **fear**

for the f. wherewith. Deut 28:67
not rather done it for f. Josh 22:24*
dwelt for f. of Abimelech. Judg 9:21
fled that day for f. of. 1 Sam 21:10
to get away for f. of Saul. 23:26
he reprove thee for f. of? Job 22:4
over to strong hold for f. Isa 31:9*
for f. of the army of. Jer 35:11
army broken up for f. 37:11
Asa had made for f. of Baasha. 41:9
for f. was round about. 46:5*
for f. of the oppressing. 50:16
for the f. wherewith he. Mal 2:5
disciples cried out for f. Mat 14:26
for f. of him keepers did shake. 28:4
hearts failing for f. Luke 21:26
no man spake openly for f. John 7:13
but secretly for f. of the Jews. 19:38
disciples assembled for f. of Jews. 20:19
off for f. of torment. Rev 18:10, 15

fear *of God*

surely f. of God is not. Gen 20:11
ruling in the f. of God. 2 Sam 23:3
the f. of God was on. 2 Chr 20:29

to walk in f. of God? Neh 5:9
because of the f. of God. 15
is no f. of God before his Ps 36:1
no f. of God before their. Rom 3:18
holiness in the f. of God. 2 Cor 7:1
to another in f. of God. Eph 5:21

fear *of the Lord*

f. of Lord fell on people. 1 Sam 11:7*; 2 Chr 17:10
f. of the Lord came. 2 Chr 14:14
let the f. of the Lord be upon. 19:7
thus do, in the f. of the Lord. 9
the f. of Lord is wisdom. Job 28:28
the f. of Lord is clean. Ps 19:9
will teach you f. of the Lord. 34:11
f. of the Lord is beginning of 111:10
f. of Lord beginning of knowledge. Pr 1:7; 9:10
did not choose f. of the Lord. 1:29
understand the f. of the Lord. 2:5
f. of the Lord is to hate evil. 8:13
f. of the Lord prolongeth days. 10:27
in the f. of the Lord is strong. 14:26
the f. of the Lord is fountain of. 27
better little with f. of the Lord. 15:16
f. of the Lord is instruction of. 33
by f. of the Lord men depart. 16:6
the f. of the Lord tendeth. 19:23
by the f. of the Lord are riches. 22:4
f. of the Lord all day long. 23:17
in dust for f. of the Lord. Isa 2:10
into caves for f. of the Lord. 19
clefts of rocks for f. of the Lord. 21
knowledge, and of the f. of the Lord. 11:2
understanding in f. of the Lord 3
f. of the Lord is his treasure. 33:6
walking in f. of the Lord. Acts 9:31

with **fear**

serve Lord with f. Ps 2:11
they departed with f. Mat 28:8
were all filled with f. Luke 5:26
were taken with great f. 8:37
how with f. ye received. 2 Cor 7:15
to masters with f. and. Eph 6:5
work out salvation with f. Phil 2:12
Noah moved with f. Heb 11:7
subject to masters with f. 1 Pet 2:18
conversation coupled with f. 3:2
and others save with f. Jude 23

without **fear**

labour is in vain without f. Job 39:16
like, who is made without f. 41:33
serve him without f. Luke 1:74
be with you without f. 1 Cor 16:10
to speak word without f. Phil 1:14
feeding themselves without f. Jude 12

fear, *verb*

shall f. every man his. Lev 19:3
neither f. ye the people. Num 14:9
they may learn to f. me. Deut 4:10
O that they would f. me. 5:29
f. this glorious name. 28:58
thou shalt f. day and night. 66
of heart wherewith thou shalt f. 67
if thou f. to go down. Judg 7:10
that they may f. thee. 1 Ki 8:40; 2 Chr 6:31
may know thy name to f. 1 Ki 8:43; 2 Chr 6:33
neither f. other gods. 2 Ki 17:38
but Lord your God ye shall f. 39
f. before him all earth. 1 Chr 16:30*; Ps 96:9
servants who desire to f. Neh 1:11
did I f. a great multitude? Job 31:34
I will f. no evil. Ps 23:4
whom shall I f.? 27:1
laid up for them that f. 31:19
and f. and shall trust in Lord. 40:3
wherefore should I f. in days? 49:5
righteous also shall see, and f. 52:6
given a banner to them that f. 60:4
heritage of those that f. 61:5
shall f. and declare the work. 64:9
shall f. thee as long as the sun. 72:5
unite my heart to f. thy name. 86:11
heathen shall f. thy name. 102:15
my reproach which I f. 119:39
a companion of them that f. 63
they that f. thee will be glad. 74
those that f. thee turn unto me. 79
men should f. before him. Eccl 3:14
neither f. ye their fear. Isa 8:12
like to women, afraid and f. 19:16
city of terrible nations shall f. 25:3
the workmen shall f. and be. 44:11
f. the name of the Lord. 59:19
thine heart shall f. and be. 60:5*
who would not f. thee? Jer 10:7
and they shall f. no more. 23:4
them one heart that may f. 32:39
they shall f. and tremble for. 33:9
your heart faint, and ye f. for. 51:46
I f. my lord the king. Dan 1:10
that men f. before God of. 6:26
inhabitants of Samaria f. Hos 10:5*
move as worms, and f. Mi 7:17
surely thou wilt f. me. Zeph 3:7
the people did f. before. Hag 1:12
Ashkelon shall see it and f. Zech 9:5
to you that f. my name. Mal 4:2
say, of men, we f. the. Mat 21:26
forewarn you whom ye shall f. Luke 12:5
of bondage again to f. Rom 8:15
be not highminded, but f. 11:20
I f. lest as the serpent. 2 Cor 11:3
I f. lest I shall not find you. 12:20
rebuke that others may f. 1 Tim 5:20
let us f. lest promise. Heb 4:1
I exceedingly f. and quake. 12:21
f. none of those things. Rev 2:10
reward to them that f. thy. 11:18

fear *God*

and live, for I f. God. Gen 42:18
men, such as f. God. Ex 18:21
but thou shalt f. thy God. Lev 19:14; 32; 25:17, 36, 43
Job f. God for nought? Job 1:9
hear, all ye that f. God. Ps 66:16
but f. thou God. Eccl 5:7
be well with them that f. God. 8:12
f. God and keep his. 12:13
shall f. God of Israel. Isa 29:23*
dost not f. God? Luke 23:40
f. God give audience. Acts 13:16
f. God, honour king. 1 Pet 2:17
f. God, and give glory to. Rev 14:7

hear and **fear**

Israel shall hear and f. Deut 13:11; 21:21
the people shall hear and f. 17:13
those shall hear and f. 19:20

fear *him*

for I f. him. Gen 32:11
after God, and f. him. Deut 13:4
him shall ye f. him shall. 2 Ki 17:36
men therefore f. him. Job 37:24
and f. him, seed of. Ps 22:23*
vows before them that f. him. 25
Lord with them that f. him. 25:14
of Lord on them that f. him. 33:18
angel encampeth about them that f. him. 34:7
no want to them that f. him. 9
ends of earth shall f. him. 67:7
is nigh them that f. him. 85:9
mercy to them that f. him. 103:11
Lord pitieth them that f. him. 13
mercy of the Lord is upon them that f. him. 17; Luke 1:50
meat to them that f. him. Ps. 111:5
desire of them that f. him. 145:19
pleasure in them that f. him. 147:11
f. him who is able to. Mat 10:28; Luke 12:5
praise God, ye that f. him. Rev 19:5

fear *the Lord*

that thou mightest f. the Lord. Deut 6:2
thou shalt f. Lord thy. 13; 10:20; 2 Ki 17:39
to f. the Lord our God. Deut 6:24
f. the Lord, walk in his ways. 10:12
learn to f. the Lord. 14:23; 17:19; 31:12, 13
that ye might f. the Lord. Josh 4:24
now therefore f. the Lord. 24:14
if ye will f. the Lord. 1 Sam 12:14
only f. the Lord and serve him. 24
I thy servant f. the Lord. 1 Ki 18:12; 2 Ki 4:1
taught them f. Lord. 2 Ki 17:28
honoureth them that f. the Lord. Ps 15:4
ye that f. the Lord, praise. 22:23
let all the earth f. the Lord. 33:8
O f. the Lord, ye his saints. 34:9
ye that f. the Lord trust. 115:11
will bless them that f. the Lord. 13
that f. the Lord, say, his. 118:4
that f. the Lord, bless the. 135:20
f. the Lord, depart from. Pr 3:7
my son, f. thou the Lord. 24:21
say, let us f. the Lord. Jer 5:24
did he not f. the Lord, and? 26:19
shall Israel f. the Lord. Hos 3:5
and I f. the Lord, the. Jonah 1:9

fear *not*

f. not, Abram, I am thy. Gen 15:1
f. not, God hath heard voice. 21:17
f. not, I am with thee. 26:24
midwife said to Rachel, f. not. 35:17
said, peace be to you, f. not. 43:23
f. not to go down into Egypt. 46:3
Joseph said, f. not, for am I? 50:19
f. not, I will nourish you and your. 21
f. not, stand and see. Ex 14:13
Moses said, f. not, God is. 20:20
Lord is with us, f. them not. Num 14:9
Lord said to Moses, f. him not. 21:34
possess the land, f. not. Deut 1:21
f. not Og. 3:2, 22
f. not your enemies. 20:3
f. not the Canaanites. 31:6; Josh 10:8, 25
Lord will go before thee, f. not. Deut 31:8; Josh 8:1; 1 Chr 28:20
turn in to me, f. not. Judg 4:18
f. not gods of the Amorites. 6:10
peace be to thee, f. not 23
now, my daughter, f. not. Ruth 3:11
women that stood by said, f. not. 1 Sam 4:20
Samuel said to people, f. not. 12:20
abide thou with me, f. not. 22:23
said unto David, f. not. 23:17
to Mephibosheth, f. not. 2 Sam 9:7
servants, kill Amnon, f. not. 13:28
Elijah said to widow, f. not. 1 Ki 17:13
f. not: for they that be. 2 Ki 6:16
unto this day, they f. not. 17:34
f. not to serve. 25:24; Jer 40:9
will be with you, f. not. 2 Chr 20:17
therefore they f. not God. Ps 55:19
do they shoot, and f. not. 64:4
f. not the tails of firebrands. Isa 7:4
are of a fearful heart, f. not. 35:4
f. thou not, I am with. 41:10; 43:5
thy God will hold thy right hand, saying to thee, f. not. 41:13
f. not, thou worm Jacob. 14
f. not, I have redeemed thee. 43:1
f. not, O Jacob, and Jeshurun I have 44:2; Jer 30:10; 46:27, 28
f. ye not, nor be afraid. Isa 44:8
f. not the reproach of men. 51:7
f. not, thou shalt not be. 54:4
f. ye not me? Jer 5:22
thou saidst, f. not. Lam 3:57
f. not, nor be dismayed. Ezek 3:
f. not, Daniel. Dan 10:12, 1
f. not, O land, be glad. Joel 2:2
said to Jerusalem, f. not. Zeph 3:1
Spirit remaineth, f. not. Hag 2:
shall be a blessing, f. not. Zech 8:1
do well to Judah, f. ye not. 1
against them that f. not me. Mal 3:
f. not to take to thee Mary. Mat 1:2
f. them not, there is nothing. 10:2
f. not them which kill the body. 2
f. not, ye are of. 31; Luke 12:
angel said to women, f. not. Mat 28:
f. not, Zacharias. Luke 1:1
f. not, Mary.
to the shepherds f. not. 2:1
Simon, f. not. 5:1
Jairus, f. not. 8:5
f. not, little flock. 12:3
though I f. not God, nor. 18
f. not, daughter of Sion. John 12:
f. not, Paul, thou must. Acts 27:
f. not, I am the first and. Rev 1:

not fear
I know ye will not yet f. Ex 9:30
not f. other gods. 2 Ki 17:35, 37
I speak, and not f. him. Job 9:35
far away, thou shalt not f. 11:15
my heart shall not f. Ps 27:3
we will not f. though earth be. 46:2
I will not f. what. 56:4; 118:6
oppression, shalt not f. Isa 54:14
who would not f. thee? Jer 10:7
roared, who will not f.? Amos 3:8
dost not thou f. God? Luke 23:40
not f. what man shall do. Heb 13:6
who shall not f. thee? Rev 15:4

feared
Lot f. to dwell in Zoar. Gen 19:30
Isaac f. to say of Rebekah. 26:7
Moses f. and said, this. Ex 2:14
he that f. the word of Lord. 9:20
Amalek smote thee, f. Deut 25:18
gods whom your fathers f. 32:17*
were it not that I f. the wrath. 27
f. Joshua as they did. Josh 4:14
Gideon f. Judg 6:27
Jether f. to slay them. 8:20
Samuel f. to shew Eli. 1 Sam 3:15
honey dropped, for people f. 14:26
because I f. the people. 15:24
answer, he f. Abner. 2 Sam 3:11
the Syrians f. to help. 10:19
David's servants f. to tell. 12:18
Adonijah f. because of. 1 Ki 1:50
Israel heard judgement, and f. 3:28
f. other gods. 2 Ki 17:7
they f. not the Lord. 25
to be f. above all gods. 1 Chr 16:25
Ps 96:4
Jehoshaphat f. and. 2 Chr 20:3
even thou, art to be f. Ps 76:7
the earth f. 8
presents to him that ought to be f. 11
safely, so that they f. not. 78:53
that thou mayest be f. 130:4
the isles saw it and f. Isa 41:5
and hast f. continually. 51:13
whom hast thou f. that thou. 57:11
sister Judah f. not. Jer 3:8
the sword which ye f. shall. 42:16
humbled, nor have they f. 44:10
ye have f. the sword. Ezek 11:8
all people and nations f. Dan 5:19
fear wherewith he f. me. Mal 2:5
Herod f. the multitude. Mat 14:5
21:46
and they f. exceedingly. Mark 4:41
Herod f. John, knowing he. 6:20
and chief priests f. Jesus. 11:18
of men, they f. people. 32; 12:12
Luke 20:19; 22:2; Acts 5:26
and they f. as they. Luke 9:34
and they f. to ask him. 45
city a judge which f. not. 18:2
f. thee because thou art. 19:21
because they f. the Jews. John 9:22
the magistrates f. when. Acts 16:38
Christ was heard in that he f.
Heb 5:7

feared *God*
but the midwives f. God. Ex 1:17
because they f. God, he made. 21
was faithful, and f. God. Neh 7:2
Job was one that f. God. Job 1:1
Cornelius f. God with his. Acts 10:2

feared *greatly*
the Canaanites f. greatly. Josh 10:2
all people greatly f. the. 1 Sam 12:18
Obadiah f. Lord greatly. 1 Ki 18:3
the thing I greatly f. is. Job 3:25
God is greatly to be f. Ps 89:7
they with him f. greatly. Mat 27:54

feared *the Lord*
the people f. the Lord. Ex 14:31
they f. the Lord. 2 Ki 17:32, 33, 41
we f. not the Lord. Hos 10:3
the men f. the Lord. Jonah 1:16
that f. Lord spake one to another . . .
that f. the Lord. Mal 3:16

fearest
know that thou f. God. Gen 22:12
even not I held my peace even of old,
and thou f. me not? Isa 57:11
and of them thou f. Jer 22:25

feareth
behold, Adonijah f. king. 1 Ki 1:51
Job, one that f. God. Job 1:8; 2:3
what man f. the Lord? Ps 25:12
blessed is man that f. Lord. 112:1
blessed is every one that f. 128:1
shall the man be blessed that f. 4
that f. commandment. Pr 13:13
walketh in his uprightness f. 14:2
a wise man f. and departeth. 16
happy is man that f. always. 28:14
woman that f. Lord shall be. 31:30
that f. God shall come. Eccl 7:18
because the wicked f. not. 8:13
as he that f. an oath. 9:2
among you f. the Lord? Isa 50:10
Cornelius, one that f. Acts 10:22
he that f. him, is accepted. 35
whosoever among you f. God. 13:26
he that f. is not perfect. 1 John 4:18

fearful
who is like thee, f. in? Ex 15:11
what man is f. let him. Deut 20:8
Judg 7:3
mayest fear this f. name. Deut 28:58
say to them of a f. heart. Isa 35:4
why are ye f. O ye of? Mat 8:26
why are ye so f.? Mark 4:40
f. sights in divers. Luke 21:11*
a certain f. looking for. Heb 10:27
f. to fall into the hands of. 31
f. have their part in the. Rev 21:8

fearfully
f. and wonderfully made. Ps 139:14

fearfulness
f. and trembling are. Ps 55:5
heart panteth, f. affrighted. Isa 21:4*
f. hath surprised hypocrites. 33:14*

fearing
children cease from f. Josh 22:25
the woman f. and. Mark 5:33
the chief captain f. lest. Acts 23:10
f. lest they fall into the. 27:17, 29
f. them which were of. Gal 2:12
in singleness of heart f. Col 3:22
forsook Egypt, not f. Heb 11:27

fears
delivered me from all my f. Ps 34:4
and when f. shall be in. Eccl 12:5*
will bring their f. upon. Isa 66:4
were fightings, within f. 2 Cor 7:5

feast
The Hebrews had a great number of feasts. The first, and most ancient of all, was the sabbath, or the seventh day of the week, instituted to preserve the memory of the world's creation, Gen 2:3.
The Passover celebration began on the evening of the fourteenth day of the first month in the ecclesiastical year, which was the seventh of the civil year. It lasted seven days, but the first and last days only were days of rest, Ex 12:14, etc.
The feast of Pentecost was celebrated on the fiftieth day after the Passover, or seven complete weeks after the consecration of the harvest season by the offering of the sheaf of the first ripe barley, Ex 23:16; Lev 23:15–22; Num 28.
The feast of Trumpets was celebrated on the first day of the civil year, in the month Tisri, *answering to our September. This day was kept solemn; all manual labour was forbidden to be done upon it: and particular sacrifices were offered,* Lev 23:24, 25.
The new moons, or first days of every month, were also celebrated as minor feasts.
The feast of Tabernacles, the feast of ingathering or real harvest festival, was kept for a week in the month Tisri, *beginning five days after the day of atonement.*
Besides these feasts mentioned by Moses, we find the feasts of lots, *or* Purim, *which celebrated the escape of the Jews from Haman; the feast of Dedication, or rather of the restoration of the temple after it had been profaned by Antiochus Epiphanes, which is thought to be the feast mentioned in the gospel,* John 10:22, *was celebrated in the winter. Josephus says it was called* the feast of lights.
The Day of Atonement, which was not a feast but a fast, was kept upon the tenth day of the month Tisri, *or September. The* Hebrews *call it* Kippur, *that is, pardon or expiation, because it was instituted for the expiation of all the sins, irreverences, and pollutions of all the Israelites, from the high priest to the lowest of the people, committed by them throughout the whole year.*

Lot made a f. Gen 19:3
Abraham made a f. 21:8
Isaac made a f. 26:30
Laban made a f. 29:22
Pharaoh made a f. to servants. 40:20
they may hold a f. Ex 5:1; 10:9
keep it a f. 12:14; Lev 23:39, 41
the seventh day shall be a f. Ex 13:6
three times thou shalt keep a f. 23:14
the f. of harvest, the firstfruits. 16
Aaron said, to-morrow is a f. 32:5
fifteenth day is the f. Num 28:17
ye shall keep a f. to the Lord. 29:12
shalt rejoice in thy f. Deut 16:14
Samson made there a f. Judg 14:10
within the seven days of the f. 12
wept before him while f. lasted. 17
Nabal held a f. in his. 1 Sam 25:36
David made Abner a f. 2 Sam 3:20
Solomon made a f. 1 Ki 3:15; 8:65
all Israel assembled at the f. 8:2
a f. like to the f. in Judah. 12:32
he ordained a f. to the children. 33
f. in the seventh month. 2 Chr 5:3
Neh 8:14
Solomon kept the f. seven. 2 Chr 7:8
9; 30:22; Neh 8:18; Ezek 45:25
Ahasuerus made f. Esth 1:3, 5; 2:18
Vashti made a f. 1:9
the Jews had a f. 8:17
heart hath continual f. Pr 15:15
f. is made for laughter. Eccl 10:19
make to all people a f. Isa 25:6
seven days of the f. Ezek 45:23
Belshazzar made a great f. Dan 5:1
at that f. the governor was wont to
release. Mat 27:15; Mark 15:6
up after custom of the f. Luke 2:42
Levi made him a great f. 5:29
but when thou makest a f. call. 14:13
release one unto them at f. 23:17
bear to governor of the f. John 2:8
when the ruler of the f. tasted. 9
things he did at Jerusalem at the f.,
for they also went to the f. 4:45
after this a f. of the Jews. 5:1
the passover, a f. of the Jews. 6:4
to this f. I go not up yet to f. 7:8
then went he also up to the f. 10
the Jews sought him at the f. 11
about midst of the f. Jesus. 14
that great day of the f. 37
at Jerusalem the f. of. 10:22
that he will not come to f.? 11:56
much people were come to f. 12:12
Greeks among them that came f. 20
we have need of against the f. 13:29
I must keep this f. Acts 18:21
let us keep the f. not. 1 Cor 5:8
believe not bid you to a f. 10:27
sporting while they f. 2 Pet 2:13
spots, when they f. with you. Jude 12*

feasted
his sons went and f. Job 1:4

feast *of the passover*
nor sacrifice of f. of passover be left.
Ex 34:25
two days f. of passover. Mat 26:2
Mark 14:1
year at f. of passover. Luke 2:41
before the f. of passover when Jesus
knew his hour was come. John 13:1

solemn **feast**
days keep a *solemn f.* *Deut* 16:15
trumpet on *solemn f.* day. *Ps* 81:3
noise as in *solemn f.* day. *Lam* 2:7*

feast *of tabernacles*
fifteenth day *f. of taber.* *Lev* 23:34
shalt observe *f. of taber.* *Deut* 16:13
three times appear in *f. of taber.* 16; 31:10; *2 Chr* 8:13
kept *f. of taber.* as it. *Ezra* 3:4
go up to keep *f. of taber.* *Zech* 14:16
not to keep *f. of taber.* 18, 19
Jews' *f. of taber.* was at. *John* 7:2

feast *of unleavened bread*
observe *f. of unl. br.* *Ex* 12:17; 23:15; 34:18
fifteenth day is *f. of unl. br.* *Lev* 23:6
appear in *f. of unl. br.* *Deut* 16:16; *2 Chr* 8:13
to keep *f. of unl. br.* *2 Chr* 30:13
children of Israel kept *f. of unl. br.* 21
f. of unl. br. seven days. 35:17; *Ezra* 6:22; *Ezek* 45:21
first day of *f. of unl. br.* *Mat* 26:17
after two days was *f. of unl. br.* *Mark* 14:1; *Luke* 22:1

feast *of weeks*
shalt observe *f. of weeks.* *Ex* 34:22; *Deut* 16:10
appear in *f. of weeks.* *Deut* 16:16
burnt offerings in *f. of weeks.* *2 Chr* 8:13

feast day, -s
will also cause her *f. days.* *Hos* 2:11
will ye do in *day* of the *f.* of? 9:5
I despise your *f. days.* *Amos* 5:21
said, not on the *f. day.* *Mat* 26:5; *Mark* 14:2
in the *f. day* many. *John* 2:23

feasting
made it a day of *f.* *Esth* 9:17, 18
should make them days of *f.* 22
days of their *f.* were gone. *Job* 1:5
than to go to house of *f.* *Eccl* 7:2
not go into house of *f.* *Jer* 16:8

feasts
these are my *f.* *Lev* 23:2, 4, 37, 44
hypocritical mockers in *f.* *Ps* 35:16
pipe, and wine in their *f.* *Isa* 5:12
I will make their *f.* *Jer* 51:39
part to give offerings in *f.* *Ezek* 45:17
in *f.* the meat offering shall. 46:11
I will turn your *f.* into. *Amos* 8:10
joy, gladness, cheerful *f.* *Zech* 8:19
love uppermost rooms at *f.* *Mat* 23:6; *Mark* 12:39; *Luke* 20:46
spots in your *f.* of charity. *Jude* 12

appointed **feasts**
your *appointed f.* my soul. *Isa* 1:14

set **feasts**
things do in your *set f.* *Num* 29:39
to offer on the *set f.* *1 Chr* 23:31; *Ezra* 3:5
king's portion for *set f.* *2 Chr* 31:3
for offering in the *set f.* *Neh* 10:33

solemn **feasts**
offering in your *solemn f.* *Num* 15:3
house for offering on *solemn f.* *2 Chr* 2:4
offering on *solemn f.* three. 8:13
none come to *solemn f.* *Lam* 1:4*
caused the *solemn f.* to be. 2:6*
Jerusalem in *solemn f.* *Ezek* 36:38
come before Lord in *solemn f.* 46:9
to cease her *solemn f.* *Hos* 2:11*
dwell as in days of *solemn f.* 12:9
Judah, keep thy *solemn f.* *Nah* 1:15
even dung of your *solemn f.* *Mal* 2:3

feathered, *see* **fowl**

feathers
away crop with his *f.* *Lev* 1:16*
goodly wings to peacock? or wings and *f.* to the ostrich? *Job* 39:13
f. covered with yellow. *Ps* 68:13*
shall cover thee with his *f.* 91:4*
long-winged, full of *f.* *Ezek* 17:3, 7
were grown like eagle's *f.* *Dan* 4:33

fed
Jacob *f.* Laban's flock. *Gen* 30:36
he *f.* the asses of Zibeon. 36:24
the seven kine *f.* in a. *Gen* 41:2, 18
he *f.* them with bread for. 47:17
the God who *f.* me all my. 48:15
bread wherewith I have *f.* *Ex* 16:32
he *f.* thee with manna. *Deut* 8:3
who *f.* thee in the wilderness. 16
concubines in ward, *f.* *2 Sam* 20:3*
f. them with bread. *1 Ki* 18:4, 13
over the herds that *f.* *1 Chr* 27:29
in Lord, thou shalt be *f.* *Ps* 37:3*
so he *f.* them, according to. 78:72
he should have *f.* them with. 81:16
full of fat of *f.* beasts. *Isa* 1:11
I had *f.* them to the full. *Jer* 5:7
were as *f.* horses in the morning. 8
honey wherewith I *f.* *Ezek* 16:19
and kill them that are *f.* 34:3
shepherds *f.* themselves, *f.* not. 8
all flesh was *f.* with it. *Dan* 4:12
they *f.* Nebuchadnezzar with. 5:21
two staves, and I *f.* flock. *Zech* 11:7
thee hungered, and *f.*? *Mat* 25:37
that *f.* the swine fled. *Mark* 5:14; *Luke* 8:34
desiring to be *f.* with. *Luke* 16:21
I have *f.* you with milk. *1 Cor* 3:2

feeble
when cattle were *f.* he. *Gen* 30:42
Amalekites smote all *f.* *Deut* 25:18
many children, waxen *f.* *1 Sam* 2:5
Ish-bosheth's hands were *f.* *2 Sam* 4:1
carried all the *f.* of. *2 Chr* 28:15
what do these *f.* Jews? *Neh* 4:2
hast strengthened the *f.* *Job* 4:4
I am *f.* and sore broken. *Ps* 38:8*
not one *f.* person amongst. 105:37
the conies are but a *f.* folk. *Pr* 30:26
remnant very small and *f.* *Isa* 16:14*
confirm *f.* knees. 35:3
fame, our hands wax *f.* *Jer* 6:24
Damascus is waxed *f.* and. 49:24
of Babylon's hands waxed *f.* 50:43
all hands shall be *f.* *Ezek* 7:17; 21:7
he that is *f.* be as David. *Zech* 12:8
which seem to be *f.* *1 Cor* 12:22
comfort the *f.*-minded. *1 Thes* 5:14
hands and *f.* knees. *Heb* 12:12*

feebler
so the *f.* were Laban's. *Gen* 30:42

feebleness
not look back for *f.* *Jer* 47:3

feed
brethren went to *f.* *Gen* 37:12
where they *f.* their flocks. 16
trade hath been to *f.* cattle. 46:32*
shall *f.* in another man's. *Ex* 22:5
neither let flocks *f.* before. 34:3
thou shalt *f.* my people. *2 Sam* 5:2†
I commanded to *f.* Israel. 7:7†; *1 Chr* 17:6†
commanded ravens to *f.* *1 Ki* 17:4
take away flocks and *f.* *Job* 24:2
the worms shall *f.* sweetly on. 20
f. them, and lift them up. *Ps* 28:9†
in grave, death *f.* on them. 49:14*
he brought David to *f.* Jacob. 78:71
lips of the righteous *f.* *Pr* 10:21
like two roes which *f.* *S of S* 4:5
my beloved is gone to *f.* in. 6:2
f. after their manner. *Isa* 5:17
the cow and the bear shall *f.* 11:7
firstborn of poor shall *f.* 14:30
there shall the calf *f.* and. 27:10
cattle *f.* in large pastures. 30:23
f. his flock as a shepherd. 40:11
they shall *f.* in the ways. 49:9
strangers shall stand and *f.* 61:5
wolf and the lamb shall *f.* 65:25
pastors who shall *f.* you. *Jer* 3:15
f. every one in his place. 6:3
pastors that *f.* my people. 23:2
shepherds which shall *f.* them. 4
Israel shall *f.* on Carmel. 50:19
they that *f.* delicately. *Lam* 4:5
woe to shepherds that *f.* *Ezek* 34:2
eat the fat, but ye *f.* not flock. 3
neither shall shepherds *f.* 10
my servant David shall *f.* them. 23
that *f.* of his meat. *Dan* 11:26*
now the Lord will *f.* them. *Hos* 4:16
the flour and winepress not *f.* 9:2
let them not *f.* nor drink. *Jonah* 3:7
f. in strength of the Lord. *Mi* 5:4
they shall *f.* thereupon. *Zeph* 2:7
they shall *f.* none make afraid. 3:13
I will not *f.* you. *Zech* 11:9
the shepherd shall not *f.* that. 16
sent him to fields to *f.* *Luke* 15:15
take heed to *f.* church of. *Acts* 20:28
all my goods to *f.* poor. *1 Cor* 13:3
for the Lamb shall *f.* *Rev* 7:17*
that they should *f.* her there. 12:6*

feed, *imperatively*
f. me with that red. *Gen* 25:30
water the sheep, go and *f.* 29:7
f. him with bread and water. *1 Ki* 22:27; *2 Chr* 18:26
f. me with food convenient. *Pr* 30:8
f. thy kids beside the. *S of S* 1:8
f. thy people with thy rod. *Mi* 7:14
saith Lord, *f.* the flock. *Zech* 11:4
f. my lambs. *John* 21:15
f. my sheep. 16*, 17
if enemy hunger, *f.* him. *Rom* 12:20
f. the flock of God. *1 Pet* 5:2*

I will **feed**
I will again *f.* and keep. *Gen* 30:31
I will f. thee with me. *2 Sam* 19:33
I will f. them that oppress. *Isa* 49:26
I will f. thee with heritage of. 58:14
I will f. them with wormwood. *Jer* 9:15; 23:15
I will f. them upon the mountains. *Ezek* 34:13
I will f. them in a good pasture. 14
I will f. my flock, and cause. 15
I will f. the fat and the strong. 16
I will f. the flock of. *Zech* 11:7

feedest
f. them with bread of tears. *Ps* 80:5
me where thou *f.* flock. *S of S* 1:7

feedeth
mouth of fools *f.* on. *Pr* 15:14
my beloved *f.* among lilies. *S of S* 2:16; 6:3
he *f.* on ashes, a deceived. *Isa* 44:20
Ephraim *f.* on wind. *Hos* 12:1
your heavenly Father *f.* *Mat* 6:26
ravens sow not, yet God *f.* them. *Luke* 12:24
who *f.* a flock, and. *1 Cor* 9:7

feeding
Joseph was *f.* his flock. *Gen* 37:2
plowing, the asses *f.* by. *Job* 1:14
to cease from *f.* flock. *Ezek* 34:10
where is the *f.* place? *Nah* 2:11
an herd of swine *f.* *Mat* 8:30; *Mark* 5:11; *Luke* 8:32
a servant *f.* cattle. *Luke* 17:7*
f. themselves without fear. *Jude* 12*

feel
peradventure will *f.* me. *Gen* 27:12
come near, that I may *f.* thee. 21
suffer me that I may *f.* *Judg* 16:26
he shall not *f.* quietness. *Job* 20:20*
before pots can *f.* thorns. *Ps* 58:9
commandment *f.* no evil. *Eccl* 8:5*
if haply they might *f.* *Acts* 17:27

feeling
being past *f.* have given. *Eph* 4:19
touched with the *f.* of. *Heb* 4:15

feet
lawgiver from between his *f.* *Gen* 49:10
Jacob gathered up *f.* in the bed. 33
thy shoes from off thy *f.* *Ex* 3:5; *Acts* 7:33
passover with shoes on *f.* *Ex* 12:1
have legs above their *f.* *Lev* 11:2
will pass through on *f.* *Deut* 2:2
cometh from between her *f.* 28:5
they sat down at thy *f.* every. 33:
the *f.* of the priests were. *Josh* 3:1
old shoes, and clouted upon *f.* 9:
put your *f.* on the necks of. 10:2
land whereon thy *f.* have. 14:
he covereth his *f.* in. *Judg* 3:2
Sisera fled away on his *f.* 4:15, 1
at her *f.* bowed, at her *f.* fell. 5:2
go in, uncover his *f.* and. *Ruth* 3:
behold a woman lay at his *f.*
he will keep the *f.* of *1 Sam* 2:

Jonathan climbed on hands and f. 1 Sam 14:13
Saul went in to cover his f. 24:3
rode with five damsels at f. 25:42
thy f. put into fetters. 2 Sam 3:34
Jonathan's son lame of f. 4:4; 9:3, 13
cut off their hands and their f. 4:12
Mephibosheth had neither dressed his f. 19:24
he maketh my f. like hinds' f. 22:34
Ps 18:33; Hab 3:19
my f. did not slip. 2 Sam 22:37
Ps 18:36
of war in shoes on his f. 1 Ki 2:5
Ahijah heard sound of her f. 14:6
when thy f. enter the city, the. 12
Asa was diseased in his f. 15:23
2 Chr 16:12
came, caught him by f. 2 Ki 4:27
not sound of his master's f.? 6:32
no more of her than the f. 9:35
man revived, stood upon his f. 13:21
nor make the f. of Israel. 21:8
David king stood on his f. 1 Chr 28:2
not old, their f. swelled. Neh 9:21
ready to slip with his f. Job 12:5
puttest my f. in stocks, thou settest a print upon heels of my f. 13:27
cast into a net by his own f. 18:8
and drive him to his f. 11
blind, f. was I to the lame. 29:15
youth rise, push away my f. 30:12
he putteth my f. in the stocks. 33:11
my hands and my f. Ps 22:16
for he shall pluck my f. out. 25:15
hast set my f. in large room. 31:8
he set my f. on rock, and. 40:2
deliver my f. from falling? 56:13
suffereth not our f. to be. 66:9
my f. were almost gone. 73:2
lift up thy f. unto perpetual. 74:3
f. they hurt with fetters. 105:18
f. have they, but they walk not. 115:7
hast delivered my f. from. 116:8
my f. unto thy testimonies. 119:59
I refrained my f. from every. 101
thy word is a lamp to my f. 105
f. shall stand within thy gates. 122:2
their f. run to evil. Pr 1:16; 6:18
Isa 59:7
ponder the path of thy f. Pr 4:26
her f. go down to death. 5:5
wicked man speaketh with his f. 6:13
on coals and his f. not be burnt? 28
her f. abide not in her house. 7:11
hasteth with his f. sinneth. 19:2
cutteth off the f. and drinketh. 26:6
spreadeth a net for his f. 29:5*
beautiful are thy f. with. S of S 7:1
tinkling with their f. Isa 3:16
away ornaments about their f. 18
with twain covered his f., with. 6:2
Lord shall shave hair of the f. 7:20
own f. shall carry her afar. 23:7
of the poor shall tread. 26:6
send forth the f. of the ox. 32:20
he had not gone with his f. 41:3
shall lick up dust of thy f. 49:23
of him that bringeth tidings. 52:7
Nah 1:15
place of my f. glorious. Isa 60:13
before your f. stumble. Jer 13:16
not refrained their f. 14:10
and hid snares for my f. 18:22
thy f. are sunk in the mire. 38:22
spread a net for my f. Lam 1:13
their f. were straight f. Ezek 1:7
son of man, stand upon thy f. 2:1
spirit set me upon my f. 2; 3:24
hast opened thy f. to. 16:25
put on thy shoes upon thy f. 24:17
your heads, shoes on your f. 23
thou hast stamped with f. 25:6
troubledst waters with thy f. 32:2
foul residue with your f. 34:18
trodden and fouled with f. 19
and stood upon their f. 37:10
part of iron. Dan 2:33, 42
stone smote image upon his f. 34
thou sawest the f. and toes. 41
stamped residue with f. of it. 7:7, 19
f. like polished brass. 10:6
Rev 1:15; 2:18
clouds are dust of his f. Nah 1:3

his f. shall stand upon. Zech 14:4
depart, shake off the dust of your f. Mat 10:14; Mark 6:11; Luke 9:5
lame and blind at Jesus' f. Mat 15:30
rather than having two f. to. 18:8
they held him by the f. and. 28:9
to guide our f. into way. Luke 1:79
she kissed his f. and. 7:38
woman not ceased to kiss my f. 45
man sitting at the f. of Jesus. 8:35
Jairus fell down at Jesus' f. 41
Mary, who sat at Jesus' f. 10:39
ring on hand, shoes on his f. 15:22
behold my hands and my f. 24:39
shewed them his hands and f. 40
wiped his f. with. John 11:2; 12:3
Mary anointed the f. of Jesus. 12:3
angel at head, the other at f. 20:12
immediately his f. received strength. Acts 3:7
laid them down at apostles' f. 4:35
37; 5:2
f. of them who have buried. 5:9
their clothes at young man's f. 7:58
shoes of his f. I am not. 13:25
they shook off the dust of their f. 51
Lystra a man impotent in his f. 14:8
stand upright on thy f. he. 10
who made their f. fast in. 16:24
Agabus bound hands and f. 21:11
brought up at f. of Gamaliel. 22:3
rise, and stand upon thy f. 26:16
f. are swift to shed. Rom 3:15
the f. of them that preach. 10:15
nor head to the f. I. 1 Cor 12:21
your f. shod with the. Eph 6:15
straight paths for f. Heb 12:13
and worship before thy f. Rev 3:9
mighty angel, his f. as pillars. 10:1
witnesses stood upon their f. 11:11
his f. were as f. of a bear. 13:2
to worship before his f. 22:8

at his feet

cast foreskin at his f. Ex 4:25
ten thousand at his f. Judg 4:10
she lay at his f. until. Ruth 3:14
Abigail fell at his f. 1 Sam 25:24
of Shunem fell at his f. 2 Ki 4:37
Esther fell down at his f. Esth 8:3
coals went forth at his f. Hab 3:5
servant fell at his f. Mat 18:29
Jairus fell at his f. Mark 5:22
Syrophenician woman fell at his f. 7:25
stood at his f. behind. Luke 7:38
Mary fell down at his f. John 11:32
Sapphira fell at his f. Acts 5:10
Cornelius met him, fell at his f. 10:25
I fell at his f. as dead. Rev 1:17
fell at his f. to worship him. 19:10

feet joined with *sole* or *soles*

soles of your f. tread. Deut 11:24
as soles of priests' f. Josh 3:13; 4:18
them under soles of his f. 1 Ki 5:3
sole of my f. dried. 2 Ki 19:24
Isa 37:25
bow at the soles of thy f. Isa 60:14
the sole of their f. was. Ezek 1:7
the place of soles of my f. 43:7
be ashes under soles of f. Mal 4:3

***under* feet**

under his f. as it were. Ex 24:10
darkness under his f. 2 Sam 22:10
Ps 18:9
fallen under my f. 2 Sam 22:39
put all things under his f. Ps 8:6
1 Cor 15:27; Eph 1:22
subdue nations under our f. Ps 47:3
dragon shalt trample under f. 91:13
carcase trodden under f. Isa 14:19
drunkards trodden under f. 28:3
to crush under his f. all. Lam 3:34
trample them under their f. Mat 7:6
bruise Satan under your f. Rom 16:20
all enemies under his f. 1 Cor 15:25
in subjection under his f. Heb 2:8
sun, moon under her f. Rev 12:1

feet with *wash*, or *washed*

fetched, wash your f. Gen 18:4
tarry all night, wash your f. 19:2
gave water to wash his f. 24:32
and they washed their f. Gen 43:24
Aaron and his sons shall wash hands and f. Ex 30:19, 21; 40:31
and concubine washed f. Judg 19:21
to wash the f. of. 1 Sam 25:41
thy house, wash thy f. 2 Sam 11:8
wash his f. in blood of. Ps 58:10
have washed my f. how. S of S 5:3
began to wash his f. Luke 7:38
hath washed my f. with tears. 44
to wash disciples' f. John 13:5
Lord dost thou wash my f.? 6
thou shalt never wash my f. 8
needeth not save to wash his f. 10
after he had washed their f. 12
if I have washed your f. 14
have washed saints' f. 1 Tim 5:10

feign

f. thyself to be a mourner. 2 Sam 14:2
f. herself to be another. 1 Ki 14:5
should f. themselves. Luke 20:20

feigned

David f. himself mad. 1 Sam 21:13
prayer that goeth not out of f. lips. Ps 17:1
with f. words make. 2 Pet 2:3

feignedly

turned to me but f. Jer 3:10

feignest

f. thou to be another? 1 Ki 14:6
but thou f. them out of. Neh 6:8

Felix

bring Paul safe to F. Acts 23:24
Lysias to excellent governor F. 26
accepted always, most noble F. 24:3
when F. came with his wife. 24
Paul reasoned of judgement, F. 25
certain man left in bonds by F. 25:14

fell

and his countenance f. Gen 4:5
of Sodom and Gomorrah f. 14:10
a deep sleep f. on Abram. 15:12
Esau ran, and f. on his. 33:4
Joseph's brethren f. before. 44:14
Joseph f. on Benjamin's neck. 45:14
Jacob f. on Joseph's neck. 46:29
f. of the people 3000. Ex 32:28
goat on which the Lord's lot f. Lev 16:9, 10
mixt multitude f. lusting. Num 11:4
dew f. on the camp, the manna f. 9
Moses and Aaron f. 14:5; 16:22, 45
20:6
that f. that day, 12,000. Josh 8:25
Joshua came and f. upon. 11:7
and wrath f. on all the. 22:20
Sisera's host f. on edge. Judg 4:16
Sisera f. 5:27
of bread smote tent that it f. 7:13
for there f. 120,000 men. 8:10
there f. of Ephraimites 42,000. 12:6
the house f. on the lords. 16:30
there f. of Benjamin 18,000. 20:44
f. of Israel 30,000. 1 Sam 4:10
Eli f. from his seat backward. 18
fear of the Lord f. on people. 11:7
Philistines f. before Jonathan. 14:13
Doeg turned, and f. upon. 22:18
Abigail f. at David's feet. 25:24
Saul f. straightway along on. 28:20
no fault in him since he f. 29:3
three days agone I f. sick. 30:13
Saul took a sword and f. 31:4
armourbearer f. 5; 1 Chr 10:4, 5
Mephibosheth f. and. 2 Sam 4:4
f. some of the people of. 11:17
Amnon f. sick for his sister. 13:2
Joab's sword f. out as he. 20:8
they f. all seven together. 21:9
f. by hand of David. 22; 1 Chr 20:8
Benaiah f. on Adonijah. 1 Ki 2:25
who f. upon two men better than. 32
Benaiah f. on Joab. 34
Benaiah f. on Shimei. 46
Abijah son of Jeroboam f. 14:1
the son of the woman f. sick. 17:17
fire of Lord f. and consumed. 18:38
a wall f. on 27,000 men. 20:30
third captain f. on knees. 2 Ki 1:13
mantle of Elijah that f. from. 2:13
it f. on a day Elisha passed. 4:8, 11

it f. on a day the child went. 2 Ki 4:18
Shunammite f. at his feet. 37
the axe head f. into water. 6:5
man of God said, where f. it ? 6
so it f. out to him, the. 7:20*
the fugitives that f. away. 25:11
f. some of Manasseh. 1 Chr 12:19
there f. of Israel 70,000. 21:14
because there f. wrath for. 27:24*
for they f. to David. 2 Chr 15:9
the fear of Lord f. on all. 17:10
inhabitants of Jerusalem f. 20:18
bowels f. out by reason of. 21:19
the soldiers of Israel f. on. 25:13
I f. on my knees and. Ezra 9:5
fear of Jews f. on. Esth 8:17; 9:2
the fear of Mordecai f. upon. 9:3
Sabeans f. on the asses. Job 1:15
Chaldeans f. on camels, and. 17
the house f. on young men, and. 19
to eat my flesh, they f. Ps 27:2
their priests f. by sword. 78:64
the fear of Israel f. on. 105:38
that f. away, f. to. Jer 39:9; 52:15
one f. upon another. 46:16
her people f. into hand. Lam 1:7
and children f. under wood. 5:13*
hand of the Lord f. Ezek 8:1; 11:5
so f. they all by the sword. 39:23
f. a voice from heaven. Dan 4:31
came up, before whom three f. 7:20
a great quaking f. upon them. 10:7
and the lot f. on Jonah. Jonah 1:7
the house f. not. Mat 7:25
house, and it f. 27; Luke 6:49
seed f. by way side. Mat 13:4
Mark 4:4; Luke 8:5
f. upon stony places. Mat 13:5
Mark 4:5; Luke 8:6
some f. among thorns. Mat 13:7
Mark 4:7; Luke 8:7
other f. into good. Mat 13:8
Mark 4:8; Luke 8:8
Jairus f. at his feet. Mark 5:22
Syrophenician woman came, f. 7:25
he f. on the ground and. 9:20
Jesus f. on the ground. 14:35
fear f. upon Zacharias. Luke 1:12
as they sailed, Jesus f. asleep. 8:23
a certain man f. among. 10:30, 36
upon whom tower in Siloam f. 13:4
his father f. on his neck. 15:20
crumbs which f. from rich. 16:21
went backward and f. to. John 18:6
Judas by transgression f. Acts 1:25
gave forth lots, and the lot f. 26
he had said this, he f. asleep. 7:60
Saul f. to the earth and. 9:4
there f. from his eyes as it had. 18
Peter became hungry, f. into. 10:10
Holy Ghost f. on them. 44; 11:15
chains f. from Peter's hands. 12:7
there f. on him a mist and. 13:11
David f. on sleep and saw. 36
and fear f. on all the Jews. 19:17
Paul went down, f. on. 20:10
they all f. on Paul's neck. 37
I f. unto the ground, and. 22:7
them which f. severity. Rom 11:22
reproaches of them f. on me. 15:3
and f. in one day. 1 Cor 10:8
whose carcases f. in the. Heb 3:17
since fathers f. asleep. 2 Pet 3:4
when I saw him I f. at. Rev 1:17
the stars of heaven f. unto. 6:13
there f. a great star from. 8:10
and great fear f. on them who. 11:11
the tenth part of the city f. by. 13
and there f. a noisome and. 16:2
and cities of nations f. 19
there f. upon men, great hail out. 21
I f. at his feet to worship him. 19:10
see **face, faces**

fell *down*

ass saw angel, she f. down.
Num 22:27*
and I f. down before. Deut 9:18, 25
shouted, wall f. down. Josh 6:20
there he f. down dead. Judg 5:27
concubine f. down at door. 19:26
Philistines f. down. 1 Sam 17:52
Israel f. down in Gilboa. 31:1
1 Chr 10:1
so they f. down together. 2 Sam 2:16
Asahel f. down there, and. 23
Ahimaaz f. down. 18:28*
Shimei f. down. 19:18
and Ahaziah f. down. 2 Ki 1:2
f. down many slain. 1 Chr 5:22
there f. down of Israel. 2 Chr 13:17
Esther f. down at. Esth 8:3
Job f. down on ground. Job 1:20
f. down there was none. Ps 107:12
all nations f. down and. Dan 3:7
these three f. down bound in. 23
wise men f. down and. Mat 2:11
servant therefore f. down, saying.
18:26, 29
unclean spirits f. down. Mark 3:11
with issue of blood f. down. 5:33
Simon Peter f. down at. Luke 5:8
which had devils f. down. 8:28
Jairus f. down. 41
the Samaritan f. down. 17:16
Mary f. down at feet. John 11:32
Ananias f. down. Acts 5:5
Sapphira f. down. 10
Cornelius f. down at his feet. 10:25
keeper f. down before Paul. 16:29
image which f. down from. 19:35
Eutychus f. down from third. 20:9
walls of Jericho f. down. Heb 11:30
elders f. down before the Lamb.
Rev 5:8, 14; 19:4
John f. down to worship. 22:8

fell

shall f. every good tree. 2 Ki 3:19

felled

and they f. all good trees. 2 Ki 3:25

feller

no f. is come up against. Isa 14:8

fellest

before wicked men, so f. 2 Sam 3:34

felling

as one was f. a beam. 2 Ki 6:5

felloes

their f. and their spokes. 1 Ki 7:33

fellow

this one f. came in to. Gen 19:9
smitest thou thy f.? Ex 2:13
told a dream to his f. Judg 7:13
Lord set every man's sword against
his f. through. 22; 1 Sam 14:20
brought this f. to play the madman;
shall this f. come. 1 Sam 21:15
in vain have I kept all this f. 25:21
make this f. return. 29:4
caught every one his f. 2 Sam 2:16
put this f. in prison. 1 Ki 22:27
2 Chr 18:26
wherefore came this mad f. to ?
2 Ki 9:11
one will lift up his f. Eccl 4:10
the satyr shall cry to his f. Isa 34:14
said every one to his f. Jonah 1:7
awake, O sword, against the man
that is my f., saith Lord. Zech 13:7
f. doth not cast out. Mat 12:24*
this f. said, I am able to. 26:61*
this f. was also with Jesus. 71*
Luke 22:59*
found this f. perverting. Luke 23:2*
as for this f. we know. John 9:29*
Didymus said to f. disciples. 11:16
this f. persuadeth men. Acts 18:13*
away with such a f. from. 22:22
this man a pestilent f. 24:5

fellow-citizens

but f.-citizens with saints. Eph 2:19

fellow-heirs

Gentiles be f.-heirs. Eph 3:6

fellow-helper

Titus my f.-helper. 2 Cor 8:23

fellow-helpers

we might be f.-helpers. 3 John 8

fellow-labourer

Timotheus our f.-labourer.
1 Thes 3:2
Philemon our f.-labourer. Philem 1

fellow-labourers

other my f.-labourers. Phil 4:3
Lucas, my f.-labourers. Philem 24

fellow-prisoner

Aristarchus my f.-prisoner. Col 4:10
Epaphras my f.-prisoner. Philem 23

fellow-prisoners

Andronicus and Junia f.-prisoners.
Rom 16:7

fellows

virginity, I and my f. Judg 11:37*
lest angry f. run on thee. 18:25
as one of the vain f. 2 Sam 6:20
with oil of gladness above f.
Ps 45:7; Heb 1:9
his f. shall be ashamed. Isa 44:11
tribes of Israel his f. Ezek 37:19*
sought Daniel and his f. Dan 2:13*
that Daniel and his f. not. 18*
was more stout than his f. 7:20
thou and thy f. that set. Zech 3:8
children calling to their f. Mat 11:16
Jews took lewd f. of. Acts 17:5

fellow-servant, or *servants*

found one of his f.-serv. Mat 18:28
his f.-serv. fell at his feet. 29
so when his f.-serv. saw what. 31
have had compassion on f.-serv. 33
begin to smite his f.-serv. 24:49
of Epaphras our f.-serv. Col 1:7
Tychicus, who is a f.-serv. in. 4:7
till their f.-serv. should. Rev 6:11
it not, I am thy f.-serv. 19:10; 22:9

fellowship

him to keep, or in f. Lev 6:2
of iniquity have f. with ? Ps 94:20
apostles' doctrine and f. Acts 2:42
called to the f. of his Son. 1 Cor 1:9
not that ye should have f. 10:20*
what f. hath righteousness with ?
2 Cor 6:14
take on us the f. of ministering. 8:4
gave to me right hand of f. Gal 2:9
make men see what is f. Eph 3:9*
have no f. with works of. 5:11
for your f. in the gospel. Phil 1:5
if there be any f. of the spirit. 2:1
that I may know the f. of. 3:10
also may have f. with us, and our f.
is with Father, and. 1 John 1:3
if we say that we have f. with. 6
if we walk in light, we have f. 7

fellow-soldier

Epaphroditus my f.-soldier.
Phil 2:25
Paul to Archippus our f.-soldier.
Philem 2

fellow-workers

only are my f.-workers. Col 4:1

felt

and Isaac f. him. Gen 27:2
darkness that may be f. Ex 10:2
beaten me, and I f. it not. Pr 23:3
she f. she was healed. Mark 5:2
shook off the beast and f. Acts 28:5

female

male and f. created. Gen 1:27; 5:
they shall be male and f. 6:1
sevens, the male and his f. 7:2,
went in two and two, male and f.
went in, went in male and f. 1
whether it be male or f. Lev 3:
offering be of flock, male or f.
a f. without blemish. 4:28, 32; 5:
that hath born a male or f. 12:
if it be a f. thy estimation shall. 27:
thy estimation for the f. ten. 5,
for the f. from a month old.
both male and f. shall. Num 5
the likeness of male or f. Deut 4:
not be a male or f. barren. 7:
made them male and f. Mat 19
Mark 10
in Christ neither male nor f.
Gal 3:

fence

wall and a tottering f. Ps 62

fenced, *verb*

f. me with bones and. Job 10:
he hath f. up my way that. 19
hath a vineyard, f. it. Isa 5

fenced

till thy high and f. walls. Deut 28:
must be f. with iron. 2 Sam 2:
ye shall smite every f. 2 Ki 3:

there are with you a f. city. 2 Ki 10:2
tower to the f. city. 17:9; 18:8
day of Lord on every f. Isa 2:15
make thee a f. brasen. Jer 15:20
ruined cities become f. Ezek 36:35

fenced *cities*
(*American Revision uses here the word* fortified)

ones dwell in f. cities. Num 32:17
all these cities were f. Deut 3:5
to possess cities great and f. 9:1
rest entered into f. cities. Josh 10:20
the cities were great and f. 14:12
number of f. cities. 1 Sam 6:18
lest he get f. cities. 2 Sam 20:6
Sennacherib came against all the f. cities of. 2 Ki 18:13; 2 Chr 12:4
lay waste f. cities. 2 Ki 19:25
Solomon built f. cities. 2 Chr 8:5
Shishak took the f. cities. 12:4
Asa built f. cities in Judah. 14:6
placed forces in f. cities. 17:2, 19
judges throughout all f. cities. 19:5
gave them f. cities in Judah. 21:3
put captains in f. cities. 33:14
impoverish thy f. cities. Jer 5:17
of north take f. cities. Dan 11:15
Judah multiplied f. cities. Hos 8:14
alarm against f. cities. Zeph 1:16

fens

in covert of reed and f. Job 40:21

ferret

f. chameleon and lizard. Lev 11:30*

ferry boat

there went a f. boat. 2 Sam 19:18

fervent

Apollos, being f. in spirit. Acts 18:25
f. in spirit, serving Lord. Rom 12:11
he told us your f. mind. 2 Cor 7:7*
f. prayer of a righteous. Jas 5:16*
above all things f. charity. 1 Pet 4:8
elements melt with f. heat. 2 Pet 3:10, 12

fervently

Epaphras labouring f. Col 4:12
love one another with a pure heart f. 1 Pet 1:22

Festus

Porcius F. come into. Acts 24:27
F. willing to do Jews a pleasure. 25:9
came to Caesarea to salute F. 13
F. declared Paul's cause unto. 14
at F.' commandment Paul was. 23
not mad, most noble F. 26:25

fetch

I will f. a morsel of bread. Gen 18:5
go, f. me two good kids. 27:9, 13
then I will send and f. thee. 45
ark, sent maid to f. it. Ex 2:5
must we f. water out? Num 20:10*
elders shall send and f. Deut 19:12
shalt not go to f. pledge. 24:10, 19
from thence will Lord f. thee. 30:4
of Gilead went to f. Judg 11:5
take men to f. victuals. 20:10
let us f. the ark. 1 Sam 4:3
come ye down, and f. it up. 6:21
Samuel said, Send and f. him. 16:11
20:31
let us come over and f. 26:22
a compass behind. 2 Sam 5:23*
doth king not f. home his. 14:13
to f. about this form of speech. 20*
me, I pray thee, a. 1 Ki 17:10
as she was going to f. it. 11
he is, that I may f. him. 2 Ki 6:13
quickly Micaiah the. 2 Chr 18:8
olive branches, pine. Neh 8:15
will f. my knowledge. Job 36:3
say they, I will f. wine. Isa 56:12
king sent Jehudi to f. Jer 36:21
come and f. us out. Acts 16:37*

fetched

water, I pray you, be f. Gen 18:4
Abraham f. a calf tender and. 7
Jacob went and f. the kids. 27:14
they f. carved image. Judg 18:18
men came and f. up ark. 1 Sam 7:1
they ran, and f. Saul thence. 10:23
they would have f. wheat. 2 Sam 4:6
David sent and f. Mephibosheth. 9:5
David sent and f. Bath-sheba. 11:27*

Joab f. from Tekoah a. 2 Sam 14:2
king Solomon f. Hiram. 1 Ki 7:13
f. from Ophir gold, 420 talents. 9:28
f. a compass of seven. 2 Ki 3:9
Jehoiada sent and f. rulers. 11:4
f. from Egypt a chariot. 2 Chr 1:17
guard came and f. the. 12:11*
and they f. forth Urijah. Jer 26:23
and from thence f. a. Acts 28:13*

fetcheth

and his hand f. a stroke. Deut 19:5

fetters

bound Samson with f. Judg 16:21
hands were not bound, nor thy feet put into f. 2 Sam 3:34
put out eyes of Zedekiah, and bound him with f. of brass. 2 Ki 25:7
Manasseh was bound with f. 2 Chr 33:11
Jehoiakim bound with f. to. 36:6
feet they hurt with f. Ps 105:18
their nobles with f. of iron. 149:8
being often bound with f. Mark 5:4
Luke 8:29

fever

shall smite thee with a f. Deut 28:22
Peter's wife's mother sick of a f. Mat 8:14; Mark 1:30; Luke 4:38
at 7th hour f. left him. John 4:52
of Publius sick of a f. Acts 28:8

few

damsel abide a f. days. Gen 24:55
tarry a f. days till thy. 27:44
I being f. in number, they. 34:30
f. and evil the days of my life. 47:9
I will make you f. Lev 26:22
Deut 4:27; 28:62
the cloud was a f. days. Num 9:20
see people whether they be f. 13:18
to f. shall give less. 26:54; 35:8
divided between many and f. 26:56
sojourned there with a f. Deut 26:5
live, let not his men be f. 33:6
to save by many or f. 1 Sam 14:6
whom hast thou left f. sheep? 17:28
but priests were too f. 2 Chr 29:34
I and some f. men with. Neh 2:12
large, but the people were f. 7:4
are not my days f.? Job 10:20
man is of f. days and full. 14:1
when a f. years are come. 16:22
let his days be f. and let. Ps 109:8
therefore let words be f. Eccl 5:2
a little city, and f. men in it. 9:14
cease, because they are f. 12:3
trees of forest shall be f. Isa 10:19
inhabitants are burned, and f. 24:6
shalt also take a f. in. Ezek 5:3
I will leave a f. men from. 12:16
f. days be destroyed. Dan 11:20
strait is gate, and f. Mat 7:14
labourers are f. 9:37; Luke 10:2
seven, and a f. little fishes. Mat 15:34; Mark 8:7
f. are chosen. Mat 20:16; 22:14
faithful in a f. things. 25:21, 23
laid hands on a f. sick. Mark 6:5
be beaten with f. stripes. Luke 12:48
are there f. that be saved? 13:23
hear us a f. words. Acts 24:4
as I wrote in f. words. Eph 3:3
for a f. days chastened. Heb 12:10
written unto you in f. words. 13:22
wherein f. that is, eight. 1 Pet 3:20
a f. things against. Rev 2:14, 20
hast a f. names even in. 3:4

but a **few**

to him but a few days. Gen 29:20
but f. years to jubile. Lev 25:52
the men of Ai are but f. Josh 7:3
when ye were but f. 1 Chr 16:19
Ps 105:12
we are left but a f. of. Jer 42:2

not a **few**

vessels, borrow not a f. 2 Ki 4:3
cut off nations not a f. Isa 10:7
and they shall not be f. Jer 30:19
chief women not a f. Acts 17:4
of men not a f. 12

fewer

to f. ye shall give less. Num 33:54

fewest

ye were f. of all people. Deut 7:7

fewness

according to f. of years. Lev 25:16

fidelity

servants shewing good f. Tit 2:10

field

the f. give I thee. Gen 23:11
the f. and cave were made sure. 20
of my son is as smell of a f. 27:27
called Rachel and Leah to f. 31:4
in f. which Abraham. 49:30; 50:13
a man shall cause a f. to. Ex 22:5
that the corn or f. be consumed. 6
shalt not sow thy f. with. Lev 19:19
six years shalt sow thy f. 25:3
seventh year shalt not sow thy f. 4
if he sanctify his f. from. 27:17, 18
redeem the f. or if he sold the f. 20
covet thy neighbour's f. Deut 5:21
ask of her father a f. Josh 15:18
Judg 1:14
not to glean in another f. Ruth 2:8
what day thou buyest f. of. 4:5
Joab's f. is near mine. 2 Sam 14:30
servants set my f. on fire? 31
upper pool, in highway of fuller's f. 2 Ki 18:17; Isa 7:3; 36:2
fled every one to his f. Neh 13:10
let the f. be joyful. Ps 96:12
I went by the f. of slothful. Pr 24:30
and goats the price of f. 27:26
considereth a f. and buyeth. 31:16
king himself is served by f. Eccl 5:9
woe to them that lay f. to f. Isa 5:8
joy is taken out of plentiful f. 16:10
herbs of every f. wither. Jer 12:4
Zion plowed like a f. 26:18; Mi 3:12
my f. in Anathoth. Jer 32:7, 8, 25
have we vineyard, nor f. 35:9
gladness is taken from plentiful f. 48:33
the f. is wasted, the. Joel 1:10
good seed in his f. Mat 13:24, 31
the f. is the world, good seed. 38
of heaven is like to treasure hid in a f.; he selleth all, buyeth that f. 44
with them the potter's f. 27:7, 10
f. was called f. of blood. 8; Acts 1:19
when come from the f. Luke 17:7
man purchased a f. with. Acts 1:18

fruitful **field**

glory of his fruitful f. Isa 10:18
Lebanon turned into fruitful f. 29:17
till wilderness be a fruitful f. and the fruitful f. be counted a. 32:15
righteousness in the fruitful f. 16
the seed in a fruitful f. Ezek 17:5

in the **field**

when they were in the f. Gen 4:8
out to meditate in the f. 24:63
and behold a well in the f. 29:2
Joseph was wandering in the f. 37:15
gather all thou hast in the f. Ex 9:19
hail smote all that was in the f. 25
ye shall not find it in the f. 16:25
found slain, lying in the f. Deut 21:1
find a betrothed damsel in f. 22:25
blessed in city and in the f. 28:3
cursed in city and in the f. 16
angel came to woman in f. Judg 13:9
stone remaineth in f. of. 1 Sam 6:18
stand beside my father in the f. 19:3
found an Egyptian in the f. 30:11
they two strove in the f. 2 Sam 14:6
two were alone in the f. 1 Ki 11:29
dieth of Jeroboam in the f. 14:11
dieth of Ahab in the f. fowls. 21:24
kings by themselves in f. 1 Chr 19:9
over them that did work in f. 27:26
every one his corn in f. Job 24:6
marvellous things in f. of Zoan. Ps 78:12, 43
it fit for thyself in the f. Pr 24:27
the hind calved in the f. Jer 14:5
O my mountain in the f. 17:3
we have treasures in the f. 41:8
is in the f. shall die. Ezek 7:15
slay thy daughters in the f. 26:6, 8
shalt dwell in the f. and. Mi 4:10
every one grass in the f. Zech 10:1

nor vine cast her fruit *in the f.* *Mal* 3:11
let him who is *in f.* return to. *Mat* 24:18; *Mark* 13:16; *Luke* 17:31
shall two be *in the f.* *Mat* 24:40; *Luke* 17:36
shepherds abiding *in f.* *Luke* 2:8
grass which is to-day *in the f.* 12:28
his elder son was *in the f.* 15:25

into the **field**

and went *into the f.* *Num* 22:23
people went *into the f.* *Judg* 9:42
cart came *into the f.* *1 Sam* 6:14
come let us go *into the f.* 20:11
men came out *into f.* *2 Sam* 11:23
removed Amasa *into the f.* 20:12
one went *into f.* and. *2 Ki* 4:39
let us go forth *into f.* *S of S* 7:11
go not forth *into f.* nor. *Jer* 6:25
if I go forth *into the f.* 14:18

of the **field**

plant and herb *of the f.* *Gen* 2:5
sons of Jacob came out *of f.* 34:7
four parts, for seed *of the f.* 47:24
trees *of the f.* yield fruit. *Lev* 26:4
no devoted thing *of the f.* 27:28
for the tree *of the f.* is. *Deut* 20:19
marchedst out *of the f.* *Judg* 5:4
old man from work out *of f.* 19:16
on a part *of the f.* *Ruth* 2:3
Saul came out *of the f.* *1 Sam* 11:5
of the f. of Naboth. *2 Ki* 9:25
as dung upon the face *of the f.* 37
league with stones *of the f.* *Job* 5:23
as a flower *of the f.* *Ps* 103:15
charge you by the roes *of the f.* *S of S* 2:7; 3:5
were as grass *of the f.* *Isa* 37:27
as the flower *of the f.* 40:6
beast *of the f.* honour me. 43:20
trees *of the f.* shall clap. 55:12
as keepers *of the f.* are. *Jer* 4:17
of Lebanon from rock *of the f.* 18:14
want of fruits *of the f.* *Lam* 4:9
multiply as bud *of the f.* *Ezek* 16:7
all trees *of the f.* shall know. 17:24
tree *of the f.* shall yield fruit. 34:27
multiply increase *of the f.* 36:30
take no wood out *of the f.* 39:10
in tender grass *of the f.* *Dan* 4:15
hemlock in furrows *of f.* *Hos* 10:4
altars as heaps in furrows *of f.* 12:11
harvest *of the f.* is. *Joel* 1:11
even all the trees *of the f.* are. 12
flame hath burnt all trees *of f.* 19
Samaria as an heap *of f.* *Mi* 1:6
consider lilies *of the f.* *Mat* 6:28
if God so clothe grass *of the f.* 30
parable of the tares *of the f.* 13:36

see **beast, beasts**

open **field**

bird loose into *open f.* *Lev* 14:7
sacrifices which they offer in *open f.* 17:5
carcases as dung upon the *open f.* *Jer* 9:22
cast out in the *open f.* *Ezek* 16:5
cast thee forth upon *open f.* 32:4
him that is in the *open f.* I. 33:27
thou shalt fall upon the *open f.* 39:5

fields

died out of houses and *f.* *Ex* 8:13
shall be counted as the *f.* *Lev* 25:31
which is not of the *f.* of. 27:22
us inheritance of *f.* *Num* 16:14
not pass through *f.* or. 20:17; 21:22
send grass into thy *f.* *Deut* 11:15
might eat increase of the *f.* 32:13
vine is as vine of the *f.* of. 32
f. and villages gave they. *Josh* 21:12
he will take your *f.* *1 Sam* 8:14
of Jesse give each of you *f.*? 22:7
wall to us when we were in *f.* 25:15
Anathoth, to thine own *f.* *1 Ki* 2:26
that dieth of Baasha in *f.* 16:4
let the *f.* rejoice, and. *1 Chr* 16:32
over storehouses in the *f.* 27:25
sendeth waters upon *f.* *Job* 5:10
sow the *f.* and plant. *Ps* 107:37
we found it in the *f.* of wood. 132:6
yet he had not made the *f.* *Pr* 8:26
into *f.* of the fatherless. *Pr.* 23:10
for *f.* of Heshbon. *Isa* 16:8
lament for pleasant *f.* 32:12
their *f.* turned to. *Jer* 6:12; 8:10
seen abominations in the *f.* 13:27
f. shall be possessed again. 32:15
f. bought. 43
men shall buy *f.* for money. 44
Nebuzar-adan gave them *f.* 39:10
captains of forces in the *f.* 40:7, 13
shall possess *f.* of Ephraim. *Ob* 19
they covet *f.* and take. *Mi* 2:2
turning away, hath divided our *f.* 4
although *f.* yield no meat. *Hab* 3:17
went through the corn *f.* *Mark* 2:23; *Luke* 6:1
your eyes, look on the *f.* *John* 4:35
which reaped down your *f.* *Jas* 5:4

open **fields**

living bird into *open f.* *Lev* 14:53
with sword in *open f.* *Num* 19:16
encamped in the *open f.* *2 Sam* 11:11
shalt fall upon *open f.* *Ezek* 29:5

fierce

be their anger, it was *f.* *Gen* 49:7
nation of *f.* countenance. *Deut* 28:50
the voice of *f.* lion and. *Job* 4:10
huntest me as a *f.* lion. 10:16
nor the *f.* lion passed by it. 28:8
none is so *f.* that dare stir. 41:10
a *f.* king shall rule over. *Isa* 19:4
shalt not see a *f.* people. 33:19
king of *f.* countenance. *Dan* 8:23
horses are more *f.* than. *Hab* 1:8
with devils, exceeding *f.* *Mat* 8:28
and they were more *f.* *Luke* 23:5
shall be incontinent, *f.* *2 Tim* 3:3
ships which are driven of *f.* winds. *Jas* 3:4*

see **anger, wrath**

fierceness

swalloweth ground with *f.* and. *Job* 39:24
land desolate for the *f.* *Jer* 25:38

fiercer

words of Judah *f.* than. *2 Sam* 19:43

fiery

the Lord sent *f.* serpents. *Num* 21:6
make thee a *f.* serpent, and set. 8
wherein were *f.* serpents. *Deut* 8:15
from his right hand a *f.* law. 33:2
make them as a *f.* oven. *Ps* 21:9
fruit a *f.* flying serpent. *Isa* 14:29
into midst of *f.* furnace. *Dan* 3:6, 11, 15, 21
God is able to deliver us from *f.* 17
three men into midst of *f.* furnace. 23
came near to mouth of *f.* furnace. 26
his throne was like the *f.* flame. 7:9
a *f.* stream issued and came. 10
able to quench *f.* darts. *Eph* 6:16
of judgement, and *f.* *Heb* 10:27*
not strange concerning *f.* *1 Pet* 4:12

fifteen

f. cubits upwards did. *Gen* 7:20
hangings to be *f.* cubits. *Ex* 27:14; 15; 38:14
shall be *f.* shekels. *Lev* 27:7
now Ziba had *f.* sons. *2 Sam* 9:10
Ziba and his *f.* sons went. 19:17
on forty-five pillars, *f.* *1 Ki* 7:3
Amaziah lived after Jehoash *f.* years. *2 Ki* 14:17
I will add to thy days *f.* years. 20:6; *2 Chr* 25:25; *Isa* 38:5
f. shekels shall be. *Ezek* 45:12
bought her to me for *f.* *Hos* 3:2
Bethany was *f.* furlongs. *John* 11:18
and found it *f.* fathoms. *Acts* 27:28
I abode with Peter *f.* days. *Gal* 1:18

fifteenth

in *f.* year of Amaziah. *2 Ki* 14:23
f. to Bilgah. *1 Chr* 24:14
f. to Jerimoth. 25:22
to Jerusalem in *f.* year. *2 Chr* 15:10
in the *f.* year of reign. *Luke* 3:1

fifteenth *day*

came to Sin, on *f. day.* *Ex* 16:1
on *f. day* of the same month. *Lev* 23:6; *Num* 28:17; 33:3
f. day of this seventh month feast of. *Lev* 23:34, 39; *Num* 29:12
on *f. day* of the eighth month was Jeroboam's. *1 Ki* 12:32, 33
on *f. day* they rested. *Esth* 9:18, 21
f. day of twelfth year. *Ezek* 32:17
in *f. day* do like in feast 45:25

fifth

Leah bare Jacob the *f.* *Gen* 30:17
f. lot came out for Asher. *Josh* 19:24
smote Asahel under *f.* *2 Sam* 2:23*
Abner under the *f.* rib. 3:27*
Joab smote Amasa in the *f.* 20:10*
Sanballat sent *f.* time. *Neh* 6:5
when he had opened *f.* seal. *Rev* 6:9
the *f.* angel sounded, and I saw. 9:1
f. angel poured out his vial. 16:10
the *f.* a sardonyx. 21:20

see **day, part**

fifth *month*

Aaron died first day of *f. month.* *Num* 33:38
f. month came Nebuzar-adan. *2 Ki* 25:8; *Jer* 52:12
fifth captain for *f. month.* *1 Chr* 27:8
Ezra came in *f. month.* *Ezra* 7:8, 9
Jerusalem captive in the *f. month.* *Jer* 1:3
in *f. month* Hananiah spake. 28:1
in *f. month* the elders. *Ezek* 20:1
I weep in *f. month*? *Zech* 7:3
fasted and mourned in *f. month.* 5
fast of fourth and of *f. month.* 8:19

fifth *year*

in *f. year* ye shall eat. *Lev* 19:25
f. year of king Rehoboam Shishak came. *1 Ki* 14:25; *2 Chr* 12:2
in the *f. year* of Joram. *2 Ki* 8:16
in *f. year* of Jehoiakim. *Jer* 36:9
f. year of Jehoiachin's. *Ezek* 1:2

fifties

place rulers of *f.* *Ex* 18:21, 25; *Deut* 1:15
appoint captains over *f.* *1 Sam* 8:12
burnt two captains of *f.* *2 Ki* 1:14

fiftieth

ye shall hallow *f.* year. *Lev* 25:10
a jubile shall that *f.* year be to. 11
in *f.* year of Azariah. *2 Ki* 15:23

fifty

breadth of ark *f.* cubits. *Gen* 6:15
not spare the place for *f.*? 18:24, 26
f. loops shalt thou make. *Ex* 26:5, 10; 36:12, 17
make *f.* taches of gold. 26:6, 11; 36:13, 18
hangings of *f.* cubits. 27:12; 38:12
two hundred and *f.* shekels, of sweet calamus two hundred *f.* 30:23
7th sabbath, number *f.* *Lev* 23:16
males thy estimation *f.* shekels. 27:3
homer of barley seed valued at *f.* 16
from thirty years old even to *f.* years. *Num* 4:3, 23, 30, 35, 39
from age of *f.* shall serve no. 8:25
two hundred and *f.* princes of. 16:2
bring two hundred and *f.* censers. 17
fire devoured two hundred *f.* 26:10
one portion of *f.* for Levites. 31:30
Moses took one portion of *f.* of. 47
give damsel's father *f.* *Deut* 22:29
a wedge of gold of *f.* *Josh* 7:21
Absalom had *f.* men to. *2 Sam* 15:1
Adonijah had *f.* men to. *1 Ki* 1:5
breadth of house of forest *f.* 7:2
hid them by *f.* in a cave. 18:4, 13
captain of *f.* with his *f.* *2 Ki* 1:9, 11, 13
fire consume thee and thy *f.* 10, 12
f. men of sons of the prophets. 2:
they sent therefore *f.* men to. 1
left to Jehoahaz but *f.* 13:
Menahem exacted of each *f.* 15:2
but Pekah slew *f.* men of. 2
weight of nails was *f.* *2 Chr* 3:
Ebed went up with *f.* *Ezra* 8:
Tirshatha gave *f.* basons. *Neh* 7:7
gallows *f.* cubits. *Esth* 5:14; 7:
Lord will take captain of *f.* *Isa* 3:
to face of porch *f.* *Ezek* 40:1
length *f.* cubits. 21, 25, 29, 33, 3
42

of north door *f.* cubits. *Ezek* 42:2
to draw out *f.* vessels. *Hag* 2:16
owed 500 pence, other *f. Luke* 7:41
sit down quickly, and write *f.* 16:6
art not yet *f.* years old. *John* 8:57

fifty-two

Azariah reigned *f.-two.* *2 Ki* 15:2
children of Nebo *f.-two.* *Ezra* 2:29 *Neh* 7:33
wall finished in *f.-two* days. *Neh* 6:15

fifty-six

of Netophah, *f.* and *six.* *Ezra* 2:22

fifty thousand

of people *f. thousand.* *1 Sam* 6:19
of camels *f. thousand.* *1 Chr* 5:21
of Zebulun *f. thousand.* 12:33
price of books *f. thousand* pieces of silver. *Acts* 19:19

fifty-three thousand

of Naphtali numbered *f.-three thousand.* *Num* 1:43; 2:30; 26:47

fifty-four thousand

of Issachar *f.-four thousand* four hundred. *Num* 1:29; 2:6

fifty-seven thousand

Zebulun *f.-seven thousand* four. *Num* 1:31; 2:8

fifty-nine thousand

of Simeon numbered *f.-nine thousand* three hundred. *Num* 1:23

fig, -s

The fig tree and its fruit are well known; they were very common in Palestine, and there is mention often made of them in scripture. Our first parents clothed themselves with fig leaves, Gen 3:7. *The prophet Isaiah gave orders to apply a lump of figs to Hezekiah's boil; and immediately after he was cured,* 2 Ki 20:7.

The cursing of the fig tree, in Mat 21:19, *is explained by the fact that the fruit of this tree appears before the leaves, and a tree so full of leaves indicated that ripe figs should be there, even though it was not yet the regular season. The meaning is then, that when one has the outward show of a good character, without its fruits, he is but a hypocrite, and of no value to the kingdom of God.*

To dwell under one's own vine, or fig tree, *represents in scripture a time of happiness and prosperity, safety and security,* 1 Ki 4:25.

sewed *f.* leaves together. *Gen* 3:7
of pomegranates and *f.* *Num* 13:23
no place of seed, or of *f.* or. 20:5
Abigail took cakes of *f.* *1 Sam* 25:18
gave Egyptian a cake of *f.* 30:12
said, take a lump of *f.* *2 Ki* 20:7 *Isa* 38:21
that were nigh brought *f.* *1 Chr* 12:40
sabbath some brought *f.* *Neh* 13:15
putteth forth green *f.* *S of S* 2:13
as a falling *f.* from. *Isa* 34:4*
there shall be no *f.* on. *Jer* 8:13
of *f.* one had very good *f.* 24:1, 2, 3
as the evil *f.* that cannot be eaten. 8
I will make them like vile *f.* 29:17
fig trees with first ripe *f.* *Nah* 3:12
men gather *f.* of thistles? *Mat* 7:16 *Luke* 6:44
bear berries, or a vine *f.*? *Jas* 3:12
casteth her untimely *f.* *Rev* 6:13

fig tree

trees said to the *f.* come, reign. *Judg* 9:10, 11
dwelt safely under his *f.* *1 Ki* 4:25 *Mi* 4:4
at every one of his *f.* *2 Ki* 18:31 *Isa* 36:16
whoso keepeth *f.* shall eat. *Pr* 27:18
fathers as firstripe in the *f.* *Hos* 9:10
he hath barked my *f.* *Joel* 1:7
vine is dried, the *f.* languisheth. 12
the *f.* and vine do yield. 2:22
the *f.* shall not blossom. *Hab* 3:17
as yet the *f.* hath not. *Hag* 2:19
call every man under *f.* *Zech* 3:10
when he saw a *f.* in way. *Mat* 21:19 *Mark* 11:13
how soon is *f.* withered! *Mat* 21:20 *Mark* 11:20, 21
a parable of the *f.* *Mat* 24:32 *Mark* 13:28
a man had a *f.* planted. *Luke* 13:6
I come, seeking fruit on this *f.* 7
behold the *f.* and all trees. 21:29
under the *f.* I saw. *John* 1:48, 50

fig trees

of wheat, vines, and *f.* *Deut* 8:8
smote their vines also and *f.* *Ps* 105:33
eat up thy vines and *f.* *Jer* 5:17
destroy her vines and *f.* *Hos* 2:12
when your gardens and *f.* *Amos* 4:9
strong holds shall be like *f.* *Nah* 3:12

fight, *substantive*

as host was going forth to the *f.* *1 Sam* 17:20
fight the good *f.* of faith. *1 Tim* 6:12
I have fought a good *f.* *2 Tim* 4:7
ye endured a great *f.* *Heb* 10:32*
strong, waxed valiant in *f.* 11:34*

fight, *verb*

we will go up and *f.* *Deut* 1:41
go not up, nor *f.*, I am not among. 42
Sihon and his people came to *f.* 2:32*
art come against me to *f.* *Judg* 11:12
yourselves like men, *f.* *1 Sam* 4:9
me a man that we may *f.* 17:10
nigh when ye did *f.*? *2 Sam* 11:20
f. not small nor great. *1 Ki* 22:31 *2 Chr* 18:30
about Jehoshaphat to *f.* *2 Chr* 18:31
ye shall not need to *f.* in. 20:17
teacheth my fingers to *f.* *Ps* 144:1
men have forborn to *f.* *Jer* 51:30
shall *f.* because Lord is. *Zech* 10:5
Judah also shall *f.* at. 14:14
would my servants *f.* *John* 18:36
so *f.* I, not as one that. *1 Cor* 9:26
f. the good fight of faith. *1 Tim* 6:12
ye kill, ye *f.* and war. *Jas* 4:2

see **battles**

fight *against*

join enemies, *f. against* us. *Ex* 1:10
to a city to *f. against* it. *Deut* 20:10
to enemies *against* whom ye *f.* *Josh* 10:25
pitched to *f. against* Israel. 11:5
Danites went up to *f. against.* 19:47
first to *f. against* them? *Judg* 1:1
that we may *f. against* Canaanites. 3
over Jordan to *f. against* Judah. 10:9
to *f. against* Ammon. 11:8, 9
against Israel, or *f. against* them? 25
come ye to *f. against* me? 12:3
set themselves to *f. against.* 20:20
f. against Amalekites. *1 Sam* 15:18
Philistines *f. against* Keilah. 23:1
not *f. against* enemies of king. 29:8
Judah with Benjamin to *f. against* Israel. *1 Ki* 12:21; *2 Chr* 11:1
not *f. against* your brethren. *1 Ki* 12:24; *2 Chr* 11:4
let us *f. against* them in plain. *1 Ki* 20:23, 25
to *f. against* Jehoshaphat. 22:32
kings were come to *f. against* them. *2 Ki* 3:21
he is come out to *f. against.* 19:9
O Israel, *f.* not *against.* *2 Chr* 13:12
Sennacherib to *f. against.* 32:2
Necho came to *f. against.* 35:20
and *f. against* Jerusalem. *Neh* 4:8
f. against them that *f. against* me. *Ps* 35:1
be many that *f. against* me. 56:2
f. every one *against* his brother. *Isa* 19:2
nations that *f. against* Ariel. 29:7
nations that *f. against* Zion. 8
f. against thee, not prevail. *Jer* 1:19 15:20
wherewith ye *f. against* king. 21:4
I myself will *f. against* you. 5
city is given to the Chaldeans that *f. against* it. 32:24, 29; 34:22; 37:8
Chaldeans that *f. against* you. 37:10
Lord shall *f. against.* *Zech* 14:3
found to *f. against* God. *Acts* 5:39
let us not *f. against* God. 23:9
f. against them with sword. *Rev* 2:16*

fight *for*

f. for you. *Ex* 14:14; *Deut* 1:30 3:22; 20:4
f. for your master's. *2 Ki* 10:3
f. for your brethren, sons. *Neh* 4:14
our God shall *f. for* us. 20
Lord shall come to *f. for.* *Isa* 31:4

fight *with*

go out, *f. with* Amalek. *Ex* 17:9
gathered to *f. with* Joshua. *Josh* 9:2
to *f. with* the Midianites. *Judg* 8:1
go out and *f. with* Abimelech. 9:38
may *f. with* children of Ammon. 11:6
gathered to *f. with* Israel. *1 Sam* 13:5; 28:1
if he be able to *f. with* me. 17:9
servant will *f. with* this Philistine. 32
disguised himself to *f. with* him. *2 Chr* 35:22
of shaking *f. with* it. *Isa* 30:32
ye *f. with* Chaldeans. *Jer* 32:5
came to *f. with* Chaldeans. 33:5
went to *f. with* Ishmael. 41:12
return to *f. with* prince of. *Dan* 10:20
south come and *f. with* him. 11:11

fighteth

Lord *f.* for them against. *Ex* 14:25
the Lord God, that *f.* for. *Josh* 23:10
my lord *f.* the battles. *1 Sam* 25:28

fighting

were *f.* Philistines. *1 Sam* 17:19
Uzziah had host of *f.* *2 Chr* 26:11
O God, he *f.* oppresseth. *Ps* 56:1

fightings

without were *f.* within. *2 Cor* 7:5
whence come wars and *f.*? *Jas* 4:1

figure

similitude of any *f.* *Deut* 4:16
maketh it after the *f.* of. *Isa* 44:13
who is the *f.* of him. *Rom* 5:14
I have in a *f.* transferred. *1 Cor* 4:6
which was a *f.* of the time. *Heb* 9:9
whence he received him in a *f.* 11:19
the like *f.* whereunto. *1 Pet* 3:21*

figures

carved with carved *f.* *1 Ki* 6:29
f. ye made to worship. *Acts* 7:43
holy places, *f.* of the true. *Heb* 9:24*

file

had a *f.* for mattocks. *1 Sam* 13:21

fill, *substantive*

shall eat *f.* in safety. *Lev* 25:19
mayest eat grapes thy *f.* *Deut* 23:24
let us take our *f.* of love. *Pr* 7:18

fill, *verb*

multiply, and *f.* waters. *Gen* 1:22
Joseph commanded to *f.* 42:25 44:1
locusts shall *f.* thy houses. *Ex* 10:6
Moses said, *f.* an homer. 16:32*
f. thine horn with oil. *1 Sam* 16:1
f. four barrels with. *1 Ki* 18:33
till he *f.* thy mouth with. *Job* 8:21
a wise man *f.* belly with east. 15:2
when he is about to *f.* his. 20:23
f. my mouth with arguments. 23:4
f. appetite of young lions. 38:39*
canst thou *f.* his skin with? 41:7
thy mouth and I will *f.* it. *Ps* 81:10
f. their faces with shame. 83:16
shall *f.* places with dead. 110:6
shall *f.* our houses with. *Pr* 1:13
I will *f.* their treasures. 8:21
wings shall *f.* breadth of. *Isa* 8:8
nor *f.* face of world with. 14:21
f. face of the world with fruit. 27:6
we will *f.* ourselves with. 56:12
I will *f.* inhabitants with. *Jer* 13:13
not I *f.* heaven and earth? 23:24
it is to *f.* them with the dead. 33:5
surely I will *f.* thee with. 51:14
f. thy bowels with this roll. *Ezek* 3:3
not satisfy their souls nor *f.* 7:19
f. the courts with the slain. 9:7
f. thine hand with coals of fire. 10:2
gather pieces, *f.* it with choice. 24:4
shall *f.* the land with slain. 30:11

f. beasts of whole earth. *Ezek* 32:4*
I will *f.* the valleys with thy. 5
f. his mountains with slain. 35:8
f. masters' house with. *Zeph* 1:9
I will *f.* this house with. *Hag* 2:7
which is put in to *f.* it up. *Mat* 9:16
have bread to *f.* such a? 15:33
f. ye up then the measure of. 23:32
f. the water-pots with. *John* 2:7
God of hope *f.* you with. *Rom* 15:13
ascended, that he might *f.* all. *Eph* 4:10
f. up what is behind of. *Col* 1:24
Jews, to *f.* up their sins. *1 Thes* 2:16
cup she hath filled, *f.* *Rev* 18:6*

filled

earth is *f.* with violence. *Gen* 6:13
Hagar went and *f.* the bottle. 21:19
Rebekah *f.* her pitcher. 24:16
Philistines had *f.* the wells. 26:15
children of Israel *f.* land. *Ex* 1:7
f. the troughs to water flock. 2:16
I have *f.* with wisdom. 28:3; 35:35
I have *f.* him with Spirit. 31:3; 35:31
of Lord *f.* tabernacle. 40:34, 35
within thy gates and be *f.* *Deut* 26:12
have eaten and *f.* themselves. 31:20
these bottles we *f.* were. *Josh* 9:13
cloud *f.* house of Lord. *1 Ki* 8:10
glory of Lord *f.* house. 11
2 Chr 5:14; 7:1, 2
he *f.* the trench also with. 18:35
but Syrians *f.* the country. 20:27
man his stone and *f.* it. *2 Ki* 3:25
Manasseh *f.* Jerusalem. 21:16; 24:4
Josiah *f.* places with bones. 23:14
which have *f.* it from end. *Ezra* 9:11
with princes who *f.* their. *Job* 3:15
hast *f.* me with wrinkles. 16:8*
yet he *f.* their houses with. 22:18
are *f.* with loathsome. *Ps* 38:7
let my mouth be *f.* with thy. 71:8
let the whole earth be *f.* 72:19
to take deep root, it *f.* the. 80:9
openest thine hand, *f.* with. 104:28*
exceedingly *f.* with contempt. 123:3
our soul is *f.* with scorning. 4
lest strangers be *f.* with. *Pr* 5:10
lest thou be *f.* with honey. 25:16
earth that is not *f.* with. 30:16*
a fool when he is *f.* with meat. 22
nor the ear *f.* with hearing. *Eccl* 1:8
his soul be not *f.* with good. 6:3
and yet the appetite is not *f.* 7
my head is *f.* with dew. *S of S* 5:2
and his train *f.* temple. *Isa* 6:1
are my loins *f.* with pain. 21:3
Lord hath *f.* Zion with. 33:5
sword of Lord is *f.* with blood. 34:6
nor *f.* me with the fat of thy. 43:24
old man that hath not *f.* 65:20
thou hast *f.* me with. *Jer* 15:17
they *f.* mine inheritance. 16:18
f. this place with blood of. 19:4
Ishmael *f.* the pit with them. 41:9
and thy cry hath *f.* the land. 46:12
he hath *f.* his belly with. 51:34
hath *f.* me with bitterness. *Lam* 3:15
he is *f.* full with reproach. 30
have *f.* the land with. *Ezek* 8:17
and the cloud *f.* the inner. 10:3
have *f.* the streets with slain. 11:6
f. the midst of thee with. 28:16
waste cities be *f.* with. 36:38
glory of Lord *f.* the house. 43:5
44:4
the stone cut out *f.* the. *Dan* 2:35
lion *f.* his holes with. *Nah* 2:12
thou art *f.* with shame. *Hab* 2:16
but are not *f.* with drink. *Hag* 1:6
I have *f.* the bow with. *Zech* 9:13
and *f.* a spunge with. *Mat* 27:48
Mark 15:36; *John* 19:29
new piece that *f.* it up. *Mark* 2:21
let the children first be *f.* 7:27
he hath *f.* the hungry. *Luke* 1:53
strong in spirit, *f.* with wisdom. 2:40
they came and *f.* both ships. 5:7
come, that my house be *f.* 14:23
f. his belly with husks. 15:16
they *f.* them up to brim. *John* 2:7
they *f.* twelve baskets with. 6:13
sorrow hath *f.* your heart. 16:6
rushing mighty wind, *f.* *Acts* 2:2
Peter, *f.* with Holy Ghost. *Acts* 4:8
why hath Satan *f.* thine heart? 5:3
f. Jerusalem with your doctrine. 28
mightest be *f.* with Holy Ghost. 9:17
Paul, *f.* with the Holy Ghost. 13:9
being *f.* with all unrighteousness. *Rom* 1:29
are *f.* with all knowledge. 15:14
if first I be somewhat *f.* with. 24*
I am *f.* with comfort. *2 Cor* 7:4
f. with the fulness of God. *Eph* 3:19
not drunk with wine, be *f.* with. 5:18
f. with the fruits of *Phil* 1:11
might be *f.* with knowledge. *Col* 1:9
that I may be *f.* with joy. *2 Tim* 1:4
in peace, be warmed and *f.* *Jas* 2:16
angel *f.* the censer with. *Rev* 8:5
for in them is *f.* up the wrath. 15:1*
cup which she hath *f.* fill. 18:6*

shall be **filled**

morning ye *shall be f.* *Ex* 16:12
earth *shall be f.* with. *Num* 14:21
valley *shall be f.* with. *2 Ki* 3:17
shall be f. with own. *Pr* 1:31
shall thy barns *be f.* with plenty. 3:10
wicked *shall be f.* with. 12:21
the backslider *shall be f.* 14:14
increase of lips *shall* he *be f.* 18:20*
his mouth *shall be f.* with. 20:17
knowledge *shall* chambers *be f.* 24:4
every bottle *shall be f.* *Jer* 13:12
shalt be f. with drunkenness. *Ezek* 23:33
ye *shall be f.* at my table. 39:20
earth *shall be f.* with. *Hab* 2:14
shall be f. like bowls. *Zech* 9:15
blessed they that hunger, they *shall be f.* *Mat* 5:6
John *shall be f.* with. *Luke* 1:15
every valley *shall be f.* 3:5
ye that hunger, ye *shall be f.* 6:21

was **filled**

earth *was f.* with violence. *Gen* 6:11
Hiram *was f.* with. *1 Ki* 7:14
country *was f.* with water. *2 Ki* 3:20
house *was f.* with a. *2 Chr* 5:13
was f. with sweet odours. 16:14
our mouth *was f.* with. *Ps* 126:2
house *was f.* with smoke. *Isa* 6:4
land *was f.* with sin. *Jer* 51:5
house *was f.* with cloud. *Ezek* 10:4
Elisabeth *was f.* with Holy Ghost. *Luke* 1:41
Zacharias *was f.* with Holy Ghost. 67
house *was f.* with odour. *John* 12:3
city *was f.* with confusion. *Acts* 19:29
temple *was f.* with smoke. *Rev* 15:8

were **filled**

so were they *f.* they *were f.* *Hos* 13:6
they *were f.* with wrath. *Luke* 4:28
were f. with fear, saying. 5:26
they *were f.* with madness. 6:11
they *were f.* with water. 8:23
when they *were f.* he. *John* 6:12
did eat of loaves, and *were f.* 26
they *were* all *f.* with the Holy Ghost. *Acts* 2:4; 4:31
they *were f.* with wonder. 3:10
and *were f.* with indignation. 5:17
the Jews *were f.* with envy. 13:45
disciples *were f.* with joy and. 52
fowls *were f.* with their. *Rev* 19:21

see **eat**

filledst

houses, which thou *f.* not. *Deut* 6:11
thou *f.* many people. *Ezek* 27:33

fillest

belly thou *f.* with hid. *Ps* 17:14

fillet

a *f.* of twelve cubits. *Jer* 52:21*

filleth

he *f.* me with bitterness. *Job* 9:18
the rain also *f.* pools. *Ps* 84:6*
he *f.* hungry soul with. 107:9
the mower *f.* not his hand. 129:7
f. thee with finest of wheat. 147:14
fulness of him that *f.* all. *Eph* 1:23

fillets

hooks of the pillars, and their *f.* be.
Ex 27:10, 11; 38:10, 11, 12, 17, 19
chapiters and *f.* with gold. 36:38

filletted

f. with silver. *Ex* 27:17; 38:17
overlaid chapiters and *f.* 38:28

filling

f. our hearts with food. *Acts* 14:17

filth

Lord washed away *f.* of. *Isa* 4:4
cast abominable *f.* upon. *Nah* 3:6
made as the *f.* of world. *1 Cor* 4:13
putting away *f.* of flesh. *1 Pet* 3:21

filthiness

f. out of the holy place. *2 Chr* 29:5
had separated from *f.* of. *Ezra* 6:21
an unclean land with the *f.* 9:11
is not washed from their *f.* *Pr* 30:12
are full of vomit and *f.* *Isa* 28:8
her *f.* is in her skirts. *Lam* 1:9
thy *f.* was poured out. *Ezek* 16:36
and I will consume thy *f.* 22:15
that the *f.* of it may be. 24:11
in thy *f.* is lewdness, shalt not be purged from thy *f.* 13
from all *f.* will I cleanse you. 36:25
cleanse ourselves from all *f.* of. *2 Cor* 7:1*
nor let *f.* be once named. *Eph* 5:4
wherefore lay apart all *f.* *Jas* 1:21
of abomination and *f.* of. *Rev* 17:4*

filthy

more abominable and *f.* *Job* 15:16*
altogether become *f.* *Ps* 14:3; 53:3
righteousness as *f.* rags. *Isa* 64:6*
woe to her that is *f.* *Zeph* 3:1*
Joshua clothed with *f.* *Zech* 3:3
take away *f.* garments from him. 4
you also put off *f.* communication. *Col* 3:8*
nor greedy of *f.* lucre. *1 Tim* 3:3*, 8
not given to *f.* lucre. *Tit* 1:7
teaching things for *f.* lucre's sake. 11
1 Pet 5:2
Lot vexed with *f.* *2 Pet* 2:7*
these *f.* dreamers defile. *Jude* 8
he that is *f.* let him be *f.* *Rev* 22:11

finally

f. my brethren, farewell. *2 Cor* 13:11
Eph 6:10; *Phil* 3:1; 4:8
2 Thes 3:1; *1 Pet* 3:8

find

wearied themselves to *f.* *Gen* 19:11
speak to Esau, when you *f.* 32:19
sin shall *f.* you out. *Num* 32:23
the revenger of blood *f.* him. 35:27
a man *f.* a damsel. *Deut* 22:25, 28
sojourn where he could *f.* a place. *Judg* 17:8, 9
Lord grant ye may *f.* rest. *Ruth* 1:9
go, *f.* out arrows. *1 Sam* 20:21, 36
if a man *f.* his enemy. 24:19
peradventure we may *f.* *1 Ki* 18:5
to *f.* out every device. *2 Chr* 2:14*
Assyria come and *f.* much. 32:4
I knew where I might *f.* *Job* 23:3
every man to *f.* according to. 34:11
seek out his wickedness till thou *f.* *Ps* 10:15
thou shalt *f.* knowledge. *Pr* 2:5
words are like to those that *f.* 4:22
right to them that *f.* knowledge. 8:9
I *f.* out knowledge of inventions. 12
a man should *f.* nothing. *Eccl* 7:14
counting one by one, to *f.* out the. 27
sought to *f.* acceptable. 12:10
if *f.* my beloved, tell him. *S of S* 5:8
screech owl shall *f.* a. *Isa* 34:14
in the day of fast you *f.* 58:3
that they may *f.* it so. *Jer* 10:18*
like harts that *f.* no. *Lam* 1:6
her prophets also *f.* no vision. 2:9
sought to *f.* occasion against Daniel, but could *f.* none. *Dan* 6:4
not *f.* except we *f.* it concerning. 5
and few there be that *f.* it. *Mat* 7:14
and if so be that he *f.* it. 18:13
if haply he might *f.* any. *Mark* 11:13
coming suddenly, *f.* you. 13:36
that they might *f.* an. *Luke* 6:7
and *f.* them so, blessed are. 12:38
I come seeking fruit and *f.* 13:7
that which is lost, till he *f.* it. 15:4
seek dilgently till she *f.* it? 8
go in and out and *f.* *John* 10:9

f. a tabernacle for God. *Acts* 7:46
might feel after him and *f.* 17:27
we *f.* no evil in this man. 23:9
why doth he yet *f.* fault ? *Rom* 9:19
and *f.* you unprepared. *2 Cor* 9:4
he may *f.* mercy of Lord. *2 Tim* 1:18

see **favour**

can or *canst* **find**

can we *f.* such a one as ? *Gen* 41:38
straw where you *can f.* it. *Ex* 5:11
and gold thou *canst f.* *Ezra* 7:16
when they *can f.* the grave. *Job* 3:22
canst thou by searching *f.* out God ?
canst thou *f.* out Almighty ? 11:7
faithful man who *can f.*? *Pr* 20:6
who *can f.* virtuous woman ? 31:10
no man *can f.* out work. *Eccl* 3:11
exceeding deep, who *can f.* it ? 7:24
can f. a man that seeketh. *Jer* 5:1

cannot **find**

said, I *cannot f.* her. *Gen* 38:22
if he *cannot f.* thee, will slay me. *1 Ki* 18:12
I *cannot f.* one wise man. *Job* 17:10
Almighty, we *cannot f.* him. 37:23
a man cannot *f.* out work. *Eccl* 8:17

find *grace*

may *f. grace* in thy sight. *Gen* 32:5 *Ex* 33:13
are to *f. grace* in sight. *Gen* 33:8
let me *f. grace.* 15
let me *f. grace* in your eyes. 34:11
f. grace in sight of my lord. 47:25
in whose sight I *f. grace.* *Ruth* 2:2
thy handmaid *f. grace.* *1 Sam* 1:18
f. grace in thy sight. *2 Sam* 16:4
we may *f. grace* to help. *Heb* 4:16

I **find**

if *I f.* in Sodom fifty. *Gen* 18:26
if *I f.* there forty-five. 28
if I *f.* thirty there. 30
till *I f.* out a place for. *Ps* 132:5
and *I f.* more bitter than. *Eccl* 7:26
when *I* should *f.* thee. *S of S* 8:1
sighing, and *I f.* no. *Jer* 45:3
Pilate said, *I f.* no fault. *Luke* 23:4 *John* 18:38; 19:4, 6
to perform good, *I f.* not. *Rom* 7:18*
I f. then a law, that when I. 21

not **find**, or **find** *not*

to-day ye shall *not f.* it. *Ex* 16:25
Saul shall *not f.* thee. *1 Sam* 23:17
sought, could *not f.* *2 Sam* 17:20
but they shall *not f.* me. *Pr* 1:28 *Hos* 5:6; *John* 7:34, 36
soul seeketh, but I *f. not.* *Eccl* 7:28
him, could *not f.* him. *S of S* 5:6
seek, but shalt *not f.* them. *Isa* 41:12 *Hos* 2:7
not f. any occasion. *Dan* 6:5
shall *not f.* her paths. *Hos* 2:6
seek the word, *not f.* it. *Amos* 8:12
not f. what way they. *Luke* 5:19
could *not f.* what they might. 19:48
that we shall *not f.* him. *John* 7:35
that which is good, I *f. not.* *Rom* 7:18
I shall *not f.* you such. *2 Cor* 12:20
death, and shall *not f.* it. *Rev* 9:6

shall, or *shalt* **find**

seek Lord thou *shalt f.* *Deut* 4:29
shalt f. no ease among these. 28:65
do as thou *shalt f.* *Judg* 9:33
ye *shall f.* him before. *1 Sam* 9:13
there *shall f.* two men by. 10:2
ye *shall f.* them at end. *2 Chr* 20:16
children *shall f.* compassion. 30:9
thou *shalt f.* in book of. *Ezra* 4:15
tried me, and *shalt f.* *Ps* 17:3
shall f. out thine enemies. 21:8
shall f. precious substance. *Pr* 1:13
that seek me early *shall f.* me. 8:17 *Jer* 29:13
matter wisely, *shall f.* good. *Pr* 16:20
understanding *shall f.* good. 19:8
for thou *shalt f.* it after. *Eccl* 11:1
in her month *shall f.* her. *Jer* 2:24
ye *shall f.* rest to your souls. 6:16 *Mat* 11:29
shall f. none iniquity in. *Hos* 12:8
seek and ye *shall f.* *Mat* 7:7 *Luke* 11:9

life for my sake *shall f.* it. *Mat* 10:39
thou *shalt f.* a piece of money. 17:27
ye *shall f.* an ass tied, and a colt. 21:2; *Mark* 11:2
as many as ye *shall f.* *Mat* 22:9
cometh, *shall f.* so doing. 24:46 *Luke* 12:37, 43
ye *shall f.* babe wrapt. *Luke* 2:12
shall he *f.* faith on earth ? 18:8
cast the net on the right side, ye *shall f.* *John* 21:6
shalt f. them no more. *Rev* 18:14

findest

with whomsover thou *f.* *Gen* 31:32
eat thou *f.* eat this roll. *Ezek* 3:1

findeth

every one that *f.* me. *Gen* 4:14
he *f.* occasions against. *Job* 33:10
as one that *f.* spoil. *Ps* 119:162
happy is man that *f.* *Pr* 3:13
whoso *f.* me, *f.* life. 8:35
scorner seeketh wisdom, *f.* it. 14:6
a froward heart, *f.* no good. 17:20
whoso *f.* a wife *f.* good. 18:22
his neighbour *f.* no favour. 21:10
that followeth after mercy *f.* life. 21
whatsoever thy hand *f.* *Eccl* 9:10
heathen, she *f.* no rest. *Lam* 1:3
in thee the fatherless *f.* *Hos* 14:3
and he that seeketh *f.* *Mat* 7:8 *Luke* 11:10
f. his life shall lose it. *Mat* 10:39
walketh, seeking rest, *f.* none. 12:43
f. it empty, swept. 44; *Luke* 11:25
he *f.* his disciples asleep. *Mat* 26:40 *Mark* 14:37
f. his own brother Simon. *John* 1:41
Jesus *f.* Philip. 43
Philip *f.* Nathanael. 45
afterward Jesus *f.* him in. 5:14

finding

any *f.* Cain kill him. *Gen* 4:15
who doeth things past *f.* *Job* 9:10
f. thine own pleasure. *Isa* 58:13
seeking rest, and *f.* *Luke* 11:24
f. nothing how they. *Acts* 4:21
Paul came *f.* certain. 19:1; 21:4
f. ship sailing over to. 21:2
his ways past *f.* out. *Rom* 11:33*
for *f.* fault with them. *Heb* 8:8

fine

for gold where they *f.* it. *Job* 28:1*

fine

and two vessels of *f.* *Ezra* 8:27
they that work in *f.* flax. *Isa* 19:9*
feet like unto brass. *Rev* 1:15; 2:18

fine *flour*

offering of *f. flour.* *Lev* 2:1; 24:5
cakes of *f. f.* mingled with oil. 2:4, 5, 7
7:12; 14:10, 21; 23:13; *Num* 6:15
7:13, 19, 25, 31, 37, 43, 49, 55, 61 8:8
tenth part of an ephah of *f. flour.* *Lev* 5:11; 6:20
measures of *f. flour* in. *1 Ki* 4:22
measure *f. flour* sold for shekel. *2 Ki* 7:1, 16, 18
appointed to oversee *f. flour.* *1 Chr* 9:29; 23:29
didst eat *f. flour,* honey. *Ezek* 16:13
I gave thee *f. flour,* and oil. 19
of oil to temper with *f. flour.* 46:14
merchandise of *f. flour.* *Rev* 18:13

fine *gold*

he overlaid with *f. gold.* *2 Chr* 3:5
most holy he overlaid with *f. gold.* 8
be for jewels of *f. gold.* *Job* 28:17
or said to *f. gold,* thou. 31:24
desired than *f. gold.* *Ps* 19:10
thy commandments above *f. gold.* 119:127
of wisdom than *f. gold.* *Pr* 3:14
better than gold, than *f. gold.* 8:19
as an ornament of *f. gold.* 25:12
head is as most *f. gold.* *S of S* 5:11
pillars set on sockets of *f. gold.* 15
more precious than *f. gold.* *Isa* 13:12
most *f. gold* changed! *Lam* 4:1*
of Zion comparable to *f. gold.* 2
image's head *f. gold.* *Dan* 2:32
loins were girded with *f. gold.* 10:5*
Tyrus heaped *f. gold.* *Zech* 9:3

fine *linen*

in vestures of *f. linen.* *Gen* 41:42
offering ye shall take, *f. linen.* *Ex* 25:4
ten curtains of *f.* twined *linen.* 26:1
the vail of *f. linen.* 31; 36:35 *2 Chr* 3:14
hanging of *f.* twined *linen.* *Ex* 26:36
27:9, 16, 18; 36:37; 38:9, 16, 18
take gold and *f. linen.* 28:5
the ephod of *f. linen.* 28:6; 39:2
girdle *f. linen.* 28:8; 39:5, 29
breastplate *f. linen.* 28:15; 39:8
the coat of *f. linen,* thou shalt make mitre of *f. linen.* 28:39
bring an offering of *f. linen.* 35:6
with whom was found *f. linen.* 23
brought scarlet and *f. linen.* 25
with wisdom to work all manner of *f. linen.* 35; 38:23, *2 Chr* 2:14
curtains of *f. linen* and. *Ex* 36:8
coats of *f. linen* for Aaron. 39:27
of *f. linen,* bonnets of *f. linen.* 28
that wrought *f. linen.* *1 Chr* 4:21
clothed with robe of *f. linen.* 15:27
with cords of *f. linen.* *Esth* 1:6
Mordecai with garment of *f. linen.* 8:15
my bed with *f. linen.* *Pr* 7:16*
she maketh *f. linen.* 31:24*
take away *f. linen.* *Isa* 3:23
girded thee with *f. linen.* *Ezek* 16:10
thy raiment was of *f. linen.* 13
f. linen from Egypt was. 27:7
occupied in thy fairs with *f. linen.* 16
Joseph bought *f. linen.* *Mark* 15:46*
in purple and *f. linen.* *Luke* 16:19
merchandise of *f. linen.* *Rev* 18:12
that city clothed in *f. linen* is. 16
to be arrayed in *f. linen.* 19:8
in heaven clothed in *f. linen.* 14

fine *meal*

measures of *f. meal.* *Gen* 18:6

finer

forth a vessel for the *f.* *Pr* 25:4†

finest

fed thee with the *f.* of. *Ps* 81:16
filleth thee with *f.* of wheat. 147:14

finger

The finger of God is used to mean his power, his working. Pharaoh's magicians discovered the finger of God in the miracles which Moses wrought, Ex 8:19. *This legislator gave the law written with the finger of God to the Hebrews,* Ex 31:18.

magicians said, this is *f.* of. *Ex* 8:19
blood on altar with thy *f.* 29:12
written with the *f.* of God. 31:18 *Deut* 9:10
priest dip his *f.* in blood. *Lev* 4:6
17, 25, 30, 34; 8:15; 9:9; 16:14, 19
his right *f.* in the oil, and sprinkle of the oil with his *f.* 14:16, 27
take of blood with his *f.* *Num* 19:4
my little *f.* thicker. *1 Ki* 12:10 *2 Chr* 10:10
the putting forth of the *f.* *Isa* 58:9
if I with the *f.* of God. *Luke* 11:20
he dip tip of his *f.* in water. 16:24
and with his *f.* wrote. *John* 8:6
put my *f.* into the print. 20:25
reach hither thy *f.* and behold. 27

fingers

on every hand six *f.* *2 Sam* 21:20 *1 Chr* 20:6
heavens, work of thy *f.* *Ps* 8:3
who teacheth my *f.* to fight. 144:1
man teacheth with his *f.* *Pr* 6:13
bind them on thy *f.* write. 7:3
f. with sweetsmelling. *S of S* 5:5
which their own *f.* have made. *Isa* 2:8; 17:8
hands defiled with blood, and *f.* 59:3
thickness of pillar four *f.* *Jer* 52:21
came forth *f.* of a man's. *Dan* 5:5
but will not move them with one of their *f.* *Mat* 23:4; *Luke* 11:46
and he put his *f.* into. *Mark* 7:33

fining

f. pot is for silver. *Pr* 17:3†; 27:21

finish

in a cubit shalt thou f. Gen 6:16
to f. transgression. Dan 9:24
Zerubbabel's hands shall f. Zech 4:9
have sufficient to f. Luke 14:28*
laid foundation, is not able to f. 29
to build, was not able to f. 30
his will, and f. his work. John 4:34
Father hath given me to f. 5:36*
I might f. my course. Acts 20:24*
for he will f. the work. Rom 9:28
f. in you the same grace. 2 Cor 8:6*

finished

heavens and earth were f. Gen 2:1
thus was the work f. Ex 39:32; 40:33
till they were f. Deut 31:24
till every thing was f. Josh 4:10
till he have f. the thing. Ruth 3:18
Solomon built house and f. 1 Ki 6:9
14, 22, 38; 2 Chr 5:1; 7:11
Solomon f. all his house. 1 Ki 7:1
9:1, 25; 2 Chr 8:16
so was work of pillars f. 1 Ki 7:22
to number, but f. not. 1 Chr 27:24
not fail thee, till thou hast f. 28:20
they had f. repairing. 2 Chr 24:14
sang, till burnt offering was f. 29:28
they f. the heaps in the. 31:7
and yet it is not f. Ezra 5:16*
elders of Jews built and f. 6:14, 15
so the wall was f. in. Neh 6:15
numbered thy kingdom and f. it.
Dan 5:26
all these things shall be f. 12:7
when Jesus had f. these. Mat 13:53
Jesus f. these sayings. 19:1; 26:1
I have f. the work thou. John 17:4*
it is f. and he bowed his head. 19:30
we had f. our course. Acts 21:7
I have f. my course. 2 Tim 4:7
were f. from foundation. Heb 4:3
sin, when it is f. bringeth. Jas 1:15*
mystery of God should be f.
Rev 10:7
witnesses have f. their testimony.
11:7
till the thousand years were f. 20:5

finisher

Jesus, author and f. of. Heb 12:2*

fins

hath f. and scales eat. Lev 11:9
Deut 14:9
all that hath not f. shall be an abomination. Lev 11:10, 12

fir

concerning timber of f. 1 Ki 5:8
covered floor with planks of f. 6:15
are cedar, rafters of f. S of S 1:17

fire

Fire is often used as a symbol of God, Deut 4:24; Ps 18:12, 13, 14; Ezek 1:4; Rev 1:14. *And it is said that Jesus will appear in the midst of fire at his second coming,* 2 Thes 1:8. *The wrath of God is compared to fire,* Ps 18:8.

Our Saviour is compared to fire, Mal 3:2. *The Holy Ghost is likewise compared to fire,* Mat 3:11. *The angels themselves, as the ministers of God, are compared to a burning fire, speedy and irresistible in the execution of his commands,* Ps. 104:4.

Fire from heaven fell frequently on the victims sacrificed to the Lord, as a mark of his presence and approbation. It is thought that God in this manner expressed his acceptance of Abel's sacrifices, Gen 4:4. *When the Lord made a covenant with Abraham, a fire, like that of a furnace, passed through the divided pieces of the sacrifices, and consumed them,* Gen 15:17. *Fire fell upon the sacrifices which Moses offered at the dedication of the tabernacle,* Lev 9:24; *and upon those of Manoah, Samson's father,* Judg 13:19, 20; *upon Solomon's, at the dedication of the temple,* 2 Chr 7:1; *and upon Elijah's, at mount Carmel,* 1 Ki 18:38.

The word of God is compared to fire, Jer 23:29.

Abraham took f. in his. Gen 22:6
behold the f. and the wood, but. 7
the bush burned with f. Ex 3:2
Lord sent hail and the f. along. 9:23
hail, and f. mingled with hail. 24
flesh in that night roast with f. 12:8, 9
upon mount Sinai in f. 19:18
if f. break out, and catch. 22:6
then I cast gold into f. and. 32:24
f. was on the tabernacle by night.
40:38; Num 9:16; Deut 1:33
the priest put f. on the altar, and lay wood in order upon f. Lev 1:7
upon the wood in f. 8, 12, 17; 3:5
green ears of corn dried by f. 2:14
f. of the altar be burning. 6:9, 10
12, 13
came a f. out from before. 9:24
the sons of Aaron put f. in. 10:1
there went out f. from Lord. 2
shall put incense upon f. 16:13
pass through f. to Molech. 18:21
Deut 18:10; 2 Ki 17:17; 23:10
hair, and put it in the f. Num 6:18
Moses prayed, the f. was. 11:2
censers, and put f. therein. 16:7, 18
take the censers, and scatter f. 37
take a censer, and put f. therein. 46
holy things reserved from f. 18:9
for there is a f. gone out. 21:28
may abide f. go through f. 31:23
mountain burnt with f. Deut 4:11
9:15
earth he shewed his great f. 4:36
afraid by reason of the f. 5:5
nor let me see this great f. 18:16
burned Achan with f. Josh 7:25
there rose up f. out of. Judg 6:21
let f. come out of bramble. 9:15
tow when it toucheth the f. 16:9
lay it on wood, put no f. under.
1 Ki 18:23, 25
the God that answereth by f. 24
then f. of Lord fell. 38; 2 Chr 7:1, 3
after earthquake a f., Lord was not in f., after f. a still small. 1 Ki 19:12
then let f. come down. 2 Ki 1:10
and the f. of God came down. 12
a chariot and horses of f. 2:11
mountain, full of chariots of f. 6:17
Ahaz made son pass through f. 16:3
have cast their gods into f. 19:18
made son pass through f. 21:6
2 Chr 33:6
make son pass through f. 2 Ki 23:10
answered him from heaven by f.
1 Chr 21:26
roasted passover with f. 2 Chr 35:13
the gates are consumed with f.
Neh 2:3, 13
the f. of God is fallen. Job 1:16
the spark of his f. shall not. 18:5
is turned up as it were f. 28:5
and sparks of f. leap out. 41:19
while I was musing the f. Ps 39:3
he burneth chariot in the f. 46:9
we went through f. and. 66:12
as wax melteth before f. so. 68:2
cast f. into thy sanctuary. 74:7
with a light of f. 78:14; 105:39
as the f. burneth the wood. 83:14
a f. goeth before him and. 97:3
gave hail and flaming f. in. 105:32
they are quenched as f. 118:12
be cast into the f. into deep. 140:10
f. and hail, stormy wind. 148:8
can a man take f. in bosom. Pr 6:27
in his lips as a burning f. 16:27
where no wood is, the f. 26:20
as wood is to f. so is contentious. 21
the grave and the f. saith not. 30:16
burning and fuel of f. Isa 9:5
wickedness burneth as the f. 18
the people shall be as fuel of f. 19
a burning like burning of a f. 10:16
light of Israel shall be for a f. 17
not be found a sherd to take f. 30:14
the pile thereof is f. and wood. 33
whose f. is in Zion. 31:9
of Assyria cast gods into f. 37:19
walkest through f. not be. Isa 43:2
in the f. he warmeth himself, saith, I have seen the f. 44:16
as stubble, the f. shall burn. 47:14
walk in light of your f. and. 50:11
when the melting f. burneth, the f. causeth the waters to boil. 64:2
a f. that burneth all the day. 65:5
the Lord will come with f. 66:15
by f. will Lord plead with all. 16
worm not die, neither f. be. 24
fury come forth like f. Jer 4:4
my words in thy mouth f. 5:14
his word was as a f. shut up. 20:9
lest my fury go out like f. 21:12
cut down choice cedars, cast in f. 22:7
king of Babylon roasted in f. 29:22
sons to pass through f. to Molech.
32:35; Ezek 16:21; 20:26, 31
was a f. on the hearth. Jer 36:22
Jehudi cut roll, cast it into f. 23
but a f. shall come forth. 48:45
labour in vain and in the f. 51:58
against Jacob like flaming f. Lam 2:3
bent his bow, poured out fury like f. 4
I looked, behold, a f. Ezek 1:4
the f. was bright, out of the f. 13
take f. from between wheels. 10:6
cherub stretched forth hand to f. 7
blow against thee in f. 21:31; 22:21
thou shalt be for fuel to f. 21:32
to blow f. upon it. 22:20
I will even make pile for f. 24:9
her scum shall be in the f. 12
will I bring forth a f. from. 28:18
in f. of my jealousy have I spoken.
36:5; 38:19
bodies the f. had no power, nor the smell of f. passed on. Dan 3:27
wheels like burning f. 7:9
his eyes as lamps of f. 10:6
burneth as a flaming f. Hos 7:6
blood, f. and pillars of smoke.
Joel 2:30; Acts 2:19
lest he break out like f. Amos 5:6
Lord God called to contend by f. 7:4
house of Jacob shall be a f. Ob 18
under him as wax before f. Mi 1:4
fury poured out like f. Nah 1:6
people shall labour in f. Hab 2:13
be unto her a wall of f. Zech 2:5
brand plucked out of f.? 3:2
hearth of f. and like torch of f. 12:6
the third part through the f. 13:9
he is like a refiner's f. Mal 3:2
bringeth not forth good fruit is cast into f. Mat 3:10; 7:19; Luke 3:9
John 15:6
baptize with Holy Ghost, and f.
Mat 3:11; Luke 3:16
cast them into a furnace of f.
Mat 13:42, 50
ofttimes falleth into f. Mat 17:15
Mark 9:22
or two feet, be cast into everlasting f.
Mat 18:8; Mark 9:43, 46
me, into everlasting f. Mat 25:41
f. is not quenched. Mark 9:44, 45
Peter warmed himself at f. 14:54
command f. to come? Luke 9:54
the same day it rained f. 17:29
beheld him as he sat by f. 22:56
cloven tongues like as of f. Acts 2:3
when Paul laid sticks on the f. 28:3
he shook off the beast into f. 5
revealed by f. and the f. shall try every man's work. 1 Cor 3:13
shall be saved, yet so as by f. 15
in flaming f. taking. 2 Thes 1:8
his ministers a flame of f. Heb 1:7
faith quenched violence of f. 11:34
to mount that burned with f. 12:18
how great matter a little f. Jas 3:5
and the tongue is a f., a world of. 6
eat your flesh as it were f. 5:3
gold, though it be tried with f.
1 Pet 1:7
reserved unto f. against. 2 Pet 3:7
heavens being on f. be dissolved. 12
vengeance of eternal f. Jude 7
others save, pulling out of the f. 23
of me gold tried in the f. Rev 3:18
seven lamps of f. burning. 4:5
angel filled the censer with f. 8:5

there followed hail and *f.* *Rev* 8:7
great mountain burning with *f.* 8
of their mouths issued *f.* 9:17; 11:5
part of men killed by the *f.* 9:18
he maketh *f.* come down. 13:13
angel which had power over *f.* 14:18
sea of glass mingled with *f.* 15:2
him to scorch men with *f.* 16:8
and *f.* came down from God. 20:9
the devil was cast into lake of *f.* 10
hell cast into the lake of *f.* 14
in book of life, cast into *f.* 15
lake which burneth with *f.* 21:8
see **brimstone, burn** *or* **burnt, coals, consume, consuming, devour, devoured, devouring, flame, hell, midst**

kindle, or *kindled* **fire**

he that *kindled* the *f.* *Ex* 22:6
kindle no *f.* on sabbath day. 35:3
a *f.* is *kindled* in my anger, and.
Deut 32:22; *Jer* 15:14; 17:4
him coals of *f.* *kindled.* *2 Sam* 22:13
so a *f.* was *kindled* against Jacob.
Ps 78:21
f. *kindled* in their company. 106:18
kindle a burning like a *f.* *Isa* 10:16
behold, all ye that *kindle* a *f.* 50:11
fathers *kindled* *f.* *Jer* 7:18
hath *kindled* *f.* on green. 11:16
then will I *kindle* a *f.* in gates. 17:27
I will *kindle* a *f.* in forest. 21:14
I will *kindle* a *f.* in houses of. 43:12
I will *kindle* a *f.* in the wall. 49:27
I will *kindle* a *f.* in his cities. 50:32
Lord hath *kindled* a *f.* in. *Lam* 4:11
kindle a *f.* in the forest. *Ezek* 20:47
heap on wood, *kindle* *f.* 24:10
I will *kindle* a *f.* in wall of Rabbah.
Amos 1:14
neither do ye *kindle* *f.* on my altar.
Mal 1:10
f. on the earth; and what if it be already *kindled* ? *Luke* 12:49
when they had *kindled* a *f.* 22:55
barbarians *kindled* a *f.* *Acts* 28:2

made with **fire**

an offering *made* by *f.* unto Lord.
Ex 29:18, 25, 41; *Lev* 1:9, 13, 17
2:2, 9, 16; 3:3, 5, 9, 11, 14, 16
7:5, 25, 8:21, 28; 21:6, 22:27
23:8, 13, 18, 25, 27, 36, 37; 24:7
Num 15:3, 10, 13, 14; 18:17; 28:3
the offerings of Lord *made* by *f.*
Lev 2:3, 10; 4:35; 5:12; 6:17, 18
7:30, 35; 10:12, 15; 21:21; 24:9
Deut 18:1; *1 Sam* 2:28
sacrifices *made* by *f.* *Lev* 10:13
Num 28:2; *Josh* 13:14
bring sacrifice *made* by *f.* unto Lord.
Num 15:25; 28:6, 8, 13, 19, 24
29:6, 13, 36

pillar of **fire**

Lord looked through *pillar of f.*
Ex 14:24
his feet as *pillars of f.* *Rev* 10:1
see, by **night**

send, or *sent* **fire**

from above he *sent* *f.* *Lam* 1:13
and I will *send* a *f.* *Ezek* 39:6
send a *f.* upon his cities. *Hos* 8:14
send a *f.* into house of. *Amos* 1:4
I will *send* a *f.* on the wall. 7
I will *send* a *f.* on wall of Tyrus. 10
send *f.* on Teman. 12
I will *send* a *f.* on Moab. 2:2
send *f.* on Judah. 5
I am come to *send* *f.* on. *Luke* 12:49

set **fire**

set on *f.* foundations of. *Deut* 32:22
set city of Ai on *f.* *Josh* 8:8
hasted, and *set* the city on *f.* 19
had *set* Jerusalem on *f.* *Judg* 1:8
the people *set* the hold on *f.* 9:49
had *set* the brands on *f.* and. 15:5
set on *f.* all the cities of. 20:48
set Joab's field on *f.* *2 Sam* 14:30
have thy servants *set* field on *f.*? 31
set strong holds on *f.* *2 Ki* 8:12
them that are *set* on *f.* *Ps* 57:4
women *set* them on *f.* *Isa* 27:11
hath *set* him on *f.* round. 42:25
set up a sign of *f.* in. *Jer* 6:1
Chaldeans shall *set* on *f.* this. 32:29
when I have *set* a *f.* in. *Ezek* 30:8
I will *set* *f.* in Zoan. 14
set *f.* in Egypt. 16
set on *f.* and burn weapons. 39:9
tongue is a fire, *setteth* on *f.* . . . it is *set* on *f.* of hell. *Jas* 3:6

strange **fire**

Abihu offered *strange* *f.* *Lev* 10:1
died when they offered *strange* *f.*
Num 3:4; 26:61

firebrand, -s

took *f.* and put a *f.* in. *Judg* 15:4
mad man who casteth *f.* *Pr* 26:18
tails of these smoking *f.* *Isa* 7:4
ye were as a *f.* plucked. *Amos* 4:11

firepans

make basons and *f.* *Ex* 27:3
f. and all vessels of brass. 38:3
f. carried he away. *2 Ki* 25:15
Jer 52:19

fires

glorify ye the Lord in *f.* *Isa* 24:15*

firkins

waterpots containing two or three *f.*
John 2:6

firm

priests stood *f.* on dry. *Josh* 3:17
place where priests' feet stood *f.* 4:3
are *f.* in themselves. *Job* 41:23
his heart is as *f.* as a stone. 24
no bands in death, their strength is *f.*
Ps 73:4
to make a *f.* decree. *Dan* 6:7*
rejoicing of the hope *f.* *Heb* 3:6

firmament

By the word firmament (Hebrew, rakiah), the Hebrews understood the heavens, which they thought to be like a solid arch between the upper and lower waters. They also believed that the stars are set in this arch, like so many precious stones in gold and silver, Gen 1:17.

let there be a *f.* in midst. *Gen* 1:6
f. waters under and above *f.* 7
God called the *f.* Heaven. 8
let there be lights in the *f.* 14, 15
God set them in *f.* of heaven. 17
fowl that fly above open *f.* 20
f. sheweth his handy work. *Ps* 19:1
praise him in *f.* of his power. 150:1
of *f.* was as crystal. *Ezek* 1:22
a voice from the *f.* over their. 25
above the *f.* was the likeness of. 26
in *f.* above the cherubims. 10:1
shine as brightness of *f.* *Dan* 12:3

fir tree

the two doors were of *f.* *1 Ki* 6:34
house he cieled with *f.* *2 Chr* 3:5
I will set in desert the *f.* *Isa* 41:19
instead of the thorn the *f.* 55:13
the *f.* the pine tree and box. 60:13
I am like a green *f.* *Hos* 14:8
howl, *f.* *Zech* 11:2

fir trees

so Hiram gave Solomon *f.*
1 Ki 5:10; 9:11
I will cut down tall *f.* *2 Ki* 19:23
Isa 37:24
send me *f.* *2 Chr* 2:8
the *f.* rejoice. *Isa* 14:8
the stork the *f.* are her. *Ps* 104:17
ship boards of *f.* of Senir. *Ezek* 27:5
the *f.* were not like his boughs. 31:8
f. shall be terribly shaken. *Nah* 2:3

fir wood

on instruments of *f.* *2 Sam* 6:5

first

the *f.* came out red. *Gen* 25:25
a famine beside the *f.* famine. 26:1
midwife said, this came out *f.* 38:28
not hearken to *f.* sign. *Ex* 4:8
the *f.* of the firstfruits bring. 23:19
the *f.* row a sardius. 28:17; 39:10
two tables like to the *f.* 34:1, 4
Deut 10:1, 3
what is for sin offering *f.* *Lev* 5:8
Judah, these shall *f.* set. *Num* 2:9
and they *f.* took their journey. 10:13
time of the *f.* ripe grapes. *Num* 13:20
offer up a cake of the *f.* of your.
15:20, 21; *Ezek* 44:30
whatsoever is *f.* ripe. *Num* 18:13
Amalek was *f.* of nations. 24:20
according to the *f.* time. *Deut* 10:10
I will give thee *f.* rain. 11:14*
thine hand shall be *f.* upon. 13:9
hands of witnesses be *f.* upon. 17:7
f. of the fleece of thy sheep. 18:4
provided *f.* part for himself. 33:21
theirs was *f.* lot. *Josh* 21:10
1 Chr 24:7; 25:9
who shall go up *f.* *Judg* 1:1; 20:18
Israel are smitten as in *f.* 20:39
f. slaughter twenty. *1 Sam* 14:14
same was *f.* altar Saul built. 35
thou *f.* bring Michal. *2 Sam* 3:13
I am come the *f.* this day to. 19:20
that advice should not be *f.* 43
captain, howbeit he attained not unto *f.* 23:19, 23; *1 Chr* 11:21, 25
thereof a little cake *f.* *1 Ki* 17:13
and dress it *f.* for ye are. 18:25
men of princes went out *f.* 20:17
now *f.* inhabitants that. *1 Chr* 9:2
smiteth the Jebusites *f.* 11:6
day David delivered *f.* this. 16:7
length by cubits after *f.* *2 Chr* 3:3
had seen glory of the *f.* *Ezra* 3:12
sat *f.* in the kingdom. *Esth* 1:14
art thou *f.* man born ? *Job* 15:7
that is *f.* in his own cause. *Ps* 18:17
the *f.* shall say to Zion. *Isa* 41:27
thy *f.* father hath sinned. 43:27
ships of Tarshish *f.* to bring. 60:9
bringeth forth her *f.* child. *Jer* 4:31
f. I will recompense iniquity. 16:18
like the figs that are *f.* ripe. 24:2
words that were in *f.* roll. 36:28
f. king of Assyria devoured. 50:17
Daniel was *f.* president. *Dan* 6:2*
the *f.* beast was like a lion. 7:4
Rev 4:7*
be diverse from the *f.* *Dan* 7:24*
horn between eyes is *f.* king. 8:21
return to my *f.* husband. *Hos* 2:7
f. ripe in fig tree at *f.* time. 9:10
go captive with the *f.* *Amos* 6:7
to thee shall come *f.* *Mi* 4:8*
like fig trees with *f.* ripe. *Nah* 3:12
that saw house in *f.* glory? *Hag* 2:3*
in the *f.* chariot red. *Zech* 6:2
shall save tents of Judah *f.* 12:7
f. be reconciled to thy. *Mat* 5:24
seek ye *f.* the kingdom of. 6:33
f. cast beam out of. 7:5; *Luke* 6:42
suffer me *f.* to go and bury. *Mat* 8:21
Luke 9:59
f. bind the strong man. *Mat* 12:29
Mark 3:27
state worse than the *f.* *Mat* 12:45
Luke 11:26
gather ye together *f.* tares. *Mat* 13:30
Elias *f.* come. 17:10, 11; *Mark* 9:12
take up fish that *f.* *Mat* 17:27
but when the *f.* came, they. 20:10
he came to the *f.* and said. 21:28
they say unto him, the *f.* 31
other servants more than *f.* 36
f. when married. 22:25
Mark 12:20; *Luke* 20:29
this is *f.* commandment. *Mat* 22:38
Mark 12:28, 29, 30
cleanse *f.* that which is. *Mat* 23:26
f. the blade, then ear. *Mark* 4:28
let the children *f.* be filled. 7:27
desire to be *f.* he shall be last. 9:35
and the gospel must *f.* be. 13:10
appeared *f.* to Mary. 16:9
perfect understanding from the *f.*
Luke 1:3
was *f.* made when Cyrenius. 2:2
second sabbath after the *f.* he. 6:1
f. say, Peace be to this house. 10:5
that he had not *f.* washed. 11:38
sitteth not down *f.* and. 14:28
f. must he suffer many. 17:25
things must *f.* come to pass. 21:9
f. findeth his brother. *John* 1:41
whosoever *f.* stepped in, made. 5:4
without sin, let him *f.* cast. 8:7
where John at *f.* baptized. 10:40
led him away to Annas *f.* 18:13

brake the legs of the f. John 19:32
disciple came f. to the. 20:4, 8
to you f. God sent him. Acts 3:26
Jacob sent out our fathers f. 7:12*
called Christians f. at. 11:26
past the f. and second ward. 12:10
when John had f. preached. 13:24
it should f. have been spoken. 46
f. unto them of Damascus. 26:20
Christ f. that should rise from. 23
cast themselves f. into sea. 27:43
f. I thank my God. Rom 1:8
of the Jew f. and also of. 2:9, 10
who hath f. given to him? 11:35
if f. I be somewhat filled. 15:24
f. apostles, secondarily. 1 Cor 12:28
let the f. hold his peace. 14:30
for I delivered f. of all that. 15:3
the f. man Adam a living soul. 45
howbeit that was not f. which. 46
the f. man is of the earth. 47
f. gave their own selves. 2 Cor 8:5
for if there be f. a willing mind. 12
who f. trusted in Christ. Eph 1:12
descended f. into lower parts. 4:9
which is the f. commandment. 6:2
in Christ shall rise f. 1 Thes 4:16
come a falling away f. 2 Thes 2:3
that in me f. Christ. 1 Tim 1:16*
for Adam was f. formed. 2:13
let these also f. be proved. 3:10
learn f. to shew piety at home. 5:4
have cast off their f. faith. 12
faith dwelt f. in thy grandmother. 2 Tim 1:5
husbandman be f. partaker of. 2:6
at my f. answer no man stood. 4:16
after f. and second. Tit 3:10
to whom it was f. preached. Heb 4:6*
teach you which be the f. 5:12
f. being by interpretation, king. 7:2
offer f. for his own sins. 27
the f. covenant. 8:7, 13; 9:1, 15, 18
f. tabernacle, wherein. 9:2, 6, 8
he taketh away the f. that. 10:9
wisdom from above, is f. Jas 3:17
if judgement f. begin at. 1 Pet 4:17
knowing this f. that no prophecy. 2 Pet 1:20; 3:3
because he f. loved us. 1 John 4:19
who kept not their f. estate. Jude 6*
thou hast left thy f. love. Rev 2:4
repent, and do the f. works. 5
the power of the f. beast. 13:12
this is the f. resurrection. 20:5
f. heaven and f. earth were. 21:1
the f. foundation was jasper. 19
see **day, last**

at the **first**

made the altar at the f. Gen 13:4
city was called Luz at the f. 28:19
of money returned at the f. 43:18
down at the f. to buy food. 20
down before Lord as at the f. Deut 9:18, 25
come against us at the f. Josh 8:5
they flee before us as at the f. 6
of city Laish at the f. Judg 18:29
smitten before us as at the f. 20:32
be overthrown at the f. 2 Sam 17:9
send for to thy servant at f. 1 Ki 20:9
ye did it not at the f. 1 Chr 15:13
which came up at the f. Neh 7:5
thy judges as at the f. Isa 1:26
when at the f. he lightly. 9:1*
I set my name at the f. Jer 7:12
I will build them as at the f. 33:7
return captivity of land, as at the f. 11
which appeared at the f. Dan 8:1
understood not at the f. John 12:16
which at the f. came by night. 19:39
God at the f. did visit. Acts 15:14
at the f. among mine own. 26:4
gospel unto you, at the f. Gal 4:13*
at the f. began to be spoken by. Heb 2:3

first *month*

f. month, the f. day of the month. Gen 8:13
the f. month of year to. Ex 12:2
f. month eat unleavened bread. 18
Lev 23:5
day of f. month set up. Ex 40:2, 17
f. month keep passover. Num 9:1
28:16; 2 Chr 35:1; Ezra 6:19
Ezek 45:21
desert of Zin in f. month. Num 20:1
from Rameses in f. month. 33:3
of Jordan in f. month. Josh 4:19
over Jordan in f. month. 1 Chr 12:15
captain that served f. month. 27:2, 3
f. month opened doors. 2 Chr 29:3
first day of f. month to sanctify and sixteenth day of f. month. 17
f. month began he to go. Ezra 7:9
the f. month we departed. 8:31
end with them by f. month. 10:17
in f. month cast Pur, on thirteenth day of the f. month. Esth 3:7, 12
f. month take a young. Ezek 45:18
and latter rain in f. month. Joel 2:23

first *year*

(In the giving of the age, as lamb of the first year, *the American Revision changes to* lamb a year old)

lambs male of the f. year. Ex 12:5
offer two lambs of f. year day by. 29:38; Lev 23:19; Num 28:3, 9
take a kid of the f. year. Lev 9:3
bring a lamb of the f. year. 12:6
Num 6:12; 7:15, 21, 27, 33, 39, 45, 51, 57, 63, 69, 75, 81; Ezek 46:13
take an ewe lamb of the f. year. Lev 14:10; Num 6:14
an he lamb of f. year. Lev 23:12
Num 6:14
seven lambs of f. year. Lev 23:18
Num 28:11, 19, 27; 29:2, 8, 36
peace offering five lambs of f. year. Num 7:17, 23, 29, 35, 41, 47, 53, 59
lambs of the f. year twelve. 87
the lambs of the f. year sixty. 88
a she goat of the f. year. 15:27
a burnt offering, fourteen lambs of f. year. 29:13, 17, 20, 23, 26, 29, 32
Hezekiah in f. year of. 2 Chr 29:3
in f. year of Cyrus. 36:22
Ezra 1:1; 5:13; 6:3
f. year of Nebuchadnezzar. Jer 25:1
f. year of Evil-merodach. 52:31
to the f. year of Cyrus. Dan 1:21
in the f. year of Belshazzar. 7:1
in the f. year of Darius I, Daniel. 9:1, 2; 11:1

first begotten

when he bringeth in the f. b. Heb 1:6
Jesus, who is f. b. of dead. Rev 1:5

firstborn

The firstborn of both man and beast was considered as belonging to God. If of man, the child was redeemed, Ex 13:13, 15; 34:20. *If of a clean beast it was sacrificed, and if unclean either had the neck broken or was replaced by a lamb,* Ex 13:13, 15; 22:30; 34:20. *Later the Levites were substituted for the Israelites' firstborn,* Num 3:12, 41, 46; 8:13–19.

To the firstborn son belonged the birthright, which included the headship of the family or tribe, and a double portion of his father's property.

f. said to younger. Gen 19:31, 34
f. went in, lay with her father. 33
f. bare a son, called name Moab. 37
said, I am Esau, thy f. 27:19, 32
to give younger before f. 29:26
f. according to his birthright. 43:33
not so my father, this is f. 48:18
Israel is my son, even my f. Ex 4:22
I will slay thy son, even thy f. 23
all the f. in Egypt shall die. 11:5
and I will smite all the f. 12:12
Lord smote all the f. in. 29; 13:15
sanctify unto me all the f. 13:2
the f. of thy sons shalt thou. 22:29
f. of thy sons. 34:20; Num 18:15
instead of all the f. Num 3:12
41, 45; 8:17, 18
the f. of Israel are mine, I hallowed to me all the f. of. 3:13
number the f. of the males of. 40
Moses numbered f. of Israel. 42
of f. of Israel took he money. Num 3:50
the Egyptians buried all their f. 33:4
if f. son be her's that. Deut 21:15
for the right of f. is his. 17
f. which she beareth, succeed. 25:6
lay foundation in his f. Josh 6:26
foundation in Abiram f. 1 Ki 16:34
Reuben f. he was the f. 1 Chr 5:1
though he was not the f. yet. 26:10
Jehoram, the f. 2 Chr 21:3
the f. to the house of. Neh 10:36
the f. of death shall. Job 18:13
he smote all the f. in. Ps 78:51
105:36; 135:8; 136:10
my f. higher than kings. 89:27
f. of the poor shall feed. Isa 14:30
Israel, Ephraim is my f. Jer 31:9
my f. for my transgression? Mi 6:7
in bitterness for his f. Zech 12:10
Mary brought forth her f. son. Mat 1:25; Luke 2:7
f. among many brethren. Rom 8:29
the f. of every creature. Col 1:15
the beginning, f. from the dead. 18
lest he that destroyed f. Heb 11:28
ye are come to the church of f. 12:23

firstfruits

The firstfruits were to be given as an offering to Jehovah, Lev 23:10, 17; Ex 23:19. *The term is used figuratively also,* Rom 8:23; Jas 1:18.

to offer f. ripe fruits. Ex 22:29
f. of thy labour thou hast. 23:16
first of f. 23:19; 34:26; Deut 26:2
of f. of wheat harvest. Ex 34:22
oblation of the f. offer. Lev 2:12
the meat offering of f. green. 14
a sheaf of the f. of harvest. 23:10
they are the f. unto the Lord. 17
wave them with bread of the f. 20
f. of oil, wine, wheat. Num 18:12
in the day of f. when ye. 28:26
the f. of thy corn, wine. Deut 18:4
brought the f. of the land. 26:10
brought man of God f. 2 Ki 4:42
brought in abundance f. 2 Chr 31:5
bring f. of our ground. Neh 10:35
should bring the f. of our dough. 37
over, chambers for f. 12:44; 13:31
honour Lord with the f. Pr 3:9
Israel was the f. of his. Jer 2:3
there will I require f. Ezek 20:40
the first of all the f. 44:30
nor exchange the f. of land. 48:14
have the f. of the Spirit. Rom 8:23
if the f. be holy. 11:16
who is the f. of Achaia. 16:5
1 Cor 16:15
Christ the f. of them that slept. 1 Cor 15:20, 23
f. of his creatures. Jas 1:18
being the f. unto God. Rev 14:4

firstling

(*The same as firstborn, but confined to the firstborn of beasts*)

shalt set apart every f. of beast, males shall be. Ex 13:12; 34:19
every f. of an ass. 13:13; 34:20
the Lord's f. no man. Lev 27:26
f. of unclean beasts. Num 18:15
the f. of a cow, sheep, or goat. 17
all the f. males sanctify. Deut 15:19
Joseph's glory is like f. of. 33:17

firstlings

Abel brought f. of his flock. Gen 4:4
instead of all the f. Num 3:41
ye shall bring f. of your. Deut 12:6
not eat within thy gates the f. 17
eat the f. in place Lord shall. 14:23
f. of our herds bring to. Neh 10:36

fish

dominion over f. Gen 1:26, 28
f. in river shall die. Ex 7:18, 21
f. we did eat in Egypt. Num 11:5
all the f. of the sea be gathered? 22
nor likeness of any f. in. Deut 4:18
of Tyre, which brought f. Neh 13:16
his head with f. spears? Job 41:7
thou hast put the f. under. Ps 8:8
waters into blood, slew f. 105:29

sluices and ponds for *f.* *Isa* 19:10*
their *f.* stinketh because there. 50:2
will cause the *f.* to stick. *Ezek* 29:4
and all the *f.* of thy rivers. 5
very great multitude of *f.* 47:9
their *f.* as the *f.* of the great sea. 10
a great *f.* to swallow Jonah, in belly of *f.* three days. *Jonah* 1:17
to Lord out of the *f.'s* belly. 2:1
Lord spake to the *f.* and it. 10
if he ask a *f.* will he give? *Mat* 7:10
take up *f.* that first cometh. 17:27
a piece of a broiled *f.* *Luke* 24:42
they saw *f.* laid thereon. *John* 21:9
bring of *f.* ye have now caught. 10
Jesus taketh bread, and *f.* 13

fish, *verb*

fishers, they shall *f.* *Jer* 16:16

fishermen

but the *f.* were gone out. *Luke* 5:2

fisher, -s

the *f.* also shall mourn. *Isa* 19:8
I will send for many *f.* *Jer* 16:16
that the *f.* shall stand. *Ezek* 47:10
for they were *f.* *Mat* 4:18; *Mark* 1:16
make you *f.* of men. *Mat* 4:19; *Mark* 1:17
Peter girt *f.'s* coat to him. *John* 21:7

fishes

you shall be on all *f.* *Gen* 9:2
creeping things and *f.* *1 Ki* 4:33
f. of the sea shall. *Job* 12:8
the *f.* that are taken in. *Eccl* 9:12
the *f.* of the sea. *Ezek* 38:20
f. of the sea shall be taken. *Hos* 4:3
makest men as *f.* of sea. *Hab* 1:14
consume the *f.* of the sea. *Zeph* 1:3
five loaves and two *f.* *Mat* 14:17; *Mark* 6:38; *Luke* 9:13; *John* 6:9
seven loaves and a few *f.* *Mat* 15:34; *Mark* 8:7
a great multitude of *f.* *Luke* 5:6
astonished at the draught of *f.* 9
not able to draw it for *f.* *John* 21:6
drew net to land full of great *f.* 11
of beasts, another of *f.* *1 Cor* 15:39

fish gate

on entering of *f. gate.* *2 Chr* 33:14
f. gate did the sons of. *Neh* 3:3
after them from above *f. gate.* 12:39
noise of a cry from *f. gate.* *Zeph* 1:10

fishhooks

your posterity with *f.* *Amos* 4:2

fishing

Peter saith unto them, I go a *f.* *John* 21:3

fishpools

thine eyes like the *f.* in. *S of S* 7:4

fist, -s

smite another with his *f.* *Ex* 21:18
gathered wind in his *f.*? *Pr* 30:4
with *f.* of wickedness. *Isa* 58:4

fit

him away by a *f.* man. *Lev* 16:21*
f. to go out to war and battle. *1 Chr* 7:11*; 12:8*
is it *f.* to say to a king? *Job* 34:18
make it *f.* for thyself. *Pr* 24:27*
vine made *f.* for no. *Ezek* 15:5
f. for kingdom of God. *Luke* 9:62
it is not *f.* for the land nor. 14:35
not *f.* that he should live. *Acts* 22:22
submit as it is *f.* in Lord. *Col* 3:18

fitches

he not cast abroad the *f.*? *Isa* 28:25
f. are not threshed, *f.* are. 27
wheat, barley, millet, *f.* *Ezek* 4:9*

fitly

a word *f.* spoken is like. *Pr* 25:11
eyes washed with milk, *f.* *S of S* 5:12
in whom building *f.* *Eph* 2:21
from whom the whole body *f.* 4:16

fitted

with gold *f.* upon carved. *1 Ki* 6:35
they shall withal be *f.* *Pr* 22:18*
vessels of wrath *f.* to. *Rom* 9:22

fitteth

the carpenter *f.* it. *Isa* 44:13*

five

Siddim, four kings with *f.* *Gen* 14:9
destroy all for lack of *f.*? 18:28
Benjamin's mess was *f.* 43:34
f. years in which no earing. 45:6, 11
to Benjamin he gave *f.* changes. 22
presented *f.* of his brethren. 47:2
thief restore *f.* oxen for. *Ex* 22:1
other *f.* curtains coupled. 26:3, 9; 36:10, 16
make *f.* bars for the boards. 26:26; 27; 36:31, 32
f. pillars. 26:37; 36:38
an altar *f.* cubits long, *f.* 27:1
height of hangings *f.* 18; 38:18
f. sockets of brass. 36:38
f. cubits breadth, *f.* the length. 38:1
f. of you chase an hundred. *Lev* 26:8
estimation be from *f.* years. 27:5
from a month old to *f.* years. 6
take *f.* shekels apiece. *Num* 3:47; 18:16
of peace offerings, *f.* rams, *f.* goats, *f.* 7:17, 23, 29, 35, 41, 47, 53
slew *f.* kings of Midian. 31:8
f. kings of Amorites. *Josh* 10:5
these *f.* kings fled and hid. 16
f. kings hid. 17
bring out the *f.* kings. 22
brought out these *f.* kings unto. 23
hanged them on *f.* trees. 26
f. lords of the Philistines. 13:3; *Judg* 3:3
children of Dan sent *f.* *Judg* 18:2
f. golden emerods, *f.* *1 Sam* 6:4
when *f.* lords of Philistines had. 16
David chose *f.* smooth stones. 17:40
give me *f.* loaves of bread. 21:3
f. sheep, *f.* measures of corn. 25:18
Abigail rode on an ass with *f.* 42
Mephibosheth was *f.* *2 Sam* 4:4
David took the *f.* sons of. 21:8
f. bases on the right, *f.* *1 Ki* 7:39
f. on right side, *f.* on. 49; *2 Chr* 4:7
cab of dove's dung sold *f.* *2 Ki* 6:25
let some take *f.* of the horses. 7:13
have smitten *f.* or six times. 13:19
f. men in king's presence. 25:19
the sons of Zera, *f.* of. *1 Chr* 2:6
Benaiah slew an Egyptian *f.* 11:23
four or *f.* in fruitful. *Isa* 17:6
f. cities in Egypt speak. 19:18
at the rebuke of *f.* shall ye. 30:17
but *f.* loaves and two. *Mat* 14:17; *Mark* 6:38; *Luke* 9:13
f. loaves of the *f.* thousand. *Mat* 16:9; *Mark* 8:19
f. were wise, *f.* foolish. *Mat* 25:2
unto one he gave *f.* talents. 15, 16
are not *f.* sparrows sold? *Luke* 12:6
f. in one house divided. 52
I have bought *f.* yoke of. 14:19
I have *f.* brethren 16:28
thy pound hath gained *f.* 19:18
be thou also over *f.* cities. 19
hast had *f.* husbands. *John* 4:18
pool Bethesda having *f.* porches 5:2
lad which had *f.* barley loaves. 6:9
fragments of *f.* barley loaves. 13
rather speak *f.* words. *1 Cor* 14:19
f. times received I forty stripes. *2 Cor* 11:24
seven kings, *f.* are fallen. *Rev* 17:10

fixed

my heart is *f.* *Ps* 57:7; 108:1
his heart is *f.*, trusting. 112:7
there is a gulf *f.* *Luke* 16:26

flag, -s

she laid the ark in the *f.* *Ex* 2:3
when she saw the ark among *f.* 5
f. grow without water? *Job* 8:11
the reeds and *f.* shall. *Isa* 19:6

flagon

each a *f.* of wine. *2 Sam* 6:19*; *1 Chr* 16:3*

flagons

stay me with *f.* *S of S* 2:5*
to all the vessels of *f.* *Isa* 22:24
to other gods, love *f.* *Hos* 3:1*

flakes

the *f.* of his flesh joined. *Job* 41:23

flame

angel appeared in a *f.* *Ex* 3:2; *Acts* 7:30
a *f.* from the city of. *Num* 21:28; *Jer* 48:45
f. went up, angel went in the *f.* *Judg* 13:20
make a great *f.* to rise. 20:38*
the *f.* of the city ascended up. 40*
the *f.* shall dry up his. *Job* 15:30
a *f.* goeth out of his mouth. 41:21
f. setteth mountains on. *Ps* 83:14
the *f.* burnt up the wicked. 106:18
which hath a vehement *f.* *S of S* 8:6
f. consumeth the chaff. *Isa* 5:24
Holy One shall be for a *f.* 10:17
with *f.* of devouring fire. 29:6
with *f.* of a devouring fire. 30:30
neither the *f.* kindle upon thee. 43:2
not deliver themselves from *f.* 47:14
flaming *f.* not quenched. *Ezek* 20:47
f. slew those men that. *Dan* 3:22
his throne was like fiery *f.* 7:9
body was given to burning *f.* 11*
shall fall by sword and by *f.* 11:33
the *f.* hath burnt all trees. *Joel* 1:19
and behind them a *f.* burneth. 2:3
like the noise of a *f.* of fire. 5
house of Joseph shall be a *f.* *Ob* 18
am tormented in this *f.* *Luke* 16:24
maketh his ministers a *f.* *Heb* 1:7
eyes as a *f.* *Rev* 1:14; 2:18; 19:12

flames

of Lord divideth the *f.* *Ps* 29:7
their faces shall be as *f.* *Isa* 13:8
to render rebuke with *f.* 66:15

flaming

at Eden a *f.* sword. *Gen* 3:24
the *f.* flame shall not be quenched. *Ezek* 20:47
chariots with *f.* torches. *Nah* 2:3

see **fire**

flanks

(*Revised Version,* loins)
the fat which is by the *f.* shall he. *Lev* 3:4, 10, 15; 4:9; 7:4
collops of fat on his *f.* *Job* 15:27

flash

as the appearance of a *f.* *Ezek* 1:14

flat

hath a *f.* nose shall not. *Lev* 21:18
Balaam bowed, fell *f.* *Num* 22:31
of city shall fall down *f.* *Josh* 6:5
people shouted, wall fell down *f.* 20

flatter

they *f.* with their tongue. *Ps* 5:9
they did *f.* him with their. 78:36

flattereth

f. himself in his own eyes. *Ps* 36:2
stranger who *f.* with. *Pr* 2:16; 7:5
meddle not with him that *f.* 20:19*
more favour than he that *f.* 28:23
a man that *f.* spreadeth a net. 29:5

flatteries

obtain the kingdom by *f.* *Dan* 11:21
do wickedly be corrupt by *f.* 32
shall cleave to them with *f.* 34

flattering

neither let me give *f.* titles to man. *Job* 32:21
for I know not to give *f.* titles. 22
with *f.* lips and double. *Ps* 12:2
the Lord shall cut off all *f.* lips. 3
with the *f.* of her lips. *Pr* 7:21
a *f.* mouth worketh ruin. 26:28
no more *f.* divination. *Ezek* 12:24
neither used we *f.* *1 Thes* 2:5

flattery

speaketh *f.* to his friends. *Job* 17:5*
from *f.* of strange woman. *Pr* 6:24

flax

f. and barley smitten, *f.* *Ex* 9:31
hid them with stalks of *f.* *Josh* 2:6
cords became as *f.* that. *Judg* 15:14
she seeks wool and *f.* *Pr* 31:13
they that work in fine *f.* *Isa* 19:9
the smoking *f.* shall he not quench. 42:3; *Mat* 12:20
a man with a line of *f.* *Ezek* 40:3
lovers that give me *f.* *Hos* 2:5
I will recover my wool and my *f.* 9

flay

f. their skins from off them. Mi 3:3

flayed

the Levites f. them. 2 Chr 35:11

flea

is king come after a f.? 1 Sam 24:14
26:20

fled

kings of Sodom and Gomorrah f.
Gen 14:10
Hagar f. 16:6
Jacob f. 31:22; Hos 12:12
Moses f. from Pharaoh. Ex 2:15
4:3; Acts 7:29
king of Egypt that people f. Ex 14:5
Egyptians f. against the sea. 27
f. at the cry of them. Num 16:34
Israel f. by way of the. Josh 8:15
these five kings f. and hid. 10:16
Adoni-bezek f. Judg 1:6
Sisera f. away. 4:15
host ran and cried, and f. 7:21*, 22
Zalmunna f. 8:12
Jotham ran and f. 9:21
to the tower f. men and. 51
Jephthah f. 11:3
the Benjamites f. 20:45, 47
and I f. to-day out of. 1 Sam 4:16
heard that Philistines f. 14:22
men of Israel f. from Goliath. 17:24
David f. and escaped. 19:10
12, 18; 20:1; 21:10
Abiathar escaped and f. 22:20; 23:6
four hundred which rode and f. 30:17
Israel f. from Philistines. 31:1, 7
2 Sam 19:8
Beerothites f. to Gittaim. 2 Sam 4:3
and his nurse f. 4
the Syrians f. 10:14, 18
Absalom and king's sons f. 13:29
34:37, 38
all Israel f. every one to tent. 18:17
came to me when I f. 1 Ki 2:7
Joab f. to the tabernacle. 28, 29
Hadad f. 11:17
Rezon f. from his lord. 23
Jeroboam f. 40
the Syrians f. 20:20; 1 Chr 19:18
2 Ki 7:7
the people f. to their. 2 Ki 8:21
prophet opened door and f. 9:10
Joram f. 23
all the men of war f. by night. 25:4
Jer 52:7
the men of Israel f. 1 Chr 10:1
11:13; 2 Chr 13:16
Ethiopians and they f. 2 Chr 14:12
the Levites f. every one. Neh 13:10
they that did see me f. Ps 31:11
the sea saw it and f. 114:3
with bread him that f. Isa 21:14
all thy rulers are f. together. 22:3
noise of tumult the people f. 33:3
birds of the heavens were f. Jer 4:25
the fowl and beast are f. 9:10
Urijah heard and f. 26:21
Egyptians are f. 46:5
also her hired men are f. 21
I f. before to Tarshish. Jonah 4:2
flee as ye f. before the. Zech 14:5
they that kept them f. Mat 8:33
disciples forsook him and f. 26:56
Mark 14:50
they went out and f. Mark 16:8
the prisoners had been f. Acts 16:27*
f. for refuge to lay hold. Heb 6:18
the woman f. Rev 12:6
every island f. away. 16:20
earth and heaven f. away. 20:11

he **fled**

told him not that he f. Gen 31:20
so he f. 21
when he f. from his brother. 35:7
he left his garment and f. 39:12
13, 15, 18
to the city of his refuge, whither he was f. Num 35:25; Josh 20:6
Abimelech chased Gaal, and he f.
Judg 9:40
they knew when he f. 1 Sam 22:17
Ahaziah fled, and he f. 2 Ki 9:27
he f. to Lachish. 14:19; 2 Chr 25:27
he f. from presence of. Jonah 1:10
he left linen cloth, and f. naked.
Mark 14:52

is **fled**

no satisfaction for him that is f.
Num 35:32
is f. before Philistines. 1 Sam 4:17
David is f. out of the. 2 Sam 19:9
Gibeah of Saul is f. Isa 10:29

they **fled**

they that remained f. Gen 14:10
they f. from before men of Ai.
Josh 7:4
as they f. Lord cast down. 10:11
Israel was smitten, they f. every man to. 1 Sam 4:10; 2 Ki 14:12
champion dead they f. 1 Sam 17:51
slew Philistines, and they f. 19:8
Joab drew nigh, they f. 2 Sam 10:13
1 Chr 19:14
Moabites, they f. before them.
2 Ki 3:24
Israel saw that they f. 1 Chr 10:7
at thy rebuke they f. Ps 104:7
they f. from swords. Isa 21:15
they f. and went forth. Jer 39:4
when they f. away. Lam 4:15
they f. to save themselves. Dan 10:7
for they have f. from me. Hos 7:13*
what was done, they f. Luke 8:34
they f. out of that house. Acts 19:16

fleddest

thou f. from Esau. Gen 35:1
ailed thee, O sea, thou f.? Ps 114:5

flee

I f. from the face of. Gen 16:8
this city is near to f. unto. 19:20
arise, f. to Laban my. 27:43
us f. from face of Israel. Ex 14:25
a place whither he shall f. 21:13
f. when none pursueth. Lev 26:17, 36
hate thee f. before thee. Num 10:55
Ps 68:1
now f. thou to thy place. Num 24:11
that the manslayer may f. 35:6
11, 15; Deut 4:42; 19:3, 4, 5
Josh 20:3, 4, 9
and f. before thee. Deut 28:7, 25
first we f. before them. Josh 8:5, 6
had no power to f. this way or. 20
let us f. and draw them. Judg 20:32
but didst f. on spoil. 1 Sam 15:19
nurse made haste to f. 2 Sam 4:4
f. else we shall not escape. 15:14
men steal away when they f. 19:3
f. three months before? 24:13
made speed to get to chariot, and f.
1 Ki 12:18; 2 Chr 10:18
then open door, and f. 2 Ki 9:3
such a man as I f.? Neh 6:11
f. from the iron weapon. Job 20:24
would fain f. out of hand. 27:22
abhor me, they f. far from. 30:10*
arrow cannot make him f. 41:28
f. as bird to your? Ps 11:1
kings of armies f. apace. 68:12
I f. from thy presence? 139:7
O Lord, I f. to thee to hide. 143:9
wicked f. when no man. Pr 28:1
he shall f. to the pit. 17
whom will ye f. for help? Isa 10:3
f. every one into his own. 13:14
his fugitives shall f. unto Zoar. 15:5
they shall f. far off. 17:13
expectation whither we f. for. 20:6
no, for we will f. on horses. 30:16
at rebuke of five shall ye f. 17
f. ye from the Chaldeans. 48:20
the city shall f. for noise. Jer 4:29
to f. out of Jerusalem. 6:1
shepherds have no way to f. 25:35
f. save your lives, and be. 48:6
wings to Moab, that it may f. 9
Edom shall f. 49:8
Damascus turned to f. 24
f. dwell deep, inhabitants of. 30
f. every one to his own land. 50:16
voice of them that f. and escape. 28
f. out of midst of Babylon. 51:6
Zech 2:6
man did f. from a lion. Amos 5:19
Jonah rose up to f. to. Jonah 1:3
that look on, shall f. Nah 3:7
take young child and f. Mat 2:13
hath warned you f. from wrath? 3:7
Luke 3:7
persecute you in city f. Mat 10:23
be in Judea f. to the mountains.
24:16; Mark 13:14; Luke 21:21
stranger not follow, but f. John 10:5
shipmen were about to f. Acts 27:30
f. fornication. 1 Cor 6:18
f. from idolatry. 10:14
O man of God, f. these. 1 Tim 6:11
f. also youthful lusts. 2 Tim 2:22
devil, he will f. from you. Jas 4:7
death shall f. from them. Rev 9:6
that the woman might f. into. 12:14

flee *away*

wherefore didst thou f. away?
Gen 31:27
if f. away, they will not. 2 Sam 18:3
my days f. away. Job 9:25
f. away as a dream. 20:8
that see, shall f. away. Ps 64:8*
day break, and shadows f. away.
S of S 2:17; 4:6
sighing f. away. Isa 35:10; 51:11
let not swift f. away. Jer 46:6
courageous shall f. away. Amos 2:16
O thou seer, go, f. away into. 7:12
fleeth of them, shall not f. away. 9:1
Nineveh shall f. away. Nah 2:8
grasshoppers in hedges f. away. 3:17

fleece

first of f. of sheep give. Deut 18:4
a f. of wool in floor. Judg 6:37
Gideon wringed dew out of f. 38
let it be dry only upon the f. 39
not warmed with f. of. Job 31:20

fleeing

flee as f. from sword. Lev 26:36
that f. to one of these. Deut 4:42
for want and famine f. to. Job 30:3*

fleeth

smite him mortally, f. Deut 19:11
he f. as a shadow. Job 14:2
he who f. from noise of. Isa 24:18
ask him that f. and. Jer 48:19
he that f. from the fear, shall. 44
f. shall not flee away. Amos 9:1*
that is an hireling f. John 10:12, 13

flesh

[1] *The muscles and other soft parts of the animal body, whether of man, beast, bird, or fish,* Ex 12:8; Mat 26:41. [2] *All beings possessed of flesh, man and the inferior animals, especially man; often in contrast with God, who is spirit,* Gen 6:13. [3] *Human nature considered as unregenerate and unsanctified,* Rom 7:5. [4] *The word is also used for one of near kindred,* Gen 37:27; 2 Sam 19:12, 13.

To be one flesh, denotes an intimate communion, as if the two were but one person or one body, Gen 2:24. *This phrase is used by the Apostle to shew the union between Christ and believers,* Eph 5:30, 31. *Flesh also signifies the human nature of Christ,* Heb 10:20.

God closed up the f. Gen 2:21
to his wife, they shall be one f. 24
not strive with man, he is f. 6:3
ye shall circumcise the f. of. 17:11
whose f. is not circumcised. 14
Abraham circumcised f. of. 23
he is our brother and our f. 37:27
turned again as his other f. Ex 4:7
burn the f. 29:14; Lev 9:11; 16:27
Num 19:5
man's f. not be poured. Ex 30:32
what shall touch f thereof. Lev 6:27
as for f., all that be clean shall. 7:19
boil the f. at the door of. 8:31
be quick raw f. 13:10, 14, 15, 16, 24
if skin of their f. have bright. 38, 39
that toucheth the f. of him. 15:7
if her issue in her f. be blood. 19
make any cuttings in their f. 21:5

while f. was between. Num 11:33
whom f. is half consumed. 12:12
the f. of them shall be thine. 18:18
my sword shall devour f. Deut 32:42
take f. and unleavened cakes. Judg 6:20
fire out of rock, and consumed f. 21
while f. was in seething. 1 Sam 2:13
give f. to roast for the priest. 15
David dealt to each f. 2 Sam 6:19
1 Chr 16:3
him bread and f. in morning, bread and f. in evening. 1 Ki 17:6
boiled f. with instruments of. 19:21
f. of the child waxed. 2 Ki 4:34
with him is an arm of f. 2 Chr 32:8
yet our f. is as the f. of. Neh 5:5
hast thou eyes of f.? Job 10:4
clothed me with skin and f. 11
I will not fear what f. can. Ps 56:4
he provide f. for his people ? 78:20
rained f. also upon them as dust. 27
remembered they were but f. 39
the f. of thy saints given to. 79:2
sayings are health to their f. Pr 4:22
not among riotous eaters of f. 23:20
and their horses are f. 31:3
I will feed them with own f. 49:26
and the holy f. is passed. Jer 11:15
spoilers come, no f. have. 12:12
cursed be man that maketh f. 17:5
nor came abominable f. Ezek 4:14
city is caldron, and we be f. 11:3
slain in midst of it, they are the f. 7
nor ye be the f. in the midst. 11
give them a heart of f. 19; 36:26
great of f. and hast increased. 16:26
whose f. is as f. of asses. 23:20
consume the f., spice it well. 24:10
I will bring f. upon you. 37:6, 8
dwelling is not with f. Dan 2:11
arise, devour much f. 7:5
neither came f. nor wine. 10:3
sacrifice f. for sacrifices. Hos 8:13
f. from off their bones. Mi 3:2
their f. shall be poured. Zeph 1:17
if one bear holy f. in. Hag 2:12
f. shall consume away. Zech 14:12
f. and blood hath not. Mat 16:17
and they twain be one f. 19:5, 6
Mark 10:8; 1 Cor 6:16; Eph 5:31
should no f. be saved. Mat 24:22
Mark 13:20
spirit willing, f. is weak. Mat 26:41
Mark 14:38
spirit hath not f. and. Luke 24:39
the Word was made f. John 1:14
the f. profiteth nothing. 6:63
of David according to f. Acts 2:30
Rom 1:3
shall no f. be justified. Rom 3:20
Abraham as pertaining to f. 4:1
with f. I serve the law of sin. 7:25
law was weak through f., God sent own Son in likeness of sinful f. 8:3
and kinsmen according to f. 9:3
of whom as concerning the f. 5
make not provision for the f. 13:14
that no f. should glory. 1 Cor 1:29
there is one f. of men, and. 15:39
f. and blood cannot inherit. 50
purpose according to f.? 2 Cor 1:17
of Jesus manifest in our f. 4:11
our f. had no rest, but. 7:5
walked according to the f. 10:2
conferred not with f. and. Gal 1:16
by works of law no f. justified. 2:16
are ye made perfect by the f.? 3:3
not liberty for occasion to the f. 5:13
f. lusteth against the Spirit, Spirit against f. 17
Christ's have crucified the f. 24
in lusts of our f. Eph 2:3
masters according to the f. 6:5
Col 3:22
wrestle not against f. and. Eph 6:12
children partakers of f. Heb 2:14
we had fathers of our f. who. 12:9
going after strange f. are. Jude 7
these filthy dreamers defile the f. 8
hating even garment spotted by f. 23
eat f. of captains, f. of. Rev 19:18
all the fowls filled with their f. 21
see **eat, eateth**

after the **flesh**

ye judge after the f. John 8:15
who walk not after the f. Rom 8:1, 4
are after the f. mind things of f. 5
debtors to flesh to live after the f. 12
if ye live after the f. ye shall die. 13
many wise men after f. 1 Cor 1:26
behold Israel after the f. 10:18
no man after the f.: though we have known Christ after f. 2 Cor 5:16
we do not war after the f. 10:3
many glory after the f. I also. 11:18
Ishmael born after the f. Gal 4:23, 29
them that walk after f. 2 Pet 2:10

all **flesh**

for all f. had corrupted. Gen 6:12
God said, the end of all f. is. 13
of all f. two of every sort bring into the ark to keep. 19; 7:15
all f. died that moved upon. 7:21
bring forth of all f. both of. 8:17
nor all f. cut off any more. 9:11, 15
covenant between me and all f. 16, 17
the life of all f. is blood. Lev 17:14
shave all their f. and. Num 8:7
God of spirits of all f. 16:22; 27:16
that openeth matrix of all f. 18:15
who of all f. heard word. Deut 5:26
all f. shall perish together. Job 34:15
to thee shall all f. come. Ps 65:2
who giveth food to all f. 136:25
let all f. bless his holy name. 145:21
all f. shall see it together. Isa 40:5
all f. is grass. 6; 1 Pet 1:24
all f. shall know I am thy Saviour.
Isa 49:26; Ezek 21:5
by fire will Lord plead with all f.
Isa 66:16
all f. shall come to worship. 23
an abhorring to all f. 24
will plead with all f. Jer 25:31
I am Lord the God of all f. 32:27
I will bring evil on all f. 45:5
all f. shall see that I. Ezek 20:48
sword go forth against all f. 21:4
and all f. was fed of it. Dan 4:12
will pour out my Spirit on all f.
Joel 2:28; Acts 2:17
be silent, O all f. Zech 2:13
all f. shall see salvation. Luke 3:6
given him power over all f. John 17:2
all f. is not same flesh. 1 Cor 15:39

his **flesh**

his f. shall not be eaten. Ex 21:28
seethe his f. in holy place. 29:31
burn all his f. with. Lev 4:11; 8:17
linen breeches on his f. 6:10; 16:4
a rising in the skin of his f. 13:2
look on plague in skin of his f. 3
spot be white in skin of his f. 4
old leprosy in skin of his f. 11, 13
also wash his f. in water. 14:9
15:16; 16:24, 28; Num 19:7
running issue out of his f. Lev 15:2
whether his f. run with his issue. 3
wash them not, nor bathe his f. 17:16
unclean, unless he wash his f. 22:6
Ahab put sackcloth on his f.
1 Ki 21:27
his f. came again, and. 2 Ki 5:14
Joram had sackcloth on his f. 6:30
touch his bone and his f. Job 2:5
his f. upon him shall have. 14:22
O that we had of his f. 31:31
his f. is consumed away. 33:21
his f. be fresher than a child's. 25
flakes of his f. are joined. 41:23
cruel troubleth his f. Pr 11:17
foldeth hands, eateth his f. Eccl 4:5
fatness of his f. wax lean. Isa 17:4
man give us his f. to eat ? John 6:52
his f. did see corruption. Acts 2:31
he that soweth to his f. Gal 6:8
abolished in his f. the. Eph 2:15
no man yet hated his own f. 5:29
members of his body, of his f. 30
reconciled in body of his f. Col 1:22
in days of his f. when. Heb 5:7
that is to say, his f. 10:20

in the **flesh,** *or in* **flesh**

Abraham was circumcised in the f.
Gen 17:24
Ishmael circumcised in the f. 25
uncircumcised in the f. Ezek 44:7
uncircumcised in the f. not enter. 9
fairer and fatter in f. Dan 1:15
circumcision outward in the f.
Rom 2:28
for when we were in the f. 7:5
for sin condemned sin in the f. 8:3
are in the f. cannot please God. 8
but ye are not in the f. but. 9
have trouble in the f. 1 Cor 7:28
in the f. not war after f. 2 Cor 10:3
given to me a thorn in the f. 12:7
which I now live in the f. Gal 2:20
to make a fair shew in the f. 6:12
Gentiles in the f. called the circumcision in the f. made. Eph 2:11
if I live in the f. this is. Phil 1:22
to abide in the f. more needful. 24
have no confidence in the f. 3:3
might have confidence in the f. 4
not seen my face in the f. Col 2:1
though I be absent in the f. 5
God manifest in the f. 1 Tim 3:16
more to thee, both in the f. Philem 16
put to death in the f. 1 Pet 3:18
Christ suffered for us in the f.: he that hath suffered in the f. 4:1
no longer live in the f. 2
judged according to men in the f. 6
denieth Christ in the f. 1 John 4:2, 3
not Christ is come in the f. 2 John 7

my **flesh**

my bread and my f.? 1 Sam 25:11
the hair of my f. stood. Job 4:15
or is my f. brass ? 6:12
my f. is clothed with worms. 7:5
I take my f. in my teeth ? 13:14
cleaveth to skin, and my f. 19:20
and not satisfied with my f.? 22
yet in my f. shall I see God. 26
trembling taketh hold of my f. 21:6
my f. shall rest in hope. Ps 16:9
Acts 2:26
no soundness in my f. Ps 38:3, 7
my f. longeth for thee in a dry. 63:1
my f. faileth, but God is my. 73:26
my heart and my f. crieth out. 84:2
my knees are weak, my f. 109:24
my f. trembleth for fear. 119:120
done to me, and to my f. Jer 51:35
my f. and my skin hath. Lam 3:4
bread I will give is my f. John 6:51
eateth my f. hath eternal. 54, 56
my f. is meat indeed. 55
in my f. dwelleth no. Rom 7:18
provoke them which are my f. 11:14
temptation which was in my f.
Gal 4:14
afflictions of Christ in my f. Col 1:24
see **bone**

of the **flesh**

carry forth aught of the f. Ex 12:46
if aught of the f. remain. 29:34
nor give of the f. Deut 28:55
sound heart is life of the f. Pr 14:30
study weariness of the f. Eccl 12:12
not of the will of the f. John 1:13
is born of the f. is flesh. 3:6
do mind the things of the f. Rom 8:5
which are children of the f. 9:8
for destruction of the f. 1 Cor 5:5
cleanse from all filthiness of the f.
2 Cor 7:1
through infirmity of the f. Gal 4:13
shall not fulfil the lust of the f. 5:16
now works of the f. are manifest. 19
soweth to flesh of the f. reap. 6:8
in lusts of our f. desires of the f.
Eph 2:3
putting off sins of the f. Col 2:11
to the satisfying of the f. 23
to the purging of the f. Heb 9:13
away the filth of the f. 1 Pet 3:21
through lusts of the f. 2 Pet 2:18
the lust of the f. the. 1 John 2:16

thy **flesh**

birds shall eat thy f. Gen 40:19
give thy f. unto fowls. 1 Sam 17:44
are thy bone and thy f. 2 Sam 5:1
1 Chr 11:1
wash, thy f. shall come. 2 Ki 5:10
when thy f. is consumed. Pr 5:11

not mouth to cause thy f. Eccl 5:6
put away evil from thy f. 11:10
hide not thyself from thine own f. Isa 58:7
lay thy f. on mountains. Ezek 32:5

your **flesh**

make cuttings in your f. Lev 19:28
then I will tear your f. Judg 8:7
stony heart out of your f. Ezek 36:26
of the infirmity of your f. Rom 6:19
they may glory in your f. Gal 6:13
uncircumcision of your f. Col 2:13
rust shall eat your f. Jas 5:3

fleshhook

servant came with a f. 1 Sam 2:13
all that the f. brought up. 14

fleshhooks

shalt make his f. and. Ex 27:3
made vessels and the f. 38:3
upon purple cloth the f. Num 4:14
pure gold for the f. 1 Chr 28:17
also the pots and f. 2 Chr 4:16

fleshly

simplicity, not f. wisdom. 2 Cor 1:12
but in f. tables of the heart. 3:3
puffed up by his f. mind. Col 2:18
abstain from f. lusts. 1 Pet 2:11

flesh pots

we sat by the f. pots. Ex 16:3

flew

people f. upon spoil. 1 Sam 14:32
f. one of the seraphims. Isa 6:6

flies

swarms of f. upon thee. Ex 8:21
he removed the swarms of f. 31
he sent divers sorts of f. Ps 78:45
there came divers sorts of f. 105:31
dead f. cause ointment. Eccl 10:1

flieth

any winged fowl that f. Deut 4:17
every creeping thing that f. 14:19*
a nation swift as the eagle f. 28:49
for arrow that f. by day. Ps 91:5
cankerworm spoileth and f. Nah 3:16

flight

go out with haste nor f. Isa 52:12
the f. shall perish from. Amos 2:14
pray f. be not in winter. Mat 24:20
Mark 13:18
to f. armies of aliens. Heb 11:34
see **put**

flint

water out of rock of f. Deut 8:15
turning f. into a fountain. Ps 114:8
horses be counted like f. Isa 5:28
have I set my face like a f. 50:7
harder than f. have I. Ezek 3:9

flinty

to suck oil out of the f. rock. Deut 32:13

floats

by sea in f. 1 Ki 5:9; 2 Chr 2:16

flock

Abel brought firstlings of his f. Gen 4:4
Abraham set ewe lambs of f. 21:28
go to f. and fetch two good. 27:9
Jacob watered the f. of Laban. 29:10
again feed and keep thy f. 30:31
I will pass through all thy f. 32
Jacob fed rest of Laban's f. 36
separate all the brown in the f. 40
Rachel and Leah to his f. 31:4
rams of thy f. have I not eaten. 38
overdrive them, the f. will die. 33:13
Joseph was feeding the f. with. 37:2
brethren went to feed their f. 12, 13
I will send a kid from the f. 38:17
water their father's f. Ex 2:16
Moses helped, watered f. 17, 19
Moses led the f. to the desert. 3:1
of your offering for f. Lev 1:2
bring a female from the f. 5:6
ram without blemish out of f. 18
6:6; Ezra 10:19; Ezek 43:23, 25
concerning tithe of the f. Lev 27:32
savour of the herd or f. Num 15:3
kill of thy herd and f. Deut 12:21
him liberally out of thy f. 15:14
all the firstling males of thy f. 19
sacrifice to Lord of the f. Deut 16:2
lion took lamb out of f. 1 Sam 17:34
spared to take of own f. 2 Sam 12:4
gave to people of the f. 2 Chr 35:7
to set with dogs of my f. Job 30:1
makest thy f. to rest at. S of S 1:7
go by the footsteps of the f. 8
hair is as a f. of goats. 4:1; 6:5
teeth are like f. of sheep. 4:2; 6:6
feed his f. like a shepherd. Isa 40:11
them with shepherd of his f. 63:11
Lord's f. is carried. Jer 13:17
where is the f., thy beautiful f.? 20
ye have scattered my f. and. 23:2
gather the remnant of my f. 3
ye principal of the f. 25:34
nor principal of the f. to escape. 35
an howling of principal of the f. 36
him as a shepherd doth his f. 31:10
shall sing for the young of the f. 12
least of f. draw them. 49:20; 50:45
in pieces shepherd and his f. 51:23
take the choice of the f. Ezek 24:5
eat the fat, ye feed not the f. 34:3*
my f. was scattered on the face. 6*
my f. became a prey, my f. meat. 8*
require my f. I will deliver my f. 10*
as a shepherd seeketh out his f. 12
I will feed my f. 15*
as for you, O my f. 17
therefore will I save my f. 22
ye my f. the f. of my pasture. 31*
the holy f. as f. of Jerusalem. 36:38
offer one lamb out of the f. 45:15
eat lambs out of the f. Amos 6:4
Lord took me as I followed f. 7:15
let not herd nor f. taste. Jonah 3:7
as the f. in the midst. Mi 2:12
O tower of the f. the strong. 4:8
thy people, f. of thine heritage. 7:14
the f. shall be cut off. Hab 3:17
save them as the f. of. Zech 9:16
they went their way as a f. 10:2*
Lord of hosts hath visited his f. 3
will feed f. of slaughter. 11:4, 7
poor of the f. that waited on. 7, 11
woe to shepherd, that leaveth f. 17
deceiver which hath in his f. a male. Mal 1:14
sheep of f. be scattered. Mat 26:31
keeping watch over their f. Luke 2:8
fear not little f. it is your. 12:32
take heed to all the f. Acts 20:28
wolves enter, not sparing f. 29
who feedeth a f. and. 1 Cor 9:7
feed the f. of God. 1 Pet 5:2
but being ensamples to the f. 3

like a **flock**

their little ones like a f. Job 21:11
leddest thy people like a f. Ps 77:20
guided them in wilderness like a f. 78:52
that leadest Joseph like a f. 80:1
maketh him families like a f. 107:41
them with men like a f. Ezek 36:37

flocks

f. of sheep lying by well, out of that they watered the f. Gen 29:2
thither were all the f. gathered. 3
we cannot until the f. be gathered. 8
Jacob set rods before the f. 30:38
the f. conceived before the rods. 39
faces of the f. towards the ringstraked, he put his own f. by. 40*
I have oxen, asses, f. and. 32:5
he divided the f. and herds. 7
whether it be well with f. 37:14
tell me where they feed their f. 16
have no pasture for their f. 47:4
in exchange for horses and f. 17
if his offering be of the f. Lev 1:10
ram without blemish out of f. 5:15
took spoil of all their f. Num 31:9
take one portion of the f. 30
our wives, our f. and cattle. 32:26
also bless f. of thy sheep. Deut 7:13
blessed be the f. of thy sheep. 28:4
cursed be the f. of thy sheep. 18
not leave the f. of thy sheep. 51
hear bleatings of the f. Judg 5:16
like two little f. of kids. 1 Ki 20:27
seek pasture for their f. 1 Chr 4:39
there was pasture for their f. 41
and over the f. was Jaziz. 1 Chr 27:31
Arabians brought him f. 2 Chr 17:11
violently take away f. Job 24:2
pastures are clothed with f. Ps 65:13
their f. to hot thunderbolts. 78:48
turn aside by the f. of. S of S 1:7
cities of Aroer be for f. Isa 17:2
palaces be a pasture of f. 32:14
all the f. of Kedar shall be. 60:7
strangers shall feed your f. 61:5
Sharon shall be a fold for f. 65:10
the shepherds with their f. Jer 6:3
all f. shall be scattered. 10:21
Judah they that go forth with f. 31:24
shepherds causing f. to lie. 33:12
the f. shall pass again under rod. 13
tents and f. shall take away. 49:29
as the he goats before the f. 50:8
a couching place for f. Ezek 25:5
not the shepherds feed the f.? 34:2*
the waste cities filled with f. 36:38
f. of sheep are desolate. Joel 1:18
as a young lion among f. of. Mi 5:8
sea coast be folds for f. Zeph 2:6
f. lie down in midst of Nineveh. 14*

flocks with herds

Lot also had f. and herds. Gen 13:5
given Abraham f. and herds. 24:35
possession of f. and herds. 26:14
Jacob divided f. and herds. 32:7
the f. and herds with young. 33:13
me, thou, thy f. and herds. 45:10
brethren, their f. and herds. 47:1
their f. and herds left they. 50:8
will go with f. and herds. Ex 10:9
let your f. and your herds be. 24
take your f. and your herds. 12:32
neither let f. nor herds feed. 34:3
f. and herds be slain. Num 11:22
thy herds and f. multiply. Deut 8:13
firstling of herds and f. 12:6, 17
14:23; Neh 10:36
took all f. and herds. 1 Sam 30:20
had exceeding many f. and herds. 2 Sam 12:2
possessions of f. and herds. 2 Chr 32:29
thy f. look to thy herds. Pr 27:23
devoured f. and herds. Jer 3:24
nation eat thy f. and herds. 5:17
go with f. and herds to. Hos 5:6

flood

[1] A great flow of water; inundation. [2] Figuratively, of dangers or sorrows or temptations which come like a flood of water. [3] Specifically, the great flood of Noah's time.

I bring a f. of water on. Gen 6:17
when the f. of waters was. 7:6
because of the waters of the f. 7
after seven days f. was on earth. 10
f. was forty days on earth. 17
any more a f. to destroy. 9:11
lived after the f. 350 years. 28
to them were sons born after f. 10:1
nations divided in earth after f. 32
your fathers on either side of f. Josh 24:2*, 3*, 14*, 15*
as the f. decayeth and. Job 14:11*
foundation overthrown with f. 22:16*
f. breaketh out from the. 28:4*
Lord sitteth upon the f. Ps 29:10
went through the f. on foot. 66:6
let not the water-f. overflow. 69:15
cleave fountain and the f. 74:15
them away as with a f. 90:5
strong one, which as a f. Isa 28:2*
enemy come in like a f. 59:19*
who cometh up as a f.? Jer 46:7*
Egypt riseth up like a f. 8*
waters be an overflowing f. 47:2*
end shall be with a f. Dan 9:26
with arms of a f. shall be. 11:22
it shall rise up wholly as a f. Amos 8:8*; 9:5*
be drowned as by the f. of. 9:5*
with an overrunning f. Nah 1:8
in days before the f. Mat 24:38
and knew not till the f. came. 39
Luke 17:27
when the f. arose the. Luke 6:48
bringing in the f. on world. 2 Pet 2:5

dragon poured out water as a *f.* *Rev* 12:15*
earth helped, swallowed up the *f.* 16*

floods

the *f.* stood upright. *Ex* 15:8
f. of ungodly made me afraid. *2 Sam* 22:5; *Ps* 18:4
not see rivers and *f.* *Job* 20:17*
bindeth *f.* from overflowing. 28:11*
established it upon the *f.* *Ps* 24:2
surely in *f.* of great waters. 32:6*
deep waters, where the *f.* 69:2
turned their *f.* into blood. 78:44*
f. have lifted up, O Lord, *f.* 93:3
let the *f.* clap their hands. 98:8
neither can *f.* drown love. *S of S* 8:7
f. upon the dry ground. *Isa* 44:3*
I restrained the *f.* *Ezek* 31:15*
f. compassed me about. *Jonah* 2:3
the *f.* came, winds. *Mat* 7:25, 27

floor, *substantive*

the threshing *f.* of Atad. *Gen* 50:10
inhabitants saw mourning in *f.* 11
priests take dust in *f.* *Num* 5:17
heave offering of threshing *f.* 15:20
as the corn of the threshing *f.* 18:27
as increase of threshing *f.* 30
furnish him out of thy *f.* *Deut* 15:14*
a fleece of wool in the *f.* *Judg* 6:37*
winnoweth in threshing *f.* *Ruth* 3:2
came to Nachon's threshing *f.* *2 Sam* 6:6; *1 Chr* 13:9
altar in threshing *f.* of. *2 Sam* 24:18
David said, to buy threshing *f.* 21
he overlaid the *f.* of. *1 Ki* 6:30
cedar from one side of the *f.* 7:7
out of the barn-*f.* or the. *2 Ki* 6:27
answered in threshing *f.* *1 Chr* 21:28
prepared in threshing *f.* of. *2 Chr* 3:1
and the corn of my *f.* *Isa* 21:10
is like a threshing *f.* *Jer* 51:33
a reward on every corn *f.* *Hos* 9:1
the *f.* and winepress shall not. 2*
as chaff driven out of the *f.* 13:3*
them as sheaves into *f.* *Mi* 4:12*
he will throughly purge his *f.* *Mat* 3:12*; *Luke* 3:17*

floor, *verb*

timber to *f.* the houses. *2 Chr* 34:11*

floors

rob the threshing *f.* *1 Sam* 23:1
of summer threshing *f.* *Dan* 2:35
f. shall be full of wheat. *Joel* 2:24

flour

of wheaten *f.* make them. *Ex* 29:2
his handful of the *f.* *Lev* 2:2; 6:15
tenth part of ephah of *f.* for a meat-. *Num* 28:5, 20, 28; 29:3, 9, 14
cakes of an ephah of *f.* *Judg* 6:19 *1 Sam* 1:24
she took *f.* and kneaded it. *1 Sam* 28:24; *2 Sam* 13:8*
brought *f.* parched corn. *2 Sam* 17:28
see **deal, fine**

flourish

in his days the righteous *f.* *Ps* 72:7
they of the city shall *f.* like. 16
the workers of iniquity *f.* 92:7
the righteous shall *f.* like the. 12
f. in the courts of our God. 13
himself shall his crown *f.* 132:18
the righteous shall *f.* *Pr* 11:28
tabernacle of upright shall *f.* 14:11
the almond tree shall *f.* *Eccl* 12:5*
let us see if vine *f.* *S of S* 7:12*
shalt make thy seed to *f.* *Isa* 17:11*
your bones shall *f.* like an. 66:14
made the dry tree to *f.* *Ezek* 17:24

flourished

to see whether vine *f.* *S of S* 6:11*
your care of me hath *f.* *Phil* 4:10*

flourisheth

in the morning it *f.* *Ps* 90:6
as a flower of field, so he *f.* 103:15

flourishing

in old age, fat and *f.* *Ps* 92:14*
I was at rest, and *f.* in. *Dan* 4:4

flow

his goods shall *f.* away. *Job* 20:28
wind blow, and waters *f.* *Ps* 147:18
spices thereof may *f.* out. *S of S* 4:16
all nations shall *f.* unto it. *Isa* 2:2
waters to *f.* out of the rock. 48:21
shalt see and *f.* together. 60:5*
mountains might *f.* down at. 64:1
f. to goodness of Lord. *Jer* 31:12
nations shall not *f.* together. 51:44
the hills shall *f.* with milk, the rivers of Judah *f.* with waters. *Joel* 3:18
people shall *f.* to mountain. *Mi* 4:1
out of his belly *f.* living. *John* 7:38

flowed

Jordan *f.* over all banks. *Josh* 4:18
the mountains *f.* down. *Isa* 64:3
the waters *f.* over mine. *Lam* 3:54

floweth

land that *f.* with milk and honey. *Lev* 20:24; *Num* 13:27; 14:8 16:13, 14; *Deut* 6:3; 11:9; 26:15 27:3; 31:20; *Josh* 5:6

flowing

to a land *f.* with milk and honey. *Ex* 3:8, 17; 13:5; 33:3; *Jer* 11:5 32:22; *Ezek* 20:6, 15
wellspring of wisdom as a *f.* *Pr* 18:4
glory of Gentiles like a *f.* *Isa* 66:12
or shall cold *f.* waters? *Jer* 18:14
gloriest thou in thy *f.* valley? 49:4

flower

increase shall die in *f.* *1 Sam* 2:33
if she pass *f.* of her age. *1 Cor* 7:36

flower

with knop and *f.* in one branch. *Ex* 25:33; 37:19
he cometh forth as a *f.* *Job* 14:2
he shall cast off his *f.* as. 15:33
as a *f.* of field, so he. *Ps* 103:15
sour grape is ripening in *f.* *Isa* 18:5
glorious beauty is a fading *f.* 28:1, 4
goodliness thereof is as *f.* of. 40:6
f. fadeth. 7, 8; *Neh* 1:4; *Jas* 1:10 11; *1 Pet* 1:24

flowers

his *f.* shall be of same. *Ex* 25:31 37:17
his knops and his *f.* 37:20
if her *f.* be upon him, he. *Lev* 15:24*
of her that is sick of her *f.* of. 33*
to the *f.* thereof was. *Num* 8:4
of house within carved with open *f.* *1 Ki* 6:18, 29, 32, 35; 7:26, 49
like brim of cup with *f.* *2 Chr* 4:5
the *f.* lamps, and tongs made. 21
the *f.* appear on earth. *S of S* 2:12
cheeks as a bed of spices, sweet *f.* 5:13*

flute

ye hear the *f.* *Dan* 3:5, 7, 10, 15

fluttereth

eagle *f.* over her young. *Deut* 32:11

flux

of Publius sick of a *f.* *Acts* 28:8

fly

Lord shall hiss for the *f.* in. *Isa* 7:18

fly, *verb*

and fowl that may *f.* *Gen* 1:20
rode upon a cherub, and did *f.* *2 Sam* 22:11; *Ps* 18:10
born to trouble as sparks *f.* *Job* 5:7
doth the hawk *f.* by thy? 39:26*
he did *f.* upon the wings. *Ps* 18:10
for then would I *f.* away. 55:6
is soon cut off, we *f.* away. 90:10
riches *f.* away as an eagle. *Pr* 23:5
with twain he did *f.* *Isa* 6:2
shall *f.* upon the shoulders of. 11:14
who are these that *f.* as a cloud. 60:8
he shall *f.* as an eagle. *Jer* 48:40
hunt the souls to make them *f.* *Ezek* 13:20
Gabriel being caused to *f.* *Dan* 9:21
their glory shall *f.* away. *Hos* 9:11
they shall *f.* as the eagle. *Hab* 1:8
I saw another angel *f.* *Rev* 14:6
to all the fowls that *f.* in. 19:17
see **flee, flieth**

flying

eat of every *f.* creeping. *Lev* 11:21*
but all other *f.* creeping things. 23*
all cattle and *f.* fowl. *Ps* 148:10
as the swallow by *f.* so. *Pr* 26:2
fruit shall be a fiery *f.* *Isa* 14:29
come viper and fiery *f.* serpent. 30:6
as birds *f.* so will the Lord. 31:5†
and behold, a *f.* roll. *Zech* 5:1, 2
fourth beast like a *f.* eagle. *Rev* 4:7
heard an angel *f.* through. 8:13

foal, -s

bulls, twenty asses, ten *f.* *Gen* 32:15
binding his *f.* to the vine. 49:11
f. of an ass. *Zech* 9:9; *Mat* 21:5

foam

of Samaria cut off as *f.* *Hos* 10:7

foameth

f. gnasheth with his teeth. *Mark* 9:18 *Luke* 9:39

foaming

on ground wallowed *f.* *Mark* 9:20
raging waves of sea, *f.* *Jude* 13

fodder

or loweth the ox over his *f.* *Job* 6:5

foes

destroyed before thy *f.* *1 Chr* 21:12
the Jews slew of their *f.* *Esth* 9:16
mine enemies and *f.* *Ps* 27:2
thou hast not made my *f.* to. 30:1
I will beat down his *f.* 89:23
a man's *f.* shall be they. *Mat* 10:36
make thy *f.* thy footstool. *Acts* 2:35

fold

as vesture shalt thou *f.* *Heb* 1:12*

fold

shepherds make their *f.* *Isa* 13:20*
Sharon shall be *f.* for flocks. 65:10
on mountains their *f.* be. *Ezek* 34:14
as flock in midst of their *f.* *Mi* 2:12*
flock be cut off from the *f.* *Hab* 3:17
hundred, some sixty, some thirty *f.* *Mat* 13:8, 23; *Mark* 4:8, 20
shall receive 100 *f.* *Mat* 19:29
other sheep which are not of this *f.* there shall be one *f.* *John* 10:16*

folden

while they be *f.* together. *Nah* 1:10

foldeth

the fool *f.* his hands. *Eccl* 4:5

folding

leaves of one door were *f.* *1 Ki* 6:34
a little *f.* of hands. *Pr* 6:10; 24:33

folds

build ye *f.* for. *Num* 32:24, 36
no he goats out of thy *f.* *Ps* 50:9
bring them again to their *f.* *Jer* 23:3
the sea coast shall be *f.* *Zeph* 2:6

folk

leave with thee some of *f.* *Gen* 33:15
conies are but a feeble *f.* *Pr* 30:26
the *f.* shall labour in fire. *Jer* 51:58*
hands upon few sick *f.* *Mark* 6:5
multitude of impotent *f.* *John* 5:3*
a multitude bringing sick *f.* *Acts* 5:16

follow

woman not willing to *f.* *Gen* 24:8
Joseph said, *f.* after the men. 44:4
out, and people that *f.* *Ex* 11:8
harden Pharaoh that he shall *f.* 14:4
the Egyptians shall *f.* them. 17*
a woman, and no mischief *f.* 21:22
and if any mischief *f.* then. 23
not *f.* a multitude to do evil. 23:2
what is altogether just *f.* *Deut* 16:20
if the thing *f.* not. 18:22
inclined to *f.* Abimelech. *Judg* 9:3
men, who *f.* my lord. *1 Sam* 25:27
faint they could not *f.* David. 30:21
people that *f.* Absalom. *2 Sam* 17:9
then I will *f.* thee. *1 Ki* 19:20
I *f.* the thing that good is. *Ps* 38:20
virgins her companions that *f.* 45:14
upright in heart shall *f.* it. 94:15
they draw nigh that *f.* 119:150
that they *f.* strong drink. *Isa* 5:11
ye that *f.* after righteousness. 51:1
being a pastor to *f.* thee. *Jer* 17:16
the famine shall *f.* close. 42:16
prophets that *f.* own spirit. *Ezek* 13:3
shall *f.* after her lovers. *Hos* 2:7
if we *f.* on to know the Lord. 6:3
Master, I will *f.* thee. *Mat* 8:19 *Luke* 9:57, 61
these signs *f.* them. *Mark* 16:17

not after them, nor *f.* *Luke* 17:23
about him saw what would *f.* 22:49
a stranger will they not *f.* *John* 10:5
why cannot I *f.* thee now? 13:37
from Samuel, and that *f.* *Acts* 3:24
f. things that make for peace.
Rom 14:19
f. after charity. *1 Cor* 14:1
but I *f.* after. *Phil* 3:12*
f. that which is good. *1 Thes* 5:15
know how ye ought to *f.* *2 Thes* 3:7*
ourselves an ensample to you to *f.* 9*
some men they *f.* after. *1 Tim* 5:24
f. righteousness. 6:11; *2 Tim* 2:22
f. peace with all men. *Heb* 12:14
whose faith *f.* considering end. 13:7*
the glory that should *f.* *1 Pet* 1:11
that ye should *f.* his steps. 2:21
f. their pernicious ways. *2 Pet* 2:2
f. not that which is evil. *3 John* 11*
are they that *f.* Lamb. *Rev* 14:4
they may rest from their labours, and their works do *f.* them. 13

follow *him*

if Lord be God, *f. him.* *1 Ki* 18:21
suffered no man to *f. him.* *Mark* 5:37
out, and his disciples *f. him.* 6:1
f. him into the house. *Luke* 22:10
Mark 14:13
before, the sheep *f. him.* *John* 10:4

follow *me*

woman will not be willing to *f. me.*
Gen 24:5, 39
Ehud said, *f.* after *me.* *Judg* 3:24
bread, to the people that *f. me.* 8:5
handfuls for people that *f. me.*
1 Ki 20:10
f. me, I will bring you to. *2 Ki* 6:19
and mercy shall *f. me.* *Ps* 23:6
Jesus saith, *f. me,* I. *Mat* 4:19*
8:22; 9:9; *Mark* 2:14; *Luke* 5:27
take up his cross, *f. me.* *Mat* 16:24
Mark 8:34; 10:21; *Luke* 9:23
sell that thou hast, *f. me.* *Mat* 19:21
Luke 18:22
he said, *f. me.* *Luke* 9:59
John 1:43; 21:22
sheep hear my voice and *f. me.*
John 10:27
if any serve me, let him *f. me.* 12:26
thou canst not *f. me* now. 13:36
garment about thee, *f. me.* *Acts* 12:8

followed

Rebekah and her damsels *f.* the.
Gen 24:61
so commanded he all that *f.* 32:19
they have wholly *f.* the Lord.
Num 32:12; *Deut* 1:36
the men that *f.* Baal-peor. *Deut* 4:3
ark of the covenant *f.* *Josh* 6:8
but I wholly *f.* Lord. 14:8, 9, 14
forsook the Lord, *f.* other. *Judg* 2:12
cut down bough, *f.* Abimelech 9:49
f. hard after Philistines. *1 Sam* 14:22
Jesse's three sons *f.* Saul. 17:13, 14
Philistines *f.* Saul. 31:2; *2 Sam* 1:6
1 Chr 10:2
house of Judah *f.* David. *2 Sam* 2:10
king David himself *f.* the bier. 3:31
Ahithophel saw counsel was not *f.*
17:23
Israel *f.* Sheba the son of. 20:2
none *f.* house of David. *1 Ki* 12:20
of people *f.* Tibni, half *f.* 16:21, 22
forsaken Lord, thou hast *f.* 18:18
and the army which *f.* them. 20:19
no water for cattle that *f.* *2 Ki* 3:9
Elisha rose and *f.* her. 4:30
so Gehazi *f.* after Naaman. 5:21
Jehu *f.* after Ahaziah. 9:27
Jehoahaz *f.* sins of Jeroboam. 13:2
and they *f.* vanity. 17:15
players on instruments *f.* *Ps* 68:25
head looked, they *f.* it. *Ezek* 10:11
Lord took me as I *f.* *Amos* 7:15
women which *f.* Jesus. *Mat* 27:55
we left all and *f.* thee. *Mark* 10:28
Luke 18:28
they *f.* they were afraid. *Mark* 10:32
Peter *f.* afar off. *Luke* 22:54
religious proselytes *f.* *Acts* 13:43
the same *f.* Paul and us. 16:17

f. not after righteousness. *Rom* 9:30
who *f.* after law of righteousness. 31
drank that rock that *f.* *1 Cor* 10:4
diligently *f.* every good. *1 Tim* 5:10
not *f.* cunningly devised. *2 Pet* 1:16
was Death, and hell *f.* *Rev* 6:8
there *f.* hail and fire mingled. 8:7
and there *f.* another angel. 14:8
and the third angel *f.* them. 9

followed *him*

elders of Israel *f. him.* *Num* 16:25
and light persons *f. him.* *Judg* 9:4
and all people *f. him.* *1 Sam* 13:7
f. him a mess of meat. *2 Sam* 11:8
they left their nets and *f. him.*
Mat 4:20; *Mark* 1:18
left the ship and *f. him.* *Mat* 4:22
f. him great multitudes. 25; 8:1
12:15; 19:2; 20:29; *Mark* 2:15
5:24; *Luke* 23:27; *John* 6:2
when entered, his disciples *f. him.*
Mat 8:23; *Luke* 22:39
two blind men *f. him.* *Mat* 9:27
but Peter *f. him* afar off. 26:58
Mark 14:54
f. him a young man. *Mark* 14:51
forsook all and *f. him.* *Luke* 5:11, 28
said unto the people that *f. him.* 7:9
Peter went out and *f. him.* *Acts* 12:9
armies *f. him* on white. *Rev* 19:14

followed *me*

Caleb hath *f. me* fully. *Num* 14:24
have not wholly *f. me.* 32:11
David who *f. me* with all. *1 Ki* 14:8
of the guard which *f. me.* *Neh* 4:23
f. me, in the regeneration. *Mat* 19:28

followedst

thou *f.* not young men. *Ruth* 3:10

followers

I beseech you, be *f.* of me.
1 Cor 4:16*; 11:1*; *Phil* 3:17*
be ye *f.* of God as dear. *Eph* 5:1*
ye became *f.* of us and. *1 Thes* 1:6*
became *f.* of the churches. 2:14*
f. of them who through. *Heb* 6:12*
f. of that which is good. *1 Pet* 3:13*

followeth

that *f.* her be killed. *2 Ki* 11:15
2 Chr 23:14
my soul *f.* hard after. *Ps* 63:8
but he that *f.* vain persons.
Pr 12:11; 28:19
that *f.* righteousness. 15:9; 21:21
one loveth gifts and *f.* *Isa* 1:23
none *f.* thee to commit. *Ezek* 16:34
Ephraim feeds on wind, *f.* *Hos* 12:1
not up his cross and *f.* *Mat* 10:38
because he *f.* not us. *Mark* 9:38
Luke 9:49
f. me shall not walk in. *John* 8:12

following

by reason of famine *f.* *Gen* 41:31
turn away thy son from *f.* *Deut* 7:4
thou be not snared by *f.* them. 12:30
from *f.* the Lord. *Josh* 22:16, 18, 23
29; *1 Sam* 12:20; *2 Ki* 17:21
2 Chr 25:27; 34:33
corrupted in *f.* other. *Judg* 2:19
to return from *f.* after. *Ruth* 1:16
if ye continue *f.* Lord. *1 Sam* 12:14
went up from *f.* Philistines. 14:46
Saul is turned back from *f.* 15:11
Saul was returned from *f.* 24:1
Asahel turned not from *f.* Abner.
2 Sam 2:19, 30
bid people return from *f.* their. 26
I took thee from *f.* the sheep, to.
7:8; *1 Chr* 17:7; *Ps* 78:71
and they *f.* Adonijah. *1 Ki* 1:7
if you shall at all turn from *f.* 9:6
Ahab did abominably in *f.* 21:26
tell it to the generation *f.* *Ps* 48:13
in generation *f.* name be. 109:13
the word with signs *f.* *Mark* 16:20
to-morrow, and day *f.* *Luke* 13:33
Jesus turned, saw them *f.* *John* 1:38
the day *f.* 43
the day *f.* when the people. 6:22
seeth disciple Jesus loved *f.* 21:20
we came day *f.* unto. *Acts* 21:1, 18
night *f.* Lord stood by him. 23:11
gone astray, *f.* way of. *2 Pet* 2:15

folly

Shechem had wrought *f.* *Gen* 34:7
f. by playing the whore. *Deut* 22:21
because Achan wrought *f.* *Josh* 7:15
I pray you, do not this *f.* *Judg* 19:23
committed lewdness and *f.* in. 20:6
according to *f.* that they wrought. 10
Nabal his name, and *f.* *1 Sam* 25:25
do not thou this *f.* *2 Sam* 13:12
angels he charged with *f.* *Job* 4:18
God layeth not *f.* to them. 24:12
lest I deal with you after *f.* 42:8
their way is their *f.* *Ps* 49:13
let them not turn again to *f.* 85:8
in the greatness of his *f.* *Pr* 5:23
but a fool layeth open his *f.* 13:16
but the *f.* of fools is deceitful. 14:8
the simple inherit *f.* 18
foolishness of fools is *f.* 24
hasty of spirit exalteth *f.* 29
f. is joy to him destitute of. 15:21
the instruction of fools is *f.* 16:22
rather than a fool in his *f.* 17:12
is *f.* and shame to him. 18:13
not a fool according to his *f.* 26:4
answer a fool according to his *f.* 5
so a fool returneth to his *f.* 11
my heart to know wisdom and *f.*
Eccl 1:17
in my heart to lay hold on *f.* 2:3
turned to behold *f.* 12
wisdom excelleth *f.* 13
to know wickedness of *f.* 7:25
so doth a little *f.* him that. 10:1
f. is set in great dignity. 6
every mouth speaketh *f.* *Isa* 9:17
seen *f.* in the prophets of. *Jer* 23:13
bear with me a little in my *f.*
2 Cor 11:1
their *f.* shall be made. *2 Tim* 3:9

food

pleasant and that is good for *f.*
Gen 2:9
woman saw tree was good for *f.* 3:6
take thou to thee of all *f.* 6:21
gather all *f.* of those good. 41:35
came to buy *f.* 42:7, 10; 43:2, 4
20, 22; 44:25
take *f.* for the famine. 42:33*
commanded to fill sacks with *f.* 44:1
your *f.* and for *f.* for your. 47:24
her *f.* not be diminished. *Ex* 21:10
the *f.* of the offering. *Lev* 3:11, 16
all manner of trees for *f.* 19:23
eat holy things, it is his *f.* 22:7*
him *f.* and raiment. *Deut* 10:18
cursed that eateth *f.* *1 Sam* 14:24, 28
that master's son have *f.* to eat.
2 Sam 9:10*
my desire, in giving *f.* for. *1 Ki* 5:9
gave Hiram wheat for *f.* to his. 11
more than necessary *f.* *Job* 23:12
wilderness yieldeth *f.* for. 24:5†
provideth for raven *f.*? 38:41†
mountains bring him forth *f.* 40:20
man did eat angels' *f.* *Ps* 78:25*
he may bring forth *f.* out. 104:14
who giveth *f.* to all flesh. 136:25
Lord who giveth *f.* to the. 146:7
he giveth to the beast his *f.* 147:9
ant gathereth her *f.* in. *Pr* 6:8
much *f.* is in the tillage of. 13:23
goats' milk enough for thy *f.* 27:27
rain which leaveth no *f.* 28:3
feed me with *f.* convenient for. 30:8
she bringeth her *f.* from afar. 31:14†
I have diminished thine ordinary *f.*
Ezek 16:27
increase thereof shall be for *f.* 48:18
filling our hearts with *f.* *Acts* 14:17
minister bread for your *f.* *2 Cor* 9:10
having *f.* and raiment. *1 Tim* 6:8
and destitute of daily *f.* *Jas* 2:15

fool

I have played *f.* and. *1 Sam* 26:21
f. hath said in heart. *Ps* 14:1; 53:1
likewise the *f.* and brutish. 49:10
neither doth a *f.* understand. 92:6
prating *f.* shall fall. *Pr* 10:8, 10
it is a sport to a *f.* to do mischief. 23
the *f.* shall be servant to. 11:29*
way of a *f.* right in own eyes. 12:15*
a *f.'s* wrath is presently known. 16

but f. layeth open his folly. Pr 13:16
the f. rageth and is confident. 14:16
f. despiseth father's instruction. 15:5
speech becometh not a f. 17:7
than a hundred stripes into a f. 10
a bear meet a man rather than f. 12
price in hand of a f. to get. 16
begetteth a f. doth it to sorrow. 21
f. when he holdeth his peace. 28
f. hath no delight in understanding. 18:2
a f.'s lips enter into contention. 6
but every f. will be meddling. 20:3
answer not a f. 26:4
answer a f. 5
so is he that giveth honour to a f. 8
the great God rewardeth the f. 10
as a dog so a f. returneth to his. 11
but a f.'s wrath is heavier. 27:3
though thou bray a f. in a mortar. 22
f. uttereth all his mind. 29:11
f. walketh in darkness. Eccl 2:14
as it happeneth to the f. so. 15
of wise man more than of f. 16
whether he be wise or a f.? 19
the f. foldeth his hands. 4:5
a f.'s voice is known by. 5:3
hath wise more than the f.? 6:8
but a f.'s heart is at his left. 10:2
f. is full of words. 14
at his end he shall be a f. Jer 17:11
whosoever shall say, Thou f. shall be in danger. Mat 5:22
f., this night thy soul. Luke 12:20*
let him become a f. 1 Cor 3:18
thou f., that thou sowest is. 15:36*
no man think me a f. 2 Cor 11:16*
to glory, I shall not be a f. 12:6*
I am become a f. in glorying. 11*

as a **fool**

died Abner *as a f.* dieth? 2 Sam 3:33
as a f. to correction of. Pr 7:22
how dieth wise? *as the f.* Eccl 2:16
yet *as a f.* receive me. 2 Cor 11:16
I speak *as a f.* I am more. 23

for a **fool**

delight not seemly *for a f.* Pr 19:10
wisdom is too high *for a f.* 24:7
honour is not seemly *for a f.* 26:1
and a rod *for the f.'s* back. 3
for a f. when filled with meat. 30:22

is a **fool**

uttereth slander *is a f.* Pr 10:18
perverse in lips, and *is a f.* 19:1
in his own heart *is a f.* 28:26
he that *is a f.* walketh, saith to every one that he *is a f.* Eccl 10:3
the prophet *is a f.*, the. Hos 9:7

of a **fool**

way *of a f.* is right in. Pr 12:15
the father *of a f.* hath no joy. 17:21
eyes *of a f.* in ends of the earth. 24
speak not in the ears *of a f.* 23:9
a message by hand *of a f.* 26:6
more hope *of a f.* than. 12; 29:20
so laughter *of the f.* Eccl 7:6
lips *of a f.* will swallow. 10:12

foolish

thus requite Lord, O f.? Deut 32:6
provoke them with a f. nation. 21
Rom 10:19
speakest as one of f. Job 2:10
for wrath killeth the f. man. 5:2
I have seen the f. taking root. 3
the f. shall not stand. Ps 5:5*
make me not reproach of f. 39:8
for I was envious at the f. 73:3*
so f. was I and ignorant. 22*
. people have blasphemed. 74:18
emember how the f. man. 22
orsake the f. and live. Pr 9:6*
f. woman is clamorous. 13
. son is heaviness of his. 10:1
nouth of f. is near destruction. 14
ut the f. plucketh it down. 14:1
n the mouth of the f. is a rod. 3
o from presence of a f. man. 7
eart of the f. doeth not so. 15:7
man despiseth his mother. 20
f. son is a grief to his father. 17:25
f. son is the calamity of. 19:13
f. man spendeth a treasure. 21:20

wise man contendeth with f. Pr 29:9
better is a wise child than a f. king. Eccl 4:13
neither be thou f. 7:17
labour of the f. wearieth. 10:15
maketh knowledge f. Isa 44:25
for my people are f. Jer 4:22
surely these are poor, they are f. 5:4
hear now this, O f. people. 21
are altogether brutish and f. 10:8
seen vain and f. things. Lam 2:14
woe unto f. prophets. Ezek 13:3
instruments of a f. shepherd. Zech 11:15
likened unto a f. man. Mat 7:26
five virgins were wise, five f. 25:2
f. heart was darkened. Rom 1:21*
an instructor of the f. 2:20
hath not God made f.? 1 Cor 1:20
O f. Galatians, who? Gal 3:1
are ye so f.? having begun. 3
filthiness, nor f. talking. Eph 5:4
be rich fall into f. lusts. 1 Tim 6:9
but f. questions avoid. 2 Tim 2:23
Tit 3:9
were sometimes f. deceived. Tit 3:3
put to silence ignorance of f. men. 1 Pet 2:15

foolishly

thou hast now done f. Gen 31:28
1 Sam 13:13; 2 Chr 16:9
wherein we have done f. Num 12:11
I have done very f. 2 Sam 24:10
1 Chr 21:8
not, nor charged God f. Job 1:22
said to fools, deal not f. Ps 75:4
soon angry dealeth f. Pr 14:17
if thou hast done f. in lifting. 30:32
I speak it as it were f. 2 Cor 11:17
I speak f. I am bold also. 21

foolishness

of Ahithophel into f. 2 Sam 15:31
stink because of my f. Ps 38:5
thou knowest my f. 69:5
of fools proclaimeth f. Pr 12:23
but the f. of fools is folly. 14:24
mouth of fools poureth out f. 15:2
mouth of fools feedeth on f. 14
the f. of man perverteth way. 19:3
f. is bound in heart of child. 22:15
the thought of f. is sin. 24:9
yet will not his f. depart. 27:22
know wickedness of f. Eccl 7:25
of the words of his mouth is f. 10:13
thefts, pride, f. come. Mark 7:22
preaching of cross to them that perish f. 1 Cor 1:18
pleased God by f. of preaching. 21
Christ crucified, to the Greeks f. 23
because the f. of God is wiser. 25
of Spirit of God are f. to him. 2:14
wisdom of world is f. with God. 3:19

fools

be as one of the f. in. 2 Sam 13:13
he maketh the judges f. Job 12:17
they were children of f. 30:8
I said to f. deal not. Ps 75:4*
ye f. when will ye be wise? 94:8
f. because of transgression. 107:17
but f. despise wisdom. Pr 1:7*
how long, f. hate knowledge? 22
prosperity of f. destroy them. 32
shame be the promotion of f. 3:35
ye f. be ye of an understanding. 8:5
f. die for want of wisdom. 10:21*
heart of f. proclaimeth. 12:23
abomination to f. to depart. 13:19
companion of f. be destroyed. 20
folly of f. is deceit. 14:8
f. make a mock at sin. 9*
foolishness of f. is folly. 24
what is in the midst of f. is. 33
mouth of f. poureth foolishness. 15:2
mouth of f. feedeth on foolishness. 14
instruction of f. is folly. 16:22
stripes are prepared for f. 19:29
a parable in mouth of f. 26:7, 9
than give sacrifice of f. Eccl 5:1
he hath no pleasure in f. 4
heart of f. is in house of. 7:4
than for man to hear the song of f. 5
anger resteth in the bosom of f. 9
of him that ruleth among f. 9:17

princes of Zoan are f. Isa 19:11*, 13
wayfaring men, though f. 35:8
ye f. and blind. Mat 23:17, 19
ye f. did not he that? Luke 11:40*
O f. and slow of heart to. 24:25*
wise, they became f. Rom 1:22
we are f. for Christ's. 1 Cor 4:10
for ye suffer f. gladly. 2 Cor 11:19*
that ye walk not as f. Eph 5:15*

foot

thee no man lift up his f. Gen 41:44
six hundred thousand on f. Ex 12:37
give f. for f. 21:24; Deut 19:21
shalt make a laver of brass and his f. 30:18, 28; 31:9*; 35:16*; 38:8* 39:39*; 40:11*; Lev 8:11*
leprosy cover from head to f. Lev 13:12
ass crushed Balaam's f. Num 22:25
nor did thy f. swell. Deut 8:4
and wateredst it with thy f. 11:10
loose his shoe from off his f. 25:9
shoe not waxen old upon thy f. 29:5
their f. shall slide in due. 32:35
let Asher dip his f. in oil. 33:24
every place your f. Josh 1:3
loose thy shoe from off thy f. 5:15
Barak was sent on f. to. Judg 5:15
Asahel was as light of f. as a roe. 2 Sam 2:18
every f. six toes. 21:20; 1 Chr 20:6
trod Jezebel under f. 2 Ki 9:33
any more remove the f. 2 Chr 33:8
my f. hath held his steps. Job 23:11
even waters forgotten of the f. 28:4
or if my f. hath hasted to. 31:5
forgetteth that f. may crush. 39:15
in net they hid is their f. Ps 9:15
my f. standeth in even place. 26:12
let not the f. of pride come. 36:11
when my f. slippeth. 38:16
went through the flood on f. 66:6
thy f. be dipped in blood. 68:23
lest thou dash thy f. against a stone. 91:12; Mat 4:6; Luke 4:11
I said my f. slippeth, thy. Ps 94:18
not suffer thy f. to be moved. 121:3
refrain thy f. from their. Pr 1:15
safely, thy f. shall not stumble. 3:23
the Lord shall keep thy f. from. 26
remove thy f. from. 4:27
withdraw thy f. from thy. 25:17
is like f. out of joint. 19
keep thy f. when goest. Eccl 5:1
mountains tread under f. Isa 14:25
meted out trodden under f. 18:7*
off thy shoe from off thy f. 20:2
the f. shall tread it down. 26:6
called righteous man to his f. 41:2
if thou turn away thy f. from. 58:13
withhold thy f. from. Jer 2:25
trodden my portion under f. 12:10
hath trodden under f. Lam 1:15*
stamp with thy f. and. Ezek 6:11
no f. of man, no f. of beast. 29:11
neither shall the f. of man. 32:13
give host to be trodden under f. Dan 8:13
that is swift of f. shall. Amos 2:15
salt trodden under f. of. Mat 5:13
the people followed him on f. 14:13
if thy f. offend thee. 18:8; Mark 9:45
bind him hand and f. Mat 22:13
many ran a f. thither. Mark 6:33
forth bound hand and f. John 11:44
so much as to set his f. on. Acts 7:5
minding himself to go a-f. 20:13
if the f. say, because I. 1 Cor 12:15
trodden under f. the Son. Heb 10:29
with a garment to the f. Rev 1:13
holy city shall tread under f. 11:2

sole of **foot**

no rest for *sole of* her f. Gen 8:9
a botch from *sole of* f. Deut 28:35
not set *sole of* her f. on ground. 56
nor the *sole of* thy f. have rest. 65
sole of your f. shall tread. Josh 1:3
Absalom, from *sole of* f. 2 Sam 14:25
with boils from *sole of* f. Job 2:7
from *sole of* f. to head. Isa 1:6
sole of f. like *sole of* a calf's f. Ezek 1:7

left **foot**
he set his *left f.* upon. *Rev* 10:2
right **foot**
he set his *right f.* on sea. *Rev* 10:2
foot breadth
not so much as *f. breadth. Deut* 2:5*
footed
whatsoever is cloven *f.* *Lev* 11:3
though he be cloven *f.* is unclean. 7
a man that is broken *f.* shall. 21:19
all manner of four *f.* beasts.
Acts 10:12; 11:6
birds and four *f.* beasts. *Rom* 1:23
footmen
six hundred thousand *f. Num* 11:21
Saul said to the *f.* *1 Sam* 22:17*
if thou hast run with *f.* and. *Jer* 12:5
footsteps
up my goings that my *f.* *Ps* 17:5*
thy way is in sea, thy *f.* are. 77:19
they reproached the *f.* of. 89:51
go thy way by the *f.* of. *S of S* 1:8
footstool
an house for *f.* of our. *1 Chr* 28:2
six steps to throne with *f.* of gold.
2 Chr 9:18
worship at his *f.* *Ps* 99:5; 132:7
hand till I make thine enemies thy *f.*
110:1; *Mat* 22:44; *Mark* 12:36
Luke 20:43; *Acts* 2:35; *Heb* 1:13
earth is my *f.* *Isa* 66:1; *Acts* 7:49
remembered not his *f.* *Lam* 2:1
swear not by earth, his *f.* *Mat* 5:35
enemies be made his *f.* *Heb* 10:13
poor, sit here under my *f.* *Jas* 2:3
for
all things we call on him *f. Deut* 4:7
all Joab had sent him *f. 2 Sam* 11:22
f. piece of bread that. *Pr* 28:21
f. he maketh his sun to. *Mat* 5:45
to be heard *f.* much speaking. 6:7
f. I was hungry, and ye. 25:35, 42
we received grace *f.* *John* 1:16
f. f. this cause ye pay. *Rom* 13:6
f. we know, if this house. *2 Cor* 5:1
f. we can do nothing against but *f.*
the truth. 13:8
looking *f.* the coming of. *2 Pet* 3:12
forasmuch
f. as God hath shewed. *Gen* 41:39
f. as he hath no inheritance with.
Deut 12:12
f. as the Lord hath taken. *Judg* 11:36
f. as we have sworn. *1 Sam* 20:42
f. as my lord is come. *2 Sam* 19:30
f. as thou hast disobeyed. *1 Ki* 13:21
f. as Reuben defiled. *1 Chr* 5:1
f. as this people draw. *Isa* 29:13
f. as there is none like. *Jer* 10:6
f. among all wise men of nations. 7
f. as iron breaketh. *Dan* 2:40
f. as he also is son of. *Luke* 19:9
f. then as God gave them. *Acts* 11:17
f. then as we are offspring. 17:29
f. as I know that thou hast. 24:10
f. as he is the image. *1 Cor* 11:7
f. as ye are zealous of. 14:12*
f. as ye know your labour is. 15:58
f. as we know ye were. *1 Pet* 1:18
f. then as Christ suffered for us. 4:1
forbad
whatsoever Lord *f.* us. *Deut* 2:37
but John *f.* him, saying. *Mat* 3:14*
casting out devils in thy name, we *f.*
him. *Mark* 9:38; *Luke* 9:49
the ass *f.* the madness. *2 Pet* 2:16*
forbare
escaped, and Saul *f.* *1 Sam* 23:13
then the prophet *f.* and. *2 Chr* 25:16
Ishmael *f.* and slew. *Jer* 41:8
forbear
if see his ass, and would *f. Ex* 23:5
if thou shalt *f.* to vow. *Deut* 23:22
shall I go, or *f.*? *1 Ki* 22:6
2 Chr 18:5, 14
f. why shouldest thou be smitten?
2 Chr 25:16
f. thee from meddling with 35:21
many years didst thou *f. Neh* 9:30*
and though I *f.* what? *Job* 16:6
thou *f.* to deliver them. *Pr* 24:11*
seem ill to thee to come, *f. Jer* 40:4
whether they will hear or *f.*
Ezek 2:5, 7; 3:11
he that forbeareth, let him *f.* 3:27
f. to cry, make no mourning. 24:17*
give me my price, if *f.* *Zech* 11:12
have not we power to *f.*? *1 Cor* 9:6
f. lest any should think. *2 Cor* 12:6
we could no longer *f.* *1 Thes* 3:1
forbearance
thou the riches of his *f.*? *Rom* 2:4
of sins, through the *f.* of God. 3:25
forbeareth
that *f.* keep passover. *Num* 9:13
he that *f.* let him forbear. *Ezek* 3:27
forbearing
by long *f.* is prince. *Pr* 25:15
I was weary with *f.* *Jer* 20:9
f. one another in love. *Eph* 4:2
Col 3:13
do the same things, *f.* *Eph* 6:9
forbid
my lord Moses, *f.* *Num* 11:28
Lord *f.* I should do. *1 Sam* 24:6
f. I should stretch forth hand. 26:11
Naboth said, the Lord *f.* *1 Ki* 21:3
my God *f.* it me. *1 Chr* 11:19
Jesus said, *f.* him not. *Mark* 9:39
Luke 9:50
suffer little children, and *f.* them not.
Mark 10:14; *Luke* 18:16
f. not to take coat also. *Luke* 6:29*
can any *f.* water? *Acts* 10:47
f. none acquaintance to come. 24:23
f. not to speak with. *1 Cor* 14:39
God **forbid**
(*American Revision renders this* far be it from me)
God f. Gen 44:7, 17; *Josh* 22:29
24:16; *1 Sam* 12:23; 14:45; 20:2
Job 27:5; *Luke* 20:16; *Rom* 3:4, 6
31; 6:2, 15; 7:7, 13; 9:14; 11:1
11; *1 Cor* 6:15; *Gal* 2:17; 3:21
6:14
forbidden
commit any of things *f.* *Lev* 5:17*
of what Lord hath *f.* *Deut* 4:23
and were *f.* to preach the. *Acts* 16:6
forbiddeth
f. them that would. *3 John* 10
forbidding
f. to give tribute to. *Luke* 23:2
preaching kingdom of God, no man *f.*
Acts 28:31
f. us to speak to the. *1 Thes* 2:16
f. to marry. *1 Tim* 4:3
forborn
men of Babylon *f.* to. *Jer* 51:30
force
wouldest take by *f.* *Gen* 31:31
nor was his natural *f.* *Deut* 34:7
if not, I will take it by *f. 1 Sam* 2:16
made them to cease by *f.* *Ezra* 4:23
by great *f.* of my disease. *Job* 30:18
and his *f.* is in the navel. 40:16
out their blood by *f.* *Jer* 18:21*
and their *f.* is not right. 23:10
under shadow, because of *f.* 48:45*
with *f.* and cruelty have. *Ezek* 34:4
hast shed blood by *f.* of. 35:5*
shall not strengthen his *f. Amos* 2:14
violent take it by *f.* *Mat* 11:12
would take him by *f.* *John* 6:15
to take Paul by *f.* *Acts* 23:10
for a testament is of *f.* *Heb* 9:17
force, *verb*
if the man *f.* her and. *Deut* 22:25
brother, do not *f.* me. *2 Sam* 13:12
will he *f.* the queen? *Esth* 7:8
forced
Ammonites *f.* children. *Judg* 1:34
my concubine have they *f.* 20:5
I *f.* myself therefore. *1 Sam* 13:12
Amnon *f.* Tamar and. *2 Sam* 13:14
hated Amnon, because he *f.* his. 22
determined from day he *f.* his. 32
flattering of lips she *f.* *Pr* 7:21
forces
placed *f.* in fenced. *2 Chr* 17:2
will not esteem all the *f.* *Job* 36:19
the *f.* of the Gentiles. *Isa* 60:5*
men may bring to thee the *f.* 11*
the captains of the *f.* that. *Jer* 40:7
13; 41:11, 13, 16; 42:1, 8; 43:4, 5
a multitude of great *f.* *Dan* 11:10
in his estate honour God of *f.* 38*
carried away captive his *f.* *Ob* 11*
forcible
how *f.* right words. *Job* 6:25
forcing
not destroy trees by *f.* *Deut* 20:19*
so the *f.* of wrath. *Pr* 30:33
ford, -s
Jacob passed over the *f.* *Gen* 32:22
men pursued spies to *f.* *Josh* 2:7
Israel took the *f.* of. *Judg* 3:28
daughters of Moab at *f.* *Isa* 16:2
forecast
shall *f.* devices. *Dan* 11:24*, 25*
forefathers
the iniquities of their *f.* *Jer* 11:10
whom I serve from my *f. 2 Tim* 1:3
forefront
six curtains in the *f.* *Ex* 26:9
on the *f.* of the mitre it shall. 28:37
upon his *f.* did he put. *Lev* 8:9*
f. of one rock was. *1 Sam* 14:5*
set Uriah in the *f.* of. *2 Sam* 11:15
the brazen altar from *f.* *2 Ki* 16:14
Jehoshaphat in the *f.* *2 Chr* 20:27
f. of lower gate to *f.* of. *Ezek* 40:19
the *f.* of the house stood. 47:1
forehead
plate shall be on Aaron's *f. Ex* 28:38
he is *f.* bald: yet is he. *Lev* 13:41
a leprosy sprung up in bald *f.* 42
if rising be reddish in bald *f.* 43
smote the Philistine in *f.*, stone sunk
in his *f.* *1 Sam* 17:49
leprosy rose up in Uzziah's *f.*
2 Chr 26:19
behold he was leprous in his *f.* 20
thou hadst a whore's *f.* *Jer* 3:3
have made thy *f.* strong. *Ezek* 3:8
harder than flint have made thy *f.* 9
put a jewel upon thy *f.* and. 16:12*
mark of beast in his *f.* *Rev* 14:9
and upon her *f.* was a name. 17:5
foreheads
forehead strong against their *f.*
Ezek 3:8
set a mark on the *f.* of them. 9:4
sealed servants of God in their *f.*
Rev 7:3
not seal of God in their *f.* 9:4
all to receive mark in their *f.* 13:16
Father's name written in their *f.* 14:1
received the mark upon their *f.* 20:4
his name shall be in their *f.* 22:4
foreigner
f. and hired servant not. *Ex* 12:45*
of a *f.* thou mayest. *Deut* 15:3
foreigners
in the day that *f.* entered. *Ob* 11
no more strangers and *f. Eph* 2:19*
foreknew
away people which he *f.* *Rom* 11:2
foreknow
whom he did *f.* he also. *Rom* 8:29
foreknowledge
being delivered by the *f.* *Acts* 2:23
elect according to *f.* of. *1 Pet* 1:2
foremost
Jacob commanded the *f. Gen* 32:17
put handmaids and children *f.* 33:2
the running of the *f.* is. *2 Sam* 18:27
foreordained
who verily was *f.* *1 Pet* 1:20*
forepart
two rings towards *f.* of. *Ex* 28:27
39:20
the oracle in the *f.* *1 Ki* 6:20*
wall on *f.* of chambers. *Ezek* 42:7
the *f.* of ship stuck. *Acts* 27:41*
forerunner
whither the *f.* is for us. *Heb* 6:20
foresaw
I *f.* the Lord always. *Acts* 2:25

foreseeing
the scripture f. God. Gal 3:8

foreseeth
a prudent man f. the evil. Pr 22:3*
27:12*

foreship
cast anchors out of f. Acts 27:30

foreskin
circumcise flesh of your f. Gen 17:11
flesh of his f. is not circumcised. 14
circumcised flesh of their f. 23, 24, 25
Zipporah cut off the f. Ex 4:25
the flesh of his f. shall. Lev 12:3
circumcise therefore f. Deut 10:16
let thy f. be uncovered. Hab 2:16*

foreskins
circumcised Israel at hill of the f.
Josh 5:3
but an hundred f. of. 1 Sam 18:25
David brought their f. 27
to me for an hundred f. 2 Sam 3:14
take away f. of your heart. Jer 4:4

forest
David came into the f. 1 Sam 22:5
Solomon built house of f. 1 Ki 7:2
them in the house of the f. 10:17
2 Chr 9:16
into the f. of his Carmel. 2 Ki 19:23
Isa 37:24
Asaph, keeper of king's f. Neh 2:8
every beast of the f. is. Ps 50:10
wherein all beasts of the f. 104:20
kindle in thickets of f. Isa 9:18
shall consume glory of his f. 10:18
the rest of the trees of his f. 19
in the f. of Arabia ye lodge. 21:13
didst look to armour of the f. 22:8
field be esteemed as a f. 29:17
32:15
hail, coming down on the f. 32:19
cypress from among trees of f. 44:14
break forth into singing, O f. 23
all ye beasts of the f. come. 56:9
a lion out of f. shall slay. Jer 5:6
one cutteth a tree out of f. 10:3
heritage is to me as a lion in f. 12:8
I will kindle a fire in the f. 21:14
become as high places of the f.
26:18; Mi 3:12
they shall cut down her f. Jer 46:23
vine tree among the trees of the f.
Ezek 15:6
prophesy against the f. of the. 20:46
say unto the f. of the south. 47
I will make them a f. Hos 2:12
will lion roar in the f.? Amos 3:4
as lion among beasts of the f. Mi 5:8
the f. of the vintage is. Zech 11:2

forests
Jotham built castles in f. 2 Chr 27:4
voice of the Lord discovereth the f.
Ps 29:9
cut down thickets of the f. Isa 10:34
cut down any out of f. Ezek 39:10

foretell
I f. you as if I were. 2 Cor 13:2*

foretold
I have f. you all things. Mark 13:23
prophets have likewise f. Acts 3:24*

forewarn
but I will f. you whom. Luke 12:5*

forewarned
as we also have f. you. 1 Thes 4:6

forfeited
his substance should be f. Ezra 10:8

forgat
remember Joseph, but f. Gen 40:23
children of Israel f. Lord. Judg 3:7
and when they f. Lord. 1 Sam 12:9
and they f. his works. Ps 78:11
soon f. his works. 106:13
. God their Saviour. 21
ar from peace, I f. Lam 3:17
after her lovers and f. me. Hos 2:13

forgave
e f. their iniquity. Ps 78:38
loosed him, and f. him. Mat 18:27
f. thee all that debt. 32
e frankly f. them. Luke 7:42
e to whom he f. most. 43

if I f. any thing to whom I f. it for
your sakes f. I it in. 2 Cor 2:10
even as Christ f. you. Col 3:13

forgavest
thou f. the iniquity of. Ps 32:5
thou wast a God that f. them. 99:8

forged
the proud have f. a lie. Ps 119:69

forgers
ye are f. of lies, are all. Job 13:4

forget
till he f. that which thou. Gen 27:45
for God hath made me f. 41:51
lest thou f. the things. Deut 4:9
lest ye f. covenant of the Lord. 23
the Lord will not f. the covenant. 31
lest thou f. Lord. 6:12; 8:11, 14, 19
f. not how thou provokedst. 9:7
out Amalek, thou shalt not f. 25:19
if thou wilt not f. thine. 1 Sam 1:11
covenant I made ye shall not f.
2 Ki 17:38
paths of all that f. God. Job 8:13
if I say, I will f. my complaint. 9:27
thou shalt f. thy misery. 11:16
the womb shall f. him. 24:20
all the nations that f. God. Ps 9:17
O Lord, f. not the humble. 10:12
how long wilt thou f. me ? 13:1
f. also thine own people. 45:10
consider this, ye that f. God. 50:22
lest my people f.: scatter. 59:11
f. not the congregation of thy. 74:19
f. not the voice of thine enemies. 23
might not f. the works of God. 78:7
so that I f. to eat my bread. 102:4
f. not all his benefits. 103:2
I will not f. thy word. 119:16
do I not f. thy statutes. 83, 109, 141
I will never f. thy precepts. 93
for I do not f. thy law. 153
I do not f. thy commandments. 176
if I f. thee let my hand f. 137:5
my son, f. not my law. Pr 3:1
wisdom, get understanding, f. 4:5
lest they drink and f. the law. 31:5
let him drink and f. poverty. 7
f. her sucking child ? yea, they may f.
yet will I not f. thee. Isa 49:15
shalt f. the shame of thy youth. 54:4
they that f. my holy mountain. 65:11
can maid f. ornaments ? Jer 2:32
think to cause my people to f. 23:27
I, even I, will utterly f. you. 39
thou f. us for ever ? Lam 5:20
forgotten law, I will also f. Hos 4:6
never f. any of their works. Amos 8:7
is not unrighteous to f. Heb 6:10
good and communicate f. not. 13:16

forgetful
not f. to entertain. Heb 13:2
he be not a f. hearer. Jas 1:25

forgetfulness
righteousness in land of f. Ps 88:12

forgettest
f. thou our affliction ? Ps 44:24
and f. the Lord thy maker. Isa 51:13

forgetteth
and f. that the foot. Job 39:15
he f. not the cry of. Ps 9:12
f. the covenant of her God. Pr 2:17
f. what manner of man. Jas 1:24

forgetting
f. those things behind. Phil 3:13

forgive
f. I pray, the trespass, f. the trespass
of servants of God. Gen 50:17
f. I pray thee, my sin. Ex 10:17
if thou wilt f. their sin. 32:32
Lord shall f. her. Num 30:5, 8, 12
he will not f. your sins. Josh 24:19
I pray, f. the trespass. 1 Sam 25:28
when thou hearest, f. 1 Ki 8:30, 39
2 Chr 6:21, 30
f. the sin of thy people. 1 Ki 8:34
f. the sin of thy servants. 36
2 Chr 6:25, 27, 39
f. thy people have sinned. 1 Ki 8:50
then will I hear and f. 2 Chr 7:14
look on my pain, and f. Ps 25:18
Lord, art good and ready to f. 86:5

man boweth, therefore f. Isa 2:9
f. not their iniquity nor. Jer 18:23
for I will f. their iniquity. 31:34
that I may f. their iniquity. 36:3
O Lord f. Lord hearken. Dan 9:19
O Lord God, f. I beseech. Amos 7:2
f. us, as we f. our debtors.
Mat 6:12; Luke 11:4
f. men trespasses, Father will f.
Mat 6:14
if ye f. not, nor will your Father f. 15
hath power to f. sin. 9:6
Mark 2:10; Luke 5:24
how oft my brother sin, and I f. him ?
Mat 18:21
if ye from your hearts f. not. 35
who can f. sins but God only ?
Mark 2:7; Luke 5:21
f. that your Father may f. you.
Mark 11:25
not f. your Father will not f. 26
f. and ye shall be. Luke 6:37*
if thy brother repent, f. him. 17:3, 4
Father, f. them, they know. 23:34
ye ought rather to f. 2 Cor 2:7
to whom ye f. any thing, I f. also. 10
not burdensome, f. me this. 12:13
faithful and just to f. 1 John 1:9

forgiven
atonement, and it shall be f. them.
Lev 4:20, 26, 31, 35; 5:10, 13, 16
18; 6:7; 19:22; Num 15:25, 26
28; Deut 21:8
thou hast f. from Egypt. Num 14:19
blessed, whose transgression is f.
Ps 32:1; Rom 4:7
hast f. the iniquity of thy. Ps 85:2
the people shall be f. Isa 33:24
cheer, thy sins be f. Mat 9:2, 5
Mark 2:5, 9; Luke 5:20, 23; 7:48
blasphemy be f.; against Holy Ghost
not be f. Mat 12:31, 32
Mark 3:28; Luke 12:10
their sins be f. them. Mark 4:12
forgive, and ye shall be f. Luke 6:37
sins are f. but to whom little is f. 7:47
of heart may be f. thee. Acts 8:22
for Christ's sake hath f. Eph 4:32
he quickened, having f. Col 2:13
sins, they shall be f. him. Jas 5:15
because your sins are f. 1 John 2:12

forgiveness
f. with thee that be. Ps 130:4
hath never f. but is in. Mark 3:29
God exalted to give f. Acts 5:31*
him is preached unto you f. 13:38*
to God, that they receive f. 26:18*
in whom we have f. of. Eph 1:7
Col 1:14

forgivenesses
God belong mercies and f. Dan 9:9

forgiveth
heals thy diseases, who f. Ps 103:3
say, who is this f. sins ? Luke 7:49

forgiving
f. iniquity, transgression. Ex 34:7
Num 14:18
forbearing, f. one another.
Eph 4:32; Col 3:13

forgot
and hast f. a sheaf in. Deut 24:19

forgotten
all the plenty shall be f. Gen 41:30
nor have I f. them. Deut 26:13
not be f. out of mouths. 31:21
hast f. God that formed thee. 32:18
familiar friends have f. Job 19:14
flood breaks out, even waters f. 28:4
needy shall not alway be f. Ps 9:18
said in his heart, God hath f. 10:11
I am f. as a dead man. 31:12
rock, why hast thou f. me ? 42:9
is come, yet have we not f. 44:17
if we have f. name of our God. 20
hath God f. to be gracious ? 77:9
I have not f. thy law. 119:61
because mine enemies have f. 139
days to come all be f. Eccl 2:16
and the wicked were f. in the. 8:10
for the memory of them is f. 9:5
thou hast f. God of thy. Isa 17:10
Tyre shall be f. seventy years. 23:15

thou harlot that hast been f. Isa 23:16
thou shalt not be f. of me. 44:21
my Lord hath f. me. 49:14
the former troubles are f. 65:16
my people have f. me. Jer 2:32
13:25; 18:15
have f. the Lord their God. 3:21
confusion never be f. 20:11; 23:40
as their fathers have f. my. 23:27
all thy lovers have f. thee. 30:14
f. wickedness of your fathers. 44:9
covenant that shall not be f. 50:5
they turned away, have f. 6
caused Sabbath to be f. Lam 2:6
thou hast f. me. Ezek 22:12
because thou hast f. me. 23:35
seeing thou hast f. the law. Hos 4:6
for Israel hath f. Maker. 8:14
exalted, therefore have f. me. 13:6
they had f. to take bread. Mat 16:5
Mark 8:14
and not one of them is f. Luke 12:6
have f. the exhortation. Heb 12:5
f. that he was purged. 2 Pet 1:9

forks

they had a file for f. 1 Sam 13:21

form

the earth was without f. Gen 1:2*
what f. is he of ? 1 Sam 28:14
about this f. of speech. 2 Sam 14:20*
I could not discern f. Job 4:16*
his f. more than sons of. Isa 52:14
he hath no f. nor comeliness. 53:2
and, lo, it was without f. Jer 4:23*
appeared the f. of man's. Ezek 10:8
shew them the f. of the house. 43:11
and the f. of his visage. Dan 3:19
the f. of the fourth is like the. 25*
appeared in another f. Mark 16:12
hast f. of knowledge. Rom 2:20
ye have obeyed that f. of. 6:17
who being in the f. of God. Phil 2:6
took upon him the f. of a servant. 7
hold fast f. of sound. 2 Tim 1:13
having f. of godliness. 3:5

formed

the Lord God f. man of. Gen 2:7
out of the ground God f. every. 19
forgotten God that f. Deut 32:18*
I have f. it. 2 Ki 19:25; Isa 37:26
dead things are f. from. Job 26:5*
hand hath f. crooked serpent. 13*
I also am f. out of the clay. 33:6
or ever thou hadst f. earth. Ps 90:2
he that f. the eye. 94:9
sea is his, his hands f. the. 95:5
the great God that f. all. Pr 26:10*
he that f. them will shew. Isa 27:11
thus saith he that f. thee. 43:1
I have f. him, yea, I have. 7
before me there was no god f. nor. 10
this people have I f. for myself. 21
that made thee, and f. thee 44:2
who hath f. a god ? 10*
art my servant, I have f. thee. 21
thus saith he that f. thee. 24
I f. the light and create. 45:7
God that f. the earth, he f. it. 18
Lord that f. me from womb to. 49:5
no weapon f. against thee. 54:17
before I f. thee I knew. Jer 1:5
Lord that f. it to establish it. 33:2
behold, he f. grasshoppers. Amos 7:1
shall the thing f. say to him that f. it?
Rom 9:20
in birth, till Christ be f. in. Gal 4:19
Adam was first f., then. 1 Tim 2:13

former

deliver cup after the f. Gen 40:13
fought against the f. king of Moab.
Num 21:26
her f. husband which. Deut 24:4
was the manner in f. time. Ruth 4:7
answered after the f. 1 Sam 17:30
the two captains of f. 2 Ki 1:14
do after the f. manner. 17:34, 40
the f. governors were. Neh 5:15
inquire, I pray, of f. age. Job 8:8
the wilderness in f. time. 30:3*
O remember not f. iniquities.
Ps 79:8
where are thy f. loving-? 89:49

no remembrance of f. Eccl 1:11
f. days were better than these. 7:10
shew the f. things. Isa 41:22; 43:9
the f. things are come to pass. 42:9
remember ye not the f. 43:18
remember f. things of old. 46:9
I have declared f. things. 48:3
raise up the f. desolations. 61:4
I will measure their f. work. 65:7*
the f. troubles are forgotten. 16
f. shall not be remembered. 17
that giveth the f. and latter rain.
Jer 5:24; Hos 6:3; Joel 2:23
is f. of all things. Jer 10:16; 51:19
the f. kings before thee. 34:5
write in it all the f. words. 36:28
thy daughter return to f. Ezek 16:55
multitude greater than f. Dan 11:13
but it shall not be as the f. or. 29
glory greater than of the f. Hag 2:9
the f. prophets have cried. Zech 1:4
7:7, 12
not be to people as in f. days. 8:11
waters go half toward the f. 14:8*
pleasant to Lord as in f. Mal 3:4*
the f. treatise have I made. Acts 1:1
concerning f. conversation. Eph 4:22
not according to f. lusts. 1 Pet 1:14
f. things are passed. Rev 21:4*

formeth

lo, he that f. mountains. Amos 4:13
and f. the spirit of man. Zech 12:1

fornication

This word is taken [1] *For the sin of impurity,* Mat 5:32; 1 Cor 7:2. [2] *For the sin of idolatry, which is infidelity to and forsaking of the true God for false gods,* 2 Chr 21:11.

caused Jerusalem to commit f.
2 Chr 21:11
Tyre shall commit f. with. Isa 23:17
hast multiplied thy f. Ezek 16:29
saving for cause of f. Mat 5:32; 19:9
we be not born of f. John 8:41
that they abstain from f. Acts 15:20
29; 21:25
being filled with all f. Rom 1:29
f. among you, and such f. 1 Cor 5:1
the body is not for f. but for. 6:13
flee f. 18
nevertheless, to avoid f. 7:2
not repented of their f. 2 Cor 12:21
works of the flesh, f. Gal 5:19
f. let it not be named. Eph 5:3
mortify therefore f. Col 3:5
will of God that ye abstain from f.
1 Thes 4:3
cities giving themselves over to f.
Jude 7
space to repent of her f. Rev 2:21
neither repented they of their f. 9:21
the wine of wrath of her f. 14:8
made drunk with wine of her f. 17:2
golden cup full of filthiness of f. 4
with wine of wrath of her f. 18:3
did corrupt earth with her f. 19:2

fornications

pouredst out thy f. on. Ezek 16:15
out of heart proceed f. thefts.
Mat 15:19; Mark 7:22

see **commit, committed**

fornicator

called a brother be a f. 1 Cor 5:11
lest there be any f. or. Heb 12:16

fornicators

you not to company with f. 1 Cor 5:9
yet not altogether with the f. of. 10
nor shall f. inherit the kingdom. 6:9

forsake

this people will f. me. Deut 31:16
in that day I will f. them. 17
God forbid we should f. Josh 24:16
if ye f. the Lord and serve. 20
should I f. my sweetness? Judg 9:11*
I will f. remnant of. 2 Ki 21:14*
if thou f. him, cast thee. 1 Chr 28:9
if ye turn away, and f. 2 Chr 7:19
but if ye f. him, he will f. you. 15:2
wrath is against them that f. him.
Ezra 8:22
father and mother f. me. Ps 27:10
cease from anger and f. wrath. 37:8

if his children f. my law. Ps 89:30
will he f. his inheritance. 94:14
because wicked f. law. 119:53
let not mercy and truth f. Pr 3:3
f. the foolish, and live. 9:6*
they that f. the law. 28:4
they that f. the Lord. Isa 1:28
let wicked f. his way. 55:7
ye are they that f. Lord. 65:11
all that f. the Lord. Jer 17:13
I will even f. you. 23:33*, 39*
f. her, and let us go every one. 51:9
wherefore dost thou f.? Lam 5:20
that f. the holy covenant. Dan 11:30
f. their own mercy. Jonah 2:8
teachest the Jews to f. Acts 21:21

forsake *not*

thou f. *not* the Levite. Deut 12:19
wickedness and f. it *not*. Job 20:13*
f. me *not*, O. Ps 38:21; 71:9, 18
thy statutes, O f. me *not*. 119:8
f. *not* works of thine own. 138:8
f. *not* law of mother. Pr 1:8; 6:20
good doctrine, f. ye *not* my. 4:2
f. her *not*, she shall preserve thee. 6
and father's friend f. *not*. 27:10

not **forsake**

he will *not* f. thee. Deut 4:31*
31:6, 8; 1 Chr 28:20
Levite, thou shalt *not* f. Deut 14:27
not fail nor f. thee. Josh 1:5
Heb 13:5
Lord will *not* f. his people.
1 Sam 12:22; 1 Ki 6:13
not leave us, nor f. us. 1 Ki 8:57
didst *not* consume, nor f. Neh 9:31
we will *not* f. the house of. 10:39
neither f. me, O God of. Ps 27:9
God of Israel, will *not* f. Isa 41:17
will I do, and *not* f. them. 42:16
nor did they f. the idols. Ezek 20:8

forsaken

because he had f. the Lord.
2 Chr 21:10; 24:24; 28:6
why is house of God f.? Neh 13:11
shall earth be f. for thee ? Job 18:4
not seen righteous f. Ps 37:25
the land shall be f. of. Isa 7:16
the cities of Aroer are f. 17:2
shall be as a f. bough, and an. 9
the habitation shall be f. 27:10
because palaces shall be f. 32:14
hath called thee as a woman f. 54:6
shalt no more be termed f. 62:4
every city shall be f. Jer 4:29
cold waters from another place be f.?
18:14*
saith Lord to cities f. Ezek 36:4
the virgin of Israel is f. Amos 5:2*
Gaza shall be f. and. Zeph 2:4

have, hast, hath **forsaken**

whereby thou *hast* f. Deut 28:20
have f. the Lord. 29:25; Judg 10:10
now the Lord *hath* f. us. Judg 6:13*
yet ye *have* f. me. 10:13
works wherewith they *have* f. me.
1 Sam 8:8
sinned, because we *have* f. 12:10
because they *have* f. me. 1 Ki 11:33
ye *have* f. commandments of. 18:18
Israel *have* f. thy covenant. 19:10, 14
have f. me and burnt. 2 Ki 22:17
2 Chr 34:25; Jer 16:11; 19:4
ye *have* f. me, I have. 2 Chr 12:5
charge of Lord ye *have* f. 13:1
ye *have* f. the Lord, he *hath* f. 24:2
have done evil, *have* f. him. 29:
for we *have* f. thy commandments.
Ezra 9:1
he *hath* oppressed and f. Job 20:1
my God, my God, why *hast* thou f.
Ps 22:1; Mat 27:46; Mark 15:3
saying, God *hath* f. him. Ps 71:1
they *have* f. the Lord. Isa 1:
the Lord *hath* f. me. 49:1
for a small moment *have* I f. 54:
have f. me, burnt. Jer 1:1
they *have* f. me, the fountain. 2:1
in that thou *hast* f. the Lord. 17,
thy children *have* f. me. 5:
answer, like as ye *have* f. me.
saith, because they *have* f. 9:1
confounded, because ye *have* f.

I have f. my house. Jer 12:7
thou hast f. me, saith Lord. 15:6*
have f. fountain of living. 17:13
because they have f. covenant. 22:9
he hath f. his covert as lion. 25:38
Lord hath f. earth. Ezek 8:12; 9:9
we have f. all and. Mat 19:27*
every one that hath f. houses. 29*
Demas hath f. me. 2 Tim 4:10
which have f. right way. 2 Pet 2:15

not forsaken

the Lord is our God, we have not f. 2 Chr 13:10
yet God hath not f. us. Ezra 9:9
thou hast not f. them. Ps 9:10
sought out, a city not f. Isa 62:12
Israel hath not been f. Jer 51:5
persecuted, but not f. 2 Cor 4:9

forsaketh

f. the fear of the Almighty. Job 6:14
for the Lord f. not his. Ps 37:28
from her f. the guide of. Pr 2:17
grievous to him that f. way. 15:10
confesseth and f. have mercy. 28:13
whoso f. not all that. Luke 14:33*

forsaking

until there be a great f. Isa 6:12
not f. the assembling of. Heb 10:25

forsook

he f. God that made. Deut 32:15
they f. the Lord God. Judg 2:12, 13 10:6
f. their cities and fled. 1 Sam 31:7 1 Chr 10:7
because they f. the Lord. 1 Ki 9:9
Rehoboam f. the counsel of old men. 12:8, 13; 2 Chr 10:8, 13
Amon f. the God of his. 2 Ki 21:22
f. God of their fathers. 2 Chr 7:22
Rehoboam f. law of Lord. 12:1
he f. tabernacle of Shiloh. Ps 78:60
but I f. not thy precepts. 119:87
f. not ordinance of God. Isa 58:2
hind calved in field and f. Jer 14:5
disciples f. him and fled. Mat 26:56*; Mark 14:50*
they f. their nets and. Mark 1:18*
they f. all and followed. Luke 5:11*
all men f. me. 2 Tim 4:16
by faith Moses f. Egypt. Heb 11:27

forsookest

God slow to anger, f. not. Neh 9:17
thou in thy mercies f. them not. 19

forswear

thou shalt not f. thyself. Mat 5:33

fort, -s

o David dwelt in the f. 2 Sam 5:9*
they built f. against Jerusalem. 2 Ki 25:1; Jer 52:4
igh f. of walls bring. Isa 25:12
nd I will raise f. against. 29:3*
he f. and towers shall be. 32:14*
nd built a f. against it. Ezek 4:2 21:22; 26:8
uilding f. to cut off. 17:17
r Jerusalem to build a f. 21:22
e shall make a f. against. 26:8
ey that be in the f. shall die. 33:27*
hall turn toward the f. Dan 11:19

forth

at time f. servants. Neh 4:16
om that time f. came they. 13:21
me of the Lord, from this time f. Ps 113:2; 115:18; 121:8
t every man right f. Jer 49:5
om that time f. began. Mat 16:21
r durst from that day f. 22:46
om that day f. took. John 11:53

forthwith

at f. expenses be. Ezra 6:8*
sprung up, because. Mat 13:5*
f. came to Jesus, and. 26:49*
when they were. Mark 1:29*
arged him, and f. sent him. 43*
d f. Jesus gave unclean. 5:13*
d f. came thereout. John 19:34*
received sight f. and. Acts 9:18*
d f. the angel departed. 12:10*
ew Paul out, and f. doors. 21:30*

fortieth

ron died there in f. Num 33:38
in f. year Moses spake. Deut 1:3
in f. year of reign of. 1 Chr 26:31
Asa died in one and f. 2 Chr 16:13

fortify

they f. the city against. Judg 9:31*
will these feeble Jews f.? Neh 4:2
houses broken down to f. Isa 22:10
she should f. height of. Jer 51:53
watch the way, f. thy. Nah 2:1
waters for siege, f. strong. 3:14*

fortified

Rehoboam f. the strong. 2 Chr 11:11
Uzziah built towers and f. 26:9
they f. Jerusalem to broad. Neh 3:8
shall come from f. cities. Mi 7:12*

fortress, -es

the Lord is my rock and my f. 2 Sam 22:2; Ps 18:2; 31:3; 71:3 91:2; 144:2
the f. also shall cease. Isa 17:3
the f. of the high fort shall. 25:12
brambles come up in the f. 34:13
I have set thee for a f. Jer 6:27
wares, O inhabitant of the f. 10:17*
O Lord, my f. in day of. 16:19*
enter into the f. of king. Dan 11:7
and be stirred up even to his f. 10
all thy f. be spoiled. Hos 10:14
spoiled come against f. Amos 5:9
day come to thee from f. Mi 7:12*

Fortunatus

glad of the coming of F. 1 Cor 16:17

forty

there shall be f. found; he said, I will not do it for f.'s sake. Gen 18:29
shalt make f. sockets. Ex 26:19
f. sockets of silver. 21; 36:24, 26
Abdon had f. sons and. Judg 12:14
Hazael went and took f. 2 Ki 8:9
governors had taken f. Neh 5:15
more than f. made. Acts 23:13, 21
see **days**

forty *baths*

one contained f. baths. 1 Ki 7:38

forty *cubits*

house before it was f. cubits long. 1 Ki 6:17
the length f. cubits. Ezek 41:2
courts joined of f. cubits. 46:22

forty *kine*

f. kine, ten bulls. Gen 32:15

forty *stripes*

f. stripes he may give. Deut 25:3
f. stripes save one. 2 Cor 11:24

forty *years*

Isaac was f. years. Gen 25:20
Esau f. years when he took. 36:34
Israel did eat manna f. years. Ex 16:35; Neh 9:21
wander in wilderness f. years. Num 14:33; 32:13
your iniquities f. years. 34
thy walking these f. years. Deut 2:7
God led thee f. years. 8:2; 29:5
thy foot swell these f. years. 4
Israel walked f. years in. Josh 5:6
f. years old was I when. 14:7
the land had rest f. years. Judg 3:11; 5:31; 8:28
hand of Philistines f. years. 13:1
Eli judged f. years. 1 Sam 4:18
Ish-bosheth f. years old. 2 Sam 2:10
David reigned f. years. 5:4 1 Ki 2:11
after f. years Absalom. 2 Sam 15:7
Solomon reigned f. years. 1 Ki 11:42
Jehoash reigned f. years. 2 Ki 12:1
Joash reigned f. years. 2 Chr 24:1
f. years was I grieved. Ps 95:10
it be inhabited f. years. Ezek 29:11
cities be desolate f. years. 12
at the end of f. years I will. 13
I led you f. years in the. Amos 2:10
ye offered sacrifices f. years. 5:25 Acts 7:42
healed was above f. years. Acts 4:22
Moses was f. years old, he. 7:23
when f. years expired, there. 30
wonders in wilderness f. years. 36
the time of f. years suffered. 13:18
them Saul by space of f. years. 21
saw my works f. years. Heb 3:9
with whom he grieved f. years? 17

forty-one *years*

Rehoboam f.-one years old when he. 1 Ki 14:21; 2 Chr 12:13
Asa reigned f.-one years. 1 Ki 15:10
Jeroboam reigned f.-one years. 2 Ki 14:23

forty-two

cities add f.-two cities. Num 35:6
two bears tare f. and two. 2 Ki 2:24
them alive, f. and two men. 10:14
f.-two years old Ahaz. 2 Chr 22:2
of Azmaveth f. and two. Ezra 2:24
Beth-azmaveth f. and two. Neh 7:28
holy city tread f.-two. Rev 11:2
to continue f.-two months. 13:5

forty-five

if I find f.-five, I will. Gen 18:28
me alive f.-five years. Josh 14:10
that lay on f.-five pillars. 1 Ki 7:3

forty-six

f.-six years was temple. John 2:20

forty-eight

cities of Levites f.-eight. Num 35:7 Josh 21:41

forty-nine

space be to thee f.-nine years. Lev 25:8

forty *thousand*

tribe of Ephraim were f. thousand. Num 1:33; 2:19; 26:18
about f. thousand prepared for war. Josh 4:13
shield or spear seen among f. thousand. Judg 5:8
David slew f. thousand horsemen. 2 Sam 10:18; 1 Chr 19:18
Solomon had f. thousand. 1 Ki 4:26
of Asher expert in war f. thousand. 1 Chr 12:36

forty-one *thousand*

Asher were f. and one thousand. Num 1:41; 2:28

forty-two *thousand*

fell of Ephraimites f.-two thousand. Judg 12:6

forward

not inherit on yonder side or f. Num 32:19
backward and not f. Jer 7:24
upon eighth day and so f. Ezek 43:27
helped f. the affliction. Zech 1:15
also to be f. year ago. 2 Cor 8:10*
but being more f. of own. 17*
same which I also was f. Gal 2:10*
whom if thou bring f. on. 3 John 6
see that **day, go, set, went**

forwardness

by occasion of the f. 2 Cor 8:8*
for I know f. of your mind. 9:2*

fought

then came Amalek and f. Ex 17:8
so Joshua f. with Amalek. 10
then king Arad f. against Israel. Num 21:1
Sihon came and f. against Israel. 23 Judg 11:20
Sihon f. against former. Num 21:26
Lord f. for Israel. Josh 10:14, 42 23:3
all Israel f. against Libnah. 10:29
f. against Lachish. 31
Amorites on the other side f. 24:8
men of Jericho f. against you. 11
found Adoni-bezek and f. Judg 1:5
Judah had f. against Jerusalem. 8
kings came, then f. kings of. 5:19
f. from heaven, stars in courses f. 20
my father f. for you and. 9:17
Gaal went out and f. with. 39
the men of Gilead f. with. 12:4
Philistines f. 1 Sam 4:10; 1 Chr 10:1
Saul f. against all his. 1 Sam 14:47
David f. with Philistines. 19:8; 23:5
people stood still, nor f. 2 Sam 2:28
f. against Hadadezer. 8:10 1 Chr 18:10
the Syrians f. against David. 2 Sam 10:17; 1 Chr 19:17

David f. against Rabbah and took. 2 Sam 12:29
Joram f. Hazael. 2 Ki 8:29; 9:15
Hazael f. against Gath. 12:17
Joash f. against Amaziah. 13:12
14:15
Lord f. against enemies. 2 Chr 20:29
f. against me without a. Ps 109:3
Tartan f. against Ashdod. Isa 20:1
turned their enemy and f. 63:10
f. against Jerusalem. Jer 34:1, 7
when he f. in day of. Zech 14:3
smite them that f. against. 12*
I have f. with beasts at. 1 Cor 15:32
I have f. a good fight. 2 Tim 4:7
Michael and his angels f. Rev 12:7*

foul, *adj.*

my face is f. with. Job 16:16
it will be f. weather. Mat 16:3
he rebuked the f. spirit. Mark 9:25*
Babylon, the hold of every f. spirit. Rev 18:2*

foul, -ed

ye must f. the residue. Ezek 34:18
they drink that ye have f. with. 19

fouledst

troubledst waters and f. Ezek 32:2

found

for Adam not f. an help. Gen 2:20
dove f. no rest for sole of her. 8:9
Isaac's servants digged and f. 26:19
Isaac's servants said we have f. 32
is it that thou hast f. it so? 27:20
Reuben went and f. mandrakes in. 30:14
tents, but f. not images. 31:33
what hast thou f. of all thy stuff? 37
Anah that f. the mules in. 36:24
coat, said, this have we f. 37:32
kid, and thou hast not f. her. 38:23
money which we f. in our. 44:8
God hath f. out the iniquity of. 16
went three days and f. no. Ex 15:22
went to gather manna and f. 16:27
or if he have f. that. Lev 6:3
f. a man that gathered. Num 15:32
f. him brought him to Moses. 33
with what thou hast f. Deut 22:3
came to her I f. her not a maid. 14, 17
f. her in field, and the. 22:27
he hath f. some uncleanness. 24:1
he f. him in a desert land. 32:10
pursuers sought, but f. them not. Josh 2:22
five kings are f. hid in a cave. 10:17
they f. Adoni-bezek and. Judg 1:5
not plowed with heifer, not f. 14:18
he f. a new jawbone of ass. 15:15
f. four hundred young virgins. 21:12
but they f. not asses. 1 Sam 9:4
they f. young maidens going to. 11
asses, they are f. 9:20; 10:2, 16
Lord is witness ye have not f. 12:5
was no smith f. in Israel. 13:19
no sword nor spear f. in hand. 22
evil hath not been f. with. 25:28
I have f. no fault in him. 29:3
they f. an Egyptian in field. 30:11
f. Saul and his three sons. 31:8
thy servant f. in his heart to pray. 2 Sam 7:27; 1 Chr 17:25
nor was weight of brass f. 1 Ki 7:47
prophet Ahijah f. Jeroboam. 11:29
he went and f. his carcase. 13:28
an oath that they f. thee not. 18:10
Elijah departed and f. Elisha. 19:19
a lion f. him and slew him. 20:36
f. me, O mine enemy? have f. 21:20
sought Elijah, but f. not. 2 Ki 2:17
f. no more of her than skull. 9:35
I f. the book of the law in. 22:8
sixty men that were f. in city. 25:19
they f. fat pasture and. 1 Chr 4:40
whom precious stones were f. 29:8
there are good things f. 2 Chr 19:3
by genealogy, but they were not f. Ezra 2:62; Neh 7:64
f. there none of sons of. Ezra 8:15
f. nothing to answer. Neh 5:8
they f. written in the law of. 8:14
nor is wisdom f. in land. Job 28:13
up myself when evil f. mine. 31:29
because they had f. no answer. 32:3
lest ye say, we have f. wisdom. Job 32:13
I have f. a ransom. 33:24
no women f. so fair as the. 42:15
looked for comforters, f. Ps 69:20
none of men of might f. their. 76:5
yea sparrow hath f. an house. 84:3
I have f. David my servant. 89:20
wandered and f. no city. 107:4
we f. it in the fields of wood. 132:6
seek thy face, and I have f. Pr 7:15
wisdom be when thou hast f. 24:14
hast thou f. honey? 25:16
this have I f. saith the preacher. Eccl 7:27
man among a thousand have I f. but woman have I not f. 28
f. that God made man upright. 29
sought him, f. him not. S of S 3:1, 2
the watchmen f. me. 3; 5:7
f. him whom my soul loveth. 3:4
hand hath f. kingdoms. Isa 10:10
my hand hath f. the riches of. 14
all that are f. in thee are. 22:3
hast f. the life of thine hand. 57:10
f. of them that sought me not. 65:1
iniquity have your fathers f.? Jer 2:5
in thy skirts is f. the blood of. 34
among my people are f. 5:26
to the pits and f. no water. 14:3
words were f. and I did eat. 15:16
house I f. their wickedness. 23:11
ten men were f. that said. 41:8
all that f. them devoured. 50:7
this is the day we have f. Lam 2:16
for man, but I f. none. Ezek 22:30
excellent spirit was f. in Daniel. Dan 5:12
weighed, and art f. wanting. 27
nor any fault f. in Daniel. 6:4
these men f. Daniel praying. 11
I f. Israel like grapes. Hos 9:10
he f. him in Beth-el, and. 12:4
Ephraim said, I have f. me out. 8
from me is thy fruit f. 14:8
he f. a ship for Tarshish. Jonah 1:3
transgressions of Israel f. Mi 1:13
when ye have f. him. Mat 2:8
I have not f. so great faith. 8:10
Luke 7:9
when a man hath f. he. Mat 13:44
when he had f. one pearl of. 46
and f. one of his fellow. 18:28
went on and f. others standing. 20:6
f. nothing thereon. 21:19
Mark 11:13; Luke 13:6
gathered all as many as they f. Mat 22:10
he f. them asleep. 26:43
Mark 14:40; Luke 22:45
sought witnesses, yet f. they none. Mat 26:60; Mark 14:55
f. a man of Cyrene. Mat 27:32
when they had f. him. Mark 1:37
ate with defiled hands, f. fault. 7:2
when she was come, f. devil gone. 30
they f. the colt tied by door. 11:4
f. the babe in a manger. Luke 2:16
after three days they f. him. 46
f. the place where it was. 4:17
returning f. the servant whole. 7:10
they f. man clothed and in. 8:35
when he hath f. the sheep. 15:5
for I have f. my sheep. 6
when she hath f. the piece. 9
are not any f. that returned. 17:18
they f. even as he had. 19:32; 22:13
f. this fellow perverting nation. 23:2
I have f. no fault in this man. 14
f. the stone rolled away. 24:2
they f. not the body of Lord Jesus. 3
when they f. not his body. 23
and they f. the eleven gathered. 33
we have found Messias. John 1:41
45
Jesus f. in the temple those. 2:14
young men came in, f. her. Acts 5:10
when the officers f. them not. 22
our fathers f. no sustenance. 7:11
that if he f. any of this way. 9:2
Peter f. many come together. 10:27
Herod sought Peter, f. him. 12:19
they f. a certain sorcerer. 13:6
I have f. David, a man after. 22
I f. an altar with this. Acts 17:23
f. this man a pestilent fellow. 24:5
if they have f. any evil doing. 20
I f. he hath done nothing. 25:25
came to Puteoli, where we f. 28:14
Abraham our father hath f. Rom 4:1
ordained to life, I f. to be to. 7:10
yea, we are f. false. 1 Cor 15:15
because I f. not Titus. 2 Cor 2:13
ourselves are f. sinners. Gal 2:17
being f. in fashion as a man. Phil 2:8
the office, f. blameless. 1 Tim 3:10
Onesiphorus sought me, f. 2 Tim 1:17
f. no place of repentance. Heb 12:17
your faith might be f. 1 Pet 1:7
I f. of thy children. 2 John 4
tried them, and hast f. Rev 2:2
I have not f. thy works perfect. 3:2
nor was their place f. any. 12:8
and mountains were not f. 16:20

***be* found**

there shall be forty f. Gen 18:29
with whomsoever it be f. 44:9
no leaven be f. in houses. Ex 12:19
stealeth a man, if he be f. in. 21:16
if a thief be f. breaking up. 22:2, 7
if theft be certainly f. in his hand. 4
lie with her, they be f. Deut 22:28
him, he could not be f. 1 Sam 10:21
on him where he be f. 2 Sam 17:12
if wickedness be f. in. 1 Ki 1:52
if thou seek him, he will be f. of thee. 1 Chr 28:9; 2 Chr 15:2
fly away and not be f. Job 20:8
but where shall wisdom be f.? 28:12
pray in time when thou mayest be f. Ps 32:6
till his iniquity be f. to be. 36:2
him, but he could not be f. 37:36
if he be f. he shall restore. Pr 6:3
be f. in way of righteousness. 16:3
reprove thee and thou be f. a. 30:6
curse thee, and thou be f. guilty. 1
not be f. a sherd to take. Isa 30:1
nor beast shall be f. there. 35:
joy and gladness shall be f. 51:
seek Lord while he may be f. 55:
I will be f. of you. Jer 29:1
sins of Judah be sought for, not be
50:2
shalt thou never be f. Ezek 26:2
and fall, and not be f. Dan 11:1
every one shall be f. written in. 12:
now shall they be f. faulty. Hos 10:
deceitful tongue be f. in. Zeph 3:1
place shall not be f. for. Zech 10:1
be f. to fight against God. Acts 5:3
that a steward be f. 1 Cor 4:
we shall not be f. naked. 2 Cor 5
they may be f. even as we. 11:1
that I shall be f. such as ye. 12:
be f. in him, not having my. Phil 3
that ye may be f. of him. 2 Pet 3:
city of Babylon be f. no. Rev 18:
no craftsman shall be f. any.

see **favour**

found *grace*

Noah f. grace in eyes of. Gen 6
thy servant hath f. grace. 19:
f. grace in thy sight. 33:10; 47:
50
Joseph f. grace in his sight. 39
hast also f. grace in. Ex 33:12,
if I have f. grace in thy sight.
34:9; Judg 6:17; 1 Sam 27
thy people have f. grace? Ex 33:
if we have f. grace in thy sight. Num 32
why have I f. grace in? Ruth 2
father knoweth I f. grace. 1 Sam 2
thy servant knoweth I have f. gra
2 Sam 14
the people f. grace in. Jer 3

***is* found**

with whom it is f. be my servant. Gen 44:10
people that is f. shall. Deut 20
is f. some good thing. 1 Ki 14
this book that is f. 2 Ki 22
2 Chr 34
is f. city hath been. Ezra 4
seeing root of matter is f. Job 19
in lips of him wisdom is f. Pr 10

every one that is f. shall. Isa 13:15
as new wine is f. in cluster. 65:8
thief is ashamed when he is f. Jer 2:26
in thy skirts is f. the blood. 34
a conspiracy is f. among the. 11:9
excellent wisdom is f. Dan 5:12, 14
from me is thy fruit f. Hos 14:8
my son lost and is f. Luke 15:24, 32
our boasting which I made is f. a truth. 2 Cor 7:14

was **found**

cup was f. in Benjamin's. Gen 44:12
gathered money that was f. 47:14
with whom was f. purple. Ex 35:23
with whom was f. shittim wood. 24
and Jonathan was f. 1 Sam 13:22
told the money that was f. 2 Ki 12:10
shewed all that was f. in treasury. 20:13; Isa 39:2
gathered the money that was f. 2 Ki 22:9; 2 Chr 34:17
read book which was f. 2 Ki 23:2
2 Chr 34:30
sought him, he was f. 2 Chr 15:4, 15
away substance that was f. 21:17
was f. at Achmetha a roll. Ezra 6:2
was f. in it a poor wise. Eccl 9:15
was he f. among thieves? Jer 48:27
perfect till iniquity was f. Ezek 28:15
none was f. like Daniel. Dan 1:19
clay broken, no place was f. 2:35
like wisdom of the gods was f. 5:11
before him innocency was f. 6:22
she was f. with child of. Mat 1:18
past, Jesus was f. alone. Luke 9:36
Philip was f. at Azotus. Acts 8:40
was f. of them that. Rom 10:20
neither was guile f. in. 1 Pet 2:22
no man was f. worthy. Rev 5:4
in their mouth was f. no guile. 14:5
in her was f. the blood of. 18:24
there was f. no place for them. 20:11

was not **found**

iniquity was not f. in his. Mal 2:6
Enoch was not f. because. Heb 11:5
was not f. written in. Rev 20:15

foundation

not been in Egypt since f. Ex 9:18
he shall lay the f. in his. Josh 6:26
hewn stones to lay the f. 1 Ki 5:17
fourth year was f. of house. 6:37
costly stones even from f. 7:9, 10
he laid the f. of Jericho in. 16:34
work was prepared of f. 2 Chr 8:16
they began to lay the f. of. 31:7
of temple not yet laid. Ezra 3:6
when the builders laid f. of. 10, 12
Sheshbazzar laid f. of house. 5:16
much less in them whose f. Job 4:19
whose f. was overflown. 22:16
his f. is in holy mountains. Ps 87:1
of old thou hast laid the f. 102:25
rase it, even to the f. thereof. 137:7
righteous an everlasting f. Pr 10:25
lay in Zion for a f. Isa 28:16
temple, thy f. shall be. 44:28
hand hath laid the f. of. 48:13
thereof be discovered. Ezek 13:14
discovering the f. to neck. Hab 3:13
from day the f. was laid. Hag 2:18
Zerubbabel hath laid f. Zech 4:9
prophets which were when f. 8:9
Lord, which layeth the f. of. 12:1
laid the f. on a rock. Luke 6:48
a man that without a f. built. 49
haply after he hath laid f. 14:29
build on another man's f. Rom 15:20
wise masterbuilder I laid the f. 1 Cor 3:10
other f. can no man lay than. 11
any man build on this f. gold. 12
on f. of prophets. Eph 2:20
in store a good f. 1 Tim 6:19
God standeth sure. 2 Tim 2:19
Lord, hast laid the f. Heb 1:10
laying the f. of repentance. 6:1
first f. jasper. Rev 21:19

foundation *of the world*

secret from the f. of the world. Mat 13:35
prepared from f. of the world. 25:34
blood shed from the f. of the world. Luke 11:50
lovedst me before f. of the world. John 17:24
chosen us in him before the f. of the world. Eph 1:4
finished from f. of world. Heb 4:3
oft suffered since f. of world. 9:26
foreordained before f. of the world. 1 Pet 1:20
slain from f. of the world. Rev 13:8
not written from f. of the world. 17:8

foundations

and set on fire the f. Deut 32:22
the f. of heaven moved. 2 Sam 22:8
f. of the world were discovered. 16
Ps 18:7, 15
set up walls and joined f. Ezra 4:12
let the f. thereof be strongly. 6:3
wast thou when I laid f.? Job 38:4
whereupon are the f. fastened. 6
if f. be destroyed, what? Ps 11:3
all the f. of the earth are out. 82:5
laid the f. of earth not to be. 104:5
when he appointed the f. Pr 8:29
for f. of Kir-hareseth. Isa 16:7*
the f. of the earth do shake. 24:18
have ye not understood from f. of earth? 40:21
Lord that laid f. of earth. 51:13
that I may lay f. of the earth. 16
I will lay thy f. with sapphires. 54:11
thou shalt raise up the f. of. 58:12
f. of earth can be searched. Jer 31:37
her f. are fallen, her walls. 50:15*
not take of thee a stone for f. 51:26
and it hath devoured the f. Lam 4:11
Egypt's f. shall be broken. Ezek 30:4
the f. of the side chambers. 41:8
and I will discover the f. Mi 1:6
and ye strong f. of earth. 6:2
f. of prison were shaken. Acts 16:26
for a city that hath f. Heb 11:10
walls of city had twelve f. Rev 21:14
f. garnished with precious stones. 19

founded

for he hath f. it upon seas. Ps 24:2
fulness thereof, thou hast f. 89:11
to place which thou hast f. 104:8
testimonies thou hast f. 119:152
Lord by wisdom f. earth. Pr 3:19
that Lord hath f. Zion. Isa 14:32
people was not till Assyrian f. 23:13†
and he hath f. his troop. Amos 9:6
fell not, for it was f. on a rock. Mat 7:25
it was f. on a rock. Luke 6:48

founder

mother gave them to f. Judg 17:4
bellows are burnt, f. Jer 6:29
work of the hands of the f. 10:9*
every f. confounded by. 14*; 51:17*

foundest

and f. his heart faithful. Neh 9:8

fountain

Is properly the source or spring-head of waters. It is often used of a well. Metaphorically, God is called the fountain of living waters, Jer 2:13. *Springs or fountains are called living, when they never cease, but are always sending forth their waters. All spiritual graces and refreshments communicated by the Spirit, are also compared to a fountain,* Joel 3:18; Zech 13:1.

found Hagar by a f. Gen 16:7
a f. wherein is water. Lev 11:36
he discovered her f. the f. of. 20:18
f. of Jacob shall be on a. Deut 33:28
Israelites pitched by a f. 1 Sam 29:1
for with thee is f. of life. Ps 36:9
bless the Lord from the f. 68:26
didst cleave the f. and the. 74:15
turned flint into a f. of water. 114:8
let thy f. be blessed. Pr 5:18
law of the wise is a f. of life. 13:14
the fear of Lord is a f. of life. 14:27
is a troubled f. and corrupt. 25:26
pitcher be broken at f. Eccl 12:6
a f. sealed. S of S 4:12
a f. of gardens. S of S 4:15
forsaken f. of living. Jer 2:13; 17:13
as a f. casteth out her waters. 6:7*
oh that mine eyes were a f. of. 9:1
a f. shall come forth of. Joel 3:18
in that day a f. shall be. Zech 13:1
the f. of her blood. Mark 5:29
doth a f. send forth sweet waters? Jas 3:11
no f. can yield salt water and. 12
I will give of the f. of life. Rev 21:6

fountains

f. of the great deep. Gen 7:11
the f. also of the deep were. 8:2
God bringeth thee into a land of f. Deut 8:7
go into land, to all f. 1 Ki 18:5
took counsel to stop waters of f. 2 Chr 32:3
much people, who stopped all the f. 4
let thy f. be dispersed. Pr 5:16*
there were no f. abounding. 8:24
when he strengthened the f. 28
I will open f. in midst. Isa 41:18
and his f. shall be dried. Hos 13:15
he shall lead them to living f. Rev 7:17
star fell upon f. of waters. 8:10
worship him that made the f. 14:7
third angel poured vial upon f. 16:4

four

river became f. heads. Gen 2:10
f. kings joined battle with five. 14:9
and f. parts shall be your. 47:24
he shall restore f. sheep. Ex 22:1
shalt make for it f. rings. 25:26
shall be f. bowls made like. 34
of one curtain f. cubits. 26:2, 8
their pillars f. their sockets f. 27:16; 38:19
in candlestick were f. bowls. 37:20
he cast f. rings for the f. ends. 38:5
f. rows of stones set in the. 39:10
fowls that creep going on all f. Lev 11:20
of beasts that go on all f. 27, 42
two wagons, f. oxen to. Num 7:7
f. wagons, eight oxen to sons of. 8
fringes on the f. quarters. Deut 22:12
a custom to lament f. Judg 11:40
these f. were born. 2 Sam 21:22
fill f. barrels with water. 1 Ki 18:33
there were f. leprous men. 2 Ki 7:3
saw his son's sons, even f. Job 42:16
f. things say not, it is. Pr 30:15
be f. things which I know not. 18
f. things which it cannot bear. 21
there be f. things which are little. 24
f. things are comely in going. 30:29
f. or five in the utmost. Isa 17:6
appoint over them f. kinds. Jer 15:3
Jehudi read three or f. leaves. 36:23
likeness of f. living creatures. Ezek 1:5
every one had f. faces. 6, 15
10:14, 21
they f. had one likeness. 1:16; 10:10
went upon their f. sides. 1:17; 10:11
every one had f. wings. 10:21
send my f. sore judgements. 14:21
and say, come from f. winds. 37:9
f. tables were on this side, f. 40:41
altar f. cubits; and f. horns. 43:15
these f. children, God. Dan 1:17
lo, I see f. men loose, walking. 3:25
the f. winds of heaven strove. 7:2
f. great beasts came from sea. 3
these f. beasts are f. kings. 17
f. notable horns towards f. 8:8
whereas f. stood up, f. kingdoms. 22
kingdom divided towards f. winds. 11:4
f. I will not turn away punishment. Amos 1:3, 6, 9, 11, 13; 2:1, 4, 6
I saw, and behold f. horns. Zech 1:18
the Lord shewed me f. carpenters. 20
there came f. chariots out. 6:1
and they shall gather elect from f. winds. Mat 24:31; Mark 13:27
sick of palsy borne of f. Mark 2:3
are yet f. months, then. John 4:35
Lazarus had lain in grave f. 11:17
the soldiers made f. parts. 19:23

f. days ago I was fasting. *Acts* 10:30
Philip had *f.* daughters. 21:9
have *f.* men which have a vow. 23
cast *f.* anchors out of stern. 27:29
about throne were *f.* beasts. *Rev* 4:6
the *f.* beasts had each of them. 8
the *f.* beasts said, amen. 5:14
a voice in the midst of *f.* beasts. 6:6
f. angels, on *f.* corners, holding *f.* 7:1
a voice from the *f.* horns of. 9:13
loose the *f.* angels bound in. 14
sung new song before *f.* beasts. 14:3
one of *f.* beasts gave seven. 15:7
elders and the *f.* beasts fell. 19:4
see **corners, days, footed, twenty, hundred, thousand**

four *times*
they sent to me *f. times.* *Neh* 6:4

fourfold
shall restore lamb *f.* *2 Sam* 12:6
taken any thing, I restore *f.* *Luke* 19:8

fourscore
Moses was *f.* years old, Aaron *f.* and three, when they spake. *Ex* 7:7
land had rest *f.* years. *Judg* 3:30
Barzillai was *f.* old. *2 Sam* 19:32, 35
ass's head was sold for *f.* *2 Ki* 6:25
Jehu appointed *f.* men. 10:24
Eliel chief, his brethren *f.* *1 Chr* 15:9
with him *f.* priests. *2 Chr* 26:17
Zebadiah, and with him *f.* *Ezra* 8:8
if by strength they be *f.* *Ps* 90:10
threescore queens, *f.* *S of S* 6:8
came from Samaria, *f.* *Jer* 41:5
widow about *f.* and four. *Luke* 2:37
take thy bill, and write *f.* 16:7

fourscore *and five*
I am this day *f. and five* years old. *Josh* 14:10
Doeg slew *f. and five.* *1 Sam* 22:18

fourscore *and six*
Abram was *f. and six.* *Gen* 16:16

one hundred and **fourscore**
days of Isaac were *one hundred and f.* *Gen* 35:28

four hundred and **fourscore**
in *four hundred f.* years after Israel were come out of Egypt. *1 Ki* 6:1

fourscore *thousand*
f. thousand hewers in mountains. *1 Ki* 5:15; *2 Chr* 2:18

fourscore *and seven thousand*
Issachar reckoned in all *f. and seven thousand.* *1 Chr* 7:5

one hundred **fourscore** *and five thousand*
angel smote in camp *one hundred f. and five thousand.* *2 Ki* 19:35

foursquare
altar shall be *f.* *Ex* 27:1
the breastplate *f.* 28:16
he measured court *f.* *Ezek* 40:47
ye shall offer holy oblation *f.* 48:20
and the city lieth *f.* *Rev* 21:16

fourteen
I served *f.* years for. *Gen* 31:41
born to Jacob, all souls were *f.* 46:22
offer for burnt offering *f.* lambs of. *Num* 29:13, 17, 20, 23, 26, 29, 32
tribe of Judah had in valley *f.* cities with their. *Josh* 15:36; 18:28
and Israel held a feast *f.* *1 Ki* 8:65
God gave to Heman *f.* *1 Chr* 25:5
waxed mighty, married *f.* wives. *2 Chr* 13:21
settle be *f.* cubits long. *Ezek* 43:17
to David *f.* from David to carrying to Babylon *f.* to Christ *f.* *Mat* 1:17
a man above *f.* years. *2 Cor* 12:2
then *f.* years after I went. *Gal* 2:1

fourteen *thousand*
Job had *f. thousand* sheep. *Job* 42:12

fourteen *thousand seven hundred*
died in plague were *f. thousand seven hundred.* *Num* 16:49

fourteenth
in the *f.* year came Chedorlaomer. *Gen* 14:5
in *f.* year of Hezekiah. *2 Ki* 18:13
Isa 36:1
the *f.* lot came forth to. *1 Chr* 24:13
f. lot came forth to Mattithiah. 25:21
in the *f.* year after city. *Ezek* 40:1
but when the *f.* night was come. *Acts* 27:27
see **day**

fourth
f. river is Euphrates. *Gen* 2:14
in *f.* generation they shall. 15:16
iniquity of fathers to the *f.* *Ex* 20:5
34:7; *Num* 14:18; *Deut* 5:9
and *f.* row a beryl. 28:20; 39:13
in *f.* year fruit shall be. *Lev* 19:24
f. lot came to Issachar. *Josh* 19:17
David's *f.* son, Adonijah. *2 Sam* 3:4
1 Chr 3:2
thy children of *f.* generation. *2 Ki* 10:30; 15:12
f. had the face of eagle. *Ezek* 10:14
f. kingdom strong as. *Dan* 2:40
form of *f.* is like Son of God. 3:25
a *f.* beast dreadful and strong. 7:7
then I would know truth of *f.* 19
the *f.* beast shall be the *f.* 23
the *f.* shall be far richer. 11:2
in the *f.* chariot were. *Zech* 6:3
Jesus came in *f.* watch. *Mat* 14:25
f. beast was like a flying eagle. *Rev* 4:7
when he had opened the *f.* seal. 6:7
the *f.* angel sounded, the sun. 8:12
the *f.* angel poured out his vial. 16:8
third, a chalcedony; *f.* an. 21:19
see **day, month, part**

fourth *year*
in the *f. year* of Solomon's reign he began. *1 Ki* 6:1, 37; *2 Chr* 3:2
Jehoshaphat began to reign in *f. year* of Ahab. *1 Ki* 22:41
in the *f. year* of Hezekiah Shalmaneser came up against. *2 Ki* 18:9
word came to Jeremiah in *f. year* of Jehoiakim. *Jer* 25:1
in the *f. year* of Zedekiah. 28:1
in the *f. year* of Jehoiakim this word came to. 36:1; 45:1; 46:2
commanded Seraiah in *f. year.* 51:59
in *f. year* of Darius. *Zech* 7:1

fowl
have dominion over *f.* *Gen* 1:26, 28
of ground God formed every *f.* 2:19
the *f.* of the heaven destroyed. 7:23
bring forth of all flesh, of *f.* 8:17
fear of you shall be on every *f.* 9:2
I establish my covenant with *f.* 10
no blood, whether of *f.* or. *Lev* 7:26
law of the beasts and *f.* 11:46
likeness of any winged *f.* *Deut* 4:17
there is a path which no *f.* *Job* 28:7*
dominion over *f.* of air. *Ps* 8:8
beasts and flying *f.* praise. 148:10
f. of heavens and beast. *Jer* 9:10
under it shall dwell all *f.* *Ezek* 17:23
speak to every feathered *f.* 39:17*
priest not eat any thing torn, *f.* 44:31
back of it four wings of a *f.* *Dan* 7:6

fowler
deliver thee from snare of *f.* *Ps* 91:3
a bird from hand of the *f.* *Pr* 6:5
prophet is a snare of a *f.* *Hos* 9:8

fowlers
escaped out of snare of *f.* *Ps* 124:7

fowls
take of *f.* also of air by. *Gen* 7:3
when the *f.* came down on. 15:11*
if the burnt sacrifice to Lord be of *f.* *Lev* 1:14
these *f.* ye shall have in. 11:13
of all clean *f.* ye may. *Deut* 14:20
carcase be meat to all *f.* of. 28:26
thy flesh to the *f.* *1 Sam* 17:44, 46
spake of beasts and of *f.* *1 Ki* 4:33
that dieth in fields, *f.* eat. 14:11
16:4; 21:24
f. were prepared for me. *Neh* 5:18
ask the *f.* they shall tell. *Job* 12:7
know all *f.* of mountains. *Ps* 50:11
he rained *f.* like as the sand. 78:27
left to the *f.* of the mountains, and the *f.* summer upon. *Isa* 18:6*
let *f.* get from branches. *Dan* 4:14
f. sow not, neither reap. *Mat* 6:26*
the *f.* devoured the seed. 13:4*
Mark 4:4*; *Luke* 8:5*
that *f.* may lodge under it. *Mark* 4:32*; *Luke* 13:19*
much better than *f.* *Luke* 12:24*
a sheet wherein were *f.* *Acts* 10:12
11:6
an angel cried to all the *f.* *Rev* 19:17*
and all the *f.* were filled with. 21*

fowls *of the heaven*
wiser than *f. of heaven.* *Job* 35:11
bodies of thy servants meat to *f. of the heaven.* *Ps* 79:2
by them the *f. of heaven.* 104:12
of people meat for *f. of the heaven.* *Jer* 7:33; 16:4; 19:7; 34:20
will appoint *f. of the heaven.* 15:3
given Pharaoh for meat to *f. of heaven.* *Ezek* 29:5
f. of heaven made their nests in Assyria. 31:6
ruin all *f. of heaven* remain. 13
will cause all *f. of heaven* to. 32:4
the *f. of heaven* shall shake. 38:20
f. of heaven given to Nebuchadnezzar. *Dan* 2:38
covenant for them with *f. of heaven.* *Hos* 2:18
languish with *f. of heaven.* 4:3
down as the *f. of heaven.* 7:12
consume *f. of the heaven.* *Zeph* 1:3
f. of heaven lodged in. *Luke* 13:19

fox
The Hebrew word Shual *is used generally of any sort of fox or of jackal, which really belongs to the dog family. Most probably jackals are intended in* Judg 15:4, *as they were much more numerous, and remained in packs, which made them easier to capture. Although several species of foxes are found in Palestine, it is impossible to decide with certainty in any particular case which species is intended, if it is not the jackal.*
a *f.* break down stone. *Neh* 4:3
go and tell that *f.* I cast. *Luke* 13:32

foxes
caught three hundred *f.* *Judg* 15:4
shall be a portion for *f.* *Ps* 63:1
take the *f.* the little *f.* *S of S* 2:1
Zion is desolate, *f.* walk. *Lam* 5:1
thy prophets are like *f.* *Ezek* 13:
f. have holes. *Mat* 8:20; *Luke* 9:5

fragments
(*Revisions substitute for this* broken pieces)
up *f.* twelve baskets full. *Mat* 14:2
Mark 6:43; *Luke* 9:17; *John* 6:1
baskets full of *f.*? *Mark* 8:19, 2
gather up *f.* that remain. *John* 6:1

frail
I may know how *f.* I am. *Ps* 39:

frame
he knoweth our *f.* *Ps* 103:1
which was as *f.* of a city. *Ezek* 40:

frame, *verb*
could not *f.* to pronounce. *Judg* 12
behold, I *f.* evil against. *Jer* 18:
will not *f.* their doings. *Hos* 5:

framed
thing *f.* say to him that *f.* it? *Isa* 29:1
building fitly *f.* groweth. *Eph* 2:
worlds *f.* by word of God. *Heb* 11

frameth
evil, thy tongue *f.* deceit. *Ps* 50:
f. mischief by a law. 94:

frankincense
spices with pure *f.* *Ex* 30:
put *f.* thereon. *Lev* 2:1, 15; 5:
24:7; *Num* 5:
oil with all the *f.* thereof. *Lev*
priest shall burn the oil with all *f*
16; 6
appointed to oversee *f.* *1 Chr* 9
where they laid the *f.* *Neh* 1
brought I the vessels and the *f.*

comes perfumed with *f.*? *S of S* 3:6
I will get me to the hill of *f.* 4:6
cinnamon, with all trees of *f.* 14
presented to him gold, *f.* *Mat* 2:11
no man buyeth *f.* wine. *Rev* 18:13

frankly

nothing to pay, he *f.* *Luke* 7:42*

fraud

his mouth is full of cursing and *f.* *Ps* 10:7*
kept back by *f.* crieth. *Jas* 5:4

fray

(*American Revision substitutes for this* frighten)
no man shall *f.* them away. *Deut* 28:26; *Jer* 7:33
these are come to *f.* them. *Zech* 1:21

freckled

a *f.* spot that groweth. *Lev* 13:39*

free

an Hebrew servant, in the seventh year shall go out *f.* *Ex* 21:2
Deut 15:12; *Jer* 34:9, 14
say, I will not go out *f.* *Ex* 21:5
then shall she go out *f.* 11*
he shall let him go *f.* for his. 26
he shall let him go *f.* for tooth's. 27
not be put to death because not *f.* *Lev* 19:20
. from this bitter water. *Num* 5:19
woman be not defiled, shall be *f.* 28
hou sendest him out *f.* *Deut* 15:13
ard when thou sendest him *f.* 18
ut he shall be *f.* at home. 24:5
is father's house *f.* *1 Sam* 17:25
he singers, who remaining were *f.* *1 Chr* 9:33
s many as were of *f.* *2 Chr* 29:31*
he servant is *f.* from. *Job* 3:19
who sent out the wild ass *f.*? 39:5
phold me with thy *f.* *Ps* 51:12†
among the dead, like slain. 88:5*
ing loosed him, let him go *f.* 105:20
o let the oppressed go *f.* *Isa* 58:6
nan let his servant go *f.* *Jer* 34:9
aused them whom they let go *f.* 11
onour not his father, he shall be *f.* *Mat* 15:6
aith, then are the children *f.* 17:26
is Corban, he shall be *f.* *Mark* 7:11
ruth shall make you *f.* *John* 8:32
ayest thou, ye shall be made *f.*? 33
ake you *f.* ye shall be *f.* indeed. 36
ut I was *f.* born. *Acts* 22:28*
ffence, so is the *f.* gift. *Rom* 5:15
ut *f.* gift is of many offences. 16
ven so the *f.* gift came upon. 18
eing made *f.* from sin. 6:18, 22
ervants of sin ye were *f.* 20
er husband be dead, she is *f.* 7:3
pirit of life made me *f.* 8:2
ayest be made *f.* use. *1 Cor* 7:21
ot an apostle ? am I not *f.*? 9:1
hough I be *f.* from all men. 19
hether bond or *f.* 12:13
here is neither bond nor *f.* *Gal* 3:28
Col 3:11
erusalem above, is *f.* *Gal* 4:26
hildren of bondwoman, but of *f.* 31
herewith Christ hath made us *f.* 5:1
ceive of Lord, bond or *f.* *Eph* 6:8
at word may have *f.* *2 Thes* 3:1*
f. and not using your liberty. *1 Pet* 2:16
useth all, *f.* and bond. *Rev* 13:16
t flesh of both bond and *f.* 19:18

free *offerings*

ought *f. offerings.* *Ex* 36:3
l publish *f. offerings.* *Amos* 4:5

freed

ll none of you be *f.* *Josh* 9:23*
t is dead is *f.* from sin. *Rom* 6:7*

freedom

h a woman, not *f.* *Lev* 19:20
at sum obtained *f.* *Acts* 22:28*

freely

every tree *f.* eat. *Gen* 2:16
fish we did eat *f.* *Num* 11:5
eople had eaten *f.* *1 Sam* 14:30
of chief fathers offered *f.* *Ezra* 2:68
which king hath offered *f.* to. 7:15
I will *f.* sacrifice unto thee. *Ps* 54:6
I will love them *f.* *Hos* 14:4
f. ye have received *f.* give. *Mat* 10:8
let me *f.* speak. *Acts* 2:29
before whom I speak *f.* 26:26
justified *f.* by his grace. *Rom* 3:24
will with him also *f.* give us. 8:32
know things *f.* given us. *1 Cor* 2:12
preached the gospel of God *f.* *2 Cor* 11:7
give of fountain of life *f.* *Rev* 21:6
whosoever will, let him take *f.* 22:17

freeman

called, is the Lord's *f.* *1 Cor* 7:22
every bondman and *f.* *Rev* 6:15

freewill

f. to go up to Jerusalem. *Ezra* 7:13

freewill *offering*

who offereth *f. off.* it. *Lev* 22:21
bullock thou mayest offer *f. off.* 23
make sacrifice in *f. off.* *Num* 15:3
with a tribute of *f. off.* *Deut* 16:10
a *f. off.* shalt thou keep. 23:23
beasts besides *f. off.* *Ezra* 1:4
that willingly offered a *f. off.* 3:5
silver thou canst find with *f. off.* 7:16
silver and gold are a *f. off.* 8:28

freewill *offerings*

offer oblation for *f. off.* *Lev* 22:18
beside all your *f. off.* 23:38
Num 29:39
thither bring your *f. off.* *Deut* 12:6
not eat within thy gates *f. off.* 17
Kore was over *f. off.* of. *2 Chr* 31:14
accept the *f. off.* of my. *Ps* 119:108

freewoman

two sons, by bondmaid, and by a *f.* *Gal* 4:22
but he of the *f.* was by promise. 23
not be heir with son of the *f.* 30
children of bondwoman, but of *f.* 31

frequent

in prisons more *f.* *2 Cor* 11:23*

fresh

manna was as taste of *f.* *Num* 11:8
my glory was *f.* in me. *Job* 29:20
anointed with *f.* oil. *Ps* 92:10
yield salt water and *f.* *Jas* 3:12*

fresher

flesh shall be *f.* than a. *Job* 33:35

fret

burn it in the fire, it is *f.* *Lev* 13:55

fret, *verb*

provoked her to make her *f.* *1 Sam* 1:6
f. not thyself. *Ps* 37:1, 7, 8
Pr 24:19
be hungry, they shall *f.* *Isa* 8:21

fretted

but thou hast *f.* me in. *Ezek* 16:43†

fretteth

and his heart *f.* against. *Pr* 19:3

fretting

the plague is a *f.* leprosy. *Lev* 13:51, 52; 14:44

fried

cakes mingled with oil of flour *f.* *Lev* 7:12*
Levites to wait about that which is *f.* *1 Chr* 23:29*

friend

The friend of the king was a high court official, probably the king's confidential adviser, Gen 26:26; 1 Ki 4:5.
The friend of God is a title given to Abraham because of his close relations with God and his faithfulness, 2 Chr. 20:7; Jas 2:23.
The word friend was used as a general salutation, whether to friend or foe, Mat 22:12; 26:50.

sent kid by hand of his *f.* *Gen* 38:20
God spake to Moses as a man to *f.* *Ex* 33:11
or if thy wife or *f.* entice. *Deut* 13:6
companion whom he used as his *f.* *Judg* 14:20
Amnon had a *f.* his. *2 Sam* 13:3
Hushai David's *f.* came into city. 15:37; 16:16
this thy kindness to thy *f.*? why went-est thou not with thy *f.*? 16:17
Zabud was principal officer, the king's *f.* *1 Ki* 4:5
gavest to the seed of Abraham thy *f.* *2 Chr* 20:7
pity be shewed from his *f.* *Job* 6:14
and ye dig a pit for your *f.* 27
as though he had been my *f.* *Ps* 35:14
my familiar *f.* hath lifted up. 41:9
lover and *f.* hast thou put far. 88:18
be surety for thy *f.* *Pr* 6:1*
hand of thy *f.*; make sure thy *f.* 3*
f. loveth at all times. 17:17
surety in the presence of his *f.* 18
a *f.* that sticketh closer. 18:24
every man is a *f.* to him that. 19:6
the king shall be his *f.* 22:11
faithful are the wounds of a *f.* 27:6
so doth sweetness of man's *f.* 9
thine own *f.* and father's *f.* 10
blesseth his *f.* with a loud voice. 14
sharpeneth countenance of his *f.* 17
this is my *f.* O daughter. *S of S* 5:16
seed of Abraham my *f.* *Isa* 41:8
neighbour and his *f.* *Jer* 6:21
eat every one flesh of his *f.* 19:9
beloved of her *f.* yet an. *Hos* 3:1
trust ye not in a *f.* put. *Mi* 7:5
behold, a *f.* of publicans. *Mat* 11:19
Luke 7:34
f. I do thee no wrong. *Mat* 20:13
f. how camest thou hither ? 22:12
f. wherefore art thou come ? 26:50
which of you have a *f.* and go at mid-night and say, *f.* lend. *Luke* 11:5
for a *f.* of mine in his journey. 6
not give him because he is his *f.* 8
bade thee say, *f.* go up higher. 14:10
the *f.* of the bridegroom. *John* 3:29
our *f.* Lazarus sleepeth. 11:11
this man go, art not Cesar's *f.* 19:12
made Blastus their *f.* *Acts* 12:20
Abraham called *f.* of God. *Jas* 2:23
will be a *f.* of the world. 4:4

friendly

Levite went to speak *f.* *Judg* 19:3*
thou hast spoken *f.* to. *Ruth* 2:13*
must shew himself *f.* *Pr* 18:24*

friends

David sent spoil to his *f.* *1 Sam* 30:26
shew kindness to Saul's *f.* *2 Sam* 3:8
thine enemies, hatest thy *f.* 19:6*
left him not one of his *f.* *1 Ki* 16:11
sent and called for his *f.* *Esth* 5:10
said his wife and all his *f.* 14
Haman told his wife and *f.* 6:13
when Job's three *f.* heard. *Job* 2:11
my *f.* scorn me, but mine eye. 16:20
speaketh flattery to his *f.* 17:5
familiar *f.* have forgotten me. 19:14
all my inward *f.* abhorred me. 19
have pity on me, O ye *f.* 21
Elihu's wrath kindled against *f.* 32:3
Lord's wrath kindled against *f.* 42:7
Lord turned when he prayed for *f.* 10
my *f.* stand aloof. *Ps* 38:11
is hated, rich hath *f.* *Pr* 14:20
whisperer separateth chief *f.* 16:28
a matter, separateth *f.* 17:9
hath *f.* shew himself friendly. 18:24
wealth maketh many *f.* but. 19:4
how much more do his *f.* go. 7
eat, O *f.*; drink, yea. *S of S* 5:1
thee a terror to thy *f.* *Jer* 20:4
shalt be buried there, thou and *f.* 6
thy *f.* have set thee on. 38:22*
f. have dealt treacherously. *Lam* 1:2
wounded in house of my *f.* *Zech* 13:6
when his *f.* heard of it. *Mark* 3:21
go home to thy *f.* 5:19
centurion sent *f.* to him. *Luke* 7:6
my *f.* be not afraid of them. 12:4
a dinner, call not thy *f.* 14:12
he calleth together his *f.* 15:6
she calleth her *f.* and neighbours. 9
make merry with my *f.* 29

f. of the mammon. *Luke* 16:9
betrayed by parents and *f.* 21:16
and Herod were made *f.* 23:12
man lay down life for *f.* *John* 15:13
ye are my *f.* if ye do what I. 14
but I have called you *f.* 15
Cornelius called together his *f.* *Acts* 10:24
certain which were his *f.* sent. 19:31
Julius gave liberty to go to *f.* 27:3
our *f.* salute thee, greet the *f.* by. *3 John* 14

friendship

make no *f.* with angry. *Pr* 22:24
the *f.* of world is enmity. *Jas* 4:4

fringe, -s

them make *f.* put on *f.* *Num* 15:38
it shall be to you for a *f.* 39
make thee *f.* on the four quarters. *Deut* 22:12

to and **fro**

raven, which went *to and f.* *Gen* 8:7
Elisha walked *to and f.* *2 Ki* 4:35
Satan said, from going *to and f.* in earth. *Job* 1:7; 2:2
I am full of tossings *to and f.* 7:4
break a leaf driven *to and f.*? 13:25
reel *to and f.* and stagger. *Ps* 107:27
vanity tossed *to and f.* *Pr* 21:6
earth shall reel *to and f.* *Isa* 24:20
running *to and f.* of locusts. 33:4
and removing *to and f.* 49:21
Javan going *to and f.* *Ezek* 27:19
Lord sent to walk *to and f.* through. *Zech* 1:10
walked *to and f.* through earth. 11
that they might walk *to and f.* so they walked *to and f.* 6:7
no more children tossed *to and f.* *Eph* 4:14

see **run**

frogs

smite thy borders with *f.* *Ex* 8:2
the magicians brought up *f.* 7
sent *f.* which destroyed. *Ps* 78:45
the land brought forth *f.* 105:30
unclean spirits like *f.* *Rev* 16:13

from

hand *f.* off you, and *f.* off. *1 Sam* 6:5
multitudes *f.* Decapolis, *f.* Jerusalem, *f.* Judea, *f.* beyond. *Mat* 4:25

front

Joab saw *f.* of battle. *2 Sam* 10:9
porch in the *f.* of house. *2 Chr* 3:4

frontiers

from cities on his *f.* *Ezek* 25:9

frontlets

These were square pieces of hard calf's skin, including four pieces of parchment, upon which the Jews wrote four passages of the law, and bound them with strings on their foreheads. The four passages which they wrote are these: On the first piece of parchment, Ex 13, *from verse* 2 *to* 10. *On the second,* Ex 13, *from verse* 11 *to* 16. *On the third,* Deut 6, *from verse* 4 *to* 9. *And on the fourth,* Deut 11, *from verse* 13 *to* 21.

it shall be for *f.* between. *Ex* 13:16
shall be a *f.* between thine eyes. *Deut* 6:8; 11:18

frost

drought consumed by day, *f.* by night. *Gen* 31:40
as small as the hoar *f.* *Ex* 16:14
by breath of God *f.* is. *Job* 37:10*
the *f.* of heaven, who hath? 38:29
destroyeth trees with *f.* *Ps* 78:47
he scattereth the hoar *f.* 147:16
body cast out to the *f.* *Jer* 36:30

froward

a very *f.* generation. *Deut* 32:20†
thyself pure, with the *f.* shew thyself *f.* *2 Sam* 22:27*; *Ps* 18:26*
the counsel of the *f.* is. *Job* 5:13†
a *f.* heart shall depart. *Ps* 101:4
man that speaketh *f.* *Pr* 2:12†
ways are crooked, and they *f.* 15*
for the *f.* is abomination. 3:32*
put away a *f.* mouth. *Pr* 4:24†
wicked walketh with *f.* mouth. 6:12†
there is nothing *f.* or perverse. 8:8*
the evil way, and the *f.* mouth. 13†
the *f.* tongue be cut out. 10:31†
of a *f.* heart, are abomination. 11:20*
a *f.* man soweth strife. 16:28†
shutteth eyes to devise *f.* things. 30†
he that hath a *f.* heart. 17:20†
the way of a man is *f.* and. 21:8*
thorns and snares in way of *f.* 22:5†
subject to masters, to *f.* *1 Pet* 2:18

frowardly

went on *f.* in way of his. *Isa* 57:17†

frowardness

who delight in the *f.* of. *Pr* 2:14†
f. is in his heart, he deviseth. 6:14†
mouth of wicked speaketh *f.* 10:32†

frozen

the face of the deep is *f.* *Job* 38:30

fruit

every tree wherein is *f.* *Gen* 1:29
Cain brought of the *f.* of the. 4:3
hath withheld from thee *f.* of. 30:2
so that her *f.* depart. *Ex* 21:22
count *f.* uncircumcised. *Lev* 19:23
in fourth year *f.* shall be holy. 24
six years thou shalt gather *f.* 25:3
the tithe of the *f.* is the. 27:30
shewed them the *f.* of. *Num* 13:26
and this is the *f.* of it. 27
they took of the *f.* in. *Deut* 1:25
he will bless the *f.* of thy land. 7:13
lest *f.* of thy seed, *f.* of thy. 22:9
take of the first of all the *f.* 26:2
blessed shall be the *f.* of thy. 28:4
plenteous in *f.* of thy body. 11; 30:9
cursed shall be the *f.* of thy. 28:18
for thine olive shall cast his *f.* 40
thy trees and *f.* shall locust. 42
forsake my sweetness and *f.*? *Judg* 9:11
summer *f.* for young. *2 Sam* 16:2
f. shalt thou destroy. *Ps* 21:10
f. thereof shall shake like. 72:16
earth is satisfied with *f.* of. 104:13
locusts devoured the *f.* 105:35
f. of the womb is his reward. 127:3
of *f.* of thy body will I set. 132:11
my *f.* better than fine gold. *Pr* 8:19
the *f.* of the wicked tendeth. 10:16
f. of the righteous is a tree. 11:30
a man is satisfied by the *f.* 12:14
satisfied with the *f.* of mouth. 18:20
with the *f.* of her hand she. 31:16
give her of the *f.* of her hands. 31
and his *f.* was sweet to. *S of S* 2:3
those that keep the *f.* thereof. 8:12
eat the *f.* of their doings. *Isa* 3:10
f. of the earth be excellent. 4:2
I will punish the *f.* of the. 10:12
no pity on the *f.* of womb. 13:18
his *f.* a fiery flying serpent. 14:29
fill face of the world with *f.* 27:6
the *f.* to take away his sin. 9
as the hasty *f.* before summer. 28:4*
I create the *f.* of the lips. 57:19
plant vineyards, eat *f.* of. 65:21
bring *f.* of their thoughts. *Jer* 6:19
my fury shall be on the *f.* of. 7:20
green olive tree, fair, and of goodly *f.* 11:16
let us destroy the tree with *f.* 19
f. of his doings. 17:10; 21:14; 32:19
cut off the *f.* thereof. *Ezek* 17:9
the east wind dried up her *f.* 19:12
which hath devoured her *f.* 14
they shall eat thy *f.* and drink. 25:4
I will multiply the *f.* of tree. 36:30
nor *f.* thereof be consumed. 47:12
the leaves fair and *f.* *Dan* 4:12, 21
and said thus, scatter his *f.* 14
ye have eaten the *f.* of lies. *Hos* 10:13
from me is thy *f.* found. 14:8
destroyed his *f.* from. *Amos* 2:9
turned *f.* of righteousness. 6:12
a gatherer of sycamore *f.* 7:14*
behold a basket of summer *f.* 8:1, 2
f. of body for sin of my? *Mi* 6:7
desolate, for the *f.* of their. 7:13
neither *f.* be in the vines. *Hab* 3:17
earth is stayed from her *f.* *Hag* 1:10
the vine shall give her *f.* *Zech* 8:12
table is polluted, and *f.* *Mal* 1:12
nor shall your vine cast her *f.* 3:11
f. good, tree corrupt, *f.* corrupt, tree is known by his *f.* *Mat* 12:33
let no *f.* grow on thee for. 21:19
when the time of *f.* drew near. 34
not drink of *f.* of the vine, till I drink it new in. 26:29; *Mark* 14:25
might receive the *f.* of. *Mark* 12:2
blessed is the *f.* of thy. *Luke* 1:42
he sought *f.* thereon. 13:6
I come seeking *f.* on this fig tree. 7
should give him of the *f.* 20:10
gathereth *f.* to life. *John* 4:36
of the *f.* of his loins. *Acts* 2:30
that I might have some *f.* *Rom* 1:13
what *f.* had ye then in those? 6:21
ye have your *f.* unto holiness. 22
have sealed to them this *f.* 15:28
but the *f.* of Spirit is love. *Gal* 5:22
the *f.* of the Spirit is in. *Eph* 5:9
this is the *f.* of my labour. *Phil* 1:22
I desire *f.* that may abound to. 4:17
by him let us offer the *f.* *Heb* 13:15
the *f.* of righteousness is. *Jas* 3:18
husbandman waiteth for *f.* 5:7
f. withereth, without *f.* *Jude* 12*

see **eat**

bear, or *beareth* **fruit**

shall *bear f.* upward. *2 Ki* 19:30; *Isa* 37:31
good soil, that it *bear f.* *Ezek* 17:8
in height of Israel it shall *bear f.* 23
they shall *bear* no *f.* *Hos* 9:16
the tree *beareth* her *f.* *Joel* 2:22
good ground, is he who *beareth f.* *Mat* 13:23
fell on good ground, and *bare f.* *Luke* 8:8
if it *bear f.* well, if not, cut. 13:9
branch that *beareth* not *f.* every branch that *beareth f.* *John* 15:2
as the branch cannot *bear f.* of. 4
that ye *bear* much *f.* so shall. 8

bring, bringeth, or *brought forth* **fruit**

it shall *bring forth f.* for. *Lev* 25:21
bring of the *f.* of land. *Num* 13:20
to *bring* the *f.* of all. *Neh* 10:35, 37
that *bringeth forth f.* *Ps* 1:3
they shall *bring forth f.* 92:14
f. was to *bring* silver. *S of S* 8:11
the wicked grow, they *bring forth f.* *Jer* 12:2
they shall increase, and *bring forth f.* *Ezek* 36:1
bring forth new *f.* for meat. 47:1
Israel *bringeth forth f.* to. *Hos* 10:
bringeth not *forth* good *f.* *Mat* 3:1 7:19; *Luke* 3:
good tree *bringeth forth* good *f.* *Mat* 7:1
good tree cannot *bring forth* evil *f.* 1
when blade *brought forth f.* 13:2
hear the word and *bring forth f.* *Mark* 4:2
for the earth *bringeth forth f.* 2
bring no *f.* to perfection. *Luke* 8:1
they keep it and *bring forth f.* 1
die, it *bringeth forth f.* *John* 12:2
it may *bring forth* more *f.* 15:
abideth, *bringeth forth* much *f.*
ordained that you *bring forth f.*
that we *bring forth f.* to. *Rom* 7:
motions did work to *bring forth f.*
the gospel *bringeth forth f.* *Col* 1:
prayed, earth *brought forth f.* *Jas* 5:

see **firstfruit**

yield, yieldeth, yielding **fruit**

fruit tree *yielding f.* *Gen* 1:11,
land shall *yield* her *f.* *Lev* 25:
trees of field shall *yield* their *f.* 26
land *yield* not her *f.* *Deut* 11:
root of the righteous *yieldeth f.* *Pr* 12:
cease from *yielding f.* *Jer* 17
tree of the field shall *yield* her *f.* *Ezek* 34:
yield your *f.* to my people. 36
choked it, it *yielded* no *f.* *Mark* 4
on good ground and did *yield f.*

yieldeth peaceable *f.* of. *Heb* 12:11
the tree *yielded* her *f.* *Rev* 22:2

fruitful

saying, Be *f.* and multiply. *Gen* 1:22
28; 8:17; 9:7; 35:11
I will make thee exceeding *f.* 17:6
I will make Ishmael *f.* 20
room for us, we shall be *f.* 26:22
bless thee, and make thee *f.* 28:3
make Jacob *f.* 48:4
Joseph is a *f.* bough, a *f.* 49:22
children of Israel were *f.* *Ex* 1:7
I will make you *f.* and. *Lev* 26:9
he turneth a *f.* land into. *Ps* 107:34
thy wife shall be as a *f.* vine. 128:3
mountains and *f.* trees, praise. 148:9
beloved hath vineyard in a *f.* hill. *Isa* 5:1
four or five in the outmost *f.* 17:6
shall lament for the *f.* vine. 32:12
f. place was a wilderness. *Jer* 4:26
they shall be *f.* and increase. 23:3
was *f.* and full of. *Ezek* 19:10
though he be *f.* an east. *Hos* 13:15
gave us rain and *f.* *Acts* 14:17
being *f.* in every good. *Col* 1:10
see **field**

fruits

take of the best *f.* in land. *Gen* 43:11
to offer first of ripe *f.* *Ex* 22:29
six years gather in the *f.* 23:10
according to years of the *f.*
Lev 25:15*, 16*
till her *f.* come in. 22
neither the trees yield their *f.* 26:20
precious *f.* brought forth. *Deut* 33:14
thy sons shall bring in *f.* *2 Sam* 9:10
restore to her all the *f.* of. *2 Ki* 8:6
and eat the *f.* thereof. 19:29
if I have eaten the *f.* *Job* 31:39
fields, which may yield *f.* *Ps* 107:37
I planted trees of all kind of *f.*
Eccl 2:5
orchard with pleasant *f.* *S of S* 4:13
my beloved eat his pleasant *f.* 16
I went down to see the *f.* of. 6:11*
gates all manner of pleasant *f.* 7:13
and Carmel shake off *f.* *Isa* 33:9*
pine away for want of *f.* *Lam* 4:9
not destroy the *f.* of your. *Mal* 3:11
bring *f.* meet for repentance.
Mat 3:8; *Luke* 3:8
know them by their *f.* *Mat* 7:16, 20
that they receive the *f.* of it. 21:34
who shall render him the *f.* in. 41
given to a nation bringing *f.* 43
I have no room where to bestow my
f. *Luke* 12:17
there will I bestow all my *f.* 18*
increase the *f.* of your. *2 Cor* 9:10
filled with the *f.* of. *Phil* 1:11
husbandman first partaker of the *f.*
2 Tim 2:6
wisdom from above full of good *f.*
Jas 3:17
f. thy soul lusted after. *Rev* 18:14
of life bare twelve manner of *f.* 22:2
see **first**

summer **fruits**

hundred of *summer f.* *2 Sam* 16:1
summer *f.* and harvest. *Isa* 16:9
e wine and *summer f.* *Jer* 40:10
wine and *summer f.* very much. 12
spoiler is fallen on *summer f.* 48:32
when they gathered the *summer f.*
Mi 7:1

fruit trees

and possessed *f. trees.* *Neh* 9:25

frustrate

hired counsellors to *f.* *Ezra* 4:5
do not *f.* grace of God. *Gal* 2:21*

frustrateth

that *f.* the tokens of liars. *Isa* 44:25

fryingpan

e a meat offering in the *f.* *Lev* 2:7
l that is dressed in the *f.* 7:9

fuel

e with burning and *f.* of. *Isa* 9:5
people shall be as *f.* of the fire. 19
the tree is cast into the fire for *f.*
Ezek 15:4, 6
ou shalt be for *f.* to the fire. 21:32

fugitive

a *f.* and a vagabond. *Gen* 4:12
I shall be a *f.* and a vagabond. 14

fugitives

Gileadites *f.* of Ephraim. *Judg* 12:4
and the *f.* that fell away. *2 Ki* 25:11
cry for Moab, his *f.* shall. *Isa* 15:5*
all his *f.* shall fall by. *Ezek* 17:21

fulfil

f. her week, and we will. *Gen* 29:27
f. your works. *Ex* 5:13
number of thy days I will *f.* 23:26
he might *f.* the word. *1 Ki* 2:27
if thou takest heed to *f.* *1 Chr* 22:13*
to *f.* threescore and. *2 Chr* 36:21
canst thou number months they *f.*?
Job 39:2
Lord grant thee, and *f.* all. *Ps* 20:4
the Lord *f.* all thy petitions. 5
he will *f.* the desire of them. 145:19
becometh us to *f.* all. *Mat* 3:15
not come to destroy, but to *f.* 5:17
David, who shall *f.* my. *Acts* 13:22*
if it *f.* the law. *Rom* 2:27
for the flesh, to *f.* the lusts. 13:14
ye shall not *f.* the lust. *Gal* 5:16
and so *f.* the law of Christ. 6:2
f. ye my joy, that ye be. *Phil* 2:2
given to me, to *f.* word. *Col* 1:25
heed ministry, that thou *f.* 4:17
f. good pleasure of his. *2 Thes* 1:11
if ye *f.* the royal law. *Jas* 2:8
put in their hearts to *f.* *Rev* 17:17*

fulfilled

to be delivered were *f.* *Gen* 25:24
my wife, for my days are *f.* 29:21
forty days were *f.* for so are *f.* 50:3
have ye not *f.* your task ? *Ex* 5:14
seven days *f.* after Lord hath. 7:25
till purification be *f.* *Lev* 12:4, 6
of his separation are *f.* *Num* 6:13
when days be *f.* and. *2 Sam* 7:12
in that the king *f.* request. 14:22
hath with his hand *f.* it. *1 Ki* 8:15
hast *f.* it with hand. 24; *2 Chr* 6:15
the Lord hath *f.* that. *2 Chr* 6:4
word of Lord might be *f.* *Ezra* 1:1
thou hast *f.* judgement. *Job* 36:17*
and your wives have *f.* *Jer* 44:25
he hath *f.* his word he. *Lam* 2:17
our days are *f.* our end is. 4:18
when days of siege are *f.* *Ezek* 5:2
the same hour was thing *f.* *Dan* 4:33
till three whole weeks were *f.* 10:3
that it might be *f.* *Mat* 1:22; 2:15
23; 8:17; 12:17; 13:35; 21:4
27:35; *John* 12:38; 15:25; 17:12
18:9, 32; 19:24, 28, 36
f. that which was spoken. *Mat* 2:17
27:9
pass from law till all be *f.* 5:18
in them is *f.* the prophecy. 13:14
not pass till these things be *f.* 24:34
the time is *f.* kingdom. *Mark* 1:15
sign when these things be *f.*? 13:4*
words which shall be *f.* *Luke* 1:20
when they had *f.* the days. 2:43
all things written may be *f.* 21:22
until times of Gentiles be *f.* 24
not eat till it be *f.* in kingdom. 22:16
all things must be *f.* 24:44
this my joy therefore is *f.* *John* 3:29†
they might have my joy *f.* in. 17:13†
God shewed, he hath *f.* *Acts* 3:18
after many days were *f.* Jews. 9:23
and Barnabas *f.* their ministry. 12:25
and as John *f.* his course. 13:25
have *f.* them in condemning. 27
had *f.* all that was written of. 29
God hath *f.* the same to us. 33
grace of God for work they *f.* 14:26
righteousness of law might be *f.* in.
Rom 8:4
loveth another hath *f.* the law. 13:8
when obedience is *f.* *2 Cor* 10:6
law is *f.* in one word. *Gal* 5:14
killing of brethren be *f.* *Rev* 6:11
plagues of seven angels *f.* 15:8*
till words of God be *f.* 17:17*
no more, till 1000 years be *f.* 20:3*
see **scripture**

fulfilling

fire, hail, stormy wind *f.* *Ps* 148:8
love is the *f.* of the law. *Rom* 13:10
f. the desires of the flesh. *Eph* 2:3*

full

of Amorites not yet *f.* *Gen* 15:16
Abraham an old man, and *f.* 25:8
Isaac old and *f.* of days. 35:29
at the end of two *f.* years. 41:1
thin ears devoured seven *f.* 7, 22
money in his sack *f.* weight. 43:21
be *f.* of swarms of flies. *Ex* 8:21
an homer *f.* of manna therein. 16:33
he should make *f.* restitution. 22:3
corn beaten out of *f.* ears. *Lev* 2:14
censer *f.* of coals, hands *f.* of. 16:12
land became *f.* of wickedness. 19:29
within a *f.* year redeem it. 25:29
if not redeemed in a *f.* year. 30
both *f.* of fine flour. *Num* 7:13, 19
25, 31, 37, 43, 49, 55, 61, 67, 73, 79
spoon of ten shekels *f.* of. 14, 20, 26
32, 38, 44, 50, 56, 62, 68, 74, 80, 86
Balak give house *f.* of. 22:18; 24:13
houses *f.* of good things, have eaten
and be *f.* *Deut* 6:11; 8:10, 12
will send grass, that thou mayest eat
and be *f.* 11:15
bewail her father a *f.* month. 21:13
Naphtali *f.* of the blessing. 33:23
Joshua was *f.* of Spirit of. 34:9
dew, a bowl *f.* of water. *Judg* 6:38
house was *f.* of men and. 16:27
I went out *f.* and Lord. *Ruth* 1:21
and a *f.* reward be given thee. 2:12
they that were *f.* hired. *1 Sam* 2:5
they gave them in *f.* tale. 18:27
in country of Philistines a *f.* 27:7
and with one *f.* line to. *2 Sam* 8:2
make valley *f.* of ditches. *2 Ki* 3:16
when vessels were *f.* she said. 4:6
mountain was *f.* of horses. 6:17
all the way was *f.* of garments. 7:15
house of Baal was *f.* from one. 10:21
grant it me for *f.* price. *1 Chr* 21:22
I will verily buy it for a *f.* price. 24
David old and *f.* of. 23:1; 29:28
was Haman *f.* of wrath. *Esth* 3:5
f. of indignation against. 5:9
come to grave in a *f.* age. *Job* 5:26
I am *f.* of tossings to and fro. 7:4
I am *f.* of confusion. 10:15
a man *f.* of talk be justified ? 11:2
man is of few days *f.* of trouble. 14:1
bones are *f.* of sins of youth. 20:11
one dieth in his *f.* strength. 21:23
his breasts are *f.* of milk, his. 24
I am *f.* of matter, the Spirit. 32:18
on thy table should be *f.* of. 36:16
Job died, old and *f.* of days. 42:17
they are *f.* of children. *Ps* 17:14*
broken my heart, I am *f.* of. 69:20
waters of a *f.* cup are wrung. 73:10
dark places *f.* of habitations of. 74:20
sent meat to the *f.* 78:25
trees of Lord are *f.* of sap. 104:16*
happy that hath quiver *f.* of. 127:5
that our garners may be *f.* 144:13
an house *f.* of sacrifices. *Pr* 17:1
the *f.* soul loatheth honeycomb. 27:7
hell and destruction are never *f.* 20
lest I be *f.* and deny thee. 30:9
yet the sea is not *f.* *Eccl* 1:7
all things are *f.* of labour. 8
than both hands *f.* with travel. 4:6*
if the clouds be *f.* of rain. 11:3
I am *f.* of burnt offerings. *Isa* 1:11
your hands are *f.* of blood. 15
faithful city *f.* of judgement. 21
earth shall be *f.* of knowledge. 11:9
houses shall be *f.* of doleful. 13:21
waters of Dimon *f.* of blood. 15:9
thou art *f.* of stirs 22:2
valleys shall be *f.* of chariots. 7
a feast *f.* of marrow. 25:6
tables are *f.* of vomit and. 28:8
his lips are *f.* of indignation. 30:27
they are *f.* of the fury of. 51:20
a *f.* wind from those. *Jer* 4:12
when I had fed them to the *f.* 5:7
I am *f.* of the fury of the Lord. 6:11
within two *f.* years will I. 28:3, 11
the Rechabites pots *f.* of wine. 35:5

city sit solitary that was *f.* *Lam* 1:1
he is filled *f.* with reproach. 3:30
their wings were *f.* of. *Ezek* 1:18
court was *f.* of the brightness. 10:4
the wheels were *f.* of eyes. 12
great eagle with wings *f.* of. 17:3
fruitful and *f.* of branches. 19:10
the sum, *f.* of wisdom and. 28:12
rivers shall be *f.* of thee. 32:6
in midst of valley which was *f.* 37:1
ye shall eat fat till ye be *f.* and. 39:19
then was Nebuchadnezzar *f.* of fury. *Dan* 3:19
transgressors are come to *f.* 8:23
Daniel mourned three *f.* weeks. 10:2
floors shall be *f.* of wheat. *Joel* 2:24
but truly I am *f.* of power. *Mi* 3:8
the rich men are *f.* of violence. 6:12
earth was *f.* of his praise. *Hab* 3:3
streets shall be *f.* of boys. *Zech* 8:5
thy body shall be *f.* of light. *Mat* 6:22; *Luke* 11:36
when it was *f.* they drew. *Mat* 13:48
twelve baskets *f.* 14:20; *Mark* 6:43
left seven baskets *f.* *Mat* 15:37
but within are *f.* of extortion. 23:25
within *f.* of dead men's bones. 27
within ye are *f.* of hypocrisy. 28
f. well ye reject commandment of. *Mark* 7:9
filled a spunge *f.* of vinegar. 15:36
now Elizabeth's *f.* time. *Luke* 1:57
Jesus being *f.* of the Holy Ghost. 4:1
behold a man *f.* of leprosy fell. 5:12
woe unto you that are *f.* 6:25
Lazarus laid at his gate *f.* of. 16:20
among us, *f.* of grace. *John* 1:14
for my time is not yet *f.* come. 7:8
that your joy be *f.* 15:11; 16:24
was set a vessel *f.* of vinegar. 19:29
men are *f.* of new wine. *Acts* 2:13
shalt make me *f.* of joy. 28
look out men *f.* of Holy Ghost. 6:3
Stephen *f.* of faith and. 5, 8; 7:55
Moses was *f.* forty years old. 7:23
Dorcas *f.* of good works. 9:36
Barnabas *f.* of the Holy Ghost. 11:24
O *f.* of all subtilty and. 13:10
they were *f.* of wrath and. 19:28
being *f.* of envy, murder. *Rom* 1:29
ye also are *f.* of goodness. 15:14
now ye are *f.* now ye are. *1 Cor* 4:8
and was *f.* of heaviness. *Phil* 2:26*
I am instructed to be *f.* and. 4:12
I have all and abound, I am *f.* 18
f. proof of thy ministry. *2 Tim* 4:5
meat to them of *f.* age. *Heb* 5:14*
tongue an unruly evil, *f.* *Jas* 3:8
wisdom from above is pure, *f.* 17
with joy unspeakable, *f.* of. *1 Pet* 1:8
eyes *f.* of adultery. *2 Pet* 2:14
that your joy may be *f.* *1 John* 1:4
that we receive a *f.* reward. *2 John* 8
to face, that our joy may be *f.* 12
four beasts *f.* of eyes. *Rev* 4:6, 8
every one golden vials *f.* of. 5:8
seven golden vials *f.* of wrath. 15:7
kingdom was *f.* of darkness. 16:10*
I saw a woman *f.* of names of. 17:3
a golden cup *f.* of abominations. 4
seven vials *f.* of seven last. 21:9
see **assurance, compassion**

is **full**

set aside that which *is f.* *2 Ki* 4:4
his mouth *is f.* of cursing. *Ps* 10:7 *Rom* 3:14
right hand *is f.* of bribes. *Ps* 26:10
of the Lord *is f.* of majesty. 29:4
earth *is f.* of goodness of the. 33:5
hand *is f.* of righteousness. 48:10
river of God, which *is f.* of. 65:9
wine is red, it *is f.* of mixture. 75:8
my soul *is f.* of troubles. 88:3
the earth *is f.* of thy riches. 104:24
earth *is f.* of thy mercy. 119:64
heart of sons of men *is f.* of. *Eccl* 9:3
a fool *is f.* of words. 10:14*
land *is f.* of silver, *is f.* of. *Isa* 2:7
their land also *is f.* of idols. 8
the whole earth *is f.* of his. 6:3
as a cage *is f.* of birds. *Jer* 5:27
with him that *is f.* of days. 6:11
the land *is f.* of adulterers. 23:10
land *is f.* of crimes, city *is f.* of. *Ezek* 7:23
land *is f.* of blood, city *is f.* of. 9:9
for the press *is f.* the fats. *Joel* 3:13
cart is pressed, that *is f.* of sheaves. *Amos* 2:13
it *is* all *f.* of lies and. *Nah* 3:1
body *is f.* of light, *is f.* of. *Luke* 11:34
inward part *is f.* of ravening. 39

to the **full**

and did eat bread *to the f.* *Ex* 16:3
when Lord shall give bread in morning *to the f.* 8
eat your bread *to the f.* *Lev* 26:5

fuller, -s

and stood in the highway of the *f.'s* field. *2 Ki* 18:17; *Isa* 7:3; 36:2
like a refiner's fire, and *f.'s.* *Mal* 3:2
so as no *f.* on earth can. *Mark* 9:3

fully

Caleb followed me *f.* *Num* 14:24
Boaz said, it hath *f.* been. *Ruth* 2:11
Solomon went not *f.* after. *1 Ki* 11:6
heart of men is *f.* set to. *Eccl* 8:11
devoured as stubble *f.* *Nah* 1:10*
day of Pentecost *f.* come. *Acts* 2:1
being *f.* persuaded, that. *Rom* 4:21
let every man be *f.* persuaded. 14:5
I have *f.* preached the gospel. 15:19
thou hast *f.* known my. *2 Tim* 3:10
by me preaching might be *f.* 4:17
thrust in sickle, grapes *f.* *Rev* 14:18

fulness

the *f.* of the winepress. *Num* 18:27
precious things of the earth, *f.* *Deut* 33:16
the sea roar and the *f.* thereof. *1 Chr* 16:32; *Ps* 96:11; 98:7
in *f.* of sufficiency shall. *Job* 20:22
in thy presence is *f.* of joy. *Ps* 16:11
earth is the Lord's and the *f.* 24:1 *1 Cor* 10:26, 28
the world is mine, and *f.* thereof. *Ps* 50:12; 89:11
iniquity of Sodom, *f.* of. *Ezek* 16:49
of his *f.* have we received grace for. *John* 1:16
how much more their *f.*? *Rom* 11:12
till *f.* of Gentiles be come in. 25
come in the *f.* of the gospel. 15:29
when *f.* of time was come. *Gal* 4:4
that in the *f.* of times he. *Eph* 1:10
the *f.* of him that filleth all in all. 23
be filled with the *f.* of God. 3:19
come to stature of *f.* of Christ. 4:13
in him should all *f.* dwell. *Col* 1:19
in him dwelleth *f.* of Godhead. 2:9

furbish

f. the spears, put on the. *Jer* 46:4

furbished

a sword is sharpened and also *f.* *Ezek* 21:9, 10
given to be *f.* 11
sword *f.* to consume. 28

furious

(*Revisions substitute* wrathful)
with *f.* man thou shalt. *Pr* 22:24
a *f.* man aboundeth in. 29:22
execute judgement in *f.* rebukes. *Ezek* 5:15; 25:17
Nebuchadnezzar the king was very *f.* *Dan* 2:12
Lord revengeth, and is *f.* *Nah* 1:2

furiously

of Jehu, he driveth *f.* *2 Ki* 9:20
they shall deal *f.* with. *Ezek* 23:25*

furlongs

(*A furlong was about an eighth of a mile*)
from Jerusalem sixty *f.* *Luke* 24:13
rowed about five and twenty *f.* *John* 6:19
nigh Jerusalem about fifteen *f.* 11:18
out by space of 1600 *f.* *Rev* 14:20
the city with reed, 12,000 *f.* 21:16

furnace

[1] *An oven for smelting iron from the ore,* Deut 4:20; 1 Ki 8:51. [2] *A crucible for refining gold and silver,* Pr 17:3; Ezek 22:20. [3] *A bake oven,* Neh 3:11; Isa 31:9.

a smoking *f.* and a. *Gen* 15:17
went up as the smoke of a *f.* 19:28
handfuls of ashes of the *f.* *Ex* 9:8
and they took ashes of the *f.* 10
ascended as the smoke of a *f.* 19:18
taken you out of the *f.* *Deut* 4:20
from the midst of the *f.* *1 Ki* 8:51 *Jer* 11:4
pure words, as silver tried in a *f.* of earth. *Ps* 12:6
as the *f.* for gold. *Pr* 17:3; 27:21
his *f.* in Jerusalem. *Isa* 31:9
chosen thee in *f.* of affliction. 48:10
dross in midst of the *f.* *Ezek* 22:18
gather you as tin in midst of *f.* 20
silver melted in midst of the *f.* 22
be cast into midst of a burning fiery *f.* *Dan* 3:6, 11
cast them into a *f.* *Mat* 13:42, 50
brass, as if burned in a *f.* *Rev* 1:15
a smoke, as smoke of a great *f.* 9:2

furnaces

Hashub repaired tower of *f.* *Neh* 3:11
from the tower of the *f.* to. 12:38

furnish

shalt *f.* him liberally. *Deut* 15:14
can God *f.* a table in? *Ps* 78:19*
that *f.* the drink offering. *Isa* 65:11*
f. thyself to go into. *Jer* 46:19

furnished

Hiram *f.* Solomon with. *1 Ki* 9:11
she hath also *f.* her table. *Pr* 9:2
wedding *f.* with guests. *Mat* 22:10*
will shew you a room *f.* *Mark* 14:15 *Luke* 22:12
throughly *f.* unto all. *2 Tim* 3:17

furniture

(*General meaning, fittings*)
put them in camels' *f.* *Gen* 31:34
tabernacle and his *f.* *Ex* 31:7; 39:33
table and his *f.* 8*
altar with all his *f.* 9*
the candlestick and his *f.* 35:14*
none end of all pleasant *f.* *Nah* 2:9

furrow

bind the unicorn in the *f.*? *Job* 39:10

furrows

or the *f.* thereof likewise. *Job* 31:38
thou settlest the *f.* *Ps* 65:10
plowed, made long their *f.* 129:3
might water it by *f.* of. *Ezek* 17:7*
it shall wither in the *f.* where. 10*
as hemlock in the *f.* of. *Hos* 10:4
bind themselves in their two *f.* 10*
their altars as heaps in the *f.* 12:11

further

angel went *f.* and stood. *Num* 22:26
officers shall speak *f.* to. *Deut* 20:8
inquired of the Lord *f.* *1 Sam* 10:22
shalt thou come, but no *f.* *Job* 38:11
yea, twice, will proceed no *f.* 40:5
f. by these, my son, be admonished. *Eccl* 12:12
f. need have we of witnesses? *Mat* 26:65; *Mark* 14:63; *Luke* 22:71
why troublest Master *f.*? *Mark* 5:35
as he would have gone *f.* *Luke* 24:28
that it spread no *f.* *Acts* 4:17
when they had *f.* threatened them. 21
Herod proceeded *f.* to take. 12:3
f. he brought Greeks also. 21:28
that I be not *f.* tedious. 24:4
they had gone a little *f.* 27:28*
they shall proceed no *f.* *2 Tim* 3:9
f. need another priest. *Heb* 7:11

further, *verb*

f. not his wicked device. *Ps* 140:8

furtherance

things which happened have fallen out unto *f.* of gospel. *Phil* 1:12
shall abide with you for your *f.* 25

furthered

f. the people and house of. *Ezra* 8:36

furthermore

the Lord said *f* to Moses. *Ex* 4:
Lord said *f.* to Ezekiel. *Ezek* 8:

gallows
to hang Mordecai on g. Esth 6:4
hanged Haman on the g. 7:10; 8:7
sons be hanged on the g. 9:13, 25

Gamaliel
of Manasseh, G. son of. Num 1:10
2:20; 7:54, 59; 10:23
a Pharisee named G. Acts 5:34
brought up at the feet of G. 22:3

Gammadims
and the G. were in thy. Ezek 27:11

gap
man that should stand in g. before.
Ezek 22:30

gaped
have g. upon. Job 16:10; Ps 22:13

gaps
not gone up into the g. Ezek 13:5

garden
man and put him in g. Gen 2:15
sent him forth from the g. 3:23
plain of Jordan was as the g. 13:10
and wateredst it as a g. Deut 11:10
I may have it for a g. 1 Ki 21:2
shooteth forth in his g. Job 8:16
g. inclosed is my sister. S of S 4:12
g. let him come into his g. 16
I am come into my g. my sister. 5:1
is gone down into his g. 6:2, 11
Zion is as a lodge in a g. Isa 1:8
ye shall be as a g. which hath. 30
desert like the g. of God. 51:3
shalt be like a watered g. 58:11
as the g. causeth things sown. 61:11
shall be as a watered g. Jer 31:12
away his tabernacle, as it were of a g.
Lam 2:6
in Eden the g. of God. Ezek 28:13
cedars in g. of God could not. 31:8
all the trees in the g. of God. 9
land is become like the g. of. 36:35
land is as the g. of Eden. Joel 2:3
took and cast into his g. Luke 13:19
Cedron, where was a g. John 18:1
did not I see thee in the g.? 26
there was a g. and in the g. 19:41

gardener
he had been the g. John 20:15

gardens
thy tents as g. by the. Num 24:6
I made me g. and orchards. Eccl 2:5
a fountain of g. a well. S of S 4:15
to feed in the g. and to gather. 6:2
thou that dwellest in the g. 8:13
be confounded for the g. Isa 1:29
a people that sacrificeth in g. 65:3
purify themselves in the g. 66:17
g. and eat the fruit. Jer 29:5, 28
sent blasting, when your g. Amos 4:9
they shall also make g. and 9:14

garlands
brought oxen and g. Acts 14:13

garlick
we remember the g. we. Num 11:5

garment
and Japhet took a g. Gen 9:23
came out red, like a hairy g. 25:25
by his g. he left his g. 39:12
he left his g. with me. 15, 18
she laid up his g. till her lord. 39:16
blood thereof on any g. Lev 6:27
g. wherein is the plague. 13:47, 49
if plague be spread in the g. in. 51
plague of leprosy in a g. 59; 14:55
every g. whereon is the seed. 15:17
nor g. mingled. 19:9; Deut 22:11*
not put on a woman's g. Deut 22:5
goodly Babylonish g. Josh 7:21
Achan, the silver, and the g. 24
they spread a g. and. Judg 8:25
Tamar had a g. of. 2 Sam 13:18
she rent her g. and went on. 19
clad himself with a new g. 1 Ki 11:29
took every man his g. 2 Ki 9:13
I heard this I rent my g. Ezra 9:3
having rent my g. and mantle I. 5
Mordecai went with a g. Esth 8:15
consumeth, as a g. that. Job 13:28
force of my disease is my g. 30:18
when I made the cloud the g. 38:9
clay to seal, they stand as a g. 14
discover the face of his g.? Job 41:13
sackcloth also my g. Ps 69:11
violence covereth them as g. 73:6
yea all of them shall wax old like a g.
102:26; Isa 50:9; 51:6, Heb 1:11
with light, as with a g. Ps 104:2
it with the deep as with a g. 6
himself with cursing as a g. 109:18
as the g. which covereth him. 19
g. that is surety. Pr 20:16; 27:13
as he that taketh away a g. in. 25:20
bound the waters in a g.? 30:4
eat them up like a g. Isa 51:8
to give g. of praise for spirit. 61:3
shepherd putteth on his g. Jer 43:12
the naked with a g. Ezek 18:7, 16
whose g. was white as. Dan 7:9
ye pull off robe with the g. Mi 2:8
holy flesh in skirt of his g. Hag 2:12
shall wear a rough g. Zech 13:4*
violence with his g. Mal 2:16
new cloth to old g. Mat 9:16
Mark 2:21; Luke 5:36
touched the hem of his g. Mat 9:20
21; 14:36; Mark 5:27; Luke 8:44
not on a wedding g. Mat 22:11, 12
back again to take up his g.
Mark 13:16
clothed with a long white g. 16:5
sell his g. and buy one. Luke 22:36
cast thy g. about thee. Acts 12:8
hating even the g. spotted. Jude 23
of man clothed with a g. Rev 1:13

garments
and change your g. Gen 35:2
Tamar put her widow's g. 38:14
washed his g. in wine, his. 49:11
may make Aaron's g. to. Ex 28:3
sprinkled the blood on Aaron's g.
29:21; Lev 8:30
them wisdom to make g. Ex 31:10
put off his g. put on other g.
Lev 6:11; 16:23, 24
borders of their g. Num 15:38
strip Aaron of his g. put. 20:26
Moses stripped Aaron of g. put. 28
Gibeonites brought old g. Josh 9:5
you thirty changes of g. Judg 14:12
gave David his g. 1 Sam 18:4
cut off their g. in the middle.
2 Sam 10:4; 1 Chr 19:4
David tare his g. 2 Sam 13:31
to receive money and g.? 2 Ki 5:26
all the way was full of g. and. 7:15
Jehoiakim's g. 25:29; Jer 52:33
one hundred priests' g. Ezra 2:69
gave 530 priests' g. Neh 7:70
gave sixty-seven priests' g. 72
how thy g. are warm. Job 37:17
they part my g. among. Ps 22:18
all thy g. smell of myrrh. 45:8
went down to skirts of his g. 133:2
let thy g. be always white. Eccl 9:8
smell of thy g. is like. S of S 4:11
every battle is with g. Isa 9:5
put on thy beautiful g. 52:1
their webs shall not become g. 59:6
he put on the g. of vengeance. 17
he hath clothed me with g. 61:10
that cometh with dyed g. 63:1
shall be sprinkled upon my g. 3
not afraid, nor rent g. Jer 36:24
could not touch their g. Lam 4:14
tookest thy broidered g. Ezek 16:18
there shall lay their g. they. 42:14
sanctify people with their g. 44:19
in their coats and other g. Dan 3:21
heart, and not your g. Joel 2:13
clothed with filthy g. Zech 3:3
take the filthy g. from him. 4
spread their g. in the way. Mat 21:8
Mark 11:8
the borders of their g. Mat 23:5
they parted his g. casting lots.
27:35; Mark 15:24
casting away his g. Mark 10:50
g. on the colt. 11:7; Luke 19:35
by them in shining g. Luke 24:4*
he laid aside his g. John 13:4
shewing coats and g. Acts 9:39
and your g. are motheaten. Jas 5:2
have not defiled their g. Rev 3:4
watcheth and keepeth his g. 16:15

holy garments
make holy g. for Aaron. Ex 28:2, 4
put wisdom to make holy g. 31:10
holy g. he shall wash. Lev 16:4, 32
lay their holy g. Ezek 42:14

garner
gather his wheat into the g.
Mat 3:12; Luke 3:17

garners
our g. may be full. Ps 144:13
the g. are laid desolate. Joel 1:17

garnish, -ed
he g. the house with. 2 Chr 3:6
by his Spirit he hath g. Job 26:13
findeth it swept and g. Mat 12:44
Luke 11:25
you g. the sepulchres of. Mat 23:29
of the wall are g. Rev 21:19*

garrison, -s
to hill where is g. of. 1 Sam 10:5
Jonathan smote the g. of the. 13:3
over to the Philistines' g. 14:1, 6
the g. and the spoilers, they also. 15
David put g. in Syria. 2 Sam 8:6
1 Chr 18:6
David put g. in Edom. 2 Sam 8:14
1 Chr 18:13
g. of Philistines in Beth-lehem.
2 Sam 23:14; 1 Chr 11:16
Jehoshaphat set g. in Judah.
2 Chr 17:2
strong g. shall go down. Ezek 26:11
kept the city with a g. 2 Cor 11:32

gat
Moses g. him up into. Ex 24:18
g. up from tabernacle. Num 16:27
and g. them up to the top. Judg 9:51
and David g. him a. 2 Sam 8:13
covered him, but he g. 1 Ki 1:1
the pains of hell g. hold. Ps 116:3
I g. men singers, and. Eccl 2:8
we g. our bread with the. Lam 5:9

gate
The gates were the important part of an ancient city. They gave the only means of passing through the wall and were usually closed at night and were strengthened by bars of brass or iron. The gate was the place of public concourse, partly because it was an open space, not usually found elsewhere in a city. Much of the legal business of the city was done there, Ruth 4:11.

The word gate is sometimes used to mean power or dominion. God promises Abraham, that his posterity should possess the gates of their enemies, their towns, their fortresses, Gen 22:17. *They should conquer them, they should have dominion over them.*

The gates of death are the brink, or mouth of the grave, Ps 9:13.

thy seed possess the g. of enemies.
Gen 22:17; 24:60
Jacob said, this is the g. of. 28:17
go in and out from g. to g. Ex 32:27
bring him to the g. Deut 21:19
bring them both out to the g. 22:24
brother's wife go up to g. 25:7
they shut the g. Josh 2:7
took the doors of the g. Judg 16:3
then went Boaz to the g. Ruth 4:1
dead be not cut off from the g. 10
by the side of the g. 1 Sam 4:18
beside the way of the g. 2 Sam 15:2
to the chamber over the g. 18:33
water by g. 23:15, 16; 1 Chr 11:18
when Elijah came to g. 1 Ki 17:10
have the charge of the g. 2 Ki 7:17
cast lots for every g. 1 Chr 26:13
porters at every g. 2 Chr 8:14
the g. should be shut. Neh 13:19
before the king's g. Esth 4:2; 6:12
when I went out to the g. Job 29:7
this g. of the Lord, the. Ps 118:20
the fish pools by the g. S of S 7:4
howl, O g. cry, O city. Isa 14:31
the g. is smitten with. 24:12

to turn the battle to the *g.* *Isa* 28:6
at the entry of new *g.* *Jer* 36:10
have ceased from the *g.* *Lam* 5:14
to door of the inner *g.* *Ezek* 8:3
at the door of the *g.* twenty-. 11:1
Lord come by way of the *g.* 43:4
this *g.* shall be shut, none. 44:2
enter by way of *g.* 3; 46:2, 8
blood on the posts of the *g.* 45:19
the *g.* of the inner court shall. 46:1
but the *g.* shall not be shut till. 2
open the *g.* one shall shut the *g.* 12
g. of Reuben, one *g.* of Judah. 48:31
the *g.* of my people. *Ob* 13
he is come into the *g.* of. *Mi* 1:9
from Lord to the *g.* of Jerusalem. 12
have passed through the *g.* 2:13
strait *g.* wide is the *g.* and broad is.
Mat 7:13, 14; *Luke* 13:24*
when he came nigh *g.* *Luke* 7:12
a beggar Lazarus laid at his *g.* 16:20
Cornelius stood before *g.* *Acts* 10:17
they came to the iron *g.* 12:10
Rhoda opened not the *g.* for. 14
suffered without the *g.* *Heb* 13:12
every several *g.* was of. *Rev* 21:21
see **entereth, entering**

gate
he that exalteth his *g.* *Pr* 17:19

at the **gate**
of all that went in *at the g.* of city.
Gen 23:10, 18
Jehu entered in *at the g.* *2 Ki* 9:31
at the g. of Sur, and a third *at the g.*
11:6; *2 Chr* 23:5
man's left hand *at the g.* *2 Ki* 23:8
set a chest *at the g.* of. *2 Chr* 24:8
I see Mordecai sitting *at the* king's
g. *Esth* 5:13
in array *at the g.* *Isa* 22:7
they laid daily *at the g.* *Acts* 3:2*
who sat for alms *at* beautiful *g.* 10
see **fish gate**

high **gate**
through the *high g.* *2 Chr* 23:20
Jotham built the *high g.* of. 27:3
in stocks in the *high g.* *Jer* 20:2
see **horse gate**

in the **gate**
and Lot sat *in the g.* *Gen* 19:1
Moses stood *in the g.* of. *Ex* 32:26
virginity to elders *in g.* *Deut* 22:15
wait for Samson *in the g.* *Judg* 16:2
people *in the g.* said, we. *Ruth* 4:11
near to Samuel *in the g.* *1 Sam* 9:18
Abner aside *in the g.* *2 Sam* 3:27
king sat *in the g.* they told all. 19:8
a shekel *in the g.* *2 Ki* 7:1, 18
the people trod on him *in the g.* 20
sat *in the* king's *g.* *Esth* 2:19, 21
saw him *in the* king's *g.* 5:9
his children are crushed *in the g.*
Job 5:4
when I saw my help *in the g.* 31:21
that sit *in the g.* speak. *Ps* 69:12
speak with the enemies *in g.* 127:5
the afflicted *in the g.* *Pr* 22:22
openeth not his mouth *in the g.* 24:7
him that reproveth *in g.* *Isa* 29:21
stand *in the g.* of the Lord's. *Jer* 7:2
stand *in the g.* of children. 17:19
when he was *in the g.* of. 37:13
king then sitting *in the g.* of. 38:7
princes of Babylon sat *in the g.* 39:3
but Daniel sat *in the g.* *Dan* 2:49
that rebuketh *in the g.* *Amos* 5:10
turn aside the poor *in the g.* 12
establish judgement *in the g.* 15

old **gate**
old g. repaired Jehoiada. *Neh* 3:6
priests went above the *old g.* 12:39

prison **gate**
stood still in the *prison g.* *Neh* 12:39

sheep **gate**
went even unto *sheep g.* *Neh* 12:39

valley **gate**
towers at the *valley g.* *2 Chr* 26:9
out by *g.* of the *valley.* *Neh* 2:13
entered by the *g.* of the *valley.* 15
the *valley g.* repaired Hanun. 3:13

water **gate**
over against *water g.* *Neh* 3:26
the street before the *water g.* 8:1
in the law before the *water g.* 3
in the street of the *water g.* 16
even to the *water g.* eastward. 12:37

gates
Levite within your *g.* *Deut* 12:12
son set up *g.* *Josh* 6:26; *1 Ki* 16:34
gods, then was war in *g.* *Judg* 5:8
the Lord shall go to the *g.* 5:11
appointed to praise in *g.* *2 Chr* 31:2
g. are burnt. *Neh* 1:3; 2:3, 13, 17
let not the *g.* of Jerusalem be. 7:3
and Levites purified the *g.* 12:30
my servants set I at the *g.* 13:19*
the Levites to keep the *g.* 22
thy praise in the *g.* *Ps* 9:14
lift up your heads, O ye *g.* 24:7, 9
the Lord loveth the *g.* of Zion. 87:2
enter into his *g.* with. 100:4
for he hath broken the *g.* of. 107:16
open to me the *g.* of. 118:19
in openings of *g.* *Pr* 1:21; 8:3
watching daily at my *g.* 8:34
the wicked at the *g.* of the. 14:19
husband is known in the *g.* 31:23
works praise her in the *g.* 31
our *g.* are all manner. *S of S* 7:13*
and her *g.* shall lament. *Isa* 3:26
they may go into the *g.* of the. 13:2
open ye the *g.* that righteous. 26:2
I shall go to the *g.* of the. 38:10
before him the two leaved *g.* 45:1*
I will break in pieces the *g.* of. 2*
go through, go through the *g.* 62:10
hear the word, all ye that enter in at
the *g.* *Jer* 7:2; 17:20; 22:2
Judah mourneth, and the *g.* 14:2
fan them with a fan in *g.* of. 15:7
go and stand in all the *g.* of. 17:19
on the sabbath by the *g.* 21, 24
there enter into the *g.* 25; 22:4
I will kindle a fire in the *g.* of. 27
and cast forth beyond the *g.* 22:19
Zion's *g.* are desolate. *Lam* 1:4
her *g.* are sunk into the ground. 2:9
should have entered the *g.* 4:12
of sword against their *g.* *Ezek* 21:15
battering rams against the *g.* 22
she is broken that was the *g.* of. 26:2
at the east side three *g.* one. 48:32
foreigners entered his *g.* *Ob* 11
the *g.* of the rivers shall. *Nah* 2:6
the *g.* of thy land shall be set. 3:13
truth and peace in your *g.* *Zech* 8:16
g. of hell shall not prevail. *Mat* 16:18
and they watched the *g.* *Acts* 9:24
priests brought oxen to the *g.* 14:13
the city had twelve *g.* at *g.* *Rev* 21:12
three *g.* on the north three *g.* 13
the twelve *g.* were twelve pearls. 21
the *g.* of it shall not be shut at. 25
see **bars, death**

thy **gates**
thy stranger within *thy g.* *Ex* 20:10
Deut 5:14
thou shalt write them on *thy g.*
Deut 6:9; 11:20
eat flesh in *thy g.* 12:15, 21
mayest not eat within *thy g.* the. 17
thou and Levite in *thy g.* 18
the stranger that is in *thy g.* 14:21
Levite within *thy g.* thou shalt. 27
up the tithe within *thy g.* 28
the widow within *thy g.* shall. 29
poor man within any of *thy g.* 15:7
eat the firstling within *thy g.* 22
the passover within *thy g.* 16:5
Levite in *thy g.* 11, 14; 26:12
shalt thou make in all *thy g.* 16:18
that man or woman to *thy g.* 17:5
Levite come from any of *thy g.* 18:6
escaped dwell in one of *thy g.* 23:16
not oppress within *thy g.* 24:14
besiege thee in all *thy g.* 28:52
distress thee in all *thy g.* 55
gather the people within *thy g.* 31:12
stand within *thy g.* O. *Ps* 122:2
I will make *thy g.* of. *Isa* 54:12
therefore *thy g.* shall be open. 60:11
thy walls salvation, and *thy g.* 18
enter *thy g.* as men. *Ezek* 26:10

Gath
ark be carried about to *G.* *1 Sam* 5:8
golden emerods, for *G.* one. 6:17
that David was fled to *G.* 27:4
tell it not in *G.* publish. *2 Sam* 1:20
giant in *G.* and fell by the hand of
David and. 21:22; *1 Chr* 20:8
Shimei ran to *G.* *1 Ki* 2:39
Shimei went to *G.* to seek. 40
and fought against *G.* *2 Ki* 12:17
drove away inhabitants of *G.*
1 Chr 8:13
David took *G.* from the. 18:1
brake down wall of *G.* *2 Chr* 26:6
then go down to *G.* of. *Amos* 6:2
declare ye it not at *G.* *Mi* 1:10

gather
Jacob said, *g.* stones, and. *Gen* 31:46
let them *g.* all the food of. 41:35
let them go and *g.* straw. *Ex* 5:7
g. stubble. 12
g. thy cattle. 9:19*
shall *g.* a certain rate. 16:4
g. twice as much. 5
six days *g.* it. 26
sow thy land and *g.* 23:10; *Lev* 25:3
not *g.* the gleanings. *Lev* 19:9; 23:22
thou shalt not *g.* every grape of. 10
nor *g.* grapes of the vine. 25:5, 11
we shall not sow, nor *g.* in our. 20
trumpet, then princes *g.* *Num* 10:4
g. seventy men of the elders. 11:16
a man that is clean shall *g.* 19:9
rain that thou mayest *g.* *Deut* 11:14
thou shalt *g.* all the spoil of. 13:16
vineyard and not *g.* grapes. 28:30, 39
carry much seed out, and *g.* but. 38
g. thee from all nations. 30:3
Ezek 36:24
into the field to *g.* herbs. *2 Ki* 4:39
g. thee to thy 22:20; *2 Chr* 34:28
Levites to *g.* *1 Chr* 13:2
g. money to repair. *2 Chr* 24:5
yet will I *g.* them from. *Neh* 1:9
some appointed to *g.* for the. 12:44
they *g.* the vintage of the. *Job* 24:6*
if he *g.* to himself his spirit. 34:14
will he bring seed, and *g.* it? 39:12
g. not my soul with sinners. *Ps* 26:9
and knoweth not who shall *g.* 39:6
that thou givest them they *g.* 104:28
save us, and *g.* us from 106:47
shall *g.* for him that will. *Pr* 28:8
to sinner travail, to *g.* *Eccl* 2:26
gone down to *g.* lilies. *S of S* 6:2
there the owl *g.* under. *Isa* 34:15
he shall *g.* the lambs with. 40:11
fear not, I will *g.* thee from. 43:5
great mercies will I *g.* thee. 54:7
yet will I *g.* others to him. 56:8
cast up the highway, *g.* out. 62:10
I will *g.* all nations and. 66:18
g. to flee. *Jer* 6:1*
the children *g.* wood. 7:18
none shall *g.* them. 9:22
g. up thy wares. 10:17
I will *g.* the remnant of my. 23:3
I will *g.* you from all the. 29:14
I will *g.* them from coasts of. 31:8
32:37; *Ezek* 20:34, 41; 34:13
he that scattered Israel will *g.*
Jer 31:10
g. ye wine, and summer. 40:10
and none shall *g.* up him that. 49:5
I will even *g.* you from. *Ezek* 11:17
I will *g.* all thy lovers against. 16:37
I will *g.* you into the midst of. 22:19
as they *g.* silver, so will I *g.* 20, 21
g. the pieces. 24:4
I will *g.* the Egyptians. 29:13
I will *g.* them on every. 37:21; 39:17
among nations, I will *g.* *Hos* 8:10
Egypt shall *g.* them up. 9:6
g. the elders and the. *Joel* 1:14
much pained, all faces shall *g.* 2:6*
g. the people, *g.* the children. 16
I will *g.* all nations, and bring. 3:2
will surely *g.* remnant. *Mi* 2:12
g. her that was driven out. 4:6
Zeph 3:19
he shall *g.* them as sheaves into. 12
g. thyself in troops, O daughter. 5:1
the faces of them all *g.* *Nah* 2:10*

they shall *g.* captivity as. *Hab* 1:9
they catch them, and *g.* them in. 15
my determination is to *g.* *Zeph* 3:8
I will *g.* them that are sorrowful. 18
even in the time that I *g.* you. 20
I will hiss for them and *g.* *Zech* 10:8
I will *g.* them out of Assyria. 10
I will *g.* all nations against. 14:2
g. his wheat into his garner.
Mat 3:12; *Luke* 3:17
they sow not, nor do they *g.* *Mat* 6:26
do men *g.* grapes ? 7:16; *Luke* 6:44
wilt that we go and *g.*? *Mat* 13:28
he said, nay, lest while ye *g.* up. 29
burn tares, but *g.* the wheat into. 30
shall *g.* out of his kingdom all. 41
and that *g.* where I have not. 25:26
as a hen doth *g.* her. *Luke* 13:34
g. up the fragments that. *John* 6:12
men *g.* them and cast them. 15:6
g. the clusters of vine. *Rev* 14:18
g. them to the battle of that. 16:14

gather *together*

few they shall *g. tog.* *Gen* 34:30
g. yourselves *tog.* ye sons. 49:1, 2*
g. the elders of Israel *tog.* *Ex* 3:16
g. congregation of Israel *tog.*
Lev 8:3*; *Num* 8:9*
g. thou the assembly *tog.* *Num* 20:8*
g. the people *tog.* 21:16; *Deut* 4:10*
31:12*
g. the rest *tog.* and. *2 Sam* 12:28
O God, and *g.* us *tog.* *1 Chr* 16:35
David commanded to *g. tog.* 22:2
in my heart to *g. tog.* *Neh* 7:5
may *g. tog.* all the fair. *Esth* 2:3
g. tog. the Jews present in. 4:16
if he *g. tog.* who can ? *Job* 11:10*
g. my saints *tog.* unto me. *Ps* 50:5
they *g.* themselves *tog.* to. 56:6
they *g. together* against the. 94:21
they *g.* themselves *tog.* 104:22*
time to *g.* stones *tog.* *Eccl* 3:5
shall *g. tog.* the dispersed. *Isa* 11:12
these *g. tog.* and. 49:18; 60:4
they shall surely *g. tog.* but. 54:15
the trumpet, cry, *g. tog.* *Jer* 4:5*
g. ye *tog.* and come against. 49:14
king sent to *g. tog.* *Dan* 3:2
g. yourselves *tog.* round. *Joel* 3:11
g. tog. yea, *g. tog.* O. *Zeph* 2:1
g. tog. first the tares. *Mat* 13:30
they shall *g. tog.* his elect. 24:31
Mark 13:27
he should *g. tog.* in one. *John* 11:52
Eph 1:10*
g. tog. to the supper of. *Rev* 19:17
g. Gog and Magog *tog.* to. 20:8

gathered

Abraham died and was *g.* *Gen* 25:8
Ishmael was *g.* 17
Isaac was *g.* to people. 35:29
Jacob was *g.* to his people. 49:29, 33
and they *g.* some more. *Ex* 16:17
that *g.* much, he that *g.* little. 18
2 Cor 8:15
they *g.* it every morning. *Ex* 16:21
hast *g.* in thy labours. 23:16
ye have *g.* in the fruits. *Lev* 23:39
the people *g.* quails. *Num* 11:32
g. sticks. 15:32
g. congregation against. 16:19*, 42*
Aaron shall be *g* to. 20:24, 26
Moses *g.* to his people. 27:13
31:2; *Deut* 32:50
kings *g.* their meat. *Judg* 1:7
that generation was *g.* to. 2:10
and Abiezer was *g.* after. 6:34
there were *g.* vain men to. 11:3
they *g.* all the lords of. *1 Sam* 5:8
every one that was in distress *g.* 22:2
which cannot be *g.* up. *2 Sam* 14:14
they *g.* all able to put. *2 Ki* 3:21
Josiah be *g.* to grave in peace. 22:20
2 Chr 34:28
all my servants were *g.* *Neh* 5:16
down, but shall not be *g.* *Job* 27:19
the mighty are *g.* against. *Ps* 59:3
and he *g.* them out of lands. 107:3
of the mountains are *g.* *Pr* 27:25
who hath *g.* the winds in his ? 30:4
I *g.* me also silver. *Eccl* 2:8
I have *g.* my myrrh with. *S of S* 5:1
he fenced it, and *g.* out. *Isa* 5:2
one gathereth eggs, have I *g.* 10:14
ye shall be *g.* one by one. 27:12
vultures be *g.* 34:15
his Spirit *g.* them. 16
though Israel be not *g.* yet. 49:5
besides those that are *g.* 56:8
but they that have *g.* it shall. 62:9*
and all nations shall be *g.* *Jer* 3:17
they shall not be *g.* 8:2; 25:33
all people *g.* against Jeremiah. 26:9
all the Jews *g.* to thee should. 40:15
I shall have *g.* house. *Ezek* 28:25
be brought together nor *g.* 29:5
hast thou *g.* thy company to ? 38:13*
have *g.* them out of their. 39:27
but I have *g.* them to their own. 28
the people shall be *g.* *Hos* 10:10
I am as when they *g.* *Mi* 7:1
tares are *g.* and burnt. *Mat* 13:40
a net cast into the sea, and *g.* of. 47
before him shall be *g.* all. 25:32
and *g.* to him the whole band. 27:27
g. chief priests a council. *John* 11:47
g. a company, set city. *Acts* 17:5
when Paul had *g.* a bundle of. 28:3
the angel *g.* the vine of. *Rev* 14:19

gathered *together*

they *g.* them *tog.* upon. *Ex* 8:14
congregation to be *g. tog.* *Num* 10:7
fish of the sea be *g. tog.*? 11:22
congregation was *g. tog.* *Judg* 20:1*
11; *Ezra* 3:1; *Neh* 8:1
Judah *g. tog.* to ask. *2 Chr* 20:4
they *g.* themselves *tog.* *Job* 16:10
under nettles were they *g. tog.* 30:7
abjects *g.* themselves *tog.* *Ps* 35:15
of the people are *g. tog.* 47:9
when people are *g. tog.* to. 102:22
are they *g. tog.* for war. 140:2
children of Judah be *g. tog.* *Hos* 1:11
nations are *g. tog.* against. *Mi* 4:11*
all people be *g. tog.* *Zech* 12:3
two or three are *g. tog.* *Mat* 18:20
I have *g.* thy children *tog.*, as a hen.
23:37; *Luke* 13:34
there will eagles be *g. tog.*
Mat 24:28; *Luke* 17:37
all the city was *g. tog.* *Mark* 1:33
younger son *g.* all *tog.* *Luke* 15:13
they found the eleven *g. tog.* 24:33
rulers were *g. tog.* *Acts* 4:26
where many were *g. tog.* 12:12
had *g.* the church *tog.* 14:27
when ye are *g. tog.* and. *1 Cor* 5:4
g. tog. into a place called. *Rev* 16:16
beast and his army *g. tog.* 19:19

gatherer, -s

thy hand as a grape *g.* *Jer* 6:9
grape *g.* come to thee. 49:9; *Ob* 5
I was a *g.* of sycamore. *Amos* 7:14*

gatherest

when thou *g.* the grapes. *Deut* 24:21

gathereth

that *g.* the ashes shall. *Num* 19:10
he *g.* the waters of sea. *Ps* 33:7
his heart *g.* iniquity to itself. 41:6
he *g.* the outcasts. 147:2; *Isa* 56:8
the ant *g.* her food in the. *Pr* 6:8
he that *g.* in summer is a wise. 10:5
but he that *g.* by labour shall. 13:11
one *g.* eggs that are left. *Isa* 10:14
as when the harvestman *g.* 17:5*
scattered, and no man *g.* *Nah* 3:18
but *g.* to him all nations. *Hab* 2:5
he that *g.* not scattereth. *Mat* 12:30
Luke 11:23
as a hen *g.* her chickens. *Mat* 23:37
he that reapeth *g.* fruit. *John* 4:36

gathering

to him shall the *g.* of. *Gen* 49:10*
they that found him *g.* *Num* 15:33
was there *g.* sticks. *1 Ki* 17:10
were three days in *g.* *2 Chr* 20:25*
vintage shall fail, the *g.* *Isa* 32:10*
your spoil like the *g.* of the. 33:4
g. where thou hast not. *Mat* 25:24
g. that the Lord had. *Acts* 16:10*
and by our *g.* together. *2 Thes* 2:1

gatherings

that there be no *g.* *1 Cor* 16:2*

gave

Adam *g.* names to all. *Gen* 2:20
the woman *g.* me of the tree. 3:12
he *g.* him tithes. 14:20; *Heb* 7:2, 4
Abraham *g.* all that he. *Gen* 25:5
land which God *g.* 28:4; 35:12
Lord *g.* the people favour. *Ex* 11:3
12:36
the cloud *g.* light by night to. 14:20
took of Spirit, and *g.* *Num* 11:25
I *g.* my daughter to. *Deut* 22:16
they *g.* him the city. *Josh* 19:50
the Lord *g.* to Israel all the. 21:43
the Lord *g.* them rest. 44
2 Chr 15:15; 20:30
I drave them out, and *g.* *Judg* 6:9
Lord *g.* her conception. *Ruth* 4:13
God *g.* to Saul another. *1 Sam* 10:9
I *g.* thee thy master's. *2 Sam* 12:8
Lord *g.* Solomon. *1 Ki* 4:29; 5:12
and the Lord *g.* Israel. *2 Ki* 13:5
God *g.* to Heman. *1 Chr* 25:5
and God *g.* Hezekiah. *2 Chr* 32:24
read book, *g.* the sense. *Neh* 8:8
Lord *g.* and the Lord. *Job* 1:21
God *g.* Job twice as much as. 42:10
and the Highest *g.* his. *Ps* 18:13
the Lord *g.* the word, great. 68:11
g. me also gall, they *g.* me. 69:21
for he *g.* them their. 78:29; 106:15
return to God that *g.* it. *Eccl* 12:7
who *g.* Jacob for a spoil ? *Isa* 42:24
I *g.* Egypt for thy ransom. 43:3
I *g.* my back to the smiters. 50:6
my meat also which I *g.* *Ezek* 16:19
I *g.* them my statutes. 20:11
moreover also, I *g.* them my. 12
I *g.* them also statutes that were. 25
God *g.* these four children. *Dan* 1:17
Daniel prayed and *g.* thanks. 6:10
she did not know that I *g.* *Hos* 2:8
g. thee a king in mine anger. 13:11
ye *g.* the Nazarites wine. *Amos* 2:12
I *g.* my covenant to Levi. *Mal* 2:5
Jesus *g.* them power against unclean.
Mat 10:1; *Mark* 6:7; *Luke* 9:1
he brake and *g.* loaves. *Mat* 14:19
15:36; 26:16; *Mark* 6:41; 8:6
14:22; *Luke* 9:16; 22:19
who *g.* thee authority ? *Mat* 21:23
Mark 11:28; *Luke* 20:2
ye *g.* me meat, ye *g.* me. *Mat* 25:35
ye *g.* me no meat, and ye *g.* me. 42
husks, and no man *g.* *Luke* 15:16
to them *g.* he power to. *John* 1:12
God so loved world that he *g.* 3:16
he *g.* them bread from heaven. 6:31
my Father who *g.* them me. 10:29
Father *g.* me commandment. 14:31
to speak as Spirit *g.* them. *Acts* 2:4
and he *g.* them no inheritance. 7:5
God *g.* Joseph favour and. 10
Cornelius *g.* much alms to the. 10:2
as God *g.* them the like gift. 11:17
smote him, because he *g.* not. 12:23
afterward God *g.* them Saul. 13:21
he did good, and *g.* us rain. 14:17
to whom we *g.* no such. 15:24
when put to death, I *g.* my. 26:10
God *g.* them over to a. *Rom* 2:28
even as the Lord *g.* to. *1 Cor* 3:5
Apollos watered, but God *g.* the. 6
but first *g.* their own. *2 Cor* 8:5
who *g.* himself. *Gal* 1:4; *Tit* 2:14
who loved me, and *g.* *Gal* 2:20
but God *g.* it to Abraham by. 3:18
and *g.* him to be head. *Eph* 1:22
he led captivity captive and *g.* 4:8
and he *g.* some apostles; some. 11
Christ loved the church, and *g.* 5:25
commandment we *g.* *1 Thes* 4:2
who *g.* himself a ransom. *1 Tim* 2:6
corrected us, we *g.* them. *Heb* 12:9
and the heavens *g.* rain. *Jas* 5:18
love one another, as he *g.* us.
1 John 3:23
believeth not the record God *g.* 5:10
Jesus Christ which God *g.* *Rev* 1:1
g. her space to repent of her. 2:21
the dragon *g.* him his power. 13:2, 4

gave *up*

Abraham *g. up* ghost. *Gen* 25:8
Isaac *g. up* the ghost. 35:29

Joab *g. up* the sum of. *2 Sam* 24:9
g. them *up* to desolation. *2 Chr* 30:7
he *g. up* their cattle. *Ps* 78:48
I *g.* them *up* to their own. 81:12*
my elders *g. up* ghost. *Lam* 1:19
a loud voice, and *g. up*. *Mark* 15:37
39; *Luke* 23:46; *John* 19:30
Ananias *g. up* the ghost. *Acts* 5:5
God *g.* them *up* to worship. 7:42
God also *g.* them *up* to. *Rom* 1:24
for this cause God *g.* them *up* to. 26
the sea *g. up* the dead. *Rev* 20:13

gavest

the woman whom thou *g.* *Gen* 3:12
land which thou *g.* *1 Ki* 8:34, 40, 48
2 Chr 6:25, 31, 38; *Neh* 9:35
thou *g.* him the name of. *Neh* 9:7
thou *g.* them right judgements. 13
g. them bread from heaven. 15
g. also thy good Spirit, *g.* water. 20
g. them kingdoms and nations. 22
thou *g.* them saviours who saved. 27
g. the goodly wings to ? *Job* 39:13*
life of thee; thou *g.* it him. *Ps* 21:4
thou *g.* him to be meat to. 74:14
thou *g.* me no water for. *Luke* 7:44
g. me no kiss, but this woman. 45
yet thou never *g.* me a kid, to. 15:29
finished work thou *g.* *John* 17:4
men whom thou *g.* me out of world,
thine they were, and thou *g.* 6
the words which thou *g.* me. 8
those that thou *g.* me I have kept. 12
the glory which thou *g.* me. 22
of them whom thou *g.* me. 18:9

gay

that weareth *g.* clothing. *Jas* 2:3*

Gaza

Samson went to *G.* and. *Judg* 16:1
brought Samson down to *G.* 21
Pharaoh smote *G.* *Jer* 47:1
baldness is come upon *G.* 5
three transgressions of *G.* *Amos* 1:6
will send a fire on the wall of *G.* 7
G. shall be forsaken. *Zeph* 2:4
G. shall see it, king shall perish from
G. *Zech* 9:5
from Jerusalem to *G.* *Acts* 8:26

gaze

through unto the Lord to *g.* *Ex* 19:21

gazing

will set thee as a *g.*-stock. *Nah* 3:6
why stand ye *g.* up into ? *Acts* 1:11
e were made a *g.*-stock. *Heb* 10:33

Geba

G. with her suburbs. *Josh* 21:17
1 Chr 6:60
ing Asa built *G.* *1 Ki* 15:22
2 Chr 16:6
osiah defiled the high places from
G. *2 Ki* 23:8
aken up lodging at *G.* *Isa* 10:29
e as a plain from *G.* *Zech* 14:10

Gebal

and Ammon are. *Ps* 83:7
e ancients of *G.* were. *Ezek* 27:9

Gebim

habitants of *G.* gather. *Isa* 10:31

Gedaliah

d *G.* sware to them. *2 Ki* 25:24
Jer 40:9
duthun, *G.* and Zeri. *1 Chr* 25:3
cond lot came forth to *G.* 9
rib and *G.* had taken. *Ezra* 10:18
the son of Pashur. *Jer* 38:1
son of Ahikam believed not. 40:14
hmael smote *G.* with sword. 41:2
ok all that were left with *G.* 43:6
n of Cushi, son of *G.* *Zeph* 1:1
see **Ahikam**

Gehazi

sha said to *G.* *2 Ki* 4:12, 36
G. came near to thrust. 27
followed after Naaman. 5:21
him, Whence comest thou, *G.*? 25
king talked with *G.* servant. 8:4

Gemariah

emiah sent by *G.* *Jer* 29:3
made intercession not to. 36:25

gender

shalt not let cattle *g.* *Lev* 19:19
knowing that they do *g.* *2 Tim* 2:23

gendereth

their bull *g.* and faileth not. *Job* 21:10
frost of heaven, who hath *g.*? 38:29
which *g.* to bondage. *Gal* 4:24

genealogies

Comes from the Greek word Genealogia, *which signifies a history of the descent of an individual or family from an ancestor. The Jews were very exact in their genealogies, partly in order that family honours and family property should descend properly; partly to keep the line wherein the Messiah was to come.*

Even the Babylonian Exile did not prevent the keeping of these, as a rule, for we find that some, who claimed Jewish descent but could not produce their genealogy, were not allowed part in the Return as were the others.

were reckoned by *g.* *1 Chr* 9:1
Shemaiah concerning *g.* *2 Chr* 12:15
to all reckoned by *g.* 31:9
fables and endless *g.* *1 Tim* 1:4
avoid foolish questions, *g.* *Tit* 3:9

genealogy

and the *g.* is not to be. *1 Chr* 5:1
these sought their *g.* *Ezra* 2:62
Neh 7:64
the *g.* of them that went. *Ezra* 8:1
I found a register of *g.* *Neh* 7:5

general

g. of the king's army. *1 Chr* 27:34*
to *g.* assembly and. *Heb* 12:23

generally

I counsel that Israel be *g.* gathered.
2 Sam 17:11*
lamentation *g.* on house. *Jer* 48:38

generation

[1] *A begetting or producing, or the person or thing produced,* Gen 2:4; 5:1. [2] *Each succession of persons from a common ancestor,* Gen 50:23; Deut 23:2. [3] *An age or period, not meaning as now the average lifetime of man, but the average period of the activity of any body of contemporaries,* Ex 1:6; Num 32:13; Judg 2:10.

seen righteous in this *g.* *Gen* 7:1
Joseph died, and all that *g.* *Ex* 1:6
war with Amalek from *g.* to *g.* 17:16
till that *g.* was consumed.
Num 32:13; *Deut* 2:14
not one of this evil *g.* *Deut* 1:35
enter even to his tenth *g.* 23:2
an Ammonite to tenth *g.* shall not. 3
Edomite and Egyptian in third *g.* 8
so that the *g.* to come shall. 29:22
perverse and crooked *g.* 32:5, 20
g. were gathered to their fathers, and
there arose another *g.* *Judg* 2:10
remembered in every *g.* *Esth* 9:28
preserve them from this *g.* *Ps* 12:7
for God is in the *g.* of the. 14:5
to the Lord for a *g.* 22:30
this is the *g.* of them that. 24:6
that ye may tell it to the *g.* 48:13
he shall go to the *g.* of his. 49:19
shewed thy strength to this *g.* 71:18
I should offend against the *g.* 73:15
shewing to the *g.* to come the. 78:4
that the *g.* to come might know. 6
a stubborn and rebellious *g.* 8
forty years grieved with this *g.*
95:10; *Heb* 3:10
this shall be written for *g.* 102:18
in *g.* following let their. 109:13
the *g.* of the upright shall be. 112:2
one *g.* shall praise thy works. 145:4
crown endure to every *g.*? *Pr* 27:24
there is a *g.* that curseth. 30:11
there is a *g.* that are pure in. 12
a *g.* lofty. 13
a *g.* whose teeth are swords. 14
g. passeth away, another *g.* *Eccl* 1:4
not dwelt in from *g.* to *g.* *Isa* 13:20
Jer 50:39
from *g.* to *g.* it shall lie. *Isa* 34:10
from *g.* to *g.* they shall dwell. 17
salvation shall be from *g.* to *g.* 51:8
who declare his *g.*? 53:8; *Acts* 8:33
O *g.* see ye the word of. *Jer* 2:31
the Lord hath rejected *g.* 7:29
remains from *g.* to *g.* *Lam* 5:19
and his dominion is from *g.* to *g.*
Dan 4:3, 34
children tell another *g.* *Joel* 1:3
shall dwell from *g.* to *g.* 3:20
the *g.* of Jesus Christ. *Mat* 1:1
O *g.* of vipers. 3:7*; 12:34*; 23:33*
Luke 3:7*
whereto shall I liken this *g.*?
Mat 11:16; *Luke* 7:31
evil and adulterous *g.* *Mat* 12:39
16:4; *Mark* 8:12; *Luke* 11:29
shall rise in judgement with this *g.*
Mat 12:41; *Luke* 11:32
queen of the south rise up with *g.*
Mat 12:42; *Luke* 11:31
also to this wicked *g.* *Mat* 12:45
O perverse *g.* 17:17; *Mark* 9:19
Luke 9:41
shall come on this *g.* *Mat* 23:36
this *g.* shall not pass. 24:34
Mark 13:30; *Luke* 21:32
of me in this sinful *g.* *Mark* 8:38
on them from *g.* to *g.* *Luke* 1:50
Son of man be to this *g.* 11:30
prophets required of this *g.* 50, 51
children of this world in their *g.* 16:8
must be rejected of this *g.* 17:25
from this untoward *g.* *Acts* 2:40
he had served his own *g.* 13:36
ye are a chosen *g.* a. *1 Pet* 2:9*
see **fourth**

generations

g. of the heavens and. *Gen* 2:4
the *g.* of Adam. 5:1
the *g.* of Noah. 6:9; 10:1
just man and perfect in his *g.* 6:9
I make for perpetual *g.* 9:12
these are the *g.* of Shem. 11:10
g. of Terah. 27
me and thy seed in their *g.* 17:7
thy seed after thee in their *g.* 9
every man child in your *g.* must. 12
g. of Ishmael. 25:12, 13; *1 Chr* 1:29
these the *g.* of Isaac. *Gen* 25:19
the *g.* of Esau. 36:1
g. of Jacob, Joseph. 37:2
memorial unto all *g.* *Ex* 3:15
of Levi according to their *g.* 6:16
to Lord throughout your *g.* 12:14
observe this day in your *g.* 17
observed by Israel in their *g.* 42
to be kept for your *g.* 16:32, 33
statute for ever to their *g.* 27:21
30:21; *Lev* 3:17; 6:18; 7:36
10:9; 17:7; 23:14, 21, 31, 41
throughout your *g.* *Ex* 29:42
burn incense throughout your *g.* 30:8
oil throughout your *g.* 31
a sign throughout your *g.* 31:13, 16
priesthood through their *g.* 40:15
of thy seed in their *g.* *Lev* 21:17
your *g.* may know that I. 23:43
for ever in *g.* 24:3; *Num* 10:8
18:23
covenant to a thousand *g.* *Deut* 7:9
consider the years of many *g.* 32:7
between you and our *g.* *Josh* 22:27
when they should say to our *g.* 28
g. of Israel might teach. *Judg* 3:2
now these are the *g.* of. *Ruth* 4:18
word which he commanded to a
thousand *g.* *1 Chr* 16:15; *Ps* 105:8
sons' sons, even four *g.* *Job* 42:16
his heart to all *g.* *Ps* 33:11
to be remembered in all *g.* 45:17
places continue to all *g.* 49:11
the king's years as many *g.* 61:6
fear thee throughout all *g.* 72:5
shew forth thy praise to all *g.* 79:13
out thine anger to all *g.*? 85:5
known thy faithfulness to all *g.* 89:1
build up thy throne to all *g.* 4
our dwelling place in all *g.* 90:1
his truth endureth to all *g.* 100:5

remembrance unto all *g*. *Ps* 102:12
thy years are throughout all *g*. 24
him for righteousness to all *g*. 106:31
thy faithfulness is unto all *g*. 119:90
memorial throughout all *g*. 135:13
dominion throughout all *g*. 145:13
O Zion, shall reign to all *g*. 146:10
calling the *g*. from the. *Isa* 41:4
O arm of the Lord as in the *g*. 51:9
up the foundations of many *g*. 58:12
make thee a joy of many *g*. 60:15
the desolations of many *g*. 61:4
to the years of many *g*. *Joel* 2:2
g. from Abraham to David are 14 *g*. *Mat* 1:17
behold, all *g*. shall call. *Luke* 1:48
been hid from ages and *g*. *Col* 1:26

Gennesaret

land of *G*. *Mat* 14:34; *Mark* 6:53
Jesus stood by lake of *G*. *Luke* 5:1

Gentile

The Hebrews call the Gentiles by the general name of Goiim, *which signifies the nations that have not received the faith, or law of God. All who are not Jews and circumcised, are comprised under the word* Goiim. *Those who were converted, and embraced Judaism, they called Proselytes.*

The apostle Paul *generally includes all Gentiles under the name of* Greeks, Rom 1:16.

The old prophets declared in a very particular manner the calling of the Gentiles. Jacob foretold, that when Shiloh, or the Messiah should come, to him should the gathering of the people be; that is, the Gentiles should yield obedience to Christ, and acknowledge him for their Lord and Saviour.

and also of the *g*. *Rom* 2:9*, 10*

Gentiles

(*The Revisions very often substitute for this the word* nations)
by these the isles of the *g*. *Gen* 10:5
dwelt in Harosheth of *g*. *Judg* 4:2
Jesse, to it shall the *g*. *Isa* 11:10
judgement to the *g*. 42:1; *Mat* 12:18
light to *g*. *Isa* 42:6; 49:6
Luke 2:32; *Acts* 13:47
will lift up mine hand to *g*. *Isa* 49:22
thy seed shall inherit the *g*. 54:3
and the *g*. shall come to thy. 60:3
the forces of the *g*. shall come. 5, 11
also suck the milk of the *g*. 16
ye shall eat the riches of the *g*. 61:6
seed shall be known among the *g*. 9
and the *g*. shall see thy. 62:2
the glory of the *g*. like a. 66:12
declare my glory among the *g*. 19
destroyer of the *g*. is on. *Jer* 4:7
any of the vanities of the *g*.? 14:22*
the *g*. shall come to thee from. 16:19
came to Jeremiah against *g*. 46:1
princes are among the *g*. *Lam* 2:9
defiled bread among *g*. *Ezek* 4:13
shall they be among the *g*. *Hos* 8:8
proclaim ye this among *g*. *Joel* 3:9
Jacob shall be among the *g*. *Mi* 5:8
cast out the horns of *g*. *Zech* 1:21
be great among the *g*. *Mal* 1:11
Jordan, Galilee of the *g*. *Mat* 4:15
these things do the *g*. seek. 6:32
go not into the way of the *g*. 10:5
testimony against them and the *g*. 18
his name shall the *g*. trust. 12:21
deliver him to the *g*. to mock. 20:19
Mark 10:33; *Luke* 18:32
of *g*. exercise dominion. *Mat* 20:25
Luke 22:25
g., until the times of *g*. *Luke* 21:24
among *g*. and teach *g*. *John* 7:35
Pilate with *g*. were. *Acts* 4:27
into the possession of the *g*. 7:45
to bear my name before the *g*. 9:15
on the *g*. also was poured out. 10:45
heard that the *g*. received. 11:1
God to *g*. granted repentance? 18
g. besought these words. 13:42
Barnabas said, lo, we turn to *g*. 46
when the *g*. heard this, they. 48
Jews stirred up the *g*. *Acts* 14:2*
assault made both of Jews and *g*. 5
opened the door of faith to the *g*. 27
conversion of the *g*. great joy. 15:3
the *g*. by my mouth should hear. 7
God had wrought among the *g*. 12
how God at first did visit *g*. 14
all the *g*. on whom my name. 17
them, which from among the *g*. 19
greeting to the brethren of the *g*. 23
henceforth I will go to the *g*. 18:6
Paul into the hands of the *g*. 21:11
God wrought among the *g*. by. 19
teachest the Jews among *g*. to. 21
as touching the *g*. which believe. 25
send thee far hence to the *g*. 22:21
thee from the people and *g*. 26:17
shewing to the *g*. that they. 20
Christ should shew light to the *g*. 23
salvation of God is sent to *g*. 28:28
fruit, as among other *g*. *Rom* 1:13
when the *g*. which have not. 2:14
God is blasphemed among the *g*. 24
have proved both Jews and *g*. 3:9
also of the *g*.? yes, of the *g*. 29
Jews only, but also of the *g*. 9:24
g. which followed not after. 30
salvation is come to the *g*. 11:11
of them the riches of the *g*. 12
you *g*. as the apostle of the *g*. 13
till the fulness of the *g*. be come. 25
g. might glorify God . . . I will confess to thee among the *g*. 15:9
he saith, rejoice, ye *g*. with his. 10
praise Lord, all ye *g*. and laud him. 11
reign over the *g*. in him shall *g*. 12
minister of Jesus Christ to the *g*. that the offering up of the *g*. 16
to make the *g*. obedient by word. 18
for if the *g*. have been made. 27
but all the churches of the *g*. 16:4
as named among the *g*. *1 Cor* 5:1
things which the *g*. sacrifice. 10:20
offence, neither to Jews nor *g*. 32
ye know ye were *g*. carried. 12:2
whether we be Jews or *g*. 13
I preach among the *g*. *Gal* 2:2
mighty in me towards the *g*. 8
he did eat with the *g*. 12
manner of *g*., why compellest *g*.? 14
Jews, and not sinners of the *g*. 15
Abraham might come on the *g*. 3:14
ye being in time past *g*. in. *Eph* 2:11
of Jesus Christ for you *g*. 3:1
that *g*. should be fellowheirs of. 6
among the *g*. the unsearchable. 8
henceforth walk not as other *g*. 4:17
this mystery among the *g*. *Col* 1:27
to speak to the *g*. *1 Thes* 2:16
lust of concupiscence, as the *g*. 4:5
a teacher of the *g*. *1 Tim* 2:7
preached to the *g*. believed on. 3:16
apostle and teacher of *g*. *2 Tim* 1:11
and that all the *g*. might hear. 4:17
honest among the *g*. *1 Pet* 2:12
wrought the will of the *g*. 4:3
taking nothing of the *g*. *3 John* 7
court is given to the *g*. *Rev* 11:2

gentle

we were *g*. among you. *1 Thes* 2:7
of the Lord must be *g*. *2 Tim* 2:24
g. shewing all meekness. *Tit* 3:2
above is pure and *g*. *Jas* 3:17
only to the good and *g*. *1 Pet* 2:18

gentleness

g. hath made me. *2 Sam* 22:36
Ps 18:35
I beseech you by the *g*. *2 Cor* 10:1
the fruit of the Spirit is *g*. *Gal* 5:22*

gently

deal *g*. with the young. *2 Sam* 18:5
he will *g*. lead those with. *Isa* 40:11

Gera

Ehud the son of *G*. *Judg* 3:15
son of *G*. *2 Sam* 16:5; 19:16, 18
1 Ki 2:8

gerahs

a shekel is twenty *g*. *Ex* 30:13
Lev 27:25; *Num* 3:47; 18:16
Ezek 45:12

Gerar

Abraham sojourned in *G*. *Gen* 20:1
Abimelech king of *G*. 2
Isaac dwelt in *G*. *Gen* 26:6
the herdmen of *G*. 20

Gergesenes

into the country of the *G*. *Mat* 8:28

Gerizim

blessing on mount *G*. *Deut* 11:29
these shall stand on mount *G*. 27:12
over against mount *G*. *Josh* 8:33
stood on top of mount *G*. *Judg* 9:7

Gershom, Gershon

sons of Levi, *G*. Kohath. *Gen* 46:11
Ex 6:16; *Num* 3:17; *1 Chr* 6:1, 16
23:6
of Moses' son was *G*. *Ex* 2:22
of *G*. Libni, Shimei. 6:17; *Num* 3:18
of *G*. was the family of. *Num* 3:21
charge of the sons of *G*. 25
sum of the sons of *G*. 4:22, 38
service of the sons of *G*. 28
four oxen gave to sons of *G*. 7:7
the sons of *G*. bearing the. 10:17
children of *G*. had. *Josh* 21:6, 27
Jonathan the son of *G*. *Judg* 18:30
of the sons of Phinehas, *G*. *Ezra* 8:2

Geshur

fled and went to *G*. *2 Sam* 13:37, 38
Joab went to *G*. 14:23
why I come from *G*. 32
thy servant vowed a vow at *G*. 15:8
Jair took *G*. and Aram. *1 Chr* 2:23

Geshurites

the *G*. dwell among the. *Josh* 13:13
his men invaded the *G*. *1 Sam* 27:8

get

saying, *g*. me this damsel. *Gen* 34:4
and so *g*. them out of the. *Ex* 1:10
and I will *g*. me honour upon. 14:17
he be poor and cannot *g*. *Lev* 14:21
such as he is able to *g*. 22, 30, 31
whose hand is not able to *g*. 32
that his hand shall *g*. *Num* 6:21
now therefore I will *g*. me. 22:34
giveth thee power to *g*. *Deut* 8:18
strangers shall *g*. up above. 28:43
g. her for me to wife. *Judg* 14:2, 3
let me *g*. away and. *1 Sam* 20:29
David made haste to *g*. 23:26
lest Sheba *g*. fenced. *2 Sam* 20:6
lord the king may *g*. *1 Ki* 1:2
Rehoboam made speed to *g*. up to his chariot. 12:18; *2 Chr* 10:18
catch them alive, and *g*. *2 Ki* 7:12
through thy precepts I *g*. *Ps* 119:104
g. wisdom, *g*. *Pr* 4:5, 7
dishonour shall he *g*. 6:33
better it is to *g*. wisdom . . . to *g*. understanding rather to be. 16:16
price in the hand of a fool to *g*. 17:16
thou learn his ways and *g*. 22:25
there is a time to *g*. and. *Eccl* 3:6
I will *g*. me to the mountains. *S of S* 4:
let us *g*. up early to vineyards. 7:1
I will *g*. me to great men. *Jer* 5:
g. a potter's earthen bottle. 19:
harness the horses, and *g*. up. 46:
wings to Moab, that it may *g*. 48:
hedged me about, I cannot *g*. out. *Lam* 3:
to destroy souls, to *g*. *Ezek* 22:2
let the beasts *g*. away. *Dan* 4:1
I will *g*. them praise. *Zeph* 3:1
to *g*. into ship. *Mat* 14:2
Mark 6:4
they may lodge and *g*. *Luke* 9:1
into sea, and *g*. to land. *Acts* 27:4
lest Satan should *g*. *2 Cor* 2:1
buy, sell, and *g*. gain. *Jas* 4:1

get *thee*

g. *thee* out of. *Gen* 12:1; *Acts* 7:
g. *thee* into the land. *Gen* 22:
g. *thee* out from this land. 31:
g. *thee* to Pharaoh in. *Ex* 7:
g. *thee* from me, take heed. 10:
g. *thee* out, and all people. 11:
Moses, away, *g*. *thee* down and th shalt. 19:24; 32:7; *Deut* 9:
g. *thee* up to mount. *Num* 27:
Deut 33:
g. *thee* up to the top. *Deut* 3:
g. *thee* up to the place the. 17
g. *thee* up, wherefore? *Josh* 7:

g. thee up to the wood. *Josh* 17:15
arise, *g. thee* down unto. *Judg* 7:9
wash thyself, *g. thee.* *Ruth* 3:3
depart, *g. thee* into. *1 Sam* 22:5
g. thee in to king David. *1 Ki* 1:13
g. thee to Anathoth to thine. 2:26
g. thee to Shiloh, behold there. 14:2
arise therefore, *g. thee* to thine. 12
g. thee hence. 17:3
g. thee to Zarephath. 9
Elijah said, *g. thee* up, eat. 18:41
g. thee down, that the rain stop. 44
g. thee to the prophets of. *2 Ki* 3:13
so didst thou *g. thee* a. *Neh* 9:10
g. thee to this treasurer, *Isa* 22:15
thou shalt say unto it, *g. thee.* 30:22
O Zion, *g. thee* up into the. 40:9
sit thou silent, and *g. thee.* 47:5
g. thee a linen girdle, put. *Jer* 13:1
son of man, *g. thee* to the. *Ezek* 3:4
and go, *g. thee* to them of the. 11
Jesus saith to him, *g. thee. Mat* 4:10
Peter, *g. thee* behind me, Satan.
16:23; *Mark* 8:33; *Luke* 4:8
g. thee out, for Herod. *Luke* 13:31
arise, *g. thee* down, go. *Acts* 10:20
g. thee quickly out of. 22:18

get *ye*

Lot said, up, *g. ye* out. *Gen* 19:14
g. ye out of the way, turn. *Isa* 30:11
arise, *g. ye* up to the. *Jer* 49:31
said, *g. ye* far from. *Ezek* 11:15
come, *g. ye* down, for the. *Joel* 3:13
he said, *g. ye* hence, walk. *Zech* 6:7

get *you*

g. you possessions. *Gen* 34:10
g. you down thither and buy. 42:2
rise up, *g. you* up in peace. 44:17
the king said, *g. you* to. *Ex* 5:4
go you, *g. you* straw where you. 11
rise up, *g. you* forth from. 12:31
turn you, *g. you* into. *Num* 14:25
g. you up from tabernacle. 16:24
Balaam said, *g. you* into your. 22:13
g. you into your tents. *Deut* 5:30
Josh 22:4
g. you to the mountain. *Josh* 2:16
to-morrow *g. you* early. *Judg* 19:9
g. you up, for ye shall. *1 Sam* 9:13
g. you down from among the. 15:6
g. you up to Carmel, and go. 25:5
flee, *g. you* off, dwell. *Jer* 49:30

Gethsemane

to a place called *G.* *Mat* 26:36
Mark 14:32

getteth

whosoever *g.* up to the. *2 Sam* 5:8
happy is the man that *g.* *Pr* 3:13
reproveth a scorner *g.* shame, rebuketh a wicked man *g.* blot. 9:7
he that heareth reproof *g.* 15:32
the heart of the prudent *g.* 18:15
he that *g.* wisdom loveth his. 19:8
so he that *g.* riches. *Jer* 17:11
he that *g.* out of the pit shall. 48:44

getting

away the cattle of his *g.* *Gen* 31:18
with all thy *g.* get. *Pr* 4:7
. of treasures by a lying. 21:6

ghost

(*American Revision renders this* spirit)

acob yielded up the *g.* *Gen* 49:33
had given up the *g.* *Job* 10:18
hall be as the giving up of *g.* 11:20
ea, man giveth up the *g.* 14:10
he hath given up the *g.* *Jer* 15:9
ried, and yielded up *g.* *Mat* 27:50
own and yielded up *g.* *Acts* 5:10
see **gave, give, holy**

Giah

mmah that lieth before *G.*
2 Sam 2:24

giant

The Hebrew Nephel *may signify monster, or a terrible man, who eats and bears down other men. he Scripture speaks of Giants who ved before the flood; they are lled* Nephilim, *mighty men which ere of old, men of renown.* en 6:4. *The words* Emim *and* Rephaim *are also used to denote these unusual men.*

The Anakims, *or the sons of Anak, were the most famous giants of Palestine. They dwelt near Hebron. Their stature was so much above what was common, that the Israelites, who were sent to view the promised land, told the people at their return, that they had seen giants of the race of Anak in that country, who were of so monstrous a size, that the Israelites, in comparison, were but grasshoppers,* Num 13:33.

sons of the *g.* *2 Sam* 21:16, 18
1 Chr 20:4
the son of the *g.* *1 Chr.* 20:6
born to the *g.* 8
runneth upon me like a *g. Job* 16:14

giants

(*The Revisions replace this word in all passages by the Hebrew word, using it as a proper name*)

were *g.* in the earth. *Gen* 6:4
the *g.* the sons of Anak. *Num* 13:33
Emims were counted *g.* *Deut* 2:11
remained of the remnant of *g.* 3:11*
Josh 12:4; 13:12
was called the land of *g. Deut* 3:13
the end of the valley of *g. Josh* 15:8
up to the land of the *g.* 17:15
came to the valley of the *g.* 18:16

Gibeah

when they were by *G.* *Judg* 19:14
of mount Ephraim sojourned in *G.* 16
the thing we will do to *G.* 20:9
the children of Belial in *G.* 13
themselves in array against *G.* 30
went home to *G. 1 Sam* 10:26; 15:34
in the uttermost part of *G.* 14:2
up to the Lord in *G.* *2 Sam* 21:6
Ramah is afraid, *G.* of Saul.
Isa 10:29
blow ye the cornet in *G.* *Hos* 5:8
themselves as in the days of *G.* 9:9
days of *G.* the battle of *G.* 10:9

Gibeon

feared, because *G.* was. *Josh* 10:2
help me, that we may smite *G.* 4
sun, stand thou still upon *G.* 12
by the pool of *G.* *2 Sam* 2:13
he had slain Asahel at *G.* 3:30
at the great stone in *G.* 20:8
in *G.* Lord appeared. *1 Ki* 3:5; 9:2
at *G.* dwelt father of *G.* *1 Chr* 8:29
9:35
burnt offering was at *G.* 21:29
as in the valley of *G.* *Isa* 28:21
the son of Azur in *G.* *Jer* 28:1
Ishmael by the waters in *G.* 41:12

Gibeonites

because Saul slew *G.* *2 Sam* 21:1
them into the hands of the *G.* 9

Gideon

G. threshed wheat by. *Judg* 6:11
G. built an altar there unto the. 24
Spirit of the Lord came upon *G.* 34
Jerubbaal, who is *G.* rose up. 7:1
nothing else, save sword of *G.* 14
sword of the Lord and of *G.* 18, 20
G. slew Zeba. 8:21
G. made an ephod thereof. 27
G. had 70 sons. 30
G. died in a good old age. 32
nor kindness to the house of *G.* 35
fail me to tell of *G.* *Heb* 11:32

Gideoni

prince of Benjamin, Abidan the son of *G.* *Num* 1:11; 2:22; 7:60, 65

gier eagle

abomination, the *g. e.* *Lev* 11:18*
Deut 14:17*

gift

so much dowry and *g.* *Gen* 34:12
take no *g.* a *g.* blindeth. *Ex* 23:8
Deut 16:19
the Levites as a *g. Num* 8:19; 18:6
office as a service of *g.* 18:7
the heave offering of their *g.* 11
given us any *g.*? *2 Sam* 19:42
Tyre shall be there with *g. Ps* 45:12
a *g.* is as a precious stone. *Pr* 17:8
a wicked man taketh a *g.* out. 23
a man's *g.* maketh room for. 18:16
a *g.* in secret pacifieth anger. 21:14
boasteth himself of a false *g.* 25:14
enjoy good, it is *g.* *Eccl* 3:13; 5:19
and a *g.* destroyeth the heart. 7:7
if a prince give a *g.* to. *Ezek* 46:16
if he give a *g.* to one of his. 17
if thou bring thy *g.* to. *Mat* 5:23
leave there thy *g.* before the. 24
and offer the *g.* that Moses. 8:4
it is a *g.* by me. 15:5; *Mark* 7:11
sweareth by the *g.* is. *Mat* 23:18, 19
if thou knewest the *g.* *John* 4:10
ye shall receive the *g.* *Acts* 2:38
thought the *g.* of God may be. 8:20
also was poured out the *g.* 10:45
God gave them the like *g.* as. 11:17
to you some spiritual *g.* *Rom* 1:11
is free *g.* of God and the *g.* by grace abounded. 5:15
so is the *g.* the free *g.* is of. 16
receive the *g.* of righteousness. 17
the free *g.* came on all men. 18
the *g.* of God is eternal life. 6:23
ye come behind in no *g.* *1 Cor* 1:7
man hath his proper *g.* of God. 7:7
though I have the *g.* of. 13:2
that for the *g.* bestowed. *2 Cor* 1:11
that we would receive the *g.* 8:4*
God for his unspeakable *g.* 9:15
it is the *g.* of God. *Eph* 2:8
a minister, according to the *g.* 3:7
the measure of the *g.* of Christ. 4:7
not because I desire a *g.* *Phil* 4:17
neglect not the *g.* that. *1 Tim* 4:14
stir up the *g.* that is in. *2 Tim* 1:6
tasted of the heavenly *g.* *Heb* 6:4
good *g.* and perfect *g.* *Jas* 1:17
man hath received the *g. 1 Pet* 4:10

gifts

Abraham gave *g.* to sons. *Gen* 25:6
shall hallow in their *g.* *Ex* 28:38
feasts, besides your *g.* *Lev* 23:38
out of all your *g.* offer. *Num* 18:29
David's servants, and brought *g.*
2 Sam 8:2, 6; *1 Chr* 18:2
Lord is no taking of *g.* *2 Chr* 19:7
Jehoshaphat gave great *g.* of. 21:3
Ammonites gave *g.* to Uzziah. 26:8
and many brought *g.* unto. 32:23
a feast and gave *g.* *Esth* 2:18
make them days of sending *g.* 9:22
hast received *g.* for men. *Ps* 68:18
Sheba and Seba shall offer *g.* 72:10
though thou givest many *g. Pr* 6:35
he that hateth *g.* shall live. 15:27
is friend to him that giveth *g.* 19:6
that receiveth *g.* overthroweth. 29:4
every one loveth *g.* *Isa* 1:23
g. to whores, *g.* to lovers. *Ezek* 16:33
polluted them in their own *g.* 20:26
when ye offer your *g.* ye pollute. 31
holy name no more with your *g.* 39
in thee have they taken *g.* 22:12
dream, ye shall receive *g.* *Dan* 2:6
king gave Daniel many great *g.* 48
then Daniel said, let thy *g.* be. 5:17
they presented to him *g.* *Mat* 2:11
how to give good *g.* 7:11
Luke 11:13
rich casting their *g.* into. *Luke* 21:1
adorned with goodly stones and *g.* 5
g. of God are without. *Rom* 11:29
having *g.* differing according. 12:6
concerning spiritual *g.* *1 Cor* 12:1
there are diversities of *g.* but the. 4
to another the *g.* of healing. 9, 28, 30
but covet earnestly the best *g.* 12:31
charity, and desire spiritual *g.* 14:1
ye are zealous of spiritual *g.* 12
captive, gave *g.* to men. *Eph* 4:8
bearing witness with *g.* *Heb* 2:4
he may offer *g.* and sacrifices. 5:1
high priest ordained to offer *g.* 8:3
there are priests that offer *g.* 4
which were offered, both *g.* and. 9:9
God testifying of Abel's *g.* 11:4
dwell on earth shall send *g. Rev* 11:10

Gihon

the second river is *G.* *Gen* 2:13

Solomon down to G. *1 Ki* 1:33, 38
anointed him king in G. 45

Gilboa

all Israel pitched in G. *1 Sam* 28:4
Saul fell down slain in mount G. 31:1
8; *2 Sam* 21:12; *1 Chr* 10:1, 8
by chance on mount G. *2 Sam* 1:6
ye mountains of G. let there be. 21

Gilead

saw the land of G. was. *Num* 32:1
G. to Machir. 40; *Deut* 3:15
shewed him land of G. *Deut* 34:1
a man of war, had G. *Josh* 17:1
Phinehas into the land of G. 22:13
the inhabitants of G. *Judg* 10:18
went with the elders of G. 11:11
Ish-bosheth king over G. *2 Sam* 2:9
Absalom pitched in land of G. 17:26
Tishbite, who was of G. *1 Ki* 17:1
G. is mine. *Ps* 60:7; 108:8
of goats from G. *S of S* 4:1; 6:5
is there no balm in G.? *Jer* 8:22
thou art G. to me. 22:6
go up into G. 46:11
shall be satisfied on mount G. 50:19
G. is the city of them. *Hos* 6:8
is there iniquity in G.? they 12:11
they have threshed G. *Amos* 1:3
up women with child of G. 13
Benjamin shall possess G. *Ob* 19
feed in Bashan and G. *Mi* 7:14
them into the land of G. *Zech* 10:10
see **Ramoth**

Gileadite, -s

G. judged Israel. *Judg* 10:3
Jephthah the G. 11:1
ye G. are fugitives of. 12:4
and the G. took the passages. 5
Barzillai the G. *2 Sam* 17:27
see **Barzillai**

Gilgal

up and encamped in G. *Josh* 4:19
Joshua unto the camp at G. 9:6
of G. sent to the camp at. 10:6
an angel came up from G. *Judg* 2:1
went in circuit to G. *1 Sam* 7:16
go down before me to G. 10:8
let us go to G. and renew. 11:14
Saul was in G. 13:7
Samuel came not to G. 8
hewed Agag in pieces in G. 15:33
come not ye to G. nor. *Hos* 4:15
their wickedness is in G. 9:15
they sacrifice bullocks in G. 12:11
G. multiply transgression. *Amos* 4:4
enter not into G. for G. shall. 5:5
him from Shittim to G. *Mi* 6:5

Gilonite

the G. *2 Sam* 15:12; 23:34

gin

the *g.* shall take him by. *Job* 18:9
for a *g.* to the inhabitants. *Isa* 8:14
fall into a snare where no *g* is?
Amos 3:5

gins

they spread a net, they set *g.* for me.
Ps 140:5
keep me from the *g.* of the. 141:9

gird

g. him with the curious. *Ex* 29:5, 9
Ehud did *g.* his dagger. *Judg* 3:16
g. ye on every man his. *1 Sam* 25:13
g. thy sword on thy thigh. *Ps* 45:3
g. yourselves, and ye shall. *Isa* 8:9
not *g.* with what. *Ezek* 44:18
g. yourselves, and lament. *Joel* 1:13
shall *g.* himself, and. *Luke* 12:37
g. thyself, and serve me, till. 17:8
another shall *g.* thee. *John* 21:18
g. thyself and bind on. *Acts* 12:8
see **loins, sackcloth**

girded

g. him with the girdle. *Lev* 8:7
when ye *g.* on every man. *Deut* 1:41
six hundred men *g.* *Judg* 18:11
Samuel *g.* with a linen. *1 Sam* 2:18
David danced, was *g.* *2 Sam* 6:14
Joab's garment was *g.* unto. 20:8
thou hast *g.* me with. 22:40; *Ps* 18:39
they *g.* sackcloth on. *1 Ki* 20:32
thou hast *g.* me with. *Ps* 30:11
setteth fast mountains, being *g.* 65:6
strength wherewith he hath *g.* 93:1
girdle wherewith he is *g.* 109:19
I *g.* thee, though thou. *Isa* 45:5
elders of Zion *g.* with. *Lam* 2:10
I *g.* thee about with fine. *Ezek* 16:10
images of the Chaldeans *g.* 23:15
lament like a virgin *g.* with. *Joel* 1:8
he took a towel and *g.* *John* 13:4
the towel wherewith he was *g.* 5
seven angels, breasts *g.* *Rev* 15:6
see **loins, sword**

girdedst

young thou *g.* thyself. *John* 21:18

girdeth

let not him that *g.* on. *1 Ki* 20:11
he *g.* their loins with. *Job* 12:18*
it is God that *g.* me. *Ps* 18:32
g. her loins with strength. *Pr* 31:17

girding

instead of a stomacher, a *g.* *Isa* 3:24
the Lord did call to *g.* with. 22:12

girdle

With the long loose robes which were commonly worn in the East a girdle was very necessary when a man wished to do any active work. When men were at ease the robes fell loosely around them, but the first thing in preparing for walking or for work was to tighten the girdle and tuck up the long skirts of the robe, 1 Ki 18:46.

The girdle was sometimes of leather, but more usually a long piece of soft cloth, or silk that could be easily wrapped around the body and tied tightly.

they shall make a *g.* *Ex* 28:4
g. of the ephod which is. 8*, 27*
28*; 29:5*; 39:5*, 20*; *Lev* 8:7*
make *g.* of needlework. *Ex* 28:39*
they made a *g.* of fine twined. 39:29
David his bow and *g.* *1 Sam* 18:4
have given thee a *g.* *2 Sam* 18:11
blood of war on his *g.* *1 Ki* 2:5
Elijah was girt with a *g.* *2 Ki* 1:8
loins of kings with a *g.* *Job* 12:18
for a *g.* wherewith he. *Ps* 109:19
instead of a *g.* there shall. *Isa* 3:24
nor shall the *g.* of their loins. 5:27
shall be the *g.* of his loins, and faithfulness the *g.* of his reins. 11:5
strengthen Eliakim with thy *g.* 22:21
get thee a linen *g.* put it. *Jer* 13:1
this people shall be as this *g.* 10
a leathern *g.* *Mat* 3:4; *Mark* 1:6
g. man that owneth this *g.* *Acts* 21:11
the paps with a golden *g.* *Rev* 1:13

girdles

make for Aaron's sons *g.* *Ex* 28:40
gird Aaron and sons with *g.* 29:9
gird Aaron's sons with *g.* *Lev* 8:13
she delivereth *g.* to the. *Pr* 31:24
of Chaldeans girded with *g.*
Ezek 23:15
girded with golden *g.* *Rev* 15:6

Girgashite, -s

begat the G. *Gen* 10:16; *1 Chr* 1:14
land of the G. *Gen* 15:21; *Neh* 9:8
Lord hath cast out the G. *Deut* 7:1
without fail drive out G. *Judg* 3:10

girl, -s

have sold a *g.* for wine. *Joel* 3:3
city be full of boys and *g.* *Zech* 8:5

girt

they that stumbled are *g.* *1 Sam* 2:4
he was *g.* with a girdle. *2 Ki* 1:8
Peter *g.* his fisher's coat. *John* 21:7
stand, having your loins *g.* *Eph* 6:14
g. about the paps with a. *Rev* 1:13

Gittite

Obed-edom the G. *2 Sam* 6:10, 11
Ittai the G. 15:19, 22; 18:2
Goliath the G. 21:19

Gittith

This is the title prefixed to Psalms 8, 81, *and* 84.

It probably means either a musical instrument in use in Gath, or a vintage song to the tune of which the psalm should be sung, or a march of the Gittite guard, 2 Sam 15:18.

give

g. me the persons, and. *Gen* 14:21
what wilt *g.* me, seeing? 15:2
the field I *g.* thee, and the. 23:11
therefore God *g.* thee of dew. 27:28
all thou shalt *g.* me I will *g.* 28:22
better I *g.* her thee, than *g.* 29:19
g. me my wife. 21
g. me children or else I die. 30:1
g. me my wives and my. 26
will we *g.* our daughters. 34:16
thou must *g.* us also. *Ex* 10:25
her father utterly refuse to *g.* 22:17
on the eighth day thou shalt *g.* 30
then they shall *g.* every man. 30:12
this they shall *g.* every one half. 13
thou shalt *g.* the Levites. *Num* 3:9
Lord *g.* thee peace. 6:26
said, who shall *g.* us flesh? 11:4, 18
if Balak would *g.* me. 22:18; 24:13
I *g.* to Phinehas my covenant. 25:12
g. thou the more inheritance, to few thou shalt *g.* 26:54; 33:54
ye shall *g.* to Levites suburbs. 35:2
thou shalt *g.* him. *Deut.* 15:10, 14
every man *g.* as he is able. 16:17
Ezek 46:5, 11
day thou shalt *g.* him. *Deut* 24:15
forty stripes he may *g.* him. 25:3
swear to me, and *g.* me. *Josh* 2:12
now therefore *g.* me this. 14:12
g. me a blessing, *g.* springs. 15:19
Judg 1:15
that fleeth, they shall *g.* *Josh* 20:4
to *g.* the Midianites into. *Judg* 7:2
answered, we will willingly *g.* 8:25
nay, but thou shalt *g.* *1 Sam* 2:16
wealth which God shall *g.* Israel. 32
they said *g.* us a king. 8:6
g. me a man that we may. 17:10
king will *g.* him his daughter. 25
David said, *g.* it me. 21:9
will the son of Jesse *g.* every? 22:7
shall I then *g.* it to men whom. 25:11
would *g.* me drink of the water of the well. *2 Sam* 23:15; *1 Chr* 11:17
these did Araunah *g.* *2 Sam* 24:23
1 Chr 21:23
g. thy servant an. *1 Ki* 3:9
O my lord, *g.* her the living. 26, 27
g. every man according to. 8:39*
if thou wilt *g.* me half. 13:8
he said, G. me thy son, and. 17:19
I said, G. thy son, that. *2 Ki* 6:29
if it be, *g.* me thine hand. 10:15
saying, G. thy daughter to my. 14:9
g. to Lord, ye kindreds of the people.
1 Chr 16:28, 29; *Ps* 29:1, 2; 96:7, 8
Lord *g.* thee wisdom. *1 Chr* 22:12
g. me now wisdom. *2 Chr* 1:10
hand of God was to *g.* them. 30:12
and to *g.* us a nail in his. *Ezra* 9:8
to *g.* us a reviving, to *g.* us a wall. 9
g. them for a prey in land. *Neh* 4:4
all that a man hath will he *g.* *Job* 2:4
g. flattering titles to man. 32:21
ask of me, and I shall *g.* *Ps* 2:8
g. them according to. 28:4
he shall *g.* thee the desires. 37:4
none can *g.* to God a ransom. 49:7
not sacrifice, else would I *g.* 51:1
g. us help from. 60:11; 108:1
can he *g.* bread also? can he? 78:2
O turn, *g.* thy strength to. 86:1
shall *g.* his angels. 91:11; *Mat* 4:
but I *g.* myself unto. *Ps* 109:
g. me. 119:34, 73, 125, 144, 16
g. instruction to a wise. *Pr* 9:
my son, *g.* me thine heart. 23:2
if enemy hunger, *g.* him. 25:2
Rom 12:2
the rod and reproof *g.* *Pr* 29:1
shall *g.* thee rest, shall *g.* delight. 1
g. me neither poverty nor. 30:
two daughters, crying, *g.* *g.* 1
that he may *g.* to him. *Eccl* 2:2
g. a portion to seven. 11:
man would *g.* substance. *S of S* 8:
then he shall *g.* the rain. *Isa* 30:2
g. place to me, that I. 49:2

may g. seed to the sower. Isa 55:10
g. unto them beauty for ashes. 61:3
g. him no rest till he establish. 62:7
shall I g. thee a pleasant? Jer 3:19
to whom shall I speak and g.? 6:10*
to g. man according. 17:10; 32:19
g. heed to me, O Lord. 18:19
I think to g. you an expected. 29:11
bring them, and g. them wine. 35:2
tears run down, g. thyself. Lam 2:18
g. them sorrow of heart, thy. 3:65
mouth, eat that I g. thee. Ezek 2:8
with this roll that I g. thee. 3:3
and g. them warning. 17
thy children, which didst g. 16:36
to land, I lifted up mine hand to g. it to them. 20:28, 42; 47:14
if wicked g. again that he. 33:15
prince g. a gift to his sons. 46:16, 17
and g. thy rewards to. Dan 5:17
I am come forth to g. 9:22*
with shame do love, g. ye. Hos 4:18
g. O Lord, what wilt thou g.? 9:14
thou saidst, g. me a king and. 13:10
shall I g. my firstborn? Mi 6:7
g. her fruit, the ground shall g. increase, and heavens g. Zech 8:12
g. me my price, if not. 11:12
g. to him that asketh thee. Mat 5:42
g. us this day our. 6:11; Luke 11:3
if he ask bread, will he g.? Mat 7:9
will he g. a serpent? 10; Luke 11:11
g. gifts unto your children, your Father g. to them that ask him? Mat 7:11; Luke 11:13
g. place. Mat 9:24
freely ye received, freely g. 10:8
shall g. to drink a cup. 42
he promised to g. her what. 14:7
g. ye them to eat. 16; Mark 6:37 Luke 9:13
what g. in exchange for his soul? Mat 16:26; Mark 8:37
and g. to them for. Mat 17:27
command to g. a writing? 19:7
g. to the poor. 19:21; Mark 10:21
call the labourers, and g. Mat 20:8
is not mine to g. 20:23; Mark 10:40
g. us of your oil, for our. Mat 25:8
what will ye g. me? 26:15
I will that thou g. me. Mark 6:25
and he will g. the vineyard. 12:9
whomsoever I will, I g. it. Luke 4:6
g. and it shall be given . . . good measure shall men g. 6:38
he will g. him as many as he. 11:8
g. alms of such things. 41; 12:33
he that bade thee say, g. this. 14:9
younger said, g. me the. 15:12
who shall g. you that which? 16:12
Jesus saith, G. me. John 4:7, 10
drinketh water I shall g. 14
the Son of man shall g. you. 6:27
said, Lord, evermore g. us. 34
how can this man g. us his? 52
. God the praise, this man. 9:24
g. to them eternal life. 10:28
thou wilt ask, God will g. 11:22
that he should g. something. 13:29
you another Comforter. 14:16
my peace I g. unto you not as world giveth, g. I unto you. 27
shall ask, he may g. it. 15:16
whatsoever ye ask he will g. 16:23
that he should g. eternal life. 17:2
such as I have g. I thee. Acts 3:6
we will g. ourselves to prayer. 6:4*
promised he would g. it for. 7:5
Simon said, G. me also. 8:19
is more blessed to g. than. 20:35
with him also freely g. us. Rom 8:32
venge not, but rather g. 12:19
may g. yourselves. 1 Cor 7:5
none offence, neither. 10:32
him g. not grudgingly. 2 Cor 9:7
God may g. you the. Eph 1:17
that he may have to g. to him. 4:28
to your servants that. Col 4:1*
attendance to reading. 1 Tim 4:13
meditate, g. thyself wholly to. 15
righteous Judge shall g. 2 Tim 4:8
ought to g. the more. Heb 2:1
life for them that sin. 1 John 5:16
me the little book. Rev. 10:9

he had power to g. life. Rev 13:15
to g. her the cup of the wine. 16:19
torment and sorrow g. her. 18:7
to g. every man according. 22:12*

see **account, charge, ear, glory, light, sware**

I will **give**

I will g. to thee and thy seed the land. Gen 17:8; 48:4; Deut 34:4
I will g. thee a son also. Gen 17:16
I will surely g. the tenth to. 28:22
shall say to me I will g. 34:11, 12
and I will g. this people. Ex 3:21
with thee, and I will g. 33:14
I will g. you rain in due season. Lev 26:4; Deut 11:14
I will g. peace in the land. Lev 26:6
I will g. him to the. 1 Sam 1:11
I will g. her, that she may be. 18:21
I will g. thy wives to. 2 Sam 12:11
not rend all, but I will g. 1 Ki 11:13
I will g. ten tribes to thee. 31
come home, and I will g. thee. 13:7
I will g. thee for it a better. 21:2
I will g. thee the vineyard of. 7
I will g. him rest, I will g. 1 Chr 22:9
I will g. thee riches. 2 Chr 1:12
O Lord, I will g. thanks. Ps 30:12
I will sing and g. 57:7*; 108:1*
to-morrow I will g. when. Pr 3:28
I will g. them children to. Isa 3:4
Zion, behold, and I will g. 41:27
I will g. thee for. 42:6; 49:8
I will g. thee the treasures. 45:3
I will g. thee for a light to the. 49:6
I will g. them an everlasting. 56:5
I will g. pastors according. Jer 3:15
I will g. them waters of gall. 9:15
I will g. you assured peace. 14:13
I will g. thy substance to the. 17:3
I will g. them an heart to. 24:7
I will g. them one heart. 32:39 Ezek 11:19
I will g. men that have. Jer 34:18
I will g. it into the hand. Ezek 7:21
and I will g. you the land of. 11:17
I will g. thee blood in fury. 16:38*
I will also g. thee into their. 39
I will g. them to thee for. 61
whose right it is, I will g. 21:27
I will g. them to be removed. 23:46
I will g. land of Egypt to. 29:19
I will g. thee the opening of the. 21
and I will g. you an heart. 36:26
I will g. her vineyards. Hos 2:15
unto me, and I will g. Mat 11:28
I will g. to thee the keys of. 16:19
is right, I will g. you. 20:4
I will g. to this last even as. 14
what thou wilt, I will g. Mark 6:22
for I will g. you a mouth. Luke 21:15
I will g. is my flesh, which I will g. for the life of the world. John 6:51
I will g. you the sure. Acts 13:34
be faithful, I will g. thee. Rev 2:10
I will g. him a white stone and. 17
I will g. to every one according. 23
I will g. him the morning star. 28
and I will g. power to my two. 11:3
I will g. to him that is athirst. 21:6

will I **give**

will I g. this land. Gen 12:7; 13:15 24:7; 28:13; 35:12; Ex 32:13 33:1
Caleb, to him will I g. Deut 1:36
go in thither, to them will I g. 39
to him will I g. Achsah. Josh 15:16 Judg 1:12
will I g. to the man of. 1 Sam 9:8
Merab, her will I g. thee. 18:17
to thee will I g. land. 1 Chr 16:18 Ps 105:11
therefore will I g. thanks. Ps 18:49
there will I g. thee my. S of S 7:12
therefore will I g. men for. Isa 43:4
them will I g. in mine house. 56:5
so will I g. Zedekiah. Jer 24:8
thy life will I g. to thee for a. 45:5
so will I g. inhabitants. Ezek 15:6
new heart also will I g. you. 36:26
and in this place will I g. Hag 2:9
all these things will I g. Mat 4:9

all this power will I g. Luke 4:6
overcometh will I g. Rev 2:7, 17, 26

Lord **give**

land which Lord will g. you. Ex 12:25 Lev 14:34; 23:10; 25:2; Num 15:2
the Lord shall g. you flesh. Ex 16:8
therefore the Lord will g. Num 11:18
Lord delight in us, he will g. 14:8
Lord refuseth to g. me leave. 22:13
Lord commanded to g. nine. 34:13
Lord commanded to g. the land. 36:2
land the Lord doth g. Deut 1:25
the Lord shall g. thee a. 28:65
Lord commanded Moses to g. Josh 9:24
Lord commanded to g. us. 17:4
the Lord commanded to g. us cities. 21:2
which the Lord shall g. Ruth 4:12
the Lord his God did g. 1 Ki 15:4
the Lord is able to g. 2 Chr 25:9
the Lord will g. strength. Ps 29:11
the Lord will g. grace and. 84:11
the Lord shall g. that which. 85:12
the Lord himself shall g. Isa 7:14
the Lord shall g. thee rest. 14:3
though the Lord g. you bread. 30:20
Lord shall g. them showers. Zech 10:1
Lord shall g. him the. Luke 1:32
Lord g. mercy to house. 2 Tim 1:16

not **give**, or **give** not

said, thou shalt not g. Gen 30:31
I will not g. you straw. Ex 5:10
shall not g. more, poor not g. 30:15
shalt not g. thy money. Lev 25:37
I will not g. you of. Deut 2:5; 9:19
thy daughter thou shalt not g. 7:3
he will not g. of the flesh of. 28:55
shall not any of us g. Judg 21:1
we have sworn we will not g. 7
we will not g. them. 1 Sam 30:22
I will not g. inheritance. 1 Ki 21:4
g. not your daughters. Ezra 9:12 Neh 10:30; 13:25
not g. sleep to mine. Ps 132:4
g. not sleep to thine eyes. Pr 6:4
g not thy strength unto. 31:3
constellations shall not g. Isa 13:10
my glory will I not g. 42:8; 48:11
I will no more g. thy corn. 62:8
let us not g. heed to any. Jer 18:18
not g. Jeremiah into the hand. 26:24
a cloud, the moon shall not g. her light. Ezek 32:7; Mat 24:29 Mark 13:24
to whom not g. honour. Dan 11:21
g. not thine heritage to. Joel 2:17
g. not that which is holy. Mat 7:6
g. or shall we not g.? Mark 12:15
neither g. place to the. Eph 4:27
g. not those things they. Jas 2:16

give thanks

I will g. thanks. 2 Sam 22:50 Ps 18:49
g. thanks to the Lord, call upon. 1 Chr 16:8; Ps 105:1; 106:1 107:1; 118:1, 29; 136:1, 3
God of our salvation, that we may g. thanks. 1 Chr 16:35; Ps 106:47
by name, to g. thanks. 1 Chr 16:41
with a harp to g. thanks. 25:3
appointed Levites to g. thanks. 2 Chr 31:2
who shall g. thee thanks? Ps 6:5
g. thanks at the remembrance of his holiness. 30:4; 97:12
Lord, I will g. thanks to thee. 30:12
I will g. thanks in the great. 35:18
do we g. thanks, do g. thanks. 75:1
people will g. thee thanks. 79:13
it is a good thing to g. thanks. 92:1
save us to g. thanks to thy. 106:47
I will rise to g. thanks. 119:62
the tribes go up to g. thanks. 122:4
g. thanks unto God of gods. 136:2
O g. thanks unto God of heaven. 26
righteous shall g. thanks to. 140:13
not only I g. thanks. Rom 16:4
for which I g. thanks. 1 Cor 10:30
I cease not to g. thanks. Eph 1:16
we g. thanks to God and. Col 1:3

g. thanks to God always. *1 Thes* 1:2
in every thing *g. thanks.* 5:18
bound to *g. thanks.* *2 Thes* 2:13
g. thee *thanks,* Lord God. *Rev* 11:17

give *up*

the Lord walketh, to *g. up* thine enemies. *Deut* 23:14; 31:5
he shall *g.* Israel *up.* *1 Ki* 14:16
did not I *g. up* the ghost? *Job* 3:11
hold my tongue, I shall *g. up.* 13:19
I will say to north, *g. up.* *Isa* 43:6
how shall I *g.* thee *up*? *Hos* 11:8
therefore will he *g.* them *up.* *Mi* 5:3
thou deliverest will I *g. up.* 6:14

given

Sarah should have *g.* *Gen* 21:7
because he hath *g.* his. *Lev* 20:3
they are *g.* as a gift for. *Num* 18:6
to the blessing *g.* *Deut* 12:15; 16:17
a full reward be *g.* thee. *Ruth* 2:12
thought I would have *g.* *2 Sam* 4:10
would have *g.* thee such and. 12:8*
I would have *g.* thee ten. 18:11
hath the king *g.* us any gift? 19:42
the man of God had *g.* *1 Ki* 13:5
thine own have we *g.* *1 Chr* 29:14
let it be *g.* them day by. *Ezra* 6:9
the silver is *g.* to thee. *Esth* 3:11
let my life be *g.* me at my. 7:3
why is light *g.* to him? *Job* 3:20
why is light *g.* to a man whose? 23
whom alone the earth was *g.* 15:19
bodies of thy servants *g.* *Ps* 79:2
he hath *g.* to the. 112:9; *2 Cor* 9:9
the earth hath he *g.* to the. *Ps* 115:16
that which he hath *g.* will. *Pr* 19:17
deliver those that are *g.* *Eccl* 8:8
are *g.* from one shepherd. 12:11
Child is born, to us Son is *g.* *Isa* 9:6
therefore hear, thou that art *g.* 47:8
g. to covetousness. *Jer* 6:13; 8:10
he said to all who had *g.* him. 44:20
we have *g.* the hand to. *Lam* 5:6
is this land *g.* *Ezek* 11:15; 33:24
they are desolate, they are *g.* 35:12
beasts, fowls hath he *g.* *Dan* 2:38
lion, and a man's heart was *g.* 7:4
she shall be *g.* up, and they. 11:6
it is *g.* to you to know the mysteries. *Mat* 13:11; *Mark* 4:11; *Luke* 8:10
save they to whom it is *g.* *Mat* 19:11
be *g.* to a nation bringing. 21:43
are *g.* in marriage. 22:30
Mark 12:25; *Luke* 20:35
sold for much and *g.* *Mat* 26:9
Mark 14:5
all power is *g.* to me in. *Mat* 28:18
hear more shall be *g.* *Mark* 4:24
to whom much is *g.* of. *Luke* 12:48
nothing, except it be *g.* *John* 3:27
hath *g.* to the Son to have life. 5:26
of all he hath *g.* me, I should. 6:39
come to me, except it were *g.* 65
except it were *g.* thee from. 19:11
is none other name *g.* *Acts* 4:12
hoped that money should be *g.* 24:26
Holy Ghost which is *g.* *Rom* 5:5
who hath first *g.* to him. 11:35
because of the grace that is *g.* 15:15
freely *g.* us of God. *1 Cor* 2:12
that thanks may be *g.* *2 Cor* 1:11
law *g.* which could have *g.* *Gal* 3:21*
dispensation, which is *g.* *Eph* 3:2
unto me, the least, is this grace *g.* 8
who have *g.* themselves over. 4:19
Christ hath loved us, and *g.* 5:2
to you it is *g.* in behalf. *Phil* 1:29*
and hath *g.* him a name above. 2:9
if Jesus had *g.* them rest. *Heb* 4:8
Spirit which he hath *g.* *1 John* 3:24
because he hath *g.* us of his. 4:13
white robes were *g.* to. *Rev* 6:11
power was *g.* to him to. 13:5
it was *g.* unto him to make war. 7

God or *Lord hath, had* **given**

the *Lord hath g.* Abraham flocks. *Gen* 24:35
and Rachel said, *God hath g.* 30:6
and Leah said, *God hath g.* me. 18
God hath g. me your father's. 31:9
G. hath graciously *g.* me. 33:5
God hath g. you treasure in. 43:23
the children *God hath g.* me. 48:9
the *Lord hath g.* you. *Ex* 16:15
for that the *Lord hath g.* you the. 29
land which the *Lord hath g.* them. *Num* 32:7, 9; *Deut* 3:18; 28:52
Josh 2:9, 14; 23:13, 15; *Jer* 25:5
shout, for *Lord hath g.* *Josh* 6:16
land which the *Lord hath g.* 18:3
Lord hath g. me my. *1 Sam* 1:27
Lord hath g. it to a neighbour. 15:28; 28:17
with what the *Lord hath g.* 30:23
the kingdom *hath God g.* me. *2 Chr* 36:23; *Ezra* 1:2
man to whom God *hath g.* *Eccl* 5:19
children *Lord hath g.* *Isa* 8:18
Heb 2:13
Lord hath g. a command. *Isa* 23:11
Lord hath g. me the tongue. 50:4
Lord hath g. knowledge. *Jer* 11:18
seeing the *Lord hath g.* it. 47:7
the *Lord had g.* thanks. *John* 6:23
whom *God hath g.* to. *Acts* 5:32
God hath g. thee all that. 27:24
God hath g. them spirit. *Rom* 11:8
the *Lord hath g.* us for edification. *2 Cor* 10:8; 13:10
but *God* who *hath g.* us. *1 Thes* 4:8
the record *God hath g.* *1 John* 5:11
see **rest**

I have, or *have I* **given**

brethren *have I g.* him. *Gen* 27:37
I have g. thee that thou. *1 Ki* 3:13
therefore *I have g.* Jacob. *Isa* 43:28*
I have g. him for a witness. 55:4
things *I have g.* shall pass. *Jer* 8:13
I have g. it to whom it seemed. 27:5
I have g. thee cow's dung. *Ezek* 4:15
I have g. him land of Egypt. 29:20
I have g. you cleanness. *Amos* 4:6
be pulled out of land *I have g.* 9:15
I have g. you example. *John* 13:15
I have g. them the words. 17:8, 14
gavest me, *I have g.* them. 22
I have g. order to the. *1 Cor* 16:1

not **given**

and she was *not g.* unto. *Gen* 38:14
I have *not g.* ought. *Deut* 26:14
Lord hath *not g.* you an heart. 29:4
hath he *not g.* you rest? *1 Chr* 22:18
Levites had *not* been *g.* *Neh* 13:10
thou hast *not g.* water to. *Job* 22:7
maidens were *not g.* *Ps* 78:63
but he hath *not g.* me over. 118:18
who hath *not g.* us as a prey. 124:6
Jerusalem *not* be *g.* into. *Isa* 37:10
thou shalt *not* be *g.* into. *Jer* 39:17
because thou hast *not g.* *Ezek* 3:20
he that hath *not g.* forth upon. 18:8
to them it is *not g.* *Mat* 13:11
Holy Ghost was *not* yet *g.* *John* 7:39
bishop *not g.* to wine. *1 Tim* 3:3*
Tit 1:7*
not g. to much wine. *1 Tim* 3:8
God hath *not g.* us the. *2 Tim* 1:7
women likewise *not g.* to. *Tit* 2:3*

shall be **given**

shall inheritance *be g.* *Num* 26:54
thy sheep *shall be g.* to. *Deut* 28:31
thy sons *shall be g.* to another. 32
commandment *shall be g.* *Ezra* 4:21
it *shall be g.* to half of. *Esth* 5:3
to him *shall be g.* of gold. *Ps* 72:15
what *shall be g.* to thee? 120:3
reward *shall be g.* him. *Isa* 3:11
bread *shall be g.* him, waters. 33:16
glory of Lebanon *shall be g.* 35:2
this city *shall be g.* into the hand of king. *Jer* 21:10; 38:3, 18
marishes, they *shall be g.* *Ezek* 47:11
the saints *shall be g.* into. *Dan* 7:25
the kingdom *shall be g.* to the. 27
ask and it *shall be g.* you in that same hour. *Mat* 7:7; *Luke* 11:9
shall be g. you in same. *Mat* 10:19
Mark 13:11
no sign *shall be g.* *Mat* 12:39
Mark 8:12; *Luke* 11:29
hath, to him *shall be g.* and more abundance. *Mat* 13:12; 25:29
Mark 4:25; *Luke* 8:18
it *shall be g.* them for. *Mat* 20:23
kingdom of God *shall be g.* 21:43
give, and it *shall be g.* *Luke* 6:38
your prayers I *shall be g.* *Philem* 22
God, and it *shall be g.* him. *Jas* 1:5

thou hast, or *hast thou* **given**

thou hast g. no seed. *Gen* 15:3
which *thou hast g.* us. *Deut* 26:15
thou hast g. me south. *Josh* 15:19*
Judg 1:15*
why *hast thou g.* me? *Josh* 17:14
thou hast g. this great. *Judg* 15:18
thou hast g. him bread. *1 Sam* 22:13
this deed *thou hast g.* *2 Sam* 12:14
thou hast g. me the shield of thy salvation. 22:36; *Ps* 18:35
thou hast g. me the necks. *2 Sam* 22:41; *Ps* 18:40
thou hast g. him a son to. *1 Ki* 3:6
land *thou hast g.* 8:36; *2 Chr* 6:27
are these *thou hast g.*? *1 Ki* 9:13
possession *thou hast g.* *2 Chr* 20:11
thou hast g. us such. *Ezra* 9:13
thou hast g. him his heart's. *Ps* 21:2
thou hast g. us like sheep. 44:11
thou hast g. a banner to them. 60:4
thou hast g. me the heritage. 61:5
thou hast g. commandment to. 71:3
thou hast g. him power. *John* 17:2
that all things *thou hast g.* me. 7
but for them which *thou hast g.* 9
thy name those *thou hast g.* me. 11
thou hast g. them blood. *Rev* 16:6

giver

taker of usury, so with *g.* *Isa* 24:2
God loveth a cheerful *g.* *2 Cor* 9:7

givest

thou *g.* him nought, and. *Deut* 15:9
not be grieved when thou *g.* him. 10
if righteous, what *g.* thou? *Job* 35:7
thou *g.* thy mouth to evil. *Ps* 50:19
thou *g.* them tears to drink. 80:5
thou *g.* them, they gather. 104:28
thou *g.* them their meat in. 145:15
rest content, though thou *g.* *Pr* 6:35
thou *g.* not warning, to. *Ezek* 3:18
but thou *g.* thy gifts to all. 16:33
that thou *g.* a reward, and none. 34
thou verily *g.* thanks. *1 Cor* 14:17

giveth

he *g.* you on sixth day. *Ex* 16:29
in land which Lord thy God *g.* thee. 20:12; *Deut* 4:40; 5:16; 25:15
every man that *g.* willingly. *Ex* 25:2*
all that any man *g.* *Lev* 27:9
the Lord our God *g.* thee. *Deut* 2:29
4:1, 21; 11:17, 31; 12:1, 10*
15:4, 7; 16:20; 17:14; 18:9; 19:1
2, 10, 14; 21:1, 23; 24:4; 26:1, 2
27:2, 3; 28:8; *Josh* 1:11, 15
he that *g.* thee power. *Deut* 8:18
God *g.* not this land for thy. 9:6
g. you rest from. 12:10; 25:19
if a prophet *g.* thee a sign or. 13:1
gates which Lord *g.* 16:5, 18; 17:2
who *g.* rain upon the earth. *Job* 5:10
he *g.* no account of any of his. 33:13
when he *g.* quietness. 34:29
who *g.* songs. 35:10
but *g.* right to the poor. 36:6
he *g.* meat. 31
great deliverance *g.* he. *Ps* 18:50
righteous sheweth mercy, *g.* 37:21
God of Israel is he that *g.* 68:35
of thy words *g.* light. 119:130
for so he *g.* his beloved. 127:2
who *g.* food to all flesh. 136:25
146:7; 147:9
g. salvation to kings. 144:10
he *g.* snow. 147:16
the Lord *g.* wisdom out. *Pr* 2:
he *g.* grace to the lowly. 3:3
Jas 4:6; *1 Pet* 5:
good understanding *g.* *Pr* 13:1
g. and spareth not. 21:26; 22:
he that *g.* to the poor shall. 28:2
g. to a man that is good, but to th sinner he *g.* travail. *Eccl* 2:2
yet God *g.* him not power to. 6:
he *g.* power to the faint. *Isa* 40:2
g. breath. 42:
g. rain. *Jer* 5:2
woe to him that *g.* him not. 22:1
g. the sun for a light. 31:3
he *g.* his cheek to him. *Lam* 3:

he g. wisdom to the wise. Dan 2:21
and g. it to whomsover. 4:17, 25, 32
woe to him that g. his. Hab 2:15
it g. light to all that are. Mat 5:15
God g. not the Spirit. John 3:34
but my Father g. you the true. 6:32
who cometh down and g. life. 33
all that the Father g. me shall. 37
the good shepherd g. his. 10:11
not as the world g. give I. 14:27
he g. to all life, breath. Acts 17:25
he that g. let him do it. Rom 12:8
he eateth to the Lord, for he g. 14:6
but God that g. the. 1 Cor 3:7
he that g. her in marriage. 7:38
God g. it a body as it hath. 15:38
but thanks be to God who g. us. 57
killeth, but the Spirit g. 2 Cor 3:6
g. us richly all things. 1 Tim 6:17
ask of God, that g. to. Jas 1:5
g. more grace, God g. grace to. 4:6
as of ability that God g. 1 Pet 4:11*
for the Lord God g. Rev 22:5

giving

loveth the stranger in g. Deut 10:18
by g. him a double portion of. 21:17
visited his people in g. Ruth 1:6
my desire, in g. food. 1 Ki 5:9
by g. him according to. 2 Chr 6:23
their hope be as the g. Job 11:20
were marrying and g. Mat 24:38
g. out that himself was. Acts 8:9
g. them the Holy Ghost, as he. 15:8
was strong in faith, g. Rom 4:20
g. of the law, and the service. 9:4
things g. sound. 1 Cor 14:7
at thy g. of thanks. 16
g. no offence in any thing. 2 Cor 6:3
concerning g. and. Phil 4:15
g. heed to seducing. 1 Tim 4:1
g. honour to the wife as. 1 Pet 3:7
g. all diligence, add to. 2 Pet 1:5
g. themselves over to. Jude 7
see **thanks**

glad

seeth thee, he will be g. Ex 4:14
the priest's heart was g. Judg 18:20
men of Jabesh were g. 1 Sam 11:9
Israel went to tents g. 1 Ki 8:66
2 Chr 7:10
Haman g. Esth 5:9
the city Shushan was g. 8:15
are g. when they can find. Job 3:22
see it and are g. 22:19; Ps 64:10
therefore my heart is g. Ps 16:9
thou hast made him g. with. 21:6
shall hear and be g. 34:2; 69:32
them be g. that favour my. 35:27
they have made thee g. 45:8
the streams shall make g. the. 46:4
let the nations be g. and sing. 67:4
make us g. 90:15
thou, Lord, hast made me g. 92:4
let the isles be g. 97:1
Zion heard, and was g. 8
wine that maketh g. the. 104:15
I will be g. in the Lord. 34*
Egypt was g. 105:38
then are they g. because. 107:30
they that fear thee will be g. 119:74
I was g. when they said unto. 122:1
whereof we are g. 126:3
a wise son maketh a g. father.
Pr 10:1; 15:20
but a good word maketh it g. 12:25
that is g. at calamities, not. 17:5
and thy mother shall be g. 23:25
let not thy heart be g. when. 24:17
wise, and make my heart g. 27:11
wilderness shall be g. Isa 35:1
Hezekiah was g. of them, and. 39:2
is born, making him very g. Jer 20:15
because ye were g. O ye. 50:11
they are g. that thou. Lam 1:21
was the king exceeding g. Dan 6:23
they make the king g. Hos 7:3
Jonah was g. because of. Jonah 4:6
shall see it and be g. Zech 10:7
were g. and promised money.
Mark 14:11; Luke 22:5
am sent to shew thee these g.
tidings. Luke 1:19*
shewing the g. tidings of the. 8:1*

make merry and be g. Luke 15:32
saw my day and was g. John 8:56
I am g. for your sakes that I. 11:15
seen grace of G. he was g. Acts 11:23
heard this, they were g. 13:48
I am g. therefore on. Rom 16:19*
I am g. of the coming. 1 Cor 16:17*
then that maketh me g.? 2 Cor 2:2
we are g. when we are weak. 13:9*
glory revealed, ye may be g. also.
1 Pet 4:13*

glad joined with rejoice

be g. and let the earth rejoice.
1 Chr 16:31; Ps 96:11
I will be g. and rejoice. Ps 9:2
rejoice, Israel shall be g. 14:7; 53:6
I will be g. and rejoice in thy. 31:7
be g. and rejoice, ye righteous.
32:11; 68:3
that seek thee, be g. and rejoice.
40:16; 70:4
rejoice, daughters of Judah be g.
48:11*
that we may be g. and rejoice. 90:14
we will rejoice and be g. in it. 118:24
we will be g. and rejoice in thee.
S of S 1:4
we will rejoice and be g. in his salvation. Isa 25:9
but be you g. and rejoice for. 65:18
rejoice ye with Jerusalem, and be g.
66:10
rejoice and be g. O Edom. Lam 4:21
O land, be g. and rejoice. Joel 2:21
g. ye children of Zion, and rejoice. 23
they rejoice and are g. Hab 1:15
be g. and rejoice, O. Zeph 3:14
rejoice and be g. great. Mat 5:12
rejoice, my tongue was g. Acts 2:26*
be g. and rejoice, the. Rev 19:7*

gladly

Herod heard John g. Mark 6:20
people heard Christ g. 12:37
that g. received the word. Acts 2:41
the brethren received us g. 21:17
ye suffer fools g. seeing. 2 Cor 11:19
most g. therefore will I rather. 12:9
I will very g. spend and be. 15

gladness

in the day of your g. ye. Num 10:10
not the Lord with g. of. Deut 28:47
brought up ark with g. 2 Sam 6:12*
strength and g. are in. 1 Chr 16:27
drink that day with great g. 29:22
sang praises with g. 2 Chr 29:30
of unleavened bread with g. 30:21
kept other seven days with g. 23
there was very great g. Neh 8:17
keep the dedication with g. 12:27
light, and g. and joy. Esth 8:16, 17
a day of feasting and g. 9:17, 18, 19
thou hast put g. in my heart. Ps 4:7
thou hast girded me with g. 30:11
thee with oil of g. 45:7; Heb 1:9
with g. and rejoicing shall. Ps 45:15
make me to hear joy and g. 51:8
and g. is sown for the upright. 97:11
serve the Lord with g.: come. 100:2
forth his chosen with g. 105:43*
that I may rejoice in the g. 106:5
the righteous shall be g. Pr 10:28
and in the day of the g. S of S 3:11
joy and g. is taken away. Isa 16:10
behold joy and g. 22:13
ye shall have a song and g. 30:29
obtain joy and g. 35:10; 51:11
joy and g. shall be found. 51:3
cease voice of mirth and g. Jer 7:34
16:9; 25:10
sing with g. for Jacob, shout. 31:7
heard a voice of joy and g. 33:11
joy and g. taken from the. 48:33
joy and g. from house. Joel 1:16
house of Judah joy and g. Zech 8:19
receive it with g. Mark 4:16*
shalt have joy and g. Luke 1:14
did eat their meat with g. Acts 2:46
opened not the gate for g. 12:14*
our hearts with food and g. 14:17
in the Lord with all g. Phil 2:29*

glass

see through a g. darkly. 1 Cor 13:12*

beholding as in a g. 2 Cor 3:18*
his natural face in a g. Jas 1:23*
there was a sea of g. like. Rev 4:6
I saw a sea of g. mingled. 15:2
pure gold, like clear g. 21:18, 21

glasses

Lord will take away g. Isa 3:23*
see **looking**

glean

thou shalt not g. vineyard.
Lev 19:10; Deut 24:21
go to field and g. ears. Ruth 2:2
they shall thoroughly g. Jer 6:9

gleaned

g. of them in highways. Judg 20:45
she came and g. after. Ruth 2:3

gleaning, -s

the g. of harvest. Lev 19:9; 23:22
is not the g. of grapes? Judg 8:2
yet g. grapes shall be left. Isa 17:6
the g. grapes when vintage is. 24:13
they not leave some g.? Jer 49:9
I am as the grape g. of the. Mi 7:1

glede

ye shall not eat the g. Deut 14:13

glistering

now I have prepared g. 1 Chr 29:2*
the g. sword cometh out. Job 20:25
raiment was white and g. Luke 9:29*

glitter, -ing

if I whet my g. sword. Deut 32:41
g. spear rattleth against. Job 39:23*
furbished that it may g. Ezek 21:10*
to consume, because of the g. 28*
lifteth up the g. spear. Nah 3:3
shining of thy g. spear. Hab 3:11

gloominess

a day of darkness and g. Joel 2:2
Zeph 1:15

gloriest

wherefore g. thou in the? Jer 49:4

glorieth

let him that g. Jer 9:24
1 Cor 1:31; 2 Cor 10:17

glorified

all the people I will be g. Lev 10:3
hast increased nation, thou art g.
Isa 26:15
for the Lord hath g. himself. 44:23
O Israel, in whom I will be g. 49:3
of Israel he hath g. thee. 55:5; 60:9
my hands, that I may be g. 60:21
of the Lord that he might be g. 61:3
said, let the Lord be g. 66:5
I will be g. in midst. Ezek 28:22
in the day I shall be g. 39:13
hast thou not g. Dan 5:23
pleasure in it, and be g. Hag 1:8
marvelled, and g. God. Mat 9:8
Mark 2:12; Luke 5:26
they g. the God of Israel. Mat 15:31
synagogues, being g. of. Luke 4:15
fear on all, and they g. God. 7:16
made straight, and g. God. 13:13
the leper g. God. 17:15
the centurion g. God. 23:47
Holy Ghost was not yet given, because Jesus not g. John 7:39
Son of God might be g. 11:4
but when Jesus was g. 12:16
the Son of man should be g. 23
I have both g. it, and will. 28
Son of man g. God is g. in. 13:31
if God be g. in him, God shall. 32
that the Father may be g. in. 14:13
herein is my Father g. that ye. 15:8
I have g. thee on earth. 17:4
and thine are mine, and I am g. 10
God of our fathers hath g. Acts 3:13
for all men g. God for what. 4:21
they held their peace, and g. 11:18
Gentiles heard this, they g. 13:48
they of Jerusalem g. the Lord. 21:20
they knew God, they g. Rom 1:21
with him, that we may be g. 8:17
whom he justified, them he also g. 30
and they g. God in me. Gal 1:24
come to be g. in saints. 2 Thes 1:10
the name of Jesus may be g. 12
word of the Lord may be g. 3:1
so Christ g. not himself. Heb 5:5

that God in all things may be g. through Jesus Christ. 1 Pet 4:11
spoken of, but on your part he is g. 14
how much she hath g. Rev 18:7

glorifieth, -ing

whoso offereth praise g. Ps 50:23
shepherds returned, g. Luke 2:20
he departed to his own house, g. 5:25
the blind man followed him, g. 18:43

glorify

all ye seed of Jacob g. Ps 22:23
thee, and thou shalt g. me. 50:15
all nations shall come and g. 86:9
and I will g. thy name for ever. 12
wherefore g. ye the Lord. Isa 24:15
shall the strong people g. thee. 25:3
and I will g. the house of. 60:7
multiply, I will also g. Jer 30:19
g. your Father which is. Mat 5:16
g. thy name, I will g. it. John 12:28
God shall also g. him in. 13:32
he shall g. me; for he shall. 16:14
g. thy Son, that thy Son also may g. 17:1
now, O Father, g. me with thine. 5
what death he should g. God. 21:19
with one mind and mouth g. God. Rom 15:6
that the Gentiles might g. God. 9
g. God in body and. 1 Cor 6:20
g. God for your professed. 2 Cor 9:13
may g. God in the day. 1 Pet 2:12
let him g. God on this behalf. 4:16
fear thee, and g. thy name. Rev 15:4

glorious

hand, O Lord, is become g. Ex 15:6
who is like thee, O Lord, g. in. 11
mayest fear this g. Deut 28:58
g. was king of Israel! 2 Sam 6:20
thank and praise thy g. 1 Chr 29:13
blessed be thy g. name. Neh 9:5
the king's daughter is all g. Ps 45:13
his honour, make his praise g. 66:2
and blessed be his g. name. 72:19
more g. than the mountains. 76:4
g. things are spoken of thee. 87:3
his work is honourable and g. 111:3*
I will speak of the g. honour. 145:5
to make known the g. majesty of. 12*
of the Lord shall be g. Isa 4:2
Jesse, and his rest shall be g. 11:10
he shall be for a g. throne. 22:23
whose g. beauty is a fading. 28:1
the g. beauty which is on head of. 4
Lord shall cause his g. voice. 30:30
the g. Lord will be to us a. 33:21*
yet shall I be g. in the eyes. 49:5*
make the place of my feet g. 60:13
who is this that is g. in his ? 63:1
led them by Moses with his g. 12
people to make thyself a g. name. 14
a g. high throne from. Jer 17:12
made very g. in midst. Ezek 27:25
he shall stand in the g. Dan 11:16
he shall enter also into the g. 41
between the seas in the g. holy. 45
people rejoiced for g. Luke 13:17
into the g. liberty of the. Rom 8:21
engraven in stones was g. 2 Cor 3:7
of the Spirit be rather g. 3:8
lest light of g. gospel should. 4:4
it to himself a g. church. Eph 5:27
like to his g. body. Phil 3:21
according to his g. power. Col 1:11
according to g. gospel. 1 Tim 1:11
looking for g. appearing. Tit 2:13

gloriously

he hath triumphed g. Ex 15:1
reign before his ancients g. Isa 24:23

glory

hath he gotten all this g. Gen 31:1
for Aaron for g. Ex 28:2, 40
inherit the throne of g. 1 Sam 2:8
g. is departed from Israel. 4:21, 22
for Lord must be of g. 1 Chr 22:5
thine is greatness, power, and g. 29:11; Mat 6:13
Haman told of the g. of. Esth 5:11
the g. of his nostrils is. Job 39:20
and array thyself with g. and. 40:10*
King of g. shall come in. Ps 24:7, 9
who is this King of g.? the Lord. 10
the God of g. thundereth. Ps 29:3
when the g. of his house. 49:16
afterward receive me to g. 73:24
help us, O God, for the g. of. 79:9
that g. may dwell in our land. 85:9
for thou art the g. of their. 89:17
they changed their g. into. 106:20
speak of the g. of thy. 145:11
let the saints be joyful in g. 149:5
the wise shall inherit g. Pr 3:35
the g. of children are their. 17:6
the g. of young men is their. 20:29
search their own g. is not g. 25:27
men rejoice there is g. 28:12
hide thee in the dust, for the g. of his majesty. Isa 2:10, 19, 21
for upon all the g. shall be a. 4:5
their g. and pomp shall descend. 5:14
where will ye leave your g.? 10:3
I will punish the g. of his high. 12
and shall consume the g. of his. 18
Babylon the g. of kingdom. 13:19
all of them lie in g. each in. 14:18
the g. of Moab shall be. 16:14
they shall be as the g. of the. 17:3
g. of Jacob shall be made thin. 4
be ashamed of Egypt their g. 20:5
and all the g. of Kedar shall. 21:16
g. of his Father's house. 22:24
to stain the pride of all g. 23:9
we heard songs, even g. to. 24:16
the g. of Lebanon shall be. 35:2
in their g. ye shall boast. 61:6
with the abundance of her g. 66:11
the g. of the Gentiles as a. 12
have changed their g. Jer 2:11
might be to me for a g. 13:11
even the crown of your g. 18
g. of all lands. Ezek 20:6, 15
take from them joy of their g. 24:25
I will open the g. of the. 25:9
I shall set g. in the land of. 26:20
whom art thou thus like in g.? 31:18
hath given thee power and g. Dan 2:37; 7:14
the g. of my kingdom returned. 4:36
and increase with g. 11:39
I will change their g. Hos 4:7
as for Ephraim, their g. shall. 9:11
priests that rejoiced for the g. 10:5
come to Adullam the g. Mi 1:15
end of the store and g. Nah 2:9
filled with shame for g. Hab 2:16
this house in her first g.? Hag 2:3
I will fill this house with g. saith. 7
g. of this latter house greater. 9
will be the g. in midst. Zech 2:5
after the g. hath he sent me to. 8
temple, he shall bear the g. 6:13
their g. is spoiled, a voice of. 11:3
g. of the house of David, g. of. 12:7
kingdoms of world, and g. Mat 4:8
trumpet, that they may have g. 6:2
shall come in the g. of his Father. Mat 16:27; Mark 8:38
Son of man coming with power and great g. Mat 24:30; Mark 13:26 Luke 21:27
saying, G. to God in the highest. Luke 2:14; 19:38
light to Gentiles, and the g. 2:32
will I give thee, and the g. 4:6
who appeared in g. and spake. 9:31
with the g. which I had. John 17:5
the g. thou gavest me, I have. 22
the God of g. appeared. Acts 7:2
he gave not God the g. 12:23
could not see for the g. of. 22:11
strong in faith, giving g. Rom 4:20
raised from the dead by the g. 6:4
to be compared with the g. 8:18
to whom pertaineth the g. and. 9:4
had afore prepared unto g. 23
of him are all things, to whom be g. 11:36; Gal 1:5; 2 Tim 4:18 Heb 13:21; 1 Pet 5:11
to God only wise be g. Rom 16:27 1 Tim 1:17
hath ordained to our g. 1 Cor 2:7
have crucified the Lord of g. 8
but the woman is the g. of the. 11:7
woman have long hair, it is a g. 15
g. of celestial is one, the g. of. 15:40
one g. of the sun, another g. of. 41
dishonour, it is raised in g. 1 Cor 15:43
for the g. of his countenance, which g. 2 Cor 3:7
be g. the ministration of righteousness doth exceed in g. 9
had no g. by reason of the g. 10
we are all changed from g. to g. 18
us an eternal weight of g. 4:17
administered to us to the g. of. 8:19
they are messengers, and the g. 23
to the praise of the g. of. Eph 1:6
the Father of g. may give you. 17
what is the riches of the g. 18
for you, which is your g. 3:13
to him be g. in the church by. 21
are by Christ to g. of. Phil 1:11
and whose g. is in their shame. 3:19
according to his riches in g. by. 4:19
now to God and our Father be g. 20
the g. of this mystery, which is Christ in you, the hope of g. Col 1:27
ye appear with him in g. 3:4
nor of men sought we g. 1 Thes 2:6
called you to his kingdom and g. 12
for ye are our g. and joy. 20
punished from the g. of. 2 Thes 1:9
to the obtaining of the g. of. 2:14
seen of angels, received up into g. 1 Tim 3:16
in Christ, with eternal g. 2 Tim 2:10
in bringing many sons to g. Heb 2:10
was counted worthy of more g. 3:3
over it the cherubims of g. 9:5
Lord Jesus, the Lord of g. Jas 2:1
joy unspeakable, full of g. 1 Pet 1:8
it testified the g. that should. 11
raised him up, and gave him g. 21
all the g. of man, as the flower. 24
for what g. is it, if when ye be ? 2:20
the Spirit of g. and of God. 4:14
a partaker of the g. that shall. 5:1
hath called us to eternal g. by. 10
that hath called us to g. 2 Pet 1:3
voice to him from the excellent g. 17
g. both now and ever. 3:18; Rev 1:6
wise God our Saviour be g. Jude 25
worthy to receive g. Rev 4:11; 5:12
blessing and g. and wisdom. 7:12
affrighted, and gave g. to God. 11:13
see **crown, honour, vain**

give **glory**

my son, *give* g. to God. Josh 7:19
ye shall *give* g. to God. 1 Sam 6:5
give to Lord g. 1 Chr 16:28, 29 Ps 29:1, 2; 96:7, 8; Jer 13:16
will *give* grace and g. Ps 84:11
but to thy name *give* the g. 115:1
let them *give* g. unto the. Isa 42:12
not lay it to heart to *give* g. Mal 2:2
that returned to *give* g. Luke 17:18
when those beasts *give* g. Rev 4:9
fear God, and *give* g. to him. 14:7
and repented not to *give* g. 16:9

glory *of God*

declare the g. *of God*. Ps 19:1
the g. *of God* to conceal. Pr 25:2
g. *of* the *God* of Israel. Ezek 8:4
the g. *of God* was gone up from. 9:3
the g. *of God* was over them. 10:19 11:22
the g. *of God* came from the. 43:2
is for the g. *of God*. John 11:4
thou shouldest see the g. *of God*. 40
up and saw the g. *of God*. Acts 7:55
come short of g. *of God*. Rom 3:23
in hope of the g. *of God*. 5:2
received us to the g. *of God*. 15:7
do all to the g. *of God*. 1 Cor 10:31
man is image and g. *of God*. 11:7
and amen, to g. *of God*. 2 Cor 1:2(
the knowledge of the g. *of God*. 4:(
many redound to g. *of God*. 1
by Christ to the g. *of God*. Phil 1:1
Jesus is Lord to the g. *of God*. 2:1
smoke from g. *of God*. Rev 15:
Jerusalem, having g. *of God*. 21:1
no need of the sun, g. *of God*. 2

his **glory**

God hath shewed us *his* g. Deut 5:2
his g. like the firstling of. 33:17
declare *his* g. among. 1 Chr 16:2 Ps 96:

his g. is great in thy. *Ps* 21:5
doth every one speak of *his g.* 29:9
his g. shall not descend after. 49:17
earth be filled with *his g.* 72:19
delivered *his g.* into the. 78:61
thou hast made *his g.* to. 89:44*
and all the people see *his g.* 97:6
Zion, he shall appear in *his g.* 102:16
and *his g.* above the. 113:4; 148:13
it is *his g.* to pass over. *Pr* 19:11
provoke the eyes of *his g.* *Isa* 3:8
the whole earth is full of *his g.* 6:3
the king of Assyria and *his g.* 8:7
under *his g.* he shall kindle. 10:16
shall fear *his g.* from rising. 59:19
and *his g.* shall be seen upon. 60:2
Ah lord, or, Ah *his g.* *Jer* 22:18
earth shined with *his g.* *Ezek* 43:2
and they took *his g.* *Dan* 5:20
God came, *his g.* covered. *Hab* 3:3
Solomon in all *his g.* *Mat* 6:29
Luke 12:27
shall sit in *his g.* *Mat* 19:28
Luke 9:26
awake, they saw *his g.* *Luke* 9:32
and to enter into *his g.* 24:26
we beheld *his g.* glory as. *John* 1:14
and manifested forth *his g.* 2:11
but he that seeketh *his g.* that. 7:18
Esaias, when he saw *his g.* 12:41
through my lie unto *his g.* *Rom* 3:7
make known riches of *his g.* 9:23
to the praise of *his g.* *Eph* 1:12, 14
according to riches of *his g.* 3:16
being brightness of *his g.* *Heb* 1:3
that when *his g.* shall be. *1 Pet* 4:13
before the presence of *his g.* *Jude* 24
was lightened with *his g.* *Rev* 18:1

***my* glory**

tell my father of all *my g.* *Gen* 45:13
be sanctified by *my g.* *Ex* 29:43
while *my g.* passeth by. 33:22
which have seen *my g.* *Num* 14:22
he hath stript me of *my g.* *Job* 19:9
my g. was fresh in me, my. 29:20
thou art *my g.* and lifter. *Ps* 3:3
how long will ye turn *my g.*? 4:2
my g. rejoiceth. 16:9
my g. may sing. 30:12
awake up *my g.* 57:8
in God is *my g.* 62:7
sing and give praise with *my g.* 108:1
my g. will I not give to another.
Isa 42:8; 48:11
have created him for *my g.* 43:7
salvation for Israel, *my g.* 46:13
glorify the house of *my g.* 60:7
shall come and see *my g.* 66:18
my g. they shall declare *my g.* 19
I will set *my g.* among. *Ezek* 39:21
have ye taken away *my g.* *Mi* 2:9
I seek not *mine* own *g.* *John* 8:50
that they may behold *my g.* 17:24

glory *of the Lord*

ye shall see *g. of the Lord.* *Ex* 16:7
g. of Lord appeared. 10; *Lev* 9:23
Num 14:10; 16:19, 42; 20:6
the *g. of the Lord* abode. *Ex* 24:16
the *g. of Lord* was like. 17
the *g. of the Lord* filled. 40:34, 35
the *g. of the Lord* shall. *Lev* 9:6
filled with *g. of the Lord.* *Num* 14:21
the *g. of the Lord* filled. *1 Ki* 8:11
2 Chr 5:14; 7:1, 2, 3; *Ezek* 43:5
44:4
g. of Lord shall endure. *Ps* 104:31
great is the *g. of the Lord.* 138:5
shall see *g. of the Lord.* *Isa* 35:2
g. of the Lord be revealed. 40:5
g. of the Lord shall be thy. 58:8
and the *g. of the Lord* is risen. 60:1
the likeness of *g. of Lord.* *Ezek* 1:28
blessed be the *g. of the Lord.* 3:12
and behold, the *g. of the Lord.* 23
the *g. of the Lord* went up. 10:4
g. of the Lord departed from. 18
the *g. of the Lord* stood upon. 11:23
g. of the Lord came into. 43:4
knowledge of *g. of Lord.* *Hab* 2:14
g. of the Lord shone. *Luke* 2:9
as in a glass *g. of the Lord.*
2 Cor 3:18

***thy* glory**

I beseech thee shew me *thy g.*
Ex 33:18
who hast set *thy g.* above. *Ps* 8:1
sword on thy thigh with *thy g.* 45:3
let *thy g.* be above. 57:5, 11; 108:5
to see thy power and *thy g.* 63:2
let *thy g.* appear unto their. 90:16
kings of the earth *thy g.* 102:15
the chariots of *thy g.* *Isa* 22:18
thy God *thy g.* 60:19
kings shall see *thy g.* 62:2
from the habitation of *thy g.* 63:15
disgrace throne of *thy g.* *Jer* 14:21
come down from *thy g.* and. 48:18
shall be on *thy g.* *Hab* 2:16
thy left hand, in *thy g.* *Mark* 10:37

glory, *verb*

g. over me, when shall I. *Ex* 8:9
g. of this, and tarry at. *2 Ki* 14:10
g. ye in his holy name. *1 Chr* 16:10
Ps 105:3
give thanks, and *g.* *1 Chr* 16:35
sweareth by him shall *g.* *Ps* 63:11
upright in heart shall *g.* 64:10
that I may *g.* with thine. 106:5
shalt *g.* in Holy One of. *Isa* 41:16
shall all the seed of Israel *g.* 45:25
and in him shall they *g.* *Jer* 4:2
let not the rich man *g.* 9:23
let him *g.* in this, that he. 24
he hath whereof to *g.* *Rom* 4:2
but we *g.* in tribulations also. 5:3*
whereof I may *g.* through. 15:17
that no flesh should *g.* *1 Cor* 1:29
he that glorieth, let him *g.* in the
Lord. 31; *2 Cor* 10:17
therefore, let no man *g.* *1 Cor* 3:21
why dost thou *g.* as if thou? 4:7
preach, I have nothing to *g.* of. 9:16
to *g.* on our behalf, to answer them
who *g.* *2 Cor* 5:12
wherein they *g.* they may be. 11:12
many *g.* after the flesh, I will *g.* 18
if I must needs *g.* I will *g.* of. 30
expedient for me doubtless to *g.* 12:1
will I *g.* of myself I will not *g.* 5
for though I would desire to *g.* I. 6
therefore I will rather *g.* in. 9
circumcised, that they may *g.* in.
Gal 6:13
should *g.* save in the cross of. 14
that we ourselves *g.* in. *2 Thes* 1:4
envying in hearts, *g.* not. *Jas* 3:14

glorying

your *g.* is not good. *1 Cor* 5:6
man should make my *g.* void. 9:15
great is my boldness, great my *g.*
of you. *2 Cor* 7:4
I am become a fool in *g.* 12:11

glutton, -s

this our son, is a *g.* *Deut* 21:20*
drunkard and *g.* shall. *Pr* 23:21

gluttonous

they said, behold a man *g.*
Mat 11:19; *Luke* 7:34

gnash

he shall *g.* with his teeth. *Ps* 112:10
thine enemies hiss and *g.* *Lam* 2:16

gnashed

they *g.* upon me with. *Ps* 35:16
and they *g.* on him with. *Acts* 7:54

gnasheth

he *g.* on me with his teeth.
Job 16:9; *Ps* 37:12
he foameth and *g.* *Mark* 9:18*

gnashing

weeping and *g.* of teeth. *Mat* 8:12
13:42, 50; 22:13; 24:51; 25:30
Luke 13:28

gnat

who strain at a *g.* and. *Mat* 23:24

gnaw

her judges *g.* not bones. *Zeph* 3:3*

gnawed

they *g.* their tongues. *Rev* 16:10

go

on thy belly shalt thou *go.* *Gen* 3:14
whither wilt thou *go*? 16:8
prosper my way which I *go.*
Gen 24:42
after that Rebekah shall *go.* 55
that I may *go* to my master. 56
go with this man? she said, I will *go.*
58
Abimelech said to Isaac, *go.* 26:16
keep me in this way that I *go.* 28:20
send me away that I may *go.* 30:25
me *go*, for the day breaketh . . . said,
I will not let thee *go.* 32:26
and I, whither shall I *go*? 37:30
and we will arise, and *go.* 43:8
will not let you *go.* *Ex* 3:19; 4:21
he will let you *go.* 3:20; 11:1
go, ye shall not *go* empty. 3:21
go; if thou refuse to let him *go*, I.
4:23; 8:2, 21; 9:2; 10:4
he let him *go*, then she said. 4:26*
let my people *go.* 5:1; 7:16; 8:1
20; 9:1, 13; 10:3
nor will I let Israel *go.* 5:2
he refuseth to let the people *go.*
7:14; 8:32; 9:35; 10:27
will let the people *go.* 8:8, 28; 9:28
let the men *go.* 10:7
who are they that shall *go*? 8
we will *go* with our young and. 9
light to *go* by day and night. 13:21
Neh 9:12, 19
we have let Israel *go* from. *Ex* 14:5
Lord said to Moses, *go* on. 17:5
shall *go* before thee. 23:23; 32:34
gods to *go* before us. 32:23
Acts 7:40
my presence shall *go.* *Ex* 33:14
have found grace in sight, *go.* 34:9
shall be, if thou *go* with. *Num* 10:32
go by the king's highway. 20:17, 19
to give me leave to *go.* 22:13
men call thee, rise up, and *go.* 20, 35
and now behold, I *go* unto. 24:14
shall make it *go* through fire. 31:23
shall your brethren *go* to war? 32:6
but we will *go* ready armed. 17
by what way ye should *go.* *Deut* 1:33
in land whither ye *go.* 4:5, 26
11:8, 11; 30:18
it may *go* well. 4:40; 5:16; 19:13
ye *go* after other gods. 11:28; 28:14
go and return to his house. 20:5, 6
7, 8
then thou shalt let her *go.* 21:14
in anywise let the dam *go.* 22:7
she may *go* and be another. 24:2
thy God, he it is that doth *go.* 31:6
for thou must *go* with this people. 7
the Lord, he it is that doth *go.* 8
the land whither they *go* to be. 16
know their imagination they *go.* 21*
sendest us we will *go.* *Josh* 1:16
the way by which ye must *go.* 3:4
but they let *go* the man. *Judg* 1:25
go with me, then I will *go.* 4:8
the Lord said to him, *go* in. 6:14
this shall *go*, the same shall *go.* 7:4
to thee, that thou mayest *go.* 11:8
then my strength will *go.* 16:17
whether our way we *go* shall? 18:5
is your way wherein ye *go.* 6
be not slothful to *go* to possess. 9
when ye *go.* 10
hold thy peace, *go* with us. 19
to spring, they let her *go.* 19:25
again, why will ye *go*? *Ruth* 1:11
she was stedfastly minded to *go.* 18
let me *go* to field and glean, *go.* 2:2
let it *go* again to its. *1 Sam* 5:11
did they not let people *go*? 6:6
ark, send it away that it may *go.* 8
let us *go* thither, he can shew. 9:6
if we *go* what shall we bring the? 7
go up before me, to-morrow I will let
thee *go.* 19
when he turned his back to *go.* 10:9
for then should ye *go.* 12:21
how can I *go*? if Saul hear it. 16:2
thou art not able to *go* against. 17:33
Saul would let him *go* no more. 18:2
he said, let me *go*, why? 19:17
but let me *go*, that I may hide. 20:5
David went whither could *go.* 23:13
driven me out, saying, *go.* 26:19
a woman, that I may *go* and. 28:7

shall *go* to him, he. *2 Sam* 12:23
I cause my shame to *go* ? 13:13
Absalom said, let me *go* and. 15:7
seeing I *go* whither I may. 20
that thou *go* to battle in thy. 17:11
thy servant will *go* a little. 19:36
that is for David, let him *go*. 20:11
go the way of all the. *1 Ki* 2:2
let me depart, that I may *go*. 11:21
nothing, howbeit, let me *go* in. 22
shall kill me, and *go* to. 12:27*
nor turn to *go* by the way. 13:17
because thou hast let *go* a. 20:42
wilt thou *go* with me to battle? 22:4
2 Chr 18:3
wilt thou *go* with me ? *2 Ki* 3:7
wherefore wilt thou *go* to ? 4:23
water, that they may *go* and. 6:22
he that letteth him *go*, his life. 10:24
it will *go* into hand. 18:21; *Isa* 36:6
in thy name we *go*. *2 Chr* 14:11*
let not the army of Israel *go*. 25:7
if thou wilt *go*, do it, be strong. 8
go to nothing and perish. *Job* 6:18
before I *go* whence I shall not return.
10:21; 16:22
it shall *go* ill with him that. 20:26*
ye not asked them that *go* by ? 21:29
righteousness I will not let *go*. 27:6
in the way thou shalt *go*. *Ps* 32:8
before I *go* hence, and be. 39:13
God, why *go* I mourning ? 42:9; 43:2
he shall *go* to the generation. 49:19
they *go* from strength to. 84:7
righteousness shall *go* before. 85:13
mercy and truth shall *go*. 89:14
that they might *go* to a city. 107:7
we will *go* into his tabernacles. 132:7
whither shall I *go* from thy ? 139:7
none that *go* unto her. *Pr* 2:19
go and come again, to-morrow. 3:28
can one *go* on hot coals ? 6:28
to call passengers who *go* right. 9:15
go from the presence of a. 14:7
neither will the scorner *go*. 15:12
much more do his friends *go*. 19:7
child in the way he should *go*. 22:6
that *go* to seek mixed wine. 23:30
be three things which *go* well. 30:29
all *go* unto one place. *Eccl* 3:20
return to *go* as he came. 5:15, 16
hath seen no good, do not all *go*? 6:6
it is better to *go* to the house. 7:2
after that, they *go* to the dead. 9:3
not how to *go* to city. 10:15
and the mourners *go* about. 12:5
I would not let him *go*. *S of S* 3:4
mincing as they *go*. *Isa* 3:16
and who will *go* for us ? 6:8
he said, *go* and tell. 9; *Acts* 28:26
I would *go* through them. *Isa* 27:4
that they might *go* and fall. 28:13
he shall let *go* my captives. 45:13
the way thou shouldest *go*. 48:17
thy righteousness shall *go*. 58:8
go through, *go* through the. 62:10
thou shalt *go* to all that. *Jer* 1:7
I might leave my people, and *go*. 9:2
ye shall *go* and pray to me. 29:12
how long wilt thou *go* about ? 31:22
go to Babylon. 34:3; *Mi* 4:10
good to *go*, there *go*. *Jer* 40:4, 5
reward, and let him *go*. 5
saying, let me *go*, and I will. 15
place whither ye desire to *go*. 42:22
the voice thereof shall *go* like. 46:22
they shall *go* and seek Lord. 50:4
they refused to let them *go*. 33
the Spirit was to *go*. *Ezek* 1:12, 20
that I should *go* far from my. 8:6
go through the midst of. 9:4, 5
high place whereto ye *go* ? 20:29
go thee one way or other. 21:16
they shall *go* with flocks. *Hos* 5:6
they call to Egypt, they *go* to. 7:11
when they shall *go* I will spread. 12
I taught Ephraim also to *go*. 11:3
who, if he *go* through. *Mi* 5:8
and sought to *go*. *Zech* 6:7
these that *go* toward the north. 8
inhabitants of one city shall *go*. 8:21
we will *go* with you, for we. 23
and shall *g*. with whirlwinds. 9:14
Joseph was afraid to *go*. *Mat* 2:22

compel thee to *go* a mile, *go* twain.
Mat 5:41; *Luke* 7:8
and I say to this man, *go*. *Mat* 8:9
he said to them, *go*, they went. 32
but *go* ye learn what that. 9:13
go rather to the lost sheep of. 10:6
he answered, I *go* sir, and. 21:30
but *go* rather to them that sell. 25:9
sit ye here, while I *go* and. 26:36
go, tell my brethren that they *go* to
Galilee. 28:10
go ye therefore and teach all. 19
go and see. *Mark* 6:38
and they let them *go*. 11:6
shall *go* before him in. *Luke* 1:17
he stedfastly set his face to *go*. 9:51
but *go* thou and preach the. 60
then said Jesus, *go* and do. 10:37
ground and must needs *go*. 14:18
I am ready to *go* with thee. 22:33
not answer me, nor let me *go*. 68
chastise him, and let him *go*. 23:22
to whom shall we *go* ? *John* 6:68
and then I *go* unto him that. 7:33
whence I came and whither I *go*. 8:14
I *go* my way, whither I *go* ye. 21
loose him, and let him *go*. 11:44
whither I *go* thou canst not. 13:36
I *go* to prepare a place for. 14:2
whither I *go* ye know, the way. 4
I *go* unto my Father. 12; 16:10
I *go* to the Father. 14:28; 16:17, 28
cried, if thou let this man *go*. 19:12
I *go* a fishing, they say, we also *go*.
21:3
that he might *go* to his. *Acts* 1:25
determined to let him *go*. 3:13
them, they let them *go*. 4:21
being let *go* they went to their. 23
not speak, and let them *go*. 5:40
should *go* as far as Antioch. 11:22
essayed to *go* into Bithynia. 16:7
saying, let those men *go*. 35
taken Jason, they let them *go*. 17:9
I *go* bound in the Spirit to. 20:22
Cesar, to Cesar shalt thou *go*. 25:12
would have let me *go*. 28:18
now I *go* to Jerusalem. *Rom* 15:25
dare you *go* to law ? *1 Cor* 6:1
bid, and ye be disposed to *go*. 10:27
that I *go* also, they shall *go*. 16:4
brethren that they *go*. *2 Cor* 9:5
I shall see how it will *go*. *Phil* 2:23
will *go* into such a city. *Jas* 4:13
see **free**

go *aside*

if any man's wife *go aside*. *Num* 5:12
shalt not *go aside* from. *Deut* 28:14
who shall *go aside* to ask ? *Jer* 15:5
commanded them to *go aside*.
Acts 4:15

go *astray*

brother's ox *go astray*. *Deut* 22:1
go astray as soon as they. *Ps* 58:3
folly he shall *go astray*. *Pr* 5:23
not to her ways, *go* not *astray*. 7:25
righteous to *go astray*. 28:10
caused them to *go astray*. *Jer* 50:6
may *go* no more *astray*. *Ezek* 14:11

go *away*

not *go* very far *away*. *Ex* 8:28
let him *go away* empty. *Deut* 15:13
if he say, I will not *go away*. 16
Samuel turned about to *go away*.
1 Sam 15:27
will he let him *go away* ? 24:19
their excellency *go away* ? *Job* 4:21*
his mouth shall he *go away*. 15:30
ye that escaped the sword, *go away*.
Jer 51:50
I will tear and *go away*. *Hos* 5:14
suffer us to *go away*. *Mat* 8:31
go away into everlasting. 25:46
will ye also *go away* ? *John* 6:67
how I said, I *go away*. 14:28; 16:7

go *back*

caused the sea to *go back*. *Ex* 14:21
do in any wise *go back*. *Josh* 23:12
mouth, I cannot *go back*. *Judg* 11:35
go back again, what ? *1 Ki* 19:20
shall the shadow *go back* ? *2 Ki* 20:9
so will not we *go back*. *Ps* 80:18

go back to Gedaliah. *Jer* 40:5
I will not *go back*, nor. *Ezek* 24:14

go *down*

let us *go down* and confound their.
Gen 11:7
I will *go down* now, and see. 18:21
the Lord said, *go* not *down*. 26:2
send him, we will not *go down*. 43:5
we cannot *go down*, then will we *go*
down. 44:26
fear not, Jacob, to *go down*. 46:3
Lord said, *go down*. *Ex* 19:21
and they *go down* quick. *Num* 16:30
nor shall sun *go down*. *Deut* 24:15
the sun hasted not to *go down* about
a whole day. *Josh* 10:13
if thou fear to *go down*. *Judg* 7:10
thou shalt *go down*. *1 Sam* 10:8
go down after Philistines by. 14:36
go down to Keilah, I will. 23:4
who will *go down* with me ? 26:6
let him not *go down* with us. 29:4
David said, *go down* to. *2 Sam* 11:8
why didst thou not *go down* ? 10
make thee *go* up and *down*. 15:20
go down to meet Ahab. *1 Ki* 21:18
go down with him, be. *2 Ki* 1:15
for the shadow to *go down*. 20:10*
to-morrow *go down*. *2 Chr* 20:16
in a moment *go down* to. *Job* 21:13
that *go down* to the dust. *Ps* 22:29
become like them that *go down*. 28:1
and let them *go down* quick. 55:15
they that *go down* to the sea. 107:23
neither any that *go down*. 115:17
I be like them that *go down*. 143:7
her feet *go down* to death. *Pr* 5:5
as those that *go down*. *Isa* 14:19
woe to them that walk to *go down*.
30:2; 31:1
they that *go down* into pit. 38:18
sun shall not *go down*, nor. 60:20
let them *go down* to. *Jer* 50:27
garrisons shall *go down*. *Ezek* 26:11
with them that *go down* to the pit.
20; 31:14; 32:18, 24, 25, 29, 30
these waters *go down* into. 47:8
then *go down* to Gath. *Amos* 6:2
I will cause the sun to *go down*. 8:9
the sun shall *go down*. *Mi* 3:6
is on housetop not *go down*.
Mark 13:15
which are able to *go down*. *Acts* 25:5
let not the sun *go down* on. *Eph* 4:26

go *forth*

go forth of the ark, thou. *Gen* 8:16
not *go forth* hence, except. 42:15
the priest shall *go forth*. *Lev* 14:3
all able to *go forth* to war.
Num 1:3; *2 Chr* 25:5
have a place to *go forth*. *Deut* 23:12
forbare to *go forth*. *1 Sam* 23:13
when kings *go forth* to. *2 Sam* 11:1
I will surely *go forth* with you. 18:2
thou *go* not *forth*, there will. 19:7
and *go* not *forth* thence. *1 Ki* 2:36
said, I will *go forth* ; *go forth*. 22:22
minds, let none *go forth*. *2 Ki* 9:15
Jerusalem shall *go forth* a remnant.
19:31; *Isa* 37:32
as wild asses *go* they *forth*. *Job* 24:5
own people to *go forth*. *Ps* 78:52
wilt not thou *go forth* with ? 108:11
go not *forth* hastily to. *Pr* 25:8
no king, yet *go* they *forth*. 30:27
go forth, O ye daughters. *S of S* 3:11
come, let us *go forth* into the. 7:11
out of Zion shall *go forth* the law.
Isa 2:3; *Mi* 4:2
the Lord shall *go forth*. *Isa* 42:13
go forth of Babylon. 48:20; *Jer* 50:8
say to prisoners, *go forth*. *Isa* 49:9
made thee waste shall *go forth*. 17
righteousness thereof *go forth*. 62:1
go not *forth* into the field. *Jer* 6:25
if I *go forth* into the field. 14:18
let them *go forth*. 15:1
whither shall we *go forth* ? 2
evil shall *go forth* from. 25:32
O Israel, thou shalt *go forth*. 31:4
measuring line shall yet *go forth*. 39
if thou wilt *go forth* to the king. 38:17
but if thou wilt not *go forth* to. 18, 21

he shall *go forth* from. Jer 43:12
go forth as they that *go forth*. Ezek 12:4
the prince shall *go forth*. 12
my sword shall *go forth*. 21:4
messengers shall *go forth*. 30:9
and he shall *go forth* by the. 46:8
shall *go forth* over against it. 9
shall *go forth* with great. Dan 11:44
let bridegroom *go forth*. Joel 2:16
judgement doth never *go forth*. Hab 1:4
four spirits which *go forth*. Zech 6:5
black horses *go forth* into the. 6
then shall the Lord *go forth*. 14:3
ye shall *go forth* and grow. Mal 4:2
behold, he is in the desert, *go* not *forth*. Mat 24:26
Paul have to *go forth*. Acts 16:3
let us *go forth* to him. Heb 13:13
devils which *go forth*. Rev 16:14

go *forward*

Israel that they *go forward*. Ex 14:15
they shall *go forward* in. Num 2:24
shall shadow *go forward*? 2 Ki 20:9
behold, I *go forward*, but. Job 23:8

go *his way*

and went to *go his way*. Judg 19:27

go *their way*

let these *go their way*. John 18:8

go *thy way*

thy wife, take her, *go thy way*. Gen 12:19
go thy way, the Lord. 1 Sam 20:22
my staff, and *go thy way*. 2 Ki 4:29
go thy way, eat thy bread. Eccl 9:7
go thy way forth by. S of S 1:8
go thy way, for words. Dan 12:9
go thy way till the end be, for. 13
go thy way, be reconciled. Mat 5:24
go thy way, shew thyself to. 8:4
that thine is, and *go thy way*. 20:14
this saying, *go thy way*. Mark 7:29
go thy way, sell whatsoever. 10:21
go thy way; thy faith hath made thee whole. 52; Luke 17:19
Jesus saith, *go thy way*. John 4:50
go thy way, for he is a. Acts 9:15
Felix answered, *go thy way*. 24:25

go *your way*, *-s*

up and *go* on *your ways*. Gen 19:2
afterward *go your way*. Josh 2:16
Judg 19:5
daughters, *go your way*. Ruth 1:12
go your way, eat the fat. Neh 8:10
go your way, make it as. Mat 27:65
go your way into village. Mark 11:2
go your way, tell his disciples. 16:7
go your way, tell John. Luke 7:22
go your ways, I send you as. 10:3
receive you not, *go your ways*. 10
go your ways, pour out. Rev 16:1

go *in*, or *into*, or *not* **go** *in*

from Ur, to *go into* land of Canaan. Gen 11:31; 12:5
when *go into* tabernacle. Ex 30:20
go in and out from gate to. 32:27
wine, when ye *go into*. Lev 10:9
house, before the priest *go in*. 14:36
neither shall he *go in* to any. 21:11
only he shall not *go in* to the vail. 23
his sons shall *go in*. Num 4:19
but they shall not *go in* to see. 20
that shall the Levites *go in*. 8:15
which may go out, and *go in*. 27:17
that they should not *go into*. 32:9
thou also shalt not *go in* thither. Deut 1:37; 4:21
son of Nun he shall *go in*. 1:38
live, and *go in* and possess. 4:1; 8:1
go in and possess. 6:18; 10:11
strong, and *go in* and possess. 11:8
not *go into* his house to fetch. 24:10
turned aside to *go in*. Judg 19:15
shalt *go in*, and uncover. Ruth 3:4
shall I then *go into*? 2 Sam 11:11
I will not *go in*, nor eat. 1 Ki 13:8
I may not return, nor *go in* with. 16
may *go in*, and dress it for. 17:12
look out Jehu, and *go in*. 2 Ki 9:2
go in and slay them, let none. 10:25
shalt *go into* an inner. 2 Chr 18:24
of the Levites shall *go in*. 23:6*
would *go into* the temple to save his life? I will not *go in*. Neh 6:11
turn was come to *go in*. Esth 2:15
her that she should *go in*. 4:8
and so will I *go in* unto the king. 16
then *go* thou *in* merrily unto. 5:14
nor will I *go in* with. Ps 26:4
open the gates, I will *go in*. 118:19
make me *go in* path of thy. 119:35
we will *go into* his tabernacle. 132:7
nor *go into* thy brother's Pr 27:10
they shall *go into* holes. Isa 2:19
and let us *go into* the. Jer 4:5
I cannot *go into* the house of. 36:5
but we will *go into* the land. 42:14
go ye not *into* Egypt. 19
when they *go in* shall *go in*. Ezek 46:10
go into clay, and tread. Nah 3:14
go into house of Josiah. Zech 6:10
take the young child, and *go into* the land of Israel. Mat 2:20
and many there be that *go in*. 7:13
go into the vineyard, and. 20:4, 7
go into village. 21:2; Luke 19:30
harlots *go into* kingdom. Mat 21:31
go ye *into* the highways. 22:9
go in, nor suffer others to *go in*. 23:13
go into the city, to such a man. 26:18
Mark 14:13
that they may *go into*. Mark 6:36
nor *go into* the town, nor tell. 8:26
go into all the world, preach. 16:15
suffered no man to *go in*. Luke 8:51
angry, and would not *go in*. 15:28
he shall *go in* and out. John 10:9
see him *go into* heaven. Acts 1:11
shall *go into* perdition. Rev 17:8

see **captivity**

go *in*

Sarai said, I pray thee, *go in* unto. Gen 16:2
drink wine, and *go* thou *in*. 19:34
behold my maid Bilhah, *go in*. 30:3
go in unto thy brother's wife. 38:8
that thou shalt *go in*. Deut 21:13
if take a wife, and *go in* unto. 22:13
husband's brother shall *go in*. 25:5
marriages, and *go in*. Josh 23:12
I will *go in* to my wife. Judg 15:1
go in unto thy father's. 2 Sam 16:21
shall not *go in* to them. 1 Ki 11:2
went to her as they *go in*. Ezek 23:44
a man and his father *go in*. Amos 2:7

go *in peace*

go to thy fathers *in peace*. Gen 15:15
to Moses, *go in peace*. Ex 4:18
shall *go* to their place *in peace*. 18:23
to Danites, *go in peace*. Judg 18:6
to Hannah, *go in peace*. 1 Sam 1:17
to David, *go in peace*. 20:42
to Abigail, *go* up *in peace*. 25:35
Achish said to David, *go in peace*. 29:7
to Absalom, *go in peace*. 2 Sam 15:9
let not his hoary head *go* down *in peace*. 1 Ki 2:6
to Naaman, *go in peace*. 2 Ki 5:19
go in peace, and be whole of thy. Mark 5:34
faith hath saved thee, *go in peace*. Luke 7:50; 8:48
they were let *go in peace*. Acts 15:33

let us **go**

say, *let us go* to Dothan. Gen 37:17
let us go three days'. Ex 3:18; 5:3
say, *let us go* sacrifice. 5:8, 17
would hardly *let us go*. 13:15
let us go after. Deut 13:2, 6, 13
he spake, *let us go*. 1 Sam 9:9, 10
let us go to Gilgal and renew. 11:14
let us go over to Philistines'. 14:1, 6
let us go to Jordan. 2 Ki 6:2
let us go into the house. Ps 122:1
let us go up to mountain. Isa 2:3
let us go into defenced. Jer 4:5
let us go by night and destroy. 6:5
let us go to Jerusalem for. 35:11
let us go again to our own. 46:16
let us go, every one to his own. 51:9
let us go to pray before. Zech 8:21
let us go into next towns. Mark 1:38
let us go, he that betrayeth. 14:42
let us go to Bethlehem. Luke 2:15
then saith he, *let us go*. John 11:7
let us go to him. 15
let us go that we may die. 16
even so I do; arise, *let us go*. 14:31
let us go again and. Acts 15:36
let us go on to perfection. Heb 6:1

I will **go**

I will go to the right, *I will go* to the. Gen 13:9
with this man? *I will go*. 24:58
let us go, *I will go*. 33:12; Isa 45:2
son is alive, *I will go* see. Gen 45:28
I will only *go* through. Num 20:19
thy burnt offering, and *I will go*. 23:3
I will go along by the. Deut 2:27
I will go likewise with. Judg 1:3
go with me, then *will I go*. 4:8
and she said, *I will* surely *go* with. 9
I will go out as at other. 16:20
thou goest, *I will go*. Ruth 1:16
he answered, *I will go*. 2 Ki 6:3
he said, *I will go*. 2 Chr 18:29
then *will I go* to the altar. Ps 43:4
I will go into thy house with. 66:13*
I will go in the strength of. 71:16*
of righteousness, *I will go* in. 118:19*
after them *I will go*. Jer 2:25
I will go to them that. Ezek 38:11
for she said, *I will go* after. Hos 2:5
I will go and return to my first. 7
I will go to my place, till they. 5:15
I will wail, *I will go*. Mi 1:8
seek the Lord; *I will go*. Zech 8:21
I will go before you into Galilee. Mat 26:32; Mark 14:28
I will arise and *go* to. Luke 15:18
henceforth *I will go* to. Acts 18:6

go *near*

go near, and hear all. Deut 5:27
David said, *go near*. 2 Sam 1:15
prince would I *go near*. Job 31:37
go near, join thyself to. Acts 8:29

go *not*, or *not* **go**

if thy presence *go not*. Ex 33:15
Hobab said, I will *not go*. Num 10:30
he said, thou shalt *not go*. 20:20
Balaam, shalt *not go*. 22:12
I *cannot go* beyond word. 18; 24:13
thou shalt *not go* over. Deut 3:27
ye shall *not go* after other gods. 6:14; 1 Ki 11:10
if he say, I will *not go*. Deut 15:16
thou shalt *not go* again to. 24:19
but thou shalt *not go* thither to. 32:52
go not far from the city. Josh 8:4
if wilt *not go* with me, I will *not go*. Judg 4:8
not go, the same shall *not go*. 7:4
we will *not* any of us *go* to his. 20:8
go not empty to thy mother-in-law. Ruth 3:17
David said, I *cannot go* with these. 1 Sam 17:39
I may *not go* fight against. 29:8
let *not* all *go*, howbeit he would *not go*. 2 Sam 13:25
not say to you, *go not*? 2 Ki 2:18
David could *not go*. 1 Chr 21:30
should *not go* to battle. 2 Chr 25:13
instruction, let her *not go*. Pr 4:13
and *go not* into the way of evil. 14
furious man thou shalt *not go*. 22:24
for ye shall *not go* out. Isa 52:12
because they *cannot go*. Jer 10:5
thou shalt *not go* into house. 16:8
go not after other gods. 25:6; 35:15
that the vessels left *go not*. 27:18
go not into Egypt. 42:19; 43:2
thou shalt *not go* unpunished. 49:12
steps, that we *cannot go*. Lam 4:18
priests shall *not go* out. Ezek 42:14
go not into the way of. Mat 10:5
go not from house to. Luke 10:7
see here or there: *go not*. 17:23; 21:8

go *over*

I pray thee let me *go over*. Deut 3:25
Joshua shall *go over* before. 28; 31:3
land whither ye *go over*. 4:14, 26
31:13; 32:47
go over Jordan, ye shall *go over*. 4:22
thou shalt not *go over* the. 24:20

who shall *go over* sea for us? *Deut* 30:13
the Lord thy God will *go over*. 31:3
but thou shalt not *go over*. 34:4
therefore arise, *go over*. *Josh* 1:2
said, let me *go over*. *Judg* 12:5
come, let us *go over*. *1 Sam* 14:1, 6
faint, they could not *go over*. 30:10
me *go over* and take. *2 Sam* 16:9
Chimham, let him *go over*. 19:37
he shall come and *go over*. *Isa* 8:7
make men *go over* dryshod. 11:15
down, that we may *go over*. 51:23
Noah should no more *go over*. 54:9
Ishmael departed to *go over* to. *Jer* 41:10
let us *go over* to other. *Luke* 8:22

go *out*

from all that *go out* of. *Gen* 9:10
time that women *go out* to. 24:11
cause every man to *go out*. 45:1
children of Israel *go out*. *Ex* 6:11
behold, I *go out* from thee, I. 8:29
after that I will *go out*, and. 11:8
let the children of Israel *go out*. 10
none of you shall *go out* at the. 12:22
people shall *go out* and gather. 16:4
let no man *go out* of his place on. 29
seventh year he shall *go out*. 21:2
go out by himself; if married, his wife shall *go out* with him. 3
her master's, and he shall *go out*. 4
if the servant say, I will not *go out*. 5
a maidservant not *go out* as. 7
then shall she *go out* free. 11
fire on altar never *go out*. *Lev* 6:13
shall not *go out* of tabernacle in. 8:33
ye shall not *go out* at the door. 10:7
then the priest shall *go out*. 14:38
seed of copulation *go out*. 15:16
shall *go out* to the altar. 16:18
he *go out* of the sanctuary. 21:12
jubile it shall *go out*. 25:28, 31, 33
it shall not *go out* in jubile. 30
he shall *go out*. 54
he shall not *go out* to war. *Deut* 24:5
thou shalt *go out* one way. 28:25
who shall *go out*, his blood. *Josh* 2:19
go out, I pray now, and. *Judg* 9:38
he said, I will *go out* as at. 16:20
shall I yet again *go out* to. 20:28
it is good thou *go out*. *Ruth* 2:22
I will *go out* and stand. *1 Sam* 19:3
come, let us *go out* into field. 20:11
Achish said, thou shalt *go out*. 28:1
then Lord shall *go out*. *2 Sam* 5:24
thou shalt *go* no more *out*. 21:17
not suffer any to *go out*, or come in to Asa. *1 Ki* 15:17; *2 Chr* 16:1
put ropes on heads, and *go out* to. *1 Ki* 20:31
at the time kings *go out*. *1 Chr* 20:1
go out and be a lying spirit, *go out*. *2 Chr* 18:21
fear not, to-morrow *go out*. 20:17
go out of sanctuary, for thou. 26:18
himself hasted also to *go out*. 20
lettest such words *go out*. *Job* 15:13
which didst not *go out* with. *Ps* 60:10
scorner, contention *go out*. *Pr* 22:10
be not hasty to *go out* of. *Eccl* 8:3
depart ye, *go* ye *out*. *Isa* 52:11
ye shall not *go out* with haste. 12
ye shall *go out* with joy, and. 55:12
lest my fury *go out* like. *Jer* 21:12
my people, *go* ye *out* of the. 51:45
they shall *go out* from. *Ezek* 15:7
prince shall *go out* the same. 44:3
entereth by north, shall *go out*. 46:9
and ye shall *go out* at. *Amos* 4:3
living waters *go out* from. *Zech* 14:8
bridegroom cometh, *go* ye *out* to. *Mat* 25:6
ye *go out* of city, shake off. *Luke* 9:5
go out quickly into the streets. 14:21
go out into the highways and. 23
must ye needs *go out*. *1 Cor* 5:10
he was called to *go out*. *Heb* 11:8
shall *go* no more *out*. *Rev* 3:12
and shall *go out* to deceive. 20:8

go *to*

go to, let us make brick. *Gen* 11:3
go to, let us build. 4
go to, let us confound. *Gen* 11:7
go to now, I will prove. *Eccl* 2:1
go to, I will tell you what. *Isa* 5:5
go to now, ye that say. *Jas* 4:13
go to now, ye rich men, weep. 5:1

go *up*

arise, *go up* to Beth-el. *Gen* 35:1, 3
and let the lad *go up* with. 44:33
how shall I *go up* to? 34; 45:9
Pharaoh said, *go up* and. 50:6
frogs shall *go up* and. *Ex* 8:3
take heed ye *go* not *up* into. 19:12
nor shalt thou *go up* by steps. 20:26
neither shall people *go up*. 24:2
a great sin, I will *go up*. 32:30
depart and *go up*, thou and. 33:1
for I will not *go up* in the midst. 3
land, when thou shalt *go up*. 34:24
shalt not *go up* and down. *Lev* 19:16
let us *go up* at once and. *Num* 13:30
we be not able to *go up* against. 31
lo, we be here, and will *go up*. 14:40 *Deut* 1:41
go not *up*. *Num* 14:42
but they presumed to *go up*. 44
his brother's wife *go up*. *Deut* 25:7
shall *go up* for us to heaven. 30:12
go up, let 3000 men *go up*. *Josh* 7:3
did not intend to *go up* against. 22:33
who shall *go up* for us to? *Judg* 1:1
said, Judah shall *go up*. 2; 20:18
an angel said, I made you *go up*. 2:1
that I may *go up* and down on. 11:37
arise, that we may *go up*. 18:9
we will *go up* by lot against. 20:9
which of us shall *go up* first to? 18
shall I *go up* again? 23
go up against him. 28
not *go up* till the child. *1 Sam* 1:22
if it *go up* by the way of his. 6:9
and to whom shall he *go up*? 20
shall find him before he *go up*. 9:13
Samuel came to *go up* to. 14, 19
say, Tarry; we will not *go up*. 14:9
come up unto us, we will *go up*. 10
shall I *go up* to any of cities of Judah? the Lord said, *go up*. *2 Sam* 2:1
shall I *go up* against the? 5:19
should I make thee *go up*? 15:20
I to live, that I should *go up*. 19:34
go up, rear an altar in floor. 24:18 *1 Chr* 21:18
ye shall not *go up*. *1 Ki* 12:24 *2 Chr* 11:4
if this people *go up* to. *1 Ki* 12:27
it is too much for you to *go up*. 28
go up, look towards the sea. 18:43
go up, for the Lord shall deliver. 22:6 12; *2 Chr* 18:11, 14
may *go up* and fall at Ramoth. *1 Ki* 22:20; *2 Chr* 18:19
go up, meet messengers. *2 Ki* 1:3
go up thou bald head, *go up*. 2:23
wilt thou *go up* with me? 3:7
which way shall we *go up*? 8
Hazael set his face to *go up* to. 12:17
Lord said, *go up* against the land. 18:25; *Isa* 36:10
third day thou shalt *go up*. *2 Ki* 20:5
sign that I shall *go up*? 8; *Isa* 38:22
go up to Hilkiah. *2 Ki* 22:4
shall I *go up*? *1 Chr* 14:10
go not *up* after them. 14
we *go up* to Ramoth? *2 Chr* 18:5
let him *go up*. 36:23; *Ezra* 1:3
he began to *go up* from. *Ezra* 7:9
all which are minded to *go up*. 13
if a fox *go up* he shall. *Neh* 4:3
go up by the mountains. *Ps* 104:8
surely I will not *go up* into. 132:3
flock of sheep that *go up*. *S of S* 6:6
I will *go up* to the palm tree. 7:8
let us *go up* to mountain of Lord. *Isa* 2:3; *Mi* 4:2
let us *go up* against Judah. *Isa* 7:6
weeping shall they *go* it *up*. 15:5
go up, O Elam. 21:2
the smoke shall *go up*. 34:10
ravenous beast shall *go up*. 35:9
go up against this land, and. 36:10
go ye *up* upon her walls. *Jer* 5:10
arise, and let us *go up* at noon. 6:4
Nebuchadnezzar may *go up*. 21:2
go up to Lebanon, and cry. *Jer* 22:20
let us *go up* to Zion, to the. 31:6
he saith, I will *go up* and. 46:8
go up into Gilead, and take. 11
continual weeping shall *go up*. 48:5
go up to Kedar, and spoil men. 49:28
go up against the land of. 50:21
I will *go up* to land of *Ezek* 38:11
were seven steps to *go up*. 40:26
neither *go up* to Beth-aven. *Hos* 4:15
go up to the mountain. *Hag* 1:8
go up from year to year. *Zech* 14:16
we *go up* to Jerusalem. *Mat* 20:18 *Mark* 10:33; *Luke* 18:31
friend, *go up* higher. *Luke* 14:10
go ye *up* to this feast, I *go* not *up*. *John* 7:8
go up to Jerusalem. *Acts* 15:2
that Paul should not *go up* to. 21:4
we besought him not to *go up* to. 12
wilt thou *go up* to Jerusalem? 25:9

go *a whoring*

lest they go *a whoring*. *Ex* 34:15
and thy sons *go a whoring* after. 16
cut off all that *go a whoring*. *Lev* 20:5
I will cut off such as *go a whoring*. 6
ye use to *go a whoring*. *Num* 15:39
people will *go a whoring*. *Deut* 31:16
Judah *go a whoring*. *2 Chr* 21:13
destroyed all that *go a whoring*. *Ps* 73:27
eyes which *go a whoring*. *Ezek* 6:9

goad, -s

slew 600 men with an ox *g*. *Judg* 3:31
a file to sharpen the *g*. *1 Sam* 13:21
words of wise are as *g*. *Eccl* 12:11

goat

take a heifer, a she *g*. *Gen* 15:9
if his offering be a *g*. *Lev* 3:12
lay his hand on the head of *g*. 4:24
eat no fat of ox, sheep, or of *g*. 7:23
he took the *g*. which was the. 9:15
Moses sought the *g*. of the. 10:16
Aaron shall bring the *g*. on. 16:9
the *g*. in the wilderness. 22
whosoever killeth a *g*. in the. 17:3
when a *g*. is brought forth. 22:27
he shall bring a *g*. *Num* 15:27
the firstling of a *g*. thou shalt. 18:17
one *g*. for a sin offering, to. 28:22 29:22, 28, 31, 34, 38
eat the ox, sheep, and *g*. *Deut* 14:4
prepare every day a *g*. *Ezek* 43:25
g. had a notable horn. *Dan* 8:5
rough *g*. is the king of Grecia. 21

he **goat**

comely in going, an *he g*. *Pr* 30:31
down like rams with *he g*. *Jer* 51:40
behold, an *he g*. came. *Dan* 8:5
therefore the *he g*. waxed very. 8

live **goat**

bring *live g*. *Lev* 16:20
lay both hands on *live g*. 21

*scape***goat**

other lot for the *scapegoat*. *Lev* 16:8
to let him go for a *scapegoat*. 10
let go *scapegoat* shall wash. 26

wild **goat**

ye shall eat the *wild g*. *Deut* 14:5

goats

from thence two kids of *g*. *Gen* 27:9
she put the skins of the *g*. on. 16
and speckled among the *g*. 30:32
is not speckled among *g*. 33
he removed *g*. 35
thy she *g*. have not cast. 31:38
she *g*. and twenty he *g*. 32:14
brethren killed a kid of the *g*. 37:31
take it from sheep or *g*. *Ex* 12:5
offering be of sheep or *g*. *Lev* 1:10
knowledge, he shall bring his offering, a kid of the *g*. 4:23, 28; 5:6
take a kid of *g*. for a sin offering. 9:3
two kids of the *g*. 16:5
two *g*. and present them. 7
offer a male of sheep or *g*. 22:19
sacrifice one kid of the *g*. for a sin offering. 23:19; *Num* 7:16; 15:24
five he *g*. five lambs. *Num* 7:17, 23 29, 35, 41, 47, 53, 59, 65, 71, 77, 83
kids of the *g*. for a sin offering. 7:87
he *g*. sixty, the lambs of first. 88

rams and he *g.* of breed. *Deut* 32:14
Nabal had a thousand *g. 1 Sam* 25:2
brought 7,700 he *g.* *2 Chr* 17:11
they brought seven he *g.* for. 29:21
the dedication twelve he *g. Ezra* 6:17
of captivity offered 12 he *g.* 8:35
I will take no he *g.* out. *Ps* 50:9
or will I drink the blood of *g.*? 13
offer to thee bullocks with *g.* 66:15
the *g.* are the price of. *Pr* 27:26
thou shalt have *g.*' milk enough. 27
hair is as a flock of *g. S of S* 4:1; 6:5
not in the blood of he *g.* *Isa* 1:11
fat with the blood of *g.* 34:6
and be as the he *g.* before. *Jer* 50:8
occupied with thee in *g.* *Ezek* 27:21
between the rams and he *g.* 34:17
drink the blood of lambs and *g.* 39:18
second day offer a kid of the *g.* 43:22
a kid of the *g.* daily for a. 45:23
kindled, I punished the *g. Zech* 10:3
divideth sheep from *g.* *Mat* 25:32
shall set the *g.* on his left hand. 33
nor entered by blood of *g. Heb* 9:12
blood of bulls and *g.* sanctifieth. 13
blood of *g.* and sprinkled book. 19
not possible that the blood of *g.* 10:4

wild **goats**

David on rocks of *wild g. 1 Sam* 24:2
knowest thou when the *wild g.* bring. *Job* 39:1
are a refuge for *wild g.* *Ps* 104:18

goats' hair

offering ye shall take *gs.' hair.* *Ex* 25:4
shalt make curtains of *gs.' hair.* 26:7
willing, let him bring *gs.' hair.* 35:6
with whom was found *gs.' hair.* 23
and all the women spun *gs.' hair.* 26
made curtains of *gs.' hair* for. 36:14
purify all works of *gs.' hair* and wood. *Num* 31:20
gs.' hair for bolster. *1 Sam* 19:13, 16

goatskins

in sheepskins and *g.* *Heb* 11:37

Gob

with Philistines at *G.* *2 Sam* 21:18

goblet

thy navel is like a round *g. S of S* 7:2

god referred to *man*

made thee a *g.* to Pharaoh. *Ex* 7:1

god for *idol*

with that which is not *g. Deut* 32:21
if he be a *g.* let him plead. *Judg* 6:31
they made Baal-berith their *g.* 8:33
went into house of their *g.* 9:27
which Chemosh thy *g.* giveth. 11:24
Philistines' *g.* was Dagon. 16:23, 24
sore on us, and our *g.* *1 Sam* 5:7
Israel worshipped the *g.* *1 Ki* 11:33
he is a *g.* either talking, or. 18:27
Baal-zebub the *g.* of Ekron. *2 Ki* 1:2, 3, 6, 16
house of Nisroch his *g.*, his sons. 19:37; *2 Chr* 32:21; *Isa* 37:38
hasten after other *g.* *Ps* 16:4
formed a *g.* or molten? *Isa* 44:10
maketh a *g.* and worshippeth. 15, 17
and that pray to a *g.* that. 45:20
he maketh it a *g.*: they fall. 46:6
vessels into house of his *g. Dan* 1:2
according to the name of my *g.* 4:8
magnify self above every *g.* 11:36
the star of your *g.* ye made. *Amos* 5:26; *Acts* 7:43
swear, and say, thy *g.* O. *Amos* 8:14
cried, every man to his *g. Jonah* 1:5
will walk in name of his *g.* *Mi* 4:5
this his power to his *g.* *Hab* 1:11
it is the voice of a *g.* *Acts* 12:22
the *g.* of this world hath blinded. *2 Cor* 4:4

any **god**

that sacrifice to *any g.* *Ex* 22:20
nor is there *any G.* beside. *2 Sam* 7:22; *1 Chr* 17:20
might not worship *any g.* *Dan* 3:28
ask a petition of *any g.* or. 6:7, 12
neither shall he regard *any g.* 11:37

other **god**

shalt worship no *other g.* *Ex* 34:14
because there is no *other g.* can deliver. *Dan* 3:29
there is none *other g.* *1 Cor* 8:4

strange **god**

there was no *strange g. Deut* 32:12
our hands to a *strange g.* *Ps* 44:20
no *strange g.* be in thee, nor worship *strange g.* 81:9
there was no *strange g.* *Isa* 43:12
he do with a *strange g.* *Dan* 11:39

God

The Creator and Father of all things, supreme Ruler of the world. The usual name given to God by the Hebrews was that which is rendered into English by the word Jehovah. *Where the older version has the word* GOD *printed in capitals the American Revision has substituted the word* Jehovah.

This word Jehovah *was so reverenced by the ancient Hebrews that it was not generally pronounced, its place being taken, in speaking, by* Adonai, *Lord,* Elohim, *or* El-Shaddai, *all of which are really expressions for the attributes of God.*

Lord, thou *G.* seest me. *Gen* 16:13
to be a *G.* to thee and thy. 17:7
I am the *G.* of Beth-el, where. 31:13
what is this that *G.* hath? 42:28
you that sent me hither, but *G.* 45:8
behold, I die, but *G.* shall be. 48:21
be to Aaron instead of *G.* *Ex* 4:16
to me, and be to you a *G.* 6:7
and *G.* shall be with thee. 18:19
what hath *G.* wrought? *Num* 23:23
alas, who shall live when *G.*? 24:23
what nation which hath *G.*? *Deut* 4:7
that he may be to thee a *G.* 29:13
G. do so and more also. *1 Sam* 3:17
14:44; 25:22; *2 Sam* 3:9, 35
19:13; *1 Ki* 2:23; *2 Ki* 6:31
know that there is a *G. 1 Sam* 17:46
till I know what *G.* will do for. 22:3
who is *G.* save the Lord? *2 Sam* 22:32; *Ps* 18:31
if the Lord be *G.* *1 Ki* 18:21
the *G.* the Lord, he is the *G.* 39
thou art the *G.* even. *2 Ki* 19:15
G., art not thou *G.* in? *2 Chr* 20:6
G. be with him, he is the *G. Ezra* 1:3
art a *G.* ready to pardon. *Neh* 9:17
sayest, how doth *G.* know? *Job* 22:13; *Ps* 73:11
art not a *G.* that hast. *Ps* 5:4
the man that made not *G.* his. 52:7
art great, thou art *G.* alone. 86:10
Isa 37:16
behold, *G.* is my salvation. *Isa* 12:2
a *G.* beside me? yea, there is no *G.* 44:8
look unto me, I am *G.* there is. 45:22
I am *G.* there is none else. 46:9
I will be their *G.* they my people. *Jer* 31:33; 32:38
a god, I sit in seat of *G.* *Ezek* 28:2
shalt be a man, and no *G.* 9
therefore it is not *G.* *Hos* 8:6
for I am *G.* and not man, the. 11:9
who is a *G.* like unto thee? *Mi* 7:18
Emmanuel, which is *G.* *Mat* 1:23
ye cannot serve *G.* and mammon. 6:24; *Luke* 16:13
good but one, that is *G.* *Mat* 19:17
Mark 10:18; *Luke* 18:19
there is one *G.* and. *Mark* 12:32
with *G.* and Word was *G. John* 1:1
can do miracles, except *G.* be. 3:2
we have one Father, even *G.* 8:41
forth, and came from *G.* 42
know thee, the only true *G.* 17:3
by wonders, which *G.* did. *Acts* 2:22
we ought to obey *G.* rather. 5:29
patriarchs sold Joseph, but *G.* 7:9
I perceive *G.* is no respecter. 10:34
let *G.* be true, and. *Rom* 3:4
if *G.* be for us, who can be? 8:31
now the *G.* of patience and. 15:5
to us there is but one *G.* *1 Cor* 8:6
that *G.* may be all in all. 15:28
hath anointed us, is *G.* *2 Cor* 1:21
G. of love and peace shall. 13:11
called *G.* so that he as *G. 2 Thes* 2:4
G. was manifest in the. *1 Tim* 3:16
profess that they know *G.* *Tit* 1:16
that built all things is *G.* *Heb* 3:4
ceased from his works, as *G.* 4:10
I will be to them a *G.*, they to. 8:10
G. is light, in him is no. *1 John* 1:5
no man hath seen *G.* at any. 4:12
and *G.* himself shall be. *Rev* 21:3
G. shall wipe away all tears. 4
I will be his *G.* and he shall be. 7

against **God**

wickedness, and sin *against G.*? *Gen* 39:9
the people spake *against G.* *Num* 21:5; *Ps* 78:19
transgressed *against G.* *1 Chr* 5:25
spake *against* the *G.* of. *2 Chr* 32:19
thy spirit *against G.* *Job* 15:13
stretcheth out his hand *against G.* 25
multiplieth his words *against G.* 34:37
speak amiss *against G.* *Dan* 3:29
marvellous things *against G.* 11:36
rebelled *against* her *G.* *Hos* 13:16
found to fight *against G.* *Acts* 5:39
blasphemous words *against G.* 6:11
let us not fight *against G.* 23:9
mind is enmity *against G. Rom* 8:7
thou that repliest *against G.*? 9:20
in blasphemy *against G.* *Rev* 13:6

see **almighty**

before **God**

was corrupt *before G.* *Gen* 6:11
Moses' father *before G.* *Ex* 18:12
themselves *before G.* *Josh* 24:1
abode till even *before G. Judg* 21:2
Israel played *before G. 1 Chr* 13:8
and there Uzza died *before G.* 10
burnt sacrifices *before G.* 16:1
Manasseh humbled himself *before G.* *2 Chr* 33:12
heart was humbled *before G.* 34:27
deliver *before* the *G.* of. *Ezra* 7:19
restrainest prayer *before G.* *Job* 15:4
shall I appear *before G.*? *Ps* 42:2
may walk *before G.* in light. 56:13
he shall abide *before G.* for. 61:7
let righteous rejoice *before G.* 68:3
in Zion appeareth *before G.* 84:7
him that is good *before G. Eccl* 2:26
to utter any thing *before G.* 5:2
he feareth not *before G.* 8:13
gave thanks *before his G. Dan* 6:10
making supplication *before G.* 11
that men tremble *before G.* 26
both righteous *before G.* *Luke* 1:6
of them is forgotten *before G.* 12:6
in deed and word *before G.* 24:19
found favour *before G.* *Acts* 7:46
come for a memorial *before G.* 10:4
we are all here present *before G.* 33*
all good conscience *before G.* 23:1
of law are just *before G. Rom* 2:13
may become guilty *before G.* 3:19
to glory, but not *before G.* 4:2
have it to thyself *before G.* 14:22
we speak *before G.* in. *2 Cor* 12:19
behold, *before G.* I lie not. *Gal* 1:20
your hearts *before G.* *1 Thes* 3:13
and acceptable *before G. 1 Tim* 5:4
thee *before G.* 21:1; *2 Tim* 4:1
and undefiled *before G.* *Jas* 1:27
words perfect *before G.* *Rev* 3:2
the horns of the altar *before G.* 9:13
which accused them *before G.* 12:10
in remembrance *before G.* 16:19
and great, stand *before G.* 20:12*

see **called, chosen, commanded**

eternal **God**

eternal G. is thy refuge. *Deut* 33:27

everlasting **God**

called on name of *ever. G. Gen* 21:33
the *ever. G.* fainteth not. *Isa* 40:28
to commandment of *ever. G.* *Rom* 16:26

see **father, fear, forbid, gave, glorify**

high **God**
was priest of the most *high G.*
Gen 14:18; *Heb* 7:1
Abraham of most *high G. Gen* 14:19
blessed be the most *high G.* 20
up my hand to the most *high G.* 22
cry unto *G.* most *high.* *Ps* 57:2
G. was their rock, the *high G.* 78:35
provoked the most *high G.* 56
servants of most *high G.* *Dan* 3:26
shew the wonders the *high G.* 4:2
high G. gave Nebuchadnezzar. 5:18
that the most *high G.* ruled. 21
before the most *high G.* *Mi* 6:6
thou Son of the most *high G.*
Mark 5:7; *Luke* 8:28
servants of most *high G. Acts* 16:17

holy **God**
he is an *holy G.* he is. *Josh* 24:19
stand before this *holy G.*?*1 Sam* 6:20
the Lord our *G.* is *holy.* *Ps* 99:9
G. that is *holy* shall be. *Isa* 5:16

God *of heaven*
all earth hath the Lord *G. of heaven* given. *2 Chr* 36:23; *Ezra* 1:2
servants of *G. of heaven. Ezra* 5:11
provoked *G. of heaven.* 12
offerings of the *G. of heaven.* 6:9, 10
law of the *G. of heaven.* 7:12, 21
commanded by the *G. of heaven.* 23
prayed before *G. of heaven. Neh* 1:4
so I prayed to the *G. of heaven.* 2:4
to the *G. of heaven.* *Ps* 136:26
desire mercies of *G. of heaven.*
Dan 2:18
Daniel blessed the *G. of heaven.* 19
the *G. of heaven* shall set up a. 44
Lord, the *G. of heaven.* *Jonah* 1:9
glory to *G. of heaven.* *Rev* 11:13
blasphemed the *G. of heaven.* 16:11

God *of hosts*
again, O *G. of hosts.* *Ps* 80:7, 19
we beseech thee, O *G. of hosts.* 14
name is the *G. of hosts. Amos* 5:27
see **Lord** *God*

God *is*
G. is with thee in all. *Gen* 21:22
see, *G. is* witness betwixt me. 31:50
fear not, for *G. is* come. *Ex* 20:20
G. is not a man, that. *Num* 23:19
G. is there in heaven? *Deut* 3:24
the eternal *G. is* thy refuge. 33:27
our holy *G. is* a jealous God.
Josh 24:19; *Nah* 1:2
G. is come into the camp. *1 Sam* 4:7
for *G. is* come. 10:7; *1 Chr* 17:2
G. is departed from me. *1 Sam* 28:15
G. is my strength and. *2 Sam* 22:33
G. is gone forth before. *1 Chr* 14:15
G. himself *is* with us. *2 Chr* 13:12
I answer thee, *G. is.* *Job* 33:12
G. is mighty and despiseth. 36:5
behold, *G. is* great, and we know. 26
G. is angry with wicked. *Ps* 7:11
G. is not in all his thoughts. 10:4
for *G. is* in the generation of. 14:5
whose *G. is* Lord. 33:12; 144:15
G. is our refuge and. 46:1; 62:8
G. is in midst of her, she shall. 46:5
G. is gone up with a shout. 47:5
for *G. is* King. 7
G. is known in her palaces. 48:3
for *G. is* judge himself. 50:6; 75:7
behold, *G. is* my helper, Lord. 54:4
this I know, for *G. is* for me. 56:9
for *G. is* my defence. 59:9, 17
in *G. is* my salvation and glory.
62:7; *Isa* 12:2
of the fatherless *is G.* *Ps* 68:5
truly *G. is* good to Israel. 73:1
G. is strength of my heart, and. 26
G. is my King of old, working. 74:12
G. is greatly to be feared in. 89:7
gracious is the Lord, our *G. is.* 116:5
G. is the Lord that hath. 118:27
for *G. is* in heaven, and. *Eccl* 5:2
G. that *is* holy shall be. *Isa* 5:16
for *G. is* with us. 8:10
surely *G. is* in thee. 45:14
we have heard that *G. is. Zech* 8:23
G. is able of these stones to raise.
Mat 3:9; *Luke* 3:8
G. is not God of dead. *Mat* 22:32
to his seal that *G. is.* *John* 3:33
G. is a Spirit. 4:24
G. is glorified in him. 13:31
G. is no respecter of. *Acts* 10:34
for *G. is* my witness. *Rom* 1:9
for *G. is* able to graff them. 11:23
for *G. is* able to make him. 14:4*
G. is faithful, by whom. *1 Cor* 1:9
G. is faithful who will not. 10:13
and report that *G. is* in you. 14:25
G. is not author of confusion, but. 33
as *G. is* true, our word. *2 Cor* 1:18
G. is able to make all grace. 9:8
but *G. is* one. *Gal* 3:20
G. is not mocked. 6:7
but *G.* who *is* rich in. *Eph* 2:4
G. is my record, how. *Phil* 1:8
whose *g. is* their belly. 3:19
G. is witness. *1 Thes* 2:5
G. is not unrighteous to. *Heb* 6:10
G. is not ashamed to be. 11:16
for our *G. is* a consuming fire. 12:29
for with such sacrifices *G. is.* 13:16
G. is light. *1 John* 1:5
for *G. is* love. 4:8, 16
G. is greater than our heart. 3:20

God *of Israel*
and saw the *G. of Israel.* *Ex* 24:10
the *G. of Israel* hath. *Num* 16:9
to give glory to the *G. of Israel.*
Josh 7:19; *1 Sam* 6:5
G. of Israel was their. *Josh* 13:33
ye committed against *G. of Israel.*
22:16
to do with the *G. of Israel*? 24
heart to the *G. of Israel.* 24:23
G. of Israel dispossessed the.
Judg 11:23
given thee of *G. of Israel. Ruth* 2:12
the *G. of Israel* grant. *1 Sam* 1:17
the ark of the *G. of Israel.* 5:11
Lord *G. of Israel,* no God like thee.
1 Ki 8:23; *2 Chr* 6:14
thing toward *G. of Israel. 1 Ki* 14:13
called on *G. of Israel.* *1 Chr* 4:10
of hosts is the *G. of Israel.* 17:24
not seek *G. of Israel*? *2 Chr* 15:13
offered to *G. of Israel.* *Ezra* 7:15
words of the *G. of Israel.* 9:4
blessed be the Lord *G. of Israel.*
Ps 41:13; 72:18; 106:48
Luke 1:68
I the *G. of Israel* will. *Isa* 41:17
call thee by name, *G. of Israel.* 45:3
themselves on the *G. of Israel.* 48:2
glory of the *G. of Israel.* *Ezek* 8:4
glorified the *G. of Israel. Mat* 15:31

living **God**
voice of the *living G.* *Deut* 5:26
hereby know *living G.* is. *Josh* 3:10
armies of *living G. 1 Sam* 17:26, 36
Assyria hath sent to reproach *living G.* *2 Ki* 19:4, 16; *Isa* 37:4, 17
soul thirsteth for God, the *living G.*
Ps 42:2
flesh crieth out for *living G.* 84:2
living G. an everlasting. *Jer* 10:10
the words of the *living G.* 23:36
living G. and stedfast. *Dan* 6:26
ye are sons of *living G.* *Hos* 1:10
art Christ, Son of *living G.*
Mat 16:16; *John* 6:69
I adjure thee by the *living G.* 26:63
vanities to *living G.* *Acts* 14:15
children of *living G.* *Rom* 9:26
Spirit of the *living G.* *2 Cor* 3:3
the temple of the *living G.* 6:16
serve *living* and true *G. 1 Thes* 1:9
church of the *living G.* *1 Tim* 3:15
trust in the *living G.* 4:10; 6:17
in departing from *living G. Heb* 3:12
conscience to serve *living G.* 9:14
to fall into hands of *living G.* 10:31
Zion, the city of *living G.* 12:22
the seal of the *living G.* *Rev* 7:2
For combinations of **Lord** *with* **God,** *see in divisions under* **Lord**

merciful **God**
Lord, the Lord *G. merciful. Ex* 34:6
God is a *merciful G.* *Deut* 4:31
Lord your *G.* is *merciful* if ye turn.
2 Chr 30:9
gracious and *merciful G.* *Neh* 9:31
gracious is the Lord, our *G.* is *merciful.* *Ps* 116:5
thou art a *G. merciful.* *Jonah* 4:2

mighty **God**
by hands of *mighty G.* *Gen* 49:24
Lord is among you, a *mighty G.*
Deut 7:21; 10:17
our God, the *mighty G.* *Neh* 9:32
G. is *mighty,* and. *Job* 36:5
the *mighty G.* the Lord. *Ps* 50:1
how he vowed to *mighty G.* 132:2
I find an habitation for *mighty G.* 5
be called the *mighty G.* *Isa* 9:6
shall return to the *mighty G.* 10:21
mighty G. Lord of hosts. *Jer* 32:18
O *mighty G.* thou hast. *Hab* 1:12

my **God**
then shall Lord be *my G.* *Gen* 28:21
he is *my G. my* father's *G.* *Ex* 15:2
my people, thy God *my G. Ruth* 1:16
I cried to *my G.* he heard.
2 Sam 22:7; *Ps* 18:6
and have not departed from *my G.*
2 Sam 22:22; *Ps* 18:21
by *my G.* I have leaped over a.
2 Sam 22:30; *Ps* 18:29
for God, even *my G.* *1 Chr* 28:20
what *my G.* saith, that. *2 Chr* 18:13
think upon me, *my G.* for good.
Neh 5:19; 13:31
remember me, *my G.* 13:14, 22
my G. my G. why hast thou forsaken me? *Ps* 22:1; *Mat* 27:46
thou art *my G.* from my. *Ps* 22:10
I said, Thou art *my G.* 31:14
O *my G.* be not far. 38:21; 71:12
thou art my Father, *my G.* 89:26
sing praise to *my G.* 104:33; 146:2
thou art *my G.* and I will. 118:28
I will extol thee, *my G.* O. 145:1
and take name of *my G.* *Pr* 30:9
but will ye weary *my G.*? *Isa* 7:13
is passed over from *my G.* 40:27
deliver me, for thou art *my G.* 44:17
soul shall be joyful in *my G.* 61:10
my G. hath sent his angel. *Dan* 6:22
they shall say, Thou art *my G.*
Hos 2:23; *Zech* 13:9
Israel shall cry to me, *my G. Hos* 8:2
my G. will cast them away. 9:17
I will wait, for *my G.* will. *Mi* 7:7
ascend to *my G.* and. *John* 20:17
and said, My Lord and *my G.* 28
I thank *my G.* *Rom* 1:8; *1 Cor* 1:4
14:18; *Phil* 1:3; *Philem* 4
lest when I come, *my G. 2 Cor* 12:21
my G. shall supply all. *Phil* 4:19
on him the name of *my G. Rev* 3:12

no **God**
I am he, there is *no G.* *Deut* 32:39
there is *no G.* like thee. *1 Ki* 8:23
2 Chr 6:14
there is *no G.* in Israel? *2 Ki* 1:16
now I know there is *no G.* in. 5:15
no g. of any nation. *2 Chr* 32:15
said, There is *no G.* *Ps* 14:1; 53:1
before me there was *no G. Isa* 43:10
beside me there is *no G.* 44:6, 8
45:5, 14, 21
shalt be a man, and *no G. Ezek* 28:9
shalt know *no G.* but me. *Hos* 13:4

O **God**
heal her now, *O G.* *Num* 12:13
only this once, *O G.* *Judg* 16:28
hear me, *O G.* of my. *Ps* 4:1
redeem Israel, *O G.* out of. 25:22
from bloodguiltiness, *O G.* 51:14
thy vows are upon me, *O G.* 56:12
nor hath eye seen, *O G.* *Isa* 64:4
to do thy will, *O G.* *Heb* 10:7, 9

of **God**
for the cause was *of G. 2 Chr* 10:15
not hear, for it came *of G.* 25:20
my defence is *of G.* who. *Ps* 7:10
esteem him smitten *of G.* *Isa* 53:4
savourest not things *of G.*
Mat 16:23; *Mark* 8:33
of will of man, but *of G.* *John* 1:13
he which is *of G.* hath seen. 6:46
of doctrine whether it be *of G.* 7:17
of G. heareth: ye are not *of G.* 8:47
this man is not *of G.* 9:16

if he were not *of G.* John 9:33
praise of men more than *of G.* 12:43
if it be *of G.* ye cannot. Acts 5:39
is not of men, but *of G.* Rom 2:29
but *of G.* that sheweth mercy. 9:16
of G. powers ordained *of G.* 13:1
of G. is made unto us. 1 Cor 1:30
which ye have *of G.* ye are. 6:19
things are *of G.* 11:12; 2 Cor 5:18
as *of G.* in the sight *of G.* 2 Cor 2:17
our sufficiency is *of G.* 3:5
salvation, and that *of G.* Phil 1:28
righteousness which is *of G.* 3:9
he that was called *of G.* Heb 5:4
not righteousness, is not *of G.* 1 John 3:10
spirits whether they are *of G.* 4:1
not that Christ is come, is not *of G.* 3
we are *of G.* 6
we know that we are *of G.* 5:19
he that doeth good is *of G.* 3 John 11
see **angel, ark, born, children, chosen, church, counsel, fear, glory, grace, hand, house, kingdom, knowledge, love, man, people, power, servant, sight, son, sons, spirit, will, words, work, works, world, wrath**

our **God**

go and sacrifice to *our G.* Ex 5:8
because *our G.* is not. Deut 31:17
ye greatness unto *our G.* 32:3
serve Lord, he is *our G.* Josh 24:18
have forsaken *our G.* Judg 10:10
any rock like *our G.* 1 Sam 2:2
people, and for the cities of *our G.* 2 Sam 10:12; 1 Chr 19:13
who is a rock, save *our G.*? 2 Sam 22:32; Ps 18:31
now therefore, *our G.* 1 Chr 29:13
for great is *our G.* 2 Chr 2:5
O Lord, thou art *our G.* 14:11
art not thou *our G.* who didst? 20:7
now, O *our G.* what? Ezra 9:10
hear, O *our G.* Neh 4:4
our G. shall fight for us. 20
work was wrought of *our G.* 6:16
our G. the great, mighty God. 9:32
our G. turned the curse into a. 13:2
song, even praise to *our G.* Ps 40:3
this God is *our G.* for ever. 48:14
our G. shall come and not. 50:3
and God, even *our* own *G.* 67:6
he that is *our G.* is the God. 68:20
so great a God as *our G.*? 77:13
he is *our G.* 95:7
our G. is in the heavens. 115:3
gracious is the Lord, *our G.* 116:5
lo, this is *our G.* we. Isa 25:9
to *our G.* for he will. 55:7
departing away from *our G.* 59:13
day of vengeance of *our G.* 61:2
our G. whom we serve. Dan 3:17
remaineth be for *our G.* Zech 9:7
by the Spirit of *our G.* 1 Cor 6:11
our G. is a consuming. Heb 12:29
hast made us to *our G.* Rev 5:10
salvation to *our G.* who sitteth. 7:10
honour, and power be to *our G.* 12
see **peace, said, saith, serve, sent, speak, speed, spoken**

their **God**

I will be *their G.* Gen 17:8
Ex 29:45; Jer 24:7; 31:33; 32:38
Ezek 11:20; 34:24; 37:23, 27
Zech 8:8; 2 Cor 6:16; Rev 21:3
to *their G.* for offerings of the Lord, and bread of *their G.* Lev 21:6
might be *their G.* 26:45; Ezek 14:11
thou art become *their G.* 2 Sam 7:24; 1 Chr 17:22
the eye of *their G.* was. Ezra 5:5
where is *their G.*? Ps 79:10
115:2; Joel 2:17
people seek to *their G.*? Isa 8:19
and curse their king, and *their G.* 21
not the ordinance of *their G.* 58:2
judgement of *their G.* Jer 5:4, 5
people that know *their G.* Dan 11:32
gone a whoring from under *their G.* Hos 4:12
their doings to turn to *their G.* 5:4
in Lord of hosts *their G.* Zech 12:5
not ashamed to be called *their G.* Heb 11:16

thy **God**

fear *thy G.* Lev 19:14; 25:17, 36, 43
praise, and he is *thy G.* Deut 10:21
this day the Lord to be *thy G.* 26:17
my people, *thy G.* my. Ruth 1:16
let not *thy G.* deceive thee. 2 Ki 19:10; Isa 37:10
peace to thee, for *thy G.* 1 Chr 12:18
because *thy G.* loved Israel made he thee king. 2 Chr 9:8
to law of *thy G.* in thy. Ezra 7:14
wisdom of *thy G.* laws of *thy G.* 25
this is *thy G.* that brought. Neh 9:18
to me, Where is *thy G.*? Ps 42:3, 10
God, *thy G.* hath anointed thee. 45:7; Heb 1:9
I am God, even *thy G.* Ps 50:7
thy G. commanded strength. 68:28
praise the Lord, praise *thy G.* 147:12
dismayed, for I am *thy G.* Isa 41:10
full of the rebuke of *thy G.* 51:20
that saith to Zion, *Thy G.* 52:7
Lord be a light, and *thy G.* 60:19
shall *thy G.* rejoice over thee. 62:5
thy G. whom thou servest. Dan 6:16
is *thy G.* whom thou servest? 20
chasten thyself before *thy G.* 10:12
forgotten the law of *thy G.* Hos 4:6
gone a whoring from *thy G.* 9:1
to *thy G.* and wait on *thy G.* 12:6
prepare to meet *thy G.* Amos 4:12
arise, call upon *thy G.* Jonah 1:6
to walk humbly with *thy G.* Mi 6:8

to, or *unto* **God**

interpretations belong *to G.*? Gen 40:8
their cry came up *unto G.* Ex 2:23
for he is holy *unto* his *G.* Lev 21:7
sacrifice to devils, not *to G.* Deut 32:17; 1 Cor 10:20
none like *unto* the *G.* of. Deut 33:26
shall be a Nazarite *unto G.* Judg 13:5, 7; 16:17
three men going up *to G.* 1 Sam 10:3
matter pertaining *to G.* 1 Chr 26:32
man be profitable *unto G.*? Job 22:2
meet to be said *unto G.* I. 34:31
power belongeth *unto G.* Ps 62:11
to G. the Lord belong issues. 68:20
shall stretch her hands *to G.* 31
for me to draw near *to G.* 73:28
I cried *to G.* even *to G.* with. 77:1
spirit shall return *unto G.* Eccl 12:7
in approaching to *G.* Isa 58:2
our heart with hands *to G.* Lam 3:41
render *unto G.* the things. Mat 22:21
Mark 12:17; Luke 20:25
from God, went *to G.* John 13:3
you more than *unto G.* Acts 4:19
not lied unto men, but *unto G.* 5:4
from power of Satan *unto G.* 26:18
turn *to G.* and do works meet. 20
he liveth *unto G.* Rom 6:10
but alive *unto G.* 11
yield yourselves *unto G.* as alive. 13
should bring forth fruit *unto G.* 7:4
a living sacrifice *unto G.* 12:1
give account of himself *to G.* 14:12
not unto men but *unto G.* 1 Cor 14:2
delivered up kingdom *to G.* 15:24
unto G. and our Father. Phil 4:20
them that come *unto G.* Heb 7:25
to G. must believe that he is. 11:6
ye are come *to G.* the Judge. 12:23
yourselves therefore *to G.* Jas 4:7
might bring us *to G.* 1 Pet 3:18
but live according *to G.* in the. 4:6
hast redeemed us *to G.* Rev 5:9
child was caught up *unto G.* 12:5
being the firstfruits *unto G.* 14:4
see **true**

with **God**

Enoch walked *with G.* Gen 5:22, 24
Noah walked *with G.* 6:9
thou hast power *with G.* 32:28
people to meet *with G.* Ex 19:17
hath wrought *with G.* 1 Sam 14:45
house be not so *with G.* 2 Sam 23:5
from meddling *with G.* 2 Chr 35:21
man be just *with G.*? Job 9:2
and I desire to reason *with G.* 13:3
might plead for a man *with G.* Job 16:21
a man be justified *with G.*? 25:4
portion of a wicked man *with G.* 27:13
should delight himself *with G.* 34:9
enter into judgement *with G.* 23
with G. is terrible majesty. 37:22
is not stedfast *with G.* Ps 78:8
Judah yet ruleth *with G.* Hos 11:12
his strength had power *with G.* 12:3
but *with G.* all things are possible. Mat 19:26; Mark 10:27
Luke 1:37; 18:27
found favour *with G.* Luke 1:30
increased in favour *with G.* 2:52
Word was *with G.* the. John 1:1
himself equal *with G.* 5:18; Phil 2:6
respect of persons *with G.* Rom 2:11
faith, we have peace *with G.* 5:1
there unrighteousness *with G.*? 9:14
labourers together *with G.* 1 Cor 3:9
this world is foolishness *with G.* 19
man therein abide *with G.* 7:24
righteous thing *with G.* 2 Thes 1:6
of world is enmity *with G.* Jas 4:4
this is acceptable *with G.* 1 Pet 2:20
would **God**, see **would**

your **God**

your G. hath given you. Gen 43:23
go ye, sacrifice to *your G.* Ex 8:25
of Egypt to be *your G.* Lev 11:45
22:33; 25:38; Num 15:41
I will be *your G.* and ye. Lev 26:12
Jer 7:23; 11:4; 30:22; Ezek 36:28
memorial before *your G.* Num 10:10
be holy to *your G.* 15:40
lest ye deny *your G.* Josh 24:27
day rejected *your G.* 1 Sam 10:19
your G. should deliver. 2 Chr 32:14
how much less shall *your G.*? 15
we seek *your G.* as ye do. Ezra 4:2
your G. will come with. Isa 35:4
ye my people, saith *your G.* 40:1
cities of Judah, behold *your G.* 9
between you and *your G.* 59:2
your G. saith the Lord. Ezek 34:31
of a truth it is, *your G.* Dan 2:47
I will not be *your G.* Hos 1:9
say that he is *your G.* John 8:54
to my God and *your G.* 20:17

goddess

after *g.* of Zidonians. 1 Ki 11:5
worshipped Ashtoreth, the *g.* 33
temple of great *g.* Diana. Acts 19:27
worshippers of the *g.* Diana. 35
nor yet blasphemers of your *g.* 37

godhead

think that *g.* is like to. Acts 17:29
eternal power and *g.* Rom 1:20*
dwelleth the fulness of *g.* Col 2:9

godliness

lead a quiet life in all *g.* 1 Tim 2:2
becometh women professing *g.* 10
great is the mystery of *g.* 3:16
exercise thyself rather unto *g.* 4:7
g. is profitable unto all things. 8
doctrine which is according to *g.* 6:3
men, supposing that gain is *g.* 5
g. with contentment is great gain. 6
follow after righteousness, *g.* 11
having a form of *g.* but. 2 Tim 3:5
the truth which is after *g.* Tit 1:1
that pertain to life and *g.* 2 Pet 1:3
add to patience *g.* to *g.* brotherly. 6, 7
of persons ought to be in all *g.* 3:11

godly

set apart him that is *g.* Ps 4:3
help, Lord, for the *g.* man. 12:1
every one that is *g.* pray. 32:6
he might seek a *g.* seed. Mal 2:15
in *g.* sincerity had our. 2 Cor 1:12
sorry after a *g.* manner. 7:9, 11
g. sorrow worketh repentance. 10
I am jealous over you with *g.* 11:2
will live *g.* in Christ. 2 Tim 3:12
that ye should live *g.* in. Tit 2:12
God with reverence and *g.* fear. Heb 12:28*
how to deliver the *g.* 2 Pet 2:9
forward after a *g.* sort. 3 John 6

gods

ye shall be as g. knowing. Gen 3:5
hast thou stolen my g.? 31:30
against all g. of Egypt. Ex 12:12
shalt not make with me g. of. 20:23
thou shalt not revile the g. 22:28
not bow down to their g. 23:24
covenant with them nor their g. 32
up, make us g. to go before us.
32:1, 23; Acts 7:40
these be thy g. O Israel. Ex 32:4, 8
they have made them g. of gold. 31
go a whoring after their g. 34:15
the sacrifices of their g. Num 25:2
upon the Egyptians' g. also. 33:4
Jer 43:12, 13; 46:25
images of their g. shall. Deut 7:25
Lord your God is God of g. 10:17
down the images of their g. 12:3
thou enquire not after their g. 30
their g. burnt their sons and daughters in the fire to their g. 31
entice thee to the g. of people. 13:7
they have done to their g. 20:18
say, where are their g.? 32:37
Lord God of g. knoweth. Josh 22:22
mention of the name of their g. 23:7
they chose new g. then. Judg 5:8
I said, fear not the g. of the. 6:10
go and cry to the g. which ye. 10:14
Micah had an house of g. 17:5
ye have taken away my g. 18:24
is gone back to her g. Ruth 1:15
are the g. that smote. 1 Sam 4:8
hand from off you and your g. 6:5
cursed David by his g. 17:43
she said, I saw g. ascending. 28:13
from Egypt and their g. 2 Sam 7:23
your heart after their g. 1 Ki 11:2
incense and sacrificed to their g. 8
to go up, behold thy g. 12:28
the name of your g. 18:24, 25
let the g. do so to me. 19:2; 20:10
their g. are g. of the hills. 20:23
every nation made g. 2 Ki 17:29
and served their own g. 33
g. delivered his land? 18:33; 19:12
2 Chr 32:13, 14; Isa 36:18; 37:12
where are the g. of Hamath?
2 Ki 18:34; Isa 36:19
g. into fire they were no g. 2 Ki 19:18
went a whoring after g. 1 Chr 5:25
armour in the house of their g. 10:10
their g. David burnt them. 14:12
Jeroboam made for g. 2 Chr 13:8
be a priest to them that are no g. 9
g. of Seir to be his g. 25:14
Ahaz sacrificed to the g. of. 28:23
the g. of the nations have not. 32:17
vessels in house of his g. Ezra 1:7
he judgeth among the g. Ps 82:1
said, ye are g. 6; John 10:34
thanks unto the God of g. Ps 136:2
before g. will I sing praise. 138:1
fallen, and her g. broken. Isa 21:9
may know that ye are g. 41:23
molten images, ye are our g. 42:17
changed her g. are no g.? Jer 2:11
g. thou hast made? . . . number of thy cities are thy g. 28; 11:13
sworn by them that are no g. 5:7
the g. that have not made the. 10:11
cry to the g. to whom they. 11:12
make g. and they are no g.? 16:20
that burneth incense to his g. 48:35
can shew it, except the g. Dan 2:11
that your God is a God of g. 47
is the spirit of the holy g. 4:8
of holy g. is in thee. 9, 18; 5:14
the g. of gold and silver. 5:4, 23
like the wisdom of the g. 11
carry captives into Egypt g. 11:8
things against God of g. 36
say any more, ye are our g. Hos 14:3
out of the house of thy g. Nah 1:14
if he called them g. to. John 10:35
the g. are come down to. Acts 14:11
they be no g. which are made. 19:26
are called g. there be g. 1 Cor 8:5
which by nature are no g. Gal 4:8
see **serve**

all **gods**

Lord is greater than all g. Ex 18:11
to be feared above all g.
1 Chr 16:25; Ps 96:4
all g. of the people are idols.
1 Chr 16:26; Ps 96:5
great is God above all g. 2 Chr 2:5
Ps 135:5
a great King above all g. Ps 95:3
worship him, all ye g 97:7
exalted above all g. 9
he will famish all the g. Zeph 2:11

among the **gods**

among the g. who is like. Ex 15:11
who among the g. could deliver?
2 Ki 18:35; 2 Chr 32:14; Isa 36:20
among the g. there is. Ps 86:8

molten **gods**

no molten g. Ex 34:17; Lev 19:4

other **gods**

shalt have no other g. before me.
Ex 20:3; Deut 5:7
of names of other g. Ex 23:13
ye shall not go after other g.
Deut 6:14; 11:28; 28:14
1 Ki 11:10; Jer 25:6; 35:15
thy son to serve other g. Deut 7:4
if thou walk after other g. 8:19
let us go after other g. 13:2, 6, 13
hath gone and served other g. 17:3
29:26; Josh 23:16; Judg 10:13
1 Sam 8:8; Jer 11:10
speak in name of other g. Deut 18:20
away, and worship other g. and serve them. Deut 30:17; Jer 22:9
they turned to other g. Deut 31:18
then will they turn to other g. 20
and followed other g. Judg 2:12
went a whoring after other g. 17
in following other g. to serve. 19
go serve other g. 1 Sam 26:19
upon other g. 1 Ki 9:9; 2 Chr 7:22
his heart after other g. 1 Ki 11:4
gone and made thee other g. 14:9
offer sacrifice to other g. 2 Ki 5:17
sinned, and had feared other g. 17:7
ye shall not fear other g. 35, 37, 38
burnt incense to other g. 22:17
2 Chr 34:25; Jer 1:16; 19:4
incense to other g. 2 Chr 28:25
nor walk after other g. Jer 7:6
walk after other g. whom. 9; 13:10
and walked after other g. 16:11
burn no incense to other g. 44:5
burning incense to other g. in. 8, 15
look to other g. and love. Hos 3:1
see **serve**

strange **gods**

the strange g. Gen 35:2; 1 Sam 7:3
they gave Jacob the strange g.
Gen 35:4; Josh 24:23
jealousy with strange g. Deut 32:16
and serve strange g. Josh 24:20
away their strange g. Judg 10:16
away altar of strange g. 2 Chr 14:3
away the strange g. and idol. 33:15
as ye served strange g. so. Jer 5:19
setter forth of strange g. Acts 17:18

God-ward

be thou for people to G. Ex 18:19
we through Christ to G. 2 Cor 3:4
your faith to G. is. 1 Thes 1:8

goest

in places whither thou g. Gen 28:15
whither g. thou? 32:17; Judg 19:17
Zech 2:2; John 13:36; 16:5
is it not in that thou g.? Ex 33:16
inhabitants whither thou g. 34:12
thou g. before them by. Num 14:14
God shall bring thee into the land whither thou g. Deut 7:1; 11:29
the land whither thou g. is. 11:10
cut off nations whither thou g. 12:29
when thou g. to battle. 20:1; 21:10
thou settest thine hand to, whither thou g. 23:20; Josh 1:7
shalt thou be when thou g. Deut 28:6
cursed shalt thou be when thou g. 19
cleave to thee whither thou g. 21
plucked off land whither thou g. 63
die in mount whither thou g. 32:50
with thee whither thou g. Josh 1:9
thou g. to take a wife of. Judg 14:3
whither thou g. I will go. Ruth 1:16
wherefore g. thou also? 2 Sam 15:19
thou g. over brook. 1 Ki 2:37, 42
but thou g. not forth with. Ps 44:9
when thou g. steps shall. Pr 4:12
when thou g. it shall lead thee. 6:22
keep thy foot when thou g. Eccl 5:1
in grave whither thou g. 9:10
a prey whither thou g. Jer 45:5
I will follow thee whither g.
Mat 8:19; Luke 9:57
when thou g. with thine. Luke 12:58
sought to stone thee, g. John 11:8
we know not whither thou g. 14:5

goeth

lo, he g. out unto the. Ex 7:15
deliver it by that the sun g. 22:26
shall bear them when he g. 28:29
on Aaron's heart when he g. 30
shall be heard when he g. in. 35
these ye may eat that g. Lev 11:21
he that g. into the house. 14:46
him whose seed g. from. 15:32; 22:4
the tabernacle when he g. in. 16:17
who g. to holy things having. 22:3
when it g. out in jubile. 27:21
when a wife g. aside. Num 5:29
the Lord which g. before. Deut 1:30
thy God is he that g. over. 9:3
as when a man g. into wood. 19:5
Lord your God is he that g. 20:4
when the host g. forth against. 23:9
pledge when the sun g. down. 24:13
as the sun when he g. Judg 5:31
as David, who g. at. 1 Sam 22:14
as his part is that g. down to. 30:24
thy master g. to house of. 2 Ki 5:18
be with the king as he g. out. 11:8
2 Chr 23:7
this work g. fast on. Ezra 5:8
that g. down to grave. Job 7:9
lo, he g. by me, and I see. 9:11
when g. in company with. 34:8
hear the sound that g. out of. 37:2
g. on to meet the armed men. 39:21
prayer that g. not out of. Ps 17:1
when he g. abroad, he telleth. 41:6
such a one as g. on in his. 68:21
thy fierce wrath g. over me. 88:16
a fire g. before him, and. 97:3
man g. forth to his work. 104:23
he that g. forth and weepeth. 126:6
his breath g. forth; he. 146:4
so he that g. in to his. Pr 6:29
g. after her, as an ox g. to the. 7:22
when it g. well with righteous. 11:10
pride g. before destruction. 16:18
g. about as a talebearer. 20:19
as a thorn g. up into hand of. 26:9
no wood is, there the fire g. out. 20
her candle g. not out by. 31:18
sun g. down, and hasteth. Eccl 1:5
man g. up, spirit of beast g. 3:21
because man g. to his long. 12:5
that g. down sweetly. S of S 7:9
from the time it g. forth. Isa 28:19
when one g. with a pipe to. 30:29
so shall my word be that g. 55:11
whoso g. therein shall not. 59:8
as a beast g. down into the. 63:14
every one that g. out. Jer 5:6
woe unto us, for the day g. 6:4
that g. out to Chaldeans. 21:9; 38:2
but weep sore for him that g. 22:10
whirlwind of the Lord g. 30:23
we will do what g. out of our. 44:17
every one that g. by it. 49:17; 50:13
have blown, but none g. Ezek 7:14
their heart g. after their. 33:31
in the day that he g. into the. 44:27
as the early dew, it g. Hos 6:4
thy judgements are as light that g. 5
this is the curse that g. Zech 5:3
he said, this is an ephah that g. 6
I say to this man go, and he g.
Mat 8:9; Luke 7:8
then g. he and taketh. Mat 12:45
Luke 11:26
for joy thereof g. and. Mat 13:44
not that which g. into mouth. 15:11
this kind g. not out but by. 17:21
Son of man g. as it is written. 26:24
Mark 14:21; Luke 22:22
he g. before you into Galilee.
Mat 28:7; Mark 16:[illegible]

not tell whither it *g.* *John* 3:8
thou hast a devil; who *g.*? 7:20
g. before them, the sheep. 10:4
she *g.* unto the grave to weep. 11:31
not whither he *g.* 12:35; *1 John* 2:11
brother *g.* to law with. *1 Cor* 6:6
who *g.* a warfare any time at. 9:7
beholdeth himself and *g.* *Jas* 1:24
Lamb whithersoever he *g.* *Rev* 14:4
and is of the seven, and *g.* 17:11
and out of his mouth *g.* a. 19:15

Gog

G. his son, Shimei his. *1 Chr* 5:4
set thy face against *G.* *Ezek* 38:2
I am against thee, O *G.* 3; 39:1
be sanctified in thee, O *G.* 38:16
when *G.* shall come against. 18
give to *G.* a place of graves. 39:11
G. and Magog, to gather. *Rev* 20:8

Golan, *see* **Bashan**

going

sun *g.* down, a deep. *Gen* 15:12
his hands steady, to *g.* *Ex* 17:12
thou meet thine enemy's ox *g.* 23:4
g. forth of border from. *Num* 34:4
sacrifice the passover at *g.* *Deut* 16:6
rejoice, Zebulun, in thy *g.* 33:18
and smote them in the *g.* *Josh* 7:5
as they were in the *g.* down. 10:11
at the *g.* down of the sun carcases. 27
I am *g.* the way of all the. 23:14
I am now *g.* to house of. *Judg* 19:18
up, let us be *g.* but none. 28
meet thee three men *g.* *1 Sam* 10:3
in *g.* turned not from. *2 Sam* 2:19
hearest a sound of *g.* in trees. 5:24
1 Chr 14:15
as she was *g.* to fetch. *1 Ki* 17:11
went a proclamation at *g.* 22:36
g. by the way, children. *2 Ki* 2:23
they smote Ahaziah at the *g.* 9:27
time of sun *g.* down, he. *2 Chr* 18:34
from *g.* to and fro in. *Job* 1:7; 2:2
deliver him from *g.* down to. 33:24
he will deliver his soul from *g.* 28
his *g.* forth is from end. *Ps* 19:6
calleth earth, from rising of sun to *g.* down. 50:1; 113:3; *Mal* 1:11
sun knoweth his *g.* down. *Ps* 104:19
g. down to the chambers. *Pr* 7:27
man looketh well to his *g.* 14:15
yea, four are comely in *g.* 30:29
shall be darkened in his *g.* *Isa* 13:10
g. up to Luhith, continual weeping shall *g.* up; in the *g.* *Jer* 48:5
g. and weeping they shall. 50:4
g. up had eight. *Ezek* 40:31, 34, 37
with every *g.* forth of the. 44:5
after his *g.* forth, one shut. 46:12
and laboured till *g.* down. *Dan* 6:14
g. forth of the commandment. 9:25
his *g.* forth is prepared. *Hos* 6:3
rise, let us be *g.* *Mat* 26:46
what king *g.* to war. *Luke* 14:31
g. through midst of. *John* 8:59
these *g.* before, tarried. *Acts* 20:5
g. about to establish. *Rom* 10:3
some men's sins *g.* *1 Tim* 5:24
disannulling of command *g.* before. *Heb* 7:18
g. after strange flesh are. *Jude* 7
see **coming**

goings

and Moses wrote their *g.* *Num* 33:2
the *g.* out of their borders. 34:5
8, 9, 12; *Josh* 15:4, 7, 11; 16:3, 8
18:12, 14
man, he seeth all his *g.* *Job* 34:21
hold up my *g.* in thy paths. *Ps* 17:5
on a rock, established my *g.* 40:2
seen thy *g.* even the *g.* of. 68:24
purposed to overthrow my *g.* 140:4
and he pondereth all his *g.* *Pr* 5:21
man's *g.* are of the Lord. 20:24
s no judgement in their *g.* *Isa* 59:8
here *g.* out were. *Ezek* 42:11
hew them the *g.* out thereof. 43:11
whose *g.* forth have been. *Mi* 5:2

gold

Havilah, where there is *g.* *Gen* 2:11
he *g.* of that land is good. 12
hain of *g.* on Joseph's neck. 41:42
make you gods of *g.* *Ex* 20:23
cast four rings of *g.* for. 25:12, 26
26:29; 28:23, 26, 27; 37:3, 13
overlay them with *g.* 25:13, 28
26:29, 37; 30:5; 37:4, 15, 28
two cherubims of *g.* 25:18; 37:7
make fifty taches of *g.* 26:6; 36:13
hooks shall be of *g.* 26:32, 37; 36:38
ephod of *g.* 28:6
girdle of *g.* 8
ouches of *g.* 11, 13; 39:6, 13, 16
breastplate of *g.* 15
chains of *g.* 28:24
thou shalt make bells of *g.* 33
who hath any *g.* let him. 32:24
have made them gods of *g.* 31
jewels of *g.* an offering of *g.* 35:22
the boards with *g.* bars with *g.* 36:34
their chapiters and fillets with *g.* 38
all the *g.* that was occupied. 38:24
they did beat the *g.* into thin. 39:3
thou shalt set the altar of *g.* 40:5
ten shekels of *g.* *Num* 7:14, 20
the altar twelve spoons of *g.* 84
all the *g.* of the spoons was 120. 86
captains' oblation, jewels of *g.* 31:50
a wedge of *g.* of 50. *Josh* 7:21
Achan and the wedge of *g.* 24
1700 shekels of *g.* *Judg* 8:26
and put the jewels of *g.* *1 Sam* 6:8
laid coffer and the mice of *g.* 11
the coffer with the jewels of *g.* 15
David took shields of *g.* *2 Sam* 8:7
1 Chr 18:7
altar, he overlaid with *g.* *1 Ki* 6:22
cherubims with *g.* 28; *2 Chr* 3:10
the altar and table of *g.* *1 Ki* 7:48
lamps and tongs of *g.* 49
hinges of *g.* 50
Tyre furnished Solomon with *g.* and. 9:11; 10:11; *2 Chr* 9:10
queen of Sheba came with *g.* *1 Ki* 10:2; *2 Chr* 9:1
the weight of *g.* came in one year. *1 Ki* 10:14; *2 Chr* 9:13
200 targets of beaten *g.* *1 Ki* 10:16
made three hundred shields of *g.* 17
the throne with the best *g.* 18
made two calves of *g.* 12:28
made ships to go for *g.* 22:48
Hezekiah cut off *g.* *2 Ki* 18:16
of *g.* by weight for *g.* *1 Chr* 28:14
and the *g.* was *g.* of. *2 Chr* 3:6
ten candlesticks of *g.* 4:7
basons of *g.* 8
censers, and spoons of pure *g.* 22
throne, with a footstool of *g.* 9:18
carried away the shields of *g.* 12:9
g. copper precious as *g.* *Ezra* 8:27
thousand drachms of *g.* *Neh* 7:70
chief of the fathers gave *g.* 71
people gave *g.* 72
lay up *g.* as dust, the *g.* *Job* 22:24*
I shall come forth like *g.* 23:10
earth, it hath the dust of *g.* 28:6
wisdom cannot be gotten for *g.* 15
it cannot be valued with the *g.* 16
the *g.* and the crystal cannot. 17
g. my hope, or said to fine *g.* 31:24
esteem thy riches? no, not *g.* 36:19*
gave Job an earring of *g.* 42:11
desired are they than *g.* *Ps* 19:10
stand the queen in *g.* of Ophir. 45:9
be given of the *g.* of Sheba. 72:15
as a jewel of *g.* in a. *Pr* 11:22
it is to get wisdom than *g.* 16:16
there is *g.* and a multitude of. 20:15
comely with chains of *g.* *S of S* 1:10*
his hands are as *g.* rings set. 5:14
of thy images of *g.* *Isa* 30:22
spreadeth it over with *g.* 40:19
for brass I will bring *g.* for. 60:17
thee with ornaments of *g.* *Jer* 4:30
g. become dim! fine *g.* *Lam* 4:1
Sheba occupied with *g.* *Ezek* 27:22
art head of *g.* *Dan* 2:38
Nebuchadnezzar made image of *g.* 3:1
hast praised the gods of *g.* 5:23
they put a chain of *g.* about. 29
a candlestick all of *g.* *Zech* 4:2
and I will try them as *g.* is. 13:9
they presented to him *g.* *Mat* 2:11
whoso shall swear by the *g.* of. 23:16
for whether is greater, the *g.* or the temple? *Mat* 23:17
not adorned with *g.* or pearls. *1 Tim* 2:9; *1 Pet* 3:3
round about with *g.* *Heb* 9:4
come a man with a *g.* ring. *Jas* 2:2
faith more precious than *g.* *1 Pet* 1:7
thee to buy of me *g.* tried. *Rev* 3:18
their heads crowns of *g.* 4:4; 9:7
woman was decked with *g.* 17:4
city that was decked with *g.* 18:16
see **beaten, crown, fine**

***pure* gold**

overlay the ark with *pure g.* within. *Ex* 25:11, 24; 30:3; 37:2, 11, 26
a mercy seat of *pure g.* 25:17; 37:6
dishes, spoons and covers of *pure g.* 25:29; 37:16, 23
make a candlestick of *pure g.* 25:31
37:17; *1 Ki* 7:49
snuffdishes *pure g.* *Ex* 25:38
1 Ki 7:50; *2 Chr* 4:22
two chains of *pure g.* at ends. *Ex* 28:14, 22; 39:15
a plate of *pure g.* 28:36; 39:30
he overlaid with *pure g.* *1 Ki* 6:20
vessels of Lebanon of *pure g.* 10:21
2 Chr 9:20
pure g. for fleshhooks. *1 Chr* 28:17
porch within with *pure g.* *2 Chr* 3:4
the throne with *pure g.* 9:17
to be valued with *pure g.* *Job* 28:19
settest a crown of *pure g.* *Ps* 21:3
city was *pure g.* *Rev* 21:18
street of *pure g.* 21

gold with *silver*

Abram was rich in *silver* and *g.* *Gen* 13:2; 24:35
my lord's house *silver* or *g.* 44:8
jewels of *silver* and *g.* *Ex* 3:22
11:2; 12:35
offering, take *silver* and *g.* 25:3
to work in *g.* *silver.* 31:4; 35:32
his house full of *silver* and *g.* *Num* 22:18; 24:13
only *g.* and *silver* that may. 31:22
not desire *silver* and *g.* *Deut* 7:25
when thy *silver* and *g.* is. 8:13
greatly multiply *silver* and *g.* 17:17
seen their idols, *silver* and *g.* 29:17
silver and *g.* are consecrated to. *Josh* 6:19, 24
your tents with *silver* and *g.* 22:8
silver and *g.* David dedicated. *2 Sam* 8:11; *1 Ki* 7:51
will have no *silver* or *g.* *2 Sam* 21:4
house of Lord *silver* and *g.* he had. *1 Ki* 15:15; *2 Chr* 15:18
Asa took all the *silver* and *g.* *1 Ki* 15:18; *2 Chr* 16:2
I have sent a present of *silver* and *g.* *1 Ki* 15:19; *2 Chr* 16:3
silver and *g.* is mine. *1 Ki* 20:3
deliver *silver* and *g.* 5
thence *silver* and *g.* *2 Ki* 7:8
Jehoash took the *silver* and *g.* *2 Ki* 14:14; *2 Chr* 25:24
Ahaz took *silver* and *g.* *2 Ki* 16:8
Hezekiah shewed them *silver* and *g.* 20:13; *Isa* 39:2
Jehoiakim gave *silver* and *g.* exacted *silver* and *g.* *2 Ki* 23:35
things of *g.* in *g.* of *silver* in *silver.* 25:15; *Jer* 52:19
good, of *g.* and *silver.* *1 Chr* 29:3
king made *silver* and *g.* *2 Chr* 1:15
place help with *silver* and *g.* *Ezra* 1:4
gave *silver* and *g.* 2:69
to carry *silver* and *g.* 7:15
weighed them *silver* and *g.* 8:25, 33
beds were of *g.* and *silver.* *Esth* 1:6
for *silver*, a place for *g.* *Job* 28:1
silver her feathers with *g.* *Ps* 68:13
them out with *silver* and *g.* 105:37
are *silver* and *g.* 115:4; 135:15
is better than *g.* and *silver.* 119:72
silver receive knowledge rather than *g.* *Pr* 8:10
silver, furnace for *g.* 17:3; 27:21
favour rather than *silver* or *g.* 22:1
of *g.* in pictures of *silver.* 25:11
me also *silver* and *g.* *Eccl* 2:8

of *g.* with studs of *silver.* *S of S* 1:11
pillars of *silver,* bottom of *g.* 3:10
is full of *silver* and *g.* *Isa* 2:7
cast his idols of *silver* and *g.* 20; 31:7
shall not regard *silver* or *g.* 13:17
g. out of the bag, and weigh *silver.* 46:6
their *silver* and *g.* with them. 60:9
deck it with *silver* and *g.* *Jer* 10:4
away their *silver* and *g. silver* and *g.* not able. *Ezek* 7:19; *Zeph* 1:18
wast thou decked with *g.* and *silver.* *Ezek* 16:13
silver and *g.* broken. *Dan* 2:35, 45
the gods of *silver* and *g.* 5:4, 23
he honour with *g.* and *silver.* 11:38
over treasures of *g.* and *silver.* 43
I multiplied her *silver* and *g.* *Hos* 2:8
of their *silver* and *g.* have they. 8:4
taken my *silver* and *g.* *Joel* 3:5
of *silver* and spoil of *g.* *Nah* 2:9
laid over with *silver* and *g.* *Hab* 2:19
silver is mine, and the *g.* *Hag* 2:8
then take *silver* and *g.* *Zech* 6:11
purge them as *g.* and *silver.* *Mal* 3:3
provide neither *g.* nor *silver.* *Mat* 10:9
Peter said, *silver* and *g.* *Acts* 3:6
Godhead like to *silver* and *g.* 17:29
coveted no man's *silver* or *g.* 20:33
this foundation *g. silver.* *1 Cor* 3:12
vessels of *silver* and *g.* *2 Tim* 2:20
your *g.* and *silver* cankered. *Jas* 5:3
were not redeemed with *silver* and *g.* *1 Pet* 1:18
of idols of *silver* and *g.* *Rev* 9:20

talent and *talents of* **gold**

of a *talent of* pure *g.* *Ex* 25:39
of a *talent of* pure *g.* made. 37:24
weight of crown a *talent of g.* *2 Sam* 12:30; *1 Chr* 20:2
Solomon 120 *talents of g.* *1 Ki* 9:14
from Ophir 420 *talents of g.* 28
she gave Solomon 120 *talents of g.* 10:10; *2 Chr* 9:9
came to Solomon 666 *talents of g.* *1 Ki* 10:14
put the land to a *talent of g.* *2 Ki* 23:33; *2 Chr* 36:3
100,000 *talents of g.* *1 Chr* 22:14
proper good 3000 *talents of g.* 29:4
fathers gave 5000 *talents of g.* 7
Ophir 450 *talents of g.* *2 Chr* 8:18
of *g.* vessels 100 *talents.* *Ezra* 8:26

vessels of **gold**

Toi sent to David *vessels of g.* *2 Sam* 8:10; *1 Chr* 18:10
Solomon's drinking *vessels* were *of g.* *1 Ki* 10:21; *2 Chr* 9:20
every man brought present, *vessels of g.* *1 Ki* 10:25; *2 Chr* 9:24
for house of Lord *vessels of g.* *2 Ki* 12:13
cut in pieces *vessels of g.* 24:13
of rest of money made they *vessels of g.* *2 Chr* 24:14
the *vessels of g.* and silver 5400. *Ezra* 1:11
vessels of g. Cyrus deliverd. 5:14
I weighed of *vessels of g.* 100. 8:26
drink in *vessels of g.* *Esth* 1:7
into Egypt *vessels of g.* *Dan* 11:8
not only *vessels of g.* *2 Tim* 2:20

golden

a *g.* crown to the border. *Ex* 25:25
a *g.* bell. 28:34
two *g.* rings, 30:4; 39:20
Aaron said, break off the *g.* 32:2
upon forefront he put *g.* *Lev* 8:9
one *g.* spoon of ten. *Num* 7:26
had *g.* earrings, because. *Judg* 8:24
the weight of *g.* earrings he. 26
g. emerods, five *g.* *1 Sam* 6:4, 17, 18
departed not from the *g.* *2 Ki* 10:29
for the *g.* basons he. *1 Chr* 28:17
there are with you *g.* *2 Chr* 13:8
and also let the *g.* vessels. *Ezra* 6:5
king shall hold out a *g.* sceptre. *Esth* 4:11; 5:2; 8:4
or the *g.* bowl be broken. *Eccl* 12:6
more precious than the *g.* *Isa* 13:12
how hath the *g.* city ceased! 14:4
Babylon hath been *g.* *Jer* 51:7
and worship *g.* image. *Dan* 3:5, 12
commanded to bring the *g.* 5:2
they brought the *g.* vessels taken. 3
g. pipes, empty the *g.* oil. *Zech* 4:12
g. censer and ark where was *g.* pot. *Heb* 9:4
turned, I saw seven *g.* *Rev* 1:12
girt about the paps with a *g.* 13
the mystery of the seven *g.* 20
who walketh in midst of the *g.* 2:1
g. vials. 5:8; 15:7
having a *g.* censer. 8:3
on his head a *g.* crown. 14:14
a *g.* cup full. 17:4
had a *g.* reed to measure the. 21:15

see **altar**

goldsmith, -s

Uzziel of the *g.* repaired. *Neh* 3:8
the *g.'s* son. 31
and merchants repaired and *g.* 32
the *g.* spreadeth it over. *Isa* 40:19
carpenter encouraged the *g.* 41:7
they hire a *g.* and he maketh. 46:6

Golgotha

come to a place called *G.* *Mat* 27:33
Mark 15:22; *John* 19:17

Goliath

G. of Gath a. *1 Sam* 17:4, 23
sword of *G.* the Philistine. 21:9
he gave him the sword of *G.* 22:10
slew the brother of *G.* *2 Sam* 21:19
1 Chr 20:5

Gomer

sons of Japheth, *G.* Magog. *Gen* 10:2; *1 Chr* 1:5
the sons of *G.* Ashkenaz, Riphath. *Gen* 10:3; *1 Chr* 1:6
G. and all his bands. *Ezek* 38:6
he took *G.* the daughter. *Hos* 1:3

Gomorrah

destroyed Sodom and *G.* *Gen* 13:10
goods of Sodom and *G.* 14:11
cry of Sodom and *G.* is. 18:20
the Lord rained on *G.* fire. 19:24
looked towards Sodom and *G.* 28
like the overthrow of Sodom and *G.* *Deut* 29:23; *Isa* 1:9; 13:19
Jer 23:14; 49:18; 50:40
Amos 4:11; *Rom* 9:29
2 Pet 2:6; *Jude* 7
vine is of fields of *G.* *Deut* 32:32
the law, ye people of *G.* *Isa* 1:10
of Ammon shall be as *G.* *Zeph* 2:9
be more tolerable for *G.* *Mat* 10:15
Mark 6:11

gone

thou wouldest needs be *g.* *Gen* 31:30
daughter, and we will be *g.* 34:17
for your households, and be *g.* 42:33
flocks and herds, and be *g.* *Ex* 12:32
seeth their power is *g.* *Deut* 32:36
not Jonathan was *g.* *1 Sam* 14:3
number now, and see who is *g.* 17
I have *g.* the way which the. 15:20
as soon as the lad was *g.* 20:41
g. in to my father's? *2 Sam* 3:7
he is quite *g.* 24
Amnon said, Arise, be *g.* 13:15
that Shimei had *g.* from. *1 Ki* 2:41
when he was *g.* a lion met. 13:24
away dung till it be all *g.* 14:10
as soon as I am *g.* Spirit. 18:12
busy here and there, he was *g.* 20:40
messenger that was *g.* to call. 22:13
but have *g.* from tent to. *1 Chr* 17:5
I rise, and the night be *g.*? *Job* 7:4
destroyed me, and I am *g.* 19:10
exalted for a while, but are *g.* 24:24
are dried up and *g.* away. 28:4*
of mine eyes, it also is *g.* *Ps* 38:10
I had *g.* with the multitude to. 42:4
me, my feet were almost *g.* 73:2
is his mercy clean *g.* for ever? 77:8
passeth over it, and it is *g.* 103:16
I am *g.* like the shadow that. 109:23
good man is *g.* a long. *Pr* 7:19
when he is *g.* his way, then. 20:14
who had come and *g.* *Eccl* 8:10*
the rain is over and *g.* *S of S* 2:11
had withdrawn, and was *g.* 5:6
whither is thy beloved *g.* O? 6:1
therefore my people are *g.* *Isa* 5:13
the mirth of the land *g.* *Isa* 24:11
the way he had not *g.* 41:3
in me, that they are *g.* *Jer* 2:5
I have not *g.* after Baalim? 23
this people are revolted and *g.* 5:23
beasts are *g.* 9:10
thou art *g.* backward. 15:6
none that are *g.* into Egypt. 44:14
all remnant that are *g.* shall. 28
they have *g.* from mountain. 50:6
Judah is *g.* *Lam* 1:3
Zion's children are *g.* 5
g. without strength. 6
my virgins are *g.* 18
from heathen whither *g.* *Ezek* 37:21
the thing is *g.* from me. *Dan* 2:5, 8
lo, they are *g.* because of. *Hos* 9:6
will new moon be *g.* *Amos* 8:5
angels were *g.* from. *Luke* 2:15
as if he would have *g.* further. 24:28
for his disciples were *g.* *John* 4:8
behold, the world is *g.* after. 12:19
saw hope of gains was *g.* *Acts* 16:19
among whom I have *g.* 20:25
who is *g.* into heaven. *1 Pet* 3:22
have *g.* in the way of Cain. *Jude* 11

gone *about*

Saul is *g. about* and. *1 Sam* 15:12
feastings were *g. about.* *Job* 1:5
city is *g. about* the. *Isa* 15:8
hath *g. about* to profane. *Acts* 24:6*

gone *aside*

if thou hast not *g. aside.* *Num* 5:19
if hast *g. aside* to another. 20
they are all *g. aside,* they. *Ps* 14:3
they were *g. aside,* they. *Acts* 26:31

gone *astray*

I have *g. astray* like. *Ps* 119:176
like sheep have *g. astray.* *Isa* 53:6
one of them be *g. astray,* he seeketh that which is *g. astray.* *Mat* 18:12
way, and are *g. astray.* *2 Pet* 2:15

gone *away*

Abner was *g. away.* *2 Sam* 3:22, 23
men of Israel were *g. away.* 23:9
the waters were *g. away.* *Job* 28:4
they are *g. away* backward. *Isa* 1:4
Levites which are *g. away* from. *Ezek* 44:10
are *g. away* from mine. *Mal* 3:7*
disciples are *g. away.* *John* 6:22

gone *back*

sister-in-law is *g. back.* *Ruth* 1:15
nor have I *g. back.* *Job* 23:12
every one is *g. back.* *Ps* 53:3
he was not yet *g. back,* he. *Jer* 40:5

gone *down*

passed, and *g. down.* *1 Sam* 15:12
Adonijah is *g. down.* *1 Ki* 1:25
Ahab *g. down* to possess. 21:18
shadow had *g. down* in the dial of Ahaz. *2 Ki* 20:11; *Isa* 38:8
my beloved is *g. down.* *S of S* 6:2
her sun is *g. down* while. *Jer* 15:9
his young men are *g. down.* 48:15
all people *g. down.* *Ezek* 31:12
the strong are *g. down,* slain. 32:21
Tubal *g. down.* 27
Zidonians *g. down.* 30
Jonah was *g. down* to. *Jonah* 1:5

gone *forth*

when Israel was *g. forth.* *Ex* 19:1
of Elisha was *g. forth.* *2 Ki* 6:15
God is *g. forth* before. *1 Chr* 14:15
my salvation is *g. forth.* *Isa* 51:5
g. forth to make thy land. *Jer* 4:7
my children are *g. forth* of me. 10:20
is profaneness *g. forth* into. 23:15
whirlwind of Lord is *g. forth.* 19
brethren that are not *g. forth.* 29:16
the morning is *g. forth.* *Ezek* 7:10
of the Lord and are *g. forth.* 36:20
g. forth to slay wise men. *Dan* 2:14
when I am *g. forth,* prince. 10:20
when he was *g. forth.* *Mark* 10:17

gone *out*

as soon as I am *g. out* I. *Ex* 9:29
there is wrath *g. out.* *Num* 16:46
certain men *g. out* *Deut* 13:13
which is *g. out* of thy lips. 23:23
is not the Lord *g. out*? *Judg* 4:14

hand of Lord is g. out. *Ruth* 1:13
when wine was g. out. *1 Sam* 25:37
the Syrians had g. out. *2 Ki* 5:2
therefore they are g. out. 7:12
afore Isaiah was g. out into. 20:4
their line is g. out. *Ps* 19:4
alter the thing that is g. out. 89:34
the word is g. out of my. *Isa* 45:23
scum is not g. out of it. *Ezek* 24:6
when unclean spirit is g. out.
Mat 12:43; *Luke* 11:24
our lamps are g. out. *Mat* 25:8
that virtue had g. out of him.
Mark 5:30; *Luke* 8:46
devil is g. out of daughter.
Mark 7:29, 30; *Luke* 11:14
he was g. out, Jesus. *John* 13:31
are all g. out of way. *Rom* 3:12*
false prophets are g. out. *1 John* 4:1

gone *over*
be g. over the brook. *2 Sam* 17:20
iniquities are g. over. *Ps* 38:4
and billows are g. over me. 42:7
then the stream had g. over. 124:4
the proud waters had g. over. 5
they are g. over passage. *Isa* 10:29
g. over the sea. 16:8; *Jer* 48:32
shall not have g. over. *Mat* 10:23

gone *up*
my son, thou art g. up. *Gen* 49:9
bed on which g. up. *2 Ki* 1:4, 6, 16
God is g. up with a shout. *Ps* 47:5
he is g. up to Bajith. *Isa* 15:2
than me, and art g. up. 57:8
she is g. up on every. *Jer* 3:6
cry of Jerusalem is g. up. 14:2
army, which are g. up. 34:21
Moab is spoiled, and g. up. 48:15
God of Israel was g. up. *Ezek* 9:3
ye have not g. up into the gaps. 13:5
are g. up to Assyria. *Hos* 8:9
his brethren were g. up. *John* 7:10
had g. up and saluted. *Acts* 18:22

gone *a whoring*
they have g. a whoring. *Lev* 17:7
thou hast g. a whoring. *Ezek* 23:30
g. a whoring from under. *Hos* 4:12
for thou hast g. a whoring from. 9:1

good, *substantive*
done to thee nothing but g. *Gen* 26:29
I will surely do thee g. 32:12
I will give you the g. of the. 45:18
for the g. of the land of Egypt. 20
God meant it unto g. to bring. 50:20
Lord hath spoken g. *Num* 10:29
after he hath done you g. *Josh* 24:20
behold, if there be g. *1 Sam* 20:12
for thou hast rewarded me g. 24:17
Lord rewarded thee g. 19
according to all the g. he. 25:30
it had been g. for me. *2 Sam* 14:32
Lord will requite g. for his. 16:12
prophets declare g. to the king.
1 Ki 22:13; *2 Chr* 18:12
of mine own proper g. *1 Chr* 29:3*
because he had done g. *2 Chr* 24:16
be strong, and eat the g. *Ezra* 9:12
who had spoken g. for. *Esth* 7:9
shall we receive g. at? *Job* 2:10
know thou it for thy g. 5:27
mine eye shall no more see g. 7:7
flee away, they see no g. 9:25
wherewith he can do no g. 15:3
lo, their g. is not in their. 21:16*
be at peace: thereby g. shall. 22:21
he doeth not g. to the widow. 24:21
who will shew us any g.? *Ps* 4:6
none doeth g., no, not one. 14:1, 3
53:1, 3; *Rom* 3:12
days, that he may see g. *Ps* 34:12
held my peace even from g. 39:2
hand, they are filled with g. 104:28
that I may see the g. of. 106:5*
of Lord I will seek thy g. 122:9
shall see the g. of Jerusalem. 128:5
withhold not g. from them. *Pr* 3:27
the merciful man doth g. to. 11:17
he that diligently seeketh g. 27
a man satisfied with g. by. 12:14
a man shall eat g. by fruit. 13:2
but to the righteous g. shall be. 21
truth be to them that devise g. 14:22
matter wisely, shall find g. 16:20

a froward heart findeth no g.
Pr 17:20
a merry heart doeth g. like a. 17:22
understanding shall find g. 19:8
soul enjoy g. *Eccl* 2:24; 3:13; 5:18
I know that there is no g. in. 3:12*
and bereave my soul of g.? 4:8
and what g. is there to the? 5:11*
his soul be not filled with g. 6:3
yet hath he seen no g. all go. 6
not a man just, that doeth g. 7:20
one sinner destroyeth much g. 9:18
ye shall eat the g. of. *Isa* 1:19
bringeth good tidings of g. 52:7
we looked for peace, no g. came.
Jer 8:15; 14:19
shall not see when g. cometh. 17:6
evil, I will repent of the g. 18:10
I stood before thee to speak g. 20
shall he behold the g. I will. 29:32
I will bring all the g. I have. 32:42
which shall hear all the g. that. 33:9
them away as I saw g. *Ezek* 16:50
I said, if ye think g. *Zech* 11:12
been g. for that man. *Mat* 26:24
that have done g. to the. *John* 5:29
who went about doing g. *Acts* 10:38
in that he did g. and gave us 14:17
every man that worketh g. *Rom* 2:10
thought it g. to be left. *1 Thes* 3:1
hath this world's g. and. *1 John* 3:17

for **good**
fear the Lord for our g. *Deut* 6:24
thee this day for thy g. 10:13
again rejoice over thee for g. 30:9
God on all of them for g. *Ezra* 8:22
think upon me, O my God, for g.
Neh 5:19; 13:31
and know thou it for thy g. *Job* 5:27
shew me a token for g. *Ps* 86:17
surety for thy servant for g. 119:122
this people for their g. *Jer* 14:11
out of this place for their g. 24:5
set mine eyes on them for g. 6
me for ever, for the g. of. 32:39
waited carefully for g. *Mi* 1:12
things work together for g. *Rom* 8:28
minister of God to thee for g. 13:4
please his neighbour for g. 15:2
see **bad, evil**

good, *adjective*
Hagar sat her down a g. *Gen* 21:16
I pray thee, send me g. 24:12
Rebekah said, what g. shall? 27:46
g. ears. 41:5
g. kine. 26
g. years. 35
our father is in g. health. 43:28
on his father's neck a g. 46:29
for g.-will of him that. *Deut* 33:16
sons, it is no g. report. *1 Sam* 2:24
I will teach you the g. and. 12:23
men were very g. to us, we. 25:15
I know that thou art g. in my. 29:9
see thy matters are g. *2 Sam* 15:3
what the king thought g. 19:18
teach them the g. way. *1 Ki* 8:36
not failed one word of all his g. 56
speak g. words. 12:7; *2 Chr* 10:7
g. is the word of the Lord.
2 Ki 20:19*; *Isa* 39:8
Lord be with the g. *2 Chr* 19:11
saying, the g. Lord pardon. 30:18
the g. hand of his God on him.
Ezra 7:9; *Neh* 2:8
the g. hand of our God. *Ezra* 8:18
them true laws, g. *Neh* 9:13
gavest thy g. Spirit to instruct. 20
is it g. that thou shouldest? *Job* 10:3
is it g. that he should search? 13:9
their young ones are in g. 39:4
g. and upright is the Lord. *Ps* 25:8
steps of a g. man are ordered. 37:23
heart is inditing a g. matter. 45:1
Lord, art g., ready. 86:5; 119:68
a g. man sheweth favour. 112:5*
thy judgements are g. 119:39
teach me g. judgement and. 66
understand every g. path. *Pr* 2:9
mayest walk in the way of g. men. 20
g. word maketh the heart. 12:25
evil bow before the g. and. 14:19
in due season, how g. is it! 15:23

g. report maketh bones fat. *Pr* 15:30
with g. advice make war. 20:18*
a g. name rather to be chosen. 22:1
they have a g. reward. *Eccl* 4:9
what g. is there to the owners? 5:11
there is one event to the g. and. 9:2
they both shall be alike g. 11:6
where is the g. way. *Jer* 6:16
g. figs. 24:2
the good figs, very g. 3
like g. figs, so will I. 5
I will perform my g. word. 29:10
planted in a g. soil. *Ezek* 17:8
gather every g. piece, thigh. 24:4
I thought it g. to shew. *Dan* 4:2
the angel with g. words. *Zech* 1:13
receiveth it with g.-will. *Mal* 2:13
know how to give g. gifts.
Mat 7:11; *Luke* 11:13
g. tree bringeth forth g. *Mat* 7:17, 18
daughter, be of g. 9:22; *Luke* 8:48
fell in g. ground. *Mat* 13:8, 23
Mark 4:8, 20; *Luke* 8:8, 15
g. seed. *Mat* 13:24
g. Master, what g. thing. 19:16
why callest thou me g.? none g. 17
eye evil because I am g.? 20:15
well done, thou g. and. 25:21
peace on earth, g.-will. *Luke* 2:14*
g. measure, pressed down. 6:38
Mary hath chosen that g. 10:42
it is your Father's g. pleasure. 12:32
hast kept the g. wine. *John* 2:10
I am the g. Shepherd, the g. 10:11
ye know how that a g. *Acts* 15:7
is holy, and just, and g. *Rom* 7:12
what is that g. and perfect. 12:2
corrupt g. manners. *1 Cor* 15:33
g. remembrance of us. *1 Thes* 3:6*
of those that are g. *2 Tim* 3:3
must be a lover of g. men. *Tit* 1:8
that have tasted the g. *Heb* 6:5
every g. gift. *Jas* 1:17
sit in a g. place. 2:3
subject not only to g. *1 Pet* 2:18
will love life, and see g. days. 3:10
see **bad, cheer, conscience, courage, day, do, old** age

as **good**
of one, and him as g. *Heb* 11:12

good *heed*
take ye g. heed. *Deut* 2:4; 4:15
Josh 23:11
preacher gave g. heed. *Eccl* 12:9

is **good**
gold of that land is g. *Gen* 2:12
thou hast spoken is g. *Deut* 1:14
do that which is g. in sight. 6:18
me in the host is g. *1 Sam* 29:6
said, the saying is g. *1 Ki* 2:38
word that I have heard is g. 42
and speak that which is g. 22:13
I have done that which is g.
2 Ki 20:3; *Isa* 38:3
Lord is g. *1 Chr* 16:34; *2 Chr* 5:13
7:3; *Ezra* 3:11; *Ps* 100:5; 106:1
107:1; 118:1, 29; 135:3; 136:1
145:9; *Jer* 33:11; *Lam* 3:25
Nah 1:7
which is g. in his sight. *1 Chr* 19:13
ourselves what is g. *Job* 34:4
see that the Lord is g. *Ps* 34:8
thy lovingkindness is g. 69:16
truly God is g. to Israel, to. 73:1
Lord shall give that which is g. 85:12
because thy mercy is g. 109:21
thy Spirit is g.; lead me into. 143:10
the righteous is only g. *Pr* 11:23
so is g. news from a far. 25:25
her merchandise is g. 31:18*
man that is g. in his sight, may give
to him that is g. *Eccl* 2:26*
who knoweth what is g. for? 6:12
wisdom is g. with an. 7:11
as is the g. so is the sinner. 9:2
eat ye that which is g. *Isa* 55:2
this girdle which is g. *Jer* 13:10
shadow thereof is g. *Hos* 4:13
thee, O man, what is g. *Mi* 6:8
one that doeth evil is g. *Mal* 2:17
salt is g. but if the salt. *Mark* 9:50
Luke 14:34

forth that which *is g.* *Luke* 6:45
none *is g.* save one, that. 18:19
then that which *is g.* *Rom* 7:13
but how to perform that *is g.* I. 18
cleave to that which *is g.* 12:9
you wise to that which *is g.* 16:19
that this *is g.* for the. *1 Cor* 7:26
but that *is g.* *Eph* 4:29
follow that which *is g.* *1 Thes* 5:15
3 John 11
hold fast that which *is g.* *1 Thes* 5:21
know that the law *is g.* *1 Tim* 1:8
is g. and acceptable in sight. 2:3
for every creature of God *is g.* 4:4
for that *is g.* and acceptable. 5:4
be followers of that which *is g.*
1 Pet 3:13

it is **good**

wait on thy name, for *it is g.*
Ps 52:9; 54:6
it is g. for me to draw near. 73:28
it is a *g.* thing to give thanks. 92:1
it is g. for me that I have. 119:71
it is g. to sing praises unto. 147:1
thou honey, because *it is g.* *Pr* 24:13
it is g. and comely for. *Eccl* 5:18
it is g. that thou shouldest. 7:18
it is g. that a man should. *Lam* 3:26
it is g. that a man bear the yoke. 27
it is g. for nothing but. *Mat* 5:13
it is g. for us to be here. 17:4
Mark 9:5; *Luke* 9:33
unto the law that *it is g.* *Rom* 7:16
it is g. neither to eat. 14:21
it is g. for a man not to touch a.
1 Cor 7:1, 8
I say, *it is g.* for a man so to be. 26
it is g. to be zealously. *Gal* 4:18

good *land*

come to bring them to *g. land.*
Ex 3:8; *Deut* 8:7
we searched is a *g. land.* *Num* 14:7
is a *g. land* which Lord. *Deut* 1:25
generation see that *g. land.* 35
over, and see the *g. land.* 3:25
not go unto that *g. land.* 4:21
over and possess that *g. land.* 22
go in and possess the *g. land.* 6:18
God bringeth thee into a *g. land.* 8:7
Lord thy God for the *g. land.* 10
giveth not this *g. land* for thy. 9:6
lest ye perish from off *g. land.* 11:17
until ye perish from this *g. land.*
Josh 23:13, 15
perish from off the *g. land.* 16
land, and it is very *g.* *Judg* 18:9
Israel out of this *g. land.* *1 Ki* 14:15
g. piece of *land.* *2 Ki* 3:19, 25
possess this *g. land.* *1 Chr* 28:8

good with *make*

the owner of pit shall *make* it *g.*
Ex 21:34; 22:14*
shall not *make* it *g.* 22:11*, 13, 15
shall *make* it *g.*; beast for. *Lev* 24:18
shall he not *make* it *g.*? *Num* 23:19
make your ways and your doings *g.*
Jer 18:11*

good *man*

Ahimaaz is a *g. man.* *2 Sam* 18:27
steps of a *g. man* are. *Ps* 37:23
a *g. man* sheweth favour. 112:5
the *g. man* is not at home. *Pr* 7:19
g. man obtaineth favour of. 12:2
a *g. man* satisfied. 12:14; 14:14
a *g. man* leaveth an. 13:22
the *g. man* is perished. *Mi* 7:2*
g. man out of good treasure.
Mat 12:35; *Luke* 6:45
against the *g. man.* *Mat* 20:11*
if the *g. man* of the house had known.
24:43*; *Luke* 12:39*
Joseph was a *g. man.* *Luke* 23:50
some said, he is a *g. man.* *John* 7:12
Barnabas was a *g. man.* *Acts* 11:24
for a *g. man* some would. *Rom* 5:7

not **good**

it is *not g.* that man. *Gen* 2:18
the counsel is *not g.* *2 Sam* 17:7
in a way that is *not g.* *Ps* 36:4
into way that is *not g.* *Pr* 16:29
punish the just is *not g.* 17:26
is *not g.* to accept the person. 18:5
without knowledge is *not g.* 19:2
and a false balance is *not g.* *Pr* 20:23
not g. to have respect. 24:23; 28:21
it is *not g.* to eat much honey. 25:27
in a way that is *not g.* *Isa* 65:2
did that which is *not g.* *Ezek* 18:18
statutes that were *not g.* 20:25
doings that were *not g.* 36:31
case be so, it is *not g.* *Mat* 19:10*
Paul thought *not g.* to. *Acts* 15:38
your glorying is *not g.* *1 Cor* 5:6

seem, seemed, seemeth **good**

as it *seemeth g.* to thee. *Josh* 9:25
Judg 10:15; *1 Sam* 14:36, 40
Ezra 7:18; *Esth* 3:11; *Jer* 26:14
40:4
do to them what *seemeth g.* unto.
Judg 19:24
do what *seemeth g.* *1 Sam* 1:23
3:18; 11:10; 24:4
Abner spake all *seemed g.* to.
2 Sam 3:19
the Lord do that *seemeth* him *g.*
10:12; 15:26
Chimham what *seem g.* 19:37, 38
and offer up what *seemeth g.* 24:22
if it *seem g.* to thee. *1 Ki* 31:2
Jer 40:4
if it *seem g.* to you, let. *1 Chr* 13:2
if it *seem g.* to the king. *Ezra* 5:17
Esth 5:4
as *seemed g.* to potter. *Jer* 18:4
so it *seemed g.* in sight.
Mat 11:26*; *Luke* 10:21*
it *seemed g.* to me. *Luke* 1:3
it *seemed g.* unto us. *Acts* 15:25
it *seemed g.* to the Holy Ghost. 28

good with *thing*

the *thing* that thou doest is not *g.*
Ex 18:17
rejoice in every *g. thing.* *Deut* 26:11
aught of any *g. thing.* *Josh* 21:45
the *thing* is not *g.* *1 Sam* 26:16
is found some *g. thing.* *1 Ki* 14:13
Hazael took of every *g. thing* of.
2 Ki 8:9
Lord not want any *g. thing.* *Ps* 34:10
I follow the *thing* that *g.* is. 38:20
no *g. thing* will he withhold. 84:11
it is a *g. thing* to give thanks. 92:1
a wife, findeth a *g. thing.* *Pr* 18:22
I will perform *g. thing.* *Jer* 33:14
cast off the *thing* that is *g.* *Hos* 8:3
what *g. thing* shall I do? *Mat* 19:16
can any *g. thing* come? *John* 1:46
flesh, dwelleth no *g. thing.* *Rom* 7:18
affected in a *g. thing.* *Gal* 4:18
his hands *thing* which is *g.* *Eph* 4:28
knowing that what *g. thing* any. 6:8
that *g. thing* committed. *2 Tim* 1:14
acknowledging every *g. thing* in you.
Philem 6
it is a *g. thing* the heart. *Heb* 13:9

good *things*

houses full of all *g. things.* *Deut* 6:11
failed of all the *g. things.* *Josh* 23:14
that as all *g. things* are come. 15
there were *g. things.* *2 Chr* 12:12
there are *g. things* found. 19:3
houses with *g. things.* *Job* 22:18
thy mouth with *g. things.* *Ps* 103:5
the upright shall have *g. things.*
Pr 28:10
have withholden *g. things.* *Jer* 5:25
give *g. things* to them? *Mat* 7:11
ye being evil speak *g. things*? 12:34
good man bringeth forth *g. things.* 35
the hungry with *g. things.* *Luke* 1:53
time receivedst thy *g. things.* 16:25
glad tidings of *g. things.* *Rom* 10:15
unto him in all *g. things.* *Gal* 6:6
be teachers of *g. things.* *Tit* 2:3
these *things* are *g.* and. 3:8
high priest of *g. things.* *Heb* 9:11
a shadow of *g. things* to come. 10:1

good *tidings*

have brought *g. tidings.* *2 Sam* 4:10
and cometh with *g. tidings.* 18:27
and bringest *g. tidings.* *1 Ki* 1:42
is a day of *g. tidings.* *2 Ki* 7:9
that bringest *g. tidings.* *Isa* 40:9
one that bringeth *g. tidings.* 41:27
him that bringeth *g. tidings.* 52:7
me to preach *g. tidings.* *Isa* 61:1
who bringeth *g. tidings.* *Nah* 1:15
I bring you *g. tidings* of. *Luke* 2:10
brought us *g. tidings* of. *1 Thes* 3:6

was **good**

God saw that it *was g.* *Gen* 1:4, 10
12, 18, 21, 25
thing, behold it *was* very *g.* 31
woman saw that the tree *was g.* 3:6
saw the interpretation *was g.* 40:16
thing *was g.* in eyes of. 41:37
Issachar saw that rest *was g.* 49:15
spared all that *was g.* *1 Sam* 15:9
did that which *was g.* *2 Chr* 14:2
wrought that which *was g.* 31:20
hand of God which *was g.* *Neh* 2:18
see what *was* that *g.* for. *Eccl* 2:3

good *understanding*

woman of *g. unders.* *1 Sam* 25:3
g. unders. have all that. *Ps* 111:10
find favour and *g. unders.* *Pr* 3:4
g. unders. giveth favour. 13:15

good *work*

hands for this *g. work.* *Neh* 2:18
she hath wrought a *g. work.*
Mat 26:10; *Mark* 14:6
for a *g. work* we stone. *John* 10:33
abound to every *g. work.* *2 Cor* 9:8
hath begun a *g. work.* *Phil* 1:6
fruitful in every *g. work.* *Col.* 1:10
every *g.* word and *work.* *2 Thes* 2:17
bishop, desireth a *g. work.* *1 Tim* 3:1
followed every *g. work.* 5:10
unto every *g. work.* *2 Tim* 2:21
every *g. work* reprobate. *Tit* 1:16
to be ready to every *g. work.* 3:1
perfect in every *g. work.* *Heb* 13:21

good *works*

his *works* to thee have been very *g.*
1 Sam 19:4
may see your *g. works.* *Mat* 5:16
many *g. works* have I. *John* 10:32
Dorcas full of *g. works.* *Acts* 9:36
not a terror to *g. works.* *Rom* 13:3
Christ Jesus unto *g. works.* *Eph* 2:10
adorned with *g. works.* *1 Tim* 2:10
well reported of for *g. works.* 5:10
the *g. works* of some are. 25
that they be rich in *g. works.* 6:18
furnished to all *g. works.* *2 Tim* 3:17
a pattern of *g. works.* *Tit* 2:7
people, zealous of *g. works.* 14
to maintain *g. works.* 3:8, 14
unto love and *g. works.* *Heb* 10:24
may by your *g. works.* *1 Pet* 2:12

goodlier

not in Israel a *g.* person. *1 Sam* 9:2

goodliest

he will take your *g.* *1 Sam* 8:16
thy children, even the *g.* *1 Ki* 20:3

goodliness

the *g.* thereof as flower of. *Isa* 40:6

goodly

Rebekah took *g.* raiment. *Gen* 27:15
Joseph was a *g.* person and. 39:6*
hind let loose, giveth *g.* words. 49:21
when she saw he was a *g.* *Ex* 2:2
they made *g.* bonnets of. 39:28
day of boughs, the *g.* *Lev* 23:40
how *g.* are thy tents. *Num* 24:5
they burnt all their *g.* castles. 31:10*
me see that *g.* mount. *Deut* 3:25
great and *g.* cities which thou. 6:10
lest when thou hast built *g.* 8:12
I saw a *g.* Babylonish. *Josh* 7:21
young man, and a *g.* *1 Sam* 9:2
David was ruddy and *g.* to. 16:12
Egyptian, a *g.* man. *2 Sam* 23:21
also was a very *g.* man. *1 Ki* 1:6
Babylon the *g.* vessels. *2 Chr* 36:10
and destroyed the *g.* vessels. 19
gavest thou *g.* wings? *Job* 39:13
yea, I have a *g.* heritage. *Ps* 16:6
boughs were like the *g.* 80:10
how shall I give thee a *g.*? *Jer* 3:1
olive tree, fair, and of *g.* fruit. 11:1
that it might be a *g.* *Ezek* 17:
shall bear fruit, and be a *g.* 2
have made *g.* images. *Hos* 10:
temples my *g.* things. *Joel* 3:
as his *g.* horse in battle. *Zech* 10:
g. price that I was prized. 11:1

man seeking g. pearls. Mat 13:45
adorned with g. stones. Luke 21:5
if there come a man in g. Jas 2:2*
all things dainty and g. Rev 18:14*

goodness

Jethro rejoiced for all g. Ex 18:9
I will make all my g. pass. 33:19
the Lord God abundant in g. 34:6
what g. the Lord shall. Num 10:32
thou promisedst this g. 2 Sam 7:28
1 Chr 17:26
joyful for all the g. that the Lord had done. 1 Ki 8:66; 2 Chr 7:10
thy saints rejoice in g. 2 Chr 6:41
Hezekiah his g. 32:32
Josiah and his g. 35:26
themselves in thy g. Neh 9:25
not served thee in thy great g. 35
my g. extendeth not to. Ps 16:2
him with blessings of g. 21:3
g. and mercy shall follow me. 23:6
remember thou me, for thy g. 25:7
I had believed to see the g. 27:13
O how great is thy g. thou. 31:19
the earth is full of the g. of. 33:5
the g. of God endureth. 52:1
shall be satisfied with the g. of. 65:4
crownest the year with thy g. 11
thou hast prepared of thy g. 68:10
praise the Lord for his g. 107:8, 15
21, 31
and filleth the hungry soul with g. 9
my g. and my fortress, my. 144:2
utter the memory of thy g. 145:7
proclaim every one his g. Pr 20:6
g. toward house of Israel. Isa 63:7
I brought you to eat the g. Jer 2:7
shall flow together to the g. 31:12
satisfied with my g. saith Lord. 14
and tremble for all the g. 33:9
fear the Lord and his g. Hos 3:5
your g. is as a morning cloud. 6:4
according to g. of his land. 10:1
for how great is his g. Zech 9:17
riches of his g. not knowing that the g. of God leadeth thee. Rom 2:4
g. and severity of God, toward thee g. if thou continue in his g. 11:22
that you are full of g. 15:14
the fruit of the Spirit is g. Gal 5:22
Eph 5:9
good pleasure of his g. 2 Thes 1:11

goods

back all the g. and Lot. Gen 14:16
the persons, and take the g. 21
the g. of his master were in. 24:10
carried away all his g. 31:18*; 46:6
o his neighbour's g. Ex 22:8, 11
earth swallowed them and their g
Num 16:32
spoil of Midian and their g. 31:9
e for Levites' cattle and g. 35:3*
hee plenteous in g. Deut 28:11
mite thy wives, thy g. 2 Chr 21:14*
et men help him with g. Ezra 1:4
trengthened their hands with g. 6
hat of king's g. expenses be. 6:8
r to confiscation of g. 7:26
ouses full of all g. Neh 9:25*
hall restore their g. Job 20:10*
hall no man look for his g. 21*
is g. shall flow away in the day. 28
hen g. increase, they. Eccl 5:11
otten cattle and g. Ezek 38:12
take away cattle and g.? 13
eir g. shall become a. Zeph 1:13*
an's house, and spoil his g.
Mat 12:29; Mark 3:27
ler over all his g. Mat 24:47
elivered to them his g. 25:14
at taketh away thy g. Luke 6:30
eepeth his palace, his g. are. 11:21
my fruits and my g. 12:18
ou hast much g. laid up for. 19
ve me the portion of g. that. 15:12*
n that he had wasted his g. 16:1
half of my g. I give to. 19:8
d their g. and parted. Acts 2:45
ugh I bestow all my g. 1 Cor 13:3
spoiling of your g. Heb 10:34*
h, and increased with g. Rev 3:17*

gopher *wood*

ark of g. wood. Gen 6:14

gore, -d

an ox g. man or woman. Ex 21:28
whether he have g. a son or a. 31

gorgeous

arrayed Jesus in a g. Luke 23:11

gorgeously

clothed most g. Ezek 23:12
are g. apparelled in. Luke 7:25

Goshen

dwell in G. Gen 45:10; 46:34
47:4, 6, 27
that day the land of G. Ex 8:22
only in the land of G. was. 9:26
smote the country of G. Josh 10:41
Joshua took all the land of G. 11:16
inheritance of Judah, G. 15:51

gospel

The English word gospel comes from the Anglo-Saxon gōdspel *which meant good tidings, through* gōdspel, *or god-story. The word in the original (Greek) in the New Testament is* euaggelion, *from which, through the Latin* evangelium, *comes our word* evangel, *with its derivatives. In the New Testament it is the Christ-message, not the books which were written to spread that message. Later it was applied to the four books which tell of the earthly life of Jesus—Matthew, Mark, Luke, and John.*

of the g. of Jesus Christ. Mark 1:1
came, saying, repent and believe g. 15
lose his life for my sake and g.'s. 8:35
his house for my sake and g.'s. 10:29
the g. must be published. 13:10
by my mouth hear g. Acts 15:7
testify the g. of grace of God. 20:24
apostle, separated to g. Rom 1:1
whom I serve with my spirit in g. 9
for I am not ashamed of g. of. 16
secrets of men according to my g.
2:16
have not all obeyed the g. 10:16
as concerning the g. they. 11:28
ministering the g. of God. 15:16
fulness of the blessing of the g. 29
stablish you according to g. 16:25
begotten you through g. 1 Cor 4:15
lest we should hinder the g. 9:12
a dispensation of the g. 17*
g. I may make the g. of Christ without charge . . . my power in g. 18
this I do for the g.'s sake. 23
if our g. be hid, it is hid. 2 Cor 4:3
lest light of glorious g. of Christ. 4
brother, whose praise is in g. 8:18
your professed subjection to g. 9:13
another Spirit or g. 11:4; Gal 1:6
and would pervert the g. Gal 1:7
I communicated to them the g. 2:2
that the truth of the g. might. 5
they saw the g. of uncircumcision. 7
according to the truth of the g. 14
of truth the g. of your. Eph 1:13
his promise in Christ by the g. 3:6
preparation of the g. of peace. 6:15
known the mystery of the g. 19
fellowship in the g. till now. Phil 1:5
and confirmation of the g. 7, 17
to the furtherance of the g. 12
becometh the g. striving together for the faith of the g. 27
served with me in the g. 2:22
laboured with me in the g. 4:3
that in the beginning of the g. 15
in word of truth of the g. Col 1:5
away from the hope of the g. 23
g. came not in word but. 1 Thes 1:5
we were bold to speak the g. 2:2
allowed to be put in trust with g. 4
to have imparted not the g. only. 8
our fellow-labourer in the g. 3:2
on them that obey not the g.
2 Thes 1:8; 1 Pet 4:17
he called you by our g. 2 Thes 2:14
g. of the blessed God. 1 Tim 1:11
of the afflictions of the g. 2 Tim 1:8
immortality to light through g. 10
raised according to my g. 2:8
to me in bonds of the g. Philem 13

gospel joined with *preach, preached, preaching*

Jesus went preaching g. Mat 4:23
9:35; Mark 1:14
the poor have the g. preached.
Mat 11:5*; Luke 7:22
this g. shall be preached.
Mat 24:14; 26:13; Mark 14:9
go, preach the g. to. Mark 16:15
me to preach the g. Luke 4:18*
they departed, preaching the g. 9:6
taught, and preached the g. 20:1
and preached the g. to. Acts 8:25
and there they preached the g. 14:7
when they had preached the g. 21
called us to preach the g. 16:10
preach the g. at Rome. Rom 1:15
feet of them that preach g. 10:15
I have fully preached the g. 15:19
I strived to preach the g. not. 20
baptize, but to preach g. 1 Cor 1:17
that preach the g. should live. 9:14
I preach the g. have nothing to glory, woe to me if I preach not g. 16
that when I preach the g. I may. 18
the g. which I preached. 15:1
Troas to preach the g. 2 Cor 2:12
as to you in preaching the g. 10:14
preached to you freely the g. 11:7
angel preach any other g. Gal 1:8, 9
the g. preached of me is not. 11
preached before the g. to. 3:8
of flesh I preached the g. 4:13
preached to you the g. 1 Thes 2:9
to us was the g. preached. Heb 4:2*
that preached the g. to. 1 Pet 1:12
which by g. is preached to you. 25
this cause was the g. preached. 4:6
g. to preach to them. Rev 14:6†

got

her and g. him out. Gen 39:12, 15
they g. not the land by. Ps 44:3
I g. me servants and. Eccl 2:7
I g. a girdle according. Jer 13:2*
take the girdle that thou hast g. 4*

gotten

she said, I have g. a. Gen 4:1
was our father's hath he g. all. 31:1
when I have g. me honour. Ex 14:18
he hath deceitfully g. Lev 6:4
what every man hath g. Num 31:50
of my hand hath g. this. Deut 8:17
moreover if he be g. 2 Sam 17:13
wisdom cannot be g. Job 28:15
because my hand had g. 31:25
his holy arm hath g. Ps 98:1
wealth g. by vanity shall. Pr 13:11
an inheritance may be g. 20:21
have g. more wisdom. Eccl 1:16
the abundance g. they. Isa 15:7
because riches he hath g. Jer 48:36
thou hast g. riches. Ezek 28:4
thou hast g. thee renown. Dan 9:15
I saw them that had g. Rev 15:2*

gourd

[1] *Hebrew* Kikayon, *used only in* Jonah 4:6. *It may mean the castor-oil plant, or a genuine gourd.* [2] *Wild gourd of* 2 Ki 4:39 *was a poisonous gourd, supposed to be the* colocynth, *which might be mistaken for the wholesome globe cucumber.*

a g. Jonah glad of the g. Jonah 4:6
a worm smote the g. that it. 7
thou hast had pity on the g. for. 16

wild **gourds**

one gathered wild g. his. 2 Ki 4:39

govern

dost thou now g. the. 1 Ki 21:7
he that hateth right g.? Job 34:17
for thou shalt g. the nations. Ps 67:4

government, -s

and the g. shall be upon. Isa 9:6
of the increase of his g. there. 7
I will commit thy g. into his. 22:21
helps, g. diversities of. 1 Cor 12:28
them that despise g. 2 Pet 2:10*

governor

Joseph was g. Gen 42:6; 45:26*
Obadiah was g. over. 1 Ki 18:3*
Solomon to be chief g. 1 Chr 29:22*

the vessels to the *g.* *Ezra* 5:14
not eaten bread of the *g.* *Neh* 5:14
I required not bread of the *g.* 18
he is the *g.* among the. *Ps* 22:28*
their *g.* shall proceed. *Jer* 30:21*
back also to Gedaliah the *g.* 40:5
smote Gedaliah the *g.* 41:2, 18
stirred up Zerubbabel *g.* *Hag* 1:14
the *g.* and to Joshua. 2:2, 21
and he shall be as a *g.* *Zech* 9:7*
offer it now to thy *g.* *Mal* 1:8
of thee shall come a *g.* *Mat* 2:6
him to Pontius Pilate the *g.* 27:2
if this come to the *g.'s* ears. 28:14
and bear to the *g.* of. *John* 2:8*
informed the *g.* against. *Acts* 24:1
g. under Aretas king. *2 Cor* 11:32
ships turned whither *g.* *Jas* 3:4*

governors

heart is towards the *g.* *Judg* 5:9
out of Machir came down *g.* 14
king's commissions to *g.* *Ezra* 8:36
letters be given me to *g.* *Neh* 2:7
the former *g.* were chargeable. 5:15
Daniel chief of the *g.* *Dan* 2:48
the *g.* of Judah shall. *Zech* 12:5*
I will make the *g.* of Judah. 6*
shall be brought before *g.* *Mat* 10:18
heir is under tutors and *g.* *Gal* 4:2*
submit yourselves to *g.* *1 Pet* 2:14

Gozan

placed Israel by the river of *G.*
2 Ki 17:6; 18:11; *1 Chr* 5:26
my fathers have destroyed, as *G.*
2 Ki 19:12; *Isa* 37:12

grace

[1] *The free mercy of God, or the enjoyment of his favour,* Rom 11:6; 2 Tim 1:9. [2] *A Christian virtue,* 2 Cor 8:7.

for a little space *g.* hath. *Ezra* 9:8
Esther obtained *g.* in. *Esth* 2:17*
g. is poured into lips. *Ps* 45:2
Lord is a sun, he will give *g.* 84:11
shall be an ornament of *g.* *Pr* 1:9
so shall they be life and *g.* to. 3:22
but he giveth *g.* to. 34; *Jas* 4:6
head an ornament of *g.* *Pr* 4:9
for the *g.* of his lips the king. 22:11
shoutings, crying, *g. g.* *Zech* 4:7
I will pour the Spirit of *g.* 12:10
of Father, full of *g.* and. *John* 1:14
we have all received, *g.* for *g.* 16
but *g.* and truth came by Jesus. 17
and great *g.* was on. *Acts* 4:33
testimony to word of his *g.* 14:3
had believed through *g.* 18:27
you to the word of his *g.* 20:32
whom we received *g.* and. *Rom* 1:5
g. and peace to you from God. 7
1 Cor 1:3; *2 Cor* 1:2; *Gal* 1:3
Eph 1:2; *Phil* 1:2; *Col* 1:2
1 Thes 1:1; *2 Thes* 1:2; *Philem* 3
justified freely by his *g.* *Rom* 3:24
reward is not reckoned of *g.* but. 4:4
faith, that it might be by *g.* 16
have access into this *g.* wherein. 5:2
who receive abundance of *g.* 17
where sin abounded *g.* did much. 20
even so might *g.* reign through. 21
shall we continue in sin, that *g.*? 6:1
not under law, but under *g.* 14
shall we sin, because under *g.*? 15
according to the election of *g.* 11:5
and if by *g.* then it is no more. 6
for I say, through the *g.* given. 12:3
gifts differing according to the *g.* 6
because of the *g.* given to. 15:15
I by *g.* be a partaker. *1 Cor* 10:30
his *g.* bestowed upon me was. 15:10
abundant *g.* might redound to.
2 Cor 4:15
finish in you the same *g.* also. 8:6
see that ye abound in this *g.* 7
to travel with us with this *g.* 19
God is able to make all *g.* 9:8
said my *g.* is sufficient for thee. 12:9
him who called you to *g.* *Gal* 1:6
God, who called me by his *g.* 15
when James perceived the *g.* 2:9
the law, ye are fallen from *g.* 5:4
praise of the glory of his *g.* *Eph* 1:6
according to the riches of his *g.* 7
by *g.* ye are saved. *Eph* 2:5, 8
the exceeding riches of his *g.* 7
least of all saints is this *g.* 3:8
every one of us is given *g.* 4:7
that it may minister *g.* to the. 29
g. be with all that love our. 6:24
ye are all partakers of my *g.* *Phil* 1:7
singing with *g.* in your. *Col* 3:16
let speech be alway with *g.* 4:6
g. be with you. 18; *2 Tim* 4:22
Tit 3:15; *Heb* 13:25
us good hope through *g.* *2 Thes* 2:16
g. mercy, and peace from. *1 Tim* 1:2
2 Tim 1:2; *Tit* 1:4; *2 John* 3
g. of our Lord was. *1 Tim* 1:14
g. be with thee. Amen. 6:21
us according to his *g.* *2 Tim* 1:9
be strong in the *g.* that is in. 2:1
being justified by his *g.* *Tit* 3:7
boldly to the throne of *g.* *Heb* 4:16
done despite to the Spirit of *g.* 10:29
let us have *g.* to serve God. 12:28
heart be established with *g.* 13:9
the *g.* of the fashion of. *Jas* 1:11
he giveth more *g.* giveth *g.* to. 4:6
g. and peace. *1 Pet* 1:2; *2 Pet* 1:2
who prophesied of the *g.* *1 Pet* 1:10
hope to the end for the *g.* 13
as being heirs of *g.* 3:7
God resisteth proud, giveth *g.* 5:5
the God of *g.* who hath called. 10
grow in *g.* and. *2 Pet* 3:18
turning the *g.* of God into. *Jude* 4
g. and peace from him. *Rev* 1:4

see **find, found**

grace *of God*

and the *g. of God* was. *Luke* 2:40
he had seen *g. of God.* *Acts* 11:23
to continue in the *g. of G.* 13:43
recommended to *g. of G.* 14:26
15:40
gospel of the *g. of God.* 20:24
much more *g. of God.* *Rom* 5:15
the *g. of God* given you. *1 Cor* 1:4
according to *g. of God* which. 3:10
g. of God I am what I am, yet not I, but the *g. of God* which. 15:10
by the *g. of God* we had. *2 Cor* 1:12
ye receive not the *g. of God* in. 6:1
of the *g. of God* bestowed on. 8:1
for the exceeding *g. of God* in. 9:14
frustrate the *g. of God.* *Gal* 2:21
dispensation of *g. of God.* *Eph* 3:2
to gift of the *g. of God* given me. 7
day ye knew *g. of God.* *Col* 1:6
according to *g. of God.* *2 Thes* 1:12
g. of God that bringeth. *Tit* 2:11
that he by *g. of God.* *Heb* 2:9
any man fail of *g. of God.* 12:15
of the manifold *g. of God.* *1 Pet* 4:10
this is true *g. of God.* 5:12

grace *of our Lord Jesus*

through *g. of Lord Jesus* we shall.
Acts 15:11
the *g. of our Lord Jesus.* *Rom* 16:20
24; *1 Cor* 16:23; *Phil* 4:23
1 Thes 5:28; *2 Thes* 3:18
know *g. of our Lord Jesus.* *2 Cor* 8:9
the *g. of our Lord Jesus* Christ, love of God, and communion. 13:14
g. of our Lord Jesus Christ be with your spirit. *Gal* 6:18; *Philem* 25
g. of Lord Jesus Christ be with you.
Rev 22:21

gracious

he said, God be *g.* to. *Gen* 43:29
I will hear, for I am *g.* *Ex* 22:27
be *g.* to whom I will be *g.* 33:19
the Lord, the Lord God, *g.* 34:6
2 Chr 30:9; *Ps* 103:8; 116:5
145:8; *Joel* 2:13
his face shine, and be *g.*, *Num* 6:25
whether God will be *g.*? *2 Sam* 12:22
the Lord was *g.* unto them. 13:23
to pardon, *g.* merciful. *Neh* 9:17, 31
then he is *g.* to him. *Job* 33:24
hath God forgotten to be *g.*? *Ps* 77:9
thou, O Lord, art a God *g.* 86:15
111:4; 112:4
a *g.* woman retaineth. *Pr* 11:16
wise man's mouth are *g.* *Eccl* 10:12
wait that he may be *g.* *Isa* 30:18
he will be very *g.* to thee. 19
be *g.* to us. *Isa* 33:2
how *g.* when pangs. *Jer* 22:23*
may be the Lord will be *g.* *Amos* 5:15
that thou art a *g.* God. *Jonah* 4:2
God that he will be *g.* to. *Mal* 1:9
wondered at *g.* words. *Luke* 4:22
tasted that the Lord is *g.* *1 Pet* 2:3

graciously

children which G. hath *g.* *Gen* 33:5
because God hath dealt *g.* with. 11
and grant me thy law *g.* *Ps* 119:29
iniquity, and receive us *g.* *Hos* 14:2*

graft, -ed

olive tree wert *g.* in. *Rom* 11:17
broken that I might be *g.* in. 19
g. in, for God is able to *g.* them. 23
and *g.* much more these be *g.* 24

grain

yet shall not least *g.* fall. *Amos* 9:9*
is like a *g.* of mustard. *Mat* 13:31
Mark 4:31; *Luke* 13:19
faith as a *g.* of mustard seed, ye shall say unto this mountain.
Mat 17:20; *Luke* 17:6
bare *g.* wheat, or some other *g.*
1 Cor 15:37*

grandmother

dwelt first in thy *g.* Lois. *2 Tim* 1:5

grant

according to the *g.* they. *Ezra* 3:7

grant

ye shall *g.* a redemption. *Lev* 25:24
Lord *g.* you that you. *Ruth* 1:9
God of Israel *g.* thee. *1 Sam* 1:17
g. me place of this threshingfloor; thou shalt *g.* it me. *1 Chr* 21:22*
but I will *g.* them some. *2 Chr* 12:7
and *g.* him mercy in. *Neh* 1:11
it please the king to *g.* *Esth* 5:8
that God would *g.* the. *Job* 6:8
g. thee according to thine. *Ps* 20:4
us thy mercy, O Lord, *g.* us. 85:7
and *g.* me thy law graciously. 119:29
g. not, O Lord, the desires. 140:8
g. my two sons may sit. *Mat* 20:21*
Mark 10:37
g. to us, that we being. *Luke* 1:74
g. that with boldness we. *Acts* 4:29
God *g.* you be likeminded.
Rom 15:5
g. you to be strengthened. *Eph* 3:16
the Lord *g.* that he may. *2 Tim* 1:18
will I *g.* to sit with me. *Rev* 3:21*

granted

God *g.* him that which. *1 Chr* 4:1[illegible]
knowledge is *g.* thee. *2 Chr* 1:1[illegible]
and the king *g.* him all. *Ezra* 7:[illegible]
g. according to good hand. *Neh* 2:[illegible]
what is thy petition? and it shall be *g*
Esth 5:6; 7:2; 9:1[illegible]
let it be *g.* to the Jews in. 9:1[illegible]
thou hast *g.* me life and. *Job* 10:1[illegible]
of righteous shall be *g.* *Pr* 10:2[illegible]
a murderer to be *g.* you. *Acts* 3:1[illegible]
God also to the Gentiles *g.* 11:1[illegible]
who *g.* signs to be done by. 14:[illegible]
to her was *g.* she should. *Rev* 19:8

grape

There was an abundance of vine-yards in Palestine from the earlie[st] times. The vines were celebrate[d] both for luxuriant growth and for th[e] immense clusters of grapes whic[h] they produced which were som[e]times carried on a staff between tw[o] men as in the case of the spie[s] Num 13:23, 24, *and as has be[en] done in some instances in mode[rn] times.*

From the abundance and exc[el]lence of the vines, it may readily [be] understood how frequently th[e] plant is the subject of metaphor [in] the Holy Scriptures.

nor gather every *g.* of. *Lev* 19:1[illegible]
drink the blood of the *g.* *Deut* 32:[illegible]
shake off his unripe *g.* *Job* 15:[illegible]
vines with tender *g.* *S of S* 2:1[illegible]
us see whether the tender *g.* 7:[illegible]
the sour *g.* is ripening in. *Isa* 1[illegible]
have eaten a sour *g.* *Jer* 31:[illegible]

that eateth the sour g. Jer 31:30
I am as the g.-gleanings. Mi 7:1

grapegatherer

turn back thy hand as a g. Jer 6:9
g. come, would they? 49:9; Ob 5

grapes

brought forth ripe g. Gen 40:10
his clothes in blood of g. 49:11
nor gather the g. of thy. Lev 25:5
in jubile, nor gather g. of thy. 11
shall he eat moist g. or. Num 6:3
the time of the firstripe g. 13:20
a branch with one cluster of g. 23
then thou mayest eat g. Deut 23:24
when thou gatherest the g. of. 24:21
vineyard, not gather the g. 28:30*, 39
their g. are g. of gall, their. 32:32
is not gleaning of the g.? Judg 8:2
they trode the g. and cursed. 9:27
bringing in wine and g. Neh 13:15
our vines have tender g. S of S 2:15*
breasts are like to clusters of g. 7:7
it should bring forth g. Isa 5:2
forth g. brought it forth wild g.? 4
yet gleaning g. shall be left. 17:6
as gleaning g. when vintage. 24:13
there shall be no g. on. Jer 8:13
as they that tread the g. 25:30
leave some gleaning g. 49:9; Ob 5
fathers have eaten sour g. Ezek 18:2
I found Israel like g. in the. Hos 9:10
treader of g. shall overtake the. Amos 9:13
men gather g. of thorns? Mat 7:16
bush gather they g. Luke 6:44
thrust in sickle, her g. Rev 14:18

grass

let earth bring forth g. Gen 1:11
and the earth brought forth g. 12
as the ox licketh up g. Num 22:4
I will send g. in thy. Deut 11:15
not sown, not any g. 29:23
distil as showers upon the g. 32:2
as the g. springeth out. 2 Sam 23:4
peradventure find g. to. 1 Ki 18:5
he g. of the field, as green herb, as g. on. 2 Ki 19:26; Isa 37:27
hine offspring is the g. of. Job 5:25
wild ass bray when he hath g.? 6:5
behold, behemoth eateth g. 40:15
e cut down like the g. Ps 37:2
lown like rain upon mown g. 72:6
hey of city shall flourish like g. 16
n the morning they are like g. 90:5
hen wicked spring as the g. 92:7
mitten, and withered like g. 102:4
shadow; I am withered like g. 11
s for man, his days are as g. 103:15
e causeth g. to grow for. 104:14
f an ox that eateth g. 106:20
t them be as the g. upon. 129:6
ho maketh g. to grow upon. 147:8
as dew upon the g. Pr 19:12
y appeareth, the tender g. 27:25
faileth, there is no. Isa 15:6
dragons, shall be g. 35:7
y, all flesh is g. 40:6; 1 Pet 1:24
withereth, surely the people is g. Isa 40:7, 8
ring up as among the g. 44:4
an which shall be made as g. 51:12
cause there was no g. Jer 14:5, 6
own fat as the heifer at g. 50:11
amp in tender g. Dan 4:15, 23
ake thee eat g. 25, 32, 33; 5:21
ade an end of eating g. Amos 7:2
showers upon the g. Mi 5:7
all give every one g. Zech 10:1
God so clothe the g. Mat 6:30
Luke 12:28
multitude to sit down on g. Mat 14:19; Mark 6:39
w there was much g. John 6:10
the flower of the g. he. Jas 1:10
risen, but it withereth the g. 11
all green g. was. Rev 8:7
y should not hurt the g. of. 9:4

grasshopper, -s

Grasshoppers or locusts are frequently mentioned in the Bible as y destructive agents. They ne over the land in huge numbers, eating every green leaf, and very often leaving famine in their path)

these ye may eat, the g. Lev 11:22
in our own sight as g. Num 13:33
as g. for multitude. Judg 6:5*; 7:12*
make him afraid as a g.? Job 39:20*
and the g. shall be a. Eccl 12:5
thereof are as g. Isa 40:22
they are more than g. Jer 46:23*
behold, he formed g. in. Amos 7:1*
captains are as great g. Nah 3:17

grave, *substantive*

(The Revisions very frequently substitute for grave *the Hebrew word* Sheol, *which means the place of the dead)*

pillar upon her g. that is the pillar of Rachel's g. unto this. Gen 35:20
I will go down to g. to my. 37:35
hairs with sorrow to g. 42:38; 44:31
bury me in the g. which I. 50:5
whosoever toucheth a g. Num 19:16
that touched one dead, or a g. 18
bringeth down to the g. 1 Sam 2:6
wept at Abner's g. 2 Sam 3:32
and be buried by the g. of. 19:37
his head go to the g. in. 1 Ki 2:6
his head bring down to the g. 9
laid his carcase in his own g. 13:30
Jeroboam shall come to g. 14:13
thou shalt be gathered into thy g. 2 Ki 22:20; 2 Chr 34:28
when they can find the g. Job 3:22
thou shalt come to thy g. in. 5:26
so he that goeth to g. shall. 7:9
been carried from womb to g. 10:19
wouldest hide me in the g. 14:13
if I wait, the g. is my house. 17:13
they go down to the g. 21:13
yet shall he be brought to the g. 32
so doth the g. those that have. 24:19
stretch out his hand to the g. 30:24
soul draweth near to the g. 33:22*
in the g. who shall give? Ps 6:5
brought up my soul from the g. 30:3
the wicked be silent in the g. 31:17
laid in the g.: consume in the g. 49:14
my soul from the power of g. 15
life draweth nigh to the g. 88:3
like slain that lie in the g. 5
be declared in the g. 11
his soul from hand of g.? 89:48
scattered at the g.'s mouth. 141:7
them alive as the g. Pr 1:12
g. and barren womb, say not. 30:16
no wisdom in g. whither. Eccl 9:10
jealousy is cruel as the g. S of S 8:6
pomp is brought down to g. Isa 14:11
thou art cast out of thy g. like. 19
go to the gates of the g. 38:10
the g. cannot praise thee, death. 18
he made his g. with wicked. 53:9
might have been my g. Jer 20:17
he went down to the g. Ezek 31:15
company is round about her g. 32:23
from the power of g.; I will redeem from death: O g. I will. Hos 13:14
I will make thy g. for. Nah 1:14
he had lain in the g. John 11:17*
saying, she goeth to the g. to. 31*
again groaning, cometh to the g. 38*
called Lazarus out of his g. 12:17*
g. where is thy victory? 1 Cor 15:55*

grave, *adjective*

deacons must be g. 1 Tim 3:8
wives must be g. 11
aged men be sober, g. Tit 2:2

grave, *verb*

g. on the onyx stones. Ex 28:9
a plate of pure gold, and g. on it. 36
a man that can skill to g. 2 Chr 2:7
sent a cunning man to g. any. 14

graveclothes

came forth bound with g. John 11:44

graved

on the borders he g. 1 Ki 7:36
and he g. cherubims on. 2 Chr 3:7

gravel

mouth be filled with g. Pr 20:17
of thy bowels like g. Isa 48:19*
broken my teeth with g. Lam 3:16

graven

was writing of God g. Ex 32:16
g. as signets are g. with the. 39:6
g. with an iron pen. Job 19:24
I have g. thee on palms of. Isa 49:16
g. upon the table of their. Jer 17:1
maker thereof hath g. it. Hab 2:18
Godhead is like gold g. Acts 17:29

graven *image*

make unto thee any g. *image*. Ex 20:4; Lev 26:1; Deut 5:8
corrupt and make a g. *image*. Deut 4:16, 25
that maketh any g. *image*. 27:15
son to make a g. *image*. Judg 17:3
founder, who made a g. *image*. 4
in these houses a g. *image*. 18:14
the g. *image*. 17
Dan set up the g. *image*. 30, 31
Manasseh set up g. *image*. 2 Ki 21:7
melteth a g. *image*. Isa 40:19
workman to prepare a g. *image*. 20
they that make a g. *image* are. 44:9
who hath molten a g. *image*? 10
thereof he maketh his g. *image*. 17
the wood of their g. *image*. 45:20
my g. *image* hath commanded. 48:5
founder confounded by g. *image*. Jer 10:14; 51:17
cut off the g. and molten *image*. Nah 1:14
profiteth the g. *image*? Hab 2:18

graven *images*

burn their g. *images* with fire. Deut 7:5, 25
hew down the g. *images* of. 12:3
nations feared the Lord, and served their g. *images*. 2 Ki 17:41
set up g. *images* before. 2 Chr 33:19
he had beaten the g. *images*. 34:7
to jealousy with g. *images*. Ps 78:58
they that serve g. *images*. 97:7
whose g. *images* did excel. Isa 10:10
fallen, and all the g. *images*. 21:9
covering of thy g. *images*. 30:22
I give my praise to g. *images*. 42:8
ashamed that trust in g. *images*. 17
anger with their g. *images*. Jer 8:19
it is the land of g. *images*. 50:38
judgement on g. *images*. 51:47, 52
incense to g. *images*. Hos 11:2
g. *images* shall be beaten. Mi 1:7
thy g. *images* also will I cut. 5:13

graves

were no g. *in* Egypt. Ex 14:11
cast powder on the g. 2 Ki 23:6
strowed it upon the g. 2 Chr 34:4
days extinct, the g. are. Job 17:1
remain among the g. Isa 65:4
priests' bones out of their g. Jer 8:1
and cast his dead body into g. 26:23
his g. are about him. Ezek 32:22
23, 25, 26
I will open your g. and cause you to come up out of your g. 37:12
opened your g. brought out of g. 13
give Gog a place of g. in. 39:11*
the g. were opened. Mat 27:52*
bodies of saints came out of g. 53*
for ye are as g. which. Luke 11:44
all that are in the g. John 5:28*
bodies to be put in g. Rev 11:9*

graveth

that g. an habitation in. Isa 22:16

graving

golden calf with a g. tool. Ex 32:4
grave any manner of g. 2 Chr 2:14
I will engrave g. thereof. Zech 3:9

gravings

on mouth of laver were g. 1 Ki 7:31

gravity

subjection with all g. 1 Tim 3:4
in doctrine shewing g. Tit 2:7

gray, *see* **hairs** *and* **head**

grayheaded

I am old and g. my. 1 Sam 12:2
with us are the g. Job 15:10
when I am old and g. Ps 71:18

grease

heart is as fat as g. Ps 119:70

great

[1] *Large in size,* 2 Chr 2:5. [2] *Considerable in degree of qualities or feelings,* Gen 39:9; Ps 14:5. [3] *Eminent or important,* Gen 24:35; 2 Chr 17:12.

and make thy name g. Gen 12:2
my master is become g. 24:35
with g. wrestlings have I. 30:8
can I do this g. wickedness? 39:9
to save your lives by a g. 45:7
my son, he also shall be g. 48:19
unwalled towns a g. many. Deut 3:5
God is a g. God. 10:17; 2 Chr 2:5
eyes have seen g. acts. Deut 11:7
neither let me see this g. fire 18:16
meaneth the heat of his g.? 29:24
wilt thou do unto thy g.? Josh 7:9
thou heardest cities were g. 14:12
there a g. altar by Jordan. 22:10
for he did those g. signs in. 24:17
divisions of Reuben g. Judg 5:15
your wickedness is g. 1 Sam 12:17
David went on, and grew g. and the Lord was with him. 2 Sam 5:10
I have made thee a g. name. 7:9
thou art g. O Lord God, none is. 22
given g. occasion to enemies. 12:14
gentleness hath made me g. 22:36
Ps 18:35
shall hear of thy g. name. 1 Ki 8:42
2 Chr 6:32
the journey is too g. for. 1 Ki 19:7
Shunem, where a g. woman. 2 Ki 4:8
g. is the wrath of the Lord. 22:13
g. is the Lord, and. 1 Chr 16:25
Ps 48:1; 96:4; 135:5; 145:3
Lord's hand, for very g. 1 Chr 21:13
thine hand it is to make g. 29:12
house I build is g. for g. 2 Chr 2:5
I am to build shall be wonderful g. 9
Jehoshaphat waxed g. 17:12
our trespass is g. 28:13
g. wrath poured. 34:21
Lord who is g. and terrible. Neh 4:14
now therefore our God, the g. 9:32
his empire, for it is g. Esth 1:20
that thy seed shall be g. Job 5:25
is not thy wickedness g.? 22:5
by g. force of my disease. 30:18
yet he knoweth it not in g. 35:15
a g. ransom. 36:18
God is g., and we know him not. 26
the number of thy days is g. 38:21
in him, because strength is g.? 39:11
were they in g. fear. Ps 14:5; 53:5
keeping of them there is g. 19:11
his glory is g. in thy salvation. 21:5
mine iniquity, for it is g. 25:11
O how g. is thy goodness! 31:19
art g. and doest wondrous. 86:10
how g. are thy works! 92:5
O God, how g. is the sum! 139:17
this wisdom seemed g. Eccl 9:13
houses even g. and fair. Isa 5:9
people that walked in darkness have seen g. light. 9:2; Mat 4:16
g. is the Holy One of. Isa 12:6
send them a Saviour and a g. 19:20*
divide him a portion with g. 53:12
and g. shall be the peace of. 54:13
are become g. and rich. Jer 5:27
art g. and thy name is g. in. 10:6
her womb to be always g. 20:17
the G., the mighty God is his. 32:18
g. in counsel, and mighty in. 19
I have sworn by my g. name. 44:26
they are new, g. is thy. Lam 3:23
increased and waxed g. Ezek 16:7
a g. eagle with g. wings. 17:3, 7
even make the pile for fire g. 24:9
to serve a g. service against. 29:18
the waters made him g. 31:4*
I will sanctify my g. name. 36:23
how g. his signs, how. Dan 4:3
ram pushing, and he became g. 8:4*
for their wickedness is g. Joel 3:13
go to Hamath the g. Amos 6:2
shall he be g. unto the ends. Mi 5:4
g. his goodness, how g. Zech 9:17
my name shall be g. Mal 1:11
exceeding glad, for g. is your reward. Mat 5:12; Luke 6:23, 35
shall be called g. in the. Mat 5:19
if light be darkness, how g. is! 6:23
one pearl of g. price. 13:46
g. is thy faith. 15:28
g. possessions. 19:22; Mark 10:42
they that are g. exercise. Mat 20:25
be g. among you. 26; Mark 10:43
Master, which is the g.? Mat 22:36
is the first and g. commandment. 38
g. in sight of Lord. Luke 1:15, 32
you, the same shall be g. 9:48
the harvest truly is g. but. 10:2*
us and you there is a g. gulf. 16:26
out that he was some g. Acts 8:9
g. is Diana of the. 19:28, 34
g. is my boldness, g. is. 2 Cor 7:4
that he hath a g. zeal for. Col 4:13
g. is mystery of. 1 Tim 3:16
in g. house not only. 2 Tim 2:20
appearing of the g. God. Tit 2:13
now consider how g. this. Heb 7:4
how g. a matter a little. Jas 3:5*
another sign in heaven, g. Rev 15:1
g. Babylon came in. 16:19
Babylon the g. mother. 17:5; 18:2
unto supper of the g. God. 19:17
see **city, company, congregation, cry, day, destruction**

great *evil*

hath done us g. evil. 1 Sam 6:9
to do all this g. evil. Neh 13:27
vanity, and a g. evil. Eccl 2:21
pronounced this g. evil. Jer 16:10
thus might we procure g. evil. 26:19
I have brought this g. evil. 32:42
why commit this g. evil? 44:7
bringing upon us a g. evil. Dan 9:12
see **exceeding, joy**

great *king* or *kings*

thus saith the g. king. 2 Ki 18:19
28; Isa 36:4, 13
which a g. king of Israel. Ezra 5:11
the Lord is a g. King. Ps 47:2
Zion, the city of the g. King. 48:2
the Lord is a g. King above. 95:3
to him that smote g. kings. 136:17
there came a g. king. Eccl 9:14
g. kings shall serve. Jer 25:14; 27:7
for I am a g. King, saith. Mal 1:14
is city of the g. King. Mat 5:35

great *men*

like name of g. men in earth.
2 Sam 7:9; 1 Chr 17:8
sons were with g. men. 2 Ki 10:6
Jehu slew all Ahab's g. men and. 11
son of one of g. men. Neh 11:14*
g. men are not always wise. Job 32:9
him before g. men. Pr 18:16
stand not in place of g. men. 25:6
get me unto the g. men. Jer 5:5
all houses of the g. men. 52:13
is sword of the g. men. Ezek 21:14
all her g. men were bound. Nah 3:10
g. men hid themselves. Rev 6:15*
merchants were the g. men. 18:23*

great *multitude, multitudes*

Gad had a g. multitude. Num 32:1
hast thou seen all this g. multitude? 1 Ki 20:13
I will deliver this g. multitude. 28
be ye a g. multitude. 2 Chr 13:8
there cometh a g. multitude. 20:2
by reason of this g. multitude. 15
carried a g. multitude captives. 28:5
did I fear a g. multitude? Job 31:34
all that g. multitude. Isa 16:14
by, even a g. multitude. Jer 44:15
very g. multitude of fish. Ezek 47:9
set forth a g. multitude. Dan 11:11
g. multitudes followed him.
Mat 4:25; 8:1; 12:15*; 19:2
20:29; Mark 3:7; John 6:2
when Jesus saw g. multitude.
Mat 8:18; 14:14; Mark 9:14
g. multitudes came. Mat 15:30
bread as to fill so g. multitude. 33
a g. multitude spread their. 21:8
with Judas a g. multitude with.
26:47; Mark 14:43
inclosed a g. multitude. Luke 5:6
a g. multitude came together to. 15
in these lay a g. multitude. John 5:3
a g. multitude of Jews. Acts 14:1
Greeks a g. multitude. Acts 17:4
a g. multitude which no. Rev 7:9
the voice of a g. multitude. 19:6

great *nation* and *nations*

a g. nation, and will bless. Gen 12:2
18:18; 46:3; Ex 32:10
Ishmael a g. nation. 17:20; 21:18
surely this g. nation is. Deut 4:6
he became there a nation g. 26:5
before you g. nations. Josh 23:9
who smote g. nations. Ps 135:10*
a g. nation shall be raised. Jer 6:22
Babylon an assembly of g. nations.
50:9
from the north, a g. nation. 41
dwelt all g. nations. Ezek 31:6

great *people*

therein, a people g. Deut 2:10
Zamzummims, a people g. many. 21
a people g. and tall, children. 9:2
seeing I am a g. people. Josh 17:14
if thou be a g. people. 15
thou art a g. people. 17
g. people that cannot be. 1 Ki 3:8
judge this g. people? 9; 2 Chr 1:10
son over this g. people. 1 Ki 5:7
mountains like as of g. people.
Isa 13:4
g. people hath not been. Joel 2:2

great *power*

out of Egypt with g. power. Ex 32:11
2 Ki 17:36; Neh 1:10
power of my lord be g. Num 14:17
people and hast g. power. Josh 17:17
against me with g. power? Job 23:6
Lord, and of g. power. Ps 147:5
man and beast upon the ground, by my g. power. Jer 27:5; 32:17
wither even without g. power.
Ezek 17:9*
slow to anger, g. in power. Nah 1:3
clouds with g. power. Mark 13:26
g. power gave the. Acts 4:33
saying, this man is the g. power. 8:10
to thee thy g. power. Rev 11:17
from heaven, having g. power. 18:1

great *sea*

shall have the g. sea. Num 34:6
wilderness unto g. sea. Josh 1:4
kings in the coasts of g. sea. 9:1
border was to the g. sea. 15:12
inheritance of Judah, to g. sea. 47
I have cut off to the g. sea. 23:4
as fish of the g. sea. Ezek 47:10
land toward north from g. sea. 15
winds strove upon g. sea. Dan 7:2
see **sin**

great *slaughter*

with a g. s. at Gibeon. Josh 10:1
end of slaying them with g. s. 2
Ammonites with g. s. Judg 11:3
smote Philistines with g. s. 15:
Israel with g. s. 1 Sam 4:10, 1
smitten people with a g. s. 6:1
David slew Philistines with a g. s.
19:8; 23:
a g. s. that day. 1 Sam 18:
slew Assyrians with g. s. 1 Ki 20:2
slew Israel with a g. s. 2 Chr 13:1
smote Ahaz with a g. s. 28:
in day of g. s. when. Isa 30:2
Lord hath a g. s. in the land. 34:

so **great**

hast brought so g. a sin. Ex 32:
what nation so g. hath? Deut 4:7,
who is able to judge so g. a people
1 Ki 3:9; 2 Chr 1:
who is so g. a God as? Ps 77:
so g. in his mercy to them. 103:
I have not found so g. faith, no, n in Israel. Mat 8:10; Luke 7
bread as to fill so g. Mat 15:
delivered us from so g. 2 Cor 1:
we neglect so g. salvation? Heb 2
are compassed with so g. a. 12
ships though so g. yet. Jas 3
earthquake and so g. Rev 16:
in one hour so g. riches come. 18:

small and **great**

blindness small and g. Gen 19
hear small as well as g. Deut 1
divers weights, a g. and small. 25

measures, a *g. and small. Deut* 25:14
smote men *small and g. 1 Sam* 5:9
do nothing *g. or small.* 20:2
not any either *g.* or *small.* 30:2
lacking neither *small* nor *g.* 19
fight not with *small* nor *g.*
1 Ki 22:31; *2 Chr* 18:30
small and g. went to house.
2 Ki 23:2; *2 Chr* 34:30
people *small and g.* *2 Ki* 25:26
lots, as well *small* as *g. 1 Chr* 26:13
he put to death, whether *small* or *g.*
2 Chr 15:13
by courses, *g. and small.* 31:15
hand vessels, *g. and small.* 36:18
feast unto *g. and small.* *Esth* 1:5
husbands honour *g. and small.* 20
small and g. are there. *Job* 3:19
the *small* rain, and to *g.* rain. 37:6*
creeping, *small and g.* *Ps* 104:25
fear the Lord, *small and g.* 115:13
possessions of *g. and small. Eccl* 2:7
g. and small shall die. *Jer* 16:6
ephah *small*, shekel *g.* *Amos* 8:5
witnessing to *small and g. Acts* 26:22
fear him, *small and g.* *Rev* 11:18
he caused *small and g.* to. 13:16
ye that fear him, *small and g.* 19:5
flesh of all men, *small and g.* 18
I saw dead, *small and g.* 20:12

great *stone* and *stones*

a *g. stone* was upon the. *Gen* 29:2
that set up *g. stones.* *Deut* 27:2
cast down *g. stones.* *Josh* 10:11
roll *g. stones* upon the mouth of. 18
Joshua took a *g. stone*, and. 24:26
there was a *g. stone.* *1 Sam* 6:14
Levites put them on the *g. stone.* 15
to the *g. stone* of Abel, whereon. 18
transgressed, roll a *g. stone.* 14:33
were at *g. stone* in. *2 Sam* 20:8
they brought *g. stones* to. *1 Ki* 5:17
was of *g. stones.* 7:10; *Ezra* 5:8
to shoot *g. stones.* *2 Chr* 26:15
three rows of *g. stones.* *Ezra* 6:4
take *g. stones* and hide. *Jer* 43:9
he rolled a *g. stone* to. *Mat* 27:60

great *thing* and *things*

thing as this *g. thing* is. *Deut* 4:32
God that hath done *g. things.* 10:21
and see this *g. thing.* *1 Sam* 12:16
consider how *g. things* he hath. 24
shalt both do *g. things* and. 26:25*
hast done *g. things.* *2 Sam* 7:21*
and to do for you *g. things* and. 23
bid thee do some *g. thing. 2 Ki* 5:13
tell me all the *g. things* Elisha. 8:4
he should do this *g. thing* ? 13
known these *g. things.* *1 Chr* 17:19
to God who doeth *g. things.*
Job 5:9; 9:10; 37:5
hast done *g. things*, who. *Ps* 71:19
God who had done *g. things.* 106:21
done *g. things* for them. 126:2, 3
g. and mighty *things.* *Jer* 33:3
and seekest thou *g. things* ? 45:5
a mouth speaking *g. things.*
Dan 7:8, 20; *Rev* 13:5
I have written *g. things.* *Hos* 8:12*
he hath done *g. things.* *Joel* 2:20
the Lord will do *g. things.* 21
heard what *g. things* he. *Mark* 3:8
tell them how *g. things* the Lord hath done. 5:19; *Luke* 8:39
hath done *g. things.* *Luke* 1:49
he published how *g. things.* 8:39
will shew how *g. things.* *Acts* 9:16*
a *g. thing* if we reap ? *1 Cor* 9:11
no *g. thing* if his ministers be.
2 Cor 11:15
member boasteth *g. things.* *Jas* 3:5

very **great**

till he became *very g.* *Gen* 26:13
man Moses was *very g.* *Ex* 11:3
people with a *very g.* plague.
Num 11:33
cities are walled and *very g.* 12:28
promote thee unto *very g.* 22:17
of young men was *very g. 1 Sam* 2:17
there was a *very g.* slaughter. 4:10
very g. trembling. 14:15
very g. discomfiture. 20
Nabal was a *very g.* man, he. 25:2
laid a *very g.* heap. *2 Sam* 18:17
for Barzillai was a *very g.* 19:32
came with a *very g.* train. *1 Ki* 10:2
very g. are his mercies. *1 Chr* 21:13
very g. burning for Asa. *2 Chr* 16:14
very g. host into their hand. 24:24
a *very g.* congregation. 30:13
Ezra 10:1
up wall a *very g.* height. *2 Chr* 33:14
and there was a *very g.* *Neh* 8:17
Job a *very g.* household. *Job* 1:3
that his grief was *very g.* 2:13
God, thou art *very g.* *Ps* 104:1
there shall be a *very g.* multitude of fish. *Ezek* 47:9
he goat waxed *very g.* *Dan* 8:8
up with a *very g.* army. 11:25
for his camp is *very g.* *Joel* 2:11
shall be a *very g.* valley. *Zech* 14:4
very g. multitude spread. *Mat* 21:8
multitude *very g.* having. *Mark* 8:1
rolled away, for it was *very g.* 16:4

was **great**

wickedness of man *was g.* *Gen* 6:5
their substance *was g.* so that. 13:6
to Gibeon, that *was g.* *1 Ki* 3:4
there *was g.* indignation. *2 Ki* 3:27
where decree came *was g. Esth* 4:3
Mordecai *was g.* in the. 9:4; 10:3
because my wealth *was g. Job* 31:25
I *was g.* and increased. *Eccl* 2:9
she that *was g.* among. *Lam* 1:1
tree's height *was g.* *Dan* 4:10
it fell, and *g. was* the fall of it.
Mat 7:27; *Luke* 6:49

great *waters*

in floods of *g. waters.* *Ps* 32:6
sea, thy path in *g. waters.* 77:19
do business in *g. waters.* 107:23
deliver me out of *g. waters.* 144:7
and by *g. waters* the seed. *Isa* 23:3
Ishmael by *g. waters.* *Jer* 41:12
do roar like *g. waters.* 51:55*
their wings like *g. waters. Ezek* 1:24
of the seed by *g. waters*, set. 17:5*
in a good soil by *g. waters.* 8*
when *g. waters* shall cover. 26:19
brought thee into *g.* waters. 27:26
his root was by *g. waters.* 31:7*
floods, the *g. waters* were stayed. 15
all beasts beside *g. waters.* 32:13
through heap of *g. waters. Hab* 3:15

great *while*

of thy servant's house for a *g. while.*
2 Sam 7:19; *1 Chr* 17:17
rising up a *g. while.* *Mark* 1:35
g. while ago repented. *Luke* 10:13
barbarians looked a *g. while.*
Acts 28:6

great *work* and *works*

Israel saw that *g. work.* *Ex* 14:31
had seen all *g. works.* *Judg* 2:7
young, and *work* is *g.* *1 Chr* 29:1
the *work* is *g.* and we. *Neh* 4:19
I am doing a *g. work*, I cannot. 6:3
the *works* of the Lord are *g.*
Ps 111:2; *Rev* 15:3
I made *g. works*, I builded. *Eccl* 2:4

greater

God made the *g.* light to. *Gen* 1:16
my punishment is *g.* than I can. 4:13
there is none *g.* in this house. 39:9
only in throne will I be *g.* than. 41:40
younger brother shall be *g.* 48:19
know the Lord is *g.* than. *Ex* 18:11
make of thee *g.* nation. *Num* 14:12
Deut 9:14
people is *g.* and taller. *Deut* 1:28
drive nations *g.* than thou. 4:38
7:1; 9:1; 11:23
because Gibeon was *g.* *Josh* 10:2
there been a much *g.* *1 Sam* 14:30
the hatred was *g.* than. *2 Sam* 13:15
this evil is *g.* than the other. 16*
make his throne *g.* *1 Ki* 1:37, 47
David waxed *g.* and *g.* *1 Chr* 11:9
the *g.* house he cieled. *2 Chr* 3:5
Mordecai waxed *g.* and *g. Esth* 9:4
answer, that God is *g.* *Job* 33:12
is *g.* than the punishment. *Lam* 4:6
g. abominations. *Ezek* 8:6, 13, 15
set forth a multitude *g.* *Dan* 11:13
or their border *g.* than. *Amos* 6:2
glory of latter house *g.* *Hag* 2:9
hath not risen a *g.* than John the Baptist. *Mat* 11:11; *Luke* 7:28
in this place is one *g.* *Mat* 12:6
g. than Jonas is. 41; *Luke* 11:32
behold a *g.* than Solomon is here.
Mat 12:42; *Luke* 11:31
receiving *g.* damnation. *Mat* 23:14
Mark 12:40; *Luke* 20:47
whether is *g.* the gold or ? *Mat* 23:17
for whether is *g.* the gift or the ? 19
sown, it becometh *g.* *Mark* 4:32
is no other commandment *g.* 12:31
my barns, and build *g.* *Luke* 12:18
whether is *g.* he that sitteth ? 22:27
thou shalt see *g.* things.
John 1:50; 5:20; 14:12
art thou *g.* than our father ? 4:12
I have a *g.* witness than that. 5:36
art thou *g.* than our father ? 8:53
Father is *g.* than all. 10:29; 14:28
the servant is not *g.* 13:16; 15:20
g. love hath no man than this. 15:13
delivered me to thee hath *g.* 19:11
to lay upon you no *g.* *Acts* 15:28
g. is he that prophesieth. *1 Cor* 14:5
of whom the *g.* part remain. 15:6
he could swear by no *g.* *Heb* 6:13
men verily swear by the *g.* 16
by a *g.* and more perfect. 9:11
reproach of Christ *g.* riches. 11:26
we shall receive *g.* *Jas* 3:1*
angels which are *g.* in. *2 Pet* 2:11
God is *g.* than our. *1 John* 3:20
g. is he that is in you, than he. 4:4
witness of God is *g.* this is the. 5:9
I have no *g.* joy than to. *3 John* 4

greatest

was over 100, *g.* over. *1 Chr* 12:14
hitherto the *g.* part had kept the. 29
this man was the *g.* of. *Job* 1:3
from least to *g.* given. *Jer* 6:13; 8:10
from least to the *g.* 31:34; *Heb* 8:11
people from least to the *g.* *Jer* 42:1
called people from least to *g.* 8
die, from the least to the *g.* 44:12
sackcloth, from the *g.* *Jonah* 3:5
when grown, it is the *g.* *Mat* 13:32
who is the *g.* in the kingdom ? 18:1
as this little child, same is *g.* 4
but he that is *g.* shall be. 23:11
disputed who should be *g.*
Mark 9:34; *Luke* 9:46
strife who should be *g.* *Luke* 22:24
but he that is *g.* let him be as. 26
heed from least to the *g.* *Acts* 8:10
but the *g.* of these is. *1 Cor* 13:13

greatly

I will *g.* multiply thy. *Gen* 3:16
Lot pressed upon them *g.* and. 19:3
hath blessed my master *g.* 24:35
then Jacob was *g.* afraid and. 32:7
whole mount quaked *g.* *Ex* 19:18
of Lord was kindled *g.* *Num* 11:10
and the people mourned *g.* 14:39
Lord shall *g.* bless thee. *Deut* 15:4*
nor shall he *g.* multiply silver. 17:17
they were *g.* distressed. *Judg* 2:15*
Israel was *g.* impoverished. 6:6*
anger was kindled *g.* *1 Sam* 11:6
all men of Israel rejoiced *g.* 15
the people *g.* feared the Lord. 12:18
he loved him *g.* became his. 16:21
Philistine, they were *g.* 17:11
Philistines his heart trembled *g.* 28:5
David was *g.* distressed, for. 30:6
the men were *g.* ashamed.
2 Sam 10:5; *1 Chr* 19:5
David's anger was *g.* kindled.
2 Sam 12:5
David said, I have sinned *g.* 24:10
1 Chr 21:8
kingdom was established *g. 1 Ki* 2:12
Solomon's words, he rejoiced *g.* 5:7
now Obadiah feared the Lord *g.* 18:3
fathers increased *g.* *1 Chr* 4:38
great is the Lord, *g.* to be. 16:25*
Ps 48:1; 96:4; 145:3
their anger was *g.* *2 Chr* 25:10
Manasseh humbled himself *g.* 33:12
latter end should *g.* *Job* 8:7
in thy salvation how *g.* *Ps* 21:1

my heart g. rejoiceth, I will. Ps 28:7
bowed down g. go mourning. 38:6
so shall the king g. desire. 45:11
earth belong to God, he is g. 47:9
my defence, I shall not be g. 62:2
thou g. enrichest it with river. 65:9
my lips shall g. rejoice when. 71:23
wroth, and g. abhorred. 78:59
his people g. 105:24; 107:38
I will g. praise the Lord. 109:30
blessed that delighteth g. in. 112:1
I was g. afflicted, I said in. 116:10
proud have had me g. in. 119:51
of righteous shall g. Pr 23:24
be g. ashamed that. Isa 42:17†
I will g. rejoice in the Lord. 61:10
shall not that land be g.? Jer 3:1
surely thou hast g. deceived. 4:10
we are g. confounded, have. 9:19
persecutors shall be g. 20:11†
my sabbaths they g. Ezek 20:13
because that Edom hath g. 25:12
was king Belshazzar g. Dan 5:9
thou art g. beloved. 9:23; 10:11, 19
made thee small, thou art g. Ob 2
day of Lord hasteth g. Zeph 1:14
g. O daughter of Zion. Zech 9:9
governor marvelled g. Mat 27:14
Jairus besought him g. Mark 5:23
them that wept and wailed g. 38
beheld, they were amazed g. 9:15
the living, ye therefore do g. 12:27
rejoiceth g. because of. John 3:29
people ran to porch, g. Acts 3:11
disciples multiplied in Jerusalem g. 6:7
I g. desired Apollos. 1 Cor 16:12
how g. I long after you all. Phil 1:8
I rejoiced in the Lord g. that. 4:10
desiring g. to see us, as. 1 Thes 3:6
g. desiring to see thee. 2 Tim 1:4
for he hath g. withstood our. 4:15
ye g. rejoice though now. 1 Pet 1:6
I rejoiced g. that I found. 2 John 4
I rejoiced g. when the. 3 John 3
see **feared**

greatness
in g. of thy excellency. Ex. 15:7
by g. of thine arm they shall be. 16
pardon according to g. Num 14:19
to shew thy servant thy g. Deut 3:24
shewed us his glory and g. 5:24
hast redeemed through thy g. 9:26
who have not seen his g. 11:2
ascribe ye g. unto our God. 32:3
hast done all this g. 1 Chr 17:19
to make thee a name of g. and. 21
O Lord is the g., the power. 29:11
half of g. of thy wisdom. 2 Chr 9:6
and the g. of the burdens. 24:27
spare me according to g. Neh 13:22
the declaration of the g. Esth 10:2
by g. of thy power. Ps 66:3
thou shalt increase my g. 71:21
according to the g. of thy. 79:11
his g. is unsearchable. 145:3
I declare thy g. 6
according to his excellent g. 150:2
in the g. of his folly he. Pr 5:23
calleth by name, by g. Isa 40:26
thou art wearied in the g. 57:10*
travelling in the g. of his. 63:1
for g. of iniquity thy. Jer 13:22
art thou like in thy g.? Ezek 31:2
thus was he fair in his g. 7
thy g. is grown and. Dan 4:22
the g. of the kingdom shall. 7:27
what is exceeding g. of. Eph 1:19

greaves
Goliath had g. of brass. 1 Sam 17:6

Grecia
rough goat is king of G. Dan 8:21
when I am gone, prince of G. 10:20
stir up all against realm of G. 11:2

Grecians
Judah sold to the G. Joel 3:6
a murmuring of the G. Acts 6:1
and disputed against the G. 9:29
spoke to the G. preaching. 11:20

Greece
against thy sons, O G. Zech 9:13
Paul came to G. and abode. Acts 20:2

greedily
he coveteth g. all day. Pr 21:26
hast g. gained of thy. Ezek 22:12
they ran g. after the error. Jude 11*

greediness
all uncleanness with g. Eph 4:19

greedy
as a lion that is g. of. Ps 17:12
every one that is g. of. Pr 1:19
he that is g. of gain troubleth. 15:27
they are g. dogs, can. Isa 56:11
not g. of filthy lucre. 1 Tim 3:3, 8

Greek
superscription written in G.
Luke 23:38; John 19:20
canst thou speak G.? Acts 21:37
G. tongue hath his name. Rev 9:11

Greek
the woman was a G. Mark 7:26
Timotheus was a G. Acts 16:1, 3
Jew first, and also to G. Rom 1:16
no difference between Jew and G.
10:12; Gal 3:28; Col 3:11
was with me, being a G. Gal 2:3
see appellatives

Greeks
certain G. came to. John 12:20
a multitude of G. believed.
Acts 14:1; 17:4, 12
persuaded the Jews and the G. 18:4
then the G. took Sosthenes. 17
Jews and G. heard the word. 19:10
this was known to all the G. 17
testifying to Jews and G. 20:21
he brought the G. also into. 21:28
both to G. and Barbarians. Rom 1:14
G. seek after wisdom. 1 Cor 1:22
preach Christ crucified, to the G. 23
unto called, Jews and G., Christ. 24

green
have given every g. herb. Gen 1:30
as the g. herb have I given you. 9:3
Jacob took rods of g. poplar. 30:37*
remained not any g. Ex 10:15
for thy firstfruits g. ears. Lev 2:14*
eat no g. ears, till ye have. 23:14*
bind me with seven g. Judg 16:7
brought to her seven g. withs. 8
inhabitants were as g. herbs.
2 Ki 19:26; Isa 37:27
where were white, g., blue. Esth 1:6
he is g. before the sun. Job 8:16
and his branch shall not be g. 15:32
searcheth after every g. thing. 39:8
maketh me lie down in g. Ps 23:2
they shall wither as the g. herb. 37:2
wicked spreading like a g. bay. 35
fair, also our bed is g. S of S 1:16
fig tree putteth forth her g. 2:13
grass faileth, there is no g. Isa 15:6
called thy name, a g. Jer 11:16
her roots, leaf shall be g. 17:8
I am like a g. fir tree. Hos 14:8
companies on g. grass. Mark 6:39
hail and fire, and all g. Rev 8:7
commanded not to hurt any g. 9:4

green *tree*
under every g. tree. Deut 12:2
images under every g. tree.
1 Ki 14:23; 2 Ki 17:10
Ahaz sacrificed under every g. tree.
2 Ki 16:4; 2 Chr 28:4
I am like a g. olive tree. Ps 52:8
under every g. tree. Isa 57:5
under every g. tree thou. Jer 2:20
under every g. tree, there played. 3:6
thy ways under every g. tree. 13
be under every g. tree. Ezek 6:13
I have dried up the g. tree. 17:24
it shall devour every g. tree. 20:47
things in a g. tree. Luke 23:31

green *trees*
groves by g. trees. Jer 17:2

greenish
if the plague be g. in. Lev 13:49
be with hollow strakes g. or. 14:37

greenness
it is yet in his g. and. Job 8:12

greet
(*The Revisions change this word to* salute *when used in the New Testament*)
go to Nabal and g. 1 Sam 25:5
g. Priscilla and Aquila. Rom 16:3
g. church. 5
g. Mary who bestowed labour. 6
g. Amplias. 8
g. the household of Narcissus. 11
all the brethren g. you. 1 Cor 16:20
Phil 4:21
g. ye one another. 1 Cor 16:20
2 Cor 13:12; 1 Pet 5:14
and Demas g. you. Col 4:14
g. the brethren with an. 1 Thes 5:26
g. them that love us in. Tit 3:15
of thy elect sister g. thee. 2 John 13
peace be to thee, g. the. 3 John 14

greeteth
Eubulus g. thee. 2 Tim 4:21*

greeting, -s
g. in markets. Mat 23:7*
Luke 11:43*; 20:46*
and brethren, send g. Acts 15:23
Lysias to Felix sendeth g. 23:26
tribes scattered abroad, g. Jas 1:1

grew
every herb before it g. Gen 2:5*
he overthrew that which g. 19:25
Isaac g. 21:8; 26:13
Ishmael g. and dwelt in. 21:20
the boys g. 25:27
Israel g. and multiplied. 47:27*
afflicted, more they g. Ex 1:12*
Moses g. 2:10
his wife's sons g. up. Judg 11:2
Samson g. and the Lord. 13:24
the child Samuel g. 1 Sam 2:21, 26
David went on and g. 2 Sam 5:10
lamb g. up together with him. 12:3
it g. and became a. Ezek 17:6
tree g. and was strong. Dan 4:11
and the thorns g. up. Mark 4:7
bettered, but rather g. worse. 5:26
child g. and waxed. Luke 1:80; 2:40
it g. and waxed a great tree. 13:19
people g. and multiplied. Acts 7:17
word of God g. and multiplied. 12:24
so mightily g. the word of. 19:20

greyhound
for comely in going, a g. Pr 30:31

grief, -s
a g. unto Isaac and. Gen 26:35
out of abundance of g. 1 Sam 1:16*
be no g. to thee, or offence. 25:31
shall know his own g. 2 Chr 6:29*
they saw that his g. was. Job 2:13
oh that my g. were throughly. 6:2*
lips should assuage your g. 16:5
speak, my g. is not assuaged. 6
my eye is consumed because of g.
Ps 6:7; 31:9
my life is spent with g. my. 31:10*
they talk to g. of those thou. 69:26*
a foolish son is a g. to. Pr 17:25
much wisdom is much g. Eccl 1:18
are sorrows, and his travail g. 2:23
be a heap in day of g. Isa 17:11
and acquainted with g. 53:3
he hath borne our g. and carried. 4
bruise him, he put him to g. 10
before me continually is g. Jer 6:7*
truly this is a g. and I must. 10:19
for the Lord hath added g. 45:3*
though he cause g. he will. Lam 3:32
a gourd, a shadow to deliver him from g. Jonah 4:6*
if any caused g. he hath. 2 Cor 2:5*
with joy and not with g. Heb 13:17
toward God endure g. 1 Pet 2:19

grievance
cause me to behold g.? Hab 1:3*

grieve
man shall be to g. 1 Sam 2:3
that it may not g. me. 1 Chr 4:10
how oft did they g.? Ps 78:4
doth not willingly g. Lam 3:3
g. not the Holy Spirit of. Eph 4:3

grieved
the earth, and it *g.* him. *Gen* 6:6
sons heard and were *g.* and. 34:7
now be not *g.* that ye sold me. 45:5
archers have sorely *g.* him. 49:23
and they were *g.* because. *Ex* 1:12
shall not be *g.* when. *Deut* 15:10
soul was *g.* for misery. *Judg* 10:16
why is thy heart *g.*? *1 Sam* 1:8
it *g.* Samuel, and he cried. 15:11*
Jonathan know this lest he be *g.* 20:3
arose, for he was *g.* for David. 34
soul of all the people was *g.* 30:6
heard how king was *g.* *2 Sam* 19:2
it *g.* them exceedingly. *Neh* 2:10
it *g.* me sore, and I cast forth. 13:8
was queen exceedingly *g.* *Esth* 4:4
commune, wilt thou be *g.*? *Job* 4:2
was not my soul *g.* for the? 30:25
thus my heart was *g.*, I. *Ps* 73:21
forty years was I *g.* with. 95:10
wicked shall see it, and be *g.* 112:10
transgressors and was *g.* 119:158
am not I *g.* with those that? 139:21
called thee as a woman *g.* *Isa* 54:6
therefore thou wast not *g.* 57:10*
them, they have not *g.* *Jer* 5:3
I Daniel was *g.* in spirit. *Dan* 7:15
therefore he shall be *g.* and. 11:30
not *g.* for the affliction. *Amos* 6:6
being *g.* for the hardness. *Mark* 3:5
he went away *g.* for he had. 10:22
Peter was *g.* because. *John* 21:17
being *g.* that they taught. *Acts* 4:2
Paul being *g.* said to spirit. 16:18*
if thy brother be *g.* *Rom* 14:15
that ye should be *g.* *2 Cor* 2:4*
caused grief, he hath not *g.* me. 5
wherefore I was *g.* with. *Heb* 3:10*
but with whom was he *g.* forty? 17*

grieveth
for it *g.* me much for. *Ruth* 1:13
it *g.* him to bring it. *Pr* 26:15

grieving
shall be no more a *g.* *Ezek* 28:24

grievous
for the famine was *g.* *Gen* 12:10*
because their sin is very *g.* 18:20
the thing was very *g.* in. 21:11
God said, let it not be *g.* in thy. 12
famine shall be very *g.* 41:31
this is a *g.* mourning to the. 50:11
came a *g.* swarm of flies. *Ex* 8:24
a *g.* murrain. 9:3
to rain a very *g.* hail. 18, 24
locusts were very *g.* before. 10:14
Shimei cursed me with a *g.* *1 Ki* 2:8
g. service lighter. 12:4; *2 Chr* 10:4
his ways always *g.* *Ps* 10:5*
speak *g.* things against. 31:18*
but *g.* words stir up anger. *Pr* 15:1
correction is *g.* unto him that. 10
wrought under sun is *g.* *Eccl* 2:17
his life shall be *g.* unto. *Isa* 15:4*
g. vision is declared unto me. 21:2
they are all *g.* revolters. *Jer* 6:28
my hurt, my wound is *g.* 10:19
people broken with a *g.* blow. 14:17
they shall die of *g.* deaths. 16:4
a *g.* whirlwind shall fall on. 23:19*
thy wound is *g.* 30:12; *Nah* 3:19
bind heavy burdens and *g.*
Mat 23:4; *Luke* 11:46
shall *g.* wolves enter in. *Acts* 20:29
Jews laid many *g.* complaints. 25:7
to me indeed is not *g.* but. *Phil* 3:1*
seemeth joyous, but *g.* *Heb* 12:11
commandments are not *g.* *1 John* 5:3
a *g.* sore on men that. *Rev* 16:2

grievously
afterward did more *g.* *Isa* 9:1*
it shall fall *g.* upon head. *Jer* 23:19*
Jerusalem hath *g.* sinned. *Lam* 1:8
turned, for I have *g.* rebelled. 20
land sinneth by trespassing *g.*
Ezek 14:13*
g. tormented. *Mat* 8:6
daughter *g.* vexed. 15:22

grievousness
that write *g.* which they. *Isa* 10:1*
they fled from the *g.* of war. 21:15

grind
Samson did *g.* in the. *Judg* 16:21
then let my wife *g.* unto. *Job* 31:10
what mean ye to *g.* the? *Isa* 3:15
take millstones and *g.* meal. 47:2
took the young men to *g.* *Lam* 5:13*
it will *g.* him to powder.
Mat 21:44*; *Luke* 20:18*

grinders
the *g.* cease, because. *Eccl* 12:3

grinding
when sound of the *g.* is. *Eccl* 12:4
two women *g.* at the mill.
Mat 24:41; *Luke* 17:35

grisled
were speckled and *g.* *Gen* 31:10, 12
in fourth chariot were *g.* *Zech* 6:3
the *g.* go forth toward the south. 6

groan
men *g.* from out of city. *Job* 24:12
her land wounded shall *g.* *Jer* 51:52
Pharaoh shall *g.* before. *Ezek* 30:24
how do the beasts *g.*! *Joel* 1:18
we ourselves *g.* within. *Rom* 8:23
in this we *g.* desiring to. *2 Cor* 5:2
we in this tabernacle do *g.* being. 4

groaned
he *g.* in the spirit. *John* 11:33

groaneth
the whole creation *g.* *Rom* 8:22

groaning, -s
God heard their *g.* and. *Ex* 2:24
the *g.* of Israel. 6:5; *Acts* 7:34
Lord because of their *g.* *Judg* 2:18
is heavier than my *g.* *Job* 23:2
I am weary with *g.* all. *Ps* 6:6
my *g.* is not hid from thee. 38:9
by reason of my *g.* my bones. 102:5
to hear the *g.* of the prisoner, to. 20
with the *g.* of a deadly. *Ezek* 30:24
Jesus *g.* in himself. *John* 11:38
for us with *g.* that. *Rom* 8:26

grope, -eth
shalt *g.* at noonday as the blind *g.*
Deut 28:29
they *g.* in noonday as. *Job* 5:14
they *g.* in the dark without. 12:25
g. for the wall like the blind, we *g.*
Isa 59:10

gross
g. darkness shall cover. *Isa* 60:2
for light, make it *g.* *Jer* 13:16
people's heart is waxed *g.*
Mat 13:15; *Acts* 28:27

ground
he *g.* the calf to powder. *Ex* 32:20
Deut 9:21
the people *g.* the manna. *Num* 11:8

ground *corn*
spread *g. corn* on the. *2 Sam* 17:19*

ground
not a man to till the *g.* *Gen* 2:5
formed man of the dust of the *g.* 7
out of the *g.* the Lord formed. 19
he said, cursed is the *g.* for. 3:17
but Cain a tiller of *g.* 4:2
blood crieth to me from the *g.* 10
because of the *g.* the Lord. 5:29
I will not again curse the *g.* 8:21
bowed himself toward the *g.* 18:2*
with his face toward *g.* 19:1*
where thou standest is holy *g.*
Ex 3:5; *Acts* 7:33
g. whereon they are shall. *Ex* 8:21
the *g.* clave asunder. *Num* 16:31
be the fruit of thy *g.* *Deut* 28:4, 11
fastened the nail into *g.* *Judg* 4:21
set them to ear his *g.* *1 Sam* 8:12
his spear stuck in the *g.* at. 26:7
was a piece of *g.* full. *2 Sam* 23:11
he stood in midst of the *g.* and. 12*
water is naught, and *g.* *2 Ki* 2:19*
cast him into the plat of *g.* 9:26
where was a parcel of *g.* *1 Chr* 11:13
did cast them in clay *g.* *2 Chr* 4:17
the firstfruits of our *g.* *Neh* 10:35
bring the tithes of our *g.* to. 37
trouble spring out of the *g.* *Job* 5:6
the stock thereof die in the *g.* 14:8
snare is laid for him in the *g.* 18:10
the desolate and waste *g.* 38:27
he swallows the *g.* with. *Job* 39:24
devoured fruit of their *g.* *Ps* 105:35
watersprings into dry *g.* 107:33
he turneth dry *g.* into water. 35*
break clods of his *g.*? *Isa* 28:24
shalt speak out of the *g.* 29:4
seed that thou shalt sow the *g.* 30:23
oxen and young asses that ear *g.* 24
and the parched *g.* shall. 35:7*
laid thy body as the *g.* 51:23
break up your fallow *g.* *Jer* 4:3
Hos 10:12
poured on fruit of the *g.* *Jer* 7:20
because the *g.* is chapt, there. 14:4
gates are sunk into the *g.* *Lam* 2:2
face, thou see not *g.* *Ezek* 12:6, 12
cieled from the *g.* up to the. 41:16
and touched not the *g.* *Dan* 8:5
face was towards *g.* 18; 10:9, 15
with them for things of *g.* *Hos* 2:18
and the *g.* shall give her. *Zech* 8:12
not destroy fruits of your *g.* *Mal* 3:11
but other fell into good *g.* *Mat* 13:8
Luke 8:8
he that received seed into good *g.*
Mat 13:23; *Luke* 8:15
cast seed into the *g.* *Mark* 4:26*
the *g.* of a certain rich. *Luke* 12:16
why cumbereth it the *g.*? 13:7
I have bought a piece of *g.* 14:18*
lay thee even with the *g.* 19:44
near the parcel of *g.* *John* 4:5
corn of wheat fall into *g.* 12:24*

see **dry, face**

on or *upon the* **ground**
he spilled it *on the g.* *Gen* 38:9
fell before him *on the g.* 44:14
cast the rod *on the g.* he cast it *on the g.* *Ex* 4:3
and fire ran along *upon the g.* 9:23*
on dry *g.* through the sea. 14:16, 22
as the hoar frost *on the g.* 16:14
pour blood *upon the g.* *Deut* 15:23
nest chance to be *on the g.* 22:6
would not set her foot *upon g.* 28:56
upon all *the g.* let there. *Judg* 6:39
there was dew *upon* all *the g.* 40
was honey *upon the g.* *1 Sam* 14:25
slew oxen and calves *on the g.* 32
son of Jesse liveth *on the g.* 20:31
water spilt *on the g.* *2 Sam* 14:14
him as dew falleth *on the g.* 17:12
said, Smite *upon the g.* *2 Ki* 13:18
Job fell *upon the g.* and. *Job* 1:20
down with him *upon the g.* 2:13
out my gall *upon the g.* 16:13
shall sit *on the g.* *Isa* 3:26
of Babylon, sit *on the g.* 47:1
be dung *upon the g.* *Jer* 25:33
man and beast *upon the g.* 27:5*
of Zion sit *on the g.* *Lam* 2:10
young and old lie *on the g.* in. 21
poured it not *upon the g.* *Ezek* 24:7
princes shall sit *upon the g.* 26:16
the multitude to sit *on the g.*
Mat 15:35; *Mark* 8:6
some fell *on* stony *g.* *Mark* 4:5, 16*
fell *on* good *g.* 8, 20; *Luke* 8:8, 15
and he fell *on the g.* *Mark* 9:20
forward, and fell *on g.* and. 14:35
he wrote *on the g.* *John* 8:6, 8
he spat *on the g.* 9:6

to or *unto the* **ground**
till thou return *unto the g.* *Gen* 3:19
Jacob bowed himself *to the g.* 33:3
his wife fell *to the g.* *Judg* 13:20
Benjamin destroyed *to the g.* 20:21
and destroyed *to the g.* of Israel. 25
bowed and fell *to the g.* *Ruth* 2:10
his words fall *to the g.* *1 Sam* 3:19
fallen on his face *to the g.* 5:4
not one hair fall *to the g.* 14:45
and fell on his face *to the g.* 20:41
Abigail bowed *to the g.* before. 25:23
with his face *to the g.* 28:14
I smite thee *to the g.*? *2 Sam* 2:22
casting him down *to the g.* 8:2
fell on her face *to the g.* 14:4
Joab fell *to the g.* 22
Absalom bowed *to the g.* 33
not thou smite him *to the g.*? 18:11
out Amasa's bowels *to the g.* 20:10
Nathan bowed *to the g.* *1 Ki* 1:23

prophets bowed *to the g.* *2 Ki* 2:15
she bowed herself *to the g.* 4:37
Ornan bowed *to the g.* *1 Chr* 21:21
Israel bowed with their faces *to g.* *2 Chr* 7:3
bowed with his face *to the g.* 20:18
with their faces *to the g.* *Neh* 8:6
casting down the dwelling place of thy name *to the g.* *Ps* 74:7
crown, by casting it *to the g.* 89:39
cast his throne down *to the g.* 44
smitten my life down *to the g.* 143:3
the wicked down *to the g.* 147:6
thou cut down *to the g.*! *Isa* 14:12
images he hath broken *to the g.* 21:9
bring *to the g.* even to dust. 25:12
city he layeth even *to the g.* 26:5
languish, are black *to the g.* *Jer* 14:2
strong holds of Judah *to g.* *Lam* 2:2
hang their heads *to the g.* 10
down the wall *to the g.* *Ezek* 13:14
mother was cast down *to the g.* 19:12
garrison shall go down *to g.* 26:11
I will cast thee *to the g.* 28:17
cast the ram down *to the g.* *Dan* 8:7
some of hosts and stars *to the g.* 10
and cast down the truth *to the g.* 12
altar shall fall *to the g.* *Amos* 3:14
bring me down *to the g.*? *Ob* 3
shall not fall *to the g.* *Mat* 10:29
blood falling *to the g.* *Luke* 22:44
went backward, and fell *to the g.* *John* 18:6
I fell *to the g.* and heard. *Acts* 22:7

ground

is the pillar and *g.* of. *1 Tim* 3:15

grounded

in every place where *g.* *Isa* 30:32*
ye being rooted and *g.* *Eph* 3:17
continue in the faith, *g.* *Col* 1:23

grove

[1] *A tamarisk tree,* Gen 21:33 (R.V.). [2] *The* Asherah (R.V.) *is in all other places, for singular,* Asherim, *for plural.*

Abraham planted a *g.* *Gen* 21:33
shalt not plant a *g.* *Deut* 16:21
and cut down the *g.* *Judg* 6:25
g. was cut down that was by. 28
she had made an idol in a *g.* *1 Ki* 15:13; *2 Chr* 15:16
Ahab made a *g.* and. *1 Ki* 16:33
there remained the *g.* *2 Ki* 13:6
Israel made a *g.* and served. 17:16
up altars, and made a *g.* 21:3
the vessels made for the *g.* 23:4
he brought out the *g.* from house. 6
burnt the high place and the *g.* 15

groves

ye shall cut down their *g.* *Ex* 34:13 *Deut* 7:5
ye shall burn their *g.* *Deut* 12:3
forgat Lord and served *g.* *Judg* 3:7; *2 Chr* 24:18
out of this good land, because they have made their *g.* *1 Ki* 14:15
built them *g.* on. 23; *2 Ki* 17:10
the prophets of the *g.* *1 Ki* 18:19
Hezekiah cut down *g.* *2 Ki* 18:4
cut down the *g.* 23:14; *2 Chr* 34:3, 4
and cut down the *g.* *2 Chr* 14:3
Jehoshaphat took away the *g.* 17:6
thou hast taken away the *g.* 19:3
all Israel cut down the *g.* 31:1
Manasseh made *g.* 33:3
where he set up *g.* 19
to purge Judah from the *g.* 34:3
broken down the altars and *g.* 7
nor shall he respect the *g.* *Isa* 17:8
the *g.* and the images shall. 27:9
remember altars and *g.* *Jer* 17:2
I will pluck up thy *g.* *Mi* 5:14

grow

God made every tree to *g.* *Gen* 2:9
them *g.* into a multitude. 48:16
let locks of his hair *g.* *Num* 6:5
hair of head began to *g.* *Judg* 16:22
he make it not to *g.* *2 Sam* 23:5
eat such things as *g.* *2 Ki* 19:29
why should damage *g.*? *Ezra* 4:22
can the rush *g.* up? *Job* 8:11
out of the earth shall others *g.* 19*
washest away things that *g.* *Job* 14:19*
thistles *g.* instead of wheat. 31:40
they *g.* up with corn, they go. 39:4
he shall *g.* like a cedar. *Ps* 92:12
causeth grass to *g.* 104:14; 147:8
nor how the bones *g.* in. *Eccl* 11:5
and a branch shall *g.* *Isa* 11:1*
shalt thou make thy plant *g.* 17:11*
he shall *g.* up before him. 53:2
they *g.* yea, they bring. *Jer* 12:2
Branch to *g.* up unto David. 33:15
suffer their locks to *g.* *Ezek* 44:20
by the river shall *g.* all trees. 47:12
shall *g.* as the lily, cast. *Hos* 14:5*
shall revive as the corn, and *g.* as. 7*
nor madest it *g.* which. *Jonah* 4:10
the Branch, he shall *g.* up. *Zech* 6:12
ye shall *g.* up as calves. *Mal* 4:2*
consider the lilies how they *g.* *Mat* 6:28; *Luke* 12:27
let both *g.* together until. *Mat* 13:30
let no fruit *g.* on thee. 21:19
seed should *g.* up, he. *Mark* 4:27
whereunto this would *g.* *Acts* 5:24
may *g.* up into him in all. *Eph* 4:15
of word, that ye may *g.* *1 Pet* 2:2
g. in grace and in. *2 Pet* 3:18

groweth

shall eat every tree that *g.* *Ex* 10:5
freckled spot that *g.* in. *Lev* 13:39*
which *g.* of its own accord. 25:5, 11
nor any grass *g.* therein. *Deut* 29:23
behold, the day *g.* to. *Judg* 19:9
the dust *g.* into hardness. *Job* 38:38*
like grass which *g.* up. *Ps* 90:5, 6
which withereth afore it *g.* up. 129:6
eat this year such as *g.* *Isa* 37:30
when it is sown, it *g.* up. *Mark* 4:32
g. unto an holy temple. *Eph* 2:21
because your faith *g.* *2 Thes* 1:3

grown

till Shelah be *g.* *Gen* 38:11
Shelah was *g.* 14
when Moses was *g.* he. *Ex* 2:11
for they were not *g.* up. 9:32
thou art *g.* thick. *Deut* 32:15
for them till they were *g.* *Ruth* 1:13
tarry until your beards be *g.* *2 Sam* 10:5; *1 Chr* 19:5
with young men *g.* *1 Ki* 12:8, 10
when the child was *g.* up. *2 Ki* 4:18
as corn blasted before it be *g.* 19:26 *Isa* 37:27
our trespass is *g.* up to. *Ezra* 9:6
sons may be as plants *g.* *Ps* 144:12
and lo, it was all *g.* over. *Pr* 24:31
because ye are *g.* fat as. *Jer* 50:11*
fashioned, thy hair is *g.* *Ezek* 16:7
art *g.* strong, thy greatness is *g.* *Dan* 4:22
his hairs were *g.* like eagles'. 33
when *g.* it is the greatest. *Mat* 13:32

growth

g. lo, it was latter *g.* *Amos* 7:1

grudge

nor bear any *g.* against. *Lev* 19:18
let them *g.* if they be. *Ps* 59:15*
g. not one against. *Jas* 5:9*

grudging

to another without *g.* *1 Pet* 4:9*

grudgingly

let him give, not *g.* or. *2 Cor* 9:7

guard

a captain of the *g.* *Gen* 37:36; 39:1
servant to a captain of the *g.* 41:12
David set him over his *g.* *2 Sam* 23:23; *1 Chr* 11:25
shields to captain of *g.* *1 Ki* 14:27 *2 Chr* 12:10
g. bare them and brought them. *1 Ki* 14:28; *2 Chr* 12:11
part at gate behind *g.* *2 Ki* 11:6
captain of *g.* came to Jerusalem. 25:8; *Jer* 52:12
captain of *g.* brake down walls. *2 Ki* 25:10; *Jer* 52:14
rest of people captain of *g.* *2 Ki* 25:11
the captain of the *g.* left of poor. 12
in night they may be a *g.* *Neh* 4:22
nor I nor men of the *g.* put off. 23
captain of *g.* concerning. *Jer* 39:11
when the captain of *g.* had. *Jer* 40:1
captain of the *g.* gave him. 5
the captain of the *g.* took. 52:30
and be a *g.* to them. *Ezek* 38:7
answered captain of *g.* *Dan* 2:14
prisoners to captain of *g.* *Acts* 28:16

guard chamber

guard bare them to *g. chamber.* *1 Ki* 14:28; *2 Chr* 12:11

guest

he was gone to be *g.* *Luke* 19:7*

guestchamber

where is the *g.*? *Mark* 14:14 *Luke* 22:11

guests

Adonijah and all the *g.* *1 Ki* 1:41
all *g.* with Adonijah were afraid. 49
her *g.* are in the depths. *Pr* 9:18
hath prepared and bid *g.* *Zeph* 1:7
was furnished with *g.* *Mat* 22:10
the king came in to see the *g.* 11

guide, -s

he will be our *g.* even. *Ps* 48:14
it was thou, a man, my *g.* 55:13
who forsaketh the *g.* of. *Pr* 2:17
which having no *g.*, overseer. 6:7
my father, thou art the *g.* *Jer* 3:4
put ye not confidence in *g.* *Mi* 7:5
to you, ye blind *g.* *Mat* 23:16, 24
who was *g.* to them. *Acts* 1:16
confident thou art a *g.* of. *Rom* 2:19

guide, *verb*

canst thou *g.* Arcturus? *Job* 38:32
the meek will he *g.* in. *Ps* 25:9
lead me and *g.* me. 31:3
I will teach and *g.* thee with. 32:8*
thou shalt *g.* me with thy. 73:24
he will *g.* his affairs with. 112:5*
of the upright shall *g.* *Pr* 11:3
be wise, and *g.* thine heart in. 23:19
of water shall he *g.* them. *Isa* 49:10
is none to *g.* her among. 51:18
the Lord shall *g.* thee. 58:11
to *g.* our feet into the way. *Luke* 1:79
he will *g.* you into all. *John* 16:13
except some man *g.* me? *Acts* 8:31
bear children, *g.* house. *1 Tim* 5:14*

guided, -ing

Israel *g.* his hands. *Gen* 48:14
thou hast *g.* them in thy. *Ex* 15:13
the Lord *g.* them on. *2 Chr* 32:22
I have *g.* her from my. *Job* 31:18
g. them in the wilderness. *Ps* 78:52
hast *g.* them by the skilfulness. 72

guile

if a man slay with *g.* *Ex* 21:14
in whose spirit there is no *g.* *Ps* 32:2
keep lips from speaking *g.* 34:13 *1 Pet* 3:10
deceit and *g.* depart not. *Ps* 55:11
indeed, in whom is no *g.* *John* 1:47
I caught you with *g.* *2 Cor* 12:16
exhortation was not in *g.* *1 Thes* 2:3
aside all malice and *g.* *1 Pet* 2:1
who did no sin, neither was *g.* 22
mouth was found no *g.* *Rev* 14:5*

guilt

g. of innocent. *Deut* 19:13; 21:9

guiltiness

have brought *g.* on us. *Gen* 26:10
me from blood-*g.* O God. *Ps* 51:14

guiltless

Lord will not hold him *g.* *Ex* 20:7 *Deut* 5:11
then shall the man be *g.* *Num* 5:31
shall return and be *g.* 32:22
on him, and he will be *g.* *Josh* 2:19
anointed and be *g.* *1 Sam* 26:9
my kingdom are *g.* *2 Sam* 3:28
king and his throne be *g.* 14:9
hold him not *g.* for thou. *1 Ki* 2:9
not have condemned the *g.* *Mat* 12:7

guilty

verily *g.* concerning. *Gen* 42:21
will by no means clear *g.* *Ex* 34:7 *Num* 14:18
not be done are *g.* *Lev* 4:13; 22:27
he shall be unclean and *g.* 5:2
knoweth of it, he shall be *g.* 3, 4
he shall be *g.*, he shall confess. 5

he wist it not, yet is he g. Lev 5:17
because he sinned and is g. he. 6:4
the slayer shall not be g. Num 35:27
no satisfaction for a murderer g. 31
that you should be g. Judg 21:22
being g. offered a ram. Ezra 10:19
and thou be found g. Pr 30:10
become g. in blood. Ezek 22:4
hold themselves not g. Zech 11:5
by the gift on it, he is g. Mat 23:18*
they said, he is g. of death. 26:66*
Mark 14:64*
world may become g. Rom 3:19*
shall be g. of the body. 1 Cor 11:27
in one point, he is g. Jas 2:10

gulf

us and you is a great g. Luke 16:26

Gur

smote Ahaziah at the going up to G. 2 Ki 9:27

gush, -ed

till the blood g. out. 1 Ki 18:28
rock, the waters g. out. Ps 78:20
opened rock, waters g. out. 105:41
clave the rock, and the waters g. out. Isa 48:21
and our eyelids g. out. Jer 9:18
and his bowels g. out. Acts 1:18

gutter, -s

Jacob set rods in the g. Gen 30:38
before the eyes of the cattle in g. 41
who getteth up to the g. 2 Sam 5:8*

H

ha

the trumpets, ha, ha. Job 39:25

habergeon

hole of an h. Ex 28:32*; 39:23*
spear, the dart, the h. Job 41:26*

habergeons

h. and bows (Uzziah). 2 Chr 26:14*
servants held bows and h. Neh 4:16*

habitable

rejoicing in the h. part. Pr 8:31

habitation

I will prepare him an h. Ex 15:2*
camp shall his h. be. Lev 13:46
even to his h. shall ye. Deut 12:5
why kick at offering, commanded in my h.? 1 Sam 2:29
thou shalt see an enemy in my h. 32
me both it, and his h. 2 Sam 15:25
built an house of h. for. 2 Chr 6:2
and have turned from the h. 29:6
God of Israel whose h. is. Ezra 7:15
but suddenly I cursed h. Job 5:3
thou shalt visit thy h. and shalt. 24
make h. of thy righteousness. 8:6
be scattered upon his h. 18:15
I have loved the h. of thy. Ps 26:8
from the place of his h. he. 33:14
let their h. be desolate. 69:25
thou my strong h. whereunto. 71:3
and judgement the h. 89:14; 97:2
made the most High thy h. 91:9
fowls of heaven have their h. 104:12
might go to a city of h. 107:7, 36
find an h. for the mighty God. 132:5
for Lord hath desired it for his h. 13
but he blesseth the h. of. Pr 3:33
and that graveth an h. Isa 22:16
and the h. shall be forsaken. 27:10
shall dwell in a peaceable h. 32:18
see Jerusalem a quiet h. 33:20
t shall be an h. of dragons. 34:13
n the h. of dragons shall be. 35:7
and behold from the h. of. 63:15
hine h. is in midst of. Jer 9:6
ave made his h. desolate. 10:25
mightily roar upon his h. 25:30
hee, O h. of justice. 31:23; 50:7
ities thereof be an h. of. 33:12
hey dwelt in the h. of. 41:17
gainst h. of strong. 49:19; 50:44
srael again to his h. 50:19
urely he shall make their h. 45
Egypt to return to their h. Ezek 29:14
whose h. is high, that saith. Ob 3
moon stood still in their h. Hab 3:11

it is written, let his h. be. Acts 1:20
the bounds of their h. 17:26
for an h. of God through. Eph 2:22
which left their own h. Jude 6
Babylon is become the h. Rev 18:2

holy **habitation**

guided them to thy holy h. Ex 15:13
down from thy holy h. Deut 26:15
is God in his holy h. Ps 68:5
his voice from holy h. Jer 25:30
up out of his holy h. Zech 2:13

habitations

cruelty are in their h. Gen 49:5*
in all your h. eat unleaven. Ex 12:20
kindle no fire through your h. 35:3
ye be come into the h. Num 15:2
places of earth full of h. Ps 74:20
fall round about their h. 78:28
forth curtains of thy h. Isa 54:2
for h. of the wilderness. Jer 9:10
who shall enter into our h.? 21:13
and the peaceable h. are cut. 25:37
surely he shall make their h. 49:20
swallowed up the h. of. Lam 2:2
in all their h. make land. Ezek 6:14
the h. of the shepherds. Amos 1:2
you into everlasting h. Luke 16:9*

Hachilah

hid in hill of H. 1 Sam 23:19; 26:1
Saul pitched in the hill of H. 26:3

had

ruled over all that he h. Gen 24:2
he knew not aught he h. save. 39:6
he that gathered much h. Ex 16:18
the Lord h. a delight in. Deut 10:15
Rahab and all that she h. Josh 6:25
Achan and all that he h. 7:24
of them shall I be h. in. 2 Sam 6:22
did this thing, and h. no pity. 12:6
mighty men whom David h. 23:8
she said, h. Zimri peace. 2 Ki 9:31
house and all he h. 1 Chr 13:14
as for me, I h. in my heart to. 28:2
and pattern of all that he h. by. 12
in safety, neither h. I rest. Job 3:26
if men said not, oh that we h. 31:31
him twice as much as he h. 42:10
I said, O that I h. wings. Ps 55:6
I h. rather be a doorkeeper. 84:10
to be h. in reverence of all. 89:7
proud have h. me greatly. 119:51
as were oppressed, they h. Eccl 4:1
behold, for peace I h. Isa 38:17
we grope as if we h. no eyes. 59:10
in my favour have I h. mercy. 60:10
and they h. no light. Jer 4:23
then h. we plenty of victuals. 44:17
pleasant things she h. in. Lam 1:7
she came down wonderfully: h. no. 9
yet h. he no wages for. Ezek 29:18
but I h. pity for mine holy. 36:21
by his strength Jacob h. Hos 12:3
yea he h. power over the angel. 4
against which thou hast h. Zech 1:12
yet h. he the residue of. Mal 2:15
he sold all that he h. Mat 13:46
seven, for they all h. her? 22:28
did cast in all she h. Mark 12:44
thou hast h. five husbands. John 4:18
of whatsoever disease he h. 5:4
Judas h. the bag, and bare. 12:6
if I h. not come, they h. not h. 15:22
the glory I h. with thee before. 17:5
all that believed h. all. Acts 2:44
shorn his head, for he h. 18:18
that after examination h., I. 25:26
faith he h. yet being. Rom 4:11, 12
what fruit h. ye in those things? 6:21
wives be as though they h. none. 1 Cor 7:29
but we h. the sentence of. 2 Cor 1:9
of entering in we h. 1 Thes 1:9
and blessed him that h. Heb 7:6
old commandment which ye h. from. 1 John 2:7
that which we h. from. 2 John 5

Hadadezer, Hadarezer

David smote H. 2 Sam 8:3; 9:10
1 Chr 18:3
came to succour H. 2 Sam 8:5
shields of gold on servants of H. 7
cities of H. 8

H. had wars with Toi. 2 Sam 8:10
the spoil of H. 12
H. sent and brought out the. 10:16
Rezon fled from H. 1 Ki 11:23

Hadadrimmon

the mourning of H. in. Zech 12:11

Hadassah

H. his uncle's daughter. Esth 2:7

Hadoram

begat H. Gen 10:27; 1 Chr 1:21
Tou sent H. his son. 1 Chr 18:10
Rehoboam sent H. 2 Chr 10:18

Hadrach

word of Lord in land of H. Zech 9:1

hadst

for it was little thou h. Gen 30:30
because thou h. a favour. Ps 44:3
thou h. a whore's forehead. Jer 3:3
neither h. pleasure therein. Heb 10:8

haft

and the h. also went in. Judg 3:22

Hagar

H. an Egyptian. Gen 16:1, 3, 8
H. bare Abram a son. 15, 16; 25:12
Sarah saw son of H. the. 21:9
Abraham gave H. bread. 14
called to H., What aileth thee, H.? 17
see **Agar**

Hagarenes

the H. are confederate. Ps 83:6

Hagarites

made war with H. 1 Chr 5:10, 19
H. were delivered into their. 20

Haggai

son of Gad, H. Shuni. Gen 46:16
H. prophesied to the Jews. Ezra 5:1
prophesying of H. the prophet. 6:14
word of the Lord by H. Hag 1:1, 3
2:1, 10, 20

Haggith

Adonijah the son of H. 2 Sam 3:4
1 Ki 1:5, 11; 2:13; 1 Chr 3:2

hail

rain a very grievous h. Ex 9:18
Lord sent thunder and h., fire. 23
of Israel were, was there no h. 26
nor shall there be any more h. 29
h. ceased. 33
remaineth from the h. 10:5, 12, 15
the treasures of the h.? Job 38:22
their vines with h. Ps 78:47
gave up their cattle also to the h. 48
he gave them h. for rain. 105:32
fire, h. snow and vapour. 148:8
which as a tempest of h. Isa 28:2
the h. shall sweep away the. 17
I smote you with h. in all. Hag 2:17
there followed h. and fire. Rev 8:7
and there was great h. 11:19
fell on men a great h. out of. 16:21

hail, *verb*

dwell when it shall h. Isa 32:19

hail

Judas said, H. master. Mat 26:49
H. King of the Jews. 27:29
Mark 15:18; John 19:3
to Mary, and said, H. Luke 1:28

hailstones

which died with h. Josh 10:11
clouds passed, h. and. Ps 18:12, 13
shew indignation with h. Isa 30:30
and ye, O great h. shall. Ezek 13:11
there shall be great h. in my. 13
I will rain great h. fire, and. 38:22

hair

when the h. in the plague. Lev 13:3
if in plague a yellow h. 30
no black h. in it. 31
there is black h. grown. 37
shave off h. 14:8, 9
the h. of his separation. Num 6:19*
sling stones h.'s breadth. Judg 20:16
not one h. of thy son. 2 Sam 14:11
because the h. was heavy on. 26
there shall not an h. of. 1 Ki 1:52
I plucked off their h. Neh 13:25
spirit passed, h. of my. Job 4:15
thy h. is as a flock. S of S 4:1; 6:5

and instead of well set *h.* *Isa* 3:24
shave the head and *h.* of feet. 7:20
to them that plucked off *h.* 50:6
cut off thy *h.* O. *Jer* 7:29
and divide the *h.* *Ezek* 5:1
thy *h.* is grown. 16:7
John had raiment of camel's *h.* *Mat* 3:4; *Mark* 1:6
canst not make one *h.* *Mat* 5:36
his feet with her *h.* *John* 11:2; 12:3
if a man have long *h.* *1 Cor* 11:14
a woman have long *h.* it is a. 15
not with broidered *h.* or. *1 Tim* 2:9
not of plaiting the *h.* *1 Pet* 3:3
black as sackcloth of *h.* *Rev* 6:12
had *h.* as the *h.* of women. 9:8
see **goats, head**

hairs

ye shall bring down my *h.* *Gen* 42:38; 44:29, 31
if there be no white *h.* *Lev* 13:21
also with man of gray *h.* *Deut* 32:25
are more than the *h.* of my head. *Ps* 40:12; 69:4
and even to hoar *h.* will. *Isa* 46:4
h. were grown like eagles'. *Dan* 4:33
gray *h.* are here and there. *Hos* 7:9
the very *h.* of your head are all numbered. *Mat* 10:30; *Luke* 12:7
did wipe them with *h.* *Luke* 7:38, 44
head and *h.* were white. *Rev* 1:14

hairy

red, all over like an *h.* *Gen* 25:25
Esau is an *h.* man. 27:11
his hands were *h.* 23
Elijah was an *h.* man. *2 Ki* 1:8
the *h.* scalp of such an one. *Ps* 68:21

hale

lest adversary *h.* thee. *Luke* 12:58†

half

Moses took *h.* the blood, *h.* *Ex* 24:6
of sweet cinnamon *h.* so much. 30:23
h. of it in morning, and *h.* *Lev* 6:20
of whom the flesh is *h.* *Num* 12:12
take it of their *h.* and give it. 31:29
h. of them over against. *Josh* 8:33
within as it were an *h.* *1 Sam* 14:14
Hanun shaved off one *h.* *2 Sam* 10:4
nor if *h.* of us die, will they. 18:3
h. the people of Israel. 19:40
h. of the child to one, *h.* *1 Ki* 3:25
h. was not told. 10:7; *2 Chr* 9:6
give me *h.* thine house. *1 Ki* 13:8
h. of people followed Tibni, *h.* 16:21
the ruler of the *h.* part. *Neh* 3:9, 12
h. part of Bethzur. 16
h. of Keilah. 17, 18
children spake *h.* in speech. 13:24
to the *h.* of the kingdom. *Esth* 5:3
7:2; *Mark* 6:23
bloody men shall not live *h.* *Ps* 55:23
Samaria committed *h.* *Ezek* 16:51
be for time, times, and an *h.* *Dan* 12:7; *Rev* 12:14
I bought her for *h.* an. *Hos* 3:2
h. of the city shall go. *Zech* 14:2
h. of mount toward the south. 4
h. toward the sea. 8
leaving him *h.* dead. *Luke* 10:30
behold, the *h.* of my goods. 19:8
silence about space of *h.* *Rev* 8:1
bodies three days and an *h.* 11:9, 11
see **shekel, tribe**

haling

Saul *h.* men and women. *Acts* 8:3†

hall

Jesus into common *h.* *Mat* 27:27*
led him away to the *h.* *Mark* 15:16*
fire in midst of the *h.* *Luke* 22:55*
see **judgement**

hallow

children of Israel shall *h.* *Ex* 28:38
h. them to minister to me in. 29:1
things which they *h.* to. *Lev* 22:2, 3
hallowed, I am the Lord which *h.* 32
h. the fiftieth year, proclaim. 25:10
and he shall *h.* his head. *Num* 6:11
same day did king *h.* court. *1 Ki* 8:64; *2 Chr* 7:7
h. ye sabbath. *Jer* 17:22, 24, 27
and *h.* my sabbaths. *Ezek* 20:20
keep laws and *h.* my sabbaths. 44:24

hallowed

the sabbath day and *h.* it. *Ex* 20:11
Aaron shall be *h.* and his. 29:21
she shall touch no *h.* *Lev* 12:4
he hath profaned the *h.* 19:8*
I will be *h.* among children. 22:32
h. me all the firstborn. *Num* 3:13
and every man's *h.* things. 5:10
censers, for they are *h.* 16:37*, 38*
of all the *h.* things I have. 18:8
the *h.* part thereof out of it. 29
have brought away *h.* *Deut* 26:13
common, but there is *h.* *1 Sam* 21:4*
the priest gave him *h.* bread. 6*
I have *h.* this house. *1 Ki* 9:3, 7
Jehoash took all the *h.* *2 Ki* 12:18
polluted the house of Lord which he had *h.* *2 Chr* 36:14
h. be thy name. *Mat* 6:9; *Luke* 11:2

halt

(*Lame, limping*)

is better to enter into life *h.* *Mat* 18:8*; *Mark* 9:45
bring in hither the *h.* *Luke* 14:21*
of *h.* waiting for moving. *John* 5:3

halt

how long *h.* ye between? *1 Ki* 18:21†
ready to *h.*, my sorrow is. *Ps* 38:17†

halted

Jacob passed, he *h.* *Gen* 32:31
I will make her that *h.* *Mi* 4:7

halteth

will assemble her that *h.* *Mi* 4:6†
I will save her that *h.* *Zeph* 3:19†

halting

familiars watched for my *h.* *Jer* 20:10†

Ham

Noah begat Shem, *H.* *Gen* 5:32
6:10; 9:18; 10:1; *1 Chr* 1:4
selfsame day *H.* *Gen* 7:13
H. is the father of Canaan. 9:18
sons of *H.* 10:6; 20; *1 Chr* 1:8
smote the Zuzims in *H.* *Gen* 14:5
they of *H.* had dwelt. *1 Chr* 4:40
in the tabernacles of *H.* *Ps* 78:51
sojourned in the land of *H.* 105:23
wonders in land of *H.* 27; 106:22

Haman

king promoted *H.* *Esth* 3:1
king's servants reverenced *H.* 2
H. full of wrath. 5
wherefore *H.* sought to destroy. 6
cast the lot before *H.* 7
and the king and *H.* sat down. 15
H. promised to pay. 4:7
H. came to banquet. 5:4, 5, 8; 7:1
went *H.* forth that day joyful. 5:9
H. told them of the glory of his. 11
the thing pleased *H.* 14
H. standeth in the court. 6:5
H. thought in his heart. 6
then *H.* took the apparel. 11
H. hasted to his house mourning. 12
H. told Zeresh his wife. 13
this wicked *H.* 7:6
H. made request. 7
H. was fallen on the bed. 8
so they hanged *H.* 10
gave Esther the house of *H.* 8:1
slew the sons of *H.* 9:10
they hanged *H.*'s ten sons. 14

Hamath

as men come to *H.* *Num* 13:21
Hor to the entrance of *H.* 34:8
Josh 13:5; *Judg* 3:3; *1 Ki* 8:65
2 Ki 14:25; *2 Chr* 7:8
king of *H.* *2 Sam* 8:9; *1 Chr* 18:9
Jeroboam recovered *H.* *2 Ki* 14:28
Assyria brought men from *H.* 17:24
the men of *H.* made Ashima. 30
the gods of *H.*? 18:34; *Isa* 36:19
where is the king of *H.*? *2 Ki* 19:13
Isa 37:13
put in bands in the land of *H.* *2 Ki* 23:33; 25:21
smote Hadarezer to *H.* *1 Chr* 18:3
built store cities in *H.* *2 Chr* 8:4
is not *H.* as Arpad? *Isa* 10:9
recover his people from *H.* 11:11
to *H.* where he gave. *Jer* 39:5; 52:9
Damascus, *H.* is confounded. 49:23
on the north, *H.* *Ezek* 47:16, 17
till a man come over against *H.* 20
H. also shall border. *Zech* 9:2

Hammedatha

the son of *H.* *Esth* 8:5; 9:10, 24

hammer

then Jael took an *h.* in. *Judg* 4:21
with *h.* she smote Sisera. 5:26
neither *h.* nor axe heard. *1 Ki* 6:7
smootheth with the *h.* *Isa* 41:7
like a *h.* that breaketh. *Jer* 23:29
how is the *h.* of whole earth. 50:23

hammers

the carved work with *h.* *Ps* 74:6
fashioneth it with *h.* *Isa* 44:12
fasten it with nails and *h.* *Jer* 10:4

Hamon-Gog

call it the valley of *H.* *Ezek* 39:11
have buried it in the valley of *H.* 15

Hamor

field of the children of *H.* Shechem's father. *Gen* 33:19; *Josh* 24:32
H. went out to commune. *Gen* 34:6, 8
to *H.* and Shechem hearkened all. 24
they slew *H.* and Shechem. 26
serve the men of *H.* *Judg* 9:28

Hanameel

H. thine uncle's son. *Jer* 32:7, 8
bought the field of *H.* my uncle's. 9
evidence to Baruch in sight of *H.* 12

Hananeel

tower of *H.* *Neh* 3:1; 12:39
Jer 31:38; *Zech* 14:10

Hanani

to Jehu son of *H.* the. *1 Ki* 16:1
H. son of Heman. *1 Chr* 25:4
18th lot to *H.* 25
at that time *H.* the seer. *2 Chr* 16:7
Jehu son of *H.* went to meet. 19:2
in book of Jehu son of *H.* 20:34
of the sons of Imman, *H.* *Ezra* 10:20
H. one of my brethren. *Neh* 1:2
I gave my brother *H.* charge. 7:2
H. with the musical. 12:36

Hananiah

Meshullam and *H.* and. *1 Chr* 3:19
the sons of *H.* 21
H. Benjamite. 8:24
H. son of Heman. 25:4
sixteenth lot to *H.* 23
Uzziah had an host under *H.* *2 Chr* 26:11
sons of Bebai; *H.* Zabbai. *Ezra* 10:28
H. the son of an. *Neh* 3:8
I gave *H.* ruler of palace. 7:2
H. sealed. 10:23
chief fathers: *H.* 12:12, 41
H. son of Azur the prophet. *Jer* 28:1
H. spake in the presence of all. 11
after that *H.* had broken. 12
H. died that year in the seventh. 17
Zedekiah son of *H.* sat in. 36:12
Irijah the son of *H.* took. 37:13
of Judah, Daniel, *H.* *Dan* 1:6
he gave to *H.* the name of. 7
Melzar was set over Daniel, *H.* 11
was found none like Daniel, *H.* 19
made the thing known to *H.* 2:17

hand

The word hand is sometimes used for power, as in 1 Sam 5:6, 7. *This is especially the case where the expression right hand is used.*

To pour water on any one's hands, meant to serve him, 2 Ki 3:11.

To wash one's hands, denoted that the person was innocent of crime, Deut 21:6, 7; Mat 27:24.

To kiss one's hand, is an act of adoration, Job 31:27.

To lift up one's hand, is a way of taking an oath in use with all nations, Gen 14:22. *It was likewise a posture used in praying for a blessing,* Lev 9:22. *To lift up the hand against one, is to rebel against him,* 2 Sam 20:21.

To give one's hand, means to swear friendship, to promise security, to make alliance, **2 Ki 10:15.**

The right hand *denotes power, strength. The scripture generally imputes to God's right hand all the effects of his omnipotence,* Ex 15:6; Ps 17:7; 20:6; 44:3.

Often, to be at one's right hand signifies to defend, to protect, to support, Ps 16:8; 109:31.

Laying on of hands is understood in different ways both in the Old and New Testaments. [1] *It is often taken for ordination and consecration of priests and ministers, as well among the Jews as the Christians,* Num 8:10; Acts 6:6; 13:3; 1 Tim 4:14. [2] *It is sometimes also made use of to signify the establishment of judges and magistrates,* Gen 48:14; Num 27:18.

into your *h.* are they. *Gen* 9:2
all that he had in Joseph's *h.* 39:6
man in whose *h.* the cup. 44:17
with a strong *h.* shall he. *Ex* 6:1
by strength of *h.* Lord brought. 13:3
Israel went out with an high *h.* 14:8
Num 33:3
stretch out thine *h.* over. *Ex* 14:16
there shall not a *h.* touch it. 19:13
h. for *h.*, foot for. 21:24; *Deut* 19:21
testimony in Moses' *h.* *Ex* 34:29
on this *h.* and that *h.* 38:15
remain in the *h.* of him. *Lev* 25:28
afterwards the *h.* of all. *Deut* 13:9
thou shalt cut off her *h.* 25:12
on our head if any *h.* *Josh* 2:19
h. of the house of Joseph. *Judg* 1:35
Lord shall sell Sisera into *h.* 4:9
now fall into the *h.* of the. 15:18
smote all that came to *h.* of. 20:48*
of whose *h.* have I? *1 Sam* 12:3
nor spear found in the *h.* of. 13:22
was no sword in the *h.* of. 17:50
when the business was in *h.* 20:19
their *h.* also is with David. 22:17
and eat it at her *h.* *2 Sam* 13:5, 6
is not the *h.* of Joab with? 14:19
h. six fingers. 21:20; *1 Chr* 20:6
let me not fall into *h.* of men.
2 Sam 24:14; *1 Chr* 21:13
kingdom established in *h.* *1 Ki* 2:46
and the king's *h.* was restored. 13:6
a cloud like a man's *h.* 18:44
Lord shall deliver it into the king's *h.*
22:6, 12, 15; *2 Chr* 28:5
lord on whose *h.* the. *2 Ki* 7:2, 17
went out from under the *h.* 13:5
hath Lord left you in *h.* *2 Chr* 12:5
according to good *h.* of his. *Ezra* 7:9
the *h.* of princes hath been. 9:2
earth is given into *h.* of. *Job* 9:24
into whose *h.* God bringeth. 12:6
in whose *h.* is the soul of every. 10
every *h.* of the wicked shall. 20:22
their good is not in their *h.* 21:16
mighty taken away without *h.* 34:20
he sealeth up the *h.* of every. 37:7
hast not shut me into *h.* *Ps* 31:8
let not the *h.* of the wicked. 36:11
deliver me out of *h.* of wicked.
71:4; 82:4; 97:10
servants look to the *h.* 123:2
as arrows are in the *h.* of. 127:4
two-edged sword be in their *h.* 149:6
thou art come into *h.* *Pr* 6:3
with a slack *h.* but the *h.* of. *Pr* 10:4
though *h.* join in *h.*, the wicked shall
not be unpunished. 11:21; 16:5
the *h.* of the diligent shall. 12:24
why a price in *h.* of a fool? 17:16
as a thorn goeth up into the *h.* 26:9
the staff in their *h.* is. *Isa* 10:5
shake the *h.* that they may go. 13:2
this is the *h.* that is stretched. 14:26
I will give over into the *h.* 19:4
down to the earth with the *h.* 28:2
dearly beloved into *h.* of. *Jer* 12:7
vessel was marred in the *h.* 18:4
as clay in the potter's *h.* so are. 6
with an outstretched *h.* I will. 21:5
h. of Ahikam was with Jeremiah, not
to give him into *h.* of people. 26:24
she hath given her *h.* 50:15*

we have given the *h.* to. *Lam* 5:6
princes are hanged up by their *h.* 12
an *h.* was sent me, and lo. *Ezek* 2:9
forth the form of an *h.* 8:3; 10:8
nor did she strengthen *h.* of. 16:49
shall be taken with the *h.* 21:24
no god in the *h.* of him that. 28:9
require my flock at their *h.* 34:10
stick which is in the *h.* of. 37:19
in man's *h.* a measuring reed. 40:5
forth fingers of a man's *h.* *Dan* 5:5
God in whose *h.* thy breath is. 23
he shall be broken without *h.* 8:25
behold, an *h.* touched me. 10:10
and daughters into *h.* *Joel* 3:8
in the power of their *h.* *Mi* 2:1
shall see plummet in *h.* *Zech* 4:10
he touched her *h.* *Mat* 8:15
bind him *h.* and foot. 22:13
a man who had a withered *h.*
Mark 3:1, 3; *Luke* 6:8
is betrayed into *h.* *Mark* 14:41
as many have taken in *h.* *Luke* 1:1
being delivered out of the *h.* 74
the *h.* of him that betrayeth. 22:21
escaped out of their *h.* *John* 10:39
dead came forth, bound *h.* 11:44
beckoning to them with *h.* *Acts* 12:17
because I am not the *h.* *1 Cor* 12:15
eye cannot say to the *h.* I have. 21
ordained by angels in the *h.* *Gal* 3:19
take little book open in *h.* *Rev* 10:8
having a golden cup in her *h.* 17:4
blood of his servants at her *h.* 19:2

at **hand**, or *at the* **hand**

at the h. of every beast, *at the h.* of
man, *at the h.* of man's. *Gen* 9:5
days of mourning for my father are
at h. 27:41
field Jacob bought *at h.* of. 33:19
year of release is *at h.* *Deut* 15:9
day of their calamity is *at h.* 32:35
I have here *at h.* fourth. *1 Sam* 9:8
Lord require it *at h.* of. 20:16
avenge blood *at the h.* of. *2 Ki* 9:7
was *at the* king's *h.* in. *Neh* 11:24
day of Lord is *at h.* *Isa* 13:6
Joel 1:15; *Zeph* 1:7
am I a God *at h.* and? *Jer* 23:23
the days are *at h.* and. *Ezek* 12:23
I require *at* watchman's *h.* 33:6
fruit, for they are *at h.* to. 36:8
cometh, it is nigh *at h.* *Joel* 2:1
kingdom of heaven is *at h.*
Mat 3:2; 4:17; 10:7
my time is *at h.* 26:18
the hour is *at h.* 45
he is *at h.* that doth. 46; *Mark* 14:42
kingdom of God is *at h.* *Mark* 1:15
Luke 21:31
summer is now nigh *at h.* *Luke* 21:30
and the Jews' passover was *at h.*
John 2:13; 11:55
feast of tabernacles was *at h.* 7:2
sepulchre was nigh *at h.* 19:42
spent, the day is *at h.* *Rom* 13:12
be known, Lord is *at h.* *Phil* 4:5
the day of Christ is *at h.* *2 Thes* 2:2*
my departure is *at h.* *2 Tim* 4:6*
end of all things is *at h.* *1 Pet* 4:7
for time is *at h.* *Rev* 1:3; 22:10

by the **hand**

send *by h.* of him whom. *Ex* 4:13
of tabernacle counted *by h.* 38:21
Lord commanded *by h.* *Lev* 8:36
10:11; 26:46; *Num* 4:37, 45, 49
9:23; 10:13; 15:23; 16:40; 27:23
36:13; *Josh* 14:2; 20:2; 21:2, 8
22:9; *Judg* 3:4; *1 Ki* 8:53, 56
2 Chr 33:8; 35:6; *Neh* 9:14
Ps 77:20
send him away *by the h.* *Lev* 16:21
by the h. of avenger of. *Josh* 20:9
lad that held *by the h.* *Judg* 16:26
David fall *by the h.* of. *1 Sam* 18:25
one day perish *by the h.* of. 27:1
by the h. of my servant. *2 Sam* 3:18
comfort him *by h.* of servants. 10:2
letter, sent it *by h.* of Uriah. 11:14
sent *by the h.* of Nathan the. 12:25
these fell *by the h.* of David. 21:22
1 Chr 20:8
Solomon sent *by the h.* *1 Ki* 2:25

by the h. of his servant. *1 Ki* 14:18
by the h. of Jehu came. 16:7
spake *by the h.* of Jonah. *2 Ki* 14:25
by the h. of Jeroboam. 27
spake *by h.* of Ahijah. *2 Chr* 10:15
not pour out wrath *by the h.* 12:7
out vessels *by the h.* of. *Ezra* 1:8
weighed *by the h.* of. 8:33
sendeth a message *by h.* *Pr* 26:6
taketh her *by the h.* *Isa* 51:18
send yokes *by the h.* of. *Jer* 27:3
in the day I took them *by the h.* 31:32
Heb 8:9
on Edom *by h.* of Israel. *Ezek* 25:14
lay the land waste *by h.* of. 30:12
took her *by the h.* *Mat* 9:25
Mark 1:31; 5:41; *Luke* 8:54
took the blind man *by h.* *Mark* 8:23
that was possessed *by the h.* 9:27
to be a deliverer *by h.* *Acts* 7:35
they led him *by the h.* 9:8
some to lead him *by the h.* 13:11
the salutation *by the h.* *Col* 4:18
see **Chaldeans, enemy**

hand joined with *enemies*.

may save us out of the *h.* of our *e.*
1 Sam 4:3; 12:10; *2 Sam* 3:18
deliver you out of *h.* of *e.*
1 Sam 12:11; *2 Ki* 17:39
saved us out of the *h.* of our *e.*
2 Sam 19:9
into the *h.* of their *e.* *2 Ki* 21:14
2 Chr 25:20; *Neh* 9:27
them in *h.* of their *e.* *Neh* 9:28
me from *h.* of mine *e.* *Ps* 31:15
this city into *h.* of their *e.* *Jer* 20:5
21:7; 34:20, 21; *Ezek* 39:23
give Pharaoh into *h.* of his *e.* 44:30
thee from the *h.* of thy *e.* *Mi* 4:10
out of the *h.* of our *e.* *Luke* 1:74

from the **hand**

deliver me *from h.* of my. *Gen* 32:11
redeemed you *from the h.* *Deut* 7:8
delivered us *from h.* of. *Judg* 8:22
my reproach *from h.* of. *1 Sam* 25:39
saveth the poor *from the h.* *Job* 5:15
redeem me *from the h.* of the. 6:23
deliver his soul *from the h.* *Ps* 89:48
from the h. of him that hated, and
redeemed them *from h.* 106:10
me *from h.* of strange. 144:7, 11
thyself as a roe *from h.* of. *Pr* 6:5
poor *from h.* of evil. *Jer* 20:13
from h. of him that was. 31:11
be saved *from the h.* *Luke* 1:71

hand *of God*

h. of God was heavy. *1 Sam* 5:11
h. of God was to give. *2 Chr* 30:12
according to the good *h. of God.*
Ezra 7:9; *Neh* 2:8
by good *h. of God* upon us. 8:18
h. of God is upon all them for. 22
the *h. of God* is upon us. 31
told them of *h. of God.* *Neh* 2:18
good at the *h. of God?* *Job* 2:10
pity on me, *h. of God* hath. 19:21
teach you by the *h. of God.* 27:11
it was from the *h. of God.* *Eccl* 2:24
works are in the *h. of God.* 9:1
diadem in *h. of* thy *God.* *Isa* 62:3
heaven, and sat on right *h. of God.*
Mark 16:19; *Rom* 8:34; *Col* 3:1
Heb 10:12; *1 Pet* 3:22
by the right *h. of God.* *Acts* 2:33
standing on right *h. of G.* 7:55, 56
under the *h. of God.* *1 Pet* 5:6

his **hand**

lest he put forth *his h.* *Gen* 3:22
his h. will be against every. 16:12
men laid hold on *his h.* 19:16
of his master were in *his h.* 24:10
that which came to *his h.* 32:13*
that he did prosper in *his h.* 39:3
Pharaoh took ring off *his h.* 41:42
his h., and caught it and it became
a rod in *his h.* *Ex* 4:4
when he took it out, *his h.* was. 6
took the rod of God in *his h.* 20
out *his h.* over the waters. 8:6, 17
Moses stretched forth *his h.* 10:22
held up *his h.* let down *his h.* 17:11
God delivered him into *his h.* 21:13

if found in *his h.* *Ex* 21:16
he die under *his h.* 20
theft be certainly found in *his h.* 22:4
he hath put *his h.* to goods. 8, 11
on the nobles he laid not *his h.* 24:11
testimony were in *his h.* 32:15; 34:4
shall put *his h.* on head. *Lev* 1:4
priest shall have in *his h.* *Num* 5:18
beside that that *his h.* shall. 6:21*
all his land out of *his h.* 21:26
his sword drawn in *his h.* 22:23, 31
1 Chr 21:16
took a javelin in *his h.* *Num* 25:7
his h. fetcheth a stroke. *Deut* 19:5
man with his sword drawn in *his h.*
Josh 5:13
Joshua drew not *his h.* back. 8:26
deliver the slayer up into *his h.* 20:5
end of the staff in *his h.* *Judg* 6:21
into *his h.* hath God delivered. 7:14
his h. is not removed. *1 Sam* 6:3
it is not *his h.* that smote us. 9
no man put *his h.* to his. 14:26
Jonathan put *his h.* to his. 27
he shall play with *his h.* 16:16
harp and played with *his h.* 23; 18:10
staff and his sling in *his h.* 17:40
head of the Philistine in *his h.* 57
he put his life in *his h.* and. 19:5
strengthened *his h.* in God. 23:16
Uzzah put *his h.* to ark. *2 Sam* 6:6
1 Chr 13:10
and hath with *his h.* *1 Ki* 8:15
whole kingdom out of *his h.* 11:34
his h. which he put forth. 13:4
strike *his h.* over place. *2 Ki* 5:11
he gave *his h.* took him up. 10:15
every man with his weapons in *his h.*
11:8, 11; *2 Chr* 23:7
was confirmed in *his h.* *2 Ki* 14:5
his h. might be with him to. 15:19
man lean, it will go into *his h.* 18:21
save us out of *his h.* 19:19
understand by *his h.* *1 Chr* 28:19
had a censer in *his h.* *2 Chr* 26:19
he gave them all into *his h.* 36:17
with open letter in *his h.* *Neh* 6:5
he would let loose *his h.* *Job* 6:9
darkness is ready at *his h.* 15:23
he stretcheth out *his h.* against. 25
his h. hath formed the. 26:13
would fain flee out of *his h.* 27:22
he putteth forth *his h.* upon. 28:9
upholdeth him with *his h.* *Ps* 37:24
will not leave him in *his h.* 33
they remembered not *his h.* 78:42
I will set *his h.* also in sea. 89:25
in *his h.* are the deep places. 95:4
sheep of *his h.* To-day, if ye will. 7
therefore he lifted up *his h.* 106:26
the mower filleth not *his h.* 129:7
a slothful man hideth *his h.* *Pr* 19:24
26:15
and nothing is in his *h.* *Eccl* 5:14
he may carry away in *his h.* 15
beloved put in *his h.* *S of S* 5:4
his h. is stretched out still. *Isa* 5:25
9:12, 17, 21; 10:4; 14:27
shall shake *his h.* against. *Isa* 10:32
Lord shall set *his h.* again. 11:11
shake *his h.* over the river. 15
thy government into *his h.* 22:21
while it is yet in *his h.* he. 28:4
Lord shall stretch out *his h.* 31:3
Lord, save us from *his h.* 37:20
waters in hollow of *his h.* 40:12
shall subscribe with *his h.* to. 44:5
in the shadow of *his h.* hath. 49:2
of Lord shall prosper in *his h.* 53:10
keepeth *his h.* from doing. 56:2
consumed them by *his h.* *Jer* 27:8
my transgression bound by *his h.*
Lam 1:14
he hath not withdrawn *his h.* 2:8
he turneth *his h.* against me. 3:3
with his censer in *his h.* *Ezek* 8:11
his destroying weapon in *his h.* 9:1
lo, he had given *his h.* 17:18
the sword to fall out of *his h.* 30:22
I will put my sword in *his h.* 24
according as *his h.* shall. 46:7*
none can stay *his h.* or. *Dan* 4:35
could deliver out of *his h.* 8:4, 7
cause craft to prosper in *his h.* 25

multitude be given into *his h.*
Dan 11:11
but these shall escape out of *his h.* 41
he stretched out *his h.* *Hos* 7:5
balances of deceit are in *his h.* 12:7
horns coming out of *his h.* *Hab* 3:4
hiss, and wag *his h.* *Zeph* 2:15
man with staff in *his h.* *Zech* 8:4
his h. rise up against hand. 14:13
whose fan is in *his h.* *Mat* 3:12
Luke 3:17
he that dippeth *his h.* *Mat* 26:23
and *his h.* was restored whole.
Mark 3:5; *Luke* 6:10
beseech him to put *his h.* *Mark* 7:32
man having put *his h.* to. *Luke* 9:62
a ring on *his h.*, and shoes. 15:22
all things into *his h.* *John* 3:35
him with the palm of *his h.* 18:22
how God by *his h.* *Acts* 7:25
a viper fastened on *his h.* 28:3
hang on *his h.* 4
pair of balances in *his h.* *Rev* 6:5
and he had in *his h.* a little. 10:2
in his forehead, or in *his h.* 14:9
crown, and in *his h.* sharp sickle. 14
with a great chain in *his h.* 20:1

hand *of the Lord,* or *Lord's* **hand**

the *h. of the Lord* is upon. *Ex* 9:3
had died by *h. of the Lord.* 16:3
is *Lord's h.* waxed? *Num* 11:23
h. of the Lord was against them to destroy. *Deut* 2:15
know that *h. of Lord* is. *Josh* 4:24
Israel out of *h. of the Lord.* 22:31
the *h. of the Lord* was against them for evil. *Judg* 2:15
h. of the Lord is gone. *Ruth* 1:13
h. of Lord was heavy. *1 Sam* 5:6
h. of Lord was against the city. 9
the *h. of the Lord* was against the Philistines. 7:13
then shall *h. of the Lord* be. 12:15
let us now fall into *h. of the Lord.*
2 Sam 24:14; *1 Chr* 21:13
h. of the Lord was on. *1 Ki* 18:46
h. of the Lord came upon. *2 Ki* 3:15
according to *h. of Lord.* *Ezra* 7:6
h. of Lord hath wrought this.
Job 12:9; *Isa* 40:20
in *h. of the Lord* there. *Ps* 75:8
heart is in *h. of the Lord.* *Pr* 21:1
shaking of the *h. of Lord.* *Isa* 19:16
mountain shall *h. of the Lord.* 25:10
received of *the Lord's h.* 40:2
hast drunk at *h. of Lord* cup. 51:17
Lord's h. is not shortened. 59:1
a crown of glory in *h. of Lord.* 62:3
h. of Lord shall be known. 66:14
the cup at the *Lord's h.* *Jer* 25:17
been a golden cup in *Lord's h.* 51:7
h. of the Lord was there. *Ezek* 1:3
the *h. of the L.* was upon me. 3:14
22; 8:1; 37:1
h. of the Lord was on me. 33:22
selfsame day the *h. of Lord.* 40:1
and the *h. of the Lord* was with him.
Luke 1:66; *Acts* 11:21
behold, the *h. of the Lord* is.
Acts 13:11

see **lay,** *or* **laid**

left **hand**

if thou wilt take *left h.* I. *Gen* 13:9
Hobah which is on *left h.* of. 14:15
to the right *h.* or to the *left.* 24:49
his right hand toward Israel's *left h.* and Manasseh in his *left h.* 48:13
Israel laid his *left h.* upon. 14
wall on right *h.* and *left.* *Ex* 14:22
oil into his own *left h.* *Lev* 14:15, 27
we will not turn to the right *h.* nor to the *left.* *Num* 20:17; *Deut* 2:27
5:32; 17:11, 20; 28:14
either to right *h.* or *left.* *Num* 22:26
from it to right *h.* or to *left.* *Josh* 1:7
23:6; *1 Sam* 6:12; *Pr* 4:27
Ehud put forth *left h.* *Judg* 3:21
held lamps in their *left h.* 7:20
hold of other pillar with *left h.* 16:29
he turned not to *left h.* *2 Sam* 2:19
none can turn to right *h.* or to *left.*
14:19
were on right *h.* and *left.* 16:6

host of heaven on his *left h.*
1 Ki 22:19; *2 Chr* 18:18
Josiah turned not to the right *h.* or *left.* *2 Ki* 22:2
which were on a man's *left h.* 23:8
Merari stood on *left h.* *1 Chr* 6:44
use both right *h.* and *left* in. 12:2
name of that on *left h.* *2 Chr* 3:17
and he put five on the *left h.* 4:6
on the right, five on the *left h.* 7
on pulpit, on his *left h.* *Neh* 8:4
on *left h.* he doth work. *Job* 23:9
and in her *left h.* riches. *Pr* 3:16
fool's heart is at his *left h.* *Eccl* 10:2
his *left h.* is under my head.
S of S 2:6; 8:3
he shall eat on *left h.* and. *Isa* 9:20
when ye turn to the *left h.* 30:21
forth on the right *h.* and *left.* 54:3
dwell at thy *left h.* *Ezek* 16:46
on the right *h.* or on the *left.* 21:16
smite thy bow out of thy *left h.* 39:3
he held up his *left h.* to. *Dan* 12:7
between right *h.* and *left.* *Jonah* 4:11
all people on right *h.* and *left.*
Zech 12:6
let not *left h.* know what. *Mat* 6:3
one on right *h.* other on *left.* 20:21
Mark 10:37
to sit on right *h.* and *left* not mine.
Mat 20:23; *Mark* 10:40
right *h.*, goats on *left.* *Mat* 25:33
shall say to them on *left h.* 41
crucified on right *h.* other on *left.*
27:38; *Mark* 15:27; *Luke* 23:33
Cyprus on the *left h.* *Acts* 21:3
righteousness on right *h.* and *left.*
2 Cor 6:7

see **lift** *hand* or *hands*

mighty **hand**

go, no not with *mighty h.* *Ex* 3:19
forth with *mighty h.* 32:11
servant thy *mighty h.* *Deut* 3:24
him a nation by a *mighty h.* 4:34
God brought thee out of Egypt through a *mighty h.* 5:15; 6:21
7:8, 19; 9:26; 11:2
26:8; 34:12
come for thy *mighty h.* *2 Chr* 6:32
a *mighty h.* will I rule. *Ezek* 20:33
bring you out with a *mighty h.* 34
you out of Egypt with *mighty h.*
Dan 9:15
under *mighty h.* of God. *1 Pet* 5:6

mine and *my* **hand**

I have lifted up *mine h.* *Gen* 14:22
lambs shalt thou take of *my h.* 21:30
it is in power of *my h.* to do. 31:29
I bear loss, of *my h.* didst thou. 39
receive my present at *my h.* 33:10
deliver him into *my h.* I will. 42:37
I will be surety, of *my h.* shalt. 43:9
with rod that is in *mine h.* *Ex* 7:17
my h. shall destroy them. 15:9
rod in *mine h.* 17:9
will cover thee with *mine h.* 33:22
I will take away *mine h.* and thou. 23
this people into *my h.* *Num* 21:2
there were a sword in *mine h.* 22:29
might of *my h.* hath. *Deut* 8:17
the two tables in *mine h.* 10:3
neither any that can deliver out of *my h.* 32:39; *Isa* 43:13
I lift up *my h.* to heaven. *Deut* 32:40
and if *mine h.* take hold on. 41
save Israel by *my h.* *Judg* 6:36, 37
lest vaunt, saying, *mine* own *h.* 7:2
delivered Zeba into *mine h.* 8:7
this people were under *my h.* 9:29
Lord delivered them into *my h.* 12:3
silver unto Lord from *my h.* 17:3
not found aught in *my h.* *1 Sam* 12:5
this day into *mine h.* 17:46
let not *mine h.* be upon him. 18:17
common bread under *mine h.* 21:4
delivered him into *mine h.* 23:7
stretch *mine h.* against Lord's. 24:6
see the skirt in *my h.*, no transgression in *mine h.* 11
mine h. shall not be upon. 12, 13
into *mine h.* to day. 24:10; 26:23
what evil is in *mine h.*? 26:18
I have put my life in *my h.* 28:21

my h. shall be with. 2 Sam 3:12
deliver Philistines into mine h.? 5:19; 1 Chr 14:10
forth mine h. against Absalom. 2 Sam 18:12
that my h. may be. 1 Ki 13:6
leaneth on my h. in. 2 Ki 5:18
Samaria out of my h.? 18:34
out of mine h., that Lord should deliver Jerusalem out of mine h.? 35
of land into my h. 1 Chr 22:18
you out of my h.? 2 Chr 32:15, 17
put my life into mine h.? Job 13:14
bow was renewed in my h. 29:20
rejoiced because mine h. had. 31:25
or my mouth hath kissed my h. 27
neither shall my h. be heavy. 33:7*
turned my h. against. Ps 81:14
with whom my h. shall be. 89:21
soul is continually in my h. 119:109
stretched out my h. Pr 1:24
I will turn my h. upon. Isa 1:25
as my h. hath found the. 10:10
by the strength of my h. I have. 13
my h. hath found as a nest the. 14
Samaria out of my h.? 36:19
deliver Jerusalem out of my h. 20
mine h. also hath laid. 48:13
is my h. shortened at all? 50:2
this ye have of my h. 11
in the shadow of mine h. 51:16
mine h. made. 66:2; Acts 7:50
I will stretch out my h. Jer 6:12
15:6; 51:25
cause them to know mine h. 16:21
so are ye in mine h. O house. 18:6
wine cup of this fury at my h. 25:15
will I stretch out my h. Ezek 6:14
digged through wall with my h. 12:7
mine h. shall be upon prophets. 13:9
mine h., saying I am the Lord. 20:5, 6
23, 28, 42; 36:7; 44:12; 47:14
withdrew my h. and wrought. 20:22
I have smitten mine h. at thy. 22:13
they shall be one in mine h. 37:19
deliver her out of mine h. Hos 2:10
I will turn mine h. Amos 1:8
into hell, thence shall mine h. 9:2
I will shake mine h. Zech 2:9
I will turn mine h. upon the. 13:7
pluck them out of my h. John 10:28
pluck them out of my Father's h. 29
except I shall thrust my h. 20:25
salutation of me Paul with mine own h. 1 Cor 16:21; 2 Thes 3:17
I have written with my h. Gal 6:11
Philem 19

our hand

let not our h. be on him. Gen 37:27
have brought it again in our h. 43:21
say, Our h. is high. Deut 32:27
Samson into our h. Judg 16:23
Lord hath delivered them into our h.
1 Sam 14:10; 30:23
thou die not by our h. Jer 11:21
made ready to our h. 2 Cor 10:16

out of hand, or out of the hand

I took out of the h. of. Gen 48:22
Egyptian delivered us out of h. of.
Ex 2:19
out of h. of Egyptians. 3:8; 14:30
offering out of woman's h. Num 5:25
kill me, I pray thee, out of h. 11:15
deliver him out of h. of the. 35:25
out of the h. of Israel. Josh 9:26
judges which delivered them out of the h. Judg 2:16
delivered you out of the h. 6:9
out of the h. of the Philistines. 13:5
out of h. of these gods? 1 Sam 4:8
me out of h. of this Philistine. 17:37
delivered thee out of h. of Saul.
2 Sam 12:7; 22:1
pear out of the Egyptian's h. 23:21
ingdom out of h. of. 1 Ki 11:12, 31
e take it not out of h. of. 22:3
ook again out of h. of. 2 Ki 13:25
ut of h. of the king of Assyria. 20:6
Isa 38:6
eliver me out of h. of. Ps 71:4
d them out of the h. of. 82:4
e delivereth them out of h. 97:10
ut of h. of the wicked. Jer 15:21

spoiled out of h. of. Jer 21:12; 22:3
not escape out of h. 32:4; 38:18, 23
deliver us out of their h. Lam 5:8
out of their h. I will not. Zech 11:6
escaped out of their h. John 10:39
out of the h. of Herod. Acts 12:11
ascended before God out of angel's h. Rev 8:4; 10:10

right hand

right h. on Ephraim's. Gen 48:14, 18
thy right h. O Lord, is. Ex 15:6
the thumb of their right h. 29:20
Lev 8:23, 24; 14:14, 17, 25, 28
from his right h. went. Deut 33:2
right h. to workman's. Judg 5:26
Amasa with right h. 2 Sam 20:9
on Solomon's right h. 1 Ki 2:19
on right h. of mount. 2 Ki 23:13
himself on the right h. Job 23:9
upon my right h. rise the. 30:12
that thine own right h. can. 40:14
he is at my right h. I. Ps 16:8
at thy right h. are pleasures for. 11
savest by thy right h. them. 17:7
thy right h. hath holden me. 18:35
saving strength of his right h. 20:6
thy right h. shall find out. 21:8
their right h. is full of bribes. 26:10
but thy right h. and thy arm. 44:3
thy right h. shall teach thee. 45:4
on thy right h. did stand queen. 9
thy right h. is full of. 48:10
save with thy right h. and. 60:5
my soul followeth, thy right h. 63:8
holden me by my right h. 73:23
withdrawest thou thy right h.? 74:11
remember years of the right h. 77:10
mountain which his right h. 78:54
the vineyard which thy right h. 80:15
upon the man of thy right h. 17
thy hand, high is thy right h. 89:13
I will also set his right h. in the. 25
thou hast set up the right h. of his. 42
shall fall at thy right h. 91:7
his right h. hath gotten him. 98:1
save with thy right h. and. 108:6
let Satan stand at his right h. 109:6
he shall stand at the right h. of. 31
sit thou at my right h. until I. 110:1
Luke 20:42; Acts 2:34; Heb 1:13
the Lord at thy right h. Ps 110:5
the right h. of the Lord. 118:15
right h. of the Lord is exalted. 16
thy shade upon thy right h. 121:5
I forget, let my right h. forget. 137:5
and thy right h. shall save. 138:7
even there thy right h. shall. 139:10
looked on my right h., no man. 142:4
right h. is a right h. of falsehood.
144:8, 11
of days is in her right h. Pr 3:16
the ointment of his right h. 27:16
heart is at his right h. Eccl 10:2
and his right h. doth. S of S 2:6
his right h. should embrace me. 8:3
thee with right h. of. Isa 41:10
Lord thy God will hold thy right h. 13
is there not a lie in my right h.? 44:20
to Cyrus whose right h. I have. 45:1
my right h. hath spanned the. 48:13
hath sworn by his right h. 62:8
that led them by the right h. 63:12
the signet on my right h. Jer 22:24
drawn back his right h. Lam 2:3
he stood with his right h. as an. 4
at right h. divination. Ezek 21:22
cup of Lord's right h. Hab 2:16
standing at his right h. Zech 3:1
if thy right h. offend thee. Mat 5:30
not left know what thy right h. 6:3
Son of man sitting on the right h. of power. Mark 14:62; Luke 22:69
to heaven, sat on right h. of God.
Mark 16:19; Heb 1:3; 8:1
10:12; 12:2; 1 Pet 3:22
man whose right h. was. Luke 6:6
he is on my right h. I. Acts 2:25
the right h. of God exalted. 33; 5:31
he took him by the right h. and. 3:7
standing on right h. of God. 7:55, 56
is even at the right h. Rom 8:34
right h. in heavenly. Eph 1:20
sitteth on the right h. of. Col 3:1

in his right h. seven stars. Rev 1:16
20; 2:1
laid right h. upon me, saying. 1:17
I saw in his right h. a book. 5:1, 7
receive mark in their right h. 13:16

see left **hand**

to stretch forth or out hand

Abraham stretched forth his h. to slay. Gen 22:10
I will stretch out my h. on Egypt.
Ex 3:20; 7:5; 9:15
stretch out thy h. over the sea.
14:16; 26:7, 19
Moses stretched out his h. 14:21, 27
who can stretch forth hand against the Lord's anointed? 1 Sam 26:9
not afraid to stretch forth thy h.
2 Sam 1:14
stretch forth thy hand. Ps 138:7
she stretcheth out her h. Pr 31:20
I will stretch out my h. Ezek 14:9
will I stretch out mine h. upon. 13
I will stretch out mine h. upon. 25:7
I will also stretch out mine h. 13
I will stretch out mine h. on the. 16
I will stretch out mine h. against.
35:3
shall stretch forth his h. Dan 11:42
stretch out mine h. upon Judah.
Zeph 1:4
stretch out his h. against Assyria.
2:13

see **strong**

thine or thy hand

blood from thy h. Gen 4:11
thy maid is in thy h., do to. 16:6
he said, lay not thine h. upon. 22:12
thy h. under my thigh. 24:2; 47:29
thy h. shall be in the neck. 49:8
what is that in thine h.? Ex 4:2
this rod in thine h. 17; 7:15; 17:5
stretch forth thine h. over. 8:5; 9:22
10:12, 21; Mat 12:13; Mark 3:5
it shall be for a sign on thine h.
Ex 13:9, 16; Deut 6:8
put not thine h. with. Ex 23:1
delivered Og into thy h. Num 21:34
in works of thy h. Deut 2:7; 14:29
15:10; 23:20; 28:8, 12, 20
I have given into thy h. 2:24
Og and his people into thy h. 3:2
thy h. shall be first on him. 13:9
nought of cursed thing to thine h. 17
bind up money in thine h. 14:25
nor shut thine h. from thy. 15:7
thou shalt open thine h. wide to. 8
pluck the ears with thine h. 23:25
be no might in thine h. 28:32
in every work of thine h. 30:9
all the saints are in thy h. 33:3
I have given into thine h. Josh 6:2
for I will give Ai into thine h. 8:18
behold, we are in thine h. to. 9:25
slack not thy h. from thy. 10:6
kings of Canaan into thy h. 8
Sisera into thine h. Judg 4:7
the Midianites into thine h. 7:7
and Zalmunna in thine h.? 8:15
hold thy peace, lay thine h. 18:19
Benjamin into thine h. 20:28
priest, withdraw thy h. 1 Sam 14:19
what is under thine h.? give. 21:3
deliver Philistines into thine h.
23:4; 2 Sam 5:19
I may eat of thine h. 2 Sam 13:10
stay thine h. 24:16; 1 Chr 21:15
let thine h., I pray thee, be against me. 2 Sam 24:17; 1 Chr 21:17
hast fulfilled it with thine h.
1 Ki 8:24; 2 Chr 6:15
of bread in thine h. 2 Ki 17:11
Syrians into thine h. 20:13, 28
hast let go out of thy h. a man. 42
take my staff in thine h. 2 Ki 4:29
take a present in thine h. 8:8
take this box of oil in thine h. 9:1
give me thine h. and he gave. 10:15
he said, put thine h. upon. 13:16
and that thine h. might. 1 Chr 4:10
in thine h. is power and might. 29:12
for house cometh of thine h. 16
in thine h. is there not? 2 Chr 20:6
law which is in thine h. Ezra 7:14

wisdom that is in *thine h.* *Ezra* 7:25
but put forth *thine h.* and touch.
Job 1:11; 2:5
himself put not forth *thine h.* 1:12
behold, he is in *thine h.* but. 2:6
can deliver out of *thine h.* 10:7
if iniquity be in *thine h.* put. 11:14
withdraw *thine h.* far from. 13:21
what receiveth he of *thine h.*? 35:7
O God, lift up *thine h.* *Ps* 10:12
spite, to requite it with *thy h.* 14
from men which are *thy h.* 17:14
thine h. shall find out all. 21:8
into *thine h.* I commit my. 31:5
my times are in *thy h.*: deliver. 15
for day and night *thy h.* was. 32:4
thy h. presseth me. 38:2
by blow of *thine h.* 39:10
why withdrawest thou *thy h.*? 74:11
thy h. be upon the man of *thy* right *h.*
80:17
they are cut off from *thy h.* 88:5
thou openest *thy h.* 104:28; 145:16
know that this is *thy h.* 109:27
let *thine h.* help me. 119:173
laid *thine h.* on me. 139:5
even there shall *thy h.* lead. 10
send *thine h.* from above. 144:7
is in power of *thine h.* *Pr* 3:27
if thou hast stricken *thy h.* 6:1
if thought evil, lay *thy h.* upon. 30:32
withdraw not *thine h.* *Eccl* 7:18
whatsoever *thy h.* findeth to do. 9:10
evening withhold not *thine h.* 11:6
ruin be under *thy h.* *Isa* 3:6
when *thy h.* is lifted up, they. 26:11
I the Lord will hold *thine h.* 42:6
my inheritance into *thine h.* 47:6
I have taken out of *thy h.* cup. 51:22
found the life of *thine h.* 57:10
we are the work of *thy h.* 64:8
thine h. as a grape. *Jer* 6:9
I sat alone because of *thy h.* 15:17
to take the cup at *thine h.* 25:28
take in *thy h.* the roll. 36:14
chains which were upon *thine h.* 40:4
his blood will I require at *thine h.*
Ezek 3:18, 20; 33:8
smite with *thine h.* and. 6:11
and fill *thine h.* with coals. 10:2
I will give her cup into *thine h.* 23:31
took hold of thee by *thy h.* 29:7
shall become one in *thine h.* 37:17
to turn *thine h.* upon the. 38:12
he given into *thine h.* *Dan* 2:38
deliver us out of *thine h.* 3:17
thine h. shall he lift up on. *Mi* 5:9
cut off witchcrafts out of *thine h.* 12
if *thy h.* or foot offend thee.
Mat 18:8; *Mark* 9:43
reach *thy h.* and thrust. *John* 20:27
thine h. and counsel. *Acts* 4:28
stretching forth *thine h.* to heal. 30

your **hand**

your h. are they delivered. *Gen* 9:2
take double money in *your h.* 43:12
your feet, staff in *your h.* *Ex* 12:11
of the land into *your h.* 23:31
rejoice in all ye put *your h.* to.
Deut 12:7
deliver it into *your h.* *Josh* 8:7, 20
delivered them into *your h.* 10:19
Amorites into *your h.* 24:8, 11
Moabites into *your h.* *Judg* 3:28
Midianites into *your h.* 7:15
his blood of *your h.*? *2 Sam* 4:11
be delivered into *your h.* *2 Chr* 18:14
hath delivered them into *your h.* 28:9
required this at *your h.*? *Isa* 1:12
I am in *your h.*: do with. *Jer* 26:14
said, behold, he is in *your h.* 38:5
and fulfilled with *your h.* 44:25
be no more in *your h.* *Ezek* 13:21
deliver my people out of *your h.* 23
an offering at *your h.* *Mal* 1:10
should I accept this of *your h.*? 13
it with good will at *your h.* 2:13

handbreadth

a border of an *h.* round about.
Ex 25:25; 37:12
a molten sea *h.* thick. *1 Ki* 7:26
2 Chr 4:5
made my days as an *h.* *Ps* 39:5

six cubits long, and an *h.* *Ezek* 40:5
the cubit is a cubit and an *h.* 43:13

hand broad

hooks an *h. broad.* *Ezek* 40:43

handful

take thereout an *h.* of flour. *Lev* 2:2
5:12; 6:15; 9:17*; *Num* 5:26
an *h.* of meal in a barrel. *1 Ki* 17:12
there shall be an *h.* of. *Ps* 72:16*
better is *h.* with quietness. *Eccl* 4:6
and as the *h.* after the. *Jer* 9:22

handfuls

earth brought forth by *h.* *Gen* 41:47
take to you *h.* of ashes of. *Ex* 9:8
fall also some *h.* of. *Ruth* 2:16*
if dust of Samaria shall suffice for *h.*
1 Ki 20:10
ye pollute me for *h.* of? *Ezek* 13:19

handkerchiefs

were brought unto sick *h.* *Acts* 19:12

handle

father of such as *h.* the. *Gen* 4:21
they that *h.* the pen of. *Judg* 5:14
men that could *h.* shield. *1 Chr* 12:8
2 Chr 25:5
hands, but they *h.* not. *Ps* 115:7
they that *h.* the law knew. *Jer* 2:8
Lybians that *h.* the shield. 46:9
all that *h.* the oar, and. *Ezek* 27:29
h. me and see. *Luke* 24:39
taste not, *h.* not. *Col* 2:21

handled

that it may be *h.* *Ezek* 21:11
him away shamefully *h.* *Mark* 12:4
our hands have *h.* of the. *1 John* 1:1

handleth

he that *h.* matter wisely. *Pr* 16:20
cut off him that *h.* sickle. *Jer* 50:16
shall he stand that *h.* *Amos* 2:15

handling

all of them *h.* swords. *Ezek* 38:4
not *h.* the word of God. *2 Cor* 4:2

handmaid

Sarai had an *h.* whose. *Gen* 16:1
Zilpah to be Leah's *h.* 29:24; 35:26
to be Rachel's *h.* 29:29; 30:4; 35:25
that son of thy *h.* may. *Ex* 23:12
wine for me and thy *h.* *Judg* 19:19
spoken friendly to thy *h.* *Ruth* 2:13
answered, I am Ruth thine *h.* 3:9
on affliction of thine *h.* *1 Sam* 1:11
count not thine *h.* for a daughter. 16
Hannah said, let thy *h.* find. 18*
let thy *h.* speak. 25:24
remember thy *h.* 31
let thy *h.* be a servant to wash. 41
thy *h.* had two sons. *2 Sam* 14:6
hear the words of thy *h.* 20:17
didst swear to thy *h.*? *1 Ki* 1:13
the Lord thy God to thy *h.* 17
she took my son while thine *h.* 3:20
thy *h.* hath not any thing. *2 Ki* 4:2
man of God, do not lie to thine *h.* 16
save the son of thy *h.* *Ps* 86:16
and the son of thy *h.* 116:16
and an *h.* that is heir to. *Pr* 30:23
caused every man his *h.* *Jer* 34:16
behold the *h.* of the. *Luke* 1:38

handmaiden

the low estate of his *h.* *Luke* 1:48

handmaids

children to the two *h.* *Gen* 33:1
he put the *h.* and their children. 2
not like to one of thy *h.* *Ruth* 2:13
himself in eyes of *h.* *2 Sam* 6:20
the *h.* to return for *h.* *Jer* 34:11
on the *h.* will I pour my spirit.
Joel 2:29; *Acts* 2:18

hands

thyself under her *h.* *Gen* 16:9
the *h.* are the *h.* of Esau. 27:22
h. were made strong by *h.* of. 49:24
but Moses' *h.* were. *Ex* 17:12
thou shalt put all in the *h.* of. 29:24
h. and on his son's *h.* *Lev* 8:27
of memorial in her *h.* *Num* 5:18
and shall put them on the *h.* 6:19
the work of men's *h.* *Deut* 4:28
27:15; *2 Ki* 19:18; *2 Chr* 32:19

of the covenant were in my two *h.*
Deut 9:15
I cast them out of my two *h.* 17
the *h.* of the witnesses shall. 17:7
through the work of your *h.* 31:29
delivered them into *h.* of. *Judg* 2:14
into *h.* of Midianites. 6:13
are *h.* of Zeba and Zalmunna? 8:6, 15
delivered them out of *h.* of enemies.
34; *1 Sam* 14:48
into *h.* of Philistines. *Judg* 10:7
given Laish into your *h.* 18:10
and her *h.* were upon the. 19:27
nor deliver me into *h.* *1 Sam* 30:15
let your *h.* be strong. *2 Sam* 2:7
Zech 8:9, 13
then the *h.* of all with. *2 Sam* 16:21
delivered them into the *h.* of. 21:9
they cannot be taken with *h.* 23:6
into the *h.* of the guard. *1 Ki* 14:27
2 Chr 12:10
poured water on the *h.* *2 Ki* 3:11
skull and the palms of her *h.* 9:35
whom I brought into your *h.* 10:24
Asaph under the *h.* of. *1 Chr* 25:2
under the *h.* of Jeduthun. 3
h. of their father. 6
let not your *h.* be weak. *2 Chr* 15:7
weakened the *h.* of people. *Ezra* 4:4
strengthened the weak *h.* *Job* 4:3
God hath turned me into the *h.* 16:11
who is he that will strike *h.*? 17:3
that hath clean *h.* shall be. 9
he that hath clean *h.* *Ps* 24:4
in whose *h.* is mischief. 26:10
clap your *h.* 47:1
ye weigh the violence of your *h.* 58:2
shall stretch out her *h.* unto. 68:31
idols, the work of men's *h.* 115:4
135:15; *Isa* 37:19
h. but handle not, feet. *Ps* 115:7
lift up your *h.* in sanctuary. 134:2
me, O Lord, from the *h.* of. 140:4
folding of the *h.* to sleep. *Pr* 6:10
24:33
h. that shed innocent blood. 6:17
the recompence of man's *h.* 12:14
plucketh it down with her *h.* 14:1
a man striketh *h.* and. 17:18
one of them that strike *h.* 22:26
spider taketh hold with her *h.* 30:28
worketh willingly with her *h.* 31:13
h. to the spindle, her *h.* hold. 19
yea, she reacheth forth her *h.* to. 20
give her the fruit of her *h.* and. 31
then both *h.* full with. *Eccl* 4:6*
her *h.* are as bands. 7:26
the idleness of *h.* 10:18
the work of the *h.* of a. *S of S* 7:1
forth your *h.* I will hide my eyes from
you; your *h.* are full. *Isa* 1:15
worship work of their own *h.* 2:8
therefore shall all *h.* be faint. 13:7
idols which your own *h.* have. 31:7
strengthen ye the weak *h.* 35:3
thy work say, he hath no *h.* 45:9
h. are defiled with blood. 59:3
that spreadeth her *h.* *Jer* 4:31
a tree, the work of the *h.* of. 10:3
and of the *h.* of the founder, blue. 9
cause them to fall by *h.* that. 19:7
weapons that are in your *h.* 21:4
the *h.* of evildoers, that none return.
23:14; *Ezek* 13:22
not with works of your *h.* *Jer* 25:6, 7
shall pass under *h.* of him. 33:13
weakeneth *h.* of men of war, *h.* 38:4
upon all the *h.* shall be. 48:37
Zion spreadeth her *h.* *Lam* 1:17
how esteemed as work of *h.* 4:2
that was overthrown, and no *h.* 6
h. of pitiful women have sodden. 10
h. shall be feeble. *Ezek* 7:17; 21:7
was cut out without *h.* *Dan* 2:34, 45
may do evil with both *h.* *Mi* 7:3
all shall clap the *h.* over. *Nah* 3:19
in all labour of your *h.* *Hag* 2:17
the *h.* of Zerubbabel laid. *Zech* 4:9
to eat with unwashen *h.* *Mat* 15:20
Mark 7:2, 5
betrayed into *h.* of men. *Mat* 17:22
26:45; *Mark* 9:31; *Luke* 9:44
having two *h.* to be cast into fire.
Mat 18:8; *Mark* 9:43

h., another without h. Mark 14:58
ye stretched forth no h. Luke 22:53
must be delivered into the h. 24:7
wicked h. have crucified. Acts 2:23
by h. of the apostles were. 5:12
in temples made with h. 48; 17:24
laying on of the apostles' h. 8:18
elders by the h. of Barnabas. 11:30
is worshipped with men's h. 17:25
gods which are made with h. 19:26
these h. have ministered to. 20:34
shall deliver him into the h. 21:11
house not made with h. 2 Cor 5:1
in flesh made by h. Eph 2:11
circumcision made without h. Col 2:11
work with your own h. 1 Thes 4:11
pray, lifting up holy h. 1 Tim 2:8
of h. of presbytery. 4:14; Heb 6:2
tabernacle not with h. Heb 9:11
into holy place made with h. 24
fearful to fall into the h. of. 10:31
wherefore lift up the h. 12:12
cleanse your h. ye sinners. Jas 4:8

see **clap**

his **hands**

his h. were hairy. Gen 27:23
guiding his h. 48:14
Hur stayed up his h. Ex 17:12
cast the tables out of his h. 32:19
his own h. shall bring. Lev 7:30
and hath not rinsed his h. in. 15:11
his h. full of sweet incense. 16:12
Aaron shall lay both his h. on. 21
Balak smote his h. Num 24:10
let his h. be sufficient. Deut 33:7
and accept the work of his h. 11
for Moses had laid his h. 34:9
the deserving of his h. Judg 9:16
both the palms of his h. 1 Sam 5:4
climbed up on his h. and his. 14:13
went and strengthened his h. 23:16
heard, his h. were feeble. 2 Sam 4:1
spread his h. toward heaven.
1 Ki 8:22; 38:54; 2 Chr 6:12, 13, 29
with the work of his h. 1 Ki 16:7
put his h. upon his h. 2 Ki 4:34
in not receiving at his h. 5:20
Elisha put his h. upon the. 13:16
who hath with his h. 2 Chr 6:4
with one of his h. Neh 4:17
blessed the work of his h. Job 1:10
he woundeth, and his h. make. 5:18
and his h. shall restore their. 20:10
all are the works of his h. 34:19
for he clappeth his h. amongst. 37
snared in work of his h. Ps 9:16
not the operation of his h. 28:5
by the skilfulness of his h. 78:72
his h. were delivered from. 81:6
the sea is his, and his h. 95:5
the works of his h. are verity. 111:7
his h. refuse to labour. Pr 21:25
foldeth his h. together. Eccl 4:5
his h. are as gold rings. S of S 5:14
the reward of his h. shall. Isa 3:11
consider the operation of his h. 5:12
to altars, the work of his h. 17:8
his h. in midst of them, as he that swimmeth spreadeth his h. 25:11
that shaketh his h. from. 33:15
every man with his h. on? Jer 30:6
king heard the report, his h. 50:43
the deep lifted up his h. Hab 3:10
his h. shall also finish. Zech 4:9
he should put his h. on them.
Mat 19:13; Mark 10:16
washed his h. before the. Mat 27:24
are wrought by his h. Mark 6:2
put his h. on his eyes. 8:23, 25
shewed them his h. and feet.
Luke 24:40; John 20:20
and he lifted up his h. Luke 24:50
given all things into his h. John 13:3
except I see in his h. the. 20:25
putting his h. on him. Acts 9:17
Herod stretched forth his h. 12:1
and his chains fell off from his h. 7
wall, and escaped his h. 2 Cor 11:33
working with his h. Eph 4:28

see **lay, laid**

mine **hands,** *my* **hands**

in innocency of my h. Gen 20:5
seen the labour of my h. Gen 31:42
I will spread abroad my h.
Ex 9:29; Ezra 9:5
I put my life in my h. Judg 12:3
according to cleanness of my h.
2 Sam 22:21; Ps 18:20, 24
he teacheth my h. to war.
2 Sam 22:35; Ps 18:34; 144:1
is no wrong in mine h. 1 Chr 12:17
O God, strengthen my h. Neh 6:9
and if I make my h. Job 9:30
any injustice in mine h. 16:17
blot hath cleaved to mine h. 31:7
there be iniquity in my h. Ps 7:3
they pierced my h. and my. 22:16
I will wash mine h. in. 26:6
when I lift up my h. toward. 28:2
I will lift up my h. in thy name. 63:4
in vain, I have washed my h. 73:13
I have stretched out my h. 88:9
my h. will I lift to thy. 119:48
lifting up of my h. as the. 141:2
I stretch forth my h. to thee. 143:6
the works that my h. Eccl 2:11
I rose, and my h. S of S 5:5
Assyria the work of my h. Isa 19:25
he seeth the work of mine h. 29:23
concerning the work of my h. 45:11
even my h. have stretched out. 12
graven thee on palms of my h. 49:16
people also the work of my h. 60:21
I have spread out my h. all. 65:2
I will also smite mine h. Ezek 21:17
you out of my h.? Dan 3:15
set me on the palms of my h. 10:10
behold my h. and my feet.
Luke 24:39; John 20:27
but also my h. and head. John 13:9
stretched forth my h. Rom 10:21
by putting on of my h. 2 Tim 1:6

our **hands**

concerning toil of our h. Gen 5:29
have we brought in our h. 43:22
into our h. Og king of. Deut 3:3
shall say, our h. have not shed. 21:7
delivered into our h. all. Josh 2:24
meat offering at our h. Judg 13:23
into our h. our enemy. 16:24
will give you into our h. 1 Sam 17:47
stretched out our h. to a. Ps 44:20
thou the work of our h. upon. 90:17
fame, our h. wax feeble. Jer 6:24
heart with our h. to God. Lam 3:41
say to work of our h. Hos 14:3
him away out of our h. Acts 24:7
working with our own h. 1 Cor 4:12
our h. have handled. 1 John 1:1

right **hands**

they gave to me and Barnabas the right h. of fellowship. Gal 2:9

their **hands**

him out of their h. Gen 37:21, 22
shall put their h. on head. Ex 29:10
shall put their h. on the. 15, 19
shalt receive them of their h. 25
Lev 8:28
Israel shall put their h. Num 8:10
the Levites shall lay their h. 12
fruit of land in their h. Deut 1:25
the elders shall wash their h. 21:6
Midianites into their h. Judg 7:2
me not out of their h. 12:2
they cut off their h. 2 Sam 4:12
they clapped their h. 2 Ki 11:12
me to anger with all the works of their h. 22:17; 2 Chr 34:25
their h. with vessels of. Ezra 1:6
on and prospereth in their h. 5:8
their h. in the work of the. 6:22
they gave their h. that they. 10:19
strengthened their h. for. Neh 2:18
their h. shall be weakened. 6:9
gavest them into their h. 9:24
their h. cannot perform. Job 5:12
strength of their h. profit me. 30:2
after work of their h. Ps 28:4
have not found their h. 76:5
bear thee up in their h. 91:12
forth their h. to iniquity. 125:3
the spoils of their h. Isa 25:11
act of violence is in their h. 59:6
shall enjoy work of their h. 65:22
works of their own h. Jer 1:16
the works of their h. Jer 25:14
Lam 3:64
with works of their h. Jer 32:30
delivered me into their h. Lam 1:14
their h. and wings. Ezek 10:12
blood is in their h. 23:37, 45
violence that is in their h. Jonah 3:8
every work of their h. Hag 2:14
with their h. they should bear thee.
Mat 4:6; Luke 4:11
they wash not their h. Mat 15:2
palms of their h. 26:67; Mark 14:65
except they wash their h. Mark 7:3
rubbing them in their h. Luke 6:1
smote him with their h. John 19:3
in the works of their h. Acts 7:41
wonders to be done by their h. 14:3
and palms in their h. Rev 7:9
not of the works of their h. 9:20
received his mark in their h. 20:4

thine or *thy* **hands**

sanctuary which thy h. Ex 15:17
bless thee in all works of thine h.
Deut 16:15; 24:19
afterward shall thine h. Judg 7:11
thy h. were not bound. 2 Sam 3:34
despise work of thine h.? Job 10:3
thine h. have made and fashioned. 8
desire to work of thine h. 14:15
by pureness of thine h. 22:30
over the works of thy h. Ps 8:6
triumph in the works of thy h. 92:4
heavens are work of thy h. 102:25
thy h. have made me and. 119:73
shalt eat labour of thine h. 128:2
the works of thine own h. 138:8
I muse on the work of thy h. 143:5
destroy work of thine h. Eccl 5:6
and thine h. on thy head. Jer 2:37
lift up thy h. for the life. Lam 2:19
smite thine h. together. Ezek 21:14
can thine h. be strong in the ? 22:14
worship work of thine h. Mi 5:13
let not thine h. be slack. Zeph 3:16
these wounds in thine h.? Zech 13:6*
Father, into thy h. I. Luke 23:46
stretch forth thy h. John 21:18
are the works of thine h. Heb 1:10
him over the works of thy h. 2:7

handstaves

and shall burn the h. Ezek 39:9

hand weapon

him with a h. weapon. Num 35:18

handwriting

blotting out the h. Col 2:14*

handywork

firmament showeth his h. Ps 19:1

hang

Pharaoh shall h. thee. Gen 40:19
h. them before the Lord. Num 25:4
if thou h. him on a tree. Deut 21:22
thy life shall h. in doubt. 28:66
we will h. them up. 2 Sam 21:6
to speak to the king to h. Esth 6:4
then the king said, H. him. 7:9
there h. a thousand. S of S 4:4
they shall h. upon him all. Isa 22:24
virgins of Jerusalem h. Lam 2:10
take pin of it to h. any? Ezek 15:3
on these two h. all law. Mat 22:40
saw venomous beast h. Acts 28:4
lift up hands h. down. Heb 12:12

hanged

h. the chief baker. Gen 40:22; 41:13
for he that is h. is. Deut 21:23
and the king of Ai he h. Josh 8:29
the five kings h. he on. 10:26
Rechab and Baanah h. 2 Sam 4:12
Ahithophel h. himself. 17:23
Absalom h. 18:10
seven sons of Saul h. they. 21:9
set up, let him be h. Ezra 6:11
chamberlains were h. Esth 2:23
they h. Haman. 7:10
they h. his ten sons. 9:14
we h. our harps on the. Ps 137:2
princes are h. up by their. Lam 5:12
they h. the shield and. Ezek 27:10
h. their shields upon thy walls. 11
millstone were h. about. Mat 18:6
Mark 9:42; Luke 17:2
Judas went and h. Mat 27:5

thieves who were *h.* *Luke* 23:39
and *h.* on a tree. *Acts* 5:30; 10:39

hangeth

and he *h.* the earth upon. *Job* 26:7
is every one that *h.* on. *Gal* 3:13

hanging

they were *h.* on trees. *Josh* 10:26

hanging

(*Revised Versions substitute for this the word* screen)
thou shalt make an *h.* *Ex* 26:36
thou shalt make for the *h.* five. 37
h. for court gate. 27:16; 38:18
39:40; 40:8, 33
the *h.* for the door at the. 35:15
36:37; 39:38; 40:5, 28

hangings

h. of an hundred cubits. *Ex* 27:9; 11
38:9, 11
shall be *h.* of fifty. 27:12; 38:12
the *h.* on either side of gate. 27:14
15; 38:14, 15
the *h.* of court. 35:17; 38:9
16, 18; 39:40; *Num* 3:26; 4:26
women wove *h.* for the. *2 Ki* 23:7
blue *h.* fastened with. *Esth* 1:6

Hannah

Elkanah's wife *H.* had. *1 Sam* 1:2
H. why weepest thou ? 8
so *H.* rose up. 9
H. spake in her heart, only her. 13
Elkanah knew *H.* 19
after *H.* conceived. 20
but *H.* went not up. 22
H. prayed, and said. 2:1
the Lord visited *H.* so that. 21

Hanoch

sons of Midian, Ephah, *H.*
Gen 25:4; *1 Chr* 1:33
H. son of Reuben. *Gen* 46:9
Ex. 6:14; *Num* 26:5; *1 Chr* 5:3

Hanun

H. his son reigned in. *2 Sam* 10:1
kindness unto *H.* 2; *1 Chr* 19:2
H. took David's servants, and.
2 Sam 10:4; *1 Chr* 19:4
the valley gate repaired *H.* *Neh* 3:13
H. sixth son of Zalaph repaired. 30

hap

and her *h.* was to light. *Ruth* 2:3

haply

if *h.* the people had. *1 Sam* 14:30
if *h.* he might find any. *Mark* 11:13
lest *h.* after he hath laid. *Luke* 14:29
lest *h.* ye be found to. *Acts* 5:39
if *h.* they might feel after. 17:27
h. if they of Macedonia. *2 Cor* 9:4*

happen

no punishment *h.* to. *1 Sam* 28:10
there shall no evil *h.* to. *Pr* 12:21
shew us what shall *h.* *Isa* 41:22
what things should *h.* *Mark* 10:32

happened

it was a chance that *h.* *1 Sam* 6:9
as I *h.* by chance upon. *2 Sam* 1:6
there *h.* to be there a man. 20:1
him of all that had *h.* *Esth* 4:7
therefore this evil is *h.* to. *Jer* 44:23
of all things that had *h.* *Luke* 24:14
wonder at that which *h.* *Acts* 3:10
blindness in part is *h.* *Rom* 11:25*
now all things *h.* to. *1 Cor* 10:11
the things which *h.* to me. *Phil* 1:12
some strange thing *h.* *1 Pet* 4:12
is *h.* to them according. *2 Pet* 2:22

happeneth

that one event *h.* to. *Eccl* 2:14
as it *h.* to the fool, so it *h.* 15
wicked men to whom it *h.* 8:14
but time and chance *h.* to. 9:11

happier

but she is *h.* if she so. *1 Cor* 7:40

happy

h. am I, for daughters. *Gen* 30:13
h. art thou, O Israel. *Deut* 33:29
h. thy men, *h.* thy servants.
1 Ki 10:8; *2 Chr* 9:7
h. is the man whom God. *Job* 5:17
h. is man who hath quiver. *Ps* 127:5
h. shalt thou be, it shall be. 128:2
h. he be that rewardeth. *Ps* 137:8, 9
h. is that people that is in such a case, yea *h.* is that. 144:15
h. is he that hath God of. 146:5
h. is man that findeth. *Pr* 3:13
h. is every one that retaineth. 18
h. is he that hath mercy on. 14:21
trusteth in the Lord, *h.* is he. 16:20
h. is the man that feareth. 28:14
he that keepeth the law, *h.* is. 29:18
are they *h.* that deal ? *Jer* 12:1
now we call the proud *h.* *Mal* 3:15
know these things, *h.* *John* 13:17
I think myself *h.* king. *Acts* 26:2
h. is he that condemneth. *Rom* 14:22
behold, we count them *h.* *Jas* 5:11
righteousness' sake, *h.* *1 Pet* 3:14
for name of Christ *h.* are ye. 4:14

Haran, *a man*

Terah begat *H.* *Gen* 11:26, 27
H. died before Terah. 28
Milcah, the daughter of *H.* 29
Terah took Lot the son of *H.* his. 31
Caleb's concubine, bare *H.* and Moza, and *H.* begat. *1 Chr* 2:46
Shimei, *H.* Shelomith. 23:9

Haran, *a place*

Terah came to *H.* *Gen* 11:31
Terah died in *H.* 32
at 75 years departed out of *H.* 12:4
souls that they had gotten in *H.* 5
flee to *H.* 27:43
from Beer-sheba toward *H.* 28:10
they said, of *H.* are we. 29:4
my fathers destroyed *H.* *2 Ki* 19:12
Isa 37:12

Harbonah

H. was one of the. *Esth* 1:10; 7:9

hard

is any thing too *h.* for ? *Gen* 18:14
travailed, and had *h.* 35:16, 17
their lives bitter with *h.* *Ex* 1:14
h. causes they brought unto. 18:26
cause that is too *h.* *Deut* 1:17
it shall not seem *h.* to thee. 15:18
if there arise matter too *h.* for. 17:8
laid upon us *h.* bondage. 26:6
of Zeruiah be too *h.* *2 Sam* 3:39
Amnon thought it *h.* to do. 13:2
to prove him with *h.* questions.
1 Ki 10:1; *2 Chr* 9:1
thou hast asked a *h.* *2 Ki* 2:10
as *h.* as a piece of the. *Job* 41:24*
hast shewed thy people *h.* *Ps* 60:3
thy wrath lieth *h.* on me. 88:7
long shall wicked speak *h.*? 94:4*
way of transgressors is *h.* *Pr* 13:15*
give thee rest from *h.* *Isa* 14:3
there is nothing too *h.* *Jer* 32:17
Lord: is there any thing too *h.*? 27
art not sent to a people of *h.*
Ezek 3:5, 6
shewing *h.* sentences. *Dan* 5:12*
that thou art an *h.* man. *Mat* 25:24
h. for them that trust. *Mark* 10:24
this is an *h.* saying. *John* 6:60
h. for thee to kick. *Acts* 9:5; 26:14
things to say, and *h.* *Heb* 5:11
which are things *h.* to. *2 Pet* 3:16
all ungodly of their *h.* *Jude* 15

hard, *adverb*

rump, shall he take off *h.* by. *Lev* 3:9
Abimelech went *h.* to. *Judg* 9:52*
Israel pursued *h.* after. 20:45
h. after Philistines in. *1 Sam* 14:22
followed *h.* upon Saul, and upon.
31:2; *2 Sam* 1:6; *1 Chr* 10:2
Naboth had a vineyard *h.* *1 Ki* 21:1
cut off garments *h.* by. *1 Chr* 19:4*
my soul followeth *h.* after. *Ps* 63:8
the men rowed *h.* to. *Jonah* 1:13
whose house joined *h.* *Acts* 18:7

harden

I will *h.* Pharaoh's heart. *Ex* 4:21
7:3; 14:4
I will *h.* the hearts of the. 14:17
shalt not *h.* thy heart. *Deut* 15:7
it was of Lord to *h.* *Josh* 11:20
wherefore then do ye *h.*? *1 Sam* 6:6
yea, I would *h.* myself. *Job* 6:10*
h. not your hearts. *Ps* 95:8
Heb 3:8, 15; 4:7

hardened

Lord *h.* Pharaoh's heart. *Ex* 7:13
9:12; 10:1, 20, 27; 11:10; 14:8
Pharaoh's heart is *h.* 7:14*
was *h.* 22; 8:19; 9:7*, 35
he *h.* his heart. 8:15, 32; 9:34
Lord thy God *h.* his. *Deut* 2:30
as Egyptians and Pharaoh *h.* their.
1 Sam 6:6
they *h.* their necks. *2 Ki* 17:14
Zedekiah *h.* heart from. *2 Chr* 36:13
they and our fathers *h.* their necks.
Neh 9:16; 17:29
who hath *h.* himself. *Job* 9:4
she is *h.* against her young. 39:16†
hast thou *h.* our heart ? *Isa* 63:17
hearkened not, but *h.* *Jer* 7:26*
have *h.* their necks not to. 19:15*
when his mind was *h.* *Dan* 5:20
for their heart was *h.* *Mark* 6:52
have ye your heart yet *h.*? 8:17
blinded their eyes, *h.* *John* 12:40
but when divers were *h.* *Acts* 19:9
lest any of you be *h.* *Heb* 3:13

hardeneth

a wicked man *h.* his. *Pr* 21:29
he that *h.* his heart shall fall. 28:14
that being often reproved *h.* 29:1
whom he will he *h.* *Rom* 9:18

harder

brother offended *h.* to. *Pr* 18:19
have made their faces *h.* *Jer* 5:3
h. than flint have I made. *Ezek* 3:9

hardhearted

house of Israel are *h.* *Ezek* 3:7*

hardly

when Sarai dealt *h.* *Gen* 16:6
when Pharaoh would *h.* *Ex* 13:15
h. bestead and hungry. *Isa* 8:21†
rich man shall *h.* enter. *Mat* 19:23*
Mark 10:23; *Luke* 18:24
bruising him, *h.* departeth. *Luke* 9:39
h. passing it, we came. *Acts* 27:8*

hardness

dust groweth into *h.* *Job* 38:38*
because of *h.* of your hearts.
Mat 19:8; *Mark* 10:5
grieved for the *h.* of. *Mark* 3:5
upbraided them with their *h.* 16:14
but after thy *h.* and. *Rom* 2:5
endure *h.* as a good. *2 Tim* 2:3*

hare

the *h.* is unclean to you. *Lev* 11:6
Deut 14:7

harlot

our sister as with *h.*? *Gen* 34:31
her, he took her to be an *h.* 38:15
daughter in law hath played *h.* 24
priest shall not take an *h.* *Lev* 21:14
spies came into an *h.*'s. *Josh* 2:1
only Rahab the *h.* shall live. 6:17
Jephthah was son of an *h.* *Judg* 11:1
Samson saw there an *h.* and. 16:1
him with attire of an *h.* *Pr* 7:10
faithful city become an *h.*? *Isa* 1:21
years shall Tyre sing as an *h.* 23:15
take an harp, thou *h.* that hast. 16
wanderest, playing the *h.* *Jer* 2:20
thou hast played the *h.* with. 3:1
tree, and there hath played *h.* 6
feared not, but went and played *h.* 8
playedst the *h.* because. *Ezek* 16:15
playedst *h.* thereon. 16
playedst *h.* with them. 28
hast not been as an *h.* 31
O *h.* hear the word. 35
thee to cease from playing the *h.* 41
Aholah played the *h.* when. 23:5
wherein she had played the *h.* 19
a woman that playeth the *h.* 44
mother hath played the *h.* *Hos* 2:5
thou shalt not play the *h.* 3:3
tho' Israel play the *h.*, let not. 4:15
have given a boy for an *h.* *Joel* 3:3
thy wife shall be an *h.* *Amos* 7:17
return to hire of an *h.* *Mi* 1:7
of the well favoured *h.* *Nah* 3:4
the members of an *h.*? *1 Cor* 6:15
that he who is joined to an *h.* is. 1
by faith the *h.* Rahab. *Heb* 11:31
not Rahab the *h.* justified ? *Jas* 2:25

harlots
came two women h. 1 Ki 3:16
keepeth company with h. Pr 29:3
assemble in h.' houses. Jer 5:7
whores, sacrifice with h. Hos 4:14
publicans and h. go. Mat 21:31
but the publicans and the h. 32
thy living with h. Luke 15:30
Babylon, mother of h. Rev 17:5

harm
this pillar unto me, for h. Gen 31:52
shall make amends for h. Lev 5:16
enemy, nor sought his h. Num 35:23
will no more do thee h. 1 Sam 26:21
shall Sheba do more h. 2 Sam 20:6
and there was no h. in. 2 Ki 4:41
do my prophets no h. 1 Chr 16:22
Ps 105:15
if he have done thee no h. Pr 3:30
him, and do him no h. Jer 39:12
do thyself no h. Acts 16:28
gained this h. 27:21
he felt no h. 28:5
saw no h. come to him. 6
spake any h. of thee. 21

harm
will h. you, if followers? 1 Pet 3:13

harmless
wise as serpents and h. Mat 10:16
ye may be h., the sons. Phil 2:15
is holy, h., undefiled. Heb 7:26*

harness, *substantive*
(*Revised Versions substitute for this the word* armour)
him that girdeth on h. 1 Ki 20:11
joints of his h. 22:34; 2 Chr 18:33
brought every man h. 2 Chr 9:24

harness, *verb*
h. the horses, and get. Jer 46:4

harnessed
Israel went up h. out of. Ex 13:18*

Harod
pitched beside well of H. Judg 7:1

Harosheth, *see* **gentiles**

harp
of them that handle h. Gen 4:21
thee away with tabret and h. 31:27
of prophets with a h. 1 Sam 10:5
is a cunning player on an h. 16:16
David took an h. and played. 23
prophesied with a h. to. 1 Chr 25:3
take the timbrel and h. Job 21:12
h. also is turned to mourning. 30:31
praise Lord with the h. Ps 33:2; 150:3
yea, on the h. will I praise thee. 43:4
my dark sayings upon the h. 49:4
awake psaltery and h. 57:8; 108:2
sing with h. 71:22; 92:3; 98:5
147:7; 149:3
bring hither the pleasant h. 81:2
he h. and the viol are in. Isa 5:12
ound like an h. for Moab. 16:11
ake an h. 23:16
he joy of the h. ceaseth. 24:8
t sound of h. Dan 3:5, 7, 10, 15
whether pipe or h. 1 Cor 14:7

harped
nown what is piped or h.? 1 Cor 14:7

harpers
e voice of h. harping. Rev 14:2
e voice of h. shall be heard. 18:22

harps
l Israel played on h. 2 Sam 6:5
ade of almug trees h. 1 Ki 10:12
e hanged our h. upon. Ps 137:2
e with tabrets and h. Isa 30:32
e sound of thy h. Ezek 26:13
very one of them h. Rev 5:8
arping with their h. 14:2
e h. of God. 15:2
see **cymbal**

harrow
will he h. the valleys? Job 39:10

harrows
der saws and h. of. 2 Sam 12:31
th saws and h. of iron. 1 Chr 20:3

hart
ay eat flesh as of the h. Deut 12:15
14:5; 15:22

as the h. panteth after. Ps 42:1
lame man leap as an h. Isa 35:6

harts
ten fat oxen, besides h. 1 Ki 4:23
princes become like h. Lam 1:6

harvest
(*This, the time for reaping, or the ingathering of the crops, is used both literally and figuratively in Scripture. The day of judgement is called the harvest time for the world*)
while earth remaineth, h. Gen 8:22
went in days of wheat h. 30:14
neither be earing nor h. 45:6
keep the feast of h. Ex 23:16; 34:22
in earing time and in h. 34:21
when ye reap h. Lev 19:9; 23:10
22; Deut 24:19
own accord of h. not reap. Lev 25:5
in beginning of barley h. Ruth 1:22
my maidens till end of h. 2:21, 23
of Beth-shemesh reaping their h.
1 Sam 6:13
will set them to reap his h. 8:12
is it not wheat h. to-day? 12:17
death in h. in barley h. 2 Sam 21:9
her from beginning of barley h. 10
whose h. the hungry eateth. Job 5:5
gathereth her food in the h. Pr 6:8
he that sleepeth in h. causeth. 10:5
as rain in h. so honour is not. 26:1
according to joy in h. Isa 9:3
for the shouting for thy h. is. 16:9
but the h. shall be a heap in. 17:11
cloud of dew in the heat of h. 18:4
for afore the h. when the bud. 5
the h. of the river is her. 23:3
they shall eat up thy h. Jer 5:17
to us the appointed weeks of h. 24
the h. is past, summer is. 8:20
O Judah, he hath set an h. Hos 6:11
because h. of the field. Joel 1:11
put in the sickle, for the h. 3:13
yet three months to h. Amos 4:7
h. is plenteous, the. Mat 9:37
pray ye Lord of h. 38; Luke 10:2
grow together until h.: in time of h.
Mat 13:30
h. is end of the world, reapers. 39
in the sickle because h. Mark 4:29
said unto them, the h. Luke 10:2
cometh h.? the fields are white to h.
John 4:35
time is come, for the h. Rev 14:15

harvestman
it shall be as when the h. Isa 17:5
fall as handful after h. Jer 9:22

harvest time
overfloweth all *time* of h. Josh 3:15
in *time* of wheat h. Judg 15:1
to David in h. *time*. 2 Sam 23:13
of snow in the *time* of h. Pr 25:13
handleth sickle in h. *time*. Jer 50:16
a little while *time* of her h. 51:33
in the *time* of h. I will. Mat 13:30

hast
Lot, h. thou here any besides? whatsoever thou h. in. Gen 19:12
Esau said, H. thou but one? 27:38
as a prince h. thou power. 32:28
Esau said, keep that thou h. 33:9
thy flock, and all that thou h. 45:10
and gather all that thou h. Ex 9:19
every firstling thou h. shall. 13:12
gold, and all thou h. is. Deut 8:13
makest thou? what h.? Judg 18:3
and all that thou h. 1 Sam 25:6
h. thou not here with? 2 Sam 15:35
tell me, what h. in house. 2 Ki 4:2
h. thou eyes of flesh, or? Job 10:4
h. thou an arm like God? 40:9
say not, Go, when thou h. Pr 3:28
what h. thou here? whom h. thou?
Isa 22:16
go and sell that thou h. Mat 19:21
Mark 10:21; Luke 18:22
thou h. that is thine. Mat 25:25
from whence then h.? John 4:11
to whom thou now h. is not. 18
thou h. words of eternal life. 6:68
said, thou h. a devil. 7:20; 8:48, 52

if I wash thee not, thou h. John 13:8
thou h. neither part nor. Acts 8:21
thou who h. the form of. Rom 2:20
h. thou faith? have it to. 14:22
what h. thou that thou? 1 Cor 4:7
may say, thou h. faith. Jas 2:18
thou h. patience, and for. Rev 2:3
but this thou h. 6
thou h. a name to live. 3:1, 4
thou h. a little strength. 8
hold that fast which thou h. 11

haste, *substantive*
for Moses and Aaron in h. Ex 10:16
ye shall eat in h. with your. 12:11
out of land in h. 33; Deut 16:3
business required h. 1 Sam 21:8
cast away in their h. 2 Ki 7:15
they went up in h. to. Ezra 4:23
I said in my h., I am cut. Ps 31:22
I said in my h., All men. 116:11
shall not go out with h. Isa 52:12
Daniel before king in h. Dan 2:25
king rose up in h. and spake. 3:24
the king went in h. unto the. 6:19
in straightway with h. Mark 6:25
the hill country with h. Luke 1:39
the shepherds came with h. 2:16

haste
h. thee, escape thither. Gen 19:22
h. ye and go up to my. 45:9, 13
speed, h., stay not. 1 Sam 20:38
h. thee, for Philistines have. 23:27
O my Strength, h. thee. Ps 22:19
see **make** *haste*

hasted
young man, and he h. Gen 18:7
drink, my lord, and she h. 24:18, 20
and taskmasters h. them. Ex 5:13
people h. and passed. Josh 4:10
the king of Ai saw it. they h. 8:14
the ambush h. and set the city. 19
the sun h. not to go down. 10:13
liers in wait h. and. Judg 20:37
David h. 1 Sam 17:48
Abigail h. 25:23, 42
except thou hadst h. and. 34
the witch at En-dor h. and. 28:24
who was of Bahurim, h. 2 Sam 19:16
the prophet h. and took. 1 Ki 20:41
they h. and put garments. 2 Ki 9:13
yea, himself h. also. 2 Chr 26:20
Haman h. to his house. Esth 6:12
they h. to bring Haman unto. 14
or if my foot hath h. to. Job 31:5
were troubled and h. away.
Ps 48:5; 104:7
Paul h. to be at. Acts 20:16

hasten
h. hither Micaiah the. 1 Ki 22:9*
and see that ye h. the. 2 Chr 24:5
sorrows multiplied that h. Ps 16:4*
I would h. my escape from. 55:8
or who else can h.? Eccl 2:25*
let him h. his work that. Isa 5:19
I the Lord will h. it in his. 60:22
I will h. my word to. Jer 1:12*

hastened, -eth
Abraham h. into the tent. Gen 18:6
angels h. Lot, saying, arise. 19:15
howbeit the Levites h. 2 Chr 24:5
posts went out, being h. by king.
Esth 3:15; 8:14
captive exile h. to. Isa 51:14
I have not h. from. Jer 17:16

hasteth
as the eagle that h. Job 9:26*
drinketh up a river, and h. 40:23*
as a bird h. to snare. Pr 7:23
and he that h. with his feet. 19:2
he that h. to be rich, hath an. 28:22
the sun h. to the place. Eccl 1:5
the affliction of Moab h. Jer 48:16
fly as eagle that h. to eat. Hab 1:8
great day of the Lord h. Zeph 1:14

hastily
brought Joseph h. out. Gen 41:14
driving them out h. Judg 2:23
Abimelech called h. unto his. 9:54
and the man came in h. 1 Sam 4:14
the men did h. catch it. 1 Ki 20:33*
may be gotten h. Pr 20:21

go not forth h. to strive, lest. Pr 25:8
Mary that she rose h. John 11:31*

hasting

judgement, and h. righteousness. Isa 16:5*
and h. unto the coming. 2 Pet 3:12*

hasty

he that is h. of spirit. Pr 14:29
every one that is h. only. 21:5
seest thou a man that is h. 29:20
let not thy heart be h. Eccl 5:2
be not h. in thy spirit to be. 7:9
be not too h. to go out of his. 8:3
as the h. fruit before. Isa 28:4*
why is decree so h.? Dan 2:15*
that bitter and h. nation. Hab 1:6

hatch

owl shall h. and gather. Isa 34:15
they h. cockatrice' eggs, weave. 59:5

hatcheth

sitteth on eggs and h. not. Jer 17:11*

hate

This word is used in the Bible frequently, as it is now, not for literal hatred, but a dislike, or even a lesser degree of love for one than for another, Deut 21:15; Pr 13:24; Luke 14:26.

gate of those that h. Gen 24:60
Joseph will peradventure h. 50:15
shalt not h. thy brother. Lev 19:17
they that h. you shall reign. 26:17
them that h. thee flee. Num 10:35
repayeth them that h. Deut 7:10
lay them upon them that h. 15; 30:7
if any man h. his neighbour. 19:11
and go in unto her and h. her. 22:13
if the latter husband h. her. 24:3
the loins of them that h. him. 33:11
and love them that h.? 2 Chr 19:2
that h. thee shall be. Job 8:22
shall find those that h. thee. Ps 21:8
they that h. the righteous. 34:21
they which h. us spoil for. 44:10
let them also that h. him flee. 68:1
they that h. thee have lifted. 83:2
and I will plague them that h. 89:23
ye that love the Lord h. evil. 97:10
he turned their heart to h. 105:25
them be turned back that h. 129:5
how long, fools, will ye h.? Pr 1:22
six things doth the Lord h. 6:16
Lord is to h. evil; pride do I h. 8:13
reprove not a scorner, lest he h. 9:8
brethren of the poor do h. 19:7
weary of thee, and so h. thee. 25:17
bloodthirsty h. the upright. 29:10
love and a time to h. Eccl 3:8
unto will of them that h. Ezek 16:27
to them that h. thee. Dan 4:19
h. him that rebuketh. Amos 5:10
h. the evil, and love the good. 15
who h. the good, and love. Mi 3:2
love thy neighbour, h. Mat 5:43
do good to them that h. you. 44
Luke 6:27
either he will h. the one. Mat 6:24
Luke 16:13
shall betray and shall h. Mat 24:10
hand of all that h. us. Luke 1:71
are ye when men shall h. you. 6:22
h. not his father, and mother. 14:26
world cannot h. you, but. John 7:7
if the world h. you, ye know that it hated me. 15:18; 1 John 3:13
ten horns, these shall h. Rev 17:16

I hate

there is one man, but I h. him. 1 Ki 22:8; 2 Chr 18:7
I h. the work of them. Ps 101:3
I h. every false way. 119:104, 128
I h. vain thoughts. 113
I h. and abhor lying. 163
do not I h. them, O Lord? 139:21
I h. them with perfect hatred. 22
froward mouth do I h. Pr 8:13
I h. robbery for burnt. Isa 61:8
abominable thing that I h. Jer 44:4
I h. I despise your feast. Amos 5:21
I h. his palaces, therefore. 6:8
these are things that I h. Zech 8:17
what I h. that do I. Rom 7:15
the Nicolaitans I h. Rev 2:6, 15*

hate me

me, seeing ye h. me? Gen 26:27
and fourth generation of them that h. me. Ex 20:5; Deut 5:9
reward them that h. me. Deut 32:41
do not ye h. me? Judg 11:7
thou dost h. me. 14:16
destroy them that h. me. 2 Sam 22:41; Ps 18:40
I suffer of them that h. me. Ps 9:13
they h. me with cruel hatred. 25:19
let them wink that h. me. 35:19
that h. me wrongfully. 38:19; 69:4
all that h. me whisper. 41:7
upon me, in wrath h. me. 55:3*
from them that h. me. 69:14
they which h. me may see. 86:17
desire upon them that h. me. 118:7
all they that h. me love. Pr 8:36

hated

Esau h. Jacob, because. Gen 27:41
the Lord saw Leah was h. 29:31
that I was h. 33
h. Joseph yet the more. 37:4, 5, 8
shot at him and h. him. 49:23*
and said, because the Lord h. us. Deut 1:27; 9:28
h. him not in times past. 4:42
19:4, 6; Josh 20:5
one loved and another h. Deut 21:15
before the son of the h. 16
shall acknowledge the son of h. 17
thou hadst utterly h. her. Judg 15:2
and blind that are h. 2 Sam 5:8
Amnon h. Tamar. 13:15
Absalom h. Amnon. 22
from my strong enemy, and from them that h. me. 22:18; Ps 18:17
rule over them that h. Esth 9:1
would unto those that h. them. 5
destruction of him that h. Job 31:29
I have h. congregation of. Ps 26:5
I have h. them that regard. 31:6
put them to shame that h. us. 44:7
neither was it he that h. me. 55:12
saved them from him that h. 106:10
and they that h. them ruled. 41
they h. knowledge, and. Pr 1:29
and say, how have I h. 5:12
man of wicked devices is h. 14:17
the poor is h. even of his own. 20
therefore I h. life. Eccl 2:17
I h. labour. 18
been forsaken and h. Isa 60:15
brethren that h. you said. 66:5
therefore have I h. mine. Jer 12:8
them that thou hast h. Ezek 16:37
sith thou hast not h. blood. 35:6
I h. them for wickedness. Hos 9:15
I loved Jacob, and h. Esau. Mal 1:3; Rom 9:13
ye shall be h. Mat 10:22
Mark 13:13; Luke 21:17
shall be h. of all nations. Mat 24:9
his citizens h. him, and. Luke 19:14
it h. me before it h. you. John 15:18
have both seen and h. both me. 24
written in their law, They h. me. 25
world hath h. them, because. 17:14
no man ever yet h. his. Eph 5:29
righteousness and h. Heb 1:9

hateful

iniquity be found to be h. Ps 36:2
we were h. and hating. Tit 3:3
every unclean and h. bird. Rev 18:2

hatefully

shall deal with thee h. Ezek 23:29

haters

the h. of Lord should. Ps 81:15
backbiters, h. of God. Rom 1:30

hatest

thine enemies, and h. 2 Sam 19:6
thou h. all workers of. Ps 5:5
lovest righteousness, and h. 45:7
thou h. instruction, and. 50:17
into hand whom thou h. Ezek 23:28
thou h. the deeds of the. Rev 2:6

hateth

if thou see ass of him that h. Ex 23:5
be slack to him that h. Deut 7:10
every abomination he h. 12:31
any image which the Lord h. 16:22
daughter unto this man, he h. 22:16
me in his wrath, who h. Job 16:9
shall even he that h. right? 34:17
loveth violence, his soul h. Ps 11:5
dwelt with him that h. peace. 120:6
and he that h. suretyship. Pr 11:15
but he that h. reproof is. 12:1
a righteous man h. lying, but. 13:5
he that spareth his rod h. his. 24
he that h. reproof shall die. 15:10
but he that h. gifts shall live. 27
he that h. dissembleth with. 26:24
a lying tongue h. those that. 28
he that h. covetousness. 28:16
is partner with a thief h. his. 29:24
feasts my soul h. Isa 1:14
Lord saith, that he h. Mal 2:16
one that doeth evil h. John 3:20
but me the world h. because. 7:7
that h. his life in this world. 12:25
world, therefore world h. you. 15:19
he that h. me h. my Father also. 23
he that h. his brother. 1 John 2:9, 11
whosoever h. his brother is. 3:15
I love God, and h. his brother. 4:20

hath

h. he given all that he h. Gen 24:36
uncleanness he h. Lev 22:5
no devoted thing of all he h. 27:28
h. the strength of. Num 23:22; 24:8
done away because he h. no. 27:4
inherit that which he h. Deut 21:16
a double portion of all he h. 17
woman and all she h. Josh 6:22
burnt with fire, and all he h. 7:15
h. the Lord as great? 1 Sam 15:22
thine handmaid h. not. 2 Ki 4:2
she h. no child, her husband is. 14
hedge about all he h. Job 1:10
touch all he h. 11
behold, all that he h. is in thy. 12
all that a man h. will he give. 2:4
so the poor h. hope. 5:16
h. the rain a father? 38:28
righteous man h. is better. Ps 37:16
catch all that he h. 109:11
happy is the man h. his quiver. 127:5
happy he that h. God of. 146:5
despised and h. a servant. Pr 12:9
the sluggard desireth, and h. 13:4
maketh himself rich, yet h. 7
is life unto him who h. it. 16:22
stone in eyes of him that h. it. 17:8
he that h. it, shall abide. 19:23
who h. woe? who h. sorrow? who h. wounds? 23:29
yea, he h. neither child. Eccl 4:8
for he h. not another to help. 10
for what h. the wise more? 6:8
neither h. he the power in the. 8:8
and she h. no breasts. S of S 8:8
and his soul h. appetite. Isa 29:8
he h. no hands. 45:9
and h. no light. 50:10
he h. no form nor comeliness. 53:2
he that h. no money, come. 55:1
prophet that h. a dream, let him tell and he that h. my word. Jer 23:28
h. Israel no sons? h. he no? 49:1
deceiver which h. in flock. Mal 1:14
h. not where to lay head. Mat 8:20
Luke 9:58
he that h. ears to hear, let him hear. Mat 11:15; 13:9, 43; Mark 4:9
Luke 8:8; 14:35; Rev 2:
they say he h. a devil. Mat 11:1
h. to him shall be given, who h. not from him shall be taken that he h. 13:12; 25:29; Mark 4:2
Luke 8:18; 19:2
selleth all that he h. and. Mat 13:4
whence h. this man? 56; Mark 6:
h. Beelzebub, and. Mark 3:2
because they said, he h. an. 3
and ye say, he h. a devil. Luke 7:3
John 10:2
ruler over all that he h. Luke 12:4
forsaketh not all that he h. 14:3
whose superscription h. it? 20:2
h. a purse, he that h. no. 22:3

spirit *h.* not flesh and bones. *Luke* 24:39
he that *h.* the bride, is. *John* 3:29
he that believeth on the Son *h.* everlasting life. 36; 5:24; 6:47, 54
Father *h.* life in himself, so *h.* 5:26
h. one that judgeth him. 12:48
he that *h.* my commandments. 14:21
prince of this world *h.* nothing. 30
greater love *h.* no man than. 15:13
all things that the Father *h.* 16:15
delivered thee unto me, *h.* 19:11
what advantage then *h.*? *Rom* 3:1
by works, he *h.* whereof to. 4:2
h. not the potter power over? 9:21
the wife *h.* not power of. *1 Cor* 7:4
but every man *h.* his proper gift. 7
h. a psalm, *h.* a doctrine, *h.* a. 14:26
h. righteousness with unrighteousness? what communion *h.* *2 Cor* 6:14
what concord *h.* Christ? 15
what agreement *h.* temple of God? 16
according to that a man *h.* 8:12
desolate *h.* more children. *Gal* 4:27
nor idolater *h.* any. *Eph* 5:5
if any thinketh he *h.* *Phil* 3:4
builder *h.* more honour. *Heb* 3:3
man *h.* an unchangeable. 7:24
your confidence, which *h.* great. 10:35
a man say he *h.* faith, and? *Jas* 2:14
denieth Son, same *h.* *1 John* 2:23
every man that *h.* this hope. 3:3
ye know that no murderer *h.* 15
whoso *h.* this world's good, and. 17
believed the love that God *h.* 4:16
no fear in love, because fear *h.* 18
believeth on Son of God *h.* 5:10
h. the Son *h.* life, *h.* not Son *h.* 12
not in the doctrine of Christ, *h.* not God. He that abideth *h.* *2 John* 9
that *h.* key of David. *Rev* 3:7
where she *h.* a place prepared. 12:6
because he knoweth that he *h.* 12
beast which *h.* the seven heads. 17:7
and there is the mind which *h.* 9
on such the second death *h.* 20:6

hating

provide men of truth, *h.* *Ex* 18:21
times past hateful, and *h.* *Tit* 3:3
h. even garment spotted by. *Jude* 23

hatred

if he thrust him off *h.* *Num* 35:20
h. wherewith he hated. *2 Sam* 13:15
hate me with cruel *h.* *Ps* 25:19
compassed me about with *h.* 109:3
they have rewarded me *h.* 5
I hate them with perfect *h.* I. 139:22
h. stirs up strifes, love. *Pr* 10:12
he that hideth *h.* with lying lips. 18
than a stalled ox, and *h.* 15:17
whose *h.* is covered by deceit. 26:26
knoweth either love or *h.* *Eccl* 9:1
their love, their *h.* and envy is. 6
destroy it for the old *h.* *Ezek* 25:15
thou hast had a perpetual *h.* 35:5
envy thou hast used out of *h.* 11
iniquity, and for great *h.* *Hos* 9:7
but the prophet is *h.* in the house. 8
works of flesh; witchcraft, *h.* *Gal* 5:20

hats

in their hosen and *h.* *Dan* 3:21*

haughtily

neither shall ye go *h.* *Mi* 2:3

haughtiness

. of men shall be bowed. *Isa* 2:11
nd the *h.* of men shall be. 17
will lay low the *h.* of the. 13:11
f the *h.* of Moab. 16:6; *Jer* 48:29

haughty

ine eyes are upon *h.* *2 Sam* 22:28
ord, my heart is not *h.* *Ps* 131:1
h. spirit before a fall. *Pr* 16:18
efore destruction heart is *h.* 18:12
roud and *h.* scorner is his. 21:24
aughters of Zion are *h.* *Isa* 3:16
gh hewn down, and *h.* 10:33*
e *h.* people of the earth. 24:4*
ere *h.* before me, I. *Ezek* 16:50
more be *h.* because. *Zeph* 3:11

haunt

s place where his *h.* *1 Sam* 23:22

men were wont to *h.* *1 Sam* 30:31
to be on all that *h.* it. *Ezek* 26:17

have

they *h.* all one language. *Gen* 11:6
h. ye another brother? 43:7
h. ye a father? 44:19
have brought all that they *h.* 46:32
thou shalt *h.* no other gods. *Ex* 20:3 *Deut* 5:7
the priest shall *h.* it. *Lev* 7:7, 8
the sons of Aaron shall *h.* 10
and a just hin, shall ye *h.* 19:36
priest's daughter *h.* no child. 22:13 *Num* 27:8, 9
whence should I *h.* flesh? *Num* 11:13
h. I now any power at all to? 22:38
peace he and his seed shall *h.* 25:13
that *h.* many, them that *h.* few. 35:8
voice of God, as we *h.*? *Deut* 5:26
father and all they *h.* *Josh* 2:13
though they *h.* iron chariots. 17:18
what *h.* you to do with Lord? 22:24
h. ye called us to take that we *h.*? *Judg* 14:15
h. taken my gods, and what *h.*? 18:24
I am too old to *h.* an husband, if I should *h.* an husband. *Ruth* 1:12
but we will *h.* a king. *1 Sam* 8:19
present to bring; what *h.* we? 9:7
utterly destroy all that they *h.* 15:3
what can he *h.* more but the? 18:8
h. I need of mad men, that ye *h.*? 21:15
Amnon said, *h.* out all. *2 Sam* 13:9
they *h.* there with them their. 15:36
what *h.* I to do with you, ye? 16:10
I *h.* no son to keep my name. 18:18
what right *h.* I yet to cry? 19:28
said unto king, how long *h.* I to? 34
Israel said, we *h.* ten parts in. 43
h. thou respect unto. *1 Ki* 8:28
saying, What portion *h.* we? 12:16
I *h.* not a cake, but an handful. 17:12
king, I am thine, and all I *h.* 20:4
that I may *h.* it for a garden. 21:2
scattered as sheep that *h.* no. 22:17
h. her forth without. *2 Ki* 11:15 *2 Chr* 23:14
this sign shalt thou *h.* *2 Ki* 20:9
shall any after thee *h.* *2 Chr* 1:12
from henceforth thou shalt *h.* 16:9
what *h.* I to do with thee? 35:21
he said, *H.* me away, for I am. 23
other men *h.* our lands. *Neh* 5:5
let it look for light but *h.* *Job* 3:9
O that I might *h.* my request. 6:8
then should I yet *h.* comfort. 10
what profit should we *h.* if? 21:15
they mar my path, they *h.* no. 30:13
profit shall I *h.* if be cleansed? 35:3
the Lord shall *h.* them. *Ps* 2:4
h. workers of iniquity? 14:4; 53:4
in pleasant places, I *h.* a. 16:6
say, Ah! so would we *h.* it. 35:25
whom *h.* I in heaven but? 73:25
sing to my God while I *h.* 104:33
a good understanding *h.* all. 111:10
they *h.* mouths; eyes *h.* they. 115:5
they *h.* ears; noses *h.* they. 6, 7 135:16, 17
so shall I *h.* wherewith to. 119:42
great peace *h.* they which love. 165
praises unto my God while I *h.* 146:2
this honour *h.* all his saints. 149:9
lot, let us all *h.* one purse. *Pr* 1:14
shall beg in harvest and *h.* 20:4
shall *h.* him become his son. 29:21
and I *h.* not the understanding. 30:2
nor *h.* the knowledge of the holy. 3
they *h.* all one breath. *Eccl* 3:19
giveth life to them that *h.* it. 7:12
h. they any more a reward. 9:5
neither *h.* they any more portion. 6
we *h.* a little sister and. *S of S* 8:8
thou, O Solomon, must *h.* a. 12
gone, because they *h.* no. *Isa* 5:13
also shalt thou *h.* no rest. 23:12
h. a strong city, salvation will. 26:1
ye shall *h.* a song as in night. 30:29
blind that *h.* eyes, deaf that *h.* 43:8
h. not I the Lord? there is no. 45:21
in the Lord *h.* I righteousness. 24
children which thou shalt *h.* 49:20

hand shortened? *h.* I no? *Isa* 50:2
h. of my hand, ye shall lie down. 11
now therefore what *h.* I here? 52:5
dogs, which can never *h.* 56:11
for your shame you shall *h.* 61:7
h. eyes and see not; which *h.* ears, and hear not. *Jer* 5:21
people love to *h.* it so, what. 31
no flesh shall *h.* peace. 12:12
h. sons nor daughters in. 16:2
said, ye shall *h.* peace. 23:17; 29:7
plant vineyard, nor *h.* any. 35:7
he shall *h.* none to sit upon. 36:30
he shall *h.* his life for a prey. 38:2
to the which they *h.* a desire. 44:14
they will destroy till they *h.* 49:9
the nation which *h.* neither gates. 31
mind, therefore *h.* I hope. *Lam* 3:21
neither will I *h.* any pity. *Ezek* 5:11 7:4; 8:18; 9:10
eye spare, neither *h.* ye pity. 9:5
h. I any pleasure that the? 18:23
I *h.* no pleasure in death. 32; 33:11
when iniquity shall *h.* 21:25, 29
any wisdom that I *h.* *Dan* 2:30
loose, and they *h.* no hurt. 3:25
shall *h.* a chain of gold. 5:7, 16
the king should *h.* no damage. 6:2
now they shall say, We *h.* *Hos* 10:3
unto you, ye shall not *h.* *Mi* 3:6
this shall they *h.* for. *Zeph* 2:10
but ye *h.* not enough. *Hag* 1:6
h. we not all one father? *Mal* 2:10
we *h.* Abraham to our father. *Mat* 3:9; *Luke* 3:8
thy coat, let him *h.* thy. *Mat* 5:40
love you, what reward *h.* ye? 46
they *h.* their reward. 6:2; 5:16
the foxes *h.* holes, birds *h.* nests. 8:20; *Luke* 9:58
what *h.* we to do with thee, Jesus? *Mat* 8:29; *Mark* 1:24; *Luke* 4:34
and he shall have more abundance. *Mat* 13:12; 25:29
it is not lawful for thee to *h.* her. 14:4; *Mark* 6:18
we *h.* so much bread? *Mat* 15:33
how many loaves *h.* ye? 34 *Mark* 6:38; 8:5
h. faith as a grain. *Mat* 17:20; 21:21
what shall I do, that I may *h.*? 19:16
followed thee what shall we *h.*? 27
h. poor always with you, but me ye *h.* 26:11; *Mark* 14:7; *John* 12:8
need *h.* we of witnesses? *Mat* 26:65
h. nothing to do with that. 27:19
deliver him now, if he will *h.* him. 43
the whole *h.* no need of. *Mark* 2:17
long as they *h.* the bridegroom. 19
if any man *h.* ears to hear. 4:23 7:16; *Rev* 13:9
so fearful, how is it ye *h.*? *Mark* 4:40
saying, It is because we *h.* 8:16
h. salt in yourselves, *h.* peace. 9:50
thou shalt *h.* treasure in heaven. 10:21; *Luke* 18:22
shall *h.* whatsoever he. *Mark* 11:23
receive them, and ye shall *h.* 24
what thank *h.* ye? *Luke* 6:32, 33, 34
taken what he seemeth to *h.* 8:18
which of you shall *h.* a friend? 11:5
alms of such things as ye *h.* 41
and after that *h.* no more. 12:4
which neither *h.* storehouse nor. 24
sell that ye *h.* and give alms. 33
I pray thee *h.* me excused. 14:18, 19
ever with me, all that I *h.* 15:31
we will not *h.* this man to. 19:14
Satan hath desired to *h.* you. 22:31
what communications ye *h.*? 24:17
flesh and bones, as ye see me *h.* 39
h. ye here any meat? 41; *John* 21:5
said, They *h.* no wine. *John* 2:3
woman, what *h.* I to do with thee? 4
but *h.* everlasting life. 3:15, 16
answered and said, I *h.* no. 4:17
hath given the Son to *h.* life. 5:26
and ye *h.* not his word abiding. 38
I know that ye *h.* not the love. 42
believeth on him, may *h.* 6:40
except ye eat his flesh, ye *h.* no. 53
tempting, that they might *h.* to. 8:6
he that followeth me, shall *h.* 12
h. one father even God. 41

I *h.* not a devil. *John* 8:49
ye were blind, ye should *h.* no. 9:41
I am come that they might *h.* 10:10
other sheep I *h.* which are not. 16
walk while ye *h.* light. 12:35, 36
might *h.* peace. In the world ye shall *h.* tribulation: I *h.* overcome. 16:33
but ye *h.* a custom that I. 18:39
we *h.* a law. 19:7
we *h.* no king but Cesar. 15
that believing ye might *h.* life. 20:31
silver and gold *h.* I none, but such as I *h.* *Acts* 3:6
said, Lord, what wilt thou *h.*? 9:6
in him we live, move, and *h.* 17:28
know that by this craft we *h.* 19:25
h. four men which *h.* a vow. 21:23
when Gentiles, which *h.* *Rom* 2:14
ye *h.* your fruit unto holiness. 6:22
if any man *h.* not the Spirit. 8:9
I will come, and Sara shall *h.* 9:9
and all members *h.* not the. 12:4
hast thou faith ? *h.* to thyself. 14:22
I *h.* whereof I may glory. 15:17
but we *h.* the mind of. *1 Cor* 2:16
are naked, and *h.* no certain. 4:11
instructors, yet *h.* ye not many. 15
that one should *h.* his father's. 5:1
is in you, which ye *h.* of God. 6:19
let every man *h.* his own wife, let every woman *h.* her own. 7:2
yet such shall *h.* trouble in the. 28
they that *h.* wives be as though. 29
h. you without carefulness. 32
I think also that I *h.* the Spirit. 40
that we all *h.* knowledge. 8:1
h. we not power to eat ? 9:4, 5, 6
if a man *h.* long hair, it is. 11:14
if a woman *h.* long hair, it is a. 15
we *h.* no such custom, nor the. 16
what, *h.* ye not houses to eat in ? 22
eye not say to hand, I *h.* no. 12:21
h. all the gifts of healing ? 30
h. not charity, I am become. 13:1
I *h.* all faith and *h.* not charity. 2, 3
your rejoicing which I *h.* 15:31
for some *h.* not the knowledge. 34
such trust *h.* we through. *2 Cor* 3:4
seeing we *h.* this ministry, we. 4:1
out of that which ye *h.* 8:11
he may *h.* to give to him. *Eph* 4:28
h. no fellowship with the. 5:11
I *h.* you in my heart. *Phil* 1:7
but I *h.* all. 4:18
love which ye *h.* to all. *Col* 1:4
what great conflict I *h.* for you. 2:1
if any man *h.* a quarrel. 3:13
ye also *h.* a Master in. 4:1
ye suffered, as they *h.* *1 Thes* 2:14
for all men *h.* not faith. *2 Thes* 3:2
not because we *h.* not power. 9
who will *h.* all men to. *1 Tim* 2:4
him with whom we *h.* to. *Heb* 4:13
seeing then that we *h.* a great. 14
by reason of use *h.* their senses. 5:14
which hope we *h.* as an. 6:19
we *h.* such a High Priest, set. 8:1
that this man *h.* somewhat also. 3
that ye *h.* in heaven a better. 10:34
with such things as ye *h.* 13:5
we *h.* an altar whereof they *h.* no. 10
here *h.* we no continuing city. 14
but let patience *h.* her. *Jas* 1:4
h. not faith of Christ with. 2:1
and *h.* not works, can faith ? 14
even so faith, if it *h.* not works. 17
thou hast faith, and I *h.* works. 18
if ye *h.* bitter envy, and strife. 3:14
ye lust and *h.* not, ye desire to *h.* ye fight and war, yet ye *h.* not. 4:2
above all things *h.* *1 Pet* 4:8
we *h.* a more sure word. *2 Pet* 1:19
a heart they *h.* exercised. 2:14
if we say, we *h.* no sin. *1 John* 1:8
h. an Advocate with the Father. 2:1
but we *h.* an unction from the. 20
and this commandment *h.* we. 4:21
that ye may know that ye *h.* 5:13
this is the confidence that we *h.* 14
we *h.* the petitions we desired. 15
I *h.* no greater joy than. *3 John* 4
Diotrephes, who loveth to *h.* the. 9
I *h.* the keys of hell. *Rev* 1:18
I *h.* somewhat against. 2:4; 14:20
and ye shall *h.* tribulation. *Rev* 2:10
to you, and to as many as *h.* not. 24
but what ye *h.* already, hold. 25
which *h.* not the seal of God. 9:4
h. the testimony of Jesus. 12:17
they *h.* no rest day nor night. 14:11
these *h.* one mind, and give. 17:13
brethren that *h.* the testimony. 19:10
liars shall *h.* their part in lake. 21:8
that they may *h.* right to tree. 22:14
see **compassion, dominion**

haven

dwell at the *h.* an *h.* *Gen* 49:13
them to their desired *h.* *Ps* 107:30
h. not commodious, an *h.* *Acts* 27:12

fair **havens**

place which is called *fair h.* *Acts* 27:8

having

h. his uncleanness. *Lev* 7:20; 22:3
h. her sickness. 20:18
h. a wen or scurvy. 22:22
into a trance, but *h.* *Num* 24:4, 16
stay for them from *h.* *Ruth* 1:13
h. a drawn sword in. *1 Chr* 21:16
h. Judah and Benjamin. *2 Chr* 11:12
mourning, and *h.* his. *Esth* 6:12
h. no guide, overseer. *Pr* 6:7
and *h.* neither bars nor. *Ezek* 38:11
pass ye away, *h.* thy. *Mi* 1:11
king cometh to thee, *h.* *Zech* 9:9
he taught as one *h.* *Mat* 7:29
h. soldiers under me. 8:9; *Luke* 7:8
were as sheep *h.* no shepherd. *Mat* 9:36; *Mark* 6:34
rather than *h.* two hands or. *Mat* 18:8
rather than *h.* two eyes to be cast. 9; *Mark* 9:43
not *h.* wedding garment ? *Mat* 22:12
if a man die, *h.* no children. 24 *Luke* 20:28
and *h.* no issue, left. *Mat* 22:25
woman *h.* an alabaster box. 26:7 *Mark* 14:3
h. nothing to eat, Jesus. *Mark* 8:1
h. eyes, see ye not ? *h.* ears ? 18
a fig tree *h.* leaves. 11:13
h. one son. 12:6
woman *h.* an issue of. *Luke* 8:43
man of you *h.* an hundred ? 15:4
either what woman *h.* ten pieces ? 8
but which of you, *h.* a servant ? 17:7
how knows he letters, *h.*? *John* 7:15
Simon Peter *h.* a sword. 18:10
h. land, sold it, and. *Acts* 4:37
h. a good report of the Jews. 22:12
h. more perfect knowledge of. 24:22
h. not the law, are a law. *Rom* 2:14
h. then gifts differing according. 12:6
h. a matter against. *1 Cor* 6:1
he that standeth stedfast, *h.* 7:37
h. the same spirit of. *2 Cor* 4:13
h. nothing, and yet possessing. 6:10
h. therefore these promises. 7:1
ye always *h.* all sufficiency in. 9:8
h. in a readiness to revenge. 10:6
but *h.* hope, when your faith is. 15
h. no hope. *Eph* 2:12
not *h.* spot or wrinkle. 5:27
h. your loins girt about. 6:14
h. a desire to depart. *Phil* 1:23
h. this confidence. 25
h. the same conflict. 30
h. the same love. 2:2
not *h.* my own righteousness. 3:9
h. made peace through. *Col* 1:20
h. nourishment ministered. 2:19
h. his children in. *1 Tim* 3:4
h. the promise of the life that. 4:8
h. damnation, because they. 5:12
and *h.* food and raiment, let. 6:8
h. this seal, the Lord. *2 Tim* 2:19
h. a form of godliness, but. 3:5
they shall heap teachers, *h.* 4:3
h. faithful children, not. *Tit* 1:6
h. conversation honest. *1 Pet* 2:12
h. a good conscience, they. 3:16
h. eyes full of adultery. *2 Pet* 2:14
these be sensual, *h.* not. *Jude* 19
h. seven horns. *Rev* 5:6
h. every one harps. 8
I saw an angel, *h.* the seal of. 7:2
h. a golden censer. 8:3
h. breastplates. 9:17
h. seven heads. *Rev* 12:3
h. great wrath. 12
h. the everlasting gospel. 14:6
h. the harps of God. 15:2
h. a golden cup. 17:4
h. great power. 18:1
h. the key of the pit. 20:1
holy Jerusalem, *h.* the glory. 21:11

havock

as for Saul, he made *h.* of. *Acts* 8:3*

hawk

h. had in. *Lev* 11:16; *Deut* 14:15
doth the *h.* fly by thy ? *Job* 39:26

hay

h. appeareth, and tender. *Pr* 27:25
the *h.* is withered away. *Isa* 15:6*
on this foundation, *h.* *1 Cor* 3:12

Hazael

anoint *H.* to be king. *1 Ki* 19:15
that escapeth the sword of *H.* 17
H. went to meet Elisha. *2 Ki* 8:9
Ben-hadad died, and *H.* reigned. 15
went with Joram against *H.* 28
kept Ramoth-gilead because of *H.* 9:14
H. smote them in all coasts. 10:32
H. set his face to go up to. 12:17
sent the hallowed things to *H.* 18
Israel into the hand of *H.* 13:3
but *H.* oppressed Israel. 22
so *H.* died. 24
Ben-hadad son of *H.* cities. 25
fire into the house of *H.* *Amos* 1:4

hazel

took him rods of *h.* and. *Gen* 30:37*

Hazelelponi

of their sister was *H.* *1 Chr* 4:3

Hazeroth

abode at *H.* *Num* 11:35; 33:17
removed from *H.* 12:16; 33:18

Hazor

Joshua took *H.* head of. *Josh* 11:10
and he burnt *H.* with fire. 11, 13
Kedesh and *H.* cities of. 15:23, 25
Ramah and *H.* cities of. 19:36
Jabin who reigned in *H.* *Judg* 4:2
raised a levy to build *H.* *1 Ki* 9:15
king of Syria took *H.* *2 Ki* 15:29
the kingdoms of *H.* *Jer* 49:28
O ye inhabitants of *H.* 30
and *H.* shall be a dwelling for. 33

he

he shall rule over thee. *Gen* 3:16
strive with man, for *he* is flesh. 6:3
he with whom it is found. 44:10
brother be greater than *he.* 48:19
art *he* whom thy brethren. 49:8
he shall be thy spokesman to the people, and *he* shall be. *Ex* 4:16
and hardened his heart, *he.* 9:34
he hath put in his heart that *he* may teach both *he* and. 35:34
he among the sons of. *Lev* 7:33
shall go out in jubile, *he* and. 25:54
cursed is *he* that. *Num* 24:9
came, *he* and all his. *Deut* 3:1
it is *he* that giveth power to. 8:18
cursed be *he.* 27:16
So to the end of the chapter
he that doth go with thee, *he* will. 31:6, 8
is not *he* thy Father that ? 32:6
I, even I am *he,* and there is. 39
Isa 41:4; 43:10, 13; 46:4; 48:12
Lord your God is *he.* *Josh* 23:3, 10
what man is *he* will ? *Judg* 10:18
I am *he* that came. *1 Sam* 4:16
not a goodlier person than *he.* 9:2
this is *he.* 16:12
as his name is so is *he.* 25:25
two men better than *he.* *1 Ki* 2:32
she and *he* and her house. 17:15
thou *he* that troubleth Israel ? 18:17
is not that *he* whose places. *2 Ki* 18:22; *Isa* 36:7
he in first year of reign. *2 Chr* 29:
where, and who is *he* ? *Job* 9:2
who is *he* that will plead ? 13:1
man dieth, and where is *he* ? 14:1
20:7; *Isa* 63:1
thou art *he* that took me. *Ps* 22:

he it is shall tread. *Ps* 60:12; 108:13
he that is our God is the God. 68:20
he is God, it is *he* that. 100:3
is *he* that giveth salvation. 144:10
Lord, happy is *he*. *Pr* 16:20; 29:18
he that is higher than. *Eccl* 5:8
untimely birth is better than *he*. 6:3
he sitteth on the circle. *Isa* 40:22
he that comforteth. 51:12; 52:6
John 18:5, 6, 8; *Rev* 1:18; 2:23
and said, it is not *he*. *Jer* 5:12
art not thou *he*, O Lord our? 14:22
the king is not *he* that can do. 38:5
he also shall be in derision. 48:26
art thou *he* of whom? *Ezek* 38:17
is more righteous than *he*. *Hab* 1:13
where is *he* that is born? *Mat* 2:2
this is *he* that was spoken of. 3:3
art thou *he* that should come? 11:3
Luke 7:19, 20
he that is not with me is against me, and *he* that. *Mat* 12:30; *Luke* 11:23
Christ? whose son is *he*? *Mat* 22:42
he is in the desert, *he* is in. 24:26
the same is *he*. 26:48; *Mark* 14:44
is none other but *he*. *Mark* 12:32
he to whom the Son. *Luke* 10:22
and *he* from within shall. 11:7
who is *he* that gave thee this? 20:2
he that sitteth at meat, or *he*? 22:27
they said, *he* is not here, but. 24:6
we trusted *he* should have. 21
this was *he* of whom. *John* 1:15, 30
I that speak to thee, am *he*. 4:26
where is *he*? 7:11
is not this *he* they seek to kill? 25
believe not that I am *he*, ye. 8:24
then shall ye know that I am *he*. 28
they said, is not this *he* that? 9:8
this is *he*, but *he* said, I am *he*. 9
who is *he*, Lord? 36
he that talketh with thee. 37
ye may believe that I am *he*. 13:19
they knew it was *he* who. *Acts* 3:10
this is *he* that was in church. 7:38
is not this *he* that destroyed? 9:21
Peter said, I am *he* whom. 10:21
he that was ordained of God. 42
ye that I am? I am not *he*. 13:25
he is not a Jew that is. *Rom* 2:28
he is a Jew that is one inwardly. 29
he that in these things. 14:18
are we stronger than *he*? *1 Cor* 10:22
that as *he* is Christ's. *2 Cor* 10:7
faithful is *he* that. *1 Thes* 5:24
he who now letteth will let, until *he* be taken. *2 Thes* 2:7
son is *he* whom the father? *Heb* 12:7
he for our profit, that we might. 10
as *he* which hath called. *1 Pet* 1:15
we walk in light, as *he* is. *1 John* 1:7
when *he* shall appear, we may. 2:28
is righteous, even as *he* is. 3:7
dwelleth in him, and *he*. 24; 4:15
he that is in you, than *he* in. 4:4
because as *he* is, so are we in. 17
he that hath the Son, hath life; and *he* that hath not the Son. 5:12
follow not evil, *he* that doeth good is of God; *he* that doeth. *3 John* 11
holy is *he* that hath part. *Rev* 20:6
he that is unjust, *he* that is. 22:11

head

it shall bruise thy *h*. *Gen* 3:15
shall lift up thy *h*. 40:13, 19
on the *h*. of Joseph, and on the top of the *h*. of him. 49:26; *Deut* 33:16
Aaron and his sons put their hands upon *h*. *Ex* 29:10; *Lev* 4:4; 8:14
put hands upon the *h*. of the ram.
Ex 29:15, 19; *Lev* 8:18, 22
shall put hand on the *h*. *Lev* 1:4
shall lay his hand on the *h*. of. 3:2
hand on *h*. of sin offering. 4:29, 33
leprous, his plague is in his *h*. 13:44
shall be rent, and his *h*. bare. 45
not make baldness on their *h*. 21:5
shall not uncover his *h*. nor rend. 10
uncover the woman's *h*. *Num* 5:18
shall no razor come upon his *h*. 6:5
of his God is on his *h*. 7
shall shave his *h*. 9, 18; *Deut* 21:12
and he shall hallow his *h*. *Num* 6:11
on his *h*., blood on our *h*. *Josh* 2:19
she smote off Sisera's *h*. *Judg* 5:26
no razor shall come on his *h*. 13:5
Goliath's *h*. *1 Sam* 17:57
of Nabal on his own *h*. 25:39
thee keeper of my *h*. for ever. 28:2
cut off Saul's *h*. 31:9
earth upon his *h*. *2 Sam* 1:2; 15:32
blood be upon thy *h*. 1:16; *1 Ki* 2:37
and said, Am I a dog's *h*.? *2 Sam* 3:8
let it rest on the *h*. of Joab, and. 29
go over, and take off his *h*. 16:9
take thy master from thy *h*. to-day.
2 Ki 2:3, 5
unto his father, My *h*. my *h*. 4:19
if the *h*. of Elisha shall. 6:31
murderer sent to take away my *h*. 32
daughter of Jerusalem hath shaken her *h*. 19:21; *Isa* 37:22
did lift up the *h*. of Jehoiachin.
2 Ki 25:27; *Jer* 52:31
his way on his *h*. *2 Chr* 6:23
are increased over our *h*. *Ezra* 9:6
reproach on their own *h*. *Neh* 4:4
return on his own *h*. *Esth* 9:25
Job arose, shaved his *h*. *Job* 1:20
yet will not I lift up my *h*. 10:15
I could shake my *h*. at you. 16:4
the lifter up of mine *h*. *Ps* 3:3
shall return on his own *h*. 7:16
out the lip, they shake the *h*. 22:7
thou anointest my *h*. with oil. 23:5
now shall my *h*. be lifted up. 27:6
iniquities are gone over mine *h*. 38:4
a shaking of the *h*. among. 44:14
is strength of mine *h*. 60:7; 108:8
God shall wound the *h*. of. 68:21
hate thee, have lift up the *h*. 83:2
therefore shall he lift up the *h*. 110:7
as for the *h*. of those that. 140:9
which shall not break my *h*. 141:5
blessings are on the *h*. of. *Pr* 10:6
blessing on the *h*. of him. 11:26
heap coals of fire on his *h*. 25:22
Rom 12:20
man's eyes are in his *h*. *Eccl* 2:14
hand is under my *h*. *S of S* 2:6; 8:3
my *h*. is filled with dew, my. 5:2
his *h*. as most fine gold. 11
thy *h*. as Carmel. 7:5
whole *h*. is sick and heart. *Isa* 1:5
joy shall be on their *h*. 51:11
is it to bow down his *h*. as a? 58:5
helmet of salvation on his *h*. 59:17
and thine hands on thy *h*. *Jer* 2:37
O that my *h*. were waters. 9:1
fall grievously on the *h*. 23:19; 30:23
their way on their *h*. *Ezek* 9:10
h. was made bald, shoulder. 29:18
O king, thou art this *h*. *Dan* 2:38
recompense on your *h*. *Joel* 3:4, 7
pant after dust on the *h*. *Amos* 2:7
will bring baldness on every *h*. 8:10
cut them in the *h*. all of them. 9:1
no man did lift up his *h*. *Zech* 1:21
then set the crowns on the *h*. 6:11
thou swear by thy *h*. *Mat* 5:36
smote him on *h*. 27:30; *Mark* 15:19
she said, The *h*. of John. *Mark* 6:24
my *h*. with oil thou didst. *Luke* 7:46
but also my hands and *h*. *John* 13:9
his *h*. covered, dishonoureth his *h*.
1 Cor 11:4
ought to have power on her *h*. 10
the *h*. to the feet, I have no. 12:21
and gave him as *h*. to the church.
Eph 1:22; 4:15; *Col* 1:18
not holding the *h*. from. *Col* 2:19
eyes flame of fire, and *h*. *Rev* 19:12
see **bald, beard, bow, bowed, cover, covered, crown**

head *of the corner*

the *h*. *of the corner*. *Mat* 21:42
Mark 12:10; *Luke* 20:17
Acts 4:11; *1 Pet* 2:7

head, for *ruler, governor*

one rod shall be for the *h*. *Num* 17:3
he was *h*. over a people of a. 25:15
Lord will make thee *h*. *Deut* 28:13
he shall be the *h*. and thou shalt. 44
each one an *h*. of house. *Josh* 22:14
he shall be *h*. over all Gilead.
Judg 10:18; 11:8
shall I be your *h*.? *Judg* 11:9
the people made him *h*. 11
thou not made the *h*.? *1 Sam* 15:17
thou hast kept me to be *h*. of the heathen. *2 Sam* 22:44; *Ps* 18:43
thou art exalted as *h*. *1 Chr* 29:11
h. of Damascus is Rezin, *h*. of.
Isa 7:8, 9
will cut off from Israel *h*. 9:14
and honourable, he is the *h*. 15
nor work which *h*. or tail, or. 19:15
art Gilead to me, *h*. of. *Jer* 22:6
themselves one *h*. *Hos* 1:11
woundedst the *h*. out of. *Hab* 3:13
thou didst strike through the *h*. 14
h. of every man is Christ; the *h*. of the woman is the man; and the *h*. of Christ is God. *1 Cor* 11:3
is the *h*. of the wife, even as Christ is *h*. of the church, and. *Eph* 5:23
h. of all principality. *Col* 2:10

head, for *top, chief*

the *h*. of fat valleys. *Isa* 28:1, 4
they lie at the *h*. of all the. 51:20*
built high places at *h*. *Ezek* 16:25
choose it at the *h*. of the. 21:19
king of Babylon stood at the *h*. of. 21

head with *hair* or *hairs*

hair is fallen off his *h*. *Lev* 13:40, 41
shave all his *hair* off his *h*. 14:9
locks of *hair* of his *h*. *Num* 6:5
and shalt take the *hair* of *h*. of. 18
the *hair* of his *h*. began. *Judg* 16:22
not an *hair* of his *h*. *1 Sam* 14:45
weighed *hair* of his *h*. *2 Sam* 14:26
plucked off *hair* of my *h*. *Ezra* 9:3
they are more than *hairs* of my *h*.
Ps 40:12; 69:4
the *hair* of thine *h*. *S of S* 7:5
nor was an *hair* of their *h*. *Dan* 3:27
hair of his *h*. like the pure. 7:9
hairs of your *h*. are numbered.
Mat 10:30; *Luke* 12:7
with *hairs* of her *h*. *Luke* 7:38, 44
not an *hair* of your *h*. perish. 21:18
not an *hair* fall from *h*. *Acts* 27:34
his *h*. and his *hairs* were. *Rev* 1:14

axe **head**

the *axe h*. slippeth. *Deut* 19:5
axe h. fell into water. *2 Ki* 6:5

bed's **head**

himself on the *bed's h*. *Gen* 47:31

hoary **head**

rise before the *hoary h*. *Lev* 19:32

spear's **head**

spear's h. weighed 600 shekels.
1 Sam 17:7; *2 Sam* 21:16

headbands

Lord will take away *h*. *Isa* 3:20*

headlong

of froward is carried *h*. *Job* 5:13
might cast him down *h*. *Luke* 4:29
falling *h*. he burst. *Acts* 1:18

heads

they bowed down their *h*. *Gen* 43:28
Ex 4:31
uncover not your *h*. lest. *Lev* 10:6
and put dust upon their *h*. *Josh* 7:6
Job 2:12
they lifted up their *h*. no. *Judg* 8:28
did God render upon their *h*. 9:57
it not be with the *h*. *1 Sam* 29:4
put ropes on our *h*. *1 Ki* 20:31
put ropes on their *h*. and came. 32
take ye the *h*. of your. *2 Ki* 10:6
they have brought the *h*. of the. 8
lift up your *h*. O ye gates. *Ps* 24:7, 9
caused men to ride over our *h*. 66:12
brakest the *h*. of the dragons. 74:13
thou brakest the *h*. of leviathan. 14
on me, they shaked their *h*. 109:25
their *h*. shall be baldness. *Isa* 15:2
everlasting joy on their *h*. 35:10
and covered their *h*. *Jer* 14:3
ashamed, they covered their *h*. 4
shall be on all their *h*. *Ezek* 7:18
their way on their *h*. 11:21; 22:31
their swords under their *h*. 32:27
have linen bonnets on their *h*. 44:18
they shall poll their *h*. 20

reviled, wagging their h. Mat 27:39
Mark 15:29
up, and lift up your h. Luke 21:28
blood be upon your own h. Acts 18:6
on their h. were as it were. Rev 9:7
were like to serpents, and had h. 19
having seven h. and on his h. 13:1
his h. as it were wounded to. 3
seven h. are seven mountains. 17:9
they cast dust on their h. 18:19

heads for *governors*
and made them h. over. Ex 18:25
were h. of thousands. Num 1:16
take all the h. of the people. 25:4*
and Gad answered the h. Josh 22:21
Joshua called for their h. and. 23:2
the h. of Israel were. 1 Chr 12:32
assembled all the h. to. 2 Chr 5:2
certain of the h. of Ephraim. 28:12
shall wound the h. over. Ps 110:6
O h. of Jacob, and. Mi 3:1, 9
h. thereof judge for reward. 11
see **fathers**

headstone
is become the h. of the. Ps 118:22
bring forth the h. with. Zech 4:7†

heady
for men shall be h. 2 Tim 3:4*

heal
h. her now, O God. Num 12:13
alive, I wound, I h. Deut 32:39
I will h. thee, and add. 2 Ki 20:5
sign that the Lord will h. me? 8
their sin, and will h. 2 Chr 7:14
O Lord, h. me, for my. Ps 6:2
h. my soul, for I have sinned. 41:4
h. the breaches thereof, for. 60:2
to kill, and a time to h. Eccl 3:3
smite and h. it, and he shall h. them.
Isa 19:22
his ways, and will h. him. 57:18, 19
return, and I will h. your. Jer 3:22
h. me, O Lord, and I shall be. 17:14
I will h. thee of thy wounds. 30:17
breach is great, who can h. thee?
Lam 2:13
yet could he not h. you. Hos 5:13
he hath torn, and will h. us. 6:1
I will h. their backsliding, I. 14:4
he shall not h. that that. Zech 11:16
I will come and h. him. Mat 8:7
to h. all manner of sickness. 10:1
Mark 3:15
h. the sick, cleanse the lepers.
Mat 10:8; Luke 9:2; 10:9
is it lawful to h. on the sabbath days?
Mat 12:10; Luke 14:3
I should h. them. Mat 13:15
John 12:40; Acts 28:27
whether he would h. on sabbath.
Mark 3:2; Luke 6:7
he hath sent me to h. the. Luke 4:18
ye will surely say, Physician, h. 23
the Lord was present to h. 5:17
that he would come and h. his. 7:3*
would come down and h. John 4:47
forth thine hand to h. Acts 4:30

healed
God h. Abimelech and. Gen 20:17
him to be thoroughly h. Ex 21:19
the bile is h. Lev 13:18
the scall is h. 37
the plague of leprosy be h. 14:3, 48
thou canst not be h. Deut 28:27
then he shall be h. 1 Sam 6:3
have h. the waters. 2 Ki 2:21
waters were h. 22
king Joram went to be h. in. 8:29
Joram was returned to be h. 9:15
2 Chr 22:6
Lord hearkened and h. 2 Chr 30:20
thee, and thou hast h. me. Ps 30:2
sent his word, and h. them. 107:20
and convert, and be h. Isa 6:10
and with his stripes we are h. 53:5
have h. the hurt. Jer 6:14; 8:11
which refuseth to be h. 15:18
O Lord, and I shall be h. 17:14
balm, if so be she may be h. 51:8
h. Babylon, but she is not h. 9
not be bound up to be h. Ezek 30:21
neither have ye h. that which. 34:4
the waters shall be h. Ezek 47:8, 9
marishes thereof shall not be h. 11
I would have h. Israel. Hos 7:1
but they knew not that I h. 11:3
the palsy, and he h. Mat 4:24
speak, and my servant shall be h.
Mat 8:8; Luke 7:7
multitudes followed him, he h.
Mat 12:15; 14:14
that she may be h. and. Mark 5:23*
all, nor could be h. of. Luke 8:43
therefore come and be h. and. 13:14
when he saw that he was h. 17:15
touched his ear, and h. him. 22:51
he that was h. wist not. John 5:13
the man who was h. Acts 4:14
and they were h. every one. 5:16
that he had faith to be h. 14:9*
Paul prayed, and h. father of. 28:8
but let it rather be h. Heb 12:13
another, that ye may be h. Jas 5:16
whose stripes ye were h. 1 Pet 2:24
deadly wound was h. Rev 13:3, 12

healer
I will not be an h. Isa 3:7

healeth
the Lord that h. thee. Ex 15:26
who h. all thy diseases. Ps 103:3
he h. the broken in heart. 147:3
and he h. the stroke. Isa 30:26

healing, *substantive*
no h. for us, the time of h. Jer 14:19
is no h. of thy bruise. Nah 3:19*
Sun of righteousness arise with h.
Mal 4:2
that had need of h. Luke 9:11
on whom this miracle of h. Acts 4:22
another the gift of h. 1 Cor 12:9, 28
have all the gifts of h.? 30
leaves of tree were for h. Rev 22:2

healing
thou hast no h. medicine. Jer 30:13
went about h. all manner. Mat 4:23
preaching gospel, and h. Luke 9:6
h. all that were oppressed of the.
Acts 10:38

health
our father is in good h. Gen 43:28
Joab said, Art thou in h.? 2 Sam 20:9
who is the h. of my countenance.
Ps 42:11†; 43:5†
thy saving h. may be known. 67:2
it shall be h. to thy navel. Pr 3:8
they are h. to all their flesh. 4:22
the tongue of the wise is h. 12:18
but a faithful ambassador is h. 13:17
sweet to the soul, and h. to. 16:24
thy h. shall spring forth. Isa 58:8
looked for a time of h. Jer 8:15
why is not the h. of my people? 22
I will restore h. unto thee. 30:17
I will bring it h. and cure. 33:6
for this is for your h. Acts 27:34*
mayest be in h. as thy soul. 3 John 2

heap, *substantive*
h. and did eat on the h. Gen 31:46
this h. be witness, and this pillar. 52
floods stood upright as an h. Ex 15:8
Josh 3:13, 16; Ps 33:7; 78:13
shall be an h. for ever. Deut 13:16
over him a great h. of. Josh 7:26
burnt Ai, and made it an h. 8:28
raise on the king of Ai a great h. 29
down at the end of the h. Ruth 3:7
they laid very great h. 2 Sam 18:17
thy belly is like an h. of. S of S 7:2
shall be a ruinous h. Isa 17:1
harvest shall be an h. in the. 11*
thou hast made of a city an h. 25:2
builded on her own h. Jer 30:18
Rabbah shall be a desolate h. 49:2
make Samaria as an h. Mi 1:6
didst walk through the h. Hab 3:15
one came to an h. of. Hag 2:16

heap
I will h. mischiefs upon. Deut 32:23
I could h. up words. Job 16:4*
though he h. up silver as. 27:16
the hypocrites in heart, h. 36:13*
thou shalt h. coals of fire. Pr 25:22
Rom 12:20
to gather and to h. up. Eccl 2:26
h. on wood, kindle fire. Ezek 24:10
for they shall h. dust. Hab 1:10
h. to themselves teachers. 2 Tim 4:3

heaped
Tyrus h. up silver as. Zech 9:3
ye have h. treasure. Jas 5:3*

heapeth
he h. up riches, and. Ps 39:6
he h. unto him all people. Hab 2:5

heaps
them together on h. Ex 8:14
bone of an ass, h. on h. Judg 15:16
lay ye them in two h. 2 Ki 10:8
fenced cities into ruinous h. 19:25
and laid them by h. 2 Chr 31:6
month they began to lay the h. 7
princes came and saw the h. 8
revive stones out of the h.? Neh 4:2
are ready to become h. Job 15:28
have laid Jerusalem on h. Ps 79:1
make Jerusalem h. Jer 9:11; 26:18
way marks, make thee high h. 31:21
cast Babylon up as h. and. 50:26
and Babylon shall become h. 51:37
their altars are as h. in. Hos 12:11
Jerusalem shall become h. Mi 3:12

hear
(*This word is often used for listening to the word of God with a firm purpose to obey his commands. It is also used of God hearing prayer, in the sense of answering, or granting it*)
that all that h. will laugh. Gen 21:6
h. us, my lord, thou art a. 23:6
that the people may h. Ex 19:9
noise of them that sing do I h. 32:18
h. I pray you, ye sons. Num 16:8
rise up, Balak, and h. 23:18
and her father h. her vow. 30:4
h. the cause between. Deut 1:16
and I will make them h. my. 4:10
h. Israel the statutes. 5:1; 6:3; 9:1
20:3; Isa 48:1; Mark 12:29
and h. all that the Lord. Deut 5:27
h. all these words which I. 12:28
if thou shalt h. say in one. 13:12
bring it, that we may h. 30:12, 13
that they may h. and fear Lord.
31:12, 13; Jer 6:10
h. the words of the Lord. Josh 3:9
when ye hear the sound of trumpet.
6:5; Neh 4:20; Dan 3:5, 15
h. O ye kings, give ear. Judg 5:3
why abodest, to h. bleatings of? 16
riddle, that we may h. it. 14:13
for I h. of your evil. 1 Sam 2:23
it is no good report that I h. 24
lowing of the oxen which I h. 15:14
how can I go? if Saul h. it. 16:2
h. the words of thy handmaid. 25:24
2 Sam 20:17
let my lord the king h. 1 Sam 26:19
no man deputed of the king to h.
2 Sam 15:3
as soon as ye h. the sound of. 10
what thing soever thou shalt h. 35
send to me every thing that ye h. 36
h. likewise what Hushai saith. 17:5
woman cried out of city, h. h. 20:16
as soon as they h., they shall be obedient. 22:45; Ps 18:44
to h. the wisdom of Solomon.
1 Ki 4:34; 10:8, 24; 2 Chr 9:7, 23
Mat 12:42; Luke 11:31
and h. thou in heaven. 1 Ki 8:30
32, 34, 36, 39, 43, 45, 49; 2 Chr 6:21
saying, O Baal, h. us. 1 Ki 18:26
made the host to h. a. 2 Ki 7:6
h. the word of the great king. 18:28
Isa 36:1
h. the words of Sennacherib.
2 Ki 19:16; Isa 37:1
when thou shalt h. a. 1 Chr 14:1
thou mayest h. prayer. Neh 1:6
h. O our God, for we are. 4:
and all that could h. with. 8:
h. it, and know thou it. Job 5:2
h. diligently my speech. 13:17; 21:
will God h. his cry? 27:
h. my words. 34:
h. I beseech thee, and I will. 42:

have mercy upon me, *h.* Ps 4:1
39:12; 54:2; 84:8; 102:1; 143:1
the Lord *h.* thee in the day. 20:1*
save, Lord, let the king *h.* us. 9*
h. O Lord, when I cry with. 27:7
h. O Lord, and have mercy. 30:10
h. this, all ye people, give ear. 49:1
h. O my people, and. 50:7; 81:8
make me to *h.* joy and. 51:8
for who, say they, doth *h.*? 59:7
h. my cry, O God, attend to. 61:1
come, and *h.*, all ye that fear. 66:16
h. groaning of the prisoner. 102:20
when they *h.* the words of. 138:4
me to *h.* thy lovingkindness. 143:8
my son, *h.* the instruction. Pr 1:8
h. ye children, the instruction. 4:1
h. O my son, and receive. 10; 19:20
h. for I will speak of excellent. 8:6
h. instruction, and be wise. 33
cease to *h.* instruction. 19:27
bow thine ear, *h.* the words. 22:17
h. thou, my son, be wise. 23:19
and be more ready to *h.* Eccl 5:1
it is better to *h.* the rebuke. 7:5
let us *h.* the conclusion of. 12:13
voice, cause me to *h.* it. S of S 8:13
h. O heavens, and give ear. Isa 1:2
h. ye indeed, but. 6:9; Mark 4:12
when he bloweth, *h.* ye. Isa 18:3
h. ye that are afar off what. 33:13
let the earth *h.* and all that. 34:1
h. ye deaf. 42:18
who will *h.* for time to come? 23
or let them *h.* and say, It is. 43:9
assemble yourselves and *h.* 48:14
h. ye this, I have not spoken. 16
h. and your soul shall live. 55:3
John 5:25
shall I *h.* the sound of? Jer 4:21
therefore *h.* ye nations. 6:18
h. O earth. 19
h. ye the words of this. 11:2, 6
who refused to *h.* 10; 13:10
h. ye, give ear, for the Lord. 13:15
then I will cause thee to *h.* 18:2
caused my people to *h.* my. 23:22
if the princes *h.* that I have. 38:25
therefore *h.* counsel of. 49:20; 50:45
h. I pray you, all. Lam 1:18
h. what I say. Ezek 2:8
h. at my mouth. 3:17; 33:7
he that heareth, let him *h.* 3:27
lying to my people, that *h.* 13:19
h. what is the word that. 33:30
they *h.* thy words, but will not. 31, 32
O God, *h.* the prayer of. Dan 9:17*
O Lord, *h.* O Lord, forgive. 19
h. ye this, O priests. Hos 5:1
h. this, ye old men. Joel 1:2
h. this word that the Lord hath
spoken. Amos 3:1; 4:1; 5:1; 8:4
h. all ye people, hearken. Mi 1:2
I said, *h.* I pray you, O. 3:1, 9
h. ye, O mountains. 6:2
h. ye the rod and him. 9
all that *h.* the bruit of. Nah 3:19
lest they should *h.* law. Zech 7:12
the things which ye *h.* Mat 11:4
lame walk, and deaf *h.* 5
Mark 7:37; Luke 7:22
to *h.* those things that ye *h.*
Mat 13:17; Luke 10:24
he said to multitude *h.* Mat 15:10
beloved Son, *h.* him. 17:5; Mark 9:7
neglect to *h.* them, to *h.* Mat 18:17
are such as *h.* the word. Mark 4:18
20; Luke 8:12, 13
heed what ye *h.* you that *h.* more.
Mark 4:24
pressed on him to *h.* Luke 5:1
multitudes came together to *h.* 15
which came to *h.* him, and to. 6:17
I say to you which *h.* love your. 27
heed therefore how ye *h.* 8:18
which *h.* the word and. 21; 11:28
but who is this of whom I *h.*? 9:9
publicans and sinners to *h.* him. 15:1
said, How is it that I *h.* this? 16:2
and prophets let them *h.* them. 29
Lord said, *H.* what the unjust. 18:6
were very attentive to *h.* him. 19:48*
to him in temple, for to *h.* him. 21:38
as I *h.* I judge. John 5:30

who can *h.* it? John 6:60
law judge a man before it *h.*? 7:51
wherefore would ye *h.* it again? 9:27
sheep *h.* his voice, and he. 10:3
if any man *h.* my words. 12:47
and the word which ye *h.* is. 14:24
how *h.* we every man? Acts 2:8
this, which ye now see and *h.* 33
send for thee, and to *h.* 10:22
to *h.* all things that are. 33
desired to *h.* the word of God. 13:7
whole city came together to *h.* 44
by my mouth should *h.* the. 15:7
either to tell or to *h.* some. 17:21
ye *h.* Paul hath turned. 19:26
h. ye my defence which I make. 22:1
that thou wouldest *h.* us of. 24:4
Agrippa said, I would *h.* 25:22
but we desire to *h.* what. 28:22
I *h.* there be divisions. 1 Cor 11:18
or else be absent, I may *h.* Phil 1:27
we *h.* that some walk. 2 Thes 3:11
thyself and them that *h.* 1 Tim 4:16
all the Gentiles might *h.* 2 Tim 4:17
let every one be swift to *h.* Jas 1:19
we know that he *h.* us. 1 John 5:15
than to *h.* my children. 3 John 4
blessed that *h.* words of. Rev 1:3
which neither can see, nor *h.* 9:20

see **ear, ears, voice**

hear *me*

shall Pharaoh *h. me*? Ex 6:12
h. me, O Lord, *h. me.* 1 Ki 18:37
h. me, my brethren. 1 Chr 28:2
h. me, thou Jeroboam. 2 Chr 13:4
h. me, Asa. 15:2
and he said, *h. me*, O Judah. 20:20
h. me, ye Levites, sanctify. 29:5
I will shew thee, *h. me*, I. Job 15:17
O that one would *h. me*, my. 31:35
h. me when I call, O God. Ps 4:1*
consider, and *h. me*, O Lord. 13:3*
upon thee, for thou wilt *h. me.* 17:6*
h. me, lest they should rejoice. 38:16
attend unto me, and *h. me.* 55:2*
thy right hand, and *h. me.* 60:5*
multitude of thy mercy *h. me.* 69:13*
trouble, *h. me* speedily. 17*; 143:7
God, my God will *h. me.* Mi 7:7
I beseech thee to *h. me.* Acts 26:3
also all that *h. me*, were such. 29
that will they not *h. me.* 1 Cor 14:21

hear *not*, or *not* **hear**

wilt *not h.* but worship. Deut 30:17
the Lord will *not h.* 1 Sam 8:18*
and thou dost *not h.* me. Job 30:20*
surely God will *not h.* vanity. 35:13
Lord will *not h.* me. Ps 66:18
the ear, shall he *not h.*? 94:9
many prayers, I will *not h.* Isa 1:15
Jer 7:16; 11:14; 14:12
Ezek 8:18; Amos 5:23
children that will *not h.* law. Isa 30:9
ear heavy that it *cannot h.* 59:1
he will *not h.* 2
when I spake ye did *not h.* 65:12
when I spake, they did *not h.* 66:4
Zech 1:4
have ears and *h. not.* Jer 5:21
Ezek 12:2; Mark 8:18
but if ye will *not h.* Jer 13:17
22:5; Mal 2:2
that they might *not h.* Jer 17:23
19:15; Zech 7:11
thou saidst, I will *not h.* Jer 22:21
praised the gods of silver, which see
not, nor *h.* Dan 5:23; Rev 9:20
Lord, but he will *not h.* Mi 3:4
I cry, and thou wilt *not h.* Hab 1:2
not receive you, *nor h.* Mat 10:14
if he will *not h.* thee, then. 18:16
if they *h. not* Moses. Luke 16:31
even because ye *cannot h.* John 8:43
therefore *h.* them *not*, because. 47
I told you, and ye did *not h.* 9:27
but the sheep did *not h.* them. 10:8
soul which will *not h.* Acts 3:23
will they *not h.* me. 1 Cor 14:21
do ye *not h.* the law? Gal 4:21

would not **hear**

besought us, we *would not h.*
Gen 42:21
against the child, ye *would not h.* 22

thou *wouldest not h.* Ex 7:16
Israel *would not h.* Deut 1:43; 3:26
2 Ki 17:14; 18:12; Neh 9:29
Zech 7:13
Amaziah *would not h.* 2 Ki 14:11
2 Chr 25:20
this is the refreshing: yet they *would
not h.* Isa 28:12
might be for praise, they *would not h.*
Jer 13:11; 29:19
he *would not h.* 36:25
I *would not h.* Zech 7:13

hear *now*, or *now* **hear**

and he said, *h. now* my words.
Num 12:6; 20:10
Saul said, *h. now*, ye. 1 Sam 22:7
h. now, thou son of Ahitub. 12
h. now my reasoning. Job 13:6
h. me *now*, therefore, O. Pr 5:7
and he said, *h.* ye *now.* Isa 7:13
now h. O Jacob my servant. 44:1
h. now, thou that art given to. 47:8
therefore, *h. now* this, thou. 51:21
h. now this, O foolish. Jer 5:21
h. now, Hananiah. 28:15
h. now, O Joshua. Zech 3:8
h. now, I pray thee, O my. 37:20
h. ye *now* what the Lord. Mi 6:1
which ye *now* see and *h.* Acts 2:33
in me, and *now h.* to be in. Phil 1:30

shall **hear**

the people *shall h.* and. Ex 15:14
Deut 13:11; 17:13; 19:20; 21:21
the Egyptians *shall h.* it. Num 14:13
ye *shall h.* small as well. Deut 1:17
who *shall h.* report of thee. 2:25
which *shall h.* all these statutes. 4:6
of the land *shall h.* of it. Josh 7:9
and thou *shalt h.* what. Judg 7:11
Israel *shall h.* that. 2 Sam 16:21
shall h. of thy great. 1 Ki 8:42
and he *shall h.* a rumour. 2 Ki 19:7
Isa 37:7
prayer to him, he *shall h.* Job 22:27
humble *shall h.* thereof. Ps 34:2
cry, and he *shall h.* my voice. 55:17
God *shall h.* and afflict them. 19
mine ears *shall h.* desire of. 92:11
they *shall h.* my words. 141:6
day *shall* the deaf *h.* Isa 29:18
when he *shall h.* it he will. 30:19
thine ears *shall h.* a word. 21
shall h. all the good. Jer 33:9
and the heaven *shall h.* Hos 2:21
the earth *shall h.* the corn and. 22
by hearing, ye *shall h.* Mat 13:14
Acts 28:26
if he *shall h.* thee thou. Mat 18:15
ye *shall h.* of wars. 24:6
Mark 13:7; Luke 21:9
dead *shall h.* voice of. John 5:25
whatsoever he *shall h.* that. 16:13
him *shall* ye *h.* in all things.
Acts 3:22; 7:37
said he, thou *shalt h.* him. 25:22
shall they *h.* without a. Rom 10:14

will **hear**

speak unto us, we *will h.* Ex 20:19
Deut 5:27
if they cry, I *will* surely *h.* 22:23, 27
I *will h.* what the Lord. Num 9:8
king *will h.* to deliver. 2 Sam 14:16
be thy God *will h.* the. 2 Ki 19:4
then *will* I *h.* from heaven.
2 Chr 7:14; Ps 20:6
wilt h. and help. 2 Chr 20:9; Ps 38:15
the Lord *will h.* Ps 4:3
thou *wilt h.* me. 17:6
I *will h.* what God the Lord. 85:8
he also *will h.* their cry, and. 145:19
man *will h.* and increase. Pr 1:5
the Lord *will h.* them. Isa 41:17*
are yet speaking, I *will h.* 65:24
house of Judah *will h.* Jer 36:3
whether they *will h.* or forbear.
Ezek 2:5, 7; 3:11
I *will h.* the heavens. Hos 2:21
God, my God *will h.* me. Mi 7:7
I am their God and *will h.* them.
Zech 10:6; 13:9
we *will h.* thee again of. Acts 17:32
for they *will h.* that thou. 21:22

I *will h.* thee, when thy. *Acts* 23:35
to the Gentiles, they *will h.* 28:28

hear *the word of the Lord*
h. therefore *the word of the Lord.* *1 Ki* 22:19; *2 Chr* 18:18
Jer 29:20; 42:15; *Amos* 7:16
Elisha said *h.* ye *word of the Lord.* *2 Ki* 7:1; *Jer* 17:20; 21:11
Hezekiah, *H. the word of Lord.* *2 Ki* 20:16; *Isa* 39:5
h. word of the Lord, ye rulers of Sodom. *Isa* 1:10
h. the word of the Lord, ye scornful men. 28:14
h. word of Lord, ye that tremble. 66:5
h. word of Lord, O house of Jacob. *Jer* 2:4; 10:1
h. the word of the Lord, all ye of. 7:2
yet *h. word of the Lord,* O ye. 9:20
h. word of Lord, O kings of Judah. 19:3; 22:2
earth, *h. the word of the Lord.* 22:29
h. the word of Lord, O ye nations. 31:10
h. word of Lord, O Zedekiah. 34:4
h. the word of the Lord, all Judah. 44:24, 26
of Israel, *h. the word of the Lord,* I will bring a. *Ezek* 6:3; 36:1, 4
prophets *h.* ye *the word of the Lord.* 13:2
O harlot, *h. the word of the Lord.* 16:35
forest of the south, *H. the word of the Lord.* 20:47
Ammonites, *h. the word of the Lord.* 25:3
shepherds, *h. the word of the Lord.* 34:7, 9
dry bones, *h. the word of the Lord.* 37:4
h. word of the Lord, ye children. *Hos* 4:1
Amaziah, *h.* thou *the word of the Lord.* *Amos* 7:16

heard
because Lord hath *h.* *Gen* 16:11
neither yet *h.* I of it, but. 21:26
because the Lord hath *h.* that. 29:33
aloud, and the Egyptians *h.* 45:2
God *h.* their groaning. *Ex* 2:24
he hath *h.* your murmurings. 16:9
neither let it be *h.* out of thy. 23:13
sound shall be *h.* when he. 28:35
people *h.* these evil tidings. 33:4
let all that *h.* him lay. *Lev* 24:14
complained, the Lord *h.* *Num* 11:1
against Moses, the Lord *h.* it. 12:2
they have *h.* thou art among. 14:14
nations which have *h.* the fame. 15
in the day that he *h.* it. 30:7, 14
they *h.* that they were. *Josh* 9:16
Samuel cried, and the Lord *h.* him. *1 Sam* 7:9*
come, as thy servant hath *h.*? 23:11
hast not *h.* that Adonijah? *1 Ki* 1:11
nor was any tool of iron *h.* in. 6:7
and prosperity exceedeth fame which I *h.* 10:7; *2 Chr* 9:6
hast thou not *h.* long ago? *2 Ki* 19:25; *Isa* 37:26
make one sound to be *h.* *2 Chr* 5:13
he was entreated and *h.* his. 33:13
the noise was *h.* afar. *Ezra* 3:13
the joy of Jerusalem *h.* *Neh* 12:43
h. the secret of God? *Job* 15:8
of wrong, but I am not *h.* 19:7
but how little a portion is *h.* 26:14
when the ear *h.* me, then it. 29:11
the Lord hath *h.* my. *Ps* 6:9
thou hast *h.* the desire of. 10:17
save me, for thou hast *h.* 22:21*
but when he cried he *h.* 24; 34:6
40:1; 120:1
I sought the Lord, and he *h.* 34:4*
but I as a deaf man *h.* not. 38:13
thou, O God, hast *h.* my vows. 61:5
verily God hath *h.* me, he. 66:19
cause judgement to be *h.* 76:8
therefore the Lord *h.* this and. 78:21
when God *h.* this, was wroth. 59
where I *h.* a language that I. 81:5
Zion *h.* and was glad, and. 97:8
their affliction, when he *h.* *Ps* 106:44
for thou hast *h.* me, and. 118:21*
lo, we *h.* of it at Ephratah. 132:6
cry himself, but not be *h.* *Pr* 21:13
to be *h.* unto Laish. *Isa* 10:30
have ye not *h.*? hath it not? 40:21
hast thou not *h.* everlasting God? 28
thou hast *h.* see all this, will? 48:6
which they had not *h.* shall. 52:15
violence shall no more be *h.* in. 60:18
men have not *h.* what he hath. 64:4
weeping shall be no more *h.* 65:19
who hath *h.* such a thing? 66:8
isles afar off, that have not *h.* 19
thou hast *h.* the sound. *Jer* 4:19
wickedness, spoil is *h.* in her. 6:7
rising early, but ye *h.* not. 7:13
hearkened and *h.* but they. 8:6
ask the heathen, who hath *h.* 18:13
let cry be *h.* from houses when. 22
howling of the flock shall be *h.* 25:36
prophesied as ye have *h.* 26:11
h. every one should let his. 34:10
spoken, but they have not *h.* 35:17
the nations have *h.* of thy. 46:12
and the cry is *h.* among. 50:46
a rumour that shall be *h.* in. 51:46
they have *h.* that I sigh. *Lam* 1:21
thou hast *h.* their reproach. 3:61
the nations *h.* of him. *Ezek* 19:4
thy harps shall be no more *h.* 26:13
h. the sound of the trumpet. 33:5
and I *h.* but I understood. *Dan* 12:8
their congregation hath *h.* *Hos* 7:12
unto Lord, and he *h.* me. *Jonah* 2:2*
such as they have not *h.* *Mi* 5:15
I *h.*, my belly trembled. *Hab* 3:16
Lord hearkened and *h.* it. *Mal* 3:16
ye have *h.* it was said. *Mat* 5:21
27, 33, 38, 43
they shall be *h.* for their much. 6:7
ye hear, and have not *h.* them. 13:17; *Luke* 10:24
offended after they *h.* *Mat* 15:12
when the king *h.* thereof. 22:7
ye have *h.* his blasphemy. 26:65
Mark 14:64
but when they have *h.* *Mark* 4:15
and when they *h.* it they. 14:11
fear not, thy prayer is *h.* *Luke* 1:13
Acts 10:31
have spoken, shall be *h.* *Luke* 12:3
when they *h.* it, they said. 20:16
what he hath *h.* that. *John* 3:32
every man that hath *h.* of the. 6:45
on ground, as though he *h.* not. 8:6
since world began was it not *h.* 9:32
I thank thee that thou hast *h.* 11:41
ask them which *h.* me, what. 18:21
when Simon Peter *h.* that it. 21:7
for the promise ye have *h.* *Acts* 1:4
h. this, they were pricked. 2:37
many of them which *h.* the. 4:4
fear came on all them that *h.* 5:5
when the Gentiles *h.* this. 13:48
the same *h.* Paul speak, who. 14:9
which worshipped God, *h.* us. 16:14
and the prisoners *h.* them. 25*
h. this, they were baptized. 19:5
of what thou hast seen and *h.* 22:15
h. him concerning the faith. 24:24
of whom they have not *h.* *Rom* 10:14
but I say, have they not *h.*? 18
they that have not *h.* shall. 15:21
not seen, nor ear *h.* *1 Cor* 2:9
h. of my conversation. *Gal* 1:13
after that ye *h.* the word. *Eph* 1:13
h. of your faith in the Lord. 15
if so be ye have *h.* him and. 4:21
that ye had *h.* that he. *Phil* 2:26
things ye have *h.* and seen. 4:9
since we *h.* of your faith. *Col* 1:4
since day ye *h.* of it, and knew. 6
since day we *h.* it, do not cease. 9
things thou hast *h.* of me. *2 Tim* 2:2
to us by them that *h.* him. *Heb* 2:3
for some when they had *h.* 3:16
with faith in them that *h.* 4:2
offered up prayers, and was *h.* 5:7
h. of the patience of Job. *Jas* 5:11
ye *h.* that antichrist shall come. *1 John* 2:18; 4:3
have *h.* from the beginning. 2:24
3:11; *2 John* 6
therefore how thou hast *h.* *Rev* 3:3
and all that are in them *h.* 5:13
I *h.* the number of them which. 7:4
and I *h.* the number of the. 9:16
I *h.* the angel of the waters. 16:5
of trumpeters shall be *h.* no. 18:22
the voice of bride shall be *h.* no. 23
things, and *h.* them, when I *h.* 22:8

I have **heard**
Ishmael *I have h.* thee. *Gen* 17:20
dreamed a dream: *I have h.* say that thou canst. 41:15; *Dan* 5:14, 16
I have h. there is corn. *Gen* 42:2
I have h. their cry. *Ex* 3:7
I have h. the groaning. 6:5
I have h. the murmuring. 16:12
Num 14:27
I have h. the voice of. *Deut* 5:28
now *I have h.* that thou. *1 Sam* 25:7
word that *I have h.* is. *1 Ki* 2:42
I have h. thy prayer thou hast. 9:3
2 Ki 20:5; *2 Chr* 7:12; *Isa* 38:5
which thou hast prayed *I have h.* *2 Ki* 19:20
I also *have h.* thee, saith Lord. 22:19; *2 Chr* 34:27
I have h. many such things. *Job* 16:2
I have h. the check of my. 20:3
I have h. of thee by the hearing. 42:5
for *I have h.* slander. *Ps* 31:13
twice *I have h.* this, power. 62:11
that which *I have h.* of. *Isa* 21:10
I have h. from the Lord a. 28:22
in an acceptable time *have I h.* 49:8*
2 Cor 6:2
I have h. what prophets. *Jer* 23:25
I have h. Ephraim bemoaning. 31:18
I have h. you, behold, I will. 42:4
I have h. a rumour from. 49:14
know *I have h.* all. *Ezek* 35:12
I have h. him and. *Hos* 14:8*
Lord, *I have h.* thy speech. *Hab* 3:2
I have h. the reproach. *Zeph* 2:8
those things *I have h.* *John* 8:26
truth, which *I have h.* of God. 40
all things that *I have h.* of. 15:15
I have h. their groaning. *Acts* 7:34
Lord, *I have h.* by many of this. 9:13

heard joined with *voice*
h. voice of the Lord walking. *Gen* 3:8
I *h.* thy *voice,* and was afraid. 10
God *h.* the *voice* of the lad. 21:17
God hath *h.* my *voice,* and. 30:6
h. that I lifted up my *voice.* 39:15
then he *h.* the *voice* of. *Num* 7:89
we cried, he *h.* our *voice.* 20:16
the Lord *h.* the *voice* of. *Deut* 1:34
similitude, only he *h.* a *voice.* 4:12
v. of God as thou hast *h.* 33; 5:26
ye *h.* the *voice* out of the. 5:23
have *h.* his *voice* out of the. 24
and the Lord *h.* the *voice* of your. 28
we cried, the Lord *h.* our *voice.* 26:7
let not thy *voice* be *h.* *Judg* 18:25
her *voice* was not *h.* *1 Sam* 1:13
the Lord *h.* the *voice.* *1 Ki* 17:22
voice was *h.* prayer. *2 Chr* 30:27
was silence, I *h.* a *voice.* *Job* 4:16
I have *h.* the *voice* of thy. 33:8
stay them when his *voice* is *h.* 37:4
Lord with my *voice,* he *h.* *Ps* 3:4
the Lord hath *h.* the *voice* of. 6:8
I called, he *h.* my *voice* out of. 18:6
no speech where their *voice* is not *h.* 19:3
because he hath *h.* the *voice* of. 28:6
the *voice* of his praise to be *h.* 66:8
love the Lord, because he hath *h.* my *voice.* 116:1
voice of the turtle is *h.* *S of S* 2:12
h. the *voice* of the Lord. *Isa* 6:8
their *voice* shall be *h.* even. 15:4
his glorious *voice* to be *h.* 30:30
nor cause his *voice* to be *h.* 42:2
to make your *voice* be *h.* on. 58:4
voice of weeping shall no more be *h.* 65:19
a *voice* was *h.* upon the. *Jer* 3:21
h. a *voice* of a woman in. 4:31
voice of wailing is *h.* out of. 9:19
h. a *voice* of trembling. 30:5
a *voice* was *h.* in Ramah. 31:15
Mat 2:18

hast h. my voice, hide. Lam 3:56
and I h. a voice of one. Ezek 1:28
ı h. behind me a voice of. 3:12
voice should no more be h. 19:9
cause their voice to be h. 27:30
I h. a man's voice between. Dan 8:16
yet h. I the voice of his words, when
I h. 10:9
voice of thy messengers no more be
h. Nah 2:13
neither h. his voice. John 5:37
h. a voice, saying, Saul, Saul.
Acts 9:4; 22:7; 26:14
h. a voice saying to me, arise. 11:7
they h. not the voice of him. 22:9
which voice they that h. Heb 12:19
voice which came from heaven we h.
2 Pet 1:18
I h. a great voice. Rev 1:10; 16:1
19:1; 21:3
the first voice I h. was as it. 4:1
I beheld, and h. the voice of. 5:11
I h. a voice in the midst of the. 6:6
I h. the voice of the fourth beast. 7
I h. a voice from the four. 9:13
I h. a voice from heaven. 10:4, 8
14:2, 13; 18:4
and I h. a loud voice, saying. 12:10
I h. the voice of harpers. 14:2
I h. as it were the voice of a. 19:6

we have **heard**

we have h. how the Lord. Josh 2:10
as soon as we had h. these. 11
we have h. the fame of him. 9:9
thee according to all we have h.
2 Sam 7:22; 1 Chr 17:20
we have h. kings of Israel are.
1 Ki 20:31
we have h. the fame thereof.
Job 28:22; Jer 6:24
we have h. with our ears. Ps 44:1
as we have h. so have we. 48:8
dark sayings which we have h. 78:3
we have h. of pride of Moab.
Isa 16:6; Jer 48:29
we have h. songs, glory. Isa 24:16
we have h. a voice. Jer 30:5
because we have h. reproach. 51:51
we have h. a rumour from. Ob 1
for we have h. that God. Zech 8:23
we have h. him say, I. Mark 14:58
whatsoever we have h. done in
Capernaum. Luke 4:23
we ourselves have h. of his. 22:71
we believe, we have h. John 4:42
we have h. out of the law. 12:34
speak things we have h. Acts 4:20
we have h. him speak. 6:11
we have h. him say, this Jesus. 14
we have h. that certain. 15:24
we have not h. whether there. 19:2
to things which we have h. Heb 2:1
that which we have h. 1 John 1:1, 3
message which we have h. of him. 5

heard joined with word or words

when he h. the words of. Gen 24:30
Abraham's servant h. their words. 52
and when Esau h. the words. 27:34
Jacob h. the words of Laban's. 31:1
when his master h. the words. 39:19
h. words of God. Num 24:4, 16
heads of Israel h. words. Josh 22:30
for it hath h. all the words of. 24:27
when Zebul h. the words. Judg 9:30
Samuel h. all the words. 1 Sam 8:21
Israel h. Goliath's words. 17:11
the same words, and David h. 23
words were h. which David. 31
the word that I have h. is good.
1 Ki 2:42
Hiram h. Solomon's words. 5:7
when Ahab h. those words. 21:27
when the king h. words. 2 Ki 6:30
e not afraid of words thou hast h.
19:6; Isa 37:6
ı. the words of book of law, he rent.
2 Ki 22:11, 18; 2 Chr 34:19
ısa h. these words. 2 Chr 15:8
h. these words, I sat. Neh 1:4
ngry when I h. these words. 5:6
wept, when they h. words. 8:9
. the voice of thy words, saying.
Job 33:8

man's words are not h. Eccl 9:16
the words of wise men are h. in. 17
words which God hath h. Isa 37:4
marked, and h. his word. Jer 23:18
ye have not h. my words. 25:8
city all the words ye have h. 26:12
all the princes h. his words. 21
them all the words he had h. 36:13
not afraid that h. these words. 24
Pashur h. the words Jeremiah. 38:1
Darius h. these words. Dan 6:14
thy words were h., and I am. 10:12
they h. these words. Mat 22:22
as soon as Jesus h. the word.
Mark 5:36
Jesus' feet, and h. his words.
Luke 10:39
fell on them who h. word. Acts 10:44
h. unspeakable words. 2 Cor 12:4
ye h. the word of truth. Eph 1:13
ye h. in the word of the. Col 1:5
word which ye h. of us. 1 Thes 2:13
sound words thou hast h. of me.
2 Tim 1:13
h. intreated that word. Heb 12:19
the word ye have h. from the.
1 John 2:7

heardest

and thou h. his words. Deut 4:36
for thou h. in that day. Josh 14:12
h. what I spake against this place.
2 Ki 22:19; 2 Chr 34:27
and thou h. their cry by. Neh 9:9
thou h. them from heaven. 27, 28
thou h. the voice of my. Ps 31:22
my ways, and thou h. me. 119:26*
the day when thou h. Isa 48:7
yea, thou h. not, yea, thou. 8
of hell I cried, thou h. Jonah 2:2

hearer

if any be a h. of the word. Jas 1:23
he being not a forgetful h. but. 25

hearers

the h. of the law are. Rom 2:13
minister grace unto h. Eph 4:29
the subverting of the h. 2 Tim 2:14
doers of word, and not h. Jas 1:22

hearest

Boaz to Ruth, h. thou ? Ruth 2:8
h. thou men's words ? 1 Sam 24:9
when h. sound in the. 2 Sam 5:4
when thou h. forgive. 1 Ki 8:30
2 Chr 6:21
daytime, but thou h. not. Ps 22:2*
thou that h. prayer, unto thee. 65:2
said unto him, h. thou ? Mat 21:16
h. thou not how many things ? 27:13
wind bloweth, and thou h. John 3:8
and I knew that thou h. me. 11:42

heareth

for that he h. your murmurings.
Ex 16:7, 8
disallow her in day that he h.
Num 30:5
when he h. the words of. Deut 29:19
for thy servant h. 1 Sam 3:9, 10
at which ears of every one that h.
11; 2 Ki 21:12; Jer 19:3
whosoever h. it will say. 2 Sam 17:9
and he h. the cry of the. Job 34:28
cry, and the Lord h. Ps 34:17
thus I was as a man that h. not. 38:14
Lord h. poor, and despiseth. 69:33
blessed is the man that h. Pr 8:34
a wise son h. his father's. 13:1
ransom his riches, but the poor h. 8
but he h. the prayer of. 15:29
that h. the reproof of life. 31, 32
a matter before he h. it. 18:13
the man that h. speaketh. 21:28
lest he that h. it put thee. 25:10
h. cursing, and bewrayeth it. 29:24
there is none that h. Isa 41:26
opening the ears, but he h. not. 42:20
shalt say, he that h. Ezek 3:27
whosoever h. the sound of the. 33:4
whoso h. these sayings. Mat 7:24
26; Luke 6:47, 49
when any one h. word. Mat 13:19
is he that h. the word. 20, 22, 23

he that h. you h. me. Luke 10:16
and h. him rejoiceth. John 3:29
h. my word, and believeth. 5:24
that is of God h. God's words. 8:47
h. not sinners, but if any man be a
worshipper of God, him he h. 9:31
one that is of the truth, h. 18:37
me above that he h. of. 2 Cor 12:6
and the world h. them. 1 John 4:5
he that knoweth God h. us. 6
according to his will, he h. us. 5:14
let him that h. say, Come. Rev 22:17
I testify to every man that h. 18

hearing

law to Israel in their h. Deut 31:11
for in our h. the king. 2 Sam 18:12
was neither voice nor h. 2 Ki 4:31
hast spoken in my h. Job 33:8
I have heard of thee by the h. 42:5
nor reprove after the h. of. Isa 11:3
I was bowed down at the h. 21:3
that stoppeth his ears from h. 33:15
to others he said in my h. Ezek 9:5
cried unto them in my h. O. 10:13
a famine of h. the word. Amos 8:11
to be reserved to the h. Acts 25:21*
entered into the place of h. 23
faith cometh by h. and h. Rom 10:17
the h.? if whole were h. 1 Cor 12:17
or by the h. of faith. Gal 3:2, 5
seeing ye are dull of h. Heb 5:11

hearing, verb

the h. ear, the Lord. Pr 20:12
turneth away the ear from h. 28:9
nor is the ear filled with h. Eccl 1:8
and h. they hear not. Mat 13:13
by h. ye shall hear, and shall. 14
their ears dull of h. 15; Acts 28:27
Heb 5:11
h. him were astonished. Mark 6:2
h. them and asking. Luke 2:46
Ananias h. these words. Acts 5:5
h. and seeing the miracles which. 8:6
men stood, h. a voice, but. 9:7
many of the Corinthians h. 18:8
h. of thy love and faith. Philem 5
Lot in seeing and h. 2 Pet 2:8

hearken

how shall Pharaoh h.? Ex 6:30
if ye h. to these judgements.
Deut 7:12
if ye will h. diligently to my. 11:13
if thou carefully h. to voice of. 15:5
Jer 17:24
to him ye shall h. Deut 18:15
if thou h. to commandments. 28:13
1 Ki 11:38
as to Moses, so will we h. Josh 1:17
to h. than the fat of. 1 Sam 15:22
for who will h. to you in ? 30:24
have thou respect to h. to cry.
1 Ki 8:28
mayest h. to the prayer. 29, 52
2 Chr 6:19, 20
shall we h. then to you ? Neh 13:27
Israel, if thou wilt h. Ps 81:8
if ruler h. to lies, servants. Pr 29:12
them that hear shall h. Isa 32:3
h. and hear for the time. 42:23
if so be they will h. and. Jer 26:3
to h. to the prophets whom I. 5
pray to me, and I will h. unto. 29:12
not receive instruction to h. 35:13
refused to h., stopped. Zech 7:11
to h. unto you more than. Acts 4:19
knocked, a damsel came to h. 12:13*

hearken, imperatively

wives of Lamech, h. to. Gen 4:23
my lord, h. to me. 23:15
h. to Israel your father. 49:2
rise up, h. unto me, thou son of.
Num 23:18
h. O Israel, to statutes. Deut 4:1
take heed, and h. O Israel. 27:9
he cried, h. to me, ye. Judg 9:7
h. to the supplication. 1 Ki 8:30
2 Chr 6:21
he said, h. O people. 1 Ki 22:28
and he said, h. all ye. 2 Chr 18:27
h. ye, all Judah, and ye. 20:15
and h. to the pleadings of. Job 13:6

Job, *h.* unto me. *Job* 32:10; 33:31
h. to all my words. 33:1
h. unto me, ye men of. 34:10
let a wise man *h.* 34
h. to this, O Job. 37:14
h. I will teach you *Ps* 34:11
h. O daughter. 45:10
h. to me, therefore, O children. *Pr* 7:24; 8:32
hear my voice, *h.* and. *Isa* 28:23
come near, ye nations, *h.* 34:1; 49:1
h. to me, O house of Jacob. 46:3
48:12; *Hos* 5:1
h. to me, stouthearted. *Isa* 46:12
h. to me, ye that follow after. 51:1
h. unto me, my people, give ear. 4
h. to me, ye that know. 7
h. diligently unto me, eat. 55:2
saying, *h.* to the sound. *Jer* 6:17
O Lord, *h.* and do; defer. *Dan* 9:19
h. O earth, and all that. *Mi* 1:2
he said, *h.* to me, every. *Mark* 7:14
ye men of Judah, *h.* to. *Acts* 2:14
men, brethren, and fathers, *h.* 7:2
saying, men and brethren, *h.* 15:13
h. my beloved brethren. *Jas* 2:5
see **voice**

hearken *not*, or *not* **hearken**

if ye will *not h.*, to be. *Gen* 34:17
Pharaoh shall *not h.* to you. *Ex* 7:4
22; 11:9
but if ye will *not h.* to me. *Lev* 26:14
18, 21, 27
thou shalt *not h.* to that. *Deut* 13:3
not h. unto him, nor shall thine. 8
the man that will *not h.* to. 17:12
that whosoever will *not h.* 18:19
chastened, he will *not h.* to. 21:18
not h. to Balaam. 23:5; *Josh* 24:10
will *not h.* to thy words. *Josh* 1:18
yet they would *not h.* to. *Judg* 2:17
king of Edom would *not h.* 11:17
men of Gibeah would *not h.* 19:25
of Benjamin would *not h.* 20:13
elders said, *h. not* to him. *1 Ki* 20:8
did *not h.* but did after. *2 Ki* 17:40
h. not to Hezekiah. 18:31; *Isa* 36:16
Rehoboam would *not h.* *2 Chr* 10:16
spake, but they would *not h.* 33:10
if *not h.* hold thy peace, I. *Job* 33:33
not h. to the voice of. *Ps* 58:5
but my people would *not h.* 81:11
ear is uncircumcised, they *cannot h.* *Jer* 6:10
said, we will *not h.* 17; 44:16
shalt speak, they will *not h.* 7:27
they cry to me, I will *not h.* 11:11
that they may *not h.* to me. 16:12
if ye will *not h.* to me. 17:27
26:4; *Ezek* 20:39
h. not to words of the prophets. *Jer.* 23:16; 27:9, 14, 16, 17; 29:8
counsel, wilt thou *not h.*? 38:15
not h. to thee, for they will *not h.* *Ezek* 3:7
rebelled, and would *not h.* 20:8
because they did *not h.* to him. *Hos* 9:17; *Zech* 1:4

hearkened

Abraham *h.* to Ephron. *Gen* 23:16
God *h.* to Leah. 30:17
God *h.* to Rachel. 22
to Hamor *h.* all that went out. 34:24
that Joseph *h.* not to her. 39:10
h. not to Moses. *Ex* 6:9; 16:20
Israel have not *h.* to me. 6:12
Pharaoh *h.* not to them. 7:13
8:15, 19; 9:12
Lord *h.* to me. *Deut* 9:19; 10:10
these nations *h.* to observers. 18:14
h. to Joshua as to Moses. 34:9
Josh 1:17
king of Ammonites *h.* *Judg* 11:28
the woman of Endor *h.* *1 Sam* 28:21
king *h.* not to people. *1 Ki* 12:15
16; *2 Chr* 10:15
h. therefore to the word. *1 Ki* 12:24
Ben-hahad *h.* to king Asa. 15:20
2 Chr 16:4
and the Lord *h.* to. *2 Ki* 13:4
king of Assyria *h.* to Asa. 16:9
Hezekiah *h.* to messengers. 20:13
Judah *h.* not to the law. 21:9
fathers *h.* not to words. *2 Ki* 22:13
Joash *h.* to princes. *2 Chr* 24:17
Amaziah *h.* not to the. 25:16
Lord *h.* to Hezekiah, and. 30:20
Josiah *h.* not to Pharaoh-necho. 35:22
and *h.* not to thy commandments. *Neh* 9:16, 29, 34; *Jer* 34:14
now when Mordecai *h.* *Esth* 3:4
that my people had *h.* *Ps* 81:13
and he *h.* diligently with. *Isa* 21:7
O that thou hadst *h.* to my. 48:18
they have not *h.* to my word. *Jer* 6:19; 7:24, 26; 25:3, 4, 7
26:5; 29:19; 32:33; 34:17; 35:14
15, 16; 36:31; 44:5
Irijah *h.* not to Jeremiah. 37:14
they would have *h.* to thee. *Ezek* 3:6
neither have we *h.* to thy. *Dan* 9:6
the Lord *h.* and heard it. *Mal* 3:16
Jer 8:6
sirs, ye should have *h.* *Acts* 27:21
see **voice**

hearkenedst

h. not to voice of Lord. *Deut* 28:45

hearkeneth

but whoso *h.* to me. *Pr* 1:33
he that *h.* to counsel is wise. 12:15

hearkening

angels *h.* to the voice of. *Ps* 103:20

heart

(*The word heart is used in Scripture as the seat of life or strength; hence it means mind, soul, spirit, or one's entire emotional nature and understanding. It is also used as the centre or inner part of a thing*)

Jacob's *h.* fainted, for. *Gen* 45:26
for ye know the *h.* of a. *Ex* 23:9
they shall be on Aaron's *h.* 28:30
whoso is of a willing *h.* let. 35:5
he filled with wisdom of *h.* 35
eyes, cause sorrow of *h.* *Lev* 26:16*
discourage ye the *h.*? *Num* 32:7
they discouraged the *h.* of the. 9
there were such an *h.* *Deut* 5:29
smite with astonishment of *h.* 28:28
the Lord with gladness of *h.* 47
give thee there a trembling *h.* 65
Lord hath not given you an *h.* to. 29:4
h. of the people melt. *Josh* 14:8
great thoughts of *h.* *Judg* 5:15
there were great searchings of *h.* 16
the priest's *h.* was glad, he. 18:20
now Hannah, she spake in her *h.* *1 Sam* 1:13
that God gave him another *h.* 10:9
but the Lord looketh on the *h.* 16:7
let no man's *h.* fail because. 17:32
David's *h.* smote him, because. 24:5
no grief, nor offence of *h.* 25:31
and Nabal's *h.* was merry within. 36
she despised him in her *h.* *2 Sam* 6:16
1 Chr 15:29
Amnon's *h.* is merry. *2 Sam* 13:28
that the king's *h.* was toward. 14:1
thrust darts through the *h.* 18:14
he bowed the *h.* of all men. 19:14
an understanding *h.* *1 Ki* 3:9
given thee an understanding *h.* 12
Solomon wisdom and largeness of *h.* 4:29
the *h.* of David. 8:17; *2 Chr* 6:7
people went to tents glad of *h.* *1 Ki* 8:66; *2 Chr* 7:10
communed with him of all that was in her *h.* *1 Ki* 10:2; *2 Chr* 9:1
perfect, as was the *h.* of. *1 Ki* 11:4
shall the *h.* of this people. 12:27
h. of king of Assyria. *2 Ki* 6:11
into any man's *h.* 12:4; *2 Chr* 29:31
were not of double *h.* *1 Chr* 12:33
let the *h.* of them rejoice. 16:10
Ps 105:3
I know thou triest the *h.* *1 Chr* 29:17
18; *Jer* 11:20
came into Solomon's *h.* *2 Chr* 7:11
turned the *h.* of king of. *Ezra* 6:22
a thing as this in the king's *h.* 7:27
else but sorrow of *h.* *Neh* 2:2
when the *h.* of the king. *Esth* 1:10
forth that day with a glad *h.* 5:9
he is wise in *h.* and. *Job* 9:4
he taketh away the *h.* of. *Job* 12:24†
I caused the widow's *h.* to. 29:13
but the hypocrites in *h.* heap. 36:13
not any that are wise of *h.* 37:24
given understanding to *h.* 38:36*
and with double *h.* do. *Ps* 12:2
are right, rejoicing the *h.* 19:8
them that are of a broken *h.* 34:18
knoweth the secrets of the *h.* 44:21
arrows are sharp in the *h.* 45:5
in *h.* ye work wickedness. 58:2
the *h.* is deep. 64:6
have more than *h.* could wish. 73:7
a froward *h.* shall depart. 101:4
an high look, and a proud *h.* will. 5
glad the *h.* of man, bread, which strengtheneth man's *h.* 104:15
a *h.* that deviseth wicked. *Pr* 6:18
met him a woman subtle of *h.* 7:10
ye of an understanding *h.* 8:5
the wise in *h.* will receive. 10:8
h. of the wicked is little worth. 20
froward *h.* are abomination. 11:20
be servant to the wise of *h.* 29
but he that is of perverse *h.* 12:8
deceit is in the *h.* of them who. 20
heaviness in the *h.* of man. 25
hope deferred maketh the *h.* 13:12
the *h.* knoweth his own. 14:10
in laughter the *h.* is sorrowful. 13
backslider in *h.* be filled with. 14
a sound *h.* is the life of the flesh. 30
wisdom resteth in *h.* of him. 33
but the *h.* of the foolish doeth. 15:7
a merry *h.* maketh a cheerful countenance; but by sorrow of the *h.* 13
h. of him that hath understanding. 14
a merry *h.* hath a continual feast. 15
the *h.* of the righteous studieth. 28
of the eyes rejoiceth the *h.* 30
the preparation of *h.* in man. 16:1
proud in *h.* is an abomination. 5
a man's *h.* deviseth his way. 9
h. of wise teacheth his mouth. 23
seeing he hath no *h.* to it. 17:16
hath a froward *h.* findeth no. 20
a merry *h.* doeth good like a. 22
before destruction the *h.* of. 18:12
the *h.* of the prudent getteth. 15
many devices in a man's *h.* 19:21
counsel in *h.* of man is like. 20:5
the king's *h.* is in the hand of. 21:1
high look, and a proud *h.* is sin. 4
he that loveth pureness of *h.* 22:11
foolishness is bound in the *h.* 15
doth not he that pondereth *h.*? 24:12
and the *h.* of kings is. 25:3
singeth songs to an heavy *h.* 20
a wicked *h.* is like a potsherd. 26:23
perfume rejoice the *h.* 27:9
h. of man answereth to man. 19
that is of a proud *h.* stirreth. 28:25*
the *h.* of her husband doth. 31:11
sadness of countenance *h.* *Eccl* 7:3
the *h.* of the wise is in the house of mourning, but the *h.* of fools. 4
and a gift destroyeth the *h.* 7*
wise man's *h.* discerneth both. 8:5
the *h.* of men is fully set in. 11
the *h.* of the sons of men is. 9:3
drink thy wine with merry *h.* 7
wise man's *h.* is at right hand, fool's *h.* at left. 10:2
make their *h.* fat. *Isa* 6:10
Mat 13:15; *Acts* 28:27
pride and stoutness of *h.* *Isa* 9:9
punish fruit of the stout *h.* 10:12
all hands faint, every man's *h.* 13:7
ye shall have gladness of *h.* 30:29
h. of rash shall understand. 32:4
to them that are of fearful *h.* 35:4
yet he laid it not to *h.* 42:25
a deceived *h.* hath turned. 44:20
and no man layeth it to *h.* 57:1
Jer 12:11
and to revive the *h.* of the. *Isa* 57:15
uttering from the *h.* words of. 59:13
servants shall sing for joy of *h.*, but ye shall cry for sorrow of *h.* 65:14
the *h.* of the king and princes. *Jer* 4:9
people hath a rebellious *h.* 5:23
Israel are uncircumcised in *h.* 9:26
triest the reins and the *h.* 11:20
the *h.* is deceitful above all. 17:9

I the Lord search the *h.* *Jer* 17:10
that seest the reins and *h.* 20:12
long shall this be in the *h.*? 23:26
and I will give them an *h.* to. 24:7
be as the *h.* of a woman in her. 48:41; 49:22
give them sorrow of *h.* *Lam* 3:65
with their whorish *h.* *Ezek* 6:9
I will take the stony *h.* out. 11:19
with lies ye made *h.* of the. 13:22
and make you a new *h.* and. 18:31
every *h.* shall melt, all hands. 21:7
rejoiced in *h.* with all thy. 25:6
vengeance with a despiteful *h.* 15*
for thee with bitterness of *h.* 27:31*
and I will give you an *h.* of. 36:26
strangers uncircumcised in *h.* 44:7
9; *Acts* 7:51
let a beast's *h.* be given. *Dan* 4:16
a man's *h.* was given to it. 7:4
wine take away the *h.* *Hos* 4:11*
like a silly dove without *h.* 7:11*
h. melteth, and the knees. *Nah* 2:10
city that said in her *h.* *Zeph* 2:15
not lay it to *h.* to give glory, because ye do not lay it to *h.* *Mal* 2:2
turn the *h.* of fathers, and *h.* 4:6
meek and lowly in *h.* *Mat* 11:29
out of the abundance of the *h.* 12:34
Luke 6:45
out of the treasure of the *h.* *Mat* 12:35; *Luke* 6:45
come forth from the *h.* *Mat* 15:18
out of *h.* proceed evil thoughts. 19
Mark 7:21
with hardness of *h.* *Mark* 16:14
pondered them in her *h.* *Luke* 2:19
kept these sayings in her *h.* 51
which in a good *h.* having. 8:15
O fools, slow of *h.* to believe. 24:25
devil having put into the *h.* *John* 13:2
eat with singleness of *h.* *Acts* 2:46
were cut to the *h.* 5:33; 7:54
purpose of *h.* they would. 11:23
impenitent *h.* treasurest. *Rom* 2:5
circumcision is that of the *h.* 29
ye have obeyed from the *h.* 6:17
with the *h.* man believeth unto. 10:10
entered into *h.* of man. *1 Cor* 2:9
so decreed in his *h.* that he. 7:37
of much anguish of *h.* I. *2 Cor* 2:4
written in fleshly tables of *h.* 3:3
appearance, and not in *h.* 5:12
earnest care in the *h.* of Titus. 8:16
will of God from the *h.* *Eph* 6:6
but in singleness of *h.* *Col* 3:22
in presence, not in *h.* *1 Thes* 2:17
of the intents of the *h.* *Heb* 4:12
us draw near with a true *h.* 10:22
h. be established with grace. 13:9
the hidden man of the *h.* *1 Pet* 3:4
an *h.* exercised with. *2 Pet* 2:14
she saith in her *h.* I sit. *Rev* 18:7

heart

depths were congealed in *h.* *Ex* 15:8
h. of Egypt shall melt in. *Isa* 19:1
so shall the Son of man be . . . in the *h.* of the earth. *Mat* 12:40

heart with *all*

serve him with *all* your *h.* and with. *Deut* 11:13; *Josh* 22:5
1 Sam 12:20, 24
love the Lord with *all* your *h.* and. *Deut* 13:3; 30:6; *Mat* 22:37
Mark 12:30, 33; *Luke* 10:27
do them with *all* thy *h.* *Deut* 26:16
return to the Lord with *all* thine *h.* 30:2; *Joel* 2:12
told her *all* his *h.* *Judg* 16:17, 18
walk before me with *all* their *h.* *1 Ki* 2:4; 8:23
return unto thee with *all* their *h.* and all. 8:48; *2 Ki* 23:25; *2 Chr* 6:38
followed me with *all* his *h.* *1 Ki* 14:8
heed to walk with *all h.* *2 Ki* 10:31
walk before the Lord with *all* their *h.* 23:3; *2 Chr* 34:31
seek God of fathers with *all* their *h.* *2 Chr* 15:12
they had sworn with *all* their *h.* 15
sought the Lord with *all* his *h.* 22:9
he did it with *all* his *h.* and. 31:21
O Lord, with *all* my *h.* *Ps* 86:12
Lord with *all* thy *h.*, lean not. *Pr* 3:5
search for me with *all* your *h.* *Jer* 29:13
with the joy of *all* their *h.* *Ezek* 36:5
be glad with *all* the *h.* *Zeph* 3:14
believest with *all* thy *h.* *Acts* 8:37

see **apply, broken, clean, evil, harden, hardened**

his **heart**

imagination of *his h.* *Gen* 6:5
Lord and grieved him at *his h.* 6
Lord said in *his h.* 8:21
Abraham in *his h.* 17:17
Esau said in *his h.*, The days. 27:41
he will be glad in *his h.* *Ex* 4:14
neither did he set *his h.* to. 7:23
that giveth willingly with *his h.* 25:2
of judgement upon *his h.* 28:29
he hath put in *his h.* that he. 35:34
made *his h.* obstinate. *Deut* 2:30
multiply wives, that *his h.* 17:17
his h. be not lifted up above his. 20
avenger pursue, while *his h.* 19:6
heart faint as well as *his h.* 20:8
he is poor, and setteth *his h.* 24:15
that he bless himself in *his h.* 29:19
his h. was merry, he went. *Ruth* 3:7
his h. trembled for the. *1 Sam* 4:13
laid up these words in *his h.* 21:12
it came to pass that *his h.* 25:37
David said in *his h.* 27:1
his h. trembled. 28:5
found in *his h.* to pray this prayer. *2 Sam* 7:27; *1 Chr* 17:25
take the thing to *his h.* *2 Sam* 13:33
which God had put in *his h.* *1 Ki* 10:24; *2 Chr* 9:23
wives turned away *his h.* *1 Ki* 11:3, 4, 9
Jeroboam said in *his h.* 12:26
arrow went out at *his h.* *2 Ki* 9:24
prepared not *his h.* to. *2 Chr* 12:14
his h. was lifted up in ways. 17:6
his h. was lifted up to his. 26:16
that prepareth *his h.* to seek. 30:19
for *his h.* was lifted up. 32:25
himself for the pride of *his h.* 26
know all that was in *his h.* 31
Ezra prepared *his h.* to. *Ezra* 7:10
foundest *his h.* faithful. *Neh* 9:8
Haman thought in *his h.* *Esth* 6:6
that durst presume in *his h.* 7:5
if he set *his h.* upon man. *Job* 34:14
his h. is as firm as a stone. 41:24
wicked boasteth of *his h.*'s. *Ps* 10:3
he hath said in *his h.* 6; 11:13
14:1; 53:1
that speaketh truth in *his h.* 15:2
hast given him *his h.*'s desire. 21:2
the thoughts of *his h.* to all. 33:11
law of his God is in *his h.* 37:31
his h. gathereth iniquity to. 41:6
smooth, but war was in *his h.* 55:21
according to integrity of *his h.* 78:72
his h. is fixed, trusting in. 112:7
his h. is established, he shall not. 8
frowardness is in *his h.* *Pr* 6:14
but that *his h.* may discover. 18:2
and *his h.* fretteth against. 19:3
thinketh in *his h.* so is he; eat and drink, saith he, but *his h.* 23:7
but he that hardeneth *his h.* 28:14
yea *his h.* taketh not rest. *Eccl* 2:23
him in the joy of *his h.* 5:20
day of gladness of *his h.* *S of S* 3:11
his h. was moved, and the h. *Isa* 7:2
neither doth *his h.* think so, but it is in *his h.* to destroy and. 10:7
his h. will work iniquity, to. 32:6
none considereth in *his h.* 44:19*
frowardly in the way of *his h.* 57:17
but in *h.* he layeth *his.* *Jer* 9:8
performed thoughts of *his h.* 23:20
engaged *his h.* to approach. 30:21*
performed the intents of *his h.* 24
heard the haughtiness of *his h.* 48:29
up his idols in *his h.* *Ezek* 14:4, 7
his h. lifted up in his height. 31:10
Dan 5:20
Daniel purposed in *his h.* *Dan* 1:8
let *his h.* be changed. 4:16; 5:21
the king set *his h.* on Daniel. 6:14
shall magnify himself in *his h.* 8:25
his h. shall be lifted up. *Dan* 11:12
his h. shall be against the holy. 28
that saith in *his h.*, Who shall? *Ob* 3
adultery with her in *his h.* *Mat* 5:28
away that was sown in *his h.* 13:19
if evil servant shall say in *his h.* 24:48; *Luke* 12:45
entereth not into *his h.* *Mark* 7:19
shall not doubt in *his h.* but. 11:23
of *his h.*; an evil man out of the evil treasure of *his h.* *Luke* 6:45
it came into *his h.* to. *Acts* 7:23
standeth stedfast in *his h.* *1 Cor* 7:37
thus are the secrets of *his h.* 14:25
as he purposeth in *his h.* *2 Cor* 9:7

mine or *my* **heart**

the integrity of *my h.* *Gen* 20:5
speaking in *mine h.* Rebekah. 24:45
imagination of *mine h.* *Deut* 29:19
word as it was in *mine h.* *Josh* 14:7
my h. is toward the. *Judg* 5:9
said, *My h.* rejoiceth. *1 Sam* 2:1
to that which is in *mine h.* 35
my eyes and *mine h.* shall be there. *1 Ki* 9:3; *2 Chr* 7:16
went not *mine h.* with? *2 Ki* 5:26
h. right as *my h.* is with thy h.? 10:15
to all that was in *mine h.* 30
if to help, *mine h.* shall. *1 Chr* 12:17
mine h. to build an house of. 28:2
it is in *mine h.* to make. *2 Chr* 29:10
what God had put in *my h.* to do. *Neh* 2:12; 7:5
thoughts of *my h.* are. *Job* 17:11
God maketh *my h.* soft, and. 23:16
my h. shall not reproach me. 27:6
and *mine h.* walked after mine. 31:7
mine h. have been deceived by. 9
and *my h.* hath been secretly. 27
of the uprightness of *my h.* 33:3
at this also *my h.* trembleth. 37:1
hast put gladness in *my h.* *Ps* 4:7
take counsel, sorrow in *my h.* 13:2
but I trusted, *my h.* shall rejoice. 5
my h. is glad. 16:9
thou hast proved *mine h.* 17:3
let the meditation of *my h.* 19:14
my h. is like wax. 22:14
try my reins and *my h.* 26:2
troubles of *my h.* are enlarged. 25:17
my h. shall not fear though. 27:3
my h. said to thee, Thy face, Lord. 8
my h. trusted in him, *my h.* 28:7
of the wicked saith in *my h.* 36:1
of the disquietness of *my h.* 38:8
my h. panteth, my strength faileth. 10; *Isa* 21:4
my h. was hot within me. 39:3
yea, thy law is within *my h.* 40:8
hid thy righteousness within *my h.* 10
able to look up, therefore *my h.* 12
my h. is inditing a good matter. 45:1
the meditation of *my h.* be of. 49:3
my h. is sore pained within me. 55:4
my h. is fixed, O God, *my h.* is. 57:7; 108:1
I will cry, when *my h.* is. 61:2
if I regard iniquity in *my h.* 66:18
reproach hath broken *my h.* 69:20
verily I have cleansed *my h.* 73:13
my h. was grieved, I was pricked. 21
my h. faileth, but God is the strength of *my h.* 26
my h. and flesh crieth out for. 84:2
unite *my h.* to fear thy name. 86:11
my h. is smitten and withered. 102:4
my h. is wounded within me. 109:22
word have I hid in *mine h.* 119:11
when thou shalt enlarge *my h.* 32
incline *my h.* to thy testimonies. 36
my h. be sound in thy statutes. 80
are the rejoicing of *my h.* 111
inclined *mine h.* to perform. 112
Lord, *my h.* is not haughty. 131:1
search me, and know *my h.* 139:23
incline not *my h.* to any evil. 141:4
my h. within me is desolate. 143:4
how hath *my h.* despised? *Pr* 5:12
can say, I have made *my h.*? 20:9
if thine heart be wise, *my h.* 23:15
I gave *my h.* to seek. *Eccl* 1:13
my h. had great experience of. 16
I gave *my h.* to know wisdom. 17

I said in *mine h.* I will prove thee.
Eccl 2:1, 15; 3:17, 18
mine h. to give myself to wine, yet
acquainting *mine h.* with. 2:3
I withheld not *my h.* from any. 10
to cause *my h.* to despair of all. 20
mine h. to know and search. 7:25
8:9, 16
this I considered in *my h.* 9:1
hast ravished *my h.* *S of S* 4:9
I sleep, but *my h.* waketh. 5:2
my h. shall cry out for. *Isa* 15:5
day of vengeance is in *mine h.* 63:4
according to *mine h.* *Jer* 3:15
pained at *my h.* *my h.* maketh. 4:19
neither came it into *my h.* 7:31*
when I comfort myself, *my h.* 8:18
hast seen me and tried *mine h.* 12:3
joy and rejoicing of *mine h.* 15:16
his word was in *mine h.* as a. 20:9
mine h. is broken. 23:9
mine h. shall mourn. 48:31
therefore *mine h.* shall sound. 36
behold, *mine h.* is turned. *Lam* 1:20
my sighs are many, and *my h.* 22
mine eye affecteth *mine h.* 3:51
kept the matter in *my h.* *Dan* 7:28
mine h. is turned within. *Hos* 11:8
did *my h.* rejoice. *Acts* 2:26
to weep, and break *mine h.*? 21:13
continual sorrow in *my h.* *Rom* 9:2
my h.'s desire to God for Israel. 10:1
because I have you in *my h.* *Phil* 1:7

see **applied**

one **heart**

was to give them *one h.* *2 Chr* 30:12
I will give them *one h.* *Jer* 32:39
Ezek 11:19
believed were of *one h.* *Acts* 4:32

own **heart**

not after your *own h.* *Num* 15:39
sought man after his *own h.*
1 Sam 13:14; *Acts* 13:22
according to thine *own h.* hast thou.
2 Sam 7:21; *1 Chr* 17:19
man plague of his *own h.* *1 Ki* 8:38
had devised of his *own h.* 12:33
them out of thine *own h.* *Neh* 6:8
your *own h.* on your bed. *Ps* 4:4
according to thine *own h.* 20:4
shall enter into their *own h.* 37:15
I commune with my *own h.* and. 77:6
trusteth in his *own h.* *Pr* 28:26
communed with mine *own h.*
Eccl 1:16
thy *own h.* knoweth thou hast. 7:22
after imagination of their *own h.*
Jer 9:14; 23:17
a vision of their *own h.* 23:16
prophesy the deceit of their *own h.*
26; *Ezek* 13:17
of Israel in their *own h.* *Ezek* 14:5
but deceiveth his *own h.* *Jas* 1:26

our **heart**

have discouraged *our h.* *Deut* 1:28
for *our h.* shall rejoice. *Ps* 33:21
our h. is not turned back. 44:18
let us lift up *our h.* with. *Lam* 3:41
the joy of *our h.* is ceased. 5:15
our h. is faint. 17
did not *our h.* burn? *Luke* 24:32
our mouth is open, *our h.* *2 Cor* 6:11
if *our h.* condemn us. *1 John* 3:20
if *our h.* condemn us not, we. 21

perfect **heart**

let your *h.* be *perfect.* *1 Ki* 8:61
his *h.* was not *perfect.* 11:4; 15:3
Asa's *h.* was *perfect* with the Lord.
15:14; *2 Chr* 15:17
have walked before thee with a *perfect h.* *2 Ki* 20:3; *Isa* 38:3
came with *perfect h.* to. *1 Chr* 12:38
serve God with a *perfect h.* 28:9
with *perfect h.* they offered. 29:9
give Solomon my son a *perfect h.* 19
them whose *h.* is *perfect.* *2 Chr* 16:9
in fear of Lord with *perfect h.* 19:9
right, but not with a *perfect h.* 25:2
my house with *perfect h.* *Ps* 101:2

pure **heart**

ascend? that hath a *pure h.* *Ps* 24:4
blessed are the *pure* in *h.* *Mat* 5:8
is charity out of *pure h.* *1 Tim* 1:5
the Lord out of a *pure h.* *2 Tim* 2:22
another with a *pure h.* *1 Pet* 1:22

their **heart**

their h. failed them. *Gen* 42:28
their h. melted, neither was there
spirit in them. *Josh* 5:1
thou hast turned *their h.* *1 Ki* 18:37
and prepare *their h.* *1 Chr* 29:18
utter words out of *their h.*? *Job* 8:10
thou hast hid *their h.* from. 17:4
wilt prepare *their h.* *Ps* 10:17
generation that set not *their h.* 78:8
they tempted God in *their h.* 18
their h. was not right with him. 37
people that do err in *their h.* 95:10
he turned *their h.* to hate. 105:25
he brought down *their h.* 107:12
their h. is as fat as grease. 119:70
imagine mischief in *their h.* 140:2
for *their h.* studieth. *Pr* 24:2
set the world in *their h.* *Eccl* 3:11
madness is in *their h.* while. 9:3
ears and understand with *their h.*
Isa 6:10; *Mat* 13:15; *Acts* 28:27
their h. is far from me. *Isa* 29:13
Mat 15:8; *Mark* 7:6
neither say they in *their h.* *Jer* 5:24
in the imagination of *their h.* 13:10
prophesy the deceit of *their h.* 14:14
is graven on table of *their h.* 17:1
their h. cried to Lord. *Lam* 2:18
up their idols in *their h.* *Ezek* 14:3
for *their h.* went after their. 20:16
that *their h.* may faint, ruins. 21:15
but *their h.* goeth after. 33:31
they set *their h.* on their. *Hos* 4:8
they have made ready *their h.* 7:6
not cried unto me with *their h.* 14
their h. is divided. 10:2
their h. was exalted. 13:6
I will rend the caul of *their h.* 8
men that say in *their h.* *Zeph* 1:12
their h. shall rejoice. *Zech* 10:7
Judah shall say in *their h.* 12:5
their h. was hardened. *Mark* 6:52
Rom 1:21
the thought of *their h.* *Luke* 9:47
their h.; they should not see, nor
understand with *their h.* *John* 12:40
were pricked in *their h.* *Acts* 2:37
the vail is upon *their h.* *2 Cor* 3:15
the blindness of *their h.* *Eph* 4:18

thine, thy **heart**

in the integrity of *thy h.* *Gen* 20:6
my plagues upon *thine h.* *Ex* 9:14
not hate thy brother in *thine h.*
Lev 19:17
they depart from *thy h.* *Deut* 4:9
if thou seek him with all *thy h.* 29
consider it in *thine h.* 4:39; 8:5
love Lord with all *thine h.* 6:5
in *thine h.* these nations are more.
7:17; 8:17; 18:21; *Jer* 13:22
know what was in *thine h.* *Deut* 8:2
then *thine h.* be lifted up, and. 14
speak not thou in *thine h.* after. 9:4
not for uprightness of *thine h.* 5
serve thy God with all *thy h.* 10:12
a thought in *thy* wicked *h.* 15:9
thine h. shall not be grieved. 10
fear of *thine h.* wherewith. 28:67
circumcise *thine h.* and the *h.* 30:6
is very nigh unto thee, in *thy h.* 14
if *thine h.* turn, so that thou. 17
when *thine h.* is not. *Judg* 16:15
and let *thine h.* be merry. 19:6, 9
1 Ki 21:7
father said, Comfort *thine h.*
Judg 19:8
why is *thy h.* grieved? *1 Sam* 1:8
thine shall be to grieve *thine h.* 2:33
tell thee all that is in *thine h.* 9:19
do all that is in *thine h.* *1 Sam* 14:7
2 Sam 7:3; *1 Chr* 17:2
thee, according to *thy h.* *1 Sam* 14:7
pride and naughtiness of *thy h.* 17:28
reign over all that *thine h.*
2 Sam 3:21
wickedness *thine h.* is. *1 Ki* 2:44
in *thine h.* to build. 8:18
2 Chr 1:11; 6:8
Jehu said, Is *thine h.* right, as my *h.*
is with *thy h.*? *2 Ki* 10:15
thine h. hath lifted thee up. 14:10
2 Chr 25:19
because *thine h.* was tender.
2 Ki 22:19; *2 Chr* 34:27
hast prepared *thine h.* *2 Chr* 19:3
thou shouldest set *thine h.* *Job* 7:17
things hast thou hid in *thine h.* 10:13
if thou prepare *thine h.* and. 11:13
why doth *thine h.* carry thee? 15:12
lay up his words in *thine h.* 22:22
shall strengthen *thine h.* *Ps* 27:14
give thee the desires of *thine h.* 37:4
thine h. to understanding. *Pr* 2:2
wisdom entereth into *thine h.* 10
my son, let *thine h.* keep my. 3:1
upon the table of *thine h.* 3; 7:3
he said, let *thine h.* retain. 4:4, 21
keep *thy h.* with all diligence. 23
them continually upon *thine h.* 6:21
after her beauty in *thine h.* 25
let not *thine h.* incline to her. 7:25
if *thine h.* be wise, my *h.* 23:15
let not *thine h.* envy sinners. 17
hear, my son, and guide *thine h.* 19
my son, give me *thine h.* 26
thine h. shall utter perverse. 33
let not *thine h.* be glad when. 24:17
let not *thine h.* be hasty to. *Eccl* 5:2
thy h. cheer thee; walk in ways of *thy h.* 11:9
remove sorrow from *thy h.* 10
thou hast said in *thine h.* *Isa* 14:13
thine h. shall meditate terror. 33:18
these things to *thy h.* 47:7; 57:11
that sayest in *thine h.* I am. 47:8, 10
shalt thou say in *thine h.* 49:21
O Jerusalem, wash *thine h.* *Jer* 4:14
because it reacheth unto *thine h.* 18
thine h. are not but for thy. 22:17
set *thine h.* toward the. 31:21
thine h. deceived thee. 49:16; *Ob* 2
pour out *thine h.* like. *Lam* 2:19
receive in *thine h.* hear. *Ezek* 3:10
how weak is *thine h.* saith. 16:30
can *thine h.* endure in days. 22:14
because *thine h.* is lifted up. 28:2, 5
hast set *thine h.* as the heart. 6
thine h. was lifted up because. 17
set *thine h.* upon all that I. 40:4
know the thoughts of *thy h.* *Dan* 2:30
hast not humbled *thine h.* 5:22
thou didst set *thine h.* to. 10:12
filled *thine h.* to lie. *Acts* 5:3
thou conceived this in *thine h.*? 4
for *thy h.* is not right in the. 8:21
thought of *thine h.* may. 22
say not in *thine h.*, Who? *Rom* 10:6
and shalt believe in *thine h.* that. 9

upright in **heart**

were more *upright in h.* *2 Chr* 29:34
saveth the *upright in h.* *Ps* 7:10
may shoot at the *upright in h.* 11:2
joy, ye that are *upright in h.* 32:11
righteousness to *upright in h.* 36:10
the *upright in h.* shall glory. 64:10
the *upright in h.* shall follow. 94:15
sown for the *upright in h.* 97:11

uprightness of **heart**

he walketh in *uprightness of h.*
1 Ki 3:6; 9:4
I will praise thee with *uprightness of h.* *Ps* 119:7

whole **heart**

I will praise thee, O Lord, with my
whole h. *Ps* 9:1; 111:1; 138:1
seek him with the *whole h.* 119:2
with my *whole h.* have I. 10
observe it with my *whole h.* 34
thy favour with my *whole h.* 58
thy precepts with my *whole h.* 69
I cried with my *whole h.* hear. 145
head is sick, the *whole h.* *Isa* 1:5
not turned with *whole h.* *Jer* 3:10
unto me with their *whole h.* 24:7
them in land with my *whole h.* 32:41

whose **heart**

whose h. stirred him up. *Ex* 35:21
29; 36:2
all the women, *whose h.* 35:26
whose h. turneth away. *Deut* 29:18
whose h. is as the heart. *2 Sam* 17:10

whose h. thou knowest. 1 Ki 8:39
2 Chr 6:30
behalf of them whose h. 2 Chr 16:9
in whose h. are the ways. Ps 84:5
woman whose h. is snares and nets.
Eccl 7:26
in whose h. is my law. Isa. 51:7
whose h. departeth from. Jer 17:5
whose h. walketh after. Ezek 11:21
whose h. the Lord. Acts 16:14

your **heart**

circumcise foreskin of your h.
Deut 10:16; Jer 4:4
your h. be not deceived. Deut 11:16
lay up these my words in your h. 18
will turn away your h. 1 Ki 11:2
set your h. and soul. 1 Chr 22:19
your h. shall live. Ps 22:26
he shall strengthen your h. 31:24
ye people, pour out your h. 62:8
if riches increase, set not your h. 10
your h. shall live that seek. 69:32
ye see this, your h. shall. Isa 66:14
and lest your h. faint. Jer 51:46
and rend your h. and not. Joel 2:13
you imagine evil in your h. Zech 7:10
there will your h. be also. Mat 6:21
Luke 12:34
have ye your h. yet? Mark 8:17
for the hardness of your h. 10:5
not your h. be troubled. John 14:1, 27
sorrow hath filled your h. 16:6
I will see you, and your h. shall. 22
in singleness of your h. Eph 6:5

hearted

many as were willing h. Ex 35:22
the stout h. are spoiled. Ps 76:5
all the merry h. do sigh. Isa 24:7
me to bind up the broken h. 61:1
of Israel are hard h. Ezek 3:7

faint **hearted**

is there that is faint h.? Deut 20:8

tender **hearted**

Rehoboam was young and tender h.
2 Chr 13:7
and be kind one to another, tender h.
Eph 4:32

wise **hearted**

unto all that are wise h. Ex 28:3
hearts of all that are wise h. 31:6
and every wise h. among you. 35:10
all the women that were wise h. 25
then wrought every wise h. man.
36:1, 2, 8

hearth

make cakes upon the h. Gen 18:6
bones are burnt as an h. Ps 102:3*
to take fire from the h. Isa 30:14
a fire on the h. burning. Jer 36:22*
roll into fire that was on the h. 23*
of Judah like h. of fire. Zech 12:6*

heartily

what ye do, do it h. as to. Col 3:23

hearts

they discouraged the h. Num 32:9
wherefore the h. of the. Josh 7:5
of men, whose h. God. 1 Sam 10:26
so Absalom stole the h. 2 Sam 15:6
the h. of the men of Israel. 13
thou only knowest the h. 1 Ki 8:39
2 Chr 6:30
the Lord searcheth all h. 1 Chr 28:9
the righteous God trieth the h.
Ps 7:9; Pr 17:3
more then the h. of men? Pr 15:11
but the Lord pondereth the h. 21:2
wine to those that be of heavy h.
31:6*
mighty men's h. of Moab. Jer 48:41
I will also vex the h. Ezek 32:9
both these kings' h. shall. Dan 11:27
turn the h. of the fathers. Luke 1:17
that the thoughts of h. may be. 2:35
signs in the sun, men's h. 21:26
which knowest the h. of all men.
Acts 1:24; 15:8
he that searcheth the h. Rom 8:27
by fair speeches deceive the h. 16:18
the counsels of the h. 1 Cor 4:5
searcheth the reins and h. Rev 2:23

our **hearts**

soon as we heard, our h. Josh 2:11
incline our h. to him. 1 Ki 8:58
filling our h. with food. Acts 14:17
love of God is shed abroad in our h.
Rom 5:5
of the Spirit in our h. 2 Cor 1:22
our epistle written in our h. 3:2
God hath shined in our h. 4:6
that you are in our h. to die. 7:3
God, who trieth our h. 1 Thes 2:4
our h. sprinkled from. Heb 10:22
and shall assure our h. 1 John 3:19

their **hearts**

a faintness into their h. Lev 26:36
if then their uncircumcised h. 41
their h. inclined to follow. Judg 9:3
when their h. were merry. 16:25
they were making their h. 19:22
thee with all their h. 2 Chr 6:14
such as set their h. to seek. 11:16
people had not prepared their h. to.
20:33
my sons have cursed God in their h.
Job 1:5
but mischief is in their h. Ps 28:3
he fashioneth their h. alike. 33:15
let them not say in their h., Ah. 35:25
said in their h., Let us destroy. 74:8
gave them up to their own h. 81:12
that are upright in their h. 125:4
hath shut their h. they. Isa 44:18
and write my law in their h.
Jer 31:33; Heb 8:10
put my fear in their h. Jer 32:40
out of their own h. Ezek 13:2
consider not in their h. Hos 7:2
yea, they made their h. Zech 7:12
and reasoning in their h. Mark 2:6
for the hardness of their h. 3:5
taketh away word sown in their h.
4:15; Luke 8:12
in imagination of their h. Luke 1:51
heard laid them up in their h. 66
all men mused in their h. of. 3:15
in their h. turned back. Acts 7:39
through lust of their h. Rom 1:24
work of law written in their h. 2:15
their h. might be comforted. Col 2:2
always err in their h. Heb 3:10
God hath put in their h. Rev 17:17

your **hearts**

comfort ye your h. after. Gen 18:5
O Israel, let not your h. Deut 20:3
set your h. to all the words. 32:46
ye know in all your h. Josh 23:14
incline your h. to the Lord. 24:23
do ye harden your h.? 1 Sam 6:6
the Lord with all your h. and prepare
your h. to the Lord to serve. 7:3
ye dissembled in your h. Jer 42:20*
imagine evil in your h. Zech 8:17
think ye evil in your h.? Mat 9:4
if ye from your h. forgive not. 18:35
of the hardness of your h. 19:8
these things in your h.? Mark 2:8
what reason ye in your h.? Luke 5:22
God knoweth your h. 16:15
settle it in your h. not to. 21:14
lest at any time your h. be. 34
thoughts arise in your h.? 24:38
of his Son into your h. Gal 4:6
Christ may dwell in your h. Eph 3:17
melody in your h. to. 5:19; Col 3:16
that he might comfort your h. 6:22
keep your h. and minds. Phil 4:7
peace of God rule in your h. Col 3:15
your estate and comfort your h. 4:8
may establish your h. 1 Thes 3:13
comfort your h. and. 2 Thes 2:17
Lord direct your h. into love. 3:5
if ye have strife in your h. Jas 3:14
your h. ye double minded. 4:8
ye have nourished your h. 5:5
be ye also patient, stablish your h. 8
the Lord God in your h. 1 Pet 3:15
day star arise in your h. 2 Pet 1:19

hearty

sweetness of a friend by h. Pr 27:9

heat

h., summer and winter. Gen 8:22
sat in the tent door in the h. of. 18:1
what meaneth the h. of? Deut 29:24
be devoured with burning h. 32:24
slew Ammonites till h. 1 Sam 11:11
they came about the h. 2 Sam 4:5
but he gat no h. 1 Ki 1:1
my lord may get h. 2
drought and h. consume. Job 24:19
my bones are burnt with h. 30:30
hid from the h. thereof. Ps 19:6
together, then they have h. Eccl 4:11
a shadow in the daytime from the h.
Isa 4:6; 25:4
like a clear h. on herbs, and like a
cloud of dew in the h. 18:4
h. in a dry place, even the h. 25:5
neither shall the h. nor sun. 49:10
shall not see when h. Jer 17:8
dead body shall be cast in the day to
h. 36:30
in their h. I will make their. 51:39
and I went in the h. of. Ezek 3:14
borne the burden and h. Mat 20:12
blow, there will be h. Luke 12:55
came a viper out of the h. Acts 28:3
no sooner risen with a burning h.
Jas 1:11
shall melt with fervent h. 2 Pet 3:10

heat

h. the furnace more. Dan 3:19

heated

more than wont to be h. Dan 3:19
adulterers, as an oven h. Hos 7:4

heath

he shall be like the h. in. Jer 17:6
flee, and be like the h. in the. 48:6

heathen

(Most frequently this word merely means the other nations as distinguished from the Hebrews, without intending any reference to religion. But it generally means idolaters. The Revisions very frequently substitute the word nations *for heathen)*

bondmen shall be of the h. round.
Lev 25:44
forth in sight of the h. 26:45
be head of h. 2 Sam 22:44; Ps 18:43
to abominations of the h. 2 Ki 16:3
17:15; 21:2; 2 Chr 28:3; 36:14
walked in statutes of h. 2 Ki 17:8
as did the h. whom the Lord. 11
deliver us from the h. 1 Chr 16:35
over all kingdoms of h. 2 Chr 20:6
the abominations of the h. 33:2
made Judah to do worse than h. 9
from filthiness of the h. Ezra 6:21
Jews who were sold to h. Neh 5:8
because of the reproach of the h. 9
all the h. that were about us. 6:16
why do the h. rage? Ps 2:1
Acts 4:25
shall give thee the h. for thy. Ps 2:8
thou hast rebuked the h. thou. 9:5
the h. are sunk in the pit that. 15
arise, let the h. be judged in. 9:19
the h. are perished out of his. 10:16
Lord bringeth the counsel of h. 33:10
how thou didst drive out the h. 44:2
the h. raged, the kingdoms. 46:6
God reigneth over the h. 47:8
awake to visit all the h. 59:5
shalt have all the h. in derision. 8
he cast out the h. also. 78:55; 80:8
the h. are come into thine. 79:1
thy wrath upon the h. 6; Jer 10:25
the h. say, where is their God? let
him be known among h. Ps 79:10
115:2
he that chastiseth the h. 94:10
openly shewed in the sight of h. 98:2
h. shall fear the name of the. 102:15
gave them the lands of the h. 105:44
gave them into hand of the h. 106:41
gave them heritage of the h. 111:6
the idols of the h. are silver. 135:15
execute vengeance upon the h. 149:7
the lords of the h. have. Isa 16:8
of the h. be not dismayed at signs of
heaven, for the h. Jer 10:2
ambassador is sent to the h. 49:14
seen that the h. entered. Lam 1:10
bring the worst of the h. Ezek 7:24

after the manners of *h*. *Ezek* 11:12
polluted before the *h*. 20:9, 14, 22
ye say, we will be as the *h*. 32
be sanctified before the *h*. 41; 28:25
thee a reproach to the *h*. 22:4
inheritance in sight of the *h*. 16
gone a whoring after the *h*. 23:30
deliver thee for a spoil to *h*. 25:7
house of Judah is like to all the *h*. 8
it shall be the time of the *h*. 30:3
hand of the mighty one of *h*. 31:11
his shadow in midst of the *h*. 17
no more be a prey to the *h*. 34:28
neither bear the shame of the *h*. 29
possession to the residue of *h*. 36:3
a derision to the residue of the *h*. 4
ye have borne the shame of the *h*. 6
when they entered unto the *h*. 20
h. know I am Lord. 23, 36; 37:28
38:16; 39:7
and all the *h*. shall see my. 39:21
that the *h*. should rule. *Joel* 2:17
and come, all ye *h*. and gather. 3:11
h. be wakened, and come up to valley
of Jehoshaphat . . . to judge all *h*. 12
possess remnant of all *h*. *Amos* 9:12
the Lord is near on all the *h*. *Ob* 15
all the *h*. drink continually. 16
execute fury upon the *h*. *Mi* 5:15
thou didst thresh the *h*. *Hab* 3:12
all the isles of the *h*. *Zeph* 2:11
destroy the strength of *h*. *Hag* 2:22
sore displeased with *h*. *Zech* 1:15
shall speak peace to the *h*. 9:10
the wealth of all the *h*. shall. 14:14
wherewith Lord will smite the *h*. 18
repetitions as the *h*. do. *Mat* 6:7
let him be to thee as an *h*. 18:17*
in perils by the *h*. *2 Cor* 11:26
we should go unto the *h*. *Gal* 2:9
that God would justify the *h*. 3:8

among the **heathen**

among the h. and land. *Lev* 26:33
Jer 9:16; *Ezek* 20:23; 22:15
perish *among the h*. and. *Lev* 26:38
few in number *among h*. *Deut* 4:27
thee, O Lord, *among h*. and sing
praises. *2 Sam* 22:50; *Ps* 18:49
declare his glory *among h*.
1 Chr 16:24; *Ps* 96:3
to us from *among the h*. *Neh* 5:17
it is reported *among the h*. 6:6
scattered us *among the h*. *Ps* 44:11
us a byword *among the h*. 14
I will be exalted *among the h*. 46:10
known *among the h*. in sight. 79:10
say *among the h*. that Lord. 96:10
were mingled *among the h*. 106:35
and gather us from *among h*. 47
judge *among the h*. he shall. 110:6
said *among the h*. Lord hath. 126:2
ask *among the h*., who. *Jer* 18:13
make thee small *among the h*. 49:15
she dwelleth *among the h*. *Lam* 1:3
said *among the h*. they shall. 4:15
shadow we shall live *among the h*. 20
have cast them far off *among the h*.
Ezek 11:16
abominations *among the h*. 12:16
went forth *among the h*. 16:14
scatter them *among the h*. 36:19
profaned *among the h*. 21, 22, 23
you from *among the h*. 24, 37:21
reproach of famine *among the h*. 30
set my glory *among the h*. 39:21
be led into captivity *among h*. 28
a reproach *among the h*. *Joel* 2:19
ambassador sent *among the h*. *Ob* 1
made thee small *among the h*. 2
behold ye *among the h*. *Hab* 1:5
a curse *among the h*. *Zech* 8:13
be great *among the h*. *Mal* 1:11
name is dreadful *among the h*. 14
preach him *among the h*. *Gal* 1:16

heave

as ye do the *h*. offering, so shall ye *h*.
it. *Num* 15:20

heaved

is *h*. of the ram of. *Ex* 29:27
ye have *h*. the best. *Num* 18:30, 32
see **offering, shoulder**

heaven

This word is used of the abode of the redeemed after death and the second resurrection. It is also used for God, without whom there would be no heaven.

It is sometimes used of the air, as in the phrase birds *or* fowls of heaven. *And for the sky, wherein the sun, moon, and stars are placed.*

the beginning God created *h*. *Gen* 1:1
and God called the firmament *h*. 8
lights in the firmament of *h*. 14, 15
fly in the open firmament of *h*. 20
and the windows of *h*. were. 7:11
windows of *h*. were stopped. 8:2
possessor of *h*. and earth. 14:19, 22
fire from the Lord out of *h*. 19:24
God called to Hagar out of *h*. 21:17
called to Abraham out of *h*. 22:11, 15
give thee of the dew of *h*. 27:28, 39
said, this is the gate of *h*. 28:17
blessings of *h*. above. 49:25
six days Lord made *h*. and earth.
Ex 20:11; 31:17
as it were the body of *h*. in. 24:10
I will make your *h*. as. *Lev* 26:19
burned to the midst of *h*. *Deut* 4:11
I call *h*. and earth. 26; 30:19; 31:28
ask from the one side of *h*. to. 4:32
out of *h*. he made thee hear his. 36
behold, the *h*. and *h*. of heavens.
10:14; *Ps* 115:16
water of the rain of *h*. *Deut* 11:11
he shut up *h*. 17; *1 Ki* 8:35
2 Chr 6:26; 7:13
multiplied as days of *h*. *Deut* 11:21
open the *h*. to give the rain. 28:12
h. that is over thy head shall. 23
scatter thee to the utmost part of *h*.
30:4; *Neh* 1:9
precious things of *h*. *Deut* 33:13
of Jeshurun rideth upon the *h*. 26
of *h*. shall he thunder. *1 Sam* 2:10
taken up between *h*. *2 Sam* 18:9
dropped on them out of *h*. 21:10
the foundations of *h*. moved. 22:8
h. and the *h*. of heavens cannot.
1 Ki 8:27; *2 Chr* 2:6; 6:18
when *h*. is shut up, and. *1 Ki* 8:35
mean while the *h*. was black. 18:45
of all kingdoms, thou hast made *h*.
2 Ki 19:15; *2 Chr* 2:12; *Neh* 9:6
angel stood between *h*. *1 Chr* 21:16
it is as high as *h*. *Job* 11:8
h. shall reveal his iniquity. 20:27
is not God in height of *h*.? 22:12
walketh in the circuit of *h*. 14
the pillars of *h*. tremble at. 26:11
the hoary frost of *h*. who? 38:29
thou the ordinances of *h*.? 33
who can stay the bottles of *h*.? 37
forth is from the end of *h*. *Ps* 19:6
hear him from his holy *h*. 20:6
let *h*. and earth praise him. 69:34
he opened the doors of *h*. 78:23
given them of the corn of *h*. 24
to endure as the days of *h*. 89:29
h. is high above the earth. 103:11
them with the bread of *h*. 105:40
the Lord who made *h*. and earth.
115:15; 121:2; 124:8; 134:3
146:6; *Isa* 37:16; *Jer* 32:17
Acts 4:24; 14:15; *Rev* 14:7
covereth *h*. with clouds. *Ps* 147:8
glory is above earth and *h*. 148:13
the *h*. for height, the earth. *Pr* 25:3
far, from the end of *h*. *Isa* 13:5
who hath meted out *h*. with. 40:12
sing, O *h*. and be. 49:13; *Rev* 18:20
h. my throne, earth my footstool.
Isa 66:1; *Acts* 7:49
cakes to the queen of *h*. *Jer* 7:18
not dismayed at the signs of *h*. 10:2
do not I fill *h*. and earth? 23:24
if *h*. above can be measured. 31:37
appointed ordinances of *h*. 33:25
to burn incense to queen of *h*. 44:17
18, 19, 25
from the four quarters of *h*. 49:36
hath stretched out the *h*. by. 51:15
the *h*. and earth shall sing for. 48
swifter than eagles of *h*. *Lam* 4:19
me between earth and *h*. *Ezek* 8:3
I will cover the *h*. and make. 32:7
the lights of *h*. will I make dark. 8
be wet with dew of *h*. *Dan* 4:15
23, 25, 33; 5:21
his will in the army of *h*. 4:35
extol and honour the King of *h*. 37
thyself against the Lord of *h*. 5:23
the four winds of *h*. strove. 7:2
of man, came with clouds of *h*. 13
towards the four winds of *h*. 8:8
divided toward four winds of *h*. 11:4
buildeth his stories in *h*. *Amos* 9:6
the *h*. over you is stayed. *Hag* 1:10
as the four winds of *h*. *Zech* 2:6
ephah between earth and *h*. 5:9
not open windows of *h*. *Mal* 3:10
till *h*. and earth pass. *Mat* 5:18
neither swear by *h*.; for it is God's
throne. 34; *Jas* 5:12
I thank thee, Father, Lord of *h*.
Mat 11:25; *Luke* 10:21
swear by *h*. sweareth by. *Mat* 23:22
coming in the clouds of *h*. 24:30
26:64; *Mark* 14:62
elect from one end of *h*. *Mat* 24:31
h. and earth shall pass away. 35
Mark 13:31; *Luke* 21:33
the angels of *h*. but my. *Mat* 24:36
from utmost part of *h*. *Mark* 13:27
Jesus praying, the *h*. *Luke* 3:21
when the *h*. was shut up. 4:25
I have sinned against *h*. 15:18, 21
it is easier for *h*. and earth. 16:17
for the powers of *h*. shall be. 21:26
hereafter ye shall see *h*. *John* 1:51
the *h*. must receive. *Acts* 3:21
I saw *h*. opened, and a vessel.
10:11; *Rev* 19:11
seeing he is Lord of *h*. *Acts* 17:24
prayed again, and the *h*. *Jas* 5:18
cometh down out of *h* *Rev* 3:12
h. departed as a scroll when. 6:14
an angel flying through the midst of *h*.
8:13; 14:6
who created *h*. and the things. 10:6
have power to shut *h*. that. 11:6
voice out of the temple of *h*. 16:17
fell on men a great hail out of *h*. 21
rejoice over her, thou *h*. 18:20
fowls that fly in midst of *h*. 19:17
came down from God out of *h*. 20:9
earth and *h*. fled away, and. 11
a new *h*. and earth, the first *h*. 21:1
Jerusalem descending out of *h*. 10
see **fowl, fowls**

from **heaven**

and the rain *from h*. was. *Gen* 8:2
rain bread *from h*. for you. *Ex* 16:4
I have talked with you *from h*.
20:22; *Neh* 9:13
look down *from h*. *Deut* 26:15
Isa 63:15; *Lam* 3:50
as dust *from h*. shall it. *Deut* 28:24
cast great stones *from h*. *Josh* 10:11
they fought *from h*. *Judg* 5:20
Lord thundered *from h*. *2 Sam* 22:14
down *from h*. and there came down
fire *from h*. *2 Ki* 1:10, 12, 14
answered him *from h*. *1 Chr* 21:26
hear thou *from h*. *2 Chr* 6:21, 23
27, 30
the fire came down *from h*. 7:1
then will I hear *from h*. and. 14
bread *from h*. for hunger. *Neh* 9:15
heardest them *from h*. 27, 28
of God is fallen *from h*. *Job* 1:16
the Lord looked down *from h*.
Ps 14:2; 53:2
the Lord looketh *from h*. *Ps* 33:13
shall send *from h*. and save. 57:3
judgement to be heard *from h*. 76:8
O God, look down *from h*. 80:14
shall look down *from h*. 85:11
from h. did the Lord behold. 102:19
from h. O Lucifer! *Isa* 14:12
as snow falleth *from h*. and. 55:10
Lord cast down *from h*. *Lam* 2:1
came down *from h*. *Dan* 4:13
an holy one coming down *from h*. 23
fell a voice *from h*. saying. 31
Mat 3:17; *Luke* 3:22; *John* 12:28
shew them a sign *from h*. *Mat* 16:1
John, whence was it? *from h*. or of?
21:25; *Mark* 11:30; *Luke* 20:4
for the angel descended *from h*.
Mat 28:2; *Rev* 10:1; 18:1; 20:1

seeking of him a sign from h. Mark 8:11; Luke 11:16
fire to come down from h. Luke 9:54
as lightning fall from h. 10:18
fire and brimstone from h. 17:29
signs shall there be from h. 21:11
appeared an angel from h. 22:43
Spirit descending from h. John 1:32
came down from h. 3:13; 6:33
except it be given him from h. 3:27
he that cometh from h. is above. 31
he gave them bread from h. to. 6:31
gave you not that bread from h. 32
I came from h. not to do. 38, 42
came down from h. 41, 50, 51, 58
came a sound from h. Acts 2:2
a light from h. shined about him. 9:3; 22:6; 26:13
sheet let down from h. 11:5
voice answered me again from h. 9
good, and gave us rain from h. 14:17
God is revealed from h. Rom 1:18
man is the Lord from h. 1 Cor 15:47
our house that is from h. 2 Cor 5:2
an angel from h. preach. Gal 1:8
wait for his Son from h. 1 Thes 1:10
himself shall descend from h. 4:16
Lord Jesus shall be revealed from h. 2 Thes 1:7
him that speaketh from h. Heb 12:25
gospel to you with the Holy Ghost sent down from h. 1 Pet 1:12
fell a great star from h. Rev 8:10
and I saw a star fall from h. 9:1
voice from h., Seal up those things. 10:4, 8; 11:12; 14:2, 13; 18:4
fire come down from h. 13:13

see **God** *of heaven*

host, or, *hosts of* **heaven**

seest the host of h. Deut 4:19
and worshipped the host of h. 17:3
Lord sitting on the throne and the host of h. 1 Ki 22:19; 2 Chr 18:18
Israel worshipped the host of h. 2 Ki 17:16
Manasseh worshipped host of h. 21:3; 2 Chr 33:3
built altars for the host of h. 2 Ki 21:5; 2 Chr 33:5
vessels made for host of h. 2 Ki 23:4
that burnt incense to host of h. 5
made the h. of heavens with their host, and the host of h. Neh 9:6
all the host of h. shall be. Isa 34:4
them before the host of h. Jer 8:2
incense to all the host of h. 19:13
as the host of h. cannot be. 33:22
even to the host of h. Dan 8:10
them that worship host of h. Zeph 1:5
up to worship the host of h. Acts 7:42

in **heaven**

nor likeness of any thing in h. Ex 20:4; Deut 5:8
what God in h. can do? Deut 3:24
that the Lord he is God in h. 4:39
in h. that thou shouldest say. 30:12
God he is God in h. Josh 2:11
is no God like thee in h. 1 Ki 8:23
2 Chr 6:14
hear thou in h. 1 Ki 8:30, 32, 34, 36, 39, 43, 45, 49
make windows in h. 2 Ki 7:2, 19
all that is in h. and. 1 Chr 29:11
art not thou God in h.? 2 Chr 20:6
my witness is in h. Job 16:19
the Lord's throne is in h. Ps 11:4
whom have I in h. but thee? 73:25
thy thunder was in the h. 77:18*
an east wind to blow in the h. 78:26
who in h. can be compared to? 89:6*
as a faithful witness in h. 37*
himself to behold things in h. 113:6
thy word is settled in h. 119:89
that did he in h. and earth. 135:6
for God is in h. and thou. Eccl 5:2
sword shall be bathed in h. Isa 34:5
the stork in h. knoweth her. Jer 8:7
there is a God in h. that. Dan 2:28
signs and wonders in h. and. 6:27
buildeth his stories in h. Amos 9:6
great is your reward in h. Mat 5:12
your Father who is in h. 16
of your Father who is in h. Mat 5:45
be perfect as your Father in h. 48
which art in h. 6:9; Luke 11:2
will be done on earth, as it is in h. Mat 6:10; Luke 11:2
yourselves treasures in h. Mat 6:20
shall your Father in h. give. 7:11
will of my Father in h. 21; 12:50
before my Father in h. 10:32
I deny before my Father in h. 33
but my Father which is in h. 16:17
shall be bound in h.: shall be loosed in h. 19; 18:18
in h. their angels do always behold the face of my Father in h. 18:10
for them of my Father in h. 19
thou shalt have treasure in h. 19:21
Luke 18:22
are as the angels of God in h. Mat 22:30; Mark 12:25
your Father who is in h. Mat 23:9
sign of the Son of man in h. 24:30
all power is given to me in h. 28:18
will your Father in h. Mark 11:26
the powers that are in h. 13:25
no, not the angels which are in h. 32
reward is great in h. Luke 6:23
your names are written in h. 10:20
joy shall be in h. over one. 15:7
peace in h. and glory in. 19:38
Son of man who is in h. John 3:13
wonders in h. above and. Acts 2:19
whether in h. or in earth. 1 Cor 8:5
gather in one, things in h. Eph 1:10
of whom the whole family in h. 3:15
your master is in h. 6:9; Col 4:1
should bow, of things in h. Phil 2:10
is in h. from whence we look. 3:20
is laid up for you in h. Col 1:5
all things created that are in h. 16
him to reconcile all things in h. 20
ye have in h. a better. Heb 10:34
born which are written in h. 12:23
inheritance reserved in h. 1 Pet 1:4
there are three that bear record in h. 1 John 5:7
door was opened in h. Rev 4:1
a throne was set in h. and one. 2
no man in h. or earth was. 5:3
creature in h. saying, Blessing. 13
was silence in h. 8:1
great voices in h. 11:15
temple of God was opened in h. 19
a great wonder in h. 12:1, 3
there was war in h.: Michael. 7
place found any more in h. 8
loud voice saying in h. 10; 19:1
them that dwell in h. 13:6
of the temple which is in h. 14:17
I saw another sign in h. great. 15:1
the tabernacle of testimony in h. 5
the armies that were in h. 19:14

into **heaven**

take up Elijah into h. 2 Ki 2:1
up by a whirlwind into h. 11
if I ascend into h. thou. Ps 139:8
who hath ascended into h.? Pr 30:4
Rom 10:6
said, I will ascend into h. Isa 14:13
was received up into h. Mark 16:19
angels were gone away into h. Luke 2:15
from them, carried up into h. 24:51
into h. taken from you into h. Jesus shall come ... go into h. Acts 1:11
looked up stedfastly into h. 7:55
was received up into h. 10:16; 11:10
into h. itself, to appear. Heb 9:24
who is gone into h. on. 1 Pet 3:22

see **kingdom**

heaven joined with *stars*

stars in the firmament of h. Gen 1:17
thy seed as stars of h. 22:17; 26:4
Ex 32:13; 1 Chr 27:23; Neh 9:23
you are this day as stars of h. Deut 1:10; 10:22
whereas ye were as stars of h. 28:62
the stars of h. shall not. Isa 13:10
cover h. and make stars. Ezek 32:7
merchants as stars of h. Nah 3:16
the stars shall fall from h. Mat 24:29; Mark 13:25
and the stars of h. fell. Rev 6:13
the third part of stars of h. 12:4

to **heaven**, or *unto* **heaven**

top may reach unto h. Gen 11:4
and the top of it reached to h. 28:12
the cities great and walled up to h. Deut 1:28; 9:1
thou lift up thine eyes unto h. 4:19
who shall go up for us to h.? 30:12
I lift up my hand to h. and. 32:40
smoke of the city ascended up to h. Josh 8:20
flame of the city ascended up to h. Judg 20:40
cry of city went up to h. 1 Sam 5:12
hands spread up to h. 1 Ki 8:54
that reacheth up unto h. 2 Chr 28:9
prayer came up even unto h. 30:27
Isaiah prayed and cried to h. 32:20
they mount up to h. Ps 107:26
her judgement reacheth unto h. Jer 51:9
height reached to h. Dan 4:11, 20
held up his left hand unto h. 12:7
they climb up to h. Amos 9:2
which art exalted to h. Mat 11:23
and looking up to h. 14:19
Mark 6:41; Luke 9:16
looking up to h. he. Mark 7:34
much as his eyes unto h. Luke 18:13
and no man hath ascended up to h. John 3:13
Jesus lifted up his eyes to h. 17:1
caught up to the third h. 2 Cor 12:2
lifted up his hand to h. Rev 10:5
and they ascended up to h. 11:12
sins have reached unto h. 18:5

toward **heaven**

look now toward h. Gen 15:5
sprinkle it toward the h. Ex 9:8
Moses sprinkled it up toward h. 10
thine hand toward h. 22; 10:21
forth his rod toward h. 9:23
forth his hand toward h. 10:22
flame went up toward h. Judg 13:20
Solomon spread forth his hands toward h. 1 Ki 8:22; 2 Chr 6:13
dust on their heads toward h. Job 2:12
as an eagle toward h. Pr 23:5
stedfastly toward h. Acts 1:10

under **heaven**

let the waters under h. Gen 1:9
destroy all flesh from under h. 6:17
high hills under the whole h. 7:19
remembrance of Amalek from under h. Ex 17:14; Deut 25:19
thee on nations under h. Deut 2:25
divided to all nations under h. 4:19
their name from under h. 7:24; 9:14
out his name from under h. 29:20
of Israel from under h. 2 Ki 14:27
seeth under the whole h. Job 28:24
directeth it under the whole h. 37:3
is under the whole h. is mine. 41:11
all things done under h. Eccl 1:13
good they should do under h. 2:3
every purpose under the h. 3:1
out of one part under h. Luke 17:24
of every nation under h. Acts 2:5
none other name under h. 4:12
every creature under h. Col 1:23

heavenly

h. Father will forgive you. Mat 6:14
yet your h. Father feedeth them. 26
your h. Father knoweth that ye. 32
every plant my h. Father. 15:13
so shall my h. Father do also. 18:35
a multitude of the h. host. Luke 2:13
your h. Father shall give the. 11:13
believe, if I tell you of h. John 3:12
not disobedient to the h. Acts 26:19
the h. such are they that are h. 1 Cor 15:48
also bear the image of the h. 49
spiritual blessings in h. Eph 1:3
right hand in h. places. 1:20; 2:6
unto the powers in h. places. 3:10
preserve me to his h. 2 Tim 4:18
partakers of the h. Heb 3:1
and have tasted of the h. gift. 6:4
example and shadow of h. 8:5

h. things with better sacrifices. *Heb* 9:23
an *h.* country. 11:16
the *h.* Jerusalem. 12:22

heavens

thus the *h.* and the earth. *Gen* 2:1
generations of the *h.* and the earth in the day that the Lord made the *h.* 4
give ear, O *h.* I will speak. *Deut* 32:1; *Isa* 1:2
also his *h.* shall drop. *Deut* 33:28
earth trembled, the *h.* *Judg* 5:4
he bowed the *h.* and came. *2 Sam* 22:10; *Ps* 18:9
the heaven of *h.* cannot. *1 Ki* 8:27
the Lord made the *h.* *1 Chr* 16:26
Neh 9:6; *Ps* 96:5; 102:25; 136:5
let the *h.* be glad, let. *1 Chr* 16:31
then hear from the *h.* *2 Chr* 6:25
33, 35, 39
is grown up to the *h.* *Ezra* 9:6
spreadeth out the *h.* *Job* 9:8
man riseth not till the *h.* be. 14:12
yea, the *h.* are not clean in. 15:15
excellency mount up to the *h.* 20:6
Spirit he hath garnished the *h.* 26:13
look to the *h.* and see, and. 35:5
thou hast set thy glory above the *h.* *Ps* 8:1; 113:4
I consider thy *h.* the work. *Ps* 8:3
the *h.* declare the glory of God. 19:1
the Lord were the *h.* made. 33:6
shall call to the *h.* from above. 50:4
h. shall declare his righteousness. 6
exalted, O God, above *h.* 57:5, 11
108:5
mercy is great unto the *h.* 57:10
108:4
him that rideth upon the *h.* 68:4, 33
h. also dropped at the presence. 8
their mouth against the *h.* 73:9
thy *h.* shall praise thy wonders. 89:5
the *h.* are thine, the earth also. 11
let the *h.* rejoice, earth be glad. 96:11; *Rev* 12:12
h. declare his righteousness. *Ps* 97:6
who stretchest out the *h.* 104:2
Isa 40:22
mercy is great above the *h.* *Ps* 108:4
the heaven, even the *h.* are. 115:16
bow thy *h.* O Lord, and come. 144:5
praise ye the Lord from the *h.* 148:1
ye *h.* of *h.* and waters above the *h.* 4
he established the *h.* *Pr* 3:19
when he prepared the *h.* I was. 8:27
will shake the *h.* and earth. *Isa* 13:13
Hag 2:6, 21
the *h.* shall be rolled. *Isa* 34:4
he that created the *h.* 42:5; 45:18
sing, O ye *h.* for the Lord. 44:23
Lord, that stretcheth forth the *h.* 24
45:12; 51:13; *Jer* 10:12; *Zech* 12:1
drop down ye *h.* from above. *Isa* 45:8
hand hath spanned the *h.* 48:13
sing, O *h.* and be joyful, O. 49:13
clothe *h.* with blackness, I. 50:3
eyes to the *h.* and look, the *h.* 51:6
that I may plant the *h.* and lay. 16
for as the *h.* are higher than. 55:9
thou wouldest rend the *h.* and. 64:1
behold, I create new *h.* and. 65:17
for as the new *h.* which I. 66:22
astonished, O ye *h.* and. *Jer* 2:12
I beheld the *h.* and they had. 4:23
birds of the *h.* were fled. 25; 9:10
shall the earth mourn, *h.* 4:28
the *h.* and the earth shall perish, and from under these *h.* 10:11
or can the *h.* give showers? 14:22
from under *h.* of the Lord. *Lam* 3:66
that the *h.* were opened. *Ezek* 1:1
Mat 3:16
known that the *h.* do. *Dan* 4:26
I will hear the *h.*, they. *Hos* 2:21
the *h.* shall tremble, sun. *Joel* 2:10
and the *h.* and the earth. 3:16
his glory covered the *h.* *Hab* 3:3
four spirits of the *h.* *Zech* 6:5
and the *h.* shall give their dew. 8:12
powers of the *h.* shall be. *Mat* 24:29
coming up, he saw the *h.* *Mark* 1:10
not ascended into the *h.* *Acts* 2:34
whom the *h.* must receive until. 3:21
behold, I see the *h.* opened *Acts* 7:56
h. are the work of thine. *Heb* 1:10
Priest that is passed into *h.* 4:14
Priest made higher than the *h.* 7:26
by word of God the *h.* *2 Pet* 3:5
but the *h.* which are now, are. 7
h. shall pass away with a great. 10
wherein the *h.* being on fire. 12

in the **heavens**

that sitteth *in the h.* *Ps* 2:4
Lord also thundered *in the h.* 18:13
mercy, O Lord, is *in the h.* 36:5
shalt thou establish *in the h.* 89:2
prepared his throne *in the h.* 103:19
God is *in the h.* he hath done. 115:3
O thou that dwellest *in the h.* 123:1
light is darkened *in the h.* *Isa* 5:30*
a multitude of waters *in the h.* *Jer* 10:13; 51:16
hearts to God *in the h.* *Lam* 3:41
shew wonders *in the h.* *Joel* 2:30
a treasure *in the h.* *Luke* 12:33
hands, eternal *in the h.* *2 Cor* 5:1
of the Majesty *in the h.* *Heb* 8:1
patterns of things *in the h.* 9:23

heavier

be *h.* than the sand of. *Job* 6:3
my stroke is *h.* than my. 23:2
a fool's wrath is *h.* than. *Pr* 27:3

heavily

so that drave them *h.* *Ex* 14:25
I bowed down *h.* as one. *Ps* 35:14*
on ancient hast thou *h.* laid. *Isa* 47:6

heaviness

sacrifice I rose from my *h.* *Ezra* 9:5*
I will leave off my *h.* *Job* 9:27*
heart, and I am full of *h.* *Ps* 69:20
soul melteth for *h.* 119:28
a foolish son is the *h.* of. *Pr* 10:1
h. in the heart of man. 12:25
the end of that mirth is *h.* 14:13
there shall be *h.* and. *Isa* 29:2*
of praise for spirit of *h.* 61:3
that I have great *h.* and. *Rom* 9:2*
come again to you in *h.* *2 Cor* 2:1*
my brother was full of *h.* *Phil* 2:26*
your joy be turned into *h.* *Jas* 4:9
if need be, ye are in *h.* *1 Pet* 1:6*

heavy

Moses' hands were *h.* *Ex* 17:12
for this thing is too *h.* for. 18:18
because it is too *h.* for. *Num* 11:14
was an old man and *h.* *1 Sam* 4:18
was *h.* on them of Ashdod. 5:6, 11
the hair was *h.* on. *2 Sam* 14:26
father's *h.* yoke lighter. *1 Ki* 12:4
10, 11, 14; *2 Chr* 10:4, 10, 11, 14
sent to thee with *h.* *1 Ki* 14:6
went to his house *h.* 20:43; 21:4
the bondage was *h.* *Neh* 5:18
shall my hand be *h.* *Job* 33:7
and night thy hand was *h.* *Ps* 32:4
h. burden they are too *h.* 38:4
singeth songs to an *h.* *Pr* 25:20
stone is *h.* and sand weighty. 27:3
wine to those that be of *h.* 31:6*
make their ears *h.*, shut. *Isa* 6:10
transgression thereof shall be *h.* 24:20
and the burden thereof is *h.* 30:27*
carriages were *h.* loaden. 46:1*
this the fast, to undo the *h.*? 58:6*
neither his ear *h.* that it. 59:1
hath made my chain *h.* *Lam* 3:7
all ye that are *h.* laden. *Mat* 11:28
for they bind *h.* burdens. 23:4
sorrowful, and very *h.* 26:37*
for their eyes were very *h.* 43
Mark 14:33*, 40*
were with him, were *h.* *Luke* 9:32

Heber

the sons of Beriah, *H.* *Gen* 46:17
1 Chr 7:31
H. the Kenite. *Judg* 4:11, 17; 5:24
which was the son of *H.* *Luke* 3:35

Hebrew, *language*

written over him in *H.* *Luke* 23:38
John 19:20
a pool called in the *H.* *John* 5:2
called in *H.* Gabbatha. 19:13
called in *H.* Golgotha. 17
Paul spake to them in *H.* *Acts* 21:40; 22:2
a voice saying in the *H.* *Acts* 26:14
in *H.* Abaddon. *Rev* 9:11
in the *H.* Armageddon. 16:16

Hebrew *man*

an *H. man,* be sold. *Deut* 15:12

Hebrew, *servant*

the *H. servant* came in. *Gen* 39:17
if thou buy an *H. servant.* *Ex* 21:2

Hebrew *woman, women*

a midwife to *H. women.* *Ex* 1:16
H. women are not as the. 19
thee a nurse of the *H. women*? 2:7
if any *H. woman* be. *Deut* 15:12

Hebrewess

man should let an *H.* *Jer* 34:9

Hebrew

told Abraham the *H.* *Gen* 14:13
see he hath brought in an *H.* 39:14
with us a young man, an *H.* 41:12
Egyptian smiting an *H.* *Ex* 2:11
H. or Hebrewess go free. *Jer* 34:9
I am an *H.* *Jonah* 1:9

Hebrews

out of the land of the *H.* *Gen* 40:15
might not eat with the *H.* 43:32
this is one of the *H.* *Ex* 2:6
two men of the *H.* strove. 13
God of the *H.* 3:18; 5:3; 7:16
9:1, 13; 10:3
shout in camp of the *H.* *1 Sam* 4:6
ye be not servants to the *H.* 9
let the *H.* hear. 13:3
lest the *H.* make swords. 19
behold the *H.* come forth. 14:11
the *H.* that were with the. 21
princes said, What do these *H.*? 29:3
Grecians against the *H.* *Acts* 6:1
they *H.* or Israelites? *2 Cor* 11:22
an Hebrew of the *H.* *Phil* 3:5

Hebron, *place*

Sarah died in Kirjath-arba, the same is *H.* *Gen* 23:2; 35:27; *Josh* 14:15
20:7; *Judg* 1:10
out of the vale of *H.* *Gen* 37:14
H. was built seven. *Num* 13:22
as he did to *H.* so he. *Josh* 10:39
Joshua gave to Caleb *H.* 14:13, 14
Judg 1:20
them which were in *H.* *1 Sam* 30:31
Go up? he said, Unto *H.* *2 Sam* 2:1
David was king in *H.* 11; 5:5
1 Ki 2:11; *1 Chr* 29:27
Joab and his men came to *H.* *2 Sam* 2:32
to David were sons born in *H.* 3:2, 5
1 Chr 3:1, 4
they buried Abner in *H.* *2 Sam* 3:32
head of Ish-bosheth in *H.* 4:12
to *H.* and David made a league with them in *H.* 5:3; *1 Chr* 11:3
wives after he was come from *H.* *2 Sam* 5:13
vowed to the Lord in *H.* 15:7
Absalom reigneth in *H.* 10
cities of Judah *H.* a. *1 Chr* 6:57
with a perfect heart to *H.* 12:38
built Zorah, *H.* in. *2 Chr* 11:10

Hebron, *person*

Amram, *H.* and Uzziel. *Ex* 6:18
Num 3:19; *1 Chr* 6:2, 18; 23:12
Mareshah father of *H.* *1 Chr* 2:42
the sons of *H.* 43; 15:9; 23:19; 24:23

hedge

hast thou not made an *h.* *Job* 1:10
of slothful is an *h.* *Pr* 15:19
breaketh a *h.*, a serpent. *Eccl* 10:8*
I will take away the *h.* *Isa* 5:5
nor made up the *h.* for. *Ezek* 13:5*
man that should make up *h.* 22:30*
sharper than a thorn *h.* *Mi* 7:4
h. about it, digged for. *Mark* 12:1

hedge

behold, I will *h.* up thy. *Hos* 2:6

hedged

whom God hath *h.* in. *Job* 3:23
hath *h.* me about, I. *Lam* 3:7*
a vineyard, and *h.* it. *Mat* 21:33

hedges

amongst plants and *h.* *1 Chr* 4:23

hast thou broken down her *h.*? *Ps* 80:12; 89:40
run to and fro by the *h.* *Jer* 49:3*
which camp in the *h.* *Nah* 3:17
the highways and *h.* *Luke* 14:23

heed

Amasa took no *h.* to. *2 Sam* 20:10
Jehu took no *h.* to. *2 Ki* 10:31
by taking *h.* according. *Ps* 119:9
wicked doer giveth *h.* *Pr* 17:4
preacher gave good *h.* *Eccl* 12:9*
diligently with much *h.* *Isa* 21:7
let us not give *h.* to any. *Jer* 18:18
h. to me, O Lord, and hearken. 19
he gave *h.* unto them. *Acts* 3:5
the people of Samaria gave *h.* 8:6
they gave *h.* to Simon from least. 10
neither give *h.* to fables. *1 Tim* 1:4 *Tit* 1:14
h. to seducing spirits. *1 Tim* 4:1
give the more earnest *h.* *Heb* 2:1
see **take**

heel, -s

thou shalt bruise his *h.* *Gen* 3:15
hold on Esau's *h.* 25:26; *Hos* 12:3
that biteth the horses' *h.* *Gen* 49:17
settest a print on the *h.* *Job* 13:27*
gin shall take him by the *h.* 18:9
friend, hath lifted up his *h.* against me. *Ps* 41:9; *John* 13:18
when iniquity of my *h.* *Ps* 49:5
iniquity are thy *h.* made. *Jer* 13:22

Hege

unto the custody of *H.* *Esth* 2:3

heifer

take me an *h.* of three. *Gen* 15:9
bring me a red *h.* *Num* 19:2
burn the *h.* in his sight. 5
gather up the ashes of the *h.* 9
that city shall take an *h.* *Deut* 21:3
shall strike off *h.*'s neck. 4
wash hands over the *h.* 6
not plowed with my *h.* *Judg* 14:18
Lord said, Take an *h.* *1 Sam* 16:2
out for Moab as an *h.* of. *Isa* 15:5*
Egypt is like a fair *h.* *Jer* 46:20
uttered their voice as an *h.* 48:34
ye are grown fat as an *h.* 50:11
back, as a backsliding *h.* *Hos* 4:16
Ephraim is as an *h.* that is. 10:11
the ashes of an *h.* *Heb* 9:13

height

the *h.* of the ark shall. *Gen* 6:15
ark of shittim wood, a cubit and a half be *h.* *Ex* 25:10, 23; 37:1, 10
h. of the altar shall. *Ex* 27:1; 38:1
h. of court shall be. 27:18; 38:18
h. of altar of incense. 30:2; 37:25
look not on the *h.* of. *1 Sam* 16:7
Goliath's *h.* was six cubits. 17:4
the *h.* of house of God. *1 Ki* 6:2
oracle twenty cubits in the *h.* 20
the *h.* of the one cherub was. 26
the *h.* of the house of Lebanon. 7:2
h. of the one chapiter was five. 16
the *h.* of the molten sea was. 23
h. of one base was three cubits. 27
with chariots I am come up to the *h.* of. *2 Ki* 19:23; *Isa* 37:24
the *h.* of one pillar was. *2 Ki* 25:17
it up a very great *h.* *2 Chr* 33:14
the *h.* of God's house. *Ezra* 6:3
is not God in the *h.* of heaven ? and behold the *h.* of the. *Job* 22:12
Lord looked from *h.* of. *Ps* 102:19
the heaven for *h.*, and earth. *Pr* 25:3
in the depth, or in the *h.* *Isa* 7:11
come and sing in the *h.* *Jer* 31:12
O thou that holdest the *h.* 49:16
though she should fortify *h.* 51:53
in mountain of the *h.* of Israel. *Ezek* 17:23; 20:40
she appeared in her *h.* with. 19:11
therefore his *h.* was exalted. 31:5*
thou hast lifted up thyself in *h.* 10*
trees exalt themselves for *h.* 14*
all the valleys with thy *h.* 32:5
image of gold whose *h.* *Dan* 3:1
saw and beheld a tree whose *h.* 4:10
and the *h.* thereof reached. 11, 20
whose *h.* was like the *h.* *Amos* 2:9
nor *h.* nor depth shall be. *Rom* 8:39

what is the *h.* of the love ? *Eph* 3:18
breadth and *h.* of the city. *Rev* 21:16

heights

Lord, praise him in the *h.* *Ps* 148:1
I will ascend above the *h.* *Isa* 14:14

heinous

for this is an *h.* crime. *Job* 31:11

heir, -s

in my house is mine *h.* *Gen* 15:3
saying, This shall not be thine *h.* 4
Ishmael shall not be *h.* with. 21:10
we will destroy the *h.* *2 Sam* 14:7
an handmaid that is *h.* *Pr* 30:23
no sons ? hath he no *h.*? *Jer* 49:1
be *h.* unto them that were his *h.* 2*
yet will I bring an *h.* *Mi* 1:15*
this is the *h.* *Mat* 21:38 *Mark* 12:7; *Luke* 20:14
that he should be *h.* of. *Rom* 4:13
which are of the law be *h.* 14
children, then *h.*; *h.* of God, and joint-*h.* with Christ; if we. 8:17
ye are *h.* according to the. *Gal* 3:29
I say, that the *h.* as long as. 4:1
if a son, then an *h.* of God. 7
bondwoman shall not be *h.* 30
Gentiles should be fellow-*h.* *Eph* 3:6
h. according to the hope. *Tit* 3:7
whom he appointed *h.* of *Heb* 1:2
for them who shall be *h.* of. 14
God willing to shew unto the *h.* 6:17
h. of the righteousness by. 11:7
and Jacob, *h.* with him of the. 9
h. of the kingdom he hath. *Jas* 2:5
as *h.* together of grace. *1 Pet* 3:7

Helam

the river came to *H.* *2 Sam* 10:16

Helbon

merchant in wine of *H.* *Ezek* 27:18

held

Joseph *h.* up his father's. *Gen* 48:17
when Moses *h.* up hand. *Ex* 17:11
the loops *h.* one curtain to. 36:12*
and *h.* the lamps in. *Judg* 7:20
Samson said unto lad that *h.* 16:26
she *h.* it, he measured. *Ruth* 3:15
Nabal *h.* a feast in his. *1 Sam* 25:36
for Joab *h.* back the. *2 Sam* 18:16
time Solomon *h.* a feast. *1 Ki* 8:65
sea *h.* three thousand. *2 Chr* 4:5
them *h.* both spears. *Neh* 4:16, 21
and with the other hand he *h.* 17
the king *h.* out the golden. *Esth* 5:2
if we have been sold, I had *h.* 7:4
my foot *h.* his steps, his. *Job* 23:11
mouth must be *h.* in. *Ps* 32:9
thy mercy, O Lord, *h.* me up. 94:18
I *h.* him, and would not. *S of S* 3:4
the king is *h.* in the galleries. 7:5
took them captives, *h.* *Jer* 50:33
he *h.* up his right hand. *Dan* 12:7
h. a council against him. *Mat* 12:14 *Mark* 15:1
the men that *h.* Jesus. *Luke* 22:63
same man that was healed, *h.* Peter. *Acts* 3:11
part *h.* with Jews, part with. 14:4
dead wherein we were *h.* *Rom* 7:6
testimony which they *h.* *Rev* 6:9

held *peace*

at her, *h.* his *peace.* *Gen* 24:21
Jacob *h.* his *peace* until they. 34:5
and Aaron *h.* his *peace.* *Lev* 10:3
her husband *h.* his *peace* at her. *Num* 30:7; 11:14
Saul, he *h.* his *peace.* *1 Sam* 10:27
people *h.* their *peace.* *2 Ki* 18:36
they *h.* their *peace,* and found. *Neh* 5:8
nobles *h.* their *peace.* *Job* 29:10
I was dumb, I *h.* my *peace.* *Ps* 39:2
h. their *peace.* *Isa* 36:21; *Mark* 3:4 9:34; *Luke* 14:4; 20:26 *Acts* 11:18; 15:13
have not I *h.* my *peace* ? *Isa* 57:11
but Jesus *h.* his *peace.* *Mat* 26:63

Heldai

captivity even of *H.* *Zech* 6:10

Heli

which was the son of *H.* *Luke* 3:23

Helkath-hazzurim

place was called *H.* *2 Sam* 2:16

hell

This word is generally used in the Old Testament to translate the Hebrew word Sheol, *which really means simply the place of the dead, without reference to happiness or the reverse, see* Gen 37:35; 42:38; 1 Sam 2:6; Job 14:13.

In other passages there is an idea of punishment. The American Revision retains the Hebrew word in all places.

In the New Testament the word hell is used to translate two words, [1] *Hades, generally meaning the same as* Sheol, *the place of the dead,* Acts 2:21; 1 Cor 15:55; Rev 20:13. [2] Gehenna, *the place of retribution for evil deeds.*

Note.—*Where this last is the meaning of a verse it is here starred.*

burn unto the lowest *h.* *Deut* 32:22
sorrows of *h.* compassed me. *2 Sam* 22:6; *Ps* 18:5
deeper than *h.* what canst ? *Job* 11:8
h. is naked before him. 26:6
shall be turned into *h.* *Ps* 9:17
thou wilt not leave my soul in *h.* 16:10; *Acts* 2:27
go down quick into *h.* *Ps* 55:15
my soul from the lowest *h.* 86:13
and the pains of *h.* gat hold. 116:3
if I make my bed in *h.* thou. 139:8
her steps take hold on *h.* *Pr* 5:5
her house is the way to *h.* 7:27
guests are in the depths of *h.* 9:18
h. and destruction are before. 15:11
depart from *h.* beneath. 24
shalt deliver his soul from *h.* 23:14
h. and destruction are never. 27:20
therefore *h.* hath enlarged. *Isa* 5:14
h. from beneath is moved. 14:9
shalt be brought down to *h.* 15
and with *h.* are we at. 28:15
debase thyself even unto *h.* 57:9
I cast him down to *h.* *Ezek* 31:16
they also went down unto *h.* 17
him out of the midst of *h.* 32:21
which are going down to *h.* with. 27
though they dig into *h.* *Amos* 9:2
out of the belly of *h.* *Jonah* 2:2
enlargeth his desire as *h.* *Hab* 2:5
shall be in danger of *h.* *Mat* 5:22*
body should be cast into *h.* 29*, 30*
to destroy soul and body in *h.* 10:28*; *Luke* 12:5*
Capernaum brought down to *h.* *Mat* 11:23; *Luke* 10:15
gates of *h.* shall not. *Mat* 16:18
having two eyes, to be cast into *h.* 18:9*; *Mark* 9:47*
twofold more child of *h.* *Mat* 23:15*
escape the damnation of *h.*? 33*
h. he lifted up his eyes. *Luke* 16:23
soul was not left in *h.* *Acts* 2:31
tongue is set on fire of *h.* *Jas* 3:6*
cast angels down to *h.* *2 Pet* 2:4*
and I have the keys of *h.* *Rev* 1:18
was Death, and *h.* followed. 6:8
death and *h.* delivered up the. 20:13
death and *h.* were cast into the. 14

helm

about with a small *h.* *Jas* 3:4*

helmet

he had a *h.* of brass. *1 Sam* 17:5, 38
and an *h.* of salvation. *Isa* 59:17
against shield and *h.* *Ezek* 23:24
they hanged the shield and *h.* 27:10
all of them with shield and *h.* 38:5
take *h.* of salvation, and. *Eph* 6:17
and for an *h.* the hope of. *1 Thes* 5:8

helmets

prepared spears and *h.* *2 Chr* 26:14
forth with your *h.* *Jer* 46:4

help, *substantive*

I will make him an *h.* *Gen* 2:18
there was not found an *h.* meet. 20
father, said he, was my *h.* *Ex* 18:4
be thou an *h.* to him. *Deut* 33:7

upon the heavens in thy *h. Deut* 33:26
saved by Lord the shield of thy *h.* 29
they came not to the *h.* *Judg* 5:23
hot, ye shall have *h.* *1 Sam* 11:9
gathered to ask *h.* of. *2 Chr* 20:4
is not my *h.* in me? *Job* 6:13
my hand, when I saw my *h.* 31:21
soul, there is no *h.* for him. *Ps* 3:2
the Lord send thee *h.* from. 20:2
thou hast been my *h.* leave. 27:9
waits for Lord, he is our *h.* 33:20
stand up for mine *h.* 35:2; 44:26
thou art my *h.* and my. 40:17; 70:5
praise him for the *h.* of his. 42:5
God is a very present *h.* in. 46:1
h. for vain is the *h.* 60:11; 108:12
because thou hast been my *h.* 63:7
my God, make haste for my *h.* 71:12
I have laid *h.* upon one that. 89:19
Lord had been my *h.* 94:17
he is their *h.* and their. 115:9, 10, 11
from whence cometh my *h.* 121:1
my *h.* cometh from Lord which. 2
our *h.* is in name of Lord. 124:8
man, in whom there is no *h.* 146:3
hath the God of Jacob for his *h.* 5
to whom will ye flee for *h.*? *Isa* 10:3
we flee for *h.* to be delivered. 20:6
nor be an *h.* nor profit, but. 30:5
that go down to Egypt for *h.* 31:1
against the *h.* of them that work. 2
failed for our vain *h.* *Lam* 4:17
holpen with a little *h.* *Dan* 11:34
but in me is thine *h.* *Hos* 13:9
having obtained *h.* of. *Acts* 26:22

help, *verb*

father, who shall *h.* thee. *Gen* 49:25
forbear to *h.* him, thou shalt surely *h.* him. *Ex* 23:5*; *Deut* 22:4
let them rise and *h.* *Deut* 32:38
your brethren, and *h.* *Josh* 1:14
come unto me, and *h.* me. 10:4
us quickly, and save us, and *h.* us. 6
king of Gezer came up to *h.* 33
then *h.* me: then I will *h.* thee. *2 Sam* 10:11; *1 Chr* 19:12
Syrians feared to *h.* Ammon. *2 Sam* 10:19; *1 Chr* 19:19
woman said, *H.*, O king. *2 Sam* 14:4; *2 Ki* 6:26
come unto me to *h.* me. *1 Chr* 12:17
day there came to David to *h.* 22
of Damascus came to *h.* 18:5
David commanded to *h.* 22:17
it is nothing with thee to *h.*, *h.* us, O Lord our God, we rest. *2 Chr* 14:11
shouldest thou *h.* the ungodly. 19:2
then thou wilt hear and *h.* 20:9
for God hath power to *h.* and. 25:8
war with mighty power to *h.* 26:13
kings of Assyria to *h.* him. 28:16
Syria *h.* them, that they may *h.* 23
the Levites did *h.* them. 29:34
and his mighty men did *h.* him. 32:3
is the Lord our God, to *h.* us. 8
the men of his place *h.* *Ezra* 1:4
to require horsemen to *h.* 8:22
will he *h.* the evil doers. *Job* 8:20*
him that had none to *h.* him. 29:12
h. Lord. *Ps* 12:1
for there is none to *h.* 22:11
haste thee to *h.* me. 22:19; 38:22; 40:13; 70:1
Lord shall *h.* them. 37:40
God shall *h.* her. 46:5
awake to *h.* me. 59:4
h. us, O God of salvation. 79:9
was none to *h.* 107:12; *Isa* 63:5
h. me, O Lord my God. *Ps* 109:26
my part with them that *h.* 118:7
h. thou me. 119:86
let thine hand *h.* me. 173
and let thy judgements *h.* me. 175
hath not another to *h.* *Eccl* 4:10
the Egyptians shall *h.* *Isa* 30:7
fear not, I will *h.* 41:10, 13, 14; 44:2
Lord God will *h.* me. 50:7, 9
army, which is come to *h.* *Jer* 37:7
people fell, and none did *h.* *Lam* 1:7
scatter all about to *h.* *Ezek* 12:14
out of hell with them that *h.* 32:21
princes came to *h.* me. *Dan* 10:13
his end, and none shall *h.* 11:45
him, saying, Lord *h.* me. *Mat* 15:25
on us and *h.* us. *Mark* 9:22
Lord, I believe, *h.* thou mine. 24
they should come and *h.* *Luke* 5:7
bid her therefore that she *h.* 10:40
into Macedonia, and *h.* us. *Acts* 16:9
crying out, men of Israel, *h.* 21:28
h. those women which. *Phil* 4:3
we may find grace to *h.* *Heb* 4:16

helped

Moses stood up and *h.* *Ex* 2:17
hath the Lord *h.* us. *1 Sam* 7:12
following Adonijah, *h.* *1 Ki* 1:7
and two kings that *h.* him. 20:16
and they were *h.* *1 Chr* 5:20
but they *h.* them not, for the. 12:19
they *h.* David against the band. 21
when God *h.* the Levites that. 15:26
the Lord *h.* Jehoshaphat. *2 Chr* 18:31
every one *h.* to destroy. 20:23
God *h.* him against the. 26:7
for he was marvellously *h.* till. 15
king of Assyria *h.* him not. 28:21
Shabbethai the Levite *h.* *Ezra* 10:15
officers of the king *h.* *Esth* 9:3
how hast thou *h.* him that? *Job* 26:2
and I am *h.* *Ps* 28:7
brought low, and he *h.* me. 116:6
but the Lord *h.* me. 118:13
they *h.* every one his. *Isa* 41:6
day of salvation have I *h.* thee. 49:8
and they *h.* forward the. *Zech* 1:15
when he was come, *h.* *Acts* 18:27
the earth *h.* the woman. *Rev* 12:16

helper

nor was there any *h.* *2 Ki* 14:26
my path, they have no *h.* *Job* 30:13
thou art the *h.* of the. *Ps* 10:14
Lord, be thou my *h.* 30:10
God is my *h.* 54:4
deliver him that hath no *h.* 72:12
and Zidon every *h.* *Jer* 47:4
salute Urbane, our *h.* *Rom* 16:9*
the Lord is my *h.* I will. *Heb* 13:6

helpers

among the mighty men, *h.* *1 Chr* 12:1
and peace be to thine *h.* 18
the proud *h.* do stoop. *Job* 9:13
when all her *h.* shall be. *Ezek* 30:8
and Lubim were thy *h.* *Nah* 3:9
and Aquila my *h.* in. *Rom* 16:3*
but are *h.* of your joy. *2 Cor* 1:24
we might be fellow-*h.* *3 John* 8

helpeth

for thy God *h.* thee. *1 Chr* 12:18
both he that *h.* shall fall. *Isa* 31:3
the Spirit also *h.* our. *Rom* 8:26
submit to every one that *h.* with us. *1 Cor* 16:16

helping

the prophets of God *h.* *Ezra* 5:2
thou so far from me? *Ps* 22:1
ye also *h.* together by. *2 Cor* 1:11

helps

used *h.* undergirding. *Acts* 27:17
gifts of healings, *h.* *1 Cor* 12:28

helve

head slippeth from the *h.* *Deut* 19:5

hem, -s

upon the *h.* of it thou shalt make. *Ex* 28:33*, 34*; 39:24*, 25*, 26*
woman touched *h.* of his garment. *Mat* 9:20*; 14:36*

Heman

wiser than Ethan, *H.* *1 Ki* 4:31
Zerah, *H.* and Calcol. *1 Chr* 2:6
H. a singer, son of Joel. 6:33; 15:17, 19; 16:42
the sons of Asaph and of *H.* 25:1, 4, 6; *2 Chr* 5:12; 29:14; 35:15
H. God gave *H.* 14 sons. *1 Chr* 25:6

hemlock

springeth up as *h.* in. *Hos* 10:4
of righteousness into *h.* *Amos* 6:12

hen

as a *h.* gathereth chickens. *Mat* 23:37; *Luke* 13:34

Hen

crown shall be for *H.* *Zech* 6:14

hence

said, they are departed *h.* *Gen* 37:17
ye shall not go forth *h.* 42:15
carry up my bones from *h.* 50:25; *Ex* 13:19
go *h.* thrust you out *h.* *Ex* 11:1
depart and go *h.* thou and. 33:1
not with me, carry us not up *h.* 15
thee down quickly from *h.* *Deut* 9:12
h. out of Jordan twelve. *Josh* 4:3
depart not *h.* I pray thee. *Judg* 6:18
nor go *h.* but abide fast by. *Ruth* 2:8
get thee *h.* *1 Ki* 17:3; *Isa* 30:22; *Mat* 4:10
O spare me, before I go *h.* *Ps* 39:13
take from *h.* thirty. *Jer* 38:10
he said, Get you *h.*, walk. *Zech* 6:7
shall say, Remove *h.* to. *Mat* 17:20
cast thyself down from *h.* *Luke* 4:9
out, and depart *h.* 13:31; *John* 7:3
pass from *h.* to you. *Luke* 16:26
take things *h.*; make not. *John* 2:16
arise, let us go *h.* 14:31
my kingdom not *h.* 18:36
sir, if thou have borne him *h.* 20:15
the H. G. not many days *h.* *Acts* 1:5
I will send thee far *h.* unto. 22:21
come they not *h.* even? *Jas* 4:1

henceforth

the ground not *h.* yield. *Gen* 4:12
neither must Israel *h.* *Num* 18:22
ye shall *h.* return no. *Deut* 17:16
shall *h.* commit no more. 19:20
I will not *h.* drive out. *Judg* 2:21
thy servant will *h.* not. *2 Ki* 5:17
from *h.* thou shalt have. *2 Chr* 16:9
about his people from *h.* *Ps* 125:2*
hope in the Lord from *h.* 131:3*
it with justice from *h.* *Isa* 9:7
h. there shall no more come. 52:1
mouth of thy seed's seed *h.* 59:21
thou shalt no more *h.* *Ezek* 36:12
in mount Zion from *h.* *Mi* 4:7
ye shall not see me *h.* *Mat* 23:39
I will not drink *h.* of this. 26:29
h. all generations shall. *Luke* 1:48
fear not, from *h.* thou shalt. 5:10
h. there shall be five in one. 12:52
h. ye know him, and. *John* 14:7
h. I call you not servants. 15:15
they speak *h.* to no man. *Acts* 4:17
I am clean, *h.* I will go unto. 18:6
that *h.* we should not. *Rom* 6:6*
should not *h.* live unto. *2 Cor* 5:15*
h. know we no man, *h.* know. 16*
from *h.* let no man. *Gal* 6:17
h. be no more children. *Eph* 4:14*
that ye *h.* walk not as other. 17
h. there is laid up for. *2 Tim* 4:8
h. expecting till enemies. *Heb* 10:13
who die in Lord, from *h.* *Rev* 14:13

henceforward

and *h.* among your. *Num* 15:23*
no fruit grow on thee *h.* *Mat* 21:19

Hephzi-bah

mother's name was *H.* *2 Ki* 21:1
thou shalt be called *H.* *Isa* 62:4

herald

then an *h.* cried aloud. *Dan* 3:4

herb

the *h.* yielding seed. *Gen* 1:11, 12
I have given you every *h.* 29
made every *h.* 2:5
thou shalt eat the *h.* 3:18
even as the *h.* I have given. 9:3
hail smote every *h.* of. *Ex* 9:22, 25
the locusts eat every *h.* 10:12, 15
rain upon the tender *h.* *Deut* 32:2
were as the green *h.* *2 Ki* 19:26; *Isa* 37:27
before any other *h.* *Job* 8:12
the bud of the tender *h.* 38:27*
wither as the green *h.* *Ps* 37:2
he causeth *h.* to grow for. 104:14
shall flourish like an *h.* *Isa* 66:14*

herbs

and with bitter *h.* eat it. *Ex* 12:8; *Num* 9:11
it as a garden of *h.* *Deut* 11:10
have it for garden of *h.* *1 Ki* 21:2
into field to gather *h.* *2 Ki* 4:39
and did eat up all the *h.* *Ps* 105:35

better is a dinner of *h.* *Pr* 15:17
and *h.* of the mountains are. 27:25
a clear heat upon *h.* *Isa* 18:4*
thy dew is as the dew of *h.* 26:19
I will dry up all their *h.* 42:15
how long the *h.* of every. *Jer* 12:4
is greatest among all *h.* *Mat* 13:32
Mark 4:32
tithe all manner of *h.* *Luke* 11:42
who is weak eateth *h.* *Rom* 14:2
and bringeth forth *h.* *Heb* 6:7

herd, -s

Abraham ran to the *h.* *Gen* 18:7
Jacob divided his *h.* into two. 32:7
my lord also hath our *h.* 47:18
our flocks and *h.* will. *Ex* 10:9
your offering of the *h.* *Lev* 1:2
h. male or female. 3:1; *Num* 15:3
the tithe of the *h.* or. *Lev* 27:32
shalt kill of thy *h.* *Deut* 12:21
males that come of thy *h.* 15:19
Saul came after the *h.* *1 Sam* 11:5*
spared to take of his *h.* *2 Sam* 12:4
the *h.* in Sharon, *h.* in. *1 Chr* 27:29
Achor a place for the *h.* *Isa* 65:10
for young of the *h.* *Jer* 31:12
h. of cattle are perplexed. *Joel* 1:18
let not the *h.* nor flock. *Jonah* 3:7
there shall be no *h.* in. *Hab* 3:17
h. of swine feeding. *Mat* 8:30
Mark 5:11; *Luke* 8:32
whole *h.* ran violently. *Mat* 8:32
Mark 5:13; *Luke* 8:33
see **flocks**

herdman

prophet, but I was an *h.* *Amos* 7:14

herdmen

the *h.* of Abram and Lot. *Gen* 13:7
no strife between my *h.* and thy *h.* 8
h. of Gerar did strive with Isaac's *h.* 26:20
chiefest of *h.* belonged. *1 Sam* 21:7
who was among the *h.* *Amos* 1:1

here

men said, hast thou *h.*? *Gen* 19:12
thy two daughters which are *h.* 15
therefore swear unto me *h.* by. 21:23
h. I am. 22:1, 7, 11; 27:1, 18; 31:11
37:13; 46:2; *Ex* 3:4; 1 *Sam* 3:4, 5
6, 8, 16; *2 Sam* 1:7; 15:26; *Isa* 6:8
abide ye *h.* with the ass. *Gen* 22:5
I stand *h.* by the well. 24:13
set it *h.* before my brethren. 31:37
and *h.* also have I done. 40:15
one of your brethren *h.* with. 42:33
lo, *h.* is seed for you, ye shall. 47:23
Tarry ye *h.* for us, until. *Ex* 24:14
saying, Lo, we be *h.* *Num* 14:40
lodge *h.* this night, I will. 22:8, 19
h. seven altars, prepare *h.* 23:1, 29
go to war, and you sit *h.*? 32:6
we will build sheepfolds *h.* for. 16
who are all of us *h.* alive. *Deut* 5:3
after all the things we do *h.* 12:8
h. and with him that is not *h.* 29:15
cast lots for you *h.* *Josh* 18:6, 8
is there any man *h.*? *Judg* 4:20
and what hast thou *h.*? 18:3
lodge *h.* 19:9
behold, *h.* is my daughter. 24
give *h.* your advice and. 20:7
but abide *h.* fast by. *Ruth* 2:8
turn aside, sit down *h.* 4:1, 2
I am the woman that stood by thee *h.* *1 Sam* 1:26
hill and said, Is the seer *h.*? 9:11
behold, *h.* I am. 12:3; 22:12
Isa 58:9
slay them *h.* and eat. *1 Sam* 14:34
Samuel said to Jesse, Are *h.*? 16:11
is there not *h.* under thine? 21:8
h. wrapped in a cloth, none save *h.* 9
behold, we be afraid *h.* in. 23:3
what do these Hebrews *h.*? 29:3
tarry *h.* to-day. *2 Sam* 11:12
turn aside *h.* 18:30
e thou *h.* present. 20:4
. be oxen. 24:22
nay, but I will die *h.* *1 Ki* 2:30
behold, Elijah is *h.* 18:8; 11:14
what doest thou *h.* Elijah? 19:9, 13
s thy servant was busy *h.* 20:40
ot *h.* a prophet? 22:7; *2 Ki* 3:11
Elijah said, Tarry *h.* *2 Ki* 2:2, 6
h. is Elisha. 3:11
why sit we *h.* until we die? 7:3
lepers said, If we sit still *h.* 4
look there be *h.* none of the. 10:23
joy thy people present *h.* *1 Chr* 29:17
h. shall thy proud. *Job* 38:11
may say unto thee, *H.* we are. 35
this is my rest, *h.* will. *Ps* 132:14
behold, *h.* cometh a. *Isa* 21:9
thou *h.*? whom hast thou *h.*? 22:16
h. a little, and there. 28:10, 13
therefore, what have I *h.*? 52:5
Israel committeth *h.* *Ezek* 8:6, 17
gray hairs are *h.* and. *Hos* 7:9
a greater than Jonas is *h.* *Mat* 12:41
Luke 11:32
a greater than Solomon is *h.*
Mat 12:42; *Luke* 11:31
give me *h.* John Baptist's. *Mat* 14:8
we have *h.* but five loaves. 17
there be some standing *h.* 16:28
Luke 9:27
to be *h.* let us make *h.* *Mat* 17:4
shall not be left *h.* one stone. 24:2
you, Lo, *h.* is Christ. 23; *Mark* 13:21
sit ye *h.* while I go and pray.
Mat 26:36 *Mark* 14:32
tarry ye *h.* and watch. *Mat* 26:38
he is not *h.*, he is risen. 28:6
Mark 16:6; *Luke* 24:6
are not his sisters *h.*? *Mark* 6:3
stones and buildings are *h.* 13:1
heard done, do *h.* in thy. *Luke* 4:23
for we are *h.* in a desert place. 9:12
neither shall they say, Lo *h.*! 17:21
say to you, See *h.*; or, see there. 23
behold, *h.* is thy pound. 19:20
h. are two swords, he said. 22:38
unto them, Have ye *h.* any? 24:41
there is a lad *h.* which. *John* 6:9
Lord, if thou hadst been *h.* 11:21, 32
h. is water. *Acts* 8:36
behold, I am *h.* Lord. 9:10
and *h.* he hath authority from. 14
are we all *h.* present before. 10:33
no harm: for we are all *h.* 16:28
who ought to have been *h.* 24:19
and all men which are *h.* 25:24
unto you all things done *h.* *Col* 4:9
h. men that die receive. *Heb* 7:8
for *h.* have we no continuing. 13:14
sit *h.* in a good place, or sit *h.* under. *Jas* 2:3
of your sojourning *h.* *1 Pet* 1:17
h. is the patience of the saints.
Rev 13:10; 14:12
h. is wisdom; let him that. 13:18
h. are they that kept the. 14:12
and *h.* is the mind which hath. 17:9
see **stand**

hereafter

things that are to come *h.* *Isa* 41:23
h. also, if ye will not. *Ezek* 20:39
should come to pass *h.* *Dan* 2:29, 45
h. shall ye see the Son. *Mat* 26:64
man eat fruit of thee *h.* *Mark* 11:14
h. shall Son of man sit. *Luke* 22:69
I say, *H.* ye shall see. *John* 1:51
not now, thou shalt know *h.* 13:7
h. I will not talk much with. 14:30
pattern to them which *h.* *1 Tim* 1:16
things which shall be *h.* *Rev* 1:19
thee things which must be *h.* 4:1
there come two woes more *h.* 9:12

hereby

h. ye shall be proved, by. *Gen* 42:15
h. shall I know that ye are. 33
h. know that the Lord. *Num* 16:28
h. know that the living. *Josh* 3:10
nothing, yet am I not *h.* *1 Cor* 4:4
h. we do know that we. *1 John* 2:3
keepeth word, *h.* know we that. 5
h. perceive we the love of God. 3:16
and *h.* we know that we are of. 19
and *h.* we know that he abideth. 24
h. know ye the Spirit of God. 4:2
h. know we the Spirit of truth. 6
h. know we that we dwell in him. 13

herein

only *h.* will the men. *Gen* 34:22*
h. thou hast done foolishly.
2 Chr 16:9
h. is that saying true. *John* 4:37
h. is a marvellous thing, that. 9:30
h. is my Father glorified. 15:8
h. do I exercise myself. *Acts* 24:16
h. I give my advice, for. *2 Cor* 8:10
h. is love. *1 John* 4:10
h. is love made perfect. 17

heresies

(*This word never appears in the New Testament in its strict modern meaning, but means sects, factions*)
also *h.* among you. *1 Cor* 11:19†
the flesh, wrath, strife, *h.* *Gal* 5:20
bring in damnable *h.* *2 Pet* 2:1

heresy

way which they call *h.* *Acts* 24:14*

heretick

an *h.* after the second. *Tit* 3:10*

heretofore

am not eloquent, neither *h.* *Ex* 4:10
straw to make brick as *h.* 5:7
not passed this way *h.* *Josh* 3:4
thou knewest not *h.* *Ruth* 2:11
not been such a thing *h.* *1 Sam* 4:7
which *h.* have sinned. *2 Cor* 13:2

hereunto

or who else can hasten *h.*? *Eccl* 2:25*
for even *h.* were ye. *1 Pet* 2:21

herewith

wast not satisfied *h.* *Ezek* 16:29
be meat in mine house, and prove me now *h.* saith the. *Mal* 3:10

heritage

I will give it you for an *h.* *Ex* 6:8
and the *h.* appointed by. *Job* 20:29
the *h.* of oppressors which. 27:13
yea, I have a goodly *h.* *Ps* 16:6
give me the *h.* of those that. 61:5
people, they afflict thy *h.* 94:5
he may give them the *h.* of. 111:6
have I taken as an *h.* 119:111
lo, children are an *h.* of the. 127:3
and gave their land for an *h.*
135:12; 136:21, 22
is the *h.* of the servants. *Isa* 54:17
I will feed thee with the *h.* 58:14
and ye made mine *h.* *Jer* 2:7
I give thee a goodly *h.*? 3:19
I have left mine *h.* 12:7
mine *h.* is as a lion. 8
mine *h.* is unto me as a speckled. 9
them again every man to his *h.* 15
discontinue from thine *h.* 17:4
O destroyers of mine *h.* 50:11
and give not thine *h.* to. *Joel* 2:17
plead with them for my *h.* 3:2
oppress a man and his *h.* *Mi* 2:2
feed the flock of thine *h.* 7:14
by the transgression of his *h.* 18
Esau's mountains and *h.* *Mal* 1:3
being lords over God's *h.* *1 Pet* 5:3*

heritages

to inherit the desolate *h.* *Isa* 49:8

Hermas, Hermes

salute *Hermas*, Patrobas, *Hermes*. *Rom* 16:14

Hermogenes

are Phygellus and *H.* *2 Tim* 1:15

Hermon

mount Sion, which is *H.* *Deut* 4:48
all mount *H.* Reuben. *Josh* 13:11
Tabor and *H.* shall. *Ps* 89:12
the dew of *H.* that descended. 133:3
top of Shenir and *H.* *S of S* 4:8

Hermonites

from the land of *H.* *Ps* 42:6

Herod

should not return to *H.* *Mat* 2:12
was there till the death of *H.* 15
H. slew all the children in. 16
for *H.* had laid hold on John. 14:3
Mark 6:17
but when *H.*'s birthday was kept.
Mat 14:6; *Mark* 6:21
H. feared John. *Mark* 6:20
beware of the leaven of *H.* 8:15
and *H.* being tetrarch. *Luke* 3:1
all the evils which *H.* had done. 19
H. heard of all that was done. 9:7

depart thence, for *H.* *Luke* 13:31
Pilate sent Jesus to *H.* 23:7
H. was glad. 8
H. with his men of war set. 11
Pilate and *H.* were made. 12
no fault in this man, nor yet *H.* 15
both *H.* and Pilate. *Acts* 4:27
H. vexed the church. 12:1
when *H.* would have brought. 6
out of the hand of *H.* 11
day *H.* made an oration to them. 21
had been brought up with *H.* 13:1
him to be kept in *H.'s.* 23:35

Herodians
see **sect**
their disciples, with *H.* saying, we.
Mat 22:16; *Mark* 12:13
took counsel with the *H.* *Mark* 3:6

Herodias
John in prison for *H.'s* sake.
Mat 14:3; *Mark* 6:17
the daughter of *H.* danced.
Mat 14:6; *Mark* 6:22
H. had a quarrel. *Mark* 6:19
reproved by John for *H.* *Luke* 3:19

Herodion
salute *H.* my kinsman. *Rom* 16:11

heron
the stork, the *h.* unclean. *Lev* 11:19
Deut 14:18

herself
number to *h.* seven days. *Lev* 15:28
if she profane *h.* by playing. 21:9
if a woman bind *h.* by a. *Num* 30:3
she returned answer to *h.* *Judg* 5:29
bowed *h.* and travailed. *1 Sam* 4:19
Abigail bowed *h.* to the earth. 25:41
a woman washing *h.* *2 Sam* 11:2
she shall feign *h.* another. *1 Ki* 14:5
she lifteth up *h.* on high. *Job* 39:18
swallow found a nest for *h.* *Ps* 84:3
h. coverings of tapestry. *Pr* 31:22
hell hath enlarged *h.* *Isa* 5:14
screech owl find for *h.* a place. 34:14
as a bride adorneth *h.* with. 61:10
Israel hath justified *h.* *Jer* 3:11
of Zion that bewaileth *h.* 4:31
is feeble and turneth *h.* to. 49:24
maketh idols against *h.* *Ezek* 22:3
their idols she defiled *h.* 23:7
she hath wearied *h.* with lies. 24:12
she decked *h.* with her. *Hos* 2:13
Tyrus did build *h.* a. *Zech* 9:3
she said within *h.* If I. *Mat* 9:21
earth bringeth forth fruit of *h.*
Mark 4:28
Elisabeth hid *h.* five. *Luke* 1:24
woman could in no wise lift up *h.*
13:11
through faith Sarah *h.* *Heb* 11:11
Jezebel who calleth *h.* a. *Rev* 2:20
she hath glorified *h.* and lived. 18:7
and his wife hath made *h.* 19:7
see **himself**

Heshbon
Israel dwelt in *H.* *Num* 21:25
H. was the city of Sihon. 26
come into *H.* 27
a fire gone out of *H.* 28
H. is perished. 30
children of Reuben built *H.* 32:37
given Sihon king of *H.* *Deut* 2:24
while Israel dwelt in *H.* *Judg* 11:26
land of the king of *H.* *Neh* 9:22
like the fish pools of *H.* *S of S* 7:4
H. shall cry. *Isa* 15:4
for field of *H.* languish. 16:8
water thee with my tears, O *H.* 9
in *H.* they have devised. *Jer* 48:2
from cry of *H.* even to Elealeh. 34
stood under the shadow of *H.*, but a fire shall come out of *H.* 45
howl, O *H.* 49:3
see **Sihon**

Heth
Canaan begat Sidon and *H.*
Gen 10:15; *1 Chr* 1:13
before the children of *H.* *Gen* 23:7
Abraham purchased of the sons of *H.*
25:10; 49:32
because of the daughters of *H.*
Gen 27:46

hew
h. thee two tables of stone. *Ex* 34:1
Deut 10:1
shall *h.* down the graven. *Deut* 12:3
man goeth with neighbour to *h.* 19:5
they *h.* me cedar trees. *1 Ki* 5:6
and Hiram's builders did *h.* 18*
David set masons to *h.* *1 Chr* 22:2
Solomon told 80,000 to *h.* *2 Chr* 2:2
h. ye down trees and. *Jer* 6:6
cried aloud, *H.* down. *Dan* 4:14, 23

hewed
he *h.* two tables like the first.
Ex 34:4; *Deut* 10:3
Saul *h.* oxen in pieces. *1 Sam* 11:7
and Samuel *h.* Agag in pieces. 15:33
h. stones to lay. *1 Ki* 5:17*
three rows of *h.* stone. 6:36; 7:12
measures of *h.* stones. 7:9, 11
buy *h.* stone to repair. *2 Ki* 12:12
thou hast *h.* thee out. *Isa* 22:16
my people have *h.* them. *Jer* 2:13
therefore have I *h.* them. *Hos* 6:5

hewer
h. of wood, unto drawer. *Deut* 29:11

hewers
be *h.* of wood and. *Josh* 9:21, 23
made them that day *h.* of wood. 27
80,000 *h.* in mountains. *1 Ki* 5:15
2 Chr 2:18
money to masons and *h.* *2 Ki* 12:12
are *h.* with thee in. *1 Chr* 22:15
to thy servants the *h.* *2 Chr* 2:10
come against Egypt as *h.* *Jer* 46:22

heweth
boast against him that *h.*? *Isa* 10:5
that *h.* him out a sepulchre. 22:16
he *h.* him down cedars, and. 44:14

hewn
she hath *h.* out her seven. *Pr* 9:1
of stature shall be *h.* down. *Isa* 10:33
Lebanon is ashamed, and *h.* 33:9*
the rock whence ye are *h.* 51:1
h. down and cast into fire. *Mat* 3:10
7:19; *Luke* 3:9
he had *h.* out in the rock. *Mat* 27:60
Mark 15:46; *Luke* 23:53
see **stone**

Hezekiah, *called* **Ezekias**
H. Ahaz's son reigned. *2 Ki* 16:20
H. sent to the king of Assyria. 18:14
H. gave him all the silver in. 15
H. hath taken away. 22; *Isa* 36:7
let not *H.* deceive you. *2 Ki* 18:29
2 Chr 32:15; *Isa* 36:14
hearken not to *H.* *2 Ki* 18:31, 32
Isa 36:16
king *H.* heard it, he rent his.
2 Ki 19:1; *Isa* 37:1
H. prayed. *2 Ki* 19:15; *2 Chr* 30:18
Isa 37:15
H. was sick to death. *2 Ki* 20:1
2 Chr 32:24; *Isa* 38:1
H. wept sore. *2 Ki* 20:3; *Isa* 38:3
turn again, tell *H.* *2 Ki* 20:5
Berodach sent a present to *H.* 12
Isa 39:1
nothing, that *H.* shewed them not.
2 Ki 20:13; *Isa* 39:2
H. said, Good is the word of the.
2 Ki 20:19; *Isa* 39:8
H. slept with his fathers. *2 Ki* 20:21
2 Chr 32:3
built what *H.* had destroyed.
2 Ki 21:3; *2 Chr* 33:3
Neariah, *H.* and. *1 Chr* 3:23
came in days of *H.* and smote. 4:41
H. commanded to offer. *2 Chr* 29:27
H. rejoiced, and all the people. 36
the Lord hearkened to *H.* 30:20
H. spake comfortably to all. 22
H. gave the congregation 1000. 24
H. appointed the courses of. 31:2
then *H.* commanded to prepare. 11
rested on the words of *H.* 32:8
so shall not the God of *H.* deliver. 17
saved *H.* from Sennacherib. 22
H. rendered not again according. 25
not on them in the days of *H.* 26
H. prospered in all his. *2 Chr* 32:30
the children of Ater of *H.* *Ezra* 2:16
Neh 7:21
which the men of *H.* copied. *Pr* 25:1
Manasseh the son of *H.* *Jer* 15:4
in days of *H.* 26:18; *Mi* 1:1
H. and all Judah put. *Jer* 26:19
to Hosea in days of *H.* *Hos* 1:1
Achaz begat *H.* *Mat* 1:9
H. begat Manasses. 10

Hezron
sons of Reuben, *H.* Carmi.
Gen 46:9; *Ex* 6:14
son of Pharez, *H.* *Gen* 46:12
Ruth 4:18; *1 Chr* 2:5; 4:1
H. begat Ram, Ram. *Ruth* 4:19
the sons of *H.* *1 Chr* 2:9
Caleb the son of *H.* 18
H. begat Segub. 21
after that *H.* was dead. 24
Jerahmeel the firstborn of *H.* 25

hid, *verb*
and Adam and his wife *h.* *Gen* 3:8
because I was naked, and I *h.* 10
Jacob *h.* them under the oak. 35:4
goodly child, she *h.* Moses. *Ex* 2:2
Moses slew the Egyptian, and *h.* 12
Moses *h.* his face, for he was. 3:6
Rahab *h.* the spies with. *Josh* 2:4, 6
because she *h.* messengers. 6:17, 25
and behold they are *h.* in the. 7:21
the five kings *h.* themselves. 10:16
Jotham was left, for he *h.* *Judg* 9:5
Samuel told Eli and *h.* *1 Sam* 3:18
Saul *h.* himself. 10:22
David *h.* himself. 20:24
Obadiah *h.* the. *1 Ki* 18:4, 13
and the Lord hath *h.* *2 Ki* 4:27
give thy son, she hath *h.* 6:29
and *h.* it, carried thence, and *h.* 7:8
h. him and his. 11:2; *2 Chr* 22:11
Ornan and four sons *h.* *1 Chr* 21:20
h. sorrow from mine eyes. *Job* 3:10
these things hast thou *h.* 10:13
thou hast *h.* their heart from. 17:4
young men saw me and *h.* 29:8
in net which they *h.* is their. *Ps* 9:15
neither hath he *h.* his face. 22:24
without cause they *h.* for me. 35:7
net that he hath *h.* catch himself. 8
I would have *h.* myself. 55:12
thy word have I *h.* in. 119:11*
the proud have *h.* a snare. 140:5
falsehood have we *h.* *Isa* 28:15
his hand, in quiver he *h.* me. 49:2
I *h.* not my face from shame. 50:6
and we *h.* as it were our. 53:3
in a little wrath I *h.* my face. 54:8
I *h.* me and was wroth, and. 57:17
your sins have *h.* his face. 59:2
for thou hast *h.* thy face from. 64:7
because they are *h.* from. 65:16
so I went and *h.* it by. *Jer* 13:5
from the place where I had *h.* it. 7
for they have *h.* snares for. 18:22
I have *h.* my face from this. 33:5
to take them, but the Lord *h.* 36:26
on these stones I have *h.* 43:10
have *h.* their eyes from. *Ezek* 22:26
h. I my face from them. 39:23, 24
thou hast *h.* from the wise.
Mat 11:25; *Luke* 10:21
h. in three measures of meal.
Mat 13:33; *Luke* 13:21
went and *h.* his lord's. *Mat* 25:18
I went and *h.* thy talent in the. 25
Elisabeth *h.* herself five. *Luke* 1:24
but Jesus *h.* himself. *John* 8:59
free man *h.* themselves. *Rev* 6:15

hid
suck of treasures *h.* in. *Deut* 33:19
and behold, it was *h.* in. *Josh* 7:22
the five kings are found *h.* 10:17
behold, he is *h.* now in. *2 Sam* 17:
no matter *h.* from king. 18:1
1 Ki 10:3; *2 Chr* 9:
he was *h.* in house of God.
2 Ki 11:3; *2 Chr* 22:1
Ahaziah was *h.* in. *2 Chr* 22:
dig for it more than for *h.* *Job* 3:2
given to a man whose way is *h.*? 2
brooks, wherein the snow is *h.* 6:1
the thing that is *h.* bringeth. 28:1

seeing it is *h.* from eyes. *Job* 28:21
the waters are *h.* as with a. 38:30
belly thou fillest with *h.* *Ps* 17:14
nothing is *h.* from the heat. 19:6
searchest for her as for *h.* *Pr* 2:4
why sayest, My way is *h.* *Isa* 40:27
they are *h.* in prison houses. 42:22
nor their iniquity *h.* from. *Jer* 16:17
bound up, his sin is *h.* *Hos* 13:12*
h. that shall not be known. *Mat* 10:26
Mark 4:22; *Luke* 8:17; 12:2
this saying was *h.* *Luke* 9:45; 18:34
but now they are *h.* from. 19:42
beginning hath been *h.* in. *Eph* 3:9
mystery which hath been *h.* *Col* 1:26
in whom are *h.* all treasures. 2:3
and your life is *h.* with Christ. 3:3
by faith Moses was *h.* *Heb* 11:23

be **hid**

thy face shall I *be h.* *Gen* 4:14
thing *be h.* from. *Lev* 4:13; 5:3, 4
it *be h.* from the eyes. *Num* 5:13
shalt *be h.* from scourge. *Job* 5:21
darkness shall *be h.* in his. 20:26
of prudent men *be h.* *Isa* 29:14
repentance shall *be h.* *Hos* 13:14
though they *be h.* *Amos* 9:3
drunken, thou shalt *be h.* *Nah* 3:11
shall *be h.* in the day. *Zeph* 2:3
if our gospel *be h.* it is. *2 Cor* 4:3*

not be **hid**

on an hill *cannot be h.* *Mat* 5:14
he entered into an house, but he could *not be h.* *Mark* 7:24
otherwise *cannot be h.* *1 Tim* 5:25

not **hid**

fathers, and *not h.* it. *Job* 15:18
iniquity have I *not h.* *Ps* 32:5
and my groaning is *not h.* 38:9
not h. thy righteousness. 40:10
and my sins are *not h.* from. 69:5
substance was *not h.* when. 139:15
they are *not h.* from my face, neither is iniquity hid from. *Jer* 16:17
Israel is *not h.* from me. *Hos* 5:3
saw that she was *not h.* *Luke* 8:47

Hiddekel

the third river is *H.* *Gen* 2:14
the side of the river *H.* *Dan* 10:4

hidden

if it be *h.* from him, he. *Lev* 5:2
it is not *h.* from thee. *Deut* 30:11
as an *h.* untimely birth. *Job* 3:16
number of years is *h.* to the. 15:20*
seeing times are not *h.* from. 24:1
in *h.* part shalt make me. *Ps* 51:6
wicked rise, a man is *h.* *Pr* 28:12
I will give thee *h.* riches. *Isa* 45:3
shewed thee new things, *h.* 48:6
how are his *h.* things sought! *Ob* 6
of these things are *h.* *Acts* 26:26
h. wisdom which God. *1 Cor* 2:7
will bring to light the *h.* things. 4:5
have renounced *h.* things. *2 Cor* 4:2
but let it be the *h.* man. *1 Pet* 3:4
I give to eat of the *h.* *Rev* 2:17

hidden *ones*

against thy *h. ones.* *Ps* 83:3

hide, *substantive*

his *h.* and flesh he. *Lev* 8:17*; 9:11*

hide

shall I *h.* from Abraham? *Gen* 18:17
we will not *h.* it from my. 47:18
she could not longer *h.* him. *Ex* 2:3
any ways *h.* their eyes. *Lev* 20:4
go astray, *h.* thyself. *Deut* 22:1, 4
lost things, thou mayest not *h.* 3
and *h.* yourselves there. *Josh* 2:16
tell what thou hast done, *h.* it. 7:19
to *h.* the wheat from. *Judg* 6:11
h. it not from me, if thou *h.* *1 Sam* 3:17; *2 Sam* 14:18
secret place, and *h.* *1 Sam* 19:2
why should my father *h.*? 20:2
let me go, that I may *h.* myself. 5
the place where thou didst *h.* 19
h. thyself by the brook. *1 Ki* 17:3
chamber to *h.* 22:25; *2 Chr* 18:24
then will I not *h.* myself. *Job* 13:20
O that thou wouldest *h.* me. 14:13
he *h.* it under his tongue. 20:12
from his purpose, and *h.* *Job* 33:17
h. them in the dust together. 40:13
h. me under the shadow. *Ps* 17:8
h. me in his pavilion, in secret of his tabernacle shall he *h.* me. 27:5*
thou didst *h.* thy face and I. 30:7
thou shalt *h.* them in secret. 31:20
and *h.* not thyself from my. 55:1
h. me from the secret counsel. 64:2
we will not *h.* them from their. 78:4
O Lord, wilt thou *h.* thyself? 89:46
h. not thy commandments. 119:19
I flee to thee to *h.* me. 143:9
h. my commandments. *Pr* 2:1*
I will *h.* my eyes from you. *Isa* 1:15
and *h.* thee in the dust, for. 2:10
they *h.* not their sin. 3:9
h. the outcasts. 16:3
h. thyself as it were for a. 26:20
to them that seek deep to *h.* 29:15
that thou *h.* not thyself from. 58:7
and *h.* it there in a hole. *Jer* 13:4
I commanded thee to *h.* there. 6
h. thee, thou, and Jeremiah. 36:19
ask thee a thing, *h.* nothing. 38:14
h. it not from us. 25
h. them in the clay. 43:9
h. not thine ear at my. *Lam* 3:56
no secret they can *h.* *Ezek* 28:3
garden of God could not *h.* 31:8
neither will I *h.* my face. 39:29
and shall *h.* a multitude. *Jas* 5:20
h. us from the face of him. *Rev* 6:16
see **face**

hide *himself*

doth not David *h. himself*? *1 Sam* 23:19; 26:1
can any *h. himself* in? *Jer* 23:24
not be able to *h. himself.* 49:10
Jesus did *h. himself.* *John* 12:36

hide *themselves*

they that *h. themselves.* *Deut* 7:20
people did *h. themselves* in caves. *1 Sam* 13:6
to *h. themselves* in field. *2 Ki* 7:12
the earth *h. themselves.* *Job* 24:4
iniquity may *h. themselves.* 34:22
they *h. themselves,* they. *Ps* 56:6
rise, men *h. themselves.* *Pr* 28:28
fled to *h. themselves.* *Dan* 10:7
h. themselves in top of. *Amos* 9:3

hidest

wherefore *h.* thou thy face? *Job* 13:24; *Ps* 44:24; 88:14
why *h.* thyself in times? *Ps* 10:1
thou *h.* thy face, they are. 104:29
art a God that *h.* thyself. *Isa* 45:15

hideth

places where he *h.* *1 Sam* 23:23
he *h.* himself on the right. *Job* 23:9
when he *h.* his face, who? 34:29
who is he that *h.* counsel? 42:3
he *h.* his face, he will. *Ps* 10:11
yea, the darkness *h.* not. 139:12
he that *h.* hatred with. *Pr* 10:18
slothful *h.* his hand. 19:24*; 26:15*
man foreseeth and *h.* 22:3; 27:12
whosoever *h.* her, *h.* the. 27:16*
he that *h.* his eyes shall. 28:27
that *h.* his face from the. *Isa* 8:17
a man hath found, he *h.* *Mat* 13:44

hiding

by *h.* mine iniquity in. *Job* 31:33
my *h.* place. *Ps* 32:7; 119:114
shall overflow the *h.* *Isa* 28:17
man shall be as an *h.* place. 32:2
and there was the *h.* of. *Hab* 3:4

Hiel

H. the Beth-elite built. *1 Ki* 16:34

Higgaion

snared in his work *H.* *Ps* 9:16

high

[1] *Lofty, tall, elevated,* Deut 3:5; Esth 5:14. [2] *Advanced,* Gen 29:7. [3] *Exalted in rank or dignity,* Deut 26:19; Ps 62:9. [4] *Arrogant, boastful,* Ps 18:27; Isa 10:12. [5] *High places were the altars built, according to custom, on conspicuous places. They are usually thought of as places of idolatry, and certainly were such in later times.*

lo, it is yet *h.* day. *Gen* 29:7
Israel went out with *h.* hand. *Ex* 14:8; *Num* 33:3
quails as it were two cubits *h.* *Num* 11:31*
were fenced with *h.* walls. *Deut* 3:5
gods on the *h.* mountains. 12:2
and to make thee *h.* above. 26:19
get up above thee very *h.* 28:43*
till thy *h.* and fenced walls. 52
should say, our hand is *h.* 32:27*
at this house which is *h.* *1 Ki* 9:8
estate of a man of *h.* *1 Chr* 17:17
this house is *h.* shall be. *2 Chr* 7:21
a gallows be made of fifty cubits *h.* *Esth* 5:14; 7:9
it is as *h.* as heaven. *Job* 11:8
he judgeth those that are *h.* 21:22
behold the stars, how *h.* 22:12
and the *h.* arm shall be. 38:15
he beholdeth all *h.* things. 41:34
wilt bring down *h.* looks. *Ps* 18:27*
give ear, both low and *h.* 49:2
men of *h.* degree are a lie. 62:9
also, O God, is very *h.* 71:19
built his sanctuary like *h.* 78:69*
strong is thy hand, *h.* is thy. 89:13
thou, Lord, art *h.* above earth. 97:9
99:2; 113:4
him that hath an *h.* look and. 101:5
for as the heaven is *h.* 103:11
I exercise in things too *h.* 131:1*
though the Lord be *h.* yet. 138:6
such knowledge, it is *h.* 139:6
let the *h.* praises of God be in. 149:6
praise him on *h.* sounding. 150:5
and as an *h.* wall in his. *Pr* 18:11
an *h.* look, and a proud heart. 21:4
wisdom is too *h.* for a fool. 24:7
afraid of that which is *h.* *Eccl* 12:5
on all cedars that are *h.* *Isa* 2:13
and upon all the *h.* mountains. 14
Lord sitting on a throne *h.* 6:1
the glory of his *h.* looks. 10:12
the *h.* ones of stature shall be. 33
of the *h.* ones that are on *h.* 24:21
the fortress of *h.* fort shall. 25:12
breach swelling out in an *h.* 30:13
my servant shall be very *h.* 52:13
for thus saith the *h.* and. 57:15
a glorious *h.* throne. *Jer* 17:12
waymarks, make thee *h.* 31:21*
thou makest thy nest *h.* 49:16
h. gates shall be burnt with. 51:58
their rings they were so *h.* *Ezek* 1:18
brought down the *h.* tree. 17:24
low, and abase him that is *h.* 21:26
behold the Assyrian was of *h.* 31:3
I will feed them on the *h.* 34:14
the two horns were *h.* *Dan* 8:3
whose habitation is *h.* that. *Ob* 3
against the *h.* towers. *Zeph* 1:16
sabbath day was an *h.* *John* 19:31
with an *h.* arm brought. *Acts* 13:17
mind not *h.* things. *Rom* 12:16
it is *h.* time. 13:11
casting down every *h.* *2 Cor* 10:5
for the prize of the *h.* *Phil* 3:14
had a wall great and *h.* *Rev* 21:12
see **gate, God, hill, hills**

most **High**

knowledge of *most H.* *Num* 24:16
when the *most H.* divided to the. *Deut* 32:8
the *most H.* uttered. *2 Sam* 22:14
sing praise to the name of the Lord *most H.* *Ps* 7:17; 9:2; 92:1
through mercy of the *most H.* 21:7
the tabernacle of the *most H.* 46:4
the Lord *most H.* is terrible. 47:2
pay thy vows to the *most H.* 50:14
against me, O thou *most H.* 56:2*
I will cry unto God *most H.* 57:2
knowledge in the *most H.*? 73:11
the right hand of the *most H.* 77:10
by provoking the *most H.* 78:17, 56
the children of the *most H.* 82:6
that thou art *most H.* over. 83:18
secret place of the *most H.* 91:1
thou hast made the *most H.* thy. 9
but thou, Lord, art *most H.* 92:8

the counsel of the *most H.* Ps 107:11
I will be like the *most H.* Isa 14:14
the face of the *most H.* Lam 3:35
of mouth of *most H.* proceedeth. 38
that the *most H.* ruleth. Dan 4:17
this is the decree of the *most H.* 24
most H. ruleth in kingdom. 25, 32
and I blessed the *most H.* and. 34
the saints of *most H.* shall. 7:18
was given to the saints of *most H.* 22
great words against the *most H.* 25
of the saints of the *most H.* 27
but not to the *most H.* Hos 7:16
called them to the *most H.* 11:7
the *most H.* dwelleth not. Acts 7:48
see **mountain**

on **high**

stretch wings *on h.* Ex 25:20; 37:9
of blue, to fasten it *on h.* 39:31*
God will set thee *on h.* Deut 28:1
hast lifted me up *on h.* 2 Sam 22:49
man who was raised up *on h.* 23:1
set Naboth *on h.* 1 Ki 21:9, 12
hast thou lifted up thine eyes *on h.*? 2 Ki 19:22; Isa 37:23
kingdom was lifted up *on h.* 1 Chr 14:2
praise God of Israel *on h.* 2 Chr 20:19*
to set up *on h.* those. Job 5:11
and my record is *on h.* 16:19
of the Almighty from *on h.*? 31:2
she lifteth up herself *on h.* 39:18
up and make her nest *on h.*? 27
sakes therefore return *on h.* Ps 7:7
thou hast ascended *on h.* 68:18
O God, set me up *on h.* 69:29
lift not up your horn *on h.* 75:5
I will set him *on h.* because. 91:14
the Lord *on h.* is mightier. 93:4
setteth he the poor *on h.* 107:41
our God, who dwelleth *on h.*? 113:5
out a sepulchre *on h.* Isa 22:16
for the windows from *on h.* 24.18
host of high ones that are *on h.* 21
down them that dwell *on h.* 26:5
be poured on us from *on h.* 32:15
he dwelleth *on h.* 33:5
he shall dwell *on h.* 16
lift up your eyes *on h.* and. 40:26
voice to be heard *on h.* 58:4
shall roar from *on h.* Jer 25:30
deep set him up *on h.* Ezek 31:4*
may set his nest *on h.* Hab 2:9
lifted up his hands *on h.* 3:10
dayspring from *on h.* Luke 1:78
endued with power from *on h.* 24:49
he ascended up *on h.* Eph 4:8
of the Majesty *on h.* Heb 1:3
see **place, places, priest, tower**

higher

his king shall be *h.* Num 24:7
Saul was *h.* than any of. 1 Sam 9:2
Jotham built *h.* gate of. 2 Ki 15:35*
on the *h.* places, I even. Neh 4:13*
clouds, which are *h.* Job 35:5
to the rock that is *h.* than I. Ps 61:2
make him *h.* than kings. 89:27*
regardeth, and there be *h.* Eccl 5:8
are *h.* than earth, so my ways *h.* than your ways, thoughts. Isa 55:9
read Baruch in the *h.* Jer 36:10*
from the way of the *h.* Ezek 9:2*
for the galleries were *h.* than. 42:5
and this shall be the *h.* place. 43:13*
one horn *h.* than other, *h.* Dan 8:3
to thee, Friend, go up *h.* Luke 14:10
soul be subject to the *h.* Rom 13:1
an High Priest made *h.* Heb 7:26

highest

Lord thundered, the *H.* Ps 18:13
H. himself shall establish her. 87:5
nor the *h.* part of the dust. Pr 8:26*
she crieth upon the *h.* places. 9:3
is higher than the *h.* Eccl 5:8
and took the *h.* branch. Ezek 17:3
I will take of the *h.* branch. 22
from lowest chamber to the *h.* 41:7
saying, Hosanna in the *h.* Mat 21:9
Mark 11:10
called the Son of the *H.* Luke 1:32
the power of the *H.* shall. 35
called the prophet of the *H.* 76

glory to God in the *h.* Luke 2:14
19:38
shall be the children of the *H.* 6:35
sit not down in the *h.* room. 14:8
and love the *h.* seats in. 20:46*

highly

angel said, thou art *h.* Luke 1:28
that which is *h.* esteemed. 16:15*
Herod was *h.* displeased. Acts 12:20
think of himself more *h.* Rom 12:3
wherefore God also hath *h.* Phil 2:9
to esteem them very *h.* 1 Thes 5:13

highminded

be not *h.* but fear. Rom 11:20
1 Tim 6:17
traitors, heady, *h.* 2 Tim 3:4*

highness

by reason of his *h.* I. Job 31:23*
that rejoice in my *h.* Isa 13:3*

highway, -s

and your *h.* shall be. Lev 26:22
by king's *h.* Num 20:17, 19; 21:22
Deut 2:27
in days of Jael *h.* were. Judg 5:6
to kill the people in the *h.* 20:31
and draw them unto the *h.* 32
gleaned of them in the *h.* 45
kine went along the *h.* 1 Sam 6:12
wallowed in blood in *h.* 2 Sam 20:12
h. of fuller's field. 2 Ki 18:17
Isa 7:3; 36:2
h. of upright to depart. Pr 16:17
an *h.* for the remnant. Isa 11:16
shall be *h.* out of Egypt to. 19:23
h. lie waste, wayfaring man. 33:8
and an *h.* shall be there. 35:8
make in the desert a *h.* for. 40:3
and my *h.* shall be exalted. 49:11
cast up, cast up the *h.* 62:10
heart toward the *h.* Jer 31:21
shall say in all the *h.* Amos 5:16*
go therefore into the *h.* Mat 22:9
Luke 14:23
Bartimaeus sat by *h.* Mark 10:46

Hilkiah

Eliakim son of *H.* 2 Ki 18:18
Eliakim son of *H.* to Hezekiah. 37
Isa 36:22
saying, Go up to *H.* 2 Ki 22:4
H. gave book to. 8, 10; 2 Chr 34:15
H. to enquire of the Lord for him. 2 Ki 22:12; 2 Chr 34:20
so *H.* went to Huldah. 2 Ki 22:14
2 Chr 34:22
commanded *H.* to bring 2 Ki 23:4
Shallum begat *H.* and *H.* 1 Chr 6:13
H. son of Amaziah. 45
H. son of Meshullam. 9:11
H. the second son of Hosah. 26:11
H. the son of Shallum. Ezra 7:1
H. stood on Ezra's right. Neh 8:4
Seraiah the son of *H.* dwelt. 11:11
H. the priest went up with. 12:7
of *H.*, Hashabiah were priests. 21
servant Eliakim son of *H.* Isa 22:20
Jeremiah the son of *H.* Jer 1:1
son of *H.* was sent to Babylon. 29:3

hill

built an altar under the *h.* Ex 24:4*
which dwelt in that *h.* Num 14:45*
were ready to go up into the *h.* Deut 1:41*, 43*
circumcised Israel at *h.* Josh 5:3
they said, The *h.* is not. 17:16*
Joshua buried on the *h.* Gaash. 24:30*; Judg 2:9
Eleazar was buried in *h.* Josh 24:33
Midianites were by *h.* Judg 7:1
house of Abinadab in *h.* 1 Sam 7:1
his servants went up the *h.* 9:11*
shalt come to *h.* of God. 10:5, 10
hid in *h.* of Hachilah. 23:19; 26:1
came down by covert of *h.* 25:20*
they were come to *h.* 2 Sam 2:24
much people came by the *h.* 13:34
Shimei went along on the *h.* 16:13
they hanged them in the *h.* 21:9*
Solomon built in the *h.* 1 Ki 11:7*
the *h.* Samaria, built on *h.* 16:24
to man of God to the *h.* 2 Ki 4:27
who shall ascend into the *h.*? Ps 24:3
remember thee from the *h.* 42:6

h. of God is as the *h.* of. Ps 68:15*
this is the *h.* which God. 16*
I will get me to the *h.* S of S 4:6
vineyard in a very fruitful *h.* Isa 5:1
shake his head against *h.* 10:32
be left an ensign on an *h.* 30:17
hosts shall fight for the *h.* 31:4
every mountain and *h.* shall. 40:4
hunt them from every *h.* Jer 16:16
measuring line upon the *h.* 31:39
holdest the height of the *h.* 49:16
gone from mountain to *h.* 50:6
make places about my *h.* Ezek 34:26
city that is set on an *h.* Mat 5:14
and every *h.* shall be. Luke 3:5
led him unto the brow of the *h.* 4:29
were come down from the *h.* 9:37*
the midst of Mars' *h.* Acts 17:22*

high **hill, -s**

all *high h.* under heaven. Gen 7:19
groves on every *high h.* 1 Ki 14:23
2 Ki 17:10
is a *high h.* as the hill. Ps 68:15
why leap ye, ye *high h.*? this is. 16
high h. are a refuge for the. 104:18
every *high h.*, rivers. Isa 30:25
when on every *high h.* Jer 2:20, 23
remember groves on *high h.* 17:2
idols on every *high h.* Ezek 6:13
then they saw every *high h.* 20:28
wandered on every *high h.* 34:6

holy **hill**

on my *holy h.* of Zion. Ps 2:6
he heard me out of his *holy h.* 3:4
shall dwell in thy *holy h.*? 15:1
me, bring me to thy *holy h.* 43:3
worship at his *holy h.* the. 99:9

hill, with *top*

stand on *top* of the *h.* Ex 17:9
Hur, went to *top* of the *h.* 10
to go up to the *h. top.* Num 14:44
them to the *top* of an *h.* Judg 16:3*
David stood on the *top* of an *h.* 1 Sam 26:13*
Abner stood on the *top* of an *h.* 2 Sam 2:25
little past the *top* of the *h.* 16:1*
sat on the *top* of an *h.* 2 Ki 1:9

hill country

inhabitants of *h. country.* Josh 13:6
of Aaron, Arba in *h. country.* 21:11
down into *h. country.* Luke 1:39
noised through all the *h. country.* 65

hills

of the everlasting *h.* Gen 49:26
and from the *h.* I behold. Num 23:9
out of the valleys and *h.* Deut 8:7
out of whose *h.* thou mayest. 9
it is a land of *h.* and valleys. 11:11
precious things of lasting *h.* 33:15
smote all country of *h.* Josh 10:40*
took all that land, the *h.* 11:16*
the gods of the *h.* 1 Ki 20:23, 28
all Israel scattered on the *h.* 22:17*
burnt incense on the *h.* 2 Ki 16:4
2 Chr 28:4
thou made before the *h.*? Job 15:7
foundations also of the *h.* Ps 18:7*
cattle on a thousand *h.* are. 50:10
the little *h.* rejoice on every. 65:12
the little *h.* by righteousness. 72:3
h. were covered with shadow. 80:10*
strength of the *h.* is his also. 95:4
the *h.* melted like wax at. 97:5†
let the *h.* be joyful together. 98:8
springs, which run among *h.* 104:10*
he watereth the *h.* from his. 13*
he toucheth the *h.* and they. 32*
and the little *h.* skipped. 114:4, 6
I will lift up mine eyes to *h.* 121:1
mountains and all *h.* praise. 148:9
before the *h.* was I brought. Pr 8:25
skipping upon the *h.* S of S 2:8
be exalted above the *h.* Isa 2:2
day of the Lord shall be on all *h.* 14
h. did tremble, their carcases. 5:25
on all *h.* shall not come the. 7:25
who hath weighed the *h.* in? 40:12
and thou shalt make the *h.* 41:15
make waste mountains and *h.* 42:15
mountains shall depart, *h.* 54:10
the *h.* shall break forth. 55:12

blasphemed me upon the *h.* *Isa* 65:7
salvation hoped for from *h.* *Jer* 3:23
I beheld, and lo, the *h.* moved. 4:24
thy abominations on the *h.* 13:27
saith Lord to the *h.* *Ezek* 6:3; 36:4
in thy *h.* shall slain fall. 35:8
and say to the *h.* to the rivers. 36:6
burn incense on the *h.* *Hos* 4:13
and they shall say to the *h.* 10:8
and the *h.* shall flow with. *Joel* 3:18
wine, and all the *h.* *Amos* 9:13
be exalted above the *h.* *Mi* 4:1
arise, and let the *h.* hear thy. 6:1
the *h.* melt, and earth. *Nah* 1:5
perpetual *h.* did bow. *Hab* 3:6
great crashing from the *h.* *Zeph* 1:10
begin to say to the *h.* *Luke* 23:30

him

me he restored, and *h.* *Gen* 41:13
whosoever hath sinned, *h.* *Ex* 32:33
Caleb, *h.* will I bring. *Num* 14:24
to come near, even *h.* whom. 16:5
h. shalt thou serve, and to *h.* *Deut* 10:20
the Lord hath chosen *h.* and. 18:5
see ye *h.* whom Lord. *1 Sam* 10:24
h. that dieth in city. *1 Ki* 14:11; 16:4; 21:24
h. that pisseth against the wall. 21:21; *2 Ki* 9:8
they hid *h.* even *h.* and. *2 Ki* 11:2
and *h.* that followed her, kill. 15
h. shall ye fear, *h.* shall ye. 17:36
h. did outlandish women. *Neh* 13:26
h. they have hanged on. *Esth* 8:7
not *h.* that is deceived. *Job* 15:31
h. that had none to help *h.* 29:12
behold, who teacheth like *h.*? 36:22
thunder with a voice like *h.*? 40:9
Job shall pray for you, for *h.* 42:8
Lord hath set apart *h.* *Ps* 4:3
h. shall he teach in the way. 25:12
worship *h.* 45:11
h. that hath no helper. 72:12
h. will I cut off, *h.* that hath. 101:5
h. that soweth discord. *Pr* 6:19
h. shall the people curse. 24:24
a little folly *h.* that is in. *Eccl* 10:1
h. that offereth in the. *Jer* 48:35
and cut off from it *h.* *Ezek* 35:7
and *h.* that holdeth the. *Amos* 1:5
cut off *h.* that offereth. *Mal* 2:12
h. only shalt thou serve. *Mat* 4:10; *Luke* 4:8
confess me before men, *h.* will I confess also. *Mat* 10:32; *Luke* 12:8
h. will I deny before my. *Mat* 10:33
h. that sent me. 40; *Mark* 9:37
this is my Son, hear ye *h.* *Mat* 17:5; *Acts* 3:22; 7:37
go tell *h.* between *h.* and. *Mat* 18:15
nor let *h.* in the field return. 24:18; *Mark* 13:6
h. they compelled to. *Mat* 27:32
let *h.* that readeth. *Mark* 13:14
let *h.* that is on the housetop. 15
h. that for sedition and. *Luke* 23:25
but *h.* they saw not. 24:24
whom he hath sent, *h.* *John* 5:38
come in his own name, *h.* ye. 43
h. hath God the Father sealed. 6:27
h. that cometh unto me, I will. 37
h. he heareth. 9:31
h. will my Father honour. 12:26
God shall also glorify *h.* in. 13:32
h. being delivered. *Acts* 2:23
h. God exalted. 5:31
h. God raised up the third. 10:40
h. would Paul have to go forth with *h.* 16:3
whom ye worship *h.* declare. 17:23
h. that is weak in faith. *Rom* 14:1
let not *h.* that eateth, despise *h.* 3
defile temple, *h.* shall. *1 Cor* 3:17
h. that thinketh he standeth. 10:12
for he hath made *h.* to. *2 Cor* 5:21
let *h.* that is taught in the. *Gal* 6:6
let *h.* that stole steal no. *Eph* 4:28
h. therefore I hope to. *Phil* 2:23
receive *h.* therefore in the Lord. 29
h. whose coming is. *2 Thes* 2:9
might destroy *h.* that. *Heb* 2:14
sprang there of one, and *h.* 11:12

about **him**

his servants were standing *about h.* *1 Sam* 22:6, 7
the footmen that stood *about h.* 17
wars which were *about h.* *1 Ki* 5:3
compassed *about h.* to. *2 Chr* 18:31
made an hedge *about h.*? *Job* 1:10
let all round *about h.* *Ps* 76:11
in reverence of all *about h.* 89:7
all ye that are *about h.* *Jer* 48:17
be a dismaying to all *about h.* 39
devour all round *about h.* 50:32
shall be round *about h.* *Lam* 1:17
scatter all that are *about h.* to help him. *Ezek* 12:14
his graves are round *about h.* 32:22, 25, 26
great multitudes *about h.* *Mat* 8:18
multitude sat *about h.* *Mark* 3:32
the Jews round *about h.* *John* 10:24
each six wings *about h.* *Rev* 4:8

above **him**

shall be strong *above h.* *Dan* 11:5

after **him**

with his seed *after h.* *Gen* 17:19
his household *after h.* 18:19
be a statute for his seed *after h.* *Ex* 28:43
shall be his son's *after h.* 29:29
that go a whoring *after h.* *Lev* 20:5
turn away from *after h.* *Num* 32:15
of blood pursue *after h.* *Josh* 20:5
fled, they pursued *after h.* *Judg* 1:6
they went *after h.* and took. 3:28
was gathered *after h.* 6:34, 35
armourbearer *after h.* *1 Sam* 14:13
I went out *after h.* and. 17:35
saw that Saul came *after h.* 26:3
followed hard *after h.* *2 Sam* 1:6
and all the people *after h.* 15:17
the people returned *after h.* 23:10
on the throne of my lord *after h.* *1 Ki* 1:20, 27
to set up his son *after h.* 15:4
I will run *after h.* and. *2 Ki* 5:20
Jehu followed *after h.* and. 9:27
sent *after h.* to. 14:19; *2 Chr* 25:27
so that *after h.* was none like him. *2 Ki* 18:5; 23:25
Zebadiah his son *after h.* *1 Chr* 27:7
priest went in *after h.* *2 Chr* 26:17
after h. repaired. *Neh* 3:16
So to the 31st *verse*
they that come *after h.* *Job* 18:20
he in his house *after h.* 21:21
every man shall draw *after h.* 33
a path to shine *after h.* 41:32
not descend *after h.* *Ps* 49:17
children are blessed *after h.* *Pr* 20:7
bring to see what shall be *after h.* *Eccl* 3:22; 6:12
should find nothing *after h.* 7:14
what shall be *after h.* who? 10:14
after h. through the city. *Ezek* 9:5
sent a message *after h.* *Luke* 19:14
world is gone *after h.* *John* 12:19
much people *after h.* *Acts* 5:37
to him, and to his seed *after h.* 7:5
if haply they might feel *after h.* 17:27
which should come *after h.* 19:4

against **him**

man's hand *against h.* *Gen* 16:12
he prevailed not *against h.* 32:25
they conspired *against h.* 37:18
1 Ki 15:27; 16:9; *2 Ki* 14:19; 15:10, 25; 21:23
which ye murmur *against h.* *Ex* 16:8; *Num* 14:36; 16:11
an adversary *against h.* *Num* 22:22
man rise up *against h.* *Deut* 19:11
witness rise to testify *against h.* 16
loins that rise *against h.* 33:11
a man over *against h.* *Josh* 5:13
lion roared *against h.* *Judg* 14:5
Philistines shouted *against h.* 15:14
Lord said, Go up *against h.* 20:23
battle was *against h.* *2 Sam* 10:9
put forth *against h.* dried. *1 Ki* 13:4
to bear witness *against h.* 21:10
went up *against h.* *2 Ki* 23:29
Lord sent *against h.* bands of. 24:2
to speak *against h.* *2 Chr* 32:17
not prevail *against h.* *Esth* 6:13
movedst me *against h.* *Job* 2:3
have sinned *against h.* 8:4
hardened himself *against h.* 9:4
prevailest for ever *against h.* 14:20
thou strive *against h.*? 33:13
what doest thou *against h.*? 35:6
sinned yet more *against h.* *Ps* 78:17
messenger shall be sent *against h.* *Pr* 17:11
if one prevail *against h.* *Eccl* 4:12
axe boast *against h.*, or saw magnify itself *against h.*? *Isa* 10:15
are called forth *against h.* 31:4
that are incensed *against h.* 45:24
lift up a standard *against h.* 59:19
we shall prevail *against h.* *Jer* 20:10
for since I spake *against h.* I. 31:20
against h. that bendeth, let. 51:3
prophesy *against h.* and Egypt. *Ezek* 29:2; 38:2
call for a sword *against h.* 38:21
I will plead *against h.* with. 22
have sinned *against h.* *Dan* 9:11
but he that cometh *against h.* 11:16
prepare war *against h.* *Mi* 3:5
I have sinned *against h.* 7:9
up a parable *against h.*? *Hab* 2:6
and held a counsel *against h.* *Mat* 12:14; *Mark* 3:6
that cometh *against h.* *Luke* 14:31
they cried so *against h.* *Acts* 22:24
what they had *against h.* 23:30
priest desired favour *against h.* 25:3
to have judgement *against h.* 15
not bring *against h.* a. *Jude* 9
sinners have spoken *against h.* 15
make war *against h.* *Rev* 19:19

at **him**

the archers shot *at h.* *Gen* 49:23
Saul cast a javelin *at h.* *1 Sam* 20:33
threw stones *at h.* and. *2 Sam* 16:13
shall clap their hands *at h.* *Job* 27:23
him that puffeth *at h.* *Ps* 12:5
the Lord shall laugh *at h.* 37:13
shall see and laugh *at h.* 52:6
do they shoot *at h.* and. 64:4
shut their mouths *at h.* *Isa* 52:15
south shall push *at h.* *Dan* 11:40
the mountains quake *at h.* *Nah* 1:5
they were offended *at h.* *Mark* 6:3
at h. they cast stones, and. 12:4
and they marvelled *at h.* 17
he marvelled *at h.* and. *Luke* 7:9
they could not come *at h.* for. 8:19
Jews then murmured *at h.* *John* 6:41
took up stones to cast *at h.* 8:59

before **him**

meat *before h.* to eat. *Gen* 24:33
messengers *before h.* to. 32:3
so went the present over *before h.* 21
and they cried *before h.* 41:43
they sat *before h.* 43:33
fell *before h.* 44:14
Lord passed by *before h.* *Ex* 34:6
have wept *before h.* *Num* 11:20
man straight *before h.* *Josh* 6:5
service of the Lord *before h.* 22:27
chased, he fled *before h.* *Judg* 9:40
wife wept *before h.* and. 14:16, 17
anointed is *before h.* *1 Sam* 16:6
came to Saul and stood *before h.* 21
a shield went *before h.* 17:7
they fled *before h.* *2 Sam* 10:13; *1 Chr* 19:14
eat and drink *before h.* *2 Sam* 11:13
they set bread *before h.* 12:20
and fifty men to run *before h.* 15:1; *1 Ki* 1:5
I was also upright *before h.* *2 Sam* 22:24; *Ps* 18:23
harlots, stood *before h.* *1 Ki* 3:16
Omri worse than all *before h.* 16:25
Ahab evil above all *before h.* 30, 33
men, sons of Belial, *before h.* 21:10
to the ground *before h.* *2 Ki* 2:15
when called, stood *before h.* 4:12
prophets were sitting *before h.* 38
king sent a man from *before h.* 6:32
kings stood not *before h.* how? 10:4
kings that were *before h.* 17:2
nor any that were *before h.* 18:5
did, which were *before h.* 21:11
there was no king *before h.* 23:25

did eat bread continually *before h.* *2 Ki* 25:29; *Jer* 52:33
and come *before h.* *1 Chr* 16:29
fear *before h.* 30; *Ps* 96:9
Eccl 3:14; 8:12
before h. like Solomon. *1 Chr* 29:5
to burn *before h.* sweet. *2 Chr* 2:4, 6
kingdom was quiet *before h.* 14:5
chosen you to stand *before h.* 29:11
that wine was *before h.* *Neh* 2:1
make a request *before h.* *Esth* 4:8
proclaim *before h.* 6:9, 11
fall *before h.* 13
I will maintain my ways *before h.* *Job* 13:15
shall not come *before h.* 16
are innumerable *before h.* 21:33
order my cause *before h.* 23:4
hell is naked *before h.* and. 26:6
judgement is *before h.* 35:14
is turned into joy *before h.* 41:22
cry came *before h.* *Ps* 18:6
brightness that was *before h.* 12
shall bow *before h.* 22:29
a fire shall devour *before h.* 50:3
pour out your heart *before h.* 62:8
that hate him flee *before h.* 68:1
God, sing and rejoice *before h.* 4
wilderness shall bow *before h.* 72:9
kings shall fall *before h.*, nations shall serve *h.* 11
righteousness shall go *before h.* 85:13
and majesty are *before h.* 96:6
worship the Lord, fear *before h.* 9
goeth *before h.* and burneth. 97:3
his chosen stood *before h.* 106:23
showed *before h.* my trouble. 142:2
rejoicing always *before h.* *Pr* 8:30
wisdom is *before h.* that hath. 17:24
reward with him, work *before h.* *Isa* 40:10; 62:11
nations *before h.* are as. 40:17
gave nations *before h.* and. 41:2
to subdue nations *before h.* 45:1
supplications *before h.* *Jer* 42:9
wilt thou say *before h.* *Ezek* 28:9
shall groan *before h.* with. 30:24
10,000 stood *before h.* *Dan* 7:10
no beasts might stand *before h.* 8:4
no power in ram to stand *before h.* 7
none shall stand *before h.* 11:16
be overflown from *before h.* 22
shall I come *before h.*? *Mi* 6:6
keep silence *before h.* *Hab* 2:20
before h. went the pestilence. 3:5
a book of remembrance written *before h.* *Mal* 3:16
before h. be gathered. *Mat* 25:32
bowed the knee *before h.* 27:29
fell down *before h.* *Mark* 3:11; 5:33
before h. in the spirit. *Luke* 1:17
and righteousness *before h.* 75
means to lay him *before h.* 5:18
I have nothing to set *before h.* 11:6
that I am sent *before h.* *John* 3:28
Paul also *before h.* *Acts* 23:33
before h. whom he believed, even. *Rom* 4:17
without blame *before h.* *Eph* 1:4
joy that was set *before h.* *Heb* 12:2
not ashamed *before h.* *1 John* 2:28
assure our hearts *before h.* 3:19
first beast *before h.* *Rev* 13:12
wrought miracles *before h.* 19:20

behind **him**

in the tent door *behind h.* *Gen* 18:10
spear came out *behind h.* *2 Sam* 2:23
his master's feet *behind h.*? *2 Ki* 6:32
leave a blessing *behind h.* *Joel* 2:14
behind h. were red horses. *Zech* 1:8
diseased with an issue of blood came *behind h.* *Mat* 9:20; *Luke* 8:44
leave his wife *behind h.* *Mark* 12:19
at his feet *behind h.* *Luke* 7:38

beside **him**

there is none *beside h.* *Deut* 4:35
his servants passed on *beside h.* *2 Sam* 15:18
beside h. stood Mattithiah. *Neh* 8:4

between **him**

Lord made *between h.* *Lev* 26:46
shall discern *between h.* *Mal* 3:18

beyond **him**

an arrow *beyond h.* *1 Sam* 20:36

by **him**

not let us pass *by h.* *Deut* 2:30
shall dwell in safety *by h.* 33:12
by h. children of Israel. *Judg* 3:15
all that stood *by h.* went out. 19
and *by h.* actions are. *1 Sam* 2:3
that evil is determined *by h.* 20:7
of heaven standing *by h.* *1 Ki* 22:19
we may enquire of the Lord *by h.* *2 Ki* 3:11; 8:8
by h. the Lord had given. 5:1
hundred slain *by h.* *1 Chr* 11:11
queen also sitting *by h.* *Neh* 2:6
the Ammonite was *by h.* 4:3
sweareth *by h.* shall glory. *Ps* 63:11
that are slain *by h.* *Isa* 27:7
by h. daily sacrifice was. *Dan* 8:11
sware *by h.* that liveth for ever. 12:7; *Rev* 10:6
rocks are thrown down *by h.* *Nah* 1:6
sweareth *by h.* who. *Mat* 23:21
sweareth *by h.* that sitteth. 22
Herod being reproved *by h.* shut up John. *Luke* 3:19
heard all that was done *by h.* 9:7
things that were done *by h.* 13:17
all things were made *by h.* *John* 1:3
the world was made *by h.* and. 10
wonders God did *by him.* *Acts* 2:22
the faith which is *by h.* 3:16; 4:10
by h. all that believe. 13:39
following the Lord stood *by h.* 23:11
ye are enriched *by h.* *1 Cor* 1:5
are all things, and we *by h.* 8:6
have been taught *by h.* *Eph* 4:21
for *by h.* were all things. *Col* 1:16
he is before all things, *by h.* all. 17
by h. to reconcile all things to himself *by h.* 20
to God the Father *by h.* 3:17
are taken captive *by h.* *2 Tim* 2:26
that come to God *by h.* *Heb* 7:25
by h. let us offer the sacrifice. 13:15
who *by h.* do believe in. *1 Pet* 1:21
are sent *by h.* for punishment. 2:14

concerning **him**

made an oath *con. h.* *Judg* 21:5
word Lord hath spoken *con. h.* *2 Ki* 19:21; *Isa* 37:22
so commanded *con. h.* *Esth* 3:2
a proclamation *con. h.* *Dan* 5:29
among people *con h.* *John* 7:12, 32
Jews did not believe *con. h.* 9:18
David speaketh *con. h.* *Acts* 2:25
enquire something *con. h.* 23:15
con. h. that hath so done. *1 Cor* 5:3

see **fear**

for **him**

an help meet *for h.* *Gen* 2:18, 20
Joseph's father wept *for h.* 37:35
I will be surety *for h.* of. 43:9
no blood shed *for h.* *Ex* 22:2
blood shed *for h.* 3
accepted *for h.* to make atonement *for h.* *Lev* 1:4; 4:26, 31; 5:13
14:18, 19, 20, 31; 15:15; 19:22
Num 5:8; 6:11; 15:28
shall ask counsel *for h.* *Num* 27:21
take no satisfaction *for h.* 35:32
lie in wait *for h.* and. *Deut* 19:11
his hands be sufficient *for h.* 33:7
he that will plead *for h.* *Judg* 6:31
shall entreat *for h.*? *1 Sam* 2:25
how he laid wait *for h.* in. 15:2
them, and Saul sent *for h.* 17:31
enquired of Lord *for h.* 22:10, 15
sought no more again *for h.* 27:4
till the land *for h.* *2 Sam* 9:10
for h. the kingdom, even *for h.* *1 Ki* 2:22
saddled *for h.* the ass, to wit. 13:23
all Israel shall mourn *for h.* 14:13
very great burning *for h.* *2 Chr* 16:14
people made no burning *for h.* 21:19
I have prepared *for h.* *Esth* 5:4
saw that he moved not *for h.* 9
there is nothing done *for h.* 6:3
gallows he had prepared *for h.* 4
talk deceitfully *for h.*? *Job* 13:7
did not I weep *for h.* that? 30:25
there is no help *for h.* *Ps* 3:2
Lord, and wait patiently *for h.* 37:7
give to God a ransom *for h.* 49:7
prayer also be made *for h.* 72:15
as *for h.* that wanteth. *Pr* 9:4, 16
he shall gather it *for h.* that. 28:8
bowels were moved *for h.* *S of S* 5:4
the Lord and look *for h.* *Isa* 8:17
for h. he will save us. 25:9
a snare *for h.* that reproveth. 29:21
are all they that wait *for h.* 30:18
his arm shall rule *for h.* 40:10
what he hath prepared *for h.* that waiteth *for h.* 64:4
shall not lament *for h.* *Jer* 22:18
my bowels are troubled *for h.* 31:20
to them that wait *for h.* *Lam* 3:25
Pharaoh make *for h.* in. *Ezek* 17:17
for h. I caused Lebanon to mourn *for h.*, and all the trees of the field fainted *for h.* 31:15
so shalt thou do *for h.* that. 45:20
nor shall she be *for h.* *Dan* 11:17
where no gin is *for h.* *Amos* 3:5
Lord nor enquired *for h.* *Zeph* 1:6
shall mourn *for h.* be in bitterness *for h.* *Zech* 12:10
not lawful *for h.* to eat. *Mat* 12:4
better *for h.* that a millstone. 18:6
Mark 9:42; *Luke* 17:2
when he looketh not *for h.* *Mat* 24:50; *Luke* 12:46
Jesus had done *for h.* *Mark* 5:20
child Jesus, to do *for h.* *Luke* 2:27
they were all waiting *for h.* 8:40
went to make ready *for h.* 9:52
made unto God *for h.* *Acts* 12:5
for I look *for h.* with. *1 Cor* 16:11
created by him and *for h.* *Col* 1:16
them that look *for h.* *Heb* 9:28

from **him**

and God went up *from h.* *Gen* 35:13
it be hid *from h.* when. *Lev* 5:3
by him, went out *from h.* *Judg* 3:19
locks, his strength went *from h.* 16:19
hid nothing *from h.* *1 Sam* 3:18
retire *from h.* *2 Sam* 11:15
went out *from h.* 13:9
thing would come *from h.* *1 Ki* 20:33
were scattered *from h.* *2 Ki* 25:5
the Lord turned *from h.* *2 Chr* 12:12
turn *from h.* that he may. *Job* 14:6
he hid his face *from h.* *Ps* 22:24
the poor *from h.* that spoileth. 35:10
have hid myself *from h.* 55:12
waiteth on God: *from h.* 62:1
of the righteous *from h.* *Isa* 5:23
hid as it were our faces *from h.* 53:3
she go *from h.* and become. *Jer* 3:1
part of hand sent *from h.* *Dan* 5:24
ye take *from h.* burdens. *Amos* 5:11
and laid his robe *from h.* *Jonah* 3:6
from h. that would borrow of thee. *Mat* 5:42
from h. shall be taken. 13:12
Mark 4:25; *Luke* 8:18
from h. that hath not shall be taken. *Mat* 25:29; *Luke* 19:26
hour might pass *from h.* *Mark* 14:35
he taketh *from h.* all. *Luke* 11:22
I am *from h.* *John* 7:29
but will flee *from h.* 10:5
soon removed *from h.* *Gal* 1:6
if we turn away *from h.* *Heb* 12:25
of compassion *from h.* *1 John* 3:17
commandment have we *from h.* 4:21
peace *from h.* which is. *Rev* 1:4

see **depart, departed**

in **him**

nations of earth shall be blessed in *h.* *Gen* 18:18
for my name is *in h.* *Ex* 23:21
Shechem put confidence *in h.* *Judg* 9:26
was no strength *in h.* *1 Sam* 28:20
no fault *in h.* 29:3; *John* 19:4, 6
in h. will I trust. *2 Sam* 22:3
Ps 91:2
he is a buckler to all that trust *in h.* *2 Sam* 22:31; *Isa* 36:6

if wickedness be *in h.* *1 Ki* 1:52
the wisdom of God was *in h.* 3:28
because *in h.* there is found. 14:13
there was no breath left *in h.* 17:17
put their trust *in h.* *1 Chr* 5:20
me, yet will I trust *in h.* *Job* 13:15
before him, trust thou *in h.* 35:14
that put their trust *in h.* *Ps* 2:12
all those that trust *in h.* 18:30
my heart trusted *in h.* and I. 28:7
our heart shall rejoice *in h.* 33:21
66:6; 149:2
man that trusteth *in h.* 34:8
none of them that trust *in h.* 22
trust also *in h.*; and he shall. 37:5
because they trust *in h.* 40
trust *in h.* at all times, ye. 62:8
shall be glad and trust *in h.* 64:10
men shall be blessed *in h.* 72:17
is no unrighteousness *in h.* 92:15
John 7:18
perceivest not *in h.* lips. *Pr* 14:7
them that put their trust *in h.* 30:5
shall not rejoice *in h.* *Eccl* 4:16
bless themselves *in h.* *Jer* 4:2
all them that trust *in h.* 46:25
his taste remained *in h.* 48:11
therefore will I hope *in h.* *Lam* 3:24
servants who trusted *in h.* *Dan* 3:28
nor any error or fault found *in h.* 6:4
none understanding *in h.* *Ob* 7
them that trust *in h.* *Nah* 1:7
soul is not upright *in h.* *Hab* 2:4
they were offended *in h.* *Mat* 13:57
do shew themselves *in h.* 14:2
no cause of death *in h.* *Luke* 23:22
in h. was life; and the life. *John* 1:4
whosoever believeth *in h.* 3:15, 16
Acts 10:43
shall be *in h.* a well of. *John* 4:14
dwelleth in me, and I *in h.* 6:56
10:38; 15:5
his brethren believe *in h.* 7:5
there is no truth *in h.* 8:44
made manifest *in h.* 9:3
no light *in h.* 11:10
God is glorified *in h.* 13:31
if God be glorified *in h.* 32
in h. we live, move. *Acts* 17:28
they believe *in h.* of. *Rom* 10:14
in h. shall the Gentiles trust. 15:12
of man which is *in h.* *1 Cor* 2:11
all things, we *in h.* 8:6; *1 John* 5:20
nay, but *in h.* was yea. *2 Cor* 1:19, 20
righteousness of God *in h.* 5:21
for we are weak *in h.* but. 13:4
chosen us *in h.* *Eph* 1:4
gather together; even *in h.* 10
Christ, and be found *in h.* *Phil* 3:9
that *in h.* should all. *Col* 1:19; 2:9
so walk ye *in h.* 2:6
rooted and built up *in h.* 7
in h. dwelleth the fulness of the. 9
ye are complete *in h.* who is the. 10
I will put my trust *in h.* *Heb* 2:13
shall have no pleasure *in h.* 10:38
the truth is not *in h.* *1 John* 2:4
in h. verily is love of God perfected,
hereby know we that we are *in h.* 5
he that saith he abideth *in h.* 6
thing is true *in h.* and in you. 8
none occasion of stumbling *in h.* 10
the Father is not *in h.* 15; 3:17
you, ye shall abide *in h.* 27, 28
man that hath this hope *in h.* 3:3
in h. is no sin. 5
who abideth *in h.* sinneth not. 6
for his seed remaineth *in h.* he. 9
hath eternal life abiding *in h.* 15
dwelleth *in h.* and he *in h.* 24; 4:13
15, 16
confidence that we have *in h.* 5:14

into **him**

child's soul come *into h.* *1 Ki* 17:21
soul of the child came *into h.* 22
many devils were entered *into h.*
Luke 8:30
Satan entered *into h.* *John* 13:27
may grow up *into h.* in. *Eph* 4:15

of **him**

Lord was entreated *of h.* *Gen* 25:21
beware *of h.* and obey. *Ex* 23:21
not what is become *of h.* 32:1, 23
flesh *of h.* hath issue. *Lev* 15:7, 33
take thou no usury *of h.* 25:36
but by the blood *of h.* *Num* 35:33
I will require it *of h.* *Deut* 18:19
not be afraid *of h.* 22; *2 Ki* 1:15
heart fail because *of h.* *1 Sam* 17:32
and take somewhat *of h.* *2 Ki* 5:20
shall be for the life *of h.* 10:24
of h. came the chief. *1 Chr* 5:2
they were the ruin *of h.* *2 Chr* 28:23
he was entreated *of h.* 33:13, 19
to seek *of h.* a right way. *Ezra* 8:21
eye *of h.* hath seen me. *Job* 7:8
despised in the thought *of h.* 12:5
is the place *of h.* that knoweth. 18:21
consider, I am afraid *of h.* 23:15
not thyself because *of h.* *Ps* 37:7
mouth craveth it *of h.* *Pr* 16:26
wise child, shall have joy *of h.* 23:24
of a fool than *of h.* 26:12; 29:20
take a pledge *of h.* for a. 27:13
shall the work say *of h.* *Isa* 29:16
feet *of h.* bringeth good tidings.
52:7; *Nah* 1:15
will not make mention *of h.* *Jer* 20:9
be not afraid *of h.* saith the. 42:11
as the punishment *of h.* *Ezek* 14:10
Babylon hath taken oath *of h.* 17:13
no pleasure in the death *of h.* 18:32
nations also heard *of h.* he. 19:4
in the hand *of h.* that slayeth. 28:9
take hold of skirt *of h.* *Zech* 8:23
I will encamp because *of h.* 9:8
as it is written *of h.* *Mat* 26:24
Mark 9:13; 14:21
in a dream because *of h.* *Mat* 27:19
should tell no man *of h.* *Mark* 8:30
of h. shall Son of man be ashamed.
38; *Luke* 9:26
of h. that taketh thy. *Luke* 6:30
much given, *of h.* shall much. 12:48
ye *of h.* whom Father. *John* 10:36
the justifier *of h.* that. *Rom* 3:26
not of works but *of h.* that. 9:11
it is not *of h.* that willeth, but. 16
for *of h.* and through him. 11:36
of h. are ye in Christ. *1 Cor* 1:30
shew forth praises *of h.* *1 Pet* 2:9
ye may be found *of h.* *2 Pet* 3:14
we have heard *of h.* *1 John* 1:5
which we have received *of h.* 2:27
doeth righteousness is born *of h.* 29
all kindreds of the earth shall wail
because *of h.* *Rev* 1:7

on, or *upon* **him**

whatsoever is laid *upon h.* *Ex* 21:30
his uncleanness *upon h.* *Lev* 7:20
if her flowers be *upon h.* he. 15:24
and not suffer sin *upon h.* 19:17
his blood shall be *upon h.* 20:9
oil of his God is *upon h.* 21:12
spirit that was *upon h.* *Num* 11:25
his iniquity shall be *upon h.* 15:31
seeing him not, cast it *upon h.* 35:23
shall be first *upon h.* *Deut* 13:9
witnesses shall be first *upon h.* 17:7
written in this book *upon h.* 29:20
if any hand be *upon h.* *Josh* 2:19
the Spirit of the Lord came *upon h.*
Judg 3:10; 14:6, 19; 15:14
Num 24:2; *1 Sam* 10:10, 19:23
Philistines be *upon h.* *1 Sam* 18:17
I will come *upon h.* *2 Sam* 17:2
an oath be laid *upon h.* *1 Ki* 8:31
2 Chr 6:22
saying, Lay hold *on h.* *1 Ki* 13:4
shut the door *upon h.* *2 Ki* 4:21
head of Elisha stand *on h.* 6:31
the people trode upon *h.* in. 7:17, 20
there was wrath *upon h.* *2 Chr* 32:25
Lord his God *upon h.* *Ezra* 7:6, 9
set thy heart *upon h.* *Job* 7:17
destroyer shall come *upon h.* 15:21
wicked shall come *upon h.* 20:22
and shall rain it *upon h.* while. 23
cometh, terrors are *upon h.* 25
when trouble cometh *upon h.*? 27:9
I will call *upon h.* as. *Ps* 116:2
nigh to all that call *upon h.* 145:18
I will pour water *upon h.* *Isa* 44:3
of our peace was *upon h.* 53:5
seek the Lord, call ye *upon h.* 55:6
and he will have mercy *upon h.* 7
have mercy *upon h.* *Jer* 31:20
will I spread *upon h.* *Ezek* 12:13
be *upon h.*, wickedness of the wicked
shall be *upon h.* 18:20
gray hairs are here and there *upon h.*
Hos 7:9
shall leave his blood *upon h.* 12:14
put my Spirit *upon h.* *Mat* 12:18
and they spit *upon h.* and. 27:30
and *on h.* they laid the. *Luke* 23:26
it abode *upon h.* *John* 1:32
remaining *on h.* 33
on h. is not condemned. 3:18; 5:24
6:40; *Rom* 9:33; *1 Pet* 2:6
look *on h.* whom they. *John* 19:37
Saul set his eyes *on h.* *Acts* 13:9
not only to believe *on h.* *Phil* 1:29
had mercy *on h.* and not *on h.* 2:27
took not *on h.* the nature. *Heb* 2:16
that sat *on h.* *Rev* 6:2, 5, 8; 19:11
and he set a seal *upon h.* 20:3

over **him**

thou shalt rule *over h.* *Gen* 4:7
and confess *over h.* all. *Lev* 16:21
thou shalt not rule *over h.* 25:43, 53
people wept again *over h.* *2 Sam* 3:34
they mourned *over h.* *1 Ki* 13:30
burnt the king's house *over h.* 16:18
a wicked man *over h.* *Ps* 109:6
spread their net *over h.* *Ezek* 19:8
times pass *over h.* *Dan* 4:16, 23
made lamentation *over h.* *Acts* 8:2
no more dominion *over h.* *Rom* 6:9
let them pray *over h.* *Jas* 5:14

through **him**

that all men *through h.* *John* 1:7
that the world *through h.* 3:17
be saved from wrath, *through h.*
Rom 5:9
than conquerors *through h.* 8:37
of him, *through h.* and to him. 11:36
through h. we have access. *Eph* 2:18
sent his Son, that we might live
through h. *1 John* 4:9

to, or *unto* **him**

to Seth, *to h.* also there. *Gen* 4:26
Lord, who appeared *unto h.* 12:7
shall a child be born *unto h.*? 17:17
of which God had spoken *to h.* 21:2
unto h. hath he given all that. 24:36
unto h. shall the gathering. 49:10
thou shalt be *to h.* *Ex* 4:16
not be *to h.* as an usurer. 22:25
it shall be a statute for ever *unto h.*
28:43; 30:21
and *to h.* will I give the. *Deut* 1:36
raise up a Prophet, *unto h.* 18:15
to do *to h.* as he hath. *Judg* 15:10
Lord hath done *to h.* *1 Sam* 28:17
David, even so I do *to h.* *2 Sam* 3:9
wilt thou go *to h.* to-day ? *2 Ki* 4:23
so it fell out *unto h.* for the. 7:20
even *to h.* and his sons. *2 Chr* 13:5
king, so shall ye say *unto h.* 34:26
to h. that is afflicted. *Job* 6:14
what doest thou *unto h.*? 35:6
to h. that rideth on. *Ps* 68:33
to h. shall be given of gold. 72:15
to h. that made great lights. 136:7
to h. that smote great kings, for. 17
one event *to h.* that sacrificeth, and *to*
h. that sacrificeth not. *Eccl* 9:2
people turneth not *to h.* *Isa* 9:13
turn *to h.* from whom Israel. 31:6
they are counted *to h.* less. 40:17
will ye compare *unto h.*? 18
even *to h.* shall men come. 45:24
thus saith the Lord *to h.* whom. 49:7
to h. that is far off, and to *h.* 57:19
look, even *to h.* that is poor. 66:2
to h. that knocketh, it. *Mat* 7:8
to h. that smiteth thee. *Luke* 6:29
whosoever hath, *to h.* shall be. 8:18
to h. that blasphemeth against. 12:10
living, for all live *unto h.* 20:38
then I go *unto h.* *John* 7:33; 16:5
to h. the porter openeth, the. 10:3
to h. they agreed, and. *Acts* 5:40
to h. they had regard, because. 8:11
to h. give all the prophets. 10:43
now *to h.* that worketh. *Rom* 4:4
to h. that worketh not, but. 5
even *to h.* who is raised. 7:4
and *to h.* are all things, to. 11:36

to h. that esteemeth, to h. *Rom* 14:14
now to h. that is of power to. 16:25
be to h. who speaketh a. *1 Cor* 14:11
it was accounted to h. for. *Gal* 3:6
unto h. be glory in the. *Eph* 3:21
I will be to h. a Father. *Heb* 1:5
to h. that was able to save him. 5:7
it was imputed unto h. *Jas* 2:23
to h. that knoweth to do good, to h. 4:17
unto h. that loved us. *Rev* 1:5
to h. that overcometh. 2:7, 17; 3:21
to h. will I give power over. 2:26
will give unto h. that is athirst. 21:6

toward **him**

it was not toward h. *Gen* 31:2
anger was abated toward h. *Judg* 8:3
heart is perfect toward h. *2 Chr* 16:9
stretch out thine hands toward h. *Job* 11:13
lift up thy hands toward h. *Lam* 2:19
branches turned toward h. *Ezek* 17:6
your love toward h. *2 Cor* 2:8

under **him**

stone and put it under h. *Ex* 17:12
mule that was under h. *2 Sam* 18:9
helpers do stoop under h. *Job* 9:13
spread sackcloth and ashes under h. *Isa* 58:5
the roots thereof were under h. *Ezek* 17:6
all things put under h. *1 Cor* 15:27, 28; *Heb* 2:8

with **him**

saw that Lord was with h. *Gen* 39:3
I have given with h. Aholiab. *Ex* 31:6; 38:23
with h. will I speak mouth to mouth. *Num* 12:8; *Jer* 32:4
his God is with h. and. *Num* 23:21
with h. that standeth here with us, also with h. that is. *Deut* 29:15
was no strange god with h. 32:12
and the Lord was with h. *1 Sam* 3:19; 18:12, 14
the Lord is with h. 16:18
folly is with h. 25:25
Lord of hosts was with h. *2 Sam* 5:10; *1 Chr* 11:9
will I be, and with h. *2 Sam* 16:18
Solomon held a feast, and all Israel with h. *1 Ki* 8:65; *2 Chr* 7:8
word of Lord is with h. *2 Ki* 3:12
his hand might be with h. 15:19
the Lord was with h. and he. 18:7; *1 Chr* 9:20; *2 Chr* 1:1; 15:9
while ye be with h. *2 Chr* 15:2
with h. fourscore priests of. 26:17
be more with us than with h. 32:7
with h. is an arm of flesh, with. 8
the Lord his God be with h. 36:23; *Ezra* 1:3
with h. 150 males. *Ezra* 8:3
with h. 200 males. 4
with h. 50 males. 6
with h. is wisdom. *Job* 12:13, 16
candle shall be put out with h. 18:6
acquaint thyself with h. and. 22:21
mercy shall be with h. *Ps* 89:24
I will be with h. in trouble. 91:15
and with h. is plenteous. 130:7
one brought up with h. *Pr* 8:30
that shall abide with h. *Eccl* 8:15
righteous, it shall be well with h. *Isa* 3:10
wicked, it shall be ill with h. 11
his reward is with h. 40:10; 62:11
with h. also that is of a. 57:15
it was well with h. *Jer* 22:15, 16
he shall deal with h. *Ezek* 31:11
covenant was with h. of. *Mal* 2:5
art in the way with h. *Mat* 5:25
they should be with h. *Mark* 3:14
he might be with h. 5:18; *Luke* 8:38
hand of Lord was with h. *Luke* 1:66
this man was also with h. 22:56
miracles, except God be with h. *John* 3:2
and make our abode with h. 14:23
but God was with h. *Acts* 7:9; 10:38
him is accepted with h. 10:35
crying, Away with h. 21:36

we are buried with h. by baptism. *Rom* 6:4; *Col* 2:12
live with h. *Rom* 6:8; *2 Cor* 13:4; *1 Thes* 5:10; *2 Tim* 2:11
shall he not with h. give? *Rom* 8:32
will God bring with h. *1 Thes* 4:14
we also shall reign with h. *2 Tim* 2:12; *Rev* 20:6
the heirs with h. of the. *Heb* 11:9
when we were with h. *2 Pet* 1:18
and I will sup with h. *Rev* 3:20
with h. 144,000 having his. 14:1
they that are with h. are. 17:14

within **him**

his soul within h. mourn. *Job* 14:22
the gall of asps within h. 20:14
layeth up deceit within h. *Pr* 26:24
his Holy Spirit within h. *Isa* 63:11
spirit of man within h. *Zech* 12:1

without **him**

and without h. was not. *John* 1:3

himself

set on for him by h. *Gen* 43:32
if he came in by h. he shall go out by h. *Ex* 21:3
sin offering which was for h. *Lev* 9:8; 16:6, 11
shall make an atonement for h. 16:11, 17, 24
to bring you near to h. *Num* 16:9
taken spoil, every man for h. 31:53
Lord hath chosen thee to h. *Deut* 7:6; 14:2; 28:9; 29:13; *2 Sam* 7:23
provided the first part for h. *Deut* 33:21
let the Lord h. require. *Josh* 22:23
he h. turned again. *Judg* 3:19
David encouraged h. *1 Sam* 30:6
Elijah h. went a day's journey, and he requested for h. *1 Ki* 19:4
God h. is with us for. *2 Chr* 13:12
thrust him out, yea, h. hasted. 26:20
h. separated from the. *Ezra* 10:8
only on h. put not forth. *Job* 1:12
wise may be profitable to h. 22:2
will he delight h. in the? 27:10
because he justified h. rather. 32:2
that he should delight h. with. 34:9
when he raiseth h. the. 41:25
him that is godly for h. *Ps* 4:3
the poor committeth h. unto. 10:14
net that he hath hid catch h. 35:8
he setteth h. in a way that is. 36:4
for God is judge h. 50:6
and the Highest h. shall. 87:5
but on h. shall his crown. 132:18
Lord hath chosen Jacob to h. 135:4
shall take wicked h. *Pr* 5:22
shall be watered also h. 11:25
h. rich, that maketh h. poor. 13:7
man shall be satisfied from h. 14:14
hath made all things for h. 16:4
that laboureth, laboureth for h. 26
he also shall cry h. but shall. 21:13
the evil, and hideth h. 22:3; 27:12
child left to h. bringeth. 29:15
beloved hath withdrawn h. *S of S* 5:6
the Lord h. shall give you. *Isa* 7:14
he hath spoken, and h. hath. 38:15
another shall call h. by the. 44:5
departeth from evil, maketh h. 59:15
make h. an everlasting name? 63:12
way of man is not in h. *Jer* 10:23
that is mad, and maketh h. 29:26
hath sworn by h. 51:14; *Amos* 6:8
prince prepare for h. *Ezek* 45:22
be cut off, but not for h. *Dan* 9:26
he hath withdrawn h. *Hos* 5:6
vine, bringeth forth fruit to h. 10:1
the mighty deliver h. *Amos* 2:14
swift of foot shall not deliver h. 15
h. shall reward thee. *Mat* 6:4
h. took our infirmities, bare. 8:17
he not root in h. but dureth. 13:21
he saved others; h. he cannot save. 27:42; *Mark* 15:31
said, He is beside h. *Mark* 3:21
let him deny h., and take up his cross. 8:34; *Luke* 9:23
love his neighbour as h. *Mark* 12:33
sent them, whither he h. *Luke* 10:1
spirits more wicked than h. 11:26
lord's will, and prepared not h. 12:47
he came to h. he said. *Luke* 15:17
nobleman went to receive for h. 19:12
saying, that he h. is Christ. 23:2
also h. waited for the kingdom. 51
the things concerning h. 24:27
Jesus h. stood in the midst of. 36
Jesus h. baptized not. *John* 4:2
God was his Father, making h. 5:18
I say, the Son can do nothing of h. 19
for as the Father hath life in h. 26
for he h. knew what he would. 6:6
when Jesus knew in h. that his. 61
and he h. seeketh to be known. 7:4
he that speaketh of h. seeketh. 18
him, he shall speak for h. 9:21
this spake he not of h. but. 11:51
God shall glorify him in h. 13:32
he shall not speak of h. 16:13
Father h. loveth you, because. 27
maketh h. a king, speaketh. 19:12
Jesus shewed h. again. 21:1, 14
durst no man join h. to. *Acts* 5:13
rose up Theudas, boasting h. 36
giving out that h. was some. 8:9
speaketh the prophet this? of h.? 34
while Peter doubted in h. 10:17
when Peter was come to h. 12:11
he left not h. without witness. 14:17
while he answered for h. 25:8; 26:1
as he spake for h. Festus said. 26:24
was suffered to dwell by h. 28:16
think of h. more highly. *Rom* 12:3
to h., no man dieth to h. 14:7
for even Christ pleased not h. 15:3
yet he h. is judged of. *1 Cor* 2:15
but he h. shall be saved, yet. 3:15
let a man examine h., and so. 11:28
then shall the Son h. be. 15:28
reconciled us to h. by Jesus. *2 Cor* 5:18, 19
man trust to h. let him of h. 10:7
for ye suffer if a man exalt h. 11:20
who gave h. for our sins. *Gal* 1:4
gave h. for me. 2:20
think h. to be something. 6:3
he have rejoicing in h. 4
to make in h. of twain. *Eph* 2:15
Jesus h. being the chief corner-. 20
hath given h. for us. 5:2
gave h. for it. 25
present it to h. a glorious church. 27
loveth h. 28
so love his wife, even as h. 33
reconcile all things to h. *Col* 1:20
sitteth, shewing h. that. *2 Thes* 2:4
who gave h. a ransom. *1 Tim* 2:6
h. for us, to purify to h. *Tit* 2:14
being condemned of h. 3:11
when he had by h. purged. *Heb* 1:3
he also h. likewise took part. 2:14
in that he h. hath suffered. 18
for that he h. also is compassed. 5:2
as for the people, so also for h. 3
no man taketh this honour to h. 4
Christ glorified not h. to be made. 5
he sware by h. 6:13
when he offered up h. 7:27
away sin by the sacrifice of h. 9:26
but committed h. to. *1 Pet* 2:23
ought to walk, even as. *1 John* 2:6
hath this hope, purifieth h. even. 3:3
believeth hath the witness in h. 5:10
nor doth he h. receive. *3 John* 10
that no man knew but h. *Rev* 19:12
God h. shall be with them. 21:3

see **bowed, hide**

hin

(*A liquid measure of the Hebrews It was the sixth part of a* Bath *o* Ephah, *and held about one gallo and three pints*)

fourth part of an h. of oil. *Ex* 29:4
unto thee of oil olive an h. 30:2
a just ephah and h. shall. *Lev* 19:3
shall be of wine, fourth part of an h 23:13; *Num* 15:4; 28:1
part of an h. of wine. *Num* 15:
the third part of an h. of oil.
half an h.
drink sixth part of an h. *Ezek* 4:1
an h. of oil for an ephah. 45:2; 46:5, 7, 1
third part of an h. of oil to. 46:1

hind, -s
Naphtali is a h. let loose. Gen 49:21
my feet like hs.' feet. and setteth me.
2 Sam 22:34; Ps 18:33; Hab 3:19
thou mark when the h.? Job 39:1
of Lord maketh the h. Ps 29:9
her be as the loving h. Pr 5:19
I charge you by the h. of the field.
S of S 2:7; 3:5
the h. calved in the field. Jer 14:5

hinder
h. me not, seeing the. Gen 24:56
let nothing h. thee from. Num 22:16
come and fight, and h. the. Neh 4:8*
away, who can h. him? Job 9:12
and shut up, who can h. him? 11:10
what doth h. me to be? Acts 8:36
should h. the gospel of. 1 Cor 9:12
who did h. you, that? Gal 5:7

hinder *end*
Abner smote him with h. end of.
2 Sam 2:23

hinder *part*
and his h. part toward. Joel 2:20
Jesus was in the h. part. Mark 4:38
the h. part was broken. Acts 27:41*

hinder *parts*
their h. parts were inward.
1 Ki 7:25; 2 Chr 4:4
enemies in the h. parts. Ps 78:66*

hinder *sea*
them toward the h. sea. Zech 14:8*

hindered
given, that they be not h. Ezra 6:8
were entering in, ye h. Luke 11:52
have been much h. Rom 15:22
have come, but Satan h. 1 Thes 2:18
that your prayers be not h. 1 Pet 3:7

hindereth
is persecuted, and none h. Isa 14:6*

hindermost, or hindmost
put Rachel and Joseph h. Gen 33:2
shall go h. with their. Num 2:31
and smote the h. of thee. Deut 25:18
pursue, and smite the h. Josh 10:19
the h. of the nations. Jer 50:12

hinges
and the h. of gold for. 1 Ki 7:50
door turneth upon his h. Pr 26:14

Hinnom
went up by valley of H. Josh 15:8
s in the valley of H. 2 Ki 23:10
ncense in the valley of H. 2 Chr 28:3
o pass through fire in H. 33:6
he valley of the son of H. Jer 19:2
laces in the valley of H. 32:35

hip
e smote them h. and. Judg 15:8

Hiram
H. king of Tyre sent messengers to.
2 Sam 5:11; 1 Chr 14:1
H. king of Tyre sent servants to Solomon, for H. was ever. 1 Ki 5:1, 8
H. gave Solomon cedar trees. 10
olomon gave H. 20,000. 11
eace between H. and Solomon. 12
olomon sent and fetched H. 7:13
H. made the lavers, H. made. 40
H. came to see the cities. 9:12
H. sent in the navy his. 27
e navy of H. brought in. 10:11
t sea a navy, with the navy of H. 22

hire, *substantive*
od hath given me my h. Gen 30:18
id of such shall be my h. 32
hen it shall come for thy h. 33
ngstraked shall be thy h. 31:8*
ing, it came for his h. Ex 22:15
alt not bring the h. Deut 23:18
ou shalt give him his h. 24:15
thee will I give h. 1 Ki 5:6
e shall turn to her h. Isa 23:17
d her h. shall be holiness to. 18
that thou scornest h. Ezek 16:31
d thou also shalt give no h. 41
of the h. of an harlot, return to
the h. of an harlot. Mi 1:7
iests thereof teach for h. 3:11
h. for man, nor any h. Zech 8:10
ve them their h. Mat 20:8
labourer is worthy of his h.
Luke 10:7
the h. of the labourers is. Jas 5:4

hire
h. a goldsmith, and he. Isa 46:6
went out to h. labourers. Mat 20:1

hired
h. thee with my son's. Gen 30:16
if it be an h. thing it. Ex 22:15
wages of him that is h. Lev 19:13
they h. against thee Balaam.
Deut 23:4; Neh 13:2
Abimelech h. vain persons. Judg 9:4
Micah hath h. me, and I am. 18:4
that were full, have h. 1 Sam 2:5
Ammon h. the Syrians. 2 Sam 10:6
1 Chr 19:7
king of Israel hath h. 2 Ki 7:6
h. masons and. 2 Chr 24:12
Amaziah h. 100,000 mighty. 25:6
h. counsellors against. Ezra 4:5
Sanballat had h. him. Neh 6:12, 13
with a razor that is h. Isa 7:20
h. men are like fatted. Jer 46:21
up, Ephraim hath h. Hos 8:9
yea, though they have h. among. 10
no man hath h. us. Mat 20:7
when they came that were h. 9
Paul dwelt two years in his own h. house. Acts 28:30

hired *servant*
an h. servant not eat thereof.
Ex 12:45; Lev 22:10
be meat for thy h. servant. Lev 25:6
but as an h. servant he shall be. 40
the time of an h. servant shall. 50
as a yearly h. servant shall he. 53
a double h. servant. Deut 15:18*
not oppress an h. servant. 24:14

hired *servants*
the ship with h. servants. Mark 1:20
many h. servants have. Luke 15:17
as one of thy h. servants. 19

hireling
days like the days of an h.? Job 7:1
as an h. looketh for the reward. 2
he shall accomplish as an h. 14:6
in three years as the years of an h.
Isa 16:14; 21:16
those that oppress the h. Mat 3:5
he that is an h. and not. John 10:12
the h. fleeth, because he is an h. 13

hires
all the h. thereof shall. Mi 1:7

hirest
thou h. them, that they. Ezek 16:33

his
(*As the neuter possessive pronoun its was hardly come into use in 1611 when the Authorised Version ("King James's Version") was translated, the possessive* his *was often used where modern usage would require* its. *In these places the Revisions change the pronoun to the modern form*)
the seed should not be h. Gen 38:9
dead beast shall be h. Ex 21:34
another challengeth to be h. 22:9
part, and it shall be h. Lev 27:15
hallowed thing shall be h. Num 5:10
the Lord will shew who are h. 16:5
and let my last end be like h. 23:10
of the firstborn is h. Deut 21:17
h. will I be, with him. 2 Sam 16:18
for it was h. from the. 1 Ki 2:15
a captain of h. conspired. 2 Ki 15:25
is one law of h. to put. Esth 4:11
and the deceiver are h. Job 12:16
because it is none of h. 18:15
Lord, all ye saints of h. Ps 30:4
strength of the hills is h. also. 95:4
ye ministers of h. that do. 103:21
is mine, and I am h. S of S 2:16
passed by; h. it was. Ezek 16:15
then it shall be h. to the year. 46:17
wisdom and might are h. Dan 2:20
h. that did escape, nor have delivered up those of h. Ob 14
him increaseth that which is not h.
Hab 2:6
is not mine, but h. that. John 7:16
baptized, he and all h. Acts 16:33
Spirit, he is none of h. Rom 8:9
knoweth them that are h. 2 Tim 2:19
works, as God did from h. Heb 4:10

hiss
(*Hiss, or hissing is generally used in the Bible with the idea of contempt or scorn. Occasionally the the word has the idea of anger*)
house every one shall h. 1 Ki 9:8
men shall h. him out of. Job 27:23
he will h. to them from. Isa 5:26
the Lord shall h. for the fly. 7:18
passeth thereby shall h. Jer 19:8
49:17; 50:13
they h. at the daughter. Lam 2:15
thy enemies h. and gnash the. 16
the merchants shall h. Ezek 27:36
passeth by her shall h. Zeph 2:15
I will h. for them and. Zech 10:8

hissing
delivered them to h. 2 Chr 29:8
their land a perpetual h. Jer 18:16
make this city an h. 19:8
make them an h. 25:9, 18; 29:18
Babylon shall be an h. 51:37
inhabitants thereof an h. Mi 6:16

hit
and the archers h. him. 1 Sam 31:3*
1 Chr 10:3*

hither
angry that ye sold me h. Gen 45:5
it was not you that sent me h. 8
bring down my father h. 13
draw not nigh h.: put off. Ex 3:5
there came men in h. Josh 2:2
bring the description h. to me. 18:6
him, who brought thee h.? Judg 18:3
we will not turn aside h. 19:12
bring h. a burnt offering. 1 Sam 13:9
Saul said, bring h. the ark. 14:18
bring me h. every man his ox. 34
let us draw near h. unto God. 36
bring h. Agag. 15:32
why camest thou h.? 17:28
Abiathar, bring h. the. 23:9; 30:7
I have brought them h. 2 Sam 1:10
hasten h. Micaiah. 1 Ki 22:9*
Jordan divided h. and. 2 Ki 2:8, 14
not bring in captives h. 2 Chr 28:13
which brought us up h. Ezra 4:2
his people return h. Ps 73:10
take a psalm, and bring h. 81:2
let him turn in h. Pr 9:4, 16
draw near h. ye sons of. Isa 57:3
he said, bring them h. Mat 14:18
Jesus said, bring him h. to me.
17:17; Luke 9:41
how camest thou in h.? Mat 22:12
bring in h. the poor. Luke 14:21
bring h. the fatted calf and. 15:23
bring h. and slay them. 19:27
colt tied, loose him, bring him h. 30
Rabbi, when camest thou h.?
John 6:25
reach h. thy finger, reach h. 20:27
that came h. for that. Acts 9:21
call h. Simon, whose surname. 10:32
have brought h. these men. 19:37
see **come**

hitherto
behold, h. thou wouldest. Ex 7:16
Lord hath blessed me h. Josh 17:14
h. thou hast mocked. Judg 16:13
grief have I spoken h. 1 Sam 1:16
and saying, H. hath the Lord. 7:12
thou hast brought me h. 2 Sam 7:18
1 Chr 17:16
thy father's servant h. 2 Sam 15:34
who h. waited in the. 1 Chr 9:18
h. the greatest part kept. 12:29
h. shalt thou come, but. Job 38:11
h. have I declared thy. Ps 71:17
terrible from their beginning h.
Isa 18:2, 7
my Father worketh h. John 5:17
h. have ye asked nothing. 16:24
to come, but was let h. Rom 1:13
for h. ye were not able. 1 Cor 3:2

Hittite
the field of Ephron the H. Gen 25:9

daughter of Beeri the *H.* *Gen* 26:34
Elon the *H.* 36:2
Abraham bought of Ephron the *H.* 49:30; 50:13
I will drive out the *H.* *Ex* 23:28
33:2; 34:11
the *H.* and Amorite. *Josh* 9:1; 11:3
to Abimelech the *H.* *1 Sam* 26:6
send me Uriah the *H.* *2 Sam* 11:6
thy servant Uriah the *H.* 21, 24
hast killed Uriah the *H.* 12:9
taken the wife of Uriah the *H.* 10
Uriah the *H.* thirty-seven. 23:39
matter of Uriah the *H.* *1 Ki* 15:5
thy mother an *H.* *Ezek* 16:3, 45

Hittites

unto thy seed have I given land of *H.* *Gen* 15:20; *Josh* 1:4
Canaanites, *H.* Amorites. *Ex* 3:8, 17
13:5; 23:23; *Deut* 7:1; 20:17
Josh 3:10; 12:8; 24:11; *Judg* 3:5
1 Ki 9:20; *Neh* 9:8
into the land of the *H.* *Judg* 1:26
Israel dwelt among the *H.* 3:5
loved women of the *H.* *1 Ki* 11:1
hired the kings of the *H.* *2 Ki* 7:6
left of *H.*, Solomon made. *2 Chr* 8:7
abominations of the *H.* *Ezra* 9:1

Hivite, much in **Hittite**

ho

to whom he said, *Ho.* *Ruth* 4:1
ho every one that thirsteth. *Isa* 55:1
ho, ho, come forth. *Zech* 2:6

hoar, *see* **frost, hairs, head**

hoary

think the deep to be *h.* *Job* 41:32

Hobab

Moses said to *H.* come. *Num* 10:29
of the children of *H.* *Judg* 4:11

hoised

they *h.* up the mainsail. *Acts* 27:40*

hold, *substantive*

(*In the Old Testament the American Revision renders this* stronghold)

they entered into a *h.* *Judg* 9:46
put them to the *h.* and set the *h.* 49
David in *h.* *1 Sam* 22:4; 24:22
2 Sam 5:17; 23:14
abide not in the *h.* *1 Sam* 22:5
came of Judah to *h.* *1 Chr* 12:16
and put them in *h.* unto. *Acts* 4:3*
is become the *h.* of every. *Rev* 18:2
see **strong**

hold

lift up the lad, *h.* him. *Gen* 21:18
that they may *h.* a feast. *Ex* 5:1
to let them go, and wilt *h.* 9:2
for we must *h.* a feast unto. 10:9
Lord will not *h.* 20:7; *Deut* 5:11
bring the vail, and *h.* it. *Ruth* 3:15
how should I *h.* up my? *2 Sam* 2:22
his hand to ark of God, and took *h.* of it, oxen shook it. 6:6; *1 Chr* 13:9
now therefore *h.* him. *1 Ki* 2:9
the king shall *h.* out. *Esth* 4:11
teach me, and I will *h.* *Job* 6:24
I know that thou wilt not *h.* 9:28
if I *h.* my tongue, I shall. 13:19
the righteous also shall *h.* on. 17:9
dart, the habergeon cannot *h.* 41:26
h. up my goings in thy. *Ps* 17:5
horror hath taken *h.* upon. 119:53
h. thou me up, and I shall. 117
and thy right hand shall *h.* 139:10
and her hands *h.* the. *Pr* 31:19
they all *h.* swords, being. *S of S* 3:8
I the Lord will *h.* thy. *Isa* 41:13
and I will *h.* thine hand. 42:6
broken cisterns, can *h.* *Jer* 2:13
astonishment hath taken *h.* 8:21
they shall *h.* the bow. 50:42
anguish took *h.* of him, and. 43
to make it strong to *h.* *Ezek* 30:21
might have *h.*, they had not *h.* 41:6
then shall he say, *H.* *Amos* 6:10
them, and *h.* themselves. *Zech* 11:5
else he will *h.* to the one. *Mat* 6:24
Luke 16:13
all *h.* John as a prophet. *Mat* 21:26
they have received to *h.* *Mark* 7:4
ye *h.* the tradition of men. *Mark* 7:8
who *h.* the truth in. *Rom* 1:18*
receive him, and *h.* such. *Phil* 2:29
h. the traditions ye. *2 Thes* 2:15
if we *h.* the beginning. *Heb* 3:14
them that *h.* the doctrine. *Rev* 2:14
that *h.* doctrine of Nicolaitanes. 15
see **caught, take**

hold *fast*

he shall *h.* it *fast,* but. *Job* 8:15
my righteousness I *h. fast,* I. 27:6
they *h. fast* deceit, they. *Jer* 8:5
prove all things, *h. fast.* *1 Thes* 5:21
h. fast the form of sound. *2 Tim* 1:13
if we *h. fast* the confidence. *Heb* 3:6
h. fast our profession. 4:14; 10:23
ye have already *h. fast.* *Rev* 2:25
h. fast and repent. 3:3
h. fast which thou hast. 11

hold *peace*

ye shall *h.* your *peace.* *Ex* 14:14
her father *h.* his *peace.* *Num* 30:4
husband altogether *h.* his *peace.* 14
h. thy *peace,* lay hand. *Judg* 18:19
h. thy *peace,* my sister. *2 Sam* 13:20
I know it, *h.* ye your *peace.* *2 Ki* 2:3, 5
tidings, and we *h.* our *peace.* 7:9
saying, *H.* your *peace.* *Neh* 8:11
lies make men *h.* their *peace?* *Job* 11:3
altogether *h.* your *peace.* 13:5
h. your *peace,* let me alone. 13
mark well, *h.* thy *peace* and. 33:31
h. thy *peace,* and I will teach. 33
O God, *h.* not thy *peace,* be not still. *Ps* 83:1; 109:1
will I not *h.* my *peace.* *Isa* 62:1
which shall never *h.* their *peace.* 6
wilt thou *h.* thy *peace* and? 64:12
I cannot *h.* my *peace.* *Jer* 4:19
h. thy *p.* at the presence. *Zeph* 1:7
because they should *h.* their *peace.* *Mat* 20:31; *Mark* 10:48; *Luke* 18:39
h. thy *peace* come out of him. *Mark* 1:25; *Luke* 4:35
should *h.* their *peace.* *Luke* 19:40
to them to *h.* their *peace.* *Acts* 12:17
but speak, and *h.* not thy *peace.* 18:9
let the first *h.* his *peace.* *1 Cor* 14:30

holden

there was not *h.* such a passover. *2 Ki* 23:22*, 23*
if they be *h.* in cords. *Job* 36:8*
thy right hand hath *h.* *Ps* 18:35
by thee have I been *h.* up. 71:6
thou hast *h.* me up by my. 73:23
shall be *h.* with the cords. *Pr* 5:22
I have long *h.* my peace. *Isa* 42:14
whose right hand I have *h.* to. 45:1
eyes were *h.* they. *Luke* 24:16
possible he should be *h.* *Acts* 2:24
yea, he shall be *h.* up. *Rom* 14:4*

holdest

if thou altogether *h.* thy. *Esth* 4:14
wherefore *h.* thou me? *Job* 13:24
h. my eyes waking, I. *Ps* 77:4
O thou that *h.* the height. *Jer* 49:16
h. thy tongue when the. *Hab* 1:13
thou *h.* fast my name. *Rev* 2:13

holdeth

and still he *h.* fast his. *Job* 2:3
h. back the face of his throne. 26:9
bless God who *h.* our. *Ps* 66:9
a man of understanding *h.* *Pr* 11:12
a fool when he *h.* his peace. 17:28
and none *h.* with me. *Dan* 10:21
I will cut off him that *h.* *Amos* 1:5, 8
that *h.* the seven stars. *Rev* 2:1

holding

shaketh his hands from *h.* *Isa* 33:15
I am weary with *h.* in, I. *Jer* 6:11
eat not, *h.* the tradition. *Mark* 7:3
h. forth the word of life. *Phil* 2:16
not *h.* the head, from. *Col* 2:19
h. faith and a good. *1 Tim* 1:19
h. the mystery of faith in a pure. 3:9
h. fast faithful word, as he. *Tit* 1:9
I saw four angels *h.* the. *Rev* 7:1

holds

have remained in their *h.* *Jer* 51:30*
brought him into *h.* *Ezek* 19:9*
see **strong**

hole

there shall be an *h.* in the. *Ex* 28:32
Jehoiada bored an *h.* in. *2 Ki* 12:9
put in his hand by the *h.* *S of S* 5:4
child shall play on the *h.* *Isa* 11:8
look to *h.* of the pit whence. 51:1
and hide it there in a *h.* of. *Jer* 13:4
I looked, behold a *h.* *Ezek* 8:7

holes

come forth out of the *h* *1 Sam* 14:11
h. of the rocks. *Isa* 2:19; 7:19
all of them snared in *h.* 42:22
hunt them out of the *h.* *Jer* 16:16
her nest in sides of the *h.* 48:28
not move out of their *h.* *Mi* 7:17*
lion filled his *h.* with prey. *Nah* 2:12*
to put it in a bag with *h.* *Hag* 1:6
shall consume in their *h.* *Zech* 14:12*
Jesus saith, The foxes have *h.* *Mat* 8:20; *Luke* 9:58

holier

come not near, for I am *h.* *Isa* 65:5

holiest

which is called the *h.* *Heb* 9:3
the way into the *h.* was not yet. 8
enter into the *h.* by blood of. 10:19*

holily

are witnesses how *h.* *1 Thes* 2:10

holiness

like thee, glorious in *h.*? *Ex* 15:11
h. to the Lord. 28:36*; 39:30*
Zech 14:20*, 21*
worship the Lord in the beauty of *h.* *1 Chr* 16:29; *Ps* 29:2; 96:9
praise the beauty of *h.* *2 Chr* 20:21
sanctified themselves in *h.* 31:18
at the remembrance of his *h.* *Ps* 30:4*; 97:12
sitteth upon throne of his *h.* 47:8*
praised in mountain of his *h.* 48:1
hath spoken in his *h.* 60:6; 108:7
once I have sworn by my *h.* 89:35
h. becometh thine house, O. 93:5
be willing, in beauties of *h.* 110:3
and her hire shall be *h.* *Isa* 23:18
shall be called the way of *h.* 35:8
drink it in the courts of my *h.* 62:9*
from habitation of thy *h.* 63:15
the people of thy *h.* have. 18*
Israel was *h.* to the Lord. *Jer* 2:3
of the words of his *h.* 23:9
bless thee, O mountain of *h.* 31:23
God hath sworn by his *h.* *Amos* 4:2
mount Zion there shall be *h.* *Ob* 17*
Judah hath profaned the *h.* *Mal* 2:11
might serve him in *h.* *Luke* 1:75
as though by our *h.* made. *Acts* 3:12*
according to Spirit of *h.* *Rom* 1:4
servants to righteousness unto *h.* 6:19
ye have your fruit unto *h.* 22
perfecting *h.* in the fear. *2 Cor* 7:1
created in righteousness and *h.* *Eph* 4:24
your hearts unblameable, in *h.* *1 Thes* 3:13
us unto uncleanness, but to *h.* 4:7*
continue in faith and *h.* *1 Tim* 2:15
in behaviour as becometh *h.* *Tit* 2:
be partakers of his *h.* *Heb* 12:1
follow peace with men, and *h.* 14

hollow

the *h.* of his thigh. *Gen* 32:25, 3
shalt make the altar *h.* with boards *Ex* 27:8; 38:
plague be in walls with *h.* *Lev* 14:3
God clave an *h.* place. *Judg* 15:1
measured waters in *h.* *Isa* 40:1
the pillar, it was *h.* *Jer* 52:2

holpen

(*American Revision,* helped)

have *h.* the children. *Ps* 83:
thou, Lord, hast *h.* me. 86:1
and he that is *h.* shall. *Isa* 31:
they shall be *h.* with a. *Dan* 11:3
hath *h.* his servant Israel. *Luke* 1:5

holy

[1] *Godly*, Deut 33:8; Ps 86:2. [2] *Dedicated*, 2 Chr 31:6, *or sacred* 1 Cor 9:13. [3] *The holy place, the inner room of the tabernacle or temple where none but priests could enter.* [4] *The Holy of Holies, the innermost part of the house of God, where only the High Priest entered, and he but once a year, on the Day of Atonement.*

thou standest is *h.* ground. *Ex* 3:5
the rest of the *h.* sabbath. 16:23
to me a *h.* nation. 19:6; *1 Pet* 2:9
sabbath day to keep it *h.* *Ex* 20:8
hallow in all their *h.* gifts. 28:38
and put the *h.* crown upon the. 29:6
because they are *h.* 33
because it is *h.* 34
make it an oil of *h.* ointment. 30:25
it is *h.* and it shall be *h.* unto. 32
tempered together, pure and *h.* 35
for it is *h.* unto you. 31:14, 15
upon Aaron the *h.* crown. *Lev* 8:9
may put difference between *h.* 10:10
he shall put on the *h.* linen. 16:4
make atonement for the *h.* 33
Lord your God am *h.* 19:2; 21:8
be ye *h.* 20:7
for he is *h.* unto his God. 21:7
man sanctify his house to be *h.* 27:14
the tithe of the land is *h.* unto. 30
the priest shall take *h.* *Num* 5:17
ye may remember, and be *h.* 15:40
all the congregation are *h.* 16:3
shew who are his, and who is *h.* 5
not redeem them, they are *h.* 18:17
sent Phinehas with the *h.* 31:6*
for there is none *h.* as. *1 Sam* 2:2
vessels of the young men are *h.* 21:5
ark and the tabernacle, and all the *h.* *1 Ki* 8:4; *2 Chr* 5:5
I perceive this is an *h.* *2 Ki* 4:9
bring the *h.* vessels into. *1 Chr* 22:19
I have prepared for the *h.* 29:3
go in, for they are *h.* *2 Chr* 23:6
Levites which were *h.* to the Lord, put the *h.* ark into the. 35:3
the other *h.* offerings sod they in. 13
h. to the Lord, vessels are *h.* also. *Ezra* 8:28
the *h.* seed mingled themselves. 9:2
known unto them thy *h.* *Neh* 9:14
hear him from his *h.* heaven. *Ps* 20:6
art *h.* O thou that inhabitest. 22:3
lift my hands towards thy *h.* 28:2
preserve my soul, for I am *h.* 86:2*
his *h.* arm hath gotten him. 98:1
his footstool, for he is *h.* 99:5
and worship at his *h.* hill. 9
remembered his *h.* promise. 105:42
the Lord is *h.* in all his. 145:17*
the knowledge of the *h.* is. *Pr* 9:10
devoureth that which is *h.* 20:25
I the knowledge of the *h.* 30:3*
Jerusalem shall be called *h.* *Isa* 4:3
one cried, *H. h. h.* is the Lord. 6:3
h. seed shall be the substance. 13
worship in the *h.* mountain. 27:13
as when a *h.* solemnity is. 30:29
Lord hath made bare his *h.* 52:10
sabbath, the *h.* of the Lord. 58:13
thy *h.* cities are a wilderness. 64:10
our *h.* and beautiful house is. 11
the *h.* flesh is passed. *Jer* 11:15
no difference between *h.* *Ezek* 22:26
increase them as the *h.* flock. 36:38*
they be *h.* chambers, where. 42:13
their garments, for they are *h.* 14
and lay them in the *h.* 44:19
shall teach difference between *h.* 23
an *h.* portion of the land. 45:1, 4
oblation of *h.* portion. 6, 7; 48:18
into the *h.* chambers of the. 46:19
for the priests shall be this *h.* 48:10
not sell firstfruits, for it is *h.* 14
shall offer the *h.* oblation. 20, 21
came in before me, in whom is the spirit of the *h.* *Dan* 4:8, 9, 18; 5:11
heart shall be against the *h.* 11:28
the *h.* covenant, intelligence with them that forsake the *h.* 30
. flesh, and with his skirt touch bread or oil, shall it be *h.*? *Hag* 2:12
inherit Judah in the *h.* *Zech* 2:12
Lord is raised up out of his *h.* 13
give not that which is *h.* *Mat* 7:6
and all the *h.* angels with. 25:31
he was a just man and *h.* *Mark* 6:20
he shall come in his own glory, and of *h.* angels. 8:38; *Luke* 9:26
by the mouth of *h.* prophets. *Luke* 1:70; *Acts* 3:21
and to remember his *h.* *Luke* 1:72
male shall be called *h.* to. 2:23
h. Father, keep those. *John* 17:11
against thy *h.* child. *Acts* 4:27
done by name of thy *h.* child. 30
thou standest is *h.* ground. 7:33
warned from God by an *h.* 10:22
had promised in the *h.* *Rom* 1:2
the commandment is *h.*, just. 7:12
fruit be *h.* if the root be *h.* 11:16
ye present your bodies a *h.* 12:1
salute one another with an *h.* kiss. 16:16; *1 Cor* 16:20; *2 Cor* 13:12 *1 Thes* 5:26; *1 Pet* 5:14
temple of God is *h.* *1 Cor* 3:17
but now are they *h.* 7:14
that she may be *h.* 34
h. and without blame. *Eph* 1:4; 5:27
to present you *h.* and. *Col* 1:22
put on, as the elect of God, *h.* 3:12
epistle be read to all *h.* *1 Thes* 5:27
lifting up *h.* hands. *1 Tim* 2:8
hath called us with an *h.* *2 Tim* 1:9
hast known *h.* scriptures. 3:15*
bishop must be sober, *h.* *Tit* 1:8
h. brethren, partakers of. *Heb* 3:1
priest became us, who is *h.* 7:26
h. in all conversation. *1 Pet* 1:15, 16
a *h.* priesthood, to offer up. 2:5
the *h.* women also who trusted. 3:5
we were with him in *h.* *2 Pet* 1:18
but *h.* men spake as moved by. 21
than to turn from the *h.* 2:21
words spoken before by the *h.* 3:2
what persons to be in all *h.* 11
things, saith he that is *h.* *Rev* 3:7
H. h. h. Lord God Almighty. 4:8
How long, O Lord, *h.* and? 6:10
tormented in presence of *h.* 14:10
not fear thee? for thou art *h.* 15:4
rejoice over her, ye *h.* 18:20*
h. is he that hath part in first. 20:6
and he shewed me the *h.* 21:10
Lord God of the *h.* prophets. 22:6*
he that is *h.* let him be *h.* still. 11
see **convocation, habitation, hill**

holy *day*

day shall be an *h. day.* *Ex* 35:2
this *day* is *h.* unto. *Neh* 8:9, 10, 11
them on sabbath or *h. day.* 10:31
multitude that kept *h. day.* *Ps* 42:4
thy pleasure on my *h. day.* *Isa* 58:13
in respect of an *h. day.* *Col* 2:16*
see **garments**

Holy *Ghost*

(*American Revision substitutes for this the words* Holy Spirit. *The starred references here refer to other changes*)

with child of the *H. Ghost.* *Mat* 1:18
conceived in her is of *H. Ghost.* 20
baptize you with *H. Ghost.* 3:11 *Mark* 1:8; *Luke* 3:16 *John* 1:33; *Acts* 1:5
blasphemy against the *H. Ghost.* *Mat* 12:31*; *Mark* 3:29 *Luke* 12:10
speaketh against the *H. Ghost.* *Mat* 12:32
baptize in name of Father, Son, and *H. Ghost.* 28:19
David said by the *H. Ghost.* *Mark* 12:36; *Acts* 1:16
speak, but the *H. Ghost.* *Mark* 13:11
filled with *H. Ghost.* *Luke* 1:15
the *H. Ghost* shall come upon. 35
and Elisabeth was filled with the *H. Ghost.* 41
Zacharias was filled with the *H. Ghost.* 67
Simeon; *H. Ghost* was upon. 2:25
revealed unto him by *H. Ghost.* 26
the *H. Ghost* descended in a. 3:22
being full of the *H. Ghost.* 4:1
H. Ghost shall teach you. *Luke* 12:12
for the *H. Ghost* was. *John* 7:39*
who is the *H. Ghost.* 14:26
he saith, receive ye the *H. Ghost.* 20:22; *Acts* 2:38
he through the *H. Ghost.* *Acts* 1:2
after that the *H. Ghost* is come. 8
filled with the *H. Ghost.* 2:4; 4:31
the promise of the *H. Ghost.* 2:33
Peter, filled with the *H. Ghost.* 4:8
heart to lie to the *H. Ghost.* 5:3
witnesses, so is also *H. Ghost.* 32
look out men full of *H. Ghost.* 6:3*
Stephen, a man full of *H. Ghost.* 5
ye always resist the *H. Ghost.* 7:51
he being full of *H. Ghost* looked. 55
might receive the *H. Ghost.* 8:15
and they received the *H. Ghost.* 17
when Simon saw that *H. Ghost.* 18
hands, he may receive *H. Ghost.* 19
be filled with the *H. Ghost.* 9:17
the comfort of the *H. Ghost.* 31
anointed Jesus with *H. Ghost.* 10:38
H. Ghost fell on all which. 44
poured the gift of the *H. Ghost.* 45
have received the *H. Ghost.* 47
H. Ghost fell on them as on. 11:15
shall be baptized with *H. Ghost.* 16
Barnabas, full of the *H. Ghost.* 24
the *H. Ghost* said, separate. 13:2
being sent forth by *H. Ghost.* 4
Paul, filled with the *H. Ghost.* 9
were filled with the *H. Ghost.* 52
giving them the *H. Ghost* as. 15:8
it seemed good to the *H. Ghost.* 28
were forbidden of *H. Ghost.* 16:6
the *H. Ghost*? . . . not heard whether there be any *H. Ghost.* 19:2
laid hands on them, the *H. Ghost.* 6
save that the *H. Ghost.* 20:23
over which *H. Ghost* hath made. 28
thus saith the *H. Ghost*, so. 21:11
well spake the *H. Ghost* by. 28:25
love of God is shed abroad in hearts by *H. Ghost.* *Rom* 5:5
me witness in the *H. Ghost.* 9:1
God is joy in the *H. Ghost.* 14:17
through power of *H. Ghost.* 15:13
being sanctified by *H. Ghost.* 16
words which *H. Ghost.* *1 Cor* 2:13*
the temple of the *H. Ghost.* 6:19
Lord, but by the *H. Ghost.* 12:3
kindness, by *H. Ghost.* *2 Cor* 6:6
communion of the *H. Ghost.* 13:14
gospel came in *H. Ghost.* *1 Thes* 1:5
word with joy of the *H. Ghost.* 6
thing keep by *H. Ghost.* *2 Tim* 1:14
renewing of the *H. Ghost.* *Tit* 3:5
with gifts of the *H. Ghost.* *Heb* 2:4
as the *H. Ghost* saith, To-day. 3:7
made partakers of the *H. Ghost.* 6:4
the *H. Ghost* this signifying. 9:8
whereof the *H. Ghost* is a. 10:15
the *H. Ghost* sent down. *1 Pet* 1:12
moved by the *H. Ghost.* *2 Pet* 1:21
Word, and the *H. Ghost.* *1 John* 5:7
praying in the *H. Ghost.* *Jude* 20
see **God**

most **holy**

place and the *most h.* *Ex* 26:33
of the testimony in the *most h.* 34
be an altar *most h.* 29:37; 40:10
it is *most h.* 30:10
that they may be *most h.* 29
perfume shall be to you *most h.* 36
offering shall be Aaron's, it is *most h.* *Lev* 2:3, 10; 6:17; 10:12
the sin offering is *most h.* 6:25, 29 10:17
trespass offering is *most h.* 7:1, 6 14:13
bread of God, both of *most h.* 21:22
cakes of fine flour are *most h.* 24:9
devoted thing is *most h.* to. 27:28
be service about *most h.* *Num* 4:4
they approach the *most h.* things. 19
render to me shall be *most h.* 18:9
in the *most h.* place shalt thou. 10
them for the *most h.* place. *1 Ki* 6:16
made vessels for the *most h.* 7:50
brought the ark unto *most h.* place. 8:6; *2 Chr* 5:7
sons for work of *most h.* *1 Chr* 6:49

to sanctify most h. 1 Chr 23:13
made the most h. house. 2 Chr 3:8
in the most h. house he made. 10
doors thereof for the most h. 4:22
Kore to distribute the most h. 31:14
not eat of the most h. things.
Ezra 2:63; Neh 7:65
limit shall be most h. Ezek 43:12
near in the most h. place. 44:13
be the sanctuary and most h. 45:3
oblation be a thing most h. 48:12
weeks to anoint the most h. Dan 9:24
yourselves on your most h. Jude 20

holy *mountain, -s*

foundation is in the h. mountains.
Ps 87:1
nor destroy in my h. mountain.
Isa 11:9; 65:25
will I bring to my h. mountain. 56:7
shall inherit my h. mountain. 57:13
that forget my h. mountain. 65:11
beasts to my h. mountain. 66:20
in my h. mountain they. Ezek 20:40
wast upon the h. mountain. 28:14
turned from thy h. mountain.
Dan 9:16
supplication for the h. mountain. 20
in glorious h. mountain. 11:45
alarm in my h. mountain. Joel 2:1
in Zion, my h. mountain. 3:17
drunk on my h. mountain. Ob 16
because of h. mountain. Zeph 3:11
Lord called h. mountain. Zech 8:3

holy *name*

to profane my h. name. Lev 20:3
profane not my h. name. 22:2
ye profane my h. name. 32
glory ye in his h. name. 1 Chr 16:10
Ps 105:3
we give thanks to thy h. name.
1 Chr 16:35; Ps 106:47
house for thy h. name. 1 Chr 29:16
trusted in his h. name. Ps 33:21
terrible name, for it is h. 99:3
bless the Lord, bless his h. name.
103:1; 145:21
h. and reverend is his name. 111:9
Luke 1:49
One, whose name is h. Isa 57:15
my h. name no more. Ezek 20:39
they profaned my h. name. 36:20
but I had pity for mine h. name. 21
sakes, but for my h. name's sake. 22
h. name known in . . . not let them pollute my h. name any more. 39:7
will be jealous for my h. name. 25
my h. name shall Israel no. 43:7
they have defiled my h. name by. 8
to profane my h. name. Amos 2:7

holy *oil*

an h. anointing oil. Ex 30:25, 31
made the h. anointing oil. 37:29
was anointed with h. oil. Num 35:25
with my h. oil have I. Ps 89:20

holy *One*

Urim be with thy h. one. Deut 33:8*
words of the H. One. Job 6:10
in hell, nor suffer thine H. One to.
Ps 16:10; Acts 2:27; 13:35
in vision to thy h. one. Ps 89:19*
and his H. One shall be. Isa 10:17
shall sanctify the H. One of. 29:23
I be equal ? saith the H. One. 40:25
I am the Lord your H. One. 43:15
Redeemer of Israel his H. One. 49:7
an h. one came down. Dan 4:13, 23
for I am the H. One in. Hos 11:9
from everlasting, O Lord my H. One.
Hab 1:12
the H. One came from mount. 3:3
I know thee who thou art, the H. One.
Mark 1:24; Luke 4:34
ye denied the H. One. Acts 3:14
unction from the H. One. 1 John 2:20

holy *One of Israel*

lifted thy eyes against the H. One of Isr. 2 Ki 19:22; Isa 37:23
sing, O thou H. One of Isr. Ps 71:22
limited the H. One of Isr. 78:41
the H. One of Isr. is our king. 89:18
provoked the H. One of Isr. Isa 1:4
counsel of the H. One of Isr. 5:19
the word of the H. One of Isr. 24
the Lord, the H. One of Isr. Isa 10:20
43:3; 45:11
great is the H. One of Isr. in. 12:6
have respect to H. One of Isr. 17:7
rejoice in the H. One of Isr. 29:19
cause the H. One of Isr. to. 30:11
saith the H. One of Isr. 12, 15
not unto the H. One of Isr. 31:1
Redeemer, the H. One of Isr. 41:14
glory in the H. One of Isr. 16
and the H. One of Isr. hath. 20
your Redeemer, the H. One of Isr.
43:14
is his name, the H. One of Isr. 47:4
saith thy Redeemer, the H. One of Isr. 48:17; 54:5
of Isr. and his H. One. 49:7
unto thee, for the H. One of Isr. 55:5
gold to the H. One of Isr. 60:9
the Zion of the H. One of Isr. 14
Babylon proud against the H. One of Isr. Jer 50:29
sin against the H. One of Isr. 51:5
Lord, the H. One in Isr. Ezek 39:7

holy *ones*

the word of the h. ones. Dan 4:17

holy *people*

thou art an h. people to the Lord.
Deut 7:6; 14:2, 21
thou mayest be an h. people. 26:19
establish thee an h. people. 28:9
call them, the h. people. Isa 62:12
and destroy the h. people. Dan 8:24
the power of the h. people. 12:7

holy *place*

in unto the h. place. Ex 28:29, 35
minister in the h. place. 43; 29:30
seeth his flesh in the h. place. 29:31
sweet incense for the h. place. 31:11
service in h. place. 35:19; 39:1, 41
all the work of the h. place. 38:24*
with unleavened bread . . . in h. place.
Lev 6:16, 26; 7:6; 10:13; 24:9
wash that in the h. place. 6:27
reconcile withal in the h. place. 30
eaten sin offering in h. place? 10:17*
not brought in within h. place. 18*
slay burnt offering in h. place. 14:13*
not at all times into the h. place. 16:2
Aaron come into the h. place. 3
atonement for the h. place. 16
atonement in the h. place. 17, 27
end of reconciling the h. place. 20
when he went into the h. place. 23
flesh with water in the h. place. 24
place whereon thou standest is h.
Josh 5:15
seen out in the h. place. 1 Ki 8:8
priests come out of the h. place. 10
2 Chr 5:11
charge of the h. place. 1 Chr 23:32
carry filthiness out of the h. place.
2 Chr 29:5
burnt offerings in the h. place. 7
up to his h. dwelling-place. 30:27
stand in the h. place according. 35:5
us a nail in his h. place. Ezra 9:8
stand in his h. place ? Ps 24:3
make glad the h. place. 46:4
as in Sinai, in the h. place. 68:17
from the place of the h. Eccl 8:10
in the high and h. place. Isa 57:15
this is the most h. place. Ezek 41:4
place is h. 42:13
not go out of the h. place. 14
it shall be an h. place for the. 45:4
the abomination stand in h. place.
Mat 24:15
blasphemous words against this h. place. Acts 6:13
hath polluted this h. place. 21:28
once into the h. place. Heb 9:12
entered every year into h. place. 25

holy *places*

because places are h. 2 Chr 8:11
out of thy h. places. Ps 68:35
h. places shall be defiled. Ezek 7:24
thy word toward the h. places. 21:2*
not entered into h. places. Heb 9:24

shall be **holy**

ye shall be h. men unto. Ex 22:31
toucheth altar shall be h. 29:37
toucheth them shall be h. Ex 30:29
Lev 6:18
holy, and it shall be h. Ex 30:32, 37
tabernacle, and it shall be h. 40:9
flesh thereof shall be h. Lev 6:27
ye shall be h. for I am holy. 11:44
45; 19:2; 20:26
fruit thereof shall be h. to. 19:24
the priests shall be h. unto. 21:6
they shall be h. to the Lord. 23:20
it is the jubile: it shall be h. 25:12
man giveth to Lord shall be h. 27:9
exchange thereof shall be h. 10, 33
field in the jubile shall be h. 21
the tenth shall be h. unto the. 32
Nazarite shall be h. unto. Num 6:5
doth choose he shall be h. 16:7
male shall eat it, it shall be h. 18:10
shall thy camp be h. Deut 23:14
towards east shall be h. Jer 31:40
holy portion shall be h. Ezek 45:1
then shall Jerusalem be h. Joel 3:17

holy *Spirit*

take not thy h. Spirit. Ps 51:11
and vexed his h. Spirit. Isa 63:10
is he that put his h. Spirit? 11
Father give h. Spirit. Luke 11:13
h. Spirit of promise. Eph 1:13
grieve not h. Spirit of God. 4:30
given us his h. Spirit. 1 Thes 4:8

holy *temple*

toward thy h. temple. Ps 5:7; 138:2
the Lord is in his h. temple. 11:4
the goodness of thy h. temple. 65:4
h. temple have they defiled. 79:1
toward thy h. temple. Jonah 2:4
in unto thee, to thy h. temple. 7
Lord from his h. temple. Mi 1:2
Lord is in his h. temple. Hab 2:20
groweth to an h. temple in. Eph 2:21

holy *thing*

eat of the h. thing. Lev 22:10
if a man eat of the h. thing. 14
thy estimation as an h. thing. 27:23
not touch any h. thing. Num 4:15*
to them a thing most h. Ezek 48:12
therefore that h. thing. Luke 1:35

holy *things*

bear iniquity of h. things. Ex 28:38
ignorance in the h. things. Lev 5:15
from the h. things of Israel. 22:2
that goeth unto the h. things. 3
h. things till he be clean. 4, 6, 12
shall afterward eat of the h. things. 7
shall not profane the h. things. 15
when they eat h. things. 16
not go in to see, when h. things are.
Num 4:20
of h. things shall be his. 5:9; 18:19
shall ye pollute the h. things. 18:32
thy h. things take and. Deut 12:26
in purifying h. things. 1 Chr 23:28
the tithe of h. things. 2 Chr 31:6*
ordinances for h. things. Neh 10:33
the h. things to the Levites. 12:47
I require your h. things. Ezek 20:40
despised mine h. things. 22:8
have profaned my h. things. 26
not kept charge of my h. things. 44:8
near to any of my h. things. 13
minister about h. things. 1 Cor 9:13*

home

until her lord came h. Gen 39:16
bring these men h. slay and. 43:16*
beast not brought h. Ex 9:19
thou shalt bring her h. Deut 21:12
but he shall be free at h. one. 24:5
father's household h. to thee.
Josh 2:18*
if ye bring me h. again. Judg 11:9
way, that thou mayest go h. 19:9
Lord hath brought me h. Ruth 1:2
went unto their own h. 1 Sam 2:2
and bring their calves h. from. 6:
men shut up their calves at h. 1
went h. to Gibeah. 10:26; 24:2
no more h. to his father's. 18:
David sent h. to Tamar. 2 Sam 13:
the king doth not fetch h. 14:1
Ahithophel gat him h. to. 17:2
Lebanon, two months at h. 1 Ki 5:1
h. with me and refresh. 13:7, 1

and tarry at *h*. *2 Ki* 14:10
2 Chr 25:19
bring the ark of God *h*. *1 Chr* 13:12
so David brought not ark *h*. to. 13
the army of Ephraim to go *h*.: they returned *h*. in great. *2 Chr* 25:10
Haman came *h*., called. *Esth* 5:10
believe he will bring *h*. *Job* 39:12
she that tarried at *h*. *Ps* 68:12
good man is not at *h*. *Pr* 7:19
come *h*. at the day appointed. 20
man goeth to his long *h*. *Eccl* 12:5
that Gedaliah should carry him *h*. *Jer* 39:14
abroad the sword, *h*. there. *Lam* 1:20
neither keepeth at *h*. *Hab* 2:5
when ye brought it *h*. I. *Hag* 1:9
servant lieth at *h*. sick. *Mat* 8:6
go *h*. to thy friends. *Mark* 5:19
farewell which are at *h*. *Luke* 9:61
he cometh *h*. he calleth his. 15:6
took her to his own *h*. *John* 19:27
went away to their own *h*. 20:10
and they returned *h*. *Acts* 21:6
hunger let him eat at *h*. *1 Cor* 11:34
ask their husbands at *h*. 14:35
at *h*. in the body. *2 Cor* 5:6
learn to show piety at *h*. *1 Tim* 5:4*
chaste, keepers at *h*. *Tit* 2:5

homeborn

be to him that is *h*. *Ex* 12:49
sister whether *born* at *h*. *Lev* 18:9
Israel a servant? is he a *h*.? *Jer* 2:14

homer

(*A measure of capacity used in both liquid and dry measure. It was equal to ten ephahs or baths, or approximately 9 gallons or 11 bushels. This word is frequently confused with omer, which was one-tenth of an ephah or about 5 pints*)

h. of barley seed at fifty. *Lev* 27:16
seed of an *h*. shall yield. *Isa* 5:10
shall be after the *h*. *Ezek* 45:11
the sixth part of an ephah of an *h*. 13
of a bath, for ten baths are an *h*. 14
for an *h*. and half an *h*. *Hos* 3:2

honest

is an *h*. and good heart. *Luke* 8:15
you seven men of *h*. *Acts* 6:3*
provide things *h*. in the. *Rom* 12:17*
providing *h*. things in. *2 Cor* 8:21*
should do that which is *h*. 13:7*
whatsoever things are *h*. *Phil* 4:8*
our conversation *h*. *1 Pet* 2:12*

honestly

let us walk *h*. as in day. *Rom* 13:13
may walk *h*. toward. *1 Thes* 4:12†
things willing to live *h*. *Heb* 13:18†

honesty

life in godliness and *h*. *1 Tim* 2:2*

honey

Palestine is often referred to in the Bible as a land flowing with milk and honey, Ex 3:8. *Bees are still abundant even in the remote parts of the wilderness, where they deposit their honey in the crevices of rocks or in hollow trees. In some places the word which is translated honey may mean a decoction of the juice of the grape,* Gen 43:11; Ezek 27:17. *Honey was not to be used in sacrifices,* Lev 2:11; *but the firstfruits of honey as of other things were to be presented to the Lord, for the use of his priests.*

carry a little *h*., spices. *Gen* 43:11
like wafers made with *h*. *Ex* 16:31
no leaven, nor any *h*. *Lev* 2:11
a land of oil olive and *h*. *Deut* 8:8
2 Ki 18:32
he made him to suck *h*. *Deut* 32:13
there was *h*. in carcase. *Judg* 14:8, 9
what sweeter than *h*.? what? 18
and there was *h*. upon. *1 Sam* 14:25
h. dropped. 26
tasted a little *h*. 29, 43
brought *h*. and butter. *2 Sam* 17:29
take a cruse of *h*. and. *1 Ki* 14:3
brought firstfruits of *h*. *2 Chr* 31:5
see the brooks of *h*. and. *Job* 20:17
sweeter than *h*. *Ps* 19:10; 119:103
with *h*. out of the rock. 81:16
my son, eat *h*. *Pr* 24:13; 25:16
it is not good to eat much *h*. 25:27
h. and milk are under. *S of S* 4:11
my honeycomb with my *h*. 5:1
butter and *h*. shall he eat. *Isa* 7:15
for butter and *h*. shall everyone. 22
we have treasures of *h*. *Jer* 41:8
was in my mouth as *h*. for. *Ezek* 3:3
eat fine flour, *h*. and oil. 16:13 19
Judah traded in *h*. and balm. 27:17
and his meat was locusts and wild *h*. *Mat* 3:4; *Mark* 1:6
in thy mouth sweet as *h*. *Rev* 10:9
see **floweth, flowing**

honeycomb

rod, and dipped it in a *h*. *1 Sam* 14:27
also than honey and *h*. *Ps* 19:10
strange woman drop as *h*. *Pr* 5:3
words are as an *h*. sweet. 16:24
eat the *h*. which is sweet. 24:13
full soul loatheth an *h*. 27:7
Thy lips drop as the *h*. *S of S* 4:11
I have eaten my *h*. with. 5:1
him a piece of an *h*. *Luke* 24:42

honour

to their assembly, my *h*. *Gen* 49:6*
will get me *h*. upon Pharaoh. *Ex* 14:17
when I have gotten me *h*. upon. 18
I will promote thee unto great *h*. *Num* 22:17, 37
hath kept thee back from *h*. 24:11
shalt put some of thine *h*. 27:20
above all nations in *h*. *Deut* 26:19
shall not be for thine *h*. *Judg* 4:9
to pass, we may do thee *h*. 13:17
shall I be had in *h*. *2 Sam* 6:22
given thee riches and *h*. *1 Ki* 3:13
glory and *h*. are in his. *1 Chr* 16:27
can David say more for *h*. 17:18
both riches and *h*. come of. 29:12
in old age, full of riches and *h*. 28
not asked riches or *h*. *2 Chr* 1:11
thee riches, and wealth, and *h*. 12
had *h*. in abundance. 17:5; 18:1
nor shall it be for thy *h*. 26:18
had much riches and *h*. 32:27
of Jerusalem did him *h*. 33
the *h*. of his excellent. *Esth* 1:4
shall give to their husbands *h*. 20
h. hath been done Mordecai? 6:3
light and gladness, joy and *h*. 8:16
sons come to *h*. he. *Job* 14:21
the enemy lay mine *h*. in. *Ps* 7:5*
crowned him with *h*. 8:5; *Heb* 2:7, 9
h. and majesty. *Ps* 21:5
loved the place where thine *h*. 26:8*
nevertheless man being in *h*. 49:12
in *h*. and understandeth not. 20
sing forth the *h*. of his name. 66:2*
thy mouth be filled with thy *h*. 71:8
h. and majesty are before him. 96:6
thou art clothed with *h*. 104:1
horn shall be exalted with *h*. 112:9
I will speak of the *h*. of thy. 145:5
h. have all his saints, praise. 149:9
left hand are riches and *h*. *Pr* 3:16
and she shall bring thee to *h*. 4:8
lest thou give thine *h*. to others. 5:9
riches and *h*. are with me. 8:18
a gracious woman retaineth *h*. 11:16
of the people is the king's *h*. 14:28*
before *h*. is humility. 15:33; 18:12
it is an *h*. for a man to cease. 20:3
followeth mercy, findeth *h*. 21:21
of the Lord are riches and *h*. 22:4
the *h*. of kings is to search. 25:2*
so *h*. is not seemly for a fool. 26:1
so is he that giveth *h*. to a fool. 8
h. shall uphold the humble. 29:23
and *h*. are her clothing. 31:25*
whom God hath given *h*. *Eccl* 6:2
that is in reputation for *h*. 10:1
h. before all nations of. *Jer* 33:9*
rewards and great *h*. *Dan* 2:6
I have built for the *h*. of my. 4:30*
mine *h*. and brightness returned. 36*
gave thy father glory and *h*. 5:18*
they shall not give the *h*. of. 11:21
father, where is mine *h*.? *Mal* 1:6
prophet is not without *h*. save in his. *Mat* 13:57; *Mark* 6:4; *John* 4:44
receive not *h*. from men. *John* 5:41*
h. one of another, and seek not *h*. 44*
if I honour myself, my *h*. is. 8:54*
seek for glory and *h*. *Rom* 2:7
but *h*. to every man that. 10
lump to make one vessel to *h*. 9:21
kindly affectioned, in *h*. 12:10
render therefore *h*. to whom *h*. 13:7
we bestow more *h*. *1 Cor* 12:23, 24
by *h*. and dishonour, by. *2 Cor* 6:8*
not in any *h*. to satisfying. *Col* 2:23*
possess his vessel in *h*. *1 Thes* 4:4
the only wise God be *h*. *1 Tim* 1:17
counted worthy of double *h*. 5:17
own masters worthy of all *h*. 6:1
to whom be *h*. and power. 16
vessels, some to *h*. *2 Tim* 2:20, 21
builded, hath more *h*. *Heb* 3:3
no man taketh this *h*. to. 5:4
be found to praise, *h*. *1 Pet* 1:7
giving *h*. to the wife as to the. 3:7
from God the Father *h*. *2 Pet* 1:17
beasts give glory and *h*. *Rev* 4:9
to receive glory and *h*. 11; 5:12
h. power and might be to him. 5:13
7:12; 19:1
be glad, rejoice, and give *h*. 19:7*
bring their glory and *h*. 21:24, 26

honour, *verb*

h. thy father and thy mother. *Ex* 20:12; *Deut* 5:16; *Mat* 15:4
19:19; *Mark* 7:10; 10:19
Luke 18:20; *Eph* 6:2
shalt not *h*. the person. *Lev* 19:15
thou shalt *h*. the face of the old. 32
they *h*. God and man. *Judg* 9:9
that *h*. me I will *h*. *1 Sam* 2:30
yet *h*. me now, I pray thee. 15:30
David doth *h*. thy father, that he. *2 Sam* 10:3; *1 Chr* 19:3
whom the king delighteth to *h*. *Esth* 6:6, 7, 9, 11
I will deliver him and *h*. *Ps* 91:15
h. Lord with thy substance. *Pr* 3:9
with their lips do *h*. me. *Isa* 29:13
the beast of the field shall *h*. 43:20
and shalt *h*. him, not doing. 58:13
I extol and *h*. the King. *Dan* 4:37
he *h*. the God . . . a god whom his fathers knew not, shall he *h*. 11:38
and *h*. not his father or. *Mat* 15:6
should *h*. Son as they *h*. *John* 5:23
but I *h*. my Father, and ye. 8:49
if I *h*. myself, my *h*. is nothing. 54
him will my Father *h*. 12:26
h. widows that are. *1 Tim* 5:3
h. all men, fear God, *h*. *1 Pet* 2:17

honourable

Shechem was more *h*. *Gen* 34:19
sent princes more *h*. *Num* 22:15
the city a man of God, and he is an *h*. man, all he saith. *1 Sam* 9:6
faithful as David, who is *h*. in. 22:14
was he not most *h*. of three? *2 Sam* 23:19; *1 Chr* 11:21
was more *h*. than the thirty, but. 23
now Naaman was *h*. with. *2 Ki* 5:1
Jabez was more *h*. than. *1 Chr* 4:9
behold, was *h*. among thirty. 11:25
had the earth, and the *h*. *Job* 22:8
king's daughters among thy *h*. *Ps* 45:9
his work is *h*. and glorious. 111:3
doth take away the *h*. man. *Isa* 3:3
behave proudly against the *h*. 5
and their *h*. men are famished. 5:13
ancient and *h*. he is the head. 9:15
whose traffickers are the *h*. of. 23:8
bring into contempt all the *h*. of. 9
magnify the law and make it *h*. 42:21
thou hast been *h*. 43:4
the holy of the Lord *h*. 58:13
cast lots for her *h*. men. *Nah* 3:10
of Arimathaea an *h*. *Mark* 15:43*
lest a more *h*. man be. *Luke* 14:8
Jews stirred up the *h*. *Acts* 13:50*
also of *h*. women not a few. 17:12
ye are strong, ye are *h*. *1 Cor* 4:10
members we think less *h*. 12:23
marriage is *h*. in all. *Heb* 13:4

honoured

I will be *h.* upon Pharaoh. *Ex* 14:4
reproof shall be *h.* *Pr* 13:18
on his master shall be *h.* 27:18
nor hast thou *h.* me with. *Isa* 43:23
all that *h.* her, despise. *Lam* 1:8
of the elders were not *h.* 5:12
I praised and *h.* him that. *Dan* 4:34
who also *h.* us with. *Acts* 28:10
or one member be *h.* *1 Cor* 12:26

honourest

and *h.* thy sons above. *1 Sam* 2:29

honoureth

but he *h.* them that fear. *Ps* 15:4
is better than he that *h.* *Pr* 12:9
he that *h.* him hath mercy. 14:31
a son *h.* his father, where? *Mal* 1:6
and *h.* me with their lips. *Mat* 15:8
Mark 7:6
he that *h.* not the Son, *h.* not the.
John 5:23
it is my Father that *h.* me, of. 8:54*

honours

honoured us with many *h.* *Acts* 28:10

hoods

I will take away the *h.* *Isa* 3:23*

hoof

there shall not an *h.* be. *Ex* 10:26
whatever parteth *h.* and. *Lev* 11:3
divide the *h.* but divideth not *h.* 4
divideth not the *h.* 5, 6; *Deut* 14:7
the swine, though he divide the *h.*
Lev 11:7, 26; *Deut* 14:6, 8

hoofs

were the horse *h.* broken. *Judg* 5:22
than an ox with *h.* *Ps* 69:31
horses' *h.* shall be counted. *Isa* 5:28
of the stamping of the *h.* *Jer* 47:3
with *h.* of horses shall. *Ezek* 26:11
nor shall the *h.* of beasts. 32:13
I will make thy *h.* brass. *Mi* 4:13

hook

I will put my *h.* in thy nose.
2 Ki 19:28; *Isa* 37:29
thou draw leviathan with an *h.*?
Job 41:1, 2*
go, and cast an *h.* and. *Mat* 17:27

hooks

their *h.* shall be of gold. *Ex* 26:32
37; 36:36
the *h.* of the pillars shall be. 27:10
11, 17; 38:10, 11, 12, 17, 19
their spears into pruning *h.* *Isa* 2:4
Mi 4:3
off the sprigs with pruning *h.* 18:5
but I will put *h.* *Ezek* 29:4; 38:4
and within were *h.*, an hand. 40:43
beat your pruning *h.* into. *Joel* 3:10
take you away with *h.* *Amos* 4:2

hope

should say, I have *h.*, if. *Ruth* 1:12
there is *h.* in Israel. *Ezra* 10:2
fear, confidence, thy *h.*? *Job* 4:6
poor hath *h.*, and iniquity. 5:16
my days are spent without *h.* 7:6
hypocrite's *h.* shall perish. 8:13, 14*
be secure, because there is *h.* 11:18
their *h.* shall be as the giving up. 20
for there is *h.* of a tree if it. 14:7
thou destroyest the *h.* of man. 19
what is *h.* of hypocrite though? 27:8
the *h.* of him is in vain. 41:9
might set their *h.* in. *Ps* 78:7
happy is he whose *h.* is in. 146:5
the *h.* of the righteous. *Pr* 10:28
h. of unjust men perisheth. 11:7
h. deferred maketh the. 13:12
but the righteous hath *h.* 14:32
thy son while there is *h.* 19:18
more *h.* of a fool than. 26:12; 29:20
to living, there is *h.* *Eccl* 9:4
is no *h.* *Isa* 57:10; *Jer* 2:25; 18:12
O the *h.* of Israel. *Jer* 14:8; 17:13
blessed is the man whose *h.* 17:7*
there is *h.* in the end, saith. 31:17
even the Lord, the *h.* of their. 50:7
therefore have I *h.* *Lam* 3:21
the dust, if so be there may be *h.* 29
she saw that her *h.* was. *Ezek* 19:5
our bones dried, our *h.* lost. 37:11
Achor for a door of *h.* *Hos* 2:15
the Lord will be the *h.* *Joel* 3:16*
hold ye prisoners of *h.* *Zech* 9:12
the *h.* of their gains. *Acts* 16:19
of the *h.* and resurrection of. 23:6
I have *h.* toward God which. 24:15
now I am judged for the *h.* 26:6
for which *h.*'s sake. I am accused. 7
h. that we should be saved. 27:20
for *h.* of Israel I am bound. 28:20
experience; experience, *h.* *Rom* 5:4
h. maketh not ashamed, because. 5
saved by *h.*: but *h.* seen is not *h.* 8:24
through patience might have *h.* 15:4
that ye may abound in *h.* through. 13
be partaker of his *h.* *1 Cor* 9:10
now abideth faith, *h.*, charity. 13:13
this life only we have *h.* in. 15:19
h. of you is stedfast. *2 Cor* 1:7
seeing that we have such *h.* 3:12
having *h.* when your faith is. 10:15
we thro' the Spirit wait for *h.* *Gal* 5:5
may know what is the *h.* *Eph* 1:18
having no *h.* and without God. 2:12
even as ye are called in one *h.* 4:4
for the *h.* laid up for you. *Col* 1:5
be not moved away from the *h.* 23
which is Christ in you, the *h.* of. 27
your patience of *h.* in. *1 Thes* 1:3
for what is our *h.* and joy? 2:19
even as others who have no *h.* 4:13
and for an helmet the *h.* of. 5:8
hath given us good *h.* *2 Thes* 2:16
Jesus, who is our *h.* *1 Tim* 1:1
looking for that blessed *h.* *Tit* 2:13
made heirs according to the *h.* 3:7
rejoicing of the *h.* firm to. *Heb* 3:6
to the full assurance of *h.* 6:11
who have fled to lay hold on *h.* 18
which *h.* we have as an anchor of. 19
bringing in of a better *h.* did. 7:19
us again to a lively *h.* *1 Pet* 1:3
that your faith and *h.* might be. 21
asketh a reason of the *h.* that. 3:15
man that hath this *h.* *1 John* 3:3

hope, *verb*

strength, that I should *h.*? *Job* 6:11*
didst make me *h.* when. *Ps* 22:9*
of courage, all ye that *h.* in. 31:24
h. in his mercy. 33:18; 147:11
on us, according as we *h.* in. 33:22
in thee, O Lord, do I *h.* 38:15
h. thou in God. 42:5, 11; 43:5
but I will *h.* continually. 71:14
thou hast caused me to *h.* 119:49
I *h.* in thy word. 81, 114; 130:5
let Israel *h.* in Lord. 130:7; 131:3
in the pit cannot *h.* for. *Isa* 38:18
therefore will I *h.* in him. *Lam* 3:24
good that a man should both *h.* 26
have made others to *h.* *Ezek* 13:6
if ye lend to them of whom ye *h.*
Luke 6:34
promise our tribes *h.* to. *Acts* 26:7
why doth he *h.* for? *Rom* 8:24
if we *h.* for that we see not. 25
him I *h.* to send presently. *Phil* 2:23
be sober, and *h.* to the. *1 Pet* 1:13

in **hope**

my flesh shall rest in *h.* *Ps* 16:9*
Acts 2:26
against hope believed *in h.* *Rom* 4:18
and rejoice *in h.* of the glory. 5:2
hath subjected the same *in h.* 8:20
rejoicing *in h.* patient in. 12:12
may abound *in h.* through. 15:13
ploweth *in h.*; that thresheth *in h.*
1 Cor 9:10
in h. of eternal life which. *Tit* 1:2

my **hope**

is now *my h.*? as for *my h.* *Job* 17:15
and *my h.* hath he removed. 19:10
if I have made gold *my h.* or. 31:24
what wait I for? *my h.* is. *Ps* 39:7
for thou art *my h.* O Lord God. 71:5
Jer 17:17
not be ashamed of *my h.* *Ps* 119:116
and *my h.* is perished. *Lam* 3:18*
according to *my h.* that in. *Phil* 1:20

hoped

enemies of the Jews *h.* *Esth* 9:1
confounded because they had *h.*
Job 6:20
have *h.* in thy judgements. *Ps* 119:43
I have *h.* in thy word. 74, 147
I have *h.* for thy salvation. 166
in vain is salvation *h.* for. *Jer* 3:23
he *h.* to have seen some. *Luke* 23:8
h. money should have. *Acts* 24:26
they did, not as we *h.* *2 Cor* 8:5
substance of things *h.* for. *Heb* 11:1

hopeth

charity *h.* all things. *1 Cor* 13:7

Hophni

two sons of Eli, *H.* *1 Sam* 1:3; 4:4
H. and Phinehas shall both. 2:34
H. and Phinehas were slain. 4:11, 17

hoping

do good, and lend, *h.* *Luke* 6:35*
I write, *h.* to come. *1 Tim* 3:14

Hor, *see* **mount**

Horeb

came to the mountain of God, even
to *H.* *Ex* 3:1; *1 Ki* 19:8
before thee on the rock in *H.* *Ex* 17:6
of ornaments by mount *H.* 33:6
spake to us in *H.* *Deut* 1:6; 4:15
stoodest before the Lord in *H.* 4:10
a covenant with us in *H.* 5:2; 29:1
also in *H.* ye provoked the. 9:8
desiredst of the Lord in *H.* 18:16
two tables which Moses put in ark at
H. *1 Ki* 8:9; *2 Chr* 5:10
they made a calf in *H.* *Ps* 106:19
commanded unto him in *H.* *Mal* 4:4

Hor-hagidgad

encamped at *H.* *Num* 33:32
went from *H.* 33

Hormah

discomfited them to *H.* *Num* 14:45
called the name of place *H.* 21:3
you in Seir, even unto *H.* *Deut* 1:44
of Judah, Eltolad, *H.* *Josh* 15:30
out of Judah, Bethul, *H.* 19:4
the city was called *H.* *Judg* 1:17
them that were in *H.* *1 Sam* 30:30
Shimei's sons dwelt at *H.* *1 Chr* 4:30

horn

This word is often used metaphorically to signify strength and honour, because horns are the chief weapons and ornaments of the animals which possess them; hence they are also used as a type of victory. In the sense of honour, the word stands both for the abstract, Lam 2:3; *and so for supreme authority, or for the concrete,* Dan 7:8, *whence it comes to mean king or kingdom.*

wont to push with his *h.* *Ex* 21:29
Hannah said, mine *h.* is. *1 Sam* 2:1
and he shall exalt the *h.* of. 10
fill thine *h.* with oil, go, I will. 16:1
Samuel took the *h.* of oil. 13
the *h.* of my salvation. *2 Sam* 22:3
Ps 18:2
priest took an *h.* of oil. *1 Ki* 1:39
God, to lift up the *h.* *1 Chr* 25:5
I have defiled my *h.* in. *Job* 16:15
lift not up the *h.* *Ps* 75:4, 5
and in thy favour our *h.* 89:17
and in my name shall his *h.* 24
h. shalt thou exalt like *h.* 92:10
his *h.* shall be exalted with. 112:9
make the *h.* of David to. 132:17
he also exalteth the *h.* of. 148:14
h. of Moab is cut off. *Jer* 48:25
cut off all the *h.* of Israel. *Lam* 2:3
he hath set up the *h.* of thine. 17
I will cause the *h.* of. *Ezek* 29:21
little *h.*; in this *h.* *Dan* 7:8, 20
the great words which the *h.* 11
the same *h.* made war with the. 21
goat had a notable *h.* between. 8:5
he was strong, the great *h.* 8
of them came forth a little *h.* 9
the great *h.* that is between his. 21
lift up their *h.* over the. *Zech* 1:21
hath raised up an *h.* of. *Luke* 1:69

hornet

(*The large species of wasp, whose sting is very severe*)

Lord will send the *h.* *Deut* 7:20
I sent the *h.* before you. *Josh* 24:12

hornets

I will send *h.* before thee. *Ex* 23:28

horns

in a thicket by his *h.* *Gen* 22:13
h. of it on the four corners, his *h.* *Ex* 27:2; 30:2; 37:25; 38:2
put of the blood on the *h.* 29:12
Lev 4:7, 18, 25, 30, 34; 8:15; 9:9 16:18
shalt overlay the *h.* *Ex* 30:3; 37:26
make an atonement on *h.* of. 30:10
his *h.* are like the *h.* *Deut* 33:17
Joab caught hold on *h.* of. *1 Ki* 2:28
Zedekiah made *h.* of iron. 22:11 *2 Chr* 18:10
heard me from the *h.* of. *Ps* 22:21
than a bullock that hath *h.* 69:31
h. of the wicked will I cut off, but the *h.* of the righteous shall. 75:10
bind the sacrifice to the *h.* 118:27
brought for a present *h.* *Ezek* 27:15
all the diseased with your *h.* 34:21
the altar and upward shall be four *h.* 43:15
fourth beast had ten *h.* *Dan* 7:7, 20
I considered the *h.*, three *h.* were. 8
the ten *h.* are ten kings that shall. 24
ram had two *h.*: the two *h.* were. 8:3
came to the ram which had two *h.* 6
the ram, and brake his two *h.* 7
two *h.* are the kings of Media. 20
have we not taken *h.* by. *Amos* 6:13
for I will make thy *h.* iron. *Mi* 4:13
he had *h.* coming out of. *Hab* 3:4
I saw, and behold, four *h.* *Zech* 1:18
the *h.* which have scattered. 19, 21
are come to cast out the *h.* 21
a Lamb having seven *h.* *Rev* 5:6
having seven heads and ten *h.* 12:3
beast having ten *h.* and on his *h.* 13:1
another beast had two *h.* like a. 11
coloured beast, having ten *h.* 17:3
hath the seven heads and ten *h.* 7
the ten *h.* thou sawest are. 12, 16
see **rams**

Horonaim

in the way of *H.* they shall. *Isa* 15:5
crying shall be from *H.* *Jer* 48:3
in going down of *H.* the enemies. 5
from Zoar to *H.* they uttered. 34

Horonite, *see* **Sanballat**

horrible

wicked he shall rain a *h.* *Ps* 11:6*
me up also out of a *h.* pit. 40:2
a *h.* thing is committed. *Jer* 5:30
virgin of Israel hath done a *h.* 18:13
seen in the prophets a *h.* 23:14
I have seen a *h.* thing in. *Hos* 6:10

horribly

be *h.* afraid, O ye heavens. *Jer* 2:12
their kings shall be *h.* *Ezek* 32:10

horror

a *h.* of great darkness. *Gen* 15:12
h. hath overwhelmed me. *Ps* 55:5
h. hath taken hold on me. 119:53*
h. shall cover them, and. *Ezek* 7:18

horse

The most striking feature of the notices of this animal in the Bible is that it invariably means a war-horse. The principal use of the horse in war was in the chariot, and because of the hilly nature of Palestine only certain localities allowed the use of chariots. The possession of a large number of horses, or their breeding, was forbidden in early times, Deut 17:16, *and was held to apply to later periods as well. David first gathered a force of cavalry or chariots,* 2 Sam 8:4, *but Solomon was the first to have them in great numbers,* 1 Ki 4:26. *They were not shod, and those with naturally hard hoofs were greatly desired,* Isa 5:28. *Horses and chariots were used in idolatrous processions,* 2 Ki 23:11.

adder that biteth the *h.* heels. *Gen* 49:17
the *h.* and rider hath he. *Ex* 15:21
were *h.* hoofs broken. *Judg* 5:22
a *h.* for 150 shekels. *1 Ki* 10:29 *2 Chr* 1:17
Ben-hadad king escaped on *h.* with. *1 Ki* 20:20
like the army lost, *h.* for *h.* 25
let *h.* the king rideth upon. *Esth* 6:8
let this *h.* be delivered to one. 9
take the apparel and *h.* as thou. 10
Haman the apparel and the *h.* 11
she scorneth the *h.* *Job* 39:18
hast thou given *h.* strength? 19
be ye not as the *h.* or as. *Ps* 32:9
h. is a vain thing for safety. 33:17
the chariot and *h.* are cast. 76:6
not in the strength of the *h.* 147:10
the *h.* is prepared against. *Pr* 21:31
a whip for the *h.* a rod for the. 26:3
forth the chariot and *h.* *Isa* 43:17
through the deep, as a *h.* 63:13
as the *h.* rusheth into. *Jer* 8:6
will I break in pieces the *h.* 51:21
nor shall he that rideth *h.* *Amos* 2:15
a man riding upon a red *h.* *Zech* 1:8
and I will cut off the *h.* from. 9:10
made them as his goodly *h.* 10:3
I will smite every *h.* with. 12:4
shall be the plague of the *h.* 14:15
behold, a white *h.* *Rev* 6:2; 19:11
h. that was red. 6:4
a black *h.* 5
behold, a pale *h.* 8
blood came even to the *h.* 14:20
against him that sat on the *h.* 19:19
sword of him that sat on the *h.* 21

horseback

there went one on *h.* to. *2 Ki* 9:18
then he sent out a second on *h.* 19
and bring him on *h.* *Esth* 6:9
Haman brought him on *h.* 11
sent letters by posts on *h.* 8:10

horse gate

to entering of *h. gate.* *2 Chr* 23:15
above *h. gate* repaired. *Neh* 3:28
corner of the *h. gate.* *Jer* 31:40

horseleech

the *h.* hath two daughters. *Pr* 30:15

horseman

Joram said, take an *h.* *2 Ki* 9:17
h. lifteth up the bright. *Nah* 3:3

horsemen

Joseph chariots and *h.* *Gen* 50:9
the *h.* of Pharaoh pursued. *Ex* 14:9
me honour on Pharaoh and his *h.* 17
Pharaoh and *h.* went into sea. 15:19 *Josh* 24:6
your sons to be his *h.* *1 Sam* 8:11
Philistines gathered 6000 *h.* 13:5
lo, the *h.* followed hard. *2 Sam* 1:6
and David took 700 *h.* 8:4
David slew 40,000 *h.*, smote. 10:18
prepared chariots and *h.* *1 Ki* 1:5
Solomon had 12,000 *h.* 4:26; 10:26
store for his chariots, and cities for his *h.* 9:19, 22; *2 Chr* 8:6, 9
escaped on an horse with his *h.* 20:20
chariots of Israel and *h.* *2 Ki* 2:12
leave to Jehoahaz but fifty *h.* 13:7
Joash said, O my father, the *h.* 14
in Egypt for chariots and *h.* 18:24
came up with 60,000 *h.* *2 Chr* 12:3
a huge host with many *h.* 16:8
ashamed to require *h.* *Ezra* 8:22
sent captains and *h.* with. *Neh* 2:9
chariot with a couple of *h.* *Isa* 21:7, 9
h. shall set themselves in array. 22:7
not bruise them with his *h.* 28:28*
and trust in *h.* because they. 31:1
put thy trust on Egypt for *h.* 36:9
flee for the noise of the *h.* *Jer* 4:29
get up, ye *h.* and stand with. 46:4
all of them *h.* riding. *Ezek* 23:6, 12
against Tyrus with *h.* 26:7
shake at the noise of the *h.* 10
Togarmah traded in fairs with *h.* 27:14*
thee forth, horses and *h.* 38:4
north shall come with *h.* *Dan* 11:40

I will not save them by horses, nor by *h.* *Hos* 1:7
as *h.* so shall they run. *Joel* 2:4
h. shall spread themselves, and their *h.* shall come from far. *Hab* 1:8
make ready *h.* threescore. *Acts* 23:23
morrow they left the *h.* to go. 32
number of the army of *h.* *Rev* 9:16

horses

bread in exchange for *h.* *Gen* 47:17
hand of Lord is upon the *h.* *Ex* 9:3
h. to himself, to the end that he should multiply *h.* *Deut* 17:16
also and straw for the *h.* *1 Ki* 4:28
they brought *h.* and mules. 10:25 *2 Chr* 9:24
Solomon had *h.* out of Egypt. *1 Ki* 10:28; *2 Chr* 1:16, 17; 9:28
find grass to save the *h.* *1 Ki* 18:5
and my *h.* are as thy *h.* 22:4 *2 Ki* 3:7
there appeared *h.* of fire. *2 Ki* 2:11
Naaman came with his *h.* and. 5:9
they left their *h.* and fled for. 7:7
but *h.* tied. 10
some take five of the *h.* 13
blood was sprinkled on the *h.* 9:33
brought Amaziah on *h.* 14:20 *2 Chr* 25:28
I will deliver thee 2000 *h.* *2 Ki* 18:23; *Isa* 36:8
Josiah took away the *h.* *2 Ki* 23:11
h. were 736. *Ezra* 2:66; *Neh* 7:68
I have seen servants on *h.* *Eccl* 10:7
land is also full of *h.* *Isa* 2:7
their *h.*' hoofs shall be counted. 5:28
no, for we will flee upon *h.* 30:16
and stay on *h.* and trust in. 31:1
and their *h.* are flesh, and not. 3
his *h.* are swifter than. *Jer* 4:13
as fed *h.* in the morning. 5:8
they ride on *h.* set in array. 6:23
snorting of his *h.* was heard. 8:16
canst thou contend with *h.*? 12:5
harness the *h.* and get up, ye. 46:4
stamping of the hoofs of his *h.* 47:3
and they shall ride upon *h.* 50:42
cause the *h.* to come up as. 51:27
they might give him *h.* *Ezek* 17:15
horsemen riding on *h.* 23:6, 12
issue is like the issue of *h.* 20
all of them riding on *h.* 23; 38:15
the abundance of his *h.* 26:10
traded in thy fairs with *h.* 27:14
forth, and all thy army, *h.* 38:4
nor by battle, by *h.* *Hos* 1:7
not save, we will not ride on *h.* 14:3
as the appearance of *h.* *Joel* 2:4
have taken away your *h.* *Amos* 4:10
shall *h.* run upon the rock? 6:12
that I will cut off thy *h.* *Mi* 5:10
their *h.* also are swifter. *Hab* 1:8
that thou didst ride on thy *h.* 3:8
walk through the sea with thy *h.* 15
I will overthrow the *h.* *Hag* 2:22
him there were red *h.* *Zech* 1:8
chariot red *h.*, in the second black *h.* 6:2
white *h.*, in fourth chariot bay *h.* 3
h. go forth into the north country. 6
the riders on *h.* shall be. 10:5
on bells of *h.* HOLINESS UNTO THE LORD. 14:20
we put bits in the *h.*' mouths. *Jas* 3:3
locusts were like *h.* *Rev* 9:7
h., the heads of *h.* as heads of. 17
buyeth the merchandise of *h.* 18:13
followed him upon white *h.* 19:14
may eat flesh of kings and *h.* 18
see **chariots**

hosanna

An Hebrew *word, meaning,* Save, we pray. *It is taken from the* 118*th Psalm, and was the cry of the multitudes as they thronged in our Lord's triumphal procession into Jerusalem,* Mat 21:9, 15; Mark 11:9, 10; John 12:13.

Hosea

(*One of the Minor Prophets. The same name as* **Hoshea**)

hosen

men were bound in their *h.* *Dan* 3:21

Hoshea

H. son of Nun. *Deut* 32:44
H. made a conspiracy. *2 Ki* 15:30
H. son of Elah began to reign. 17:1
H. became Assyria's servant. 3
ninth year of *H.* Samaria. 6; 18:10
ruler of Ephraim was *H. 1 Chr* 27:20
H. sealed the covenant. *Neh* 10:23

hospitality

This virtue has always been very much esteemed by civilized peoples. The Jewish laws with regard to strangers are framed in accordance with the spirit of hospitality, Lev 19:33, 34, etc.; *and before the giving of the law there were many instances of the entertaining of strangers,* Gen 18:2, 3; Heb 13:2. *It was more necessary in those times of difficult travel and few inns, but the spirit of modern hospitality is the same.*

In Apostolic times the virtue was strongly enjoined on the followers of Christ, although the higher civilization and larger population made it less of a necessity than in patriarchal times.

distributing, given to *h.* *Rom* 12:13
1 Tim 3:2
but a lover of *h.* a lover. *Tit* 1:8
use *h.* one to another. *1 Pet* 4:9

host

two pence, gave them to *h.Luke* 10:35
Gaius mine *h.* and of. *Rom* 16:23

host

[1] *The word very frequently means camp or army. In these passages, easily discovered by the context, the Revisions use these other words.* [2] *It means in some cases merely a vast number.*

earth was finished, and all *h. Gen* 2:1
chief captain of his *h.* 21:22, 32
he said, This is God's *h.* 32:2
honoured on all his *h.* *Ex* 14:4, 17
h. of Egyptians through pillar of fire and of cloud, and troubled *h.* 24
the waters covered all the *h.* 28
dew lay round about the *h.* 16:13
h. and those that were numbered.
Num 2:4, 6, 8, 11, 13, 15, 19, 21, 23
all that entered into *h.* *Num* 4:3*
over the *h.* of Judah. 10:14
the *h.* of Issachar. 15
over *h.* of Zebulun. 16
over *h.* of Reuben 18
over *h.* of Simeon. 19
wroth with the officers of *h.* 31:14
the officers of the *h.* came near. 48
war were wasted from *h. Deut* 2:14
to destroy them from among *h.* 15
when the *h.* goeth forth against. 23:9
pass through the *h.* and. *Josh* 1:11
the officers went through the *h.* 3:2
as captain of the *h.* of the Lord. 5:14
came again to Joshua to the *h.* 18:9
the captain of whose *h.* *Judg* 4:2
and all the *h.* of Sisera fell on. 16
the *h.* of Midian was beneath. 7:8
arise, get thee down unto the *h.* 9, 10
cake of bread tumbled into the *h.* 13
and all the *h.* ran, and cried 21
up and smote the *h.*, the *h.* 8:11
pursued and discomfited all the *h.* 12
Saul came into the *h.* *1 Sam* 11:11
there was trembling in the *h.* 14:15
the noise of the *h.* went on and. 19
the captain of Saul's *h.* was Abner. 50
David came as the *h.* was. 17:20
when Saul saw the *h.* of the. 28:5
deliver the *h.* of Israel to. 19
coming in with me in the *h.* is. 29:6
Lord shall smite the *h.* *2 Sam* 5:24
David had smitten all the *h.* of Hadadezer. 8:9; *1 Chr* 18:9
David smote Shobach captain of their *h. 2 Sam* 10:18; *1 Chr* 19:18
Amasa captain of *h.* *2 Sam* 17:25
if thou be not captain of *h.* 19:13
Joab was over all the *h.* 20:23
1 Chr 18:15
these three brake through the *h.*
2 Sam 23:16; *1 Chr* 11:18
son of Ner captain of *h.* of Israel and Amasa captain of *h. 1 Ki* 2:32
Benaiah over the *h.* 35, 4:4
Omri captain of the *h.*, king. 16:16
gathered all his *h.* together. 20:1
hand and carry me out of *h.* 22:34
was no water for the *h.* *2 Ki* 3:9
spoken for to captain of the *h.*? 4:13
sent he horses and great *h.* 6:14
Ben-hadad gathered his *h.* and. 24
come and let us fall unto the *h.* 7:4
h. to hear the noise of a great *h.* 6
behold the captains of the *h.* 9:5
Sennacherib sent a great *h.* 18:17
Nebuchadnezzar came and his *h.* 25:1
scribe of the *h.* 19; *Jer* 52:25
their fathers over the *h. 1 Chr* 9:19
was a great *h.* like the *h.* 12:22
of all the captains of the *h.* 27:3
Zerah came with an *h.* *2 Chr* 14:9
not relied, therefore is the *h.* 16:7
Ethiopians and Lubims a huge *h.*? 8
and carry me out of the *h.* 18:33
delivered a great *h.* into. 24:24
Uzziah had an *h.* of fighting. 26:11
Oded went out before the *h.* 28:9
though an *h.* should encamp. *Ps* 27:3
all *h.* of them made by breath. 33:6
by the multitude of an *h.* 16
Pharaoh and *h.* in Red sea. 136:15
hosts mustereth the *h.* of. *Isa* 13:4
Lord shall punish the *h.* of. 24:21
that bringeth out their *h.* 40:26
and all their *h.* have I. 45:12
destroy ye utterly all her *h. Jer* 51:3
speech, as noise of an *h.* *Ezek* 1:24
cast down some of the *h.* *Dan* 8:10
himself to the prince of the *h.* 11
an *h.* was given him against the. 12
to give the *h.* to be trodden. 13
the captivity of this *h.* shall. *Ob* 20
multitude of heavenly *h. Luke* 2:13
see **heaven**

hostages

all the gold and silver and *h.* and.
2 Ki 14:14; *2 Chr* 25:24

hosts

the *h.* of Lord went out. *Ex* 12:41
of Canaan and all their *h. Josh* 10:5
11:4
Zalmunna with their *h.* *Judg* 8:10
sent the captains of the *h. 1 Ki* 15:20
the Lord, all ye his *h.* *Ps* 103:21
O God, go forth with *h.*? 108:11
all his angels, all his *h.* 148:2
a goodly heritage of the *h. Jer* 3:19
see **God, Lord**

hot

when the sun waxed *h.* *Ex* 16:21
there is a *h.* burning. *Lev* 13:24
afraid of anger and *h.* *Deut* 9:19
pursue, while his heart is *h.* 19:6
this our bread we took *h. Josh* 9:12
Lord was *h.* against Israel, and he.
Judg 2:14*, 20*; 3:8*; 10:7*
not thine anger be *h.* against. 6:39*
time sun be *h.*, ye. *1 Sam* 11:9
put *h.* bread in day when it. 21:6
be opened till the sun be *h. Neh* 7:3
when it is *h.* they are. *Job* 6:17
neither chasten in thy *h. Ps* 6:1; 38:1
my heart was *h.* within me. 39:3
he gave their flocks to *h.* 78:48
can one go upon *h.* coals? *Pr* 6:28
brass of it may be *h.* *Ezek* 24:11
furnace was exceeding *h.* *Dan* 3:22
they are all *h.* as an oven. *Hos* 7:7
seared with a *h.* iron. *1 Tim* 4:2
thou art neither cold nor *h.*: I would thou wert cold or *h.* *Rev* 3:15, 16
see **wax,** *verb*

hotly

thou hast so *h.* pursued. *Gen* 31:36

hottest

Uriah in forefront of *h. 2 Sam* 11:15

hough

Lord said, thou shalt *h.* *Josh* 11:6

houghed

h. their horses, burnt. *Josh* 11:9
and David *h.* all the. *2 Sam* 8:4

hour

(*The day was not divided into hours by the ancient Hebrews. Only the natural divisions of morning, noon, and evening were noted. After the Exile there was a somewhat clearer division which, it is supposed, was learned from the Babylonians. The length of the hour was dependent usually upon the season, as people commonly reckoned it as the twelfth part of the natural day, from sunrise to sunset, and this would differ according to season*)

was astonied for one *h.* *Dan* 4:19*
made whole from that *h.* *Mat* 9:22
made whole from that very *h.* 15:28
was cured from that very *h.* 17:18
about the third *h.* and saw. 20:3
about the sixth and ninth *h.* 5
the eleventh *h.* 6
have wrought but one *h.* 12
that *h.* knoweth no man. 24:36, 42
Mark 13:32
such an *h.* as ye think not.
Mat 24:44, 50; *Luke* 12:40, 46
neither the day nor the *h. Mat* 25:13
could ye not watch one *h.*? 26:40
Mark 14:37
the *h.* is at hand, the. *Mat* 26:45
h. was darkness over land to ninth *h.*
27:45; *Mark* 15:33; *Luke* 23:44
about the ninth *h.* Jesus cried.
Mat 27:46; *Mark* 15:34
be given you in that *h.* *Mark* 13:11
that if possible the *h.* might. 14:35
it was the third *h.* and they. 15:25
in that *h.* Jesus rejoiced. *Luke* 10:21
had known what *h.* the thief. 12:39
and when the *h.* was come. 22:14
but this is your *h.* and the power. 53
space of one *h.* after another. 59
for it was about tenth *h.* *John* 1:39
Jesus saith, Woman, mine *h.* is. 2:4
it was about the sixth *h.* 4:6; 19:14
believe me, the *h.* cometh. 4:21, 23
he the *h.* when he began to amend, yesterday at seventh *h.* 52
h. is coming, and. 5:25, 28; 16:32
his *h.* was not yet come. 7:30; 8:20
the *h.* is come, Son. 12:23; 17:1
Father, save me from this *h.*: but for this cause came I to this *h.* 12:27
when Jesus knew that his *h.* 13:1
hath sorrow, because her *h.* 16:21
from that *h.* that disciple. 19:27
seeing it is third *h.* of. *Acts* 2:15
h. of prayer being the ninth *h.* 3:1
about the ninth *h.* an angel. 10:3
up to pray about the sixth *h.* 9
ago I was fasting until this *h.* 30
make ready at the third *h.* of. 23:23
to this present *h.* both. *1 Cor* 4:11
conscience of idol unto this *h.* 8:7
stand we in jeopardy every *h.*? 15:30
gave place, no not for an *h.* *Gal* 2:5
not know what *h.* I will. *Rev* 3:3
I will keep thee from the *h.* of. 10
silence about space of half an *h.* 8:1
which were prepared for an *h.* 9:15
the *h.* of his judgement is come. 14:7
receive power as kings one *h.* 17:12
for in one *h.* is thy judgement. 18:10
in one *h.* so great riches come. 17
that great city in one *h.* she is. 19

same **hour**

the *same h.* be cast. *Dan* 3:6, 15
the *same h.* was the thing. 4:33
the *same h.* came forth fingers. 5:5
was healed the *same h.* *Mat* 8:13
it shall be given you the *same h.*
10:19; *Luke* 12:12
the *same h.* said Jesus. *Mat* 26:55
that *same h.* cured many. *Luke* 7:21
scribes *same h.* sought to lay. 20:19
they rose up the *same h.* 24:33
that it was at the *same h. John* 4:53
he came out the *same h. Acts* 16:18
he took them *same h.* of night. 33

the *same h.* I looked up. *Acts* 22:13
the *same h.* was there a. *Rev* 11:13

hours

are there not twelve *h.*? *John* 11:9
about space of thre *h.* *Acts* 5:7
about two *h.*, Great is Diana. 19:34

house

[1] *A place to dwell in,* Gen 19:3; *hence used also of the body as the dwelling place of the soul of man.* 2 Cor 5:1. [2] *The household, or persons dwelling in the house,* Acts 10:2; Heb 11:7. [3] *Kindred or lineage,* 2 Sam 7:18; Luke 1:27. [4] *Wealth, riches, or estates,* Mat 23:14. [5] *The grave,* Job 30:23; Isa 14:18. [6] *The house of God, the building erected for the worship of God, in which his spirit is most frequently considered as dwelling,* Judg 18:31; 2 Chr 5:14; 1 Tim 3:15.

Sodom compassed the *h.* *Gen* 19:4
to the *h.* of my master's. 24:27
I have prepared the *h.* 31
go to the *h.* of Bethuel, thy. 28:2
Lord blessed the Egyptian's *h.* 39:5
the Egyptians and the *h.* of. 45:2
frogs shall come into *h.* of. *Ex* 8:3
a lamb according to the *h.* of. 12:3*
not an *h.* where there was not. 30
carry of the flesh out of the *h.* 46
came out from Egypt, out of *h.* of bondage. 13:3, 14; *Deut* 5:6; 6:12
shalt not covet neighbour's *h.* *Ex* 20:17; *Deut* 5:21
command they empty *h.* *Lev* 14:36
priest shall go out of the *h.* 38
break down *h.* and mortar of *h.* 45
he that goeth into the *h.* shall. 46
he shall take to cleanse the *h.* 49
h. sold in walled city, not go. 25:30
if she vowed in her husband's *h.* *Num* 30:10
redeemed you out of *h.* *Deut* 7:8
of the land of Egypt, from the *h.* of. 8:14; 13:5, 10; *Josh* 24:17 *Judg* 6:8; *Jer* 34:13; *Mi* 6:4
h. of him that hath his shoe loosed. *Deut* 25:10
for her *h.* was upon the. *Josh* 2:15
neither shewed kindness to *h.* of. *Judg* 8:35
h. of Millo made Abimelech. 9:6
let fire come from *h.* of Millo. 20
Ammon fought against the *h.* 10:9
may feel pillars whereon *h.* 16:26
the *h.* was full of men. 27
h. fell on the lords. 30
Micah had an *h.* of gods. 17:5
and they came unto the *h.* 18:13
no man receiveth me to *h.* 19:18
Belial beset the *h.* round. 22; 20:5
sworn unto *h.* of Eli. *1 Sam* 3:14
brought the ark into the *h.* 5:2
and brought the ark into the *h.* 7:1
thee, where the seer's *h.* is. 9:18
Nabal was churlish, and of *h.* 25:3
certainly make my lord a sure *h.* 28
war between *h.* of Saul and *h.* of David. *2 Sam* 3:1
shew kindness to the *h.* of Saul. 8
let there not fail from the *h.* of. 29
came to *h.* of Ish-bosheth, who. 4:5
lame shall not come into the *h.* 5:8
h. of Obed-edom, David brought ark from his *h.* 6:11,12; *1 Chr* 13:14
I have not dwelt in any *h.* *2 Sam* 7:6; *1 Chr* 17:5
he will make thee an *h.* *2 Sam* 7:11
to bless the *h.* of thy servant. 29 *1 Chr* 17:27
is left of the *h.* of Saul? *2 Sam* 9:1
I gave thee thy master's *h.* 12:8
now to thy brother Amnon's *h.* 13:7
a man of the family of the *h.* 16:5
who made me an *h.* as. *1 Ki* 2:24
which he spake concerning the *h.* 27
and the whole *h.* he overlaid. 6:22
so Solomon finished the *h.* 9:25
Pharaoh, who gave him an *h.* 11:18
made an *h.* of his high places. 12:31
bring an evil on the *h.* of. 14:10, 14
Baasha smote all the *h.* of. 15:29
Zimri slew all the *h.* of. *1 Ki* 16:11
and he, and her *h.* did eat. 17:15
I will make thy *h.* like the *h.* 21:22
cry to king for her *h.* and. *2 Ki* 8:3
as did the *h.* of Ahab. 18, 27 *2 Chr* 21:6; 22:4
for the whole *h.* of Ahab. *2 Ki* 9:8
best, fight for your master's *h.* 10:3
h. of Baal was full from one end. 21
made the *h.* of Baal a draught *h.* 27
for all that was laid out for *h.* 12:12
h. of his precious things, all the *h.* of his armour. 20:13; *Isa* 39:2
h. of which I said, My. *2 Ki* 23:27
every great man's *h.* he burnt. 25:9
of Salma; Ataroth the *h.* *1 Chr* 2:54*
sons, the *h.* of Asuppim. 26:15*
glory of Lord filled the *h.* *2 Chr* 7:1 *Ezek* 43:4, 5
chosen this place to myself for *h.* of. *2 Chr* 7:12
so the *h.* of Ahaziah had no. 22:9
but against the *h.* wherewith. 35:21
that we went to the *h.* of. *Ezra* 5:8
let the *h.* be builded, the place. 6:3
and for the *h.* which I. *Neh* 2:8
gather all virgins to the *h.* *Esth* 2:3
king did give *h.* of Haman. 8:1, 7
drinking wine in eldest brother's *h.* *Job* 1:13, 18
and smote the corners of the *h.* 19
hath taken away a *h.* which. 20:19
for ye say, Where is the *h.* of? 21:28
and to the *h.* appointed for. 30:23
shouldest know paths to the *h.* 38:20
whose *h.* I have made the. 39:6
my rock be for a *h.* of. *Ps* 31:2
the sparrow hath found an *h.* 84:3
stork, fir trees are her *h.* 104:17
her *h.* inclineth to death. *Pr* 2:18
young man went way to her *h.* 7:8
her feet abide not in her *h.* 11
her *h.* is the way to hell. 27
wisdom hath builded her *h.* 9:1
but the *h.* of the righteous shall. 12:7
the *h.* of the wicked shall be. 14:11
the Lord will destroy the *h.* of. 15:25
than an *h.* full of sacrifices. 17:1
h. and riches are inheritance. 19:14
dwell in corner of *h.* top. 21:9; 25:24
wisely considereth the *h.* 21:12
through wisdom is an *h.* built. 24:3
foot from thy neighbour's *h.* 25:17
nor go into brother's *h.* in day. 27:10
to go to *h.* of mourning, than *h.* of feasting. *Eccl* 7:2
through idleness of hands *h.* 10:18
when the keepers of the *h.* 12:3
the beams of our *h.* are. *S of S* 1:17
me to the banqueting *h.* his. 2:4
brought him into my mother's *h.* 3:4
bring thee into my mother's *h.* 8:2
woe to them that join *h.* to *h.*, field. *Isa* 5:8
the *h.* was filled with smoke. 6:4
that opened not the *h.* of. 14:17*
so that there is no *h.* 23:1
every *h.* shut. 24:10
he will arise against the *h.* of. 31:2
and I will glorify the *h.* of. 60:7
our holy and beautiful *h.* is. 64:11
enter not into the *h.* of. *Jer* 16:5
thou shalt not go into *h.* of. 8
h. of the king of Judah. 21:11; 22:1
go to the *h.* of the Rechabites. 35:2
to *h.* of Jonathan. 37:20; 38:26
rebellious *h.* yet shall know a. *Ezek* 2:5; 3:9, 26, 27; 12:3
rebellious like that rebellious *h.* 2:8
he said to them, Defile the *h.* go. 9:7
the midst of a rebellious *h.* 12:2
in your days, O rebellious *h.* 25
say now to the rebellious *h.* 17:12
a parable to the rebellious *h.* 24:3
shew them the form of the *h.* 43:11
this is the law of *h.*; Upon the top. 12
so shall ye reconcile the *h.* 45:20
which he carried to the *h.* *Dan* 1:2
blood of Jezreel on the *h.* *Hos* 1:4
a fire into the *h.* of Hazael. *Amos* 1:4
that holdeth the sceptre from the *h.* 5
the winter *h.* with summer *h.* 3:15
or went into *h.* and leaned his. 5:19
the great *h.* and the little *h.* 6:11
I will rise against *h.* of. *Amos* 7:9
drop not thy word against the *h.* 16
the *h.* of Esau shall be for. *Ob* 18
heaps, and the mountain of the *h.* shall be as high places. *Mi* 3:12
let us go up to the *h.* of the. 4:2
works of the *h.* of Ahab. 6:16
out of the *h.* of thy gods. *Nah* 1:14
enter into the *h.* of the thief, into *h.* of him that sweareth. *Zech* 5:4
family of the *h* of Nathan. 12:12
and beat upon that *h.* *Mat* 7:25, 27 *Luke* 6:48
when ye come into a *h.* *Mat* 10:12
if *h.* be worthy, let. 13; *Luke* 10:5
every *h.* divided against itself. *Mat* 12:25; *Mark* 3:25
how can one enter into a strong man's *h.*? *Mat* 12:29; *Mark* 3:27
against good man of *h.* *Mat* 20:11*
your *h.* is left to you desolate. *Mat* 23:38; *Luke* 13:25
man of the *h.* had known in what watch. *Mat* 24:43; *Luke* 12:39
h. divided against itself, that *h.* *Mark* 3:25
that hath left *h.* or brethren. 10:29
is the guestchamber? say ye to the good man of *h.* 14:14; *Luke* 22:11
that *h.* remain, go not from *h.* to *h.* *Luke* 10:7
Martha, received him into her *h.* 38
not light candle and sweep *h.*? 15:8
h. was filled with odour. *John* 12:3
from heaven filled all *h.* *Acts* 2:2
breaking bread from *h.* to *h.* 46*
every *h.* ceased not to teach. 5:42*
Simon a tanner, whose *h.* is. 10:6
entered into the man's *h.* 11:12
he came to the *h.* of Mary. 12:12
but the Jews assaulted the *h.* 17:5
whose *h.* joined hard to the. 18:7
they fled out of that *h.* naked. 19:16
publicly, and from *h.* to *h.* 20:20
entered into the *h.* of Philip. 21:8
greet the church in their *h.* *Rom* 16:5 *1 Cor* 16:19
which are of the *h.* of. *1 Cor* 1:11*
ye know the *h.* of Stephanas. 16:15
earthly *h.* be dissolved, we have an *h.* *2 Cor* 5:1
desiring to be clothed upon with *h.* 2*
wandering about from *h.* to *h.* and. *1 Tim* 5:13
younger women guide the *h.* 14*
Lord give mercy to *h.* of. *2 Tim* 1:16
in a great *h.* there are vessels. 2:20
he who built the *h.* more honour than *h.* *Heb* 3:3
h. is built by some man, he. 4
whose *h.* are we, if we hold fast. 6
receive him not into your *h.* nor. *2 John* 10

see **Aaron, born, build, built, chief, David, door, dwell**

house joined with *father*

get thee from thy *father's h.* *Gen* 12:1
to wander from *father's h.* 20:13
took me from my *father's h.* 24:7
thou shalt go to my *father's h.* 38
wife for my son of my *father's h.* 40
portion for us in our *father's h.*? 31:14
at thy *father's h.* till Shelah be grown . . . dwelt in her *father's h.* 38:11
made me forget my *father's h.* 41:51
my brethren and *father's h.* 46:31
in Egypt, he and his *father's h.* 50:22
a lamb, according to *h.* of their *fathers.* *Ex* 12:3
returned to her *father's h.* *Lev* 22:13
Israel by *h.* of their *fathers,* with. *Num* 1:2, 18, 20, 22, 24
tribe, every one head of the *h.* of his *fathers.* 1:4, 44; *Josh* 22:14
numbered by the *h.* of their *fathers.* *Num* 1:45
pitch with ensign of their *father's h.* 2:2
children of Levi after the *h.* of their *fathers,* by. 3:15, 20; 4:46
Gershon by *h.* of their *fathers.* 4:38

Merari after *h.* of their *fathers.* *Num* 4:42
according to *h.* of their *fathers* twelve rods. 17:2, 3
and *father's h.* bear iniquity of. 18:1
vow a vow, being in her *father's h.* 30:3, 16
Reuben, Gad, according to the *h.* of their *fathers.* 34:14
whore in her *father's h.* *Deut* 22:21
kindness to my *father's h.* *Josh* 2:12
the least in my *father's h.* *Judg* 6:15
risen up against my *father's h.* 9:18
not inherit in our *father's h.* 11:2
burn thee and thy *father's h.* 14:15
all the *h.* of his *father* came. 16:31
went to his *father's h.* 19:2
brought him into her *father's h.* 3
plainly appear to *h.* of thy *father.* *1 Sam* 2:27
said the *h.* of thy *f.* should walk. 30
thee, and on all thy *father's h.*? 9:20
king will make his *father's h.* 17:25
no more home to his *father's h.* 18:2
king sent to call all his *father's h.* 22:11
thou and all thy *father's h.* shall. 16
destroy my name out of *father's h.* 24:21
rest on Joab and all his *father's h.* *2 Sam* 3:29
iniquity be on me, and on my *father's h.* 14:9
my *father's h.* were but dead. 19:28
pray thee, be against me and against my *father's h.* 24:17; *1 Chr* 21:17
innocent blood from me and *father's h.* *1 Ki* 2:31
father's h. have troubled Israel. 18:18
Hemath *father* of the *h.* of Rechab. *1 Chr* 2:55
h. of their *fathers* increased. 4:38
son of Guni, chief of *h.* of their *fathers.* 5:15, 24; 7:2, 7, 9, 40
with them after the *h.* of *fathers.* 7:4
chief in the *h.* of their *fathers.* 9:9 13; 12:30
of Zadok, his *father's h.* 12:28
me before the *h.* of my *father.* 28:4
slain thy brethren of thy *father's h.* *2 Chr* 21:13
could not shew their *father's h.* *Ezra* 2:59; *Neh* 1:6
chief of *h.* of their *father.* *Ezra* 10:16
both I and my *father's h.* *Neh* 1:6
thou and thy *father's h.* shall be destroyed. *Esth* 4:14
forget thy people and thy *father's h.* *Ps* 45:10
take hold of his brother of the *h.* of his *father.* *Isa* 3:6
bring on thy *father's h.* days. 7:17
throne to his *father's h.* 22:23
all the glory of his *father's h.* 24
the *h.* of thy *fathers* dealt treacherously. *Jer* 12:6
send him to my *father's h.* *Luke* 16:27
not my *Father's h.* a house of merchandise. *John* 2:16
Father's h. are many mansions. 14:2
nourished in his *father's h.* *Acts* 7:20

house *of God*

other but the *h. of God.* *Gen* 28:17
stone which I set shall be *God's h.* 22
drawers of water for *h. of God.* *Josh* 9:23
all the time *h. of God.* *Judg* 18:31
and went up to the *h. of God.* 20:18*
people came unto the *h. of God.* 26* 21:2*
which one goeth up to *h. of God.* 31*
Azariah ruler of *h. of God.* *1 Chr* 9:11; *Neh* 11:11
governors of *h. of God.* *1 Chr* 24:5
glory filled the *h. of God.* *2 Chr* 5:14
with them hid in *h. of God.* 22:12
they set the *h. of God* in. 24:13
a carved image in the *h. of God.* 33:7
they burnt the *h. of God.* 36:19
to the *h. of* the great *God.* *Ezra* 5:8
let the *h. of God* be builded. 15; 6:7
needed for the *h. of God*? *Ezra* 7:20
it be done for the *h. of* the *God.* 23
let us meet in *h. of God.* *Neh* 6:10
I said, Why is the *h. of God*? 13:11
I went with them to the *h. of God.* *Ps* 42:4; 55:14
olive tree in the *h. of God.* 52:8
be doorkeeper in *h. of God.* 84:10
thou goest to *h. of God.* *Eccl* 5:1
let us go up to the *h. of God.* *Isa* 2:3; *Mi* 4:2
is hated in the *h. of God.* *Hos* 9:8
withholden from *h. of God.* *Joel* 1:13
cut off from the *h. of God.* 16
to *h. of God* men to pray. *Zech* 7:2*
into the *h. of God,* and did eat the. *Mat* 12:4; *Mark* 2:26; *Luke* 6:4
to behave thyself in the *h. of God.* *1 Tim* 3:15
high priest over the *h. of God.* *Heb* 10:21
begin at the *h. of God.* *1 Pet* 4:17

his **house**

Lord plagued Pharaoh and *his h.* *Gen* 12:17
of *his h.* were circumcised. 17:27
him overseer over *his h.* 39:4, 5
made me lord of all *his h.* 45:8 *Acts* 7:10
atonement for *his h.* *Lev* 16:6, 11
a man shall sanctify *his h.* 27:14
sanctified it will redeem *his h.* 15
would give me *his h.* full of silver. *Num* 22:18; 24:13
let him go and return to *his h.* *Deut* 20:5, 6, 7, 8
him send her out of *his h.* 24:1
go into *his h.* to fetch his pledge. 10
became a snare to *his h.* *Judg* 8:27
with Jerubbaal and *his h.* 9:16, 19
spoken concerning *his h.* *1 Sam* 3:12
I will judge *his h.* for ever. 13
Ramah, for there was *his h.* 7:17
Israel buried Samuel in *his h.* 25:1
departed every one to *his h.* *2 Sam* 6:19
before thy father and *his h.* 21
pass, when the king sat in *his h.* 7:1
concerning *his h.* 25; *1 Chr* 17:23
went not down to *his h.* 11:9, 10, 13
fetched her to *his h.* became. 27
bring the king back to *his h.*? 19:11
it is for Saul and *his* bloody *h.* 21:1
silver nor gold of Saul, nor of *his h.* 4
his h. there shall be peace. *1 Ki* 2:33
building, and finished all *his h.* 7:1
man to *his h.* for thing. 12:24; 22:17 *1 Chr* 16:43; *2 Chr* 11:4; 18:16
did eat bread in *his h.* *1 Ki* 13:19
sword against Baasha and *his h.* 16:7
of Israel went to *his h.* 20:43; 21:4
Elisha sat in *his h.* and. *2 Ki* 6:32
nothing in *his h.* Hezekiah. 20:13
it went evil with *his h.* *1 Chr* 7:23
Saul, his sons, and all *his h.* 10:6
the ark remained in *his h.* 13:14
toward God and *his h.* *2 Chr* 24:16
his h. be made a dunghill. *Ezra* 6:11
one repaired over against *his h.* *Neh* 3:28
out every man from *his h.* 5:13
to be over against *his h.* 7:3
an hedge about *his h.*? *Job* 1:10
shall return no more to *his h.* 7:10
he shall lean on *his h.* it shall. 8:15
the increase of *his h.* shall. 20:28
pleasure hath he in *his h.*? 21:21
he buildeth *his h.* as a moth. 27:18
when the glory of *his h.* *Ps* 49:16
made him Lord of *his h.* 105:21
and riches shall be in *his h.* 112:3
give the substance of *his h.* *Pr* 6:31 *S of S* 8:7
not depart from *his h.* *Pr* 17:13
even punish that man and *his h.* *Jer* 23:34
oppress a man and *his h.* *Mi* 2:2
evil covetousness to *his h.* *Hab* 2:9
in the midst of *his h.* *Zech* 5:4
then he shall spoil *his h.* *Mat* 12:29 *Mark* 3:27
to take any thing out of *his h.* *Mat* 24:17; *Mark* 13:15
not have suffered *his h.* *Mat* 24:43
he would come into *his h.* *Luke* 8:41
went down to *his h.* justified. 18:14
believed and *his* whole *h.* *John* 4:53
feared God with all *his h.* *Acts* 10:2
to send for thee into *his h.* 22
he had seen an angel in *his h.* 11:13
to him and to all in *his h.* 16:32
into *his h.* he rejoiced, believing in God with all *his h.* 34; 18:8
church which is in *his h.* *Col* 4:15
faithful in all *his h.* *Heb* 3:2, 5
an ark for the saving of *his h.* 11:7

house *of Israel*

let *h. of Israel* bewail. *Lev* 10:6
be of *h. of Israel* that killeth an ox or lamb. 17:3, 8, 10; 22:18
all *h. of Israel* mourned. *Num* 20:29
h. of Israel lamented. *1 Sam* 7:2
they mourned for the *h. of Israel.* *2 Sam* 1:12
all the *h. of Israel* played. 6:5
David and the *h. of Israel.* 15
the *h. of Israel* and Judah. 12:8
shall *h. of Israel* restore the. 16:3
kings of *h. of Israel* are. *1 Ki* 20:31
truth toward *h. of Israel.* *Ps* 98:3
us, he will bless *h. of Israel.* 115:12
bless ye Lord, O *h. of Israel.* 135:19
vineyard of Lord is the *h. of Israel.* *Isa* 5:7
the *h. of Israel* shall possess. 14:2
remnant of the *h. of Israel.* 46:3
goodness toward *h. of Israel.* 63:7
families of *h. of Israel.* *Jer* 2:4
as a thief, so is the *h. of Israel.* 26
Judah shall walk with *h. of Israel.* 3:18
treacherously, *h. of Israel.* 20; 5:11
h. of Israel are uncircumcised. 9:26
the *h. of Israel* have broken. 11:10
evil for evil, of the *h. of Israel.* 17
cleave to me the whole *h. of Israel.* 13:11
liveth, who led the *h. of Israel.* 23:8
I will sow the *h. of Israel.* 31:27
covenant with *h. of Israel.* 31, 33
I promised to the *h. of Israel.* 33:14
the *h. of Israel* was ashamed. 48:13
speak to *h. of Israel.* *Ezek* 3:1; 17:2 20:27, 30; 24:21; 33:10; 36:22
get thee unto the *h. of Israel.* 3:4
thou art sent to the *h. of Israel.* 5
h. of Israel will not hearken to me, for all the *h. of Israel* are. 7
watchman to *h. of Israel.* 17; 33:7
be a sign to the *h. of Israel.* 4:3
iniquity of the *h. of Israel* upon. 4
bear iniquity of the *h. of Israel.* 5
a fire shall come forth into the *h. of Israel.* 5:4
abominations of the *h. of Israel.* 6:11
all the idols of the *h. of Israel.* 8:10
the ancients of *h. of Israel.* 11, 12
the iniquity of the *h. of Israel.* 9:9
ye said, O *h. of Israel,* for. 11:5
the *h. of Israel* wholly are they. 15
the *h. of Israel* said. 12:9, 27; 18:29
divination within *h. of Israel.* 12:24
hedge for the *h. of Israel.* 13:5
the writing of the *h. of Israel.* 9
h. of Israel that setteth up idols. 14:4, 7
h. of Israel may go no more. 11
eyes to idols of *h. of Israel.* 18:6, 15
O *h. of Israel,* is not my way? 25
will I judge you, O *h. of Israel.* 30
ye die, O *h. of Israel*? 31; 33:11
but the *h. of Israel* rebelled. 20:13
O *h. of Israel,* go ye, serve ye every one his idols, if ye will not. 39
all the *h. of Israel* serve me. 40
corrupt doings, O *h. of Israel.* 44
h. of Israel is to me become. 22:18
briar to the *h. of Israel.* 28:24
have gathered the *h. of Israel.* 25
staff of a reed to *h. of Israel.* 29:6
the confidence of *h. of Israel.* 16
the horn of the *h. of Israel* to. 21
that they, even the *h. of Israel.* 34:30
multiply all the *h. of Israel.* 36:1
when the *h. of Israel* dwelt in. 1
which the *h. of Israel* profaned. 2

your sakes, O *h. of Israel. Ezek* 36:22
for your ways, O *h. of Israel.* 32
be enquired of by the *h. of Israel.* 37
bones are whole *h. of Israel.* 37:11
write on it, for the *h. of Israel.* 16
months shall *h. of Israel* be. 39:12
the *h. of Israel* shall know I. 22
h. of Israel went into captivity. 23
mercy on whole *h. of Israel.* 25
poured my Spirit on *h. of Israel.* 29
thou seest to the *h. of Israel.* 40:4
shew house to *h. of Israel.* 43:10
rebellious, even to *h. of Israel.* 44:6
caused the *h. of Israel* to fall. 12
of the seed of the *h. of Israel.* 22
for the whole *h. of Israel.* 45:6
land shall they give to *h. of Israel.* 8
reconciliation for the *h. of Israel.* 17
kingdom of *h. of Israel. Hos* 1:4
have mercy on the *h. of Israel.* 6
and hearken, ye *h. of Israel.* 5:1
horrible thing in *h. of Israel.* 6:10
h. of Israel compasseth me. 11:12
leave ten to *h. of Israel. Amos* 5:3
saith the Lord to the *h. of Israel.* 4
sacrifices 40 years, O *h. of Israel*? 25
nations, to whom *h. of Israel.* 6:1
you a nation, O *h. of Israel.* 14
against thee in the *h. of Israel.* 7:10
I will sift the *h. of Israel.* 9:9
sins of the *h. of Israel. Mi* 1:5
princes of the *h. of Israel.* 3:1, 9
a curse, O *h. of Israel. Zech* 8:13
go to lost sheep of the *h. of Israel.*
Mat 10:6; 15:24
all the *h. of Israel* know. *Acts* 2:36
O *h. of Israel,* have ye offered? 7:42
a new covenant with *h. of Israel.*
Heb 8:8, 10

house *of Jacob*

souls of *h. of Jacob. Gen* 46:27
say to the *h. of Jacob. Ex* 19:3
h. of Jacob from people. *Ps* 114:1
O *h. of Jacob,* let us walk. *Isa* 2:5
forsaken thy people, *h. of Jacob.* 6
his face from *h. of Jacob.* 8:17
escaped of the *h. of Jacob.* 10:20
cleave to the *h. of Jacob.* 14:1
Lord concerning *h. of Jacob.* 29:22
O *h. of Jacob* and Israel. 46:3
hear ye this, O *h. of Jacob.* 48:1
shew the *h. of Jacob* their sins. 58:1
word of Lord, O *h. of Jacob. Jer* 2:4
declare this in the *h. of Jacob.* 5:20
my hand to *h. of Jacob. Ezek* 20:5
testify in *h. of Jacob. Amos* 3:13
utterly destroy the *h. of Jacob.* 9:8
the *h. of Jacob* shall possess. *Ob* 17
h. of Jacob shall be a fire. 18
named the *h. of Jacob. Mi* 2:7
pray, ye heads of the *h. of Jacob.* 3:9
reign over *h. of Jacob. Luke* 1:33

house *of Joseph*

men into *Joseph's h. Gen* 43:17
h. of Joseph shall abide. *Josh* 18:5
the *h. of Joseph* went up. *Judg* 1:22
the *h. of Joseph* sent to descry. 23
hand of the *h. of Joseph.* 35
I am come the first this day of all the
h. of Joseph. *2 Sam* 19:20
charge of *h. of Joseph. 1 Ki* 11:28
break out like fire in *h. of Joseph.*
Amos 5:6
h. of Joseph shall be a flame. *Ob* 18
will save the *h. of Joseph. Zech* 10:6

house *of Judah*

David king over *h. of Judah.*
2 Sam 2:4, 7, 11; *1 Chr* 2:84
I gave thee *h. of Judah. 2 Sam* 12:8
he assembled all the *h. of Judah.*
1 Ki 12:21
speak to all the *h. of Judah.* 23
escaped of the *h. of Judah* shall take.
2 Ki 19:30; *Isa* 37:31
ruler of *h. of Judah. 2 Chr* 19:11
behind the *h. of Judah. Neh* 4:16
a father to *h. of Judah. Isa* 22:21
h. of Judah shall walk. *Jer* 3:18
the *h. of Judah* hath dealt. 5:11
the *h. of Judah* hath broken. 11:10
for evil of the *h. of Judah* that. 17
I will pluck *h. of Judah.* 12:14
cleave to me the *h. of Judah.* 13:11
I will sow the *h. of Judah. Jer* 31:27
a new covenant with *h. of Judah.* 31
I promised to *h. of Judah.* 33:14
may be *h. of Judah* will hear. 36:3
bear the iniquity of *h. of Judah* forty
days. *Ezek* 4:6
light thing to *h. of Judah*? 8:17
iniquity of *h. of Judah* is great. 9:9
Aha, against the *h. of Judah.* 25:3
the *h. of Judah* is like to all the. 8
dealt against the *h. of Judah.* 12
mercy upon *h. of Judah. Hos* 1:7
I will be to the *h. of Judah.* 5:12
young lion to the *h. of Judah.* 14
for remnant of *h. of Judah. Zeph* 2:7
a curse, O *h. of Judah. Zech* 8:13
to do well to the *h. of Judah.* 15
the fast shall be to *h. of Judah.* 19
Lord hath visited *h. of Judah.* 10:3
strengthen the *h. of Judah.* 6
eyes unto the *h. of Judah.* 12:4
covenant with *h. of Judah. Heb* 8:8

king's **house**

on roof of the *king's h. 2 Sam* 11:2
departed out of the *king's h.* 8
hear out of the *king's h.* 15:35
finished the *king's h. 1 Ki* 9:1
treasure of *king's h.* 14:26; 15:18
2 Ki 16:8; *2 Chr* 12:9; 25:24
Zimri burnt the *king's h. 1 Ki* 16:18
told it to the *king's h. 2 Ki* 7:11*
he burnt the *king's h.* 25:9
Jer 39:8; 52:13
shall be at the *king's h. 2 Chr* 23:5
son was over the *king's h.* 26:21
portion out of *h.* of the *king.* 28:21
given out of the *king's h. Ezra* 6:4
maidens out of *king's h. Esth* 2:9
shalt escape in the *king's h.* 4:13
was great in the *king's h.* 9:4
give ear, O *h.* of the *king. Hos* 5:1

house *of Levi*

a man of the *h. of Levi. Ex* 2:1
rod of Aaron for *h. of Levi* was.
Num 17:8
the Lord, O *h. of Levi. Ps* 135:20
family of the *h. of Levi. Zech* 12:13

in the **house**

of Esau that were *in h. Gen* 27:15
even all that was *in the h.* 34:29
blessing was on all *in the h.* 39:5
not what is with me *in the h.* 8
was heard *in* Pharaoh's *h.* 45:16
in one *h.* shall passover. *Ex* 12:46
of leprosy *in a h. Lev* 14:34, 35
again and break out *in the h.* 43
the plague be spread *in the h.* 44
he that lieth, that eateth *in the h.* 47
plague hath not spread *in the h.* 48
whoso with thee *in the h. Josh* 2:19
all that are with her *in the h.* 6:17
in the h. of Micah. *Judg* 17:4, 12
find rest, each *in h.* of. *Ruth* 1:9
she tarried a little *in the h.* 2:7
had a fat calf *in the h. 1 Sam* 28:24
sent to publish it *in the h.* of. 31:9
they put his armour *in the h.* of. 10
dwell *in one h.* . . . of a child with her
in the h. *1 Ki* 3:17
any tool of iron heard *in the h.* 6:7
is found some good *in the h.* 14:13
drinking himself drunk *in the h.* 16:9
in the h.? thine handmaid hath not
any thing *in the h.* *2 Ki* 4:2
he returned, and walked *in the h.* 35
leaneth on my hand, bow *in h.* 5:18
and bestowed them *in the h.* 24
in h. of Nisroch. 19:37; *Isa* 37:38
a graven image *in the h. 2 Ki* 21:7
slew young men *in the h. 2 Chr* 36:17
had put them *in the h.* of. *Ezra* 1:7
search was made *in the h.* of. 6:1
the queen also *in the h.*? *Esth* 7:8
the gallows standeth *in the h.* of. 9
my songs *in the h.* of my. *Ps* 119:54
curse of Lord is *in the h. Pr* 3:33
thy labours be *in the h.* of a. 5:10
her feet abide not *in* her *h.* 7:11
in the h. of the righteous is. 15:6
wise is *in h.* of mourning . . . fools is
in the h. of mirth. *Eccl* 7:4
it may remain *in the h. Isa* 44:13
set their abominations *in the h.*
Jer 7:30; 32:34
covenant before me *in the h.* 34:15
put him *in the h.* of Jonathan. 37:15
remain ten men *in* one *h. Amos* 6:9
in the h. of Aphrah roll. *Mi* 1:10*
of wickedness *in the h.* of. 6:10
I was wounded *in the h. Zech* 13:6
unto all that are *in the h. Mat* 5:15
that he was *in the h. Mark* 2:1
being *in the h.* he asked them. 9:33
in the h. his disciples asked. 10:10
in Bethany, *in the h.* of Simon. 14:3
nor abode *in* any *h.* but. *Luke* 8:27
abideth not *in the h. John* 8:35
Mary sat still *in the h.* 11:20
enquire *in the h.* of Judas. *Acts* 9:11
Peter is lodged *in the h.* of. 10:32

house joined with *Lord*

shalt bring into the *h.* of the *Lord.*
Ex 23:19; 34:26; *Neh* 10:35
of a dog into *h.* of *Lord. Deut* 23:18
treasury of *h.* of the *Lord. Josh* 6:24
going to *h.* of the *Lord. Judg* 19:18
up to the *h.* of the *Lord. 1 Sam* 1:7
unto *h.* of the *Lord.* 24; *2 Ki* 12:4
9, 13; 22:4; *2 Chr* 34:14
came into *h.* of *Lord. 2 Sam* 12:20
of building *h. of Lord. 1 Ki* 3:1
foundation of *h.* of *Lord* laid. 6:37
2 Chr 8:16; *Ezra* 3:11; *Zech* 8:9
made for *h.* of the *Lord. 1 Ki* 7:40
45:51; *2 Chr* 4:16; 5:1; 24:14
cloud filled *h.* of *Lord. 1 Ki* 8:10, 11
2 Chr 5:13; 7:2; *Ezek* 44:4
dedicated *h.* of the *Lord. 1 Ki* 8:63
he went up unto the *h.* of *Lord.*
10:5; *2 Chr* 9:4
hid in the *h.* of *Lord* six. *2 Ki* 11:3
oath of them in *h.* of the *Lord.* 4
let her not be slain in *h.* of *Lord.* 15
2 Chr 23:14
appointed officers over *h.* of *Lord.*
2 Ki 11:18; *2 Chr* 23:18
brought from the *h.* of the *Lord.*
2 Ki 11:19; 23:6
found in *h.* of the *Lord.* 12:10
14:14; 16:8; 18:15
oversight of the *h.* of the *Lord.* 12:11
was not brought into *h. of Lord.* 16
turned he from *h. of Lord.* 16:18
shalt go up unto *h. of Lord.* 20:5
will heal me, and that I shall go up to
the *h.* of the *Lord.* 8; *Isa* 38:22
covenant which were found in *h.* of
Lord. 2 Ki 23:2, 24; *2 Chr* 34:17, 30
Sodomites that were by *h.* of *Lord.*
2 Ki 23:7
entering in of *h.* of the *Lord.* 11
burnt the *h.* of the *Lord.* 25:9
Jer 52:13
song in the *h.* of the *Lord. 1 Chr* 6:31
said, This is the *h.* of the *Lord.* 22:1
build the *h.* of the *Lord* thy God. 11
prepared for the *h.* of the *Lord.* 14
the work of the *h.* of the *Lord.* 23:4
minister in the *h.* of the *Lord.* 26:12
so the *h.* of the *Lord. 2 Chr* 8:16
he was cut off from *h.* of *Lord.*
26:21; *Joel* 1:9
sanctify *h.* of the *Lord. 2 Chr* 29:5
cleanse the *h.* of the *Lord.* 15
the idol out of *h.* of *Lord.* 33:15
book of the law in *h.* of *Lord.* 34:15
polluted the *h.* of the *Lord.* 36:14
beautify *h.* of the *Lord. Ezra* 7:27
will dwell in the *h.* of *Lord. Ps* 23:6
I may dwell in the *h.* of *Lord.* 27:4
planted in the *h.* of the *Lord.* 92:13
vows in courts of *Lord's h.* 116:19
you out of the *h.* of *Lord.* 118:26
let us go into *h.* of the *Lord.* 122:1
because of the *h.* of *Lord* I will. 9
stand in the *h.* of the *Lord.* 134:1
135:2
mountain of the *Lord's h. Isa* 2:2
Mi 4:1
up into *h.* of the *Lord. Isa* 37:14
praise to *h.* of the *Lord. Jer* 17:26
governor in the *h.* of the *Lord.* 20:1
which was by *h.* of the *Lord.* 2
to worship in the *Lord's h.* 26:2
words in the *h.* of the *Lord.* 7

spake to me in *h.* of *Lord.* *Jer* 28:1
that stood in the *h.* of the *Lord.* 5
officers in the *h.* of the *Lord.* 29:26
Rechabites into *h.* of the *Lord.* 35:2
I cannot go into *h.* of *Lord.* 36:5
read in the *Lord's h.* upon the. 6
entry that is in *h.* of the *Lord.* 38:14
them to the *h.* of the *Lord.* 41:5
the sanctuaries of *Lord's h.* 51:51
a noise in the *h.* of the *Lord.* *Lam* 2:7
the time that the *Lord's h.* *Hag* 1:2
see **court, door, gate, treasures, vessels**

mine, or *my* **house**

the steward of *my h.* is. *Gen* 15:2
one born in *my h.* is mine heir. 3
be destroyed, I and *my h.* 34:30
thou shalt be over *my h.* 41:40
faithful in all *mine h.* *Num* 12:7
things out of *mine h.* *Deut* 26:13
my h. we will serve Lord. *Josh* 24:15
forth of doors of *my h.* *Judg* 11:31
this man come into *mine h.* 19:23
kindness from *my h.* *1 Sam* 20:15
fellow come into *my h.*? 21:15
what is my *h.* that thou hast ? *2 Sam* 7:18; *1 Chr* 17:16
go into *mine h.* to eat ? *2 Sam* 11:11
my h. be not so with God. 23:5
it is near to my *h.* *1 Ki* 21:2
all in *mine h.* have they seen. *2 Ki* 20:15; *Isa* 39:4
settle him in *mine h.* *1 Chr* 17:14
the grave is *mine h.* *Job* 17:13
I will walk in *my h.* with. *Ps* 101:2
into the tabernacle of *my h.* 132:3
at the window of *my h.* *Pr* 7:6
in *my h.* is neither bread. *Isa* 3:7
them will I give in *mine h.* 56:5
in *my h.* of prayer, *mine h.* shall be called an *h.* of. 7; *Mat* 21:13
Mark 11:17; *Luke* 19:46
beloved to do in *mine h.*? *Jer* 11:15
forsaken *mine h.* I left mine. 12:7
in *my h.* have I found their. 23:11
I sat in *mine h.* and. *Ezek* 8:1
done in midst of *mine h.* 23:39
to pollute it, even *my h.* 44:7
was at rest in *mine h.* *Dan* 4:4
drive them out of *mine h.* *Hos* 9:15
why ? because of *mine h.* *Hag* 1:9
shalt also judge *my h.* *Zech* 3:7
I will encamp about *mine h.* 9:8
may be meat in *mine h.* *Mal* 3:10
I will return into *my h.* *Mat* 12:44
Luke 11:24
them farewell at *my h.* *Luke* 9:61
compel them, that *my h.* 14:23
hour I prayed in *my h.* *Acts* 10:30
saying, Come into *my h.* and. 16:15

own **house**

servants born in *own h.* *Gen* 14:14
I provide for mine *own h.* 30:30
bring it unto thine *own h.* *Deut* 22:2
and come unto his *own h.* *Josh* 20:6
and dwelt in his *own h.* *Judg* 8:29
person in his *own h.* *2 Sam* 4:11
against thee out of thy *own h.* 12:11
own h. and not see my face, so Absalom returned to *own h.* 14:24
again in peace to his *own h.* 19:30
Joab buried in his *own h.* *1 Ki* 2:34
an end of building his *own h.* 3:1
building his *own h.* 13 years. 7:1
a levy to build his *own h.* 9:15
own h. David. 12:16; *2 Chr* 10:16
thee into thine *own h.* *1 Ki* 14:12
was buried in the garden of his *own h.* *2 Ki* 21:18; *2 Chr* 33:20
slew the king in his *own h.* *2 Ki* 21:23; *2 Chr* 33:24
came in his heart to make in his *own h.* *2 Chr* 7:11
wherein Solomon had built the house of the Lord and his *own h.* 8:1
bear rule in his *own h.* *Esth* 1:22
troubleth his *own h.* shall. *Pr* 11:29
of gain troubleth his *own h.* 15:27
every one in his *own h.* *Isa* 14:18
are the men of his *own h.* *Mi* 7:6
run every man to his *own h.* *Hag* 1:9
a prophet is not without honour, save in his *own h.* *Mat* 13:57; *Mark* 6:4

to his *own h.* *Luke* 1:23; 5:25
Mary returned to her *own h.* 1:56
a great feast in his *own h.* 5:29
return to thy *own h.* and shew. 8:39
man went unto his *own h.* *John* 7:53
two years in his *own h.* *Acts* 28:30*
that ruleth well his *own h.* *1 Tim* 3:4
know not how to rule his *own h.* 5
for those of his *own h.* 5:8
as a Son over his *own h.* *Heb* 3:6

this **house**

greater in *this h.* than I. *Gen* 39:9
and bring me out of *this h.* 40:14
this h. thou art building. *1 Ki* 6:12
how much less *this h.* that I. 8:27
opened toward *this h.* 29; *2 Chr* 6:20
before thine altar in *this h.* *1 Ki* 8:31; *2 Chr* 6:22
make supplication to thee in *this h.* *1 Ki* 8:33, 42; *2 Chr* 6:24, 32
his hands towards *this h.* *1 Ki* 8:38
hallowed *this h.* 9:3; *2 Chr* 7:16, 20
at *this h.* every one shall hiss. *1 Ki* 9:8; *2 Chr* 7:21
this h. which I have chosen. *2 Ki* 21:7; *2 Chr* 33:7
upon us we stand before *this h.* for thy name is in this *h.* *2 Chr* 20:9
foundation of *this h.* was. *Ezra* 3:12
who destroyed *this h.* 5:12
this h. was finished on third. 6:15
stand before me in *this h.* *Jer* 7:10
is *this h.* become a den of ? 11
therefore will I do to *this h.* 14
enter in by the gates of *this h.* 22:4
this h. shall become a desolation. 5
will I make *this h.* like Shiloh. 26:6
this h. shall be like Shiloh. 9
me to prophesy against *this h.* 12
and *this h.* lie waste. *Hag* 1:4
who is left that saw *this h.* in? 2:3
I will fill *this h.* with glory, saith. 7
the glory of *this* latter *h.* greater. 9
laid foundation of *this h.* *Zech* 4:9
say, Peace be to *this h.* *Luke* 10:5
is salvation come to *this h.* 19:9

thine or *thy* **house**

all *thy h.* into the ark. *Gen* 7:1
been twenty years in *thy h.* 31:41
up and come into *thine h.* *Ex* 8:3
that is clean in *thy h.* *Num* 18:11, 13
when thou sittest in *thine h.* *Deut* 6:7; 11:19
on the posts of *thy h.* 6:9; 11:20
an abomination into *thine h.* 7:26
he loveth thee and *thine h.* 15:16
bring her home to *thine h.* 21:12
remain in *thine h.* and bewail. 13
bring not blood upon *thine h.* 22:8
not have in *thine h.* divers. 25:14
given to thee and *thine h.* 26:11
are entered into *thine h.* *Josh* 2:3
shall go out of doors of *thy h.* 19
we will burn *thine h.* on. *Judg* 12:1
man that came into *thine h.* 19:22
woman that is come into *thine h.* *Ruth* 4:11
let *thy h.* be like the house. 12
that *thy h.* should walk. *1 Sam* 2:30
not be an old man in *thine h.* 31
the increase of *thine h.* shall die. 33
one in *thine h.* shall crouch to. 36
is honourable in *thine h.* 22:14
peace be to *thine h.* and to. 25:6
her, Go up in peace to *thine h.* 35
thine h. shall be established for. *2 Sam* 7:16
go down to *thy h.* and wash. 11:8
didst not thou go down to *thine h.*? 10
never depart from *thine h.* 12:10
go to *thine h.* 14:8; *1 Ki* 1:53
give me half *thine h.* *1 Ki* 13:8
back with thee into *thine h.* 18
make *thy h.* like the *h.* of Jeroboam. 16:3; 21:22
they shall search *thine h.* 20:6
set *thine h.* in order. *2 Ki* 20:1
Isa 38:1
what have they seen in *thine h.*? *2 Ki* 20:15; *Isa* 39:4
all in *thine h.* shall be carried. *2 Ki* 20:17; *Isa* 39:6
come to *thy h.* in multitude. *Ps* 5:7

loved the habitation of *thy h.* *Ps* 26:8
satisfied with fatness of *thy h.* 36:8
no bullock out of *thy h.* 50:9
satisfied with goodness of *thy h.* 65:4
will go into *thy h.* with burnt. 66:13
zeal of *thine h.* hath eaten me up. 69:9; *John* 2:17
holiness becometh *thine h.* *Ps* 93:5
fruitful vine by sides of *thine h.* 128:3
that are cast out to *thy h.* *Isa* 58:7
thou shalt live and *thine h.* *Jer* 38:17
shut thyself within *thine h.* *Ezek* 3:24
blessing to rest in *thine h.* 44:30
consulted shame to *thy h.* *Hab* 2:10
arise, go unto *thine h.* *Mat* 9:6
Mark 2:11; *Luke* 5:24
the passover at *thy h.* *Mat* 26:18
I entered *thine h.* thou. *Luke* 7:44
to-day I must abide at *thy h.* 19:5
thou and all *thy h.* shall be saved. *Acts* 11:14; 16:31
to the church in *thy h.* *Philem* 2
see **tops**

household, *or* **households**

he will command his *h.* *Gen* 18:19
Jacob said to his *h.* Put away. 35:2
famine of your *h.* be gone. 42:33*
lest thou and thy *h.* come to. 45:11
take your father and your *h.* and. 18
nourished his father's *h.* 47:12
shall be food for your *h.* 24
man and his *h.* came. *Ex* 1:1
if the *h.* be too little for the. 12:4
made an atonement for his *h.* *Lev* 16:17
every place, and your *h.* *Num* 18:31
wonders upon all his *h.* *Deut* 6:22*
swallowed them and their *h.* 11:6
rejoice, thou and thy *h.* 14:26
eat it before the Lord, thou and thy *h.* 15:20
bring all thy father's *h.* *Josh* 2:18
Rahab, her father's *h.* and all. 6:25
and the family shall come by *h.* 7:14
brought his *h.* man by man. 18
he feared his father's *h.* *Judg* 6:27
life, with the lives of thy *h.* 18:25
evil is determined against his *h.* *1 Sam* 25:17*
man with his *h.* 27:3; *2 Sam* 2:3
Lord blessed him and all his *h.* *2 Sam* 6:11*
David returned to bless his *h.* 20
king went forth and all his *h.* 15:16
asses be for the king's *h.* to. 16:2
put his *h.* in order, and. 17:23*
to carry over the king's *h.* 19:18
Judah brought the king and his *h.* 41
Abishai was over the *h.* *1 Ki* 4:6
victuals for the king and his *h.* 7
in giving food for my *h.* 5:9
Hiram wheat for food to his *h.* 11
Genubath was in Pharaoh's *h.* 11:20*
go and tell the king's *h.* *2 Ki* 7:9
go and thine *h.* to sojourn. 8:1
Eliakim son of Hilkiah who was over *h.* 18:18; 19:2; *Isa* 36:22; 37:2
principal *h.* being taken. *1 Chr* 24:6*
camels and a great *h.* *Job* 1:3
milk for food of thy *h.* *Pr* 27:27
and giveth meat to her *h.* 31:15
not afraid of the snow for her *h.*: for all her *h.* are clothed with scarlet. 21
well to the ways of her *h.* 27
they call them of his *h.*? *Mat* 10:25
foes shall be they of his own *h.* 36
ruler over his *h.* 24:45; *Luke* 12:42
was baptized and her *h.* *Acts* 16:15
are of Aristobulus' *h.* *Rom* 16:10
that be of the *h.* of Narcissus. 11
I baptized also the *h.* of. *1 Cor* 1:16
to them who are of the *h.* *Gal* 6:10
no more strangers, but of the *h.* of God. *Eph* 2:19
that are of Cesar's *h.* *Phil* 4:22
salute the *h.* of. *2 Tim* 4:19*

householder

so the servants of the *h.* *Mat* 13:27
unto a man that is an *h.* 52; 20:1
was a certain *h.* planted. 21:33

household servants

two of his *h. servants.* *Acts* 10:7

household stuff

found of all thy *h. stuff* ? *Gen* 31:37
I cast out all the *h. stuff*. *Neh* 13:8

houses

carry corn for the famine of your *h.* *Gen* 42:19
God, he made them *h.* *Ex* 1:21†
heads of their fathers' *h.* 6:14
frogs from thee and thy *h.* 8:9, 11
and the frogs died out of the *h.* 13
swarms of flies into thy *h.* 21, 24
and cattle flee into the *h.* 9:20
fill thy *h.* and the *h.* of all thy servants, and the *h.* of all. 10:6
on the upper door post of the *h.* 12:7
blood be for a token upon the *h.* 13
away leaven out of your *h.* 15
no leaven found in your *h.* 19
destroyer to come in unto your *h.* 23
passed over and delivered our *h.* 27
h. of villages be counted. *Lev* 25:31
the *h.* of the cities of their. 32, 33
sum of the sons of Gershon throughout their *h.* *Num* 4:22
swallowed them up and their *h.* 16:32*
according to their father's *h.* 17:6
we will not return unto our *h.* 32:18
to give thee *h.* full of all. *Deut* 6:11
when hast built goodly *h.* and. 8:12
dwellest in their cities and *h.* 19:1
Neh 9:25
hot provision out of our *h.* *Josh* 9:12
that there is in these *h.* *Judg* 18:14
men that were in the *h.* near. 22
he cried against the *h.* *1 Ki* 13:32
they shall search the *h.* of thy. 20:6
put them in the *h.* of. *2 Ki* 17:29
which sacrificed in the *h.* of the. 32
he brake down the *h.* of the. 23:7
the *h.* of the high places, Josiah. 19
he burnt all the *h.* of Jerusalem. 25:9; *Jer* 52:13
David made *h.* in city. *1 Chr* 15:1
Solomon pattern of the *h.* 28:11
to overlay the walls of the *h.* 29:4
timber to floor the *h.* *2 Chr* 34:11
and prepare yourselves by *h.* 35:4
your wives and your *h.* *Neh* 4:14
mortgaged our lands and *h.* 5:3
them their vineyards and *h.* 11
the people were few, and *h.* not. 7:4
we cast lots after the *h.* of our. 10:34
and feasted in their *h.* *Job* 1:4
princes, who filled their *h.* 3:15
them that dwell in *h.* of clay. 4:19
he dwelleth in *h.* which no. 15:28
their *h.* are safe from fear, nor. 21:9
yet he filled their *h.* with. 22:18
the dark they dig through *h.* 24:16
that their *h.* shall continue. *Ps* 49:11
let us take the *h.* of God. 83:12*
fill our *h.* with spoil. *Pr* 1:13
make they their *h.* in rocks. 30:26
I builded me *h.* I planted. *Eccl* 2:4
the poor is in your *h.* *Isa* 3:14
of a truth, many *h.* shall. 5:9; 6:11
rock of offence to both *h.* of. 8:14
h. be spoiled, their wives. 13:16
their *h.* shall be full of doleful. 21
shall cry in their desolate *h.* 22
on the tops of their *h.* every. 15:3
the *h.* of Jerusalem, and the *h.* 22:10
yea, upon all the *h.* of joy in. 32:13
shall build *h.* and inhabit. 65:21
troops in the harlots' *h.* *Jer* 5:7
as cage is full of birds, are their *h.* 27
and their *h.* shall be turned. 6:12
cry be heard from their *h.* 18:22
the *h.* of Jerusalem and the *h.* of. 19:13
build ye *h.* and dwell in. 29:5, 28
h. and fields shall be possessed. 32:15
h. on whose roofs they offered. 29
concerning *h.* of this city, and *h.* 33:4
they burnt the *h.* of the people. 39:8
I will kindle a fire in *h.* of. 43:12, 13
h. are turned to aliens. *Lam* 5:2
shall possess their *h.* *Ezek* 7:24
it is not near, let us build *h.* 11:3
burn thine *h.* with fire. 16:41; 23:47
destroy thy pleasant *h.* 26:12
shall build *h.* and plant. *Ezek* 28:26
thee in the doors of the *h.* 33:30
shall be a place for their *h.* 45:4
your *h.* shall be made a dunghill. *Dan* 2:5
their *h.* shall be made a dunghill. 3:29
I will place them in their *h.* saith. *Hos* 11:11
climb up upon the *h.* *Joel* 2:9
and summer house, *h.* of ivory shall perish, great *h.* shall. *Amos* 3:15
the *h.* of Achzib shall be. *Mi* 1:14
and they covet *h.* and take. 2:2
cast out from their pleasant *h.* 9
which fill their masters' *h.* *Zeph* 1:9
h. shall become a desolation, they shall build *h.* but not inhabit. 13
in the *h.* of Ashkelon shall. 2:7
to dwell in your cieled *h.*? *Hag* 1:4
h. shall be rifled, and the. *Zech* 14:2
wear soft clothing are in kings' *h.* *Mat* 11:8
one that hath forsaken *h.* or. 19:29
devour widows' *h.* 23:14*
Mark 12:40; *Luke* 20:47
fasting to their own *h.* *Mark* 8:3*
receive me into their *h.* *Luke* 16:4
were possessors of *h.* sold. *Acts* 4:34
have ye not *h.* to eat in? *1 Cor* 11:22
ruling their own *h.* well. *1 Tim* 3:12
they which creep into *h.* *2 Tim* 3:6
who subvert whole *h.* *Tit* 1:11

how

and *h.* saidst thou, she? *Gen* 26:29
h. is it thou hast found it? 27:20
Jacob said, *h.* dreadful is. 28:17
h. then can I do this great? 39:9
h. then should we steal out? 44:8
what shall we speak? *h.* shall? 16
h. shall I go to my father, lad? 34
h. is that ye are come so? *Ex* 2:18
h. then shall Pharaoh hear? 6:12
and *h.* shall Pharaoh hearken? 30
Moses told *h.* the Lord. 18:8
seen *h.* I bare you. 19:4; *Deut* 1:31
h. we are to encamp in. *Num* 10:31
h. shall I curse, whom God hath not cursed? *h.* 23:8
h. goodly are thy tents, O! 24:5
h. can I myself bear? *Deut* 1:12
if thou shalt say, *H.* can I? 7:17
h. the earth opened her mouth. 11:6
h. did these nations serve? 12:30
h. he met thee by the way. 25:18
h. we have dwelt in Egypt, and *h.* we came through nations. 29:16
h. should one chase a. 32:30
h. shall we make a league with? *Josh* 9:7
h. shall we order the child, *h.* do to him? *Judg* 13:12
she said, *H.* canst thou say? 16:15
they said, Tell us, *h.* was this? 20:3
h. do for wives for them? 21:7, 16
know *h.* the matter will. *Ruth* 3:18
said, *H.* shall this man? *1 Sam* 10:27
see *h.* mine eyes have been. 14:29
h. can I go? if Saul hear he. 16:2
h. went the matter, I. *2 Sam* 1:4
h. knowest thou that Saul and? 5
h. are the mighty fallen! 19, 25, 27
h. Joab did, *h.* the people did, and *h.* 11:7
h. then will he vex himself? 12:18
I know not *h.* to go out. *1 Ki* 3:7
h. do you advise, that I may? 12:6
h. Jeroboam warred, and *h.* 14:19
h. I hid an hundred men of. 18:13
and see *h.* the man seeketh. 20:7
h. he seeketh a quarrel. *2 Ki* 5:7
two kings stood not, *h.* then? 10:4
taught them *h.* they should. 17:28
h. then wilt thou turn away? 18:24
Isa 36:9
heard long ago, *h.* I have done it.
2 Ki 19:25; *Isa* 37:26
h. I have walked before thee.
2 Ki 20:3; *Isa* 38:3
behold, I say, *H.* they. *2 Chr* 20:11
his prayer, and *h.* God was. 33:19
to know *h.* Esther did. *Esth* 2:11
h. can I endure to see evil that? 8:6
h. should a man be just? *Job* 9:2
and thou sayest, *H.* doth? 22:13
h. hast thou helped him that is without power? *h.* savest thou? 26:2
h. little a portion is heard of! 14
h. say ye to my soul, Flee. *Ps* 11:1
h. thou didst drive out heathen, *h.* 44:2
say to God, *H.* terrible art thou. 66:3
h. doth God know? 73:11
h. amiable are thy tabernacles. 84:1
h. short my time is. 89:47
O Lord, *h.* manifold are! 104:24
O *h.* love I thy law, it is. 119:97
h. sweet are thy words unto. 103
consider *h.* I love thy precepts. 159
h. he sware unto the Lord. 132:2
h. precious are thy thoughts. 139:17
a word in due season, *h.* good! *Pr* 15:23
there is a generation, O *h.* 30:13
he knoweth not *h.* to go. *Eccl* 10:15
knowest not *h.* the bones. 11:5
h. fair is thy love, my sister, my spouse! *S of S* 4:10; 7:6
I have put off my coat, *h.* shall? 5:3
h. beautiful are thy feet with. 7:1
h. art thou fallen from! *Isa* 14:12
shall say in that day, and *h.*? 20:6
for *h.* should my name be? 48:11
h. to speak a word in season. 50:4
h. beautiful are the feet of him. 52:7; *Rom* 10:15
h. canst thou say, I am? *Jer* 2:23
I said, *h.* shall I put thee? 3:19
h. shall I pardon thee for this? 5:7
h. do ye say? 8:8; 48:14
h. are we spoiled? 9:19
to ask *h.* thou doest? 15:5
h. can it be quiet, seeing the? 47:7
h. is the hammer of the whole? 50:23
h. doth city sit solitary. *Lam* 1:1
h. weak is thy heart. *Ezek* 16:30
if we pine away in sins, *h.*? 33:10
h. shall I give thee up, Ephraim? *h.* deliver thee? *h.* make? *Hos* 11:8
h. do the beasts groan? *Joel* 1:18
if thieves came to thee, *h.* art. *Ob* 5
h. is she become a desolation. *Zeph* 2:15
h. do you see it now? *Hag* 2:3
h. great is his goodness! *Zech* 9:17
if light be darkness *h.* *Mat* 6:23
h. wilt thou say to thy brother? 7:4
if ye know *h.* to give good gifts. 11
Luke 11:13
take no thought *h.* or. *Mat* 10:19
h. they might destroy him. 12:14
Mark 3:6; 11:18
h. shall his kingdom stand?
Mat 12:26; *Luke* 11:18
h. can ye, being evil, speak? *Mat* 12:34
h. is it that ye do not understand that I spake it not? 16:11
h. think ye? if a man have. 18:12
h. soon is the fig tree. 21:20
h. camest thou in hither not? 22:12
if call him Lord, *h.* is he his son? 45
Luke 20:44
h. can ye escape the? *Mat* 23:33
h. then shall the scriptures? 26:54
h. is it that he eateth? *Mark* 2:16
h. he went into house. 26; *Luke* 6:4
grow up, he knoweth not *h.* *Mark* 4:27
he said, *H.* is it that ye have? 40
h. hardly shall they that. 10:23
sought *h.* they might take him. 14:1
sought *h.* he might betray him. 11
Luke 22:4
h. shall this be, seeing I? *Luke* 1:34
h. is it that ye sought me? 2:49
take heed *h.* ye hear. 8:18
h. readest thou? 10:26
and *h.* am I straitened till it. 12:50
h. is it that ye do not discern? 56
he said, *h.* is it that I hear? 16:2
remember *h.* he spake unto? 24:6
h. he was known of them in. 35
h. can a man be born? *John* 3:4
h. can these things be? 9
h. can ye believe? 5:44
if not his writing, *h.* believe? 47
h. can this man give us his? 6:52

h. knoweth this man? *John* 7:15
h. were thy eyes opened? 9:10
h. opened eyes? 26
h. loved him. 11:36
h. can we know the way? 14:5
h. is it thou wilt manifest? 22
finding nothing *h.* they. *Acts* 4:21
h. is it that ye have agreed? 5:9
h. God by his hand would. 7:25
h. can I, except some man? 8:31
told, *h.* he had seen the Lord. 9:27
h. God anointed Jesus of. 10:38
h. he had seen an angel. 11:13
h. he had opened the door. 14:27
let us go again, and see *h.* 15:36
h. I kept back nothing that. 20:20
h. so labouring, ye ought to. 35
h. shall God judge the? *Rom* 3:6
h. we that are dead to sin? 6:2
h. to perform what is good. 7:18
h. shall he not with him freely? 8:32
h. shall they call? *h.* shall they believe? *h.* shall they hear? 10:14
h. he maketh intercession to. 11:2
h. unsearchable his judgements. 33
take heed *h.* he buildeth. *1 Cor* 3:10
unmarried careth *h.* he may. 7:32
that is married careth *h.* he. 33
she careth *h.* she may please. 34
h. shall it be known what is piped? 14:7
h. shall be known what is spoken? 9
h. say some that there is no? 15:12
man will say, *h.* are the dead? 35
h. with fear and. *2 Cor* 7:15
h. that in a great trial of. 8:2
know ye not *h.* that Jesus? 13:5
h. turn ye again to weak? *Gal* 4:9
ye see *h.* large a letter I have. 6:11
also may know *h.* I do. *Eph* 6:21
see *h.* it will go with me. *Phil* 2:23
h. to be abased, and know *h.* to. 4:12
h. ye ought to answer. *Col* 4:6
and *h.* ye turned to God. *1 Thes* 1:9
h. holily we behaved ourselves. 2:10
h. we exhorted you. 11
h. ye ought to walk. 4:1
should know *h.* to possess his. 4:4
h. ye ought to follow us. *2 Thes* 3:7
not *h.* to rule his own house, *h.* shall he take care of the? *1 Tim* 3:5
know *h.* thou oughtest to behave. 15
h. shall we escape if we? *Heb* 2:3
now consider *h.* great this man. 7:4
ye see *h.* that by works. *Jas* 2:24
h. great a matter a little fire. 3:5
Lord knoweth *h.* to. *2 Pet* 2:9
h. dwelleth the love of? *1 John* 3:17
h. can he love God whom he? 4:20
h. that the Lord having. *Jude* 5
h. thou canst not bear them. *Rev* 2:2
h. thou hast received. 3:3
see **do**

how *long*

h. long wilt refuse to? *Ex* 10:3
h. long shall this man be a snare? 7
h. long refuse to keep my? 16:28
h. long will this people provoke me? *h. long* will it be ere? *Num* 14:11
h. long shall I bear with this? 27
h. long are ye slack to? *Josh* 18:3
Eli said, *H. long* wilt? *1 Sam* 1:14
h. long wilt thou mourn for? 16:1
Barzillai said, *H. long*? *2 Sam* 19:34
h. long halt ye between? *1 Ki* 18:21
for *h. long* shall thy journey be? *Neh* 2:6
h. long wilt thou not depart from? *Job* 7:19
h. long wilt thou speak? *h. long* shall words of thy mouth be like? 8:2
h. long will it be ere you? 18:2
h. long will ye vex my soul? 19:2
h. long will ye turn my glory into shame? *h. long* will ye? *Ps* 4:2
vexed; but thou, O Lord, *h. long*? 6:3
h. long wilt thou forget me? 13:1
h. long shall I take counsel in my soul? *h. long* shall my enemy? 2
Lord, *h. long* wilt thou look? 35:17
h. long will ye imagine? 62:3
among us that knoweth *h. long*. 74:9
h. long shall adversary? *Ps* 74:10
h. long wilt thou be angry for? 79:5; 80:4
h. long wilt judge unjustly? 82:2
h. long, Lord, wilt thou hide? 89:46
return, O Lord, *h. long*? let. 90:13
the proud, Lord, *h. long* shall the wicked, *h. long* shall? 94:3
h. long shall they utter and? 4
h. long, simple ones, will? *Pr* 1:22
h. long wilt thou sleep, O? 6:9
then said I, Lord, *h. long*? *Isa* 6:11
h. long shall vain? *Jer* 4:14
h. long shall I see standard? 21
h. long shall land mourn? 12:4
h. long shall this be in heart? 23:26
baldness on Gaza, *h. long* wilt? 47:5
O sword of the Lord, *h. long* ere? 6
h. long shall be vision? *Dan* 8:13
h. long shall it be to end of? 12:6
h. long will it be ere they? *Hos* 8:5
h. long shall I cry, and? *Hab* 1:2
increaseth what not his, *h. long*? 2:6
h. long wilt thou not have mercy on Jerusalem? *Zech* 1:12
h. long shall I be with you, *h. long*? *Mat* 17:17; *Mark* 9:19; *Luke* 9:41
h. long is it ago since? *Mark* 9:21
h. long dost thou make? *John* 10:24
h. long, O Lord, holy and? *Rev* 6:10

how *many*

h. many are mine iniquities and? *Job* 13:23
h. many are the days? *Ps* 119:84
h. many loaves have ye? *Mat* 15:34 *Mark* 6:38; 8:5
h. many baskets ye took up? *Mat* 16:9; *Mark* 8:19, 20
h. many things they. *Mark* 15:4
h. many hired servants. *Luke* 15:17
in *h. many* things he. *2 Tim* 1:18

how *many times*

h. many times shall I adjure thee? *1 Ki* 22:16; *2 Chr* 18:15

how *much*

h. much rather when. *2 Ki* 5:13
without prescribing *h. much*. *Ezra* 7:22
h. much better is it to get. *Pr* 16:16
h. much better is thy love. *S of S* 4:10
h. much is a man better? *Mat* 12:12
h. much owest thou to? *Luke* 16:5, 7
h. much every man hath. 19:15
h. much evil he hath. *Acts* 9:13
h. much he is the Mediator. *Heb* 8:6
of *h. much* sorer punishment. 10:29
h. much she hath glorified. *Rev* 18:7

how *much less*

contain thee, *h. much less* this house? *1 Ki* 8:27; *2 Chr* 6:18
h. much less shall your God? *2 Chr* 32:15
h. much less in them that dwell in houses of clay? *Job* 4:19
h. much less shall I answer? 9:14
h. much less is man that is? 25:6
h. much less to him that accepteth? 34:19
h. much less shall it be meet for? *Ezek* 15:5

how *much more*

and *h. much more* after my death? *Deut* 31:27
h. much more if people? *1 Sam* 14:30
h. much more then if we? 23:3
h. much more when wicked men? *2 Sam* 4:11
h. much more now may this? 16:11
h. much more abominable and? *Job* 15:16
h. much more then the hearts of? *Pr* 15:11
h. much more do his friends? 19:7
h. much more when with a? 21:27
h. much more when I send my four sore judgements? *Ezek* 14:21
h. much more shall your heavenly Father? *Mat* 7:11; *Luke* 11:13
h. much more shall call? *Mat* 10:25
h. much more are ye better than? *Luke* 12:24
h. much more will he clothe you? *Luke* 12:28
h. much more their fulness? *Rom* 11:12
h. much more these which be? 24
h. much more things that pertain to? *1 Cor* 6:3
brother to me, *h. much more* to? *Philem* 16

how *oft, often*

h. oft is the candle of the wicked put out? *h. oft* cometh? *Job* 21:17
h. oft did they provoke? *Ps* 78:40
h. oft shall my brother? *Mat* 18:21
h. often would I have gathered thy children as a. 23:37; *Luke* 13:34

howbeit

h. Sisera fled on his feet. *Judg* 4:17
h. the king of Ammonites. 11:28
h. the hair of his head began. 16:22
h. the name of the city was. 18:29
h. we may not give them wives of. 21:18
h. there is a kinsman. *Ruth* 3:12
h. yet protest solemnly. *1 Sam* 8:9
h. Asahel refused to. *2 Sam* 2:23
h. because by this deed hast. 12:14
h. he would not hearken. 13:14
h. he would not go, but blessed. 25
h. he attained not unto the first three. 23:19; *1 Chr* 11:21
h. the kingdom is turned. *1 Ki* 2:15
h. I believed not the words. 10:7 *2 Chr* 9:6
h. I will not rend all the kingdom. *1 Ki* 11:13, 34
I have lacked nothing, *h.* let. 11:22
h. slingers went about it. *2 Ki* 3:25
h. Lord shewed me, that he. 8:10
h. from sins of Jeroboam, Jehu. 10:29
h. there were not made for. 12:13
h. high places were not taken away. 14:4; 15:35; *2 Chr* 20:33
h. every nation made. *2 Ki* 17:29
h. they did not hearken, but. 40
h. there was no reckoning. 22:7
h. the Lord God of Israel. *1 Chr* 28:4
h. the king of Israel stayed himself. *2 Chr* 18:34
h. the Levites hastened it not. 24:5
h. he entered not into temple. 27:2
h. in business of ambassadors. 32:31
h. thou art just in all. *Neh* 9:33
h. our God turned the curse. 13:2
h. he will not stretch out. *Job* 30:24
h. he meaneth not so. *Isa* 10:7
h. I sent to you all my. *Jer* 44:4
h. this kind goeth not. *Mat* 17:21
h. Jesus suffered him. *Mark* 5:19
h. in vain do they worship me. 7:7
h. there came boats from. *John* 6:23
h. no man spake openly of. 7:13
h. we know this man whence he. 27
h. Jesus spake of his death. 11:13
h. when he the Spirit of truth. 16:13
h. many who heard the. *Acts* 4:4
h. the Most High dwelleth not. 7:48
h. he rose up and came into. 14:20
h. certain men clave to him. 17:34
h. we must be cast upon a. 27:26
h. they looked when he should have swollen. 28:6
h. we speak wisdom. *1 Cor* 2:6
h. there is not in every man. 8:7
h. in the Spirit he speaketh. 14:2
h. in malice be children, in. 20
h. that was not first which. 15:46
h. wherein soever any is. *2 Cor* 11:21
h. when ye knew not God. *Gal* 4:8
h. for this cause I obtained mercy. *1 Tim* 1:16
h. not all that came out of. *Heb* 3:16

howl

(*American Revision usually substitutes the word* wail)
h. ye, for the day of the. *Isa* 13:6
h. O gate. 14:31
Moab shall *h.* 15:2, 3; 16:7
h. ye ships of Tarshish, for it. 23:1
pass over to Tarshish, *h.* ye. 6
make them to *h.* 52:5
h. for vexation. 65:14
lament and *h.* *Jer* 4:8; 48:20

h. ye shepherds. *Jer* 25:34
inhabitants of the land shall *h.* 47:2
I will *h.* for Moab. 48:31
they shall *h.* 39
h. O Heshbon. 49:3
h. for Babylon. 51:8
cry and *h.* son of man. *Ezek* 21:12
prophesy and say, *H.* ye, woe. 30:2
h. ye drinkers. *Joel* 1:5
h. yo vinedressers. 11
lament and *h.* ye ministers of. 13
I will wail and *h.*, will go. *Mi* 1:8
h. ye inhabitants of. *Zeph* 1:11
h. fir tree, *h.* O ye oaks. *Zech* 11:2
ye rich men, weep and *h.* *Jas* 5:1

howled

not cried to me, when they *h.* on. *Hos* 7:14

howling

in waste *h.* wilderness. *Deut* 32:10
h. thereof is gone to Eglaim and. *Isa* 15:8
an *h.* of principal of the. *Jer* 25:36
h. from the second gate. *Zeph* 1:10
there is a voice of the *h.* *Zech* 11:3

howlings

songs of the temple shall be *h.* *Amos* 8:3

huge

and Lubims a *h.* host. *2 Chr* 16:8

humble

[1] *Not proud or assertive. The word does not have its modern sense of undue self-depreciation.* [2] *To humble is to humiliate.*

and he shall save the *h.* *Job* 22:29
not the cry of the *h.* *Ps* 9:12*
O God, forget not the *h.* 10:12*
hast heard the desire of the *h.* 17*
the *h.* shall hear thereof and. 34:2
h. shall see this and be glad. 69:32
better be of a *h.* spirit. *Pr* 16:19*
honour shall uphold the *h.* 29:23*
of a contrite and *h.* spirit, to revive the spirit of the *h.* *Isa* 57:15
but giveth grace to the *h.* *Jas* 4:6 *1 Pet* 5:5

humble

refuse to *h.* thyself ? *Ex* 10:3
to *h.* thee and to prove. *Deut* 8:2, 16
h. ye them, and do. *Judg* 19:24
my people shall *h.* *2 Chr* 7:14
because thou didst *h.* thyself. 34:27
go, *h.* thyself, and make. *Pr* 6:3
h. yourselves, sit down. *Jer* 13:18
shall *h.* himself. *Mat* 18:4; 23:12
my God will *h.* me. *2 Cor* 12:21
h. yourselves in the sight. *Jas* 4:10
h. yourselves under. *1 Pet* 5:6

humbled

if their uncircumcised hearts be *h.* *Lev* 26:41
h. thee and suffered thee. *Deut* 8:3
because thou hast *h.* her. 21:14 22:29
hath *h.* his neighbour's wife. 22:24
because hast *h.* thyself. *2 Ki* 22:19
princes and the king *h.* *2 Chr* 12:6
when the Lord saw that they *h.* 7
he *h.* himself, wrath turned. 12
divers of Asher and Zebulun *h.* 30:11
Hezekiah *h.* himself for pride. 32:26
Manasseh *h.* himself greatly. 33:12
graven images before he was *h.* 19
Amon *h.* not himself before the Lord, as Manasseh his father *h.* 23
Zedekiah *h.* not himself. 36:12
as for me, I *h.* my soul. *Ps* 35:13*
looks of man shall be *h.* *Isa* 2:11*
h., eyes of the lofty shall be *h.* 5:15
and the haughty shall be *h.* 10:33*
they are not *h.* even to. *Jer* 44:10
remembrance and is *h.* *Lam* 3:20*
in thee have they *h.* *Ezek* 22:10
and another in thee hath *h.* 11
thou his son hast not *h.* *Dan* 5:22
he *h.* himself and became. *Phil* 2:8

humbledst

because thou *h.* thyself. *2 Chr* 34:27

humbleness

put on kindness, *h.* of. *Col* 3:12

humbleth

seest thou how Ahab *h.*? because he *h.* himself. *1 Ki* 21:29
he croucheth and *h.* *Ps* 10:10*
who *h.* himself to behold. 113:6
man boweth, great man *h.* *Isa* 2:9*
he that *h.* himself shall be exalted. *Luke* 14:11; 18:14

humbly

I *h.* beseech thee that. *2 Sam* 16:4
love mercy, and to walk *h.* *Mi* 6:8

humiliation

in his *h.* his judgement. *Acts* 8:33

humility

before honour is *h.* *Pr* 15:33; 18:12
by *h.* are riches, and honour. 22:4
Lord with all *h.* of mind. *Acts* 20:19*
beguile you in a voluntary *h.* *Col* 2:18
wisdom in will worship and *h.* 23
another, clothed with *h.* *1 Pet* 5:5

hundred

Shem was an *h.* years. *Gen* 11:10
child be born to him that is an *h.*? 17:17; 21:5; *Rom* 4:19
Jacob bought for an *h.* pieces. *Gen* 33:19; *Josh* 24:32
hangings *h.* cubits long. *Ex* 27:9, 11 38:9, 11
the court shall be an *h.* cubits. 18
h. sockets were cast of the *h.* 38:27
five shall chase an *h.* and an *h.* put to. *Lev* 26:8
shall amerce him in an *h.* *Deut* 22:19
so Gideon and the *h.* men. *Judg* 7:19
ten of an *h.* an *h.* of a 1000. 20:10
of Benjamin 25,000 and an *h.* 35
but an *h.* foreskins. *1 Sam* 18:25 *2 Sam* 3:14
an *h.* clusters of raisins. *1 Sam* 25:18 *2 Sam* 16:1
reserved for an *h.* chariots. *2 Sam* 8:4; *1 Chr* 18:4
provision for one day *h.* *1 Ki* 4:23
house of the forest an *h.* cubits. 7:2
Obadiah took *h.* prophets. 18:4, 13
this before an *h.* men ? *2 Ki* 4:43
Jehoahaz in bands, and put land to a tribute of an *h.* 23:33; *2 Chr* 36:3
least was over an *h.* *1 Chr* 12:14
Simeon seven thousand and one *h.* 25
Lord make his people an *h.* 21:3
Solomon made an *h.* *2 Chr* 3:16
made an *h.* basons of gold. 4:8
men for an *h.* talents of silver. 25:6
what shall we do for the *h.* talents ? 9
Jotham an *h.* talents of silver. 27:5
brought an *h.* rams. 29:32
they gave one *h.* priests'. *Ezra* 2:69
offered at the dedication an *h.* 6:17
an *h.* talents of silver, *h.* measures of wheat and wine, and an *h.* 7:22
h. talents of gold, an *h.* 8:26
restore to them the *h.* *Neh* 5:11
more than an *h.* stripes. *Pr* 17:10
man beget an *h.* children. *Eccl* 6:3
though sinner do evil *h.* times. 8:12
h. years old, but the sinner being an *h.* years old shall. *Isa* 65:20
measured an *h.* cubits. *Ezek* 40:19
gate to gate an *h.* cubits. 23, 27
h. cubits long, an *h.* cubits broad. 47
house an *h.* cubits long. 41:13
place toward east, an *h.* cubits. 14
one side and other, an *h.* cubits. 15
the temple were an *h.* cubits. 42:8
shall leave an *h.*, that which went forth by an *h.* shall. *Amos* 5:3
if a man have an *h.* sheep. *Mat* 18:12; *Luke* 15:4
owed him an *h.* pence. *Mat* 18:28
an *h.* measures of oil. *Luke* 16:6
thou ? an *h.* measures of wheat. 7
myrrh and aloes, an *h.* *John* 19:39

hundredfold, see fold

one **hundred** *and five*

Seth lived *one h. and five* years. *Gen* 5:6

one **hundred** *and ten*

Joseph lived *one h. and ten* years. *Gen* 50:22, 26
Joshua died, being an *h. and ten* years old. *Josh* 24:29; *Judg* 2:8
Johanan an *h. and ten.* *Ezra* 8:12

one **hundred** *and twelve*

Uzziel an *h. and twelve.* *1 Chr* 15:10
Jorah, an *h. and twelve.* *Ezra* 2:18
Hariph, an *h. and twelve.* *Neh* 7:24

one **hundred** *and nineteen*

Terah *h. and nineteen.* *Gen* 11:25

one **hundred** *and twenty*

his days shall be *h. and twenty* years. *Gen* 6:3
the gold of the spoons was an *h. and twenty* shekels. *Num* 7:86
an *h. and twenty* years. *Deut* 31:2
Moses an *h. and twenty* years. 34:7
an *h. and twenty* talents of gold. *1 Ki* 10:10; *2 Chr* 9:9
and brethren an *h. and twenty.* *1 Chr* 15:5
porch an *h. and twenty.* *2 Chr* 3:4
an *h. and twenty* priests. 5:12
kingdom an *h. and twenty.* *Dan* 6:1
names were about an *h. and twenty.* *Acts* 1:15

one **hundred** *twenty two*

men of Michmash, *h. twenty two.* *Ezra* 2:27; *Neh* 7:31

one **hundred** *twenty three*

Aaron *h. twenty three.* *Num* 33:39
of captivity an *h. twenty and three.* *Ezra* 2:21; *Neh* 7:32

one **hundred** *and twenty seven*

Sarah was an *h. twenty seven.* *Gen* 23:1
reigned over an *h.* and *twenty seven.* *Esth* 1:1; 8:9; 9:30

one **hundred** *and twenty eight*

men of Anathoth *h. twenty eight.* *Ezra* 2:23; *Neh* 7:27
Asaph an *h. twenty eight.* *Ezra* 2:41
brethren an *h.* and *twenty eight.* *Neh* 11:14

one **hundred** *and thirty*

Adam lived *h. thirty* years. *Gen* 5:3
pilgrimage are an *h. and thirty.* 47:9
weight thereof was an *h. and thirty.* *Num* 7:13, 19, 25
charger weighing an *h. and thirty.* 85
brethren an *h. and thirty.* *1 Chr* 15:7
Jehoiada was an *h. and thirty* years. *2 Chr* 24:15

one **hundred** *thirty three*

Kohath an *h. thirty three.* *Ex* 6:18

one **hundred** *thirty seven*

Ishmael an *h.* and *thirty seven.* *Gen* 25:17
of Levi were *h.* and *thirty seven.* *Ex* 6:16
Amram were an *h. thirty seven.* 20

one **hundred** *thirty eight*

children of Shobai of Ater, *h. thirty eight.* *Neh* 7:45

one **hundred** *thirty nine*

of Shobai in all an *h. thirty nine.* *Ezra* 2:42

one **hundred** *forty*

Job an *h. forty* years. *Job* 42:16

one **hundred** *forty four*

the wall an *h. forty four* cubits. *Rev* 21:17

one **hundred** *forty seven*

Jacob an *h. forty seven.* *Gen* 47:28

one **hundred** *forty eight*

the children of Asaph *h. forty eight.* *Neh* 7:44

one **hundred** *and fifty*

waters prevailed an *h. and fifty* days. *Gen* 7:24; 8:3
and an horse for an *h. andfifty.* *1 Ki* 10:29; *2 Chr* 1:17
sons' sons an *h. andfifty.* *1 Chr* 8:40
reckoned of males, an *h. and fifty.* *Ezra* 8:3
table an *h. and fifty* Jews. *Neh* 5:17

one **hundred** *fifty three*

net full of fishes an *h. and fifty and three.* *John* 21:11

one **hundred** *fifty six*
Magbish, and *h. fifty six.* *Ezra* 2:30
one **hundred** *sixty*
with him *h. sixty* males. *Ezra* 8:10
one **hundred** *sixty two*
Jared lived *h. sixty two* years. *Gen* 5:18
one **hundred** *seventy two*
brethren *h. seventy two.* *Neh* 11:19
one **hundred** *seventy five*
life was an *h. seventy five.* *Gen* 25:7
one **hundred** *eighty*
of Isaac an *h.* and *eighty* years. *Gen* 35:28
feast for an *h.* and *eighty* days. *Esth* 1:4
one **hundred** *eighty two*
Lamech lived *h. eighty two* and. *Gen* 5:28
one **hundred** *eighty seven*
Methuselah lived *h. eighty seven.* *Gen* 5:25
one **hundred** *eighty eight*
of Beth-lehem an *h. eighty eight.* *Neh* 7:26
hundred *thousand*
Judah were an *h. thous.* *Num* 2:9
the camp of Reuben an *h. thous.* 16
slew of Syrians *h. thous.* *1 Ki* 20:29
to king of Israel an *h. thous.* lambs, an *h. thous.* rams. *2 Ki* 3:4
from Hagarites an *h. thous.* men. *1 Chr* 5:21
thousand and *h. thous.* 21:5
for house of Lord *h. thous.* 22:14
an *h. thous.* talents of iron. 29:7
he hired an *h. thous.* *2 Chr* 25:6
one **hundred** *and eight thousand and an* **hundred**
of camp of Ephraim, 108,100. *Num* 2:24
an **hundred** *twenty thousand*
the Midianites 120,000. *Judg* 8:10
a sacrifice of an 120,000 sheep. *1 Ki* 8:63; *2 Chr* 7:5
Gad, and Manasseh, 120,000. *1 Chr* 12:37
slew in Judah in one day 120,000. *2 Chr* 28:6
Nineveh were about 120,000 persons. *Jonah* 4:11
an **hundred** *forty four thousand*
were sealed 144,000 of all. *Rev* 7:4
with him 144,000, having his. 14:1
learn that song but the 144,000. 3
an **hundred** *fifty thousand*
strangers in the land of Israel were found 150,000. *2 Chr* 2:17
an **hundred** *eighty thousand*
with Benjamin 180,000. *1 Ki* 12:21 *2 Chr* 11:1
with Jehozabad were 180,000, for. *2 Chr* 17:18
an **hundred** *eighty five thousand*
of the Lord smote of the Assyrians, 185,000. *2 Ki* 19:35; *Isa* 37:36
two **hundred**
begat Nahor *two h.* years. *Gen* 11:23
two h. she goats, and *two h.* 32:14
Achan saw *two h.* shekels. *Josh* 7:21
his mother took *two h.* *Judg* 17:4
slew of Philistines *two h.* men. *1 Sam* 18:27
two h. abode by. 25:13; 30:10, 21
two h. loaves, *two h.* cakes. 25:18
weighed hair *two h.* *2 Sam* 14:26
with Absalom went *two h.* 15:11
Ziba brought David *two h.* 16:1
pomegranates were *two h.* *1 Ki* 7:20
Solomon made *two h.* targets. 10:16 *2 Chr* 9:15
burnt offerings *two h.* *2 Chr* 29:32
were among them *two h.* *Ezra* 2:65
offered at dedication *two h.* 6:17
the fruit thereof *two h.* *S of S* 8:12
one lamb out of *two h.* *Ezek* 45:15
two h. pennyworth is not. *John* 6:7
make ready *two h.* soldiers, and spearmen *two h.* *Acts* 23:23

two **hundred** *five*
the days of Terah were *two h. five* years. *Gen* 11:32
two **hundred** *seven*
Reu lived *two h. seven.* *Gen* 11:21
two **hundred** *nine*
Peleg lived *two h. nine.* *Gen* 11:19
two **hundred** *twelve*
gates were *two h. twelve.* *1 Chr* 9:22
two **hundred** *eighteen*
Obadiah *two h. eighteen.* *Ezra* 8:9
two **hundred** *twenty*
service of Levites *two h. twenty.* *Ezra* 8:20
two **hundred** *twenty three*
Beth-el and Ai *two h. twenty three.* *Ezra* 2:28
two **hundred** *thirty two*
of provinces *two h. thirty two.* *1 Ki* 20:15
two **hundred** *forty two*
fathers *two h. forty two.* *Neh* 11:13
two **hundred** *forty five*
their mules *two h.* and *forty five.* *Ezra* 2:66; *Neh* 7:68
and *two h. forty five* singing men. *Neh* 7:67
two **hundred** *fifty*
cinnamon *two h.* and *fifty*, of calamus *two h.* and *fifty.* *Ex* 30:23
two h. and *fifty* princes. *Num* 16:2
two h. and *fifty* censers. 17
consumed the *two h.* and *fifty.* 35
two h. and *fifty* that bare. *2 Chr* 8:10
north *two h. fifty.* *Ezek* 48:17
two **hundred** *seventy six*
ship *two h. seventy six* souls. *Acts* 27:37
two **hundred** *eighty four*
in the holy city *two h. eighty four.* *Neh* 11:18
two **hundred** *eighty eight*
songs *two h. eighty eight.* *1 Chr* 25:7
two **hundred** *fifty thousand*
sheep *two h. fifty thous.* *1 Chr* 5:21
three **hundred**
Enoch walked with God *three h.* *Gen* 5:22
the ark shall be *three h.* 6:15
Benjamin *three h.* pieces of. 45:22
lapped were *three h.* men. *Judg* 7:6
and he retained those *three h.* 8
the *three h.* men that were. 8:4
coast of Arnon *three h.* years. 11:26
and caught *three h.* foxes. 15:4
spear weighed *three h.* shekels. *2 Sam* 21:16
Abishai lifted up his spear against *three h.* 23:18; *1 Chr* 11:11, 20
made *three h.* shields. *1 Ki* 10:17
Solomon had *three h.* 11:3
Hezekiah *three h.* talents. *2 Ki* 18:14
three h. shekels of gold. *2 Chr* 9:16
against Asa with *three h.* 14:19
passover offerings *three h.* 35:8
with Shechaniah *three h.* *Ezra* 8:5
the Jews slew *three h.* *Esth* 9:15
sold for *three h.* pence. *John* 12:5
three **hundred** *eighteen*
with *three h. eighteen* servants. *Gen* 14:14
three **hundred** *twenty*
Harim *three h.* and *twenty.* *Ezra* 2:32; *Neh* 7:35
three **hundred** *twenty three*
the children of Bezai 323. *Ezra* 2:17 *Neh* 7:23
three **hundred** *twenty eight*
of Hashum *three h. twenty eight.* *Neh* 7:22
three **hundred** *forty five*
children of Jericho 345. *Ezra* 2:34 *Neh* 7:36
three **hundred** *fifty*
flood *three h. fifty* years. *Gen* 9:28

three **hundred** *sixty*
of Israel *three h. sixty* men died. *2 Sam* 2:31
three **hundred** *sixty five*
Enoch's days were *three h. sixty five* years. *Gen* 5:23
three **hundred** *seventy two*
the children of Shephatiah 372. *Ezra* 2:4; *Neh* 7:9
three **hundred** *ninety*
to number of days 390. *Ezek* 4:5, 9
three **hundred** *thousand*
went out to war 300,000. *Num* 31:36
Israel were 300,000. *1 Sam* 11:8 *2 Chr* 14:8
with Adnah mighty men 300,000. *2 Chr* 17:14
and Benjamin to be 300,000. 25:5
three **hundred** *and seven thousand five* **hundred**
an army of 307,500. *2 Chr* 26:13
three **hundred** *and thirty seven thousand five* **hundred**
pertained unto the congregation was 337,500 sheep. *Num* 31:43
four **hundred**
afflict them *four h.* years. *Gen* 15:13; *Acts* 7:6
four h. shekels of silver. 23:15, 16
Esau cometh to thee with *four h.* 32:6; 33:1
found *four h.* virgins of. *Judg* 21:12
there were with David about *four h.* men. *1 Sam* 22:2; 25:13; 30:10
save *four h.* young men on. 30:17
four h. pomegranates. *1 Ki* 7:42
prophets of the groves *four h.* 18:19
gathered of the prophets about *four h.* and said. 22:6; *2 Chr* 18:5
brake down wall of Jerusalem *four h.* cubits. *2 Ki* 14:13; *2 Chr* 25:23
of house *four h.* lambs. *Ezra* 6:17
to whom about *four h.* *Acts* 5:36
four **hundred** *and three*
Arphaxad lived 403. *Gen* 11:13
lived after he begat Eber 403. 15
four **hundred** *and ten*
second sort *four h. ten.* *Ezra* 1:10
four **hundred** *and twenty*
from thence gold, 420. *1 Ki* 9:28
four **hundred** *and thirty*
Eber lived 430 years. *Gen* 11:17
in Egypt 430 years. *Ex* 12:40, 41
law which was 430 years. *Gal* 3:17
four **hundred** *thirty five*
their camels were 435. *Ezra* 2:67 *Neh* 7:69
four **hundred** *and fifty*
prophets of Baal 450. *1 Ki* 18:19, 22
gave judges about *four h. fifty* years. *Acts* 13:20
four **hundred** *fifty four*
Adin *four h. fifty four* *Ezra* 2:15
four **hundred** *sixty eight*
of Perez were 468 men. *Neh* 11:6
four **hundred** *eighty*
in 480 years Solomon. *1 Ki* 6:1
four **hundred** *thousand*
Benjamin 400,000. *Judg* 20:2, 17
array with 400,000 men. *2 Chr* 13:3
four **hundred** *seventy thousand*
Judah was 470,000 that. *1 Chr* 21:5
five **hundred**
Noah was *five h.* years. *Gen* 5:32
Shem lived after *five h.* years. 11:11
of pure myrrh *five h.* *Ex* 30:23
of cassia *five h.* shekels after. 24
levy one soul of *five h.* *Num* 31:28
offerings *five h.* oxen. *2 Chr* 35:9
Shushan *five h.* men. *Esth* 9:6, 12
five h. yoke of oxen, *five h.* she asses. *Job* 1:3
he measured *five h.* reeds. *Ezek* 42:16, 17, 18, 19, 20
be for the sanctuary *five h.* in length, with *five h.* in breadth. 45:2
one owed *five h.* pence. *Luke* 7:41
above *five h.* brethren at. *1 Cor* 15:6

five **hundred** *and thirty*
gave *five h. and thirty* priests'. *Neh* 7:70
five **hundred** *and fifty*
five hundred fifty bare rule over. *1 Ki* 9:23
five **hundred** *thousand*
men of Judah were 500,000 men. *2 Sam* 24:9
slain of Israel 500,000 men. *2 Chr* 13:17
six **hundred**
Noah *six h.* years old when flood. *Gen* 7:6, 11
Pharaoh took *six h.* *Ex* 14:7
slew with an ox goad *six h.* *Judg* 3:31
out of Eshtaol *six h.* 18:11, 16, 17
six h. Benjamites fled to. 20:47
Saul numbered the people *six h.* *1 Sam* 13:15; 14:2
spear head weighed *six h.* 17:7
David and his men about *six h.* 23:13; 27:2; 30:9
all the Gittites were *six h.* men. *2 Sam* 15:18
six h. shekels of gold went to one target. *1 Ki* 10:16; *2 Chr* 9:15
a chariot went for *six h.* shekels. *1 Ki* 10:29; *2 Chr* 1:17
Ornan *six h.* shekels. *1 Chr* 21:25
house with gold to *six h.* talents. *2 Chr* 3:8
consecrated things were *six h.* oxen. 29:33
six **hundred** *twenty one*
children of Ramah *six h. twenty one.* *Ezra* 2:26; *Neh* 7:30
six **hundred** *twenty three*
Bebai *six h. twenty three. Ezra* 2:11
six **hundred** *twenty eight*
Bebai, *six h. twenty eight. Neh* 7:16
six **hundred** *forty two*
of Bani, *six h. forty two.* *Ezra* 2:10
Nekoda, *six h. forty two.* *Neh* 7:62
six **hundred** *forty eight*
Binnui, *six h. forty eight. Neh* 7:15
six **hundred** *and fifty*
weighed unto their hand *six h. fifty* talents. *Ezra* 8:26
six **hundred** *fifty two*
Nekoda, *six h. fifty two.* *Ezra* 2:60
Arah, *six h.* and *fifty two. Neh* 7:10
six **hundred** *sixty six*
gold to Solomon in year 666 talents. *1 Ki* 10:14
of Adonikam, 666. *Ezra* 2:13
and his number is 666. *Rev* 13:18
six **hundred** *sixty seven*
of Adonikam, 667. *Neh* 7:18
six **hundred** *seventy five*
tribute of sheep was 675. *Num* 31:37
six **hundred** *ninety*
Jeuel and brethren 690. *1 Chr* 9:6
six **hundred** *thousand*
journeyed about 600,000. *Ex* 12:37
for every man for 600,000. 38:26
numbered were 600,000. *Num* 1:46
people are 600,000 footmen. 11:21
six **hundred** *seventy five thousand*
prey was 675,000 sheep. *Num* 31:32
seven **hundred**
of Gibeah were *seven h.* chosen. *Judg* 20:15, 16
David took from him *seven h.* *2 Sam* 8:4
David slew men of *seven h.* 10:18
had *seven h.* wives. *1 Ki* 11:3
Moab took *seven h.* *2 Ki* 3:26
the Lord *seven h.* oxen. *2 Chr* 15:11
seven **hundred** *twenty one*
Lod, Hadid, Ono, 721. *Neh* 7:37
seven **hundred** *twenty five*
Lod, Hadid, Ono, 725. *Ezra* 2:33
seven **hundred** *thirty six*
their horses were 736. *Ezra* 2:66 *Neh* 7:68
seven **hundred** *forty three*
of Kirjath-arim, 743. *Ezra* 2:25
seven **hundred** *forty five*
captive of the Jews 745. *Jer* 52:30
seven **hundred** *sixty*
the children of Zaccai 760. *Ezra* 2:9; *Neh* 7:14
seven **hundred** *seventy five*
children of Arah, 775. *Ezra* 2:5
seven **hundred** *seventy seven*
of Lamech were 777. *Gen* 5:31
seven **hundred** *eighty two*
Methuselah lived 782. *Gen* 5:26
eight **hundred**
he begat Seth lived 800. *Gen* 5:4
after he begat Enoch lived 800. 19
his spear against 800. *2 Sam* 23:8
eight **hundred** *seven*
after he begat Enos 807. *Gen* 5:7
eight **hundred** *fifteen*
after he begat Cainan 815. *Gen* 5:10
eight **hundred** *twenty two*
that did work were 822. *Neh* 11:12
eight **hundred** *thirty*
he begat Jared 830 years. *Gen* 5:16
eight **hundred** *thirty two*
carried captive 832. *Jer* 52:29
eight **hundred** *forty*
he begat Mahalaleel 840. *Gen* 5:13
eight **hundred** *forty five*
children of Zattu were 845. *Neh* 7:13
eight **hundred** *ninety five*
Mahalaleel were 895. *Gen* 5:17
nine **hundred**
Jabin had *nine h.* *Judg* 4:3, 13
nine **hundred** *five*
days of Enos were 905. *Gen* 5:11
nine **hundred** *ten*
days of Cainan 910 years. *Gen* 5:14
nine **hundred** *twelve*
days of Seth were 912. *Gen* 5:8
nine **hundred** *twenty eight*
him Gabbai, Sallai, 928. *Neh* 11:8
nine **hundred** *thirty*
that Adam lived were 930. *Gen* 5:5
nine **hundred** *forty five*
children of Zattu 945. *Ezra* 2:8
nine **hundred** *fifty*
of Noah were 950 years. *Gen* 9:29
nine **hundred** *fifty six*
brethren according to generations 956. *1 Chr* 9:9
nine **hundred** *sixty two*
Jared were 962 years. *Gen* 5:20
nine **hundred** *sixty nine*
days of Methuselah were 969 years. *Gen* 5:27
nine **hundred** *seventy three*
the children of Jedaiah 973. *Ezra* 2:36; *Neh* 7:39

hundreds
be rulers of *h.* and tens. *Ex* 18:21 25; *Deut* 1:15
was wroth with captains over *h.* *Num* 31:14
took gold of the captains of *h.* 54
will son of Jesse make you captains of *h.*? *1 Sam* 22:7
the Philistines passed on by *h.* 29:2
set captains of *h.* over. *2 Sam* 18:1
all the people came out by *h.* 4
and set the rulers over *h.* *2 Ki* 11:4
captains over *h.* did the priest give spears and. 10; *2 Chr* 23:9
with the captains of *h.* *1 Chr* 13:1
which the captains over *h.* 26:26
the captains over the *h.* 28:1
then the captains of *h.* offered. 29:6
Jehoiada took captains of *h.* into. *2 Chr* 23:1
made them captains over *h.* 25:5
sat down in ranks by *h.* *Mark* 6:40

hunger, *substantive*
whole assembly with *h.* *Ex* 16:3
serve thine enemies in *h. Deut* 28:48
they shall be burnt with *h.* 32:24
bread from heaven for their *h.* *Neh* 9:15
young lions do lack and suffer *h.* *Ps* 34:10
an idle soul shall suffer *h. Pr* 19:15
he is like to die for *h.* *Jer* 38:9*
see no war, nor have *h.* of. 42:14
that faint for *h.* in top of. *Lam* 2:19
than they that be slain with *h.* 4:9
be no more consumed with *h.* *Ezek* 34:29
and I perish with *h.* *Luke* 15:17
been in *h.* and thirst. *2 Cor* 11:27
given them to kill with *h.* *Rev* 6:8

hunger, *verb*
he suffered thee to *h.* *Deut* 8:3
shall not *h.* nor thirst. *Isa* 49:10
blessed are they that *h.* *Mat* 5:6 *Luke* 6:21
are full, for ye shall *h.* *Luke* 6:25
he that cometh to me shall never *h.* *John* 6:35
if thine enemy *h.* feed. *Rom* 12:20
we both *h.* and thirst. *1 Cor* 4:11
and if any man *h.* let him eat. 11:34
they shall *h.* no more. *Rev* 7:16

hungerbitten
his strength shall be *h.* *Job* 18:12

hungered
he was afterwards an *h.* *Mat* 4:2 *Luke* 4:2
his disciples were an *h.* *Mat* 12:1
did when he was an *h.* 3; *Mark* 2:25
returned into city, he *h.* *Mat* 21:18
for I was an *h.* and ye gave. 25:35
Lord, when saw we thee an *h.*? 37, 44
for I was an *h.* and ye gave. 42
did when himself was an *h. Luke* 6:3

hungry
they that were *h.* ceased. *1 Sam* 2:5
the people is *h.*, weary. *2 Sam* 17:29
they know that we be *h.* *2 Ki* 7:12
h. eateth up and taketh it. *Job* 5:5
withholden bread from the *h.* 22:7
away the sheaf from the *h.* 24:10
if I were *h.* I would not. *Ps* 50:12
h. and thirsty, their soul. 107:5
filleth the *h.* soul with goodness. 9
and there he maketh the *h.* to. 36
who giveth food to the *h.* 146:7
satisfy his soul when he is *h. Pr* 6:30
if thine enemy be *h.* give. 25:21
to the *h.* soul every bitter. 27:7
bestead and *h.*: when they shall be *h.*, they shall fret. *Isa* 8:21
snatch on right hand, and be *h.* 9:20
it shall even be as when a *h.* 29:8
empty the soul of the *h.* 32:6
yea, he is *h.* and his strength. 44:12
to deal thy bread to the *h.*? 58:7
draw out thy soul to the *h.* 10
shall eat, but ye shall be *h.* 65:13
his bread to the *h.* *Ezek* 18:7, 16
from Bethany he was *h. Mark* 11:12
he hath filled the *h.* with. *Luke* 1:53
Peter became very *h.* *Acts* 10:10
one is *h.* and another is. *1 Cor* 11:21
to be full and to be *h.* *Phil* 4:12

hunt
(*Hunting as a matter of necessity, whether for the extermination of dangerous beasts or for procuring food, betokens a rude and semi-civilized state; as an amusement, it indicates an advanced state. As a pastoral people the Hebrews did little hunting as a sport; and their rules of eating prevented their doing so for food, after the Law was given*)
Esau went to field to *h.* *Gen* 27:5
as when one doth *h.* *1 Sam* 26:20
wilt thou *h.* the prey? *Job* 38:39
evil shall *h.* violent man. *Ps* 140:11
the adulteress will *h.* *Pr* 6:26
shall *h.* them from every. *Jer* 16:16
they *h.* our steps that we. *Lam* 4:18
will ye *h.* the souls? *Ezek* 13:18
pillows wherewith ye there *h.* 20
h. every man his brother. *Mi* 7:2

hunted
in your hand to be *h.* *Ezek* 13:21

subjection to your own *h.* *1 Pet* 3:1
ye *h.* dwell with them according. 7

Hushai

H. the Archite came. *2 Sam* 15:32
so *H.* David's friend came into. 37
H. came to Absalom and. 16:16
said to *H.*, Is this thy kindness ? 17
call *H.* 17:5
for, said *H.* thou knowest thy. 8
the counsel of *H.* is better than. 14
then said *H.* to Zadok and to. 15
Baanah the son of *H.* *1 Ki* 4:16
and *H.* was the king's. *1 Chr* 27:33

husk, -s

kernels even to the *h.* *Num* 6:4
full ears of corn in *h.* *2 Ki* 4:42
filled his belly with *h.* *Luke* 15:16

Huzzab

H. be led away captive. *Nah* 2:7

Hymenaeus

of whom is *H.* and. *1 Tim* 1:20
is *H.* and Philetus. *2 Tim* 2:17

hymn, -s

when they had sung an *h.* *Mat* 26:30
Mark 14:26
to yourselves in psalms and *h.*
Eph 5:19
one another in psalms and *h.* *Col* 3:16

hypocrisies

aside all malice and *h.* *1 Pet* 2:1

hypocrisy

(*A false assumption of virtue; canting pretence of goodness or religion. The word is frequently used in the Bible with the meaning of godlessness*)

iniquity, to practise *h.* *Isa* 32:6
within ye are full of *h.* *Mat* 23:28
knowing their *h.* said. *Mark* 12:15
of Pharisees, which is *h.* *Luke* 12:1
speaking lies in *h.* their. *1 Tim* 4:2
is pure and without *h.* *Jas* 3:17

hypocrite

the *h.*'s hope shall perish. *Job* 8:13*
for an *h.* shall not come. 13:16*
shall stir up himself against *h.* 17:8*
and the joy of the *h.* is but. 20:5*
what is the hope of the *h.*? 27:8*
h. reign not, lest the people. 34:30*
an *h.* with his mouth destroyeth.
Pr 11:9*
for every one is an *h.* *Isa* 9:17*
thou *h.*, first cast out beam. *Mat* 7:5
thou *h.*, cast beam out. *Luke* 6:42
thou *h.*, doth not each one ? 13:15

hypocrites

congregation of *h.* shall. *Job* 15:34*
the *h.* in heart heap up. 36:13*
fearfulness hath surprised the *h.*
Isa 33:14*
not sound a trumpet, as *h.* *Mat* 6:2
prayest, thou shalt not be as *h.* 5
when ye fast, be not as the *h.* 16
ye *h.* well did Esaias prophesy. 15:7
Mark 7:6
O ye *h.* ye can discern the face of.
Mat 16:3; *Luke* 12:56
why tempt ye me, ye *h.*? *Mat* 22:18
scribes and Pharisees, *h.* ye shut up.
23:13, 14, 15, 23, 25, 27, 29
him his portion with the *h.* 24:51
scribes and Pharisees, *h.* *Luke* 11:44

hypocritical

with *h.* mockers in feasts. *Ps* 35:16*
him against an *h.* nation. *Isa* 10:6*

hyssop

(*A bushy herb in common use among the Hebrews. It is not known whether it was or was not the shrub now known by the name*)

shall take a bunch of *h.* *Ex* 12:22
take cedar wood, scarlet, and *h.*
Lev 14:4, 6, 49, 51
cleanse the house with the *h.* 52
shall cast *h.* into midst. *Num* 19:6
a clean person shall take *h.* 18
cedar tree even unto the *h.* *1 Ki* 4:33
purge me with *h.* and I. *Ps* 51:7
spunge, and put it on *h.* *John* 19:29
he took blood with *h.* *Heb* 9:19

I

I

behold *I*, even *I*, do bring a flood.
Gen 6:17
I, behold *I*, establish my. 9:9
I shall be destroyed, *I* and. 34:30
shall *I*, thy mother and ? 37:10
and *I*, whither shall *I* go ? 30
in this house greater than *I*. 39:9
who am *I*, that *I* should go to ?
Ex 3:11
Lord is righteous, *I* and my. 9:27
and *I*, behold *I* will harden. 14:17
I thy father in law Jethro am. 18:6
I, behold *I*, have given with. 31:6
I, even *I*, will chastise. *Lev* 26:28
I, behold *I*, have taken the Levites.
Num 3:12; 18:6
nations more than *I*, how can *I*.?
Deut 7:17
I, even *I*, am he, there is no. 32:39
forty years old was *I*. *Josh* 14:7
I, even *I*, will sing to the. *Judg* 5:3
till *I* Deborah arose, that *I* arose. 7
when *I* blow, *I* and all that. 7:18
may bewail my virginity, *I*. 11:37
I and my people were at strife. 12:2
I came to Gibeah, *I* and my. 20:4
more righteous than *I*. *1 Sam* 24:17
I and my kingdom are. *2 Sam* 3:28
I, whither shall *I* cause my ? 13:13
I and my son Solomon be. *1 Ki* 1:21
I, even *I*, only remain a prophet.
18:22; 19:10, 14
who am *I*, and what my people that we should ? *1 Chr* 29:14; *2 Chr* 2:6
what *I* and fathers have. *2 Chr* 32:13
I, even *I* Artaxerxes. *Ezra* 7:21
but so did not *I*, because. *Neh* 5:15
I also and my maidens. *Esth* 4:16
I only am escaped to tell thee.
Job 1:15, 16, 17, 19
condemneth thee, and not *I*. 15:6
refuse or choose, and not *I*. 34:33
rock that is higher than *I*. *Ps* 61:2
they are stronger than *I*. 142:6
hereunto more than *I* ? *Eccl* 2:25
I am the rose of Sharon. *S of S* 2:1
I am my beloved's. 6:3; 7:10
I am a wall. 8:10
I and children Lord hath given me.
Isa 8:18; *Heb* 2:13
I the Lord, the first; *I* am he.
Isa 41:4; 43:11, 25
I am with thee, for *I*. 41:10; 43:5
I am the first, *I* am the last. 44:6
48:12; *Rev* 1:17
who as *I* shall call, and ? *Isa* 44:7
I, even my hands have. 45:12
even to your old age *I* am he, *I*. 46:4
I am God, and there is none else, *I*. 9
I, even *I* have spoken, *I* have. 48:15
it was, there am *I*. 16; *Mat* 18:20
yet shall *I* be glorious in. *Isa* 49:5
I, even *I* am he. 51:12; 52:6
behold, it is *I*. 52:6
stand by thyself, for *I* am. 65:5
thou art stronger than *I*. *Jer* 20:7
behold *I*, even *I*, will utterly. 23:39
behold *I*, even *I*, am against thee.
Ezek 5:8
behold *I*, even *I*, will bring a. 6:3
behold *I*, even *I*, will search. 34:11
I, even *I*, will judge between fat. 20
I am their inheritance, *I* am. 44:28
when *I*, even *I* Daniel. *Dan* 8:15
I, even *I*, will tear, *I* will. *Hos* 5:14
Haggai spoke, *I* am with. *Hag* 1:13
I was but little displeased. *Zech* 1:15
I accept of your hands ? *Mal* 1:13
after me is mightier than *I*.
Mat 3:11; *Mark* 1:7
it is *I*, be not afraid. *Mat* 14:27
Mark 6:50; *John* 6:20
men say that *I* the Son ? *Mat* 16:13
two or three, there am *I* in. 18:20
in name, saying, *I* am Christ. 24:5
began to say, Lord, is it *I*? 26:22
offended, yet will not *I*. *Mark* 14:29
father and *I* sought thee. *Luke* 2:48
if *I* by Beelzebub cast out. 11:19
if *I* with the finger of God cast. 20
name saying, *I* am Christ. *Luke* 21:8
but *I* am among you as he. 22:27
that it is *I* myself, handle me. 24:39
he confessed, *I* am not the Christ.
John 1:20; 3:28
I knew him not. 33
I that speak am he. 4:26
I am not alone, but *I* and. 8:16
I am from above, *I* am not of. 23
I am he, *I* do nothing of myself. 28
verily, before Abraham was, *I*. 58
I and my Father are one. 10:30
the Father in me, and *I* in him. 38
17:21
and *I*, if *I* be lifted up, will. 12:32
if *I* then your Lord and. 13:14
I in my Father. 14:20
I go unto Father: for my Father is greater than *I*. 28
abide in me, and *I* in you. 15:4
I in them. 17:23, 26
but *I* have known thee. 25
Pilate answered, am *I* a Jew ? 18:35
what was *I*, that *I* could ? *Acts* 11:17
I obtained this freedom; *I* was. 22:28
no more *I*, that do it. *Rom* 7:17, 20
I am of Paul, *I* of Apollos, *I* of.
1 Cor 1:12; 3:4
and *I*, brethren, when *I* came to. 2:1
and *I*, brethren, could not speak. 3:1
I would that all men even as *I*. 7:7
if they abide even as *I*. 8
yet not *I*, but Lord. 10
or *I* only and Barnabas, have. 9:6
I therefore so run, so fight *I*, not. 26
of me, even as *I* am of Christ. 11:1
I am what *I* am, yet not *I*. 15:10
whether it were *I* or they, so. 11
work of Christ, even as *I*. 16:10
Hebrews ? so am *I*. *2 Cor* 11:22
I am more. 23
I burn not ? 29
dead to the law, that *I*. *Gal* 2:19
I live, yet not *I*, but Christ liveth. 20
brethren, be as *I* am, for *I* am. 4:12
I, brethren, if *I* yet preach. 5:11
I should glory in cross, and *I* to. 6:14
I also, after *I* heard of. *Eph* 1:15
I therefore, prisoner of the Lord. 4:1
be ye holy, for *I* am. *1 Pet* 1:16
I love in the truth, and not *I* only.
2 John 1
I am Alpha and Omega. *Rev* 1:8
as many as *I* love, *I* rebuke. 3:19
as *I* also overcame. 21
I John saw. 21:2; 22:8
see thou do it not, *I* am thy. 22:9
I Jesus have sent my angel to testify these things, *I* am the root and. 16

Ibhar

David's son *I*. *2 Sam* 5:15
1 Chr 3:6; 14:5

ice

blackish by reason of *ice*. *Job* 6:16
womb came the *ice* and frost. 38:29
forth his *ice* like morsels. *Ps* 147:17

Ichabod

child *I*., glory departed. *1 Sam* 4:21
Ahiah, the son of Ahitub, *I*. 14:3

Iconium

Barnabas came unto *I*. *Acts* 13:51
in *I*. they went both into the. 14:1
thither certain Jews from *I*. 19
of by the brethren at *I*. 16:2
which came to me at *I*. *2 Tim* 3:11

Iddo

Abinadab son of *I*. had. *1 Ki* 4:14
Joash his son, *I*. his. *1 Chr* 6:21
half tribe of Manasseh *I*. 27:21
acts of Solomon written in visions of *I*. the. *2 Chr* 9:29; 12:15; 13:22
Zechariah son of *I*. prophesied.
Ezra 5:1; *Zech* 1:1, 7
prophesying of Zechariah son of *I*.
Ezra 6:14
I. the chief, and told them what they should say to *I*. and his. 8:17
I. with priests went up. *Neh* 12:4

idle

[1] *One who is slothful or lazy*, Ex 5:8, 17. [2] *One that would*

work, but is not hired, Mat 20:3, 6.
[3] *Unprofitable,* Mat 12:36.
they be *i.*; therefore they cry. *Ex* 5:8
are *i.* ye are *i.*: ye say, Let us go. 17
and *i.* soul shall suffer. *Pr* 19:15
every *i.* word that men. *Mat* 12:36
standing *i.* in marketplace. 20:3, 6
words seemed *i.* tales. *Luke* 24:11
they learn to be *i.* and not only *i.*
1 Tim 5:13

idleness

eateth not the bread of *i.* *Pr* 31:27
i. the house droppeth. *Eccl* 10:18
and abundance of *i.* *Ezek* 16:49*

idol

woe to the *i.* shepherd. *Zech* 11:17

idol

she made an *i.* in grove. *1 Ki* 15:13
2 Chr 15:16
he set the *i.* in house of. *2 Chr* 33:7
he took the *i.* out of the house. 15
say my *i.* hath done them. *Isa* 48:5
incense as if he blessed an *i.* 66:3
a despised broken *i.* *Jer* 22:28*
offered sacrifice to the *i.* *Acts* 7:41
we know an *i.* is nothing in world.
1 Cor 8:4; 10:19
some with conscience of the *i.* 8:7

idolater

a brother be an *i.* not to. *1 Cor* 5:11
an *i.* hath any inheritance. *Eph* 5:5

idolaters

with the covetous or *i.* *1 Cor* 5:10
i. shall not inherit the kingdom. 6:9
neither be ye *i.* as were some. 10:7
but *i.* shall have their part. *Rev* 21:8
without are murderers and *i.* 22:15

idolatries

walked in abominable *i.* *1 Pet* 4:3

idolatrous

Josiah put down the *i.* *2 Ki* 23:5

idolatry

is as iniquity and *i.* *1 Sam* 15:23*
city wholly given to *i.* *Acts* 17:16*
beloved, flee from *i.* *1 Cor* 10:14
works of the flesh are *i.* *Gal* 5:20
covetousness, which is *i.* *Col* 3:5

idols

turn ye not unto *i.* *Lev* 19:4
shall make no *i.* 26:1
carcases upon carcases of your *i.* 30
their *i.* wood and stone. *Deut* 29:17
in the house of their *i.* *1 Sam* 31:9
Asa removed the *i.* his. *1 Ki* 15:12
abominable in following *i.* 21:26
for they served *i.* *2 Ki* 17:12
2 Chr 24:18
Judah to sin with his *i.* *2 Ki* 21:11
Amon served the *i.* that his. 21
the *i.* that were spied in the. 23:24
carry tidings to their *i.* *1 Chr* 10:9
gods of the people are *i.* 16:26
Asa put away abominable *i.* out.
2 Chr 15:8
Josiah cut down all the *i.* in. 34:7*
gods of the nations are *i.* *Ps* 96:5
that boast themselves of *i.* 97:7
they served their *i.* that. 106:36
whom they sacrificed to the *i.* of. 38
their *i.* are silver. 115:4; 135:15
their land is full of *i.* *Isa* 2:8
the *i.* he shall utterly abolish. 18
cast away his *i.* of silver. 20; 31:7
hath found kingdoms of *i.* 10:10
i., so do to Jerusalem and her *i.*? 11
i. of Egypt shall be moved at. 19:1
they shall seek to the *i.* and to. 3
the makers of *i.* shall go to. 45:16
their *i.* were on the beasts. 46:1
inflaming yourselves with *i.* 57:5
her *i.* are confounded. *Jer* 50:2*
and they are mad upon their *i.* 38
I will cast down your slain men before your *i.* *Ezek* 6:4, 5, 13
laid waste, your *i.* may be broken. 6
go a whoring after their *i.* 9
offer sweet savour to all their *i.* 13
the *i.* of Israel pourtrayed. 8:10
up their *i.* in their heart. 14:3, 4, 7
estranged from me through their *i.* 5
repent, and turn from your *i.* 6
i. of thy abominations. *Ezek* 16:36
eyes to the *i.* of Israel. 18:6, 15
hath lifted up his eyes to the *i.* 12
yourselves with *i.* of Egypt. 20:7, 18
nor did they forsake the *i.* of. 8
for their heart went after *i.* 16
their eyes went after father's *i.* 24
pollute yourselves with all your *i.*
20:31; 22:4; 23:7, 30, 37
my holy name no more with *i.* 20:39
city maketh *i.* against herself. 22:3
slain their children to their *i.* 23:39
ye shall bear the sins of your *i.* 49
I will destroy *i.* and will. 30:13
up your eyes towards your *i.* 33:25
i. wherewith they polluted it. 36:18
from *i.* will I cleanse you. 25; 37:23
astray from me after their *i.* 44:10
ministered to them before their *i.* 12
Ephraim is joined to *i.* *Hos* 4:17
gold have they made them *i.* 8:4
have made *i.* according to. 13:2
I to do any more with *i.* 14:8
i. thereof will I lay. *Mi* 1:7
therein to make dumb *i.* *Hab* 2:18
i. have spoken vanity. *Zech* 10:2*
I will cut off names of the *i.* 13:2
from pollutions of *i.* *Acts* 15:20
from meats offered to *i.* 29; 21:25
thou that abhorrest *i.* *Rom* 2:22
things offered to *i.* *1 Cor* 8:1, 4, 10
10:19, 28; *Rev* 2:14, 20
carried away to dumb *i.* *1 Cor* 12:2
temple of God with *i.*? *2 Cor* 6:16
ye turned to God from *i.* *1 Thes* 1:9
keep yourselves from *i.* *1 John* 5:21
not worship devils and *i.* *Rev* 9:20

Idumea

shall come down on *I.* *Isa* 34:5, 6
I. shall be desolate. *Ezek* 35:15
have I spoken against all *I.* 36:5
followed him from *I.* *Mark* 3:8

if

she said, *if* it be so? *Gen* 25:22
if he said thus. 31:8
if ye will be as we be. 34:15
if it must be so now, take of. 43:11
if so be the Lord will. *Josh* 14:12
if they say to us, Tarry. *1 Sam* 14:9
if we say thus, it is well. 20:7
2 Sam 15:26
if we say, *if* we sit still here; *if* they save us, *if* they kill us. *2 Ki* 7:4
if ye be mine, *if* ye will. 10:6
if I be wicked. *Job* 9:29; 10:15
if it be not so. 24:25
if I have done this, *if* there. *Ps* 7:3
if they be prophets, *if*. *Jer* 27:18
take balm for her pain, *if* so. 51:8
if it be so, our God is. *Dan* 3:17
if it may be a lengthening. 4:27
if so be it yield, strangers. *Hos* 8:7
if thou be the Son of God. *Mat* 4:3
27:40; *Luke* 4:3
if it be thou, bid me come. *Mat* 14:28
let him deliver him, *if* he. 27:43
if thou wilt, thou canst. *Mark* 1:40
if we shall say, Of men. 11:32
if he be Christ. *Luke* 23:35, 39
John 10:24
if thou be not Elias. *John* 1:25
if the world hate you. 15:18
1 John 3:13
if thou let this man go. *John* 19:12
if it be of God ye cannot. *Acts* 5:39
if in this life only we. *1 Cor* 15:19
if a son, then an heir of. *Gal* 4:7
if any consolation, *if* any. *Phil* 2:1
if they shall enter. *Heb* 4:3, 5
if they had been of us. *1 John* 2:19

if *not*

if not I will know. *Gen* 18:21
if not tell me. 24:49
if not, blot me, I pray. *Ex* 32:32
if not, let fire come out. *Judg* 9:15, 20
and *if not,* I will take. *1 Sam* 2:16
if not, then we shall know it is. 6:9
if not, I pray thee. *2 Sam* 13:26
after his saying? *if not* speak. 17:6
but *if not,* it shall not. *2 Ki* 2:10
if not, where, and who? *Job* 9:24
if not, hearken unto me, hold. 33:33
if not, be it known to. *Dan* 3:18
give me my price; *if not.* *Zech* 11:12
but *if not,* it shall turn. *Luke* 10:6
if not, after that thou shalt. 13:9

if *now*

if now I have found favour. *Gen* 18:3
O God, *if now* thou do. 24:42
if now ye will deal kindly with. 49
if now I have found grace in thy.
33:10; 47:29; *Ex* 34:9; *Judg* 6:17
if now thou didst receive it.
1 Cor 4:7

ignominy

and with *i.* reproach. *Pr* 18:3

ignorance

if a soul shall sin through *i.* *Lev* 4:2*
5:15; *Num* 15:24*, 27*, 28*, 29*
of Israel sin through *i.* *Lev* 4:13*
hath done somewhat through *i.* 22*
common people sin through *i.* 27*
forgiven them, for it is *i.* *Num* 15:25*
I wot that through *i.* ye. *Acts* 3:17
and the times of this *i.* God. 17:30
alienated through the *i.* *Eph* 4:18
to former lusts in your *i.* *1 Pet* 1:14
ye may put to silence *i.* of. 2:15

ignorant

foolish was I, and *i.*; I was. *Ps* 73:22
they are all *i.* they are. *Isa* 56:10*
though Abraham be *i.* of us. 63:16
that they were *i.* men. *Acts* 4:13
I would not have you *i.* brethren.
Rom 1:13; *1 Cor* 10:1; 12:1
2 Cor 1:8; *1 Thes* 4:13
i. of God's righteousness. *Rom* 10:3
should be *i.* of this mystery. 11:25
man be *i.* let him be *i.* *1 Cor* 14:38
not *i.* of Satan's devices. *2 Cor* 2:11
have compassion on the *i.* *Heb* 5:2
they are willingly *i.* of. *2 Pet* 3:5*
but, beloved, be not *i.* of this one. 8

ignorantly

soul that sinneth *i.* *Num* 15:28*
killeth his neighbour *i.* *Deut* 19:4*
ye *i.* worship, declare I. *Acts* 17:23
because I did it *i.* in. *1 Tim* 1:13

ill

kine came up *i.* favoured. *Gen* 41:3
4, 19, 20, 21
why dealt ye so *i.* with me? 43:6
hath any *i.* blemish. *Deut* 15:21
it shall go *i.* with him. *Job* 20:26*
it went *i.* with Moses. *Ps* 106:32
the wicked, it shall be *i.* *Isa* 3:11
if it seem *i.* to thee to. *Jer* 40:4
his stink and his *i.* *Joel* 2:20
behaved themselves *i.* *Mi* 3:4*
love worketh no *i.* to. *Rom* 13:10

illuminated

ye were *i.* ye endured. *Heb* 10:32*

Illyricum

round about unto *I.* *Rom* 15:19

image

make man in our *i.* *Gen* 1:26, 27
9:6
a son in his own *i.* after his *i.* 5:3
nor rear up a standing *i.* *Lev* 26:1*
Deut 16:22*
Michal took an *i.* and. *1 Sam* 19:13*
behold there was an *i.* in bed. 16*
put away the *i.* of Baal. *2 Ki* 3:2*
they brake down the *i.* and. 10:27*
Manasseh set carved *i.* *2 Chr* 33:7
an *i.* was before mine. *Job* 4:16*
shalt despise their *i.* *Ps* 73:20
seat of the *i.* of jealousy. *Ezek* 8:3, 5
behold, a great *i.* stood. *Dan* 2:31
stone that smote *i.* became a. 35
the king made an *i.* of gold. 3:1
worship the golden *i.* 5, 10, 15
many days without an *i.* *Hos* 3:4*
whose is this *i.*? *Mat* 22:20
Mark 12:16; *Luke* 20:24
of the *i.* which fell down. *Acts* 19:35
glory of God into an *i.* *Rom* 1:23
to be conformed to the *i.* of. 8:29
bowed the knee to *i.* of Baal. 11:4
is the *i.* and glory of God. *1 Cor* 11:7
as we have borne the *i.* of. 15:49
changed into same *i.* *2 Cor* 3:18

the *i.* of God. *2 Cor* 4:4; *Col* 1:15
after the *i.* of him that. *Col* 3:10
by his Son, the express *i.* *Heb* 1:3
a shadow, not the very *i.* of. 10:1
they should make an *i.* *Rev* 13:14
had power to give life unto the *i.* 15
man worship beast and his *i.* 14:9
rest, who worship beast and his *i.* 11
victory over beast and his *i.* 15:2
fell on them that worshipped *i.* 16:2
them that worshipped his *i.* 19:20
not worshipped beast nor his *i.* 20:4
see **graven**

molten **image**
made them a *molten i.* *Deut* 9:12
son to make a *molten i.* *Judg* 17:3
and worshipped *molten i.* *Ps* 106:19
for his *molten i.* is falsehood.
Jer 10:14; 51:17
graven and *molten i.* *Hab* 2:18

imagery
in the chambers of his *i.* *Ezek* 8:12

images
Rachel had stolen her father's *i.*
Gen 31:19* 34*
searched but found not the *i.* 35*
quite break down their *i.* *Ex* 23:24*
34:13*; *Deut* 7:5*; *Num* 33:52
I will cut down your *i.* *Lev* 26:30
make *i.* of your emerods. *1 Sam* 6:5
they laid the *i.* of their emerods. 11
they left their *i.*, David. *2 Sam* 5:21
hast made molten *i.* to. *1 Ki* 14:9
built them high places, *i.* and. 23*
i. out of house of Baal. *2 Ki* 10:26
his *i.* brake they in pieces. 11:18
18:4*; 23:14*
set up *i.* 17:10*
they made molten *i.* 16
Josiah put away *i.* that were. 23:24*
broke down the *i.* *2 Chr* 14:3, 5
Jehoiada brake *i.* 23:17
Hezekiah brake *i.* 31:1*
Ahaz made also molten *i.* 28:2
sacrificed to all the carved *i.* 33:22
down carved and molten *i.* 34:3, 4
not look to groves or *i.* *Isa* 17:8
the groves and *i.* shall not. 27:9
the ornament of molten *i.* 30:22
their molten *i.* are wind and. 41:29
he shall break the *i.* *Jer* 43:13*
idols confounded, her *i.* are. 50:2
altars desolate, and your *i.* *Ezek* 6:4
idols broken, and that your *i.* may. 6
but they made the *i.* of their. 7:20
madest to thyself *i.* of men. 16:17
of Babylon consulted with *i.* 21:21
the *i.* of the Chaldeans. 23:14
cause their *i.* to cease out of. 30:13
they have made goodly *i.* *Hos* 10:1*
their altars, spoil their *i.* 2*
have made their molten *i.* of. 13:2
the tabernacle of your *i.* *Amos* 5:26
graven and standing *i.* *Mi* 5:13*

image work
he made two cherubims of *i. work.*
2 Chr 3:10

imagination
(*An old meaning of the word is a plotting or a devising of evil. Another, which is much used in the Bible, is stubbornness*)
every *i.* of his heart was. *Gen* 6:5
the *i.* of man's heart is evil. 8:21
though I walk in the *i.* *Deut* 29:19*
for I know their *i.* 31:21
1 Chr 28:9
this for ever in the *i.* *1 Chr* 29:18
the *i.* of his own heart. *Jer* 23:17*
scattered the proud in *i.* *Luke* 1:51

imaginations
Lord understandeth all *i.* *1 Chr* 28:9
heart that deviseth wicked *i.* *Pr* 6:18
hast seen all their *i.* *Lam* 3:60*
thou hast heard all their *i.* 61*
became vain in their *i.* *Rom* 1:21*
casting down *i.* that. *2 Cor* 10:5
see **heart**

imagine
do ye *i.* to reprove words? *Job* 6:26
the devices ye wrongfully *i.* 21:27
why do the people *i.* a? *Ps* 2:1
they seek my hurt and *i.* 38:12
how long will ye *i.* mischief? 62:3*
i. mischief in their heart. 140:2†
heart of them that *i.* evil. *Pr* 12:20*
yet do they *i.* mischief. *Hos* 7:15†
what do ye *i.* against? *Nah* 1:9†
let none *i.* evil against neighbour.
Zech 7:10†; 8:17†
why do the people *i.*? *Acts* 4:25

imagined
which they have *i.* *Gen* 11:6*
in devices they have *i.* *Ps* 10:2†
they *i.* mischievous device. 21:11†

imagineth
there is one that *i.* evil. *Nah* 1:11†

Imlah, *see* **Micaiah**; **Immanuel**, *see* **Emmanuel**

immediately
they *i.* left the ship and. *Mat* 4:22
i. his leprosy was cleansed. 8:3
Mark 1:42; *Luke* 5:13
i. received sight. *Mat* 20:34
Mark 10:52; *Luke* 18:43
i. the cock crew. *Mat* 26:74
Luke 22:60; *John* 18:27
i. the Spirit driveth him. *Mark* 1:12
he lifted her up, and *i.* the. 31
Satan cometh *i.* and taketh. 4:15
when affliction ariseth, *i.* they. 17
mouth was opened *i.* *Luke* 1:64
i. it fell. 6:49
i. her issue of blood staunched. 8:44
i. she was made straight. 13:13
kingdom of God should *i.* 19:11
and *i.* the man was made. *John* 5:9
Aeneas arose *i.* *Acts* 9:34
I sent *i.* to thee. 10:33
i. the angel of the Lord smote. 12:23
and *i.* all the doors were. 16:26
i. I conferred not with. *Gal* 1:16
and *i.* I was in the Spirit. *Rev* 4:2

immortal
King eternal, *i.*, invisible. *1 Tim* 1:17*

immortality
to them who seek for *i.* *Rom* 2:7*
mortal must put on *i.* *1 Cor* 15:53
this mortal shall have put on *i.* 54
only hath *i.* dwelling. *1 Tim* 6:16
who brought *i.* to light. *2 Tim* 1:10*

immutability
the *i.* of his counsel. *Heb* 6:17

immutable
that by two *i.* things, in. *Heb* 6:18

impart
two coats, let him *i.* to. *Luke* 3:11
that I may *i.* to you some. *Rom* 1:11

imparted
nor hath he *i.* to her. *Job* 39:17
were willing to have *i.* *1 Thes* 2:8

impediment
bring one that had *i.* in. *Mark* 7:32

impenitent
thou, after thy *i.* heart. *Rom* 2:5

imperious
work of an *i.* whorish. *Ezek* 16:30

implacable
without natural affection, *i.* *Rom* 1:31

implead
law is open, let them *i.* *Acts* 19:38*

importunity
of his *i.* he will rise and. *Luke* 11:8

impose
it shall not be lawful to *i.* *Ezra* 7:24

imposed
in carnal ordinances *i.* on. *Heb* 9:10

impossible
and nothing shall be *i.* *Mat* 17:20
with men this is *i.*; but. 19:26
Mark 10:27; *Luke* 18:27
for with God nothing shall be *i.*
Luke 1:37*; 18:27
it is *i.* but that offences will. 17:1
it is *i.* for those who were. *Heb* 6:4*
it was *i.* for God to lie. 18
without faith it is *i.* to please. 11:6

impotent
a great multitude of *i.* *John* 5:3*
deed done to the *i.* man. *Acts* 4:9
there sat a man at Lystra *i.* in. 14:8

impoverish
shall *i.* thy fenced cities. *Jer* 5:17*

impoverished
Israel was greatly *i.* *Judg* 6:6*
he that is so *i.* chooseth. *Isa* 40:20
Edom saith, We are *i.* but. *Mal* 1:4*

imprisoned
they know that I *i.* *Acts* 22:19

imprisonment
death, banishment, or *i.* *Ezra* 7:26
of mockings, bonds, *i.* *Heb* 11:36

imprisonments
in stripes, in *i.*, in tumults. *2 Cor* 6:5

impudent
and with an *i.* face she. *Pr* 7:13
for they are *i.* children *Ezek* 2:4
the house of Israel are *i.* 3:7*

impute
[1] *To charge or credit another with*, 2 Sam 19:19. [2] *To ascribe vicariously*, Rom 4:11. *The Revisions frequently substitute* reckon.
let not the king *i.* any. *1 Sam* 22:15
let not my lord *i.* *2 Sam* 19:19
the Lord will not *i.* sin. *Rom* 4:8

imputed
nor shall it be *i.* to him. *Lev* 7:18
blood shall be *i.* to that man. 17:4
righteousness might be *i.* *Rom* 4:11
i. to him for righteousness. 22, 23
Jas 2:23
shall be *i.* if we believe. *Rom* 4:24
but sin is not *i.* when there. 5:13

imputeth
blessed, to whom Lord *i.* not. *Ps* 32:2
God *i.* righteousness. *Rom* 4:6

imputing
pass over, *i.* his power. *Hab* 1:11*
Christ, not *i.* their trespasses unto.
2 Cor 5:19

in
and the Lord shut him *in.* *Gen* 7:16
I am *in* Father. *John* 14:10, 11, 20

inasmuch
i. as he hated him not. *Deut* 19:6
i. as thou followedst not. *Ruth* 3:10
i. as have done it to one. *Mat* 25:40
i. as ye did it not to one of the. 45
i. as both in bonds. *Phil* 1:7
i. as he who builded. *Heb* 3:3
i. as ye are partakers of. *1 Pet* 4:13

incense
A rich perfume used in sacrifices, Ex 37:29.
shall burn a perpetual *i.* *Ex* 30:8
ye shall offer no strange *i.* thereon. 9
he made the pure *i.* of sweet. 37:29
set the altar of gold for *i.* 40:5
his censer, and put *i.* *Lev* 10:1
he shall put *i.* on the fire. 16:13
ten shekels full of *i.* *Num* 7:14, 86
put *i.* in them before Lord. 16:7, 17
the 250 men that offered *i.* 35
Moses said to Aaron, put on *i.* 46
on *i.* and made an atonement. 47
shall put *i.* before thee. *Deut* 33:10
the altars of *i.* took. *2 Chr* 30:14
forsaken me, and burned *i.* 34:25
I will offer to thee the *i.* *Ps* 66:15
be set forth before thee as *i.* 141:2
i. is an abomination to me. *Isa* 1:13
not wearied thee with *i.* 43:23*
bring gold and *i.* and shew. 60:6*
sacrificeth and burneth *i.* on. 65:3
burneth *i.* as if he blessed. 66:3*
cometh there to me *i.*? *Jer* 6:20*
the gods to whom they offer *i.* 11:12
provoke me to anger, in offering *i.* 16
offerings and *i.* in their. 41:5*
and him that burneth *i.* to. 48:35
and a thick cloud of *i.* *Ezek* 8:11
thou hast set mine oil and *i.* 16:18
thou hast set mine *i.* and oil. 23:41
i. shall be offered to my. *Mal* 1:11
praying at time of *i.* *Luke* 1:10

given to him much *i.* to. *Rev* 8:3
the smoke of thy *i.* ascended up. 4
see **altar, burn, burnt**

sweet incense

spices for *sweet i.* *Ex* 25:6
35:8, 28; *Num* 4:16
to make oil and *sweet i.* *Ex* 31:11
brought the oil and *sweet i.* 39:38
a censer, hands full of *sweet i.*
Lev 16:12

incensed

are *i.* against thee be ashamed.
Isa 41:11
all that are *i.* against him. 45:24

incline

i. your heart to Lord. *Josh* 24:23
he may *i.* our hearts. *1 Ki* 8:58
i. your ears to the words. *Ps* 78:1
i. my heart unto thy testimonies.
119:36
i. not my heart to any thing. 141:4
see **ear**

inclined

i. to follow Abimelech. *Judg* 9:3
Lord *i.* unto me, and heard my cry.
Ps 40:1; 116:2
I have *i.* mine heart to. 119:112
nor *i.* mine ear to them. *Pr* 5:13
nor *i.* ear. *Jer* 7:24, 26; 11:8; 17:23
34:14
but ye have not *i.* your ear. 25:4
35:15; 44:5

inclineth

her house *i.* to death. *Pr* 2:18

inclose

we will *i.* her with cedar. *S of S* 8:9

inclosed

onyx stones *i.* in ouches. *Ex* 39:6, 13
Israel *i.* the Benjamites. *Judg* 20:43
they are *i.* in their own fat. *Ps* 17:10
of the wicked have *i.* me. 22:16
a garden *i.* is my sister. *S of S* 4:12*
he hath *i.* my ways with. *Lam* 3:9*
i. great multitude of fishes. *Luke* 5:6

inclosings

stones shall be set in gold in *i.*
Ex 28:20*; 39:13*

incontinency

tempt you not for your *i.* *1 Cor* 7:5

incontinent

natural affection, *i.* *1 Tim* 3:3*

incorruptible

the glory of the *i.* God. *Rom* 1:23
to obtain an *i.* crown. *1 Cor* 9:25
the dead shall be raised *i.* 15:52
us to an inheritance, *i.* *1 Pet* 1:4
being born of *i.* seed, by the. 23

incorruption

it is raised in *i.* *1 Cor* 15:42
neither doth corruption inherit *i.* 50
this corruptible must put on *i.* 53
corruptible shall have put on *i.* 54

increase, *substantive*

yield you the *i.* thereof. *Lev* 19:25
for thy cattle shall all the *i.* 25:7
take thou no usury of him or *i.* 36
usury, lend him victuals for *i.* 37
the land shall yield her *i.* 26:4
land shall not yield her *i.* or. 20
i. of the threshingfloor. *Num* 18:30
risen up in father's stead an *i.* 32:14
I will also bless the *i.* of thy kine.
Deut 7:13; 28:4
shalt truly tithe all the *i.* 14:22
shall bring forth all tithe of the *i.* 28
shall bless thee in all thy *i.* 16:15
be the *i.* of thy kine. 28:18, 51
i. of thy house shall die. *1 Sam* 2:33
it yieldeth much *i.* to. *Neh* 9:37
i. of his house shall. *Job* 20:28
would root out all mine *i.* 31:12
earth shall yield her *i.* *Ps* 67:6
he gave also their *i.* to the. 78:46
and our land shall yield her *i.* 85:12
much *i.* is by the strength. *Pr* 14:4
and with the *i.* of his lips he. 18:20
not be satisfied with *i.* *Eccl* 5:10
of the *i.* of his government. *Isa* 9:7
firstfruits of his *i.* was. *Jer* 2:3
nor hath taken any *i.* *Ezek* 18:8, 17
upon usury, and taken *i.* 18:13; 22:12
earth shall yield her *i.* *Ezek* 34:27
ground shall give her *i.* *Zech* 8:12
but God gave the *i.* *1 Cor* 3:6, 7
maketh *i.* of the body to. *Eph.* 4:16
increaseth with *i.* of God. *Col* 2:19

increase, *verb*

by years thou shalt *i.* *Lev* 25:16
O Israel, that ye may *i.* *Deut* 6:3
lest beasts of the field *i.* on. 7:22
i. thy army, and come. *Judg* 9:29
he would *i.* Israel like. *1 Chr* 27:23
strange wives to *i.* *Ezra* 10:10
latter end should greatly *i.* *Job* 8:7
dost not *i.* thy wealth by. *Ps* 44:12
if riches *i.* set not your heart. 62:10
thou shalt *i.* my greatness. 71:21
in the world, they *i.* in riches. 73:12
the Lord shall *i.* you more. 115:14
a wise man will *i.* *Pr* 1:5; 9:9
that oppresseth poor to *i.* 22:16
they perish, the righteous *i.* 28:28
goods *i.* they are increased that.
Eccl 5:11
there be many things that *i.* 6:11
meek shall *i.* their joy. *Isa* 29:19
and didst *i.* thy perfumes. 57:9
I will *i.* the famine on. *Ezek* 5:16
will *i.* it, and lay no famine. 36:29
I will *i.* them with men like a. 37
he shall *i.* with glory. *Dan* 11:39
commit whoredom, and shall not *i.*
Hos 4:10
they shall *i.* as they have. *Zech* 10:8
unto Lord, *I.* our faith. *Luke* 17:5
he must *i.*, but I must. *John* 3:30
and *i.* the fruits of your. *2 Cor* 9:10
make you to *i.* in love. *1 Thes* 3:12
we beseech you, that ye *i.* 4:10*
they will *i.* to more. *2 Tim* 2:16*

increased

the waters *i.* and bare. *Gen* 7:17, 18
thou hadst, and it is now *i.* 30:30
Jacob *i.* 43
Israel *i.* abundantly. *Ex* 1:7
till thou be *i.* and inherit. 23:30
the host went on and *i.* *1 Sam* 14:19
people *i.* with Absalom. *2 Sam* 15:12
the battle *i.* that day. *1 Ki* 22:35
2 Chr 18:34
house of their fathers *i.* *1 Chr* 4:38
for our iniquities are *i.* *Ezra* 9:6
are they *i.* that trouble me. *Ps* 3:1
that their corn and wine *i.* 4:7
glory of his house is *i.* 49:16
and he *i.* his people greatly. 105:24
years of thy life shall be *i.* *Pr* 9:11
I *i.* more than all before. *Eccl* 2:9
goods increase, they are *i.* that. 5:11
nation, and not *i.* the joy. *Isa* 9:3
thou hast *i.* the nation. 26:15
their backslidings are *i.* *Jer* 5:6
widows are *i.* above the sand. 15:8
take wives, that ye may be *i.* 29:6
because thy sins were *i.* 30:14, 15
i. in daughter of Judah. *Lam* 2:5*
and hast *i.* thy whoredoms.
Ezek 16:26*; 23:14
wisdom hast thou *i.* thy riches. 28:5
and knowledge shall be *i.* *Dan* 12:4
were *i.* so they sinned. *Hos* 4:7*
according to fruit, he hath *i.* 10:1*
increase, as they have *i.* *Zech* 10:8
fruit, that sprang up and *i.* *Mark* 4:8
Jesus *i.* in wisdom and. *Luke* 2:52*
and the word of God *i.* *Acts* 6:7
Saul *i.* the more in strength. 9:22
churches *i.* in number daily. 16:5
when your faith is *i.* *2 Cor* 10:15*
rich, and *i.* with goods. *Rev* 3:17*

increasest

i. thine indignation upon. *Job* 10:17

increaseth

my affliction *i.* *Job* 10:16*
he *i.* the nations. 12:23
the tumult of those *i.* *Ps* 74:23*
scattereth, and yet *i.* *Pr* 11:24
she *i.* the transgressors. 23:28
man of knowledge *i.* strength. 24:5
he that by unjust gain *i.* his. 28:8*
multiplied, transgression *i.* 29:16
i. knowledge, *i.* sorrow. *Eccl* 1:18
no might, he *i.* strength. *Isa* 40:29
he daily *i.* lies and. *Hos* 12:1*
woe to him that *i.* that. *Hab* 2:6
body *i.* with the increase. *Col* 2:19

increasing

i. in the knowledge of God. *Col* 1:10

incredible

thought *i.* God should? *Acts* 26:8

incurable

him with an *i.* disease. *2 Chr* 21:18
my wound is *i.* without. *Job* 34:6
why is my wound *i.*? *Jer* 15:18
thy bruise is *i.* 30:12
thy sorrow is *i.* 15
for her wound is *i.*; for it is. *Mi* 1:9

indebted

every one that is *i.* to us. *Luke* 11:4

indeed

wife shall bear a son *i.* *Gen* 17:19
yet *i.* she is my sister. 20:12
i. reign over us, shalt thou *i.*? 37:8
mother and brethren *i.* come. 10
for *i.* I was stolen away out. 40:15
if you will obey my voice *i.*
Ex 19:5; 23:22
ye should *i.* have eaten it. *Lev* 10:18
hath the Lord *i.* spoken? *Num* 12:2
if thou wilt *i.* deliver this. 21:2
am I not able *i.* to promote? 22:37
i. the hand of the Lord. *Deut* 2:15
son of the hated, which is *i.* 21:16
i. I have sinned against. *Josh* 7:20
if thou wilt *i.* look on. *1 Sam* 1:11
but will God *i.* dwell on the earth?
1 Ki 8:27, *2 Chr* 6:18
thou hast *i.* smitten. *2 Ki* 14:10
wouldest bless me *i.* *1 Chr* 4:10
have sinned and done evil *i.* 21:17
i. that I have erred. *Job* 19:4
i. speak righteousness. *Ps* 58:1
hear ye *i.*, see ye *i.* but. *Isa* 6:9
for if ye do this thing *i.* *Jer* 22:4
I *i.* baptize. *Mat* 3:11; *Mark* 1:8
Luke 3:16
that he was a prophet *i.* *Mark* 11:32
we *i.* justly. *Luke* 23:41
the Lord is risen *i.* 24:34
behold an Israelite *i.* *John* 1:47
that this is *i.* the Christ. 4:42
meat *i.*, my blood is drink *i.* 6:55
the rulers know *i.* that this is? 7:26
then are ye my disciples *i.* 8:31
make you free, ye shall be free *i.* 36
that *i.* a notable miracle. *Acts* 4:16
law, neither *i.* can be. *Rom* 8:7
all things *i.* are pure, but it. 14:20
and *i.* bear with me. *2 Cor* 11:1
some *i.* preach Christ. *Phil* 1:15
you to me *i.* is not grievous. 3:1
i. have a shew of wisdom. *Col* 2:23
i. ye do it towards all. *1 Thes* 4:10
honour widows that are widows *i.*
1 Tim 5:3
she that is a widow *i.* 5, 16
disallowed *i.* of men. *1 Pet* 2:4

indignation

great *i.* against Israel. *2 Ki* 3:27
Sanballat took great *i.* *Neh* 4:1
Haman was full of *i.* *Esth* 5:9
there increasest thine *i.* *Job* 10:17
pour out thy *i.* on them. *Ps* 69:24
he cast upon them wrath, *i.* 78:49
thine *i.* and thy wrath. 102:10
in their hand is mine *i.* *Isa* 10:5
for yet a little while, and the *i.* 25
even the Lord, and the weapons of
his *i.* 13:5, *Jer* 50:25
hide thyself till the *i.* be. *Isa* 26:20
full of *i.* his tongue as fire. 30:27
with the *i.* of his anger. 30
for the *i.* of the Lord is on. 34:2
i. shall be known towards. 66:14
not be able to abide his *i.* *Jer* 10:10
for thou hast filled me with *i.* 15:17
despised in *i.* of his anger. *Lam* 2:6
I will pour out mine *i.* *Ezek* 21:31
not rained on in day of his *i.* 22:24
therefore I poured out mine *i.* 31
i. against holy covenant. *Dan* 11:30
will bear the *i.* of the Lord. *Mi* 7:9
who can stand before his *i.*? *Nah* 1:6
march through land in *i.* *Hab* 3:12
i. these seventy years. *Zech* 1:12

whom the Lord hath *i.* *Mal* 1:4
they were moved with *i.* *Mat* 20:24
they had *i.* saying, To what? 26:8
ruler of synagogue answered with *i.* *Luke* 13:14
they were filled with *i.* *Acts* 5:17*
obey unrighteousness, *i.* *Rom* 2:8
what *i.*, yea, what fear! *2 Cor* 7:11
looking for of fiery *i.* *Heb* 10:27
into the cup of his *i.* *Rev* 14:10

inditing

my heart is *i.* a good. *Ps* 45:1*

industrious

man that he was *i.* *1 Ki* 11:28

inexcusable

therefore thou art *i.* O. *Rom* 2:1*

infallible

himself by many *i.* proofs. *Acts* 1:3

infamous

mock thee which art *i.* *Ezek* 22:5

infamy

thine *i.* turn not away. *Pr* 25:10
an *i.* of the people. *Ezek* 36:3*

infant

slay man, woman, *i.* *1 Sam* 15:3
no more thence an *i.* of. *Isa* 65:20

infants

as *i.* which never saw light. *Job* 3:16
i. shall be dashed in. *Hos* 13:16
brought also *i.* to him. *Luke* 18:15

inferior

I am not *i.* to you. *Job* 12:3; 13:2
another kingdom *i.* to thee. *Dan* 2:39
ye *i.* to other churches? *2 Cor* 12:13

infidel

believeth with an *i.*? *2 Cor* 6:15*
and is worse than an *i.* *1 Tim* 5:8*

infinite

not thine iniquities *i.*? *Job* 22:5*
his understanding is *i.* *Ps* 147:5
her strength, and it was *i.* *Nah* 3:9

infirmities

himself took our *i.* and. *Mat* 8:17
healed by him of their *i.* *Luke* 5:15
cured many of their *i.* 7:21; 8:2
Spirit also helpeth our *i.* *Rom* 8:26
strong ought to bear the *i.* of. 15:1
which concern mine *i.* *2 Cor* 11:30
I glory not, but in mine *i.* 12:5*, 9
I take pleasure in mine *i.* 10
wine for thine often *i.* *1 Tim* 5:23
with the feeling of our *i.* *Heb* 4:15

infirmity

(*Disease or disability, ordinarily applied to the body, but in the Bible used frequently for mental or moral weakness*)

separation for her *i.* *Lev* 12:2
this is mine *i.* but I will. *Ps* 77:10
a man will sustain his *i.* *Pr* 18:14
which had a spirit of *i.* *Luke* 13:11
thou art loosed from thine *i.* 12
an *i.* thirty-eight years. *John* 5:5
of the *i.* of your flesh. *Rom* 6:19
ye know how through *i.* I. *Gal* 4:13
also is compassed with *i.* *Heb* 5:2
high priests which have *i.* 7:28

inflame

continue till wine *i.* them. *Isa* 5:11

inflaming

i. yourselves with idols. *Isa* 57:5

inflammation

an *i.* of the burning. *Lev* 13:28*
smite thee with an *i.* *Deut* 28:22

inflicted

punishment which was *i.* *2 Cor* 2:6

influences

canst thou bind the *i.*? *Job* 38:31*

infolding

a fire *i.* itself, and a. *Ezek* 1:4

inform

to all that they *i.* thee. *Deut* 17:10*

informed

me, and talked with. *Deut* 9:22*
are *i.* of thee that thou teachest. *Acts* 21:21, 24
the governor. 24:1; 25:2, 15

ingathering

feast of the *i.* in the end. *Ex* 23:16

ingrafted

with meekness the *i.* word. *Jas* 1:21

inhabit

land which ye shall *i.* *Num* 35:34
the wicked shall not *i.* *Pr* 10:30
villages that Kedar doth *i.* *Isa* 42:11
shall build houses and *i.* 65:21
shall not build, and another *i.* 22
shall *i.* the parched. *Jer* 17:6
thou daughter, that dost *i.* 48:18
i. those wastes of Israel. *Ezek* 33:24
waste cities and *i.* them. *Amos* 9:14
houses, but not *i.* them. *Zeph* 1:13

inhabitant

great and fair without *i.* *Isa* 5:9
cities be wasted without *i.* 6:11
Ephraim and the *i.* of Samaria. 9:9
cry out and shout, thou *i.* of. 12:6
the *i.* of this isle shall say in. 20:6
snare, are upon thee, O *i.* of. 24:17
i. shall not say, I am sick. 33:24
cities are burned without *i.* *Jer* 2:15
cities shall be laid waste without an *i.* 4:7; 9:11; 26:9; 33:10; 34:22
gather thy wares, O *i.* of the. 10:17*
i. of the valley. 21:13
i. of Lebanon. 22:23
is a curse, without an *i.* 44:22
desolate, without *i.* 46:19; 51:29, 37
O *i.* of Aroer. 48:19
O *i.* of Moab. 43
be upon Babylon, shall the *i.* 51:35
I will cut off the *i.* from plain of Aven. *Amos* 1:5
I will cut off the *i.* from Ashdod. 8
i. of Saphir, *i.* of Zaanan. *Mi* 1:11
the *i.* of Maroth waited carefully. 12
O thou *i.* of Lachish, bind the. 13
will bring an heir to thee, O *i.* 15
destroy, that there shall be no *i.* *Zeph* 2:5
destroyed, so that there is none *i.* 3:6

inhabitants

he overthrew all the *i.* *Gen* 19:25
take hold of the *i.* of. *Ex* 15:14
all the *i.* of Canaan shall melt. 15
itself vomiteth out her *i.* *Lev* 18:25
proclaim liberty to all the *i.* 25:10
land that eateth up the *i.* *Num* 13:32
have withdrawn the *i.* *Deut* 13:13
thou shalt surely smite the *i.* of. 15
even the *i.* of the country. *Josh* 2:24
peace, save the *i.* of Gibeon. 11:19
drive out the *i.* 17:12; *Judg* 1:19, 27
no league with the *i.* of. *Judg* 2:2
the *i.* of the villages ceased. 5:7*
curse ye bitterly the *i.* thereof. 23
be head over all the *i.* of Gilead. 10:18; 11:8
the *i.* of Jabesh-gilead there. 21:9
smite the *i.* of Jabesh-gilead. 10
buy it before the *i.* and. *Ruth* 4:4*
Elijah who was of the *i.* *1 Ki* 17:1*
i. were of small power. *2 Ki* 19:26
first *i.* that dwelt in. *1 Chr* 9:2
the *i.* of mount Seir. *2 Chr* 20:23
from under the *i.* thereof. *Job* 26:5
all the *i.* of world stand. *Ps* 33:8
looketh on all the *i.* of the earth. 14
give ear, all ye *i.* of the world. 49:1
all the *i.* thereof are dissolved. 75:3
put down the *i.* like a. *Isa* 10:13*
all ye *i.* of the world, see ye. 18:3
be still, ye *i.* of the isle. 23:2, 6
and scattereth abroad the *i.* 24:1
the earth is defiled under the *i.* 5
therefore the *i.* of the earth are. 6
the *i.* of the world will learn. 26:9
have the *i.* of the world fallen. 18
behold man no more with the *i.* 38:11
i. thereof are as grasshoppers. 40:22
isles and *i.* sing to the Lord. 42:10
let the *i.* of the rock sing, let. 11
too narrow by reason of the *i.* 49:19
fill the *i.* with drunkenness. *Jer* 13:13
will I do to the *i.* thereof. 19:12
I will smite the *i.* of this city. 21:6
as Sodom, and the *i.* thereof. 23:14
for a sword upon the *i.* thereof. 25:29
50:35
innocent blood on the *i.* *Jer* 26:15
dwell deep, O *i.* of Dedan. 49:8, 30
the Lord will disquiet the *i.* 50:34
and my blood upon the *i.* of. 51:35
i. of the world would not. *Lam* 4:12
i. of Egypt shall know. *Ezek* 29:6
i. of earth are reputed as. *Dan* 4:35
i. thereof have spoken lies. *Mi* 6:12
I should make the *i.* thereof an. 16
come *i.* of many cities. *Zech* 8:20
the *i.* of one city shall go to. 21
the *i.* of the earth have. *Rev* 17:2
see **Jerusalem**

inhabitants *of the land*

stink among the *i. of land.* *Gen* 34:30
I will deliver *i. of land.* *Ex* 23:31
a covenant with *i. of land.* 34:12, 15
because of the *i. of land.* *Num* 32:17
shall drive out the *i. of land.* 33:52
55; *2 Chr* 20:7
all the *i. of the land* faint. *Josh* 2:9
all the *i. of land* shall hear of. 7:9
to destroy all the *i. of the land.* 9:24
of old the *i. of land.* *1 Sam* 27:8
he hath given *i. of land.* *1 Chr* 22:18
forth on all *i. of land.* *Jer* 1:14
will fling out the *i. of land.* 10:18
and the *i. of land* shall howl. 47:2
controversy with *i. of land.* *Hos* 4:1
the *i. of the land* tremble. *Joel* 2:1
no more pity *i. of the l.* *Zech* 11:6

inhabited

till they came to a land *i.* *Ex* 16:35
iniquities to a land not *i.* *Lev* 16:22
it shall never be *i.* nor. *Isa* 13:20
thou shalt be *i.* 44:26
formed it to be *i.* 45:18
the desolate cities to be *i.* 54:3
make thee a land not *i* *Jer* 6:8
in a salt land and not *i.* 17:6
thee cities which are not *i.* 22:6
afterward it shall be *i.* as in. 46:26
it shall not be *i.* 50:13
no more *i.* for ever. 39
the cities that are *i.* *Ezek* 12:20
set thee, that thou be not *i.* 26:20
nor shall it be *i.* forty years. 29:11
the cities shall be *i.* and the. 36:10
desolate places that are now *i.* 38:12
Jerusalem be *i.* as towns. *Zech* 2:4
and Askelon shall not be *i.* 9:5
Jerusalem shall be *i.* again. 12:6
it shall be lifted up, and *i.* in. 14:10
but Jerusalem shall be safely *i.* 11

inhabiters

woe, woe, woe, to *i.* of. *Rev* 8:13
woe to the *i.* of the earth. 12:12

inhabitest

thou that *i.* the praises. *Ps* 22:3

inhabiteth

houses which no man *i.* *Job* 15:28
lofty One that *i.* eternity. *Isa* 57:15

inhabiting

be meat to the people *i.* *Ps* 74:14

inherit

know that I shall *i.* it? *Gen* 15:8
and they shall *i.* it for ever. *Ex* 32:13
it to the Levites to *i.* *Num* 18:24
names of tribes they shall *i.* 26:55
we will not *i.* on yonder side. 32:19
cause Israel to *i.* it. *Deut* 1:38
Lord God giveth you to *i.* 12:10
he maketh his sons to *i.* 21:16
not *i.* in our father's. *Judg* 11:2
them *i.* the throne of. *1 Sam* 2:8
seed shall *i.* the earth. *Ps* 25:13
that wait on the Lord shall *i.* 37:9
but the meek shall *i.* the earth. 11
Mat 5:5
be blessed of him shall *i.* *Ps* 37:22
also of his servants shall *i.* it. 69:36
O God, for thou shalt *i.* all. 82:8
the wise shall *i.* glory. *Pr* 3:35
cause those who love me to *i.* 8:21
own house, shall *i.* the wind. 11:29
the simple *i.* folly, but the. 14:18
to cause to *i.* the desolate. *Isa* 49:8
thy seed shall *i.* the Gentiles. 54:3*
and mine elect shall *i.* it, and. 65:9
my people Israel to *i.* *Jer* 12:14
doth their king *i.* Gad? 49:1*
ye shall *i.* it, one as well. *Ezek* 47:14

the Lord shall i. Judah. Zech 2:12
shall i. everlasting life. Mat 19:29
i. the kingdom prepared for. 25:34
i. eternal life. Mark 10:17
Luke 10:25; 18:18
unrighteous not i. the. 1 Cor 6:9
neither shall extortioners i. 10
Gal 5:21
cannot i. the kingdom of God, nor doth corruption i. 1 Cor 15:50
who through faith i. the. Heb 6:12
called, that ye should i. 1 Pet 3:9
he that overcometh shall i. Rev 21:7

inherit *land*

give thee this land to i. it. Gen 15:7
that thou mayest i. land. 28:4
ye shall i. their land. Lev 20:24
land ye shall i. by lot. Num 34:13
thou mayest i. his land. Deut 2:31
i. land Lord giveth thee. 16:20; 19:3
righteous shall i. the land. Ps 37:29
shall exalt thee to i. the land. 34
they i. the land for ever. Isa 60:21
border, whereby ye shall i. the land. Ezek 47:13

inheritance

any portion or i. for us ? Gen 31:14
of their brethren in their i. 48:6
in mountain of thine i. Ex 15:17
take them as an i. for. Lev 25:46
or given us i. of fields. Num 16:14
i. for I am thy part and thine i. 18:20
shall cause his i. to pass to. 27:8
i. to brethren. 9
i. to father's brethren. 10
our i. is fallen. 32:19, 32; 34:15
prince, to divide the land by i. 34:18
put to the i. of the tribe. 36:3, 4
Israel may enjoy the i. 8
nor i. remove from one tribe to. 9
a people of i. as ye are. Deut 4:20
destroy not thine i. 9:26
they are thine i. 29
Jacob is the lot of his i. 32:9
sacrifices of Lord their i. Josh 13:14
18:7
God of Israel was their 13:33
by lot was their i. 14:2; Ps 78:55
Hebron therefore became the i. of. Josh 14:14
daughters of Manasseh had i. 17:6
every man to his i. 24:28; Judg 2:6
21:24
i. for them that escaped. Judg 21:27
lest I mar mine own i. Ruth 4:6
thee captain over his i. 1 Sam 10:1
from abiding in the i. of. 26:19
neither i. in son of Jesse. 2 Sam 20:1
1 Ki 12:16
that ye may bless the i. 2 Sam 21:3
thy people and thy i. 1 Ki 8:51, 53
give the i. of my fathers. 21:3, 4
the remnant of mine i. 2 Ki 21:14
Canaan, the lot of your i. 1 Chr 16:18
every one in his i. Neh 11:20
what i. of the Almighty? Job 31:2
is the portion of mine i. Ps 16:5
bless thine i. 28:9
chosen for his i. 33:12
their i. shall be for ever. 37:18
he shall choose our i. for us. 47:4
thou didst confirm thine i. 68:9
the rod of thine i., thou hast. 74:2
and was wroth with his i. 78:62
him to feed Israel his i. 71
heathen are come into thine i. 79:1
neither will he forsake his i. 94:14
Canaan, the lot of your i. 105:11
that I may glory with thine i. 106:5
he abhorred his own i. 40
good man leaveth an i. Pr 13:22
have part of the i. among. 17:2
house and riches are the i. of. 19:14
an i. may be gotten hastily. 20:21
wisdom is good with an i. Eccl 7:11
blessed be Israel mine i. Isa 19:25
I have polluted mine i. and. 47:6
sake, the tribes of thine i. 63:17
Israel is the rod of his i. Jer 10:16
51:19
right of i. is thine, redemption. 32:8
i. is turned to strangers. Lam 5:2
thou shalt be their i. Ezek 36:12
for an i.: I am their i. Ezek 44:28
i. thereof shall be his son's. 46:16, 17
shall not take of the people's i. 18
i. among you with tribes. 47:22, 23
let us seize on his i. Mat 21:38
and the i. shall be ours. Mark 12:7
Luke 20:14
that he divide the i. Luke 12:13
to give you an i. among. Acts 20:32
and i. among them sanctified. 26:18
if the i. be of the law, it. Gal 3:18
we have obtained an i. Eph 1:11
which is the earnest of our i. 14
the riches of the glory of his i. in. 18
i. in the kingdom of Christ. 5:5
to be partakers of the i. of. Col 1:12
shall receive the reward of i. 3:24
as he hath by i. obtained. Heb 1:4
the promise of eternal i. 9:15
begotten us to an i. 1 Pet 1:4

for **inheritance**

and take us for thine i. Ex 34:9
all the tenth in Israel for an i. Num 18:21, 26
shall be divided for an i. 26:53
33:54; 34:2; 36:2; Deut 4:21, 38
15:4; 19:10; Josh 13:6, 7, 32
14:1; 19:49, 51; Ezek 45:1
47:22; 48:29
the Lord doth give thee for an i. Deut 20:16; 21:23; 24:4; 25:19
26:1; Josh 11:23; 13:6; 14:13
1 Ki 8:36; 2 Chr 6:27; Jer 3:18
leave it for an i. for children. 1 Chr 28:8; Ezra 9:12
give thee heathen for thine i. Ps 2:8
is given us for an i. Ezek 33:24
it shall be to them for an i. I. 44:28
shall fall unto you for an i. 47:14
after receive for an i. Heb 11:8

no or *none* **inheritance**

thou shalt have no i. Num 18:20
23:24; 26:62; Deut 10:9; 14:27
29; 18:1, 2; Josh 13:14, 33; 14:3
no i. in the son of Jesse. 2 Chr 10:16
he gave him none i. in it. Acts 7:5

inheritances

these are the i. Joshua. Josh 19:51

inherited

return till Israel have i. Num 32:18
children of Israel i. in. Josh 14:1
they i. the labour of. Ps 105:44
our fathers have i. lies. Jer 16:19
one, and he i. the land. Ezek 33:24
have i. the blessing. Heb 12:17

inheriteth

inheriting which he i. Num 35:8

inheritor

out of Judah an i. of my. Isa 65:9

iniquities

over the goat all the i. Lev 16:21
in the i. of their fathers shall. 26:39
our i. are increased over. Ezra 9:6
for our i. have we, our kings. 7
punished us less than our i. 13
Israel confessed the i. Neh 9:2
how many are mine i.? Job 13:23
thou makest me to possess the i. 26
great, and thine i. infinite. 22:5
and mine i. are gone over. Ps 38:4
i. have taken hold on me. 40:12
my sins, and blot out all i. 51:9
they search out i. 64:6
i. prevail against. 65:3
not against us former i. 79:8
hast set our i. before thee. 90:8
Lord, who forgiveth all thine i. 103:3
rewarded us according to our i. 10
if thou, Lord shouldest mark i. 130:3
redeem Israel from all his i. 8
his own i. shall take the. Pr 5:22
wearied me with thine i. Isa 43:24
but he was bruised for our i. 53:5
as for our i. we know them. 59:12
our i. like the wind have taken. 64:6
consumed us because of our i. 7
turned back to i. of their. Jer 11:10
O Lord, though our i. testify. 14:7
for i. of her priests that. Lam 4:13
multitude of thine i. Ezek 28:18
break off thine i. by. Dan 4:27
from our i. and understand. 9:13
for our sins, and for the i. of. 16
turn, he will subdue our i. Mi 7:19
bless in turning every one from his i. Acts 3:26
blessed are they whose i. Rom 4:7
hath remembered her i. Rev 18:5

their **iniquities**

bear on him all their i. Lev 16:22
fools because of their i. Ps 107:17
he shall bear their i. Isa 53:11
will pardon all their i. Jer 33:8
sinned, we have borne their i. Lam 5:7
their i. shall be on their. Ezek 32:27
may be ashamed of their i. 43:10
their i. will I remember no more. Heb 8:12; 10:17

your **iniquities**

shall ye bear your i. Num 14:34
for your i. have you sold. Isa 50:1
your i. separated between you. 59:2
your i. I will recompense. 65:7
your i. have turned away. Jer 5:25
pine away for your i. Ezek 24:23
loathe youselves for your i. 36:31
cleansed you from all your i. 33
punish you for all your i. Amos 3:2

iniquity

i. of the Amorites is not. Gen 15:16
thou be consumed in the i. of. 19:15
God hath found out the i. of. 44:16
visiting the i. of fathers. Ex 20:5
34:7; Num 14:18; Deut 5:9
forgiving i. and transgression. Ex 34:7; Num 14:18
and pardon our i. and. Ex 34:9
therefore I do visit the i. Lev 18:25
an offering bringing i. to. Num 5:15
shall the man be guiltless from i. 31
pray thee, the i. of this people. 14:19
he hath not beheld i. in Jacob. 23:21
against a man for any i. Deut 19:15
God of truth and without i. 32:4
i. of Peor too little for ? Josh 22:17
judge for the i. which. 1 Sam 3:13
the i. of Eli's house shall not. 14
and stubbornness is as i. 15:23*
if there be in me i. slay me. 20:8
upon me let this i. be. 25:24
2 Sam 14:9
if there be i. in me, let. 2 Sam 14:32
let not my lord impute i. to. 19:19
to take away i. of thy servant. 24:10; 1 Chr 21:8
for there is no i. with. 2 Chr 19:7
they that plow i. reap. Job 4:8
poor hath hope, and i. stoppeth. 5:16
I pray you, let it not be i. 6:29*
is there i. in my tongue ? 30*
God exacteth less than thine i. 11:6
if i. be in thy hand, put it far. 14
for thy mouth uttereth thine i. 15:5
filthy is man which drinketh i. 16
thou shalt put away i. far. 22:23
it is an i. to be punished. 31:11, 28
innocent, nor is there i. in me. 33:9
if I have done i. I will do. 34:32
that they return from i. 36:10
take heed, regard not i. for this. 21
can say, Thou hast wrought i.? 23
O Lord, if there be i. in. Ps 7:3
behold, he travaileth with i. 14
whom the Lord imputeth not i. 32:2
thou forgavest the i. of my sin. 5
the words of his mouth are i. 36:3
thou dost correct man for i. 39:1
heart gathereth i. to itself. 41:
when the i. of my heels shall. 49:
behold I was shapen in i. and. 51:
and have done abominable i. 53:
they cast i. upon me, and in. 55:
shall they escape by i.? 56:
if I regard i. in my heart. 66:1
thou hast forgiven the i. of thy. 85:
throne of i. have fellowship. 94:2
all i. shall stop her mouth. 107:4
let the i. of his fathers be. 109:1
they also do no i.: they walk. 119:
let not any i. have dominion. 13
put forth their hands to i. 125:
by mercy and truth i. Pr 16:

of the wicked devoureth i. Pr 19:28
he that soweth i. shall reap. 22:8
of righteousness that i. Eccl 3:16
a people laden with i. a. Isa 1:4
it is i. even the solemn meeting. 13
woe to them that draw i. 5:18
i. is taken away, and thy sin. 6:7
prepare for the i. of their. 14:21
this i. shall not be purged. 22:14
by this shall the i. of Jacob. 27:9
all that watch for i. are cut off. 29:20
this i. shall be to you as a. 30:13
cry unto her, her i. is pardoned. 40:2
Lord hath laid on him the i. 53:6
for the i. of his covetousness. 57:17
fingers are defiled with i. 59:3
they bring forth i. 4
their works are works of i. 6
their thoughts are thoughts of i. 7
not wroth, nor remember i. 64:9
what i. have your fathers? Jer 2:5
thine i. is marked before me. 22
only acknowledge thine i. 3:13
the greatness of thine i. are. 13:22
we acknowledge the i. of our. 14:20
what is our i.? 16:10
i. hid from mine eyes. 17
for multitude of thine i. 30:14, 15
Hos 9:7
recompensest i. of fathers. Jer 32:18
the i. of Israel be sought for. 50:20
Babylon, be not cut off in her i. 51:6
not discovered thine i. Lam 2:14
for the punishment of the i. of. 4:6
thine i. is accomplished, he will visit thine i. O daughter of Edom. 22
lay i. of the house of. Ezek 4:4
nor strengthen himself in i. 7:13
the i. of the house of Israel. 9:9
this was the i. of thy sister. 16:49
withdrawn his hand from i. 18:8
he shall not die for the i. of his. 17
repent, so i. shall not be your. 30
to remembrance your i. 21:23, 24
i. shall have an end. 25, 29; 35:5
wast perfect, till i. was found. 28:15
defiled thy sanctuaries by i. of. 18
house of Israel to fall into i. 44:12
make reconciliation for i. Dan 9:24
the i. of Ephraim was. Hos 7:1
against children of i. 10:9
ye reaped i. 13
find no i. in me. 12:8
is there i. in Gilead? 11
the i. of Ephraim is bound up. 13:12
for thou hast fallen by thine i. 14:1
take away all i. and receive us. 2
woe to them that devise i. Mi 2:1
they build up Jerusalem with i. 3:10
who is a God like to thee, that pardoneth i.? 7:18
why dost thou shew me i.? Hab 1:3
and thou canst not look on i. 13*
that establisheth a city by i. 2:12
Lord, he will not do i. Zeph 3:5
of Israel shall not do i. 13
I have caused thine i. to. Zech 3:4
I will remove the i. of that land. 9
i. was not found in his lips, did turn many away from i. Mal 2:6
gather them which do i. Mat 13:41
ye are full of hypocrisy and i. 23:28
because i. shall abound, love. 24:12
field with the reward of i. Acts 1:18
thou art in the bond of i. 8:23
servants to i. unto i. Rom 6:19
rejoiceth not in i. but in. 1 Cor 13:6
the mystery of i. doth. 2 Thes 2:7*
Christ, depart from i. 2 Tim 2:19
redeem us from all i. Tit 2:14
hast hated i. therefore God. Heb 1:9
tongue is a fire, a world of i.
Jas 3:6
see **bear, commit, committed**

his **iniquity**

his i. shall be upon him. Num 15:31
that man perished not alone in his i.
Josh 22:20
heavens shall reveal his i. Job 20:27
God layeth up his i. for his. 21:19
until his i. be found to be. Ps 36:2
die for his i. Jer 31:30; Ezek 3:18
19; 7:16; 18:26

the stumblingblock of his i.
Ezek 14:7, 14
shall die in his i. 18:18; 33:8, 9
he is taken away in his i. but. 33:6
was rebuked for his i. 2 Pet 2:16*

mine **iniquity**

what is mine i. and? 1 Sam 20:1
I kept myself from mine i.
2 Sam 22:24; Ps 18:23
thou not take away mine i.? Job 7:21
thou enquirest after mine i. 10:6
not acquit me from mine i. 14
bag, thou sewest up mine i. 14:17
if I covered, by hiding mine i. 31:33
pardon mine i. for it is. Ps 25:11
faileth because of mine i. 31:10
and mine i. have I not hid. 32:5
for I will declare mine i. I. 38:18
me throughly from mine i. 51:2

their **iniquity**

pine away in their i. Lev 26:39
confess their i. and iniquity of. 40
the punishment of their i. 41, 43
cover not their i. let not. Neh 4:5
add iniquity unto their i. Ps 69:27
he forgave their i. 78:38
I will visit their i. 89:32
bring upon them their i. 94:23
brought low for their i. 106:43
punish wicked for their i. Isa 13:11
inhabitants of earth for their i. 26:21
people shall be forgiven their i. 33:24
now remember their i. Jer 14:10
I will recompense their i. 16:18
forgive not their i. nor blot. 18:23
punish that nation for their i. 25:12
for I will forgive their i. 31:34
cleanse them from all their i. 33:8
I may forgive their i. and sin. 36:3
punish his servants for their i. 31
thee the years of their i. Ezek 4:5
may consume away for their i. 17
the stumblingblock of their i. 7:19
14:3
bear the punishment of their i. 14:10
which bringeth their i. to. 29:16
went into captivity for their i. 39:23
set their heart on their i. Hos 4:8
Israel fall in their i. 5:5
he will remember their i. he. 9:9

work **iniquity**

with men that work i. Ps 141:4
help of them that work i. Isa 31:2
heart will work i. to practise. 32:6
a city of them that work i. Hos 6:8
from me, ye that work i. Mat 7:23

workers of **iniquity**

punishment to the w. of i. Job 31:3
company with the w. of i. 34:8
where the w. of i. may hide. 22
stand, thou hatest all w. of i. Ps 5:5
depart from me all ye w. of i. 6:8
Luke 13:27
have all w. of i. no? Ps 14:4; 53:4
not away with the w. of i. 28:3
there are the w. of i. fallen. 36:12
envious against the w. of i. 37:1
deliver me from the w. of i. 59:2
insurrection of the w. of i. 64:2
all the w. of i. do flourish. 92:7
the w. of i. shall be scattered. 9
the w. of i. boast themselves. 94:4
stand up for me against the w. of i. 16
them forth with the w. of i. 125:5
from the gins of the w. of i. 141:9
destruction shall be to w. of i.
Pr 10:29; 21:15

injured

ye have not i. me at all. Gal 4:12

injurious

a persecutor and i. 1 Tim 1:13

injustice

not for i. in my hands. Job 16:17

ink

I wrote them with i. Jer 36:18
written not with i. but. 2 Cor 3:3
I would not write with i. 2 John 12
3 John 13

inkhorn

with a writer's i. Ezek 9:2, 3, 11

inn

ass provender in the i. Gen 42:27*
we came to the i. we opened. 43:21*
by the way in the i., the. Ex 4:24*
no room for them in the i. Luke 2:7
brought him to an i. and took. 10:34

inner

cherubims in i. house. 1 Ki 6:27
gave patterns of the i. 1 Chr 28:11
to the king into the i. court. Esth 4:11
Esther stood in the i. court. 5:1
and the cloud filled the i. Ezek 10:3
end of measuring the i. house. 42:15
the gate of the i. court shall be. 46:1
thrust them into the i. Acts 16:24
with might in the i. man. Eph 3:16
see **chamber**

innermost

into the i. parts of the belly.
Pr 18:8; 26:22

innocency

in the i. of my hands. Gen 20:5
wash my hands in i. so. Ps 26:6
have washed my hands in i. 73:13
before him i. was found. Dan 6:22
be ere they attain to i.? Hos 8:5

innocent

the i. and the righteous. Ex 23:7
reward to slay the i. Deut 27:25
whoever perished being i.? Job 4:7
laugh at the trial of the i. 9:23
that thou wilt not hold me i. 28
i. shall stir up the hypocrite. 17:8
i. laugh them to scorn. 22:19
deliver the island of the i. 30
i. shall divide the silver. 27:17
I am i. nor is iniquity in me. 33:9
doth he murder the i. Ps 10:8
taketh reward against the i. 15:5
I shall be i. from the great. 19:13*
let us lurk privily for the i. Pr 1:11
toucheth her shall not be i. 6:29*
haste to be rich shall not be i. 28:20*
sayest, Because I am i. Jer 2:35
I am i. of the blood of. Mat 27:24
see **blood**

innocents

the blood of the poor i. Jer 2:34
place with the blood of i. 19:4

innumerable

after him, as there are i. Job 21:23
i. evils have compassed. Ps 40:12
are things creeping i. 104:25
grasshoppers, and are i. Jer 46:23
i. multitude gathered. Luke 12:1*
is by the sea shore i. Heb 11:12
an i. company of angels. 12:22

inordinate

corrupt in her i. love. Ezek 23:11*
fornication, i. affection. Col 3:8*

inquisition

shall make diligent i. Deut 19:18
when i. was made of the. Esth 2:23
he maketh i. for blood. Ps 9:12

inscription

found an altar with this i. Acts 17:23

inside

covered the walls on i. 1 Ki 6:15

inspiration

i. of Almighty giveth. Job 32:8*
all scripture is given by i. 2 Tim 3:16

instant

[1] *A short moment of time,* Isa 29:5. [2] *Very eager, or pressing,* Luke 23:23.

yea, it shall be at an i. Isa 29:5
cometh suddenly at an i. 30:13
at what i. I speak. Jer 18:7, 9
she coming in that i. Luke 2:38*
and they were i. with loud. 23:23*
patient, continuing i. Rom 12:12*
preach the word, be i. 2 Tim 4:2

instantly

they besought him i. Luke 7:4*
our twelve tribes i. Acts 26:7*

instruct

that he might i. thee. Deut 4:36
thy good Spirit to i. Neh 9:20
that contendeth i. him? Job 40:2*

my reins also *i.* me in. *Ps* 16:7
I will *i.* thee and teach thee. 32:8
mother's house, who will *i.* *S of S* 8:2
his God doth *i.* him to. *Isa* 28:26
understand shall *i.* many. *Dan* 11:33
Lord, that he may *i.* *1 Cor* 2:16

instructed

led him about, he *i.* *Deut* 32:10*
Jehoiada the priest *i.* him. *2 Ki* 12:2
Chenaniah *i.* about the. *1 Chr* 15:22
that were *i.* in the songs of. 25:7
Solomon was *i.* for the. *2 Chr* 3:3*
behold thou hast *i.* many. *Job* 4:3
be *i.* ye judges of the. *Ps* 2:10
mine ear to them that *i.* *Pr* 5:13
the wise is *i.* he receiveth. 21:11
spake thus to me and *i.* *Isa* 8:11
who *i.* him, and taught him? 40:14
be *i.* O Jerusalem, lest my. *Jer* 6:8
after that I was *i.* I smote. 31:19
every scribe who is *i.* to. *Mat* 13:52
and she, being before *i.* of. 14:8*
wherein thou hast been *i.* *Luke* 1:4
man was *i.* in the way. *Acts* 18:25
his will, being *i.* out of. *Rom* 2:18
and in all things, I am *i.* *Phil* 4:12*

instructing

i. those that oppose *2 Tim* 2:25

instruction

the ears, and sealeth *i.* *Job* 33:16
seeing thou hatest *i.* and. *Ps* 50:17
to know wisdom and *i.* *Pr* 1:2
to receive the *i.* of wisdom. 3
despise wisdom and *i.* 7; 15:5
hear the *i.* of thy father. 1:8; 4:1
take fast hold of *i.*, let her. 4:13
how have I hated *i.* and my. 5:12
he shall die without *i.* and. 23
and reproofs of *i.* are the. 6:23
receive my *i.* 8:10
hear *i.* and be wise. 33
give *i.* to a wise man and he. 9:9
way of life that keepeth *i.* 10:17*
loveth *i.* loveth knowledge. 12:1*
son heareth his father's *i.* 13:1
shall be to him that refuseth *i.* 18*
he that refuseth *i.* hateth his. 15:32*
the fear of the Lord is the *i.* of. 33
but the *i.* of fools is folly. 16:22*
hear counsel, and receive *i.* 19:20
cease to hear the *i.* that causeth. 27
apply thy heart to *i.* and. 23:12
buy the truth, also *i.* and. 23
upon it and received *i.* 24:32
not hear, nor receive *i.* *Jer* 17:23
not hearkened to receive *i.* 32:33
receive *i.* to hearken to my. 35:13
a reproach, a taunt, an *i.* *Ezek* 5:15
surely thou wilt receive *i.* *Zeph* 3:7*
all scripture is profitable for *i.*
2 Tim 3:16

instructor

Tubal-Cain, an *i.* of. *Gen* 4:22*
i. of foolish, a teacher. *Rom* 2:20*

instructors

ye have 10,000 *i.* in. *1 Cor* 4:15

instrument

smite him with an *i.* of. *Num* 35:16
sing to him with an *i.* of ten strings.
Ps 33:2; 92:3
new song, O God, on an *i.* 144:9
threshed with a threshing *i.* *Isa* 28:27
thee a sharp threshing *i.* 41:15
that bringeth forth an *i.* for. 54:16*
one that can play on an *i.* *Ezek* 33:32

instruments

i. of cruelty are in their. *Gen* 49:5*
pattern of all the *i.* *Ex* 25:9*
shall keep all the *i.* of. *Num* 3:8
they shall take all the *i.* of. 4:12*
sanctified all the *i.* 7:1*
with the holy *i.* 31:6*
make *i.* of war, and *i.* *1 Sam* 8:12
king Saul with *i.* of music. 18:6
their flesh with *i.* of oxen. *1 Ki* 19:21
to oversee all the *i.* of. *1 Chr* 9:29*
make a sound with musical *i.* 16:42
singing with loud *i.* to. *2 Chr* 30:21
Hanani with musical *i.* *Neh* 12:36
prepared for him the *i.* *Ps* 7:13
players on *i.* followed after. 68:25*
as the players on *i.* shall be. 87:7*
praise him with stringed *i.* *Ps* 150:4
as musical *i.* and that of. *Eccl* 2:8†
i. also of the churl are evil. *Isa* 32:7
my songs to the stringed *i.* 38:20
nor *i.* of music brought. *Dan* 6:18
Gilead with threshing *i.* *Amos* 1:3
and invent to themselves *i.* of. 6:5
singer on my stringed *i.* *Hab* 3:19
take thee *i.* of a foolish. *Zech* 11:15
yield members *i.* of unrighteousness,
members as *i.* of. *Rom* 6:13

insurrection

this city hath made *i.* *Ezra* 4:19
from the *i.* of the workers. *Ps* 64:2*
that had made *i.* who had committed
murder in the *i.* *Mark* 15:7
Jews made *i.* with one. *Acts* 18:12*

integrity

in *i.* of my heart I have. *Gen* 20:5
I know that thou didst this in the *i.* 6
thy father walked in *i.* *1 Ki* 9:4
he holdeth fast his *i.* *Job* 2:3
dost thou still retain thine *i.* 9
I will not remove my *i.* from. 27:5
that God may know my *i.* 31:6
according to my *i.* that. *Ps* 7:8
i. and uprightness preserve. 25:21
I walked in my *i.* 26:1
I will walk in *i.* 11
thou upholdest me in my *i.* 41:12
he fed them according to *i.* 78:72
the *i.* of the upright shall. *Pr* 11:3
poor that walketh in his *i.* 19:1
just man walketh in his *i.* 20:7

intelligence

i. with them that forsake covenant.
Dan 11:30*

intend

did not *i.* to go up. *Josh* 22:23*
ye *i.* to add more to. *2 Chr* 28:13
ye *i.* to bring this man's. *Acts* 5:28
what ye *i.* to do as touching. 35

intended

for they *i.* evil against. *Ps* 21:11

intendest

i. thou to kill me, as the? *Ex* 2:14

intending

which of you *i.* to build? *Luke* 14:28
i. after Easter to bring. *Acts* 12:4
sailed to Assos, there *i.* to. 20:13

intent

to the *i.* the Lord might. *2 Sam* 17:14
to *i.* he might destroy. *2 Ki* 10:19
to the *i.* he might let. *2 Chr* 16:1
to the *i.* that I might. *Ezek* 40:4
to the *i.* that the living. *Dan* 4:17
not there to the *i.* ye. *John* 11:15
for what *i.* he spake this to. 13:28
and came hither for that *i.* *Acts* 9:21
I ask for what *i.* ye have? 10:29
to the *i.* we should not. *1 Cor* 10:6
to the *i.* that now to the. *Eph* 3:10

intents

till he have performed *i.* *Jer* 30:24
is a discerner of the *i.* *Heb* 4:12

intercession

and made *i.* for the. *Isa* 53:12
cry, nor make *i.* to me. *Jer* 7:16
let them now make *i.* to the. 27:18
Gemariah had made *i.* 36:25
but the Spirit maketh *i.* for us.
Rom 8:26, 27, 34
how he maketh *i.* to God. 11:2*
he ever liveth to make *i.* *Heb* 7:25

intercessions

that prayers and *i.* be. *1 Tim* 2:1

intercessor

he wondered that there was no *i.*
Isa 59:16

intermeddle

a stranger doth not *i.* *Pr* 14:10

intermeddleth

seeketh and *i.* with all. *Pr* 18:1*

intermission

ceaseth not without any *i.* *Lam* 3:49

interpret

none that could *i.* them. *Gen* 41:8
according to his dream he did *i.* 12
do all *i.*? *1 Cor* 12:30
except he *i.* 14:5
pray that he may *i.* *1 Cor* 14:13
let one *i.* 27

interpretation

[1] *A translation, or turning from one language into another,* 1 Cor 12:10. [2] *The gift of explaining visions and dreams, etc.,* Gen 40:8; 2 Pet 1:20.

each man according to the *i.* of his
dream. *Gen* 40:5; 41:11
the *i.* of it. 40:12, 18; *Dan* 4:24; 5:26
baker saw that the *i.* *Gen* 40:16
when Gideon heard the *i.* *Judg* 7:15
a proverb and the *i.* *Pr* 1:6*
we shall shew the *i.* *Dan* 2:4, 7, 36
the dream is certain, and the *i.* 45
and the *i.* thereof be to thy. 4:19
he will shew the *i.* 5:12
not shew the *i.* 15
and he made me to know the *i.* 7:16
Cephas, which is by *i.* a. *John* 1:42
of Siloam, which is by *i.* Sent. 9:7
by *i.* is called Dorcas. *Acts* 9:36
sorcerer, so is his name by *i.* 13:8
to another the *i.* of. *1 Cor* 12:10
every one of you hath an *i.* 14:26
being by *i.* king of. *Heb* 7:2
is of any private *i.* *2 Pet* 1:20

interpretations

Joseph said, do not *i.*? *Gen* 40:8
that thou canst make *i.* *Dan* 5:16

interpreted

as Joseph had *i.* *Gen* 40:22; 41:13
written and *i.* in the. *Ezra* 4:7*
being *i.* is, God with us. *Mat* 1:23
being *i.*, Damsel, arise. *Mark* 5:41
which is, being *i.* the place of. 15:22
i. My God, my God, why hast? 34
being *i.* Master. *John* 1:38
which is, being *i.*, the Christ. 41
is, being *i.* the son of. *Acts* 4:36

interpreter

and there is no *i.* of it. *Gen* 40:8
spake to them by an *i.* 42:23
i., one among a thousand. *Job* 33:23
but if there be no *i.* let. *1 Cor* 14:28

interpreting

i. of dreams was found. *Dan* 5:12

intreat

[1] *To supplicate or pray to,* Ex 8:8; Judg 13:8. [2] *To intercede, or speak in one's behalf,* Gen 23:8; 1 Sam 2:25. [3] *To seek,* Pr 19:6.

i. for me to Ephron the. *Gen* 23:8
called for Moses, and said, *i.* the.
Ex 8:8, 28; 9:28; 10:17
when shall I *i.* for thee? 8:9
I will *i.* the Lord that the flies. 29
i. me not to leave thee. *Ruth* 1:16
who shall *i.* for him? *1 Sam* 2:25
i. the face of the Lord. *1 Ki* 13:6
among the people, shall *i.* *Ps* 45:12
many will *i.* the favour of. *Pr* 19:6
being defamed, we *i.* *1 Cor* 4:13
I *i.* thee also, true yoke-. *Phil* 4:3*
rebuke not, but *i.* him. *1 Tim* 5:1*

intreated

i. for his wife, Lord was *i.* *Gen* 25:21
out and *i.* the Lord. *Ex* 8:30; 10:18
then Manoah *i.* the Lord. *Judg* 13:8
after that God was *i.* *2 Sam* 21:14
Lord was *i.* for the land. 24:25
cried and he was *i.* of. *1 Chr* 5:2
prayed, and God was *i.* *2 Chr* 33:1
God, and he was *i.* of us. *Ezra* 8:2
I called, I *i.* him with. *Job* 19:1
though I *i.* for the children's. 17
I *i.* thy favour with my. *Ps* 119:5
he shall be *i.* of them. *Isa* 19:2
his father out, and *i.* *Luke* 15:2
i. the word should not. *Heb* 12:1
from above is easy to be *i.* *Jas* 3:1
see also **entreat,** *etc.*

intreaties

the poor useth *i.* but the. *Pr* 18:2
praying us with much *i.* *2 Cor* 8:

intruding

i. into things he hath not. *Col* 2:18

invade

wouldest not let Israel *i.* *2 Chr* 20:1
will *i.* them with troops. *Hab* 3:1

will I establish with *I.* *Gen* 17:21
heir with my son, even *I.* 21:10
for in *I.* shall thy seed be called.
12; *Rom* 9:7; *Heb* 11:18
take thine only son *I.* *Gen* 22:2
Abraham bound *I.* 9
take a wife for *I.* 24:4
appointed for *I.* 14
I. went out to meditate in the. 63
I. was comforted after his. 67
all that he had unto *I.* 25:5
his sons *I.* and Ishmael buried. 9
God blessed *I.* 11
I. forty years old when he took. 20
I. intreated the Lord for his wife. 21
I. was sixty years old when. 26
I. loved Esau. 28
I. went to Abimelech king of. 26:1
I. was sporting with Rebekah his. 8
I. sowed and received an. 12
I.'s servants digged in valley and. 19
grief of mind to *I.* and Rebekah. 35
as *I.* had made an end of. 27:30
I. called Jacob, blessed him. 28:1
I. sent Jacob away, he went to. 5
except the fear of *I.* had. 31:42
the God of *I.* 32:9; *Ex* 3:6, 15, 16
4:5; *1 Ki* 18:36; *1 Chr* 29:18
2 Chr 30:6; *Mat* 22:32
Mark 12:26; *Luke* 20:37
Acts 3:13; 7:32
Jacob came to *I.* *Gen* 35:27
I. gave up the ghost. 29
to the God of his father *I.* 46:1
God, before whom my father *I.* 48:15
let the name of my father *I.* 16
there they buried *I.* 49:31
he sware to *I.* 50:24
remembered his covenant with Abraham, with *I.* *Ex* 2:24; *Lev* 26:42
his seed and gave him *I.* *Josh* 24:3
I gave unto *I.* Jacob and Esau. 4
his oath unto *I.* *1 Chr* 16:16; *Ps* 105:9
rulers over the seed of *I.* *Jer* 33:26
high places of *I.* shall be desolate.
Amos 7:9
word against the house of *I.* 16
I., and *I.* begat Jacob. *Mat* 1:2
Luke 3:34; *Acts* 7:8
shall sit down with *I.* in. *Mat* 8:11
when ye shall see *I.* in. *Luke* 13:28
conceived by our father *I.* *Rom* 9:10
we, brethren, as *I.* was. *Gal* 4:28
in tabernacles with *I.* and. *Heb* 11:9
Abraham offered up *I.* 17; *Jas* 2:21
by faith *I.* blessed Jacob. *Heb* 11:20

Isaiah *or* **Esaias**

Hezekiah sent Eliakim to *I.*
2 Ki 19:2; *Isa* 37:2
Hezekiah was sick, *I.* came to him.
2 Ki 20:1; *Isa* 38:1
and *I.* cried unto the Lord.
2 Ki 20:11; *2 Chr* 32:20
acts did *I.* write. *2 Chr* 26:22; 32:32
I. hath walked naked. *Isa* 20:3
spoken by the prophet *E.* *Mat* 3:3
4:14; 8:17; 12:17; 13:14
Luke 3:4; *John* 1:23; 12:38
well did *E.* prophesy of you.
Mat 15:7; *Mark* 7:6
him book of prophet *E.* *Luke* 4:17
because that *E.* said. *John* 12:39
these things said *E.* when he. 41
the eunuch read *E.* *Acts* 8:28, 30
spake the Holy Ghost by *E.* 28:25
E. also crieth concerning. *Rom* 9:27
E. said before, Except the Lord. 29
E. saith, Lord, who hath? 10:16
E. is very bold, and saith, I. 20
again *E.* saith, There shall be. 15:12

Iscariot, *see* **Judas**

Ish-bosheth

Abner took *I.* and set. *2 Sam* 2:8
wroth for the words of *I.* 3:8
David sent messengers to *I.* 14
they brought the head of *I.* 4:8
but they took the head of *I.* 12

Ishmael

call his name *I.* *Gen* 16:11, 15
old when Hagar bare *I.* 16
said to God, O that *I.* might. 17:18
as for *I.* I have heard thee, I. 20
I. was 13 years old when. 25
his sons Isaac and *I.* buried. *Gen* 25:9
the generations of *I.* 12, 13, 16
1 Chr 1:29, 31
years of the life of *I.* 137. *Gen* 25:17
went Esau unto *I.* and took. 28:9
I. came to Gedaliah. *2 Ki* 25:23
Jer 40:8
I. came and ten men with him.
2 Ki 25:25; *Jer* 41:1
Abraham, Isaac and *I.* *1 Chr* 1:28
and *I.* were sons of Azel. 8:38; 9:44
Zebadiah son of *I.* the. *2 Chr* 19:11
Jehoiada took *I.* into covenant. 23:1
I. Elasah, had taken. *Ezra* 10:22
Ammonites hath sent *I.* *Jer* 40:14
I will slay *I.* 15
for thou speakest falsely of *I.* 16
I. smote Gedaliah. 41:2
I. went forth to meet them. 6
then *I.* carried away captive. 10
then Johanan went to fight with *I.* 12
but *I.* escaped from Johanan. 15

Ishmaelites

let us sell him to the *I.* *Gen* 37:27
bought him of the hand of *I.* 39:1
because they were *I.* *Judg* 8:24
Edomites and *I.* confederate against.
Ps 80:3

island

he shall deliver the *i.* of. *Job* 22:30
the wild beasts of the *i.* *Isa* 34:14
under a certain *i.* Clauda. *Acts* 27:16
must be cast on a certain *i.* 26
the *i.* was called Melita. 28:1
of the chief man of the *i.* 7
others who had diseases in the *i.* 9
every *i.* was moved out. *Rev* 6:14
every *i.* fled away, mountains. 16:20

islands

his people from the *i.* of. *Isa* 11:11
wild beasts of the *i.* shall. 13:22
keep silence before me, O *i.* 41:1
his praise in the *i.* 42:12
I will make the rivers *i.* and. 15
i. he will repay recompence. 59:18
wild beasts of the *i.* shall. *Jer* 50:39

isle

inhabitants of the *i.* say. *Isa* 20:6
be still, ye inhabitants of the *i.* 23:2
Tarshish, howl, inhabitants of the *i.* 6
through the *i.* to Paphos. *Acts* 13:6
which had wintered in the *i.* 28:11
I John was in the *i.* that is. *Rev* 1:9

isles

the *i.* of the Gentiles. *Gen* 10:5
laid a tribute on the *i.* *Esth* 10:1
the kings of the *i.* shall. *Ps* 72:10
let the multitude of the *i.* be. 97:1
ye the Lord in the *i.* of. *Isa* 24:15
he taketh up the *i.* as a very. 40:15
the *i.* saw it and feared, the. 41:5
the *i.* shall wait for his law. 42:4
the *i.* and the inhabitants thereof. 10
listen, O *i.* unto me, and. 49:1
the *i.* shall wait upon me. 51:5; 60:9
the *i.* afar off that have not. 66:19
over the *i.* of Chittim. *Jer* 2:10
the kings of the *i.* shall drink. 25:22
hear and declare it in the *i.* 31:10
shall not *i.* shake at? *Ezek* 26:15
the *i.* tremble, the *i.* shall. 18
of the people for many *i.* 27:3
benches of ivory, brought out of *i.* 6
blue and purple from the *i.* of. 7
many *i.* were the merchandise. 15
inhabitants of the *i.* shall be. 35
dwell carelessly in the *i.* 39:6
turn his face to the *i.* *Dan* 11:18
the *i.* of the heathen. *Zeph* 2:11

Israel

be no more Jacob but *I.* *Gen* 32:28
but *I.* shall be thy name. 35:10
1 Ki 18:31
I. dwelt in land of Egypt. *Gen* 47:27
and *I.* bowed himself upon the. 31
in thee shall *I.* bless, saying. 48:20
the shepherd, the stone of *I.* 49:24
I. is my son. *Ex* 4:22
obey his voice to let *I.* go? 5:2
that we have let *I.* go from. 14:5
from *I.*, for Lord fighteth. 25
Lord saved *I.* that day from. 30
I. prevailed. *Ex* 17:11
Isaac, and *I.* thy servant. 32:13
her son and a man of *I.* *Lev* 24:10
good concerning *I.* *Num* 10:29
to the many thousands of *I.* 36
thus saith thy brother *I.*, Let. 20:14
I. vowed a vow unto the Lord. 21:2
then *I.* sang this song, Spring up. 17
defy *I.* 23:7
shall be said of *I.* What hath! 23
a Sceptre rise out of *I.* 24:17
Edom a possession, and *I.* 18
Phinehas went after man of *I.* 25:8
name be not put out of *I.* *Deut* 25:6
shall teach *I.* thy law, Jacob. 33:10
I. then shall dwell in safety. 28
when *I.* turned their backs. *Josh* 7:8
I. hath sinned. 11
took the mountain of *I.* 11:16
and *I.* he shall know. 22:22
I. served the Lord all days. 24:31
it came to pass when *I.* *Judg* 1:28
them I may prove *I.* 2:22; 3:1, 4
toward the governors of *I.* 5:9
I. was greatly impoverished by. 6:1
save *I.* 14, 15, 36, 37
lest *I.* vaunt themselves. 7:2
so that *I.* was sore distressed. 10:9
grieved for the misery of *I.* 16
because *I.* took away my land. 11:13
smote Benjamin before *I.* 20:35
I. was smitten. *1 Sam* 4:2, 10
I. is fled. 17
on whom is the desire of *I.*? 9:20
heard that *I.* also was had. 13:4
also the strength of *I.* will. 15:29
of the God of the armies of *I.* 17:45
the beauty of *I.* is slain. *2 Sam* 1:19
broughtest in *I.* 5:2; *1 Chr* 11:2
nation is like thy people *I.*? *2 Sam* 7:23
the ark, and *I.* and Judah. 11:11
for *I.* had fled every man to. 19:8
Judah and *I.* were many. *1 Ki* 4:20
I. dwelt safely. 25; *Jer* 23:6
I. shall be a proverb among. *1 Ki* 9:7
he abhorred *I.* 11:25
so *I.* rebelled. 12:19
Lord shall smite *I.* as a reed. 14:15
art thou he that troubleth *I.*? 18:17
began to cut *I.* short. *2 Ki* 10:32
was put to the worse before *I.* 14:12
would blot out the name of *I.* 27
carried *I.* away into Assyria. 17:6
23, 27
of Jacob, whom he named *I.* 34
the Lord concerning *I.* *1 Chr* 11:10
they of *I.* were a thousand. 21:5
the God of *I.* 29:18; *1 Ki* 18:36
2 Chr 6:16; 30:6; *Jer* 31:1
because thy God loved *I.* *2 Chr* 9:8
whether they were of *I.* *Ezra* 2:59
Neh 7:61
for ever towards *I.* *Ezra* 3:11
to increase the trespass of *I.* 10:10
Jacob shall rejoice, *I.* shall be glad.
Ps 14:7; 53:6
fear him, all ye seed of *I.* 22:23
redeem *I.* O God, out of all. 25:22
Lord, from the fountain of *I.* 68:26
heard this, he abhorred *I.* 78:59
would not hearken, *I.* would. 81:11
O that my people *I.* had walked. 13
that name of *I.* may be no more. 83:4
Judah was his sanctuary, *I.* 114:2
he that keepeth *I.* shall. 121:4
peace shall be upon *I.* 125:5; 128:6
I. hope in the Lord. 130:7; 131:3
Lord hath chosen *I.* for his. 135:4
together the outcasts of *I.* 147:2
let *I.* rejoice in him that made. 149:2
but *I.* doth not know nor. *Isa* 1:3
blessed be *I.* mine inheritance. 19:25
I. shall blossom and bud. 27:6
but thou *I.* art my servant. 41:8
who gave *I.* to robbers? 42:24
have given *I.* to reproaches. 43:28
himself by the name of *I.* 44:5
for *I.* mine elect's sake, I. 45:4
I. shall be saved in Lord with. 17
in the Lord shall the seed of *I.* 25
called by the name of *I.* 48:1
though *I.* be not gathered, *I.* 49:5
to restore the preserved of *I.* 6
gathereth the outcasts of *I.* 56:8

I. acknowledge us not. Isa 63:16
I. was holiness to the Lord. Jer 2:3
is I. a servant? 14
the salvation of I. 3:23
I. is the rod of his. 10:16; 51:19
of I., saviour in trouble. 14:8; 17:13
for was not I. a derision? 48:27
hath I. no sons? hath he no? 49:1
I. shall be heir to them that were. 2
I. is a scattered sheep, lions. 50:17
I will bring I. again to his. 19
iniquity of I. be sought for and. 20
I. hath not been forsaken of. 51:5
Lord hath swallowed up I. Lam 2:5
you in the border of I. Ezek 11:10
wilt thou make a full end of I.? 13
I the Lord do sanctify I. 37:28
are gone from me, when I. 44:10
though thou I. play harlot. Hos 4:15
I. slideth back as a backsliding. 16
I. is not hid from me, I. 5:3; 6:10
I. shall fall. 5:5
I. shall cry to me, My God. 8:2
I. hath cast off the thing that. 3
I. is swallowed up. 8
I. shall know it. 9:7
I. hath forgotten his Maker. 14
I found I. like grapes in the. 9:10
I. is an empty vine. 10:1
I. shall be ashamed of his own. 6
the sin of I. be destroyed. 8
when I. was a child, then I. 11:1
how shall I deliver thee, I.? 8
I. served and kept sheep. 12:12
with them for my heritage I. Joel 3:2
I. shall surely be led. Amos 7:11, 17
Adullam the glory of I. Mi 1:15
they shall smite the judge of I. 5:1
holpen his servant I. Luke 1:54
art thou a master of I.? John 3:10
that for the hope of I. Acts 28:20
not all I. which are of I. Rom 9:6
concerning I. though number of I. 27
I. which followed the law of. 31
but I say, did not I. know? 10:19
I. hath not obtained what he. 11:7
behold I. after the flesh. 1 Cor 10:18
on them and on I. of God. Gal 6:16
of the stock of I. of the. Phil 3:5
see **children, congregation, elders, God, Holy** One of Israel, **house**

against **Israel**

Arad fought ag. I. Num 21:1
Sihon fought ag. I. 23
is there any divination ag. I.? 23:23
anger of Lord was kindled ag. I. 25:3
32:13; Judg 2:14, 20; 3:8; 10:7
2 Sam 24:1; 2 Ki 13:3; 1 Chr 27:24
2 Chr 28:13; Ps 78:21
of Canaan ag. I. Josh 8:14; 11:5
Balak of Moab warred ag. I. 24:9
Eglon ag. I. Judg 3:12
Midian ag. I. 6:2
Ammon made war ag. I. 11:4, 5, 20
Balak, did he ever strive ag. I.? 25
Philistines put themselves in array against I. 1 Sam 4:2; 7:7, 10
31:1; 1 Chr 10:1
Ben-hadad ag. I. 1 Ki 20:26
2 Ki 6:8
Moab rebelled ag. I. 2 Ki 1:1
was great indignation ag. I. 3:27
yet the Lord testified ag. I. 17:13
stood up against I. 1 Chr 21:1
Rehoboam went out ag. I. 2 Chr 11:1
words I have spoken ag. I. Jer 36:2
prophesy not ag. I. Amos 7:16
maketh intercession ag. I. Rom 11:2

all **Israel**

able men out of all I. Ex 18:25
all I. round about fled. Num 16:34
all I. shall hear. Deut 13:11; 21:21
all I. stoned Achan with. Josh 7:25
all I. went a whoring. Judg 8:27
that his sons did to all I. 1 Sam 2:22
all I. knew that Samuel was. 3:20
word of Samuel came to all I. 4:1
lay it for a reproach on all I. 11:2
but all I. and Judah loved. 18:16
all I. had lamented Samuel. 28:3
to bring about all I. 2 Sam 3:12
all I. understood that it was not. 37
will do this thing before all I.
2 Sam 12:12
in all I. none so much praised. 14:25
all I. shall hear that thou art. 16:21
all I. know thy father. 17:10
and all I. fled every one to. 18:17
speech of all I. is come to me. 19:11
the eyes of all I. are. 1 Ki 1:20
thou knowest that all I. set. 2:15
all I. heard of the judgement. 3:28
king and all I. offered sacrifice. 8:62
all I. stoned Adoram with. 12:18
all I. shall mourn for him. 14:13
gather to me all I. unto. 18:19
I saw all I. scattered. 22:17
2 Chr 18:16
David and all I. went to. 1 Chr 11:4
David and all I. played. 13:8
all I. brought up the ark of. 15:28
I have walked with all I. 17:6
all I. and the princes obeyed. 29:23
all I. forsook the law. 2 Chr 12:1
hear me, Jeroboam, and all I. 13:4
God smote Jeroboam and all I. 15
ruin of him and of all I. 28:23
to make an atonement for all I.
29:24; Ezra 6:17
all I. went out and brake. 2 Chr 31:1
all I. dwelt in their cities. Ezra 2:70
Neh 7:73
made all I. swear to do. Ezra 10:5
all I. gave the portions. Neh 12:47
belongeth to us, to all I. Dan 9:7
yea, all I. have transgressed. 11
the law of Moses for all I. Mal 4:4
not all I. which are of I. Rom 9:6
so all I. shall be saved, as it. 11:26

camp of **Israel**

went before the camp of I. Ex 24:19
Egyptians and the camp of I. 20
the camp of I. a curse. Josh 6:18
them without the camp of I. 23
out of the camp of I. am I escaped.
2 Sam 1:3
came to the camp of I. 2 Ki 3:24

for **Israel**

God had done for I. Ex 18:1, 8
Josh 24:31; Judg 2:7, 10; 1 Ki 8:66
Lord fought for I. Josh 10:14, 42
left no sustenance for I. Judg 6:4
cried unto Lord for I. 1 Sam 7:9
made it an ordinance for I. 30:25
not any helper for I. 2 Ki 14:26
atonement for I. as Moses had.
1 Chr 6:49; 22:1; Neh 10:33
statute for I., a law of God. Ps 81:4
salvation in Zion for I. Isa 46:13
word of the Lord for I. Zech 12:1
my prayer to God for I. Rom 10:1

from **Israel**

shalt be cut off from I. Ex 12:15
Num 19:13
be turned away from I. Num 25:4
put evil from I. Deut 17:12; 22:22
Judg 20:13
one tribe cut off from I. Judg 21:6
the glory is departed from I.
1 Sam 4:21, 22
the cities taken from I. were. 7:14
away the reproach from I. 17:26
the plague was stayed from I.
2 Sam 24:25
they separated from I. all the mixed multitude. Neh 13:3
cut off from I. head and. Isa 9:14
for from I. was it also, the. Hos 8:6

in **Israel**

he had wrought folly in I. Gen 34:7
Deut 22:21; Josh 7:15
Judg 20:6, 10
Jacob, scatter them in I. Gen 49:7
strangers sojourn in I. Lev 20:2
22:18; Ezek 14:7
able to go forth to war in I.
Num 1:3, 45; 26:2
heads of thousands in I. 1:16; 10:4
to me all the firstborn in I. 3:13
every thing devoted in I. 18:14
given all the tenth in I. for an. 21
nor seen perverseness in I. 23:21
abomination is wrought in I.
Deut 17:4; 22:21
up his brother a name in I. 25:7
his name be called in I. Deut 25:10
arose not a prophet since in I. 34:10
Rahab dwelleth in I. Josh 6:25
in I. till that I Deborah arose, that I arose a mother in I. Judg 5:7
spear seen among 40,000 in I.? 8
in I. to lament Jephthah. 11:39
was no king in I. 17:6, 18:1
19:1; 21:25
be priest to a family in I. 18:19
in I., one tribe lacking in I.? 21:3
times in I. concerning redeeming, this was a testimony in I. Ruth 4:7
his name may be famous in I. 14
I will do a thing in I. 1 Sam 3:11
beforetime in I. when a man. 9:9
wrought salvation in I. 11:13; 14:45
father's house free in I. 17:25
know that there is a God in I. 46
is my father's family in I. 18:18
who is like to thee in I.? 26:15
great man fallen in I. 2 Sam 3:38
ought to be done in I. 13:12
be as one of the fools in I. 13
put to death this day in I.? 19:22
and peaceable in I., thou seekest to destroy a mother in I. 20:19
shalt thou kill any man in I. 21:4
cut off him that is shut up and left in I. 1 Ki 14:10; 21:21; 2 Ki 9:8
that thou art God in I. 1 Ki 18:36
left me seven thousand in I. 19:18
because there is not a God in I.
2 Ki 1:3, 6, 16
that there is a prophet in I. 5:8
no God in all the earth but in I. 15
the prophet in I. telleth the. 6:12
for there was joy in I. 1 Chr 12:40
a man to be ruler in I. 2 Chr 7:18
because he had done good in I. 24:16
for them that are left in I. 34:21
Josiah made all present in I. to. 33
passover like to that kept in I. 35:18
made them an ordinance in I. 25
yet there is hope in I. Ezra 10:2
Judah, his name is great in I. Ps 76:1
and he appointed law in I. 78:5
signs and for wonders in I. Isa 8:18
hath glorified himself in I. 44:23
committed villany in I. Jer 29:23
set signs and wonders in I. 32:20
it as a proverb in I. Ezek 12:23
18:3
I am the holy One in I. 39:7
Gog a place of graves in I. 11
give them no possession in I. 44:28
every dedicated thing in I. 29
shall be his possession in I. 45:8
oblation for the prince in I. 16
he exalted himself in I. Hos 13:1
that is to be ruler in I. Mi 5:2
is committed in I. Mal 2:11
so great faith, no not in I. Mat 8:10
Luke 7:9
it was never so seen in I. Mat 9:33
and rising of many in I. Luke 2:34
many widows were in I. 4:25
lepers in I. 27
see **king, kings**

land of **Israel**

no smith found in all the land of I.
1 Sam 13:19
little maid out of land of I. 1 Ki 5:2
came no more into land of I. 6:23
brethren left in land of I. 1 Chr 13:2
strangers that were in land of I.
22:2; 2 Chr 2:17; 30:25
idols through land of I. 2 Chr 34:7
the Lord to the land of I. Ezek 7:2
I will give you the land of I. 11:17
the Lord of the land of I. 12:19
enter into land of I. 13:9; 20:38
bring you into the land of I. 20:42
37:12
prophesy against the land of I. 21:2
Aha, against the land of I. 25:3
with despite against land of I. 6
Judah and land of I. were. 27:17
shall come against land of I. 38:18
great shaking in the land of I. 19
brought me into land of I. 40:2
go into the land of I. for. Mat 2:20
and came into the land of I. 21

made **Israel** *sin*
Jeroboam *made I.* to *sin. 1 Ki* 14:16
15:26, 30, 34; 16:19, 26; 22:52
Baasha *made* my people *I.* to *sin.*
16:2, 13
Ahab *made I.* to *sin.* 21:22
son of Nebat who *made I.* to *sin.*
2 Ki 3:3; 10:29, 31; 13:2, 6, 11
14:24; 15:9, 18, 24, 28; 23:15

men of **Israel**
called for all *men of I.* *Josh* 10:24
men of I. gathered. *Judg* 20:11
men of I. went out. 20
men of I. encouraged themselves. 22
the *men of I.* gave place to the. 36
men of I. were distressed that day.
1 Sam 14:24
the *men of I.* fled from the. 31:1
beaten and the *men of I. 2 Sam* 2:17
hearts of the *men of I.* are. 15:13
whom the *men of I.* choose. 16:18
words of men of Judah fiercer than
of the *men of I.* 19:43
men of I. were gone away. 23:9
down the chosen *men of I. Ps* 78:31
fear not, ye *men of I.* I. *Isa* 41:14
ye *men of I.* hear these. *Acts* 2:22
ye *men of I.* why marvel ? 3:12
ye *men of I.* take heed to. 5:35
Paul said, *Men of I.* give. 13:16
crying out, *Men of I.* help. 21:28

O **Israel**
these be thy gods, *O I.* *Ex* 32:4
are thy tabernacles, *O I. Num* 24:5
hearken, *O I.* *Deut* 4:1; 27:9
Isa 48:12
hear, *O I.*, the statutes. *Deut* 5:1
6:3, 4; 9:1; 20:3; *Ps* 50:7
81:8; *Isa* 44:1; *Mark* 12:29
happy art thou, *O I.* *Deut* 33:29
in the midst of thee, *O I. Josh* 7:13
every man to his tents, *O I.*
2 Sam 20:1; *1 Ki* 12:16
2 Chr 10:16
behold thy gods, *O I.* *1 Ki* 12:28
O I. trust thou in Lord. *Ps* 115:9
why speakest thou, *O I.*? *Isa* 40:27
O I. fear not. 43:1; *Jer* 30:10
46:27
been weary of me, *O I.* *Isa* 43:22
O I. for thou art my servant, *O I.*
thou shalt not be. 44:21; 49:3
if thou wilt return, *O I.* *Jer* 4:1
Hos 14:1
O I. thy prophets are. *Ezek* 13:4
rejoice not, *O I.* for joy. *Hos* 9:1
O I. thou hast sinned from. 10:9
O I. thou hast destroyed. 13:9
to meet thy God, *O I.* *Amos* 4:12
shout, *O I.* be glad and. *Zeph* 3:14

over **Israel**
Abimelech reigned three years *over*
I. *Judg* 9:22
had dominion *over I.* 14:4
his sons judges *over I.* *1 Sam* 8:1
reigned two years *over I.* 13:1
thee from being king *over I.* 13:26
Ish-bosheth Saul's son reigned *over*
I. *2 Sam* 2:10
throne of David *over I.* 3:10
5:2, 3, 17; 6:21; *1 Chr* 11:3
hosts is the God *over I. 2 Sam* 7:26
Solomon king *over I.* *1 Ki* 1:34
Jeroboam king *over I.* 11:37
shall raise up a king *over I.* 14:14
Nadab reigned *over I.* 15:25
Elah reigned *over I.* 16:8
Omri king *over I.* 16
Ahab reigned *over I.* 29
Ahaziah reigned *over I.* 22:51
Jehoram reigned *over I.* *2 Ki* 3:1
Jehu king *over I.* 9:3, 6, 12; 10:36
Jehoahaz reigned *over I.* 13:1
Jehoash reigned *over I.* 10
Zechariah reigned *over I.* 15:8
Menahem reigned *over I.* 15:17
Pekahiah reigned *over I.* 23
Hoshea reigned *over I.* 17:1
Chenaniah for outward business *over*
I. *1 Chr* 26:29
times that went *over I.* are. 29:30
his excellency is *over I.* *Ps* 68:34
preacher was king *over I. Eccl* 1:12

Israel joined with *people*
much *people* of *I.* died. *Num* 21:6
O Lord, to thy *people I.* *Deut* 21:8
and bless thy *people I.* 26:15
should bless *people* of *I.* *Josh* 8:33
before his *people I.* *Judg* 11:23
offerings of *I.* my *people. 1 Sam* 2:29
Saul captain over my *people I.* 9:16
made his *people I.* utterly. 27:12
I will save my *people I. 2 Sam* 3:18
to feed my *people I.* 5:2; 7:7
1 Chr 11:2
for his *people I.'s* sake. *2 Sam* 5:12
for my *people I.* that they may dwell
and move no. 7:10; *1 Chr* 17:9
to thyself thy *people I.* *2 Sam* 7:24
not forsake my *people I.* *1 Ki* 6:13
when thy *people I.* be smitten. 8:33
2 Chr 6:24
what prayer soever be made by all
thy *people I.* *1 Ki* 8:38
fear thee, as do thy *people I.* 43
given rest to his *people I.* 56
because of his *people I.* *1 Chr* 14:2
be ruler over my *people I.* 17:7
2 Chr 6:5
earth is like thy *people I. 1 Chr* 17:21
people I. didst thou make. 22
shewed *I.* his *people.* *2 Chr* 7:10
blessed Lord and his *people I.* 31:8
serve now the Lord your God and his
people I. 35:3
all they of the *people* of *I.* *Ezra* 7:13
people of *I.* have not separated. 9:1
heritage to *I.* his *people.* *Ps* 135:12
people I. be as the sand. *Isa* 10:22
wickedness of my *people I. Jer* 7:12
which I caused my *people I.* 12:14
caused my *people I.* to err. 23:13
again the captivity of my *people I.*
and Judah. 30:3; *Amos* 9:14
Edom by my *people I.* *Ezek* 25:14
your fruit to my *people I.* 36:8
will cause my *people I.* to walk. 12
when my *people I.* dwelleth. 38:14
come up against my *people I.* 16
the sin of my *people I.* *Dan* 9:20
go, prophesy unto my *people I.*
Amos 7:15
is come upon my *people I.* 8:2
shall rule my *people I.* *Mat* 2:6
glory of thy *people I.* *Luke* 2:32
people of *I.* were gathered against.
Acts 4:27
God of this *people I.* chose. 13:17
repentance to all *people* of *I.* 24

princes of **Israel**
the *princes of I.* being. *Num* 1:44
the *princes of I.* heads and princes of
the tribes offered at the. 7:2, 84
princes of I. to help. *1 Chr* 22:17
David assembled the *princes of I.*
23:2; 28:1
princes of I. humbled. *2 Chr* 12:6
slew divers of *princes of I.* 21:4
lamentation for the *princes of I.*
Ezek 19:1
be upon all the *princes of I.* 21:12
the *princes of I.* were on thee. 22:6
it suffice you, O *princes of I.* 45:9

to or *unto* **Israel**
God spake *unto I.* in. *Gen* 46:2
hear and hearken *unto I.* 49:2
the Lord hath done *to I.* *Ex* 18:9
Joshua gave it for inheritance *to I.*
Josh 11:23; 21:43
Lord hath given rest *unto I.* 23:1
he hath shewed *unto I.* *Judg* 8:35
what Amalek did *to I.* *1 Sam* 15:2
that seemed good *to I.* *2 Sam* 3:19
an adversary *to I.* *1 Ki* 11:25
for a law, and *to I.* for an everlasting
covenant. *1 Chr* 16:17; *Ps* 105:10
a cause of trespass *to I.*? *1 Chr* 21:3
I will give quietness *to I.* in. 22:9
ordinance for ever *to I.* *2 Chr* 2:4
scribe of his statutes *to I. Ezra* 7:11
Lord had commanded *to I. Neh* 8:1
truly God is good *to I.* *Ps* 73:1
heritage *unto I.* 135:12; 136:22
sheweth his judgements *to I.* 147:19
as it was *to I.* in the day. *Isa* 11:16
a wilderness *unto I.*? *Jer* 2:31

a father *to I.* Ephraim is. *Jer* 31:9
I will be as the dew *to I.* *Hos* 14:5
to declare *to I.* his sin. *Mi* 3:8
the word of the Lord *to I.* *Mal* 1:1
day of his shewing *unto I. Luke* 1:80
be made manifest *to I.* *John* 1:31
restore the kingdom *to I.*? *Acts* 1:6
to give repentance *to I.* 5:31
God hath raised *unto I.* 13:23
to I. he saith, All day. *Rom* 10:21
in part is happened *to I.* 11:25

tribes of **Israel**
Dan shall judge as one of *tribes of I.*
Gen 49:16
are the twelve *tribes of I.* 28
according to 12 *tribes of I.* *Ex* 24:4
through all *tribes of I.* to war.
Num 31:4
to any of the other *tribes of I.* 36:3
every one of *tribes of I.* shall keep. 9
evil out of *tribes of I.* *Deut* 29:21
when the *tribes of I.* were. 33:5
men out of *tribes of I.* *Josh* 3:12
to number of *tribes of I.* 4:5, 8
brought *I.* by their *tribes.* 7:16
Joshua gave to the *tribes of I.* 12:7
fathers of *tribes of I.* divided. 19:51
princes through *tribes of I.* 22:14
Joshua gathered all *tribes of I.* 24:1
Dan not among *tribes of I. Judg* 18:1
chief of *tribes of I.* presented. 20:2
of an 100 out of all *tribes of I.* 10
tribes of I. came not up. 21:5, 8
a breach in the *tribes of I.* 15
him out of all *tribes of I. 1 Sam* 2:28
the smallest of the *tribes of I.* 9:21
Samuel caused all *tribes of I.* 10:20
made head of the *tribes of I.*? 15:17
came all the *tribes of I.* to David.
2 Sam 5:1
word with any of *tribes of I.* 7:7
servant is of one of *tribes of I.* 15:2
spies through all the *tribes of I.* 10
strife through the *tribes of I.* 19:9
all the *tribes of I.* and number. 24:2
no city out of all the *tribes of I.* to
build. *1 Ki* 8:16; *2 Chr* 6:5
Jerusalem out of all the *tribes of I.*
1 Ki 11:32; 14:21; *2 Ki* 21:7
2 Chr 12:13; 33:7
out of all the *tribes of I. 2 Chr* 11:16
goats according to *tribes of I.*
Ezra 6:17
made *tribes of I.* to dwell. *Ps* 78:55
I will take *tribes of I.* *Ezek* 37:19
the twelve *tribes of I.* 47:13, 21, 22
city out of all the *tribes of I.* 48:19
after the names of the *tribes of I.* 31
among *tribes of I.* have I. *Hos* 5:9
the eyes of all *tribes of I.* *Zech* 9:1
judging the twelve *tribes of I.*
Mat 19:28; *Luke* 22:30
with names of twelve *tribes of I.*
Rev 21:12

with **Israel**
Amalek fought *with I.* *Ex* 17:8
a covenant *with* thee and *I.* 34:27
have no inheritance *with I. Deut* 18:1
his judgements *with I.* 33:21
of Canaan fought *with I.* *Josh* 9:2
Gibeon made peace *with I.* 10:1
themselves together to fight *with I.*
1 Sam 13:5; 28:1; *2 Sam* 21:15
Syrians made peace *with I.*
2 Sam 10:19
was very angry *with I.* *2 Ki* 17:18
for Lord is not *with I.* *2 Chr* 25:7
Lord will plead *with I.* *Mi* 6:2

Israelite
the *I.* was slain, Zimri. *Num* 25:14
the son of Ithra an *I.* *2 Sam* 17:25
behold an *I.* indeed, in. *John* 1:47
I also am an *I.* of seed. *Rom* 11:1

Israelites
the cattle of the *I.* dead. *Ex* 9:7
I. born shall dwell in. *Lev* 23:42
all the *I.* passed over on. *Josh* 3:17
only divide it by lot to the *I.* 13:6
destroyed of the *I.* *Judg* 20:21
servants did to all *I.* *1 Sam* 2:14
I. went to the Philistines to. 13:20
turned to be with the *I.* 14:21
all the *I.* lamented Samuel. 25:1

the I. pitched by a. 1 Sam 29:1
the I. were troubled at. 2 Sam 4:1
the I. rose and smote. 2 Ki 3:24
as all the multitude of the I. 7:13
inhabitants were the I. 1 Chr 9:2
who are I.; to whom. Rom 9:4
are they I.? so am I. 2 Cor 11:22

Israelitish

the son of an I. woman. Lev 24:10
I. woman's son blasphemed the. 11

Issachar

Leah called his name I. Gen 30:18
Leah's son, I. 35:23
sons of I. 46:13; 1 Chr 7:1
I. is a strong ass. Gen 49:14
Israel's sons, I., Zebulun. Ex 1:3
1 Chr 2:1
the princes of I., Nethaneel.
Num 1:8; 2:5; 7:18
I. and Joseph shall stand to bless.
Deut 27:12
rejoice, Zebulun and I. in. 33:18
they met together in I. Josh 17:10
Manasseh had in I. and Asher. 11
the princes of I. were with Deborah, even I. and also. Judg 5:15
Tola a man of I. arose to. 10:1
was an officer in I. 1 Ki 4:17
Ahijah of the house of I. 15:27
they that were nigh to I. 1 Chr 12:40
I. the seventh son of. 26:5
captain of I. Omri the son of. 27:18
of I. had not cleansed. 2 Chr 30:18
of Simeon, I. a portion. Ezek 48:25
by the border of I., Zebulun a. 26
south side, one gate of I., one. 33

tribe of **Issachar**

were numbered of the *tribe of I.*
Num 1:29
Judah shall be the *tribe of I.* 2:5
over the *tribe of I.* was. 10:15
of the *tribe of I.* to spy the. 13:7
prince of the *tribe of I.* 34:26
inheritance of the *tribe of I.*
Josh 19:23
lot out of the families of the *tribe of I.*
21:6, 28; 1 Chr 6:62, 72
of *tribe of I.* were sealed. Rev 7:7

issue

[1] *A passage, way, or outlet,* Ps 68:20. [2] *Children or posterity,* Gen 48:6. [3] *A flux or running,* Lev 12:7. [4] *To flow,* Ezek 47:8. [5] *To come forth hastily and violently,* Josh 8:22.

issue, *substantive*

i. which thou begettest. Gen 48:6
the i. of her blood. Lev 12:7; 15:25
Mat 9:20; Mark 5:25
Luke 8:43, 44
running i. Lev 15:2, 3; 22:4
hath the i. 15:8, 28
of Joab, one hath an i. 2 Sam 3:29
on him the offspring and i. Isa 22:24
whose i. is like the i. Ezek 23:20
having no i. left his wife. Mat 22:25

issue

thy sons that i. from thee. 2 Ki 20:18
Isa 39:7
these waters i. toward. Ezek 47:8*

issued

other i. out of the city. Josh 8:22
break forth as if it i. Job 38:8
waters i. from under. Ezek 47:1
because their waters i. out of. 12
fiery stream i. and. Dan 7:10
of their mouths i. fire. Rev 9:17, 18

issues

to God belong the i. Ps 68:20
out of it are the i. of life. Pr 4:23

Italian

centurion of the I. band. Acts 10:1

Italy

Jew lately come from I. Acts 18:2
that we should sail into I. 27:1
they of I. salute you. Heb 13:24

itch

will smite thee with i. Deut 28:27

itching

teachers having i. ears. 2 Tim 4:3

Ithamar

Aaron's sons, Abihu, and I.
Ex 6:23; 1 Chr 6:3
counted by the hand of I. 38:21
charge under hand of I. Num 4:28
Ahimelech of sons of I. 1 Chr 24:3
chief men among the sons of I. 4
of the sons of I. Daniel. Ezra 8:2
see **Eleazar**

Ithiel

I. son of Jesaiah dwelt. Neh 11:7
man spake to I. even to I. Pr 30:1

itself

the fruit tree, whose seed is in i.
Gen 1:11
the beast that dieth of i. Lev 7:24
17:15; 22:8; Deut 14:21
land i. vomiteth out. Lev 18:25
nor reap what groweth of i. 25:11
Isa 37:30
undersetters were of the base i.
1 Ki 7:34
darkness, as darkness i. Job 10:22
gathereth iniquity to i. Ps 41:6
even Sinai i. was moved at. 68:8
his heart may discover i. Pr 18:2
wine when it moveth i. aright. 23:31
ointment which bewrayeth i. 27:16
the tender grass sheweth i. 25
shall axe boast i. against him that heweth, saw magnify i., rod shake i., staff lift up i. Isa 10:15
your soul delight i. in fatness. 55:2
shall thy moon withdraw i. 60:20
shall dwell in Judah i. Jer 31:24
a fire unfolding i. and. Ezek 1:4
not eaten what dieth of i. 4:14; 44:31
be base, that it might not lift i. 17:14
nor exalt i. any more above. 29:15
it raised up i. on the one. Dan 7:5
thought for the things of i. Mat 6:34
every kingdom divided against i.
12:25; Mark 3:24, 25; Luke 11:17
branch cannot bear fruit of i.
John 15:4
together in a place by i. 20:7
i. could not contain the books. 21:25
Spirit i. beareth witness. Rom 8:16
creature i. also shall be delivered. 21
Spirit i. maketh intercession for. 26
there is nothing unclean of i. 14:14
not even nature i. teach? 1 Cor 11:14
charity vaunteth not i., is not. 13:4
charity doth not behave i. 5
every thing that exalts i. 2 Cor 10:5
edifying of i. in love. Eph 4:16
into heaven i. to appear. Heb 9:24
good report of truth i. 3 John 12

Iturea

brother Philip tetrarch of I. Luke 3:1

Ivah

the gods of Hena and I.? 2 Ki 18:34
is the king of I.? 19:13; Isa 37:13

ivory

king made a throne of i. 1 Ki 10:18
2 Chr 9:17
bringing gold, silver, and i.
1 Ki 10:22; 2 Chr 9:21
the i. house which Ahab. 1 Ki 22:39
out of the i. palaces. Ps 45:8
his belly is as bright i. S of S 5:14
thy neck is as a tower of i. 7:4
made thy benches of i. Ezek 27:6
thee for a present horns of i. 15
houses of i. shall perish. Amos 3:15
lie upon beds of i. and stretch. 6:4
man buyeth vessels of i. Rev 18:12

J

Jaazaniah

J. came to Gedaliah. 2 Ki 25:23
J. of the house of the. Jer 35:3
J. stood with his censer. Ezek 8:11
J. and Pelatiah princes of. 11:1

Jabal

J. was the father of such. Gen 4:20

Jabbok

passed over the ford J. Gen 32:22
not to any place of river J. Deut 2:37
Reuben and Gad border to J. 3:16
Gilead to the river J. Josh 12:2

Jabesh

told Saul the tidings of men of J.
1 Sam 11:5
shewed to the men of J. and. 9
came to J. and burned the. 31:12
their bones at J. 13; 1 Chr 10:12
Shallum the son of J. conspired.
2 Ki 15:10
Shallum the son of J. began to. 13
smote Shallum the son of J. 14

Jabesh-gilead

none to the camp from J. Judg 21:8
smite the inhabitants of J. 10
found 400 young virgins of J. 12
Benjamites wives of women of J. 14
Nahash came and encamped against J. 1 Sam 11:1
the inhabitants of J. heard what.
31:11; 1 Chr 10:12
men of J. were they that buried Saul.
2 Sam 2:4
bones of Saul from men of J. 21:12

Jabez

scribes who dwelt at J. 1 Chr 2:55

Jabez

honourable than his brethren, mother called his name J. 1 Chr 4:9
J. called on God of Israel, saying. 10

Jabin

when J. king of Hazor. Josh 11:1
sold them into hand of J. Judg 4:2
peace between J. and the house. 17
God subdued that day, J. king. 23
of Israel prevailed against J. 24
do to them as unto J. Ps 83:9

Jachin

he called the pillar on the right hand J. 1 Ki 7:21; 2 Chr 3:17

jacinth

breastplates of fire, j. Rev 9:17*
foundation of city was a j. 21:20

Jacob

he was called J. Gen 25:26
J. was a plain man. 27
J. sod pottage. 29
J. gave Esau pottage. 34
the voice is J.'s. 27:22
J. was scarce gone out. 30
is not he rightly named J.? 36
Esau hated J. 41
if J. take a wife of Heth. 46
Isaac sent away J. 28:5
J. obeyed his father. 7
J. awaked out of sleep. 16
J. vowed a vow. 20
J. saw Rachel the daughter. 29:10
J. served seven years for Rachel. 20
and J. did so, and fulfilled her. 28
J. came out of the field in. 30:16
and J. took him rods of green. 37
were Laban's, the stronger J.'s. 42
J. hath taken all that was. 31:1
J. stole away unawares to Laban. 20
J. sware by the fear of his father. 53
J. sent messengers before. 32:3
J. saith, Thus have I sojourned. 4
then J. was greatly afraid. 7
say, They be thy servant J.'s. 18
J. was left alone, and there. 24
be no more J. but Israel. 28; 35:10
J. called the name of place. 32:30
J. looked, and behold, Esau. 33:1
J. journeyed to Succoth. 17
J. came to Shalem. 18
J. held his peace until they. 34:5
sons of J. 7, 13, 25; 35:26; 49:1, 2
1 Ki 18:31
J. came to Luz. Gen 35:6
J. called the place Beth-el. 15
these are the generations of J. 37:2
J. rent his clothes, put sackcloth. 34
J.'s heart fainted, for he. 45:26
J. and all his seed came into. 46:6
that came with J. were sixty-six. 26
J. blessed Pharaoh. 47:10
the whole age of J. 28
the mighty God of J. 49:24; Ex 3:6
15, 16; 4:5; 2 Sam 23:1; Ps 20:1

remembered his covenant with *J.*
Ex 2:24; *Lev* 26:42
come, curse me *J.* and. *Num* 23:7
can count dust of *J* and number? 10
enchantment against *J.* it shall be
said of *J.* and Israel, what? 23
shall come a star out of *J.* 24:17
out of *J.* come he that shall have. 19
J. is the lot of his. *Deut* 32:9
they shall teach *J.* thy. 33:10
fountain of *J.* shall be on land. 28
Israel his servant, ye children of *J.*
1 Chr 16:13; *Ps* 105:6
J. shall rejoice. *Ps* 14:7; 53:6
the name of the God of *J.* 20:1
all ye seed of *J.* glorify him. 22:23
command deliverances for *J.* 44:4
the god of *J.* 46:7, 11; 75:9; 76:6
81:1, 4; 84:8; 94:7; 114:7; 132:2
5; 146:5
the excellency of *J.* whom he loved.
47:4; *Nah* 2:2
fire was kindled against *J.* *Ps* 78:21
he brought him to feed *J.* his. 71
for they have devoured *J.* and. 79:7
brought back the captivity of *J.* 85:1
gates of Zion more than all the dwellings of *J.* 87:2
J. sojourned in the land of. 105:23
the Lord hath chosen *J.* 135:4
the God of *J.* *Isa* 2:3; 41:21
Mi 4:2; *Mat* 22:32; *Mark* 12:26
Luke 20:37; *Acts* 3:13; 7:32, 46
remnant of *J.* shall return. *Isa* 10:21
Lord will have mercy on *J.* 14:1
in that day the glory of *J.* shall. 17:4
shall cause them that come of *J.* 27:6
by this shall the iniquity of *J.* be. 9
sanctify the Holy One of *J.* 29:23
J. whom I have chosen, the. 41:8
fear not, thou worm *J.* and ye. 14
who gave *J.* for a spoil? 42:24
therefore I have given *J.* to. 43:28
call himself by the name of *J.* 44:5
Lord hath redeemed *J.* 23; *Jer* 31:11
for *J.* my servant's sake. *Isa* 45:4
hath redeemed his servant *J.* 48:20
that formed me to bring *J.* 49:5
servant to raise up the tribes of *J.* 6
the mighty One of *J.* 26; 60:16
feed thee with heritage of *J.* 58:14
bring forth a seed out of *J.* 65:9
the portion of *J.* not like them.
Jer 10:16; 51:19
they have eaten up *J.* and. 10:25
even the time of *J.'s* trouble. 30:7
fear thou not, O my servant *J.* 10
bring again the captivity of *J.* 18
sing with the gladness for *J.* 31:7
will I cast away the seed of *J.* 33:26
J. shall return to be in rest. 46:27
commanded concerning *J.* *Lam* 1:17
he burned against *J.* like a. 2:3
Judah shall plow, *J.* shall. *Hos* 10:11
I will punish *J.* 12:2
J. fled into Syria. 12
abhor the excellency of *J.* *Amos* 6:8
shall *J.* arise, for he is small? 7:2, 5
sworn by the excellency of *J.* 8:7
for the transgression of *J.* *Mi* 1:5
hear, I pray you, O heads of *J.* 3:1
remnant of *J.* shall be among. 5:8
Esau *J.'s* brother? yet I loved *J.*
Mal 1:2
therefore, ye sons of *J.* are not. 3:6
Isaac begat *J.* *Mat* 1:2
Matthan begat *J.* 15
sit down with Abraham, Isaac, and *J.*
8:11
J. in kingdom of God. *Luke* 13:28
now *J.'s* well was there. *John* 4:6
Joseph called his father *J.* *Acts* 7:14
J. have I loved, but. *Rom* 9:13
turn away ungodliness from *J.* 11:26
in tabernacles with *J.* *Heb* 11:9
by faith Isaac blessed *J.* 20
J. blessed the sons of Joseph. 21

see **house**

in **Jacob**

I will divide them *in J.* *Gen* 49:7
not beheld iniquity *in J.* *Num* 23:21
know that God ruleth *in J.* *Ps* 59:13
established a testimony *in J.* 78:5
and righteousness *in J.* *Ps* 99:4
from transgression *in J.* *Isa* 59:20

O **Jacob**

how goodly are thy tents, *O J.*!
Num 24:5
that seek thy face, *O J.* *Ps* 24:6
why sayest thou, *O J.*? *Isa* 40:27
Lord that created thee, *O J.* 43:1
hast not called upon me, *O J.* 22
yet hear, *O J.* 44:1
fear not, *O J.* my servant. 2
Jer 46:27, 28
remember these, *O J.* for. *Isa* 44:21
hearken unto me, *O J.* 48:12
I will surely assemble, *O J.* *Mi* 2:12

to or *unto* **Jacob**

speak not *to J.* *Gen* 31:24, 29
God appeared *unto J.* and. 35:9
land which he sware to give *to J.*
50:24; *Ex* 6:8; 33:1; *Num* 32:11
Deut 6:10; 29:13; 30:20; 34:4
Ezek 37:25
confirmed the same *to J.* for a law.
1 Chr 16:17; *Ps* 105:10
shewed his word *unto J.* *Ps* 147:19
Lord sent a word *unto J.* *Isa* 9:8
declare *unto J.* his transgression.
Mi 3:8
wilt perform truth *to J.* and. 7:20

Jael

fled away to tent of *J.* *Judg* 4:17
J. took a nail of the tent and. 21
J. came out to meet Barak. 22
in days of *J.* the highways. 5:6
blessed above women shall *J.* 24

Jah

extol him by his name *J.* *Ps* 68:4

Jahaz

his people and came and fought at *J.*
Num 21:23; *Deut* 2:32
Judg 11:20
shall be heard even to *J.* *Isa* 15:4
to *J.* have they uttered. *Jer* 48:34

Jahazah

out of Reuben *J.* given. *Josh* 21:36
judgement is come upon Holon and
J. *Jer* 48:21

jailer

charging the *j.* to keep. *Acts* 16:23

Jair

J. took the small towns. *Num* 32:41
Deut 3:14
J. the Gileadite judged. *Judg* 10:3
J. died. 5
Segub begat *J.* *1 Chr* 2:22
Elhanan the son of *J.* slew. 20:5
Mordecai the son of *J.* *Esth* 2:5

Jairus

J. a ruler of the synagogue.
Mark 5:22; *Luke* 8:41

Jakeh, *see* **Agur**

Jambres

as Jannes and *J.* withstood Moses.
2 Tim 3:8

James

saw two brethren *J.* and John.
Mat 4:21; *Mark* 1:19
J. the son of Zebedee. *Mat* 10:2
Mark 3:17
J. the son of Alpheus. *Mat* 10:3
Mark 3:18; *Acts* 1:13
and his brethren *J.* and Joses.
Mat 13:55; *Mark* 6:3
after six days Jesus taketh Peter, *J.*
and John. *Mat* 17:1; *Mark* 5:37
9:2; 14:33; *Luke* 8:51
Mary mother of *J.* *Mat* 27:56
Mark 15:40; 16:1; *Luke* 24:10
much displeased with *J.* *Mark* 10:41
Peter, *J.* and John asked him. 13:3
J. was astonished at. *Luke* 5:10
abode both Peter, *J.* and. *Acts* 1:13
Herod killed *J.* brother of. 12:2
Peter said, shew these things to *J.* 17
J. answered, saying, Hearken. 15:13
Paul went in with us unto *J.* 21:18
after that was seen of *J.* *1 Cor* 15:7
save *J.* the Lord's brother. *Gal* 1:19
J. perceived the grace given. 2:9
before certain came from *J.* did. 12

jangling

turned aside to vain *j.* *1 Tim* 1:6

Janna

Melchi the son of *J.* *Luke* 3:24

Jannes, *see* **Jambres**

Japheth

J. the sons of Noah. *Gen* 5:32
6:10; 7:13; 9:18; *1 Chr* 1:4
Shem and *J.* took a garment and.
Gen 9:23
God shall enlarge *J.* he shall. 27
unto *J.* were sons born. 10:1
1 Chr 1:4, 5
Eber, brother of *J.* *Gen* 10:21

Jareb

saw, and sent to king *J.* *Hos* 5:13
for a present to king *J.* 10:6

Jared

begat *J.* *Gen* 5:15; *Luke* 3:37

Jasher

written in the book of *J.* *Josh* 10:13
2 Sam 1:18

Jashubites

the family of the *J.* *Num* 26:24

Jason

assaulted the house of *J.* *Acts* 17:5
they drew *J.* 6
whom *J.* hath received. 7
had taken security of *J.* 9
Lucius, *J.* and Sosipater. *Rom* 16:21

jasper

fourth row an onyx and a *j.*
Ex 28:20; 39:13
topaz, the diamond and *j.* *Ezek* 28:13
was to look upon like a *j.* *Rev* 4:3
light was like to a *j.* stone. 21:11
of the wall of city was of *j.* 18
stones, the first foundation was *j.* 19

Javan

sons of Japheth, *J.*, Tubal. *Gen* 10:2
1 Chr 1:5
those that escape to *J.* *Isa* 66:19
J. and Tubal were. *Ezek* 27:13, 19

javelin

(*A variety of spear. Revisions use the general word* spear)
and Phinehas took a *j.* *Num* 25:7
there was a *j.* in Saul's hand.
1 Sam 18:10; 19:9
Saul cast the *j.* for he said. 18:11
he smote the *j.* into the wall. 19:10

jaw

an hollow place in the *j.* *Judg* 15:19*
canst thou bore his *j.*? *Job* 41:2

jawbone

Samson found a new *j.* *Judg* 15:15
with the *j.* of an ass have. 16
he cast away the *j.* out of his. 17

jaws

and I brake the *j.* of. *Job* 29:17
tongue cleaveth to my *j.* *Ps* 22:15
shall be a bridle in *j.* *Isa* 30:28
off the yoke on their *j.* *Hos* 11:4

jaw teeth

their *j. teeth* as knives. *Pr* 30:14

Jazer

saw the land of *J.* *Num* 32:1, 3
are come even unto *J.* *Isa* 16:8
I will bewail with weeping of *J.* 9

jealous

Lord thy God am a *j.* God. *Ex* 20:5
34:14; *Deut* 4:24; 5:9; 6:15
Josh 24:19
j. of his wife. *Num* 5:14, 30
j. for Lord of hosts. *1 Ki* 19:10, 14
and will be *j.* for my. *Ezek* 39:25
will the Lord be *j.* for. *Joel* 2:18
God is *j.* and the Lord. *Nah* 1:2
I am *j.* for Jerusalem. *Zech* 1:14
was *j.* for Zion. 8:2
for I am *j.* over you. *2 Cor* 11:2

jealousies

is law of *j.* when a wife. *Num* 5:29

jealousy

(*In addition to its modern meaning this word also used to mean zeal, solicitude*)
the spirit of *j.* come. *Num* 5:14, 30
for it is an offering of *j.* and. 15, 18

then priest shall take *j.* offering.
Num 5:25
consumed not Israel in my *j.* 25:11
j. shall smoke against. *Deut* 29:20
they provoked him to *j.* 32:16
1 Ki 14:22
moved me to *j.*: I will move them to *j.* *Deut* 32:21
they moved him to *j.* *Ps* 78:58
how long, Lord, shall thy *j.*? 79:5
for *j.* is the rage of man. *Pr* 6:34
j. is cruel as the grave. *S of S* 8:6
he shall stir up *j.* like. *Isa* 42:13
seat of the image of *j.*? *Ezek* 8:3
gate of altar this image of *j.* in. 5
give thee blood in fury and *j.* 16:38
my *j.* shall depart from thee. 42
I will set my *j.* against thee. 23:25
in the fire of *j.* have I spoken. 36:5
6; 38:19
whose land devoured by fire of his *j.*
Zeph 1:18; 3:8
for Zion with great *j.* *Zech* 1:14; 8:2
provoke you to *j.* by them.*Rom* 10:19
Gentiles, to provoke them to *j.* 11:11
provoke the Lord to *j.*? *1 Cor* 10:22
over you with godly *j.* *2 Cor* 11:2

Jebusite
Canaan begat the *J.* *Gen* 10:16
1 Chr 1:14
drive out the *J.* *Ex* 33:2; 34:11
the threshingplace of Araunah the *J.*
2 Sam 24:16; *1 Chr* 21:15
Judah, and Ekron as a *J.* *Zech* 9:7

Jebusites
the *J.* dwell in the. *Num* 13:29
J. dwell with the children of Judah.
Josh 15:63
drive *J.* that inhabited. *Judg* 1:21
turn into this city of the *J.* 19:11
up and smiteth the *J.* *2 Sam* 5:8
see **Hittites**

Jeconiah
sons of Jehoiakim, *J.* *1 Chr* 3:16
the sons of *J.* Assir and. 17
away captive *J.* *Jer* 24:1; 27:20
will bring again to this place *J.* 28:4

Jedidiah
called Solomon *J.* *2 Sam* 12:24, 25

Jeduthun
Heman and *J.* to give. *1 Chr* 16:41
the sons of *J.* 42; 25:3; *2 Chr* 29:14
the king's order to *J.* *1 Chr* 25:6

Jegar-sahadutha
Laban called the heap *J.* *Gen* 31:47

Jehoahaz, *called* **Ahaziah**
J. son of Jehu reigned. *2 Ki* 10:35
J. son of Jehu began to reign. 13:1
people of the land took *J.* the son of Josiah. 23:30; *2 Chr* 36:1
Pharaoh-necho took *J.* away.
2 Ki 23:34; *2 Chr* 36:4
never a son save *J.* *2 Chr* 21:17

Jehoash, *or* **Joash**
J. seven years old when. *2 Ki* 11:21
J. did what was right in sight. 12:2
J. sent all the hallowed things. 18
his servant slew *J.* in the house. 20
J. the son of Jehoahaz. 13:10
sent messengers to *J.* 14:8
J. slept with his fathers and. 16

Jehoiachin
J. was 18 years old. *2 Ki* 24:8
J. king of Judah went to. 12
up the head of *J.* 25:27; *Jer* 52:31
J. was eight years old. *2 Chr* 36:9

Jehoiada
Benaiah the son of *J.* *2 Sam* 8:18
20:23; 23:20, 22; *1 Chr* 11:22, 24
18:17
king sent Benaiah son of *J.* *1 Ki* 1:44
Benaiah the son of *J.* was over. 4:4
J. made a covenant. *2 Ki* 11:17
2 Chr 23:16
J. the priest instructed. *2 Ki* 12:2
J. was leader of the. *1 Chr* 12:27
after Ahithophel was *J.* a. 27:34
right all the days of *J.* *2 Chr* 24:2
after the death of *J.* came the. 17
remembered not the kindness *J.* 22
for the blood of the sons of *J.* 25

old gate repaired *J.* son. *Neh* 3:6
thee priest instead of *J.* *Jer* 29:26

Jehoiakim
turned his name to *J.* *2 Ki* 23:34
2 Chr 36:4
J. gave silver and gold. *2 Ki* 23:35
J. became his servant three. 24:1
the Lord concerning *J.* *Jer* 22:18
J. sent men after Urijah into. 26:22
the roll which *J.* the king. 36:28
thus saith the Lord of *J.* king of. 30
Zedekiah did what was evil as *J.*
52:2
and the Lord gave *J.* *Dan* 1:2

Jehonadab
lighted on *J.* the son. *2 Ki* 10:15
Jehu and *J.* went into the house. 23

Jehoram
J. son of Jehoshaphat. *1 Ki* 22:50
2 Ki 8:16
J. the son of Ahab. *2 Ki* 1:17
Elishama and *J.* priests. *2 Chr* 17:8
J. went forth and smote the. 21:9
the Lord stirred up against *J.* 16
went with *J.* to war against. 22:5
Ahaziah went out with *J.* against. 7

Jehoshaphat
J. the son of Ahilud. *2 Sam* 8:16, 20
24; *1 Ki* 4:3; *1 Chr* 18:15
J. son of Paruah was. *1 Ki* 4:17
J. the son of Asa. 15:24; *2 Chr* 17:1
J. came down to Ahab. *1 Ki* 22:2
Ahab and *J.* sat each on his throne.
10; *2 Chr* 18:9
J. went up to Ramoth-gilead.
1 Ki 22:29; *2 Chr* 18:28
J. cried out. *1 Ki* 22:32
J. slept with his fathers. 50
let my servants go, but *J.* would. 49
I regard presence of *J.* *2 Ki* 3:14
look out there Jehu the son of *J.* 9:2
J. blew with trumpet. *1 Chr* 15:24
Lord was with *J.* because. *2 Chr* 17:3
they made no war against *J.* 10
J. waxed great exceedingly. 12
J. had riches and honour in. 18:1
J. feared and set himself to. 20:3
returned, and *J.* in the forefront. 27
after this did *J.* join with Ahaziah. 35
Eliezer prophesied against *J.* 37
walked in the ways of *J.* 21:12
said they, He is the son of *J.* 22:9
down to the valley of *J.* *Joel* 3:2
come up to the valley of *J.* 12

Jehoshua
Oshea, son of Nun, *J.* *Num* 13:16
Non his son, *J.* his son. *1 Chr* 7:27

Jehovah
by my name *J.* was I not. *Ex* 6:3
whose name alone is *J.* *Ps* 83:18
Lord *J.* is my strength. *Isa* 12:2
Lord *J.* is everlasting strength. 26:4

Jehovah-jireh
called the name of the place *J.*
Gen 22:14

Jehovah-nissi
name of the altar *J.* *Ex* 17:15

Jehovah-shalom
and called the altar *J.* *Judg* 6:24

Jehu
J. son of Hanani. *1 Ki* 16:1, 7, 12
J. son of Nimshi shalt thou. 19:16
J. slay; that escapeth sword of *J.* 17
look out there *J.* *2 Ki* 9:2
J. is king. 13
J. son of Nimshi conspired. 14
a watchman spied company of *J.* 17
driving is like the driving of *J.* 20
J. drew a bow with his full. 24
J. slew all that remained of. 10:11
Ahab served Baal, *J.* shall serve. 18
J. departed not from the sins. 29
J. took no heed to walk in the. 31
word which he spake to *J.* 15:12
Obed begat *J.* and *J.* *1 Chr* 2:38
J. son of Josibiah. 4:35
J. son of Azmaveth. 12:3
J. went out to meet. *2 Chr* 19:2
written in the book of *J.* son. 20:34
J. was executing judgement. 22:8
the blood of Jezreel on *J.* *Hos* 1:4

jeoparded
were people that *j.* their. *Judg* 5:18

jeopardy
went in *j.* of their lives. *2 Sam* 23:17
1 Chr 11:19
will fall to Saul, to *j.* *1 Chr* 12:19
with water, and were in *j.* *Luke* 8:23
and why stand we in *j.*? *1 Cor* 15:30

Jephthah
J. the Gileadite was a mighty . . . and Gilead begat *J.* *Judg* 11:1
J. fled from his brethren, and. 3
J. uttered all his words before. 11
hearkened not to words of *J.* 28
the Spirit came on *J.* 29
J. vowed a vow. 30
to lament the daughter of *J.* 40
J. judged Israel six years, then died *J.* 12:7
the Lord sent *J.* and. *1 Sam* 12:11
would fail me to tell of *J.* *Heb* 11:32

Jephunneh
Caleb the son of *J.* *Num* 13:6
the sons of Jether, *J.* *1 Chr* 7:38
see **Caleb**

Jerahmeel
Hezron, *J.* and Ram. *1 Chr* 2:9
the sons of *J.* 33
J. the son of Kish. 24:29
king commanded *J.* to. *Jer* 36:26

Jeremiah
Hamutal, the daughter of *J.* of.
2 Ki 23:31; 24:18; *Jer* 52:1
J. a mighty. *1 Chr* 5:24; 12:4, 10, 13
and *J.* lamented for. *2 Chr* 35:25
humbled not himself before *J.* 36:12
of Lord by the mouth of *J.* till land enjoyed her. 21, 22; *Ezra* 1:1
Azariah, *J.* sealed the. *Neh* 10:2
Seraiah, *J.* went up with. 12:1
days of Joiakim, of *J.*, Hananiah. 12
J. and Shemaiah went after. 34
the words of *J.* the son. *Jer* 1:1
the word that came to *J.* 7:1; 11:1
14:1; 18:1
devise devices against *J.* 18:18
Pashur smote *J.* and put him. 20:2
the Lord, What seest thou, *J.*? 24:3
people were gathered against *J.* 26:9
the hand of Ahikam was with *J.* 24
yoke from the prophet *J.* 28:10
why hast thou not reproved *J.*? 29:27
J. was shut up in court of. 32:2
J. spake all these words to. 34:6
Jaazaniah the son of *J.* 35:3
said, Go hide thee, thou and *J.* 36:19
Lord hid Baruch the scribe and *J.* 26
J. came in and went out. 37:4
so Irijah took *J.* and brought. 14
princes were wroth with *J.* 15
when *J.* was entered into the. 16
to commit *J.* into the court of. 21
they cast *J.* into the dungeon. 38:6
drew up *J.* with cords out of the. 13
the king sware secretly to *J.* 16
gave charge concerning *J.* 39:11
then went *J.* to Gedaliah son of. 40:6
J. wrote in a book all the evil. 51:60
thus far are the words of *J.* 64
was spoken by *J.* *Mat* 2:17; 27:9
others say Thou art *J.* or one. 16:14

Jericho
go view *J.* *Josh* 2:1
passed over right against *J.* 3:16
J. was straitly shut up. 6:1
I have given into thine hand *J.* 2
the man that buildeth the city *J.* 26
Joshua sent men from *J.* to. 7:2
to *J.* and the men of *J.* fought. 24:11
tarry at *J.* till your beard be grown.
2 Sam 10:5; *1 Chr* 19:5
days did Hiel build *J.* *1 Ki* 16:34
Lord hath sent me to *J.* *2 Ki* 2:4
Chaldees overtook him in the plains of *J.* 25:5; *Jer* 39:5; 52:8
the captives to *J.* *2 Chr* 28:15
man went down to *J.* *Luke* 10:30
by faith the walls of *J.* *Heb* 11:30

Jeroboam
J. was a mighty man of. *1 Ki* 11:28
Solomon sought to kill *J.* and *J.* 40
J. dwelt in Egypt. 12:2

J. was come again. *1 Ki* 12:20
J. built Shechem and dwelt. 25
J. ordained a feast in the eighth. 32
J. stood by the altar to burn. 13:1
after this *J.* returned not from. 33
became sin to the house of *J.* 34
at that time Abijah the son of *J.* 14:1
come in, thou wife of *J.* 6
bring evil upon the house of *J.* 10
him that dieth of *J.* shall the. 11
for he only of *J.* shall come to. 13
of the sins of *J.* 16; 15:30
between Rehoboam and *J.* 14:30
Baasha left not to *J.* any. 15:29
evil and walked in the way of *J.* 34
2 Ki 10:31; 13:6; 14:24; 17:22
J. son of Joash sat on. *2 Ki* 13:13
saved Israel by the hand of *J.* 14:27
J. drave Israel from following. 17:21
genealogies in days of *J.* *1 Chr* 5:17
J. had cast off Levites. *2 Chr* 11:14
golden calf which *J.* made for. 13:8
God smote *J.* and all Israel. 15
neither did *J.* recover strength. 20
prophesied in the days of *J.* *Hos* 1:1
Amos 1:1
rise against house of *J.* *Amos* 7:9
thus Amos saith, *J.* shall die. 11

Jeroboam joined with *Nebat*
J. son of *Nebat* lifted. *1 Ki* 11:26
spake by Ahijah the Shilonite to *J.* son of *Nebat.* 12:15; *2 Chr* 10:15
like house of *J.* the son of *Nebat.*
1 Ki 16:3; 21:22; *2 Ki* 9:9
in all the way of *J.* the son of *Nebat.*
1 Ki 16:26, 31; 22:52; *2 Ki* 3:3
Jehu departed not from the sins of *J.* son of *Nebat.* *2 Ki* 10:29; 13:2
11; 14:24; 15:9, 18, 24, 28

Jerubbaal
he called him *J.* saying. *Judg* 6:32
then *J.* (who is Gideon) rose up. 7:1
and *J.* went and dwelt in his. 8:29
they kindness to the house of *J.* 35
either that all sons of *J.* reign. 9:2
slew his brethren the sons of *J.* 5
if ye dealt well with *J.* 16
if sincerely with *J.* 19
is not he the son of *J.*? 28
the Lord sent *J.* and. *1 Sam* 12:11

Jerubbesheth
Abimelech son of *J.* *2 Sam* 11:21

Jerusalem, *or* **Hierusalem**
Jebusi, which is *J.* *Josh* 18:28
Judg 19:10
Goliath's head to *J.* *1 Sam* 17:54
and his men went to *J.* *2 Sam* 5:6
the shields of gold to *J.* 8:7
all the people returned to *J.* 12:31
shall bring me again to *J.* 15:8
carried the ark of God again to *J.* 29
my lord went out of *J.* 19:19
they came to *J.* at the end of. 24:8
stretched out his hand on *J.* to. 16
1 Chr 21:15
of building the wall of *J.* *1 Ki* 3:1
she came to *J.* with a very. 10:2
for *J.*'s sake which I have chosen.
11:13; *2 Chr* 6:6
him and to establish *J.* *1 Ki* 15:4
country, that Lord should deliver *J.*
2 Ki 18:35; *Isa* 36:20
out of *J.* shall go forth a remnant.
2 Ki 19:31; *Isa* 37:32
bring such evil upon *J.* *2 Ki* 21:12
I will wipe *J.* as a man wipeth a. 13
blood till he had filled *J.* 16; 24:4
I will cast off *J.* when. *2 Ki* 23:27
he carried away all *J.* and. 24:14
burnt all the houses of *J.* 25:9
not be poured on *J.* *2 Chr* 12:7
came to *J.* with psalteries. 20:28
wrath was upon *J.* 24:18; 29:8
32:25
altars in every corner of *J.* 28:24
spake against the God of *J.* 32:19
Josiah began to purge *J.* from. 34:3
to inquire concerning *J.* *Ezra* 7:14
thou before the God of *J.* 19
so I came to *J.* *Neh* 2:11; 7:6; 13:7
merchants lodged without *J.* 13:20
Zion, build thou walls of *J.* *Ps* 51:18
the heathen have laid *J.* on. *Ps* 79:1
have they shed round about *J.* 3
J. is builded as a city. 122:3
pray for the peace of *J.* they. 6
mountains are round about *J.* 125:2
thou shalt see the good of *J.* 128:5
if I prefer not *J.* above my. 137:6
children of Edom in the day of *J.* 7
the Lord doth build up *J.* he. 147:2
comely, O my love, as *J.* *S of S* 6:4
he saw concerning *J.* *Isa* 1:1; 2:1
for *J.* is ruined. 3:8
have purged the blood of *J.* 4:4
so will I do to *J.* 10:11
performed whole work on *J.* 12
numbered the houses of *J.* 22:10
Lord of hosts defend *J.* 31:5
thine eyes see *J.* a quiet. 33:20
speak ye comfortably to *J.* 40:2
give to *J.* one that bringeth. 41:27
that saith to *J.* Thou shalt. 44:26
of *J.* for Lord hath comforted his people, he hath redeemed *J.* 52:9
for *J.*'s sake I will not rest till. 62:1
give him no rest till he make *J.* 7
Zion is a wilderness, *J.* a. 64:10
for behold, I create *J.* a. 65:18
rejoice ye with *J.* and be glad. 66:10
and cry in the ears of *J.* *Jer* 2:2
they shall call *J.* the throne of. 3:17
fro through the streets of *J.* 5:1
to flee out of the midst of *J.* 6:1
why then is this people of *J.*? 8:5
I will make *J.* heaps, and a. 9:11
words in the streets of *J.* 11:6
great pride of Judah and *J.* 13:9
Judah mourneth, the cry of *J.* 14:2
come from the places about *J.* 17:26
make void the counsel of *J.* 19:7
the houses of *J.* shall be defiled. 13
have seen in prophets of *J.* an. 23:14
J. shall become heaps. 26:18
Mi 3:12
about *J.* shall flocks pass. *Jer* 33:13
in those days *J.* shall dwell. 16
let us go to *J.* for fear of. 35:11
till day that *J.* was taken. 38:28
brake down the walls of *J.* 39:8
the evil I have brought on *J.* 44:2
was kindled in the streets of *J.* 6
let *J.* come into your mind. 51:50
J. hath grievously sinned. *Lam* 1:8
J. is as a menstruous woman. 17
this is *J.* *Ezek* 5:5
go through the midst of *J.* 9:4
son of man cause *J.* to know. 16:2
of Babylon is come to *J.* 17:12
sword may come to Judah in *J.* 21:20
right hand the divination for *J.* 22
gather you into the midst of *J.* 22:19
one that had escaped out of *J.* 33:21
flock of *J.* in her solemn. 36:38
being open toward *J.* *Dan* 6:10
as hath been done upon *J.* 9:12
of the commandment to build *J.* 25
again the captivity of *J.* *Joel* 3:1
then shall *J.* be holy. 17
J. shall dwell. 20
entered and cast lots upon *J.* *Ob* 11
are they not *J.*? *Mi* 1:5
build up Zion with blood, *J.* 3:10
search *J.* with candles. *Zeph* 1:12
not have mercy on *J.*? *Zech* 1:12
I am jealous for *J.* and Zion. 14
comfort Zion, and choose *J.* 17; 2:12
horns which have scattered *J.* 1:19
goest thou? I go to measure *J.* 2:2
J. shall be inhabited as towns. 4
I will dwell in the midst of *J.* 8:3
have I thought to do well to *J.* 15
behold, I will make *J.* a cup. 12:2
make *J.* a burdensome stone. 3
J. shall be safely inhabited. 14:11
the offering of *J.* shall be. *Mal* 3:4
then went out to him *J.* *Mat* 3:5
Mark 1:5
neither swear by *J.* *Mat* 5:35
to shew how he must go to *J.* 16:21
when he was come into *J.* 21:10
parents brought him to *J.* *Luke* 2:22
they turned back again to *J.* 45
a great multitude out of *J.* 6:17
as though he would go to *J.* 9:53
that a prophet perish out of *J.* 13:33
because he was nigh to *J.* *Luke* 19:11
ye shall see *J.* compassed. 21:20
J. shall be trodden down of the. 24
tarry ye in *J.* till ye be. 24:49
and they returned to *J.* with. 52
Jesus was coming to *J.* *John* 12:12
ye have filled *J.* with. *Acts* 5:28
might bring them bound unto *J.* 9:2
bound in the Spirit to *J.* 20:22
tidings came that all *J.* was. 21:31
get thee quickly out of *J.* 22:18
him whether he would go to *J.*? 25:20
that my service for *J.* *Rom* 15:31
your liberality unto *J.* *1 Cor* 16:3
Agar answereth to *J.* *Gal* 4:25
J. which is above is free. 26
the new *J.* *Rev* 3:12; 21:2
the holy *J.* 21:10
see **dwell**

against **Jerusalem**
Judah had fought *ag. J.* *Judg* 1:8
Shishak came *ag. J.* *1 Ki* 14:25
2 Chr 12:9
Sennacherib *ag. J.* *2 Ki* 18:17
2 Chr 32:2
the king of Babylon came *ag. J.*
2 Ki 24:10; 25:1; *Jer* 34:1, 7
39:1; 52:4; *Ezek* 24:2
Shimshai, wrote *ag. J.* *Ezra* 4:8
to come and fight *ag. J.* *Neh* 4:8
publish *ag. J.* *Jer* 4:16
cast a mount *ag. J.* 6:6
that Tyrus hath said *ag. J.* *Ezek* 26:2
destroy nations that come *ag. J.*
Zech 12:9; 14:12

at **Jerusalem**
dwelt with Judah *at J.* *Josh* 15:63
came to his house *at J.* *2 Sam* 20:3
sacrifice in house of the Lord *at J.*
1 Ki 12:27; *2 Chr* 9:25; *Isa* 27:13
fathers dwelt *at J.* *1 Chr* 9:34, 38
to build the house of the Lord *at J.*
2 Chr 3:1; *Ezra* 1:2; 5:2
offered themselves to dwell *at J.*
Neh 11:2
this time was not I *at J.* 13:6
because of thy temple *at J.* *Ps* 68:29
the Lord who dwelleth *at J.* 135:21
shall dwell in Zion *at J.* *Isa* 30:19
into *J.*, so we dwell *at J.* *Jer* 35:11
also shall fight *at J.* *Zech* 14:14
should accomplish *at J.* *Luke* 9:31
Herod himself was also *at J.* 23:7
all nations, beginning *at J.* 24:47
nor yet *at J.* shall ye worship.
John 4:21
all things that he did *at J.* 45
to all the dwellers *at J.* *Acts* 1:19
against the church *at J.* 8:1
hath done to thy saints *at J.* 9:13
they that dwell *at J.* have. 13:27
be *at J.* the day of Pentecost. 20:16
so shall the Jews *at J.* bind. 21:11
but also to die *at J.* for the name. 13
to them of Damascus *at J.* 26:20
for the saints *at J.* *Rom* 15:26
see **daughters**

from **Jerusalem**
Shimei had gone *from J.* *1 Ki* 2:41
Hazael went away *from J.* *2 Ki* 12:18
carried into captivity *from J.* to.
24:15; *Esth* 2:6; *Jer* 24:1; 27:20
29:1; 52:29
the word of the Lord *from J.*
Isa 2:3; *Mi* 4:2
take away *from J.* the stay. *Isa* 3:1
the Lord utter his voice *from J.*
Joel 3:16; *Amos* 1:2
cut off the horse *from J.* *Zech* 9:10
waters shall go out *from J.* 14:8
followed him *from J.* *Mat* 4:25
man went down *from J.* *Luke* 10:30
which was *from J.* about sixty. 24:13
should not depart *from J.* *Acts* 1:4
way that goeth down *from J.* 8:26
there came prophets *from J.* 11:27
from J. to Illyricum I. *Rom* 15:19

in **Jerusalem**
dwell with Benjamin *in J.* *Judg* 1:21
feed thee with me *in J.* *2 Sam* 19:33
thee an house *in J.* *1 Ki* 2:36
a light alway before me *in J.* 11:36
15:

worship before this altar *in J.* *2 Ki* 18:22
Lord said, *In J.* will I put. 21:4
now Huldah dwelt *in J.* in. 22:14
these dwelt *in J. 1 Chr* 8:28, 32; 9:3
that they may dwell *in J.* 23:25
king made silver *in J.* *2 Chr* 9:27
away the altars that were *in J.* 30:14
great joy *in J.* not the like *in J.* 26
house of the Lord which is *in J.* *Ezra* 1:3
Israel, whose habitation is *in J.* 7:15
us a wall in Judah and *in J.* 9:9
no right nor memorial *in J.* *Neh* 2:20
let every one lodge *in J.* 4:22
bring one of ten to dwell *in J.* 11:1
Zion and his praises *in J.* *Ps* 102:21
that have been before me *in J.* *Eccl* 1:16; 2:7, 9
that remaineth *in J.* be. *Isa* 4:3
Lord of hosts shall reign *in J.* 24:23
scornful men that rule *in J.* 28:14
is in Zion, his furnace *in J.* 31:9
I will rejoice *in J.* and joy. 65:19
shall be comforted *in J.* 66:13
publish *in J.* and say. *Jer* 4:5
which Manasseh did *in J.* 15:4
the staff of bread *in J.* *Ezek* 4:16
in mount Zion and *in J.* *Joel* 2:32
J. be inhabited in her place, even *in J.* *Zech* 12:6
every pot *in J.* shall be. 14:21
is committed *in J.* *Mal* 2:11
a man *in J.* whose name. *Luke* 2:25
that looked for redemption *in J.* 38
Jesus tarried behind *in J.* 43
sinners above all that dwelt *in J.* 13:4
art thou only a stranger *in J.*? 24:18
in J. is the place where. *John* 4:20
shall be witnesses to me *in J.* *Acts* 1:8; 10:39
the disciples multiplied *in J.* 6:7
hast testified of me *in J.* 23:11
which thing I also did *in J.* 26:10

inhabitants of **Jerusalem**

ye *inhabitants of J.* be not afraid. *2 Chr* 20:15
Lord saved *inhabitants of J.* 32:22
inhabitants of J. did him honour. 33
inhabitants of J. did according to. 34:32
O *inhabitants of J.* judge. *Isa* 5:3
snare to *inhabitants of J.* 8:14
father to the *inhabitants of J.* 22:21
inhabitants of J. shall remain for. *Jer* 17:25
and tell Judah and *inhabitants of J.* 35:13
to whom *inhabitants of J.* have said. *Ezek* 11:15
I give the *inhabitants of J.* for. 15:6
the *inhabitants of J.* shall be my strength. *Zech* 12:5
the glory of the *inhabitants of J.* 7
shall defend the *inhabitants of J.* 8
pour upon *inhabitants of J.* the. 10
opened to the *inhabitants of J.* 13:1

O **Jerusalem**

vows in midst of thee, *O J.* *Ps* 116:19
stand within thy gates, *O J.* 122:2
if I forget thee, *O J.* 137:5
praise the Lord, *O J.* 147:12
O J. that bringest good. *Isa* 40:9
stand up, *O J.* 51:17
beautiful garments, *O J.* 52:1
arise, and sit down, *O J.* 2
O J. wash thy heart from. *Jer* 4:14
be thou instructed, *O J.* lest. 6:8
cut off thine hair, *O J.* and. 7:29
woe to thee, *O J.* Wilt thou not? 13:27
who have pity upon thee, *O J.*? 15:5
O J. J. thou that killest the prophets. *Mat* 23:37; *Luke* 13:34

up to **Jerusalem**

up with the king *to J.* *2 Sam* 19:34
for you to go *up to J.* *1 Ki* 12:28
his face to go *up to J.* *2 Ki* 12:17
Pekah came *up to J.* to war. 16:5
let him go *up to J.* *Ezra* 1:3; 7:13
we go *up to J.*; Son of man. *Mat* 20:18; *Mark* 10:33 *Luke* 18:31
the way going *up to J.* *Mark* 10:32
ascending *up to J.* *Luke* 19:28
Peter was come *up to J.* *Acts* 11:2
go *up to J.* to the apostles. 15:2
he should not go *up to J.* 21:4, 12
wilt thou go *up to J.* and ? 25:9
neither went I *up to J.* to. *Gal* 1:17
I went *up to J.* to see Peter and. 18
I went *up to J.* with Barnabas. 2:1

Jeshua

came with Zerubbabel, *J.* *Ezra* 2:2
stood up *J.* son of Jozadak. 3:2

Jeshurun

but *J.* waxed fat and. *Deut* 32:15
he was king in *J.* when Israel. 33:5
none like to the God of *J.* 26
fear not, thou *J.* whom. *Isa* 44:2

Jesse

Obed, he is the father of *J.* *Ruth* 4:17; *Mat* 1:5
Obed begat *J.* and *J.* begat David. *Ruth* 4:22; *Mat* 1:6
I will send thee to *J.* *1 Sam* 16:1
he sanctified *J.* and his sons and. 9
I have seen a son of *J.* that is. 18
Saul sent messengers unto *J.* 19
I am the son of thy servant *J.* 17:58
hast chosen the son of *J.* 20:30
as long as the son of *J.* liveth. 31
will the son of *J.* give every.? 22:7
made a league with the son of *J.* 8
Doeg said, I saw the son of *J.* 9
and who is the son of *J.*? 25:10
inheritance in son of *J.* *2 Sam* 20:1 *1 Ki* 12:16; *2 Chr* 10:16
to David the son of *J.* *1 Chr* 10:14
thine are we, thou son of *J.* 12:18
rod out of the stem of *J.* *Isa* 11:1
shall be a root of *J.* 10; *Rom* 15:12
found David the son of *J.* *Acts* 13:22

jesting

nor filthiness, nor *j.* not. *Eph* 5:4

Jesus

J. for he shall save his people from. *Mat* 1:21, 25; *Luke* 1:31; 2:21
J. was led up of the Spirit. *Mat* 4:1
from that time *J.* began to. 17
J. put forth his hand and. 8:3
when *J.* heard it, he marvelled. 10
do with thee, *J.* thou Son of God ? 29; *Mark* 1:24; 5:7; *Luke* 8:28
city came out to meet *J.* *Mat* 8:34
J. seeing their faith. 9:2
as *J.* sat at meat. 10
J. turned him about. 22
J. departed thence. 27
J. knew their thoughts. 12:25
these things spake *J.* to the. 13:24
Herod heard of the fame of *J.* 14:1
walked on the water, to go to *J.* 29
they saw no man save *J.* only. 17:8 *Mark* 9:8
J. rebuked the devil and. *Mat* 17:18
when come into the house, *J.* 25
J. called a little child to him. 18:2
two blind men heard that *J.* 20:30
J. had compassion on them. 34
is *J.* the prophet of Nazareth. 21:11
J. perceived their wickedness. 22:18
they might take *J.* by subtilty. 26:4
the disciples did as *J.* had. 19
J. took bread and. 26; *Mark* 14:22
thou also wast with *J.* *Mat* 26:69 71; *Mark* 14:67
remembered words of *J.* *Mat* 26:75
written, This is *J.* the king. 27:37
J. cried with a loud voice. 46 *Mark* 15:37
Joseph, who also himself was *J.*' disciple. *Mat* 27:57
fear not ye, I know ye seek *J.* *Mat* 28:5; *Mark* 16:6
J. met them. *Mat* 28:9
J. came and spake to them. 18
J. could no more enter. *Mark* 1:45
J. withdrew himself with his. 3:7
J. gave them leave. 5:13
J. suffered him not. 19
J. knowing that virtue had gone. 30
Elias and Moses talking with *J.* 9:4
then *J.* beholding him. 10:21
J. saw that he answered. *Mark* 12:34
bound *J.* and carried him. 15:1
in the midst before *J.* *Luke* 5:19
what they might do to *J.* 6:11
who sat at *J.*' feet and heard. 10:39
Zacchaeus sought to see *J.* who. 19:3
bear the cross after *J.* 23:26
J. himself drew near and. 24:15
they said, Is not this *J.*? *John* 6:42
that is called *J.* made clay. 9:11
J. spake of his death. 11:13
J. wept. 35
sir, we would see *J.* 12:21
when *J.* knew that his hour. 13:1
leaning on *J.*' bosom. 23
whom seek ye ? they said, *J.* 18:7
officers that stood by struck *J.* 22
came *J.* forth, wearing crown. 19:5
there stood by the cross of *J.* 25
J. knowing that all things were. 28
took the body of *J.* 40
there laid they *J.* 42
knew not that it was *J.* 20:14; 21:4
of all that *J.* began to. *Acts* 1:1
this same *J.* which is taken up. 11
was guide to them who took *J.* 16
this *J.* hath God raised up. 2:32 3:26; 5:30
hath glorified his Son *J.* 3:13
through *J.* resurrection from. 4:2
that they had been with *J.* 13
not to teach in the name of *J.* 18
against thy holy child *J.* 27
the name of thy holy child *J.* 30
not speak in the name of *J.* 5:40
this *J.* shall destroy this place. 6:14
he saw *J.* standing on the right. 7:55
Philip preached unto him *J.* 8:35
I am *J.* whom thou persecutest. 9:5 22:8; 26:15
even *J.*, that appeared to thee. 9:17
at Damascus in the name of *J.* 27
how God anointed *J.* with. 10:38
raised to Israel a Saviour *J.* 13:23
there is another king, one *J.* 17:7
because he preached *J.* and the. 18
adjure you by *J.* whom Paul. 19:13
J. I know, and Paul I know, but. 15
had questions of one *J.* who. 25:19
persuading them concerning *J.* 28:23
of him that believeth in *J.* *Rom* 3:26
Spirit of him that raised up *J.* 8:11
by Spirit calleth *J.* *1 Cor* 12:3
your servants for *J.*' sake. *2 Cor* 4:5
the life of *J.* might be made. 10
we are delivered to death for *J.* 11
J. shall raise up us also by *J.* 14
that cometh, preach another *J.* 11:4
him as the truth is in *J.* *Eph* 4:21
at name of *J.* every knee. *Phil* 2:10
J. who delivered us. *1 Thes* 1:10
them that sleep in *J.* will God. 4:14
we see *J.* who was made. *Heb* 2:9
great high priest, *J.* son. 4:14; 6:20
was *J.* made surety of better. 7:22
the holiest by the blood of *J.* 10:19
looking unto *J.* the author of. 12:2
to *J.* the Mediator of the new. 24
wherefore *J.* suffered without. 13:12
confess *J.* is Son of God. *1 John* 4:15
that *J.* is the Son of God. 5:5
that keep the faith of *J.* *Rev* 14:12
with blood of martyrs of *J.* 17:6
beheaded for the witness of *J.* 20:4
I *J.* have sent mine angel to. 22:16

see **Christ**

Jesus joined with *Lord*

all the time the *Lord J.* *Acts* 1:21
same *J.* both *Lord* and Christ. 2:36
Stephen saying, *Lord J.* 7:59
in the name of the *Lord J.* 8:16
boldly in the name of *Lord J.* 9:29
Grecians, preaching *Lord J.* 11:20
believe on the *Lord J.* Christ. 16:31
heard the word of the *Lord J.* 19:10
and the name of the *Lord J.* was. 17
the words of the *Lord J.* 20:35
Lord J. same night he. *1 Cor* 11:23
no man can say that *J.* is *Lord.* 12:3
are ours in the day of the *Lord J.* *2 Cor* 1:14
about the dying of *Lord J.* 4:10
the marks of *Lord J.* *Gal* 6:17

who both killed *Lord J. 1 Thes* 2:15
exhort you by the *Lord J.* 4:1
we gave you by *Lord J.* 2
Lord J. shall be revealed. *2 Thes* 1:7
from dead our *Lord J.* *Heb* 13:20
knowledge of *J.* our *Lord. 2 Pet* 1:2
even so, come *Lord J.* *Rev* 22:20
see **grace, name**

Jesus *said*
mind the word *J. said.* *Mark* 14:72
believed the word *J. said. John* 2:22
the same hour in which *J. said.* 4:53
when *J.* had thus *said*, he was. 13:21
yet *J. said* not unto him. 21:23

Jesus, for *Joshua*
with *J.* into possession. *Acts* 7:45
if *J.* had given them rest. *Heb* 4:8

Jesus
J. who is called Justus. *Col* 4:11

Jethro, called *Reuel*
Moses kept the flock of *J.* *Ex* 3:1
Moses returned to *J.* his. 4:18
when *J.* heard of all that God. 18:1
J. came with his sons and his wife. 5
I thy father in law *J.* am come. 6
J. rejoiced for the goodness. 9, 10
J. took a burnt offering and. 12

Jew
a certain *J.* whose name. *Esth* 2:5
told them that he was a *J.* 3:4
do even so to Mordecai the *J.* 6:10
of them, to wit, of a *J.* *Jer* 34:9
take hold of skirt of a *J. Zech* 8:23
is it that thou, being a *J.*? *John* 4:9
Pilate answered am I a *J.*? 18:35
for a man that is a *J.* *Acts* 10:28
sorcerer, a *J.* named Bar-jesus. 13:6
certain *J.* named Aquila. 18:2
a *J.* named Apollos. 24
sons of Sceva a *J.* 19:14
Alexander a *J.* 33, 34
Paul a *J.* 21:39; 22:3
to the *J.* first. *Rom* 1:16; 2:9, 10
behold, thou art called a *J.*, and. 2:17
he is not a *J.* 28
he is a *J.* who is one inwardly. 29
what advantage then hath the *J.*? 3:1
no difference between the *J.* and.
10:12; *Gal* 3:28; *Col* 3:11
to the *J.* I became as a *J. 1 Cor* 9:20
if thou being a *J.* livest as. *Gal* 2:14

Jewel
as a *j.* of gold in a. *Pr* 11:22
of knowledge are a precious *j.* 20:15
put a *j.* on thy forehead. *Ezek* 16:12*

Jewels
servant brought forth *j.* *Gen* 24:53
shall borrow *j.* of gold. *Ex* 3:22
11:2; 12:35
they brought all *j.* of gold. 35:22
Num 31:50
gold, even all wrought *j. Num* 31:51
put the *j.* of gold in. *1 Sam* 6:8, 15
riches and precious *j.* *2 Chr* 20:25
for all manner of pleasant *j.* 32:27*
of it shall not be for *j.* *Job* 28:17
comely with rows of *j. S of S* 1:10*
joints of thy thighs are like *j.* 7:1
bride adorneth herself with her *j.*
Isa 61:10
taken thy *j.* of my gold. *Ezek* 16:17
shall take thy fair *j.* 39; 23:26
with earrings and *j.* *Hos* 2:13
when I make up my *j.* *Mal* 3:17*

Jewess
Timotheus was son of a *J. Acts* 16:1
Felix' wife Drusilla was a *J.* 24:24

Jewish
not giving heed to *J.* *Tit* 1:14

Jewry
my father brought out of *J. Dan* 5:13

Jews
king Rezin drave the *J.* *2 Ki* 16:6
the *J.* are come up to. *Ezra* 4:12
I asked concerning the *J.* *Neh* 1:2
what do these feeble *J.*? 4:2
table one hundred and fifty *J.* 5:17
thou and the *J.* think to rebel. 6:6
I saw *J.* that married wives. 13:23
mourning among the *J.* *Esth* 4:3
deliverance arise unto *J.* *Esth* 4:14
Mordecai be of seed of the *J.* 6:13
laid his hand upon the *J.* 8:7
write ye for the *J.*, in king's name. 8
J. had light, and gladness. 16, 17
for the fear of the *J.* fell upon. 17
officers of the king helped the *J.* 9:3
should not fail from among *J.* 28
was great among the *J.* 10:3
said, I am afraid of the *J. Jer* 38:19
captive 3023 of the *J.* 52:28, 30
near and accused the *J.* *Dan* 3:8
is reported among the *J. Mat* 28:15
John's disciples and *J.* *John* 3:25
the *J.* have no dealings with. 4:9
salvation is of the *J.* 22
feast of the *J.* 5:1
did the *J.* persecute Jesus. 16
J. sought the more to kill him. 18
the *J.* therefore strove among. 6:52
openly of him, for fear of *J.* 7:13
the *J.* did not believe that. 9:18
the *J.* took up stones again. 10:31
master, the *J.* of late sought. 11:8
when Jesus saw her and the *J.* 33
J. went away and believed. 12:11
I taught in temple, whither *J.* 18:20
not be delivered to the *J.* 36
of Jesus as the manner of *J.* 19:40
to none, but the *J.* only. *Acts* 11:19
Herod saw it pleased the *J.* 12:3
because of the *J.* that were. 16:3
these men being *J.* do trouble. 20
J. and Greeks heard the word. 19:10
certain of the vagabond *J.* 13
the *J.* laid wait for him. 20:3, 19
so shall the *J.* at Jerusalem. 21:11
certain of the *J.* banded. 23:12
this man was taken of the *J.* 27
certain *J.* from Asia found. 24:18
to the *J.* have done no wrong. 25:10
is he God of *J.* only? *Rom* 3:29
Christ, to the *J.* a. *1 Cor* 1:23
to *J.* I became as a Jew, that. 9:20
of *J.* five times received. *2 Cor* 11:24
and not as do the *J.* *Gal* 2:14
we who are *J.* by nature, and. 15
have suffered of the *J. 1 Thes* 2:14
which say they are *J.* and are not.
Rev 2:9; 3:9
see **Gentiles**

all the **Jews**
Haman sought to destroy *all the J.*
Esth 3:6, 13
more than *all the J.* 4:13
go, gather *all the J.* 16
when *all the J.* in Moab. *Jer* 40:11
even *all the J.* returned out of. 12
Ishmael slew *all the J.* that. 41:3
the word concerning *all the J.* 44:1
all the J. except they wash, they.
Mark 7:3
all the Jews to depart. *Acts* 18:2
this was known to *all the J.* 19:17
thou teachest *all the J.* to. 21:21
a good report of *all the J.* 22:12
of sedition among *all the J.* 24:5
manner of life at Jerusalem know *all the J.* 26:4

King of the **Jews**
that is born *King of the J.*? *Mat* 2:2
Jesus, Art thou *King of the J.*?
27:11; *Mark* 15:2; *Luke* 23:3
John 18:33
Hail, *King of the J.* *Mat* 27:29
Mark 15:18; *John* 19:3
accusation, This is the *King of the Jews.* *Mat* 27:37; *Mark* 15:26
Luke 23:38; *John* 19:19
will ye that I release to you *King of the J.*? *Mark* 15:9; *John* 18:39
call the *King of the J.*? *Mark* 15:12
if thou be the *King of the J.* save thyself. *Luke* 23:37
the *King of the J.* but that he said, I am *King of the J.* *John* 19:21

Jezebel
Ahab took to wife *J.* *1 Ki* 16:31
when *J.* cut off the prophets. 18:4
when *J.* slew the prophets of. 13
of Baal which eat at *J.'s* table. 19
Ahab told *J.* all that Elijah. 19:1
the elders did as *J.* had sent. 21:11
when *J.* heard Naboth. *1 Ki* 21:15
dogs shall eat *J.* 23; *2 Ki* 9:10, 36
none like Ahab, whom *J. 1 Ki* 21:25
avenge at the hand of *J.* *2 Ki* 9:7
whoredoms of thy mother *J.* 22
J. shall be as dung upon face of field, so they shall not say, this is *J.* 37
sufferest that woman *J.* *Rev* 2:20

Jezreel, name of place and person
pitched in the valley of *J. Judg* 6:33
also took Ahinoam of *J. 1 Sam* 25:43
by a fountain which is in *J.* 29:1
Ish-bosheth king over *J.* *2 Sam* 2:9
rode and went to *J.* *1 Ki* 18:45
before Ahab to entrance of *J.* 46
a vineyard which was in *J.* 21:1
dogs shall eat Jezebel by the wall of *J.* 23; *2 Ki* 9:10, 36
Joram went back to *J.* *2 Ki* 8:29
2 Chr 22:6
in a chariot and went to *J. 2 Ki* 9:16
come to me to *J.* by to-morrow. 10:6
heads of the king's sons to *J.* 7
of the father of Etam, *J.* *1 Chr* 4:3
call his name *J.* for I will avenge the blood of *J.* on house. *Hos* 1:4
break bow of Israel in valley of *J.* 5
for great shall be the day of *J.* 11
wine and oil shall hear *J.* 2:22

Jezreelite, *see* **Naboth**

Joab
three sons of Zeruiah, *J. 2 Sam* 2:18
should I hold up my face to *J.*? 22
J. also and Abishai pursued. 24
of Abner rest on the head of *J.* 3:29
so *J.* and Abishai his brother. 30
J. son of Zeruiah was. 8:16; 20:23
1 Chr 11:6; 18:15; 27:34
demanded of Uriah how *J.* did.
2 Sam 11:7
abide in tents, and my lord *J.* 11
David wrote a letter to *J.* 14
J. fought against Rabbah of. 12:26
J. put the words in widow's. 14:3
is not the hand of *J.* with thee? 19
Absalom sent for *J.* 29
J.'s field is near. 30
J. killed Amasa. 20:9
woman said, Art thou *J.*? 17
the king's word prevailed against *J.*
24:4; *1 Chr* 21:4
Adonijah conferred with *J. 1 Ki* 1:7
moreover thou knowest what *J.* 2:5
J. fled to tabernacle of Lord. 28
six months *J.* remain, every. 11:16
Seraiah begat *J.* *1 Chr* 4:14
J. led the army. 20:1
word was abominable to *J.* 21:6
all that Abner and *J.* had. 26:28
of children of Jeshua and *J.*
Ezra 2:6; *Neh* 7:11
of the sons of *J.* Obadiah. *Ezra* 8:9

Joah
J. son of Asaph the recorder.
2 Ki 18:18; *Isa* 36:3
J. son of Zimmah. *1 Chr* 6:21
J. son of Obed-edom. 26:4

Joanna
which was the son of *J.* *Luke* 3:27
J. the wife of Chuza, Herod's. 8:3
J. and Mary 24:10

Joash
that pertaineth to *J.* the. *Judg* 6:11
sword of Gideon the son of *J.* 7:14
carry him back to Amon and *J.* the.
1 Ki 22:26; *2 Chr* 18:25
Jehosheba stole *J.* *2 Ki* 11:2
2 Chr 22:11
J. the son of Jehoahaz. *2 Ki* 13:9
J. the king of Israel wept over. 14
J. beat Ben-hadad three times. 25
of Jeroboam the son of *J.* 14:27
Becher, Zemira, and *J.* *1 Chr* 7:8
J. the son of Shemaiah the. 12:3
over the cellars of oil was *J.* 27:28
J. remembered not the. *2 Chr* 24:22
executed judgement against *J.* 24

Job
the sons of Issachar, *J.* *Gen* 46:13
Uz whose name was *J.* *Job* 1:1
considered my servant *J.*? 8; 2:3
Satan said, Doth *J.* fear God? 1:9

J. sinned not with his lips. *Job* 1:22; 2:10
Satan went and smote *J.* with. 2:7
three men ceased to answer *J.* 32:1
against *J.* was Elihu's wrath. 2
no answer and condemned *J.* 3
none of you that convinced *J.* 12
mark well, O *J.* hearken. 33:31
man is like *J.* who drinketh? 34:7
J. hath spoken without. 35
my desire is that *J.* may be tried. 36
doth *J.* open his mouth in vain? 35:16
spoken as my servant *J.* hath. 42:7, 8
bullocks and go to my servant *J.* 8
the Lord also accepted *J.* 9
the Lord gave *J.* twice as much. 10
Lord blessed the latter end of *J.* 12
so fair as the daughters of *J.* 15
after this lived *J.* 140 years. 16
so *J.* died, being old and full. 17
Noah, Daniel and *J.* *Ezek* 14:14, 20
heard of the patience of *J.* *Jas* 5:11

Joel
Samuel's firstborn was *J.* *1 Sam* 8:2
Simeon, *J.* and Jehu. *1 Chr* 4:35
Reubenites, the sons of *J.* 5:4, 8
of the Gadites, *J.* the chief, and. 12
Heman, a singer, son of *J.* 6:33
Elkanah the son of *J.* a. 36
Michael, Obadiah and *J.* 7:3
J. and Mibhar were valiant. 11:38
of the sons of Gershom, *J.* 15:7
David called for Isaiah and *J.* 11
Laadan, the chief was *J.* 23:8
Jehuli, Zetham and *J.* 26:22
half tribe of Manasseh, *J.* 27:20
J. and Benaiah had. *Ezra* 10:43
J. son of Zichri was. *Neh* 11:9
word came to *J.* the son. *Joel* 1:1
spoken by the prophet *J.* *Acts* 2:16

Johanan
J. came to Gedaliah. *2 Ki* 25:23
Jer 40:8, 13
Josiah, the firstborn *J.* *1 Chr* 3:15
into the chamber of *J.* *Ezra* 10:6
but when *J.* heard of all. *Jer* 41:11
so *J.* obeyed not the voice of. 43:4

John son of *Zacharias*
J. had raiment of camel's hair.
Mat 3:4; *Mark* 1:6
came to be baptized, but *J.* *Mat* 3:14
when *J.* was cast into prison. 4:12
Mark 1:14
then came to him the disciples of *J.*
Mat 9:14; *Mark* 2:18; *Luke* 5:33
7:18; 11:1; *John* 3:25
J. had heard the works of Christ.
Mat 11:2; *Luke* 7:19
go and shew *J.* these things.
Mat 11:4; *Luke* 7:22
Jesus began to say concerning *J.*
Mat 11:7; *Luke* 7:24
the law prophesied till *J.* *Mat* 11:13
Luke 16:16
Herod beheaded *J.* *Mat* 14:10
Mark 6:16; *Luke* 9:9
all hold *J.* as a prophet. *Mat* 21:26
Mark 11:32; *Luke* 20:6
J. came in way of righteousness.
Mat 21:32
Herod feared *J.* knowing. *Mark* 6:20
thou shalt call his name *J.*
Luke 1:13, 60
mused in their hearts of *J.* 3:15
it was said, that *J.* was risen. 9:7
a man, whose name was *J.* *John* 1:6
and this is the record of *J.* 19, 32
next day *J.* seeth Jesus coming. 29
J. also was baptizing in Enon. 3:23
for *J.* was not yet cast into. 24
made more disciples than *J.* 4:1
sent to *J.* and he bare witness. 5:33
greater witness than that of *J.* 36
J. did no miracle; but all that *J.* spake. 10:41
for *J.* truly baptized with water.
Acts 1:5; 11:16
J. had first preached before. 13:24
and as *J.* fulfilled his course, he. 25
see **baptism, baptist**

John *the apostle*
James and *J.* the sons of. *Mat* 4:21
10:2; *Mark* 1:19; 3:17
Jesus sent Peter and *J.* *Luke* 22:8
Peter and *J.* went up. *Acts* 3:1
lame man held Peter and *J.* 11
the boldness of Peter and *J.* 4:13
sent to Samaria Peter and *J.* 8:14
James the brother of *J.* 12:2
his angel to his servant *J.* *Rev* 1:1
J. to the seven churches which. 4
J. who also am your brother. 9:1
I *J.* saw the holy city. 21:2
see **James**

John
J. and Alexander. *Acts* 4:6

John, surnamed *Mark*
Peter came to house of *J.* *Acts* 12:12
with them *J.* whose surname. 25
and they had also *J.* to their. 13:5
J. departing from them, returned. 13
to take with them *J.* 15:37

join
they *j.* to our enemies. *Ex* 1:10
did Jehoshaphat *j.* *2 Chr* 20:35
and *j.* in affinity with. *Ezra* 9:14
hand *j.* in hand. *Pr* 11:21; 16:5
woe to them that *j.* house. *Isa* 5:8
the Lord shall *j.* his enemies. 9:11*
sons of stranger that *j.* 56:6
come, let us *j.* ourselves. *Jer* 50:5
j. them one to another. *Ezek* 37:17
they shall *j.* in the end. *Dan* 11:6
the rest durst no man *j.* *Acts* 5:13
go near and *j.* thyself to this. 8:29
Saul assayed to *j.* himself. 9:26

joined
kings were *j.* together in. *Gen* 14:3
they *j.* battle with them in the. 8*
will my husband be *j.* to me. 29:34
of Levi be *j.* to thee. *Num* 18:2, 4
they *j.* battle, Israel. *1 Sam* 4:2
day the battle was *j.* *1 Ki* 20:29
Jehoshaphat *j.* affinity. *2 Chr* 18:1
he *j.* with Ahaziah to. 20:36, 37
set up walls, and *j.* the. *Ezra* 4:12*
all the wall was *j.* *Neh* 4:6
j. should keep these days. *Esth* 9:27
let it not be *j.* to the days. *Job* 3:6*
Leviathan's scales are *j.* one. 41:17
the flakes of his flesh are *j.* 23
Assur also is *j.* with them. *Ps* 83:8
to him that is *j.* to all. *Eccl* 9:4
every one *j.* to them. *Isa* 13:15*
and the strangers shall be *j.* 14:1
thou shalt not be *j.* with them. 20
nor him that hath *j.* to the. 56:3
their wings were *j.* one. *Ezek* 1:9
were courts *j.* of forty. 46:22*
Ephraim is *j.* to idols. *Hos* 4:17
many nations shall be *j.* *Zech* 2:11
what God hath *j.* together.
Mat 19:6; *Mark* 10:9
he went and *j.* himself. *Luke* 15:15
about four hundred *j.* *Acts* 5:36
whose house *j.* hard to the. 18:7
ye be perfectly *j.* in. *1 Cor* 1:10
he which is *j.* to an harlot. 6:16
he that is *j.* to the Lord is one. 17
the whole body fitly *j.* *Eph* 4:16*
and shall be *j.* to his wife. 15:31*
see **Baal-peor**

joining, -s
prepared iron for the *j.* *1 Chr* 22:3*
j. to the wing of the. *2 Chr* 3:12

joint
thigh was out of *j.* *Gen* 32:25*
all my bones are out of *j.* *Ps* 22:14
is like a foot out of *j.* *Pr* 25:19
by that which every *j.* *Eph* 4:16

joint-heirs
heirs of God, and *j.-heirs.* *Rom* 8:17

joints
king of Israel between the *j.* of the.
1 Ki 22:34; *2 Chr* 18:33
the *j.* of thy thighs are. *S of S* 7:1†
that the *j.* of his loins. *Dan* 5:6
all the body by *j.* knit. *Col* 2:19
to dividing asunder of *j.* *Heb* 4:12

Jonadab, *called* **Jehonadab**
J. was Amnon's friend. *2 Sam* 13:3
J. son of Rechab came. *2 Ki* 10:15
J. our father commanded. *Jer* 35:6
obeyed the voice of *J.* *Jer* 35:8, 18
J. shall not want a man to stand. 19

Jonah, *or* **Jonas**
spake by his servant *J.* *2 Ki* 14:25
J. rose to flee to Tarshish. *Jonah* 1:3
lots, and the lot fell upon *J.* 7
they cast *J.* into the sea, the. 15
J. was in the belly of the fish. 17
J. prayed. 2:1
the fish vomited out *J.* 10
J. went to Nineveh. 3:3
it displeased *J.* 4:1
the gourd to come up over *J.* 4:6
to it, but the sign of the prophet *J.*
Mat 12:39; 16:4; *Luke* 11:29, 30
as *J.* was three days in. *Mat* 12:40
repented at the preaching of *J.* 41
Simon son of *J.* lovest thou me?
John 21:15, 16, 17

Jonathan
J. and his sons were. *Judg* 18:30
men were with *J.* in. *1 Sam* 13:2
with Saul and *J.* were swords. 22
knew not that *J.* was gone. 14:3
J. climbed up upon his hands. 13
J. heard not when his father. 27
though it be in *J.* my son, he. 39
I and *J.* my son will be on the. 40
J. was taken. 42
thou shalt surely die, *J.* 44
so the people rescued *J.* that he. 45
the soul of *J.* was knit with. 18:1
but *J.* Saul's son delighted. 19:2
J. spake good of David to Saul. 4
let not *J.* know this lest he. 20:3
do so and much more to *J.* 13
J. made a covenant with the. 16
anger was kindled against *J.* 30
J. knew it was determined to. 33
J. cried after the lad. 37
J. and David knew. 39
J. arose and went to David. 23:16
the Philistines slew *J.* 31:2
1 Chr 10:2
Saul and *J.* his son. *2 Sam* 1:4
the bow of *J.* turned not back. 22
Saul and *J.* were lovely in. 23
distressed for thee, my brother *J.* 26
J. had a son that was lame. 4:4; 9:3
shew thee kindness for *J.*'s sake. 9:7
J. the son of Abiathar. 15:27, 36
1 Ki 1:42, 43
now *J.* and Ahimaaz. *2 Sam* 17:17
Mephibosheth the son of *J.* 21:7
took the bones of Saul and *J.* 12
J. the son of Shimea slew him. 21
1 Chr 20:7
of sons of Jashen, *J.* *2 Sam* 23:32
Jada, Jether and *J.* *1 Chr* 2:32
sons of Hashem, *J.* Ahiam. 11:34
also *J.* David's uncle was a. 27:32
Ebed the son of *J.* went. *Ezra* 8:6
only *J.* and Jehaziah were. 10:15
Joiada begat *J.* *Neh* 12:11
of Melicu, *J.* 14
Zechariah the son of *J.* with a. 35
in prison in the house of *J.* *Jer* 37:15
return to the house of *J.* 20; 38:26
Johanan and *J.* came to. 40:8
see **David, Saul**

Joppa
bring it by sea in floats to *J.*
2 Chr 2:16; *Ezra* 3:7
Jonah went down to *J.* *Jonah* 1:3
at *J.* a disciple named. *Acts* 9:36
it was known throughout all *J.* 42
Peter tarried many days in *J.* 43
send men to *J.* and call. 10:5, 32
certain brethren from *J.* 23
I was in the city of *J.* praying. 11:5

Joram, *called* **Jehoram**
Toi sent *J.* his son to. *2 Sam* 8:10
J. of Ahab; *J.* son of. *2 Ki* 8:16
Syrians wounded *J.* 28
J. went to Jezreel. 29
Jehoshaphat conspired against *J.* 9:14
a bow and smote *J.* between. 24
Jehosheba the daughter of *J.* 11:2
of the Levites, *J.* over. *1 Chr* 26:25
destruction of Ahaziah was of God by coming to *J.* *2 Chr* 22:7
Josaphat begat *J.* and *J.* *Mat* 1:8

Jordan

him all the plain of *J.* *Gen* 13:11
go down to *J.* and goings out at the. *Num* 34:12; *Josh* 13:27; 18:12
come to *J.* stand still in *J.* *Josh* 3:8
passeth over before you into *J.* 11
J. overfloweth all his banks in. 15
stones out of the midst of *J.* 4:3
priests, come ye up out of *J.* 17
God dried the waters of *J.* 23
Lord hath made *J.* a border. 22:25
they took the fords of *J.* *Judg* 3:28
7:24; 12:5
slew him at the passages of *J.* 12:6
king returned and came to *J.* *2 Sam* 19:15
down to meet me at *J.* *1 Ki* 2:8
in plain of *J.* did the king cast them in clay ground. 7:46; *2 Chr* 4:17
brook Cherith before *J.* *1 Ki* 17:3, 5
Lord hath sent me to *J.* *2 Ki* 2:6
they two stood by *J.* 7
Elisha stood by *J.* 13
go and wash in *J.* seven times. 5:10
dipped himself sever times in *J.* 14
let us go, we pray thee, to *J.* 6:2
went after the Syrians to *J.* 7:15
that he can draw up *J.* *Job* 40:23
thee from the land of *J.* *Ps* 42:6
sea fled, *J.* was driven. 114:3, 5
do in the swelling of *J.*? *Jer* 12:5
from the swelling of *J.* 49:19; 50:44
pride of *J.* is spoiled. *Zech* 11:3
were baptized of him in *J.* *Mat* 3:6
Mark 1:5, 9
cometh Jesus from Galilee to *J.* *Mat* 3:13

beyond **Jordan**

Atad which is *beyond J.* *Gen* 50:10
Abel-mizraim, which is *beyond J.* 11
land that is *beyond J.* *Deut* 3:25
kings of Amorites *beyond J.* *Josh* 9:10
gave them *beyond J.* 13:8; 18:7
Gilead abode *beyond J.* *Judg* 5:17
Zebulun and land of Naphtali *beyond J.* in. *Isa* 9:1; *Mat* 4:15
in Bethabara *beyond J.* *John* 1:28
he that was with thee *beyond J.* 3:26

on the other side **Jordan**

Ebal, are they not *on other side J.*? *Deut* 11:30
content and dwelt *on the other side J.* *Josh* 7:7
and half the tribe *on the other side J.* 12:1; 13:27, 32; 14:3; 17:5; 22:4
on other side J. Bezer. 20:8
who dwelt *on the other side J.* 24:8
of Oreb, Zeeb *on other side J.* *Judg* 7:25
Israel *on other side J.* oppressed. 10:8
on other side J. forsook. *1 Sam* 31:7
of Merari cities *on other side J.* *1 Chr* 6:78
on the other side J. 120,000. 12:37

on this side **Jordan**

is fallen *on this side J.* *Num* 32:19
32; 34:15; *Josh* 1:14, 15; 22:7
give three cities *on this side J.* *Num* 35:14; *Deut* 4:41
on this side J. Moses. *Deut* 1:5
we took the land *on this side J.* 3:8
kings *on this side J.* *Josh* 9:1
1700 officers *this side J.* *1 Chr* 26:30

over **Jordan**

I passed *over* this *J.* *Gen* 32:10
land, bring us not *over J.* *Num* 32:5
go all of you armed *over J.* 21
we will pass *over J.* armed. 32
passed *over J.* into the land. 33:51
35:10; *Deut* 12:10; 27:4, 12
thou shalt not go *over J.* *Deut* 3:27
4:21; 31:2
this land, I must not go *over J.* 4:22
pass *over J.* this day. 9:1; 11:31
go *over J.* thou and all. *Josh* 1:2
three days ye shall pass *over J.* 11
were passed clean *over J.* 3:17; 4:1
Israel came *over* this *J.* on. 4:22
brought this people *over J.* to. 7:7
ye went *over J.* and came. 24:11
Ammon passed *over J.* *Judg* 10:9
Hebrews went *over J.* *1 Sam* 13:7
his men passed *over J.* *2 Sam* 2:29
the people passed *over J.* 17:22
and all Israel passed *over J.* 24
conduct the king *over J.* 19:15, 31
they that passed *over J.* *1 Chr* 12:15
David passed *over J.* against. 19:17

Jorim, Jose

Jose the son of Eliezer, the son of *Jorim.* *Luke* 3:29

Josedech, *see* **Joshua**

Joseph

she called his name *J.* *Gen* 30:24
Jacob put Rachel and *J.* 33:2
the sons of Rachel, *J.* and Benjamin. 35:24; 46:19; *1 Chr* 2:2
J. brought to his father. *Gen* 37:2
Israel loved *J.* 3
J. dreamed a dream. 5
his brethren sold *J.* 28
J. is rent in pieces. 33
but the Lord was with *J.* 39:2, 21
Egyptian's house for *J.'s* sake. 5
wife cast her eyes upon *J.* 7
J.'s master took him and put him. 20
butler told his dream to *J.* 40:9
not the chief butler remember *J.* 23
they brought *J.* out of the. 41:14
Pharaoh put his ring on *J.'s* hand. 42
J. 30 years old when he stood. 46
J. gathered corn as the sand of. 49
go to *J.* 41:55
J. knew his brethren. 42:8
J. is not. 36
the man did as *J.* bade. 43:17
J. made haste, for his bowels. 30
I am *J.* 45:3, 4
say, Thus saith thy son *J.* 9
they told him, saying, *J.* is. 26, 28
J. shall put his hand upon thine. 46:4
J. went up to meet Israel his. 29
J. nourished his father and. 47:12
all the Egyptians came to *J.* 15
die, and he called his son *J.* 29
one told Jacob, thy son *J.* 48:2
J. brought them from between. 12
Jacob blessed *J.* and said, God. 15
J. is a fruitful bough, even a. 49:22
blessings shall be on head of *J.* 26
J. went up to bury his father. 50:7
J. will peradventure hate us. 15
and they sent a messenger to *J.* 16
J. wept when they spake unto. 17
J. took an oath of the children. 25
new king which knew not *J.* *Ex* 1:8; *Acts* 7:18
Moses took the bones of *J.* *Ex* 13:19
sons of *J.* Manasseh. *Num* 26:28, 37
these on Gerizim to bless, Judah, *J.* *Deut* 27:12
of *J.* he said, Blessed of the. 33:13
blessing come upon head of *J.* 16
but the birthright was *J.'s.* *1 Chr* 5:2
sons of Jacob and *J.* *Ps* 77:15
refused the tabernacle of *J.* 78:67
give ear, thou that leadest *J.* 80:1
this he ordained in *J.* for a. 81:5
even *J.* who was sold for a. 105:17
write for *J.* the stick. *Ezek* 37:16, 19
tribes of Israel, *J.* shall have. 47:13
one gate of *J.* one gate of. 48:32
be gracious to the remnant of *J.* *Amos* 5:15
not grieved for the affliction of *J.* 6:6
near the ground that Jacob gave to *J.* *John* 4:5
the patriarchs sold *J.* into. *Acts* 7:9
at the second time *J.* was made. 13
then *J.* called his father Jacob. 14
Jacob blessed sons of *J.* *Heb* 11:21
J. made mention of Israel's. 22
see **house**

Joseph with *tribe* and *children*

of the *children* of *J.* of Ephraim. *Num* 1:10, 32
of the *tribe* of *J.* namely of. 13:11
princes of the *children* of *J.* 34:23
the *tribe* of the sons of *J.* hath. 36:5
the *children* of *J.* two tribes. *Josh* 14:4; 16:4
the lot of *children* of *J.* fell. 16:1
the *children* of *J.* spake. 17:14, 16
dwelt the *children* of *J.* *1 Chr* 7:29
of the *tribe* of *J.* were sealed 12,000. *Rev* 7:8

Joseph, husband of *Mary*

Jacob begat *J.* the. *Mat* 1:16
mother Mary was espoused to *J.* 18
J. her husband being a just man. 19
J. did as angel of the Lord hath. 24
the Lord appeared to *J.* 2:13, 19
name was *J.* of house. *Luke* 1:27
J. also went up from Galilee. 2:4
the shepherds found Mary, *J.* 16
and *J.* and his mother knew. 43
as we supposed, the son of *J.* 3:23
this *J.'s* son? 4:22; *John* 1:45; 6:42

Joseph, the name of divers men

Issachar, Igal son of *J.* *Num* 13:7
of Asaph, Zaccur, *J.* *1 Chr* 25:2, 9
Shallum, *J.* had taken. *Ezra* 10:42
of Shebaniah, *J.* was a. *Neh* 12:14
J. of Arimathaea, Jesus' disciple. *Mat* 27:57, 59; *Mark* 15:43, 45
Luke 23:50; *John* 19:38
Janna, son of *J.* *Luke* 3:24, 26, 30
two, *J.* called Barsabas. *Acts* 1:23

Joses

James and *J.* *Mat* 13:55; *Mark* 6:3
Mary the mother of *J.* *Mat* 27:56
Mark 15:40, 47
J. by apostles was surnamed. *Acts* 4:36

Joshua, called **Jehoshua,** and **Oshea**

J. discomfited Amalek. *Ex* 17:13
rehearse it in the ears of *J.* 14
rose up and his minister *J.* 24:13
when *J.* heard the noise of. 32:17
J. departed not out of the. 33:11
of the tribe of Ephraim, *Oshea* son of Nun. *Num* 13:8
Oshea the son of Nun, Jehoshua. 16
save Caleb and *J.* 14:30, 38; 26:65
32:12
take thee *J.* 27:18
he set *J.* before Eleazar. 22
Eleazar and *J.* shall divide. 34:17
but *J.* shall go in. *Deut* 1:38; 31:3
charge *J.* and encourage him. 3:28
31:23
J. was full of the spirit of. 34:9
J. commanded officers. *Josh* 1:10
J. sent two men to spy secretly. 2:1
Lord said to *J.* 3:7; 5:9; 6:2
7:10; 8:18; 10:8
children of Israel did so as *J.* 4:8
day the Lord magnified *J.* in. 14
children, them *J.* circumcised. 5:7
J. fell on his face to the earth. 14
and *J.* did so. 15
so the Lord was with *J.* 6:27
J. rent his clothes. 7:6
pursued after *J.* 8:16
then *J.* built an altar to the. 30
which *J.* read not before all the. 35
then spake *J.* Sun, stand still. 10:12
their land did *J.* take at one. 42
J. did unto them as the Lord. 11:9
now *J.* was old and. 13:1; 23:1
so *J.* blessed Caleb and gave. 14:13
J. cast lots for them before. 18:10
gave an inheritance to *J.* 19:49
J. blessed the Reubenites. 22:6
J. gathered the tribes of. 24:1
so *J.* made a covenant with. 25
J. the servant of the Lord died. 29
Judg 2:8
days of *J.* and of elders that overlived *J.* *Josh* 24:31; *Judg* 2:7
into the field of *J.* *1 Sam* 6:14, 18
which he spake by *J.* *1 Ki* 16:34
in of the gate of *J.* *2 Ki* 23:8
J. son of Josedech. *Hag* 1:1, 12, 14
2:2, 4
and he shewed me *J.* the. *Zech* 3:1
now *J.* was clothed with filthy. 3
stone that I have laid before *J.* 9
set them upon the head of *J.* 6:11

Josiah

a child shall be born, *J.* *1 Ki* 13:2
the people made *J.* king. *2 Ki* 21:24
2 Chr 33:25
J. was eight years old. *2 Ki* 22:1

did *J.* take away. *2 Ki* 23:19, 24
2 Chr 34:33
J. went. *2 Ki* 23:29; *2 Chr* 35:22
sons of *J.* were Johanan. *1 Chr* 3:15
J. kept a passover. *2 Chr* 35:1
keep such a passover as *J.* 18
in the 18th year of *J.* was this. 19
archers shot at king *J.* and. 23
and Jerusalem mourned for *J.* 24
lamented for *J.*.. men spake of *J.* 25
came in days of *J.* *Jer* 1:2; 3:6
Zephaniah in days of *J.* *Zeph* 1:1
go into the house of *J.* *Zech* 6:10
Amon begat *J.* *Mat* 1:10
J. begat Jechonias. 11

jot

one *j.* or tittle shall in. *Mat* 5:18

Jotham

J. youngest son of. *Judg* 9:5, 21
on them came the curse of *J.* 57
J. judged the people. *2 Ki* 15:5
2 Chr 26:21
of Jahdai, Regem and *J.* *1 Chr* 2:47
Azariah his son, *J.* his son. 3:12
genealogies in the days of *J.* 5:17
J. became mighty. *2 Chr* 27:6
in the days of *J.* *Isa* 1:1; *Hos* 1:1
Mi 1:1
Ozias begat *J.* and *J.* *Mat* 1:9

journey

Lord hath made his *j.* *Gen* 24:21
Jacob went on his *j.* and. 29:1
after him seven days' *j.* 31:23
let us take our *j.* 33:12
Israel took his *j.* 46:1
they took their *j.* from. *Ex* 13:20
Israelites took their *j.* from. 16:1
a *j.* yet shall keep the. *Num* 9:10
is not in a *j.* and forbeareth to. 13
they first took their *j.* 10:13
there are eleven days' *j.* *Deut* 1:2
arise, take thy *j.* before the. 10:11
take victuals with you for your *j.*
Josh 9:11
by reason of the very long *j.* 13
the *j.* thou takest is not. *Judg* 4:9
Lord sent thee on a *j.* *1 Sam* 15:18
thou not from thy *j.*? *2 Sam* 11:10
or he is in a *j.* *1 Ki* 18:27
the *j.* is great. 19:7
compass of seven days' *j.* *2 Ki* 3:9
for how long shall thy *j.* be? *Neh* 2:6
man is gone a long *j.* *Pr* 7:19
nor scrip for your *j.* nor. *Mat* 10:10
take nothing for their *j.* *Mark* 6:8
Luke 9:3
a friend of mine in his *j.* *Luke* 11:6
the younger took his *j.* into a. 15:13
Jesus wearied with his *j.* *John* 4:6
might have a prosperous *j.* *Rom* 1:10
I trust to see you in my *j.* 15:24*
may bring me on my *j.* *1 Cor* 16:6
and Apollos on their *j.* *Tit* 3:13
bring forward on their *j.* *3 John* 6

day's **journey**

the quails fall a *day's j.* *Num* 11:31
himself went a *day's j.* *1 Ki* 19:4
to enter city a *day's j.* *Jonah* 3:4
went a *day's j.* among. *Luke* 2:44
from Jerusalem a sabbath *day's j.*
Acts 1:12

see three **days**

journeyed

that as they *j.* they. *Gen* 11:2
Abram *j.* going on toward. 12:9, 20:1
Lot *j.* east. 13:11
Jacob *j.* to Succoth. 33:17
Israel *j.* toward Beth-el. 35:5
j. from Beth-el. 16
j. to the tower of Edar. 21
cloud not taken up, then they *j.* not.
Ex 40:37; *Num* 9:21
after that the children of Israel *j.*
Num 9:17, 18
charge of the Lord, and *j.* not. 19
commandment of Lord they *j.* 20, 23
j. not till Miriam was brought. 12:15
house of Micah as he *j.* *Judg* 17:8
as Saul *j.* he came near. *Acts* 9:3
which *j.* with him stood. 7; 26:13

journeying

make trumpets for *j.* of. *Num* 10:2

we are *j.* to the place. *Num* 10:29
as he was *j.* towards. *Luke* 13:22
in *j.* often, in perils. *2 Cor* 11:26

journeyings

were the *j.* of Israel's. *Num* 10:28

journeys

Abram went on his *j.* *Gen* 13:3
j. according to the. *Ex* 17:1
cloud was taken up, they went on in their *j.* 40:36; *Num* 10:12
for the cloud was upon the tabernacle through all their *j.* *Ex* 40:38
blow an alarm for their *j.* *Num* 10:6
these are the *j.* of Israel. 33:1, 2

joy, *substantive*

to meet Saul with *j.* *1 Sam* 18:6
for there was *j.* in *1 Chr* 12:40
by lifting up the voice with *j.* 15:16
bring ark of the covenant with *j.* 25
now have I seen with *j.* the. 29:17
to Jerusalem with *j.* *2 Chr* 20:27
noise of the shout of *j.* *Ezra* 3:13
of the house of God with *j.* 6:16
the feast seven days with *j.* 22
the *j.* of the Lord is. *Neh* 8:10
j. of Jerusalem was heard. 12:43
the Jews had light, *j.* *Esth* 8:16
sorrow to *j.* they should make them days of feasting and *j.* 9:22*
this is the *j.* of his way. *Job* 8:19
the *j.* of the hypocrite is but. 20:5
widow's heart to sing for *j.* 29:13
he will see his face with *j.* 33:26
and sorrow is turned into *j.* 41:22*
presence is fulness of *j.* *Ps* 16:11
his tabernacles sacrifices of *j.* 27:6
but *j.* cometh in the morning. 30:5
I went with the voice of *j.* and. 42:4
unto God my exceeding *j.* 43:4
the *j.* of the whole earth is. 48:2
restore to me the *j.* of thy. 51:12
nations be glad and sing for *j.* 67:4
forth his people with *j.* 105:43
sow in tears shall reap in *j.* 126:5
Jerusalem above my chief *j.* 137:6
counsellors of peace is *j.* *Pr* 12:20
not intermeddle with his *j.* 14:10
folly is *j.* to him destitute. 15:21
a man hath *j.* by the answer of. 23
father of a fool hath no *j.* 17:21
it is *j.* to the just to do. 21:15
a wise child shall have *j.* 23:24
not my heart from *j.* *Eccl* 2:10
him wisdom, knowledge, and *j.* 26
God answereth him in the *j.* 5:20
way, eat thy bread with *j.* 9:7
the *j.* according to the *j.* *Isa* 9:3
Lord shall have no *j.* in their. 17*
with *j.* shall ye draw water. 12:3
j. is taken out of the plentiful. 16:10
j. of the harp ceaseth. 24:8
j. is darkened. 11
meek shall increase their *j.* 29:19
on all houses of *j.* 32:13
a *j.* of wild asses. 14
and rejoice even with *j.* and. 35:2
j. on their heads. 10; 51:11
break forth into *j.* 52:9
go out with *j.* 55:12
I will make thee a *j.* of many. 60:15
to give them the oil of *j.* for. 61:3
everlasting *j.* shall be unto them. 7
my servants shall sing for *j.* 65:14
I create her people a *j.* 18
but he shall appear to your *j.* 66:5
rejoice for *j.* with her, all ye. 10
the word was to me the *j.* *Jer* 15:16
turn their mourning into *j.* 31:13
to me a name of *j.*, a praise. 33:9
shall be heard the voice of *j.* 11
spakest, thou skippedst for *j.* 48:27*
j. is taken from the plentiful. 33
praise, the city of my *j.* 49:25
city, the *j.* of the whole. *Lam* 2:15
the *j.* of our heart is ceased. 5:15
take from them the *j.* *Ezek* 24:25
appointed, with the *j.* of all. 36:5
rejoice not, O Israel, for *j.* *Hos* 9:1
because *j.* is withered. *Joel* 1:12
rejoice over thee with *j.* *Zeph* 3:17
anon with *j.* receiveth it. *Mat* 13:20
Luke 8:13
for *j.* thereof goeth and. *Mat* 13:44

enter thou into the *j.* *Mat* 25:21, 23
leaped in my womb for *j.* *Luke* 1:44
in that day, and leap for *j.* 6:23
seventy returned again with *j.* 10:17
j. shall be in heaven over one. 15:7
there is *j.* in the presence of. 10
they yet believed not for *j.* 24:41
this my *j.* therefore is. *John* 3:29
to you, that my *j.* might remain in you, and that your *j.* might. 15:11
sorrow shall be turned into *j.* 16:20
for *j.* that a man is born into. 21
and your *j.* no man taketh from. 22
ye shall receive, that your *j.* 24
might have my *j.* fulfilled. 17:13
make me full of *j.* with. *Acts* 2:28*
disciples filled with *j.* in the. 13:52
might finish my course with *j.* 20:24
kingdom of God is *j.* in. *Rom* 14:17
God fill you with all *j.* in. 15:13
may come to you with *j.* by the. 32
are helpers of your *j.* *2 Cor* 1:24
that my *j.* is the *j.* of you all. 2:3
joyed we for the *j.* of Titus. 7:13
the abundance of their *j.* 8:2
Spirit is love, *j.* peace. *Gal* 5:22
making request with *j.* *Phil* 1:4
furtherance and *j.* of faith. 25
fulfil ye my *j.* 2:2
my *j.* and crown. 4:1
received the word with *j.* *1 Thes* 1:6
what is our hope or *j.*? 2:19
ye are our *j.* 20
for the *j.* wherewith we joy. 3:9
I may be filled with *j.* *2 Tim* 1:4
let me have *j.* of thee. *Philem* 20
who for the *j.* that was. *Heb* 12:2
they may do it with *j.* and. 13:17
count it *j.* when ye fall into. *Jas* 1:2
and your *j.* be turned into. 4:9
ye rejoice with *j.* *1 Pet* 1:8
be glad also with exceeding *j.* 4:13
that your *j.* may be full. *1 John* 1:4
2 John 12
I have no greater *j.* than. *3 John* 4
you faultless with exceeding *j.*
Jude 24

see **gladness**

joy, *verb*

the king shall *j.* in thy. *Ps* 21:1
j. before thee according. *Isa* 9:3
I will rejoice and *j.* in my. 65:19
I will *j.* in the God of my. *Hab* 3:18
he will *j.* over thee with. *Zeph* 3:17
we also *j.* in God through. *Rom* 5:11*
I *j.* and rejoice with. *Phil* 2:17
for the same cause also do ye *j.* 18
wherewith we *j.* for you. *1 Thes* 3:9

great **joy**

the people rejoiced with *great j.*
1 Ki 1:40
David the king rejoiced with *great j.*
1 Chr 29:9
so there was *great j.* *2 Chr* 30:26
them rejoice with *great j.* *Neh* 12:43
they rejoiced with *great j.* *Mat* 2:10
sepulchre with fear and *great j.* 28:8
good tidings of *great j.* *Luke* 2:10
to Jerusalem with *great j.* 24:52
and there was *great j.* in. *Acts* 8:8
they caused *great j.* to all. 15:3
for we have *great j.* in thy. *Philem* 7

shout, or *shouted for* **joy**

many *shouted* aloud *for j.* *Ezra* 3:12
sons of God *shouted for j.* *Job* 38:7
trust in thee rejoice: let them ever *shout for j.* *Ps* 5:11; 35:27
shout for j. all ye that are. 32:11
the valleys *shout for j.* they. 65:13
thy saints *shout for j.* 132:9, 16

joyed

more *j.* we for the joy. *2 Cor* 7:13

joyful

went to their tents *j.* *1 Ki* 8:66
Lord hath made them *j.* *Ezra* 6:22
went forth that day *j.* *Esth* 5:9
let no *j.* voice come therein. *Job* 3:7
love thy name be *j.* in. *Ps* 5:11
soul shall be *j.* in the Lord. 35:9
shall praise thee with *j.* lips. 63:5
make a *j.* noise to God, all. 66:1
make a *j.* noise to the God of. 81:1

that know the *j.* sound. *Ps* 89:15
make a *j.* noise to the rock of. 95:1
a *j.* noise to him. 2; 98:4; 100:1
make a *j.* noise before the. 98:6
let the hills be *j.* together before. 8*
the barren to be a *j.* mother. 113:9
let the children of Zion be *j.* 149:2
let the saints be *j.* in glory; let. 5*
of prosperity be *j.* but in. *Eccl* 7:14
heavens, and be *j.* earth. *Isa* 49:13
make them *j.* in my house of. 56:7
soul shall be *j.* in my God. 61:10
I am exceeding *j.* in all. *2 Cor* 7:4*

joyfully

live *j.* with the wife. *Eccl* 9:9
down and received him *j.* *Luke* 19:6
ye took *j.* the spoiling of. *Heb* 10:34

joyfulness

not the Lord with *j.* *Deut* 28:47
to longsuffering with *j.* *Col* 1:11

joying

with you in the spirit, *j.* *Col* 2:5

joyous

art full of stirs, a *j.* city. *Isa* 22:2
is this your *j.* city, whose. 23:7
houses of joy in the *j.* city. 32:13
no chastening seemeth to be *j.* *Heb* 12:11

jubile

cause trumpet of the *j.* to. *Lev* 25:9
j. it shall be holy to you. 10, 12
a *j.* shall that fiftieth year be. 11
in the year of *j.* ye shall return. 13
a field shall go out in the year of *j.* 25:28; 27:21, 24
house shall not go out in the *j.* 25:30
they shall go out in the year of *j.* 31, 33, 54
his field from year of *j.* 27:17, 18
j. then their inheritance. *Num* 36:4

Judah

called his name *J.* *Gen* 29:35
sons of Leah, *J.* Issachar. 35:23
J. thought Tamar to be an. 38:15
J. acknowledged the signet and. 26
sons of *J.* 46:12; *Num* 26:19
1 Chr 2:3; 4:1
Jacob sent *J.* before him. *Gen* 46:28
J. thou art he whom thy. 49:8
J. is a lion's whelp, he couched. 9
sceptre shall not depart *J.* until. 10
the sons of Israel, Levi, *J.* *Ex* 1:2
1 Chr 2:1
J. Nashan son of. *Num* 1:7
the camp of *J.* shall pitch on. 2:3
numbered in the camp of *J.* 9
Simeon, Levi, *J.* shall. *Deut* 27:12
blessing of *J.* the voice of *J.* 33:7
brought the family of *J.* *Josh* 7:17
J. shall abide in their coast. 18:5
the Lord said, *J.* shall go. *Judg* 1:2
the Lord was with *J.* 19
fight against *J.* 10:9
whom Tamar bare to *J.* *Ruth* 4:12
search him out throughout all the thousands of *J.* *1 Sam* 23:23
J. do shew kindness. *2 Sam* 3:8
David reigned over *J.* seven. 5:5
the ark, Israel, and *J.* abide. 11:11
J. came to Gilgal to meet. 19:15
go number Israel and *J.* 24:1
captain of host of *J.* *1 Ki* 2:32
J. and Israel were many, as. 4:20
J. and Israel dwelt safely. 25
of God out of *J.* by the word of the Lord to Beth-el. 13:1; *2 Ki* 23:17
J. did evil in the sight of. *1 Ki* 14:22
Abijam reigned over *J.* 15:1
reigned Asa over *J.* 9
went up against *J.* 17; *2 Chr* 16:1
Jehoshaphat began to reign over *J.* *1 Ki* 22:41
Lord would not destroy *J.* *2 Ki* 8:19
Edom revolted from *J.* 20, 22
2 Chr 21:8, 10
Ahaziah began to reign over *J.* *2 Ki* 9:29
to fall, thou and *J.* with thee. 14:10
2 Chr 25:19
J. was put to the worse. *2 Ki* 14:12; *2 Chr* 25:22
Azariah restored Elath to *J.* *2 Ki* 14:22; *2 Chr* 26:2
to send against *J.* Rezin. *2 Ki* 15:37
testified against Israel and *J.* 17:13
J. kept not the commandments. 19
Manasseh made *J.* to sin. 21:11, 16
2 Chr 33:9
bringing such evil upon *J.* *2 Ki* 21:12
his anger kindled against *J.* 23:26
2 Chr 25:10
I will remove *J.* also. *2 Ki* 23:27
bands of Chaldees against *J.* 24:2
of the Lord came this on *J.* 3
so *J.* was carried away. 25:21
1 Chr 6:15
J. prevailed above his. *1 Chr* 5:2
of *J.*, Elihu, one of David's. 27:18
for he hath chosen *J.* to be. 28:4
so they were before *J.* *2 Chr* 13:13
children of Israel fled before *J.* 16
Asa commanded *J.* to seek. 14:4
took the groves out of *J.* 17:6
Jehoram compelled *J.* to. 21:11
hast made *J.* and Jerusalem. 13
wrath came upon *J.* 24:18; 28:9
29:8; 32:25
Lord brought *J.* low, made *J.* 28:19
lambs for a sin offering for *J.* 29:21
all the congregation of *J.* 30:25
Manasseh commanded *J.* to. 33:16
Josiah began to purge *J.* 34:3, 5
sons of *J.* to set forward. *Ezra* 3:9
sent to enquire concerning *J.* 7:14
J. and Eliezer had taken. 10:23
wouldst send me to *J.* *Neh* 2:5
convey me till I come into *J.* 7
the nobles of *J.* sent letters. 6:17
J. son of Senuah was second. 11:9
for *J.* rejoiced for the priests. 12:44
Gilead is mine, *J.* *Ps* 60:7; 108:8
J. was his sanctuary, Israel. 114:2
he saw concerning *J.* *Isa* 1:1; 2:1
Lord doth take from *J.* the stay. 3:1
J. is fallen. 8
let us go up against *J.* 7:6
that Ephraim departed from *J.* 17
pass through *J.* shall overflow. 8:8
together shall be against *J.* 9:21
together the dispersed of *J.* 11:12
J. shall be cut off; Ephraim shall not envy *J.* and *J.* not vex. 13
discovered the covering of *J.* 22:8
forth out of the waters of *J.* 48:1
and out of *J.* an inheritor of . 65:9
cities are thy gods, O *J.* *Jer* 2:28
treacherous sister *J.* saw it. 3:7, 8
Egypt, and *J.* and Edom. 9:26
will I mar the pride of *J.* 13:9
J. shall be carried away captive. 19
J. mourneth. 14:2
hast thou utterly rejected *J.* 19
the sin of *J.* is written with. 17:1
I will void the counsel of *J.* 19:7
J. shall be saved. 23:6
do this to cause *J.* to sin. 32:35
I will cause the captivity of *J.* 33:7
I have spoken against *J.* 36:2
the Lord, ye remnant of *J.* 42:15
in mouth of any man of *J.* 44:26
sins of *J.* shall not be found. 50:20
J. hath not been forsaken of. 51:5
J. was carried away captive. 52:27
Lam 1:3
sword may come to *J.* *Ezek* 21:20
J. and Israel were thy. . 27:17
write upon it for *J.* and for. 37:16
of Reuben, a portion for *J.* 48:7
gate of Reuben, one gate of *J.* 31
harlot, yet let not *J.* *Hos* 4:15
J. shall fall. 5:5
when *J.* saw his wound. 13
O *J.* what shall I do unto thee ? 6:4
J. shall plow, Jacob shall. 10:11
but *J.* ruleth yet with God. 11:12
also a controversy with *J.* 12:2
but *J.* shall dwell for ever. *Joel* 3:20
three transgressions of *J.* *Amos* 2:4
I will send a fire on *J.*. it shall. 5
incurable, it is come to *J.* *Mi* 1:9
little among the thousands of *J.* 5:2
out mine hand upon *J.* *Zeph* 1:4
have scattered *J.* *Zech* 1:19, 21
Lord shall inherit *J.* his. 2:12
when I have bent *J.* for me. 9:13
save the tents of *J.* first. *Zech* 12:7
J. also shall fight at. 14:14
J. hath dealt treacherously; *J.* hath profaned the holiness. *Mal* 2:11
then shall the offering of *J.* 3:4
Jacob begat *J.* *Mat* 1:2
J. begat Phares. 3
which was the son of *J.* *Luke* 3:33
our Lord sprang of *J.* *Heb* 7:14

all **Judah**

but all Israel and *all J.* *1 Sam* 18:16
33 years over *all J.* *2 Sam* 5:5
all J. rejoiced at the. *2 Chr* 15:15
all J. stood before the Lord. 20:13
all J. did honour Hezekiah. 32:33
all J. and Jerusalem mourned. 35:24
all J. brought the tithe. *Neh* 13:12
give *all J.* to the king of. *Jer* 20:4
set my face to cut off *all J.* 44:11
see **Benjamin, Beth-lehem, children, cities, daughter, daughters, house**

in **Judah**

be afraid here *in J.* *1 Sam* 23:3
the feast that is *in J.* *1 Ki* 12:32
it came to pass *in* Jerusalem and *J.* *2 Ki* 24:20; *Jer* 52:3
cunning men that are with me *in J.* *2 Chr* 2:7
in J. things went well. 12:12
they taught *in J.* and had book. 17:9
Pekah slew *in J.* 120,000 in. 28:6
in J. hand of God was to give. 30:12
for them that are left *in J.* 34:21
the Jews that were *in J.* *Ezra* 5:1
mercy to give us a wall *in J.* 9:9
saying, There is a king *in J.* *Neh* 6:7
I saw *in J.* some treading. 13:15
in J. is God known. *Ps* 76:1
declare ye *in J.* publish in Jerusalem. *Jer* 4:5; 5:20
prosper, ruling any more *in J.* 22:30
shall be as a governor *in J.* *Zech* 9:7
every pot *in J.* be holiness. 14:21
see **king, kings**

land of **Judah**

Lord shewed him all the *land of J.* *Deut* 34:2
went to return unto the *land of J.* *Ruth* 1:7
thee into the *land of J.* *1 Sam* 22:5
remained in *land of J.* *2 Ki* 25:22
garrisons in *land of J.* *2 Chr* 17:2
the *land of J.* shall be a. *Isa* 19:17
shall be sung in the *land of J.* 26:1
speech in the *land of J.* *Jer* 31:23
had nothing in the *land of J.* 39:10
committed in the *land of J.* 44:9
should return into the *land of J.* 14
seer, into the *land of J.* *Amos* 7:12
horn over the *land of J.* *Zech* 1:21
Bethlehem, in the *land of J.* *Mat* 2:6

men of **Judah**

men of J. said, Why are ? *Judg* 15:10
the *men of J.* anointed. *2 Sam* 2:4
the heart of all the *men of J.* 19:14
the words of the *men of J.* 43
men of J. clave to their king. 20:2
assemble the *men of J.* within. 4
men of J. were five hundred. 24:9
men of J. gave a shout. *2 Chr* 13:15
men of J. gathered. *Ezra* 10:9
men of J. are his pleasant. *Isa* 5:7
your hearts, ye *men of J.* *Jer* 4:4
is found among the *men of J.* 11:9
bring upon the *men of J.* all. 36:31
the sight of the *men of J.* 43:9
men of J. shall be consumed. 44:27
belongeth to the *men of J.* *Dan* 9:7
see **princes**

tribe of **Judah**

Bezaleel of the *tribe of J.* *Ex* 31:2
35:30; 38:22
numbered of *tribe of J.* *Num* 1:27
the prince of the *tribe of J.* 7:12
of the *tribe of J.* Caleb. 13:6; 34:19
Achan of *tribe of J.* took. *Josh* 7:1
and the *tribe of J.* was taken. 16, 18
lot of the *tribe of J.* 15:1, 20
Levites out of the *tribe of J.* 21:4, 9
1 Chr 6:65
the *tribe of J.* only. *1 Ki* 12:20

left but *tribe of J.* only. *2 Ki* 17:18
but he chose the *tribe of J. Ps* 78:68
Lion of the *tribe of J.* hath. *Rev* 5:5
of the *tribe of J.* were sealed. 7:5

Judas

Joses, Simon, and *J.* *Mat* 13:55
J. one of the twelve came, and a.
26:47; *Mark* 14:43
Luke 22:47; *John* 18:3, 5
then *J.* repented himself. *Mat* 27:3
some thought because *J. John* 13:29
J. said unto him, not Iscariot. 14:22
spake before concerning *J. Acts* 1:16
J. by transgression, fell. 25
after this man rose up *J.* of. 5:37
enquire in the house of *J.* for. 9:11
J. surnamed Barsabas. 15:22, 27
J. and Silas exhorted the. 32

Judas *Iscariot*

J. Iscariot, who betrayed him.
Mat 10:4; *Mark* 3:19
Luke 6:16; *John* 6:71; 13:2
J. Iscariot went to chief priests.
Mat 26:14; *Mark* 14:10
Satan into *J. Iscariot.* *Luke* 22:3
the sop to *J. Iscariot.* *John* 13:26

Judea

into the province of *J.* *Ezra* 5:8
in *J.* flee into mountains. *Mat* 24:16
Mark 13:14; *Luke* 21:21
he left *J.* and departed. *John* 4:3
depart hence and go into *J.* again.
7:3; 11:7
in *J.* ye shall be witnesses. *Acts* 1:8
ye men of *J.* be this known. 2:14
had rest throughout *J.* 9:31
was published through *J.* 10:37
went down from *J.* to Cesarea. 12:19
received letters out of *J.* 28:21
that do not believe in *J. Rom* 15:31
on my way toward *J.* *2 Cor* 1:16
churches which are in *J.* are in Christ.
1 Thes 2:14

judge, *substantive*

shall not the *J.* of all? *Gen* 18:25
came, and will needs be a *j.* 19:9
who made thee a *j.* over us? *Ex* 2:14
Acts 7:27, 35
come to the *j.* that shall. *Deut* 17:9
will not hearken to the *j.* 12
that the *j.* shall cause him to. 25:2
the Lord was with the *j.* *Judg* 2:18
the *j.* was dead, they corrupted. 19
the Lord the *J.* be *j.* this. 11:27
if a man sin, the *j.* *1 Sam* 2:25*
O that I were made *j.* *2 Sam* 15:4
supplication to my *j.* *Job* 9:15*
delivered for ever from my *j.* 23:7
to be punished by the *j.* 31:28
declare, for God is *j.* *Ps* 50:6
a *j.* of the widows. 68:5
God is the *j.* 75:7
lift up thyself, thou *J.* of. 94:2
away from Jerusalem the *j. Isa* 3:2
I will cut off the *j.* from. *Amos* 2:3
shall smite the *J.* of Israel. *Mi* 5:1
prince asketh, and the *j.* asketh. 7:3
deliver thee to the *j.*, the *j.* deliver.
Mat 5:25; *Luke* 12:58
man, who made me a *j.*? *Luke* 12:14
saying, There was in a city a *j.* 18:2
hear what the unjust *j.* saith. 6
be the *j.* of quick and. *Acts* 10:42
for I will be no *j.* of such. 18:15
hast been of many years a *j.* 24:10
the Lord, the righteous *j. 2 Tim* 4:8
come to God the *J.* of. *Heb* 12:23
a doer of the law, but a *j.* *Jas* 4:11
behold, the *J.* standeth before. 5:9

judge, *verb, applied to* **God** *and* **Christ**

j. between me and thee. *Gen* 16:5
1 Sam 24:12, 15
God of their father *j.* *Gen* 31:53
Lord look on you, and *j.* *Ex* 5:21
Lord shall *j.* his people. *Deut* 32:36
Ps 50:4; 135:14; *Heb* 10:30
Lord shall *j.* the ends. *1 Sam* 2:10
hear and *j.* thy servants. *1 Ki* 8:32
2 Chr 6:23
cometh to *j.* the earth. *1 Chr* 16:33
Ps 96:13; 98:9
wilt thou not *j.* them? *2 Chr* 20:12
sayest, Can he *j.* through? *Job* 22:13
Lord shall *j.* the people righteously.
Ps 7:8; 9:8; 50:4; 96:10
j. the fatherless and poor. 10:18
Isa 11:4
j. me, O Lord. *Ps* 7:8; 26:1; 35:24
43:1; 54:1; *Lam* 3:59
arise, O God, *j.* the earth. *Ps* 82:8
shall *j.* the world with righteousness.
96:13; 98:9; *Acts* 17:31
shall *j.* among the heathen. *Ps* 110:6
God shall *j.* the righteous. *Eccl* 3:17
and he shall *j.* among the. *Isa* 2:4
the Lord standeth to *j.* the. 3:13
he shall not *j.* after the sight. 11:3
mine arm shall *j.* the people. 51:5
and will *j.* thee according. *Ezek* 7:3
I *j.* between cattle and cattle. 34:17
there will I sit to *j.* the. *Joel* 3:12
j. among many people. *Mi* 4:3
I hear, I *j.*: my judgement. *John* 5:30
I *j.* no man. 8:15
and yet if I *j.* 16
things to say and to *j.* of you. 26
I *j.* him not, I came not to *j.* 12:47
when God shall *j.* the. *Rom* 2:16
how shall God *j.* the world? 3:6
who shall *j.* quick and dead.
2 Tim 4:1; *1 Pet* 4:5
and adulterers God will *j. Heb* 13:4
dost thou not *j.* and? *Rev* 6:10
in righteousness he doth *j.* 19:11
see further, I *will* **judge**

judge, *applied to* **man,** *or other things*

that they may *j.* betwixt. *Gen* 31:37
Dan shall *j.* his people as. 49:16
that Moses sat to *j.* the. *Ex* 18:13
I *j.* between one and another. 16
small matter they shall *j.* 22
in righteousness shalt thou *j.* thy.
Lev 19:15; *Deut* 1:16; 16:18
the congregation *j.* *Num* 35:24
the judges may *j.* them. *Deut* 25:1
sin, the judge shall *j.* *1 Sam* 2:25
make us a king to *j.* us. 8:5, 6, 20
heart to *j.* thy people: for who is able to *j.* this? *1 Ki* 3:9; *2 Chr* 1:10
throne where he might *j.* *1 Ki* 7:7
mayest *j.* my people. *2 Chr* 1:11
for ye *j.* not for man, but for. 19:6
set judges which may *j.* *Ezra* 7:25
do ye *j.* uprightly, O ye? *Ps* 58:1
he shall *j.* thy people with. 72:2
he shall *j.* the poor of. 4; *Pr* 3:9
how long will ye *j.* unjustly? *Ps* 82:2
j. the fatherless, plead. *Isa* 1:17
j. not the fatherless. 23; *Jer* 5:28
j. I pray you betwixt me. *Isa* 5:3
wilt thou *j.* them? *Ezek* 20:4; 22:2
they shall *j.* thee. 23:24, 45; 24:14
Son of man, wilt *j.* Aholah? 23:36
they shall *j.* it according to. 44:24
saviours come to *j.* the. *Ob* 21
the heads thereof *j.* for. *Mi* 3:11
then thou shalt also *j.* *Zech* 3:7
j. not that ye be not. *Mat* 7:1
what judgement ye *j.* 2; *Luke* 6:37
yea, and why *j.* ye not? *Luke* 12:57
j. not according to the appearance, but *j.* righteous. *John* 7:24
doth our law *j.* any man before? 51
ye *j.* after flesh. 8:15
same shall *j.* him. 12:48
take and *j.* him according to. 18:31
j. ye. *Acts* 4:19
j. yourselves unworthy. 13:46
for sittest thou to *j.* me after? 23:3
if it fulfil the law, *j.* thee. *Rom* 2:27
j. him that eateth. 14:3
why dost thou *j.* thy brother? 10
let us not *j.* one another, but *j.* 13
I *j.* not mine own self. *1 Cor* 4:3
j. nothing before the time. 5
I to do to *j.* them that are without? do not ye *j.* them that are within? 5:12
not know that saints shall *j.*? 6:2
know ye not that we shall *j.*? 3
to *j.* who are least esteemed. 4
shall be able to *j.* between. 5*
j. ye what I say. 10:15
j. in yourselves. 11:13
we would *j.* ourselves. *1 Cor* 11:31*
speak, and the other *j.* 14:29*
because we thus *j.* that. *2 Cor* 5:14
let no man therefore *j.* *Col* 2:16
but if thou *j.* the law. *Jas* 4:11

I will **judge**

I told him that *I will j.* *1 Sam* 3:13
receive, *I will j.* uprightly. *Ps* 75:2
I will j. thee according to thy ways.
Ezek 7:3, 8, 27; 33:20
I will j. you in the border. 11:10, 11
I will j. thee as women that. 16:38
therefore *I will j.* you, O. 18:30
I will j. thee in the place. 21:30
I, even *I, will j.* between. 34:20, 22

will I **judge**

the nation they shall serve *will I j.*
Gen 15:14; *Acts* 7:7
own mouth *will I j.* thee. *Luke* 19:22

judged

God hath *j.* me and. *Gen* 30:6
j. the people, small matter they *j.*
Ex 18:26
Othniel *j.* Israel. *Judg* 3:10
Deborah *j.* Israel. 4:4
Tola *j.* Israel. 10:2
Jair *j.* Israel. 3
Jephthah *j.* Israel. 12:7
Ibzan *j.* Israel. 8
Elon *j.* Israel. 11
Abdon *j.* Israel. 14
Samson *j.* Israel. 15:20; 16:31
Eli *j.* Israel. *1 Sam* 4:18
Samuel *j.* Israel. 7:6, 15, 16, 17
judgement the king had *j. 1 Ki* 3:28
of the judges that *j.* *2 Ki* 23:22
let the heathen be *j.* in. *Ps* 9:19
condemn him when he is *j.* 37:33
when he shall be *j.* let him. 109:7
j. the cause of the poor. *Jer* 22:16
that shed blood are *j.* *Ezek* 16:38
thou also who hast *j.* thy sisters. 52
and the wounded shall be *j.* 28:23
known, when I have *j.* thee. 35:11
to their doings I *j.* them. 36:19
our judges that *j.* us. *Dan* 9:12
that ye be not *j.* *Mat* 7:1
shall be *j.* 2; *Luke* 6:37
him, thou hast rightly *j.* *Luke* 7:43
prince of this world is *j.* *John* 16:11
if ye have *j.* me to be. *Acts* 16:15
we would have *j.* according. 24:6
and there be *j.* of these. 25:9, 20
stand, where I ought to be *j.* 25:10
and am *j.* for the hope of the. 26:6
shall be *j.* by the law. *Rom* 2:12
Jas 2:12
overcome when thou art *j. Rom* 3:4
why yet am I also *j.* as a sinner? 7
yet he himself is *j.* of. *1 Cor* 2:15
a small thing that I should be *j.* 4:3
I have *j.* already, as though I. 5:3
and if the world shall be *j.* by. 6:2
for why is my liberty *j.* of? 10:29
judge we should not be *j.* 11:31
when we are *j.* we are chastened. 32
convinced of all, he is *j.* of. 14:24
she *j.* him faithful. *Heb* 11:11*
be *j.* according to men. *1 Pet* 4:6
time of the dead, that they should be *j.* *Rev* 11:18
because thou hast *j.* thus. 16:5
righteous, for he hath *j.* the. 19:2
the dead were *j.* out of those. 20:12
were *j.* every man according to. 13

judgement

[1] *The sentence, or decision of a judge,* 1 Ki 3:28. [2] *The spirit of wisdom and prudence, enabling to know and discern right from wrong, and good from evil,* Ps 72:1. [3] *The righteous statutes and commandments of God,* Ps 119:7, 20. [4] *Justice and equity,* Isa 1:17; Luke 11:42. [5] *God's decrees and purposes concerning nations, or persons,* Rom 11:33. [6] *Courts of judgement,* Mat 5:21. [7] *The last judgement,* Mat. 25:31-46.

gods I will execute *j.* *Ex* 12:12
according to this *j.* be it done. 21:31
after many, to wrest *j.* 23:2, 6

make the breastplate of j. Ex 28:15
names in breastplate of j. 29, 30
a statute of j. Num 27:11; 35:29
after the j. of Urim before the. 27:21
afraid of man, for the j. Deut 1:17
he doth execute the j. of the. 10:18
judge the people with just j. 16:18
not wrest j. 19
shew thee sentence of j. 17:9
according to the j. 11
thou shalt not pervert the j. 24:17
and they come unto j. 25:1
cursed be he that perverteth j. 27:19
for all his ways are j.; a God. 32:4†
if my hand take hold on j. I. 41
the congregation for j. Josh 20:6
up to Deborah for j. Judg 4:5
bribes and perverted j. 1 Sam 8:3
David executed j. 2 Sam 8:15
1 Chr 18:14
came to king for j. 2 Sam 15:2, 6
understanding to discern j. 1 Ki 3:11
all Israel heard of the j. the. 28
the porch of j. 7:7
so shall thy j. be. 20:40
took king and gave j. 2 Ki 25:6
chief of fathers for j. 2 Chr 19:8
cometh on us as the sword, j. 20:9
when Jehu was executing j. 22:8
executed j. against Joash. 24:24
let j. be executed. Ezra 7:26
all that knew law and j. Esth 1:13
doth God pervert j.? Job 8:3
if I speak of j. 9:19
but there is no j. 19:7
that ye may know there is a j. 29
do the aged understand j. 32:9
let us choose to us j. 34:4
will the Almighty pervert j. 12
yet j. is before him, trust. 35:14*
fulfilled the j. of the wicked, j. and justice take hold on thee. 36:17
awake for me to the j. thou. Ps 7:6
hath prepared his throne for j. 9:7
shall minister j. to the people. 8
the Lord is known by the j. he. 16
he loveth righteousness and j. 33:5†
37:28
he shall bring forth thy j. as. 37:6
and his tongue talketh of j. 30
shall judge thy poor with j. 72:2
thou didst cause j. to be heard. 76:8*
when God arose to j. to save the. 9
justice and j. are the. 89:14†; 97:2†
but j. shall return to. 94:15
also loveth j.; thou executest j. and. 99:4†
I will sing of mercy and j. to. 101:1
Lord executeth j. for. 103:6; 146:7
blessed are they that keep j. 106:3
Phinehas stood up and executed j. 30
the works are verity and j. 111:7
teach me good j. and. 119:66
I have done j. and justice. 121†
quicken me according to thy j. 149
for there are set thrones of j. 122:5
to execute upon them the j. 149:9
instruction of wisdom and j. Pr 1:3†
he keepeth the paths of j. and. 2:8†
then shalt thou understand j. and. 9†
the midst of the paths of j. 8:20
that is destroyed for want of j. 13:23
gift to pervert the ways of j. 17:23
an ungodly witness scorneth j. 19:28
that sitteth in the throne of j. 20:8
evil men understand not j. but. 28:5
the king by j. establisheth the. 29:4
every man's j. cometh from. 26
nor pervert the j. of any of. 31:5
the sun the place of j. Eccl 3:16
violent perverting of j. and. 5:8
man discerneth both time and j. 8:5
every purpose there is time and j. 6
seek j. Isa 1:17
it was full of j. 21
Zion shall be redeemed with j. 27†
purged Jerusalem by spirit of j. 4:4
and looked for j. 5:7†
and to establish it with j. 9:7
to turn aside the needy from j. 10:2†
execute j. 16:3; Jer 21:12; 22:3
Ezek 18:8; 45:9; Zech 7:9; 8:12
seeking j. Isa 16:5
for a spirit of j. 28:6
I will lay j. to the line. Isa 28:17†
for the Lord is a God of j. 30:18
then j. shall dwell in the. 32:16†
Lord hath filled Zion with j. 33:5†
the people of my curse to j. 34:5
taught him in the path of j.? 40:14
let us come near together to j. 41:1
he shall bring forth j. to the. 42:1
he shall bring forth j. unto truth. 3
he shall not fail, till he have set j. 4
from prison and from j. 53:8
keep ye j. and do justice. 56:1
Hos 12:6†
is no j. in their goings. Isa 59:8†
therefore is j. far from us. 9†
we look for j. but there is none. 11†
j. is turned away backward. 14†
him that there was no j. 15†
I the Lord love j. I hate. 61:8†
be any that executeth j. Jer 5:1
not the j. of their God. 4; 8:7*
they have known the j. of their. 5:5
if ye throughly execute j. 7:5
exercise j. and righteousness. 9:24†
correct me, but with j. not in. 10:24
execute j. in the morning. 21:12
branch shall execute j. 23:5; 33:15
to Riblah, where he gave j. upon Zedekiah. 39:5; 52:9
and j. is come upon the. 48:21
thus far is the j. of Moab. 47
whose j. was not to drink. 49:12*
forsake her, for her j. reacheth. 51:9
for they had executed j. Ezek 23:10
I will set j. before them, they. 24
all whose ways are j. Dan 4:37
j. was set. 7:10
but the j. shall sit. 26
j. was given to the saints of the. 22
give ye ear, for j. is. Hos 5:1
thus j. springeth up as hemlock. 10:4
turn j. into wormwood. Amos 5:7
love the good, and establish j. in. 15
but let j. run down as waters and. 24
for ye have turned j. into gall. 6:12
is it not to know j.? Mi 3:1
I am full of j. 8
that abhor j. 9
and execute j. for me. 7:9
law is slacked, j. doth. Hab 1:4
j. shall proceed of themselves. 7
thou hast ordained them for j. 12
have wrought his j. Zeph 2:3
every morning doth he bring j. 3:5
where is the God of j.? Mal 2:17
in danger of the j. Mat 5:21, 22
with what j. ye judge, ye shall. 7:2
shew j. to the Gentiles. 12:18
till he send forth j. unto victory. 20
and have omitted j., mercy. 23:23†
pass over j. and love of. Luke 11:42†
but hath committed all j. John 5:22
him authority to execute j. also. 27
but judge righteous j. 7:24
j. I am come into this world. 9:39
now is the j. of this world. 12:31
reprove the world of j. 16:8, 11
in his humiliation his j. Acts 8:33
as he reasoned of j., Felix. 24:25
the Jews desiring to have j. 25:15
knowing the j. of God. Rom 1:32*
sure that the j. of God is. 2:2
that thou shalt escape the j. of ? 3
and revelation of the righteous j. 5
for the j. was by one to. 5:16
j. came on all men to. 18
be joined together in j. 1 Cor 1:10
should be judged of man's j. 4:3
token of the righteous j. 2 Thes 1:5
open, going before to j. 1 Tim 5:24
and of eternal j. Heb 6:2
after this the j. 9:27
certain fearful looking for of j. 10:27
j. without mercy, shewed no mercy, mercy rejoiceth against j. Jas 2:13
we shall receive greater j. 3:1
that j. must begin at the. 1 Pet 4:17
whose j. lingereth not. 2 Pet 2:3*
angels reserved unto j. 4
to j. of the great day. Jude 6
to execute j. 15
fear God, for the hour of his j. is come. Rev 14:7
will shew thee j. of the great. 17:1
for in one hour is thy j. come. Rev 18:10
and j. was given to them. 20:4
see **bear, day**

do judgement

to do justice and j. Gen 18:19†
1 Ki 10:9; Pr 21:3†; Jer 22:15
God was in him to do j. 1 Ki 3:28
them to do justice and j. 2 Chr 9:8
they refuse to do j. Pr 21:7†
it is joy to the just to do j. but. 15†
I will do j. on the graven images. Jer 51:47
I will do j. on her graven images. 52

in judgement

unrighteousness in j. Lev 19:15, 35
the congregation in j. Num 35:12
not respect persons in j. Deut 1:17
matter too hard for thee in j. 17:8
ye that sit in j. and. Judg 5:10*
who is with you in j. 2 Chr 19:6
come together in j. Job 9:32
excellent in power and in j. 37:23
shall not stand in j. Ps 1:5
the meek will he guide in j. 25:9
trangresseth not in j. Pr 16:10
overthrow the righteous in j. 18:5
have respect of persons in j. 24:23
hosts shall be exalted in j. Isa 5:16
him that sitteth in j. 28:6
they stumble in j. 7
behold princes shall rule in j. 32:1
that shall rise against thee in j. 54:17
Lord liveth in righteousness and in j. Jer 4:2†
they stand in j. Ezek 44:24
betroth thee to me in j. Hos 2:19
oppressed and broken in j. 5:11
come near to you in j. Mal 3:5
Nineveh shall rise in j. Mat 12:41
queen of south shall rise in j. 42
Luke 11:31, 32
your love may abound in j. Phil 1:9*

into judgement

bringest me into j. with. Job 14:3
will he enter with thee into j.? 22:4
that he should enter into j. 34:23
enter not into j. with. Ps 143:2
God will bring thee into j. Eccl 11:9
bring every work into j. 12:14
Lord will enter into j. Isa 3:14

my judgement

taken away my j. Job 27:2*; 34:5*
my j. was as a robe. 29:14*
wilt thou also disannul my j.? 40:8
up thyself, awake to my j. Ps 35:23
my j. is passed over from. Isa 40:27
yet surely my j. is with Lord. 49:4
I will make my j. to rest for a. 51:4
heathen shall see my j. Ezek 39:21
and my j. is just. John 5:30
my j. is true. 8:16
yet I give my j. 1 Cor 7:25
happier in my j. 40

judgement hall

Jesus to the hall of j. . . . went not into the j. hall. John 18:28*
Pilate entered into the j. hall. 33*
into the j. hall, and saith. 19:9*
kept in Herod's j. hall. Acts 23:35*

judgements

I will redeem you with great j. Ex 6:6; 7:4
these are the j. thou shalt set. 21:1
told the people all the j. 24:3
gods the Lord executed j. Num 33:4
judge according to these j. 35:24
are the j. which the Lord. 36:13
if ye hearken to these j. Deut 7:12
they shall teach Jacob thy j. 33:10
he executed the j. of the Lord. 21
his j. were before me. 2 Sam 22:23
Ps 18:22
remember j. of his mouth. 1 Chr 16:12; Ps 105:5
his j. are in all the earth. 1 Chr 16:14; Ps 105:7
but sinned against thy j. Neh 9:29
thy j. are far above out. Ps 10:5
the j. of the Lord are true. 19:9
thy j. are a great deep. 36:6
be glad because of thy j. 48:11

give the king thy *j.* O God. *Ps* 72:1
Judah rejoiced, because of thy *j.* 97:8
learned thy righteous *j.* 119:7
with my lips I declared all *j.* of. 13
longing that it hath unto thy *j.* 20
thy *j.* have I laid before me. 30
away my reproach, for thy *j.* are. 39
I hoped in thy *j.* 43
I remembered thy *j.* 52
because of thy righteous *j.* 62, 164
I know, O Lord, that thy *j.* are. 75
I have not departed from thy *j.* 102
I will keep thy righteous *j.* 106
teach me thy *j.* 108
I am afraid of thy *j.* 120
art thou, and upright are thy *j.* 137
quicken me according to thy *j.* 156
every one of thy righteous *j.* 160
let my soul live, and let thy *j.* 175
his *j.* they have not known. 147:20
j. are prepared for. *Pr* 19:29
way of thy *j.* we waited. *Isa* 26:8
for when thy *j.* are in the earth. 9
me talk with thee of thy *j.* *Jer* 12:1*
nor done according to *j.* *Ezek* 5:7*
j. in midst of thee. 8; 10:15; 11:9
execute *j.* on thee in sight. 16:41
shall judge thee according to their *j.* 23:24
I will execute *j.* on Moab. 25:11
executed *j.* on all those that. 28:26
I will execute *j.* in No. 30:14
thus will I execute *j.* in Egypt. 19
I will feed them with *j.* 34:16
by departing from thy *j.* *Dan* 9:5
thy *j.* are as the light that. *Hos* 6:5
hath taken away thy *j.* *Zeph* 3:15
unsearchable are his *j.* *Rom* 11:33
if ye have *j.* of things. *1 Cor* 6:4
j. are made manifest. *Rev* 15:4*
righteous are thy *j.* 16:7; 19:2

my judgements

ye shall do *my j.* I am. *Lev* 18:4
therefore keep *my j.* 5; 25:18
if your soul abhor *my j.* so. 26:15
because they despised *my j.* 43
constant to do *my j.* *1 Chr* 28:7
children walk not in *my j.* *Ps* 89:30
I will utter *my j.* against. *Jer* 1:16
she changed *my j.* into wickedness. *Ezek* 5:6
neither have kept *my j.* nor. 5:7
when I send *my* four sore *j.* 14:21
and ye shall keep *my j.* 36:27
judge it according to *my j.* 44:24

statutes and judgements

keep my *st. and* my *j.* *Lev* 18:5, 26
20:22; *Deut* 7:11; 11:1; 26:16, 17
30:16; *1 Ki* 2:3; 8:58; 9:4; 11:33
observe all my *st. and j.* *Lev* 19:37
Deut 11:32; 12:1; *2 Chr* 7:17
these are the *st. and j.* Lord made. *Lev* 26:46; *Deut* 4:45
hearken to *st. and j.* *Deut* 4:1; 5:1
I have taught you *st. and j.* 4:5
hath *st. and j.* so righteous as all? 8
commanded to teach *st. and j.* 14
6:1; *Ezra* 7:10
I will speak the *st. and j.* *Deut* 5:31
thee, What mean the *st. and j.*? 6:20
forget Lord in not keeping his *st. and j.* 8:11; *Neh* 1:7
my *st. and* execute my *j.* *1 Ki* 6:12
heed to fulfil *st. and j.* *1 Chr* 22:13
come between *st. and j.* *2 Chr* 19:10
thou gavest them right *st. and j.* *Neh* 9:13
a curse, to do all his *st. and j.* 10:29
sheweth his *st. and j.* to. *Ps* 147:19
refused my *j. and* my *st.* *Ezek* 5:6
not walked in my *st.* nor executed my *j.* 11:12; 20:13, 16, 21
walked in my *st. and j.* 18:9, 17
20:19; 37:24
my *st. and* shewed my *j.* 20:11
st. of fathers, nor observe their *j.* 18
them *st.* not good, *and j.* 25
of Moses with *st. and j.* *Mal* 4:4

judgement seat

he was set down on *j. seat.*
Mat 27:19; *John* 19:13
brought him to the *j. seat.* *Acts* 18:12
drave them from the *j. seat.* 16
beat Sosthenes before the *j. seat.* 17
I stand at Cesar's *j. seat.* 25:10
I sat on *j. seat.* 17
we shall all stand before the *j. seat* of Christ. *Rom* 14:10; *2 Cor* 5:10
draw you before *j. seats.* *Jas* 2:6

judges

shall bring him to the *j.* *Ex* 21:6*
and he shall pay as the *j.* 22
shall be brought to the *j.* 22:8*
both shall come before the *j.* 9*
Moses said to the *j.* Slay. *Num* 25:5
I charged your *j.* at that. *Deut* 1:16
j. shalt thou make in all. 16:18
stand before priests and *j.* 19:17
the *j.* shall make diligent. 18
thy elders and thy *j.* shall. 21:2
they come that the *j.* may. 25:1
enemies themselves being *j.* 32:31
their *j.* stood on this side. *Josh* 8:33
Joshua called for their heads and *j.* 23:2; 24:1
Lord raised up *j.* *Judg* 2:16, 18
would not hearken to their *j.* 17
when the *j.* ruled a famine. *Ruth* 1:1
he made his sons *j.* *1 Sam* 8:1, 2
I commanded *j.* to be. *2 Sam* 7:11
from the days of the *j.* *2 Ki* 23:22
word to any of the *j.* *1 Chr* 17:6, 10
thousand were officers and *j.* 23:4
and his sons were for *j.* 26:29
Solomon spake to the *j.* *2 Chr* 1:2
he set *j.* in the land. 19:5
said to the *j.* 6
set *j.* which may judge. *Ezra* 7:25
and with them the *j.* of every. 10:14
covereth the face of the *j.* *Job* 9:24
and he maketh the *j.* fools. 12:17
iniquity to be punished by *j.* 31:11
be instructed, ye *j.* of the. *Ps* 2:10
when *j.* are overthrown in. 141:6
princes, and all *j.* of the earth. 148:11
princes rule, and all *j.* of. *Pr* 8:16
I will restore thy *j.* as at. *Isa* 1:26
he maketh the *j.* of the earth. 40:23
sent to gather the *j.* *Dan* 3:2, 3
his words against our *j.* that. 9:12
they have devoured their *j.* *Hos* 7:7
where are thy *j.* of whom? 13:10
her *j.* are evening wolves. *Zeph* 3:3
they shall be your *j.* *Mat* 12:27
Luke 11:19
that he gave to them *j.* *Acts* 13:20
and are become *j.* of evil. *Jas* 2:4

judgest

be clear when thou *j.* *Ps* 51:4
Lord of hosts, that *j.* *Jer* 11:20
whosoever thou art that *j.* *Rom* 2:1
O man, that *j.* them which do. 3
that *j.* another man's servant? 14:4
who art thou that *j.*? *Jas* 4:12

judgeth

seeing he *j.* those that. *Job* 21:22
for by them *j.* he the people. 36:31
God *j.* the righteous, is. *Ps* 7:11
verily he is a God that *j.* in. 58:11
in congregation of mighty, he *j.* 82:1
king that faithfully *j.* *Pr* 29:14
for the Father *j.* no man. *John* 5:22
there is one that *j.* 8:50
one that *j.* him. 12:48
he that is spiritual *j.* all. *1 Cor* 2:15
but he that *j.* me is the Lord. 4:4
that are without, God *j.* 5:13
he that *j.* his brother, *j.* *Jas* 4:11
respect of persons *j.* *1 Pet* 1:17
committed himself to him that *j.* 2:23
strong is the Lord that *j.* *Rev* 18:8

judging

j. the people of the land. *2 Ki* 15:5
2 Chr 26:21
satest in the throne *j.* right. *Ps* 9:4
he shall sit *j.* and seeking. *Isa* 16:5
j. the twelve tribes. *Mat* 19:28
Luke 22:30

juice

to drink wine of the *j.* *S of S* 8:2

jumping

noise of horses and the *j.* *Nah* 3:2†

juniper

and sat under a *j.* tree. *1 Ki* 19:4, 5
who cut up *j.* roots. *Job* 30:4*
the mighty with coals of *j.* *Ps* 120:4

Jupiter

called Barnabas, *J.* *Acts* 14:12
then the priests of *J.* brought. 13
image which fell down from *J.* 19:35

jurisdiction

he belonged to Herod's *j.* *Luke* 23:7

just

[1] *One who is righteous before God,* Gen 6:9. [2] *Exact, accurate,* Lev 19:36. [3] *Honest, upright,* Luke 23:50. *The word is in most places replaced in the Revisions by the word* righteous.

Noah was a *j.* man. *Gen* 6:9
j. balances, *j.* weights, a *j.* ephah, and a *j.* hin shall ye have.
Lev 19:36; *Deut* 25:15; *Ezek* 45:10
judge people with *j.* *Deut* 16:18
that is altogether *j.* shalt thou. 20
a God without iniquity, *j.* and. 32:4
over men must be *j.* *2 Sam* 23:3
thou art *j.* in all that is. *Neh* 9:33
mortal man be more *j.*? *Job* 4:17
but how should man be *j.* with? 9:2
j. upright man is laughed to. 12:4
he may prepare it, but the *j.* 27:17
in this thou art not *j.* 33:12
end, but establish the *j.* *Ps* 7:9
wicked plotteth against the *j.* 37:12
the habitation of the *j.* *Pr* 3:33
the path of the *j.* is as the. 4:18
a *j.* man, and he will increase. 9:9
are upon the head of the *j.* 10:6
the memory of the *j.* is blessed. 7
tongue of the *j.* is as choice. 20
the mouth of the *j.* bringeth forth. 31
but *j.* weight is his delight. 11:1
but through knowledge shall the *j.* 9
but the *j.* shall come out of. 12:13
shall no evil happen to the *j.* 21
the sinner is laid up for the *j.* 13:22
a *j.* weight and balance are. 16:11
he that condemneth the *j.* is. 17:15
also to punish the *j.* is not good. 26
in his own cause seemeth *j.* 18:17
j. man walketh in his integrity. 20:7
joy to the *j.* to do judgement. 21:15
a *j.* man falleth seven times. 24:16
hate the upright, but the *j.* 29:10
man is an abomination to the *j.* 27
j. man that perisheth in. *Eccl* 7:15
not a *j.* man upon earth that. 20
there be *j.* men to whom it. 8:14
j. is uprightness, thou most upright dost weigh path of *j.* *Isa* 26:7
turn aside the *j.* for a thing. 29:21
I the Lord, a *j.* God, and a. 45:21
shed the blood of the *j.* *Lam* 4:13
but if a man be *j.* and. *Ezek* 18:5
he is *j.* he shall surely live. 9
ways of Lord right, *j.* *Hos* 14:9
they afflict the *j.* they. *Amos* 5:12
the *j.* shall live by faith. *Hab* 2:4
Rom 1:17; *Gal* 3:11; *Heb* 10:38
j. Lord is in the midst. *Zeph* 3:5
j. and having salvation. *Zech* 9:9
husband, being a *j.* man. *Mat* 1:19
sendeth rain on the *j.* and on. 5:45
the wicked from among the *j.* 13:49
to do with that *j.* man. 27:19
innocent of the blood of this *j.* 24
knowing that he was a *j.* *Mark* 6:20
the wisdom of the *j.* *Luke* 1:17
Simeon was *j.* and devout. 2:25
the resurrection of the *j.* 14:14
over ninety and nine *j.* persons. 15:7
should feign themselves *j.* 20:20
Joseph was a good man and *j.* 23:50
and my judgement is *j.* *John* 5:30
the centurion a *j.* man. *Acts* 10:22
shall be resurrection both of *j.* 24:15
hearers of the law are *j.* *Rom* 2:13
whose damnation is *j.* 3:8
he might be *j.* 26
the commandment holy, *j.* 7:12
whatsoever things are *j.* *Phil* 4:8
give servants that which is *j.* *Col* 4:1

a bishop must be *j.*, holy. *Tit* 1:8
received a *j.* recompence. *Heb* 2:2
spirits of *j.* men made perfect. 12:23
condemned and killed the *j. Jas* 5:6
Christ suffered, the *j.* *1 Pet* 3:18
delivered *j.* Lot, vexed. *2 Pet* 2:7
if we confess, he is *j.* to. *1 John* 1:9
j. and true are thy ways. *Rev* 15:3

most **just**

condemn him that is *most j.*? *Job* 34:17

Just *One*

Holy One and the *J.* *Acts* 3:14
of the coming of the *J. One.* 7:52
his will, and see that *J. One.* 22:14

justice

(*Uprightness, just treatment. The Revisions often change this word to* righteousness)

keep way of Lord to do *j. Gen* 18:19
he executeth *j.* of Lord. *Deut* 33:21
David executed *j.* *2 Sam* 8:15
1 Chr 18:14
judge, I would do *j.* *2 Sam* 15:4
Almighty pervert *j.*? *Job* 8:3
judgement and *j.* take hold. 36:17
is excellent in plenty of *j.* 37:23
do *j.* to the afflicted and. *Ps* 82:3
j. and judgement are habitation. 89:14
have done judgement and *j.* 119:121
receive the instruction of *j.* *Pr* 1:3
reign, and princes decree *j.* 8:15
seest the perverting of *j.* *Eccl* 5:8
establish his throne with *j.* *Isa* 9:7
keep ye judgement, and do *j.* 56:1
ask of me the ordinances of *j.* 58:2
none calleth for *j.* 59:4
neither doth *j.* overtake us. 9
j. standeth afar off, truth is. 14
execute judgement and *j.* in earth. *Jer* 23:5
bless thee, O habitation of *j.* 31:23
the Lord, the habitation of *j.* 50:7
princes, execute judgement and *j.* *Ezek* 45:9
see do **judgement,** before

justification

raised again for our *j.* *Rom* 4:25
gift is of many offences to *j.* 5:16
free gift came upon all men to *j.* 18
see **sanctify**

justified

a man full of talk be *j.*? *Job* 11:2
I know that I shall be *j.* 13:18
then can man be *j.* with God? 25:4
because he *j.* himself rather. 32:2
thou mightest be *j.* when. *Ps* 51:4
sight shall no man living be *j.* 143:2
they may be *j.* *Isa* 43:9
thou mayest be *j.* 26
all the seed of Israel be *j.* 45:25
backsliding Israel hath *j.* *Jer* 3:11
j. thy sisters in all. *Ezek* 16:51, 52
wisdom is *j.* of her children. *Mat* 11:19; *Luke* 7:35
thy words thou shalt be *j. Mat* 12:37
and publicans *j.* God. *Luke* 7:29
this man went down *j.* rather. 18:14
are *j.* from all things from which ye could not be *j.* by. *Acts* 13:39
doers of the law shall be *j. Rom* 2:13
mightest be *j.* in thy sayings. 3:4
shall no flesh be *j.* in his sight. 20
j. freely by his grace. 24; *Tit* 3:7
a man is *j.* by faith. *Rom* 3:28; 5:1
Gal 2:16; 3:24
if Abraham were *j.* by. *Rom* 4:2
being *j.* by faith we have peace. 5:1
being now *j.* by his blood, we. 9
he *j.* them he also glorified. 8:30
yet am I not hereby *j.* *1 Cor* 4:4
ye are *j.* in the name of Lord. 6:11
a man is not *j.* by the works of the law. *Gal* 2:16; 3:11
whosoever of you is *j.* by law. 5:4
God manifest in the flesh, *j.* in the spirit. *1 Tim* 3:16
our father *j.* by works? *Jas* 2:21
that by works a man is *j.* 24
was not Rahab the harlot *j.* by? 25

justifier

j. of him who believeth. *Rom* 3:26

justifieth

he that *j.* the wicked is. *Pr* 17:15
he is near that *j.* me. *Isa* 50:8
believeth on him that *j.* *Rom* 4:5
of God's elect? it is God that *j.* 8:33

justify

(*To show to be just or righteous; to vindicate*)

I will not *j.* the wicked. *Ex* 23:7
then they shall *j.* the. *Deut* 25:1
if I *j.* myself, my own. *Job* 9:20
God forbid that I should *j.* 27:5
speak, for I desire to *j.* thee. 33:32
which *j.* the wicked for. *Isa* 5:23
my righteous servant *j.* many. 53:11
he willing to *j.* himself. *Luke* 10:29
are they which *j.* yourselves. 16:15
God shall *j.* circumcision. *Rom* 3:30
foreseeing that God would *j. Gal* 3:8

justifying

and *j.* the righteous. *1 Ki* 8:32
2 Chr 6:23

justle

the chariots shall *j.* one. *Nah* 2:4†

justly

Lord require but to do *j.*? *Mi* 6:8
indeed *j.* for we receive. *Luke* 23:41
how holily and *j.* we. *1 Thes* 2:10

Justus

Joseph, who was surnamed *J.* and. *Acts* 1:23
certain man's house, named *J.* 18:7
Jesus, who is called *J.* *Col* 4:11

K

Kadesh

Enmishpat, which is *K.* *Gen* 14:7
to wilderness of Paran to *K.* *Num* 13:26
behold, we are in *K.* a city. 20:16
me at water of Meribah in *K.* 27:14
Deut 32:51; *Ezek* 47:19; 48:28
of Zin, which is *K.* *Num* 33:36
abode in *K.* many days. *Deut* 1:46
shaketh the wilderness of *K. Ps* 29:8

Kadesh-barnea

I sent them from *K.* to see the land.
Num 32:8; *Deut* 9:23; *Josh* 14:7
them from *K.* to Gaza. *Josh* 10:41
concerning me and thee in *K.* 14:6

Kareah, *see* **Johanan**

Kedar

the son of Ishmael, *K.* *Gen* 25:13
1 Chr 1:29
I dwell in the tents of *K.* *Ps* 120:5
comely as the tents of *K. S of S* 1:5
glory of *K.* shall fail. *Isa* 21:16, 17
the villages that *K.* doth. 42:11
the flocks of *K.* shall be. 60:7
send to *K.* and consider. *Jer* 2:10
K., thus saith the Lord; Arise ye, go up to *K.* 49:28
princes of *K.* occupied. *Ezek* 27:21

keep

[1] *To retain or hold fast,* 2 Tim 1:14. [2] *To defend and protect,* Ps 127:1. [3] *To observe and practise,* Ps 119:4; Acts 16:4. [4] *To celebrate,* Mat 26:18. [5] *To perform as a duty; observe,* Mat 19:17.

the garden of Eden to *k.* *Gen* 2:15
and they shall *k.* the way of. 18:19
I am with thee, to *k.* thee. 28:15, 20
I will again feed and *k.* thy. 30:31
my brother, *k.* that thou hast. 33:9
and let them *k.* food in the. 41:35
whom the Egyptians *k.* *Ex* 6:5
shall *k.* it till the fourteenth. 12:6
k. it a feast to the Lord through.
14; 23:15; 34:18; *Lev* 23:41
that ye shall *k.* this service.
Ex 12:25; 13:5
of Israel shall *k.* it. 12:47
thou shalt *k.* this ordinance in. 13:10
sabbath day to *k.* it holy. 20:8
31:13, 14, 16; *Deut* 5:12, 15
money or stuff to *k.* *Ex* 22:7, 10
k. thee far from a false matter. 23:7
three times shalt thou *k.* a feast. 14
I send an Angel to *k.* thee in. 20
that delivered him to *k.* *Lev* 6:2, 4
ye shall *k.* my ordinances, I am the Lord. 18:4, 30; 22:9; *Ezek* 11:20
shall *k.* my sabbaths. *Lev* 19:3, 30
26:2; *Isa* 56:4
shall *k.* a feast seven days.
Lev 23:39; *2 Chr* 30:13
ye shall *k.* my judgements and do.
Lev 25:18
Lord bless thee and *k.* *Num* 6:24
14th day at even ye shall *k.* it. 9:3
month at even they shall *k.* it. 11
thy sons shall *k.* your priests'. 18:7
ye shall *k.* a feast to the. 29:12
k. himself to inheritance. 36:7*, 9*
k. therefore and do them. *Deut* 4:6
5:1*
loved you, would *k.* the oath. 7:8
if ye *k.* them, the Lord shall *k.* 12
k. the feast of weeks to the. 16:10
shalt *k.* a solemn feast to Lord. 15
may learn to *k.* all the words. 17:19
k. thee from every wicked. 23:9
gone out of thy lips thou shalt *k.* 23*
k. therefore the words of this. 29:9
k. yourselves from the. *Josh* 6:18
set men by the cave, for to *k.* 10:18
to *k.* all that is written in the. 23:6
whether they will *k.* the. *Judg* 2:22
thou shalt *k.* fast by my. *Ruth* 2:21
he will *k.* the feet of his. *1 Sam* 2:9
Eleazar his son, to *k.* the ark. 7:1
women which were concubines to *k.*
2 Sam 15:16; 16:21; 20:3
no son to *k.* my name. 18:18
k. with thy servant David.
1 Ki 8:25; *2 Chr* 6:16
man to me and said, *K.* *1 Ki* 20:39
that thou wouldest *k.* me. *1 Chr* 4:10
which could *k.* rank. 12:33*, 38*
that thou mayest *k.* the law. 22:12
k. this for ever in imagination. 29:18
had no power to *k.* still the kingdom.
2 Chr 22:9*
ye purpose to *k.* under the. 28:10
for they could not *k.* it at. 30:3
assembly took counsel to *k.* other. 23
watch and *k.* them till. *Ezra* 8:29
to *k.* the dedication with. *Neh* 12:27
that the Levites should *k.* 13:22
nor *k.* they the king's. *Esth* 3:8
that they would *k.* those two. 9:27
that thou wouldest *k.* me. *Job* 14:13
though he *k.* it still within. 20:13
k. them, O Lord. *Ps* 12:7; 31:20
k. me as the apple of the eye. 17:8
k. back thy servant also from presumptuous sins. 19:13
O *k.* my soul, and deliver me. 25:20
k. thy tongue from evil, and. 34:13
and *k.* his way. 37:34
I will *k.* my mouth. 39:1
my mercy will I *k.* for him. 89:28
his angels charge, to *k.* thee. 91:11
nor chide, nor will he *k.* his. 103:9
observe and *k.* his laws. 105:45
blessed are they that *k.* judgement.
106:3
barren woman to *k.* house. 113:9
blessed are they that *k.* his. 119:2
thou hast commanded us to *k.* 4
may live and *k.* thy word. 17, 101
teach me, and I shall *k.* it to. 33
I shall *k.* thy law. 34, 44
I have said, that I would *k.* 57
I am a companion of them that *k.* 63
I will *k.* thy precepts with. 69, 134
so shall I *k.* the testimony of thy. 88
I understand, because I *k.* thy. 100
k. thy righteous judgements. 106
therefore doth my soul *k.* them. 129
down my eyes, because they *k.* 136
save me, and I shall *k.* thy. 146
except the Lord *k.* the city. 127:1
k. me from the hands of the. 140:4
k. the door of my lips. 141:3
k. me from the snares they have. 9
understanding shall *k.* thee. *Pr* 2:11
thou mayest *k.* the paths of the. 20
my son, *k.* sound wisdom and. 3:21

Lord shall *k.* thy foot from. *Pr* 3:26
love wisdom, and she shall *k.* 4:6
k. instruction, let her not go, for. 13
k. my sayings in the midst of. 21
k. thy heart with all diligence. 23
and that thy lips may *k.* 5:2
when thou sleepest it shall *k.* 6:22
to *k.* thee from the evil woman. 24
my son, *k.* my words, and lay. 7:1
may *k.* thee from the strange. 5
for blessed are they that *k.* 8:32
he that doth *k.* his soul shall. 22:5
it is pleasant if thou *k.* them. 18
such as *k.* the law contend. 28:4
there is a time to *k.* and. *Eccl* 3:6
k. thy foot when thou goest to. 5:1
k. the fruit thereof, two. *S of S* 8:12
wilt *k.* him in perfect. *Isa* 26:3
I the Lord do *k.* it, I will *k.* it. 27:3
have called thee, I will *k.* thee. 42:6
k. not back. 43:6
k. ye judgement. 56:1
k. his anger to the end ? *Jer* 3:5
and I will not *k.* anger for ever. 12
k. him as a shepherd doth. 31:10
I will *k.* nothing back from. 42:4
k. my judgements and do them.
Ezek 20:19; 36:27
that they may *k.* the whole. 43:11
k. mercy and judgement. *Hos* 12:6
k. the doors of thy mouth. *Mi* 7:5
k. thy feasts. *Nah* 1:15
k. the munition. 2:1
shalt also *k.* my courts. *Zech* 3:7
man taught me to *k.* cattle. 13:5*
k. the feast of tabernacles. 14:16
18, 19
the priests' lips should *k.* *Mal* 2:7
k. your own tradition. *Mark* 7:9
his angels charge to *k.* *Luke* 4:10
having heard the word *k.* it. 8:15
that hear the word and *k.* it. 11:28
thy enemies shall *k.* thee in. 19:43
if *k.* my saying shall. *John* 8:51, 52
but I know him, and *k.* his. 55
his life in this world shall *k.* 12:25
if a man love me he will *k.* 14:23
my saying, they will *k.* yours. 15:20
k. through thy name. 17:11
k. from the evil. 15
and to *k.* back part of the. *Acts* 5:3
for a man that is a Jew to *k.* 10:28
him to soldiers to *k.* him. 12:4
command them to *k.* the law. 15:5
ye must be circumcised, and *k.* 24
from which, if ye *k.* yourselves. 29
them the decrees for to *k.* 16:4
charging the jailer to *k.* them. 23
I must by all means *k.* this. 18:21
k. themselves from things. 21:25
a centurion to *k.* Paul. 24:23*
if thou *k.* the law. *Rom* 2:25
k. the righteousness of law. 26
let us *k.* the feast. *1 Cor* 5:8
not *k.* company. 11
decreed that he will *k.* his. 7:37
I *k.* under my body and bring. 9:27*
that ye *k.* the ordinances, as. 11:2
if ye *k.* in memory what I. 15:2*
and so will I *k.* myself. *2 Cor* 11:9
neither do circumcised *k.* *Gal* 6:13
endeavouring to *k.* unity. *Eph* 4:3
peace of God shall *k.* *Phil* 4:7
who shall stablish and *k.* *2 Thes* 3:3
nor partaker of sins, *k.* *1 Tim* 5:22
k. that which is committed to. 6:20
able to *k.* that which I have committed unto him. *2 Tim* 1:12
good thing committed to thee *k.* 14
and to *k.* himself unspotted. *Jas* 1:27
whosoever shall *k.* whole law. 2:10
k. yourselves from idols. *1 John* 5:21
k. yourselves in the love. *Jude* 21
to him that is able to *k.* you. 24
blessed are they that hear and *k.*
Rev 1:3
I will *k.* thee from the hour of. 3:10
of them who *k.* the sayings of. 22:9

keep *alive*

ark to *k.* them *alive.* *Gen* 6:19, 20
to *k.* seed *alive* on the face of. 7:3
women, children *k. alive.* *Num* 31:18
full line to *k. alive.* *2 Sam* 8:2
none can *k. alive* his own soul.
Ps 22:29
deliver and *k.* them *alive* in. 33:19
preserve him and *k.* him *alive.* 41:2

keep *charge*

and *k.* the *charge* of the Lord.
Lev 8:35; *1 Ki* 2:3
k. charge of tabernacle. *Num* 1:53
18:4; 31:30; *1 Chr* 23:32
they shall *k.* his *charge.* *Num* 3:7
8:26; 18:3; *Deut* 11:1
k. the *charge* of children of Israel.
Num 3:8
k. charge of the sanctuary. 32
18:5; *1 Chr* 23:32
to me, and *k.* my *charge.* *Ezek* 44:16
if thou wilt *k.* my *charge.* *Zech* 3:7

keep *commandments*

refuse ye to *k.* my *com.*? *Ex* 16:28
to them that *k.* my *com.* 20:6
Deut 5:10; 7:9; *Dan* 9:4
ye *k.* my *com.* and do them.
Lev 22:31; *Deut* 4:40; 6:17; 7:11
if ye *k.* my *com.* *Lev* 26:3
Deut 11:22; 19:9; 28:9; 30:10
1 Ki 3:14
may *k.* the *com.* of Lord. *Deut* 4:2
would fear me and *k.* my *com.* 5:29
thou wouldest *k.* his *com.* 8:2
thou shalt *k.* the *com.* 6; 11:1, 8
13:4, 18
to *k.* the *com.* of the Lord. 10:13
27:1; 30:16
avouched Lord to *k.* his *com.* 26:17
thee, that thou shouldest *k. com.* 18
hearkenedst not to *k.* his *com.* 28:45
to *k.* his *com.* to cleave. *Josh* 22:5
charge of Lord to *k.* his *com.* *1 Ki* 2:3
k. my *com.* 6:12; *2 Ki* 17:13
Pr 4:4; 7:2
incline our hearts to *k.* his *com.*
1 Ki 8:58
be perfect to *k.* his *com.* 61
if ye will not *k.* my *com.* I will. 9:6
if thou wilt *k.* my *com.* 11:38
Neh 1:9; *John* 15:10
made a covenant to *k. com.*
2 Ki 23:3; *2 Chr* 34:31
k. and seek for all the *com.* of the.
1 Chr 28:8
a perfect heart to *k.* thy *com.* 29:19
of God, but *k.* his *com.* *Ps* 78:7
delayed not to *k.* thy *com.* 119:60
for I will *k. com.* of my God. 115
let thy heart *k.* my *com.* *Pr* 3:1
my son, *k.* thy father's *com.* 6:20
to *k.* the king's *com.* *Eccl* 8:2
fear God and *k.* his *com.* this. 12:13
enter into life, *k.* the *com.* *Mat* 19:17
love me, *k.* my *com.* *John* 14:15
k. this *com.* without spot. *1 Tim* 6:14
we do know that we know him if we *k.* his *com.* *1 John* 2:3
receive, because we *k.* his *com.* 3:22
love God and *k.* his *com.* 5:2
love of God, that we *k.* his *com.* 3
her seed which *k. com.* *Rev* 12:17
are they which *k.* the *com.* 14:12
see **covenant**

keep *passover*

k. pass. to Lord . . . be circumcised, then let him *k. pass.* *Ex* 12:48
of Israel *k. pass.* in its season.
Num 9:2, 4; *Deut* 16:1
2 Ki 23:21
could not *k.* the *pass.* *Num* 9:6
yet he shall *k. pass.* 10
ordinances of *pass.* they shall *k.* 12
and forbeareth to *k.* the *pass.* 13
if a stranger will *k.* the *pass.* to. 14
come to *k.* the *pass.* to. *2 Chr* 30:1
taken counsel, to *k. pass.* in the. 2
was prepared to *k. pass.* 35:16
kings of Israel *k.* such a *pass.* 18
say to him, I will *k. pass.* *Mat* 26:18

keep *silence*

who said, *K. silence,* and. *Judg* 3:19
k. not *silence.* *Ps* 35:22; 83:1
come and not *k. silence.* 50:3
a time to *k. silence* and. *Eccl* 3:7
k. silence before me, O. *Isa* 41:1
k. not *silence.* 62:6
behold, I will not *k. silence.* *Isa* 65:6
elders of daughter of Zion *k. silence.*
Lam 2:10
prudent shall *k. silence.* *Amos* 5:13
let the earth *k. silence.* *Hab* 2:20
let him *k. silence* in the. *1 Cor* 14:28
let your women *k. silence* in the. 34

keep *statutes*

if thou wilt *k.* all his *stat.* *Ex* 15:26
Deut 30:10; *1 Ki* 9:4; 11:38
k. my *stat.* and judgements.
Lev 18:5, 26; 19:19; 20:8, 22
Ezek 44:24
thou shalt *k.* therefore his *stat.*
Deut 4:10; 26:16
fear Lord to *k.* his *stat.* 6:2
avouched Lord to *k.* his *stat.* 26:17
hearkenedst not to *k.* his *stat.* 28:45
in my ways to *k.* my *stat.* *1 Ki* 11:33
were directed to *k.* thy *stat.* *Ps* 119:5
I will *k.* thy *stat.*, forsake. 8, 145
will turn and *k.* my *stat.* *Ezek* 18:21

keeper

Abel was a *k.* of sheep. *Gen* 4:2
am I my brother's *k.*? 9
Joseph favour in sight of *k.* 39:21
the *k.* of the prison committed. 22
the *k.* of the prison looked not to. 23
left sheep with a *k.* *1 Sam* 17:20
carriage in the hand of the *k.* 22
I will make thee *k.* of mine. 28:2
k. of the wardrobe. *2 Ki* 22:14
2 Chr 34:22
Asaph the *k.* of the king's. *Neh* 2:8
after him Shemaiah *k.* of the. 3:29
Hege *k.* of women. *Esth* 2:3, 8, 15
and as a booth that the *k.* *Job* 27:18
Lord is thy *k.*, the Lord. *Ps* 121:5
they made me the *k.* of. *S of S* 1:6
the son of Shallum *k.* of *Jer* 35:4
k. of prison awaking. *Acts* 16:27*
the *k.* of the prison told this. 36*

keepers

a third part shall be *k.* *2 Ki* 11:5
k. of the gates of the. *1 Chr* 9:19
when the *k.* of the house. *Eccl* 12:3
k. took away my vail. *S of S* 5:7
let out the vineyard to *k.* 8:11
as *k.* of the field are. *Jer* 4:17
k. of charge of house. *Ezek* 40:45
46; 44:8, 14
for fear of him the *k.* *Mat* 28:4
k. standing before doors. *Acts* 5:23
k. kept the prison. 12:6*
Herod examined the *k.* 19*
discreet, chaste, *k.* at home. *Tit* 2:5*
see **door**

keepest

who *k.* covenant and. *1 Ki* 8:23
2 Chr 6:14; *Neh* 9:32
orderly and *k.* the law. *Acts* 21:24

keepeth

and he die not, but *k.* *Ex* 21:18
faithful God which *k.* covenant.
Deut 7:9; *Neh* 1:5
behold he *k.* the sheep. *1 Sam* 16:11
he *k.* back his soul from. *Job* 33:18
he *k.* all his bones, none. *Ps* 34:20
he that *k.* thee will not. 121:3, 4
Lord God, which *k.* truth. 146:6
he *k.* the paths of. *Pr* 2:8
is in the way of life that *k.* 10:17*
he that *k.* his mouth *k.* 13:3; 21:23
righteousness *k.* him upright in. 13:6
k. his way preserveth. 16:17; 19:16
he that *k.* understanding. 19:8
that *k.* thy soul, doth not he. 24:12
whoso *k.* the fig tree shall. 27:18
whoso *k.* the law is a wise. 28:7
that *k.* company with harlots. 29:3
but a wise man *k.* it in till. 11
but he that *k.* the law, happy. 18
k. the commandments. *Eccl* 8:5
nation which *k.* truth. *Isa* 26:2
k. the sabbath from polluting it, and *k.* his hand from doing. 56:2, 6
that *k.* back his sword. *Jer* 48:10
he sitteth alone and *k.* *Lam* 3:28
man, neither *k.* at home. *Hab* 2:5
a strong man armed *k.* *Luke* 11:21
yet none of you *k.* the. *John* 7:19
is not of God, because he *k.* 9:16

that hath my commandments and *k.* them. *John* 14:21
he that loveth me not, *k.* not. 24
I know him, and *k.* not. *1 John* 2:4
whoso *k.* his word, in him. 5; 3:24
he that is begotten of God *k.* 5:18
that overcometh and *k.* *Rev* 2:26
blessed is he that *k.* his. 16:15
blessed is he that *k.* sayings. 22:7

keeping

Lord God *k.* mercy for. *Ex* 34:7
k. the charge of the. *Num* 3:28, 38
forget not God, in not *k.* *Deut* 8:11
with them *k.* sheep. *1 Sam* 25:16
were porters *k.* the ward. *Neh* 12:25
and in *k.* of them is great. *Ps* 19:11
by *k.* of his covenant. *Ezek* 17:14
O Lord the great God, *k.* *Dan* 9:4
there were shepherds *k.* *Luke* 2:8
k. the commandments. *1 Cor* 7:19
commit the *k.* of their. *1 Pet* 4:19

Keilah

K. and Achzib, cities. *Josh* 15:44
Philistines fight against *K.* *1 Sam* 23:1
arise, go down to *K.* 4
David saved *K.* 5
son of Ahimelech fled to *K.* 6
K. deliver me to Saul ? 11, 12
the ruler of the half part of *K.* repaired. *Neh* 3:17, 18

Kenaz, *see* **Othniel**

Kenites

seed have I given the *K.* *Gen* 15:19
Balaam looked on the *K.* *Num* 24:21
Saul said to the *K.* *1 Sam* 15:6
road against south of the *K.* 27:10

kept

Abraham *k.* my charge. *Gen* 26:5
with sheep, for she *k.* them. 29:9
nor hath he *k.* back any thing. 39:9
send one, and ye shall be *k.* 42:16
now Moses *k.* the flock. *Ex* 3:1
lay up for you to be *k.* until. 16:23
pot of manna *k.* for. 32, 33, 34
the owner hath not *k.* 21:29, 36
and it be *k.* close, and. *Num* 5:13
they *k.* the passover. 9:5
why are we *k.* back ? 7
then Israel *k.* the charge. 19, 23
bring Aaron's rod to be *k.* 17:10
k. for a water of separation. 19:9
Lord hath *k.* thee back. 24:11
which *k.* the charge of the. 31:47
k. them as the apple. *Deut* 32:10
they observed thy word, and *k.* 33:9
Israel *k.* the passover. *Josh* 5:10
k. me alive these 45 years. 14:10
ye have *k.* all that Moses. 22:2
ye have *k.* the charge of. 3
k. fast by the maidens. *Ruth* 2:23
time it hath been *k.* *1 Sam* 9:24
not *k.* the commandment. 13:13, 14
David said, Thy servant *k.* his. 17:34
k. themselves from women. 21:4
surely in vain have I *k.* all. 25:21
blessed be thou who hast *k.* me. 33
the Lord God hath *k.* me. 34, 39
why hast thou not *k.* thy ? 26:15
because ye have not *k.* your. 16
the young man that *k.* *2 Sam* 13:34
I have *k.* the ways of the Lord. 22:22
Ps 18:21
I have *k.* myself from iniquity. *2 Sam* 22:24; *Ps* 18:23
hast *k.* me to be head of the heathen. *2 Sam* 22:44
not *k.* the oath of Lord ? *1 Ki* 2:43
thou hast *k.* for him this great. 3:6
k. with thy servant David my father. 8:24; *2 Chr* 6:15
Solomon *k.* not that the Lord. *1 Ki* 11:10
thou hast not *k.* my covenant and. 11
because David *k.* my commandments. 34; 14:8
man of God from Judah not *k.* 13:21
Judah *k.* not the. *2 Ki* 17:19
Hezekiah *k.* commandments. 18:6
the word of the Lord Saul *k.* not. *1 Chr* 10:13
while David *k.* himself close. 12:1
Solomon *k.* the feast. *2 Chr* 7:8
k. the dedication of altar. 9
k. feast of unleavened bread. 30:21; *Ezra* 6:22
and they *k.* other seven days. *2 Chr* 30:23
our fathers have not *k.* the. 34:21
Josiah and Israel *k.* the passover. 35:1, 17, 19
was no passover like to that *k.* 18
they *k.* also the feast of. *Ezra* 3:4
k. the dedication of this house. 6:16
children of the captivity *k.* the. 19
we have not *k.* the commandments. *Neh* 1:7
they *k.* the feast seven days. 8:18
nor our fathers *k.* thy law. 9:34
days of Purim be *k.* *Esth* 9:28
ways have I *k.* and not. *Job* 23:11
k. close from the fowls of air. 28:21
I have *k.* me from paths. *Ps* 17:4
hast *k.* me alive. 30:3
a multitude that *k.* holy day. 42:4
they *k.* not the covenant of. 78:10
they tempted God, and *k.* not. 56
they *k.* his testimonies and. 99:7
have *k.* thy testimonies. 119:22, 167
I have *k.* thy law. 55
because I *k.* thy precepts. 56, 168
now have I *k.* thy word. 67
they *k.* not thy word. 158
eyes desired, I *k.* not. *Eccl* 2:10
riches *k.* for owners thereof. 5:13
vineyard have I not *k.* *S of S* 1:6
a holy solemnity is *k.* *Isa* 30:29
not *k.* my laws. *Jer* 16:11
and *k.* his precepts. 35:18
neither have *k.* my judgements. *Ezek* 5:7; 20:21
hath *k.* my judgements. 18:9
hath *k.* my statutes. 19
ye have not *k.* the charge of. 44:8
that *k.* the charge of my. 15; 48:11
would, he *k.* alive, he set. *Dan* 5:19
I *k.* the matter in my heart. 7:28
for a wife, and *k.* sheep. *Hos* 12:12
and Edom *k.* his wrath. *Amos* 1:11
Judah hath not *k.* his. 2:4
statutes of Omri are *k.* *Mi* 6:16
as ye have not *k.* my ways. *Mal* 2:9; 3:7
what profit is it that we have *k.*? 3:14
they that *k.* the swine. *Mat* 8:33
which have been *k.* secret. 13:35
Herod's birthday was *k.* 14:6
these have I *k.* from my youth. 19:20; *Luke* 18:21
nor was any thing *k.* secret, but. *Mark* 4:22
and they *k.* that saying. 9:10
Luke 9:36
Mary *k.* these things. *Luke* 2:19, 51
he was *k.* bound with chains. 8:29
thy pound, which I have *k.* 19:20
but thou hast *k.* good. *John* 2:10
of my burying hath she *k.* this. 12:7
as I have *k.* my father's. 15:10
if they have *k.* my saying. 20
thine they were, and have *k.* 17:6
k. in thy name, those thou gavest me I have *k.* 12
and spake to her that *k.* the. 18:16
saith the damsel that *k.* the door. 17
sold, and *k.* back part of. *Acts* 5:2
law, and have not *k.* it. 7:53
Eneas had *k.* his bed eight. 9:33
Peter was *k.* in prison. 12:5
keepers *k.* the prison. 6
I *k.* back nothing profitable. 20:20
and *k.* the raiment of them. 22:20
and he commanded him to be *k.* 23:35; 25:21
that Paul should be *k.* 25:4
the centurion *k.* them from. 27:43
with a soldier that *k.* him. 28:16
mystery *k.* secret since. *Rom* 16:25
I *k.* myself from being. *2 Cor* 11:9
the governor *k.* the city with. 32
we were *k.* under law. *Gal* 3:23
my course, I *k.* the faith. *2 Tim* 4:7
through faith Moses *k.* *Heb* 11:28
the hire that is *k.* back. *Jas* 5:4
who are *k.* by the power. *1 Pet* 1:5
by the same word are *k.* *2 Pet* 3:7
angels which *k.* not their. *Jude* 6
hast *k.* my word, and not. *Rev* 3:8
because thou hast *k.* the word. 10

kept *silence*

men gave ear, and *k. sil.* *Job* 29:21
great multitude, that I *k. sil.* 31:34
when I *k. sil.* my bones. *Ps* 32:3
hast thou done, and I *k. sil.* 50:21
the multitude *k. sil.* *Acts* 15:12
Hebrew, they *k.* the more *sil.* 22:2

kerchiefs

k. on head of every. *Ezek* 13:18
your *k.* will I tear, and deliver. 21

Kerioth

judgement is come on *K.* *Jer* 48:24
K. is taken. 41
devour the palaces of *K.* *Amos* 2:2

kernels

eat nothing from the *k.* *Num* 6:4

kettle

servant struck into the *k.* *1 Sam* 2:14

Keturah

wife, her name was *K.* *Gen* 25:1
children of *K.* 4; *1 Chr* 1:32, 33

key

therefore they took a *k.* *Judg* 3:25
k. of house of David lay. *Isa* 22:22
have taken away the *k.* *Luke* 11:52
saith he that hath the *k.* *Rev* 3:7
given *k.* of bottomless pit. 9:1; 20:1

keys

give the *k.* of kingdom. *Mat* 16:19
k. of hell and of death. *Rev* 1:18

kick

wherefore *k.* ye at my ? *1 Sam* 2:29
it is hard to *k.* against the pricks. *Acts* 9:5; 26:14

kicked

but Jeshurun waxed fat and *k.* *Deut* 32:15

kid

(*Kid of the goats is frequently changed in Revisions to* he goat)

brethren killed a *k.* of. *Gen* 37:31
I will send thee a *k.* from. 38:17
not seethe *k.* in his mother's milk. *Ex* 23:19; 34:26; *Deut* 14:21
bring his offering, a *k.* of the goats. *Lev* 4:23, 28; 9:3; *Ezek* 43:22
45:23
or a *k.* for a sin offering. *Lev* 5:6
then ye shall sacrifice one *k.* 23:19
Num 7:16, 22, 28; 15:24; 28:15
30; 29:5, 11, 16, 19, 25
done for a lamb or a *k.* *Num* 15:11
and made ready a *k.* *Judg* 6:19
so Manoah took a *k.* with a. 13:19
Samson rent lion as a *k.* 14:6
visited his wife with a *k.* 15:1
an ass laden, and a *k.* *1 Sam* 16:20
lie down with the *k.* *Isa* 11:6
never gavest me a *k.* *Luke* 15:29

kidneys

thou shalt take the two *k.* and burn. *Ex* 29:13, 22; *Lev* 3:4, 10, 15; 4:9
7:4; 8:16, 25
but fat and *k.* burnt on. *Lev* 9:10, 19
rams, with the fat of *k.* *Deut* 32:14
the sword of Lord, with fat of *k.* of rams. *Isa* 34:6

Kidron, *see* **brook**

kids

fetch me from thence two *k.* *Gen* 27:9
she put the skins of the *k.* on. 16
take two *k.* of the goats. *Lev* 16:5
the *k.* of the goats for. *Num* 7:87
one carrying three *k.* *1 Sam* 10:3
two little flocks of *k.* *1 Ki* 20:27
Josiah gave lambs and *k.* *2 Chr* 35:7
feed thy *k.* beside the. *S of S* 1:8

kill

Cain, should *k.* him. *Gen* 4:15
they will *k.* me, but will save. 12:12
men of the place should *k.* me. 26:7
himself, purposing to *k.* thee. 27:42
and said, Let us not *k.* him. 37:21
a son, then ye shall *k.* him. *Ex* 1:16
thou to *k.* me ? 2:14; *Acts* 7:28
him, and sought to *k.* him. *Ex* 4:24

of Israel shall *k.* it. *Ex* 12:6, 21
to *k.* this whole assembly. 16:3
to *k.* us and our children. 17:3
thou shalt not *k.* 20:13*; *Deut* 5:17*
Mat 5:21; *Rom* 13:9
steal an ox or sheep, and *k. Ex* 22:1
I will *k.* you with the sword. 24
k. bullock before the Lord. 29:11
Lev 1:5; 4:4
then thou shalt *k.* the ram. *Ex* 29:20
shall *k.* it on the side of the altar.
Lev 1:11; 16:15
and *k.* it at the door of the. 3:2
shall *k.* it before the tabernacle. 8, 13
k. it in the place where they *k.* 4:24
k. the burnt offering. 33; 7:2
k. the sin offering. 14:13; 16:11
he shall *k.* the lamb of the. 14:25
shall *k.* the one of the birds. 50
seed to Molech, and *k.* him not. 20:4
thou shalt *k.* the woman and the. 16
cow or ewe, ye shall not *k.* it. 22:28
thus with me, *k.* me. *Num* 11:15
if thou *k.* all this people as. 14:15
hast brought us to *k.* us in. 16:13
for now would I *k.* thee. 22:29
k. every male among the little ones, *k.* every woman that hath. 31:17
revenger of blood *k.* slayer. 35:27
should *k.* his neighbour unawares.
Deut 4:42
thou mayest *k.* and eat flesh. 12:15
then thou shalt *k.* of thy herd. 21
but thou shalt surely *k.* him. 13:9
I *k.* and I make alive, I. 32:29
if Lord were pleased to *k. Judg* 13:23
saying, Surely we will not *k.* 15:13
it is day, we shall *k.* him. 16:2
they began to *k.* as at other times.
20:31, 39
hear it, he will *k.* me. *1 Sam* 16:2
if he be able to *k.* me, then. 17:9
that they should *k.* David. 19:1
Saul my father seeketh to *k.* thee. 2
why should I *k.* thee? 17
bade me *k.* thee. 24:10
swear thou wilt neither *k.* me. 30:15
smite Amnon, then *k.* *2 Sam* 13:28
that we may *k.* him, for the life. 14:7
iniquity be in me, let him *k.* me. 32
nor for us shalt thou *k.* any. 21:4
Solomon sought to *k.* *1 Ki* 11:40
and they shall *k.* me, and go. 12:27
am I God, to *k.* and? *2 Ki* 5:7
and if they *k.* us, we shall. 7:4
him that followeth her *k.* 11:15
k. the passover, sanctify. *2 Chr* 35:6
by posts to *k.* all Jews. *Esth* 3:13
a time to *k.* and a time. *Eccl* 3:3
and I will *k.* thy root. *Isa* 14:30
year to year, let them *k.* 29:1*
ye *k.* them that are fed. *Ezek* 34:3
shall *k.* shall be in danger. *Mat* 5:21
fear not them which *k.* the body.
10:28; *Luke* 12:4
and they shall *k.* him. *Mat* 17:23
Mark 9:31; 10:34
come let us *k.* him. *Mat* 21:38
Mark 12:7; *Luke* 20:14
ye shall *k.* and crucify. *Mat* 23:34
deliver you up, and shall *k.* you. 24:9
take Jesus by subtilty and *k.* 26:4
to save life, or to *k.*? *Mark* 3:4
do not *k.* 10:19; *Luke* 18:20
Jas 2:11
for Herod will *k.* thee. *Luke* 13:31
hither the fatted calf and *k.* it. 15:23
and scribes sought how to *k.* 22:2
Jews sought the more to *k.* him.
John 5:18; 7:1
why go ye about to *k.* me? 7:19
who goeth about to *k.* thee? 20
he whom they seek to *k.*? 25
will he *k.* himself? 8:22
ye seek to *k.* me. 37, 40
not but to steal and *k.* 10:10
Jews took counsel to *k.* Paul.
Acts 9:23; 26:21
day and night to *k.* him. 9:24
to him, Rise, Peter, *k.* and eat. 10:13
they went about to *k.* him. 21:31
near, are ready to *k.* him. 23:15
laying wait in the way to *k.* 25:3
soldiers' counsel was to *k.* 27:42
no adultery, yet if thou *k.* *Jas* 2:11
ye *k.* and desire to have, and. 4:2
I will *k.* her children. *Rev* 2:23
that they should *k.* one another. 6:4
power was given them to *k.* with. 8
that they should not *k.* them. 9:5
overcome them and *k.* them. 11:7

killed

Joseph's coat, and *k.* a kid.
Gen 37:31
the beast hath *k.* a man. *Ex* 21:29
bullock shall be *k.* before. *Lev* 4:15
where the burnt offering is *k.* shall the sin offering be *k.* before. 6:25
the ram he *k.* 8:19
one of the birds be *k.* 14:5
in the blood of the bird *k.* 6
ye have *k.* the people. *Num* 16:41
whosoever hath *k.* any person. 31:19
skirt of thy robe, and *k. 1 Sam* 24:11
take my flesh I have *k.* for. 25:11
woman hasted and *k.* the calf. 28:24
thou hast *k.* Uriah with. *2 Sam* 12:9
smote the Philistine and *k.* 21:17
and because he *k.* him. *1 Ki* 16:7
and smote Ela, and *k.* him. 10
hast thou *k.* and also taken? 21:19
Pekah *k.* Pekahiah. *2 Ki* 15:25
David *k.* Shophach. *1 Chr* 19:18
Ahab *k.* sheep and. *2 Chr* 18:2
he slew those that had *k.* the. 25:3
so they *k.* the bullocks, rams. 29:22
the priests *k.* them and made. 24
k. the passover. 30:15; 35:1, 11
Ezra 6:20
for thy sake are we *k.* *Ps* 44:22
k. her beasts, mingled. *Pr* 9:2
hast *k.* and not pitied. *Lam* 2:21
and be *k.* and be raised again.
Mat 16:21; *Mark* 8:31; 9:31
beat one, and *k.* another. *Mat* 21:35
Mark 12:5
oxen and my fatlings are *k. Mat* 22:4
are children of them that *k.* 23:31
Herodias would have *k. Mark* 6:19
k. him and cast him out of the. 12:8
the first day, when they *k.* 14:12
fathers *k.* them. *Luke* 11:47, 48
after he hath *k.* hath power. 12:5
hath *k.* the fatted calf. 15:27, 30
when the passover must be *k.* 22:7
k. the Prince of life. *Acts* 3:15
he *k.* James. 12:2
and would have *k.* himself. 16:27
drink till they had *k.* Paul. 23:12
Jews, and should have been *k.* 27
for thy sake we are *k.* all. *Rom* 8:36
Lord, they have *k.* thy prophets. 11:3
as chastened and not *k.* *2 Cor* 6:9
who *k.* the Lord Jesus. *1 Thes* 2:15
ye have condemned and *k.* *Jas* 5:6
brethren who should be *k. Rev* 6:11
was the third part of men *k.* 9:18
the rest which were not *k.* by. 20
he must in this manner be *k.* 11:5
killeth with sword, must be *k.* 13:10
image of the beast, should be *k.* 15

killedst

to kill me, as thou *k.* the. *Ex* 2:14
forasmuch as thou *k.* *1 Sam* 24:18

killest

Jerusalem, which *k.* the prophets.
Mat 23:37; *Luke* 13:34

killeth

k. an ox, or lamb, or goat, in the camp, or *k.* it out. *Lev* 17:3
k. any man shall surely be put to death. 24:17, 21; *Num* 35:30
he that *k.* a beast. *Lev* 24:18, 21
k. any person unawares. *Num* 35:11
15; *Deut* 19:4; *Josh* 20:3, 9
the Lord *k.* and maketh. *1 Sam* 2:6
man who *k.* him, king. 17:25; 26:27
wrath *k.* the foolish man. *Job* 5:2
the murderer *k.* the poor and. 24:14
of the slothful *k.* him. *Pr* 21:25
he that *k.* an ox, as if he. *Isa* 66:3
who *k.* you will think. *John* 16:2
letter *k.*, but the Spirit. *2 Cor* 3:6
he that *k.* with sword. *Rev* 13:10

killing

which aided him in *k.* *Judg* 9:24
charge of *k.* passover. *2 Chr* 30:17
oxen, and *k.* sheep. *Isa* 22:13
by swearing, lying, *k.* and. *Hos* 4:2
beating some, and *k.* *Mark* 12:5

kin

approach to any near of *k. Lev* 18:6
uncovereth his near *k.* 20:19
for his *k.* that is near, he. 21:2
if any of his *k.* come to. 25:25*, 49
the man is near of *k.* to. *Ruth* 2:20
the king is near of *k.* *2 Sam* 19:42
not, but among his own *k. Mark* 6:4

kind, *substantive*

herb yielding seed, and the fruit tree yielding fruit after his *k.*
Gen 1:11, 12
forth abundantly after their *k.* and every winged fowl after his *k.* 21
beast of earth after their *k.* 24
beast of the earth after his *k.* 25
k. and of cattle after their *k.*, every creeping thing after his *k.* 6:20
cattle and fowl, after their *k.* 7:14
raven, hawk after his *k.* *Lev* 11:14
15, 16, 19; *Deut* 14:14
and tortoise after his *k.* *Lev* 11:29
cattle gender with a diverse *k.* 19:19
instruments of every *k. 1 Chr* 28:14
sellers of all *k.* of ware. *Neh* 13:20
I planted trees of all *k.* *Eccl* 2:5
the multitude of all *k.* of. *Ezek* 27:12
and gathered of every *k. Mat* 13:47
this *k.* goeth not out but by prayer.
17:21; *Mark* 9:29
there is one *k.* of flesh. *1 Cor* 15:39
that we should be a *k.* *Jas* 1:18
for every *k.* of beasts and birds. 3:7

kind

saying, If thou be *k.* to. *2 Chr* 10:7
God is *k.* to unthankful. *Luke* 6:35
suffereth long and is *k.* *1 Cor* 13:4
be *k.* one to another. *Eph* 4:32

kindle

a contentious man to *k.* *Pr* 26:21*
k. in the thickets of the. *Isa* 9:18
k. a burning like the burning. 10:16
breath of the Lord doth *k.* it. 30:33
nor shall the flame *k.* upon. 43:2
never want a man to *k.* *Jer* 33:18*
fire and flame shall *k.* in. *Ob* 18

kindled

Potiphar's wrath was *k.* *Gen* 39:19
burning the Lord hath *k.* *Lev* 10:6
wrath of the Lord was *k. Num* 11:33
Deut 11:17; *2 Ki* 22:13, 17
Ps 106:40
coals were *k.* by it. *2 Sam* 22:9
Ps 18:8
also *k.* his wrath against. *Job* 19:11
k. the wrath of Elihu, against Job was his wrath *k.* because. 32:2
three friends was his wrath *k.* 3, 5
my wrath is *k.* against thee. 42:7
when his wrath is *k.* but. *Ps* 2:12
when their wrath is *k.* 124:3
the sparks that ye have *k. Isa* 50:11
wrath was *k.* in the cities. *Jer* 44:6
I the Lord have *k.* it. *Ezek* 20:48
my repentings are *k.* *Hos* 11:8
if it be already *k.* *Luke* 12:49
see **anger, fire**

kindleth

his breath *k.* coals. *Job* 41:21
yea, he *k.* it, and baketh. *Isa* 44:15
a matter a little fire *k.*! *Jas* 3:5*

kindly

if you will deal *k.* with me.
Gen 24:49; 47:29
Shechem spake *k.* to the. 34:3
Joseph spake *k.* to his. 50:21
deal *k.* and truly with. *Josh* 2:14
the Lord deal *k.* with you. *Ruth* 1:8
thou shalt deal *k.* with. *1 Sam* 20:8
spake *k.* to Jehoiachin. *2 Ki* 25:28
Jer 52:32
be *k.* affectioned one. *Rom* 12:10*

kindness

this is thy *k.* thou shalt. *Gen* 20:13
according to the *k.* I have. 21:23
O Lord, shew *k.* to my master. 24:12
know that thou hast shewed *k.* 14
think on me, and shew *k.* 40:14

I have shewed you *k.* that ye will also shew *k.* to my father's. *Josh* 2:12
nor shewed *k.* to house. *Judg* 8:35
not left off his *k.* to living. *Ruth* 2:20
thou hast shewed more *k.* 3:10
ye shewed *k.* to Israel. *1 Sam* 15:6
thou shalt shew me the *k.* of. 20:14
thou shalt not cut off thy *k.* 15
this *k.* unto your lord. *2 Sam* 2:5
k. to you, I also will requite you this *k.* because ye have done this. 6
against Judah shew *k.* to house. 3:8
that I may shew him *k.* for. 9:1
any, that I may shew the *k.* of. 3
shew thee *k.* for Jonathan's sake. 7
k. to Hanun son of Nahash, as his father shewed *k.* 10:2; *1 Chr* 19:2
Absalom said, Is this thy *k.* to thy? *2 Sam* 16:17
shew *k.* to the sons of. *1 Ki* 2:7
kept for David this great *k.* 3:6
Joash remembered not *k.* of. *2 Chr* 24:22
God gracious, of great *k.* *Neh* 9:17*
the maiden obtained *k.* of. *Esth* 2:9
me his marvellous *k.* *Ps* 31:21
for his merciful *k.* is great. 117:2
let thy merciful *k.* be for. 119:76
smite me, it shall be a *k.* 141:5
desire of a man is his *k.* *Pr* 19:22
in her tongue is the law of *k.* 31:26
with everlasting *k.* will I. *Isa* 54:8
but my *k.* shall not depart. 10
I remember thee, the *k.* of. *Jer* 2:2
for he is gracious, of great *k.* *Joel* 2:13* *Jonah* 4:2*
people shewed us no little *k.* *Acts* 28:2
by longsuffering, by *k.* *2 Cor* 6:6
in his *k.* toward us. *Eph* 2:7
put on *k.* humbleness of. *Col* 3:12
k. of God our Saviour. *Tit* 3:4
godliness brotherly *k.*; to *k.* charity. *2 Pet* 1:7

see **lovingkindness**

kindred

God said, Get thee from thy *k.* *Gen* 12:1; *Acts* 7:3
go to *k.* and take a wife. *Gen* 24:4; 38:40
Lord who took me from my *k.* 7*
when thou comest to my *k.* if they. 41
the Lord said, Return to thy *k.* 31:3 13*; 32:9
asked us straitly of our *k.* 43:7
to my own land and *k.* *Num* 10:30
brought out all her *k.* *Josh* 6:23
of the *k.* of Elimelech. *Ruth* 2:3; 3:2
the *k.* of Saul 3000. *1 Chr* 12:29
Esther shewed not her people or *k.* *Esth* 2:10, 20
to see the destruction of my *k.* 8:6
Elihu, of the *k.* of Ram. *Job* 32:2
men of thy *k.* said, Get. *Ezek* 11:15
none of thy *k.* called by. *Luke* 1:61
the *k.* of the high priest. *Acts* 4:6
Joseph's *k.* was made known. 7:13
Jacob to him and all his *k.* 14
dealt subtilly with our *k.* 19
redeemed us out of every *k.* and. *Rev* 5:9
gospel to preach to every *k.* 14:6

kindreds

give to the Lord, ye *k.* *1 Chr* 16:28 *Ps* 96:7
all *k.* of nations shall. *Ps* 22:27
k. of the earth be blessed. *Acts* 3:25
k. of the earth shall wail. *Rev* 1:7
a great multitude of all *k.* 7:9
of *k.* shall see their dead. 11:9
was given him over all *k.* 13:7

kinds

creepeth after their *k.* *Gen* 8:19*
divers *k.* of spices. *2 Chr* 16:14
appoint over them four *k.* *Jer* 15:3
be according to their *k.* *Ezek* 47:10
dulcimer, and all *k.* of music. *Dan* 3:5, 7, 10, 15
to another divers *k.* of. *1 Cor* 12:10
are, it may be, so many *k.* of. 14:10

kine

Is taken, [1] *Literally, for cows.* Deut 7:13. [2] *Figuratively, for the proud and wealthy rulers of Israel,* Amos 4:4.

forty *k.* ten bulls, a. *Gen* 32:15
up seven well favoured *k.* 41:2, 18
seven other *k.* came out. 3, 4, 19, 20
seven good *k.* are seven years. 26
the seven thin ill favoured *k.* are. 27
bless the increase of thy *k.* *Deut* 7:13
blessed shall be the increase of thy *k.* 28:4
cursed shall be the increase of thy *k.* 18
not leave the increase of thy *k.* 51
butter of *k.*, milk of sheep. 32:14
milch *k.* and tie the *k.* *1 Sam* 6:7
took two *k.* 10
the *k.* took the straight way. 12
wood of cart, and offered the *k.* 14
butter, and cheese of *k.* *2 Sam* 17:29
hear ye this word, ye *k.* *Amos* 4:1

king

Melchizedek *k.* of Salem. *Gen* 14:18; *Heb* 7:1
in Edom, before there reigned any *k.* *Gen* 36:31; *1 Chr* 1:43
arose up a new *k.* over. *Ex* 1:8
the shout of a *k.* is. *Num* 23:21
and his *k.* shall be higher. 24:7
I will set a *k.* over me. *Deut* 17:14
shalt in any wise set him *k.* over. 15
bring thee, and thy *k.* which. 28:36
and he was *k.* in Jeshurun. 33:5
the children of a *k.* *Judg* 8:18
the trees went to anoint a *k.* 9:8
no *k.* in Israel, but every man did. 17:6; 18:1; 19:1; 21:25
give strength to his *k.* *1 Sam* 2:10
go make us a *k.* to judge us. 8:5
give us a *k.* 6
shew the manner of the *k.* 8:9, 11
cry in that day because of your *k.* 18
we will have a *k.* 19
that our *k.* may judge us, and. 20
and make them a *k.* 22
nay, but set a *k.* over us. 10:19
God save the *k.* 24; *2 Sam* 16:16 *2 Ki* 11:12; *2 Chr* 23:11
I have made a *k.* over. *1 Sam* 12:1
the *k.* walketh before you. 2
nay; but a *k.* shall reign over us: when Lord your God was your *k.* 12
behold the *k.* whom ye have. 13
wickedness is great in asking a *k.* 17
our sins this evil, to ask us a *k.* 19
consumed, both you and your *k.* 25
sent me to anoint thee to be *k.* 15:1
rejected thee from being *k.* 23, 26
I have provided me a *k.* 16:1
let not the *k.* sin against his. 19:4
I should not fail to sit with *k.* 20:5
let not the *k.* impute any. 22:15
that thou shalt surely be *k.* 24:20
a feast like the feast of a *k.* 25:36
enemies of my lord the *k.* 29:8
he made Ish-bosheth *k.* *2 Sam* 2:9
what the *k.* did, pleased all. 3:36
not of the *k.* to slay Abner. 37
Lord had established him *k.* over. 5:12
him a mess of meat from *k.* 11:8
I anointed thee *k.* over. 12:7
I pray thee, speak to the *k.* 13:13
and the *k.* and his throne be. 14:9
of God so is my Lord the *k.* 17; 19:27
controversy, came to the *k.* 15:2
there is none deputed of the *k.* 3
abide with the *k.* for thou art. 19
in what place my lord the *k.* 21
this dead dog curse the *k.*? 16:9
flee, I will smite the *k.* only. 17:2
is no matter hid from the *k.* 18:13
k. saved us out of the hand of. 19:9
of all Israel is come to the *k.* 11
the *k.* should take it to his heart. 19
I know that I am this day *k.* 22
I yet to cry any more to the *k.*? 28
because the *k.* is near of kin. 42
we have ten parts in the *k.* 43
tower of salvation for his *k.* 22:51
Araunah as a *k.* give to *k.* 24:23
Adonijah said. I will be *k.* *1 Ki* 1:5
for Solomon shall be *k.* in my. 35
I will speak for thee to the *k.* 2:18
as *k.* hath said, so will thy. *1 Ki* 2:38
made thy servant *k.* instead of. 3:7
women spake before the *k.* 22
Israel heard the judgement the *k.* 28
k. and all Israel offered. 8:62
not any thing hid from the *k.* 10:3
lifted up his hand against *k.* 11:26
thou shalt reign and shalt be *k.* 37
who told me I should be *k.* 14:2
the Lord shall raise up a *k.* over. 14
conspired and hath slain the *k.* 16:16
blaspheme God and the *k.* 21:10
prophets declare good to the *k.* 22:13 *2 Chr* 18:12
there was then no *k.* in Edom: a deputy was *k.* *1 Ki* 22:47
O man of God, *k.* said. *2 Ki* 1:9, 11
be spoken for to the *k.*? 4:13
lord on whose hand the *k.* 7:2
she went to cry to the *k.* for. 8:3
shewed that thou shalt be *k.* 13
Edom revolted, made a *k.* over. 20
we will not make any *k.* 10:5
with the *k.* as he goeth out and. 11:8
a covenant between the Lord and *k.*, between the *k.* also and the. 17
had slain the *k.* his father. 14:5 *2 Chr* 25:3
brought the *k.* word. *2 Ki* 22:9 20; *2 Chr* 34:16, 28
Shaphan read it before the *k.* *2 Ki* 22:10; *2 Chr* 34:18
they took the *k.* and brought him. *2 Ki* 25:6; *Jer* 52:9
they dwelt with the *k.* *1 Chr* 4:23
Shemaiah wrote them before *k.* 24:6
worshipped the Lord and *k.* 29:20
hath made thee *k.* *2 Chr* 2:11; 9:8
so the *k.* hearkened not to. 10:15
for he thought to make him *k.* 11:22
him at the command of the *k.* 24:21
thou made of the *k.*'s counsel? 25:16
be it known to the *k.* *Ezra* 4:12 13; 5:8
and pray for the life of *k.* and. 6:10
who will not do the law of the *k.* 7:26
who hath put in the *k.*'s heart to. 27
to require of the *k.* a band of. 8:22
was the *k.*'s cupbearer. *Neh* 1:11
will ye rebel against the *k.*? 2:19
mayest be their *k.* according to. 6:6
to preach, saying, There is a *k.* 7
nations was there no *k.* like him, God made him *k.* over all Israel. 13:26
so I will go in unto the *k.* *Esth* 4:16
whom the *k.* delighteth to. 6:6, 7
as the word went out of the *k.* 7:8
who had spoken good for the *k.* 9
prevail, as a *k.* ready to. *Job* 15:24
bring him to the *k.* of terrors. 18:14
I sat chief, and dwelt as a *k.* in. 29:25
is it fit to say to the *k.*, Thou? 34:18
he is a *k.* over all children. 41:34
I set my *k.* upon my holy. *Ps* 2:6
hearken to my cry, my *K.* 5:2; 84:3
the Lord is *K.* for ever. 10:16; 29:10
deliverance giveth he to his *k.* 18:50
let the *k.* hear us when we call. 20:9
k. shall joy in thy strength. 21:1
for the *k.* trusteth in the Lord. 7
and the *K.* of glory shall come. 24:7, 9
K. of glory? the Lord strong. 8
the Lord of hosts, he is the *K.* 10
no *k.* saved by the multitude. 33:16
art my *K.* O God, command. 44:4
I have made touching the *k.* 45:1
so shall the *k.* greatly desire. 11
she shall be brought to the *k.* 14
sing praises to our *K.* 47:6
God is the *K.* 7
thou wilt prolong the *k.*'s life. 61:6
the *k.* shall rejoice in God. 63:11
the goings of my God, my *K.* 68:24
give the *k.* thy judgements. 72:1
God is my *K.* of old, working. 74:12
Holy One of Israel is our *k.* 89:18
noise before the Lord, the *K.* 98:6
the *k.*'s strength also loveth. 99:4
the *k.* sent and loosed him. 105:20
of Zion be joyful in their *K.* 149:2
of people is the *k.*'s honour. *Pr* 14:28
the *k.*'s favour is toward a wise. 35
and truth preserve the *k.* 20:28
for grace of his lips, the *k.* 22:11

fear thou the Lord, and *k.* *Pr* 24:21
the wicked from before the *k.* 25:5
the locusts have no *k.* yet go. 30:27
and a *k.* against whom there is. 31
what can the man do that cometh after the *k.*? *Eccl* 2:12
the *k.* himself is served by the. 5:9
where the word of a *k.* is, there. 8:4
O land, when thy *k.* is a child. 10:16
blessed when thy *k.* is the son. 17
curse not the *k.* no, not in thy. 20
the *k.* brought me into. *S of S* 1:4
while the *k.* sitteth at his table. 12
k. Solomon with the crown. 3:11
the *k.* is held in the galleries. 7:5
mine eyes have seen the *K.* *Isa* 6:5
let us set a *k.* in the midst of it. 7:6
curse their *k.* and their God. 8:21
and a fierce *k.* shall rule over. 19:4
according to days of one *k.* 23:15
for Tophet; yea, for the *k.* it. 30:33
behold, a *k.* shall reign in. 32:1
thine eyes shall see the *k.* 33:17
Lord is our *k.*, he will save us. 22
your reasons, saith the *k.* of. 41:21
Creator of Israel, your *K.* 43:15
and thou wentest to the *k.* 57:9
the heart of *k.* shall perish. *Jer* 4:9
Lord in Zion ? is not her *k.* in ? 8:19
the true God, an everlasting *k.* 10:10
to the *k.* and queen, Humble. 13:18
a *K.* shall reign and prosper. 23:5
thus saith the Lord, of the *k.* 29:16
for the *k.* is not he that can do. 38:5
hast said to the *k.* the *k.*...to thee. 25
saith the *K.* whose name is the Lord. 46:18; 48:15; 51:57
why doth their *k.* inherit Gad ? 49:1*
I will destroy from thence the *k.* 38
Lord hath despised the *k.* *Lam* 2:6
the *k.* shall mourn and. *Ezek* 7:27
taken the *k.* and the princes. 17:12
hath taken of the *k.'s* seed and. 13
k. dwelleth that made him *k.* 16
I will bring a *k.* of kings from. 26:7
k. shall be *k.* to them all. 37:22, 24
there is no *k.* asked such. *Dan* 2:10
none that can shew it before *k.* 11
before the *k.* and I will shew the *k.* 24
these men before the *k.* 3:13
is come upon my lord the *k.* 4:24
while the word was in the *k.'s.* 31
and honour the *K.* of heaven. 37
the *k.* saw the part of the hand. 5:5
assembled together to the *k.* 6:6
k. of fierce countenance shall. 8:23
and a mighty *k.* shall stand. 11:3
the *k.* shall do according to his. 36
many days without a *k.* *Hos* 3:4
seek the Lord, and David their *k.* 5
sent to *k.* Jareb. 5:13; 10:6
they made the *k.* glad with. 7:3
in the day of our *k.* princes made. 5
no *k.*; what then should a *k.* do ? 10:3
her *k.* is cut off, as the foam. 7
the Assyrian shall be his *k.* 11:5
I will be thy *k.*; give me a *k.* 13:10
I gave thee a *k.* in mine anger. 11
k. shall go into captivity. *Amos* 1:15
for it is the *k.'s* chapel, the *k.'s.* 7:13
and their *k.* shall pass. *Mi* 2:13
cry ? is there no *k.* in thee ? 4:9
k. shall perish from Gaza. *Zech* 9:5
thy *K.* cometh to thee. 9; *Mat* 21:5
into the hand of his *k.* *Zech* 11:6
shall be *k.* over all the earth. 14:9
even go up to worship the *K.* 16, 17
kingdom likened to a certain *k.* *Mat* 18:23; 22:2
k. came in to see the guests. 22:11
with haste to the *k.* *Mark* 6:25
what *k.* going to war against another *k.*? *Luke* 14:31
K. that cometh in name of. 19:38
he himself is Christ, a *K.* 23:2
to make him a *k.* *John* 6:15
thy *K.* cometh. 12:15
to him, Art thou a *k.* then ? 18:37
maketh himself a *k.* speaketh. 19:12
saith to the Jews, Behold your *K.* 14
crucify your *K.*? have no *k.* but. 15
till another *k.* arose, who. *Acts* 7:18
afterward they desired a *k.* 13:21
that there is another *k.* one. 17:7
the *k.* knoweth of these. *Acts* 26:26
now to the *K.*, eternal. *1 Tim* 1:17
who is the *K.* of kings, and. 6:15
and not afraid of the *k.'s.* *Heb* 11:23
not fearing the wrath of the *k.* 27
to the *k.* as supreme. *1 Pet* 2:13
fear God, honour the *k.* 17
they had a *k.* over them. *Rev* 9:11
just are thy ways, thou *K.* 15:3
of lords, *K.* of kings. 17:14; 19:16
see **David, great, house, Jews**

king *of the Amorites, see* **Sihon**

king *of Assyria*

Pul the *k. of A.* came. *2 Ki* 15:19
exacted money to give *k. of A.* 20
from house of Lord to *k. of A.* 16:18
Hoshea *k. of A.* took Samaria. 17:6
k. of A. did carry away Israel. 18:11
thus saith great king the *k. of A.* 19
land out of hand of *k. of A.* 33
saith Lord concerning *k. of A.* 19:32 *Isa* 37:33
turned heart of *k. of A.* to. *Ezra* 6:22
bring upon thee the *k. of A.* *Isa* 7:17
shave by *k. of A.* the head and. 20
k. of A. hath devoured. *Jer* 50:17
will punish Babylon as I punished *k. of A.* 18
shepherds slumber, O *k. of A.* *Nah* 3:18
see **Bashan, Babylon**

king *of Egypt*

midwives did not as *k. of E.* *Ex* 1:17
sure the *k. of E.* will not let. 3:19
them a charge to the *k. of E.* 6:13
k. of E. came not again any more ... pertained to *k. of E.* *2 Ki* 24:7
k. of E. came up. *2 Chr* 12:2
the *k. of E.* put him down. 36:3
k. of E. made Eliakim his brother. 4
so is the *k. of E.* to all that. *Isa* 36:6
see **Pharaoh**

king *of Israel*

after whom is the *k. of Isr.* come ? *1 Sam* 24:14
k. of Isr. is come out to. 26:20
glorious was the *k. of Isr.* to day! *2 Sam* 6:20
thee, go out to *k. of Isr.* *1 Ki* 20:31
not, save only with *k. of Isr.* 22:31 *2 Chr* 18:30
they said, Surely it is *k. of Isr.* *1 Ki* 22:32; *2 Chr* 18:31
shew me which of us is for *k. of Isr.*? *2 Ki* 6:11
out of the hand of *k. of Isr.* 16:7
that it was not *k. of Isr.* *2 Chr* 18:32
son of David *k. of Isr.* did build. 35:3 *Ezra* 5:11
not Solomon *k. of Isr.* sin? *Neh* 13:26
saith the Lord, the *k. of Isr.* *Isa* 44:6
the *k. of Isr.* be cut off. *Hos* 10:15
k. of Isr. is in the midst. *Zeph* 3:15
if he be *k. of Isr.* let him descend. *Mat* 27:42; *Mark* 15:32
thou art the *k. of Isr.* *John* 1:49
blessed is the *k. of Isr.* 12:13

king *of Judah*

being then *k. of J.* *2 Ki* 8:16
to *k. of J.* which sent you to. 22:18
as for *k. of J.* who sent. *2 Chr* 34:26
to do with thee, thou *k. of J.*? 35:21
hear the word of the Lord O *k. of J.* *Jer* 34:4
thus shall ye say to *k. of J.* 37:7

king *of Moab*

Balak *k. of M.* brought. *Num* 23:7
the *k. of M.* warred. *Josh* 24:9
Israel served the *k. of M.* *Judg* 3:14
like manner sent to *k. of M.* 11:17
better than Balak *k. of M.*? 25
into hand of *k. of M.* *1 Sam* 12:9
father and mother to *k. of M.* 22:4
and Mesha *k. of M.* *2 Ki* 3:4
k. of M. rebelled against Israel. 5, 7
when the *k. of M.* saw battle. 26
and yokes to the *k. of M.* *Jer* 27:3

O king

Abner said, *O k.* I. *1 Sam* 17:55
therefore, *O k.* come down. 23:20
lord, *O k.* *1 Sam* 26:17; *2 Sam* 14:9, 22; 16:4; 19:26; *1 Ki* 1:13, 20, 24; 20:4; *2 Ki* 6:12, 26; 8:5
Tekoah said, Help, *O k.* *2 Sam* 14:4
I will be thy servant, *O k.* 15:34
O k. let not the army. *2 Chr* 25:7
extol thee, my God, *O k.* *Ps* 145:1
would not fear thee, *O k.*? *Jer* 10:7
O k. live for ever. *Dan* 2:4; 3:9; 5:10; 6:21
as for thee, *O k.* 2:29
thou *O k.* sawest an image. 31
thou *O k.* art a king of kings, for. 37
O k. hast made a decree. 3:10
deliver us out of thy hand, *O k.* 17
be it known to thee, *O k.* 18
true, *O k.* 24
it is thou, *O k.* 4:22
O k. let my counsel be. 27
O k. Nebuchadnezzar, to thee it. 31
O thou *k.*, the most high God. 5:18
a petition save of thee, *O k.* 6:7
now, *O k.* establish the decree. 8
regardeth not thee, *O k.* 13
know, *O k.* 15
also before thee, *O k.* have I. 22
at midday, *O k.* I saw. *Acts* 26:13
O k. I was not disobedient. 19

king *of Persia*

as Cyrus, *k. of P.* hath. *Ezra* 4:3
till the reign of Darius *k. of P.* 5
Bishlam wrote unto Artaxerxes *k. of P.* 7; 6:14
mercy in sight of the *k. of P.* 9:9
see **Cyrus**

king *of Syria*

Ben-hadad *k. of S.* *1 Ki* 20:20
k. of S. will come up against. 22
captain of host of *k. of S.* *2 Ki* 5:1
k. of S. was sick. 8:7
k. of S. hath sent me to thee. 9
the *k. of S.* oppressed them. 13:4
k. of S. had destroyed them. 7
out of the hand of the *k. of S.* 16:7
hast relied on *k. of S.* the host of the *k. of S.* is escaped. *2 Chr* 16:7
see **Ben-hadad, Hazael, Rezin**

king *of Tyre*

Hiram *k. of T.* sent messengers to. *2 Sam* 5:11; *1 Chr* 14:1
the *k. of T.* sent servants. *1 Ki* 5:1
Hiram the *k. of T.* had. 9:11
sent to Huram the *k. of T.* *2 Chr* 2:3
Huram the *k. of T.* answered. 11

kingdom

ye shall be to me a *k.* *Ex* 19:6
Gad, Reuben, and Manasseh the *k.* of Sihon and the *k.* of. *Num* 32:33; *Deut* 3:13; *Josh* 13:12, 21, 27, 30
took the *k.* of Og in. *Deut* 3:4
matter of *k.* he told. *1 Sam* 10:16
Samuel told the manner of the *k.* 25
renew the *k.* there. 11:14
Saul took *k.* 14:47
rent the *k.* of Israel. 15:28; 28:17
can he have more but the *k.*? 18:8
to translate the *k.* *2 Sam* 3:10
Israel shall restore me the *k.* 16:3
hath delivered the *k.* into hand. 8
thou knowest that the *k.* *1 Ki* 2:15
ask for him the *k.* for he is my. 22
not like made in any *k.* 10:20 *2 Chr* 9:19
I will surely rend the *k.* from thee. *1 Ki* 11:11; 31:35
not rend away all *k.* 11:13, 34
to bring *k.* again to Rehoboam. 12:21; *2 Chr* 11:1
k. return again to house. *1 Ki* 12:26
I rent the *k.* away from the. 14:8
no *k.* where my lord hath not. 18:10
dost thou now govern the *k.*? 21:7
as the *k.* was confirmed. *2 Ki* 14:5
with him, to confirm the *k.* 15:19
and turned the *k.* to David. *1 Chr* 10:14; 12:23
from one *k.* to another people. 16:20; *Ps* 105:13
earth is thine, thine is the *k.* O Lord. *1 Chr* 29:11; *Ps* 22:28; *Mat* 6:13
think to withstand the *k.* *2 Chr* 13:8
and the *k.* was quiet before. 14:5

k. gave he to Jehoram. *2 Chr* 21:3
Jehoram was risen up to the *k.* 4
no power to keep still the *k.* 22:9
for a sin offering for the *k.* 29:21
no god of any nation or *k.* 32:15
not served thee in their *k. Neh* 9:35
which sat first in the *k.* *Esth* 1:14
thou art come to the *k.* for. 4:14
given to the half of the *k.* 5:3, 6; 7:2
shall fight, *k.* against *k.* *Isa* 19:2
Mat 24:7; *Mark* 13:8; *Luke* 21:10
call nobles thereof to *k.* *Isa* 34:12
the *k.* that will not serve thee. 60:12
Jer 27:8
I speak concerning a *k.* *Jer* 18:7
concerning a *k.*, to build and to. 9
he hath polluted the *k.* and. *Lam* 2:2
didst prosper into a *k.* *Ezek* 16:13
that the *k.* might be base. 17:14
shall be there a base *k.* 29:14
heaven hath given thee a *k. Dan* 2:37
shall God of heaven set up a *k.* 44
Most High ruleth in *k.* 4:17, 25, 32
O king, the *k.* is departed. 31
Daniel concerning the *k.* 6:4
take the *k.* and possess the *k.* 7:18
the saints possessed the *k.* 22
whose *k.* is an everlasting *k.* 27
give the honour of the *k.* 11:21
cause to cease the *k.* of. *Hos* 1:4
Lord are upon sinful *k.* *Amos* 9:8
the *k.* shall be the Lord's. *Ob* 21
k. shall come to daughter. *Mi* 4:8
the gospel of the *k.* *Mat* 4:23
9:35; 24:14
the children of the *k.* shall. 8:12
k. divided against itself is brought.
12:25; *Mark* 3:24; *Luke* 11:17
seed are children of *k.* *Mat* 13:38
shall shine as the sun in the *k.* 43
inherit the *k.* prepared for. 25:34
drink it new in my Father's *k.* 26:29
blessed be *k.* of our. *Mark* 11:10
pleasure to give you *k.* *Luke* 12:32
to receive for himself a *k.* 19:12
having received the *k.* 15
I appoint unto you a *k.* as. 22:29
thou restore again the *k.*? *Acts* 1:6
have delivered up the *k. 1 Cor* 15:24
translated us into the *k.* *Col* 1:13
we receiving a *k.* that. *Heb* 12:28
heirs of the *k.* which he. *Jas* 2:5
an entrance ministered into everlasting *k.* *2 Pet* 1:11
k. and patience of Jesus. *Rev* 1:9
have received no *k.* as yet. 17:12
to agree, and give their *k.* to. 17
see **establish, established, throne**

kingdom *of God*
but seek ye first the *k. of God.*
Mat 6:33; *Luke* 12:31
k. of God is come unto. *Mat* 12:28
Luke 10:9, 11; 11:20
eye of a needle, than for a rich man to enter into *k. of God. Mat* 19:24
Mark 10:23; *Luke* 18:24
harlots go into *k. of God. Mat* 21:31
k. of God shall be taken from. 43
preaching *k. of God.* *Mark* 1:14
Acts 8:12; 20:25; 28:31
k. of God is at hand. *Mark* 1:15
to know the mystery of *k. of God.*
4:11; *Luke* 8:10
so is the *k. of God* as if. *Mark* 4:26
whereunto shall liken *k. of God*?
30; *Luke* 13:18, 20
have seen *k. of God.* *Mark* 9:1
better to enter into the *k. of God.* 47
children, for of such is *k. of God.*
10:14; *Luke* 18:16
whoso shall not receive *k. of God.*
Mark 10:15; *Luke* 18:17
trust in riches to enter into *k. of God.*
Mark 10:24, 25; *Luke* 18:25
far from the *k. of God. Mark* 12:34
I drink it new in the *k. of God.* 14:25
which waited for the *k. of God.*
15:43; *Luke* 23:51
I must preach *k. of God. Luke* 4:43
poor, for yours is the *k. of God.* 6:20
that is least in the *k. of God.* 7:28
glad tidings of *k. of God.* 8:1
them to preach *k. of God.* 9:2, 60
and spake to them of *k. of God.*
Luke 9:11
of death, till they see *k. of God.* 27
back, is fit for the *k. of God.* 62
the prophets in the *k. of God.* 13:28
sit down in the *k. of God.* 29
shall eat bread in *k. of God.* 14:15
since that time the *k. of God.* 16:16
demanded when *k. of God.* 17:20
the *k. of God* cometh not with. 20
behold the *k. of God* is within. 21
children for *k. of God's* sake. 18:29
that *k. of God* should appear. 19:11
the *k. of God* is nigh at hand. 21:31
it be fulfilled in the *k. of God.* 22:16
I will not drink until *k. of God.* 18
cannot see the *k. of God.* *John* 3:3
cannot enter into the *k. of God.* 5
things pertaining to *k. of God.*
Acts 1:3; 8:12; 19:8
much tribulation enter into *k. of God.*
14:22
and testified *k. of God.* 28:23
k. of God is not meat. *Rom* 14:17
k. of God is not in word. *1 Cor* 4:20
shall not inherit the *k. of God.* 6:9
nor extortioners inherit *k. of God.*
10; *Gal* 5:21; *Eph* 5:5
cannot inherit *k. of God. 1 Cor* 15:50
workers unto the *k. of God. Col* 4:11
worthy of the *k. of God. 2 Thes* 1:5
come the *k. of* our *God.* *Rev* 12:10

kingdom *of heaven*
repent, for *k. of h.* is at hand.
Mat 3:2; 4:17; 10:7
in spirit, their's is *k. of h.* 5:3, 10
least in *k. of h.* great in *k. of h.* 19
no case enter into *k. of h.* 20; 18:3
Lord, shall enter into *k. of h.* 7:21
with Abraham in *k. of h.* 8:11
in *k. of h.* is greater than. 11:11
k. of h. suffereth violence, violent. 12
know mysteries of the *k. of h.* 13:11
the *k. of h.* is like. 24, 31, 33, 44, 45
47, 52; 18:23; 20:1; 22:2; 25:1, 14
to thee the keys of *k. of h.* 16:19
is the greatest in *k. of h.*? 18:1, 4
for ye shut up the *k. of h.* 23:13

his **kingdom**
the beginning of *his k.* *Gen* 10:10
his k. shall be exalted. *Num* 24:7
on the throne of *his k.* *Deut* 17:18
may prolong his days in *his k.* 20
he had exalted *his k.* *2 Sam* 5:12
with him in *his k.* *1 Chr* 11:10
for *his k.* was lifted up on high. 14:2
strengthened in *his k.* *2 Chr* 1:1
to build a house for *his k.* 2:1, 12
again to Jerusalem into *his k.* 33:13
his k. ruleth over all. *Ps* 103:19
glorious majesty of *his k.* 145:12
that is born in *his k.* *Eccl* 4:14
upon *his k.* to order and. *Isa* 9:7
his k. is an everlasting *k.* *Dan* 4:3
his k. from generation to generation.
34; 6:26; 7:14
his k. shall be broken and. 11:4
south shall come into *his k.* 9
how shall *his k.* stand? *Mat* 12:26
Luke 11:18
gather out of *his k.* all. *Mat* 13:41
Son of man coming in *his k.* 16:28
of *his k.* there shall be. *Luke* 1:33
hath called you to *his k. 1 Thes* 2:12
at his appearing and *his k. 2 Tim* 4:1
and *his k.* was full of. *Rev* 16:10

my **kingdom**
brought on me and *my k.* *Gen* 20:9
I and *my k.* are guiltless. *2 Sam* 3:28
settle him in *my k.* for. *1 Chr* 17:14
glory of *my k.* in *my k.* *Dan* 4:36
in every dominion of *my k.* 6:26
it to the half of *my k.* *Mark* 6:23
eat and drink at my table in *my k.*
Luke 22:30
my k. is not of this world, if *my k.* were, but now *my k.* *John* 18:36

thy **kingdom**
but now *thy k.* shall. *1 Sam* 13:14
sceptre of *thy k.* a right sceptre.
Ps 45:6; *Heb* 1:8
speak of glory of *thy k.* *Ps* 145:11
thy k. is an everlasting kingdom. 13
thy k. shall be sure to. *Dan* 4:26
there is a man in *thy k.* 5:11
God numbered *thy k.* 26
thy k. is divided. 28
thy k. come, thy will be done.
Mat 6:10; *Luke* 11:2
on the left in *thy k.* *Mat* 20:21
thou comest to *thy k.* *Luke* 23:42

kingdoms
Lord do to all the *k.* *Deut* 3:21
be removed into all the *k.* of. 28:25
the head of all those *k.* *Josh* 11:10
you out of hand of all *k. 1 Sam* 10:18
reigned over all *k.* from. *1 Ki* 4:21
the God of all the *k.* of. *2 Ki* 19:15
all the *k.* may know. 19; *Isa* 37:20
went over all the *k.* *1 Chr* 29:30
know the service of the *k. 2 Chr* 12:8
fear fell upon all the *k.* 17:10; 20:29
thou rulest over all the *k.* of. 20:6
all *k.* hath the Lord. 36:23; *Ezra* 1:2
thou gavest them *k.* and. *Neh* 9:22
the heathen raged, the *k.* *Ps* 46:6
sing unto God, ye *k.* of the. 68:32
thy wrath on the *k.* that have. 79:6
k. are gathered to serve. 102:22
smote all the *k.* of Canaan. 135:11
my hand hath found the *k. Isa* 10:10
the noise of the *k.* of nations. 13:4
Babylon the glory of *k.* 19; 47:5
man that did shake *k.*? 14:16
he shook the *k.* 23:11
God of all *k.* 37:16
and over the *k.* I have. *Jer* 1:10
and in all their *k.* none like. 10:7*
to be removed into all *k.* 15:4; 24:9
34:17
all the *k.* of the world shall. 25:26
prophesied against great *k.* 28:8
them a terror to all *k.* 29:18
all the *k.* fought against. 34:1
concerning Kedar and the *k.* 49:28
with thee will I destroy *k.* 51:20
call together against her the *k.* 27
be the basest of the *k.* *Ezek* 29:15
neither be divided into two *k.* 37:22
consume all these *k.* *Dan* 2:44
shall be diverse from all *k.* 7:23
four *k.* shall stand up out of. 8:22
better than these *k.*? *Amos* 6:2
and I will shew the *k.* thy. *Nah* 3:5
I may assemble the *k.* to. *Zeph* 3:8
throne of *k.* and I will destroy the strength of the *k.* of. *Hag* 2:22
shewed him all the *k.* of world.
Mat 4:8; *Luke* 4:5
through faith subdued *k. Heb* 11:33
k. of this world become *k. Rev* 11:15

kingly
he was deposed from his *k.* throne.
Dan 5:20

kings
k. shall come out of thee. *Gen* 17:6
16; 35:11
these are the *k.* that reigned. 36:31
slew the *k.* of Midian. *Num* 31:8
hath done to these two *k. Deut* 3:21
he shall deliver their *k.* into. 7:24
five *k.* of Amorites. *Josh* 10:5
these five *k.* fled. 16
bring out those five *k.* 22
put your feet on necks of these *k.* 24
Joshua smote all their *k.* 40; 11:17
all these *k.* thirty and one. 12:24
seventy *k.* having their thumbs cut off. *Judg* 1:7
hear, O ye *k.* 5:3
the *k.* came and fought. 19
time when *k.* go forth to. *2 Sam* 11:1
not be any among the *k.* *1 Ki* 3:13
10:23; *2 Chr* 1:12; 9:22
Solomon over all the *k.* on. *1 Ki* 4:24
Ben-hadad and thirty-two *k.* 20:1
these three *k.* together. *2 Ki* 3:10
this is blood, the *k.* are surely. 23
hired against us the *k.* of the. 7:6
behold, two *k.* stood not before. 10:4
he reproved *k.* for them. *1 Chr* 16:21
Ps 105:14
k. sought the presence of. *2 Chr* 9:23
but not in the sepulchres of the *k.*
21:20; 24:25
burial which belonged to *k.* 26:23

the revenue of the *k*. *Ezra* 4:13
this city hath been hurtful to *k*. 15
made insurrection against *k*. 19
there have been mighty *k*. over. 20
God destroy *k*. that shall. 6:12
Artaxerxes, king of *k*. to Ezra. 7:12
k. and priests have been delivered. 9:7; *Neh* 9:24
little to us and our *k*. *Neh* 9:32
nor have our *k*. or princes. 34
had I been at rest with *k*. *Job* 3:14
he looseth the bond of *k*. 12:18
with *k*. are they on the throne. 36:7
k. of the earth set themselves. *Ps* 2:2; *Acts* 4:26
be wise, therefore, O ye *k*. *Ps* 2:10
k.' daughters among thy. 45:9
lo, the *k*. were assembled. 48:4
k. of armies did flee apace. 68:12
when the Almighty scattered *k*. 14
shall *k*. bring presents to thee. 29
yea, all *k*. shall fall down. 72:11
he is terrible to the *k*. of. 76:12
make him higher than the *k*. 89:27
the *k*. of the earth shall fear. 102:15
he shall strike through *k*. in. 110:5
of thy testimonies before *k*. 119:46
nations, and slew mighty *k*. 135:10
which smote great *k*. 136:17, 18
all *k*. of the earth. 138:4; 148:11
that giveth salvation to *k*. 144:10
to bind their *k*. with chains. 149:8
by me *k*. reign, and princes. *Pr* 8:15
abomination for *k*. to commit. 16:12
righteous lips are the delight of *k*. 13
the diligent in business shall stand before *k*. 22:29
honour of *k*. to search a. 25:2
heart of *k*. is unsearchable. 3
the spider is in *k*.' palaces. 30:28
to that which destroyeth *k*. 31:3
it is not for *k*. O Lemuel, to drink. 4
the peculiar treasure of *k*. *Eccl* 2:8
be forsaken of both her *k*. *Isa* 7:16
my princes altogether *k*.? 10:8
raised all the *k*. of the nations. 14:9
all the *k*. of the nations lie in. 18
I am the son of ancient *k*. 19:11
Lord shall punish the *k*. of. 24:21
and made him ruler over *k*. 41:2
I will loose the loins of *k*. to. 45:1
k. shall see and arise, princes. 49:7
k. shall be thy nursing fathers. 23
the *k*. shall shut their mouths. 52:15
and *k*. to the brightness of. 60:3
their *k*. shall minister to thee. 10
thy gates open, that their *k*. 11
also suck the breast of *k*. 16
and all *k*. shall see thy glory. 62:2
they, their *k*. and princes. *Jer* 2:26
even *k*. that sit upon David's. 13:13
into the gates of this city, *k*. 17:25
k. sitting upon the throne of. 22:4
I made Judah and *k*. drink. 25:18
k. of Tyrus. 22
all the *k*. of Arabia. 24
the *k*. of Zimri. 25
all the *k*. of the north. 26
me to anger, they, their *k*. 32:32
burnings of former *k*. before. 34:5
as we, our *k*. and princes to. 44:17
your *k*. and princes burnt. 21
I will punish their *k*. and. 46:25
k. shall go into captivity. 49:3
many *k*. shall be raised up. 50:41
the spirit of *k*. of the Medes. 51:11
k. of the earth would not. *Lam* 4:12
their *k*. shall be sore afraid. *Ezek* 27:35; 32:10
I will lay thee before *k*. to. 28:17
there is Edom, her *k*. and. 32:29
their *k*. shall no more defile. 43:7
k. and setteth up *k*. *Dan* 2:21
these *k*. shall God set up a. 44
that your God is a Lord of *k*. 47
the four beasts are four *k*. 7:17
ten *k*.; he shall subdue three *k*. 24
spake in thy name to our *k*. 9:6
to our *k*. and princes belongs. 8
I remained there with the *k*. 10:13
stand up three *k*. 11:2
both these *k*.' hearts. 27
hot as an oven, all their *k*. *Hos* 7:7
they have set up *k*. but not. 8:4
they shall scoff at *k*. *Hab* 1:10
brought before governors and *k*. for my sake. *Mat* 10:18; *Mark* 13:9; *Luke* 21:12
clothing are in *k*.' houses. *Mat* 11:8
of whom do *k*. of the earth? 17:25
prophets and *k*. have. *Luke* 10:24
k. of Gentiles exercise. 22:25
a chosen vessel to bear my name before *k*. *Acts* 9:15
ye have reigned as *k*. *1 Cor* 4:8
prayers be made for *k*. *1 Tim* 2:2
King of *k*., Lord of lords. 6:15; *Rev* 17:14; 19:16
from slaughter of the *k*. *Heb* 7:1
Christ the prince of the *k*. *Rev* 1:5
hath made us *k*. and priests. 6*; 5:10*
k. of the earth hid themselves. 6:15
prophesy again before *k*. 10:11
way of the *k*. of east might. 16:12
spirits which go forth to the *k*. 14
whom *k*. of earth committed. 17:2
there are seven *k*., five are fallen. 10
ten *k*. which receive power as *k*. 12
city which reigneth over *k*. of. 18
k. of earth have committed. 18:3
k. of earth who shall bewail her. 9
ye may eat the flesh of *k*. 19:18
k. of the earth gathered to make. 19
the *k*. of the earth do bring. 21:24

kings *of the Amorites*

two *k*. of *Am*. *Deut* 4:47; 31:4; *Josh* 2:10; 9:10; 24:12
when all *k*. *of Am*. heard. *Josh* 5:1
five *k*. *of Am*. gathered. 10:5, 6
see **book, great**

kings *of Israel*

book of the Chronicles of the *k*. *of Isr*. *1 Ki* 14:19; 15:31; 16:5, 14, 20, 27; 22:39; *2 Ki* 1:18; 10:34; 13:8, 12; 14:15, 28; 15:11, 15, 21, 26, 31
more than all *k*. *of Isr*. *1 Ki* 16:33
we heard that *k*. *of Isr*. are. 20:31
Jehoram walked in way of *k*. *of Isr*. *2 Ki* 8:18
Joash was buried with the *k*. *of Isr*. 13:13; 14:16
Jeroboam slept with his fathers *k*. *of Isr*. 14:29
Ahaz walked in the way of the *k*. *of Isr*. 16:3
Hoshea did evil, but not as the *k*. *of Isr*. 17:2
Israel walked in the statutes of the *k*. *of Isr*. 8
away houses the *k*. *of Isr*. 23:19
passover in days of the *k*. *of Isr*. 22
written in book of *k*. *of Isr*. *1 Chr* 9:1; *2 Chr* 16:11; 25:26; 27:7; 28:26; 32:32; 33:18
is mentioned in the book of the *k*. *of Isr*. *2 Chr* 20:34; 35:27; 36:8
Ahaz was not brought into sepulchres of *k*. *of Isr*. 28:27
houses of Achzib shall be a lie to *k*. *of Isr*. *Mi* 1:14

kings *of Judah*

Ziklag pertained to the *k*. *of J*. *1 Sam* 27:6
acts of Rehoboam in the Chronicles of the *k*. *of J*. *1 Ki* 14:29; 15:7, 23; 22:45; *2 Ki* 8:23; 15:6, 36; 16:19; 20:20; 21:17, 25; 23:28; 24:5
hallowed things the *k*. *of J*. had dedicated. *2 Ki* 12:18, 19
written in the Chronicles of the *k*. *of J*. 14:18; *2 Chr* 25:26; 28:26; 32:32; 35:27; 36:8
like him of all the *k*. *of J*. *2 Ki* 18:5
priests *k*. *of J*. ordained. 23:5
took horses *k*. *of J*. had given. 11
beat down altars which *k*. *of J*. 12
passover in all days of *k*. *of J*. 22
floor houses *k*. *of J*. *2 Chr* 34:11
Isaiah in days of the *k*. *of J*. *Isa* 1:1
iron pillar against *k*. *of J*. *Jer* 1:18
bring out bones of the *k*. *of J*. 8:1
in gate, whereby *k*. *of J*. 17:19
word of Lord ye *k*. *of J*. 20; 19:3
burnt incense to gods *k*. *of J*. 19:4
houses of the *k*. *of J*. shall. 13
treasures of *k*. *of J*. will. 20:5
concerning houses of *k*. *of J*. *Jer* 33:4
wickedness of *k*. *of J*.? 44:9
word of Lord that came to Hosea in days of *k*. *of J*. *Hos* 1:1; *Mi* 1:1
see **kings** *of Israel*

kinsfolk

my *k*. have failed and. *Job* 19:14
Jesus among their *k*. *Luke* 2:44

kinsfolks

left none of Baasha's *k*. *1 Ki* 16:11
Jehu slew Ahab's *k*. *2 Ki* 10:11*
shall be betrayed by *k*. *Luke* 21:16

kinsman

if the man have no *k*. to. *Num* 5:8
give his inheritance to his *k*. 27:11
Naomi had a *k*. his name. *Ruth* 2:1
thou art a near *k*. 3:9
near *k*.: a *k*. nearer than I. 12
to thee the part of a *k*. well; if not, I will do the part of a *k*. to. thee 13
behold the *k*. of whom Boaz. 4:1
the *k*. said, I cannot redeem it. 6
the *k*. said unto Boaz, Buy it. 8
not left thee this day without a *k*. 14
being his *k*. whose ear. *John* 18:26
salute Herodion my *k*. *Rom* 16:11

kinsmen

of kin one of our next *k*. *Ruth* 2:20
my lovers and *k*. stood. *Ps* 38:11
friends, brethren, nor *k*. *Luke* 14:12
called together his *k*. *Acts* 10:24
accursed, for my *k*. according to the. *Rom* 9:3
salute my *k*. 16:7
my *k*. salute you. 21

kinswoman

is my father's near *k*. *Lev* 18:12
she is thy mother's near *k*. 13
call understanding thy *k*. *Pr* 7:4

kinswomen

they are her near *k*. *Lev* 18:17

Kir

the people captive to *K*. *2 Ki* 16:9
in the night *K*. of Moab. *Isa* 15:1
Elam bare the quiver, *K*. 22:6
go into captivity to *K*. *Amos* 1:5
brought the Assyrians from *K*.? 9:7

Kir-haraseth

only in *K*. left they. *2 Ki* 3:25
for the foundations of *K*. *Isa* 16:7
inward parts shall sound for *K*. 11

Kiriathaim

smote Emims in Shavah *K*. *Gen* 14:5
saith Lord, *K*. is confounded and. *Jer* 48:1
judgement is come upon *K*. and. 23

Kirjath-arba

Sarah died in *K*. the. *Gen* 23:2; *Josh* 14:15; 20:7; *Judg* 1:10

Kirjath-jearim

K. a city of the Hivites. *Josh* 9:17
was to Baalah, which is *K*. 15:9, 60
K. a city of Judah. 18:14; *1 Chr* 13:6
the men of *K*. came. *1 Sam* 7:1
ark of God from *K*. *1 Chr* 13:5
brought the ark from *K*. *2 Chr* 1:4

Kish

a man of Benjamin whose name was *K*. *1 Sam* 9:1
asses of *K*. Saul's father. 3; 14:51
that is come to the son of *K*.? 10:11
and Saul the son of *K*. was. 21
Saul in sepulchre of *K*. *2 Sam* 21:14
K. the son of Gibeon. *1 Chr* 8:30
Ner begat *K*. 33
K. son of Mahli. 23:21
K. son of Abdi. *2 Chr* 29:12
of Shimei, son of *K*. *Esth* 2:5
them Saul the son of *K*. *Acts* 13:21

kiss, -es

In the Bible times and countries the kiss was given as a sign. [1] *Of reverence and subjection to a superior,* 1 Sam 10:1. [2] *Of love and affection,* Gen 27:26, 27; 1 Sam 20:41. [3] *Of idolatrous reverence and adoration,* Hos 13:2.

the *k*. of an enemy are. *Pr* 27:6
k. me with the *k*. of. *S of S* 1:2
thou gavest me no *k*. *Luke* 7:45

Son of man with a *k.*? *Luke* 22:48
another with an holy *k.* *Rom* 16:16
greet with an holy *k.* *1 Cor* 16:20
2 Cor 13:12
brethren with an holy *k.* *1 Thes* 5:26
one another with a *k.* *1 Pet* 5:14

kiss, *verb*

come near now and *k.* *Gen* 27:26
not suffered me to *k.* my sons. 31:28
Amasa by beard to *k.* *2 Sam* 20:9
let me *k.* my father. *1 Ki* 19:20
k. the Son, lest he be angry. *Ps* 2:12
every man shall *k.* his. *Pr* 24:26
him *k.* me with kisses. *S of S* 1:2
I would *k.* thee, yea I should. 8:1
let men that sacrifice *k.* *Hos* 13:2
saying, Whomsoever I *k.* the same.
Mat 26:48; *Mark* 14:44
not ceased to *k.* my feet. *Luke* 7:45
drew near to Jesus to *k.* him. 22:47

kissed

Jacob came near and *k.* *Gen* 27:27
Jacob *k.* Rachel and wept. 29:11
Laban *k.* Jacob. 13
Laban *k.* his sons and his. 31:55
Esau *k.* Jacob. 33:4
Joseph *k.* all his brethren. 45:15
Jacob *k.* and embraced. 48:10
on his father's face and *k.* him. 50:1
Moses in the mount and *k.* *Ex* 4:27
his father in law and *k.* him. 18:7
k. her daughters in law. *Ruth* 1:9
Orpah *k.* her mother in law. 14
poured oil and *k.* Saul. *1 Sam* 10:1
Jonathan and David *k.* one. 20:41
the king *k.* Absalom. *2 Sam* 14:33
Absalom *k.* any man that. 15:5
the king *k.* Barzillai, and. 19:39
which hath not *k.* him. *1 Ki* 19:18
mouth hath *k.* my hand. *Job* 31:27
righteousness and peace *k.* *Ps* 85:10
she caught him and *k.* him. *Pr* 7:13
hail, Master, and *k.* him. *Mat* 26:49
Mark 14:45
Mary *k.* his feet and. *Luke* 7:38
fell on his neck and *k.* him. 15:20
Paul's neck and *k.* him. *Acts* 20:37

kite

the *k.* after his kind unclean.
Lev 11:14*; *Deut* 14:13*

Kittim

sons of Javan, Tarshish, *K.*
Gen 10:4; *1 Chr* 1:7
see **Chittim**

knead

k. it, and make cakes. *Gen* 18:6
women *k.* their dough. *Jer* 7:18

kneaded

Endor took flour and *k.* *1 Sam* 28:24
Tamar took flour and *k.* *2 Sam* 13:8
the baker *k.* the dough. *Hos* 7:4

kneadingtroughs

frogs shall come into thy *k.* *Ex* 8:3
their *k.* being bound up in. 12:34

knee

before him, bow the *k.* *Gen* 41:43
every *k.* shall bow, every tongue.
Isa 45:23; *Rom* 14:11; *Phil* 2:10
they bowed the *k.* before him.
Mat 27:29*; *Mark* 15:19
who have not bowed the *k.* *Rom* 11:4

kneel

he made his camels *k.* *Gen* 24:11
let us *k.* before the Lord. *Ps* 95:6

kneeled

Solomon *k.* down on. *2 Chr* 6:13
Daniel *k.* three times. *Dan* 6:10
and Jesus *k.* down and. *Luke* 22:41
Stephen *k.* and cried with. *Acts* 7:60
Peter *k.* and prayed. 9:40
Paul *k.* and prayed. 20:36
and we *k.* down on the shore. 21:5

kneeling

Solomon rose up from *k.* *1 Ki* 8:54
a man *k.* to him saying. *Mat* 17:14
Mark 10:17
there came a leper *k.* *Mark* 1:40

knees

Bilhah shall bear on my *k.* *Gen* 30:3
out from between his *k.* 48:12
brought up on Joseph's *k.* *Gen* 50:23
shall smite thee in the *k.* *Deut* 28:35
on his *k.* to drink. *Judg* 7:5, 6
made Samson sleep on her *k.* 16:19
from kneeling on his *k.* *1 Ki* 8:54
put his face between his *k.* 18:42
k. which have not bowed. 19:18
third captain fell on his *k.* *2 Ki* 1:13
sat on his mother's *k.* till noon. 4:20
kneeled down on his *k.* *2 Chr* 6:13
I fell on my *k.* and spread. *Ezra* 9:5
why did the *k.* prevent? *Job* 3:12
strengthened the feeble *k.* 4:4
my *k.* are weak through. *Ps* 109:24
confirm the feeble *k.* *Isa* 35:3
and be dandled upon her *k.* 66:12
all *k.* shall be weak as water.
Ezek 7:17; 21:7
the waters were to the *k.* 47:4
his *k.* smote one against. *Dan* 5:6
kneeled on his *k.* three times. 6:10
an hand set me upon my *k.* 10:10
she is empty, and the *k.* *Nah* 2:10
bowing their *k.* worshipped him.
Mark 15:19
Simon Peter fell down at Jesus' *k.*
Luke 5:8
for this cause I bow my *k.* *Eph* 3:14
hang down and feeble *k.* *Heb* 12:12

knew

Adam *k.* Eve his wife. *Gen* 4:1, 25
Cain *k.* his wife. 17
Judah *k.* her no more. 38:26
Jephthah's daughter *k.* no man.
Judg 11:39
they *k.* her and abused her. 19:25
Elkanah *k.* Hannah his. *1 Sam* 1:19
but the king *k.* her not. *1 Ki* 1:4
Joseph *k.* her not, till. *Mat* 1:25

knew

Adam and Eve *k.* that. *Gen* 3:7
Noah *k.* what his younger. 9:24
Jacob *k.* it, and said, It is. 37:33
Onan *k.* the seed should not. 38:9
Joseph saw and *k.* his. 42:7, 8
and *k.* the knowledge. *Num* 24:16
from the day I *k.* you. *Deut* 9:24
a prophet whom the Lord *k.* 34:10
such as before *k.* nothing. *Judg* 3:2
Manoah *k.* that he was an. 13:21
they *k.* the voice of the. 18:3
all Israel *k.* Samuel. *1 Sam* 3:20
Saul *k.* that the Lord was. 18:28
for if I *k.* then would I not. 20:9
Jonathan *k.* that it was. 33
only David and Jonathan *k.* 39
for the servant *k.* nothing of. 22:15
slay the priests, because they *k.* 17
David said to Abiathar, I *k.* it. 22
David *k.* that Saul secretly. 23:9
Saul *k.* David's voice, and. 26:17
he *k.* that valiant men. *2 Sam* 11:16
Obadiah *k.* Elijah, and. *1 Ki* 18:7
then Manasseh *k.* the. *2 Chr* 33:13
manner to all that *k.* law. *Esth* 1:13
O that I *k.* where I might! *Job* 23:3
because I *k.* that thou. *Isa* 48:4
shouldest say, Behold, I *k.* them. 7
I *k.* that thou wouldest deal very. 8
I formed thee, I *k.* thee. *Jer* 1:5
then I *k.* this was the word of. 32:8
Gedaliah, and no man *k.* it. 41:4
men which *k.* their wives. 44:15
I *k.* that they were the cherubims.
Ezek 10:20
he *k.* their desolate palaces. 19:7
he *k.* that the most high. *Dan* 5:21
when Daniel *k.* the writing was. 6:10
I *k.* thou art a gracious. *Jonah* 4:2
k. that it was the word of. *Zech* 11:11
profess I never *k.* you. *Mat* 7:23
when Jesus *k.* he withdrew. 12:15
Jesus *k.* their thoughts. 25; *Luke* 6:8
I *k.* thee that thou art an. *Mat* 25:24
he *k.* that for envy they. 27:18
speak because they *k.* *Mark* 1:34
ship, straightway they *k.* him. 6:54
k. he had spoken the parable. 12:12
the devils, for they *k.* *Luke* 4:41
servant which *k.* his lord's. 12:47
nor *k.* they the things that. 18:34
were opened, and they *k.* 24:31
but the servants *k.* *John* 2:9
not commit himself unto them, because he *k.* *John* 2:24
and testify, for he *k.* what was. 25
the father *k.* it was at the. 4:53
Jesus *k.* he had been long in. 5:6
for he himself *k.* what he. 6:6
Jesus *k.* that his disciples. 61
Jesus *k.* from the beginning who. 64
I *k.* that thou hearest me. 11:42
that if any man *k.* where he. 57
when Jesus *k.* that his hour. 13:1
for he *k.* who should betray him. 11
no man at the table *k.* for what. 28
Jesus *k.* that they were. 16:19
Judas which betrayed him *k.* 18:2
k. that it was he that sat. *Acts* 3:10
which when the brethren *k.* 9:30
when Rhoda *k.* Peter's voice. 12:14
they *k.* all that his father was. 16:3
they *k.* that he was a Jew. 19:34
k. that he was a Roman. 22:29
which *k.* me from the beginning. 26:5
k. the island was called Melita. 28:1
that when they *k.* God. *Rom* 1:21
the princes of this world *k.* *1 Cor* 2:8
to be sin, who *k.* no sin. *2 Cor* 5:21
I *k.* a man in Christ. 12:2, 3
in you since ye *k.* grace of. *Col* 1:6
you *k.* what great conflict I. 2:1
though ye once *k.* this. *Jude* 5
written that no man *k.* *Rev* 19:12

knew *not*

place, and I *k.* it *not.* *Gen* 28:16
Jacob *k.* *not* that Rachel had. 31:32
Judah *k.* *not* she was his. 38:16
he *k.* *not* aught he had. 39:6
but they *k.* *not* him. 42:8
king which *k.* *not* Joseph. *Ex* 1:8
I *k.* *not* that thou stoodest.
Num 22:34
which thy fathers *k.* *not.* *Deut* 8:16
thy fathers *k.* *not.* 29:26; 32:17
a generation which *k.* *not* the Lord.
Judg 2:10
Manoah *k.* *not* that he was. 13:16
his father *k.* *not* that it was. 14:4
Benjamin *k.* *not* that evil. 20:34
of Eli *k.* *not* the Lord. *1 Sam* 2:12
people *k.* *not* that Jonathan. 14:3
the lad *k.* *not* any thing. 20:39
sent messengers after Abner, but David *k.* it *not.* *2 Sam* 3:26
k. ye *not* they would shoot? 11:20
simplicity, and *k.* *not* any. 15:11
I saw a tumult, but I *k.* *not.* 18:29
a people which I *k.* *not* shall. 22:44
gathered gourds for they *k.* them *not.* *2 Ki* 4:39
the rulers *k.* *not* whither. *Neh* 2:16
Job's friends *k.* him *not.* *Job* 2:12
the cause which I *k.* *not* I. 29:16
things which I *k.* *not.* 42:3
my charge things I *k.* *not.* *Ps* 35:11
against me, and I *k.* it *not.* 15
behold, we *k.* it *not.* *Pr* 24:12
blind by a way they *k.* *not.* *Isa* 42:16
set him on fire, yet he *k.* *not.* 25
and nations that *k.* *not* thee. 55:5
handle the law *k.* me *not.* *Jer* 2:8
k. *not* that they had devised. 11:19
other gods whom they *k.* *not.* 44:3
honour a god whom his fathers *k.* *not.* *Dan* 11:38
made princes and I *k.* it *not.* *Hos* 8:4
but they *k.* *not* that I healed. 11:3
nations whom they *k.* *not.* *Zech* 7:14
and they *k.* him *not.* *Mat* 17:12
k. *not* till flood came. 24:39
his mother *k.* *not* of it. *Luke* 2:43
that *k.* *not* and did commit. 12:48
the world *k.* him *not.* *John* 1:10
I *k.* him *not.* 31, 33
governor *k.* *not* whence it was. 2:9
yet they *k.* *not* the scriptures. 20:9
k. *not* that it was Jesus. 14; 21:4
because they *k.* him *not.* *Acts* 13:27
more part *k.* *not* wherefore. 19:32
when it was day, they *k.* *not.* 27:39
world by wisdom *k.* *not.* *1 Cor* 1:21
howbeit then, when ye *k.* *not* God.
Gal 4:8
world knoweth us not, because it *k.* him *not.* *1 John* 3:1

knewest
manna, which thou *k.* not. *Deut* 8:3
people which thou *k. not. Ruth* 2:11
thou *k.* that they dealt. *Neh* 9:10
then thou *k.* my path in. *Ps* 142:3
heardest not, yea, thou *k.* *Isa* 48:8
thy heart, thou *k.* all this. *Dan* 5:22
thou *k.* I reaped where. *Mat* 25:26
Luke 19:22
thou *k.* not the time of. *Luke* 19:44
if thou *k.* the gift of God. *John* 4:10

knife
Abraham took the *k.* *Gen* 22:6, 10
took a *k.* and laid hold. *Judg* 19:29
put a *k.* to thy throat. *Pr* 23:2
take thee a sharp *k.* *Ezek* 5:1
and smite about it with a *k.* 2

knit
Israel were *k.* together. *Judg* 20:11
soul of Jonathan was *k. 1 Sam* 18:1
my heart shall be *k.* *1 Chr* 12:17
I saw a sheet *k.* at the. *Acts* 10:11
hearts being *k.* together. *Col* 2:2
body *k.* together increaseth with. 19

knives
make thee sharp *k.* and. *Josh* 5:2
Joshua made him sharp *k.* and. 3
cut themselves with *k.* *2 Ki* 18:28
nine and twenty *k.* Cyrus. *Ezra* 1:9
jaw teeth as *k.* to devour. *Pr* 30:14

knock
k. and it shall be opened. *Mat* 7:7
Luke 11:9
ye begin to *k.* at door. *Luke* 13:25
stand at the door and *k.* *Rev* 3:20

knocked
and as Peter *k.* at door. *Acts* 12:13

knocketh
of my beloved that *k.* *S of S* 5:2
to him that *k.* shall be opened.
Mat 7:8; *Luke* 11:10
when he cometh and *k.* *Luke* 12:36

knocking
Peter continued *k.* and. *Acts* 12:16

knop, -s
his *k.* and his flowers. *Ex* 25:31, 34
36; 37:17
with a *k.* and flower in. 25:33; 37:19
and *k.* branches of the same. 25:36
37:17, 20, 22
cedar carved with *k.* *1 Ki* 6:18
were *k.* compassing it, *k.* cast. 7:24

know
God doth *k.* that your eyes. *Gen* 3:5
man is become as one of us, to *k.* 22
said to Abram, *K.* thy seed. 15:13
and see, and if not, I will *k.* 18:21
if thou restore her not, *k.* 20:7
make them *k.* the statutes. *Ex* 18:16
hast not let me *k.* whom thou. 33:12
they shall *k.* the land. *Num* 14:31
k. this day and. *Deut* 4:39; 11:2
to prove thee and *k.* what was. 8:2
fathers *k.* he might make thee *k.* 3
proveth you, to *k.* whether ye. 13:3
shall let your children *k.* *Josh* 4:22
and Israel he shall *k.* 22:22
k. whether they would. *Judg* 3:4
city of my people doth *k.* *Ruth* 3:11
she rose up before one could *k.* 14*
sit still, my daughter, till thou *k.* 18
this assembly shall *k.* *1 Sam* 17:47
he saith, Let not Jonathan *k.* 20:3
let no man *k.* any thing of. 21:2
k. and see that there is no. 24:11
therefore *k.* and consider. 25:17
Achish said to David, *k.* 28:1
surely thou shalt *k.* what thy. 2
to *k.* thy going out, to *k. 2 Sam* 3:25
things to make thy servant *k.* 7:21
to *k.* all things that are in. 14:20
thy servant doth *k.* that I. 19:20
k. every man the plague. *1 Ki* 8:38
2 Chr 6:29
he shall *k.* that there is. *2 Ki* 5:8
they *k.* that we be hungry. 7:12
k. now that there shall fall. 10:10
Issachar, to *k.* what Israel ought.
1 Chr 12:32
my son, *k.* thou the God of. 28:9
ought ye not to *k.* that. *2 Chr* 13:5
k. that this city is a. *Ezra* 4:15
all such as *k.* the laws of thy. 7:25
Mordecai walked to *k.* *Esth* 2:11
to *k.* what it was, and why it. 4:5
people *k.* whosoever shall come. 11
shalt *k.* thy tabernacle. *Job* 5:24
shalt *k.* that thy seed shall. 25
hear it, and *k.* thou it for thy. 27
nor shall his place *k.* him. 7:10
but of yesterday, and *k.* 8:9
k. therefore that God exacteth. 11:6
than hell, what canst thou *k.*? 8
to *k.* my transgression. 13:23
k. that God hath overthrown. 19:6
him, and he shall *k.* it. 21:19
sayest, How doth God *k.*? 22:13
do they that *k.* him not see? 24:1
one *k.* them, they are in terrors. 17
let us *k.* among ourselves. 34:4
dost thou *k.* when God? 37:15
dost thou *k.* the balancings of? 16
caused the dayspring to *k.* 38:12
that thou shouldest *k.* the paths. 20*
k. the Lord hath set apart. *Ps* 4:3
that *k.* thy name put their. 9:10
lovingkindness to them *k.* 36:10
Lord, make me to *k.* mine end. 39:4
be still, and *k.* that I am God. 46:10
part thou shalt make me to *k.* 51:6
k. that God ruleth in Jacob. 59:13
How doth God *k.*? 73:11
I thought to *k.* this. 16
Babylon to them that *k.* me. 87:4
blessed are they that *k.* the. 89:15
the place thereof shall *k.* it. 103:16
k. my heart, try me, and *k.* 139:23
no man that would *k.* me. 142:4
cause me to *k.* the way wherein. 143:8
k. wisdom and instruction. *Pr* 1:2
attend to *k.* understanding. 4:1
the lips of righteous *k.* what. 10:32
be thou diligent to *k.* the. 27:23
I gave my heart to *k.* *Eccl* 1:17
I applied my heart to *k.* 7:25
when I applied my heart to *k.* 8:16
though a wise man think to *k.* 17
the living *k.* they shall die, but. 9:5
but *k.* that God will bring thee. 11:9
before the child shall *k.* *Isa* 7:16
and all the people shall *k.* even. 9:9
Egyptians shall *k.* the Lord. 19:21
that they may see and *k.* 41:20
that we may *k.* the latter end. 22
all flesh shall *k.* that I am. 49:26
k. how to speak in season. 50:4
therefore my people shall *k.* 52:6
seek me, and delight to *k.* my. 58:2
thou shalt *k.* that I the Lord. 60:16
k. and see that it is an evil. *Jer* 2:19
see thy way in valley, *k.* what. 23
and *k.* O congregation, what is. 6:18
through deceit they refuse to *k.* 9:6
k. that for thy sake I have. 15:15
to *k.* my hand and my might, and
they shall *k.* that my name. 16:21
deceitful, who can *k.* it? 17:9
was not this to *k.* me? saith. 22:16
give them an heart to *k.* me. 24:7
they shall all *k.* me. 31:34; *Heb* 8:11
go, hide thee, let no man *k.* *Jer* 36:19
he said, Let no man *k.* of. 38:24
and no man shall *k.* it. 40:15
Judah shall *k.* whose words. 44:28
k. that there hath been a prophet.
Ezek 2:5; 33:33
k. that I the Lord hath spoken. 5:13
k. her abomination. 16:2; 20:4
they shall *k.* my vengeance. 25:14
all that *k.* thee shall be. 28:19
thus shall they *k.* that I am. 34:30
heathen shall *k.* 37:28; 39:23
givest knowledge to them who *k.*
Dan 2:21
k. that the Most High. 4:25, 32
made me *k.* the interpretation. 7:16
k. the truth of the fourth beast. 19
make thee *k.* what shall be. 8:19
k. therefore and understand. 9:25
people that *k.* their God. 11:32
thou shalt *k.* the Lord. *Hos* 2:20
Israel shall *k.* it. 9:7
and thou shalt *k.* no god. 13:4
prudent, and he shall *k.* them. 14:9
is it not for you to *k.*? *Mi* 3:1
thou shalt *k.* that the Lord sent me.
Zech 2:11; 4:9
shall *k.* that I have sent. *Mal* 2:4
let not thy left hand *k.* *Mat* 6:3
if ye *k.* how to give good gifts. 7:11
Luke 11:13
see no man *k.* it. *Mat* 9:30
Mark 5:43; 7:24; 9:30
it is given unto you to *k. Mat* 13:11
Mark 4:11; *Luke* 8:10
k. that it [desolation] is near.
Mat 24:33; *Mark* 13:29; *Luke* 21:20
k. this, if the goodman. *Mat* 24:43
Luke 12:39
k. that this is indeed. *John* 4:42
if any do his will, he shall *k.* 7:17
do the rulers *k.* indeed. 26
and *k.* what he doeth? 51
sheep follow him, for they *k.* 10:4
I *k.* my sheep. 14
thou shalt *k.* hereafter. 13:7
by this shall all men *k.* ye are. 35
behold, they *k.* what I said. 18:21
not for you to *k.* times. *Acts* 1:7
let all the house of Israel *k.* 2:36
shouldest *k.* his will and see. 22:14
they *k.* I imprisoned them that. 19
life from my youth *k.* all Jews. 26:4
I speak to them that *k.* *Rom* 7:1
but I say, Did not Israel *k.*? 10:19
neither can he *k.* them. *1 Cor* 2:14
nothing as he ought to *k.* 8:2
but I would have you *k.* that. 11:3
to *k.* the love of Christ. *Eph* 3:19
for this cause I sent to *k. 1 Thes* 3:5
one should *k.* how to possess. 4:4
to *k.* them who labour among. 5:12
them which believe and *k. 1 Tim* 4:3
this *k.* also that in last. *2 Tim* 3:1
they profess that they *k.* *Tit* 1:16
but wilt thou *k.* O vain? *Jas* 2:20
let him *k.* he which converteth. 5:20
but what they *k.* naturally. *Jude* 10
all churches shall *k.* that. *Rev* 2:23
I will make them to *k.* that I. 3:9
see **certain, certainly, certainty**

I know
now *I k.* that thou art a. *Gen* 12:11
whereby shall *I k.* that I shall? 15:8
I k. that he will command. 18:19
I k. thou didst this in integrity. 20:6
now *I k.* that thou fearest. 22:12
thereby shall *I k.* that thou. 24:14
I k. it, my son, *I k.* it. 48:19
Lord said, *I k.* their sorrows. *Ex* 3:7
Aaron thy brother *I k.* he can. 4:14
I k. that ye will not yet fear. 9:30
I k. that the Lord is greater. 18:11
thou hast said, *I k.* thee. 33:12, 17
I k. their imagination. *Deut* 31:21
for *I k.* thy rebellion and thy. 27
I k. that after my death ye will. 29
I k. the Lord hath given. *Josh* 2:9
I k. that thou wilt save. *Judg* 6:37
now *k. I* that the Lord will. 17:13
I k. thy pride and. *1 Sam* 17:28
do not *I k.* thou hast chosen? 20:30
till *I k.* what God will do for. 22:3
I k. well that thou shalt. 24:20
I k. that thou art good in my. 29:9
yea *I k.* it, hold you. *2 Ki* 2:3, 5
I k. that there is no God. 5:15
I k. the evil that thou wilt do. 8:12
I k. thy abode and. 19:27; *Isa* 37:28
I k. that thou triest. *1 Chr* 29:17
I k. that God hath. *2 Chr* 25:16
I k. it is so of a truth, but. *Job* 9:2
I k. thou wilt not hold me. 28
things hast hid, *I k.* that this. 10:13
what ye know, the same do *I k.* 13:2
behold, *I k.* that I shall be. 18
I k. that my Redeemer liveth. 19:25
I k. your thoughts and devices. 21:27
for *I k.* that thou wilt bring. 30:23
I k. that thou canst do every. 42:2
I k. that the Lord saveth. *Ps* 20:6
this *I k.* that thou favourest. 41:11
I k. all the fowls of the. 50:11
this *I k.* for God is for me. 56:9
I k. O Lord, that thy. 119:75
for *I k.* the Lord is great and. 135:5
I k. the Lord will maintain. 140:12
I k. that there is no good. *Eccl* 3:12

I k. that whatsoever God. *Eccl* 3:14
I k. it shall be well with. 8:12
nor shall *I k.* the loss of. *Isa* 47:8
and *I k.* that I shall not. 50:7
I k. their works and their. 66:18
I k. the way of man is. *Jer* 10:23
given me knowledge, and *I k.* 11:18
for *I k.* the thoughts that I. 29:11
I k. and am a witness, saith. 23
I k. his wrath, saith the. 48:30
I k. things that come. *Ezek* 11:5
the dream, and *I* shall *k.* *Dan* 2:9
I k. Ephraim, and Israel. *Hos* 5:3
I did *k.* thee in the wilderness. 13:5
I k. your manifold. *Amos* 5:12
I k. that for my sake. *Jonah* 1:12
fear not ye, *I k.* that ye. *Mat* 28:5
I k. thee who thou art. *Mark* 1:24
Luke 4:34
whereby shall *I k.* this. *Luke* 1:18
I k. that Messias cometh. *John* 4:25
but *I k.* you. 5:42
I k. whence I came. 8:14
I k. that ye are Abraham's. 37
but *I k.* him. 55
one thing *I k.* 9:25
Father knoweth me, so *I k.* 10:15
I k. my sheep, and they follow. 27
I k. that what thou wilt ask. 11:22
Martha said, *I k.* that he shall. 24
I k. his commandment is. 12:50
I speak not of all, *I k.* whom. 13:18
now *I k.* of a surety. *Acts* 12:11
Jesus *I k.* and Paul *I k.* 19:15
I k. that ye shall see my face. 20:25
I k. this, that after my departing. 29
I will *k.* the uttermost of. 24:22
because *I k.* thee to be expert. 26:3
king Agrippa, *I k.* that thou. 27
I k. that in me dwelleth. *Rom* 7:18
I k. nothing by myself. *1 Cor* 4:4
I k. in part, then shall *I k.* as. 13:12
I k. the forwardness of. *2 Cor* 9:2
I k. this shall turn to. *Phil* 1:19
I k. that I shall abide with you. 25
be of good comfort, when *I k.* 2:19
I k. how to be abased, *I k.* 4:12
for *I k.* whom I have believed.
2 Tim 1:12
I k. him, and keepeth. *1 John* 2:4
I k. thy works. *Rev* 2:2, 9, 13, 19
3:1, 8, 15
I k. the blasphemy of them. 2:9

know *not*, or *not* **know**

is Abel ? he said, I *k. not*. *Gen* 4:9
I am old, I *k. not* the day. 27:2
I *k. not* the Lord, nor will. *Ex* 5:2
we *k. not* with what we must. 10:26
or if thou *k.* him *not*. *Deut* 22:2
Samuel did *not* yet *k.* *1 Sam* 3:7
give to men whom I *k. not* ? 25:11
I *k. not* how to go out. *1 Ki* 3:7
carry thee whither I *k. not*. 18:12
they *k. not* the manner. *2 Ki* 17:26
them that *k.* them *not*. *Ezra* 7:25
they shall *not k.* nor see. *Neh* 4:11
would I *not k.* my soul. *Job* 9:21*
knowest thou that we *k. not* ? 15:9
do ye *not k.* their tokens ? 21:29
they *k. not* the ways thereof. 24:13
the dark, they *k. not* the light. 16
for I *k. not* to give flattering. 32:22
great, and we *k.* him *not*. 36:26
for I *k. not* the numbers. *Ps* 71:15
they *k. not*, neither will they. 82:5
teacheth man, shall he *not k.*? 94:10
I will *not k.* a wicked person. 101:4
k. not at what they stumble. *Pr* 4:19
that thou canst *not k.* them. 5:6
doth *not* he *k.* it, and shall ? 24:12
k. not what to do in the end. 25:8
wicked regardeth *not* to *k.* it. 29:7
four things which I *k. not*. 30:18
dead *k. not* any thing. *Eccl* 9:5
if thou *k. not*, O fairest. *S of S* 1:8
Israel doth *not k.* nor. *Isa* 1:3
shall ye *not k.* it ? 43:19
there is no God; I *k. not* any. 44:8
thou shalt *not k.* from whence. 47:11
and thou didst *not k.* them. 48:6
they *k. not*, shall *not k.* peace. 59:8
for they *k. not* the way. *Jer* 5:4
other gods, whom ye *k. not* ? 7:9

k. not the judgements of. *Jer* 8:7
k. not me, saith the Lord. 9:3
the heathen that *k.* thee *not*. 10:25
into a land that they *k. not*. 14:18
22:28
dwelleth safely shalt thou *not k.* it ?
Ezek 38:14
she did *not k.* that I gave. *Hos* 2:8
they *k. not* to do right. *Amos* 3:10
k. not the thoughts of. *Mi* 4:12
unto you, I *k.* you *not*. *Mat* 25:12
Peter said, I *k. not* what thou sayest.
26:70; *Luke* 22:60
curse and swear, saying, I *k. not*.
Mat 26:72, 74; *Mark* 14:68, 71
Jesus said, Ye *k. not*. *Mark* 10:38
ye err, because ye *k. not* the. 12:24
seeing I *k. not* a man. *Luke* 1:34
I *k. not* whence you are. 13:25, 27
woman, I *k.* him *not*. 22:57
forgive them; for they *k. not*. 23:34
that they should *not k.* him. 24:16
standeth one among you whom ye *k. not*. *John* 1:26
if I should say, I *k.* him *not*. 8:55
blind man said, I *k. not*. 9:12, 25
opened his eyes, we *k. not*. 21
for this fellow, we *k. not* from. 29
for they *k. not* the voice of. 10:5
Lord, we *k. not* whither thou. 14:5
because they *k. not* him that. 15:21
we *k. not* where they have laid. 20:2
I *k. not* where they have laid. 13
could *not k.* the certainty. *Acts* 21:34
for we *k. not* what we should pray for. *Rom* 8:26
I *k. not* whether I baptized any other.
1 Cor 1:16
I determined *not* to *k.* any. 2:2
if I *k. not* the meaning of. 14:11
which *k. not* God. *1 Thes* 4:5
vengeance on them that *k. not* God.
2 Thes 1:8
k. not how to rule his. *1 Tim* 3:5
evil of things they *k. not*. *Jude* 10
shalt *not k.* what hour I. *Rev* 3:3

see, ye **know**

know *that I am the Lord*

ye shall *k. that I am the Lord*. *Ex* 6:7
16:12; *1 Ki* 20:28; *Ezek* 6:7, 13
7:4, 9; 11:10, 12; 12:20; 13:9, 14
21, 23; 14:8; 15:7; 20:38, 42, 44
23:49; 24:24; 25:5; 35:9; 36:11
37:6, 13; *Joel* 3:17
Egyptians shall *k. that I am Lord*.
Ex 7:5; 14:4, 18
thou shalt *k. I am Lord*. *Ex* 7:17
1 Ki 20:13; *Isa* 49:23; *Ezek* 16:62
22:16; 25:7; 35:4, 12
to the end that thou mayest *k. that I am the Lord*. *Ex* 8:22
that ye may *k. that I am Lord*.
10:2; 31:13; *Ezek* 20:20
they shall *k. that I am the Lord*.
Ex 29:46; *Ezek* 6:10, 14; 7:27
12:15, 16; 24:27; 25:11, 17; 26:6
28:22, 23, 24, 26; 29:9, 16, 21
30:8, 19, 25, 26; 32:15; 33:29
34:27; 35:15; 36:38; 38:23
39:6, 28
that ye might *k. that I am the Lord*.
Deut 29:6
I will give them an heart to *k.* me *that I am the Lord*. *Jer* 24:7
my sabbaths that they might *k. that I am the Lord*. *Ezek* 20:12, 26
and the heathen shall *k. that I am the Lord*. 36:23; 39:7
the house of Israel shall *k. that I am the Lord*. 39:22

may, mayest, or *might* **know**

mayest k. there is none like God.
Ex 8:10; 9:14
mayest k. that the earth. 9:29
ye *may k.* the Lord doth put. 11:7
that I *may k.* what to do to. 33:5
thy way, that I *may k.* thee. 13
generations *may k.* that. *Lev* 23:43
may k. what the Lord. *Num* 22:19
that thou *mightest k.* that the Lord he is God. *Deut* 4:35
ye *may k.* the way by. *Josh* 3:4
may k. that as I was with Moses. 7

people *might k.* the hand. *Josh* 4:24
Israel *might k.* to teach. *Judg* 3:2
we *may k.* whether our way. 18:5
tell me, that I *may k.* *Ruth* 4:4
that all the earth *may k.* there is a God in Israel. *1 Sam* 17:46
1 Ki 8:43, 60; *2 Ki* 19:19
I *may k.* the number. *2 Sam* 24:2
this people *may k.* that. *1 Ki* 18:37
may k. thy name, and *may k.* that this house is. *2 Chr* 6:33
his servants, that they *may k.* 12:8
that ye *may k.* there is. *Job* 19:29
be weighed, that God *may k.* 31:6
that all men *may k.* his work. 37:7
nations *may k.* themselves. *Ps* 9:20
measure of days, that *may k.* 39:4
generation to come *might k.* 78:6
that men *may k.* that thou. 83:18
may k. that this is thy hand. 109:27
I *may k.* thy testimonies. 119:125
draw nigh that we *may k.* *Isa* 5:19
may k. to refuse the evil. 7:15
that all *may k.* that thou art. 37:20
that we *may k.* ye are gods. 41:23
declared, that we *may k.* and. 26
ye *may k.* and believe me. 43:10
that thou *mayest k.* that I am. 45:3
that they *may k.* from the rising. 6
thou *mayest k.* and try. *Jer* 6:27
that ye *may k.* that my words. 44:29
flesh *may k.* that I have. *Ezek* 21:5
that heathen *may k.* me. 38:16
mightest k. the thoughts. *Dan* 2:30
intent that the living *may k.* 4:17
cast lots, that we *may k.* *Jonah* 1:7
ye *may k.* the righteousness. *Mi* 6:5
that ye *may k.* that the Son of man.
Mat 9:6; *Mark* 2:10; *Luke* 5:24
ye *may k.* and believe. *John* 10:38
the world *may k.* 14:31; 17:23
might k. thee the only true God. 17:3
ye *may k.* that I find no fault. 19:4
may we *k.* what this new? *Acts* 17:19
all *may k.* that those things. 21:24
we *might k.* the things. *1 Cor* 2:12
that ye *might k.* the love. *2 Cor* 2:4
that I *might k.* the proof of you. 9
that ye *may k.* the hope. *Eph* 1:18
whom I sent, that ye *might k.* 6:22
may k. him and the power. *Phil* 3:10
may k. how to answer. *Col* 4:6
whom I sent, that he *might k.* 8
thou *mayest k.* how thou oughtest to behave. *1 Tim* 3:15
may k. ye have eternal. *1 John* 5:13
that we *may k.* him that is true. 20

we **know**, or **know** *we*

Laban ? they said, *We k.* *Gen* 29:5
shall *we k.* the word ? *Deut* 18:21
we k. it is not his hand. *1 Sam* 6:9
nor *k. we* what to do. *2 Chr* 20:12
God is great, and *we k.* him not.
Job 36:26
our iniquities, *we k.* them. *Isa* 59:12
we k. if we follow on to. *Hos* 6:3
cry to me, My God, *we k.* thee. 8:2
we k. thou art true, and. *Mat* 22:16
Mark 12:14; *Luke* 20:21
we k. thou art a teacher. *John* 3:2
to thee, we speak that *we* do *k.* 11
we k. what we worship. 4:22
father and mother *we k.*? 6:42
howbeit, *we k.* whence this. 7:27
we k. that thou hast a devil. 8:52
we k. that this is our son and. 9:20
said to him, *we k.* that this man. 24
we k. that God spake to Moses. 29
now *we k.* that God heareth. 31
Lord *we k.* not whither thou goest, and how can *we k.* the way ? 14:5
and *we k.* that his testimony. 21:24
we would *k.* what these. *Acts* 17:20
we k. it is every where. 28:22
we k. that what things. *Rom* 3:19
we k. that the law is spiritual. 7:14
we k. that the whole creation. 8:22
we k. that all things work. 28
we k. that we all have. *1 Cor* 8:1
we k. that an idol is nothing in. 4
we k. in part, and prophesy. 13:9
we k. that if our earthly. *2 Cor* 5:1
k. we no man after flesh, *k. we.* 16

we k. that the law is. *1 Tim* 1:8
for *we k.* him that hath. *Heb* 10:30
hereby *we k.* that *we k. 1 John* 2:3
hereby *k. we* that we are in him. 5
we k. that it is the last time. 18
but *we k.* that when he shall. 3:2
we k. that we have passed from. 14
hereby *we k.* that we are of the. 19
hereby *we k.* that he abideth. 24
hereby *k. we* the spirit of. 4:6
hereby *k. we* that we dwell in. 13
by this *we k.* that we love the. 5:2
we k. that he heareth us, *we k.* that we have petitions that we. 15
we k. whosoever is born of God. 18
we k. that we are of God, and. 19
we k. that the Son of God is come, that *we* may *k.* him that. 5:20

ye **know,** or **know** *ye*

he said, *K. ye* Laban the ? *Gen* 29:5
ye k. that with all my power. 31:6
ye k. that my wife bare me. 44:27
at even *ye* shall *k.* the. *Ex* 16:6
ye k. the heart of a stranger. 23:9
ye shall *k.* my breach. *Num* 14:34
ye shall *k.* that the Lord. 16:28
ye shall *k.* the living God is among. *Josh* 3:10
and *ye k.* in all your hearts. 23:14
ye k. there is in these houses an ephod. *Judg* 18:14
k. ye that Ramoth is ? *1 Ki* 22:3
ye k. the man and his. *2 Ki* 9:11
what *ye k.* the same do. *Job* 13:2
k. ye that the Lord he is God. *Ps* 100:3
hearken, *ye* that *k. Isa* 51:7
k. ye for certain, if ye. *Jer* 26:15
all *ye* that *k.* his name, say. 48:17
ye shall *k.* that I have not done. *Ezek* 14:23
ye shall *k.* I the Lord have spoken. 17:21; 37:14
ye shall *k.* that I am in. *Joel* 2:27
ye shall *k.* the Lord hath sent me. *Zech* 2:9; 6:15
ye shall *k.* them by their fruits. *Mat* 7:16, 20
ye k. that the princes of the Gentiles. 20:25; *Mark* 10:42
ye k. that summer is nigh. *Mat* 24:32 *Mark* 13:28; *Luke* 21:30
watch, for *ye k.* neither. *Mat* 25:13
k. ye not this parable ? *Mark* 4:13
k. ye that the kingdom of God. *Luke* 21:31
ye both *k.* me, and know. *John* 7:28
ye shall *k.* that I am he. 8:28
ye shall *k.* the truth. 32
k. ye nothing. 11:49
k. ye what I have done. 13:12
if *ye k.* these things, happy. 13:17
I go *ye k.* and the way *ye k.* 14:4
from henceforth *ye k.* him. 7, 17
ye shall *k.* I am in my Father. 20
ye k. that it hated me before. 15:18
as *ye* yourselves also *k. Acts* 2:22
ye k. how that it is unlawful. 10:28
brethren, *ye k.* how that a good. 15:7
ye k. that by this craft we. 19:25
ye k. from the first day that. 20:18
ye k. that ye were Gentiles, carried. *1 Cor* 12:2
ye k. your labour is not in. 15:58
brethren, *ye k.* the house of. 16:15
ye k. the grace of our Lord. *2 Cor* 8:9
I trust *ye* shall *k.* we are not. 13:6
k. ye that they which are of faith. *Gal* 3:7
ye k. how through infirmities. 4:13
ye k. that no whoremonger. *Eph* 5:5
ye k. the proof of him. *Phil* 2:22
as *ye k.* what manner. *1 Thes* 1:5
shamefully entreated, as *ye k.* 2:2
neither flattering words, as *ye k.* 5
ye k. how we exhorted and. 11
it came to pass, and *ye k.* 3:4
ye k. what commandments we. 4:2
and now *ye k.* what withholdeth. *2 Thes* 2:6
ye k. how when he would have inherited the blessing. *Heb* 12:17
k. ye that our brother. 13:23
ye k. that ye were not redeemed. *1 Pet* 1:18
put you in remembrance, though *ye k.* them. *2 Pet* 1:12
seeing *ye k.* these things. 3:17
ye k. all things. *1 John* 2:20
because *ye k.* it. 21
if *ye k.* he is righteous, *ye k.* 29
ye k. he was manifested to. 3:5
ye k. no murderer hath eternal. 15
hereby *k. ye* the Spirit of God. 4:2
and *ye k.* that our record. *3 John* 12

ye **know** *not,* or **know** *ye not*

k. ye not that there is a prince fallen? *2 Sam* 3:38
k. ye not what I and my fathers ? *2 Chr* 32:13
do *ye not k.* their tokens. *Job* 21:29
k. ye not what these things mean ? *Ezek* 17:12
Jesus said, *Ye k. not* what ye ask. *Mat* 20:22
ye k. not what hour your Lord. 24:42
K. ye not this parable ? *Mark* 4:13
ye err, because *ye k. not.* 12:24
watch, for *ye k. not* when. 13:33, 35
ye k. not what manner. *Luke* 9:55
standeth one among you, whom *ye k. not. John* 1:26
ye worship *ye k. not* what. 4:22
meat *ye k. not* of. 32
is true, whom *ye k. not.* 7:28
ye neither *k.* me nor my. 8:19
that *ye k. not* from whence. 9:30
k. ye not that so many ? *Rom* 6:3*
k. ye not that to whom ye yield ? 16
k. ye not, brethren, for I speak. 7:1*
k. ye not that ye are the temple of God ? *1 Cor* 3:16; 6:15, 19
k. ye not that a little leaven ? 5:6
do *ye not k.* the saints shall ? 6:2
k. ye not that we shall judge ? 3
k. ye not, the unrighteous shall ? 9
k. ye not that he which is ? 16
do *ye not k.* that they which ? 9:13
k. ye not that they which run ? 24
k. ye not yourselves ? *2 Cor* 13:5
k. ye not that the friendship of ? *Jas* 4:4
ye k. not what shall be on the. 14
not written, because *ye k. not* the truth. *1 John* 2:21

knowest

thou *k.* my service that. *Gen* 30:26
thou *k.* how I have served thee. 29
thou *k.* any man of activity. 47:6
k. thou not yet that Egypt ? *Ex* 10:7
thou *k.* the people are set on. 32:22
for thou *k.* how we are. *Num* 10:31
thou *k.* the travel that hath. 20:14
Egypt, which thou *k. Deut* 7:15
the Anakims, whom thou *k.* 9:2
nation thou *k.* not, shall eat. 28:33
thou *k.* the thing that the. *Josh* 14:6
k. thou not Philistines ? *Judg* 15:11
woman said, Thou *k.* what Saul hath done. *1 Sam* 28:9
how *k.* thou that Saul ? *2 Sam* 1:5
k. thou not that it will be ? 2:26
thou *k.* Abner the son of Ner. 3:25
thou, Lord, *k.* thy servant. 7:20 *1 Chr* 17:18
For, said Hushai, thou *k. 2 Sam* 17:8
the king, thou *k.* it not. *1 Ki* 1:18
thou *k.* also what Joab did to. 2:5
thou *k.* what thou oughtest to do. 9
thou *k.* that the kingdom was. 15
thou *k.* all the wickedness. 44
whose heart thou *k.* thou only *k.* 8:39 *2 Chr* 6:30
k. thou the Lord will ? *2 Ki* 2:3, 5
thou *k.* that thy servant did. 4:1
k. that I am not wicked. *Job* 10:7
k. thou that we know not ? 15:9
k. thou not this of old, since ? 20:4
therefore speak what thou *k.* 34:33
measures thereof, if thou *k.*? 38:5
earth, declare, if thou *k.* it all. 18
k. thou it, because thou wast ? 21
k. thou the ordinances of heaven ? 33
k. thou when the wild goats. 39:1, 2
not refrained, O Lord thou *k.* *Ps* 40:9; *Jer* 15:15
thou *k.* my foolishness. *Ps* 69:5
thou *k.* my downsitting and. 139:2
O Lord, thou *k.* it altogether. 4
k. not what a day may. *Pr* 27:1
k. not what evil shall. *Eccl* 11:2
k. not what is the way of the Spirit, even so thou *k.* not the works. 5
k. not whether shall prosper. 6
a nation that thou *k.* not. *Isa* 55:5
whose language thou *k.* not. *Jer* 5:15
but thou, O Lord, *k.* me. 12:3
land which thou *k.* not. 15:14; 17:4
desired woeful day, thou *k.* 17:16
thou *k.* all their counsel to. 18:23
thee things which thou *k.* not. 33:3
O Lord God, thou *k. Ezek* 37:3
k. thou wherefore I ? *Dan* 10:20
angel said, *K.* thou not ? *Zech* 4:5, 13
k. thou that Pharisees ? *Mat* 15:12
thou *k.* commandments. *Mark* 10:19 *Luke* 18:20
deny that thou *k.* me. *Luke* 22:34
Nathanael said, Whence *k.* thou me ? *John* 1:48
art thou a master, and *k.* not ? 3:10*
Jesus said, What I do, thou *k.* 13:7
we are sure thou *k.* 16:30; 21:17
k. thou not I have power ? 19:10
thou *k.* that I love thee. 21:15, 16
which *k.* the hearts of. *Acts* 1:24
no wrong, as thou very well *k.* 25:10
k. his will, and approvest. *Rom* 2:18
what *k.* thou, O wife, *k.*? *1 Cor* 7:16
k. that all they in Asia. *2 Tim* 1:15
how he ministered to me, thou *k.* 18
and *k.* not that thou art. *Rev* 3:17
I said unto him, Sir, thou *k.* 7:14

knoweth

my lord *k.* the children. *Gen* 33:13
when he *k.* of it, he shall. *Lev* 5:3, 4
he *k.* thy walking through. *Deut* 2:7
no man *k.* of Moses' sepulchre. 34:6
Lord God of gods, he *k. Josh* 22:22
the iniquity which he *k. 1 Sam* 3:13
thy father certainly *k.* that. 20:3
that also Saul my father *k.* 23:17
thy servant *k.* that I. *2 Sam* 14:22
all Israel *k.* thy father is a. 17:10
he *k.* vain men, he seeth. *Job* 11:11
he *k.* the day of darkness is. 15:23
he *k.* the way that I take. 23:10
there is a path which no fowl *k.* 28:7
God understandeth and *k.* the. 23
therefore he *k.* their works. 34:25
Lord *k.* way of righteous. *Ps* 1:6
the Lord *k.* the days of the. 37:18
for he *k.* the secrets of the. 44:21
is there any among us that *k.* 74:9
Lord *k.* the thoughts of man. 94:11
k. our frame, remembereth. 103:14
moon for seasons, the sun *k.* 104:19
but the proud he *k.* afar off. 138:6
that my soul *k.* right well. 139:14
woman is simple and *k. Pr* 9:13
heart *k.* his own bitterness. 14:10
poor, that *k.* to walk. *Eccl* 6:8
thine own heart *k.* thou hast. 7:22
no man *k.* either love or hatred. 9:1
the ox *k.* his owner, the ass. *Isa* 1:3
the stork *k.* her appointed. *Jer* 8:7
he understandeth and *k.* me. 9:24
k. what is in the darkness. *Dan* 2:22
Lord is good, he *k.* them. *Nah* 1:7
the unjust *k.* no shame. *Zeph* 3:5
your Father *k.* what. *Mat* 6:8
k. ye have need of. 32; *Luke* 12:30
no man *k.* the Son but the Father, nor any *k. Mat* 11:27; *Luke* 10:22
of that day *k.* no man. *Mat* 24:36 *Mark* 13:32
ye justify, but God *k. Luke* 16:15
how *k.* this man letters ? *John* 7:15
when Christ cometh, no man *k.* 27
as the Father *k.* me. 10:15
nor *k.* him. 14:17
he saw it, and he *k.* that he. 19:35
God which *k.* the hearts. *Acts* 15:8
for the king *k.* of these things. 26:26
he *k.* what is the mind. *Rom* 8:27
k. the things of a man, even so the things of God *k.* no. *1 Cor* 2:11
he *k.* any thing, he *k.* nothing. 8:2
I love you not ? God *k. 2 Cor* 11:11

God *k.* I lie not. 2 Cor 11:31
I cannot tell, God *k.* 12:2, 3
the Lord *k.* them that. 2 Tim 2:19
him that *k.* to do good. Jas 4:17
Lord *k.* how to deliver. 2 Pet 2:9
and *k.* all things. 1 John 3:20
he that *k.* God. 4:6
loveth is born of God, and *k.* 7
written, which no man *k.* Rev 2:17
because he *k.* that he hath. 12:12

who **knoweth**, or **knoweth** *not*

David our lord *k.* it *not.* 1 Ki 1:11
who k. whether thou art? Esth 4:14
who k. not such things? Job 12:3
who k. not in all these, that the? 9
come to honour, he *k.* it *not.* 14:21
place of him that *k. not* God. 18:21
man *k. not* the price thereof. 28:13
in anger, yet he *k.* it *not.* 35:15*
riches, and *k. not* who. Ps 39:6
who k. the power of thine? 90:11
a brutish man *k. not*, nor a fool. 92:6
k. not that it is for his life. Pr 7:23
but he *k. not* that the dead. 9:18
and *who k.* the ruin of them? 24:22
who k. whether he be wise? Eccl 2:19
who k. the spirit of man that? 3:21
for *who k.* what is good for? 6:12
who k. the interpretation of? 8:1
for he *k. not* that which shall be. 7
for man also *k. not* his time. 9:12
because he *k. not* how to go. 10:15
who seeth us? *who k.* us? Isa 29:15
and there, yet he *k. not.* Hos 7:9
who k. if he will return? Joel 2:14
grow up, he *k. not* how. Mark 4:27
this people, who *k. not.* John 7:49
walketh in darkness, *k. not.* 12:35
servant *k. not* what his lord. 15:15
k. not that Ephesians. Acts 19:35
walketh in darkness, *k. not.* whither. 1 John 2:11
therefore the world *k.* us *not.* 3:1
he that loveth not, *k. not* God. 4:8

knowing

ye shall be as gods, *k.* Gen 3:5
my father David not *k.* 1 Ki 2:32
Jesus *k.* their thoughts. Mat 9:4
Luke 11:17
ye err, not *k.* scriptures. Mat 22:29
Jesus immediately *k.* in. Mark 5:30*
the woman *k.* what was done. 33
feared John, *k.* that he was. 6:20
but he *k.* their hypocrisy. 12:15
they laughed, *k.* that she. Luke 8:53
and one for Elias, not *k.* what. 9:33
Jesus *k.* the Father had. John 13:3
Jesus *k.* all things that should. 18:4
Jesus *k.* that all things were. 19:28
none durst ask him, *k.* that it. 21:12
k. that God had sworn. Acts 2:30
his wife not *k.* what was done. 5:7
he taught, *k.* only the baptism. 18:25
not *k.* the things that shall. 20:22
who *k.* the judgement of. Rom 1:32
not *k.* that the goodness of God. 2:4
k. that tribulation worketh. 5:3
k. this, that our old man is. 6:6
k. Christ being raised from dead. 9
k. the time, now it is high. 13:11
k. that as ye are partakers. 2 Cor 1:7
k. that he which raised Lord. 4:14
k. that whilst we are at home. 5:6
k. the terror of the Lord, we. 11
k. that a man is not. Gal 2:16
k. that whatsoever good. Eph 6:8
k. that your master is. 9; Col 4:1
k. that I am set for. Phil 1:17
k. that of the Lord ye. Col 3:24
k. beloved, your election. 1 Thes 1:4
k. this, that the law is. 1 Tim 1:9
is proud, *k.* nothing, but doting. 6:4
k. that they do gender. 2 Tim 2:23
k. of whom thou hast learned. 3:14
k. that he that is such. Tit 3:11
k. that thou wilt do more. Philem 21
k. ye have in heaven a. Heb 10:34
he went out, not *k.* whither. 11:8
k. this, that the trying of. Jas 1:3
k. we shall receive greater. 3:1
blessing, *k.* that ye are. 1 Pet 3:9*
k. that the same afflictions are. 5:9
k. that shortly I must put. 2 Pet 1:14
k. this, that no prophecy. 2 Pet 1:20
k. there shall come scoffers in. 3:3

knowledge

tree of *k.* of good and. Gen 2:9, 17
filled Bezaleel in *k.* Ex 31:3; 35:31
sin come to his *k.* Lev 4:23, 28
and knew the *k.* of the. Num 24:16
thou shouldest take *k.* Ruth 2:10
blessed be he that did take *k.* 19
the Lord is a God of *k.* 1 Sam 2:3
take *k.* of all the lurking. 23:23
shipmen that had *k.* of sea. 1 Ki 9:27; 2 Chr 8:18
give me *k.* that I may. 2 Chr 1:10
but hast asked *k.* 11
k. is granted thee. 12
every one having *k.* Neh 10:28
wise man utter vain *k.*? Job 15:2
for we desire not the *k.* of. 21:14
shall any teach God *k.* seeing? 22
and my lips shall utter *k.* 33:3*
ear unto me, ye that have *k.* 34:2
I will fetch my *k.* from afar. 36:3
he that is perfect in *k.* is. 4; 37:16
night unto night sheweth *k.* Ps 19:2
is there *k.* in the most High? 73:11
he that teacheth man *k.* shall. 94:10
me good judgement and *k.* 119:66
such *k.* is too wonderful for. 139:6
that thou takest *k.* of him? 144:3
to give the young man *k.* Pr 1:4
fear of Lord is the beginning of *k.* 7
fools hate *k.* 22
if thou criest after *k.* 2:3*
for that they hated *k.* and did. 29
out of his mouth cometh *k.* and. 2:6
and when *k.* is pleasant to thy. 10
his *k.* the depths are broken. 3:20
and that thy lips may keep *k.* 5:2
right to them that find *k.* 8:9
k. rather than gold. 10
and find out *k.* 12
k. of the holy is understanding. 9:10
wise men lay up *k.*: but the. 10:14
but through *k.* shall the just. 11:9
loveth instruction loveth *k.* 12:1
a prudent man concealeth *k.* 23
prudent man dealeth with *k.* 13:16
k. is easy to him that. 14:6
not in him the lips of *k.* 7
prudent are crowned with *k.* 18
the tongue of the wise useth *k.* 15:2
the lips of the wise disperse *k.* 7
hath understanding seeketh *k.* 14
he that hath *k.* spareth his. 17:27
the prudent getteth *k.* and the ear of the wise seeketh *k.* 18:15
and he will understand *k.* 19:25
to err from the words of *k.* 27
lips of *k.* are a precious jewel. 20:15
when the wise is instructed, he receiveth *k.* 21:11
eyes of the Lord preserve *k.* 22:12
and apply thine heart unto my *k.* 17
excellent things in counsels and *k.* 20
thine ears to the words of *k.* 23:12
by *k.* shall the chambers be. 24:4
man of *k.* increaseth strength. 5
so shall the *k.* of wisdom be to. 14
by a man of *k.* the state. 28:2
wisdom, nor have *k.* of holy. 30:3
heart had experience of *k.* Eccl 1:16
he that increaseth *k.* increaseth. 18
is a man whose labour is in *k.* 2:21
God giveth to a man wisdom, *k.* 26
but the excellency of *k.* is. 7:12
nor *k.* in the grave, whither. 9:10
still taught the people *k.* 12:9
before the child shall have *k.* Isa 8:4
spirit of *k.* and of the fear. 11:2
whom shall he teach *k.*? them. 28:9
the rash shall understand *k.* 32:4
wisdom and *k.* shall be stability. 33:6
who taught him *k.* 40:14
nor is there *k.* 44:19
and maketh their *k.* foolish. 25
thy wisdom and thy *k.* hath. 47:10
by his *k.* my righteous. 53:11
which shall feed you with *k.* Jer 3:15
every man is brutish in his *k.* 10:14
51:17
Lord hath given me *k.* of it. 11:18
favoured and cunning in *k.* Dan 1:4
God gave them *k.* Dan 1:17
he giveth *k.* to them. 2:21
excellent spirit and *k.* were. 5:12
many run to and fro, and *k.* 12:4
destroyed for lack of *k.*: because thou hast rejected *k.*, I will. Hos 4:6
the earth filled with the *k.* Hab 2:14
priest's lips should keep *k.* Mal 2:7
that place had *k.* of him. Mat 14:35
k. of salvation by remission of sins. Luke 1:77
taken away the key of *k.* 11:52
marvelled and took *k.* Acts 4:13
having more perfect *k.* of. 24:22
to retain God in their *k.* Rom 1:28
which hast the form of *k.* 2:20
justified, for by law is the *k.* 3:20
zeal, but not according to *k.* 10:2
ye also are filled with all *k.* 15:14
in all utterance and all *k.* 1 Cor 1:5
we know that we all have *k.* *K.* 8:1
there is not in every man that *k.* 7
if any man see thee which hast *k.* 10
through thy *k.* shall thy weak. 11
to another the word of *k.* by the. 12:8
understand all mysteries and all *k.* 13:2
whether there be *k.* it shall vanish. 8
speak to you by revelation or *k.* 14:6
the savour of his *k.* 2 Cor 2:14
to give the light of the *k.* of the. 4:6
by *k.*, by longsuffering, by. 6:6
abound in faith, utterance, and *k.* 8:7
I be rude in speech, yet not in *k.* 11:6
give you wisdom in the *k.* Eph 1:17
ye may understand my *k.* 3:4*
love of Christ which passeth *k.* 19
we come in the unity of the *k.* 4:13
love may abound more in *k.* Phil 1:9
things but loss for *k.* of Christ. 3:8
ye might be filled with *k.* Col 1:9
hid treasures of wisdom and *k.* 2:3
new man which is renewed in *k.* 3:10
all men to come to the *k.* 1 Tim 2:4
never able to come to *k.* 2 Tim 3:7
after we have received *k.* Heb 10:26
man, and endued with *k.*? Jas 3:13*
husbands dwell with them according to *k.* 1 Pet 3:7
through the *k.* of him. 2 Pet 1:3
add to virtue *k.* and to *k.* 5
nor unfruitful in the *k.* of our. 8
grow in grace and in the *k.* of. 3:18

knowledge *of God*

shalt thou find the *k. of God.* Pr 2:5
is no truth, nor *k. of God.* Hos 4:1
desired the *k. of God* more. 6:6
the riches both of the wisdom and *k. of God.* Rom 11:33
have not the *k. of God.* 1 Cor 15:34
exalteth itself against *k. of God.* 2 Cor 10:5
increasing in the *k. of God.* Col 1:10
through the *k. of God.* 2 Pet 1:2

knowledge *of the Lord*

the good *k. of the Lord.* 2 Chr 30:22*
full of the *k. of the Lord.* Isa 11:9
escaped pollution through the *k. of the Lord.* 2 Pet 2:20

no **knowledge**

your children which in that day had *no k.* Deut 1:39
have all the workers of iniquity *no k.*? Ps 14:4; 53:4
captivity because they have *no k.* Isa 5:13
have *no k.* that set up their images. 45:20
our soul, and thou takest *no k.* 58:3
do good, they have *no k.* Jer 4:22

without **knowledge**

committed *without k.* of. Num 15:24
Job hath spoken *without k.* and. Job 34:35
multiplieth words *without k.* 35:16
perish by sword, and die *without k.* 36:12
by words *without k.* 38:2; 42:3
the soul be *without k.* Pr 19:2

known

nor had any man *k.* her. Gen 24:1
surely this thing is *k.* Ex 2:1

if it be *k.* that the ox hath. *Ex* 21:36
for wherein shall it be *k.* 33:16
sin they have sinned is *k.* *Lev* 4:14
whether he hath seen or *k.* of it. 5:1
woman that hath *k.* man. *Num* 31:17
take wise men, and *k.* *Deut* 1:13, 15
be not *k.* who hath slain him. 21:1
which had *k.* the works. *Josh* 24:31
k. to you why his hand. *1 Sam* 6:3
let it be *k.* that thou art God in. *1 Ki* 18:36
it *k.* to the king. *Ezra* 4:12, 13; 5:8
enemies heard it was *k.* to. *Neh* 4:15
thing was *k.* to Mordecai. *Esth* 2:22
Lord is *k.* by the judgement. *Ps* 9:16
hast *k.* my soul in adversities. 31:7
God is *k.* in her palaces for. 48:3
thy way may be *k.* on earth. 67:2
thou hast *k.* my reproach. 69:19
in Judah is God *k.*: his name. 76:1
sea, thy footsteps are not *k.* 77:19
which we have heard and *k.* 78:3
be *k.* among the heathen in. 79:10
shall thy wonders be *k.* in ? 88:12
because he hath *k.* my name. 91:14
that have *k.* thy testimonies. 119:79
I have *k.* of old thou hast. 152
hast searched me, and *k.* me. 139:1
that perverteth his ways shall be *k.* *Pr* 10:9
a fool's wrath is presently *k.* 12:16
a child is *k.* by his doings. 20:11
her husband is *k.* in the gates. 31:23
a fool's voice is *k.* by. *Eccl* 5:3
and it is *k.* that it is man, nor. 6:10
excellent things, this is *k.* *Isa* 12:5
and the Lord shall be *k.* to. 19:21
their seed shall be *k.* among. 61:9
hand of the Lord shall be *k.* to. 66:14
they have *k.* the way of. *Jer* 5:5
then shall prophet be *k.* the. 28:9
saith Lord God, be it *k.* *Ezek* 36:32
Acts 4:10; 13:38; 28:28
I will be *k.* in the eyes. *Ezek* 38:23
but if not, be it *k.* to thee. *Dan* 3:18
after thou shalt have *k.* the. 4:26
have I *k.* of all families. *Amos* 3:2
a day which shall be *k.* *Zech* 14:7
ye had *k.* what this meant. *Mat* 12:7
tree is *k.* by his fruit. 33; *Luke* 6:44
goodman of house had *k.* *Mat* 24:43
Luke 12:39
prophet, he would have *k.* *Luke* 7:39
saying, If thou hadst *k.* in. 19:42
how he was *k.* of them in. 24:35
himself seeketh to be *k.* *John* 7:4
nor my Father: if ye had *k.* me, ye should have *k.* my. 8:19; 14:7
I know my sheep, and am *k.* 10:14
now they have *k.* 17:7
and have *k.* surely. 8
I have *k.* thee, these have *k.* 25
that disciple which was *k.* 18:15, 16
was *k.* to all dwellers. *Acts* 1:19
this *k.* unto you, and hearken. 2:14
but their laying await was *k.* of. 9:24
it was *k.* throughout all Joppa. 42
k. unto God are all his works. 15:18
this was *k.* to all the Jews and. 19:17
have *k.* the certainty. 22:30; 23:28
which may be *k.* of God. *Rom* 1:19
for who hath *k.* the mind of the Lord ? 11:34; *1 Cor* 2:16
for had they *k.* it. *1 Cor* 2:8
same is *k.* of him. 8:3
know, even as I also am *k.* 13:12
how shall it be *k.* what is piped ? 14:7
how shall it be *k.* what is spoken ? 9
Ye are our epistle, *k.* and. *2 Cor* 3:2
though we have *k.* Christ. 5:16
as unknown, and yet well *k.*; as. 6:9
have *k.* God or are *k.* of. *Gal* 4:9
might be *k.* by church the. *Eph* 3:10
Let your moderation be *k.* *Phil* 4:5
thou hast fully *k.* my. *2 Tim* 3:10
from a child thou hast *k.* the. 15
preaching might be fully *k.* 4:17
because ye have *k.* him. *1 John* 2:13
we have *k.* and believed the. 4:16
that have *k.* the truth. *2 John* 1:1

made or *madest* **known**

Joseph *made* himself *k.* *Gen* 45:1
and *madest* *k.* to them. *Neh* 9:14
the Lord hath *made k.* his. *Ps* 98:2
make k. his ways to Moses. 103:7
that which is in the midst of fools is *made k.* *Pr* 14:33
have *made k.* to thee this day. 22:19
made myself *k.* to. *Ezek* 20:5, 9
Arioch *made* the thing *k.* *Dan* 2:15
Daniel *made* the thing *k.* to. 17
hast *made k.* to me, *made k.* to. 23
God hath *made k.* to the king. 45
made k. that which shall surely be. *Hos* 5:9
Lord hath *made k.* to us. *Luke* 2:15
seen it, they *made k.* abroad. 17
I have *made k.* to you. *John* 15:15
made k. to me the ways. *Acts* 2:28
Joseph was *made k.* to his brethren; and Joseph's kindred *made k.* 7:13
made k. to all nations. *Rom* 16:26
made k. to us the mystery. *Eph* 1:9
how by revelation he *made k.* 3:3
requests be *made k.* to. *Phil* 4:6
we *make k.* the coming. *2 Pet* 1:16

make **known**

I will *make* myself *k.* *Num* 12:6
thou mayest *make k.* to me what I. *1 Sam* 28:15
make k. his deeds among people. *1 Chr* 16:8; *Ps* 105:1
in *making k.* all these great. 17:19
they should *make* them *k.* *Ps* 78:5
with my mouth will I *make k.* 89:1
that he might *make k.* his. 106:8
to *make k.* to sons of men. 145:12
I will *make k.* my words. *Pr* 1:23
the father to children shall *make k.* thy truth. *Isa* 38:19
to *make* thy name *k.* to thy. 64:2
I will *make* myself *k.* *Ezek* 35:11
I *make* my holy name *k.* in. 39:7
a man that will *make k.* *Dan* 2:25
art thou able to *make k.* to me ? 26
Lord *maketh k.* to the king. 28, 29
shall *make k.* the interpretation. 30
5:15, 16, 17
midst of the years *make k.* *Hab* 3:2
God willing to *make* his power *k.* *Rom* 9:22
that he might *make k.* riches of. 23
to *make k.* the mystery of. *Eph* 6:19
Tychicus shall *make k.* to you. 21
whom God will *make k.* *Col* 1:27
shall *make k.* to you all things. 4:9

not **known**

I have two daughters which have *not k.* man. *Gen* 19:8; *Num* 31:18
35; *Judg* 21:12
not be *k.* they had. *Gen* 41:21
and the plenty shall *not* be *k.* in. 31
Jehovah was I *not k.* *Ex* 6:3
with children which have *not k.* *Deut* 11:2; 31:13
to go after gods which ye have *not k.* 11:28; 13:6, 13
nor thy fathers have *k.* 28:36, 64
as had *not k.* the wars. *Judg* 3:1
withs, so his strength was *not k.* 16:9
but make *not* thyself *k.* *Ruth* 3:3
let it *not* be *k.* that a woman. 14
and the thing was *not k.* *2 Sam* 17:19
be *not k.* to be the wife. *1 Ki* 14:2
people whom I have *not k.* *Ps* 18:43
and thy footsteps are *not k.* 77:19
heathen that have *not k.* thee. 79:6
not k. my ways. 95:10; *Heb* 3:10
they have *not k.* them. *Ps* 147:20
he hath not seen the sun, *nor k.* any thing. *Eccl* 6:5
have ye *not k.*? *Isa* 40:21
hast thou *not k.*? 28
paths that they have *not k.* 42:16
have *not k.* nor understood. 44:18
though thou hast *not k.* me. 45:4, 5
foolish, they have *not k.* me. *Jer* 4:22
countries thou hast *not k.* *Ezek* 32:9
not make *k.* the dream. *Dan* 2:5, 9
they did *not* make *k.* to. 4:7; 5:8
they have *not k.* the Lord. *Hos* 5:4
their place is *not k.* *Nah* 3:17
for there is nothing hid that shall *not* be *k.* *Mat* 10:26; *Luke* 8:17; 12:2
they should *not* make him *k.* *Mat* 12:16; *Mark* 3:12
a stranger, and hast *not k.* the things which ? *Luke* 24:18
yet ye have *not k.* him. *John* 8:55
and yet hast thou *not k.* me. 14:9
because they have *not k.* the. 16:3
the world hath *not k.* thee. 17:25
of peace have they *not k.* *Rom* 3:17
I had *not k.* sin but by the law: for I had *not k.* 7:7
other ages was *not* made *k.* *Eph* 3:5
been better *not* to have *k.* *2 Pet* 2:21
hath not seen *nor k.* him. *1 John* 3:6
which have *not k.* depths. *Rev* 2:24

Kohath

the sons of Levi, Gershon, *K.* and. *Gen* 46:11; *Ex* 6:16; *Num* 3:17
the sons of *K.* *Ex* 6:18; *Num* 3:19
27, 29, 30; 16:1; *1 Chr* 6:2, 22, 61
life of *K.* were 133 years. *Ex* 6:18
sum of the sons of *K.* of. *Num* 4:2
service of the sons of *K.* 4, 15; 7:9
the sons of *K.* Uriel. *1 Chr* 15:5

Kohathites

off the family of the *K.* *Num* 4:18
Aaron numbered sons of *K.* 34, 37
the *K.* set forward bearing. 10:21
the lot came out for *K.* *Josh* 21:4
1 Chr 6:54
sons of *K.* sanctified. *2 Chr* 29:12
the sons of the *K.* to set the. 34:12

Korah

Aholibamah bare *K.* *Gen* 36:5
duke *K.* 16, 18
sons of Izhar, *K.* Nepheg. *Ex* 6:21
Num 16:1
take censers, *K.* and all. *Num* 16:6
K. gathered all the congregation. 19
from about the tabernacle of *K.* 24
that he be not as *K.* and as. 40
strove in the company of *K.* 26:9
the children of *K.* died not. 11
not in the company of *K.* 27:3
Esau, Jaalam and *K.* *1 Chr* 1:35
sons of Hebron, *K.* 2:43
Amminadab his son, *K.* his. 6:22
son of *K.* and his brethren. 9:19
in the gainsaying of *K.* *Jude* 11

L

Laban

a brother, his name was *L.* *Gen* 24:29
flee thou to *L.* my brother. 27:43
a wife of the daughters of *L.* 28:2
know ye *L.*? 29:5
L. gave Rachel, Bilhah. 29
Jacob fed the rest of *L.'s* flocks. 30:36
so the feebler were *L.'s*, the. 42
beheld the countenance of *L.* 31:2
seen all that *L.* doth to thee. 12
Jacob stole away unawares to *L.* 20
God came to *L.* in a dream by. 24
L. searched all the tent, but. 34
Jacob chode with *L.* 36
L. kissed his sons. 55
I have sojourned with *L.* and. 32:4

Laban

between Paran and *L.* *Deut* 1:1

labour, *substantive*

God hath seen the *l.* *Gen* 31:42
travailed and had hard *l.* 35:16, 17
and looked on our *l.* *Deut* 26:7
out every man from his *l.* *Neh* 5:13
or wilt thou leave thy *l.*? *Job* 39:11
her *l.* is in vain without fear. 16
he gave their *l.* to locust. *Ps* 78:46
yet is their strength *l.* and. 90:10
man goeth to his *l.* until. 104:23
they inherited the *l.* of the people. 105:44
down their heart with *l.* 107:12
let the stranger spoil his *l.* 109:11
thou shalt eat the *l.* of thy. 128:2
the *l.* of the righteous. *Pr* 10:16
he that gathereth by *l.* shall. 13:11
in all *l.* there is profit, but. 14:23
what profit hath a man of all his *l.*? *Eccl* 1:3
all things are full of *l.*; man. 8*
all my *l.* my portion of all my *l.* 2:10

I hated all my l. which I. Eccl 2:18
he have rule over all my l. 19
my heart to despair of the l. I. 20
a man whose l. is in wisdom. 21
what hath man of all his l. under? 22
soul enjoy good in l. 24; 3:13; 5:18
yet there is no end of all his l. 4:8
have a good reward for their l. 9
nothing of his l. which he may. 5:15
to rejoice in his l.; this is the gift. 19
all the l. of man is for his mouth. 6:7
shall abide with him of his l. 8:15
thy portion in thy l. under. 9:9
the l. of the foolish wearieth. 10:15
l. of Egypt shall come. Isa 45:14
spend your l. for that which? 55:2
shame devoured the l. of. Jer 3:24
came I forth to see l. and? 20:18
take away all thy l. Ezek 23:29
the land of Egypt for his l. 29:20*
though the l. of the olive. Hab 3:17
a drought on all the l. of. Hag 1:11
whereon ye bestowed no l. John 4:38
who bestowed much l. on. Rom 16:6
every man shall receive according to his l. 1 Cor 3:8
that your l. is not in vain. 15:58
lest I bestowed l. in vain. Gal 4:11
flesh, this is fruit of my l. Phil 1:22
my brother and companion in l. 2:25
remembering your l. of. 1 Thes 1:3
for ye remember, brethren, our l. 2:9
you, and our l. be in vain. 3:5
but wrought with l. and. 2 Thes 3:8
to forget your l. of love. Heb 6:10
I know thy works, and l. Rev 2:2

labour, *verb*

work, that they may l. Ex 5:9
days shalt thou l. 20:9; Deut 5:13
not all the people to l. Josh 7:3
a land, for which he did not l. 24:13
be a guard to us, and l. Neh 4:22
I be wicked, why then l.? Job 9:29
Lord build, they l. in vain. Ps 127:1
oxen may be strong to l. 144:14*
his hands refuse to l. Pr 21:25
L. not to be rich, cease from. 23:4*
he, For whom do I l.? Eccl 4:8
though a man l. to seek it out. 8:17
I will weep bitterly, l. not. Isa 22:4
they shall not l. in vain, nor. 65:53
the people shall l. in vain. Jer 51:58
under persecution we l. Lam 5:5*
be in pain, and l. to bring. Mi 4:10
that the people should l. Hab 2:13
come unto me all ye that l. Mat 11:28
l. not for the meat that. John 6:27
and Tryphosa who l. Rom 16:12
and l. working with our. 1 Cor 4:12
we l. to be accepted of. 2 Cor 5:9*
but rather l. working. Eph 4:28
whereunto I also l. striving. Col 1:29
to know them which l. 1 Thes 5:12
therefore we both l. and. 1 Tim 4:10
especially they that l. in word. 5:17
let us l. therefore to. Heb 4:11*

laboured

so we l. in the work. Neh 4:21
that which he l. for. Job 20:18
on the labour I had l. to. Eccl 2:11
all my labour wherein I have l. 19
yet to a man that hath not l. 21
of his heart wherein he hath l. 22
what profit hath he that hath l.? 5:16
thy sorceries wherein thou hast l. Isa 47:12
to thee with whom thou hast l. 15
I said, I have l. in vain. 49:4
drink, for which thou hast l. 62:8
king l. to deliver Daniel. Dan 6:14
for which thou hast not l. Jonah 4:10
other men l. and ye are. John 4:38
salute Persis, who l. Rom 16:12
but I l. more abundantly. 1 Cor 15:10
I have not run nor l. in. Phil 2:16
help those that l. with me in. 4:3
and for my name's sake l. Rev 2:3

labourer

the l. is worthy of his hire. Luke 10:7
l. is worthy of his reward. 1 Tim 5:18

labourers

harvest plenteous, but l. few. Mat 9:37; Luke 10:2
pray the Lord that he will send l. Mat 9:38; Luke 10:2
went out early to hire l. Mat 20:1
when he had agreed with the l. 2
call the l. 8
for we are l. together. 1 Cor 3:9*
behold the hire of the l. Jas 5:4

laboureth

he that l. l. for himself. Pr 16:26*
in that wherein he l.? Eccl 3:9
one that helpeth and l. 1 Cor 16:16
the husbandman that l. 2 Tim 2:6

labouring

the sleep of a l. man. Eccl 5:12
l. ye ought to support. Acts 20:35
l. for you in prayer. Col 4:12*
l. night and day we. 1 Thes 2:9

labours

of thy l. when thou hast gathered in thy l. out of the field. Ex 23:16
all thy l. shall a nation. Deut 28:33
and thy l. be in the house. Pr 5:10
fast, ye exact all your l. Isa 58:3
I will deliver all their l. Jer 20:5*
in my l. shall they find no. Hos 12:8
I smote you in all the l. Hag 2:17
entered into their l. John 4:38
in tumults, in l. in. 2 Cor 6:5
not boasting of other men's l. 10:15
in l. more abundant, in. 11:23
may rest from their l. Rev 14:13

lace

breastplate with l. of blue. Ex 28:28
thou shalt put it on a blue l. 37
tied it to a l. of blue to fasten. 39:31

Lachish

the Lord delivered L. Josh 10:32
the king of L. one. 12:11
Judah had L. 15:39
Amaziah fled to L. 2 Ki 14:19; 2 Chr 25:27
king of Assyria to L. 2 Ki 18:14
Assyria sent Rab-shakeh from L. with a great host. 17; Isa 36:2
Rehoboam built L. and. 2 Chr 11:9
Babylon fought against L. Jer 34:7
O inhabitant of L. bind. Mi 1:13

lack, *substantive*

destroy all for l. of five? Gen 18:28
that gathered little had no l. Ex 16:18; 2 Cor 8:15
old lion perisheth for l. Job 4:11
ones wander for l. of meat. 38:41
my people are destroyed for l. of. Hos 4:6
his life to supply your l. Phil 2:30
that ye may have l. of. 1 Thes 4:12

lack, *verb*

there shall l. five of? Gen 18:28
not l. any thing in it. Deut 8:9
the young lions do l. Ps 34:10
to the poor shall not l. Pr 28:27
thy head l. no ointment. Eccl 9:8
have I kept, what l. I yet? Mat 19:20
if any of you l. wisdom. Jas 1:5

lacked

thou hast l. nothing. Deut 2:7
l. of David's servants. 2 Sam 2:30
provided victual, they l. 1 Ki 4:27
but what hast thou l. with me? 11:22
sustain them, they l. Neh 9:21
because it l. moisture. Luke 8:6
without purse, l. ye any? 22:35
any among them that l. Acts 4:34
more honour to that part which l. 1 Cor 12:24
ye were careful, but l. Phil 4:10

lackest

but one thing thou l. Mark 10:21; Luke 18:22

lacketh

there l. not one man of. Num 31:49
not fail one that l. bread. 2 Sam 3:29
committeth adultery, l. Pr 6:32*
honoureth himself, and l. bread. 12:9
he that l. these things. 2 Pet 1:9

lacking

thou suffer salt to be l. Lev 2:13
a lamb that hath any thing l. 22:23
should be one tribe l. in. Judg 21:3
there was nothing l. to. 1 Sam 30:19
they shall fear no more, nor shall be l. Jer 23:4
for that which was l. 1 Cor 16:17
was l. to me the brethren. 2 Cor 11:9
might perfect what is l. 1 Thes 3:10

lad, -s

This word is used [1] *Of a boy of about thirteen,* Gen 21:12, 17. [2] *Of a boy of about seventeen,* Gen 37:2. [3] *Of a married man,* Gen 43:8 *compared with* 46:21. [4] *Of a servant,* 1 Sam 20:36.

grievous because of the l. Gen 21:12
God heard the voice of the l. 17
arise, lift up the l. 18
she gave the l. drink. 19
God was with the l. and he. 20
I and the l. will go yonder. 22:5
lay not thine hand upon the l. 12
l. was with the sons of Bilhah. 37:2
send the l. with me, and we. 43:8
we said, The l. cannot leave. 44:22
the l. be not with us, his life is bound up in the l.'s life. 30, 31, 34
became surety for the l. 32
abide instead of the l.; let the l. 33
who redeemed me, bless the l. 48:16
Samson said to the l. Judg 16:26
behold I will send a l. 1 Sam 20:21
unto the l. Run, and as the l. ran. 36
Jonathan cried after the l. 37, 38
l. knew not any thing, only. 39
gave his artillery to his l. 40
a l. saw them and told. 2 Sam 17:18
a l. here hath five barley. John 6:9

ladder

dreamed, and behold a l. Gen 28:12

lade

l. your beasts and go to. Gen 45:17
my father did l. you. 1 Ki 12:11
ye l. men with grievous. Luke 11:46

laded

they l. their asses with the corn. Gen 42:26; 44:13
those that l. wrought. Neh 4:17
l. us with such things. Acts 28:10*

laden

sent ten asses l. with. Gen 45:23
Jesse took an ass l. with bread. 1 Sam 16:20
a people l. with iniquity. Isa 1:4
labour and are heavy l. Mat 11:28
silly women, l. with sins. 2 Tim 3:6

ladeth

woe to him that l. himself. Hab 2:6

lading

on the sabbath l. asses. Neh 13:15
damage not only of l. Acts 27:10

ladies

wise l. answered her, yea. Judg 5:29
shall l. of Persia and. Esth 1:18*

lady

no more be called a l. Isa 47:5†
and thou saidst, I shall be a l. 7†
the elder to the elect l. 2 John 1
now I beseech thee, l., that we. 5

laid

and l. it on both their. Gen 9:23
Abraham took wood and l. it. 22:6
Jacob l. the rods before. 30:41
she went away, and l. by her. 38:19
right hand, and l. it on. 48:14
she l. it in the flags by. Ex 2:3
let more work be l. on the men. 5:9
he shall give whatsoever is l. 21:30
Egyptians l. on us hard. Deut 26:6
stalks of flax she had l. Josh 2:6
they took and l. them out. 7:23
blood be l. on Abimelech. Judg 9:24
took the child and l. it in. Ruth 4:16
l. a great heap of stones on Absalom. 2 Sam 18:17
my son and l. it in her bosom, and l. her dead child in my. 1 Ki 3:20
an oath be l. on him. 8:31; 2 Chr 6:2
the prophet l. the carcase. 1 Ki 13:2
l. his carcase in his own grave. 3
he carried him up, and l. him. 17:1
she went and l. him on. 2 Ki 4:2
Lord l. this burden on him. 9:2
took and l. it on the boil. 20:

l. upon Israel in the. 2 Chr 24:9
where they l. the meat. Neh 13:5
and my calamity l. in. Job 6:2
the snare is l. for him in. 18:10*
or who l. the corner-stone. 38:6
and majesty hast l. on. Ps 21:5
out of the net they have l. for. 31:4
like sheep they are l. in the. 49:14
to be l. in the balance, they. 62:9
they have l. Jerusalem on. 79:1
l. me in the lowest pit. 88:6
I have l. help upon one that. 89:19
hurt with fetters, he was l. 105:18
thy judgements have I l. 119:30
wicked have l. a snare. 110; 141:19
thou hast l. thine hand upon. 139:5
they have privily l. a snare. 142:3
he l. it upon my mouth. Isa 6:7*
burned him, yet l. it. 42:25; 57:11
thou hast very heavily l. 47:6
Lord l. on him the iniquity of. 53:6
I have l. a snare for thee. Jer 50:24
be thou l. with the uncircumcised. Ezek 32:19
when I have l. the land. 33:29
spoken, saying, They are l. 35:12
I drew them, and I l. Hos 11:4
garners are l. desolate. Joel 1:17
on clothes l. to pledge. Amos 2:8
they have l. a wound. Ob 7
he arose and l. his robe. Jonah 3:6
now gather, he hath l. siege. Mi 5:1
it is l. over with gold. Hab 2:19
from before a stone was l. Hag 2:15
the stone that I have l. Zech 3:9
for they l. the pleasant land. 7:14
now the axe is l. to the root. Mat 3:10; Luke 3:9
l. it in his own new tomb. Mat 27:60
and her daughter l. on. Mark 7:30
Mary beheld where he was l. 15:47
behold the place where they l. 16:6
her firstborn, and l. Luke 2:7
Lazarus was l. at his gate. 16:20
wherein never man before was l. 23:53; John 19:41
said, Where have ye l.? John 11:34
l. aside his garments, and. 13:4
there l. they Jesus therefore. 19:42
not where they have l. him. 20:2, 13
whom they l. at the gate. Acts 3:2
and l. the money at the. 4:37; 5:2
l. them on beds and couches. 5:15
when washed, they l. her in. 9:37
David was l. to his fathers. 13:36
nothing l. to his charge. 23:29
. many complaints they could. 25:7
concerning the crime l. against. 16
necessity is l. upon me. 1 Cor 9:16
I pray it be not l. to. 2 Tim 4:16
see **foundation**

laid *down*

efore they were l. down. Josh 2:8
arried them, and l. them down. 4:8
is feet and l. her down. Ruth 3:7
li was l. down. 1 Sam 3:2
amuel l. down to sleep. 3
mnon was l. down. 2 Sam 13:8
id eat, and l. him down. 1 Ki 19:6
hab came and l. him down. 21:4
l. me down and slept. Ps 3:5
ince thou art l. down no feller is. Isa 14:8
o that I l. not down. Luke 19:22
them down at the. Acts 4:35
itnesses l. down their clothes. 7:58
or my life l. down their. Rom 16:4
e l. down his life for. 1 John 3:16

laid *hand*

obles he l. not his hand. Ex 24:11
amar l. her hand on. 2 Sam 13:19
ecause he l. his hand on. Esth 8:7
not their hand on spoil. 9:10, 15, 16
inces l. their hand on. Job 29:9
ou hast l. thine hand. Ps 139:5
y hand that I have l. Ezek 39:21
l. his right hand upon. Rev 1:17

laid *hands*

s sons l. their h. Lev 8:14, 18, 22
oses l. his hands on Joshua. Num 27:23; Deut 34:9
d they l. hands on her. 2 Ki 11:16; 2 Chr 23:15*
l. their hands on the he goats. 2 Chr 29:23
nor have l. hands on their. Ob 13
l. hands, and took him. Mat 18:28
and he l. his hands on them. 19:15
they came and l. hands on Jesus. 26:50; Mark 14:46
save that he l. hands on. Mark 6:5
he l. his hands on every. Luke 4:40
he l. his hands on her, she. 13:13
but no man l. hands on him. John 7:30, 44; 8:20
and they l. hands on the apostles. Acts 4:3; 5:18
and prayed, they l. hands on. 6:6
then l. they their hands on. 8:17
they l. their hands on Paul. 13:3
when Paul had l. his hands. 19:6
up the people, and l. hands. 21:27
Paul l. hands on Publius'. 28:8

laid *hold*

men l. hold on Lot's. Gen 19:16
took a knife, and l. hold. Judg 19:29
Saul l. hold on Samuel's skirt, and. 1 Sam 15:27
l. hold on other gods. 2 Chr 7:22
Herod had l. hold on John. Mat 14:3; Mark 6:17
l. no hold on me. Mat 26:55
l. hold on Jesus. 57; Mark 14:51
l. hold on one Simon. Luke 23:26
he l. hold on the dragon. Rev 20:2

laid *up*

she l. up his garments. Gen 39:16
Joseph l. up food in the. 41:48
l. it up till the morning. Ex 16:24
Aaron l. up the pot of manna. 34
Moses l. up the rods. Num 17:7
not this l. up in store? Deut 32:34
Samuel l. it up before. 1 Sam 10:25
David l. up these words. 21:12
which thy fathers l. up. 2 Ki 20:17
treasures were l. up. Ezra 6:1
thou hast l. up for them. Ps 31:19
wealth of sinners is l. up. Pr 13:22
fruits which I have l. up. S of S 7:13
at Michmash he l. up. Isa 10:28
that l. up shall they carry. 15:7
shall not be treasured or l. up. 23:18
which fathers l. up be carried. 39:6
they l. up the roll in the. Jer 36:20
l. them up in their hearts. Luke 1:66
hast much goods l. up for. 12:19
thy pound I have kept l. up in. 19:20
for the hope which is l. up. Col 1:5
is l. up for me a crown. 2 Tim 4:8

laid *wait*

l. wait against Shechem. Judg 9:34
l. wait all night for Samson. 16:2
Amalek l. wait for him. 1 Sam 15:2
Saul came and l. wait in the valley. 5
l. wait at my neighbour's. Job 31:9
they l. wait for us in the wilderness. Lam 4:19
when the Jews l. wait for him. Acts 20:3; 23:30

laid *waste*

l. waste his dwelling place. Ps 79:7
Ar and Kir l. waste. Isa 15:1
Tyre, it is l. waste. 23:1
your strength is l. waste. 23:14
kings of Assyria l. waste all. 37:18
pleasant things are l. waste. 64:11
thy cities shall be l. waste. Jer 4:7
Ezek 6:6; 12:20; 19:7; 29:12
should this city be l. waste? Jer 27:17
now she is l. waste. Ezek 26:2
l. my vine waste, and. Joel 1:7
Israel shall be l. waste. Amos 7:9
say, Nineveh is l. waste. Nah 3:7
I l. his heritage waste. Mal 1:3

laidest

l. affliction on our loins. Ps 66:11
takest up that thou l. Luke 19:21

lain

he had l. in the grave. John 11:17
the body of Jesus had l. 20:12
see **lien**

Laish

to spy the country of L. Judg 18:14
the name of the city was L. 29
cause thy voice to be heard unto L. Isa 10:30

Laish, *person*

given to Phalti son of L. 1 Sam 25:44
Ish-bosheth took her from the son of L. 2 Sam 3:15

lake

Jesus stood by the l. Luke 5:1
two ships standing by the l. 2
over to the other side of the l. 8:22
down a storm of wind on the l. 23
violently down a steep place into l. 33
were cast into a l. of fire. Rev 19:20
devil was cast into l. of fire. 20:10
hell were cast into the l. of. 14
not in the book of life, cast into l. 15
their part in the l. burneth. 21:8

lamb

(The word is used most often literally, of a young sheep. Jesus is called the Lamb of God because he was sacrificed for us, as was the lamb in the Jewish ritual)

where is the l. for a? Gen 22:7
God will provide himself a l. 8
to them every man a l. Ex 12:3, 21
your l. shall be without blemish. 5
thou redeem with a l. 13:13; 34:20
l. thou shalt offer in morning, and the other l. 29:39, 41; Num 28:4
with a l. a tenth deal of. Ex 29:40
Num 28:21, 29; 29:4, 10, 15
if he offer a l. Lev 3:7; 4:32; 5:6
22:23; 23:12
as the fat of a l. is taken away. 4:35
if not able to bring a l. 5:7; 12:8
take a l. of the first year. 9:3
14:10; Num 6:12; 7:15, 21
the priest shall take the l. Lev 14:12
slay the l. 13, 25
l. of trespass offering. 24
that killeth an ox, or a l. or. 17:3
offer a l. without blemish. 23:12
one he l. of first year for a burnt offering, ewe l. of. Num 6:14
prepare with sacrifice for one l. 15:5
thus done for one l. 11; 28:7, 13
14; Ezek 46:15
offered a sucking l. to. 1 Sam 7:9
lion and bear and took a l. 17:34
took the poor man's l. 2 Sam 12:4
he shall restore the l. fourfold. 6
shall dwell with the l. Isa 11:6
send ye the l. to the ruler of. 16:1
l. to the slaughter. 53:7; Jer 11:19
wolf and the l. shall feed. 65:25
that sacrificeth a l. as if he. 66:3
one l. out of flock for. Ezek 45:15
a l. of the first year thou. 46:13
Lord will feed them as l. Hos 4:16
behold l. of God that. John 1:29, 36
l. dumb before the shearer. Acts 8:32
as of a l. without blemish. 1 Pet 1:19
the elders stood a l. slain. Rev 5:6
beasts fell down before the l. 8
saying, Worthy is the l. that was. 12
glory, and power, be to the l. for. 13
I saw when the l. opened one. 6:1
hide us from the wrath of the l. 16
multitude stood before the l. 7:9
salvation to our God and to the l. 10
white in the blood of the l. 14
for the l. shall feed and lead. 17
by the blood of the l. 12:11
l. slain from the foundation. 13:8
he had two horns like a l. and. 11
I looked, and lo, a l. stood on. 14:1
these are they that follow the l. 4
presence of angels and the l. 10
of Moses and song of the l. 15:3
war with the l. and the l. shall. 17:14
for the marriage of the l. is. 19:7
the marriage supper of the l. 9
I will shew thee the bride, the l.'s wife. 21:9
the twelve apostles of the l. 14
God Almighty and the l. are the. 22
God did lighten it, and the l. is. 23
but they are written in the l.'s book. 27
of throne of God and of l. 22:1, 3

lambs
did separate the l. Gen 30:40
rams twelve, l. of the. Num 7:87
sixty l. 88
fourteen l. 29:13, 17, 20, 23
for the bullocks, l. and rams. 29:18
with fat of l. and rams. Deut 32:14
spared the best of the l. 1 Sam 15:9
to Israel 100,000 l. 2 Ki 3:4
to the Lord a thousand l. 1 Chr 29:21
priests killed l. and. 2 Chr 29:22
burnt offerings two hundred l. 32
Josiah gave to the people l. 35:7
mayest buy speedily l. Ezra 7:17
shall be as the fat of l. Ps 37:20
little hills skipped like l. 114:4
ye little hills that skipped like l. 6
l. are for thy clothing. Pr 27:26
delight not in blood of l. Isa 1:11
then shall the l. feed after. 5:17
sword filled with blood of l. 34:6
he shall gather the l. with. 40:11
I will bring them like l. Jer 51:40
occupied with thee in l. Ezek 27:21
ye shall drink the blood of l. 39:18
in the sabbath six l. 46:4
in new moons six l. 6
and meat offering for the l. 5, 7
eat the l. out of the flock. Amos 6:4
I send you forth as l. Luke 10:3
to Peter, Feed my l. John 21:15

five **lambs**
five l. of the first year. Num 7:17
23, 29, 35, 41, 47

seven **lambs**
Abraham set *seven* ewe l. Gen 21:28
what mean these *seven* ewe l. set? 29
these *seven* ewe l. thou shalt. 30
offer with bread *seven* l. Lev 23:18
seven l. of the first year without.
Num 28:11, 19, 27; 29:2, 8, 36
a tenth deal throughout *seven* l.
28:21, 29; 29:4, 10
they brought *seven* l. 2 Chr 29:21

two **lambs**
two l. of the first year offer.
Ex 29:38; Num 28:3
day he shall take *two* l. Lev 14:10
then ye shall sacrifice *two* l. of. 23:19
and on the sabbath *two* l. Num 28:9

lame
a blind or l. man shall. Lev 21:18
if it be l. thou shalt. Deut 15:21
Jonathan had a son that was l. of his feet. 2 Sam 4:4; 9:3, 13
away the blind and the l. 5:6
whosoever smiteth the l. 8
because thy servant is l. 19:26
to the blind, feet to the l. Job 29:15
legs of the l. are not equal. Pr 26:7
then is prey divided, the l. Isa 33:23
then shall the l. man leap as. 35:6
them the blind and the l. Jer 31:8
offer the l. for sacrifice. Mal 1:8
that which was torn and l. 13
the l. walk. Mat 11:5; 15:31
21:14; Luke 7:22
call the poor, the l. and. Luke 14:13
certain man, l. from womb. Acts 3:2
L. man held Peter and John. 11
with palsies and that were l. 8:7
lest the l. be turned out. Heb 12:13

Lamech
Methusael begat L. Gen 4:18
L. took two wives. 19
Methuselah begat L. 5:25
1 Chr 1:3
Noe, which was son of L. Luke 3:36

lament
Israel went yearly to l. Judg 11:40*
and her gates shall l. Isa 3:26
fishers also shall mourn and l. 19:8
l. for the teats and pleasant. 32:12*
for this l. and howl, for. Jer 4:8
to l. nor bemoan them. 16:5, 6
they shall not l. for him. 22:18
l. thee saying, Ah Lord. 34:5
ye daughters of Rabbah, l. and. 49:3
rampart and the wall to l. Lam 2:8
they shall l. over Tyrus. Ezek 27:32
of the nations shall l. her. 32:16
l. like a virgin girded. Joel 1:8
gird yourselves, and l. ye priests. 13
l. with a doleful lamentation, and.
Mi 2:4
say, ye shall weep and l. John 16:20
kings of the earth shall l. Rev 18:9*

lamentable
king cried with a l. voice. Dan 6:20

lamentation
mourned with a sore l. Gen 50:10
lamented with this l. 2 Sam 1:17
their widows made no l. Ps 78:64
in ashes, make bitter l. Jer 6:26
and take up a l. on the high. 7:29
habitations of wilderness a l. 9:10
every one her neighbour l. 20
in Ramah l. and weeping. 31:15
Mat 2:18
shall be l. generally on. Jer 48:38
increased mourning and l. Lam 2:5
take thou up a l. for. Ezek 19:1
this is a l. and shall be for a l. 14
they shall take up a l. for Tyrus.
26:17; 27:2, 32
a l. upon the king of Tyrus. 28:12
take up a l. for Pharaoh. 32:2, 16
l. against you, O house. Amos 5:1
shall call such as are skilful of l. 16
turn all your songs into l. 8:10
lament with a doleful l. Mi 2:4
great l. over Stephen. Acts 8:2

lamentations
Josiah in their l. and, behold, they are written in the l. 2 Chr 35:25
was written therein l. Ezek 2:10

lamented
people l. because the. 1 Sam 6:19
all the house of Israel l. after. 7:2
Israelites l. Samuel. 25:1; 28:3
David l. over Saul. 2 Sam 1:17
king l. over Abner and said. 3:33
and Jeremiah l. for. 2 Chr 35:25
die and not be l. Jer 16:4; 25:33
to you, but ye have not l. Mat 11:17
company of people l. Luke 23:27

lamp
In Bible times [1] *a small cup-like vessel, usually of earthenware, containing oil in which a cotton wick floated. It gave a very faint light.* [2] *A torch,* Judg 7:16, 20. *The word is frequently used symbolically, the special meaning being easily gained from the context.*

a burning l. that passed. Gen 15:17
to cause the l. to burn. Ex 27:20
ere l. went out, Samuel. 1 Sam 3:3
thou art my l. O Lord. 2 Sam 22:29
God gave him a l. in. 1 Ki 15:4
a l. despised in thought. Job 12:5*
thy word is a l. to my. Ps 119:105
I have ordained a l. for. 132:17
commandment is a l. the. Pr 6:23
l. of the wicked shall be put. 13:9
curseth his father, his l. shall. 20:20
salvation thereof as a l. Isa 62:1
star burning as it were a l. Rev 8:10

lamps
light the l. thereof. Ex 25:37; 40:4
dresseth the l. burn incense on. 30:7
when Aaron lighteth the l. at even. 8
and his l. with the oil for. 35:14
and they brought l. to Moses. 39:37
he lighted the l. before the Lord.
40:25; Num 8:2, 3
l. to burn continually. Lev 24:2
2 Chr 13:11
order the l. Lev 24:4
and cover his l. Num 4:9
l. within the pitchers. Judg 7:16
and held the l. in their left hand. 20
he made l. of gold. 1 Ki 7:49
2 Chr 4:20, 21
of his mouth go burning l. Job 41:19
like the appearance of l. Ezek 1:13
and his eyes as l. of fire. Dan 10:6
which took their l. Mat 25:1; 3:4
arose and trimmed their l. 7
give us of your oil; for our l. 8

seven **lamps**
make the *seven* l. thereof. Ex 25:37
his *seven* l. of pure gold. 37:23
seven l. shall give light. Num 8:2
a candlestick and *seven* l. Zech 4:2
seven l. of fire burning. Rev 4:5

lance
they that hold the l. are. Jer 50:42

lancets
cut themselves with l. 1 Ki 18:28

land
[1] *The earth, as distinguished from sea,* Mat 23:15. [2] *One particular country,* Mat 9:26. [3] *Arable ground,* Gen 26:12. [4] *The inhabitants of a country,* Isa 37:11. [5] *A certain possession,* 2 Sam 19:29; Acts 4:37.

gold of that l. is good. Gen 2:12
out of that l. went forth Ashur. 10:11
get thee into a l. I will shew. 12:1
Acts 7:3
and the l. was not able to. Gen 13:6
is not the whole l. before thee? 9
I will give thee and seed the l. 17:8
28:13; 35:12
behold, my l. is before thee. 20:15
of the Canaanite, in whose l. 24:37
Isaac sowed in that l. and. 26:12
bought the l. so the l. became. 47:20
only the l. of the priests bought. 22
the l. was corrupted by. Ex 8:24
so that l. was darkened. 10:15
days may be long upon the l. 20:12
goat bear iniquities into a l. not.
Lev 16:22
and the l. is defiled. 18:25, 27
that the l. spue not you. 28; 20:22
then shall the l. keep. 25:2; 26:34
l. shall yield her fruit. 25:19; 26:4
l. shall not be sold, for the l. 25:23
l. of your enemies shall eat. 26:38
and I will remember the l. 42
the l. also shall be left of them. 43
see the l. what it is, and. Num 13:18
the l. is a l. that eateth up the. 32
surely they shall not see the l. 14:23
Caleb will I bring to the l. 24
when ye be come into the l. 15:2, 18
Deut 17:14; 18:9; 26:1
delivered into thy hand his l.
Num 21:34; Deut 3:2
country Lord smote is a l. for cattle.
Num 32:4
blood defileth the l. and the l. 35:33
to him will I give the l. Deut 1:36
accounted a l. of giants. 2:20; 3:13
a l. of wheat, and barley, and. 8:8
l. wherein eat bread, l. whose. 9
not able to bring them into the l. 9:28
to Jotbath, a l. of rivers. 10:7
a l. which the Lord thy God. 11:12
whole l. thereof is brimstone. 29:23
cast them into another l. as at. 28
he found him in a desert l. 32:10
he will be merciful to his l. 43
blessed of the Lord be his l. 33:13
Lord shewed him all the l. 34:1
saying, Go view the l. Josh 2:1
Lord hath given you the l. 9; 21:43
Joshua took all that l. 11:16, 23
and the l. had rest from war. 14:15
given you a l. for which ye did. 24:13
l. had rest forty. Judg 3:11; 5:31
l. had rest fourscore years. 30
to fight against me in my l. 11:12
ye shall come to a large l. 18:1
day of the captivity of the l. 3
hath troubled the l. 1 Sam 14:2
David the king of the l.? 21:1
saying, Whose is the l.? 2 Sam 3:1
restore thee all the l. of Saul. 9:
entreated for the l. 21:14: 24:2
them the l. of Cabul. 1 Ki 9:1
victuals, and gave him l. 11:1
cry to the king for her l. 2 Ki 8:
since the day that she left the l.
manner of the God of l. 17:26, 2
take you to a l. of corn and wine.
18:32; Isa 36:1
hath any of the gods delivered at a his l. 2 Ki 18:33; Isa 36:1

neither move any more out of the l.
2 Ki 21:8; 2 Chr 33:8
the king of Egypt came no more out of his l. 2 Ki 24:7
left of the poor of the l. 25:12
Jer 52:16
and the l. was wide. 1 Chr 4:40
Gath, who were born in that l. 7:21
pluck them out of my l. 2 Chr 7:20
make walls, while the l. is. 14:7
when he had purged the l. 34:8
that ye may eat the good of l.
Ezra 9:12; Isa 1:19
nor brought we any l. Neh 5:16
l. behold, we are servants in. 9:36
if my l. cry against me. Job 31:38
for correction, or his l., or for. 37:13
barren l. his dwellings. 39:6
are perished out of his l. Ps 10:16
remember thee from the l. of. 42:6
got not the l. in possession. 44:3
root thee out of the l. of the. 52:5
deep root, and it filled the l. 80:9
be on the faithful of the l. 101:6
destroy all the wicked of the l. 8
called for a famine on the l. 105:16
the l. brought forth frogs in. 30
despised the pleasant l. 106:24
l. was polluted with blood. 38
he turneth the fruitful l. into. 107:34
thirsts after thee as a thirsty l. 143:6
into the l. of uprightness. 10
that tilleth his l. shall be. Pr 12:11
28:19
for the trangression of a l. 28:2
woe to thee, O l. when. Eccl 10:16
blessed art thou, O l. when thy. 17
if one look unto the l. Isa 5:30
l. that thou abhorrest shall be. 7:16
all l. shall become briers. 24
l. of Zebulun, l. of Naphtali. 9:1
Mat 4:15
thro' wrath of the Lord is l. Isa 9:19
come to destroy the whole l. 13:5
break the Assyrian in my l. 14:25
woe to the l. shadowing with. 18:1
whose l. the rivers have spoiled. 2, 7
blessing in the midst of the l. 19:24
the desert, from a terrible l. 21:1
l. of Chittim it is revealed. 23:1
the l. shall be utterly emptied. 24:3
darkened, the mirth of the l. 11
l. of trouble and anguish. 30:6
of a great rock in a weary l. 32:2
the l. of my people shall come. 13
behold the l. that is very. 33:17
the l. thereof shall become. 34:9
thirsty l. springs of water. 35:7
these from the l. of Sinim. 49:12
the l. of thy destruction be too. 19
he was cut off out of the l. of. 53:8
pillar against the whole l. Jer 1:18
wentest after me, in a l. that. 2:2
led us through a l. of deserts, a l. 6
ye entered, ye defiled my l. 7; 3:9
young lions made his l. waste. 2:15
I give thee a pleasant l.? 3:19
for the whole l. is spoiled. 4:20
serve strangers in a l. that is. 5:19
make thee a l. not inhabited. 6:8
l. trembled at the sound. 8:16
l. perisheth and is burnt. 9:12
we have forsaken the l. 19
let us cut him off from l. 11:19
the l. mourn, herbs wither? 12:4
from the one end of the l. even to. 12
bring again every man to his l. 15
brought Israel from l. of the north.
16:15; 31:16
because they defiled my l. 16:18
inhabit wilderness into a salt l. 17:6
the l. whereunto they desire. 22:27
s profaneness gone forth into the l.
23:15
I will bring on that l. all my. 25:13
very time of his l. come. 27:7
all the l. is before thee. 40:4
and thy cry hath filled the l. 46:12
he king of Babylon and his l. 50:18
or it is the l. of graven images. 38
a dry l., a l. wherein no man. 51:43
er whole l. shall be confounded. 47
. is full of bloody. Ezek 7:23
lled the l. with violence. 8:17

l. is full of blood, and city. Ezek 9:9
the l. sinneth against me. 14:13
bring a sword on l. 17
a pestilence into l. 19
took also of the seed of the l. 17:5
hath taken the mighty of the l. 13
shall come forth out of one l. 21:19
thou art the l. is not cleansed. 22:24
in the gap before me for the l. 30
will I leave thee upon the l. 32:4
I bring the sword upon a l. 33:2
seeth the sword come upon the l. 3
l. is given us for inheritance. 24
have appointed my l. into their. 36:5
thou l. devourest up men, and. 13
like a cloud to cover the l. 38:9, 16
I will go up to the l. of unwalled. 11
I will bring thee against my l. 16
they may cleanse the l. 39:12
thus shall they cleanse the l. 16
shall be the border of the l. 47:15
he shall stand in the glorious l.
Dan 11:16, 41
shall the l. mourn and. Hos 4:3
for a nation is come up upon my l.
Joel 1:6
the l. is as the garden of Eden. 2:3
the Lord be jealous for his l. 18
fear not, O l. be glad. 21
and parted my l. 3:2
she is forsaken upon her l. Amos 5:2
the l. is not able to bear all. 7:10
make the poor of the l. to fail 8:4
shall not the l. tremble for this? 8
hosts is he that toucheth the l. 9:5
all things from off the l. Zeph 1:2
whole l. shall be devoured by fire. 18
praise and fame in every l. 3:19*
Ho, ho, flee from the l. of. Zech 2:6
remove the iniquity of that l. in. 3:9
up, as an ensign upon his l. 9:16
l. shall mourn, every family. 12:12
unclean spirit to pass out of l. 13:2
in all the l. two parts therein. 8
all the l. shall be turned as a. 14:10
shall be a delightsome l. Mal 3:12
went abroad into all that l. Mat 9:26
for the l. of Sodom. 10:15; 11:24
ye compass sea and l. to. 23:15
was darkness over all the l. 27:45
Mark 15:33
sea, and he alone on the l. Mark 6:47
neither fit for the l. nor. Luke 14:35
a great famine in that l. 15:14
the ship was at the l. John 6:21
Peter drew the net to l. full. 21:11
having l. sold it, and. Acts 4:37
tell me whether ye sold the l. for? 5:8
day, they knew not the l. 27:39
into the sea, and get to l. 43
that they escaped all safe to l. 44
see **Benjamin, Canaan, Chaldeans, darkness, desolate, divide, divided, inhabitants, inherit, Israel, Judah, strange**

dry **land**

let dry l. appear. Gen 1:9
called dry l. earth. 10
that was in the dry l. died. 7:22
water on dry l. and the waters shall become blood on dry l. Ex 4:9
Lord made the sea dry l. 14:21
Israel walked on dry l. 29; 15:19
Neh 9:11
the priests' feet were lifted up on dry l. Josh 4:18
came over this Jordan on dry l. 22
longeth for thee in a dry l. Ps 63:1
he turned the sea into dry l. 66:6
rebellious dwell in a dry l. 68:6
and his hands formed the dry l. 95:5
I will make dry l. springs. Isa 41:18
of nations shall be a dry l. Jer 50:12
her cities are a dry l. and. 51:43
lest I set her as a dry l. Hos 2:3
who made sea and dry l. Jonah 1:9
vomited out Jonah on the dry l. 2:10
shake the sea and dry l. Hag 2:6
the Red sea as by dry l. Heb 11:29
see **dwelt, Egypt, good**

in the **land**

Canaanite dwelt then in the l.
Gen 13:7
shall be fruitful in the l. Gen 26:22
plenty not be known in the l. 41:31
and ye shall traffiick in the l.
42:34
for to sojourn in the l. are. 47:4
go ye, sacrifice to your God in the l.
Ex 8:25
Lord shall do this thing in the l. 9:5
they are entangled in the l. 14:3
give peace in the l. and. Lev 26:6
ye may do them in the l. Deut 4:14
go well with thee in the l. 5:16
that ye may prolong days in the l.
11:9, 21; 25:15
hath given thee rest in the l. 25:19
bless thee in the l. 28:8, 11; 30:16
as long as ye live in the l. 31:13
no magistrate in the l. Judg 18:7
and if he be in the l. I. 1 Sam 23:23
made judge in the l. 2 Sam 15:4
if there be famine in the l. 1 Ki 8:37
2 Chr 6:28
long as they live in the l. 2 Chr 6:31
set judges in the l. 19:5
wonder that was done in the l. 32:31
nor is it found in the l. of. Job 28:13
goodness of the Lord in the l. of the.
Ps 27:13
devise deceitful matter in the l.
35:20
the synagogues of God in the l. 74:8
walk before the Lord in the l. 116:9
thou art my portion in the l. 142:5
shall every one eat in the l. Isa 7:22
in the l. of uprightness he. 26:10
not see the Lord in the l. of. 38:11
them in the l. serve me. Ezek 20:40
I shall set glory in the l. of. 26:20
caused terror in the l. of the living.
32:23; 24:32
make them one nation in the l. 37:22
in the l. shall be his possession. 45:8
there is no truth in the l. Hos 4:1
up a Shepherd in the l. Zech 11:16
great distress in the l. Luke 21:23
by faith he sojourned in the l. of.
Heb 11:9

our **land**

buy us and our l. for bread, and we and our l. Gen 47:19
and our l. shall yield her. Ps 85:12
turtle is heard in our l. S of S 2:12
the Assyrian shall come into our l.
Mi 5:5
us when he cometh into our l. 6

own **land**

Jethro went into his own l. Ex 18:27
Num 10:30
a true report I heard in mine own l.
1 Ki 10:6; 2 Chr 9:5
carried out of their own l. 2 Ki 17:23
take you to a land like your own l.
18:32; Isa 36:17
shall return to his own l. 2 Ki 19:7
with shame to his own l. 2 Chr 32:21
every one to his own l. Isa 13:14
and set them in their own l. 14:1
fall by the sword in his own l. 37:7
they that dwell in their own l.
Jer 25:8; 27:11
Egypt, into their own l. 37:7; 42:12
flee every one to his own l. 50:16
them into their own l. Ezek 34:13
36:24; 37:14, 21; 39:28
Israel dwelt in their own l. 36:17
captive out of their own l. Amos 7:11
see **people, possess, possession**

their **land**

people sold not their l. Gen 47:22
ye shall inherit their l. Lev 20:24
no inheritance in their l. Num 18:20
not give you of their l. Deut 2:5, 9
bring thee, and give thee their l. 4:38
Judg 6:9
we took their l. and gave it.
Deut 29:8; Josh 10:42
Lord rooted them out of their l.
Deut 29:28
and pray unto thee toward their l.
1 Ki 8:48
sin and heal their l. 2 Chr 7:14
flaming fire in their l. Ps 105:32

and gave *their l.* for an heritage. *Ps* 135:12; 136:21
their l. is full of silver. *Isa* 2:7
their l. also is full of idols. 8
their l. shall be soaked with. 34:7
I will pluck them out of *their l.* *Jer* 12:14
bring them again into *their l.* 16:15
forsaken, though *their l.* was. 51:5
shall be safe in *their l.* *Ezek* 34:27
they dwelt safely in *their l.* 39:26
will plant them on *their l.* *Amos* 9:15

this **land**

the Lord said, Unto thy seed I will give *this l.* *Gen* 12:7; 15:18; 24:7
48:4; *Ex* 32:13
thee again into *this l.* *Gen* 28:15
get thee out from *this l.* and. 31:13
will bring you out of *this l.* 50:24
brought us unto *this l.* *Num* 14:3
then he will bring us into *this l.* 8
this l. be given to thy servants. 32:5
this l. shall be your possession. 22
this l. shall fall to you. 34:2, 13
Josh 13:2
but I must die in *this l.* *Deut* 4:22
and he hath given us *this l.* 26:9
Josh 1:13
Lord done thus to *this l.*? *Deut* 29:24
27; *1 Ki* 9:8; *2 Chr* 7:21
the inhabitants of *this l.* *Judg* 2:2
Lord said, Go up against *this l.*
2 Ki 18:25; *Isa* 36:10
come again into *this l.* *2 Chr* 30:9
sword shall not be in *this l.* *Jer* 14:15
that begat them in *this l.* 16:3
and small shall die in *this l.* 6
I will cast you out of *this l.* 13
he shall see *this l.* no more. 22:12
will bring them again to *this l.* 24:6
bring them against *this l.* 25:9
and *this* whole *l.* shall be a. 11
prophesied against *this l.* 26:20
be possessed again in *this l.* 32:15
and I will plant them in *this l.* 41
Babylon shall destroy *this l.* 36:29
come against you, nor *this l.* 37:19
if ye will abide in *this l.* I. 42:10
we will not dwell in *this l.* 13
pluck up even *this* whole *l.* 45:4
to us is *this l.* given in. *Ezek* 11:15
this l. shall fall unto you for. 47:14
this is the *l.* which ye shall. 48:29
removed him into *this l.* *Acts* 7:4

thy **land**

years thou shalt sow *thy l.* *Ex* 23:10
cast their young in *thy l.* 26
they shall not dwell in *thy l.* 33
nor shall any man desire *thy l.* 34:24
let me pass through *thy l.* *Num* 21:22
Deut 2:27; *Judg* 11:17, 19
bless the fruit of *thy l.* *Deut* 7:13
bury him; that *thy l.* be not. 21:23
give the rain to *thy l.* in. 28:12
shall be the fruit of *thy l.* 18, 42
do great things for *thy l.* *2 Sam* 7:23
famine come to thee in *thy l.*? 24:13
been favourable to *thy l.* *Ps* 85:1
fill the breadth of *thy l.* *Isa* 8:8
thou hast destroyed *thy l.* 14:20
through *thy l.* as a river, O. 23:10
no more be heard in *thy l.* 60:18
thy l. be termed desolate; the Lord delighteth in thee, and *thy l.* 62:4
set darkness upon *thy l.* *Ezek* 32:8
thy l. shall be divided. *Amos* 7:17
cut off the cities of *thy l.* *Mi* 5:11
the gates of *thy l.* shall. *Nah* 3:13

your **land**

bought you and *your l.* *Gen* 47:23
when ye reap the harvest of *your l.*
Lev 19:9; 23:22
which they begat in *your l.* 25:45
and dwell in *your l.* safely. 26:5
nor the sword go through *your l.* 6
for *your l.* shall not yield her. 20
you go to war in *your l.* *Num* 10:9
get into *your l.* 22:13
this shall be *your l.* 34:12
give you rain of *your l.* *Deut* 11:14
his hand from off *your l.* *1 Sam* 6:5
strange gods in *your l.* *Jer* 5:19
remove you far from *your l.* *Jer* 27:10
is *your l.* a desolation and. 44:22

landed

we had *l.* at Caesarea. *Acts* 18:22
into Syria, and *l.* at Tyre. 21:3

landing

l. at Syracuse we. *Acts* 28:12*

landmark, -s

not remove thy neighbour's *l.*
Deut 19:14; *Pr* 22:28; 23:10
removeth neighbour's *l.* *Deut* 27:17
some remove the *l.* and. *Job* 24:2

lands

dearth was in all *l.* *Gen* 41:45
left but our bodies and *l.* 47:18
wherefore they sold not their *l.* 22
restore those *l.* again. *Judg* 11:13
the kings of Assyria have done to all *l.* *2 Ki* 19:11; *Isa* 37:11
David went into all *l.* *1 Chr* 14:17
the manner of other *l.* *2 Chr* 13:9
fear fell on all *l.* round about. 17:10
as the gods of other *l.* have. 32:17
separated from people of *l.* *Ezra* 9:1
with the people of those *l.* 2, 11
have mortgaged our *l.* *Neh* 5:3, 4
men have our *l.* and vineyards. 5
I pray you, this day their *l.* 11
separated from people of the *l.* 10:28
they call their *l.* after their. *Ps* 49:11
a joyful noise, all ye *l.* 66:1; 100:1
and gave them the *l.* of. 105:44
hand, to scatter them in the *l.* 106:27
gathered them out of the *l.* 107:3
brought up Israel from *l.* *Jer* 16:15
all these *l.* to Nebuchadnezzar. 27:6
into a land which is the glory of all *l.* *Ezek* 20:6, 15
them out of their enemies' *l.* 39:27
hath forsaken houses, *l.* *Mat* 19:29
Mark 10:29
an hundredfold, *l.* *Mark* 10:30
were possessors of *l.* sold. *Acts* 4:34

lanes

go out quickly into the *l.* *Luke* 14:21

language

whole earth was of one *l.* *Gen* 11:1
one, and they have all one *l.* 6
and there confound their *l.* 7, 9
speak in the Syrian *l.* *2 Ki* 18:26
Isa 36:11
Rab-shakeh cried in the Jews' *l.*
2 Ki 18:28; *Isa* 36:13
could not speak in the Jews' *l.* but according to the *l.* of. *Neh* 13:24
to every people after their *l.*
Esth 1:22; 3:12; 8:9
no *l.* where their voice is. *Ps* 19:3
where I heard a *l.* that I. 81:5
from a people of strange *l.* 114:1
five cities speak the *l.* of. *Isa* 19:18
a nation, whose *l.* thou. *Jer* 5:15
not sent to a people of hard *l.*
Ezek 3:5, 6
I decree, every *l.* that. *Dan* 3:29
turn to the people a pure *l.* *Zeph* 3:9
them speak in his own *l.* *Acts* 2:6

languages

O people, nations, and *l.* *Dan* 3:4
all *l.* fell down and worshipped. 7
Nebuchadnezzar to all *l.* 4:1
all *l.* trembled and feared. 5:19
Darius to all *l.* 6:25
all people, nations, and *l.* 7:14
ten men out of all *l.* *Zech* 8:23

languish

for the fields of Hebron *l.* *Isa* 16:8
spread nets on waters shall *l.* 19:8
haughty people of the earth do *l.* 24:4
gates of Judah *l.* and. *Jer* 14:2
that dwelleth therein shall *l.* *Hos* 4:3

languished

and wall to lament, *l.* *Lam* 2:8

languisheth

the world *l.* and fadeth. *Isa* 24:4
the vine *l.* 7
the earth mourneth and *l.* 33:9
she that hath borne seven *l.* *Jer* 15:9
the oil *l.* *Joel* 1:10
the fig tree *l.* 12
l. and Carmel, the flower *l.* *Nah* 1:4

languishing

Lord will strengthen him on the bed of *l.* *Ps* 41:3

lanterns

Judas cometh with *l.* *John* 18:3

Laodicea

conflict I have for them at *L.* *Col* 2:1
zeal for them that are in *L.* 4:13
salute brethren which are in *L.* 15
likewise read the epistle from *L.* 16

Laodiceans

read in the church of the *L.* *Col* 4:16
angel of church of the *L.* *Rev* 3:14

lap

wild gourds, his *l.* full. *2 Ki* 4:39
I shook my *l.* and said. *Neh* 5:13
the lot is cast into the *l.* *Pr* 16:33

lapped

the number that *l.* were. *Judg* 7:6
the Lord said, By them that *l.* I. 7

lappeth

that *l.* of the water as. *Judg* 7:5

large

the land, behold it is *l.* *Gen* 34:21
them into a good and *l.* land. *Ex* 3:8
shall come into a *l.* land. *Judg* 18:10
he brought me forth also into a *l.* place. *2 Sam* 22:20; *Ps* 18:19
the work is great and *l.* *Neh* 4:19
the city was *l.* and great. 7:4*
have not served thee in the *l.* 9:35
set my feet in a *l.* room. *Ps* 31:8
and set me in a *l.* place. 118:5
he will toss thee into a *l.* *Isa* 22:18
shall thy cattle feed in *l.* 30:23
ordained, he made it deep and *l.* 33
I will build *l.* chambers. *Jer* 22:14*
sister's cup deep and *l.* *Ezek* 23:32
as a lamb in a *l.* place. *Hos* 4:16
they gave *l.* money to. *Mat* 28:12
will shew you a *l.* upper room.
Mark 14:15; *Luke* 22:12
ye see how *l.* a letter I. *Gal* 6:11
the length is as *l.* as. *Rev* 21:16*

largeness

God gave Solomon *l.* *1 Ki* 4:29

lasciviousness

heart of men proceed *l.* *Mark* 7:22
not repented of the *l.* *2 Cor* 12:21
of the flesh are manifest, *l.* *Gal* 5:19
given themselves over to *l.* *Eph* 4:19
walked in *l.*, lusts, excess. *1 Pet* 4:3
grace of our God into *l.* *Jude* 4

last

(*Frequently used where modern writers would use* latter)

shall overcome at the *l.* *Gen* 49:19*
my *l.* end be like his. *Num* 23:10
why are ye the *l.* to bring the king back? *2 Sam* 19:11, 12
now these be the *l.* words of. 23:1
for by the *l.* words of. *1 Chr* 23:27
David the king, first and *l.* 29:29
of Solomon, first and *l.* *2 Chr* 9:29
of Rehoboam, first and *l.* 12:15
the acts of Asa, first and *l.* 16:11
acts of Jehoshaphat, first and *l.* 20:34
acts of Amaziah, first and *l.* 25:26
the acts of Uzziah, first and *l.* 26:22
the acts of Ahaz, first and *l.* 28:26
Josiah's deeds, first and *l.* 35:27
the *l.* sons of Adonikam. *Ezra* 8:13
from the first day to the *l.* *Neh* 8:18
and thou mourn at the *l.* *Pr* 5:11*
the *l.* it biteth like a serpent. 23:32
the Lord, the first, and with the *l.*
Isa 41:4; 44:6; 48:12; *Rev* 1:11
17; 2:8; 22:13
he shall not see our *l.* end. *Jer* 12:4
at *l.* Nebuchadnezzar hath. 50:17
remembered not her *l.* *Lam* 1:9
at the *l.* Daniel came in. *Dan* 4:8
and the higher came up *l.* 8:3
what shall be in the *l.* end. 19
I will slay the *l.* of them. *Amos* 9:1
l. state of that man is worse.
Mat 12:45; *Luke* 11:26
many that are first shall be *l.* and the *l.* first. *Mat* 19:30; 20:16
Mark 10:31; *Luke* 13:30
beginning from the *l.* to. *Mat* 20:8

l. have wrought one hour. Mat 20:12
I will give to this l. even as unto. 14
l. of all he sent his son, saying.
21:37*; Mark 12:6
l. of all the woman died. Mat 22:27
Mark 12:22; Luke 20:32*
at the l. came two false. Mat 26:60*
the l. error shall be worse. 27:64
desire to be first, the same shall be l.
Mark 9:35
hast paid the l. mite. Luke 12:59
the eldest even to the l. John 8:9
set forth us the apostles l. 1 Cor 4:9
and l. of all he was seen of. 15:8
the l. enemy is death. 26
the l. Adam. 45
changed in a moment, at the l. 52
at l. your care of me. Phil 4:10*
the l. works to be more. Rev 2:19
having the seven l. plagues. 15:1
seven vials full of the seven l. 21:9

last *day, days*
befall you in the l. days. Gen 49:1
come to pass in l. days. Isa 2:2
Mi 4:1; Acts 2:17
should raise it up at the l. day.
John 6:39, 40, 44, 54
in the l. day, the great day. 7:37
he shall rise again at the l. day. 11:24
judge him in the l. day. 12:48
in l. days perilous times. 2 Tim 3:1
hath spoken in these l. days by his Son. Heb 1:2
treasure for the l. days. Jas 5:3
come in l. days scoffers. 2 Pet 3:3

last *time, times*
revealed in the l. time. 1 Pet 1:5
manifest in these l. times for. 20
is the l. time: are there many antichrists ... it is the l. time.
1 John 2:18
be mockers in the l. time. Jude 18

lasted
wept while the feast l. Judg 14:17

lasting
things of the l. hills. Deut 33:15

latchet
nor the l. of their shoes. Isa 5:27
the l. of whose shoes. Mark 1:7
Luke 3:16

late
is vain for you to sit up l. Ps 127:2
of l. my people is risen up. Mi 2:8
the Jews of l. sought to. John 11:8

lately
Aquila a Jew l. come. Acts 18:2

Latin
written in Hebrew, and Greek, and L.
Luke 23:38*; John 19:20

latter
he voice of the l. sign. Ex 4:8
ive thee the first rain, and l. rain.
Deut 11:14
f her l. husband hate her or. 24:3
tand at the l. day. Job 19:25
heir mouth as for the l. rain. 29:23
s a cloud of the l. rain. Pr 16:15
nayest be wise in the l. end. 19:20
nd there hath been no l. Jer 3:3
oth the former and l. rain in. 5:24
i the l. years thou shalt. Ezek 38:8
i the l. time of their. Dan 8:23
ot be as the former or the l. 11:29
s the l. and former rain. Hos 6:3
rain in the first month. Joel 2:23
eginning of the l. growth. Amos 7:1
e glory of the l. house. Hag 2:9
e time of the l. rain. Zech 10:1
at in the l. times. 1 Tim 4:1
see **days, end**

lattice
ied through the l. Judg 5:28
ll down through the l. 2 Ki 1:2
ewing himself through the l.
S of S 2:9

laud
aise the Lord, and l. Rom 15:11

laugh
(Used both for the laugh of joy and the laugh of derision)
erefore did Sarah l.? Gen 18:13
said, Nay, but thou didst l. Gen 18:15
hath made me to l., all will l. 21:6
and famine thou shalt l. Job 5:22
he will l. at the trial of the. 9:23*
and the innocent l. them to. 22:19
in the heavens shall l. Ps 2:4
all they that see me l. me to. 22:7
the Lord shall l. at him, for. 37:13
righteous also shall l. at him. 52:6
but thou, O Lord, shalt l. at. 59:8
and our enemies l. among. 80:6
will l. at your calamity. Pr 1:26
whether he rage or l. there is. 29:9
weep, and a time to l. Eccl 3:4
ye that weep, ye shall l. Luke 6:21
woe unto you that l. now! for ye. 25

laughed
Abraham l. Gen 17:17
Sarah l. in herself. 18:12
Sarah denied, saying, I l. not. 15
daughter of Zion hath l. 2 Ki 19:21
Isa 37:22
they l. them to scorn. 2 Chr 30:10
they l. us to scorn, and. Neh 2:19
just and upright man is l. Job 12:4
if I l. on them, they. 29:24
thou shalt be l. to scorn. Ezek 23:32
they l. him to scorn. Mat 9:24
Mark 5:40; Luke 8:53

laugheth
he l. at the shaking of. Job 41:29

laughing
till he fill thy mouth with l. Job 8:21

laughter
our mouth filled with l. Ps 126:2
even in l. the heart is. Pr 14:13
I said of l. It is mad. Eccl 2:2
sorrow is better than l. 7:3
so is l. of the fool. 6
let your l. be turned to. Jas 4:9

launch
he said to Simon, L. out. Luke 5:4*

launched
go over, and they l. forth. Luke 8:22
after we had l. Acts 21:1*; 27:2*, 4*

laver
make a l. of brass. Ex 30:18
the l. and his foot. 28; 31:9
35:16; 39:39
he made the l. of brass and. 38:8
thou shalt set the l. 40:7
and he set the l. 30
anoint the l. and his foot. 11
he anointed both the l. and. Lev 8:11
under the l. were undersetters.
1 Ki 7:30
l. was forty baths, and every l. 38
Ahaz removed the l. 2 Ki 16:17

lavers
then made he ten l. of. 1 Ki 7:38
Hiram make the l. and shovels. 40
l. on the bases. 43; 2 Chr 4:6, 14

lavish
l. gold out of the bag. Isa 46:6

law
(When used alone it most frequently refers to the Mosaic Law, and, in the New Testament, the additions to that Law made by the Jewish teachers)
Joseph made it a l. over. Gen 47:26
l. to him that is homeborn. Ex 12:49
Lev 24:22; Num 15:16, 29
I will give thee a l. and. Ex 24:12
to the sentence of the l. Deut 17:11
hand went a fiery l. for them. 33:2
Moses commanded us a l. even. 4
according to all the l. Josh 1:7
stones a copy of the l. of Moses. 8:32
he read the words of the l. 34
take heed to the l. 22:5
2 Ki 17:13, 37; 21:8
nor do after the l. and. 2 Ki 17:34
perform the words of the l. 23:24
according to all the l. of Moses. 25
to Jacob for a l. 1 Chr 16:17
that thou mayest keep the l. 22:12
Judah to do the l. 2 Chr 14:4
l. and commandment. 19:10
in their place according to l. 30:16
in every work, and in the l. 31:21
do according to the whole l. 33:8
heard the words of the l. 34:19
ready scribe in the l. Ezra 7:6; 12:21
according to the l. of thy God. 14
will not do the l. of God and l. of. 26
be done according to the l. 10:3
the priest brought the l. Neh 8:2
the people to understand the l. 7
when they heard the words of l. 9
together to understand the l. 13
themselves to l. of God. 10:28
an oath to walk in God's l. 29
into them the portions of the l. 12:44
when they had heard the l. 13:3
was according to the l. Esth 1:8
queen Vashti according to l.? 15
one l. of his to put him to death. 4:11
which is not according to the l. 16
receive the l. from his. Job 22:22
in his l. he meditates day. Ps 1:2
l. of his God is in his heart. 37:31
he appointed a l. in Israel. 78:5
and they refused to walk in his l. 10
was a l. of the God of Jacob. 81:4
frameth mischief by a l. 94:20
the same to Jacob for a l. 105:10
the l. of thy mouth is better. 119:72
forsake not the l. of thy mother.
Pr 1:8; 6:20
is a lamp, and the l. is light. 6:23
l. of the wise is a fountain. 13:14
the l. praise the wicked, but such as keep the l. contend with. 28:4
keepeth the l. is a wise son. 7
away his ear from hearing the l. 9
but he that keepeth the l. 29:18
they drink and forget the l. 31:5
her tongue is the l. of kindness. 26
and give ear to the l. of. Isa 1:10
out of Zion shall go forth the l. 2:3
Mi 4:2
seal the l. Isa 8:16
to the l. and the testimony. 20
the isles shall wait for his l. 42:4
the Lord will magnify the l. 21
were they obedient to his l. 24
for a l. shall proceed from me. 51:4
they that handle the l. Jer 2:8
the l. shall not perish from. 18:18
was sealed according to l. 32:11
obeyed, nor walked in his l. 44:23
the l. is no more, prophets. Lam 2:9
the l. shall perish from. Ezek 7:26
concerning the l. of his God. Dan 6:5
according to l. of the Medes. 12, 15
thou hast forgotten the l. Hos 4:6
therefore the l. is slacked. Hab 1:4
done violence to the l. Zeph 3:4
priests concerning the l. Hag 2:11
they should hear the l. Zech 7:12
the l. of truth was in his. Mal 2:6
and they should seek the l. at. 7
caused many to stumble at the l. 8
ways, but have been partial in l. 9
remember the l. of Moses my. 4:4
am come to destroy the l. Mat 5:17
shall in no wise pass from the l. 18
any man will sue thee at the l. 40
the l. prophesied until John. 11:13
Luke 16:16
have ye not read in the l.? Mat 12:5
the great commandment in l. 22:36
commandments hang all the l. 40
the weightier matters of the l. 23:23
after the custom of the l. Luke 2:27
there were doctors of the l. 5:17
than for one tittle of the l. to. 16:17
l. was given by Moses. John 1:17
of whom Moses in the l. did. 45
give you the l. and yet none of you keepeth the l.? Why go ye? 7:19
l. of Moses should not be broken. 23
people who knoweth not the l. 49
doth our l. judge any man before? 51
Moses in the l. commanded. 8:5
is it not written in your l.? 10:34
we have heard out of the l. 12:34
what is written in their l. 15:25
judge him according to your l. 18:31
we have a l. and by our l. he. 19:7

Gamaliel, a doctor of the *l.* *Acts* 5:34
blasphemous words against *l.* 6:13
received the *l.* by angels. 7:53
reading of the *l.* and prophets. 13:15
could not be justified by the *l.* 39
to command them to keep the *l.* 15:5
circumcised and keep the *l.* 24
God contrary to the *l.* 18:13
but if it be a question of your *l.* 15
the *l.* is open. 19:38
zealous of the *l.* 21:20
thou thyself keepest the *l.* 24
man that teacheth against the *l.* 28
to the manner of the *l.* 22:3
devout man according to the *l.* 12
me after the *l.* and commandest me to be smitten contrary to *l.*? 23:3
have judged according to our *l.* 24:6
nor against the *l.* of the Jews. 25:8
persuading them out of the *l.* 28:23
without *l.*: ... have sinned in the *l.* shall be judged by the *l.* *Rom* 2:12
not the hearers of the *l.* are just. 13
Gentiles, which have not *l.*, do by nature things contained in *l.*, these, having not *l.*, are a *l.* unto. 14
shew the work of the *l.* written. 15
called a Jew, and restest in the *l.* 17
being instructed out of the *l.* 18
the form of the truth in *l.* 20
makest thy boast of the *l.* through breaking the *l.* dishonourest? 23
profiteth if thou keep the *l.* but if thou be a breaker of the *l.* 25
keep the righteousness of the *l* 26
it fulfil the *l.* judge thee who by circumcision dost trangress the *l.* 27
what things soever the *l.* saith. 3:19
l. no flesh be justified, for by the *l.* is the knowledge. 20, 28; *Gal* 2:16
righteousness of God is witnessed by the *l.* *Rom* 3:21
by what *l.* excluded? by the *l.* 27
void the *l.*? we establish the *l.* 31
promise was not through the *l.* 4:13
for if they which are of the *l.* 14
l. worketh wrath, for where no *l.* 15
not to that only which is of the *l.* 16
l. sin was in the world, but sin is not imputed when there is no *l.* 5:13
the *l.* entered, that the offence. 20
speak to them which know the *l.*, the *l.* hath dominion over a man. 7:1
the *l.* to her husband; if he be dead, she is loosed from the *l.* 2, 3
ye also are become dead to the *l.* 4
of sins which were by the *l.* 5
now we are delivered from the *l.* 6
is the *l.* sin? I had not known sin, but by *l.* nor lust, except *l.* had said. 7
for without the *l.* sin was dead. 8
the *l.* is holy, and commandment. 12
the *l.* is spiritual. 14
the *l.* is good. 16; *1 Tim* 1:8
I find then a *l.* *Rom* 7:21
I delight in the *l.* of God. 22
l. warring against the *l.* of my mind, bringing me into captivity to *l.* 23
I serve *l.* of God: flesh *l.* of sin. 25
l. of life made me free from the *l.* 8:2
for what the *l.* could not do, in. 3
righteousness of the *l.* might be. 4
carnal mind is not subject to the *l.* 7
pertaineth the giving of the *l.* 9:4
Israel followed after the *l.* of. 31
sought it by the works of the *l.* 32
Christ is the end of the *l.* for. 10:4
righteousness which is of the *l.* 5
loveth another, hath fulfilled *l.* 13:8
love is the fulfilling of the *l.* 10
dare any of you go to *l.*? *1 Cor* 6:1
brother goeth to *l.* with brother. 6
because ye go to *l.* one with. 7
wife is bound by the *l.* as long. 7:39
saith not the *l.* the same also? 9:8
obedience, as also saith the *l.* 14:34
sin, and strength of sin is the *l.* 15:56
not justified by the works of the *l.* *Gal* 2:16
I through the *l.* am dead to the *l.* 19
righteousness come by the *l.* then. 21
Spirit by the works of the *l.*? 3:2
doeth he it by the works of the *l.*? 5
as are of the works of the *l.* 10
no man is justified by the *l.* *Gal* 3:11
l. is not of faith, but the man. 12
redeemed us from the curse of *l.* 13
covenant in Christ, the *l.* cannot. 17
if the inheritance be of the *l.* not. 18
wherefore then serveth the *l.*? 19
l. .... promises? if a *l.* had been given, righteousness had been by the *l.* 21
the *l.* was our schoolmaster to. 24
tell me, do ye not hear the *l.*? 4:21
he is a debtor to do the whole *l.* 5:3
of you are justified by the *l.* 4
all the *l.* is fulfilled in one word. 14
against such there is no *l.* 23
bear ye, and so fulfil the *l.* of. 6:2
nor themselves keep the *l.* but. 13
abolished in his flesh the *l.* *Eph* 2:15
as touching the *l.* a. *Phil* 3:5
touching the righteousness in the *l.* 6
mine own righteousness, of the *l.* 9
to be teachers of the *l.* *1 Tim* 1:7
the *l.* is not made for a righteous. 9
contentions about the *l.* *Tit* 3:9
people according to the *l.* *Heb* 7:5
it the people received the *l.* 11
of necessity a change of the *l.* 12
not after the *l.* of a carnal. 16
for the *l.* made nothing perfect. 19
l. maketh men high priests, but word of the oath which was since *l.* 28
priests offer gifts according to *l.* 8:4
had spoken according to the *l.* 9:19
are by the *l.* purged with blood. 22
the *l.* having a shadow of good. 10:1
he that despised Moses' *l.* died. 28
into perfect *l.* of liberty. *Jas* 1:25
if ye fulfil the royal *l.* 2:8
and are convinced of the *l.* as. 9
shall keep the whole *l.* 10
thou art a transgressor of the *l.* 11
they that shall be judged by the *l.* 12
evil of the *l.* and judgeth the *l.* 4:11
sin transgresseth also the *l.* for sin is the transgression of *l.* *1 John* 3:4

see **book**

law *of the Lord*

that *the Lord's l.* may be. *Ex* 13:9
Jehu took no heed to walk in *l. of Lord.* *2 Ki* 10:31
Rehoboam forsook *l. of Lord* and. *2 Chr* 12:1
be encouraged in the *l. of Lord.* 31:4
Josiah's goodness according to the *l. of Lord.* 35:26
prepared his heart to seek the *l. of Lord.* *Ezra* 7:10
his delight is in the *l. of L.* *Ps* 1:2
the *l. of the Lord* is perfect. 19:7
who walk in the *l. of the Lord.* 119:1
cast away the *l. of Lord.* *Isa* 5:24
will not hear the *l. of the Lord.* 30:9
l. of the Lord is with us. *Jer* 8:8
despised the *l. of the Lord.* *Amos* 2:4
according to the *l. of Lord.* *Luke* 2:39

my **law**

will walk in *my l.* or no. *Ex* 16:4
children walk in *my l.* *2 Chr* 6:16
O my people, to *my l.* *Ps* 78:1
if his children forsake *my l.* 89:30
forget not *my l.* but keep. *Pr* 3:1
forsake not *my l.* 4:2
keep *my l.* as the apple. 7:2
in whose heart is *my l.* *Isa* 51:7
not hearkened unto *my l.* *Jer* 6:19
they have forsaken *my l.* 9:13
and have not kept *my l.* 16:11
not hearken to walk in *my l.* 26:4
put *my l.* in their inward parts. 31:33
feared nor walked in *my l.* 44:10
her priests have violated *my l.* *Ezek* 22:26
trespassed against *my l.* *Hos* 8:1
to him the great things of *my l.* 12

this **law**

this shall be the *l.* of leper. *Lev* 14:2
execute on her *this l.* *Num* 5:30
this is the ordinance of the *l.* 19:2; 31:21
Moses to declare *this l.* *Deut* 1:5
all *this l.* which I set before you. 4:8
shall write him a copy of *this l.* 17:18
to keep all the words of *this l.* 19
them the words of *this l.* 27:3, 8
confirmeth not the words of *this l.* *Deut* 27:26
not observe words of *this l.* 28:58
all the words of *this l.* 29:29; 31:12
Moses wrote *this l.* 31:9
thou shalt read *this l.* 11
of writing the words of *this l.* in. 24
children to do the words of *this l.* 32:46
read the words of *this l.* *Josh* 8:34

this is the **law**

this is the l. of the burnt offering. *Lev* 6:9; 7:37
this is the l. of meat offering. 6:14
this is the l. of sin offering. 25
this is the l. of the trespass. 7:1
this is the l. of the beasts. 11:46
this is the l. of her that hath. 12:7
this is the l. of the plague of leprosy. 13:59; 14:32, 57
this is the l. for all manner. 14:54
this is the l. of him that hath an issue. 15:32
this is the l. of jealousies. *Num* 5:29
this is the l. of the Nazarite. 6:13
this is the l. when a man dieth. 19:14
this is the l. which Moses. *Deut* 4:44
this is the l. of the house. *Ezek* 43:12
this is the l. and prophets. *Mat* 7:12

thy **law**

shall teach Israel *thy l.* *Deut* 33:10
they cast *thy l.* behind. *Neh* 9:26
bring them again to *thy l.* 29
kings, nor our princes kept *thy l.* 34
yea, *thy l.* is within my. *Ps* 40:8
teachest him out of *thy l.* 94:12
things out of *thy l.* 119:18
way of lying, and grant me *thy l.* 29
give me understanding, and I shall keep *thy l.* 34
I keep *thy l.* continually for ever. 44
have I not declined from *thy l.* 51
the wicked that forsake *thy l.* 53
thy name, and kept *thy l.* 55
but I have not forgotten *thy l.* 61
is fat, but I delight in *thy l.* 70
I may live, for *thy l.* is my delight. 77, 92, 174
pits, which are not after *thy l.* 85
O how I love *thy l.* 97
yet do I not forget *thy l.* 109
but *thy l.* do I love. 113, 163
made void *thy l.* 126
down, because they keep not *thy l.* 136
and *thy l.* is the truth. 142
are far from *thy l.* 150
peace have they who love *thy l.* 165
not, nor walked in *thy l.* *Jer* 32:23
have transgressed *thy l.* *Dan* 9:11

under the **law**

them that are *under the l.* *Rom* 3:19
for ye are not *under the l.* 6:1
because we are not *under l.* 1
under the l. as *under the l.* that ... that are *under the l.* *1 Cor* 9:2
without law to God, but *under l.* 2
we were kept *under the l.* *Gal* 3:2
made *under the l.* 4:
redeem them that were *under l.*
ye that desire to be *under the l.* 2
if ye be led of the Spirit, ye are no *under the l.* 5:1

without **law**

a long season, Israel hath been *with out l.* *2 Chr* 15:
as many as sinned *without l.* peris *without l.* *Rom* 2:1
righteousness of God *without l.* 3:2
for *without l.* sin was dead. 7:
I was alive *without* the *l.* once.
that are *without l.*, as *without l.*, n *without l.* to God. *1 Cor* 9:

written in the **law**

as it is *w. in the l.* of Moses. *1 Ki* 2:3; *2 Chr* 23:18; 25:4; 31 *Ezra* 3:2; *Neh* 10:34, *Dan* 9:13; *Luke* 2:
do according to all *w. in the l.* *1 Chr* 16:40; *2 Chr* 35:
found *w. in the l.* that. *Neh* 8:
oath that is *w. in l.* of. *Dan* 9:

what is w. in the l.? Luke 10:26
fulfilled, which were w. in l. 24:44
things that are w. in l. Acts 24:14
it is w. in the l. 1 Cor 9:9
in the l. it is w. 14:21

lawful

shall not be l. to impose. Ezra 7:24
shall the l. captive be? Isa 49:24
do that which is l. Ezek 18:5; 21:27; 33:14, 19
the son hath done that which is l. 18:19; 33:16
do what is not l. Mat 12:2; Mark 2:24; Luke 6:2
was not l. for him to eat. Mat 12:4; Mark 2:26; Luke 6:4
l. to heal on the sabbath? Mat 12:10, 12; Mark 3:4; Luke 6:9; 14:3
it is not l. for thee to have her. Mat 14:4; Mark 6:18
is it l. for man to put away wife? Mat 19:3; Mark 10:2
l. to give tribute to? Mat 22:17; Mark 12:14; Luke 20:22
it is not l. to put them in the treasury. Mat 27:6
not l. for thee to carry. John 5:10
not l. for us to put any man. 18:31
which are not l. to receive. Acts 16:21
shall be determined in a l. 19:39
is it l. for you to scourge? 22:25
all things are l. unto me: all things l. for me. 1 Cor 6:12; 10:23
is not l. for a man to. 2 Cor 12:4

lawfully

good, if a man use it l. 1 Tim 1:8
yet is not crowned, except he strive l. 2 Tim 2:5

lawgiver

l. from between his feet. Gen 49:10*
digged the well by direction of the l. Num 21:18*
in a portion of the l. Deut 33:21
Judah is my l. Ps 60:7*; 108:8*
the Lord is our l. and. Isa 33:22
there is one l. who is able. Jas 4:12

lawless

the law is for the l. and. 1 Tim 1:9

laws

my statutes and my l. Gen 26:5
refuse ye to keep my l.? Ex 16:28
I do make them know the l. 18:16
teach them ordinances and l. 20
. which the Lord made. Lev 26:46
know the l. of thy God. Ezra 7:25
hou gavest them true l. Neh 9:13
commandedst them statutes and l. 14
vritten among the l. of. Esth 1:19
heir l. are diverse from all people, neither keep they the king's l. 3:8
hey might keep his l. Ps 105:45
ave transgressed the l. Isa 24:5
hew them all the l. Ezek 43:11
ear all the l. 44:5
hey shall keep my l. 24
o change times and l. Dan 7:25
ve obeyed to walk in his l. 9:10
will put my l. into their. Heb 8:10
ut my l. into their hearts. 10:16

lawyer

(One skilled in the interpretation of the Mosaic Law)

ne that was a l. asked him. Mat 22:35; Luke 10:25
ring Zenas the l. and. Tit 3:13

lawyers

rejected the counsel. Luke 7:30
en answered one of the l. 11:45
oe unto you, l. 46, 52
esus spake to l.. 14:3

lay, *as with a woman*

e firstborn l. with her father. Gen 19:33, 34, 35
d Jacob l. with Leah. 30:16
echem l. with Dinah. 34:2
euben went and l. with. 35:22
an that l. with woman. Deut 22:22
e man only that l. with her. 25
an that l. with her give fifty. 29
i heard they l. with. 1 Sam 2:22
e came, and he l. with her. 2 Sam 11:4; 12:24
Amnon forced Tamor and l. 2 Sam 13:14
for in her youth they l. Ezek 23:8

lay

tale of bricks ye shall l. Ex 5:8
as woman's husband will l. 21:22
neither shalt thou l. upon. 22:25
and l. the wood in order. Lev 1:7
the priests shall l. the parts. 8, 12
thou shalt l. the frankincense. 2:15
and l. the burnt offering in. 6:12
Lord, l. not the sin upon. Num 12:11
l. them on them that hate. Deut 7:15
shall l. the fear of you upon. 11:25
l. not innocent blood to thy. 21:8*
l. thee an ambush for the city. Josh 8:2
Samson l. till midnight. Judg 16:3
behold, a woman l. at his. Ruth 3:8
and Samuel l. till the. 1 Sam 3:15
and l. it for a reproach on. 11:2
Saul l. in the trench, people. 26:5, 7
Ish-bosheth, who l. on a. 2 Sam 4:5*
lamb eat of his meat, and l. 12:3
David l. all night on the. 16; 13:31
l. my bones beside his. 1 Ki 13:31
l. it on wood and put no fire. 18:23
and as he l. and slept under. 19:5
Ahab fasted and l. in. 21:27
he went up and l. upon. 2 Ki 4:34
l. ye them in two heaps at. 10:8
long as she l. desolate. 2 Chr 36:21
many l. in sackcloth and. Esth 4:3
the dew l. all night. Job 29:19
he will not l. on man more. 34:23*
let him l. mine honour in. Ps 7:5
they that seek my life, l. 38:12
found a nest, where she may l. 84:3
and the living will l. it to. Eccl 7:2
woe to them that l. field. Isa 5:8
to l. the land desolate. 13:9; Ezek 33:28
I will l. low haughtiness. Isa 13:11
key of house of David l. on. 22:22
fortress shall he l. low. 25:12
behold, I will l. in Zion a. 28:16
judgement will I l. to the line. 17*
that l. a snare for him that. 29:21
staff which the Lord shall l. 30:32
there shall the great owl l. 34:15
a lump of figs, and l. it for. 38:21
thou didst not l. these things. 47:7
I will l. thy stones with fair. 54:11
I will l. stumblingblocks. Jer 6:21; Ezek 3:20
take thee a tile, and l. it. Ezek 4:1
l. siege against it. 2, 3
l. the iniquity of the house of. 4
I will l. bands upon thee. 8
I will l. my vengeance on. 25:14, 17
I will l. thee before kings. 28:17
l. thy flesh on the mountains. 32:5
and I will l. no famine upon. 36:29
be tilled, whereas it l. desolate. 34
I will l. sinews upon you. 37:6
there l. the most holy things. 42:13; 14; 44:19
O Lord, l. not on us. Jonah 1:14
idols thereof will I l. Mi 1:7
l. it to heart, I will send a curse upon you; because ye do not l. Mal 2:2
hath not where to l. his head. Mat 8:20; Luke 9:58
and lay them on men's. Mat 23:4
see the place where the Lord l. 28:6
the sick of the palsy l. Mark 2:4
shall l. thee even with. Luke 19:44*
l. impotent folk, blind. John 5:3
it was a cave, and a stone l. 11:38
Lord, l. not this sin to. Acts 7:60
l. on you no greater burden. 15:28
and no small tempest l. on. 27:20
l. any thing to the charge. Rom 8:33
I l. in Sion a stumblingstone. 9:33
let every one l. by him. 1 Cor 16:2
l. aside every weight. Heb 12:1
wherefore l. apart all. Jas 1:21
I l. in Sion a chief. 1 Pet 2:6
see **foundation**

lay *down*

before they l. down men. Gen 19:4
and Lot perceived not when she l. down. 33, 35
Jacob l. down in that place. Gen 28:11
he l. down as a lion. Num 24:9
he l. down at her feet. Judg 5:27
his feet, and l. thee down. Ruth 3:4
lie down, and Samuel went and l. down. 1 Sam 3:5, 9
Saul l. down naked all that. 19:24
Jonadab said, L. thee down on thy. 2 Sam 13:5
so Amnon l. down and made. 6
l. down now, put me in surety with. Job 17:3*
l. me down in peace. Ps 4:8
young lions l. them down. 104:22
thy mother l. down. Ezek 19:2*
l. themselves down on clothes. Amos 2:8
and I l. down my life for my sheep. John 10:15, 17
l. it down of myself, have power to l. it down. 18
I will l. down my life for. 13:37, 38
that a man l. down his life. 15:13
to l. down our lives. 1 John 3:16

lay *hand*

l. not thy hand on the lad. Gen 22:12
shed no blood, l. no hand. 37:22
l. my hand upon Egypt. Ex 7:4
l. his hand on the head of his offering. Lev 3:2, 8
l. his hand on the head of the goat. 13; 4:24
he shall l. his hand on the bullock's head. 4:4, 15
he shall l. his hand on the sin offering. 29, 33
l. thy hand on Joshua. Num 27:18
l. thy hand upon thy mouth, and go. Judg 18:19
to l. hand on the king. Esth 2:21
to l. hand on such as sought. 9:2
daysman might l. his hand. Job 9:33
mark me, and l. your hand. 21:5
I will l. my hand on my mouth. 40:4
l. thy hand upon him. 41:8
thought evil, l. hand upon. Pr 30:32
l. their hand on Edom. Isa 11:14
shall l. their hand on their mouth. Mi 7:16
and l. thy hand on her. Mat 9:18

lay *hands*

Aaron shall l. both his hands on. Lev 16:21
him l. their hands on head. 24:14
the Levites l. their h. Num 8:12
I will l. hands on you. Neh 13:21
scorn to l. hands on. Esth 3:6
they sought to l. hands on him. Mat 21:46; Luke 20:19
come and l. thy hands. Mark 5:23
l. hands on the sick, and they. 16:18
shall l. hands on you. Luke 21:12
on whomsoever I l. hands. Acts 8:19
l. hands suddenly on. 1 Tim 5:22

lay *hold*

shall his father l. hold. Deut 21:19
and l. hold on her, and lie. 22:28
l. thee hold on one of. 2 Sam 2:21
hand, saying, L. hold on. 1 Ki 13:4
life to them that l. hold. Pr 3:18
I sought to l. hold on folly. Eccl 2:3
shall roar, and l. hold on. Isa 5:29
they shall l. hold on bow. Jer 6:23
l. hold on his neighbour. Zech 14:13
will he not l. hold on it? Mat 12:11
out to l. hold on him. Mark 3:21
they sought to l. hold on him. 12:12
l. hold on eternal life. 1 Tim 6:12, 19
to l. hold on the hope. Heb 6:18

lay *up*

l. up corn under the hand. Gen 41:35
l. up manna for you till. Ex 16:23
l. up a pot of manna to be kept. 33
l. them up in tabernacle. Num 17:4
l. them up without the camp. 19:9
l. up these my words. Deut 11:18
shall l. it up within thy gates. 14:28
l. up his words in thy. Job 22:22
then shalt l. up gold as dust and. 24
l. up my commandments. Pr 7:1
wise men l. up knowledge. 10:14
l. not up for yourselves treasures upon earth. Mat 6:19

l. up for yourselves treasures in heaven. Mat 6:20
children not to *l. up* for. 2 Cor 12:14

lay *wait*
from such as *l.* in *wait.* Ezra 8:31
that *l. wait* for my soul. Ps 71:10
let us *l. wait* for blood. Pr 1:11
l. wait for their own blood. 18
l. not *wait* against the. 24:15
they *l. wait* as he that. Jer 5:26

lay *waste*
that shouldest be to *l. waste.* 2 Ki 19:25; Isa 37:26
I will *l.* it *waste,* it shall. Isa 5:6
I will *l.* thy cities *waste.* Ezek 35:4

layest
thou *l.* the burden of. Num 11:11
l. thou a snare for my? 1 Sam 28:9

layeth
God *l.* up his iniquity. Job 21:19
soul crieth out, yet God *l.* 24:12*
the sword of him that *l.* at. 41:26
he *l.* up the depth in. Ps 33:7
l. the beams of his chambers. 104:3
he *l.* up wisdom for the. Pr 2:7
with knowledge, but a fool *l.* 13:16*
dissembleth, and *l.* up deceit. 26:24
l. her hands to the spindle. 31:19
the lofty city he *l.* low to. Isa 26:5
blessed is the man that *l.* 56:2*
perisheth, and no man *l.* it to. 57:1
but in heart he *l.* his wait. Jer 9:8
l. it to heart. 12:11
Lord *l.* the foundation. Zech 12:1
he that *l.* up treasure. Luke 12:21
he *l.* it on his shoulders. 15:5

laying
hurl at him by *l.* wait. Num 35:20
him any thing without *l.* wait. 22
commune of *l.* snares. Ps 64:5
l. aside the commandment of God. Mark 7:8
l. wait for him, and. Luke 11:54
l. on of the apostles'. Acts 8:18
but their *l.* wait was known. 9:24*
kinsmen heard of their *l.* in. 23:16
l. wait in the way to kill him. 25:3
with *l.* on of the hands. 1 Tim 4:14
l. up in store a good foundation. 6:19
not *l.* again the foundation. Heb 6:1
doctrine of baptisms, and of *l.* on. 2
l. aside all malice, guile. 1 Pet 2:1

Lazarus
certain beggar named *L.* Luke 16:20
seeth *L.* in Abraham's bosom. 23
send *L.* that he may dip the tip. 24
likewise *L.* received evil things. 25
Mary whose brother *L.* John 11:2
Jesus loved *L.* 5
our friend *L.* sleepeth. 11
L. is dead. 14
he cried, *L.* come forth. 43
L. was one of them that sat. 12:2
came that they might see *L.* 9
when he called *L.* out of grave. 17

lead, *substantive*
sank as *l.* in the mighty. Ex 15:10
l. that may abide fire. Num 31:22
graven with iron and *l.* Job 19:24
l. is consumed of the fire. Jer 6:29
they are *l.* in the midst. Ezek 22:18
as they gather *l.* so will I gather. 20
with iron, tin, and *l.* Tarshish. 27:12
lifted up a talent of *l.* Zech 5:7
he cast the weight of *l.* on the. 8

lead
I will *l.* on softly as the. Gen 33:14
a pillar of cloud to *l.* Ex 13:21
go, *l.* the people to the place. 32:34
l. them out and bring. Num 27:17
whither the Lord shall *l.* you. Deut 4:27; 28:37
shall make captains to *l.* the. 20:9
so the Lord alone did *l.* him. 32:12
Barak, *l.* thy captivity. Judg 5:12
they may *l.* them away. 1 Sam 30:22
find compassion before them that *l.* 2 Chr 30:9
pillar of cloud to *l.* Neh 9:19
l. me, O Lord, in thy. Ps 5:8
l. me in thy truth. 25:5
l. me in a plain path. 27:11
for thy name's sake *l.* me. Ps 31:3
light and truth, let them *l.* me. 43:3
l. me into Edom? 60:9*; 108:10
l. me to the rock that is. 61:2
l. them forth with workers of. 125:5
there shall thine hand *l.* me. 139:10
l. me in the way everlasting. 24
l. me into the land of. 143:10
goest, it shall *l.* thee. Pr 6:22
l. in way of righteousness. 8:20*
l. thee to my mother's. S of S 8:2
l. thee cause thee to err. Isa 3:12
a little child shall *l.* them. 11:6
the king of Assyria *l.* 20:4
gently *l.* those that are with. 40:11
I will *l.* them in paths not. 42:16
hath mercy on them, shall *l.* 49:10
I will *l.* him, and restore. 57:18
so didst thou *l.* thy people. 63:14
with supplications will I *l.* Jer 31:9
shall *l.* Zedekiah to Babylon. 32:5
maids *l.* her, as with voice. Nah 2:7*
l. us not into temptation. Mat 6:13*; Luke 11:4*
if the blind *l.* the blind. Mat 15:14 Luke 6:39
when they shall *l.* you. Mark 13:11
take him and *l.* him away. 14:44
loose his ox and *l.* him. Luke 13:15
seeking some to *l.* him. Acts 13:11
have we not power to *l.*? 1 Cor 9:5
we may *l.* a quiet life. 1 Tim 2:2
l. captive silly women. 2 Tim 3:6*
to *l.* them out of the land. Heb 8:9
shall feed and *l.* them. Rev 7:17

leader
Jehoiada was *l.* of the. 1 Chr 12:27
David consulted with captains and every *l.* 13:1
I have given him a *l.* Isa 55:4

leaders
angel which cut off *l.* 2 Chr 32:21
the *l.* of this people. Isa 9:16
they be blind *l.* of the. Mat 15:14*

leadest
that *l.* Joseph like a flock. Ps 80:1

leadeth
turned to the way that *l.* 1 Sam 13:17
he *l.* counsellors away. Job 12:17
he *l.* princes away spoiled, and. 19
he *l.* me beside the still. Ps 23:2
he *l.* me in the paths of. 3
l. him into the way that. Pr 16:29
Lord thy God which *l.* Isa 48:17
wide is the way that *l.* to. Mat 7:13
narrow is the way that *l.* to life. 14
Jesus *l.* them into a high. Mark 9:2*
he calleth his sheep and *l.* John 10:3
the iron gate that *l.* Acts 12:10
the goodness of God *l.* to. Rom 2:4
he that *l.* shall go into. Rev 13:10

leaf
her mouth was an olive *l.* Gen 8:11
sound of a shaken *l.* Lev 26:36
wilt thou break a *l.* driven to and fro? Job 13:25
his *l.* also shall not wither. Ps 1:3
be as an oak, whose *l.* Isa 1:30
their host fall as a *l.* 34:4
we all do fade as a *l.* 64:6
no grapes, the *l.* shall. Jer 8:13
but her *l.* shall be green, and. 17:8
l. shall not fade, the *l.* Ezek 47:12

league
(*The Revisions frequently change this word to* covenant)
make therefore a *l.* Josh 9:6, 11
Joshua made a *l.* with the. 15, 16
no *l.* with the inhabitants. Judg 2:2
my son hath made a *l.* 1 Sam 22:8
king David made a *l.* 2 Sam 5:3
Solomon made a *l.* 1 Ki 5:12
is a *l.* between me and thee. 15:19
go break thy *l.* with. 2 Chr 16:3
be in *l.* with the stones. Job 5:23
men of the land that is in *l.* shall. Ezek 30:5
after the *l.* he shall work. Dan 11:23

Leah
elder daughter was *L.* Gen 29:16
L. was tender eyed, but Rachel. 17
in the morning, behold it was *L.* 25
the Lord saw that *L.* Gen 29:31
L. conceived and bare. 32; 30:19
out of the field, *L.* met him. 30:16
Jacob called Rachel and *L.* 31:4
Jacob put *L.* and her children. 33:2
Dinah the daughter of *L.* went. 34:1
L.; Reuben, Simeon. 35:23; 46:15
Abraham, there I buried *L.* 49:31
make this woman like *L.* Ruth 4:11

lean
kine came out of the river *l.*fleshed. Gen 41:3, 19
the *l.*fleshed eat up the. 4, 20
land is, whether fat or *l.* Num 13:20
being the king's son *l.* 2 Sam 13:4
of his flesh shall wax *l.* Isa 17:4
between fat cattle and *l.* Ezek 34:20

lean, *verb*
I may *l.* on the pillars. Judg 16:26
on which if a man *l.* 2 Ki 18:21 Isa 36:6
shall *l.* on his house. Job 8:15
l. not to thine own. Pr 3:5
yet will they *l.* on the Lord. Mi 3:11

leaned
behold, Saul *l.* upon. 2 Sam 1:6
on whose hand the king *l.* 2 Ki 7:2
when they *l.* on thee. Ezek 29:7
l. his hand on the wall. Amos 5:19
who also *l.* on his breast. John 21:20

leaneth
not fail one that *l.* on. 2 Sam 3:29
l. on my hand in the. 2 Ki 5:18

leaning
that cometh up *l.* on. S of S 8:5
there was *l.* on Jesus'. John 13:23
Jacob worshipped, *l.* on. Heb 11:21

leanness
my *l.* rising up in me. Job 16:8
gave request, but sent *l.* Ps 106:15
among his fat ones *l.* Isa 10:16
but I said, My *l.*, my *l.*, woe. 24:16*

leap
all the rams which *l.* on. Gen 31:12
have legs to *l.* withal. Lev 11:21
and of Dan, he shall *l.* Deut 33:22
and sparks of fire *l.* out. Job 41:19
why *l.* ye, ye high hills? Ps 68:16*
then shall the lame man *l.* Isa 35:6
of chariots shall they *l.* Joel 2:5
shall punish those that *l.* Zeph 1:9
in that day, and *l.* for joy. Luke 6:23

leaped
the rams which *l.* upon. Gen 31:10
by my God, I *l.* over a wall. 2 Sam 22:30; Ps 18:29
they *l.* upon the altar. 1 Ki 18:26
babe *l.* in her womb. Luke 1:41, 44
stand upright, and he *l.* Acts 14:10
he in whom evil spirit was, *l.* 19:16

leaping
Michal saw David *l.* 2 Sam 6:1
behold he cometh *l.* on. S of S 2:
l. up, stood and walked. Acts 3:

learn
that they may *l.* to fear me. Deut 4:10; 14:2
that ye may *l.* them, and keep. 5:
therein, that he may *l.* to fear. 17:1
shalt not *l.* to do after the. 18:
they may hear, and *l.* and. 31:1
that their children may *l.* to. 1
I might *l.* thy statutes. Ps 119:71, 7
lest thou *l.* his ways. Pr 22:2
l. to do well, seek. Isa 1:1
neither shall they *l.* war. 2:4; Mi 4:
the inhabitants of world shall righteousness. Isa 26:
not the wicked *l.* righteousness.
murmured shall *l.* doctrine. 29:24
l. not the way of heathen. Jer 10:
if they will diligently *l.* ways. 12:
but go and *l.* what that. Mat 9:
l. of me, for I am meek and. 11:
l. a parable of the fig tree. 24: Mark 13:
l. in us not to think. 1 Cor 4
one by one, that all may *l.* 14:
if they will *l.* any thing, let them.
would *l.* of you, received ye? Gal 3

l. not to blaspheme. *1 Tim* 1:20*
let the woman *l.* in silence. 2:11
let them *l.* first to shew piety. 5:4
and withal they *l.* to be idle. 13
let ours *l.* to maintain. *Tit* 3:14
no man could *l.* that song. *Rev* 14:3

learned

tarry, for I have *l.* by. *Gen* 30:27*
among the heathen, and *l.* *Ps* 106:35
l. thy righteous judgements. 119:7
I neither *l.* wisdom, nor. *Pr* 30:3
deliver to one that is *l.* *Isa* 29:11
is not *l.* he saith, I am not *l.* 12
given me tongue of the *l.* he wakeneth mine ear to hear as *l.* 50:4*
it *l.* to catch the prey. *Ezek* 19:3, 6
every man that hath *l.* *John* 6:45
man letters, having never *l.* 7:15
Moses was *l.* in all. *Acts* 7:22*
the doctrine ye have *l.* *Rom* 16:17
have not so *l.* Christ. *Eph* 4:20
those things ye have *l.* and. *Phil* 4:9
l., therewith to be content. 11
as ye *l.* of Epaphras our. *Col* 1:7
in the things thou hast *l.* knowing of whom thou hast *l.* *2 Tim* 3:14
though he were a son, yet *l.* *Heb* 5:8

learning

will hear and increase *l.* *Pr* 1:5
man, and he will increase in *l.* 9:9
of the lips increaseth *l.* 16:21
the heart of the wise addeth *l.* 23
whom they might teach *l.* *Dan* 1:4
God gave them skill in all *l.* 17
Festus said, Much *l.* *Acts* 26:24
were written for our *l.* *Rom* 15:4
ever *l.* and never able. *2 Tim* 3:7

leasing

long will ye seek after *l.*? *Ps* 4:2*
destroy them that speak *l.* 5:6*

least

[1] *The smallest quantity,* Num 11:32. [2] *Most humble and lowly,* Luke 9:48. [3] *The meanest person, or one of the least judgement, skill, and experience,* Judg 6:15.

not worthy of the *l.* of. *Gen* 32:10
gathered *l.* gathered. *Num* 11:32
l. in my father's house. *Judg* 6:15
my family, the *l.* of. *1 Sam* 9:21
one captain of *l.* of. *2 Ki* 18:24
l. of flock shall draw them. *Jer* 49:20*; 50:45*
not the *l.* grain fall upon. *Amos* 9:9
art not the *l.* among the princes of Judah. *Mat* 2:6
of these *l.* commandments, shall be called the *l.* in the kingdom. 5:19
that is *l.* in the kingdom of heaven, is greater. 11:11*; *Luke* 7:28*
is the *l.* of all seeds. *Mat* 13:32*
have done it to the *l.* 25:40, 45
he that is *l.* among you. *Luke* 9:48
not able to do that which is *l.* 12:26
faithful in the *l.*: unjust in *l.* 16:10*
them to judge who are *l.* *1 Cor* 6:4*
for I am the *l.* of the apostles. 15:9
who am less than the *l.* *Eph* 3:8

see **greatest**

at the **least**

damsel abide with us, *at the l.* *Gen* 24:55
at the l. such as before. *Judg* 3:2
if kept themselves *at l.* *1 Sam* 21:4*
hadst known *at l.* in. *Luke* 19:42
that *at the l.* the shadow of Peter. *Acts* 5:15

leather

man, girt with a girdle of *l.* *2 Ki* 1:8

leathern

John had a *l.* girdle. *Mat* 3:4

leave

[1] *Permission,* Num 22:13; Mark 5:13. [2] *To depart from,* John 6:28. [3] *Farewell,* Acts 18:18. [4] *To lay down,* Mat 5:24.

leave, *substantive*

refuseth to give me *l.* *Num* 22:13
asked *l.* of me. *1 Sam* 20:6, 28
certain days obtained I *l.* *Neh* 13:6
Jesus gave them *l.* *Mark* 5:13
Pilate gave him *l.* to. *John* 19:38
Paul took his *l.* of the. *Acts* 18:18
when we had taken our *l.* one. 21:6
l. I went to Macedonia. *2 Cor* 2:13

leave

l. father and mother and. *Gen* 2:24
Mat 19:5; *Mark* 10:7; *Eph* 5:31
let me *l.* with thee some of the folk. *Gen* 33:15
l. one of your brethren here. 42:33
cannot *l.* his father, if he *l.* 44:22
let no man *l.* manna till. *Ex* 16:19
what they *l.* the beasts of. 23:11
not *l.* any of the peace offering. *Lev* 7:15; 22:30
shall put off garments and *l.* 16:23
thou shalt *l.* them for the poor. 19:10; 23:22
l. none of the passover. *Num* 9:12
he said, *L.* us not, I pray. 10:31
will yet again *l.* them in the. 32:15
not *l.* thee either corn. *Deut* 28:51
of children which he shall *l.* 54
and *l.* them in the lodging. *Josh* 4:3*
olive said, Should I *l.* my? *Judg* 9:9
vine said, Should I *l.* my vine? 13
Entreat me not to *l.* *Ruth* 1:16
lest my father *l.* caring. *1 Sam* 9:5
Saul said, Let us not *l.* a. 14:36
if I *l.* of all that pertain to. 25:22
shall not *l.* to my husband neither name nor. *2 Sam* 14:7
let him not *l.* us nor. *1 Ki* 8:57
shall eat and shall *l.* *2 Ki* 4:43
did he *l.* of the people but fifty. 13:7
this good land, and *l.* it. *1 Chr* 28:8
to *l.* us a remnant to. *Ezra* 9:8
l. it for an inheritance to your. 12
I pray you let us *l.* off this. *Neh* 5:10
the work cease whilst I *l.* it? 6:3
would *l.* the seventh year. 10:31*
wilt thou *l.* thy labour? *Job* 39:11
thou wilt not *l.* my soul in hell. *Ps* 16:10; *Acts* 2:27
they *l.* their substance to. *Ps* 17:14
thou hast been my help, *l.* me not. 27:9; 119:121
they die and *l.* their wealth. 49:10
O God, my trust, *l.* not my. 141:8
l. the paths of uprightness. *Pr* 2:13
l. off contention, before it be. 17:14
I should *l.* it to the man. *Eccl* 2:18
yet shall he *l.* it for his portion. 21
if ruler rise up against thee, *l.* 10:4
will ye *l.* your glory? *Isa* 10:3
shall *l.* your name for a curse. 65:15
I might *l.* my people, and. *Jer* 9:2
called by thy name, *l.* us not. 14:9
riches, he shall *l.* them in. 17:11
will a man *l.* the snow of? 18:14
child and suckling, to *l.* you. 44:7
l. the cities, and dwell in. 48:28
not *l.* some gleaning grapes? 49:9
l. thy fatherless children, I will. 11
and *l.* thee naked and bare. *Ezek* 16:39; 23:29
will turn thee, and *l.* but a. 39:2*
l. the stump of his. *Dan* 4:15, 23, 26
he *l.* his blood upon him. *Hos* 12:14
return, and *l.* a blessing. *Joel* 2:14
l. an hundred, shall *l.* *Amos* 5:3
who *l.* off righteousness in the. 7*
would they not *l.* grapes? *Ob* 5
it shall *l.* them neither. *Mal* 4:1
l. there thy gift before. *Mat* 5:24
doth he not *l.* the ninety and nine? 18:12; *Luke* 15:4
to have done, and not *l.* *Mat* 23:23
and *l.* his wife, and *l.* *Mark* 12:19
they shall not *l.* in thee. *Luke* 19:44
my peace I *l.* with you. *John* 14:27
I *l.* the world and go to the. 16:28
ye shall *l.* me alone, yet I am not. 32
not reason we should *l.* *Acts* 6:2
her, let her not *l.* him. *1 Cor* 7:13
I will never *l.* thee, nor. *Heb* 13:5*
the court *l.* out, and. *Rev* 11:2

I will, or *will I* **leave**

if I say, *I will l.* off my. *Job* 9:27
I will l. my complaint upon. 10:1*
yet *will I l.* a remnant. *Ezek* 6:8
but *I will l.* a few. 12:16
I will l. you there, and melt. 22:20*
I will l. thee thrown into. *Ezek* 29:5
I will l. thee upon the land. 32:4
I will l. in midst of thee. *Zeph* 3:12

I will not **leave**

I will not l. thee until I. *Gen* 28:15
as the Lord liveth, *I will not l.* thee. *2 Ki* 2:2; 4:30
As thy soul liveth, *I will not l.* 2:4, 6
Lord *I will not l.* him in. *Ps* 37:33
I will not l. thee together. *Jer* 30:11; 46:28
I will not l. you comfortless. *John* 14:18

leaved

before him the two-*l.* gates. *Isa* 45:1

leaven

A piece of dough salted and soured, to ferment and relish a mass of dough for bread, Hos 7:4; 1 Cor 5:6. *The word is also used figuratively in the New Testament for* teachings.

ye shall put away *l.* *Ex* 12:15, 19
neither shall be *l.* seen in all. 13:7
blood of my sacrifice with *l.* 34:25
shall be made with *l.* *Lev* 2:11
it shall not be baken with *l.* 6:17
eat meat offering without *l.* 10:12
they shall be baken with *l.* 23:17
of thanksgiving with *l.* *Amos* 4:5
kingdom of heaven is like *l.* *Mat* 13:33; *Luke* 13:21
the *l.* of the Pharisees. *Mat* 16:6
11; *Mark* 8:15; *Luke* 12:1
not beware of the *l.* *Mat* 16:12
little *l.* leaveneth the whole lump. *1 Cor* 5:6; *Gal* 5:9
purge out therefore the old *l.* that. *1 Cor* 5:7
let us keep the feast, not with old *l.* 8

leavened

for whosoever eateth *l.* *Ex* 12:15, 19
shall eat nothing *l.* in all your. 20
their dough before it was *l.* 34, 39
there shall no *l.* be eaten. 13:3, 7
after he hath kneaded the dough till it be *l.* *Hos* 7:4
till the whole was *l.* *Mat* 13:33; *Luke* 13:21

see **bread**

leaveneth

little leaven *l.* the whole lump. *1 Cor* 5:6; *Gal* 5:9

leaves

sewed fig *l.* and made. *Gen* 3:7
when they cast their *l.* *Isa* 6:13*
read three or four *l.* *Jer* 36:23
it shall wither in all the *l.* *Ezek* 17:9
l. thereof fair. *Dan* 4:12, 21
shake off his *l.* 14
nothing thereon but *l.* *Mat* 21:19; *Mark* 11:13
his branch putteth forth *l.* *Mat* 24:32; *Mark* 13:28
l. were for the healing of. *Rev* 22:2

leaves *for doors*

the two *l.* of the one door. *1 Ki* 6:34
two *l.* apiece, two *l.* for. *Ezek* 41:24

leaveth

the ostrich *l.* her eggs. *Job* 39:14
a good man *l.* an. *Pr* 13:22
like a sweeping rain which *l.* 28:3
idol shepherd, that *l.* *Zech* 11:17
then the devil *l.* him. *Mat* 4:11
the hireling *l.* the sheep. *John* 10:12

leaving

Jesus *l.* Nazareth, dwelt. *Mat* 4:13
thieves departed, *l.* *Luke* 10:30
men *l.* the natural use. *Rom* 1:27
l. the principles of the. *Heb* 6:1*
Christ suffered for us, *l.* *1 Pet* 2:21

Lebanon

goodly mountain and *L.* *Deut* 3:25
that dwelt in mount *L.* *Judg* 3:3
ten thousand a month to *L.* *1 Ki* 5:14
the forest of *L.* 7:2; 10:17, 21
was in *L.* sent to cedar in *L.* give thy. *2 Ki* 14:9; *2 Chr* 25:18
I am come up to the sides of *L.* *2 Ki* 19:23; *Isa* 37:24
skill to cut timber in *L.* *2 Chr* 2:8
L. and Sirion like a. *Ps* 29:6

thereof shall shake like *L.* *Ps* 72:16
shall grow like a cedar in *L.* 92:12
Solomon made a chariot of the wood of *L.* *S of S* 3:9
from *L.* my spouse, from *L.* 4:8
garments is like the smell of *L.* 11
waters, and streams from *L.* 15
his countenance is as *L.* 5:15
thy nose is as the tower of *L.* 7:4
L. shall fall. *Isa* 10:34
L. shall be turned into a. 29:17
L. is ashamed. 33:9
the glory of *L.* shall be given. 35:2
L. is not sufficient to burn for. 40:16
the glory of *L.* shall come. 60:13
leave the snow of *L.*? *Jer* 18:14
Gilead and the head of *L.* 22:6
go up to *L.* and cry, lift up thy. 20
longwinged, came to *L.* *Ezek* 17:3
and I caused *L.* to mourn. 31:15
cast forth his roots as *L.* *Hos* 14:5
his smell as *L.* 6
the scent as the wine of *L.* 7
Bashan and the flower of *L.* *Nah* 1:4
violence of *L.* shall cover. *Hab* 2:17
them into the land of *L.* *Zech* 10:10
open thy doors, O *L.* that fire. 11:1
see **cedars**

Lebbaeus

L. whose surname was Thaddaeus. *Mat* 10:3

led

the way, the Lord *l.* me. *Gen* 24:27
blessed the Lord, who had *l.* me. 48
Moses *l.* flock to backside. *Ex* 3:1
God *l.* them not through the. 13:17
but God *l.* them about, through. 18
thou in mercy hast *l.* forth. 15:13
Lord *l.* thee forty years. *Deut* 8:2
who *l.* thee through that great. 15
I have *l.* you forty years in. 29:5
l. him about, he instructed. 32:10*
l. him through all land. *Josh* 24:3
enemies, which *l.* them. *1 Ki* 8:48*
but Elisha *l.* them to. *2 Ki* 6:19
Joab *l.* forth the power. *1 Chr* 20:1
and Amaziah *l.* forth. *2 Chr* 25:11
in the day he *l.* them. *Ps* 78:14
he *l.* them on safely, so that. 53
l. them through the depths as through a. 106:9; 136:16; *Isa* 63:13
he *l.* them forth by right. *Ps* 107:7
I have *l.* thee in right. *Pr* 4:11
they that are *l.* of them. *Isa* 9:16
they thirsted not when they *l.* 48:21
for ye shall be *l.* forth in. 55:12
that *l.* them by the right hand. 63:12
where is the Lord that *l.* us? *Jer* 2:6
hath forsaken God, when he *l.* 17
the place whither they have *l.* 22:12
the Lord liveth which *l.* the. 23:8
he hath *l.* me into darkness. *Lam* 3:2
and *l.* them with him. *Ezek* 17:12*
who caused them to be *l.* 39:28
l. me about to the outer. 47:2
also I *l.* you 40 years. *Amos* 2:10
Israel shall surely be *l.* captive. 7:11
and Huzzah shall be *l.* *Nah* 2:7*
then was Jesus *l.* of the Spirit. *Mat* 4:1; *Luke* 4:1
they *l.* him to Caiaphas the high. *Mat* 26:57; *Mark* 14:53 *Luke* 22:54; *John* 18:13
they *l.* him to Pontius Pilate the. *Mat* 27:2, 31; *Mark* 15:16, 20 *Luke* 22:54; *John* 18:13
the blind man and *l.* *Mark* 8:23*
l. Jesus to the brow. *Luke* 4:29
they shall be *l.* away captive. 21:24
and *l.* him into their council. 22:66
the whole multitude *l.* him. 23:1*
two other malefactors were *l.* 32
l. them out as far as Bethany. 24:50
l. Jesus unto the hall. *John* 18:28
he was *l.* as a sheep to. *Acts* 8:32
they *l.* Saul by the hand. 9:8; 22:11
as Paul was to be *l.* into. 21:37*
as many as are *l.* by the. *Rom* 8:14
idols, even as ye were *l.* *1 Cor* 12:2
but if ye be *l.* by the Spirit. *Gal* 5:18
silly women, *l.* away. *2 Tim* 3:6
being *l.* away with the error of the wicked, fall from. *2 Pet* 3:17*

leddest

wast he that *l.* out Israel. *2 Sam* 5:2; *1 Chr* 11:2
l. them in the day by a. *Neh* 9:12
thou *l.* thy people like. *Ps* 77:20
l. into the wilderness. *Acts* 21:38

ledges

were between the *l.* *1 Ki* 7:28
the *l.* and borders thereof were. 35*
on plates of the *l.* he graved. 36*

leeks

we remember the *l.* *Num* 11:5

lees

a feast of wine on the *l.* *Isa* 25:6
hath settled on his *l.* *Jer* 48:11
men settled on their *l.* *Zeph* 1:12

left

had *l.* communing with. *Gen* 18:33
who hath not *l.* destitute my. 24:27
Judah, and *l.* bearing. 29:35; 30:9
other company which is *l.* 32:8
l. all that he had in Joseph's. 39:6
he *l.* his garment in. 12, 13, 15, 18
Joseph gathered corn till he *l.* 41:49
at the eldest, and *l.* at the. 44:12
not enough *l.* but our bodies. 47:18
little ones *l.* they in Goshen. 50:8
why is it that ye have *l.*? *Ex* 2:20
l. his servants and his cattle. 9:21
herb, all that the hail *l.* 10:12, 15
there shall not an hoof be *l.* 26
but some of them *l.* of it till. 16:20
nor sacrifice of passover be *l.* 34:25
l. of the meat offering. *Lev* 2:10
Ithamar, his sons that were *l.* 10:12
are *l.* of you shall pine away. 26:39
the land also shall be *l.* of them. 43
not *l.* a man of them. *Num* 26:65 *Josh* 8:17; *Judg* 4:16; *Hos* 9:12
we *l.* none to remain. *Deut* 2:34 *Josh* 10:33, 37, 39, 40; 11:8, 11, 14
ye shall be *l.* few in number among the heathen. *Deut* 4:27; 28:62 *Isa* 24:6; *Jer* 42:2
that are *l.* be destroyed. *Deut* 7:20
he hath nothing *l.* him in. 28:55
there is none shut up or *l.* 32:36
and *l.* them without the camp of. *Josh* 6:23*
they *l.* the city open, and. 8:17
he *l.* nothing undone of all. 11:15
was none of the Anakims *l.* 22
ye have not *l.* your brethren. 22:3
of nations which Joshua *l.* when. *Judg* 2:21
the Lord *l.* those nations. 23; 3:1
l. no sustenance for Israel. 6:4
Jotham the youngest son was *l.* 9:5
she was *l.*, and her two. *Ruth* 1:3, 5
was minded to go, then she *l.* 18
how thou hast *l.* thy father. 2:11
eat and was sufficed, and *l.* 14
Lord hath not *l.* thee this day. 4:14
that is *l.* in thy house. *1 Sam* 2:36
the stump of Dagon was *l.* 5:4
that *l.*! set before thee and eat. 9:24*
thy father hath *l.* the care. 10:2
two of them were not *l.* 11:11
David rose up and *l.* sheep. 17:20
David *l.* his carriage in the hand. 22
not been *l.* any that pisseth. 25:34
David *l.* neither man nor. 27:9*
they *l.* their images. *2 Sam* 5:21
any *l.* of the house of Saul? 9:1
sons, there is not one of them *l.* 13:30
quench my coal which is *l.* 14:7
l. ten concubines. 15:16; 16:21
shall not be *l.* so much as one. 17:12
their children that were *l.* *1 Ki* 9:21 *2 Chr* 8:8
cut off him that is shut up and *l.* *1 Ki* 14:10; *2 Ki* 9:8
he *l.* not Jeroboam any. *1 Ki* 15:29
l. Baasha not one that pisseth. 16:11
there was no breath *l.* in. 17:17
and *l.* his servant, 19:3
I only am *l.* 10
yet I have *l.* me 7000. 18
he *l.* oxen and ran. 20
they did eat and *l.* *2 Ki* 4:44
they arose and *l.* tents. 7:7
all that are *l.* 13
since the day she *l.* the land even. *2 Ki* 8:6
Jehu slew all, till he *l.* him. 10:11
so that there was not a man *l.* 21
for there was not any *l.* nor. 14:26
they *l.* the commandments of. 17:16
lift up thy prayer for the remnant that are *l.* 19:4; *Isa* 37:4
nothing shall be *l.* saith. *2 Ki* 20:17
l. of the poor of the land. 25:12 *Jer* 39:10; 52:16
our brethren that are *l.* *1 Chr* 13:2
for the Levites *l.* their. *2 Chr* 11:14
I have also *l.* you in the hand. 12:5
was never a son *l.* him. 21:17
and they *l.* the house of Lord. 24:18
l. Joash in great diseases. 25
enough to eat, and have *l.* 31:10
God *l.* him to try him, that he. 32:31
enquire for them that are *l.* 34:21
concerning the Jews which had *l.* *Neh* 1:2
the remnant that are *l.* are. 3
there was no breach *l.* therein. 6:1
none of his meat be *l.* *Job* 20:21
it shall go ill with him that is *l.* 26
was not one of them *l.* *Ps* 106:11
a child *l.* to himself. *Pr* 29:15
Zion is *l.* as a cottage in a. *Isa* 1:8
except Lord had *l.* us. 9; *Rom* 9:29
he that is *l.* in Zion shall. *Isa* 4:3
butter and honey shall every one eat that is *l.* 7:22
gathereth eggs that are *l.* 10:14
for the remnant that shall be *l.* 11:16
yet gleaning grapes shall be *l.* 17:6
in the city is *l.* desolation. 24:12
till ye be *l.* as a beacon on. 30:17
shall be *l.* saith the Lord. 39:6
I *l.* my heritage. *Jer* 12:7
l. of the sword. 31:2
how is the city of praise not *l.*! 49:25
let nothing of her be *l.* 50:26
shall be *l.* a remnant. *Ezek* 14:22
nor *l.* her whoredoms brought. 23:8
cut him off and have *l.* him. 31:12
the kingdom shall not be *l.* to other. *Dan* 2:44
worm *l.* the locust hath *l.* *Joel* 1:4
who is *l.* that saw this house in her glory? *Hag* 2:3
part shall be *l.* therein. *Zech* 13:8
l. their nets. *Mat* 4:20
they *l.* their ships. 22
he touched her, and the fever *l.* her. 8:15; *Mark* 1:31
took up of the meat that was *l.* *Mat* 15:37; *Mark* 8:8
he *l.* his wife to his brother. *Mat* 22:25; *Mark* 12:20
your house is *l.* unto you. *Mat* 23:38
there shall not be *l.* one stone upon. 24:2; *Mark* 13:2; *Luke* 21:6
one shall be taken, and the other *l.* *Mat* 24:40, 41; *Luke* 17:34, 35, 36
Jesus *l.* them, and prayed the third. *Mat* 26:44
l. all and followed. *Mark* 10:28
no man that hath *l.* house. 29 *Luke* 18:28, 29
had her, and *l.* no seed. *Mark* 12:22
he *l.* all, rose up, and. *Luke* 5:28
that my sister hath *l.* me to. 10:40
woman then *l.* her waterpot. *John* 4:28
at the seventh hour the fever *l.* 52
that his soul was not *l.* in. *Acts* 2:31
l. not himself without witness. 14:17
captain, they *l.* beating of Paul. 21:32
and Felix *l.* Paul. 24:27; 25:14
we thought good to be *l.* *1 Thes* 3:1
the cloak that I *l.* at. *2 Tim* 4:13
Trophimus have I *l.* sick at. 20
this cause *l.* I thee at Crete. *Tit* 1:5
he *l.* nothing that is not. *Heb* 2:8
us fear, lest a promise being *l.* 4:1
the angels which *l.* their. *Jude* 6
thou hast *l.* thy first love. *Rev* 2:4
see **alone, hand**

left *off*

l. off to build the city. *Gen* 11:8
l. off talking with him, and. 17:22
not *l. off* his kindness. *Ruth* 2:20

Baasha *l. off* building. *1 Ki* 15:21
2 Chr 16:5
they *l. off* speaking. *Job* 32:15*
he hath *l. off* to be wise. *Ps* 36:3
so they *l. off* speaking. *Jer* 38:27
since we *l. off* to burn incense. 44:18
have *l. off* to take heed. *Hos* 4:10

left *corner*
guard stood to the *l. corner* about.
2 Ki 11:11

lefthanded
raised Ehud, a man *l.* *Judg* 3:15
seven hundred chosen men *l.* 20:16

left *pillar*
he set up the *l. pillar.* *1 Ki* 7:21

left *side*
five bases on the *l. side.* *1 Ki* 7:39
five candlesticks on the *l. side.* 49
with his weapon from right to *l. side.*
2 Chr 23:10
had the face of an ox on the *l. side.*
Ezek 1:10
lie also on thy *l. side,* and lay. 4:4
olive tree upon *l. side. Zech* 4:3, 11

leg, -s
with fire his head and *l.* *Ex* 12:9
wash the inwards and his *l.* 29:17
Lev 9:14
his head, and his *l.* burn. *Lev* 4:11
he washed the inwards and *l.* 8:21
which have *l.* above their feet. 11:21
shall smite thee in the knees and *l.*
Deut 28:35
of brass upon his *l.* *1 Sam* 17:6
pleasure in the *l.* of a man. *Ps* 147:10
the *l.* of the lame are not. *Pr* 26:7
his *l.* are as pillars of. *S of S* 5:15
take away ornaments of *l. Isa* 3:20*
make bare the *l.* uncover the. 47:2*
his *l.* of iron, his feet. *Dan* 2:33
two *l.*, or piece of an ear. *Amos* 3:12
their *l.* might be broken. *John* 19:31
and brake the *l.* of the first. 32
he was dead, brake not his *l.* 33

Legion
my name is *L.* for we are many.
Mark 5:9; *Luke* 8:30

legions
me more than twelve *l.* *Mat* 26:53

leisure
had no *l.* so much as to. *Mark* 6:31

Lemuel
the words of king *L.* *Pr* 31:1
not for kings, O *L.* to drink. 4

lend
if thou *l.* money to any. *Ex* 22:25
not *l.* him thy victuals. *Lev* 25:37*
shalt *l.* to many nations. *Deut* 15:6
thou shalt surely *l.* him sufficient. 8
thou shalt not *l.* upon usury. 23:19
to a stranger thou mayest *l.* 20
thou dost *l.* thy brother any. 24:10
the man to whom thou dost *l.* 11
thou shalt *l.* to many nations. 28:12
l. to thee, thou shalt not *l.* him. 44
if ye *l.* to them of whom ye . . . for
sinners also *l.* to sinners.
Luke 6:34
your enemies, do good and *l.* 35
and say to him, Friend, *l.* me. 11:5

lender
is servant to the *l.* *Pr* 22:7
as with the *l.* so with. *Isa* 24:2

lendeth
every creditor that *l.* *Deut* 15:2
merciful, and *l.*; his seed. *Ps* 37:26
man sheweth favour and *l.* 112:5
pity on the poor *l.* to Lord. *Pr* 19:17

length
through the land in the *l. Gen* 13:17
he is thy life, and the *l. Deut* 30:20
l. of days, understanding. *Job* 12:12
even *l.* of days for ever. *Ps* 21:4
for *l.* of days shall they. *Pr* 3:2
l. of days is in her right hand. 16
and to see what is the *l.* *Zech* 2:2
l. of the roll is twenty cubits. 5:2
be able to comprehend *l. Eph* 3:18
l. as large as the breadth. *Rev* 21:16

at **length**
him become his son *at l.* *Pr* 29:21
if now at *l.* I may have a journey.
Rom 1:10

lengthen
then will I *l.* thy days. *1 Ki* 3:14
l. thy cords and strengthen. *Isa* 54:2

lengthened
that thy days may be *l. Deut* 25:15*

lengthening
a *l.* of thy tranquillity. *Dan* 4:27

lent
they *l.* to them such as. *Ex* 12:36*
thing that is *l.* on usury. *Deut* 23:19
I *l.* him to the Lord, he shall be *l.*
1 Sam 1:28*
for the loan which is *l.* to. 2:20†
I have not *l.* on usury nor have men *l.*
me. *Jer* 15:10

lentiles
gave Esau pottage of *l.* *Gen* 25:34
piece of ground full of *l. 2 Sam* 23:11
see **beans**

leopard
(*A large and ferocious spotted animal*)
the *l.* shall lie down with. *Isa* 11:6
a *l.* watch over their cities. *Jer* 5:6
can the *l.* change his spots? 13:23
and lo, another like a *l.* *Dan* 7:6
I will be to them as a *l.* *Hos* 13:7
the beast was like to a *l.* *Rev* 13:2

leopards
the mountains of the *l.* *S of S* 4:8
horses are swifter than *l.* *Hab* 1:8

leper
l. in whom the plague is. *Lev* 13:45
shall be the law of the *l.* in. 14:2
the leprosy be healed in the *l.* 3
man of the seed of Aaron is a *l.* 22:4
out of the camp every *l.* *Num* 5:2
from the house of Joab, one that is a
l. *2 Sam* 3:29
Naaman was a *l.* *2 Ki* 5:1
recover the *l.* 11
went from his presence a *l.* as. 27
Azariah was a *l.* to the day. 15:5
the king was a *l.* *2 Chr* 26:21
him, for they said, He is a *l.* 23
and behold, there came a *l.*
Mat 8:2; *Mark* 1:40
in the house of Simon the *l.*
Mat 26:6; *Mark* 14:3

lepers
when the *l.* came to the. *2 Ki* 7:8
heal the sick, cleanse *l.* *Mat* 10:8
the lame walk, the *l.* are cleansed.
11:5; *Luke* 7:22
many *l.* were in Israel. *Luke* 4:27
met him ten men that were *l.* 17:12

leprosy
skin like the plague of *l.* *Lev* 13:2
it is a plague of *l.* 3, 8, 11, 15, 25
27, 30, 42, 49
when the plague of *l.* is in a man. 9
if a *l.* break out. 12
if the *l.* covered his flesh. 13
as the *l.* appeareth in the skin. 43
that the plague of *l.* is in. 47
this is the law of the plague of *l.*
59; 14:54, 55, 57
if the plague of *l.* be healed. 14:3
him that is to be cleansed from *l.* 7
him in whom is the plague of *l.* 32
heed in the plague of *l.* *Deut* 24:8
recover him of his *l.* *2 Ki* 5:3, 7
mayest recover him of his *l.* 6
the *l.* of Naaman shall cleave. 27
the *l.* rose up in his. *2 Chr* 26:19
his *l.* was cleansed. *Mat* 8:3
Mark 1:42; *Luke* 5:13
behold, a man full of *l.* *Luke* 5:12
see **fretting**

leprous
behold, his hand was *l.* *Ex* 4:6
l. man he is unclean. *Lev* 13:44
Miriam became *l.* behold she was *l.*
Num 12:10
there were four *l.* men. *2 Ki* 7:3
and Uzziah was *l.* in. *2 Chr* 26:20

less
some more, some *l.* *Ex* 16:17
the poor shall not give *l.* than. 30:15
word of the Lord to do *l. Num* 22:18
to few thou shalt give *l.* inheritance.
26:54; 33:54
thy servant knew nothing *l.* or more.
1 Sam 22:15
Abigail told him nothing *l.* 25:36
punished us *l.* than our. *Ezra* 9:13
exacteth *l.* than iniquity. *Job* 11:6
much *l.* do lying lips a. *Pr* 17:7
much *l.* for a servant to rule. 19:10
all nations are counted *l.* *Isa* 40:17
when it is sown is *l.* *Mark* 4:31
mother of James the *l.* 15:40
members we think *l.* *1 Cor* 12:23
the more I love, the *l.* *2 Cor* 12:15
l. than the least of all. *Eph* 3:8
and that I may be the *l.* *Phil* 2:28
the *l.* is blessed of better. *Heb* 7:7

lesser
made the *l.* light to rule. *Gen* 1:16
for the treading of *l.* *Isa* 7:25*
l. settle to the greater. *Ezek* 43:14

lest
ye touch it, *l.* ye die. *Gen* 3:3
Lev 10:6, 7, 9; *Num* 18:32
l. we be scattered abroad. *Gen* 11:4
l. thou say, I have made. 14:23
l. thou be consumed in the. 19:15
l. I die. 19; 26:9
l. he come and smite me. 32:11
l. he die, as his brethren did. 38:11
Deut 20:5, 6, 7
let her take it to her, *l.* *Gen* 38:23
l. thou and thy household. 45:11
go, *l.* he fall on us with. *Ex* 5:3
l. peradventure the people. 13:17
l. they break through to the. 19:21
sanctify, *l.* the Lord break forth. 22
let not God speak with us, *l.* 20:19
I will not go, *l.* I consume thee. 33:3
shall not go in to see, *l.* they die.
Num 4:20; 18:22
l. ye perish quickly. *Deut* 11:17
l. he cry against thee to. 24:15
l. if he should exceed and. 25:3
let them live, *l.* wrath. *Josh* 9:20
shall be a witness, *l.* ye deny. 24:27
l. Israel vaunt themselves. *Judg* 7:2
let him not know, *l.* he. *1 Sam* 20:3
l. I take the city, and. *2 Sam* 12:28
l. he take thee away. *Job* 36:18
l. I deal with you after your. 42:8
kiss the Son *l.* he be angry. *Ps* 2:12
lighten mine eyes, *l.* I sleep. 13:3
consider this, *l.* I tear you. 50:22
l. thou dash thy foot. 91:12
Mat 4:6; *Luke* 4:11
Moses stood, *l.* he should. *Ps* 106:23
grant not, *l.* they exalt. 140:8
l. I be like them that go down. 143:7
reprove not a scorner, *l.* he. *Pr* 9:8
love not sleep, *l.* thou come. 20:13
l. thou learn his ways, and. 22:25
l. the Lord see it, and it. 24:18
l. thou know not what to do. 25:8
l. he that heareth it, put thee to. 10
l. he be weary of thee, and so. 17
answer not a fool, *l.* thou also. 26:4
add not to his words, *l.* he. 30:6
l. I be full and deny thee, or *l.* 9
l. they see with their eyes. *Isa* 6:10
Acts 28:27
l. any hurt it, I will keep it. *Isa* 27:3
not mockers, *l.* your bands. 28:22
l. thou shouldest say, My idol hath.
48:5, 7
be not dismayed, *l.* I. *Jer* 1:17
l. my fury come forth. 4:4; 21:12
instructed, *l.* my soul depart. 6:8
cause me not to return, *l.* I. 37:20
l. I strip her naked, and. *Hos* 2:3
seek the Lord, *l.* he break. *Amos* 5:6
as an adamant, *l.* they. *Zech* 7:12
l. I come and smite the. *Mal* 4:6
l. we should offend, go. *Mat* 17:27
l. there be not enough for us. 25:9
take heed, *l.* any man. *Mark* 13:5
l. coming suddenly, he find you. 36
watch and pray, *l.* ye enter. 14:38
l. they should believe. *Luke* 8:12

l. your hearts be overcharged. *Luke* 21:34
sin no more, *l.* a worse. *John* 5:14
they went out *l.* they should. 18:28
l. ye be found to fight. *Acts* 5:39
beware therefore, *l.* that. 13:40
take heed, *l.* he spare not thee. *Rom* 11:21, 44
l. we hinder the gospel. *1 Cor* 9:12
standeth take heed *l.* he fall. 10:12
l. Satan should get. *2 Cor* 2:11
l. I should be exalted above. 12:7
l. by any means I should. *Gal* 2:2
considering thyself, *l.* thou. 6:1
not of works, *l.* any man. *Eph* 2:9
l. any man beguile you. *Col* 2:4
provoke not children, *l.* they. 3:21
l. being lifted up with. *1 Tim* 3:6
l. at any time we should let them slip. *Heb* 2:1
l. there be in any an evil heart. 3:12
l. any of you be hardened. 13
l. any man fall after the same. 4:11
l. ye be weary and faint in. 12:3
l. what is lame be turned out. 13
l. any man fail of the grace. 15
grudge not, *l.* ye be. *Jas* 5:9
swear not, *l.* ye fall into. 12
beware, *l.* ye also being. *2 Pet* 3:17
keepeth his garments, *l.* *Rev* 16:15

let
(*Used occasionally in the now obsolete sense of* hinder)
Naphtali is a hind *l.* *Gen* 49:21
king of Egypt will not *l.* you go. *Ex* 3:19; 4:21; 7:14; 8:32; 9:7
17, 35; 10:20, 27; 11:10
after that he will *l.* you go. 3:20
l. my people go. 5:1; 7:16; 8:1, 20
9:1, 13; 10:3
why do ye *l.* the people from? 5:4*
I will *l.* you go. 8:28; 9:28; 13:17
why have we *l.* Israel go? 14:5
and Moses *l.* his father in law. 18:27
shall he *l.* her be redeemed. 21:8
l. him go free for his eye. 26, 27
seventh year thou shalt *l.* it. 23:11
hast not *l.* me know whom. 33:12
and shall *l.* the living bird. *Lev* 14:7
not *l.* seed pass through. 18:21*
not *l.* cattle gender with a. 19:19
thou shalt *l.* him go. *Deut* 15:12
thou shalt not *l.* him go away. 13
and all therein, he *l.* none remain. *Josh* 10:28*, 30*
so Joshua *l.* the people. 24:28*
they *l.* the man go and. *Judg* 1:25
Saul would *l.* him go no. *1 Sam* 18:2
to-morrow I will *l.* *2 Sam* 11:12
I pray thee, *l.* Tamar my. 13:6
Elijah said, *L.* none of. *1 Ki* 18:40
thou wouldest not *l.* *2 Chr* 20:10
queen did *l.* no man. *Esth* 5:12
even that he would *l.* loose. *Job* 6:9
my righteousness I will not *l.* 27:6
l. not those that wait on thee be ashamed, *l.* not those. *Ps* 69:6
and *l.* Satan stand at his right. 109:6
l. me not wander from thy. 119:10
and would not *l.* him go. *S of S* 3:4
l. out the vineyard to keepers. 8:11
work, and who shall *l.* it? *Isa* 43:13
those will I *l.* remain. *Jer* 27:11
I will not *l.* them pollute. *Ezek* 39:7
planted a vineyard and *l.* *Mat* 21:33
Mark 12:1; *Luke* 20:9
answer me nor *l.* me. *Luke* 22:68*
the Jews cried, If thou *l.* *John* 19:12
ship could not bear up, we *l.* her. *Acts* 27:15*
you, but was *l.* hitherto. *Rom* 1:13*
who now letteth, will *l.* *2 Thes* 2:7*
lest at any time we should *l.* *Heb* 2:1
see **alone**

let *down*
l. down thy pitcher, I pray thee. *Gen* 24:14; 18:46
when he *l. down* his hands, Amalek. *Ex* 17:11
Rahab *l.* them *down.* *Josh* 2:15, 18
Michal *l.* David *down.* *1 Sam* 19:12
the man was *l. down.* *2 Ki* 13:21
they *l. down* Jeremiah. *Jer* 38:6
they stood they *l. down* their wings. *Ezek* 1:24, 25
they *l. down* the bed wherein. *Mark* 2:4; *Luke* 5:19
and *l. down* your nets. *Luke* 5:4
at thy word I will *l. down* the net. 5
and *l.* him *down* in a basket. *Acts* 9:25; *2 Cor* 11:33
l. down to the earth. *Acts* 10:11
had *l. down* the boat. 27:30

letter
David wrote a *l.* to. *2 Sam* 11:14
I will send a *l.* to the. *2 Ki* 5:5
now when this *l.* is come to thee. 6
as soon as this *l.* cometh to. 10:2
Hezekiah received the *l.* 19:14
Isa 37:14
the *l.* was written in. *Ezra* 4:7
Rehum wrote a *l.* against. 8
now this is the copy of the *l.* 7:11
5:6, 7
a *l.* to Asaph the keeper. *Neh* 2:8
sent to me with an open *l.* in. 6:5
wrote to confirm this *l.* of. *Esth* 9:29
the words of the *l.* that. *Jer* 29:1
Zephaniah priest read this *l.* in. 29
Claudius wrote a *l.* to. *Acts* 23:25
the governor had read the *l.* he. 34
l. dost transgress the law. *Rom* 2:27
circumcision of heart, not in the *l.* 29
serve, not in the oldness of the *l.* 7:6
ministers not of the *l.* *2 Cor* 3:6
you sorry with *l.* I do not repent. 7:8
ye see how large a *l.* I. *Gal* 6:11*
shaken by word or by *l.* *2 Thes* 2:2
I have written a *l.* to. *Heb* 13:22

letters
l. in Ahab's name. *1 Ki* 21:8, 9
Jehu wrote *l.* and sent. *2 Ki* 10:1
Babylon sent *l.* to Hezekiah. 20:12
Hezekiah wrote *l.* also. *2 Chr* 30:1
so the posts went with the *l.* 6
Sennacherib wrote *l.* to rail on. 32:17
let *l.* be given me to the. *Neh* 2:7
sent *l.* to Tobiah, and *l.* came. 6:17
and Tobiah sent *l.* to put me. 19
Ahasuerus sent *l.* to the. *Esth* 1:22
the *l.* were sent by posts. 3:13; 8:10
to reverse *l.* devised by Haman. 8:5
Mordecai sent *l.* to all. 9:20, 30
because thou hast sent *l.* *Jer* 29:25
was written in *l.* of. *Luke* 23:38
how knoweth this man *l.*? *John* 7:15
of him *l.* to Damascus. *Acts* 9:2
the apostles wrote *l.* after. 15:23*
I received *l.* to the brethren. 22:5
we neither received *l.* out of. 28:21
shall approve by your *l.* *1 Cor* 16:3
we *l.* of commendation. *2 Cor* 3:1
as if I would terrify you by *l.* 10:9
for his *l.* are weighty and. 10
such as we are in word, by *l.* 11

lettest
l. such words go out of. *Job* 15:13
with a cord thou *l.* down? 41:1*
now *l.* thou thy servant. *Luke* 2:29

letteth
he that *l.* him go, his life. *2 Ki* 10:24
strife is as when one *l.* out. *Pr* 17:14
only he that now *l.* will. *2 Thes* 2:7*

letting
deal deceitfully in not *l.* the people. *Ex* 8:29

Levi
was his name called *L.* *Gen* 29:34
the sons of *L.* 46:11; *Ex* 6:16
Num 3:17
Simeon, *L.* are brethren. *Gen* 49:5
years of the life of *L.* *Ex* 6:16
upon you, ye sons of *L.* *Num* 16:7
Jochebed, daughter of *L.* 26:59
L. hath no part with his. *Deut* 10:9
priests the sons of *L.* shall. 21:5
L. he said, Let thy Thummim. 33:8
made priests which were not of *L.* *1 Ki* 12:31
but *L.* and Benjamin. *1 Chr* 21:6
none of the sons of *L.* *Ezra* 8:15
bless Lord, O house of *L.* *Ps* 135:20
the sons of Zadok among the sons of *L.* *Ezek* 40:46
of Judah, one gate of *L.* *Ezek* 48:31
family of the house of *L.* *Zech* 12:13
covenant might be with *L.* *Mal* 2:4
corrupted the covenant of *L.* 8
purify the sons of *L.* 3:3
L. the son of Alpheus. *Mark* 2:14
Matthat, which was the son of *L.* *Luke* 3:24, 29
he saw a publican named *L.* 5:27
L. made him a great feast in his. 29
L. who received tithes. *Heb* 7:9

tribe of **Levi**
not number *tribe of L.* *Num* 1:49
bring the *tribe of L.* near and. 3:6
tribe of L. bring, that they. 18:2
separated the *tribe of L.* *Deut* 10:8
tribe of L. shall have no part nor. 18:1; *Josh* 13:14, 33
Moses' sons were named of the *tribe of L.* *1 Chr* 23:14
of *tribe of L.* were sealed. *Rev* 7:7

leviathan
thou draw out *l.* with? *Job* 41:1
heads of *l.* in pieces. *Ps* 74:14
l. thou hast made to play. 104:26
punish *l.* even *l.* that crooked serpent. *Isa* 27:1

Levite
is not Aaron the *l.* thy? *Ex* 4:14
rejoice before the Lord your God, ye and the *l.* *Deut* 12:12, 18
16:11, 14; 26:11, 13
l. shall come and eat. 14:29; 26:12
if a *l.* come from any of thy. 18:6
a young man a *l.* *Judg* 17:7, 9
so the *l.* went in. 10
the *l.* was content to dwell. 11
Micah consecrated the *l.* 12
a *l.* to my priest. 13
voice of the young man the *l.* 18:3
certain *l.* sojourning on mount. 19:1
the *l.* said, I came into Gibeah. 20:4
on Jahaziel a *l.* came. *2 Chr* 20:14
Cononiah the *l.* was ruler. 31:12
Kore the *l.* over the freewill. 14
Shabbethai the *l.* helped. *Ezra* 10:15
likewise a *l.* came and. *Luke* 10:32
Barnabas a *l.* having. *Acts* 4:36

Levites
of the fathers of the *l.* *Ex* 6:25
for the service of the *l.* 38:21
cities of *l.* may redeem. *Lev* 25:32
the cities of the *l.* are their. 33
l. not numbered. *Num* 1:47; 2:33
shalt appoint the *l.* over the. 1:50
the *l.* shall take it down. 51
the *l.* shall pitch. 53
and thou shalt give the *l.* 3:9
I have taken the *l.*: the *l.* shall. 12
chief over chief of the *l.* 32
were numbered of the *l.* 39; 4:46
and thou shall take the *l.* for me. 3:41, 45; 8:14
shalt give wagons unto the *l.* 7:5
take the *l.* from Israel and. 8:6
bring the *l.* before tabernacle. 9, 10
Aaron shall offer the *l.* before the. 11
after that shall the *l.* go in. 15, 22
this is it that belongeth unto the *l.* 24
thou do to the *l.* touching their. 26
the *l.* to do service. 18:6, 23
tithes I have given to the *l.* 24
give to the *l.* cities round. 35:2, 8
minister, as his brethren the *l.* do. *Deut* 18:7
to the *l.* he gave none. *Josh* 14:3
gave these cities to the *l.* 21:3, 8
all the cities of the *l.* were. 41
l. took down the ark. *1 Sam* 6:15
Zadok and the *l.* were. *2 Sam* 15:24
the children of the *l.* *1 Chr* 15:15
when God helped the *l.* that. 26
l. wrote them before the king. 24:6
the *l.* which were singers stood. *2 Chr* 5:12; 7:
the *l.* left their suburbs and. 11:14
cast out the sons of Aaron and *l.* 13:
also the *l.* shall be officers. 19:1
the *l.* shall compass the king. 23:6,
the *l.* hastened it not. 24:
hear me, ye *l.* sanctify now. 29:
spake comfortably to the *l.* 30:2
of the *l.* there were scribes. 34:1

Josiah said to *l.* which. *2 Chr* 35:3
of the *l.* gave to the *l.* 500 oxen. 9
l. prepared for themselves. 14, 15
set the *l.* in their courses. *Ezra* 6:18
after him repaired the *l.* *Neh* 3:17
l. caused people to understand. 8:7
the *l.* stilled the people, saying. 11
the overseer of the *l.* was. 11:22
dedication they sought the *l.* 12:27
portions of *l.* had not been given them, for the *l.* were fled. 13:10
defiled the priesthood of the *l.* 29
I will multiply the *l.* *Jer* 33:22
l. that are gone shall bear iniquity. *Ezek* 44:10
went not astray when the *l.* 48:11

***priests and* Levites**

shalt come to *p.* the *l.* *Deut* 17:9
to do all that *p.* and *l.* shall. 24:8
p. and l. bearing the ark. *Josh* 3:3
p. and l. brought up ark. *1 Ki* 8:4
p. and l. shall be porters. *2 Chr* 23:4
p. and l. were more upright. 29:34
p. and l. were ashamed, and. 30:15
l. and the *p.* praised the Lord. 21
then the *p. and l.* blessed the. 27
questioned with the *p. and l.* 31:9
gave willingly to the *p. and l.* 35:8
so *p. and l.* dwelt in. *Ezra* 2:70
for the *p. and l.* were purified. 6:20
went up of the *p. and* the *l.* 7:7
p. and l. have not separated. 9:1
made the *p. and l.* to swear. 10:5
our princes, *l. and p.* *Neh* 9:38
we cast lots among *p. and l.* 10:34
p. and l. purified themselves. 12:30
Judah rejoiced for the *p. and l.* 44
take of them for *p. and l.* *Isa* 66:21
p. and l. not want a man. *Jer* 33:18
with *l.* the *p.* my ministers. 21
the *p. and l.* that kept. *Ezek* 44:15
the Jews sent *p. and l.* *John* 1:19

Levitical

if perfection were by the *L.* *Heb* 7:11

levy, *substantive*

Solomon raised a *l.* of. *1 Ki* 5:13
and Adoniram was over the *l.* 14
reason of the *l.* Solomon raised. 9:15

levy, *verb*

l. a tribute to the Lord. *Num* 31:28
did Solomon *l.* a tribute. *1 Ki* 9:21*

lewd

ashamed of thy *l.* way. *Ezek* 16:27
unto Aholibah, the *l.* women. 23:44
l. fellows of baser sort. *Acts* 17:5*

lewdly

l. defiled his daughter. *Ezek* 22:11

lewdness

they have committed *l.* *Judg* 20:6
she hath wrought *l.* *Jer* 11:15
I have seen the *l.* of thy. 13:27
shalt not commit this *l.* *Ezek* 16:43
thou hast borne thy *l.* and. 58
in midst of thee they commit *l.* 22:9
calledst to remembrance *l.* 23:21
I make thy *l.* to cease. 27, 48
shall be discovered, both thy *l.* 29
therefore bear thou also thy *l.* and. 35
shall recompense your *l.* on you. 49
n thy filthiness is *l.* 24:13
ow will I discover her *l.* *Hos* 2:10
murder in way, they commit *l.* 6:9
matter of wicked *l.* *Acts* 18:14*

liar

who will make me a *l.*? *Job* 24:25
giveth ear to a naughty. *Pr* 17:4
oor man is better than a *l.* 19:22
nd thou be found a *l.* 30:6
ltogether to me as a *l.*? *Jer* 15:18*
e is a *l.* and the father. *John* 8:44
shall be a *l.* like to. 55
nd every man a *l.* *Rom* 3:4
nned, we make him a *l.* *1 John* 1:10
and truth is not in him. 2:4; 4:20
who is a *l.* but he that denieth? 22
ot God, hath made him a *l.* 5:10

liars

hall be found *l.* to thee. *Deut* 33:29
haste, all men are *l.* *Ps* 116:11
e tokens of the *l.* *Isa* 44:25

a sword is upon the *l.* *Jer* 50:36*
law is made for *l.* for. *1 Tim* 1:10
the Cretians are alway *l.* *Tit* 1:12
and hast found them *l.* *Rev* 2:2
all *l.* shall have their part in. 21:8

liberal

l. soul shall be made fat. *Pr* 11:25
vile person shall not be called *l.* *Isa* 32:5†
the *l.* deviseth *l.* things, and by *l.* 8
for your *l.* distribution. *2 Cor* 9:13*

liberality

your *l.* to Jerusalem. *1 Cor* 16:3*
to the riches of their *l.* *2 Cor* 8:2

liberally

furnish him *l.* out of. *Deut* 15:14
who giveth to all men *l.* *Jas* 1:5

Libertines

called synagogue of the *L.* *Acts* 6:9

liberty

ye shall proclaim *l.* *Lev* 25:10
and I will walk at *l.* *Ps* 119:45
he sent me to proclaim *l.* *Isa* 61:1
a covenant to proclaim *l.* *Jer* 34:8
in my sight, in proclaiming *l.* 15
his servant whom he had set at *l.* 16*
not hearkened to me in proclaiming *l.*: I proclaim a *l.* for you. 17
be his to the year of *l.* *Ezek* 46:17
l. them that are bruised. *Luke* 4:18
Paul, and let him have *l.* *Acts* 24:23*
man might have been set at *l.* 26:32
gave him *l.* to go to his friends. 27:3*
glorious *l.* of children of. *Rom* 8:21
she is at *l.* to marry. *1 Cor* 7:39*
take heed lest this *l.* of yours. 8:9
for why is my *l.* judged of? 10:29
where the Spirit of the Lord is, there is *l.* *2 Cor* 3:17
privily, to spy out our *l.* *Gal* 2:4
stand fast in the *l.* wherewith. 5:1*
called unto *l.*; only use not *l.* 13*
Timothy is set at *l.* *Heb* 13:23
looketh into the law of *l.* *Jas* 1:25
shall be judged by the law of *l.* 2:12
as free, and not using *l.* *1 Pet* 2:16*
they promise them *l.* *2 Pet* 2:19

Libnah

pitched in *L.* *Num* 33:20
removed from *L.* 21
passed to *L.* *Josh* 10:29
gave *L.* to Levites. 21:13
then *L.* revolted. *2 Ki* 8:22
2 Chr 21:10
found the king of Assyria warring against *L.* *2 Ki* 19:8; *Isa* 37:8
Hammutal, daughter of Jeremiah of *L.* *2 Ki* 23:31; 24:18; *Jer* 52:1

Libya

L. shall fall with them. *Ezek* 30:5
parts of *L.* about Cyrene. *Acts* 2:10

Libyans

L. that handled the shield. *Jer* 46:9
L. and Ethiopians shall. *Dan* 11:43

lice

that dust may become *l.* *Ex* 8:16
smote dust, it became *l.* in man. 17
so with their enchantments to bring forth *l.*: so there were *l.* upon. 18
l. in all their coasts. *Ps* 105:31

licence

given him *l.* Paul stood. *Acts* 21:40*
accused have *l.* to answer. 25:16*

lick

now shall this company *l.* *Num* 22:4
dogs *l.* thy blood, even. *1 Ki* 21:19
his enemies shall *l.* dust *Ps* 72:9
l. up the dust of thy feet. *Isa* 49:23
l. up the dust like a serpent. *Mi* 7:17

licked

fire *l.* up the water in. *1 Ki* 18:38
dogs *l.* the blood of Naboth. 21:19
and the dogs *l.* up his blood. 22:38
the dogs came and *l.* his sores. *Luke* 16:21

licketh

lick up all, as the ox *l.* *Num* 22:4

lid

bored a hole in the *l.* *2 Ki* 12:9

lie

drink wine, we will *l.* *Gen* 19:32
go thou in, and *l.* with him. 34
he shall *l.* with thee to-night. 30:15
she said, Come *l.* with me. 39:7, 12
2 Sam 13:11
he came in unto me to *l.* *Gen* 39:14
if a man *l.* with a maid. *Ex* 22:16
man shall *l.* with seed. *Lev* 15:18
if a man *l.* with her at all. 24
not *l.* carnally with thy. 18:20
shalt not *l.* with mankind. 22
nor *l.* with beasts. 23
l. with his daughter in law. 20:12
if *l.* with mankind. 13
if *l.* with a beast. 15
if a man *l.* with a woman having. 18
man *l.* with his uncle's wife. 20
if a man *l.* with her. *Num* 5:13
man find her, and *l.* *Deut* 22:23
if the man force her, and *l.* with. 25
damsel not betrothed, and *l.* with. 28
betroth a wife, and another *l.* 28:30
go to *l.* with my wife? *2 Sam* 11:11
shall *l.* all night betwixt. *S of S* 1:13

lie

I will *l.* with my fathers. *Gen* 47:30*
let the ground *l.* still. *Ex* 23:11
curses in this book shall *l.* on him. *Deut* 29:20
went to *l.* in ambush. *Josh* 8:9*, 12
all thy wants *l.* on me. *Judg* 19:20
mark the place where he shall *l.* *Ruth* 3:4
let her *l.* in thy bosom. *1 Ki* 1:2
I *l.* among them that are. *Ps* 57:4
like slain that *l.* in the grave. 88:5
if two *l.* together they have heat. *Eccl* 4:11
beasts of the desert shall *l.* there. *Isa* 13:21
kings of the nations *l.* in. 14:18*
thy sons *l.* at the head of all. 51:20
the young and old *l.* on. *Lam* 2:21
l. thou also upon thy left. *Ezek* 4:4
l. again on thy right side. 6
shalt *l.* 390 days. 9
shalt *l.* in the midst of the. 31:18
they *l.* uncircumcised. 32:21, 30
shall not *l.* with the mighty. 27
l. with the slain. 28
l. with uncircumcised. 29
shall they *l.* in a good fold. 34:14
come, *l.* all night in. *Joel* 1:13
that *l.* on beds of ivory. *Amos* 6:4
when Jesus saw him *l.* he. *John* 5:6
Peter seeth the linen clothes *l.* 20:6

lie *down*

before a beast, to *l. down* thereto. *Lev* 18:23; 20:16
ye shall *l. down* and none. 26:6
Israel shall not *l. down.* *Num* 23:24
cause him to *l. down.* *Deut* 25:2
Boaz went to *l. down* at. *Ruth* 3:7
tarry this night, *l. down* until. 13
Eli said, I called not, *l. down* again. *1 Sam* 3:5, 6, 9
even he went to *l. down.* *2 Sam* 11:13
when I *l. down* I say, When? *Job* 7:4
thou shalt *l. down* and none. 11:19
which shall *l. down* with him. 20:11
they shall *l. down* alike in. 21:26
the rich man shall *l. down.* 27:19
he maketh me *l. down* in. *Ps* 23:2
l. down and thy sleep be. *Pr* 3:24
leopard shall *l. down.* *Isa* 11:6
their young ones shall *l. down.* 7
and the needy shall *l. down.* 14:30
for flocks which shall *l. down.* 17:2
the calf feed and *l. down.* 27:10
power shall *l. down* together. 43:17
ye shall *l. down* in sorrow. 50:11
place for herds to *l. down* in. 65:10
we *l. down* in our shame. *Jer* 3:25
shepherds causing their flocks to *l. down.* 33:12
cause them to *l. down.* *Ezek* 34:15
them to *l. down* safely. *Hos* 2:18
l. down in the evening. *Zeph* 2:7
flocks shall *l. down.* 14
for beasts to *l. down* in. 15
Israel shall feed and *l. down.* 3:13

lie *in wait*
if a man *l.* not *in wait.* *Ex* 21:13
neighbour and *l. in wait.* *Deut* 19:11
l. in wait against the city . *Josh* 8:4
l. in wait in the field. *Judg* 9:32
saying, Go and *l. in wait* in. 21:20
hast stirred up my servant to *l. in wait.* *1 Sam* 22:8, 13
in the covert to *l. in wait.* *Job* 38:40
for lo, they *l. in wait.* *Ps* 59:3
the wicked are to *l. in wait.* *Pr* 12:6
oven, whiles they *l. in wait.* *Hos* 7:6
all *l. in wait* for blood. *Mi* 7:2
l. in wait for him more. *Acts* 23:21
whereby they *l. in wait* to. *Eph* 4:14

lie *waste*
the highways *l. waste.* *Isa* 33:8
it shall *l. waste.* 34:10
and this house *l. waste.* *Hag* 1:4

lie, *verb*
soul *l.* to his neighbour. *Lev* 6:2*
ye shall not steal, nor *l.* 19:11
a man, that he should *l.* *Num* 23:19
Strength of Israel will not *l.* nor. *1 Sam* 15:29
my lord, do not *l.* to thy. *2 Ki* 4:16
is evident to you if I *l.* *Job* 6:28
should I *l.* against my right. 34:6
sworn that I will not *l.* *Ps* 89:35
faithful witness will not *l.* *Pr* 14:5
children that will not *l.* *Isa* 63:8*
walking in falsehood do *l.* *Mi* 2:11
shall speak and not *l.* *Hab* 2:3
filled thy heart to *l.*? *Acts* 5:3
I say the truth in Christ, I *l.* not. *Rom* 9:1; *1 Tim* 2:7
Lord knoweth I *l.* not. *2 Cor* 11:31
to you, behold I *l.* not. *Gal* 1:20
l. not one to another. *Col* 3:9
God, that cannot *l.*, promised. *Tit* 1:2
impossible for God to *l.* *Heb* 6:18
glory not, *l.* not against. *Jas* 3:14
have fellowship with him and walk in darkness, we *l.* and. *1 John* 1:6
say they are Jews, but do *l.* *Rev* 3:9

lie, *substantive*
men of high degree are a *l.* *Ps* 62:9
the proud have forged a *l.* 119:69
a *l.* in my right hand ? *Isa* 44:20
they prophesy a *l.* to you to remove. *Jer* 27:10, 14, 15*, 16; 29:21
this people to trust in a *l.* 28:15
caused you to trust in a *l.* 29:31
whilst they divine a *l.* *Ezek* 21:29
houses of Achzib shall be a *l.* to. *Mi* 1:14
for the diviners have seen a *l.* and. *Zech* 10:2
when he speaketh a *l.* he. *John* 8:44
truth of God into a *l.* *Rom* 1:25
more abounded through my *l.* 3:7
they should believe a *l.* *2 Thes* 2:11
ye know that no *l.* is. *1 John* 2:21
you of all things, and is no *l.* 27
whatsoever maketh a *l.* *Rev* 21:27
whosoever loveth and maketh a *l.* 22:15

lied
prophet, but he *l.* unto. *1 Ki* 13:18
they *l.* unto him with. *Ps* 78:36
afraid, that thou hast *l.* *Isa* 57:11
thou hast not *l.* unto men. *Acts* 5:4

lien, *or* **lain**
one might have *l.* with. *Gen* 26:10
if no man have *l.* with. *Num* 5:19
if some man have *l.* with thee. 20
woman that hath *l.* *Judg* 21:11
for now should I have *l.* *Job* 3:13
though ye have *l.* among. *Ps* 68:13
thou hast not been *l.* with. *Jer* 3:2

liers *in wait*
there were *l. in* ambush. *Josh* 8:14
Shechem set *l. in wait.* *Judg* 9:25
there were *l. in wait* abiding. 16:12
Israel set *l. in wait* round. 20:29
the *l. in wait* came forth. 33
l. in wait hasted and rushed. 37
they trusted in the *l. in wait.* 36

lies
thou hast told me *l.* *Judg* 16:10, 13
should thy *l.* make men ? *Job* 11:3*
ye are forgers of *l.* 13:4
such as turn aside to *l.* *Ps* 40:4
and go astray, speaking *l.* 58:3
they delight in *l.*, they curse. 62:4
the mouth that speaketh *l.* 63:11
that telleth *l.* shall not tarry. 101:7
hates a false witness that speaketh *l.* *Pr* 6:19
but a false witness will utter *l.* 14:5
deceitful witness speaketh *l.* 25
and he that speaketh *l.* shall. 19:5
speaketh *l.* shall perish. 9
if a ruler hearken to *l.* his. 29:12
far from me vanity and *l.* 30:8
prophet that teacheth *l.* *Isa* 9:15
pride of Moab, but his *l.* 16:6*
we have made *l.* our refuge. 28:15
sweep away the refuge of *l.* 17
your lips have spoken *l.*, your. 59:3
they trust in vanity, and speak *l.* 4
bend their tongues like their bow for *l.* *Jer* 9:3
taught their tongue to speak *l.* 5
prophesy *l.* 14:14; 23:25, 26
fathers have inherited *l.* 16:19
thou hast prophesied *l.* 20:6
adultery, and walk in *l.* 23:14
to err by their *l.* and lightness. 32
his *l.* shall not so affect it. 48:30*
spoken vanity and seen *l.* *Ezek* 13:8
upon the prophets that divine *l.* 9
my people that hear your *l.* 19
with *l.* ye have made the. 22
divining *l.* unto them, saying. 22:28
hath wearied herself with *l.* 24:12*
speak *l.* at one table. *Dan* 11:27
princes glad with their *l.* *Hos* 7:3
yet they have spoken *l.* against. 13
eaten the fruit of *l.* because. 10:13
compasseth me about with *l.* 11:12
increaseth *l.* and desolation. 12:1
and their *l.* caused them. *Amos* 2:4
thereof have spoken *l.* *Mi* 6:12
bloody city, it is full of *l.* *Nah* 3:1
image, and a teacher of *l.* *Hab* 2:18
Israel shall not speak *l.* *Zeph* 3:13
speakest *l.* in the name. *Zech* 13:3
speak *l.* in hypocrisy. *1 Tim* 4:2

liest
the land whereon thou *l.* *Gen* 28:13
when thou *l.* down. *Deut* 6:7; 11:19
Get thee up; wherefore *l.* thou thus upon thy face ? *Josh* 7:10*
l. down, shalt not be afraid. *Pr* 3:24

lieth
doest not well, sin *l.* *Gen* 4:7*
of the deep that *l.* under. 49:25*
found that which was lost, and *l.* concerning it. *Lev* 6:3
he that *l.* in the house. 14:47
every bed whereon he *l.* is. 15:4
every thing that she *l.* upon shall be unclean. 20, 26
all the bed whereon he *l.* 24, 33
sabbaths, as long as it *l.* 26:34, 35
sabbaths, while she *l.* desolate. 43
his great strength *l.* *Judg* 16:5
wherein thy great strength *l.* 6, 15
l. under the shady trees. *Job* 40:21
he *l.* he shall rise no more. *Ps* 41:8
thy wrath *l.* hard on me, thou. 88:7
my servant *l.* at home sick. *Mat* 8:6
my daughter *l.* at point. *Mark* 5:23
as much as *l.* in you, live. *Rom* 12:8
the whole world *l.* in. *1 John* 5:19

lieth *down*
it shall be when he *l. down.* *Ruth* 3:4
so man *l. down* and riseth. *Job* 14:12
that *l. down* in the midst. *Pr* 23:34

lieth *in wait*
l. in wait secretly as a lion: *l. in wait* to catch the poor. *Ps* 10:9*
and *she l. in wait* at every. *Pr* 7:12
she also *l. in wait* as for a. 23:28

lieth *waste*
the place of my fathers' sepulchres *l. waste.* *Neh* 2:3
you see how Jerusalem *l. waste.* 17

lieth, as with a woman
whoso *l.* with a beast. *Ex* 22:19
whoso *l.* carnally with a. *Lev* 19:20
man that *l.* with his father's. 20:11
lie with mankind as he *l.* with. 13
cursed be he that *l.* with. *Deut* 27:20
l. with beast. 21
l. with his sister. 22
l. with his mother in law 23
her that *l.* in thy bosom. *Mi* 7:5

lieutenants
(*Revised Versions*, satraps)
king's commissions to *l.* *Ezra* 8:36
commanded the king's *l.* *Esth* 3:12
had commanded to the *l.* 8:9
all the rulers and *l.* helped. 9:3

life
[1] *Literally, animate existence, as distinguished from dead matter,* Gen 1:20. [2] *Conscious existence with the powers derived from it,* Job 3:20. [3] *The existence of the soul after the death of the body,* John 5:29. *Other passages correspond with modern uses of the word, or are derived from these heads.*
creature that hath *l.* *Gen* 1:20
every thing wherein there is *l.* 30
into his nostrils the breath of *l.* 2:7
the tree of *l.* in the midst. 9; 3:22
keep the way of the tree of *l.* 3:24
wherein is the breath of *l.* 6:17; 7:22
flesh with the *l.* shall ye not eat. 9:4; *Lev* 17:14
man will I require *l.* of man. *Gen* 9:5
according to time of *l.* 18:10*, 14*
these were the years of the *l.* 23:1
the years of Abraham's *l.* 25:7
by the *l.* of Pharaoh. 42:15, 16
send me before to preserve *l.* 45:5
not attained to the years of *l.* 47:9
of the *l.* of Levi were 137. *Ex* 6:16
years of the *l.* of Kohath. 18
l. of Amram. 20
shall give *l.* for *l.* 21:23; *Deut* 19:21
for the *l.* of the flesh is. *Lev* 17:11
the other in her *l.* time. 18:18
blood is the *l.*; and thou mayest not eat the *l.* with flesh. *Deut* 12:23
tree of the field is man's *l.* 20:19
taketh a man's *l.* to pledge. 24:6
I have set before thee *l.* 30:15, 19 *Jer* 21:8
it is not a vain thing, because it is your *l.* *Deut* 32:47
the men answered, Our *l.* *Josh* 2:14
up in the bundle of *l.* *1 Sam* 25:29
for the *l.* of his brother. *2 Sam* 14:7
whether in death or *l.* there. 15:21
for thyself long *l.* nor asked the *l.* of. *1 Ki* 3:11; *2 Chr* 1:11
time of *l.* thou shalt. *2 Ki* 4:16*, 17*
left camp, and fled for their *l.* 7:7
they may pray for the *l.* *Ezra* 6:10
Jews to stand for their *l.* *Esth* 8:11
why is *l.* given to the bitter in soul ? *Job* 3:20
thou hast granted me *l.* and. 10:12
and no man is sure of *l.* 24:22
owners thereof to lose their *l.* 31:3
the Almighty hath given me *l.* 33:
he preserveth not the *l.* of the. 36:
their *l.* is among the unclean. 1
shew me the path of *l.* *Ps* 16:1
he asked *l.* of thee, thou. 21:
in his favour is *l.*: weeping. 30:5
man is he that desireth *l.*? 34:1
with thee is the fountain of *l.* 36:
thou wilt prolong the king's *l.* 61:
kindness is better than *l.* 63:
who holdeth our soul in *l.* 66:
but gave their *l.* over to the. 78:5
with long *l.* will I satisfy him. 91:1
the blessing, even *l.* for. 133:
which taketh away the *l.* *Pr* 1:1
nor take hold of the paths of *l.* 2:1
long *l.* and peace shall they. 3:
she is a tree of *l.* to them that. 1
so shall they be *l.* to thy soul. 2
they are *l.* to those that find. 4:2
for out of it are the issues of *l.* 2
shouldest ponder the path of *l.* 5:
of instruction are the way of *l.* 6:2
will hunt for the precious *l.* 2
whoso findeth me findeth *l.* and. 8:
the righteous is a well of *l.* 10:
is in the way of *l.* that keepeth.

the righteous is a tree of l. Pr 11:30
righteous regardeth the l. of. 12:10
in the way of righteousness is l. 28
the ransom of a man's l. are. 13:8
desire cometh, it is a tree of l. 12
law of the wise is a fountain of l. 14
of the Lord is a fountain of l. 14:27
a sound heart is the l. of the flesh. 30
wholesome tongue is a tree of l. 15:4
way of l. is above to the wise. 24
reproof of l. abideth among. 31
of the king's countenance is l. 16:15
understanding is wellspring of l. 22
death and l. are in the power. 18:21
followeth mercy, findeth l. 21:21
are riches, honour, and l. 22:4
good all the days of her l. 31:12
good they should do all the days of their l. Eccl 2:3
therefore I hated l. 17
wisdom giveth l. 7:12
in all these things is the l. Isa 38:16
sing songs all the days of our l. 20
found the l. of thy hand. 57:10*
and death shall be chosen rather than l. Jer 8:3
into the hand of those that seek their l. 21:7; 34:20, 21
I set before you the way of l. 21:8
dismayed before their enemies, before them that seek their l. 49:37
lift up thy hands for the l. Lam 2:19
strengthened the hands of wicked, by promising him l. Ezek 13:22*
walk in the statutes of l. 33:15
perish for this man's l. Jonah 1:14
my covenant was with him of l. and peace. Mal 2:5
which sought the child's l. Mat 2:20
take no thought for your l. 6:25
Luke 12:22
to enter into l. halt or maimed.
Mat 18:8; Mark 9:43, 45
enter into l. with one eye. Mat 18:9
if wilt enter into l. keep. Mat 19:17
is it lawful to save l. or to kill?
Mark 3:4; Luke 6:9
all the days of our l. Luke 1:75
for a man's l. consisteth not. 12:15
the l. is more than meat. 23
in him was l. and the l. John 1:4
believeth not, shall not see l. 3:36
Father hath l. in himself, so hath he given to the Son to have l. 5:26
good, to the resurrection of l. 29
to me that ye might have l. 40; 10:10
giveth l. unto the world. 6:33
I am the bread of l. 35, 48
which I will give for the l. of the. 51
and drink his blood, ye have no l. 53
words I speak to you, they are l. 63
but shall have the light of l. 8:12
resurrection and the l. 11:25; 14:6
believing ye might have l. 20:31
known to me the ways of l. Acts 2:28
killed the Prince of l. whom. 3:15
seeing he giveth to all l. 17:25
the manner of l. from my youth. 26:4
be no loss of any man's l. 27:22
in l. by one, Jesus Christ. Rom 5:17
all men to justification of l. 18
should walk in newness of l. 6:4
the Spirit of l. in Christ Jesus. 8:2
to be spiritually minded is l. 6
the Spirit is l. because of. 10
that neither death nor l. 38
the receiving them be but l.? 11:15
the world, or l.. or death. 1 Cor 3:22
things without l. giving sound. 14:7
ye despaired even of l. 2 Cor 1:8
the savour of l. unto l. 2:16
killeth, but the Spirit giveth l. 3:6
that the l. of Jesus might be. 4:10
death worketh in us, but l. in you. 12
might be swallowed up of l. 5:4
the l. which I now live. Gal 2:20
which could have given l. 3:21*
alienated from the l. Eph 4:18
whether it be by l. or by. Phil 1:20
holding forth the word of l. 2:16
is hid with Christ in God. Col 3:3
when Christ who is our l. shall. 4
may lead a peaceable l. 1 Tim 2:2
having the promise of l. 4:8

the promise of l. in Christ. 2 Tim 1:1
and he hath brought l. to light. 10
fully known my manner of l. 3:10
beginnning of days, nor end of l.
Heb 7:3
after the power of an endless l. 16
receive the crown of l. Jas 1:12
for what is your l.? it is even. 4:14
as being heirs together of the grace of l. 1 Pet 3:7
for he that will love l. and see. 10
for the time past of our l. may. 4:3
all things pertaining to l. 2 Pet 1:3
handled the word of l. 1 John 1:1
for the l. was manifested, and we. 2
pride of l. is not of the Father. 2:16
hath Son hath l.; and he that hath not the Son of God hath not l. 5:12
he shall give him l. for them. 16
I give to eat of the tree of l. Rev 2:7
I will give thee a crown of l. 10
of the creatures that had l. died. 8:9
Spirit of l. from God entered. 11:11
he had power to give l. to. 13:15*
to thirsty of the water of l. 21:6
me a pure river of water of l. 22:1
tree of l. bare twelve manner of. 2
have right to the tree of l. 14
let him take the water of l. 17
see **book, eternal, everlasting**

his **life**

seeing his l. is bound. Gen 44:30
for the ransom of his l. Ex 21:30
read therein all the days of his l.
Deut 17:19
feared him all the days of his l.
Josh 4:14
father adventured his l. Judg 9:17
they which he slew in his l. 16:30
put his l. in his hand. 1 Sam 19:5
was come out to seek his l. 23:15
this word against his l. 1 Ki 2:23
he arose and went for his l. 19:3
thy life be for his l. 20:39, 42
his l. shall be for the life. 2 Ki 10:24
the temple to save his l. Neh 6:11
to make request for his l. Esth 7:7
all that a man hath will he give for his l. Job 2:4
he is in thy hand, but save his l. 6
and his l. from perishing by. 33:18
his l. abhorreth bread. 20
his l. to destroyers. 22
he will deliver, and his l. shall. 28
not that it is for his l. Pr 7:23
his mouth, keepeth his l. 13:3
man to rejoice and do good in his l.
Eccl 3:12
man that prolongeth his l. 7:15
labours all the days of his l. 8:15
Moab, his l. shall be. Isa 15:4
his l. shall be to him for a prey.
Jer 21:9; 38:2
hand of them that seek his l. 44:30
to warn, to save his l. Ezek 3:18
himself in iniquity of his l. 7:13
tremble, every man for his l. 32:10
findeth his l. shall lose it: he that loseth his l. shall find it. Mat 10:39
16:25; Mark 8:35; Luke 9:24
17:33; John 12:25
to give his l. a ransom for many.
Mat 20:28; Mark 10:45
hate not his own l. also. Luke 14:26
good Shepherd giveth his l. for.
John 10:11
that a man lay down his l. for. 15:13
for his l. is taken from. Acts 8:33
trouble not yourselves, his l. 20:10
shall be saved by his l. Rom 5:10
regarding his l. to supply. Phil 2:30
he laid down his l. 1 John 3:16
see **days**

my **life**

shewed in saving my l. Gen 19:19
of my l.: what good shall my l.? 27:46
my l. is preserved. 32:30
fed me all my l. 48:15
I put my l. in my hands. Judg 12:3
what is my l. or my father's family?
1 Sam 18:18
that he seeketh my l.? 20:1
he that seeketh my l. seeketh. 22:23

my l. be much set by. 1 Sam 26:24
layest thou a snare for my l.? 28:9
I put my l. in my hand, and. 21
because my l. is yet whole in me.
2 Sam 1:9
my son of my bowels seeketh my l.
16:11
falsehood against my l. 18:13
now, take away my l. 1 Ki 19:4
they seek my l. to take it away.
10, 14; Rom 11:3
let my l. be precious. 2 Ki 1:13, 14
let my l. be given me at my petition.
Esth 7:3
I should prolong my l. Job 6:11
O remember that my l. is but. 7:7
chooseth death rather than my l. 15
yet I would despise my l. 9:21
my soul is weary of my l. 10:1
wherefore do I put my l. in? 13:14
let him tread down my l. Ps 7:5
follow me all the days of my l. 23:6
gather not my l. with bloody. 26:9
Lord is the strength of my l. 27:1
house of the Lord all days of my l. 4
my l. is spent with grief. 31:10
they devised to take away my l. 13
seek after my l. lay snares. 38:12
my prayer to the God of my l. 42:8
preserve my l. from fear of the. 64:1
and my l. draweth nigh to. 88:3
he hath smitten my l. to the. 143:3
cut off like a weaver my l. Isa 38:12
cut off my l. in dungeon. Lam 3:53
Lord, thou hast redeemed my l. 58
hast brought up my l. Jonah 2:6
take, I beseech thee, my l. 4:3
and I lay down my l. for the sheep.
John 10:15
me, because I lay down my l. 17
Lord, I will lay down my l. 13:37
nor count I my l. dear. Acts 20:24

this **life**

have their portion in this l. Ps 17:14
good for a man in this l. Eccl 6:12
this is thy portion in this l. and. 9:9
are choked with the cares of this l.
Luke 8:14
hearts overcharged with the cares of this l. 21:34
speak all words of this l. Acts 5:20
that pertain to this l. 1 Cor 6:3
of things pertaining to this l. 4
if in this l. only we have hope. 15:19
entangleth himself with affairs of this l. 2 Tim 2:4
eternal life, and this l. 1 John 5:11

thy **life**

Escape for thy l.; look. Gen 19:17
dead which sought thy l. Ex 4:19
thy l. shall hang in doubt before thee, no assurance of thy l. Deut 28:66
thee, and thou lose thy l. Judg 18:25
thee a restorer of thy l. Ruth 4:15
if thou save not thy l. 1 Sam 19:11
seeketh my life seeketh thy l. 22:23
thy l. was much set by this. 26:24
enemy that sought thy l. 2 Sam 4:8
which this day saved thy l. 19:5
thou mayest save thy l. 1 Ki 1:12
if I make not thy l. as the life. 19:2
peradventure he will save thy l. 20:31
if he be missing thy l. be. 39, 42
who redeemeth thy l. Ps 103:4
and the years of thy l. shall be.
Pr 4:10; 9:11
keep her, for she is thy l. 4:13
and the years of thy l. shall. 9:11
will I give people for thy l. 43:4
they will seek thy l. Jer 4:30
of the men that seek thy l. 11:21
22:25; 38:16
thy l. shall be for a prey to thee.
39:18; 45:5
wilt thou lay down thy l.? John 13:38

to or unto **life**

he had restored to l. 2 Ki 8:1, 5
the righteous tendeth to l. Pr 10:16
as righteousness tendeth to l. 11:19
fear of the Lord tendeth to l. 19:23
the way that leadeth unto l. Mat 7:14
but is passed from death unto l.
John 5:24; 1 John 3:14

granted repentance unto l. Acts 11:18
ordained to l. Rom 7:10
their dead raised to l. Heb 11:35

lift

To lift up the eyes, frequently means to direct and make known our desires to God by prayer, Ps 121; 123:1. *To lift up the head, is* [1] *To restore a person to his former dignity,* Gen 40:13. [2] *To recover former strength and courage, so as to oppress others,* Judg 8:28. [3] *To rejoice and be glad,* Luke 21:28. [4] *To be advanced above others, and obtain a complete victory over them,* Ps 27:6. *To lift up the hand, is* [1] *To swear, or by oath to confirm a thing,* Gen 14:22. [2] *To bless,* Lev 9:22. [3] *To pray,* Ps 28:2. [4] *To rise in rebellion,* 2 Sam 18:28; 20:21. [5] *To oppress, threaten, injure, or wrong in any way,* Job 31:21.

Hath lift up his heel against me, Ps 41:9. *Hath behaved himself insolently, contemptuously and injuriously towards me. It is a phrase taken from an unruly horse, who kicks at one who owns and feeds him.*

Lift not up the horn, Ps 75:4. *Carry not yourselves arrogantly, scornfully, or maliciously towards me or any of God's people.*

Lift up thy feet, Ps 74:3. *Come speedily to our help, and for our deliverance.*

To lift up one's self in height, that is to grow proud, insolent, and oppressive, Ezek 31:10.

the ark was l. up above. Gen 7:17
l. up the lad, and hold him in. 21:18
shall l. up thine head. 40:13, 19
if thou l. up a tool on it. Ex 20:25
Lord l. up his countenance upon thee. Num 6:26
wherefore then l. ye up? 16:3
l. up himself as a young lion. 23:24
shalt help him to l. Deut 22:4
not l. up an iron tool. 27:5; Josh 8:31
he l. up his spear against 800. 2 Sam 23:8
l. up thy prayer for the remnant. 2 Ki 19:4; Isa 37:4
l. up head of Jehoiachin. 2 Ki 25:27
were to l. up the horn. 1 Chr 25:5
I blush to l. up my face. Ezra 9:6
if righteous, yet will I not l. up. Job 10:15
then shalt thou l. up thy face. 11:15; 22:26
l. up the light of thy. Ps 4:6
arise, O Lord, in thine anger, l. 7:6
l. up your heads, O ye gates, be l. 24:7, 9
unto thee, O Lord, do I l. up my soul. 25:1; 86:4; 143:8
hear, when I l. up my hands. 28:2
feed them also, and l. them up. 9*
l. up thy feet to perpetual. 74:3
and to the wicked, l. not up. 75:4, 5
the floods l. up their waves. 93:3
l. up thyself, thou judge of. 94:2
shall he l. up the head. 110:7
if they fall, the one will l. Eccl 4:10
not l. up sword against nation. Isa 2:4; Mi 4:3
he will l. up an ensign. Isa 5:26
as if staff should l. up itself. 10:15
smite, and shall l. up his staff. 24
so shall l. it up after the manner. 26
l. ye up a banner upon the. 13:2*
now will I rise, now will I l. 33:10
Lord shall l. up a standard. 59:19*
l. up a standard for the. 62:10
nor l. up cry nor prayer for them. Jer 7:16; 11:14
they shall l. up a shout. 51:14
let us l. up our heart. Lam 3:41
it might not l. itself up. Ezek 17:14
and shall l. up the buckler. 26:8
so that no man did l. up his head. Zech 1:21
will he not l. it out on the sabbath? Mat 12:11
in no wise l. up herself. Luke 13:11
l. up your heads; for your. 21:28
and he shall l. you up. Jas 4:10*

see **eyes**

lift *hand* or *hands*

I have l. up mine hand. Gen 14:22
shall no man l. up his hand. 41:44
I l. up my h., and say. Deut 32:40
l. up thine hand, forget. Ps 10:12
when I l. up my hands toward. 28:2
I will l. up my hands in thy. 63:4
my h. will I l. up to thy. 119:48
l. up your hands in sanctuary. 134:2
I will l. up mine hand to the Gentiles. Isa 49:22
l. up thy hands toward. Lam 2:19
wherefore l. up the h. Heb 12:12

lift *voice*

Hagar l. up her voice. Gen 21:16
canst thou l. up thy voice? Job 38:34
l. up thy voice, O daughter. Isa 10:30*
they shall l. up their voice. 24:14
l. up thy voice with strength. 40:9
not cry, nor l. up his voice. 42:2
and cities l. up their voice. 11
shall l. up the voice. 52:8
cry, spare not, l. up thy voice 58:1
cry, and l. up thy voice. Jer 22:20
to l. up the voice with. Ezek 21:22

lifted

Lot l. up his eyes and. Gen 13:10
Abraham l. up his eyes. 18:2; 22:13
Esau l. up voice. 27:38
and Jacob l. up his voice. 29:11
I l. up mine eyes, saw. 31:10; 33:1
l. up Joseph out of the pit. 37:28
as I l. up my voice. 39:18
Pharaoh l. up the head of. 40:20
l. up the rod and smote waters. Ex 7:20; 14:16
Aaron l. up his hand. Lev 9:22
the congregation l. up. Num 14:1
Moses l. up his hand and. 20:11
then thy heart be l. up. Deut 8:14
that his heart be not l. above. 17:20
of the priests' feet were l. Josh 4:18
the people l. up their voice and wept. Judg 2:4; 21:2; 1 Sam 11:4
so they l. up their heads. Judg 8:28
Jotham l. up his voice and. 9:7
Orpah and Ruth l. up their voice and wept. Ruth 1:9, 14
Saul l. up his voice and wept. 1 Sam 24:16
David and people l. up voice. 30:4
2 Sam 3:32
king's sons came and l. 2 Sam 13:36
Sheba hath l. up his hand. 20:21
also hast l. me up on high. 22:49
he l. up his spear against 300. 23:18
1 Chr 11:11
Jeroboam l. up hand against king. 1 Ki 11:26, 27
he l. up his face to the. 2 Ki 9:32
thine heart hath l. thee. 14:10
his kingdom was l. up. 1 Chr 14:2*
and singers l. up voice. 2 Chr 5:13
his heart was l. up in the ways. 17:6
heart was l. up to destruction. 26:16; 32:25
l. up their voice and wept. Job 2:12
if I have l. up my hand against. 31:21
or l. up myself when evil found. 29
who hath not l. up his soul. Ps 24:4
shall my head be l. up above. 27:6
for thou hast l. me up. 30:1
102:10
hath l. up his heel against me. 41:9
John 13:18
as he l. up axes upon the. Ps. 74:5
they that hate thee have l. up. 83:2
floods have l. up their voice. 93:3
therefore he l. up his hand. 106:26
and their eyelids are l. up. Pr 30:13
day of the Lord of hosts shall be on every one that is l. up. Isa 2:12
on cedars that are high and l. up. 13
mountains l. up. 14
sitting on a throne high and l. up. 6:1
when thy hand is l. up they. 26:11
against whom hast thou l. up thine eyes on high? Isa 37:23
her judgement is l. up to. Jer 51:9
creatures were l. up. Ezek 1:19
wheels were l. up. 20, 21; 10:17*
so the Spirit l. me up and. 3:14
Spirit l. me up between the earth. 8:3; 11:1
l. up their wings. 10:16, 19; 11:22
and l. up my hand to the. 20:5, 6
yet l. up mine hand in the. 15, 23
into the land for the which I l. up mine hand. 28, 42; 47:14
because thine heart is l. up. 28:2
5, 17; 31:10*
thus saith the Lord, I have l. 36:7
have I l. up my hand against. 44:12
when his heart was l. up. Dan 5:20
but hast l. up thyself against. 23
the first beast was l. up from. 7:4
then I l. up mine eyes. 8:3; 10:5
thine hand shall be l. up. Mi 5:9
his soul which is l. up is. Hab 2:4*
deep l. up his hands on high. 3:10
which l. up their horn. Zech 1:21
behold, there was l. up a. 5:7
they l. up the ephah between. 5:9
the stones of a crown, l. up. 9:16
the land shall be l. up. 14:10
by the hand, and l. her up. Mark 1:31
but Jesus l. him up, and. 9:27
he l. up his eyes on his. Luke 6:20
a certain woman l. up her. 11:27
ten lepers l. up their voices. 17:13
and he l. up his hands and. 24:50
l. up the serpent in the wilderness, . . . the Son of man be l. John 3:14
when ye have l. up the Son. 8:28
I, if I be l. up, will draw all. 12:32
Son of man must be l. up. 34
Peter l. up his voice. Acts 2:14
l. up their voice to God with. 4:24
they l. up their voices saying. 14:11
and then l. up their voices. 22:22
being l. up with pride. 1 Tim 3:6*
the angel l. up his hand. Rev 10:5

lifter

my glory, and the l. up. Ps 3:3

liftest

thou l. me up to the wind. Job 30:22
l. me up from the gates. Ps 9:13
l. above those that rise up. 18:48
and l. up thy voice for. Pr 2:3

lifteth

bringeth low, and l. up. 1 Sam 2:7, 8
thine heart l. thee up. 2 Chr 25:19
what time the ostrich l. Job 39:18
wind which l. up the. Ps 107:25
he l. the needy out of the. 113:7
the Lord l. up the meek. 147:6*
when he l. up an ensign. Isa 18:3
that l. himself up in his. Jer 51:3
horseman l. up his bright. Nah 3:3*

lifetime

Absalom in his l. had. 2 Sam 18:18
thou in thy l. receivedst. Luke 16:25
were all their l. subject. Heb 2:15

lifting

Abishai chief, for l. up. 1 Chr 11:20
sounding, by l. up the voice. 15:16
answered, Amen, with l. Neh 8:6
shalt say, There is l. up. Job 22:29
l. up of my hands as. Ps 141:2
hast done foolishly in l. Pr 30:32
shall mount up like the l. Isa 9:18
at l. up of thyself nations were. 33:3
men pray every where, l. 1 Tim 2:8

light

morning was l., the men. Gen 44:3
of the house, till it was l. Judg 19:2
them till the morning l. 1 Sam 14:3
night shall be l. about. Ps 139:1
when morning is l. they. Mi 2:1
evening time it shall be l. Zech 14:

light

our soul loatheth this l. Num 21:
and my burden is l. Mat 11:3
our l. affliction worketh. 2 Cor 4:1

light

hired vain and l. persons. Judg 9:
her prophets are l. and. Zeph 3:

light, *adj.*
Asahel was *l.* of foot. *2 Sam* 2:18
light, *adv.*
cursed that setteth *l.* *Deut* 27:16
they set *l.* by father. *Ezek* 22:7
but made *l.* of it, and. *Mat* 22:5
light *thing*
seemeth it a *l. thing*? *1 Sam* 18:23
it had been a *l. thing.* *1 Ki* 16:31
a *l. thing* in sight of Lord. *2 Ki* 3:18
it is a *l. thing* for the shadow. 20:10
l. thing that thou shouldest. *Isa* 49:6
a *l. thing* they commit? *Ezek* 8:17
light
there be *l.* and there was *l. Gen* 1:3
God saw the *l.* 4
God called the *l.* day. 5
the greater *l.* to rule . . . lesser *l.* 16
Israel had *l.* in their. *Ex* 10:23
pillar gave *l.* by night to these. 14:20
offering, oil for the *l.* 25:6; 27:20
35:8, 14, 28; 39:37; *Lev* 24:2
pertaineth oil for the *l.* *Num* 4:16
as ye have *l.* depart. *1 Sam* 29:10
thou quench not the *l. 2 Sam* 21:17*
he shall be as the *l.* of the. 23:4
l. was against *l.* in. *1 Ki* 7:4, 5
my servant may have a *l.* 11:36*
nor pillar of fire by night to shew them *l.* *Neh* 9:19
the Jews had *l.*, joy. *Esth* 8:16
neither let the *l.* shine. *Job* 3:4
let it look for *l.* but have none. 9
as infants which never saw *l.* 16
l. given to him in misery. 20, 23
without order, where the *l.* 10:22
bringeth out to *l.* the shadow. 12:22
they grope in the dark without *l.* 25
the *l.* of the wicked shall be. 18:5
the *l.* shall be dark in his. 6
l. shall shine on thy ways. 22:28
those that rebel against the *l.* 24:13
the murderer rising with the *l.* 14
daytime, they know not the *l.* 16
upon whom doth not his *l.*? 25:3
that is hid bringeth he to *l.* 28:11
and his life shall see the *l.* 33:28
to be enlightened with the *l.* of. 30
behold he spreadeth his *l.* 36:30
with clouds he covereth *l.* and. 32*
the *l.* of his cloud to shine? 37:15*
men see not the bright *l.* in. 21
wicked their *l.* is withholden. 38:15
where is way where *l.* dwelleth? 19
by what way is the *l.* parted? 24
his neesings a *l.* doth shine. 41:18
lift up the *l.* of thy. *Ps* 4:6
Lord is my *l.* and my salvation. 27:1
forth thy righteousness as *l.* 37:6
l. of mine eyes, it also is gone. 38:10
they shall never see *l.* 49:19
thou hast prepared the *l.* 74:16
all the night with a *l.* of fire. 78:14
l. is sown for the righteous. 97:11
who coverest thyself with *l.* 104:2
Lord, who hath shewed us *l.* 118:27
thy word is a lamp, and a *l.* 119:105
entrance of thy words giveth *l.* 130
darkness and *l.* are both. 139:12
sun, and all ye stars of *l.* 148:3
just is as the shining *l.* *Pr* 4:18
is a lamp, the law is *l.* 6:23
l. of righteous rejoiceth, but. 13:9
the *l.* of the eyes rejoiceth. 15:30
truly the *l.* is sweet. *Eccl* 11:7
while the sun or the *l.* be not. 12:2
put darkness for *l.* and *l.* *Isa* 5:20
the *l.* is darkened in the heavens. 30
it is because there is no *l.* 8:20*
a great *l.*; on them hath *l.* shined. 9:2
l. of Israel shall be for fire. 10:17
moon shall not cause her *l.* to shine. 13:10; *Mat* 24:29; *Mark* 13:24
l. of moon be as *l.* of sun, *l.* of sun as the *l.* of seven days. *Isa* 30:26
my judgement to rest for a *l.* 51:4
we wait for *l.* but behold. 59:9
be to thee an everlasting *l.* 60:19
heavens, and they had no *l. Jer* 4:23
I will take from them the *l.* 25:10
sun for a *l.* by day, and ordinances of the moon and stars for *l.* 31:35
and the *l.* dwelleth with. *Dan* 2:22
l. and understanding. *Dan* 5:11, 14
thy judgements as *l.* that. *Hos* 6:5
bring me forth to the *l.* *Mi* 7:9
brightness was as the *l.* *Hab* 3:4
at the *l.* of thine arrows they. 11
bring judgement to *l.* *Zeph* 3:5
in that day the *l.* shall. *Zech* 14:6
in darkness saw great *l.* *Mat* 4:16
ye are the *l.* of the world. 5:14
it giveth *l.* unto all that are in. 15*
let your *l.* so shine before men. 16
l. of body is the eye, if eye . . . full of *l.* 6:22*; *Luke* 11:34*, 36
raiment was white as the *l. Mat* 17:2
a *l.* to lighten Gentiles. *Luke* 2:32
enter in may see the *l.* 8:16; 11:33
wiser than the children of *l.* 16:8
and life was the *l.* of men. *John* 1:4
to bear witness of that *l.* 7, 8
that was the true *l.* which. 9
condemnation, that *l.* is come. 3:19
that doeth evil hateth the *l.* 20
doeth truth cometh to the *l.* 21
a shining *l.*: and ye were willing for a season to rejoice in his *l.* 5:35*
I am the *l.* of the world, he that followeth me shall have *l.* 8:12; 9:5
because he seeth the *l.* 11:9
stumbleth, because there is no *l.* 10
yet a little while is the *l.* 12:35
ye have *l.*, believe in the *l.* that. 36
I am come a *l.* into the world. 46
shined about him a *l.* *Acts* 9:3
a *l.* shined in the prison, and. 12:7
I have set thee to be a *l.* to. 13:47
he called for a *l.* and sprang. 16:29
there shone a great *l.* round. 22:6
were with me saw indeed the *l.* 9
not see for the glory of that *l.* 11
O king, I saw in the way a *l.* 26:13
should shew *l.* to the people and. 23
a *l.* of them which are in. *Rom* 2:19
put on the armour of *l.* 13:12
who will bring to *l.* hidden. *1 Cor* 4:5
lest the *l.* of the gospel. *2 Cor* 4:4
who commanded *l.* to shine out. 6
transformed into an angel of *l.* 11:14
now are ye *l.* in the Lord: walk as children of *l.* *Eph* 5:8
made manifest by the *l.*: for whatsoever doth make manifest is *l.* 13
inheritance of saints in *l.* *Col* 1:12
ye are all children of the *l.* and day. *1 Thes* 5:5
dwelling in *l.* no man. *1 Tim* 6:16
and immortality to *l.* *2 Tim* 1:10
into his marvellous *l.* *1 Pet* 2:9
take heed, as unto a *l.* that shineth in a dark place. *2 Pet* 1:19*
God is *l.* and in him. *1 John* 1:5
the *l.* of a candle shall. *Rev* 18:23
her *l.* was like a stone most. 21:11
lighten it, and the Lamb is the *l.* 23*
l. of the sun, the Lord giveth *l.* 22:5
see **countenance, darkness**
give **light**
and let them be to *give l.* *Gen* 1:15
and God set the stars to *give l.* 17
of fire to *give* them *l.* *Ex* 13:21
the lamps may *give l.* over against. 25:37; *Num* 8:2
he promised to *give* him alway a *l.* *2 Ki* 8:19*; *2 Chr* 21:7*
to *give* them *l.* in the way. *Neh* 9:12
and fire to *give l.* in the. *Ps* 105:39
stars of heaven shall not *give* their *l.* *Isa* 13:10
I will *give* thee for a *l.* to. 42:6; 49:6
nor shall the moon *give l.* to thee. 60:19; *Ezek* 32:7
it *giveth l.* unto all in the house. *Mat* 5:15; *Luke* 11:36
to *give* the *l.* of the knowledge of. *2 Cor* 4:6
Christ shall *give* thee *l.* *Eph* 5:14*
in the **light**
that I may walk *in the l.* *Ps* 56:13
come, let us walk *in the l.* *Isa* 2:5
walk *in the l.* of your fire. 50:11*
the light, believe *in the l. John* 12:36
we walk *in the l.* as he is *in the l.* *1 John* 1:7
he that saith he is *in the l.*, and. 2:9
brother, abideth *in the l. 1 John* 2:10
saved shall walk *in l.* *Rev* 21:24
thy **light**
in *thy l.* shall we see light. *Ps* 36:9
O send out *thy l.* and thy truth. 43:3
then shall *thy l.* break forth. *Isa* 58:8
then shall *thy l.* rise in obscurity. 10
arise, shine, for *thy l.* is come. 60:1
the Gentiles shall come to *thy l.* 3
the sun shall be no more *thy l.* 19
Lord shall be *thy* everlasting *l.* 20
light, -ed
shall *l.* the lamps. *Ex* 25:37; 40:4
he *l.* the lamps before the Lord. 40:25; *Num* 8:3
for thou wilt *l.* my candle. *Ps* 18:28
nor do men *l.* a candle. *Mat* 5:15
no man when he hath *l.* a candle. *Luke* 8:16; 11:33
doth not *l.* a candle, and? 15:8
nor shall the sun *l.* on. *Rev* 7:16*
light (*to come upon*)
her hap was to *l.* on a. *Ruth* 2:3
and we will *l.* on him. *2 Sam* 17:12
lighted (*came down*)
she saw Isaac, she *l.* off. *Gen* 24:64
and she *l.* off her ass. *Josh* 15:18
Judg 1:14
Sisera *l.* off his chariot. *Judg* 4:15
Abigail hasted and *l.* off the ass. *1 Sam* 25:23
Naaman *l.* down from. *2 Ki* 5:21
lighted (*came upon*)
Jacob *l.* on a certain. *Gen* 28:11
Jehu *l.* on Jehonadab. *2 Ki* 10:15
word to Jacob and it *l.* on. *Isa* 9:8
lighten
the Lord will *l.* my. *2 Sam* 22:29
that our God may *l.* our. *Ezra* 9:8
l. mine eyes, lest I sleep. *Ps* 13:3
a light to *l.* the Gentiles. *Luke* 2:32
glory of God did *l.* it. *Rev* 21:23
lighten
peradventure he will *l.* *1 Sam* 6:5
cast wares into the sea, to *l.* it of. *Jonah* 1:5
lightened
looked unto him and were *l. Ps* 34:5
the lightnings *l.* the world. 77:18
earth was *l.* with his glory. *Rev* 18:1
see **enlightened**
lightened
being tossed, next day they *l.* ship. *Acts* 27:18*, 38
lighteneth
Lord *l.* both their eyes. *Pr* 29:13
for as lightning that *l.* *Luke* 17:24
lighter
make heavy yoke which he put upon us, *l. 1 Ki* 12:4, 9, 10; *2 Chr* 10:10
altogether *l.* than vanity. *Ps* 62:9
lightest
say to him, When thou *l.* *Num* 8:2
lighteth
when Aaron *l.* the lamps. *Ex* 30:8
the true light which *l.* *John* 1:9
lighteth
axe head slippeth and *l.* *Deut* 19:5
lighting
Lord shall shew the *l.* down of his arm. *Isa* 30:30
like a dove, and *l.* on him. *Mat* 3:16
lightly
one might *l.* have lien. *Gen* 26:10
when at first he *l.* afflicted. *Isa* 9:1*
and all the hills moved *l.* *Jer* 4:24*
can *l.* speak evil of me. *Mark* 9:39*
see **esteemed**
lightness
l. of her whoredoms she. *Jer* 3:9
my people to err by their *l.* 23:22*
minded, did I use *l.*? *2 Cor* 1:17*
lightning
he sent *l.* and discomfited them. *2 Sam* 22:15
he made a way for the *l.* *Job* 28:26
he directeth his *l.* to the ends. 37:3
who divided a way for the *l.* 38:25
cast forth *l.* and scatter. *Ps* 114:6

out of fire went forth *l.* *Ezek* 1:13
ran as the appearance of *l.* 14
face as the appearance of *l.* *Dan* 10:6
his arrow shall go forth as the *l.* *Zech* 9:14
as *l.* cometh out of the east. *Mat* 24:27; *Luke* 17:24
his countenance was as *l.* *Mat* 28:3
I beheld Satan as *l.* fall. *Luke* 10:18

lightnings

thunders, *l.* and thick. *Ex* 19:16
all the people saw the *l.* and. 20:18
canst thou send *l.* that? *Job* 38:35
he shot out *l.* and. *Ps* 18:14
l. lighted the world. 77:18; 97:4
he maketh *l.* for the rain. 135:7
he maketh *l.* with rain. *Jer* 10:13
51:16
chariots shall run like the *l.* *Nah* 2:4
out of throne proceeded *l.* *Rev* 4:5
were voices, thunderings, and *l.* 8:5
11:19
l. and a great earthquake. 16:18

lights

be *l.* in the firmament. *Gen* 1:14
let them be for *l.* in firmament. 15
God made two great *l.* greater. 16
windows of narrow *l.* *1 Ki* 6:4*
that made great *l.* for. *Ps* 136:7
all the bright *l.* will I make dark. *Ezek* 32:8
girded, your *l.* burning. *Luke* 12:35*
l. in the upper chamber. *Acts* 20:8
whom ye shine as *l.* in. *Phil* 2:15
from the Father of *l.* *Jas* 1:17

lign aloes

as the trees of *l. a.* which. *Num* 24:6

ligure

(*Revised Versions*, jacinth)
the third row a *l.*, an agate and an amethyst. *Ex* 28:19; 39:12*

like

Sodom was *l.* the land. *Gen* 13:10
who is *l.* unto thee? *Ex* 15:11
Deut 33:29; *1 Ki* 8:23; *2 Chr* 6:14
Ps 35:10; 71:19
manna was *l.* coriander. *Ex* 16:31
the glory of the Lord was *l.* 24:17
make any ointment *l.* it. 30:32
compoundeth any thing *l.* it. 33
of each shall there be a *l.* weight. 34
hew two tables *l.* unto the first. 34:1
Deut 10:1, 3
my last end be *l.* his. *Num* 23:10
hath been heard *l.* it. *Deut* 4:32
lest thou be a cursed thing *l.* it. 7:26
set king over me *l.* all nations. 17:14; *1 Sam* 8:5, 20
they shall have *l.* portions to eat. *Deut* 18:8
prophet of thy brethren *l.* me. 15
Acts 3:22; 7:37
raise a prophet from brethren *l.* to thee. *Deut* 18:18
l. the overthrow of Sodom. 29:23
not a prophet *l.* unto Moses. 34:10
no day *l.* that before. *Josh* 10:14
countenance *l.* an angel. *Judg* 13:6
brake them from his arms *l.* 16:12
I shall become weak and *l.* any. 17
though I be not *l.* to one of thy. *Ruth* 2:13
woman *l.* Rachel and *l.* Leah. 4:11
let thy house be *l.* the house. 12
nor is there any rock *l.* *1 Sam* 2:2
be strong, quit yourselves *l.* men. 4:9
1 Cor 16:13
staff of his spear was *l.* a. 17:7
Nabal held a feast *l.* the feast. 25:36
a valiant man, and who is *l.* 26:15
l. to name of great men. *2 Sam* 7:9
what one nation in earth is *l.*? 23
he maketh my feet *l.* hinds'. 22:34
none *l.* thee before thee, nor after thee arise *l.* thee. *1 Ki* 3:12, 13
there was not the *l.* made in. 10:20
Jeroboam ordained a feast *l.* 12:32
l. the house of Jeroboam. 16:3, 7
21:22; *2 Ki* 9:9
ariseth a little cloud *l.* *1 Ki* 18:44*
number thee an army *l.* the. 20:25
pitched before them *l.* two little. 27
word *l.* word of one of those. *1 Ki* 22:13; *2 Chr* 18:12
but not *l.* his father and *l.* *2 Ki* 3:2
his flesh came again *l.* flesh of a. 5:14
l. the house of Baasha son of. 9:9
made them *l.* dust by threshing. 13:7
yet not *l.* David his father. 14:3
16:2; *2 Chr* 28:1
the Lord charged they should not do *l.* them. *2 Ki* 17:15
take you to a land *l.* your own. 18:32; *Isa* 36:17
l. to him was there no king. *2 Ki* 23:25; *Neh* 13:26
host *l.* the host of God. *1 Chr* 12:22
would increase Israel *l.* stars. 27:23
over a people *l.* the dust. *2 Chr* 1:9
no burning for him *l.* burning. 21:19
be not ye *l.* your fathers and. 30:7
l. to the abominations of the. 33:2
there was no passover *l.* to. 35:18
to grave *l.* as a shock of. *Job* 5:26
hast thou not curdled me *l.*? 10:10
though man be born *l.* a wild. 11:12
he maketh them to stagger *l.* 12:25
your remembrances are *l.* 13:12*
he cometh forth *l.* a flower. 14:2
who drinketh iniquity *l.* water. 15:16
he runneth upon me *l.* a giant. 16:14
he shall perish for ever *l.* his. 20:7
they send their little ones *l.* 21:11
what man is *l.* Job, who? 34:7
power: who teacheth *l.* him? 36:22
gird up now thy loins *l.* a man. 38:3
40:7
hast thou an arm *l.* God? or. 40:9
on earth there is not his *l.* 41:33
ye have not spoken right *l.* my. 42:8
he shall be *l.* a tree planted. *Ps* 1:3
ungodly are not so, but are *l.* 4
lest he tear my soul *l.* a lion. 7:2
l. a lion that is greedy of his. 17:12
out *l.* water, my heart *l.* wax. 22:14
I become *l.* them that go down. 28:1
I am forgotten, I am *l.* a. 31:12
thy righteousness is *l.* the. 36:6
shall be soon cut down *l.* grass. 37:2
spreading himself *l.* a green bay. 35
beauty to consume *l.* a moth. 39:11
thou hast given us *l.* sheep. 44:11
man is *l.* the beasts that. 49:12, 20
tongue is *l.* a sharp razor. 52:2
but I am *l.* a green olive tree. 8
O that I had wings *l.* a dove! 55:6
l. the poison of a serpent, *l.* 58:4
make a noise *l.* a dog. 59:6, 14
whet their tongue *l.* a sword. 64:3
he shall come down *l.* rain. 72:6
neither plagued *l.* other men. 73:5
leddest thy people *l.* a flock. 77:20
78:52
unfaithfully *l.* their fathers. 78:57
their blood have shed *l.* water. 79:3
thereof *l.* the goodly cedars. 80:10
shall die *l.* men, and fall *l.* one. 82:7
make them *l.* a wheel. 83:13
who is a strong Lord *l.* unto thee? 89:8; 113:5; *Mi* 7:18
flourish *l.* the palm tree, he shall grow *l.* a cedar in. *Ps* 92:12
heart withered *l.* grass. 102:4, 11
I am *l.* a pelican, *l.* an owl of the. 6
shall wax old *l.* a garment. 26
l. as a father pitieth his. 103:13
out the heavens *l.* a curtain. 104:2
the dry places *l.* a river. 105:41
stagger *l.* a drunken man. 107:27
l. water, and *l.* oil into. 109:18
they that make them are *l.* to them. 115:8; 135:18
we were *l.* them that dream. 126:1
lest I be *l.* them that go down. 143:7
man is *l.* to vanity, his days. 144:4
l. wool, hoar frost *l.* ashes. 147:16
l. the bars of a castle. *Pr* 18:19
counsel in the heart of man is *l.* 20:5
biteth *l.* a serpent, stingeth *l.* 23:32
unfaithful man is *l.* a broken tooth. 25:19
l. a city broken down, and. 28
fool, lest thou be *l.* to him. 26:4
my beloved is *l.* a roe. *S of S* 2:9
turn, my beloved, and be thou *l.* a roe. 17; 8:14
cometh *l.* pillars of smoke? *S of S* 3:6
thy teeth are *l.* a flock of sheep. 4:2
thy lips *l.* scarlet, temples *l.* a. 3
thy neck is *l.* the tower of David. 4
breasts are *l.* two young. 5; 7:3
his lips *l.* lilies dropping sweet. 5:13
my soul made me *l.* chariots. 6:12
joints of thy thighs are *l.* jewels. 7:1
l. a goblet, thy belly is *l.* wheat. 2
stature *l.* a palm tree. 7
smell of thy nose *l.* apples. 8
would have been *l.* unto Gomorrah. *Isa* 1:9; *Rom* 9:29
red *l.* crimson, shall be. *Isa* 1:18
inhabitants *l.* a valiant man. 10:13
lion shall eat straw *l.* the ox. 11:7
and shall be an highway, *l.* as it. 16
art thou become *l.* to us? 14:10
I will be *l.* the most High. 14
out *l.* an abominable branch. 19
sound *l.* an harp for Moab. 16:11
in that day shall Egypt be *l.* 19:16
l. as my servant Isaiah hath. 20:3
will toss thee *l.* a ball into a. 22:18
l. a woman with child that. 26:17
breath of the Lord *l.* a stream. 30:33
Sharon is *l.* a wilderness. 33:9
I have cut off *l.* a weaver my. 38:12
l. a crane or swallow so did I. 14
will I cry *l.* a travailing. 42:14
to whom will ye compare me that we may be *l.*? 46:5
wicked are *l.* the troubled sea. 57:20
lift up thy voice *l.* a trumpet. 58:1
be *l.* a watered garden, and *l.* 11
for the wall *l.* the blind. 59:10
all *l.* bears, and mourn sore *l.* 11
enemy shall come in *l.* a flood. 19
l. him that treadeth in the. 63:2
our iniquities *l.* wind have. 64:6
peace to her *l.* a river. 66:12
lest my fury come forth *l.* fire. *Jer* 4:4; 21:12
l. as ye have forsaken me. 5:19
portion of Jacob is not *l.* them. 10:16
I was *l.* a lamb brought to. 11:19
for he shall be *l.* the heath in. 17:6
word *l.* fire and *l.* a hammer? 23:29
make this house *l.* Shiloh. 26:6, 9
Zion shall be plowed *l.* a field. 18
l. Zedekiah and *l.* Ahab. 29:22
were added besides to them many *l.* words. 36:32
he is *l.* to die with hunger. 38:9
Egypt is *l.* a very fair heifer. 46:20
flee, be *l.* the heath in the. 48:6
be *l.* the dove that maketh nest. 28
shall come *l.* a lion. 49:19; 50:44
is *l.* me, who will appoint? 49:19
of Jacob is not *l.* them. 51:19
not do any more the *l.* *Ezek* 5:9
l. as I have done, so shall. 12:11
and doeth the *l.* to any of. 18:10
the house of Judah is *l.* to all. 25:8
thou *l.* in thy greatness? 31:2, 18
nor any tree was *l.* unto him in his. 8
month shall he do the *l.* 45:25
form of the fourth is *l.* the Son of God. *Dan* 3:25
made *l.* the beasts, *l.* oxen. 5:21
one *l.* the Son of man came. 7:13
shall be *l.* people, *l.* priest. *Hos* 4:9
princes *l.* them that remove. 5:10
they *l.* men have transgressed. 6:7
I am *l.* a green fir tree, from. 14:8
hath not been ever the *l.* *Joel* 2:2
lest he break out *l.* fire. *Amos* 5:6
instruments of music *l.* David. 6:5
l. as the Lord of hosts. *Zech* 1:6
the governors of Judah *l.* a. 12:6
l. a dove, and lighting. *Mat* 3:16
Mark 1:10; *Luke* 3:22; *John* 1:32
be not ye therefore *l.* unto. *Mat* 6:8
was not arrayed *l.* one of these. 29; *Luke* 12:27
l. children sitting in the market. *Mat* 11:16; *Luke* 7:32
it was restored whole *l.* *Mat* 12:13
kingdom is *l.* to a grain of mustard 13:31; *Mark* 4:31; *Luke* 13:19
kingdom of heaven is *l.* leaven. *Mat* 13:33; *Luke* 13:21
is *l.* unto treasure. *Mat* 13:44
is *l.* unto a merchant. 45

that did wear a *l.* ephod. *1 Sam* 22:18
David was girded with a *l.* ephod. *2 Sam* 6:14
l. yarn . . . merchants received the *l.* *1 Ki* 10:28*; *2 Chr* 1:16*
get thee a *l.* girdle, put. *Jer* 13:1
wrapped it in a *l.* cloth. *Mat* 27:59; *John* 19:40
a *l.* cloth cast about his. *Mark* 14:51
left the *l.* cloth and fled naked. 52
Peter beheld the *l.* clothes. *Luke* 24:12; *John* 20:6
John saw the *l.* clothes. *John* 20:5
see **fine**

lines

with two *l.* measured. *2 Sam* 8:2
l. are fallen in pleasant. *Ps* 16:6

lingered

while Lot *l.* the men. *Gen* 19:16
except we had *l.* surely we. 43:10

lingereth

whose judgement *l.* not. *2 Pet* 2:3

lintel

and strike the *l.* and two. *Ex* 12:22
when he seeth blood on the *l.* he. 23
l. and side posts were. *1 Ki* 6:31
smite *l.* that the posts. *Amos* 9:1*

lintels

lodge in the upper *l.* of it. *Zeph* 2:14

lion

(*This word is often used as a synonym of strength and power*)
Judah couched as a *l.* *Gen* 49:9
Israel lay down as a *l.*, as a great *l.* *Num* 24:9
Gad dwelleth as a *l.* *Deut* 33:20
of *l.* there was a swarm of bees and honey in carcase of *l.* *Judg* 14:8
what is stronger than a *l.*? 18
a *l.* and took a lamb. *1 Sam* 17:34
is as the heart of a *l.* *2 Sam* 17:10
slew a *l.* in the midst of a pit. 23:20; *1 Chr* 11:22
a *l.* met him by the way and slew him, the *l.* also stood by. *1 Ki* 13:24
l. standing by the carcase. 25, 28
hath delivered him to the *l.* 26
art departed from me, a *l.* shall slay thee; a *l.* found him and. 20:36
roaring of the *l.*, and the voice of the fierce *l.* *Job* 4:10
huntest me as a fierce *l.* 10:16
nor the fierce *l.* passed by it. 28:8
hunt the prey for the *l.*? 38:39
lest he tear my soul like a *l.* *Ps* 7:2
he lieth in wait secretly as a *l.* 10:9
like a *l.* that is greedy of his. 17:12
gaped on me as a roaring *l.* 22:13
save me from the *l.*'s mouth. 21
thou shalt tread on the *l.* 91:13
king's wrath is as the roaring of a *l.* *Pr* 19:12
king is as the roaring of a *l.* 20:2
the slothful saith, There is a *l.* 22:13
there is a *l.* in the way, a *l.* 26:13
the righteous are bold as a *l.* 28:1
l. which is strongest among. 30:30
dog is better than a dead *l.* *Eccl* 9:4
their roaring shall be like a *l.* *Isa* 5:29
l. shall eat straw like the ox. 11:7; 65:25
he cried, A *l.*: My lord, I stand. 21:8
no *l.* shall be there, nor. 35:9
as a *l.* so will be break all 38:13
your prophets like a *l.* *Jer* 2:30
l. is come up from his thicket. 4:7
a *l.* out of the forest shall slay. 5:6
my heritage is to me as a *l.* in. 12:8
forsaken his covert as the *l.* 25:38
shall come up like a *l.* 49:19; 50:44
as a *l.* in secret places. *Lam* 3:10
and the face of a *l.* on. *Ezek* 1:10
third was the face of a *l.* 10:14
prophets like a roaring *l.* 22:25
the first was like a *l.* and. *Dan* 7:4
will be to Ephraim as a *l.* *Hos* 5:14
he shall roar like a *l.* when. 11:10
I will be to them as *l.* 13:7
I will devour as a *l.* 8
cheek teeth of a great *l.* *Joel* 1:6
will a *l.* roar when he? *Amos* 3:4
l. hath roared, who will not? *Amos* 3:8
taketh out of mouth of *l.* 12
of Jacob shall be as a *l.* *Mi* 5:8
l. did tear in pieces enough for his. *Nah* 2:12
out of the mouth of the *l.* *2 Tim* 4:17
the devil as a roaring *l.* *1 Pet* 5:8
first beast was like a *l.* *Rev* 4:7
the *l.* of the tribe of Judah. 5:5
loud voice, as when a *l.* roareth. 10:3
mouth as the mouth of a *l.* 13:2
see **bear**

old **lion**

as an *old l.* who shall rouse him? *Gen* 49:9
the *old l.* perisheth for. *Job* 4:11
come the young and *old l.*? *Isa* 30:6
lion, even *old l.* walked. *Nah* 2:11

young **lion**

up himself as a *young l.* *Num* 23:24
behold, a *young l.* roared. *Judg* 14:5
young l. lurking in secret. *Ps* 17:12
young l. shalt thou trample. 91:13
calf and *young l.* lie down. *Isa* 11:6
like the *young l.* roaring on. 31:4
became a *young l.* and learned to catch the prey. *Ezek* 19:3, 6
another, and made him a *young l.* 5
thou art like a *young l.* of the. 32:2
face of a *young l.* was towards. 41:19
as a *young l.* to the house of Judah. *Hos* 5:14
will a *young l.* cry out of his den, if he has taken nothing? *Amos* 3:4
Jacob as a *young l.* among the flocks. *Mi* 5:8

lioness

what is thy mother? A *l.* *Ezek* 19:2

lionesses

lion strangled for his *l.* *Nah* 2:12

lionlike

slew two *l.* men of Moab. *2 Sam* 23:20*; *1 Chr* 11:22*

lions

Saul and Jonathan stronger than *l.* *2 Sam* 1:23
on the borders were *l.*, oxen: beneath the *l.* were. *1 Ki* 7:29
cherubims, *l.* and palm trees. 36
two *l.* stood beside the stays. 10:19; *2 Chr* 9:18
twelve *l.* stood on the one side. *1 Ki* 10:20; *2 Chr* 9:19
the Lord sent *l.* among. *2 Ki* 17:25
therefore he hath sent *l.* among. 26
were like faces of *l.* *1 Chr* 12:8
rescue my darling from *l.* *Ps.* 35:17
my soul is among *l.*: I lie even. 57:4
look from top of Amana, from the *l.*' dens. *S of S* 4:8
l. upon him that escapeth. *Isa* 15:9
the *l.* have driven Israel. *Jer* 50:17
roar together like *l.* 51:38
she lay down among *l.* *Ezek* 19:2
went up and down among the *l.* 6
the *l.* had the mastery, *Dan* 6:24
Daniel from the power of the *l.* 27
the dwelling of the *l.*? *Nah* 2:11
her princes within are roaring *l.* *Zeph* 3:3
faith stopped the mouths of *l.* *Heb* 11:33
were as the teeth of *l.* *Rev* 9:8
the horses were as the heads of *l.* 17
see **den**

lion's *whelp, whelps*

Judah is a *l. whelp.* *Gen* 49:9
Dan is a *l. whelp.* *Deut* 33:22
the stout *l. whelps* are. *Job* 4:11
l. whelps have not trodden it. 28:8
they shall yell as *l. whelps.* *Jer* 51:38

young **lions**

teeth of the *young l.* are. *Job* 4:10
the appetite of the *young l.*? 38:39
the *young l.* do lack and. *Ps* 34:10
great teeth of the *young l.* 58:6
young l. roar after their prey. 104:21
shall roar like *young l.* *Isa* 5:29
young l. roared upon him. *Jer* 2:15
whelps among *young l.* *Ezek* 19:2
with all the *young l.* shall. 38:13
the feedingplace of the *young l.*? *Nah* 2:11
sword shall devour thy *young l.* 13
voice of the roaring of *young l.* *Zech* 11:3

lip

put a covering on his *l.* *Lev* 13:45
they shoot out the *l.* *Ps* 22:7
the *l.* of truth shall be. *Pr* 12:19

lips

of uncircumcised *l.* *Ex* 6:12, 30
aught out of her *l.* *Num* 30:6; 8:12
heart, only her *l.* moved. *1 Sam* 1:13
with flattering *l.* do they. *Ps* 12:2
shall cut off all flattering *l.* 3
our *l.* are our own, who is lord? 4
goeth not out of feigned *l.* 17:1
let lying *l.* be put to silence. 31:18
behold, swords are in their *l.* 59:7
for the words of their *l.* let. 12
praise thee with joyful *l.* 63:5
soul, O Lord, from lying *l.* 120:2
adders' poison is under their *l.* 140:3
mischief of their own *l.* cover. 9
and perverse *l.* put far. *Pr* 4:24
l. of a strange woman drop as. 5:3
with flattering of her *l.* she. 7:21
in the *l.* of him that hath. 10:13
hideth hatred with lying *l.* is a. 18
the *l.* of the righteous feed many. 21
the *l.* of righteous know what is. 32
lying *l.* are an abomination. 12:22
but the *l.* of the wise shall. 14:3
when perceivest not in him the *l.* 7
the talk of the *l.* tendeth only to. 23
the *l.* of the wise disperse. 15:7
a divine sentence is in the *l.* 16:10
righteous *l.* are the delight of. 13
sweetness of the *l.* increaseth. 21
doer giveth heed to false *l.* 17:4
less do lying *l.* become a prince. 7
a fool's *l.* enter into contention. 18:6
the *l.* of knowledge are a. 20:15
and their *l.* talk of mischief. 24:2
burning *l.* are like a potsherd. 26:23
l. of a fool will swallow himself. *Eccl* 10:12
causing the *l.* of those asleep to. *S of S* 7:9
undone, a man of unclean *l.* . . . of a people of unclean *l.* *Isa* 6:5
for with stammering *l.* will. 28:11
this people with their *l.* do. 29:13
I create the fruit of the *l.* 57:19
your *l.* have spoken lies. 59:3
l. of those that rose. *Lam* 3:62
cover your *l.* nor eat. *Ezek* 24:22
taken up in the *l.* of talkers. 36:3
render the calves of our *l.* *Hos* 14:2
seers shall cover their *l.* *Mi* 3:7
priest's *l.* should keep. *Mal* 2:7
honoureth me with their *l.* *Mat* 15:8; *Mark* 7:6
of asps is under their *l.* *Rom* 3:13
other *l.* will I speak to. *1 Cor* 14:21
fruit of our *l.* giving. *Heb* 13:15

his **lips**

pronouncing with *his l.* *Lev* 5:4
did not Job sin with *his l.* *Job* 2:10
O that God would open *his l.* 11:5
from commandment of *his l.* 23:12
the request of *his l.* *Ps* 21:2
spake unadvisedly with *his l.* 106:33
he that refraineth *his l.* *Pr* 10:19
by transgression of *his l.* 12:13
openeth wide *his l.* shall have. 13:3
wise addeth learning to *his l.* 16:23
in *his l.* there is as a burning fire. 27
moving *his l.* he bringeth evil. 30
shutteth *his l.* is a man of. 17:28
his l. are the snare of his soul. 18:7
with the increase of *his l.* shall. 20
he that is perverse in *his l.* 19:1
that flattereth with *his l.* 20:19
for grace of *his l.* the king. 22:11
shall kiss *his l.* that giveth. 24:26
hateth dissembleth with *his l.* 26:24
his l. like lilies dropping. *S of S* 5:13
with breath of *his l.* shall. *Isa* 11:4
his l. are full of indignation. 30:27
was not found in *his l.* *Mal* 2:6
his l. that they speak. *1 Pet* 3:10

***my* lips**
to the pleading of *my l.* *Job* 13:6
moving of *my l.* should assuage. 16:5
my l. shall not speak wickedness. 27:4
I will speak, I will open *my l.* 32:20
my l. shall utter knowledge. 33:3
up their names into *my l.* *Ps* 16:4
lo, I have not refrained *my l.* 40:9
open thou *my l.* 51:15
my l. shall praise thee. 63:3
I will pay vows, which *my l.* 66:14
my l. shall greatly rejoice. 71:23
thing that is gone out of *my l.* 89:34
with *my l.* have I declared. 119:13
my l. shall utter thy praise. 171
Lord, keep the door of *my l.* 141:3
the opening of *my l.* *Pr* 8:6
is an abomination to *my l.* 7
which came out of *my l.* *Jer* 17:16
the sons of men touched *my l.* *Dan* 10:16
I heard, *my l.* quivered. *Hab* 3:16

***thy* lips**
which is gone out of *thy l.* perform. *Deut* 23:23
I will put my bridle in *thy l.* *2 Ki* 19:28; *Isa* 37:29
fill *thy l.* with rejoicing. *Job* 8:21
thy own *l.* testify against thee. 15:6
the word of *thy l.* I have. *Ps* 17:4
keep *thy l.* from speaking. 34:13
grace is poured into *thy l.* 45:2
thy l. may keep knowledge. *Pr* 5:2
withal be fitted in *thy l.* 22:18
rejoice when *thy l.* speak. 23:16
deceive not with *thy l.* 24:28
praise thee, and not *thine* own *l.* 27:2
thy l. are like a thread. *S of S* 4:3
thy l. O my spouse, drop as the. 11
this hath touched *thy l.* *Isa* 6:7
cover not *thy l.* and eat. *Ezek* 24:17

liquor
nor shall he drink any *l.* *Num* 6:3
a round goblet, which wanteth not *l.* *S of S* 7:2*

liquors
offer the first of thy *l.* *Ex* 22:29

listed
done unto him whatsoever they *l.* *Mat* 17:12; *Mark* 9:13

listen
l. O isles, unto me, and. *Isa* 49:1

listeth
wind bloweth where it *l.* *John* 3:8
whithersoever the governor *l.* *Jas* 3:4*

litters
bring your brethren in chariots and *l.* *Isa* 66:20

little
l. water, I pray you. *Gen* 18:4
let me drink a *l.* water of. 24:17
it was but *l.* thou hadst. 30:30
a *l.* way to Ephrath. 35:16; 48:7
buy us a *l.* food. 43:2; 44:25
a *l.* balm, a *l.* honey. 43:11
if the household be too *l.* *Ex* 12:4
he that gathered *l.* had no lack. 16:18
2 Cor 8:15
by *l.* and *l.* I will drive them out. *Ex* 23:30; *Deut* 7:22
and gather but *l.* in. *Deut* 28:38
Dan went out too *l.* for. *Josh* 19:47
is the iniquity of Peor too *l.*? 22:17
give me *l.* water to drink. *Judg* 4:19
1 Ki 17:10
that she tarried a *l.* in. *Ruth* 2:7
mother made him a *l.* *1 Sam* 2:19
because I tasted a *l.* of this honey. 14:29, 43
when thou wast *l.* in thine. 15:17
save one *l.* ewe lamb. *2 Sam* 12:3
if that had been too *l.* I would. 8
thy servant will go a *l.* way. 19:36*
brasen altar was too *l.* *1 Ki* 8:64
my *l.* finger thicker than. 12:10
2 Chr 10:10
and a *l.* oil in a cruse. *1 Ki* 17:12
make a *l.* cake. 13
there ariseth a *l.* cloud like. 18:44
like two *l.* flocks of kids. 20:27
l. children out of the city mocked. *2 Ki* 2:23†
away captive a *l.* maid. 5:2
Ahab served Baal a *l.* but. 10:18
a *l.* space, give us a *l.* *Ezra* 9:8
all the trouble seem *l.* *Neh* 9:32
and my ear received a *l.* *Job* 4:12*
that I may take comfort a *l.* 10:20
but how *l.* a portion is heard? 26:14
suffer me a *l.* and I will shew. 36:2
wrath is kindled but a *l.* *Ps* 2:12*
made him a *l.* lower than the angels. 8:5; *Heb* 2:7
l. that righteous man hath. *Ps* 37:16
l. hills rejoice on every side. 65:12*
there is *l.* Benjamin, with. 68:27
l. hills by righteousness. 72:3*
l. hills skipped like lambs. 114:4, 6
a *l.* sleep, a *l.* slumber, a *l.* folding. *Pr* 6:10; 24:33
heart of the wicked is *l.* 10:20
better is a *l.* with the fear of. 15:16
better is a *l.* with righteousness. 16:8
four things that are *l.* on the. 30:24
sweet, whether he eat *l.* *Eccl* 5:12
there was a *l.* city, and few. 9:14
so doth a *l.* folly him that is in. 10:1
take us the foxes, the *l.* *S of S* 2:15
was but a *l.* that I passed. 3:4
we have a *l.* sister, and she. 8:8
hide thyself for a *l.* moment till. *Isa* 26:20
here a *l.* and there a *l.* 28:10, 13
the isles as a very *l.* thing. 40:15
in a *l.* wrath I hid my face. 54:8*
I will be to them a *l.* *Ezek* 11:16
but as if that were a very *l.* 16:47
and sent out her *l.* rivers. 31:4*
up another *l.* horn. *Dan* 7:8; 8:9
shall be holpen with a *l.* help. 11:34
they shall sorrow a *l.* *Hos* 8:10*
the *l.* house with clefts. *Amos* 6:11
l. among the thousands. *Mi* 5:2
sown much, and bring in *l.* *Hag* 1:6
for much, and lo, it came to *l.* 9
was but a *l.* displeased. *Zech* 1:15
clothe you, O ye of *l.* faith? *Mat* 6:30
8:26; 16:8; *Luke* 12:28
O thou of *l.* faith. *Mat* 14:31
seven, and a few *l.* fishes. 15:34
he went a *l.* further. 26:39
Mark 1:19; 14:35
my *l.* daughter lieth at. *Mark* 5:23
to whom *l.* is forgiven, the same loveth *l.* *Luke* 7:47
fear not, *l.* flock. 12:32
he was *l.* of stature. 19:3
been faithful in a very *l.* 19:17
of them may take a *l.* *John* 6:7
put the apostles forth a *l.* *Acts* 5:54
man alive, and were not a *l.* 20:12
barbarians shewed us no *l.* 28:2*
a *l.* leaven leaveneth the whole lump. *1 Cor* 5:6; *Gal* 5:9
could bear with me a *l.* *2 Cor* 11:1
that I may boast myself a *l.* 16
bodily exercise profiteth *l.* *1 Tim* 4:8
use a *l.* wine for thy. 5:23
who was made a *l.* lower. *Heb* 2:9
tongue is a *l.* member ... a *l.* *Jas* 3:5
vapour that appeareth for a *l.* 4:14
thou hast a *l.* strength. *Rev* 3:8
rest a *l.* season. 6:11
be loosed a *l.* season. 20:3
see **book, chambers, child, children**

little *one,* or *ones*
a *l. one,* is it not a *l. one*? *Gen* 19:20
l. ones took they captive. 34:29
we, and thou, and our *l. ones.* 43:8
l. one, and his brother is dead. 44:20
out of Egypt for your *l. ones.* 45:19
carried their *l. ones.* 46:5
food for your *l. ones.* 47:24
l. ones left they in Goshen. 50:8
will nourish you and your *l. ones.* 21
go, and your *l. ones.* *Ex* 10:10, 24
l. ones, them will I bring. *Num* 14:31
Midian captives and *l. ones.* 31:9
every male among the *l. ones.* 17
build cities for our *l. ones.* 32:16
our *l. ones* shall dwell in. 17, 26
we destroyed men, women, and *l. ones.* *Deut* 2:34
the women and *l. ones.* *Deut* 20:14
Joshua read before the women and *l. ones.* *Josh* 8:35
put the *l. ones* before. *Judg* 18:21
over and all the *l. ones.* *2 Sam* 15:22
Judah stood before Lord and *l. ones.* *2 Chr* 20:13
genealogy of all their *l. ones.* 31:18
right way for our *l. ones.* *Ezra* 8:21
cause to perish *l. ones.* *Esth* 8:11
their *l. ones* like a flock. *Job* 21:11
that dasheth thy *l. ones.* *Ps* 137:9
a *l. one* shall become a. *Isa* 60:22
nobles sent their *l. ones.* *Jer* 14:3
her *l. ones* have caused a cry. 48:4
my hand on the *l. ones.* *Zech* 13:7
give to drink to one of these *l. ones.* *Mat* 10:42
whoso shall offend one of these *l. ones.* 18:6; *Mark* 9:42
despise not one of these *l. ones.* *Mat* 18:10
of these *l. ones* should perish. 14
that he should offend one of these *l. ones.* *Luke* 17:2

little *while*
exalted for a *l. while.* *Job* 24:24
yet a *l. while* and wicked. *Pr* 37:10
l. while and indignation. *Isa* 10:25
a very *l. while,* and Lebanon. 29:17
possessed it but a *l. while.* 63:18
l. while and her harvest. *Jer* 51:33
yet a *l. while* and I will avenge the blood. *Hos* 1:4
a *l. while* and I will shake. *Hag* 2:6
and after a *l. while* another saw him. *Luke* 22:58
yet a *l. while* and I am with you. *John* 7:33; 13:33
yet a *l. while* is the light. 12:35
a *l. while,* and the world. 14:19
a *l. while,* and ye shall not see me, and again a *l. while.* 16:16, 17, 19
a *l. while*? we cannot tell. 18
for yet a *l. while* and he. *Heb* 10:37

live
they shall sell the *l.* ox. *Ex* 21:35
a seraphim, having a *l.* coal. *Isa* 6:6
see **goat**

live
tree of life, and *l.* for. *Gen* 3:22
and my soul shall *l.* because. 12:13
O that Ishmael might *l.*! 17:18
escape, and my soul shall *l.* 19:20
for thee, and thou shall *l.* 20:7
by sword shalt thou *l.* and. 27:40
thy goods, let him not *l.* 31:32
Joseph said, This do, and *l.* 42:18
Joseph, doth my father yet *l.*? 45:3
daughter, then she shall *l.* *Ex* 1:16
no man see me and *l.* 33:20
he shall *l.* in them, I am. *Lev* 18:5
Neh 9:29; *Ezek* 20:11, 13, 21
upon serpent, shall *l.* *Num* 21:8
alas, who shall *l.* when God? 24:23
all the days they shall *l.* *Deut* 4:10
people hear, as thou hast, and *l.*? 33
word of the Lord doth man *l.* 8:3
days that ye *l.* on the earth. 12:1
to one of these cities and *l.* 19:5
learn to fear Lord as long as ye *l.* 31:13; *1 Ki* 8:40
let Reuben *l.* and not die. *Deut* 33:6
only Rahab harlot shall *l.* *Josh* 6:17
league with them to let them *l.* 9:15
we will let them *l.* lest wrath. 20, 21
not only while I *l.* shew. *1 Sam* 20:14
l. thou and thy children. *2 Ki* 4:7
they save us alive, we shall *l.* 7:4
ways so long as they *l.* *2 Chr* 6:31
if a man die, shall he *l.*? *Job* 14:14
wherefore do the wicked *l.*? 21:7
your heart shall *l.* for ever. *Ps* 22:26
still *l.* and not see corruption. 49:9
will I bless thee while I *l.* 63:4
hearts shall *l.* that seek God. 69:32
he shall *l.* 72:15
I shall not die but *l.* 118:17
understanding and I shall *l.* 119:144
let my soul *l.* and it shall. 175
I *l.* will I praise the Lord. 146:2
commandments and *l.* *Pr* 4:4; 7:2

forsake the foolish and *l.* *Pr* 9:6
he that hateth gifts shall *l.* 15:27
if a man *l.* many years. *Eccl* 6:3, 6
11:8
madness is in their heart while they *l.*
9:3
l. joyfully with the wife whom. 9
thy dead men shall *l.* *Isa* 26:19
by these things men *l.*: make me to *l.* 38:16
hear, and your soul shall *l.* 55:3
he that falleth to Chaldeans, shall *l.*
Jer 21:9; 27:12, 17; 38:2, 17
obey . . . and thy soul shall *l.* 38:20
his shadow we shall *l.* *Lam* 4:20
he shall surely *l.* *Ezek* 3:21; 18:9
17; 33:13, 15, 16
when thou wast in thy blood, *L.* 16:6
kept all my statutes, shall surely *l.*
18:19, 21, 22; 20:11, 25
shall he *l.* 18:24
turn yourselves and *l.* 32; 33:11
on us, how should we then *l.*? 33:10
is lawful and right, he shall *l.* 19
Son of man, can these bones *l.*? 37:3
enter you, and ye shall *l.* 5, 6, 14
which liveth and moveth shall *l.*; every thing shall *l.* whither. 47:9
revive us, we shall *l.* in. *Hos* 6:2
seek me, and ye shall *l.* *Amos* 5:4, 6
me to die than to *l.* *Jonah* 4:3, 8
the just shall *l.* by his faith.
Hab 2:4; *Rom* 1:17
l. with their children. *Zech* 10:9
man shall not *l.* by bread alone.
Mat 4:4; *Luke* 4:4
lay thy hand upon her, and she shall *l.*
Mat 9:18; *Mark* 5:23
they which *l.* delicately. *Luke* 7:25
this do, and thou shalt *l.* 10:28
of dead, for all *l.* unto him. 20:38
dead shall hear voice of the Son of God, and *l.* *John* 5:25
sent me, and I *l.* by Father: so he that eateth me, even shall *l.* 6:57
he were dead, yet he shall *l.* 11:25
because I *l.* ye shall *l.* also. 14:19
in him we *l.* and move. *Acts* 17:28
not fit that he should *l.* 22:22
that are dead to sin, *l.* *Rom* 6:2
we believe that we shall also *l.* 8
we are debtors, not to *l.* after. 8:12
ye *l.* after flesh ye shall die . . . mortify deeds of body, ye shall *l.* 13
doeth these things shall *l.* by them.
10:5; *Gal* 3:12
if possible, *l.* peaceably. *Rom* 12:18*
l. we *l.* to the Lord; whether we *l.* therefore or die, we are. 14:8
they *l.* of the things of. *1 Cor* 9:13*
preach gospel, should *l.* of gospel. 14
l. are delivered to death. *2 Cor* 4:11
as dying, and behold we *l.* 6:9
in our hearts to die and *l.* with. 7:3
we shall *l.* with him by the. 13:4
brethren, be of one mind, *l.* in. 11
Gentiles to *l.* as Jews. *Gal* 2:14
dead to the law, that I might *l.* 19
I *l.*, yet not I, but Christ liveth in me, the life I now *l.* in flesh, I *l.* by. 20
the just shall *l.* by faith. 3:11
Heb 10:38
if we *l.* in the Spirit, let. *Gal* 5:25
for me to *l.* is Christ. *Phil* 1:21
if I *l.* in the flesh, this is fruit. 22
now we *l.* if ye stand. *1 Thes* 3:8
died, that we should *l.* 5:10
if dead, we shall also *l.* *2 Tim* 2:11
all that will *l.* godly shall suffer. 3:12
that we should *l.* soberly. *Tit* 2:12
to Father of spirits and *l.*? *Heb* 12:9
things willing to *l.* honestly. 13:18
if the Lord will we shall *l.* *Jas* 4:15
should *l.* to righteousness. *1 Pet* 2:24
no longer should *l.* in the flesh. 4:2
but *l.* according to God in spirit. 6
ensample to those that *l.* *2 Pet* 2:6
escaped from them that *l.* in. 18
his Son, that we might *l.* *1 John* 4:9
had the wound and did *l.* *Rev* 13:14
see for **ever**

as I **live**
as truly *as I l.*, earth. *Num* 14:21, 28
so long *as I l.* *Job* 27:6; *Ps* 104:33
116:2
As I l. saith the Lord. *Isa* 49:18
Jer 22:24; *Ezek* 5:11; 14:16, 18
20; 16:48; 17:16, 19; 18:3; 20:3
33; 33:11, 27; 34:8; 35:6, 11
Zeph 2:9; *Rom* 14:11
As I l. saith the king. *Jer* 46:18

may, might, or *mayest* **live**
that we *may l.* and not die.
Gen 42:2; 43:8; 47:19
that he *may l.* with thee. *Lev* 25:35
no usury, that thy brother *may l.* 36
to them that they *may l.* *Num* 4:19
for to do to them, that ye *may l.*
Deut 4:1; 5:33; 8:1; 30:6, 16
one of these cities he *might l.* 4:42
follow, that thou *mayest l.* 16:20
that thou and thy seed *may l.* 30:19
that the child *may l.* *2 Sam* 12:22
bread, that you *may l.* *2 Ki* 18:32
sceptre, that he *may l.* *Esth* 4:11
bountifully, that I *may l.* *Ps* 119:17
mercies come to me, that I *may l.* 77
to thy word, that I *may l.* 116
dwell in tents, that ye *may l.* many.
Jer 35:7
slain, that they *may l.* *Ezek* 37:9
not evil, that ye *may l.* *Amos* 5:14
and thou *mayest l.* long. *Eph* 6:3

not **live**
the mountain shall *not l.* *Ex* 19:13
not suffer a witch to *l.* 22:18
not l. by bread only, but by the word.
Deut 8:3; *Mat* 4:4; *Luke* 4:4
sure that he could *not l.* *2 Sam* 1:10
is wanting he shall *not l.* *2 Ki* 10:19
set house in order, thou shalt *not l.*
20:1; *Isa* 38:1
I loath it, I would *not l.* *Job* 7:16
wicked shall *not l.* half. *Ps* 55:23
dead, they shall *not l.* *Isa* 26:14
souls that should *not l.* *Ezek* 13:19
then live ? he shall *not l.* 18:13
whereby they should *not l.* 20:25
to him, thou shalt *not l.* *Zech* 13:3
cast out children, that they might *not l.* *Acts* 7:19
crying, that he ought *not* to *l.* 25:24
vengeance suffereth *not* to *l.* 28:4
not l. to themselves. *2 Cor* 5:15

lived
his son, while he yet *l.* *Gen* 25:6
Jacob *l.* in the land of Egypt. 47:28
and Caleb *l.* still. *Num* 14:38
beheld the serpent of brass he *l.* 21:9
the voice of God and *l.* *Deut* 5:26
if Absalom had *l.* and. *2 Sam* 19:6
before Solomon his father while he yet *l.* *1 Ki* 12:6; *2 Chr* 10:6
Amaziah *l.* after death of Jehoash.
2 Ki 14:17; *2 Chr* 25:25
while he *l.* he blessed. *Ps* 49:18
breath came into them, and they *l.*
Ezek 37:10
had *l.* with a husband. *Luke* 2:36
l. in all good conscience. *Acts* 23:1
sect of our religion I *l.* a. 26:5
ye also walked sometime, when ye *l.* in them. *Col* 3:7
ye have *l.* in pleasure. *Jas* 5:5
how much she hath *l.* *Rev* 18:7, 9
they *l.* with Christ. 20:4
the rest *l.* not again. 5

lively
Hebrew women are *l.* *Ex* 1:19
but my enemies are *l.* *Ps* 38:19
received the *l.* oracles. *Acts* 7:38*
us again to a *l.* hope. *1 Pet* 1:3*
ye, as *l.* stones, are built up a. 2:5*

liver
the caul above the *l.* *Ex* 29:13, 22
Lev 3:4, 10, 15; 4:9; 7:4; 8:16
25; 9:10, 19
strike through his *l.* *Pr* 7:23
my *l.* is poured upon. *Lam* 2:11
he looked in the *l.* *Ezek* 21:21
see **caul**

lives
your blood of your *l.* *Gen* 9:5
to save your *l.* by a great. 45:7
thou hast saved our *l.*: let us. 47:25
they made their *l.* bitter. *Ex* 1:14
deliver our *l.* from death. *Josh* 2:13
were sore afraid of our *l.* 9:24
that jeoparded their *l.* *Judg* 5:18
thou lose thy life with *l.* of. 18:25
Saul and Jonathan lovely in their *l.*
2 Sam 1:23
saved *l.* of thy sons, wives. 19:5
that went in jeopardy of their *l.*
23:17; *1 Chr* 11:19
and stood for their *l.* *Esth* 9:16
they lurk privily for their *l.* *Pr* 1:18
fall by them which seek their *l.*
Jer 19:7; 46:26
seek their *l.* shall straiten them. 19:9
flee, save your *l.*, be like the. 48:6
with the peril of our *l.* *Lam* 5:9
their *l.* were prolonged. *Dan* 7:12
Son of man is not come to destroy men's *l.* *Luke* 9:56
hazarded their *l.* for our. *Acts* 15:26
will be with damage of our *l.* 27:10
to lay down our *l.* for. *1 John* 3:16
they loved not their *l.* to. *Rev* 12:11

livest
Levite as long as thou *l.* *Deut* 12:19
if thou being a Jew *l.* after. *Gal* 2:14
a name that thou *l.* and. *Rev* 3:1

liveth
that *l.* shall be meat for. *Gen* 9:3
talk with man, and he *l.* *Deut* 5:24
have lent him to the Lord as long as he *l.* *1 Sam* 1:28
for as long as son of Jesse *l.* 20:31
thus shall say to him that *l.* 25:6
as God *l.* unless thou. *2 Sam* 2:27
as my lord the king *l.* surely. 15:21
Lord *l.* blessed be my rock. 22:47
Ps 18:46
this is my son that *l.* *1 Ki* 3:23
Elijah said, See thy son *l.* 17:23
that my Redeemer *l.* *Job* 19:25
as God *l.* who hath taken. 27:2
what man that *l.* and shall? *Ps* 89:48
shalt swear, the Lord *l.* *Jer* 4:2
though they say, The Lord *l.* they. 5:2
swear by my name, the Lord *l.* 12:16
no more be said, The Lord *l.* 16:14
15; 23:7, 8
Egypt, saying, The Lord *l.* 44:26
every thing that *l.* and. *Ezek* 47:9
nor swear, the Lord *l.* *Hos* 4:15
Thy God, O Dan, *l.*; and, The manner of Beer-sheba *l.* *Amos* 8:14
Jesus said, Go thy way, thy son *l.*
John 4:50, 51, 53
whosoever *l.* and believeth in. 11:26
that he *l.* he *l.* to God. *Rom* 6:10
over man as long as he *l.* 7:1, 2
so if while her husband *l.* she be. 3
for none of us *l.* or dieth to. 14:7
wife is bound as long as her husband *l.* *1 Cor* 7:39
l. by the power of God. *2 Cor* 13:4
yet not I, but Christ *l.* *Gal* 2:20
she that *l.* in pleasure is dead while she *l.* *1 Tim* 5:6*
it is witnessed that he *l.* *Heb* 7:8
he ever *l.* to make intercession. 25
no strength while testator *l.* 9:17
I am he that *l.* and was. *Rev* 1:18
see for **ever**

as the Lord **liveth**
as the Lord l. if ye have saved.
Judg 8:19
part of kinsman, *as the Lord l.*
Ruth 3:13
for, *as the Lord l.*, . . . though it be in Jonathan. *1 Sam* 14:39
as the Lord l. 45; 19:6; 20:21
25:26; 26:10, 16; 28:10; 29:6
2 Sam 4:9; 12:5; 14:11; *1 Ki* 1:29
2:24; *2 Ki* 5:20; *2 Chr* 18:13
Jer 38:16
as the Lord l. there is but a step.
1 Sam 20:3
as the Lord God of Israel *l.* 25:34
1 Ki 17:1; 18:15
as the Lord l. and as my lord the king *l.* *2 Sam* 15:21
as the Lord thy God *l.* *1 Ki* 17:12
18:10

as the Lord l. and thy soul liveth. *2 Ki* 2:2, 4, 6; 4:30
as the Lord of hosts *l.* before whom I stand. 3:14; 5:16

as thy soul liveth

as thy soul l. I am the woman who stood praying. *1 Sam* 1:26
Abner said, *As thy soul l.* O. 17:55
as soul l. there is but one step. 20:3
as thy soul l. seeing Lord. 25:26
as thy soul l. I will not do this thing. *2 Sam* 11:11
as thy soul l. none can turn to the right hand or left. 14:19
as thy soul l., I will not leave thee. So they went. *2 Ki* 2:2

living

[1] *One who is alive, or enjoys life,* 1 Ki 3:22. [2] *Of a well, or water always running,* John 4:10; 7:38. [3] *Spiritual,* Rom 12:1. [4] *A person's wealth, goods, or estate,* Luke 15:12.

having dominion over every *l.* thing. *Gen* 1:28
man became a *l.* soul. 2:7
Eve, mother of all *l.* 3:20
every *l.* thing of all flesh, two. 6:19
and every *l.* substance I have. 7:4
and every *l.* substance was. 23
Noah and every *l.* thing. 8:1
any more every thing *l.* 21
of any *l.* thing which is in the water. *Lev* 11:10
as for the *l.* bird, he shall take it. 14:6, 7, 53
not made abominable by any *l.* 20:25
he stood between the dead and the *l.* *Num* 16:48
off his kindness to the *l.* *Ruth* 2:20
shut up *l.* in widowhood. *2 Sam* 20:3
the *l.* is my son, the dead thy son. *1 Ki* 3:22, 23
divide the *l.* child in two, and. 25
l. child was, give her the *l.* 26
king said, Give her the *l.* child. 27
in whose hand is soul of every *l.* thing. *Job* 12:10
found in the land of the *l.* 28:13
is hid from the eyes of all *l.* 21
house appointed for all *l.* 30:23
enlightened with light of *l.* 33:30
of the Lord in land of *l.* *Ps* 27:13
thee out of the land of the *l.* 52:5
walk in the light of the *l.* 56:13
away both *l.*, and in his wrath. 58:9*
blotted out of the book of the *l.* 69:28
I will walk before the Lord in the land of the *l.* 116:9
thou art my portion in the land of the *l.* 142:5
in thy sight shall no man *l.* be justified. 143:2
the desire of every *l.* thing. 145:16
dead, more than the *l.* *Eccl* 4:2
I considered all the *l.* under the. 15
knoweth to walk before the *l.* 6:8
end of all men, and the *l.* will lay. 7:2
joined to all the *l.*, for a *l.* dog is. 9:4
for the *l.* know that they shall die. 5
a well of *l.* water. *S of S* 4:15
is written among the *l.* in. *Isa* 4:3
seek to their God for the *l.* to. 8:19
Lord in the land of the *l.* 38:11
the *l.* the *l.* he shall praise thee. 19
out of the land of the *l.* 53:8
forsaken fountain of *l.* waters. *Jer* 2:13; 17:13
off from the land of the *l.* 11:19
wherefore doth a *l.* man? *Lam* 3:39
glory in the land of the *l.* 26:20
caused terror in the land of the *l.* 32:23, 24, 25, 26, 27, 32
I have more than any *l.* *Dan* 2:30
to the intent that the *l.* may. 4:17
l. waters shall go out. *Zech* 14:8
not the God of the dead, but of the *l.* *Mat* 22:23; *Mark* 12:27 *Luke* 20:38
she had, even all her *l.* *Mark* 12:44
woman had spent all her *l.* *Luke* 8:43
he divided unto them his *l.* 15:12
substance with riotous *l.* *Luke* 15:13, 30
why seek ye the *l.* among? 24:5
given thee *l.* water. *John* 4:10
whence hast thou that *l.* water? 11
I am the *l.* bread which came. 6:51
as the *l.* Father hath sent me. 57
shall flow rivers of *l.* water. 7:38
your bodies a *l.* sacrifice. *Rom* 12:1
be Lord both of dead and *l.* 14:9
first man Adam was made a *l.* soul. *1 Cor* 15:45
l. in the world, are ye? *Col* 2:20
l. in malice, envy, and. *Tit* 3:3
enter by a new and *l.* *Heb* 10:20
coming as to a *l.* stone. *1 Pet* 2:4
Lamb shall lead them to *l.* *Rev* 7:17*
every *l.* soul died in the sea. 16:3
see **bird, creature, God**

lizard

the *l.*, snail, and mole. *Lev* 11:30

lo

l. Sarah thy wife shall. *Gen* 18:10
l. it is yet high day, water ye. 29:7
l. I die. 50:5
l. I come in a cloud. *Ex* 19:9
l. we be here, and will. *Num* 14:40
l. the Lord hath kept thee. 24:11
I did but taste honey, and *l.* I must die. *1 Sam* 14:43
l. I have sinned and. *2 Sam* 24:17
strength, *l.* he is strong. *Job* 9:19
away, and *l.* he was not. *Ps* 37:36
l. I come. 40:7
l. we heard it at Ephratah. 132:6
l. the man that made not God. 52:7
l. they that are far from. 73:27
l. thine enemies, for *l.* thine. 92:9
l. this only have I found. *Eccl* 7:29
l. the winter is past. *S of S* 2:11
l. this is our God, we. *Isa* 25:9
the earth, and *l.* it was. *Jer* 4:23
I beheld, and *l.* there was no. 25
l. certainly in vain made he it. 8:8
for *l.* I begin to bring evil. 25:29
when *l.* he had given. *Ezek* 17:18
for *l.* it cometh. 30:9
l. it will come. 33:33
for *l.* they are gone. *Hos* 9:6
l. the days shall come. *Amos* 4:2
ye looked for much, and *l.* *Hag* 1:9
and *l.* the heavens were. *Mat* 3:16
l., here is Christ, or there. 24:23
l. I have told you. 28:7
l. I am with you. 20
Satan bound, *l.* these. *Luke* 13:16
l. nothing worthy of death. 23:15
unworthy, *l.* we turn to. *Acts* 13:46
l. I come to do thy will. *Heb* 10:7, 9

loaden

carriages were heavy *l.* *Isa* 46:1*

loadeth

Lord, who daily *l.* us. *Ps* 68:19*

loaf

(*A loaf in Palestine in Bible times was a round, flat, crisp cake of dough baked on the hearth*)

one *l.* of bread, one cake. *Ex* 29:23
every one a *l.* of bread. *1 Chr* 16:3
they more than one *l.* *Mark* 8:14

Lo-ammi

call his name *L.* for ye. *Hos* 1:9

loan

for the *l.* which is lent. *1 Sam* 2:20†

loath, *see* **lothe**

loaves

take ten *l.* and run. *1 Sam* 17:17
made haste and took 200 *l.* 25:18
take with thee ten *l.* *1 Ki* 14:3
the man of God 20 *l.* *2 Ki* 4:42
have here but five *l.* *Mat* 14:17
and he took the five *l.* 19 *Mark* 6:38; *Luke* 9:13
said, How many *l.* have ye? *Mat* 15:34; *Mark* 6:38; 8:5
he took the seven *l.* and the fishes. *Mat* 15:36; *Mark* 8:6
the five *l.* of the 5000. *Mat* 16:9
nor the seven *l.* of the 4000. 10
eat of the *l.* were 5000. *Mark* 6:44
not the miracle of the *l.* 52
Friend, lend me three *l.* *Luke* 11:5
who hath five barley *l.* *John* 6:9
Jesus took the *l.* and distributed. 11
fragments of the barley *l.* 13
because ye did eat of the *l.* 26
see **bread**

***wave* loaves**

shall bring two *wave l.* *Lev* 23:17

lock

myrrh on the handles of the *l.* *S of S* 5:5*

locked

the doors and *l.* them. *Judg* 3:23
doors of the parlour were *l.* 24

locks

let the *l.* of the hair of his. *Num* 6:5
seven *l.* of my head. *Judg* 16:13
to shave off the seven *l.* 19
set up doors, and *l.* thereof. *Neh* 3:3*, 6*, 13*, 14*, 15*
doves' eyes within thy *l.* *S of S* 4:1*
pomegranate within thy *l.* 3*
my *l.* are filled with the drops. 5:2
his *l.* are bushy, and black as. 11
thy temples within thy *l.* 6:7*
uncover thy *l.*, make bare. *Isa* 47:2
nor suffer their *l.* to. *Ezek* 44:20
see **bars**

locust

(*An insect of the grasshopper family, which travels in swarms, and commits great ravages on vegetation. It has been used as food from the earliest times, and resembles the shrimp in taste. At the present time it is eaten by only the poorest people*)

remained not one *l.* in. *Ex* 10:19
l. after his kind, and bald *l.* ye. *Lev* 11:22
all thy trees shall the *l.* *Deut* 28:42
if there be in the land *l.* *1 Ki* 8:37 *2 Chr* 6:28
also their labour to the *l.* *Ps* 78:46
tossed up and down as the *l.* 109:23
l. eaten, and that which *l.* *Joel* 1:4
restore the years that the *l.* 2:25

locusts

to-morrow I will bring *l.* *Ex* 10:4
hand over Egypt for the *l.* 12
the east wind brought the *l.* 13
no such *l.* 14
the west wind took away the *l.* 19
l. shall consume it. *Deut* 28:38
if I command the *l.* to. *2 Chr* 7:13
he spake, and *l.* came. *Ps* 105:34
the *l.* have no king, yet. *Pr* 30:27
running to and fro of *l.* *Isa* 33:4
thyself many as the *l.* *Nah* 3:15
thy crowned are as the *l.* and. 17
his meat was *l.* and wild honey. *Mat* 3:4; *Mark* 1:6
came out of the smoke *l.* *Rev* 9:3
shapes of *l.* were like to horses. 7

lodge

daughter of Zion is left as a *l.* in garden. *Isa* 1:8

lodge

the house for us to *l.* in. *Gen* 24:23
enough, and room to *l.* 25
them, *l.* here this night. *Num* 22:8
place where ye shall *l.* *Josh* 4:3
l. here, that thy heart. *Judg* 19:9
to *l.* in Gibeah or in Ramah. 13, 15 20:4
the old man said, Only *l.* not. 19:20
thou lodgest I will *l.* *Ruth* 1:16
thy father will not *l.* *2 Sam* 17:8
l. not this night in the plains. 16
let every one *l.* within. *Neh* 4:22
why *l.* ye about the wall? 13:21
they cause the naked to *l.* *Job* 24:7*
stranger did not *l.* in street. 31:32
my beloved, let us *l.* *S of S* 7:11
of Arabia shall ye *l.* *Isa* 21:13
and *l.* in monuments, and eat. 65:4
shall thy vain thoughts *l.*? *Jer* 4:14
beasts shall *l.* in upper. *Zeph* 2:14
birds of the air come and *l.* in the. *Mat* 13:32; *Mark* 4:32
with whom we should *l.* *Acts* 21:16

lodged
Jacob *l.* there that same. *Gen* 32:13
and himself *l.* that night in the. 21
into harlot's house, and *l.* *Josh* 2:1*
he and all Israel, and *l.* there. 3:1
over to the place where they *l.* 4:8
came to the camp, and *l.* in. 6:11
but Joshua *l.* that night among. 8:9
of Micah, they *l.* there. *Judg* 18:2
eat and drink, and *l.* there. 19:4
urged him, therefore he *l.* 7
into a cave, and *l.* there. *1 Ki* 19:9
they *l.* round about the. *1 Chr* 9:27
merchants *l.* without. *Neh* 13:20
righteousness *l.* in it, but. *Isa* 1:21
to Bethany and *l.* there. *Mat* 21:17
Simon were *l.* there. *Acts* 10:18
called he them in, and *l.* them. 23
Publius *l.* us three days. 28:7*
if she have *l.* strangers. *1 Tim* 5:10*

lodgest
Ruth said, Where thou *l.* *Ruth* 1:16

lodgeth
l. with one Simon a. *Acts* 10:6

lodging
leave them in the *l.* *Josh* 4:3
them to his house to *l.* *Judg* 19:15
have taken up their *l.* at. *Isa* 10:29
the wilderness a *l.* place. *Jer* 9:2
many to him into his *l.* *Acts* 28:23
prepare me also a *l.* *Philem* 22

lodgings
I will enter into the *l.* *2 Ki* 19:23

loft
and carried him into a *l.* *1 Ki* 17:19*
Eutychus fell down from the third *l.*
Acts 20:9*

loftily
corrupt, they speak *l.* *Ps* 73:8

loftiness
l. of man shall be bowed. *Isa* 2:17
the pride of Moab, his *l.* *Jer* 48:29

lofty
haughty, nor mine eyes *l.* *Ps* 131:1
a generation, O how *l.* are ! *Pr* 30:13
the *l.* looks of man shall. *Isa* 2:11
5:15
Lord be on every one that is *l.* 12*
the *l.* city he layeth low to. 26:5
on a *l.* mountain hast thou. 57:7
thus saith high and *l.* One. 15

log
(*A measure; two-thirds of a pint*)
the priest shall take a *l.* of oil.
Lev 14:10, 12, 24
shall take some of the *l.* of oil. 15
then he shall take a *l.* of oil. 21

loins
(*The word is used often in the phrase to gird up the loins, which means to prepare for active work, since the eastern peoples commonly wore flowing garments and when they wished to be active tucked them up out of the way*)
shall come out of thy *l.* *Gen* 35:11
put sackcloth upon his *l.* 37:34
the souls which came out of his *l.*
46:26; *Ex* 1:5
eat it, with your *l.* girded. *Ex* 12:11
breeches reach from the *l.* 28:42
smite through the *l.* of. *Deut* 33:11
sword fastened on his *l.* *2 Sam* 20:8
the girdle about his *l.* *1 Ki* 2:5
son shall come forth of thy *l.* 8:19
2 Chr 6:9
thicker than my father's *l.* *1 Ki* 12:10
2 Chr 10:10
Elijah girded up his *l.* *1 Ki* 18:46
put sackcloth on our *l.* 20:31
girded sackcloth on their *l.* 32
girt with girdle of leather about his *l.*
2 Ki 1:8; *Mat* 3:4; *Mark* 1:6
gird up thy *l.* *2 Ki* 4:29; 9:1
Job 38:3; 40:7; *Jer* 1:17
he girdeth the *l.* of kings. *Job* 12:18
if his *l.* have not blessed me. 31:20
his strength is in his *l.* 40:16
my *l.* are filled with a. *Ps* 38:7
affliction upon our *l.* 66:11
and make their *l.* continually. 69:23
girdeth her *l.* with strength. *Pr* 31:17
girdle of their *l.* be loosed. *Isa* 5:27
shall be the girdle of his *l.* 11:5
sackcloth from off thy *l.*, put. 20:2
are my *l.* filled with pain. 21:3
gird sackcloth upon your *l.* 32:11
I will loose the *l.* of kings to. 45:1
girdle and put it upon thy *l.* *Jer* 13:1
as the girdle cleaveth to the *l.* 11
man with his hands on his *l.* 30:6
and upon the *l.* shall be. 48:37
appearance of his *l.* upward.
Ezek 1:27
l. downward, fire; from his *l.* 8:2
sigh with the breaking of thy *l.* 21:6
with girdles upon their *l.* 23:15
thou madest all their *l.* to be. 29:7
have linen breeches on their *l.* 44:18
the waters were to the *l.* 47:4
so the joints of his *l.* were. *Dan* 5:6
l. were girded with fine gold. 10:5
bring sackcloth on your *l.* *Amos* 8:10
make thy *l.* strong. *Nah* 2:1
pain is in all *l.* 10
let your *l.* be girded. *Luke* 12:35
of his *l.* he would raise. *Acts* 2:30
having your *l.* girt about. *Eph* 6:14
they came out of the *l.* of. *Heb* 7:5
for he was yet in the *l.* of his. 10
wherefore gird up the *l.* *1 Pet* 1:13

Lois
in thy grandmother *L.* *2 Tim* 1:5

long
fed me all my life *l.* *Gen* 48:15
trumpet soundeth *l.* *Ex* 19:13, 19
that thy days may be *l.* on. 20:12
when the cloud tarried *l.* *Num* 9:19
ye dwelt *l.* enough. *Deut* 1:6; 2:3
and shalt have remained *l.* 4:25
if the way be too *l.* for thee. 14:24
overtake him, because way is *l.* 19:6
make great plagues and of *l.* 28:59
when they make a *l.* blast. *Josh* 6:5
old, by reason of the very *l.* 9:13
ye dwelt in the wilderness a *l.* 24:7*
there was *l.* war between. *2 Sam* 3:1
and hast not asked *l.* life. *1 Ki* 3:11
2 Chr 1:11
for a *l.* season Israel. *2 Chr* 15:3
l. life will I satisfy him. *Ps* 91:16
forty years *l.* was I grieved. 95:10
my soul *l.* dwelt with him. 120:6
plowers made *l.* their furrows. 129:3
those that have been *l.* dead. 143:3
and *l.* life shall they. *Pr* 3:2*
the goodman is gone a *l.* 7:19
that tarry *l.* at the wine. 23:30
by *l.* forbearing is a prince. 25:15
man goeth to his *l.* home. *Eccl* 12:5
my elect shall *l.* enjoy. *Isa* 65:22
this captivity is *l.*: build. *Jer* 29:28
shall the women eat their children of a span *l.*? *Lam* 2:20*
a great eagle *l.*-winged. *Ezek* 17:3
his branches became *l.* because. 31:5
suffer their locks to grow *l.* 44:20
time appointed was *l.* *Dan* 10:1*
not stay *l.* in the place of. *Hos* 13:13
repented *l.* ago in sackcloth and.
Mat 11:21
and for pretence make *l.* prayers.
23:14; *Mark* 12:40; *Luke* 20:47
who go in *l.* clothing. *Mark* 12:38
Luke 20:46
sitting clothed in a *l.* *Mark* 16:5
avenge, though he bear *l.* *Luke* 18:7*
to see him of a *l.* season. 23:8
as Paul was *l.* preaching. *Acts* 20:9*
l. after there arose a tempest. 27:14
but after *l.* abstinence Paul. 21
if a man have *l.* hair. *1 Cor* 11:14
if a woman have *l.* hair it is a. 15
that thou mayest live *l.* *Eph* 6:3
if I tarry *l.* that thou. *1 Tim* 3:15
the husbandman hath *l.* *Jas* 5:7*
see **ago, cubits, day**

long, *verb*
which *l.* for death, but. *Job* 3:21
grant me thing that I *l.* for! 6:8
for I *l.* to see you, that. *Rom* 1:11
by their prayer which *l.* *2 Cor* 9:14
how greatly I *l.* after you. *Phil* 1:8

as **long** *as*
as l. as she is put apart. *Lev* 18:19
enjoy sabbaths, *as l. as* it. 26:34, 35
as l. as the cloud abode. *Num* 9:18
forsake not the Levite *as l. as* thou.
Deut 12:19
fear the Lord *as l. as* you live. 31:13
lent to the Lord, *as l. as*. *1 Sam* 1:28
as l. as son of Jesse liveth. 20:31
any thing *as l. as* we were. 25:15
as l. as he sought the Lord he prospered. *2 Chr* 26:5
as l. as she lay desolate she. 36:21
fear thee *as l. as* sun and. *Ps* 72:5
be continued *as l. as* the sun. 17
to the Lord *as l. as* I live. 104:33
call upon him *as l. as* I live. 116:2
as l. as they, and as broad as they.
Ezek 42:11*
as l. as bridegroom is with them.
Mat 9:15; *Mark* 2:19
as l. as I am in the world. I am the.
John 9:5*
dominion over a man *as l. as* he.
Rom 7:1
wife is bound *as l. as* her. *1 Cor* 7:39
heir *as l. as* he is a child. *Gal* 4:1
daughters ye are *as l. as*. *1 Pet* 3:6*
as l. as I am in this tabernacle.
2 Pet 1:13

so **long**
is his chariot *so l.* in? *Judg* 5:28
found in thy servant, *so l.* *1 Sam* 29:8
so l. as the whoredoms. *2 Ki* 9:22
they may fear thee *so l.* *2 Chr* 6:31
so l. as I see Mordecai. *Esth* 5:13
shall not reproach me *so l.* *Job* 27:6
peace *so l.* as the moon. *Ps* 72:7
that he tarried *so l.* *Luke* 1:21
bound to her husband *so l.* *Rom* 7:2
to-day, after *so l.* a time. *Heb* 4:7

long *time*
been there a *l. time.* *Gen* 26:8
dwelt in Egypt a *l. time.* *Num* 20:15
besiege a city a *l. time.* *Deut* 20:19
war a *l. time* with kings. *Josh* 11:18
a *l. time* after that Joshua. 23:1*
ark abode the *time* was *l.* *1 Sam* 7:2
woman that had *l. time.* *2 Sam* 14:2
not done it of a *l. time.* *2 Chr* 30:5*
l. time holden my peace. *Isa* 42:14
and forsake us so *l. time.* *Lam* 5:20
after a *l. time* the lord of those servants. *Mat* 25:19; *Luke* 20:9
which had devils *l. time.* *Luke* 8:27
into a far country for a *l. time.* 20:9
that he had been a *l. time.* *John* 5:6
have I been so *l. time* with? 14:9
because of *l. time* he had. *Acts* 8:11
l. time abode they with. 14:3, 28
judgement of *l. time.* *2 Pet* 2:3*

long *while*
he talked a *l. while* till. *Acts* 20:11

longed
David *l.* to go forth. *2 Sam* 13:39
David *l.* and said, O that one. 23:15
1 Chr 11:17
behold, I have *l.* after. *Ps* 119:40
l. for thy commandments. 131
I have *l.* for thy salvation. 174
for he *l.* after you all. *Phil* 2:26
brethren dearly beloved and *l.* 4:1

longedst
thou sore *l.* after thy. *Gen* 21:30

longer
she could no *l.* hide him. *Ex* 2:3
you go, and ye shall stay no *l.* 9:28
could not any *l.* stand. *Judg* 2:14
he tarried *l.* than the. *2 Sam* 20:5
wait for the Lord any *l.*? *2 Ki* 6:33
the measure thereof is *l.* *Job* 11:9
Lord could no *l.* bear. *Jer* 44:22
for thou mayest be no *l.* *Luke* 16:2
desired him to tarry *l.* *Acts* 18:20
he ought not to live any *l.* 25:24
dead to sin, live any *l.* *Rom* 6:2
no *l.* under a schoolmaster. *Gal* 3:25
when we could no *l.* forbear.
1 Thes 3:1, 5
drink no *l.* water, but. *1 Tim* 5:23
that he no *l.* live the rest. *1 Pet* 4:2
should be time no *l.* *Rev* 10:6

longeth

my son Shechem *l.* for. *Gen* 34:8
because thy soul *l.* to. *Deut* 12:20
my flesh *l.* for thee in. *Ps* 63:1
my soul *l.* for the courts of. 84:2

longing

fail with *l.* for them. *Deut* 28:32
satisfieth the *l.* soul. *Ps* 107:9
my soul breaketh for the *l.* 119:20

longsuffering

Lord God merciful and gracious, *l.* *Ex* 34:6*; *Num* 14:18* *Ps* 86:15*; *2 Pet* 3:9
O Lord, take me not away in thy *l.* *Jer* 15:15
thou the riches of his *l.* *Rom* 2:4
endured with much *l.* vessels. 9:22
by knowledge, by *l.* *2 Cor* 6:6
of the Spirit is love, *l.* *Gal* 5:22
l., forbearing one another. *Eph* 4:2
strengthened to all *l.* with. *Col* 1:11
as elect of God, meekness, *l.* 3:12
Christ might shew all *l.* *1 Tim* 1:16
fully known my faith, *l.* *2 Tim* 3:10
rebuke, exhort with all *l.* and. 4:2
when *l.* of God waited. *1 Pet* 3:20
l. of our Lord is salvation. *2 Pet* 3:15

look, -s

bring down high *l.* *Ps* 18:27
that hath a high *l.* I will not. 101:5
a proud *l.*, a lying tongue. *Pr* 6:17*
high *l.* and proud heart is sin. 21:4
the lofty *l.* of man shall be. *Isa* 2:11
punish the glory of his high *l.* 10:12
dismayed at their *l.* *Ezek* 2:6; 3:9
whose *l.* was more stout. *Dan* 7:20

look, *verb*

l. from the place where. *Gen* 13:14
l. towards heaven, and tell. 15:5
thy life, *l.* not behind thee. 19:17
l. ye so sadly to-day? 40:7
now let Pharaoh *l.* out a man. 41:33
Jacob said, Why *l.* ye one? 42:1
l. to it; for evil is. *Ex* 10:10
and their faces shall *l.* 25:20
l. that thou make them after. 40
then the priest shall *l.* *Lev* 13:39
priest shall *l.* and behold. 53, 56
shall *l.* if the plague. 14:3, 39, 44
l. not to the stubbornness. *Deut* 9:27
thine eyes shall *l.* and fail. 28:32
ruddy, and goodly to *l.* *1 Sam* 16:12
l. how thy brethren fare. 17:18
go up now, *l.* toward. *1 Ki* 18:43
I would not *l.* toward. *2 Ki* 3:14
l. when messenger cometh. 6:32
l. out there Jehu, and go in. 9:2
l. even out best and meetest. 10:3
l. there be none of the servants. 23
come, let us *l.* one another. 14:8
God of our fathers *l.* *1 Chr* 12:17
let it *l.* for light, but. *Job* 3:9
therefore shall no man *l.* 20:21*
l. to heavens and see, and. 35:5
my prayer to thee, and *l.* *Ps* 5:3*
that I am not able to *l.* up. 40:12
as the eyes of servants *l.* to. 123:2
let thine eyes *l.* right on. *Pr* 4:25
to know thy flocks, and *l.* well. 27:23
l. out at the windows. *Eccl* 12:3
l. from top of Amana. *S of S* 4:8
if one *l.* unto the land. *Isa* 5:30
on the Lord, I will *l.* for him. 8:17
curse their king and God, and *l.* 21
they shall *l.* unto earth, and. 22
in that day shall a man *l.* 17:7
he shall not *l.* to the altars. 8
l. away from me; I will weep. 22:4
l. in that day to the armour. 8
l. not to the Holy One of Israel. 31:1
hear ye deaf, *l.* ye blind, that. 42:18
l. unto me, and be saved, all. 45:22
l. to the rock whence ye are. 51:1
l. to Abraham your father and to. 2
they all *l.* to their own way. 56:11*
we *l.* for judgement, but. 59:11
but to this man will I *l.* that. 66:2
and while ye *l.* for light. *Jer* 13:16
take and *l.* well to him, do. 39:12
come with me and I will *l.* well. 40:4
mighty ones are fled, and *l.* 46:5
the fathers shall not *l.* back. 47:3
all of them princes to *l.* *Ezek* 23:15
remembrance when they *l.* 29:16
who *l.* to other gods, and. *Hos* 3:1
I will *l.* again towards. *Jonah* 2:4
I will *l.* unto the Lord. *Mi* 7:7
but none shall *l.* back. *Nah* 2:8
or do we *l.* for another? *Mat* 11:3 *Luke* 7:19, 20
hands on eyes, and made him *l.* up. *Mark* 8:25
things begin, then *l.* up. *Luke* 21:28
search and *l.*: for out of. *John* 7:52
l. ye out seven men of. *Acts* 6:3
be a question of words, *l.* ye. 18:15
I *l.* for him with the brethren. *1 Cor* 16:11
Israel could not stedfastly *l.* to the end. *2 Cor* 3:13
while we *l.* not at things which. 4:18
from whence we *l.* for. *Phil* 3:20
to them that *l.* for him. *Heb* 9:28
angels desire to *l.* into. *1 Pet* 1:12
we *l.* for new heavens. *2 Pet* 3:13
seeing ye *l.* for such things, be. 14
l. to yourselves, that we. *2 John* 8
and no man was able to *l.* *Rev* 5:3
worthy to read the book nor *l.* 4

look *down*

l. down from thy holy. *Deut* 26:15
l. down, behold, and visit. *Ps* 80:14
righteousness shall *l. down.* 85:11
l. down from heaven, and. *Isa* 63:15
till Lord *l. down* and behold from heaven. *Lam* 3:50

look *on*, or *upon*

be in cloud, and I will *l. upon* it. *Gen* 9:16
art a fair woman to *l. upon.* 12:11
Rebekah was very fair to *l. upon.* 24:16; 26:7
afraid to *l. upon* God. *Ex* 3:6
Lord *l. upon* you and judge. 5:21
and Moses did *l. upon* all. 39:43
l. on the plague in the skin of the flesh. *Lev* 13:3, 21, 25, 26, 31 32, 34, 43, 50
the priest shall *l. on* him. 3, 5, 6 27, 36
the priest shall *l. upon* it. 14:48
for a fringe, that ye may *l. upon* it. *Num* 15:39
Gideon said, *L. on* me. *Judg* 7:17
if thou wilt indeed *l. on.* *1 Sam* 1:11
l. not *on* his countenance or. 16:7
l. upon such a dead dog. *2 Sam* 9:8
very beautiful to *l upon.* 11:2
Lord will *l. on* my affliction. 16:12
Lord *l. upon* it and require it. *2 Chr* 24:22
queen was fair to *l. on.* *Esth* 1:11
be content, *l. upon* me. *Job* 6:28
l. on every one that is proud. 40:12
stare and *l. upon* me. *Ps* 22:17
l. upon mine affliction and. 25:18*
how long wilt thou *l. on*? 35:17
and *l. upon* the face of thine. 84:9
l. thou *upon* me, and be. 119:132*
let thine eyes *l.* right *on.* *Pr* 4:25
l. not thou *upon* the wine. 23:31
l. not *upon* me, because I am black. *S of S* 1:6
return, that we may *l. upon.* 6:13
narrowly *l. upon* thee. *Isa* 14:16
l. upon Zion. 33:20
l. upon the earth beneath. 51:6
forth and *l. upon* the carcases. 66:24
let our eye *l. upon* Zion. *Mi* 4:11
l. upon thee, shall flee. *Nah* 3:7
purer eyes than to *l. upon* iniquity. *Hab* 1:13
mayest *l. upon* their nakedness. 2:15
l. upon me whom they pierced. *Zech* 12:10
I beseech thee, *l. upon.* *Luke* 9:38
your eyes, and *l. upon.* *John* 4:35
l. upon him whom they pierced. 19:37
Peter and John said, *L. on us.* *Acts* 3:4, 12*
l. upon things after outward appearance. *2 Cor* 10:7
l. not every man *on* his. *Phil* 2:4
he that sat was to *l. upon.* *Rev* 4:3

looked

God *l.* on the earth and it. *Gen* 6:12
the men rose up, and *l.* 18:16
his wife *l.* back. 19:26
l. out at a window. 26:8
the Lord hath *l.* upon my. 29:32
the keeper of the prison *l.* not. 39:23
Joseph *l.* on them, behold they. 40:6
Moses went and *l.* on. *Ex* 2:11
he *l.* this way and that way. 12
and God *l.* upon the children. 25
Lord had *l.* on their affliction. 4:31 *Deut* 26:7
the Lord *l.* on the host of. *Ex* 14:24
l. toward the wilderness. 16:10
the people *l.* after Moses till. 33:8
Aaron *l.* on Miriam. *Num* 12:10
l. towards the tabernacle. 16:42
he *l.* on Amalek, he took up. 24:20
l. on the Kenites, and took up. 21
when the men of Ai *l.* *Josh* 8:20
mother of Sisera *l.* out. *Judg* 5:28
the Lord *l.* upon him, and said. 6:14
Manoah and his wife *l.* on. 13:19, 30
Benjamites *l.* behind them. 20:40
they had *l.* into the ark. *1 Sam* 6:19
I have *l.* on my people. 9:16
the watchmen of Saul *l.* and. 14:16
when they were come, he *l.* 16:6
the Philistines *l.* about, and. 17:42
Saul *l.* behind him, David stood. 24:8; *2 Sam* 1:7
Abner *l.* behind him. *2 Sam* 2:20
Michal *l.* through a window. 6:16
they *l.* but there was none. 22:42
servant went up and *l.* *1 Ki* 18:43
turned back and *l.* on. *2 Ki* 2:24
the people *l.* and behold he. 6:30
Jezebel painted, and *l.* out at. 9:30
l. one another in the face at. 14:11
when Judah *l.* back. *2 Chr* 13:14
l. on him, and behold he was. 26:20
sight of all who *l.* on her. *Esth* 2:15
troops of Tema *l.*, Sheba. *Job* 6:19
the Lord *l.* to see if any. *Ps* 14:2
l. to him, and were lightened. 34:5
God *l.* down on the children of. 53:2
l. down from his sanctuary. 102:19
l. they shaked their heads. 109:25
because the sun hath *l.* *S of S* 1:6*
he *l.* that it should bring. *Isa* 5:2
he *l.* for judgement, but behold. 7
ye have not *l.* to the maker. 22:11
terrible things which we *l.* not. 64:3
we *l.* for peace, no good came. *Jer* 8:15; 14:19
certainly this is the day that we *l.* for. *Lam* 2:16
whither the head *l.* they. *Ezek* 10:11
consulted with images, he *l.* 21:21
let our countenance be *l.* *Dan* 1:13
not have *l.* on the day. *Ob* 12
thou shouldest not have *l.* on. 13
ye *l.* for much, and lo it. *Hag* 1:9
when he *l.* round about. *Mark* 3:5 5:32; 10:23
he *l.* up to heaven, and blessed. 6:41
he *l.* and said, I see men as. 8:24
they *l.* they saw the stone. 16:4
l. on me to take away. *Luke* 1:25
to all that *l.* for redemption. 2:38
likewise a Levite came and *l.* 10:32
the Lord turned, and *l.* 22:61
then the disciples *l.* one. *John* 13:22
while they *l.* stedfastly. *Acts* 1:10
after they had *l.* a great while. 28:6*
for he *l.* for a city which. *Heb* 11:10
which we have *l.* upon. *1 John* 1:1

looked with *eyes*

Jacob lifted up his *eyes* and *l.* *Gen* 33:1
lifted up their *eyes* and *l.* 37:25
I lifted up mine *eyes* and *l.* *Dan* 10:5
Zechariah lifted his *eyes* and *l.* *Zech* 2:1; 5:9; 6:1

***I* looked**

have *I* also here *l.* after. *Gen* 16:13
I l. and behold ye had sinned. *Deut* 9:16
when *I l.* for good, then. *Job* 30:26
I l. for some to take pity. *Ps* 69:20
I l. on my right hand, and. 142:4
at the window, *I l.* through. *Pr* 7:6

I l. upon it, and received. *Pr* 24:32
I l. on all the works that. *Eccl* 2:11
I l. that it should bring forth grapes. *Isa* 5:4
and *I l.* and there was none to. 63:5
I l. and behold. *Ezek* 1:4; 2:9; 8:7 10:1, 9; 44:4
I Daniel *l.* and behold. *Dan* 12:5
I have *l.* and behold a candlestick. *Zech* 4:2
and the same hour *I l.* up. *Acts* 22:13
I l. and behold. *Rev* 4:1; 6:8; 14:1 14; 15:5

lookest

thou *l.* narrowly to all. *Job* 13:27*
why *l.* on them that deal? *Hab* 1:13

looketh

if leprosy cover wheresoever priest *l.* *Lev* 13:12*
when he *l.* on the serpent. *Num* 21:8
Pisgah, which *l.* toward. 20; 23:28
man *l.* on the outward. *1 Sam* 16:7
as an hireling *l.* for the. *Job* 7:2
l. to the ends of the earth. 28:24
he *l.* on men, and if any say. 33:27*
the Lord *l.* from heaven. *Ps* 33:13
he *l.* on all the inhabitants of. 14
he *l.* on the earth, and it. 104:32
the prudent *l.* well to. *Pr* 14:15
she *l.* well to the ways of. 31:27
he *l.* forth at the window. *S of S* 2:9
that *l.* forth as the morning? 6:10
as the tower which *l.* toward. 7:4
when he that *l.* upon it. *Isa* 28:4
the door that *l.* toward. *Ezek* 8:3
gate which *l.* eastward. 11:1; 40:6 22*; 43:1; 44:1; 46:1, 12; 47:2
gate of the court that *l.* 40:20
l. on a woman to lust. *Mat* 5:28
lord come when that servant *l.* not for him. 24:50; *Luke* 12:46
l. into the perfect law of. *Jas* 1:25

looking

three oxen *l.* toward the north. *1 Ki* 7:25
Michal *l.* out at a window, saw David. *1 Chr* 15:29
three oxen *l.* toward the south. *2 Chr* 4:4
mine eyes fail with *l.* upward. *Isa* 38:14
l. up to heaven, he blessed. *Mat* 14:19; *Luke* 9:16
and *l.* up to heaven, he. *Mark* 7:34
there were also women *l.* on. 15:40
l. round about them all. *Luke* 6:10
and *l.* back, is fit for the. 9:62
hearts failing them for *l.* 21:26*
John *l.* on Jesus saith. *John* 1:36
l. in, saw linen clothes lying. 20:5
l. stedfastly on him, saw. *Acts* 6:15
they ready, *l.* for a promise. 23:21
l. for that blessed hope. *Tit* 2:13
but a certain fearful *l.* for. *Heb* 10:27
l. unto Jesus the author and. 12:2
l. diligently, lest any fail of the. 15
l. for the coming of the. *2 Pet* 3:12
l. for the mercy of our Lord. *Jude* 21

lookingglass, -es

(*Properly, as in Revisions,* mirror, mirrors, *as they were made of polished metal, not of glass*)
laver and foot of *l.-glasses.* *Ex* 38:8
sky as a molten *l.-glass.* *Job* 37:18

loops

make *l.* of blue. *Ex* 26:4, 5
l. shalt thou make. 5, 10
put taches in the *l.* 11
made *l.* of blue. 36:11
fifty *l.* made he. 12, 17

loose

Naphtali is a hind let *l.* *Gen* 49:21
let the living bird *l.* into. *Lev* 14:7
he would let *l.* his hand and cut me. *Job* 6:9
they have let *l.* the bridle. 30:11
lo I see four men *l.* *Dan* 3:25

loose, *verb*

and *l.* his shoe from. *Deut* 25:9
l. thy shoe from off thy. *Josh* 5:15
canst thou *l.* the bands of? *Job* 38:31
l. those that are appointed to death. *Ps* 102:20
go and *l.* the sackcloth. *Isa* 20:2
I will *l.* the loins of kings. 45:1
O Jerusalem, *l.* thyself from. 52:2
to *l.* the bands of wickedness. 58:6
and now behold I *l.* thee. *Jer* 40:4
whatsoever ye *l.* on earth. *Mat* 16:9; 18:18
an ass tied and colt, *l.* and bring. 21:2; *Mark* 11:2, 4; *Luke* 19:30
why do ye *l.* him? *Luke* 19:31, 33
Jesus said, *L.* him. *John* 11:44
shoes of his feet I am not worthy to *l.* *Acts* 13:25
been given, that he might *l.* 24:26
who is worthy to *l.* the seals? *Rev* 5:2
hath prevailed to *l.* the seven. 5
l. the four angels bound in. 9:14

loosed

that the breastplate be not *l.* *Ex* 28:28; 39:21
him that hath his shoe *l.* *Deut* 25:10
his bands *l.* from off. *Judg* 15:14
because he *l.* my cord. *Job* 30:11
l. the bands of the wild ass? 39:5
the king sent and *l.* him. *Ps* 105:20
thy servant, thou hast *l.* 116:16
silver cord be *l.*, or bowl. *Eccl* 12:6
girdle of their loins be *l.* *Isa* 5:27
tacklings are *l.* they could. 33:23
hasteneth that he may be *l.* 51:14
joints of his loins were *l.* *Dan* 5:6
thou shalt loose on earth, shall be *l.* in heaven. *Mat* 16:19; 18:18
with compassion, and *l.* him. 18:27*
the string of his tongue was *l.* *Mark* 7:35; *Luke* 1:64
woman, thou art *l.* from. *Luke* 13:12
ought not this woman to be *l.*? 16
raised up, having *l.* the. *Acts* 2:24
when Paul and his company *l.* 13:13
every one's bands were *l.* 16:26
on the morrow he *l.* him from. 22:30
hearkened, and not have *l.* 27:21
l. the rudder bands, and hoised. 40
be dead, she is *l.* from. *Rom* 7:2*
art thou *l.* from wife? *1 Cor* 7:27
the four angels were *l.* *Rev* 9:15
after that he must be *l.* a. 20:3, 7

looseth

he *l.* the bond of kings. *Job* 12:18
food to hungry, the Lord *l.* *Ps* 149:7

loosing

what do ye, *l.* the colt? *Mark* 11:5
as they were *l.* the colt. *Luke* 19:33
l. from Troas, we came. *Acts* 16:11*
l. thence, they sailed close. 27:13

lop

behold the Lord shall *l.* *Isa* 10:33

Lord

(*This word means, in general, one with power and authority, a master or ruler. The Hebrew word transliterated Jehovah is usually rendered in the Old Testament by* LORD *written in small capitals. This the American Revision changes to* Jehovah. *Otherwise the word is used for Jesus Christ, for the Holy Spirit, for a husband, and for any one whom it was desired to address deferentially*)
too hard for the *L.*? *Gen* 18:14
the *L.* before whom I walk. 24:40
we saw certainly the *L.* 26:28
again, then shall the *L.* be. 28:21
L. was with Joseph. 39:2, 21, 23
who is the *L.* that I should obey? *Ex* 5:2
and the *L.* did so, and there. 8:24
the earth is the *L.'s.* 9:29; *Ps* 24:1 *1 Cor* 10:26
the *L.* be so with you, as I. *Ex* 10:10
because of that which the *L.* 13:8
beast the male shall be the *L.'s.* 12
be unto thee holy for the *L.* 30:37
on the *L.'s* side? let him come. 32:26
for *L.* whose name is jealous. 34:14
all the fat is the *L.'s.* *Lev* 3:16
Aaron shall cast one lot for the *L.* 16:8; 25:4; 27:2
thou *L.* art among this people, that thou *L.* art seen face. *Num* 14:14
therefore the *L.* will not be. 43
are given as a gift for the *L.* 18:6
that I may know what the *L.* 22:19
all that the *L.* speaketh that. 23:26
the *L.* hath kept thee back. 24:11
brought oblation for the *L.* 31:50
for they have wholly followed the *L.* 32:12; *Deut* 1:36
so shall the *L.* do to all kingdoms. *Deut* 3:21
know that the *L.* he is God. 4:35 39; *1 Ki* 18:39
I stood between the *L.* and you. *Deut* 5:5
heaven of heavens is the *L.'s.* 10:14
L. of lords, a great God, a. 17
ye have seen all that the *L.* 29:2
L. hath not given you an heart to. 4
hath the *L.* done thus to this land? 24; *1 Ki* 9:8; *2 Chr* 7:21
L. shall do to them as he did to Sihon. *Deut* 31:4
do ye thus requite the *L.*? 32:6
to flight, except the *L.* had. 30
O people, saved by the *L.* 33:29
swear unto me by the *L.* *Josh* 2:12 *1 Sam* 24:21
even the *L.* of all the. *Josh* 3:11, 13
the *L.* do to all your enemies. 10:25
if so be the *L.* will be with me. 14:12
the *L.* was with Judah. *Judg* 1:19
and the *L.* was with the house. 22
which knew not the *L.* 2:10
is not the *L.* gone out before? 4:14
if the *L.* be with us, why is? 6:13
meet me shall surely be the *L.* 11:31
now know I that the *L.* will. 17:13
L. do so to me and more. *Ruth* 1:17 *1 Sam* 20:13
the *L.* be with you. *Ruth* 2:4 *2 Chr* 20:17; *2 Thes* 3:16
none holy as the *L.* *1 Sam* 2:2
pillars of the earth are the *L.'s.* 8
it is the *L.* let him do what seemeth. 3:18; *John* 21:7
Samuel grew, and the *L.* *1 Sam* 3:19; 18:12, 14; *2 Ki* 18:7 *1 Chr* 9:20
this great thing which the *L.* will do. *1 Sam* 12:16
the *L.* be with thee. 17:37; 20:13 *1 Chr* 22:11, 16
the *L.* be between thee and me. *1 Sam* 20:23, 42
L. art become their God. *2 Sam* 7:24; *1 Chr* 17:22
L. do what seemeth him good. *2 Sam* 10:12; *1 Chr* 19:13
if the *L.* be God, follow. *1 Ki* 18:21
if the *L.* do not help. *2 Ki* 6:27
what should I wait for the *L.*? 33
and see my zeal for the *L.* 10:16
am I now come up without the *L.*? 18:25; *Isa* 36:10
for great is the *L.* *1 Chr* 16:25 *Ps* 48:1; 145:3
now *L.* thou art God. *1 Chr* 17:26
that which is thine for the *L.* 21:24
for man, but for the *L.* *2 Chr* 19:6
and the *L.* shall be with the good. 11
Manasseh knew that the *L.* 33:13
even that thou art *L.* alone. *Neh* 9:6 *Isa* 37:20
L. hath set apart the godly. *Ps* 4:3
nation, whose God is the *L.* 33:12
my bones say, *L.* who is? 35:10
for he is thy *L.*; worship. 45:11
if I regard iniquity, the *L.* will. 66:18
for thou *L.* art good, ready. 86:5
thou *L.* art most high for ever. 92:8 97:9
know ye that the *L.* he is God. 100:3
do thou for me, O God the *L.* 109:21; 140:7
they may know that thou *L.* 109:27
gracious is the *L.* and. 116:5
this is the *L.'s* doing; it is. 118:23
God is the *L.* 27
if it had not been the *L.* 124:1, 2
L. shouldest mark iniquity. 130:3
find out a place for the *L.* 132:5
lest the *L.* see it, and it. *Pr* 24:18

against the **Lord**

before the **Lord**

from the **Lord**

my help cometh *from the L.* *Ps* 121:2
of the tongue is *from the L.* *Pr* 16:1
prudent wife is *from the L.* 19:14
but every man's judgement cometh *from the L.* 29:26
their counsel *from the L.* *Isa* 29:15
my way is hid *from the L.* 40:27
word came to Jeremiah *from the L.* *Jer* 7:1; 11:1; 18:1; 21:1; 26:1; 27:1; 30:1; 32:1; 34:1, 8, 12; 35:1; 36:1; 40:1
heart departeth *from the L.* 17:5
is there any word *from the L.*? 37:17
heard a rumour *from the L.* 49:14
no vision *from the L.* *Lam* 2:9
hope is perished *from the L.* 3:18
get ye far *from the L.* *Ezek* 11:15
word that cometh *from the L.* 33:30
whoredom, departing *from the L.* *Hos* 1:2
a rumour *from the L.* arise. *Ob* 1
evil came down *from the L.* *Mi* 1:12
Jacob shall be as dew *from the L.* 5:7
turned back *from the L.* *Zeph* 1:6
tumult *from the L.* shall. *Zech* 14:13
told her *from the L.* *Luke* 1:45
we are absent *from the L.* *2 Cor* 5:6

Lord *God*

blessed be the *L. God.* *Gen* 9:26
Abram said, *L. God,* what wilt? 15:2
L. God, whereby shall I know? 8
the *L. God* of my master. 24:27
I am the *L. God* of Abraham. 28:13
the *L. God* of Israel. *Ex* 32:27; *Josh* 9:18, 19; 10:40, 42; 13:14, 33; 14:14
the *L. God* merciful and. 34:6
Joshua said, Alas, O *L. God.* *Josh* 7:7
L. God of gods, the *L. God* of. 22:22
ye to do with the *L. God* of? 24
the *L. God* of Israel. 24:2; *Judg* 4:6; 5:3, 5; 11:21, 23; 21:3; *Ruth* 2:12; *1 Sam* 2:30; 14:41; 20:12; 23:10; 25:32, 34; *1 Ki* 1:30; *1 Chr* 23:25; 24:19
alas, O *L. God,* because. *Judg* 6:22
O *L. God,* remember me only. 16:28
who is able to stand before this holy *L. God*? *1 Sam* 6:20
L. God of hosts was with him. *2 Sam* 5:10
who am I, O *L. God,* and? 7:18
manner of man, O *L. God*? 19
for thou, *L. God,* knowest thy. 20
thou art great, O *L. God.* 22
the *L. God* of my lord the king. *1 Ki* 1:36
king said, Blessed be the *L. God.* 48; 8:15; *1 Chr* 16:36; 29:10
good thing toward the *L. God.* *1 Ki* 14:13
As the *L. God* of Israel liveth. 17:1
may know thou art *L. God.* 18:37; *2 Ki* 19:19
where is *L. God* of Elijah? *2 Ki* 2:14
state of a man of high degree, O *L. God.* *1 Chr* 17:17
fight ye not against *L. God* of fathers. *2 Chr* 13:12
house of the *L. God* of fathers. 24:18
for thy honour from *L. God.* 26:18
spake more against *L. God.* 32:16
thou art the *L. God,* who didst choose Abram. *Neh* 9:7
redeemed me, O *L. God* of. *Ps* 31:5
L. God of Israel from everlasting to. 41:13; 72:18; 106:48; *Luke* 1:68
L. God might dwell. *Ps* 68:18
thou art my hope, O *L. God.* 71:5
for *L. God* is a sun and. 84:11
I will hear what the *L. God.* 85:8
heard from the *L. God.* *Isa* 28:22
for the *L. God* will help me. 50:7, 9
for *L. God* shall slay thee. 65:15
saying, The *L. God* liveth. *Jer* 44:26
As I live, saith the *L. God.* *Ezek* 5:11, 14, 16
I am the *L. God.* 13:9; 23:49; 24:24
thus it was, saith the *L. God.* 16:19
Woe unto thee, saith the *L. God.* 23
to his ways, saith the *L. God.* 18:30
to pass, saith the *L. God.* *Ezek* 21:7
no more, saith the *L. God.* 13
forgotten me, saith the *L. God.* 22:12
wrought for me, saith *L. God.* 29:20
your God, saith the *L. God.* 34:31
am the Lord, saith the *L. God.* 36:23
sakes do I this, saith the *L. God.* 32
and I answered, O *L. God.* 37:3
spoken it, saith the *L. God.* 39:5; 23:34; 26:14; 28:10
it is done, saith the *L. God.* 8
accept you, saith the *L. God.* 43:27
face unto the *L. God* to. *Dan* 9:3
even *L. God* of hosts is. *Hos* 12:5
Philistines shall perish, saith *L. God.* *Amos* 1:8
L. God will do nothing, but. 3:7
the *L. God* hath spoken, who? 8
liketh you, saith the *L. God.* 4:5
L. God of hosts is he that. 9:5
let the *L. God* be witness. *Mi* 1:2
L. God is my strength. *Hab* 3:19
sanctify the *L. God* in. *1 Pet* 3:15
holy, holy, *L. God* Almighty. *Rev* 4:8; 11:17; 16:7
thy works, *L. God* Almighty. 15:3
for strong is the *L. God* who. 18:8
for the *L. God* omnipotent. 19:6
the *L. God* and the Lamb. 21:22
the *L. God* giveth them light. 22:5
see **fathers**

Lord *his God*

besought the *L. his God.* *Ex* 32:11
against the commandments of the *L. his God.* *Lev* 4:22
L. his God is with him. *Num* 23:21
learn to fear the *L. his G.* *Deut* 17:19
in name of the *L. his God.* 18:7
encouraged himself in *L. his G.* *1 Sam* 30:6
an house unto the name of *L. his G.* *1 Ki* 5:3
heart was not perfect with *L. his G.* 11:4; 15:3
L. his God give a lamp in. 15:4
the sight of *L. his God.* *2 Ki* 16:2
L. his God was with him. *2 Chr* 1:1
right in eyes of the *L. his God.* 14:2
Asa cried unto the *L. his God.* 11
when they saw that *L. his G.* 15:9
Uzziah transgressed against the *L. his G.* 26:16
his ways before *L. his God.* 27:6
L. his G. delivered Ahaz. 28:5
Hezekiah wrought right before *L. his God.* 31:20
Manasseh in affliction besought *L. his God.* 33:12
repair house of the *L. his God.* 34:8
evil in sight of *L. his God.* 36:5, 12
the *L. his G.* be with him, and. 23
to hand of *L. his G.* *Ezra* 7:6
happy he whose hope is in the *L. his God.* *Ps* 146:5
prayed to the *L. his God.* *Jonah* 2:1
of the name of *L. his God.* *Mi* 5:4

Lord *my God*

the word of *L. my God.* *Num* 22:18
L. my God commanded. *Deut* 4:5
again voice of *L. my God.* 18:16
hearkened to voice of *L. my God.* 26:14
followed the *L. my God.* *Josh* 14:8
offerings to *L. my God.* *2 Sam* 24:24
O *L. my G.* *1 Ki* 3:7; 8:28; 17:20, 21; *1 Chr* 21:17; *2 Chr* 6:19; *Ps* 7:1, 3; 13:3; 30:2, 12; 35:24; 38:15; 40:5; 86:12; 109:26; *Jonah* 2:6; *Hab* 1:12
the *L. my God* hath given. *1 Ki* 5:4
house unto the name of the *L. my God.* 5; *1 Chr* 22:7; *2 Chr* 2:4
hand of the *L. my God.* *Ezra* 7:28
out my hands to the *L. my God.* 9:5
the *L. my God* will. *Ps* 18:28
for thou art *L. my God.* *Jer* 31:18
I prayed unto the *L. my God.* *Dan* 9:4
supplication before *L. my God.* 20
L. my God, Feed the flock. *Zech* 11:4
and the *L. my God* shall come. 14:5

Lord *our God*

sacrifice to *L. our God.* *Ex* 3:18; 5:3; 8:27; 10:25
there is none like to *L. our God.* *Ex* 8:10; *Ps* 113:5
to serve the *L. our God.* *Ex* 10:26
L. our God spake unto. *Deut* 1:6
all that wilderness, as the *L. our God* commanded us. 19, 41; 6:20
which *L. our God* doth give unto us. 1:20, 25; 2:29
L. our God delivered him. 2:33
unto whatsoever *L. our God.* 37
so nigh to them, as *L. our God.* 4:7
L. our God made a covenant. 5:2
the *L. our God* hath shewed. 24
hear the voice of *L. our God.* 25
hear all that the *L. our God.* 27
O Israel, *L. our God* is one Lord. 6:4; *Mark* 12:29
to fear *L. our God.* *Deut* 6:24
to do before *L. our God.* 25
day before the *L. our God.* 29:15
things belong to the *L. our God.* 29
you before the *L. our God.* *Josh* 18:6
the altar of *L. our God.* 22:19, 29
L. our God, he it is that brought us up. 24:17
the people said, The *L. our God.* 24
whomsoever *L. our God.* *Judg* 11:24
cry to the *L. our God* for. *1 Sam* 7:8
L. our God be with us. *1 Ki* 8:57
words be nigh unto *L. our God.* 59
we trust *Lord our God.* *2 Ki* 18:22
O *L. our God,* save thou us. 19:19
that it be of *L. our God.* *1 Chr* 13:2
the *L. our God* made a breach. 15:13
he is the *L. our God*; his judgements. 16:14; *Ps* 105:7
O *L. our God.* *1 Chr* 29:16; *2 Chr* 14:11; *Ps* 99:8; 106:47; *Isa* 26:13; 37:20; *Jer* 14:22; *Dan* 9:15
keep the charge of the *L. our God.* *2 Chr* 13:11
have sought the *L. our God.* 14:7
iniquity with the *L. our God.* 19:7
but with us is the *L. our God.* 32:8
L. our God shall deliver us. 11
been shewed from the *L. our God.* *Ezra* 9:8
name of the *L. our God.* *Ps* 20:7
beauty of the *L. our God.* 90:17
yea, the *L. our God* shall cut. 94:23
exalt ye the *L. our God.* 99:5, 9
for the *L. our God* is holy. 9
for he is the *Lord our God.* 105:7
house of the *L. our God.* 122:9
wait on the *L. our God.* 123:2
come to thee, for thou art the *L. our God.* *Jer* 3:22
L. our God is the salvation. 23
sinned against the *L. our God* . . . not obeyed voice of *L. our God.* 25
doeth *L. our God* these things? 5:19
let us now fear the *L. our God.* 24
for the *L. our God* hath put. 8:14
committed against the *L. our God.* 16:10
us in the name of *L. our God.* 26:16
up to Zion, to the *L. our God.* 31:6
pray now to *L. our God* for us. 37:3; 42:20
the voice of the *L. our God.* 42:6
the *L. our God* hath not sent. 43:2
vengeance of *L. our God.* 50:28
Zion the work of *L. our God.* 51:10
to the *L. our God* belong. *Dan* 9:9
obeyed voice of the *L. our God.* 10
for the *L. our God* is righteous in. 14
in the name of the *L. our G.* *Mi* 4:5
afraid of the *L. our God.* 7:17
as *L. our God* shall call. *Acts* 2:39
power to the *L. our God.* *Rev* 19:1

Lord *their God*

may serve *L. their God.* *Ex* 10:7; *2 Chr* 34:33; *Jer* 30:9
know that I am the *L. their God.* *Ex* 29:46; *Ezek* 28:26; 34:30; 39:22, 28
break covenant, I am *L. their God.* *Lev* 26:44; *Zech* 10:6
forgat *L. their God.* *Judg* 3:7; 8:34; *1 Sam* 12:9; *Jer* 3:21
because they forsook *L. their God.* *1 Ki* 9:9; *Jer* 22:9

Israel had sinned against the *L. their God.* *2 Ki* 17:7
right against the *L. their God.* 9
did not believe in the *L. their God.* 14
left all the commandments of the *L. their God.* 16
Judah kept not commandments of the *L. their God.* 19
obeyed not voice of the *L. their God.* 18:12; *Jer* 7:28
were consecrated to the *L. their God.* *2 Chr* 31:6
sacrifice unto *L. their God.* 33:17
words of the *L. their God* for which the *L. their God* had. *Jer* 43:1
they shall go and seek the *L. their God.* 50:4; *Hos* 3:5
save them by *L. their God.* *Hos* 1:7
not return to the *L. their God.* 7:10
obeyed the voice of the *L. their God.* *Hag* 1:12
L. their God shall save. *Zech* 9:16
he turn to *L. their God.* *Luke* 1:16

Lord *thy God*

I am the *L. thy God.* *Ex* 20:2
Ps 81:10; *Isa* 51:15; *Hos* 12:9
13:4
for I the *L. thy God* am a jealous God. *Ex* 20:5; *Deut* 5:9
L. thy God hath been. *Deut* 2:7
L. thy God is a consuming fire. 4:24
L. thy God is a merciful God. 31
that the *L. thy God,* he is God. 7:9
L. thy God is among. 21; 23:14
so the *L. thy God* chasteneth. 8:5
not do so to the *L. thy God.* 12:31
for the *L. thy God* is with thee. 20:1
say before the *L. thy God.* 26:5, 13
fear this fearful name, the *L. thy God.* 28:58
L. thy God is with thee. *Josh* 1:9
only the *L. thy God* be with. 17
L. thy God will be with thee. *2 Sam* 14:17
Araunah said, The *L. thy God.* 24:23
face of the *L. thy God.* *1 Ki* 13:6
as the *L. thy God* liveth I have not a cake. 17:12; 18:10
L. thy God, the Holy One. *Isa* 43:3
because of the *L. thy God.* 55:5
pray for us to *L. thy God.* *Jer* 42:2
that the *L. thy God* may shew us. 3
where is the *L. thy God*? *Mi* 7:10
the *L. thy God* in midst. *Zeph* 3:17
thou shalt not tempt the *L. thy God.* *Mat* 4:7; *Luke* 4:12

Lord *your God*

holy, for I the *L. your God.* *Lev* 19:2
Lord your God hath multiplied you. *Deut* 1:10
L. your God he shall fight. 30; 3:22
not tempt the *L. your God.* 6:16
L. your God is God of gods. 10:17
L. your God is he that goeth. 20:4
L. your God is God in. *Josh* 2:11
the *L. your God* is he that hath fought for you. 23:3, 10
when *L. your God* was your king. *1 Sam* 12:12
L. your God ye shall fear. *2 Ki* 17:39
is not the *L. your God* with you? *1 Chr* 22:18
believe in *L. your God.* *2 Chr* 20:20
sent me to *L. your God.* *Jer* 42:20
ye know that I am the *L. your God.* *Joel* 3:17
prophet shall the *L. your God* raise. *Acts* 3:22; 7:37
see, I am the **Lord** *your God*

Lord *of hosts*

O *L. of hosts.* *1 Sam* 1:11
Ps 59:5; 84:1, 3, 12; *2 Sam* 7:27
Jer 11:20; 20:12
name of the *L. of hosts.* *2 Sam* 6:2
the *L. of hosts* is God over. 7:26
Elijah said, As *L. of hosts* liveth. *1 Ki* 18:15; *2 Ki* 3:14
the zeal of the *L. of hosts* shall do. *2 Ki* 19:31; *Isa* 9:7; 37:32
greater, for the *L. of h.* *1 Chr* 11:9
the *L. of h.* God of Israel. 17:24
L. of hosts, he is the King. *Ps* 24:10
the *L. of h.* is with us. 46:7, 11
in city of *L. of hosts.* *Ps* 48:8
the Lord, the *L. of hosts.* *Isa* 1:24
the day of the *L. of hosts.* 2:12
Holy, holy is the *L. of hosts.* 6:3
seen the King, the *L. of hosts.* 5
sanctify the *L. of hosts* himself. 8:13
for the *L. of hosts* hath purposed. 14:27; 23:9
swear to the *L. of hosts.* 19:18
L. of hosts is his name. 47:4; 48:2
51:15; 54:5; *Jer* 10:16; 31:35
32:18; 50:34; 51:19
king, whose name is the *L. of hosts.* *Jer* 46:18; 48:15
L. of hosts saith, I will punish. 46:25
is it not of the *L. of hosts*? *Hab* 2:13
I am with you, saith *L. of hosts.* *Hag* 2:4
the *L. of hosts* thought. *Zech* 1:6
the *L. of hosts* sent me. 2:9, 11; 4:9
wrath from the *L. of hosts.* 7:12
not hear, saith the *L. of hosts.* 13
and to seek the *L. of hosts.* 8:21
come to seek the *L. of hosts.* 22
the King, *L. of hosts.* 14:16, 17
be holiness unto the *L. of hosts.* 21
I am a great King, saith *L. of hosts.* *Mal* 1:14
see, saith the **Lord**

I the **Lord**

for *I the L.* your God am holy. *Lev* 19:2; 20:26; 21:8
for *I the L.* do sanctify him. 21:15
23; 22:9, 16
I the L. have said it, I will do it. *Num* 14:35; *Ezek* 21:17
I the L. do keep it, I will. *Isa* 27:3
I the L. the first, and with. 41:4
when the needy seek, *I the L.* 17
I the L. have called thee in. 42:6
I the L. which call thee by. 45:3
I the L. do all these things. 7
I the L. created it. 8
I the L. speak righteousness. 19
who hath told? have not *I the L.*? 21
that *I the L.* am thy Saviour. 60:16
I the L. will hasten it in his time. 22
for *I the L.* love judgement. 61:8
I the L. search the heart. *Jer* 17:10
I the L. have spoken it. *Ezek* 5:13
15, 17; 17:21; 21:32; 22:14
24:14; 26:14; 30:12
I the L. will answer him. 14:4, 7
I the L. have deceived that. 9
I L. have brought down, *I L.* 17:24
I the L. have kindled it. 20:48
I the L. have drawn forth. 21:5
I the L. will be their God. 34:24
know that *I the L.* their God. 30
I the L. do build, *I the L.* 36:36
I the L. have performed it. 37:14
I the L. do sanctify Israel. 28

I am the **Lord**

I am the L. that brought. *Gen* 15:7
I am the L. *Ex* 6:2, 6, 8, 29; 12:12
Lev 18:5, 6, 21; *Num* 3:13
Isa 43:11, 15
I am the L. thy God which. *Ex* 20:2
I am L. which hallow you. *Lev* 22:32
I am L.: that is my name. *Isa* 42:8
shall say, *I am the L.'s.* 44:5
knoweth that *I am the L.* *Jer* 9:24
behold, *I am the L.* the God. 32:27
I am the L., I change not. *Mal* 3:6
see **know**

I am the **Lord** *your God*

ye shall know that *I am L. your God.* *Ex* 6:7; 16:12
I am the L. your God. *Lev* 11:44
18:30; 19:3; 20:7; 23:22
Judg 6:10; *Ezek* 20:5, 7, 19, 20
Joel 2:27

Lord *Jesus, see* **Jesus**

in the **Lord**

he believed *in the L.* *Gen* 15:6
children of Reuben, Gad; ye have no part *in the L.* *Josh* 22:25, 27
rejoiceth *in the L.,* mine horn is exalted *in the L.* *1 Sam* 2:1
put your trust *in the L.* *Ps* 4:5
in the L. put I my trust. 11:1
26:1; 31:6; 73:28
all ye that hope *in the L.* *Ps* 31:24
be glad *in the L.* 32:11
make her boast *in the L.* 34:2
be joyful *in the L.* 35:9
delight also thyself *in the L.* 37:4
Isa 58:14
rest *in the L.* *Ps* 37:7
in the L. will I praise his. 56:10
righteous shall be glad *in the L.* 64:10; 104:34
trust *in the L.* with all thine heart. *Pr* 3:5
putteth his trust *in the L.* 29:25
in the L. Jehovah is. *Isa* 26:4
increase their joy *in the L.* 29:19
shall be saved *in the L.* 45:17
in the L. have I righteousness. 24
in the L. shall all the seed of. 25
in the L. is the salvation. *Jer* 3:23
she trusted not *in the L.* *Zeph* 3:2
be my strength *in the L.* *Zech* 12:5
many believed *in the L.* *Acts* 9:42
speaking boldly *in the L.* 14:3
ye receive her *in the L.* *Rom* 16:2
greet Amplias *in the L.* 8
who laboured much *in the L.* 12
salute Rufus, chosen *in the L.* 13
I Tertius salute you *in the L.* 22
glorieth, let him glory *in the L.* *1 Cor* 1:31; *2 Cor* 10:17
and faithful *in the L.* *1 Cor* 4:17
called *in the L.* 7:22
whom she will; only *in the L.* 39
are ye not my work *in the L.*? 9:1
seal of apostleship are ye *in the L.* 2
without the man, *in the L.* 11:11
labour is not in vain *in the L.* 15:58
an holy temple *in the L.* *Eph* 2:21
and testify *in the L.* 4:17
now are ye light *in the L.* 5:8
obey your parents *in the L.* 6:1
brethren, be strong *in the L.* 10
faithful minister *in the L.* 21
brethren *in the L.* waxing. *Phil* 1:14
I trust *in the L.* I shall come. 2:24
receive him therefore *in the L.* 29
stand fast *in the L.* 4:1; *1 Thes* 3:8
the same mind *in the L.* *Phil* 4:2
rejoice *in the L.* alway. 4
but I rejoiced *in the L.* greatly. 10
own husbands *in the L.* *Col* 3:18
is a fellow-servant *in the L.* 4:7
thou hast received *in the L.* 17
which are over you *in L.* *1 Thes* 5:12
confidence *in the L.* *2 Thes* 3:4
in the flesh and *in the L.* *Philem* 16
joy of thee *in the L.*: refresh my bowels *in the L.* 20
dead which die *in the L.* *Rev* 14:13
see **rejoice, trust**

Lord *is*

the *L. is* in this place. *Gen* 28:16
the *L. is* righteous, I and my people wicked. *Ex* 9:27; *2 Chr* 12:6
L. is my strength and. *Ex* 15:2
the *L. is* a man of war, the *L. is.* 3
I know that *L. is* greater than. 18:11
the *L. is* with us, fear. *Num* 14:9
the *L. is* longsuffering. 18; *Nah* 1:3
go not up, for the *L. is.* *Num* 14:42
holy every one, and the *L. is.* 16:3
the *L. is* his inheritance. *Deut* 10:9
the *L. is* their inheritance. 18:2
witness, that *L. is* God. *Josh* 22:34
and said, The *L. is* with thee. *Judg* 6:12; *Luke* 1:28
for the *L. is* a God of. *1 Sam* 2:3
L. is with David. 16:18; *2 Sam* 7:3
seeing *L. is* departed. *1 Sam* 28:16
he said, The *L. is* my rock. *2 Sam* 22:2; *Ps* 18:2
know that *L. is* God. *1 Ki* 8:60
L. is the God of the hills. 20:28
the *L. is* our God. *2 Chr* 13:10
the *L. is* with you while ye. 15:2
L. is known by judgement. *Ps* 9:16
L. is king for ever and ever. 10:16
the *L. is* in his holy temple. 11:4
because the *L. is* his refuge. 14:6
the *L. is* the portion of mine. 16:5
the *L. is* my shepherd, I shall. 23:1
L. is my light and my salvation, the *L. is* the strength of my life. 27:1

the *L. is* my strength. *Ps* 28:7; 118:14
the *L. is* their strength, and he. 28:8
O taste and see that the *L. is.* 34:8
for the *L.* most high *is* terrible. 47:2
L. is our defence and Holy. 89:18
to shew that *L. is* upright. 92:15
the *L. is* clothed with strength. 93:1
the *L. is* my defence and. 94:22
the *L. is* a great God. 95:3; 96:4 99:2; 135:5
the *L. is* good. 100:5; 34:8; 135:3 145:9; *Jer* 33:11; *Lam* 3:25 *Nah* 1:7
L. is merciful and gracious. *Ps* 103:8; 111:4; 145:8
the *L. is* high. 113:4
the *L. is* on my side. 118:6
the *L. is* thy keeper, the *L. is.* 121:5
so the *L. is* round about his. 125:2
L. is righteous. 129:4; 145:17 *Lam* 1:18; *Dan* 9:14
the *L. is* nigh to all them. *Ps* 145:18
L. is far from the wicked. *Pr* 15:29
the *L. is* the maker of them. 22:2
L. is a God of judgement. *Isa* 30:18
the *L. is* exalted. 33:5
L. is our judge, our. 22
L. is well pleased for his. 42:21
the *L. is* the true God. *Jer* 10:10
whose hope the *L. is.* 17:7
the *L. is* with me. 20:11
the *L. is* my portion. *Lam* 3:24
the city, the *L. is* there. *Ezek* 48:35
maketh the stars the *L. is* his name. *Amos* 5:8; 9:6
L. is in his holy temple. *Hab* 2:20
the just *L. is* in the midst thereof. *Zeph* 3:5, 15
fight, because *L. is* with. *Zech* 10:5
shall say, The *L. is* my God. 13:9
the *L. is* risen indeed. *Luke* 24:34
the *L. is* that Spirit. *2 Cor* 3:17
known, the *L. is* at hand. *Phil* 4:5
the *L. is* the avenger of. *1 Thes* 4:6
but the *L. is* faithful. *2 Thes* 3:3
the *L. is* my helper, I. *Heb* 13:6
L. is very pitiful, and. *Jas* 5:11
tasted that *L. is* gracious. *1 Pet* 2:3
L. is not slack concerning. *2 Pet* 3:9

my **Lord**

said, Oh, not so, *my L.* *Gen* 19:18
Moses said. O *my L.* I. *Ex* 4:10
O *my L.* send by hand of whom. 13
let the power of *my L.* *Num* 14:17
saith *my L.* to his servant? *Josh* 5:14
O *my L.* if the *L.* be with us. *Judg* 6:13
O *my L.* wherewith shall I? 15
O *my L.* let the man of God. 13:8
to the *L.* thou art *my L.* *Ps* 16:2
stir up thyself, my God, *my L.* 35:23 *John* 20:28
the *L.* said to *my L.* *Ps* 110:1 *Mat* 22:44; *Mark* 12:36 *Luke* 20:42; *Acts* 2:34
a lion: *My L.* I stand. *Isa* 21:8
but Zion said. *My L.* hath. 49:14
O *my L.* by the vision. *Dan* 10:16
of *my L.* talk with this *my L.*? 17
and I said, Let *my L.* speak. 19
O *my L.* what shall be end of? 12:8
said I, O *my L.* what are these? *Zech* 1:9; 4:4; 6:4
knowest thou? No, *my L.* 4:5, 13
the mother of *my L.* *Luke* 1:43
have taken away *my L.* *John* 20:13
of Christ Jesus *my L.* *Phil* 3:8

O **Lord**

for thy salvation, *O L.* *Gen* 49:18
who is like to thee, *O L.*? *Ex* 15:11
return, *O L.* unto Israel. *Num* 10:36 *Ps* 6:4
O L. hast given me. *Deut* 26:10
O L. what shall I say? *Josh* 7:8
thine enemies perish, *O L.* *Judg* 5:31
O L. turn counsel of. *2 Sam* 15:31
thou art my lamp, *O L.* and. 22:29
be it far from me, *O L.* that. 23:17
O L. there is none like. *1 Chr* 17:20
O L. is greatness, thine, *O L.* 29:11
help us, *O L.* our God; *O L.* thou art our God. *2 Chr* 14:11
arise, *O L.*; save me. *Ps* 3:7
lead me, *O L.* 5:8
O L. heal me. 6:2
but thou, *O L.* how long? 3
arise, *O L.* 7:6; 9:19; 10:12; 17:13
judge me, *O L.* according. 7:8; 26:1
O L. our *L.* 8:1, 9
I will praise thee, *O L.* 9:1
O L.: consider my trouble. 13 31:9; 86:3; 123:3
O L. my strength. 18:1; 19:14
be not thou far from me, *O L.* 22:19 35:22
hear, *O L.* 27:7; 30:10; 39:12 69:16; 86:6; 102:1; 119:145 140:6
I trusted in thee, *O L.* I said. 31:14
gods none like to thee, *O L.* 86:8
teach me thy way, *O L.* I walk. 11 25:4; 27:11
not unto us, *O L.* not unto. 115:1
O L. thy commandments. 119:151
hear my prayer, *O L.* 143:1, 7 *Isa* 37:17; *Dan* 9:19
O L. thou art my God. *Isa* 25:1
O L. art our Father. 63:16; 64:8
O L. thou art great. *Jer* 10:6
so be it, *O L.* 11:5
but thou, *O L.* knowest me. 12:3
O L. art in the midst of us. 14:9
O L. the hope of Israel. 17:13
heal me, *O L.* and I shall be. 14
see, *O L.*, and consider; for I am become vile. *Lam* 1:11; 2:20
thou, *O L.* remainest for ever. 5:19
turn us unto thee, *O L.* we. 21
we beseech thee, *O L.* *Jonah* 1:14
O L. thou hast ordained. *Hab* 1:12
O L. revive thy work in. 3:2
O L. thou Son of David. *Mat* 15:22 20:30, 31
I am a sinful man, *O L.* *Luke* 5:8
thou art worthy, *O L.* to. *Rev* 4:11
saying, How long, *O L.*? 6:10
who shall not fear thee, *O L.*? 15:4
O L. which art, and wast. 16:5

see **Lord** *God*

anger of the **Lord**

anger of the L. was kindled against Moses. *Ex* 4:14
anger of the L. was kindled against Israel. *Num* 11:10; 25:3 *Josh* 7:1; *Judg* 2:14, 20; 3:8 10:7; *2 Sam* 24:1; *2 Ki* 13:3 *Isa* 5:25
anger of the L. kindled against Aaron. *Num* 12:9
that the fierce *anger of L.* may. 25:4
augment yet the *anger of L.* 32:14
lest the *anger of L.* be. *Deut* 6:15
so will *anger of the L.* be. 7:4
anger of Lord shall smoke. 29:20
anger of the L. was kindled. 27
anger of L. be kindled against you. *Josh* 23:16
anger of L. kindled against Uzzah. *2 Sam* 6:7; *1 Chr* 13:10
through *anger of the L.* it came to. *2 Ki* 24:20; *Jer* 52:3
anger of the L. kindled against Amaziah. *2 Chr* 25:15
fierce *anger of the L.* is not turned back from us. *Jer* 4:8
of the fierce *anger of the L.* 12:13
anger of the L. shall not return till. 23:20; 30:24
his soul from *anger of the L.* 51:45
in day of *L.'s anger* none. *Lam* 2:22
anger of L. hath divided them. 4:16
before the fierce *anger of L.* *Zeph* 2:2
hid in day of the *anger of the L.* 3
see **commandment, congregation, counsel, day, eyes, face, fear, feast, glory, hand, house, knowledge, law**

mouth of the **Lord**

word that proceedeth out of *mouth of L.* *Deut* 8:3
counsel at *mouth of L.* *Josh* 9:14
disobeyed *mouth of L.* *1 Ki* 13:21
for the *mouth of L.* hath spoken it. *Isa* 1:20; 40:5; 58:14; *Jer* 9:12 *Mi* 4:4
by a new name, which the *mouth of the L.* shall name. *Isa* 62:2
speak not out of *mouth of the L.* *Jer* 23:16

name of the **Lord**

Abram called on the *name of the L.* *Gen* 12:8
she called the *name of L.* 16:13
Isaac called on *name of L.* 26:25
shall not take *name of L.* in vain. *Ex* 20:7; *Deut* 5:11
proclaim *name of the L.* *Ex* 33:19
proclaimed the *name of the L.* 34:5
woman's son blasphemed the *name of the L.* *Lev* 24:11, 16
minister in *name of L.* *Deut* 18:5, 7
speaketh in the *name of the L.* 22
chosen to bless in *name of L.* 21:5
art called by the *name of L.* 28:10
publish *name of L.*: ascribe. 32:3
thy servants are come because of *name of the L.* *Josh* 9:9
in *name of L.* of hosts. *1 Sam* 17:45
both of us in *name of L.* 20:42
called by *name of the L.* *2 Sam* 6:2
blessed the people in the *name of L.* 18; *1 Chr* 16:2
no house built to the *name of the L.* *1 Ki* 3:2; 5:3, 5; 8:17, 20 *1 Chr* 22:7, 19; *2 Chr* 2:1, 4; 6:10
Sheba heard concerning *name of L.* *1 Ki* 10:1
altar in the *name of the L.* 18:32
that which is true in *name of L.* 22:16 *2 Chr* 18:15
cursed them in *name of the L.* *2 Ki* 2:24
which he spake in *name of L.* *1 Chr* 21:19; *2 Chr* 33:18
blessed be the *name of the L.* *Job* 1:21; *Ps* 113:2
sing praises to *name of L.* *Ps* 7:17
remember *name of the L.* our. 20:7
shall fear the *name of the L.* 102:15
to declare *name of the L.* in. 21
praise the *name of L.* 113:1; 135:1 148:5, 13; *Joel* 2:26
rising of sun *L.'s name* is. *Ps* 113:3
called I upon *name of L.* 116:4
in the *name of L.* will I destroy. 118:10, 11, 12
cometh in the *name of the L.* 26
thanks unto *name of the L.* 122:4
our help is in *name of L.* 124:8
we bless you in *name of L.* 129:8
name of L. is a strong. *Pr* 18:10
place of the *name of the L.* *Isa* 18:7
glorify the *name of the L.* in. 24:15
name of L. cometh from far. 30:27
which swear by *name of L.* 48:1
let him trust in *name of the L.* 50:10
and to love the *name of L.* to. 56:6
they fear the *name of L.* 59:19
and gold to *name of the L.* 60:9
all nations gathered to *name of the L.* *Jer* 3:17
prophesy not in the *name of L.* 11:21
prophesied in the *name of L.* 26:9
he hath spoken to us in the *name of L.* 16; 44:16
Urijah that prophesied in the *name of the L.* 26:20
mention of *name of L.* *Amos* 6:10
will walk in *name of Lord.* *Mi* 4:5
majesty of the *name of the L.* 5:4
trust in *name of the L.* *Zeph* 3:12
lies in *name of the L.* *Zech* 13:3
that cometh in the *name of L.* *Mat* 21:9; 23:39; *Mark* 11:9, 10 *Luke* 13:35; 19:38; *John* 12:13
spake boldly in *name of the L.* Jesus. *Acts* 9:29
to be baptized in *name of L.* 10:48
to call over them the *name of the L.* 19:13
and the *name of the L.* Jesus. 17
to die for the *name of L.* 21:13
sins, calling on the *name of L.* 22:16
that the *name of L.* Jesus may be glorified. *2 Thes* 1:12
command you in the *name of L.* 3:6
have spoken in *name of L.* *Jas* 5:10
with oil in the *name of the L.* 14

of the **Lord**

of the L. to harden. *Josh* 11:20
asked him *of the L.* *1 Sam* 1:20
them in the ears *of the L.* 8:21
Saul said, Blessed be ye *of L.* 23:21 *2 Sam* 2:5
his name Jedidiah because *of the L.* *2 Sam* 12:25
the saying *of the L.* *1 Ki* 15:29
this evil is *of the L.* *2 Ki* 6:33
man of God and enquire *of L.* 8:8
saying *of the L.* to Elijah. 10:17
we may enquire *of L.* *2 Chr* 18:7
go, enquire *of the L.* for me. 34:21
I will say *of the L.* He. *Ps* 91:2
disposing thereof is *of the L.* *Pr* 16:33
man's goings are *of the L.* 20:24
safety is *of L.* 21:31
worship, because *of the L.* *Isa* 49:7
O arm *of the L.* awake as. 51:9
pray thee, *of the L.* for us. *Jer* 21:2
it is *of the L.'s* mercies. *Lam* 3:22
salvation is *of the L.* *Jonah* 2:9
the will *of L.* be done. *Acts* 21:14
I have received *of the L.* *1 Cor* 11:23
opened to me *of the L.* *2 Cor* 2:12
shall he receive *of the L.* *Eph* 6:8
knowing that *of the L.* *Col* 3:24
may find mercy *of the L.* *2 Tim* 1:18
receive any thing *of the L.* *Jas* 1:7
seen the end *of the L.* 5:11
longsuffering *of the L.* *2 Pet* 3:15

see **angel**

prophet and *prophets of the* **Lord**

Samuel established to be a *p. of the L.* *1 Sam* 3:20
Jezebel cut off *p. of the L.* *1 Ki* 18:4
Jezebel slew the *p. of the L.* 13
I only remain *a p. of the L.* 22
is there not here a *p. of the L.* to? 22:7; *2 Ki* 3:11; *2 Chr* 18:6
a p. of the L. was there. *2 Chr* 28:9

see **sabaoth, sabbath**

servant, servants of the **Lord**

Moses the *s. of the L.* died there. *Deut* 34:5
death of Moses *s. of the L.* *Josh* 1:1
which Moses the *s. of the L.* commanded. 1:13; 8:31, 33; 11:12 22:2, 5; *2 Ki* 18:12
which Moses the *s. of the L.* gave. *Josh* 1:15; 12:6; 13:8; 18:7; 22:4
Moses the *s. of the L.* smite. 12:6
s. of L. sent me from Kadesh. 14:7
Joshua son of Nun the *s. of the L.* died. 24:29; *Judg* 2:8
blood of all the *s. of the L.* *2 Ki* 9:7
here none of the *s. of the L.* 10:23
Moses *s. of the L.* made. *2 Chr* 1:3
to commandment of Moses the *s. of the L.* 24:6
praise the Lord, praise, O ye *s. of the L.* *Ps* 113:1; 135:1
bless Lord, O all ye *s. of L.* 134:1
blind or deaf as the *L.'s s.* *Isa* 42:19
heritage of the *s. of the L.* 54:17
and the *s. of the L.* must not strive. *2 Tim* 2:24

sight of the **Lord**

Er was wicked in *s. of L.* and he slew him. *Gen* 38:7
been accepted in *s. of L.* *Lev* 10:19
do that which is good in *s. of L.* *Deut* 6:18; 12:28
do what is right in *s. of the L.* 12:25 21:9; *2 Ki* 12:2; 14:3; 15:3, 24 18:3; 22:2; *2 Chr* 20:32; 24:2 25:2; 26:4; 27:2; 29:2; 34:2
wickedness is great ye have done in the *s. of L.* *1 Sam* 12:17 *1 Ki* 21:25; *2 Ki* 21:6
a light thing in *s. of L.* *2 Ki* 3:18
did not what was right in *s. of L.* 16:2 *2 Chr* 28:1
precious in *s. of L.* is death of his saints. *Ps* 116:15
that doeth evil, is good in *s. of L.* *Mal* 2:17
great in *the s. of the L.* *Luke* 1:15
not only in *s. of the L.* *2 Cor* 8:21

humble yourselves in the *s. of the L.* *Jas* 4:10

see **evil**

Spirit of the **Lord**

S. of L. came on Othniel. *Judg* 3:10
S. of L. came on Gideon. 6:34
S of L. came on Jephtha. 11:29
S. of L. began to move Samson. 13:25; 14:6, 19; 15:14
S. of L. will come on Saul. *1 Sam* 10:6
S. of L. came upon David. 16:13
S. of L. departed from. 14
S. of L. spake by me. *2 Sam* 23:2
S. of L. shall carry thee. *1 Ki* 18:12
went *S. of the L.* from me to speak unto? 22:24; *2 Chr* 18:23
S. of the L. hath taken. *2 Ki* 2:16
Jahaziel came *S. of L.* *2 Chr* 20:14
S. of L. shall rest upon. *Isa* 11:2
S. of L. bloweth upon it. 40:7
who hath directed *S. of L.*? 13
the *S. of L.* shall lift. 59:19
S. of L. is upon me, because the. 61:1; *Luke* 4:18
S. of L. caused him to rest. *Isa* 63:14
S. of L. fell upon me. *Ezek* 11:5
carried in *S. of L.* 37:1
house of Jacob, is the *S. of L.*? *Mi* 2:7
full of power by the *S. of L.* 3:8
agreed to tempt *S. of L.* *Acts* 5:9
the *S. of L.* caught away Philip. 8:39
where the *S. of L.* is, there is liberty. *2 Cor* 3:17
glory, even as by the *S. of L.* 18

temple of the **Lord**

by a post of the *t. of L.* *1 Sam* 1:9
lamp of God went out in the *t. of the L.* 3:3
people into *t. of L.* *2 Ki* 11:13
gold off from doors of *t. of L.* 18:16
bring out of the *t. of L.* vessels. 23:4
Solomon had made in *t. of L.* 24:13
Uzziah went into *t. of L.* *2 Chr* 26:16
not into *the t. of the L.* 27:2
uncleanness found in *t. of L.* 29:16
foundation of the *t. of L.* *Ezra* 3:6
laid foundation of *t. of the L.* 10
The *t. of L.*, The *t. of L.* *Jer* 7:4
were set before the *t. of the L.* 24:1
t. of L. were 25 men, with their backs toward *t. of L.* and. *Ezek* 8:16
stone was laid in *t. of L.* *Hag* 2:15
and he shall build the *t. of the L.* *Zech* 6:12; 13:15
for a memorial in *t. of L.* 6:14
Zacharias went into *t. of L.* *Luke* 1:9

voice of the **Lord**

and obey *v. of L.* *Deut* 30:8 *Jer* 26:13; 38:20
obeyed not the *v. of L.* *Josh* 5:6 *1 Sam* 28:18; *1 Ki* 20:36; *Jer* 3:25 7:28; 42:13, 21; 43:4, 7; 44:23 *Dan* 9:10
thou not obey *v. of L.*? *1 Sam* 15:19
yea, I have obeyed the *v. of the L.* 20
in obeying the *v. of the L.* 22
the *v. of the L.* is upon. *Ps* 29:3
the *v. of the L.* is powerful. 4
the *v. of the L.* divideth the. 7
v. of L. shaketh the wilderness. 8
v. of the L. maketh the hinds. 9
not to the *v. of the L.* 106:25
I heard the *v. of the L.* *Isa* 6:8
v. of the L. shall Assyrians. 30:31
a *v. of the L.* that rendereth 66:6
v. of the L. our God that it may be well . . . obey the *v. of L.* *Jer* 42:6
the *L.'s v.* crieth unto the. *Mi* 6:9
people obeyed *v. of the L.* *Hag* 1:12
diligently obey the *v. of L.* *Zech* 6:15
v. of L. came to Moses. *Acts* 7:31

way of the **Lord**

command his household to keep *w. of L.* *Gen* 18:19
will keep the *w. of the L.* *Judg* 2:22
Amon walked not in the *w. of the L.* *2 Ki* 21:22
who walk in *w. of the L.* *Ps* 119:1
w. of the L. is strength. *Pr* 10:29
prepare ye *w. of the L.* *Isa* 40:3 *Mat* 3:3; *Mark* 1:3; *Luke* 3:4

know not *way of the L.* *Jer* 5:4
they have known *way of the L.* 5
the *w. of the L.* is not equal. *Ezek* 18:25, 29; 33:17, 20
make straight *way of L.* *John* 1:23
instructed in *w. of L.* *Acts* 18:25

ways of the **Lord**

for I have kept the *w. of L.* *2 Sam* 22:22; *Ps* 18:21
lifted up in *w. of L.* *2 Chr* 17:6
sing in the *w. of the L.* *Ps* 138:5
the *w. of the L.* are right. *Hos* 14:9
cease to pervert the right *w. of the L.* *Acts* 13:10

word of the **Lord**

feared the *w. of the L.* *Ex* 9:20
regarded not the *w. of the L.* left. 21
according to *w. of the L.* *Num* 3:16 51; 4:45; 36:5; *Deut* 34:5 *Josh* 8:27; 19:50; 22:9; *1 Ki* 12:24 13:26; 14:18; 16:12, 34; 17:5, 16 22:38; *2 Ki* 1:17; 4:44; 7:16 9:26; 14:25
he hath despised the *w. of the L.* *Num* 15:31
beyond the *w. of L.* my God. 22:18
to shew you the *w. of L.* *Deut* 5:5
w. of L. was precious. *1 Sam* 3:1
w. of the L. yet revealed to. 7
hast rejected the *w. of L.* 15:23, 26
the *w. of L.* is tried. *2 Sam* 22:31 *Ps* 18:30
might fulfil *w. of the L.* *1 Ki* 2:27 *2 Chr* 36:21
to the *w. of the L.* and returned. *1 Ki* 12:24; *2 Chr* 11:4; *Jer* 37:2
a man of God by *w. of L.* *1 Ki* 13:1
the altar in the *w. of the L.* 2
man of God had given by *w. of L.* 5
charged me by *w. of L.* saying. 9
angel spake by *w. of L.* saying. 18
disobedient unto the *w. of L.* 26
he cried by the *w. of the L.* 32
according to the *w. of L.* 14:18
w. of the L. in my mouth. 17:24
prophet said, in *w. of L.*, Smite. 20:35
enquire, I pray thee, at *w. of L.* 22:5; *2 Chr* 18:4
Jehoshaphat said, *W. of L.* *2 Ki* 3:12
this is *w. of L.* 9:36
nothing of the *w. of the L.* fall. 10:10
this was the *w. of L.* 15:12
good is the *w. of L.* 20:19; *Isa* 39:8
according to *w. of L.* *2 Ki* 23:16 24:2; *1 Chr* 11:3, 10; 12:23 15:15; *Jer* 13:2; 32:8; *Jonah* 3:3
against *w. of the L.* *1 Chr* 10:13
of king by *w. of L.* *2 Chr* 30:12
not kept the *w. of the L.* 34:21
that *w. of L.* might be accomplished. 36:22; *Ezra* 1:1
for the *w. of L.* is right. *Ps* 33:4
by *w. of L.* were heavens made. 6
word came, the *w. of L.* 105:19
and the *w. of L.* from Jerusalem. *Isa* 2:3; *Mi* 4:2
the *w. of L.* was to them. 28:13
see ye the *word of the L.* *Jer* 2:31
w. of the L. is to them a reproach. 6:10; 20:8
have rejected the *w. of L.* 8:9
to me, Where is the *w. of L.*? 17:15
to this day the *w. of L.* hath. 25:3
if the *w. of L.* be with them. 27:18
that this was the *word of the L.* 32:8
the *w. of L.* that came to Hosea. *Hos* 1:2
wander to seek *w. of L.* *Amos* 8:12
w. of L. is against you. *Zeph* 2:5
this is *w. of the L.* to Zerubbabel. *Zech* 4:6
w. of the L. in the land of Hadrach. 9:1; 12:1; *Mal* 1:1
poor of the flock knew that it was *w. of L.* *Zech* 11:11
Peter remembered *w. of L.* *Luke* 22:61; *Acts* 11:16
preached the *w. of the L.* *Acts* 8:25 13:49; 15:35, 36; 16:32
glorified the *w. of the L.* 13:48
heard the *w. of the L.* Jesus. 19:10

sounded out the *w. of L.* *1 Thes* 1:8
say to you by the *w. of the L.* 4:15
pray that the *w. of the L.* may have free course. *2 Thes* 3:1
w. of L. endureth for. *1 Pet* 1:25

words of the **Lord**

Moses told people all *w. of L.* *Ex* 24:3; *Num* 11:24
Moses wrote all the *w. of L.* and. *Ex* 24:4
heard all the *w. of the L.* *Josh* 24:27
told people *w. of the L.* *1 Sam* 8:10
the voice of the *w. of the L.* 15:1
came by *w. of L.* to cleanse the. *2 Chr* 29:15
w. of the L. are pure. *Ps* 12:6
Baruch wrote all *w. of L.* *Jer* 36:4
roll thou hast written *w. of L.* 6, 8
of the book all the *w. of the L.* 11
hearing the *w. of the L.* *Amos* 8:11

see **came, hear**

work of the **Lord**

see the *w. of the L.* *Ex* 34:10
regard not the *w. of L.* *Isa* 5:12
cursed that doeth the *w. of L.* *Jer* 48:10
this is the *w. of L.* 50:25
declare the *w. of L.* 51:10
abounding in the *w. of the L.* *1 Cor* 15:58
he worketh the *w. of the L.* 16:10

works of the **Lord**

known all the *w. of the L.* *Josh* 24:31
seen all the great *w. of the L.* *Judg* 2:7
regard not the *w. of L.* *Ps* 28:5
come, behold the *w. of the L.* 46:8
I will remember the *w. of L.* 77:11
these see the *w. of the L.* 107:24
the *w. of L.* are great. 111:2
declare *w. of L.* 118:17

wrath of the **Lord**

w. of L. was kindled. *Num* 11:33
the *L.'s w.* be kindled. *Deut* 11:17
for great is the *w. of L.* *2 Ki* 22:13 *2 Chr* 34:21
the *w. of L.* turned. *2 Chr* 12:12
the *w. of L.* was upon Judah. 29:8
so that the *w. of the L.* 32:26
until *w. of the L.* arose. 36:16
was *w. of the L.* kindled. *Ps* 106:40
through the *w. of the L.* *Isa* 9:19
remove in the *w. of the L.* 13:13
because of *w. of the L.* *Jer* 50:13
gold shall not be able to . . . day of *w. of the L.* *Ezek* 7:19; *Zeph* 1:18

see **praise**

Lord *said*

L. said in his heart. *Gen* 8:21
he hearkened not as the *L. said.* *Ex* 7:13; 22; 8:15, 19; *Deut* 9:3 *Judg* 2:15; 6:27
is that which the *L. said.* *Ex* 16:23
all the words the *L. said.* 24:3
all *L. said* we will do. 7; *Num* 32:31
place of which *L. said.* *Num* 10:29
as the *L. said* to him by the. 16:40
for the *L.* had *said,* They shall. 26:65
as the *L.* hath *said.* *Deut* 31:3 *Josh* 14:12; *Joel* 2:32
all the *L. said* to Moses. *Josh* 11:23
thing that the *L. said.* 14:6
what is the thing that *L. said* to thee? *1 Sam* 3:17
tell thee what the *L. said.* 15:16
day of which the *L. said* to thee. 24:4
because the *L. said* to him, Curse David. *2 Sam* 16:10
L. said he would dwell. *1 Ki* 8:12 *2 Chr* 6:1
nations, concerning which *L. said* to Israel. *1 Ki* 11:2
L. said not that he would blot out. *2 Ki* 14:27
whereof the *L.* had *said,* Ye. 17:12
which *L. said* in Jerusalem. 21:4, 7 *2 Chr* 33:4
Solomon had made in temple as the *L. said.* *2 Ki* 24:13
the *L.* hath *said* unto me. *Ps* 2:7
the *L. said* unto my Lord. 110:1 *Mat* 22:44; *Mark* 12:36 *Luke* 20:42; *Acts* 2:34
then *said* the *L.* *Isa* 7:3; 8:3 *Ezek* 44:2; *Hos* 3:1; *Jonah* 4:10 *Luke* 20:13
for so *L. said* unto me, I. *Isa* 18:4
thus hath *L. said* unto me. 21:16 *Jer* 4:27; 6:6
L. said, Forasmuch. *Isa* 29:13
rest, I the *L.* have *said.* *Ezek* 21:17
said the *L.* in a vision. *Acts* 9:10
the word of *L.* how he *said.* 11:16

saith the **Lord**

thus *saith the L.* *Ex* 4:22; 5:1 7:17; *1 Sam* 2:27; *2 Sam* 12:11 24:12
what the *L. saith,* that will I speak. *Num* 24:13
thus *saith the L.* God of. *Josh* 7:13 24:2; *Judg* 6:8; *2 Sam* 12:7
but now the *L. saith,* Be it far from me. *1 Sam* 2:30
saith L. of hosts. 15:2; *2 Sam* 7:8 *1 Chr* 17:7; *Jer* 6:9; 7:3, 21
L. saith, that will I speak. *1 Ki* 22:14
not be purged, *saith the L.* *Isa* 22:14 *Jer* 5:14; 35:17; 49:5; 50:31
now will I rise, *saith the L.*; now will I be exalted. *Isa* 33:10 *Ps* 12:5
now *saith the L.* that formed me. *Isa* 49:5
saith the L. that hath mercy. 54:10
for I am with thee, *saith the L.* *Jer* 1:8, 19; 30:11
fear is not in thee, *saith the L.* 2:19
yet return unto me, *saith the L.* 3:1
if thou wilt return, *saith the L.* 4:1
fear ye not me, *saith L.* 5:22
I have seen it, *saith L.* 7:11
evil, they know not me, *saith the L.* 9:3
to know me? *saith the L.* 22:16
I a God at hand, *saith the L.*? 23:23
I shall not see him, *saith the L.* 24
even forsake you, *saith the L.* 33
not sent him, *saith the L.* 27:15
not sent them, *saith the L.* 29:9
L. saith and the Lord hath not sent them. *Ezek* 13:6, 7
I am against you, *saith L.* 8
thus it was, *saith L.* 16:19
be no more, *saith the L.* God. 21:13
and I am your God *saith L.* 34:31
it is done, *saith the L.* God. 39:8
accept you, *saith the L.* God. 43:27
is it not even thus, O Israel? *saith the L.* *Amos* 2:11
this liketh you, *saith the L.* 4:5
shall not be, *saith L.* 7:3
called by my name, *saith L.* 9:12
the *L. saith,* Arise thou. *Mi* 6:1
behold, I am against thee, *saith the L.* *Nah* 2:13; 3:5
wait ye upon me, *saith L.* *Zeph* 3:8
why? *saith L.* of hosts. *Hag* 1:9
I am with you, *saith L.* 13
for I, *saith the L.* will be. *Zech* 2:5
but by my Spirit, *saith the L.* 4:6
loved you, *saith the L.* *Mal* 1:2
this of your hand, *saith the L.* 13
great King, *saith the L.* of hosts. 14
fear not me, *saith the L.* of. 3:5
now herewith, *saith the L.* of. 10
shall be mine, *saith the L.* of. 17
shall do this, *saith the L.* of. 4:3
saith the L. who doeth. *Acts* 15:17
I will repay, *saith the L.* *Rom* 12:19
hear me for all this, *saith the L.* *1 Cor* 14:21
ye separate, *saith the L.* *2 Cor* 6:17
regarded them not, *saith the L.* *Heb* 8:9
I will recompense, *saith the L.* 10:30
and the ending, *saith the L.* *Rev* 1:8

see **live, saved**

Lord joined with *seek*

thence thou shalt *seek L.* *Deut* 4:29
heart rejoice, that *seek L.* *1 Chr* 16:10; *Ps* 105:3
seek the *L.* and his strength. *1 Chr* 16:11; *Ps* 105:4
set your heart to *seek* the *L.* *1 Chr* 22:19; *2 Chr* 11:16
his heart to *seek* the *L.* *2 Chr* 12:14
Judah to *seek* the *L.* God. 14:4
a covenant to *seek* the *L.* 15:12
would not *seek* the *L.* God. 13
set himself to *seek* the *L.* 20:3
Judah they came to *seek L.* 4
were come to *seek* the *L.* *Ezra* 6:21
praise the *L.* that *seek.* *Ps* 22:26
they that *seek* the *L.* shall not want any good. 34:10
that *seek L.* understand. *Pr* 28:5
neither do they *seek L.* *Isa* 9:13 31:1; *Hos* 7:10
ye that *seek* the *L.* look to. *Isa* 51:1
seek ye *L.* while he may be. 55:6
shall go and *seek* the *L.* *Jer* 50:4
return and *seek* the *L.* *Hos* 3:5
with their herds to *seek* the *L.* 5:6
to *seek* the *L.* till he come. 10:12
seek the *L.* and ye shall live, lest. *Amos* 5:6
seek ye the *L.* all ye meek. *Zeph* 2:3
go to *seek* the *L.* of hosts. *Zech* 8:21
people shall come to *seek* the *L.* 22
the *L.* whom ye *seek* shall suddenly come. *Mal* 3:1
of men might *seek* the *L.* *Acts* 15:17
seek the *L.* if haply they might. 17:27

Lord joined with *sent*

the *L. sent* him forth from the garden. *Gen* 3:23
the *L. sent* us to destroy it. 19:13
words of *L.* who had *sent.* *Ex* 4:28
L. God of the Hebrews *sent.* 7:16
and *L. sent* thunder and hail. 9:23
that the *L.* hath *sent* me. *Num* 16:28
death, then *L.* hath not *sent.* 29
cried, the *L. sent* an angel. 20:16
the *L. sent* fiery serpents. 21:6
L. sent you from Kadesh-barnea. *Deut* 9:23
wonders which the *L. sent.* 34:11
the *L. sent* a prophet. *Judg* 6:8
then the *L. sent* Moses. *1 Sam* 12:8
and the *L. sent* Jerubbaal. 11
the *L. sent* thunder. 18
L. sent me to anoint thee. 15:1
the *L. sent* thee on a journey. 18
way which the *L. sent* me. 20
the *L.* hath *sent* thee away. 20:22
L. sent Nathan to David. *2 Sam* 12:1
L. sent pestilence on Israel. 24:15 *1 Chr* 21:14
tarry, for the *L.* hath *sent* me to Beth-el. *2 Ki* 2:2
L. hath *sent* me to Jericho. 4
L. sent me to Jordan. 6
therefore the *L. sent* lions. 17:25
the *L. sent* against him bands. 24:2
the *L. sent* an angel. *2 Chr* 32:21
L. sent a word into Jacob. *Isa* 9:8
L. sent him to prophesy. *Jer* 19:14
L. hath *sent* to you all his servants. 25:4
drink to whom the *L.* had *sent* me. 17
L. sent me to prophesy. 26:12, 15
L. hath truly *sent* him. 28:9
the *L.* hath not *sent* thee. 15
L. hath not *sent* them. *Ezek* 13:6
the *L. sent* out a great wind into. *Jonah* 1:4
L. their God had *sent* him. *Hag* 1:12
L. hath *sent* to walk to. *Zech* 1:10
know *L.* of hosts hath *sent* me 2:9 11; 4:9; 6:15
words which *L.* hath *sent.* 7:12
Saul, the *L.* Jesus hath *sent* me. *Acts* 9:17
the *L.* hath *sent* his angel. 12:11

serve the **Lord**

let the men go, that they may *serve the L.* their God. *Ex* 10:7
Pharaoh said, Go *serve the L.* your God. 8; 11:24; 12:31
take to *serve the L.* our God . . . with what we must *serve the L.* 10:26
ye shall *serve the L.* your. 23:25
to *serve the L.* thy God. *Deut* 10:12
fear and *serve the L.* *Josh* 24:14
seem evil unto you to *serve the L.* 15
will we *serve the L.*; he is our God. 18, 21, 24
Joshua said, Ye cannot *serve L.* 19

ye have chosen you the *L.* to *serve* him. *Josh* 24:22
serve the L. with all your heart. *1 Sam* 12:20
if the Lord shall bring me again, then will I *serve the L.* *2 Sam* 15:8
but yield, and *serve the L.* your God. *2 Chr* 30:8; 35:3
Judah to *serve the L.* 33:16; 34:33
serve the L. with fear. *Ps* 2:11
serve the L. with gladness. 100:2
gathered to *serve the L.* 102:22
for ye *serve the L.* Christ. *Col* 3:24

Lord *spake*
name of *L.* that *spake* to. *Gen* 16:13
L. spake, saying, I will. *Lev* 10:3
in the day the *L. spake* with Moses. *Num* 3:1; 9:1
as the *L. spake* unto Moses. 5:4
whereof *L. spake* to Moses. 21:16
L. spake to you out of the midst of fire. *Deut* 4:12
similitude in the day the *L. spake.* 15
these words the *L. spake* to. 5:22
the words which the *L. spake.* 9:10
commandments which *L. spake.* 10:4
the *L. spake* this word to. *Josh* 14:10
this mountain whereof *L. spake.* 12
Samuel did that which the *L. spake.* *1 Sam* 16:4
L. may continue his word which he *spake.* *1 Ki* 2:4
word of the *L.* which he *spake.* 27
as the *L. spake* to David my. 5:5
L. hath performed word he *spake.* 8:20; *2 Ki* 10:10
perform his saying, which the *L. spake.* *1 Ki* 12:15; *2 Chr* 10:15
to the word of the *L.* which he *spake.* *1 Ki* 13:26; 14:18; 16:12, 34 17:16; 22:38; *2 Ki* 10:10; 24:2
the *L.* which he *spake* by his servant Ahijah. *1 Ki* 15:29; *2 Ki* 10:17
spake the *L.* saying, The dogs shall eat Jezebel. *1 Ki* 21:23
word of *L.* which he *spake.* *2 Ki* 9:36
L. which he *spake* to Jehu. 15:12
L. spake by his servants. 21:10
L. spake unto Gad. *1 Chr* 21:9
L. spake to Manasseh. *2 Chr* 33:10
moreover, the *L. spake.* *Isa* 7:10
L. spake also unto me again. 8:5
for the *L. spake* thus to me with. 11
time *spake* the *L.* by Isaiah. 20:2
words that the *L. spake.* *Jer* 30:4
the word that the *L. spake.* 50:1
L. hath done that which he *spake.* 51:12
L. spake unto the fish. *Jonah* 2:10
then *spake* the *L.* to Paul. *Acts* 18:9

Lord joined with *spoken*
Abram departed as *L.* had *spoken.* *Gen* 12:4; 21:1; 24:51; *Ex* 9:12 35; *Deut* 6:19
words the *L.* had *spoken.* *Ex* 4:30
all that the *L.* hath *spoken.* 19:8
gave in commandment all that the *L.* had *spoken.* 34:32
statutes *L.* hath *spoken.* *Lev* 10:11
for *L.* had *spoken* to Moses, saying. *Num* 1:48; 15:22
the *L.* hath *spoken* good. 10:29
hath the *L.* indeed *spoken* only by Moses? 12:2
what hath the *L. spoken*? 23:17
L. hath not *spoken.* *Deut* 18:21, 22
failed not aught which *L.* had *spoken.* *Josh* 21:45
L. have done the good he hath *spoken.* *1 Sam* 25:30
now then do it, for the *L.* hath *spoken.* *2 Sam* 3:18
for thou, O *L.* hath *spoken* it. 7:29
sign which *L.* hath *spoken.* *1 Ki* 13:3
for the *L.* hath *spoken* it. 14:11
Isa 21:17; 22:25; 24:3; 25:8 *Joel* 3:8; *Ob* 18
after the *L.* had *spoken* these words to Job. *Job* 42:7
the *L.* hath *spoken*, and called the earth. *Ps* 50:1
for thus hath the *L. spoken* to me. *Isa* 31:4
L. will do this thing that he hath *spoken.* 38:7
mouth of *L.* hath *spoken.* *Jer* 9:12
proud, for the *L.* hath *spoken.* 13:15
say, What hath *L. spoken*? 23:35, 37
L. hath *spoken* against nation. 27:13
destroyed, as *L.* hath *spoken.* 48:8
I the *L.* have *spoken* it. *Ezek* 5:13 15, 17; 17:21, 24; 21:32; 22:14 24:14; 26:14; 30:12; 34:24 36:36; 37:14
when the *L.* hath not *spoken.* 22:28
for I have *spoken* it, saith *L.* 26:5; 28:10; 39:5
hear this word that the *L.* hath *spoken.* *Amos* 3:1
the *L.* God hath *spoken*, who? 8
L. of hosts hath *spoken* it. *Mi* 4:4
fulfilled which was *spoken* of the *L.* *Mat* 1:22; 2:15
so then after the *L.* had *spoken* to them. *Mark* 16:19
had seen the *L.* and that he had *spoken.* *Acts* 9:27
at the first began to be *spoken* by the *L.* *Heb* 2:3

to or *unto the* **Lord**
I have lift up my hands *to L.* most high. *Gen* 14:22
I have taken on me to speak *to the L.* 18:27, 31
let us go, and do sacrifice *to L.* *Ex* 5:17; 8:8, 29
we must hold a feast *to L.* 10:9 12:14; *Num* 29:12
sing *to the L.* *Ex* 15:1, 21; *Judg* 5:3 *1 Chr* 16:23; *Ps* 13:6; 30:4; 68:32 95:1; 96:1, 2; 98:1, 5; 104:33 147:7; 149:1; *Isa* 12:5; 42:10 *Jer* 20:13
for to-day is a sabbath *to the L.* *Ex* 16:25; 35:2; *Lev* 25:2
sacrificeth save *unto the L.* *Ex* 22:20
holy *unto the L.* 30:10; 31:15 *Lev* 23:20; 27:21, 30, 32 *Num* 6:8; *Ezra* 8:28
We have sinned; pray *unto L.* *Num* 21:7; *Jer* 29:7; *Acts* 8:24
do *to the L.* in feasts. *Num* 29:39
not do so *to the L.* thy. *Deut* 12:31
I have opened my mouth *to the L.* *Judg* 11:35, 36
dedicated the silver *to the L.* 17:3
not up *to the L.* to Mizpeh. 21:8
Hannah prayed *to the L.* *1 Sam* 1:10
and he prayed *to the L.* 8:6
is no restraint *to the L.* to. 14:6
hang them up *to the L.* *2 Sam* 21:6
being priest *to the L.* *1 Ki* 2:27
Elisha shut door, prayed *to the L.* *2 Ki* 4:33; 6:18
Hezekiah clave *to the L.* 18:6
unto the wall, and prayed *to L.* 20:2 *2 Chr* 32:24; *Isa* 37:15; 38:2
passover holden *to the L.* *2 Ki* 23:23
but poured it out *to L.* *1 Chr* 11:18
give thanks *to L.*, call upon his name. 16:8, 41; *Ps* 92:1
burn *to L.* morning and. *2 Chr* 13:11
bring *to the L.* the collection. 24:9
but yield yourselves *to the L.* 30:8
salvation belongeth *to the L.* *Ps* 3:8
they cried *unto the L.* 18:41
and *to the L.* I made. 30:8; 142:1
compared *to L.* be likened *to L.*? 89:6
shall I render *to the L.* for? 116:12
I said *to the L.* Thou art my. 140:6
abomination *to the L.* *Pr* 3:32 11:1, 20; 12:22; 15:8, 9, 26; 16:5 17:15; 20:10, 23
commit thy works *to L.* 16:3
giveth to poor lendeth *to L.* 19:17
vow a vow *to the L.* *Isa* 19:21
even *to the L.* and he shall heal. 22
shall be holiness *to L.* 23:18 *Jer* 2:3; *Zech* 14:20
to the L. for a name. *Isa* 55:13
joined himself *to the L.* 56:3, 6
acceptable day *to the L.* 58:5
Jeremiah prayed *to the L.* *Jer* 32:16
to take heed *to the L.* *Hos* 4:10
Jonah prayed *to the L.* *Jonah* 4:2
their gain *unto the L.* and their substance *unto the L.* of. *Mi* 4:13
therefore I will look *to the L.* I. 7:7
shall be known *to the L.* *Zech* 14:7
but shalt perform *to the L.* *Mat* 5:33
to present him *to the L.* *Luke* 2:22
shall be called holy *to the L.* 23
the more added *to the L.* *Acts* 5:14
they would cleave *to the L.* 11:23
they ministered *unto the L.* 13:2
commended them *to the L.* 14:23
judged me faithful *to the L.* 16:15
eateth, eateth *to the L.* *Rom* 14:6
live *to the L.*; we die *to the L.* 8
their own selves *to the L.* *2 Cor* 8:5
is acceptable *to the L.* *Eph* 5:10
submit yourselves, as *to the L.* 22 6:7; *Col* 3:23
see **cry, cried, give, turn**

lord, as applied to *man*
after I am old, my *l.* *Gen* 18:12
nay, my *l.* hear me. 23:11
my *l.* hearken to me. 15
Drink, my *l.*; and she hasted. 24:18
be *l.* over thy brethren, let. 27:29
I have made him thy *l.* 37
let it not displease my *l.* 31:35
shall ye speak to my *l.* Esau. 32:4
I have sent to tell my *l.* that I. 5
it is a present sent to my *l.* Esau. 18
his garment, until his *l.* 39:16*
had offended their *l.* the king. 40:1
nay, my *l.* but to buy food. 42:10
who is the *l.* of the land. 30, 33
is not this it, in which my *l.*? 44:5
should we steal out of thy *l.*'s house. 8
will be my *l.*'s bondmen. 9
we told him the words of my *l.* 24
and he hath made me *l.* of all. 45:8
God hath made me *l.* of all. 9
my *l.* how that there is nothing left in sight of my *l.* but our. 47:18
anger of my *l.* wax hot. *Ex* 32:22
and said, My *l.* Moses. *Num* 11:28
my *l.* I beseech thee, lay not. 12:11
as my *l.* commandeth. 32:25, 27
the Lord commanded my *l.* 36:2
their *l.* was fallen down. *Judg* 3:25
Turn in, my *l.*, turn in to me. 4:18
fell down where her *l.* was. 19:26
and her *l.* rose up in morning. 27
favour in thy sight, my *l.* *Ruth* 2:13
l. I am of a sorrowful. *1 Sam* 1:15
O my *l.* as thy soul liveth, my *l.* 26
here I am, my *l.* 22:12
Saul, saying, My *l.* the king. 24:8
on me, my *l.* on me let this. 25:24
let not my *l.* regard this man. 25
seek evil to my *l.* be as Nabal. 26
young men that follow my *l.* 27
shall have dealt with my *l.* 31
not kept thy *l.* the king? 26:15
David said, It is my voice, my *l.* 17
why doth my *l.* thus pursue after? 18
fight against enemies of my *l.* 29:8
them hither to my *l.* *2 Sam* 1:10
I will gather all Israel to my *l.* 3:21
according to all that my *l.* hath. 9:11
Uriah slept with all the servants of his *l.* 11:9, 13
let not my *l.* suppose they. 13:32
handmaid speak to my *l.* 14:12
angel of God, so is my *l.* 17
none can turn from aught my *l.* 19
l. is wise according to wisdom. 20
dead dog curse my *l.* the king. 16:9
Cushi said, Tidings, my *l.* 18:31
let not my *l.* impute iniquity to me, the day my *l.* the king. 19:19
first to go down to meet my *l.* 20
my *l.* is come again in peace. 30
be a burden to my *l.* 35
go over with my *l.* 37
take thou thy *l.*'s servants, and. 20:6
my *l.* the king may see it, but why doth my *l.* delight in? 24:3
let my *l.* take and offer what. 22
that my *l.* the king may. *1 Ki* 1:2
thing done by my *l.* the king? 27
the Lord God of my *l.* the king. 36
the Lord hath been with my *l.* 37

as my *l.* the king hath said. *1 Ki* 2:38
O my *l.* I and this woman. 3:17
O my *l.* give her the living child. 26
fled from his *l.* Hadadezer. 11:23
art thou that my *l.* Elijah ? 18:7
was it not told my *l.* what I did? 13
Go tell thy *l.* Behold Elijah is. 14
my *l.* I am thine, and all. 20:4
tell my *l.* all thou didst send for. 9
pleasant as my *l.* seeth. *2 Ki* 2:19
nay, my *l.* do not lie to thine. 4:16
did I desire a son of my *l.*? 28
would God my *l.* were with the. 5:3
went in and told his *l.* saying. 4
servants said, None, my *l.* 6:12
saying, Help, my *l.* O king. 26
then a *l.* on whose hand. 7:2*, 17*
my *l.* O king, this is the woman. 8:5
said, Why weepeth my *l.*? 12
forth to the servants of his *l.* 9:11
thee, give pledges to my *l.* 18:23*
cunning men of my *l.* *2 Chr* 2:14
the counsel of my *l.* *Ezra* 10:3
our own, who is *l.* over us ? *Ps* 12:4
Ah *l.*, or Ah his glory. *Jer* 22:18; 34:5
now, I pray thee, my *l.* 37:20
my *l.* the king, these men. 38:9
I fear my *l.* the king. *Dan* 1:10
is no king nor *l.* that asked. 2:10
my *l.* the dream be to them. 4:19
decree which is come upon my *l.* 24
servant above his *l.* *Mat* 10:24
that the servant be as his *l.* 25
L., have patience with me. 18:26
they came and told their *l.* all. 31
my *l.* delayeth his coming. 24:48
Luke 12:45
his *l.* *said* unto him, Well done.
Mat 25:21, 23
men that wait for their *l.* *Luke* 12:36
that servant shewed his *l.* 14:21
my *l.* taketh away from me. 16:3
and he said to the first, How much owest thou unto my *l.*? 5
not what his *l.* doeth. *John* 15:15
servant is not greater than his *l.* 20
thing to write to my *l.* *Acts* 25:26
a servant, though *l.* of all. *Gal* 4:1
Abraham, calling him *l.* *1 Pet* 3:6

lords

Behold now, my *l.*, turn in. *Gen* 19:2
consumed *l.* of high places of Arnon.
Num 21:28
is Lord of *l.* *Deut* 10:17
1 Tim 6:15; *Rev* 17:14
five *l.* of the Philistines. *Josh* 13:3
Judg 3:3
l. of the Philistines. *Judg* 16:5
and the house fell upon the *l.* 30
they gathered *l.* of the Philistines.
1 Sam 5:8, 11
plague on you all, and on your *l.* 6:4
l. of the Philistines went after 12
l. of the Philistines went up. 7:7
the *l.* passed on by hundreds. 29:2
nevertheless, the *l.* favour thee not. 6
that thou displease not the *l.* 7
offerings which *l.* offered. *Ezra* 8:25*
the *l.* of the heathen. *Isa* 16:8
other *l.* have had dominion. 26:13
say my people, We are *l.*? *Jer* 2:31*
great *l.* renowned. all. *Ezek* 23:23*
my counsellors and *l.* *Dan* 4:36
feast to a thousand of his *l.* 5:1
thy *l.* have drunk wine in them. 23
with his own signet and of his *l.* 6:17
made a supper to his *l.* *Mark* 6:21
gods many, and *l.* many. *1 Cor* 8:5
nor as being *l.* over God's. *1 Pet* 5:3

lordship

kings of Gentiles exercise *l.*
Mark 10:42; *Luke* 22:25

Lo-ruhamah

God said, Call her name *L.* *Hos* 1:6
weaned *L.* she conceived and. 8

lose

run on thee, and thou *l.* *Judg* 18:25
mules alive, that we *l.* *1 Ki* 18:5
caused owners to *l.* life. *Job* 31:39
shalt vomit up, and *l.* *Pr* 23:8
to get, and a time to *l.* *Eccl* 3:6
findeth his life shall *l.* it. *Mat* 10:39
16:25; *Mark* 8:35; *Luke* 9:24
he shall in no wise *l.* his reward.
Mat 10:42; *Mark* 9:41
and *l.* his own soul. *Mat* 16:26*
Mark 8:36*; *Luke* 9:25
if he *l.* one sheep. *Luke* 15:4
if she *l.* one piece. 8
whosoever shall *l.* his life. 17:33
Father's will I should *l.* *John* 6:39
loveth his life shall *l.* it. 12:25
look to yourselves, we *l.* *2 John* 8

loseth

and he that *l.* his life. *Mat* 10:39

loss

torn, I bare the *l.* of. *Gen* 31:39
pay for the *l.* of time. *Ex* 21:19
nor shall I know the *l.* *Isa* 47:8
come in one day *l.* of children. 9
gained this harm and *l.* *Acts* 27:21
there shall be no *l.* of any man's. 22
burned, he shall suffer *l.* *1 Cor* 3:15
I counted *l.* for Christ. *Phil* 3:7
and I count all things but *l.* for Christ, for whom I suffered the *l.* of. 8

lost

for any manner of *l.* thing. *Ex* 22:9
Deut 22:3
found that which was *l.* *Lev* 6:3
restore the *l.* thing he found. 4
the days that were before shall be *l.*
Num 6:12*
with all *l.* thing of thy brother's.
Deut 22:3
asses of Kish, Saul's father, were *l.*
1 Sam 9:3
as for thine asses that were *l.* 20
army like that thou hast *l.* *1 Ki* 20:25
astray like a *l.* sheep. *Ps* 119:176
thou hast *l.* the other. *Isa* 49:20*
seeing I have *l.* my children. 21*
people hath been *l.* sheep. *Jer* 50:6
saw that her hope was *l.* *Ezek* 19:5
sought that which was *l.* 34:4
I will seek that which was *l.* 16
they say, Our hope is *l.*, we. 37:11
if the salt have *l.* his savour. *Mat* 5:13
Mark 9:50; *Luke* 14:34
rather to the *l.* sheep. *Mat* 10:6
not sent but to the *l.* sheep. 15:24
Son of man is come to save that which was *l.* 18:11; *Luke* 19:10
go after that which is *l.* *Luke* 15:4
found my sheep which was *l.* 6
found the piece which I had *l.* 9
this my son was *l.* 24
thy brother was *l.* 32
Gather up fragments that nothing be *l.* *John* 6:12
none of them is *l.* but the. 17:12
them thou gavest me, I have *l.* 18:9
our gospel is hid, to them that are *l.*
2 Cor 4:3*

lot

Many things were decided in olden times by casting lots, and the term was used in rather a figurative sense in connection with other things. As examples, lots were cast, [1] *To find out a person,* 1 Sam 14:41; Jonah 1:7. [2] *To divide lands,* Num 26:55, 56. [3] *To choose a church officer,* Acts 1:26. [4] *To order and regulate the courses of men in office,* 1 Chr 24:5; 25:8. [5] *To decide a controversy,* Ps 22:8.

one *l.* for Lord, other for scapegoat.
Lev 16:8, 9, 10
land shall be divided by *l.*
Num 26:55; *Ezek* 48:29
divide the land by *l.* *Num* 33:54
36:2; *Josh* 13:6; *Ezek* 47:22
land ye shall inherit by *l.* *Num* 34:13
Jacob is the *l.* of his. *Deut* 32:9
was the *l.* of the tribe. *Josh* 15:1
the *l.* of Joseph. 16:1
was a *l.* for Manasseh. 17:1
thou given me but one *l.*? 14
thou shalt not have one *l.* only. 17
l. of the tribe of Benjamin. 18:11
and the second *l.* came forth. 19:1
the third *l.* came for the children. 10
fourth *l.* came out to Issachar. 17
fifth *l.* to Asher. *Josh* 19:24
sixth *l.* to Naphtali. 32
seventh *l.* came for tribe of Dan. 40
l. for families of Kohathites. 21:4
1 Chr 6:54
Gershon had by *l.* *Josh* 21:6
gave by *l.* to the Levites. 8
my *l.* to fight against Canaanites, likewise go . . . into thy *l.* *Judg* 1:3
we will go up by *l.* against it. 20:9
God, give a perfect *l.* *1 Sam* 14:41
Merari were given by *l.* *1 Chr* 6:63
I give the land of Canaan, the *l.* of.
16:18; *Ps* 105:11
they were divided by *l.* *1 Chr* 24:5
first *l.* came forth to Jehoiarib. 7
first *l.* came forth for Asaph. 25:9
Pur, that is *l.* before. *Esth* 3:7
cup, thou maintainest my *l.* *Ps* 16:5
shall not rest on the *l.* of the. 125:3
cast in thy *l.* among us. *Pr* 1:14
l. is cast into lap, but disposing. 16:33
l. causeth contentions to cease. 18:18
l. of them that rob us. *Isa* 17:14
and he hath cast the *l.* for. 34:17
stones of the stream are thy *l.* 57:6
this is thy *l.* from me. *Jer* 13:25
bring it out, let no *l.* fall. *Ezek* 24:6
stand in thy *l.* at end. *Dan* 12:13
none that shall cast a cord by *l.*
Mi 2:5
his *l.* was to burn incense. *Luke* 1:9
the *l.* fell on Matthias. *Acts* 1:26
no *l.* or part in this matter. 8:21
their land to them by *l.* 13:19*

Lot

Haran begat *L.* *Gen* 11:27
Terah took *L.* 31
L. went with him. 12:4; 13:1
L. had flocks. 13:5
strife between herdmen of Abram and *L.* 7
L. chose him all the plain of. 11
they took *L.* prisoner. 14:12
L. sat in the gate of Sodom; *L.* 19:1
pulled *L.* into house. 10
the angels hastened *L.* 15
God sent *L.* out of the midst of. 29
both the daughters of *L.* were. 36
I have given Ar to the children of *L.*
Deut 2:9, 19
holpen the children of *L.* *Ps* 83:8
was in the days of *L.* *Luke* 17:28
remember *L.*'s wife. 32
delivered just *L.* vexed. *2 Pet* 2:7

lothe (loathe)

Egyptians shall *l.* to drink. *Ex* 7:18
I *l.* it, I would not live. *Job* 7:16
l. themselves for evils. *Ezek* 6:9
ye shall *l.* yourselves in your. 20:43
l. yourselves for your iniquities.
36:31

lothed (loathed)

hath thy soul *l.* Zion ? *Jer* 14:19
soul *l.* them, their soul. *Zech* 11:8*

lotheth (loatheth)

soul *l.* this light bread. *Num* 21:5
full soul *l.* an honeycomb. *Pr* 27:7
l. her husband and her. *Ezek* 16:45

lothing (loathing)

wast cast out to the *l.* *Ezek* 16:5*

lothsome (loathsome)

month, till it be *l.* to you. *Num* 11:20
skin is broken and become *l.* *Job* 7:5
are filled with a *l.* disease. *Ps* 38:7
a wicked man is *l.* and. *Pr* 13:5

lots

cast *l.* between me and Jonathan.
1 Sam 14:42
cast *l.* over against. *1 Chr* 24:31
parted garments, casting *l.*
Mat 27:35; *Mark* 15:24
they gave forth their *l.* *Acts* 1:26
see **cast**

loud

l. instruments to Lord. *2 Chr* 30:21
people shouted with a *l.* *Ezra* 3:13
the singers sang *l.* with. *Neh* 12:12
cried with a *l.* cry. *Esth* 4:1
play skilfully with a *l.* *Ps* 33:3
make a *l* noise and rejoice. 98:4*
praise him on *l.* cymbals. 150:5

she is *l.* and stubborn. *Pr* 7:11*
angel cried with a *l.* cry. *Rev* 14:18

loud joined with *voice*

I cried with a *l. voice.* *Gen* 39:14
voice of the trumpet exceeding *l.* *Ex* 19:16
speak with a *l. voice.* *Deut* 27:14
wept with a *l. voice.* *2 Sam* 15:23
blessed congregation with a *l. voice.* *1 Ki* 8:55
sware to the Lord with a *l. voice.* *2 Chr* 15:14
to praise Lord with a *l. voice.* 20:19
Luke 19:37
many wept with a *l. voice.* *Ezra* 3:12
answered with a *l. voice.* 10:12
his friend with a *l. voice.* *Pr* 27:14
they cry with a *l. voice.* *Ezek* 8:18
he cried with a *l. voice,* saying. 9:1
spake out with a *l. voice.* *Luke* 1:42
unclean spirit cried with a *l. voice.* 8:28; *Acts* 8:7
back and with a *l. voice.* *Luke* 17:15
said with a *l. voice,* Stand. *Acts* 14:10
Festus said with a *l. voice.* 26:24
proclaiming with a *l. voice.* *Rev* 5:2*
with a *l. voice,* Worthy is. 12*
angel saying with a *l. voice,* Woe, woe. 8:13*; 14:7*, 9*, 15*
a *l. voice* saying in heaven. 12:10*

loud *voices*

instant with *l. voices.* *Luke* 23:23

louder

trumpet waxed *l.* and *l.* *Ex* 19:19

love

In a number of verses in the Authorized Version of the New Testament the word charity *is used where the true meaning is* love. *In the 17th century when the Bible was translated the word charity had this meaning, which the French* cher, chère, *from the same root* (*Latin,* carus, dear) *still retains. As charity now often means something quite different, both the Revisions substitute for it the word which expresses the true idea*—love. *These references are:* 1 Cor 8:1; 13:1, 2, 3, 4, 8, 13; 14:1; 16:14; Col. 3:14; 1 Thes 3:6; 2 Thes 1:3; 1 Tim 1:5; 2:15; 4:12; 2 Tim 2:22; 3:10; 1 Pet 4:8; 5:14; 2 Pet 1:7; 3 John 6; Jude 12; Rev 2:19. *See also* Rom 14:15.

a few days for the *l.* *Gen* 29:20
passing the *l.* of women. *2 Sam* 1:26
greater than the *l.* he had. 13:15
be thou ravished always with her *l.* *Pr* 5:19
let us take our fill of *l.* till. 7:18
hatred stirreth up strifes, but *l.* 10:12
dinner of herbs where *l.* is. 15:17
a transgression seeketh *l.* 17:9
rebuke is better than secret *l.* 27:5
no man knoweth either *l.* *Eccl* 9:1
also their *l.* and hatred is now. 6
banner over me was *l.* *S of S* 2:4
apples, for I am sick of *l.* 5; 5:8
thereof being paved with *l.* 3:10
how pleasant art thou, O *l.*! 7:6
l. is strong as death, jealousy. 8:6
many waters cannot quench *l.*: if a man would give all . . . for *l.* 7
I remember thee, the *l.* *Jer* 2:2
trimmest thy way to seek *l.*? 33
loved thee with everlasting *l.* 31:3
time was the time of *l.* *Ezek* 16:8
corrupt in her inordinate *l.* 23:11*
came to her into bed of *l.* 17
mouth they shew much *l.* 33:31
Daniel into tender *l.* *Dan* 1:9*
l. of Lord toward Israel. *Hos* 3:1
I drew them with bands of *l.* 11:4
l. of many shall wax cold. *Mat* 24:12
if ye have *l.* one to. *John* 13:35
greater *l.* hath no man than. 15:13
l. wherewith thou hast loved. 17:26
who shall separate us from the *l.* of Christ? *Rom* 8:35
let *l.* be without dissimulation. 12:9
affectioned with brotherly *l.* 10
l. worketh no ill, therefore *l.* *Rom* 13:10
I beseech you for the *l.* of the. 15:30
you may know the *l.* *2 Cor* 2:4
that ye would confirm your *l.* 8
l. of Christ constraineth us. 5:14
Holy Ghost, by *l.* unfeigned. 6:6
prove the sincerity of your *l.* 8:8
churches the proof of your *l.* 24
and the God of *l.* shall be. 13:11
faith which worketh by *l.* *Gal* 5:6
but brethren, by *l.* serve one. 13
fruit of the Spirit is *l.*, joy. 22
after I heard of your *l.* *Eph* 1:15
l. of Christ, passeth knowledge. 3:19
and *l.* with faith, from God. 6:23
that your *l.* may abound. *Phil* 1:9
other of *l.* doth preach Christ. 17
therefore any comfort of *l.* 2:1
likeminded, having the same *l.* 2
l. which ye have to all the saints. *Col* 1:4
who declared to us your *l.* in. 1:8
your labour of *l.* *1 Thes* 1:3
touching brotherly *l.*, ye need. 4:9
breastplate of faith and *l.* 5:8
they received not the *l.* *2 Thes* 2:10
abundant with faith and *l.* *1 Tim* 1:14
the *l.* of money is the root. 6:10
righteousness, *l.*, patience. 11
not given the spirit of fear, but of *l.* *2 Tim* 1:7
yet for *l.'s* sake I rather beseech thee. *Philem* 9
work and labour of *l.* *Heb* 6:10
to provoke unto *l.* and to. 10:24
let brotherly *l.* continue. 13:1
to unfeigned *l.* of the. *1 Pet* 1:22
the *l.* of the Father is. *1 John* 2:15
behold what manner of *l.* the. 3:1
let us love one another, for *l.* 4:7
God is *l.* 8
herein is *l.* not that we loved God. 10
l. that God hath to us; God is *l.* 16
herein is our *l.* made perfect. 17
there is no fear in *l.*; perfect *l.* 18
this is *l.*, that we walk after. *2 John* 6
mercy to you, peace and *l.* *Jude* 2
hast left thy first *l.* *Rev* 2:4

love, *verb*

l. thy neighbour as. *Lev* 19:18, 34
Mat 19:19; 22:39; *Mark* 12:31
l. the Lord thy God with. *Deut* 6:5
10:12; 11:1, 13, 22; 19:9; 30:6
God, which keepeth covenant with them that *l.* him. 7:9; *Dan* 9:4
he will *l.* thee, bless thee. *Deut* 7:13
delight in thy fathers to *l.* 10:15
l. therefore the stranger, for ye. 19
know whether ye *l.* the Lord. 13:3
command thee to *l.* Lord thy. 30:16
that thou mayest *l.* the Lord. 20
take heed to *l.* the Lord your God. *Josh* 22:5; 23:11
l. him be as the sun. *Judg* 5:31
king's servants *l.* thee. *1 Sam* 18:22
shouldest thou *l.* them? *2 Chr* 19:2
mercy for them that *l.* him. *Neh* 1:5
how long will ye *l.* vanity? *Ps* 4:2
let them that *l.* thy name be. 5:11
I will *l.* thee, O Lord my. 18:1
O *l.* the Lord, all ye saints. 31:23
l. thy salvation say. 40:16; 70:4
they that *l.* his name shall. 69:36
ye that *l.* the Lord, hate evil. 97:10
usest to do to those that *l.* 119:132
great peace have they who *l.* 165
shall prosper that *l.* thee. 122:6
preserveth them that *l.* him. 145:20
long, ye simple, will ye *l.*? *Pr* 1:22
l. wisdom, and she shall keep. 4:6
all they that hate me, *l.* death. 8:36
a wise man and he will *l.* thee. 9:8
kings *l.* him that speaketh. 16:13
that *l.* it shall eat the fruit. 18:21
a time to *l.* and a time. *Eccl* 3:8
therefore do the virgins *l.* *S of S* 1:3
than wine, the upright *l.* thee. 4
to serve and *l.* the name. *Isa* 56:6
I the Lord *l.* judgement, I. 61:8
Jerusalem all ye that *l.* her. 66:10
and my people *l.* to have. *Jer* 5:31
l. a woman beloved, *l.* *Hos* 3:1
her rulers with shame, do *l.* *Hos* 4:18
drive them out, I will *l.* them. 9:15
I will *l.* them freely, for mine. 14:4
hate evil and *l.* the good. *Amos* 5:15
hate the good and *l.* the. *Mi* 3:2
to *l.* mercy and to walk. 6:8
l. no false oath. *Zech* 8:17
l. the truth. 19
it hath been said, *L.* thy. *Mat* 5:43
but I say, *L.* your enemies. 44
Luke 6:27, 35
if ye *l.* them which *l.* you. *Mat* 5:46; *Luke* 6:32
they *l.* to pray standing. *Mat* 6:5
hate the one and *l.* the other. 24
Luke 16:13
l. the Lord thy God with all thy heart. *Mat* 22:37; *Mark* 12:30, 33
Luke 10:27
l. the uppermost rooms. *Mat* 23:6
scribes, who *l.* to go. *Mark* 12:38
which of them will *l.*? *Luke* 7:42
ye *l.* greetings in the markets. *Luke* 11:43; 20:46
will *l.* him and manifest. *John* 14:21
l. me, my Father will *l.* him. 23
my commandment, That ye *l.* one another. 15:12, 17
the world would *l.* his own. 19
for good, to them *l.* God. *Rom* 8:28
owe nothing to any, but to *l.* 13:8
shalt *l.* thy neighbour as thyself. *Rom* 13:9; *Gal* 5:14; *Jas* 2:8
prepared for them that *l.* *1 Cor* 2:9
if any man *l.* God the same is. 8:3
husbands, *l.* your wives, as Christ also. *Eph* 5:25, 28, 33; *Col* 3:19
grace be with all them that *l.* our Lord Jesus. *Eph* 6:24
are taught of God to *l.* *1 Thes* 4:9
but to all them that *l.* *2 Tim* 4:8
teach young women to *l.* *Tit* 2:4
greet them that *l.* us in the. 3:15
Lord promised to them that *l.* him. *Jas* 1:12; 2:5
whom having not seen ye *l.* *1 Pet* 1:8
see ye *l.* one another with a. 22
l. the brotherhood. 2:17
l. as brethren. 3:8
he that will *l.* life. 10
l. not the world, if any man *l.* the. *1 John* 2:15
from the beginning that we should *l.* 3:11; 4:7, 11; *2 John* 5
to life, because we *l.* *1 John* 3:14
l. one another, as he gave us. 23
if we *l.* one another, God. 4:12
l. him, because he first loved us. 19
can he *l.* God whom he hath not? 20
loveth God, *l.* his brother also. 21
l. the children of God, when we *l.* 5:2

love *of God*

ye pass over judgement and *l. of God.* *Luke* 11:42
not *l. of God* in you. *John* 5:42
l. of God is shed abroad. *Rom* 5:5
separate us from the *l. of God.* 8:39
l. of God be with you. *2 Cor* 13:14
hearts into the *l. of God.* *2 Thes* 3:5
kindness and *l. of God.* *Tit* 3:4
the *l. of God* perfected. *1 John* 2:5
hereby perceive we *l. of God.* 3:16
dwelleth the *l. of God* in him? 17
was manifested the *l. of God.* 4:9
this is *l. of God* that we keep. 5:3
keep yourselves in the *l. of God.* *Jude* 21

his **love**

Lord did not set *his l.* *Deut* 7:7
because he hath set *his l.* *Ps* 91:14
in *his l.* and in his pity he. *Isa* 63:9
will rest in *his l.* he will. *Zeph* 3:17
and abide in *his l.* *John* 15:10
but God commendeth *his l.* *Rom* 5:8
if love one another *his l.* *1 John* 4:12

in **love**

clave unto these *in l.* *1 Ki* 11:2
in l. to my soul delivered. *Isa* 38:17
to you with a rod, or *in l.* *1 Cor* 4:21
as ye abound *in* your *l.* to. *2 Cor* 8:7
be without blame before him *in l.* *Eph* 1:4
rooted and grounded *in l.* 3:17

forbearing one another *in l.* *Eph* 4:2
the truth *in l.* may grow up to. 15
to edifying of itself *in l.* 16
walk *in l.* as Christ hath loved. 5:2
being knit together *in l.* *Col* 2:2
you to increase *in l.* *1 Thes* 3:12
esteem them highly *in l.* 5:13
in faith and *l.* which is. *2 Tim* 1:13
he that dwelleth *in l.* *1 John* 4:16
no fear *in l.*: he that feareth is not made perfect *in l.* 18
Father *in* truth and *l.* *2 John* 3

my love

for *my l.* they are mine. *Ps* 109:4
rewarded me hatred for *my l.* 5
compared thee, O *my l.* *S of S* 1:9
behold, thou art fair, *my l.* 15; 4:1
as lily, so is *my l.* among. 2:2
my l. till he please. 7; 3:5; 8:4
rise up, *my l.* 2:10, 13
all fair, *my l.*; there is no spot. 4:7
open to me, *my l.* my dove. 5:2
beautiful, O *my l.* as Tirzah. 6:4
continue ye in *my l.* *John* 15:9
abide in *my l.* 10
my l. be with you all in Christ Jesus. *1 Cor* 16:24

thy love

thy l. was wonderful. *2 Sam* 1:26
for *thy l.* is better. *S of S* 1:2; 4:10
we will remember *thy l.* more. 1:4
how fair is *thy l.* my sister! 4:10
hearing of *thy l.* and faith. *Philem* 5
joy and consolation in *thy l.* 7
hast left *thy* first *l.* *Rev* 2:4

I love

savoury meat, such as *I l.* *Gen* 27:4
if servant shall say, *I l.* *Ex* 21:5
canst thou say, *I l.* thee? *Judg* 16:15
I l. Tamar my brother. *2 Sam* 13:4
I l. the Lord, because. *Ps* 116:1
O how *l.* *I* thy law. 119:97
thy law do *I l.* 113, 163
therefore *I l.* thy testimonies. 119
I l. thy commands above gold. 127
consider how *I l.* thy precepts. 159
thy testimonies *I l.* exceedingly. 167
I l. them that *l.* me. *Pr* 8:17
world may know that *I l.* *John* 14:31
knowest that *I l.* thee. 21:15, 16, 17
the more *I l.* you, the. *2 Cor* 12:15
if a man say, *I l.* God. *1 John* 4:20
I l. in the truth. *2 John* 1; *3 John* 1
as *I l.* I rebuke and. *Rev* 3:19

love me

my husband will *l. me.* *Gen* 29:32
showing mercy to thousands of them that *l. me.* *Ex* 20:6; *Deut* 5:10
I love them that *l. me.* *Pr* 8:17
cause those that *l. me* to inherit. 21
Father ye would *l. me.* *John* 8:42
doth my Father *l. me.* 10:17
if ye *l. me,* keep my. 14:15
if a man *l. me,* he will keep. 23

love not

l. not sleep, lest thou. *Pr* 20:13
if any man *l. not* the. *1 Cor* 16:22
because I *l.* you *not*? *2 Cor* 11:11
l. not the world. *1 John* 2:15
let us *not l.* in word. 3:18

loved

Rebekah to wife, and *l.* *Gen* 24:67
Isaac *l.* Esau, but Rebekah *l.* 25:28
meat such as his father *l.* 27:14
Jacob *l.* Rachel more. 29:18, 30
Shechem *l.* Dinah, and spake. 34:3
Israel *l.* Joseph more than. 37:3, 4
because he *l.* thy fathers. *Deut* 4:37
but because the Lord *l.* you. 7:8
23:5; 33:3
Samson *l.* a woman in. *Judg* 16:4
Elkanah *l.* Hannah. *1 Sam* 1:5
Saul *l.* David. 16:21
Jonathan *l.* David as his own soul. 18:1, 3; 20:17
Israel and Judah *l.* David. 18:16
Saul's daughter, *l.* David. 20
Lord *l.* Solomon, and. *2 Sam* 12:24
son of David, *l.* Tamar. 13:1
than love wherewith he *l.* her. 15
Solomon *l.* the Lord. *1 Ki* 3:3
because the Lord *l.* Israel. 10:9
2 Chr 9:8
Solomon *l.* many strange. *1 Ki* 11:1
the Lord *l.* his people. *2 Chr* 2:11
Isa 48:14
Rehoboam *l.* Maacah. *2 Chr* 11:21
Uzziah had husbandmen, he *l.* 26:10
the king *l.* Esther above. *Esth* 2:17
they whom I *l.* are turned against. *Job* 19:19
excellency of Jacob whom he *l.* *Ps* 47:4
the mount Zion which he *l.* 78:68
as he *l.* cursing, so let it. 109:17
heaven whom they have *l.* *Jer* 8:2
thus have they *l.* to wander. 14:10
them that thou hast *l.* *Ezek* 16:37
thou hast *l.* a reward on. *Hos* 9:1
their abominations were according as they *l.* 10
was a child, then I *l.* him. 11:1
wherein hast thou *l.* us.? *Mal* 1:2
holiness of Lord which he *l.* 2:11
beholding him, *l.* him. *Mark* 10:21
forgiven, for she *l.* much. *Luke* 7:47
God so *l.* the world. *John* 3:16
Jesus *l.* Martha, and her sister. 11:5
Jews, behold how he *l.* him. 36
for they *l.* praise of men more. 12:43
having *l.* his own, he *l.* them to. 13:1
disciple whom Jesus *l.* 23; 19:26
20:2; 21:7, 20
he that loveth me shall be *l.* 14:21
if ye *l.* me, ye would rejoice. 28
Father *l.* me, so have I *l.* you. 15:9
loveth you, because ye *l.* 16:27
l. them, as thou hast *l.* me. 17:23
love wherewith thou hast *l.* me. 26
more than conquerors through him that *l.* us. *Rom* 8:37
love you, the less I be *l.* *2 Cor* 12:15
l. me, and gave himself. *Gal* 2:20
great love wherewith he *l.* *Eph* 2:4
as Christ also *l.* us. 5:2
Christ *l.* the church. 25
Father, which hath *l.* us. *2 Thes* 2:16
Demas having *l.* this. *2 Tim* 4:10
hast *l.* righteousness. *Heb* 1:9
Balaam *l.* the wages of. *2 Pet* 2:15
l. God, but that he *l.* us. *1 John* 4:10
if God so *l.* us. 11
because he first *l.* us. 19
to him that *l.* us and. *Rev* 1:5
l. not their lives to the death. 12:11

***I have* loved**

I have l. the habitation. *Ps* 26:8
commandments *I have l.* 119:47, 48
I have l. thee, therefore. *Isa* 43:4
I have l. strangers, and. *Jer* 2:25
I have l. thee with an everlasting love. 31:3
I have l. you, yet ye say. *Mal* 1:2
as *I have l.* you, that ye also love. *John* 13:34; 15:12
Father loved me, so *have I l.* 15:9
written, Jacob *I have l.* *Rom* 9:13
make them know that *I have l.* *Rev* 3:9

lovedst

thou *l.* their bed where. *Isa* 57:8
l. me before foundation. *John* 17:24

lovely

and Jonathan were *l.* *2 Sam* 1:23
he is altogether *l.* O. *S of S* 5:16
them as a very *l.* song. *Ezek* 33:32
whatsoever things are *l.* *Phil* 4:8

lover

for Hiram was ever a *l.* *1 Ki* 5:1
l. and friend hast thou. *Ps* 88:18
a *l.* of hospitality, a *l.* of good men. *Tit* 1:8*

lovers

my *l.* and friends stand. *Ps* 38:11
the harlot with many *l.* *Jer* 3:1
thy *l.* will despise thee, they. 4:30
go up and cry, for all thy *l.* 22:20
thy *l.* shall go into captivity. 22
all thy *l.* have forgotten thee. 30:14
l. hath none to comfort. *Lam* 1:2
called for my *l.* but they deceived. 19
thy gifts to all thy *l.* *Ezek* 16:33
discovered with thy *l.* and idols. 36
I will gather thy *l.* 37
doted on her *l.* 23:5
her into the hand of her *l.* *Exek* 23:9
behold, I will raise up thy *l.* 22
I will go after my *l.* *Hos* 2:5
shall follow her *l.* 7
her lewdness in the sight of *l.* 10
these rewards that my *l.* have. 12
and she went after her *l.* and. 13
Ephraim hath hired *l.* 8:9
be *l.* of their own selves. *2 Tim* 3:2
l. of pleasures more than *l.* of. 4

loves

us solace ourselves with *l.* *Pr* 7:18
will I give thee my *l.* *S of S* 7:12

lovest

son Isaac whom thou *l.* *Gen* 22:2
thou dost but hate me, and *l.* me not. *Judg* 14:16
thou *l.* thine enemies. *2 Sam* 19:6
thou *l.* righteousness. *Ps* 45:7
thou *l.* evil more than good. 52:3
thou *l.* all devouring words. 4
with wife whom thou *l.* *Eccl* 9:9
he whom thou *l.* is sick. *John* 11:3
Simon, son of Jonas, *l.* thou me? 21:15, 16, 17

loveth

for thy father, such as he *l.* *Gen* 27:9
little one, and his father *l.* him. 44:20
Lord *l.* the stranger in. *Deut* 10:18
go away because he *l.* thee. 15:16
daughter in law who *l.* *Ruth* 4:15
and him that *l.* violence. *Ps* 11:5
Lord *l.* righteousness. 7; 33:5
what man is he that *l.* many days? 34:12
Lord *l.* judgement. 37:28; 99:4
the Lord *l.* gates of Zion. 87:2
word is very pure, therefore thy servant *l.* 119:140
The Lord *l.* the righteous. 146:8
the Lord *l.* he correcteth. *Pr* 3:12
l. instruction, *l.* knowledge. 12:1
but he that *l.* him, chasteneth. 13:24
he *l.* him that followeth after. 15:9
a scorner *l.* not one that. 12
a friend *l.* at all times. 17:17
l. transgression that *l.* strife. 19
he that getteth wisdom *l.* his. 19:8
l. pleasure, he that *l.* wine. 21:17
he that *l.* pureness of heart. 22:11
whoso *l.* wisdom rejoiceth his. 29:3
that *l.* silver, he that *l.* *Eccl* 5:10
O thou whom my soul *l.* *S of S* 1:7
bed I sought him whom soul *l.* 3:1
seek him whom my soul *l.* 2
saw ye him whom my soul *l.*? 3
I found him whom my soul *l.* 4
every one *l.* gifts and. *Isa* 1:23
Ephraim as heifer *l.* to. *Hos* 10:11
he is a merchant, he *l.* to. 12:7
l. father or mother, he that *l.* son or daughter more than me. *Mat* 10:37
he *l.* our nation. *Luke* 7:5
the same *l.* little. 47
the Father *l.* the Son, and hath given all things. *John* 3:35; 5:20
l. his life shall lose it. 12:25
commandments, he it is that *l.* me, and he that *l.* me shall be. 14:21
he that *l.* me not, keepeth not. 24
Father himself *l.* you, because. 16:27
he that *l.* another hath. *Rom* 13:8
for God *l.* a cheerful giver. *2 Cor* 9:7
that *l.* his wife, *l.* himself. *Eph* 5:28
for whom the Lord *l.* he. *Heb* 12:6
he that *l.* his brother. *1 John* 2:10
he that *l.* not his brother, is not of God. 3:10
l. not his brother, abideth in death. 14; 4:8, 20
every one that *l.* is born of God. 4:7
that he who *l.* God, love his. 21
that *l.* him that begat, *l.* him. 5:1
Diotrephes *l.* to have. *3 John* 9
l. and maketh a lie. *Rev* 22:15

loving

let her be as the *l.* hind. *Pr* 5:19
l. favour rather than silver. 22:1
lying down, *l.* to slumber. *Isa* 56:10

lovingkindness

thy marvellous *l.* *Ps* 17:7; 92:2
thy *l.* is before mine eyes. 26:3
how excellent is thy *l.* O God! 36:7

O continue thy *l.* to them. *Ps* 36:10
I have not concealed thy *l.* 40:10
let thy *l.* continually preserve. 11
the Lord will command his *l.* 42:8
we have thought of thy *l.* O. 48:9
mercy on me according to thy *l.* 51:1
because thy *l.* is better than. 63:3
O Lord, for thy *l.* is good. 69:16
l. be declared in the grave ? 88:11
l. will I not utterly take. 89:33
to shew forth thy *l.* in the. 92:2
who crowneth thee with *l.* and. 103:4
shall understand *l.* of Lord. 107:43
quicken me after thy *l.* 119:88, 159
hear my voice according to thy *l.* 149
praise thy name for thy *l.* 138:2
cause me to hear thy *l.* in. 143:8
the Lord which exercise *l.* *Jer* 9:24
taken away my peace, even *l.* 16:5
with *l.* have I drawn thee. 31:3
shewest *l.* unto thousands. 32:18
betroth thee to me in *l.* *Hos* 2:19

lovingkindnesses

Lord thy mercies and *l.* *Ps* 25:6
where are thy former *l.*? 89:49
mention the *l.* of the Lord according to the multitude of his *l.* *Isa* 63:7

low

shalt come down very *l.* *Deut* 28:43
the Lord bringeth *l.* *1 Sam* 2:7
sycamore trees in the *l.* *2 Chr* 9:27
Uzziah had much cattle in *l.* 26:10
Philistines invaded cities of *l.* 28:18
on high those that be *l.* *Job* 5:11
look on proud, and bring him *l.* 40:12
high and *l.* rich and poor. *Ps* 49:2
surely men of *l.* degree. 62:9
remembered us in our *l.* 136:23
pride shall bring him *l.* *Pr* 29:23
rich sit in *l.* place. *Eccl* 10:6
sound of the grinding is *l.* 12:4
will lay *l.* the haughtiness. *Isa* 13:11
fort of thy walls shall he lay *l.* 25:12
the lofty city he layeth it *l.* to. 26:5
thy speech shall be *l.* out of. 29:4
city shall be *l.* in a *l.* place. 32:19
I called on thy name out of *l.* dungeon. *Lam* 3:55
spreading vine of *l.* *Ezek* 17:6
that I have exalted the *l.* tree. 24
exalt him that is *l.*, abase. 21:26
shall set thee in the *l.* parts. 26:20*
regarded *l.* estate of his. *Luke* 1:48
hath exalted them of *l.* degree. 52
condescend to men of *l.* *Rom* 12:16
let the brother of *l.* degree. *Jas* 1:9
but the rich in that he is made *l.* 10
see **brought**

lower

second and third stories. *Gen* 6:16
f rising be in sight *l.* *Lev* 13:20
t be no *l.* than the skin. 21, 26
set in the *l.* places the. *Neh* 4:13
made him a little *l.* than the angels. *Ps* 8:5; *Heb* 2:7, 9
shall go into the *l.* parts of the. 63:9
out *l.* in presence of prince. *Pr* 25:7
waters of the *l.* pool. *Isa* 22:9
Shout, ye *l.* parts. 44:23
bottom even to the *l.* *Ezek* 43:14
descended first into the *l.* *Eph* 4:9

lower *parts of the earth*

[1] *The valleys*, Isa 44:23. [2] *The state of the dead*, Ps 63:9. [3] *The mother's womb*, Ps 139:15. [4] *The earth, as the lowest part of the visible world, or the grave and state of the dead*, Eph 4:9.

lowest

hall burn to the *l.* hell. *Deut* 32:22†
made priests *l.* *1 Ki* 12:31; 13:33
2 Ki 17:32
my soul from the *l.* hell. *Ps* 86:13†
hou hast laid me in the *l.* pit. 88:6
uriously wrought in the *l.* 139:15
ncreased from the *l.* *Ezek* 41:7
traitened more than the *l.* 42:6
hame to take *l.* room. *Luke* 14:9
it down in the *l.* room. 10

loweth

wild ass bray, or *l.* the ox? *Job* 6:5

lowing

along the highway *l.* *1 Sam* 6:12
then the *l.* of the oxen ? 15:14

lowliness

that ye walk with all *l.* *Eph* 4:2
but in *l.* of mind, let each. *Phil* 2:3

lowly

yet hath he respect to *l.* *Ps* 138:6
but he giveth grace to *l.* *Pr* 3:34
then cometh shame, but with *l.* 11:2
humble spirit with the *l.* 16:19*
he is just, *l.* and riding. *Zech* 9:9
for I am meek and *l.* *Mat* 11:29

lowring

for the sky is red and *l.* *Mat* 16:3

Lucas

Marcus, Demas, *L.* my. *Philem* 24

Lucifer

fallen from heaven, O *L.* *Isa* 14:12

Lucius

L. of Cyrene was a. *Acts* 13:1
L. Jason and Sosipater. *Rom* 16:21

lucre

Samuel's sons turned after *l.*, took. *1 Sam* 8:3
greedy of filthy *l.* *1 Tim* 3:3, 8
not be given to filthy *l.* *Tit* 1:7
they ought not for filthy *l.* 11
feed flock not for filthy *l.* *1 Pet* 5:2

Luke

L. the beloved physician. *Col* 4:14
only *L.* is with me. *2 Tim* 4:11

lukewarm

because thou art *l.* *Rev* 3:16

lump

take a *l.* of figs and lay. *2 Ki* 20:7* *Isa* 38:21*
of the same *l.* one vessel. *Rom* 9:21
firstfruit be holy the *l.* is. 11:16
a little leaven leaveneth the whole *l.* *1 Cor* 5:6; *Gal* 5:9
that ye may be a new *l.* *1 Cor* 5:7

lunatick

and those which were *l.* *Mat* 4:24*
mercy on my son, for he is *l.* 17:15*

lurk

come, let us *l.* privily. *Pr* 1:11
l. privily for their own lives. 18

lurking

knowledge of all the *l.* *1 Sam* 23:23
he sitteth in the *l.* places. *Ps* 10:8
as it were a young lion *l.* in. 17:12

lust

(*Formerly often used with a general meaning of pleasure, desire, with no idea of evil*)

my *l.* shall be satisfied. *Ex* 15:9
asking meat for their *l.* *Ps* 78:18
not estranged from their *l.* 30
to their own hearts' *l.* 81:12*
burned in their *l.* one. *Rom* 1:27
not known *l.* except the law. 7:7*
ye shall not fulfil *l.* of flesh. *Gal* 5:16
not in *l.* of concupiscence. *1 Thes* 4:5
he is drawn of his own *l.* *Jas* 1:14
l. hath conceived, it bringeth. 15
that is in world through *l.* *2 Pet* 1:4
that walk after flesh in the *l.* of. 2:10
l. of the flesh, the *l.* of. *1 John* 2:16
world passeth away, and the *l.* 17

lust, *verb*

l. not after her beauty. *Pr* 6:25
on a woman to *l.* after her. *Mat* 5:28
not *l.* after evil things. *1 Cor* 10:6
ye *l.* and have not, ye kill. *Jas* 4:2

lusted

buried the people that *l.* *Num* 11:34
but they *l.* exceedingly. *Ps* 106:14
not lust as they also *l.* *1 Cor* 10:6
fruits thy soul *l.* after. *Rev* 18:14

lusteth

what thy soul *l.* after. *Deut* 12:15 20, 21; 14:26
flesh *l.* against the Spirit. *Gal* 5:17
dwelleth in us *l.* to envy. *Jas* 4:5

lusting

mixed multitude fell a *l.* *Num* 11:4

lusts

the *l.* of other things. *Mark* 4:19
and the *l.* of your father. *John* 8:44
gave them up to uncleanness through *l.* *Rom* 1:24
obey it in the *l.* thereof. 6:12
provision for flesh, to fulfil *l.* 13:14
have crucified flesh with *l.* *Gal* 5:24
our conversation in the *l.* of. *Eph* 2:3
according to the deceitful *l.* 4:22
into foolish and hurtful *l.* *1 Tim* 6:9
flee youthful *l.* but. *2 Tim* 2:22
silly women led away with *l.* 3:6
own *l.* shall they heap teachers. 4:3
that denying worldly *l.* *Tit* 2:12
disobedient, serving divers *l.* 3:3
not hence, even of your *l.*? *Jas* 4:1
ye may consume it on your *l.* 3
according to former *l.* *1 Pet* 1:14
abstain from fleshly *l.* that. 2:11
no longer should live to the *l.* 4:2
in lasciviousness, *l.* excess of. 3
they allure through the *l.* *2 Pet* 2:18
walking after their own *l.* 3:3
complainers, walking after *l.* *Jude* 16
walk after their own ungodly *l.* 18

lusty

Moab 10,000 men, all *l.* *Judg* 3:29

Luz

the city was called *L.* at the first. *Gen* 28:19; *Judg* 1:23
Jacob came to *L.* in the. *Gen* 35:6
Almighty appeared to me at *L.* 48:3

Lycaonia

and Derbe, cities of *L.* *Acts* 14:6
voices, saying in the speech of *L.* 11

Lydda

down to the saints at *L.* *Acts* 9:32
dwelt at *L.* turned to the Lord. 35
forasmuch as *L.* was nigh. 38

Lydia

L. shall fall with them. *Ezek* 30:5

Lydia

L. whose heart the Lord. *Acts* 16:14
entered into the house of *L.* 40

lying

hated them that regard *l.* vanities, but I trust in the Lord. *Ps* 31:6
let the *l.* lips be put to silence. 18
thou lovest *l.* rather than. 52:3
and for cursing and *l.* which. 59:12
spoken against me with *l.* 109:2
remove from me the way of *l.* 119:29
I hate and abhor *l.* but thy law. 163
soul, O Lord, from *l.* lips. 120:2
hateth a proud look, a *l.* *Pr* 6:17
that hideth hatred with *l.* lips. 10:18
but a *l.* tongue is but for a. 12:19
l. lips are abomination to the. 22
a righteous man hateth *l.* but a wicked man is loathsome. 13:5
much less do *l.* lips become a. 17:7
getting of treasures by a *l.* 21:6
a *l.* tongue hateth those. 26:28
rebellious people, *l.* *Isa* 30:9
wicked devices with *l.* words. 32:7
in transgressing and *l.* against. 59:13
trust ye not in *l.* words. *Jer* 7:4
behold, ye trust in *l.* words that. 8
because have spoken *l.* words. 29:23
vanity and *l.* divination. *Ezek* 13:6
spoken a *l.* divination? 7
by your *l.* to my people that. 19
ye have prepared *l.* words. *Dan* 2:9
by swearing, *l.* and killing. *Hos* 4:2*
that observe *l.* vanities forsake. *Jonah* 2:8
away *l.* speak truth. *Eph* 4:25
whose coming is with *l.* *2 Thes* 2:9

lying *spirit*

l. spirit in the mouth of all his. *1 Ki* 22:22; *2 Chr* 18:21
Lord hath put a *l. spirit* in prophets. *1 Ki* 22:23; *2 Chr* 18:22

lying, *verb*

three flocks of sheep *l.* *Gen* 29:2
him that hateth thee, *l.* *Ex* 23:5
if one be found slain, *l.* *Deut* 21:1
my path and *l.* down. *Ps* 139:3
sleeping, *l.* down, loving. *Isa* 56:10

man sick of the palsy, *l.* *Mat* 9:2
where the damsel was *l.* *Mark* 5:40
babe *l.* in a manger. *Luke* 2:12, 16
then *l.* on Jesus' breast. *John* 13:25*
he saw the linen clothes *l.* yet. 20:5
napkin not *l.* with the linen. 7

lying *in wait*

rose up from *l. in wait.* *Judg* 9:35
now there were men *l. in wait.* 16:9
as a bear *l. in wait,* as. *Lam* 3:10
me by the *l. in wait* of Jews. *Acts* 20:19
when Paul's kinsmen heard of their *l. in wait.* 23:16

lying *with*

l. with Jacob's daughter. *Gen* 34:7
kill woman that hath known man by *l. with* him. *Num* 31:17
not known man by *l. with* him, keep alive. 18; *Judg* 21:12
women had not known man by *l. with* him. *Num* 31:35
if a man be found *l. with. Deut* 22:22

Lysanias

reign of Tiberius, *L.* *Luke* 3:1

Lysias

L. unto the most excellent Felix. *Acts* 23:26

Lystra

were ware of it, and fled unto *L.* *Acts* 14:6
a certain man at *L.* impotent. 8
Paul came to *L.* 16:1
by the brethren at *L.* 2
afflictions which came unto me at *L.* *2 Tim* 3:11

M

Maachah

Reumah Nahor's concubine bare *M.* *Gen* 22:24
M. mother of Absalom. *2 Sam* 3:3
1 Chr 3:2
M. the mother of Abijam, the daughter of. *1 Ki* 15:2, 10; *2 Chr* 11:22
M. Caleb's concubine. *1 Chr* 2:48
M. the wife of Machir bare. 7:16
Hanan the son of *M.* 11:43

Maaseiah

Zichri slew *M.* *2 Chr* 28:7
Rehum and *M.* sealed. *Neh* 10:25
Zephaniah the son of *M.* *Jer* 21:1
29:25; 37:3
Lord of Zedekiah son of *M.* 29:21
Neriah son of *M.* 32:12; 51:59
above the chamber of *M.* son. 35:4

Maath

which was the son of *M. Luke* 3:26

Macedonia

come over into *M.* and. *Acts* 16:9
Timotheus were come from *M.* 18:5
when he had passed through *M.* 19:21
hath pleased them of *M. Rom* 15:26
were come into *M.* *2 Cor* 7:5
bestowed on the churches of *M.* 8:1
boast of you to them of *M.* 9:2
lest if they of *M.* find you. 4
brethren which came from *M.* 11:9
to all that believe in *M.* *1 Thes* 1:7
sounded the word, not only in *M.* 8
the brethren that are in *M.* 4:10

Machir

M. the son of Manasseh. *Gen* 50:23; *Num* 32:39
M. begat Gilead. *Num* 26:29; 27:1
36:1; *Josh* 17:1
Moses gave Gilead unto *M.* *Num* 32:40; *Deut* 3:15
out of *M.* came down. *Judg* 5:14
M. the son of Ammiel. *2 Sam* 9:4
5; 17:27

Machpelah

give me cave of *M.* *Gen* 23:9, 17
buried Sarah in the cave of *M.* 19
buried Abraham in *M.* 25:9
buried Jacob in *M.* 49:30; 50:13

mad

be *m.* for the sight of. *Deut* 28:34
feigned himself *m.* *1 Sam* 21:13
servants, Ye see the man is *m.* 14
this *m.* fellow to thee? *2 Ki* 9:11
m. against me are sworn. *Ps* 102:8
I said of laughter, It is *m.* *Eccl* 2:2
maketh a wise man *m.* 7:7*
that maketh diviners *m.* *Isa* 44:25
be moved, and be *m.* *Jer* 25:16
for every man that is *m.* put. 29:26
they are *m.* upon their idols. 50:38
therefore the nations are *m.* 51:7
fool, the spiritual man is *m. Hos* 9:7
he hath a devil and is *m. John* 10:20
to Rhoda, Thou art *m.* *Acts* 12:15
being exceedingly *m.* against them. 26:11
learning doth make thee *m.* 24
I am not *m.* most noble Festus. 25
not say that ye are *m.*? *1 Cor* 14:23

made

who *m.* thee prince over us? *Ex* 2:14; *Acts* 7:27
hath *m.* man's mouth? *Ex* 4:11
m. his servants and cattle flee. 9:20
after he had *m.* it a molten. 32:4
Aaron had *m.* them naked. 25
m. them gods of gold. 31; *Hos* 8:4
of Israel *m.* all the work. *Ex* 39:42
why have ye *m.* us to come from Egypt? *Num* 20:5
and calf which he had *m.* *Deut* 9:21
Joshua and Israel *m.* as if. *Josh* 8:15
went and *m.* as if they had been. 9:4
m. the heart of the people. 14:8
altar which our fathers *m.* 22:28
m. Samson sleep upon. *Judg* 16:19
Samson *m.* the Philistines. 25, 27
away the gods which I *m.* 18:24
his sons *m.* themselves vile. *1 Sam* 3:13*
that Samuel *m.* his sons judges. 8:1
have *m.* a king over you. 12:1
wast thou not *m.* the head? 15:17
sword hath *m.* women childless. 33
Whither have ye *m.* road? 27:10
m. himself sick. *2 Sam* 13:6*
calves that he had *m.* *1 Ki* 12:32
idols which his fathers *m.* 15:12
she had *m.* an idol in a grove. 13
2 Chr 15:16
streets as my fathers *m.* in. 20:34
they *m.* him king and. *2 Ki* 11:12
so Urijah the priest *m.* it. 16:11
yet his father *m.* him. *1 Chr* 26:10
art thou *m.* of the king's counsel? *2 Chr* 25:16
for Ahab *m.* Judah naked. 28:19
set the idol he had *m.* in the. 33:7
Josiah *m.* all present to serve. 34:33
whom he *m.* governor. *Ezra* 5:14
we *m.* our prayer unto. *Neh* 4:9
Ahasuerus *m.* her queen. *Esth* 2:17
they *m.* it a day of feasting. 9:17, 18
wast thou *m.* before the? *Job* 15:7
m. a pit, and is fallen into pit he *m.* *Ps* 7:15
are sunk into the pit they *m.* 9:15
is the man that *m.* not God. 52:7
I *m.* me great works. *Eccl* 2:4
I *m.* me gardens. 5
I *m.* me pools of water. 6
they *m.* me the keeper. *S of S* 1:6
he *m.* the pillars of silver. 3:10
my soul *m.* me like chariots. 6:12
their own fingers have *m.* *Isa* 2:8
is this the man that *m.* earth? 14:16
for we have *m.* lies our refuge. 28:15
of him that *m.* it, he *m.* me not. 29:16
which your hands have *m.* unto. 31:7
they have *m.* them crooked. 59:8
gods that have not *m.* *Jer* 10:11
have *m.* my pleasant portion a wilderness. 12:10
vessel that *m.* was marred in hand of potter, so he *m.* it again. 18:4
had *m.* that the prison. 37:15
which Asa the king had *m.* 41:9
Nebuchadnezzar *m.* me an. 51:34
ye *m.* the heart of the. *Ezek* 13:22*
the king dwelleth that *m.* 17:16
m. their sweet savour. 20:28
ye have *m.* your iniquity to be. 21:24
waters *m.* him great, deep set. 31:4
thy father *m.* master of. *Dan* 5:11
yet *m.* we not prayer before. 9:13
princes have *m.* him sick. *Hos* 7:5
the workman *m.* it, therefore. 8:6
the god which ye *m.* *Amos* 5:26
they *m.* their hearts as. *Zech* 7:12
thy faith hath *m.* thee whole. *Mat* 9:22; *Mark* 5:34; 10:52
Luke 8:48; 17:19
have *m.* commandment of God of none effect. *Mat* 15:6
prayer, but ye have *m.* it a den of. 21:13; *Mark* 11:17; *Luke* 19:46
m. them other five talents. *Mat* 25:16
who *m.* me a judge? *Luke* 12:14
and his name hath *m.* *Acts* 3:16
as for Saul, he *m.* havock of. 8:3*
who had *m.* this conspiracy. 23:13
they hoised up sail, and *m.* 27:40
m. free from law of sin. *Rom* 8:2
concerning faith have *m.* *1 Tim* 1:19
law *m.* nothing perfect. *Heb* 7:19
believeth not, hath *m.* God a liar. *1 John* 5:10
m. them white in blood. *Rev* 7:14
m. all nations drink of wine. 14:8

see **covenant, end, fire**

made, referring to *God, Lord, Christ*

God *m.* the firmament. *Gen* 1:7
m. two great lights, he *m.* stars. 16; *Ps* 136:7, 9
m. the beast of the earth. *Gen* 1:25
every thing that he had *m.* 31
from all his work he had *m.* 2:2
God *m.* the earth and heavens. 4
Ex 20:11; 31:17; *Ps* 146:6
Isa 45:18; *Jer* 10:12
m. to grow every tree. *Gen* 2:9
m. he a woman. 22
in the likeness of God *m.* 5:1; 9:6
Lord he had *m.* man. 6:6, 7
God *m.* a wind to pass over. 8:1
Sarah said, God hath *m.* me. 21:6
m. his journey prosperous. 24:21
Lord hath *m.* room for us. 26:22
the Lord *m.* all Joseph did. 39:3, 23
God hath *m.* me to forget. 41:51
God hath *m.* me a father. 45:8
God hath *m.* me lord of all. 9
feared God, he *m.* houses. *Ex* 1:21
Lord *m.* the sea dry land. 14:21
I *m.* Israel to dwell in. *Lev* 23:43
Lord your God and I have *m.* 26:13
he *m.* them wander in. *Num* 32:13
for the Lord *m.* his heart. *Deut* 2:30
out of heaven he *m.* thee to. 4:36
the Lord hath *m.* thee as. 10:22
m. the water of the Red sea. 11:4
nations which he hath *m.* 26:19
m. thee, and established thee. 32:6
he *m.* him ride, *m.* him suck. 13
then he forsook God which *m.* 15
Lord *m.* Jordan border. *Josh* 22:25
m. him have dominion. *Judg* 5:13*
the Lord had *m.* a breach in. 21:15
and *m.* them dwell in. *1 Sam* 12:8
Lord repented that he had *m.* 15:35
Lord had *m.* a breach. *2 Sam* 6:8*
he *m.* darkness pavilions. 22:12
thy gentleness hath *m.* me great. 36
Ps 18:35
who hath *m.* me a house. *1 Ki* 2:24
Lord loved Israel, therefore he *m.* 10:9; 14:7; 16:2; *2 Chr* 1:11
but the Lord *m.* the heavens. *1 Chr* 16:26; *Neh* 9:6; *Ps* 33:6
96:5; 121:2; 124:8; 134:3
Lord had *m.* them to rejoice. *2 Chr* 20:27
he sought the Lord, God *m.* 26:5
Lord had *m.* them joyful. *Ezra* 6:22; *Neh* 12:43
thy hands have *m.* me. *Job* 10:8
m. me weary, thou hast *m.* 16:7
he hath *m.* me a byword of. 17:6
he *m.* a decree for the rain. 28:26
that *m.* me in the womb make. 31:15
the Spirit of God *m.* me, and. 33:4
m. him can make his sword. 40:19
hast not *m.* my foes to. *Ps* 30:1
what desolations he hath *m.* in. 46:8
the sea is his and he *m.* it. 95:5
he *m.* us. 100:3
darkness, and *m.* it dark. 105:28

the day the Lord hath *m.* *Ps* 118:24
thy hands have *m.* me and. 119:73
that by wisdom *m.* the heavens. 136:5; *Acts* 14:15
m. Israel pass through. *Ps* 136:14
he hath *m.* a decree which. 148:6
rejoice in him that *m.* him. 149:2
the Lord *m.* all things. *Pr* 16:4
the Lord hath *m.* even both. 20:12
he hath *m.* every thing. *Eccl* 3:11
I found that God hath *m.* man. 7:29
he that *m.* them will not. *Isa* 27:11
he hath *m.* Tophet deep and. 30:33
thus saith the Lord that *m.* 44:2
he *m.* intercession for the. 53:12
things hath mine hand *m.* 66:2
lo, certainly in vain *m.* he it. *Jer* 8:8
Lord *m.* thee priest instead. 29:26
and hast *m.* thee a name as. 32:20
as the Lord liveth, that *m.* 38:16
he hath *m.* me desolate and faint. *Lam* 1:13; 3:11
the Lord hath *m.* my strength. 1:14
my skin hath he *m.* old. 3:4
hath *m.* my chain heavy. 7
m. my paths crooked. 9
he hath *m.* me drunken with. 15
I *m.* nations to shake at. *Ezek* 31:16
fear God who hath *m.* sea. *Jonah* 1:9
I *m.* their streets waste. *Zeph* 3:6
he *m.* them male and female. *Mat* 19:4; *Mark* 10:6
did not he that *m.* that? *Luke* 11:40
was not any thing *m.* *John* 1:3
Jesus *m.* more disciples. 4:1
he *m.* water wine. 46
he that *m.* me whole said. 5:11
m. clay of the spittle. 9:6; 11:14
m. himself the Son of God. 19:7
know that God hath *m.* *Acts* 2:36
know that God *m.* choice. 15:7
God that *m.* the world and. 17:24
hath *m.* of one blood all nations. 26
the Holy Ghost hath *m.* you. 20:28
m. foolish the wisdom. *1 Cor* 1:20
m. us able ministers of. *2 Cor* 3:6
hath *m.* him to be sin for us. 5:21
Christ hath *m.* us free. *Gal* 5:1
he hath *m.* us accepted. *Eph* 1:6
God hath *m.* us sit together. 2:6
he is our peace who hath *m.* 14
but *m.* himself of no. *Philem* 2:7
who hath *m.* us meet to. *Col* 1:12
he *m.* a shew of them openly. 2:15
by whom also he *m.* *Heb* 1:2
for when God *m.* promise to. 6:13
and hath *m.* us kings and. *Rev* 1:6
and worship him that *m.* 14:7

I have, or *have I* **made**

living substance *I have m.* *Gen* 7:4
lest thou say, *I have m.* 14:23
a father of nations *have I m.* thee. 17:5; *Rom* 4:17
Isaac said, Behold, *I have m.* him thy lord. *Gen* 27:37
see *I have m.* thee a god. *Ex* 7:1
I have m. thee a great name. *2 Sam* 7:9; *1 Chr* 17:8
I have m. supplication. *1 Ki* 8:59
I have m. provision. *1 Chr* 29:19
I Darius *have made* a decree. *Ezra* 6:11, 12
I have m. my bed in. *Job* 17:13
if *I have m.* gold my hope. 31:24
I have m. the wilderness. 39:6
things which *I have m.* *Ps* 45:1
who can say, *I have m.* my? *Pr* 20:9
I have m. their shouting. *Isa* 16:10
the sighing thereof *have I m.* 21:2
yea, *I have m.* him. 43:7; 46:4
I have m. the earth, and created. 45:12; *Jer* 27:5
the souls which *I have m.* *Isa* 57:16
behold *I have m.* thee a. *Jer* 1:18
but *I have m.* Esau bare. 49:10
ehold, *I have m.* thy face strong. *Ezek* 3:8, 9
have m. thee a watchman to. 17
whom *I have* not *m.* sad. 13:22
and *I have m.* the dry tree. 17:24
ave I m. thee a reproach. 22:4
have m. it for myself. 29:3, 9
have m. **him fair by multitude.** 31:9

image which *I have m.* *Dan* 3:15
I have m. the stink of camps to. *Amos* 4:10
I have m. thee small among the. *Obad* 2
have I m. you contemptible. *Mal* 2:9
because *I have m.* a man every whit whole. *John* 7:23
yet *have I m.* myself. *1 Cor* 9:19

thou hast **made**

plant them in the place which *thou hast m.* *Ex* 15:17
thou hast m. an atonement for. 29:36
this oath which *thou hast m.* us swear. *Josh* 2:17, 20
thou hast m. thy servant king instead of David. *1 Ki* 3:7
supplication that *thou hast m.* 9:3
thou hast m. heaven and earth. *2 Ki* 19:15; *Isa* 37:16; *Jer* 32:17
word came, saying, *Thou hast m.* great wars. *1 Chr* 22:8
thou hast m. an hedge. *Job* 1:10
remember that *thou hast m.* 10:9
thou hast m. desolate all my. 16:7
thou hast m. him little lower than angels. *Ps* 8:5
thou hast m. me the head of. 18:43
thou hast m. him most blessed. 21:6
thou hast m. my mountain. 30:7
behold, *thou hast m.* my days. 39:5
thou hast m. the earth to tremble. 60:2
thou hast m. us drink the wine. 3
thou hast m. summer and. 74:17
all nations whom *thou hast m.* 86:9
thou hast m. me an abomination to them. 88:8
thou hast m. all his enemies. 89:42
thou hast m. his glory to cease. 44
hast thou m. all men in vain? 47
thou hast m. the Lord thy habitation. 91:9
thou, Lord, *hast m.* me glad. 92:4
wisdom *hast thou m.* them. 104:24
Leviathan, whom *thou hast m.* 26
thou hast m. me wiser than. 119:98
for *thou hast m.* of a city. *Isa* 25:2
but *thou hast m.* me to serve. 43:24
O Lord, why *hast thou m.* us to err from thy ways? 63:17
where are thy gods that *thou hast m.* thee? *Jer* 2:28
wait on thee, for *thou hast m.* 14:22
thou hast m. us as the offscouring and refuse. *Lam* 3:45
nor *hast thou m.* up the hedge in the house. *Ezek* 13:5
thou hast m. thee an high place in every street. 16:24
thou hast m. thy beauty to be. 25
thy idols which *thou hast m.* 22:4
at thy dishonest gain which *thou hast m.* 13
but one hour, and *thou hast m.* them equal to us. *Mat* 20:12
why *hast thou m.* me thus. *Rom* 9:20
thou hast m. us to our God kings and priests. *Rev* 5:10

made *haste*

Rebekah *m. haste* and. *Gen* 24:46
Joseph *m. haste.* 43:30
Moses *m. haste.* *Ex* 34:8
Manoah's wife *m. haste.* *Judg* 13:10
David *made h.* *1 Sam* 23:26
Abigail *m. haste.* 25:18
nurse *m. haste* to flee. *2 Sam* 4:4
I *m. haste,* and delayed. *Ps* 119:60
Zacchaeus *m. haste.* *Luke* 19:6

see **Israel, sin, known**

made *manifest*

secret that shall not be *m. manifest.* *Luke* 8:17
he should be *m. manifest.* *John* 1:31
his deeds may be *m. manifest.* 3:21
God should be *m. manifest* in. 9:3
I was *m. manifest* to them that asked not. *Rom* 10:20
m. manifest to all nations for the obedience of faith. 16:26
every man's work shall be *m. manifest.* *1 Cor* 3:13
are approved may be *m. manifest.* *1 Cor* 11:19
secrets of his heart *m. manifest.* 14:25
life of Jesus should be *m. manifest.* *2 Cor* 4:10, 11
been throughly *m. manifest.* 11:6
m. manifest by the light. *Eph* 5:13
but now is *m. manifest* to. *Col* 1:26
now *m. manifest* by the appearing of Christ. *2 Tim* 1:10
way into the holiest was not yet *m. manifest.* *Heb* 9:8
went out, that they they might be *m. manifest.* *1 John* 2:19
judgements are *m. manifest.* *Rev* 15:4

made *peace*

and Joshua *m. peace* with them. *Josh* 9:15; 10:1, 4
was not a city that *m. peace* with Israel. 11:19
of Hadarezer were smitten, they *m. peace.* *2 Sam* 10:19; *1 Chr* 19:19
Jehoshaphat *m. peace.* *1 Ki* 22:44

made *ready*

m. ready the present. *Gen* 43:25
Joseph *m. ready* his chariot. 46:29
m. ready his chariot, and. *Ex* 14:6
in and *m. ready* a kid. *Judg* 6:19
till we have *m. ready* a kid. 13:15
m. ready before it was. *1 Ki* 6:7
chariot was *m. ready.* *2 Ki* 9:21
m. ready for the building. *1 Chr* 28:2
afterward they *m. ready* for themselves. *2 Chr.* 35:14
his bow and *m.* it *ready.* *Ps* 7:12
have *m. ready* their heart. *Hos* 7:6
the disciples *m. ready.* *Mat* 26:19; *Mark* 14:16; *Luke* 22:13
they *m. ready* Peter fell. *Acts* 10:10
boast of things *m. ready.* *2 Cor* 10:16
wife hath *m.* herself *ready.* *Rev* 19:7

made *speed*

Rehoboam *m. speed* to get. *1 Ki* 12:18; *2 Chr* 10:18

made *void*

hath utterly *m. void.* *Num* 30:12
thou hast *m. void* covenant. *Ps* 89:39
they have *m. void* thy law. 119:126
be heirs, faith is *m. void.* *Rom* 4:14

made, *passively*

hands were *m.* strong. *Gen* 49:24
may be *m.* unclean. *Lev* 22:5
shall bear all that is *m.* for them. *Num* 4:26
that is *m.* of the vine tree. 6:4
what supplication be *m.* *1 Ki* 8:38; *2 Chr* 6:29
ears attend to prayer *m.* *2 Chr* 6:40
let there be search *m.* in. *Ezra* 5:17
and arch was *m.* in the house. 6:1
let house be *m.* a dunghill. 11
gallows be *m.* of fifty. *Esth* 5:14
I am *m.* to possess months. *Job* 7:3
his like on earth, who is *m.* 41:33
when one is *m.* rich. *Ps* 49:16
fearfully and wonderfully *m.* 139:14
the righteous is *m.* plain. *Pr* 15:19
the simple is *m.* wise. 21:11
trust in Lord shall be *m.* fat. 28:25
cannot be *m.* straight. *Eccl* 1:15
countenance the heart is *m.* 7:3
a feast is *m.* for laughter. 10:19
which shall be *m.* as grass. *Isa* 51:12
shall earth be *m.* to bring forth. 66:8
a vessel that cannot be *m.* *Jer* 19:11
the word of the Lord was *m.* 20:8
his heart was *m.* like. *Dan* 5:21
these stones be *m.* bread. *Mat* 4:3
and the rent is *m.* worse. 9:16; *Mark* 2:21
and payment to be *m.* *Mat* 18:25
is *m.* ye make him twofold. 23:15
there was a cry *m.* behold. 25:6
rather a tumult was *m.* 27:24
the sepulchre be *m.* sure. 64
sabbath was *m.* for man. *Mark* 2:27
a recompence be *m.* thee. *Luke* 14:12
Pilate and Herod were *m.* 23:12
m. by him, and without him was not any thing *m.* that was *m.* *John* 1:3
the world was *m.* **by him.** 10

Word was *m.* flesh, and. *John* 1:14
the water that was *m.* wine. 2:9
wilt thou be *m.* whole? 5:6
Behold, thou art *m.* whole. 14
ye shall be *m.* free. 8:33
might be *m.* blind. 9:39
that they may be *m.* perfect. 17:23
distribution was *m.* to. *Acts* 4:35
prayer *m.* without ceasing. 12:5
promise which was *m.* 13:32; 26:6
prayer was wont to be *m.* 16:13
they be no gods which are *m.* 19:26
Jesus who was *m.* of the. *Rom* 1:3
by the things that are *m.* 20
thy circumcision is *m.* 2:25
were *m.* sinners, many *m.* 5:19
being *m.* free from sin. 6:18, 22
that which is good, *m.* death. 7:13
we had been *m.* like to Sodom. 9:29
the mouth confession is *m.* 10:10
let their table be *m.* a snare. 11:9
thy brother is *m.* weak. 14:21
cross of Christ be *m.* *1 Cor* 1:17
are in Christ, who of God is *m.* 30
m. a spectacle to the world. 4:9
we are *m.* as filth of world. 13
I am *m.* all things to all men. 9:22
have been all *m.* to drink. 12:13
in Christ shall all be *m.* alive. 15:22
first man Adam was *m.* a living soul,
last Adam was *m.* a. 45
which was *m.* glorious. *2 Cor* 3:10
an house not *m.* with hands. 5:1
might be *m.* the righteousness. 21
my strength is *m.* perfect in. 12:9
are ye now *m.* perfect by? *Gal* 3:3
Christ redeemed us, being *m.* 13
his seed were the promises *m.* 16
to whom the promise was *m.* 19
sent his Son, *m.* of a woman, *m.* 4:4
circumcision in flesh *m.* *Eph* 2:11
were far off, are *m.* nigh by the. 13
whereof I was *m.* a minister. 3:7
Col 1:23, 25
and was *m.* in the likeness. *Phil* 2:7
m. conformable to his death. 3:10
m. peace through blood. *Col* 1:20
with the circumcision *m.* 2:11
the law is not *m.* for a. *1 Tim* 1:9
and giving of thanks be *m.* for. 2:1
grace, we should be *m.* heirs. *Tit* 3:7
being *m.* so much better. *Heb* 1:4
it behoved him to be *m.* like. 2:17
for we are *m.* partakers of. 3:14
himself to be *m.* an high priest. 5:5
being *m.* perfect, he became the. 9
m. like to the Son of God. 7:3
m. of necessity a change. 12
m. not after law of a carnal. 16
an oath he was *m.* priest. 20
those priests were *m.* without. 21
Jesus was *m.* a surety of a better. 22
there was a tabernacle *m.* 9:2
a perfect tabernacle not *m.* 11
not entered into holy places *m.* 24
is a remembrance *m.* of sins. 10:3
expecting till his enemies be *m.* 13
ye were *m.* a gazingstock. 33
were not *m.* of things which. 11:3
weakness were *m.* strong. 34
us should not be *m.* perfect. 40
the spirits of just men *m.* 12:23
rich, in that he is *m.* low. *Jas* 1:10
by works was faith *m.* perfect. 2:22
m. after similitude of God. 3:9
m. head of the corner. *1 Pet* 2:7
but these *m.* to be taken. *2 Pet* 2:12
they were *m.* bitter. *Rev* 8:11
been *m.* drunk with wine of. 17:2

madest

thou *m.* him to have dominion over.
Ps 8:6
visit the branch that thou *m.* 80:15
son of man, whom thou *m.* 17
m. to thyself images of. *Ezek* 16:17
thou *m.* all their loins to be. 29:7
neither *m.* it grow. *Jonah* 4:10
art not thou that Egyptian which *m.*
an uproar? *Acts* 21:38
thou *m.* him a little lower. *Heb* 2:7

madman

fellow to play the *m.* *1 Sam* 21:15
as a *m.* who casteth. *Pr* 26:18

madmen

have I need of *m.*? *1 Sam* 21:15
O *m.* the sword shall. *Jer* 48:2

madness

shall smite thee with *m.* *Deut* 28:28
heart to know wisdom and *m.*
Eccl 1:17
to behold wisdom and *m.* 2:12
wickedness of folly, and *m.* 7:25
m. is in their heart, while. 9:3
his talk is mischievous *m.* 10:13
horse and rider with *m.* *Zech* 12:4
were filled with *m.* *Luke* 6:11
dumb ass forbade the *m.* *2 Pet* 2:16

Magdala

into the coasts of *M.* *Mat* 15:39

magician

such things at any *m.* *Dan* 2:10

magicians

and called for the *m.* *Gen* 41:8
I told this to the *m.* but none. 24
m. of Egypt did so in like manner.
Ex 7:11, 22; 8:7, 18
the *m.* said to Pharaoh, This. 8:19
m. could not stand before. 9:11
ten times better than all *m.* *Dan* 1:20
king commanded to call the *m.* 2:2
the secret cannot the *m.* shew. 27
then came in the *m.* but did not. 4:7
master of the *m.* tell me. 9
father made master of the *m.* 5:11

magistrate

was no *m.* in the land. *Judg* 18:7
goest to the *m.* give. *Luke* 12:58

magistrates

set *m.* and judges, who. *Ezra* 7:25
bring you to the *m.* *Luke* 12:11*
Paul and Silas to the *m.* *Acts* 16:20
m. commanded to beat them. 22
the *m.* sent the serjeants. 35, 36
told these words to the *m.* 38
in mind to obey *m.* and. *Tit* 3:1*

magnifical

the house must be exceeding *m.*
1 Chr 22:5

magnificence

m. should be destroyed. *Acts* 19:27

magnified

thou hast *m.* thy mercy. *Gen* 19:19
Lord *m.* Joshua in sight. *Josh* 4:14
let thy name be *m.* *2 Sam* 7:26
1 Chr 17:24
and the Lord *m.* Solomon.
1 Chr 29:25; *2 Chr* 1:1
Hezekiah was *m.* in sight of all.
2 Chr 32:23*
say, Let the Lord be *m.* *Ps* 35:27
say continually, The Lord be *m.*
40:16; 70:4
thou hast *m.* thy word above. 138:2
for he *m.* himself against the Lord.
Jer 48:26, 42; *Dan* 8:11
the enemy hath *m.* himself. *Lam* 1:9
and *m.* themselves against their border.
Zeph 2:8
m. themselves against people. 10
Lord will be *m.* from the. *Mal* 1:5
but the people *m.* them. *Acts* 5:13
name of Lord Jesus was *m.* 19:17
Christ be *m.* in my body. *Phil* 1:20

magnify

[1] *To declare and shew forth one's greatness and glory,* Luke 1:46. [2] *To increase one's esteem, reputation, and authority,* Josh 3:7; 4:14; 1 Chr 29:25.

day will I begin to *m.* thee. *Josh* 3:7
thou shouldest *m.* him? *Job* 7:17
if indeed ye will *m.* yourselves. 19:5
remember that thou *m.* his. 36:24
O *m.* the Lord with me. *Ps* 34:3
clothed with shame that *m.* 35:26
my foot slippeth, they *m.* 38:16
did *m.* himself against me. 55:12
m. him with thanksgiving. 69:30
Shall the saw *m.* itself? *Isa* 10:15
he will *m.* the law and make. 42:21
thus will I *m.* myself. *Ezek* 38:23
and he shall *m.* himself. *Dan* 8:25
the king shall *m.* himself. 11:36
shall *m.* himself above all. 37

they *m.* not themselves. *Zech* 12:
soul doth *m.* the Lord. *Luke* 1:4
tongues, and *m.* God. *Acts* 10:4
I am an apostle, I *m.* *Rom* 11:1

Magog

the son of Japheth, *M.* *Gen* 10:
1 Chr 1:
against the land of *M.* *Ezek* 38:
I will send a fire on *M.* and. 39:
to gather Gog and *M.* *Rev* 20:

Mahanaim

called name of place *M.* *Gen* 32:
out of Gad to Levites, *M.*
Josh 21:38; *1 Chr* 6:8
Ish-bosheth to *M.* *2 Sam* 2:
then David came to *M.* 17:24, 2
provided sustenance at *M.* 19:3
Shimei cursed me when I went to *M*
1 Ki 2:
the son of Iddo had *M.* 4:1

Maher-shalal-hash-baz

in the roll concerning *M.* *Isa* 8:
then said Lord, Call his name *M.*

Mahlon

Elimelech's sons, *M.* *Ruth* 1:
M. and Chilion died also both.
have bought all that was *M.* 4:
wife of *M.* have I purchased. 1

maid

(*The Revisions frequently substitute for this word the wor handmaid. The handmaids o maidservants of those days wer usually slaves*)

go in unto my *m.* Hagar. *Gen* 16:
behold, thy *m.* is in thy hand.
Hagar, Sarai's *m.* whence?
Laban gave Zilpah his *m.* 29:2
Bilhah, to be Rachel's *m.* 2
m. Bilhah, go in unto her. 30:
Rachel's *m.* conceived.
gave Zilpah her *m.*
Zilpah, Leah's *m.* bare Jacob. 10, 1
she sent her *m.* to fetch. *Ex* 2:
the *m.* went and called the.
smite his *m.* with a rod. 21:2
or the eye of his *m.* that it. 2
if a man entice a *m.* not. 22:16
shall be meat for thy *m.* *Lev* 25:
I came to her, I found her not a *m*
Deut 22:14*, 17
away captive a little *m.* *2 Ki* 5:
thus said the *m.* that is of Israel.
m. was fair and beautiful. *Esth* 2:
should I think upon a *m.*? *Job* 31:
way of a man with a *m.* *Pr* 30:1
with *m.* so with mistress. *Isa* 24:
m. forget her ornaments? *Jer* 2:3
the young man and the *m.* 51:2
father go in to the same *m.* *Amos* 2:
for the *m.* is not dead. *Mat* 9:2
by the hand, and the *m.* arose. 2
another *m.* saw him. 26:7
Mark 14:69; *Luke* 22:5
called, saying, *M.*, arise. *Luke* 8:5

maid child

if she bear a *m. child.* *Lev* 12:

maiden

I have given my *m.* to. *Gen* 30:1
is my daughter a *m.* *Judg* 19:2
on young man or *m.* *2 Chr* 36:1
every *m.* to the king. *Esth* 2:1
as the eyes of a *m.* to her mistress
Ps 123:
and mother of the *m.* *Luke* 8:5

maidens

her *m.* walked along by. *Ex* 2:
abide here fast by my *m.* *Ruth* 2:
that thou go out with his *m.* 2
kept fast by the *m.* of Boaz. 2
they found *m.* going to. *1 Sam* 9:1
I and my *m.* will fast. *Esth* 4:1
thou bind him for thy *m.*? *Job* 41:
their *m.* were not given. *Ps* 78:6
young men and *m.* praise. 148:1
hath sent forth her *m.* *Pr* 9:
maintenance for thy *m.* 27:2
giveth a portion to her *m.* 31:1
I got me servants and *m.* *Eccl* 2:
m. of seed of Israel. *Ezek* 44:22
begin to beat menservants and *m.*
Luke 12:4

maids

preferred her and her *m.* *Esth* 2:9
my *m.* count me for a. *Job* 19:15
ravished the *m.* in cities. *Lam* 5:11
slay utterly both *m.* and. *Ezek* 9:6
her *m.* shall lead her with. *Nah* 2:7
young men cheerful, and new wine the *m.* *Zech* 9:17

maidservant

the firstborn of the *m.* *Ex* 11:5
thy *m.* shall do no work. 20:10
Deut 5:14
not covet thy neighbour's wife, nor *m.* *Ex* 20:17
sell his daughter to be a *m.* 21:7
if he smite out his *m.*'s tooth. 27
if an ox push a *m.* he shall give. 32
that thy *m.* may rest as. *Deut* 5:14
desire thy neighbour's *m.* 21
eat them, thou and thy *m.* 12:18
16:11, 14
to thy *m.* thou shalt do. 15:17
son of his *m.* king. *Judg* 9:18
despise cause of my *m.* *Job* 31:13
his *m.* go free. *Jer* 34:9, 10

maidservants

Abram had *m.* and she asses.
Gen 12:16; 24:35
Abimelech's wife and *m.* 20:17
had much cattle and *m.* 30:43
entered into the two *m.*' tents. 31:33
rejoice, ye and your *m.* *Deut* 12:12
he shall take your *m.* *1 Sam* 8:16
of the *m.* shall I be had. *2 Sam* 6:22
time to receive *m.*? *2 Ki* 5:26

mail

he was armed with a coat of *m.*
1 Sam 17:5, 38

maimed

blind or *m.* ye shall not. *Lev* 22:22
them those that were *m.* *Mat* 15:30
wondered when they saw the *m.* 31
better to enter into life *m.* 18:8*
Mark 9:43
makest a feast, call *m.* *Luke* 14:13
bring in hither the poor and *m.* 21

main

hoised up the *m.*-sail. *Acts* 27:40*

maintain

[1] *To support and preserve*, 1 Chr 26:27; Ps 16:5. [2] *To defend by argument*, Job 13:15. [3] *To persevere in*, Tit 3:8, 14.

m. their cause. *1 Ki* 8:45, 49, 59
2 Chr 6:35, 39
they dedicate to *m.* the house of the Lord. *1 Chr* 26:27*
I will *m.* mine own ways. *Job* 13:15
Lord will *m.* the cause of. *Ps* 140:12
careful to *m.* good works. *Tit* 3:8
learn to *m.* good works for uses. 14

maintained

for thou hast *m.* my right. *Ps* 9:4

maintainest

portion, and thou *m.* my lot. *Ps* 16:5

maintenance

have *m.* from the king. *Ezra* 4:14*
the *m.* for thy maidens. *Pr* 27:27

majesty

the power and *m.* *1 Chr* 29:11
upon him such royal *m.* 25
shewed the honour of his *m.* *Esth* 1:4
with God is terrible *m.* *Job* 37:22
deck thyself now with *m.* 40:10
honour and *m.* hast thou. *Ps* 21:5
voice of the Lord is full of *m.* 29:4
with thy glory and *m.* 45:3
thy *m.* ride. 4
reigneth, he is clothed with *m.* 93:1
honour and *m.* are before him. 96:6
clothed with honour and *m.* 104:1
speak of the honour of thy *m.* 145:5
make known the glorious *m.* 12
hide thee for the glory of his *m.*
Isa 2:10; 19:21
they shall sing for the *m.* of. 24:14
behold the *m.* of the Lord. 26:10
ornament he set it in *m.* *Ezek* 7:20
for the honour of my *m.* *Dan* 4:30
excellent *m.* was added unto me. 36
Nebuchadnezzar thy father *m.* 5:18
the *m.* he gave him, all people. 19
feed in *m.* of the name. *Mi* 5:4
on the right hand of *m.* *Heb* 1:3; 8:1
eyewitnesses of his *m.* *2 Pet* 1:16
wise God be glory and *m.* *Jude* 25

make

let us *m.* man. *Gen* 1:26
I will *m.* him an help. 2:18
and a tree to be desired to *m.* 3:6
m. coats of skins. 21
m. thee an ark. 6:14
let us *m.* brick. 11:3
let us *m.* us a name. 4
I will *m.* of thee a great nation.
12:2; 21:18; 46:3; *Ex* 32:10
let us *m.* a name, lest. *Gen* 12:4
I will *m.* thy seed as the dust. 13:16
I will *m.* thee exceeding fruitful.
17:6; 48:4
m. Ishmael fruitful, I will *m.* 17:20
let us *m.* our father drink wine.
19:32, 34
I will *m.* thy seed as the stars. 26:4
Isaac said, *M.* me savoury. 27:4
bless thee, and *m.* thee fruitful. 28:3
I will *m.* thy seed as the sand. 32:12
m. ye marriages with us and. 34:9
ye *m.* me to stink among the. 30
go to Beth-el, and *m.* there an. 35:1
m. there an altar unto God. 3
m. mention of me to Pharaoh. 40:14
land *m.* thy father to dwell. 47:6
God *m.* thee as Ephraim and. 48:20
they say to us, *M.* brick. *Ex* 5:16
m. your count for the lamb. 12:4
m. them know the statutes. 18:16
not *m.* unto thee any graven image.
20:4; *Lev* 26:1; *Deut* 5:8
not *m.* with me gods of. *Ex* 20:23
an altar of earth shalt thou *m.* 24
if thou wilt *m.* me an altar. 25
m. full restitution. 22:3, 5, 6, 12
m. no mention of other gods. 23:13
Josh 23:7
I will *m.* enemies turn. *Ex* 23:27
shall not dwell, lest they *m.* thee. 33
m. me a sanctuary. 25:8
so shall ye *m.* it. 9
shalt *m.* holy garments. 28:2, 4
garments which they shall *m.* 4
for Aaron's sons thou shalt *m.* 40
m. them linen breeches. 42
m. him an altar of shittim. 30:1
m. it an oil of holy ointment. 25
perfume, you shall not *m.* like. 37
that they *m.* all that. 31:6; 35:10
up, *m.* us gods which shall go before us. 32:1, 23; *Acts* 7:40
I will *m.* of thee a great. *Ex* 32:10
I will *m.* my goodness pass. 33:19
and *m.* thy sons go a whoring. 34:16
m. no molten gods. 17; *Lev* 19:4
neither man nor woman *m.* *Ex* 36:6
he shall *m.* amends for. *Lev* 5:16
not *m.* yourselves abominable.
11:43; 20:25
not *m.* any cuttings in your. 19:28
not *m.* baldness. 21:5; *Deut* 14:1
I will *m.* you fruitful. *Lev* 26:9
I will *m.* your heaven as iron. 19
beasts, which shall *m.* you few. 22
man shall *m.* a singular vow. 27:2
the Lord *m.* thee a curse, *m.* thy.
Num 5:21
he shall not *m.* himself unclean. 6:7
the Lord *m.* his face to shine. 25
so *m.* themselves clean. 8:7
let us *m.* a captain, and return. 14:4
will *m.* of thee a greater nation. 12
thou *m.* thyself a prince. 16:13
if the Lord *m.* a new thing. 30
let them *m.* them broad plates. 38
I will *m.* to cease from me. 17:5
m. thee a fiery serpent, and. 21:8
he shall *m.* her vow of none. 30:8
ye shall *m.* it go through fire. 31:23
Lord *m.* you a thousand. *Deut* 1:11
I will *m.* them rulers over you. 13
I will *m.* them hear my words. 4:10
ye *m.* you a graven image. 16, 23
nor shalt thou *m.* marriages.
Deut 7:3
m. thee know that man liveth. 8:3
if it *m.* thee answer of peace. 20:11
if it will *m.* no peace with thee. 12
m. thee high above all nations. 26:19
shall *m.* thee plenteous. 28:11; 30:9
Lord shall *m.* thee the head. 13
m. the remembrance of. 32:26
I kill, and I *m.* alive, I wound. 39
thou shalt *m.* thy way. *Josh* 1:8
m. yourselves accursed, and *m.* the camp of Israel a curse. 6:18
m. confession. 7:19; *Ezra* 10:11
so shall your children *m.* *Josh* 22:25
m. marriages with them. 23:12
Samson, that he may *m.* *Judg* 16:25
m. the woman like Rachel and Leah.
Ruth 4:11
provoked her sore, to *m.* *1 Sam* 1:6
m. them inherit the throne. 2:8
ye *m.* the Lord's people to. 2:24
to *m.* yourselves fat with. 29
ye shall *m.* images of your. 6:5
m. a new cart. 7
m. us a king to judge us. 8:5
hearken to them, and *m.* 22
because it hath pleased the Lord to *m.* you his. 12:22; *1 Chr* 17:22
Lord will *m.* my lord. *1 Sam* 25:28
I will *m.* thee keeper of mine. 28:2
m. this fellow return that he. 29:4
will *m.* thee an house. *2 Sam* 7:11
things, to *m.* thy servant know. 21
to *m.* him a name. 23
and *m.* thyself sick. 13:5
should I *m.* thee go up and? 15:20
all my desire, though he *m.* it. 23:5
m. his throne greater. *1 Ki* 1:37
God *m.* the name of Solomon. 47
did I not *m.* thee to swear? 2:42
prayer which thy servant shall *m.*
8:29; *2 Chr* 6:21
pray, and *m.* supplication to thee in.
1 Ki 8:33, 47; *2 Chr* 6:24
I will *m.* him prince all. *1 Ki* 11:34
m. the yoke lighter. 12:9, 10
2 Chr 10:10
m. thy house like the house of.
1 Ki 16:3; 21:22; *2 Ki* 9:9
and after *m.* for thee. *1 Ki* 17:13
if I *m.* not thy life as the life. 19:2
us *m.* a little chamber. *2 Ki* 4:10
am I God to kill and to *m.* alive? 5:7
let us *m.* a place, where we. 6:2
if Lord would *m.* windows. 7:2, 19
m. him arise up, and anoint. 9:2
we will not *m.* any king, do. 10:5
m. an agreement with me. 18:31
Isa 36:16
nor will I *m.* feet of Israel move.
2 Ki 21:8
m. his son or daughter to pass.
23:10; *Ezek* 20:31
all Israel to *m.* him king.
1 Chr 11:10; 12:31, 38
m. thee a name of greatness. 17:21
Lord *m.* his people 100 times. 21:3
he liked me to *m.* me king. 28:4
thine hand it is to *m.* great. 29:12
m. it a proverb among. *2 Chr* 7:20
thought to *m.* him king. 11:22
God shall *m.* thee fall before. 25:8
I *m.* a decree what ye shall do.
Ezra 6:8; 7:13, 21
branches of thick trees to *m.* booths.
Neh 8:15
the king to *m.* supplication. *Esth* 4:8
Haman stood up to *m.* request. 7:7
m. them days of feasting and. 9:22
and his hands *m.* whole. *Job* 5:18
m. thy supplication to. 8:5; 22:27
and if I *m.* my hands never. 9:30
should thy lies *m.* men hold? 11:3
m. me to know my transgression.
13:23
that ye *m.* yourselves strange. 19:3
now, who will *m.* me a liar? 24:25
made me in womb *m.* him? 31:15
quietness, who then can *m.*? 34:29
they *m.* the oppressed to cry. 35:9
can *m.* his sword to approach. 40:19
will he *m.* many supplications? 41:3
m. thy way straight before. *Ps* 5:8

night *m.* I my bed to swim. *Ps* 6:6
m. them as a fiery oven in. 21:9
shalt *m.* them turn their back. 12
m. me hope when on breasts. 22:9
m. thy face shine on thy servant. 31:16; 119:135
my soul shall *m.* her boast in. 34:2
m. me to know mine end. 39:4
m. me not the reproach of the. 8
m. no tarrying. 40:17; 70:5
will *m.* all his bed. 41:3
I will *m.* thy name to be. 45:17
the streams shall *m.* glad the. 46:4
in hidden part shalt *m.* me. 51:6
m. me to hear joy and gladness. 8
wings will I *m.* my refuge. 57:1
sing forth his name, *m.* his. 66:2
ye people, *m.* the voice of his. 8
thine enemies *m.* a tumult. 83:2
m. their nobles like Oreb. 11
O my God, *m.* them like a wheel. 13
valley of Baca, *m.* it a well. 84:6
will *m.* him my firstborn. 89:27
his seed also will I *m.* to endure. 29
m. us glad, according to the. 90:15
until I *m.* thine enemies thy. 110:1
Mat 22:44; *Mark* 12:36
Luke 20:43; *Acts* 2:35; *Heb* 1:13
they that *m.* them are like unto.
Ps 115:8; 135:18
m. me to understand the. 119:27
m. me go in the path of thy. 35
there will I *m.* the horn of. 132:17
if I *m.* my bed in hell, thou. 139:8
to the Lord did I *m.* my. 142:1
go humble thyself, and *m.* *Pr* 6:3
fools *m.* a mock at sin, but. 14:9
and with good advice *m.* war. 20:18
after vows to *m.* enquiry. 25
m. thee know the certainty. 22:21
m. no friendship with an angry. 24
riches certainly *m.* themselves. 23:5
be wise, and *m.* my heart glad. 27:11
yet *m.* they their houses. 30:26
who can *m.* that straight? *Eccl* 7:13
nor *m.* thyself over wise. 16
when ye *m.* many prayers. *Isa* 1:15
wash you, *m.* you clean. 16
m. me not a ruler. 3:7
m. the heart of this people fat. 6:10
let us *m.* a breach therein. 7:6
the Lord of hosts shall *m.* 10:23
and shall *m.* him of quick. 11:3
m. men go over dry shod. 15
m. mention that his name is. 12:4
will *m.* a man more precious. 13:12
m. thy shadow as the night. 16:3
Lord *m.* to all people a feast. 25:6
that he may *m.* peace with me. 27:5
m. to understand doctrine? 28:9
that *m.* a man an offender. 29:21
to *m.* empty the soul of the. 32:6
wilt thou recover me and *m.* 38:16
m. straight in the desert a. 40:3
Mat 3:3; *Mark* 1:3; *Luke* 3:4
I will *m.* the wilderness. *Isa* 41:18
I will *m.* the rivers islands. 42:15
I will *m.* darkness light before. 16
he will magnify and *m.* the law. 21
m. a way in the wilderness. 43:19
they that *m.* a graven image. 44:9
m. the crooked places straight. 45:2
m. peace and create evil, I the. 7
they shall *m.* supplication. 14
to whom will ye *m.* me equal? 46:5
m. bare the leg, uncover the. 47:2
m. his way prosperous. 48:15
m. all my mountains a way. 49:11
m. the rivers a wilderness. 50:2
I will *m.* my judgements to rest. 51:4
they that rule over them, *m.* 52:5
when thou shalt *m.* his soul. 53:10
m. thy windows of agates. 54:12
I will *m.* them joyful in my. 56:7
m. ye a wide mouth? 57:4
to *m.* your voice to be heard. 58:4
Lord shall *m.* fat thy bones. 11
I will *m.* the place of my feet. 60:13
m. thee an eternal excellency. 15
I will also *m.* thy officers peace. 17
till he *m.* Jerusalem a praise. 62:7
m. them drunk in my fury. 63:6
m. himself an everlasting name. 12
people to *m.* thyself a glorious. 14

to *m.* thy name known to thy. *Isa* 64:2
as new earth which I will *m.* 66:22
shalt thou *m.* thyself fair. *Jer* 4:30
m. my words in thy mouth. 5:14
m. thee mourning, as for an. 6:26
nor *m.* intercession to me. 7:16
m. Jerusalem heaps and den. 9:11
he turn it, and *m.* it gross. 13:16
m. thee a fenced brasen wall. 15:20
a man *m.* gods to himself. 16:20
good to the potter to *m.* it. 18:4
m. void counsel of Judah. 19:7
even *m.* this city as Tophet. 12
m. thee a terror to thyself. 20:4
I will *m.* thee a wilderness. 22:6
prophets, they *m.* you vain. 23:16
m. this house like Shiloh. 26:6
m. thee bonds and yokes, put. 27:2
now *m.* intercession to the Lord. 18
I will *m.* them like vile figs. 29:17
Lord *m.* thee like Zedekiah. 22
I will *m.* you be removed. 34:17
m. her cakes to worship her? 44:19
m. ye him drunken: for he. 48:26
I will *m.* thee small among. 49:15
m. thee a burnt mountain. 51:25
and *m.* her springs dry. 36
m. them drunken. 39
I will *m.* drunk her princes. 57
m. bread thereof. *Ezek* 4:9
m. a chain. 7:23
m. him a sign and a proverb. 14:8
I will *m.* my fury toward. 16:42
and *m.* you a new heart. 18:31
should we then *m.* mirth? 21:10
that should *m.* up the hedge. 22:30
m. no mourning for the dead. 24:17
m. her like the top of a. 26:4, 14
I will *m.* thee a terror, thou. 21
m. the stars thereof dark. 32:7, 8
I will *m.* them and places. 34:26
m. them one stick, shall be. 37:19
m. them one nation in the land. 22
m. them keepers of charge. 44:14
shall *m.* thee to eat grass as oxen.
Dan 4:25, 32
m. this man to understand the vision.
8:16; 10:14
weeks to *m.* reconciliation for. 9:24
fall to *m.* them white. 11:35
shall go utterly to purge and *m.* 44
I *m.* her as a wilderness. *Hos* 2:3
m. a wall, that she shall not find. 6
m. them to lie down safely. 18
m. the king glad with their. 7:3
m. Ephraim ride, Judah. 10:11
how shall I *m.* thee as Admah? 11:8
m. thee dwell in tabernacles. 12:9
nor will I *m.* you a reproach.
Joel 2:19
m. the poor of the land to. *Amos* 8:4
m. gardens, and eat fruit. 9:14
that *m.* my people err. *Mi* 3:5
her that halted a remnant. 4:7
I will *m.* thee sick in smiting. 6:13
I will *m.* thy grave, for. *Nah* 1:14
filth on thee, and *m.* thee vile. 3:6
m. thyself many, as the canker-. 15
write the vision, and *m.* *Hab* 2:2
m. my feet like hinds' feet. 3:19
shall *m.* even a speedy riddance.
Zeph 1:18
for I will *m.* you a name. 3:20
I will *m.* thee as a signet. *Hag* 2:33
m. bright clouds. *Zech* 10:1
I will *m.* Jerusalem a cup of. 12:2
I *m.* Jerusalem a burdensome. 3
did not he *m.* one? yet. *Mal* 2:15
when I *m.* up my jewels. 3:17
m. her a publick example. *Mat* 1:19
I will *m.* you fishers of men. 4:19
Mark 1:17
m. one hair white or black. *Mat* 5:36
Lord, if thou wilt, thou canst *m.* me.
8:2; *Mark* 1:40; *Luke* 5:12
m. the tree good, *m.* the. *Mat* 12:33
let us *m.* here three tabernacles.
17:4; *Mark* 9:5; *Luke* 9:33
for pretence *m.* long prayers.
Mat 23:14; *Mark* 12:40
to *m.* one proselyte, and. *Mat* 23:15
ye *m.* clean the outside of the cup.
25; *Luke* 11:39
I will *m.* thee ruler. *Mat* 25:21

your way, *m.* it as sure. *Mat* 27:65
why *m.* ye this ado? *Mark* 5:39
can ye *m.* children of? *Luke* 5:34
did he not *m.* that which is? 11:40
consent began to *m.* excuse. 14:18
m. me as one of thy hired. 15:19
m. friends of the mammon of. 16:9
m. straight the way of. *John* 1:23
m. not my Father's house. 2:16
by force to *m.* him a king. 6:15
the truth shall *m.* you free. 8:32
if the Son *m.* you free, ye shall. 36
dost thou *m.* us to doubt? 10:24
will come and *m.* our abode. 14:23
m. me full of joy with. *Acts* 2:28
him, arise and *m.* thy bed. 9:34
to *m.* thee a minister and a. 26:16
much learning doth *m.* thee mad. 24
m. the faith of God without effect.
Rom 3:3
do we then *m.* void the law? 31
power to *m.* one vessel unto. 9:21
short work will the Lord *m.* 28
m. not provision for the flesh. 13:14
God is able to *m.* him stand. 14:4
things which *m.* for peace. 19
to *m.* a certain contribution. 15:26
and *m.* them the members. *1 Cor* 6:15
meat *m.* my brother to offend. 8:13
temptation also *m.* a way to. 10:13
if I *m.* you sorry, who? *2 Cor* 2:2
m. up beforehand your bounty. 9:5
able to *m.* all grace abound. 8
did I *m.* gain of you by any? 12:17
m. myself a transgressor. *Gal* 2:18
m. the promise of none effect. 3:17
desire to *m.* a fair show in. 6:12
to *m.* in himself of twain. *Eph* 2:15
the Lord *m.* you to increase in love.
1 Thes 3:12
m. ourselves an ensample to you.
2 Thes 3:9
scriptures which are able to *m.* thee wise unto salvation. *2 Tim* 3:15
m. full proof of thy ministry. 4:5
to *m.* the Captain of their. *Heb* 2:10
to *m.* reconciliation for the sins. 17
liveth to *m.* intercession. 7:25
m. all things according to. 8:5
could not *m.* him that did. 9:9
m. comers thereunto perfect. 10:1
m. straight paths for your. 12:13
m. you perfect in every good. 13:21
of them that *m.* peace. *Jas* 3:18
the God of all grace *m.* *1 Pet* 5:10
m. your calling and. *2 Pet* 1:10
we *m.* him a liar, his. *1 John* 1:10
I will *m.* them worship. *Rev* 3:9
m. a pillar in the temple of my. 12
eat it, and it shall *m.* thy belly. 10:9
shall *m.* war against them. 11:7
went to *m.* war with the. 12:17
saying, Who is able to *m.* war? 13:4
that they should *m.* an image. 14
he doth judge and *m.* war. 19:11
behold, I *m.* all things new. 21:5
see **afraid, atonement, covenant, desolate, desolation, end, fire, good, known, mention, noise**

make *haste*

come on them, *m. haste*. *Deut* 32:35
and said, *M. haste* and do as I have.
Judg 9:48
is before you, *m. haste*. *1 Sam* 9:12
me to *m. haste*. *2 Chr* 35:21
cause Haman to *m. haste*.
Esth 5:5; 6:1
for this I *m. haste*. *Job* 20:2
m. haste to help me, O Lord, my.
Ps 38:22; 40:13; 70:1; 71:1
I am poor and needy, *m. haste* unt
me. 70:5; 141:
they *m. haste* to shed blood.
Pr 1:16; *Isa* 59:
m. haste, my beloved. *S of S* 8:1
he that believeth shall not *m. haste*.
Isa 28:1
thy children shall *m. haste*. 49:1
let them *m. haste*, and. *Jer* 9:1
m. haste to the wall. *Nah* 2:
said, Zacchaeus, *m. haste* *Luke* 19:
m. haste and get quickly out.
Acts 22:1

make *manifest*
m. manifest the counsels. *1 Cor* 4:5
doth *m. manifest* is light. *Eph* 5:13
that I may *m.* it *manifest.* *Col* 4:4

make *ready*
m. ready three measures. *Gen* 18:6
m. ready, for these men. 43:16
and Joram said, *M. ready.* *2 Ki* 9:21
m. ready their arrow on. *Ps* 11:2
m. ready thine arrows. 21:12
the trumpet to *m. ready.* *Ezek* 7:14
there *m. ready* for us. *Mark* 14:15
Luke 22:12
to *m. ready* a people. *Luke* 1:17
m. ready, wherewith I may sup. 17:8
m. ready 200 soldiers to. *Acts* 23:23

make *speed*
m. speed, haste. *1 Sam* 20:38
m. speed to depart. *2 Sam* 15:14
let him *m. speed* and. *Isa* 5:19

make *waste*
m. your cities *waste.* *Lev* 26:31
will *m. waste* mountains. *Isa* 42:15
will *m.* Jerusalem *waste.* *Ezek* 5:14
m. land of Egypt utterly *waste.*
29:10; 30:12

maker, or makers
more pure than his *M.*? *Job* 4:17
in so doing my *M.* will soon. 32:22
where is God my *M.*? 35:10
righteousness to my *M.* 36:3
before the Lord our *M.* *Ps* 95:6
oppresseth the poor, reproacheth his *M.* *Pr* 14:31
mocketh the poor reproacheth his *M.*
17:5
rich and poor, Lord is the *M.* 22:2
the *m.* of it as a spark. *Isa* 1:31*
shall a man look to his *M.* 17:7
ye have not looked to the *m.* 22:11*
that striveth with his *M.* 45:9
Holy One of Israel and his *M.* 11
confusion that are *m.* of idols. 16
forgettest the Lord thy *M.* 51:13
thy *m.* is thy husband, and. 54:5
saith the Lord the *M.* *Jer* 33:2
hath forgotten his *M.* *Hos* 8:14
graven image that *m.* hath graven, *m.* of his work? *Hab* 2:18
builder and *M.* is God. *Heb* 11:10

makest
and what *m.* thou in? *Judg* 18:3
m. me possess the iniquities of my youth. *Job* 13:26
is it gain to him that thou *m.*? 22:3
thou only *m.* me to dwell. *Ps* 4:8
m. his beauty to consume. 39:11
thou *m.* us to turn back. 44:10
thou *m.* us a reproach to our. 13
thou *m.* us a byword among. 14
m. the outgoings of morning. 65:8
m. the earth soft with showers. 10
thou *m.* us a strife to our. 80:6
thou *m.* darkness, and it. 104:20
that thou *m.* account of him? 144:3
m. thy flock to rest at. *S of S* 1:7
fashioneth it, what *m.* thou? *Isa* 45:9
that *m.* thy nest in cedars. *Jer* 22:23
thou *m.* this people to trust. 28:15
thou *m.* thy high place. *Ezek* 16:31
and *m.* men as the fishes. *Hab* 1:14
bottle to him, and *m.* him. 2:15
when thou *m.* a dinner. *Luke* 14:12
but when thou *m.* a feast, call. 13
prophets are dead, whom *m.* thou thyself? *John* 8:53
because thou being a man *m.* 10:33
and *m.* thy boast of God. *Rom* 2:17
m. thy boast of the law. 23

maketh
who *m.* the dumb, or deaf? *Ex* 4:11
priest that *m.* atonement clean.
Lev 7:7; 14:11
blood that *m.* an atonement. 17:11
that *m.* his son to pass. *Deut* 18:10
against the city that *m.* war. 20:20
he *m.* his sons to inherit. 21:16
m. merchandise of him. 24:7
cursed be the man that *m.* 27:15
cursed be he that *m.* the blind. 18
hath which the Lord *m.* with. 29:12
Lord killeth and *m.* *1 Sam* 2:6
the Lord *m.* poor, and *m.* rich.
1 Sam 2:7
God *m.* my way perfect.
2 Sam 22:33; *Ps* 18:32
he *m.* my feet like hinds' feet.
2 Sam 22:34; *Ps* 18:33
m. sore, and bindeth up. *Job* 5:18
Lord *m.* Arcturus, Orion. 9:9
he *m.* the judges fools. 12:17
he *m.* to stagger. 25
he *m.* collops of fat on his. 15:27
God *m.* my heart soft, and. 23:16
he *m.* peace in his high places. 25:2
booth that the keeper *m.* 27:18
m. us wiser than the fowls. 35:11
m. small the drops of water. 36:27
m. the deep to boil like a pot. 41:31
he *m.* a path to shine after him. 32
when he *m.* inquisition. *Ps* 9:12
he *m.* me to lie down in green. 23:2
Lord *m.* the hinds to calve 29:9
he *m.* the devices of people of. 33:10
blessed is the man that *m.* the. 40:4
he *m.* wars to cease to the end. 46:9
who *m.* the clouds his chariot. 104:3
m. his angels spirits. 4; *Heb* 1:7
wine that *m.* glad heart. *Ps* 104:15
m. the storm a calm, the. 107:29
he *m.* the hungry to dwell. 36
m. him families like a flock. 41
he *m.* the barren woman to. 113:9
m. lightnings for rain, bringeth. 135:7
who *m.* grass to grow on the. 147:8
he *m.* peace in thy borders. 14
a wise son *m.* a glad father. *Pr* 10:1
15:20
but the hand of the diligent *m.* 10:4
blessing of the Lord, it *m.* rich. 22
m. ashamed is as rottenness. 12:4
heart of a man *m.* it to stoop, but a good word *m.* it glad. 25
m. himself rich, yet hath nothing, there is that *m.* himself. 13:7
hope deferred *m.* the heart sick. 12
a merry heart *m.* a cheerful. 15:13
good report *m.* the bones fat. 30
he *m.* even his enemies to be. 16:7
a man's gift *m.* room for. 18:16
wealth *m.* many friends, but. 19:4
she *m.* herself coverings. 31:22
she *m.* fine linen and selleth it. 24
the work that God *m.* *Eccl* 3:11
oppression *m.* a wise man mad. 7:7
wisdom *m.* his face to shine. 8:1
not works of God, who *m.* all. 11:5
Lord *m.* the earth empty. *Isa* 24:1
he *m.* the judges of the earth. 40:23
which *m.* a way in the sea. 43:16
he *m.* a god, and worshippeth it.
44:15, 17; 46:6
I am the Lord that *m.* all. 44:24
he *m.* diviners mad. 25
watereth earth, and *m.* it. 55:10
m. himself a prey. 59:15
he *m.* lightnings. *Jer* 10:13; 51:16
cursed be the man that *m.* 17:5
m. himself a prophet. 29:26, 27
m. idols against herself. *Ezek* 22:3
but *m.* his petition three. *Dan* 6:13
that *m.* desolate. 11:31; 12:11
that *m.* the morning. *Amos* 4:13
seek him that *m.* the seven stars. 5:8
sea, and *m.* it dry. *Nah* 1:4
he *m.* his sun to rise on. *Mat* 5:45
he *m.* both deaf to hear. *Mark* 7:37
m. himself a king. *John* 19:12
Aeneas, Jesus Christ *m.* *Acts* 9:34
hope *m.* not ashamed. *Rom* 5:5
Spirit *m.* intercession. 8:26, 27, 34
m. intercession to God. 11:2
who *m.* thee to differ? *1 Cor* 4:7
he that *m.* me glad, but? *2 Cor* 2:2
m. manifest the savour of his. 14
it *m.* no matter to me. *Gal* 2:6
m. increase of the body. *Eph* 4:16
m. men high priests, but the word of ... the law *m.* the Son. *Heb* 7:28
he *m.* fire come down. *Rev* 13:13
whatsoever *m.* a lie. 21:27; 22:15

maketh *haste*
m. haste to be rich. *Pr* 28:20

making
m. confession to the. *2 Chr* 30:22
testimony of Lord is sure, *m.* wise.
Ps 19:7
of *m.* many books there. *Eccl* 12:12
walking and *m.* a tinkling. *Isa* 3:16
that brought tidings, *m.* *Jer* 20:15
m. ephah small, and the. *Amos* 8:5
m. the word of God of. *Mark* 7:13
m. himself equal with. *John* 5:18
as poor, yet *m.* many. *2 Cor* 6:10
give thanks for you, *m.* mention of.
Eph 1:16; *1 Thes* 1:2; *Philem* 4
new man, so *m.* peace. *Eph* 2:15
m. melody in your heart. 5:19
you *m.* request with joy. *Phil* 1:4
m. them an ensample. *2 Pet* 2:6
compassion, *m.* a difference. *Jude* 22

making
wares of thy *m.* *Ezek* 27:16, 18

Malcham
by the Lord and by *M.* *Zeph* 1:5

Malchus
servant's name was *M.* *John* 18:10

male
every *m.* circumcised. *Gen* 17:23
34; 15:22, 24
for the passover a *m.* of. *Ex* 12:5
the *m.* shall be the Lord's. 13:12
34:19; *Luke* 2:23
a *m.* without blemish. *Lev* 1:3, 10
4:23; 22:19
every *m.* among the priests. 7:6
thy estimation shall be of the *m.* 27:3
5, 6, 7
every *m.* by their polls. *Num* 1:2
every *m.* from 20 years old. 20
every *m.* from a month old. 3:15
now kill every *m.* among. 31:17
smite every *m.* thereof. *Deut* 20:13
destroy every *m.* *Judg* 21:11
he had smitten every *m.* in Edom.
1 Ki 11:15, 16
hath in his flock a *m.* *Mal* 1:14
see **female**

male children
were the *m. children* of. *Josh* 17:2

malefactor
if he were not a *m.* *John* 18:30*

malefactors
there were two *m.* *Luke* 23:32
they crucified him, and the *m.* 33
one of the *m.* railed on him. 39

males
Levi slew all the *m.* *Gen* 34:25
m. be circumcised. *Ex* 12:48
to the Lord all being *m.* 13:15
three times a year all thy *m.* shall appear before. 23:17; *Deut* 16:16
all the *m.* of Aaron. *Lev* 6:18, 29
number of all *m.* from a month old.
Num 3:22; 28:34; 26:62
the firstborn of the *m.* 3:40, 43
Midianites, and slew the *m.* 31:7
all firstling *m.* sanctify. *Deut* 15:19
m. that came out of Egypt died.
Josh 5:4
their genealogy of *m.* *2 Chr* 31:16
to all the *m.* among priests. 19
by genealogy of the *m.* *Ezra* 8:3

malice
not with leaven of *m.* *1 Cor* 5:8
howbeit in *m.* be ye children. 14:20
from you with all *m.* *Eph* 4:31
also put off all these; *m.* *Col* 3:8
living in *m.* and envy. *Tit* 3:3
laying aside all *m.* *1 Pet* 2:1*

malicious
prating against us with *m.* *3 John* 10*

maliciousness
all unrighteousness, *m.* *Rom* 1:29
liberty for a cloke of *m.* *1 Pet* 2:16*

malignity
murder, debate, *m.* *Rom* 1:29

mallows
cut up *m.* by the bushes. *Job* 30:4

mammon
ye cannot serve God and *m.*
Mat 6:24; *Luke* 16:13
make friends of *m.* of. *Luke* 16:9
if not faithful in unrighteous *m.* 11

Mamre

Abram dwelt in the plain of *M*. *Gen* 13:18; 14:13
Eshcol, *M*. let them take. 14:24
appeared to Abraham in *M*. 18:1
Machpelah before *M*. 23:17, 19
49:30; 50:13
Jacob came to Isaac to *M*. 35:27

man

[1] *A human being,* 1 Cor 10:13. [2] *The human race; mankind,* Job 5:7. [3] *The adult male, as distinguished from a woman or a child,* Acts 4:22.

God said, Let us make *m*. in our image. *Gen* 1:26, 27; 9:6
God formed *m*. of the dust. 2:7
it is not good that *m*. should. 18
they were both naked, the *m*. 25
the *m*. is become as one of us. 3:22
not always strive with *m*. 6:3
I will destroy *m*. whom I have. 7
curse the ground for *m.'s* sake. 8:21
m.'s blood, by *m*. shall his. 9:6
which have not known *m*. 19:8
Num 31:35
restore the *m*. his wife. *Gen* 20:7
the *m*. wondering at her held. 24:21
Laban ran out to the *m*. to. 29
what *m*. is this that walketh? 65
give her to another *m*. 29:19
by the *m*. whose these are. 38:25
arise, go again to the *m*. 43:13
the *m*. in whose hand cup. 44:17
that ye have left the *m*.? *Ex* 2:20
content to dwell with the *m*. 21
who hath made *m.'s* mouth? 4:11
upon *m*., flesh shall it not be. 30:32
m. that brought us out of. 32:1, 23
be imputed to that *m*. and that *m*. shall be cut off from. *Lev* 17:4
m. bring his wife to. *Num* 5:15
but the *m*. that is clean, and. 9:13
the *m*. Moses was very meek. 12:3
the *m*. shall be put to death. 15:35
Deut 22:25
m. whom the Lord doth. *Num* 16:7
but *m*. that shall be unclean. 19:20
day that God created *m*. *Deut* 4:32
God doth talk with *m*. and he. 5:24
m. doth not live by bread only, but. 8:3; *Mat* 4:4; *Luke* 4:4
tree of the field is *m.'s*. *Deut* 20:19
and they shall come *m*. by *m*. *Josh* 7:14, 17, 18
but they let go the *m*. *Judg* 1:25
I will shew thee the *m*. whom. 4:22
for as the *m*. is, so is his. 8:21
me they honour God and *m*. 9:9
cheereth God and *m*. 13
what *m*. will fight against? 10:18
m. hath appeared that came. 13:10
the *m*. spakest to the woman? 11
and as another *m*. 16:7, 11, 17
bring forth the *m*. that came. 19:22
the *m*. took her on an ass and. 28
m. was Elimelech. *Ruth* 1:2; 2:19
for the *m*. will not be in rest. 3:18
m. of thine whom I. *1 Sam* 2:33
m. came in hastily, and told. 4:14
a *m*. of God. and he is an honourable *m*. 9:6
behold the *m*. whom I spake. 17
if the *m*. should yet come. 10:22
Lord seeth not as *m*. seeth. 16:7
what be done to the *m*.? 17:26
lo, ye see the *m*. is mad. 21:14
anger kindled against the *m*. said to Nathan, the *m*. that. *2 Sam* 12:5
David, Thou art the *m*. 7
come out, thou bloody *m*. 16:7*, 8
the *m*. thou seekest is as if. 17:3
m. that consumed us, and. 21:5
the *m*. who was raised up on. 23:1
slew every one his *m*. *1 Ki* 20:20
when *m*. turned again. *2 Ki* 5:26
I will bring you to the *m*. 6:19
you know the *m*. and his. 9:11
tell the *m*. that sent you. 22:15
2 Chr 34:23
Levites *m*. by *m*. 38,000. *1 Chr* 23:3
the palace is not for *m*. but. 29:1
let not *m*. prevail. *2 Chr* 14:11
for ye judge not for *m*. but. *2 Chr* 19:6
what shall be done unto the *m*.? *Esth* 6:6, 7, 9
m. be more just than? *Job* 4:17
yet *m*. is born to trouble, as. 5:7
happy is the *m*. whom God. 17
appointed time for *m*. on earth? 7:1
what is *m*. that thou shouldest? 17
15:14; *Ps* 8:4; 144:3; *Heb* 2:6
but how should *m*. be just? *Job* 9:2
or seest thou as *m*. seeth? 10:4
days of *m*.? years as *m.'s* days? 5
vain *m*. would be wise, though *m*. 11:12
m. that is born of a woman. 14:1
m. dieth and wasteth away, *m*. 10
so *m*. lieth down, and riseth not. 12
first *m*. that was born? 15:7
what is *m*. that he should be? 14
abominable and filthy is *m*. 16
m. was first placed on the. 20:4
me is my complaint to *m*.? 21:4
can *m*. be justified with God? 25:4
m. that is a worm, and son of *m*. 6
but there is a spirit in *m*. 32:8
God thrusteth him down, not *m*. 13
that God is greater than *m*. 33:12
God speaketh, yet *m*. perceiveth it not. 14
that he may withdraw *m*. from purpose, and hide pride from *m*. 17
if a messenger, to shew to *m*. 23
worketh God often with *m*. 29
m. is like Job, who drinketh? 34:7
his heart upon *m*. if he gather. 14
for he will not lay on *m*. more. 23
arise, O Lord, let not *m*. *Ps* 9:19
that the *m*. of earth may no. 10:18
what *m*. is he that feareth? 25:12
what *m*. is he that desireth? 34:12
when thou dost correct *m*. 39:11
m. being in honour. 49:12, 20
I will not be afraid what *m*. 56:11
m. did eat angels' food, he. 78:25
thy hand be on the *m*. of. 80:17
what *m*. is he that liveth? 89:48
thou turnest *m*. to destruction. 90:3
that teacheth *m*. knowledge? 94:10
for *m*. his days are as grass. 103:15
m. goeth forth to his work. 104:23
I will not fear what *m*. can. 118:6
than put confidence in *m*. 8
m. is like to vanity, his days. 144:4
from *m*. that speaketh. *Pr* 2:12
come as an armed *m*. 6:11; 24:34
preparations of the heart in *m*. 16:1
m.'s goings are of the Lord, how can a *m*.? 20:24
so is the *m*. that deceiveth. 26:19
things full of labour, *m*. *Eccl* 1:8
can the *m*. do that cometh? 2:12
hath *m*. of all his labour? 22
it is known that it is *m*. 6:10
what is *m*. better? 11
what is good for *m*.? 12
because *m*. goeth to his long. 12:5
from *m*. whose breath is. *Isa* 2:22
I said, I shall behold *m*. no. 38:11
the *m*. that executeth my. 46:11
it is not in *m*. to direct. *Jer* 10:23
I am the *m*. that hath. *Lam* 3:1
cows' dung for *m.'s* dung. *Ezek* 4:15
judgement between *m*. and *m*. 18:8
be changed from *m.'s*. *Dan* 4:16
O *m*. greatly beloved. 10:19
for I am God, and not *m*. *Hos* 11:9
declareth to *m*. what is. *Amos* 4:13
that tarrieth not for *m*. *Mi* 5:7
he hath shewed thee, O *m*. 6:8
the *m*. of wisdom shall see. 9
the wicked devoureth *m*. *Hab* 1:13
I will cut off the *m*. *Zeph* 1:3
the *m*. whose name is. *Zech* 6:12
m. taught me to keep cattle. 13:5*
awake, O sword, against *m*. that. 7
Lord will cut off the *m*. *Mal* 2:12
what *m*. is there of you, if his son? *Mat* 7:9; 12:11; *Luke* 15:4
and they defile the *m*. *Mat* 15:18
let not *m*. put asunder. 19:6
Mark 10:9
I do not know the *m*. *Mat* 26:72, 74
sabbath was made for *m*. not *m*. *Mark* 2:27
colt tied, whereon never *m*. sat. 11:2
he said, *M*. thy sins are. *Luke* 5:20
m. who made me a judge? 12:14
fear not God, nor regard *m*. 18:4
Peter said, *M*., I am not. 22:58
Peter said, *M*., I know not. 60
he asked, whether the *m*. was. 23:6
never *m*. was laid. 53; *John* 19:41
knew what was in *m*. *John* 2:25
what *m*. is that which said? 5:12
not testimony from *m*. 34
which none other *m*. did. 15:24
unto them, Behold the *m*. 19:5
for the *m*. was above. *Acts* 4:22
how can I, except some *m*.? 8:31
himself, or of some other *m*.? 34
the *m*. in whom the evil. 19:16
what *m*. is there that knoweth? 35
m. that owneth this girdle. 21:11
Jews laid wait for the *m*. 23:30
I would also hear the *m*. 25:22
inexcusable, O *m*. *Rom* 2:1
thinkest thou, O *m*. 3
of God after the inward *m*. 7:22
O wretched *m*. that I am, who? 24
but O *m*. who art thou that? 9:20
the *m*. who doeth. 10:5; *Gal* 3:12
with heart *m*. believeth. *Rom* 10:10
what *m*. knoweth the things of a *m*.? *1 Cor* 2:11
how knowest thou, O *m*.? 7:16*
such as is common to *m*. 10:13
head of the woman is the *m*. 11:3
m. is not of the woman. 8
but woman for the *m*. 9
m. without the woman, nor the woman without the *m*. 11
the *m*. also by the woman. 12
by *m*. came death, by *m*. 15:21
the first *m*. Adam was made. 45
the first *m*. is of the earth, earthy; the second *m*. is the Lord. 47
outward *m*. perish, yet the inward *m*. is renewed day by. *2 Cor* 4:16
not of men, neither by *m*. *Gal* 1:1
I preached is not after *m*. 11
of twain one new *m*. *Eph* 2:15
his Spirit in the inner *m*. 3:16
that ye put on new *m*. created. 4:24
new *m*. which is renewed. *Col* 3:10
despiseth not *m*. but God. *1 Thes* 4:8
men, the *m*. Christ Jesus. *1 Tim* 2:5
usurp authority over the *m*. 12
Saviour toward *m*. appeared. *Tit* 3:4
house is built by some *m*. *Heb* 3:4
Lord pitched, and not *m*. 8:2
I will not fear what *m*. shall. 13:6
a double minded *m*. is unstable in all his ways. *Jas* 1:8
wilt thou know, O vain *m*.? 2:20
let it be the hidden *m*. *1 Pet* 3:4
see **beast, blessed, cursed, each, evil, foolish, good, old, poor, rich, understanding**

a man

not *a m*. to till the ground. *Gen* 2:5
shall *a m*. leave his father. 24
Mat 19:5; *Mark* 10:7; *Eph* 5:31
I have gotten *a m*. from the Lord. *Gen* 4:1
slain *a m*. to my wounding. 23
if *a m*. can number the dust. 13:16
there is not *a m*. to come in. 19:31
dead man; she is *a m.'s* wife. 20:3
Esau a cunning hunter, *a m*. 25:27
there wrestled *a m*. with him. 32:24
let Pharaoh look out *a m*. discreet and wise. 41:33
a m. in whom the Spirit of God. 38
wot ye not such *a m*. as I can? 44:1
in their anger they slew *a m*. 49:
face, as *a m*. speaketh. *Ex* 33:1
plague of leprosy is in *a m*. *Lev* 13:
if *a m*. do he shall live. 18:
Neh 9:29; *Ezek* 20:11, 13, 2
and *a m*. of Israel strove. *Lev* 24:1
caused a blemish in *a m*. 2
no devoted thing *a m*. shall. 27:2
be *a m*. of every tribe. *Num* 1:
tribe shall ye send *a m*. 13:
a m. that gathered sticks. 15:3

is law when *a m.* dieth. *Num* 19:14
God is not *a m.* that he should lie. 23:19; *1 Sam* 15:29
among these there was not *a m.* of. *Num* 26:64
was not left *a m.* save Caleb. 65
a m. over the congregation. 27:16
take thee Joshua, *a m.* in whom. 18
Lord bare thee, as *a m.* *Deut* 1:31
after the cubit of *a m.* 3:11
that as *a m.* chasteneth his son. 8:5
shall not rise against *a m.* 19:15
take ye out of every tribe *a m.* *Josh* 3:12; 4:2, 4
a m. over against him with. 5:13
shall not *a m.* of them stand. 10:8
hearkened to the voice of *a m.* 14
Arba was *a* great *m.* among. 14:15
not *a m.* of all their enemies. 21:44
the spies saw *a m.* *Judg* 1:24
escaped not *a m.* 3:29
was not *a m.* left. 4:16
was *a m.* that told a dream. 7:13
save the sword of Gideon *a m.* 14
Tola *a m.* of Issachar. 10:1
she called *a m.* 16:19
a m. plucked off his shoe. *Ruth* 4:7
I will send thee *a m.* *1 Sam* 9:16
there shall not *a m.* be put. 11:13
the Lord hath sought him *a m.* 13:14
not leave *a m.* of them. 14:36
a m. who is a cunning player. 16:16
provide me *a m.* that can play. 17
choose you *a m.* for you, let. 17:8
give me *a m.* that we may fight. 10
such that *a m.* cannot speak. 25:17
and there escaped not *a m.* 30:17
as *a m.* falleth before. *2 Sam* 3:34
prince and *a* great *m.* is fallen. 38
a m. enquired at the oracle. 16:23
happened to be there *a m.* 20:1*
and shew thyself *a m.* *1 Ki* 2:2
not fail thee *a m.* on throne. 4; 8:25
a m. turned aside, and brought *a m.* 20:39
a m. whom I appointed to. 42
came *a m.* to meet us. *2 Ki* 1:6
a m. from Baal-shalisha. 4:42
not *a m.* left that came not. 10:21
as they were burying *a m.*. 13:21
shall be *a m.* of rest. *1 Chr* 22:9
here shall not fail thee *a m.* *2 Chr* 6:16; 7:18
m. to seek the welfare. *Neh* 2:10
hould such *a m.* as I flee? 6:11
ll that *a m.* hath will he. *Job* 2:4
why is light given to *a m.*? 3:23
hall *a m.* be more pure than? 4:17
e is not *a m.* as I am, that. 9:32
nd should *a m.* full of talk? 11:2
e shutteth up *a m.* 12:14
a m. die. 14:14
ne might plead for *a m.* with God, as *a m.* pleadeth for. 16:21
an *a m.* be profitable to God? 22:2
one against a nation or *a m.* 34:29
ny wickedness may hurt *a m.* 35:8
a m. speak he shall be swallowed. 37:20
ird up now thy loins like *a m.* 38:3
40:7
was as *a m.* that. *Ps* 38:14
ut it was thou, *a m.* mine. 55:13
nagine mischief against *a m.*? 62:3
m. was famous according. 74:5
m. that hath no strength. 88:4
e sent *a m.* before them. 105:17
easure in the legs of *a m.* 147:10
rive not with *a m.* *Pr* 3:30
r jealousy is the rage of *a m.* 6:34
ere is a way that seemeth right unto *a m.* 14:12; 16:25
l ways of *a m.* are clean. 16:2
m.'s ways please the Lord. 7
w can *a m.* understand? 20:24
m. given to appetite. 23:2
a contentious *m.* to kindle. 26:21
is *a m.* that wandereth. 27:8
the furnace, so is *a m.* to. 21
en the wicked rise *a m.* 28:12
that rebuketh *a m.* shall find. 23
est thou *a m.* that is hasty? 29:20
n. whose labour is in wisdom and knowledge, yet to *a m.* *Eccl* 2:21
God giveth to *a m.* that is good. *Eccl* 2:26
for this *a m.* is envied of his. 4:4
a m. to whom God hath given. 6:2
who can tell *a m.* what shall? 12
a m. cannot tell what shall. 10:14
if *a m.* live many years. 11:8
if *a m.* would give all. *S of S* 8:7
I am *a m.* of unclean lips. *Isa* 6:5
a m. more precious than. 13:12
at that day shall *a m.* look. 17:7
than that *a m.* can stretch. 28:20
that make *a m.* an offender. 29:21
a m. shall be an hiding place. 32:2
not meet thee as *a m.* 47:3
he is *a m.* of sorrows and. 53:3
for *a m.* to afflict his soul? 58:5
an ox, is as if he slew *a m.* 66:3
forsaken, and not *a m.* *Jer* 4:29
places, if ye can find *a m.* 5:1
why shouldest thou be as *a m.*? 14:9
that thou hast borne me *a m.* 15:10
a m. made gods to himself? 16:20
a m. that shall not prosper. 22:30
I am like *a m.* whom wine. 23:9
see whether *a m.* doth travail? 30:6
a woman shall compass *a m.* 31:22
David shall never want *a m.* 33:17
shall the priests want *a m.* 18
Jonadab shall not want *a m.* 35:19
man put in array like *a m.* to. 50:42
good for *a m.* to hope. *Lam* 3:26
it is good for *a m.* that he bear. 27
complain, *a m.* for punishment. 39
sought for *a m.* among. *Ezek* 22:30
art *a m.* and not God. 28:2, 9
people of the land take *a m.* 33:2
not *a m.* on earth that. *Dan* 2:10
found *a m.* of the captives. 25
there is *a m.* in thy kingdom. 5:11
stand as *a m.* and *a m.'s* heart. 7:4
O Daniel, *a m.* greatly. 10:11
robbers wait for *a m.* *Hos* 6:9
there shall not be *a m.* left. 9:12
drew them with cords of *a m.* 11:4
a m. and his father go. *Amos* 2:7
as if *a m.* did flee from a lion. 5:19
a m. and his house, even *a m.* *Mi* 2:2
if *a m.* walking in spirit and. 11
a m.'s enemies are the men of his own house. 7:6; *Mat* 10:36
as *a m.* spareth his own. *Mal* 3:17
I am *a m.* under authority. *Mat* 8:9 *Luke* 7:8
to set *a m.* at variance. *Mat* 10:35
how much is *a m.* better? 12:12
spirit is gone out of *a m.* 43
the mouth defileth *a m.* 15:11
unwashen hands defileth not *a m.* 20
is it lawful for *a m.* to put away? 19:3; *Mark* 10:2
if *a m.* die having no. *Mat* 22:24
the city, to such *a m.* and say to him. 26:18; *Mark* 14:13; *Luke* 22:10
seeing I know not *a m.*? *Luke* 1:34
depart, for I am *a* sinful *m.* 5:8
which *a m.* took and cast. 13:19
to be guest with *a m.* that is. 19:7
there was *a m.* sent from. *John* 1:6
after me cometh *a m.* who is. 30
except *a m.* be born again. 3:3, 5
how can *a m.* be born when? 4
a m. can receive nothing, except. 27
come, see *a m.* which told me. 4:29
I have made *a m.* whole. 7:23
a m. that hath told you the. 8:40
a m. that is called Jesus. 9:11
how can *a m.* a sinner, do such? 16
a m. makest thyself God. 10:33
if *a m.* love me, he will keep. 14:23
for joy that *a m.* is born into. 16:21
Jesus *a m.* approved of. *Acts* 2:22
I myself also am *a m.* 10:26
I found David, *a m.* after. 13:22
not believe, though *a m.* declare. 16:41
there stood *a m.* of Macedonia. 16:9
I am *a m.* who am a Jew. 21:39
preachest *a m.* should. *Rom* 2:21
sayest, *a m.* should not commit. 22
I speak as *a m.* 3:5
dominion over *a m.* 7:1
let *a m.* so account of us. *1 Cor* 4:1
it is required, that *a m.* be found. 2
every sin that *a m.* doeth is. 6:18
it is good for *a m.* not to touch. *1 Cor* 7:1
I say that it is good for *a m.* so. 26
say I these things as *a m.*? or. 9:8
a m. indeed ought not to. 11:7
if *a m.* have long hair, it is a. 14
but let *a m.* examine himself. 28
when I became *a m.*, I put. 13:11
sufficient to such *a m.* is. *2 Cor* 2:6
according to that *a m.* hath. 8:12
if *a m.* bring you into bondage, if *a m.* smite. 11:20
I knew *a m.* in Christ caught. 12:2, 3
which it is not lawful for *a m.* 4
a m. is not justified by. *Gal* 2:16
brethren, if *a m.* be overtaken. 6:1
if *a m.* think himself to be. 3
found in fashion as *a m.* *Phil* 2:8
the law is good, if *a m.* *1 Tim* 1:8
if *a m.* desire the office of a. 3:1
if *a m.* know not how to rule his. 5
if *a m.* also strive for. *2 Tim* 2:5
if *a m.* therefore purge himself. 21
a m. that is a heretic. *Tit* 3:10
he is like *a m.* beholding. *Jas* 1:23
if there come *a m.* with a gold. 2:2
what profit, though *a m.* say. 14
a m. may say, Thou hast faith. 18
ye see how that by works *a m.* 24
Elias was *a m.* subject to like. 5:17
if *a m.* for conscience. *1 Pet* 2:19
for of whom *a m.* is. *2 Pet* 2:19
if *a m.* say, I love God. *1 John* 4:20
beast had a face as *a m.* *Rev* 4:7
scorpion, when he striketh *a m.* 9:5

a certain **man**

a cer. m. found him. *Gen* 37:15
a cer. m. saw it, and. *2 Sam* 18:10
a cer. m. drew a bow at a venture. *1 Ki* 22:34; *2 Chr* 18:33
a cer. m. had two sons. *Mat* 21:28 *Luke* 15:11
a cer. m. went down. *Luke* 10:30
the ground of *a cer.* rich *m.* 12:16
a cer. m. had a fig tree planted. 13:6
a cer. m. made a great supper. 14:16
there was *a cer. m.* which had. 16:1
a cer. blind *m.* sat by the way. 18:35
a cer. noble-*m.* went into a. 19:12
a cer. m. planted a vineyard. 20:9
a cer. noble-*m.* whose son was sick. *John* 4:46
a cer. m. was sick, named. 11:1
a cer. m. lame from his. *Acts* 3:2
a cer. m. named Ananias, sold. 5:1
a cer. m. called Simeon, who. 8:9
there he found *a cer. m.* 9:33
there was *a cer. m.* in Caesarea. 10:1
there sat *a cer. m.* at Lystra. 14:8
entered into *a cer. m.'s* house. 18:7
a cer. m. named Demetrius. 19:24
a cer. m. left in bonds. 25:14

any **man**

a virgin, nor had *any m.* known her. *Gen* 24:16
if thou knowest *any m.* of activity. 47:6
if *any m.* have any. *Ex* 24:14
nor let *any m.* be seen through. 34:3
nor shall *any m.* desire thy land. 24
any m. hath a running. *Lev* 15:2
if *any m.'s* seed of copulation go. 16
if *any m.* lie with her at all, he. 24
killeth *any m.* shall surely. 24:17
any m. giveth the priest. *Num* 5:10
if *any m.'s* wife go aside, and. 12
if *any m.* die very suddenly. 6:9
the dead body of *any m.* 19:11, 13
if a serpent had bitten *any m.* 21:9
if *any m.* hate his neighbour and. *Deut* 19:11
witness rise up against *any m.* 16
blood on thy house, if *any m.* 22:8
be *any m.* among you that is not clean. 23:10
not *any m.* be able to stand before. *Josh* 1:5
remain courage in *any m.* 2:11
when *any m.* doth enquire, Is there *any m.* here? *Judg* 4:20
weak and be like *any* other *m.* 16:17
no business with *any m.* **18:7, 28**

that when *any m.* offered sacrifice. *1 Sam* 2:13
if *any m.* said, Fail not to burn. 16
taken aught at *any m.'s* hand. 12:4
when *any m.* that had a controversy. *2 Sam* 15:2
it was so, that when *any m.* came. 5
shall *any m.* be put to death. 19:22
for us shalt thou kill *any m.* 21:4
if *any m.* trespass. *1 Ki* 8:31
what supplication soever be made by *any m.* 38; *2 Chr* 6:29
if thou meet *any m.* *2 Ki* 4:29
chose I *any m.* to be ruler. *2 Chr* 6:5
nor told I *any m.* what God put in my heart. *Neh* 2:12
let me not accept *any m.* *Job* 32:21
more brutish than *any m.* *Pr* 30:2
marred more than *any m.* *Isa* 52:14
in mouth of *any m.* *Jer* 44:26
come not near *any m.* on. *Ezek* 9:6
ask a petition of *any* god or *m.* *Dan* 6:7, 12
if *any m.* sue thee at law. *Mat* 5:40
knoweth *any m.* the Father. 11:27
nor shall *any m.* hear his voice. 12:19
if *any m.* will come after me. 16:24 *Luke* 9:23
if *any m.* say aught to you, say. *Mat* 21:3; *Mark* 11:3; *Luke* 19:31
carest thou for *any m.* *Mat* 22:16
nor durst *any m.* from that day. 46
if *any m.* say, Lo, here is Christ. 24:23; *Mark* 13:21
nothing to *any m.* but go. *Mark* 1:44
if *any m.* hath ears to hear. 4:23 7:16; *Rev* 13:9
neither could *any m.* tame. *Mark* 5:4
not that *any m.* should know it. 9:30
if *any m.* desire to be first, the. 35
take heed, lest *any m.* deceive. 13:5
nor said any thing to *any m.* 16:8
art bidden of *any m.* to. *Luke* 14:8
if *any m.* come to me, and hate. 26
taken any thing from *any m.* 19:8
if *any m.'s* brother die, having. 20:28
hath *any m.* brought him aught to eat? *John* 4:33
not that *any m.* hath seen. 6:46
if *any m.* eat of this bread he. 51
if *any m.* do his will he shall. 7:17
if *any m.* thirst, let him come. 37
doth our law judge *any m.*? 51
never in bondage to *any m.* 8:33
if *any m.* did confess that he. 9:22
if *any m.* be a worshipper of. 31
that *any m.* opened the eyes of. 32
by me, if *any m.* enter in, he. 10:9
nor shall *any m.* pluck them out. 28
if *any m.* walk in the day. 11:9
if *any m.* knew where he were. 57
if *any m.* serve me, let him. 12:26
if *any m.* hear my words. 47
that *any m.* should ask thee. 16:30
for us to put *any m.* to death. 18:31
not call *any m.* common. *Acts* 10:28
can *any m.* forbid water, these? 47
matter against *any m.* law. 19:38
me disputing with *any m.* 24:12
Romans to deliver *any m.* 25:16
shall be no loss of *any m.'s* life. 27:22
if *any m.* have not the Spirit of. *Rom* 8:9
if *any m.* build on this. *1 Cor* 3:12
if *any m.'s* work abide. 14
if *any m.'s* work be burnt. 15
if *any m.* defile the temple of. 17
if *any m.* among you seemeth. 18
any m. that is called a brother. 5:11
is *any m.* called, being circumcised? 7:18
if *any m.* think that he knoweth. 8:2
if *any m.* love God. 3
if *any m.* see thee which hast. 10
that *any m.* should make my. 9:15
if *any m.* say that this is offered. 10:28
any m. seem to be contentious. 11:16
if *any m.* hunger let him. 34
any m. speak in an unknown. 14:27
if *any m.* think himself to be a. 37
if *any m.* be ignorant, let him. 38
if *any m.* love not the Lord. 16:22
if *any m.* be in Christ. *2 Cor* 5:17
if *any m.* trust to himself that. *2 Cor* 10:7
lest *any m.* should think of. 12:6
if *any m.* preach any other. *Gal* 1:9
not of works, lest *any m.* *Eph* 2:9
whatsoever good thing *any m.* 6:8
lest *any m.* should beguile. *Col* 2:4
beware lest *any m.* spoil you. 8
if *any m.* hath a quarrel. 3:13
none render evil for evil to *any m.* *1 Thes* 5:15
did eat *any m.'s* bread. *2 Thes* 3:8
if *any m.* obey not our word. 14
any m. teach otherwise. *1 Tim* 6:3
lest *any m.* fall after. *Heb* 4:11
but if *any m.* draw back, my. 10:38
lest *any m.* fail of the grace. 12:15
nor tempteth *any m.* *Jas* 1:13
if *any m.* among you seem. 26
if *any m.* offend not in word. 3:2
if *any m.* speak, let him. *1 Pet* 4:11
yet if *any m.* suffer as christian. 16
if *any m.* sin, we have. *1 John* 2:1
if *any m.* love the world, the. 15
and ye need not that *any m.* 27
if *any m.* see his brother sin. 5:16
if *any m.* hear my voice. *Rev* 3:20
if *any m.* will hurt them, fire. 11:5
if *any m.* worship the beast. 14:9
if *any m.* shall add to these. 22:18
if *any m.* shall take away from. 19

man child

every *m. child* shall be circumcised. *Gen* 17:10, 12
the uncircumcised *m. child* shall. 14
born a *m. child,* then. *Lev* 12:2
handmaid a *m. child.* *1 Sam* 1:11
said, There is a *m. child* conceived. *Job* 3:3; *Jer* 20:15
she was delivered of a *m. child.* *Isa* 66:7; *Rev* 12:5
brought forth a *m. child.* *Rev* 12:13

every **man**

on earth, and *every m.* *Gen* 7:21
at hand of *every m.'s* brother. 9:5
hand be against *every m.* and *every m.'s* hand. 16:12
to restore *every m.'s* money. 42:25
every m.'s money was in his sack. 35; 43:21
took down *every m.* his sack. 44:11
and laded *every m.* his ass, and. 13
Joseph cried, Cause *every m.* 45:1
the Egyptians sold *every m.* 47:20
every m. and his household. *Ex* 1:1
for they cast down *every m.* 7:12
let *every m.* borrow of his. 11:2
take to them *every m.* a lamb. 12:3
every m. according to his eating. 4 16:16; 18:21
that which *every m.* must eat. 12:16
abide ye *every m.* in his place. 16:29
every m. that giveth it. 25:2
give *every m.* a ransom for. 30:12
every m. a sword by his side, slay *every m.* his brother, *every m.* his. 32:27
stood *every m.* at his tent door. 33:8
they worshipped *every m.* in his. 10
came *every m.* from his work. 36:4
a bekah for *every m.* that is. 38:26
fear *every m.* his mother. *Lev* 19:3
ye shall return *every m.* 25:10, 13
pitch *every m.* by his standard. *Num* 1:52; 2:2, 17
every m.'s hallowed things. 5:10
give to *every m.* according to. 7:5
take *every m.* his censer. 16:17
they took *every m.* his censer. 18
write thou *every m.'s* name. 17:2
took *every m.* his rod. 9
men of war had taken spoil, *every m.* 31:53
Israel inherited *every m.* his. 32:18
pass over *every m.* armed. 27, 29
judge righteously between *every m.* *Deut* 1:16
shall ye return *every m.* to his. 3:20
not do *every m.* what is right. 12:8
every m. shall give as he. 16:17
every m. shall die for his own sin. *Deut* 24:16; *2 Ki* 14:6; *2 Chr* 25:4
every m. of you a stone. *Josh* 4:5
ascend *every m.* straight. 6:5, 20
every m. to his inheritance. 24:28 *Judg* 2:6
to *every m.* a damsel or. *Judg* 5:30
go *every m.* unto his place. 7:7, 8
and he put a trumpet in *every m.'s.* 16
set *every m.'s* sword against his fellow. 22; *1 Sam* 14:20
give me *every m.* his earrings. *Judg* 8:24, 25
the people cut down *every m.* 9:49
every m. did what was right in. 17:6; 21:25
catch you *every m.* his wife. 21:21
every m. to his tribe, *every m.* to. 24
every m. into his tent. *1 Sam* 4:10
Samuel said, Go ye *every m.* 8:22
every m. his ox, *every m.* his. 14:34
that break away *every m.* 25:10
David said, Gird you on *every m.* 13
the Lord render to *every m.* his righteousness. 26:23; *2 Chr* 6:30
grieved *every m.* for his sons. *1 Sam* 30:6
save to *every m.* his wife and. 22
they went out *every m.* *2 Sam* 13:9
every m. gat him upon his mule. 29
that *every m.* which hath any. 15:4
covered *every m.* his head, and. 30
for Israel hath fled *every m.* 19:8
Sheba said, *Every m.* to his. 20:1
dwelt safely *every m.* *1 Ki* 4:25
every m. the plague of heart. 8:38
give to *every m.* according to his. 39; *Job* 34:11; *Jer* 17:10
brought *every m.* his present. *1 Ki* 10:25; *2 Chr* 9:24
not go up, return *every m.* to his. *1 Ki* 12:24; 22:17, 36; *2 Chr* 11:4
take the kings, *every m.* *1 Ki* 20:24
thence *every m.* a beam. *2 Ki* 6:2
every m. with his weapons. 11:8
Judah fled *every m.* to their. 14:12
and then eat ye *every m.* of. 18:31
God shake out *every m.* *Neh* 5:13
do according to *every m.'s.* *Esth* 1:8
every m. should bear rule in his. 22
and *every m.* shall draw. *Job* 21:23
the hand of *every m.* that. 37:7
every m. at his best state is vanity. *Ps* 39:5, 1
every m. walketh in a vain shew.
renderest to *every m.* according t his work. 62:12; *Pr* 24:1
every m. is a friend to. *Pr* 19:
every m. shall kiss his lips. 24:2
every m.'s judgement cometh. 29:2
eat *every m.* the flesh. *Isa* 9:2
therefore *every m.'s* heart shall. 13:
in that day *every m.* shall cast. 31:
every m. is brutish in knowledge. *Jer* 10:14; 51:1
turn *every m.* from his evil way. 26:3; 35:15; 36:
for *every m.* that is mad, and. 29:2
teach no more *every m.* his neigh bour. 31:34; *Heb* 8:1
in proclaiming liberty *every m.* to hi neighbour. *Jer* 34:15, 1
rise up *every m.* in his tent. 37:1
deliver ye *every m.* his soul. 51:4
with *every m.* his censer. *Ezek* 8:1
every m. in the chambers. 1
every m. with his destroying. 9:1,
away *every m.* abominations. 20:
they did not *every m.* cast away.
every m. shall tremble for. 32:
not scattered *every m.* from. 46:1
every m. that shall hear. *Dan* 3:
that *every m.* that shall ask. 6:
mariners cried *every m.* *Jonah* 1:
shall sit *every m.* under. *Mi* 4
hunt *every m.* his brother. 7
and ye run *every m.* to his ow house. *Hag* 1
every m. his neighbour. *Zech* 3:
every m. with his staff in his. 8
speak *every m.* truth to his neig bour. 16; *Eph* 4:
why do we deal treacherously *eve* *m.*? *Mal* 2:

shall reward *every m.* according to. *Mat* 16:27; *Rom* 2:6; *Rev* 22:12
received *every m.* a penny. *Mat* 20:9, 10
he gave to *every m.* according. 25:15
saw *every m.* clearly. *Mark* 8:25
and gave to *every m.* his work. 13:34
casting lots, what *every m.* 15:24
give to *every m.* that. *Luke* 6:30
every m. presseth into it. 16:16
much *every m.* had gained. 19:15
which lighteth *every m.* *John* 1:9
every m. at beginning doth set. 2:10
every m. that hath heard and. 6:45
ye shall be scattered *every m.* 16:32
how hear we *every m.* in? *Acts* 2:8
parted to all men, as *every m.* had need. 45; 4:35
every m. determined to send. 11:29
peace to *every m.* that. *Rom* 2:10
be true, but *every m.* a liar. 3:4
as God dealt to *every m.* the. 12:3
every m. be fully persuaded. 14:5
Lord gave to *every m.* *1 Cor* 3:5; 7:17
every m.'s work shall be made. 3:13
then shall *every m.* have praise. 4:5
nevertheless, let *every m.* have. 7:2
but *every m.* hath his proper gift. 7
let *every m.* abide in the. 20, 24
there is not in *every m.* that. 8:7
let *every m.* seek another's. 10:24*
know that the head of *every m.* 11:3
Spirit is given to *every m.* to. 12:7
every m. in his order, Christ. 15:23
commending ourselves to *every m.* *2 Cor* 4:2
I testify again to *every m.* *Gal* 5:3
let *every m.* prove his own work. 6:4
for *every m.* shall bear his own. 5
look not *every m.* on his. *Phil* 2:4
teaching *every m.* in all wisdom; to present *every m.* *Col* 1:28
ye ought to answer *every m.* 4:6
taste death for *every m.* *Heb* 2:9
but *every m.* is tempted. *Jas* 1:14
let *every m.* be swift to hear. 19
who judgeth according to *every m.'s* work. *1 Pet* 1:17
to give reason to *every m.* that. 3:15
every m. hath received the gift. 4:10
every m. that hath this hope in him. *1 John* 3:3
judged *every m.* according to their works. *Rev* 20:13
I testify to *every m.* that heareth. 22:18

man *of God*

Moses the *m. of God.* *Deut* 33:1
Josh 14:6
woman told, saying, A *m. of God* came to me. *Judg* 13:6
et the *m. of God* come again to. 8
. *m. of God* to Eli. *1 Sam* 2:27
s in this city a *m. of God.* 9:6
resent to bring the *m. of God.* 7
ive to the *m. of God* to tell us. 8
Shemaiah the *m. of God.* *1 Ki* 12:22
m. of God out of Judah. 13:1
n. of God who was disobedient. 26
o with thee, O *m. of God*? 17:18
know that thou art a *m. of God.* 24
ı. of God and spake to Ahab. 20:28
hou *m. of God,* king said, Come down. *2 Ki* 1:9, 11
) *m. of God,* I pray thee, let my life be precious. 13
he came and told *m. of God.* 4:7
his is *m. of God.* 9
hou *m. of God,* do not lie to. 16
hat I may run to *m. of God.* 22
he came unto the *m. of God.* 25, 27
thou *m. of God,* there is death. 40
rought the *m. of God* bread. 42
the saying of *m. of God.* 5:14
Elisha, the *m. of God.* 20; 8:4
place which *m. of God.* 6:10
hen the servant of the *m. of God.* 15
rd answered the *m. of God.* 7:2, 19
ode on him as the *m. of God* said. 17, 18
ter the saying of *m. of God.* 8:2
. *of God* is come hither. 7
the *m. of God* wept. *2 Ki* 8:11
and go, meet the *m. of God.* 8
and the *m. of God* was wroth. 13:19
word which the *m. of God.* 23:16
it is the sepulchre of *m. of God.* 17
Moses *m. of God.* *1 Chr* 23:14
2 Chr 30:16; *Ezra* 3:2
David the *m. of God.* *2 Chr* 8:14
Neh 12:24, 36
came a *m. of God* to Amaziah. *2 Chr* 25:7
m. of God answered, The Lord is. 9
of Igdaliah a *m. of God.* *Jer* 35:4
thou, O *m. of God,* flee. *1 Tim* 6:11
that the *m. of God* may be perfect. *2 Tim* 3:17

mighty **man**

Lord is with thee, thou *mighty m.* *Judg* 6:12
now Jephthah was a *mighty m.* 11:1
a kinsman a *mighty m.* of. *Ruth* 2:1
Benjamite, a *mighty m.* of power *1 Sam* 9:1
David a *mighty m.* and a man of war. 16:18; *2 Sam* 17:10
Jeroboam was a *mighty m.* *1 Ki* 11:28
Naaman was also a *mighty m.* *2 Ki* 5:1
Ismaiah a *mighty m.* among. *1 Chr* 12:4
Eliada a *mighty m.* of valour. *2 Chr* 17:17
Zichri, a *mighty m.* of. 28:7
as for the *mighty m.* he. *Job* 22:8
a *mighty m.* is not delivered by. *Ps* 33:16
thou in mischief, O *mighty m.* 52:1
Lord awaked like a *mighty m.* 78:65
in the hand of a *mighty m.* 127:4
take away the *mighty m.* *Isa* 3:2
mighty m. shall be humbled. 5:15
the sword, not of a *mighty m.* 31:8
go forth as a *mighty m.* 42:13
nor let the *mighty m.* glory. *Jer* 9:23
shouldest be as a *mighty m.* 14:9
nor *mighty m.* escape. 46:6
mighty m. stumbled. 12
the *mighty m.* shall cry. *Zeph* 1:14
as sword of a *mighty m.* *Zech* 9:13
Ephraim shall be like a *mighty m.* 10:7

no **man**

no m. is with us, see. *Gen* 31:50
without thee shall *no m.* lift. 41:44
stood *no m.* while Joseph made. 45:1
saw that there was *no m.* *Ex* 2:12
let *no m.* leave of it till the. 16:19
let *no m.* go out of his place on. 29
hurt or driven away, *no m.* 22:10
no m. did put on him his. 33:4
shall *no m.* see me and live. 20
no m. shall come up with thee. 34:3
there shall be *no m.* in. *Lev* 16:17
no m. that hath a blemish. 21:21
no m. shall sanctify it, it is. 27:26
if *no m.* hath lain with. *Num* 5:19
no m. able to stand before thee. *Deut* 7:24; 11:25
oppressed, and *no m.* shall save. 28:29, 68
no m. knoweth of his sepulchre. 34:6
no m. hath been able to stand before. *Josh* 23:9
daughter knew *no m.* *Judg* 11:39
no m. that took them to his house. 19:15, 18
virgins that had known *no m.* 21:12
for by strength shall *no m.* *1 Sam* 2:9
and then if there be *no m.* 11:3
let *no m.'s* heart fail because. 17:32
let *no m.* know any thing of. 21:2
and *no m.* saw nor knew it. 26:12
no m. deputed of king. *2 Sam* 15:3
for there is *no m.* that sinneth not. *1 Ki* 8:46; *2 Chr* 6:36
behold, there was *no m.* in camp. *2 Ki* 7:5, 10
let him alone, let *no m.* move. 23:18
no m. do them wrong, he reproved. *1 Chr* 16:21; *Ps* 105:14
queen did let *no m.* come. *Esth* 5:12
may *no m.* reverse. 8:8
no m. could withstand. *Esth* 9:2
shall *no m.* make thee ashamed? *Job* 11:3
in houses which *no m.* 15:28
therefore shall *no m.* look. 20:21
he riseth, and *no m.* is sure. 24:22
where *no m.* is, wherein there is *no m.* 38:26
I am a worm, and *no m.* *Ps* 22:6
there was *no m.* 142:4; *Isa* 41:28
59:16; *Jer* 4:25
in thy sight shall *no m.* be justified. *Ps* 143:2
and *no m.* regarded. *Pr* 1:24
flee when *no m.* pursueth. 28:1
the pit, let *no m.* stay him. 17
no m. hath power over. *Eccl* 8:8
no m. knoweth either love. 9:1
no m. remembered that same. 15
no m. shall spare his. *Isa* 9:19
no m. may come in. 24:10
he regardeth *no m.* 33:8
when I came, was there *no m.* 50:2
and *no m.* layeth it to heart. 57:1
Jer 12:11
so that *no m.* went. *Isa* 60:15
and where *no m.* dwelt. *Jer* 2:6
no m. repented. 8:6
for *no m.* of his seed shall. 22:30
this is Zion, whom *no m.* 30:17
go hide, and let *no m.* know. 36:19
Zedekiah said, Let *no m.* 38:24
and *no m.* shall know it. 40:15
no m. knew it. 41:4
and *no m.* dwelleth. 44:2; 51:43
no m. shall abide there. 49:18, 33
50:40
ask bread, and *no m.* *Lam* 4:4
no m. may pass through. *Ezek* 14:15
no m. shall enter in by this. 44:2
yet let *no m.* strive or. *Hos* 4:4
is scattered, and *no m.* *Nah* 3:18
so that there is *no m.* *Zeph* 3:6
so that *no m.* did lift up. *Zech* 1:21
that *no m.* passed through nor. 7:14
no m. can serve two masters. *Mat* 6:24; *Luke* 16:13
tell *no m.* *Mat* 8:4; 16:20
Mark 7:36; *Luke* 5:14; 9:21
see that *no m.* know it. *Mat* 9:30
Mark 5:43; 7:24; 8:30; 9:9
no m. knoweth the Son, but the Father. *Mat* 11:27; *Luke* 10:22
saw *no m.* save Jesus. *Mat* 17:8
tell the vision to *no m.* till the. 9
no m. was able to answer. 22:46
call *no m.* father on the earth. 23:9
that day and hour knoweth *no m.* 24:36; *Mark* 13:32
no m. that hath left house. *Mark* 10:29; *Luke* 18:29
no m. eat fruit of thee. *Mark* 11:14
that thou carest for *no m.* 12:14
do violence to *no m.* *Luke* 3:14
salute *no m.* 10:4
with the husks, and *no m.* 15:16
no m. hath seen God. *John* 1:18
1 John 4:12
no m. can do these miracles. *John* 3:2
no m. hath ascended up to. 13
for the Father judgeth *no m.* 5:22
no m. can come to me. 6:44, 65
but *no m.* laid hands. 7:30, 44; 8:20
she said, *No m.* Lord. 8:11
I judge *no m.* 15
the night cometh when *no m.* 9:4
no m. taketh it from me. 10:18
no m. is able to pluck them out. 29
no m. at the table knew. 13:28
no m. cometh to the Father. 14:6
greater love hath *no m.* 15:13
and your joy *no m.* taketh. 16:22
let *no m.* dwell therein. *Acts* 1:20
that they speak to *no m.* 4:17
of the rest durst *no m.* join. 5:13
we had opened, we found *no m.* 23
voice, but seeing *no m.* 9:7, 8
no m. shall set on thee to. 18:10
preaching kingdom of God, *no m.* 28:31
recompense to *no m.* *Rom* 12:17
owe *no m.* any thing, but. 13:8
and *no m.* dieth to himself. 14:7
that *no m.* put a stumblingblock. 13

of God knoweth no m. 1 Cor 2:11
himself is judged of no m. 15
other foundation can no m. lay. 3:11
let no m. deceive himself. 18, 21
let no m. seek his own, but. 10:24
henceforth know we no m. after the flesh. 2 Cor 5:16
no m., we have corrupted no m. 7:2
God accepteth no m. Gal 2:6
but that no m. is justified by. 3:11
let no m. deceive you. Eph 5:6
2 Thes 2:3
for no m. ever yet hated. Eph 5:29
no m. likeminded, who. Phil 2:20
let no m. beguile you of. Col 2:18
that no m. go beyond. 1 Thes 4:6
suddenly on no m. 1 Tim 5:22
at my first answer no m. 2 Tim 4:16
to speak evil of no m. Tit 3:2
no m. taketh this honour. Heb 5:4
no m. gave attendance at. 7:13
without which no m. shall see. 12:14
let no m. say when he is. Jas 1:13
the tongue can no m. tame, it. 3:8
little children, let no m. 1 John 3:7
a new name, which no m. Rev 2:17
he that shutteth, and no m. 3:7
and no m. can shut it. 8
that no m. take thy crown. 11
and no m. was able to open. 5:3, 4
multitude which no m. could. 7:9
that no m. might buy or sell. 13:17
no m. could learn that song. 14:3
no m. was able to enter into. 15:8
no m. buyeth their merchandise. 18:11
a name written, that no m. 19:12

of man

of m. will I require life of m. Gen 9:5
all the firstborn of m. Ex 13:13
Num 18:15
afraid of the face of m. Deut 1:17
is this the manner of m.? 2 Sam 7:19
not fall into the hands of m. 24:14
1 Chr 21:13
what manner of m. was he ? 2 Ki 1:7
no man there, nor voice of m. 7:10
days as the days of m.? Job 10:5
destroyest the hope of m. 14:19
for vain is the help of m. Ps 60:11
108:12
wrath of m. shall praise thee. 76:10
the ways of m. are before. Pr 5:21
the spirit of m. will sustain. 18:14
the discretion of m. deferreth. 19:11
the desire of m. is his kindness. 22
so the heart of m. answereth. 27:19
fear of m. bringeth a snare. 29:25
not the understanding of m. 30:2
way of a m. with a maid. 19
all the labour of m. is. Eccl 6:7
misery of m. is great upon. 8:6
this is the whole duty of m. 12:13
after the figure of a m., according to the beauty of a m. Isa 44:13
shouldest be afraid of a m. 51:12
I know the way of m. is. Jer 10:23
aside the right of a m. Lam 3:35
they four had the face of a m. Ezek 1:10; 10:14
no foot of m. shall pass. 29:11
neither shall the foot of m. 32:13
appearance of a m. Dan 8:15; 10:18
when the eyes of m. shall. Zech 9:1
who formeth the spirit of m. 12:1
of m. is this that the winds. Mat 8:27
Mark 4:41; Luke 8:25
of m. be so with his wife. Mat 19:10
he said, Come out of the m. Mark 5:8; Luke 8:29
nor of the will of m. but. John 1:13
any should testify of m. 2:25
voice of a god, not of m. Acts 12:22
upon every soul of m. Rom 2:9
the blessedness of the m. 4:6
entered into heart of m. 1 Cor 2:9
knoweth the things of a m. save the spirit of m. which is in him, so. 11
judged of you, or of m. 4:3
woman is the glory of the m. 11:7
but the woman is of the m. 8, 12
neither received it of m. Gal 1:12
wrath of m. worketh not. Jas 1:20
forgetteth what manner of m. Jas 1:24
all the glory of m. as. 1 Pet 1:24
old time by the will of m. 2 Pet 1:21
is the number of a m. Rev 13:18
to the measure of a m. 21:17

one man

we all one m.'s sons. Gen 42:11, 13
two homers for one m. Ex 16:22
if one m.'s ox hurt another's. 21:35
this people as one m. Num 14:15
shall one m. sin, and wilt ? 16:22
lacketh not one m. of us. 31:49
one m. shall chase a. Josh 23:10
Midianites as one m. Judg 6:16
priest to the house of one m. 18:19
was gathered as one m. 20:1
all the people arose as one m. 8
if one m. sin against. 1 Sam 2:25
as the heart of one m. 2 Sam 19:14
there is yet one m. Micaiah. 1 Ki 22:8; 2 Chr 18:7
gathered together as one m. Ezra 3:1; Neh 8:1
as one m. mocketh. Job 13:9
one m. among a thousand have. Eccl 7:28
one m. ruleth over another. 8:9
shall take hold of one m. Isa 4:1
one m. was clothed with. Ezek 9:2
one m. should die for the people. John 11:50; 18:14
by one m. sin entered into. Rom 5:12
grace, which is by one m. Jesus. 15
if by one m.'s offence death. 17
as by one m.'s disobedience many. 19
one m. esteemeth one day. 14:5
been the wife of one m. 1 Tim 5:9

son of man

nor son of m. that he Num 23:19
and the son of m. which. Job 25:6
may profit the son of m. 35:8
and son of m. that thou visitest. Ps 8:4; Heb 2:6
on son of m. whom thou. Ps 80:17
son of m. that thou makest. 144:3
trust in the son of m. 146:3
not afraid of the son of m. Isa 51:12
blessed is the son of m. that. 56:2
nor shall son of m. dwell in it. Jer 49:18, 33; 50:40
any son of m. pass thereby. 51:43
hast thou seen this, O son of m.? Ezek 8:15, 17
sigh therefore, thou son of m. 21:6
one like the Son of m. Dan 7:13
Rev 1:13; 14:14
Son of m. hath not where to lay. Mat 8:20; Luke 9:58
Son of m. hath power on earth to. Mat 9:6; Mark 2:10; Luke 5:24
not gone over, till the Son of m. be. Mat 10:23
the Son of m. came eating. 11:19
Luke 7:34
Son of m. is Lord even of sabbath. Mat 12:8; Mark 2:28; Luke 5:5
whosoever speaketh against Son of m. Mat 12:32; Luke 12:10
shall Son of m. be three. Mat 12:40
good seed is the Son of m. 13:37
the Son of m. shall send forth. 41
say, that I, the Son of m. am ? 16:13
until the Son of m. be risen again. 17:9; Mark 9:9
the Son of m. shall be betrayed. Mat 17:22; 20:18; 26:2, 45
Mark 14:41; Luke 9:44
also the coming of the Son of m. Mat 24:27, 37, 39; Luke 17:26
see Son of m. coming. Mat 24:30
Mark 13:26; Luke 21:27
hour ye think not Son of m. cometh. Mat 24:44; Luke 12:40
when the Son of m. shall. Mat 25:31
the Son of m. goeth. 26:24
Mark 14:21; Luke 22:22
Son of m. be ashamed. Mark 8:38
written of the Son of m. 9:12
the Son of m. is delivered. 31
10:33; Luke 24:7
Son of m. is as a man. Mark 13:34*
for the Son of m.'s sake. Luke 6:22
the Son of m. must suffer. Luke 9:22, 26
S. of man is not come to destroy. 56
so shall Son of m. be to this generation. 11:30; 17:24
him shall the Son of m. confess. 12:8
of the days of the Son of m. 17:22
when the Son of m. cometh. 18:8
the Son of m. is come to seek. 19:10
stand before the Son of m. 21:36
betrayest thou the Son of m.? 22:48
descending on Son of m. John 1:51
even the Son of m. which is. 3:13
even so must the Son of m. be. 14
because he is the Son of m. 5:27
which the Son of m. shall give. 6:27
eat the flesh of the Son of m. 53
ye shall see the Son of m. ascend. 62
when ye have lifted up the Son of m. then shall. 8:28
Son of m. should be glorified. 12:23
Son of m. must be lifted up, who is this Son of m.? 34
now is the Son of m. glorified. 13:31
see the Son of m. standing. Acts 7:56
see son

that man

even that m. shall be cut off from. Lev 17:9
I will set my face against that m. 20:3, 5; Ezek 14:8
brought not offering that m. shall. Num 9:13
stone that m. or. Deut 17:5, 12
elders shall take that m. and. 22:18
so shall it be done to that m. 25:9
shall smoke against that m. 29:20
that m. perisheth not. Josh 22:20
and that m. was perfect. Job 1:1
for the end of that m. is. Ps 37:37
blessed is that m. who maketh. 40:4
this and that m. was born in. 87:5
for bread that m. will. Pr 28:21
that m. be as cities Lord. Jer 20:16
I will even punish that m. 23:34
last state of that m. is worse. Mat 12:45; Luke 11:26
woe to that m. by whom. Mat 18:7
that m. by whom the Son of man is ... good were it for that m. 26:24
Mark 14:21; Luke 22:22
to do with that just m. Mat 27:19
by that m. whom he hath ordained. Acts 17:31
evil for that m. who. Rom 14:20
that m. of sin be revealed, the son of perdition. 2 Thes 2:3
note that m. and have no. 3:14
let not that m. think he. Jas 1:7

this man

wilt thou go with this m.? Gen 24:38
he that toucheth this m. or. 26:11
how long shall this m. be ? Ex 10:7
gave my daughter to this m. to wife. Deut 22:16
seeing this m. is come. Judg 19:23
to this m. do not so vile a thing. 24
this m. went up early. 1 Sam 1:3
said, How shall this m. save ? 10:27
seen this m. that is come ? 17:25
not my lord regard this m. 25:25
how this m. seeketh. 1 Ki 20:7
to me, and said, Keep this m. 39
this m. sends to me to. 2 Ki 5:7
mercy in sight of this m. Neh 1:11
this m. Mordecai waxed. Esth 9:4
this m. was the greatest. Job 1:3
this m. made not God. Ps 52:7
this m. was born there. 87:4, 5, 6
is this the m. that made ? Isa 14:16
this m. will I look, even to. 66:2
is this m. Coniah a despised broken idol ? Jer 22:28
Lord, Write ye this m. childless. 30
saying, This m. is worthy. 26:11, 1
let this m. be put to death, this m. seeketh not the welfare of. 38:4
make this m. understand. Dan 8:1
not perish for this m.'s life. Jonah 1:1
this m. shall be the peace. Mi 5:
I say to this m. Go, and he. Mat 8:
scribes said, This m. blasphemeth. 9:3; Mark 2:

whence hath this m. this wisdom ?
Mat 13:54; Mark 6:2
some said, This m. calleth.
Mat 27:47
I know not this m. of. Mark 14:71
this m. was the Son of God. 15:39
this m. if he were a prophet.
Luke 7:39
say to thee, Give this m. place. 14:9
saying, This m. began to build. 30
this m. receiveth sinners, and. 15:2
I tell you, this m. went down. 18:14
will not have this m. to reign. 19:14
said, This m. was also with. 22:56
I find no fault in this m. 23:4, 14
away with this m. 18
but this m. hath done nothing. 41
this m. went to Pilate and. 52
this m. give us his flesh ? John 6:52
how knoweth this m. letters ? 7:15
howbeit, we know this m. whence. 27
never man spake like this m. 46
Master, who did sin, this m.? 9:2
neither hath this m. sinned, nor. 3
this m. is not of God, he keepeth. 16
praise God, we know that this m. 24
if this m. were not of God he. 33
all that John spake of this m. 10:41
this m. which opened the eyes of blind, caused that this m.? 11:37
what do we ? for this m. doeth. 47
art not thou one of this m.'s ? 18:17
bring ye against this m.? 29
not this m. but Barabbas, now. 40
if let this m. go, thou art not. 19:12
and what shall this m. do ? 21:21
this m. purchased a field. Acts 1:18
had made this m. to walk. 3:12, 16
even by him doth this m. stand. 4:10
intend to bring this m.'s blood. 5:28
after this m. rose up Judas of. 37
this m. ceaseth not to speak. 6:13
saying, This m. is the great. 8:10
I heard of this m. how much. 9:13
of this m.'s seed hath God. 13:23
through this m. is preached to. 38
this m. was instructed in way. 18:25
this is the m. that teacheth all. 21:28
this m. is a Roman. 22:26
find no evil in this m. 23:9
this m. was taken of the Jews.
23:27
this m. a pestilent fellow. 24:5
accuse this m. if there be any. 25:5
ye see this m. about whom. 24
this m. doeth nothing worthy. 26:31
this m. might have been set at. 32
this m. is a murderer. 28:4
this m. was counted worthy. Heb 3:3
now consider how great this m. 7:4
this m. because he continueth. 24
that this m. have somewhat. 8:3*
this m. after he had offered. 10:12
this m. shall be blessed. Jas 1:25
but deceiveth, this m.'s religion. 26

man *of war*

the Lord is a m. of war. Ex 15:3
son of Manasseh, was a m. of war.
Josh 17:1
David a m. of war. 1 Sam 16:18
2 Sam 17:8; 1 Chr 28:3
Goliath was a m. of war from his.
1 Sam 17:33
take away the m. of war. Isa 3:2
jealousy like a m. of war. 42:13

wicked **man**

if the wicked m. be worthy to be.
Deut 25:2
wicked m. travaileth. Job 15:20
the portion of a wicked m. from.
20:29; 27:13
set thou a wicked m. over. Ps 109:6
a wicked m. walketh with. Pr 6:12
he that rebuketh a wicked m. 9:7
when a wicked m. dieth, his. 11:7
a wicked m. is loathsome, and. 13:5
a wicked m. taketh a gift out. 17:23
wicked m. hardeneth his face. 21:29
ay not wait, O wicked m. 24:15
a wicked m. that prolongeth his.
Eccl 7:15
wicked m. shall die in iniquity.
Ezek 3:18

which wicked m. doeth. Ezek 18:24
when a wicked m. turneth from. 27
O wicked m. thou shalt surely die,
that wicked m. shall die in. 33:8

wise **man**

m. discreet and wise. Gen 41:33
for thou art a wise m. 1 Ki 2:9
David's uncle, was a wise m.
1 Chr 27:32
a wise m. utter vain ? Job 15:2
I cannot find one wise m. 17:10
let a wise m. hearken to me. 34:34
a wise m. will hear and. Pr 1:5
rebuke a wise m. and he will. 9:8
give instruction to a wise m. he. 9
a wise m. feareth, and. 14:16
a wise m. will pacify wrath. 16:14
entereth more into a wise m. 17:10
a wise m. scaleth the city of. 21:22
seest thou a m. wise in his ? 26:12
if a wise m. contendeth with. 29:9
but a wise m. keepeth it in. 11
the wise m.'s eyes are in. Eccl 2:14
and how dieth the wise m.? 16
whether he shall be wise m. or. 19
maketh a wise m. mad. 7:7
who is as the wise m.? 8:1
a wise m.'s heart discerneth time. 5
though a wise m. think to know. 17
found in it a poor wise m. 9:15
a wise m.'s heart is at his right. 10:2
the words of a wise m.'s mouth. 12
who is the wise m. that ? Jer 9:12
let not the wise m. glory in. 23
liken him to a wise m. Mat 7:24
not a wise m. amongst. 1 Cor 6:5
who is a wise m. endued ? Jas 3:13

man joined with *woman*

the m. said, the woman whom thou.
Gen 3:12
dead m., for the woman thou. 20:3
every m. and woman. Ex 35:29
let no m. nor woman make. 36:6
if a m. or woman have. Lev 13:29
if m. or woman have in the skin. 38
woman also with whom the m. 15:18
issue of the m. and woman. 33
if m. lie with a woman. 20:18
a m. or woman that hath a familiar spirit. 27
when m. or woman shall commit any sin. Num 5:6
when either m. or woman shall. 6:2
kill woman that hath known m.
31:17; Judg 21:11
m. or woman that hath. Deut 17:2
bring forth that m. or woman. 5
woman . . . that pertaineth to a m. nor shall m. put on a woman's. 22:5
if a m. . . . with a woman, both m. that lay with woman, and woman. 22
be among you m. or woman. 29:18
utterly destroyed both m. and woman. Josh 6:21
but slay both m., woman. 1 Sam 15:3
David left neither m. nor woman alive. 27:9, 11
m. and woman a loaf. 1 Chr 16:3
m. or woman shall die. 2 Chr 15:13
whether m. or woman come to the king. Esth 4:11
from you, m. and woman. Jer 44:7
in pieces m. and woman. 51:22
of the woman is the m. 1 Cor 11:3
woman is the glory of the m. 7
the m. is not of the woman, but woman of the m. 8
nor is the m. without the woman. 11
as woman is of the m. so is the m. by the woman. 12
if any m. or woman. 1 Tim 5:16

young **man**

I have slain a young m. Gen 4:23
Abraham gave it to a young m. 18:7*
the young m. deferred not to. 34:19
was with us a young m. an. 41:12
Joshua a young m. Ex 33:11
there ran a young m. Num 11:27
destroy both the young m. and.
Deut 32:25
caught a young m. of the men of Succoth. Judg 8:14

hastily to the young m. and his young m. thrust him through. Judg 9:54
young m. of Beth-lehem-judah. 17:7
the young m. became his priest. 12
knew the voice of the young m. 18:3
Saul was a choice young m. and.
1 Sam 9:2
Jonathan said to the young m. 14:1
whose son art thou, young m.?
17:58
I say thus to the young m. 20:22*
David, I am young m. of. 30:13
David said to the young m. that told.
2 Sam 1:5, 13
bring the young m. Absalom. 14:21
for my sake with the young m. 18:5
young m. Absalom safe ? 29, 32
enemies be as that young m. is. 32
Solomon seeing young m. industrious. 1 Ki 11:28
the eyes of the young m. 2 Ki 6:17
so the young m. even young m. went to Ramoth. 9:4
and Zadok, a young m. 1 Chr 12:28
compassion on young m. 2 Chr 36:17
wherewith shall young m.? Ps 119:9
to young m. knowledge. Pr 1:4
discerned a young m. void of. 7:7
rejoice, O young m. in. Eccl 11:9
as young m. marrieth a. Isa 62:5
break in pieces the young m. and maid. Jer 51:22
speak to this young m. Zech 2:4
young m. said, All these. Mat 19:20
followed him a certain young m.
Mark 14:51
saw a young m. sitting on the. 16:5
Young m. I say unto thee, arise.
Luke 7:14
clothes at young m.'s feet. Acts 7:58
young m. named Eutychus. 20:9
brought the young m. alive. 12*
bring this young m. to the. 23:17, 18
captain then let the young m. 22

Manaen

M. who had been brought. Acts 13:1

Manasseh

called the firstborn M. Gen 41:51
thy two sons M. and Ephraim. 48:5
God make thee as Ephraim and M. and he set Ephraim before M. 20
of M. Gamaliel was. Num 1:10
Gamaliel prince of M. offered. 7:54
these are the families of M. 26:34
27:1
married into the family of M. 36:12
the thousands of M. Deut 33:17
two tribes, M. Ephraim. Josh 14:4
the male children of M. 17:2
Zelophehad son of M. had no. 3
there fell ten portions to M. 5
the daughters of M. had an. 6
M. had in Issachar, Beth-shean. 11
children of M. could not drive out. 12
my family is poor in M. Judg 6:15
Jonathan son of Gershom, son of M.
18:30
M. his son reigned. 2 Ki 20:21
2 Chr 32:33
and M. seduced them to do more evil. 2 Ki 21:9
M. shed innocent blood, till he. 16
the altars M. made did Josiah. 23:12
M. had provoked him withal. 26
for the sins of M. this came. 24:3
dwelt of the children of M. 1 Chr 9:3
fell some of M. to David. 12:19
strangers out of M. fell. 2 Chr 15:9
letters to Ephraim and M. 30:1
yet divers of M. humbled. 11
cut down the groves in M. 31:1
M. made Judah and Jerusalem. 33:9
Lord spake to M. he would not. 10
the captains took M. among. 11
then M. knew that the Lord he. 13
humbled not himself, as M. 23
so did Josiah in the cities of M. 34:6
M. had taken strange wives.
Ezra 10:30, 33
Gilead is mine, M. Ps 60:7; 108:8
before M. stir up thy strength. 80:2
M. shall eat Ephraim. Isa 9:21
removed, because of M. Jer 15:4

side a portion for M. Ezek 48:4
Ezekias begat M. and M. Mat 1:10

tribe of **Manasseh**

numbered of the tribe of M. 32,200. Num 1:35
tribe of M. and the captain of the children of M. 2:20; 10:23
of the tribe of M., Gaddi. 13:11
to half tribe of M. the kingdom of Og. 32:33
half tribe of M. have received. 34:14
for the tribe of M., Hanniel. 23
half tribe of M. passed. Josh 4:12
nine tribes and half tribe of M. 13:7
tribe of M. this was possession of half tribe of M. 29; 12:6; 18:7
also a lot for the tribe of M. 17:1
gave Golan out of the tribe of M. 20:8; 21:27
the half tribe of M. built. 22:10
Gad, and half tribe of M. 1 Chr 5:18
tribe of M. to the Levites. 6:70, 71
half tribe of M. 18,000 to. 12:31
rulers over Gad half tribe of M. 26:32; 27:20, 21
tribe of M. were sealed. Rev 7:6

mandrakes

(The Hebrew word for mandrake means love-plant, *and it is supposed to have power to excite voluptuousness. Its roots are forked and sometimes bear a resemblance to a human being. It is a powerful narcotic)*

Reuben found m. Rachel said, Give me of thy m. Gen 30:14
son's m. also? Therefore he shall lie with thee for thy son's m. 15
hired thee with my son's m. 16
m. give a smell, and at. S of S 7:13

Maneh

shekels shall be your M. Ezek 45:12

manger

laid him in a m. Luke 2:7
shall find him in a m. 12
found the babe lying in a m. 16

manifest

that God might m. Eccl 3:18*
love him, and m. myself. John 14:21
m. thyself to us, and not unto? 22
the miracle is m. to all. Acts 4:16
known of God is m. in. Rom 1:19
m. counsels of hearts. 1 Cor 4:5
it is m. that he is excepted. 15:27
makes m. the savour of. 2 Cor 2:14
works of the flesh are m. Gal 5:19
my bonds in Christ are m. Phil 1:13
that I may make it m. Col 4:4
a m. token of righteous. 2 Thes 1:5
God was m. in the flesh. 1 Tim 3:16
good works of some are m. 5:25*
their folly shall be m. 2 Tim 3:9
creature that is not m. Heb 4:13
but was m. in these last. 1 Pet 1:20
children of God are m. 1 John 3:10
see **made**

manifestation

waiteth for the m. of the. Rom 8:19
the m. of the Spirit is. 1 Cor 12:7
but by m. of the truth. 2 Cor 4:2

manifested

hid which shall not be m. Mark 4:22
miracles did Jesus, and m. forth his glory. John 2:11
I have m. thy name unto the. 17:6
the righteousness of God is m. Rom 3:21
but hath in due time m. Tit 1:3
the life was m. and we. 1 John 1:2
that he was m. to take away. 3:5
purpose was the Son of God m. 8
in this was m. the love of God. 4:9

manifestly

are m. declared to be. 2 Cor 3:3

manifold

in thy m. mercies forsookest them not. Neh 9:19
according to m. mercies gavest. 27
O Lord, how m. are thy! Ps 104:24
I know your m. transgressions and sins. Amos 5:12

shall not receive m. Luke 18:30
might be known the m. Eph 3:10
ye are in heaviness through m. temptations. 1 Pet 1:6
good stewards of the m. grace. 4:10

mankind

shall not lie with m. as. Lev 18:22
if a man lie with m. as. 20:13
is the breath of all m. Job 12:10
them that defile with m. 1 Tim 1:10
hath been tamed of m. Jas 3:7

manna

(The word means "what is this?" *It was the food by which Israel was sustained during the* 40 *years in the wilderness. There is a modern substance now called* manna, *but it does not answer all the conditions)*

to another, it is m. Ex 16:15
put a homer full of m. therein. 33
Israel did eat m. forty years. 35
nothing besides this m. Num 11:6
the m. was as coriander seed. 7
fell upon camp the m. fell on it. 9
and fed thee with m. Deut 8:3, 16
Neh 9:20; Ps 78:24
m. ceased, they had m. Josh 5:12
our fathers did eat m. John 6:31, 49
not as your fathers did eat m. 58*
golden pot that had m. Heb 9:4
give to eat of the hidden m. Rev 2:17

manner

two m. of people shall. Gen 25:23
was of all m. of bake-meats. 40:17
their lives bitter in all m. Ex 1:14
no m. of work shall be done. 12:16
all m. of trespass, any m. 22:9*
in wisdom, and in all m. of. 31:3, 5
35:31, 33, 35; 36:1; 1 Chr 28:21
burnt offering according to m. Lev 5:10*; Num 9:14*
no m. of fat of ox or sheep. Lev 7:23
no m. of blood. 26, 27; 17:10, 14
law for all m. of plague. 14:54
ye shall do no m. of work. 23:31
ye shall have one m. of law. 24:22
Num 15:16*
she be taken with the m. Num 5:13
offering according to the m. 15:24*
do no m. of servile work. 28:18
saw no m. of similitude. Deut 4:15
this is the m. of the release. 15:2
that lieth with any m. of beast. 27:21
what m. of men were they? Judg 8:18
now this was the m. in. Ruth 4:7*
and shew them the m. of the king. 1 Sam 8:9, 11
Samuel told the people the m. 10:25
bread is in a m. common. 21:5*
so will be his m. all the while. 27:11
is this the m. of man? 2 Sam 7:19
what m. of man was he? 2 Ki 1:7
by a pillar, as the m. was. 11:14
know not the m. of the God. 17:26
let him teach them the m. of God. 27
all m. of measure. 1 Chr 23:29
for so was the king's m. Esth 1:13
abhorreth all m. of meat. Ps 107:18
full, affording all m. of store. 144:13
at our gates are all m. S of S 7:13
shall feed after their m. Isa 5:17*
this hath been thy m. Jer 22:21
and no m. of hurt was. Dan 6:23
the m. of Beer-sheba. Amos 8:14
and healing all m. of sickness. Mat 4:23; 10:1
shall say all m. of evil against. 5:11
What m. of man is this, that even wind? 8:27; Mark 4:41; Luke 8:25
all m. of sin shall be forgiven to. Mat 12:31
what m. of stones are! Mark 13:1
what m. of salutation. Luke 1:29
saying, What m. of child shall? 66
have known what m. of woman. 7:39
ye know not what m. of spirit. 9:55
ye tithe mint, rue, and all m. 11:42
what m. of communications? 24:17
what m. of saying is this? John 7:36
m. of the Jews is to bury. 19:40*
Paul, as his m. was, went. Acts 17:2*
ye know after what m. I have. 20:18
to the perfect m. of the law. 22:3

it is not m. of Romans. Acts 25:16*
my m. of life from my youth. 26:4
wrought in me all m. of. Rom 7:8
sorry after a godly m. 2 Cor 7:9*
m. of men we were. 1 Thes 1:5
what m. of entering in we had. 9
known my m. of life. 2 Tim 3:10*
assembling, as the m. Heb 10:25*
forgetteth what m. of man. Jas 1:24
m. of time the Spirit. 1 Pet 1:11
holy in all m. of conversation. 15
what m. of persons. 2 Pet 3:11
behold what m. of love. 1 John 3:1
in this m. be killed. Rev 11:5
which bare twelve m. of fruits. 22:2
see **like**

after the **manner**

Sarah after the m. of women. Gen 18:11
to come in to us after the m. 19:31
after the former m. when. 40:13
deal with her after the m. Ex 21:9
number, after the m. Num 29:18
city after the same m. Josh 6:15
careless, after the m. of. Judg 18:17
turned and spake after the same m. 1 Sam 17:30
after the m. of the nations. 2 Ki 17:33; 2 Chr 13:9
and I answered them after the same m. Neh 6:4
after the m. of Egypt. Isa 10:24
Amos 4:10
polluted after the m. Ezek 20:30
after the m. of Babylonians. 23:15
after the m. of adulteresses, and after the m. of women. 45*
after the m. of the purifying of the. John 2:6
circumcised after the m. Acts 15:1*
I speak after the m. of men. Rom 6:19; 1 Cor 15:32; Gal 3:15
after the same m. also he took the cup. 1 Cor 11:25
being a Jew, livest after the m. of. Gal 2:14*

after this **manner**

far from thee to do after this m. Gen 18:25
saying, After this m. did thy. 39:19
he sent after this m. ten asses. 45:23
after this m. ye shall offer daily. Num 28:24
spoken after this m. 2 Sam 17:6
after this m. will I mar. Jer 13:9
after this m. therefore pray ye. Mat 6:9
one after this m. and. 1 Cor 7:7
after this m. in old time. 1 Pet 3:5

on this **manner**

saying, On this m. shall ye speak to. Gen 32:19
told Saul, saying, On this m. spake David. 1 Sam 18:24
on this m. did Absalom. 2 Sam 15:6
one said on this m., another on that m. 1 Ki 22:20; 2 Chr 18 19
persuade you on this m. 2 Chr 32:15

manners

shall not walk in the m. Lev 20:23*
do after the former m. 2 Ki 17:34†
have done after the m. Ezek 11:12*
suffered he their m. Acts 13:18†
corrupt good m. 1 Cor 15:33†
God in divers m. spake. Heb 1:1

Manoah

M. intreated the Lord. Judg 13:8
God hearkened to the voice of M. 9
M. arose and went after his wife. 11
M. knew not that he was an angel. 16
M. took a kid, and offered it. 19
M. and his wife looked on it. 20
M. knew that he was an angel. 21
in the buryingplace of M. 16:31

manservant

not do any work, thou nor thy m. Ex 20:10; Deut 5:14
not covet thy neighbour's m. Ex 20:17; Deut 5:21
smite out his m.'s tooth. Ex 21:27
if the ox shall push a m. he shall. 32

must eat them, thou and thy m. Deut 12:18
rejoice, thou and m. 16:11, 14
despise cause of my m. Job 31:13
let his m. go free. Jer 34:9, 10

mansions

house are many m. John 14:2

manslayer

ye shall appoint for m. Num 35:6
the m. die not, until he stand. 12

manslayers

law was made for m. 1 Tim 1:9

mantle

Sisera with a m. Judg 4:18*
and covered with a m. 1 Sam 28:14
wrapped his face in his m. 1 Ki 19:13
Elijah cast his m. upon Elisha. 19
Elijah took his m. and. 2 Ki 2:8
Elisha took Elijah's m. that. 13, 14
heard this, I rent my m. Ezra 9:3, 5
arose and rent his m. Job 1:20
rent every one his m. 2:12
confusion, as with a m. Ps 109:29

mantles

I will take away the m. Isa 3:22

many

thou shalt be a father of m. nations. Gen 17:4, 5; Rom 4:17, 18
he made him a coat of m. colours. Gen 37:3; 23:32
to gaze, and m. perish. Ex 19:21
Moses said, Return, O Lord, to the m. thousands of. Num 10:36
whether they be few or m. 13:18
to m. thou shalt give more. 26:54
divided between m. and few. 56
have m. cities, shall give m. 35:8
hath cast out m. nations. Deut 7:1
lend to m. nations. 15:6; 28:12
and m. evils shall befall. 31:17, 21
and chariots very m. Josh 11:4
m. were overthrown. Judg 9:40
the destroyer which slew m. 16:24
she that hath m. children. 1 Sam 2:5
the Lord to save by m. or few. 14:6
Judah and Israel were m. 1 Ki 4:20
they were exceeding m. 7:47
dress it first, for ye are m. 18:25
witchcrafts are so m. 2 Ki 9:22
Rehabiah were very m. 1 Chr 23:17
hath given me m. sons. 28:5
Rehoboam desired m. 2 Chr 11:23
to help whether with m. 14:11
there were m. in congregation. 30:17
m. of Ephraim and Manasseh. 18
we are m. that have. Ezra 10:13
and our daughters are m. Neh 5:2
there were m. in Judah sworn. 6:18
and feared God above m. 7:2
among m. nations was no king. 13:26
and m. lay in sackcloth. Esth 4:3
thou hast instructed m. Job 4:3
yea, m. shall make suit unto. 11:19
m. are they that rise up. Ps 3:1
there be m. that say of my. 2; 4:6
consider mine enemies, they are m. 25:19; 56:2
heard the slander of m. 31:13
m. sorrows shall be to the. 32:10
m. are the afflictions of the. 34:19
better than the riches of m. 37:16
m. shall see it and fear, and. 40:3
delivered, for there were m. 55:18
I am a wonder to m.; but thou. 71:7
m. are my persecutors. 119:157
years of thy life shall be m. Pr 4:10
for she hath cast down m. 7:26
the righteous feed m. 10:21
the rich hath m. friends. 14:20
wealth maketh m. friends. 19:4
for transgression of land m. are. 28:2
his eyes, shall have m. a curse. 27
darkness shall be m. Eccl 11:8
trust in chariots because they are m. Isa 31:1
knowledge shall he justify m. 56:11
he bare the sin of m. and made. 12
slain of the Lord shall be m. 66:16
their transgressions are m. Jer 5:6
for our backslidings are m. 14:7
for we are left but few of m. 42:2
he made m. to fall. 46:16
for my sighs are m. my. Lam 1:22
but we are m.; the land. Ezek 33:24
by peace shall destroy m. Dan 8:25
m. stand up against the king. 11:14
understand shall instruct m. 33
utterly to make away m. 44
m. that sleep in the dust shall. 12:2
m. shall run to and fro, and. 4
Ephraim hath made m. Hos 8:11
be quiet, and likewise m. Nah 1:12
inhabitants of m. cities. Zech 8:20
but did turn m. away. Mal 2:6
and m. there be that go. Mat 7:13
m. will say to me in that day. 22
m. shall come from the east. 8:11
he did not m. mighty works. 13:58
m. that are first shall be last. 19:30; Mark 10:31
for m. be called, but few chosen. Mat 20:16; 22:14
for m. shall come in my name, and shall deceive m. 24:5; Mark 13:6 Luke 21:8
love of m. shall wax. Mat 24:12
this is my blood, shed for m. 26:28
they appear to m. 27:53
name is Legion, for we are m. Mark 5:9; Luke 8:30
m. shall he turn to Lord. Luke 1:16
fall and rising of m. in Israel. 2:34
m. widows were in Israel. 4:25
m. lepers were in Israel. 27
and devils also came out of m. 41
her sins which are m. 7:47
great supper, and bade m. 14:16
are they among so m.? John 6:9
m. therefore of his disciples. 60, 66
and m. resorted to him, and. 10:41
for all so m., the net was not. 21:11
I have heard by m. of this. Acts 9:13
where m. were gathered. 12:12
m. brought their books. 19:19
m. of the saints did I shut up. 26:10
m. be dead . . . the grace of God hath abounded unto m. Rom 5:15
m. were made sinners, m. be. 19
so we, being m. are one body. 12:5
she hath been a succourer of m. 16:2
not m. wise, not m. mighty are. 1 Cor 1:26
yet have ye not m. fathers. 4:15
there be gods m. and lords m. 8:5
but with m. God was not. 10:5
we being m. are one bread. 17
seeking the profit of m. 33
m. are weak and m. sleep. 11:30
not one member, but m. 12:14
great door, and there are m. 16:9
may be given by m. 2 Cor 1:11
punishment was inflicted of m. 2:6
m. which corrupt the word. 17
m. redound to glory. 4:15
as poor, yet making m. rich. 6:10
zeal hath provoked very m. 9:2
and profited above m. Gal 1:14
and to seeds, as of m. 3:16
m. brethren waxing confident by. Phil 1:14
m. walk, of whom I have told. 3:18
bringing m. sons to glory. Heb 2:10
they truly were m. priests. 7:23
offered to bear the sins of m. 9:28
sprang of one, so m. as stars. 11:12
my brethren be not m. Jas 3:1
m. shall follow pernicious. 2 Pet 2:2
are there m. antichrists. 1 John 2:18
because m. false prophets are. 4:1
see **believed, days, how, waters**

after **many**

cause to decline after m. Ex 23:2

as **many** *as*

and as m. as were willing. Ex 35:22
as m. as had not known. Judg 3:1
as m. as came to the place stood. 2 Sam 2:23
as m. as were of free. 2 Chr 29:31
as m. as ye find bid to. Mat 22:9
and gathered together as m. as. 10
as m. as touched him. Mark 6:56
rise and give as m. as he needeth. Luke 11:8
but as m. as received him. John 1:12
give eternal life to as m. as. 17:2
even to as m. as the Lord. Acts 2:39
as m. as have spoken have. 3:24
fear came upon as m. as heard. 5:11
and as m. as obeyed him. 36, 37
were astonished, as m. as. 10:45
as m. as were ordained to. 13:48
as m. as have sinned without law, and as m. as have. Rom 2:12
for as m. as are led by the Spirit. 8:14
as m. as are of the works. Gal 3:10
as m. as desire to make a fair shew in the flesh. 6:12
and as m. as walk according. 16
as m. as be perfect be. Phil 3:15
and for as m. as have not. Col 2:1
as m. servants as are. 1 Tim 6:1
but to as m. as have not. Rev 2:24
as m. as I love I rebuke. 3:19
cause that as m. as would not. 13:15

many *people*

people of the land now are m. Ex 5:5
a people great and m. Deut 2:21
the people are too m. . . . yet too m. for me. Judg 7:2, 4
Lord had smitten m. of the people. 1 Sam 6:19
m. of the people are fallen and dead. 2 Sam 1:4
but the people are m. Ezra 10:13
m. people of land became. Esth 8:17
m. people shall go and say. Isa 2:3
judge and rebuke m. people. 4
multitude of m. people. 17:12
m. people of a strange. Ezek 3:6
without m. people to pluck it. 17:9
vex the hearts of m. people. 32:9
I will make m. people amazed. 10
and m. people with thee. 38:9, 15
judge among m. people. Mi 4:3
beat in pieces m. people. 13
shall be in midst of m. people. 5:7
m. people shall come. Zech 8:22
thou must prophesy before m. peoples, nations and tongues. Rev 10:11

many *things*

I have heard m. such things. Job 16:2
and m. such things are with. 23:14
there be m. things that. Eccl 6:11
seeing m. things, but. Isa 42:30
spake m. things to them. Mat 13:3
suffer m. things of the elders and chief priests. 16:21; Mark 8:31 9:12; Luke 9:22; 17:25
make thee ruler over m. things. Mat 25:21, 23
hearest thou not how m. things they witness? 27:13; Mark 15:4
have suffered m. things this day in a dream. Mat 27:19
suffered m. things of many physicians. Mark 5:26
he did m. things, and heard. 6:20
m. things there be, as washing of cups. 7:4, 8, 13
accused him of m. things. 15:3
thou art troubled about m. things. Luke 10:41
to speak of m. things. 11:53
I have m. things to say. John 8:26 16:12
there are m. other things. 21:25
that I ought to do m. things contrary. Acts 26:9
diligent in m. things. 2 Cor 8:22
suffered so m. things. Gal 3:4
in how m. things he. 2 Tim 1:18
have m. things to say. Heb 5:11
in m. things we offend. Jas 3:2
having m. things to write to you. 2 John 12; 3 John 13

many *a time*

m. a time turned he his. Ps 78:38
m. a time have they afflicted me. 129:1, 2

many *times*

how m. times shall I adjure thee? 1 Ki 22:16
m. times didst deliver them. Neh 9:28; Ps 106:43

many *years*
if there be yet *m. years.* *Lev* 25:51
that was builded *m. years* ago. *Ezra* 5:11
yet *m. years* didst thou. *Neh* 9:30
children, and live *m. years. Eccl* 6:3
man live *m. years,* and rejoice. 11:8
m. days and *years* shall. *Isa* 32:10
prophesied *m. years.* *Ezek* 38:17
done these so *m. years.* *Zech* 7:3
hast goods laid up for *m. years.* *Luke* 12:19
he said, Lo, these *m. years.* 15:29
of *m. years* a judge. *Acts* 24:10
now after *m. years* I came to. 17
a great desire *m. years. Rom* 15:23

mar
nor *m.* the corners of. *Lev* 19:27
lest I *m.* mine own. *Ruth* 4:6
images of your mice that *m.* the land. *1 Sam* 6:5
and *m.* every good. *2 Ki* 3:19
they *m.* my path, they. *Job* 30:13
I *m.* the pride of Judah. *Jer* 13:9

Mara
not Naomi, call me *M.* *Ruth* 1:20

Marah
not drink of waters of *M. Ex* 15:23
days, and pitched in *M.* *Num* 33:8
removed from *M.* and came. 9

Maran-atha
(*An Aramaic or Syriac expression used by St. Paul at the conclusion of his First Epistle to the Corinthians,* 1 Cor 16:22, *meaning* our Lord cometh)

marble
I have prepared *m.* in. *1 Chr* 29:2
pillars of *m.*: pavement of red, blue, white, and black *m.* *Esth* 1:6
his legs are as pillars of *m.* set. *S of S* 5:15
the vessels of *m.* no man. *Rev* 18:12

march
thou didst *m.* through. *Ps* 68:7
shall *m.* with an army. *Jer* 46:22
m. every one on his ways. *Joel* 2:7
which shall *m.* through. *Hab* 1:6
didst *m.* through the land. 3:12

marched
behold, the Egyptians *m.* *Ex* 14:10

marchedst
when thou *m.*, the earth. *Judg* 5:4

Marcus
M. sister's son to Barnabas. *Col* 4:10
M. saluteth. *Philem* 24; *1 Pet* 5:13

mariners
of Zidon were thy *m.* *Ezek* 27:8*
ships of the sea with their *m.* were. 9
thy *m.* shall fall into the midst of. 27
the *m.* shall come down from. 29
then the *m.* were afraid. *Jonah* 1:5

marishes
miry places and *m.* shall. *Ezek* 47:11

Mark
John, surnamed *M.* *Acts* 12:12
John, whose surname was *M.* 25
Barnabas took *M.* and. 15:39
take *M.* and bring. *2 Tim* 4:11

mark, *substantive*
the Lord set a *m.* upon. *Gen* 4:15*
though I shot at a *m.* *1 Sam* 20:20
hast thou set me as a *m.* against thee? *Job* 7:20; 16:12; *Lam* 3:12
set a *m.* on the men. *Ezek* 9:4
any man on whom is the *m.* 6
I press toward the *m.* *Phil* 3:14*
all to receive a *m.* *Rev* 13:16
save he that had the *m.* 17
if any man receive his *m.* 14:9
whosoever receiveth his *m.* 11
his image, and over his *m.* 15:2
sore on them that had the *m.* 16:2
that received *m.* of beast. 19:20
nor received his *m.* upon their. 20:4

mark, *verb*
thou shalt *m.* the place. *Ruth* 3:4
m. when Amnon's heart is merry. *2 Sam* 13:28
m. how this man. *1 Ki* 20:7
the prophet said, *M.* and see. 22
m. and afterwards we will. *Job* 18:2
m. me and be astonished, and. 21:5
m. well, O Job, hearken to me. 33:31
canst thou *m.* when the hinds? 39:1
m. the perfect man. *Ps* 37:37
m. well her bulwarks. 48:13
they *m.* my steps, when they. 56:6
if thou, Lord, shouldest *m.* 130:3
m. well, *m.* the entering. *Ezek* 44:5
m. them who cause. *Rom* 16:17
m. them who walk so. *Phil* 3:17

marked
as she prayed, Eli *m.* *1 Sam* 1:12
hast thou *m.* the old way? *Job* 22:15
which they had *m.* in the day. 24:16
yet thine iniquity is *m.* *Jer* 2:22
who hath *m.* his word and? 23:18
m. how they chose rooms. *Luke* 14:7

markest
if I sin, then thou *m.* *Job* 10:14

market
they traded in thy *m.* *Ezek* 27:13* 17*, 19*, 25*
standing idle in the *m.* *Mat* 20:3
they come from the *m.* *Mark* 7:4*
salutations in the *m.* places. 12:38
sitting in the *m.* place. *Luke* 7:32
is a pool at Jerusalem by the sheep *m.* *John* 5:2*
them into the *m.* place. *Acts* 16:19
he disputed in the *m.* daily. 17:17*

marketh
my feet in stocks, he *m.* *Job* 33:11
the carpenter *m.* it out. *Isa* 44:13

markets
(*Revisions,* marketplaces)
children sitting in the *m. Mat* 11:16
love greetings in the *m.* 23:7
Luke 11:43; 20:46

marks
ye shall not print any *m.* *Lev* 19:28
I bear in my body the *m.* *Gal* 6:17

marred
his visage was so *m.* *Isa* 52:14
girdle was *m.* *Jer* 13:7
the vessel was *m.* 18:4
m. their vine branches. *Nah* 2:2
the bottles will be *m.* *Mark* 2:22

marriage
(*The word marriage is used* [1] *literally; and* [2] *figuratively to represent the union of God with his people or of Christ with his church*)
her duty of *m.* shall he. *Ex* 21:10
were not given to *m.* *Ps* 78:63*
a king who made a *m.* *Mat* 22:2
come to the *m.* 4
all ye find, bid to the *m.* 9
not given in *m.* but as the angels. 22:30; *Mark* 12:25; *Luke* 20:35
given in *m.* until day. *Mat* 24:38
went in with him to the *m.* 25:10
they did eat, they were given in *m.* *Luke* 17:27; 20:34
there was a *m.* in Cana. *John* 2:1
Jesus and his disciples to the *m.* 2
her in *m.* doeth well, but he that giveth her not in *m.* *1 Cor* 7:38
m. is honourable in all. *Heb* 13:4
m. of the Lamb is come. *Rev* 19:7
called to the *m.* supper of Lamb. 9

marriages
and make ye *m.* with us. *Gen* 34:9
neither shalt thou make *m. Deut* 7:3
else if he shall make *m.* *Josh* 23:12

married
Lot spake to them that *m. Gen* 19:14
if *m.* his wife shall go out. *Ex* 21:3
if *m.* to a stranger, she. *Lev* 22:12
woman whom he had *m.* *Num* 12:1
if they be *m.* to the sons of. 36:3
m. to their father's brothers'. 11
lying with a woman *m.* *Deut* 22:22
m. when sixty years old. *1 Chr* 2:21
Abijah *m.* fourteen. *2 Chr* 13:21
Jews that had *m.* wives. *Neh* 13:23
woman when she is *m.* *Pr* 30:23
of desolate than of *m.* *Isa* 54:1
in thee, thy land shall be *m.* 62:4
children, for I am *m.* to. *Jer* 3:14
hath *m.* the daughter of. *Mal* 2:11
the first when he had *m.* *Mat* 22:25
for he had *m.* her. *Mark* 6:17
be *m.* to another, committeth. 10:12
I have *m.* a wife, and. *Luke* 14:20
they drank, they *m.* wives. 17:27
husband liveth, she be *m.* *Rom* 7:3
dead, that ye should be *m.* 4
to the *m.* I command. *1 Cor* 7:10
he that is *m.* 33
she that is *m.* careth for. 34
to be *m.* to whom she will, only. 39

marrieth
young man *m.* a virgin. *Isa* 62:5
m. her who is put away, doth. *Mat* 19:9; *Luke* 16:18

marrow
(*A soft tissue which fills the cavities of most bones; hence, the choicest of food*)
are moistened with *m.* *Job* 21:24
be satisfied as with *m.* *Ps* 63:5
it shall be health and *m.* *Pr* 3:8
feast of fat things full of *m. Isa* 25:6
asunder of joints and *m.* *Heb* 4:12

marry
brother's wife, and *m.* *Gen* 38:8*
m. to whom they think best...father's tribe shall they *m.* *Num* 36:6
wife of dead shall not *m. Deut* 25:5
so shall thy sons *m.* thee. *Isa* 62:5
m. her that is divorced committeth. *Mat* 5:32; 19:9; *Mark* 10:11
so, it is not good to *m.* *Mat* 19:10
his brother shall *m.* his wife. 22:24
they neither *m.* nor are given. 30
Mark 12:25; *Luke* 20:35
let them *m.*, for it is better to *m.* *1 Cor* 7:9
if thou *m.* if a virgin *m.*: she hath. 28
he sinneth not, let them *m.* 36
forbidding to *m.* and. *1 Tim* 4:3
to wax wanton, they will *m.* 5:11
the younger women *m.*, bear. 14

marrying
do this great evil in *m.* *Neh* 13:27
they were *m.* and giving. *Mat* 24:38

Mars' hill
in the midst of *M. hill.* *Acts* 17:22

mart
Tyre, and she is a *m.* of. *Isa* 23:3

Martha
a woman named *M.* *Luke* 10:38
M. was cumbered about. 40
M. M. thou art careful. 41
Mary and her sister *M.* *John* 11:1
now Jesus loved *M.* Mary, and. 5
Jesus was in that place where *M.* 30
made him a supper, and *M.* 12:2

martyr
blood of thy *m.* Stephen. *Acts* 22:20*
wherein Antipas was my faithful *m.* *Rev* 2:13*

martyrs
drunken with blood of *m.* *Rev* 17:6

marvel
no *m.*; for Satan himself. *2 Cor* 11:14

marvel
if thou seest, *m.* not at. *Eccl* 5:8
and all men did *m.* *Mark* 5:20
m. not that I said, Ye must be born. *John* 3:7
greater works, that ye may *m.* 5:20
m. not at this. 28
done one work, and ye *m.* 7:21
men of Israel, why *m.*? *Acts* 3:12
I *m.* that ye are so soon. *Gal* 1:6
m. not if the world. *1 John* 3:13
wherefore didst thou *m.*? *Rev* 17:7*

marvelled
and the men *m.* one. *Gen* 43:33
they saw it, and so they *m.* *Ps* 48:5
when Jesus heard it, he *m. Mat* 8:10
the men *m.* 27
m. and glorified God. 9:8*, 33
disciples saw it, they *m.* 21:20

they *m.*, and left him. *Mat* 22:22
Mark 12:17; *Luke* 20:26
that the governor *m.* *Mat* 27:14
Mark 15:5, 44
m. because of their unbelief.
Mark 6:6
people *m.* that he tarried. *Luke* 1:21
his name is John, and they *m.* 63
Joseph and his mother *m.* at. 2:33
Jesus heard these things he *m.* 7:9
Pharisee saw it, he *m.* 11:38
disciples *m.* he talked. *John* 4:27
Jews *m.*, How knoweth this ? 7:15
m. saying, Are not these ? *Acts* 2:7
they *m.* and took knowledge. 4:13

marvellous

who doeth *m.* things. *Job* 5:9
thou shewest thyself *m.* upon. 10:16
thy *m.* lovingkindness. *Ps* 17:7
he hath shewed me his *m.* 31:21
m. things did he in the sight. 78:12
for he hath done *m.* things. 98:1
Lord's doing; it is *m.* in our eyes.
118:23; *Mat* 21:42; *Mark* 12:11
shall speak *m.* things. *Dan* 11:36
will I shew unto him *m.* *Mi* 7:15
if it be *m.* should it be *m.*? *Zech* 8:6
herein is a *m.* thing. *John* 9:30
darkness into his *m.* light. *1 Pet* 2:9
heaven, great and *m.* *Rev* 15:1

marvellous *work*

proceed to do a *m. work.* *Isa* 29:14

marvellous *works*

remember his *m. works.*
1 Chr 16:12; *Ps* 105:5
declare his *m. works.* *1 Chr* 16:24
forth all thy *m. works.* *Ps* 9:1
great and *m.* are thy *works.* 139:14
Rev 15:3

marvellously

he was *m.* helped till. *2 Chr* 26:15
God thundereth *m.* with. *Job* 37:5
regard, and wonder *m.* *Hab* 1:5

marvels

I will do *m.* such as have. *Ex* 34:10

Mary

Joseph the husband of *M.* *Mat* 1:16
his mother *M.* was espoused. 18
take unto thee *M.* thy wife. 20
saw the young child with *M.* 2:11
mother called *M.*? 13:55; *Mark* 6:3
M. the mother of James. *Mat* 27:56
Mark 15:40, 47; 16:1
virgin's name was *M.* *Luke* 1:27
fear not, *M.* 30
heard the salutation of *M.* 41
M. abode three months. 56
went to be taxed with *M.* his. 2:5
shepherds found *M.* and the. 16
but *M.* kept all these things in. 19
had a sister called *M.* 10:39
M. hath chosen that good part. 42
the town of *M.* *John* 11:1
M. that anointed the Lord. 2
but *M.* sat still. 20
she called *M.* her sister secretly. 28
M. took a pound of ointment. 12:3
M. the wife of Cleophas. 19:25
M. stood without at the. 20:11
Jesus saith to her, *M.* She turned. 16
in prayer with *M.* *Acts* 1:14
Peter came to house of *M.* 12:12
greet *M.* who bestowed. *Rom* 16:6

Mary *Magdalene*

women were there, among whom was *M. Magdalene.* *Mat* 27:56
Mark 15:40; *John* 19:25
M. Magdalene sitting. *Mat* 27:61
came *M. Magdalene* to see the sepulchre. 28:1; *John* 20:1
M. Magdalene and Mary the.
Mark 16:1; *Luke* 24:10
he appeared first to *M. Magdalene.*
Mark 16:9
M. Magdalene told the. *John* 20:18

masons

Hiram sent to David *m.* *2 Sam* 5:11
1 Chr 14:1
gave money to *m.* and hewers of.
2 Ki 12:12; 22:6; *Ezra* 3:7
he set *m.* to hew. *1 Chr* 22:2
they hired *m.* to repair. *2 Chr* 24:12

Massah

name of the place *M.* *Ex* 17:7
shall not tempt the Lord, as ye tempted him in *M.* *Deut* 6:16; 9:22
whom thou didst prove at *M.* 33:8

mast, -s

lieth on the top of a *m.* *Pr* 23:34
not strengthen their *m.* *Isa* 33:23
Lebanon to make *m.* *Ezek* 27:5

master

Joseph's *m.* put him in. *Gen* 39:20
if she please not her *m.* *Ex* 21:8
give to their *m.* thirty shekels. 32
m. of the house shall be. 22:8
and spake to the *m.* of. *Judg* 19:22
the *m.* of the house went out. 23
David sent messengers to salute our *m.* *1 Sam* 25:14
determined against our *m.* 17
have not kept your *m.* 26:16*
m. Saul is dead. *2 Sam* 2:7*
these have no *m.* *1 Ki* 22:17
2 Chr 18:16
he cried, Alas, *m.* for it *2 Ki* 6:5
drink, and go to their *m.* 22
and they went to their *m.* 23
seeing your *m.'s* sons are with. 10:2
look out the best of your *m.'s* sons. 3
take the heads of your *m.'s* sons. 6
ye say to your *m.* 19:6; *Isa* 37:6
and Chenaniah, *m.* of. *1 Chr* 15:27
servant, so with his *m.* *Isa* 24:2
king spake to the *m.* *Dan* 1:3
m. of the magicians. 4:9; 5:11
and if I be a *m.* where is ? *Mal* 1:6
the Lord will cut off the *m.* 2:12*
m. I will follow thee. *Mat* 8:19
eateth your *m.* with publicans ? 9:11
they have called the *m.* 10:25
m. we would see a sign from. 12:38
fall from their *m.'s* table. 15:27
they said, Doth not your *m.*? 17:24
m. we know that thou art true.
22:16; *Mark* 12:14
one is your *m.* even. *Mat* 23:8*, 10
the *m.* saith, My time is at. 26:18
M. is it I ? 25*
Hail, *m.* and kissed him. 49*
Mark 14:45*
why troublest thou the *m.* any more ?
Mark 5:35
m. it is good for us to be here. 9:5*
Luke 9:33
m. what shall I do ? *Mark* 10:17
Luke 10:25
for ye know not when the *m.*
Mark 13:35
the publicans said, *M.*? *Luke* 3:12
m. say on. 7:40
saying, *M.* we perish. 8:24
is dead; trouble not the *m.* 49
when once *m.* of the house. 13:25
thou a *m.* in Israel ? *John* 3:10*
the *m.* is come and calleth. 11:28
ye call me *M.* and ye say. 13:13
if I then your *m.* have washed. 14
believed the *m.* of ship. *Acts* 27:11
knowing your *m.* is in heaven.
Eph 6:9; *Col* 4:1
meet for the *m.'s* use. *2 Tim* 2:21

his **master**

under the thigh of *his m.* *Gen* 24:9
of *his m.*, for goods of *his m.* 10
Joseph was in house of *his m.* 39:2
when *his m.* heard the words. 19
if *his m.* have given him. *Ex* 21:4
his m. shall bore his ear through. 6
to *his m.* the servant which is escaped from *his m.* *Deut* 23:15
servant said to *his m.* *Judg* 19:11
the arrows and came to *his m.*
1 Sam 20:38
servants break away every one from *his m.* 25:10
reconcile himself to *his m.* 29:4*
a great man with *his m.* *2 Ki* 5:1
went in, and stood before *his m.* 25
not the sound of *his m.'s* feet ? 6:32
departed and came to *his m.* 8:14
Zimri peace, who slew *his m.*? 9:31
his m. hath sent to reproach God.
19:4; *Isa* 37:4

will fall to *his m.* Saul. *1 Chr* 12:19
servant is free from *his m.* *Job* 3:19
that waiteth on *his m.* *Pr* 27:18
accuse not a servant to *his m.* 30:10
ass knoweth *his m.'s* crib. *Isa* 1:3
servant honoureth *his m.* *Mal* 1:6
the disciple is not above *his m.*
Mat 10:24; *Luke* 6:40
disciple be as *his m.* *Mat* 10:25
perfect shall be as *his m.* *Luke* 6:40
his own *m.* he standeth. *Rom* 14:4*

my **master**

my m. Abraham shew kindness to *my m.* *Gen* 24:12, 27, 42, 48
shewed kindness to *my m.* 24:14
the Lord hath blessed *my m.* 35
Lord hath appointed for *my m.* 44
deal truly and kindly with *my m.* 49
send me away to *my m.* 54, 56
servant had said, It is *my m.* 65
my m. wotteth not what. 39:8
shall say, I love *my m.* *Ex* 21:5
should do this to *my m.* *1 Sam* 24:6*
my m. left me because I fell. 30:13
me into the hands of *my m.* 15
my m. goeth into house of. *2 Ki* 5:18
my m. hath spared Naaman. 20
my m. hath sent me, saying. 22
and he said, Alas, *my m.*, how ? 6:15
I conspired against *my m.* 10:9
turn away one captain of the least of *my m.'s* servants. 18:24; *Isa* 36:9
hath *my m.* sent me to thy master ?
2 Ki 18:27; *Isa* 36:12
I pray thee, to *my m.* *Isa* 36:8

thy **master**

be *thy m.'s* son's wife. *Gen* 24:51
rise up early with *thy m.'s* servants.
1 Sam 29:10
I give *thy m.'s* son all. *2 Sam* 9:9
thy m.'s house, *thy m.'s* wives. 12:8
where is *thy m.'s* son ? 16:3
away *thy m.* to-day. *2 Ki* 2:3, 5
we pray thee, and seek *thy m.* 16
the house of Ahab *thy m.* 9:7
master sent me to *thy m.* and. 18:27

masterbuilder

as wise *m.* I have laid. *1 Cor* 3:10

masteries

if a man also strive for *m.*, yet is he not crowned. *2 Tim* 2:5

masters

children shall be her *m.* *Ex* 21:4
eyes of servants look to their *m.*
Ps 123:2
refresheth soul of his *m.* *Pr* 25:13
as nails fastened by *m.* of. *Eccl* 12:11
them to say to their *m.* *Jer* 27:4
their *m.*, Let us drink. *Amos* 4:1*
who fill their *m.'s* houses. *Zeph* 1:9
no man can serve two *m.* *Mat* 6:24
Luke 16:13
neither be ye called *m.* *Mat* 23:10
her *m.* much gain. *Acts* 16:16
her *m.* saw the hope of their gains. 19
to them that are your *m.* *Eph* 6:5
Col 3:22; *Tit* 2:9; *1 Pet* 2:18
ye *m.* do the same things to them.
Eph 6:9; *Col* 4:1
count their *m.* worthy. *1 Tim* 6:1
believing *m.*, let them not despise. 2
be not many *m.* knowing. *Jas* 3:1*

mastery

them that shout for *m.* *Ex* 32:18
the lions had the *m.* of. *Dan* 6:24
that striveth for the *m.* *1 Cor* 9:25*

mate

every one with her *m.* *Isa* 34:15
fail, none shall want her *m.* 16

matrix

set apart unto the Lord all that openeth the *m.* *Ex* 13:12, 15
all that openeth the *m.* is. 34:19
firstborn that open the *m.* *Num* 3:12
every thing that openeth *m.* 18:15

Mattan

slew *M.* priest of Baal. *2 Ki* 11:18
2 Chr 23:17

Mattathias

which was the son of *M.* *Luke* 3:25

matter
him concerning that *m.* *Gen* 24:9
small *m.* that thou hast taken. 30:15
when they have a *m.* they. *Ex* 18:16
every great *m.* they shall bring to thee, but every small *m.* they. 22
but every small *m.* they judged. 26
keep thee far from a false *m.* 23:7
that died about the *m.* of Korah. *Num* 16:49
you in *m.* of Peor, in *m.* 25:18
trespass in the *m.* of Peor. 31:16
arise a *m.* too hard. *Deut* 17:8
mouth of three witnesses *m.* 19:15
how the *m.* will fall out. *Ruth* 3:18
m. of the kingdom he. *1 Sam* 10:16
touching the *m.* thou and I. 20:23
and David knew the *m.* 39
how went the *m.*? I pray. *2 Sam* 1:4
no *m.* hid from the king. 18:13
they ended the *m.* 20:18
the *m.* is not so. 21
at all times as the *m.* *1 Ki* 8:59*
save in the *m.* of Uriah the. 15:5
for every *m.* pertaining. *1 Chr* 26:32
served the king in any *m.* 27:1
from command in any *m.* *2 Chr* 8:15
see ye hasten the *m.* 24:5
to cease, till the *m.* *Ezra* 5:5
sat down to examine the *m.* 10:16
have *m.* for evil report. *Neh* 6:13
inquisition was made of the *m.* *Esth* 2:23
seeing the root of the *m.* *Job* 19:28
answer, for I am full of *m.* 32:18*
heart is inditing a good *m.* *Ps* 45:1
themselves in an evil *m.* 64:5*
spirit concealeth the *m.* *Pr* 11:13
that handleth a *m.* wisely. 16:20*
that repeateth a *m.* separateth. 17:9
that answereth a *m.* before. 18:13*
kings is to search out a *m.* 25:2
marvel not at the *m.* *Eccl* 5:8
wings shall tell the *m.* 10:20
the conclusion of the *m.* 12:13
the *m.* was not perceived. *Jer* 38:27
inkhorn, reported the *m.* *Ezek* 9:11
whoredoms a small *m.*? 16:20
can shew the king's *m.* *Dan* 2:10
known to us the king's *m.* 23
end of the *m.*: I kept the *m.* 7:28
understand the *m.* and. 9:23
to blaze abroad the *m.* *Mark* 1:45
him again of the same *m.* 10:10
Peter rehearsed the *m.* *Acts* 11:4
came to consider of this *m.* 15:6
Gallio said, If it were a *m.* of. 18:14
if Demetrius have a *m.* 19:38
the uttermost of your *m.* 24:22
any of you having a *m.*? *1 Cor* 6:1
might be ready as a *m.* *2 Cor* 9:5
it were, it maketh no *m.* *Gal* 2:6
defraud brother in any *m.* *1 Thes* 4:6
great a *m.* a little fire! *Jas* 3:5*

this **matter**
speak no more to me of *this m.* *Deut* 3:26
his neighbour, so is *this m.* 22:26
who will hearken to you in *this m.*? *1 Sam* 30:24
ye angry for *this m.*? *2 Sam* 19:42
answer concerning *this m.* *Ezra* 5:5
pleasure to us concerning *this m.* 17
arise, for *this m.* belongeth. 10:4
sat trembling because of *this m.* 9
were employed about *this m.* 15
seen concerning *this m.* *Esth* 9:26
Melzar consented to them in *this m.* *Dan* 1:14
to answer thee in *this m.* 3:16
this m. is by the decree of. 4:17*
part nor lot in *this m.* *Acts* 8:21
hear thee again of *this m.* 17:32
approved yourselves clear in *this m.* *2 Cor* 7:11

matters
if any have *m.* let him. *Ex* 24:14*
if arise *m.* of controversy. *Deut* 17:8
son of Jesse that is prudent in *m.* *1 Sam* 16:18*
end of telling the *m.* *2 Sam* 11:19
Absalom said, See thy *m.* are. 15:3
thou any more of thy *m.*? 19:29
you in *m.* of the Lord, and Zebadiah for all the king's *m.* *2 Chr* 19:11
Pethahiah in all *m.* concerning. *Neh* 11:24
whether Mordecai's *m.* *Esth* 3:4
the *m.* of the fastings. 9:31, 32
not account of his *m.* *Job* 33:13
thus devise deceitful *m.* *Ps* 35:20*
exercise myself in great *m.* 131:1
in *m.* of wisdom he found. *Dan* 1:20
and told the sum of the *m.* 7:1
omitted the weightier *m.* *Mat* 23:23
be no judge of such *m.* *Acts* 18:15
any thing concerning other *m.* 19:39
there be judged of these *m.* 25:20
judge the smallest *m.*? *1 Cor* 6:2
a busybody in other men's *m.* *1 Pet* 4:15

Matthew
a man named *M.* and saith. *Mat* 9:9
Philip, Thomas, and *M.* the. 10:3
Mark 3:18; *Luke* 6:15; *Acts* 1:13

Matthias
called Barsabas, and *M.* *Acts* 1:23
the lot fell on *M.* and he was. 26

mattock
sharpen every man his axe and *m.* *1 Sam* 13:20
be digged with the *m.* *Isa* 7:25

mattocks
had a file for the *m.* *1 Sam* 13:21
Josiah with their *m.* *2 Chr* 34:6*

maul
false witness, is a *m.* *Pr* 25:18

maw
two cheeks and the *m.* *Deut* 18:3

may
seeing I go whither I *m.* return thou. *2 Sam* 15:20
she said, If I *m.* but touch. *Mat* 9:21
if this cup *m.* not pass away. 26:42
as I *m.* so say, Levi also. *Heb* 7:9

may *be*
that it *m. be* well with. *Gen* 12:13
it *m. be* that I may obtain. 16:2
that the Lord's law *m. be.* *Ex* 13:9
that his fear *m. be* before. 20:20
of all meat which *m. be.* *Lev* 11:34
for his sister a virgin he *m. be.* 21:3
that it *m. be* an holy. 23:21
m. be for a memorial. *Num* 10:10
the possession *m. be* ours. 32:32
m. be well with you. *Deut* 5:33; 6:3
18; 22:7; *Ruth* 3:1; *Jer* 7:23
m. be to thee a God. *Deut* 29:13
m. be there for a witness. 31:26
it *m. be* a witness between us. *Josh* 22:27
it *m. be* the Lord will. *1 Sam* 14:6
m. be a snare, Philistines *m. be.* 18:21
it *m. be* that the king. *2 Sam* 14:15
it *m. be* Lord will look on. 16:12
m. be Lord thy God will hear. *2 Ki* 19:4; *Isa* 37:4
m. be before thee for. *1 Chr* 17:27
that ye *m. be* strong. *Ezra* 9:12
it *m. be* that my sons have sinned. *Job* 1:5
consume them, that they *m.* not *be.* *Ps* 59:13
that Israel *m. be* no more. 83:4
our sons *m. be* as plants. 144:12
that our garners *m. be* full. 13
that our oxen *m. be* strong. 14
that thy trust *m. be* in. *Pr* 22:19
whereof it *m. be* said, See this is new. *Eccl* 1:10
that it *m. be* for the time. *Isa* 30:8
the Lord waiteth that he *m. be.* 18
that we *m. be* like. 46:5
I *m. be* glorified. 60:21
name *m. be* no more. *Jer* 11:19
it *m. be* the house of Judah. 36:3
it *m. be* they will present their. 7
that it *m. be* well with us. 42:6
take balm, if so *be* she *m.* 51:8
put his mouth in the dust; if so be there *m. be* hope. *Lam* 3:29
it *m. be* they will consider. *Ezek* 12:3
that they *m. be* my people. 14:11
it *m. be* a lengthening. *Dan* 4:27
that they *m. be* cut off. *Hos* 8:4
it *m. be* the Lord will. *Amos* 5:15
it *m. be* ye shall be hid. *Zeph* 2:3
that ye *m. be* children of. *Mat* 5:45
that thine alms *m. be* in secret. 6:4
it *m. be* they will reverence him. *Luke* 20:13
the inheritance *m. be* ours. 14
ye *m. be* the children. *John* 12:36
there ye *m. be* also. 14:3
that they *m. be* one. 17:11, 21, 22
that the love *m. be* in them. 26
that he *m. be* wise. *1 Cor* 3:18
that ye *m. be* a new lump. 5:7
that she *m. be* holy in body. 7:34
are, it *m. be,* so many kinds. 14:10
be subject, that God *m. be.* 15:28
m. be that I will winter. 16:6
see that he *m. be* with you. 10
power *m. be* of God. *2 Cor* 4:7
so there *m. be* a performance. 8:11
your abundance *m. be* a supply. 14
as I said, ye *m. be* ready. 9:3
that it *m. be* well with thee. *Eph* 6:3
that ye *m. be* blameless. *Phil* 2:15
that I *m. be* of good comfort. 19
I *m. be* the less sorrowful. 28
charge that they *m. be.* *1 Tim* 5:7
man of God *m. be.* *2 Tim* 3:17
that they *m. be* found in. *Tit* 1:13
that ye *m. be* perfect. *Jas* 1:4

mayest
with all thy heart thou *m.* *Acts* 8:37

mayest *be*
thou *m. be* a multitude. *Gen* 28:3
m. be to us instead of. *Num* 10:31
m. be an holy people. *Deut* 26:19
thou *m. be* their king. *Neh* 6:6
that thou *m. be* justified. *Job* 40:8
that thou *m. be* feared. *Ps* 130:4
sing songs, that thou *m. be.* *Isa* 23:16
that thou *m. be* my salvation. 49:6
that thou *m. be* saved. *Jer* 4:14
that thou *m. be* bound up. 30:13
for thou *m. be* no longer. *Luke* 16:2

Mazzaroth
canst thou bring forth *M.*? *Job* 38:32

me
serpent beguiled *me.* *Gen* 3:13
put in ward both *me* and. 41:10
me restored, and him he hanged. 13
me have ye bereaved of. 42:36
there is none like *me* in. *Ex* 9:14
they have rejected *me.* *1 Sam* 8:7
when Joab sent *me* thy. *2 Sam* 18:29
me, even *me* thy servant. *1 Ki* 1:26
thyself to another than *me.* *Isa* 57:8
let not *me* be dismayed. *Jer* 17:18
me, and who will appoint *me*? 50:44
know no God but *me.* *Hos* 13:4
mother more than *me.* *Mat* 10:37
receiveth *me,* and he that receiveth *me.* 40; *Mark* 9:37; *John* 13:20
why callest thou *me* good? *Mat* 19:17; *Luke* 18:19
me ye have not always. *Mat* 26:11
Mark 14:7; *John* 12:8
he that despiseth *me,* despiseth him that sent *me.* *Luke* 10:16
would have believed *me.* *John* 5:46
world cannot hate you, but *me.* 7:7
ye neither know *me,* nor my. 8:19
though ye believe not *me.* 10:38
yet hast thou not known *me*? 14:9
hateth *me* hateth my Father. 15:23
hated both *me* and my Father. 24
known the Father nor *me.* 16:3
O Father, glorify thou *me.* 17:5
me? ask them who heard *me.* 18:21
if well, why smitest thou *me*? 23
he that delivered *me* to thee. 19:11
Simon, son of Jonas, lovest thou *me*? 21:15, 16, 17
Saul, why persecutest thou *me*? *Acts* 9:4; 22:7
what advantageth it *me*? *1 Cor* 15:32

about **me**
like the nations that are *about me.* *Deut* 17:14
children were *about me.* *Job* 29:5
came round *about me* daily. *Ps* 88:17
night shall be light *about me.* 139:11

not thy riding *for me.* *2 Ki* 4:24
the brasen altar be *for me* to. 16:15
enquire of the Lord *for me.* 22:13
2 Chr 34:21
was prepared *for me* daily. *Neh* 5:18
graves are ready *for me.* *Job* 17:1
thing appointed *for me.* 23:14
waited *for me* as for the rain. 29:23
things too wonderful *for me.* 42:3
art a shield *for me.* *Ps* 3:3
awake *for me.* 7:6
net they have laid privily *for me.*
31:4; 35:7; 119:110; 140:5
141:9; 142:3
as *for me.* 41:12; 55:16; 69:13
Isa 59:21; *Jer* 17:16; 26:14
40:10; *Ezek* 9:10; *Dan* 2:30
7:28; 10:17
this I know, God is *for me.* *Ps* 56:9
performeth all things *for me.* 57:2
hast been a shelter *for me.* 61:3
it was too painful *for me.* 73:16
rise up *for me,* who will stand up for *me* ? 94:16
but do thou *for me,* O God. 109:21
it is good *for me.* 119:71
the proud digged pits *for me.* 85
wicked have waited *for me* to. 95
things too high *for me.* 131:1
is too wonderful *for me.* 139:6
food convenient *for me.* *Pr* 30:8
things too wonderful *for me.* 18
undertake *for me.* *Isa* 38:14
set it in order *for me* ? 44:7
the place is too strait *for me.* 49:20
not be ashamed that wait *for me.* 23
the isles shall wait *for me.* 60:9
of them that asked not *for me.* 65:1
search *for me* with all. *Jer* 29:13
any thing too hard *for me* ? 32:27
they wrought *for me.* *Ezek* 29:20
thou shalt abide *for me.* *Hos* 3:3
better *for me* to die. *Jonah* 4:3, 8
execute judgement *for me.* *Mi* 7:9
bent Judah *for me.* *Zech* 9:13
and give *for me* and. *Mat* 17:27
weep not *for me,* but. *Luke* 23:28
pray ye to the Lord *for me.* *Acts* 8:24
intent ye have sent *for me.* 10:29
prayers to God *for me.* *Rom* 15:30
are lawful *for me.* *1 Cor* 6:12; 10:23
it were better *for me* to die. 9:15
and gave himself *for me.* *Gal* 2:20
for me, that utterance. *Eph* 6:19
laid up *for me* a crown. *2 Tim* 4:8

from me

I pray thee, *from me.* *Gen* 13:9
thine only son *from me.* 22:12
steal away *from me* ? 31:27
take thy daughters *from me.* 31
kept back any thing *from me.* 39:9
the one went out *from me.* 44:28
if ye take this also *from me.* 29
every man to go out *from me.* 45:1
get thee *from me,* see. *Ex* 10:28
tell me, hide it not *from me.*
Josh 7:19; *1 Sam* 3:17
strength will go *from me.* *Judg* 16:17
why should my father hide this thing *from me* ? *1 Sam* 20:2
said, Have out all men *from me.*
2 Sam 13:9
put this woman out *from me.* 17
far be it *from me.* 20:20
this thing is *from me.* *1 Ki* 12:24
went Spirit of Lord *from me.* 22:24
2 Chr 18:23
Lord hath hid it *from me.* *2 Ki* 4:27
offended, return *from me.* 18:14
I chased him *from me.* *Neh* 13:28
driven quite *from me* ? *Job* 6:13
his rod away *from me.* 9:34
thine hand far *from me.* 13:21
put my brethren far *from me.* 19:13
of the wicked is far *from me.* 21:16
mine integrity *from me.* 27:5
hide thy face *from me* ? *Ps* 13:1
away his statutes *from me.* 18:22
O Lord, be not far *from me.* 35:22
light of eyes, gone *from me.* 38:10
thy stroke away *from me.* 39:10
tender mercies *from me.* 40:11
take not Holy Spirit *from me.* 51:11
turned his mercy *from me.* *Ps* 66:20
hidest thou thy face *from me* ? 88:14
hide not thy face *from me* in trouble.
102:2; 143:7
commandments *from me.* 119:19
away my vail *from me.* *S of S* 5:7
turn away thine eyes *from me.* 6:5
look away *from me,* I will. *Isa* 22:4
age is removed *from me.* 38:12
a law shall proceed *from me.* 51:4
anger shall turn *from me.* *Jer* 2:35
shalt not turn away *from me.* 3:19
of thy measures *from me.* 13:25
hide nothing *from me.* 38:14
from me shall spoilers come. 51:53
warning *from me.* *Ezek* 3:17; 33:7
are all estranged *from me.* 14:5
separateth himself *from me.* 7
go no more astray *from me.* 11
went astray *from me* after. 44:10
Israel went astray *from me.* 15
thing is gone *from me.* *Dan* 2:5, 8
Israel is not hid *from me.* *Hos* 5:3
for they have fled *from me.* 7:13
bent to backsliding *from me.* 11:7
like a fir tree, *from me* is thy. 14:8
take away *from me* the noise of.
Amos 5:23
let this cup pass *from me.* *Mat* 26:39
Mark 14:36; *Luke* 22:22
not pass away *from me.* *Mat* 26:42
my lord taketh *from me.* *Luke* 16:3
man taketh it *from me.* *John* 10:18
all in Asia be turned away *from me.*
2 Tim 1:15

see **depart, departed**

in me

it is not *in me.* *Gen* 41:16
if there be iniquity *in me.*
1 Sam 20:8; *2 Sam* 14:32
life is yet whole *in me.* *2 Sam* 1:9
because he delighted *in me.* 22:20
Ps 18:19
is not my help *in me* ? *Job* 6:13
the matter is found *in me.* 19:28
would put strength *in me.* 23:6
my breath is *in me.* 27:3
saith, It is not *in me.* 28:14
nor is there iniquity *in me.* 33:9
to mine integrity *in me.* *Ps* 7:8
arrows stick fast *in me.* 38:2
I pour out my soul *in me.* 42:4
why art thou disquieted *in me* ? 5
be any wicked way *in me.* 139:24
fury is not *in me,* who. *Isa* 27:4
trust *in me* shall possess. 57:13
have fathers found *in me* ? *Jer* 2:5
hast put thy trust *in me.* 39:18
thy widows trust *in me.* 49:11
soul is humbled *in me.* *Lam* 3:20
innocency found *in me.* *Dan* 6:22
no strength *in me.* 10:8, 17
find none iniquity *in me.* *Hos* 12:8
thyself, but *in me* is thy help. 13:17
shall not be offended *in me.*
Mat 11:6; *Luke* 7:23
little ones which believe *in me.*
Mat 18:6; *Mark* 9:42
be accomplished *in me.* *Luke* 22:37
he dwelleth *in me,* and I. *John* 6:56
he that believeth *in me.* 11:25, 26
believe also *in me.* 14:1
Father that dwelleth *in me.* 10
ye *in me,* and I in you. 20
prince hath nothing *in me.* 30
every branch *in me.* 15:2
abide *in me.* 4
he that abideth *in me.* 5
if a man abide not *in me* he is. 6
if ye abide *in me.* 7
in me ye might have peace. 16:33
as thou, Father, art *in me.* 17:21
I in them, and thou *in me,* that. 23
any evil doing *in me.* *Acts* 24:20
by faith that is *in me.* 26:18
no cause of death *in me.* 28:18
as *in me* is, I am ready. *Rom* 1:15
wrought *in me* all manner of. 7:8
sin working death *in me* by. 13
but sin that dwelleth *in me.* 17, 20
that *in me* dwelleth no good thing. 18
truth of Christ is *in me.* *2 Cor* 11:10
proof of Christ speaking *in me.* 13:3
to reveal his Son *in me.* *Gal* 1:16
and they glorified God *in me.* 24
was mighty *in me* towards. 2:8
but Christ liveth *in me.* 20
conflict which ye saw *in me,* and now hear to be *in me.* *Phil* 1:30
heard and seen *in me,* do. 4:9
which worketh *in me.* *Col* 1:29
that *in me* Christ Jesus. *1 Tim* 1:16

of me

of me, He is my brother. *Gen* 20:13
he will accept *of me.* 32:20
men say not *of me,* A woman slew.
Judg 9:54
take knowledge *of me.* *Ruth* 2:10
Saul shall despair *of me.* *1 Sam* 27:1
then dost thou ask *of me* ? 28:16
this thing is done *of me.* *2 Chr* 11:4
not spoken *of me* the thing. *Job* 42:7
ask *of me,* and I shall give. *Ps* 2:8
in thy book it is written *of me.* 40:7
Heb 10:7
enemies speak evil *of me.* *Ps* 41:5
triumph thou because *of me.* 60:8
and Israel would none *of me.* 81:11
not take counsel *of me.* *Isa* 30:1
thou make an end *of me.* 38:12, 13
weary *of me,* O Israel. 43:22
not be forgotten *of me.* 44:21
and their righteousness *of me.* 54:17
they ask *of me* the ordinances. 58:2
are gone forth *of me.* *Jer* 10:20
sent you to enquire *of me.* 37:7
come to enquire *of me* ? *Ezek* 20:3
say *of me,* Doth he not speak ? 49
more than me, is not worthy *of me.*
Mat 10:37, 38
and learn *of me,* for I am. 11:29
ye shall be offended because *of me* this night. 26:31; *Mark* 14:27
whoso shall be ashamed *of me.*
Mark 8:38; *Luke* 9:26
lightly speak evil *of me.* *Mark* 9:39
virtue is gone out *of me.* *Luke* 8:46
do in remembrance *of me.* 22:19
Jew, askest drink *of me* ? *John* 4:9
beareth witness *of me.* 5:32, 37
they which testify *of me.* 39
for Moses wrote *of me.* 46
this voice came not because *of me.*
12:30
he shall testify *of me.* 15:26
did others tell it thee *of me* ? 18:34
promise ye have heard *of me.*
Acts 1:4
as thou hast testified *of me.* 23:11
be ye followers *of me.* *1 Cor* 4:16
11:1; *Phil* 3:17
this do in remembrance *of me.*
1 Cor 11:24, 25
he was seen *of me* also. 15:8
the salutation *of me* Paul. 16:21
Col 4:18
think *of me* above that which he . . . or heareth *of me.* *2 Cor* 12:6
which is preached *of me.* *Gal* 1:11
care *of me* hath flourished. *Phil* 4:10
the testimony *of me* his. *2 Tim* 1:8
which thou hast heard *of me.* 13
thou hast heard *of me,* commit. 2:2
had compassion *of me.* *Heb* 10:34

on me, or *upon* me

I have taken *upon me.* *Gen* 18:27, 31
thou hast brought *on me.* 20:9
I shall bring a curse *upon me.* 27:12
upon me be thy curse, my son. 13
custom of women is *upon me.* 31:35
think *on me* when it shall be. 40:14
ye will not fall *upon me.* *Judg* 15:12
all thy wants lie *upon me.* 19:20
come down *upon me.* *1 Sam* 13:12
upon me, my lord, *upon me.* 25:24
the iniquity be *on me.* *2 Sam* 14:9
set their faces *on me.* *1 Ki* 2:15
I pray thee, be *on me.* *1 Chr* 21:17
writing by his hand *upon me.* 28:19
hand of the Lord *upon me.*
Ezra 7:28; *Neh* 2:8, 18
think *upon me,* my God. *Neh* 5:19
feared is come *upon me.* *Job* 3:25
fear came *upon me.* 4:14
be content, look *upon me.* 6:28

thine eyes are *upon me.* *Job* 7:8
thyself marvellous *upon me.* 10:16
runneth *upon me* like a giant. 16:14
have pity *upon me,* O ye. 19:21
have mercy *upon me.* *Ps* 4:1; 6:2
9:13; 25:16; 27:7; 30:10; 31:9
51:1; 86:16
look and stare *upon me.* 22:17
thy hand was heavy *upon me.* 32:4
the Lord thinketh *upon me.* 40:17
they cast iniquity *upon me.* 55:3
thy vows are *upon me.* 56:12
hath set his love *upon me.* 91:14
he shall call *upon me.* 15
look thou *upon me.* 119:132
laid thine hand *upon me.* 139:5
look not *upon me,* sun hath looked *upon me.* *S of S* 1:6
hast not called *upon me.* *Isa* 43:22
the isles shall wait *upon me.* 51:5
Spirit of the Lord God is *upon me.* 61:1; *Luke* 4:18
these things *upon me*? *Jer* 13:22
cast a stone *upon me.* *Lam* 3:53
Lord was strong *upon me.* *Ezek* 3:14
the hand of the Lord was there *upon me.* 22; 33:22; 37:1; 40:1
hand fell there *upon me.* 8:1
Spirit of the Lord fell *upon me.* 11:5
therefore wait ye *upon me.* *Zeph* 3:8
then cried he *upon me.* *Zech* 6:8
flock that waited *upon me.* 11:11
they shall look *upon me* whom they pierced. 12:10
have mercy *upon me.* *Mat* 15:22
Mark 10:47, 48; *Luke* 18:38, 39
wrought a good work *upon me.* *Mat* 26:10; *Mark* 14:6
days wherein he looked *on me.* *Luke* 1:25
that believeth *on me.* *John* 6:35
47; 7:38; 12:44, 46; 14:12
they believe not *on me.* 16:9
who shall believe *on me.* 17:20
things come *upon me.* *Acts* 8:24
reproaches of them that reproached thee fell *on me.* *Rom* 15:3
necessity is laid *upon me.* *1 Cor* 9:16
cometh *upon me* daily. *2 Cor* 11:28
of Christ may rest *upon me.* 12:9
God had mercy *on me.* *Phil* 2:27
right hand *upon me.* *Rev* 1:17
see **call**

over **me**

to Pharaoh, Glory *over me.* *Ex* 8:9
will set a king *over me.* *Deut* 17:14
settest a watch *over me.* *Job* 7:12
enemy be exalted *over me.* *Ps* 13:2
let them not have dominion *over me.* 19:13; 119:133
enemies triumph *over me.* 25:2
doth not triumph *over me.* 41:11
billows are gone *over me.* 42:7
banner *over me* was love. *S of S* 2:4
waves passed *over me.* *Jonah* 2:3

to or *unto* **me**

blood crieth *unto me.* *Gen* 4:10
to me thou hast given no seed. 15:3
said he not *unto me*? 20:5
swear *unto me* by God. 21:23
spake the man *unto me.* 24:30
wherefore come ye *to me*? 26:27
Lord hath brought it *to me.* 27:20
thou hast done *unto me*? 29:25
hath given them *to me.* 31:9
unto me, Return to thy country. 32:9
what ye shall say *unto me.* 34:11, 12
shew kindness *unto me.* 40:14
brethren are come *unto me.* 46:31
the cry of the children of Israel is come *unto me.* *Ex* 3:9
bloody husband art thou *to me.* 4:25
feast *unto me* in the wilderness. 5:1
take you *to me* for a people. 6:7
have not hearkened *unto me.* 12
sanctify *unto me* all firstborn. 13:2
criest thou *unto me*? 14:15
matter, they come *unto me.* 18:16
peculiar treasure *unto me.* 19:5
ye shall be *unto me* a kingdom. 6
they cry at all *unto me.* 22:23, 27
sons shalt thou give *unto me.* 29
shall be holy men *unto me.* *Ex* 22:31
that he may minister *unto me.* 28:1
3; 29:1; 30:30; 40:13; *Jer* 33:22
Ezek 43:19
let him come *unto me.* *Ex* 32:26
thou sayest *unto me.* 33:12
present thyself there *to me.* 34:2
for *unto me* Israel are. *Lev* 25:55
raise up a prophet like *unto me*
Deut 18:15; *Acts* 3:22; 7:37
to me belongeth vengeance and recompence. *Deut* 32:35
are ye come *unto me*? *Judg* 11:7
as they did *unto me,* so have. 15:11
and be *unto me* a father. 17:10
Lord do so *to me,* and. *Ruth* 1:17
2 Sam 3:35; 19:13; *1 Ki* 2:23
cry is come *unto me.* *1 Sam* 9:16
anoint *unto me* him whom. 16:3
and *to me* they ascribed but. 18:8
very pleasant hast thou been *unto me.* *2 Sam* 1:26
he shall not return *to me.* 12:23
man might come *unto me.* 15:4
what Joab did *to me.* *1 Ki* 2:5
so let the gods do *to me* and more. 19:2; 20:10
Lord saith *unto me* that will. 22:14
send *unto me* to recover a man of his leprosy. *2 Ki* 5:7
let him come now *to me.* 8
God do so *to me.* 6:31
thus and thus spake he *to me.* 9:12
and come *to me* to Jezreel. 10:6
tell the man that sent you *to me.* 22:15; *2 Chr* 34:23
ark of God home *to me*? *1 Chr* 13:12
prophesy good *unto me.* *2 Chr* 18:17
extended mercy *unto me.* *Ezra* 7:28
then were assembled *unto me.* 9:4
but if ye turn *unto me.* *Neh* 1:9
afraid of is come *unto me.* *Job* 3:25
nights are appointed *to me.* 7:3
do not two things *unto me.* 13:20
unto me men gave ear. 29:21
declare *unto me.* 40:7; 42:4
lines are fallen *unto me.* *Ps* 16:6
incline thine ear *unto me.* 17:6; 31:2; 102:2
turn thee *unto me.* 25:16
merciful *unto me.* 26:11; 41:4, 10
56:1; 57:1; 86:3; 119:58, 132
be not silent *to me.* 28:1
he inclined *unto me.* 40:1; 77:1
what flesh can do *unto me.* 56:4
what man can do *unto me.* 11; 118:6
wilt hearken *unto me.* 81:8
he shall cry *unto me,* Thou. 89:26
wilt thou come *unto me*? 101:2
when they said *unto me,* Let. 122:1
are thy thoughts *unto me*! 139:17
thee, make haste *unto me.* 141:1
whoso hearkeneth *unto me* shall dwell safely. *Pr* 1:33
will do so to him as he hath done *to me.* 24:29
as to the fool, so it happeneth even *to me.* *Eccl* 2:15
bundle of myrrh is my beloved *unto me.* *S of S* 1:13, 14
abomination *unto me.* *Isa* 1:13
they are a trouble *unto me.* 14
he calleth *to me* out of Seir. 21:11
shall be *unto me* as Ariel. 29:2
unto me, for I have redeemed. 44:22
look *unto me,* and be saved. 45:22
unto me every knee shall bow. 23
let him come near *to me.* 50:8
as the waters of Noah *unto me.* 54:9
come not near *to me,* I am. 65:5
return, O Israel, *unto me.* *Jer* 4:1
though they shall cry *unto me.* 11:11
mine heritage is *unto me.* 12:8, 9
that they might be *unto me.* 13:11
thy word was *unto me* the joy. 15:16
be altogether *unto me* as a liar? 18
them *unto me* as Sodom. 23:14
this city hath been *to me* a. 32:31
shall be *to me* a name of joy. 33:9
who shall come *unto me*? 49:4
the violence done *to me* be. 51:35
shall be like *unto me.* *Lam* 1:21
as thou hast done *unto me.* 22
thou hast borne *unto me.* *Ezek* 16:20
house of Israel is *to me.* *Ezek* 22:18
they have done *unto me.* 23:38
she is turned *unto me.* 26:2
office of a priest *unto me.* 44:13
to me to minister *unto me.* 15
is not revealed *to me.* *Dan* 2:30
my reason returned *unto me;* lords sought *unto me.* 4:36
betroth thee *unto me.* *Hos* 2:19, 20
and I will sow her *unto me* in. 23
I bought her *to me* for fifteen 3:2
thou shalt be no priest *to me.* 4:6
them that calleth *unto me.* 7:7
they have not cried *unto me* with. 14
Israel shall cry *unto me.* 8:2
as Ethiopians *unto me*? *Amos* 9:7
shall come forth *unto me.* *Mi* 5:2
shall be a light *unto me.* 7:8
see what he will say *unto me.* *Hab* 2:1
yet ye turned not *to me.* *Hag* 2:17
turn ye *unto me,* saith. *Zech* 1:3
at all fast *unto me,* even *to me*? 7:5
and comest thou *to me*? *Mat* 3:14
to me in that day, Lord. 7:22
come *unto me* all ye that. 11:28
bring them *to me.* 14:18; 17:17
21:2; *Mark* 9:19
forbid them not to come *unto me.* *Mat* 19:14; *Mark* 10:14
and ye came *unto me.* *Mat* 25:36
ye have done it *unto me.* 40
not to these, ye did it not *to me.* 45
all power is given *unto me.* 28:18
it be *unto me* according. *Luke* 1:38
for that is delivered *unto me.* 4:6
whoso cometh *to me.* 6:47; 14:26
all things are delivered *to me.* 10:22
God be merciful *to me* a. 18:13
come *to me* to have life. *John* 5:40
he that cometh *to me.* 6:35, 37
no man can come *to me.* 44, 65
of the Father cometh *unto me.* 45
let him come *unto me* and. 7:37
I will draw all men *unto me.* 12:32
the Father said *unto me.* 50
speakest thou not *unto me*? 19:10
be witnesses *unto me.* *Acts* 1:8
known *unto me* the ways of life. 2:28
he is a chosen vessel *unto me.* 9:15
vessel descend, and it came even *to me.* 11:5
a voice speaking *unto me.* 26:14
made death *unto me*? *Rom* 7:13
the grace given *unto me.* 12:23
1 Cor 3:10
things are lawful *unto me.* *1 Cor* 6:12
should be so done *unto me.* 9:15
woe is *unto me* if I preach not. 16
gospel is committed *unto me.* 17
be a barbarian *unto me.* 14:11
a great door and effectual is open *unto me.* 16:9; *2 Cor* 2:12
was lacking *to me.* *2 Cor* 11:9
maketh no matter *to me.* *Gal* 2:6
and have given them *to me.* 4:15
unto me who am less. *Eph* 3:8
for *to me* to live is Christ. *Phil* 1:21
to me indeed is not grievous. 3:1
but what things were gain *to me.* 7
been a comfort *unto me.* *Col* 4:11
not *to me* only. *2 Tim* 4:8
is profitable *to me.* 11
now profitable to thee and *to me.* *Philem* 11
especially *to me.* 16
thou owest *to me* thyself. 19
belongeth *unto me,* saith. *Heb* 10:30
what man shall do *unto me.* 13:6

toward **me**

countenance is not *toward me* as. *Gen* 31:5
thy mercy *toward me.* *Ps* 86:13
all his benefits *toward me.* 116:12
I am my Beloved's, his desire is *toward me.* *S of S* 7:10
fear *toward me* is taught. *Isa* 29:13
bowels and mercies *toward me.* 63:15
high God hath wrought *toward me.* *Dan* 4:2
fervent mind *toward me.* *2 Cor* 7:7
of service *toward me.* *Phil* 2:30

under **me**
enlarged my steps *under me*. *2 Sam* 22:37; *Ps* 18:36
thou hast subdued *under me*. *2 Sam* 22:40; *Ps* 18:39
bringeth down the people *under me*. *2 Sam* 22:48; *Ps* 18:47
was *under me* to pass. *Neh* 2:14
my people *under me*. *Ps* 144:2
having soldiers *under me*. *Mat* 8:9 *Luke* 7:8

with **me**
it may be well *with me*. *Gen* 12:13
if God will be *with me* and keep. 28:20; *Josh* 14:12
thy cattle was *with me*. *Gen* 30:29
God hath been *with me*. 31:5
discern thou what is thine *with me*. 32
and she said, Lie *with me*. 39:7 12, 14; *2 Sam* 13:11
send lad *with me*. *Gen* 43:8
lad be not *with me*. 44:34
why chide ye *with me*? *Ex* 17:2
not make *with me* gods of. 20:23
thy presence go not *with me*. 33:15
deal thus *with me*, kill. *Num* 11:15
laid up in store *with me*? *Deut* 32:34
and there is no God *with me*. 39
the people that are *with me*. *Josh* 8:5
if thou wilt go *with me*. *Judg* 4:8
I and all that are *with me*. 7:18
hast thou to do *with me*? 11:12
when thy heart is not *with me*. 16:15
behold, the silver is *with me*. 17:2
dwell *with me*. 10
as ye have dealt *with me*. *Ruth* 1:8
why will ye go *with me*? 11
eat *with me* to-day. *1 Sam* 9:19
if he be able to fight *with me*. 17:9
but *with me* thou shalt be in safeguard. 22:23
hast dealt well *with me*. 24:18
and thy sons be *with me*. 28:19
wentest not *with me*? *2 Sam* 19:25
feed thee *with me* in Jerusalem. 33
made *with me* an everlasting. 23:5
hand might be *with me*. *1 Chr* 4:10
even so deal *with me*. *2 Chr* 2:3
are *with me* in Judah. 7
God, who is *with me*. 35:21
but it is not so *with me*. *Job* 9:35
sea saith, It is not *with me*. 28:14
Almighty was yet *with me*. 29:5
that was at peace *with me*. *Ps* 7:4
thou art *with me*. 23:4
his song shall be *with me*. 42:8
made a covenant *with me*. 50:5
there were many *with me*. 55:18
they may dwell *with me*. 101:6
for they are ever *with me*. 119:98
honour are *with me*, yea. *Pr* 8:18
come *with me* from Lebanon. *S of S* 4:8
shall make peace *with me*. *Isa* 27:5
who will contend *with me*? 50:8
there was none *with me*. 63:3
the Lord is *with me*. *Jer* 20:11
do *with me* as seemeth good. 26:14
none holdeth *with me*. *Dan* 10:21
then it was better *with me*. *Hos* 2:7
have ye to do *with me*? *Joel* 3:4
walked *with me* in peace. *Mal* 2:6
he that is not *with me* is against me, he that gathereth not *with me*. *Mat* 12:30; *Luke* 11:23
Lord, have patience *with me*, and I will pay thee all. *Mat* 18:26, 29
not thou agree *with me* for? 20:13
and watch *with me*. 26:38, 40
my children are *with me* in bed. *Luke* 11:7
saying, Rejoice *with me*. 15:6, 9 *Phil* 2:18
thou art ever *with me*. *Luke* 15:31
hand ... is *with me* on the table. 22:21
have continued *with me*. 22:28
thou be *with me* in paradise. 23:43
that sent me is *with me*. *John* 8:29
thou hast no part *with me*. 13:8
he that eateth bread *with me*. 18
have been *with me* from the. 15:27
because the Father is *with me*. 16:32
that they also be *with me*. 17:24
that were *with me*. *Acts* 20:34
with me saw the light. 22:9, 11
evil is present *with me*. *Rom* 7:21
strive *with me* in your. 15:30
but *with me* it is a very. *1 Cor* 4:3
of God that was *with me*. 15:10
I go, they shall go *with me*. 16:4
that *with me* there should be yea. *2 Cor* 1:17
served *with me* in the. *Phil* 2:22
see how it will go *with me*. 23
women, who laboured *with me*. 4:3
no church communicated *with me*. 15
only Luke is *with me*. *2 Tim* 4:11
none stood *with me*. 16
the Lord stood *with me* and. 17
have retained *with me*. *Philem* 13
walk *with me* in white. *Rev* 3:4
sup with him, and he *with me*. 20
to sit *with me* in my throne. 21
and my reward is *with me*. 22:12

within **me**
arrows of the Almighty are *within me*. *Job* 6:4
reins be consumed *within me*. 19:27
spirit *within me* constraineth. 32:18
heart was hot *within me*. *Ps* 39:3
soul is cast down *within me*. 42:6
why disquieted *within me*? 11; 43:5
a right spirit *within me*. 51:10
of my thoughts *within me*. 94:19
all that is *within me* bless. 103:1
my spirit was overwhelmed *within me*. 142:3; 143:4
with my spirit *within me*. *Isa* 26:9
my heart *within me* is broken. *Jer* 23:9
my heart is turned *within me*. *Lam* 1:20; *Hos* 11:8
soul fainted *within me*. *Jonah* 2:7

without **me**
without me they shall. *Isa* 10:4
for *without me* ye can. *John* 15:5

meadow
and they fed in a *m*. *Gen* 41:2*

meadows
came even out of the *m*. *Judg* 20:33*

meal
an ephah of barley *m*. *Num* 5:15
bring *m*. and cast it into. *2 Ki* 4:41
were nigh brought *m*. *1 Chr* 12:40
millstones and grind *m*. *Isa* 47:2
the bud shall yield no *m*. *Hos* 8:7
see **barrel, measures**

mealtime
at *m*. come thou hither. *Ruth* 2:14

mean, *verb*
what *m*. these seven? *Gen* 21:9
what *m*. ye by this? *Ex* 12:26
thy son asketh what *m*.? *Deut* 6:20
ask, what *m*. ye by? *Josh* 4:6, 21
what *m*. ye that ye beat? *Isa* 3:15
what these things *m*.? *Ezek* 17:12
what *m*. ye, that ye use this proverb? 18:2
from the dead should *m*. *Mark* 9:10
this vision should *m*. *Acts* 10:17
know what these things *m*. 17:20
what *m*. ye to weep and? 21:13*
I *m*. not that other men. *2 Cor* 8:13

mean, *adjective*
stand before *m*. men. *Pr* 22:29
m. man boweth down. *Isa* 2:9
m. man shall be brought down. 5:15
sword not of a *m*. man shall. 31:8*
a citizen of no *m*. city. *Acts* 21:39

meanest
what *m*. thou by all this drove I met? *Gen* 33:8
what *m*. thou by these? *2 Sam* 16:2 *Ezek* 37:18
what *m*. thou, O sleeper? *Jonah* 1:6

meaneth
what *m*. the heat of? *Deut* 29:24
what *m*. the noise? *1 Sam* 4:6, 14
what *m*. then this bleating? 15:14
howbeit he *m*. not so. *Isa* 10:7
and learn what that *m*. *Mat* 9:13
had known what this *m*. 12:7
to another, What *m*. this? *Acts* 2:12

meaning
had sought for the *m*. *Dan* 8:15*
not the *m*. of the voice. *1 Cor* 14:11

meaning
we launched, *m*. to sail. *Acts* 27:2*

means
that will by no *m*. clear the guilty. *Ex* 34:7; *Num* 14:18
broken by the *m*. of the. *Judg* 5:22*
by what *m*. we may prevail. 16:5
but doth he devise *m*. *2 Sam* 14:14
by any *m*. he be missing. *1 Ki* 20:39
by this *m*. thou shalt have no portion. *Ezra* 4:16
by any *m*. redeem his. *Ps* 49:7
for by *m*. of a whorish. *Pr* 6:26*
bear rule by their *m*. *Jer* 5:31
this hath been by your *m*. *Mal* 1:9
by no *m*. come out thence. *Mat* 5:26
they sought *m*. to bring. *Luke* 5:18
nothing shall by any *m*. hurt. 10:19*
by what *m*. he now seeth. *John* 9:21
we be examined, by what *m*. *Acts* 4:9
must by all *m*. keep this feast. 18:21
if by any *m*. they might attain. 27:12
by any *m*. I might have a. *Rom* 1:10
by any *m*. I may provoke. 11:14
take heed, lest by any *m*. *1 Cor* 8:9
that I might by all *m*. save. 9:22
lest by any *m*. when I have. 27
by *m*. of many, thanks. *2 Cor* 1:11
lest by any *m*. as the serpent. 11:3
lest by any *m*. I should run in vain. *Gal* 2:2
if by any *m*. I attain to. *Phil* 3:11
some *m*. the tempter. *1 Thes* 3:5
deceive you by any *m*. *2 Thes* 2:3*
peace always by all *m*. 3:16*
that by *m*. of death. *Heb* 9:15*
deceiveth them by *m*. *Rev* 13:14*

meant
but God *m*. it unto good. *Gen* 50:20
what these things *m*. *Luke* 15:26
pass by, he asked what it *m*. 18:36

mean time
in the *m*. *time* when there were gathered. *Luke* 12:1

mean while
m. *while* the heaven. *1 Ki* 18:45*
in *m*. *while* his disciples. *John* 4:31
their thoughts *m*. *while* accusing. *Rom* 2:15*

measure
curtains shall have one *m*. *Ex* 26:2, 8
no unrighteousness in *m*. *Lev* 19:35
and a just *m*. shalt. *Deut* 25:15
cubits one *m*. *1 Ki* 6:25
bases had one *m*. 7:37
a *m*. of fine flour. *2 Ki* 7:1, 16, 18
the *m*. thereof is longer. *Job* 11:9
weigheth the waters by *m*. 28:25
make me to know the *m*. *Ps* 39:4
tears to drink in great *m*. 80:5
her mouth without *m*. *Isa* 5:14
in *m*. when it shooteth forth. 27:8
dust of earth in a *m*. 40:12
correct thee in *m*. *Jer* 30:11; 46:28
the end is come, and *m*. of. 51:13
drink water by *m*. *Ezek* 4:11, 16
and scant *m*. that is. *Mi* 6:10
m. ye mete, it shall be measured. *Mat* 7:2; *Mark* 4:24; *Luke* 6:38
fill ye up the *m*. of your. *Mat* 23:32
were amazed beyond *m*. *Mark* 6:51
beyond *m*. astonished. 7:37; 10:26
good *m*. pressed down. *Luke* 6:38
giveth not the Spirit by *m*. *John* 3:34
dealt to every man the *m*. *Rom* 12:3
were pressed out of *m*. *2 Cor* 1:8
not boast of things without our *m*. but to *m*. of the rule. 10:13, 14, 15
stripes above *m*., in prisons. 11:23
should be exalted above *m*. 12:7*
beyond *m*. I persecuted. *Gal* 1:13
according to the *m*. of the. *Eph* 4:7
m. of the stature of the fulness. 13
the effectual working in the *m*. 16
a voice saying, A *m*. of. *Rev* 6:6
to the *m*. of a man, that is. 21:17

measure, *verb*
shall *m*. from without. *Num* 35:5
shall *m*. to their cities. *Deut* 21:2

I will *m.* their former. *Isa* 65:7
them *m.* the pattern. *Ezek* 43:10
a measuring line to *m.* *Zech* 2:2
m. the temple of God. *Rev* 11:1
court leave out and *m.* not. 2
golden reed to *m.* the city. 21:15

measured

m. six measures of barley. *Ruth* 3:15
m. with a line, with two lines *m.* he. *2 Sam* 8:2
m. waters in hollow? *Isa* 40:12
heaven above can be *m.* *Jer* 31:37
sand of the sea cannot be *m.* 33:22
he *m.* the breadth of. *Ezek* 40:5
m. the threshold. 6
he *m.* also the porch. 8, 9
he *m.* the entry. 11
m. the gate. 13, 24
m. the wall. 41:5
he *m.* the house. 13
he *m.* the length of the building. 15
he *m.* the east side with. 42:16
he *m.* north side. 17, 18, 19
he *m.* a thousand cubits. 47:3, 4
be as sand of sea which cannot be *m.* *Hos* 1:10
he stood and *m.* the earth. *Hab* 3:6
measure ye mete, it shall be *m.* to. *Mat* 7:2; *Mark* 4:24; *Luke* 6:38
he *m.* the city. *Rev* 21:16
he *m.* the wall. 17

measures

three *m.* of fine meal. *Gen* 18:6
not have divers *m.* *Deut* 25:14
Abigail took five *m.* of. *1 Sam* 25:18
provision for one day was thirty *m.* of flour, and sixty *m.* of. *1 Ki* 4:22
20 thousand *m.* of wheat, and twenty *m.* of pure oil. 5:11; *2 Chr* 2:10
m. of hewed stones. *1 Ki* 7:9, 11*
contain two *m.* of seed. 18:32
for all manner of *m.* *1 Chr* 23:29
done to an hundred *m.* *Ezra* 7:22
who hath laid the *m.*? *Job* 38:5
divers *m.* are like. *Pr* 20:10
is the portion of thy *m.* *Jer* 13:25
the arches according to these *m.* *Ezek* 40:24, 29
gate according to these *m.* 28, 32
are the *m.* of the altar. 43:13
the *m.* of the profane place. 48:16
to an heap of twenty *m.* *Hag* 2:16
leaven, which a woman hid in three *m.* of meal. *Mat* 13:33; *Luke* 13:21
an hundred *m.* of oil. *Luke* 16:6
he said, An hundred *m.* of wheat. 7
see **barley**

measuring

the *m.* line shall yet go. *Jer* 31:39
man with a *m.* reed. *Ezek* 40:3, 5
he had made an end of *m.* 42:15
he measured with *m.* reed. 16, 17, 18, 19
a man with a *m.* line in. *Zech* 2:1
they *m.* themselves. *2 Cor* 10:12

meat

[1] *Food of any sort, especially any solid food. The Revisions generally change the word to food.* [2] *Flesh, as distinct from fish, fowl, or vegetables and grains.*

to you it shall be for *m.* *Gen* 1:29
I have given every herb for *m.* 30
every moving thing shall be *m.* 9:3
savoury *m.* such as I love. 27:4, 7
Esau also made savoury *m.* 31
bread and *m.* for his father. 45:23
of all *m.* which may be. *Lev* 11:34
his house, shall eat of his *m.* 22:11*
she shall eat of her father's *m.* 13*
sabbath of land shall be *m.* 25:6, 7
buy *m.* of them for money. *Deut* 2:6
thou shalt sell me *m.* for money. 28
destroy trees not for *m.* 20:20
kings gathered their *m.* *Judg* 1:7
out of the eater came forth *m.* 14:14
it with the king at *m.* *1 Sam* 20:5
Jonathan did eat no *m.* the. 34
cause David to eat *m.* *2 Sam* 3:35
there followed him a mess of *m.* 11:8
eat of his own *m.* and drank. 12:3*
let Tamar dress the *m.* in. 13:5*

she saw the *m.* of his table. *1 Ki* 10:5; *2 Chr* 9:4
strength of that *m.* forty. *1 Ki* 19:8
were nigh brought *m.* *1 Chr* 12:40
they gave *m.* and drink. *Ezra* 3:7
are as my sorrowful *m.* *Job* 6:7
the mouth taste his *m.*? 12:11
m. in his bowels is turned. 20:14
shall none of his *m.* be left. 21*
juniper roots for their *m.* 30:4
soul abhorreth dainty *m.* 33:20
words, as the mouth tasteth *m.* 34:3
he giveth *m.* in abundance. 36:31
they wander for lack of *m.* 38:41
my tears have been my *m.* *Ps* 42:3
given us like sheep for *m.* 44:11
wander up and down for *m.* 59:15
gave me also gall for my *m.* 69:21
thou gavest him to be *m.* 74:14
tempted God by asking *m.* 78:18
he sent them *m.* to the full. 25
but while their *m.* was yet in. 30
the young lions seek their *m.* 104:21
thou mayest give them their *m.* 27
abhorreth all manner of *m.* 107:18
he hath given *m.* to them. 111:5
them *m.* in due season. 145:15
ant provideth her *m.* in. *Pr* 6:8
for they are deceitful *m.* 23:3
when he is filled with *m.* 30:22
yet they prepare their *m.* in the. 25
giveth *m.* to her household. 31:15
no more give thy corn to be *m.* for thine enemies. *Isa* 62:8
dust shall be the serpent's *m.* 65:25
pleasant things for *m.* *Lam* 1:11
while they sought their *m.* 19
children, they were their *m.* 4:10
m. shall be by weight. *Ezek* 4:10
my *m.* which I gave thee. 16:19
I have given thee for *m.* to beasts. 29:5; 34:5, 8
that they may not be *m.* 34:10
grow trees for *m.*, fruit for *m.* 47:12
would not defile himself with the king's *m.* *Dan* 1:8†
king who hath appointed your *m.* 10
and in it was *m.* for all. 4:12, 21
feed of his *m.*, shall destroy. 11:26†
and I laid *m.* unto them. *Hos* 11:4
not *m.* cut off before? *Joel* 1:16
portion fat, *m.* plenteous. *Hab* 1:16
fields shall yield no *m.* 3:17
if one do touch any *m.*? *Hag* 2:12
in that ye say, His *m.* *Mal* 1:12
tithes, that there may be *m.* 3:10
and his *m.* was locusts. *Mat* 3:4
life more than *m.*? 6:25; *Luke* 12:23
as Jesus sat at *m.* in. *Mat* 9:10; 26:7 *Mark* 2:15; 14:3; 16:14 *Luke* 24:30
workman is worthy of his *m.* *Mat* 10:10
which sat with him at *m.* 14:9
took up of the broken *m.* 15:37* *Mark* 8:8*
to give them *m.* in due season. *Mat* 24:45; *Luke* 12:42
I was an hungered, and ye gave me *m.* *Mat* 25:35
hungered, and ye gave me no *m.* 42
that hath *m.*, let him do. *Luke* 3:11
commanded to give her *m.* 8:55
except we should go and buy *m.* 9:13
presence of them that sit at *m.* 14:10
servant, Go and sit down to *m.* 17:7
greater, he that sitteth at *m.*? 22:27
he said, Have ye here any *m.*? 24:41; *John* 21:5
were gone to buy *m.* *John* 4:8
m. to eat that ye know not of. 32
my *m.* is to do the will of him. 34
labour not for the *m.* which perisheth, but for that *m.* which. 6:27
my flesh is *m.* indeed, my. 55
they did eat their *m.* with. *Acts* 2:46
when he had received *m.* he. 9:19
jailor set *m.* before them. 16:34
them all to take *m.* 27:33, 34
and they also took some *m.* 36
be grieved with thy *m.*, destroy not him with thy *m.* for. *Rom* 14:15
for the kingdom of God is not *m.* 17*
for *m.* destroy not the work of. 20

milk, and not with *m.* *1 Cor* 3:2
m. commendeth us not to God. 8:8
if any man see thee sit at *m.* in. 10
if *m.* make my brother to offend. 13
did eat the same spiritual *m.* 10:3
let no man judge you in *m.* *Col* 2:16
of milk, not of strong *m.* *Heb* 5:12*
but strong *m.* belongeth to them. 14*
who for one morsel of *m.* sold. 12:16
see **fowls**

meat offering

(*This offering did not contain flesh, but was usually a preparation of flour with spices and other ingredients. The Revisions usually change the word to meal offering*)

according to *m. off.* of. *Ex* 29:41
offer no *m. off.* thereon. 30:9
Moses offered the *m. off.* 40:29
offer a *m. off.* *Lev* 2:1, 4, 5, 7, 14
remnant of *m. off.* 3, 10; 5:13
law of the *m. off.* 6:14; 7:37
deals of flour for a *m. off.* 14:10
pertaineth daily *m. off.* *Num* 4:16
fine flour mingled with oil for *m. off.* 7:13, 19; 28:12, 13
m. off. two tenths. 15:6; 28:9, 12
the *m. off.* of the morning. 28:8
when ye bring a new *m. off.* 26
besides his *m. off.* and burnt offering. 29:6, 22, 25, 34
to offer thereon *m. off.* *Josh* 22:23
took a kid with a *m. off.* *Judg* 13:19
not have received a *m. off.* 23
m. off. was offered. *2 Ki* 3:20*
wheat for the *m. off.* *1 Chr* 21:23
for continual *m. off.* *Neh* 10:33
thou offered a *m. off.* *Isa* 57:6
they lay the *m. off.* *Ezek* 42:13
they shall eat the *m. off.* 44:29
prepare the *m. off.* 45:17, 24
do like according to the *m. off.* 25
m. off. shall be an ephah for a ram. 46:5
a *m. off.* and an ephah for a bullock. 7, 11
they prepare the *m. off.* and. 15
m. off. and the drink offering is cut off. *Joel* 1:9
the *m. off.* and drink offering is withholden. 13
leave a blessing, even a *m. off.* 2:14

meat offerings

do for your *m. off.* *Num* 29:39
build an altar for *m. off.* *Josh* 22:29
because altar was too little to receive *m. off.* *1 Ki* 8:64; *2 Chr* 7:7
lambs with their *m. off.* *Ezra* 7:17
they laid their *m. off.* *Neh* 13:5
Judah to bring *m. off.* *Jer* 17:26
want a man to kindle *m. off.* 33:18
princes to give *m. off.* *Ezek* 45:17
though ye offer *m. off.* *Amos* 5:22

meats

desire thou his dainty *m.* *Pr* 23:6*
draught, purging all *m.* *Mark* 7:19
m. offered to idols. *Acts* 15:29*
m. for the belly, and the belly for *m.* *1 Cor* 6:13
to abstain from *m.*, which. *1 Tim* 4:3
which stood only in *m.* *Heb* 9:10
established with grace, not *m.* 13:9

Medad

told Moses, Eldad and *M.* prophesy in camp. *Num* 11:26, 27

meddle

m. not with them of mount Seir. *Deut* 2:5*
m. not with the children of. 19*
why *m.* to thy hurt? *2 Ki* 14:10 *2 Chr* 25:19
m. not with him that. *Pr* 20:19
m. not with them that are. 24:21

meddled

contention before it be *m.* *Pr* 17:14*

meddleth

that *m.* with strife not. *Pr* 26:17*

meddling

forbear thee from *m.* *2 Chr* 35:21
but every fool will be *m.* *Pr* 20:3*

Mede, -s

cities of the *M.* *2 Ki* 17:6; 18:11
the province of the *M.* *Ezra* 6:2
among the laws of the *M.* *Esth* 1:19
I will stir up *M.* against them. *Isa* 13:17; *Jer* 51:11
all the kings of the *M.* *Jer* 25:25
kingdom is given to the *M.* *Dan* 5:28
the law of the *M.* 6:8, 12, 15
Ahasuerus of the seed of the *M.* 9:1
year of Darius the *M.* 11:1

Media

power of Persia and *M.* *Esth* 1:3
seven princes of Persia and *M.* 14
the ladies of *M.* shall say this. 18
book of the kings of *M.* 10:2
O *M.* all the sighing. *Isa* 21:2
two horns are kings of *M.* *Dan* 8:20

mediator

(*This word, when applied to Moses, has the meaning of intermediary. When applied to Christ it has somewhat of that meaning, with probably a little of the meaning of intercessor*)
angels in the hand of a *m.* *Gal* 3:19
a *m.* is not a *m.* of one, but. 20
one *m.* between God. *1 Tim* 2:5
he is the *m.* of a better. *Heb* 8:6
for this cause he is *m.* of. 9:15
and to Jesus the *m.* of the. 12:24

medicine

heart doeth good like a *m.* *Pr* 17:22
thereof shall be for *m.* *Ezek* 47:12*

medicines

thou hast no healing *m.* *Jer* 30:13
in vain shalt thou use many *m.* 46:11

meditate

Isaac went out to *m.* *Gen* 24:63
shalt *m.* therein day. *Josh* 1:8
in his law doth he *m.* day. *Ps* 1:2
and *m.* on thee in the night. 63:6
I will *m.* also of all thy work. 77:12
will *m.* in thy precepts. 119:15, 78
did *m.* in thy statutes. 23
I will *m.* in thy statutes. 48
night watches, that I might *m.* 148
I *m.* on all thy works, I muse. 143:5
heart shall *m.* terror. *Isa* 33:18*
not to *m.* before what ye shall answer. *Luke* 21:14
m. upon these things. *1 Tim* 4:15

meditation

my words, consider my *m.* *Ps* 5:1
let the *m.* of my heart be. 19:14
the *m.* of my heart shall be. 49:3
my *m.* of him shall be sweet. 104:34
I love thy law, it is my *m.* 119:97
for thy testimonies are my *m.* 99

meek

(*Gentle, kind, not easily provoked, ready to yield rather than cause trouble; but not used in the Bible in the bad sense of tamely submissive and servile*)
man Moses was very *m.* *Num* 12:3
the *m.* shall eat and. *Ps* 22:26
m. will he guide in judgement. 25:9
m. shall inherit the earth. 37:11
God arose to save all the *m.* 76:9
the Lord lifteth up the *m.* 147:6
he will beautify the *m.* with. 149:4
equity, for the *m.* of. *Isa* 11:4
the *m.* shall increase their. 29:19
preach good tidings to the *m.* 61:1
aside the way of the *m.* *Amos* 2:7
seek ye the Lord, all ye *m.* *Zeph* 2:3
blessed are the *m.* *Mat* 5:5
for I am *m.* and lowly. 11:29
thy king cometh to thee, *m.* 21:5
the ornament of a *m.* *1 Pet* 3:4

meekness

because of truth and *m.* *Ps* 45:4
seek *m.* shall be hid. *Zeph* 2:3
come in the spirit of *m.*? *1 Cor* 4:21†
by the *m.* of Christ. *2 Cor* 10:1
fruit of the Spirit is *m.* *Gal* 5:23
restore in the spirit of *m.* 6:1
with all lowliness and *m.* *Eph* 4:2
put on therefore *m.*, longsuffering. *Col* 3:12
faith, love, patience, *m.* *1 Tim* 6:11
in *m.* instructing those. *2 Tim* 2:25
gentle, shewing all *m.* *Tit* 3:2
receive with *m.* the ingrafted word. *Jas* 1:21
him shew his works with *m.* 3:13
of your hope with *m.* *1 Pet* 3:15

meet

(*As an adjective*, fit, suitable)
I will make an help *m.* *Gen* 2:18
found an help *m.* for Adam. 20
Moses said, It is not *m.* *Ex* 8:26
pass over, all that are *m.* for war. *Deut* 3:18*
m. for the necks of them. *Judg* 5:30
it was not *m.* to see the king's dishonour. *Ezra* 4:14
surely it is *m.* to be said. *Job* 34:31*
more than is *m.* *Pr* 11:24
do with me as seemeth *m.* to you. *Jer* 26:14*
to whom it seemed *m.* to me. 27:5*
is it *m.* for any work? *Ezek* 15:4*
it was *m.* for no work. 5
fruits *m.* for repentance. *Mat* 3:8*
it is not *m.* to take the children's bread. 15:26; *Mark* 7:27
it was *m.* we should make merry. *Luke* 15:32
do works *m.* for repentance. *Acts* 26:20*
receiving that recompence which was *m.* *Rom* 1:27*
am not *m.* to be called an. *1 Cor* 15:9
if it be *m.* that I go also. 16:4
is *m.* for me to think this. *Phil* 1:7*
made us *m.* to be partakers. *Col* 1:12
bound to thank God for you, as it is *m.* *2 Thes* 1:3
he shall be vessel *m.* *2 Tim* 2:21
herbs *m.* for them by. *Heb* 6:7
m. to stir you up. *2 Pet* 1:13*

meet

Sodom went out to *m.* *Gen* 14:17
them, and ran to *m.* them. 18:2
Lot seeing them, rose up to *m.* 19:1
servant ran to *m.* Rebekah. 24:17
what man walketh to *m.* us? 65
Laban ran to *m.* Jacob. 29:13
Leah went out to *m.* Jacob. 30:16
Esau cometh to *m.* thee. 32:6; 33:4
Joseph went up to *m.* Israel. 46:29
Aaron cometh forth to *m.* *Ex* 4:14
go into wilderness to *m.* Moses. 27
Moses went out to *m.* his. 18:7
brought forth the people to *m.* 19:17
if thou *m.* thine enemy's ox. 23:4
there I will *m.* with thee. 25:22
29:42, 43; 30:6, 36; *Num* 17:4
Balak went out to *m.* *Num* 22:36
Lord will come to *m.* me. 23:3
stand here, while I *m.* the Lord. 15
went forth to *m.* them without. 31:13
lest the pursuers *m.* you. *Josh* 2:16*
with you, and go to *m.* them. 9:11
Jael went out to *m.* Sisera. *Judg* 4:18, 22
they came up to *m.* Gideon. 6:35
out of the doors to *m.* me. 11:31
his daughter came to *m.* him. 34
father of damsel rejoiced to *m.* 19:3
that they *m.* thee not in any other field. *Ruth* 2:22
shall *m.* thee three men. *1 Sam* 10:3
m. a company of prophets. 5
Saul went to *m.* Samuel. 13:10
Samuel rose up early to *m.* 15:12
Philistine drew nigh to *m.* 17:48
the women came to *m.* Saul. 18:6
sent thee this day to *m.* me. 25:32
to *m.* David and to *m.* people. 30:21
Michal came out to *m.* *2 Sam* 6:20
David sent to *m.* the men. 10:5
1 Chr 19:5
Archite came to *m.* him. *2 Sam* 15:32
Mephibosheth came to *m.* 19:24
Shimei came down to *m.* *1 Ki* 2:8
Solomon rose up to *m.* 19
went to *m.* Ahab, to *m.* Elijah. 18:16
arise, go down to *m.* Ahab. 21:18
go up to *m.* messengers. *2 Ki* 1:3
there came a man to *m.* us. 6
what man came up to *m.* you? 7
prophets came to *m.* Elisha. *2 Ki* 2:15
run now, I pray thee, to *m.* her. 4:26
if thou *m.* any man, salute. 29
the chariot to *m.* him. 5:21, 26
go *m.* the man of God. 8:8
Hazael went to *m.* him. 9
horseman, and send to *m.* 9:17
one on horseback to *m.* him. 18
Jonadab coming to *m.* him. 10:15
Ahaz went to *m.* the king. 16:10
let us *m.* together. *Neh* 6:2, 10
they *m.* with darkness. *Job* 5:14
the horse goeth on to *m.* 39:21
came I forth to *m.* thee. *Pr* 7:15
bear robbed of her whelps *m.* 17:12
rich and poor *m.* together. 22:2
poor and deceitful *m.* together. 29:13
go forth to *m.* Ahaz. *Isa* 7:3
hell is moved for thee to *m.* 14:9
beasts of desert shall also *m.* 34:14
vengeance, and I will not *m.* 47:3*
went forth to *m.* them. *Jer* 41:6
messenger run to *m.* another. 51:31
I will *m.* them as a bear bereaved. *Hos* 13:8
prepare to *m.* thy God. *Amos* 4:12
angel went out to *m.* *Zech* 2:3
city came out to *m.* Jesus. *Mat* 8:34
to *m.* the bridegroom. 25:1
cometh, go ye out to *m.* him. 6
there shall *m.* you a man. *Mark* 14:13; *Luke* 22:10
with ten thousand to *m.* *Luke* 14:31
people went forth to *m.* *John* 12:13
to *m.* us as far as Appii-forum. *Acts* 28:15
clouds to *m.* the Lord. *1 Thes* 4:17

meetest

look out the *m.* of your. *2 Ki* 10:3
m. him that rejoiceth. *Isa* 64:5

meeteth

Esau my brother *m.* *Gen* 32:17
slay murderer when he *m.* him. *Num* 35:19, 21

meeting

afraid at *m.* of David. *1 Sam* 21:1
even the solemn *m.* *Isa* 1:13

Megiddo

would dwell in *M.* *Judg* 1:27
Canaan fought by waters of *M.* 5:19
pertained Taanach and *M.* *1 Ki* 4:12
raised a levy to build *M.* 9:15
Ahaziah fled to *M.* and. *2 Ki* 9:27
Josiah was slain at *M.* 23:29, 30
2 Chr 35:22

Megiddon

in the valley of *M.* *Zech* 12:11

Melchi

which was the son of *M.* *Luke* 3:24

Melchizedek

king *M.* brought forth. *Gen* 14:18
priest for ever after the order of *M.* *Ps* 110:4; *Heb* 5:6, 10; 6:20
7:17, 21
this *M.* king of Salem. *Heb* 7:1
loins of his father, when *M.* 10
should rise after the order of *M.* 11
after the similitude of *M* ariseth. 15

melody

make sweet *m.* sing. *Isa* 23:16
found therein, the voice of *m.* 51:3
I will not hear the *m.* *Amos* 5:23
making *m.* in your heart. *Eph* 5:19

melons

we remember the *m.* *Num* 11:5

melt

(*Frequently used in the old sense of to be prostrate because of fear*)
of Canaan shall *m.* *Ex* 15:15
things, our hearts did *m.* *Josh* 2:11
made the heart of the people *m.* 14:8
lion, shall utterly *m.* *2 Sam* 17:10
let them *m.* away as waters. *Ps* 58:7
with his teeth, and *m.* away. 112:10
every man's heart shall *m.* *Isa* 13:7
Ezek 21:7
the heart of Egypt shall *m.* *Isa* 19:1
behold, I will *m.* them. *Jer* 9:7
m. it; so will I *m.* you. *Ezek* 22:20
the land, and it shall *m.* *Amos* 9:5

all hills shall m. Amos 9:13; Nah 1:5
and the elements shall m. with heat. 2 Pet 3:10*, 12

melted

when sun waxed hot, it m. Ex 16:21
their heart m. Josh 5:1
hearts of Israel m. 7:5
the mountains m. before. Judg 5:5*
multitude m. away. 1 Sam 14:16
my heart is m. in midst. Ps 22:14
his voice, and the earth m. 46:6
the hills m. like wax. 97:5
their soul m. 107:26
mountains shall be m. Isa 34:3
ye shall be m. in the. Ezek 22:21
as silver is m. in the midst. 22

melteth

as a snail which m., let. Ps 58:8
as wax m. so let wicked perish. 68:2
my soul m. for heaviness. 119:28
out his word and m. them. 147:18
workman m. a graven. Isa 40:19†
burnt, the founder m. Jer 6:29
the heart of Nineveh m. Nah 2:10

melting

as when the m. fire. Isa 64:2

member

(*Generally used in the archaic sense of limb, or other part of the body. In this sense it is often also used figuratively*)
that hath his privy m. Deut 23:1
body is not one m. but. 1 Cor 12:14
if they were all one m., where ? 19
whether one m. suffer; one m. 26
the tongue is a little m. Jas 3:5

members

my m. are as a shadow. Job 17:7
in thy book all my m. Ps 139:16
thy m. should perish. Mat 5:29, 30
nor your m. as instruments. Rom 6:13
as ye yielded your m. servants. 19
sins did work in our m. 7:5
another law in my m. . . . law of sin which is in my m. 23
many m. in one body, and all m. have not the same office. 12:4
every one m. one of another. 5
bodies are the m. of Christ? shall I then take the m. of? 1 Cor 6:15
body hath many m. and all m. 12:12
now hath God set the m. in. 18
are they many m., yet one body. 20
m. which seem more feeble. 22
but that the m. should have. 25
one member suffer, all the m. 26
ye are the body of Christ, and m. 27
for we are m. one of. Eph 4:25
m. of his body, of his flesh. 5:30
mortify your m. which are. Col 3:5
so is tongue among our m. Jas 3:6
lusts that war in your m. 4:1

memorial

this is my m. unto all. Ex 3:15
shall be to you for a m. 12:14
it shall be for a m. between. 13:9
write this for a m. in a book. 17:14
stones of m. to the children. 28:12
for a m. before the Lord. 29; 39:7
money may be for a m. 30:16
burn the m. of it on altar. Lev 2:2
9:16; 5:12; 6:15; Num 5:26
a m. of blowing trumpets.
Lev 23:24; Num 10:10
on the bread for a m. Lev 24:7
for it is an offering of m. Num 5:15
priest put the offering of m. 18
took brasen censers to be a m. 16:40
gold of the captains for m. 31:54
stones shall be for a m. Josh 4:7
ye have no portion nor m. Neh 2:20
nor the m. of them perish. Esth 9:28
their m. is perished. Ps 9:6
and thy m. throughout all. 135:13
the Lord is his m. Hos 12:5
crowns be for a m. in. Zech 6:14
this be told for a m. of her.
Mat 26:13; Mark 14:9
alms are come up for a m. Acts 10:4

memory

he may cut off the m. Ps 109:15
utter the m. of thy great. 145:7
m. of the just is blessed. Pr 10:7
m. of them is forgotten. Eccl 9:5
and made all their m. to. Isa 26:14
if ye keep in m. what. 1 Cor 15:2

Memphis

M. shall bury them. Hos 9:6

men

then began m. to call on. Gen 4:26
when m. began to multiply on. 6:1
looked, and lo, three m. stood. 18:2
the m. of the city, m. of Sodom. 19:4
where are m. which came into ? 5
only to these m. do nothing. 8
smote the m. 11
power with God and m. 32:28
m. are peaceable with us. 34:21
only herein will the m. consent. 22
we are true m. 42:11, 31
bring these m. home. 43:16
said, Up, follow after the m. 44:4
m. are shepherds, for their. 46:32
saved the m.-children. Ex 1:17, 18
go now ye that are m. and. 10:11
thrice in the year shall m. 34:23
Aaron took these m. Num 1:17
all the people are m. of great. 13:32
m. that did bring evil report. 14:37
put out the eyes of these m.? 16:14
if these m. die the common death. 29
God said, What m. are these? 22:9
said to Balaam, Go with the m. 35
slay ye every one his m. that. 25:5
not one of these m. shall. Deut 1:35
to cease from among m. 32:26
Reuben live, let not his m. 33:6
there came m. in hither. Josh 2:2
bring forth the m. 3; 1 Sam 11:12
because he feared the m. Judg 6:27
Penuel answered as the m. 8:8
should give bread to thy m. 15
m. say not of me, A woman. 9:54
there were m. lying in wait. 16:9
therefore deliver us the m. 20:13
with the Lord and m. 1 Sam 2:26
he smote the m. of the city. 5:9
m. that died not were smitten. 12
hearest thou m.'s words ? 24:9
but the m. were very good. 25:15
m. the sons of Zeruiah. 2 Sam 3:39
and let us play the m. for. 10:12
but dead men before my. 19:28
he that ruleth over m. must. 23:3
two lionlike m. of. 20; 1 Chr 11:22
happy thy m. that hear. 1 Ki 10:8
m. come out of Samaria. 20:17
now the m. did diligently. 33
open the eyes of these m. 2 Ki 6:20
they reckoned not with m. 12:15
the m. of Babylon . . . m. of Cuth, Nergal, m. of Hamath. 17:30
hath he not sent me to the m.?
18:27; Isa 36:12
what said these m.? 2 Ki 20:14
Isa 39:3
drink blood of these m.? 1 Chr 11:19
let m. say among the nations. 16:31
m. were greatly ashamed. 19:5
will God dwell with m.? 2 Chr 6:18
the m. expressed by name. 28:15
and the m. did the work. 34:12
let m. of his place help. Ezra 1:4
to cause these m. to cease. 4:21
expenses be given to these m. 6:8
nor m. of the guard. Neh 4:23
other m. have our lands and. 5:5
sleep falleth on m. Job 4:13; 33:15
they are gone away from m. 28:4
if the m. of my tabernacle. 31:31
m. do therefore fear him. 37:24
themselves to be but m. Ps 9:20
m. which are thy hand, from m. 17:14
m. will praise thee when. 49:18
m. of low degree are vanity, m. 62:9
hast received gifts for m. 68:18
and m. shall be blessed in. 72:17
as other m., neither are they plagued like other m. 73:5
but ye shall die like m. 82:7
that m. may know that thou. 83:18
O that m. would praise the Lord.
107:8, 15, 21, 31
on our side, when m. rose. 124:2
m. shall speak of the might. 145:6
m. do not despise a thief. Pr 6:30
to you, O m. I call. 8:4
m. depart from evil. 16:6
most m. proclaim each his own. 20:6
which the m. of Hezekiah. 25:1
m. to search their own glory. 27
when the wicked rise, m. hide. 28:28
God doeth it that m. may. Eccl 3:14
m. shall fall by the sword. Isa 3:25
the Lord have removed m. 6:12
thing for you to weary m.? 7:13
now the Egyptians are m. 31:3
by these things m. live. 38:16
wherefore I will give m. for. 43:4
even to him shall m. come. 45:24
and shew yourselves m. 46:8
that m. may bring to thee. 60:11
m. shall call you the ministers. 61:6
m. have not heard, nor. 64:4
set a trap, they catch m. Jer 5:26
horses set in array, as m. for. 6:23
neither can m. hear the voice. 9:10
let their m. be put to death. 18:21
I will give the m. that transgressed my covenant. 34:18
m. have done evil to prophet. 38:9
to Gedaliah, they and their m. 40:8
then the m. shall cry and. 47:2
arise ye, and spoil the m. of. 49:28
surely I will fill thee with m. 51:14
m. call the perfection. Lam 2:15
m. that devise mischief. Ezek 11:2
these m. set up their idols. 14:3
though these three m., Noah, Daniel, Job. 14, 16, 18
sent for m. to come from. 23:40
I will deliver thee to the m. 25:4, 10
ye are m., and I am God. 34:31
mountains with his slain m. 35:8
multiply m. upon you. 36:10, 37
m. have not regarded. Dan 3:12
fire slew those m. that took. 22
these m., upon whose bodies fire. 27
drive thee from m. 4:25, 32
m. we shall not find occasion. 6:5
that m. fear before the God. 26
but they like m. trangressed the covenant. Hos 6:7
m. that were at peace. Ob 7
pass securely, as m. averse. Mi 2:8
man's enemies are the m. of. 7:6
makest m. as the fishes. Hab 1:14
they are m. wondered at. Zech 3:8
had sent their m. to pray. 7:2
but lo, I will deliver the m. 11:6
light so shine before m. Mat 5:16
shall teach m. so, shall be called. 19
do not your alms before m. 6:1
they may appear to m. to fast. 16
thou appear not unto m. to fast. 18
that m. should do to you, do ye even so to them. 7:12; Luke 6:31
given such power to m. Mat 9:8
whoso shall confess me before m.
10:32; Luke 12:8
whoso shall deny me before m.
Mat 10:33; Luke 12:9
but while m. slept, his enemy.
Mat 13:25
whom do m. say that I am ? 16:13
Mark 8:27
ye appear righteous to m. Mat 23:28
and said, I see m. as. Mark 8:24
with m. it is impossible. 10:27
Luke 18:27
good will toward m. Luke 2:14
thou shalt catch m. 5:10
shall rise up with the m. of. 11:31
to whom m. have committed. 12:48
I am not as other m. are. 18:11
not honour from m. John 5:41
manifested thy name to the m. 17:6
of these m. which have companied.
Acts 1:21
others said, These m. are full. 2:13
what shall we do to these m.? 4:16
thou hast not lied unto m. 5:4
the m. ye put in prison are in. 25
obey God rather than m. 29
to do, as touching these m. 35
refrain from these m. 38
Spirit said, Behold three m. 10:19
also are m. of like passions. 14:15
m. that hazarded their lives. 15:26

these *m.* are servants of. *Acts* 16:17
serjeants, saying, Let those *m.* go. 35
brought hither these *m.* 19:37
also of yourselves shall *m.* 20:30
of offence toward God and *m.* 24:16
m. with *m.* working. *Rom* 1:27
condescend to *m.* of low. 12:16
we are made a spectacle unto world and to angels and *m.* *1 Cor* 4:9
for he speaketh not to *m.* 14:2
but in understanding be *m.* 20
with *m.* of other tongues and lips. 21
we persuade *m.* *2 Cor* 5:11
for I mean not that other *m.* 8:13
persuade *m.*? or seek to please *m.*? *Gal* 1:10
he gave gifts unto *m.* *Eph* 4:8
so ought *m.* to love their wives. 5:28
to Lord and not to *m.* 6:7; *Col* 3:23
not as pleasing *m.* but. *1 Thes* 2:4
I will that *m.* pray every. *1 Tim* 2:8
m. shall be lovers of. *2 Tim* 3:2
priest taken from among *m.* *Heb* 5:1
for *m.* verily swear by the. 6:16
here *m.* that die receive tithes. 7:8
as it is appointed unto *m.* 9:27
to the spirits of just *m.* 12:23
therewith curse we *m.* *Jas* 3:9
judged according to *m.* *1 Pet* 4:6
but holy *m.* of God. *2 Pet* 1:21
for there are certain *m.* crept. *Jude* 4
only those *m.* which have. *Rev* 9:4
their power was to hurt *m.* 10
redeemed from among *m.* 14:4
not since *m.* were on the earth. 16:18
tabernacle of God is with *m.* 21:3
see **brethren, chief, chosen, evil, great, Israel, Judah, old, rich, righteous, singing**

all **men**

all the *m.* of his house. *Gen* 17:27
all the *m.* are dead. *Ex* 4:19
die the common death of *all m.* *Num* 16:29
all the *m.* that followed. *Deut* 4:3
said, Have out *all m.* *2 Sam* 13:9
was wiser than *all m.* *1 Ki* 4:31
all m. may know his work. *Job* 37:7
all m. shall fear, and. *Ps* 64:9
thou made *all m.* in vain? 89:47
I said in my haste, *All m.* 116:11
that is the end of *all m.* *Eccl* 7:2
so with *all* the *m.* that set. *Jer* 42:17
I set *all m.* every one against his neighbour *Zech* 8:10
ye shall be hated of *all m.* *Mat* 10:22
Mark 13:13; *Luke* 21:17
all m. cannot receive. *Mat* 19:11
tho' *all m.* shall be offended. 26:33
all m. seek thee. *Mark* 1:37
all m. did marvel. 5:20
all m. counted John a. 11:32
all m. speak well of you. *Luke* 6:26
sinners above *all m.* that dwelt. 13:4
that *all m.* through him. *John* 1:7
himself, because he knew *all m.* 2:24
the same baptizeth, and *all m.* 3:26
all m. should honour the Son. 5:23
if we let alone, *all m.* will. 11:48
I will draw *all m.* unto me. 12:32
by this shall *all m.* know that. 13:35
Lord, who knowest the hearts of *all m.* *Acts* 1:24
all m. glorified God for what. 4:21
but now commandeth *all m.* 17:30
hath given assurance to *all m.* 31
all the *m.* were about twelve. 19:7
burned their books before *all m.* 19
pure from the blood of *all m.* 20:26
be his witness to *all m.* 22:15
death passed upon *all m.* *Rom* 5:12
on *all m.* to condemnation, the free gift came on *all m.* to. 18
honest in the sight of *all m.* 12:17
live peaceably with *all m.* 18
is come abroad to *all m.* 16:19
I would that *all m.* were. *1 Cor* 7:7
for though I be free from *all m.* 9:19
I am made all things to *all m.* 22
even as I please *all m.* in. 10:33
of *all m.* most miserable. 15:19
known and read of *all m.* *2 Cor* 3:2
let us do good to *all m.* *Gal* 6:10
to make *all m.* see what is. *Eph* 3:9
let your moderation be known to *all m.* *Phil* 4:5
and contrary to *all m.* *1 Thes* 2:15
abound in love toward *all m.* 3:12
be patient toward *all m.* 5:14
follow that which is good to *all m.* 15
all m. have not faith. *2 Thes* 3:2
thanks be made for *all m.* *1 Tim* 2:1
who will have *all m.* to be saved. 4
who is the Saviour of *all m.* 4:10
but be gentle to *all m.* *2 Tim* 2:24
shall be made manifest to *all m.* 3:9
man stood with me, but *all m.* 4:16
God hath appeared to *all m.* *Tit* 2:11
shewing all meekness to *all m.* 3:2
follow peace with *all m.* *Heb* 12:14
God, that giveth to *all m.* *Jas* 1:5
Honour *all m.*, Love the. *1 Pet* 2:17
hath good report of *all m.* *3 John* 12

in **men**

let no man glory *in m.* *1 Cor* 3:21

like **men**

quit yourselves *like m.* *1 Sam* 4:9
1 Cor 16:13
but ye shall die *like m.* *Ps* 82:7
like m. have transgressed. *Hos* 6:7
yourselves *like* unto *m.* that wait for their lord. *Luke* 12:36

mighty **men**

mighty m. which were of old. *Gen* 6:4
mighty m. of Moab. *Ex* 15:15
the *mighty m.* of valour. *Josh* 1:14
Jericho and the *mighty m.* 6:2
thirty thousand *mighty m.* 8:3
m. of Gibeon were *mighty.* 10:2
ascended from Gilgal with *mighty m.* of valour. 7
bows of the *mighty m.* *1 Sam* 2:4
Joab and all the host of the *mighty m.* *2 Sam* 10:7; 20:7; *1 Chr* 19:8
mighty m. were on his right hand. *2 Sam* 16:6
his *m.*, that they be *mighty m.* 17:8
be names of the *mighty m.* 23:8
Eleazar one of the three *mighty m.* 9
the three *mighty m.* brake. 16, 17
name among three *mighty m.* 22
the *mighty m.* were not with Adonijah. *1 Ki* 1:8
the *mighty m.* and Solomon. 10
exacted of all *mighty m.* *2 Ki* 15:20
carried away all the *mighty m.* 24:14
these were *mighty m.* of valour. *1 Chr* 5:24; 7:7, 9, 1., 40
sons of Ulam were *mighty m.* 8:40
the chief of the *mighty m.* 11:10, 11
were among the *mighty m.* 12:1
were all *mighty m.* of valour. 21, 25
30; 26:6, 31
mighty m. submitted themselves to Solomon. 29:24
battle against Abijah, being *mighty m.* *2 Chr* 13:3; 14:8; 17:13, 14, 16
an hundred thousand *mighty m.* 25:6
counsel with his *mighty m.* 32:3
angel cut off all the *mighty m.* 21
their brethren *mighty m.* *Neh* 11:14
break in pieces *mighty m.* *Job* 34:24
more than ten *mighty m.* *Eccl* 7:19
all shields of *mighty m.* *S of S* 4:4
mighty m. of Kedar shall. *Isa* 21:17
quiver is an open sepulchre, they are all *mighty m.* *Jer* 5:16
king, with all his *mighty m.* 26:21
recovered *mighty m.* of war. 41:16
let *mighty m.* come forth. 46:9
we are *mighty m.* 48:14
hearts of *mighty m.* of Moab. 41
heart of *mighty m.* of Edom. 49:22
sword is upon her *mighty m.* 50:36
mighty m. of Babylon have. 51:30
mighty m. are taken, their bows. 56
I will make drunk her *mighty m.* 57
under foot my *mighty m.* *Lam* 1:15
table with *mighty m.* *Ezek* 39:20
mighty m. to bind. *Dan* 3:20
trust in the multitude of thy *mighty m.* *Hos* 10:13
shall run like *mighty m.* *Joel* 2:7
wake up the *mighty m.* 3:9
thy *mighty m.* O Teman. *Ob* 9
the shield of his *mighty m.* *Nah* 2:3
as *mighty m.* that tread. *Zech* 10:5
mighty m. hid themselves in the dens. *Rev* 6:15
eat the flesh of *mighty m.* 19:18

of **men**

saw the daughters *of m.* *Gen* 6:2
came in to the daughters *of m.* 4
none devoted *of m.* *Lev* 27:29
whether it be *of m.* *Num* 18:15
prey both *of m.* and beasts. 31:11
what manner *of m.* were. *Judg* 8:18
went with a band *of m.* *1 Sam* 10:26
him with the rod *of m.* *2 Sam* 7:14
spied a band *of m.* *2 Ki* 13:21
places with the bones *of m.* 23:14
they took away *of m.* *1 Chr* 5:21
the band *of m.* had slain. *2 Chr* 22:1
O thou Preserver *of m.*? *Job* 7:20
then he openeth the ears *of m.* 33:16
concerning the works *of m.* *Ps* 17:4
but I am a reproach *of m.* 22:6
haughtiness *of m.* shall be bowed down. *Isa* 2:11
the haughtiness *of m.* shall be made low. 17
taught by the precept *of m.* 29:13
workmen, they are *of m.* 44:11
fear ye not the reproach *of m.* 51:7
is despised and rejected *of m.* 53:3
carcases *of m.* shall fall. *Jer* 9:22
with the dead bodies *of m.* 33:5
to thyself images *of m.* *Ezek* 16:17
eat not the bread *of m.* 24:17, 22
traded the persons *of m.* in. 27:13
no more bereave them *of m.* 36:12
cities be filled with flocks *of m.* 38
mingle with the seed *of m.* *Dan* 2:43
Most High ... *of m.* and setteth up ... basest *of m.* 4:17, 25, 32; 5:21
by reason of multitude *of m.* *Mi* 2:12; *Zech* 2:4
make you fishers *of m.* *Mat* 4:19
trodden under foot *of m.* 5:13
they may have glory *of m.* 6:2
seen *of m.* 5; 23:5
beware *of m.* 10:17
for doctrines, commandments *of m.* 15:9; *Mark* 7:7
but the things that be *of m.* *Mat* 16:23; *Mark* 8:33
betrayed into hands *of m.* *Mat* 17:22
Mark 9:31; *Luke* 9:44; 24:7
made eunuchs *of m.* *Mat* 19:12
baptism of heaven or *of m.*? 21:25
if we say *of m.* 26; *Mark* 11:30
32; *Luke* 20:4, 6
regardest not person *of m.* *Mat* 22:16; *Mark* 12:14
be called *of m.* Rabbi. *Mat* 23:7
out of the heart *of m.* *Mark* 7:21
life was the light *of m.* *John* 1:4
they loved the praise *of m.* 12:43
Judas received a band *of m.* 18:3
to whom a number *of m.* *Acts* 5:36
if this work be *of m.* it will. 38
come down in likeness *of m.* 14:11
the residue *of m.* might seek. 15:17
honourable women, and *of m.* 17:12
unrighteousness *of m.* *Rom* 1:18
judge the secrets *of m.* 2:16
whose praise is not *of m.* 29
brethren, I speak after the manner *of m.* 6:19; *Gal* 3:15
Christ is approved *of m.* *Rom* 14:18
stand in the wisdom *of m.* *1 Cor* 2:5
learn in us not to think *of m.* 4:6
be not the servants *of m.* 7:23
speak with tongues *of m.* and. 13:1
if, after the manner *of m.*, I. 15:32
things in the sight *of m.* *2 Cor* 8:21
Paul an apostle, not *of m.* *Gal* 1:1
doctrine, by sleight *of m.* *Eph* 4:14
made in the likeness *of m.* *Phil* 2:7
after the tradition *of m.* *Col* 2:8
and doctrines *of m.* 22
manner *of m.* we were. *1 Thes* 1:5
nor *of m.* sought we glory. 2:6
it not as the word *of m.* 13
disputings *of m.* of. *1 Tim* 6:5
commandments *of m.* *Tit* 1:14
disallowed indeed *of m.* *1 Pet* 2:4
to silence ignorance *of* foolish *m.* 15
no longer live to the lusts *of m.* 4:2

receive the witness *of m. 1 John* 5:9
were as the faces *of m.* *Rev* 9:7
slay the third part *of m.* 15, 18
were slain *of m.* 7000. 11:13
fire come down in sight *of m.* 13:13
of slaves and souls *of m.* 18:13
see **children**

sons of **men**

ye *sons of m.* how long will ye turn my glory into? *Ps* 4:2; 58:1
thee, before the *sons of m.* 31:19
beholdeth all the *sons of m.* 33:13
I lie among the *sons of m.* 57:4
to make known to *sons of m.* 145:12
and my delights were with the *sons of m.* *Pr* 8:31
travail hath God given to the *sons of m.* *Eccl* 1:13; 3:10
good for *sons of m.* 2:3
delights of the *sons of m.* 8
the estate of the *sons of m.* 18
which befalleth the *sons of m.* 19
heart of *sons of m.* is set in. 8:11
the heart of the *sons of m.* 9:3
so are the *sons of m.* snared. 12
more than the *sons of m.* *Isa* 52:14
ways of the *sons of m.* *Jer* 32:19
driven from the *sons of m.* *Dan* 5:21
similitude of the *sons of m.* 10:16
joy is withered away from the *sons of m.* *Joel* 1:12
nor waiteth for the *sons of m.* *Mi* 5:7
be forgiven to *sons of m.* *Mark* 3:28
not known to *sons of m.* *Eph* 3:5

men *of war*

taken sum of *m. of w.* *Num* 31:49
till *m. of w.* came out of Egypt were. *Deut* 2:14, 16; *Josh* 5:6
the city, ye *m. of w.* *Josh* 6:3
drew sword, all these were *m. of w.* *Judg* 20:17
set over the *m. of w.* *1 Sam* 18:5
they were *m. of w.* and chief captains. *1 Ki* 9:22; *2 Chr* 8:9
and all the *m. of w.* fled. *2 Ki* 25:4; *Jer* 52:7
took an officer set over *m. of w.* *2 Ki* 25:19; *Jer* 52:25
Gadites *m. of w.* came to. *1 Chr* 12:8
these *m. of w.* came to Hebron. 38
set battle in array with *m. of w.* *2 Chr* 13:3
and the *m. of w.* were in. 17:13
the hands of *m. of w.* *Jer* 38:4
Ishmael slew *m. of w.* 41:3
Johanan took the *m. of w.* 16
all the *m. of w.* shall be cut off. 49:26; 50:30
m. of w. are affrighted. 51:32
Phut were thy *m. of w.* *Ezek* 27:10
all thy *m. of w.* that are in thee. 27
at my table with *m. of w.* 39:20
climb wall like *m. of w.* *Joel* 2:7
all the *m. of w.* draw near. 3:9
Herod with his *m. of w.* *Luke* 23:11

wicked **men**

but the *m.* of Sodom were *wicked.* *Gen* 13:13
tents of these *wicked m.* *Num* 16:26
then answered all the *wicked m.* *1 Sam* 30:22
as a man falleth before *wicked m.* *2 Sam* 3:34*
when *wicked m.* have slain. 4:11
marked old way that *wicked m.* have trodden. *Job* 22:15
walketh with *wicked m.* 34:8
he striketh them as *wicked m.* 26
of his answers for *wicked m.* 36
there be *wicked m.* to whom it happeneth. *Eccl* 8:14
people are found *wicked m.* *Jer* 5:26
destroy those *wicked m.* *Mat* 24:41
be delivered from *wicked m.* *2 Thes* 3:2

wise **men**

Pharaoh called for all *wise m.* *Gen* 41:8; *Ex* 7:11
wise m. that wrought. *Ex* 36:4
take ye *wise m.* and. *Deut* 1:13
chief of your tribes, *wise m.* 15
king said to *wise m.* *Esth* 1:13
then said Haman's *wise m.* 6:13
which *wise m.* have told. *Job* 15:18
hear my words, O ye *wise m.* 34:2
he seeth that *wise m.* die. *Ps* 49:10
wise m. lay up knowledge. *Pr* 10:14
he that walketh with *wise m.* 13:20
but *wise m.* turn away wrath. 29:8
the words of *wise m.* are. *Eccl* 9:17
where are thy *wise m.*? *Isa* 19:12
the wisdom of their *wise m.* 29:14
turneth *wise m.* backward. 44:25
the *wise m.* are ashamed. *Jer* 8:9
as among all the *wise m.* of. 10:7
Babylon, and on her *wise m.* 50:35
make drunken her *wise m.* 51:57
thy *wise m.* O Tyrus. *Ezek* 27:8
wise m. thereof were thy calkers. 9
destroy all the *wise m.* of. *Dan* 2:12
cannot the *wise m.* shew unto. 27
decree to bring in all the *wise m.* 4:6
king spake to the *wise m.* 5:7
even destroy the *wise m.* out. *Ob* 8
came *wise m.* from east. *Mat* 2:1
he had privily called the *wise m.* 7
was mocked of *wise m.* 16
I send *wise m.* 23:34
not many *wise m.* called. *1 Cor* 1:26
speak as to *wise m.*; judge ye. 10:15

men joined with *women*

both *m.* and *women* brought bracelets. *Ex* 35:22
destroyed the *m.* and *women* and. *Deut* 2:34; *Josh* 8:25
thousand *m.* and *women.* *Judg* 9:49
fled all the *m.* and *women.* 51
m. and *women,* upon the roof about 3000 *m* and *women.* 16:27
well to the *women* as *m.* *2 Sam* 6:19
brought the law before *m.* and *women.* *Neh* 8:2, 3
Jeremiah said to the *m.* and *women.* *Jer* 44:20
added to Lord both *m.* and *women.* *Acts* 5:14
Saul haling *m.* and *women.* 8:3
baptized, both *m.* and *women.* 12
whether *m.* or *women* he might bring them bound. 9:2
prison both *m.* and *women.* 22:4

men, *women* and *children, see* **children**

ye **men**

hearken unto me, *ye m.* *Judg* 9:7
ye m. of understanding. *Job* 34:10
ye m. of Galilee. *Acts* 1:11
ye m. of Judea. 2:14
ye m. of Israel. 5:35
ye m. and brethren, if ye. 13:15
ye m. of Athens. 17:22
ye m. of Ephesus, what man? 19:35

young **men**

that which the *young m.* *Gen* 14:25
Moses sent *young m.* *Ex* 24:5
Joshua one of the *young m.* *Num* 11:28
young m. that were spies. *Josh* 6:23
so used the *young m.* *Judg* 14:10
charged the *young m.* *Ruth* 2:9
followedst not *young m.* 3:10
the sin of the *young m.* *1 Sam* 2:17
your goodliest *young m.* 8:16
the *young m.* kept themselves. 21:4
and the vessels of the *young m.* 5
ask thy *young m.* and they. 25:8
handmaid saw not the *young m.* 25
let one of the *young m.* come. 26:22
save 400 *young m.* which rode. 30:17
David called one of the *young m.* *2 Sam* 1:15
let the *young m.* arise and. 2:14
hold on one of the *young m.* 21
have slain all the *young m.* 13:32
and ten *young m.* that bare. 18:15
consulted with *young m.* *1 Ki* 12:8
spake after counsel of *young m.* 14
2 Chr 10:8, 14
by *young m.* of princes. *1 Ki* 20:14
send, I pray thee, one of the *young m.* *2 Ki* 4:22*
there be come two *young m.* 5:22
their *young m.* wilt thou slay. 8:12
slew their *young m* with. *2 Chr* 36:17
it fell upon the *young m.* *Job* 1:19
the *young m.* saw me, and hid. 29:8
consumed their *young m.* *Ps* 78:63
praise the Lord, *young m.* 148:12
the glory of *young m.* is. *Pr* 20:29
no joy in their *young m.* *Isa* 9:17
bows also shall dash *young m.* 13:18
do I nourish up *young m.* 23:4
young m. shall be discomfited. 31:8
young m. shall utterly fall. 40:30
pour fury on assembly of *young m.* *Jer* 6:11
to cut off the *young m.* from. 9:21
the *young m.* shall die by. 11:22
against the mother of the *young m.* 15:8
let their *young m.* be slain. 18:21
young m. and old rejoice. 31:13
his chosen *young m.* are gone. 48:15
her *young m.* shall fall in the streets. 49:26; 50:30
spare ye not her *young m.* 51:3
assembly to crush my *young m.* *Lam* 1:15
my virgins and *young m.* are. 18
the *young m.* and old lie on. 2:21
took the *young m.* to grind. 5:13
the *young m.* have ceased from. 14
all of them desirable *young m.* *Ezek* 23:6, 12, 23
young m. of Aven shall fall. 30:17
your *young m.* shall see visions. *Joel* 2:28; *Acts* 2:17
and of your *young m.* *Amos* 2:11
your *young m.* have I slain. 4:10
your *young m.* shall faint. 8:13
the *young m.* cheerful. *Zech* 9:17
and the *young m.* laid. *Mark* 14:51
and the *young m.* arose. *Acts* 5:6
the *young m.* came in and found. 10
young m. likewise exhort. *Tit* 2:6
I write to you, *young m.* because. *1 John* 2:13, 14

Menahem

M. smote Shallum in. *2 Ki* 15:14
M. smote Tiphsah. 16
M. exacted money. 20

mend

brass to *m.* the house. *2 Chr* 24:12
gave it the workmen to *m.* 34:10

mending

James and John, with Zebedee, *m.* their nets. *Mat* 4:21; *Mark* 1:19

Mene

M. M. God hath numbered thy. *Dan* 5:25, 26

menpleasers

not with eye service, as *m.* *Eph* 6:6
Col 3:22

menservants

Abram had *m.* and. *Gen* 12:16
Abimelech gave *m.* to. 20:14
God hath given my master *m.* 24:35
Jacob had *m.* and camels. 30:43
32:5
shall not go out as *m.* do. *Ex* 21:7
rejoice before Lord, ye and your *m.* *Deut* 12:12
king will take you *m.* *1 Sam* 8:16
is it a time to receive *m.*? *2 Ki* 5:26
shall begin to beat the *m.* *Luke* 12:45
see **two**

menstealers

law is made for *m.* *1 Tim* 1:10

menstruous

cast them away as a *m.* *Isa* 30:22*
Jerusalem is as a *m.* *Lam* 1:17*
near to a *m.* woman. *Ezek* 18:6

mention

m. of me unto Pharaoh. *Gen* 4:14
make no *m.* of other gods. *Ex* 23:13
Josh 23:7
he made *m.* of the ark. *1 Sam* 4:18
no *m.* shall be made of coral or of pearls. *Job* 28:18
m. of thy righteousness. *Ps* 71:16
m. of Rahab and Babylon. 87:4
make *m.* that his name. *Isa* 12:4
that maketh *m.* thereof shall. 19:17
by thee only we will make *m.* 26:13

make *m.* of God of Israel. *Isa* 48:1
from bowels hath he made *m.* 49:1
ye that make *m.* of the Lord. 62:6
make ye *m.* to nations. *Jer* 4:16
I will not make *m.* of him. 20:9
we may not make *m.* of. *Amos* 6:10
I make *m.* of you always. *Rom* 1:9
Eph 1:16; *1 Thes* 1:2
making *m.* of thee always. *Philem* 4
Joseph made *m.* of the. *Heb* 11:22

mention

I will *m.* the lovingkindnesses of. *Isa* 63:7
burden of the Lord shall ye *m.* no more. *Jer* 23:36

mentioned

these cities, which are *m.* *Josh* 21:9
these *m.* by name. *1 Chr* 4:38
Jehu is *m.* in the book. *2 Chr* 20:34*
sister Sodom was not *m.* *Ezek* 16:56
his transgressions shall not be *m.* 18:22*
his righteousness shall not be *m.* 24*
none of his sins shall be *m.* 33:16*

Mephibosheth

son, his name was *M.* *2 Sam* 4:4
but *M.* shall eat bread at. 9:10, 11
M. had a young son Micha . . . of Ziba were servants to *M.* 12
are all that pertained unto *M.* 16:4
wentest thou not with me, *M.*? 19:25
but the king spared *M.* the. 21:7
sons of Rizpah, Armoni and *M.* 8

Merab

Saul's eldest daughter *M.* *1 Sam* 14:49; 18:17
M. should have been given. 18:19

Merari

Gershon, Kohath, *M.* *Gen* 46:11
Ex 6:16; *Num* 3:17; *1 Chr* 6:1, 16
23:6
sons of *M.* *Ex* 6:19; *Num* 3:20
1 Chr 6:19, 29; 23:21; 24:26
charge of the sons of *M.* *Num* 3:36
were numbered of *M.* 4:42
M. set forward. 10:17
oxen given to the sons of *M.* 7:8
cities given to *M.* *Josh* 21:7, 40
1 Chr 6:63, 77

merchandise

thou shalt not make *m.* *Deut* 21:14
and maketh *m.* of him. 24:7
m. of it is better than the *m.* *Pr* 3:14
perceiveth that her *m.* is good. 31:18
her *m.* shall be holiness. *Isa* 23:18
the *m.* of Ethiopia shall come. 45:14
make a prey of thy *m.* *Ezek* 26:12
were in thee to occupy thy *m.* 27:9
isles were the *m.* of thy hands. 15*
by the multitude of thy *m.* 28:16*
farm, another to his *m.* *Mat* 22:5
make not my Father's house an house of *m.* *John* 2:16
feigned words make *m.* *2 Pet* 2:3
no man buyeth their *m.* *Rev* 18:11
the *m.* of gold, and silver. 12

merchant

current money with *m.* *Gen* 23:16
she is like the *m.* ships. *Pr* 31:14
delivereth girdles to the *m.* 24
all powders of the *m.* *S of S* 3:6
against the *m.* city. *Isa* 23:11*
art a *m.* of the people. *Ezek* 27:3
Tarshish was thy *m.* by reason. 12
Syria was thy *m.* 16, 18, 20*
he is a *m.*, the balances. *Hos* 12:7*
for all the *m.* people. *Zeph* 1:11*

merchantman, men

passed by Midianites *m.* *Gen* 37:28
he had of the *m.* *1 Ki* 10:15
like a *m.* seeking. *Mat* 13:45

merchants

traffic of spice *m.* *1 Ki* 10:15
the king's *m.* received linen yarn. 28; *2 Chr* 1:16
besides that which *m.* *2 Chr* 9:14
the goldsmiths and the *m.* *Neh* 3:32
so the *m.* lodged without. 13:20
part him among the *m.*? *Job* 41:6
m. of Zidon replenished. *Isa* 23:2
city, whose *m.* are princes. 8
thy *m.* they shall wander. 47:15*
cropt the twigs, he set it in a city of *m.* *Ezek* 17:4
Meshech, were thy *m.* 27:13
Judah and Israel thy *m.* 17
in these were thy *m.* 21
m. of Sheba. 22, 23
there were thy *m.* in all sorts. 24
m. shall hiss at thee. 36
m. of Tarshish. 38:13
hast multiplied thy *m.* *Nah* 3:16
for the *m.* of the earth. *Rev* 18:3
the *m.* of the earth shall weep. 11
for thy *m.* were the great men. 23

Mercurius

called Paul, *M.*, because. *Acts* 14:12

mercies

of the least of thy *m.* *Gen* 32:10
for his *m.* are great. *2 Sam* 24:14
1 Chr 21:13
remember the *m.* of David thy servant. *2 Chr* 6:42
in thy manifold *m.* *Neh* 9:19
according to thy *m.* thou gavest. 27
deliver according to thy *m.* 28
m. thou didst not consume. 31
according to thy *m.* blot out. *Ps* 51:1
in the multitude of thy *m.* 69:13
according to thy tender *m.* 16
I will sing of the *m.* of Lord. 89:1
not multitude of thy *m.* 106:7
according to multitude of his *m.* 45
let thy *m.* come also to me. 119:41
with great *m.* will I gather. *Isa* 54:7
sure *m.* of David. 55:3; *Acts* 13:34
on them according to his *m.* *Isa* 63:7
where is thy zeal and thy *m.*? 15*
I have taken away my *m.* *Jer* 16:5
shew *m.* to you, that he may. 42:12
it is of the Lord's *m.* we. *Lam* 3:22
according to multitude of his *m.* 32
desire *m.* concerning. *Dan* 2:18
to the Lord our God belong *m.* 9:9
righteousness, but thy great *m.* 18
betroth thee unto me in *m.* *Hos* 2:19
to Jerusalem with *m.* *Zech* 1:16
I beseech you by the *m.* *Rom* 12:1
the Father of *m.* and. *2 Cor* 1:3
if any fellowship of the Spirit, if any bowels and *m.* *Phil* 2:1*
put on therefore, holy and beloved, bowels of *m.* *Col* 3:12*

tender **mercies**

remember, O Lord, thy *tender m.* *Ps* 25:6; 51:1
withhold not thy *tender m.* 40:11
in anger shut up his *tender m.* 77:9
let thy *tender m.* speedily. 79:8
crowneth thee with *tender m.* 103:4
let thy *tender m.* come unto. 119:77
great are thy *tender m.* O Lord. 156
tender m. are over all his. 145:9
tender m. of the wicked. *Pr* 12:10

merciful

Lord being *m.* unto Lot. *Gen* 19:16
Lord God, *m.* and gracious. *Ex* 34:6*
be *m.* O Lord, to thy. *Deut* 21:8*
and will be *m.* to his land. 32:43*
with the *m.* thou wilt shew thyself *m.* *2 Sam* 22:26; *Ps* 18:25
of Israel are *m.* kings. *1 Ki* 20:31†
God is gracious and *m.* *2 Chr* 30:9
pardon, gracious and *m.* *Neh* 9:17*
and be *m.* to me. *Ps* 26:11; 41:4
10; 56:1; 57:1; 86:3; 119:58, 132
the righteous is ever *m.* 37:26*
be not *m.* to any wicked. 59:5
God be *m.* to us, and bless us. 67:1
Lord is *m.* and gracious. 103:8*
for his *m.* kindness is great. 117:2
let thy *m.* kindness be for. 119:76
the *m.* man doeth good. *Pr* 11:17†
m. men are taken away. *Isa* 57:1†
Return, for I am *m.* saith. *Jer* 3:12
he is gracious and *m.* *Joel* 2:15*
that thou art a *m.* God. *Jonah* 4:2*
blessed are the *m.*: for they. *Mat* 5:7
be ye *m.* as your Father also is *m.* *Luke* 6:36
publican saying, God be *m.* 18:13
be a *m.* High Priest. *Heb* 2:17
m. to their unrighteousness. 8:12
see **God**

mercy

(*Compassion; pity for the undeserving and the guilty. Used of both God and man. The word is frequently changed in the Revisions to* lovingkindness)
not destitute of his *m.* *Gen* 24:27
and God give you *m.* before. 43:14
keeping *m.* for thousands. *Ex* 34:7
Dan 9:4
Lord is longsuffering and of great *m.* *Num* 14:18; *Ps* 103:11; 145:8
covenant and *m.* *Deut* 7:9, 12
my *m.* shall not depart. *2 Sam* 7:15
1 Chr 17:13; *Ps* 89:24
m. and truth be with. *2 Sam* 15:20
keepest covenant and *m.* *1 Ki* 8:23
Neh 1:5; 9:32
m. endureth for ever. *1 Chr* 16:34
41; *2 Chr* 5:13; 7:3, 6; 20:21
Ezra 3:11; *Ps* 106:1; 107:1
118:1; 136:1, *to the end*
Jer 33:11
extended *m.* to me. *Ezra* 7:28
extended *m.* to us in sight of. 9:9
grant him *m.* in the sight. *Neh* 1:11
correction or for *m.* *Job* 37:13
and through the *m.* of. *Ps* 21:7
goodness and *m.* shall follow. 23:6
the paths of the Lord are *m.* 25:10
that trusteth in Lord, *m.* shall. 32:10
them that hope in his *m.* 33:18
I trust in the *m.* of God for. 52:8
God shall send forth his *m.* 57:3
the God of my *m.* shall prevent me. 59:10, 17
O prepare *m.* and truth. 61:7
O Lord, belongeth *m.* 62:12
which hath not turned his *m.* 66:20
is his *m.* clean gone for ever? doth *m.* fail? 77:8
m. and truth are met together. 85:10
art plenteous in *m.* 86:5, 15; 103:8
I said, *m.* shall be built up. 89:2
m. and truth shall go before. 14
my *m.* will I keep for him for. 28
he hath remembered his *m.* 98:3
the Lord is good, his *m.* is. 100:5
sing of *m.* and judgement. 101:1
the *m.* of the Lord is from. 103:17
there be none to extend *m.* 109:12
with the Lord there is *m.* and. 130:7
in those that hope in his *m.* 147:11
let not *m.* and truth forsake. *Pr* 3:3
he that hath *m.* on the poor. 14:21*
m. and truth shall be to them. 22
he that honoureth God hath *m.* 31
by *m.* and truth iniquity is. 16:6
m. and truth preserve the king . . . is upholden by *m.* 20:28; *Isa* 16:5
he that followeth after *m.* *Pr* 21:21
he that hath *m.* on them. *Isa* 49:10
saith the Lord that hath *m.* 54:10
in my favour have I had *m.* on. 60:10
are cruel, and have no *m.* *Jer* 6:23
there is no truth, nor *m.* *Hos* 4:1†
for I desired *m.* and not sacrifice. 6:6†
reap in *m.* 10:12†
keep *m.* and wait on God. 12:6†
the fatherless findeth *m.* 14:3
they forsake their own *m.* *Jonah* 2:8†
do justly, and to love *m.* *Mi* 6:8†
because he delighteth in *m.* 7:18
perform the *m.* to Abraham. 20
in wrath remember *m.* *Hab* 3:2
merciful, shall obtain *m.* *Mat* 5:7
omitted judgement and *m.* 23:23
m. is on them that fear. *Luke* 1:50
in remembrance of his *m.* 54
to perform the *m.* promised to. 72
remission through the tender *m.* 78
his glory on vessels of *m.* *Rom* 9:23
have now obtained *m.* 11:30
your *m.* they also may obtain *m.* 31
might glorify God for his *m.* 15:9
that hath obtained *m.* *1 Cor* 7:25
as we have received *m.* *2 Cor* 4:1
peace be on them, and *m.* *Gal* 6:16
God who is rich in *m.* *Eph* 2:4
death, but God had *m.* on. *Phil* 2:27
m. and peace from God. *1 Tim* 1:2
2 Tim 1:2; *Tit* 1:4; *2 John* 3
I obtained *m.* because I. *1 Tim* 1:13
for this cause I obtained *m.* 16

mess, or **messes**
sent *m.* to them, but Benjamin's *m.* five times so much. *Gen* 43:34
a *m.* of meat. *2 Sam* 11:8

Messiah
(*Literally, the Anointed One. It means the expected king and deliverer of the Hebrews, who should free them from the yoke of aliens, and make them a great nation ruling over the whole world.* Christ *is the same word in the Greek. Jesus of Nazareth, believed by his followers to be this long-promised Messiah of the Jews, is for that reason called Christ. The first promise of the Messiah, although not using that name, is that to Eve in* Gen 3:15. *The same promise was, in varying phraseology, repeated to many individuals through the ages, notably to Abraham and David*)
to build Jerusalem unto the *M.* the Prince. *Dan* 9:25*
and after 62 weeks shall *M.* be. 26*
found *M.* which is Christ. *John* 1:41
woman saith, I know that *M.* 4:25

met
and the angels of God *m.* *Gen* 32:1
thou by this drove I *m.*? 33:8
God of the Hebrews hath *m.* with us. *Ex* 3:18; 5:3
the Lord *m.* him, and sought. 4:24
Aaron went and *m.* Moses in. 27
they *m.* Moses and Aaron who. 5:20
God *m.* Balaam. *Num* 23:4, 16
because they *m.* you not. *Deut* 23:4 *Neh* 13:2
Amalek *m.* thee by way. *Deut* 25:18
all these kings were *m.* *Josh* 11:5
of prophets *m.* Saul. *1 Sam* 10:10
behold, Abigail *m.* David. 25:20
Ziba *m.* David with. *2 Sam* 16:1
Absalom *m.* the servants of. 18:9
a lion *m.* him. *1 Ki* 13:24
Elijah *m.* Obadiah, and he. 18:7
Ahaziah *m.* Jehu. *2 Ki* 9:21*
Jehu *m.* with the brethren. 10:13
mercy and truth are *m.* *Ps* 85:10
there *m.* him a woman. *Pr* 7:10
a lion, and bear *m.* him. *Amos* 5:19
m. him two possessed. *Mat* 8:28
behold, Jesus *m.* them, saying. 28:9
where two ways *m.* *Mark* 11:4*
much people *m.* him. *Luke* 9:37 *John* 12:18
there *m.* him ten men. *Luke* 17:12
then Martha went and *m.* him. *John* 11:20, 30
Cornelius *m.* him, and. *Acts* 10:25
damsel possessed *m.* us. 16:16
he disputed with them that *m.* 17:17
place where two seas *m.* 27:41
who *m.* Abraham. *Heb* 7:1
when Melchizedek *m.* him. 10

mete
when they did *m.* it with. *Ex* 16:18
I will *m.* out valley. *Ps* 60:6; 108:7
with what measure ye *m.* it shall be. *Mat* 7:2; *Mark* 4:24; *Luke* 6:38

meted
go to a nation *m.* out. *Isa* 18:2, 7
m. out heaven with a span. 40:12

meteyard
no unrighteousness in *m.* *Lev* 19:35

Metheg-ammah
David took *M.* from. *2 Sam* 8:1

Methuselah
Enoch begat *M.* *Gen* 5:21
M. begat Lamech. 25
days of *M.* were 969 years. 27
Henoch, *M.* Lamech. *1 Chr* 1:3
which was the son of *M.* *Luke* 3:37

Micah
mount Ephraim called *M.* *Judg* 17:1
man *M.* had an house of gods. 5
M. consecrated the Levite for. 12
thus dealeth *M.* 18:4
they set up *M.*'s graven image. 31
M. his son, Reaia his. *1 Chr* 5:5
Merib-baal begat *M.* 8:34; 9:40
sons of *M.* were Pithon, and Melech. *1 Chr* 8:35; 9:41
Mattaniah the son of *M.* 9:15
Abdon the son of *M.* *2 Chr* 34:20
M., Rehob, sealed the. *Neh* 10:11
M. the Morasthite prophesied in. *Jer* 26:18; *Mi* 1:1

Micaiah
M. the son of Imlah. *1 Ki* 22:8, 9 *2 Chr* 18:8
Zedekiah smote *M.* on. *1 Ki* 22:24
Take *M.*, and carry him back to Amon. 26; *2 Chr* 18:23, 25

mice
five golden *m.* *1 Sam* 6:4, 18
images of your emerods and *m.* 5

Michael
M. one of the chief. *Dan* 10:13
none holdeth with me but *M.* 21
at that time shall *M.* stand. 12:1
yet *M.* the archangel. *Jude* 9
M. and angels fought. *Rev* 12:7

Michaiah
mother was *M.* of Uriel. *2 Chr* 13:2
Jehoshaphat sent *M.* to teach. 17:7
son of *M.* to give. *Neh* 12:35, 41
M. heard what Baruch. *Jer* 36:11, 13

Michal
younger daughter *M.* *1 Sam* 14:49
M. Saul's daughter. 18:20, 28
so *M.* let David down. 19:12
M. took an image and laid. 13
Saul had given *M.* David's. 25:44
thou first bring *M.* *2 Sam* 3:13
deliver me my wife *M.* whom. 14
M. Saul's daughter looked . . . and despised. 6:16; *1 Chr* 15:29
M. had no child to. *2 Sam* 6:23
king took five sons of *M.* 21:8

midday
when *m.* was past. *1 Ki* 18:29
from morning to *m.* *Neh* 8:3
at *m.* O king, I saw in. *Acts* 26:13

middle
beginning of *m.* watch. *Judg* 7:19
there come people by the *m.* 9:37
hold of the two *m.* pillars. 16:29
of the *m.* of a sling. *1 Sam* 25:29
their garments in the *m.* *2 Sam* 10:4
the king did hallow the *m.* of the court. *1 Ki* 8:64; *2 Chr* 7:7
gone into the *m.* court. *2 Ki* 20:4
princes sat in the *m.* gate. *Jer* 39:3
were a wheel in the *m.* *Ezek* 1:16
broken down the *m.* wall. *Eph* 2:14

middlemost
higher than the *m.* *Ezek* 42:5, 6

Midian
dwelt in the land of *M.* *Ex* 2:15
Jethro priest of *M.* heard all. 18:1
said to the elders of *M.* *Num* 22:4
Zur of a chief house in *M.* 25:15
go and avenge the Lord of *M.* 31:3
they slew the kings of *M.* beside. 8
Israel took all the women of *M.* 9
delivered them to *M.* *Judg* 6:1, 2
hand hath God delivered *M.* 7:14
delivered us from *M.* 8:22; 9:17
M. subdued before Israel. 28
Edomites arose out of *M.* *1 Ki* 11:18
the yoke, as in day of *M.* *Isa* 9:4
the slaughter of *M.* at Oreb. 10:26
the dromedaries of *M.* shall. 60:6
curtains of the land of *M.* *Hab* 3:7

Midianites
by *M.* merchantmen. *Gen* 37:28
the *M.* sold him into Egypt to. 36
vex *M.* and smite them. *Num* 25:17
avenge Israel of the *M.* 31:2
to the Lord because of *M.* *Judg* 6:7
and thou shalt smite the *M.* 16
Israel pursued after the *M.* 7:23
princes of the *M.* Oreb, Zeeb. 25
wentest to fight with the *M.* 8:1
do to them as to the *M.* *Ps* 83:9

Midianitish
brought a *M.* woman. *Num* 25:6
of the *M.* woman was Cozbi. 15

midnight
at *m.* will I go into the. *Ex* 11:4
at *m.* the Lord smote the. 12:29
till *m.* and rose at *m.* *Judg* 16:3
at *m.* the man was afraid. *Ruth* 3:8
she arose at *m.* and. *1 Ki* 3:20
shall be troubled at *m.* *Job* 34:20
at *m.* I will rise to. *Ps* 119:62
at *m.* there was a cry. *Mat* 25:6
come at even, or *m.* *Mark* 13:35
at *m.* and say, Lend me. *Luke* 11:5
and at *m.* Paul and. *Acts* 16:25
continued his speech till *m.* 20:7

midst
dry through *m.* of sea. *Ex* 14:16 *Num* 33:8; *Neh* 9:11; *Ps* 136:14
take sickness from *m.* *Ex* 23:25
mountain burnt to the *m.* *Deut* 4:11
evil away from the *m.* of thee. 13:5
raise up a Prophet from *m.* 18:15
from the *m.* of the furnace of iron. *1 Ki* 8:51
brook that ran through the *m.* of. *2 Chr* 32:4
m. thereof being paved. *S of S* 3:10
purged blood from the *m.* *Isa* 4:4
breath shall reach to the *m.* 30:28
take away from the *m.* of thee. 58:9
proceed from the *m.* of. *Jer* 30:21
come from the *m.* of Sihon. 48:45
through the *m.* of the city. *Ezek* 9:4
glory went up from *m.* of city. 11:23
I will cut him off from *m.* 14:8, 9
m. of it is burnt, is it meet? 15:4
have filled the *m.* of thee. 28:16
I will bring forth a fire from *m.* of. 18
of the *m.* of the fire. *Dan* 3:26
judge from *m.* thereof. *Amos* 2:3
passing through the *m.* *Luke* 4:30
about the *m.* of the feast. *John* 7:14
going through the *m.* of them. 8:59
angel flying through the *m.* *Rev* 8:13

in the **midst**
be a firmament *in the m.* *Gen* 1:6
the tree of life *in the m.* 2:9; 3:3
Abram divided them *in the m.* 15:10
wonders I will do *in the m.* *Ex* 3:20
I am the Lord *in the m.* of. 8:22
overthrew Egyptians *in the m.* 14:27
walked on dry land *in the m.* of sea. 29; 15:19
for I will not go up *in the m.* 33:3
in the m. of their uncleanness. *Lev* 16:16
set forward *in the m.* of camp. *Num* 2:17
defile not the camp *in the m.* 5:3
and the city shall be *in the m.* 35:5 *Ezek* 48:15
acts which he did *in the m.* of. *Deut* 11:3
swallowed them up *in the m.* 6
separate three cities *in the m.* 19:2
God walketh *in the m.* of. 23:14
priests stood firm *in the m.* of Jordan. *Josh* 3:17; 4:10
set up twelve stones *in the m.* 4:9
accursed thing *in the m.* of. 7:13
are hid in the earth *in the m.* 21
anointed him *in the m.* *1 Sam* 16:13
was yet alive *in the m.* *2 Sam* 18:14
stood *in the m.* of the ground. 23:12
a lion *in the m.* of a pit in time. 20
they were *in the m.* of Samaria. *2 Ki* 6:20
their garments *in the m.* *1 Chr* 19:4
till we come *in the m.* *Neh* 4:11
it is melted *in the m.* of. *Ps* 22:14
will declare thy name: *in the m.* of the congregation. 22; *Heb* 2:12
God is *in the m.* of her, she. *Ps* 46:5
mischief *in the m.* 55:10
wickedness *in the m.* 11
enemies roar *in the m.* of. 74:4
working salvation *in the m.* 12
and he let it fall *in the m.* 78:28
take me not away *in the m.* 102:24
rule thou *in the m.* of thine. 110:2
pay vows *in the m.* of thee. 116:19
I walk *in the m.* of trouble. 138:7
keep them *in the m.* of. *Pr* 4:21
I was in all evil *in the m.* 5:14
I lead *in the m.* of the paths. 8:20
which is *in the m.* of fools. 14:33
he that lieth down *in the m.* 23:34
the way of a ship *in the m.* 30:19

enemies wrongfully are *m.* *Ps* 69:4
thou driest up *m.* rivers. 74:15
in the congregation of the *m.* 82:1
among sons *m.* can be likened? 89:6
thou hast a *m.* arm. 13
laid help upon one that is *m.* 19
bosom the reproach of the *m.* 50
mightier than the *m.* waves. 93:4
make his *m.* power known. 106:8
his seed shall be *m.* upon. 112:2
sharp arrows of the *m.* with. 120:4
nations, and slew *m.* kings. 135:10
he that is slow to anger is better than the *m.* *Pr* 16:32
the lot parteth between the *m.* 18:18
scaleth the city of the *m.* 21:22
for their Redeemer is *m.* 23:11*
m. shall fall in the war *Isa* 3:25
that are *m.* to drink wine. 5:22
his *m.* wind shall he shake. 11:15
like the rushing of *m.* waters. 17:12
away with a *m.* captivity. 22:17
prey be taken from the *m.*? 49:24
in righteousness, *m.* to save. 63:1
a *m.* and an ancient nation. *Jer* 5:15
great in counsel and *m.* 32:19
shew thee great and *m.* things. 33:3
hath also taken the *m.* *Ezek* 17:13
by the swords of the *m.* will. 32:12
the strong among the *m.* shall. 21
shall not lie with the *m.* that. 27
with a great and *m.* army. 38:15
eat the flesh of the *m.* and. 39:18
how great and *m.* are his. *Dan* 4:3
his power shall be *m.* but not. 8:24
a *m.* king shall stand up that. 11:3
a very great and *m.* army. 25
the *m.* deliver himself. *Amos* 2:14
courageous among the *m.* 2:16
I know your *m.* sins. 5:12
righteousness as a *m.* stream. 24
a *m.* tempest in the sea. *Jonah* 1:4
howl, because the *m.* *Zech* 11:2
most of his *m.* works. *Mat* 11:20
if the *m.* works which were. 21, 23
this man these *m.* works? 13:54
he did not many *m.* works there. 58
Mark 6:5
Baptist risen; therefore *m.* works do shew forth. *Mat* 14:2; *Mark* 6:14
m. works are wrought by. *Mark* 6:2
he that is *m.* hath done. *Luke* 1:49
he hath put down the *m.* from. 52
amazed at *m.* power of God. 9:43
there arose a *m.* famine in. 15:14
praised God for the *m.* works. 19:37
who was a prophet *m.* in deed. 24:19
as of a rushing *m.* wind. *Acts* 2:2
Moses was *m.* in words and. 7:22
Apollos, *m.* in the scriptures. 18:24
Gentiles obedient through *m.* signs. *Rom* 15:19
not many *m.* not many. *1 Cor* 1:26
weak, to confound things *m.* 27
weapons of our warfare are *m.* through God. *2 Cor* 10:4
is not weak, but *m.* in you. 13:3
same was *m.* in me toward. *Gal* 2:8
working of his *m.* power. *Eph* 1:19
Jesus shall be revealed with his *m.* angels. *2 Thes* 1:7
shaken of a *m.* wind. *Rev* 6:13
I saw another *m.* angel. 10:1; 18:21
so *m.* an earthquake and. 16:18
Alas, Babylon, that *m.* city! 18:10
voice of *m.* thunderings. 19:6
see **acts, God, hand, man, men**

mighty *one*

Nimrod began to be a *m. one.* *Gen* 10:8
the *m. one* of Israel. *Isa* 1:24
30:29; 49:26; 60:16
Lebanon shall fall by *m. one.* 10:34
Lord hath a *m.* and strong *one.* 28:2
me as a *m.* terrible *one.* *Jer* 20:11
him into hand of *m. one.* *Ezek* 31:11

mighty *ones*

prancing of their *m. ones.* *Judg* 5:22
I have called my *m. ones.* *Isa* 13:3
their *m. ones* are beaten. *Jer* 46:5
thither cause thy *m. ones.* *Joel* 3:11

Milcah

M. daughter of Haran. *Gen* 11:29
M. also bare children. *Gen* 22:20, 23
Bethuel son of *M.* the wife. 24:15
daughter's name was *M.* *Num* 26:33

milch

thirty *m.* camels with. *Gen* 32:15
make a new cart, take two *m.* kine. *2 Sam* 6:7, 10

Milcom

Solomon went after *M.* *1 Ki* 11:5
they have worshipped *M.* god. 33
had builded for *M.* *2 Ki* 23:13

mildew, *see* **blasting**

mile

compel thee to go a *m.* *Mat* 5:41

Miletum

have I left at *M.* sick. *2 Tim* 4:20

Miletus

next day we came to *M.* *Acts* 20:15
from *M.* he sent to Ephesus to. 17

milk

An important article of food in the East. Not only the milk of cows, but also that of sheep, Deut 32:14, *of camels,* Gen 32:15, *and of goats,* Pr 27:27, *was used. The latter was most highly esteemed.*

took butter and *m.* *Gen* 18:8
teeth shall be white with *m.* 49:12
butter of kine and *m.* *Deut* 32:14
Jael opened a bottle of *m.* *Judg* 4:19
water, and she gave him *m.* 5:25
poured me out as *m.*? *Job* 10:10
his breasts are full of *m.* 21:24
thou shalt have goats' *m.* *Pr* 27:27
the churning of *m.* bringeth. 30:33
honey and *m.* are under. *S of S* 4:11
drunk my wine with my *m.* 5:1
his eyes washed with *m.* and. 12
for abundance of *m.* that. *Isa* 7:22
are weaned from the *m.* 28:9
come, buy wine and *m.* without. 55:1
thou shalt suck the *m.* of. 60:16
were whiter than *m.* *Lam* 4:7
fruit, and drink thy *m.* *Ezek* 25:4
hills shall flow with *m.* *Joel* 3:18
I have fed you with *m.* *1 Cor* 3:2
flock, and eateth not of the *m.*? 9:7
such as have need of *m.* *Heb* 5:12
that useth *m.* is a babe. 13
desire sincere *m.* of word. *1 Pet* 2:2
see **flowing**

milk

that ye may *m.* out and. *Isa* 66:11

mill, -s

that is behind the *m.* *Ex* 11:5
ground the manna in *m.* *Num* 11:8
shall be grinding at the *m.* *Mat* 24:41

millet

take lentiles, *m.* and. *Ezek* 4:9

millions

be thou mother of thousands of *m.* *Gen* 24:60

Millo

all the house of *M.* *Judg* 9:6
let fire devour the house of *M.* 20
built round about from *M.* *2 Sam* 5:9
of the levy to build *M.* *1 Ki* 9:15
did Solomon build *M.* 24; 11:27
Joash in the house of *M.* *2 Ki* 12:20

millstone

no man shall take the *m.* *Deut* 24:6
woman cast a piece of *m.* *Judg* 9:53
2 Sam 11:21
a piece of the nether *m.* *Job* 41:24
a *m.* were hanged about his neck. *Mat* 18:6; *Mark* 9:42; *Luke* 17:2
a stone like a great *m.* *Rev* 18:21
sound of a *m.* shall be heard. 22

millstones

the *m.* and grind meal. *Isa* 47:2
away the sound of the *m.* *Jer* 25:10

mincing

wanton eyes, walking and *m.* *Isa* 3:16

mind, *substantive*

a grief of *m.* to Isaac. *Gen* 26:35
m. of the Lord might. *Lev* 24:12*
all the desire of his *m.* *Deut* 18:6*
give thee sorrow of *m.* 28:65*
shalt call them to *m.* among. 30:1
him with a willing *m.* *1 Chr* 28:9
people had a *m.* to work. *Neh* 4:6
but he is in one *m.* who? *Job* 23:13
dead man out of *m.* *Ps* 31:12
with a wicked *m.* *Pr* 21:27
all his *m.* but a wise man. 29:11*
perfect peace, whose *m.* *Isa* 26:3
bring it again to *m.* O ye. 46:8
shall not come into *m.* 65:17
covenant shall not come to *m.* *Jer* 3:16
and came it not into his *m.*? 44:21
his *m.* was hardened. *Dan* 5:20*
then shall his *m.* change. *Hab* 1:11
clothed, and in his right *m.* *Mark* 5:15; *Luke* 8:35
called to *m.* the words. *Mark* 14:72
Mary cast in her *m.* *Luke* 1:29
neither be ye of doubtful *m.* 12:29
received word with all readiness of *m.* *Acts* 17:11
serve with humility of *m.* 20:19
given up to a reprobate *m.* *Rom* 1:28
with the *m.* I serve the law. 7:25
carnal *m.* is enmity against. 8:7
he knoweth what is the *m.* of. 27
who hath known the *m.* of? 11:34
be of the same *m.* one toward. 12:16
fully persuaded in his own *m.* 14:5
with one *m.* glorify God. 15:6
together in the same *m.* *1 Cor* 1:10
known the *m.* of the Lord? . . . but we have the *m.* of Christ. 2:16
your fervent *m.* toward me. *2 Cor* 7:7
there be first a willing *m.* 8:12*
brethren, be of one *m.* 13:11
Phil 1:27*; 2:2
desires of the flesh and *m.* *Eph* 2:3
walk in vanity of their *m.* 4:17
in lowliness of *m.* let each. *Phil* 2:3
let this *m.* be in you which. 5
that they be of the same *m.* 4:2
puffed up by his fleshly *m.* *Col* 2:18
humbleness of *m.*, meekness. 3:12*
not soon shaken in *m.* *2 Thes* 2:2
God hath given us the spirit of a sound *m.* *2 Tim* 1:7*
their *m.* and conscience. *Tit* 1:15
put them in *m.* to be subject. 3:1
put my laws into their *m.* *Heb* 8:10
be ye all of one *m.* *1 Pet* 3:8
likewise with the same *m.* 4:1
not for lucre, but of a ready *m.* 5:2
here is the *m.* which hath. *Rev* 17:9
these have one *m.* and shall give. 13
see **alienated**

mine or *my* **mind**

not done them of *mine* own *m.* *Num* 16:28
good or bad of *mine* own *m.* 24:13
that which is in *my m.* *1 Sam* 2:35
was in *my m.* to build. *1 Chr* 22:7*
my m. could not be toward. *Jer* 15:1
nor came it into *my m.* 19:5; 32:35
this I recall to *my m.* *Lam* 3:21
another law warring against the law of *my m.* *Rom* 7:23

thy **mind**

not *thy m.* on the asses. *1 Sam* 9:20
be according to *thy m.*? *Job* 34:33
things come into *thy m.* *Ezek* 38:10
thoughts came into *thy m.* *Dan* 2:29
love the Lord thy God with all *thy m.* *Mat* 22:37; *Mark* 12:30
Luke 10:27
without *thy m.* would. *Philem* 14

your **mind**

if it be *your m.* I should. *Gen* 23:8
let Jerusalem come into *your m.* *Jer* 51:50
that come into *your m.* *Ezek* 11:5
which cometh into *your m.* 20:32
by renewing of *your m.* *Rom* 12:2
of *your* ready *m.* *2 Cor* 8:19
forwardness of *your m.* 9:2
in the spirit of *your m.* *Eph* 4:23
sometime alienated and enemies in *your m.* *Col* 1:21
up the loins of *your m.* *1 Pet* 1:13

mind, *verb*

are after flesh, *m.* things. *Rom* 8:5
m. not high things, but. 12:16
nevertheless let us *m.* *Phil* 3:16
for many walk, who *m.* earthly. 19

minded
stedfastly *m.* to go with. *Ruth* 1:18
Joash was *m.* to repair. *2 Chr* 24:4
which are *m.* of their own free will. *Ezra* 7:13
Joseph was *m.* to put. *Mat* 1:19
for to be carnally *m.* is death, but to be spiritually *m.* is. *Rom* 8:6*
be not high-*m.* but fear. 11:20
grant you to be like *m.* one. 15:5
this confidence I was *m.* *2 Cor* 1:15
when I was thus *m.* did I use. 17
will be no otherwise *m.* *Gal* 5:10
that ye be like *m.* having. *Phil* 2:2
no man like *m.* who will care. 20
be thus *m.* if in any thing ye be otherwise *m.* God will reveal. 3:15
comfort the feeble-*m.* *1 Thes* 5:14
the rich be not high-*m.* *1 Tim* 6:17
shall be heady, high-*m.* *2 Tim* 3:4
exhort to be sober *m.* *Tit* 2:6
a double *m.* man is unstable. *Jas* 1:8
your hearts, ye double *m.* 4:8

mindful
be ye *m.* always of his. *1 Chr* 16:15*
our fathers were not *m.* of. *Neh* 9:17
what is man, that thou art *m.* of him, and son of man? *Ps* 8:4; *Heb* 2:6
be *m.* of his covenant. *Ps* 111:5
Lord hath been *m.* of us, he. 115:12
not been *m.* of the rock. *Isa* 17:10
being *m.* of thy tears. *2 Tim* 1:4*
if they had been *m.* of that country. *Heb* 11:15
m. of the words spoken. *2 Pet* 3:2

minding
Paul *m.* himself to go afoot. *Acts* 20:13

minds
and speak your *m.* *Judg* 19:30
be chafed in their *m.* *2 Sam* 17:8
if it be your *m.* let none go forth. *2 Ki* 9:15
they set their *m.* *Ezek* 24:25*
with despiteful *m.* to cast it. 36:5*
and made their *m.* evil. *Acts* 14:2
they changed their *m.*, and said. 28:6
but their *m.* were blinded. *2 Cor* 3:14
world hath blinded the *m.* 4:4
your *m.* should be corrupted. 11:3
God shall keep your *m.* *Phil* 4:7
men of corrupt *m.* *1 Tim* 6:5 *2 Tim* 3:8
in their *m.* will I write. *Heb* 10:16
wearied and faint in your *m.* 12:3*
I stir up your pure *m.* by. *2 Pet* 3:1

mine
that thou seest is *m.* *Gen* 31:43
m. as Reuben and Simeon shall be *m.* 48:5
firstborn, both of man and beast, it is *m.* *Ex* 13:2; 34:19; *Num* 3:13
for all the earth is *m.* *Ex* 19:5 *Ps* 50:12
that ye should be *m.* *Lev* 20:26 *Isa* 43:1
the land is *m.* for ye are. *Lev* 25:23
the Levites shall be *m.* *Num* 3:12 45; 8:14
of children of Israel are *m.* 8:17
Joab's field is near *m.* *2 Sam* 14:30
the kingdom was *m.* *1 Ki* 2:15
let it be neither *m.* nor thine. 3:26
gold, and wives, are *m.* 20:3
if ye will be *m.* and if. *2 Ki* 10:6
is under heaven is *m.* *Job* 41:11
myself from *m.* iniquity. *Ps* 18:23
beast of the forest is *m.* 50:10
wild beasts of field are *m.* 11
Gilead is *m.* and Manasseh is *m.* 60:7; 108:8
counsel is *m.* and sound. *Pr* 8:14
my beloved is *m.* and I am his. *S. of S.* 2:16; 6:3
my vineyard, which is *m.* 8:12
word shall stand, *m.* or. *Jer* 44:28
thee, thou becamest *m.* *Ezek* 16:8
souls are *m.*; soul of son is *m.* 18:4
and they were *m.* 23:4
when she was *m.* 5
the river is *m.* 29:9
these countries be *m.* 35:10
is *m.* and the gold is *m.* *Hag* 2:8

they shall be *m.* saith. *Mal* 3:17
heareth sayings of *m.* *Mat* 7:24
heareth these sayings of *m.* and. 26
my right hand and on my left, is not *m.* to give. 20:23; *Mark* 10:40
for a friend of *m.* in his journey is come to me. *Luke* 11:6
Jesus saith, *M.* hour. *John* 2:4
my doctrine is not *m.* 7:16
am known of *m.* 10:14
word which ye hear is not *m.* 14:24
he shall receive of *m.* 16:14
that the Father hath are *m.* 15
m. are thine, and thine are *m.* 17:10
vengeance is *m.*, I will repay. *Rom* 12:19
in every prayer of *m.* *Phil* 1:4

mingle
men of strength to *m.* *Isa* 5:22
m. with the seed of. *Dan* 2:43

mingled
there was fire *m.* with. *Ex* 9:24
sow thy field with *m.* *Lev* 19:19
holy seed have *m.* *Ezra* 9:2
and *m.* my drink with. *Ps* 102:9
m. among the heathen. 106:35
she hath *m.* her wine. *Pr* 9:2
the wine which I have *m.* 5
Lord hath *m.* a perverse. *Isa* 19:14
cup to all *m.* people. *Jer* 25:20, 24
a sword on all the *m.* people. 50:37 *Ezek* 30:5
gave him vinegar *m.* *Mat* 27:34
gave him wine *m.* with. *Mark* 15:23
blood Pilate had *m.* *Luke* 13:1
followed hail and fire *m.* *Rev* 8:7
as it were a sea of glass *m.* 15:2

minish, -ed
(*American Revision*, diminish)
ye shall not *m.* aught of. *Ex* 5:19
are *m.* and brought low. *Ps* 107:39

minister
Used in the Bible mainly in the archaic sense of one who serves, waits on, or attends another, Ex 24:13; 1 Ki 10:5. *It is applied,* [1] *To Christ, when comparing him with the Hebrew high priest,* Heb 8:2. [2] *To those who were to care for the work of the gospel,* 1 Cor 14:1. [3] *To magistrates,* Rom 13:6. [4] *To the angels,* Ps 104:4.
rose, and his *m.* Joshua. *Ex* 24:13
spake to Joshua, Moses' *m.* *Josh* 1:1
let him be your *m.* *Mat* 20:26 *Mark* 10:43
book again to the *m.* *Luke* 4:20*
also John to their *m.* *Acts* 13:5*
to make thee a *m.* and a. 26:16
the *m.* of God to thee. *Rom* 13:4, 6
Christ was a *m.* of the. 15:8
I should be the *m.* of Jesus to. 16
is Christ the *m.* of sin? *Gal* 2:17
whereof I was made a *m.* *Eph* 3:7 *Col* 1:23, 25
Tychicus, a faithful *m.* of the Lord. *Eph* 6:21; *Col* 4:7
who is for you a faithful *m.* *Col* 1:7
brother and *m.* of God. *1 Thes* 3:2
a good *m.* of Christ. *1 Tim* 4:6
a *m.* of the sanctuary. *Heb* 8:2

minister, *verb*
m. to me in the priest's. *Ex* 28:1
3, 4, 41; 29:1, 44; 30:30; 31:10
35:19; 39:41; 40:13, 15
shall be upon Aaron to *m.* 28:35
when they come to altar to *m.* 43 29:30; 30:20
I will sanctify Aaron to *m.* 29:44
he presented them to *m.* *Lev* 7:35
whom he shall consecrate to *m.* 16:32; *Num* 3:3
m. with their brethren. *Num* 8:26
tribe of Levi to *m.* to. *Deut* 10:8
to stand to *m.* in the name. 18:5, 7
God hath chosen them to *m.* 21:5
child did *m.* to the. *1 Sam* 2:11
could not stand to *m.* because of the. *1 Ki* 8:11; *2 Chr* 5:14
chosen to *m.* before him. *1 Chr* 15:2

to *m.* and to give thanks. *1 Chr* 23:13 *2 Chr* 31:2
priests which *m.* are. *2 Chr* 13:10
he shall *m.* judgement to. *Ps* 9:8
rams of Nebaioth shall *m.* *Isa* 60:7
their kings shall *m.* to thee. 10
multiply Levites that *m.* *Jer* 33:22
which come near to *m.* *Ezek* 40:46 41:15, 16
stand before them to *m.* 44:11
not to be ministered unto, but to *m.* *Mat* 20:28; *Mark* 10:45
sick, and did not *m.*? *Mat* 25:44
his acquaintance to *m.* to him. *Acts* 24:23
I go to *m.* to the saints. *Rom* 15:25
duty is to *m.* to them in carnal. 27
they which *m.* about holy. *1 Cor* 9:13
both *m.* bread for your. *2 Cor* 9:10*
that it may *m.* grace. *Eph* 4:29*
which *m.* questions. *1 Tim* 1:4
angels sent to *m.* to. *Heb* 1:14*
to the saints, and do *m.* 6:10
but to us they did *m.* the. *1 Pet* 1:12
even so *m.* the same one to. 4:10
if any man *m.* let him do it as. 11

ministered
Eleazar and Ithamar *m.* *Num* 3:4 *Deut* 10:6
Samuel *m.* before. *1 Sam* 2:18; 3:1
his servant that *m.* *2 Sam* 13:17
Abishag *m.* to David. *1 Ki* 1:4, 15
after Elijah, and *m.* to him. 19:21
snuffers, and all vessels wherewith they *m.* *2 Ki* 25:14; *Jer* 52:18
m. to them before their. *Ezek* 44:12
thousand thousands *m.* *Dan* 7:10
angels came and *m.* to him. *Mat* 4:11; *Mark* 1:13
she arose and *m.* unto them. *Mat* 8:15; *Mark* 1:31
which *m.* to him of their substance. *Luke* 8:3
as they *m.* and fasted. *Acts* 13:2
these hands have *m.* to my. 20:34
epistle of Christ *m.* by us. *2 Cor* 3:3
he that *m.* to my wants. *Phil* 2:25
having nourishment *m.* *Col* 2:19*
how many things he *m.* *2 Tim* 1:18
stead he might have *m.* *Philem* 13
m. to the saints, and. *Heb* 6:10
an entrance shall be *m.* *2 Pet* 1:11*

ministereth
now he that *m.* seed. *2 Cor* 9:10
he that *m.* to you the Spirit. *Gal* 3:5*

ministering
charge of *m.* vessels. *1 Chr* 9:28*
gates of house, *m.* to. *Ezek* 44:11
women followed Jesus *m.* to him. *Mat* 27:55
let us wait on our *m.* *Rom* 12:7
m. the gospel. 15:16
on us the *m.* to the saints. *2 Cor* 8:4
for as touching *m.* to the saints. 9:1
are they not all *m.* spirits? *Heb* 1:14
priest standeth daily *m.* 10:11

ministers
the attendance of his *m.* *1 Ki* 10:5 *2 Chr* 9:4
to impose toll on *m.* *Ezra* 7:24*
bring unto us *m.* for house. 8:17
ye *m.* of his that do. *Ps* 103:21
who maketh his *m.* a flaming fire. 104:4; *Heb* 1:7
men shall call you the *m.* *Isa* 61:6
covenant be broken with David my servant, and with my *m.* *Jer* 33:21
be *m.* in my sanctuary. *Ezek* 44:11
holy portion for the *m.* of. 45:4
the Lord's *m.* mourn. *Joel* 1:9
howl, ye *m.* 13
m. weep between the porch. 2:17
beginning were *m.* of word. *Luke* 1:2
God's *m.* attending. *Rom* 13:6
m. by whom ye believed. *1 Cor* 3:5
us as of the *m.* of Christ. 4:1
who made us able *m.* *2 Cor* 3:6
approving ourselves as the *m.* 6:4
no great thing, if his *m.* also be transformed as the *m.* of. 11:15
are they *m.* of Christ? I am more. 23

ministration

as the days of his *m.* *Luke* 1:23
neglected in the daily *m.* *Acts* 6:1
but if the *m.* of death. *2 Cor* 3:7
m. of the Spirit be rather? 8, 9
by the experiment of this *m.* 9:13

ministry

instruments of the *m.* *Num* 4:12
came to do the service of the *m.* 47
praised by their *m.* *2 Chr* 7:6
similitudes, by the *m.* of the prophets. *Hos* 12:10
obtained part of this *m.* *Acts* 1:17
that may take part of this *m.* 25
we will give ourselves to *m.* 6:4
they had fulfilled their *m.* 12:25
might finish my course, and *m.* 20:24
God had wrought by his *m.* 21:19
or *m.*, let us wait on our. *Rom* 12:7
to the *m.* of saints. *1 Cor* 16:15
seeing we have this *m.* *2 Cor* 4:1
hath given to us the *m.* of. 5:18
giving no offence, that the *m.* 6:3
for work of the *m.* for. *Eph* 4:12
take heed to the *m.* thou. *Col* 4:17
putting me into the *m.* *1 Tim* 1:12*
make full proof of thy *m.* *2 Tim* 4:5
profitable to me for the *m.* 11
he obtained a more excellent *m.* *Heb* 8:6
with blood the vessels of the *m.* 9:21

minstrel, -s

me a *m.* when *m.* played. *2 Ki* 3:15
when Jesus saw the *m.* *Mat* 9:23*

mint

pay tithe of *m.* anise. *Mat* 23:23
ye tithe *m.* and all. *Luke* 11:42

miracle

(*An event beyond the power of any known physical laws to produce; a supernatural occurrence produced by the power of God; a marvel, wonder. In the Revisions the word is generally rendered in the* Old Testament wonder, *or* mighty work; *and in the New Testament* sign)

speak, saying, Shew a *m.* *Ex* 7:9
considered not the *m.* *Mark* 6:52
no man which shall do a *m.* 9:39
hoped to have seen some *m.* done. *Luke* 23:8
this is the second *m.* *John* 4:54
and said, John did no *m.* 10:41
a notable *m.* hath been. *Acts* 4:16
forty years on whom this *m.* 22

miracles

which have seen *m.* *Num* 14:22
that have not seen his *m.* *Deut* 11:3
seen those signs and great *m.* 29:3
where be all his *m.* our. *Judg* 6:13
beginning of *m.* did. *John* 2:11
when they saw the *m.* he did. 23
no man can do these *m.* except. 3:2
because they saw his *m.* 6:2
not because ye saw the *m.* 26
will he do more *m.* than? 7:31
that is a sinner do such *m.*? 9:16
for this man doeth many *m.* 11:47
he had done so many *m.* 12:37
approved of God by *m.* *Acts* 2:22
Stephen did great *m.* among. 6:8
hearing and seeing the *m.* 8:6
wondered, beholding the *m.* 13
declaring what *m.* God had. 15:12
God wrought special *m.* by. 19:11
another the working *m.* *1 Cor* 12:10
after that *m.* 28
are all workers of *m.*? 29
he that worketh *m.* among. *Gal* 3:5
them witness with *m.* *Heb* 2:4
by the means of those *m.* *Rev* 13:14
spirits of devils working *m.* 16:14
false prophet that wrought *m.* 19:20

mire

I did stamp them as *m.* of the. *2 Sam* 22:43; *Isa* 10:6; *Mi* 7:10
rush grow up without *m.*? *Job* 8:11
he hath cast me into the *m.* 30:19
pointed things on the *m.* 41:30
I sink in deep *m.* where. *Ps* 69:2
deliver me out of the *m.*: let me. 14
whose waters cast up *m.* *Isa* 57:20
was no water, but *m.* *Jer* 38:6
thy feet are sunk in the *m.* 22
and fine gold as the *m.* *Zech* 9:3
tread their enemies in *m.* of. 10:5
her wallowing in the *m.* *2 Pet* 2:22

Miriam

M. took a timbrel. *Ex* 15:20
M. and Aaron spake. *Num* 12:1
M. became leprous white. 10
M. was shut up seven days. 15
M. died there. 20:1
were born Aaron, Moses, *M.* 26:59
remember what God did to *M.* by the way *Deut* 24:9
thee Moses, Aaron, and *M.* *Mi* 6:4

mirth

sent thee away with *m.* *Gen* 31:27
away to make great *m.* *Neh* 8:12
us desired of us *m.* *Ps* 137:3
and the end of that *m.* *Pr* 14:13
I will prove thee with *m.* *Eccl* 2:1
I said of *m.* What doeth it? 2
of fools is in the house of *m.* 7:4
then I commended *m.* because. 8:15
m. of tabrets the joy of *Isa* 24:8
joy is darkened, the *m.* of the. 11
the voice of *m.* from. *Jer* 7:34
16:9; 25:10; *Hos* 2:11
we then make *m.*? *Ezek* 21:10

miry

me out of the *m.* clay. *Ps* 40:2
the *m.* places shall not. *Ezek* 47:11
iron mixed with *m.* *Dan* 2:41, 43

miscarrying

give them a *m.* womb. *Hos* 9:14

mischief

(*Very frequently used to mean wickedness, iniquity*)

for he said, Lest some *m.* *Gen* 42:4
if *m.* befall him by the way in which ye go. 38; 44:29
depart, and yet no *m.* *Ex* 21:22
for *m.* did he bring them out. 32:12*
people that are set on *m.* 22*
that Saul practised *m.* *1 Sam* 23:9
art taken in thy *m.* *2 Sam* 16:8
the *m.* that Hadad did. *1 Ki* 11:25
see how this man seeketh *m.* 20:7
some *m.* will come upon us. *2 Ki* 7:9*
they thought to do me *m.* *Neh* 6:2
Esther besought to put away *m.* of. *Esth* 8:3
conceive *m.* and bring. *Job* 15:35
he conceived *m.* brought. *Ps* 7:14
his *m.* shall return upon his. 16
under his tongue is *m.* and. 10:7
thou beholdest *m.* and spite, to. 14
hands is *m.*, their hand is. 26:10
which speak peace, but *m.* 28:3
the wicked deviseth *m.* 36:4*
why boastest thyself in *m.*? 52:1
m. and sorrow are in the. 55:10
imagine *m.* against a man? 62:3
the throne, which frameth *m.*? 94:20
nigh that follow after *m.* 119:150*
let the *m.* of their own lips. 140:9
except they have done *m.* *Pr* 4:16
he deviseth *m.* continually. 6:14*
be swift in running to *m.* 18
sport to a fool to do *m.* 10:23*
he that seeketh *m.* it shall. 11:27
wicked shall be filled with *m.* 12:21
messenger falleth into *m.* 13:17*
perverse tongue falleth into *m.* 17:20
and their lips talk of *m.* 24:2
wicked shall fall into *m.* 16*; 28:14
therefore *m.* shall fall. *Isa* 47:11
in vanity, they conceive *m.* 59:4
m. shall come upon *m.* *Ezek* 7:26
are the men that devise *m.* 11:2*
kings' hearts shall be to do *m.* *Dan* 11:27
yet do they imagine *m.* *Hos* 7:15
full of all *m.* thou child. *Acts* 13:10*

mischiefs

I will heap *m.* on them. *Deut* 32:23
thy tongue deviseth *m.* *Ps* 52:2*
imagine *m.* in their heart. 140:2

mischievous

imagined a *m.* device. *Ps* 21:11
that seek my hurt, speak *m.* 38:12
he shall be called a *m.* *Pr* 24:8
the end of his talk is *m.* *Eccl* 10:13
man uttereth his *m.* desire. *Mi* 7:3

miserable

Job said, *m.* comforters. *Job* 16:2
of all men most *m.* *1 Cor* 15:19*
knowest not that thou art *m.* *Rev* 3:17

miserably

he will *m.* destroy those. *Mat* 21:41

miseries

Jerusalem remembered in days of her *m.* *Lam* 1:7
howl for your *m.* that shall. *Jas* 5:1

misery

was grieved for the *m.* *Judg* 10:16
given to him that is in *m.*? *Job* 3:20
thou shalt forget thy *m.* 11:16
remember his *m.* no more. *Pr* 31:7
the *m.* of a man is great. *Eccl* 8:6
mine affliction and *m.* *Lam* 3:19
destruction and *m.* are. *Rom* 3:16

Mishael

of Uzziel, *M.* Elzaphan and Zithri. *Ex* 6:22; *Lev* 10:4
Ezra's left hand stood *M.* *Neh* 8:4
children of Judah, *M.* *Dan* 1:6

miss

hair breadth and not *m.* *Judg* 20:16
if thy father at all *m.* *1 Sam* 20:6

missed

thou shalt be *m.* *1 Sam* 20:18
neither *m.* any thing as long. 25:15
nothing was *m.* of all that. 21

missing

neither was there aught *m.* unto them. *1 Sam* 25:7
any means he be *m.* *1 Ki* 20:39

mist

up a *m.* from the earth. *Gen* 2:6
there fell on him a *m.* *Acts* 13:11
to whom the *m.* of darkness is. *2 Pet* 2:17*

mistress

her *m.* was despised in. *Gen* 16:4
I flee from my *m.* Sarai. 8
return to thy *m.* 9
son of the *m.* of house. *1 Ki* 17:17
her *m.* Would God my lord. *2 Ki* 5:3
maiden to hand of her *m.* *Ps* 123:2
that is heir to her *m.* *Pr* 20:23
the maid so with her *m.* *Isa* 24:2
m. of witchcrafts, that. *Nah* 3:4

misused

they despised and *m.* *2 Chr* 36:16*

mite, -s

a widow threw in two *m.* *Mark* 12:42; *Luke* 21:2
paid the very last *m.* *Luke* 12:59

mitre

they shall make a *m.* *Ex* 28:4, 39
39:28
a blue lace upon the *m.* 28:37; 39:31
shalt put the *m.* upon his head. 29:6
the holy crown on the *m.* *Lev* 8:9
linen *m.* shall he be attired. 16:4
a fair *m.* on his head, so they set a fair *m.* *Zech* 3:5

mixed

a *m.* multitude went up. *Ex* 12:38
the *m.* multitude fell a. *Num* 11:4
they separated from Israel all *m.* *Neh* 13:3
that go to seek *m.* wine. *Pr* 23:30
thy wine *m.* with water. *Isa* 1:22
the iron *m.* with miry. *Dan* 2:41
Ephraim *m.* himself among. *Hos* 7:8
not being *m.* with faith. *Heb* 4:2*

mixture

wine red, it is full of *m.* *Ps* 75:8
Nicodemus, and brought a *m.* of myrrh and aloes. *John* 19:39
is poured out without *m.* *Rev* 14:10

Mizar

thee from the hill of *M.* *Ps* 42:6

Mizpah

the heap was called *M.* *Gen* 31:49

those stones Geba of Benjamin, and *M.* *1 Ki* 15:22; *2 Chr* 16:6
son of Nethaniah came to Gedaliah to *M.* *2 Ki* 25:23; *Jer* 41:1
men of Gibeon and *M.* *Neh* 3:7
Shallum ruler of *M.* 15
Ezer ruler of *M.* 19
went to Gedaliah to *M.* *Jer* 40:6
behold, I will dwell at *M.* 10
the Jews that were at *M.* 41:3
carried away captive from *M.* 14
been a snare on *M.* *Hos* 5:1

Mizpeh

Dilean and *M.* cities. *Josh* 15:38
M. Chephirah, cities of. 18:26
and encamped in *M.* *Judg* 10:17
uttered all his words in *M.* 11:11
gathered to the Lord in *M.* 20:1
up to the Lord to *M.* shall die. 21:5
gather all Israel to *M.* *1 Sam* 7:5
judged Israel in *M.* 6, 16
the people to the Lord to *M.* 10:17
David went thence to *M.* 22:3

Mnason

M. an old disciple. *Acts* 21:16

Moab

daughter's son was *M.* *Gen* 19:37
smote Midian in field of *M.* 36:35
1 Chr 1:46
take hold on men of *M.* *Ex* 15:15
woe to thee, *M.* *Num* 21:29
Jer 48:46
M. was sore afraid, and *M.* was distressed. *Num* 22:3
smite the corners of *M.* 24:17
whoredom with daughters of *M.* 25:1
through the coast of *M.* *Deut* 2:18
Moses died in the land of *M.* 34:5
slew of *M.* about 10,000. *Judg* 3:29
so *M.* was subdued under the. 30
served gods of Syria and *M.* 10:6
took not away the land of *M.* 11:15
into the country of *M.* *Ruth* 1:2
took wives of the women of *M.* 4
Saul fought against *M.* and Ammon. *1 Sam* 14:47
David smote *M.* and. *2 Sam* 8:2
slew two lionlike men of *M.* 23:20
the abomination of *M.* *1 Ki* 11:7
M. rebelled against. *2 Ki* 1:1
wilt thou go with me against *M.*? 3:7
kings are slain, therefore *M.* 23
had the dominion in *M.* *1 Chr* 4:22
gold he brought from *M.* 18:11
M. came against Jehoshaphat. *2 Chr* 20:1
behold, how the children of *M.* 10
had married wives of *M.* *Neh* 13:23
M. is my washpot. *Ps* 60:8; 108:9
M. is confederate against thee. 83:6
lay their hand upon *M.* *Isa* 11:14
the burden of *M.* Ar of *M.* laid waste. 15:1; 16:13; *Jer* 48:1; *Ezek* 25:8
Amos 2:2
heart shall cry out for *M.* *Isa* 15:5
we have heard the pride of *M.* 16:6
Jer 48:29
like an harp for *M.* *Isa* 16:11
and the glory of *M.* shall be. 14
M. shall be trodden down. 25:10
I will punish Egypt, Judah, and *M.* *Jer* 9:26
I made Edom and *M.* to. 25:21
Jews returned from *M.* 40:11
shall be no more praise of *M.* 48:2
give wings to *M.* that it may flee. 9
M. hath been at ease from his. 11
tell ye it in Arnon, that *M.* is. 20
M. shall wallow in his vomit. 26
gladness is taken from land of *M.* 33
how hath *M.* turned the back! 39
bring again the captivity of *M.* 47
send a fire upon *M.* *Amos* 2:2
M. shall be as Sodom. *Zeph* 2:9
see **king**

Moabite

a *M.* shall not enter into the congregation. *Deut* 23:3; *Neh* 13:1
Ithmah the *M.* a valiant. *1 Chr* 11:46

Moabites

is the father of the *M.* *Gen* 19:37
said, Distress not the *M.* *Deut* 2:9
delivered the *M.* to you. *Judg* 3:28
M. became David's servants and. *2 Sam* 8:2; *1 Chr* 18:2
loved women of the *M.* *1 Ki* 11:1
Chemosh god of the *M.* 33
he will deliver the *M.* *2 Ki* 3:18
rose up and smote the *M.* 24
the bands of the *M.* invaded. 13:20
sent against him bands of *M.* 24:2
abominations of the *M.* *Ezra* 9:1

Moabitess, *see* **Ruth**

mock

[1] *To deride or laugh at,* 2 Chr 30:10. [2] *To speak in jest,* Gen 19:14. [3] *To disappoint, deceive,* Num 22:29.

Hebrew to *m.* us. *Gen* 39:14, 17
mocketh, do ye so *m.* him. *Job* 13:9
after I have spoken, *m.* on. 21:3
I will *m.* when your fear. *Pr* 1:26
fools make a *m.* at sin. 14:9
deliver me, and they *m.* *Jer* 38:19
adversary did *m.* at her. *Lam* 1:7
m. thee who art infamous. *Ezek* 22:5
deliver him to Gentiles to *m.* him. *Mat* 20:19
they shall *m.* him and. *Mark* 10:34
behold, begin to *m.* him. *Luke* 14:29

mocked

seemed as one that *m.* to. *Gen* 19:14
thou hast *m.* me. *Num* 22:29
hast *m.* me, and told me lies. *Judg* 16:10, 13, 15.
at noon, Elijah *m.* *1 Ki* 18:27
out of the city *m.* Elisha. *2 Ki* 2:23
them to scorn and *m.* *2 Chr* 30:10
but they *m.* the messengers. 36:16
wroth, and *m.* the Jews. *Neh* 4:1
I am as one *m.* of his. *Job* 12:4*
saw that he was *m.* he. *Mat* 2:16
they bowed the knee and *m.* 27:29
31; *Mark* 15:20
be *m.* and spitefully. *Luke* 18:32
men that held Jesus *m.* him. 22:63
Herod *m.* him. 23:11
the soldiers also *m.* him. 36
the resurrection, some *m.* *Acts* 17:32
deceived, God is not *m.* *Gal* 6:7

mocker

wine is a *m.*, strong drink. *Pr* 20:1

mockers

are there not *m.* with me? *Job* 17:2
with hypocritical *m.* *Ps* 35:16
be not *m.* lest bands be. *Isa* 28:22*
not in the assembly of *m.* *Jer* 15:17*
be *m.* in the latter times. *Jude* 18

mockest

when thou *m.* shall no man. *Job* 11:3

mocketh

as one *m.* another, do. *Job* 13:9*
he *m.* at fear, and is not. 39:22
m. poor reproacheth his. *Pr* 17:5
eye that *m.* at his father. 30:17
a derision, every one *m.* me. *Jer* 20:7

mocking, -s

saw the son of Hagar *m.* *Gen* 21:9
I made thee a *m.* to all. *Ezek* 22:4
the chief priests *m.* *Mat* 27:41
Mark 15:31
m. said. These men are. *Acts* 2:13
had trial of cruel *m.* *Heb* 11:36

moderately

you the former rain *m.* *Joel* 2:23*

moderation

m. be known to all men. *Phil* 4:5*

modest

themselves in *m.* apparel. *1 Tim* 2:9

moist

shall he eat *m.* grapes. *Num* 6:3*

moistened

and his bones are *m.* *Job* 21:24*

moisture

my *m.* is turned into. *Ps* 32:4
because it lacked *m.* *Luke* 8:6

mole

lizard, snail, and *m.* are. *Lev* 11:30*

Molech

pass through fire to *M.* *Lev* 18:21
that giveth of his seed to *M.* shall surely be. 20:2; 3, 4; *Jer* 32:35
built an high place for *M.* *1 Ki* 11:7
son pass through to *M.* *2 Ki* 23:10

moles, *see* **bats**

mollified

neither bound up, nor *m.* *Isa* 1:6

Moloch

have borne the tabernacle of *M.* *Amos* 5:26; *Acts* 7:43

molten

after he had made *m.* calf. *Ex* 32:4
8; *Deut* 9:12, 16; *Neh* 9:18
shalt make thee no *m.* gods. *Ex* 34:17; *Lev* 19:4
chapiters of *m.* brass. *1 Ki* 7:16
he made a *m.* sea. 23
undersetters *m.* 30
their spokes were all *m.* 33
and brass is *m.* out of. *Job* 28:2
sky is strong, and as a *m.* 37:18
filthiness of it may be *m.* *Ezek* 24:11
the mountains shall be *m.* *Mi* 1:4

moment

midst of thee in a *m.* *Ex* 33:5
that I may consume them in a *m.* *Num* 16:21, 45
try him every *m.* *Job* 7:18
hypocrite is but for a *m.* 20:5
and in a *m.* they go down to. 21:13
in a *m.* shall they die, people. 34:20
anger endureth but a *m.* *Ps* 30:5
into desolation as in a *m.* 73:19
tongue is but for a *m.* *Pr* 12:19
as it were for a *m.* *Isa* 26:20
I will water it every *m.* 27:3
two things shall come in a *m.* 47:9
small *m.* have I forsaken. 54:7
I hid my face from thee for a *m.* 8
my curtains in a *m.* *Jer* 4:20
was overthrown in a *m.* *Lam* 4:6
and shall tremble at every *m.* *Ezek* 26:16; 32:10
kingdoms of world in a *m.* *Luke* 4:5
all be changed in a *m.* *1 Cor* 15:52
which is but for a *m.* *2 Cor* 4:17

money

(*Coined money was unknown until late in Bible times. Gold and silver in the form of rings or ingots were weighed in payment where we would count coins*)

give it for as much *m.* *Gen* 23:9*
I will give thee *m.* for the field. 13*
quite devoured also our *m.* 31:15
to restore every man's *m.* 42:25
he espied his *m.* 27
my *m.* is restored. 28
double *m.* in your hand. 43:12, 15
fear not, I had your *m.* 23
and put every man's *m.* in his. 44:1
Joseph gathered all the *m.* 47:14
for *m.* faileth. 15
how that our *m.* is spent. 18
go out free without *m.* *Ex* 21:11
for he is his *m.* 21
be laid on him a sum of *m.* 30*
and divide the *m.* 35*
deliver to his neighbour *m.* 22:7
if thou lend *m.* to any of my. 25
shalt take the atonement *m.* 30:16
not give him *m.* on usury. *Lev* 25:37; *Deut* 23:19
took the redemption *m.* *Num* 3:49
meat and water for *m.* *Deut* 2:6, 28
turn it into *m.* 14:25
shalt bestow that *m.* 26
not sell her at all for *m.* 21:14
they took no gain of *m.* *Judg* 5:19
lords of Philistines brought *m.* 16:18
yet he restored the *m.* to his. 17:4
the worth of it in *m.* *1 Ki* 21:2
is it a time to receive *m.*? *2 Ki* 5:26
m. of the dedicated things. 12:4
therefore receive no more *m.* 7
m. in the chest, and told the *m.* that was found 10; *2 Chr* 24:11
trespass *m.* and sin *m.* *2 Ki* 12:16
Menahem exacted the *m.* of. 15:20
Jehoiakim gave *m.* to. 23:35

gave m. also to masons. Ezra 3:7
buy speedily with this m. 7:17
we have borrowed m. Neh 5:4
servants might exact of them m. 10
of the sum of m. Haman. Esth 4:7
the fruits without m. Job 31:39
also gave him a piece of m. 42:11
put not out his m. to usury. Ps 15:5
he hath taken a bag of m. Pr 7:20
for wisdom and m. is a. Eccl 7:12
wine maketh merry, but m. 10:19
redeemed without m. Isa 52:3
no m., come, buy without m. 55:1
wherefore spend ye m. for that? 2
I weighed him the m. Jer 32:9, 10
men shall buy fields for m. and. 44
drunken our water for m. Lam 5:4
thereof divine for m. Mi 3:11
received the tribute m. Mat 17:24*
thou shalt find a piece of m. 27*
shew me the tribute m. 22:19
earth, and hid his lord's m. 25:18
to have put my m. to the exchangers, and at my. 27; Luke 19:23
large m. to the soldiers. Mat 28:12
so they took m. and did as they. 15
they took no m. in their purse. Mark 6:8; Luke 9:3
the people cast m. into. Mark 12:41
and promised to give him m. 14:11 Luke 22:5
changers of m. sitting. John 2:14
he poured out changers' m. 15
brought the m. and laid. Acts 4:37
sorcerer offered them m. 8:18
but Peter said, Thy m. perish. 20*
he hoped that m. should have. 24:26
the love of m. is the root. 1 Tim 6:10
see **brought**

moneychangers

overthrew tables of m. and seats of them. Mat 21:12; Mark 11:15

monsters

even the sea m. draw out. Lam 4:3*

month

(The Jews reckoned by the year of 360 days, and in all probability made an adjustment by adding a thirteenth month occasionally. They had two New Years, the Civil, in Tisri (October), and the Sacred, in Abib or Nisan, the month in which they left Egypt under Moses. The following table gives the months in order, beginning with the Sacred New Year. The numbers in parentheses are those of the months according to the civil reckoning; and the modern names given are approximately the corresponding months according to our calendar. The exact period in modern terms differs each year)

Civil	Sacred month	Answering to our
(7)	1. Nisan, Abib,	April.
(8)	2. Iar, Zif,	May.
(9)	3. Sivan,	June.
(10)	4. Tammuz,	July.
(11)	5. Ab,	Aug.
(12)	6. Elul,	Sept.
(1)	7. Tisri, Ethanim,	Oct.
(2)	8. Marchesvan,	Nov.
(3)	9. Chisleu (Kislev),	Dec.
(4)	10. Tebeth,	Jan.
(5)	11. Sebat,	Feb.
(6)	12. Adar,	Mar.

Laban space of a m. Gen 29:14
ye out in the m. Abib. Ex 13:4
keep the feast in the m. Abib. 23:15
m. Abib thou camest out. 34:18 Deut 16:1; Josh 5:10
if it be from a m. old to. Lev 27:6
every male from m. old. Num 3:15 22, 28, 34, 39, 40, 43; 26:62
a m. or year that the cloud. 9:22
flesh, even a whole m. 11:20, 21
from a m. old shalt thou. 18:16
the burnt offering of every m. 28:14 29:6*
thine house a full m. Deut 21:13
each man his m. made provision. 1 Ki 4:7, 27
a m. they were in Lebanon. 5:14
in the m. Zif. 1 Ki 6:37
in the m. Bul. 38
feast in m. Ethanim. 8:2
in m. Chisleu. Neh 1:1
in m. Nisan. 2:1; Esth 3:7
m. Elul. Neh 6:15
Jews gathered in m. Adar. Esth 9:15, 17, 19, 21
m. which was turned from. 22
in her m. they shall find. Jer 2:24
now shall a m. devour. Hos 5:7*
I cut off in one m. Zech 11:8
prepared for a day and m. Rev 9:15
yielded her fruit every m. 22:2
see **first**

second **month**

in *second* m. the fountains were. Gen 7:11
second m. was the earth dried. 8:14
wilderness of Sin in *second* m. Ex 16:1
in *second* m. take sum. Num 1:1
in *second* m. shall keep passover. 9:11; 2 Chr 30:2
of *second* m. cloud was taken up. Num 10:11
second m. Solomon began to build. 1 Ki 6:1; 2 Chr 3:2
the course of *second* m. 1 Chr 27:4
second m. began Zerubbabel to. Ezra 3:8

third **month**

in *third* m. came into wilderness of. Ex 19:1
captain for *third* m. 1 Chr 27:5
gathered at Jerusalem in the *third* m. 2 Chr 15:10
in *third* m. they began to lay. 31:7
king's scribes were called in *third* m. Esth 8:9
in *third* m. word of Lord. Ezek 31:1

fourth **month**

fourth m. the famine. 2 Ki 25:3
fourth captain for *fourth* m. was. 1 Chr 27:5
fourth m. the city was. Jer 39:2
in *fourth* m. the famine was. 52:6
in *fourth* m. Ezekiel saw. Ezek 1:1
fast of the *fourth* m. Zech 8:19
see **fifth**

sixth **month**

captain for *sixth* m. 1 Chr 27:9
in *sixth* m. the elders of. Ezek 8:1
in *sixth* m. word of Lord. Hag 1:1
in *sixth* m. they did work in. 15
in *sixth* m. the angel. Luke 1:26
this is the *sixth* m. with her, who. 36
see **seventh**

eighth **month**

in *eighth* m. came word. Zech 1:1

ninth **month**

the *ninth* m. the people. Ezra 10:9
in the *ninth* m. they. Jer 36:9
winter house in the *ninth* m. 22
in *ninth* m. came word. Hag 2:10
from the *ninth* m. consider it. 18
to Zechariah in *ninth* m. Zech 7:1

tenth **month**

waters decreased until the *tenth* m. Gen 8:5
sat down in *tenth* m. Ezra 10:16
to the king in *tenth* m. Esth 2:16
tenth m. came Nebuchadrezzar. Jer 39:1; 52:4
in *tenth* m. came word. Ezek 24:1 29:1
in the *tenth* m. one that had escaped. 33:21

eleventh **month**

in the *eleventh* m. Moses. Deut 1:3
in *eleventh* m. came word. Zech 1:7

twelfth **month**

Haman to the *twelfth* m. Esth 3:7
thirteenth day of the *twelfth* m. 13 8:12; 9:1
twelfth m. Evil-merodach. Jer 52:31
in *twelfth* m. the word of. Ezek 32:1

this **month**

this m. shall be beginning. Ex 12:2
this m. shall take every man a. 3
keep this service in *this* m. Ex 13:5 Num 9:3; 28:17
tenth day of *this* m. an. Num 29:7
this m. Israel assembled. Neh 9:1

monthly

the m. prognosticators. Isa 47:13

months

in beginnings of your m. Num 10:10
in beginnings of m. offer a. 28:11
burnt offering through the m. 14
let me alone two m. Judg 11:37
at the end of two m. she returned. 39
was with her father four m. 19:2
in the rock Rimmon four m. 20:47
ark was in country of Philistines seven m. 1 Sam 6:1
Philistines a year and four m. 27:7
over Judah seven years and six m. 2 Sam 2:11; 5:5; 1 Chr 3:4
ark was with Obed-edom three m. 2 Sam 6:11
Jerusalem at end of nine m. 24:8
and two m. they were. 1 Ki 5:14
for six m. did Joab remain. 11:16
reigned over Israel six m. 2 Ki 15:8
by month through the m. 1 Chr 27:1
twelve m. purified, six m. with oil of myrrh, six m. with. Esth 2:12
into the number of the m. Job 3:6
so am I made to possess m. of. 7:3
number of his m. are with. 14:5
when the number of his m. 21:21
O that I were as in m. past, as. 29:2
canst thou number the m. that? 39:2
seven m. Israel shall be. Ezek 39:12
after the end of seven m. shall. 14
new fruit according to his m. 47:12
at the end of twelve m. Dan 4:29
and hid herself five m. Luke 1:24
heaven was shut up three years and six m. 4:25; Jas 5:17
are yet four m. then. John 4:35
there a year and six m. Acts 18:11
observe days, and m. Gal 4:10
tormented five m. Rev 9:5, 10
under foot forty-two m. 11:2
him to continue forty-two m. 13:5
see **three**

monuments

people which lodge in the m. Isa 65:4*

moon

put forth by the m. Deut 33:14
m. in valley of Ajalon. Josh 10:12
m. and it shineth not. Job 25:5
when I consider the m. Ps 8:3
and peace so long as the m. 72:7
established for ever as the m. 89:37
he appointeth the m. for. 104:19
while the sun, m. or stars. Eccl 12:2
fair as m., clear as the. S of S 6:10
round tires like the m. Isa 3:18
see **sun**

new **moon**

is the *new* m. 1 Sam 20:5, 18
it is neither *new* m. 2 Ki 4:23
trumpet in the *new* m. Ps 81:3
that from one *new* m. to. Isa 66:23
in the day of *new* m. it. Ezek 46:1
in the day of *new* m. offer a. 6
will the *new* m. be gone? Amos 8:5
in respect of the *new* m. Col 2:16

new **moons**

sacrifices in the *new* m. 1 Chr 23:31 2 Chr 2:4; 31:3; Ezra 3:5 Neh 10:33; Ezek 46:3
new m. and sabbaths I. Isa 1:13
your *new* m. and feasts my soul. 14
offerings in the *new* m. Ezek 45:17
to cease her *new* m. Hos 2:11

Mordecai

M. came up with Zerubbabel. Ezra 2:2; Neh 7:7
Jew, whose name was M. Esth 2:5
M. sat in the king's gate. 19, 21
the thing was known to M. 22
Haman saw that M. bowed not. 3:5
shewed him the people of M. 6
M. rent his clothes, and put. 4:1
told Esther the words of M. 9
Esther bade them return M. 15
so long as I see M. the Jew. 5:13

gallows made, that M. Esth 5:14
honour hath been done to M.? 6:3
make haste, and do even so to M. 10
Haman had made for M. 7:9
his ring and gave it to M. Esther set
M. over the house of Haman. 8:2
M. went out from the king in. 15
because the fear of M. fell. 9:3
M. the Jew was next to king. 10:3

more

Jacob loved Rachel m. Gen 29:30
riches m. than that they might. 36:7
Israel loved Joseph m. than all. 37:3
brethren hated him yet the m. 5, 8
Israel are m. than we. Ex 1:9
the m. they afflicted them, the m. 12
let there m. work be laid upon. 5:9
Pharaoh sinned yet m. and. 9:34
yet will I bring one plague m. 11:1
they gathered some m. some. 16:17
rich shall not give m. nor. 30:15
add the fifth part m. thereto. Lev 6:5
shut him up seven days m. 13:5
33, 54
you seven times m. 26:18, 21
firstborn which are m. Num 3:46
princes m. honourable than. 22:15
word of Lord, to do less or m. 18
what the Lord will say to me m. 19
thou shalt give the m. 26:54; 33:54
a thousand times m. Deut 1:11
on you, not because ye were m. 7:7
nations are m. than I. 17; 20:1
add three cities m. for thee. 19:9
were m. which died. Josh 10:11
corrupted themselves m. Judg 2:19
m. than they which he slew. 16:30
and what have I m.? 18:24
Lord do so to me and m. Ruth 1:17
1 Sam 14:44; 2 Sam 3:35; 19:13
shewed m. kindness in. Ruth 3:10
God do so to thee and m. 1 Sam 3:17
what can ye have m. but the ? 18:8
and much m. to Jonathan. 20:13
knew nothing less or m. 22:15
said, Thou art m. righteous. 24:17
m. do God to the enemies. 25:22
she told him nothing less or m. 36
to Abner, and m. also. 2 Sam 3:9
David took him m. concubines. 5:13
I will yet be m. vile than. 6:22
what can David say m. unto ? 7:20
we have also m. right in. 19:43
God do so to me, and m. also.
1 Ki 2:23; 20:10; 2 Ki 6:31
Ahab did m. to provoke. 1 Ki 16:33
gods do to me, and m. also. 19:2
there is not a vessel m. 2 Ki 4:6
m. than they that be with them.
6:16; 2 Chr 32:7
seduced them to do m. evil. 2 Ki 21:9
his people so many m. 1 Chr 21:3
there were m. chief men found. 24:4
put m. to your yoke. 2 Chr 10:11
m. spoil than they could. 20:25
Lord is able to give thee m. 25:9
intend to add m. to our sins. 28:13
Ahaz did trespass yet m. against. 22
the Levites were m. upright. 29:34
his servants spake m. against. 32:16
Amon trespassed m. and m. 33:23
whatsoever m. shall be. Ezra 7:20
yet ye bring m. wrath. Neh 13:18
Esther obtained favour m. than all.
Esth 2:17
delight to do honour m. than ? 6:6
dig for it m. than for hid. Job 3:21
m. than my necessary food. 23:12
nor regardeth the rich m. 34:19
for he will not lay on man m. 23
saidst, My righteousness is m. 35:2
teacheth us m. than the beasts. 11
latter end of Job m. than. 42:12
m. than when their corn. Ps 4:7
m. to be desired are they. 19:10
thy thoughts are m. than can. 40:5
iniquities are m. than the hairs. 12
lovest evil m. than good. 52:3
that hate me are m. than hairs. 69:4
yet praise thee m. and m. 71:14
they have m. than heart could. 73:7
they sinned yet m. against. 78:17
gates of Zion m. than all. 87:2
increase you m. and m. Ps 115:14
I have m. understanding. 119:99
understand m. than the ancients. 100
m. than they that watch for. 130:6
wisdom is m. precious. Pr 3:15
shineth m. and m. unto the. 4:18
there is that withholdeth m. 11:24
a reproof entereth m. into a. 17:10
there is m. hope of a fool than of him.
26:12; 29:20
I increased m. than all. Eccl 2:9
remembrance of wise m. than. 16
or who can hasten hereunto m.? 25
the dead m. than the living. 4:2
and be m. ready to hear than. 5:1
remember thy love m. S of S 1:4
what is thy beloved m.? 5:9
what could be done m. to? Isa 5:4
afterward did m. grievously. 9:1
I will bring m. upon Dimon. 15:9
his visage so marred m. than. 52:14
for m. are the children of the. 54:1
Israel justified herself m. Jer 3:11
because they are m. than the. 46:23
changed judgements into wickedness
m. than nations. Ezek 5:6
because he multiplied m. than the. 7
thou wast corrupted m. than they in
all thy ways. 16:47, 51, 52; 23:11
not for any wisdom that I have m.
than any living. Dan 2:30
the furnace seven times m. 3:19
continue m. years than the king. 11:8
knowledge of God m. Hos 6:6
now they sin m. and m. and. 13:2
wicked devoureth man m. Hab 1:13
what is m. than these. Mat 5:37
brethren only, what do you m.? 47
is not the life m. than meat? 6:25
Luke 12:23
of m. value than many sparrows.
Mat 10:31; Luke 12:7
loveth father or mother m. Mat 10:37
and m. than a prophet. 11:9
seven spirits m. wicked than. 12:45
he shall have m. abundance. 13:12
he rejoiceth m. of that sheep. 18:13
take with thee one or two m. 16
they should have received m. 20:10
cried the m. Have mercy. 31; 27:23
Mark 10:48; 15:14; Luke 18:39
give me m. than twelve. Mat 26:53
to you that hear shall m. Mark 4:24
m. he charged them, so much the m.
7:36
poor widow cast in m. than all.
12:43; Luke 21:3
have been sold for m. Mark 14:5
what thou spendest m. Luke 10:35
of him they will ask m. 12:48
not receive manifold m. in. 18:30
many m. believed. John 4:41
Jews sought the m. to kill. 5:18
will he do m. miracles than? 7:31
praise of men m. than. 12:43
that it may bring forth m. fruit. 15:2
Simon, lovest thou me m.? 21:15
to hearken to you m. Acts 4:19
believers were the m. added. 5:14
but Saul increased the m. in. 9:22
the m. part knew not why. 19:32
it is m. blessed to give. 20:35
there were m. than forty. 23:13, 21
believed the master m. than. 27:11
served the creature m. Rom 1:25
if the truth of God hath m. 3:7
we are m. than conquerors. 8:37
that I might gain the m. 1 Cor 9:19
I speak with tongues m. than. 14:18
so I rejoiced the m. 2 Cor 7:7
I boast the m. 10:8
am m.; in prisons m. frequent. 11:23
the desolate hath many m. Gal 4:27
love may abound m. and m.
Phil 1:9; 1 Thes 4:10
trust in the flesh, I m. Phil 3:4
God, abound m. and m. 1 Thes 4:1
lovers of pleasure m. 2 Tim 3:4
also do m. than I say. Philem 21
I m. say? time would fail. Heb 11:32
much m. shall not we escape. 12:25
yet once m. I shake not the. 26, 27
he giveth m. grace. Jas 4:6
m. sure word of prophecy. 2 Pet 1:19
and the last to be m. Rev 2:19
there come two woes m. 9:12
see **abundantly**

***any* more**

returned not again any m. Gen 8:12
curse the ground any m. 21; 9:11
nor shall thy name any m. 17:5
not any m. be called Jacob. 35:10
deal deceitfully any m. Ex 8:29
neither shall there be any m. 9:29
a cry, none like it any m. 11:6
man nor woman make any m. 36:6
not be redeemed any m. Lev 27:20
be no wrath any m. Num 18:5
voice of the Lord any m. Deut 5:25
see this great fire any m. 18:16
had Israel manna any m. Josh 5:12
nor will I be with you any m. 7:12
any m. sons in my womb? Ruth 1:11
Saul shall despair to seek me any m.
1 Sam 27:1
children of wickedness afflict any m.
2 Sam 7:10
feared to help Ammon any m.
10:19; 1 Chr 19:19
speakest thou any m.? 2 Sam 19:29
make the feet of Israel move any m.
2 Ki 21:8; 2 Chr 33:8
nor shall his place know him any m
Job 7:10; 20:9
I will not offend any m. 34:31
neither have they any m. Eccl 9:5
be stricken any m.? Isa 1:5
nor shall they learn war any m. 2:4
Mi 4:3
teachers be removed any m.
Isa 30:20
be termed desolate any m. 62:4
that be done any m. Jer 3:16
nor walk any m. after imagination. 17
stretch forth my tent any m. 10:20
I will not speak any m. in. 20:9
not return thither any m. 22:11
ruling any m. in Judah. 30
shall not sorrow any m. at. 31:12
thrown down any m. for ever. 40
themselves of them any m. 34:10
not do any m. the like. Ezek 5:9
words be prolonged any m. 12:28
shalt give no hire any m. 16:41
never open thy mouth any m. 63
shall not return any m. 21:5
not remember Egypt any m. 23:27
from thy filthiness any m. 24:13
thou shall be a terror, and never shalt
be any m. 27:36; 28:19
nor shall exalt itself any m. 29:15
nor foot of man trouble them any m.
32:13; 37:23
none of them any m. there. 39:28
hide my face any m. from them. 29
nor say any m. to the work. Hos 14:3
what I to do any m. with idols? 8
pass through her any m. Joel 3:17
not again pass by them any m.
Amos 7:8; 8:2
prophesy not again any m. at. 7:13
not see evil any m. Zeph 3:15
durst any ask him any m. Mat 22:46
not any m. than one loaf. Mark 8:14
they saw no man any m. save. 9:8
nor can they die any m. Luke 20:36
I will not eat any m. thereof. 22:16
let us not judge one another any m.
Rom 14:13
be spoken to them any m. Heb 12:19
shall they thirst any m. Rev 7:16
place in heaven found any m. 12:8
buyeth her merchandise any m. 18:11
nor shall there be any m. pain. 21:4

***much* more**

people being much m. Ex 36:5
much m. the wicked and. Pr 11:31
as this day, and much m. Isa 56:12
not much m. clothe you? Mat 6:30
so much m. went a fame. Luke 5:15
I say unto you, and much m. 7:26
much m. being now justified by his.
Rom 5:9
much m. being reconciled, we. 10
much m. they that receive. 17
grace did much m. abound. 20
much m. doth ministration. 2 Cor 3:9

much m. that which remaineth. *2 Cor* 3:11
proved *much m.* diligent. 8:22
are *much m.* bold to. *Phil* 1:14
have obeyed, now *much m.* 2:12
so *much m.* as you see day. *Heb* 10:25
much m. shall not we escape. 12:25
being *much m.* precious. *1 Pet* 1:7

no **more**

waters shall *no m.* *Gen* 9:15
be called *no m.* Jacob. 32:28
Judah knew her again *no m.* 38:26
ye shall see my face *no m.* 44:23
Ex 10:28
no m. give the people. *Ex* 5:7
see thy face again *no m.* 10:29
ye shall see them again *no m.* 14:13
shall *no m.* offer their. *Lev* 17:7
fifty they shall serve *no m.* *Num* 8:25
speak *no m.* to me of this. *Deut* 3:26
Lord spake, and added *no m.* 5:22
circumcise, and be *no m.* stiff-. 10:16
do *no m.* such wickedness. 13:11
17:13
henceforth return *no m.* 17:16
thou shalt see it *no m.* again. 28:68
I am 120 years, I can *no m.* go. 31:2
God will *no m.* drive out. *Josh* 23:13
up their heads *no m.* *Judg* 8:28
I will deliver you *no m.* 10:13
was *no m.* sad. *1 Sam* 1:18
talk *no m.* so exceeding proudly. 2:3
came *no m.* into the coast of. 7:13
and Samuel came *no m.* to. 15:35
let him go *no m.* home to his. 18:2
return, for I will *no m.* do. 26:21
and he sought *no m.* again. 27:4
and answereth me *no m.* 28:15
after Israel *no m.* *2 Sam* 2:28
dwell in a place of their own, and move *no m.* 7:10; *1 Chr* 17:9
shalt go *no m.* out with us to battle. *2 Sam* 21:17
there was *no m.* spirit in her. *1 Ki* 10:5; *2 Chr* 9:4
Elisha saw Elijah *no m.* *2 Ki* 2:12
bands of Syria came *no m.* 6:23
no m. of her than the skull. 9:35
shall *no m.* carry the tabernacle. *1 Chr* 23:26
us build, that we be *no m.* *Neh* 2:17
no m. on the sabbath. 13:21
Vashti came *no m.* *Esth* 1:19
she came *no m.* in to the king. 2:14
eyes shall *no m.* see good. *Job* 7:7
shall see me *no m.* 8
shall come up *no m.* 9
return *no m.* to his house. 10
till the heavens be *no m.* 14:12
saw him shall see him *no m.* 20:9
shall be *no m.* remembered. 24:20
they answered *no m.* 32:15, 16
iniquity, I will do *no m.* 34:32
the battle, do *no m.* 41:8
earth may *no m.* oppress. *Ps* 10:18
I go hence, and be *no m.* 39:13
he shall rise up *no m.* 41:8
see not signs, there is *no m.* 74:9
and be favourable *no m.* 77:7
name of Israel be *no m.* in. 83:4
thou rememberest *no m.* 88:5
thereof shall know it *no m.* 103:16
let the wicked be *no m.* 104:35
so is the wicked *no m.* *Pr* 10:25
remember his misery *no m.* 31:7
king, who will *no m.* be. *Eccl* 4:13
bring *no m.* vain oblations. *Isa* 1:13
shall *no m.* stay on him that. 10:20
driven away, and be *no m.* 19:7
there is *no m.* strength. 23:10
no m. rejoice. 12
the earth shall *no m.* cover. 26:21
shall weep *no m.* 30:19
vile person shall be *no m.* 32:5
I shall behold man *no m.* 38:11
shalt *no m.* be called tender. 47:1
shalt *no m.* be called the lady. 5
shalt *no m.* drink it again. 51:22
no m. come into thee the uncircumcised. 52:1
violence shall *no m.* be heard. 60:18
the sun shall be *no m.* thy light. 19
sun shall *no m.* go down. *Isa* 60:20
thou shalt *no m.* be termed. 62:4
I will *no m.* give thy corn to. 8
weeping shall be *no m.* heard. 65:19
there shall be *no m.* thence an. 20
will come *no m.* unto thee. *Jer* 2:31
they shall say *no m.* The ark. 3:16
no m. be called Tophet. 7:32; 19:6
his name may be *no m.* 11:19
shall *no m.* be said, The Lord liveth. 16:14; 23:7
shall return *no m.* 22:10
see this land *no m.* 12
fear *no m.* nor be dismayed. 23:4
of Lord shall ye mention *no m.* 36
fall and rise *no m.* because of. 25:27
teach *no m.* every man his neighbour, and I . . . their sin *no m.* 31:34
should be *no m.* a nation. 33:24
shall see this place *no m.* 42:18
name shall be *no m.* named. 44:26
saith Lord, Is wisdom *no m.*? 49:7
it shall *no m.* be inhabited. 50:39
law is *no m.* her prophets. *Lam* 2:9
he will *no m.* carry thee away. 4:22
no m. any vain vision. *Ezek* 12:24
and my word shall be *no m.* 25
the wall is *no m.* 13:15
and they shall be *no m.* in. 21
ye shall see *no m.* vanity. 23
go *no m.* astray. 14:11
and will be *no m.* angry. 16:42
that his voice should be *no m.* 19:9
ye my holy name *no m.* 20:39
it shall be *no m.* saith. 21:13, 27
shalt be *no m.* remembered. 32
speak, and be *no m.* dumb. 24:27
thou shalt be *no m.* built. 26:14
shalt be *no m.* 21
be *no m.* a pricking brier. 28:24
they shall *no m.* rule over. 29:15
shall be *no m.* the confidence of. 16
there shall be *no m.* a prince. 30:13
shall be *no m.* a prey. 34:22, 28, 29
shalt devour men *no m.* 36:14
shall be *no m.* two nations. 37:22
house of Israel *no m.* defile. 43:7
my princes shall *no m.* oppress. 45:8
I will *no m.* have mercy. *Hos* 1:6
shalt call me *no m.* Baali. 2:16
they shall *no m.* be remembered. 17
out, I will love them *no m.* 9:15
I will *no m.* make you a. *Joel* 2:19
fallen, she shall *no m.* rise. *Amos* 5:2
they shall *no m.* be pulled out. 9:15
have *no m.* soothsayers. *Mi* 5:12
thou shalt *no m.* worship work. 13
I will afflict thee *no m.* *Nah* 1:12
a command that *no m.* of thy. 14
the wicked shall *no m.* pass. 15
thy messengers shall *no m.* 2:13
shalt *no m.* be haughty. *Zeph* 3:11
I will *no m.* pity the. *Zech* 11:6
shall *no m.* be remembered. 13:2
be *no m.* utter destruction. 14:11
be *no m.* the Canaanite in the. 21
they are *no m.* twain, but one. *Mat* 19:6; *Mark* 10:8
and ye suffer him *no m.* *Mark* 7:12
and enter *no m.* into him. 9:25
I will drink *no m.* of the fruit. 14:25
exact *no m.* than what. *Luke* 3:13
we have *no m.* but five loaves. 9:13
after that have *no m.* that. 12:4
thou art made whole, sin *no m.* *John* 5:14; 8:11
back, and walked *no m.* with. 6:66
the world seeth me *no m.* 14:19
no m. can ye, except ye abide. 15:4
Father, and ye see me *no m.* 16:10
no m. the anguish, for joy. 21
when I shall *no m.* speak in. 25
now I am *no m.* in the world. 17:11
eunuch saw him *no m.* *Acts* 8:39
now *no m.* to return to corruption. 13:34
shall see my face *no m.* 20:25, 38
dieth *no m.*; death hath *no m.* *Rom* 6:9
now then it is *no m.* I that. 7:17, 20
no m. of works: otherwise grace is *no m.* grace. 11:6
know we him *no m.* *2 Cor* 5:16
it is *no m.* of promise. *Gal* 3:18
thou art *no m.* a servant. *Gal* 4:7
ye are *no m.* strangers. *Eph* 2:19
we be *no m.* children tossed. 4:14
let him that stole steal *no m.* 28
iniquities I will remember *no m.* *Heb* 8:12; 10:17
had *no m.* conscience of sins. 10:2
no m. offering for sin. 18, 26
overcometh shall go *no m.* *Rev* 3:12
no m., neither thirst any more. 7:16
find them *no m.* at all. 18:14
be heard *no m.* in thee. 22, 23
deceive the nations *no m.* 20:3
no m. sea. 21:1
no m. death. 4
no m. curse. 22:3

moreover

m. by them is thy servant. *Ps* 19:11
he said, *M.* there shall be. *Isa* 39:8
thou hast *m.* multiplied. *Ezek* 16:29
m. this is their resemblance. *Zech* 5:6
mockings, *m.* of bonds. *Heb* 11:36

Moriah

into the land of *M.* *Gen* 22:2
the house of Lord in *M.* *2 Chr* 3:1

morning

m. arose, the angels. *Gen* 19:15
servants rose up in the *m.* 24:54
they rose betimes in the *m.* 26:31
the *m.* behold it was Leah. 29:25
came in unto them in the *m.* 40:6
in the *m.* he shall devour. 49:27
thee to Pharaoh in the *m.* *Ex* 7:15
in the *m.* the east wind. 10:13
to his strength in the *m.* 14:27
in the *m.* ye shall see the glory. 16:7
shall give you in the *m.* bread. 8, 12
in the *m.* the dew lay round. 13
one lamb thou shalt offer in the *m.* 29:39; *Num* 28:4
meat offering of the *m.* *Ex* 29:41
m. and come up in the *m.* 34:2
nor sacrifice be left to the *m.* 25
altar all night to the *m.* *Lev* 6:9
taken up in the *m.* *Num* 9:21
Balaam rose in the *m.* and. 22:21, 22
in *m.*, would God it were. *Deut* 28:67
death whilst it is yet *m.* *Judg* 6:31
in the *m.* when it is day, we. 16:2
her lord rose in the *m.* and. 19:27
Israel rose up in the *m.* 20:19
as the light of the *m.* when the sun riseth, even a *m.* *2 Sam* 23:4
was up in the *m.* word came. 24:11
considered it in the *m.* *1 Ki* 3:21
name of Baal from *m.* to noon. 18:26
some laboured from *m.* *Neh* 4:21
he read therein from *m.* to. 8:3
seek me in the *m.* but. *Job* 7:21
shine forth, and be as the *m.* 11:17
m. is to them as the shadow. 24:17
hast thou commanded the *m.*? 38:12
like eyelids of the *m.* 41:18
thou hear in the *m.*, O Lord; in the *m.* will I direct my prayer. *Ps* 5:3
but joy cometh in the *m.* 30:5
dominion over them in the *m.* 49:14
sing of thy mercy in the *m.* 59:16
in the *m.* shall my prayer. 88:13
in the *m.* they are like grass. 90:5
in the *m.* it flourisheth and. 6
the dawning of the *m.* 119:147
they that watch for the *m.* 130:6
if I take the wings of the *m.* 139:9
thy lovingkindness in the *m.* 143:8
and princes eat in the *m.* *Eccl* 10:16
in *m.* sow thy seed, and in the. 11:6
looketh forth as the *m.*? *S of S* 6:10
O Lucifer, son of the *m.* *Isa* 14:12
before the *m.* he is not. 17:14
the watchman said, The *m.* 21:12
for *m.* by *m.* shall it pass. 28:19
he wakeneth *m.* by *m.* he. 50:4
thy light break forth as the *m.* 58:8
were as fed horses in the *m.* *Jer* 5:8
hear the cry in the *m.* 20:16
execute judgement in the *m.* 21:12
the *m.* is come on thee. *Ezek* 7:7
the *m.* is gone forth, the rod. 10
in the *m.* came the word of. 12:8
I spake to the people in the *m.*: . . I did in the *m.* as I was. 24:18

came to me in the *m*. *Ezek* 33:22
is prepared as the *m*. *Hos* 6:3
for your goodness is as a *m*. 4
m. it burneth as a flaming fire. 7:6
a *m*. shall the king of Israel. 10:15*
as the *m*. spread upon the. *Joel* 2:2*
maketh the *m*. darkness. *Amos* 4:13
the shadow of death into the *m*. 5:8
a worm when the *m*. rose. *Jonah* 4:7
when the *m*. is light. *Mi* 2:1
in the *m*. it will be foul. *Mat* 16:3
when *m*. was come, the elders. 27:1
the *m*. as they passed. *Mark* 11:20
the cockcrowing, or in *m*. 13:35
see **cloud, evening**

early in the **morning**
Abraham gat up *early in m*.
Gen 19:27; 21:14; 22:3
Abimelech rose *early in the m*. 28:8
Jacob rose up *early in m*. 28:18
Laban rose *early in m*., kissed. 31:55
rise up *early in m*., stand. *Ex* 8:20
9:13
Moses rose *early in m*. 24:4; 34:4
Joshua rose *early in m*. *Josh* 3:1
6:12; 7:16; 8:10
city rose *early in the m*. *Judg* 6:28
Gideon rose *early in m*. 38
Levite rose *early in m*. 19:5, 8
they rose up *early in the m*.
1 Sam 1:19; 29:11; *2 Ki* 3:22
19:35; *2 Chr* 20:20; *Isa* 37:36
Samuel rose *early in m*. *1 Sam* 15:12
David rose *early in m*. 17:20
wherefore rise up *early in m*. 29:10
Job rose up *early in the m*. *Job* 1:5
friend, rising *early in m*. *Pr* 27:14
rise *early in m*. to follow. *Isa* 5:11
arose *early in m*. they were. 37:36
king Darius rose very *early in m*.
Dan 6:19
went *early in m*. to hire. *Mat* 20:1
early in m. came to sepulchre.
Mark 16:2; *Luke* 24:1*
the people came *early in m*.
Luke 21:38; *John* 8:2
entered into the temple *early in m*.
Acts 5:21*

every **morning**
gathered manna *every m*. *Ex* 16:21
thereon sweet incense *every m*. 30:7
free offerings *every m*. 36:3
burn wood on it *every m*. *Lev* 6:12
opening *every m*. pertaineth to.
1 Chr 9:27
to stand *every m*. to thank. 23:30
they burn to the Lord *every m*.
2 Chr 13:11
visit him *every m*. *Job* 7:18
been chastened *every m*. *Ps* 73:14
be thou our arm *every m*. *Isa* 33:2
mercies are new *every m*. *Lam* 3:23
prepare a lamb *every m*. *Ezek* 46:13
meat offering *every m*. 14
every m. a burnt offering. 15
your sacrifices *every m*. *Amos* 4:4
every m. doth he bring judgement to light. *Zeph* 3:5

morning *light*
let us spoil them until *m. light*.
1 Sam 14:36
pertain to him by *m. light*. 25:22
told him nothing until *m. light*. 36
over Jordan by *m. light*. *2 Sam* 17:22
if we tarry until *m. light*. *2 Ki* 7:9

morning *star* and *stars*
when *m. stars* sang together.
Job 38:7
give him the *m. star*. *Rev* 2:28
I am the bright and *m. star*. 22:10

until the **morning**
let nothing of it remain *until the m*.
Ex 12:10; 16:19; 23:18; 29:34
Lev 7:15; *Num* 9:12
at the door *until the m*. *Ex* 12:22
left of it *until the m*. 16:20
to be kept *until the m*. 23
not abide *until the m*. *Lev* 19:13
flesh remain *until the m*. *Deut* 16:4
her all night *until the m*. *Judg* 19:25
lie down *until the m*. *Ruth* 3:13
she lay *until the m*. 14
Samuel lay *until the m*. *1 Sam* 3:15
heed to thyself *until m*. *1 Sam* 19:2
kings in two heaps *until m*. *2 Ki* 10:8
fill of love *until the m*. *Pr* 7:18
I reckoned *until the m*. *Isa* 38:13

morning *watch*
in *m. watch* the Lord. *Ex* 14:24
of host in *m. watch*. *1 Sam* 11:11

morrow
Lord did that thing on the *m*. *Ex* 9:6
on *m*. the remainder. *Lev* 7:16; 19:6
none of it until the *m*. 22:30*
on *m*. after sabbath the priest. 23:11
ye shall count from the *m*. after. 15
on *m*. the congregation. *Num* 16:41
manna ceased on *m*. after. *Josh* 5:12
on the *m*. he took a thick. *2 Ki* 8:15
not the bones till the *m*. *Zeph* 3:3
no thought for the *m*., for the *m*. shall take thought for. *Mat* 6:34
to depart on the *m*. *Acts* 20:7
know not what shall be on the *m*.
Jas 4:14

to-**morrow**
to-m shall this sign be. *Ex* 8:23
to-m. the Lord shall do this. 9:5
to-m. is the rest of the holy. 16:23
sanctify them to-day and *to-m*. 19:10
Aaron said, *To-m*. is a feast. 32:5
sanctify yourselves against *to-m*. ye.
Num 11:18; *Josh* 7:13
to-m. the Lord will shew. *Num* 16:5*
be thou, they and Aaron *to-m*. 16
to-m. Lord will do wonders. *Josh* 3:5
to-m. he will be wroth with. 22:18
to-m. get you early on. *Judg* 19:9
go up, for *to-m*. I will. 20:28
to-m. by that time sun. *1 Sam* 11:9
to-m. is the new moon. 20:5, 18
to-m. shalt thou and thy. 28:19
my servants to thee *to-m*. *1 Ki* 20:6
we will eat my son *to-m*. *2 Ki* 6:28
to-m. a measure of fine flour be. 7:1
to Jezreel by *to-m*. this time. 10:6
to-m. go ye down against them.
2 Chr 20:16, 17
I will do *to-m*. as the king. *Esth* 5:8
to-m. am I invited to her with. 12
to-m. I will give, when. *Pr* 3:28
boast not thyself *to-m*. thou. 27:1
let us eat, for *to-m*. we die.
Isa 22:13; *1 Cor* 15:32
to-m. shall be as this day. *Isa* 56:12
to-m. is cast into the oven. *Mat* 6:30
Luke 12:28
cures to-day and *to-m*. *Luke* 13:32
I must walk to-day and *to-m*. 33
to-m. said he, thou shalt. *Acts* 25:22
to-day or *to-m*. we will go. *Jas* 4:13

morsel
I will fetch a *m*. of bread. *Gen* 18:5
heart with a *m*. of bread. *Judg* 19:5
eat bread, and dip thy *m*. *Ruth* 2:14
or have eaten my *m*. *Job* 31:17
better is a dry *m*. and. *Pr* 17:1
the *m*. thou hast eaten shalt. 23:8
who for one *m*. sold his. *Heb* 12:16*
see **bread**

morsels
forth his ice like *m*. *Ps* 147:17

mortal
m. man be more just? *Job* 4:17
reign in your *m*. body. *Rom* 6:12
shall also quicken your *m*. 8:11
this *m*. must put on. *1 Cor* 15:53, 54
manifest in our *m*. flesh. *2 Cor* 4:11

mortality
m. might be swallowed. *2 Cor* 5:4

mortally
smite his neighbour *m*. *Deut* 19:11

mortar
mills, or beat it in a *m*. *Num* 11:8
bray a fool in a *m*. *Pr* 27:22

morter (*mortar*)
slime had they for *m*. *Gen* 11:3
made them serve in *m*. *Ex* 1:14
take other *m*. and plaster. *Lev* 14:42
and shall break down the *m*. of. 45
upon princes as upon *m*. *Isa* 41:25
lo, others daubed it with untempered *m*. *Ezek* 13:10, 11, 14, 15; 22:28
clay, and tread the *m*. *Nah* 3:14

mortgaged
also said, We have *m*. *Neh* 5:3

mortify
if ye *m*. deeds of body. *Rom* 8:13†
m. your members which. *Col* 3:5†

Moses
called his name *M*. *Ex* 2:10
M. feared, and said, This thing. 14
sought to slay *M*. but *M*. fled. 15
called to him and said, *M*. *M*. 3:4
M. hid his face, he was afraid. 6
anger was kindled against *M*. 4:14
go to meet *M*. 27
M. returned unto the Lord. 5:22
according to the word of *M*. 8:13, 31
9:12, 35; 12:35
M. stretched forth his hand. 10:22
M. was very great. 11:3
the Lord and his servant *M*. 14:31
the people murmured against *M*.
15:24; 17:3
they hearkened not to *M*. 16:20
M. cried to the Lord. 17:4
M. did so. 6; *Num* 17:11
M.' hands were heavy. *Ex* 17:12
M. built an altar. 15
M. sat to judge. 18:13
M. went up unto God. 19:3
M. returned the words of the. 8
called *M*. up to mount Sinai. 20
M. drew near unto the thick. 20:21
M. alone shall come near. 24:2
M. wrote all the words of the. 4
and *M*. went into the midst of. 18
as for *M*. we wot not what. 32:1, 23
M. besought the Lord. 11
M.' anger waxed hot. 19
the Lord talked with *M*. 33:9
M. went up. 34:4
M. put the vail upon his face. 34:35
M. did look on all work; *M*. 39:43
M. was not able to enter. 40:35
M. sought the goat of. *Lev* 10:16
the blasphemer to *M*. 24:11
as the Lord spake to *M*. *Num* 5:4
the people cried to *M*., and *M*. 11:2
M. heard people weep through. 10
indeed spoken only by *M*.? 12:2
M. was very meek above all. 3
M. is not so, who is faithful in. 7
ark and *M*. departed not out. 14:44
when *M*. heard it, he fell upon. 16:4
M. laid up the rods before the. 17:7
the people chode with *M*. 20:3
against God and against *M*. 21:5
M. made a serpent of brass and. 9
Midianitish woman in sight of *M*.
25:6
M. sent them to war, them. 31:6
M. was wroth with the officers. 14
M. wrote their goings out by. 33:2
M. charged the people. *Deut* 27:11
M. wrote this law and. 31:9
M. wrote this song, and taught. 22
wherewith *M*. the man of God. 33:1
M. the servant of the Lord. 34:5
since in Israel like to *M*. 10
as I was with *M*. so I. *Josh* 1:5; 3:7
as we hearkened to *M*. so. 1:17
Joshua, as they feared *M*. 4:14
Lord spake this word to *M*. 14:10
as I was in the day *M*. sent me. 11
as it is written in the law of *M*.
1 Ki 2:3; *2 Ki* 23:25; *2 Chr* 23:18
Ezra 3:2; *Dan* 9:11, 13
Luke 24:44; *1 Cor* 9:9
the two tables which *M*. *1 Ki* 8:9
M. the man of God. *1 Chr* 23:14
the son of *M*. was ruler. 26:24
known his ways unto *M*. *Ps* 103:7
he sent *M*. his servant. 105:26
they envied *M*. also in the. 106:16
had not *M*. stood before him. 23
so that it went ill with *M*. for. 32
the right hand of *M*. *Isa* 63:12
though *M*. and Samuel. *Jer* 15:1
remember the law of *M*. *Mal* 4:4
appeared *M*. and Elias talking with.
Mat 17:3; *Mark* 9:4; *Luke* 9:30
let us make one tabernacle for *M*.
Mat 17:4; *Mark* 9:5
did *M*. then command? *Mat* 19:7
M. suffered you to put away. 8

Pharisees sit in *M.'* seat. *Mat* 23:2
did *M.* command you ? *Mark* 10:3
M. wrote, If a man's brother die. 12:19; *Luke* 20:28
M. and the prophets. *Luke* 16:29
if they hear not *M.* and the. 31
dead are raised, *M.* shewed. 20:37
beginning at *M.* and all the prophets, he expounded. 24:27
law was given by *M.* *John* 1:17
have found him of whom *M.* 45
as *M.* lifted up the serpent. 3:14
one accuseth you, even *M.* 5:45
had ye believed *M.* ye had. 46
M. gave you not that bread. 6:32
did not *M.* give you the law ? 7:19
not because it is of *M.* but of. 22
that the law of *M.* should not. 23
disciple, we are *M.'* disciples. 9:28
we know that God spake unto *M.* 29
for *M.* truly said unto. *Acts* 3:22
blasphemous words against *M.* 6:11
change the customs which *M.* 14
in which time *M.* was born. 7:20
then *M.* trembled and durst not. 32
this *M.* whom they refused, did. 35
M. that said unto Israel. 37
be justified by the law of *M.* 13:39
circumcised after manner of *M.* 15:1
them to keep the law of *M.* 5
M. hath in every city them that. 21
the Jews to forsake *M.* 21:21
things which *M.* did say. 26:22
out of the law of *M.* and. 28:23
from Adam to *M.* *Rom* 5:14
M. describeth righteousness of. 10:5
all baptized to *M.* in. *1 Cor* 10:2
not behold the face of *M.* *2 Cor* 3:7
not as *M.* who put a vail over. 13
when *M.* is read, the vail is. 15
and Jambres withstood *M.* *2 Tim* 3:8
M. was faithful in all. *Heb* 3:2, 5
worthy of more glory than *M.* 3
that came out of Egypt by *M.* 16
which tribe *M.* spake nothing. 7:14
for when *M.* had spoken. 9:19
that despised *M.'* law. 10:28
by faith *M.* was hid three. 11:23
M. refused to be called son of. 24
M. said, I exceedingly fear. 12:21
about the body of *M.* *Jude* 9
song of *M.* and the Lamb. *Rev* 15:3
see **Aaron, book, commanded, law**

most

m. men proclaim every. *Pr* 20:6
m. of mighty works. *Mat* 11:20
them will love him *m.*? *Luke* 7:42
that he to whom he forgave *m.* 43
sorrowing *m.* of all for. *Acts* 20:38
it be by two, or at *m.* *1 Cor* 14:27

mote

m. that is in thy brother's eye, but not beam ? *Mat* 7:3; *Luke* 6:41
let me pull out the *m.* *Mat* 7:4
to cast out the *m.* out of thy brother's eye. 5; *Luke* 6:42

moth

are crushed before the *m.* *Job* 4:19
buildeth his house as a *m.* 27:18
beauty to consume like a *m.* *Ps* 39:11
the *m.* shall eat them up. *Isa* 50:9
51:8
I be to Ephraim as a *m.* *Hos* 5:12
treasures, where *m.* and rust doth corrupt. *Mat* 6:19
neither *m.* nor rust corrupt. 20
Luke 12:33

motheaten

garment that is *m.* *Job* 13:28
your garments *m.* *Jas* 5:2

mother

was the *m.* of all living. *Gen* 3:20
shall be a *m.* of nations. 17:16
told them of her *m.'s* house. 24:28
brother and *m.* precious things. 53
thou the *m.* of thousands of. 60
lest he smite the *m.* with. 32:11
called the child's *m.* *Ex* 2:8
to take a wife and her *m.* *Lev* 20:14
Deborah arose a *m.* *Judg* 5:7
m. of Sisera looked out. 28
go, return each to her *m.'s*. *Ruth* 1:8
to Zeruiah, Joab's *m.* *2 Sam* 17:25
seekest to destroy a *m.* in. 20:19
be set for the king's *m.* *1 Ki* 2:19
child, she is the *m.* thereof. 3:27
away the king's *m.* *2 Ki* 24:15
and to be a joyful *m.* *Ps* 113:9
doth not bless their *m.* *Pr* 30:11
the only one of her *m.* *S of S* 6:9
of your *m.'s* divorcement ? *Isa* 50:1
your *m.* shall be sore. *Jer* 50:12
as is the *m.* so is the. *Ezek* 16:44
your *m.* was an Hittite, father. 45
women the daughters of one *m.* 23:2
plead with your *m.* for she. *Hos* 2:2
their *m.* hath played the harlot. 5
m. was dashed in pieces upon. 10:14
up against her *m.* a man's enemies. *Mi* 7:6; *Mat* 10:35; *Luke* 12:53
saw Peter's wife's *m.* sick. *Mat* 8:14; *Luke* 4:38
instructed of her *m.* *Mat* 14:8
brought it to her *m.* 11; *Mark* 6:28
born from their *m.'s* womb. *Mat* 19:12
m. of Zebedee's children. 20:20
the *m.* of my Lord should ? *Luke* 1:43
the *m.* of Jesus was there. *John* 2:1
Acts 1:14
house of Mary *m.* of. *Acts* 12:12
Jerusalem which is the *m.* *Gal* 4:26
the *m.* of harlots. *Rev* 17:5
see **father**

***his* mother**

his m. took him a wife. *Gen* 21:21
into *his m.* Sarah's tent, and . . . after the death of *his m.* 24:67
brought them to *his m.* 27:14
brought mandrakes to *his m.* 30:14
brother Benjamin, *his m.'s* son. 43:29
he alone is left of *his m.* 44:20
seethe a kid in *his m.'s* milk. *Ex* 23:19; 34:26; *Deut* 14:21
take *his m.'s* daughter. *Lev* 20:17
his m.'s name was Shelomith. 24:11
out of *his m.'s* womb. *Num* 12:12
the daughter of *his m.* *Deut* 27:22
Abimelech went to *his m.'s*. *Judg* 9:1
he said to *his m.* 17:2
he restored it to *his m.* 3
his m. made him a little. *1 Sam* 2:19
and *his m.* bare him. *1 Ki* 1:6
his m. he removed from. 15:13
Elijah delivered him to *his m.* 17:23
walked in the way of *his m.* 22:52
lad, Carry him to *his m.* *2 Ki* 4:19
his m. called his name. *1 Chr* 4:9
his m. was his counsellor. *2 Chr* 22:3
mourneth for *his m.* *Ps* 35:14
sin of *his m.* be blotted out. 109:14
is weaned of *his m.* 131:2
is the heaviness of *his m.* *Pr* 10:1
foolish man despiseth *his m.* 15:20
a child left bringeth *his m.* 29:15
prophecy that *his m.* taught. 31:1
forth of *his m.'s* womb. *Eccl* 5:15
crown wherewith *his m.* *S of S* 3:11
whom *his m.* comforteth. *Isa* 66:13
his m. was espoused. *Mat* 1:18
young child and *his m.* 2:13, 20
his m. stood without. 12:46
Mark 3:31; *Luke* 8:19
is not this the carpenter's son? is not *his m.* called Mary? *Mat* 13:55
with Holy Ghost from *his m.'s* womb. *Luke* 1:15
his m. said, He shall be called. 60
Joseph and *his m.* knew not. 2:43*
but *his m.* kept these sayings. 51
the only son *of his m.* and. 7:12
he delivered him to *his m.* 15
second time into *his m.'s* womb ? *John* 3:4
his m. stood by the cross of. 19:25
saw *his m.* he saith to *his m.* 26
man lame from *his m.'s* womb. *Acts* 3:2; 14:8
salute Rufus and *his m.* *Rom* 16:13

mother in law

lieth with his *m. in law.* *Deut* 27:23
kissed her *m. in law.* *Ruth* 1:14
hast done to thy *m. in law.* 2:11
Ruth dwelt with her *m. in law.* 23
all that her *m. in law* bade. 3:6
go not empty to thy *m. in law.* *Ruth* 3:17
riseth up against the *m. in law.* *Mi* 7:6; *Mat* 10:35; *Luke* 12:53

***my* mother**

the daughter of *my m.* *Gen* 20:12
even the sons of *my m.* *Judg* 8:19
Nazarite from *my m.'s* womb. 16:17
to her, Ask on, *my m.* *1 Ki* 2:20
naked came I out of *my m.'s*. *Job* 1:21
up the doors of *my m.'s* womb. 3:10
the worm, Thou art *my m.* 17:14
guided her from *my m.'s* womb. 31:18
when on *my m.'s* breasts. *Ps* 22:9
thou art my God from *my m.'s*. 10
and in sin did *my m.* conceive. 51:5
become an alien to *my m.'s*. 69:8
he that took me out of *my m.'s*. 71:6
hast covered me in *my m.'s*. 139:13
beloved in sight of *my m.* *Pr* 4:3
my m.'s children were angry with me. *S of S* 1:6
brought him to *my m.'s* house. 3:4
sucked the breasts of *my m.* 8:1
bring thee into *my m.'s* house. 2
the bowels of *my m.* he. *Isa* 49:1
woe is me, *my m.* that. *Jer* 15:10
not the day wherein *my m.* 20:14
or that *my m.* might have been. 17
Jesus said, Who is *my m.*? *Mat* 12:48; *Mark* 3:33
behold *my m.* and my brethren. *Mat* 12:49; *Mark* 3:34
my m. and my brethren are these. *Luke* 8:21
separated me from *my m.'s*. *Gal* 1:15

***thy* mother**

thy m.'s sons bow down. *Gen* 27:29
shall I and *thy m.* come to ? 37:10
nakedness of *thy m.* *Lev* 18:7
nakedness of daughter of *thy m.* 9
not uncover nakedness of sister of *thy m.* 13; 20:19
the son of *thy m.* entice. *Deut* 13:6
so shall *thy m.* be childless among. *1 Sam* 15:33
to the confusion of *thy m.'s*. 20:30
whoredoms of *thy m.* *2 Ki* 9:22
thou slanderest *thine* own *m.'s* son. *Ps* 50:20
forsake not the law of *thy m.* *Pr* 1:8; 6:20
and despise not *thy m.* 23:22
thy m. brought thee forth. *S of S* 8:5
cast thee out, and *thy m.* *Jer* 22:26
father an Amorite, *thy m.* *Ezek* 16:3
thy m.'s daughter that loatheth. 45
and say, What is *thy m.*? 19:2
thy m. is like a vine in thy. 10
and I will destroy *thy m.* *Hos* 4:5
behold *thy m.* and thy brethren. *Mat* 12:47; *Mark* 3:32
Luke 8:20; *John* 19:27
dwelt in *thy m.* Eunice. *2 Tim* 1:5

mothers

shall be thy nursing *m.* *Isa* 49:23
Lord, concerning their *m.* *Jer* 16:3
m. where is corn and wine? soul was poured out into their *m.'* *Lam* 2:12
we are fatherless, our *m.* are. 5:3
hundredfold, sisters, *m.* *Mark* 10:30
for murderers of *m.* *1 Tim* 1:9
elder women as *m.*; younger. 5:2

motions

the *m.* of sins did work. *Rom* 7:5*

mouldy

bread of provision was dry and *m.* *Josh* 9:5, 12

mount, -ing

though his excellency *m.* *Job* 20:6
doth the eagle *m.* up at thy ? 39:27
they *m.* up to heaven. *Ps* 107:26
shall *m.* up as the lifting. *Isa* 9:18*
by the *m.* of Luhith shall. 15:5
they shall *m.* up with wings. 40:31
though Babylon should *m.* up to. *Jer* 51:5
when the cherubims lifted up wings to *m.* up. *Ezek* 10:16, 1

mount

(*This word very frequently means hill country, and is so rendered by the Revisions*)

sacrifice on the *m.* *Gen* 31:54
encamped at the *m.* of. *Ex* 18:5
whoso toucheth the *m.* shall. 19:12
Moses went down from the *m.* 14
32:15; 34:29
thick cloud upon the *m.* 16; 24:15
m. Sinai on a smoke. 18
bounds about the *m.* 23
Lord abode upon *m.* Sinai. 24:16
devouring fire on the top of *m.* 17
Lord gave Moses on *m.* Sinai. 31:18
brake them beneath the *m.* 32:19
in the morning to *m.* Sinai. 34:2
man be seen through all the *m.* 3
departed from the *m.* *Num* 10:33
and came unto *m.* Hor. 20:22
bring up to *m.* Hor. 25
Aaron died in *m.* Hor. 28
point out for you *m.* Hor. 34:7
long enough in this *m.* *Deut* 1:6
go to the *m.* of the Amorites. 7
the *m.* burned with fire. 9:15
shall stand upon *m.* Ebal. 27:13
get thee to *m.* Nebo, which. 32:49
shined forth from *m.* Paran. 33:2
draw towards *m.* Tabor. *Judg* 4:6
depart early from *m.* Gilead. 7:3
gat him up to *m.* Zalmon. 9:48
up by the ascent of *m.* *2 Sam* 15:30
the top of the *m.* where he. 32*
to Horeb, the *m.* of God. *1 Ki* 19:8
go and stand on the *m.* before. 11
on right hand the *m.* *2 Ki* 23:13
go to the *m.* and fetch. *Neh* 8:15
down also on *m.* Sinai. 9:13
of goats from *m.* Gilead. *S of S* 4:1
the *m.* of the daughter of Zion.
Isa 10:32; 16:1
I will sit on the *m.* of the. 14:13
shall worship in the holy *m.* 27:13
siege against thee with a *m.* 29:3
hew ye trees, and cast a *m.* against.
Jer 6:6; *Ezek* 4:2; 21:22; 26:8
north shall cast up a *m.* *Dan* 11:15
understanding out of *m.* Esau. *Ob* 8
come to judge the *m.* of Esau. 21
Holy One from *m.* Paran. *Hab* 3:3
n wilderness of *m.* Sinai. *Acts* 7:30
he one from the *m.* Sinai. *Gal* 4:24
Agar is *m.* Sinai in Arabia. 25
not come to the *m.* *Heb* 12:18
ee **Carmel, Ephraim, Gerizim Gilboa, Seir, Zion**

before the **mount**

srael camped *before the m.* *Ex* 19:2
he flocks feed *before the m.* 34:3

in, or *into the* **mount**

n *the m.* of the Lord. *Gen* 24:14
vertook Jacob *in the m.* Gilead.
31:23
nd tarried all night *in the m.* 54
et him *in the m.* of God. *Ex* 4:27
o not up *into the m.* 19:12
ord said to Moses, Come up to me
into the m. 24:12; *Deut* 10:1
Moses went up *into the m.* of God.
Ex 24:13, 15, 18
Moses was *in the m.* forty days.
24:18; *Deut* 9:9; 10:10
eir pattern shewed thee *in the m.*
Ex 25:40; 26:30; 27:8; *Heb* 8:5
et thee up *into m.* *Num* 27:12
e *in the m.* as Aaron died *in m.*
Hor. *Deut* 32:50
tar to Lord *in m.* Ebal. *Josh* 8:30
e sepulchres *in the m.* *2 Ki* 23:16
build house of Lord *in m.* Moriah.
2 Chr 3:1
e up as *in m.* Perazim. *Isa* 28:21
ake to him *in m.* Sinai. *Acts* 7:38
th him *in the* holy *m.* *2 Pet* 1:18

mount *of Olives*

nd on the *m. of Olives*, and the *m.*
of Olives shall cleave. *Zech* 14:4
ey were come to *m. of Olives.*
Mat 21:1; *Luke* 19:29
d as he sat upon *m. of Olives.*
Mat 24:3; *Mark* 13:3
sung an hymn, they went out into *m.*
of Olives. *Mat* 26:30
Mark 14:26; *Luke* 22:39
descent of *m. of Olives.* *Luke* 19:37
and abode in *m. of Olives.* 21:37
went unto *m. of Olives.* *John* 8:1
returned from the *m. of Olives.*
Acts 1:12

mountain

(*Used as now both literally and figuratively for a great mass, or a vast quantity. The Revisions frequently change it to* hill, *or* hill country)

A Catalogue of the most famous mountains mentioned in Scripture

Abarim, *on the East of Jordan, in Moab. Nebo and Pisgah were parts of this,* Num 27:12; Deut 34:1.

Ararat, *on which Noah's ark rested,* Gen 8:4.

Bashan, *probably a whole district of hill country.*

Carmel, *on the Mediterranean Sea on the border of Phoenicia,* 1 Ki 18:20–42.

Ebal, *in Samaria near Shechem,* Deut 11:26–29.

Gerizim, *separated by a valley from Ebal,* Deut 11:26–29.

Gilboa, *on which King Saul met his death,* 1 Sam 31:1.

Gilead, *a mountainous region east of Jordan.*

Hermon, *probably the scene of the Transfiguration,* Mat 17:1.

Hor, *on which Aaron died,* Num 20:25, 27.

Hor (*another*), Num 34:7, 8. *Probably Lebanon.*

Horeb *or* Sinai, *the Mount of God, or of the Law.*

Lebanon, *the most important range in Syria, to the north,* Josh 1:4; 1 Ki 5:2–7.

Moab, Mts. of, *a general term for the hill country east of Jordan.*

Moriah, *the site of the temple in Jerusalem.*

Nebo (Pisgah), *the place of Moses' death,* Deut. 34:1.

Olivet *or* Mt. of Olives, *near Jerusalem, associated much with our Saviour.*

Seir, *the mountainous district east of the Dead Sea,* Gen 14:6.

Sinai. *See* Horeb.

Tabor, *on the Plain of Esdraelon,* Judg 4:6–15; 19:22.

Zion *or* Sion, *one the mountains on which Jerusalem was built, the south-east corner.*

remained fled to the *m.* *Gen* 14:10
escape to the *m.* 19:17
I cannot escape to the *m.* 19
came to the *m.* of God. *Ex* 3:1
Egypt, shall serve God on this *m.* 12
to him out of the *m.* saying. 19:3
people saw the *m.* smoking. 20:18
up into top of the *m.* *Num* 14:40
ye are come to the *m.* *Deut* 1:20
ye have compassed this *m.* 2:3
goodly *m.* and Lebanon. 3:25
the *m.* burnt with fire. 4:11; 5:23
call the people to the *m.* 33:19
get ye to the *m.* and hide. *Josh* 2:16
plain and the *m.* of Israel. 11:16
give me this *m.* 14:12
the *m.* shall be thine. 17:18
drave out the inhabitants of the *m.*
Judg 1:19
forced children of Dan into *m.* 34
on a *m.* on the one side, and Israel
stood on a *m.* on. *1 Sam* 17:3
this side of the *m.* and David and his
men on that side of the *m.* 23:26
cast him on some *m.* *2 Ki* 2:16
the *m.* was full of horses. 6:17
surely the *m.* falling. *Job* 14:18
flee as a bird to your *m.*? *Ps* 11:1
thou hast made my *m.* to. 30:7
brought to this *m.* his right. 78:54
the *m.* of the Lord's house established. *Isa* 2:2; *Mi* 4:1
let us go up to the *m.* of the Lord.
Isa 2:3; *Mi* 4:2
a beacon on top of a *m.* *Isa* 30:17
goeth with a pipe to *m.* of Lord. 29
every *m.* shall be made low. 40:4
Luke 3:5
hunt them from every *m.* *Jer* 16:16
O my *m.* in the field, I will give. 17:3
the *m.* of the house as high places of.
26:18; *Mi* 3:12
people have gone from *m.* *Jer* 50:6
O *m.* saith the Lord . . . and I will
make thee a burnt *m.* 51:25
eyes are dim, because of *m.* of Zion.
Lam 5:18
Lord stood on the *m.* *Ezek* 11:23
as profane out of *m.* of God. 28:16
the house on top of the *m.* 43:12
stone became a great *m.* *Dan* 2:35
the stone was cut out of the *m.* 45
to thee from *m.* to *m.* *Mi* 7:12
go up to *m.*, bring wood. *Hag* 1:8
who art thou, O great *m.*? *Zech* 4:7
m. of the Lord, the holy *m.* 8:3
half of *m.* shall remove. 14:4
he went up into a *m.* *Mat* 5:1
14:23; 15:29; *Mark* 3:13; 6:46
Luke 6:12; 9:28; *John* 6:3, 15
come down from the *m.* *Mat* 8:1
them into an high *m.* apart. 17:1
down from the *m.* 9; *Mark* 9:9
a grain of mustard, shall say to this
m. *Mat* 17:20; 21:21; *Mark* 11:23
into a *m.* where Jesus. *Mat* 28:16
swine feeding on *m.* *Luke* 8:32
as a beast touch the *m.* *Heb* 12:20
every *m.* and island were. *Rev* 6:14
as it were a great *m.* burning. 8:8
see **holy**

high **mountain**

banner upon the *high m.* *Isa* 13:2
upon every *high m.* rivers. 30:25
get thee up into the *high m.* 40:9
on a lofty and *high m.* hast. 57:7
gone up upon every *high m.* *Jer* 3:6
plant it on a *high m.* *Ezek* 17:22
set me on a very *high m.* 40:2
taketh him up into an exceeding *high*
m. and. *Mat* 4:8; *Luke* 4:5
Peter, James, and John, and bringeth
into *high m.* *Mat* 17:1; *Mark* 9:2
in the Spirit to *high m.* *Rev* 21:10

in the, or *in this* **mountain**

Zoar, and dwelt *in the m.* *Gen* 19:30
plant them *in the m.* *Ex* 15:17
go up *into the m.* *Num* 13:17
up *in this m.* Abarim. *Deut* 32:49
he blew a trumpet *in the m.* of.
Judg 3:27
David remained *in a m.* *1 Sam* 23:14
80,000 to hew *in the m.* *2 Chr* 2:2
God is to be praised *in the m.* of.
Ps 48:1
in this m. shall the Lord. *Isa* 25:6
he will destroy *in this m.* the face. 7
in this m. shall the hand of. 10
in the m. of Israel I. *Ezek* 17:23
ye kine, that are *in the m.* *Amos* 4:1
woe to them that trust *in the m.* 6:1
worshipped *in this m.* *John* 4:20
neither *in this m.* nor Jerusalem. 21

mountains

m. were covered. *Gen* 7:20
ark rested on the *m.* 8:4
in tenth month tops of the *m.* 5
departed from the *m.* *Num* 33:48
destroy places on the high *m.*
Deut 12:2
the Anakims from the *m.* *Josh* 11:21
the *m.* melted from. *Judg* 5:5
go up and down on the *m.* 11:37
her virginity upon the *m.* 38
ye *m.* of Gilboa, let. *2 Sam* 1:21
strong wind rent the *m.* *1 Ki* 19:11
as the roes on the *m.* *1 Chr* 12:8
all Israel scattered on the *m.*
2 Chr 18:16
which removeth the *m.* *Job* 9:5
he overturneth the *m.* by the. 28:9
m. bring forth food. 40:20
is like the great *m.* *Ps* 36:6

though the *m.* be carried into. *Ps* 46:2
though the *m.* shake with the. 3
strength setteth fast the *m.* 65:6
the *m.* shall bring peace. 72:3
glorious than *m.* of prey. 76:4
flames setteth the *m.* on fire. 83:14
before the *m.* were brought. 90:2
waters stood above the *m.* 104:6
they go up by the *m.*; go down by. 8
m. skipped like rams. 114:4, 6
as the *m.* are round about. 125:2
that descended on the *m.* 133:3
touch the *m.* and they shall. 144:5
grass to grow on the *m.* 147:8
m. and all hills praise the. 148:9
before the *m.* were settled. *Pr* 8:25
leaping on the *m.* *S of S* 2:8
be like a roe on the *m.* 17; 8:14
look from Amana and the *m.* 4:8
the day of the Lord shall be upon all the high *m.* *Isa* 2:14
and on my *m.* tread him. 14:25
up an ensign on the *m.* 18:3
the *m.* shall be melted with. 34:3
who hath weighed the *m.*? 40:12
thou shalt thresh the *m.* and. 41:15
and I will make waste *m.* 42:15
into singing, ye *m.* 44:23; 49:13
make all my *m.* a way. 49:11
how beautiful upon the *m.* are the feet of him that. 52:7; *Nah* 1:15
for the *m.* shall depart. *Isa* 54:10
m. shall break forth before. 55:12
the *m.* might flow down at. 64:1, 3
burnt incense on the *m.* 65:7
out of Judah an inheritor of my *m.* 9
I beheld the *m.* and. *Jer* 4:24
for the *m.* will I take up a. 9:10
stumble on the dark *m.* 13:16
from the *m.* bringing offerings. 17:26
vines on the *m.* of Samaria. 31:5
as Tabor among the *m.* so. 46:18
turned them away on the *m.* 50:6
pursued us on the *m.* *Lam* 4:19
set thy face toward the *m.* *Ezek* 6:2
and say, Ye *m.* of Israel, hear the. 3
shall be on the *m.* like doves. 7:16
not eaten upon the *m.* 18:6, 15
but hath eaten upon the *m.* 11
no more be heard on the *m.* 19:9
in thee they eat upon the *m.* 22:9
upon the *m.* his branches. 31:12
I will lay thy flesh on the *m.* 32:5
the *m.* of Israel shall be. 33:28
wandered through all the *m.* 34:6
feed them on the *m.* of Israel. 13, 14
I will fill his *m.* with his slain. 35:8
spoken against the *m.* of Israel. 12
m. of Israel, and say, Ye *m.* of Israel, hear the word of the. 36:1, 4
but ye, O *m.* of Israel, shall shoot. 8
one nation on the *m.* of Israel. 37:22
out against the *m.* of Israel. 38:8
m. shall be thrown down. 20
I will call for a sword against him throughout all my *m.* 21
and will bring thee on the *m.* 39:2
thou shalt fall on the *m.* of Israel. 4
even a great sacrifice on the *m.* 17
morning spread upon the *m.* *Joel* 2:2
m. shall drop down new wine. 3:18
assemble yourselves on the *m.* of. *Amos* 3:9
he that formeth the *m.* the. 4:13
the *m.* shall drop sweet wine. 9:13
the *m.* shall be molten. *Mi* 1:4
arise, contend thou before the *m.* 6:1
hear ye, O ye *m.* the Lord's. 2
the *m.* quake at him. *Nah* 1:5
people scattered on the *m.* 3:18
m. were scattered, the hills. *Hab* 3:6
m. saw thee, and they trembled. 10
a drought on the *m.* *Hag* 1:11
between the *m.* of brass. *Zech* 6:1
and laid his *m.* waste. *Mal* 1:3
goeth into the *m.* and. *Mat* 18:12
be in Judaea flee into the *m.* 24:16
that I could remove *m.* *1 Cor* 13:2
the *m.* were not found. *Rev* 16:20
heads are seven *m.* on which. 17:9

in the **mountains**

to slay them *in the m.* *Ex* 32:12
pitched *in m.* of Abarim. *Num* 33:47
not to the cities *in the m.* *Deut* 2:37
kings that dwell *in the m.* *Josh* 10:6
made them dens *in the m.* *Judg* 6:2
as doth hunt a partridge *in the m.* *1 Sam* 26:20
hewers *in the m.* *1 Ki* 5:15
made high places *in m.* *2 Chr* 21:11
had vine dressers *in the m.* 26:10
multitude *in the m.* like. *Isa* 13:4
day he was *in the m.* *Mark* 5:5
in deserts and *in the m.* *Heb* 11:38

of the **mountains**

tops *of the m.* were seen. *Gen* 8:5
offer him on one *of m.* I will. 22:2
Balak brought me out *of the m.* *Num* 23:7
foundations *of the m.* *Deut* 32:22
things *of the* ancient *m.* 33:15
liers in wait for him in top *of the m.* *Judg* 9:25
down from the top *of the m.* thou seest the shadow *of the m.* as. 36
I am come up to height *of m.* *2 Ki* 19:23; *Isa* 37:24
with the showers *of the m.* *Job* 24:8
range *of the m.* is his pasture. 39:8
I know all the fowls *of the m.* *Ps* 50:11
of corn on top *of the m.* 72:16
and herbs *of the m.* *Pr* 27:25
shall be established in top *of the m.* *Isa* 2:2; *Mi* 4:1
as the chaff *of the m.* *Isa* 17:13
left to the fowls *of the m.* 18:6
shout from the top *of the m.* 42:11
the multitude *of the m.* *Jer* 3:23
cities *of the m.* shall flocks. 33:13
be in the tops *of the m.* *Ezek* 6:13
sounding again *of the m.* 7:7
on the tops *of the m.* *Hos* 4:13
chariots on tops *of the m.* *Joel* 2:5
to the bottom *of the m.* *Jonah* 2:6
flee to the valley *of the m.* *Zech* 14:5
in the rocks *of the m.* *Rev* 6:15

to the **mountains**

I will get me *to the m.* *S of S* 4:6
and crying *to the m.* *Isa* 22:5
thus saith the Lord *to the m.* *Ezek* 6:3; 36:4
thy blood even *to the m.* 32:6
man, prophesy *to the m.* 36:1, 6
they shall say *to the m.* *Hos* 10:8
nigh *to the m.* a herd. *Mark* 5:11
let them that be in Judaea flee *to the m.* 13:14; *Luke* 21:21
begin to say *to m.* Fall on us. *Luke* 23:30; *Rev* 6:16

mounts

(*American Revision.* mounds)
m. are come to the city. *Jer* 32:24
houses thrown down by the *m.* 33:4
him, by casting up *m.* *Ezek* 17:17

mourn

Abraham came to *m.* *Gen* 23:2
how long wilt thou *m.*? *1 Sam* 16:1
rend clothes, and *m.* *2 Sam* 3:31
came into the city to *m.* *1 Ki* 13:29
all Israel shall *m.* for him. 14:13
holy to the Lord, *m.* not. *Neh* 8:9
an appointment to *m.* *Job* 2:11
that those which *m.* may be. 5:11
soul within him shall *m.* 14:22
I *m.* in my complaint. *Ps* 55:2*
and thou *m.* at the last. *Pr* 5:11
bear rule, the people *m.* 29:2*
a time to *m.* and a time. *Eccl* 3:4
gates shall lament and *m.* *Isa* 3:26
of Kir-hareseth shall ye *m.* 16:7
the fishers also shall *m.* 19:8
I did *m.* as a dove. 38:14
we roar like bears, we *m.* 59:11
sent me to comfort all that *m.* 61:2
m. in Zion, give beauty for ashes. 3
all ye that *m.* for her. 66:10
for this shall earth *m.* *Jer* 4:28
how long shall the land *m.*? 12:4
my heart shall *m.* for men. 48:31
ways of Zion do *m.* *Lam* 1:4
let not the seller *m.* *Ezek* 7:12
the king shall *m.* and the prince. 27
yet neither shalt thou *m.* nor. 24:16
ye shall pine away and *m.* one. 23
I caused Lebanon to *m.* *Ezek* 31:15
therefore shall the land *m.* *Hos* 4:3
for the people shall *m.* over. 10:5
the Lord's ministers *m.* *Joel* 1:9
of the shepherds shall *m.* *Amos* 1:2
every one *m.* that dwelleth. 8:8; 9:5
shall *m.* for him as one mourneth. *Zech* 12:10
and the land shall *m.* every. 12
blessed are they that *m.* *Mat* 5:4
children of bridechamber *m.*? 9:15
all the tribes of the earth *m.* 24:30
that laugh, for ye shall *m.* *Luke* 6:25
afflicted, and *m.* and weep. *Jas* 4:9
the merchants shall weep and *m.* *Rev* 18:11

mourned

Jacob *m.* for his son. *Gen* 37:34
Egyptians *m.* for Jacob. 50:3, 10
people heard these evil tidings, they *m.* *Ex* 33:4; *Num* 14:39
the congregation *m.* *Num* 20:29
nevertheless, Samuel *m.* for Saul. *1 Sam* 15:35
and they *m.* for Saul. *2 Sam* 1:12
Bath-sheba *m.* for Uriah. 11:26
David *m.* for his son. 13:37
as one that had long time *m.* 14:2
m. over the man of God. *1 Ki* 13:30
all Israel *m.* for Jeroboam's. 14:18
Ephraim their father *m.* *1 Chr* 7:22
and all Judah *m.* for. *2 Chr* 35:24
m. for the transgression. *Ezra* 10:6
I sat down and *m.* *Neh* 1:4
when ye fasted and *m.* *Zech* 7:5
we have *m.* unto you, and ye have. *Mat* 11:17; *Luke* 7:32
told them as they *m.* *Mark* 16:10
and have not rather *m.* *1 Cor* 5:2

mourner

feign thyself to be a *m.* *2 Sam* 14:2

mourners

that comforteth the *m.* *Job* 29:25
m. go about the streets. *Eccl* 12:5
restore comforts to him and his *m.* *Isa* 57:18
be to them as bread of *m.* *Hos* 9:4

mourneth

behold, the king *m.* *2 Sam* 19:1
I bowed as one that *m.* *Ps* 35:14
mine eye *m.* by reason of. 88:9*
the earth *m.* *Isa* 24:4; 33:9
the new wine *m.* 24:7
being desolate *m.* to me. *Jer* 12:11
Judah *m.* and the gates. 14:2
of swearing the land *m.* 23:10
the land *m.* for the corn. *Joel* 1:10
m. for his firstborn. *Zech* 12:10

mournfully

that we have walked *m.* *Mal* 3:14

mourning, *substantive*

days of *m.* for my father. *Gen* 27:41
and when the days of his *m.* 50:4
made a *m.* for his father Jacob. 10
m., this is a grievous *m.* 1
eaten thereof in my *m.* *Deut* 26:1
so the days of *m.* for Moses. 34:
when the *m.* was past. *2 Sam* 11:2
that day was turned into *m.* 19:
there was great *m.* among. *Esth* 4:
was turned to them from *m.* 9:2
to raise up their *m.* *Job* 3:
my harp also is turned to *m.* 30:3
thou hast turned my *m.* *Ps* 30:1
to go to the house of *m.* *Eccl* 7:
wise is in the house of *m.*
the Lord did call to *m.* *Isa* 22:1
and sorrow and *m.* shall flee. 51:1
and the days of thy *m.* shall. 60:2
them the oil of joy for *m.* 61:
make thee *m.* as for. *Jer* 6:2
enter not into the house of *m.* 16:
turn their *m.* into joy. 31:1
daughter of Judah *m.* *Lam* 2
our dance is turned into *m.* 5:1
written lamentations, *m.* and woe. *Ezek* 2:1
make no *m.* for the dead. 24:1
I caused a *m.* 31:
with weeping and *m.* *Joel* 2:
the husbandmen to *m.* *Amos* 5:

turn your feasts into m. and I will make it as the m. of an. Amos 8:10
came not forth in the m. Mi 1:11
m. in Jerusalem, as m. Zech 12:11
great m., Rachel weeping. Mat 2:18
us your desire, your m. 2 Cor 7:7
laughter be turned into m. Jas 4:9
in one day death and m. Rev 18:8

mourning, verb

to the grave to my son m. Gen 37:35
I pray thee, put on m. 2 Sam 14:2
hasted to his house m. Esth 6:12
went m. without the sun. Job 30:28
I am troubled, I go m. Ps 38:6
why go I m. because of oppression? 42:9; 43:2
call for the m. women. Jer 9:17
in m. to comfort them for. 16:7
all of them m. for their iniquities. Ezek 7:16
I Daniel was m. 3 weeks. Dan 10:2
will make a m. as the owls. Mi 1:8

mouse

weasel and m. shall be. Lev 11:29
abomination, and the m. Isa 66:17

mouth

and lo, in her m. was. Gen 8:11
and enquire at her m. 24:57
stone was upon the well's m. 29:2
stone from the well's m. 3, 10
his money was in his sack's m. 42:27; 43:12, 21
who hath made man's m.? Ex 4:11
be to thee instead of a m. 16
will I speak m. to m. Num 12:8
the earth open her m. and. 16:30
put a word in Balaam's m. 23:5
put to death by the m. of witnesses. 35:30; Deut 17:6; 19:15
roll great stones on the m. Josh 10:18, 27
open m. of cave, and bring out. 22
Eli marked her m. 1 Sam 1:12
the words in her m. 2 Sam 14:3, 19
a covering over the well's m. 17:19
every m. that hath not. 1 Ki 19:18
prophets declare good to the king with one m. 22:13
a lying spirit in m. of his prophets. 22, 23; 2 Chr 18:21, 22
Necho from m. of God. 2 Chr 35:22
word of the Lord by the m. of Jeremiah. 36:21, 22; Ezra 1:1
went out of the king's m. Esth 7:8
iniquity stoppeth her m. Job 5:16
doth not the m. taste? 12:11*; 34:3*
there was no answer in the m. 32:5
out of the m. of babes hast. Ps 8:2 Mat 21:16
save me from the lion's m. Ps 22:21
whose m. must be held in. 32:9*
the m. of the righteous. 37:30
in whose m. are no reproofs. 38:14
but m. that speaketh lies. 63:11
let not the pit shut her m. 69:15
iniquity shall stop her m. 107:42
m. of wicked, m. of deceitful. 109:2
then was our m. filled with. 126:2
scattered at the grave's m. 141:7
whose m. speaketh vanity. 144:8, 11
from thee a froward m. Pr 4:24
and her m. is smoother than oil. 5:3
walketh with froward m. 6:12; 10:32
the froward m. do I hate. 8:13
violence covereth the m. of. 10:6, 11
the m. of the foolish is near. 14
the m. of the just bringeth. 31
the city is overthrown by m. 11:11
the m. of the upright shall. 12:6
n the m. of the foolish is a. 14:3
ne m. of fools poureth out. 15:2
ne m. of fools feedeth on. 14
ne m. of the wicked poureth out. 28
ne words of a man's m. are. 18:4
fool's m. is his destruction. 7
n. of the wicked devoureth. 19:28
he m. of a strange woman. 22:14
o is a parable in the m. 26:7, 9
nd a flattering m. worketh ruin. 28
ateth, and wipeth her m. 30:20
vords of a wise man's m. Eccl 10:12
srael with open m. Isa 9:12
n evil doer, and every m. 17

make ye a wide m.? Isa 57:4
Spirit not depart out of m. 59:21
shall speak with him m. to m. Jer 32:4; 34:3
Baruch wrote from m. of Jeremiah. 36:4, 27, 32; 45:1
goeth forth out of our m. 44:17
no more named in m. of any. 26
out of the m. of Most. Lam 3:38
to open the m. in the slaughter. Ezek 21:22
thee the opening of the m. 29:21
came near to the m. of. Dan 3:26
word was in the king's m. 4:31
brought, and laid on the m. of. 6:17
it had three ribs in m. of it. 7:5
there was a m. speaking. 8, 20
of Baalim out of her m. Hos 2:17
taketh out of the m. Amos 3:12
shall even fall into the m. Nah 3:12
of lead on the m. of it. Zech 5:8
out of the m. of God. Mat 4:4
abundance of the heart the m. 12:34
goeth into the m. defileth not. 15:11
in the m. of two or three witnesses every word. 18:16; 2 Cor 13:1
as he spake by m. of his. Luke 1:70
for I will give you a m. and. 21:15
Holy Ghost spake by m. of David. Acts 1:16; 4:25
by m. of all his prophets. 3:18, 21
you the same things by m. 15:27
them to smite him on the m. 23:2
m. is full of cursing. Rom 3:14
that every m. may be stopped. 19
with the m. confession is. 10:10
that ye may with one m. 15:6
muzzle the m. of the ox. 1 Cor 9:9*
I was delivered out of m. 2 Tim 4:17
out of the same m. Jas 3:10
given to him a m. Rev 13:5
the spirits came out of m. of. 16:13
see **Lord**

his **mouth**

his m.: I will be with his m. Ex 4:15
put a word in his m. Num 23:16
proceedeth out of his m. 30:2
put my words in his m. Deut 18:18
no man put his hand to his m. 1 Sam 14:26, 27
delivered it out of his m. 17:35
there is tidings in his m. 2 Sam 18:25
and fire out of his m. devoured. 22:9; Ps 18:8
spake with his m. to David. 1 Ki 8:15; 2 Chr 6:4
he put his m. on his m. 2 Ki 4:34
judgements of his m. 1 Chr 16:12
by the breath of his m. Job 15:30
be sweet in his m. 20:12
keep it still within his m. 13
pray thee, the law from his m. 22:22
esteemed the words of his m. 23:12
sound that goeth out of his m. 37:2
draw up Jordan into his m. 40:23
out of his m. go burning. 41:19
and a flame goeth out of his m. 21
his m. is full of cursing. Ps 10:7
made by breath of his m. 33:6
words of his m. are iniquity. 36:3
man that openeth not his m. 38:13
words of his m. are smoother. 55:21
remember the judgements of his m. 105:5
his m. cometh knowledge. Pr 2:6
hypocrite with his m. 11:9
good by the fruit of his m. 12:14
eat good by the fruit of his m. 13:2
he that keepeth his m. keepeth. 3
joy by the answer of his m. 15:23
his m. transgresseth not. 16:10
of the wise teacheth his m. 23
for himself, for his m. craveth. 26
and his m. calleth for strokes. 18:6
satisfied with the fruit of his m. 20
not so much as bring it to his m. 19:24; 26:15
but his m. shall be filled. 20:17
whoso keepeth his m. 21:23
labour of a man is for his m. Eccl 6:7
beginning of words of his m. 10:13
with the kisses of his m. S of S 1:2
his m. is most sweet, this is. 5:16
earth with the rod of his m. Isa 11:4
was any deceit in his m. 53:9
peaceably with his m. Jer 9:8
ear receive the word of his m. 20
write all these words at his m. 36:17
bring out of his m. that. 51:44
putteth his m. in the dust. Lam 3:29
cleaveth to the roof of his m. 4:4
his blood out of his m. Zech 9:7
law of truth was in his m. Mal 2:6
should seek the law at his m. 7
and his m. was opened. Luke 1:64
words proceeded out of his m. 4:22
abundance of heart his m. 6:45
catch somewhat out of his m. 11:54
have heard of his own m. 22:71
filled a spunge and put it to his m. John 19:29
hear the voice of his m. Acts 22:14
with the spirit of his m. 2 Thes 2:8
guile found in his m. 1 Pet 2:22
out of his m. went a sharp sword. Rev 1:16; 19:15, 21
cast out of his m. water. 12:15
the dragon cast out of his m. 16
and his m. was as the mouth. 13:2

my **mouth**

my m. that speaketh. Gen 45:12
the word God putteth in my m. Num 22:38; 23:12
the words of my m. Deut 32:1
my m. is enlarged over. 1 Sam 2:1
I will not refrain my m. Job 7:11
mine own m. shall condemn. 9:20
strengthen you with my m. 16:5
my servant with my m. 19:16
fill my m. with arguments. 23:4
my m. hath kissed my hand. 31:27
neither have I suffered my m. 30
tongue hath spoken in my m. 33:2
will lay my hand upon my m. 40:4
purposed that my m. Ps 17:3
words of my m. be acceptable. 19:14
shall continually be in my m. 34:1
I said, I will keep my m. 39:1
he hath put a new song in my m. 40:3
hear this, my m. shall speak. 49:3
and my m. shall shew forth. 51:15
give ear to the words of my m. 54:2
my m. shall praise thee with. 63:5
my m. hath spoken, when I. 66:14
I cried to him with my m., he. 17
let my m. be filled with thy. 71:8
my m. shall shew forth thy. 15
ears to the words of my m. 78:1
I will open my m. in a parable. 2
with my m. will I make known. 89:1
praise the Lord with my m. 109:30
word of truth out of my m. 119:43
sweeter than honey to my m. 103
freewill offerings of my m. 108
cleave to the roof of my m. 137:6
O Lord, before my m. 141:3
my m. shall speak praise. 145:21
nor decline from the words of my m. Pr 4:5; 5:7
attend to the words of my m. 7:24
for my m. shall speak truth. 8:7
the words of my m. are in. 8
he laid the coal on my m. Isa 6:7
and have not asked at my m. 30:2
my m. it hath commanded. 34:16
word is gone out of my m. 45:23
things went forth out of my m. 48:3
my m. like a sharp sword. 49:2
word that goeth out of my m. 55:11
hand and touched my m. Jer 1:9
shalt be as my m. 15:19
written from my m. 36:6
in my m. like honey for. Ezek 3:3
hear the word at my m. 17; 33:7
abominable flesh into my m. 4:14
flesh nor wine in my m. Dan 10:3
by the words of my m. Hos 6:5
open my m. in parables. Mat 13:35
time entered into my m. Acts 11:8
the Gentiles by my m. should. 15:7
I may open my m. boldly. Eph 6:19
with the sword of my m. Rev 2:16
I will spue thee out of my m. 3:16
the book was in my m. sweet. 10:10

mouth with opened

earth opened her m. to. Gen 4:11

earth *opened* her *m.* and swallowed.
Num 16:32; 26:10; *Deut* 11:6
opened the *m.* of ass. *Num* 22:28
I have *opened* my *m.* *Judg* 11:35, 36
opened Job his *m.* and. *Job* 3:1
and they *opened* their *m.* wide.
29:23; *Ps* 35:21
now I have *opened* my *m.* *Job* 33:2
I *opened* not my *m.* *Ps* 39:9
m. of the deceitful are *opened.* 109:2
I *opened* my *m.* and panted. 119:131
hell hath *opened* her *m.* *Isa* 5:14
there was none that *opened m.* 10:14
yet he *opened* not his *m.* 53:7
I *opened* my *m.* and he caused me.
Ezek 3:2
thy *m.* be *opened* to him which is.
24:27; 33:22
opened my *m.* and spake. *Dan* 10:16
opened his *m.* and taught. *Mat* 5:2
when thou hast *opened* his *m.* 17:27
his *m.* was *opened* immediately.
Luke 1:64
like a lamb dumb, so *opened* he not his *m.* *Acts* 8:32
Philip *opened* his *m.* 35
Peter *opened* his *m.* 10:34
our *m.* is *opened* to you. *2 Cor* 6:11
earth *opened* her *m.* and helped.
Rev 12:16
he *opened* his *m.* in blasphemy. 13:6

mouth with *openeth*

dumb man that *openeth* not his *m.*
Ps 38:13
a fool *openeth* not his *m.* *Pr* 24:7
openeth her *m.* with wisdom. 31:26

their **mouth**

their hand to *their m.* *Judg* 7:6
thy manna from *their m.* *Neh* 9:20
the poor from *their m.* *Job* 5:15
gaped upon me with *their m.* 16:10
laid their hand on *their m.* 29:9
cleaved to the roof of *their m.* 10
no faithfulness in *their m.* *Ps* 5:9
with *their m.* they speak. 17:10
O God, in *their m.*: break out. 58:6
they belch out with *their m.* 59:7
for the sin of *their m.* and words. 12
they bless with *their m.* but. 62:4
their m. against the heavens. 73:9
flatter him with *their m.* 78:36
praises of God be in *their m.* 149:6
draw near me with *their m.* *Isa* 29:13
cut off from *their m.* *Jer* 7:28
thou art near in *their m.* far. 12:2
enemies have opened *their m.*
Lam 2:16
with *their m.* they shew much love.
Ezek 33:31
my flock from *their m.* 34:10
is deceitful in *their m.* *Mi* 6:12
lay their hand on *their m.* 7:16
tongue found in *their m.* *Zeph* 3:13
shall consume away in *their m.*
Zech 14:12
nigh to me with *their m.* *Mat* 15:8
their m. speaketh great. *Jude* 16
power is in *their m.* and. *Rev* 9:19
fire proceedeth out of *their m.* 11:5
and in *their m.* was found. 14:5

thy **mouth**

I will be with *thy m.* *Ex* 4:12, 15
Lord's law may be in *thy m.* 13:9
of other gods out of *thy m.* 23:13
promised with *thy m.* *Deut* 23:23
word is nigh to thee, in *thy m.* 30:14
Rom 10:8
not depart out of *thy m.* *Josh* 1:8
where is now *thy m.*? *Judg* 9:38
if thou hast opened *thy m.* 11:36
lay thine hand upon *thy m.* 18:19
Pr 30:32
thy m. hath testified. *2 Sam* 1:16
thou spakest with *thy m.* *1 Ki* 8:24
2 Chr 6:15
word in *thy m.* is truth. *1 Ki* 17:24
words of *thy m.* be like a *Job* 8:2
till he fill *thy m.* with laughing. 21
thy m. uttereth thine iniquity. 15:5
thine own *m.* condemneth thee. 6
such words go out of *thy m.* 13
my covenant in *thy m.* *Ps* 50:16
thou givest *thy m.* to evil. 19

open *thy m.* *Ps* 81:10
who satisfieth *thy m.* with. 103:5†
all the judgements of *thy m.* 119:13
the law of *thy m.* is better. 72
the testimony of *thy m.* 88
hear the words of *thy m.* 138:4
snared with the words of *thy m.*
Pr 6:2
praise thee, and not *thine* own *m.*
27:2
open *thy m.* for the dumb, in. 31:8
open *thy m.*, judge righteously. 9
be not rash with *thy m.* *Eccl* 5:2
suffer not *thy m.* to cause thy. 6
roof of *thy m.* like the. *S of S* 7:9
I have put my words in *thy m.*
Isa 51:16; *Jer* 1:9
my words which I put in *thy m.* shall not depart out of *thy m.* *Isa* 59:21
my words in *thy m.* fire. *Jer* 5:14
open *thy m.* and eat. *Ezek* 2:8
tongue cleave to roof of *thy m.* 3:26
I will open *thy m.* and thou shalt. 27
was not mentioned by *thy m.* 16:56
never open *thy m.* any more. 63
set the trumpet to *thy m.* *Hos* 8:1
keep doors of *thy m.* *Mi* 7:5
out of *thine* own *m.* will I judge.
Luke 19:22
if thou confess with *thy m.* *Rom* 10:9
it shall be in *thy m.* sweet. *Rev* 10:9

your **mouth**

proceeded out of *your m.* *Num* 32:24
not arrogancy come out of *your m.*
1 Sam 2:3
lay your hand on *your m.* *Job* 21:5
thus with *your m.* ye have boasted.
Ezek 35:13
is cut off from *your m.* *Joel* 1:5
no corrupt communication proceed out of *your m.* *Eph* 4:29; *Col* 3:8

mouths

song, put it in their *m.* *Deut* 31:19
not be forgotten out of *m.* of. 21
they gaped upon me with their *m.*
Ps 22:13
meat was yet in their *m.* 78:30
they have *m.* but they speak not.
115:5; 135:16
there any breath in their *m.* 135:17
kings shall shut their *m.* at. *Isa* 52:15
ye and wives have spoken with your *m.* *Jer* 44:25
enemies opened their *m.* *Lam* 3:46
hath shut the lions' *m.* *Dan* 6:22
putteth not into their *m.* *Mi* 3:5
deceivers, whose *m.* must. *Tit* 1:11
stopped the *m.* of lions. *Heb* 11:33
put bits in the horses' *m.* *Jas* 3:3
their *m.* issued fire. *Rev* 9:17, 18

move

[1] *To change position*, 2 Ki 21:8. [2] *To rouse, or influence*, Deut 32:21; Judg 13:25. [3] *To affect, as by pity or other feeling*, Ruth 1:19.

not a dog *m.* his tongue. *Ex* 11:7
that *m.* in the waters. *Lev* 11:10
not *m.* a sickle into. *Deut* 23:25
I will *m.* them to jealousy. 32:21
Spirit of the Lord began to *m.*
Judg 13:25
may dwell and *m.* no more.
2 Sam 7:10; *2 Ki* 21:8*
let no man *m.* his bones. *2 Ki* 23:18
with nails that it *m.* not. *Jer* 10:4
m. out of their holes. *Mi* 7:17*
will not *m.* them. *Mat* 23:4
for in him we live, *m.* *Acts* 17:28
none of these things *m.* me. 20:24

moveable

her ways are *m.*, canst not. *Pr* 5:6*

moved

the Spirit of God *m.* on. *Gen* 1:2
all flesh died that *m.* on the. 7:21
have *m.* me to jealousy. *Deut* 32:21
none *m.* his tongue. *Josh* 10:21
she *m.* him to ask of her father a field. 15:18; *Judg* 1:14
that all the city was *m.* *Ruth* 1:19
heart, only her lips *m.* *1 Sam* 1:13
the king was much *m.* *2 Sam* 18:33

foundations of heaven *m.* *2 Sam* 22:8
m. David against them. 24:1
world shall be stable, that it be not *m.*
1 Chr 16:30; *Ps* 93:1; 96:10
dwell, and shall be *m.* no. *1 Chr* 17:9
God *m.* them to depart. *2 Chr* 18:31
they have *m.* sedition. *Ezra* 4:15
saw that Mordecai *m.* not. *Esth* 5:9
at this my heart is *m.* *Job* 37:1
flesh, they cannot be *m.* 41:23
I shall not be *m.* *Ps* 10:6; 16:8
30:6; 62:2, 6
those rejoice when I am *m.* 13:4
these things shall never be *m.* 15:5
foundations of the hills *m.* 18:7†
in Lord, and shall not be *m.* 21:7
she shall not be *m.* God shall. 46:5
the kingdoms were *m.* 6
suffer the righteous to be *m.* 55:22
suffereth not our feet to be *m.* 66:9
m. at the presence of God. 68:8*
they *m.* him to jealousy. 78:58
reigneth, let the earth be *m.* 99:1
surely he shall not be *m.* 112:6
not suffer thy foot to be *m.* 121:3
righteous shall not be *m.* *Pr* 12:3
and my bowels were *m.* *S of S* 5:4
the posts of the door *m.* *Isa* 6:4
heart was *m.* as trees are *m.* 7:2
and there was none that *m.* 10:14
hell from beneath is *m.* for. 14:9
the idols of Egypt shall be *m.* 19:1
earth is broken down, and *m.* 24:19
image that shall not be *m.* 40:20
it should not be *m.* 41:7
all the hills *m.* lightly. *Jer* 4:24
they shall drink, and be *m.* 25:16*
whose waters are *m.* as. 46:7*, 8*
earth is *m.* at the noise of. 49:21*
Babylon the earth is *m.* 50:46*
he was *m.* with choler. *Dan* 8:7
king of the south shall be *m.* 11:11
was *m.* with compassion. *Mat* 9:36
14:14; 18:27; *Mark* 1:41; 6:34
m. with indignation. *Mat* 20:24
all the city was *m.* saying. 21:10*
but the chief priests *m.* *Mark* 15:11*
that I should not be *m.* *Acts* 2:25
patriarchs, *m.* with envy. 7:9
but the Jews *m.* with envy. 17:5
the city was *m.* and people. 21:30
be not *m.* from the hope. *Col* 1:23
that no man be *m.* by. *1 Thes* 3:3
Noah *m.* with fear. *Heb* 11:7
kingdom which cannot be *m.* 12:28*
they spake as *m.* by. *2 Pet* 1:21
mountain and island *m.* *Rev* 6:14

movedst

though thou *m.* me against him.
Job 2:3

mover

found this fellow a *m.* of sedition.
Acts 24:5

moveth

living creature that *m.* *Gen* 1:21
every thing that *m.* on earth. 28
be on all that *m.* on earth. 9:2*
of every creature that *m.* *Lev* 11:46
Behemoth *m.* his tail. *Job* 40:17
thing that *m.* praise him. *Ps* 69:34
when it *m.* itself aright. *Pr* 23:31*
m. whithersoever the rivers come.
Ezek 47:9*

moving, *substantive*

the *m.* of my lips should. *Job* 16:5*
blind, waiting for the *m.* *John* 5:3

moving

the waters bring forth *m.* *Gen* 1:20
every *m.* thing shall be meat. 9:3
m. his lips, he bringeth. *Pr* 16:30*

mower

wherewith the *m.* filleth. *Ps* 129:7

mowings

growth after the king's *m.* *Amos* 7:1

mown

rain upon the *m.* grass. *Ps* 72:[illegible]

much

for thou art *m.* mightier. *Gen* 26:1[illegible]
it is a night to be *m.* *Ex* 12:4[illegible]
he that gathered *m.* 16:18; *2 Cor* 8:1[illegible]
if the scab spread *m.* abroad.
Lev 13:7, 22, 27, 3[illegible]

soul of people was *m.* *Num* 21:4
shall carry *m.* seed out. *Deut* 28:38
return with *m.* riches. *Josh* 22:8
it grieveth me *m.* for. *Ruth* 1:13
a *m.* greater slaughter. *1 Sam* 14:30
his name was *m.* set by. 18:30
but Jonathan delighted *m.* in. 19:2
as thy life was *m.* set by this day, so let my life be *m.* set by. 26:24
had understanding exceeding *m.* *1 Ki* 4:29
Jehu shall serve him *m.* *2 Ki* 10:18
m. wickedness in sight of Lord. 21:6
of Ophel he built *m.* *2 Chr* 27:3
Manasseh wrought *m.* evil in. 33:6
it is a time of *m.* rain. *Ezra* 10:13
it yieldeth *m.* increase. *Neh* 9:37
mine hand had gotten *m.* 31:25
m. less do lying lips. *Pr* 17:7
m. less for a servant to have. 19:10
whether he eat little or *m.* *Eccl* 5:12
he hath *m.* sorrow and wrath. 17
sinner destroyeth *m.* good. 9:18
thou take thee *m.* sope [soap]. *Jer* 2:22
it containeth *m.* *Ezek* 23:32
shew *m.* love. 33:31
fruit thereof was *m.* *Dan* 4:12, 21
ye have sown *m.* *Hag* 1:6
ye looked for *m.* 9
not *m.* better than they? *Mat* 6:26
where they had not *m.* earth. 13:5 *Mark* 4:5
might have been sold for *m.* *Mat* 26:9
sins are forgiven, for she loved *m.* *Luke* 7:47
m. is given, of him shall *m.* be required ... committed *m.* 12:48
is faithful also in *m.*: unjust in least is unjust in *m.* 16:10
forth *m.* fruit. *John* 12:24; 15:5
I will not talk *m.* with you. 14:30
her masters *m.* gain. *Acts* 16:16
them *m.* which had believed. 18:27
Festus said, *M.* learning doth. 26:24
m. every way. *Rom* 3:2
laboured *m.* in the Lord. 16:12
out of *m.* affliction I. *2 Cor* 2:4
m. rather be in subjection. *Heb* 12:9
m. more shall not we escape. 25
the righteous availeth *m.* *Jas* 5:16
I wept *m.* because no man. *Rev* 5:4
see **how** *much*, **how** *much less*, **how** *much more*, *much* **more**, **people**

as **much**

as m. money as it is worth. *Gen* 23:9
mess was five times *as m.* 43:34
fill sacks with food *as m.* 44:1
twice *as m.* as they gather daily. *Ex* 16:5, 22
sons have, one *as m.* as. *Lev* 7:10
for *as m.* as the Lord. *Josh* 17:14
take *as m.* as thy soul. *1 Sam* 2:16
cut wood *as m.* as. *2 Chr* 2:16
gave Job twice *as m.* as. *Job* 42:10
joy in testimonies, *as m.* *Ps* 119:14
to receive *as m.* again. *Luke* 6:34
likewise of fishes *as m.* *John* 6:11
as m. as in me is, I am. *Rom* 1:15
in *as m.* as I am the apostle. 11:13
as m. as lieth in you, live. 12:18
in *as m.* as not without an oath. *Heb* 7:20

so **much**

remained not *so m.* *Ex* 14:28
sweet cinnamon half *so m.* 30:23
poor and cannot get *so m.* *Lev* 14:21
not give you *so m.* as a. *Deut* 2:5
none to be *so m.* praised as Absalom. *2 Sam* 14:25
there shall not be left *so m.* 17:12
the spoil, it was *so m.* *2 Chr* 20:25
will not *so m.* as bring it. *Pr* 19:24
eat *so m.* as is sufficient for. 25:16
why gaddest thou *so m.*? *Jer* 2:36
have we spoken *so m.*? *Mal* 3:13
we have *so m.* bread? *Mat* 15:33
was no room, no, not *so m.* as about. *Mark* 2:2
not *so m.* as eat. 3:20; 6:31
so m. more a great deal they. 7:36
so m. the more went there a fame. *Luke* 5:15
have ye not read *so m.* as this? 6:3
would not lift up *so m.* as his. 18:13
he cried *so m.* the more, Have. 39
sold it for *so m.* she said, Yea, for *so m.* *Acts* 5:8
no inheritance, not *so m.* as to. 7:5
not *so m.* as heard whether. 19:2
not *so m.* as named. *1 Cor* 5:1
being made *so m.* better. *Heb* 1:4
by *so m.* Jesus made surety. 7:22
so m. more as ye see day. 10:25
if *so m.* as a beast touch. 12:20
so m. torment and sorrow. *Rev* 18:7

too **much**

sufficient, and *too m.* *Ex* 36:7
them, ye take *too m.* *Num* 16:3, 7
the part of children of Judah was *too m.* for them. *Josh* 19:9
too m. for you to go up to. *1 Ki* 12:28
arise *too m.* contempt. *Esth* 1:18

very **much**

corn as sand, *very m.* *Gen* 41:49
very m. cattle went up. *Ex* 12:38
remaineth *very m.* land. *Josh* 13:1
with *very m.* cattle, *very m.* 22:8
Sheba came with *very m.* *1 Ki* 10:2
innocent blood *very m.* *2 Ki* 21:16
David *very m.* brass. *1 Chr* 18:8
away *very m.* spoil. *2 Chr* 14:13
given him substance *very m.* 32:29
people transgressed *very m.* 36:14
I am afflicted *very m.* *Ps* 119:107
summer fruits *very m.* *Jer* 40:12

mufflers

away the chains, the *m.* *Isa* 3:19

mulberry trees

upon them over against the *m. trees.* *2 Sam* 5:23; *1 Chr* 14:14
the sound in tops of the *m. trees.* *2 Sam* 5:24; *1 Chr* 14:15

mule

gat him upon his *m.* *2 Sam* 13:29
Absalom rode on a *m.*, the *m.* 18:9
to ride on my *m.* *1 Ki* 1:33; 38:44
not as the horse or *m.* *Ps* 32:9
plague of the horse, of the *m.* *Zech* 14:15

mules

Anah that found *m.* in. *Gen* 36:24*
brought horses and *m.*, a rate year by year. *1 Ki* 10:25; *2 Chr* 9:24
grass to save the *m.* *1 Ki* 18:5
to thy servant two *m.* *2 Ki* 5:17
brought bread on camels and on *m.* *1 Chr* 12:40
their *m.* were 245. *Ezra* 2:66 *Neh* 7:68
sent letters by riders on *m.* *Esth* 8:10*, 14*
your brethren on *m.* *Isa* 66:20
traded in thy fairs with *m.* *Ezek* 27:14

multiplied

Israel grew and *m.* *Gen* 47:27 *Ex* 1:7, 20
more afflicted, they *m.* *Ex* 1:12
my wonders may be *m.* in. 11:9
your God hath *m.* you. *Deut* 1:10
m. and all that thou hast is *m.* 8:13
that your days may be *m.* 11:21
I *m.* his seed, and gave. *Josh* 24:3
their cattle were *m.* *1 Chr* 5:9
if his children be *m.* it is. *Job* 27:14
if thy transgressions be *m.* 35:6
their sorrows shall be *m.* *Ps* 16:4
hate me wrongfully are *m.* 38:19
them, so that they are *m.* 107:38
thy days shall be *m.* *Pr* 9:11
wicked are *m.* transgression. 29:16
thou hast *m.* the nation. *Isa* 9:3
for our transgressions are *m.* 59:12
when ye be *m.* they shall. *Jer* 3:16
m. more than the nations. *Ezek* 5:7*
ye have *m.* your slain in. 11:6
thou hast *m.* thy whoredoms. 16:25 23:19
m. thy fornication. 16:29
m. thine abominations. 51
faint, and ruins be *m.* *Ezek* 21:15
his boughs were *m.* 31:5
m. your words. 35:13
peace be *m.* to you. *Dan* 4:1; 6:25 *1 Pet* 1:2; *2 Pet* 1:2; *Jude* 2
I *m.* her silver and gold. *Hos* 2:8
Judah hath *m.* fenced cities. 8:14
I have *m.* visions, and used. 12:10
hast *m.* thy merchants. *Nah* 3:16
when the number of the disciples was *m.* *Acts* 6:1, 7
people grew and *m.* in Egypt. 7:17
the fear of the Lord were *m.* 9:31
word of God grew and *m.* 12:24

multipliedst

children also *m.* thou as. *Neh* 9:23

multiplieth

he *m.* my wounds without. *Job* 9:17
he *m.* words against God. 34:37
m. words without knowledge. 35:16

multiply

be fruitful and *m.* *Gen* 1:22, 28 8:17; 9:7; 35:11
I will *m.* thy sorrow. 3:16
when men began to *m.* on. 6:1
I will *m.* Hagar's seed. 16:10; 17:20
and I will *m.* thee. 17:2; 48:4
I will *m.* thy seed. 22:17; 26:4, 24 *Heb* 6:14
bless thee, and *m.* thee. *Gen* 28:3
deal wisely with them; lest they *m.* *Ex* 1:10
I will *m.* my signs and. 7:3
lest the beast of the field *m.* 23:29
whom thou saidst, I will *m.* 32:13 *Lev* 26:9; *Deut* 7:13; 13:17 28:63; 30:5
that ye may live and *m.* and go in and possess. *Deut* 8:1; 30:16
the king shall not *m.* horses. 17:16
neither shall he *m.* wives, nor. 17
did all their family *m.* *1 Chr* 4:27
I shall *m.* my days as. *Job* 29:18
I will *m.* them, they shall. *Jer* 30:19
so will I *m.* the seed of David. 33:22
I have caused thee to *m.* *Ezek* 16:7
I will *m.* men. 36:10
m. man and beast. 11
I will *m.* the fruit of the tree. 30
I will place them and *m.* 37:26
Gilgal *m.* transgression. *Amos* 4:4
and *m.* your seed sown. *2 Cor* 9:10

multiplying

in *m.* I will multiply. *Gen* 22:17 *Heb* 6:14

multitude

[1] *A great company or number of persons or things*, Gen 30:30; 48:4. [2] *The common people*, Mat 9:33. [3] *The whole assembly, both common people and senators*, Acts 23:7. [4] *The church, or a company of the faithful*, Acts 15:12, 22; 21:22. [5] *Great store, or plenty*, Ps 5:7; Hos 9:7. [6] *Much variety*, Eccl 5:3, 7.

not numbered for *m.* *Gen* 16:10 32:12; *1 Ki* 3:8
God Almighty make thee a *m.* *Gen* 28:3*
now increased unto a *m.* 30:30
I will make of thee a *m.* of people. 48:4*; 16:19
a mixed *m.* went up also. *Ex* 12:38
thou shalt not follow a *m.* 23:2
according to the *m.* of. *Lev* 25:16
mixed *m.* fell a lusting. *Num* 11:4
ye are as the stars for *m.* *Deut* 1:10 10:22; 28:62; *Heb* 11:12
as sand on sea shore for *m.* *Josh* 11:4; *Judg* 7:12; *1 Sam* 13:5 *2 Sam* 17:11; *1 Ki* 4:20
grasshoppers for *m.* *Judg* 6:5; 7:12
m. melted away. *1 Sam* 14:16
he dealt among the whole *m.* of Israel. *2 Sam* 6:19
could not be told for *m.* *1 Ki* 8:5
they are as all the *m.* *2 Ki* 7:13
hast said, With the *m.* of my chariots. 19:23; *Isa* 37:24
people like dust for *m.* *2 Chr* 1:9
we go against this *m.* 14:11

the *m.* were dead bodies. *2 Chr* 20:24
for a *m.* had not cleansed. 30:18
be not afraid of all the *m.* 32:7
from Israel the mixed *m.* *Neh* 13:3
Haman told of the *m.* *Esth* 5:11
Mordecai accepted of the *m.* 10:3
should not the *m.* of words? *Job* 11:2
and *m.* of years should teach. 32:7
by reason of *m.* of oppressions. 35:9
he scorneth the *m.* of the city. 39:7*
I will come in the *m.* of. *Ps* 5:7
cast them out in *m.* of their. 10
no king saved by the *m.* of. 33:16
I had gone with the *m.* to the. 42:4
that boast themselves in *m.* 49:6
according to the *m.* of thy. 51:1
rebuke the *m.* of bulls, with. 68:30
O God, in the *m.* of thy. 69:13
turn to me, according to *m.* of. 16
deliver me not to the *m.* of. 74:19
in the *m.* of my thoughts. 94:19
they remembered not *m.* of. 106:7
and repented, according to *m.* 45
praise him among the *m.* 109:30
in the *m.* of words. *Pr* 10:19
in the *m.* of counsellors. 11:14; 24:6
in *m.* of people is the king's. 14:28
in *m.* of counsellors they are. 15:22
gold, and a *m.* of rubies. 20:15
the *m.* of business, a fool's voice is known by the *m.* of. *Eccl* 5:3
in the *m.* of dreams there are. 7
to what purpose is the *m.*? *Isa* 1:11
m. dried up with thirst. 5:13
m. and pomp shall descend. 14
woe to *m.* of many people. 17:12
so *m.* of nations be that fight. 29:8
when *m.* of shepherds is called. 31:4
shall come on thee for *m.* of. 47:9
stand now with the *m.* of thy. 12
thou art wearied in the *m.* of thy. 13
m. of camels shall cover thee. 60:6
according to *m.* of his loving. 63:7
is a *m.* of waters. *Jer* 10:13*; 51:16*
yea, they have called a *m.* 12:6*
I have wounded thee for *m.* 30:14
I will punish the *m.* of No. 46:25*
afflicted her, for *m.* of. *Lam* 1:5
compassion according to *m.* of. 3:32
wrath is on all the *m.* *Ezek* 7:12, 14
touching the whole *m.* thereof. 13
answer him according to the *m.* 14:4
by reason of the *m.* 27:12, 18, 33
the *m.* of the wares. 16, 18
Pharaoh and all his *m.* 31:18; 32:32
Elam and her *m.* 32:24
Tubal and all her *m.* 26
bury Gog, and all his *m.* 39:11
words like voice of a *m.* *Dan* 10:6
north shall set forth a *m.* 11:13
for *m.* of thine iniquity. *Hos* 9:7
thou didst trust in the *m.* 10:13
there is a *m.* of slain. *Nah* 3:3
the *m.* of the whoredoms of. 4
he feared the *m.* *Mat* 14:5; 21:46
I have compassion on the *m.* 15:32 *Mark* 8:2
thou seest the *m.* thronging thee. *Mark* 5:31; *Luke* 8:45
was with the angel a *m.* *Luke* 2:13
together an innumerable *m.* 12:1
him in the absence of the *m.* 22:6
yet spake, behold, a *m.* 47
whole *m.* of them arose. 23:1
a *m.* being present in. *John* 5:13
not able to draw it for the *m.* 21:6
m. that believed were of. *Acts* 4:32
saying pleased the whole *m.* 6:5
the *m.* rose up together. 16:22
m. must needs come together. 21:22
and shall hide a *m.* of sins. *Jas* 5:20
shall cover the *m.* of sins. *1 Pet* 4:8
see **great**

multitudes

draw her and all her *m.* *Ezek* 32:20
m. in the valley of decision. *Joel* 3:14
dumb spake; and the *m.* *Mat* 9:33
when he saw the *m.* he was. 36
m. cried, saying, Hosanna to. 21:9
m. were added both of. *Acts* 5:14
Jews saw *m.* they were. 13:45
the waters are *m.* *Rev* 17:15
see **great**

munition

against her and her *m.* *Isa* 29:7*
keep the *m.*, watch the. *Nah* 2:1†

munitions

his defence shall be *m.* *Isa* 33:16

murder

[1] *The taking away of a man's life unlawfully,* Mark 15:7. [2] *All cruelty in thought, word, or deed,* Mat 19:18; 1 John 3:15.

(*Intentional* murder *was always punished with death, but accidental* murder, *among the Hebrews, was only punished by banishment. Cities of refuge were appointed for manslaughter, whither a man might retire, and continue in safety, till the death of the high priest; then the offender was at liberty to return to his own city, and his own house, if he pleased. But as for the murderer, he was put to death without any remission, and the kinsmen of the murdered person might kill him with impunity*)

in secret doth he *m.* the. *Ps* 10:8
they slay the widow, and *m.* 94:6
ye steal, *m.* and commit? *Jer* 7:9
so priests *m.* in the way. *Hos* 6:9

murder

thou shalt do no *m.* *Mat* 19:18
who had committed *m.* *Mark* 15:7
and for *m.* was cast. *Luke* 23:19, 25
full of envy, *m.* debate. *Rom* 1:29

murderer

he is a *m.*: the *m.* shall surely be put to death. *Num* 35:16, 17, 18, 21
of blood shall slay the *m.* 19, 21
m. shall be put to death by. 30
no satisfaction for the life of a *m.* 31
see how this son of a *m.* *2 Ki* 6:32
m. rising with the light. *Job* 24:14
his children to the *m.* *Hos* 9:13
he was a *m.* from the. *John* 8:44
ye desired a *m.* to be. *Acts* 3:14
no doubt this man is a *m.* 28:4
of you suffer as a *m.* *1 Pet* 4:15
his brother is a *m.*; ye know that no *m.* hath eternal life. *1 John* 3:15

murderers

the children of the *m.* *2 Ki* 14:6
lodged in it, but now *m.* *Isa* 1:21
wearied, because of *m.* *Jer* 4:31
and destroyed those *m.* *Mat* 22:7
have been now the *m.* *Acts* 7:52
led 4000 men that were *m.* 21:38
law made for *m.* of fathers and. *1 Tim* 1:9
m. shall have their part. *Rev* 21:8
are whoremongers and *m.* 22:15

murders

out of the heart proceed *m.* *Mat* 15:19; *Mark* 7:21
the flesh are envyings, *m.* *Gal* 5:21
repented they of their *m.* *Rev* 9:21

murmur

that ye *m.* against us? *Ex* 16:7
murmurings ye *m.* 8; *Num* 14:27
the congregation to *m.* *Num* 14:36
what is Aaron, that ye *m.*? 16:11
of Israel, whereby they *m.* 17:5
Jesus said, *M.* not among. *John* 6:43
neither *m.* as some of. *1 Cor* 10:10

murmured

the people *m.* *Ex* 15:24; 17:3
congregation of Israel *m.* against. 16:2; *Num* 14:2; 16:41
years old, which have *m.* *Num* 14:29
ye *m.* in your tents. *Deut* 1:27
all the congregation *m.* *Josh* 9:18
believed not, but *m.* in. *Ps* 106:25
they that *m.* shall learn. *Isa* 29:24
received a penny, they *m.* *Mat* 20:11
and they *m.* against her. *Mark* 14:5
and Pharisees *m.* *Luke* 5:30
m. saying, This man receiveth. 15:2
m. that he was gone to be. 19:7
Jews *m.* at him, because. *John* 6:41
he knew that his disciples *m.* 61
heard that the people *m.* 7:32
as some of them *m.* *1 Cor* 10:10

murmurers

m. complainers, walking. *Jude* 16

murmuring

m. among the people. *John* 7:12
a *m.* of Grecians against. *Acts* 6:1

murmurings

he heareth your *m.* *Ex* 16:7, 8, 9 12; *Num* 14:27
your *m.* are not against us. *Ex* 16:8
cease the *m.* of Israel. *Num* 17:5
shalt quite take away their *m.* 10
do all things without *m.* *Phil* 2:14

murrain

be a very grievous *m.* *Ex* 9:3

muse

I *m.* on the work of thy. *Ps* 143:5

mused

men *m.* in their hearts. *Luke* 3:15*

music

to meet king Saul with *m.* *1 Sam* 18:6
with instruments of *m.* *1 Chr* 15:16 *2 Chr* 5:13; 23:13; 34:12
Levites with instruments of *m.* *2 Chr* 7:6
daughters of *m.* shall be. *Eccl* 12:4
rising, I am their *m.* *Lam* 3:63*
have ceased from their *m.* 5:14
ye hear the sound of cornet, and all kinds of *m.* *Dan* 3:5, 7, 10, 15
neither were instruments of *m.* 6:18
invent instruments of *m.* *Amos* 6:5
elder son heard *m.* and. *Luke* 15:25

musical

with *m.* instruments. *1 Chr* 16:42
with the *m.* instruments. *Neh* 12:36
as *m.* instruments, and. *Eccl* 2:8†

musicians

voice of *m.* shall be. *Rev* 18:22

musing

while I was *m.* the fire. *Ps* 39:3

must

m. I needs bring thy son? *Gen* 24:5
it *m.* not be so done in our. 29:26
thou *m.* come in to me. 30:16
if it *m.* be so. 43:11
it *m.* be put in water. *Lev* 11:32
seven days ye *m.* eat. 23:6
he *m.* do after the law. *Num* 6:21
m. we fetch you water out of? 20:10
m. I not take heed to speak? 23:12
Lord speaketh that I *m.* do. 26
by what way we *m.* go. *Deut* 1:22
I *m.* die in this land, I *m.* 4:22
thou *m.* eat them before. 12:18
approach that thou *m.* die. 31:14
way by which ye *m.* go. *Josh* 3:4
thou *m.* offer it to the. *Judg* 13:16
there *m.* be an inheritance. 21:17
a little, and lo I *m.* die. *1 Sam* 14:43
ruleth over men *m.* *2 Sam* 23:3
shall touch them *m.* be fenced. 7
he sleepeth, and *m.* be. *1 Ki* 18:27
hast said, so *m.* we do. *Ezra* 10:12
they *m.* needs be borne. *Jer* 10:5
fulfilled, that thus it *m.*? *Mat* 26:54
new wine *m.* be put into new bottles. *Mark* 2:22; *Luke* 5:38
Son of man *m.* suffer many things. *Mark* 8:31; 9:12
say the scribes that Elias *m.*? 9:11
of wars, be ye not troubled, for such things *m.* be. 13:7; *Luke* 21:9
gospel *m.* first be published. *Mark* 13:10
m. be about my Father's. *Luke* 2:49
I *m.* preach kingdom of God. 4:43
I bought ground, and *m.* go. 14:18
Zacchaeus, to-day I *m.* abide. 19:5
day when the passover *m.* 22:7
the things written *m.* be. 37; 24:44
he *m.* release one to them. 23:17
Son of man *m.* be delivered. 24:7
ye *m.* be born again. *John* 3:7
the serpent, so *m.* the Son of. 14
m. increase, but I *m.* decrease. 30
and he *m.* needs go through. 4:4
God is a spirit, *m.* worship him. 24
I *m.* work the works of him. 9:4
sheep I have, them also I *m.* 10:16
knew not that he *m.* rise again. 20:9

m. have been fulfilled. Acts 1:16
m. one be ordained to be a. 22
other name whereby we m. 4:12
told thee what thou m. do. 9:6
m. through much tribulation. 14:22
ye m. be circumcised and. 15:24
said, Sirs, what m. I do to? 16:30
I m. by all means keep this. 18:21
the multitude m. needs come. 21:22
so m. thou bear witness also. 23:11
fear not, thou m. be brought. 27:24
we m. be cast on a certain island. 26
wherefore ye m. needs. Rom 13:5
m. ye needs go out of. 1 Cor 5:10
there m. also be heresies. 11:19
for he m. reign till he hath. 15:25
for we m. all appear. 2 Cor 5:10
I m. needs glory, I will glory. 11:30
a bishop then m. be blameless.
1 Tim 3:2; Tit 1:7
he m. have a good report. 1 Tim 3:7
likewise m. deacons be grave. 8
husbandman m. be first. 2 Tim 2:6
the servant of the Lord m. not. 24
it remaineth that some m. Heb 4:6
there m. be the death of the. 9:16
cometh to God, m. believe that. 11:6
as they that m. give account. 13:17
shew thee things which m. Rev 4:1
if any will hurt, he m. in this. 11:5
that he m. be loosed a little. 20:3
to shew things which m. shortly. 22:6

mustard seed, *see* grain

mustered

he took the scribe which m. the people. 2 Ki 25:19; Jer 52:25

mustereth

the Lord m. the host of. Isa 13:4

mutter, -ed

that peep, and that m. Isa 8:19
tongue hath m. perverseness. 59:3

mutual

comforted by the m. faith. Rom 1:12

muzzle

thou shalt not m. the ox. Deut 25:4
1 Cor 9:9; 1 Tim 5:18

Myra

M. a city of Lycia. Acts 27:5

myrrh

bearing balm and m. Gen 37:25
the man a present, m., nuts. 43:11
pure m. five hundred. Ex 30:23
six months with oil of m. Esth 2:12
thy garments smell of m. Ps 45:8
perfumed my bed with m. Pr 7:17
a bundle of m. is my. S of S 1:13
perfumed with m. and. 3:6
get me to the mountain of m. 4:6
m. and aloes with all the chief. 14
I have gathered my m. with. 5:1
with m., my fingers with sweet m. 5
lilies, dropping sweet smelling m. 13
to him gifts, gold and m. Mat 2:11
wine mingled with m. Mark 15:23
brought a mixture of m. John 19:39

myrtle

fetch m. olive branches. Neh 8:15
in the wilderness the m. Isa 41:19
brier shall come up the m. 55:13

myrtle trees

and he stood among the m. trees.
Zech 1:8, 10, 11

myself

because naked, and hid m. Gen 3:10
by m. have I sworn, in blessing.
22:16; Isa 45:23; Jer 22:5; 49:13
brought you unto m. Ex 19:4
I sanctified them for m. Num 8:17
I the Lord will make m. known. 12:6
not able to bear you m. Deut 1:9. 12
go out and shake m. Judg 16:20
I cannot redeem it for m. Ruth 4:6
I forced m. therefore. 1 Sam 13:12
that I may hide m. in the field. 20:5
kept me from avenging m. 25:33
go forth with you m. 2 Sam 18:2
kept m. from mine iniquity. 22:24
shew m. unto him. 1 Ki 18:15
I will disguise m. 22:30
2 Chr 18:29
I bow m. in the house of. 2 Ki 5:18
chosen this place to m. 2 Chr 7:12
I consulted with m. and. Neh 5:7
come with the king but m. Esth 5:12
do honour more than to m. 6:6
harden m. in sorrow. Job 6:10
so that I am a burden to m. 7:20
if I justify m. 9:20
I will comfort m. 27
if I wash m. with snow water. 30
leave my complaint upon m. 10:1
will I not hide m. from thee. 13:20
mine error remained with m. 19:4
whom I shall see for m. and eyes. 27
or have eaten my morsel m. 31:17
or if I lift up m. when evil found. 29
wherefore I abhor m. and. 42:6
I behaved m. as though he had been.
Ps 35:14
glory, I m. awake early. 57:8; 108:2
I will behave m. wisely in. 101:2
but I give m. to prayer. 109:4
I will delight m. in thy. 119:16
delight m. in thy commandments. 47
thy judgement and comforted m. 52
nor do I exercise m. in. 131:1
behaved and quieted m. as child. 2
heart to give m. to wine. Eccl 2:3
labour wherein I have shewed m. 19
now will I lift up m. Isa 33:10
people have I formed for m. 43:21
abroad the earth by m. 44:24
comfort m. against sorrow. Jer 8:18
I m. will fight against you. 21:5
will answer him by m. Ezek 14:7
in the day I made m. known. 20:5, 9
river is mine, I have made it for m.
29:3
will make m. known amongst. 35:11
I magnify m. and sanctify m. 38:23
nor did I anoint m. at all. Dan 10:3
bow m. before the high God. Mi 6:6
heard, I trembled in m. Hab 3:16
separated m. as I have. Zech 7:3
I m. worthy to come. Luke 7:7
I m.; handle me and see. 24:39
if I bear witness of m. John 5:31
know whether I speak of m. 7:17
I am not come of m. but he that. 28
though I bear record of m. 8:14
I am one that bear witness of m. 18
know that I do nothing of m. 28
nor came I of m. but he sent me. 42
if I honour m. my honour is. 54
I lay it down of m. 10:18
spoken of m.; Father sent me. 12:49
again, and receive you unto m. 14:3
that I speak, I speak not of m. 10
love him, and manifest m. to him. 21
for their sakes I sanctify m. 17:19
stand up, I m. also am. Acts 10:26
count I my life dear unto m. 20:24
more cheerfully answer for m. 24:10
herein do I exercise m. to have. 16
I would hear the man m. 25:22
I verily thought with m. I. 26:9
I could wish that m. were. Rom 9:3
I have reserved to m. 7000. 11:4
and I m. also am persuaded. 15:14
succourer of many, and of m. 16:2
for I know nothing by m. 1 Cor 4:4
I have in a figure transferred to m. 6
that all men were even as I m. 7:7
yet have I made m. servant. 9:19
lest that I m. should be cast. 27
now I Paul m. beseech. 2 Cor 10:1
an offence in abasing m.? 11:7
kept m. from being burdensome. 9
receive me, that I may boast m. a. 16
of m. I will not glory but. 12:5
m. was not burdensome to you. 13
I make m. a transgressor. Gal 2:18
I also m. shall come. Phil 2:24
not m. to have apprehended. 3:13
receive Onesimus as m. Philem 17

Mysia

come to M. Acts 16:7
they passing by M. came to Troas. 8

mysteries

(Something secret, hidden, not known to all)

you to know the m. of the kingdom.
Mat 13:11; Luke 8:10
as stewards of the m. 1 Cor 4:1
though I understand all m. 1 Cor 13:2
the Spirit he speaketh m. 14:2

mystery

know the m. of kingdom. Mark 4:11
be ignorant of this m. Rom 11:25
the revelation of the m. 16:25
wisdom of God in a m. 1 Cor 2:7
I shew you a m.; We shall. 15:51
made known to us the m. Eph 1:9
made known to me the m. 3:3
knowledge in the m. of Christ. 4
what is the fellowship of the m. 9
this is a great m. but I speak. 5:32
boldly, to make known the m. of.
6:19; Col 1:26, 27; 4:3
acknowledgement of the m. Col 2:2
the m. of iniquity doth. 2 Thes 2:7
holding m. of faith in. 1 Tim 3:9
great is the m. of godliness. 16
the m. of the seven stars. Rev 1:20
m. of God should be finished. 10:7
m., Babylon the great. 17:5
m. of the woman. 7

N

Naaman

Benjamin, N. and. Gen 46:21
the son of Bela, N. Num 26:40
1 Chr 8:4
N. captain of Syria. 2 Ki 5:1
N. was wroth and went away. 11
my master hath spared N. the. 20
the leprosy of N. shall cleave. 27
was cleansed, saving N. Luke 4:27

Naamathite, *see* Zophar

Naashon, or Nahshon

Elisheba the sister of N. Ex 6:23
N. son of Amminadab. Num 1:7
2:3; 10:14
offered the first day was N. 7:12
this was the offering of N. son. 17
Amminadab begat N. and N. begat.
Ruth 4:20; 1 Chr 2:10, 11
Mat 1:4
which was the son of N. Luke 3:32

Nabal

name of the man was N. 1 Sam 25:3
N. did shear his sheep. 4
go to N. and greet him. 5
N. is his name, and folly is. 25
Lord smote N. that he died. 38
returned the wickedness of N. 39
Abigail N.'s wife. 27:3; 30:5
2 Sam 2:2; 3:3

Naboth

N. the Jezreelite had. 1 Ki 21:1
give thee vineyard of N. the. 7
set N. on high. 9, 12
heard N. was stoned. 14
Ahab heard that N. was dead. 16
Ahab is in the vineyard of N. 18
dogs licked the blood of N. 19
him in the portion of N. 2 Ki 9:21, 25
seen yesterday the blood of N. 26

Nadab

the sons of Aaron, N. Abihu.
Ex 6:23; Lev 10:1
N. and Abihu, seventy. Ex 24:1, 9
N. and Abihu died. Num 3:4; 26:61
N. son of Jeroboam reigned.
1 Ki 14:20; 15:25
N. son of Shammai. 1 Chr 2:28
the sons of N. 30
Baal and N. the sons. 8:30; 9:36

Nagge

was the son of N. Luke 3:25

Nahash

N. came up against Jabesh.
1 Sam 11:1; 12:12
shew kindness to Hanun the son of
N. 2 Sam 10:2; 1 Chr 19:2
the daughter of N. 2 Sam 17:25
Shobi son of N. brought beds. 27

Nahor

Serug begat N. Gen 11:22
N. lived 29 years. 24; 1 Chr 1:26
Terah begat Abraham, N. and Haran.
Gen 11:26, 27

N.'s wife Milcah. *Gen* 11:29
hath born children to thy brother *N.* 22:20, 23; 24:15, 24
went to the city of *N.* 24:10
God of Abraham and *N.* 31:53

nail

(*A finger-nail; a tent-peg, usually of wood; a metal pin, perhaps of gold*)
n. of tent, and smote *n.* *Judg* 4:21
Sisera lay dead, the *n.* was. 22
she put her hand to the *n.* 5:26
give us a *n.* in his holy. *Ezra* 9:8
I will fasten him as a *n.* *Isa* 22:23
shall the *n.* that is fastened be. 25
out of him came the *n.* *Zech* 10:4

nailing

took it out of the way, *n.* *Col* 2:14

nails

her head, and pare her *n.* *Deut* 21:12
iron in abundance for *n.* *1 Chr* 22:3
the weight of the *n.* *2 Chr* 3:9
n. fastened by the. *Eccl* 12:11
he fastened his idol with *n.* *Isa* 41:7; *Jer* 10:4
his *n.* were grown like. *Dan* 4:33
fourth beast, whose *n.* were. 7:19
into the print of the *n.* *John* 20:25

Nain

into a city called *N.* *Luke* 7:11

Naioth

Samuel and David dwelt at *N.* *1 Sam* 19:18, 19, 22
Saul went to *N.* 23
David fled from *N.* 20:1

naked

[1] *Altogether unclothed or uncovered,* Gen 2:25; 3:7. [2] *With few clothes on, having put off the greatest part of them,* 1 Sam 19:24; John 21:7. [3] *Not clothed with the righteousness of Christ,* Rev 3:17. [4] *Destitute of all worldly goods,* Job 1:21. [5] *Discovered, known, and manifest,* Job 26:6; Heb 4:13.

they were *n.* and were. *Gen* 2:25
knew that they were *n.* 3:7, 10, 11
people were *n.* for Aaron had made them *n.* to their. *Ex* 32:25*
Saul lay down *n.* all. *1 Sam* 19:24
spoil clothed all the *n.* *2 Chr* 28:15
Ahaz made Judah *n.* and. 19*
n. came I out of my mother's womb, and *n.* shall I return. *Job* 1:21
thou hast stripped the *n.* of. 22:6
they cause the *n.* to lodge. 24:7, 10
hell is *n.* before him and. 26:6
n. shall he return, to go. *Eccl* 5:15
when thou seest the *n.* *Isa* 58:7
shalt make thyself *n.* *Lam* 4:21
hath covered the *n.* *Ezek* 18:7, 16
lest I strip her *n.* and set. *Hos* 2:3
shall flee away *n.* in. *Amos* 2:16
I will go stripped and *n.* *Mi* 1:8
having thy shame *n.* 11*
bow was made quite *n.* *Hab* 3:9
I was *n.* and ye clothed. *Mat* 25:36 43
when saw we thee *n.* and? 38, 44
linen cloth about his *n.* *Mark* 14:51
linen cloth, fled from them *n.* 52
Peter was *n.* and cast. *John* 21:7
fled out of that house *n.* *Acts* 19:16
present hour we are *n.* *1 Cor* 4:11
we shall not be found *n.* *2 Cor* 5:3
but all things are *n.* to. *Heb* 4:13
if a brother or sister be *n.* *Jas* 2:15
poor, and blind, and *n.* *Rev* 3:17
garments, lest he walk *n.* 16:15
make her desolate and *n.* 17:16
see **bare**

nakedness

and Ham saw the *n.* of. *Gen* 9:22
n., they saw not their father's *n.* 23
to see the *n.* of the land. 42:9, 12
thy *n.* be not discovered. *Ex* 20:26
breeches to cover their *n.* 28:42
none shall uncover their *n.* *Lev* 18:6
the *n.* of father or mother. 7, 8, 11 15; 20:11
the *n.* of thy sister. *Lev* 18:9
n. of thy son's daughter. 10
n. of father's wife's daughter. 11
n. of father's sister. 12
n. of mother's sister. 13; 20:19
n. of father's brother. 18:14
n. of daughter in law. 15
n. of thy brother's wife, it is thy brother's *n.* 16
n. of a woman and her daughter. 17
n. of a woman as long as. 19; 20:18
sister's *n.* and she see his *n.* 20:17
uncovered his uncle's *n.* 20
uncovered his brother's *n.* 21
serve thine enemies in *n.* *Deut* 28:48
of thy mother's *n.* *1 Sam* 20:30
thy *n.* shall be uncovered. *Isa* 47:3
they have seen her *n.* *Lam* 1:8
I covered thy *n.*, yea. *Ezek* 16:8
thy *n.* discovered through. 36 23:18
and will discover thy *n.* 16:37
discovered their father's *n.* 22:10
these discovered her *n.* and. 23:10
the *n.* of thy whoredom shall. 29
flax given to cover her *n.* *Hos* 2:9
shew the nations thy *n.* *Nah* 3:5
mayest look on their *n.* *Hab* 2:15
who shall separate us from the love of Christ? shall *n.* *Rom* 8:35
often, in cold and *n.* *2 Cor* 11:27
that the shame of thy *n.* *Rev* 3:18

name

Name *is frequently used to designate the entire person, his individuality and his power. This is usually the case when the reference is to God.*

The word is also used to mean a race, as descended from some one man.

that was the *n.* thereof. *Gen* 2:19
call the *n.* of the city after *n.* 4:17
and called their *n.* Adam. 5:2
let us make us a *n.* lest we. 11:4
therefore the *n.* of the city. 19:22
the *n.* of the city was Luz. 28:19
shall be called after the *n.* of. 48:6
whose *n.* is Jealous. *Ex* 34:14
neither profane the *n.* of thy God. *Lev* 18:21; 19:12; 21:6; 22:2, 32
n. of one Eldad, of the. *Num* 11:26
write thou every man's *n.* 17:2
the *n.* of the Israelite that. 25:14
n. of Midianitish woman slain. 15
why should *n.* of our father? 27:4
Nobah, after his own *n.* 32:42
shalt destroy their *n.* *Deut* 7:24
and blot out their *n.* from. 9:14
bring up an evil *n.* on her. 22:14
he hath brought up an evil *n.* 19
firstborn shall succeed in *n.* 25:6
to raise up to his brother a *n.* 7
to make thee high in *n.* and in. 26:19
this glorious and fearful *n.* 28:58
nor make mention of *n.* *Josh* 23:7
man's *n.* with whom I. *Ruth* 2:19
raise up the *n.* of the dead. 4:5, 10
neighbours gave it a *n.* 17
n. of the man was Nabal. *1 Sam* 25:3
they spake to Nabal in the *n.* of. 9
whose *n.* is called by the *n.* of the Lord. *2 Sam* 6:2
a great *n.* like the *n.* of the great men in the earth. 7:9; *1 Chr* 17:8
God redeemed to make him a *n.* *2 Sam* 7:23; *1 Chr* 17:21
David gat him a *n.* when. *2 Sam* 8:13
to my husband neither *n.* nor. 14:7
Abishai had the *n.* among. 23:18
Benaiah, and had the *n.* among three mighty men. 22; *1 Chr* 11:20, 24
n. of Solomon better than thy *n.* and his throne greater. *1 Ki* 1:47
chose to put his *n.* there. 14:21 *2 Chr* 12:13
call ye on the *n.* of your gods. *1 Ki* 18:24, 25
wrote letters in Ahab's *n.* 21:8
not blot out the *n.* of. *2 Ki* 14:27
and was called after their *n.* *Ezra* 2:61; *Neh* 7:63
prophesied in the *n.* of. *Ezra* 5:1
and gavest him the *n.* of. *Neh* 9:7
so didst thou get thee a *n.* as. 10
the king in Mordecai's *n.* *Esth* 2:22
for the Jews in the king's *n.* 8:8
he shall have no *n.* in the. *Job* 18:17
thou hast put out their *n.* *Ps* 9:5
the *n.* of the God of Jacob. 20:1
in the *n.* of God we will set up. 5
if we have forgotten the *n.* 44:20
I will praise the *n.* of God. 69:30
the *n.* of Israel be no more. 83:4
whose *n.* alone is Jehovah. 18
let them praise thy great *m.* 99:3
n. be blotted out. 109:13
Lord's *n.* is to be praised. 113:3
the *n.* of the wicked. *Pr* 10:7
n. of the Lord is a strong. 18:10
good *n.* is rather to be chosen. 22:1
lest I take the *n.* of my God. 30:9
a good *n.* is better than. *Eccl* 7:1
off from Babylon the *n.* *Isa* 14:22
it shall be to the Lord for a *n.* 55:13
them a *n.*, an everlasting *n.* 56:5
whose *n.* is holy. 57:15
called by a new *n.* 62:2
himself an everlasting *n.* 63:12
to make thyself a glorious *n.* 14
n. for a curse to my chosen, and call his servants by another *n.* 65:15
seed and your *n.* remain. 66:22
that they might be to me for a *n.* *Jer* 13:11; 33:9
which hast made thee a *n.* 32:20
this is the *n.* wherewith she. 33:16
saith the King, whose *n.* is the Lord. 46:18; 48:15; 51:57
n. thereof is called Bamah. *Ezek* 20:29
son of man, write thee the *n.* 24:2
the *n.* of the city shall be. 48:35
blessed be the *n.* of God. *Dan* 2:20
Daniel came, according to the *n.* 4:8
call her *n.* Lo-ruhamah. *Hos* 1:6
be remembered by their *n.* 2:17
saith Lord, whose *n.* is. *Amos* 5:27
every one in the *n.* of his god, we will walk in the *n.* of our. *Mi* 4:5
I will cut off the *n.* of the. *Zeph* 1:4
make you a *n.* and a praise. 3:20
whose *n.* is the Branch. *Zech* 6:12
prophet in the *n.* of a prophet, a righteous man in *n.* of. *Mat* 10:41
give a cup of water only in *n.* 42
baptizing them in the *n.* of. 28:19
kindred is called by this *n.* *Luke* 1:61
saying, His *n.* is John. 63
shall cast out your *n.* as evil. 6:22
from God, whose *n.* was. *John* 1:6
not believed in the *n.* of the. 3:18
I am come in my Father's *n.* 5:43
I do in my Father's *n.* 10:25
be baptized in the *n.* of. *Acts* 2:38
in the *n.* of Jesus Christ, rise up. 3:6
by what power or *n.* have ye? 4:7
there is none other *n.* under. 12
henceforth to no man in this *n.* 17, 18
may be done by the *n.* of Jesus. 30
should not teach in this *n.* 5:28, 40
preaching, concerning the *n.* 8:12
them that called on this *n.* 9:21
boldly in the *n.* of Jesus. 27
their lives for the *n.* of Jesus. 15:26
said, In the *n.* of Jesus. 16:18
they were baptized in the *n.* 19:5
contrary to the *n.* of Jesus of. 26:9
for the *n.* of God is. *Rom* 2:24
ye baptized in the *n.*? *1 Cor* 1:13
in the *n.* of our Lord Jesus. 5:4 *Eph* 5:20
are justified in the *n.* of. *1 Cor* 6:11
far above every *n.* that. *Eph* 1:21
him a *n.* above every *n.* *Phil* 2:9
at the *n.* of Jesus every knee. 10
do all in the *n.* of Lord. *Col* 3:17
that the *n.* of God be not. *1 Tim* 6:1
the *n.* of Christ, depart. *2 Tim* 2:19
obtained a more excellent *n.* *Heb* 1:4
blaspheme that worthy *n.*? *Jas* 2:7
if reproached for the *n.* *1 Pet* 4:14
should believe on *n.* of his Son. *1 John* 3:23; 5:13
a *n.* written, which no. *Rev* 2:17
thou hast a *n.* that thou livest. 3:1
I will write on him the *n.* of. 12

the *n.* of the star is called. *Rev* 8:11
n. in the Hebrew tongue is. 9:11
and on his heads the *n.* of. 13:1
his Father's *n.* written in. 14:1
blasphemed the *n.* of God. 16:9
was a *n.* written, Mystery. 17:5
a *n.* written no man knew but. 19:12
on his thigh a *n.* written, King of. 16
see **called**

name, *verb*

shalt anoint to me him whom I *n.* *1 Sam* 16:3
bring him up whom I shall *n.* 28:8
mouth of the Lord shall *n.* *Isa* 62:2

by **name,** or *by the* **name**

I appeared *by the n.* of God. *Ex* 6:3
called *by n.* Bezaleel. 31:2; 35:30
I know thee *by n.* 33:12, 17
by n. ye shall reckon. *Num* 4:32
cities mentioned *by n.* *Josh* 21:9
of Gath, Goliath *by n.* *1 Sam* 17:23
Sheba, son of Bichri *by n.* hath lifted up his hand. *2 Sam* 20:21
be born, Josiah *by n.* *1 Ki* 13:2
these written *by n.* *1 Chr* 4:41
which were expressed *by n.* 12:31
16:41; *2 Chr* 28:15; 31:19
she were called *by n.* *Esth* 2:14
by the n. of Jacob, and surname himself *by the n.* *Isa* 44:5; 48:1
which call thee *by* thy *n.* 45:3
calleth his own sheep *by n.* *John* 10:3
by the n. of Jesus this. *Acts* 4:10
I beseech you *by the n.* *1 Cor* 1:10
our friends salute thee. Greet the friends *by n.* *3 John* 14
see **expressed**

his **name**

shall say, What is *his n.*? *Ex* 3:13
Pr 30:4
the Lord is *his n.* *Ex* 15:3
Jer 33:2; *Amos* 5:8; 9:6
not hold him guiltless that taketh *his n.* in vain. *Ex* 20:7; *Deut* 5:11
every stone with *his n.* shall they be. *Ex* 28:21; 39:14
Jair called them after *his* own *n.* *Deut* 3:14
and shalt swear by *his n.* 6:13
to bless in *his n.* to this day. 10:8
1 Chr 23:13
shall choose to put *his n.* *Deut* 12:5
21; *1 Ki* 14:21; *2 Chr* 12:13
choose to cause *his n.* *Deut* 12:11
choose to place *his n.* there. 14:23
16:6, 11; 26:2
shall choose to set *his n.* 14:24
that *his n.* be not put out. 25:6
his n. shall be called in Israel. 10
Lord shall blot out *his n.* 29:20
neither told he me *his n.* *Judg* 13:6
his n. may be famous. *Ruth* 4:14
for *his* great *n.*'s sake. *1 Sam* 12:22
Ps 23:3; 106:8; *1 John* 2:12
3 John 7
so that *his n.* was much. *1 Sam* 18:30
as *his n.* is, so is he, Nabal is *his n.* 25:25
give thanks to Lord, call upon *his n.* *1 Chr* 16:8; *Ps* 105:1; *Isa* 12:4
give the glory due to *his n.* *1 Chr* 16:29; *Ps* 29:2; 96:8
God that caused *his n.* *Ezra* 6:12
let us exalt *his n.* *Ps* 34:3; 66:2
when shall he die and *his n.*? 41:5
the heavens by *his n.* Jah. 68:4
they that love *his n.* shall. 69:36
his n. shall endure for ever. 72:17
and blessed be *his* glorious *n.* 19
his n. is great in Israel. 76:1
bless *his n.* 96:2; 100:4
among them that call on *his n.* 99:6
holy and reverend is *his n.* 111:9
sing praises to *his n.* for it. 135:3
praise *his n.*, for *his n.* alone. 148:13
praise *his n.* in the dance. 149:3
haughty scorner is *his n.* *Pr* 21:24
his n. shall be covered. *Eccl* 6:4
shall call *his n.* Immanuel. *Isa* 7:14
Mat 1:23
and *his n.* shall be called. *Isa* 9:6
make mention that *his n.* is 12:4

the Lord of hosts is *his n.* *Isa* 47:4
48:2; 51:15; 54:5; *Jer* 10:16
31:35; 32:18; 50:34; 51:19
his n. should not have been cut off. *Isa* 48:19
his n. may be no more. *Jer* 11:19
speak any more in *his n.* 20:9
this is *his n.* whereby he. 23:6
all ye that know *his n.* say. 48:17
God of hosts is *his n.* *Amos* 4:13
shall walk up and down in *his n.* *Zech* 10:12
shall be one Lord, and *his n.* 14:9
thought on *his n.* a book. *Mal* 3:16
shalt call *his n.* Jesus. *Mat* 1:23
Luke 1:31; 2:21
his n. shall the Gentiles. *Mat* 12:21
for *his n.* was spread. *Mark* 6:14
thou shalt call *his n.* *Luke* 1:13
remission of sins should be preached in *his n.* 24:47
that believe on *his n.* *John* 1:12
many believed in *his n.* when. 2:23
shall come in *his* own *n.* 5:43
might have life through *his n.* 20:31
his n. through faith in *his n.* hath. *Acts* 3:16
worthy to suffer for *his n.* 5:41
through *his n.* shall receive. 10:43
sorcerer, for so is *his n.* 13:8
them a people for *his n.* 15:14
all nations for *his n.* *Rom* 1:5
ye shewed towards *his n.* *Heb* 6:10
giving thanks to *his n.* 13:15
not blot out *his n.* but will confess *his n.* *Rev* 3:5
and *his n.* that sat on him. 6:8
hath *his n.* Apollyon. 9:11
to blaspheme *his n.* 13:6
number of *his n.* 17; 15:2
receiveth the mark of *his n.* 14:11
and *his n.* shall be in their. 22:4
see **holy, Lord**

my **name**

dost ask after *my n.*? *Gen* 32:29
let *my n.* be named on them. 48:16
this is *my n.* for ever. *Ex* 3:15
raised thee up, that *my n.* 9:16
where I record *my n.* I will. 20:24
provoke him not, for *my n.* 23:21
swear by *my n.* falsely. *Lev* 19:12
Molech, to profane *my* holy *n.* 20:3
my n. on the children. *Num* 6:27
shall speak in *my n.* *Deut* 18:19 20
thou thus after *my n.*? *Judg* 13:18
wilt not destroy *my n.* *1 Sam* 24:21
Nabal, and greet him in *my n.* 25:5
an house for *my n.* *2 Sam* 7:13
1 Ki 5:5; 8:18, 19; *1 Chr* 22:10
lest I take the city, and it be called after *my n.* *2 Sam* 12:28
I have no son to keep *my n.* 18:18
my n. might be therein. *1 Ki* 8:16
29; 11:36; *2 Ki* 21:4, 7; *2 Chr* 6:5
6; 7:16; 33:4, 7
have hallowed for *my n.* *1 Ki* 9:7
not build an house to *my n.* *1 Chr* 22:8; 28:3
it was in thine heart to build an house for *my n.* *2 Chr* 6:8
build the house for *my n.* 9
I have sanctified for *my n.* 7:20
I have chosen to set *my n.* there. *Neh* 1:9; *Jer* 7:12
in *my n.* shall his horn. *Ps* 89:24
he hath known *my n.* 91:14
they shall sanctify *my n.* *Isa* 29:23
sun shall he call on *my n.* 41:25
I am the Lord, that is *my n.* 42:8
for *my n.*'s sake will I defer. 48:9
should *my n.* be polluted ? 11
made mention of *my n.* 49:1
my n. continually every day. 52:5
my people shall know *my n.* 6
cast you out for *my n.*'s sake. 66:5
they prophesy lies in *my n.* *Jer* 14:14, 15; 23:25
know that *my n.* is the Lord. 16:21
to forget *my n.* as their fathers have forgotten *my n.* for Baal. 23:27
a lie in *my n.* 27:15; 29:9, 21, 23
turned and polluted *my n.* 34:16
sworn by *my* great *n.*, *my n.* no. 44:26

but I wrought for *my n.*'s sake. *Ezek* 20:9, 14, 22, 44
sanctify *my* great *n.* 36:23
shall call on *my n.* I. *Zech* 13:9
priests, that despise *my n.* *Mal* 1:6
my n. shall be great among Gentiles, and ... shall be offered to *my n.* 11
my n. is dreadful among. 14
heart, to give glory unto *my n.* 2:2
and was afraid before *my n.* 5
to you that fear *my n.* shall. 4:2
hated of all men for *my n.*'s sake. *Mat* 10:22; 24:9; *Mark* 13:13
Luke 21:17
receive a child in *my n.* *Mat* 18:5
Mark 9:37; *Luke* 9:48
gathered together in *my n.* *Mat* 18:20
forsaken houses for *my n.*'s. 19:29
many shall come in *my n.* 24:5
Mark 13:6; *Luke* 21:8
saying, *My n.* is Legion. *Mark* 5:9
do a miracle in *my n.* 9:39
cup of water to drink in *my n.* 41
in *my n.* shall they cast out. 16:17
rulers for *my n.*'s sake. *Luke* 21:12
ye shall ask in *my n.* *John* 14:13
14; 15:16; 16:23, 24, 26
whom he will send in *my n.* 14:26
will they do for *my n.*'s sake. 15:21
vessel to bear *my n.* *Acts* 9:15
he must suffer for *my n.*'s sake. 16
Gentiles upon whom *my n.* is. 15:17
my n. might be declared. *Rom* 9:17
I baptized in *mine* own *n.* *1 Cor* 1:15
and for *my n.*'s sake hast. *Rev* 2:3
thou holdest fast *my n.* and. 13
and hast not denied *my n.* 3:8
see **called**

thy **name**

and make *thy n.* great. *Gen* 12:2
thy n. Abram, but *thy n.* shall. 17:5
what is *thy n.*? 32:27, 29; *Judg* 13:17
thy n. shall be no more called Jacob. *Gen* 32:28; 35:10; *1 Ki* 18:31
Pharaoh to speak in *thy n.* *Ex* 5:23
thou do to *thy* great *n.*? *Josh* 7:9
thy n. be magnified. *2 Sam* 7:26
will sing praise to *thy n.* 22:50
Ps 9:2; 18:49; 61:8; 66:4; 92:1
Solomon better than *thy n.* *1 Ki* 1:47
turn and confess *thy n.* 8:33
2 Chr 6:24, 26
but cometh for *thy n.*'s sake. *1 Ki* 8:41; *2 Chr* 6:32
shall hear of *thy* great *n.* *1 Ki* 8:42
earth may know *thy n.*; this house is called by *thy n.* 43; *2 Chr* 6:33
house I built for *thy n.* *1 Ki* 8:44
48; *2 Chr* 6:34, 38
thy n. may be magnified. *1 Chr* 17:24
praise *thy n.* 29:13; *Ps* 44:8
wouldest put *thy n.* there. *2 Chr* 6:20
in *thy n.* we go against this. 14:11
a sanctuary for *thy n.* 20:8
before this house, for *thy n.* is. 9
who desire to fear *thy n.* *Neh* 1:11
blessed be *thy* glorious *n.* 9:5
let them that love *thy n.* *Ps* 5:11
how excellent is *thy n.* in. 8:1, 9
they that know *thy n.* will. 9:10
I will declare *thy n.* to my brethren. 22:22; *Heb* 2:12
for *thy n.*'s sake pardon. *Ps* 25:11
for *thy n.*'s sake lead me and. 31:3
through *thy n.* will we tread. 44:5
I will make *thy n.* to be. 45:17
according to *thy n.* so is. 48:10
I will wait on *thy n.* 52:9
save me by *thy n.* 54:1
heritage of those that fear *thy n.* 61:5
will lift up my hands in *thy n.* 63:4
defiled dwelling place of *thy n.* 74:7
enemy blaspheme *thy n.*? 10
people have blasphemed *thy n.* 18
needy praise *thy n.* 21
thy n. is near, thy works. 75:1
that have not called on *thy n.* 79:6
Jer 10:25
for the glory of *thy n.* and purge away our sins for *thy n.*'s sake. *Ps* 79:9
we will call upon *thy n.* 80:18
may seek *thy n.* O Lord. 83:16
come and glorify *thy n.* 86:9, 12

unite my heart to fear *thy n.* *Ps* 86:11
shall rejoice in *thy n.* 89:12, 16
O Lord, for *thy n.'s* sake. 109:21
but unto *thy n.* give glory. 115:1
I have remembered *thy n.* 119:55
do to those that love *thy n.* 132
thy n. O Lord, endureth. 135:13
n. for thy lovingkindness: for thou hast . . . word above all *thy n.* 138:2
take *thy n.* in vain. 139:20
shall give thanks to *thy n.* 140:13
that I may praise *thy n.* 142:7
O Lord, for *thy n.'s* sake. 143:11
I will bless *thy n.* for ever. 145:1, 2
praise *thy n.* for ever. 2; *Isa* 25:1
thy n. is as ointment. *S of S* 1:3
our soul is to *thy n.* *Isa* 26:8
will make mention of *thy n.* 13
thy n. is from everlasting. 63:16
make *thy n.* known to thine. 64:2
none that calleth on *thy n.* 7
art great and *thy n.* is. *Jer* 10:6
Lord calleth *thy n.* a green. 11:16
do thou it for *thy n.'s* sake. 14:7
do not abhor us for *thy n.'s* sake. 21
sent letters in *thy n.* to all. 29:25
I called upon *thy n.* *Lam* 3:55
prophets spake in *thy n.* *Dan* 9:6
wisdom shall see *thy n.* *Mi* 6:9
that no more of *thy n.* be. *Nah* 1:14
have we despised *thy n.*? *Mal* 1:6
hallowed be *thy n.* *Mat* 6:9
Luke 11:2
in *thy n.* have we cast out. *Mat* 7:22
he asked him, What is *thy n.*?
Mark 5:9; *Luke* 8:30
casting out devils in *thy n.* *Mat* 9:38
Luke 9:49
subject through *thy n.* *Luke* 10:17
Father, glorify *thy n.* *John* 12:28
I have manifested *thy n.* 17:6, 26
keep through *thine* own *n.* 11, 12
bind all that call on *thy n.* *Acts* 9:14
and sing unto *thy n.* *Rom* 15:9
to them that fear *thy n.* *Rev* 11:18
not fear and glorify *thy n.*? 15:4
see **called**

named, -eth

silver which he had *n.* *Gen* 23:16
Is not he rightly *n.* Jacob ? 27:36
my name be *n.* on them. 48:16
n. the child Ichabod. *1 Sam* 4:21
Jacob whom he *n.* Israel. *2 Ki* 17:34
Moses' sons *n.* of the. *1 Chr* 23:14
what hath been, is *n.* *Eccl* 6:10
ye shall be *n.* the priests. *Isa* 61:6
name shall no more be *n.* *Jer* 44:26
which are *n.* chief of. *Amos* 6:1
that art *n.* of the house. *Mi* 2:7
Jesus was so *n.* of the. *Luke* 2:21
twelve, whom he *n.* apostles. 6:13
not where Christ was *n.* *Rom* 15:20
such fornication not *n.* *1 Cor* 5:1
every name that is *n.* *Eph* 1:21
family in heaven and earth *is n.* 3:15
covetousness, let it not be once *n.*
5:3
let every one that *n.* *2 Tim* 2:19

namely

sore evil, *n.* riches kept. *Eccl* 5:13
razor that is hired, *n.* *Isa* 7:20
the second is like, *n.* *Mark* 12:31

names

Adam gave *n.* to all cattle. *Gen* 2:20
called their *n.* after the *n.* 26:18
make no mention of the *n.* of other.
Ex 23:13; *Deut* 12:3
grave on them the *n.* of children of.
Ex 28:9, 21
bear their *n.* before the. 12, 29
the number of their *n.* *Num* 1:2
n. of the men that shall stand. 5
number of *n.* of the Levites. 3:43
n. of the men which Moses. 13:16
n. of men which shall divide. 34:17
the *n.* of mighty men. *2 Sam* 23:8
what are the *n.* of the man ? *Ezra* 5:4
nor take up their *n.* into. *Ps* 16:4
lands after their own *n.* 49:11
the stars; he calleth them all by their *n.* 147:4; *Isa* 40:26
n. of them were Aholah. *Ezek* 23:4
I will take away the *n.* of. *Hos* 2:17
cut off the *n.* of the idols. *Zech* 13:2
your *n.* are written in. *Luke* 10:20
the number of the *n.* 120. *Acts* 1:15
question of words and *n.* 18:15
whose *n.* are in the book. *Phil* 4:3
thou hast a few *n.* in Sardis. *Rev* 3:4
whose *n.* are not written. 13:8; 17:8
I saw a woman full of *n.* 17:3
n. written thereon, *n.* of the. 21:12
in them the *n.* of twelve apostles. 14

Naomi

Elimelech's wife was *N.* *Ruth* 1:2
is this *N.*? 19
call me not *N.*, call me Mara. 20
N. had a kinsman of her. 2:1
buyest the field of hand of *N.* 4:5
bought all at the hand of *N.* 9
there is a son born to *N.* 17

Naphtali

called his name *N.* *Gen* 30:8
Rachel's handmaid. Dan, *N.* 35:25
sons of *N.* 46:24; *Num* 1:42
26:48; *1 Chr* 7:13
N. is a hind let loose. *Gen* 49:21
Israel, *N.* Gad, and Asher. *Ex* 1:4
of *N.* Ahira was prince. *Num* 1:15
2:29; 7:78
Ebal to curse; Dan, *N.* *Deut* 27:13
of *N.* he said, O *N.* satisfied. 33:23
sixth lot came out to *N.* *Josh* 19:32
in Galilee, in mount *N.* 20:7
nor did *N.* drive out the. *Judg* 1:33
called Zebulun and *N.* to. 4:10
Zebulun and *N.* jeoparded. 5:18
Gideon sent messengers to *N.* 6:35
themselves together out of *N.* 7:23
was officer in *N.* *1 Ki* 4:15
Ben-hadad smote *N.* 15:20
2 Chr 16:4
carried *N.* captive to. *2 Ki* 15:29
N. brought bread on. *1 Chr* 12:40
captain of *N.* was Jerimoth. 27:19
Josiah in *N.* brake. *2 Chr* 34:6
princes of Zebulun and *N.* *Ps* 68:27
afflicted the land of *N.* *Isa* 9:1
a portion for *N.* *Ezek* 48:3
one gate of *N.* 34
dwelt in the borders of *N.* *Mat* 4:13
the land of *N.* by the way of. 15

tribe of **Naphtali**

the *tribe of N.* 53,400 *Num* 1:43
host of the *tribe of N.* Ahira. 10:27
of the *tribe of N.* Nahbi. 13:14
of the *tribe of N.* Pedaheel. 34:28
inheritance of *tribe of N.* *Josh* 19:39
cities out of *tribe of N.* 21:32
1 Chr 6:62, 76
widow's son of *tribe of N.* *1 Ki* 7:14
tribe of N. were sealed. *Rev* 7:6

napkin

I have kept in a *n.* *Luke* 19:20
bound about with a *n.* *John* 11:44
n. that was about his head. 20:7

narrow

Lord stood in a *n.* way. *Num* 22:26
mount Ephraim be too *n.* *Josh* 17:15
made windows of *n.* *1 Ki* 6:4*
strange woman is a *n.* pit. *Pr* 23:27
destruction shall be too *n.* *Isa* 49:19*
n. is the way which. *Mat* 7:14*

narrowed

in wall he made *n.* rests. *1 Ki* 6:6*

narrower

covering *n.* than he can. *Isa* 28:20

narrowly

thou lookest *n.* to all. *Job* 13:27*
shall *n.* look upon thee. *Isa* 14:16

Nathan

son of David, *N.* *2 Sam* 5:14
N. the prophet. 7:2
so did *N.* speak. 17
the Lord sent *N.* 12:1, 25
Igal son of *N.* one of David's. 23:36
but *N.* the prophet he. *1 Ki* 1:10
talked with David, *N.* came in. 22
let Zadok and *N.* anoint him king. 34
Azariah son of *N.* was over. 4:5
Artai begat *N.* and *N.* *1 Chr* 2:36
Joel the brother of *N.* a. 11:38
written in the book of *N.* 29:29
Solomon in book of *N.* *2 Chr* 9:29
Ahava for *N.* and Ariel. *Ezra* 8:16
Shelemiah, *N.* had taken. 10:39
of the house of *N.* *Zech* 12:12
which was the son of *N.* *Luke* 3:31

Nathanael

Philip findeth *N.* *John* 1:45
N. of Cana. 21:2

nation

[1] *All the inhabitants of a particular country,* Deut 4:34. [2] *A country or kingdom,* Ex 34:10; Rev 7:9. [3] *Countrymen, natives of the same stock,* Acts 26:4. [4] *The heathen or Gentiles,* Isa 55:5.

also that *n.* they serve. *Gen* 15:14
wilt thou slay a righteous *n.*? 20:4
bondwoman I will make a *n.* 21:13
a *n.* and kings shall come. 35:11
Egypt, since it became a *n.* *Ex* 9:24
ye shall be unto me an holy *n.* 19:6
1 Pet 2:9
to sell her to a strange *n.* *Ex* 21:8*
that this *n.* is thy people. 33:13
have not been done in any *n.* 34:10
nor any of your *n.* commit abominations. *Lev* 18:26*
walk in the manners of the *n.* 20:23
I will make of thee a great *n.*
Num 14:12; *Deut* 9:14
assayed to take him a *n.* from the midst of another *n.*? *Deut* 4:34
thy land shall a *n.* eat up. 28:33
bring thee and thy king to a *n.* 36
bring a *n.* against thee. 49
a *n.* of fierce countenance shall. 50
are a *n.* void of counsel. 32:28
what *n.* like thy people ? *2 Sam* 7:23
1 Chr 17:21
n. whither my lord hath not sent . . . took an oath of the *n.* *1 Ki* 18:10
every *n.* made gods. *2 Ki* 17:29
they went from *n.* to *n.* *1 Chr* 16:20
n. was destroyed of *n.* *2 Chr* 15:6
no god of any *n.* or kingdom. 32:15
it be done against a *n.* *Job* 34:29
blessed is *n.* whose God. *Ps* 33:12
my cause against an ungodly *n.* 43:1
cut them off from being a *n.* 83:4
they went from one *n.* to. 105:13
rejoice in gladness of thy *n.* 106:5
dealt so with any *n.* 147:20
righteousness exalteth a *n.* *Pr* 14:34
ah sinful *n.*, a people laden. *Isa* 1:4
n. shall not lift up sword against *n.*
2:4; *Mi* 4:3
thou hast multiplied the *n.* *Isa* 9:3
against an hypocritical *n.* 10:6
messengers of the *n.*? 14:32
swift messengers, to a *n.* scattered and peeled, a *n.* meted. 18:2, 7
open that the righteous *n.* may. 26:2
increased the *n.* O Lord, the *n.* 15
to him whom the *n.* abhorreth. 49:7
give ear to me, O my *n.* 51:4
thou shalt call a *n.* thou. 55:5
seek me, as a *n.* that did. 58:2
the *n.* that will not serve thee. 60:12
small one become a strong *n.* 22
a *n.* that was not called by. 65:1
or shall a *n.* be born at once ? 66:8
n. changed their gods ? *Jer* 2:11
avenged on such a *n.* 5:9, 29; 9:9
n. on you from far . . . it is a mighty *n.*, it is an ancient *n.* 5:15
a *n.* that obeyeth not the. 7:28
pluck up and destroy that *n.* 12:17
speak concerning a *n.* to. 18:7, 9
if that *n.* against whom I have. 8
punish that *n.* for their. 25:12; 27:8
shall go forth from *n.* to *n.* 25:32
n. which will not serve. 27:8, 13
cease from being a *n.* 31:36; 33:24
cut off Moab from being a *n.* 48:2
get you up to the wealthy *n.* 49:31
no *n.* whither Elam shall. 36
out of the north cometh a *n.* 50:3
have watched for a *n.* *Lam* 4:17
Israel, a rebellious *n.* *Ezek* 2:3
I will make them one *n.* in. 37:22
four kingdoms shall stand up out of the *n.* *Dan* 8:22
never was since there was a *n.* 12:1
for a *n.* is come up upon. *Joel* 1:6

N. the king made an image. *Dan* 3:1
N. was full of fury. 19
N. was astonished. 24
came upon the king *N.* 4:28, 33
at end of days I *N.* lifted up mine. 34
I *N.* praise and extol. 37
most high God gave *N.* a. 5:18

Nebuzar-adan

N. captain of guard. *2 Ki* 25:8
N. left of the poor of. *Jer* 39:10

necessary

his words more than *n.* *Job* 23:12
was *n.* that the word first. *Acts* 13:46
greater burden than these *n.* 15:28
with such things as were *n.* 28:10*
which seem feeble are *n.* *1 Cor* 12:22
I thought it *n.* to exhort. *2 Cor* 9:5
I supposed it *n.* to send. *Phil* 2:25
good works for *n.* uses. *Tit* 3:14
n. patterns should be. *Heb* 9:23

necessities

have ministered to my *n.* *Acts* 20:34
ministers of God in *n.* *2 Cor* 6:4
I take pleasure in *n.*, in. 12:10

necessity

[1] *Something that must needs be, when it is contrary to its very nature and principles to be otherwise,* Heb 9:16. [2] *Poverty, or want of temporal good things,* Rom 12:13. [3] *Force or constraint,* 2 Cor 9:7.

of *n.* he must release. *Luke* 23:17
distributing to the *n.* *Rom* 12:13
having no *n.* and hath. *1 Cor* 7:37
for *n.* is laid upon me, yea. 9:16
not grudgingly, or of *n.* *2 Cor* 9:7
once and again to my *n.* *Phil* 4:16
not be as it were of *n.* *Philem* 14
made of *n.* a change of. *Heb* 7:12
n. this man have somewhat. 8:3
there must of *n.* be the death. 9:16

neck

skins on smooth of his *n.* *Gen* 27:16
break the yoke from off thy *n.* 40
Esau fell on his *n.* and. 33:4
gold chain about Joseph's *n.* 41:42
Ezek 16:11; *Dan* 5:7, 16, 29
fell on Benjamin's *n.* and. *Gen* 45:14
Jacob's *n.*; he wept on his *n.* 46:29
thy hand shall be on the *n.* 49:8
break his *n.* *Ex* 13:13; 34:20
off his head from his *n.* *Lev* 5:8
strike off the heifer's *n.* *Deut* 21:4
a yoke of iron upon thy *n.* 28:48
and his *n.* brake, and. *1 Sam* 4:18
Zedekiah stiffened his *n.* *2 Chr* 36:13
hardened their *n.* and. *Neh* 9:29
on him, even on his *n.* *Job* 15:26
he hath taken me by the *n.* 16:12
hast thou clothed his *n.* with? 39:19
in his *n.* remaineth strength. 41:22
speak not with a stiff *n.* *Ps* 75:5
be chains about thy *n.* *Pr* 1:9
bind them about thy *n.* 3:3; 6:21
life and grace to thy *n.* 3:22
thy *n.* is comely with. *S of S* 1:10
thy *n.* is like the tower of. 4:4
my heart with one chain of thy *n.* 9
thy *n.* is a tower of ivory. 7:4
reach even to the *n.* *Isa* 8:8
be taken from off thy *n.* 10:27
to the midst of the *n.* 30:28
thy *n.* is an iron sinew. 48:4
from the bands of thy *n.* 52:2
as if he cut off a dog's *n.* 66:3
not, made their *n.* stiff. *Jer* 17:23
and put them on thy *n.* 27:2
will not put *n.* under yoke of. 8, 11
the yoke from off Jeremiah's *n.* 28:10, 12
I have put a yoke on the *n.* 14
break his yoke from off thy *n.* 30:8
are come upon my *n.* *Lam* 1:14
over on her fair *n.* *Hos* 10:11
the foundation unto the *n.* *Hab* 3:13
a millstone were hanged about his *n.*
Mat 18:6; *Mark* 9:42; *Luke* 17:2
his father fell on his *n.* *Luke* 15:20
put a yoke on the *n.* *Acts* 15:10
they fell on Paul's *n.* and. 20:37
see **harden**

necks

put your feet on the *n.* *Josh* 10:24
for the *n.* of them that. *Judg* 5:30
were on their camel's *n.* 8:21, 26
given me *n.* of enemies.
2 Sam 22:41*; *Ps* 18:40*
the nobles put not their *n.* *Neh* 3:5
walk with stretched forth *n.* *Isa* 3:16
bring your *n.* under yoke. *Jer* 27:12
n. are under persecution. *Lam* 5:5
to bring thee on the *n.* *Ezek* 21:29
shall not remove your *n.* *Mi* 2:3
life laid down their own *n.* *Rom* 16:4

necromancer

found among you a *n.* *Deut* 18:11

need

him sufficient for his *n.* *Deut* 15:8
have I *n.* of madmen? *1 Sam* 21:15
much as thou shalt *n.* *2 Chr* 2:16
ye shall not *n.* to fight in. 20:17
and let what they have *n.* *Ezra* 6:9
so he shall have no *n.* *Pr* 31:11
I have *n.* to be baptized. *Mat* 3:14
Father knoweth what things ye have
n. of. 6:8, 32; *Luke* 12:30
that be whole *n.* not a physician.
Mat 9:12; *Mark* 2:17; *Luke* 5:31
they *n.* not depart, give. *Mat* 14:16
the Lord hath *n.* of them. 21:3
Mark 11:3; *Luke* 19:31, 34
n. have we of witnesses? *Mat* 26:65
Mark 14:63; *Luke* 22:71
David did when he had *n.* *Mark* 2:25
healed them that had *n.* *Luke* 9:11
over just persons which *n.* 15:7
things we have *n.* of. *John* 13:29
as every man had *n.* *Acts* 2:45; 4:35
her in what she hath *n.* *Rom* 16:2
if *n.* so require, let him. *1 Cor* 7:36
to the hand, I have no *n.* 12:21
our comely parts have no *n.* 24
or *n.* we epistles of? *2 Cor* 3:1
to abound and to suffer *n.* *Phil* 4:12
God shall supply all your *n.* 19
so that we *n.* not speak. *1 Thes* 1:8
of brotherly love ye *n.* not that. 4:9
of the times ye have no *n.* that. 5:1
grace to help in time of *n.* *Heb* 4:16
have *n.* that one teach you again;
such as have *n.* of milk. 5:12
what *n.* that another priest? 7:11
for ye have *n.* of patience. 10:36
though now, if *n.* be. *1 Pet* 1:6
ye *n.* not that any man. *1 John* 2:27
and see his brother have *n.* 3:17
I am rich, and have *n.* *Rev* 3:17
the city had no *n.* of sun. 21:23
and they *n.* no candle, nor. 22:25

needed

he *n.* not that any should. *John* 2:25
as though he *n.* any thing. *Acts* 17:25

needest, -eth

Jacob said What *n.* it. *Gen* 33:15
give him as many as he *n.* *Luke* 11:8
is washed, *n.* not save. *John* 13:10
and *n.* not that any man. 16:30
to give to him that *n.* *Eph* 4:28
a workman that *n.* not. *2 Tim* 2:15
who *n.* not daily to offer. *Heb* 7:27

needful

shall be *n.* for the house. *Ezra* 7:20
one thing is *n.* and Mary. *Luke* 10:42
n. to circumcise them. *Acts* 15:5
the flesh is more *n.* for you. *Phil* 1:24
these things which are *n.* *Jas* 2:16
it was *n.* for me to write. *Jude* 3

needle

for a camel to go through the eye of
a *n.* *Mat* 19:24; *Mark* 10:25
Luke 18:25

needlework

an hanging wrought with *n.*
Ex 26:36; 27:16; 36:37; 38:18
make the girdle of *n.* 28:39; 39:29
divers colours of *n.* *Judg* 5:30
brought in raiment of *n.* *Ps* 45:14

needs

must *n.* be circumcised. *Gen* 17:13
said, This one fellow will *n.* 19:9
must I *n.* bring thy son again? 24:5
thou wouldest *n.* be gone. 31:30
we must *n.* die, and. *2 Sam* 14:14
must *n.* be borne, because. *Jer* 10:5
it must *n.* be that offences. *Mat* 18:7
for such things must *n.* *Mark* 13:7
ground, and I must *n.* *Luke* 14:18
n. go through Samaria. *John* 4:4
this scripture must *n.* *Acts* 1:16
must *n.* have suffered. 17:3
the multitude must *n.* come. 21:22
ye must *n.* be subject. *Rom* 13:5
must *n.* go out of world. *1 Cor* 5:10
if I must *n.* glory. *2 Cor* 11:30

needy

open thy hand to the *n.* *Deut* 15:11
servant that is poor and *n.* 24:14
they turn the *n.* out of. *Job* 24:4
killeth the poor and *n.* 14
the *n.* shall not alway. *Ps* 9:18
for the sighing of the *n.* now. 12:5
the poor and *n.* 35:10; 72:4, 13
bow, to cast down the *n.* 37:14
I am poor and *n.*, make. 40:17; 70:5
he shall deliver the *n.* 72:12; 82:4
the poor and *n.*, save the *n.* 72:13
let the poor and *n.* praise. 74:21
justice to the afflicted and *n.* 82:3
deliver the poor and *n.* rid from. 4
for I am poor and *n.* 86:1; 109:22
the poor and *n.* man. 109:16
he lifteth the *n.* out of the. 113:7
devour the *n.* from. *Pr* 30:14
cause of the poor and *n.* 31:9
forth her hands to the *n.* 20
to turn aside the *n.* *Isa* 10:2
n. shall lie down in safety. 14:30
been a strength to the *n.* in. 25:4
steps of the *n.* shall tread. 26:6
when the *n.* speaketh right. 32:7
when the poor and *n.* seek. 41:17
and the right of *n.* do. *Jer* 5:28
cause of the poor and *n.* 22:16
the hands of the *n.* *Ezek* 16:49
oppressed the poor and *n.* 18:12
vexed the poor and *n.* 22:29
Bashan, which crush the *n.* *Amos* 4:1
O ye that swallow up the *n.* 8:4
buy the *n.* for a pair of shoes. 6

neesings

by his *n.* a light doth. *Job* 41:18†

neglect

n. to hear them, tell it to the church,
but if he *n.* to hear. *Mat* 18:17*
n. not the gift that. *1 Tim* 4:14
how shall we escape, if *n.*? *Heb* 2:3

neglected

their widows were *n.* *Acts* 6:1

neglecting

n. the body, not in any. *Col* 2:23*

negligent

my sons, be not now *n.* *2 Chr* 29:11
not be *n.* to put you in. *2 Pet* 1:12*

Nehelamite, *see* **Shemaiah**

Nehemiah

N. came with Zerubbabel. *Ezra* 2:2
Neh 7:7
the words of *N.* the son. *Neh* 1:1
N. son of Azbuk repaired. 3:16
N. which is the. 8:9; 10:1
Israel in the days of *N.* 12:47

Nehushtan

the brasen serpent *N.* *2 Ki* 18:4

neighbour

[1] *One who dwells or is placed near to another,* 2 Ki 4:3. [2] *Every man, to whom we have an opportunity of doing good,* Mat 22:39. [3] *A fellow-labourer, of one and the same people,* Acts 7:27. [4] *One who does us good, and who pities and relieves us in distress,* Luke 10:36.

every woman borrow of her *n.*
Ex 3:22; 11:2
hath given it to a *n.* *1 Sam* 15:28
better is a *n.* that is near. *Pr* 27:10
the *n.* and his friends. *Jer* 6:21
and teach every one her *n.* 9:20
was *n.* to him that fell. *Luke* 10:36

neighbour, *adjective*

overthrow of Sodom and Gomorrah
and the *n.* *Jer* 49:18; 50:40

his **neighbour**
and *his n.* take a lamb. *Ex* 12:4
come on *his n.* to slay him. 21:14
if a man deliver to *his n.* 22:7
hand to *his n.*'s goods. 8, 11
deliver to *his n.* an ass or ox. 10
if borrow aught of *his n.* and it. 14
camp, slay every man *his n.* 32:27
or hath deceived *his n.* *Lev* 6:2
adultery with *his n.*'s wife, shall. 20:10; *Deut* 22:24
cause a blemish in *his n.* *Lev* 24:19
should kill *his n.* *Deut* 4:42; 19:4
lendeth aught to *his n.* he shall not exact of *his n.* or his. 15:2
if any hate *his n.* and lie. 19:11
a man riseth against *his n.* 22:26
removeth *his n.*'s landmark. 27:17
cursed be he that smiteth *his n.* 24
shoe, and gave to *his n.* *Ruth* 4:7
trespass against *his n.* *1 Ki* 8:31
man sin against *his n.* *2 Chr* 6:22
one mocked of *his n.* *Job* 12:4
as a man pleadeth for *his n.* 16:21
speak vanity with *his n.* *Ps* 12:2
nor doeth evil to *his n.* 15:3*
privily slandereth *his n.* 101:5
goeth in to *his n.*'s wife. *Pr* 6:29
his mouth destroyeth *his n.* 11:9
despiseth *his n.* 12; 14:21
is more excellent than *his n.* 12:26
poor is hated even of *his n.* 14:20
a violent man enticeth *his n.* 16:29
but *his n.* cometh and. 18:17
separated from *his n.* 19:4*
his n. findeth no favour. 21:10
false witness against *his n.* 25:18
man that deceiveth *his n.* 26:19
that flattereth *his n.* spreadeth. 29:5
a man is envied of *his n.* *Eccl* 4:4
oppressed every one by *his n. Isa* 3:5
fight every one against *his n.* 19:2
they helped every one *his n.* 41:6
neighed after *his n.*'s wife. *Jer* 5:8
between a man and *his n.* 7:5
every one of *his n.*, trust not. 9:4
deceive every one *his n.* 5
speak peaceably to *his n.* 8
every man to *his n.* 22:8; 23:35
useth *his n.*'s service without. 22:13
tell every one to *his n.* 23:27
words every one from *his n.* 30
teach no more every man *his n.* 31:34; *Heb* 8:11*
liberty to *his n.* *Jer* 34:15, 17
defiled *his n.*'s wife. *Ezek* 18:6, 15
hath defiled *his n.*'s wife. 11; 22:11 33:26
that giveth *his n.* drink. *Hab* 2:15
call every man *his n.* *Zech* 3:10
every one against *his n.* 8:10
every man the truth to *his n.* 16
imagine evil against *his n.* 17
love *his n.* as himself. *Mark* 12:33
he that did *his n.* wrong. *Acts* 7:27
worketh no evil to *his n.* *Rom* 13:10
let every one please *his n.* 15:2
speak every man truth with *his n.* *Eph* 4:25

my **neighbour**
wait at *my n.*'s door. *Job* 31:9
to Jesus, Who is *my n.*? *Luke* 10:29

thy **neighbour**
not bear false witness against *thy n.* *Ex* 20:16; *Deut* 5:20
take *thy n.*'s raiment to. *Ex* 22:26
carnally with *thy n.*'s wife. *Lev* 18:20
thou shalt not defraud *thy n.* 19:13
shalt thou judge *thy n.* 15
stand against the blood of *thy n.* 16
in any wise rebuke *thy n.* 17
love *thy n.* as thyself. 18
buyest aught of *thy n.* 25:14, 15
or covet *thy n.*'s wife. *Deut* 5:21
thou shalt not remove *thy n.*'s. 19:14
comest into *thy n.*'s vineyard. 23:24
and given it to *thy n.* *1 Sam* 28:17
give them to *thy n.* *2 Sam* 12:11
say not to *thy n.* Go. *Pr* 3:28
devise not evil against *thy n.* 29
be not witness against *thy n.* 24:28
when *thy n.* hath put thee to. 25:8
debate thy cause with *thy n.* 9
withdraw thy foot from *thy n.*'s. *Pr* 25:17
shalt love *thy n.* *Mat* 5:43; 19:19 22:39; *Mark* 12:31; *Luke* 10:27 *Rom* 13:9; *Gal* 5:14; *Jas* 2:8

neighbours
that they were their *n.* *Josh* 9:16
her *n.* gave it a name. *Ruth* 4:17
borrow vessels abroad of all thy *n.* *2 Ki* 4:3
speak peace to their *n.* *Ps* 28:3
reproach among all my *n.* 31:11
us a reproach to our *n.* 44:13
become a reproach to our *n.* 79:4
render unto our *n.* sevenfold. 12
makest us a strife to our *n.* 80:6
he is a reproach to his *n.* 89:41
against all my evil *n.* *Jer* 12:14
adultery with their *n.*' wives. 29:23
his seed is spoiled and his *n.* 49:10
fornication with Egypt, thy *n.* *Ezek* 16:26
gained of thy *n.* by extortion. 22:12
the Assyrians her *n.* 23:5, 12
n. and her cousins heard. *Luke* 1:58
a supper, call not thy rich *n.* 14:12
together his friends and *n.* 15:6, 9
n. and they who before had seen him blind. *John* 9:8

neighed
n. after his neighbour's wife. *Jer* 5:8

neighing, -s
land trembled at the *n.* *Jer* 8:16
seen thine adulteries and *n.* 13:27

neither
the tree, *n.* shall ye touch. *Gen* 3:3
fight *n.* with small nor. *1 Ki* 22:31
n. tell I you by what. *Mat* 21:27

nephew
(*Most frequently this means* son's son, *grandchild, and is so rendered in Revisions*)
neither have son nor *n.* *Job* 18:19*
from Babylon son and *n.* *Isa* 14:22*

nephews
forty sons and thirty *n.* *Judg* 12:14*
have children or *n.* *1 Tim* 5:4*

Ner
N. begat Kish. *1 Chr* 8:33; 9:36, 39
see **Abner**

Nereus
salute Julia, *N.* and. *Rom* 16:15

Nergal
Cuth made *N.* their god. *2 Ki* 17:30

Neriah, *see* **Baruch**

nest
thou puttest thy *n.* in a. *Num* 24:21
if a bird's *n.* chance to. *Deut* 22:6
as an eagle stirreth up her *n.* 32:11
I shall die in my *n.* *Job* 29:18
command, make *n.* on high ? 39:27
swallow hath found a *n.* *Ps* 84:3
wandereth from her *n.* *Pr* 27:8
hath found as *n.* riches. *Isa* 10:14
bird cast out of the *n.* 16:2
the great owl made her *n.* 34:15
thy *n.* in the cedars. *Jer* 22:23
the dove makes her *n.* in the. 48:28
thy *n.* as high as the eagle. 49:16
set thy *n.* among the stars. *Ob* 4
he may set his *n.* on high. *Hab* 2:9

nests
the birds make their *n.* *Ps* 104:17
fowls of heaven made their *n.* *Ezek* 31:6
and the birds of the air have *n.* *Mat* 8:20; *Luke* 9:58

net
(*A woven fabric for catching fish or birds; hence a snare, trap. It is also used figuratively, as for difficulties in which one is caught; or the traps set by one's enemies*)
he is cast into a *n.* by. *Job* 18:8
compassed me with his *n.* 19:6
in the *n.* they hid, is. *Ps* 9:15
draweth him into his *n.* 10:9
pluck my feet out of *n.* 25:15; 31:4
they have hid for me their *n.* 35:7
let his *n.* that he hath hid catch. 8
they have prepared a *n.* for. *Ps* 57:6
thou broughtest us into the *n.* 66:11
they have spread a *n.* by. 140:5
surely in vain the *n.* *Pr* 1:17
the wicked desireth the *n.* of. 12:12
that flattereth spreadeth a *n.* 29:5
fishes are taken in an evil *n.* *Eccl* 9:12
as a wild bull in a *n.* *Isa* 51:20
he hath spread a *n.* *Lam* 1:13
my *n.* will I spread on him. *Ezek* 12:13; 17:20
nations shall spread their *n.* 19:8
I will spread out my *n.* over. 32:3
ye have been a *n.* spread. *Hos* 5:1
I will spread my *n.* upon them. 7:12
hunt his brother with a *n.* *Mi* 7:2
catch them in their *n.* *Hab* 1:15
therefore they sacrifice to their *n.* 16
therefore empty their *n.*? 17
casting *n.* into the sea. *Mat* 4:18 *Mark* 1:16
of heaven is like a *n.* cast. *Mat* 13:47
I will let down the *n.* *Luke* 5:5
multitude of fishes, and their *n.* 6
the *n.* on the right side. *John* 21:6
came in a ship, dragging the *n.* with. 8
n. to land, yet was not the *n.* 11

Nethaneel
N. the son of Zuar was prince. *Num* 1:8; 2:5; 7:18, 23; 10:15
N. the fourth son of. *1 Chr* 2:14
N. and Amasai blew with. 15:24
the son of *N.* the scribe, one. 24:6
Obed-edom, Joah and *N.* 26:4
Jehoshaphat sent *N.* to. *2 Chr* 17:7
N. gave to the Levites for. 35:9
Ishmael, *N.* had taken. *Ezra* 10:22
in days of Joiakim *N.* *Neh* 12:21
N. with musical instruments. 36

Nethaniah
Ishmael son of *N.* *2 Ki* 25:23, 25 *Jer* 40:8; 41:1
Asaph, Joseph and *N.* *1 Chr* 25:2
fifth lot came forth to *N.* he. 12
Levites to teach, even *N. 2 Chr* 17:8
princes sent the son of *N. Jer* 36:14
Ishmael the son of *N.* slew. 41:2
but Ishmael son of *N.* escaped. 15

nether
they stood at the *n.* part. *Ex* 19:17
no man shall take *n.* millstone to. *Deut* 24:6*
gave her the upper springs and the *n.* *Josh* 15:19; *Judg* 1:15
built Gezer and Beth-horon the *n.* *1 Ki* 9:17; *1 Chr* 7:24
as a piece of *n.* millstone. *Job* 41:24
delivered to death to *n.* parts. *Ezek* 31:14
be comforted in the *n.* parts. 16
shalt be brought down to *n.* parts. 18
them down to the *n.* parts. 32:18
Elam gone down to the *n.* parts. 24

nethermost
the *n.* chamber was. *1 Ki* 6:6

Nethinims
inhabitants were the *N.* *1 Chr* 9:2
the *N.* went up with. *Ezra* 2:43
N. and the children of Solomon's servant were 392. 58; *Neh* 7:60
the *N.* went to Jerusalem. *Ezra* 7:7
not lawful to impose toll on *N.* 24
to Iddo and brethren the *N.* 8:17
the *N.* whom David appointed. 20
N. dwelt in Ophel. *Neh* 3:26; 11:21
the *N.* had separated from. 10:28
and Gispa were over the *N.* 11:21

nets
n. of checker work. *1 Ki* 7:17
wicked fall into their own *n.* *Ps* 141:10
heart is snares and *n.* *Eccl* 7:26
they that spread *n.* shall. *Isa* 19:8
spreading of *n.* in the. *Ezek* 26:5
place to spread *n.* on. 14; 47:10
James and John mending their *n.* *Mat* 4:21; *Mark* 1:19; *Luke* 5:2
they forsook their *n.* *Mark* 1:18
your *n.* for a draught. *Luke* 5:4

nettles
under the *n.* they were. *Job* 30:7

and *n.* had covered the. *Pr* 24:31
n. and brambles in the. *Isa* 34:13
n. shall possess the. *Hos* 9:6
shall be the breeding of *n.* *Zeph* 2:9

network

grate of *n.* of brass. *Ex* 27:4; 38:4
round about on *n.* *1 Ki* 7:18, 42
n. on the chapiters. *Jer* 52:22
all the pomegranates on *n.* were. 23

networks

the two *n.* upon the. *1 Ki* 7:41
pomegranates for the two *n.* 42
they that weave *n.* shall. *Isa* 19:9*

never

kine, such as I *n.* saw. *Gen* 41:19
the fire shall *n.* go out. *Lev* 6:13
upon which *n.* came yoke. *Num* 19:2
the poor shall *n.* cease. *Deut* 15:11
n. break my covenant. *Judg* 2:1
is there *n.* a woman among? 14:3
green withs that were *n.* dried. 16:7
if bind with new ropes that *n.* 11
sword shall *n.* depart. *2 Sam* 12:10
he *n.* prophesieth good. *2 Chr* 18:7
was *n.* a son left him, save. 21:17
infants which *n.* saw light. *Job* 3:16
make my hands *n.* so clean. 9:30
n. eateth with pleasure. 21:25
I shall *n.* be in adversity. *Ps* 10:6
his face, he will *n.* see it. 11
these things shall *n.* be moved. 15:5
in prosperity I said, I shall *n.* 30:6
in thee do I trust, let me *n.* 31:1
they shall *n.* see light. 49:19
Lord will *n.* suffer righteous. 55:22
O Lord, let me *n.* be put to. 71:1
I will *n.* forget thy precepts. 119:93
the righteous shall *n.* be. *Pr* 10:30
destruction are *n.* full, so the eyes of a man are *n.* satisfied. 27:20
three things that are *n.* 30:15
Babylon *n.* be inhabited. *Isa* 13:20
the seed of evil doers shall *n.* 14:20
no city, it shall *n.* be built. 25:2
are greedy dogs which can *n.* 56:11
watchmen that shall *n.* hold. 62:6
we are thine: Thou *n.* barest. 63:19
their confusion shall *n.* *Jer* 20:11
David shall *n.* want a man. 33:17
n. open thy mouth. *Ezek* 16:63
Tyrus shall *n.* be found. 26:21
terror and *n.* shall be. 27:36; 28:19
a kingdom that shall *n.* *Dan* 2:44
trouble, such as *n.* was. 12:1
my people shall *n.* be ashamed. *Joel* 2:26, 27
I will *n.* forget any of. *Amos* 8:7
they shall fall and *n.* rise. 14
judgement doth *n.* go. *Hab* 1:4
profess unto them, I *n.* *Mat* 7:23
it was *n.* so seen in Israel. 9:33
have ye *n.* read, Out of the mouth of babes? 21:16, 42; *Mark* 2:25
Peter said, Yet will I *n.* *Mat* 26:33
he answered him to *n.* a word. 27:14
we *n.* saw it on this. *Mark* 2:12
Holy Ghost, hath *n.* forgiveness. 3:29
into fire that *n.* shall be. 9:43, 45
colt tied, whereon *n.* man sat. 11:2; *Luke* 19:30
good for that man if he had *n.* been born. *Mark* 14:21
n. gavest me a kid to. *Luke* 15:29
the wombs that *n.* bare. 23:29
wherein *n.* man before was laid. 53 *John* 19:41
I give, shall *n.* thirst. *John* 4:14
shall *n.* hunger, and he that believeth on me shall *n.* thirst. 6:35
man, having *n.* learned? 7:15
n. man spake like this man. 46
and we were *n.* in bondage. 8:33
he shall *n.* see death. 51, 52; 10:28 11:26
thou shalt *n.* wash my feet. 13:8
I have *n.* eaten any. *Acts* 10:14
being a cripple, who *n.* had. 14:8
charity *n.* faileth, but. *1 Cor* 13:8
n. able to come to. *2 Tim* 3:7
n. with those sacrifices. *Heb* 10:1
the same sacrifices which can *n.* 11
I will *n.* leave thee, nor forsake. 13:5
things ye shall *n.* fall. *2 Pet* 1:10

never *so*

charming *n. so* wisely. *Ps* 58:5

never *so much*

ask me *n. so m.* dowry. *Gen* 34:12

nevertheless

n. in the day when I. *Ex* 32:34
n. these ye shall not eat. *Lev* 11:4 *Deut* 14:7
n. a fountain or pit shall. *Lev* 11:36
n. the people be strong. *Num* 13:28
n. the ark of the covenant. 14:44
n. the firstborn of man shalt. 18:15
n. the Kenite shall be wasted. 24:22
n. it shall be purified with. 31:23
n. the Lord thy God. *Deut* 23:5
n. children of Israel expelled not. *Josh* 13:13
n. my brethren that went up. 14:8
n. the inhabitants of. *Judg* 1:33
n. the Lord raised up judges. 2:16
n. the people refused. *1 Sam* 8:19
n. Samuel mourned for Saul. 15:35
n. Saul spake not any thing. 20:26
n. the lords favour thee not. 29:6
n. David took the strong. *2 Sam* 5:7
n. a lad saw them and told. 17:18
n. he would not drink thereof. 23:16
n. thou shalt not build. *1 Ki* 8:19
n. for David's sake did the. 15:4
n. Asa his heart was perfect. 14
n. in his old age he was. 23
n. the high places were not. 22:43
n. if thou see me when. *2 Ki* 2:10
n. he cleaved to the sins of. 3:3
n. they departed not from sins. 13:6
n. the priests of the high. 23:9
n. David took the castle. *1 Chr* 11:5
n. the king's word prevailed. 21:4
n. they shall be his. *2 Chr* 12:8
n. the heart of Asa was. 15:17
n. there are good things found. 19:3
n. divers of Asher humbled. 30:11
n. the people did sacrifice in. 33:17
n. Josiah would not turn. 35:22
n. we made our prayer. *Neh* 4:9
n. they were disobedient. 9:26
n. for thy mercies' sake thou. 31
n. him did outlandish women. 13:26
n. Haman refrained. *Esth* 5:10
n. thou heardest my. *Ps* 31:22
n. man being in honour. 49:12
n. I am continually with thee. 73:23
n. they did flatter him with. 78:36
n. my lovingkindness will I not. 89:33
n. he saved them for his. 106:8
n. he regarded their affliction. 44
n. the counsel of the Lord. *Pr* 19:21
n. the poor man's wisdom. *Eccl* 9:16
n. the dimness shall not be. *Isa* 9:1
n. in those days I will not. *Jer* 5:18
n. the hand of Ahikam was. 26:24
n. hear thou this word that. 28:7
n. Elnathan and Delaiah. 36:25
n. if thou warn the. *Ezek* 3:21
n. I will remember my. 16:60
n. mine eye spared them. 20:17
n. I withdrew my hand, and. 22
n. if thou warn the wicked. 33:9
n. leave the stump of. *Dan* 4:15
n. the men rowed hard. *Jonah* 1:13
n. for the oath's sake. *Mat* 14:9
from me, *n.* not as I will, but. 26:39
n. hereafter ye shall see the. 64
n. not what I will. *Mark* 14:36 *Luke* 22:42
n. at thy word I will. *Luke* 5:5
n. I must walk to-day. 13:33
n. when Son of man cometh. 18:8
Lazarus is dead, *n.* let. *John* 11:15
n. among the chief rulers. 12:42
n. I tell you the truth; it is. 16:7
n. he left not himself. *Acts* 14:17
n. the centurion believed. 27:11
n. death reigned from. *Rom* 5:14
n. I have written more boldly. 15:15
n. to avoid fornication. *1 Cor* 7:2
n. such shall have trouble in. 28
n. he that standeth stedfast. 37
n. we have not used this. 9:12
n. neither is the man. 11:11
n. when it shall turn. *2 Cor* 3:16
n. God comforteth those that. 7:6
n. being crafty, I caught. 12:16
n. I live, yet not I, but. *Gal* 2:20
n. what saith scripture, cast. 4:30
n. let every one so love his wife. *Eph* 5:33
n. to abide in the flesh. *Phil* 1:24
n. whereto we have already. 3:16
n. I am not ashamed. *2 Tim* 1:12
n. the foundation of God. 2:19
n. it yieldeth peaceable. *Heb* 12:11
n. we look for new. *2 Pet* 3:13
n. I have somewhat. *Rev* 2:4

new

[1] *Fresh, newly made,* Judg 15:13; Mat 9:17. [2] *Sweet, as new wine, not yet fermented,* Joel 1:5. [3] *Undressed, as cloth,* Mat 9:16.

there arose up a *n.* king. *Ex* 1:8
offer a *n.* meat offering. *Lev* 23:16 *Num* 28:26
old, because of the *n.* *Lev* 26:10
Lord make a *n.* thing. *Num* 16:30
what man is there that hath built a *n.* house? *Deut* 20:5; 22:8
when taken a *n.* wife, he shall. 24:5
sacrificed to devils, to *n.* 32:17
bottles of wine were *n.* *Josh* 9:13
they chose *n.* gods, then. *Judg* 5:8
they bound him with *n.* cords. 15:13 16:11, 12
make a *n.* cart, and. *1 Sam* 6:7
set the ark on a *n.* cart. *2 Sam* 6:3 *1 Chr* 13:7
being girded with a *n.* *2 Sam* 21:16
clad with a *n.* garment. *1 Ki* 11:29
Ahijah caught the *n.* garment. 30
bring a *n.* cruse, and. *2 Ki* 2:20
stood in the *n.* court. *2 Chr* 20:5
it is ready to burst like *n.* *Job* 32:19
a *n.* song. *Ps* 33:3; 96:1; 98:1 144:9; 149:1; *Isa* 42:10
put a *n.* song in my mouth. *Ps* 40:3
is no *n.* thing under the. *Eccl* 1:9
whereof may be said, This is *n.*? 10
all pleasant fruits, *n.* *S of S* 7:13
behold *n.* things do. *Isa* 42:9; 48:6
behold, I will do a *n.* thing. 43:19
be called by a *n.* name. 62:2
n. heavens and a *n.* 65:17; 66:22
the *n.* gate of the Lord's house. *Jer* 26:10; 36:10
the Lord hath created a *n.* 31:22
mercies are *n.* every. *Lam* 3:23
I will put a *n.* spirit within you. *Ezek* 11:19; 36:26
a *n.* heart and *n.* spirit. 18:31
shall bring forth *n.* fruit. 47:12
a piece of *n.* cloth to an. *Mat* 9:16* *Mark* 2:21*; *Luke* 5:36
but they put *n.* wine into *n.* bottles. *Mat* 9:17; *Mark* 2:22; *Luke* 5:38
of his treasure things *n.* *Mat* 13:52
for this is my blood of the *n.* 26:28 *Mark* 14:24; *Luke* 22:20 *1 Cor* 11:25
until I drink it *n.* with you. *Mat* 26:29; *Mark* 14:25
body in his own *n.* tomb. *Mat* 27:60
saying, What *n.* doctrine? *Mark* 1:27
speak with *n.* tongues. 16:17
a *n.* commandment give. *John* 13:34
a *n.* sepulchre, wherein. 19:41
what this *n.* doctrine is? *Acts* 17:19
to tell or to hear some *n.* thing. 21
ye may be a *n.* lump. *1 Cor* 5:7
able ministers of the *n.* *2 Cor* 3:6
in Christ, he is a *n.* creature; behold, all things are become *n.* 5:17
but a *n.* creature. *Gal* 6:15
of twain, one *n.* man. *Eph* 2:15
put on the *n.* man. 4:24; *Col* 3:10
the Mediator of the *n.* *Heb* 9:15
by a *n.* and living way hath. 10:20
as *n.* born babes desire. *1 Pet* 2:2
n. heavens and a *n.* *2 Pet* 3:13
I write no *n.* commandment unto. *1 John* 2:7
a *n.* commandment I write. 8
I wrote a *n.* commandment. *2 John* 5
n. name written, which. *Rev* 2:17
n. Jerusalem. 3:12; 21:2
I will write my *n.* name. 3:12
and they sung a *n.* song. 5:9; 14:3

n. heaven and a *n.* earth. *Rev* 21:1
I make all things *n.* 5
see **covenant, moon**

new *wine*
offering of the *n. wine.* *Neh* 10:39
chamber where the *n. wine.* 13:5
brought tithe of *n. wine* unto the. 12
burst out with *n. wine.* *Pr* 3:10
the *n. wine* mourneth, the. *Isa* 24:7
as the *n. wine* is found in. 65:8
wine and *n. wine* take. *Hos* 4:11
n. wine shall fail in her. 9:2
the *n. wine* is cut off. *Joel* 1:5
n. wine is dried up. 10
mountains shall drop *n. wine.* 3:18
drought on the *n. wine.* *Hag* 1:11
n. wine shall make the maids cheerful. *Zech* 9:17
n. wine into old bottles, but *n. wine.* *Mat* 9:17; *Mark* 2:22; *Luke* 5:37
men are full of *n. wine.* *Acts* 2:13

newly
gods that came *n.* up. *Deut* 32:17*
but *n.* set the watch. *Judg* 7:19

newness
should walk in *n.* of life. *Rom* 6:4
we should serve in *n.* of spirit. 7:6

news
so is good *n.* from afar. *Pr* 25:25

next
bear at this set time *n.* *Gen* 17:21
neighbour *n.* take a lamb. *Ex* 12:4
stood up all the *n.* day. *Num* 11:32
inheritance to his kinsman *n.* 27:11
the city which is *n.* to. *Deut* 21:3
the elders of the city *n.* to the. 6
is one of our *n.* kinsmen. *Ruth* 2:20
and I shall be *n.* to thee. *1 Sam* 23:17
them to the evening of *n.* day. 30:17
Elkanah that was *n.* *2 Chr* 28:7
Mordecai was *n.* to king. *Esth* 10:3
worm the *n.* day smote. *Jonah* 4:7
the *n.* day that followed. *Mat* 27:62
us go into the *n.* towns. *Mark* 1:38
the *n.* day John seeth. *John* 1:29
in hold unto the *n.* day. *Acts* 4:3
the *n.* day Moses shewed. 7:26
be preached *n.* sabbath. 13:42, 44

Nicanor
Stephen, Philip and *N.* *Acts* 6:5

Nicodemus
N. a ruler of the Jews. *John* 3:1
N. came to Jesus by. 7:50; 19:39

Nicolaitanes
hatest the deeds of the *N.* *Rev* 2:6
hold the doctrine of the *N.* 15

Nicopolis
to come unto me to *N.* *Tit* 3:12

Niger
Simeon who was called *N.* *Acts* 13:1

nigh
virgin that is *n.* to him. *Lev* 21:3
any that is *n.* of kin may. 25:49
him, but not *n.*, a star. *Num* 24:17
hath God so *n.* to them. *Deut* 4:7
gods of the people *n.* to the. 13:7
if thy brother be not *n.* 22:2
the word is *n.* unto thee. 30:14
Rom 10:8
wherefore approached ye so *n.*? *2 Sam* 11:20, 21
my words be *n.* to the. *1 Ki* 8:59
Lord is *n.* unto them that. *Ps* 34:18
his salvation is *n.* them that. 85:9
the Lord is *n.* unto all that. 145:18
day of the Lord is *n.* *Joel* 2:1
ye know that summer is *n.* *Mat* 24:32; *Luke* 21:30
that it is *n.* even at the. *Mark* 13:29
desolation thereof is *n.* *Luke* 21:20
your redemption draweth *n.* 28
kingdom of God is *n.* at hand. 31
a feast of Jews was *n.* *John* 6:4
passover was *n.* at hand. 11:55
sepulchre was *n.* at hand. 19:42
n. by the blood of Christ. *Eph* 2:13
peace to them that were *n.* 17
sick, *n.* unto death. *Phil* 2:27
is rejected, is *n.* unto. *Heb* 6:8
see **came, draw**

night
[1] *The time while the sun is below our horizon,* Ex 12:30, 31; Mat 27:64. [2] *A time of ignorance and unbelief,* Rom 13:12. [3] *Adversity and affliction,* Isa 21:12. [4] *Death,* John 9:4.
darkness he called *n.* *Gen* 1:5
lights, to divide the day from *n.* 14
lesser light to rule the *n.* 16
tarry all *n.* 19:2; *Num* 22:19
Judg 19:6, 9
men which came in to thee this *n.*? *Gen* 19:5
drink wine that *n.* 33, 34, 35
tarried all *n.* 24:54; 28:11; 31:54
32:13, 21
appeared to Isaac the same *n.* 26:24
shall lie with thee to-*n.* 30:15, 16
each man his dream in one *n.* 40:5
41:11
Israel in visions of the *n.* 46:2
and at *n.* he shall divide. 49:27*
eat the flesh that *n.* roast. *Ex* 12:8
the land of Egypt this *n.* 12
n. to be much observed to the Lord, this is that *n.* of the Lord to be. 42
not near the other all *n.* 14:20
the burning on the altar all *n.* *Lev* 6:9
not abide with thee all *n.* 19:13
the people stood up all that *n.* *Num* 11:32
and the people wept that *n.* 14:1
to them, Lodge here this *n.* 22:8, 19
God came to Balaam at *n.* 20
shall no leavened bread remain all *n.* *Deut* 16:4
body shall not remain all *n.* 21:23
came men in hither to-*n.* *Josh* 2:2
that *n.* for it was dry on. *Judg* 6:40
all *n.* and were quiet all *n.* 16:2
man would not tarry that *n.* 19:10
and abused her all the *n.* until. 25
an husband also to-*n.* *Ruth* 1:12
Boaz winnoweth barley to-*n.* 3:2
cried to the Lord all *n.* *1 Sam* 15:11
Lord hath said to me this *n.* 16
fled and escaped that *n.* 19:10
if thou save not thy life to-*n.* 11
rose up and went away that *n.* 28:25
men of Jabesh went all *n.* 31:12
men walked all *n.* *2 Sam* 2:29
Joab and his men went all *n.* 32
away through the plain all *n.* 4:7
David went and lay all *n.* 12:16
pursue after David this *n.* 17:1
lodge not this *n.* in the plain. 16
tarry one with thee this *n.* 19:7
that *n.* the angel of the. *2 Ki* 19:35
that *n.* did God appear. *2 Chr* 1:7
n. could not the king sleep. *Esth* 6:1
let the *n.* perish in which it. *Job* 3:3
let that *n.* be solitary. 7
the visions of the *n.* 4:13
arise, and the *n.* be gone? 7:4
and the dew lay all *n.* on my. 29:19
desire not the *n.* when people. 36:20
all the *n.* make I my bed. *Ps* 6:6
n. unto *n.* sheweth knowledge. 19:2
may endure for a *n.*, but joy. 30:5
he led them all *n.* with a. 78:14
forth thy faithfulness every *n.* 92:2
darkness, and it is *n.* 104:20
even the *n.* shall be light. 139:11
the black and dark *n.* *Pr* 7:9
ariseth also while it is yet *n.* 31:15
shall lie all *n.* between my breasts. *S of S* 1:13
with the drops of the *n.* 5:2
continue until *n.* till wine. *Isa* 5:11
make thy shadow as the *n.* 16:3
the *n.* of my pleasure he. 21:4*
what of the *n.*? what of the *n.*? 11
morning cometh, and also the *n.* 12
shall be a dream of a *n.* 29:7
aside to tarry for a *n.* *Jer* 14:8
secret revealed in a *n.* *Dan* 2:19
in that *n.* was Belshazzar. 5:30
king passed the *n.* fasting. 6:18
baker sleepeth all the *n.* *Hos* 7:6
howl, come, lie all *n.* in. *Joel* 1:13
the day dark with *n.* *Amos* 5:8
up in a *n.* perished in a *n.* *Jonah* 4:10
therefore *n.* shall be to you. *Mi* 3:6
fourth watch of *n.* Jesus went to. *Mat* 14:25; *Mark* 6:48
be offended because of me this *n.* *Mat* 26:31; *Mark* 14:27
this *n.* before cockcrow. *Mat* 26:34
we have toiled all *n.* *Luke* 5:5
continued all *n.* in prayer to. 6:12
this *n.* thy soul shall be. 12:20
in that *n.* two shall be in. 17:34
at *n.* he went out and abode. 21:37
the *n.* cometh when no. *John* 9:4
went out, and it was *n.* 13:30
that *n.* they caught nothing. 21:3
the same *n.* Peter was. *Acts* 12:6
the same hour of the *n.* 16:33
n. following the Lord stood. 23:11
soldiers at third hour of the *n.* 23
stood by me this *n.* the angel. 27:23
the *n.* is far spent, the. *Rom* 13:12
the same *n.* in which. *1 Cor* 11:23
we are not of the *n.* nor. *1 Thes* 5:5
there shall be no *n.* there. *Rev* 21:25; 22:5

by **night**
to Abimelech in a dream *by n.* *Gen* 20:3
to Laban in a dream *by n.* 31:24
stolen by day, or stolen *by n.* 39
consumed me, and the frost *by n.* 40
Moses and Aaron *by n.* *Ex* 12:31
before them *by n.* in a. 13:21, 22
14:20; 40:38; *Neh* 9:12
appearance of fire *by n.* *Num* 9:16
cloud taken up by day or *by n.* 21
in fire *by n.* to shew. *Deut* 1:33
forth out of Egypt *by n.* 16:1
that chanceth him *by n.* 23:10
Joshua sent them away *by n.* *Josh* 8:3
that he did it *by n.* *Judg* 6:27
up *by n.* thou and thy people. 9:32
house round about *by n.* 20:5
after Philistines *by n.* *1 Sam* 14:36
Abishai came to people *by n.* 26:7
Saul came to the woman *by n.* 28:8
beasts of the field *by n.* *2 Sam* 21:10
Lord appeared to Solomon *by n.* *1 Ki* 3:5; *2 Chr* 7:12
by n. and compassed. *2 Ki* 6:14
rose *by n.* and smote Edomites. 8:21; *2 Chr* 21:9
all the men of war fled *by n.* *2 Ki* 25:4; *Jer* 52:7
not be afraid of terror *by n.* *Ps* 91:5
nor the moon smite thee *by n.* 121:6
that *by n.* stand in the house. 134:1
moon and stars to rule *by n.* 136:9
Jer 31:35
candle goeth not out *by n.* *Pr* 31:18
by n. on my bed I. *S of S* 3:1
of a flaming fire *by n.* *Isa* 4:5
let us go *by n.* and destroy. *Jer* 6:5
forth out of the city *by n.* 39:4
if thieves *by n.* they will. 49:9
I saw in my vision *by n.* *Dan* 7:2
if robbers *by n.* came to thee. *Ob* 5
and his mother *by n.* *Mat* 2:14
lest his disciples come *by n.* 27:64
28:13
watch over their flock *by n.* *Luke* 2:8
Nicodemus came to Jesus *by n.* *John* 3:2; 19:39
the angel *by n.* opened. *Acts* 5:19
they took Paul *by n.* and let. 9:25
sent away Paul and Silas *by n.* 17:10
see **day**

in the **night**
his servants rose *in the n.* *Ex* 12:30
dew fell on the camp *in the n.* *Num* 11:9
child died *in the n.* *1 Ki* 3:19
king arose *in the n.* and. *2 Ki* 7:12
I arose *in the n.* *Neh* 2:12
I went up *in the n.* 15
in the n. they may be a guard. 4:22
yea, *in the n.* will they come. 6:10
noonday, as *in the n.* *Job* 5:14
in the n. the murderer. 24:14
stealeth him away *in the n.* 27:20
overturneth them *in the n.* 34:25
who giveth songs *in the n.*? 35:10
instruct me *in the n.* seasons. *Ps* 16:7

hast visited me *in the n.* *Ps* 17:3
I cry *in the n.* season, and. 22:2
and *in the n.* his song shall. 42:8
my sore ran *in the n.* and. 77:2
to remembrance my song *in the n.* 6
are but as a watch *in the n.* 90:4
fire to give light *in the n.* 105:39
thy name *in the n.* 119:55
taketh not rest *in the n.* *Eccl* 2:23
because of fear *in the n.* *S of S* 3:8
in the n. Ar and Kir of. *Isa* 15:1
have I desired thee *in the n.* 26:9
have a song as *in the n.* 30:29
at noonday as *in the n.* 59:10*
shall be cast out *in the n.* *Jer* 36:30
she weepeth sore *in the n.* *Lam* 1:2
cry out *in the n.* 2:19
fall with thee *in the n.* *Hos* 4:5
if a man walk *in the n.* *John* 11:10
a vision appeared to Paul *in the n.*
Acts 16:9; 18:9
as a thief *in the n.* *1 Thes* 5:2
2 Pet 3:10
sleep *in the n.* are drunken *in the n.*
1 Thes 5:7

nighthawk
owl and *n.* ye shall not eat.
Lev 11:16; *Deut* 14:15

nights
rain forty days, forty *n.* *Gen* 7:4, 12
wearisome *n.* are appointed. *Job* 7:3
set in my ward whole *n.* *Isa* 21:8
see **days**

nightwatches
meditate on thee in the *n.* *Ps* 63:6
mine eyes prevent the *n.* 119:148

Nimrod
Cush begat *N.* *Gen* 10:8
1 Chr 1:10
as *N.* the mighty hunter. *Gen* 10:9
land of Assyria and *N.* *Mi* 5:6

Nimshi, *see* **Jehu**

nine
fifth day *n.* bullocks. *Num* 29:26
Lord commanded to give to the *n.*
34:13; *Josh* 13:7; 14:2
Og's bedstead was *n.* *Deut* 3:11
Joab came to Jerusalem at end of *n.*
months. *2 Sam* 24:8
n. parts to dwell in other. *Neh* 11:1
but where are the *n.*? *Luke* 17:17
see **hundred**

nineteen
David's servants *n.* men. *2 Sam* 2:30

nineteenth
in the *n.* year of Nebuchadnezzar.
2 Ki 25:8; *Jer* 52:12

ninety
Enos lived *n.* years, and. *Gen* 5:9
shall Sarah, that is *n.* years ? 17:17
of the building *n.* cubits. *Ezek* 41:12

ninety-five
children of Gibbar *n.-five.* *Ezra* 2:20
children of Gibeon *n.-five.* *Neh* 7:25

ninety-six
Israel *n.-six* rams. *Ezra* 8:35
n.-six pomegranates. *Jer* 52:23

ninety-eight
Eli was *n.-eight* years. *1 Sam* 4:5
the children of Ater *n.-eight.*
Ezra 2:16; *Neh* 7:21

ninety-nine
Abram was *n.-nine* years. *Gen* 17:1
was *n.-nine* years old when he. 24
doth he not leave the *n.* and *nine*?
Mat 18:12, 13; *Luke* 15:4, 7

Nineveh
went and builded *N.* *Gen* 10:11
Sennacherib dwelt at *N.* *2 Ki* 19:36
Isa 37:37
go to *N.* *Jonah* 1:2; 3:2
now *N.* was an exceeding great. 3:3
should not I spare *N.*? 4:11
the burden of *N.* *Nah* 1:1
N. is like a pool. 2:8
N. is laid waste, who will ? 3:7
N. a desolation, and. *Zeph* 2:13
N. shall rise in judgement and condemn. *Mat* 12:41; *Luke* 11:32

Ninevites
a sign unto the *N.* *Luke* 11:30

ninth
of old fruit till the *n.* year. *Lev* 25:22
in *n.* year of Hoshea Samaria taken.
2 Ki 17:6; 18:10
in the *n.* year of Zedekiah. 25:1
Jer 39:1; 52:4; *Ezek* 24:1
Elzabad the *n.* captain. *1 Chr* 12:12
the *n.* lot came forth to. 24:11
n. captain for the *n.* month. 27:12
the sixth and *n.* hour. *Mat* 20:5
was darkness over all the land unto
the *n.* hour. 27:45; *Mark* 15:33
n. hour Jesus gave up the ghost.
Mat 27:46; *Mark* 15:34
prayer, being the *n.* hour. *Acts* 3:1
a vision about the *n.* hour. 10:3, 30
n. foundation was a. *Rev* 21:20
see **day, month**

Nisan
in the month *N.* *Neh* 2:1
first month *N.* *Esth* 3:7

Nisroch
worshipping in the house of *N.* his.
2 Ki 19:37; *Isa* 37:38

nitre
as vinegar upon *n.* so is. *Pr* 25:20
wash thee with *n.* and. *Jer* 2:22*

no
let there be *no* strife. *Gen* 13:8
me thou hast given *no* seed. 15:3
that thou wilt do us *no* hurt. 26:29
shed *no* blood, and lay *no.* 37:22
there was *no* harlot in. 38:21, 22
no interpreter. 40:8
we are *no* spies. 42:11, 31, 34
have *no* pasture. 47:4; *Lam* 1:6
is *no* straw given to. *Ex* 5:16, 18
that *no* swarms of flies. 8:22
no work shall be done. 12:16
Lev 16:29; 23:3, 7, 21, 28, 31
Num 29:1; *Deut* 16:8
seven days *no* leaven shall be.
Ex 12:19; 13:3, 7
were *no* graves in Egypt. 14:11
gathered little had *no* lack. 16:18
hurt a woman, and *no.* 21:12
there shall *no* blood be shed. 22:2
no gift; gift blindeth the wise. 23:8
thou shalt make *no* covenant. 32
ye shall offer *no* strange. 30:9
that there be *no* plague amongst. 12
for thou shalt worship *no.* 34:14
make thee *no* molten gods. 17
ye shall kindle *no* fire in your. 35:3
ye shall burn *no* leaven. *Lev* 2:11
put *no* oil upon it. 5:11
ye shall eat *no* fat. 7:23
ye shall eat *no* manner of blood.
26; 17:12, 14
touch *no* hallowed thing. 12:4
be *no* white hairs therein. 13:21, 26
no black hair. 31
there be *no* yellow hair. 32
do *no* unrighteousness. 19:15, 35
that there be *no* wickedness. 20:14
but there shall *no* stranger. 22:13
shall be *no* blemish therein. 21
houses which have *no* walls. 25:31
take thou *no* usury of him. 36
ye shall make you *no* idols. 26:1
no devoted thing shall. 27:28
if the man have *no.* *Num* 5:8
there be *no* witness against. 13
and shall drink *no* vinegar. 6:3
there shall *no* razor come upon. 5
he shall come at *no* dead body. 6
that *no* stranger come near. 16:40
Zelophehad had *no* sons. 26:33; 27:3
4; *Josh* 17:3; *1 Chr* 23:22; 24:28
if a man die and *no* son. *Num* 27:8
and if he have *no* daughter. 9
be not as sheep that have *no* 17
Ezek 34:5; *Mat* 9:36
no satisfaction for the life of a murderer. *Num* 35:31, 32
saw *no* similitude. *Deut* 4:12, 15
thine eye shall have *no* pity. 7:16
Levi hath *no* part with. 10:9; 14:27
29; 18:1; *Josh* 14:4; 18:7
there shall be *no* poor. *Deut* 15:4
if it will make *no* peace. 20:12

there shall be *no* might. *Deut* 28:32
nations thou shalt find *no* ease. 65
children in whom is *no* faith. 32:20
there was *no* day like. *Josh* 10:14
no part in the Lord. 22:25, 27
there was *no* king in Israel.
Judg 17:6; 18:1; 21:25
there was *no* magistrate. 18:7
where there is *no* want. 10; 19:19
no deliverer. 18:28
for it is *no* good report. *1 Sam* 2:24
there was *no* open vision. 3:1
take it, for there is *no* other. 21:9
because he had *no* pity. *2 Sam* 12:6
no such thing ought to be. 13:12
if he say, I have *no* delight. 15:26
I have *no* son to keep my. 18:18
Sheba said, We have *no* part. 20:1
there is *no* God like. *1 Ki* 8:23
he would prophesy *no* good. 22:18
there is *no* God in Israel. *2 Ki* 1:16
because Ahaziah had *no* son. 17
Jehu took *no* heed to walk. 10:31
Sheshan had *no* sons. *1 Chr* 2:34
do my prophets *no* harm. 16:22
Ps 105:15
that have *no* shepherd. *2 Chr* 18:16
Zech 10:2
there is *no* iniquity with. *2 Chr* 19:7
we have *no* might against. 20:12
people made *no* burning for. 21:19
there was *no* passover like. 35:18
till there was *no* remedy. 36:16
that there should be *no.* *Ezra* 9:14
ye have *no* portion in. *Neh* 2:20
no king like Solomon. 13:26
he put *no* trust in his. *Job* 4:18
in seven there shall *no* evil. 5:19
see *no* good. 9:25
that *no* eye had seen me. 10:18
and there can be *no* opening. 12:14
wander where there is *no* way. 24
physicians of *no* value. 13:4
let my cry have *no* place. 16:18
he shall have *no* name in. 18:17
servant, he gave me *no.* 19:16
no eye shall see me. 24:15
have *no* helper. 30:13
there is *no* help for him. *Ps* 3:2
spirit there is *no* guile. 32:2
there is *no* want to them. 34:9
there is *no* fear of God. 36:1
in fear where *no* fear was. 53:5
they have *no* changes. 55:19
no good will he withhold. 84:11
there shall *no* evil befall thee. 91:10
there is *no* unrighteousness. 92:15
do *no* iniquity, they walk. 119:3
in whom there is *no* help. 146:3
shall *no* evil happen to. *Pr* 12:21
seeing he hath *no* heart to it. 17:16
there is *no* wisdom against. 21:30
they had *no* comforter. *Eccl* 4:1
is *no* work in the grave. 9:10
my love, there is *no.* *S of S* 4:7
sister, and she hath *no* breasts. 8:8
there is *no* soundness in it. *Isa* 1:6
field, till there be *no* place. 5:8
it is because there is *no* light. 8:20
government there shall be *no.* 9:7
no one of these shall fail. 34:16
to them that have *no* might. 40:29
beside me there is *no* saviour. 43:11
no peace to wicked. 48:22; 57:21
in darkness, and hath *no* light. 50:10
hath *no* form nor comeliness. 53:2
no weapon formed against. 54:17
and he that hath *no* money. 55:1
there is *no* hope. 57:10; *Jer* 2:25
there is *no* judgement. *Isa* 59:8
that there was *no* intercessor. 16
which are yet *no* gods. *Jer* 2:11
received *no* correction. 30
when there is *no* peace. 6:14; 8:11
cruel, and have *no* mercy. 6:23
looked for peace, but *no* good. 8:15
14:19
and there is *no* breath in them.
10:14; 51:17
wherein is *no* pleasure. 22:28; 48:38
I will do you *no* hurt. 25:6
do him *no* harm. 39:12
shall see *no* war. 42:14
spoiler shall come, and *no.* 48:8

no sons ? hath he *no* heir ? *Jer* 49:1
she had *no* comforter. *Lam* 1:9
peace, and there was *no* peace. *Ezek* 13:10, 16
I have *no* pleasure in death of him. 18:32; 33:11
yet had he *no* wages, nor. 29:18
is *no* other god that can. *Dan* 3:29
because there is *no* truth. *Hos* 4:1
thou shalt be *no* priest to me. 6
shall say, We have *no* king. 10:3
I was *no* prophet. *Amos* 7:14
there is *no* answer of God. *Mi* 3:7
is there *no* king in thee ? 4:9
there is *no* healing of thy. *Nah* 3:19
things that have *no* ruler. *Hab* 1:14
unjust knoweth *no* shame. *Zeph* 3:5
love *no* false oath. *Zech* 8:17
no oppressor shall pass. 9:8
I have *no* pleasure in you. *Mal* 1:10
ye shall in *no* case enter. *Mat* 5:20
thou shalt by *no* means come. 26
take therefore *no* thought. 6:34
10:19; *Mark* 13:11; *Luke* 12:11, 22
there is *no* resurrection. *Mat* 22:23
Mark 12:18; *Acts* 23:8
1 Cor 15:12, 13
days, *no* flesh be saved. *Mark* 13:20
need *no* repentance. *Luke* 15:7
I find *no* fault in him. 23:4, 14
John 18:38; 19:4, 6
I have *no* husband. *John* 4:17
ye have *no* life. 6:53
of Galilee ariseth *no* prophet. 7:52
ye should have *no* sin. 9:41
there is *no* light in him. 11:10
if I wash thee not, thou hast *no*. 13:8
now they have *no* cloak for. 15:22
we have *no* king but Caesar. 19:15
no difference between. *Acts* 15:9
for I will be *no* judge of. 18:15
written they observe *no*. 21:25
Jews have I done *no* wrong. 25:10
the people shewed us *no* little. 28:2
for there is *no* difference. *Rom* 3:22
for where *no* law is, *no*. 4:15; 5:13
flesh dwelleth *no* good thing. 7:18
them that are *no* people. 10:19
love worketh *no* ill to his. 13:10
that *no* flesh glory. *1 Cor* 1:29
no certain dwelling place. 4:11
I will eat *no* flesh while the. 8:13
there hath *no* temptation. 10:13
we have *no* such custom. 11:16
I have *no* need of thee. 12:21
no charity. 13:2
if there be *no* interpreter. 14:28
for us, who knew *no* sin. *2 Cor* 5:21
giving *no* offence in any thing. 6:3
I pray to God that ye do *no* evil. 13:7
against such there is *no* law. *Gal* 5:23
have *no* fellowship. *Eph* 5:11
but made himself of *no*. *Phil* 2:7
and have *no* confidence in. 3:3
which have *no* hope. *1 Thes* 4:13
and have *no* company. *2 Thes* 3:14
shall proceed *no* further. *2 Tim* 3:9
could swear by *no* greater. *Heb* 6:13
no place have been sought. 8:7
without shedding of blood is *no*. 9:22
have *no* pleasure in him. 10:38
no chastening for the present. 12:11
found *no* place of repentance. 17
have we *no* continuing city. 13:14
whom is *no* variableness. *Jas* 1:17
and have *no* works, can faith ? 2:14
who did *no* sin, nor. *1 Pet* 2:22
no prophecy of private. *2 Pet* 1:20
in him is *no* darkness. *1 John* 1:5
if we say, we have *no* sin, we. 8
in him is *no* sin. 3:5
there is *no* fear in love. 4:18
I have *no* greater joy. *3 John* 4
mouth was found *no* guile. *Rev* 14:5
received *no* kingdom as yet. 17:12
no widow, and shall see *no*. 18:7
found *no* place for them. 20:11
no temple therein. 21:22
no need of the sun. 23
no night there, they need *no*. 25; 22:5
see **bread, child, children, inheritance, knowledge, man, more, power, water, wise, wrath**

no *rain*
that there be *no rain*. *Deut* 11:17
1 Ki 8:35; *2 Chr* 6:26; 7:13
there had been *no rain* in land.
1 Ki 17:7; *Jer* 14:4
they rain *no rain* upon it. *Isa* 5:6
hath been *no* latter *rain*. *Jer* 3:3
even upon them shall be *no rain*.
Zech 14:17
and if Egypt that have *no rain*. 18

no *rest*
but the dove found *no rest*. *Gen* 8:9
my sinews take *no rest*. *Job* 30:17
or laugh there is *no rest*. *Pr* 29:9
shalt thou have *no rest*. *Isa* 23:12
no rest till he establish. 62:7
sighing, and find *no rest*. *Jer* 45:3
heathen she findeth *no rest*. *Lam* 1:3
give thyself *no rest*. 2:18
we have *no rest*. 5:5
I had *no rest* in my spirit. *2 Cor* 2:13
our flesh had *no rest*. 7:5
they have *no rest* day. *Rev* 14:11

no *strength*
no strength in Saul. *1 Sam* 28:20
arm that hath *no strength*. *Job* 26:2
man that hath *no strength*. *Ps* 88:4
there remained *no strength* in me.
Dan 10:8, 17
I have retained *no strength*. 16
it is of *no strength* at all. *Heb* 9:17

no *where*
they were *no where*. *1 Sam* 10:14

no, *opposite of yes*
not let you go, *no* not by. *Ex* 3:19
whether walk in my law or *no*. 16:4
Deut 8:2
here, thou shalt say, *No*. *Judg* 4:20
no, but we will bind thee. 15:13
no, my lord, I am of. *1 Sam* 1:15
no, not when the Lord hath. 20:15
no, but he would put strength in me.
Job 23:6
no, not gold, nor the forces. 36:19
there is none that doeth good, *no*, not one. *Ps* 14:3; 53:3
curse not king, *no* not. *Eccl* 10:20
no, for we will flee. *Isa* 30:16
no, for I have loved. *Jer* 2:25
no, but we will go into the. 42:14
thee ? he shall say, *No*. *Amos* 6:10
answered and said, *No*. *Hag* 2:12
knowest what these be, I said, *No*.
Zech 4:5, 13
so great faith, *no* not in Israel.
Mat 8:10; *Luke* 7:9
to this time, *no*, nor ever. *Mat* 24:21
no not the angels, but my. 36
no room, *no* not so much. *Mark* 2:2
bind him, *no* not with chains. 5:3
tribute to Caesar, or *no* ? *Luke* 20:22
no nor yet Herod: for I sent. 23:15
that Prophet? he said, *No*. *John* 1:21
whether he be a sinner or *no*. 9:25
meat ? they answered, *No*. 21:5
no not so much as to set. *Acts* 7:5
than they? *no*, in no wise. *Rom* 3:9
none righteous, *no* not one. 10, 12
with such an one, *no* not. *1 Cor* 5:11
no, not one that shall be able. 6:5
place by subjection, *no*. *Gal* 2:5

No
I will punish *N*. *Jer* 46:25
Ezek 30:14, 15, 16
better than populous *N*.? *Nah* 3:8

Noadiah
N. the son of Binnui. *Ezra* 8:33
think on the prophetess *N*. *Neh* 6:14

Noah, Noe
N. saying, This same. *Gen* 5:29
Lamech begat *N*. 30
N. found grace. 6:8
these are generations of *N*. 9; 10:1
32; *1 Chr* 1:4
N. only remained alive. *Gen* 7:23
God remembered *N*. and every. 8:1
N. opened the window of the ark. 6
N. builded an altar to the Lord. 20
N. awoke from his wine. 9:24
the days of *N*. 29
this is as the waters of *N*. *Isa* 54:9
these three, *N*. Daniel, Job.
Ezek 14:14, 20
as it was in the days of *N*.
Mat 24:37; *Luke* 17:26
was the son of *N*. *Luke* 3:36
by faith *N*. being warned. *Heb* 11:7
waited in the days of *N*. *1 Pet* 3:20
spared not the old world, but saved *N*. *2 Pet* 2:5

Noah
of Zelophehad were *N*. *Num* 26:33
27:1; 36:11; *Josh* 17:3

Nob
David came to *N*. *1 Sam* 21:1
son of Jesse coming to *N*. 22:9
to call the priests in *N*. 11
Doeg smote *N*. the city of. 19
of Benjamin dwelt at *N*. *Neh* 11:32
yet shall he remain at *N*. *Isa* 10:32

noble
whom the *n*. Asnapper. *Ezra* 4:10
king's most *n*. princes. *Esth* 6:9
planted thee a *n*. vine. *Jer* 2:21
Bereans more *n*. than. *Acts* 17:11
always, most *n*. Felix. 24:3; 26:25
how that not many *n*. *1 Cor* 1:26

nobleman
n. went into a far country. *Luke* 19:12
n. whose son was sick. *John* 4:46, 49

nobles
on the *n*. of Israel he. *Ex* 24:11
the *n*. of the people. *Num* 21:18
dominion over the *n*. *Judg* 5:13
letters to the *n*. in his city. *1 Ki* 21:8
Jehoiada took the *n*. *2 Chr* 23:20
as yet told it to the *n*. *Neh* 2:16
the *n*. put not their necks. 3:5
and I rebuked the *n*. and the. 5:7
the *n*. of Judah sent letters. 6:17
mine heart to gather the *n*. 7:5
their brethren, their *n*. 10:29
I contended with the *n*. of. 13:17
the *n*. held their peace. *Job* 29:10
make their *n*. like Oreb. *Ps* 83:11
bind their *n*. with fetters. 149:8
by me princes rule, and *n*. *Pr* 8:16
king is the son of *n*. *Eccl* 10:17
into the gates of the *n*. *Isa* 13:2
they shall call the *n*. to the. 34:12
brought down all their *n*. 43:14
n. sent their little ones to. *Jer* 14:3
carried captive *n*. of Judah. 27:20
and their *n*. shall be of. 30:21
king of Babylon slew all the *n*. of Judah. 39:6
of the king and his *n*. *Jonah* 3:7
Assyria, thy *n*. shall dwell. *Nah* 3:18

noise
the people heard the *n*. *Ex* 20:18*
he said, There is a *n*. of war. 32:17
but the *n*. of them that sing. 18
not shout nor make any *n*. *Josh* 6:1
delivered from the *n*. *Judg* 5:1
what meaneth the *n*. of this shout ?
1 Sam 4:6, 14
n. in the host of Philistines. 14:19
wherefore is this *n*. of ? *1 Ki* 1:4
is the *n*. that ye have heard. 4
n. of chariots, and a *n*. of. *2 Ki* 7:
Athaliah heard *n*. of guard. 11:1
2 Chr 23:1
a *n*. with psalteries. *1 Chr* 15:2
discern *n*. of joy, from *n*. *Ezra* 3:1
any understand the *n*. *Job* 36:29
n. thereof sheweth concerning it. 3
attentively the *n*. of his voice. 37:
skilfully with a loud *n*. *Ps* 33:
deep calleth at the *n*. of thy. 42:
my complaint, and make a *n*. 55:2
they make a *n*. like a dog. 59:6, 1
stilleth the *n*. of the seas, *n*. 65:7
make a joyful *n*. to God. 66:1; 81:
95:1, 2; 98:4*, 6; 100:
Lord is mightier than the *n*. 93:4
battle is with confused *n*. *Isa* 9:5
n. of a multitude in the mountains, tumultuous *n*. of the. 13:
the *n*. of thy viols is brought. 14:1
which make a *n*. like the *n*. 17:12
n. of them that rejoice endeth. 24:
he who fleeth from the *n*. of fear. 1
thou shalt bring down the *n*. 25:
visited of the Lord with great *n*. 29:

nor abase himself for the n. Isa 31:4
at the n. of the tumult the. 33:3
a voice of n. from the city. 66:6*
heart maketh a n. in me. Jer 4:19*
the city shall flee for the n. 29
behold, the n. of the bruit. 10:22*
with the n. of a great tumult. 11:16
a n. shall come to the ends. 25:31
king of Egypt is but a n. 46:17
at the n. of the stamping of. 47:3
at the n. of their fall, at the cry the n. was heard in the Red sea. 49:21
the n. of taking of Babylon. 50:46
a n. of their voice is uttered. 51:55
enemy made n. in house. Lam 2:7
I heard the n. of their wings, like the n. of great. Ezek 1:24; 43:2
the n. of the wheels, the n. of. 3:13
the land was desolate by the n. 19:7
thy walls shall shake at the n. 26:10
I will cause the n. of my songs. 13
as I prophesied, there was a n. 37:7
n. of chariots, like the n. of fire. Joel 2:5
take from me the n. of. Amos 5:23
they shall make a great n. Mi 2:12
the n. of a whip, n. of. Nah 3:2
the n. of a cry from the. Zeph 1:10
drink and make a n. Zech 9:15
people making a n. Mat 9:23*
pass away with great n. 2 Pet 3:10
I heard as it were the n. Rev 6:1*

noised

Joshua, his fame was n. Josh 6:27
it was n. that he was. Mark 2:1
all these sayings were n. Luke 1:65
when this was n. abroad. Acts 2:6*

noisome

deliver thee from the n. pestilence. Ps 91:3
when I send the sword and n. beast. Ezek 14:21†
fell a n. and grievous. Rev 16:2

none

this is n. other but the. Gen 28:17
n. of you shall go out. Ex 12:22
put n. of these diseases. 15:26
7th day, in it there shall be n. 16:26
to gather, and they found n. 27
shalt have n. other gods before me. 20:3; Deut 5:7
n. shall appear before me empty. Ex 23:15; 34:20
n. shall approach to any. Lev 18:6
there shall n. be defiled. 21:1
shall leave n. of it until morrow. 22:30; Num 9:12
and if the man have n. Lev 25:26
shall lie down, and n. shall. 26:6
flee when n. pursueth. 17, 36, 37
sons of Kohath he gave n. Num 7:9
n. that came out of Egypt. 32:11
we destroyed, and left n. Deut 2:34
3:3; Josh 8:22; 10:28, 30, 33
11:8
will put n. of diseases of. Deut 7:15
be given, and n. to rescue. 28:31
thou shalt have n. assurance. 66
n. went out of Jericho, n. Josh 6:1
n. of you be freed from being. 9:23
n. moved his tongue against. 10:21
came n. to the camp. Judg 21:8
there is n. holy as. 1 Sam 2:2
let n. of his words fall. 3:19
beware that n. touch. 2 Sam 18:12
all vessels of pure gold; n. were of silver. 1 Ki 10:21; 2 Chr 9:20
proclamation, n. was exempted. 1 Ki 15:22
blessing, I will receive n. 2 Ki 5:16
n. but Elisha tells the king of. 6:12
shall be n. to bury Jezebel. 9:10
let n. go forth or escape. 15; 10:25
till Jehu left Ahab n. 10:11
the prophets of Baal, let n. be. 19
look there be n. of the servants. 23
n. ought to carry ark of. 1 Chr 15:2
honour, such as n. of. 2 Chr 1:12
he might let n. go out or. 16:1
so that n. is able to withstand. 20:6
they were dead bodies fallen, n. 24
n. which was unclean should. 23:19
found there n. of the sons. Ezra 8:15
n. of us put off our clothes. Neh 4:23
drinking according to law, n. did compel. Esth 1:8
n. might enter the king's gate. 4:2
sat down, and n. spake. Job 2:13
let it look for light but have n. 3:9
n. shall make him afraid. 11:19
Jer 30:10; 46:27
tabernacle, because it is n. Job 18:15
shall n. of his meat be left. 20:21
him that had n. to help him. 29:12
but n. saith, Where is God? 35:10
they cry, but n. giveth answer. 12
wickedness till thou find n. Ps 10:15
n. can keep alive his own. 22:29
let n. that wait on thee be. 25:3
n. that trust in him shall. 34:22
law in his heart, n. of his. 37:31
n. of them can redeem his. 49:7
and there be n. to deliver. 50:22
comforters, but found n. 69:20
and let n. dwell in their tents. 25
n. of the men of might found. 76:5
Israel would n. of me. 81:11
let there be n. to extend. 109:12
and ye would n. of my. Pr 1:25
they would n. of my counsel. 30
n. that go unto her return. 2:19
envy not, and choose n. of his. 3:31
bear twins, and n. is. S of S 4:2
they shall burn and n. Isa 1:31
n. shall be weary, n. shall. 5:27
carry it away safe, and n. shall. 29
persecuted, and n. hindereth. 14:6
n. shall be alone in his. 31
n. shall make them afraid. 17:2
Zeph 3:13
and n. shall shut, n. open. Isa 22:22
n. shall pass through it. 34:10
they shall call the nobles but n. 12
no one shall fail, n. shall want. 16
n. delivereth, and n. saith. 42:22
n. considereth in his heart. 44:19
I am, and n. else beside. 47:8, 10
n. seeth me. 10
n. shall save thee. 15
n. considering that righteous. 57:1
n. calleth for justice, nor. 59:4
I called, n. did answer. 66:4
that n. can quench it. Jer 4:4; 21:12
for the beasts, and n. shall. 7:33
burnt up, so that n. can pass. 9:10
a wilderness that n. passeth. 12
shall fall as dung, and n. shall. 22
cities shall be shut, and n. 13:19
shall have n. to bury them. 14:16
and n. doth return from. 23:14
that n. should serve himself. 34:9
n. should serve themselves. 10
to this day they drink n. but. 35:14
n. to sit on the throne of. 36:30
n. shall remain or escape. 42:17
n. shall return, but such as. 44:14
n. shall tread with shouting. 48:33
n. shall gather up him that. 49:5
land desolate, and n. shall. 50:3
arrows, n. shall return in vain. 9
and there shall be n. 20
camp against it, let n. thereof. 29
shall fall, and n. shall raise. 32
that n. shall remain in it. 51:62
Ezek 7:11
n. to comfort her. Lam 1:2, 17
n. come to the solemn feasts. 4
fell, and n. did help her. 7
there is n. to comfort me. 21
but n. goeth to the battle. Ezek 7:14
peace, and there shall be n. 25
n. of my words shall be. 12:28
n. followeth thee to commit. 16:34
hath spoiled n. by violence. 18:7
for a man, but found n. 22:30
n. of his sins shall be. 33:16
mountains desolate, that n. 28
and n. did search or seek. 34:6
dwell safely, and n. make afraid. 28
39:26; Mi 4:4; Nah 2:11
and have left n. of them. Ezek 39:28
n. found like Daniel. Dan 1:19
n. stay his hand, or say to him. 4:35
the vision, but n. understood it. 8:27
n. shall stand before him. 11:16
shall come to his end, and n. 45
n. of the wicked shall. 12:10
n. shall deliver her out of my hands. Hos 2:10; 5:14
they called, n. at all would. 11:7
Lord your God, and n. Joel 2:27
there be n. to quench it. Amos 5:6
n. that shall cast a cord by lot. Mi 2:5
will say, n. evil can come. 3:11
he teareth in pieces, and n. 5:8
they cry, Stand, but n. Nah 2:8
let n. of you imagine evil. Zech 7:10; 8:17
let n. deal treacherously. Mal 2:15
dry places, seeking rest and findeth n. Mat 12:43; Luke 11:24
witnesses came, yet found n. Mat 26:60; Mark 14:55
impart to him that hath n. Luke 3:11
to n. of them was Elias sent. 4:26
n. of them was cleansed save. 27
n. of them shall taste of. 14:24
n. is good, save one, that. 18:19
n. of you keepeth the law. John 7:19
if I had not done the works n. 15:24
n. is lost but the son of. 17:12
thou gavest me, I have lost n. 18:9
silver and gold have I n. Acts 3:6
he was fallen on n. of them. 8:16
Pray, that n. of these things. 24
the word to n. but Jews. 11:19
Gallio cared for none of. 18:17
n. of these things move me. 20:24
he should forbid n. of his. 24:23
if there be n. of these things. 25:11
n. other than the prophets. 26:22
not the Spirit, he is n. Rom 8:9
n. of us liveth, and n. dieth. 14:7
I thank God, I baptized n. 1 Cor 1:14
whom n. of the princes of this. 2:8
wives be as though they had n. 7:29
but I have used n. of these. 9:15
give n. offence to the Jews. 10:32
and n. of them is without. 14:10
of the apostles saw I n. Gal 1:19
see that n. render evil. 1 Thes 5:15
give n. occasion to. 1 Tim 5:14
let n. of you suffer as a. 1 Pet :15
fear n. of these things. Rev 2:10
see **effect, like**

there is none

there is n. greater in. Gen 39:9
there is n. that can interpret. 41:15
there is n. so discreet and wise. 39
Lord is God, there is n. else. Deut 4:35, 39; 1 Ki 8:60; Isa 45:5
6, 14, 18, 22; 46:9; Mark 12:32
for there is n. to redeem. Ruth 4:4
there is n. holy as the Lord; there is n. beside. 1 Sam 2:2
there is n. that sheweth me, there is n. 22:8
a shadow, there is n. abiding. 1 Chr 29:15
there is n. that can deliver. Job 10:7; Ps 7:2; 71:11
they are corrupt, there is n. that. Ps 14:1, 3; 53:1, 3; Rom 3:12
for there is n. to help. Ps 22:11
there is n. on earth I desire. 73:25
seek water, there is n. Isa 41:17
there is n. sheweth, there is n. 26
there is n. that can deliver. 43:13
and there is n. to guide. 51:18
judgement, but there is n. 59:11
and there is n. that calleth on. 64:7
there is n. to stretch. Jer 10:20
there is n. to plead. 30:13
there is n. that doth deliver us. Lam 5:8
there is n. that holdeth. Dan 10:21
there is n. of them that. Hos 7:7
is forsaken, there is n. Amos 5:2
there is n. upright among. Mi 7:2
that said in her heart, I am, and there is n. Zeph 2:15
but there is n. warm. Hag 1:6
there is n. good but one. Mat 19:17
Mark 10:18
there is n. other commandment. Mark 12:31
there is n. of thy kindred. Luke 1:61
there is n. other name. Acts 4:12
there is n. righteous, no. Rom 3:10

there is n. that understandeth, *there is n.* seeketh God. *Rom* 3:11
there is n. other God. *1 Cor* 8:4

there was **none**
there was n. of men. *Gen* 39:11
there was n. that could interpret. 41:8
but *there was n.* that could. 24
until *there was n.* left. *Num* 21:35
and *there was n.* to save. *Deut* 22:27
there was n. to part them. *2 Sam* 14:6
there was n. to be so much praised as Absalom. 25
they looked, but *there was n.* to save. 22:42; *Ps* 18:41
there was n. that followed the house. *1 Ki* 12:20; *2 Ki* 17:18
to have pity, but *there was n.* *Ps* 69:20
and *there was n.* to bury them. 79:3
and *there was n.* to help. 107:12
when as yet *there was n.* of. 139:16
there was n. moved the. *Isa* 10:14
there was n. to answer. 50:2
winepress alone, and of the people *there was n.* with me. 63:3
and I wondered that *there was n.* 5
there was n. that could deliver. *Dan* 8:7

noon
shall dine with me at *n.* *Gen* 43:16
against Joseph came at *n.* 25
tarried until after *n.* *Judg* 19:8
who lay on a bed at *n.* *2 Sam* 4:5
on Baal even until *n.* *1 Ki* 18:26
at *n.* Elijah mocked them, and. 27
and they went out at *n.* 20:16
he sat on her knees till *n.* *2 Ki* 4:20
at *n.* will I pray, and. *Ps* 55:17
thy flock to rest at *n.* *S of S* 1:7
arise, let us go up at *n.* *Jer* 6:4
the sun to go down at *n.* *Amos* 8:9
about *n.* there shone. *Acts* 22:6

noonday
thou shalt grope at *n.* *Deut* 28:29
they grope in the *n.* as in. *Job* 5:14
be clearer than the *n.* 11:17
bring forth judgement as *n.* *Ps* 37:6
destruction that wasteth at *n.* 91:6
as the night, in midst of *n.* *Isa* 16:3
darkness shall be as the *n.* 58:10
we stumble at *n.* as in the. 59:10
have brought a spoiler at *n.* *Jer* 15:8
drive out Ashdod at *n.* *Zeph* 2:4

noontide
hear the shouting at *n.* *Jer* 20:16

Noph
the princes of *N.* are. *Isa* 19:13
the children of *N.* have. *Jer* 2:16
publish in *N.* 46:14
for *N.* shall be waste. 19
I will cause their images to cease out of *N.* *Ezek* 30:13
N. shall have distresses daily. 16

north
spread abroad to the *n.* *Gen* 28:14
three oxen looking toward the *n.* *1 Ki* 7:25; *2 Chr* 4:4
were toward the *n.* *1 Chr* 9:24
he stretcheth out the *n.* *Job* 26:7
and cold cometh out of the *n.* 37:9
cometh out of the *n.*: with God is. 22
the sides of the *n.*, the city. *Ps* 48:2
n. and south, thou hast. 89:12
turneth about to the *n.* *Eccl* 1:6
if the tree fall toward the *n.* 11:3
sit in the sides of the *n.* *Isa* 14:13
I will say to the *n.* Give up. 43:6
pot's face is toward the *n.* *Jer* 1:13
out of *n.* an evil break forth. 14; 4:6 46:20
of the kingdoms of the *n.* 15
these words toward the *n.* 3:12
together out of the land of the *n.* 18
for evil appeareth out of the *n.* 6:1
led Israel out of the *n.* country. 23:8; 31:8
take all the families of the *n.* 25:9
all the kings of the *n.* far and. 26
stumble and fall toward the *n.* 46:6
sacrifice in the *n.* country. 10
delivered to people of *n.* *Jer* 46:24
waters rise up out of the *n.* 47:2
out of *n.* cometh up a nation. 50:3
whirlwind came out of *n.* *Ezek* 1:4
mine eyes the way toward the *n.* 8:5
toward the *n.* sat women weeping. 14
all faces from south to *n.* 20:47
all flesh from south to *n.* will. 21:4
princes of the *n.* all of them. 32:30
the prospect toward the *n.* 40:44, 46
door was toward the *n.* 41:11; 42:4
and building toward the *n.* 42:1
their doors *n.* 4
chambers toward the *n.* 11, 13
chambers looked toward the *n.* 46:19
this holy oblation toward *n.* 48:10
suburbs shall be toward the *n.* 17
come to the king of the *n.* *Dan* 11:6
more years than the king of the *n.* 8
fight with the king of the *n.* 11
the king of the *n.* shall return. 13
the king of the *n.* shall cast. 15, 40
but tidings out of the *n.* shall. 44
his hand against the *n.* *Zeph* 2:13
black horses go into the *n.* *Zech* 6:6
quieted my spirit in the *n.* 8
shall remove toward the *n.* 14:4
n. were three gates. *Rev* 21:13

from the **north**
gathered *from the n.* *Ps* 107:3 *Isa* 49:12; *Jer* 16:15; 23:8
from the n. a smoke. *Isa* 14:31
I raised up one *from the n.* 41:25
evil *from the n.* and great. *Jer* 4:6 6:22; 10:22; 50:9, 41; 51:48
a king of kings *from the n.* *Ezek* 26:7
to come up *from the n.* parts. 39:2
wander *from the n.* to the east. *Amos* 8:12
from the land of *the n.* *Zech* 2:6
from the n. and sit. *Luke* 13:29

north *border*
and this shall be your *n. border.* *Num* 34:7, 9

north *quarter*
Judah's border in *n. quarter.* *Josh* 15:5
Togarmah of *n. quarter.* *Ezek* 38:6

north *side*
tabernacle on the *n. side.* *Ex* 26:20
put the table on the *n. side.* 35
for *n. side* hangings of 100 cubits. 27:11; 38:11
Dan shall be on *n. side.* *Num* 2:25
pitched on *n. side* of Ai. *Josh* 8:11
on the *n. side* of them. *Judg* 7:1
feast on the *n. side* of Beth-el. 21:19
altar on *n. side* of altar. *2 Ki* 16:14
the *n. side* 500 reeds. *Ezek* 42:17
of the city on the *n. side.* 48:30

northern
break the *n.* iron, and. *Jer* 15:12
remove from you the *n.* *Joel* 2:20

northward
lift up thine eyes *n.* and eastward. *Gen* 13:14; *Deut* 3:27
tabernacle *n.* without. *Ex* 40:22
the side of the altar *n.* *Lev* 1:11
mountain, turn you *n.* *Deut* 2:3
rock was situate *n.* *1 Sam* 14:5
lot came out *n.* *1 Chr* 26:14
n. were four Levites a day. 17
n. was this image of. *Ezek* 8:5
brought me out of the gate *n.* 47:2
three gates *n.*; one gate of. 48:31

nose
that hath a flat *n.* shall. *Lev* 21:18
put my hook in thy *n.* *2 Ki* 19:28 *Isa* 37:29
his *n.* pierceth through. *Job* 40:24
canst thou put a hook into his *n.*? 41:2
the wringing of the *n.* *Pr* 30:33
thy *n.* is as the tower. *S of S* 7:4
smell of thy *n.* like apples. 8*
a smoke in my *n.*, a fire. *Isa* 65:5
the branch to their *n.* *Ezek* 8:17
they shall take away thy *n.* 23:25

nose jewels
take away their tinkling ornaments, the rings and *n. jewels.* *Isa* 3:21

noses
n. have they, but they. *Ps* 115:6
it shall stop the *n.* *Ezek* 39:11*

nostrils
God breathed into man's *n.* *Gen* 2:7
all in whose *n.* was breath of. 7:22
with blast of thy *n.* waters. *Ex* 15:8
it come out at your *n.* *Num* 11:20
went a smoke out of his *n.* *2 Sam* 22:9; *Ps* 18:8
the blast of the breath of his *n.* *2 Sam* 22:16; *Ps* 18:15
by breath of his *n.* they. *Job* 4:9*
Spirit of God is in my *n.* 27:3
glory of his *n.* is terrible. 39:20*
out of his *n.* goeth smoke. 41:20
whose breath is in his *n.* *Isa* 2:22
the breath of our *n.* *Lam* 4:20
stink of your camps to come into your *n.* *Amos* 4:10

not
I will afflict, but *n.* for. *1 Ki* 11:39
upon me, and I am *n.* *Job* 7:8
he knoweth it *n.* 14:21; 35:15
n. unto us, O Lord, *n.* *Ps* 115:1
to thy testimonies, and *n.* 119:36
the wicked are *n.* *Pr* 12:7
buy the truth and sell it *n.* 23:23
riches are *n.* for ever, doth. 27:24
n. be an healer, make me *n.* *Isa* 3:7
n. as I have done to Samaria. 10:11
Moab, but his lies shall *n.* 16:6
but *n.* of me, *n.* of my spirit. 30:1
chosen thee, and *n.* cast. 41:9
thou shalt *n.* be forgotten. 44:21
let go my captives, *n.* for. 45:13
but *n.* in truth and. 48:1
they may forget, yet will I *n.* 49:15
peace, and thou fearest me *n.* 57:11
of them that sought me *n.* 65:1
a wind, *n.* to fan. *Jer* 4:11
and they are *n.* 10:20
I commanded, but they did them *n.* 11:8
leave us *n.* 14:9
I sent them *n.* neither have. 14, 15 23:32; 29:9, 31; *Ezek* 13:6
and *n.* for good. *Jer* 21:10; 39:16
and *n.* out of the mouth. 23:16
of peace, and *n.* of evil. 29:11
n. of peace. 30:5
because they were *n.* 31:15 *Mat* 2:18
darkness, but *n.* into light. *Lam* 3:2
have sinned, and are *n.* 5:7
things shall *n.* come. *Ezek* 16:16
but *n.* by thy covenant. 61
n. according to your wicked. 20:44
art a man, and *n.* God. 28:2
they will *n.* do them. 33:31, 32
I do *n.* this for your sakes. 36:22, 32
shall be mighty, but *n.* by. *Dan* 8:24
but *n.* for himself. 9:26
shall *n.* stand. 11:25
ye are *n.* my people, I will *n.* *Hos* 1:9
they return, but *n.* to the Most. 7:16
it shall *n.* be, saith. *Amos* 7:3, 6
shall speak, and *n.* lie. *Hab* 2:3
be ye *n.* as your fathers. *Zech* 1:4
n. by might nor power, but by. 4:6
I am the Lord, I change *n.* *Mal* 3:6
be *n.* like hypocrites. *Mat* 6:5, 8, 16
and it fell *n.* 7:25
and doeth them *n.* 26
n. as the scribes. 29; *Mark* 1:22
have mercy, and *n.* *Mat* 9:13; 12:7
shall *n.* be forgiven to men. 12:31, 32; *Luke* 12:10
saying, Lord, this shall *n.* *Mat* 16:22
but it shall *n.* be so among. 20:26
came *n.* to be ministered unto. 28
said, I go, sir, and went *n.* 21:30
but do *n.* ye after their works. 23:3
to have done, and *n.* to leave. 23
the end is *n.* yet. 24:6
let him *n.* come down. 17
clothed me *n.*, ye visited me *n.* 25:43
n. to one of these, did it *n.* to me. 45
n. on the feast day, lest there. 26:5
n. as I will, but as thou wilt. 39 *Mark* 14:36
see ye *n.*? hear ye *n.*? do ye *n.* remember? *Mark* 8:18

so it shall *n.* be among. *Mark* 10:43
but me ye have *n.* always. 14:7
he were the Christ or *n.* *Luke* 3:15
be healed, and *n.* on the. 13:14
I am *n.* as other men are. 18:11
woman, I know him *n.* 22:57
Peter said, Man, I am *n.* 58
I am *n.* the Christ. *John* 1:20; 3:28
n. because of thy saying. 4:42
ye will *n.* come to me, that ye. 5:40
I know ye have *n.* the love. 42
ye seek me *n.* because ye saw. 6:26
I came down, *n.* to do mine. 38
for I am *n.* alone, but I and the Father that sent me. 8:16; 16:32
I am *n.* of this world. 23
hireling, and *n.* the shepherd. 10:12
ye believe *n.*, because ye are *n.* 26
said I *n.* unto thee, if thou? 11:40
this spake he, *n.* of himself, but. 51
and *n.* for that nation only. 52
this he said, *n.* that he cared. 12:6
I judge him *n.* for I came *n.* 47
Lord, *n.* my feet only, but. 13:9
ye are clean, but *n.* all. 10
if it were *n.* so. 14:2
Judas, *n.* Iscariot, . . . and *n.* unto? 22
n. as the world giveth, give I. 27
I call you *n.* servants, but. 15:15
n. away, the Comforter will *n.* 16:7
for he shall *n.* speak of himself. 13
saying, *N.* this man. 18:40
touch me *n.* 20:17
n. to speak at all in the. *Acts* 4:18
have *n.* kept it. 7:53
he opened *n.* his mouth. 8:32
and shewed him, *n.* to all. 10:41
it is the voice of a god, and *n.* 12:22
I am *n.* he. 13:25
he be *n.* far from every one. 17:27
hold *n.* thy peace. 18:9
n. knowing the things that. 20:22
wolves enter in, *n.* sparing. 29
for I am ready *n.* to be. 21:13
I wist *n.* that he was the. 23:5
n. the hearers of the law. *Rom* 2:13
these having *n.* the law, are a. 14
and *n.* in the letter. 29
but *n.* before God. 4:2
to him that worketh *n.* but. 5
n. in circumcision, but. 10
and *n.* as it was by one that. 5:16
n., what I would, that do I *n.* 7:15
but ye are *n.* in the flesh, but. 8:9
how shall he *n.* with him give? 32
n. of the Jews only, but of. 9:24
was said, Ye are *n.* my people. 26
have they *n.* heard? yes. 10:18
n. to think of himself more. 12:3
ought to bear, and *n.* to please. 15:1
to preach, *n.* where Christ was. 20
to whom *n.* only I give thanks. 16:4
things which are *n.* *1 Cor* 1:28
eye hath *n.* seen, nor ear heard. 2:9
n. with meat. 3:2
ye *n.* carnal, and walk as men? 3, 4
n. to think of men above that. 4:6
and I will know, *n.* the speech. 19
n. with old leaven. 5:8
n. before the saints. 6:1
yet *n.* I, but the Lord. 7:10
to the rest speak I, *n.* the Lord. 12
am I *n.* an apostle? am I *n.* free? have I *n.* seen? 9:1
I therefore so run, *n.* as. 26
conscience, I say, *n.* thine. 10:29
have ye *n.* houses to eat in? 11:22
I am *n.* the eye, I am *n.* of. 12:16
yet *n.* I, but the grace of God. 15:10
n. as many which corrupt. *2 Cor* 2:17
n. with ink, *n.* in tables of. 3:3
n. that we are sufficient of. 5
n. as Moses, which put a vail. 13
we faint *n.* 4:1, 16
may be of God, and *n.* of us. 7
n. forsaken, cast down, but *n.* 9
we have an house *n.* made. 5:1
we walk by faith, *n.* by sight. 7
in appearance and *n.* in heart. 12
God comforted us, *n.* by his. 7:7
I rejoice, *n.* that ye were made. 9
I did it *n.* for his cause that had. 12
and this they did, *n.* as we hoped. 8:5
and *n.* according to that he hath *n.* 12

dare *n.* make ourselves. *2 Cor* 10:12
walked we *n.* in same spirit? 12:18
Paul an apostle, *n.* of men. *Gal* 1:1
I live, yet *n.* I. 2:20
and *n.* in another. 6:4
through faith, and that *n.* *Eph* 2:8
n. of works. 9
n. as fools, but as wise. 5:15
as to the Lord, and *n.* to men. 6:7
for we wrestle *n.* against flesh. 12
it is given to you, *n.* only. *Phil* 1:29
have obeyed, *n.* as in my. 2:12
and *n.* on him only, but on. 27
found in him, *n.* having mine. 3:9
n. as though I had already. 12
n. holding the head, from. *Col* 2:19
touch *n.* taste *n.* handle *n.* 21
on things above, *n.* on things. 3:2
to the Lord, and *n.* unto men. 23
that it was *n.* in vain. *1 Thes* 2:1
ye received it *n.* as word of. 13
therefore let us *n.* sleep as do. 5:6
all men have *n.* faith. *2 Thes* 3:2
n. because we have *n.* power. 9
n. given to wine, *n.* *1 Tim* 3:3
n. according to our works. *2 Tim* 1:9
Tit 3:5
and *n.* to me only, but. *2 Tim* 4:8
please them, *n.* answering. *Tit* 2:9
n. now as a servant. *Philem* 16
n. without an oath, he. *Heb* 7:20
Lord pitched, and *n.* man. 8:2
n. without blood, which he. 9:7
n. made with hands, *n.* of this. 11
evidence of things *n.* seen. 11:1
died, *n.* having received the. 13
us should *n.* be made perfect. 40
then are ye bastards, *n.* sons. 12:8
n. with grief. 13:17
be a hearer, and *n.* a doer. *Jas* 1:23
n. by faith only. 2:24
offend *n.* in word. 3:2
yet ye have *n.*, because ye ask *n.* 4:2
and doeth it *n.*, to him it is sin. 17
n. a people, had *n.* *1 Pet* 2:10
be subject, *n.* only to the good. 18
reviled *n.* again, he threatened *n.* 23
better for them *n.* to. *2 Pet* 2:21
same hath *n.* the Father. *1 John* 2:23
n. as Cain. 3:12
n. that we loved God. 4:10
hath *n.* the Son, hath *n.* life. 5:12
there is a sin *n.* unto death. 17
these be sensual, having *n.* *Jude* 19
are apostles, and are *n.* *Rev* 2:2, 9
see thou do it *n.* 19:10; 22:9
see **able, afraid, ashamed, answered, believe, confounded, departed, destroy, die, eat, enter, fear, few, find, forsaken, give, given, hear, hearken, hid, is, knew, know, no, obey, obeyed, passed, see, seek, so, will, would**

***if* not**

I will go down, and *if n.* *Gen* 18:21
and *if n.* tell me, that I. 24:49
if n. blot me, I pray, out. *Ex* 32:32
if n. let fire come. *Judg* 9:15, 20
and *if n.* I will take it. *1 Sam* 2:16
but *if n.* then we shall know. 6:9
if n. let Amnon go. *2 Sam* 13:26
if n.; speak thou. 17:6
but *if n.* it shall not be. *2 Ki* 2:10
if n. where, and who is he? *Job* 9:24
if n. hearken to me, hold. 33:33
and *if n.* forbear. *Zech* 11:12
if n. it shall turn to you. *Luke* 10:6
and *if n.* then thou shalt. 13:9

***or* not**

journey prosperous *or n.* *Gen* 24:31
is Lord among us, *or n.*? *Ex* 17:7
word come to pass *or n.* *Num* 11:23
be wood therein *or n.* 13:20
fathers did keep it, *or n.* *Judg* 2:22

notable

(*Worthy of notice; remarkable*)
the goat had a *n.* horn. *Dan* 8:5
for it came up four *n.* ones. 8
had then a *n.* prisoner. *Mat* 27:16
before that *n.* day of the. *Acts* 2:20
a *n.* miracle hath been done. 4:16

note, -d

write it, and *n.* it in a. *Isa* 30:8*
that is *n.* in scripture. *Dan* 10:21*
n. that man, and have. *2 Thes* 3:14

note

of *n.* among the apostles. *Rom* 16:7

nothing

now *n.* will be restrained. *Gen* 11:6
only unto these men do *n.* for. 19:8
as we have done to thee *n.* 26:29
here also have I done *n.* to. 40:15
n. die that is the children's. *Ex* 9:4
let *n.* of it remain until. 12:10
ye shall eat *n.* leavened in. 20
gathered much, had *n.* over. 16:18
2 Cor 8:15
if he have *n.* then he shall. *Ex* 23:3
there shall *n.* cast their young. 26
eat *n.* that is made of. *Num* 6:4
touch *n.* of theirs, lest ye be. 16:26
let *n.* hinder thee from. 22:16
lacked *n.* *Deut* 2:7; *Neh* 9:21
thou shalt save alive *n.* *Deu* 20:36
to the damsel thou shalt do *n.* 22:26
because he hath *n.* left him. 28:55
Joshua left *n.* undone. *Josh* 11:15
at the least such as before knew *n.* thereof. *Judg* 3:2
he rent him, and had *n.* in his. 14:6
Samuel told, and hid *n.* *1 Sam* 3:18
my father will do *n.* but will. 20:2
servant knew *n.* of all this. 22:15
n. was missed of all. 25:21; 30:19
she told him *n.* less or more. 36
poor man had *n.* save. *2 Sam* 12:3
that which doth cost me *n.* 24:24
victuals, they lacked *n.* *1 Ki* 4:27
there was *n.* in the ark save. 8:9
silver was *n.* accounted of in. 10:21
he answered *n.* 11:22; *Luke* 23:35
tell me *n.* but that which is true. *1 Ki* 22:16; *2 Chr* 18:15
fall *n.* to earth of word. *2 Ki* 10:10
n. in his house that he. 20:13
be carried into Babylon, *n.* shall be left. 17; *Isa* 39:2, 6
n. hid from Solomon. *2 Chr* 9:2
ye have *n.* to do with us. *Ezra* 4:3
they found *n.* to answer. *Neh* 5:8
we will restore, and require *n.* 12
for whom *n.* is prepared. 8:10
so that they lacked *n.* 9:21
Esther required *n.* but. *Esth* 2:15
yet all this availeth me *n.* 5:13
let *n.* fail of all that thou. 6:10
they go to *n.* and perish. *Job* 6:18
for ye are *n.* 21
of yesterday, and know *n.* 8:9
make my speech *n.* worth. 24:25
he hangeth the earth upon *n.* 26:7
it profiteth a man *n.* that he should delight himself with. 34:9
tried me and shalt find *n.* *Ps* 17:3
and mine age is as *n.* before. 39:5
he shall carry *n.* away. 49:17
who love thy law, and *n.* 119:165
simple, and knoweth *n.* *Pr* 9:13
of wickedness profit *n.* 10:2
desireth, and hath *n.* 13:4; 20:4
maketh himself rich, yet hath *n.* 13:7
if thou hast *n.* to pay, why? 22:27
whatsoever God doeth, *n.* *Eccl* 3:14
and he shall take *n.* of his. 5:15
so that he wanteth *n.* for his. 6:2
man should find *n.* after him. 7:14
all her princes shall be *n.* *Isa* 34:12
are as *n.* they are counted to him less than *n.* and vanity. 40:17; 41:29
the princes to *n.* 40:23; 41:11, 12
lest thou bring me to *n.* *Jer* 10:24
done *n.* of all that thou. 32:23
thee a thing, hide *n.* from me. 38:14
left of the poor which had *n.* 39:10
I will keep *n.* back from you. 42:4
destroy her utterly, let *n.* 50:26
is it *n.* to you, all ye? *Lam* 1:12
prophets that have seen *n.* *Ezek* 13:3
earth reputed as *n.* *Dan* 4:35
a wilderness, yea, and *n.* *Joel* 2:3
will a young lion cry out if he have taken *n.*? *Amos* 3:4
take up a snare, and have taken *n.* 5
surely the Lord will do *n.* 7

in comparison of it as n.? Hag 2:3
they have n. to eat. Mat 15:32
Mark 6:36; 8:1, 2
n. shall be impossible to you.
Mat 17:20; Luke 1:37
he found n. thereon but leaves.
Mat 21:19; Mark 11:13
answerest thou n.? Mat 26:62
he answered n. 27:12; Mark 14:60
61; 15:3, 4, 5
n. to do with that just. Mat 27:19
saw that he could prevail n. 24
see thou say n. to any. Mark 1:44
and had spent all, and was n. 5:26
take n. for their journey. 6:8
Luke 9:3
forth by n. but by prayer. Mark 9:29
those days he did eat n. Luke 4:2
toiled all night and taken n. 5:5
John 21:3
they had n. to pay, he. Luke 7:42
and n. shall by any means. 10:19
I have n. to set before him. 11:6
and lo, n. worthy of death. 23:15
Acts 23:29; 25:25; 26:31
man hath done n. amiss. Luke 23:41
man can receive n. except. John 3:27
Son can do n. of himself. 5:19, 30
gather, that n. be lost. 6:12
I should lose n. 39
quickeneth, the flesh profiteth n. 63
and they say n. unto him. 7:26
I do n. of myself. 8:28
he could do n. 9:33
ye know n. at all. 11:49
how ye prevail n.? behold. 12:19
this world hath n. in me. 14:30
for without me ye can do n. 15:5
that day ye shall ask me n. 16:23
have ye asked n. in my name. 24
in secret have I said .. 18:20
could say n. against it. Acts 4:14
finding n. how they might. 21
and go with them, doubting n. 10:20
11:12
be quiet, and do n. rashly. 19:36
I kept back n. that was. 20:20
that those things are n. 21:24
we will eat n. until we have. 23:14
fasting, having taken n. 27:33
to n. the understanding. 1 Cor 1:19
I know n. by myself. 4:4
judge n. before the time. 5
he knoweth n. yet as he ought. 8:2
for though I preach, I have n. 9:16
not charity, I am n. 13:2; 2 Cor 12:11
charity, it profiteth me n. 1 Cor 13:3
having n. yet possessing. 2 Cor 6:10
for we can do n. against. 13:8
in confidence added n. Gal 2:6
heir when a child, differeth n. 4:1
Christ shall profit you n. 5:2
n. be done through strife. Phil 2:3
every creature is good, n. 1 Tim 4:4
doing n. by partiality. 5:21
proud, knowing n. 6:4
brought n. and we can carry n. out. 7
n. be wanting unto them. Tit 3:13
thy mind would I do n. Philem 14
he left n. that is not put. Heb 2:8
Moses spake n. concerning. 7:14
for the law made n. perfect. 19
and entire, wanting n. Jas 1:4
let him ask in faith, n. wavering. 6
they went forth taking n. 3 John 7

for **nothing**

shall go out free for n. Ex 21:2
that is profitable for n. Isa 44:10
was profitable for n. Jer 13:7, 10
salt have lost his savour, it is good
for n. Mat 5:13
lend, hoping for n. again. Luke 6:35
be careful for n. but by prayer.
Phil 4:6

in **nothing**

their time in n. else. Acts 17:21
receive damage by us in n. 2 Cor 7:9
in n. am I behind chiefest, though I
be n. 12:11
in n. I shall be ashamed. Phil 1:20
and in n. terrified by your. 28

is **nothing**

there is n. at all beside. Num 11:6
is n. else save the sword. Judg 7:14
there is n. better than. 1 Sam 27:1
and said, There is n. 1 Ki 18:43
there is n. among my treasures.
2 Ki 20:15; Isa 39:4
it is n. with thee to help. 2 Chr 14:11
this is n. else but sorrow. Neh 2:2
said, There is n. done. Esth 6:3
there is n. hid from the. Ps 19:6
there is n. froward or. Pr 8:8
there is n. better for a man.
Eccl 2:24; 3:22
begetteth a son, and there is n. 5:14
there is n. too hard. Jer 32:17
is n. covered that shall. Mat 10:26
Mark 4:22; Luke 12:2
swear by temple, it is n. Mat 23:16
swear by the altar, it is n. 18
there is n. from without a man that
can defile. Mark 7:15
myself, my honour is n. John 8:54
that there is n. unclean. Rom 14:14
is n., uncircumcision is n. 1 Cor 7:19
we know that an idol is n. in. 8:4
when he is n. he deceiveth. Gal 6:3
are defiled is n. pure. Tit 1:15

of **nothing**

of n. your work nought. Isa 41:24
ye may have lack of n. 1 Thes 4:12
increased, and have need of n.
Rev 3:17

notwithstanding

n. they hearkened not to. Ex 16:20
1 Sam 2:25; 2 Ki 17:14
n. if he continue a day. Ex 21:21
n. ye would not go up. Deut 1:26
n. in thy days I will. 1 Ki 11:12
n. I have spoken unto. Jer 35:14
n. being warned of God. Mat 2:22
n. he that is least in kingdom. 11:11
n. lest we should offend. 17:27
n. be sure of this that. Luke 10:11
n. in this rejoice, that spirits. 20
n. whether in pretence or. Phil 1:18
n. have well done, that ye. 4:14
n. she shall be saved in. 1 Tim 2:15
n. Lord stood with me. 2 Tim 4:17
n. ye give not those things. Jas 2:16
n. I have a few things. Rev 2:20

nought, *see* **naught**

nourish

[1] *To feed or maintain*, Gen 47:12. [2] *To educate or bring up*, Acts 7:21. [3] *To instruct*, 1 Tim 4:6. [4] *To cherish and comfort*, Ruth 4:15; Jas 5:5.

will I n. thee. Gen 45:11; 50:21
that man shall n. young. Isa 7:21†
nor do I n. up young men, nor. 23:4
an ash, the rain doth n. it. 44:14

nourished

Joseph n. his father. Gen 47:12
he brought and n. up. 2 Sam 12:3
I have n. and brought up. Isa 1:2
she n. her whelps among. Ezek 19:2
n. in his father's house. Acts 7:20
Pharaoh's daughter n. him. 21
their country was n. by the. 12:20*
n. up in words of faith. 1 Tim 4:6
have n. your hearts as in. Jas 5:5
n. for a time, times. Rev 12:14

nourisher

he shall be n. of thy old. Ruth 4:15

nourisheth

n. his flesh, as the Lord. Eph 5:29

nourishing

so n. them three years. Dan 1:5

nourishment

joints and bands having n. Col 2:19*

novice

not a n. lest being lifted. 1 Tim 3:6

now

Adam said, This is n. Gen 2:23
I will go down n. and see. 18:21
n. will we deal worse with. 19:9
n. I know that thou fearest. 22:12
thou art n. the blessed of the. 26:29
what shall I do n. to thee? 27:37
n. will I praise the Lord. 29:35
Laban, and stayed there till n. 32:4
if it be so n. do this. Gen 43:11
so n. it was not you that sent. 45:8
about cattle from youth till n. 46:34
not such hail been in Egypt even till
n. Ex 9:18
go n. ye that are men, and. 10:11
yet n. if thou wilt forgive. 32:32
heal her n. O God, I. Num 12:13
this people from Egypt till n. 14:19
I shall see him, but not n. 24:17
Lord's host am I n. come. Josh 5:14
tell me n. what thou hast done. 7:19
are ye come to me n.? Judg 11:7
n. I know that the Lord will. 17:13
thou shalt give it me n. 1 Sam 2:16
but n. the Lord saith, Be it far. 30
honour me n. I pray thee. 15:30
what have I n. done? 17:29
son, let us not all n. go. 2 Sam 13:25
I n. also be thy servant. 15:34
let us n. fall into the hand. 24:14
cut off, but what? even n. 1 Ki 14:14
it is enough, n. O Lord, take. 19:4
he said, Why are ye n. turned back?
2 Ki 1:5
was her's since she went till n. 8:6
know n. there shall fall to. 10:10
am I n. come up without the Lord.
18:25; Isa 36:10
n. have I brought it to pass.
2 Ki 19:35; Isa 37:26
remember n. how I have walked.
2 Ki 20:3; Isa 38:3
it n. known to the king. Ezra 4:13
even till n. hath it been building. 5:16
n. for a little space grace been. 9:8
n. there is hope in Israel. 10:2
put forth thy hand n. Job 1:11; 2:5
n. it is come upon thee. 4:5
for n. ye are nothing, ye see. 6:21
lay down n. 17:3
where is n. my hope? 15
and if it be not so n. 24:25
n. I am their son. 30:9
heard of thee, but n. my eye. 42:5
n. will I arise, saith the. Ps 12:5
n. know I that the Lord saveth. 20:6
n. Lord, what wait I for, my. 39:7
why heathen say, Where is n.? 115:2
save n. I beseech thee, O. 118:25
but n. have I kept thy word. 119:67
do this n. my son, and. Pr 6:3
n. she is without, n. in the. 7:12
go to n. Eccl 2:1
that which n. is shall all be. 16
what hath been is n. 3:15
I will rise n. and go. S of S 3:2
n. go to, I will tell you. Isa 5:5
but n. the Lord hath spoken. 16:14
let them tell thee n. 19:12
what aileth thee n. that thou? 22:1
n. will I rise, n. will I lift up. 33:10
but n. O Lord, thou art our. 64:8
n. what hast thou to do? Jer 2:18
n. will I give sentence against. 4:12
the word of the Lord let it n. 17:15
turn n. every one from his. 25:5
ask ye n. and see whether a. 30:6
ye were n. turned, and had. 34:15
return ye n. every man from. 35:15
woe is me n.! for the Lord hath. 45:3
Daniel, to thee am I n. Dan 10:11
it better with me than n. Hos 2:7
and n. they sin more and more. 13:2
turn ye n. from your evil. Zech 1:4
n. have I seen with mine eyes. 9:8
prove me n. herewith. Mal 3:10
n. all this was done. Mat 1:22
days of John the Baptist, till n. 11:12
Sleep on n. 26:45
thinkest that I cannot n. pray. 53
let him n. come down from. 27:42
let him deliver him n. 43
so that the ship was n. Mark 4:37
n. lettest thy servant. Luke 2:29
which n. of these three was? 10:36
all things are n. ready. 14:17
but n. he that hath a purse. 22:36
draw out n. and bear. John 2:8
hast kept the good wine until n. 10
he whom thou n. hast is not. 4:18
hour cometh, and n. is. 23; 5:25
blind, how then doth he n. see? 9:19
what I do thou knowest not n. 13:7

ye cannot bear them *n.* *John* 16:12
ye *n.* therefore have sorrow. 22
lo, *n.* speakest thou plainly. 29
n. are we sure. 30
do ye *n.* believe? 31
I kept them, and *n.* come I. 17:13
this is *n.* the third time that. 21:14
shed forth this which ye *n.* *Acts* 2:33
n. when they heard this, were. 37
and *n.* Lord, behold their. 4:29
n. I know of a surety, the Lord. 12:11
n. as soon as it was day. 18
n. why tarriest thou? arise. 22:16
the Gentiles, to whom *n.* I. 26:17
but *n.* being made free. *Rom* 6:22
n. then it is no more I that do it. 7:17
n. it is high time to awake. 13:11
n. ye are full, *n.* ye are. *1 Cor* 4:8
n. are they holy. 7:14
n. I know in part. 13:12
for I will not see you *n.* by. 16:7
said before, so say I *n.* *Gal* 1:9
do I *n.* persuade men or God? 10
I *n.* live in the flesh, I live. 2:20
n. made perfect by the flesh? 3:3
desire to be present with you *n.* 4:20
but as then, even so it is *n.* 29
n. to principalities. *Eph* 3:10
were darkness, but *n.* are ye. 5:8
from the first day until *n.* *Phil* 1:5
obeyed, but *n.* much more. 2:12
but *n.* ye also put off. *Col* 3:8
n. we live, if ye stand. *1 Thes* 3:8
promise of the life that *n.* *1 Tim* 4:8
for I am *n.* ready to be. *2 Tim* 4:6
not *n.* as a servant, but. *Philem* 16
n. we see not yet all things. *Heb* 2:8
go to *n.* ye that say, to-day. *Jas* 4:13
go to *n.*, ye rich men, weep and. 5:1
though *n.* ye see him not. *1 Pet* 1:8
but are *n.* the people of God. 2:10
because the true light *n.* *1 John* 2:8
n. are we the sons of God, it. 3:2
and even *n.* already is it in the. 4:3

now *therefore*

n. therefore restore the. *Gen* 20:7
n. therefore my husband. 29:32
n. therefore and let us slay. 37:20
n. therefore fear Lord. *Josh* 24:14
n. therefore behold king ye have. *1 Sam* 12:13
n. therefore stand and see this. 16
shall I not *therefore n.* require? *2 Sam* 4:11
n. therefore let my life. *2 Ki* 1:14
n. therefore advise thyself, what word I shall bring. *1 Chr* 21:12
send me *n. therefore* a man cunning to work in gold. *2 Chr* 2:7
n. therefore, O God. *Neh* 6:9
n. therefore be content. *Job* 6:28
be wise *n. therefore*, O ye kings. *Ps* 2:10
n. therefore be not mockers. *Isa* 28:22
n. therefore what have I here? 52:5
n. therefore amend your. *Jer* 26:13
n. therefore why hast thou not reproved Jeremiah? 29:27
n. therefore know certainly. 42:22
n. therefore, O our God. *Dan* 9:17
therefore also *n.* saith the Lord. *Joel* 2:12
therefore n. shall they go captive. *Amos* 6:7
n. therefore hear thou word. 7:16
n. therefore are we all present. *Acts* 10:33
n. therefore why tempt ye? 15:10
n. therefore depart, and go. 16:36
n. therefore there is a fault. *1 Cor* 6:7
n. therefore perform. *2 Cor* 8:11
n. therefore ye are no more. *Eph* 2:19

number, *substantive*

I being few in *n.* they. *Gen* 34:30
for it was without *n.* 41:49
lamb according to *n.* *Ex* 12:4
gather manna, according to *n.* 16:16
nothing barren, *n.* of thy days. 23:26
n. of years after the jubile, the *n.* of years of the. *Lev* 25:15, 16, 50
shall make you few in *n.* *Lev* 26:22
n. of their names. *Num* 1:2, 18, 22
n. of males from. 3:22, 28, 34, 40, 43
odd *n.* of them is to be redeemed. 48
your whole *n.* from twenty. 14:29
after the *n.* of days ye searched. 34
n. ye shall prepare . . . to every one according to their *n.* 15:12
who can count the *n.* of fourth? 23:10
offerings shall be according to their *n.* 29:18; 21:24, 27, 30, 33, 37
of their portion was in *n.* 31:36
left few in number among heathen. *Deut* 4:27; 28:62
ye were more in *n.* than. 7:7
him to be beaten by a certain *n.* 25:2
according to the *n.* of Israel. 32:8
every man of you a stone, according to *n.* *Josh* 4:5, 8
they and their camels without *n.* *Judg* 6:5; 7:12
the *n.* of them that lapped. 7:6
to the *n.* of them that danced. 21:23
the *n.* of the lords of the. *1 Sam* 6:4
to the *n.* of all the cities. 18
went over by *n.* twelve. *2 Sam* 2:15
and toes twenty-four in *n.* 21:20
may know the *n.* of the people. 24:2*
Joab gave up the sum of the *n.* 9
12 stones according to *n.* *1 Ki* 18:31
n. was in the days of. *1 Chr* 7:2
the *n.* of them after their. 9*, 40
the *n.* of mighty men whom. 11:11
and silver, there is no *n.* 22:16
their *n.* by their polls, man. 23:3
set feasts by *n.* 31
n. of the workmen. 25:1
the *n.* that were instructed in. 7
but David took not the *n.* of. 27:23
people were without *n.* *2 Chr* 12:3
the whole *n.* of the chief of. 26:12
n. of the burnt offerings. 29:32
a great *n.* of priests sanctified. 30:24
is the *n.* of the vessels. *Ezra* 1:9
the *n.* of the men of the people. 2:2
daily burnt offerings by *n* 3:4
according to the *n.* of tribes. 6:17
by *n.* and by weight of. 8:34
the *n.* of those slain in Shushan. *Esth* 9:11
offered according to the *n.* *Job* 1:5
let it not come into the *n.* 3:6
things without *n.* 5:9; 9:10
n. of his months are with thee. 14:5
the *n.* of years is hidden to. 15:20
is there any *n.* of his armies? 25:3
declare to him the *n.* of my. 31:37
pieces mighty men without *n.* 34:24*
neither can the *n.* of his years. 36:26
n. of thy days is great. 38:21
were but a few men in *n.* *Ps* 105:12
caterpillars, and that without *n.* 34
are more in *n.* than the sand. 139:18
he telleth the *n.* of the stars. 147:4
queens and virgins without *n.* *S of S* 6:8
residue of *n.* of archers. *Isa* 21:17
bringeth out their host by *n.* 40:26
furnish the drink offering to that *n.* 65:11*
n. of thy cities are thy gods. *Jer* 2:28
forgotten me days without *n.* 32
n. of thy cities, *n.* of streets. 11:13
a small *n.* that escape sword. 44:28
the *n.* of the days. *Ezek* 4:4; 5:9
thou shalt take a few in *n.* and. 5:3
understood by books the *n.* *Dan* 9:2
n. of Israel shall be as the sand. *Hos* 1:10; *Rom* 9:27
up strong and without *n.* *Joel* 1:6
is a great *n.* of carcases. *Nah* 3:3*
Judas, being of the *n.* of. *Luke* 22:3
the men sat down, in *n.* 5000. *John* 6:10; *Acts* 4:4
the *n.* of the names. *Acts* 1:15*
to Theudas a *n.* of men. 5:36
when the *n.* of disciples. 6:1, 7
a great *n.* believed and. 11:21
were increased in *n.* daily. 16:5
dare not make ourselves of the *n.* *2 Cor* 10:12
not a widow be taken into the *n.* *1 Tim* 5:9*
n. of them was 10,000. *Rev* 5:11
I heard the *n.* of them which. *Rev* 7:4
the *n.* of the army of the. 9:16
n. of his name. 13:17
count the *n.* of the beast; for it is the *n.* of a man; and his *n.* is 666. 18
had victory over *n.* of beast. 15:2
n. of Gog is as the sand of. 20:8

number, *verb*

if a man can *n.* the dust. *Gen* 13:16
if thou be able to *n.* them. 15:5
he shall *n.* seven days for. *Lev* 15:13
shall *n.* to herself seven days. 28
seventh sabbath shall ye *n.* 23:16
thou shalt *n.* seven sabbaths. 25:8
Aaron shall *n.* them by. *Num* 1:3
only thou shalt not *n.* the tribe. 49
n. the children of Levi. 3:15
n. all the firstborn of the males. 40
till 50 years old *n.* them. 4:23, 30
of Merari thou shalt *n.* them. 29
Moses and Aaron did *n.* 37, 41
shalt thou *n.* begin to *n.* *Deut* 16:9
n. and see who is gone. *1 Sam* 14:17
to say, Go *n.* Israel. *2 Sam* 24:1
go now and *n.* the people. 2, 4 *1 Chr* 21:2
n. thee an army like. *1 Ki* 20:25
David to *n.* Israel. *1 Chr* 21:1
Joab began to *n.* but he. 27:24
who can *n.* the clouds? *Job* 38:37
canst thou *n.* the months? 39:2
So teach us to *n.* our days. *Ps* 90:12
therefore will I *n.* you. *Isa* 65:12*
which no man could *n.* *Rev* 7:9

numbered

thy seed also be *n.* *Gen* 13:16
it shall not be *n.* for. 16:10; 32:12
them that are *n.* *Ex* 30:13, 14
n. of the congregation. 38:25, 26
n. them in the wilderness. *Num* 1:19
those that were *n.* 21, 23, 44, 46; 2:4 13, 15, 19, 21, 23, 26, 28, 30
the Levites were not *n.* 1:47; 2:33
all that were *n.* in the camp. 2:9
were *n.* in camp of Reuben. 16
n. of Ephraim. 24
n. in camp of Dan. 31
Moses *n.* them. 3:16, 42
n. of the Levites were 22,000. 3:39
they *n.* of the sons of the. 4:34, 37
n. of the Gershonites. 38, 41
n. of the sons of Merari. 42, 45
these whom Moses and Aaron *n.* 45
and over them that were *n.* 7:2
in wilderness, all that were *n.* 14:29
these were *n.* of the children. 26:51
n. of the Levites. 57
Moses and Eleazar *n.* 63
Joshua rose early and *n.* *Josh* 8:10*
of Benjamin were *n.* *Judg* 20:15
he *n.* them in Bezek. *1 Sam* 11:8
Saul *n.* people in Telaim. 15:4
David *n.* the people. *2 Sam* 18:1
smote him after he had *n.* 24:10
people that cannot be *n.* *1 Ki* 3:8
sheep and oxen that could not be *n.* 8:5; *2 Chr* 5:6
then he *n.* the princes. *1 Ki* 20:15*
Ben-haded *n.* the Syrians. 26*
Israel were *n.* and were like. 27
and king Jehoram *n.* all. *2 Ki* 3:6
the people to be *n.* *1 Chr* 21:17
were *n.* from thirty years. 23:3, 27
Solomon *n.* all the. *2 Chr* 2:17
n. them from twenty years old. 25:5
Cyrus *n.* the vessels. *Ezra* 1:8
more than can be *n.* *Ps* 40:5
is wanting cannot be *n.* *Eccl* 1:15
ye have *n.* the houses of. *Isa* 22:10
he was *n.* with the transgressors; and he bare. 53:12; *Mark* 15:28
as the host of heaven cannot be *n.* *Jer* 33:22
God hath *n.* thy kingdom. *Dan* 5:26
sand, which cannot be *n.* *Hos* 1:10
hairs of your head are all *n.* *Mat* 10:30; *Luke* 12:7
for he was *n.* with us. *Acts* 1:17
Matthias was *n.* with the eleven. 26

numberest

when thou *n.* that there be no plague when thou *n.* *Ex* 30:12
for now thou *n.* my steps. *Job* 14:16

numbering
corn until he left *n.* *Gen* 41:49
after the *n.* wherewith. *2 Chr* 2:17

numbers
these are the *n.* of the. *1 Chr* 12:23
are the *n.* of them. *2 Chr* 17:14
for I know not the *n.* *Ps* 71:15

Nun, *see* **Joshua**

nurse, *substantive*
Rebekah and her *n.* *Gen* 24:59
but Deborah, Rebekah's *n.* 35:8
call to thee a *n.* of Hebrew ? *Ex* 2:7
the child, and became *n.* *Ruth* 4:16
n. took him up and fled. *2 Sam* 4:4
they hid him and his *n.* *2 Ki* 11:2
2 Chr 22:11
were gentle, as a *n.* *1 Thes* 2:7

nurse
she may *n.* the child. *Ex* 2:7
child away, and *n.* it for me. 9

nursed
took the child, and *n.* it. *Ex* 2:9
thy daughters shall be *n.* *Isa* 60:4*

nursing
carry them in thy bosom, as a *n.*
Num 11:12
kings shall be thy *n.* fathers, queens thy *n.* mothers. *Isa* 49:23

nurture
bring them up in the *n.* of. *Eph* 6:4*

nuts
carry down a present, *n.* *Gen* 43:11
into the garden of *n.* *S of S* 6:11

Nymphas
salute *N.* and the church. *Col* 4:15

O

oak
hid the gods under the *o.* *Gen* 35:4
Deborah was buried under an *o.* 8
up there under an *o.* *Josh* 24:26
angel of the Lord sat under an *o.*
Judg 6:11
mule went under an *o.* *2 Sam* 18:9
Absalom hanged in an *o.* 10
alive in the *o.* 14
man of God under an *o.* *1 Ki* 13:14
their bones under *o.* in. *1 Chr* 10:12
as an *o.* whose leaf fadeth. *Isa* 1:30
teil tree, or *o.* whose substance. 6:13
he taketh the cypress and *o.* 44:14
idols under every thick *o.* *Ezek* 6:13

oaks
be ashamed of the *o.* *Isa* 1:29
day of the Lord on all the *o.* 2:13
of *o.* of Bashan have they. *Ezek* 27:6
burn incense upon the hills under *o.*
Hos 4:13
was strong as the *o.* *Amos* 2:9
fir tree, howl, O ye *o.* *Zech* 11:2

oar
all that handle the *o.* *Ezek* 27:29

oars
shall go no galley with *o.* *Isa* 33:21
Bashan they made thy *o.* *Ezek* 27:6

oath
(A solemn appeal to God to witness the truth of a declaration. It is also used of a solemn affirmation not invoking the Deity. The modern use of the word for profanity is not found in the Bible)

Oaths were forbidden to be taken by the Israelites. [1] *Idolatrously, in the name of any false gods, or in the name of inanimate things,* Josh 23:7; Jas 5:12. [2] *Deceitfully,* Jer 42:5, 20. [3] *Falsely,* Lev 6:3; 19:12. [4] *Rashly,* Lev 5:4; Mat 14:7.

clear from this my *o.* *Gen* 24:8, 41
o. which I sware to Abraham. 26:3
Deut 7:8; *Ps* 105:9; *Jer* 11:5
let there be now an *o.* betwixt us.
Gen 26:28
Joseph took an *o.* of children. 50:25
o. of the Lord shall be. *Ex* 22:11
shall pronounce with an *o.* *Lev* 5:4
shall charge her by an *o.* *Num* 5:19*
Lord make thee a curse and an *o.* 21
an *o.* to bind his soul. 30:2, 10
every binding *o.* to afflict soul. 13
his *o.* which the Lord maketh with.
Deut 29:12
you only do I make this *o.* 14
blameless of this thine *o.* *Josh* 2:17
be on us, because of the *o.* 9:20
Israel had made a great *o.* *Judg* 21:5
people feared the *o.* *1 Sam* 14:26
charged them with the *o.* 27, 28
king spared Mephibosheth, because of *o.* *2 Sam* 21:7
hast thou not kept the *o.*? *1 Ki* 2:43
o. be laid on him, and the *o.* come.
8:31; *2 Chr* 6:22
he took an *o.* of the. *1 Ki* 18:10
Jehoiada took an *o.* of. *2 Ki* 11:4
be mindful of his *o.* to. *1 Chr* 16:16
Judah rejoiced at the *o.* *2 Chr* 15:15
Nehemiah took an *o.* of. *Neh* 5:12
they entered into an *o.* to walk. 10:29
in regard of the *o.* of God. *Eccl* 8:2
as he that feareth an *o.* 9:2
which hast despised the *o.*
Ezek 16:59; 17:18, 19
hath taken an *o.* of him. 17:13
that made him king, whose *o.* 16
us, and *o.* written in law. *Dan* 9:11
love no false *o.* for this. *Zech* 8:17
he promised with an *o.* *Mat* 14:7
for the *o.*'s sake. 9; *Mark* 6:26
he denied with an *o.* *Mat* 26:72
the *o.* which he sware. *Luke* 1:73
sworn with an *o.* to him. *Acts* 2:30
bound themselves with an *o.* 23:21*
an *o.* for confirmation is. *Heb* 6:16
God confirmed it by an *o.* 17
an *o.* he was made priest. 7:20, 21
the *o.* which was since the law. 28
the earth, nor any other *o.* *Jas* 5:12

oaths
them that have sworn *o.* *Ezek* 21:23
naked, according to the *o.* *Hab* 3:9
to the Lord thine *o.* *Mat* 5:33

Obadiah
Ahab called *O.*, now *O.* *1 Ki* 18:3
O. took an hundred prophets. 4
as *O.* was in the way, behold. 7
so *O.* went to meet Ahab, and. 16
sons of *O.* *1 Chr* 3:21
son of Izrahiah, *O.* 7:3
O. son of Azel. 8:38; 9:44
O. the son of Shemaiah, the. 9:16
of Gadites men of might, *O.* 12:9
Ishmaiah son of *O.* 27:19
to his princes, to *O.* to. *2 Chr* 17:7
Jahath and *O.* the Levites. 34:12
O. son of Jehiel went up. *Ezra* 8:9
O. sealed. *Neh* 10:5
O. was a porter. 12:25
the vision of *O.* Thus saith. *Ob* 1

Obed
called his name *O.* *Ruth* 4:17
Boaz begat *O.* 21; *1 Chr* 2:12
Mat 1:5
Ephlal begat *O.* *1 Chr* 2:37
O. one of David's valiant. 11:47
Shemaiah begat *O.* 26:7
took Azariah son of *O.* *2 Chr* 23:1
which was the son of *O.* *Luke* 3:32

Obed-edom
the ark into the house of *O.*
2 Sam 6:10, 11; *1 Chr* 13:13, 14
Lord blessed the house of *O.*
2 Sam 6:11, 12; *1 Chr* 13:14
ark from house of *O.* into city of.
2 Sam 6:12; *1 Chr* 15:25
O. a porter. *1 Chr* 15:18, 24
O. with harp. 21
O.; and Jeiel with psalteries. 16:5
O. with their brethren, *O.* also. 38
sons of *O.* 26:4, 8
sons of *O.* fit for service. 8
the lot southward fell to *O.* 15
vessels found with *O.* *2 Chr* 25:24

obedience
(Subjection to the authority of another, whether to God or to a human being. In the Bible the word is used most often in the sense of subjection to the will of God, and to his commands. It is used in speaking of Jesus, who always did the will of God.

It is also used of hearts and inanimate things, which are subject to God's controlling power)

for *o.* to the faith among. *Rom* 1:5
by the *o.* of one shall many. 5:19
of sin to death, or of *o.* unto. 6:16
your *o.* is come abroad unto. 16:19
known to all nations for the *o.* 26
women are commanded to be under *o.* *1 Cor* 14:34*
he remembereth the *o.* *2 Cor* 7:15
bringing every thought to the *o.* 10:5
all disobedience, when your *o.* 6
confidence in thy *o.* *Philem* 21
learned he *o.* by the things. *Heb* 5:8
through sanctification of the Spirit to *o.* *1 Pet* 1:2

obedient
we will do, and be *o.* *Ex* 24:7
that Israel may be *o.* *Num* 27:20
shall be *o.* to his voice. *Deut* 4:30
because ye would not be *o.* 8:20*
strangers shall be *o.* *2 Sam* 22:45
reprover upon an *o.* ear. *Pr* 25:12
if *o.* ye shall eat the good. *Isa* 1:19
nor were they *o.* to his law. 42:24
priests were *o.* to the faith. *Acts* 6:7
to make Gentiles *o.* *Rom* 15:18*
know whether ye be *o.* *2 Cor* 2:9
servants, be *o.* to your masters.
Eph 6:5; *Tit* 2:9*
Christ became *o.* unto. *Phil* 2:8
wives, be *o.* *Tit* 2:5*
children, be *o.* *1 Pet* 1:14

obeisance
(A bodily movement in token of respect and submission)
your sheaves made *o.* *Gen* 37:7
eleven stars made *o.* to me. 9
bowed and made *o.* to Joseph. 43:28
Moses did *o.* to his. *Ex* 18:7
fell down and did *o.* to. *2 Sam* 1:2
the woman of Tekoah did *o.* 14:4
man came nigh to do him *o.* 15:5
Bath-sheba did *o.* to king. *1 Ki* 1:16
the princes of Judah made *o.* to the king. *2 Chr* 24:17

obey
(Revisions frequently substitute for this the word hearken*)*
therefore, my son, *o.* my voice.
Gen 27:8, 13, 43
Lord, that I should *o.* him ? *Ex* 5:2
now if ye will *o.* my voice. 19:5
o. his voice. 23:21
if thou shalt indeed *o.* his voice. 22
ye *o.* commands of Lord. *Deut* 11:27
o. his voice. 13:4; 27:10; 30:2, 8
1 Sam 12:14
thou mayest *o.* his voice. 30:20
Lord's voice will we *o.* *Josh* 24:24
to *o.* voice of Samuel. *1 Sam* 8:19
to *o.* is better than sacrifice. 15:22
and refused to *o.* neither. *Neh* 9:17
if they *o.* and serve him. *Job* 36:11
hear, they shall *o.* me. *Ps* 18:44
eye that despiseth to *o.* *Pr* 30:17
of Ammon shall *o.* them. *Isa* 11:14
o. my voice, and I will be your God.
Jer 7:23; 11:4, 7
o. the voice of the Lord your God.
26:13; 38:20; *Zech* 6:15
Rechabites *o.* their. *Jer* 35:14
o. the voice of Lord our God . . . well with us when we *o.* the. 42:6
dominions shall serve and *o.* him.
Dan 7:27
is this, that even winds and sea *o.*?
Mat 8:27; *Mark* 4:41; *Luke* 8:25
the unclean spirits *o.* *Mark* 1:27
plucked up, and it shall *o.* *Luke* 17:6
ought to *o.* God rather. *Acts* 5:29
hath given to them that *o.* him. 32
that *o.* unrighteousness. *Rom* 2:8
that ye should *o.* it in the. 6:12
yourselves servants to *o.*, his servants ye are to whom ye *o.* 16

children, *o.* your parents. *Eph* 6:1
Col 3:20
servants, *o.* in all things. *Col* 3:22
put them in mind to *o.* *Tit* 3:1
salvation to all that *o.* him. *Heb* 5:9
o. them that have the rule. 13:17
bits in horses' mouths, that they may *o.* *Jas* 3:3

not obey, obey not

if ye will *not o.* the commandments. *Deut* 11:28; 28:62; *1 Sam* 12:15
Job 36:12; *Jer* 12:17; 18:10
will *not o.* the voice. *Deut* 21:18, 20
didst thou *not o.*? *1 Sam* 15:19
will *not o.* the Lord. *Jer* 42:13
might *not o.* thy voice. *Dan* 9:11
our fathers would *not o.* *Acts* 7:39
and do *not o.* the truth. *Rom* 2:8
who hath bewitched you, that ye should *not o.*? *Gal* 3:1; 5:7
vengeance on them that *o. not* the gospel. *2 Thes* 1:8
if any man *o. not* our word. 3:14
if any *o. not* the word. *1 Pet* 3:1
be of them that *o. not* gospel ? 4:17

obeyed

all nations be blessed, because thou hast *o.* *Gen* 22:18; 26:5
that Jacob *o.* his father. 28:7
have *o.* my voice in all. *Josh* 22:2
Saul said, I have *o.* *1 Sam* 15:20
I feared the people, and *o.* 24
handmaid hath *o.* thy voice. 28:21
all Israel *o.* Solomon. *1 Chr* 29:23
they *o.* the words of. *2 Chr* 11:4
then they *o.* and let. *Jer* 34:10
thus have we *o.* the voice. 35:8, 10
because ye *o.* the commandment. 18
neither have we *o.* voice. *Dan* 9:10
the people *o.* the voice. *Hag* 1:12
many as *o.* Theudas. *Acts* 5:36, 37
have *o.* from heart that. *Rom* 6:17
ye have *o.*, not as in my presence only. *Phil* 2:12
by faith Abraham *o.* *Heb* 11:8
Sarah *o.* Abraham. *1 Pet* 3:6

not obeyed

because they *o. not.* *Josh* 5:6
but ye have *not o.* my voice. *Judg* 2:2; 6:10
thou hast *not o.* the voice. *1 Ki* 20:36
because they *o. not* the. *2 Ki* 18:12
not o. the voice of my teachers. *Pr* 5:13
ye have *not o.* my voice. *Jer* 3:13
25; 42:21; 43:4, 7; 44:23
have *not o.* my voice. 9:13; 11:8
17:23; 32:23; 40:3; *Dan* 9:10, 14
she *o. not* the voice. *Zeph* 3:2
not all *o.* the gospel. *Rom* 10:16

obeyedst

because thou *o.* not the voice of. *1 Sam* 28:18
that thou *o.* not my voice. *Jer* 22:21

obeyeth

who that *o.* the voice ? *Isa* 50:10
this is a nation that *o.* *Jer* 7:28
cursed be the man that *o.* not. 11:3

obeying

their fathers *o.*, but they. *Judg* 2:17
in sacrifice, as in *o.* *1 Sam* 15:22
your souls in *o.* the truth. *1 Pet* 1:22

object

and *o.* if they had aught. *Acts* 24:19

oblation

(*An offering. From the Latin* oblatus, *offered*)
an *o.* of a meat offering baken. *Lev* 2:4, 5, 7, 13
as for *o.* of the firstfruits. 2:12
if his *o.* be a sacrifice of. 3:1
offer one out of the whole *o.* 7:14
he shall bring his *o.* to the Lord. 29
that will offer his *o.* for all. 22:18
every *o.* of theirs shall. *Num* 18:9
we have brought an *o.* for. 31:50
Egyptians shall do *o.* *Isa* 19:21
impoverished that he hath no *o.* 40:20
offereth an *o.* as if he offered. 66:3
they offer an *o.* I will. *Jer* 14:12†
o. shall be the priest's. *Ezek* 44:30
divide the land, offer an *o.* *Ezek* 45:1
this is the *o.* ye shall offer. 13; 48:9
20, 21
give this *o.* for the prince in. 45:16
they should offer an *o.* to. *Dan* 2:46
time of the evening *o.* 9:21
shall cause *o.* to cease. 27

oblations

Israel to offer their *o.* *Lev* 7:38
to distribute the *o.* of. *2 Chr* 31:14
bring no more vain *o.* unto. *Isa* 1:13
require the firstfruits of your *o.* *Ezek* 20:40
every sort of your *o.* shall be. 44:30

obscure

lamp shall be put out in *o.* darkness. *Pr* 20:20*

obscurity

blind shall see out of *o.* *Isa* 29:18
then shall thy light rise in *o.* 58:10*
we wait for light, but behold *o.* 59:9*

observation

God cometh not with *o.* *Luke* 17:20

observe

(*Frequently means to keep, or to celebrate, and is so rendered in the Revisions*)
ye shall *o.* the feast of unleavened. *Ex* 12:17, 24; *Deut* 16:1
o. the sabbath. *Ex* 31:16
o. thou that which I command thee. 34:11; *Deut* 12:28; 24:8
o. feast of weeks. *Ex* 34:22
nor shall ye use enchantments, *o.* times. *Lev* 19:26
ye shall *o.* all my statutes. 37
2 Chr 7:17; *Neh* 1:5; *Ps* 105:45
Ezek 37:24
sacrifice shall ye *o.* *Num* 28:2
o. the feast of tabernacles seven days. *Deut* 16:13
men did diligently *o.* *1 Ki* 20:33
whoso is wise, and will *o.* *Ps* 107:43
o. it with my whole heart. 119:34
and let thine eyes *o.* *Pr* 23:26*
crane and swallow *o.* time. *Jer* 8:7
neither *o.* their judgements nor. *Ezek* 20:18
as a leopard by the way will I *o.* them. *Hos* 13:7
that *o.* lying vanities, *Jonah* 2:8
teaching them to *o.* all. *Mat* 28:20
customs not lawful to *o.* *Acts* 16:21
Gentiles *o.* no such thing. 21:25
ye *o.* days, and months. *Gal* 4:10
then *o.* these things. *1 Tim* 5:21
see **do**

observed

father *o.* the saying. *Gen* 37:11*
it is a night to be much *o.* *Ex* 12:42
not *o.* commandments. *Num* 15:22
Levi *o.* thy word, kept. *Deut* 33:9
when Joab *o.* city, he. *2 Sam* 11:16
Manasseh *o.* times. *2 Ki* 21:6
2 Chr 33:6
I heard him, and *o.* him. *Hos* 14:8
feared John and *o.* him. *Mark* 6:20*
have I *o.* from my youth. 10:20

observer

not be found an *o.* of times. *Deut* 18:10*

observers

nations hearkened to *o.* of times. *Deut* 18:14*

observest

things, but thou *o.* not. *Isa* 42:20

observeth

he that *o.* the wind shall. *Eccl* 11:4

obstinate

God made his heart *o.* *Deut* 2:30
I knew that thou art *o.* *Isa* 48:4

obtain

I may *o.* children by. *Gen* 16:2
and shall *o.* favour of. *Pr* 8:35
they shall *o.* joy and gladness. *Isa* 35:10; 51:11
he shall *o.* the kingdom. *Dan* 11:21
accounted worthy to *o.* *Luke* 20:35*
they may *o.* mercy. *Rom* 11:31
so run that ye may *o.* *1 Cor* 9:24*
they do it to *o.* a corruptible. 25*
but to *o.* salvation by. *1 Thes* 5:9
may *o.* salvation which. *2 Tim* 2:10
that we may *o.* mercy. *Heb* 4:16*
that they might *o.* a better. 11:35
desire to have, and cannot *o.* *Jas* 4:2

obtained

after certain days I *o.* *Neh* 13:6*
Esther *o.* kindness. *Esth* 2:9
she *o.* grace. 17
her that had not *o.* mercy. *Hos* 2:23
o. part of this ministry. *Acts* 1:17*
with a great sum *o.* I this. 22:28
o. help of God I continue. 26:22
supposing that they had *o.* 27:13
Israel hath not *o.* that which he seeketh for . . . hath *o.* it. *Rom* 11:7
ye have now *o.* mercy through. 30
one that hath *o.* mercy. *1 Cor* 7:25
have *o.* an inheritance. *Eph* 1:11*
o. mercy, because I did it ignorantly. *1 Tim* 1:13, 16
o. a more excellent name. *Heb* 1:4
he had patiently endured, he *o.* 6:15
o. a more excellent ministry. 8:6
having *o.* eternal redemption. 9:12
elders *o.* a good report. 11:2*, 39*
Abel *o.* witness that he was. 4*
who *o.* promises, stopped. 11:33
not *o.* mercy, but now have *o.* *1 Pet* 2:10
have *o.* like precious. *2 Pet* 1:1
see **favour**

obtaining

to *o.* of the glory of. *2 Thes* 2:14

occasion

may seek *o.* against us. *Gen* 43:18
mayest do as thou shalt find *o.* *Judg* 9:33; *1 Sam* 10:7
Samson sought *o.* against. 14:4
great *o.* to enemies. *2 Sam* 12:14
which thou shalt have *o.* *Ezra* 7:20
o. who can turn her away ? *Jer* 2:24
not have *o.* any more. *Ezek* 18:3
sought to find *o.* and could find none *o.* *Dan* 6:4, 5
sin taking *o.* by the. *Rom* 7:8, 11
put not an *o.* to fall in his. 14:13
we give you *o.* to glory. *2 Cor* 5:12
by *o.* of the frowardness of. 8:8*
cut off *o.* from them which desire *o.* 11:12
use not liberty for an *o.* *Gal* 5:13
younger give none *o.* to. *1 Tim* 5:14
o. of stumbling in him. *1 John* 2:10

occasioned

I have *o.* the death of. *1 Sam* 22:22

occasions

and give *o.* of speech against her. *Deut* 22:14*, 17*
findeth *o.* against me. *Job* 33:10

occupation

shall say, What is your *o.*? *Gen* 46:33; 47:3; *Jonah* 1:8
for by *o.* they were tentmakers. *Acts* 18:3*
with the workmen of like *o.* 19:25

occupied

the gold that was *o.* *Ex* 38:24*
ropes that never were *o.* *Judg* 16:11*
Syria *o.* *Ezek* 27:16*
Dan and Javan *o.* 19*
Arabia *o.* 21*
Sheba *o.* in thy fairs. 22*
profited them that have *o.* *Heb* 13:9

occupiers

o. of thy merchandise. *Ezek* 27:27†

occupieth

he that *o.* the room of. *1 Cor* 14:16*

occupy

with mariners to *o.* thy. *Ezek* 27:9†
servants, *o.* till I come. *Luke* 19:13*

occurrent

adversary nor evil *o.* *1 Ki* 5:4

Ocran, *see* **Pagiel**

odd

the *o.* number is to be. *Num* 3:48

Oded

came on Azariah son of *O.* *2 Chr* 15:1
prophet of the Lord, called *O.* 28:9

odious
made themselves *o*. *1 Chr* 19:6
for an *o*. woman when. *Pr* 30:23

odour
house was filled with *o*. *John* 12:3
an *o*. of a sweet smell. *Phil* 4:18

odours
savour of your sweet *o*. *Lev* 26:31
in a bed of sweet *o*. *2 Chr* 16:14
oil of myrrh and sweet *o*. *Esth* 2:12
so shall they burn *o*. for thee. *Jer* 34:5*
offer sweet *o*. to Daniel. *Dan* 2:46
golden vials full of *o*. *Rev* 5:8
no man buyeth their *o*. 18:13

offence
[1] *Any thing that a man finds in his way, that may occasion him to stumble or fall, whether physically or morally. The Revisions often translate it* stumblingblock, *or* occasion of stumbling. [2] *A sin, or trespass.*
o. of heart to my lord. *1 Sam* 25:31
but a rock of *o*. to both. *Isa* 8:14
till they acknowledge their *o*. *Hos* 5:15
Satan, thou art *o*. to me. *Mat* 16:23
man by whom the *o*. cometh. 18:7
a conscience void of *o*. *Acts* 24:16
o. so also is the free gift, for if through the *o*. of. *Rom* 5:15, 18
by one man's *o*. death reigned. 17
the law entered that the *o*. 20
stumbling stone, and rock of *o*. 9:33
that man who eateth with *o*. 14:20
give none *o*. in any thing. *1 Cor* 10:32; *2 Cor* 6:3
an *o*. in abasing myself? *2 Cor* 11:7
then is the *o*. of the cross. *Gal* 5:11
may be without *o*. till. *Phil* 1:10
a rock of *o*. to them. *1 Pet* 2:8

offences
yielding pacifieth great *o*. *Eccl* 10:4
because of *o*., for it must needs be that *o*. *Mat* 18:7; *Luke* 17:1
was delivered for our *o*. *Rom* 4:25
of many *o*. unto justification. 5:16
mark them which cause *o*. 16:17

offend
[1] *To commit any sin in thought, word, or deed,* Jas 3:2. [2] *To displease, thus the Pharisees were offended at Christ,* Mat 15:12. [3] *To be scandalized, or made to stumble by the example of another,* 1 Cor 8:13.
I will not *o*. any more. *Job* 34:31
I should *o*. against generation of. *Ps* 73:15
law, nothing shall *o*. them. 119:165
all that devour him shall *o*. *Jer* 2:3
adversaries said, We *o*. not. 50:7
harlot, let not Judah *o*. *Hos* 4:15
pass over and *o*. *Hab* 1:11
if thy right eye *o*. thee. *Mat* 5:29
if thy right hand *o*. thee. 30; 18:8, 9 *Mark* 9:43, 45, 47
gather all things that *o*. *Mat* 13:41
lest we should *o*. them, go. 17:27
whoso shall *o*. one of these little ones. 18:6; *Mark* 9:42; *Luke* 17:2
them, doth this *o*. you? *John* 6:61
my brother *o*.... lest he *o*. *1 Cor* 8:13
yet *o*. in one point, he. *Jas* 2:10
we *o*. all. If any man *o*. not. 3:2

offended
and what have I *o*. thee? *Gen* 20:9 *Jer* 37:18
the butler and baker had *o*. 40:1
saying, I have *o*.; return. *2 Ki* 18:14
we have *o*. against the. *2 Chr* 28:13
a brother *o*. is harder. *Pr* 18:19
Edom hath greatly *o*. *Ezek* 25:12
when Ephraim *o*. in Baal. *Hos* 13:1
blessed is he whosoever shall not be *o*. *Mat* 11:6; *Luke* 7:23
persecution ariseth . . . by and by he is *o*. *Mat* 13:21; *Mark* 4:17
and they were *o*. in him. *Mat* 13:57 *Mark* 6:3
the Pharisees were *o*. *Mat* 15:12
shall many be *o*. and betray. 24:10
all ye shall be *o*. because of. 26:31
all men shall be *o*. because of thee. *Mat* 26:33; *Mark* 14:29
that ye should not be *o*. *John* 16:1
against Caesar have I *o*. *Acts* 25:8
whereby thy brother is *o*. *Rom* 14:21
who is *o*. and I burn? *2 Cor* 11:29

offender
that make a man an *o*. *Isa* 29:21
if I be an *o*. or have. *Acts* 25:11

offenders
I and my son Solomon shall be counted *o*. *1 Ki* 1:21

offer
(*Revisions commonly use the word* sacrifice, *as having a more definite meaning*)
not delay to *o*. the first. *Ex* 22:29
not *o*. the blood. 23:18; 34:25
shalt *o*. every day a bullock. 29:36
thou shalt *o*. on altar two lambs. 38
one lamb thou shalt *o*. in the morning. 39, 41; *Num* 28:4, 8
shall *o*. no strange incense. *Ex* 30:9
every one that did *o*. silver. 35:24
o. a male without blemish. *Lev* 1:3; 3:6; 22:19, 20
will *o*. a meat offering to the Lord. 2:1, 14; 23:16; *Num* 6:17
offerings thou shalt *o*. salt. *Lev* 2:13
if he *o*. a peace offering, he shall *o*. 3:1, 6; 9:2; 19:5
if he *o*. a lamb for his. 3:7; 14:12
the goat he shall *o*. before. 3:12
o. a young bullock. 4:14; *Num* 15:24
o. that for sin offering. *Lev* 5:8; 9:7
the sons of Aaron shall *o*. 6:14, 22 14:19; 15:15, 30; *Num* 6:11
o. of it all the fat. *Lev* 7:3
o. it for a thanksgiving. 12; 22:29
Israel to *o*. their oblations to. 38
o. their sacrifice to devils. 17:7
bringeth it not to the door to *o*. 9
eaten the same day ye *o*. it. 19:6
bread of their God they do *o*. 21:6
blemish shall not come nigh to *o*. 21
o. for a freewill offering. 22:23
they *o*. their offering. *Num* 7:11
shall *o*. the Levites. 8:11, 13, 15
kept back, that we may not *o*.? 9:7
shalt *o*. the third part of an. 15:7
if a stranger will *o*. an offering. 14
o. an heave offering. 19; 18:24 26, 28, 29
come near to *o*. incense. 16:40
shall ye observe to *o*. to me. 28:2
of your months ye shall *o*. 11
after this manner ye shall *o*. 24
shall choose, there *o*. *Deut* 12:14
priest's due from them that *o*. 18:3
o. sacrifices of righteousness. 33:19; *Ps* 4:5
he made an end to *o*. *Judg* 3:18
o. a great sacrifice to Dagon. 16:23
Elkanah went up to *o*. *1 Sam* 1:21
her husband to *o*. sacrifice. 2:19
did I choose him my priest to *o*.? 28
I *o*. thee three things. *2 Sam* 24:12 *1 Chr* 21:10
on thee shall he *o*. priests. *1 Ki* 13:2
should be able to *o*. so willingly. *1 Chr* 29:14, 17
vessels to *o*. withal. *2 Chr* 24:14
to *o*. sacrifices of sweet. *Ezra* 6:10
of blood will I not *o*. *Ps* 16:4
will I *o*. in his tabernacle. 27:6
o. to God thanksgiving, pay. 50:14
then shall they *o*. bullocks. 51:19
o. to thee burnt sacrifices. 66:15
Sheba and Seba shall *o*. gifts. 72:10
I will *o*. the sacrifice of. 116:17
wentest thou up to *o*. *Isa* 57:7
to whom they *o*. incense. *Jer* 11:12
when ye *o*. your gifts. *Ezek* 20:31
when ye *o*. my bread, the. 44:7
they shall *o*. to me the fat and. 15
ye shall *o*. an oblation to the Lord. 45:1, 13; 48:9
should *o*. an oblation. *Dan* 2:46
o. wine offerings to Lord. *Hos* 9:4
o. a sacrifice of. *Amos* 4:5
that which they *o*. there. *Hag* 2:14
ye *o*. polluted bread. *Mal* 1:7
if ye *o*. the blind, *o*. it now to. 8
o. to the Lord an offering in. 3:3
come and *o*. thy gift. *Mat* 5:24
o. gift Moses commanded. 8:4 *Mark* 1:44 *Luke* 5:14
smiteth on one cheek, *o*. *Luke* 6:29
if shall ask an egg, will he *o*.? 11:12
that he may *o*. both gifts. *Heb* 5:1
for himself to *o*. for sins. 3
needeth not to *o*. sacrifice, first. 7:27
to *o*.: it is of necessity that this man have somewhat also to *o*. 8:3
nor yet that he should *o*. 9:25
o. sacrifice of praise to God. 13:15
to *o*. spiritual sacrifices. *1 Pet* 2:5
he should *o*. it with prayers. *Rev* 8:3
see **burnt offerings**

offered
Jacob *o*. sacrifice on the mount. *Gen* 31:54; 46:1
every man *o*. an offering. *Ex* 35:22
he slew the goat, and *o*. *Lev* 9:15
Nadab and Abihu *o*. strange fire. 10:1; 16:1; *Num* 3:4; 26:61
the princes *o*. for the dedication. *Num* 7:2, 10
Aaron *o*. them as an offering. 8:21
250 men that *o*. incense. 16:35
Balak *o*. oxen and sheep. 22:40 23:2, 4, 14, 30
people willingly *o*. *Judg* 5:2, 9
Manoah took a kid and *o*. 13:19
was that Elkanah *o*. *1 Sam* 1:4
when any *o*. the priest's. 2:13
David *o*. peace. *2 Sam* 6:17; 24:25
and all Israel *o*. *1 Ki* 8:62, 63
Jeroboam *o*. in Beth-el. 12:32, 33
the people *o*. yet in the high. 22:43
meat offering was *o*. *2 Ki* 3:20
to the altar and *o*. 16:12
with the rulers *o*. *1 Chr* 29:6
rejoiced for that they *o*. willingly. 9
Asa *o*. to the Lord of. *2 Chr* 15:11
Amaziah willingly *o*. himself. 17:16
all that was willingly *o*. *Ezra* 1:6
some of fathers *o*. freely for. 2:68
o. at the dedication of this. 6:17
his counsellors freely *o*. to the. 7:15
Israel there present had *o*. 8:25
they *o*. a ram of the flock. 10:19
willingly *o*. themselves. *Neh* 11:2
day they *o*. great sacrifices. 12:43
hast *o*. a meat offering. *Isa* 57:6
as if he *o*. swine's blood. 66:3
o. incense unto Baal. *Jer* 32:29
o. there their sacrifices. *Ezek* 20:28
cause the reproach *o*. *Dan* 11:18
have ye *o*. to me sacrifices and offerings? *Amos* 5:25
o. a sacrifice to Lord. *Jonah* 1:16
every place incense be *o*. *Mal* 1:11
Simon *o*. them money. *Acts* 8:18
abstain from meats *o*. to idols. 15:29; 21:25
an offering should be *o*. for. 21:26
things *o*. unto idols. *1 Cor* 8:1, 4, 7 10; 10:19, 28
if I be *o*. on the service. *Phil* 2:17
am now ready to be *o*. *2 Tim* 4:6
he had *o*. up prayers. *Heb* 5:7
this he did once, when he *o*. 7:27
not without blood, which he *o*. 9:7
were *o*. gifts. 9
o. himself without spot to God. 14
Christ was once *o*. to bear the. 28
by faith Abel *o*. to God a more. 11:4
Abraham, when tried, *o*. up. 17
justified by works when he *o*. *Jas* 2:21

offereth
priest that *o*. it for sin. *Lev* 6:26
be imputed to him that *o*. it. 7:18
for he *o*. the bread of thy God. 21:8
whoso *o*. praise glorifieth. *Ps* 50:23
he that *o*. oblation as if. *Isa* 66:3

offering
(*From earliest times in all known peoples and races, a sacrifice, generally by fire, was held to be pleasing to the God they worshipped, whether a heathen*

divinity or the true God. Sacrifices were, therefore, not originated by the Israelites, but regulated for them by the law. They were public, as the regular sacrifices of the tabernacle or temple, or were private, as expressive of thanks for some blessing or sorrow for some sin. As the laws of the sacrifices occupy practically the whole of Leviticus and are touched upon in other books also, the details are too long for a concordance, and should be studied in a Bible Dictionary)

Cain brought an *o.* unto. *Gen* 4:3
respect to Abel and to his *o.* 4
o. of every man, take my *o. Ex* 25:2
o. which ye shall take. 3; 35:5
an half shekel shall be the *o.* 30:13
an *o.* to the Lord to make. 15
ye shall bring your *o.* of. *Lev* 1:2
o. to Lord be of fowls. 14
o. of fine flour. 2:1
no meat *o.* shall be made. 11
his hand on the head of his *o.* 3:2, 8
lamb for his *o.* 7; *Num* 6:14
and if his *o.* be a goat. *Lev* 3:12
4:23, 28
o. of Aaron and of his sons. 6:20
o. be a vow, or a voluntary *o.* 7:16
an *o.* of jealousy, an *o.* *Num* 5:15
princes offered their *o.* before. 7:10
offer their *o.* each prince on his. 11
Levites before the Lord for an *o.*
8:11, 21
o. of the Lord in his appointed. 9:13
respect not thou their *o.* 16:15
kick ye at mine *o.*? *1 Sam* 2:29
purged with sacrifice nor *o.* 3:14
stirred thee up against me, let him accept an *o.* 26:19
o. of evening sacrifice. *1 Ki* 18:29
bring an *o.* and come. *1 Chr* 16:29
Ps 96:8
Israel shall bring the *o.* *Neh* 10:39
I have not caused thee to serve with an *o.* *Isa* 43:23
make his soul an *o.* for sin. 53:10
your brethren for an *o.* 66:20
provocation of their *o.* *Ezek* 20:28
my dispersed bring my *o.* *Zeph* 3:10
nor will I accept an *o.* *Mal* 1:10
an *o.*: should I accept this? 13
that he regardeth not the *o.* 2:13
offer to the Lord an *o.* in. 3:3
the *o.* up of Gentiles. *Rom* 15:16
o. and a sacrifice to God. *Eph* 5:2
o. thou wouldest not. *Heb* 10:5, 8
through the *o.* of the body of. 10
by one *o.* he hath perfected for. 14
there is no more *o.* for sin. 18
see **burnt** *offering,* **free** *offering,* **meat** *offerings,* **burnt, drink, fire, free, made, make**

offering, *verb*

as Samuel was *o.* the. *1 Sam* 7:10
David made an end of *o.*
2 Sam 6:18; *1 Chr* 16:2
Jehu had made an end of *o.*
2 Ki 10:25
o. according to commandment of Moses. *2 Chr* 8:13
made an end of *o.*, the king. 29:29
seven days, *o.* peace offerings. 30:22
of Aaron were busied in *o.* 35:14
priests *o.* willingly for the. *Ezra* 7:16
me to anger in *o.* to Baal. *Jer* 11:17
and *o.* him vinegar. *Luke* 23:36
every priest *o.* often the. *Heb* 10:11

heave **offering**

shoulder of the *heave o.* *Ex* 29:27
oblation for an *heave o.* *Lev* 7:14
offer up an *heave o.* *Num* 15:19, 20
of first of dough give an *heave o.* 21
they offer as an *heave o.* 18:24
Lord's *heave o.* to Aaron. 28
to Eleazar for an *heave o.* of. 31:29
which was the Lord's *heave o.* 41
see **burnt** *offering*

peace **offering**

sacrifice of *peace o.* *Lev* 3:1, 3, 6, 9

sin **offering**

shalt thou burn, it is a *sin o.* *Ex* 29:14
Lev 4:21, 24; 5:9, 11, 12
the blood of the *sin o.* *Ex* 30:10
bullock without blemish for a *sin o.*
Lev 4:3; 16:3, 27; *Num* 8:8
priest shall take of the blood of *sin o.*
Lev 4:25; 5:9
hand on the head of the *sin o.*, slay the *sin o.* in the place. 4:29, 33
a lamb for a *sin o.* 32; *Num* 6:14
a kid of goats for a *sin o.* *Lev* 5:6
9:3; 16:5, 15, 27; 23:19
which is for the *sin o.* first. 5:8
bring fine flour for a *sin o.* 11
is the law of the *sin o.* 6:25; 7:37
as the *sin o.* is, so is. 7:7; 14:13
thee a young calf for a *sin o.* 9:2
sought goat of the *sin o.* 10:16
why have ye not eaten *sin o.* in? 17
a turtle dove for a *sin o.* 12:6
fat of the *sin o.* shall be. 16:25
kid of the goats for a *sin o.* *Num* 7:16
22, 28; 15:24; 28:15; 29:5
sin o. should be made. *2 Chr* 29:24
he goats for a *sin o.* *Ezra* 8:35
sin o. hast thou not required. *Ps* 40:6
a bullock for a *sin o.* *Ezek* 43:19
day offer a kid for a *sin o.* 22
every day a goat for a *sin o.* 25
he shall offer his *sin o.* 44:27
meat offering and *sin o.* 29
where priest shall boil *sin o.* 46:20

trespass **offering**

shall bring his *trespass o.* *Lev* 5:6
without blemish for *trespass o.* 15
atonement with the ram of the *trespass o.* 16, 18; 6:6; 19:21, 22
in the day of his *trespass o.* 6:5
law of *trespass o.* 7:37
he lamb for *trespass o.* 14:12
21, 24, 25; *Num* 6:12
trespass o. is most holy. *Lev* 14:13
any wise return him a *trespass o.*
1 Sam 6:3
shall be the *trespass o.*? 4, 8, 17
two tables to slay the *trespass o.* on.
Ezek 40:39; 42:13
eat the *trespass o.* and every. 44:29
priests shall boil *trespass o.* 46:20

wave **offering**

wave them for a *wave o.* *Ex* 29:24
26; *Lev* 7:30; 8:27, 29; 9:21
10:15; 14:12, 24; 23:20
Num 6:20
the breast of the *wave o.* *Ex* 29:27
sheaf of the *wave o.* *Lev* 23:15

wood **offering**

cast lots for the *wood o.* *Neh* 10:34
wood o. at times appointed. 13:31

offerings

if his *o.* be of the flocks. *Lev* 1:10
o. thou shalt offer salt. 2:13
with chief of all the *o.* *1 Sam* 2:29
no dew nor fields of *o.* *2 Sam* 1:21
people brought in the *o.* *2 Chr* 31:12
the priests for passover, *o.* 35:8, 9
other holy *o.* sod they in pots. 13
should bring the firstfruits of *o.*
Neh 10:37; 12:44
remember all thy *o.* *Ps* 20:3
with *o.* and incense. *Jer* 41:5
will I require your *o.* *Ezek* 20:40
sacrifice flesh for mine *o.* *Hos* 8:13
me *o.* forty years? *Amos* 5:25
o. of Judah and Jerusalem. *Mal* 3:4
robbed thee? in tithes and *o.* 8
cast in unto the *o.* *Luke* 21:4
bring alms to my nation and *o.*
Acts 24:17
see **burnt, drink, free** *made by* **fire**

heave **offerings**

charge of mine *heave o.* *Num* 18:8
shall bring your *heave o.* *Deut* 12:6

offerings *of the Lord*

men abhorred the *o. of the Lord.*
1 Sam 2:17

peace **offerings**

shalt sacrifice thereon thy *peace o.*
Ex 20:24
sacrificed *peace o* of oxen. 24:5
heave offering of *peace o.* *Ex* 29:28
people brought *peace o.* and. 32:6
from the bullock of *peace o.* *Lev* 4:10
as fat of *peace o.* 26, 31, 35; 6:12
law of sacrifice of *peace o.* 7:11
13, 37
and a ram for *peace o.* 9:4, 18
out of the sacrifice of *peace o.* 10:14
offer them for *peace o.* 17:5; 23:19
offer a sacrifice of *peace o.* 19:5
22:21
a lamb for *peace o.* *Num* 6:14
a ram for *peace o.* 17
peace o., two oxen, five lambs.
7:17, 23, 29, 35, 41; 29:39
sacrifice of your *peace o.* 10:10
Joshua sacrificed *peace o.* *Josh* 8:31
offer *peace o.*, let the Lord. 22:23
all Israel offered *peace o.*
Judg 20:26; 21:4
I will come and offer *peace o.*
1 Sam 10:8; 11:15
David offered *peace o.* *2 Sam* 6:17
24:25; *1 Chr* 21:26
Solomon offered *peace o.* *1 Ki* 3:15
8:63; 9:25
appointed priests for *peace o.*
2 Chr 31:2
Manasseh offered *peace o.* 33:16
I have *peace o.* with me. *Pr* 7:14
peace o. to make reconciliation.
Ezek 45:15, 17
priest prepare *peace o.* 46:2
prince his *peace o.* 12
not regard *peace o.* of. *Amos* 5:22

sin **offerings**

sin o. to make an. *Neh* 10:33

thank **offerings**

bring *thank o.* to house. *2 Chr* 29:31
sacrificed thereon *thank o.* 33:16

wave **offerings**

all the *wave o.* I have. *Num* 18:11

wine **offerings**

wine o. to be pleasing. *Hos* 9:4

office

me he restored to mine *o.* *Gen* 41:13
do the *o.* of a midwife. *Ex* 1:16
to the *o.* of Eleazar. *Num* 4:16*
they waited on their *o.* *1 Chr* 6:32
ordain in their set *o.* 9:22
chief porters were in their set *o.* 26
brought to the king's *o.* *2 Chr* 24:11
in their set *o.* they sanctified. 31:18
o. was to distribute to. *Neh* 13:13*
let another take his *o.* *Ps* 109:8
near to do *o.* of priest. *Ezek* 44:13
I magnify mine *o.* *Rom* 11:13*
have not the same *o.* 12:4
if a man desire the *o.* *1 Tim* 3:1
the *o.* of a deacon. 10*, 13
who receive the *o.* of the. *Heb* 7:5

priest's **office**

minister to me in the *priest's o.*
Ex 28:1, 3, 4, 41; 29:1, 44; 30:30
35:19; 40:13, 15; *Lev* 7:35
16:32*; *Num* 3:3
priest's o. shall be theirs. *Ex* 29:9*
in the *priest's o.* 31:10; 39:41
ministered in *priest's o.* *Num* 3:4*
thy sons keep your *priest's o.* 18:7*
son ministered in the *priest's o.*
Deut 10:6
executed *priest's o.* in. *1 Chr* 6:10
cast them off from executing *priest's o.* *2 Chr* 11:14
while Zacharias executed the *priest's o.* *Luke* 1:8

officer

Potiphar an *o.* of Pharaoh.
Gen 37:36; 39:1
and Zebul his *o.*? *Judg* 9:28
Nathan, was the principal *o.* *1 Ki* 4:5
Geber, son of Uri, was the only *o.* 19
Ahab called an *o.* and said. 22:9
king appointed an *o.* to. *2 Ki* 8:6
Nebuzaradan took an *o.* out. 25:19
judge deliver thee to the *o.* and the *o.* cast. *Mat* 5:25; *Luke* 12:58

officers

wroth with two of his *o.* *Gen* 40:2
Joseph asked Pharaoh's *o.* Why? 7
let Pharaoh appoint *o.* over. 41:34*

the *o.* of Israel cried to. *Ex* 5:15
the *o.* did see that they were in. 19
gather unto me the *o.* *Num* 11:16
Deut 31:28
I made them *o.* among. *Deut* 1:15
judges and *o.* shalt thou. 16:18
the *o.* shall speak to the. 20:5, 8
and give to his *o.* *1 Sam* 8:15
Nathan, over the *o.* *1 Ki* 4:5
Solomon had twelve *o.* over. 7
place where the *o.* were. 28
chief of Solomon's *o.* 5:16; 9:23
Jehoiada commanded *o.* *2 Ki* 11:15*
appointed *o.* over the house. 18
2 Chr 23:18
went out with his *o.* *2 Ki* 24:12
the *o.* and mighty men carried. 15
six thousand were *o.* *1 Chr* 23:4
Chenaniah and his sons were for *o.*
26:29
Solomon's *o.* 250 that. *2 Chr* 8:10
the Levites shall be *o.* before. 19:11
the *o.* of the king helped. *Esth* 9:3*
I will make thine *o.* peace. *Isa* 60:17
be *o.* in the house of. *Jer* 29:26
the chief priests sent *o.* *John* 7:32
the *o.* answered, Never man. 46
Judas having received *o.* 18:3
o. took Jesus. 12
one of the *o.* struck Jesus. 22
the *o.* found them not in. *Acts* 5:22

offices

into one of the priests' *o.* *1 Sam* 2:36
priests according to *o.* *1 Chr* 24:3*
waited on their *o.* *2 Chr* 7:6
my good deeds for *o.* *Neh* 13:14*

offscouring

hast made us as the *o.* *Lam* 3:45
are the *o.* of all things. *1 Cor* 4:13

offspring

thy *o.* as the grass of. *Job* 5:25
their *o.* is established before. 21:8
and his *o.* shall not be satisfied. 27:14
yea, let my *o.* be rooted out. 31:8*
hang on him the *o.* and. *Isa* 22:24
my blessing upon thine *o.* 44:3
the *o.* of thy bowels like the. 48:19
o. shall be known among the. 61:9
seed of the blessed, and *o.* 65:23
are also his *o.* *Acts* 17:28, 29
I am the Root and the *O.* *Rev* 22:16

oft

as *o.* as he passed by. *2 Ki* 4:8
how *o.* cometh their destruction?
Job 21:17
how *o.* did they provoke him. *Ps* 78:40
the Pharisees fast *o.*? *Mat* 9:14
for *o.* times he falleth into the fire,
and *o.* into. 17:15; *Mark* 9:22
o. shall my brother sin? *Mat* 18:21
except they wash *o.* eat not. *Mark* 7:3
I punished them *o.* in. *Acts* 26:11
do ye as *o.* as ye drink. *1 Cor* 11:25
in deaths *o.* *2 Cor* 11:23
for he *o.* refreshed me. *2 Tim* 1:16
up rain that cometh *o.* *Heb* 6:7

often

that being *o.* reproved. *Pr* 29:1
feared the Lord spake *o.* *Mal* 3:16
how *o.* would I have gathered thy.
Mat 23:37; *Luke* 13:34
o. bound with fetters. *Mark* 5:4
disciples of John fast *o.*? *Luke* 5:33
for as *o.* as ye eat this. *1 Cor* 11:26
journeyings *o.*, in perils. *2 Cor* 11:26
watchings *o.*, in fastings *o.* 27
of whom I have told you *o.* *Phil* 3:18
a little wine for thine *o.* infirmities.
1 Tim 5:23
should offer himself *o.* *Heb* 9:25
then he must *o.* have suffered. 26
to smite the earth as *o.* *Rev* 11:6

oftener

Felix sent for him *o.* *Acts* 24:26

oftentimes

worketh God *o.* with. *Job* 33:29
o. also thine own heart. *Eccl* 7:22
for *o.* it had caught him. *Luke* 8:29
for Jesus *o.* resorted. *John* 18:2
that *o.* I purposed to. *Rom* 1:13
have *o.* proved diligent. *2 Cor* 8:22
and *o.* offering the same. *Heb* 10:11

Og

to them as he did to *O.* *Deut* 31:4
heard what you did to *O.* *Josh* 2:10
the cities of *O.* pertaining. 13:21
in the country of *O.* *1 Ki* 4:19
see **Bashan**

oil

The most common oil in use was that made from the olive berry. This was used [1] *as food*, Ex 29:2. [2] *As a cosmetic, for anointing the body after a bath*, etc., Ps 104:15. [3] *Medicinal, as referred to in* Isa 1:6; Luke 10:34; Jas 5:14. [4] *For light*, Ex 27:20. [5] *Ritual, in the anointing of kings and priests*, Lev 8:12. [6] *In offerings.*

Jacob poured *o.* *Gen* 28:18; 35:14
take *o.* for the light. *Ex* 25:6
35:14; 39:37
tempered with *o.* 29:2, 40
shalt make it an *o.* of holy. 30:25
pour *o.* upon it. *Lev* 2:1, 6
flour mingled with *o.* 4, 5; 14:10
21; 23:13; *Num* 6:15; 7:13, 19
25, 31, 37, 43, 49, 55, 61, 67, 73, 79
8:8; 28:13; 29:3, 9, 14
thy meat offering put *o.* upon it.
Lev 2:15; 6:21
shall burn part of the *o.* 2:16
he shall put no *o.* on it. 5:11
Num 5:15
meat offering mingled with *o.*
Lev 7:10; 9:4; 14:10
shall offer cakes mingled with *o.*
7:12; *Num* 6:15
his right finger in the *o.* *Lev* 14:16
rest of the *o.* that is in. 17, 18, 29
all the *o.* vessels. *Num* 4:9
was as the taste of fresh *o.* 11:8
fourth part of an hin of *o.* 15:4
third part of an hin of *o.* 6
o. for one bullock, and *o.* 28:12
not anoint thyself with *o.* *Deut* 28:40
2 Sam 14:2; *Mi* 6:15
made him suck *o.* out of the flinty
rock. *Deut* 32:13
let Asher be acceptable, . . . and dip
his foot in *o.* 33:24
Samuel took a vial of *o.* *1 Sam* 10:1
horn with *o.* and go. 16:1, 13
priest took an horn of *o.* *1 Ki* 1:39
Hiram twenty measures of *o.* 5:11
o. in a cruse. 17:12
nor cruse of *o.* fail. 14, 16
house save a pot of *o.* *2 Ki* 4:2
the *o.* stayed. 6
go sell the *o.* and pay thy debt. 7
box of *o.* go to Ramoth-gilead. 9:1, 3
he poured the *o.* on his head. 6
over the cellars of *o.* *1 Chr* 27:28
gave drink and *o.* to them. *Ezra* 3:7
with *o.* of myrrh. *Esth* 2:12
which make *o.* within. *Job* 24:11
poured me out rivers of *o.* 29:6
my head with *o.* *Ps* 23:5
words were softer than *o.* 55:21
and *o.* to make his face. 104:15
come like *o.* into his bones. 109:18
kindness, an excellent *o.* 141:5
is smoother than *o.* *Pr* 5:3
and *o.* in the dwelling of. 21:20
to give to them the *o.* of joy. *Isa* 61:3
we have treasures of *o.* *Jer* 41:8
flour, honey, and *o.* *Ezek* 16:13, 19
hast set mine *o.* and incense. 18
Judah traded in honey and *o.* 27:17
their rivers to run like *o.* 32:14
ordinance of *o.*, bath of *o.* 45:14
ephah for a ram, an hin of *o.* 24
give me my bread and *o.* *Hos* 2:5
Assyrians, and *o.* is carried. 12:1
with 10,000 rivers of *o.*? *Mi* 6:7
empty the golden *o.* out. *Zech* 4:12
the foolish took no *o.* *Mat* 25:3
the wise took *o.* 4
give us of your *o.* 8
my head with *o.* thou. *Luke* 7:46
an hundred measures of *o.* 16:6
see **anointed, anointing, beaten, log**

wine with **oil**

best of the *o.* and *w.* *Num* 18:12
bless thy *w.* and thy *o.* *Deut* 7:13
gather thy *w.* and *o.* 11:14
tithe of thy *w.* and *o.* 12:17; 14:23
the firstfruits of *w.* and *o.* 18:4
2 Chr 31:5
not leave thee either *w.* or *o.*
Deut 28:51
oversee the *w.* and *o.* *1 Chr* 9:29
nigh brought *w.* and *o.* 12:40
20,000 baths of *w.* and *o.*
2 Chr 2:10, 15
in strong holds *o.* and *w.* 11:11
storehouses for *w.* and *o.* 32:28
give *w.* and *o.* according. *Ezra* 6:9
of *w.* and 100 baths of *o.* 7:22
restore *w.* and *o.* that ye. *Neh* 5:11
firstfruits of *w.* and *o.* 10:37
offering of the corn, new *w.* and *o.* 39
tithes of corn, new *w.* and *o.* 13:5, 12
that loveth *w.* and *o.* shall not be
rich. *Pr* 21:17
to Lord for *w.* and *o.* *Jer* 31:12
w. and summer fruits and *o.* 40:10
drought on new *w.* and *o.* *Hag* 1:11
touch bread, *w.* or *o.* shall? 2:12
poured in *o.* and *w.* *Luke* 10:34
hurt not the *w.* and the *o.* *Rev* 6:6
no man buyeth their *w.* and *o.* 18:13

oiled

one cake of *o.* bread. *Ex* 29:23
Lev 8:26

oil olive

pure *o.* *olive* beaten for. *Ex* 27:20
unto thee of *o.* *olive* an hin. 30:24
unto thee pure *o.* *olive.* *Lev* 24:2
land of *o.* *olive*, and honey.
Deut 8:8; *2 Ki* 18:32

oil tree

wilderness, the *o.* *tree.* *Isa* 41:19

ointment

(*This word often means oil and is so put in the Revisions*)

make oil of holy *o.* and *o.* *Ex* 30:25*
house of his precious things and
precious *o.* *2 Ki* 20:13; *Isa* 39:2
the *o.* of the spices. *1 Chr* 9:30*
sea to boil like pot of *o.* *Job* 41:31
it is like the precious *o.* *Ps* 133:2
o. and perfume rejoice. *Pr* 27:9
the *o.* of his right hand. 16
is better than precious *o.* *Eccl* 7:1
and let thy head lack no *o.* 9:8
dead flies cause the *o.* of. 10:1
thy name is as *o.* poured. *S of S* 1:3
nor mollified with *o.* *Isa* 1:6
thou wentest to the king with *o.* 57:9
a box of precious *o.* *Mat* 26:7
Mark 14:3; *Luke* 7:37
o. might have been sold for much.
Mat 26:9; *John* 12:5
hath poured out this *o.* *Mat* 26:12
waste of the *o.* made? *Mark* 14:4
his feet with *o.* *Luke* 7:38, 46
anointed the Lord with *o.* *John* 11:2
o. and anointed the feet of Jesus,
house . . . odour of the *o.* 12:3

ointments

savour of thy good *o.* *S of S* 1:3
the smell of thine *o.* is better. 4:10
anoint themselves with the chief *o.*
Amos 6:6
prepared spices and *o.* *Luke* 23:56
their odours and *o.* *Rev* 18:13

old

Noah was 500 years *o.* *Gen* 5:32
Noah was 600 years *o.* when. 7:6
Shem was 100 years *o.* and. 11:10
Abraham 75 years *o.* when. 12:4
a ram of three years *o.* 15:9
Abram was fourscore and six years
o. when Hagar bare. 16:16
he that is eight days *o.* shall. 17:12
that is an hundred years *o.* 17
Abraham 99 years *o.* when. 24
Ishmael thirteen years *o.* when. 25
Abraham and Sarah were *o.* 18:11
waxed *o.* my lord being *o.* also. 12
of surety bear a child, who am *o.*? 13
compassed the house, *o.* and. 19:4
our father is *o.* 31
Isaac being eight days *o.* 21:4
Abraham 100 years *o.* 5

Sarah was 127 years *o.* *Gen* 23:1
Abraham was *o.* 24:1
Isaac 40 years *o.* when took. 25:20
Isaac was 60 years *o.* when she. 26
Esau forty years *o.* when he. 26:34
when Isaac was *o.*, he called Esau. 27:1, 2; 35:29
Joseph being 17 years *o.* was. 37:2
Pharaoh said to Jacob, How *o.*? 47:8
couched as an *o.* lion, who. 49:9
Joseph died, being 110 years *o.* 50:26
Moses was eighty years *o.* and Aaron eighty-three years *o.* when. *Ex* 7:7
our young and our *o.* with sons. 10:9
are numbered from twenty years o. 30:14; 38:26; *Num* 1:3, 18; 14:29 *1 Chr* 23:27; *2 Chr* 25:5; 31:17 *Ezra* 3:8
it is an *o.* leprosy in the. *Lev* 13:11
shall eat *o.* fruit. 25:22
shall eat *o.* store. 26:10
the male from 20 years *o.* even. 27:3
from five even to twenty years *o.* 5
month *o.* to five years *o.* 6
male, from a month *o.* *Num* 3:15 22, 28, 34, 39, 40, 43
from thirty years *o.* to fifty. 4:3 23:20; *1 Chr* 23:3
Levites from 25 years *o.* *Num* 8:24
redeemed, from month *o.* 18:16
23,000 from month *o.* and. 26:62
Aaron was 123 years old. 33:39
thy raiment waxed not *o.* *Deut* 8:4 29:5; *Neh* 9:21
not regard the person of the *o.* *Deut* 28:50
I am 120 years *o.* this day. 31:2
Moses was an 120 years *o.* 34:7
eat of the *o.* corn. *Josh* 5:11, 12
men and women, young and *o.* 6:21
they took *o.* sacks. 9:4
o. shoes on their feet. 5, 13
Joshua was *o.* and. 13:1; 23:1, 2
forty years *o.* was I, when. 14:7
this day eighty-five years *o.* 10
Joshua died, being 110 years *o.* 24:29; *Judg* 2:8
too *o.* to have a husband. *Ruth* 1:12
now Eli was very *o.* *1 Sam* 2:22
Eli was ninety and eight years *o.* 4:15
Samuel was *o.*, he made. 8:1, 5; 12:2
Saul's son was forty years *o.* when. *2 Sam* 2:10
lame, and five years *o.* 4:4
David thirty years *o.* when he. 5:4
now Barzillai was eighty years *o.* 19:32, 35
king David was *o.* *1 Ki* 1:1, 15 *1 Chr* 23:1
Solomon was *o.* his wives. *1 Ki* 11:4
dwelt an *o.* prophet in. 13:11
child, and her husband is *o.* *2 Ki* 4:14
married when sixty years *o.* *1 Chr* 2:21
males from three years *o.* and. *2 Chr* 31:16
destroy all the Jews, young and *o.* *Esth* 3:13
wicked live, become *o.*? *Job* 21:7
am young, and ye are very *o.* 32:6
my bones waxed *o.* through. *Ps* 32:3
young, and now am *o.* 37:25
now when I am *o.* O God. 71:18
when *o.* he will not depart. *Pr* 22:6
remove not *o.* landmark. 23:10
thy mother when she is *o.* 22
wise child than an *o.* king. *Eccl* 4:13
pleasant fruits new and *o.* *S of S* 7:13
an heifer of three years *o.* *Isa* 15:5 *Jer* 48:34
young and *o.* naked. *Isa* 20:4
they shall wax *o.* as garment. 50:9
the *o.* waste places. 58:12; 61:4
child shall die 100 years *o.*, but the sinner being 100 years o. 65:20
ask for the *o.* paths. *Jer* 6:16
thence *o.* clouts, *o.* rags. 38:11, 12
break in pieces young and *o.* 51:22
the young and *o.* lie on. *Lam* 2:21
my skin hath he made *o.* 3:4
slay utterly *o.* and young. *Ezek* 9:6
said to her that was *o.* in adulteries. 23:43
destroy it for *o.* hatred. *Ezek* 25:15
you after your *o.* estates. 36:11
kingdom, being 62 years *o.* *Dan* 5:31
with calves of year *o.* *Mi* 6:6
children from two years *o.* *Mat* 2:16
new cloth unto an *o.* garment. 9:16
new wine into *o.* bottles. 17 *Mark* 2:21, 22; *Luke* 5:36, 37
out of his treasure things new and *o.* *Mat* 13:52
Jesus twelve years *o.* *Luke* 2:42
for he saith, The *o.* is better. 5:39
one of the *o.* prophets is risen. 9:8
man be born when he is *o.*? *John* 3:4
thou art not yet fifty years *o.* 8:57
be *o.* another shall lead thee. 21:18
above forty years *o.* *Acts* 4:22
was full forty years *o.* 7:23
Mnason, an *o.* disciple. 21:16
went about 100 years *o.* *Rom* 4:19
purge out therefore the *o.* *1 Cor* 5:7
the feast, not with *o.* leaven. 8
of the *O.* Testament. *2 Cor* 3:14
o. things are passed away, all. 5:17
and *o.* wives' fables. *1 Tim* 4:7
not taken under sixty years *o.* 5:9
he hath made the first *o.* That which decayeth and waxeth *o.* *Heb* 8:13
purged from his *o.* sins. *2 Pet* 1:9
God spared not the *o.* world. 2:5
o. commandment is word. *1 John* 2:7
o. serpent, called the devil. *Rev* 12:9
the dragon, that *o.* serpent. 20:2
see **wax**

days of **old**, *see of* **old**

old *age*

buried in a good *o. age.* *Gen* 15:15
Abraham a son of his *o. age.* 21:2, 7
Abraham died in a good *o. age.* 25:8
Joseph was the son of his *o. age.* 37:3; 44:20
Gideon died in a good *o. age.* *Judg* 8:32
nourisher in thine *o. age.* *Ruth* 4:15
Asa in *o. age* was. *1 Ki* 15:23
David died in a good *o. age*, full of days and honour. *1 Chr* 29:28
in whom *o. age* perished. *Job* 30:2
not off in the time of *o. age.* *Ps* 71:9
bring forth fruit in *o. age.* 92:14
to your *o. age* I am he. *Isa* 46:4
conceived a son in her *o. age.* *Luke* 1:36

old *gate, see* **gate**

old *man*

Abraham died an *o. man.* *Gen* 25:8
the *o. man* of whom ye spake ? 43:27
we have a father, an *o. man.* 44:20
honour face of *o. man.* *Lev* 19:32
there came an *o. man* from his work. *Judg* 19:16
o. man said, Whither goest ? 17, 20
spake to the *o. man.* 22
not be an *o. man* in thy house. *1 Sam* 2:31, 32
Eli was an *o. m.* 4:18
Jesse was an *o. m.* 17:12
an *o. man* cometh up, and. 28:14
compassion on *o. man.* *2 Chr* 36:17
nor *o. man* that hath not. *Isa* 65:20
I am an *o. man*, my wife. *Luke* 1:18
our *o. man* is crucified. *Rom* 6:6
put off the *o. man* which. *Eph* 4:22
ye have put off the *o. man.* *Col* 3:9

old *men*

Rehoboam consulted with the *o. men.* *1 Ki* 12:6
forsook counsel of *o. men.* 8, 13 *2 Chr* 10:6, 8, 13
o. men and children. *Ps* 148:12
the crown of *o. men.* *Pr* 17:6
beauty of *o. men* is the grey. 20:29
dance, young *men* and *o.* *Jer* 31:13
hear this, ye *o. men*, and. *Joel* 1:2
o. men shall dream dreams. 2:28 *Acts* 2:17
o. men and women dwell. *Zech* 8:4

of **old**

of o., men of renown. *Gen* 6:4
those nations were *of o.* *1 Sam* 27:8
Ham had dwelt there *of o.* *1 Chr* 4:40
of o. there were chief. *Neh* 12:46
knowest thou not this *of o.*? *Job* 20:4
mercies have been ever *of o.* *Ps* 25:6
thou didst in the times *of o.* 44:1
even he that abideth *of o.* 55:19
heavens which were *of o.* 68:33
which hast purchased *of o.* 74:2
for God is my king *of o.* working. 12
I have considered the days *of o.* 77:5
remember thy wonders *of o.* 11
I will utter dark sayings *of o.* 78:2
thy throne is established *of o.* 93:2
of o. hast laid the foundation. 102:25
thy judgements *of o.* O Lord. 119:52
testimonies I have known *of o.* 152
I remember the days *of o.* 143:5 *Isa* 63:11
me before his works *of o.* *Pr* 8:22
counsels *of o.* are faithfulness and. *Isa* 25:1
for Tophet is ordained *of o.* 30:33
consider the things *of o.* 43:18
former things *of o.*: I am God. 46:9
awake, as in generations *of o.* 51:9
not I held my peace even *of o.*? 57:11
carried them all the days *of o.* 63:9
prophets before me and thee *of o.* *Jer* 28:8
Lord hath appeared *of o.* to. 31:3
be inhabited as in days *of o.* 46:26
she had in the days *of o.* *Lam* 1:7
he commanded in days *of o.* 2:17
as they that be dead *of o.* 3:6
Lord, renew our days as *of o.* 5:21
down with people *of o.* *Ezek* 26:20
build it as in days *of o.* *Amos* 9:11
forth have been from *of o.* *Mi* 5:2
in Bashan, as in the days *of o.* 7:14
to our fathers from the days *of o.* 20
Nineveh is *of o.* like a pool. *Nah* 2:8
pleasant to the Lord, as in the days *of o.* *Mal* 3:4
the heavens were *of o.* *2 Pet* 3:5
who were *of o.* ordained to. *Jude* 4

old *time*

giants dwelt there in *o. time.* *Deut* 2:20
o. time set in thy inheritance. 19:14
fathers dwelt on other side in *o. time.* *Josh* 24:2
to speak in *o. time.* *2 Sam* 20:18
moved sedition of *o. time.* *Ezra* 4:15
been already of *o. time.* *Eccl* 1:10
of *o. time* I have broken. *Jer* 2:20
bring thee down with people of *o. time.* *Ezek* 26:20
I have spoken in *o. time.* 38:17
said by them of *o. time.* *Mat* 5:21 27, 33
Moses of *o. time* hath. *Acts* 15:21
in *o. time* holy women. *1 Pet* 3:5
prophecy came not in *o. time* by man. *2 Pet* 1:21

old *way*

o. way which wicked men. *Job* 22:15

oldness

should not serve in *o.* of. *Rom* 7:6

olive

(*Olives are one of the most common trees of Palestine, and the uses of the tree are many. The tree is often used as a figure for Israel*)
in mouth was an *o.* leaf. *Gen* 8:11
for thine *o.* shall cast. *Deut* 28:40
the mount, and fetch *o.* *Neh* 8:15
off his flower as the *o.* *Job* 15:33
children like *o.* plants. *Ps* 128:3
the labour of the *o.* shall. *Hab* 3:17
be these two *o.* branches ? *Zech* 4:12
can fig tree, my brethren, bear *o.* berries ? *Jas* 3:12
see **oil**

olives

foxes burnt up the vineyards and *o.* *Judg* 15:5
shalt tread the *o.* but shalt. *Mi* 6:15
see **mount**

Olivet

by ascent to mount *O.* *2 Sam* 15:30
returned from the mount called *O.* *Acts* 1:12

olive tree

beatest thine *o. tree.* *Deut* 24:20
o. tree, Reign over us. *Judg* 9:8
the *o. tree* said, Should I leave? 9
two cherubims of *o. tree.* *1 Ki* 6:23
he made doors of *o. tree.* 31, 32
posts of *o. tree.* 33
like a green *o. tree* in the. *Ps* 52:8
shaking of an *o. tree. Isa* 17:6; 24:13
thy name a green *o. tree. Jer* 11:16
shall be as the *o. tree.* *Hos* 14:6
as yet the *o. tree* hath not. *Hag* 2:19
of the fatness of *o. tree.* *Rom* 11:17
o. tree, graffed in a good *o. tree.* 24

wild **olive tree**

thou being *wild o. tree.* *Rom* 11:17

olive trees

o. trees which thou plantedst not. *Deut* 6:11
thou shalt have *o. trees,* but. 28:40
over the *o. trees* was Baal-hanan. *1 Chr* 27:28
o. trees increased, palmer-. *Amos* 4:9
two *o. trees* by it on the. *Zech* 4:3
are the two *o. trees.* *Rev* 11:4

oliveyard

shalt thou do with thy *o.* *Ex* 23:11

oliveyards

and *o.* which ye planted not, do ye eat. *Josh* 24:13; *Neh* 9:25
king shall take your *o.* *1 Sam* 8:14
to receive money and *o.*? *2 Ki* 5:26
pray, to them their *o.* *Neh* 5:11

Olympas

salute Julia, *O.* and all. *Rom* 16:15

omitted

o. weightier matters. *Mat* 23:23*

omnipotent

Lord God *o.* reigneth. *Rev* 19:6*

Omri

all Israel made *O.* king. *1 Ki* 16:16
half followed *O.* 21
but *O.* wrought evil. 25
Ahab son of *O.* did evil in the. 30
Athaliah daughter of *O.* *2 Ki* 8:26; *2 Chr* 22:2
O. son of Becher. *1 Chr* 7:8
O. son of Imri. 9:4
O. son of Michael. 27:18
for statutes of *O.* are kept. *Mi* 6:16

On

priest of *O.* *Gen* 41:45, 50; 46:20
O. the son of Peleth. *Num* 16:1

Onan

and called his name *O.* *Gen* 38:4
O. knew that the seed should. 9
sons of Judah, Er, *O.* 46:12; *Num* 26:19; *1 Chr* 2:3
Er and *O.* died in the. *Num* 26:19

once

speak yet but this *o.* *Gen* 18:32
forgive my sin only this *o.* *Ex* 10:17
atonement . . . altar of incense *o.* a. 30:10; *Lev* 16:34; *Heb* 9:7, 12
let us go up at *o.* and. *Num* 13:30
not consume them at *o.* *Deut* 7:22
go round the city *o.* *Josh* 6:3, 11, 14
this *o.*: prove but this *o.* *Judg* 6:39
come up *o.* 16:18
strengthen me this *o.* 28
let me smite him to the earth at *o.* *1 Sam* 26:8*
o. in three years came the navy of Tarshish. *1 Ki* 10:22; *2 Chr* 9:21
he saved himself not *o.* *2 Ki* 6:10
o. in ten days all store of. *Neh* 5:18
merchants lodged *o.* or twice. 13:20
God speaks *o.*, yea twice. *Job* 33:14
o. have I spoken, but I will. 40:5
God hath spoken *o.* *Ps* 62:11
down the carved work at *o.* 74:6
in sight when *o.* art angry? 76:7
o. have I sworn by my. 89:35
perverse shall fall at *o.* *Pr* 28:18
destroy and devour at *o.* *Isa* 42:14
shall a nation be born at *o.*? 66:8
out the inhabitants at *o.* *Jer* 10:18*
be clean? when shall it *o.* be? 13:27
behold, I will *o.* cause. 16:21
yet *o.* it is a little while, and I will shake. *Hag* 2:6; *Heb* 12:26
when *o.* the master of. *Luke* 13:25
they cried all at *o.* saying. 23:18
died, he died unto sin *o.* *Rom* 6:10
I was alive without the law *o.* 7:9
above 500 brethren at *o.* *1 Cor* 15:6
rods, *o.* was I stoned. *2 Cor* 11:25
the faith he *o.* destroyed. *Gal* 1:23
let it not be *o.* named. *Eph* 5:3
ye sent *o.* and again to. *Phil* 4:16
have come to you *o.* *1 Thes* 2:18
who were *o.* enlightened. *Heb* 6:4
this he did *o.* when he offered. 7:27*
but now *o.* in end of the world. 9:26*
it is appointed to men *o.* to die. 27
Christ was *o.* offered to bear sins. 28; 10:10
that the worshippers *o.* purged. 10:2
o. more signifieth the. 12:27
hath suffered *o.* for our. *1 Pet* 3:18
o. longsuffering of God waited. 20
the faith *o.* delivered to. *Jude* 3*
though ye *o.* knew this. 5

one

[1] *One only, there being no other of that kind,* 1 Tim 2:5; Heb 10:14. [2] *The very same,* Gen 11:1; 40:5; 1 Sam 6:4. [3] *Some body, any one,* 2 Sam 23:15.

cleave to his wife, and they shall be *o.* flesh. *Gen* 2:24; *Mat* 19:5; *Mark* 10:8; *1 Cor* 6:16
hast thou but *o.* blessing? *Gen* 27:38
not give our sister to *o.* that. 34:14
o. is not. 42:13, 32
o. went out from me. 44:28
yet will bring *o.* plague. *Ex* 11:1
in *o.* house shall it be eaten. 12:46
o. law shall be to him that is home-. 49; *Lev* 24:22; *Num* 15:16, 29
drive them out in *o.* year. *Ex* 23:29
every *o.* of the curtains shall have *o.* measure. 26:2; 36:9, 15
o. tabernacle. 26:6; 36:13
o. loaf of bread, *o.* cake, and *o.* 29:23
then he shall be guilty in *o.* of these. *Lev* 5:4, 5, 13
o. of your own country. 16:29; 17:15
bake your bread in *o.* oven. 26:26
if they blow but with *o.* *Num* 10:4
I have not taken *o.* as. 16:15
o. rod shall be for the head. 17:3
of the tribe shall be wife to *o.* 36:8
I took twelve men, *o.* of. *Deut* 1:23
o. of these cities. 4:42; 19:5, 11
o. witness shall not rise up. 19:15
be free at home *o.* year. 24:5
should *o.* chase a thousand? 32:30
Joshua took at *o.* time. *Josh* 10:42
Jericho *o.*, the king of Ai *o.* 12:9
Jerusalem *o.*, king of Hebron *o.* 10
but *o.* lot and *o.* portion? 17:14
thou shalt not have *o.* lot only. 17
that *o.* reign over you? *Judg* 9:2
what *o.* is there of the tribes? 21:8
o. plague was on you all. *1 Sam* 6:4
o., for Gaza *o.*, for Askelon *o.* 17
and they came out with *o.* 11:7
son in law in *o.* of the twain. 18:21
what *o.* nation is like? *2 Sam* 7:23
with *o.* full line to keep alive. 8:2
there will not tarry *o.* with. 19:7
slew at *o.* time. 23:8; *1 Chr* 11:11
O that *o.* would give me to drink. *2 Sam* 23:15; *1 Chr* 11:17
given me *o.* to sit on. *1 Ki* 1:48
I ask *o.* petition of thee, deny. 2:16
were of *o.* measure, *o.* size. 6:25
there hath not failed *o.* word. 8:56
o. tribe to thy son. 11:13, 32, 36
prophets declare good to the king with *o.* mouth. 22:13; *2 Chr* 18:12
carry thither *o.* of the. *2 Ki* 17:27
o. of the priests came and. 28
will turn away face of *o.* captain. 18:24; *Isa* 36:9
for asking counsel of *o.* *1 Chr* 10:13
o. of the least was over an. 12:14
worship before *o.* altar. *2 Chr* 32:12
Hanani, *o.* of my brethren. *Neh* 1:2
bring *o.* of ten to dwell. 11:1
he cannot answer him *o.* *Job* 9:3
o. dieth in his full strength. 21:23
he is in *o.* mind, and who? *Job* 23:13
if an interpreter *o.* among. 33:23
be not afraid when *o.* is. *Ps* 49:16
fall like *o.* of the princes. 82:7
I have laid help on *o.* that is. 89:19
sing us *o.* of the songs of Zion. 137:3
let us all have *o.* purse. *Pr* 1:14
is like *o.* that taketh a dog. 26:17
o. generation passeth away. *Eccl* 1:4
that *o.* event happeneth to. 2:14
yea, they have all *o.* breath. 3:19
all go unto *o.* place, all are. 20; 6:6
two better than *o.* 4:9
how can *o.* be warm? 11
if *o.* prevail against him, two. 12
counting *o.* by *o.* to find out. 7:27
but *o.* sinner destroyeth much. 9:18
are given from *o.* shepherd. 12:11
with *o.* of thy eyes, with *o.* chain of thy neck. *S of S* 4:9
but *o.*; she is the only *o.* 6:9
vineyard shall yield *o.* bath. *Isa* 5:10
what shall *o.* answer messengers of nation? 14:32
o. shall be called the city of. 19:18
to the days of *o.* king. 23:15
shall be gathered *o.* by *o.* 27:12
o. thousand shall flee at the rebuke of *o.* 30:17
no *o.* of these shall fail. 34:16
I have raised up *o.* from the. 41:25
I will give Jerusalem *o.* that. 27
o. shall say, I am the Lord's. 44:5
surely, shall *o.* say, in Lord. 45:24
o. saith, Destroy it not, a. 65:8
they four had *o.* likeness. *Ezek* 1:16
brought up *o.* of her whelps. 19:3
come forth out of *o.* land. 21:19
that they took both *o.* way. 23:13
that *o.* that had escaped. 33:21
Abraham was *o.*: we are many. 24
as a lovely song of *o.* 32
will set up *o.* shepherd. 34:23; 37:24
shall become *o.* in thy hand. 37:17
make them *o.* stick. 19
o. nation, *o.* king. 22
o. gate of Reuben. 48:31
o. gate of Joseph. 32
but *o.* decree for you. *Dan* 2:9
Daniel was astonied for *o.* hour. 4:19
o. like the Son of. 7:13; 10:16, 18
the covenant for *o.* week. 9:27
out of a branch shall *o.* stand. 11:7
o. shall certainly come and. 10
they shall speak lies at *o.* table. 27
Israel shall appoint themselves *o.* head. *Hos* 1:11
cities wandered to *o.* city. *Amos* 4:8
remain ten men in *o.* house. 6:9
the Lord with *o.* consent. *Zeph* 3:9
on *o.* stone shall be seven. *Zech* 3:9
three shepherds in *o.* month. 11:8
be *o.* Lord, and his name *o.* 14:9
did not he make *o.*? And wherefore *o.*? *Mal* 2:15
the voice of *o.* crying in. *Mat* 3:3; *Mark* 1:3; *Luke* 3:4; *John* 1:23
o. jot, or *o.* tittle shall not pass. *Mat* 5:18
whoso shall break *o.* of these. 19
that *o.* of thy members. 29, 30
canst not make *o.* hair white. 36
which of you can add *o.* cubit? 6:27
was not arrayed like *o.* of these. 29; *Luke* 12:27
shall give to drink to *o.* *Mat* 10:42
you shall have *o.* sheep? 12:11
Elias; and Jeremias, or *o.* of. 16:14; *Mark* 6:15; 8:28; *Luke* 9:8, 19
o. for thee, *o.* for Moses, and *o.* for. *Mat* 17:4; *Mark* 9:5; *Luke* 9:33
shall offend *o.* of these. *Mat* 18:6; *Mark* 9:42; *Luke* 17:2
heed ye despise not *o.* *Mat* 18:10
o. of these little ones should. 14
if not hear, then take with thee *o.* 16
none good but *o.* 19:17; *Mark* 10:18; *Luke* 18:19
last have wrought but *o.* hour. *Mat* 20:12
they beat *o.* and killed another. 21:35
went their ways, *o.* to his farm. 22:5
they will not move them with *o.* of their fingers. 23:4; *Luke* 11:46

for *o.* is your Master. *Mat* 23:8, 10
o. is your Father. 9
he gave to *o.* five talents, to. 25:15
he that had received the *o.* 18, 24
as ye have done it to *o.* 40
did it not to *o.* of the least. 45
o. of you shall betray me. 26:21
Mark 14:18; *John* 13:21
could ye not watch with me *o.* hour? *Mat* 26:40; *Mark* 14:37
they more than *o.* loaf. *Mark* 8:14
whoever shall receive *o.* of. 9:37
o. casting out devils. 38; *Luke* 9:49
ask of you *o.* question. *Mark* 11:29
having yet *o.* son, he sent him. 12:6
to say, *o.* by *o.*, Is it I? 14:19
at the feast he released *o.* 15:6
Luke 23:17
o. mightier than I. *Luke* 3:16
I say to *o.*, Go, and he goeth. 7:8
he had *o.* only daughter, and. 8:42
there shall be five in *o.* house. 12:52
joy in heaven over *o.* 15:7, 10
to pass, than *o.* tittle of the. 16:17
if *o.* went from the dead. 30, 31
to see *o.* of the days of the. 17:22
sell his garment, and buy *o.* 22:36
standeth *o.* among you. *John* 1:26
o. of you is a devil. 6:70
have done *o.* work. 7:21
went out *o.* by *o.* beginning at. 8:9
I am *o.* that bear witness of. 18
they said, We have *o.* Father. 41
be *o.* fold, and *o.* shepherd. 10:16
I and my Father are *o.* 30
in *o.* the children of God. 11:52
he hath *o.* that judgeth him. 12:48
that they may be *o.* 17:11, 21, 22
they may be made perfect in *o.* 23
thou not *o.* of this man's? 18:17, 25
o. be ordained to be. *Acts* 1:22
of *o.* heart and of *o.* soul. 4:32
go and enquire for *o.* Saul of. 9:11
there cometh *o.* after me. 13:25
there is another king, *o.* Jesus. 17:7
God hath made of *o.* blood all. 26
except it be for this *o.* voice. 24:21
had questions of *o.* Jesus. 25:19
Paul had spoken *o.* word. 28:25
for a righteous man will *o.* die. *Rom* 5:7
for if through the offence of *o.* 15
by *o.* that sinned, for the judgement was by *o.* to condemnation. 16
death reigned by *o.*; . . . they shall reign in life by *o.*, Jesus Christ. 17
by the offence of *o.*; . . . even so by the righteousness of *o.* 18
so by obedience of *o.* shall many. 19
Rebekah also had conceived by *o.* 9:10
o. saith, I am of Paul. *1 Cor* 3:4
planteth and that watereth are *o.* 8
such fornication, that *o.* have. 5:1
there is none other God but *o.* 8:4
but *o.* God, and *o.* Lord Jesus. 6
all run, but *o.* receiveth the. 9:24
are *o.* bread and *o.* body. 10:17
o. is hungry. 11:21
to *o.* is given by the Spirit the. 12:8
o. Spirit are baptized into *o.* body. 13
o. that believeth not, or *o.* 14:24
let *o.* interpret. 27
for ye may all prophesy *o.* by *o.* 31
was seen of me as of *o.* born. 15:8
if *o.* died for all, then. *2 Cor* 5:14
I have espoused you to *o.* 11:2
received I forty stripes save *o.* 24
of good comfort, be of *o.* mind. 13:11; *Phil* 2:2; *1 Pet* 3:8
Rev 17:13
but as of *o.*, And to thy seed, which is Christ. *Gal* 3:16
ye are all *o.* in Christ. 28
law is fulfilled in *o.* word. 5:14
gather together in *o.* all things. *Eph* 1:10
who hath made both *o.* 2:14
o. new man. 15
both have access by *o.* Spirit. 18
as ye are called in *o.* hope of. 4:4
o. faith, *o.* Lord, *o.* baptism. 5
o. God and Father of all. 6
with *o.* spirit, with *o.* *Phil* 1:27
the husband of *o.* wife. *1 Tim* 3:2
Tit 1:6
bishop, *o.* that ruleth well. *1 Tim* 3:4
be the husbands of *o.* wife. 12
o. of themselves, even a. *Tit* 1:12
but *o.* in a certain place. *Heb* 2:6
that are sanctified are all of *o.* 11
ye have need that *o.* teach you. 5:12
but this man after he had offered *o.* sacrifice. 10:12
by *o.* offering he hath perfected. 14
sprang there even of *o.* so. 11:12
for *o.* morsel of meat sold. 12:16
no city, but we seek *o.* to. 13:14
yet offend in *o.* point, he is. *Jas* 2:10
if any err, and *o.* convert him. 5:19
these three are *o.* *1 John* 5:7
these agree in *o.* 8
o. woe is past, there. *Rev* 9:12
o. of his heads as wounded. 13:3
on the cloud *o.* sat like unto. 14:14
power as kings *o.* hour. 17:12
in *o.* hour is thy judgement. 18:10
in *o.* hour so great riches come. 17
that great city, for in *o.* hour. 19
several gate was of *o.* pearl. 21:21
see **accord, another, day, every, God, heart, little, man, mighty, people**

as one

man is become *as o.* of us. *Gen* 3:22
seemed *as o.* that mocked. 19:14
Dan shall judge *as o.* of the. 49:16
shall be *as o.* that is born in the land. *Ex* 12:48; *Lev* 19:34; 24:22
let her not be *as o.* dead. *Num* 12:12
Gibeon a great city, *as o.* *Josh* 10:2
young man was to him *as o.* of his. *Judg* 17:11
this Philistine shall be *as o.* of them. *1 Sam* 17:36
as when *o.* doth hunt a partridge. 26:20
uncovered *as o.* of the. *2 Sam* 6:20
he shall eat at my table *as o.* 9:11
thou shalt be *as o.* of the fools. 13:13
the king speaketh this *as o.* 14:13
not be left so much *as o.* 17:12
as o. was felling a beam. *2 Ki* 6:5
and singers were *as o.* *2 Chr* 5:13
speakest *as o.* of the foolish women. *Job* 2:10
I am *as o.* mocked of his. 12:4
he counteth me to him *as o.* of. 19:11
as o. that mourneth for. *Ps* 35:14
then the Lord awaked *as o.* 78:65
hast broken Rahab, *as o.* 89:10
I rejoice *as o.* that findeth. 119:162
thy poverty *as o.* that. *Pr* 6:11; 24:3
as the *o.* dieth, so dieth. *Eccl* 3:19
for why should I be *as o.*? *S of S* 1:7
then was I in his eyes *as o.* 8:10
as o. that gathereth eggs. *Isa* 10:14
thy voice *as o.* that hath a. 29:4
as o. whom his mother. 66:13
I will break *as o.* breaketh. *Jer* 19:11
mourn *as o.* in bitterness. *Zech* 12:10
as o. having authority. *Mat* 7:29
Mark 1:22
or *as o.* of the prophets. *Mark* 6:15
he was *as o.* dead. 9:26
as o. of thy hired servants. *Luke* 15:19
as o. that perverteth the people. 23:14
as o. that hath obtained. *1 Cor* 7:25
so fight I, not *as o.* that. 9:26

is one

the people *is o.* *Gen* 11:6
the dream *is o.* 41:25, 26
this *is o.* of the Hebrew. *Ex* 2:6
the Lord our God *is o.* Lord. *Deut* 6:4; *Mark* 12:29
Boaz *is o.* of our next. *Ruth* 2:20
in this place *is o.* greater. *Mat* 12:6
it *is o.* of the twelve. *Mark* 14:20
he is not a Jew that *is o.* *Rom* 2:28
a Jew who *is o.* inwardly. 29
seeing it *is o.* God who shall. 3:30
unto the Lord *is o.* spirit. *1 Cor* 6:17
as body *is o.* and hath many. 12:12
glory of the celestial *is o.* and. 15:40
not a mediator of one, but God *is o.* *Gal* 3:20
who *is o.* of you. *Col* 4:9, 12

not one

if they give *not* thee *o.* *Gen* 24:41
remained *not o.* *Ex* 8:31; 10:19
cattle of Israel died *not o.* 9:6, 7
where there was *not o.* dead. 12:30
shall *not o.* of these men. *Deut* 1:35
was *not o.* city too strong for. 2:36
is *not o.* of them left. *2 Sam* 13:30
there be *not o.* small stone. 17:13
he left him *not o.* that. *1 Ki* 16:11
out of an unclean, *not o.* *Job* 14:4
and did *not o.* fashion us in? 31:15
shall *not o.* be cast down at the? 41:9
there is none that doeth good, *not o.* *Ps* 14:3; 53:3; *Rom* 3:12
was *not o.* feeble person. *Ps* 105:37
strong in power, *not o.* *Isa* 40:26
take heed ye despise *not o.* of these little ones. *Mat* 18:10
none righteous, no *not o.* *Rom* 3:10
no *not o.* that shall be able. *1 Cor* 6:5
for the body is *not o.* member. 12:14

one in reference to *other*

o. was Adah, of *other* Zillah. *Gen* 4:19
the *o.* from the *other.* 13:11
o. end of Egypt to the *other.* 47:21
o. Shiphrah, of the *other.* *Ex* 1:15
o. came not near the *other.* 14:20
hands on *o.* side, and the *other.* 17:12
o. Gershom, of the *other.* 18:3
o. for a sin offering, the *other* for a. *Lev* 5:7; 12:8; *Num* 6:11; 8:12
o. lot for the Lord, *other.* *Lev* 16:8
o. Eldad, the *other.* *Num* 11:26
o. lamb in morning, the *other* at. 28:4
o. side of heaven to *other.* *Deut* 4:32
o. end of earth to *other.* 13:7; 28:64
o. pillar and of the *other.* *Judg* 16:29
o. was Orpah, of *other.* *Ruth* 1:4
o. Hannah, the *other.* *1 Sam* 1:2
o. Baanah, of the *other.* *2 Sam* 4:2
men, *o.* rich, the *other* poor. 12:1
o. saith, This is my son: the *other* saith, Nay. *1 Ki* 3:23
half to *o.* and half to the *other.* 25
pitched *o.* against the *other.* 20:29
o. hand wrought, with *other.* *Neh* 4:17
o. dieth, so dieth the *other.* *Eccl* 3:19
the *o.* over against the *other.* 7:14
Lord shall devour from *o.* end of the land to the *other.* *Jer* 12:12; 25:33
o. basket had good figs, *other.* 24:2
go thee *o.* way or *other.* *Ezek* 21:16
o. horn was higher than the *other.* *Dan* 8:3
o. on this side of river, the *other.* 12:5
o. I called Beauty, the *other.* *Zech* 11:7
o. and love the *other*, or hold to the *o.* and despise the *other.* *Mat* 6:24
Luke 16:13
the *o.* on thy right hand, and the *other* on. *Mat* 20:21; *Mark* 10:37
o. end of heaven to *other.* *Mat* 24:31
o. taken, the *other* left. 40, 41
Luke 17:34, 35, 36
thieves, the *o.* on his right hand, the *other.* *Mark* 15:27; *Luke* 23:33
o. cheek, offer the *other.* *Luke* 6:29
o. owed 500 pence, the *other.* 7:41
o. part, shineth to the *other.* 17:24
the *o.* a Pharisee, the *other.* 18:10
o. angel at the head, *other* at the. *John* 20:12
departed asunder *o.* from *other.* *Acts* 15:39
o. part Sadducees, the *other.* 23:6
defraud ye not *o.* the *other.* *1 Cor* 7:5
to *o.* the savour of life, to *other* of. *2 Cor* 2:16
o. by bondmaid, *other.* *Gal* 4:22
contrary, the *o.* to the *other.* 5:17
and *o.* is, the *other* is not yet come. *Rev* 17:10

there is one

trespass offering, *there is o.* *Lev* 7:7
there is o. tribe cut off. *Judg* 21:6
there is o. law of his to put. *Esth* 4:11
there is o. alone, and there. *Eccl* 4:8
there is o. event to righteous. 9:2
this is an evil, that *there is o.* 3
if ye will not, *there is o.* *Dan* 2:9
there is o. come out of thee. *Nah* 1:11

there is o. God. Mark 12:32
1 Tim 2:5; Jas 2:19
there is o. that accuseth. John 5:45
there is o. that seeketh and. 8:50
there is o. kind of flesh. 1 Cor 15:39
there is o. glory of sun, another. 41
there is o. lawgiver, who. Jas 4:12

one *of them*

as o. of them opened his sack. Gen 42:27
not so much as o. of them. Ex 14:28
have I hurt o. of them. Num 16:15
if o. of them die, and. Deut 25:5
thou art o. of them that. Judg 11:35
shall be as o. of them. 1 Sam 17:36
lacked not o. of them. 2 Sam 17:22
I am o. of them that are. 20:19
three things, choose o. of them. 24:12; 1 Chr 21:10
Baal, let not o. of them escape. 1 Ki 18:40
life as the life of o. of them. 19:2
like the word of o. of them. 22:13
not o. of them is broken. Ps 34:20
every o. of them is gone back. 53:3
as a snail let every o. of them. 58:8
of every o. of them is deep. 64:6
o. of them in Zion appeareth. 84:7
there was not o. of them left. 106:11
be not thou o. of them that strike. Pr 22:26
the labour of the foolish wearieth every o. of them. Eccl 10:15
yet every o. of them doth curse me. Jer 15:10
things, every o. of them. Ezek 11:5
out of o. of them came forth. Dan 8:9
even thou wast as o. of them. Ob 11
o. of them sold for a farthing. Mat 10:29; Luke 12:6
have 100 sheep, and o. of them be gone. Mat 18:12; Luke 15:4
surely thou art o. of them. Mat 26:73; Mark 14:69, 70
o. of them when he saw. Luke 17:15
o. of them may take a little. John 6:7
Jesus by night, being o. of them. 7:50
Lazarus was o. of them that sat. 12:2
seeing o. of them suffer. Acts 7:24
and there stood up o. of them. 11:28

one *thing*

not o. thing hath failed. Josh 23:14
this is o. thing, therefore I said it. Job 9:22
o. thing have I desired of the Lord. Ps 27:4
o. thing befalleth them. Eccl 3:19
I will ask you o. thing. Mat 21:24
Luke 6:9; 20:3
o. thing thou lackest. Mark 10:21
Luke 18:22
but o. thing is needful. Luke 10:42
o. thing I know, that. John 9:25
some cried o. thing, some another. Acts 19:32; 21:34
this o. thing I do, I press. Phil 3:13
ignorant of this o. thing. 2 Pet 3:8

wicked **one**

then cometh the wicked o. Mat 13:19
the children of the wicked o. 38
ye have overcome the wicked o. 1 John 2:13, 14
Cain, who was of that wicked o. 3:12
and that wicked o. toucheth. 5:18

ones

my sanctified o. I have also called my mighty o. for mine. Isa 13:3
came up four notable o. Dan 8:8
face to enter, and upright o. 11:17

Onesimus

O. a faithful and beloved. Col 4:9
beseech thee for my son O. Philem 10

Onesiphorus

mercy to the house of O. 2 Tim 1:16
and the household of O. 4:19

onions

we remember the o. and the garlick. Num 11:5

only

thoughts of his heart are o. Gen 6:5
Noah o. remained alive, and. 7:23
o. to these men do nothing. 19:8
thy son, thine o. son Isaac. Gen 22:2
withheld thy son, thine o. son. 12, 16
o. bring not my son thither. 24:8
o. obey my voice, and go. 27:13
o. herein will the men. 34:22, 23
o. in the throne will I be. 41:40
o. the land of priests. 47:22, 26
remain in the river o. Ex 8:9, 11
I will let you go, o. ye shall not. 28
o. this once, that he may take away from me this death o. 10:17
o. let your flocks and your herds. 24
every man must eat, that o. 12:16
o. he shall pay for the loss. 21:19
to any, save to the Lord o. 22:20
for that is his covering, o. it is. 27
o. he shall not go in unto the vail. Lev 21:23
o. the firstling of the beasts, it. 27:26
o. thou shalt not number. Num 1:49
hath the Lord indeed o. spoken? 12:2
rebel not ye against the Lord o. 14:9
o. they shall not come nigh. 18:3
I will o. go through on my feet. 20:19; Deut 2:28
o. the word that I shall. Num 22:35
o. the gold and the silver. 31:22
o. marry to the family of their. 36:6
o. take heed to thyself. Deut 4:9
saw no similitude, o. ye heard. 12
man doth not live by bread o 8:3
o. the Lord had a delight in. 10:15
o. ye shall not eat the blood. 12:16
23; 15:23
the man o. that lay with her. 22:25
shalt be above o. not beneath. 28:13
thou shalt be o. oppressed. 29, 33
nor with you o. I make this. 29:14
o. be thou strong and very. Josh 1:7, 18
o. Lord thy God be with thee. 17
o. that day compassed the city. 6:15
o. Rahab shall live. 17
burned Hazor o. 11:13
shalt not have one lot o. 17:17
might o. know to teach. Judg 3:2
if dew be on the fleece o. and. 6:37
let it not be dry o. upon the. 39, 40
deliver us o. we pray thee. 10:15
and she was his o. child. 11:34
I pray thee, o. this once. 16:28
the man said, O. lodge not. 19:20
Hannah o. moved her lips. 1 Sam 1:13
o. the Lord establish his word. 23
o. the stump of Dagon was left. 5:4
and serve him o. 7:3, 4; Mat 4:10
Luke 4:8
o. fear the Lord, and. 1 Sam 12:24
o. be thou valiant for me. 18:17
not o. while I live, shew. 20:14
o. Jonathan and David knew. 39
o. Amnon is dead. 2 Sam 13:32, 33
and I will smite the king o. 17:2
deliver him o. and I will. 20:21
returned after him o. to spoil. 23:10
o. the people sacrificed in. 1 Ki 3:2
Gebar was the o. officer who. 4:19
followed David, but Judah o. 12:20
David did that o. which was. 14:8
he o. of Jeroboam shall come. 13
save o. in the matter of Uriah. 15:5
I o. am left, and they. 19:10, 14
fight not, save o. with the. 22:31
worshippers of Baal o. 2 Ki 10:23
left but the tribe of Judah o. 17:18
art the Lord, even thou o. 19:19
Isa 37:20
o. the Lord give thee. 1 Chr 22:12
save o. to burn sacrifice. 2 Chr 2:6
thou o. knowest the hearts of. 6:30
yet to the Lord their God o. 33:17
not done wrong to king o. Esth 1:16
o. on himself put not forth. Job 1:12
I o. am escaped to tell. 15, 16, 17, 19
o. do not two things to me. 13:20
against a nation, or a man o. 34:29
thou, Lord, o. makest me. Ps 4:8
against thee o. have I sinned. 51:4
he o. is my rock and my. 62:2, 6
o. consult to cast him down. 4
my soul, wait thou o. upon God. 5
righteousness, even thine o. 71:16
God of Israel o. doth wondrous. 72:18
o. with thine eyes shalt thou. 91:8
tender and o. beloved in. Pr 4:3
let them be o. thine own, and. 5:17
the righteous is o. good. 11:23
o. by pride cometh contention. 13:10
the talk of the lips tendeth o. 14:23
evil man seeketh o. rebellion. 17:11
tend o. to plenteousness, o. to. 21:5
o. have I found, that God. Eccl 7:29
the o. one of her mother. S of S 6:9
o. let us be called by thy. Isa 4:1
we will o. make mention of. 26:13
it shall be a vexation o. to. 28:19
o. acknowledge thine. Jer 3:13
make mourning as for an o. son. 6:26; Amos 8:10
o. done evil, o. provoked. Jer 32:30
and evil, an o. evil. Ezek 7:5
they o. shall be delivered. 14:16, 18
they shall o. poll their heads. 44:20
you o. have I known of all families. Amos 3:2
salute your brethren o. Mat 5:47
Lord, speak the word o. 8:8
give a cup of cold water o. 10:42
not lawful for him to eat, but o. 12:4
they might o. touch hem of. 14:36
they saw no man, save Jesus o. 17:8
Mark 9:8
nothing thereon but leaves o. Mat 21:19
shall not o. do this which is done. 21
in heaven, but my Father o. 24:36
forgive sins, but God o.? Mark 2:7
Jesus saith, Be not afraid, o. believe. 5:36; Luke 8:50
for journey, save a staff o. Mark 6:8
was a dead man, o. son. Luke 7:12
one o. daughter. 8:42
he is my o. child. 9:38
art thou o. a stranger in. 24:18
not o. because he had broken sabbath. John 5:18
honour that cometh from God o. 44
die, not for that nation o. 11:52
came not for Jesus' sake o. but. 12:9
Lord, not my feet o. but also. 13:9
know thee the o. true God. 17:3
o. they were baptized in. Acts 8:16
the word to none but Jews o. 11:19
Apollos taught, knowing o. 8:25
not o. our craft is in danger to. 19:27
ready not to be bound o. but to. 21:13
o. that they keep themselves from. 25
I would to God, that not o. 26:29
not o. do same, but have. Rom 1:32
is he God of Jews o.? is he? 3:29
this blessedness on circumcision o.? 4:9, 12
not to that o. which is of law. 16
not o. so, but we glory in. 5:3, 11
not o. they, but ourselves. 8:23
he called, not of Jews o. but. 9:24
ye must be subject, not o. for. 13:5
to whom not o. I give thanks. 16:4
to God o. wise be glory. 27
1 Tim 1:17; Jude 25
o. in the Lord. 1 Cor 7:39
I o. and Barnabas. 9:6
came word of God to you o.? 14:36
if in this life o. we have hope. 15:19
us, not by his coming o. 2 Cor 7:7
have begun not o. to do. 8:10
not that o. but was also chosen. 19
not o. in sight of Lord, but in. 21
heard o., he who persecuted. Gal 1:23
o. would that we should. 2:10
this o. would I learn of you. 3:2
not o. when I am present. 4:18
o. use not liberty for an occasion. 5:13
o. lest they should suffer. 6:12
every name named, not o. Eph 1:21
o. let your conversation be. Phil 1:27
is given not o. to believe on him. 29
obeyed, not as in my presence o. 2:12
God had mercy not on him o. 27
no church communicated with me, but ye o. 4:15
o. are my fellow-workers. Col 4:11
gospel came not in word o. 1 Thes 1:5
to you not gospel of God o. 2:8
o. he who now letteth. 2 Thes 2:7
not o. idle, but tattlers. 1 Tim 5:13
is the blessed and o. Potentate. 6:15
who o. hath immortality. 16

ot to me *o.* *2 Tim* 4:8
. Luke is with me. 11
which stood *o.* in meats. *Heb* 9:10
shake not the earth *o.* 12:26
word, and not hearers *o.* *Jas* 1:22
y works, and not faith *o.* 2:24
ot *o.* to good and gentle. *1 Pet* 2:18
ot for our sins *o.* *1 John* 2:2
ot by water *o.* 5:6
ove in the truth, and not I *o.* *2 John* 1
enying the *o.* Lord God. *Jude* 4
ut *o.* those which have. *Rev* 9:4
hee ? for thou *o.* art holy. 15:4
see **begotten**

onward

loud was taken up, Israel went *o.* *Ex* 40:36

onycha

ake thee spices, *o.* and. *Ex* 30:34

onyx

ourth row a beryl and an *o.* *Ex* 28:20; 39:13
wisdom cannot be valued with the *o.* *Job* 28:16
he topaz and the *o.* was. *Ezek* 28:13
see **stones**

open, *adjective*

nd fowl that may fly in *o.* *Gen* 1:20
Tamar sat in an *o.* place by. 38:14*
very *o.* vessel not covered is unclean. *Num* 19:15
he man whose eyes are *o.* hath. 24:3, 4, 15
eft Ai *o.* and pursued. *Josh* 8:17
was no *o.* vision. *1 Sam* 3:1†
arved with *o.* flowers. *1 Ki* 6:18 29:32, 35
yes may be *o.* towards this house. 8:29, 52; *2 Chr* 6:20, 40; 7:15
yes be *o.*, ear attentive. *Neh* 1:6
anballat with an *o.* letter sent. 6:5
s wicked men in the *o.* *Job* 34:26
heir throat is an *o.* sepulchre. *Ps* 5:9; *Rom* 3:13
ighteous, his ears are *o.* *Ps* 34:15
ool layeth *o.* his folly. *Pr* 13:16
. rebuke is better than secret. 27:5
evour Israel with *o.* mouth. *Isa* 9:12
windows from on high are *o.* 24:18
ate shall be *o.* continually. 60:11
uiver is an *o.* sepulchre. *Jer* 5:16
oth what was sealed and *o.* 32:11
yes are *o.* on all the ways. 19
many bones in *o.* valley. *Ezek* 37:2
is windows being *o.* in chamber to Jerusalem. *Dan* 6:10
ates shall be set wide *o.* *Nah* 3:13
ee heaven *o.*, angels. *John* 1:51
eeing prison doors *o.* *Acts* 16:27
he law is *o.* and there are. 19:38
ve all with *o.* face beholding. *2 Cor* 3:18*
nouth is *o.* to you, our heart. 6:11
ome men's sins are *o.* *1 Tim* 5:24*
ut him to an *o.* shame. *Heb* 6:6
is ears are *o.* to their. *1 Pet* 3:12
have set before thee an *o.* *Rev* 3:8
n his hand a little book *o.* 10:2, 8
see **field, fields**

open, *verb*
(*This word is frequently used in a figurative sense*)

f a man shall *o.* a pit. *Ex* 21:33
f such as *o.* every womb. *Num* 8:16
earth *o.* her mouth, and. 16:30
hou shalt *o.* thy hand wide. *Deut* 15:8, 11
answer of peace, and *o.* to thee. 20:11
Lord shall *o.* to thee his good. 28:12
. mouth of cave and. *Josh* 10:22
hen *o.* door and flee. *2 Ki* 9:3
nd he said, *O.* the window. 13:17
God would *o.* his lips. *Job* 11:5
will *o.* my lips, and answer. 32:20
loth Job *o.* his mouth in vain. 35:16
who can *o.* the doors of his ? 41:14
will *o.* my dark saying. *Ps* 49:4
will *o.* my mouth in a parable. 78:2
. thy mouth wide and I will. 81:10
. to me the gates of. 118:19
. thy mouth for the dumb. *Pr* 31:8
. thy mouth, judge righteously. 9
o. to me, my sister, my. *S of S* 5:2
I rose up to *o.* to my beloved. 5
he shall *o.*, and none shall shut, shut and none shall *o.* *Isa* 22:22
o. the gates, that the righteous. 26:2
doth he *o.* and break clods ? 28:24
I will *o.* rivers in high places. 41:18
to *o.* blind eyes, to bring out. 42:7
o. before him the two leaved. 45:1
let the earth *o.*, let them bring. 8
be shut up, none shall *o.* *Jer* 13:19
o. her storehouses, cast her. 50:26
o. thy mouth and eat that. *Ezek* 2:8
I speak with thee, I will *o.* thy. 3:27
confounded and never *o.* 16:63
o. the mouth in the slaughter. 21:22
I will *o.* the side of Moab. 25:9
I will *o.* your graves, and cause. 37:12
one shall *o.* him the gate. 46:12
o. thy doors, O Lebanon. *Zech* 11:1
will not *o.* you windows. *Mal* 3:10
I will *o.* my mouth in. *Mat* 13:35
Lord, *o.* to us. 25:11; *Luke* 13:25
he knocketh, they may *o.* *Luke* 12:36
Paul was about to *o.* his. *Acts* 18:14
that I may *o.* my mouth. *Eph* 6:19
that God would *o.* to us door. *Col* 4:3
is worthy to *o.* the book ? *Rev* 5:2
no man was able to *o.* book. 3
no man was found worthy to *o.* and. 4
Root of David prevailed to *o.* book. 5
to take the book, and *o.* seals. 9
see **eyes**

opened

windows of heaven were *o.* *Gen* 7:11
Noah *o.* the window of the ark. 8:6
God *o.* Leah's womb. 29:31
he *o.* Rachel's. 30:22
Joseph *o.* all storehouses. 41:56
one of them *o.* his sack. 42:27 43:21; 44:11
when she had *o.* ark. *Ex* 2:6
earth *o.* her mouth, and swallowed. *Num* 16:32; *Ps* 106:17
o. not the doors, they *o.* *Judg* 3:25
she *o.* a bottle of milk and. 4:19
her lord *o.* doors, went out. 19:27
and Elisha *o.* the door. *2 Ki* 9:10
they *o.* not to him, therefore. 15:16
Hezekiah *o.* doors of. *2 Chr* 29:3
not gates of Jerusalem be *o.* *Neh* 7:3
Ezra *o.* book; when he *o.* it. 8:5
charged gates not to be *o.* till. 13:19
o. my doors to traveller. *Job* 31:32
the gates of death been *o.*? 38:17*
mine ears hast thou *o.* *Ps* 40:6
though he had *o.* the doors. 78:23
he *o.* the rock, and the. 105:41
I *o.* to my beloved. *S of S* 5:6
that *o.* not the house of. *Isa* 14:17*
time that thine ear was not *o.* 48:8
Lord God hath *o.* mine ear, not. 50:5
thee have I *o.* my cause. *Jer* 20:12*
Lord hath *o.* his armoury. 50:25
that the heavens were *o.* *Ezek* 1:1 *Mat* 3:16; *Mark* 1:10*; *Luke* 3:21 *Acts* 7:56
thou hast *o.* thy feet to. *Ezek* 16:25
when I have *o.* your graves. 37:13
gate shall not be *o.*, no man. 44:2
new moon it shall be *o.* 46:1
was set, the books were *o.* *Dan* 7:10
rivers shall be *o.*, palace. *Nah* 2:6
shall be a fountain *o.* to. *Zech* 13:1
when they had *o.* their. *Mat* 2:11
knock, and it shall be *o.* unto you. 7:7 *Luke* 11:9, 10
the graves were *o.* and many bodies arose. *Mat* 27:52
Ephphatha, that is, Be *o.* *Mark* 7:34
his ears were *o.* 35
when he *o.* book, he found. *Luke* 4:17
o. to us the scriptures. 24:32
then *o.* he their understanding. 45
the angel by night *o.* the. *Acts* 5:19
but when we had *o.* we found. 23
Peter saw heaven *o.* and a. 10:11
the iron gate which *o.* 12:10
o. not the gate, but ran in. 14
when they had *o.* the door. 16
he had *o.* the door of faith. 14:27
Lydia, whose heart the Lord *o.* 16:14
immediately all the doors were *o.* 26
door and effectual is *o.* unto me. *1 Cor* 16:9; *2 Cor* 2:12
are naked and *o.* to him. *Heb* 4:13
a door was *o.* in heaven. *Rev* 4:1
the Lamb *o.* one of the seals. 6:1
had *o.* the second. 3, 5, 7, 9, 12; 8:1
he *o.* the bottomless pit, and. 9:2
the temple of God was *o.* 11:19
of the testimony was *o.* 15:5
I saw heaven *o.* and behold. 19:11
were *o.*: the book of life was *o.* 20:12
see **days, mouth**

openest

thou *o.* thy hand, they are. *Ps* 104:28
o. thine hand and satisfiest. 145:16

openeth

whatsoever *o.* the womb. *Ex* 13:2
set apart all that *o.* 12, 15; 34:19 *Num* 3:12; 18:15; *Luke* 2:23
the rich man *o.* his eyes. *Job* 27:19
he *o.* ears of men, and sealeth. 33:16
he *o.* their ear to discipline. 36:10
he delivereth poor, *o.* their ears. 15
I as a dumb man that *o.* *Ps* 38:13
he that *o.* wide his lips. *Pr* 13:3
o. not his mouth in the gate. 24:7
she *o.* her mouth with wisdom. 31:26
brought as a lamb, so he *o.* *Isa* 53:7
the fire, all that *o.* womb. *Ezek* 20:26
the porter *o.*; sheep hear. *John* 10:3
he that *o.* and no man shutteth, and shutteth and no man *o.* *Rev* 3:7

opening

o. ears, but he heareth not. *Isa* 42:20
o. and alleging that Christ. *Acts* 17:3

opening, -s

o. of house of God. *1 Chr* 9:27
a man, there can be no *o.* *Job* 12:14
in the *o.* of the gates. *Pr* 1:21*
and the *o.* of my lips shall be. 8:6
proclaim the *o.* of the prison. *Isa* 61:1
I will give thee the *o.* of. *Ezek* 29:21

openly

harlot that was *o.* by the way side ? *Gen* 38:21*
hath he *o.* shewed. *Ps* 98:2
thy Father shall reward thee *o.* *Mat* 6:4, 6, 18
spake that saying *o.* *Mark* 8:32
seeketh to be known *o.* *John* 7:4
to the feast, not *o.* but in secret. 10
no man spake of him *o.* for fear. 13
Jesus walked no more *o.* 11:54
I spake *o.* to the world. 18:20
raised up, and shewed him *o.* *Acts* 10:40
they have beaten us *o.* 16:37
shew of them *o.* triumphing. *Col* 2:15

operation

they regard not the *o.* *Ps* 28:5
nor consider the *o.* of his. *Isa* 5:12
the faith of the *o.* of God. *Col* 2:12*

operations

there are diversity of *o.* *1 Cor* 12:6*

Ophel

much on the wall of *O.* *2 Chr* 27:3
Manasseh compassed about *O.* 33:14
Nethinims dwelt in O. *Neh* 3:26 11:21
repaired to the wall of *O.* 27

Ophir

Joktan begat *O.* *Gen* 10:29 *1 Chr* 1:23
they came to *O.* and fetched gold. *1 Ki* 9:28; *2 Chr* 8:18; 9:10
brought from *O.* great. *1 Ki* 10:11
made ships to go to *O.* for. 22:48
talents of gold of *O.* *1 Chr* 29:4
lay up the gold of *O.* *Job* 22:24
valued with the gold of *O.* 28:16
the queen in gold of *O.* *Ps* 45:9
precious than wedge of *O.* *Isa* 13:12

opinion

durst not shew you mine *o.* *Job* 32:6
I also will shew you mine *o.* 10, 17

opinions

halt ye between two *o.*? *1 Ki* 18:21

opportunity

he sought *o.* to betray him. *Mat* 26:16; *Luke* 22:6

as we have o. let us do good. Gal 6:10
careful, but ye lacked o. Phil 4:10
they might have had o. to. Heb 11:15

oppose
instructing those that o. 2 Tim 2:25

opposed
when they o. themselves. Acts 18:6

opposest
thy strong hand thou o. Job 30:21*

opposeth
o. and exalteth himself. 2 Thes 2:4

oppositions
avoiding o. of science. 1 Tim 6:20

oppress
the Egyptians o. them. Exod 3:9
vex nor o. a stranger. 22:21; 23:9
ye shall not o. one. Lev 25:14*, 17*
shalt not o. servant that. Deut 23:16
thou shalt not o. an hired. 24:14
Moabites did o. you. Judg 10:12
thee that thou shouldest o.? Job 10:3
earth may no more o. Ps 10:18
from the wicked that o. me. 17:9†
good, let not proud o. me. 119:122
nor o. the afflicted in. Pr 22:22
will feed them that o. thee. Isa 49:26
if ye o. not the stranger. Jer 7:6
I will punish all that o. them. 30:20
princes shall no more o. Ezek 45:8
merchant, he loveth to o. Hos 12:7
ye kine of Bashan which o. Amos 4:1
they o. a man and his house. Mi 2:2
o. not the widow nor the. Zech 7:10
witness against those that o. Mal 3:5
do not rich men o. you? Jas 2:6

oppressed
thou shalt be only o. Deut 28:29, 33
by reason of them that o. Judg 2:18
Jabin o. Israel. 4:3
out of the hand of the Egyptians, and of all that o. 6:9; 1 Sam 10:18
Philistines and Ammon o. Judg 10:8
whose ox have I taken? whom have I o.? 1 Sam 12:3
thou hast not defrauded, nor o. us. 4
Assyria o. them. 2 Ki 13:4
king of Syria o. Israel. 22
Asa o. some of the people the same time. 2 Chr 16:10
because he hath o. and. Job 20:19
they made the o. to cry. 35:9*
will be a refuge for the o. Ps 9:9
judge the fatherless and o. 10:18
103:6; 146:7
not the o. return ashamed. 74:21
enemies o. them, brought. 106:42
the tears of such as were o. Eccl 4:1
learn to do well, seek judgement, relieve o. Isa 1:17
the people shall be o. every. 3:5
O thou o. virgin, daughter. 23:12
O Lord, I am o., undertake. 38:14
Assyrian o. them without. 52:4
he was o. and afflicted, yet he. 53:7
fast? to let the o. go free. 58:6
Israel and Judah were o. Jer 50:33
hath not o. any, but. Ezek 18:7*, 16*
because he hath o. 12*
he cruelly o. 18
they have o. the stranger. 22:29
Ephraim is o. and broken. Hos 5:11
o. in the midst thereof. Amos 3:9
avenged him that was o. Acts 7:24
Jesus healed all that were o. 10:38

oppresseth
against him that o. you. Num 10:9
he fighting daily o. me. Ps 56:1
he that o. the poor. Pr 14:31; 22:16
a poor man that o. the poor. 28:3

oppressing
go from the o. sword. Jer 46:16
for fear of the o. sword. 50:16
woe to o. city, she obeyed. Zeph 3:1

oppression
I have seen o. wherewith. Ex 3:9
and looked on our o. Deut 26:7
the Lord saw the o. of. 2 Ki 13:4
openeth their ears in o. Job 36:15
for the o. of the poor. Ps 12:5*
o. of the enemy. 42:9; 43:2; 55:3
forgettest our o. 44:24
trust not in o. Ps 62:10
speak wickedly concerning o. 73:8
brought low through o. 107:39
me from the o. of man. 119:134
seest the o. of the poor. Eccl 5:8
o. maketh a wise man mad. 7:7*
but behold o. Isa 5:7
because ye trust in o. 30:12
thou shalt be far from o. 54:14
speaking o. and revolt. 59:13
she is wholly o. in the midst. Jer 6:6
eyes and heart are for o. 22:17
they dealt by o. with. Ezek 22:7
people of the land have used o. 29
not take inheritance by o. 46:18

oppressions
of the multitude of o. Job 35:9
I considered the o. done. Eccl 4:1
despiseth the gain of o. Isa 33:15

oppressor
not the voice of the o. Job 3:18*
of years is hidden to the o. 15:20
break in pieces the o. Ps 72:4
envy not o., choose none. Pr 3:31*
wanteth understanding is an o. 28:16
broken the rod of his o. Isa 9:4
how hath the o. ceased! 14:4
because of the fury of the o. 51:13
deliver him that is spoiled out of the hand of the o. Jer 21:12; 22:3
of the fierceness of the o. 25:38
no o. shall pass through. Zech 9:8
out of him came every o. 10:4*

oppressors
this is the heritage of o. Job 27:13
strangers risen and o. seek. Ps 54:3
leave me not to mine o. 119:121
on the side of their o. there. Eccl 4:1
children are their o., women. Isa 3:12
they shall rule over their o. 14:2
the o. are consumed out of. 16:4
cry to Lord because of the o. 19:20

oracle
[1] *A place of communication from God, as the Jewish Holy of Holies,* 1 Ki 6:16. [2] *The word of God, the Scriptures,* Acts 7:38. *The word, in the sense in which it is used in Greek history, is not found in the Bible, although there are instances where the thing itself seems referred to in other words.*
had enquired at the o. of God. 2 Sam 16:23
for it within, for the o. 1 Ki 6:16
the ark of Lord into the o. 8:6
should burn before the o. 2 Chr 4:20
my hands toward thy holy o. Ps 28:2

oracles
who received the lively o. Acts 7:38
committed the o. of God. Rom 3:2
principles of the o. of God. Heb 5:12
speak as the o. of God. 1 Pet 4:11

oration
Herod made an o. to them. Acts 12:21

orator
from Judah the eloquent o. Isa 3:3*
certain o. named Tertullus. Acts 24:1

orchard
an o. of pomegranates. S of S 4:13

orchards
I made me gardens and o. Eccl 2:5*

ordain
[1] *To command or enjoin,* 1 Cor 9:14. [2] *To appoint or design to a certain end or use,* Rom 7:10. [3] *To choose or set apart for an office or employment,* Mark 3:14.
David and Samuel did o. 1 Chr 9:22
I will o. a place for my people. 17:9*
Lord, thou wilt o. peace. Isa 26:12
so o. I in all churches. 1 Cor 7:17
thou shouldest o. elders. Tit 1:5*

ordained
an offering that was o. in. Num 28:6
Jeroboam o. a feast. 1 Ki 12:32, 33
idolatrous priests o. 2 Ki 23:5
Jeroboam o. priests for. 2 Chr 11:15*
offer the offerings as it was o. 23:18*
instruments o. by David. 2 Chr 29:27
o. the feast of Purim. Esth 9:27
mouth of babes hast thou o. Ps 8:2*
the stars which thou hast o. 3
this he o. in Joseph for a. 81:5*
I have o. a lamp for mine. 132:17
Tophet is o. of old, he. Isa 30:33*
I o. thee to be a prophet. Jer 1:5*
king had o. to destroy. Dan 2:24*
O Lord, thou hast o. them. Hab 1:12
Jesus o. twelve to be. Mark 3:14*
I have o. that ye should. John 15:16*
one o. to be witness with. Acts 1:22*
o. of God to be the judge of. 10:42
as many as were o. to eternal. 13:48
when they had o. them elders. 14:23*
decrees that were o. of apostles. 16:4
he will judge the world by that man whom he hath o. 17:31
which was o. to life. Rom 7:10
powers that be, are o. of God. 13:1
hidden wisdom which God o. 1 Cor 2:7*
the Lord hath o. that they. 9:14
the law was o. by angels. Gal 3:19
which God hath before o. Eph 2:10*
I am o. a preacher and. 1 Tim 2:7*
priest is o. for men. Heb 5:1*; 8:3*
things were thus o., the priests. 9:6*
who were of old o. to this. Jude 4*

ordaineth
he o. his arrows against. Ps 7:13*

order
priests of second o. 2 Ki 23:4
according to their o. 1 Chr 6:32
him not after the due o. 15:13*
the o. commanded to them. 23:31*
according to the o. of David. 25:2, 6
2 Chr 8:14*
darkness, without any o. Job 10:22
priest for ever, after the o. Ps 110:4
Heb 5:6, 10; 6:20; 7:11, 17, 21
given o. to churches of. 1 Cor 16:1
joying and beholding your o. Col 2:5
not be called after o. of. Heb 7:11

***in* order**
Abraham laid wood in o. Gen 22:9
two tenons in o. Ex 26:17*
lamps set in o. 39:37
in o. the things that are to be set in o. 40:4; Lev 1:7, 8, 12; 6:12; 24:8
and he set bread in o. Ex 40:23
stalks of flax she had laid in o. upon the roof. Josh 2:6
put his house in o. 2 Sam 17:23
Elijah put wood in o. 1 Ki 18:33
set thine house in o. 2 Ki 20:1
Isa 38:1
shew bread also set they in o. 2 Chr 13:11
house of the Lord set in o. 29:35
set thy words in o. before. Job 33:5
reckoned up in o. to thee. Ps 40:5
I will set them in o. before. 50:21
the preacher set in o. Eccl 12:9
who declare it, and set it in o.? Isa 44:7
chambers were thirty in o. Ezek 41:6
in hand to set forth in o. Luke 1:1, 3
served before God in his o. 8
country of Phrygia in o. Acts 18:23
the rest will I set in o. 1 Cor 11:34
be done decently and in o. 14:40
shall rise in his o., Christ. 15:23
I left thee to set in o. Tit 1:5

order, *verb*
Aaron and sons shall o. it. Ex 27:21
Lev 24:3, 4*
shall we o. the child? Judg 13:12
who shall o. the battle? 1 Ki 20:14*
o. my cause before him. Job 23:4
teach us, for we cannot o. 37:19
o. my steps in thy word. Ps 119:133
his kingdom to o. it. Isa 9:7*
o. ye the buckler and the. Jer 46:3*

ordered, -eth
to Lord in the o. place. Judg 6:26*
covenant o. and sure. 2 Sam 23:5
now, I have o. my cause. Job 13:18
steps of a good man are o. Ps 37:23*
to him who o. his conversation. 50:23

orderings
their *o.* under Aaron. *1 Chr* 24:19

orderly
walkest *o.* and keepest. *Acts* 21:24

ordinance
[1] *Any decree, statute, or law, made by civil governors,* 1 Pet 2:13. [2] *A law, statute, or commandment of God,* Lev 18:4. *The Revisions frequently substitute the words* charge *or* statute.
Lord the feast of the passover, for an *o.* *Ex* 12:14, 24, 43; 13:10
for them a statute and an *o.* 15:25
according to *o.* of passover. *Num* 9:14
2 Chr 35:13
to you for an *o.* for ever. *Num* 10:8
o. shall be for you in your. 15:15
and to thy sons by an *o.* for ever.
18:8*; *2 Chr* 2:4
o. of law the Lord. *Num* 19:2; 31:21
and he set them an *o.* *Josh* 24:25
made it an *o.* for ever. *1 Sam* 30:25
and made them an *o.* *2 Chr* 35:25
after the *o.* of David. *Ezra* 3:10*
the law, changed the *o.* *Isa* 24:5
forsook not the *o.* of their God. 58:2
concerning the *o.* of oil. *Ezek* 45:14
an offering by a perpetual *o.* 46:14
that we have kept his *o.*? *Mal* 3:14
resisteth the *o.* of God. *Rom* 13:2
to every *o.* of man. *1 Pet* 2:13

ordinances
shalt teach them *o.* and. *Ex* 18:20
shall ye walk in their *o.* *Lev* 18:3
ye shall keep mine *o.* 4, 30; 22:9
2 Chr 33:8; *Ezek* 11:20; 43:11
1 Cor 11:2*
the *o.* of the passover. *Num* 9:12, 14
do they after their *o.* *2 Ki* 17:34
o. which he wrote for you. 37
made *o.* for us to charge. *Neh* 10:32
guide Arcturus? knowest thou the *o.*?
Job 38:33; *Jer* 31:35; 33:25
they kept the *o.* that he. *Ps* 99:7
according to thine *o.* 119:91
the *o.* of justice, delight. *Isa* 58:2
if those *o.* depart from. *Jer* 31:36
he said, These are the *o.* *Ezek* 43:18
o. of the house of the Lord. 44:5
are gone away from mine *o.* *Mal* 3:7
Zacharias and Elisabeth walking in all commandments and *o.* *Luke* 1:6
law of commandments contained in *o.*
Eph 2:15
the handwriting of *o.* *Col* 2:14
in the world, are ye subject to *o.*? 20
the first covenant had *o.* of. *Heb* 9:1
stood in carnal *o.* imposed on. 10

ordinary
diminished thine *o.* food. *Ezek* 16:27

Oreb
slew princes of Midian, Zeeb, *O.*
Judg 7:25; 8:3
nobles like *O.* and Zeeb. *Ps* 83:11
Midian at the rock of *O.* *Isa* 10:26

organ, -s
(*Not the organ as we know it, but a perforated wind instrument, a pipe. It may be the ancient* pipes of Pan, *known to the Greeks. The Revisions translate it by the word* pipe)
father of such as handle *o.* *Gen* 4:21
rejoice at sound of the *o.* *Job* 21:12
o. turned into voice of them. 30:31
with the timbrel and *o.* *Ps* 150:4

Orion
who maketh *O.* and Pleiades.
Job 9:9; *Amos* 5:8
or canst thou loose the bands of *O.*?
Job 38:31

ornament
an *o.* of grace to thy head. *Pr* 1:9*
to thine head an *o.* of grace. 4:9*
an *o.* of fine gold, so is a wise. 25:12
ye shall defile *o.* of thy. *Isa* 30:22*
clothe thee with them all as with an *o.*
49:18
the beauty of his *o.* he set. *Ezek* 7:20
even the *o.* of a meek. *1 Pet* 3:4*

ornaments
no man did put on him his *o.* *Ex* 33:4
now put off thy *o.* from thee. 5, 6
Gideon took *o.* that. *Judg* 8:21*
rings that he requested, beside *o.* 26*
Saul, who put *o.* on your. *2 Sam* 1:24
shall take away tinkling *o.* *Isa* 3:18*
bonnets, and the *o.* of the legs. 20*
decketh himself with *o.* 61:10*
can maid forget her *o.* or? *Jer* 2:32
deckest thee with *o.* of gold. 4:30
art come to excellent *o.* *Ezek* 16:7
decked thee with *o.*, put bracelets. 11
deckedst thyself with *o.* 23:40

Ornan
the threshingfloor of *O.*
1 Chr 21:15, 18, 28
and *O.* turned back, and saw. 20
David gave to *O.* for the place. 25

Orpah
the name of the one was *O.* *Ruth* 1:4
O. kissed Naomi, but Ruth. 14

orphans
we are *o.*, our mothers. *Lam* 5:3

Oshea, *see* **Joshua**

osprey, ossifrage
(*Revisions,* the gier eagle)
eagle, *osp.* and *ossif.* not eat.
Lev 11:13; *Deut* 14:12

ostrich
wings and feathers to *o.*? *Job* 39:13*

ostriches
become cruel, like *o.* in. *Lam* 4:3

other
Noah stayed yet *o.* *Gen* 8:10, 12
is none *o.* but the house. 28:17
me yet *o.* seven years. 29:27, 30
if thou take *o.* wives beside. 31:50
then the *o.* company that is left. 32:8
seven *o.* kine came up. 41:3, 19
send away your *o.* brother. 43:14
o. money have we brought down. 22
was turned again as his *o.* *Ex* 4:7
they asked each *o.* of their. 18:7
the *o.* lamb offer thou at even. 29:41
Num 28:8
ye shall not make any *o.* *Ex* 30:32
put off his garments, and put on *o.*
Lev 6:11; *Ezek* 42:14; 44:19
fat be used in any *o.* use. *Lev* 7:24
take *o.* stones and *o.* mortar. 14:42
take a wife beside the *o.* in. 18:18
separated you from *o.* 20:24, 26
and the *o.* did set up. *Num* 10:21
he went not as at *o.* times. 24:1
they gave *o.* names to the. 32:38
married to any of the *o.* tribes. 36:3
all *o.* cities they took. *Josh* 11:19
came to me the *o.* day. *Judg* 13:10
and be like any *o.* man. 16:17
I will go out as at *o.* times. 20
began to kill as at *o.* times. 20:31
Lord called as at *o.* times, Samuel.
1 Sam 3:10
with his hand as at *o.* times. 18:10
Saul sat on his seat as at *o.* 20:25
for there is no *o.* save. 21:9
evil is greater than *o.* *2 Sam* 13:16
to keep *o.* seven days. *2 Chr* 30:23
Hezekiah from hand of all *o.* 32:22
the *o.* half of them held. *Neh* 4:16
for *o.* men have our lands and. 5:5
flag withereth before any *o.* herb.
Job 8:12
out of the way, as all *o.* 24:24
in trouble as *o.* men, neither are they plagued like *o.* men. *Ps* 73:5
and peace kissed each *o.* 85:10
more rest than the *o.* *Eccl* 6:5
o. lords have had. *Isa* 26:13
after thou hast lost the *o.* 49:20
in thee from *o.* women. *Ezek* 16:34
none *o.* can shew it. *Dan* 2:11
not be left to *o.* people. 44
joy, O Israel, as *o.* people. *Hos* 9:1
where is any *o.* to save? 13:10
he saw *o.* two brethren. *Mat* 4:21
cheek, turn to him the *o.* also. 5:39
restored whole as *o.* 12:13
Mark 3:5; *Luke* 6:10
then he taketh seven *o.* spirits.
Mat 12:45; *Luke* 11:26
o. fell into good ground. *Mat* 13:8
Mark 4:8; *Luke* 8:8
o. servants more. *Mat* 21:36; 22:4
he will let out his vineyard to *o.* 21:41
and not to leave *o.* undone. 23:23
Luke 11:42
came also the *o.* virgins. *Mat* 25:11
and made them *o.* five talents. 16
and the lusts of *o.* *Mark* 4:19
and many *o.* things there be. 7:4, 8
o. commandment is greater. 12:31
God, and there is none *o.* but. 32
preach kingdom of God to *o.* cities.
Luke 4:43
Lord appointed *o.* seventy also. 10:1
or else while the *o.* is yet a. 14:32
that I am not as *o.* men. 18:11
down justified rather than the *o.* 14
o. things blasphemously. 22:65
o. men laboured. *John* 4:38
o. sheep I have. 10:16
not done works none *o.* man. 15:24
went out that *o.* disciple. 18:16
there are many *o.* things. 21:25
to speak with *o.* tongues *Acts* 2:4
and with many *o.* words. 40
salvation in any *o.* none *o.* name under heaven whereby we must be. 4:12
of himself, or of some *o.* man.? 8:34
nor *o.* creature, shall be. *Rom* 8:39
any *o.* commandment, it is. 13:9
whether I baptized any *o.* *1 Cor* 1:16
o. foundation can no man lay. 3:11
lead about sister, as well as *o.* 9:5
every one taketh before *o.* 11:21
but the *o.* is not edified. 14:17
of *o.* tongues and *o.* lips I. 21
speak, and let the *o.* judge. 29
of wheat, or some *o.* grain. 15:37
for I mean not that *o.* *2 Cor* 8:13
not boasting of *o.* men's. 10:15
I robbed *o.* churches to do. 11:8
I write to them and to all *o.* 13:2
o. apostles saw I none. *Gal* 1:19
and the *o.* Jews dissembled. 2:13
which in *o.* ages was not. *Eph* 3:5
that ye walk not as *o.* Gentiles. 4:17
but the *o.* preach Christ. *Phil* 1:17
let each esteem *o.* better than. 2:3
if any *o.* thinketh that he might. 3:4
with Clement and with *o.* my. 4:3
charity toward each *o.* *2 Thes* 1:3
teach no *o.* doctrine. *1 Tim* 1:3
be any *o.* thing contrary to. 10
partaker of *o.* men's sins. 5:22
swear by any *o.* oath. *Jas* 5:12
as a busybody in *o.* *1 Pet* 4:15
they wrest, as they do *o.* *2 Pet* 3:16
on you none *o.* burden. *Rev* 2:24
by reason of the *o.* voices. 8:13
see **God, gods, one, side**

others
of the earth shall *o.* grow. *Job* 8:19
o. bow down upon her. 31:10
shall set *o.* in their stead. 34:24
them in the open sight of *o.* 26
leave their wealth to *o.* *Ps* 49:10
give thine honour to *o.* *Pr* 5:9
likewise hast cursed *o.* *Eccl* 7:22
yet will I gather *o.* to him. *Isa* 56:8
shall be turned to *o.* *Jer* 6:12
I will give their wives unto *o.* 8:10
and they have made *o.* *Ezek* 13:6
o. daubed it with untempered. 10
was diverse from all *o.* *Dan* 7:19
kingdom shall be plucked up for *o.*
11:4
do ye more than *o.*? *Mat* 5:47
o. say, that thou art Jeremias. 16:14
Mark 6:15; 8:28; *Luke* 9:8, 19
he saw *o.* standing idle. *Mat* 20:3
o. cut down branches from trees.
21:8; *Mark* 11:8
o. smote him with the palms of.
Mat 26:67
will give vineyard to *o.* *Mark* 12:9
Luke 20:16
He saved *o.*; himself he cannot save.
Mark 15:31; *Luke* 23:35
o. which ministered to. *Luke* 8:3
did *o.* tell it thee of me? *John* 18:34
if I be not an apostle to *o.* *1 Cor* 9:2
if *o.* be partakers of this power. 12

I have preached to *o.* *1 Cor* 9:27
not thine own, but of the *o.* 10:29
by my voice I might teach *o* 14:19
or need we, as some *o.*, epistles of commendation? *2 Cor* 3:1
of the forwardness of *o.* 8:8
children of wrath, even as *o.* *Eph* 2:3
also on the things of *o.* *Phil* 2:4
nor yet of *o.* sought we. *1 Thes* 2:6
that ye sorrow not, as *o.* which. 4:13
let us not sleep as do *o.* but. 5:6
sin rebuke, that *o.* may. *1 Tim* 5:20
be able to teach *o.* also. *2 Tim* 2:2
every year with blood of *o.* *Heb* 9:25
o. were tortured, not. 11:35
o. had trial of cruel mockings. 36
o. save with fear, pulling. *Jude* 23

otherwise

o. I should have wrought falsehood against mine own. *2 Sam* 18:13
o. it shall come to pass. *1 Ki* 1:21
they eat passover *o.* *2 Chr* 30:18
lest *o.* they should. *Ps* 38:16
o. have no reward of. *Mal* 6:1
o. grace is no more grace; then is it no more grace: *o.* *Rom* 11:6
toward thee goodness: *o.* thou. 22
if *o.* yet as a fool. *2 Cor* 11:16
will be none *o.* minded. *Gal* 5:10
any thing you be *o.* minded *Phil* 3:15
and they that are *o.* *1 Tim* 5:25
if any man teach *o.* and consent. 6:3
o. it is of no strength at. *Heb* 9:17

Othniel

O. son of Kenaz took it. *Josh* 15:17
Judg 1:13
Lord raised a deliverer, *O.* *Judg* 3:9
O. died. 11
sons of Kenaz, *O.* Seraiah, sons of *O.* *1 Chr* 4:13
captain was Heldai of *O.* 27:15

ouches

(*Ornaments set with jewels. American Revision changes to* setting *except in starred reference*)

set the stones in *o.* of gold. *Ex* 28:11; 39:6, 13
shalt make *o.* of gold. 28:13
fasten wreathen chains to the *o.* 14; 39:18*
fasten in the two *o.* 28:25

ought, *see* **owed**

ought

that *o.* not to be done. *Gen* 20:9
34:7; *Lev* 4:2, 27
no such thing *o.* to be. *2 Sam* 13:12
to know what Israel *o.* *1 Chr* 12:32
none *o.* to carry the ark but. 15:2
o. ye not to know Lord. *2 Chr* 13:5
o. ye not to walk in the? *Neh* 5:9
to him who *o.* to be feared. *Ps* 76:11
these *o.* ye to have done. *Mat* 23:23; *Luke* 11:42
desolation standing where it *o.* not. *Mark* 13:14
hour what ye *o.* to say. *Luke* 12:12
days in which men *o.* to work. 13:14
o. not this man to be loosed? 16
that men *o.* always to pray. 18:1
O fools, *o.* not Christ to? 24:26
the place where men *o.* *John* 4:20
o. to wash one another's feet. 13:14
and by our law he *o.* to die. 19:7
we *o.* to obey God. *Acts* 5:29
o. not to think the Godhead. 17:29
ye *o.* to be quiet, and to do. 19:36
how so labouring ye *o.* to. 20:35
that they *o.* not to circumcise. 21:21
who *o.* to have been here. 24:19
judgement seat, where I *o.* to. 25:10
crying, that he *o.* not to live. 24
that I *o.* to do many things. 26:9
what to pray for as we *o.* *Rom* 8:26
more highly than he *o.* 12:3
we *o.* to bear the infirmities of. 15:1
nothing as he *o.* to know. *1 Cor* 8:2
o. not to cover his head. 11:7
the woman *o.* to have power. 10
of whom I *o.* to rejoice. *2 Cor* 2:3
ye *o.* rather to forgive him. 7
I *o.* to have been commended. 12:11
the children *o.* not to lay up. *2 Cor* 12:14
so *o.* men to love their. *Eph* 5:28
may speak boldly, as I *o.* to speak. 6:20; *Col* 4:4
know how ye *o.* to answer. *Col* 4:6
how ye *o.* to walk. *1 Thes* 4:1
know how ye *o.* to follow. *2 Thes* 3:7
speaking things which they *o.* not. *1 Tim* 5:13
teaching things which they *o.* not. *Tit* 1:11
we *o.* to give the more. *Heb* 2:1
he *o.* for people and for himself. 5:3
for when for the time ye *o.* 12
these things *o.* not so to be. *Jas* 3:10
for that ye *o.* to say, If the. 4:15
persons *o.* ye to be? *2 Pet* 3:11
o. himself also to walk. *1 John* 2:6
o. to lay down our lives for. 3:16
if God loved us, we *o.* also. 4:11
we therefore *o.* to receive. *3 John* 8

ought, *substantive*

(*Practically everywhere the Revisions have changed this to* aught)

he knew not *o.* that he had. *Gen* 39:6
there is not *o.* left, but our bodies. 47:18
ye shall not diminish *o.* thereof. *Ex* 5:8; 11:19
thou shalt not carry forth *o.* 12:46
if a man borrow *o.* of his. 22:14
o. of flesh of the consecrations. 29:34
beareth *o.* of carcase. *Lev* 11:25
if *o.* remain unto third day. 19:6
if thou sellest *o.* or buyest *o.* 25:14
redeem *o.* of his tithes. 27:31
if *o.* be committed by. *Num* 15:24
the soul that doeth *o.* 30
when she vowed, or uttered *o.* 30:6
add or diminish *o.* from it. *Deut* 4:2
lendeth *o.* to his neighbour. 15:2
neither have I taken away *o.* for any unclean use, nor given *o.* 26:14
there failed not *o.* of any. *Josh* 21:45
if *o.* but death part thee. *Ruth* 1:17
nor hast thou taken *o.* *1 Sam* 12:4
that ye have not found *o.* in. 5
neither was there *o.* missing. 25:7
we will not give them *o.* 30:22
if I taste bread or *o.* *2 Sam* 3:35
whoso saith *o.* to thee. 14:10
none can turn from *o.* my lord. 19
that thy brother hath *o.* *Mat* 5:23
if any man say *o.* to you, ye. 21:3
him no more to do *o.* *Mark* 7:12
and asked him if he saw *o.* 8:23
if ye have *o.* against any. 11:25
brought him *o.* to eat? *John* 4:33
neither said any that *o.* *Acts* 4:32
and object, if they had *o.* 24:19
that I had *o.* to accuse my. 28:19
if he oweth thee *o.* put to. *Philem* 18

oughtest

what thou *o.* to do to him. *1 Ki* 2:9
thou *o.* to have put my. *Mat* 25:27
thee what thou *o.* to do. *Acts* 10:6
how thou *o.* to behave. *1 Tim* 3:15

our, *see* **brother, father, Lord**

ours

saying, The water is *o.* *Gen* 26:20
from our father that is *o.* 31:16
every beast of theirs be *o.*? 34:23
side Jordan may be *o.* *Num* 32:32
Ramoth in Gilead is *o.* *1 Ki* 22:3
ancient high places are *o.* *Ezek* 36:2
and inheritance shall be *o.* *Mark* 12:7; *Luke* 20:14
Jesus, both theirs and *o.* *1 Cor* 1:2
ye also are *o.* in the day. *2 Cor* 1:14
let *o.* also learn to maintain. *Tit* 3:14

ourselves

and bow down *o.*? *Gen* 37:10
how shall we clear *o.*? 44:16
o. will go ready armed. *Num* 32:17
for a prey unto *o.* *Deut* 2:35; 3:7
we will discover *o.* *1 Sam* 14:8
we *o.* together will build. *Ezra* 4:3
that we might afflict *o.* before. 8:21
among *o.* what is good. *Job* 34:4
let us take to *o.* houses. *Ps* 83:12
made us, and not we *o.* *Ps* 100:3
come, let us solace *o.* *Pr* 7:18
falsehood have we hid *o.* *Isa* 28:15
we will fill *o.* with strong. 56:12
come let us join *o.* to. *Jer* 50:5
we *o.* have heard. *Luke* 22:71
John 4:42
we will give *o.* to prayer. *Acts* 6:4
we have bound *o.* under a. 23:14
we *o.* groan within *o.* *Rom* 8:23
bear and not to please *o.* 15:1
if we would judge *o.* *1 Cor* 11:31
wherewith we *o.* are. *2 Cor* 1:4
that we should not trust in *o.* 9
again to commend *o.* to you? 3:1
not that we are sufficient of *o.* to think any thing as of *o.*, but our. 5
commending *o.* to every man's. 4:2
for we preach not *o.* but Christ Jesus the Lord, and *o.* your servants. 5
for we commend not *o.* again. 5:12
whether we be beside *o.* it is. 13
in all things approving *o.* 6:4
let us cleanse *o.* from all. 7:1
or compare *o.* with some. 10:12
we stretch not *o.* beyond. 14
think ye we excuse *o.*? 12:19
we *o.* also are found. *Gal* 2:17
how holily we behaved *o.* *1 Thes* 2:10
so that we *o.* glory in. *2 Thes* 1:4
we behaved not *o.* disorderly. 3:7
make *o.* an ensample unto you. 9
for we *o.* were sometimes. *Tit* 3:3
the assembling of *o.* *Heb* 10:25
we deceive *o.*, the truth. *1 John* 1:8

out

o. of ground made Lord. *Gen* 2:9
she was taken *o.* of man. 23
for *o.* of it wast thou taken. 3:19
your sin will find you *o.* *Num* 32:23
as for the earth, *o.* of it. *Job* 28:5
o. of the mouth of babes. *Ps* 8:2
foundations of the earth are *o.* 82:5
thou teachest *o.* of thy law. 94:12
blessed you *o.* of house. 118:26
keep thy heart, for *o.* of it. *Pr* 4:23
candle goeth not *o.* by night. 31:18
sinners thereof *o.* of it. *Isa* 13:9
see *o.* of obscurity, *o.* of. 29:18
shall be saved *o.* of it. *Jer* 30:7
and *o.* of them shall proceed. 19
behold I will seek *o.* *Ezek* 34:11
that they bear them not *o.* into. 46:20
yet *o.* of thee shall he come forth to. *Mi* 5:2; *Mat* 2:6
o. of him came forth. *Zech* 10:4
o. of the abundance of. *Mat* 12:34
o. of good treasure: . . . *o.* of evil. 35
o. of the heart proceed evil. 15:19
they were astonished *o.* *Mark* 10:26
nor enter to take any thing *o.* 13:15
o. of whom he had cast seven. 16:9
o. of thine own mouth. *Luke* 19:22
I have chosen you *o.* *John* 15:19
devout men, *o.* of every. *Acts* 2:5
both *o.* of the law, and *o.* 28:23
seen of me, as of one born *o.* of due time. *1 Cor* 15:8
for *o.* of much affliction. *2 Cor* 2:4
be a performance *o.* of that. 8:11
recover themselves *o.* of. *2 Tim* 2:26
but *o.* of them all the Lord. 3:11
instant in season, *o.* of season. 4:2
o. of same mouth proceedeth blessing and cursing. *Jas* 3:10
see **camp, captivity, city, darkness, way, Zion**

outcast

they called thee an *o.* *Jas* 30:17

outcasts

he gathereth *o.* of Israel. *Ps* 147:2
Isa 56:8
he shall assemble the *o.* *Isa* 11:12
hide the *o.* 16:3
let my *o.* dwell with thee. 4
the *o.* in the land of Egypt. 27:13
whither the *o.* of Elam. *Jer* 49:36

outer

into the *o.* court. *Ezek* 46:21
way without to the *o.* gate. 47:2
be cast into *o.* darkness. *Mat* 8:12
22:13; 25:30

outgoings
the *o.* of it were at the sea. *Josh* 17:9; 19:39
o. of it shall be thine. 18
the *o.* of the border were. 18:19
o. thereof are in the valley. 19:14
the *o.* of their border were. 22, 33
thou makest the *o.* of the. *Ps* 65:8

outlandish
(*This word formerly meant strictly out-landish;* i.e. *anything which was from another country with other customs, hence* strange, *as the Revisions put it*)
even *o.* women caused Solomon to sin. *Neh* 13:26

outlived
elders that *o.* Joshua. *Judg* 2:7

outrageous
cruel and anger is *o.* *Pr* 27:4†

outrun
disciple did *o.* Peter. *John* 20:4

outside
Gideon went to *o.* of the. *Judg* 7:11
and when I come to the *o.* of. 17
came to the *o.* of the camp. 19
and so on *o.* toward the. *1 Ki* 7:9
behold a wall on the *o.* *Ezek* 40:5
make clean *o.* of the cup. *Mat* 23:25; *Luke* 11:39
o. of them may be clean also. 26

outstretched
out with an *o.* arm. *Deut* 26:8
against you with an *o.* hand. *Jer* 21:5
made the earth by my *o.* arm. 27:5

outward
for man looketh on the *o.* *1 Sam* 16:7
Chenaniah for the *o.* *1 Chr* 26:29
Levites for *o.* business. *Neh* 11:16
come into the *o.* court. *Esth* 6:4
me into the *o.* court. *Ezek* 40:17
which appear beautiful *o.* *Mat* 23:27
nor circumcision, which is *o.* *Rom* 2:28
though our *o.* man perish. *2 Cor* 4:16
on things after *o.* appearance? 10:7
not that *o.* adorning of. *1 Pet* 3:3

outwardly
ye *o.* appear righteous. *Mat* 23:28
for he is not a Jew which is one *o.* *Rom* 2:28

outwent
afoot thither, and *o.* *Mark* 6:33

oven
(*The word frequently means* furnace)
offering baken in the *o.* *Lev* 2:4; 7:9
be unclean, whether it be *o.* 11:35
bake your bread in one *o.* 26:26
make them as a fiery *o.* *Ps* 21:9
skin was black like an *o.* *Lam* 5:10
adulterers, as an *o.* heated. *Hos* 7:4
made ready their heart like an *o.* 6
are all hot as an *o.*, have devoured. 7
that shall burn as an *o.* *Mal* 4:1
grass, which to-morrow is cast into the *o.* *Mat* 6:30; *Luke* 12:28

ovens
frogs shall come into thine *o.* *Ex* 8:3

over
first red, all *o.* like an. *Gen* 25:25
lord *o.* thy brethren, let them. 27:29
Pharaoh said, Thou shalt be *o.* 41:40
gathered much had nothing *o.* *Ex* 16:18; *2 Cor* 8:15
what remaineth *o.* lay up. *Ex* 16:23
the mercy seat *o.* the testimony. 30:6; *Heb* 9:5
the cherubims covered *o.* the mercy seat. *Ex* 37:9
cloud was taken up from *o.* 40:36
one be killed *o.* running water. *Lev* 14:5; 6:50
shalt appoint Levites *o.* *Num* 1:50
o. and above them that were. 3:49
trumpets *o.* burnt offerings. 10:10
let the Lord set a man *o.* 27:16
dominion *o.* the nobles, *o.* *Judg* 5:13
and go to be promoted *o.* the trees. 9:9, 11, 13
o. Saul and Jonathan. *2 Sam* 1:17, 24
king *o.* Gilead, *o.* Ashurites, *o.* Jezreel, *o.* Ephraim and *o.* *2 Sam* 2:9
Edom made a king *o.* *2 Ki* 8:20
o. and above all I have. *1 Chr* 29:3
increased *o.* our heads. *Ezra* 9:6
not watch *o.* my sin? *Job* 14:16
he is a king *o.* the children. 41:34
my cup runneth *o.* *Ps* 23:5
deliver me not *o.* to the will. 27:12
but he hath not given me *o.* 118:18
his tender mercies are *o.* all. 145:9
neither make thyself *o.* wise. *Eccl* 7:16
past, rain is *o.* and gone. *S of S* 2:11
set thee *o.* nations and *o.* *Jer* 1:10
he setteth up *o.* it the basest of men. *Dan* 4:17
king thought to set him *o.* the. 6:3
people shall mourn *o.* it. *Hos* 10:5
shall be dark *o.* them. *Mi* 3:6
thee ruler *o.* many. *Mat* 25:21, 23
together, and running *o.* *Luke* 6:38
more joy *o.* one sinner. 15:7, 10
this man to reign *o.* us. 19:14
thou authority *o.* ten cities. 17
he beheld city, and wept *o.* it. 41
appoint *o.* this business. *Acts* 6:3
hath dominion *o.* a man. *Rom* 7:1
the potter power *o.* the clay? 9:21
given *o.* to lasciviousness. *Eph* 4:19
authority *o.* the man. *1 Tim* 2:12
eyes of the Lord are *o.* *1 Pet* 3:12
to him will I give power *o.* *Rev* 2:26
see **all, him, Jordan, Israel, me, thee, them, us, you**

over *against*
candlestick *o. against* table. *Ex* 26:35; 40:24
o. against candlestick. *Num* 8:2*, 3*
come on them *o. against* mulberry. *2 Sam* 5:23; *1 Chr* 14:14
pitched one *o. against.* *1 Ki* 20:29
one to be *o. against* house. *Neh* 7:3
set one *o. against* the. *Eccl* 7:14*
line shall yet go forth *o. against* it. *Jer* 31:39*
go into village *o. against.* *Mat* 21:2
Mark 11:2; *Luke* 19:30
and Mary sitting *o. against* the sepulchre. *Mat* 27:61

overcame
evil spirit was, *o.* them. *Acts* 19:16
even as I also *o.* and am. *Rev* 3:21
and they *o.* him by the blood. 12:11

overcharge
that I may not *o.* you all. *2 Cor* 2:5*

overcharged
lest your hearts be *o.* *Luke* 21:34

overcome
o. him, but he shall *o.* *Gen* 49:19*
that cry for being *o.* *Ex* 32:18
we are well able to *o.* it. *Num* 13:30
peradventure I be able to *o.* 22:11*
Ahaz, could not *o.* him. *2 Ki* 16:5
eyes, for they have *o.* me. *S of S* 6:5
head of them that are *o.* with wine. *Isa* 28:1
man whom wine hath *o.* *Jer* 23:9
a stronger shall *o.* him. *Luke* 11:22
I have *o.* the world. *John* 16:33
and mightest *o.* when. *Rom* 3:4*
be not *o.* of evil, but *o.* evil. 12:21
of whom a man is *o.*, of same is he brought. *2 Pet* 2:19
for if they are again entangled therein and *o.* 20
o. the wicked one. *1 John* 2:13, 14
ye are of God and have *o.* them. 4:4
beast shall *o.* witnesses. *Rev* 11:7
the saints, and to *o.* them. 13:7
and the Lamb shall *o.* them. 17:14

overcometh
of God, *o.* the world: this is victory that *o.* world, even. *1 John* 5:4
who is he that *o.* world, but he? 5
to him that *o.* will I give. *Rev* 2:7
he that *o.* shall not be hurt. 11
to him that *o.* will I give to eat. 17
to him that *o.* will I give power. 26
he that *o.* shall be clothed. 3:5
him that *o.* will I make pillar. 12
to him that *o.* will I grant. 21
he that *o.* shall inherit all. 21:7

overdrive
if men should *o.* them all. *Gen* 33:13

overflow
of Red sea to *o.* them. *Deut* 11:4
where the floods *o.* me. *Ps* 69:2
let not water flood *o.* me, nor. 15*
pass through Judah, *o.* *Isa* 8:8
consumption decreed shall *o.* 10:22
waters shall *o.* hiding place. 28:17
rivers they shall not *o.* thee. 43:2
north shall *o.* the land. *Jer* 47:2
one shall certainly come and *o.* *Dan* 11:10; 26:40
fats shall *o.* with wine and oil. *Joel* 2:24; 3:13

overflowed
rock, and streams *o.* *Ps* 78:20
world being *o.* with water. *2 Pet* 3:6

overfloweth
Jordan *o.* all his banks. *Josh* 3:15

overflowing
bindeth the floods from *o.* *Job* 28:11*
water course for *o.* of waters. 38:25
flood of mighty waters *o.* *Isa* 28:2
when the *o.* scourge shall. 15, 18
his breath as an *o.* stream. 30:28
north shall be an *o.* flood. *Jer* 47:2
be an *o.* shower. *Ezek* 13:11, 13
I will rain on him an *o.* rain. 38:22
o. of the water passed. *Hab* 3:10*

overflown
Jordan when it had *o.* *1 Chr* 12:15†
whose foundation was *o.* *Job* 22:16
flood shall they be *o.* *Dan* 11:22*

overlaid
shittim wood *o.* with gold. *Ex* 26:32
o. the staves of shittim wood. 38:6
died, because she *o.* it. *1 Ki* 3:19
he *o.* the doors of them. *2 Chr* 4:9
belly is as bright ivory *o.* *S of S* 5:14

overlay
shalt *o.* ark with pure gold. *Ex* 25:11, 24; 30:3
o. the horns of the altar with brass. 27:2; 38:2
see **gold**

overlaying
the *o.* of their chapiters. *Ex* 38:17
o. of their chapiters and fillets. 19

overlived
elders that *o.* Joshua. *Josh* 24:31*

overmuch
be not righteous *o.* *Eccl* 7:16
be not *o.* wicked. 17
be swallowed up with *o.* sorrow. *2 Cor* 2:7

overpass
they shine: they *o.* the deeds. *Jer* 5:28

overpast
until these calamities be *o.* *Ps* 57:1
until indignation be *o.* *Isa* 26:20

overplus
let him restore the *o.* *Lev* 25:27

overran
by plain and *o.* Cushi. *2 Sam* 18:23

overrunning
with an *o.* flood he will. *Nah* 1:8

oversee
some appointed to *o.* *1 Chr* 9:29*
and 3600 to *o.* them. *2 Chr* 2:2

overseer
he made him *o.* over. *Gen* 39:4, 5
Joel was their *o.* *Neh* 11:9
Zabdiel was *o.* 14
o. of Levites was Uzzi. 22
Jezrahiah was *o.* 12:42
the ant having no guide, *o.* *Pr* 6:7

overseers
let Pharaoh appoint *o.* *Gen* 41:34
Solomon set 3600 *o.* of the work. *2 Chr* 2:18
o. under hand of Cononiah. 31:13*
o. of all them that wrought. 34:12, 13
money into hand of *o.* 17
H. G. hath made you *o.* *Acts* 20:28

overshadow
Highest shall *o.* thee. *Luke* 1:35
of Peter might *o.* them. *Acts* 5:15

overshadowed
a cloud *o.* them. *Mat* 17:5
Mark 9:7; *Luke* 9:34

oversight
peradventure it was an *o. Gen* 43:12
have the *o.* of them. *Num* 3:32
pertaineth the *o.* of all the. 4:16*
of them that had the *o.* *2 Ki* 12:11
22:5, 9; *2 Chr* 34:10
had the *o.* of the gates. *1 Chr* 9:23
o. of outward business. *Neh* 11:16
o. of the chamber of the house. 13:4*
taking *o.* not by constraint. *1 Pet* 5:2

overspread
was the whole earth *o.* *Gen* 9:19

overspreading
for the *o.* of abominations. *Dan* 9:27*

overtake
up, when thou dost *o.* *Gen* 44:4
I will pursue, I will *o.* *Ex* 15:9
lest avenger of blood *o.* *Deut* 19:6
shall come and *o.* thee. 28:2
these curses shall *o.* thee. 15, 45
them, for ye shall *o.* them. *Josh* 2:5
Shall I *o.* them? Pursue: for thou shalt surely *o.* them. *1 Sam* 30:8
lest Absalom *o.* us. *2 Sam* 15:14
neither doth justice *o.* us. *Isa* 59:9
ye feared shall *o.* you. *Jer* 42:16
she shall not *o.* her lovers. *Hos* 2:7
Gibeah did not *o.* them. 10:9
not *o.* nor prevent us. *Amos* 9:10
behold, the plowman shall *o.* 13
should *o.* you as a thief. *1 Thes* 5:4

overtaken
mine enemies and *o.* *Ps* 18:37
brethren, if a man be *o.* *Gal* 6:1

overtaketh
while sword *o.* thee. *1 Chr* 21:12

overthrew
God *o.* these cities. *Gen* 19:25, 29
Lord *o.* the Egyptians. *Ex* 14:27
Ps 136:15
Lord *o.* in his anger. *Deut* 29:23
as when God *o.* Sodom. *Isa* 13:19
Jer 50:40; *Amos* 4:11
be as the cities Lord *o.* *Jer* 20:16
Jesus *o.* tables of the. *Mat* 21:12
Mark 11:15; *John* 2:15

overthrow
I will not *o.* this city. *Gen* 19:21
thou shalt utterly *o.* them. *Ex* 23:24
ye shall *o.* their altars. *Deut* 12:3*
sent to spy it out and *o.* *2 Sam* 10:3
battle more strong, and *o.* it. 11:25
David hath sent to *o.* and. *1 Chr* 19:3
his hand to *o.* them in the. *Ps* 106:26
to *o.* their seed also among the. 27
who have purposed to *o.* 140:4*
the violent man to *o.* him. 11
not good to *o.* righteous. *Pr* 18:5*
I will *o.* the throne of kingdoms, I will *o.* the chariots. *Hag* 2:22
of God, ye cannot *o.* it. *Acts* 5:39
and *o.* the faith of some. *2 Tim* 2:18

overthrow, *substantive*
out of the midst of the *o. Gen* 19:29
as in the *o.* of Sodom. *Deut* 29:23
Jer 49:18
the cities with an *o.* *2 Pet* 2:6

overthroweth
princes, and *o.* the mighty. *Job* 12:19
but wickedness *o.* the. *Pr* 13:6
God *o.* the wicked for. 21:12
he *o.* the words of the. 22:12
but he that receiveth gifts *o.* 29:4

overthrown
hast *o.* them that rose up. *Ex* 15:7
and many were *o.* *Judg* 9:40*
when some of them be *o.* at the first.
2 Sam 17:9*
Ethiopians were *o.* *2 Chr* 14:13*
that God hath *o.* me. *Job* 19:6
judges are *o.* in stony places.
Ps 141:6
city is *o.* by the mouth. *Pr* 11:11
the wicked are *o.*, and are not. 12:7
house of wicked shall be *o.* 14:11
your land is desolate, as *o.* *Isa* 1:7
but let them be *o.* before. *Jer* 18:23
sin of Sodom, that was *o.* *Lam* 4:6
countries shall be *o.* *Dan* 11:41
I have *o.* some of you. *Amos* 4:11
and Nineveh shall be *o.* *Jonah* 3:4
o. in the wilderness. *1 Cor* 10:5

overtook
they *o.* Jacob in the. *Gen* 31:23
Laban *o.* Jacob. 25
the steward *o.* them. 44:6
Egyptians *o.* them. *Ex* 14:9
Micah *o.* the children. *Judg* 18:22
but the battle *o.* the men. 20:42*
the army of Chaldees *o.* *2 Ki* 25:5
Jer 39:5; 52:8
all her persecutors *o.* her. *Lam* 2:3

overturn
waters, they *o.* earth. *Job* 12:15
I will *o.*, *o.*, *o.* it, until. *Ezek* 21:27

overturned
tent that it fell and *o.* it. *Judg* 7:13*

overturneth
which *o.* the mountains. *Job* 9:5
o. the mountains by the roots. 28:9
knoweth their works and *o.* 34:25

overwhelm
ye *o.* fatherless, dig a pit. *Job* 6:27*

overwhelmed
and horror hath *o.* me. *Ps* 55:5
when my heart is *o.* lead me. 61:2
and my spirit was *o.* 77:3; 142:3
143:4
but the sea *o.* their enemies. 78:53
then the waters had *o.* us. 124:4

owe
o. no man any thing. *Rom* 13:8

owed
o. him 10,000 talents. *Mat* 18:24
and found one which *o.* him an. 28
the one *o.* 500 pence. *Luke* 7:41

owest
pay me that thou *o.* *Mat* 18:28
how much *o.* thou unto my lord?
Luke 16:5, 7
thou *o.* to me even thine. *Philem* 19

oweth
hath wronged thee, or *o.* *Philem* 18

owl
(*While different sorts of owls are found in Palestine, the word so translated more often means some other bird or animal, usually the* ostrich)
o. and cuckow unclean. *Lev* 11:16*
Deut 14:15*, 16
the little *o.* and cormorant.
Lev 11:17; *Isa* 34:11, 15*
I am like an *o.* of desert. *Ps* 102:6

owls
(*Revisions in all cases,* ostriches)
companion to *o.*, a brother. *Job* 30:29
the wild beasts shall lie there, and *o.*
Isa 13:21; 34:13; *Jer* 50:39
the dragons and *o.* shall. 43:20
a mourning as the *o.* *Mi* 1:8

own
man in his *o.* image. *Gen* 1:27
begat a son in his *o.* likeness. 5:3
shall come of thine *o.* bowels. 15:4
I may go to mine *o.* place. 30:25
four parts shall be your *o.* 47:24
dead shall be his *o.* *Ex* 21:36
of the best of his *o.* field shall. 22:5
he shall offer it of his own. *Lev* 1:3
his *o.* hands shall bring the. 7:30
palm of his *o.* left hand. 14:15, 26
theirs is thine *o.* nakedness. 18:10
nor any of your *o.* nation, nor. 26
groweth of its *o.* accord. 25:5
and he shall return to his *o.* 41
his *o.* camp, by his *o.* *Num* 1:52
them of mine *o.* mind. 16:28; 24:13
sinners against their *o.* souls. 16:38
he called it after his *o.* name. 32:42
Deut 3:14
shall keep himself to his *o. Num* 36:9
eat grapes at thine *o.* *Deut* 23:24
sleep in his *o.* raiment. 24:13
every man shall be put to death for *o.* sin. 16; *2 Ki* 14:6; *2 Chr* 25:4
fruit of thine *o.* body. *Deut* 28:53
nor knew he his *o.* children. 33:9
even among their *o.* stuff. *Josh* 7:11
from their *o.* doings. *Judg* 2:19
saying, Mine *o.* hand hath. 7:2
went to their *o.* home. *1 Sam* 2:20
ark go again to his *o.* place. 5:11
wast little in thine *o.* sight. 15:17
avenging with thine *o.* hand. 25:26
base in mine *o.* sight. *2 Sam* 6:22
dwell in a place of their *o.* 7:10
did eat of his *o.* meat, and. 12:3
to battle in thine *o.* person. 17:11
falsehood against mine *o.* life. 18:13
word against his *o.* life. *1 Ki* 2:23
blood on his *o.* head. 32, 37
carcase in his *o.* grave. 13:30
laid him upon his *o.* bed. 17:19
made gods of their *o.* *2 Ki* 17:29
and of thine *o.* have. *1 Chr* 29:14
store we prepared, is all thine *o.* 16
his way on his *o.* head. *2 Chr* 6:23
reproach on their *o.* head. *Neh* 4:4
should return on *o.* head. *Esth* 9:25
perish for ever like his *o.* *Job* 20:7
let them fall by their *o.* *Ps* 5:10
our lips are our *o.*: who is? 12:4
God, even our *o.* God, shall. 67:6
he gave them their *o.* desire. 78:29
up to their *o.* hearts' lust. 81:12
their *o.* iniquity, and shall cut them off in their *o.* wickedness. 94:23
let them be only thy *o.* *Pr* 5:17
for mine *o.* sake. *Isa* 37:35; 43:25
48:11
o. pleasure, nor *o.* words. 58:13
my river is mine *o.* *Ezek* 29:3
to his *o.* righteousness. 33:13
now their *o.* doings have. *Hos* 7:2
forsake their *o.* mercy. *Jonah* 2:8
what I will with mine *o.*? *Mat* 20:15
hate not his *o.* life also. *Luke* 14:26
you that which is your *o.*? 16:12
o., his *o.* received him not. *John* 1:11
a lie, he speaketh of his *o.* 8:44
an hireling, whose *o.* the sheep. 10:12
having loved his *o.* that were in. 13:1
the world would love his *o.* 15:19
every man to his *o.* 16:32
as though by our *o.* power. *Acts* 3:12
thine *o.*? was it not in thine *o.*? 5:4
purchased with his *o.* blood. 20:28
he considered not his *o.* *Rom* 4:19
he that spared not his *o.* Son. 8:32
to his *o.* master he standeth. 14:4
ye are not your *o.* for ye. *1 Cor* 6:19
every man have his *o.* wife. 7:2
let no man seek his *o.* but. 10:24
conscience, I say, not thine *o.* 29
charity seeketh not her *o.* 13:5
for all seek their *o.* things. *Phil* 2:21
having mine *o.* righteousness. 3:9
provide not for his *o.*, his *o. 1 Tim* 5:8
a prophet of their *o.* *Tit* 1:12
but by his *o.* blood he. *Heb* 9:12
our sins in his *o.* blood. *Rev* 1:5
see **counsel, country, eyes, heart, house, land, people, self, selves, soul, way, ways, will**

owner
but the *o.* of the ox. *Ex* 21:28
testified to his *o.*, his *o.* shall. 29
the *o.* of the pit shall make it. 34
and his *o.* hath not kept him in. 36
o. of it shall accept thereof. 22:11
make restitution to the *o.* 12
o. thereof not being with it. 14
but if *o.* thereof be with it, not. 15
after name of Shemer, *o. 1 Ki* 16:24
ox knoweth his *o.*, the ass. *Isa* 1:3
centurion believed the *o.* *Acts* 27:11

owners
or have caused the *o.* to. *Job* 31:39
life of *o.* thereof. *Pr* 1:19
there to the *o.* thereof? *Eccl* 5:11
a sore evil, riches kept for *o.* 13
the *o.* said, Why loose? *Luke* 19:33

owneth
o. the house shall tell. *Lev* 14:35
bind man that *o.* this. *Acts* 21:11

ox
shalt not covet thy neighbour's *ox.*
Ex 20:17; *Deut* 5:21
if *ox* gore a man. *Ex* 21:28, 29, 32

if *ox* were wont to push. *Ex* 21:29, 36
if *ox* push a manservant or. 32
if an *ox* or ass shall fall into a pit. 33
if a man shall steal an *ox*. 22:1
whether it be *ox* or ass, he shall. 4
trespass for an *ox*. 9
deliver an *ox* to keep. 10
enemy's *ox* going astray. 23:4
that thine *ox* and thine ass. 12
every firstling of an *ox* or. 34:19
no manner of fat of *ox* or. *Lev* 7:23
what man soever killeth an *ox*. 17:3
each of princes an *ox*. *Num* 7:3
as the *ox* licketh up the grass. 22:4
thine *ox* shall do no work. *Deut* 5:14
the *ox*, the sheep, and goat. 14:4
whether it be *ox* or sheep. 18:3
thy brother's *ox* go astray. 22:1
thy brother's *ox* fall down. 4
shalt not plow with an *ox* and ass. 10
thou shalt not muzzle the *ox*. 25:4
1 Cor 9:9; *1 Tim* 5:18
thine *ox* shall be slain. *Deut* 28:31
they destroyed *ox* and sheep.
Josh 6:21; *1 Sam* 15:15
600 men with an *ox* goad. *Judg* 3:31
they left neither sheep nor *ox*. 6:4
Samuel said, Whose *ox* or ass have I taken? *1 Sam* 12:3
every man his *ox* and sheep. 14:34
me daily one *ox*, six sheep. *Neh* 5:18
or loweth the *ox* over? *Job* 6:5
they take the widow's *ox* for. 24:3
eateth grass as an *ox*. 40:15
Lord better than an *ox*. *Ps* 69:31
glory into similitude of an *ox*. 106:20
goeth after her as an *ox*. *Pr* 7:22
is by strength of the *ox*. 14:4
better than a stalled *ox*, and. 15:17
the *ox* knoweth his owner. *Isa* 1:3
lion shall eat straw like the *ox*. 11:7
thither the feet of the *ox*. 32:20
that killeth an *ox*, as if he. 66:3
a lamb or an *ox* brought. *Jer* 11:19
had the face of an *ox*. *Ezek* 1:10
of you loose his *ox* on. *Luke* 13:15
shall have an *ox* or an ass. 14:5

wild ox

wild ox and chamois. *Deut* 14:5*

oxen

Abram had sheep, and *o*. *Gen* 12:16
gave Abraham sheep and *o*. 20:14
gave Abimelech sheep and *o*. 21:27
Jacob said thus, I have *o*. 32:5
Jacob took Shechem's *o*. 34:28*
hand of Lord is upon the *o*. *Ex* 9:3*
sacrifice thereon thine *o*. 20:24
shall restore five *o*. for one. 22:1
thou do with thine *o*. and sheep. 30
princes brought twelve *o*. *Num* 7:3
four *o*. he gave to the sons of. 7
and eight *o*. he gave to the sons. 8
Balak offered *o*. and sheep. 22:40
prepare me here seven *o*. 23:1*
money for *o*. or sheep. *Deut* 14:26
Joshua took Achan, his *o*. *Josh* 7:24
yoke of *o*. in pieces, and sent them . . . done to his *o*. *1 Sam* 11:7
which yoke of *o*. might plow. 14:14*
the people took sheep and *o*. 32
Agag and the best of the *o*. 15:9
lowing of *o*. which I hear? 14
spared the best of the sheep and *o*. 15
Doeg smote the *o*. and sheep. 22:19
took away the sheep, and *o*. 27:9
Uzza took hold of it, for *o*. *2 Sam* 6:6
David sacrificed *o*. and fatlings. 13
be *o*. for burnt sacrifice. 24:22
the threshingfloor and *o*. 24
Adonijah slew sheep and *o*.
1 Ki 1:9, 19, 25
provision, 10 fat *o*. 100 sheep. 4:23
one sea, 12 *o*. under it. 7:25, 44
2 Chr 4:4, 15
sacrificing sheep and *o*. *1 Ki* 8:5
a sacrifice to the Lord of 22,000 *o*. and 120,000. 63; *2 Chr* 7:5
plowing with twelve yoke of *o*.
1 Ki 19:19
Elisha left the *o*. and ran. 20
he took a yoke of *o*. and slew. 21
to receive sheep and *o*.? *2 Ki* 5:26
bread on mules and on *o*. *1 Chr* 12:40

of the spoil 700 *o*. *2 Chr* 15:11
Ahab killed sheep and *o*. for. 18:2
consecrated things were 600 *o*. 29:33
they brought in the tithes of *o*. 31:6
passover three hundred *o*. 35:8
3000 camels, 500 yoke of *o*. *Job* 1:3
the *o*. were plowing, and the. 14
1000 yoke of *o*. 1000 asses. 42:12
to have dominion over *o*. *Ps* 8:7
that our *o*. may be strong. 144:14
where no *o*. are the crib. *Pr* 14:4
for the sending forth of *o*. *Isa* 7:25
joy and gladness, slaying *o*. 22:13
the *o*. and asses shall eat. 30:24
husbandman and his *o*. *Jer* 51:23
they shall make thee to eat grass as *o*.
Dan 4:25, 32, 33; 5:21
one plow there with *o*.? *Amos* 6:12
my *o*. and my fatlings. *Mat* 22:4
bought five yoke of *o*. *Luke* 14:19
temple those that sold *o*. *John* 2:14
out, the sheep and the *o*. 15
priest of Jupiter brought *o*. and.
Acts 14:13
God take care for *o*.? *1 Cor* 9:9

Ozem

O., sixth son of Jesse. *1 Chr* 2:15

Ozias

Joram begat *O*. *Mat* 1:8
O. begat Joatham. 9

P

Paarai

P. the Arbite, a mighty. *2 Sam* 23:35

paces

when gone six *p*. he. *2 Sam* 6:13

pacify, -ed, -eth

was king's wrath *p*. *Esth* 7:10
wise man will *p*. the wrath. *Pr* 16:14
a gift in secret *p*. anger. 21:14
p. great offences. *Eccl* 10:4*
when I am *p*. toward. *Ezek* 16:63*

Padan-aram

daughter of Bethuel of *P*. *Gen* 25:20
Isaac sent Jacob away to *P*. 28:6
Jacob was gone to *P*. 7
what he had gotten in *P*. 31:18
Jacob when he came from *P*. 35:9
sons born to him in *P*. 26; 46:15

paddle

shalt have a *p*. on thy. *Deut* 23:13

Pagiel

P. son of Ocran, prince of Asher.
Num 1:13; 7:72

paid

custom, was *p*. them. *Ezra* 4:20
this day have I *p*. vows. *Pr* 7:14
so he *p*. fare thereof. *Jonah* 1:3
not come out thence till thou hast *p*. uttermost. *Mat* 5:26; *Luke* 12:59
received tithes, *p*. tithes. *Heb* 7:9

pain

(*Used as now of great discomfort either of mind or body*)

flesh on him shall have *p*. *Job* 14:22
man travaileth with *p*. 15:20
he is chastened also with *p*. 33:19*
mine affliction and my *p*. *Ps* 25:18
p. as a woman in travail. 48:6
Isa 13:8; 26:17
my loins filled with *p*. *Isa* 21:3
child, we have been in *p*. 26:18
before her *p*. came, she was. 66:7
taken hold of us, and *p*. as of a woman in. *Jer* 6:24; 22:23
put themselves to *p*. but. 12:13
why is my *p*. perpetual? 15:18
it shall fall with *p*. on head. 30:23*
Babylon, take balm for her *p*. 51:8
great *p*. shall be in Ethiopia.
Ezek 30:4, 9
Sin shall have great *p*., No shall. 16
be in *p*. and labour to. *Mi* 4:10
p. is in all loins, faces. *Nah* 2:10
creation travaileth in *p*. *Rom* 8:22
their tongues for *p*. *Rev* 16:10
nor shall there be any more *p*. 21:4
see **pangs**

pained

my heart is sore *p*. within. *Ps* 55:4
p. at report of Tyre. *Isa* 23:5
I am *p*. at my very heart. *Jer* 4:19
people shall be much *p*. *Joel* 2:6
travailing in birth, and *p*. *Rev* 12:2

painful

it was too *p*. for me. *Ps* 73:16

painfulness

in weariness and *p*., in. *2 Cor* 11:27

pains

she travailed, for her *p*. *1 Sam* 4:19
and the *p*. of hell gat. *Ps* 116:3
having loosed *p*. of death. *Acts* 2:24
they blasphemed, because of their *p*.
Rev 16:11

painted

Jezebel *p*. her face, and. *2 Ki* 9:30
cieled with cedar, and *p*. *Jer* 22:14

paintedst

thou *p*. thy eyes. *Ezek* 23:40

painting

rentest thy face with *p*. *Jer* 4:30*

pair

offer a *p*. of turtle doves. *Luke* 2:24
he had a pair of balances. *Rev* 6:5

palace

Revisions usually replace this by castle *or* court, *as the word generally suggests a fortified house. The word occasionally includes the entire city,* Esth 9:12; *again, it is restricted to a part of the royal apartments,* 1 Ki 16:18. *It is applied to the temple in Jerusalem in* 1 Chr 29:1.

Zimri burnt the king's *p*. *1 Ki* 16:18
vineyard hard by the *p*. 21:1
Pekaiah in the *p*. *2 Ki* 15:25
shall be eunuchs in *p*. of king. 20:18
p. is not for man, but. *1 Chr* 29:1
a perfect heart to build the *p*. 19
terraces to the king's *p*. *2 Chr* 9:11
maintenance from the *p*. *Ezra* 4:14
at Achmetha, in the *p*. a roll. 6:2
as I was in Shushan the *p*. *Neh* 1:1
beams for the gates of the *p*. 2:8
I gave Hanani, ruler of the *p*. 7:2
young virgins to the *p*. *Esth* 2:3
decree was given in Shushan, the *p*.
3:15; 8:14
500 men in Shushan the *p*. 9:12
enter into the king's *p*. *Ps* 45:15
after the similitude of a *p*. 144:12
build on her *p*. of silver. *S of S* 8:9
hast made a *p*. of strangers. *Isa* 25:2
flourishing in my *p*. *Dan* 4:4
king went to his *p*. and passed. 6:18
he shall plant his *p*. between. 11:45
ye shall cast them into *p*. *Amos* 4:3*
and *p*. shall be dissolved. *Nah* 2:6
Jesus afar off to the high priest's *p*.
Mat 26:58; *Mark* 14:54
strong man keepeth his *p*. *Luke* 11:21
bonds are manifest in all the *p*.
Phil 1:13*

palaces

and burnt all the *p*. *2 Chr* 36:19
of myrrh, out of ivory *p*. *Ps* 45:8
God is known in her *p*. for. 48:3
bulwarks, consider her *p*. 13
his sanctuary like high *p*. 78:69*
prosperity within thy *p*. 122:7
spider is in king's *p*. *Pr* 30:28
cry in their pleasant *p*. *Isa* 13:22
p. shall be forsaken. 32:14
thorns come up in her *p*. 34:13
and let us destroy her *p*. *Jer* 6:5
come and is entered into our *p*. 9:21
devour the *p*. of Jerusalem. 17:27
consume the *p*. of Ben-hadad. 49:27
swallowed up all her *p*. *Lam* 2:5
knew their desolate *p*. *Ezek* 19:7
they shall set their *p*. in thee. 25:4*
in *p*. at Ashdod, in *p*. of Egypt.
Amos 3:9
violence and robbery in their *p*. 10
thy *p*. shall be spoiled. 11
I hate his *p*. 6:8
when he shall tread in our *p*. *Mi* 5:5
see **devour**

pale
his face now wax *p.* *Isa* 29:22
behold a *p.* horse: and his name was Death. *Rev* 6:8

paleness
all faces turned into *p.* *Jer* 30:6

Palestina
(*This word refers to the land of the Philistines and not to the whole of what we know as Palestine. Revisions change to* Philistia)
sorrow on men of *P.* *Ex* 15:14
rejoice not, thou whole *P.* *Isa* 14:29
thou whole *P.* art dissolved. 31

palm
pour it into *p.* of his. *Lev* 14:15, 26
struck Jesus with the *p.* *John* 18:22

palm branches
to mount and fetch *p. b.* *Neh* 8:15

palmerworm
(*The English word is one used for a variety of caterpillar. It is not however known to which variety the word refers*)
what the *p.* left, the locust. *Joel* 1:4
the years that *p.* hath eaten. 2:25
the *p.* devoured them. *Amos* 4:9

palms
both the *p.* of his hands. *1 Sam* 5:4
they found skull and *p.* *2 Ki* 9:35
I have graven thee on *p.* of my hands *Isa* 49:16
on the *p.* of my hands. *Dan* 10:10
smote him with the *p.* of their hands. *Mat* 26:67; *Mark* 14:65*
and *p.* in their hands. *Rev* 7:9

palm tree
(*The palm, especially the date-palm, is one of the most important trees in the East. The fruit is the daily food of millions; wine is made of the sap; the seeds are made into a food for camels; the fibres of the leaf-stems are woven into ropes and rigging; the tall trunk is a valuable timber; its leaves are made into many different articles.*)
The palm is also used as a symbol of victory, Rev 7:9.
under the *p.* of Deborah. *Judg* 4:5
shall flourish like the *p.* *Ps* 92:12
stature is like to a *p.* *S of S* 7:7
go up to the *p.*, I will take hold. 8
they are upright as the *p.* *Jer* 10:5
man was toward the *p.* *Ezek* 41:19
the *p.* and the apple tree. *Joel* 1:12

palm trees
where were seventy *p.* *Ex* 15:27
take you branches of *p.* *Lev* 23:40
city of *p.* unto Zoar. *Deut* 34:3
out of the city of *p.* *Judg* 1:16
and possessed city of *p.* 3:13
carved figures of *p.* *1 Ki* 6:29, 32, 35
7:36; *2 Chr* 3:5; *Ezek* 40:16
them to the city of *p.* *2 Chr* 28:15
took branches of *p.* *John* 12:13

palsies
many taken with *p.*, healed. *Acts* 8:7

palsy
(*An old word for the various sorts of paralysis*)
and those that had the *p.* *Mat* 4:24
9:2; *Mark* 2:3; *Luke* 5:18
lieth at home sick of the *p.* *Mat* 8:6
faith, said to the sick of the *p.*, Son.
9:2; *Mark* 2:5
Jesus saith to the sick of *p.*, Arise.
Mark 2:10; *Luke* 5:24
Aeneas, who was sick of the *p.* *Acts* 9:33

Pamphylia
Paphos to Perga in *P.* *Acts* 13:13
John departed from *P.* 15:38
sailed over the sea of *P.* 27:5

pan
meat offering baken in a *p.* *Lev* 2:5
in a *p.* it shall be made with oil. 6:21
all that is dressed in *p.* shall be. 7:9
priest's servant stuck it into the *p.* *1 Sam* 2:14
Tamar took a *p.* and. *2 Sam* 13:9
take unto thee an iron *p.* *Ezek* 4:3

pangs
p. and sorrows shall take. *Isa* 13:8
p. have taken hold on me, as *p.* 21:3
woman crieth out in her *p.* 26:17
thou be when *p.* come. *Jer* 22:23
as the heart of a woman in her *p.*
48:41; 49:22
and *p.* as of a woman in travail.
50:43; *Mi* 4:9

pannag
traded in thy market, *p.* *Ezek* 27:17

pans
thou shalt make *p.* to. *Ex* 27:3
they baked manna in *p.* *Num* 11:8*
over the things made in the *p.*
1 Chr 9:31; 23:29
offerings sod they in *p.* *2 Chr* 35:13

pant
that *p.* after the dust of. *Amos* 2:7

panted
I opened my mouth and *p.* *Ps* 119:131
my heart *p.*, fearfulness. *Isa* 21:4

panteth
my heart *p.*, my strength. *Ps* 38:10*
as hart *p.* so *p.* my soul after. 42:1

paper
(*The meaning in the Bible is either the papyrus, made into a sort of paper, or some preparation of skin*)
the *p.* reeds by the. *Isa* 19:7*
not write with *p.* and ink. *2 John* 12

Paphos
through the isle unto *P.* *Acts* 13:6, 13

paps
lewdness for the *p.* of. *Ezek* 23:21
blessed are *p.* which. *Luke* 11:27
blessed are the *p.* which never. 23:29
and girt about the *p.* with. *Rev* 1:13

parable
(*The word comes from the Greek* parabolé *which means a placing beside. It is therefore the placing of one subject by another as an illustration. Especially is it used for the illustration of spiritual things by familiar earthly objects or incidents. In the Bible the word is used more generally than elsewhere, being applied even to short proverbs*)
The prophets made use of Parables, to give a stronger impression to prince and people of the threatenings or of the promises they made to them. Nathan reproved David under the parable of a rich man that had taken away and killed the lamb of a poor man, 2 Sam 12:2, 3, etc. *Jotham, son of Gideon, proposed to the men of Shechem, the parable of the bramble, whom the trees had a mind to choose for their king,* Judg 9:7, 8, etc.
Our Saviour in the gospels often speaks to the people in parables, Mat 13:10, 13, etc. *He made use of them to veil the truth from those who were not willing to see it. Those who really desired to know would not rest till they had found out the meaning. This is given by Jesus as an illustration of* Isa 6:9, 10.
Baalam took up his *p.* and said.
Num 23:7; 24:3, 15, 20, 21, 23
took up his *p.*, Rise up, Balak. 23:18
Job continued his *p.* *Job* 27:1; 29:1
incline mine ear to a *p.* *Ps* 49:4
my mouth, in a *p.*, I will utter. 78:2
so is a *p.* in the mouth. *Pr* 26:7, 9
speak a *p.* to the house. *Ezek* 17:2
utter a *p.* to the rebellious. 24:3
one shall take up a *p.* *Mi* 2:4
shall not all these take up a *p.* against him! *Hab* 2:6
the *p.* of the sower. *Mat* 13:18
another *p.* put he. 24, 31, 33; 21:33
without a *p.* spake. 13:34; *Mark* 4:34
the *p.* of the tares. *Mat* 13:36; 15:15
learn a *p.* of the fig tree. *Mat* 24:32
Mark 13:28; *Luke* 21:29
they asked him of *p.* *Mark* 4:10
7:17; *Luke* 8:9
know ye not this *p.*? *Mark* 4:13
he had spoken the *p.* against them.
12:12; *Luke* 20:19
he spoke a *p.* to them. *Luke* 5:36
6:39; 8:4; 12:16; 13:6; 14:7
15:3; 18:1, 9; 19:11; 20:9; 21:29
John 10:6
this *p.* to us, or to all? *Luke* 12:41

parables
doth he not speak *p.*? *Ezek* 20:49
spake many things to them in *p.*
Mat 13:3, 13, 34; 22:1; *Mark* 3:23
4:2, 13, 33; 12:1
will ye know all *p.*? *Mark* 4:13
but others in *p.* that. *Luke* 8:10

paradise
thou be with me in *p.* *Luke* 23:43
was caught up into *p.* *2 Cor* 12:4
midst of the *p.* of God. *Rev* 2:7

paramours
she doted upon their *p.* *Ezek* 23:20

Paran
Ishmael dwelt in the wilderness of *P.* *Gen* 21:21
the wilderness of *P.* *Num* 10:12
12:16; 13:3, 26; *1 Sam* 25:1
shined from mount *P.* *Deut* 33:2
Holy One came from *P.* *Hab* 3:3

Parbar
the causeway, two at *P.* *1 Chr* 26:18

parcel
Jacob bought a *p.* of a field. *Gen* 33:19
Josh 24:32; *John* 4:5
Naomi selleth a *p.* of land. *Ruth* 4:3
p. of ground full. *1 Chr* 11:13*, 14*

parched
the *p.* ground shall. *Isa* 35:7*
but he shall inhabit the *p.* *Jer* 17:6
see **corn**

parchments
but especially the *p.* *2 Tim* 4:13

pardon
he will not *p.* your. *Ex* 23:21
p. our iniquity and our sin. 34:9
Num 14:19
I pray thee, *p.* my sin. *1 Sam* 15:25
in this thing the Lord *p.* *2 Ki* 5:18
which Lord would not *p.* 24:4
the good Lord *p.* *2 Chr* 30:18
thou art a God ready to *p.* *Neh* 9:17
why dost thou not *p.* my? *Job* 7:21
for thy name's sake *p.* *Ps* 25:11
for he will abundantly *p.* *Isa* 55:7
and I will *p.* it. *Jer* 5:1
how shall I *p.* thee for this? 7
I will *p.* all their iniquities. 33:8
for I will *p.* them whom. 50:20

pardoned
I have *p.* according to. *Num* 14:20
that her iniquity is *p.* *Isa* 40:2
rebelled, thou hast not *p.* *Lam* 3:42

pardoneth
to thee, that *p.* iniquity? *Mi* 7:18

pare
her head and *p.* her nails. *Deut* 21:12

parents
rise up against their *p.* and cause.
Mat 10:21; *Mark* 13:12
when the *p.* brought in. *Luke* 2:27
her *p.* were astonished, but. 8:56
man that hath left *p.* or wife. 18:29
ye shall be betrayed both by *p.* 21:16
sin, this man or his *p.*? *John* 9:2
these words spake *p.* 22, 23
proud, disobedient to *p.* *Rom* 1:30
2 Tim 3:2
not to lay up for the *p.* *2 Cor* 12:14
children, obey your *p.* *Eph* 6:1
Col 3:20
learn to requite their *p.* *1 Tim* 5:4
three months of his *p.* *Heb* 11:23

parlour
sitting in a summer *p.* *Judg* 3:20*
Ehud shut the doors of the *p.* 23*
Samuel brought them into the *p.*
1 Sam 9:22*

parlours
David gave Solomon a pattern of *p.* *1 Chr* 28:11*

Parmenas
Timon, *P.*, and Nicolas. *Acts* 6:5

part, *noun*
they stood at the nether *p.* *Ex* 19:17
the breast, it shall be thy *p.* 29:26
p. of the beaten corn, *p.* *Lev* 2:16
right shoulder for his *p.* 7:33
consecration was Moses' *p.* 8:29
if any *p.* of their carcase. 11:37, 38
his hair fallen off from the *p.* 13:41
nor have *p.* among them. *Num* 18:20
Deut 10:9; 12:12; 14:27, 29
18:1; *Josh* 14:4; 18:7
I am thy *p.* and thine. *Num* 18:20
might see utmost *p.* of the people.
Num 22:41; 23:13
he provided the first *p.* *Deut* 33:21
the *p.* of Judah was. *Josh* 19:9
have no *p.* in the Lord. 22:25, 27
her hap was to light on a *p.* *Ruth* 2:3
unto thee the *p.* of a kinsman. 3:13
tarried in the utmost *p.* *1 Sam* 14:2
our *p.* shall be to deliver. 23:20
as his *p.* is that goeth down to battle, so shall his *p.* be that. 30:24
we have no *p.* in David. *2 Sam* 20:1
come to uttermost *p.* *2 Ki* 7:5, 8
on thy *p.* to set riders. 18:23
Isa 36:8
greatest *p.* had kept. *1 Chr* 12:29
went into the inner *p.* *2 Chr* 29:16
cast out to the uttermost *p.* *Neh* 1:9
restore the hundredth *p.* of. 5:11
I will answer also my *p.* *Job* 32:17
their inward *p.* is very. *Ps* 5:9
in hidden *p.* shalt make me. 51:6
Lord taketh my *p.* with them. 118:7
nor highest *p.* of the dust. *Pr* 8:26
rejoicing in the habitable *p.* of. 31
shall have *p.* of inheritance. 17:2
fly that is in the utmost *p.* *Isa* 7:18
from utmost *p.* of earth. 24:16
he burneth *p.* thereof in the fire, with *p.* thereof he eateth. 44:16, 19
drink sixth *p.* of an hin. *Ezek* 4:11
leave but the sixth *p.* of thee. 39:2
sixth *p.* of an ephah of an. 45:13
it shall be the prince's *p.* to. 17
a meat offering the sixth *p.* 46:14
p. iron, and *p.* clay. *Dan* 2:33, 41, 42
the king saw *p.* of the hand. 5:5, 24
arms shall stand on his *p.* 11:31
great deep, did eat up a *p.* *Amos* 7:4
he was in the hinder *p.* of. *Mark* 4:38
is not against us, is on our *p.* 9:40
hath chosen that good *p.* *Luke* 10:42
inward *p.* is full of ravening. 11:39
as lightning that lighteneth out of one *p.* shining to other *p.* 17:24
hast no *p.* with me. *John* 13:8
four parts, every soldier a *p.* 19:23
and had obtained *p.* of. *Acts* 1:17
that he may take *p.* of this. 25
Ananias kept back *p.* of the price, and brought a certain *p.* 5:2, 3
thou hast neither *p.* nor lot in. 8:21
p. held with the Jews, *p.* with. 14:4
the chief city of that *p.* of. 16:12*
more *p.* knew not wherefore. 19:32
perceived that the one *p.* 23:6
the more *p.* advised to depart. 27:12
honour to that *p.* which. *1 Cor* 12:24
of whom the greater *p.* remain. 15:6
what was lacking on your *p.* 16:17
what *p.* he that believeth. *2 Cor* 6:15
the measure of every *p.* *Eph* 4:16
he of the contrary *p.* may. *Tit* 2:8
himself likewise took *p.* *Heb* 2:14*
on their *p.* he is evil spoken of, but on your *p.* he is. *1 Pet* 4:14
holy that hath *p.* in the. *Rev* 20:6
all liars shall have their *p.* 21:8
God shall take away his *p.* 22:19

part, *verb*
thou *p.* the meat offering. *Lev* 2:6
if aught but death *p.* *Ruth* 1:17
they shall *p.* alike. *1 Sam* 30:24
was none to *p.* them. *2 Sam* 14:6
shall they *p.* him among? *Job* 41:6
they *p.* my garments. *Ps* 22:18

in **part**
blindness *in p.* is happened.
Rom 11:25
we know *in p.* and we prophesy *in p.*
1 Cor 13:9
then that which is *in p.* shall be. 10
I know *in p.* but then shall I know. 12
acknowledged us *in p.* *2 Cor* 1:14
hath not grieved me but *in p.* 2:5

third **part**
flour mingled with the *third p.* of an.
Num 15:6; 28:14; *Ezek* 46:14
shalt offer the *third p.* of. *Num* 15:7
David sent a *third p.* *2 Sam* 18:2
a *third p.* that enter in. *2 Ki* 11:5
a *third p.* of you shall be porters.
2 Chr 23:4
with *third p.* of shekel. *Neh* 10:32
fire a *third p.*, a *third p.*, smite about it, a *third p.* *Ezek* 5:2, 12
third p. shall be left. *Zech* 13:8
the *third p.* through the fire. 9
third p. of the trees. *Rev* 8:7
and the *third p.* of the sea. 8
third p. of creatures died, *third p.* 9
it fell upon the *third p.* of. 10
third p. of the waters became. 11
third p. of the sun, moon, and stars, was smitten . . . for a *third p.* 12
for to slay the *third p.* of men. 9:15
was the *third p.* of men killed. 18
his tail drew *third p.* of the. 12:4

fourth **part**
flour mingled with the *fourth p.* of.
Ex 29:40; *Num* 15:4; 28:5
fourth p. of an hin of wine for a.
Lev 23:13; *Num* 15:5; 28:7, 14
have here the *fourth p.* of a shekel.
1 Sam 9:8
olive tree *fourth p.* of. *1 Ki* 6:33
the *fourth p.* of a cab. *2 Ki* 6:25
read one *fourth p.*; another *fourth p.*
Neh 9:3
over *fourth p.* of earth. *Rev* 6:8

fifth **part**
up *fifth p.* of the land. *Gen* 41:34
give *fifth p.* to Pharaoh. 47:24, 26
shall add the *fifth p.* *Lev* 5:16; 6:5
22:14; 27:13, 19, 27, 31; *Num* 5:7
posts were a *fifth p.* *1 Ki* 6:31

tenth **part**
an homer is the *tenth p.* *Ex* 16:36
offering the *tenth p.* of an ephah.
Lev 5:11; 6:20; *Num* 28:5
tenth p. of an ephah of. *Num* 5:15
shall offer even the *tenth p.* 18:26
may contain *tenth p.* *Ezek* 45:11
ye shall offer the *tenth p.* of a. 14
Abraham gave a *tenth p.* *Heb* 7:2
tenth p. of the city fell. *Rev* 11:13

partaker
and hast been *p.* with. *Ps* 50:18
should be *p.* of his hope. *1 Cor* 9:10
that I might be *p.* thereof. 23
if I by grace be *p.* why am I? 10:30
neither be *p.* of other. *1 Tim* 5:22
be thou *p.* of afflictions. *2 Tim* 1:8*
the husbandman must be first *p.* 2:6
who am also a *p.* of the glory.
1 Pet 5:1
is *p.* of his evil deeds. *2 John* 11

partakers
not been *p.* in blood. *Mat* 23:30
if Gentiles have been made *p.* of.
Rom 15:27
others be *p.* of this power. *1 Cor* 9:12
who wait at altar, are *p.* 13
for we are all *p.* of that one. 10:17
are not they which eat *p.* of? 18
be *p.* of the Lord's table, and. 21
are *p.* of the sufferings. *2 Cor* 1:7
and *p.* of his promise in. *Eph* 3:6
be not ye therefore *p.* with. 5:7
ye all are *p.* of my grace. *Phil* 1:7
meet to be *p.* of inheritance. *Col* 1:12
are *p.* of the benefit. *1 Tim* 6:2
as the children are *p.* of. *Heb* 2:14*
brethren, *p.* of the heavenly. 3:1
for we are made *p.* of Christ. 14
were made *p.* of the Holy Ghost. 6:4
chastisement, whereof all are *p.* 12:8
might be *p.* of his holiness. 10

as ye are *p.* of Christ's. *1 Pet* 4:13
p. of the divine nature. *2 Pet* 1:4
that ye be not *p.* of her. *Rev* 18:4

partakest
with them *p.* of root. *Rom* 11:17

parted
the river was *p.* into. *Gen* 2:10
a chariot *p.* them. *2 Ki* 2:11
the waters *p.* hither and. 14
what way is the light *p.*? *Job* 38:24
scattered, and *p.* my land. *Joel* 3:2
crucified him, and *p.* his garments.
Mat 27:35; *Mark* 15:24
Luke 23:34; *John* 19:24
blessed them, was *p.* *Luke* 24:51
p. them to all men, as. *Acts* 2:45

parteth
whatsoever *p.* the hoof. *Lev* 11:3
Deut 14:6
the lot *p.* between the. *Pr* 18:18

Parthians
P., we hear them speak in. *Acts* 2:9

partial
but have been *p.* in law. *Mal* 2:9*
are ye not then *p.* in? *Jas* 2:4*

partiality
observe these things, doing nothing by *p.* *1 Tim* 5:21
without *p.* and without. *Jas* 3:17*

particular
Christ, members in *p.* *1 Cor* 12:27*
every one of you in *p.* so. *Eph* 5:33*

particularly
Paul declared *p.* what. *Acts* 21:19*
we cannot now speak *p.* *Heb* 9:5*

parties
cause of both *p.* shall. *Ex* 22:9

parting
king of Babylon stood at the *p.* of the way. *Ezek* 21:21

partition
and he made a *p.* by. *1 Ki* 6:21*
broken down middle wall of *p.*
Eph 2:14

partly
be *p.* strong, *p.* broken. *Dan* 2:42
divisions, I *p.* believe it. *1 Cor* 11:18
p. whilst ye were made a . . . by afflictions, *p.* whilst ye. *Heb* 10:33

partner
whoso is *p.* with thief. *Pr* 29:24
Titus, he is my *p.* and. *2 Cor* 8:23
if count me a *p.* receive. *Philem* 17

partners
they beckoned to their *p.* *Luke* 5:7
James and John who were *p.* 10

partridge
one doth hunt a *p.* in. *1 Sam* 26:20
as the *p.* sitteth on eggs. *Jer* 17:11

parts
four *p.* shall be your. *Gen* 47:24
Aaron's sons shall lay the *p.* in.
Lev 1:8
any thing lacking in his *p.* 22:23
the prey into two *p.* *Num* 31:27
of the land into three *p.* *Deut* 19:3
if any be driven to utmost *p.* 30:4
they shall divide it into seven *p.*
Josh 18:5, 6, 9
emerods in their secret *p.* *1 Sam* 5:9*
ten *p.* in the king. *2 Sam* 19:43
divided into two *p.* *1 Ki* 16:21
two *p.* keep watch. *2 Ki* 11:7*
and nine *p.* to dwell in. *Neh* 11:1
lo, these are *p.* of his. *Job* 26:14
I will not conceal his *p.* nor. 41:12*
uttermost *p.* of earth for. *Ps* 2:8
shall go into lower *p.* of the. 63:9
that dwell in utmost *p.* 65:8
divided the Red sea into *p.* 136:13
uttermost *p.* of the sea. 139:9
into innermost *p.* *Pr* 18:8; 26:22
will discover their secret *p.* *Isa* 3:17
lower *p.* of the earth. 44:23
passed between the *p.* *Jer* 34:18, 19
in the low *p.* of earth. *Ezek* 26:20
delivered to the nether *p.* of earth.
31:14, 18
in nether *p.* of earth. 16; 32:18, 24

we are cut off for our p. Ezek 37:11*
out of the north p. 38:15; 39:2
length as one of the other p. 48:8
saith the Lord, two p. therein shall be cut off. Zech 13:8
turned aside into the p. Mat 2:22
came from uttermost p. 12:42
Luke 11:31
and made four p. John 19:23
he had gone over those p. Acts 20:2
more place in those p. Rom 15:23
uncomely p. have more. 1 Cor 12:23
for our comely p. have no need. 24
descended first into lower p. Eph 4:9
city was divided into three p. Rev 16:19
see **back, hinder, inward**

Pashur

P. the son of Malchijah. 1 Chr 9:12
Neh 11:12
the children of P. Ezra 2:38; 10:22
Neh 7:41
P. sealed. Neh 10:3
P. the son of Immer. Jer 20:1, 2
Lord called not thy name P. but. 3
P. go into captivity. 6
Zedekiah sent unto him P. 21:1
son of P. and P. the son of. 38:1

pass

after that ye shall p. on. Gen 18:5
shortly bring it to p. 41:32
will make my goodness p. Ex 33:19
father to p. to them. Num 27:7, 8
ye shall p. before your. Josh 1:14
he said to people, P. on. 6:7
bid the servants p. 1 Sam 9:27
Jesse made Abinadab p. 16:8
Jesse made seven of his sons p. 10
no place for the beast to p. Neh 2:14
brooks they p. away. Job 6:15
waters that p. away. 11:16
troubled, and p. away. 34:20
every one of them p. away. Ps 58:8
lips he bringeth evil to p. Pr 16:30
the simple p. on and are punished. 22:3; 27:12
grounded staff shall p. Isa 30:32
shall gallant ship p. thereby. 33:21
now have I brought it to p. 37:26
have given shall p. away. Jer 8:13
I will make thee to p. with. 15:14
the flocks shall p. again under. 33:13
nor doth any son of man p. 51:43
cause barber's razor to p. Ezek 5:1
cause you to p. under rod. 20:37
whom dost thou p. in beauty? 32:19
p. ye unto Calneh and. Amos 6:2
p. ye away, thou inhabitant. Mi 1:11
and their king shall p. before. 2:13
the day p. as the chaff. Zeph 2:2
thy iniquity to p. from. Zech 3:4
Till heaven and earth p., one tittle shall in no wise p. Mat 5:18
Father, let this cup p. from me. 26:39; Mark 14:35
would p. from hence to you cannot; nor can they p. to. Luke 16:26*
for he was to p. that way. 19:4
if she p. the flower of her. 1 Cor 7:36
grass he shall p. away. Jas 1:10
p. time of your sojourning here. 1 Pet 1:17
heavens shall p. away. 2 Pet 3:10
see **came, come**

pass *by*

my hand while I p. by. Ex 33:22
not let us p. by him. Deut 2:30
Shammah to p. by. 1 Sam 16:9
all they that p. by the. Ps 80:12
all that p. by the way spoil. 89:41
many nations shall p. by. Jer 22:8
all ye that p. by, behold. Lam 1:12
all that p. by clap their hands. 2:15
sight of all that p. by. Ezek 5:14
and caused me to p. by them. 37:2
caused me to p. by four. 46:21
I will not again p. by. Amos 7:8; 8:2
garments of them that p. by. Mi 2:8
that no man might p. by. Mat 8:28
hearing the multitude p. by. Luke 18:36
and to p. by you into. 2 Cor 1:16

not **pass**

we will not p. through. Num 20:17
thou shalt not p. by me. 18
his bounds he cannot p. Job 14:5
my way, that I cannot p. 19:8
decree, which shall not p. Ps 148:6
waters should not p. Pr 8:29
decree, that it cannot p. Jer 5:22
that shall not p. away. Dan 7:14
generation shall not p. Mat 24:34
Mark 13:30; Luke 21:32
my word shall not p. Mat 24:35
Mark 13:31; Luke 21:33

pass *not*

my lord, p. not away. Gen 18:3
beware that thou p. not. 2 Ki 6:9
avoid it, p. not by it. Pr 4:15
seek not Beth-el, p. not. Amos 5:5

pass *over*

wind to p. over the earth. Gen 8:1
will not p. over this heap. 31:52
p. over before me, and put. 32:16
let my lord p. over before. 33:14
blood, I will p. over you. Ex 12:13, 23
stone, till thy people p. over. 15:16
but thy servants will p. over. Num 32:27, 29, 32
if they will not p. over with. 30
thou art to p. over through Ar. Deut 2:18
p. over Arnon. 24
until I shall p. over Jordan. 29
ye shall p. over armed before. 3:18
thou art to p. over Jordan. 9:1; 11:31
27:2; Josh 1:11; 3:6, 14; 4:5
p. over into the land. Josh 22:19
not a man to p. over. Judg 3:28
we will p. over to Gibeah. 19:12
behold, we will p. over unto these men. 1 Sam 14:8
Ittai, Go and p. over. 2 Sam 15:22
plains, but speedily p. over. 17:16
they may not p. over. Ps 104:9
it is a glory to p. over. Pr 19:11
p. over to Tarshish. Isa 23:6
p. over to Chittim. 12
by morning shall p. over. 28:19
he shall p. over to his strong. 31:9
unclean shall not p. over. 35:8
uncover the thigh, p. over. 47:2
way for ransomed to p. over. 51:10
for p. over the isles of. Jer 2:10
yet can they not p. over it. 5:22
river that I could not p. over. Ezek 47:5
times p. over him. Dan 4:16, 25
the north shall p. over. 11:40
change, he shall p. over. Hab 1:11
and p. over judgement. Luke 11:42

pass *through*

I will p. through all thy. Gen 30:32
I will p. through land. Ex 12:12
the Lord will p. through to smite. 23
seed p. through the fire. Lev 18:21
Deut 18:10; 2 Ki 17:17
let us, I pray thee, p. through thy. Num 20:17
let me p. through thy land. 21:22
Deut 2:27
not suffer Israel to p. through. Num 21:23; Judg 11:20
ye are to p. through the coasts. Deut 2:4
only I will p. through on my feet. 28
p. through the host and. Josh 1:11
p. through brickkiln. 2 Sam 12:31
the land to p. through it. 1 Ki 18:6
to p. through the fire. 2 Ki 16:3
21:6; 23:10; 2 Chr 33:6
Jer 32:35; Ezek 20:26, 31
caused them to p. through the sea. Ps 78:13; 136:14
shall p. through Judah. Isa 8:8*
p. through it hardly bestead. 21
as whirlwinds in the south p. through, so it cometh. 21:1
p. through thy land as a river. 23:10
scourge shall p. through. 28:15, 18
none shall p. through it for. 34:10
that none can p. through. Jer 9:10
prayers should not p. through Lam 3:44
also shall p. through to thee. 4:21
pestilence and blood shall p. through thee. Ezek 5:17
beasts p. through land, no man may p. through. 14:15; 29:11; 33:28
passengers that p. through. 39:15
one shall come, p. through, and overflow. Dan 11:10
stranger shall p. through. Joel 3:17
I will p. through thee. Amos 5:17
when he shall p. through. Nah 1:12
no more p. through thee. 15
no oppressor shall p. through them. Zech 9:8
p. through Macedonia. 1 Cor 16:5

passage

refused to give Israel p. Num 20:21
altar at the p. of Israel. Josh 22:11*
garrison of Philistines went out to p. 1 Sam 13:23
they are gone over the p. Isa 10:29

passages

slew him at the p. of Jordan. Judg 12:6*
between the p. there. 1 Sam 14:4
and cry from the p. Jer 22:20*
to shew Babylon that the p. 51:32

passed

a lamp that p. between. Gen 15:17
have p. thy borders. Num 20:17
ye have not p. this way. Josh 3:4
the seven priests p. on before. 6:8
in all the way we went, among all people through whom we p. 24:17
Ehud escaped and p. Judg 3:26
Saul is gone about and p. on. 1 Sam 15:12
Philistines p. on by hundreds. 29:2
David's servants p. on. 2 Sam 15:18
it fell, that Elisha p. to. 2 Ki 4:8
Gehazi p. on before them, and. 31
Solomon p. all the kings. 2 Chr 9:22
then a spirit p. before. Job 4:15
my days are p. away as the. 9:26
and no stranger p. among. 15:19
his thick clouds p. Ps 18:12
yet he p. away, and lo. 37:36
all our days are p. away in. 90:9
was but a little that I p. S of S 3:4
come to Aiath, he is p. Isa 10:28
he pursued them, and p. 41:3
and the holy flesh is p. Jer 11:15
and p. between the parts. 34:18, 19
hath p. the time appointed. 46:17
nor smell of fire had p. Dan 3:27
the king went and p. the night. 6:18
hath not thy wickedness p.? Nah 3:19
now the time is far p. Mark 6:35
but is p. from death unto life. John 5:24; 1 John 3:14
so death p. on all men. Rom 5:12
high priest that is p. Heb 4:14
first earth were p. away. Rev 21:1
former things are p. away. 4

passed *by*

there p. by Midianites. Gen 37:28
Lord p. by before him. Ex 34:6
nations which ye p. by. Deut 29:16
behold, men p. by and. 1 Ki 13:25
the Lord p. by. 19:11
Elijah p. by Elisha. 19
as the king p. by he cried. 20:39
that as oft as he p. by. 2 Ki 4:8
the king p. by on the wall. 6:30
and there p. by a wild beast. 14:9
2 Chr 25:18
fierce lion p. by it. Job 28:8
for lo, the kings p. by. Ps 48:4
when I p. by and saw. Ezek 16:6
on every one that p. by. 15, 25
in sight of all that p. by. 36:34
of the waters p. by. Hab 3:10
heard that Jesus p. by. Mat 20:30
they that p. by reviled him. 27:39
Mark 15:29
as he p. by he saw Levi. Mark 2:14
would have p. by them. 6:48
in the morning as they p. by. 11:20
Simon who p. by to bear. 15:21
he p. by on the other side. Luke 10:31, 32
through midst of them, and so p. by. John 8:59
as I p. by and beheld. Acts 17:23

passed *over*
and *p. over* the river. *Gen* 31:21
for with my staff I *p. over.* 32:10
who *p. over* houses of. *Ex* 12:27
when ye are *p. over* Jordan. *Num* 33:51; *Deut* 27:3
they *p. over* right against. *Josh* 3:16
all the Israelites *p. over* on. 17
people were clean *p. over.* 4:1, 11
people hasted and *p. over.* 10
the ark *p. over.* 11
Reubenites and Gadites *p. over.* 12
Gideon *p. over* and 300. *Judg* 8:4
Ammon *p. over* Jordan. 10:9
Jephthah *p. over* to fight. 11:29, 32
the battle *p. over* to. *1 Sam* 14:23
David *p. over* with 600 men. 27:2
men *p. over* Jordan. *2 Sam* 2:29
Ittai *p. over.* 15:22
king and people *p. over.* 23
my judgement is *p. over. Isa* 40:27
could not be *p. over.* *Ezek* 47:5
but I *p. over* upon her. *Hos* 10:11
and waves *p. over* me. *Jonah* 2:3

passed *through*
Abram *p. through* the. *Gen* 12:6
land which we *p. through. Num* 14:7
p. through midst of the sea. 33:8
p. through mount Ephraim. *1 Sam* 9:4
posts *p. through* country of. *2 Chr* 30:10
they *p. through* the gate. *Mi* 2:13
that no man *p. through.* *Zech* 7:14
he *p. through* the midst of Samaria. *Luke* 17:11
as Peter *p. through* all quarters. *Acts* 9:32
p. through one street. 12:10
all our fathers *p. through* the sea. *1 Cor* 10:1
p. through the Red sea. *Heb* 11:29

passedst
why *p.* thou over to fight? *Judg* 12:1

passengers
she standeth to call *p.* *Pr* 9:15*
I will give Gog valley of *p.*: it shall stop noses of the *p.* *Ezek* 39:11*
to bury with *p.* those that. 14*
when *p.* see a man's bone. 15*

passest
kingdoms whither thou *p. Deut* 3:21
on land whither thou *p.* over. 30:18
if thou *p.* on, thou shalt. *2 Sam* 15:33
day thou *p.* over the. *1 Ki* 2:37
when thou *p.* through waters. *Isa* 43:2

passeth
every one that *p.* *Ex* 30:13, 14
while my glory *p.* by. 33:22
whatsoever *p.* under the. *Lev* 27:32
even the Lord *p.* over. *Josh* 3:11
every one that *p.* by it shall be. *1 Ki* 9:8; *2 Chr* 7:21
of God, which *p.* by us. *2 Ki* 4:9
money of every one that *p.* 12:4
he *p.* on also, but I. *Job* 9:11
against him, and he *p.* 14:20
and my welfare *p.* away. 30:15
but the wind *p.* and cleanseth. 37:21
whatever *p.* through seas. *Ps* 8:8
are a wind that *p.* away. 78:39
for the wind *p.* over it. 103:16
as a shadow that *p.* away. 144:4
as whirlwind *p.* so is. *Pr* 10:25
he that *p.* by and meddleth. 26:17
one generation *p.* away. *Eccl* 1:4
be as chaff that *p.* away. *Isa* 29:5
a land that no man *p. Jer* 2:6; 9:12
as stubble that *p.* away. 13:24
every one that *p.* shall be astonished. 18:16; 19:8
cut off from it him that *p. Ezek* 35:7
as early dew that *p.* away. *Hos* 13:3
God that *p.* by transgression. *Mi* 7:18
every one that *p.* by her. *Zeph* 2:15
streets waste, that none *p.* by. 3:6
because of him that *p.* by. *Zech* 9:8
told him that Jesus *p.* by. *Luke* 18:37
fashion of this world *p.* away. *1 Cor* 7:31; *1 John* 2:17
love of Christ which *p.* *Eph* 3:19
the peace of God which *p.* understanding. *Phil* 4:7

passing
we are *p.* from Beth-lehem-judah. *Judg* 19:18
thy love to me *p.* love. *2 Sam* 1:26
the people had done *p.* out. 15:24
as king of Israel was *p.* *2 Ki* 6:26
p. through valley of Baca. *Ps* 84:6
p. through the street near. *Pr* 7:8
and *p.* over he will preserve. *Isa* 31:5
p. through land to bury. *Ezek* 39:14
he *p.* through midst of. *Luke* 4:30
shadow of Peter *p.* by. *Acts* 5:15
Philip *p.* through, preached. 8:40
they *p.* by Mysia, came down. 16:8
and hardly *p.* Crete we came. 27:8

passion
(In the singular, the suffering and death of Christ. In the plural it means desires)
himself alive after his *p.* *Acts* 1:3

passions
men of like *p.* with you. *Acts* 14:15
man subject to like *p.* as. *Jas* 5:17

passover
This word comes from the Hebrew verb, pasach, *which signifies* to pass, to leap, or skip over. *They gave the name of* Passover *to the feast which was established in commemoration of the coming forth out of Egypt, because the night before their departure, the destroying angel, who slew the firstborn of the Egyptians, passed over the Israelites, who were marked with the blood of the lamb which was killed the evening before; and which for this reason was called the Paschal Lamb.*
The feast was kept for seven days, from the 14th to the 21st Nisan, corresponding to our March–April. As the beginning of the month was dependent on the moon there was nearly a month's difference between the possible times of beginning. This is the reason for the varying dates of our Easter, which must, as the commemoration of Christ's resurrection, be determined by the date of the Passover.
There were many rules as to the Passover Supper, some given in Exodus being for the first celebration only.
it is the Lord's *p.*, ye. *Ex* 12:11
27; *Lev* 23:5; *Num* 28:16
kill the *p.* *Ex* 12:21
this is ordinance of the *p.* 43
they kept the *p.* at even. *Num* 9:5
Josh 5:10
on the morrow of the *p.* *Num* 33:3
Josh 5:11
sacrifice the *p.* to Lord. *Deut* 16:2, 6
thou mayest not sacrifice *p.* 5
holden such a *p.* from days of judges, nor in days of kings. *2 Ki* 23:22
wherein this *p.* was holden. 23
then they killed *p.* in second month. *2 Chr* 30:15; 35:1, 11; *Ezra* 6:20
Mark 14:12; *Luke* 22:7
yet did they *eat p.* *2 Chr* 30:18
Josiah kept a *p.* unto the Lord. 35:1
17:19; *Ezra* 6:19
Josiah gave all for *p. 2 Chr* 35:7, 8, 9
they roasted *p.* with fire. 13
ye shall have *p.* a feast. *Ezek* 45:21
prepare for thee to eat *p.*? *Mat* 26:17
Mark 14:12; *Luke* 22:8, 11
and they made ready *p. Mat* 26:19
Mark 14:16; *Luke* 22:13
desired to eat this *p.* *Luke* 22:15
p. was at hand. *John* 2:13; 11:55
was in Jerusalem at the *p.* 2:23
Jerusalem before *p.* to purify. 11:55
six days before *p.* to Bethany. 12:1
that they might eat the *p.* 18:28
release to you one at the *p.* 39
preparation of the *p.* 19:14
Christ our *p.* is sacrificed. *1 Cor* 5:7
thro' faith he kept the *p.* *Heb* 11:28
see **feast, keep**

passovers
charge of killing of *p.* *2 Chr* 30:17

past
days of mourning were *p. Gen* 50:4
2 Sam 11:27
with horn in time *p.* *Ex* 21:29, 36
go along, until we be *p. Num* 21:22
Emims dwelt therein in times *p.* *Deut* 2:10
now of the days which are *p.* 4:32
hated him not in times *p.* 42; 19:4, 6
bitterness of death is *p. 1 Sam* 15:32
his presence as in times *p.* 19:7
for David in time *p.* to be king. *2 Sam* 3:17
also in time *p.* when Saul was. 5:2
David was a little *p.* the top. 16:1
when midday was *p.* *1 Ki* 18:29
was ruler in time *p.* *1 Chr* 9:20
which doeth great things *p. Job* 9:10
secret, until thy wrath be *p.* 14:13
my days are *p.*, my purposes. 17:11
O that I were as in months *p.* 29:2
as yesterday when it is *p. Ps* 90:4
requireth that which is *p. Eccl* 3:15
for lo the winter is *p.* *S of S* 2:11
the harvest is *p.*, the. *Jer* 8:20
the time is now *p.*, send. *Mat* 14:15
sabbath was *p.*, Mary. *Mark* 16:1
the voice was *p.*, Jesus. *Luke* 9:36
when they were *p.* first. *Acts* 12:10
who in times *p.* suffered all. 14:16
fast was now already *p.*, Paul. 27:9
for remission of sins that are *p.* *Rom* 3:25
for as ye in times *p.* have. 11:30
and his ways are *p.* finding out 33
old things *p.* away; all. *2 Cor* 5:17
my conversation in time *p. Gal* 1:13
persecuted us in times *p.* 23
I have also told you in time p. 5:21
in time *p.* ye walked. *Eph* 2:2
our conversation in times *p.* 3
who being *p.* feeling have. 4:19
that resurrection is *p.* *2 Tim* 2:18
who in time *p.* was to. *Philem* 11
who spake in time *p.* to. *Heb* 1:1
to conceive seed, when she was *p.* 11:11
p. were not a people. *1 Pet* 2:10
for the time *p.* of our life may. 4:3
darkness is *p.*, true. *1 John* 2:8
one woe is *p.* *Rev* 9:12
the second woe is *p.* 11:14

pastor
(The original meaning of this word was shepherd, and in this sense it is sometimes used in the Bible. The Eastern shepherd must both protect and feed his sheep—so there is a derived meaning of spiritual leader, minister, one given charge of a church of Christ, to care for spiritual interests of the people and feed their souls with spiritual food. This meaning also is found in the Bible)
hastened from being a *p. Jer* 17:16*

pastors
p. also transgressed. *Jer* 2:8*
I will give you *p.* according. 3:15*
for *p.* are become brutish. 10:21*
many *p.* have destroyed my. 12:10*
wind shall eat up all thy *p.* 22:22*
woe to the *p.* that destroy. 23:1*
thus saith Lord against *p.* that. 2*
and he gave some *p.* *Eph* 4:11

pasture
thy servants have no *p.* *Gen* 47:4
they went to seek *p.* *1 Chr* 4:39
they found fat *p.* 40
because there was *p.* 41
of the mountains is his *p. Job* 39:8
why doth thine anger smoke against sheep of thy *p.*? *Ps* 74:1
so we sheep of thy *p.* will. 79:13
people of his *p.* 95:7; 100:3
wild asses, a *p.* of flocks. *Isa* 32:14
scatter sheep of my *p.* *Jer* 23:1
hath spoiled their *p.* 25:36
like harts that find no *p.* *Lam* 1:6
them in a good *p.*, a fat *p. Ezek* 34:14

small thing to have eaten good *p.* *Ezek* 34:18
ye my flock, the flock of my *p.*, are. 31
according to their *p.* so. *Hos* 13:6
because they have no *p.* *Joel* 1:18
go in and out and find *p.* *John* 10:9

pastures

twenty oxen out of *p.* *1 Ki* 4:23
to lie down in green *p.* *Ps* 23:2
they drop upon the *p.* of. 65:12
p. are clothed with flocks. 13
cattle shall feed in large *p. Isa* 30:23
p. shall be in all high places. 49:9*
down residue of your *p.* *Ezek* 34:18
one lamb out of flock of fat *p.* 45:15
fire hath devoured *p.* *Joel* 1:19, 20
for the *p.* of the wilderness. 2:22

Patara

Rhodes we came unto *P.* *Acts* 21:1

pate

come down upon his own *p. Ps* 7:16

path

[1] *A beaten way by which men can walk,* Gen 49:17. [2] *The regular methods by which one lives, or shows his character. This is used of both God and man.*

Dan a serpent, an adder in *p.* that. *Gen* 49:17
the Lord stood in a *p.* *Num* 22:24*
there is a *p.* which no fowl. *Job* 28:7
mar my *p.* they set forward. 30:13
he maketh a *p.* to shine. 41:32
thou wilt shew me the *p.* *Ps* 16:11
thy way, lead me in a plain *p.* 27:11
thy way in sea, thy *p.* is. 77:19
make me to go in *p.* of thy. 119:35
lamp, and a light to my *p.* 105
thou compassest my *p.* and. 139:3
then thou knewest my *p.* 142:3
thy foot from their *p.* *Pr* 1:15
understand every good *p.* 2:9
enter not into the *p.* of the. 4:14
the *p.* of the just is as the. 18
ponder the *p.* of thy feet, and. 26
thou shouldest ponder the *p.* 5:6
thou dost weigh the *p.* of. *Isa* 26:7
the way, turn aside out of *p.* 30:11
and taught him in the *p.* 40:14
a *p.* in the mighty waters. 43:16
walk every one in his *p.* *Joel* 2:8

Pathros

of his people from *P.* *Isa* 11:11
return into the land of *P. Ezek* 29:14
will make *P.* desolate, I will. 30:14

paths

the *p.* of their way are. *Job* 6:18
so are the *p.* of all that forget. 8:13
narrowly to all my *p.* 13:27
he hath set darkness in my *p.* 19:8
neither abide they in the *p.* 24:13
in stocks, marketh all my *p.* 33:11
that thou shouldest keep the *p.* 38:20
through the *p.* of the seas. *Ps* 8:8
I have kept me from the *p.* 17:4
hold up my goings in thy *p.* that. 5
he leadeth me in the *p.* of. 23:3
O Lord, teach me thy *p.* 25:4
p. of the Lord are mercy. 10
and thy *p.* drop fatness. 65:11
he keepeth *p.* of judgement. *Pr* 2:8
leave *p.* of uprightness to walk. 13
they froward in their *p.* 15
her *p.* incline unto the dead. 18
nor take they hold of the *p.* of life. 19
thou mayest keep the *p.* of the. 20
he shall direct thy *p.* 3:6
all her *p.* are peace. 17
I have led thee in right *p.* 4:11
go not astray in her *p.* 7:25
in places of *p.* 8:2
I lead in the midst of the *p.* 20
and we will walk in his *p.* *Isa* 2:3 *Mi* 4:2
destroy the way of thy *p.* *Isa* 3:12
I will lead them in *p.* they. 42:16
he called, the restorer of *p.* 58:12
destruction are in their *p.* 59:7
have made them crooked *p.* 8
way, and ask for old *p.* *Jer* 6:16
from ancient *p.* to walk in *p.* 18:15
made my *p.* crooked. *Lam* 3:9
wall, she shall not find her *p. Hos* 2:6
make his *p.* straight. *Mat* 3:3 *Mark* 1:3; *Luke* 3:4
straight *p.* for your feet. *Heb* 12:13

pathway

in the *p.* thereof there is. *Pr* 12:28

patience

servant worshipped him, saying, Lord, have *p.* with. *Mat* 18:26, 29
bring forth fruit with *p.* *Luke* 8:15
in your *p.* possess ye your. 21:19
tribulation worketh *p.* *Rom* 5:3
and *p.* experience, and. 4
do we with *p.* wait for it. 8:25
we through *p.* and comfort. 15:4
the God of *p.* grant you to be. 5
as ministers of God in much *p.* *2 Cor* 6:4
wrought among you in all *p.* 12:12
with all might to all *p.* *Col* 1:11
remembering your *p.* of. *1 Thes* 1:3
glory in you for your *p.* *2 Thes* 1:4
and follow after love, *p. 1 Tim* 6:11
hast fully known my *p.* *2 Tim* 3:10
be sound in faith, in *p.* *Tit* 2:2
who through faith and *p.* *Heb* 6:12
ye have need of *p.* that after. 10:36
let us run with *p.* the race set. 12:1
of your faith worketh *p.* *Jas* 1:3
but let *p.* have her perfect work. 4
husbandman hath long *p.* for it. 5:7
for an example of *p.* 10
have heard of *p.* of Job. 11
to temperance *p.*; to *p.* *2 Pet* 1:6
companion in *p.* of Jesus. *Rev* 1:9
I know thy *p.* 2:2, 19
and thou hast *p.* 3
hast kept word of my *p.* 3:10
the *p.* of the saints. 13:10; 14:12

patient

p. in spirit is better than. *Eccl* 7:8
who by *p.* continuance. *Rom* 2:7
rejoicing in hope, *p.* in. 12:12
be *p.* toward all men. *1 Thes* 5:14*
and unto the *p.* waiting. *2 Thes* 3:5
not greedy of lucre, but *p.* *1 Tim* 3:3*; *2 Tim* 2:24*
be *p.* brethren. *Jas* 5:7
be ye also *p.* 8

patiently

Lord, and wait *p.* for him. *Ps* 37:7
I waited *p.* for the Lord, and. 40:1
beseech thee to hear me *p. Acts* 26:3
after he had *p.* endured. *Heb* 6:15
buffeted for faults ye take it *p.* . . . suffer, ye take it *p.* *1 Pet* 2:20

Patmos

isle that is called *P.* *Rev* 1:9

patriarch

(*This name is given to the heads, or princes of the family, chiefly to those that lived before Moses. The name Patriarch comes from the Greek word,* Patriarchēs, *which signifies* Head of a family)

speak of the *p.* David. *Acts* 2:29
p. Abraham paid tithes. *Heb* 7:4

patriarchs

Jacob begat the twelve *p.* *Acts* 7:8
p. moved with envy sold Joseph. 9

patrimony

cometh from sale of his *p. Deut* 18:8

pattern

after the *p.* of all the. *Ex* 25:9
thou make them after their *p.* 40
candlestick was made after the *p.* *Num* 8:4
behold the *p.* of the altar. *Josh* 22:28
to Urijah the *p.* of altar. *2 Ki* 16:10
David gave Solomon *p. 1 Chr* 28:11 12, 18, 19
let them measure the *p. Ezek* 43:10
that in me first Jesus Christ might shew for a *p.* *1 Tim* 1:16*
thyself a *p.* of good works. *Tit* 2:7*
according to *p.* I shewed. *Heb* 8:5

patterns

necessary that the *p.* of. *Heb* 9:23*

Paul

Saul, called *P.* filled. *Acts* 13:9
religious proselytes follow *P.* 43
P. waxed bold. 46
raised persecution against *P.* 50
the same heard *P.* 14:9
P. Mercurius, was chief speaker. 12
having stoned *P.* drew him out. 19
P. thought not good to take. 15:38
P. chose Silas. 40
him would *P.* have to go. 16:3
a vision appeared to *P.* in the. 9
to the things spoken of *P.* 14
followed *P.* 17
but *P.* being grieved. 18
P. and Silas prayed, and sang. 25
but *P.* cried, saying, Do thyself. 28
P. as his manner was, went. 17:2
consorted with *P.* and Silas. 4
brethren sent *P.* away. 10, 14
while *P.* waited at Athens. 16
P. was pressed in spirit, and. 18:5
Lord spake to *P.* in the night. 9
miracles by the hands of *P.* 19:11
P. I know. 15
P. purposed in spirit to go to. 21
this *P.* hath persuaded and. 26
P. preached unto them, ready. 20:7
P. went down, and embracing. 10
wept sore, and fell on *P.*'s neck. 37
said to *P.* through the Spirit. 21:4
Agabus took *P.*'s girdle and. 11
the day following *P.* went in. 18
took *P.* and drew him out of. 30
saw soldiers, they left beating *P.* 32
P. stood on the stairs. 40
P. beholding. 23:1
lest *P.* should have been pulled. 10
be of good cheer, *P.* 11
not eat till they had killed *P.* 12, 14
P. prayed me to bring this. 18
soldiers brought *P.* to Antipatris. 31
informed governor against *P.* 24:1
that money should have been given him of *P.* 26
Felix left *P.* bound. 27
one Jesus, whom *P.* affirmed. 25:19
Festus said, *P.* thou art. 26:24
Julius courteously entreated *P.* 27:3
saying, Fear not, *P.* 24
P. besought them all to take meat. 33
the centurion, willing to save *P.* 43
but *P.* was suffered to dwell. 28:16
I am of *P.* *1 Cor* 1:12; 3:4
is Christ divided? was *P.*? 1:13
who then is *P.*? 3:5
whether *P.*, or Apollos, or. 22
the salutation of me *P.* 16:21 *Col* 4:18; *2 Thes* 3:17
come to you, even I *P. 1 Thes* 2:18
such an one as *P.* the aged. *Philem* 9
as our beloved brother *P. 2 Pet* 3:15

Paulus

the deputy Sergius *P.* *Acts* 13:7

paved

as it were a *p.* work. *Ex* 24:10
midst thereof being *p.* *S of S* 3:10

pavement

he put the sea on a *p.* *2 Ki* 16:17
Israel bowed themselves upon the *p.* *2 Chr* 7:3
the beds were on a *p.* of. *Esth* 1:6
p. made for the court, thirty chambers were upon the *p. Ezek* 40:17
p. by the side of the gates, was the lower *p.* 18
over against the *p.* was gallery. 42:3
a place called the *p.* *John* 19:13

pavilion, -s

he made darkness his *p.* *2 Sam* 22:12; *Ps* 18:11
kings drinking in *p.* *1 Ki* 20:12
drinking himself drunk in *p.* 16
he shall hide me in his *p.* *Ps* 27:5
keep them secretly in a *p.* 31:20
spread his royal *p.* *Jer* 43:10

paw

delivered me out of *p. 1 Sam* 17:37

paweth

the horse *p.* in the valley. *Job* 39:21

paws

whatsoever goeth on *p.* *Lev* 11:27

pay

only he shall p. for loss. *Ex* 21:19
and he shall p. as the judges. 22
he shall surely p. ox for ox. 36
found, let him p. double. 22:7, 9
p. according to the dowry. 17
water, I will p. for it. *Num* 20:19
vow, shall not slack to p. *Deut* 23:21
me go and p. my vow. *2 Sam* 15:7
p. a talent of silver. *1 Ki* 20:39
sell oil, and p. thy debt. *2 Ki* 4:7
did Solomon make to p. tribute. *2 Chr* 8:8
did children of Ammon p. to. 27:5
will they not p. toll and. *Ezra* 4:13
will p. 10,000 talents. *Esth* 3:9; 4:7
thou shalt p. thy vows. *Job* 22:27
I will p. my vows. *Ps* 22:25; 66:13; 116:14, 18
and p. thy vows to the Most. 50:14
vow and p. to the Lord your. 76:11
given, will he p. again. *Pr* 19:17
if thou hast nothing to p. why? 22:27
defer not to p. it, p. that. *Eccl* 5:4
that thou shouldest vow and not p. 5
I will p. that which I have vowed. *Jonah* 2:9
doth not your master p.? *Mat* 17:24
as he had not to p., his lord forgave him. 18:25, 27; *Luke* 7:42
I will p. thee all. *Mat* 18:26, 29
p. me that thou owest. 28
till he should p. debt. 30
till he should p. all that was due. 34
for ye p. tithe of mint, anise. 23:23
p. ye tribute also. *Rom* 13:6

payeth

borroweth and p. not. *Ps* 37:21

payment

all to be sold, and p. *Mat* 18:25

peace

(This word is used in the Bible as we use it to-day. It was, however, much used as a salutation, with no stress on the meaning, although that meaning was most probably the origin of its use in that way)

Pharaoh an answer of p. *Gen* 41:16
I will give p. in land. *Lev* 26:6
the Lord lift up his countenance and give thee p. *Num* 6:26
give to him my covenant of p. 25:12
Sihon with words of p. *Deut* 2:26
city, proclaim p. to it. 20:10
if it make thee answer of p. 11
if it will make no p. with thee. 12
thou shalt not seek their p. 23:6
I shall have p. though I walk. 29:19
was p. between Jabin. *Judg* 4:17
there was p. between Israel and. *1 Sam* 7:14
well, thy servant shall have p. 20:7
there is p. to thee, no hurt. 21
throne shall there be p. *1 Ki* 2:33
Solomon had p. on all sides. 4:24
there was p. between Hiram. 5:12
whether they come for p. 20:18
let him say, Is it p.? *2 Ki* 9:17, 18
what hast thou to do with p.? 19, 22
p. so long as her witchcrafts? 22
she said, Had Zimri p., who slew? 31
is it not good, if p. be in my days? 20:19; *Isa* 39:8
I will give p. to Israel. *1 Chr* 22:9
there was no p. to him. *2 Chr* 15:5
beyond the river, p. *Ezra* 4:17
unto Darius the king, all p. 5:7
to Ezra perfect p. 7:12
nor seek their p. or their. 9:12
letters with words of p. *Esth* 9:30
Mordecai, speaking p. to all. 10:3
beasts of field shall be at p. *Job* 5:23
with him, and be at p. 22:21
maketh p. in his high places. 25:2
him that was at p. with. *Ps* 7:4
which speak p. to neighbours. 28:3
bless his people with p. 29:11
do good, seek p. and pursue it. 34:14; *1 Pet* 3:11
they speak not p. but they devise. *Ps* 35:20
themselves in abundance of p. 37:11
end of the upright man is p. *Ps* 37:37
such as be at p. with him. 55:20
the mountains shall bring p. 72:3
in days abundance of p. so long. 7
he will speak p. to his people. 85:8
righteousness and p. have kissed. 10
great p. have they which. 119:165
dwelt with him that hateth p. 120:6
I am for p., but when I speak they. 7
pray for p. of Jerusalem. 122:6
but p. shall be upon Israel. 125:5
shalt see p. upon Israel. 128:6
he maketh p. in thy borders. 147:14
pleasantness, her paths p. *Pr* 3:17
to the counsellors of p. is joy. 12:20
maketh his enemies to be at p. 16:7
of war, and a time of p. *Eccl* 3:8
The Prince of P. *Isa* 9:6
of the increase of his p. no end. 7
thou wilt ordain p. for us. 26:12
p. with me, and he shall make p. 27:5
righteousness shall be p. 32:17
the ambassadors of p. shall. 33:7
for p. I had great bitterness. 38:17
I make p. and create evil. 45:7
then had thy p. been as river. 48:18
no p. to the wicked. 22; 57:21
feet of him that publisheth p. 52:7; *Nah* 1:15
the chastisement of our p. *Isa* 53:5
nor shall covenant of my p. 54:10
shall be the p. of thy children. 13
with joy, led forth with p. 55:12
he shall enter into p. 57:2
fruit of the lips; P. p. to him. 19
the way of p. they know not. 59:8; *Rom* 3:17
I will make thine officers p. *Isa* 60:17
behold, I will extend p. to her. 66:12
ye shall have p. whereas. *Jer* 4:10
P. p. when there is no p. 6:14; 8:11
we looked for p. but no. 8:15; 14:19
if in land of p. they wearied. 12:5
sword devour, no flesh shall have p. 12
you assured p. in this place. 14:13
I have taken away my p. from. 16:5
prophet which prophesied of p. 28:9
seek p. of the city whither. 29:7
thoughts of p., and not of evil. 11
a voice of fear, and not of p. 30:5
reveal to them abundance of p. 33:6
hast removed my soul far from p. *Lam* 3:17
they shall seek p. there. *Ezek* 7:25
P. and there was no p. 13:10, 16
them a covenant of p. 34:25; 37:26
by p. he shall destroy. *Dan* 8:25*
men at p. with thee have. *Ob* 7
with their teeth and cry P. *Mi* 3:5
this man shall be the p. when. 5:5
I will give p. saith the Lord. *Hag* 2:9
counsel of p. be between. *Zech* 6:13
nor was there any p. to him. 8:10
execute judgement of truth and p. 16
love p. 19
shall speak p. to the heathen. 9:10
with him of life and p. *Mal* 2:5
worthy, let your p. come upon it; if not, let your p. return. *Mat* 10:13
am come to send p. on earth. 34
he arose and said to the sea, P. be still. *Mark* 4:39
have p. one with another. 9:50
feet into the way of p. *Luke* 1:79
and on earth p., good will. 2:14
if son of p. be there, your p. 10:6
to give p. on the earth? 12:51
desireth conditions of p. 14:32
p. in heaven, and glory in. 19:38
things which belong to thy p. 42
p. I leave with you, my p. *John* 14:27
that in me ye might have p. 16:33
preaching p. by Jesus Christ. *Acts* 10:36
Blastus their friend desired p. 12:20
p. from God the Father. *Rom* 1:7; *1 Cor* 1:3; *2 Cor* 1:2; *Gal* 1:3; *Eph* 1:2; *Phil* 1:2
but p. to every man that. *Rom* 2:10
justified, we have p. with God. 5:1
spiritually minded is life and p. 8:6
that preach the gospel of p. 10:15
kingdom of God is joy and p. 14:17
follow the things that make for p. 19
fill you with all joy and p. *Rom* 15:13
hath called us to p. *1 Cor* 7:15
but author of p. as in. 14:33
Spirit is love, joy, p. *Gal* 5:22
for he is our p. *Eph* 2:14
so making p. 15
Christ came and preached p. 17
the Spirit in the bond of p. 4:3
preparation of gospel of p. 6:15
p. of God, which passeth. *Phil* 4:7
grace and p. from God. *Col* 1:2; *1 Thes* 1:1; *2 Thes* 1:2; *1 Tim* 1:2; *2 Tim* 1:2; *Tit* 1:4; *Philem* 3; *2 John* 3
let the p. of God rule in. *Col* 3:15
when they shall say, P. *1 Thes* 5:3
be at p. among themselves. 13
Lord of p. give you p. *2 Thes* 3:16
follow p. with all men. *2 Tim* 2:22; *Heb* 12:14
Salem, that is, king of p. *Heb* 7:2
and received spies in p. 11:31
p. of them that make p.? *Jas* 3:18
p. from him that is, was. *Rev* 1:4
was given to him to take p. 6:4

see **held, hold, made, offerings**

peace *be*

and he said, P. *be* to you. *Gen* 43:23
Lord, said, P. *be* to thee. *Judg* 6:23
and the old man said, P. *be*. 19:20
p. *be* to thee, p. *be* to house, p. *be*. *1 Sam* 25:6
p. *be* to thee, and p. *be*. *1 Chr* 12:18
p. *be* within thy walls. *Ps* 122:7
I will now say, P. *be* within thee. 8
p. *be* multiplied to you. *Dan* 4:1; 6:25; *1 Pet* 1:2; *2 Pet* 1:2; *Jude* 2
p. *be* to thee, be strong. *Dan* 10:19
first say, P. *be* to this. *Luke* 10:5
he saith, P. *be* to you. 24:36; *John* 20:19, 21, 26
p. *be* on them, and mercy. *Gal* 6:16
p. *be* to brethren, and. *Eph* 6:23
p. *be* with you all that. *1 Pet* 5:14
p. *be* to thee, our friends. *3 John* 14

God of **peace**

the *God of* p. be with. *Rom* 15:33
the *God of* p. shall bruise. 16:20
God of p. shall be with you. *2 Cor* 13:11; *Phil* 4:9
very *God of* p. sanctify. *1 Thes* 5:23
now the *God of* p. make. *Heb* 13:20

in **peace**

sent thee away *in* p. *Gen* 26:29
departed from Isaac *in* p. 31
to my father's house *in* p. 28:21
as for you, get you up *in* p. 44:17
at Makkedah, *in* p. *Josh* 10:21
when I come again *in* p. *Judg* 8:9
when I return *in* p. whatever. 11:31
Abner went *in* p. *2 Sam* 3:21, 22
he is gone *in* p. 23
return to the city *in* p. and. 15:27
so all the people shall be *in* p. 17:3
until the day he came *in* p. 19:24
king is come again *in* p. 30
the blood of war *in* p. *1 Ki* 2:5
return every man *in* p. 22:17; *2 Chr* 18:16
in prison until I come *in* p. *1 Ki* 22:27; *2 Chr* 18:26
if thou return at all *in* p. *1 Ki* 22:28; *2 Chr* 18:27
shalt be gathered to thy grave *in* p. *2 Ki* 22:20; *2 Chr* 34:28
returned *in* p. *2 Chr* 19:1
tabernacle shall be *in* p. *Job* 5:24
I will lay me down *in* p. *Ps* 4:8
my soul *in* p. from the battle. 55:18
keep him *in* perfect p. *Isa* 26:3
in the p. thereof shall ye. *Jer* 29:7
but thou shalt die *in* p. 34:5
he walked with me *in* p. *Mal* 2:6
thy servant depart *in* p. *Luke* 2:29
palace his goods are *in* p. 11:21
conduct him forth *in* p. *1 Cor* 16:11
be of one mind, live *in* p. *2 Cor* 13:11
depart *in* p., be ye. *Jas* 2:16
righteousness is sown *in* p. 3:18
found of him *in* p. *2 Pet* 3:14

see **go**

peaceable
these men are p. with. Gen 34:21
of them that are p. in 2 Sam 20:19
wide, quiet, and p. 1 Chr 4:40
my people dwell in a p. Isa 32:18
the p. habitations are. Jer 25:37
lead a quiet and p. life. 1 Tim 2:2*
it yieldeth the p. fruit. Heb 12:11
above is pure, p., gentle. Jas 3:17

peaceably
speak p. to him. Gen 37:4
restore those lands again p. Judg 11:13
send some to call p. to the. 21:13
comest thou p.? 1 Sam 16:4
he said, P. 5; 1 Ki 2:13
if ye be come p. to me. 1 Chr 12:17
one speaketh p. to his. Jer 9:8
he shall come in p. Dan 11:21*, 24*
live p. with all men. Rom 12:18

peacemakers
blessed are the p. for they. Mat 5:9

peacocks
navy came, bringing p. 1 Ki 10:22
2 Chr 9:21
the goodly wings to p.? Job 39:13*

pearl
(Pearls were considered by the ancients among the most precious of gems and were highly esteemed as ornaments. This is probably the reason the word is used metaphorically for anything of great value, and especially for wise sayings)
he found one p. of great. Mat 13:46
gate was of one p. Rev 21:21

pearls
be made of coral or p. Job 28:18*
neither cast ye your p. Mat 7:6
man seeking goodly p. 13:45
not with gold, or p. or. 1 Tim 2:9
decked with gold and p. Rev 17:4
the merchandise of p. 18:12, 16
twelve gates were twelve p. 21:21

peculiar
be a p. treasure to me. Ex 19:5†
to be a p. people. Deut 14:2†
26:18†; 1 Pet 2:9*
chosen Israel for his p. treasure. Ps 135:4†
I gathered the p. treasure. Eccl 2:8
purify to himself p. people. Tit 2:14*

pedigree
they declared their p. Num 1:18

peeled
nation scattered and p. Isa 18:2*, 7*
every shoulder was p. Ezek 29:18†

peep
to wizards that p. and. Isa 8:19*

peeped
opened the mouth or p. Isa 10:14*

Pekah
P. conspired against. 2 Ki 15:25
in days of P. came Tiglath-pileser. 29
a conspiracy against P. 15:30
against Judah came P. 37; 16:5
P. slew in Judah 120,000. 2 Chr 28:6
Rezin and P. went towards. Isa 7:1

Pekahiah
P. son of Manahem. 2 Ki 15:22, 23

Pelatiah
Hananiah, P. of Judah. 1 Chr 3:21
having for their captian P. 4:42
P. and Hanan sealed. Neh 10:22
P. the son of Benaiah. Ezek 11:13

pelican
swan and p. unclean. Lev 11:18
Deut 14:17
I am like a p. of the. Ps 102:6

pen
they that handle the p. Judg 5:14*
graven with an iron p. Job 19:24
my tongue is the p. of a. Ps 45:1
write in it with a man's p. Isa 8:1
p. of the scribes is in vain. Jer 8:8
is written with a p. of iron. 17:1
I will not with ink and p. 3 John 13

pence
(The denarius, worth about 16 or 17 cents, or between 8d. and 9d., was the usual wage of an unskilled labourer for one day. American Revision changes to shillings)
owed him an hundred p. Mat 18:28
sold for more than 300 p.
Mark 14:5; John 12:5
the one owed 500 p. the. Luke 7:41
on morrow he took out two p. 10:35

Peniel
the name of the place P. Gen 32:30

penknife
Jehudi cut roll with a p. Jer 36:23

penny
with labourers for a p. Mat 20:2
they received every man a p. 9
not agree with me for a p.? 13
brought unto him a p. 22:19
he said, Bring me a p. Mark 12:15
Luke 20:24
of wheat for a p. and three measures of barley for a p. Rev 6:6

pennyworth
two hundred p. of bread. Mark 6:37
two hundred p. is not. John 6:7

Pentecost
This word is derived from the Greek word Pentecoste, fiftieth, *because the feast of Pentecost was celebrated the fiftieth day after the sixteenth of* Nisan, *which was the second day of the feast of the passover. The Hebrews call it* the Feast of Weeks, Ex 34:22, *because it was kept seven weeks after the passover.*
It was the Jewish harvest-home.
when the day of P. was. Acts 2:1
at Jerusalem the day of P. 20:16
tarry at Ephesus until P. 1 Cor 16:8

Penuel
as Jacob passed over P. Gen 32:31
Gideon went up thence to P. and. Judg 8:8
he beat down the tower of P. 17
then Jeroboam went and built P. 1 Ki 12:25
P. the father of Gedor. 1 Chr 4:4
Iphediah and P. the sons of. 8:25

penury
lips tendeth only to p. Pr 14:23
she of her p. hath cast. Luke 21:4*

people
(The Revisions often change the singular to the plural. In this case it has more distinctly the idea of nations or of people grouped together. In the New Testament the singular is more often changed to multitude)
let p. serve thee, and. Gen 27:29
he also shall become a p. 48:19
I will take you for a p. and be to you a God. Ex 6:7; Deut 4:20
2 Sam 7:24; Jer 13:11
thou art a stiffnecked p. Ex 33:3, 5
34:9; Deut 9:6
I separated you from other p. Lev 20:24, 26
thou art undone, O p. Num 21:29
a p. come out from Egypt. 22:5, 11
head over a p. in Midian. 25:15
did ever p. hear voice? Deut 4:33
chosen thee to be a special p. 7:6
chosen thee to be a peculiar p. 14:2
a p. more than thou, be not. 20:1
shall be given to another p. 28:32
may establish thee for a p. to. 29:13
with those that are not a p. 32:21
who is like to thee, O p.? 33:29
gone back to her p. Ruth 1:15
ye make the Lord's p. 1 Sam 2:24
to us, to slay us and our p. 5:10
let it slay us not, and our p. 11
went to redeem for a p. 2 Sam 7:23
afflicted p. thou wilt save. 22:28
Ps 18:27
a p. I knew not shall serve me.
2 Sam 22:44; Ps 18:43
hearken, O p. every one. 1 Ki 22:28
the p., that they should be the Lord's p. 2 Ki 11:17; 2 Chr 23:16
from one kingdom to another p.
1 Chr 16:20; Ps 105:13
valiantly for our p. 1 Chr 19:13
made me king over a p. 2 Chr 1:9
letters to every p. after. Esth 1:22
3:12; 8:9; Neh 13:24
Esther had not shewed her p. nor. Esth 2:10
there is a certain p. scattered. 3:8
request before him for her p. 4:8
when p. are cut off in. Job 36:20
ye p. pour out your hearts. Ps 62:8
O bless our God, ye p. 66:8
a p. that do err. 95:10
from a p. of a strange. 114:1
happy is that p. 144:15
a p. near to him. 148:14
a reproach to any p. Pr 14:34
wicked ruler over the poor p. 28:15
ants are a p. not strong. 30:25
a p. laden with iniquity. Isa 1:4
give ear to the law, ye p. of. 10
be broken, that it be not a p. 7:8
should not a p. seek unto? 8:19
is a p. of no understanding. 27:11
this is a rebellious p. 30:9; 65:2
I will give p. for thy life. 43:4
bring forth the blind p. that. 8
a p. that provoketh me to. 65:3
a rejoicing, and her p. a joy. 18
a p. cometh from the north.
Jer 6:22; 50:41
destroyed from being a p. 48:42
her p. fell into the hand. Lam 1:7
and there shall be, like p. Hos 4:9
O Israel, for joy as other p. 9:1
tell us, of what p. art? Jonah 1:8
it shall be exalted, and p. Mi 4:1
there shall come p. Zech 8:20
to make ready a p. Luke 1:17
to take out of them a p. Acts 15:14
by them that are no p. Rom 10:19
to himself a peculiar p. Tit 2:14
they shall be to me a p. Heb 8:10
but ye are a peculiar p. 1 Pet 2:9
p. of God, time past were not a p. 10
redeemed us out of every p. Rev 5:9

all **people**
treasure above all p. Ex 19:5
Deut 7:6, 14; 10:15; Ps 99:2
the fewest of all p. Deut 7:7
scatter thee among all p. 28:64
came of all p. to hear. 1 Ki 4:34
all p. may know thy name. 8:43
2 Chr 6:33
byword among all p. 1 Ki 9:7
are diverse from all p. Esth 3:8
was published to all p. 14; 8:13
fear of them fell upon all p. 9:2
O clap your hands, all ye p. Ps 47:1
wonders among all p. 96:3
all ye nations, praise him, all ye p.
117:1; 148:11; Rom 15:11
to all p. a feast of fat. Isa 25:6
covering cast over all p. 7
called house of prayer for all p. 56:7
all her p. sigh, they. Lam 1:11
hear, I pray you, all p. 18; Mi 1:2
all p. and nations feared. Dan 5:19
all p. and nations should. 7:14
all p. will walk each in. Mi 4:5
heapeth unto him all p. Hab 2:5
a praise among all p. of earth. Zeph 3:20
a burdensome stone for all p. Zech 12:3*
tidings of joy, which shall be to all p. Luke 2:10
before the face of all p. 31

all the **people**
all the p. of Sodom compassed. Gen 19:4
he and all the p. with him. 35:6
that sold to all the p. of. 42:6
get thee out, and all the p. Ex 11:8
all the p. stand by thee from. 18:14
out of all the p. able men. 21

all the p. answered. *Ex* 19:8; 24:3
come down in sight of *all the p.* 11
all the p. saw thunderings. 20:18
glory of the Lord appeared to *all the p.* *Lev* 9:23
and before *all the p.* I will. 10:3
that *all the* Lord's *p.* were prophets. *Num* 11:29
and *all the p.* we saw are. 13:32
all the p. were in ignorance. 15:26
afterwards the hand of *all the p.* *Deut* 13:9; 17:7
all the p. shall hear and fear. 17:13
all the p. shall say, Amen. 27:15
16, 17, 18, 19, 20, 21
all the p. of the earth shall. 28:10
that *all the p.* of the earth. *Josh* 4:24
all the p. that came out were. 5:4, 5
all the p. shall shout. 6:5
let not *all the p.* go. 7:3
from before us *all the p.* 24:18
house fell upon *all the p.* *Judg* 16:30
and *all the p.* arose as one. 20:8
him among *all the p.* *1 Sam* 10:24
all the p. wept. 11:4
all the p. feared greatly. 12:18
because the soul of *all the p.* 11:4
all the p. stood, and. *2 Sam* 2:28
Abner's grave, *all p.* wept. 3:32, 34
and *all the p.* took notice of it. 36
bring back *all the p.* unto thee, so *all the p.* shall be in peace. 17:3
and *all the p.* were at strife. 19:9
woman went to *all the p.* in. 20:22
separate them from *all p.* *1 Ki* 8:53
that *all the p.* of the earth may. 60
handfuls for *all the p.* 20:10
all the p. stood to the covenant. *2 Ki* 23:3
all the p. said, Amen. *1 Chr* 16:36
all the p. will be wholly at. 28:21
king and *all the p.* offered. *2 Chr* 7:4
may judge *all the p.* *Ezra* 7:25
in sight of *all p.* for he was above *all p.* *Neh* 8:5
so the Levites stilled *all the p.* 11
O God, let *all the p.* *Ps* 67:3, 5
and *all the p.* see his glory. 97:6
blessed be the Lord God of Israel: let *all the p.* say, Amen. 106:48
is no end of *all the p.* *Eccl* 4:16
to speak to *all the p.* *Jer* 26:8
all the p. were gathered against. 9
all the p. fought against. 34:1
a covenant with *all the p.* 8, 10
the hands of *all the p.* 38:4
all the p. obeyed the voice of. 43:4
all the p. are gone. *Ezek* 31:12
when *all the p.* heard the. *Dan* 3:7
covenant I made with *all the p.* *Zech* 11:10
a cup of trembling to *all the p.* 12:2
the Lord will smite *all the p.* 14:12
base before *all the p.* *Mal* 2:9
unto him before *all the p.* *Luke* 8:47
all the p. rejoiced for the. 13:17
all the p. when they saw, gave. 18:43
all the p. were very attentive. 19:48
but if we say, Of men, *all the p.* 20:6
favour with *all the p.* *Acts* 2:47
reputation among *all the p.* 5:34
not to *all the p.* but unto witnesses. 10:41
of repentance to *all the p.* 13:24
stirred up *all the p.* and laid. 21:27
all the p., he sprinkled both book and *all the p.* *Heb* 9:19

among the **people**

off from *among the p.* *Lev* 18:29
be a curse *among the p.* *Num* 5:27
yourselves *among the p.* *1 Sam* 14:34
ye brutish *among the p.* *Ps* 94:8
know thee *among the p.* *Ezek* 28:19
understand *among the p.* *Dan* 11:33
they say *among the p.* *Joel* 2:17
sow them *among the p.* *Zech* 10:9
all manner of disease *among the p.* *Mat* 4:23; 9:35
be an uproar *among the p.* 26:5
murmuring *among the p.* *John* 7:12
was a division *among the p.* 43
be destroyed from *among the p.* *Acts* 3:23
no further *among the p.* *Acts* 4:17
wrought *among the p.* 5:12; 6:8
Paul ran in *among the p.* 14:14
false prophets also *among the p.* *2 Pet* 2:1

see **common, foolish, many, men**

people *of God*

assembly of the *p. of God.* *Judg* 20:2
thing against *p. of God.* *2 Sam* 14:13
p. of the *God* of Abraham. *Ps* 47:9
a rest to the *p. of God.* *Heb* 4:9
affliction with *p. of God.* 11:25
but are now *p. of God.* *1 Pet* 2:10

see **great**

his **people**

be cut off from *his p.* *Gen* 17:14
Ex 30:33, 38; 31:14; *Lev* 7:20, 21
25, 27; 17:4, 9; 19:8; 23:29
Num 9:13; 15:30
was gathered to *his p.* *Gen* 25:8
Ishmael was gathered to *his p.* 17
Isaac was gathered to *his p.* 35:29
Dan shall judge *his p.* as one of. 49:16, 33
depart from *his p.* *Ex* 8:29, 31
Amalek and *his p.* 17:13
Moses and for Israel *his p.* 18:1
blood, I will cut him off from among *his p.* *Lev* 17:10; 20:3, 6; 23:30
for the dead among *his p.* 21:1
profane his seed among *his p.* 15
gathered to *his p.* *Num* 20:24, 26
delivered him into thy hand, and all *his p.* 21:34, 35; *Deut* 2:33
Og and all *his p.* *Deut* 3:2, 3
thee to be *his* peculiar *p.* 26:18
for Lord's portion is *his p.* 32:9
shall judge *his p.* 36; *Ps* 135:14
with *his p.* he will be merciful to his . . . *his p.* *Deut* 32:43; *Rom* 15:10
was gathered to *his p.* *Deut* 32:50
and bring Judah to *his p.* 33:7
Ai, the king and *his p.* *Josh* 8:1
Amorites before *his p.* *Judg* 11:23
Lord had visited *his p.* *Ruth* 1:6
forsake *his p.* for his great name's . . . make you *his p.* *1 Sam* 12:22
to be king over all *his p.* 15:1
make *his p.* Israel utterly to. 27:12
David executed justice to all *his p.* *2 Sam* 8:15; *1 Chr* 18:14
people shall go for *his p.* *1 Ki* 20:42
The Lord make *his p.* a hundred times so many more. *1 Chr* 21:3
land is subdued before Lord and *his p.* 22:18
God hath given rest to *his p.* 23:25
Lord hath loved *his p.* *2 Chr* 2:11
Lord hath blessed *his p.* 31:10
that could deliver *his p.*? 32:14, 15
to Manasseh and *his p.* 33:10
had compassion on *his p.* 36:15
wrath of Lord arose against *his p.* 16
who among you of all *his p.* go up. 23 *Ezra* 1:3
seeking wealth of *his p.* *Esth* 10:3
nor nephew among *his p.* *Job* 18:19
captivity of *his p.* *Ps* 14:7; 53:6
give strength to *his p.*; the Lord will bless *his p.* with. 29:11; 68:35
that he may judge *his p.* 50:4
therefore *his p.* return hither. 73:10
he provide flesh for *his p.*? 78:20
he gave *his p.* over also to. 62
him to feed Jacob *his p.* 71
will speak peace to *his p.* and. 85:8
will not cast off *his p.* 94:14
we are *his p.* 100:3
he increased *his p.* greatly. 105:24
turned their heart to hate *his p.* 25
he brought forth *his p.* 43
wrath of the Lord kindled against *his p.* 106:40; *Isa* 5:25
shewed *his p.* the power. *Ps* 111:6
he sent redemption to *his p.*: holy. 9
with the princes of *his p.* 113:8
the presence of all *his p.* 116:14, 18
the Lord round about *his p.* 125:2
his p. through the wilderness. 136:16
exalteth the horn of *his p.* 148:14
Lord taketh pleasure in *his p.* 149:4
with the ancients of *his p.* *Isa* 3:14
and the heart of *his p.* *Isa* 7:2
remnant of *his p.* left. 11:11
highway for the remnant of *his p.* 16
the poor of *his p.* shall trust. 14:32
the rebuke of *his p.* shall he. 25:8
beauty to residue of *his p.* 28:5
bindeth up breach of *his p.* 30:26
hath comforted *his p.* 49:13; 52:9
pleadeth the cause of *his p.* 51:22
separated me from *his p.* 56:3
days of old, Moses and *his p.* 63:11
and serve him and *his p.* *Jer* 27:12
return every one to *his p.* 50:16
not good among *his p.* *Ezek* 18:18
he and *his p.* with him. 30:11
be jealous and pity *his p.* *Joel* 2:18
answer and say to *his p.* 19
Lord will be the hope of *his p.* 3:16
controversy with *his p.* *Mi* 6:2
them as a flock of *his p.* *Zech* 9:16
Jesus: he shall save *his p.* *Mat* 1:21
hath visited and redeemed *his p.* *Luke* 1:68
knowledge of salvation to *his p.* 77
and that God hath visited *his p.* 7:16
hath God cast away *his p.*? *Rom* 11:1
God hath not cast away *his p.* 2
Lord shall judge *his p.* *Heb* 10:30
they shall be *his p.*, and God. *Rev* 21:3

see **holy, Israel**

people *of the land*

himself to *p. of the l.* *Gen* 23:7, 12
that sold to all *p. of the land.* 42:6
p. of the l. are many, ye. *Ex* 5:5
p. of the l. shall stone him. *Lev* 20:2
if *p. of the land* do hide their. 4
neither fear ye *p. of the l.* *Num* 14:9
all *p. of the l.* rejoiced and blew with trumpets. *2 Ki* 11:14, 20
Jotham judged *p. of the land.* 15:5 *2 Chr* 26:21
p. of the l. slew all them that had killed Amon, and *p. of the l.* made. *2 Ki* 21:24; *2 Chr* 33:25
p. of l. took Jehoahaz and anointed him. *2 Ki* 23:30; *2 Chr* 36:1
was no bread for *p. of the l.* *2 Ki* 25:3; *Jer* 52:6
mustered *p. of the l.* and sixty men of *p. of land.* *2 Ki* 25:19; *Jer* 52:25
gods of *p. of the land.* *1 Chr* 5:25
p. of l. weakened hands. *Ezra* 4:4
wives of the *p. of the land.* 10:2
from the *p. of the land.* 11
daughters to *p. of the l.* *Neh* 10:30
if the *p. of the l.* bring ware. 31
many of the *p. of the l.* *Esth* 8:17
iron pillar against *p. of l.* *Jer* 1:18
all the *p. of the land* which. 34:19
hands of *p. of the land.* *Ezek* 7:27
p. of the l. have used oppression. 22:29
if *p. of the land* take man to. 33:2
and all the *p. of the land* shall. 39:13
p. of the land shall give this. 45:16
prince prepare for *p. of the land.* 22
p. of the l. shall worship at. 46:3
when *p. of the land* shall come. 9
spake to the *p. of the land.* *Dan* 9:6
be strong, all ye *p. of the l.* *Hag* 2:4
speak to all the *p. of the land.* *Zech* 7:5

much **people**

Edom came out against him with *much p.* *Num* 20:20
they went with *much p.* *Josh* 11:4
came *much p.* by way. *2 Sam* 13:34
at Jerusalem *much p.* *2 Chr* 30:13
there was gathered *much p.* 32:4
praise thee among *much p.* *Ps* 35:18
much p. gathered unto. *Mark* 5:21
Jesus went with him, and *much p.* 24
Jesus saw *much p.*, was moved. 6:34
much p. of Jews knew. *John* 12:9
next day *much p.* took branches. 12
and drew away *much p.* *Acts* 5:37
and *much p.* was added unto. 11:24
for I have *much p.* in this city. 18:10
hath turned away *much p.* 19:26
I heard a voice of *much p.* *Rev* 19:1

my **people**

sons of *my p.* give I it. *Gen* 23:11
to thy word shall all *my p.* 41:10

to be gathered to *my p.* *Gen* 49:29
I have seen the affliction of *my p.*
Ex 3:7; *Acts* 7:34
mayest bring forth *my p.* *Ex* 3:10; 7:4
let *my p.* go. 5:1; 7:16; 8:1, 20
9:1, 13; 10:3
frogs from me and from *my p.* 8:8
wilt not let *my p.* go. 21; 10:4
land in which *my p.* dwell. 8:22, 23
thou thyself against *my p.* 9:17
I and *my p.* are wicked. 27
you forth from among *my p.* 12:31
money to any of *my p.* 22:25
I will be your God, ye shall by *my p.*
Lev 26:12 *Jer* 11:4; 30:22
behold I go unto *my p.* *Num* 24:14
my p. were at great strife. *Judg* 12:2
a woman among all *my p.*? 14:3
a riddle to children of *my p.* 16
people shall be *my p.* *Ruth* 1:16
for all the city of *my p.* doth. 3:11
captain over *my p.* that he may serve
my p. . . . on *my p.* *1 Sam* 9:16
I will save *my p.* *2 Sam* 3:18
I took thee to be ruler over *my p.* 7:8
2 Chr 6:5
art, *my p.* as thy people. *1 Ki* 22:4
2 Ki 3:7; *2 Chr* 18:3
the captain of *my p.* *2 Ki* 20:5
I commanded to feed *my p.*
1 Chr 17:6
David said, Hear me, *my p.* 28:2
who am I, and what *my p.*? 29:14
thou mayest judge *my p.* *2 Chr* 1:11
brought forth *my p.* out of Egypt. 6:5
pestilence among *my p.* 7:13
if *my p.* shall humble themselves. 14
let *my p.* be given me at. *Esth* 7:3
for we are sold, I and *my p.* to. 4
see evil shall come to *my p.* 8:6
who eat up *my p.* as. *Ps* 14:4; 53:4
hear, O *my p.* I will. 50:7; 81:8
slay them not, least *my p.* 59:11
I will bring *my p.* again. 68:22
give ear, O *my p.* to my law. 78:1
but *my p.* would not hearken. 81:11
O that *my p.* had hearkened. 13
my shield, who subdueth *my p.* 144:2
but Israel not know, *my p.* *Isa* 1:3
as for *my p.*, children are their oppressors, O *my p.* they which. 3:12
what mean ye that ye beat *my p.*? 15
my p. are gone into captivity. 5:13
right from poor of *my p.* 10:2
O *my p.* that dwellest in Zion. 24
blessed be Egypt, *my p.* and. 19:25
come, *my p.* enter thou into. 26:20
my p. shall dwell in a. 32:18
comfort ye, comfort ye *my p.* 40:1
drink to *my p.* my chosen. 43:20
I was wroth with *my p.* 47:6
hearken unto me, *my p.* and. 51:4
say to Zion, Thou art *my p.* 16
my p. went down into Egypt. 52:4
saith Lord, that *my p.* is taken. 5
therefore *my p.* shall know my. 6
for transgression of *my p.* was. 53:8
out of the way *of my p.* 57:14
shew *my p.* their transgression. 58:1
surely they are *my p.*, children. 63:8
Sharon a fold for *my p.* that. 65:10
Jerusalem, and joy in *my p.* 19
of a tree, are the days of *my p.* 22
but *my p.* have changed. *Jer* 2:11
for *my p.* have committed two. 13
why say *my p.*, We are lords? 31
yet *my p.* have forgotten. 32; 18:15
for *my p.* is foolish, they have. 4:22
for among *my p.* are found. 5:26
and *my p.* love to have it so, 31
for a fortress among *my p.* 6:27
and ye shall be *my p.* 7:23
my p. know not the judgement. 8:7
that I might leave *my p.* and go. 9:2
diligently learn the ways of *my p.* as they taught *my p.* to. 12:16
I will destroy *my p.*, since they. 15:7
the pastors that feed *my p.* 23:2
if they had caused *my p.* to hear. 22
cause *my p.* to forget my name. 27
cause *my p.* to err by their lies. 32
they shall be *my p.* 24:7; 31:1, 33
32:38; *Ezek* 11:20; 36:28; 37:23
27; *Zech* 8:8

behold good that I will do for *my p.*
Jer 29:32
my p. shall be satisfied with. 31:14
they have despised *my p.* 33:24
my p. hath been lost sheep. 50:6
my p. go ye out of midst of her.
51:45; *Rev* 18:4
derision to all *my p.* and. *Lam* 3:14
be in assembly of *my p.* *Ezek* 13:9
have seduced *my p.* 10
Will ye hunt the souls of *my p.*? 18
among *my p.* by lying to *my p.* 19
I will deliver *my p.* out of. 21, 23
off from the midst of *my p.* 14:8
but that they may be *my p.* and. 11
sword shall be upon *my p.* 21:12
even house of Israel are *my p.* 34:20
my p., I will open your. 37:12, 13
up against *my p.* Israel. 38:16
they shall teach *my p.* the. 44:23
shall no more oppress *my p.* 45:8
exactions from *my p.* saith Lord. 9
that *my p.* be not scattered. 46:18
God, are ye not *my p.*? *Hos* 1:9, 10
them which were not *my p.* 2:23
my p. are destroyed for lack. 4:6
they eat up the sin of *my p.* 8
my p. ask counsel at their stocks. 12
returned the captivity of *my p.* 6:11
my p. are bent to backsliding. 11:7
my p. shall never be. *Joel* 2:26, 27
with them there for *my p.* 3:2
they have cast lots for *my p.* 3
sinners of *my p.* shall die. *Amos* 9:10
into the gate of *my p.* *Ob* 13
come to the gate of *my p.* *Mi* 1:9
changed the portion of *my p.* 2:4
of late *my p.* is risen up as an. 8
the women of *my p.* have ye. 9
eat the flesh of *my p.* and flay. 3:3
prophets that make *my p.* err. 5
O *my p.* what have I done? 6:3, 5
bear the reproach of *my p.* 16
they reproached *my p.* *Zeph* 2:8
the residue of *my p.* shall spoil. 9*
nations shall be *my p.* *Zech* 2:11
I will save *my p.* from the east. 8:7
I will say, It is *my p.* and. 13:9
I will call them *my p.*, which were not *my p.* *Rom* 9:25
it was said, Ye are not *my p.* 26
they shall be *my p.* *2 Cor* 6:16

see **daughter**

of the **people**

two manner *of p.* shall. *Gen* 25:23
one *of the p.* might lightly. 26:10
the gathering *of the p.* be. 49:10
all the heads *of the p.* *Num* 25:4
take the sum *of the p.* from. 26:4
twelve men out *of the p.* *Josh* 4:2
he was higher than any *of the p.*
1 Sam 9:2; 10:23
for there is a sacrifice *of the p.* 9:12
none *of the p.* tasted any food. 14:24
then answered one *of the p.* 28
of the p. to destroy king. 26:15
nor did he leave *of the p.* *2 Ki* 13:7
of the p. of those countries. *Ezra* 3:3
there was great cry *of the p.* *Neh* 5:1
and some *of the p.* dwelt in. 7:73
the tumult *of the p.* *Ps* 65:7
judge the poor *of the p.* 72:4
one chosen out *of the p.* 89:19
a present *of a p.* scattered. *Isa* 18:7
for a covenant *of the p.* 42:6
to rest for a light *of the p.* 51:4
and *of the p.* there was none. 63:3
prince not take *of the p.* *Ezek* 46:18
boil the sacrifice *of the p.* 24
and many *of the p.* *John* 7:31
because *of the p.* that stand. 11:42
punish, because *of the p.* *Acts* 4:21
himself, and errors *of the p.* *Heb* 9:7
they *of the p.* shall see their dead.
Rev 11:9

see **ears, elders**

one **people**

one p. shall be stronger. *Gen* 25:23
with you, and become *one p.* 34:16
dwell with us, to be *one p.* 22

own **people**

fault is in thine *own p.* *Ex* 5:16
virgin of his *own p.* *Lev* 21:14
went to redeem to be his *own p.*
1 Chr 17:21
deliver their *own p.* *2 Chr* 25:15
forget also thine *own p.* *Ps* 45:10
made his *own p.* to go forth. 78:52
man turn to his *own p.* *Isa* 13:14
us go again to our *own p.* *Jer* 46:16

the **people**

behold *the p.* is one. *Gen* 11:6
why do ye let *the p.* from their work?
Ex 5:4
behold, *the p.* of the land now. 5
and *the p.* bowed the head. 12:27
God led *the p.* about. 13:18
was told that *the p.* fled. 14:5
the p. feared the Lord, and. 31
the p. shall hear and be afraid. 15:14
till *the p.* pass over which thou. 16
the p. murmured, saying, What? 24
the p. rested on the seventh. 16:30
there was no water for *the p.* 17:1
the p. did chide. 2; *Num* 20:3
there shall come water out of it, that *the p.* may drink. *Ex* 17:6
thou for *the p.* to God-ward. 18:19
the p. may hear when I speak. 19:9
Moses brought forth *the p.* out. 17
charge *the p.*, lest they break. 21
let not *the p.* break through. 24
when *the p.* saw it, they. 20:18, 21
neither shall *the p.* go up. 24:2
blood and sprinkled it on *the p.* 8
atonement for thyself and *the p.*
Lev 9:7
offering for *the p.* 15, 18; 16:15
Moses and Aaron blessed *the p.* 9:23
the p. complained. *Num* 11:1
the p. cried to Moses. 2
and see *the p.* that dwelleth. 13:18
the p. be strong. 28
Caleb stilled *the p.* 30
the p. wept that night. 14:1
the p. mourned. 39
the p. spake against God and. 21:5
lo, *the p.* shall dwell alone. 23:9
behold, *the p.* shall rise up as. 24
gather me *the p.* together. *Deut* 4:10
priest's due from *the p.* 18:3
yea, he loved *the p.* 33:3
he shall push *the p.* 17
call *the p.* to the mountain. 19
the p. hasted and passed. *Josh* 4:10
so *the p.* shouted. 6:20
let *the p.* depart. 24:28
the p. that are with thee are too many. *Judg* 7:2, 4
up thou, and *the p.* that are. 9:32
custom with *the p.* was. *1 Sam* 2:13
so *the p.* sent to Shiloh to. 4:4
did they not let *the p.* go? 6:6
the p. refused to obey the voice. 8:19
for *the p.* will not eat until. 9:13
the p. said to Saul, Shall Jonathan die? so *the p.* rescued. 14:45
for *the p.* spared the best. 15:15
the p. took of the spoil, sheep. 21
the p. answered after. 17:27, 30
David distressed, for *the p.* 30:6
that *the p.* are fled from. *2 Sam* 1:4
the p. have made me afraid. 14:15
for *the p.* increased. 15:12
and *the p.* piped with pipes. *1 Ki* 1:40
for *the p.* went to worship. 12:30
the p. that followed Omri . . . *the p.* that followed Tibni. 16:22
the p. answered him not. 18:21
pour out for *the p.* that. *2 Ki* 4:41
he said, Give *the p.* that they. 43
the p. trode upon him in the. 7:17
between the king and *the p.* 11:17
as yet *the p.* did sacrifice. 12:3
14:4; 15:4, 35
the p. held their peace. 18:36
Lord for me and for *the p.* 22:13
the p. were without. *2 Chr* 12:3
as yet *the p.* had not prepared.
20:33; 30:3
and *the p.* did yet corruptly. 27:2
Lord hearkened to Hezekiah and healed *the p.* 30:20
since *the p.* began to bring. 31:10
the p. rested on the words. 32:8
and *the p.* transgressed. 36:14

but *the p.* are many. *Ezra* 10:13
for *the p.* had a mind to. *Neh* 4:6
and *the p.* did according to. 5:13
city was large, but *the p.* were. 7:4
the p. stood in their place. 8:7
so *the p.* went and brought palm. 16
the p. blessed all that offered. 11:2
had shewed him *the p.* *Esth* 3:6
the p. also, to do with them as. 11
the p. of the king's provinces. 4:11
no doubt but ye are *the p.* *Job* 12:2
hypocrite reign not, lest *the p.* 34:30
why do *the p.* imagine? *Ps* 2:1
blessed are *the p.* whom he. 33:12
how thou didst afflict *the p.* 44:2
arrows, whereby *the p.* fall. 45:5
therefore shall *the p.* praise. 17
in thine anger cast down *the p.* 56:7
let *the p.* praise thee. 67:3, 5
blessed is *the p.* that know. 89:15
we are *the p.* of his pasture. 95:7
he shall judge *the p.* with his truth. 96:13
he shall judge *the p.* with equity. 98:9
the Lord reigneth, let *the p.* 99:1
his deeds among *the p.* 105:1
no counsel is, *the p.* fall. *Pr* 11:14
withholdeth corn, *the p.* 26; 24:24
the p. rejoiced, *the p.* mourn. 29:2
is no vision, *the p.* perish. 18
the p. shall be oppressed. *Isa* 3:5
the p. that walked in darkness. 9:2
the p. turneth not to him that. 13
and *the p.* shall be as the fuel. 19
against *the p.* of my wrath. 10:6
the p. shall take them and. 14:2
it shall be as with *the p.* so. 24:2
for *the p.* shall dwell in Zion. 30:19
the p. shall be forgiven their. 33:24
my sword shall come on *the p.* 34:5
the p. is grass. The grass. 40:7
the p. in whose heart is my. 51:7
I will tread down *the p.* in. 63:6
the p. of thy holiness have. 18
the p. that shall say, The burthen. *Jer* 23:34
the p. which were left of sword. 31:2
and went out among *the p.* 37:4
so he dwelt among *the p.* 39:14
dwell with him among *the p.* 40:5, 6
woe to thee, O Moab, *the p.* of. 48:46
the p. shall labour in vain. 51:58
gather you from *the p.* *Ezek* 11:17
I will bring you out from *the p.* 20:34
34:13
cut thee off from *the p.* 25:7
bring thee down with *the p.* 26:20
see sword come, and *the p.* 33:6
they come unto thee as *the p.* 31
these are *the p.* of the Lord. 36:20
thou shalt fall, and *the p.* that. 39:4
things which are for *the p.* 42:14
slay the sacrifice for *the p.* 44:11
shall not sanctify *the p.* with. 19
the p. of the prince. *Dan* 9:26
the p. that know their God. 11:32
the p. that doth not understand. *Hos* 4:14
for *the p.* thereof shall mourn. 10:5
and *the p.* shall be gathered. 10
the p. shall be much pained. *Joel* 2:6
the p. of Syria shall go. *Amos* 1:5
trumpet be blown, and *the p.*? 3:6
so *the p.* of Nineveh. *Jonah* 3:5
that *the p.* shall labour in the fire, and *the p.* shall weary. *Hab* 2:13
against *the p.* of Lord. *Zeph* 2:10
the p. did fear before. *Hag* 1:12
the p. against whom Lord hath indignation. *Mal* 1:4
the p. that sat in darkness. *Mat* 4:16
we fear *the p.* for all hold John as a prophet. 21:26; *Mark* 11:32
and *the p.* waited for. *Luke* 1:21
as *the p.* were in expectation. 3:15
the p. sought him. 4:42
the p. pressed upon him. 5:1
when returned, *the p.* gladly. 8:40
Whom say *the p.* that I am? 9:18
feared *the p.* 20:19; 22:2
he stirreth up *the p.* 23:5
one that perverteth *the p.* 14
the p. saw that Jesus. *John* 6:24
but he deceiveth *the p.* *John* 7:12
should die for *the p.* 11:50; 18:14
the p. magnified them. *Acts* 5:13
the p. with one accord gave. 8:6
the p. gave shout, saying, It. 12:22
the p. saw what Paul had. 14:11
scarce restrained they *the p.* 18
persuaded *the p.* and stoned. 19
delivering thee from *the p.* 26:17
nothing against *the p.* 28:17
as for *the p.* so also. *Heb* 5:3; 7:27
for under it *the p.* received. 7:11
that he might sanctify *the p.* 13:12
Lord having saved *the p.* *Jude* 5

this **people**

I will give *this p.* favour. *Ex* 3:21
so evil entreated *this p.*? 5:22
hath done evil to *this p.* 23
what shall I do to *this p.*? 17:4
thou wilt wear away, both thou and *this p.* 18:18
all *this p.* shall also go to their. 23
I have seen *this p.* 32:9
what did *this p.* unto thee? 21
this p. have sinned a great sin. 31
sayest to me, Bring up *this p.* 33:12
the burden of all *this p.* on me. *Num* 11:11
have I conceived all *this p.*? 12
flesh to give unto all *this p.* 13
able to bear all *this p.* alone. 14
long will *this p.* provoke me? 14:11
thou art among *this p.* 14
if thou shalt kill all *this p.* as. 15
was not able to bring *this p.* 16
this p., as thou hast forgiven *this p.* 19
indeed deliver *this p.* 21:2
I pray thee, curse *this p.* 22:6, 17
what *this p.* shall do to thy. 24:14
ye shall destroy all *this p.* 32:15
go over before *this p.* *Deut* 3:28
voice of the words of *this p.* 5:28
saying, I have seen *this p.* 9:13
stubbornness of *this p.* 27
thou must go with *this p.* 31:7
this p. will rise up and go. 16
to *this p.* thou shalt. *Josh* 1:6
because *this p.* have. *Judg* 2:20
would to God *this p.* were. 9:29
this the *p.* thou hast despised? 38
evil doings by *this p.* *1 Sam* 2:23
Lord and *this p.*, choose. *2 Sam* 16:18
that I may answer *this p.* *1 Ki* 12:6, 9; *2 Chr* 10:6, 9
a servant to *this p.* this. *1 Ki* 12:7
if *this p.* go up to do sacrifice . . . the heart of *this p.* shall turn. 27
I should be king over *this p.* 14:2
O Lord, that *this p.* may. 18:37
I pray thee, smite *this p.* *2 Ki* 6:18
come in before *this p.* *2 Chr* 1:10
was heavy on *this p.* *Neh* 5:18
that I have done for *this p.* 19
Go and tell *this p.*, Hear. *Isa* 6:9
make the heart of *this p.* fat. 10; *Mat* 13:15; *Acts* 28:26, 27
this p. refuseth the waters. *Isa* 8:6
walk in the way of *this p.* 11
to whom *this p.* shall say. 12
the leaders of *this p.* cause. 9:16
this p. was not till Assyrian. 23:13
tongue will speak to *this p.* 28:11
men, that rule *this p.* 14
this p. draw near me with. 29:13
work among *this p.* 14
but *this* is a *p.* robbed and. 42:22
this p. have I formed for. 43:21
greatly deceived *this p.* *Jer* 4:10
words fire and *this p.* wood. 5:14
this p. hath a revolting heart. 23
I will bring evil on *this p.* 6:19
stumblingblocks before *this p.* 21
pray not thou for *this p.* 7:16
11:14; 14:11
carcases of *this p.* meat for. 7:33
why is *this p.* of Jerusalem? 8:5
I will feed even *this p.* with. 9:15
this evil *p.* who refuse to. 13:10
could not be toward *this p.* 15:1
away my peace from *this p.* 16:5
even so will I break *this p.* 19:11
they shall not profit *this p.* 23:32
and when *this p.* shall ask thee. 33
makest *this p.* to trust. *Jer* 28:15
a man to dwell among *this p.* 29:32
great evil upon *this p.* 32:42
considerest not what *this p.* 33:24
this p. have not hearkened. 35:16
pronounced against *this p.* 36:7
offended against *this p.*? 37:18
seeketh not welfare of *this p.* 38:4
the prophet of *this p.* *Mi* 2:11
this p. say, The time is. *Hag* 1:2
Haggai said, So is *this p.* 2:14
the remnant of *this p.* *Zech* 8:6
I will not be to *this p.* as in. 11
cause the remnant of *this p.* 12
this p. draweth nigh with. *Mat* 15:8
this p. honoureth me. *Mark* 7:6
buy meat for *this p.* *Luke* 9:13
be wrath upon *this p.* 21:23
but *this p.* who knoweth. *John* 7:49
the God of *this p.* chose. *Acts* 13:17
lips I will speak to *this p.* *1 Cor* 14:21

thy **people**

thou delivered *thy p.* *Ex* 5:23
frogs upon *thy p.* 8:3, 4
swarms of flies upon *thy p.* 21
all my plagues upon *thy p.* 9:14
that I smite thee and *thy p.* 15
till *thy p.* pass over, O Lord. 15:16
nor shalt curse the ruler of *thy p.* 22:28; *Acts* 23:5
the poor of *thy p.* may eat. *Ex* 23:11
that this nation is *thy p.* 33:13
I and *thy p.* have found grace. 16
covenant before all *thy p.* 34:10
talebearer among *thy p.* *Lev* 19:16
and an oath among *thy p.* *Num* 5:21
this people shall do to *thy p.* 24:14
shalt be gathered to *thy p.* 27:13
31:2; *Deut* 32:50
for *thy p.* have corrupted. *Deut* 9:12
destroy not *thy p.* 26
yet they are *thy p.* and inheritance. 29; *Neh* 1:10
return with thee to *thy p.* *Ruth* 1:10
thy p. shall be my people. 16
like *thy p.* . . . before *thy p.* which thou? *2 Sam* 7:23; *1 Chr* 17:21
in the midst of *thy p.* *1 Ki* 3:8
heart to judge *thy p.* 9; *2 Chr* 1:10
if *thy p.* go out to battle. *1 Ki* 8:44
forgive *thy p.* that have sinned. 50
2 Chr 6:34, 39
they be *thy p.* *1 Ki* 8:51
thy p. for his people. 20:42
I am as thou art, my people as *thy p.*, my. 22:4; *2 Ki* 3:7
thy hand be on *thy p.* *1 Chr* 21:17
thoughts of heart of *thy p.* 29:18
with a plague will the Lord smite *thy p.*, and thy children. *2 Chr* 21:14
thy blessing is upon *thy p.* *Ps* 3:8
save *thy p.* and bless. 28:9; *Jer* 31:7
sellest *thy p.* for nought. *Ps* 44:12
shewed *thy p.* hard things. 60:3
wentest forth before *thy p.* 68:7
he shall judge *thy p.* with. 72:2
thine arm redeemed *thy p.* 77:15
thou leddest *thy p.* like a flock. 20
so we *thy p.* will give thee. 79:13
angry against prayer of *thy p.*? 80:4
crafty counsel against *thy p.* 83:3
forgiven the iniquity of *thy p.* 85:2
revive us, that *thy p.* may rejoice. 6
they break in pieces *thy p.* 94:5
thou bearest to *thy p.* 106:4
thy p. shall be willing in the. 110:3
thou hast forsaken *thy p.* *Isa* 2:6
bring on thee and *thy p.* days. 7:17
destroyed thy land and *thy p.* 14:20
thy p. shall be all righteous. 60:21
so didst thou lead *thy p.* 63:14
we are *thy p.* 64:9
hear, thou and *thy p.* *Jer* 22:2
will ye die, thou and *thy p.*? 27:13
get thee to *thy p.* and. *Ezek* 3:11
set thy face against the daughters of *thy p.* 13:17
he shall slay *thy p.* with. 26:11
speak to children of *thy p.* 33:2, 12
children of *thy p.* say, The way. 17
the children of *thy p.* still are. 30
when the children of *thy p.* 37:18
thy p. are become a. *Dan* 9:16

thy city and *thy p.* are. *Dan* 9:19
are determined upon *thy p.* 24
what shall befall *thy p.* 10:14
standeth for the children of *thy p.* and at that time *thy p.* shall. 12:1
thy p. as they that strive. *Hos* 4:4
tumult arose among *thy p.* 10:14
spare *thy p.* *Joel* 2:17
feed *thy p.* *Mi* 7:14
thy p. in the midst of. *Nah* 3:13
thy p. is scattered on the. 18
forth for salvation of *thy p. Hab* 3:13

to or *unto the* **people**

be spokesman *to the p.* *Ex* 4:16
he said, What is this thing that thou doest *to the p.*? 18:14
go *to the p.* 19:10
thou shalt set bounds *to the p.* 12
down from mount *to the p.* 14, 25
priest shall speak *to the p. Deut* 20:2
officers shall speak *to the p.* 5, 8
loaves of bread *to the p.* *Judg* 8:5
shall come *to a p.* secure. 18:10, 27
and art come *to a p.* *Ruth* 2:11
all the words *to the p.* *1 Sam* 8:10
Abishai came *to the p.* by. 26:7
David cried *to the p.* and to. 14
David came near *to the p.* 30:21
thy God add *to the p.* *2 Sam* 24:3
hearkened not *to the p.* *1 Ki* 12:15
Elijah came *to the p.* and. 18:21
Elisha gave *to the p.* and. 19:21
he said, Give *to p.* that. *2 Ki* 4:42
Athaliah came *to the p.* 11:13 *2 Chr* 23:12
to carry tidings *to the p. 1 Chr* 10:9
Josiah gave *to the p.* *2 Chr* 35:7*
princes gave willingly *unto the p.* 8
said I *to the p.* Lodge. *Neh* 4:22
were chargeable *to the p.* 5:15
minister judgement *to the p. Ps* 9:8
shall bring peace *to the p.* 72:3
breath *to the p.* upon it. *Isa* 42:5
set up my standard *to the p.* 49:22
for a witness *to the p.*, a leader and commander *to the p.* 55:4
so I spake *to the p.* in. *Ezek* 24:18
kingdom be given *to the p. Dan* 7:27
shall sell them *to the p.* far. *Joel* 3:8
cometh up *to the p.* he. *Hab* 3:16
I will turn *to the p.* a. *Zeph* 3:9
Lord's message *to the p.* *Hag* 1:13
talked *to the p.*, behold. *Mat* 12:46
was wont to release *to the p.* 27:15
began to speak *to the p. Luke* 7:24
as they spake *to the p.* *Acts* 4:1
speak in the temple *to the p.* 5:20
which gave alms *to the p.* and. 10:2
us to preach *to the p.* 42
bring Peter forth *to the p.* 12:4
who are his witnesses *to the p.* 13:31
to bring them out *to the p.* 17:5
have entered in *to the p.* 19:30
made his defence *to the p.* 33
suffer me to speak *to the p.* 21:39
beckoned with the hand *to the p.* 40
suffer, and shew light *to the p.* 26:23

peoples

prophesy before many *p.* *Rev* 10:11
waters thou sawest are *p.* 17:15

Peor

Balaam to top of *P.* *Num* 23:28
beguiled you in the matter of *P.* 25:18; 31:16
iniquity of *P.* too little? *Josh* 22:17

peradventure

(*Perhaps, supposing, possibly*)

p. there be fifty righteous. *Gen* 18:24
p. there shall lack five of the. 28
p. there be forty. 29, 30, 31
I will speak this once, *p.* ten. 32
p. the woman shall not. 24:5, 39
Jacob said. My father *p.* 27:12
p. thou wouldest take by. 31:31
I will see his face, *p.* he will. 32:20
for he said, Lest, *p.*, mischief. 42:4
carry it again, *p.* it was an. 43:12
lest *p.* I see evil shall come. 44:34
Joseph will *p.* hate us, and. 50:15
lest *p.* the people repent. *Ex* 13:17
p. I shall make an atonement. 32:30
curse this people, *p.* I. *Num* 22:6, 11
p. the Lord will come to. *Num* 23:3
p. it will please God that thou. 27
men of Israel said, *P.* ye. *Josh* 9:7
p. he will lighten his hand. *1 Sam* 6:5
p. he can shew us our way that. 9:6
p. we may find grass to. *1 Ki* 18:5
or *p.* he sleepeth, and must be. 27
go out to the king, *p.* he will. 20:31
lest *p.* the Spirit of Lord. *2 Ki* 2:16
watched for halting, *p.* *Jer* 20:10
p. for a good man some. *Rom* 5:7
p. God will give them. *2 Tim* 2:25

perceive

given you a heart to *p.* *Deut* 29:4
this day we *p.* the Lord. *Josh* 22:31
that ye may *p.* your. *1 Sam* 12:17
p. if Absalom had lived. *2 Sam* 19:6
I *p.* that this is an holy. *2 Ki* 4:9
but I *p.* him not. *Job* 9:11
I cannot *p.* him. 23:8
to *p.* the words of. *Pr* 1:2
I *p.* that there is nothing. *Eccl* 3:22
and see ye indeed, but *p.* *Isa* 6:19
speech than thou canst *p.* 33:9
shall see, and shall not *p.* *Mat* 13:14 *Mark* 4:12; *Acts* 28:26
do ye not *p.* that whatsoever entereth into the man? *Mark* 7:18
he said, *p.* ye not yet, neither? 8:17
I *p.* that virtue is gone. *Luke* 8:46
p. that thou art a prophet. *John* 4:19
p. ye how ye prevail nothing? 12:19
I *p.* thou art in the gall. *Acts* 8:23
I *p.* God is no respecter of. 10:34
I *p.* in all things ye are too. 17:22
p. the same epistle made. *2 Cor* 7:8
hereby *p.* we the love. *1 John* 3:16

perceived

he *p.* not when she lay down. *Gen* 19:33, 35
when Gideon *p.* he was. *Judg* 6:22
Eli *p.* that Lord had. *1 Sam* 3:8
Saul *p.* that it was Samuel. 28:14
David *p.* that the Lord had. *2 Sam* 5:12; *1 Chr* 14:2
David *p.* that the child. *2 Sam* 12:19
Joab *p.* the king's heart was. 14:1
captains of chariots *p.* that it was. *1 Ki* 22:33; *2 Chr* 18:32
lo, I *p.* that God had. *Neh* 6:12
they *p.* that this work was. 16
I *p.* portions of Levites had. 13:10
when Mordecai *p.* all. *Esth* 4:1
hast thou *p.* the breadth? *Job* 38:18
I *p.* that this also is vexation of. *Eccl* 1:17
I myself *p.* that one event. 2:14
nor *p.* by the ear what God. *Isa* 64:4
who hath *p.* and heard. *Jer* 23:18
for the matter was not *p.* 38:27
p. that he spake of them. *Mat* 21:45 *Luke* 20:19
Jesus *p.* their wickedness. *Mat* 22:18
Jesus *p.* in spirit that. *Mark* 2:8
they *p.* that he had seen. *Luke* 1:22
Jesus *p.* their thoughts. 5:22
was hid, that they *p.* it not. 9:45
but he *p.* their craftiness. 20:23
Jesus *p.* they would make him a king. *John* 6:15
they *p.* that they were unlearned. *Acts* 4:13
when Paul *p.* that one part. 23:6
when James *p.* the grace. *Gal* 2:9

perceivest

p. not in him lips of. *Pr* 14:7
but *p.* not beam that is. *Luke* 6:41

perceiveth

are brought low, but he *p.* *Job* 14:21
once, yet man *p.* it not. 33:14
p. that her merchandise. *Pr* 31:18

perceiving

p. that he had answered. *Mark* 12:28
Jesus *p.* the thought. *Luke* 9:47
and *p.* he had faith to. *Acts* 14:9

perdition

lost but the son of *p.* *John* 17:12
an evident token of *p.* *Phil* 1:28
sin be revealed, son of *p. 2 Thes* 2:3
men in destruction and *p. 1 Tim* 6:9
who draw back to *p.* *Heb* 10:39
and *p.* of ungodly men. *2 Pet* 3:7*
the beast was, and is not, and shall go into *p.* *Rev* 17:8, 11

perfect

Noah was *p.* *Gen* 6:9
and be thou *p.* 17:1
offering shall be *p.* *Lev* 22:21
thou shalt be *p.* with. *Deut* 18:13
a *p.* weight, a *p.* measure. 25:15
Saul said, Give a *p.* lot. *1 Sam* 14:41
he maketh my way *p.* *2 Sam* 22:33 *Ps* 18:32
tongs made he of *p.* gold. *2 Chr* 4:21
king, to Ezra, *p.* peace. *Ezra* 7:12
that man was *p.* and upright. *Job* 1:1, 8; 2:3
not cast away a *p.* man. 8:20
if I say, I am *p.* 9:20
though I were *p.* 21
he destroyeth the *p.* and the. 22
thou makest thy ways *p.*? 22:3
mark the *p.* man, his end. *Ps* 37:37
shoot in secret at the *p.* 64:4
myself wisely in a *p.* way. 101:2
he that walketh in a *p.* way shall. 6
Lord will *p.* what concerneth. 138:8
I hate them with *p.* hatred. 139:22
p. shall remain in it. *Pr* 2:21
shineth more and more unto *p.* 4:18
righteousness of the *p.* shall. 11:5
wilt keep him in *p.* peace. *Isa* 26:3
for it was *p.* through. *Ezek* 16:14
said, I am of *p.* beauty. 27:3
made thy beauty *p.* 11; 28:12
thou wast *p.* in thy ways. 28:15
p. even as your Father is *p. Mat* 5:48
if thou wilt be *p.* go and sell. 19:21
had *p.* understanding. *Luke* 1:3*
may be made *p.* in one. *John* 17:23
him this *p.* soundness. *Acts* 3:16
to the *p.* manner of law. 22:3*
having more *p.* knowledge of. 24:22*
is that *p.* will of God. *Rom* 12:2
among them that are *p.* *1 Cor* 2:6†
my strength is made *p.* *2 Cor* 12:9
be *p.*, be of good comfort, be. 13:11
are ye made *p.* by flesh? *Gal* 3:3
till we come to *p.* man. *Eph* 4:13*
I were already *p.* *Phil* 3:12
let us, as many as be *p.* be. 15
every man *p.* in Christ. *Col* 1:28
may stand *p.* and complete in. 4:12
might *p.* that lacking in. *1 Thes* 3:10
man of God may be *p.* *2 Tim* 3:17
make Captain of their salvation *p.* *Heb* 2:10
being made *p.* he became Author. 5:9
for law made nothing *p.* but. 7:19
him that did the service *p.* 9:9
greater and more *p.* tabernacle. 11
make the comers thereunto *p.* 10:1
should not be made *p.* 11:40
spirits of just men made *p.* 12:23
God make you *p.* in every. 13:21
let patience have her *p.* work, that ye may be *p.* and. *Jas* 1:4
every good and *p.* gift is from. 17
whoso looketh into the *p.* law. 25
by works was faith made *p.* 2:22
in word, same is a *p.* man. 3:2
suffered, make you *p.* *1 Pet* 5:10
is our love made *p.* *1 John* 4:17
p. love casteth out fear, because fear hath torment . . . not made *p.* 18

see **heart**

is **perfect**

He the Rock, his work *is p. Deut* 32:4
as for God, his way *is p.* *2 Sam* 22:31; *Ps* 18:30
he that *is p.* in knowledge. *Job* 36:4; 37:16
law of the Lord *is p.* *Ps* 19:7
when the bud *is p.* *Isa* 18:5
who is blind as he that *is p.*? 42:19*
which is in heaven *is p.* *Mat* 5:48
every one that *is p.* shall. *Luke* 6:40
when that which *is p.* *1 Cor* 13:10

perfected

house of God was *p.* *2 Chr* 8:16
and work was *p.* by them. 24:13
thy builders have *p.* *Ezek* 27:4
babes thou hast *p.* praise. *Mat* 21:16
third day I shall be *p.* *Luke* 13:32
by one offering he hath *p. Heb* 10:14

is the love of God p. 1 John 2:5
another, his love is p. in us. 4:12

perfecting

p. holiness in the fear. 2 Cor 7:1
for p. of the saints, for. Eph 4:12

perfection

out the Almighty to p.? Job 11:7
nor prolong the p. thereof. 15:29*
he searcheth out all p. 28:3*
out of Zion, the p. of. Ps 50:2
I have seen an end of p. 119:96
upon thee in their p. Isa 47:9*
city that men call the p. of. Lam 2:15
and bring no fruit to p. Luke 8:14
we wish, even your p. 2 Cor 13:9
let us go on to p. Heb 6:1
if p. were by the Levitical. 7:11

perfectly

we shall consider it p. Jer 23:20
were made p. whole. Mat 14:36
way of God more p. Acts 18:26
something more p. 23:15*, 20*
he p. joined together in. 1 Cor 1:10
for yourselves know p. 1 Thes 5:2

perfectness

which is the bond of p. Col 3:14

perform

(*Generally used with the idea of carrying out to completion something that had been promised, or what had been commanded*)

I will p. the oath which I sware.
Gen 26:3; Deut 9:5; Luke 1:72
thou art not able to p. Ex 18:18
all that enter in to p. Num 4:23*
he commanded you to p. Deut 4:13
gone out of thy lips shalt p. 23:23
and p. duty of a husband's. 25:5
not p. duty of my husband's. 7
if he will p. the part of. Ruth 3:13
in that day I will p. against Eli.
1 Sam 3:12
that the king will p. 2 Sam 14:15
then I will p. my word. 1 Ki 6:12
that he might p. his saying. 12:15
2 Chr 10:15
to p. the words of this covenant.
2 Ki 23:3, 24; 2 Chr 34:31
if it please the king to p. Esth 5:8
their hands cannot p. Job 5:12
they are not able to p. Ps 21:11
that I may daily p. my vows. 61:8
I have sworn, and I will p. 119:106
I have inclined my heart to p. 112
Lord of hosts will p. this. Isa 9:7
vow to the Lord, and p. it. 19:21
Cyrus my shepherd shall p. 44:28
hasten my word to p. it. Jer 1:12
I may p. the oath which I. 11:5
Lord p. thy words thou hast. 28:6
I will p. my good word toward you.
29:10; 33:14
ye will p. your vows. 44:25
word, and will p. it. Ezek 12:25
thou wilt p. the truth. Mi 7:20
keep thy solemn feasts, p. Nah 1:15
thou shalt p. to the Lord. Mat 5:33
he was able also to p. Rom 4:21
how to p. that which is good. 7:18
now therefore p. the. 2 Cor 8:11
he will p. it until the day. Phil 1:6

performance

be a p. of those things. Luke 1:45
so may be a p. also out. 2 Cor 8:11*

performed

Saul hath not p. my. 1 Sam 15:11
I have p. the commandment. 13
they p. all that the king. 2 Sam 21:14
Lord hath p. his word. 1 Ki 8:20
2 Chr 6:10 Neh 9:8
Vashti hath not p. Esth 1:15
kingdom it shall be p. 5:6; 7:2
to thee shall the vow be p. Ps 65:1
when the Lord hath p. Isa 10:12
p. the thoughts. Jer 23:20; 30:24
who have not p. words. 34:18
words of Jonadab are p. 35:14, 16
purpose of the Lord shall be p. 51:29
have spoken and p. it. Ezek 37:14
these things shall be p. Luke 1:20
when they had p. all things by. 2:39
when I have p. this, I. Rom 15:28

performeth

every man that p. not. Neh 5:13
he p. the thing that is. Job 23:14
I will cry to God that p. Ps 57:2
that p. the counsel of his. Isa 44:26

performing

sacrifice in p. a vow. Num 15:3, 8

perfume, -s

thou shalt make it a p. Ex 30:35, 37
ointment and p. rejoice. Pr 27:9
thou didst increase thy p. Isa 57:9

perfumed

I have p. my bed with. Pr 7:17
cometh p. with myrrh? S of S 3:6

Perga

company came to P. Acts 13:13
preached the word in P. 14:25

Pergamos

send it to P. and Thyatira. Rev 1:11
to the angel of the church in P. 2:12

perhaps

if p. thy thought may. Acts 8:22
lest p. such a one be. 2 Cor 2:7*
p. he therefore departed. Philem 15

peril

bread with p. of our lives. Lam 5:9
shall famine, p., or sword? Rom 8:35

perilous

in last days p. times. 2 Tim 3:1*

perils

in p. of waters, in p. of robbers, in p. by countrymen, in p. by heathen, in p. in city, in p. in wilderness, in p. in sea, in p. among false brethren. 2 Cor 11:26

perish

that the land p. not. Gen 41:36
and many of them p. Ex 19:21
eye of his maid, that it p. 21:26
die, we p., we all p. Num 17:12
latter end shall be that he p. 24:20
lest ye p. quickly from. Deut 11:17
a Syrian ready to p. was. 26:5
until thou p. quickly. 28:20, 22
Josh 23:13
let all thine enemies p. Judg 5:31
shall descend into battle, and p.
1 Sam 26:10
and to cause to p. Esth 3:13; 7:4
and if I p. I p. 4:16
to cause to p. all power. 8:11
nor the memorial of them p. 9:28
let the day p. wherein I. Job 3:3
by the blast of God they p. 4:9
they p. for ever, without any. 20
way go to nothing and p. 6:18
him that was ready to p. 29:13
any p. for want of clothing. 31:19
lest he be angry, and ye p. Ps 2:12
of the poor shall not p. 9:18
and the brutish person p. 49:10
like the beasts that p. 12, 20
so let the wicked p. 68:2; 83:17
they p. at the rebuke of thy. 80:16
in that day his thoughts p. 146:4
when the wicked p. Pr 11:10; 28:28
no vision, the people p. 29:18*
to him that is ready to p. 31:6
but those riches p. by. Eccl 5:14
all their memory to p. Isa 26:14
which were ready to p. 27:13
the law shall not p. Jer 18:18
you out, and ye should p. 27:10, 15
remnant in Judah should p. 40:15
I will cause thee to p. Ezek 25:7
and fellows should not p. Dan 2:18
on us that we p. not. Jonah 1:6; 3:9
O Lord, let us not p. for this. 14
members should p. Mat 5:29, 30
saying, Lord, save us, we p. 8:25
Luke 8:24
out, and the bottles p. Mat 9:17
little ones should p. 18:14
carest thou not that we p.? Mark 4:38
that a prophet p. out. Luke 13:33
have bread enough, and I p. 15:17
not an hair of your head p. 21:18
whoso believeth in him should not p.
John 3:15, 16
the whole nation p. not. 11:50

thy money p. with thee. Acts 8:20
despisers, and wonder, and p. 13:41
cross is to them that p. foolishness.
1 Cor 1:18
Christ in them that p. 2 Cor 2:15
but though our outward man p. 4:16
which all are to p. with. Col 2:22
unrighteousness in them that p.
2 Thes 2:10
that any should p. but. 2 Pet 3:9

shall **perish**

ye *shall* p. among the heathen.
Lev 26:38
also *shall* p. for ever. Num 24:24
ye *shall* soon utterly p. Deut 4:26
8:19, 20; 30:18; Josh 23:16
I *shall* one day p. by. 1 Sam 27:1
house of Ahab *shall* p. 2 Ki 9:8
hypocrite's hope *shall* p. Job 8:13
his remembrance *shall* p. 18:17
20:7; 36:12
all flesh *shall* p. together. 34:15
way of the ungodly *shall* p. Ps 1:6
wicked *shall* p. 37:20
are far from thee *shall* p. 73:27
thine enemies *shall* p. 92:9
shall p. but thou shalt endure. 102:26
desire of the wicked *shall* p. 112:10
expectation of wicked *shall* p.
Pr 10:28; 11:7
that speaketh lies *shall* p. 19:9
a false witness *shall* p. but. 21:28
their wise men *shall* p. Isa 29:14
strive with thee *shall* p. 41:11
not serve thee *shall* p. 60:12
heart of the king *shall* p. Jer 4:9
friend *shall* p. 6:21
gods *shall* p. 10:11, 15; 51:18
valley also *shall* p. and plain. 48:8
but the law *shall* p. from. Ezek 7:26
the Philistines *shall* p. Amos 1:8
flight *shall* p. from the swift. 2:14
and the houses of ivory *shall* p. 3:15
and the king *shall* p. Zech 9:5
take the sword *shall* p. Mat 26:52
and bottles *shall* p. Luke 5:37
ye *shall* all likewise p. 13:3, 5
sheep *shall* never p. nor. John 10:28
sinned without law, *shall* p. without.
Rom 2:12
shall weak brother p.? 1 Cor 8:11
they *shall* p. but thou. Heb 1:11
and *shall* p. in their. 2 Pet 2:12

perished

p. from the congregation. Num 16:33
Heshbon is p. even to Dibon. 21:30
that man p. not alone. Josh 22:20
weapons of war p.! 2 Sam 1:27
whoever p. being innocent. Job 4:7
in whom old age was p. 30:2
their memorial is p. Ps 9:6
the heathen are p. out of. 10:16
as Sisera and Jabin, which p. 83:10
I should have p. in mine. 119:92
their envy is p. Eccl 9:6
truth is p. Jer 7:28
riches that hath gotten are p. 48:36
is counsel p. from the prudent? 49:7
strength and hope is p. Lam 3:18
harvest of the field is p. Joel 1:11
which came up and p. Jonah 4:10
is thy counsellor p.? Mi 4:9
the good man is p. out of. 7:2
herd of swine ran and p. Mat 8:32
p. between the altar. Luke 11:51
he also p. and as many. Acts 5:37
asleep in Christ are p. 1 Cor 15:18
harlot Rahab p. not. Heb 11:31
overflowed with water p. 2 Pet 3:6
and p. in the gainsaying. Jude 11

perisheth

lion p. for lack of prey. Job 4:11
hope of unjust men p. Pr 11:7
there is a just man that p. Eccl 7:15
righteous p. and no man. Isa 57:1
for what the land p. and. Jer 9:12
people of Chemosh p. 48:46
for the meat which p. John 6:27
of the fashion of it p. Jas 1:11
more precious than gold p. 1 Pet 1:7

perishing

his life from p. by sword. Job 33:18

Perizzite
the *P.* dwelled then in. *Gen* 13:7
and I will drive out the *P.* *Ex* 33:2
34:11
when the *P.* and Hivite. *Josh* 9:1
Jabin sent to the *P.* and. 11:3

Perizzites
given to thy seed the land of the *P.*
Gen 15:20; *Ex* 3:8, 17; 23:23
to stink among the *P.* *Gen* 34:30
wood in the land of the *P.* *Josh* 17:15
Lord delivered the *P.* to Judah.
Judg 1:4, 5
Israel dwelt among the *P.* 3:5
Solomon made the *P.* *2 Chr* 8:7
abominations of *P.* *Ezra* 9:1

perjured
for liars and *p.* persons. *1 Tim* 1:10*

permission
I speak this by *p.* not by. *1 Cor* 7:6

permit
awhile, if the Lord *p.* *1 Cor* 16:7
will we do, if God *p.* *Heb* 6:3

permitted
Agrippa said, Thou art *p.* *Acts* 26:1
it is not *p.* to women. *1 Cor* 14:34

pernicious
follow their *p.* ways. *2 Pet* 2:2*

perpetual
[1] *Continual, or uninterrupted*, Ezek 35:5. [2] *Final*, Ps 9:6. [3] *Lasting to the end of the world*, Gen 9:12. [4] *During the continuance of the legal dispensation*, Ex 29:9; 30:8.

token of the covenant for *p.* *Gen* 9:12
priest's office be theirs for a *p.* statute. *Ex* 29:9
a *p.* incense before the Lord. 30:8
keep the sabbath for a *p.* 31:16
a *p.* statute not to eat fat. *Lev* 3:17
a *p.* meat offering for Aaron. 6:20
Aaron's by a *p.* statute. 24:9
not be sold, for it is their *p.* 25:34
a *p.* statute, that he. *Num* 19:21
destructions are come to a *p.* *Ps* 9:6*
lift up thy feet to the *p.* 74:3
he put them to a *p.* reproach. 78:66
by a *p.* decree, that it. *Jer* 5:22
people slidden back by a *p.*? 8:5
why is my pain *p.* and my? 15:18
land desolate and *p.* hissing. 18:16
bring upon you a *p.* shame. 23:40
make them *p.* desolations. 25:9, 12*
the cities thereof shall be *p.* 49:13
let us join to the Lord in a *p.* 50:5*
may sleep a *p.* sleep. 51:39, 57
hast had a *p.* hatred. *Ezek* 35:5
thee *p.* desolations. 9; *Zeph* 2:9
p. ordinance to the Lord. *Ezek* 46:14
he beheld, and the *p.* hills. *Hab* 3:6*

perpetually
my heart shall be there *p.*
1 Ki 9:3; *2 Chr* 7:16
his anger did tear *p.* *Amos* 1:11

perplexed
city Shushan was *p.* *Esth* 3:15
the herds of cattle are *p.* *Joel* 1:18
Herod was *p.* *Luke* 9:7
as they were *p.* 24:4
p. but not in despair. *2 Cor* 4:8

perplexity
for it is a day of *p.* *Isa* 22:5
now shall be their *p.* *Mi* 7:4
on earth distress of nations, with *p*
Luke 21:25

persecute
why do ye *p.* me as God? *Job* 19:22
why *p.* we him, seeing the root? 28
all them that *p.* me. *Ps* 7:1*
let the enemy *p.* my soul. 5*
wicked in his pride doth *p.* 10:2*
deliver me from them that *p.* 31:15
against them that *p.* me. 35:3*
angel of the Lord *p.* them. 6*
they *p.* him whom thou hast. 69:26
p. and take him, there is. 71:11*
so *p.* them with thy tempest. 83:15*
execute judgement on them that *p.* me. 119:84
they *p.* me wrongfully. *Ps* 119:86
be confounded that *p.* me. *Jer* 17:18
I will *p.* them with the sword. 29:18*
p. and destroy them in. *Lam* 3:66*
when men shall *p.* you. *Mat* 5:11
pray for them which *p.* you. 44
when they *p.* you in one city. 10:23
ye shall *p.* them from city. 23:34
they shall *p.* *Luke* 11:49; 21:12
did the Jews *p.* Jesus. *John* 5:16
me, they will also *p.* you. 15:20
bless them which *p.* you. *Rom* 12:14

persecuted
curses on them that *p.* *Deut* 30:7
because he *p.* the poor. *Ps* 109:16
princes have *p.* me without. 119:161
enemy hath *p.* my soul. 143:3
nations in anger is *p.* *Isa* 14:6
covered with anger, and *p.* us.
Lam 3:43*
blessed which are *p.* for. *Mat* 5:10
so *p.* they the prophets before. 12
if they have *p.* me, they. *John* 15:20
have not your fathers *p.*? *Acts* 7:52
p. this way unto the death. 22:4
I *p.* them even to strange. 26:11
reviled, we bless; being *p.* we suffer it. *1 Cor* 4:12
because I *p.* the church of God.
15:9; *Gal* 1:13
are *p.* but not forsaken. *2 Cor* 4:9*
he which *p.* us in times. *Gal* 1:23
born after the flesh *p.* him. 4:29
have killed the Lord and *p.* us.
1 Thes 2:15*
dragon *p.* woman that. *Rev* 12:13

persecutest
Saul, Saul, why *p.* thou me?
Acts 9:4; 22:7; 26:14
I am Jesus, whom thou *p.* 9:5; 22:8
26:15

persecuting
zeal, *p.* the church. *Phil* 3:6

persecution
our necks are under *p.* *Lam* 5:5*
for when *p.* ariseth. *Mat* 13:21
Mark 4:17
at that time there was great *p.*
Acts 8:1
scattered abroad upon the *p.* 11:19*
and raised *p.* against Paul and. 13:50
p. or sword, separate us? *Rom* 8:35
why do I yet suffer *p.*? *Gal* 5:11
suffer *p.* for cross of Christ. 6:12
live godly shall suffer *p.* *2 Tim* 3:12

persecutions
lands, with *p.* *Mark* 10:30
I take pleasure in *p.* for. *2 Cor* 12:10
your faith in all your *p.* *2 Thes* 1:4
my *p.* at Antioch, what *p.* *2 Tim* 3:11

persecutor
who was before a *p.* *1 Tim* 1:13

persecutors
their *p.* thou threwest. *Neh* 9:11*
his arrows against the *p.* *Ps* 7:13*
many are my *p.* 119:157
deliver me from my *p.* 142:6
and revenge me of my *p.* *Jer* 15:15
therefore my *p.* shall stumble. 20:11
all her *p.* overtook her. *Lam* 1:3
our *p.* are swifter than the. 4:19*

perseverance
thereunto with all *p.* *Eph* 6:18

Persia
the reign of the kingdom of *P.*
2 Chr 36:20
a feast to the power of *P.* *Esth* 1:3
the seven princes of *P.* which. 14
the ladies of *P.* shall say to. 18
of *P.* and Lud were. *Ezek* 27:10
P. Ethiopia, and Libya with. 38:5
kings of Media and *P.* *Dan* 8:20
prince of *P.* withstood me; and I remained with the kings of *P.* 10:13
to fight with the prince of *P.* 20
stand up yet three kings in *P.* 11:2
see **king**

Persians, *see* **Medes**

Persis
salute *P.* which laboured. *Rom* 16:12

person
Joseph was a goodly *p.* *Gen* 39:6
no uncircumcised *p.* *Ex* 12:48
nor honour the *p.* *Lev* 19:15
any sin, that *p.* be guilty. *Num* 5:6
for an unclean *p.* shall take. 19:17
clean *p.* shall take hyssop and. 18
whatsoever unclean *p.* toucheth. 22
whosoever hath killed any *p.* 31:19
35:11, 15, 30; *Josh* 20:3 9
not testify against any *p.* *Num* 35:30
unclean and clean *p.* *Deut* 15:22
to slay an innocent *p.* 27:25
shall not regard the *p.* 28:60
a goodlier *p.* than he. *1 Sam* 9:2
David a comely *p.* 16:18
I have accepted thy *p.* 25:35
have slain a righteous *p.* *2 Sam* 4:11
nor doth God respect any *p.* 14:14
go to battle in thine own *p.* 17:11
shall save the humble *p.* *Job* 22:29
in whose eyes a vile *p.* *Ps* 15:4*
fool and the brutish *p.* perish. 49:10
will not know a wicked *p.* 101:4
not one feeble *p.* among. 105:37
naughty *p.* walketh with. *Pr* 6:12
shall be called mischievous *p.* 24:8
violence to the blood of any *p.* 28:17
the vile *p.* shall be no more. *Isa* 32:5†
vile *p.* will speak villany. 6†
Johanan took every *p.* *Jer* 43:6
that were near the king's *p.* 52:25
the loathing of thy *p.* *Ezek* 16:5
if sword come and take any *p.* 33:6
come at no dead *p.* 44:25
shall stand up a vile *p.* *Dan* 11:21
regardest not *p.* of men. *Mat* 22:16
Mark 12:14
of the blood of this just *p.* *Mat* 27:24
from you that wicked *p.* *1 Cor* 5:13
forgave I it in the *p.* *2 Cor* 2:10
p. hath inheritance in. *Eph* 5:5
express image of his *p.* *Heb* 1:3
or profane *p.* as Esau, who. 12:16
saved Noah, the eighth *p.* *2 Pet* 2:5

persons
give me *p.* and take the. *Gen* 14:21
to number of your *p.* *Ex* 16:16
p. shall be for the Lord. *Lev* 27:2
shall sprinkle it upon *p.* *Num* 19:18
both of the *p.*, beeves, asses. 31:28
thirty and two thousand *p.* in all. 35
which regardeth not *p.* *Deut* 10:17
into Egypt with seventy *p.* 22
Jerubbaal which were 70 *p.* *Judg* 9:2
Abimelech hired vain and light *p.* 4
slew threescore and ten *p.* 5, 18
to kill of Israel about 30 *p.* 20:39
which were about 30 *p.* *1 Sam* 9:22
Doeg slew on that day 85 *p.* 22:18
the death of all the *p.* 22
king's sons being 70 *p.* *2 Ki* 10:6
king's sons and slew 70 *p.* 7
I have not sat with vain *p.* *Ps* 26:4†
followeth vain *p.* *Pr* 12:11; 28:19
from Jerusalem 832 *p.* *Jer* 52:29
away captive of Jews 745 *p.* 30
forts to cut off many *p.* *Ezek* 17:17
they traded the *p.* of men. 27:13
more than 120,000 *p.* *Jonah* 4:11
are treacherous *p.* *Zeph* 3:4
over ninety-nine just *p.* *Luke* 15:7
with the devout *p.* *Acts* 17:17
us by means of many *p.* *2 Cor* 1:11
made for perjured *p.* *1 Tim* 1:10*
what manner of *p.* ought? *2 Pet* 3:11
having men's *p.* in admiration.
Jude 16
see **respect**

persuade
who shall *p.* Ahab, to? *1 Ki* 22:20*
I will *p.* him. 21*
thou shalt *p.* him and prevail. 22*
doth not Hezekiah *p.*? *2 Chr* 32:11
beware, lest Hezekiah *p.* *Isa* 36:18
will *p.* him and secure. *Mat* 28:14
we *p.* men. *2 Cor* 5:11
do I now *p.* men? *Gal* 1:10†

persuaded
Ahab *p.* Jehoshaphat. *2 Chr* 18:2*
forbearing is a prince *p.* *Pr* 25:15
the chief priests *p.* the. *Mat* 27:20

will not be p. if one rose. Luke 16:31
for they be p. that John was. 20:6
p. them to continue in. Acts 13:43
who p. the people, and having. 14:19
Paul p. the Jews and the. 18:4
this Paul hath p. much people. 19:26
when he would not be p. 21:14
I am p. none of these things. 26:26
being p. that what he had promised. Rom 4:21
p. that nothing can separate us. 8:38
let every man be fully p. in. 14:5
I know and am p. there is. 14
I myself also am p. of you. 15:14
I am p. that in thee. 2 Tim 1:5
I am p. that he is able to keep. 12
are p. better things of you. Heb 6:9
seen them afar off, were p. of. 11:13

persuadest

almost thou p. me to. Acts 26:28*

persuadeth

when Hezekiah p. you. 2 Ki 18:32
Paul p. men to worship. Acts 18:13

persuading

p. things concerning. Acts 19:8
p. them concerning Jesus. 28:23

persuasion

this p. cometh not of him. Gal 5:8

pertain

peace offerings p. to Lord. Lev 7:20
and eat of the sacrifice which p. 21
if I leave all that p. 1 Sam 25:22
in those things which p. Rom 15:17
things p. to this life. 1 Cor 6:3
things that p. to life. 2 Pet 1:3

pertained

the half that p. to the. Num 31:43
buried in a hill that p. Josh 24:33
an oak that p. to Joash. Judg 6:11
of all that p. to Nabal. 1 Sam 25:21
which p. to Ish-bosheth. 2 Sam 2:15
all that p. to Obed-edom. 6:12
master's son all that p. to Saul. 9:9
all that p. to Mephibosheth. 16:4
vessels that p. to house. 1 Ki 7:48
all that p. to the king. 2 Ki 24:7
morning p. to them. 1 Chr 9:27
cities which p. to Judah. 2 Chr 12:4
abominations p. to Israel. 34:33

pertaineth

which p. to cleansing. Lev 14:32
to the office of Eleazar p. Num 4:16
not wear what p. to a man. Deut 22:5
Ziklag p. to the kings. 1 Sam 27:6
it p. not to thee, Uzziah. 2 Chr 26:18
to whom p. the adoption. Rom 9:4
he p. to another tribe. Heb 7:13

pertaining

half Gilead and cities p. Josh 13:31
every matter p. to God. 1 Chr 26:32
things p. to kingdom of God. Acts 1:3
of things p. to this life. 1 Cor 6:4
priest in things p. to God. Heb 2:17
for men in things p. to God. 5:1
not make him perfect, as p. to. 9:9

perverse

because thy way is p. Num 22:32
are a p. and crooked. Deut 32:5
thou son of the p. 1 Sam 20:30
cannot my taste discern p. things? Job 6:30*
shall also prove me p. 9:20
p. lips put far from thee. Pr 4:24
is nothing froward or p. in. 8:8
he that is of a p. heart shall. 12:8
p. in his ways despiseth him. 14:2
that hath p. tongue falleth. 17:20
than he that is p. in his lips. 19:1
thine heart shall utter p. 23:33*
than he that is p. in his ways. 28:6
he that is p. in his ways shall. 18
hath mingled a p. spirit. Isa 19:14
O p. generation. Mat 17:17
Luke 9:41
arise, speaking p. things. Acts 20:30
midst of a p. nation. Phil 2:15
p. disputings of men of. 1 Tim 6:5*

perversely

what servant did p. 2 Sam 19:19
and have done p. 1 Ki 8:47
they dealt p. with me. Ps 119:78*

perverseness

neither hath he seen p. Num 23:21
but p. of transgressors. Pr 11:3
but p. therein is a breach in. 15:4
ye trust in p. and stay. Isa 30:12
tongue hath muttered p. 59:3*
the land is full of blood, and the city full of p. Ezek 9:9*

pervert

a gift doth p. words of. Deut 16:19
shalt not p. the judgement. 24:17*
doth God p. judgement? Job 8:3
nor will the Almighty p. 34:12
to p. ways of judgement. Pr 17:23
and p. the judgement of any. 31:5
you, ye that p. equity. Mi 3:9
not cease to p. right? Acts 13:10
and would p. the gospel. Gal 1:7

perverted

took bribes, p. judgement. 1 Sam 8:3
I have p. what was right. Job 33:27
and knowledge, it hath p. Isa 47:10
they have p. their way. Jer 3:21
ye have p. the words of the. 23:36

perverteth

the gift p. the words of. Ex 23:8
cursed be he that p. Deut 27:19*
but he that p. his ways. Pr 10:9
the foolishness of a man p. 19:3*
this man as one that p. people. Luke 23:14

perverting

if thou seest the violent p. Eccl 5:8*
found this fellow p. the. Luke 23:2

pestilence

he fall on us with p. or. Ex 5:3
smite thee and thy people with p. 9:15
send the p. among you. Lev 26:25
smite them with the p. Num 14:12
the Lord shall make p. Deut 28:21
there be three days' p. 2 Sam 24:13
1 Chr 21:12
the Lord sent a p. on Israel. 2 Sam 24:15; 1 Chr 21:14
in the land of famine, p. 1 Ki 8:37
2 Chr 6:28; 7:13; 20:9
their life over to the p. Ps 78:50
thee from the noisome p. 91:3
nor for the p. that walketh in. 6
I will consume them by p. Jer 14:12
24:10; 27:8
of this city shall die by p. 21:6
Zedekiah from the p. 7
in city shall die by p. 9; 38:2
Why die by the sword and p.? 27:13
prophesied of war and of p. 28:8
will send upon them the p. 29:17
them with the famine and p. 18
the city is given because of the p. 32:24, 36
liberty for you to the p. 34:17
Egypt shall die by the p. 42:17, 22
punished Jerusalem by the p. 44:13
shall die with the p. Ezek 5:12
p. and blood shall pass through. 17
sword, famine, and the p. 6:11
that is far off shall die by the p. 12
a sword without, p. and. 7:15
few men of them from the p. 12:16
or if I send a p. into that land. 14:19
I send the p. to cut off man. 21
I will send to her p. and blood. 28:23
in caves shall die of the p. 33:27
plead against him with p. and. 38:22
sent among you the p. Amos 4:10
before him went the p. Hab 3:5

pestilences

and there shall be p. Mat 24:7
Luke 21:11

pestilent

this man a p. fellow. Acts 24:5

pestle

in a mortar with a p. Pr 27:22

Peter

when P. was come down out of the ship. Mat 14:29
I say, That thou art P. 16:18
he said to P., Get thee behind me. 23
Mark 8:33
he taketh P. James and. Mat 17:1
26:37; Mark 5:37; 9:2; 14:33
Luke 8:51; 9:28
they that received tribute money came to P. Mat 17:24
P. followed him to the high. 26:58
P. remembered words of Jesus. 75
Mark 14:72
tell his disciples and P. Mark 16:7
and looked upon P. Luke 22:61
city of Andrew and P. John 1:44
whose ear P. cut off. 18:26
P. was grieved because he. 21:17
in those days P. stood. Acts 1:15
seeing P. and John about to go. 3:3
P. filled with the Holy Ghost. 4:8
when they saw the boldness of P. 13
at least the shadow of P. might. 5:15
the apostles sent unto them P. 8:14
the disciples had heard that P. 9:38
P. put them all forth, and. 40
Rise, P. kill and eat. 10:13; 11:7
while P. spake these words. 10:44
as many as came with P. 45
further to take P. also. 12:3
P. was sleeping between two. 6
the angel of the Lord smote P. 7
as P. knocked at the door of. 13
what was become of P. 18
up to Jerusalem to see P. Gal 1:18
circumcision was committed to P. 2:7
wrought effectually in P. to the. 8
I said unto P. before them all. 14

Simon **Peter**

saw Simon called P. Mat 4:18
first Simon, who is called P. 10:2
Simon he surnamed P. Mark 3:16
Simon P. fell down at. Luke 5:8
Simon, whom he also named P. 6:14
cometh he to Simon P. John 13:6
and cometh to Simon P. 20:2
Jesus saith to Simon P., Simon. 21:15
one Simon, whose surname is P. Acts 10:5, 32; 11:13

petition

Israel grant thee thy p. 1 Sam 1:17
Lord hath given me my p. which. 27
now I ask one p. of thee. 1 Ki 2:16
I desire one small p. of thee, say. 20
the king said, What is thy p.? Esth 5:6; 7:2; 9:12
then Esther said, My p. and. 5:7
if it please the king to grant my p. 8
let my life be given me at my p. 7:3
ask a p. of any god. Dan 6:7, 12
his p. three times a day. 13

petitions

the Lord fulfil all thy p. Ps 20:5
we know we have the p. 1 John 5:15

Phalec

which was the son of P. Luke 3:35

Pharaoh

Sarai before P. Gen 12:15
plagued P. and his house. 17
Potiphar an officer of P. 39:1
P. was wroth against two. 40:2
shall P. lift up thine head. 13, 19
make mention of me to P. 14
P. dreamed. 41:1
so P. awoke. 4, 7
God shall give P. answer of. 16
let P. do this. 34
I am P. and without thee. 44
people cried to P. 55
by the life of P. 42:15, 16
thou art as P. 44:18
made me a father to P. 45:8
I will go up and shew P. 46:31
P. and went out from P. 47:10
and we will be P.'s servants. 25
of the priests became not P.'s. 26
in the ears of P. saying. 50:4
when P. heard, he sought. Ex 2:15
and I will send thee to P. 3:10
all those wonders before P. 4:21
P. said, Who is the Lord that? 5:2
officers came and cried unto P. 15
since I came to P. to speak. 23
see what I will do to P. 6:1
how then shall P. hear me? 12, 30
I have made thee a god to P. 7:1

I will harden *P.'s* heart. *Ex* 7:3
13, 14, 22; 8:19; 9:12
stand before *P.* 8:20; 9:13
P. sent for Moses. 9:27
bring one plague more upon *P.* 11:1
did all these wonders before *P.* 10
from the firstborn of *P.* 12:29
when *P.* had let people go. 13:17
will be honoured upon *P.* 14:4, 17
covered all the host of *P.* 28
made affinity with *P.* *1 Ki* 3:1
an house for *P.'s* daughter. 7:8
favour in the sight of *P.* 11:19
them from under *P.* *2 Ki* 17:7
so is *P.* to all that trust in him.
18:21; *Isa* 36:6
to commandment of *P.* *2 Ki* 23:35
signs and wonders on *P.* *Neh* 9:10
tokens and wonders on *P.* *Ps* 135:9
overthrew *P.* and his host. 136:15
of horses in *P.'s* chariots. *S of S* 1:9
how say ye to *P.* I am. *Isa* 19:11
themselves in strength of *P.* 30:2
the strength of *P.* shall be your. 3
P. and his servants. *Jer* 25:19
broken for fear of *P.'s* army. 37:11
did cry, *P.* king of Egypt. 46:17
word that came, before that *P.* 47:1
P. with his army not. *Ezek* 17:17
set thy face against *P.* king. 29:2
I am against thee, *P.* king. 3; 30:22
broken the arm of *P.* 30:21, 24, 25
this is *P.* and his multitude. 31:18
take up a lamentation for *P.* 32:2
kindred made known to *P.* *Acts* 7:13
P.'s daughter took him up and. 21
for scripture saith to *P.* *Rom* 9:17
the son of *P.'s* daughter. *Heb* 11:24

Pharaoh-hophra

will give *P.* into hand of. *Jer* 44:30

Pharaoh-nechoh

P. went against Assyria. *2 Ki* 23:29
P. put Jehoahaz in bands at. 33
P. make Eliakim king. 34
he taxed to give money to *P.* 35
word to Jeremiah against *P.* *Jer* 46:2

Pharez

name was called *P.* *Gen* 38:29
sons of Judah, *P.* and. 46:12
1 Chr 2:4; *Mat* 1:3; *Luke* 3:33
and the sons of *P.* were Hezron and Hamul. *Gen* 46:12; *Num* 26:20, 21
Ruth 4:18; *1 Chr* 2:5; 9:4
be like the house of *P.* *Ruth* 4:12

Pharisee

The Pharisees were a religious party or school among the Jews at the time of Christ, so called from the Aramaic form of the Hebrew perûshim, *the separated ones. This name may have been given them by their enemies, as they usually called themselves* Haberim, *associates. They were formalists, very patriotic but bigoted in their patriotism as in their religion. Their political influence was great, though they were only about* 6000 *to* 7000 *in number.*

Jesus denounced the Pharisees for their hypocrisy, which was shown by their care for the minutest formalities imposed by the traditions of the elders, but not for the mind and heart which should correspond. They were ambitious, arrogant, and proudly self-righteous, all of which qualities were contrary to the teachings of Jesus. This explains in part their intense hostility to him. And their influence over the people, who had come to believe as they did, led to their demand for the crucifixion of Jesus.

thou blind *p.* cleanse. *Mat* 23:26
a certain *p.* besought. *Luke* 11:37
went to pray, one a *p.* the. 18:10
the *p.* stood and prayed thus. 11
one in the council, a *p.* *Acts* 5:34
I am a *p.* the son of a *p.* 23:6
after the most straitest sect of our religion I lived a *p.* *Acts* 26:5
as touching the law, a *p.* *Phil* 3:5

Pharisees

righteousness of the *p.* *Mat* 5:20
why do we and the *p.* fast oft ? 9:14
Mark 2:18
p. said, He casteth out devils.
Mat 9:34
knowest thou that the *p.*? 15:12
beware of the leaven of the *p.* 16:6
11; *Mark* 8:15; *Luke* 12:1
the *p.* also came to him. *Mat* 19:3
the scribes and *p.* sit in. 23:2
scribes and *p.* hypocrites. 13, 14, 15
23, 25, 27, 29; *Luke* 11:42, 43, 44
the scribes and *p.* *Luke* 5:30; 15:2
the scribes and *p.* watched. 6:7
but the *p.* rejected the counsel. 7:30
now do ye *p.* make clean. 11:39
p. who were covetous, heard. 16:14
sent were of the *p.* *John* 1:24
there was a man of the *p.* 3:1
p. and priests sent officers. 7:32
have any of the rulers or *p.*? 48
the *p.* gathered a council. 11:47
p. had given a commandment. 57
certain of sect of the *p.* *Acts* 15:5
arose a dissension between *p.* and Sadducees. 23:7
there is no resurrection, but the *p.* 8

Pharpar, *see* **Abana**

Phebe

I commend unto you *P.* *Rom* 16:1

Phenice

travelled as far as *P.* *Acts* 11:19
Barnabas passed through *P.* 15:3
finding ship sailing over to *P.* 21:2
they might attain to *P.* 27:12

Philadelphia

write and send it unto *P.* *Rev* 1:11
to the angel of the church in *P.* 3:7

Philetus, *see* **Hymenaeus**

Philip

P. and Bartholomew. *Mat* 10:3
Mark 3:18; *Luke* 6:14; *Acts* 1:13
for Herodias' sake his brother *P.'s*
Mat 14:3; *Mark* 6:17; *Luke* 3:19
P. tetrarch of Iturea. *Luke* 3:1
Jesus findeth *P.* and. *John* 1:43
now *P.* was of Bethsaida, the. 44
P. findeth Nathanael, and saith. 45
the same came to *P.* and. 12:21
P. telleth Andrew; Andrew and *P.* 22
Hast thou not known me, *P.*? 14:9
P. the deacon. *Acts* 6:5
the Spirit said to *P.* 8:29
P. went down to Samaria. 5
to those things which *P.* spake. 6
believed *P.* preaching things. 12
Simon continued with *P.* and. 13
P. ran to him, and heard him read. 30
the Lord caught away *P.* 39
we entered into the house of *P.* 21:8

Philippi

from Neapolis we came to *P.* of Macedonia. *Acts* 16:12
we sailed away from *P.* and. 20:6
we were shamefully entreated at *P.*
1 Thes 2:2

Philistia

P. triumph thou because. *Ps* 60:8
behold *P.* and Tyre, this man. 87:4
Moab my washpot, over *P.* 108:9

Philistim

out of whom came *P.* *Gen* 10:14
1 Chr 1:12

Philistine

am not I a *P.*? *1 Sam* 17:8
servant will fight with this *P.* 32
the *P.* cursed David. 43
David smote the *P.* in his. 49
sword of Goliath the *P.* 21:9; 22:10
Abishai smote the *P.* *2 Sam* 21:17

Philistines

sojourned in the *P.s'* land. *Gen* 21:34
Isaac had flocks, and the *P.* 26:14
P. stopped the wells. 15, 18
not through the land of *P.* *Ex* 13:17
the borders of *P.* not. *Josh* 13:2
Ekron five lords of *P.* 3; *Judg* 3:3
Shamgar slew of the *P.* *Judg* 3:31
served the gods of the *P.* 10:6
into the hands of the *P.* 7; 13:1
you from Egyptians and *P.* 11
an occasion against the *P* 14:4
be more blameless than the *P.* 15:3
the *P.* came up and burnt her. 6
that the *P.* are rulers over us ? 11
Samson judged Israel in the days of the *P.* 20
the *P.* be upon thee. 16:9, 12, 14, 20
the *P.* took Samson and put out. 21
at once avenged of the *P.* 28
Samson said, Let me die with *P.* 30
went out against the *P.* *1 Sam* 4:1
Lord smitten us before the *P.*? 3
yourselves like men, O ye *P.*! 9
the *P.* took the ark of God and. 5:1
the ark was in the land of *P.* 6:1
P. have brought again the ark. 21
us out of the hand of the *P.* 7:8
the *P.* drew near to battle. 10
the *P.* were subdued, and came. 13
the *P.* will come down upon. 13:12
Israelites went down to the *P.* 20
and let us go over to the *P.* 14:1
noise in the host of the *P.* went on. 19
was sore war against the *P.* all. 52
the *P.* saw their champion. 17:51
from chasing after the *P.* 53
hand of the *P.* be on him. 18:17, 21
then the princes of the *P.* went. 30
David fought with the *P.* 19:8
23:5; *2 Sam* 21:15
from following the *P.* *1 Sam* 24:1
escape into land of the *P.* 27:1
for the *P.* make war against. 28:15
displease not lords of the *P.* 29:7
P. followed hard upon Saul. 31:2
1 Chr 10:2
sent into land of the *P.* *1 Sam* 31:9
all the *P.* came up to. *2 Sam* 5:17
shall I go up to the *P.*? 19
David smote the *P.* 25; 8:1
gold got from *P.* 8:12
Eleazar smote the *P.* 23:10
Shammah slew *P.* 12
brake through the host of the *P.* 16
sojourned in land of the *P.* *2 Ki* 8:2
Jehoram the spirit of *P.* *2 Chr* 21:16
helped Uzziah against the *P.* 26:7
P. had invaded the cities of. 28:18
P. with the inhabitants. *Ps* 83:7
soothsayers like the *P.* *Isa* 2:6
Syrians before, and the *P.* 9:12
shall fly on shoulders of the *P.* 11:14
the kings of the *P.* shall. *Jer* 25:20
the Lord came against the *P.* 47:1
for the Lord will spoil the *P.* 4
to the daughters of *P.* *Ezek* 16:27
because the *P.* have dealt. 25:15
stretch mine hand upon the *P.* 16
the remnant of the *P.* *Amos* 1:8
go down to Gath of the *P.* 6:2
have not I brought the *P.*? 9:7
plain shall possess the *P.* *Ob* 19
O land of the *P.* I will. *Zeph* 2:5
cut off the pride of the *P.* *Zech* 9:6
see **daughters**

Philologus

salute *P.* Julia, and. *Rom* 16:15

philosophers

certain *p.* encountered. *Acts* 17:18

philosophy

man spoil you through *p.* *Col* 2:8

Phinehas

Eleazar's wife bare him *P.* *Ex* 6:25
P. hath turned my wrath from Israel.
Num 25:11
Moses sent them and *P.* to. 31:6
Israel sent *P.* to the. *Josh* 22:13
in a hill that pertained to *P.* 24:33
P. stood before the ark. *Judg* 20:28
Hophni and *P.* the priests. *1 Sam* 1:3
Hophni and *P.* shall both die. 2:34
thy two sons Hophni and *P.* 4:17
P.'s wife was with child, near. 19
son of *P.* the Lord's priest. 14:3
Eleazar begat *P.* *1 Chr* 6:4
P. begat Abishua. 50
P. son of Eleazar was ruler. 9:20

Abishua son of P. the son. Ezra 7:5
of the sons of P. Gershom went. 8:2
was Eleazar the son of P. 33
then stood up P. and. Ps 106:30

Phlegon

salute Asyncritus, P. Rom 16:14

Phrygia

had gone throughout P. Acts 16:6
over all the country of P. 18:23

Phurah

he went down with P. Judg 7:11

Phygellus, *see* **Hermogenes**

phylacteries

The same as frontlets. *They were strips of parchment on which were written four passages of Scripture,* Ex 13:2-10, 11-17; Deut 6:4-9, 13-23. *These were put in cases of black calfskin and bound on the forehead and the arm, in obedience to their understanding of* Ex 13:16. *The Pharisees affected to have the cases of their phylacteries broader than the other Jews wore, as a badge of distinction, and through ostentation, which is what our Saviour denounced.*

made broad their p. Mat 23:5

physician

(*These were not like our physicians, as the science had not progressed far. But they were* healers, *according to their ability. The word is also used of healers of the mind, comforters, and also of embalmers, as having to do with the human body*)

is there no balm in Gilead; is there no p. there? Jer 8:22
that be whole need not a p. but the. Mat 9:12; Mark 2:17; Luke 5:31
p. heal thyself. Luke 4:23
Luke the p. Col 4:14

physicians

his servants the p. to embalm his father; the p. Gen 50:2
to the Lord, but p. 2 Chr 16:12
ye are all p. of no value. Job 13:4
had suffered many things of p. Mark 5:26; Luke 8:43

pick

the ravens shall p. it out. Pr 30:17

pictures

shall destroy all their p. Num 33:52*
of gold in p. of silver. Pr 25:11*
Lord on all pleasant p. Isa 2:16*

piece

he laid one p. against. Gen 15:10
beaten out of one p. Ex 37:7*
trumpets of a whole p. Num 10:2*
woman cast a p. of a millstone upon. Judg 9:53*; 2 Sam 11:21
crouch to him for a p. of silver, that I may eat a p. of. 1 Sam 2:36
they gave him a p. of a cake. 30:12
to every one a p. of flesh. 2 Sam 6:19; 1 Chr 16:3
was a p. of ground full of lentiles. 2 Sam 23:11
mar every good p. 2 Ki 3:19, 25
repaired the other p. Neh 3:11
next Ezer another p. 19, 20, 21, 24 27, 30
as hard as a p. of the. Job 41:24*
every man also gave him a p. 42:11
brought to a p. of bread. Pr 6:26
for a p. of bread that man. 28:21
temples are a p. of pomegranate. S of S 4:3; 6:7
daily a p. of bread. Jer 37:21
every good p., the thigh. Ezek 24:4
bring it out p. by p., let no lot fall. 6
mouth of lion, a p. of ear. Amos 3:12
p. was rained on, and the p. 4:7
no man putteth a p. of new cloth to. Mat 9:16; Mark 2:21; Luke 5:36
find a p. of money. Mat 17:27*
I have bought a p. of. Luke 14:18
if she lose one p. she doth. 15:8
for I have found the p. that 9
him a p. of a broiled fish. 24:42

pieces

passed between those p. Gen 15:17
thy brother 1000 p. of silver. 20:16
bought for 100 p. of money. 33:19 Josh 24:32
Joseph for twenty p. of silver. 37:28
Joseph is rent in p. 33; 44:28
to Benjamin thirty p. of silver. 45:22
if it be torn in p. let. Ex 22:13
have the two shoulder p. 28:7
on the shoulder p. 25; 39:4, 18
part the meat offering in p. Lev 2:6
Moses burnt the p. and fat. 8:20
burnt offering with the p. 9:13
Abimelech seventy p. of silver. Judg 9:4
give thee 1100 p. of silver. 16:5
concubine into twelve p. 19:29
a yoke of oxen in p. 1 Sam 11:7
Samuel hewed Agag in p. 15:33
new garment in twelve p. 1 Ki 11:30
to Jeroboam, Take thee ten p. 31
a strong wind brake in p. the. 19:11
Elisha rent his clothes in two p. 2 Ki 2:12
with him 6000 p. of gold. 5:5
sold for eighty p. of silver. 6:25
images of Baal in p. 11:18; 23:14
brake in p. the brasen serpent. 18:4
of Baal, and brake the images in p. 2 Chr 23:17; 31:1; 34:4; Mi 1:7
also shaken me in p. Job 16:12
his bones as strong p. of. 40:18*
rending in p. while none. Ps 7:2
lest I tear you in p. 50:22
submit with p. of silver. 68:30
heads of Leviathan in p. 74:14
the fruit bring 1000 p. S of S 8:11
ye beat my people to p.? Isa 3:15
that goeth out shall be torn in p.? Jer 5:6
breaketh the rock in p. 23:29
aside and pulled me in p. Lam 3:11
that which is torn in p. Ezek 4:14
pollute me for p. of bread? 13:19
gather the p. thereof into. 24:4
brake the image in p. Dan 2:34, 45
forasmuch as iron breaketh in p. 40
brake all their bones in p. 6:24
devoured and brake in p. 7:7, 19
to me for fifteen p. of silver. Hos 3:2
who chop my people in p. Mi 3:3
thou shalt beat in p. many. 4:13
as a lion teareth in p. and none. 5:8
lion did tear in p. enough. Nah 2:12
for my price thirty p. Zech 11:12
I took the thirty p. of silver. 13 Mat 27:6, 9
what woman having ten p. of silver? Luke 15:8
price 50,000 p. of silver. Acts 19:19
lest Paul be pulled in p. 23:10
broken p. of the ship. 27:44*

see **break, broken, cut, dash, dashed**

pierce

he shall p. them through. Num 24:8*
a man lean, it will go into his hand and p. it. 2 Ki 18:21; Isa 36:6
a sword shall p. through. Luke 2:35

pierced

when she had p. through. Judg 5:26
my bones are p. in me. Job 30:17
they p. my hands and. Ps 22:16
look on me whom they have p. Zech 12:10; John 19:37
the soldiers p. his side. John 19:34
and p. themselves with. 1 Tim 6:10
they also which p. him. Rev 1:7

pierceth

behemoth's nose p. Job 40:24

piercing

punish the p. serpent. Isa 27:1*
word of God is quick, p. Heb 4:12

piercings

that speaketh like the p. Pr 12:18

piety

let them learn to shew p. 1 Tim 5:4

pigeon, *see* **young**

Pi-hahiroth, *see* **Baal-zephon**

Pilate

they delivered him to Pontius P. Mat 27:2; Mark 15:1
P. saw that he could. Mat 27:24
so that P. marvelled. Mark 15:5, 44
so P. willing to content the. 15
Pontius P. being governor. Luke 3:1
whose blood P. had mingled. 13:1
same day P. and Herod were. 23:12
this man went to P. and begged. 52
P. then went out to them. John 18:29
entered into the judgement hall. 33
when P. heard that, he was. 19:8
from thenceforth P. sought to. 12
P. wrote a title, and put it on. 19
Joseph besought P. and P. gave. 38
ye denied him in the presence of P. Acts 3:13
against Jesus, Herod and P. 4:27
yet desired they P. that he. 13:28
who before P. witnessed. 1 Tim 6:13

pile

the p. of it is fire and. Isa 30:33
make the p. for fire. Ezek 24:9

pilgrimage

years of my p. are 130 years . . . the days of their p. Gen 47:9
them the land of their p. Ex 6:4*
in the house of my p. Ps 119:54

pilgrims

were strangers and p. Heb 11:13
I beseech you, as p. 1 Pet 2:11

pillar

(*That which supports, either actually or metaphorically. The word is used of the cloud and fire which led the Israelites through the wilderness. It is also used in other places where the form is intended, not the idea of support*)

and became a p. of salt. Gen 19:26
Jacob set it up for a p. 28:18, 22 35:14
thou anointedst the p. 31:13
behold this p. 51
and this p. be witness. 52
Jacob set a p. upon Rachel's grave, that is the p. 35:20
cloudy p. descended and. Ex 33:9
people saw the cloudy p. stand. 10
king, by the plain of the p. Judg 9:6
the flame arose with a p. 20:40
up a p.: he called the p. 2 Sam 18:18
the right p., the left p. 1 Ki 7:21
king stood by p. 2 Ki 11:14; 23:3 2 Chr 23:13
in day by a cloudy p. Neh 9:12
to them in the cloudy p. Ps 99:7
and a p. at the border. Isa 19:19
thee this day an iron p. Jer 1:18
the height of one p. was. 52:21
church, the p. and ground of the truth. 1 Tim 3:15
that overcometh will I make a p. Rev 3:12

see **cloud, fire**

pillars

an altar and twelve p. Ex 24:4
hang the vail upon four p. 26:32
for the hanging five p. 37; 36:38
the 20 p.; hooks of the p. of silver. 27:10, 11; 38:10, 11, 12, 17
their p. ten. 27:12
their p. three. 14, 15; 38:14, 15
p. shall be four. 27:16
sockets for p. were of brass. 38:17
Samson between the p. Judg 16:25
the p. of the earth are. 1 Sam 2:8
he cast two p. of brass. 1 Ki 7:15
made of the almug trees p. 10:12
cut off gold from the p. 2 Ki 18:16
brake in pieces the p. of brass and. 25:13, 16; Jer 52:17, 20
to rings and p. of marble. Esth 1:6
and the p. thereof tremble. Job 9:6 26:11
dissolved, I bear up the p. Ps 75:3
hewn out her seven p. Pr 9:1
cometh like p. of smoke? S of S 3:6
he made the p. thereof of silver. 10
legs are as p. of marble set. 5:15
fire, and p. of smoke. Joel 2:30

Cephas who seemed to be *p.* *Gal* 2:9
his feet were as *p.* of fire. *Rev* 10:1

pilled

(*Revisions substitute the modern form* peeled)
Jacob *p.* white strakes. *Gen* 30:37
he set rods which he had *p.* 38

pillow, -s

put stones for his *p.* *Gen* 28:11
that he had put for his *p.* 18
a *p.* of goats' hair. *1 Sam* 19:13, 16
women that sew *p.* and. *Ezek* 13:18
I am against your *p.* 20
in the ship asleep on a *p.* *Mark* 4:38

pilots

O Tyrus, were thy *p.* *Ezek* 27:8
sound of the cry of thy *p.* 28

pin

with a *p.*. . . Samson awaked and went away with *p.* of. *Judg* 16:14
a *p.* of the vine tree? *Ezek* 15:3

pine

p. away, in iniquities of their fathers shall they *p.* away. *Lev* 26:39
fetch olive and *p.* *Neh* 8:15*
these *p.* away, stricken. *Lam* 4:9
ye shall *p.* away for. *Ezek* 24:23
if sins be upon us, and we *p.* 33:10

pineth

his teeth, and *p.* away. *Mark* 9:18

pine tree

p. and box tree together. *Isa* 41:19
the *p.* and box tree shall come. 60:13

pining

he will cut me off with *p.* *Isa* 38:12*

pinnacle

setteth him on a *p.* of temple.
Mat 4:5; *Luke* 4:9

pins

make all the *p.* of the tabernacle.
Ex 27:19; 35:18; 38:20, 31; 39:40
their sockets, their *p.* and their cords.
Num 3:37; 4:32

pipe, -s

of prophets with *p.* *1 Sam* 10:5
the people piped with *p.* *1 Ki* 1:40
the harp and *p.* are in. *Isa* 5:12
when one goeth with a *p.* 30:29
sound for Moab like *p.* *Jer* 48:36
workmanship of thy *p.* *Ezek* 28:13
and seven *p.* to the seven. *Zech* 4:2
through the golden *p.* empty. 12*
life, whether *p.* or harp. *1 Cor* 14:7

piped

people *p.* with pipes. *1 Ki* 1:40
saying, We have *p.* unto you.
Mat 11:17; *Luke* 7:32
be known what is *p.*? *1 Cor* 14:7

pipers

voice of *p.* shall be. *Rev* 18:22*

Pisgah

Balaam to the top of *P.* *Num* 23:14
get thee up into the top of *P.*
Deut 3:27; 34:1
plain, under the springs of *P.* 4:29

Pisidia

came to Antioch in *P.* *Acts* 13:14
had passed throughout *P.* 14:24

piss

drink own *p.* with you. *2 Ki* 18:27*
Isa 36:12*

pit, -s

(*This word is used metaphorically for deep trouble, and for the depths of hell*)
was full of slime *p.* *Gen* 14:10
us cast him into some *p.* 37:20*, 24
owner of the *p.* shall. *Ex* 21:34
a *p.* wherein is water. *Lev* 11:36
quick into the *p.* *Num* 16:30, 33
hid themselves in *p.* *1 Sam* 13:6
is now hid in some *p.* *2 Sam* 17:9
cast Absalom into a great *p.* 18:17
Benaiah slew a lion in a *p.* 23:20
1 Chr 11:22
Jehu slew them at the *p.* *2 Ki* 10:14
down to the bars of the *p.* *Job* 17:16
back his soul from the *p.* 33:18, 30
from going down into the *p.* 24, 28
sunk down into the *p.* *Ps* 9:15
them that go down into *p.* 28:1
not go down to the *p.* 30:3
blood, when I go down to the *p.*? 9
hid from me their net in a *p.* 35:7
up out of an horrible *p.* 40:2
to the *p.* of destruction. 55:23
let not the *p.* shut her mouth. 69:15
with them that go down into *p.* 88:4
hast laid me in the lowest *p.* 6
the proud have digged *p.* 119:85
let them be cast into deep *p.* 140:10
like unto them that go down into the *p.* 143:7 *Pr* 1:12
strange women is a deep *p.* *Pr* 22:14
woman is a narrow *p.* 23:27
fall himself into his own *p.* 28:10
a man shall flee to the *p.*; let no. 17
down to the sides of the *p.* *Isa* 14:15
to the stones of the *p.* 19
fear, and the *p.* and the snare. 24:17
Jer 48:43, 44
cometh out of the midst of *p.* *Isa* 24:18
prisoners are gathered in the *p.* 22
water withal out of the *p.* 30:14*
hast delivered it from the *p.* 38:17
they that go down into the *p.* 18
he should not die in the *p.* 51:14
led us through a land of *p.* *Jer* 2:6
they came to the *p.* and found. 14:3†
into the midst of the *p.* 41:7
the *p.* which Asa made for fear. 9
anointed taken in their *p.* *Lam* 4:20
was taken in their *p.* *Ezek* 19:4, 8
with them that descend into the *p.*
26:20; 28:8; 31:14, 16; 32:18, 24
25, 29, 30
are set in the sides of the *p.* 32:23
of nettles and salt *p.* *Zeph* 2:9
prisoners out of the *p.* *Zech* 9:11
if it fall into a *p.* on sabbath.
Mat 12:11; *Luke* 14:5*
see **bottomless, dig, digged**

pitch

p. it within and without with *p.*
Gen 6:14
with slime and with *p.* *Ex* 2:3
turned to *p.*, and the land thereof shall become burning *p.* *Isa* 34:9

pitch, *verb*

Israel shall *p.* every man. *Num* 1:52
the Levites shall *p.* round the. 53
man shall *p.* by his own standard. 2:2
camp of Judah *p.* 3
the Gershonites *p.* 3:23
sons of Kohath *p.* 29
Merari shall *p.* 35
you out a place to *p.* in. *Deut* 1:33
Joshua did *p.* twelve stones.
Josh 4:20
nor shall the Arabian *p.* *Isa* 13:20
shepherds shall *p.* their. *Jer* 6:3

pitched

(*American Revision changes this word, when used intransitively, to* encamped)
Abram *p.* his tent, and. *Gen* 12:8
Lot *p.* 13:12
Isaac *p.* in valley. 26:17, 25
Jacob *p.* in mount, Laban *p.* 31:25
Jacob *p.* his tent before. 33:18
from Sin, Israel *p.* in. *Ex* 17:1
come to desert, and had *p.* 19:2
Moses took tabernacle, *p.* it. 33:7
when tabernacle is *p.* *Num* 1:51
so they *p.* by their standards. 2:34
at commandment of the Lord they *p.*
9:18
the people *p.* in the wilderness. 12:16
Israel *p.* in Oboth. 21:10
p. in Ije-abarim. 11
Israel *p.* in Succoth. 33:5
they *p.* in Etham. 6
ambush *p.* on north side. *Josh* 8:11
set ark in tabernacle David had *p.*
2 Sam 6:17
Israel and Absalom *p.* in land. 17:26
Israel *p.* before them. *1 Ki* 20:27, 29
Nebuchadnezzar *p.* against it.
2 Ki 25:1; *Jer* 52:4
a place for the ark, and *p.* for it a tent. *1 Chr* 15:1; 16:1; *2 Chr* 1:4
tabernacle which Lord *p.* *Heb* 8:2

pitcher, -s

let down *p.* I pray thee. *Gen* 24:14
Rebekah came with her *p.* 15, 45
empty *p.* and lamps within the *p.*
Judg 7:16
they brake *p.* that were in. 19, 20
or the *p.* be broken at. *Eccl* 12:6
esteemed as earthen *p.*? *Lam* 4:2
man bearing a *p.* of water.
Mark 14:13; *Luke* 22:10

pitied

also to be *p.* of all. *Ps* 106:46
and the Lord hath not *p.* *Lam* 2:2
17, 21; 3:43
none eye *p.* thee, to do. *Ezek* 16:5

pitieth

like as a father *p.* his children, so the Lord *p.* them that. *Ps* 103:13
I will profane what your soul *p.*
Ezek 24:21

pitiful

hands of *p.* women have. *Lam* 4:10
that the Lord is very *p.* *Jas* 5:11
love as brethren, be *p.* *1 Pet* 3:8*

pity

thine eye shall have no *p.* *Deut* 7:16
because he had no *p.* *2 Sam* 12:6
to the afflicted, *p.* should. *Job* 6:14*
have *p.* on me, *p.* on me. 19:21
looked for some to take *p.* *Ps* 69:20
that hath *p.* on poor. *Pr* 19:17
they shall have no *p.* on. *Isa* 13:18
in his love and in his *p.* he. 63:9
for who shall have *p.* upon? *Jer* 15:5
nor have *p.* nor mercy. 21:7
nor will I have *p.* *Ezek* 5:11; 7:4, 9
8:18; 9:10
eye spare, neither have ye *p.* 9:5
but I had *p.* for mine holy. 36:21
Edom did cast off all *p.* *Amos* 1:11
had *p.* on the gourd. *Jonah* 4:10
as I had *p.* on thee. *Mat* 18:33*

pity, *verb*

nor shall thine eye *p.* him. *Deut* 13:8
19:13, 21
thine eye shall not *p.* 25:12
for him that will *p.* the poor. *Pr* 28:8
I will not *p.* nor spare. *Jer* 13:14
Lord will *p.* his people. *Joel* 2:18
their own shepherds *p.* *Zech* 11:5
for I will no more *p.* inhabitants. 6

place

Lord said, Look from *p.* *Gen* 13:14
destroy and not spare the *p.*? 18:24
spare the *p.* for their sakes. 26
thou shalt shew at every *p.* 20:13
third day Abraham saw the *p.* 22:4
I may go unto mine own *p.* 30:25
into prison, the *p.* where. 40:3
p. whereon thou standest is holy.
Ex 3:5; *Josh* 5:15
this people shall go to their *p.* in peace. *Ex* 18:23
to bring thee into the *p.* I. 23:20
he shall cast it by the *p.* *Lev* 1:16
first *p.* went standard. *Num* 10:14
ye shall eat it in every *p.* ye. 18:31
every *p.* whereon the soles of your.
Deut 11:24; *Josh* 1:3
p. the Lord God shall choose.
Deut 12:5, 14; 16:16
thy burnt offering in every *p.* 12:13
if the *p.* be too far. 21; 14:24
through thy land to my *p.* *Judg* 11:19
men of Israel gave *p.* to. 20:36
thou shalt mark the *p.* *Ruth* 3:4
and one of the same *p.* *1 Sam* 10:12
went to their own *p.* 14:46
and David's *p.* was empty. 20:25, 27
and died in the same *p.* *2 Sam* 2:23
in what *p.* my lord the king. 15:21
pit, or in some other *p.* 17:9
come upon him in some *p.* 12
to this day Absalom's *p.* 18:18*
eyes may be open toward *p.* *1 Ki* 8:29
strike his hand over the *p.* *2 Ki* 5:11
behold, *p.* where we dwell is. 6:1
grant me the *p.* of. *1 Chr* 21:22
to Ornan for the *p.* 600 shekels. 25
the priests stood in their *p.*
2 Chr 30:16; 35:10
sons of Asaph, were in their *p.* 35:15

. of my father's sepulchre. Neh 2:3
here was no p. for beast under. 14
n what p. ye hear sound of. 4:20
nd Levites in their p. 13:11
er maids to the best p. Esth 2:9
eliverance from another p. 4:14
onsumed out of their p. Job 6:17
hake the earth out of her p. 9:6
et my cry have no p. 16:18
here is the p. of understanding? 28:12, 20
nd he knoweth the p. thereof. 23
eople are cut off in their p. 36:20
r darkness, where is the p.? 38:19
e wicked in their p. 40:12*
e p. where thine honour. Ps 26:8
y foot standeth in an even p. 12
ou art my hiding p. 32:7; 119:114
om the p. of his habitation. 33:14
e p. thereof shall know it. 103:16
e p. of judgement, p. Eccl 3:16
l go unto one p.; all are of. 20; 6:6
field, till there be no p. Isa 5:8
hall remove out of her p. 13:13
nd bring them to their p. 14:2
that there is no p. clean. 28:8
arley and rye in their p.? 25
every p. where grounded. 30:32*
is too strait for me, give p. 49:20
nlarge the p. of thy tent. 54:2
will make the p. of my feet. 60:13
here is the p. of my rest? 66:1
ye now unto my p. Jer 7:12
l there be no p. 32; 19:11
orious throne is the p. of. 17:12
aters come from another p. 18:14*
where they did offer. Ezek 6:13
of my throne shall Israel. 43:7
shall burn it in the appointed p. 21
at no p. was found. Dan 2:35
e p. of his sanctuary was. 8:11
and return to my p. Hos 5:15
ead bodies in every p. Amos 8:3
eir p. is not known. Nah 3:17
shall not be found. Zech 10:10
ain in her own p. 12:6; 14:10
offered in every p. Mal 1:11
me, see the p. where the Lord lay. Mat 28:6; Mark 16:6
what p. soever ye. Mark 6:10
where it was written. Luke 4:17
o and two unto every p. 10:1
Levite, when he was at the p. 32
thee, Give this man p. 14:9
rusalem is the p. of. John 4:20
cause my word hath no p. 8:37*
o days still in the same p. 11:6
mans shall take away our p. 48
trayed him, knew the p. 18:2
th one accord in one p. Acts 2:1
hen they had prayed, the p. 4:31
e p. whereon thou standest. 7:33
what is the p. of my rest? 49
e p. of scripture which he. 8:32
ther give p. unto wrath. Rom 12:19
t now having no more p. 15:23
th all that in every p. call on Jesus Christ. 1 Cor 1:2
me together into one p. 11:20*
urch be come into one p. 14:23*
s knowledge in every p. 2 Cor 2:14
whom we gave p. . . . no. Gal 2:5
r give p. to the devil. Eph 4:27
every p. your faith God-ward. 1 Thes 1:8
another p., Thou a priest. Heb 5:6
p. should have been sought. 8:7
found no p. of repentance. 12:17
e same p. sweet water. Jas 3:11*
r was their p. found any. Rev 12:8
into wilderness to her p. 14
d there was found no p. 20:11
see **dwelling, holy,** most **holy**

a place

p. where king's prisoners were. Gen 39:20
point thee a p. to flee. Ex 21:13
hold, there is a p. by me. 33:21
ace was a p. for cattle. Num 32:1
arch you out a p. to pitch your. Deut 1:33
p. without the camp. 23:12
ve him a p. in the city. Josh 20:4
where he could find a p. Judg 17:8
a p. where is no want of. 18:10
Saul set him up a p. 1 Sam 15:12*
my servants to such a p. 21:2
let them give me a p. in. 27:5
a p. for Israel, that they may dwell in a p. 2 Sam 7:10; 1 Chr 17:9
assigned Uriah to a p. 2 Sam 11:16
I set there a p. for ark. 1 Ki 8:21
1 Chr 15:1
let us make us a p. 2 Ki 6:2
in such a p. shall be my camp. 8
beware thou pass not such a p. 9
I have built a p. for thy. 2 Chr 6:2
there is a p. for gold. Job 28:1
until I find out a p. for. Ps 132:5
have a p. of refuge. Pr 14:26
a p. of refuge from rain. Isa 4:6
Lord will be to us a p. of. 33:21
for herself a p. of rest. 34:14
and within my walls a p. 56:5*
Achor a p. for the herds. 65:10
a p. for the spreading. Ezek 26:5, 14
I will give to Gog a p. of. 39:11
she is become a p. for. Zeph 2:15
that is to say, a p. of a skull. Mat 27:33; John 19:17
found colt in a p. where. Mark 11:4*
I go to prepare a p. John 14:2, 3
in a certain p. testified. Heb 2:6*
he spake in a certain p. of the. 4:4*
called to go out into a p. he. 11:8
hath a p. prepared of God. Rev 12:6
into a p. called Armageddon. 16:16
see **choose**

high place

went up to an high p. Num 23:3*
is a sacrifice to-day in high p. 1 Sam 9:12
prophets coming from high p. 10:5
an end, Saul came to high p. 13
that was great high p. 1 Ki 3:4
1 Chr 16:39
Solomon built an high p. 1 Ki 11:7
high p. that Jeroboam . . . the high p., burnt the high p. 2 Ki 23:15
went to the high p. 2 Chr 1:3
journey to high p. at Gibeon. 13
is weary on the high p. Isa 16:12
made a high p. in every street. Ezek 16:24, 25, 31
the high p. whereunto ye go? 20:29

his place

and Abraham returned to his p. Gen 18:33
rose up and returned to his p. 31:35
neither rose from his p. Ex 10:23
in his p., none go out of his p. 16:29
bright spot stay in his p. Lev 13:23
every man in his p. by. Num 2:17
Balaam rose up and returned to his p. 24:25
to the gate of his p. Deut 21:19
be not cut off from his p. Ruth 4:10
laid down in his p. 1 Sam 3:2
went and lay down in his p. 9
set Dagon in his p. again. 5:3
ark go down to his own p. 11; 6:2
go and see his p. where. 23:22
and Saul returned to his p. 26:25
that he may go again to his p. 29:4
ark of the Lord in his p. 2 Sam 6:17
returned to his own p. 19:39
priests brought ark to his p. 1 Ki 8:6; 2 Chr 5:7
every man out of his p. 1 Ki 20:24
ark of the Lord to his p. 1 Chr 15:3
and gladness are in his p. 16:27
chest to his p. again. 2 Chr 24:11
king stood in his p. and made. 34:31
let men of his p. help. Ezra 1:4
for house of God to set it in his p. 2:68; 5:15; 6:7
every one from his own p. Job 2:11
neither shall his p. know him. 7:10
if he destroy him from his p. 8:18
is removed out of his p. 14:18
rock be removed out of his p.? 18:4
nor shall his p. any more. 20:9
hurleth him out of his p. 27:21
hands and hiss him out of his p. 23
is removed out of his p. 37:1
dayspring to know his p. 38:12
diligently consider his p. Ps 37:10
wandereth from his p. Pr 27:8
the sun hasteth to his p. Eccl 1:5
Lord cometh out of his p. Isa 26:21
his p. of defence shall be. 33:16
set him in his p.; from his p. shall he not remove. 46:7
he is gone from his p. Jer 4:7
feed every one in his p. 6:3
glory of Lord from his p. Ezek 3:12
Lord cometh out of his p. Mi 1:3
worship every one from his p. Zeph 2:11
grow up out of his p. Zech 6:12
thy sword into his p. Mat 26:52
might go to his own p. Acts 1:25
candlestick out of his p. Rev 2:5

in the place

not, am I in the p. of God? Gen 50:19
plant them in the p. Ex 15:17
kill it in the p. where they kill. Lev 4:24, 29, 33; 6:25; 7:2
in the p. of the boil there. 13:19
in the p. where the cloud. Num 9:17
inheritance be in the p. 33:54
twelve stones in the p. Josh 4:9
drunk water in the p. 1 Ki 13:22
in the p. where dogs licked. 21:19
in the p. that David. 2 Chr 3:1
sore broken us in the p. Ps 44:19
and stand not in the p. Pr 25:6
in the p. where the tree. Eccl 11:3
but he shall die in the p. Jer 22:12
38:9; 42:22
in the p. where the king dwelleth. Ezek 17:16
judge thee in the p. where. 21:30
that in the p. where it was said. Hos 1:10; Rom 9:26
not stay long in the p. of. Hos 13:13
in the p. where crucified. John 19:41

of the place

men of the p. asked him; lest men of p. should kill. Gen 26:7
all the men of the p. 29:22
the name of the p. Peniel. 32:30
name of p. Succoth. 33:17
name of p. Beth-el. 35:15
name of the p. Massah. Ex 17:7
name of the p. Taberah. Num 11:3
of the p. twelve stones. Josh 4:3
name of the p. Gilgal. 5:9
of p. called valley of Achor. 7:26
the men of the p. were. Judg 19:16
Naomi went forth out of the p. Ruth 1:7
called name of the p. Perez-uzzah. 2 Sam 6:8
pattern of the p. of. 1 Chr 28:11
name of the p., valley. 2 Chr 20:26
breadth of the p. left. Ezek 41:11
raise them out of the p. Joel 3:7
end of the p. thereof. Nah 1:8

that place

called that p. Beer-sheba. Gen 21:31
that p. Jehovah-jireh. 22:14
called name of that p. Beth-el. 28:19
name of that p. Mahanaim. 32:2
asked men of that p. 38:21
name of that p. Kibroth. Num 11:34
of them out of that p. Deut 12:3
the sentence they of that p. 17:10
name of that p. Bochim. Judg 2:5
that p. Ramath-lehi. 15:17
called that p. Selah-. 1 Sam 23:28
that p. was called Helkath-hazzurim. 2 Sam 2:16
called that p. Baal-perazim. 5:20
1 Chr 14:11
that p. is called Perez-. 1 Chr 13:11
men of that p. had. Mat 14:35
ye depart from that p. Mark 6:10
multitude being in that p. John 5:13
was in that p. where Martha. 11:30
both we and they of that p. Acts 21:12

this place

bring them out of this p. Gen 19:12
we will destroy this p. 13
get out of this p. 14
fear of God is not in this p. 20:11
Lord is in this p. 28:16

dreadful is this p. Gen 28:17
no harlot in this p. 38:21, 22
God hath given me in this p. 48:9
brought you out from this p. Ex 13:3
us unto this evil p. Num 20:5
bare thee till ye came to this p.
Deut 1:31; 9:7; 11:5
he hath brought us into this p. 26:9
when ye came unto this p. 29:7
makest thou in this p.? Judg 18:3
prayer toward this p. 1 Ki 8:29, 30
35; 2 Chr 6:20, 21, 26, 40; 7:15
nor drink water in this p. 1 Ki 13:8, 16
come not against this p. 2 Ki 18:25
I will bring evil on this p. 22:16, 17
20; 2 Chr 34:24, 25, 28
and have chosen this p. 2 Chr 7:12
this the p. of him that. Job 18:21
innocent blood in this p. Jer 7:6
be poured out on this p. 20
you assured peace in this p. 14:13
sons nor daughters in this p. 16:2
cause to cease out of this p. the. 9
will bring evil upon this p. 19:3
they estranged this p., filled this p. 4
that this p. shall no more be. 6
thus will I do unto this p. 12; 40:2
went forth out of this p. 22:11; 24:5
restore them to this p. 27:22; 32:37
I will bring to this p. all. 28:3, 6
I will bring again to this p. 4
you to return to this p. 29:10
again be heard in this p. the. 33:10
ye shall see this p. no more. 42:18
punish you in this p. 44:29
hast spoken against this p. 51:62
this is the p. where the priests shall
boil the offering. Ezek 46:20
of Baal from this p. Zeph 1:4
in this p. will I give peace. Hag 2:9
in this p. one greater. Mat 12:6
into this p. of torment. Luke 16:28
from Galilee to this p. 23:5
shall destroy this p. Acts 6:14
forth and serve me in this p. 7:7
against the law and this p. 21:28
and in this p. again, if they. Heb 4:5

thy **place**
restore thee to thy p. Gen 40:13*
flee thou to thy p. Num 24:11
return to thy p. and. 2 Sam 15:19
rise against thee, leave not thy p.
Eccl 10:4
shalt remove from thy p. Ezek 12:3
38:15

to or *unto the* **place**
Abram went unto the p. Gen 13:3, 4
went unto the p. of which. 22:3, 9
to bring you unto the p. Ex 3:8
lead people unto the p. of. 32:34
journeying to the p. of. Num 10:29
go up to the p. which Lord. 14:40
carried stones to the p. Josh 4:8
come to the p. where. 1 Sam 20:19
as many as came to the p. stood.
2 Sam 2:23
sent to the p. which man. 2 Ki 6:10
bring ark to the p. that. 1 Chr 15:12
I will bring them to the p. Neh 1:9
they go to the p. that. Ps 104:8
present brought to the p. Isa 18:7
I will do to the p. which I. Jer 7:14
will bring you again to the p. 29:14
was entered into the p. Acts 25:23

place, *verb*
and p. such over them. Ex 18:21
in the p. which he shall choose to p.
Deut 14:23; 16:2, 6, 11; 26:2
and p. them in the house. Ezra 6:5
and I will p. salvation in. Isa 46:13
I shall p. you in your. Ezek 37:14, 26
shall p. the abomination. Dan 11:31
p. them in their houses. Hos 11:11*
bring them again to p. them. Zech 10:6

placed
God p. at east of the. Gen 3:24
Joseph p. his father and his. 47:11
Jeroboam p. in Beth-el. 1 Ki 12:32
and p. them in Halah. 2 Ki 17:6
and p. them in the cities of. 24, 26
he p. in the chariot cities. 2 Chr 1:14
he made tables, p. them in the. 4:8
he p. forces in all the. 2 Chr 17:2
of old, since man was p. Job 20:4
the tent which he had p. Ps 78:60
that they may be p. alone. Isa 5:8*
which p. sand for the. Jer 5:22
eagle p. it by the great. Ezek 17:7

places
will keep thee in all p. Gen 28:15
in all p. where I record. Ex 20:24
utterly destroy all the p. Deut 12:2
abode in their p. till. Josh 5:8
delivered in the p. of. Judg 5:11
to one of these p. to lodge. 19:13
Israel in all those p. 1 Sam 7:16
sent presents to all the p. 30:31
in all the p. wherein? 2 Sam 7:7
put down priests in p. 2 Ki 23:5
he filled their p. with the bones. 14
from all p. whence ye. Neh 4:12
in lower p. and on higher p. 13
Levites out of all their p. 12:27
where are the dwelling p.? Job 21:28*
dens and remain in their p. 37:8*
he sitteth in lurking p. of. Ps 10:8
fallen to me in pleasant p. 16:6
afraid out of their close p. 18:45
set them in slippery p. 73:18
the dark p. of the earth are. 74:20
all his works, in all p. 103:22
they ran in the dry p. like. 105:41
he shall fill the p. with the. 110:6
she standeth in the p. of. Pr 8:2*
that art in the secret p. S of S 2:14
dwell in quiet resting p. Isa 32:18
straight, and rough p. plain. 40:4
I will make the crooked p. 45:2
a wind from those p. shall. Jer 4:12
in all p. whither I have. 8:3; 29:14
from p. about Jerusalem. 17:26
to be a taunt and a curse in all p. 24:9
take witnesses in the p. 32:44
Jews returned out of all p. 40:12
give for a prey in all p. 45:5
he hath destroyed his p. Lam 2:6
deliver them out of all p. Ezek 34:12
I will make the p. round my hill. 26
he said, These are the p. of. 46:24*
but the miry p. thereof. 47:11
of bread in all your p. Amos 4:6
I will give thee p. to walk. Zech 3:7
he walketh through dry p.
Mat 12:43; Luke 11:24
some fell on stony p. Mat 13:5, 20
famines and earthquakes in divers p.
24:7; Mark 13:8; Luke 21:11
we accept it in all p. Acts 24:3
blessed us in heavenly p. Eph 1:3
at his own right hand in heavenly p. 20
together in heavenly p. in Christ. 2:6
to powers in heavenly p. might. 3:10
Christ are manifest in all p. Phil 1:13
island moved out of their p. Rev 6:14
see **desolate, holy**

high **places**
will destroy your high p. Lev 26:30
consumed lords of high p. of.
Num 21:28
up into the high p. of Baal. 22:41
pluck down all their high p. 33:52
made him ride on high p. Deut 32:13
tread upon their high p. 33:29
their lives in the high p. Judg 5:18
people hide themselves in high p.
1 Sam 13:6*
of Israel slain in high p. 2 Sam 1:19
thou wast slain in thy high p. 25
setteth me on my high p. 22:34
Ps 18:33
people sacrificed in high p. 1 Ki 3:2
2 Ki 17:32; 2 Chr 33:17
incense in high p. 1 Ki 3:3; 22:43
2 Ki 12:3; 15:4, 35; 16:4; 17:11
made an house of high p. 1 Ki 12:31
in Beth-el the priests of high p. 32
offer the priests of the high p. 13:2
all the houses of the high p. 32
the lowest of the people priests of
the high p. 33; 2 Ki 17:32
but the high p. were. 1 Ki 15:14
22:43; 2 Ki 12:3; 14:4; 15:4, 35
in houses of high p. 2 Ki 17:29
removed the high p. 18:4, 22
burn incense in the high p. 23:5
defiled the high p. . . and brake down
the high p. of gates. 2 Ki 23:8, 13
2 Chr 31:1; 32:12; Isa 36:7
priests of high p. came. 2 Ki 23:9
all the priests of the high p. 20
ordained priests for high p.
2 Chr 11:15
Asa took away the high p. 14:3, 5
the high p. were not taken away.
15:17; 20:33
took away the high p. 17:6
Jehoram made high p. 21:11
Ahaz made high p. 28:25
purge Jerusalem from high p. 34:3
peace in his high p. Job 25:2
provoked him with their high p.
Ps 78:58
on the top of the high p. Pr 8:2
seat in the high p. of the city. 9:14
is gone up to the high p. Isa 15:2
I will open rivers in high p. 41:18*
pastures shall be in all high p. 49:9*
cause thee to ride on high p. 58:14
thine eyes to the high p. Jer 3:2*
a voice was heard on the high p. 21*
a dry wind in the high p. of. 4:11*
a lamentation in the high p. 7:29
come up on all the high p. 12:12
did stand in the high p. 14:6*
I will give thy high p. for sin. 17:3
become as the high p. of the forest.
26:18; Mi 3:12
I will cause to cease in Moab him
that offereth in high p. Jer 48:35
I will destroy your high p. Ezek 6:3
deckedst thy high p. with. 16:16
break down thy high p. 39
the ancient high p. are ours. 36:2
the high p. of Aven. Hos 10:8
treadeth on high p. of earth.
Amos 4:13; Mi 1:3
the high p. of Isaac shall. Amos 7:9
what are the high p. of? Mi 1:5
to walk on mine high p. Hab 3:19
wickedness in high p. Eph 6:12
see **built**

waste **places**
waste p. of fat ones shall. Isa 5:17
comfort all her waste p. 51:3
sing together, ye waste p. 52:9
build the old waste p. 58:12

plague
and I will p. them that. Ps 89:23*

plague, *substantive*
yet I will bring one p. Ex 11:1
the p. shall not be on you to. 12:13
there be no p. among them. 30:12
when the hair in the p. Lev 13:3, 17
if the p. spread not in. 5, 6; 14:48
a p. then priest shall see the p.
13:30, 31, 32, 50, 51, 55; 14:37
he is a leprous man, his p. is. 13:44
and shut up it that hath the p. 50
or woof, it is a spreading p. 57*
if p. be departed from them. 58
there is as it were a p. in. 14:35
be no p. among Israel. Num 8:19
people with a very great p. 11:33
died by the p. before the Lord. 14:37
wrath is gone out, the p. 16:46, 47
the p. was stayed. 48, 50; 25:8
that died in the p. 16:49; 25:9
every p. which is not. Deut 28:61
not cleansed, although there was p.
Josh 22:17
one p. was on you all. 1 Sam 6:4
that p. may be stayed. 2 Sam 24:2
1 Chr 21:2
whatever p. or sickness. 1 Ki 8:3
shall know every man the p. of. 3
with a great p. will the. 2 Chr 21:1
nor any p. come nigh. Ps 91:1
p. brake in upon them. 106:2
judgement, so p. was stayed. 3
this shall be the p. Zech 14:12, 1
she was healed of that p. Mark 5:2
and be whole of thy p. 3
because of the p. of hail. Rev 16:2

plagued
the Lord p. Pharaoh. Gen 12:1
Lord p. the people for. Ex 32:35
p. Egypt, and afterwards. Josh 24:5

player
who is a cunning *p*. *1 Sam* 16:16

players
the *p*. on instruments. *Ps* 68:25*
as well the singers as the *p*. 87:7*

playeth
as to a woman that *p*. *Ezek* 23:44

playing
seen a son of Jesse cunning in *p*. *1 Sam* 16:18
David dancing and *p*. *1 Chr* 15:29
were the damsels *p*. *Ps* 68:25
boys and girls *p*. in the. *Zech* 8:5

plea
too hard between *p*. and *p*. *Deut* 17:8

plead
ye *p*. for Baal ? he that will *p*. for. *Judg* 6:31†
saying, Let Baal *p*. against him. 32†
set me a time to *p*.? *Job* 9:19*
who is he that will *p*. with? 13:19*
O that one might *p*. for a man. 16:21*
p. against me my reproach. 19:5
will he *p*. against me with his ? 23:6*
seek judgement, *p*. for the widow. *Isa* 1:17
Lord standeth up to *p*. and. 3:13†
let us *p*. together, declare. 43:26
by fire will the Lord *p*. 66:16
p. with you, and with your children's children will I *p*. *Jer* 2:9†, 35*
wherefore will ye *p*. with me? 29
righteous art thou, O Lord, when I *p*. with thee. 12:1†
Lord will *p*. with all flesh, 25:31†
will *p*. with him there. *Ezek* 17:20†
I *p*. with you face to face. 20:35†
so will I *p*. with you, saith the. 36†
I will *p*. against him with. 38:22†
p. with your mother, *p*. *Hos* 2:2†
I will *p*. with them for my people. *Joel* 3:2†
Lord will *p*. with Israel. *Mi* 6:2
see **cause**

pleaded
Lord that *p*. the cause. *1 Sam* 25:39
hast *p*. causes of my soul. *Lam* 3:58
like as I *p*. with your fathers in the. *Ezek* 20:36*

pleadeth
with God, as a man *p*. *Job* 16:21*
that *p*. cause of his people. *Isa* 51:22
justice, nor any *p*. for truth. 59:4

pleading
hearken to the *p*. of my lips. *Job* 13:6

pleasant
every tree grow that *is p*. *Gen* 2:9
was *p*. to the eyes, and a tree. 3:6*
saw the land that it was *p*. 49:15
Saul and Jonathan were *p*. in their lives. *2 Sam* 1:23
Jonathan, very *p*. hast thou. 26
whatever is *p*. they. *1 Ki* 20:6
situation of this city is *p*. *2 Ki* 2:19
made treasuries for *p*. jewels. *2 Chr* 32:27*
fallen to me in *p*. places. *Ps* 16:6
bring hither the *p*. harp with. 81:2
they despised the *p*. land. 106:24
how *p*. for brethren to dwell. 133:1
to his name, for it is *p*. 135:3
147:1
when knowledge is *p*. to. *Pr* 2:10
the loving hind and *p*. roe. 5:19
bread eaten in secret is *p*. 9:17
words of the pure are *p*. 15:26
p. words are as honeycomb. 16:24
for it is *p*. if thou keep them. 22:18
shall be filled with all *p*. riches. 24:4
p. it is for the eyes to behold the sun. *Eccl* 11:7
my beloved, yea *p*. *S of S* 1:16
an orchard with *p*. fruits. 4:13*
come and eat his *p*. fruits. 16*
fair and *p*. art thou, O love. 7:6
are all manner of *p*. fruits. 13
Lord upon all *p*. pictures. *Isa* 2:16
men of Judah his *p*. plant. 5:7
shall cry in their *p*. palaces. 13:22
shalt thou plant *p*. plants. 17:10
they lament for *p*. fields. 32:12
thy borders of *p*. stones. *Isa* 54:12†
p. things are laid waste. 64:11
I give thee a *p*. land ? *Jer* 3:19
my *p*. portion a desolate. 12:10
p. places of the wilderness. 23:10
shall fall like a *p*. vessel. 25:34
dear son ? is he a *p*. child ? 31:20†
she remembered all her *p*. *Lam* 1:7
spread his hand on her *p*. things. 10
they have given their *p*. things. 11
slew all that were *p*. to the eye. 2:4
they shall destroy thy *p*. houses. *Ezek* 26:12
song of one that hath *p*. voice. 33:32
great toward the *p*. land. *Dan* 8:9*
ate no *p*. bread, nor came flesh. 10:3
honour a god with *p*. things. 11:38
p. places nettles shall. *Hos* 9:6
Ephraim is planted in a *p*. place. 13
your temples my *p*. things. *Joel* 3:5†
ye planted *p*. vineyards. *Amos* 5:11
ye cast out from *p*. houses. *Mi* 2:9
glory out of all the *p*. *Nah* 2:9†
laid the *p*. land desolate. *Zech* 7:14
offering of Jerusalem be *p*. *Mal* 3:4

pleasantness
her ways are ways of *p*. *Pr* 3:17

please
if she *p*. not her master. *Ex* 21:8
peradventure it will *p*. God that thou mayest curse. *Num* 23:27
if it *p*. my father to. *1 Sam* 20:13
let it *p*. thee to bless the house. *2 Sam* 7:29; *1 Chr* 17:27
if it *p*. I will give thee. *1 Ki* 21:6
if thou *p*. they will be thy servants. *2 Chr* 10:7
if it *p*. the king, and if thy servant have found. *Neh* 2:5, 7; *Esth* 1:19
3:9; 5:8; 7:3; 8:5; 9:13
it *p*. God to destroy me. *Job* 6:9
his children shall seek to *p*. 20:10
this also shall *p*. the Lord. *Ps* 69:31
man's ways *p*. the Lord. *Pr* 16:7
nor awake my love till he *p*. *S of S* 2:7; 3:5; 8:4
p. themselves in children. *Isa* 2:6
accomplish that which I *p*. 55:11
choose the things that *p*. me. 56:4
those things that *p*. him. *John* 8:29
in the flesh cannot *p*. God. *Rom* 8:8
and not to *p*. ourselves. 15:1
let every one *p*. his neighbour. 2
careth how he may *p*. *1 Cor* 7:32
p. his wife. 33
how she may *p*. her husband. 34
p. all men in all things. 10:33
do I seek to *p*. men ? *Gal* 1:10
p. not God are contrary. *1 Thes* 2:15
ought to walk and to *p*. God. 4:1
may *p*. him who hath chosen him. *2 Tim* 2:4
and to *p*. them well in all things. *Tit* 2:9
but without faith it is impossible to *p*. him. *Heb* 11:6

pleased
Esau seeing daughters of Canaan *p*. not Isaac. *Gen* 28:8
and thou wast *p*. with me. 33:10
and their words *p*. Hamor. 34:18
it *p*. Pharaoh well and his. 45:16
Balaam saw it *p*. the Lord. *Num* 24:1
the saying *p*. me well. *Deut* 1:23
Israel . . . it *p*. them. *Josh* 22:30
if Lord were *p*. to kill us. *Judg* 13:23
he talked with her, and she *p*. 14:7
it *p*. Lord to make you his people. *1 Sam* 12:22
it *p*. Saul that Michal loved. 18:20
it *p*. David to be the king's. 26
what the king did *p*. all. *2 Sam* 3:36
saying *p*. Absalom well, and. 17:4
if all we had died, then it had *p*. 19:6
Solomon's speech *p*. the. *1 Ki* 3:10
Solomon gave, *p*. not Hiram. 9:12
the thing *p*. the king. *2 Chr* 30:4*
Neh 2:6; *Esth* 1:21; 2:4
the maiden *p*. the king. *Esth* 2:9
the thing *p*. Haman, he caused. 5:14
be *p*. O Lord, to deliver. *Ps* 40:13
be *p*. with sacrifices. 51:19
he hath done whatsoever he *p*. *Ps* 115:3; 135:6; *Jonah* 1:1
yet it *p*. the Lord to bruise. *Isa* 53:1
it *p*. Darius to set over. *Dan* 6:
will Lord be *p*. with thousands o rams ? *Mi* 6:
offer it, will he be *p*.? *Mal* 1:
daughter of Herodias danced befor them, and *p*. *Mat* 14:6; *Mark* 6:2
saying *p*. whole multitude. *Acts* 6:
because Herod saw it *p*. the. 12:
for even Christ *p*. not. *Rom* 15:
hath *p*. them of Macedonia. 26, 2
it *p*. God by foolishness. *1 Cor* 1:2
and she be *p*. to dwell with him. 7:1
and if he be *p*. to dwell with her. 1
set members as it hath *p*. him. 12:1
a body as it hath *p*. him. 15:3
for if I yet *p*. men, I. *Gal* 1:1
when it *p*. God to reveal his Son. 1
it *p*. Father that in him all. *Col* 1:1
testimony, that he *p*. God. *Heb* 11:

well **pleased**
Lord is *well* p. for his. *Isa* 42:2
beloved Son, in whom I am *well p*. *Mat* 3:17; 12:18; 17:5; *Mark* 1:1 *Luke* 3:22; *2 Pet* 1:1
them God was not *well p*. *1 Cor* 10:
sacrifices God is *well p*. *Heb* 13:1

men **pleasers**
not with eye service, as *men p*. *Eph* 6:6; *Col* 3:2

pleaseth
do to her as it *p*. thee. *Gen* 16:
dwell where it *p*. thee. 20:1
for she *p*. me well. *Judg* 14:
maiden which *p*. the king. *Esth* 2:
p. God shall escape. *Eccl* 7:2
he doeth whatsoever *p*. him. 8:

pleasing
if I be *p*. in his eyes. *Esth* 8:
shall they be *p*. to him. *Hos* 9:
worthy of the Lord to all *p*. *Col* 1:1
so we speak, not as *p*. *1 Thes* 2:
those things that are *p*. *1 John* 3:2

well-**pleasing**
acceptable, *well-p*. to God. *Phil* 4:1
obey, for this is *well-p*. *Col* 3:2
working in you that which is *well-* in his sight. *Heb* 13:2

pleasure
after I am waxed old, shall I hav *p*.? *Gen* 18:1
thy fill at thine own *p*. *Deut* 23:2
I know thou hast *p*. in. *1 Chr* 29:1
king send his *p*. to us. *Ezra* 5:1
to Lord God, and do his *p*. 10:1
over our cattle at their *p*. *Neh* 9:3
according to every man's *p*. *Esth* 1:
what *p*. hath he in his house after ? *Job* 21:2
dieth, and never eateth with *p*. 2
is it any *p*. to Almighty that ? 22:
that hath *p*. in wickedness. *Ps* 5:
hath *p*. in the prosperity. 35:2
good in thy good *p*. to Zion. 51:
for thy servants take *p*. in. 102:1
bless Lord ye ministers of his, th do his *p*. 103:2
to bind his princes at his *p*. 105:2
all them that have *p*. therein. 111:
he taketh not *p*. in the legs. 147:
the Lord taketh *p*. in them that.
Lord taketh *p*. in his people. 149:
he that loveth *p*. shall. *Pr* 21:
therefore enjoy *p*. *Eccl* 2:
he hath no *p*. in fools. 5:
thou shalt say, I have no *p*. 12:
the night of my *p*. he. *Isa* 21
shall perform all my *p*. 44:
stand, I will do all my *p*. 46:
he will do his *p*. on Babylon. 48:
p. of the Lord shall prosper. 53:
day of your fast ye find *p*. 58
p. on my holy day, and call the sa bath a delight . . . thine own *p*.
up the wind at her *p*. *Jer* 2:
a vessel wherein is no *p*.? 22:
at liberty at their *p*. to return. 34:
like a vessel wherein is no *p*. 48:
whom thou hast taken *p*. *Ezek* 16:

ave I any p. that the wicked die? *Ezek* 18:23, 32; 33:11
vessel wherein is no p. *Hos* 8:8
nd I will take p. in it. *Hag* 1:8
have no p. in you. *Mal* 1:10
'ather's good p. to give. *Luke* 12:32
'elix, willing to shew the Jews a p. left Paul. *Acts* 24:27*
villing to do the Jews a p. 25:9*
ut have p. in them that. *Rom* 1:32
herefore I take p. in infirmities. *2 Cor* 12:10
ood p. of his will. *Eph* 1:5, 9
nd to do of his good p. *Phil* 2:13
ulfil the good p. of. *2 Thes* 1:11
elieved not, but had p. in. 2:12
ut she that liveth in p. *1 Tim* 5:6
n sacrifices thou hast no p. *Heb* 10:6, 8
ny soul shall have no p. in him. 38
s after their own p. 12:10
e have lived in p. on earth. *Jas* 5:5
hat count it p. to riot. *2 Pet* 2:13
or thy p. they are and. *Rev* 4:11

pleasures

pend their years in p. *Job* 36:11
t thy right hand are p. *Ps* 16:11
rink of river of thy p. 36:8
hou that art given to p. *Isa* 47:8
re choked with the p. *Luke* 8:14
overs of p. more than. *2 Tim* 3:4
erving divers lusts and p. *Tit* 3:3
han to enjoy the p. of sin. *Heb* 11:25

pledge

vilt thou give me a p.? *Gen* 38:17
vhat p. shall I give thee? 18
udah sent to receive his p. 20
ake thy neighbour's raiment to p. *Ex* 22:26
r upper millstone to p. for he taketh a man's life to p. *Deut* 24:6
nto his house to fetch his p. 10, 11
halt not sleep with his p. 12, 13
widow's raiment to p. 17
ow thy brethren fare, take their p. *1 Sam* 17:18
ast taken a p. from thy brother. *Job* 22:6
ake the widow's ox for a p. 24:3
nd they take a p. of the poor. 9
ake p. for a strange woman. *Pr* 20:16; 27:13
o the debtor his p. *Ezek* 18:7, 16
ath not restored the p., shall he? 12
f the wicked restore the p., he. 33:15
n clothes laid to p. by. *Amos* 2:8

pledges

pray thee, give p. to the king of Assyria. *2 Ki* 18:23; *Isa* 36:8

Pleiades

rcturus, Orion, and P. *Job* 9:9
he sweet influences of P.? 38:31

plenteous

fth part in the p. years. *Gen* 41:34
n the p. years the earth brought. 47
hall make thee p. *Deut* 28:11; 30:9
old as p. as stones. *2 Chr* 1:15
rt p. in mercy to all. *Ps* 86:5, 15
racious, and p. in mercy. 103:8
vith him is p. redemption. 130:7
read shall be fat and p. *Isa* 30:23
at, and their meat p. *Hab* 1:16
he harvest truly is p. *Mat* 9:37

plenteousness

he seven years of p. *Gen* 41:53*
f the diligent tend to p. *Pr* 21:5

plentiful

lidst send a p. rain. *Ps* 68:9
ut of the p. field. *Isa* 16:10*
nd I brought you to a p. *Jer* 2:7
s taken from the p. field. 48:33*

plentifully

ow hast thou p. declared! *Job* 26:3
nd p. rewardeth. *Ps* 31:23
ich man brought forth p. *Luke* 12:16

plenty

God give thee p. of corn. *Gen* 27:28
even years of great p. 41:29
ll the p. shall be forgotten in. 30
nd the p. shall not be known. 31
pit, wherein there is p. *Lev* 11:36*

Ophir p. of almug trees. *1 Ki* 10:11
to eat, have left p. *2 Chr* 31:10
shalt have p. of silver. *Job* 22:25*
excellent in power and in p. 37:23
barns be filled with p. *Pr* 3:10
land shall have p. of bread. 28:19
had we p. of victuals. *Jer* 44:17
shall eat in p. and praise. *Joel* 2:26

plotteth

wicked p. against the just. *Ps* 37:12

plough

put his hand to the p. *Luke* 9:62

plow

shalt not p. with an ox. *Deut* 22:10
yoke of oxen might p. *1 Sam* 14:14*
they that p. iniquity. *Job* 4:8
sluggard will not p. *Pr* 20:4
doth the plowman p.? *Isa* 28:24
Judah shall p. Jacob. *Hos* 10:11
one p. there with oxen? *Amos* 6:12
plougheth should p. in hope. *1 Cor* 9:10

plowed, -ers

not p. with my heifer. *Judg* 14:18
the plowers p. on my. *Ps* 129:3
Zion shall be p. as a field. *Jer* 26:18
Mi 3:12
ye have p. wickedness. *Hos* 10:13

ploweth

that p. should plow in. *1 Cor* 9:10

plowing, *verb*

Elisha, who was p. *1 Ki* 19:19
the oxen were p. and the. *Job* 1:14
having a servant p. *Luke* 17:7

plowing

and the p. of the wicked. *Pr* 21:4*

plowman

doth the p. plow all day? *Isa* 28:24
the p. shall overtake the. *Amos* 9:13

plowmen

alien shall be your p. *Isa* 61:5
the p. were ashamed. *Jer* 14:4

plowshares

shall beat their swords into p. *Isa* 2:4; *Mi* 4:3
beat your p. into swords. *Joel* 3:10

pluck

shall p. away his crop. *Lev* 1:16
and quite p. down their. *Num* 33:52*
then thou mayest p. the ears with. *Deut* 23:25
then will I p. them up. *2 Chr* 7:20
p. the fatherless from. *Job* 24:9
he shall p. my feet out. *Ps* 25:15
p. thee out of thy dwelling. 52:5
thy right hand, p. it out of. 74:11
pass by the way do p. her. 80:12
to p. up what is planted. *Eccl* 3:2
p. out the house of Judah. *Jer* 12:14
I will utterly p. up and destroy. 17
a kingdom, to p. it up. 18:7
yet would I p. thee thence. 22:24
and not p. them up. 24:6; 42:10
watched over them to p. up. 31:28
I have planted I will p. up. 45:4
without many people to p. *Ezek* 17:9
p. off thine own breasts. 23:34
who p. off the skin from. *Mi* 3:2
I will p. up thy groves out of. 5:14
if thy right eye offend thee, p. it. *Mat* 5:29; 18:9; *Mark* 9:47
began to p. the ears of corn. *Mat* 12:1; *Mark* 2:23
nor shall any p. them. *John* 10:28
no man is able to p. them out. 29

plucked

was an olive leaf p. off. *Gen* 8:11
and he p. his hand out. *Ex* 4:7
ye shall be p. from off. *Deut* 28:63
a man p. off his shoe. *Ruth* 4:7
p. the spear out of Egyptian's hand. *2 Sam* 23:21; *1 Chr* 11:23
I p. off the hair of my. *Ezra* 9:3
I cursed them, and p. off. *Neh* 13:25
p. the spoil out of his. *Job* 29:17
my cheeks to them that p. *Isa* 50:6
wicked are not p. away. *Jer* 6:29
after I have p. them out. 12:15
it shall not be p. up, nor. 31:40
she was p. up in fury. *Ezek* 19:12

the wings thereof were p. *Dan* 7:4
three of the first horns p. up. 8
for his kingdom shall be p. 11:4
as a firebrand p. out of. *Amos* 4:11
is not this a brand p.? *Zech* 3:2
the chains had been p. *Mark* 5:4
his disciples p. ears of corn. *Luke* 6:1
be thou p. up by the root. 17:6
would have p. out your own eyes. *Gal* 4:15
twice dead, p. up by the roots. *Jude* 12

plucketh

the foolish p. it down. *Pr* 14:1

plumbline

behold the Lord stood upon a wall made by a p. with a p. *Amos* 7:7
and I said, A p. . . . Behold, I will set a p. in the midst of my people. 8

plummet

over Jerusalem the p. *2 Ki* 21:13
righteousness to the p. *Isa* 28:17
shall see the p. in hand. *Zech* 4:10

plunge

yet shalt thou p. me in the. *Job* 9:31

poets

of your own p. have said. *Acts* 17:28

point

p. out for you mount. *Num* 34:7*
p. out your border. 8*
p. out your east border. 10*

point, *substantive*

I am at the p. to die. *Gen* 25:32
is written with the p. of. *Jer* 17:1
my daughter lieth at the p. of death. *Mark* 5:23
was at the p. of death. *John* 4:47
offend in one p. is guilty. *Jas* 2:10

pointed

he spreadeth sharp p. *Job* 41:30*

points

in all p. as he came so. *Eccl* 5:16
but was in all p. tempted. *Heb* 4:15

poison

with the p. of serpents. *Deut* 32:24
their wine is p. of dragons. 33
the p. whereof drinketh. *Job* 6:4
he shall suck p. of asps. 20:16
their p. is like the p. of. *Ps* 58:4
like a serpent, adders' p. is. 140:3
the p. of asps is under. *Rom* 3:13
is an evil, full of deadly p. *Jas* 3:8

pole

set it upon a p. *Num* 21:8*
Moses put it on a p. 9*

policy

through his p. shall cause craft to. *Dan* 8:25

polished

p. after the similitude. *Ps* 144:12*
he hath made me a p. shaft. *Isa* 49:2
in colour to p. brass. *Dan* 10:6*

polishing

Nazarites purer, their p. *Lam* 4:7

poll, -s

of their names, every male by the p. *Num* 1:2; 18:20, 22; *1 Chr* 23:3
24
take five shekels a piece by the p. *Num* 3:47

poll

only p. their heads. *Ezek* 44:20†
make thee bald, and p. *Mi* 1:16†

polled

p. his head, at year's end he p. *2 Sam* 14:26†

pollute

neither shall ye p. the. *Num* 18:32*
so shall ye not p. the land. 35:33
called by name, to p. it. *Jer* 7:30
p. my secret place. *Ezek* 7:21*, 22*
will ye p. me among my? 13:19*
ye p. yourselves with idols. 20:31
23:30; 36:18
p. ye my holy name. 20:39*; 39:7*
in my sanctuary to p. it. 44:7*
shall p. the sanctuary. *Dan* 11:31*

polluted

upon it, thou hast p. it. *Ex* 20:25

Josiah *p.* the altar. *2 Ki* 23:16
the priests *p.* the house. *2 Chr* 36:14
therefore were they as *p.*
Ezra 2:62; *Neh* 7:64
and the land was *p.* with. *Ps* 106:38
I was wroth, I have *p.* *Isa* 47:6*
how should my name be *p.*? 48:11*
thou say, I am not *p.*? *Jer* 2:23
that land be greatly *p.*? 3:1, 2
turned and *p.* my name. 34:16*
he hath *p.* the kingdom. *Lam* 2:2*
they have *p.* themselves with. 4:14
my soul hath not been *p.* *Ezek* 4:14
nor be *p.* with all their. 14:11
I saw thee *p.* in thine own blood.
16:6*, 22*
that it should not be *p.* 20:9*, 14, 22
they greatly *p.* 13*, 16*, 21*, 24*
I *p.* them in their own gifts. 26*
are ye *p.* after the manner of? 30
was *p.* with the Babylonians. 23:17
Gilead is a city that is *p.* *Hos* 6:8*
all that eat thereof shall be *p.* 9:4
shalt die in a *p.* land. *Amos* 7:17*
it is *p.*, it shall destroy you. *Mi* 2:10
that is filthy and *p.* *Zeph* 3:1
her priests have *p.* sanctuary. 4*
p. bread upon mine altar, and say, Wherein have we *p.* thee? *Mal* 1:7
the table of the Lord is *p.* 12
p. this holy place. *Acts* 21:28

polluting
sabbath from *p.* it. *Isa* 56:2, 6

pollution
have they humbled her that was set apart for *p.* *Ezek* 22:10

pollutions
abstain from *p.* of idols. *Acts* 15:20
escaped *p.* of the world. *2 Pet* 2:20

pollux, ***see*** **sign**

pomegranate
A kind of apple, covered without with a reddish rind, and red within, which opens lengthways, and shews red grains within, full of juice like wine, with little kernels. God gave orders to Moses *to put embroidered pomegranates, with golden bells between, at the bottom of the high priest's blue robe or ephod,* Ex 28:33, 34.
a golden bell and a *p.* upon the hem.
Ex 28:34; 39:26
Saul tarried under a *p.* tree.
1 Sam 14:2
thy temples are like a piece of *p.*
S of S 4:3; 6:7
to drink of juice of my *p.* 8:2
the *p.* tree and all trees. *Joel* 1:12
p. hath not brought forth. *Hag* 2:19

pomegranates
thou shalt make *p.* of blue.
Ex 28:33; 39:24, 25
they brought of the *p.* *Num* 13:23
of seed, figs, vines, or *p.* 20:5
a land of *p.*, oil olive. *Deut* 8:8
chapiters on top with *p.* *1 Ki* 7:18*
2 Ki 25:17; *2 Chr* 3:16; *Jer* 52:22
plants are an orchard of *p.* with.
S of S 4:13
whether the *p.* budded. 6:11; 7:12

pommels
the pillars and *p.* of the. *2 Chr* 4:12*

pomp
and their *p.* shall descend. *Isa* 5:14
thy *p.* is brought down to. 14:11
p. of the strong to cease. *Ezek* 7:24*
the *p.* of her strength shall cease.
30:18*; 33:28*
shall spoil the *p.* of Egypt. 32:12*
when Agrippa was come, and Bernice, with great *p.* *Acts* 25:23

ponder
p. the path of thy feet. *Pr* 4:26*
shouldest *p.* the path of life. 5:6*

pondered
Mary *p.* them in her heart. *Luke* 2:19

pondereth
ways of man, the Lord *p.* *Pr* 5:21*
Lord *p.* the heart. 21:2*
he that *p.* the heart. 24:12*

ponds
thy hand on their *p.* *Ex* 7:19*; 8:5
purposes, that make *p.* *Isa* 19:10*

Pontius, ***see*** **Pilate**

Pontus
dwellers in *P.* *Acts* 2:9; 18:2
1 Pet 1:1

pool
the one side of the *p.* *2 Sam* 2:13
hanged them up over the *p.* 4:12
washed chariot in *p.* of. *1 Ki* 22:38
stood by the conduit of the upper *p.*
2 Ki 18:17; *Isa* 7:3; 36:2
made a *p.* and conduit. *2 Ki* 20:20
went on to the king's *p.* *Neh* 2:14
repaired the wall of the *p.* 3:15
the waters of the lower *p.* *Isa* 22:9
ditch for the water of the old *p.* 11
ground shall become a *p.* 35:7
the wilderness a *p.* of water. 41:18
Nineveh of old is like a *p.* of water.
Nah 2:8
by the sheep market a *p.* *John* 5:2
an angel went down into the *p.* 4
no man to put me into the *p.* 7
wash in the *p.* of Siloam. 9:7, 11

pools
thy hand on all their *p.* *Ex* 7:19
rain also filleth the *p.* *Ps* 84:6
I made me *p.* of water. *Eccl* 2:6
make it for the *p.* of water. *Isa* 14:23
and I will dry up the *p.* and. 42:15

poor
(*Used in the Bible both of those poor in this world's goods, and of those spiritually poor*)
after them seven *p.* kine. *Gen* 41:19
that the *p.* of thy people. *Ex* 23:11
p. shall not give less than. 30:15
if he be *p.* and cannot. *Lev* 14:21
leave them for the *p.* and. 19:10
respect the person of the *p.* 15
if thy brother be waxen *p.* 25:25
35, 39, 47
there be no *p.* among you. *Deut* 15:4
for the *p.* shall never cease out. 11
not young men, *p.* or rich. *Ruth* 3:10
the Lord maketh *p.* and. *1 Sam* 2:7
p. out of the dust. 8; *Ps* 113:7
rich, and the other *p.* *2 Sam* 12:1
the guard left of the *p.* of. *2 Ki* 25:12
Jer 39:10; 40:7; 52:15, 16
the *p.* from the sword. *Job* 5:15
so the *p.* hath hope, and. 16
seek to please the *p.* 20:10
oppressed and forsaken the *p.* 19
the *p.* of the earth hide. 24:4
and they take a pledge of the *p.* 9
the murderer killeth the *p.* 14
because I delivered the *p.* 29:12
soul grieved for the *p.*? 30:25
if I withheld the *p.* from. 31:16
seen any *p.* without covering. 19
the rich more than the *p.* 34:19
they cause the cry of the *p.* 28
he delivereth the *p.* in affliction.
36:15*; *Ps* 72:12
the expectation of the *p.* *Ps* 9:18
pride doth persecute the *p.* 10:2
are privily set against the *p.* 8
wait secretly to catch the *p.* 9
that the *p.* may fall by his. 10*
the *p.* committeth himself to. 14
for the oppression of the *p.* I. 12:5
the counsel of the *p.* 14:6
delivereth the *p.* from him. 35:10
their bow to cast down the *p.* 37:14
but I am *p.* 40:17; 69:29; 70:5
86:1; 109:22
he that considereth the *p.* 41:1
both low and high, rich and *p.* 49:2
of thy goodness for the *p.* 68:10
Lord heareth *p.* and despiseth. 69:33
he shall judge the *p.* of. 72:4
he shall spare the *p.* 13
let the *p.* and needy praise. 74:21
defend the *p.* 82:3
deliver the *p.* and needy. 4
yet setteth he *p.* on high. 107:41
at the right hand of the *p.* 109:31
will satisfy her *p.* with. 132:15
maintain the right of the *p.* 140:12

he becometh *p.* that dealeth. *Pr* 10:
the destruction of the *p.* is. 1
that maketh himself *p.* 13:
his riches, but the *p.* heareth.
in the tillage of the *p.* but. 2
the *p.* is hated even of his. 14:2
he that hath mercy on the *p.* 2
p. reproacheth his maker; he tha honoureth him hath mercy on *p.* 3
whoso mocketh the *p.* 17:
the *p.* useth entreaties, but. 18:2
the *p.* is separated from his. 19:
all brethren of the *p.* do hate him.
his ears at the cry of the *p.* 21:1
the rich and *p.* meet together. 22:
the rich ruleth over the *p.* and the.
oppresseth the *p.* to increase. 1
for him that will pity the *p.* 28:
the *p.* that hath understanding. 1
ruler over the *p.* people. 1
the cause of the *p.* 29:7, 1
that faithfully judgeth the *p.* 1
lest I be *p.* and steal, and. 30:
as swords, to devour the *p.* 1
and plead the cause of the *p.* 31:
his kingdom, becometh *p.* *Eccl* 4:1
the oppression of the *p.* 5:
what hath the *p.* that knoweth? 6:
the spoil of the *p.* is in. *Isa* 3:1
that ye grind faces of the *p.*? 1
take away the right from the *p.* 10:
cause it to be heard to Laish, O *p.* 3
shall he judge the *p.* 11:
the firstborn of the *p.* shall. 14:3
and the *p.* of his people shall. 32
even the feet of the *p.* shall. 26:
p. among men shall rejoice. 29:1
to destroy the *p.* with lying. 32:7
when the *p.* and needy seek. 41:1
bring the *p.* that are cast out. 58:
blood of the *p.* innocents. *Jer* 2:3
these are *p.*; they are foolish. 5:
delivered the soul of the *p.* 20:1
he judged the cause of the *p.* 22:1
strengthen hand of the *p.* *Ezek* 16:4
hath oppressed *p.* and needy. 18:1
taken off his hand from the *p.* 1
and they have vexed the *p.* 22:2
they sold the *p.* for a pair. *Amos* 2:
the dust on the head of the *p.*
which oppress the *p.* and crush. 4:
your treading is on the *p.* 5:1
turn aside the *p.* in the gate. 1
even to make the *p.* of the land. 8:
that we may buy the *p.* for silver.
was to devour the *p.* *Hab* 3:1
the *p.* people shall trust. *Zeph* 3:1
and oppress not the widow nor *p.*
Zech 7:1
I will feed even you, O *p.* 11:
the *p.* of the flock that waited. 1
blessed are the *p.* in spirit. *Mat* 5:
p. have the gospel preached. 11:5
for ye have the *p.* always with you.
26:11; *Mark* 14:7; *John* 12:
a certain *p.* widow. *Mark* 12:4
p. widow hath cast. 43; *Luke* 21:
blessed be ye *p.* for yours. *Luke* 6:2
call the *p.* the maimed. 14:13, 2
that he cared for the *p.* *John* 12:
a contribution for the *p.* *Rom* 15:2
as *p.* yet making many. *2 Cor* 6:1
yet for your sakes he became *p.* 8:
should remember the *p.* *Gal* 2:1
hath not God chosen the *p.*? *Jas* 2:
but ye have despised the *p.*
knowest not that thou art *p.* *Rev* 3:1
he causeth rich and *p.* to. 13:1

is **poor**
of my people that *is p.* *Ex* 22:2
thou shalt not oppress hired servan that *is p.* *Deut* 24:1
for he *is p.* and setteth his heart. 1
behold, my family *is p.* *Judg* 6:1
better *is* the *p.* that walketh in his in tegrity, than he. *Pr* 19:1; 28:
rob not poor because he *is p.* 22:2
better *is* a *p.* and wise child, tha an old. *Eccl* 4:1
to him that *is p.* and of a. *Isa* 66:

poor *man*
countenance a *p. man* in. *Ex* 23:

if a p. man, harden not. Deut 15:7
if a man be p., sleep not with. 24:12
seeing I am a p. man. 1 Sam 18:23
p. man had nothing. 2 Sam 12:3
but took the p. man's ewe lamb. 4
this p. man cried, and the. Ps 34:6
the p. and needy man. 109:16
and a p. man is better than a liar. Pr 19:22
pleasure shall be a p. man. 21:17
a p. man that oppresseth poor. 28:3
the p. and deceitful man. 29:13
a p. wise man, yet no man remembered that same p. man. Eccl 9:15
the p. man's wisdom is despised. 16
a p. man in vile raiment. Jas 2:2

to the **poor**

to the p. and stranger. Lev 23:22
of sending gifts to the p. Esth 9:22
I was a father to the p. Job 29:16
but he giveth right to the p. 36:6
he hath given to the p. Ps 112:9
2 Cor 9:9
of his bread to the p. Pr 22:9
giveth to the p. shall not lack. 28:27
out her hand to the p. 31:20
been a strength to the p. Isa 25:4
by shewing mercy to the p. Dan 4:27
sell all, and give to the p. Mat 19:21
Mark 10:21
sold for much, and given to the p.
Mat 26:9; Mark 14:5; John 12:5
the gospel to the p. Luke 4:18; 7:22
and distribute to the p. 18:22
half of my goods I give to the p. 19:8
give something to the p. John 13:29
my goods to feed the p. 1 Cor 13:3
say to the p., Stand thou. Jas 2:3

thy **poor**

the judgement of thy p. Ex 23:6
hand from thy p. brother. Deut 15:7
be evil against thy p. brother. 9
thine hand wide to thy p. 11
he shall judge thy p. Ps 72:2
congregation of thy p. for ever. 74:19

poorer

if he be p. than thy. Lev 27:8

poorest

none remained, save p. 2 Ki 24:14

poplar, -s

took rods of green p. Gen 30:37
incense under oaks and p. Hos 4:13

populous

great, mighty, and p. Deut 26:5
art thou better than p. No? Nah 3:8

porch

forth through the p. Judg 3:23
Solomon pattern of p. 1 Chr 28:11
shut up doors of the p. 2 Chr 29:7
month came they to the p. 17
between the p. and altar. Ezek 8:16
enter by way of p. of the gate. 44:3
46:2, 8
priests weep between p. Joel 2:17
gone out into the p. Mat 26:71
the p.; and cock crew. Mark 14:68
temple in Solomon's p. John 10:23
together in Solomon's p. Acts 3:11
one accord in Solomon's p. 5:12

porches

with the temple and p. Ezek 41:15
Bethesda, having five p. John 5:2

Porcius

P. Festus came into. Acts 24:27

porter

(Revisions render this door-keeper)
called to the p. and said. 2 Sam 18:26
lepers called to the p. 2 Ki 7:10
Zechariah was p. of door. 1 Chr 9:21
and Kore the p. toward. 2 Chr 31:14
and commanded the p. Mark 13:34
to him the p. openeth. John 10:3

porters

the p. were Shallum. 1 Chr 9:17
and Jehiel the p. 15:18
and Hosah to be p. 16:38
the sons of Jeduthun were p. 42
four thousand were p. 23:5
the divisions of the p. 26:1, 12, 19
the p. by their courses. 2 Chr 8:14
p. waited at every gate. 35:15
p. and Nethinims went up. Ezra 7:7
the Levites and p. dwelt. Neh 7:73

portion

let them take their p. Gen 14:24
any p. or inheritance for us? 31:14
priest had a p. assigned, and did eat their p. 47:22
I have given thee one p. above. 48:22
have given it them for p. Lev 6:17
this is the p. of the anointing. 7:35
of Israel's half take thou one p. Num 31:30, 36
Moses took one p. of fifty for the. 47
by giving him a double p. Deut 21:17
for Lord's p. is his people. 32:9
in a p. of the lawgiver was. 33:21
given me but one p.? Josh 17:14
but to Hannah he gave a worthy p. 1 Sam 1:5
Samuel said, Bring the p. which. 9:23
what p. have we in David? 1 Ki 12:16
2 Chr 10:16
let a double p. of thy. 2 Ki 2:9
dogs shall eat Jezebel in p. of Jezreel. 9:10, 36, 37
Joram met him in p. of Naboth. 21
in the p. of Naboth's field. 25
Ahaz took a p. out of. 2 Chr 28:11
Hezekiah appointed king's p. 31:3
to give the p. of the priests. 4, 16
no p. on this side the river. Ezra 4:16
p. nor right in Jerusalem. Neh 2:20
that a certain p. should be. 11:23
and porters, every day his p. 12:47
the p. of a wicked man. Job 20:29
p. is cursed in the earth. 24:18
little a p. is heard of? 26:14*; 27:13
for what p. of God is there? 31:2
be the cup of their cup. Ps 11:6
the Lord is the p. of mine. 16:5
from men who have their p. 17:14
shall be a p. for foxes. 63:10
God is my p. 73:26
art my p. O Lord. 119:57; 142:5
giveth a p. to her maidens. Pr 31:15*
was my p. of all my labour. Eccl 2:10
shall he leave it for his p. 21
should rejoice, for that is his p. 3:22
5:18; 9:9
him power to take his p. 5:19
nor have they any more p. for. 9:6
give a p. to seven, and also. 11:2
this is the p. of them. Isa 17:14
I will divide him a p. with. 53:12
among smooth stones of the stream is thy p. 57:6
they shall rejoice in their p. 61:7
the p. of Jacob is not like them. Jer 10:16; 51:19
my p. under foot, they have made my pleasant p. a desolate. 12:10
this is the p. of thy measures. 13:25
every day a p. until the day. 52:34
the Lord is my p. saith. Lam 3:24
shall offer an holy p. Ezek 45:1, 4
a p. shall be for prince on one. 7
to the coast of Hethlon, a p. 48:1
border of Dan a p. of Asher. 2
a p. for Naphtali. 3
a p. for Manasseh. 4
not defile himself with p. Dan 1:8
his p. be with the beasts. 4:15, 23
feed of the p. of his meat. 11:26
changed the p. of my people. Mi 2:4
by them their p. is fat. Hab 1:16
shall inherit Judah his p. Zech 2:12
shall appoint him his p. Mat 24:51
to give them their p. in. Luke 12:42
will appoint him his p. with. 46
give me the p. of goods that. 15:12

portions

they shall have like p. to eat. Deut 18:8
ten p. to Manasseh. Josh 17:5
sons and daughters p. 1 Sam 1:4
to give p. to all the. 2 Chr 31:19
eat the fat, and send p. Neh 8:10, 12
p. for the priests. 12:44
p. of the singers. 47
that the p. of the Levites had. 13:10
a day of sending p. to. Esth 9:19, 22
Joseph shall have two p. Ezek 47:13
against the p. for the prince. 48:21
devour them with their p. Hos 5:7

possess

thy seed shall p. the gate. Gen 22:17
24:60
let us go up at once and p. it, for we. Num 13:30; Deut 1:21
next kinsman shall p. it. Num 27:11
I give it, they shall p. it. Deut 1:39
begin to p. that thou mayest. 2:31
ye shall p. greater nations. 11:23†
12:2†, 29†; 18:14†; 31:3†
thou passest over Jordan to p. it. 30:18; 31:13†
Esau mount Seir to p. it. Josh 24:4
shouldest thou p. it? Judg 11:23
wilt not thou p. what Chemosh? 24
he is gone down to p. 1 Ki 21:18
to p. months of vanity. Job 7:3
thou makest me p. iniquities. 13:26
and bittern shall p. it. Isa 34:11, 17
shall p. their houses. Ezek 7:24
shall be mine, we will p. 35:10
my people Israel to p. thee. 36:12
the saints shall p. the. Dan 7:18
for silver, nettles shall p. Hos 9:6
p. the remnant of Edom. Amos 9:12
shall p. their possessions. Ob 17
shall p. mount Esau, and Benjamin p. Gilead. 19
captivity of Israel shall p. that . . . and Jerusalem shall p. the. 20
the Chaldeans to p. the. Hab 1:6
my people shall p. them. Zeph 2:9
will cause remnant to p. Zech 8:12
give tithes of all that I p. Luke 18:12
in patience p. ye your souls. 21:19
know how to p. vessel. 1 Thes 4:4

possess *with land*

I will give you their land to p. Lev 20:24; Num 33:53
Deut 3:18; 5:31; 17:14
shall p. it, I will bring into land. Num 14:24
go in and p. the land. Deut 1:8
4:1; 6:18; 8:1; 9:5, 23; 10:11
11:31; Josh 1:11
land whither ye go to p. it. Deut 4:5
14, 26; 5:33; 6:1; 7:1; 11:10, 11
29; 23:20
go over and p. that good land. 4:22
brought me to p. this land. 9:4
giveth not this land to p. for thy. 6
be strong and p. the land. 11:8
land which Lord God of thy fathers giveth thee to p. 12:1; 15:4
19:2, 14; 21:1; 25:19
consumed from off land thou goest to p. 28:21
plucked from off the land whither thou goest to p. it. 63
ye slack to p. the land? Josh 18:3
and ye shall p. their land. 23:5
that ye might p. their land. 24:8
every man to p. the land. Judg 2:6
to enter to p. the land. 18:9
may p. this good land. 1 Chr 28:8
to p. is an unclean land. Ezra 9:11
they should p. the land. Neh 9:15
them in to p. the land. 23
p. them in the land of the Lord. Isa 14:2
do not rise nor p. the land. 21
trust in me shall p. the land. 57:13
land shall they p. the double. 61:7
return to land and p. it. Jer 30:3
shall ye p. the land? Ezek 33:25, 26
I brought you to p. land. Amos 2:10

possessed

Israel p. Sihon's land. Num 21:24
and people, and have p. the land. 35
Deut 3:12; 4:47; Neh 9:22
to land thy fathers p. Deut 30:5
brethren have p. the land. Josh 1:15
they p. their land on the other. 12:1
yet very much land to be p. 13:1
Dan took Leshem and p. it. 19:47
they p. it and dwelt. 21:43; 22:9
Eglon king of Moab p. Judg 3:13
Israel p. all the land of. 11:21, 22
men of Ava p. Samaria. 2 Ki 17:24
for thou hast p. my reins. Ps 139:13

Lord *p.* me in the beginning. *Pr* 8:22
people hath *p.* it a little. *Isa* 63:18
vineyards shall be *p.* *Jer* 32:15*
they came in and *p.* it, but obeyed. 23
time came that saints *p.* *Dan* 7:22
told them by what means he that was *p.* was healed. *Luke* 8:36
none said that aught he *p.* *Acts* 4:32
a damsel *p.* with a spirit of. 16:16
as though they *p.* not. *1 Cor* 7:30
see **devils**

possessest
into land and *p.* it. *Deut* 26:1

possesseth
every daughter that *p.* *Num* 36:8
man's life consists not in things he *p.* *Luke* 12:15

possessing
as having nothing, yet *p.* *2 Cor* 6:10

possession
I will give all the land of Canaan for an everlasting *p.* *Gen* 17:8; 48:4
give me a *p.* of a buryingplace. 23:4, 9, 18, 20; 49:30; 50:13
Isaac had *p.* of flocks, of herds. 26:14
Edom in the land of their *p.* 36:43
and gave them a *p.* in the land. 47:11
Canaan, which I give to you for a *p.* *Lev* 14:34
ye shall return every man to his *p.* 25:10, 13, 27, 28, 41; *Deut* 3:20
sold away some of his *p.* *Lev* 25:25
the Levites' *p.* shall go out in. 33
strangers shall be your *p.* 45, 46
sanctify some part of his *p.* 27:16
p. thereof shall be the priest's. 21
return to whom the *p.* of the land. 24
be a *p.*, Seir also a *p.* *Num* 24:18
to the lot shall the *p.* be. 26:56*
give us a *p.* among brethren. 27:4
daughters of Zelophehad give a *p.* 7
given to thy servants for *p.* 32:5
this land shall be your *p.* before. 22
Levites of their *p.* cities. 35:2, 8
return to the land of his *p.* 28
given mount Seir to Esau for a *p.* *Deut* 2:5
given Ar to Lot for a *p.* 9, 19
in land of his *p.* Lord gave them. 12
swallowed up all in their *p.* 11:6
which I gave Israel for a *p.* 32:49
for a *p.* to Reubenites. *Josh* 12:6
get ye into the land of your *p.* 22:4
to Manasseh Moses had given a *p.* 7
returned to the land of their *p.* 9
if your *p.* be unclean, take *p.* 19
take *p.* of the vineyard. *1 Ki* 21:15
killed, and also taken *p.*? 19
cast out of thy *p.* *2 Chr* 20:11
dwelt every one in his *p.* *Neh* 11:3
parts of earth for thy *p.* *Ps* 2:8
got not the land in *p.* by their. 44:3
may dwell and have it in *p.* 69:35
take the houses of God in *p.* 83:12
the upright have good things in *p.* *Pr* 28:10*
I will make it a *p.* for. *Isa* 14:23
is this land given in *p.* *Ezek* 11:15
thee to men of the east for *p.* 25:4
high places are ours in *p.* 36:2
appointed my land into their *p.* 5
no *p.* in Israel, I am their *p.* 44:28
inheritance out of his own *p.* 46:18
with Sapphira sold a *p.* *Acts* 5:1
give it to him for a *p.* 7:5
with Jesus into *p.* of Gentiles. 45
redemption of the purchased *p.* *Eph* 1:14

possessions
and get you *p.* therein. *Gen* 34:10
Israel had *p.* therein and. 47:27
shall have *p.* among you. *Num* 32:30
you to the land of your *p.* *Josh* 22:4
whose *p.* were in Carmel. *1 Sam* 25:2
that dwelt in their *p.* *1 Chr* 9:2
the Levites left their *p.* *2 Chr* 11:14
provided *p.* of flocks and. 32:29
I had great *p.* of great. *Eccl* 2:7
Jacob shall possess their *p.* *Ob* 17
for he had great *p.* *Mat* 19:22; *Mark* 10:22
and sold their *p.* and. *Acts* 2:45
in the same quarters were *p.* 28:7*

possessor
most high God *p.* of. *Gen* 14:19, 22

possessors
whose *p.* slay them, and. *Zech* 11:5
as many as were *p.* of. *Acts* 4:34

possible
with God all things are *p.* *Mat* 19:26; *Mark* 10:27
if *p.*, shall deceive the very elect. *Mat* 24:24; *Mark* 13:22
if *p.* let this cup pass from me. *Mat* 26:39; *Mark* 14:35
all things are *p.* to him. *Mark* 9:23
all things are *p.* to thee. 14:36; *Luke* 18:27
was not *p.* he should be. *Acts* 2:24
if *p.* be at Jerusalem the day. 20:16
if it be *p.* live peaceably. *Rom* 12:18
p. ye would have plucked. *Gal* 4:15
not *p.* the blood of bulls. *Heb* 10:4

post, -s
(*The old meaning of* courier)
so the *p.* went with the letters from. *2 Chr* 30:6; *Esth* 3:13, 15; 8:10
p. rode on mules and. *Esth* 8:14
days are swifter than a *p.* *Job* 9:25
one *p.* shall run to meet. *Jer* 51:31

post
Eli sat on a seat by a *p.* *1 Sam* 1:9*
on each *p.* were palm. *Ezek* 40:16

posterity
to preserve you a *p.* in. *Gen* 45:7*
or if any of your *p.* be. *Num* 9:10
I will take away the *p.* *1 Ki* 16:3
take away the *p.* of Ahab. 21:21*
yet their *p.* approve. *Ps* 49:13*
his *p.* be cut off and blotted 109:13
not be divided to his *p.* *Dan* 11:4
your *p.* with fishhooks. *Amos* 4:2

posts
on the *p.* of thy house. *Deut* 6:9*
Samson took the two *p.* *Judg* 16:3
all the doors and *p.* were. *1 Ki* 7:5
waiting at the *p.* of my doors. *Pr* 8:34
the *p.* of the door moved. *Isa* 6:4*
behind the *p.* thou set up thy. 57:8
the *p.* had one measure. *Ezek* 40:10
setting of their *p.* by my *p.* 43:8*
smite the lintel, that the *p.* may. *Amos* 9:1*
see **door**

side **posts**
strike the blood on the two *side p.* *Ex* 12:7, 22
seeth the blood on the *side p.* 23
lintel and *side p.* were a. *1 Ki* 6:31

pot
(*The English word is used to translate a number of Hebrew words, some of which have different meanings. These are substituted for pot in the Revisions*)
take a *p.* and put an. *Ex* 16:33
be sodden in a brazen *p.* *Lev* 6:28*
put the broth in a *p.* *Judg* 6:19
into the caldron or *p.* *1 Sam* 2:14
thing, save a *p.* of oil. *2 Ki* 4:2
set on great *p.* 38
there is death in the *p.* 40
meal into the *p.*, no harm in the *p.* 41
as out of a seething *p.* *Job* 41:20
the deep to boil like a *p.* 31*
the fining *p.* is. *Pr* 17:3; 27:21
I see a seething *p.* *Jer* 1:13*
saith Lord, Set on a *p.* *Ezek* 24:3*
woe to bloody city, to the *p.* whose. 6
in pieces, as for the *p.* *Mi* 3:3
every *p.* in Jerusalem. *Zech* 14:21
wherein was the golden *p.* *Heb* 9:4

water-**pot**
then left her *water-p.* *John* 4:28

potentate
the blessed and only *P.* *1 Tim* 6:15

Potiphar
the Midianites sold Joseph to *P.* *Gen* 37:36; 39:1

Poti-pherah
the daughter of *P.* *Gen* 41:45, 50

pots
made the *p.* and shovels. *Ex* 38:3
oven, or rangers for *p.* *Lev* 11:35
p. and shovels of brass. *1 Ki* 7:45; *2 Chr* 4:16
Huram made the *p.* *2 Chr* 4:11
holy offerings sod they in *p.* 35:13
before your *p.* can feel the. *Ps* 58:9
ye have lien among the *p.* 68:13*
were delivered from the *p.* 81:6*
Rechabites *p.* full of wine. *Jer* 35:5*
washing of cups and *p.* *Mark* 7:4, 8
see **flesh**

water-**pots**
set there six *water-p.* *John* 2:6
Jesus saith to them, Fill *water-p.* 7

potsherd, -s
(*A broken piece of earthenware*)
him a *p.* to scrape himself. *Job* 2:8
my strength is dried up like a *p.* *Ps* 22:15
are like a *p.* covered. *Pr* 26:23*
let the *p.* strive with *p.* of. *Isa* 45:9

pottage
Jacob sod *p.* and Esau. *Gen* 25:29
feed me with *p.* 30
Jacob gave Esau *p.* 34
seethe *p.* for sons of the. *2 Ki* 4:38
shred them into the pot of *p.* 39
as they were eating the *p.* they. 40
skirt do touch bread or *p.* *Hag* 2:12

potter
in pieces like a *p.*'s vessel. *Ps* 2:9
it as the breaking of the *p.*'s vessel. *Isa* 30:14; *Jer* 19:11; *Rev* 2:27
down to the *p.*'s house. *Jer* 18:2
go and get a *p.*'s earthen bottle. 19:1
of the hands of the *p.* *Lam* 4:2
said, Cast it unto the *p.* *Zech* 11:13
them for the *p.*'s field. *Mat* 27:10
see **clay**

potters
these were the *p.* and. *1 Chr* 4:23

pound, -s
three *p.* of gold went. *1 Ki* 10:17
treasure 5000 *p.* of silver. *Ezra* 2:69
treasure 2200 *p.* of silver. *Neh* 7:71
the rest gave 2000 *p.* of silver. 72
to his servants ten *p.* *Luke* 19:13
thy *p.* hath gained ten *p.* 16
hath gained five *p.* 18
behold, here is thy *p.* 20
take from him the *p.* 24
he hath ten *p.* 25
then Mary took a *p.* of. *John* 12:3
aloes about a 100 *p.* weight. 19:39

pour
shall take and *p.* water on. *Ex* 4:9
shall *p.* the anointing oil on. 29:7
thou shalt *p.* the blood of the bullock. 12; *Lev* 4:7, 18, 25, 30, 34
nor *p.* drink offerings. *Ex* 30:9
he shall *p.* oil on the. *Lev* 2:1, 6
p. it into the palm of his. 14:15, 26
p. it on head of him that is to. 18
they shall *p.* out the dust that. 41
he shall *p.* out blood thereof. 17:13
he shall *p.* no oil upon. *Num* 5:15
he shall *p.* water out of his. 24:7*
p. blood out as water. *Deut* 12:16, 24; 15:23
take the flesh, and *p.* out. *Judg* 6:20
p. water on the burnt. *1 Ki* 18:33
p. out the oil into those. *2 Ki* 4:4
p. out for the people, that they. 41
and *p.* the oil on Jehu's head. 9:3
p. down rain according. *Job* 36:27*
I *p.* out my soul. *Ps* 42:4
ye people, *p.* out your heart. 62:8
p. out thine indignation on. 69:24
p. out thy wrath on the heathen 79:6
I will *p.* out my Spirit unto you. *Pr* 1:23; *Isa* 44:3; *Joel* 2:28, 29; *Acts* 2:17, 18
I will *p.* water on him. *Isa* 44:3
skies *p.* down righteousness. 45:8
I will *p.* it out on the children abroad. *Jer* 6:11
and to *p.* out drink offerings. 7:18
p. out thy fury on heathen. 10:25
I will *p.* their wickedness. 14:16
p. out their blood by force. 18:21*

to *p.* out drink offerings to the queen
of heaven. *Jer* 44:17, 18, 19, 25
p. out thine heart like. *Lam* 2:19
now will I shortly *p.* out. *Ezek* 7:8
14:19; 20:8, 13, 21; 30:15
I will *p.* out mine indignation. 21:31
Zeph 3:8
set on the pot and *p.* *Ezek* 24:3
I will *p.* out my wrath. *Hos* 5:10
I will *p.* down the stones. *Mi* 1:6
p. on house of David. *Zech* 12:10
if I will not *p.* you out. *Mal* 3:10
p. out the vials of wrath of. *Rev* 16:1

poured

Jacob *p.* oil on the top. *Gen* 28:18
Jacob *p.* a drink offering. 35:14
the rain was not *p.* on *Ex* 9:33
upon flesh shall it not be *p.* 30:32
where ashes are *p.* he. *Lev* 4:12
Moses *p.* anointing oil on. 8:12
he *p.* the blood at the bottom. 15; 9:9
head the anointing oil was *p.* 21:10
to be *p.* to the Lord for a. *Num* 28:7
sacrifices shall be *p.* out. *Deut* 12:27
but I have *p.* out my soul. *1 Sam* 1:15
drew water, and *p.* it out. 7:6
Samuel *p.* oil on Saul's head. 10:1
Tamar *p.* them out. *2 Sam* 13:9
David would not drink thereof, but *p.*
it out unto. 23:16; *1 Chr* 11:18
rent, and ashes *p.* out. *1 Ki* 13:3, 5
p. water on the hands. *2 Ki* 3:11
vessels to her, and she *p.* out. 4:5
they *p.* out for the men to eat. 40
and Ahaz *p.* his drink offering. 16:13
my wrath not be *p.* out. *2 Chr* 12:7
wrath that is *p.* out on us. 34:21
wrath shall be *p.* out on this place. 25
my roarings are *p.* out like. *Job* 3:24
not thou *p.* me out as milk? 10:10
rock *p.* me out rivers of oil. 29:6
my soul is *p.* out upon me. 30:16
I am *p.* out like water. *Ps* 22:14
grace is *p.* into thy lips. 45:2
clouds *p.* out water, skies. 77:17
I *p.* out my complaint before. 142:2
as ointment *p.* forth. *S of S* 1:3
they *p.* out a prayer. *Isa* 26:16
Lord hath *p.* on you the spirit. 29:10
till the spirit be *p.* on us from. 32:15
he hath *p.* on him the fury of. 42:25
hath *p.* out his soul to death. 53:12
hast *p.* out a drink offering. 57:6
my fury shall be *p.* out. *Jer* 7:20
they have *p.* out drink offerings.
19:13; 32:29
so shall it [fury] be *p.* out. 42:18
mine anger was *p.* forth. 44:6
when we *p.* drink offerings to. 19
he *p.* out his fury like fire.
Lam 2:4; 4:11
my liver is *p.* upon earth. 11
their soul was *p.* out. 12
of the sanctuary are *p.* out. 4:1
filthiness was *p.* out. *Ezek* 16:36
p. out their drink offerings. 20:28
with fury *p.* out will I rule. 33, 34
that I the Lord have *p.* out. 22:22
therefore I *p.* out mine. 31
p. their whoredom upon her. 23:8
she *p.* it not on the ground to. 24:7
wherefore I *p.* out my fury. 36:18
p. out my spirit on the house. 39:29
therefore the curse is *p.* *Dan* 9:11
and that determined shall be *p.* 27
as waters that are *p.* down. *Mi* 1:4
fury is *p.* out like fire. *Nah* 1:6
their blood shall be *p.* out. *Zeph* 1:17
p. ointment on his head. *Mat* 26:7
12; *Mark* 14:3
he *p.* out the changers' money.
John 2:15
on the Gentiles was *p.* *Acts* 10:45
wine of wrath of God *p.* *Rev* 14:10*
went and *p.* out his vial. 16:2, 3, 4
8, 10, 12, 17

pouredst

p. out thy fornications. *Ezek* 16:15

poureth

he *p.* contempt on princes. *Job* 12:21
Ps 107:40
he *p.* out my gall upon. *Job* 16:13
eye *p.* out tears unto God. 20

wine is red, and he *p.* *Ps* 75:8
but mouth of fools *p.* out. *Pr* 15:2
the mouth of the wicked *p.* out. 28
p. out waters on the. *Amos* 5:8; 9:6
he *p.* water into a bason. *John* 13:5

pouring

in *p.* thy fury on Jerusalem? *Ezek* 9:8
his wounds, *p.* in oil. *Luke* 10:34

pourtray

and *p.* upon it the city. *Ezek* 4:1

pourtrayed

all the idols of Israel *p.* *Ezek* 8:10
men *p.* on the wall, the images of the
Chaldeans *p.* with. 23:14

poverty

all thou hast come to *p.* *Gen* 45:11
so thy *p.* come as an armed man.
Pr 6:11; 24:34
destruction of poor is their *p.* 10:15
but it tendeth to *p.* 11:24*
p. be to him that refuseth. 13:18
sleep, lest thou come to *p.* 20:13
and glutton come to *p.* 23:21
persons, shall have *p.* enough. 28:19
considereth not that *p.* shall come. 22
give me neither *p.* nor riches. 30:8
let him drink and forget his *p.* 31:7
their deep *p.* abounded to. *2 Cor* 8:2
became poor, that ye through his *p.* 9
I know thy works and *p.* *Rev* 2:9

powder

calf and ground it to *p.* *Ex* 32:20
the rain of thy land *p.* *Deut* 28:24
grove to *p.*, cast the *p.* *2 Ki* 23:6
the altar to *p.* 15; *2 Chr* 34:7
it will grind him to *p.* *Mat* 21:44*
Luke 20:18*

powders

perfumed with all the *p.* *S of S* 3:6

power

(*Generally for rule, or authority; frequently for might and strength*)
hast thou *p.* with God. *Gen* 32:28*
dignity, excellency of *p.* 49:3
break the pride of your *p.* *Lev* 26:19
have I now any *p.* to say? *Num* 22:38
brought thee with his mighty *p.*
Deut 4:37
it is he that giveth thee *p.* to. 8:18
seeth that their *p.* is gone. 32:36
is my strength and *p.* *2 Sam* 22:33
the inhabitants were of small *p.*
2 Ki 19:26
Joab led forth the *p.* *1 Chr* 20:1
thine is the *p.* and glory. 29:11
Mat 6:13
in thine hand is *p.* *1 Chr* 29:12
2 Chr 20:6
God hath *p.* to help. *2 Chr* 25:8
siege, and all his *p.* with him. 32:9
cease by force and *p.* *Ezra* 4:23
his *p.* and wrath against all. 8:22
nor is it in our *p.* to redeem them.
Neh 5:5
he made a feast to *p.* of. *Esth* 1:3
perish the *p.* of the people. 8:11
the Jews hoped to have *p.* 9:1
redeem in war from the *p.* *Job* 5:20
also the mighty with his *p.* 24:22
helped him that is without *p.* 26:2
he divided the sea with his *p.* 12
the thunder of his *p.* who can? 14
God exalteth by his *p.* 36:22
conceal his parts nor his *p.* 41:12
my darling from the *p.* of. *Ps* 22:20
redeem my soul from the *p.* 49:15
p. belongeth unto God. 62:11
mountains girded with *p.* 65:6
he ruleth by his *p.* for ever. 66:7
he giveth strength and *p.* to. 68:35
by his *p.* he brought in the south
wind. 78:26
who knoweth the *p.* of thine? 90:11
his mighty *p.* to be known. 106:8
he shewed his people the *p.* 111:6
in the firmament of his *p.* 150:1
oppressors there was *p.* *Eccl* 4:1
and hath given him *p.* to eat. 5:19
God giveth him not *p.* to eat. 6:2
word of a king is, there is *p.* 8:4
no man hath *p.* over the spirit. 8
their inhabitants were of small *p.*
Isa 37:27

he giveth *p.* to the faint. *Isa* 40:29
bringeth forth the army and *p.* 43:17
from the *p.* of the flame. 47:14
the earth by his *p.* *Jer* 10:12; 51:15
were in thee to their *p.* *Ezek* 22:6
and the pride of her *p.* shall. 30:6
God hath given thee *p.* *Dan* 2:37
Daniel from the *p.* of lions. 6:27
ran in fury of his *p.* 8:6
but not in his *p.* 22
p. shall be mighty, but not by his *p.* 24
not retain the *p.* of the arm. 11:6
he shall stir up his *p.* and his. 25
but he shall have *p.* over the. 43
to scatter the *p.* of the holy. 12:7
he had *p.* with God. *Hos* 12:3
yea, he had *p.* over the angel. 4
I will ransom them from the *p.* 13:14
in the *p.* of their hand. *Mi* 2:1
I am full of *p.* by the Spirit of. 3:8
imputing this his *p.* unto. *Hab* 1:11
delivered from the *p.* of evil. 2:9
there was the hiding of his *p.* 3:4
not by might, nor by my *p.* *Zech* 4:6
Lord will smite her *p.* in the sea. 9:4
Son of man hath *p.* on earth to.
Mat 9:6; *Mark* 2:10; *Luke* 5:24
had given such *p.* to men. *Mat* 9:8
gave *p.* against unclean spirits. 10:1
Luke 9:1
coming in the clouds with *p.*
Mat 24:30; *Luke* 21:27
sitting on right hand with *p.*
Mat 26:64; *Mark* 14:62
all *p.* is given unto me in heaven and
in earth. *Mat* 28:18
p. to heal sicknesses. *Mark* 3:15
kingdom of God come with *p.* 9:1
p. of the Highest shall. *Luke* 1:35
the devil said, All this *p.* will. 4:6
for his word was with *p.* 32
p. he commandeth unclean spirits. 36
the *p.* of the Lord was present. 5:17
I give you *p.* to tread on serpents,
and over all the *p.* of the. 10:19
fear him that hath *p.* to cast. 12:5
they might deliver him to *p.* 20:20
and the *p.* of darkness. 22:53
until ye be endued with *p.* 24:49
to them gave he *p.* to become sons
of God. *John* 1:12*
I have *p.* to lay it down, and *p.* 10:18
thou hast given him *p.* over. 17:2
I have *p.* to crucify thee, *p.* to. 19:10
the Father hath put in his own *p.*
Acts 1:7*
shall receive *p.* after Holy Ghost. 8
as though by our own *p.* or. 3:12
they asked, By what *p.* have ye? 4:7
was it not in thine own *p.*? 5:4
faith and *p.*, did great wonders. 6:8
saying, Give me also this *p.* 8:19
Jesus with Holy Ghost and *p.* 10:38
from the *p.* of Satan to God. 26:18
be the Son of God with *p.* *Rom* 1:4
his eternal *p.* and Godhead. 20
hath not the potter *p.* over? 9:21
willing to make his *p.* known. 22
resisteth the *p.*, resisteth. 13:2
then not be afraid of the *p.*? 3
through *p.* of the Holy Ghost. 15:13
wonders, by the *p.* of the Spirit. 19
that is of *p.* to establish you. 16:25*
of the Spirit and *p.* *1 Cor* 2:4
know, not the speech, but the *p.* 4:19
with the *p.* of our Lord Jesus. 5:4
brought under the *p.* of any. 6:12
will raise us up by his own *p.* 14
wife and husband have not *p.* of. 7:4
but hath *p.* over his own will. 37
we *p.* to eat and to drink? 9:4*
p. to lead about a sister, a wife? 5*
not *p.* to forbear working? 6
if others be partakers of this *p.* over
you, we have not used this *p.* 12
the woman ought to have *p.* on. 11:10
put down all authority and *p.* 15:24
that the excellency of *p.* *2 Cor* 4:7
p. yea, and beyond their *p.* 8:3
that the *p.* of Christ may rest. 12:9
according to the *p.* God hath. 13:10
his *p.* toward us, according to the
working of his mighty *p.* *Eph* 1:19*
far above all principality, *p.* and. 21

prince of the *p.* of the air. *Eph* 2:2
by the effectual working of his *p.* 3:7
to the *p.* that worketh in us. 20
I may know the *p.* of his. *Phil* 3:10
according to his glorious *p.* *Col* 1:11*
us from the *p.* of darkness. 13
of all principality and *p.* 2:10
from the glory of his *p.* *2 Thes* 1:9
the work of faith with *p.* 11
working of Satan with all *p.* 2:9
not *p.* but to make ourselves. 3:9
whom be honour and *p.* *1 Tim* 6:16
God hath given us spirit of *p.* *2 Tim* 1:7
of godliness, but denying the *p.* 3:5
things by word of his *p.* *Heb* 1:3
him that had *p.* of death. 2:14
after the *p.* of an endless life. 7:16
as his divine *p.* hath given. *2 Pet* 1:3
known the *p.* of our Lord. 16
to the only wise God our Saviour be glory and *p.* *Jude* 25
I give *p.* over the nations. *Rev* 2:26
to receive honour and *p.* 4:11; 5:12
blessing, honour, glory, and *p.* 5:13
p. was given to him that sat on. 6:4
p. was given them over fourth. 8
honour, *p.*, and might be unto. 7:12
given *p.* as scorpions have *p.* 9:3
and their *p.* was to hurt men. 10
for their *p.* is in their mouth. 19
give *p.* to my two witnesses. 11:3
p. to shut heaven, *p.* over waters. 6
the *p.* of his Christ come. 12:10
gave him *p.* and his seat. 13:2, 4
p. was given to him to. 5, 7
he exerciseth all the *p.* of the. 12
had *p.* to give life. 15
had *p.* over fire. 14:18
filled with smoke from his *p.* 15:8
p. was given him to scorch. 16:8
blasphemed God who hath *p.* over. 9
receive *p.* as kings one hour. 17:12
shall give their *p.* and strength. 13
glory, honour, and *p.*, unto the. 19:1

see **great** *power*

power *of God*
the scriptures, nor the *p. of God.* *Mat* 22:29; *Mark* 12:24
all amazed at the mighty *p. of God.* *Luke* 9:43*
the right hand of *p. of God.* 22:69
this man is the great *p. of God.* *Acts* 8:10*
gospel is the *p. of God.* *Rom* 1:16
are saved, it is the *p. of God.* *1 Cor* 1:18
Christ the *p. of God,* and. 24
stand but by the *p. of God.* 2:5
of truth, by the *p. of God.* *2 Cor* 6:7
liveth by *p. of God,* but we shall live with him by *p. of God.* 13:4
of the afflictions of the gospel, according to the *p. of God.* *2 Tim* 1:8
kept by the *p. of God.* *1 Pet* 1:5

in **power**
it is *in p.* of my hand. *Gen* 31:29
become glorious *in p.* *Ex* 15:6
the wicked mighty *in p.*? *Job* 21:7
he is excellent *in p.* and in. 37:23
when it is *in p.* of thy. *Pr* 3:27
death and life are *in* the *p.* 18:21
that he is strong *in p.* not. *Isa* 40:26
slow to anger, great *in p.* *Nah* 1:3
go before him *in* the *p.* of Elias. *Luke* 1:17
in the *p.* of the Spirit. 4:14
kingdom of God not in word, but *in p.* *1 Cor* 4:20
in weakness, it is raised *in p.* 15:43
be strong *in* the Lord and *p.* *Eph* 6:10
came in word, and also *in p.* *1 Thes* 1:5
greater *in p.* and might. *2 Pet* 2:11

my **power**
all *my p.* I have served. *Gen* 31:6
to shew in thee *my p.* *Ex* 9:16
My p. hath gotten me. *Deut* 8:17
built by the might of *my p.* *Dan* 4:30
that I might shew *my p.* *Rom* 9:17
that I abuse not *my p.* in. *1 Cor* 9:18*

no **power**
sell her he shall have *no p.* *Ex* 21:8
shall have *no p.* to stand. *Lev* 26:37
men of Ai had *no p.* to. *Josh* 8:20
people had *no p.* to weep. *1 Sam* 30:4
with them that have *no p.* *2 Chr* 14:11
house of Ahaziah had *no p.* to. 22:9
or have I *no p.* to deliver? *Isa* 50:2
bodies the fire had *no p.* *Dan* 3:27
there was *no p.* in the ram to. 8:7
no p. against me, except. *John* 19:11
for there is *no p.* but. *Rom* 13:1
second death hath *no p.* *Rev* 20:6

thy **power**
out by *thy* mighty *p.* *Deut* 9:29
all that he hath is in *thy p.* *Job* 1:12
sing, and praise *thy p.* *Ps* 21:13
scatter them by *thy p.* 59:11
will sing of *thy p.* 16
to see *thy p.* and thy glory. 63:2
through greatness of *thy p.* 66:3
and *thy p.* to every one that. 71:18
to the greatness of *thy p.* 79:11
be willing in day of *thy p.* 110:3
they shall talk of *thy p.* 145:11
fortify *thy p.* mightily. *Nah* 2:1

powerful
Lord is *p.* full of majesty. *Ps* 29:4
for his letters, say they, are *p.* *2 Cor* 10:10*
word of God is quick, *p.* *Heb* 4:12*

powers
p. of heaven be shaken. *Mat* 24:29 *Mark* 13:25; *Luke* 21:26
when brought before *p.* *Luke* 12:11*
nor *p.* can separate from. *Rom* 8:38
the *p.* that be are ordained of. 13:1
p. in heavenly places. *Eph* 3:10
against principalities and *p.* 6:12
p. were created by him. *Col* 1:16
having spoiled *p.* he made a. 2:15
in mind to be subject to *p.* *Tit* 3:1*
tasted the *p.* of the world. *Heb* 6:5
on right hand of God, *p.* *1 Pet* 3:22

practices
heart exercised with covetous *p.* *2 Pet* 2:14*

practise
not to *p.* wicked works. *Ps* 141:4*
person shall *p.* hypocrisy. *Isa* 32:6
destroy, prosper, and *p.* *Dan* 8:24*
morning is light, they *p.* it. *Mi* 2:1

practised
that Saul secretly *p.* mischief. *1 Sam* 23:9*
the little horn *p.* and. *Dan* 8:12*

praise
(*Most frequently used with regard to praise rendered to God. The verb is frequently changed in the Revisions to* bless, *or* give thanks)
he is thy *p.* and he is. *Deut* 10:21
to make thee high in *p.* and. 26:19
I will sing *p.* to the Lord. *Judg* 5:3 *Ps* 7:17; 9:2; 57:7; 61:8; 104:33
we may glory in thy *p.* *1 Chr* 16:35
as taught to sing *p.* *2 Chr* 23:13
above all blessing and *p.* *Neh* 9:5
of David were songs of *p.* 12:46
shew forth all thy *p.* *Ps* 9:14
my *p.* shall be of thee in the. 22:25
that my glory may sing *p.* 30:12
p. is comely for the upright. 33:1
his *p.* shall be continually in. 34:1
tongue shall speak of thy *p.* 35:28
even *p.* to our God. 40:3
with voice of *p.* 42:4
so is thy *p.* to the ends of. 48:10
offereth *p.* glorifieth me. 50:23
mouth shall shew forth thy *p.* 51:15
p. waiteth for thee, O God. 65:1
honour, make his *p.* glorious. 66:2
and make the voice of his *p.* 8
my *p.* shall be continually of. 71:6
let my mouth be filled with thy *p.* 8
we will shew forth thy *p.* 79:13
rejoice and sing *p.* 98:4
enter into his courts with *p.* 100:4
declare his *p.* in Jerusalem. 102:21
who can shew forth all his *p.*? 106:2
then they sang his *p.* 12
triumph in thy *p.* 47
give *p.* even with my glory. *Ps* 108:1
O God of my *p.* 109:1
his *p.* endureth. 111:10
lips shall utter *p.* when. 119:171
before the gods will I sing *p.* 138:1
my mouth shall speak the *p.* 145:21
p. is comely. 147:1
sing *p.* on the harp. 7
the *p.* of all his saints. 148:14
sing his *p.* in the congregation. 149:1
so is a man to his *p.* *Pr* 27:21
I will not give my *p.* to. *Isa* 42:8
sing his *p.* from the end of the. 10
let them declare his *p.* in the. 12
they shall shew forth my *p.* 43:21
my *p.* will I refrain for thee. 48:9
thou shalt call thy gates *P.* 60:18
the garment of *p.* for the spirit. 61:3
will cause righteousness and *p.* 11
till he made Jerusalem a *p.* in. 62:7
might be to me for a *p.* *Jer* 13:11
O Lord, for thou art my *p.* 17:14
bringing sacrifices of *p.* 26; 33:11
it shall be to me a joy, a *p.* 33:9
there shall be no more *p.* of. 48:2
how is the city of *p.* not left? 49:25
how is the *p.* of whole earth? 51:41
earth was full of his *p.* *Hab* 3:3
will get them *p.* and fame. *Zeph* 3:19
make you a *p.* among all people. 20
thou hast perfected *p.* *Mat* 21:16
saw it, gave *p.* to God. *Luke* 18:43
unto him, Give God the *p.* *John* 9:24
p. of men more than *p.* of. 12:43
whose *p.* is not of men. *Rom* 2:29
thou shalt have *p.* of same. 13:3
every man have *p.* of God. *1 Cor* 4:5
whose *p.* is in the gospel. *2 Cor* 8:18
to *p.* of glory of his grace. *Eph* 1:6
to *p.* of glory who first. 12, 14
unto the *p.* of God. *Phil* 1:11
if there be any *p.* think on. 4:8
of the church will I sing *p.* *Heb* 2:12
him let us offer sacrifice of *p.* 13:15
faith might be found to *p.* *1 Pet* 1:7
and for the *p.* of them that do. 2:14
to whom be *p.* and dominion. 4:11

praise, *verb*
whom thy brethren shall *p.* *Gen* 49:8
fruit holy to *p.* the Lord. *Lev* 19:24
instruments I made to *p.* *1 Chr* 23:5
and *p.* thy glorious name. 29:13
Levites to *p.* before the. *2 Chr* 8:14
that should *p.* the beauty. 20:21
began to sing and to *p.* 22
to *p.* in the gates of the tents. 31:2
so will we sing and *p.* *Ps* 21:13
ye that fear the Lord, *p.* him. 22:23
pit, shall the dust *p.* thee? 30:9
hope in God, for I shall yet *p.* him. 42:5, 11; 43:5
God we boast, and *p.* thy name. 44:8
shall the people *p.* thee. 45:17
men will *p.* thee, when doest. 49:18
my lips shall *p.* thee. 63:3
mouth shall *p.* thee. 5
let the people *p.* thee. 67:3
let all the people *p.* thee. 5
heaven and the earth *p.* him. 69:34
I will yet *p.* thee more and. 71:14
let the poor and needy *p.* 74:21
wrath of man shall *p.* thee. 76:10
dead arise and *p.* thee? 88:10
the heavens shall *p.* thy. 89:5
p. thy great and terrible name. 99:3
p. him in the assembly of. 107:32
p. him, O ye servants of the Lord. 113:1; 135:1
the dead *p.* not the Lord. 115:17
seven times a day do I *p.* 119:164
let my soul live and it shall *p.* 175
I will *p.* thy name for thy. 138:2
of the earth shall *p.* thee. 4
out of prison that I may *p.* 142:7
one generation shall *p.* thy. 145:4
all thy works shall *p.* thee. 10
p. the Lord, Jerusalem, *p.* 147:12
p. ye the Lord, *p.* him in the. 148:1
p. him, all his angels, *p.* him, ye. 2
p. him, sun and moon, *p.* him. 3
p. him, ye heavens of heavens. 4
p. his name in the dance. 149:3
p. God in his sanctuary, *p.* 150:1

p. him for his mighty acts, *p.* him. *Ps* 150:2
p. him with trumpet. 3
p. him with timbrel. 4
p. him upon the loud and. 5
let another man *p.* thee. *Pr* 27:2
they that forsake the law *p.* the. 28:4
let her own works *p.* her in. 31:31
the grave cannot *p.* thee. *Isa* 38:18
the living he shall *p.* thee, as. 19
publish, *p.* ye and say. *Jer* 31:7
I thank and *p.* thee, O. *Dan* 2:23
I *p.* extol, and honour the king. 4:37
p. the name of the Lord. *Joel* 2:26
disciples began to *p.* God with loud. *Luke* 19:37
now I *p.* you that ye. *1 Cor* 11:2
I declare, I *p.* you not. 17, 22
saying, *P.* our God, all ye. *Rev* 19:5

I will, or *will I* **praise**

Leah said, Now *will I p.* *Gen* 29:35
I will p. Lord according. *Ps* 7:17
I will p. thee, O Lord, with my whole heart. 9:1; 111:1; 138:1
congregation *will I p.* thee. 22:22
with my song *will I p.* him. 28:7
I will give thee thanks, *I will p.* 35:18
57:9; 108:3; 109:30
on the harp *will I p.* thee. 43:4
I will p. thee for ever, because. 52:9
I will p. thy name, O Lord. 54:6
in God *I will p.* his word. 56:4, 10
I will p. the name of God. 69:30
I will also *p.* thee with the. 71:22
I will p. thee, O Lord my. 86:12
I will go into them, and will *p.* 118:19
I will p. thee, for thou hast heard. 21
thou art my God, and *I will p.* 28
I will p. thee with uprightness. 119:7
I will p. thee, for I am wonderfully made. 139:14
I will p. thy name for ever. 145:2
I will p. thee, though. *Isa* 12:1
I will p. thy name, thou hast. 25:1

praise *ye the Lord*, or **praise** *the Lord*

p. ye the Lord, for the avenging of Israel. *Judg* 5:2
Levites to *p. the Lord.* *1 Chr* 16:4
morning to *p. the Lord.* 23:20
with a harp to *p. the Lord.* 25:3
stood up to *p. the Lord.* *2 Chr* 20:19
p. the Lord, for his mercy. 21
cymbals to *p. the Lord.* *Ezra* 3:10
they shall *p. the Lord.* *Ps* 22:26
p. the Lord with harp, sing. 33:2
be created shall *p. the Lord.* 102:18
p. ye the Lord. 104:35; 106:1, 48
111:1; 112:1; 113:1, 9; 115:18
116:19; 117:2; 135:1; 146:1, 10
147:20; 148:1, 14; 149:1, 9
150:1, 6; *Jer* 20:13
Oh that men would *p. the Lord.* *Ps* 107:8, 15, 21, 31
I will greatly *p. the Lord.* 109:30
I will *p. the Lord.* 118:19
p. the Lord; for Lord is good. 135:3
while I live will I *p. the Lord.* 146:2
p. ye the Lord, for it is good. 147:1
p. the Lord, O Jerusalem, praise. 12
p. the Lord from the earth. 148:7
p. the Lord, call upon his. *Isa* 12:4
eat it, and *p. the Lord.* 62:9
p. the Lord of hosts, for. *Jer* 33:11
p. the Lord, all ye Gentiles. *Rom* 15:11

praised

the people *p.* their god. *Judg* 16:24
none *p.* as Absalom. *2 Sam* 14:25
the Lord is worthy to be *p.* 22:4
Ps 18:3
Lord is great and greatly to be *p.*
1 Chr 16:25; *Ps* 48:1; 96:4; 145:3
the people *p.* the Lord. *1 Chr* 16:36
and four thousand *p.* the Lord.
23:5; *2 Chr* 7:3; *Neh* 5:13
of music *p.* the Lord. *2 Chr* 5:13
David *p.* by the ministry. 7:6
Levites and priests *p.* the. 30:21
when they *p.* the Lord. *Ezra* 3:11
and daily shall he be *p.* *Ps* 72:15
of sun Lord's name is to be *p.* 113:3
feareth Lord shall be *p.* *Pr* 31:30
I *p.* the dead more than. *Eccl* 4:2
and concubines *p.* her. *S of S* 6:9
where our fathers *p.* thee. *Isa* 64:11
I *p.* and honoured him. *Dan* 4:34
they *p.* the gods of gold and. 5:4, 23
and Zacharias spake and *p.* God. *Luke* 1:64

praises

like thee, fearful in *p.*? *Ex* 15:11
sing *p.* to thy name. *2 Sam* 22:50
Ps 18:49; 92:1; 135:3
Levites to sing *p.* to the Lord, and they sang *p.* with. *2 Chr* 29:30
sing *p.* to the Lord that. *Ps* 9:11
thou that inhabitest *p.* of Israel. 22:3
yea, I will sing *p.* to God. 27:6
47:6; 68:32; 75:9; 108:3
God is king, sing ye *p.* with. 47:7
I will render *p.* unto. 56:12; 144:9
sing to God, sing *p.* to his. 68:4
generation to come *p.* of Lord. 78:4
I will sing *p.* to my God while. 146:2
for it is good to sing *p.* to. 147:1
let them sing *p.* to him. 149:3
let the high *p.* of God be in their. 6
shew forth the *p.* of Lord. *Isa* 60:6
mention of the *p.* of the Lord. 63:7
prayed and sang *p.* to. *Acts* 16:25
shew forth the *p.* of him. *1 Pet* 2:9

praiseth

husband also, and he *p.* *Pr* 31:28

praising

one sound to be heard in *p.* the Lord. *2 Chr* 5:13
Athaliah heard the people *p.* 23:12
they sang by course in *p.* *Ezra* 3:11
they will be still *p.* thee. *Ps* 84:4
heavenly host *p.* God. *Luke* 2:13
the shepherds returned, *p.* God. 20
in the temple *p.* God. 24:53
eat with gladness, *p.* God. *Acts* 2:47
and leaping, and *p.* God. 3:8, 9

prancing

the noise of the *p.* horses. *Nah* 3:2

prancings

broken by means of *p.* *Judg* 5:22

prating

but a *p.* fool shall fall. *Pr* 10:8, 10
p. against us with. *3 John* 10

pray

(*Revisions frequently change to* beseech)

and shall *p.* for thee. *Gen* 20:7
Samuel said, I will *p.* *1 Sam* 7:5
p. for thy servants to the. 12:19
that I should sin in ceasing to *p.* 23
found in his heart to *p.* this prayer.
2 Sam 7:27; *1 Chr* 17:25
when they shall *p.* toward. *1 Ki* 8:30
35, 42, 44, 48; *2 Chr* 6:26, 34, 38
p. that my hand may be. *1 Ki* 13:6
shall *p.* and make. *2 Chr* 6:24, 32
and turn and *p.* in the land of. 37
if my people shall *p.* and. 7:14
and *p.* for the life of. *Ezra* 6:10
hear the prayer which I *p.* *Neh* 1:6
what profit should we have, if we *p.* unto him? *Job* 21:15
p. to God, and he will be. 33:26
my servant Job shall *p.* for. 42:8
God, for to thee will I *p.* *Ps* 5:2
and at noon will I *p.* 55:17*
p. for the peace of Jerusalem. 122:6
come to his sanctuary to *p.* *Isa* 16:12
p. to a god that cannot save. 45:20
p. not thou for this people. *Jer* 7:16
11:14; 14:11
seek peace of the city, *p.* to. 29:7
ye shall *p.* to me, and I will. 12
p. now to the Lord. 37:3; 42:2, 20
behold, I will *p.* to the Lord. 42:4
they sent men to *p.* *Zech* 7:2*
go speedily to *p.* before. 8:21*, 22*
and *p.* for them that despitefully.
Mat 5:44; *Luke* 16:27
they love to *p.* standing. *Mat* 6:5
p. to thy Father which is in. 6
when ye *p.* use not vain. 7
after this manner *p.* ye, Our. 9
p. ye the Lord of the harvest. 9:38
Luke 10:2
he went . . . apart to *p.* *Mat* 14:23
Mark 6:46; *Luke* 6:12; 9:28
his hands on them and *p.* *Mat* 19:13
p. your flight be not in winter.
24:20; *Mark* 13:18
sit ye here while I go and *p.* yonder.
Mat 26:36; *Mark* 14:32
watch and *p.* that ye enter not.
Mat 26:41; *Mark* 13:33; 14:38
Luke 21:36; 22:40, 46
thinkest thou I cannot *p.*? *Mat* 26:53
to *p.* him to depart. *Mark* 5:17
things ye desire when ye *p.* 11:24
Lord, teach us to *p.* as. *Luke* 11:1
he said to them, When ye *p.* say. 2
that men ought always to *p.* 18:1
went up into the temple to *p.* 10
p. the Father. *John* 14:16; 16:26
I *p.* for them, I *p.* not for. 17:9
I *p.* not that thou take them. 15
neither *p.* I for these alone, but. 20
p. God, if perhaps the. *Acts* 8:22
Simon said, *P.* ye to the Lord. 24
up on the housetop to *p.* 10:9
not what we should *p.* for. *Rom* 8:26
a woman *p.* uncovered? *1 Cor* 11:13
wherefore let him *p.* that he. 14:13
for if I *p.* in unknown tongue. 14
I will *p.* with spirit, *p.* with. 15
ambassadors for Christ, we *p.* you be reconciled. *2 Cor* 5:20
now I *p.* to God, that ye do. 13:7
this I *p.* that your love. *Phil* 1:9
we do not cease to *p.* for. *Col* 1:9
p. without ceasing. *1 Thes* 5:17
I *p.* God your whole spirit be. 23
brethren, *p.* for us. 25; *2 Thes* 3:1
Heb 13:18
wherefore we *p.* always. *2 Thes* 1:11
I will that men *p.* every. *1 Tim* 2:8
I *p.* God it be not laid to. *2 Tim* 4:16
is any afflicted? let him *p.* *Jas* 5:13
p. over him, anointing him. 14
confess your faults, and *p.* one. 16
I do not say that he shall *p.* for it.
1 John 5:16*

prayed

Abraham *p.* and God healed Abimelech. *Gen* 20:17
when Moses *p.* the fire. *Num* 11:2
and Moses *p.* for the people. 21:7
Deut 9:26
I *p.* for Aaron also the. *Deut* 9:20
Hannah *p.* to Lord. *1 Sam* 1:10, 21
for this child I *p.* 27
Samuel *p.* unto the Lord. 8:6
Elisha *p.* unto the Lord. *2 Ki* 4:33
6:17, 18
Hezekiah *p.* 19:15; 20:2
2 Chr 30:18; 32:24
that which thou hast *p.* to me.
2 Ki 19:20; *Isa* 37:21
Isaiah *p.* *2 Chr* 32:20
Manasseh *p.* 33:13
now when Ezra had *p.* *Ezra* 10:1
Neh 1:4; 2:4
the captivity when Job *p.* *Job* 42:10
Jeremiah *p.* *Jer* 32:16
Jonah *p.* *Jonah* 2:1; 4:2
Daniel *p.* three times. *Dan* 6:10; 9:4
p. let this cup pass from. *Mat* 26:39
42:44; *Mark* 14:35, 39; *Luke* 22:41
a solitary place and *p.* *Mark* 1:35
he *p.* him that he might be. 5:18
Jesus *p.* him he would thrust out a.
Luke 5:3
into the wilderness and *p.* 16
as he *p.* his countenance was. 9:29
the Pharisee stood and *p.* 18:11
but I have *p.* that thy faith. 22:32
being in an agony he *p.* more. 44
his disciples *p.* him. *John* 4:31
the disciples *p.* and said. *Acts* 1:24
when they *p.* they laid their. 4:31
Peter and John when come *p.* 8:15
Peter *p.* 9:40
Cornelius *p.* always. 10:2, 30
then they *p.* him to tarry. 48
they had fasted and *p.* 13:3; 14:23
man of Macedonia *p.* him. 16:9
at midnight Paul and Silas *p.* 25
Paul kneeled down and *p.* 20:36
kneeled down on shore and *p.* 21:5
while I *p.* in the temple, I. 22:17

Paul p. me to bring this young. Acts 23:18
to whom Paul entered in and p. 28:8
Elias p. that it might. Jas 5:17
and he p. again, and the heaven. 18

prayer

heart to pray this p. 2 Sam 7:27
have respect to the p. 1 Ki 8:28
hearken to the p. 29; 2 Chr 6:19, 20
p. shall be made by any man. 1 Ki 8:38; 2 Chr 6:29
hear their p. 1 Ki 8:45, 49
2 Chr 6:35, 39, 40
end of praying this p. 1 Ki 8:54
lift up thy p. for remnant. 2 Ki 19:4
Isa 37:4
be attent to the p. 2 Chr 7:15
their p. came to his holy. 30:27
Manasseh's p. unto God. 33:18, 19
thou mayest hear the p. Neh 1:6
nevertheless we made our p. 4:9
yea thou restrainest p. Job 15:4
thou shalt make thy p. to him. 22:27
O thou that hearest p. Ps 65:2
p. shall be made for him. 72:15
how long be angry against p.? 80:4
he will regard the p. of the destitute, and not despise their p. 102:17
but I give myself unto p. 109:4
and let his p. become sin. 7
the p. of the upright is. Pr 15:8
heareth the p. of the righteous. 29
his p. shall be abomination. 28:9
poured out a p. when. Isa 26:16
joyful in my house of p.: for mine house shall be called an house of p. 56:7; Mat 21:13; Mark 11:17
Luke 19:46
cry nor p. for them. Jer 7:16; 11:14
that our p. should not pass. Lam 3:44
I set my face to the Lord, to seek by p. Dan 9:3
yet made we not our p. before. 13
now, O our God, hear the p. of. 17
a p. of Habakkuk the. Hab 3:1
howbeit, this kind goeth not out but by p. Mat 17:21; Mark 9:29
Zacharias, thy p. is. Luke 1:13
temple at the hour of p. Acts 3:1
ourselves continually to p. 6:4
Cornelius, thy p. is heard. 10:31
p. was made without ceasing. 12:5
we went out where p. was. 16:13*
as we went to p. a certain. 16
give yourselves to p. 1 Cor 7:5
helping together by p. 2 Cor 1:11
by their p. for you, which. 9:14
praying always with all p. Eph 6:18
always in every p. of mine. Phil 1:4
my salvation through your p. 19
in every thing by p. let requests. 4:6
by the word and p. 1 Tim 4:5
the p. of faith shall save. Jas 5:15
the effectual p. of a righteous. 16*
sober, and watch unto p. 1 Pet 4:7

see **heard**

in **prayer**

the thanksgiving in p. Neh 11:17
speaking in p. Gabriel. Dan 9:21
whatever ye ask in p. Mat 21:22
all night in p. to God. Luke 6:12
with one accord in p. Acts 1:14
continuing instant in p. Rom 12:12
continue in p. and watch. Col 4:2

my **prayer**

also my p. is pure. Job 16:17
have mercy upon me, and hear my p. Ps 4:1; 17:1; 39:12; 54:2
in the morning will I direct my p. 5:3
the Lord will receive my p. 6:9
and my p. returned to mine. 35:13
and my p. to the God of my. 42:8
give ear unto my p. O God. 55:1
O God, attend to my p. 61:1; 64:1*
84:8; 86:6; 102:1; 143:1
attended to the voice of my p. 66:19
hath not turned away my p. 20
my p. is unto thee in an. 69:13
let my p. come before thee. 88:2
in the morning shall my p. 13
let my p. be set before thee. 141:2
for yet my p. shall be in their. 5
he shutteth out my p. Lam 3:8
my p. came in to thee. Jonah 2:7
brethren, my p. to God. Rom 10:1

prayers

p. of David, son of. Ps 72:20
when ye make many p. Isa 1:15
pretence make long p. Mat 23:14
Mark 12:40; Luke 20:47
Anna continued in p. Luke 2:37
disciples of John make p.? 5:33
breaking of bread and in p. Acts 2:42
thy p. and alms are come up. 10:4
make mention of you always in my p. Rom 1:9; Eph 1:16; 1 Thes 1:2
2 Tim 1:3; Philem 4
strive with me in your p. Rom 15:30
fervently for you in p. Col 4:12
I exhort that p. be made. 1 Tim 2:1
continueth in p. night and day. 5:5
I trust through your p. I. Philem 22
when he had offered up p. Heb 5:7
heirs of life, that your p. 1 Pet 3:7
his ears are open to their p. but. 12
full of odours, which are the p. of saints. Rev 5:8
he should offer it with the p. 8:3
the smoke which came with the p. 4

prayest

when thou p. be not. Mat 6:5, 6

prayeth, -ing

as Hannah continued p. 1 Sam 1:12
woman that stood p. by thee. 26
hearken to prayer which thy servant p. 1 Ki 8:28; 2 Chr 6:19, 20
Solomon had made an end of p. 1 Ki 8:54; 2 Chr 7:1
he worshippeth it and p. Isa 44:17
and found Daniel p. Dan 6:11
while I was speaking and p. 9:20
ye stand p., forgive. Mark 11:25
people were p. without. Luke 1:10
and Jesus p., the heaven. 3:21
he was alone p., his disciples. 9:18
as he was p. in certain place. 11:1
behold he p. Acts 9:11
I was at Joppa p. 11:5
were gathered together p. 12:12
every man p. with his. 1 Cor 11:4
every woman that p. uncovered. 5
spirit p. but my understanding. 14:14
p. us with much entreaty. 2 Cor 8:4
p. always with all prayer. Eph 6:18
p. always for you. Col 1:3
p. also for us. 4:3
night and day p. exceedingly that we might see your face. 1 Thes 3:10
but ye, beloved, p. in the. Jude 20

preach

(To proclaim or publish abroad)

prophets to p. of thee. Neh 6:7
the Lord hath anointed me to p. good tidings. Isa 61:1
p. to it the preaching. Jonah 3:2
time Jesus began to p. Mat 4:17
p. saying, The kingdom of God. 10:7
what ye hear, that p. ye upon. 27
he departed thence to p. in. 11:1
John did p. the baptism. Mark 1:4
that I may p. there. 38; Luke 4:43
he might send them forth to p. Mat 3:14; Luke 9:2
to p. deliverance to. Luke 4:18, 19
go thou and p. the kingdom. 9:60
they ceased not to p. Acts 5:42
he commanded us to p. to. 10:42
and p. unto you that ye should. 14:15
in every city them that p. him. 15:21
forbidden by Holy Ghost to p. 16:6
Jesus whom I p. to you is. 17:3
word of faith which we p. Rom 10:8
and how shall they p. except? 15
we p. Christ crucified. 1 Cor 1:23
though I p. gospel, I have nothing to glory, woe is to me if I p. not. 9:16
I or they, so we p. and so. 15:11
we p. not ourselves, but. 2 Cor 4:5
that I might p. him among. Gal 1:16
the gospel which I p. among the. 2:2
if I yet p. circumcision. 5:11
should p. among Gentiles. Eph 3:8
some indeed p. Christ of. Phil 1:15
the one p. Christ of contention. 16
whom we p., warning. Col 1:28
p. the word, be instant. 2 Tim 4:2

preached

I have p. righteousness in. Ps 40:9
poor have the gospel p. Mat 11:5
p. saying, There cometh. Mark 1:7
he p. in their synagogues. 39
many were gathered, he p. the. 2:2
went and p. that men should. 6:12
went forth and p. every where. 16:20
many other things p. he. Luke 3:18
he p. in the synagogues of. 4:44
time the kingdom of God is p. 16:16
remission of sin should be p. 24:47
who before was p. to you. Acts 3:20
p. through Jesus resurrection. 4:2
p. Christ to Samaria. 8:5
p. the word of the Lord, p. 25
p. Jesus to eunuch. 35
Philip p. in all cities till he came. 40
Saul p. Christ in synagogues. 9:20
Barnabas told how Saul had p. 27
the baptism which John p. 10:37
they p. the word of God in. 13:5
when John had first p. before. 24
through this man is p. to you. 38
these words might be p. the next. 42
had p. the word in Perga. 14:25
and visit where we have p. 15:36
word was p. of Paul at Berea. 17:13
because he p. Jesus and the. 18
Paul p., ready to depart on. 20:7
lest when I have p. to. 1 Cor 9:27
keep in memory what I p. 15:2
if Christ be p. that he rose from. 12
Jesus who was p. among you by us. 2 Cor 1:19
Jesus, whom we have not p. 11:4
than that we have p. to you. Gal 1:8
p. peace to you who were. Eph 2:17
Christ is p. and I therein. Phil 1:18
which was p. to every. Col 1:23
p. to Gentiles, believed. 1 Tim 3:16
but the word p. did not. Heb 4:2
they to whom it was first p. 6
went and p. to the spirits. 1 Pet 3:19

see **gospel**

preacher

the words of the p. the son. Eccl 1:1
of vanities, saith the p. all. 2; 12:8
I the p. was king over Israel. 2:12
have I found, saith the p. 7:27
because p. was wise, he still. 12:9
p. sought to find out acceptable. 10
how hear without a p.? Rom 10:14
whereunto I am ordained a p. 1 Tim 2:7; 2 Tim 1:11
but saved Noah, a p. of. 2 Pet 2:5

preachest, -eth, -ing

preach to it the p. that I. Jonah 3:2
in those days came John p. Mat 3:1
Luke 3:3
p. the gospel of the. Mat 4:23; 9:35
rise in judgement, because they repented at p. 12:41; Luke 11:32
Jesus came into Galilee p. the gospel. Mark 1:14
p. and shewing glad. Luke 8:1
they went through the towns p. 9:6
went every where p. the. Acts 8:4
p. the things concerning the. 12
p. peace by Jesus Christ, he. 10:36
p. the word to none but to. 11:19
to the Greeks, p. the Lord. 20
continued in Antioch p. 15:35
by Jesus, whom Paul p. 19:13
Paul was long p., Eutychus. 20:9
among whom I have gone p. 25
p. the kingdom of God. 28:31
p. a man should not steal. Rom 2:21
according to the p. of Jesus. 16:25
for the p. of the cross. 1 Cor 1:18
by the foolishness of p. to save. 21
my p. was not with enticing. 2:4
not risen, then is our p. vain. 15:14
far as to you, p. gospel. 2 Cor 10:14
that cometh p. another Jesus. 11:4
he p. the faith which. Gal 1:23
p. might be fully known. 2 Tim 4:17
hath in due times manifested his word through p. Tit 1:3

precept, -s

commandedst them p. Neh 9:14*
hast commanded us to keep thy p. Ps 119:4

I will meditate in thy *p.* *Ps* 119:15, 78
understand the way of thy *p.* 27
I have longed after thy *p.* 40
for I seek thy *p.* 45
because I kept thy *p.* 56, 100, 168
them that keep thy *p.* 63, 69, 134
I forsook not thy *p.* 87
I will never forget thy *p.* 93
for I have sought thy *p.* 94
thro' thy *p.* I get understanding. 104
yet I erred not from thy *p.* 110
esteem all thy *p.* to be right. 128
yet do not I forget thy *p.* 141
consider how I love thy *p.* 159
for I have chosen thy *p.* 173
for *p.* must be upon *p.*, *p.* upon *p.* *Isa* 28:10, 13
taught by the *p.* of men. 29:13*
have kept all Jonadab's *p.* *Jer* 35:18
by departing from thy *p.* *Dan* 9:5
for the hardness of your heart he wrote you this *p.* *Mark* 10:5*
had spoken every *p.* *Heb* 9:19*

precious

to Rebekah's mother *p.* *Gen* 24:53
for the *p.* things of. *Deut* 33:13
p. fruits brought forth by sun. 14
p. things of the lasting hills. 15
for *p.* things of the earth, and. 16
word of the Lord was *p.* *1 Sam* 3:1
because my soul was *p.* in. 26:21
let my life be *p.* in. *2 Ki* 1:13, 14
shewed them *p.* things. 20:13
Isa 39:2
and *p.* jewels which. *2 Chr* 20:25
gave them gifts of *p.* things. 21:3
their hands with *p.* things. *Ezra* 1:6
two vessels of fine copper, *p.* 8:27
eye seeth every *p.* thing. *Job* 28:10
cannot be valued with the *p.* onyx. 16
of their soul is *p.* *Ps* 49:8*
and *p.* shall their blood be. 72:14
p. in the sight of Lord is the. 116:15
goeth forth bearing *p.* seed. 126:6*
it is like *p.* ointment on the. 133:2
how *p.* also are thy thoughts. 139:17
find all *p.* substance. *Pr* 1:13
wisdom is more *p.* than rubies. 3:15
adulteress will hunt for the *p.* 6:26
substance of a diligent man is *p.* 12:27
of knowledge are a *p.* jewel. 20:15
chambers filled with all *p.* and. 24:4
good name is better than *p.* *Eccl* 7:1
I will make a man *p.* *Isa* 13:12
I lay in Zion a *p.* corner stone. 28:16; *1 Pet* 2:6
thou wast *p.* in my sight. *Isa* 43:4
take the *p.* from the vile. *Jer* 15:19
I will deliver all the *p.* things. 20:5
the *p.* sons of Zion. *Lam* 4:2
treasure and *p.* things. *Ezek* 22:25
Dedan was thy merchant in *p.* 27:20
with their *p.* vessels of. *Dan* 11:8
power over all *p.* things of Egypt. 43
woman, having an alabaster box of very *p.* *Mat* 26:7; *Mark* 14:3
waiteth for the *p.* fruit. *Jas* 5:7
faith much more *p.* than gold. *1 Pet* 1:7
but with the *p.* blood of Christ. 19
stone, chosen of God, and *p.* 2:4
therefore which believe, he is *p.* 7
like *p.* faith with us. *2 Pet* 1:1
great and *p.* promises. 4
buyeth their *p.* vessels. *Rev* 18:12
was like unto a stone most *p.* 21:11

predestinate
(*Revisions*, foreordain)

did foreknow, he did *p.* *Rom* 8:29
and whom he did *p.* them. he 30

predestinated
(*Revisions*, foreordained)

p. us to the adoption of. *Eph* 1:5
being *p.* according to the purpose. 11

preeminence

a man hath no *p.* above. *Eccl* 3:19
things he might have the *p.* *Col* 1:18
loveth to have the *p.* *3 John* 9

prefer

if I *p.* not Jerusalem. *Ps* 137:6

preferred, -ing

p. her and her maidens. *Esth* 2:9*
Daniel was *p.* above the. *Dan* 6:3*
cometh after me is *p.* before me. *John* 1:15*, 27*
who is *p.* before me, for he was. 30*
in honour *p.* one. *Rom* 12:10
observe, without *p.* *1 Tim* 5:21*

premeditate

neither do ye *p.*: but whatsoever shall be given you. *Mark* 13:11

preparation

now make *p.* for it. *1 Chr* 22:5
torches in the day of *p.* *Nah* 2:3
followed the day of *p.* *Mat* 27:62
Mark 15:42; *Luke* 23:54
John 19:14, 31, 42
p. of the gospel of peace. *Eph* 6:15

preparations

p. of the heart in man. *Pr* 16:1

prepare

my God, and I will *p.* *Ex* 15:2*
on sixth day they shall *p.* that. 16:5
for a drink offering *p.* *Num* 15:5
or for a ram *p.* thou for a meat. 6
the number that ye shall *p.* 12
Balaam said, *P.* me seven oxen. 23:1
build me seven altars, and *p.* 29
thou shalt *p.* thee a way. *Deut* 19:3
p. you victuals to pass. *Josh* 1:11
we said, Let us now *p.* to. 22:26
p. your hearts to the Lord. *1 Sam* 7:3
say to Ahab, *P.* chariot. *1 Ki* 18:44
to *p.* shewbread every. *1 Chr* 9:32
O Lord God, *p.* their heart. 29:18
to *p.* me timber in. *2 Chr* 2:9
p. chambers in house of. 31:11
and *p.* yourselves. 35:4
sanctify yourselves, and *p.* 6
banquet that I shall *p.* *Esth* 5:8
p. thyself to the search. *Job* 8:8*
if thou *p.* thine heart toward. 11:13*
though he *p.* raiment as clay. 27:16
he may *p.* it. 17
thou wilt *p.* their heart. *Ps* 10:17
they *p.* themselves without. 59:4
O *p.* mercy and truth, which. 61:7
that they *p.* a city for. 107:36
p. thy work without. *Pr* 24:27
yet they *p.* their meat in. 30:25
p. slaughter for his. *Isa* 14:21
p. the table, watch in the. 21:5
of him that crieth, *P.* ye the way of the Lord. 40:3; *Mal* 3:1; *Mat* 3:3
Mark 1:2, 3; *Luke* 3:4; 7:27
workman to *p.* a graven. *Isa* 40:20
shall say, Cast ye up, *p.* the. 57:14
p. ye the way of the people. 62:10
p. a table for that troop. 65:11
p. ye war against her, arise. *Jer* 6:4
and *p.* them for the day of. 12:3
I will *p.* destroyers against. 22:7
say ye, Stand fast and *p.* thee. 46:14
set up watchmen, *p.* the. 51:12
blow the trumpet, *p.* nations. 27
thou shalt *p.* thy bread. *Ezek* 4:15
p. thee stuff for removing. 12:3
I will *p.* thee to blood, and blood. 35:6
p. for thyself, thou and all. 38:7
p. every day a goat, they shall also *p.* 43:25
shall *p.* the sin offering. 45:17
on that day shall prince *p.* 22; 46:12
p. a meat offering. 45:24; 46:7, 14
shall *p.* his burnt offering. 46:2, 13
they shall *p.* the lamb and. 15
p. war, wake up. *Joel* 3:9
p. to meet thy God. *Amos* 4:12
even *p.* war against him. *Mi* 3:5
messenger, who shall *p.* *Mat* 11:10
we *p.* for thee to eat the passover? 26:17; *Mark* 14:12; *Luke* 22:8, 9
to *p.* his ways. *Luke* 1:76
I go to *p.* a place for. *John* 14:2, 3
who shall *p.* himself to the battle? *1 Cor* 14:8
but withal *p.* me also a. *Philem* 22

prepared

I *p.* the house and room. *Gen* 24:31
neither had they *p.* any. *Ex* 12:39
into the place I have *p.* 23:20
Sihon be built and *p.* *Num* 21:27*
I have *p.* seven altars. *Num* 23:4
Absalom *p.* chariots. *2 Sam* 15:1
Adonijah *p.* *1 Ki* 1:5
they *p.* timber. 5:18
the oracle he *p.* in the house. 6:19
he *p.* provision and sent. *2 Ki* 6:23
brethren had *p.* for. *1 Chr* 12:39
David *p.* a place for ark of God. 15:1
3:12; *2 Chr* 1:4; 3:1
David *p.* iron in abundance for the nails. *1 Chr* 22:3
David *p.* abundantly before his. 5, 14; 29:2
work of Solomon was *p.* *2 Chr* 8:16
Rehoboam *p.* not his heart. 12:14
Jehoshaphat *p.* his heart to. 19:3
for as yet the people had not *p.* 20:33
Uzziah *p.* shields and spears. 26:14
Jotham *p.* his ways before the. 27:6
Ahaz cast away we have *p.* 29:19
that God had *p.* the people. 36
they *p.* chambers in the house. 31:11
the service was *p.*, the. 35:10, 16
when Josiah had *p.* the temple. 20
Ezra had *p.* his heart. *Ezra* 7:10
now that which was *p.* *Neh* 5:18
for whom nothing is *p.* 8:10
p. for him a great chamber. 13:5
to the banquet that I have *p.* *Esth* 5:4, 12; 6:14
on gallows Haman *p.* 6:4; 7:10
p. it, yea, and searched. *Job* 28:27
when I *p.* my seat in the. 29:7
he *p.* for him the instruments of. *Ps* 7:13
p. his throne for judgement. 9:7
p. a net for my steps. 57:6
p. of thy goodness for the. 68:10
thou hast *p.* the light and. 74:16
the Lord hath *p.* his throne. 103:19
when he *p.* the heavens. *Pr* 8:27
judgements are *p.* for scorners. 19:29
horse is *p.* against the day. 21:31
of old, for the king it is *p.* *Isa* 30:33
eye seen what he hath *p.* 64:4*
bed, and a table *p.* *Ezek* 23:41
of the pipes was *p.* in thee. 28:13
be thou *p.* and prepare for. 38:7
for ye have *p.* lying words. *Dan* 2:9
gold which they *p.* for Baal. *Hos* 2:8
his going forth is *p.* as the. 6:3
now the Lord had *p.* a. *Jonah* 1:17
God *p.* a gourd. 4:6
God *p.* a worm. 7
God *p.* a vehement east wind. 8
the defence shall be *p.* *Nah* 2:5
for the Lord hath *p.* a. *Zeph* 1:7
shall be given to them for whom it is *p.* *Mat* 20:23; *Mark* 10:40
I have *p.* my dinner. *Mat* 22:4
inherit the kingdom *p.* 25:34
into fire *p.* for devil. 41
a large upper room *p.* *Mark* 14:15
ready a people *p.* for. *Luke* 1:17
which thou hast *p.* before face. 2:31
his Lord's will, but *p.* not. 12:47
they *p.* spices, and rested the. 23:56; 24:1
he had afore *p.* to glory. *Rom* 9:23
things God hath *p.* for. *1 Cor* 2:9
vessel *p.* unto every. *2 Tim* 2:21
body hast thou *p.* me. *Heb* 10:5
Noah *p.* an ark to the saving. 11:7
their God, for he hath *p.* for. 16
and the seven angels *p.* *Rev* 8:6
the locusts were like to horses *p.* 9:7
which were *p.* for an hour, a day. 15
and the woman hath a place *p.* 12:6
kings of east may be *p.* 16:12
the holy city, *p.* as a bride for. 21:2

preparedst

thou *p.* room before it. *Ps* 80:9

preparest

when thou *p.* a bullock. *Num* 15:8
thou *p.* a table before me. *Ps* 23:5
earth, thou *p.* them corn. 65:9*

prepareth

that *p.* his heart to. *2 Chr* 30:19
their belly *p.* deceit. *Job* 15:35
who *p.* rain for earth. *Ps* 147:8

preparing

p. him a chamber in. *Neh* 13:7
while the ark was *p.* *1 Pet* 3:20

presbytery
laying on of hands of p. 1 Tim 4:14

prescribed, -ing
salt without p. how. Ezra 7:22
grievousness which they have p.
Isa 10:1*

presence
hid themselves from p. Gen 3:8
Cain went out from the p. of. 4:16
gone from the p. of Isaac. 27:30
brethren were troubled at his p. 45:3
why should we die in thy p.? 47:15
out from Pharaoh's p. Ex 10:11
my p. shall go with thee. 33:14
if thy p. go not with me, carry. 15
Israel departed from the p. 35:20
shall be cut off from my p. Lev 22:3
Moses went from the p. Num 20:6
avoided out of his p. 1 Sam 18:11
slipped away out of Saul's p. 19:10
to play the madman in my p. 21:15
as I served in thy father's p. so will
I be in thy p. 2 Sam 16:19
from the p. of Solomon. 1 Ki 12:2
I regard p. of Jehoshaphat. 2 Ki 3:14
went out from his p. a leper. 5:27
neither cast them from his p. 13:23
cast them out from his p. 24:20
that were in the king's p. 25:19*
honour are in his p. 1 Chr 16:27
trees sing at the p. of God. 33*
the king sought the p. of. 2 Chr 9:23
before this house in thy p. 20:9
altars of Baalim in his p. 34:4
before sad in his p. Neh 2:1
Mordecai went from the p. Esth 8:15
Satan went from the p. Job 1:12; 2:7
I am troubled at his p. 23:15
fall and perish at thy p. Ps 9:3
in thy p. is fulness of joy. 16:11
come forth from thy p. 17:2
them in the secret of thy p. 31:20
cast me not away from thy p. 51:11
perish at the p. of God. 68:2
Sinai moved at the p. of God. 8
come before his p. with. 95:2
hills melted like wax at the p. 97:5
before his p. with singing. 100:2
tremble, thou earth, at the p. 114:7
shall I flee from thy p.? 139:7
upright shall dwell in thy p. 140:13
go from the p. of a foolish. Pr 14:7
devour your land in your p. Isa 1:7
Egypt shall be moved at his p. 19:1
angel of his p. saved them. 63:9
that mountains might flow (flowed)
down at thy p. 64:1, 3
nations may tremble at thy p. 2
the cities broken down at p. Jer 4:26
will ye not tremble at my p.? 5:22
cast you out of my p. 23:39; 52:3
men shall shake at my p. Ezek 38:20
Jonah rose to flee from the p. of.
Jonah 1:3
men knew he fled from the p. 10
earth is burnt at his p. Nah 1:5
hold thy peace at the p. Zeph 1:7
eaten and drunk in thy p. Luke 13:26
times of refreshing come from the p.
Acts 3:19
they departed from the p. of. 5:41
should glory in his p. 1 Cor 1:29
who in p. am base. 2 Cor 10:1
letters weighty, but his bodily p. 10
have obeyed, not as in my p. only.
Phil 2:12
being taken from you in p. not in
heart. 1 Thes 2:17
destruction from the p. 2 Thes 1:9
present you faultless before p. of his
glory. Jude 24

in the **presence**
he shall dwell in the p. of. Gen 16:12
in the p. of my people I give. 23:11
in the p. of the children of Heth. 18
Ishmael died in the p. of all. 25:18
brother's wife come unto him in the
p. of the elders. Deut 25:9
should I not serve in the p. of his
son? 2 Sam 16:19
Solomon stood in the p. 1 Ki 8:22
against Naboth, in the p. of. 21:13
these cast lots in the p. 1 Chr 24:31
in the p. of Ahasuerus. Esth 1:10
a table in the p. of mine. Ps 23:5
now in the p. of all his. 116:14, 18
become surety in the p. Pr 17:18
put not forth thyself in the p. 25:6
than be put lower in the p. of. 7
Hananiah spake in the p. Jer 28:1
in the p. of people. 11
in the p. of witnesses. 32:12
I am Gabriel, that stand in the p. of
God. Luke 1:19
worship in the p. of them. 14:10
joy in the p. of the angels. 15:10
signs did Jesus in the p. John 20:30
denied him in the p. of. Acts 3:13
soundness in the p. of you all. 16
he gave thanks to God in the p. 27:35
in the p. of our Lord. 1 Thes 2:19
appear in the p. of God. Heb 9:24
in the p. of holy angels, in the p.
Rev 14:10

present, *substantive*
he took a p. for Esau. Gen 32:13, 18
I will appease him with the p. 20
so went the p. over before him. 21
if I have found grace in thy sight,
then receive my p. at. 33:10
carry down the man a p. 43:11
men took the p. 15
they made ready the p. 25
brought him the p. in their hand. 26
Israel sent a p. to Eglon. Judg 3:15
he brought the p. 17
made an end to offer the p. 18
come and bring forth my p. 6:18
not a p. for the man of. 1 Sam 9:7
a p. of the spoil of the. 30:26
a p. to his daughter. 1 Ki 9:16*
they brought every man his p. 10:25
2 Chr 9:24
sent thee a p. of silver. 1 Ki 15:19
the king said, Take a p. 2 Ki 8:8
so Hazael went ... and took a p. 9
sent it for a p. to the king of. 16:8
brought no p. to the king. 17:4
make an agreement by a p. 18:31*
Isa 36:16*
sent letters and a p. to Hezekiah.
2 Ki 20:12; Isa 39:1
a p. brought to Lord of. Isa 18:7
a p. of ivory and ebony. Ezek 27:15
carried to Assyria for a p. Hos 10:6

present, *adjective*
the people p. with him. 1 Sam 13:15
loaves, or what there is p. 21:3
and be thou here p. 2 Sam 20:4
Israel were numbered, and were all
p. 1 Ki 20:27*
people p. here to offer. 1 Chr 29:17
priests p. were sanctified. 2 Chr 5:11
Israel p. at Jerusalem. 30:21
all p. went out and brake the. 31:1
all that were p. to stand. 34:32*
and all Israel p. offered. Ezra 8:25
the Jews p. in Shushan. Esth 4:16
God is a very p. help in. Ps 46:1
power of the Lord was p. Luke 5:17
there were p. at that season. 13:1
manifold more in this p. life. 18:30
being yet p. with you. John 14:25
are we all p. before God. Acts 10:33
and all elders were p. 21:18
received us because of p. rain. 28:2
to will is p. with me, but. Rom 7:18
would do good, evil is p. with. 21
sufferings of this p. time. 8:18
nor things p. nor things to come. 38
1 Cor 3:22
even at this p. time there. Rom 11:5
even to this p. hour we both hunger.
1 Cor 4:11
but p. in spirit, have judged as
though I were p. 5:3
good for the p. distress. 7:26
greater part remain to this p. 15:6
willing rather to be p. 2 Cor 5:8*
that whether p. or absent. 9*
that I may not be bold when p. 10:2
was p. with you and wanted. 11:9
I foretell, as if I were p. the. 13:2
I write, lest being p. I should. 10
might deliver us from this p. world.
Gal 1:4
not only when I am p. with. Gal 4:18
I desire to be p. with you. 20
loved this p. world. 2 Tim 4:10
godly in this p. world. Tit 2:12
figure for the time then p. Heb 9:9
for the p. seemeth joyous. 12:11
be established in the p. truth.
2 Pet 1:12*

present, -ed, *verb*
Joseph p. himself to his. Gen 46:29
he p. five of his brethren to. 47:2
and p. thyself there to me. Ex 34:2
meat offering, when it is p. Lev 2:8
in the day when he p. them. 7:35
Aaron's sons p. to him the. 9:12, 18
and they p. the burnt offering. 13
the priest shall p. the man. 14:11*
the two goats, and p. them. 16:7*
the scapegoat shall be p. 10
p. himself before the priest. 27:8*
then he shall p. the beast. 11*
and p. the tribe of Levi. Num 3:6*
p. yourselves before the. Deut 31:14
p. themselves before God. Josh 24:1
it under oak, and p. it. Judg 6:19
the tribes of Israel p. 20:2
now p. yourselves. 1 Sam 10:19
Goliath the Philistine p. 17:16
sons of God came to p. Job 1:6
Satan came to p. himself. 2:1
will p. their supplication. Jer 36:7
I p. my supplication before. 38:26
ye sent to p. your supplication. 42:9
they p. the provocation. Ezek 20:28
do not p. our supplications. Dan 9:18
they p. to him gifts, gold. Mat 2:11
they brought him to p. Luke 2:22
called the saints, p. her. Acts 9:41
they p. Paul also before. 23:33
that ye p. your bodies a. Rom 12:1
by Jesus and p. us with. 2 Cor 4:14
that I may p. you as a chaste. 11:2
he might p. it to himself. Eph 5:27
to p. you holy and. Col 1:22
we may p. every man perfect. 28
is able to p. you faultless. Jude 24*

presenting
p. my supplication before. Dan 9:20

presently
let them not fail to burn the fat p.
1 Sam 2:16
a fool's wrath is p. known. Pr 12:16
and p. the fig tree. Mat 21:19*
he shall p. give me more. 26:53*
him I hope to send p. Phil 2:23*

presents
brought him no p. 1 Sam 10:27
they brought p. and. 1 Ki 4:21
gave Shalmanezer p. 2 Ki 17:3
p. to Jehoshaphat. 2 Chr 17:5, 11
p. to Hezekiah. 32:23*
kings shall bring p. unto. Ps 68:29
and the isles shall bring p. 72:10
let all bring p. to him that. 76:11
give p. to Moresheth-gath. Mi 1:14*

preserve
that we may p. seed. Gen 19:32, 34
send me before you to p. life. 45:5
God sent me to p. you a posterity. 7
that he might p. us alive. Deut 6:24
thou shalt p. them from. Ps 12:7
p. me, O God, for in thee do. 16:1
and uprightness p. me. 25:21
my hiding place, shalt p. me. 32:7
let thy truth continually p. me. 40:11
Lord will p. him and keep. 41:2
mercy and truth which may p. 61:7
p. my life from fear of enemy. 64:1
p. thou those that are. 79:11
p. my soul, for I am holy. 86:2
p. thee from all evil, he shall p. thy.
121:7*
p. thy going out and coming in. 8*
p. me from violent man. 140:1, 4
discretion shall p. thee. Pr 2:11*
and she shall p. thee. 4:6
lips of the wise shall p. them. 14:3
mercy and truth p. king. 20:28
eyes of Lord p. knowledge. 22:12
he will p. Jerusalem. Isa 31:5
I will p. thee, and give thee. 49:8
thy children, I will p. Jer 49:11

lose his life shall *p.* it. *Luke* 17:33
the Lord will *p.* me unto his heavenly kingdom. *2 Tim* 4:18*

preserved, -eth

God, and my life is *p.* *Gen* 32:30
and *p.* us in all the way. *Josh* 24:17
us, who hath *p.* us. *1 Sam* 30:23
Lord *p.* David whithersoever he. *2 Sam* 8:6*; *1 Chr* 18:6*, 13*
thy visitation hath *p.* my. *Job* 10:12
as in days when God *p.* me. 29:2*
he *p.* not the life of the wicked. 36:6
for the Lord *p.* the faithful. *Ps* 31:23
his saints; they are *p.* for. 37:28
he *p.* the souls of his saints. 97:10
the Lord *p.* the simple. 116:6
Lord *p.* all them that love. 145:20
the Lord *p.* the strangers. 146:9
p. the way of his saints. *Pr* 2:8
keepeth his way *p.* his soul. 16:17
to restore the *p.* of Israel. *Isa* 49:6
by a prophet was he *p.* *Hos* 12:13
new wine into new bottles, and both are *p.* *Mat* 9:17; *Luke* 5:38
soul and body *p.* blameless. *1 Thes* 5:23
and *p.* in Jesus Christ, and. *Jude* 1

preserver

thee, O thou *p.* of men ? *Job* 7:20*

preservest

thou Lord hast made . . . and thou *p.* *Neh* 9:6
thou *p.* man and beast. *Ps* 36:6

presidents

three *p.*; Daniel was first. *Dan* 6:2
this Daniel was preferred above *p.* 3
the *p.* sought to find occasion. 4
these *p.* and princes assembled. 6, 7

press

[1] *To squeeze,* Gen 40:11. [2] *To crowd,* Luke 8:45. [3] *To urge,* Gen 19:3. [4] *A crowd or throng,* Luke 19:3.

could not come nigh for the *p.* *Mark* 2:4; *Luke* 8:19
came in *p.* behind him. *Mark* 5:27
Jesus turned him about in the *p.* 30
not see Jesus for the *p.* *Luke* 19:3

press

(*Wine press*)

for the *p.* is full, the fats. *Joel* 3:13
fifty vessels out of the *p.* *Hag* 2:16

see **wine**

press, -ed, -eth

Lot *p.* on the two angels. *Gen* 19:3
they *p.* sore on Lot, and came near. 9
took the grapes and *p.* them. 40:11
Delilah *p.* him daily. *Judg* 16:16
Absalom *p.* him. *2 Sam* 13:25, 27
posts *p.* on by the king's. *Esth* 8:14
and thy hand *p.* me sore. *Ps* 38:2
were their breasts *p.* *Ezek* 23:3
I am *p.* under you as a cart is *p.* *Amos* 2:13
p. on him for to touch. *Mark* 3:10
people *p.* to hear the word. *Luke* 5:1
measure, *p.* down and shaken. 6:38
throng thee and *p.* thee. 8:45
every man *p.* into it. 16:16*
Paul was *p.* in spirit, and. *Acts* 18:5*
were *p.* above measure. *2 Cor* 1:8*
I *p.* toward the mark. *Phil* 3:14

presses

thy *p.* shall burst with. *Pr* 3:10
tread out no wine in their *p. Isa* 16:10

pressfat

when one came to the *p.* *Hag* 2:16*

presume

prophet who shall *p.* to. *Deut* 18:20*
he that durst *p.* in his. *Esth* 7:5

presumed

they *p.* to go up to hill. *Num* 14:44

presumptuous

servant also from *p.* sins. *Ps* 19:13
p. are they, selfwilled. *2 Pet* 2:10*

presumptuously

if a man come *p.* on his. *Ex* 21:14
the soul that doeth aught *p.* *Num* 15:30*; *Deut* 17:12

went *p.* up into the hill. *Deut* 1:43
shall hear, and do no more *p.* 17:13
prophet hath spoken it *p.* 18:22

pretence

for a *p.* make long prayers. *Mat* 23:14; *Mark* 12:40
every way, whether in *p.* or in truth, Christ is preached. *Phil* 1:18

prevail

upward did the waters *p.* *Gen* 7:20
peradventure I shall *p.* *Num* 22:6
by what means we may *p. Judg* 16:5
strength shall no man *p.* *1 Sam* 2:9
if I *p.* against him, then ye. 17:9
great things and shalt still *p.* 26:25
thou shalt persuade him, and *p.* *1 Ki* 22:22; *2 Chr* 18:21
O Lord, let not man *p.* *2 Chr* 14:11
thou shalt not *p.* against. *Esth* 6:13
they shall *p.* against him. *Job* 15:24
robber shall *p.* against him. 18:9*
arise, O Lord, let not man *p. Ps* 9:19
with our tongue will we *p.* 12:4
iniquities *p.* against me. 65:3
if one *p.* against him. *Eccl* 4:12
to war, but could not *p.* *Isa* 7:1
to pray, but he shall not *p.* 16:12
he shall *p.* against his enemies. 42:13*
if so be thou mayest *p.* 47:12
they shall not *p.* against thee, for. *Jer* 1:19; 15:20; 20:11
toss, yet can they not *p.* 5:22
will be enticed, and we shall *p.* 20:10
who shall deal against him and shall *p.* *Dan* 11:7
gates of hell shall not *p.* *Mat* 16:18
Pilate saw he could *p.* nothing. 27:24
perceive ye how ye *p.* nothing. *John* 12:19

prevailed

the waters *p.* and. *Gen* 7:18, 19
the waters *p.* on the earth. 24
with my sister and have *p.* 30:8
when he saw he *p.* not against. 32:25
as a prince hast thou power with God and men, and hast *p.* 28
the famine *p.* over them. 47:20
blessings of thy father have *p.* 49:26
Israel *p.*: when he let down his hand, Amalek *p.* *Ex* 17:11
of the house of Joseph *p* *Judg* 1:35
Othniel's hand *p.* against. 3:10
Israel *p.* against Jabin. 4:24
Midian *p.* against Israel. 6:2
David *p.* over Goliath. *1 Sam* 17:50
the men *p.* against us. *2 Sam* 11:23
king's word *p.* against Joab. 24:4
that followed Omri *p.* *1 Ki* 16:22
the famine *p.* in the city. *2 Ki* 25:3
for Judah *p.* above his. *1 Chr* 5:2
p. against Hamath-zobah. *2 Chr* 8:3
Judah *p.* because they relied. 13:18
p. against the Ammonites. 27:5
lest mine enemy say, I have *p.* *Ps* 13:4
they have not *p.* against me. 129:2
thou art stronger than I, and hast *p.* *Jer* 20:7
friends have *p.* against thee. 38:22
I weep because the enemy *p.* *Lam* 1:16
the same horn *p.* against. *Dan* 7:21
power over angel and *p.* *Hos* 12:4
have deceived thee and *p.* *Ob* 7
of the chief priests *p.* *Luke* 23:23
in whom the evil spirit was, leaped on them and *p.* *Acts* 19:16
so grew word of God and *p.* 20
of David hath *p.* to open. *Rev* 5:5
dragon and his angels *p.* not. 12:8

prevailest

p. for ever against him. *Job* 14:20

prevaileth

into my bones, and it *p.* *Lam* 1:13

prevent

(*Usually used in its original sense of going before, either actually or symbolically*)

why did the knees *p.* me ? *Job* 3:12*
my mercy shall *p.* me. *Ps* 59:10†
mercies speedily *p.* us. 79:8†
morning shall my prayer *p.* 88:13*

eyes *p.* nightwatches. *Ps* 119:148*
The evil shall not *p.* us. *Amos* 9:10
we shall not *p.* them who are asleep. *1 Thes* 4:15*

prevented

the snares of death *p.* me. *2 Sam* 22:6*; *Ps* 18:5*
they *p.* me in the day of my calamities. 19*; *Ps* 18:18*
days of affliction *p.* me. *Job* 30:27*
who hath *p.* me that I ? 41:11*
I *p.* the dawning of. *Ps* 119:147†
they *p.* with their bread. *Isa* 21:14*
Jesus *p.* him, saying, Simon, of. *Mat* 17:25*

preventest

thou *p.* him with blessings. *Ps* 21:3†

prey

from the *p.* my son. *Gen* 49:9
he shall devour the *p.* 27
that our wives and children shall be a *p.*? *Num* 14:3, 31; *Deut* 1:39
lie down till he eat of *p. Num* 23:24
captives and *p.* to Moses. 31:12
take the sum of the *p.* that. 26
and divide the *p.* into two parts. 27
booty being the rest of the *p.* 32
only the cattle we took for a *p.* to. *Deut* 2:35; 3:7; *Josh* 8:2, 27; 11:14
divided the *p.*; to Sisera a *p.* of. *Judg* 5:30
give me the earrings of his *p.* 8:24
man the earrings of his *p.* 25
Judah shall become a *p.* *2 Ki* 21:14
a *p.* in the land of captivity. *Neh* 4:4
take the spoil of them for a *p.* *Esth* 3:13; 8:11
on the *p.* they laid not. 9:15, 16
perisheth for lack of *p.* *Job* 4:11
eagle that hasteth to the *p.* 9:26
as wild asses; rising betimes for a *p.* 24:5*
wilt thou hunt the *p.* for ? 38:39
thence she seeketh the *p.* 39:29
like a lion greedy of his *p. Ps* 17:12
than the mountains of *p.* 76:4
lions roar after their *p.* 104:21
not given us for a *p.* to their. 124:6
lieth in wait as for a *p.* *Pr* 23:28
roar and lay hold of the *p. Isa* 5:29
that widows may be their *p.* 10:2
the *p.* of an hypocritical nation. 6
young lion roaring on his *p.* 31:4
the *p.* of a great spoil divided. 33:23
for a *p.* and none delivereth. 42:22
p. be taken from the mighty ? 49:24
the *p.* of the terrible shall be. 25
he that departeth from evil a *p.* 59:15
his life shall be to him for a *p.* *Jer* 21:9; 38:2; 39:18; 45:5
p. on thee will I give for a *p.* 30:16
hands of strangers for *p.* *Ezek* 7:21
it learned to catch the *p.* 19:3
like wolves ravening the *p.* 22:27
make a *p.* of thy merchandise. 26:12
take her spoil, and take her *p.* 29:19
because my flock became a *p.* 34:8
flock shall no more be a *p.* 22, 28
to the cities that became a *p.* 36:4
minds, to cast it out for a *p.* 5
to take a spoil and a *p.* 38:12, 13
scatter among them the *p. Dan* 11:24
will lion roar when no *p.*? *Amos* 3:4
lion filled his holes with *p.* *Nah* 2:12
I will cut off thy *p.* from. 13
city, the *p.* departeth not. 3:1
that I rise up to the *p.* *Zeph* 3:8

price

[1] *The sum asked for a thing when selling it,* 2 Sam 24:24. [2] *The worth or value of a thing,* Job 28:18. [3] *Wages or hire,* Zech 11:12.

thou shalt increase the *p.* . . . thou shalt diminish the *p. Lev* 25:16, 50
shall give him again the *p.* of. 52
not bring *p.* of a dog. *Deut* 23:18*
I will buy it at a *p.* *2 Sam* 24:24
1 Chr 21:22, 24
merchants received the linen yarn at a *p.* *1 Ki* 10:28; *2 Chr* 1:16
man knoweth not the *p. Job* 28:13, 15
p. of wisdom is above rubies. 18

increase wealth by their *p.* *Ps* 44:12
a *p.* in hand of a fool? *Pr* 17:16
goats are the *p.* of the field. 27:26
virtuous woman, for her *p.* 31:10
go my captives not for *p.* *Isa* 45:13
buy wine and milk without *p.* 55:1
to the spoil without *p.* *Jer* 15:13
p. weighed for my *p.* *Zech* 11:12*
a goodly *p.* that I was prized at. 13
one pearl of great *p.* *Mat* 13:46
because it is the *p.* of blood. 27:6
took *p.* of him that was valued. 9
kept back part of the *p.* *Acts* 5:2, 3
they counted the *p.* of them. 19:19
for ye are bought with a *p.*
1 Cor 6:20; 7:23
in sight of God of great *p.* *1 Pet* 3:4

prices

brought *p.* of the things. *Acts* 4:34

pricked

I was *p.* in my reins. *Ps* 73:21
they were *p.* in their heart. *Acts* 2:37

pricking

a *p.* briar to Israel. *Ezek* 28:24

pricks

those that remain be *p.* *Num* 33:55
it is hard to kick against the *p.*
Acts 9:5*; 26:14*

pride

I will break the *p.* of. *Lev* 26:19
I know thy *p.* and. *1 Sam* 17:28
humbled himself for *p.* *2 Chr* 32:26
that he may hide *p.* from man.
Job 33:17
they cry because of the *p.* 35:12
his scales are his *p.* shut up. 41:15
king over all children of *p.* 34
the wicked in his *p.* *Ps* 10:2
through *p.* of his countenance. 4
hide them from the *p.* of man. 31:20*
let not the foot of *p.* come. 36:11
let them be taken in their *p.* 59:12
p. compasseth them as chain. 73:6
p. . . . do I hate. *Pr* 8:13
when *p.* cometh. 11:2
by *p.* cometh contention. 13:10
the foolish is a rod of *p.* 14:3
p. goeth before destruction. 16:18
man's *p.* shall bring him low. 29:23
in the *p.* of their hearts. *Isa* 9:9
p. of Moab, even of his haughtiness
and his *p.* 16:6; *Jer* 48:29
stain the *p.* of all glory. *Isa* 23:9
shall bring down their *p.* 25:11
woe to the crown of *p.* 28:1, 3
I will mar the *p.* of Judah. *Jer* 13:9
my soul shall weep for your *p.* 17
the *p.* of thy heart hath. 49:16
blossomed, *p.* hath. *Ezek* 7:10
iniquity of thy sister Sodom, *p.* 16:49
not mentioned in the day of thy *p.* 56
and the *p.* of her power shall. 30:6
those that walk in *p.* he is. *Dan* 4:37
mind was hardened in *p.* 5:20
the *p.* of Israel doth testify.
Hos 5:5; 7:10
p. of thine heart hath deceived. *Ob* 3
they have for their *p.* *Zeph* 2:10
them away that rejoice in thy *p.* 3:11
the *p.* of the Philistines. *Zech* 9:6
the *p.* of Assyria shall be. 10:11
the *p.* of Jordan is spoiled. 11:3
the heart proceedeth *p.* *Mark* 7:22
lifted up *p.* he fall into. *1 Tim* 3:6
the *p.* of life, is not of. *1 John* 2:16

priest

There were priests in every nation, since the term is used of all who have charge of the religious life of a people. The Jewish priesthood as a definite body, dated from the appointment of Aaron and his sons as Priests of Jehovah at the time of the Exodus. At about the same time the entire tribe of Levi was set apart to do the non-priestly duties of the tabernacle, and the religious services. The priests were all descendants of Aaron, the legal head of the house of Aaron in each generation being High Priest. The priestly duties included the instruction of the people, sanitary and medicinal care for their welfare, and the services at the house of God.

Jesus Christ, as the fulfilment of the old dispensation, is called the High Priest of those who have accepted him.

p. of the most high God. *Gen* 14:18
Heb 7:1
p. of Midian had seven. *Ex* 2:16
that son that is *p.* in his stead.
29:30; *Lev* 16:32
the *p.* shall burn it all on the altar.
Lev 1:9, 13, 17; 2:2, 9, 16; 3:11
16; 4:10, 31, 35; 7:5, 31
the *p.* shall lay them in order. 1:12
when it is presented to the *p.* 2:8
if the *p.* that is anointed do sin. 4:3
the *p.* shall dip his finger. 6, 17
the *p.* shall make an atonement. 4:20
26; 5:6; 6:7; 12:8; 15:15, 30
16:30; 19:22
p. shall take of blood. 4:25; 30, 34
he shall bring them to the *p.* 5:8
the remnant shall be the *p.'s*. 13
p. shall put on his linen. 6:10
p. shall have to himself the skin. 7:8
it shall be the *p.'s* that offereth it. 9
14; 14:13
the *p.* shall look on the plague. 13:3
5, 6, 17, 20, 21, 25, 26, 27, 30, 31, 32
p. shall look on him and pronounce
unclean. 13:8, 11, 20, 22, 25, 30, 44
the *p.* shall shut him up. 4, 5, 31, 33
the *p.* shall pronounce him clean.
13:6, 17, 23, 28, 34
brought to the *p.* 13:9
come to the *p.* 16; 14:2
p. that maketh him clean. 14:11
the *p.* shall dip his right finger. 16
the house, shall come and tell *p.* 35
the *p.* shall pronounce the house. 48
if the daughter of a *p.* profane. 21:9
if the *p.* buy any soul with. 22:11
if *p.'s* daughter be married. 12, 13
a sheaf of firstfruits to the *p.* 23:10
the *p.* shall wave it before the. 11
p. shall value him, according. 27:8
possession thereof shall be *p.'s*. 21
trespass be recompensed to the *p.*
Num 5:8
man shall bring wife to the *p.* 15
the *p.* shall execute upon her. 30
this is holy for the *p.* with the. 6:20
p. shall wash and be unclean. 19:7
in land till death of high *p.* 35:32
will not hearken to *p.* *Deut* 17:12
the *p.'s* due from people. 18:3
are come nigh to battle, the *p.* 20:2
go to the *p.* in those days. 26:3
sons who became his *p.* *Judg* 17:5
and be unto me a father and a *p.* 10
seeing I have a Levite to my *p.* 13
Micah hired me, and I am his *p.*18:4
a father and a *p.*: better a *p.* unto one
man, or a *p.* unto a tribe? 19
all that the *p.* took for. *1 Sam* 2:14
give flesh to roast for the *p.* 15
choose him out of Israel to be my *p.*
28
I will raise me up a faithful *p.* 35
while Saul talked to the *p.* 14:19
said the *p.*, Let us draw near to. 36
the *p.* answered, There is no. 21:4
p. gave them hallowed bread. 6
Abiathar from being *p.* *1 Ki* 2:27
p. had said, Let her not be slain.
2 Ki 11:15
the same may be a *p.* of them that
are no gods. *2 Chr* 13:9
Israel without a teaching *p.* 15:3
till there stood up a *p.* *Ezra* 2:63
Neh 7:65
a *p.* for ever after the order of.
Ps 110:4; *Heb* 5:6; 7:17, 21
Uriah the *p.* and Zechariah. *Isa* 8:2
as with people, so with the *p.* 24:2
p. and prophet have erred. 28:7
from prophet to the *p.* every one
dealeth falsely. *Jer* 6:13; 8:10
prophet and *p.* go to a land. 14:18
law shall not perish from *p.* 18:18
prophet and *p.* are profane. *Jer* 23:11
prophet and *p.* shall. 33, 34
thee *p.* instead of Jehoiada. 29:26
despised the king and the *p.* *Lam* 2:6
shall the *p.* and prophets be slain? 20
but the law shall perish from the *p.*
Ezek 7:26
near to do the office of a *p.* 44:13
nor shall any *p.* drink wine when. 21
a widow that had a *p.* before. 22
to the *p.* the first of your dough. 30
p. shall not eat of any thing. 31
that strive with the *p.* *Hos* 4:4
thou shalt be no *p.* to me. 6
shall be, like people, like *p.* 9
the *p.* of Beth-el sent to. *Amos* 7:10
and he shall be *p.* on. *Zech* 6:13
the *p.'s* lips should keep. *Mal* 2:7
go thy way, shew thyself to the *p.*
Mat 8:4; *Mark* 1:44; *Luke* 5:14
p. named Zacharias. *Luke* 1:5
there came down a certain *p.* 10:31
the *p.* of Jupiter brought oxen and
garlands. *Acts* 14:13
abideth a *p.* continually. *Heb* 7:3
what need another *p.* should rise? 11
Melchizedek ariseth another *p.* 15
not without oath he was made *p.* 20
on earth, he should not be a *p.* 8:4
every *p.* standeth daily. 10:11

see **chief**

high **priest**

high p. shalt not uncover. *Lev* 21:10
city of refuge till the death of the
high p. *Num* 35:25; *Josh* 20:6
much money in chest, the *high p.*
came. *2 Ki* 12:10; *2 Chr* 24:11
to Hilkiah the *high p.* *2 Ki* 22:4
Eliashib the *high p.* rose up. *Neh* 3:1
Joshua the *high p.* standing.
Zech 3:1, 8; 6:11
to the palace of the *high p.*
Mat 26:3; *Luke* 22:54
struck servant of *high p.* *Mat* 26:51
Luke 22:50; *John* 18:10
led him to Caiaphas the *high p.*
Mat 26:57; *John* 18:24
the *high p.* rent his clothes.
Mat 26:65; *Mark* 14:63
days of Abiathar *high p.* *Mark* 2:26
Caiaphas being *high p.* *John* 11:49
51; 18:13
disciple was known to *high p.* 18:15
answerest thou the *high p.* so? 22
of the kindred of *high p.* *Acts* 4:6
said *high p.*, Are these things? 7:1
Saul went to the *high p.* and. 9:1
high p. doth bear me witness. 22:5
revilest thou God's *high p.*? 23:4
might be a faithful *high p.* *Heb* 2:17
consider Apostle, *High P.* of. 3:1
great *high p.* that is passed. 4:14
not an *high p.* which cannot be. 15
every *high p.* is ordained. 5:1
Christ glorified not himself to be an
high p. 5
an *high p.* after the order. 10; 6:20
such an *high p.* became us. 7:26
we have such an *high p.* who. 8:1
high p. is ordained to offer gifts. 3
into second went *high p.* alone. 9:7
Christ being come an *high p.* of. 11
as *high p.* entereth holy place. 25
having an *high p.* over house. 10:21
into sanctuary by *high p.* 13:11

see **office**

priesthood

anointing shall be an everlasting *p.*
Ex 40:15; *Num* 25:13
and seek ye the *p.* also? *Num* 16:10
shall bear iniquity of your *p.* 18:1
for *p.* of the Lord is their. *Josh* 18:7
therefore were they, as polluted, put
from the *p.* *Ezra* 2:62; *Neh* 7:64
the *p.*, the covenant of *p.* *Neh* 13:29
who receive the office of *p.* *Heb* 7:5
were by the Levitical *p.* 11
for the *p.* being changed, there. 12
spake nothing concerning the *p.* 14
this man hath an unchangeable *p.* 24
an holy *p.* *1 Pet* 2:5
ye are a royal *p.* 9

priests

land of p. bought he not, for the p. had portion assigned. Gen 47:22
except land of p. only, not. 26
be to me a kingdom of p. Ex 19:6
the p. shall sprinkle. Lev 1:11; 3:2
males among the p. shall eat. 6:29
unto one of his sons the p. 13:2
make an atonement for the p. 16:33
holy to the Lord for the p. 23:20
shall stand before p. Deut 19:17
p. that bare the ark stood. Josh 3:17
where the p.' feet stood. 4:3, 9
the p. bare seven trumpets. 6:4, 13
p. took up the ark of the Lord. 12
were p. to tribe of Dan. Judg 18:30
Hophni and Phinehas p. 1 Sam 1:3
nor the p. of Dagon tread on. 5:5
Philistines called for the p. 6:2
king said, Turn and slay the p. 22:17
Doeg, Turn thou and fall on the p. 18
that Saul had slain the Lord's p. 21
and the p. took up the ark. 1 Ki 8:3
made p. of the lowest. 12:31; 13:33
on thee shall he offer the p. of. 13:2
Jehu slew Ahab's p., he. 2 Ki 10:11
call me all Baal's p., let none. 19
p. had not repaired breaches. 12:6
carry thither one of the p. ye. 17:27
put down idolatrous p. of king. 23:5
slew all the p. of the high places. 20
sea was for p. to wash in. 2 Chr 4:6
p. sounding with trumpets. 5:12
p. could not stand to minister. 14
let thy p. be clothed with. 6:41
appointed the courses of the p. 8:14
ordained p. for high places. 11:15
have ye not cast out the p.? 13:9
p. with trumpets to cry alarm. 12
into house of Lord save the p. 23:6
with him fourscore p. of the. 26:17
Uzziah was wroth with the p. 19
p. were too few, they could. 29:34
p. had not sanctified. 30:3
Josiah burnt bones of the p. 34:5
Josiah set p. in their charges. 35:2
to the p. for passover offerings. 8
set the p. in their divisions. Ezra 6:18
and killed the passover for p. 20
offering of the people and p. 7:16
and our p. been delivered into. 9:7
as yet told it to the p. Neh 2:16
repaired the p., men of the plain. 3:22
hath come on us and our p. 9:32
we nor our p. kept thy law. 34
laid the offerings of the p. 13:5
their p. fell by the sword. Ps 78:64
Moses and Aaron among his p. 99:6
let thy p. be clothed with. 132:9
clothe her p. with salvation. 16
he sent elders of p. covered. Isa 37:2
but ye shall be named the p. of. 61:6
against the p. thereof. Jer 1:18
p. said not, Where is the Lord? 2:8
Israel ashamed; their kings, p. 26
p. shall be astonished. 4:9
p. bare rule by their means. 5:31
bones of the p. they shall bring. 8:1
fill the p. with drunkenness. 13:13
I will satiate the souls of the p. 31:14
me to anger, they and their p. 32:32
into captivity with his p. 48:7; 49:3
her p. sigh, her virgins. Lam 1:4
p. and elders gave up the ghost. 19
for the iniquities of her p. 4:13
respected not persons of p. 16
her p. violated my law. Ezek 22:26
said, This chamber is for p. 40:45
shall be for the p. 45:4; 48:10, 11
hear this, O p.; and hearken, ye house of Israel. Hos 5:1
p. murder in the way by. 6:9
p., the Lord's ministers, mourn. Joel 1:9, 13; 2:17
p. thereof teach for hire. Mi 3:11
I will cut off names of p. Zeph 1:4
her p. have polluted the. 3:4
ask p. concerning the law. Hag 2:11
O p. that despise my name. Mal 1:6
O ye p., this commandment is. 2:1
only for the p. to eat. Mat 12:4
p. in temple profane the sabbath, and. 5; Mark 2:26; Luke 6:4
not lawful to eat but for p. Mark 2:26
shew yourselves to the p. Luke 17:14
the p. and captain came. Acts 4:1
company of p. were obedient. 6:7
sons of Sceva chief of the p. 19:14
those p. were made without an oath. Heb 7:21
they truly were many p. 23
seeing there are p. that offer. 8:4
p. went always into the first. 9:6
hath made us kings and p. to God. Rev 1:6; 5:10
be p. of God and of Christ. 20:6
see **chief, Levites, office**

high **priests**

and Caiaphas being high p. Luke 3:2
daily as those high p. to. Heb 7:27
for the law maketh men high p. 28

prince

This name is given, [1] *To God, who is the supreme Ruler and Governor,* Dan 8:11. [2] *To Christ, who is called the* Prince of Peace, Isa 9:6; the Prince of Life, Acts 3:15; the Prince of the kings of the earth, Rev 1:5. [3] *To the chief of the priests, called the* princes *of the sanctuary,* Isa 43:28. [4] *To men of princely excellency and worth,* Eccl 10:7. [5] *To the nobles, counsellors, and officers in a kingdom,* Isa 10:8. [6] *To the chief, or principal men of families, or tribes,* Num 17:6. [7] *To the devil, called* the prince of this world, *John* 12:31; *who boasts of having all the kingdoms of the earth at his disposal,* Mat 4:9.

thou art a mighty p. Gen 23:6
as a p. hast power with God. 32:28
when Shechem, p. of the. 34:2
who made thee a p. over? Ex 2:14
each p. shall offer on. Num 7:11
thyself altogether a p. over. 16:13
for each p. a rod, even twelve. 17:6
Cozbi the daughter of a p. 25:18
take one p. of every tribe to. 34:18
of each chief house a p. Josh 22:14
is a p. fallen in Israel? 2 Sam 3:38
I will make him a p. all. 1 Ki 11:34
a p. over my people. 14:7; 16:2
Sheshbazzar p. of Judah. Ezra 1:8
where is house of the p.? Job 21:28
as a p. would I go near unto. 31:37
but in want of people is destruction of p. Pr 14:28
much less do lying lips a p. 17:7
put lower in presence of the p. 25:7
by long forbearing is a p. 15*
p. that wanteth understanding. 28:16
how beautiful are thy feet, O p.'s daughter. S of S 7:1
the P. of Peace. Isa 9:6
Seraiah was a quiet p. Jer 51:59*
the p. shall be clothed. Ezek 7:27
this burden concerneth the p. 12:10
p. shall bear on his shoulder. 12
profane wicked p. of Israel. 21:25
son of man, say to p. of Tyrus. 28:2
be no more a p. of Egypt. 30:13
David a p. among them. 34:24
David shall be their p. for. 37:25
against Gog, the land of Magog, the chief p. of. 38:2, 3; 39:1
this gate is for the p.; the p. 44:3
and a portion shall be for the p. 45:7
it shall be the p.'s part to give. 17
shall the p. prepare a bullock. 22
p. shall enter by the porch. 46:2
the burnt offering that the p. shall. 4
and when the p. shall enter he. 8
and the p. in the midst of them. 10
p. prepares a voluntary burnt. 12
if the p. give a gift to any of his. 16
after, it shall return to the p. but. 17
p. shall not take of the people's. 18
residue shall be for the p. on. 48:21
to whom p. of the eunuchs. Dan 1:7
requested of p. of the eunuchs. 8
favour with the p. of the eunuchs. 9
magnified himself even to p. 8:11
up against the p. of princes. 25
unto the Messiah the P. 9:25
people of the p. that shall come. 26
p. of Persia withstood me. Dan 10:13
p. of Persia, p. of Grecia come. 20
with me, but Michael your p. 21
but a p. for his own behalf. 11:18
also the p. of the covenant. 22
Michael stand up, the great p. 12:1
Israel shall abide without p. Hos 3:4
the p. and the judge ask. Mi 7:3
casteth out devils by p. of devils. Mat 9:34; 12:24; Mark 3:22
p. of this world shall be. John 12:31
the p. of this world cometh. 14:30
the p. of this world is judged. 16:11
killed P. of life, whom. Acts 3:15
hath God exalted to be a P. 5:31
p. of the power of the air. Eph 2:2
Jesus Christ the P. of. Rev 1:5*

princes

the p. also of Pharaoh. Gen 12:15
twelve p. shall Ishmael beget. 17:20; 25:16
a wagon for two p. Num 7:3
the p. offered. 10
rose up 250 p. 16:2
the p. digged a well. 21:18
and the p. of Moab abode with. 22:8
Balak sent yet again p. more. 15
p. of the congregation. Josh 9:15
whom Moses smote with p. 13:21*
with Phinehas ten p. sent to. 22:14
kings, give ear, O ye p. Judg 5:3
and the p. of Issachar were with. 15
the two p. of the Midianites. 7:25
he described the p. of Succoth. 8:14
poor, to set them among p. 1 Sam 2:8
p. of the Philistines were wroth. 29:4
young men of the p. 1 Ki 20:14
p. in their families. 1 Chr 4:38
p. and people will be at thy. 28:21*
left spoil before the p. 2 Chr 28:14
do the commandment of p. 30:12
p. gave a thousand bullocks. 24
p. gave willingly to the people. 35:8
treasures of his p. brought. 36:18
all the king's mighty p. Ezra 7:28
hand of p. hath been chief. 9:2
according to the counsel of p. 10:8
our p. kept thy law. Neh 9:34
our p. Levites, and priests seal. 38
he made a feast to all his p. Esth 1:3; 2:18
advanced him above the p. 5:11
of one of the king's noble p. 6:9
with p. that had gold. Job 3:15
leadeth p. away spoiled. 12:19*
he poureth contempt on p. and. 21
the p. refrained talking, and. 29:9
is it fit to say to p., Ye are? 34:18*
accepteth not the persons of p. 19
thou mayest make p. in all the earth. Ps 45:16
p. of the people are gathered. 47:9
the p. of Zebulun, the p. 68:27
p. shall come out of Egypt. 31
he shall cut off the spirit of p. 76:12
and fall like one of the p. 82:7
to bind his p. at his pleasure. 105:22
he poureth contempt upon p. 107:40
set him with p. even with the p. 113:8
than to put confidence in p. 118:9
p. also did sit and speak. 119:23
p. have persecuted me without. 161
put not your trust in p. nor in. 146:3
p. and all judges of the earth. 148:11
by me p. decree justice. Pr 8:15
p. rule. 16
it is not good to strike p. 17:26*
a servant to rule over p. 19:10
many are the p. thereof. 28:2
not for p. to drink strong drink. 31:4
p. walking as servants. Eccl 10:7
thy p. eat in the morning. 16
blessed art thou, when thy p. eat. 17
thy p. are rebellious. Isa 1:23
give children to be their p. 3:4
enter into judgement with the p. 14
are not my p. altogether kings? 10:8
p. of Zoan fools, p. of. 19:11, 13
ye p. and anoint the shield. 21:5
Tyre, whose merchants are p. 23:8
his p. were at Zoan, his. 30:4
his p. shall be afraid of the. 31:9
and p. shall rule in judgement. 32:1

seed which shall *p.* out. *2 Sam* 7:12
but I will *p.* no further. *Job* 40:5
p. to do a marvellous. *Isa* 29:14
give ear, for a law shall *p.* 51:4
for they *p.* from evil to evil. *Jer* 9:3
of them shall *p.* thanksgiving. 30:19
governor shall *p.* from midst. 21
and dignity shall *p.* of themselves. *Hab* 1:7
things which *p.* out of the mouth defile the man. *Mat* 15:18
out of the heart *p.* 19; *Mark* 7:21
corrupt communication *p.* *Eph* 4:29
they shall *p.* no further. *2 Tim* 3:9

proceeded

whatever *p.* out of her. *Num* 30:12
do that which hath *p.* out. 32:24
do that which *p.* out of. *Judg* 11:36
Elihu also *p.* and said. *Job* 36:1
gracious words which *p.* *Luke* 4:22
I *p.* forth from God. *John* 8:42
he *p.* further to take Peter. *Acts* 12:3
which sword *p.* out of. *Rev* 19:21

proceedeth

thing *p.* from the Lord. *Gen* 24:50
that *p.* out of his mouth. *Num* 30:2
by every word that *p.* out of the mouth of God. *Deut* 8:3; *Mat* 4:4
wickedness *p.* from. *1 Sam* 24:13
an error which *p.* from. *Eccl* 10:5
out of most High *p.* not. *Lam* 3:38
wrong judgement *p.* *Hab* 1:4*
Spirit of truth which *p.* *John* 15:26
same mouth *p.* blessing. *Jas* 3:10
fire *p.* out of their mouth. *Rev* 11:5

proceeding

water of life *p.* out of. *Rev* 22:1

process

in *p.* of time Cain. *Gen* 4:3
in *p.* of time Shuah Judah's. 38:12
in *p.* of time the king. *Ex* 2:23*
in *p.* of time, Ammon. *Judg* 11:4*

proclaim

I will *p.* the name of. *Ex* 33:19
feast of the Lord ye shall *p.* *Lev* 23:2, 4, 21, 37
p. liberty. 25:10
p. peace unto it. *Deut* 20:10
go to *p.* in the ears of. *Judg* 7:3
p. a fast, and set Naboth. *1 Ki* 21:9
Jehu said, *P.* a solemn. 2 *Ki* 10:20*
p. that they fetch pine. *Neh* 8:15
p. before him, Thus shall. *Esth* 6:9
most men *p.* their own. *Pr* 20:6
he hath sent me to *p.* liberty. *Isa* 61:1
to *p.* the acceptable year. 2
go and *p.* these words. *Jer* 3:12
11:6; 19:2
stand in gate of the Lord, and *p.* 7:2
a covenant to *p.* liberty. 34:8
I *p.* a liberty for you to sword. 17
p. ye this among Gentiles. *Joel* 3:9
and *p.* and publish the. *Amos* 4:5

proclaimed

and *p.* the name of. *Ex* 34:5, 6
they caused it to be *p.* 36:6
p. a fast, set Naboth. *1 Ki* 21:12
assembly, and they *p.* it. *2 Ki* 10:20
the man of God *p.* who 23:16, 17
feared and *p.* a fast. *2 Chr* 20:3
I *p.* a fast there at the river Ahava. *Ezra* 8:21
Haman *p.* before him. *Esth* 6:11
p. thy salvation cometh. *Isa* 62:11
they *p.* a fast before Lord. *Jer* 36:9
they *p.* a fast, and put. *Jonah* 3:5
p. and published through Nineveh. 7
p. upon the housetops. *Luke* 12:3

proclaimeth, -ing

the heart of fools *p.* *Pr* 12:23
in *p.* liberty every. *Jer* 34:15, 17
I saw a strong angel *p.* *Rev* 5:2

proclamation

Aaron made *p.* and said. *Ex* 32:5
king Asa made a *p.* *1 Ki* 15:22
went a *p.* throughout the host. 22:36
Joash made a *p.* through. *2 Chr* 24:9
p. throughout all Israel. 30:5
Cyrus made a *p.* throughout all his kingdom. 36:22; *Ezra* 1:1
Ezra and princes made *p.* *Ezra* 10:7
Belshazzar made *p.* *Dan* 5:29

procure

thus might we *p.* great. *Jer* 26:19*
prosperity that I *p.* unto it. 33:9

procured

hast thou not *p.* this to? *Jer* 2:17
thy doings have *p.* these. 4:18

procureth

seeketh good *p.* favour. *Pr* 11:27*

produce

p. your cause, saith Lord. *Isa* 41:21

profane

(*As an adjective it means not holy, sometimes having merely the idea of* secular.
As a verb it means to treat with contempt, usually referring to sacred things. At times it simply means to make common)

shall not take a wife that is *p.* *Lev* 21:7, 14
prophets and priests are *p.* *Jer* 23:11
thou *p.* wicked prince of Israel. *Ezek* 21:25*
difference between holy and *p.* 22:26*; 44:23*
thee as *p.* out of mountain. 28:16
between sanctuary and the *p.* 42:20*
shall be a *p.* place for city. 48:15*
made for unholy and *p.* *1 Tim* 1:9
refuse *p.* and old wives' fables. 4:7
avoid *p.* and vain babblings. 6:20
2 Tim 2:16
any *p.* person, as Esau. *Heb* 12:16

profane, *verb*

neither shalt thou *p.* name. *Lev* 18:21
19:12; 20:3; 21:6; 22:2, 32
his people to *p.* himself. 21:4
any priest, if she *p.* herself. 9
shall not *p.* the sanctuary of. 12, 23
nor shall he *p.* his seed among. 15
if they do *p.* my ordinance. 22:9
not *p.* holy things of Israel. 15
and *p.* the sabbath day. *Neh* 13:17
to my sanctuary to *p.* *Ezek* 23:39
I will *p.* my sanctuary. 24:21
maid, to *p.* my holy name. *Amos* 2:7
priests in the temple *p.* *Mat* 12:5
hath gone about to *p.* the. *Acts* 24:6

profaned

p. the hallowed things. *Lev* 19:8
thou hast *p.* his crown. *Ps* 89:39
I have *p.* the princes of. *Isa* 43:28
p. my sabbaths. *Ezek* 22:8; 23:38
p. my holy things, I am *p.* 22:26
sanctuary, when it was *p.* 25:3
they *p.* my holy name, when. 36:20
name which Israel had *p.* 21, 22, 23
but ye have *p.* it, in that. *Mal* 1:12
Judah hath *p.* the holiness. 2:11

profaneness

for from the prophets of Jerusalem is *p.* gone forth. *Jer* 23:15†

profaneth

she *p.* her father, she. *Lev* 21:9

profaning

wrath by *p.* the sabbath. *Neh* 13:18
by *p.* the covenant of our. *Mal* 2:10

profess

I *p.* this day to the Lord. *Deut* 26:3
will I *p.* I never knew. *Mat* 7:23
they *p.* that they know. *Tit* 1:16

professed, -ing

p. themselves to be wise. *Rom* 1:22
glorify God for your *p.* *2 Cor* 9:13*
women *p.* godliness. *1 Tim* 2:10
hath *p.* a good profession. 6:12*
some *p.* have erred concerning. 21

profession

hast professed a good *p.* *1 Tim* 6:12
the High Priest of our *p.* *Heb* 3:1*
let us hold fast our *p.* 4:14* 10:23*

profit, *substantive*

what *p.* shall this do? *Gen* 25:32
what *p.* is it if we slay? 37:26
it is not for the king's *p.* *Esth* 3:8
p. should we have if we? *Job* 21:15
might their strength *p.* me? 30:2
what *p.* if I be cleansed from? 35:3
p. is there in my blood? *Ps* 30:9
in all labour there is *p.* *Pr* 14:23
what *p.* hath a man of all his labour? *Eccl* 1:3; 3:9; 5:16
there was no *p.* under the sun. 2:11
moreover the *p.* of the earth. 5:9
by wisdom there is *p.* to. 7:11*
nor be any help nor *p.* *Isa* 30:5
things wherein is no *p.* *Jer* 16:19
what *p.* that we have kept? *Mal* 3:14
what *p.* is there of circumcision? *Rom* 3:1
I speak for your own *p.* *1 Cor* 7:35
own *p.* but the *p.* of many. 10:33
about words to no *p.* *2 Tim* 2:14
chasteneth us for our *p.* *Heb* 12:10

profit, *verb*

things which cannot *p.* *1 Sam* 12:21
thy righteousness may *p.* *Job* 35:8
wickedness *p.* nothing. *Pr* 10:2
riches *p.* not in the day. 11:4
were ashamed of people that could not *p.* *Isa* 30:5, 6
delectable things shall not *p.* 44:9
thou shalt be able to *p.* 47:12
Lord which teacheth thee to *p.* 48:17
for they shall not *p.* thee. 57:12
after things that do not *p.* *Jer* 2:8
glory for that which doth not *p.* 11
in lying words that cannot *p.* 7:8
to pain, but shall not *p.* 12:13
they shall not *p.* this people. 23:32
what *p.* if he gain the? *Mark* 8:36
every man to *p.* withal. *1 Cor* 12:7
tongues, what shall I *p.* you? 14:6
Christ shall *p.* you nothing. *Gal* 5:2
preached did not *p.* them. *Heb* 4:2
doth it *p.*, my brethren? *Jas* 2:14
things needful, what doth it *p.*? 16

profitable

can a man be *p.* to God, as wise is *p.* to himself? *Job* 22:2
wisdom is *p.* to direct. *Eccl* 10:10
image that is *p.* for nothing. *Isa* 44:10
girdle was *p.* for nothing. *Jer* 13:7
p. for thee that one of thy members perish. *Mat* 5:29, 30
I kept back nothing *p.* to. *Acts* 20:20
godliness is *p.* to all. *1 Tim* 4:8
all scripture is *p.* for. *2 Tim* 3:16
Mark is *p.* to me for the. 4:11*
these things are *p.* to men. *Tit* 3:8
but now *p.* to thee and. *Philem* 11

profited, -eth

have sinned, and it *p.* not. *Job* 33:27
it *p.* nothing to delight in God. 34:9
what *p.* the graven image? *Hab* 2:18
a gift by whatever thou mightest be *p.* *Mat* 15:5; *Mark* 7:11
is a man *p.* if he gain? *Mat* 16:26
spirit quickeneth, flesh *p.* *John* 6:63
circumcision *p.* if thou. *Rom* 2:25
not charity, it *p.* nothing. *1 Cor* 13:3
I *p.* in the Jews' religion. *Gal* 1:14*
for bodily exercise *p.* little. *1 Tim* 4:8
not *p.* them that have been occupied. *Heb* 13:9

profiting

that thy *p.* may appear. *1 Tim* 4:15*

profound

revolters are *p.* to make. *Hos* 5:2*

progenitors

the blessings of my *p.* *Gen* 49:26

prognosticators

let monthly *p.* stand up. *Isa* 47:13

prolong, -ed

ye shall not *p.* your days. *Deut* 4:26
30:18
that thou mayest *p.* thy days upon the earth. 4:40; 5:16*, 33; 6:2
11:9; 17:20; 22:7
through this thing ye shall *p.* 32:47
that I should *p.* my life? *Job* 6:11*
the wicked shall not *p.* the. 15:29*
wilt *p.* the king's life. *Ps* 61:6
the state shall be *p.* *Pr* 28:2
covetousness, shall *p.* his days. 16
though a sinner's days be *p.* *Eccl* 8:12
neither shall the wicked *p.* his. 13
her days shall not be *p.* *Isa* 13:22
see his seed, he shall *p.* his. 53:10
days are *p.* and vision. *Ezek* 12:22
I will speak, and word shall come to pass, it shall be no more *p.* 25*

none of my words be *p.* *Ezek* 12:28*
yet their lives were *p.* for. *Dan* 7:12

prolongeth

fear of the Lord *p.* days. *Pr* 10:27
wicked man that *p.* his life. *Eccl* 7:15

promise

The word in the New Testament is often taken for those promises that God made to Abraham *and the other patriarchs of sending the* Messiah. *It is in this sense that the apostle* Paul *commonly uses the word* promise, Rom 4:13, 14; Gal 3:16. *The Holy Spirit of promise,* Eph 1:13, *is the Holy Ghost, which God has promised to those that shall believe in him. The first commandment with promise is* Honour thy father and mother, Eph 6:2. *To which God has added this* promise, *that their days shall be long upon the earth,* Ex 20:12.

know my breach of *p.* *Num* 14:34*
failed one word of good *p.* *1 Ki* 8:56
let thy *p.* to David be. *2 Chr* 1:9
do according to this *p.* *Neh* 5:12
not this *p.* even thus be he shaken out. People did . . . to *p.* 13
doth his *p.* fail for? *Ps* 77:8
he remembered his holy *p.* 105:42*
I send *p.* of my Father. *Luke* 24:49
wait for the *p.* of Father. *Acts* 1:4
received *p.* of Holy Ghost. 2:33
p. is to you and to your children. 39
the time of the *p.* drew nigh. 7:17
to his *p.* hath raised a Saviour. 13:23
the *p.* made to fathers, God hath. 32
looking for a *p.* from thee. 23:21
for hope of the *p.* made of God. 26:6
to which *p.* our tribes, serving God. 7
p. that he shall be the heir. *Rom* 4:13
the *p.* is made of none effect. 14
p. might be sure to all the seed. 16
he staggered not at the *p.* 20
but children of the *p.* counted. 9:8
this is word of *p.* at this time. 9
that we might receive *p.* *Gal* 3:14
make the *p.* of none effect. 17
if of law, it is no more of *p.*: but God gave it to Abraham by *p.* 18
to whom the *p.* was made. 19
p. by faith of Jesus Christ might. 22
ye heirs according to the *p.* 29
we are the children of *p.* 4:28
with that Holy Spirit of *p.* *Eph* 1:13
strangers from covenants of *p.* 2:12
Gentiles be partakers of his *p.* 3:6
first commandment with *p.* 6:2
having the *p.* of the life. *1 Tim* 4:8
according to the *p.* of life. *2 Tim* 1:1
lest a *p.* left us of entering. *Heb* 4:1
for when God made *p.* to. 6:13
patiently endured, he obtained *p.* 15
to shew unto the heirs of *p.* 17
the *p.* of eternal life. 9:15; 10:36
sojourned in land of *p.* . . . heirs with him of the same *p.* 11:9
and these all received not the *p.* 39
saying, Where is the *p.* of? *2 Pet* 3:4
is not slack concerning his *p.* 9
according to his *p.* we look for. 13
p. that he hath promised. *1 John* 2:25

promise, *verb*

while they *p.* liberty. *2 Pet* 2:19

promised

according as he hath *p.* *Ex* 12:25
to the place the Lord *p.* *Num* 14:40
the Lord bless you as he hath *p.* *Deut* 1:11; 15:6
increase as the Lord *p.* thee. 6:3
bring them to the land he *p.* 9:28
is his inheritance, as he *p.* 10:9*
enlarge thy border, as he *p.* 12:20
give thee the land he *p.* to give. 19:8; 27:3
that which thou hast *p.* to God. 23:23
peculiar people, as he *p.* thee. 26:18
live, as the princes had *p.* *Josh* 9:21*
rest to your brethren, as he *p.* 22:4*
possess their land, as Lord *p.* 23:5*
for you, as he hath *p.* you. 10*
things are come the Lord *p.* you. 15*
hast *p.* this goodness to. *2 Sam* 7:28
me an house, as he *p.* *1 Ki* 2:24
Solomon wisdom, as he *p.* 5:12
throne of Israel as the Lord *p.* 8:20
rest to people, as he *p.* by Moses. 56
as I *p.* to David thy father. 9:5
as he *p.* to give a light. *2 Ki* 8:19 *2 Chr* 21:7
hast *p.* this goodness. *1 Chr* 17:26
the throne as Lord *p.* *2 Chr* 6:10
which thou hast *p.* David. 15, 16
thou hadst *p.* to fathers. *Neh* 9:23*
that Haman had *p.* to pay. *Esth* 4:7
will bring on them all the good I *p.* *Jer* 32:42; 33:14*
Herod *p.* with oath to. *Mat* 14:7
p. to give him money. *Mark* 14:11
mercy *p.* to our fathers. *Luke* 1:72*
he *p.* to betray him unto them. 22:6*
he *p.* to give it to him. *Acts* 7:5
which he had *p.* afore. *Rom* 1:2
that what he *p.* he was able to. 4:21
eternal life, *p.* before world. *Tit* 1:2
he is faithful that *p.* *Heb* 10:23
judged him faithful that had *p.* 11:11
he hath *p.* saying, Yet once. 12:26
Lord *p.* to them. *Jas* 1:12; 2:5
this is the promise that he hath *p.* us, even eternal. *1 John* 2:25

promisedst

David that thou *p.* him. *1 Ki* 8:24, 25
and *p.* that they should go into the land. *Neh* 9:15*

promises

to whom pertain the *p.* *Rom* 9:4
to confirm the *p.* made to the. 15:8
all *p.* of God in him are. *2 Cor* 1:20
having therefore these *p.* dearly. 7:1
to his seed were *p.* made. *Gal* 3:16
law against the *p.* of God? 21
and patience inherit *p.* *Heb* 6:12
blessed him that had the *p.* 7:6
was established upon better *p.* 8:6
died, not having received *p.* 11:13
had received the *p.*, offered up. 17
who through faith obtained *p.* 33
great and precious *p.* *2 Pet* 1:4

promising

wicked way, by *p.* life. *Ezek* 13:22*

promote

I will *p.* thee to great honour. *Num* 22:17; 24:11
am I not able indeed to *p.* thee? 37
and she shall *p.* thee. *Pr* 4:8

promoted

p. over the trees. *Judg* 9:9*, 11*, 13*
the king had *p.* him. *Esth* 5:11
then the king *p.* Shadrach. *Dan* 3:30

promotion

p. cometh neither from. *Ps* 75:6*
shame shall be the *p.* of. *Pr* 3:35

pronounce

man shall *p.* with an oath. *Lev* 5:4*
priest shall *p.* him unclean. 13:3, 6 8, 11, 15, 20, 22, 25, 27, 30, 44
shall *p.* him clean. 13:13, 17, 23, 28 34, 37; 14:7
law, to *p.* it clean or unclean. 13:59
priest shall *p.* the house clean. 14:48
could not frame to *p.* it. *Judg* 12:6

pronounced

but he *p.* this prophecy. *Neh* 6:12
the Lord hath *p.* evil. *Jer* 11:17
p. this great evil. 16:10; 19:15 35:17; 40:2
nation against whom I *p.*, turn. 18:8*
word which I have *p.* against. 25:13
Lord will repent of evil he *p.* 26:13
repented of the evil he had *p.* 19
for I have *p.* the word, saith. 34:5*
Lord hath *p.* against this people. 36:7
Jeremiah *p.* all these words. 18, 31

pronouncing

if a soul swear, *p.* to do. *Lev* 5:4*

proof

I might know the *p.* of you. *2 Cor* 2:9
shew ye to them the *p.* of your. 8:24
ye seek a *p.* of Christ speaking. 13:3
but ye know the *p.* of him. *Phil* 2:22
full *p.* of thy ministry. *2 Tim* 4:5†

proofs

alive by many infallible *p.* *Acts* 1:3

proper

(*Used with the old meaning of* one's own; *still retained in the French* propre)

mine own *p.* good. *1 Chr* 29:3*
called in their *p.* tongue. *Acts* 1:19*
hath his *p.* gift of God. *1 Cor* 7:7
saw he was a *p.* child. *Heb* 11:23*

prophecies

but whether *p.*, they. *1 Cor* 13:8
according to the *p.* that. *1 Tim* 1:18

prophecy

in the *p.* of Ahijah. *2 Chr* 9:29
when Asa heard *p.* of Obed. 15:8
he pronounced this *p.* *Neh* 6:12
p. man spake to Ithiel. *Pr* 30:1*
p. that his mother taught him. 31:1*
in them is fulfilled the *p.* of Esaias. *Mat* 13:14
p., by the same Spirit. *1 Cor* 12:10
though I have the gift of *p.* and. 13:2
the gift given thee by *p.* *1 Tim* 4:14
more sure word of *p.* *2 Pet* 1:19
no *p.* of scripture is of private. 20
p. came not in old time by the will. 21
hear the words of this *p.* *Rev* 1:3
rain not in the days of their *p.* 11:6
for the testimony of Jesus is the spirit of *p.* 19:10
keepeth the sayings of this *p.* 22:7
sayings of the *p.* of this book. 10
that heareth words of the *p.* of. 18
take from the words of this *p.* 19

prophesied

they *p.* and did not. *Num* 11:25
Eldad and Medad they *p.* in. 26
of God came upon Saul, and he *p.* *1 Sam* 10:10, 11; 18:10; 19:23, 24
messengers of Saul also *p.* 19:20, 21
they *p.* until the evening. *1 Ki* 18:29
prophets *p.* before them. 22:10, 12 *2 Chr* 18:9
sons of Asaph *p.* *1 Chr* 25:2
the sons of Jeduthun who *p.* 3
Eliezer *p.* against. *2 Chr* 20:37
Haggai and Zechariah *p.* *Ezra* 5:1
prophets *p.* by Baal. *Jer* 2:8
Pashur heard that Jeremiah *p.* 20:1
and all to whom thou *p.* lies. 6
the prophets of Samaria *p.* 23:13
not spoken to them, yet they *p.* 21
all that Jeremiah hath *p.* 25:13
why hast thou *p.* in the name of? 26:9
he hath *p.* against this city. 11, 20
Micah *p.* in days of Hezekiah. 18
Urijah *p.* 20
perform the words thou hast *p.* 28:6
p. against many countries. 8
Shemaiah hath *p.* to you. 29:31
prophets which *p.* to you? 37:19
when I *p.* Pelatiah died. *Ezek* 11:13
so I *p.* as I was commanded, and as I *p.* 37:7, 10
who *p.* I would bring thee. 38:17
be ashamed when they *p.* *Zech* 13:4
Lord, have we not *p.*? *Mat* 7:22
prophets and law *p.* until John. 11:13
well hath Esaias *p.* of you. *Mark* 7:6
Zachariah *p.* saying. *Luke* 1:67
Caiaphas *p.* that Jesus. *John* 11:51
spake with tongues and *p.* *Acts* 19:6
I would rather that ye *p.* *1 Cor* 14:5
Enoch also *p.* of these things. *Jude* 14

prophesieth

he never *p.* good to me. *2 Chr* 18:7
prophet which *p.* of peace. *Jer* 28:9
p. of times far off. *Ezek* 12:27
him through when he *p.* *Zech* 13:3
that *p.* with her head. *1 Cor* 11:5
he that *p.* speaketh unto men. 14:3
he that *p.* edifieth the church. 4
greater is he that *p.* than he. 5

prophesy, *verb*

Eldad and Medad do *p.* *Num* 11:27
they shall *p.* *1 Sam* 10:5
thou shalt *p.* 6
doth not *p.* good of me. *1 Ki* 22:8
would not *p.* good. 18; *2 Chr* 18:17
who should *p.* with harps. *1 Chr* 25:1
p. not right things, *p.* *Isa* 30:10

the prophets *p.* falsely. *Jer* 5:31
p. not in the name of the Lord. 11:21
prophets *p.* lies, they *p.* false. 14:14
concerning the prophets that *p.* 15
people to whom they *p.* shall be. 16
Tophet, whither Lord sent to *p.* 19:14
not to the prophets that *p.* 23:16
that *p.* lies in my name. 25; 26:32
27:10, 14, 15, 16; 29:9, 21
p. against the inhabitants of. 25:30
Lord sent me to *p.* against. 26:12
why dost *p.* and say, I will? 32:3
shalt *p.* against Jerusalem. *Ezek* 4:7
p. against the mountains. 6:2; 36:1
p. against them, *p.* O son. 11:4
p. against prophets that *p.* 13:2, 17
p. against the forest of the. 20:46
p. against land of Israel. 21:2, 9
son of man, *p.* and smite thy. 14
p. and say concerning. 28; 25:2
p. against Zidon. 28:21
p. against Pharaoh. 29:2
p. against Egypt. 30:2
p. against the shepherds of. 34:2
p. against mount Seir. 35:2
p. concerning the land of. 36:6
p. upon these bones. 37:4
p. to the wind. 9
p. against Gog. 38:2, 14; 39:1
your sons shall *p.* *Joel* 2:28
Acts 2:17, 18
commanded the prophets, saying, *P.* not. *Amos* 2:12; *Mi* 2:6
who can but *p.*? *Amos* 3:8
eat bread and *p.* 7:12
p. not again at Beth-el. 13
Go *p.* to my people Israel. 15
p. not against Israel and the. 16
I will *p.* to thee of wine. *Mi* 2:11
that when any shall yet *p.* then his father. *Zech* 13:3
well did Esaias *p.* of you. *Mat* 15:7
p. thou Christ. 26:68; *Mark* 14:65
Luke 22:64
virgins, which did *p.* *Acts* 21:9
whether prophecy, let us *p.* *Rom* 12:6
know in part, and we *p.* *1 Cor* 13:9
rather that ye may *p.* 14:1
if all *p.* 24
we may all *p.* one by one. 31
covet to *p.* 39
thou must *p.* again before. *Rev* 10:11
my two witnesses shall *p.* 11:3

prophesying

had made an end of *p.* *1 Sam* 10:13
company of the prophets *p.* 19:20
prospered through *p.* of. *Ezra* 6:14
man *p.* having his head. *1 Cor* 11:4
except by *p.* or by doctrine. 14:6
p. serveth not for them that. 22
despise not *p.*, prove. *1 Thes* 5:20

prophet

Ordinarily this word is understood as meaning one who foretells future events. It meant, at the time our English Bible was translated, also a preacher—and prophesying meant preaching. A meaning of the word less often recognized, but really as common, is one who tells —a forth-teller—who speaks for another, most usually for God. It is in this sense that many Bible characters are called prophets, as for example, Aaron, Moses, and Jesus Christ. Those prophets who wrote their prophecies, which are preserved to us in our Bible, are divided into two groups: four major prophets—Isaiah, Jeremiah, Ezekiel and Daniel—and 12 minor prophets, whose names are given to the last 12 books of the Old Testament. There are also a number of prophets named in the Old Testament who were important in their day, but who left no writings behind them. The most important of these are Elijah and Elisha, whose deeds are related in 1 Ki 17-21; 2 Ki 1-9, 13. *The periods of the prophecies preserved to us are in some cases a little uncertain. The following is, at least, approximately correct.*

1. Isaiah *began to prophesy near the time of the death of Uzziah, king of* Judah. *He continued to prophesy to the reign of* Manasseh, *who caused him to be put to death.*

2. Jeremiah *began in the thirteenth year of the reign of* Josiah *king of* Judah. *He continued to prophesy till the taking of Jerusalem by the Chaldeans; and it is thought he died two years after in* Egypt; Baruch *was his disciple and amanuensis.*

3. Ezekiel *was carried captive to Babylon, along with* Jeconiah *king of* Judah, *11 years before the destruction of Jerusalem. He preached during the captivity for about 22 years. We do not know when he died.*

4. Daniel *was taken into Chaldea in the third year of Jehoiakim king of Judah, and prophesied at Babylon to the end of the captivity.*

5. Hosea *prophesied under Jeroboam II. king of* Israel, *and his successors, perhaps to the destruction of* Samaria.

6. Joel *prophesied under Josiah about the same time as Jeremiah.*

7. Amos *began to prophesy the second year before the earthquake, which was in the reign of king Uzziah, about six years before the death of Jeroboam II. king of* Israel.

8. Obadiah *dwelt in Judea, probably after the taking of Jerusalem, and before the desolation of Idumea.*

9. Jonah *lived in the kingdom of* Israel *under the kings* Joash *and* Jeroboam II. *about the same time as* Hosea, Isaiah, *and* Amos.

10. Micah *lived under* Jotham, Ahaz, *and* Hezekiah, *kings of* Judah; *he was contemporary with* Isaiah, *but began later to prophesy.*

11. Nahum *appeared in* Judah *under the reign of Hezekiah, and after the expedition of* Sennacherib.

12. Habakkuk *lived* in Judea *during the reign of Jehoiakim, before the coming of Nebuchadnezzar into the country.*

13. Zephaniah *appeared at the beginning of the reign of* Josiah, *and before the twenty-eighth year of this prince.*

14. Haggai *was the great prophet of the Return to Jerusalem, and the rebuilding of the temple. He is supposed to have been an old man, as* Hag 2:3 *is taken to mean that he had seen the old temple before its destruction by Nebuchadnezzar.*

15. Zechariah *prophesied in Judea at the same time as Haggai, and continued to prophesy after him, being younger.*

16. Malachi, *the author of the last book in the Old Testament, lived about the time of Nehemiah's second visit to Jerusalem. Nothing whatever is known of him.*

Aaron shall be thy *p.* *Ex* 7:1
but the *p.* which shall presume. *Deut* 18:20, 22
p. Gad said to David. *1 Sam* 22:5
word of the Lord came to the *p.* *2 Sam* 24:11
call me Nathan the *p.* *1 Ki* 1:32
sent with him Nathan the *p.* 44
Ahijah the *p.* found Jeroboam. 11:29
an old *p.* in Beth-el. 13:11, 25
p. whom he had brought back. 23
p. took up the carcase of the man of God, and the old *p.* came to. 29
by *p.* Jehu came the word. 16:7, 12
Elijah *p.* came near and said. 18:36
p. came to king of Israel. 20:22
my lord were with the *p.* *2 Ki* 5:3
p. had bid thee do some great. 13
Elisha the *p.* telleth what thou. 6:12
young man the *p.* went to. 9:4
Isaiah the *p.* cried to Lord. 20:11
with bones of *p.* that came out. 23:18
came Shemaiah the *p.* *2 Chr* 12:5
in the story of the *p.* Iddo. 13:22
the prophecy of the *p.* Oded. 15:8
a writing from Elijah the *p.* 21:12
then the *p.* forbare, and said. 25:16
the *p.* Isaiah prayed and cried. 32:20
from the days of Samuel the *p.* 35:18
not himself before Jeremiah *p.* 36:12
Haggai the *p.* prophesied. *Ezra* 5:1
prophesying of Haggai the *p.* 6:14
there is no more any *p.* *Ps* 74:9
Lord doth take away the *p.* *Isa* 3:2
the *p.* that teacheth lies. 9:15
priest and *p.* have erred. 28:7
from the *p.* even unto the priest dealeth falsely. *Jer* 6:13; 8:10
nor shall word perish from *p.* 18:18
both *p.* and priests are profane. 23:11
p. that hath a dream let him. 28
the *p.* Jeremiah said, Amen. 28:6
p. which prophesieth of peace, when the word of the *p.* shall . . . *p.* 9
so Hananiah the *p.* died the. 17
Baruch and Jeremiah the *p.* 36:26
nor his servants hearken to *p.* 37:2
take up Jeremiah the *p.* out. 38:10
shall the *p.* be slain? *Lam* 2:20
they seek a vision of *p.* *Ezek* 7:26
and cometh to the *p.* I will. 14:4
if *p.* be deceived, I the Lord have deceived that *p.* 9
punishment of the *p.* shall be. 10
p. also shall fall with thee. *Hos* 4:5
the *p.* is a fool. 9:7
p. is a snare of a fowler. 8*
I was no *p.* nor *p.*'s son. *Amos* 7:14
he shall even be the *p.* *Mi* 2:11
prayer of Habakkuk the *p.* *Hab* 3:1
he shall say, I am no *p.* *Zech* 13:5
will send you Elijah the *p.* *Mal* 4:5
spoken by the *p.* Isaiah. *Mat* 1:22
2:15; 3:3; 4:14; 8:17; 21:4
Luke 3:4; *John* 1:23; 12:38
Acts 28:25
thus it is written by the *p.* *Mat* 2:5
spoken by Jeremy the *p.* 17; 27:9
but the sign of the *p.* Jonas. 12:39
Luke 11:29
spoken by the *p.* *Mat* 13:35
27:35
Jesus the *p.* of Nazareth of. 21:11
spoken of by Daniel the *p.* 24:15
Mark 13:14
child be called *p.* of the Highest. *Luke* 1:76
to him book of the *p.* Esaias. 4:17
no *p.* is accepted in his own. 24
in the time of Eliseus the *p.* 27
not a greater *p.* than John. 7:28
of a truth this is the *p.* *John* 7:40
out of Galilee ariseth no *p.* 52
was spoken by the *p.* Joel. *Acts* 2:16
made with hands, as saith *p.* 7:48
he read Esaias the *p.* 8:28, 30
of whom speaketh the *p.* this? 34
judges until Samuel the *p.* 13:20
the ass forbad the madness of the *p.* *2 Pet* 2:16

see **priest, Lord**

***a* prophet**

restore man his wife, for he is *a p.* *Gen* 20:7
if there be *a p.* among. *Num* 12:6
arise *a p.* or dreamer. *Deut* 13:1
I will raise up *a p.* from among. 18:15, 18; *Acts* 3:22; 7:37
when *a p.* speaketh in. *Deut* 18:22
arose not *a p.* in Israel like. 34:10
sent *a p.* to the children. *Judg* 6:8
established to be *a p.* *1 Sam* 3:20
now called *a p.*, was called. 9:9
he said, I am *a p.* also. *1 Ki* 13:18
I, even I only remain *a p.* of. 18:22
anoint Elisha to be *a p.* 19:16
there came *a p.* unto Ahab. 20:13
is there not here *a p.* of the Lord? 22:7; *2 Ki* 3:11; *2 Chr* 18:6

there is *a p.* in Israel. *2 Ki* 5:8
sent *a p.* to Amaziah. *2 Chr* 25:15
a p. of Lord was there, Oded. 28:9
thee *a p.* to the nations. *Jer* 1:5
maketh himself *a p.* 29:26, 27
there hath been *a p. Ezek* 2:5; 33:33
cometh to *a p.* to enquire of. 14:7
by *a p.* the Lord brought Israel out of Egypt, and by *a p.* *Hos* 12:13
a p. in the name of *a p.* shall receive *a p.*'s reward. *Mat* 10:41
went ye out for to see? *a p.*? 11:9
a p. is not without honour save. 13:57
Mark 6:4; *John* 4:44
they accounted him as *a p. Mat* 14:5
21:26; *Mark* 11:32; *Luke* 20:6
they took him for *a p.* *Mat* 21:46
others said, That it is *a p. Mark* 6:15
a great *p.* is risen. *Luke* 7:16
this man, if he were *a p.* would. 39
cannot be that *a p.* perish out. 13:33
Jesus, who was *a p.* mighty. 24:19
perceive that thou art *a p. John* 4:19
the blind man said, He is *a p.* 9:17
being *a p.* and knowing. *Acts* 2:30
a certain *p.* named Agabus. 21:10
think himself to be *a p. 1 Cor* 14:37
a p. of their own land. *Tit* 1:12

false prophet

a *false p.*, a Jew named. *Acts* 13:6
out of mouth of *false p.* *Rev* 16:13
taken, with him the *false p.* 19:20
where beast and *false p.* are. 20:10

that prophet

to the words of *that p.* *Deut* 13:3
that p. or that dreamer. 5; 18:20
have deceived *that p.* *Ezek* 14:9
Art thou *that p.*? *John* 1:21, 25
this is of a truth *that p.* that. 6:14
will not hear *that p.* *Acts* 3:23

prophetess

Miriam *p.* took a timbrel. *Ex* 15:20
and Deborah a *p.* judged. *Judg* 4:4
went to Huldah the *p.* *2 Ki* 22:14
2 Chr 34:22
think on the *p.* Noadiah. *Neh* 6:14
p. and she conceived a son. *Isa* 8:3
there was one Anna a *p.* *Luke* 2:36
who called herself a *p.* *Rev* 2:20

prophets

Lord's people were *p.* *Num* 11:29
meet a company of *p.* *1 Sam* 10:5
company of *p.* met him. 10
prophesied among the *p.* 11
is Saul among the *p.*? 12; 19:24
answered him not by *p.* 28:6, 15
Obadiah hid 100 *p.* by 50. *1 Ki* 18:4
Jezebel slew the *p.* 13
gather *p.* of Baal 450. 19, 22
take the *p.* of Baal, let none. 40
have slain *p.* with the sword. 19:10
14; *Neh* 9:26
of Israel gathered the *p.* *1 Ki* 22:6
a lying spirit in *p.* 22; *2 Chr* 18:21
to *p.* of thy father, and *p. 2 Ki* 3:13
Josiah went and *p.*, to house. 23:2
believe his *p.* so shall. *2 Chr* 20:20
Yet he sent *p.* to them. 24:19
they misused his *p.* 36:16
were the *p.* of God helping. *Ezra* 5:2
appointed *p.* to preach. *Neh* 6:7
by thy Spirit in thy *p.* 9:30
trouble that hath come on our *p.* 32
the *p.* and seers hath he. *Isa* 29:10
say to the *p.*, Prophesy not. 30:10
Amos 2:12
and *p.* prophesied by Baal. *Jer* 2:8
their priests and *p.* are ashamed. 26
sword hath devoured your *p.* 30
the *p.* shall wonder. 4:9
p. become wind. 5:13
p. prophesy falsely, and. 31
bring out the bones of the *p.* 8:1
will fill *p.* with drunkenness. 13:13
the *p.* say, Ye shall not see. 14:13
p. prophesy lies in my name. 14
sword and famine shall those *p.* 15
folly in the *p.* of Samaria. 23:13
seen in *p.* an horrible thing. 14
from *p.* is profaneness gone forth. 15
I have not sent these *p.*, yet. 21
I have heard what the *p.* *Jer* 23:25
p. of deceit of their own heart. 26
the *p.* that steal my word. 30, 31
priests and *p.* heard Jeremiah. 26:7
p. and people took Jeremiah. 8
the *p.*, This man is worthy to die. 11
hearken not to your *p.* 27:9, 16
ye and the *p.* might perish. 15
if they be *p.* and word of Lord. 18
p. that have been before me. 28:8
Jeremiah sent to the *p.* 29:1
saith the Lord, Let not your *p.* 8
Lord hath raised us up *p.* in. 15
they and their *p.* provoke me. 32:32
where are now your *p.*? 37:19
her *p.* also find no vision. *Lam* 2:9
thy *p.* have seen vain things. 14
for the sins of her *p.* that have. 4:13
prophesy against the *p.* *Ezek* 13:2
Woe unto the foolish *p.* 3
O Israel, thy *p.* are like foxes. 4
my hand shall be upon the *p.* that. 9
there is a conspiracy of her *p.* 22:25
p. daubed them with untempered. 28
I have hewed them by *p.* *Hos* 6:5
I have spoken by *p.* and. 12:10
raised up of your sons *p. Amos* 2:11
and commanded the *p.* saying. 12
sun shall go down over *p.* *Mi* 3:6
p. thereof divine for money. 11
her *p.* are light and. *Zeph* 3:4
to whom the former *p.* *Zech* 1:4
the *p.* do they live for ever? 5
Lord hath cried by former *p.* 7:7
word Lord sent by former *p.* 12
I will cause the *p.* to pass out. 13:2
the *p.* shall be ashamed, each. 4
so persecuted they the *p.* *Mat* 5:12
Luke 6:23
not come to destroy the law and the *p.* *Mat* 5:17
for this is the law and the *p.* 7:12
many *p.* have desired to see. 13:17
Luke 10:24
on these hang all the law and the *p.*
Mat 22:40
of them who killed the *p.* 23:31
I send unto you *p.* 34; *Luke* 11:49
thou that killest the *p.* *Mat* 23:37
written in *p.*, Behold I. *Mark* 1:2
Luke 18:31; 24:25; *John* 6:45
as he spake by his holy *p.*
Luke 1:70; *2 Pet* 3:2
and *p.* were until John. *Luke* 16:16
They have Moses and *p.* 29, 31
slow to believe what the *p.* 24:25
found him of whom the *p. John* 1:45
Abraham is dead, and *p.* 8:52, 53
by the mouth of his *p. Acts* 3:18, 21
p. came from Jerusalem to. 11:27
in church at Antioch certain *p.* 13:1
after reading of law and the *p.* 15
which is spoken of in the *p.* 40
Judas and Silas being *p.* 15:32
things written in law and *p.* 24:14
none other things than *p.* did. 26:22
Agrippa, believest thou the *p.*? 27
promised afore by his *p.* *Rom* 1:2
witnessed by law and the *p.* 3:21
Lord, they have killed thy *p.* 11:3
apostles, secondarily *p. 1 Cor* 12:28
are all *p.*? 29
let *p.* speak two or three. 14:29
on foundation of the *p.* *Eph* 2:20
as it is now revealed to his *p.* 3:5
and he gave some *p.* and. 4:11
killed Lord, and own *p. 1 Thes* 2:15
spake to fathers by the *p.* *Heb* 1:1
take, my brethren, the *p.* *Jas* 5:10
which salvation the *p.* *1 Pet* 1:10
two *p.* tormented them. *Rev* 11:10
rejoice, ye holy apostles and *p.* 18:20
in her was found blood of *p.* and. 24
for I am of thy brethren the *p.* 22:9

all the prophets

he had slain *all the p.* *1 Ki* 19:1
throne, and *all the p.* prophesied.
22:10, 12; *2 Chr* 18:9, 11
call *all the p.* of Baal. *2 Ki* 10:19
against Israel by *all the p.* 17:13
all the p. prophesied until. *Mat* 11:13
that blood of *all the p.* *Luke* 11:50
see *all the p.* in kingdom. 13:28
all the p. he expounded. *Luke* 24:27
all the p. from Samuel. *Acts* 3:24
to him give *all the p.* witness. 10:43

false prophets

false p. in sheep's. *Mat* 7:15
many *false p.* shall rise. 24:11, 24
Mark 13:22
their fathers to *false p.* *Luke* 6:26
there were *false p.* also. *2 Pet* 2:1
because many *false p.* *1 John* 4:1

my prophets

mine anointed, and do *my p.* no.
1 Chr 16:22; *Ps* 105:15

of the prophets

company *of the p.* met. *1 Sam* 10:10
saw the company *of the p.* 19:20
man of the sons *of the p. 1 Ki* 20:35
that he was *of the p.* 41
words *of the p.* 22:13; *2 Chr* 18:12
sons *of the p.* at Beth-el. *2 Ki* 2:3
the sons *of the p.* at Jericho. 5
sons *of the p.* went to view afar. 7
sons *of the p.* said, The spirit. 15
woman of wives of sons *of the p.* 4:1
pottage for the sons *of the p.* 38
think of the rest *of the p.* *Neh* 6:14
because *of the p.* all my. *Jer* 23:9
to the words *of the p.* 16; 27:14
this be in the heart *of the p.*? 23:26
by ministry *of the p.* *Hos* 12:10
by the mouth *of the p.* *Zech* 8:9
Elias or one *of the p.* *Mat* 16:14
Mark 6:15; 8:28
ye build the tombs *of the p.*
Mat 23:29; *Luke* 11:47
them in blood *of the p.* *Mat* 23:30
of the p. might be fulfilled 26:56
one *of the p.* was risen. *Luke* 9:8, 19
ye are children *of the p.* *Acts* 3:25
written in the book *of the p.* 7:42
of the p. have not your fathers? 52
reading *of* the law and *the p.* 13:15
they knew not voice *of the p.* 27
to this agree words *of the p.* 15:15
concerning Jesus out *of the p.* 28:23
by scriptures *of the p.* *Rom* 16:26
spirits *of the p.* are subject to the prophets. *1 Cor* 14:32
on the foundation *of the p. Eph* 2:20
fail me to tell *of the p.* *Heb* 11:32
shed the blood *of the p.* *Rev* 16:6
Lord God *of the* holy *p.* sent. 22:6

servants the prophets

blood of my *serv. the p.* *2 Ki* 9:7
I sent by my *serv. the p.* 17:13
Lord said by all his *serv. the p.* 23
spake by his *serv. the p.* 21:10; 24:2
commanded by *serv. the p. Ezra* 9:11
sent you my *serv. the p.* *Jer* 7:25
25:4; 29:19; 35:15
to the words of my *serv. the p.* 26:5
spoken by my *serv. the p. Ezek* 38:17
hearkened to *serv. the p.* *Dan* 9:6
set before us by his *serv. the p.* 10
his secret to his *serv. the p. Amos* 3:7
which I commanded my *serv. the p.*
Zech 1:6
declared to his *serv. the p. Rev* 10:7
give reward *to serv. the p.* 11:18

propitiation

hath set forth to be a *p.* *Rom* 3:25
and he is the *p.* *1 John* 2:2; 4:10

proportion

according to the *p.* *1 Ki* 7:36*
not conceal his comely *p. Job* 41:12†
according to *p.* of faith. *Rom* 12:6

proselyte

This term comes from the Greek *word,* Proselytos, *which signifies a* stranger, *one that comes from abroad, or from another place. The* Hebrew *word* Ger *or* Necher, *has the same signification. It means a convert to Judaism from among the Gentiles.*

The Talmud distinguishes between Proselytes of the Gate, *and* Proselytes of Righteousness. *The first are those who dwelt in the land of Israel and were not bound by circumcision. The term is derived*

from the expression the stranger that is within thy gates, Ex 20:10, etc.
The Proselytes of Righteousness *are those that were converted to Judaism, who received circumcision, and observed the whole law of Moses. They were therefore perfect Israelites.*
compass sea and land to make one *p.* *Mat* 23:15
Nicholas a *p.* of Antioch. *Acts* 6:5

proselytes

Jews and *p.*, we do hear. *Acts* 2:10
Jews and religious *p.* followed Paul. 13:43

prospect

chambers whose *p.* was. *Ezek* 40:44
p. to the north. 46
p. to the east. 42:15; 43:4

prosper

his angel and *p.* thee. *Gen* 24:40
if now thou do *p.* my way. 42
that Joseph did to *p.* 39:3, 23
but it shall not *p.* *Num* 14:41
not *p.* in thy ways. *Deut* 28:29
that ye may *p.* 29:9; *Josh* 1:7* *1 Ki* 2:3
Go up to Ramoth-gilead and *p.* *1 Ki* 22:12, 15; *2 Chr* 18:11, 14
son, the Lord *p.* thee. *1 Chr* 22:11
shalt thou *p.* if thou takest heed. 13
fight ye not, for ye shall not *p.* *2 Chr* 13:12
prophets, so shall ye *p.* 20:20
Why transgress ye, that ye cannot *p.*? 24:20
Lord God made Uzziah to *p.* 26:5
p. I pray thee, thy servant. *Neh* 1:11
God of heaven, he will *p.* us. 2:20
tabernacles of robbers *p.* *Job* 12:6
whatsoever he doeth shall *p.* *Ps* 1:3
ungodly who *p.* in the world. 73:12*
they shall *p.* that love thee. 122:6
his sins, shall not *p.* *Pr* 28:13
whether shall *p.* *Eccl* 11:6
pleasure of Lord shall *p.* *Isa* 53:10
formed against thee shall *p.* 54:17
shall *p.* in the thing whereunto. 55:11
thou shalt not *p.* in them. *Jer* 2:37
yet they *p.* 5:28
they shall not *p.* 10:21; 20:11
doth the way of wicked *p.*? 12:1
not *p.* in his days, for no man of his seed shall *p.* 22:30
a King shall reign and *p.* 23:5*
with Chaldeans ye shall not *p.* 32:5
are chief, her enemies *p.* *Lam* 1:5
thou didst *p.* *Ezek* 16:13
shall it *p.*? 17:9, 10
shall he *p.*? shall he escape? 17:15
destroy wonderfully and *p.* *Dan* 8:24
shall cause craft to *p.* in his hand. 25
lies, but it shall not *p.* 11:27, 36
all that thou mayest *p.* *3 John* 2

prospered

seeing the Lord hath *p.* *Gen* 24:56
the hand of Israel *p.* *Judg* 4:24*
demanded how war *p.* *2 Sam* 11:7
Hezekiah *p.* *2 Ki* 18:7; *2 Chr* 31:21 32:30
Solomon *p.* *1 Chr* 29:23
Asa *p.* *2 Chr* 14:7
Jews *p.* through the prophesying of Haggai. *Ezra* 6:14
against him and hath *p.*? *Job* 9:4
Daniel *p.* in the reign of. *Dan* 6:28
truth to the ground and it *p.* 8:12
lay by, as God hath *p.* *1 Cor* 16:2

prospereth

work *p.* in their hands. *Ezra* 5:8
fret not because of him that *p.* *Ps* 37:7
a gift, whithersoever it turneth it *p.* *Pr* 17:8
health, even as thy soul *p.* *3 John* 2

prosperity

thou shalt not seek their *p.* *Deut* 23:6
shall say to him that liveth in *p.* *1 Sam* 25:6
and *p.* exceedeth fame. *1 Ki* 10:7
in *p.*, the destroyer shall. *Job* 15:21
shall spend their days in *p.* *Job* 36:11
in my *p.* I said, I shall. *Ps* 30:6
Lord hath pleasure in the *p.* of. 35:27
when I saw the *p.* of wicked. 73:3
I beseech thee, send now *p.* 118:25
peace be within thy walls, *p.* 122:7
the *p.* of fools shall. *Pr* 1:32
in the day of *p.* be joyful. *Eccl* 7:14
I spake to thee in thy *p.* *Jer* 22:21
all the *p.* that I procure to. 33:9*
far from peace, I forgat *p.* *Lam* 3:17
my cities through *p.* shall. *Zech* 1:17
when Jerusalem in *p.* 7:7

prosperous

Lord made his journey *p.* *Gen* 24:21
Joseph, he was a *p.* man. 39:2
thou make thy way *p.* *Josh* 1:8
way we go shall be *p.* *Judg* 18:5
would make the habitation of thy righteousness *p.* *Job* 8:6
he shall make his way *p.* *Isa* 48:15
for the seed shall be *p.* *Zech* 8:12*
I might have a *p.* journey. *Rom* 1:10

prosperously

Solomon *p.* effected all. *2 Chr* 7:11
majesty ride *p.* because. *Ps* 45:4

prostitute

do not *p.* thy daughter. *Lev* 19:29*

protection

rise up and be your *p.* *Deut* 32:38

protest, -ed

the man did solemnly *p.* *Gen* 43:3
hearken, yet *p.* solemnly. *1 Sam* 8:9
and I *p.* unto thee. *1 Ki* 2:42
I earnestly *p.* to your. *Jer* 11:7
the angel of the Lord *p.* *Zech* 3:6
I *p.* by your rejoicing. *1 Cor* 15:31

protesting

p. saying, Obey my voice. *Jer* 11:7

proud

p. helpers do stoop. *Job* 9:13*
he smiteth through the *p.* 26:12*
shall thy *p.* waves be stayed. 38:11
behold *p.* and abase him. 40:11
look on *p.*, bring him low. 12
that speaketh *p.* things. *Ps* 12:3*
plentifully rewardeth the *p.* 31:23
man who respecteth not the *p.* 40:4
the *p.* are risen against me. 86:14
render a reward to the *p.* 94:2
him that hath a *p.* heart will I. 101:5
thou hast rebuked the *p.* 119:21
p. have had me greatly in derision. 51
p. have forged a lie against me. 69
let *p.* be ashamed, for they dealt. 78
the *p.* digged pits for me, not. 85
let not the *p.* oppress me. 122
filled with contempt of the *p.* 123:4
the *p.* waters had gone over. 124:5
the *p.* he knoweth afar off. 138:6
p. have hid a snare for me. 140:5
Lord hateth a *p.* look. *Pr* 6:17
destroy the house of the *p.* 15:25
one *p.* in heart is abomination. 16:5
to divide the spoil with the *p.* 19
an high look and *p.* heart is. 21:4
p. scorner . . . deals in *p.* wrath. 24
p. heart stirreth up strife. 28:25*
patient better than the *p.* *Eccl* 7:8
Lord on every one that is *p.* *Isa* 2:12
arrogancy of the *p.* to cease. 13:11
the *p.* wrath of Moab. 16:6
be not *p.*: for the Lord. *Jer* 13:15
p. men answered Jeremiah. 43:2
Moab, he is exceeding *p.* 48:29
she hath been *p.* 50:29
O thou most *p.* 31
most *p.* shall stumble and fall. 32
he is a *p.* man, neither. *Hab* 2:5
we call the *p.* happy. *Mal* 3:15
p. as stubble. 4:1
he hath scattered the *p.* *Luke* 1:51
despiteful, *p.*, boasters. *Rom* 1:30
he is *p.* knowing nothing. *1 Tim* 6:4
covetous, boasters, *p.* *2 Tim* 3:2
God resisteth the *p.* *Jas* 4:6 *1 Pet* 5:5

proudly

dealt *p.* he was above. *Ex* 18:11
no more so exceeding *p.* *1 Sam* 2:3
thou knewest that they dealt *p.* *Neh* 9:10, 16, 29
their mouth they speak *p.* *Ps* 17:10
which speak grievous things *p.* 31:18
child shall behave *p.* *Isa* 3:5
shouldest thou have spoken *p.* *Ob* 12

prove

[1] *To try and examine,* 2 Cor 13:5. [2] *To show to be true by argument,* Acts 9:22; Rom 3:9. [3] *To find true,* Eccl 7:23.
that I may *p.* them. *Ex* 16:4 *Deut* 8:16
God is come to *p.* you. *Ex* 20:20
humble thee, and to *p.* *Deut* 8:2
whom thou didst *p.* at Massah 33:8
that through them I may *p.* Israel. *Judg* 2:22; *Isa* 3:1, 4
let me *p.* thee but this once with fleece. *Judg* 6:39
she came to *p.* Solomon. *1 Ki* 10:1 *2 Chr* 9:1
it shall *p.* me perverse. *Job* 9:20
O Lord, and *p.* me. *Ps* 26:2
I will *p.* thee with mirth. *Eccl* 2:1
p. thy servants, I beseech. *Dan* 1:12
bring the tithes, *p.* me now herewith. *Mal* 3:10
oxen, I go to *p.* them. *Luke* 14:19
this he said to *p.* him. *John* 6:6
neither can they *p.* the things. *Acts* 24:13; 25:7
p. what is that good will. *Rom* 12:2
to *p.* the sincerity of your. *2 Cor* 8:8
p. your own selves, know ye? 13:5
let every man *p.* his own. *Gal* 6:4
p. all things; hold fast. *1 Thes* 5:21

proved

hereby ye shall be *p.* *Gen* 42:15
that your words may be *p.* 16
and there he *p.* them. *Ex* 15:25
he had not *p.* his sword, David said, I have not *p.* them. *1 Sam* 17:39
thou hast *p.* my heart. *Ps* 17:3
thou, O God, hast *p.* us. 66:10
p. thee at waters of Meribah. 81:7
fathers *p.* me and saw my. 95:9
this have I *p.* by wisdom. *Eccl* 7:23
and *p.* them ten days. *Dan* 1:14
we before *p.* both Jews. *Rom* 3:9
ye have often *p.* diligent. *2 Cor* 8:22
these also be first *p.* *1 Tim* 3:10
p. me, and saw my works. *Heb* 3:9

provender

we have both straw and *p.* *Gen* 24:25
the man gave straw and *p.* for. 32
opened sack to give his ass *p.* 42:27
the man gave their asses *p.* 43:24
there is both straw and *p.* *Judg* 19:19
him and gave *p.* to the asses. 21*
asses shall eat clean *p.* *Isa* 30:24

proverb

(*This word has in the Bible, besides its ordinary modern use, that of a short parable, or a saying with a hidden meaning*)
a *p.* and a byword. *Deut* 28:37
a *p.*, Is Saul among? *1 Sam* 10:12
as saith *p.* of the ancients. 24:13
Israel shall be a *p.* and. *1 Ki* 9:7
will I make to be a *p.* *2 Chr* 7:20
I became a *p.* to them. *Ps* 69:11
understand a *p.* and words. *Pr* 1:6
take up this *p.* against. *Isa* 14:4*
deliver them to be a *p.* *Jer* 24:9
what is that *p.* ye have? *Ezek* 12:22
I will make this *p.* cease . . . no more use it as a *p.* in. 23; 18:2, 3
will make him a sign, and a *p.* 14:8
these take up a taunting *p.* *Hab* 2:6
surely say this *p.*, Physician heal thyself. *Luke* 4:23*
thou plainly, and no *p.* *John* 16:29†
according to the *p.* *2 Pet* 2:22

proverbs

that speak in *p.* say. *Num* 21:27
spake three thousand *p.* *1 Ki* 4:32
the *p.* of Solomon. *Pr* 1:1; 10:1 25:1
preacher set in order many *p.* *Eccl* 12:9
every one that useth *p.* *Ezek* 16:44
I have spoken in *p.* . . . I shall no more speak in *p.* *John* 16:25†

proveth
for Lord your God *p.* you. *Deut* 13:3

provide
God will *p.* himself a lamb. *Gen* 22:8
when shall I *p.* for mine own? 30:30
shalt *p.* out of the people able men. *Ex* 18:21
p. me a man that can play well. *1 Sam* 16:17
men whom David did *p.* *2 Chr* 2:7
can he *p.* flesh for his? *Ps* 78:20
p. neither gold nor silver. *Mat* 10:9
p. yourselves bags. *Luke* 12:33
and *p.* them beasts to set. *Acts* 23:24
p. things honest in sight. *Rom* 12:17
but if any *p.* not for his. *1 Tim* 5:8

provided
he *p.* the first part. *Deut* 33:21
I have *p.* me a king. *1 Sam* 16:1
he had *p.* the king of. *2 Sam* 19:32
which *p.* victuals for. *1 Ki* 4:7, 27
Hezekiah *p.* possessions of flocks. *2 Chr* 32:29
corn, when thou hast *p.* *Ps* 65:9
whose shall those things be, which thou hast *p.*? *Luke* 12:20*
God having *p.* better. *Heb* 11:40

providence
to this nation by thy *p.* *Acts* 24:2

provideth
p. for the raven his food. *Job* 38:41
p. her meat in summer. *Pr* 6:8

providing
p. for honest things. *2 Cor* 8:21*

province, -s
by the princes of the *p.* *1 Ki* 20:14
15, 17, 19
hurtful to kings and *p.* *Ezra* 4:15
found in the *p.* of the Medes. 6:2
gold thou canst find in the *p.* 7:16
are the children of the *p.* *Neh* 7:6
these are the chief of the *p.* 11:3
reigned over 127 *p.* *Esth* 1:1
wrong to people in all *p.* 16, 22
appoint officers in all the *p.* 2:3
king made a release to the *p.* 18
a people scattered in all *p.* of. 3:8
sent by posts to all the king's *p.* 13
all the people of the king's *p.* 4:11
127 *p.* and do every *p.* 8:9
in all *p.* of king Ahasuerus. 12
fame went through all the *p.* 9:4
they done in the rest of the *p.* 12
these days should be kept through every *p.* 28
the treasure of the *p.* *Eccl* 2:8
oppression in a *p.* marvel not. 5:8
princess among the *p.* *Lam* 1:1
against him from the *p.* *Ezek* 19:8
Daniel ruler over the *p.* *Dan* 2:48
image in the *p.* of Babylon. 3:1
promoted Shadrach in the *p.* of. 30
at Shushan in the *p.* of Elam. 8:2
on the fattest places of the *p.* 11:24
asked of what *p.* he was. *Acts* 23:34
Festus was come into the *p.* 25:1

proving
Saul *p.* that this is very. *Acts* 9:22
p. what is acceptable to. *Eph* 5:10

provision
give them *p.* for the way. *Gen* 42:25
gave them *p.* for the way. 45:21
all the bread of their *p.* *Josh* 9:5
bread we took hot for our *p.* 12
each man made *p.* *1 Ki* 4:7
Solomon's *p.* for one day was. 22
he prepared great *p.* *2 Ki* 6:23
for which I have made *p.* *1 Chr* 29:19
abundantly bless her *p.* *Ps* 132:15
appointed them a daily *p.* *Dan* 1:5*
make not *p.* for the flesh. *Rom* 13:14

provocation
Israel sin by his *p.* *1 Ki* 15:30
for the *p.* wherewith Ahab. 21:22
because of the *p.*, Manasseh. *2 Ki* 23:26
had wrought great *p.* *Neh* 9:18, 26
eye continue in their *p.*? *Job* 17:2
harden not your hearts as in *p.* *Ps* 95:8*; *Heb* 3:8, 15
hath been to me as a *p.* *Jer* 32:31
presented *p.* of offering. *Ezek* 20:28

provoke
obey his voice, and *p.* *Ex* 23:21
will this people *p.* me? *Num* 14:11*
if ye *p.* and break. *Deut* 31:20*
that *p.* God are secure. *Job* 12:6
how oft did they *p.* him? *Ps* 78:40*
their doings are against Lord, to *p.* the eyes of his glory. *Isa* 3:8
do they *p.* me to anger? *Jer* 7:19
in that ye *p.* me to wrath. 44:8
began to urge and *p.* *Luke* 11:53
I will *p.* you to jealousy by them that are no people. *Rom* 10:19
for to *p.* them to jealousy. 11:11, 14
do we *p.* the Lord to? *1 Cor* 10:22
ye fathers, *p.* not your children to wrath. *Eph* 6:4
they had heard, did *p.* *Heb* 3:16
to *p.* to love and to good. 10:24

see **anger**

provoked
nor shall any of them that *p.* me see. *Num* 14:23*
these men have *p.* the Lord. 16:30*
in Horeb ye *p.* the Lord. *Deut* 9:8
at Taberah and Massah ye *p.* 22
her adversary also *p.* *1 Sam* 1:6
so she *p.* her, therefore she wept. 7
Judah *p.* him to jealousy. *1 Ki* 14:22
Manasseh had *p.* him. *2 Ki* 23:26
Satan *p.* David to number Israel. *1 Chr* 21:1*
our fathers had *p.* God. *Ezra* 5:12
tempted and *p.* the most high God. *Ps* 78:56*
but *p.* him at the sea. 106:7*
they *p.* him with their own. 29
because they *p.* the spirit. 33*, 43
when your fathers *p.* *Zech* 8:14
charity is not easily *p.* *1 Cor* 13:5
your zeal *p.* very many. *2 Cor* 9:2*

provokedst
forget not how thou *p.* *Deut* 9:7

provoketh
whoso *p.* him to anger. *Pr* 20:2
people that *p.* me to anger. *Isa* 65:3
where was image which *p.* *Ezek* 8:3

provoking
because of *p.* his sons. *Deut* 32:19
groves, *p.* Lord to anger. *1 Ki* 14:15
Baasha in *p.* the Lord. 16:7, 13
by *p.* the most High. *Ps* 78:17*
desirous of vain glory, *p.* *Gal* 5:26

prudence
son endued with *p.* *2 Chr* 2:12*
I wisdom dwell with *p.* *Pr* 8:12*
abounded in all wisdom and *p.* *Eph* 1:8

prudent
David *p.* in matters. *1 Sam* 16:18
p. man covereth shame. *Pr* 12:16
p. man concealeth knowledge. 23
every *p.* man dealeth with. 13:16
wisdom of the *p.* is to. 14:8
the *p.* man looketh well to his. 15
p. are crowned with knowledge. 18
he that regardeth reproof is *p.* 15:5
in heart shall be called *p.* 16:21
the heart of the *p.* getteth. 18:15
a *p.* wife is from the Lord. 19:14
p. man foreseeth evil. 22:3; 27:12
take away the *p.* and the. *Isa* 3:2*
woe to them that are *p.* in. 5:21
I have done it, for I am *p.* 10:13*
understanding of their *p.* men. 29:14
counsel perished from *p.*? *Jer* 49:7
who is *p.* and he shall? *Hos* 14:9
the *p.* shall keep silence. *Amos* 5:13
hid these things from *p.* *Mat* 11:25* *Luke* 10:21*
Sergius Paulus, a *p.* *Acts* 13:7*
understanding of the *p.* *1 Cor* 1:19

prudently
my servant shall deal *p.* *Isa* 52:13*

prune
six years shalt thou *p.* *Lev* 25:3
not sow thy field nor *p.* 4

pruned
waste, it shall not be *p.* *Isa* 5:6

pruning
beat spears into *p.* hooks. *Isa* 2:4 *Mi* 4:3
beat your *p.* hooks into. *Joel* 3:10

psalm
delivered first this *p.* *1 Chr* 16:7
take a *p.* *Ps* 81:2
with the voice of a *p.* 98:5
written in the second *p.* *Acts* 13:33
saith also in another *p.*, Thou. 35
how is it every one of you hath a *p.*? *1 Cor* 14:26

psalmist
David, sweet *p.* of Israel. *2 Sam* 23:1

psalms
sing *p.* to him. *1 Chr* 16:9* *Ps* 105:2*
noise to him with *p.* *Ps* 95:2
David saith in book of *p.* *Luke* 20:42
written in *p.* concerning me. 24:44
written in the book of *p.* *Acts* 1:20
speaking to yourselves in *p.* and. *Eph* 5:19
admonishing one another in *p.* and. *Col* 3:16
any merry? let him sing *p.* *Jas* 5:13*

psaltery
of prophets with a *p.* *1 Sam* 10:5
sing to him with the *p.* *Ps* 33:2
144:9
awake *p.* and harp. 57:8; 108:2
praise thee with the *p.* 71:22; 92:3
pleasant harp with the *p.* 81:2
trumpet, the *p.* and harp. 150:3
when ye hear sound of the *p.* *Dan* 3:5, 7, 10, 15

public
to make her a *p.* example. *Mat* 1:19

publican, -s
A tax-gatherer. The taxes were farmed by the Roman Senate to the highest bidders. These delegated their duties to others, the one condition being that they should raise as much money as possible.
They were especially detested by the Jews, not so much on account of their frequent dishonesty, but because they were paid servants of the hated Romans. They were therefore considered as traitors and apostates.
the *p.* the same? *Mat* 5:46, 47*
many *p.* sat with him. 9:10 *Mark* 2:15; *Luke* 5:29
eateth master with *p.* and sinners? *Mat* 9:11; *Mark* 2:16; *Luke* 5:30
and Matthew the *p.* *Mat* 10:3
a friend of *p.* 11:19; *Luke* 7:34
as an heathen and a *p.* *Mat* 18:17
p. go into the kingdom of God. 21:31
p. and the harlots believed. 32
came *p.* to be baptized. *Luke* 3:12
saw a *p.* named Levi sitting. 5:27
p. justified God, being baptized. 7:29
then drew near to him the *p.* 15:1
one a Pharisee, and other a *p.* 18:10
thank thee, I am not as this *p.* 11
p. standing afar off, said, God. 13
Zacchaeus was chief among *p.* 19:2

publicly
p. convinced the Jews. *Acts* 18:28
have taught you *p.* 20:20

publish
I will *p.* name of Lord. *Deut* 32:3*
to *p.* it in the house. *1 Sam* 31:9*
p. it not in streets of. *2 Sam* 1:20
should *p.* that they bring. *Neh* 8:15
may *p.* with the voice. *Ps* 26:7*
p. in Jerusalem. *Jer* 4:5
p. against Jerusalem. 16
declare this, *p.* it in Judah. 5:20
p. ye and say, O Lord, save. 31:7
p. in Migdol, *p.* in Noph. 46:14
p. and conceal not, Babylon. 50:2
p. in palaces of Ashdod. *Amos* 3:9
proclaim and *p.* free offerings. 4:5
began to *p.* it much. *Mark* 1:45; 5:20

published
king's decree be *p.* through all. *Esth* 1:20, 22

Haman's decree was *p.* *Esth* 3:14; 8:13
ompany that *p.* it. *Ps* 68:11*
aused it to be *p.* through Nineveh. *Jonah* 3:7
great deal they *p.* it. *Mark* 7:36
ospel must first be *p.* 13:10
e went and *p.* through. *Luke* 8:39
hat word which was *p.* *Acts* 10:37
vord of the Lord was *p.* 13:49*

publisheth

hat *p.* peace, that *p.* *Isa* 52:7
oice *p.* affliction from. *Jer* 4:15
eet of him that *p.* peace. *Nah* 1:15

Publius

he father of *P.* lay sick. *Acts* 28:8

Pudens

reeteth thee and *P.* *2 Tim* 4:21

puffed *up*

o one of you be *p. up.* *1 Cor* 4:6
ome are *p. up,* as though I. 18
peech of them that are *p. up.* 19
re *p. up,* and have not rather. 5:2
aunteth not itself, is not *p. up.* 13:4
ainly *p. up* by his fleshly. *Col* 2:18

puffeth *at*

nemies, he *p. at* them. *Ps* 10:5
afety from him that *p. at* him. 12:5

puffeth *up*

nowledge *p. up,* charity. *2 Cor* 8:1

Pul

P. king of Assyria came against Israel . . . gave *P.* *2 Ki* 15:19
tirred up the spirit of *P.* *1 Chr* 5:26
hose that escape to *P.* *Isa* 66:19

pull, -ed

Noah *p.* the dove to him. *Gen* 8:9*
ut the men *p.* Lot into the. 19:10*
eroboam could not *p.* *1 Ki* 13:4
et timber be *p.* down. *Ezra* 6:11
me out of net they have. *Ps* 31:4*
rom thy state shall *p.* *Isa* 22:19
et thee to *p.* down and destroy. *Jer* 1:10*; 18:7*
them out like sheep for. 12:3
hem and not *p.* down. 24:6; 42:10
me in pieces, hath. *Lam* 3:11
hall he not *p.* up? *Ezek* 17:9
hall no more be *p.* up. *Amos* 9:15*
e *p.* off the robe with. *Mi* 2:8*
away the shoulder. *Zech* 7:11
et me *p.* out the mote out of thine eye. *Mat* 7:4*; *Luke* 6:42*
will *p.* down my barns. *Luke* 12:18
nd will not *p.* out on the? 14:5*
ave been *p.* in pieces. *Acts* 23:10*

pulling

nighty to the *p.* down. *2 Cor* 10:4*
thers save with fear, *p.* *Jude* 23*

pulpit

tood upon *p.* of wood. *Neh* 8:4

pulse

eans and parched *p.* *2 Sam* 17:28
et them give *p.* to eat. *Dan* 1:12, 16

punish

you seven times more for your sins. *Lev* 26:18, 24
o *p.* the just is not good. *Pr* 17:26
the stout heart of king. *Isa* 10:12
will *p.* world for their evil. 13:11
ord shall *p.* host of high ones. 24:21
ord cometh to *p.* inhabitants. 26:21
word shall *p.* leviathan. 27:1
will *p.* all them that are circumcised. *Jer* 9:25
will *p.* men of Anathoth. 11:22
ay when he shall *p.* thee? 13:21*
vill *p.* you according to fruit. 21:14
will even *p.* that man. 23:34
king of Babylon. 25:12; 50:18
vill *p.* that nation. 27:8
will *p.* Shemaiah. 29:32
all that oppress them. 30:20
Jehoiakim and his seed. 36:31
will *p.* them in Egypt, as I *p.* 44:13
ign that I will *p.* you in this. 29
will *p.* the multitude of No. 46:25
nd I will *p.* Bel in Babylon. 51:44
vill *p.* them for their ways. *Hos* 4:9
will not *p.* your daughters. 14

p. Jacob according to his. *Hos* 12:2
I will *p.* you for your iniquities. *Amos* 3:2
day I will *p.* the princes. *Zeph* 1:8
I will *p.* all those that leap on. 9
I will *p.* men that are settled. 12
I thought to *p.* when your fathers. *Zech* 8:14*
how they might *p.* them. *Acts* 4:21

punished

he shall be surely *p.* *Ex* 21:20, 22
he shall not be *p.* for he is his. 21
thou hast *p.* less than. *Ezra* 9:13
it is an iniquity to be *p.* by judges. *Job* 31:11, 28
when scorner is *p.*, simple. *Pr* 21:11
but the simple pass on and are *p.* 22:3; 27:12
as I have *p.* Jerusalem. *Jer* 44:13
I have *p.* the king of Assyria. 50:18
howsoever I *p.* them. *Zeph* 3:7
shepherds, I *p.* the goats. *Zech* 10:3
to bring them bound to Jerusalem to be *p.* *Acts* 22:5
I *p.* them oft in every. 26:11
be *p.* with everlasting. *2 Thes* 1:9
day of judgement to be *p.* *2 Pet* 2:9

punishment

my *p.* is greater than. *Gen* 4:13
than accept the *p.* of their iniquity. *Lev* 26:41, 43
Saul sware, No *p.* shall. *1 Sam* 28:10
and a strange *p.* to the workers of. *Job* 31:3*
great wrath shall suffer *p.* *Pr* 19:19
a man for *p.* of his sins. *Lam* 3:39
p. of my people is greater than the *p.* of Sodom. 4:6
the *p.* of thine iniquity is. 22
bear *p.* of their iniquity, *p.* of prophets as *p.* of. *Ezek* 14:10*
I will not turn away the *p.* *Amos* 1:3
6, 9, 11, 13; 2:1, 4, 6
the *p.* of Egypt. *Zech* 14:19
go into everlasting *p.* *Mat* 25:46
to such a man is this *p.* *2 Cor* 2:6
of how much sorer *p.*? *Heb* 10:29
sent by him for the *p.* *1 Pet* 2:14

punishments

wrath bringeth the *p.* *Job* 19:29
to execute *p.* upon the. *Ps* 149:7

pur

they cast *p.* that is, the lot. *Esth* 3:7
Haman had cast *p.* for to. 9:24
Purim, after the name of *p.* 26

see **Purim**

purchase, *substantive*

p. of field and cave. *Gen* 49:32
evidence of the *p.* *Jer* 32:11
I gave evidence of *p.* to. 12, 14, 16

purchase, -ed

field Abraham *p.* of. *Gen* 25:10
which thou hast *p.* *Ex* 15:16
if a man *p.* of the Levites. *Lev* 25:33*
Ruth have I *p.* to be my. *Ruth* 4:10
congregation thou hast *p.* *Ps* 74:2
his right hand had *p.* 78:54
this man *p.* a field with iniquity. *Acts* 1:18*
gift of God may be *p.* by. 8:20*
which he hath *p.* with his own. 20:28
redemption of the *p.* *Eph* 1:14*
office of deacon well, *p.* *1 Tim* 3:13*

pure

that they bring the *p.* oil. *Ex* 27:20
Lev 24:2
take *p.* myrrh. *Ex* 30:23
with *p.* frankincense. 34
the *p.* candlestick. 31:8; 39:37
Lev 24:4
set cakes on the *p.* table. *Lev* 24:6
thou shalt put *p.* frankincense on. 7
didst drink the *p.* blood. *Deut* 32:14*
with the *p.* thou wilt shew thyself *p.* *2 Sam* 22:27; *Ps* 18:26
measures of *p.* oil. *1 Ki* 5:11
set on the *p.* table. *2 Chr* 13:11
all were *p.* and killed. *Ezra* 6:20
shall a man be more *p.*? *Job* 4:17
if thou wert *p.* and upright. 8:6
hast said, My doctrine is *p.* 11:4
also my prayer is *p.* 16:17

stars are not *p.* in his sight. *Job* 25:5
words of the Lord are *p.* *Ps* 12:6
commandment of Lord is *p.* 19:8
word is very *p.*: therefore I. 119:140
the words of the *p.* are. *Pr* 15:26
say, I am *p.* from my sin? 20:9
whether his work be *p.* 11
the *p.* his work is right. 21:8
every word of God is *p.* 30:5*
generation that are *p.* in their. 12
head like the *p.* wool. *Dan* 7:9
shall I count them *p.*? *Mi* 6:11
turn to the people a *p.* *Zeph* 3:9
in every place a *p.* offering. *Mal* 1:11
I am *p.* from the blood. *Acts* 20:26
all things indeed are *p.* *Rom* 14:20
whatsoever things are *p.* *Phil* 4:8
mystery of faith in a *p.* *1 Tim* 3:9
of sins, keep thyself *p.* 5:22
with a *p.* conscience. *2 Tim* 1:3
to the *p.* all things are *p.*, but to . . . nothing is *p.* *Tit* 1:15
our bodies washed with *p.* water. *Heb* 10:22
p. religion and undefiled. *Jas* 1:27
wisdom from above is first *p.* 3:17
I stir up your *p.* minds. *2 Pet* 3:1
himself even as he is *p.* *1 John* 3:3
angels clothed in *p.* linen. *Rev* 15:6
a *p.* river of water of life. 22:1

see **heart, gold**

purely

I will *p.* purge away. *Isa* 1:25

pureness

it is delivered by the *p.* *Job* 22:30
he that loveth *p.* of heart. *Pr* 22:11
approving ourselves, by *p.* *2 Cor* 6:6

purer

Nazarites *p.* than snow. *Lam* 4:7
thou art of *p.* eyes than. *Hab* 1:13

purge

Josiah began to *p.* Judah. *2 Chr* 34:3
p. me with hyssop. *Ps* 51:7
transgressions thou shalt *p.* 65:3†
and *p.* away our sins for thy. 79:9†
and purely *p.* away thy. *Isa* 1:25
I will *p.* from among. *Ezek* 20:38
shalt thou cleanse and *p.* it. 43:20*
seven days shall they *p.* altar. 26*
shall fall to *p.* them. *Dan* 11:35*
and *p.* them as gold. *Mal* 3:3*
he will throughly *p.* his floor, and. *Mat* 3:12*; *Luke* 3:17*
p. out therefore the old. *1 Cor* 5:7
if a man therefore *p.* *2 Tim* 2:21
p. your conscience from. *Heb* 9:14*

purged

Eli's house shall not be *p.* *1 Sam* 3:14
when he had *p.* the land. *2 Chr* 34:8
and truth, iniquity is *p.* *Pr* 16:6
shall have *p.* the blood of. *Isa* 4:4
taken away, and thy sin *p.* 6:7†
iniquity shall not be *p.* 22:14†
the iniquity of Jacob be *p.* 27:9†
have *p.* thee, and thou wast not *p.*, thou shalt not be *p.* *Ezek* 24:13†
when he had by himself *p.* our sins. *Heb* 1:3*
are by the law *p.* by blood. 9:22*
the worshippers once *p.* 10:2*
hath forgotten he was *p.* *2 Pet* 1:9*

purgeth

beareth fruit, he *p.* it. *John* 15:2*

purging

draught, *p.* all meats. *Mark* 7:19*

purification, -s

it is a *p.* for sin. *Num* 19:9*
burnt heifer of *p.* for sin. 17*
according to *p.* of the. *2 Chr* 30:19
the ward of their *p.* *Neh* 12:45
their things for *p.* be. *Esth* 2:3
so were the days of their *p.* 12
when days of her *p.* were. *Luke* 2:22
the accomplishment of the days of *p.* *Acts* 21:26

purified

and *p.* the altar, and. *Lev* 8:15
the Levites were *p.* *Num* 8:21
Ezra 6:20
shall be *p.* with water. *Num* 31:23
Bath-sheba was *p.* from. *2 Sam* 11:4

are pure words, as silver p. Ps 12:6
many shall be p. and. Dan 12:10
from Asia found me p. Acts 24:18
things in the heavens be p. Heb 9:23
seeing ye have p. your. 1 Pet 1:22

purifier

as refiner and p. of silver. Mal 3:3

purifieth

dead body and p. not. Num 19:13
that hath this hope p. 1 John 3:3

purify

shall p. himself with. Num 19:12, 19
and shall not p. himself. 20
p. yourselves and your captives. 31:19
p. all your raiment, and all made. 20
by reason of breakings they p. Job 41:25
they p. themselves in. Isa 66:17
seven days shall they p. Ezek 43:26
and he shall p. the sons. Mal 3:3
went to Jerusalem to p. John 11:55
take and p. thyself. Acts 21:24
and p. to himself a people. Tit 2:14
p. your hearts, ye double. Jas 4:8

purifying

the blood of her p. Lev 12:4
when the days of her p. are. 6
sprinkle water of p. on. Num 8:7*
office was in p. all holy. 1 Chr 23:28
with other things for p. of women. Esth 2:12
after the manner of the p. John 2:6
arose a question about p. 3:25
sanctifieth to the p. of. Heb 9:13

purifying, *verb*

p. their hearts by faith. Acts 15:9
and the next day p. himself. 21:26

Purim

(*Plural form of Hebrew* pur, *a lot. The annual festival instituted to commemorate the preservation of the Jews in Persia from the massacre designed by Haman. Haman, in his superstition, cast lots to determine the favourable day for the massacre*)

called these days P. Esth 9:26
that these days of P. should. 28
this sacred letter of P. 29, 31
Esther confirmed these P. 32

purity

example in faith, in p. 1 Tim 4:12
younger as sisters, with all p. 5:2

purloining

not p. but shewing all good. Tit 2:10

purple

offering, blue, p. and scarlet. Ex 25:4
curtains of fine linen and p. 26:1
wires, to work in the p. 39:3
and spread a p. cloth. Num 4:13
p. raiment was on kings. Judg 8:26
cunning to work in p. 2 Chr 2:7, 14
the vail of blue, and p. and. 3:14
cords of fine linen and p. Esth 1:6
with garment of linen and p. 8:15
clothing is silk and p. Pr 31:22
covering of it of p. S of S 3:10
hair of thine head like p. 7:5
and p. is their clothing. Jer 10:9
p. was that which covered thee. Ezek 27:7
in thy fairs with emeralds, p. 16
clothed him with p. Mark 15:17
they took off the p. from him. 20
rich man clothed in p. Luke 16:19
put on him a p. robe. John 19:2
forth wearing the p. robe. 5
Lydia, a seller of p. Acts 16:14
woman was arrayed in p. Rev 17:4
buyeth the merchandise or p. 18:12
that was clothed in p. and scarlet. 16

purpose

handfuls of p. for her. Ruth 2:16*
to frustrate their p. Ezra 4:5
they made for the p. Neh 8:4
withdraw man from his p. Job 33:17
every p. is established. Pr 20:18
and a time to every p. Eccl 3:1, 17
8:6
to what p. is multitude? Isa 1:11
this is the p. that is purposed. 14:26
shall help in vain, and to no p. 30:7
to what p. cometh to me incense? Jer 6:20
Nebuchadnezzar conceived a p. 49:30
for every p. of the Lord shall stand. 51:29
that p. be not changed. Dan 6:17
To what p. is this waste? Mat 26:8
with p. of heart, they. Acts 11:23
appeared to thee for this p. 26:16
that they had obtained their p. 27:13
centurion kept them from their p. 43
called according to his p. Rom 8:28
that the p. of God according to. 9:11
even for this same p. have I. 17
according to p. of him. Eph 1:11
according to the eternal p. in. 3:11
to you for the same p. 6:22; Col 4:8
according to his own p. 2 Tim 1:9
thou hast fully known my p. 3:10
for this p. Son of God. 1 John 3:8

purpose, -ed, *verb*

I p. to build an house. 1 Ki 5:5
p. to keep under Judah. 2 Chr 28:10
Sennacherib p. to fight against. 32:2
I am p. my mouth shall. Ps 17:3
who have p. to overthrow my. 140:4
as I have p., so shall it. Isa 14:24
this is the purpose p. upon the. 26
the Lord hath p., who shall? 27
what the Lord hath p. upon. 19:12
Lord hath p. to stain the pride. 23:9
p. it, and I will also do it. 46:11
I have p. it, and will not. Jer 4:28
repent me of the evil which I p. 26:3
will hear all evil which I p. to. 36:3
purposes that he hath p. 49:20
50:45
Lord hath p. to destroy. Lam 2:8
Daniel p. in his heart not. Dan 1:8
Paul p. in spirit to go to. Acts 19:21
Paul p. to return through. 20:3*
oftentimes I p. to come. Rom 1:13
things I p., do I p. according to the flesh? 2 Cor 1:17
will which he hath p. in. Eph 1:9
eternal purpose which he p. in. 3:11

purposes

days are past, my p. are. Job 17:11
without counsel p. are. Pr 15:22
broken in the p. thereof. Isa 19:10
hear counsel of the Lord and p. Jer 49:20; 50:45

purposeth

every man as he p. in his. 2 Cor 9:7

purposing

comfort himself, p. to kill. Gen 27:42

purse

lot, let us have one p. Pr 1:14
carry neither p. nor scrip. Luke 10:4
I sent you without p. and. 22:35
he that hath a p., let him take it. 36

purses

nor brass in your p. Mat 10:9
take no money in their p. Mark 6:8

pursue

they did not p. after. Gen 35:5
enemy said, I will p., I. Ex 15:9
lest the avenger of blood p. Deut 19:6; Josh 20:5
they shall p. thee until thou perish. Deut 28:22, 45
p. after them, ye shall. Josh 2:5
Ai were called together to p. 8:16
stay not, but p. after your. 10:19
whom dost thou p.? 1 Sam 24:14
a man is risen to p. thee. 25:29
doth my lord thus p. me? 26:18
shall I p. after this troop? 30:8
arise and p. after David. 2 Sam 17:1
servants, p. after Sheba. 20:6, 7
flee while enemies p. thee? 24:13
p. the dry stubble? Job 13:25
terrors p. my soul as the. 30:15*
seek peace and p. it. Ps 34:14
they that p. you be swift. Isa 30:16
the sword shall p. thee. Jer 48:2
blood shall p. thee. Ezek 35:6
enemy shall p. him. Hos 8:3
because Edom did p. his broth
with the sword. Amos 1:
darkness shall p. his. Nah 1

pursued

Abram p. them to Dan and Hobah
Gen 14:14,
brethren p. Jacob. 31:23,
the Egyptians p. after Israel. Ex 14
9:23; Deut 11:4; Josh 24
p. the spies. Josh 2
they of Ai p. 8:16,
p. after Adoni-bezek. Judg 1
Barak p. after chariots. 4:16,
Gideon p. after. 7:23, 25; 8:
Israel p. Benjamin unto. 20:
Israel p. the Philistines. 1 Sam 7:
17:
Saul p. David. 23:
David p. Amalekites. 30:
Asahel p. after Abner. 2 Sam 2:
Joab p. Abner.
Joab p. Israel no more.
so Joab and Abishai p. 20:
I have p. mine enemies. 22:
Ps 18:
fled, and Israel p. after. 1 Ki 20:
army of Chaldees p. the king.
2 Ki 25:5; Jer 39:5; 52
Abijah p. after. 2 Chr 13:
Asa and people p. Ethiopians. 14:
he p. them, and passed. Isa 41
they p. us upon the mountains, th
laid wait for us. Lam 4:1

pursuer, -s

lest p. meet you. Josh 2:
until the p. returned, the p.
turned back upon the p. 8:
without strength before p. Lam 1

pursueth, -ing

flee when none p. you. Lev 26:
shall fall when none p. 36,
faint, yet p. them. Judg 8
I am p. Zebah and Zalmunna.
Saul returned from p. 1 Sam 23:
Joab came from p. a. 2 Sam 3:
returned from p. after Israel. 18:
your god is p. or on a. 1 Ki 18:2
turned back from p. Jehoshaphat.
22:33; 2 Chr 18:
he that p. evil, p. it to. Pr 11:
p. sinners, to the righteous. 13:
he p. them with words, yet. 19:
wicked flee when no man p. 28:

purtenance

his head, legs, and p. Ex 12:

push

ox were wont to p. Ex 21:29*, 3
if the ox p. a manservant or. 3
with them he shall p. Deut 33:
with these thou shalt p. Syrians.
1 Ki 22:11; 2 Chr 18:
they p. away my feet. Job 30:
through thee will we p. down o
enemies. Ps 44:
king of south p. at him. Dan 11:4

pushed

p. all the diseased with. Ezek 34:2

pushing

I saw the ram p. westward. Dan 8:

put

there God p. the man. Gen 2:8,
I will p. enmity between thee. 3:1
p. thy hand under my thigh. 24:2,
47:2
and I p. the earring upon her. 24:4
p. them upon Jacob her. 27:
she p. the skins of the kids.
Jacob p. the stones for his. 28:1
p. stone again on well's mouth. 29:
p. own flocks by themselves. 30:4
when cattle were feeble, he p. not. 4
Rachel p. them in the camels'. 31:3
p. space betwixt drove and. 32:
Tamar p. off her widow's. 38:
all he had p. into Joseph's hand. 39:
that they should p. me into. 40:
he p. them altogether in ward. 42:
Joseph shall p. his hand on. 46:
p. thy right hand upon his. 48:
p. off thy shoes from off thy feet.
Ex 3:5; Isa 20:2; Acts 7:3

all p. them on your sons. Ex 3:22
ord said, P. now thy hand in. 4:6
eak to him, and p. words in. 15
p. a sword in their hand. 5:21
will p. a division between. 8:23
ay know the Lord doth p. 11:7
ill p. none of these diseases. 15:26
an homer full of manna. 16:33
his beast in another man's. 22:5
hether he have p. his hand. 8
oath that he hath not p. his. 11
not thine hand with wicked. 23:1
ou shalt p. all in the hands of. 29:24
of the perfume before the. 30:36
every man his sword by his side. 32:27
ow p. off thy ornaments. 33:5
thee in a cleft of the rock. 22
p. all on Aaron's and. Lev 8:27
or p. a stumblingblock. 19:14
the blasphemer in ward. 24:12
ten thousand to flight. 26:8
Deut 32:30
all p. my name on the. Num 6:27
irit which is on thee, and p. 11:17
e Lord would p. his Spirit. 29
rpent of brass, and p. it on a. 21:9
ord p. word in Balaam's. 23:5, 16
ou shalt p. them in ark. Deut 10:2
the tables in the ark. 5:1
ou shalt p. the blessing on. 11:29
ace he shall choose to p. 12:5, 21
shall rejoice in all ye p. 7
my words in his mouth. 18:18
ou shalt not p. any grapes. 23:24
it even among their. Josh 7:11
p. my life in my hands. Judg 12:3
me into one of the priests' offices. 1 Sam 2:36
will p. your asses to work. 8:16
man p. his hand to his. 14:26
id David p. them off him. 17:39
Goliath's armour in his tent. 54
id p. his life in his hand. 19:5
have p. my life in my hand. 28:21
ord p. them under the soles. 1 Ki 5:3
p. my name there. 9:3; 11:36
14:21
the calves p. he in Dan. 12:29
wood, and p. no fire under. 18:23
ing, P. this fellow in prison. 22:27
p. his mouth upon. 2 Ki 4:34
ing's son, they p. the crown. 11:12
thine hand upon bow, he p. 13:16
ill p. hook in thy nose. 19:28
Isa 37:29
erusalem will I p. my name. 21:7
2 Chr 6:20; 12:13; 33:7
hat have p. their lives. 1 Chr 11:19
p. his hand to the ark. 13:10
nd the angel p. up his sword. 21:27
ouse have I p. the ark. 2 Chr 6:11
he king of Egypt p. him down. 36:3
yrus p. the decree in writing. 22
Ezra 1:1
estroy kings that p. Ezra 6:12
such a thing in the king's heart. 7:27
hat God had p. in. Neh 2:12
obles p. not their necks to. 3:5
hat every one p. them off. 4:23
obiah would have p. me in fear. 6:14, 19
ecree drew near to be p. Esth 9:1
ehold, he p. no trust in. Job 4:18
herefore do I p. my life in? 13:14
me in a surety with thee. 17:3
my brethren far from me. 19:13
ut he would p. strength in me. 23:6
wisdom in inward parts. 38:36
anst thou p. an hook into his? 41:2
hou hast p. gladness in. Ps 4:7
all things under his feet. 8:6
1 Cor 15:25, 27; Eph 1:22; Heb 2:8
in fear, O Lord, that. Ps 9:20
hou hast p. off my sackcloth. 30:11
et the lying lips be p. to. 31:18
e hath p. a new song in my. 40:3
to shame. 14; 44:7; 53:5
ast cast off and p. us to shame. 44:9
thou my tears into thy. 56:8
e p. them to a perpetual. 78:66
over and friend hast thou p. 88:18

it is better to trust in the Lord than to p. confidence in man. Ps 118:8
than to p. confidence in princes. 9
O Lord, p. me not to shame. 119:31
p. a knife to thy throat. Pr 23:2
when thy neighbour hath p. 25:8
lest he that heareth it p. thee. 10
then must he p. to more. Eccl 10:10
I have p. off my coat, how shall I p.? S of S 5:3
my beloved p. in his hand by. 4
that p. darkness for light. Isa 5:20
p. down the inhabitants. 10:13
weaned child p. his hand on. 11:8
I have p. my Spirit upon him. 42:1
Mat 12:18
p. me in remembrance. Isa 43:26
thou shalt not be able to p. 47:11
I have p. my words in thy mouth and covered thee. 51:16; Jer 1:9
p. it into the hand of them. Isa 51:23
to bruise him, he hath p. 53:10
words I p. in thy mouth shall. 59:21
where is he that p. his Spirit? 63:11
how shall I p. thee among? Jer 3:19
our God hath p. us to silence. 8:14
have p. themselves to pain. 12:13
will p. my law in their inward. 31:33
p. my fear in their hearts. 32:40
O sword, p. up thyself into. 47:6
they p. the branch to. Ezek 8:17
I will p. a new spirit within. 11:19
36:26, 27; 37:14
comeliness I had p. upon thee. 16:14
priests have p. no difference. 22:26
I will p. hooks in thy jaws. 29:4; 38:4
I will p. a fear in Egypt. 30:13
and p. breath in you, and ye. 37:6
would, he p. down. Dan 5:19
p. in the sickle, for the. Joel 3:13
I will p. them together. Mi 2:12
trust not a friend, p. ye not. 7:5
where they have been p. Zeph 3:19
wages to p. it in a bag. Hag 1:6
light candle and p. it. Mat 5:15
nor do men p. new wine into. 9:17
let no man p. asunder. 19:6
Mark 10:9
p. the Sadducees to. Mat 22:34
p. my money to exchangers. 25:27
p. up again thy sword. 26:52
John 18:11
not lawful to p. them into. Mat 27:6
p. his hands on them. Mark 10:16
p. down mighty from. Luke 1:52
best robe, p. it on him, and p. 15:22
none to p. me into pool. John 5:7
he p. clay upon mine eyes. 9:15
p. it upon hyssop, and p. it to. 19:29
p. my finger into the print. 20:25
Father hath p. in his own. Acts 1:7
they p. the apostles in hold. 4:3
p. them in common prison. 5:18
the men whom ye p. in prison. 25
seeing ye p. the word of God. 13:46
and p. no difference between. 15:9
to p. a yoke upon the neck. 10
p. a stumblingblock. Rom 14:13
he shall have p. down. 1 Cor 15:24
till he p. all his enemies under. 25
God, which p. the same earnest care. 2 Cor 8:16
that ye p. off the old man. Eph 4:22
Col 3:9
ye also p. off all these. Col 3:8
if thou p. the brethren in remembrance. 1 Tim 4:6; 2 Tim 2:14
wherefore I p. thee in. 2 Tim 1:6
p. them in mind to be subject. Tit 3:1
if he oweth, p. that on. Philem 18
to angels hath he not p. Heb 2:5
p. him to an open shame. 6:6
p. my laws into their mind. 8:10
p. my laws into their hearts. 10:16
we p. bits in the horses'. Jas 3:3
ye may p. to silence. 1 Pet 2:15
to p. you always in. 2 Pet 1:12
knowing that I must p. off this. 14
p. you also in remembrance. Jude 5
I will p. on you none. Rev 2:24
God hath p. in their hearts. 17:17

put *away*

p. away the strange gods. Gen 35:2
p. away the leaven out. Ex 12:15
nor take a woman p. away. Lev 21:7
p. away guilt of innocent blood. Deut 19:13; 21:9
he may not p. away all his days. 22:19, 29
p. away the strange gods. Josh 24:14
23; Judg 10:16; 1 Sam 7:3
Eli said, p. away thy. 1 Sam 1:14
Saul had p. away. 28:3
Saul whom I p. away. 2 Sam 7:15
Lord hath p. away thy sin. 12:13
Jehoram p. away the. 2 Ki 3:2
did Josiah p. away. 23:24
Asa p. away the abominable idols. 2 Chr 15:8
covenant to p. away the wives. Ezra 10:3
they gave their hands to p. away. 19
in thine hand, p. it away. Job 11:14
p. away iniquity from thy. 22:23
I did not p. away his statutes from. Ps 18:22
p. not thy servant away. 27:9
p. away mine acquaintance. 88:8
p. away from thee a froward. Pr 4:24
have p. away? for transgressions is your mother p. away. Isa 50:1
if a man p. away his wife. Jer 3:1
I had p. her away and given her. 8
if thou wilt p. away thine. 4:1
let them p. away their. Ezek 43:9
take her that is p. away. 44:22
let her p. away her whoredoms. Hos 2:2
p. far away the evil day. Amos 6:3
to p. her away privily. Mat 1:19
shall p. away his wife. 5:31, 32
19:9; Mark 10:11; Luke 16:18
man to p. away his wife? Mark 10:2
if a woman shall p. away her. 12
p. away from you that wicked person. 1 Cor 5:13
husband p. away his wife. 7:11, 12
I p. away childish things. 13:11
evil speaking be p. away. Eph 4:31
some having p. away. 1 Tim 1:19
to p. away sin by the. Heb 9:26
see **death, evil**

put *forth*

lest he p. forth and take. Gen 3:22
Noah p. forth his hand and took. 8:9
men p. forth their hand and. 19:10
p. forth thine hand and. Ex 4:4
precious things p. forth. Deut 33:14
Ehud p. forth his left. Judg 3:21
angel p. forth the end of staff. 6:21
I will now p. forth a riddle. 14:12, 13
Samson p. forth and took. 15:15
Jonathan p. forth rod. 1 Sam 14:27
servants not p. forth to slay. 22:17
not p. forth mine hand against. 24:10
Uzzah p. forth his hand to the ark of God. 2 Sam 6:6; 1 Chr 13:9
Absalom p. forth his hand. 2 Sam 15:5
ye not p. forth my hand. 18:12
and his hand, which he p. forth against him, dried up. 1 Ki 13:4
p. forth thine hand now and touch all that he hath. Job 1:11; 2:5
upon himself p. not forth thy. 12
p. forth his hands against. Ps 55:20
lest the righteous p. forth. 125:3
and understanding p. forth her voice? Pr 8:1
p. not forth thyself in presence. 25:6
Lord p. forth his hand and touched. Jer 1:9
p. forth form of an hand. Ezek 8:3
Son of man, p. forth a riddle. 17:2
Jesus p. forth his hand and. Mat 8:3
Mark 1:41; Luke 5:13
people were p. forth, he. Mat 9:25
parable p. he forth. 13:24, 31
Luke 14:7
to p. the apostles forth. Acts 5:34
but Peter p. them all forth. 9:40

put *on*

and raiment to p. on. Gen 28:20
Tamar p. on garments of her. 38:19
priest, shall p. them on. Ex 29:30
no man did p. on him his. 33:4

the priest shall p. on his. Lev 6:10
he shall p. on other garments. 11
p. on the holy linen coat. 16:4
he shall p. on his garments. 24
consecrated to p. on garment. 21:10
p. on incense, and go. Num 16:46
nor a man p. on a woman's. Deut 22:5
weep for Saul, who p. on. 2 Sam 1:24
I pray p. on now mourning. 14:2
Joab's garment he had p. on. 20:8
but p. thou on thy robes. 1 Ki 22:30
2 Chr 18:29
able to p. on armour. 2 Ki 3:21
Mordecai p. on sackcloth. Esth 4:1
Esther p. on her royal apparel. 5:1
the just shall p. it on. Job 27:17
I p. on righteousness, and it. 29:14
how shall I p. it on? S of S 5:3
p. on strength. Isa 51:9; 52:1
p. on thy beautiful garments. 52:1
he p. on righteousness as a breastplate, he p. on garments. 59:17
and p. it on thy loins. Jer 13:1, 2
and p. on the brigandines. 46:4
p. on thy shoes upon thy. Ezek 24:17
p. on other garments. 42:14; 44:19
Nineveh p. on sackcloth. Jonah 3:5
nor what ye shall p. on. Mat 6:25
Luke 12:22
they p. on the ass and. Mat 21:7
and p. on him a scarlet robe. 27:28
platted a crown of thorns, they p. it on his head. 29; Jer 19:2
them p. a spunge on a reed.
Mat 27:48; Mark 15:36
sandals, not p. on two coats.
Mark 6:9
p. on him the best robe. Luke 15:22
a title and p. it on cross. John 19:19
p. on armour of light. Rom 13:12
but p. ye on the Lord Jesus. 14
corruptible must p. on. 1 Cor 15:53
shall have p. on immortality. 54
Christ, have p. on Christ. Gal 3:27
that ye p. on the new man.
Eph 4:24; Col 3:10
p. on whole armour of. Eph 6:11
p. on therefore as elect. Col 3:12
p. on charity, which is the bond. 14

put out

one p. out his hand. Gen 38:28
p. out the remembrance. Ex 17:14
fire shall not be p. out. Lev 6:12
p. out of the camp every leper.
Num 5:2, 4
and female shall ye p. out. 3
wilt thou p. out the eyes? 16:14
the Lord will p. out those. Deut 7:22
name be not p. out of Israel. 25:6
the Philistines p. out Samson's eyes.
Judg 16:21
p. now this woman out. 2 Sam 13:17
he p. out his hand and. 2 Ki 6:7
p. out the eyes of Zedekiah and.
25:7; Jer 39:7; 52:11
have p. out the lamps. 2 Chr 29:7
wicked shall be p. out. Job 18:5
and his candle be p. out. 6; 21:17
Pr 13:9; 20:20; 24:20
hast p. out their name. Ps 9:5
when I p. thee out I will cover heaven. Ezek 32:7
when he had p. them all out.
Mark 5:40; Luke 8:54
p. out of the stewardship. Luke 16:4
he should be p. out of the synagogue.
John 9:22
lest they should be p. out of the synagogue. 12:42
p. you out of the synagogues. 16:2

put trust

come and p. your trust in my shadow.
Judg 9:15
p. thy trust on Egypt. 2 Ki 18:24
Isa 36:9
p. their trust in him. 1 Chr 5:20
p. your trust in the Lord. Ps 4:5
p. their trust in thee rejoice. 5:11
my God, in thee do I p. my trust. 7:1
16:1; 25:20; 71:1
thy name, will p. trust in thee. 9:10
in the Lord p. I my trust. Ps 11:1
31:1; 71:1
savest them which p. their trust. 17:7
p. their trust under the shadow. 36:7
in God I have p. my trust, I. 56:4
I have p. my trust in the Lord. 73:28
p. not your trust in princes. 146:3
that p. their trust in him. Pr 30:5
hast p. thy trust in me. Jer 39:18
p. in trust with gospel. 1 Thes 2:4
I will p. my trust in him. Heb 2:13

put, participle

Joseph was p. in a coffin. Gen 50:26
the vessel, it must be p. Lev 11:32
but if any water be p. on seed. 38
shall be p. apart seven days. 15:19
as long as she is p. apart. 18:19
nor feet p. in fetters. 2 Sam 3:34
the kings having p. on their robes.
1 Ki 22:10
Judah was p. to the worse.
2 Ki 14:12; 2 Chr 25:22
the Syrians saw that they were p. to the worse. 1 Chr 19:16, 19
neither was the number p. in. 27:24
every device shall be p. 2 Chr 2:14
Israel be p. to the worse. 6:24
were p. from the priesthood.
Ezra 2:62; Neh 7:64
be p. to shame that seek after my.
Ps 35:4; 83:17
be p. to confusion, that desire. 70:2
let me never be p. to confusion. 71:1
shouldest be p. lower. Pr 25:7
nothing can be p. to it. Eccl 3:14
shalt not be p. to shame. Isa 54:4
ride, every one p. in array. Jer 50:42
have been p to shame. Zeph 3:19
is p. in to fill it up. Mat 9:16
John was p. in prison. Mark 1:14
new wine must be p. into new bottles.
2:22; Luke 5:38
no man having p. his hand to plough.
Luke 9:62
Judas bare what was p. in. John 12:6
devil having now p. into the. 13:2
that is not p. under him, but now we see not yet all things p. Heb 2:8
bodies to be p. in graves. Rev 11:9

Puteoli

came the next day to P. Acts 28:13

putrifying

bruises, and p. sores. Isa 1:6*

puttest

p. thy nest in a rock. Num 24:21
bless all thou p. thine hands to.
Deut 12:18; 15:10
thou p. on me will I bear. 2 Ki 18:14
thou p. my feet in stocks. Job 13:27
p. away the wicked like dross.
Ps 119:119
that p. thy bottle to him. Hab 2:15*

putteth

who p. any on a stranger. Ex 30:33
word that God p. in my. Num 22:38
woman p. forth her hand. Deut 25:11
graven image, and p. it in a. 27:15
as he that p. off harness. 1 Ki 20:11
he p. no trust in his saints. Job 15:15
he p. forth his hand upon. 28:9
he p. my feet in the stocks. 33:11
p. not out his money to. Ps 15:5
God p. down one and setteth. 75:7
that p. his trust in Lord. Pr 28:25
who p. his trust in the Lord. 29:25
fig tree p. forth her. S of S 2:13*
p. his trust in me shall. Isa 57:13
as a shepherd p. on. Jer 43:12
he p. his mouth in dust. Lam 3:29
p. the stumblingblock. Ezek 14:4, 7
he that p. not into their. Mi 3:5
no man p. new cloth. Mat 9:16
Luke 5:36
tender and p. forth leaves ye know.
Mat 24:32; Mark 13:28
no man p. new wine into old.
Mark 2:22; Luke 5:37
immediately he p. in sickle.
Mark 4:29
no man p. a candle under. Luke 8:16
no man, when he hath lighted a candle, p. it in a secret place. 11:33
whoso p. away his wife. Luke 16:
when he p. forth his own. John 10

putting

p. it on Hagar's shoulder. Gen 21:
p. them upon the head. Lev 16:
p. their hand to their mouth and.
Judg 7:
p. forth of the finger. Isa 58
he hateth p. away. Mal 2:
Ananias p. his hand. Acts 9:12,
they drew Alexander, Jews p. 19:
as p. you in mind. Rom 15:
p. away lying, speak truth. Eph 4:
in p. off the body of the sins. Col 2:
p. on the breastplate of. 1 Thes 5
p. me into the ministry. 1 Tim 1:
by p. on of my hands. 2 Tim 1:
not p. on of apparel, but. 1 Pet 3
not p. away the filth of the flesh.
to stir you up by p. you. 2 Pet 1:

Q

quails

God gave quails *to the Israelit upon two occasions:* First, *in th wilderness of* Sin, *or* Zin, *a few da after they had passed over the Re Sea,* Ex 16:13. *The* second *tim was at the encampment, called* Hebrew, Kibroth-hataavah, *or* th graves of lust, Num 11:31, 32.

at even q. came up. Ex 16:
the Lord brought q. Num 11:3
and they gathered the q. 3
and he brought q. Ps 105:4

quake

earth shall q. before. Joel 2:
the mountains q. at him. Nah 1:
earth did q. and rocks. Mat 27:5
I exceedingly fear and q. Heb 12:2

quaked

whole mount q. greatly. Ex 19:
host trembled, and the earth q.
1 Sam 14:1

quaking

eat thy bread with q. Ezek 12:1
but a great q. fell on them. Dan 10:

quantity

on him vessels of small q. Isa 22:24

quarrel

a sword shall avenge q. Lev 26:25
see how he seeketh a q. 2 Ki 5:
Herodias had a q. against John.
Mark 6:19
if any man have a q. Col 3:13

quarries

Ehud turned from the q. Judg 3:
escaped and passed beyond q. 2

quarter

all people from every q. Gen 19:
this was the west q. Josh 18:1
shall wander to his q. Isa 47:1
for his gain from his q. 56:1
to him from every q. Mark 1:4
see **south**

quarters

no leaven in thy q. Ex 13:7
fringes on the four q. Deut 22:12
in four q. were porters. 1 Chr 9:24
winds from four q. of. Jer 49:3
as Peter passed through all q.
Acts 9:32
Jews which were in those q. 16:3
in same q. were possessions. 28:7
nations in four q. of earth. Rev 20:8

Quartus

Q. a brother saluteth. Rom 16:2

quaternions

Peter to four q. of soldiers. Acts 12:

queen

[1] *A sovereign princess, or chie ruler of a kingdom,* 1 Ki 10:1 [2] *The* queen of heaven, *a tern applied to the moon by idolatrou moon-worshippers,* Jer 44:17, 25 *They set up altars to her upon th platforms or roofs of their house*

the corners of the streets, near
eir doors, and in groves. They
fered cakes to her kneaded up with
l and honey, and made libations
her with wine and other liquors.
of Sheba heard of the fame of.
1 Ki 10:1; *2 Chr* 9:1
had seen all Solomon's wisdom.
1 Ki 10:4
such spices as these the *q.* of
Sheba gave. 10; *2 Chr* 9:9
ng Solomon gave *q.* of Sheba all
her desire. *1 Ki* 10:13; *2 Chr* 9:12
adad the sister of the *q.* *1 Ki* 11:19
sa removed Maachah from being *q.*
15:13; *2 Chr* 15:16
lute children of the *q.* *2 Ki* 10:13
e *q.* sitting by him. *Neh* 2:6
ashti the *q.* made a feast. *Esth* 1:9
bring the *q.* 11
e *q.* refused to come. 12
all we do to the *q.* Vashti? 15
hath not done wrong to the. 16
eed of *q.* shall come abroad. 17
ve heard the deed of the *q.* 18
at pleaseth the king be *q.* 2:4
sther *q.* instead of Vashti. 17
e *q.* exceedingly grieved. 4:4
hat wilt thou, *q.* Esther? 5:3
let no man to the banquet. 12
hat is thy petition, *q.* Esther? 7:2
as afraid before king and *q.* 6
quest to the *q.* for his life. 7
ill he force *q.* also before me? 8
use of Haman to Esther the *q.* 8:1
Mordecai and Esther the *q.* 9:31
d stand the *q.* in gold. *Ps* 45:9
y to the king and *q.*, Humble yourselves. *Jer* 13:18*
cense to the *q.* of heaven. 44:17, 25
came into the banquet-. *Dan* 5:10
of the south shall rise up in the.
Mat 12:42; *Luke* 11:31
andace *q.* of Ethiopians. *Acts* 8:27
sit a *q.* and am no widow. *Rev* 18:7

queens
ere are threescore *q.* *S of S* 6:8, 9
thy nursing mothers. *Isa* 49:23

quench
all *q.* my coal. *2 Sam* 14:7
at thou *q.* not the light of. 21:17
ses *q.* their thirst. *Ps* 104:11
aters cannot *q.* love. *S of S* 8:7
ne shall *q.* them. *Isa* 1:31
x shall he not *q.* 42:3; *Mat* 12:20
st my fury come forth, and burn
that none can *q.* it. *Jer* 4:4; 21:12
ne to *q.* it in Beth-el. *Amos* 5:6
le to *q.* the fiery darts. *Eph* 6:16
not Spirit, despise. *1 Thes* 5:19

quenched
oses prayed, fire was *q.*
Num 11:2*; *2 Chr* 34:25
rath shall not be *q.* *2 Ki* 22:17
ey are *q.* as the fire. *Ps* 118:12
shall not be *q.* night. *Isa* 34:10
ey are *q.* as tow. 43:17
r shall their fire be *q.* 66:24
y fury shall burn, and shall not be
q. *Jer* 7:20; 17:27
me shall not be *q.* *Ezek* 20:47, 48
at never shall be *q.* *Mark* 9:43, 45
here the fire is not *q.* 44, 46, 48
the violence of fire. *Heb* 11:34

question, *substantive*
wyer asked him a *q.* *Mat* 22:35
will ask you one *q.* *Mark* 11:29
man after that durst ask him any
q. 12:34; *Luke* 20:40
ere arose a *q.* between. *John* 3:25
postles about this *q.* *Acts* 15:2
of words and names. 18:15
danger to be called in *q.* 19:40*
am called in *q.* 23:6; 24:21
q. for conscience. *1 Cor* 10:25, 27

question, *verb*
egan to *q.* him. *Mark* 8:11
cribes, What *q.* ye with them? 9:16

questioned, -ing
ezekiah *q.* priests. *2 Chr* 31:9
among themselves. *Mark* 1:27
what rising from the dead. 9:10

and scribes *q.* with them. *Mark* 9:14
Pilate *q.* with him in. *Luke* 23:9

questions
to prove him with *q.* *1 Ki* 10:1
told her all her *q.* 3; *2 Chr* 9:1, 2
durst any ask him more *q.* *Mat* 22:46
and asking them *q.* *Luke* 2:46
accused of *q.* of their law. *Acts* 23:29
had certain *q.* against him. 25:19
doubted of such manner of *q.* 20*
I know thee to be expert in *q.* 26:3
which minister *q.* rather. *1 Tim* 1:4
but doting about *q.* and strifes. 6:4
but unlearned *q.* avoid. *2 Tim* 2:23
Tit 3:9

quick
(*Very frequently used with the old meaning of* living)
there be *q.* raw flesh. *Lev* 13:10
the *q.* flesh that burneth have a. 24
down *q.* into the pit. *Num* 16:30*
go down *q.* into hell. *Ps* 55:15*
swallowed us up *q.* 124:3*
him of *q.* understanding. *Isa* 11:3*
judge of the *q.* and dead. *Acts* 10:42*
shall judge the *q.* and the dead.
2 Tim 4:1; *1 Pet* 4:5
the word of God is *q.* *Heb* 4:12*

quicken
(*To bring back to life, either literally, as to restore life to the body, or figuratively, to stimulate the spirit which was deadened*)
thou shalt *q.* me again. *Ps* 71:20
q. us, and we will call on thy. 80:18
q. me according to thy word.
119:25, 107, 149, 154, 156
turn me from vanity, *q.* me in. 37
q. me in thy righteousness. 40
q. me after thy. 88, 159
q. me, O Lord, for thy. 143:11
shall also *q.* your mortal. *Rom* 8:11

quickened
thy word hath *q.* me. *Ps* 119:50
thy precepts thou hast *q.* me. 93
thou sowest, is not *q.* *1 Cor* 15:36
you hath he *q.*, who were. *Eph* 2:1
hath *q.* us together with Christ. 5
Col 2:13
but *q.* by the Spirit. *1 Pet* 3:18

quickeneth
as the Father *q.* them; even so the Son *q.* whom. *John* 5:21
it is the Spirit that *q.* 6:63
even God who *q.* the dead. *Rom* 4:17
God, who *q.* all things. *1 Tim* 6:13

quickening
was made a *q.* spirit. *1 Cor* 15:45

quickly
ready *q.* three measures. *Gen* 18:6
hast found it so *q.* my son? 27:20
aside *q.* out of the way. *Ex* 32:8
Deut 9:12, 16; *Judg* 2:17
put on incense and go *q.* *Num* 16:46
shalt thou destroy them *q.* *Deut* 9:3
get thee down *q.* 12
lest ye perish *q.* 11:17
till thou perish *q.* because of. 28:20
pursue *q.* for ye shall. *Josh* 2:5
the ambush arose *q.* out of. 8:19
come up to us *q.* and save us. 10:6
shall perish *q.* from off the. 23:16
thou shalt go down *q.* *1 Sam* 20:19
send *q.* and tell David. *2 Sam* 17:16
went both of them away *q.* 18
David, Arise and pass *q.* over. 21
king said, Come down *q.* *2 Ki* 1:11
fetch *q.* Micaiah the. *2 Chr* 18:8
threefold cord is not *q.* *Eccl* 4:12
with thine adversary *q.* *Mat* 5:25
go *q.* and tell his disciples. 28:7
they departed *q.* with. 8; *Mark* 16:8
go *q.* into the streets. *Luke* 14:21
sit down *q.* and write fifty. 16:6
Mary arose *q.* and came. *John* 11:29
That thou doest, do *q.* 13:27
saying, Arise up *q.* *Acts* 12:7
get thee *q.* out of Jerusalem. 22:18
I will come to thee *q.* *Rev* 2:5, 16
behold, I come *q.* 3:11; 22:7, 12
behold third woe cometh *q.* 11:14
Surely I come *q.* Even so. 22:20

quicksands
should fall into the *q.* *Acts* 27:17*

quiet
laid wait and were *q.* *Judg* 16:2
Zidonians, *q.* and secure. 18:7
to a people that were at *q.* 27
rejoiced, and the city was in *q.*
2 Ki 11:20; *2 Chr* 23:21
land was wide and *q.* *1 Chr* 4:40
land was *q.* ten years. *2 Chr* 14:1
the kingdom was *q.* before. 5; 20:30
should I have been *q.* *Job* 3:13
neither was I *q.*, yet trouble. 26
being wholly at ease and *q.* 21:23
against them that are *q.* *Ps* 35:20
glad, because they be *q.* 107:30
hearkeneth to me shall be in *q.*
Pr 1:33
wise men are heard in *q.* *Eccl* 9:17
Take heed and be *q.*; fear. *Isa* 7:4
earth is at rest, and is *q.* 14:7
shall dwell in *q.* resting places. 32:18
Jerusalem a *q.* habitation. 33:20
and be in rest and *q.* *Jer* 30:10
long will it be ere thou be *q.*? 47:6
how be *q.* seeing the Lord hath? 7
sorrow on sea, it cannot be *q.* 49:23
Seraiah was a *q.* prince. 51:59*
I will be *q.* and will be. *Ezek* 16:42
though they be *q.* they. *Nah* 1:12*
ye ought to be *q.* and do. *Acts* 19:36
that ye study to be *q.* *1 Thes* 4:11
lead a *q.* and peaceable. *1 Tim* 2:2
a meek and *q.* spirit. *1 Pet* 3:4

quieted
behaved and *q.* myself. *Ps* 131:2
these *q.* my spirit in the. *Zech* 6:8

quieteth
when he *q.* the earth. *Job* 37:17*

quietly
took Abner to speak *q.* *2 Sam* 3:27
q. wait for the salvation. *Lam* 3:26

quietness
was in *q.* forty years. *Judg* 8:28*
I will give *q.* to Israel. *1 Chr* 22:9
not feel *q.* in his belly. *Job* 20:20
when he giveth *q.* who can? 34:29
dry morsel and *q.* *Pr* 17:1
better is an handful with *q.* *Eccl* 4:6
in *q.* and confidence shall. *Isa* 30:15
effect of righteousness, *q.* 32:17
thee we enjoy great *q.* *Acts* 24:2*
we exhort that with *q.* *2 Thes* 3:12

quit
he that smote him be *q.* *Ex* 21:19
owner of the ox shall be *q.* 28
will be *q.* of thine oath. *Josh* 2:20*
q. yourselves like men. *1 Sam* 4:9
1 Cor 16:13

quite
q. devoured also our. *Gen* 31:15
thou shalt *q.* break down. *Ex* 23:24*
q. take away their murmurings.
Num 17:10*
and *q.* pluck down all their. 33:52*
and he is *q.* gone. *2 Sam* 3:24
and is wisdom driven *q.*? *Job* 6:13
bow was made *q.* naked. *Hab* 3:9

quiver
therefore take thy *q.* and. *Gen* 27:3
q. rattleth against him. *Job* 39:23
man that hath his *q.* full. *Ps* 127:5
Elam bare the *q.* with. *Isa* 22:6
in his *q.* hath he hid me. 49:2
q. is as an open sepulchre. *Jer* 5:16
arrows of his *q.* to enter. *Lam* 3:13

quivered
when I heard, my lips *q.* *Hab* 3:16

R

Rabbah, *or* **Rabbath**
is it not in *R.* of the children of?
Deut 3:11
Israel besieged *R.* *2 Sam* 11:1
Joab fought against *R.* and. 12:26
Shobi of *R.* brought beds. 17:27
Joab smote *R.* and. *1 Chr* 20:1

an alarm to be heard in *R. Jer* 49:2
cry, ye daughters of *R.*, gird with. 3
sword may come to *R. Ezek* 21:20
I will make *R.* a stable for. 25:5
a fire in the wall of *R. Amos* 1:14

Rabbi

(*A title of respect meaning* master, teacher, *given by the Jews to their teachers and spiritual leaders, and often addressed to our Lord. Another form of the title was* Rabboni. *The titles were used with different degrees of honour—the lowest being* rab, *master; second,* rabbi, *my master; and greatest of all,* rabboni, *my lord, master.*
The term rab *was also used in Babylonia and Assyria to mean* chief—*as* Rab-mag, *the chief of the magi, etc.*)

called of men, *r. r. Mat* 23:7
be not ye called *r.*, for one is. 8
R. where dwellest thou? *John* 1:38
R. thou art the Son of God. 49
R. we know thou art a teacher. 3:2
R. he that was with thee. 26
they said, *R.* when camest? 6:25

Rabboni

Mary saith, *R. John* 20:16
R., [R.V.] that I may receive my sight. *Mark* 10:51

Rab-shakeh

(*Properly a title of a court officer*)

the king of Assyria sent *R.* *2 Ki* 18:17; *Isa* 36:2
they told him the words of *R.* *2 Ki* 18:37; *Isa* 36:22
God will hear the words of *R.* *2 Ki* 19:4; *Isa* 37:4

raca

(*A term of reproach and contempt meaning* empty, *and hence* worthless. *It is a weaker word than* fool)

shall say to his brother, *R. Mat* 5:22

race

strong man to run a *r. Ps* 19:5*
the *r.* is not to the swift. *Eccl* 9:11
run in a *r.* run all. *1 Cor* 9:24
run with patience the *r. Heb* 12:1

Rachel

Jacob told *R.* that he. *Gen* 29:12
name of the younger was *R.* 16
R. was beautiful and well. 17
Jacob loved *R.* 18, 30
R. was barren. 31
seven years for *R.* 20, 25
Laban gave him *R.* his. 28
R. bare no children, *R.* envied. 30:1
kindled against *R.*: he said. 2
God remembered *R.* and opened. 22
R. had stolen her father's. 31:19, 34
then Laban went into *R.*'s tent. 33
Jacob put *R.* and Joseph. 33:2
R. died. 35:19; 48:7
sons of *R.* 35:24; 46:19, 22
make the woman like *R. Ruth* 4:11
find two men by *R.*'s. *1 Sam* 10:2
R. weeping. *Jer* 31:15; *Mat* 2:18

rafters

cedar, and our *r.* of fir. *S of S* 1:17

Ragau

was the son of *R. Luke* 3:35

rage, *substantive*

turned away in a *r. 2 Ki* 5:12
I know thy *r.* against me. 19:27
Isa 37:28
Asa was in a *r.* with. *2 Chr* 16:10
and ye have slain them in a *r.* 28:9
swalloweth the ground with *r.* *Job* 39:24
cast abroad *r.* of thy wrath. 40:11*
thyself because of *r.* of. *Ps* 7:6
jealousy is *r.* of a man. *Pr* 6:34
Nebuchadnezzar commanded in his *r.* to bring. *Dan* 3:13
they shall fall for the *r. Hos* 7:16

rage, *verb*

why do the heathen *r.*? *Ps* 2:1
Acts 4:25
whether he *r.* or laugh. *Pr* 29:9
ye horses, *r.* ye chariots. *Jer* 46:9
chariots shall *r.* in streets. *Nah* 2:4

raged

heathen *r.*, the kingdoms. *Ps* 46:6

rageth

fool *r.* and is confident. *Pr* 14:16*

ragged

tops of the *r.* rocks. *Isa* 2:21

raging

thou rulest the *r.* of the sea. *Ps* 89:9
strong drink is *r. Pr* 20:1*
sea ceased from her *r. Jonah* 1:15
wind and *r.* of the water. *Luke* 8:24
r. waves of the sea foaming. *Jude* 13

rags

clothe a man with *r. Pr* 23:31
all our righteousnesses are as filthy *r.* *Isa* 64:6*
took old rotten *r. Jer* 38:11
put *r.* under thine arm holes. 12

Rahab, *person, place*

entered into house of *R. Josh* 2:1
only *R.* shall live. 6:17
Joshua saved *R.* 25
make mention of *R. Ps* 87:4
thou hast broken *R.* in pieces. 89:10
not it that hath cut *R.*? *Isa* 51:9
Salmon begat Booz of *R. Mat* 1:5
by faith the harlot *R. Heb* 11:31
was not *R.* also justified? *Jas* 2:25

rail

he wrote letters to *r. 2 Chr* 32:17

railed

our master *r.* on them. *1 Sam* 25:14*
they that passed by *r. Mark* 15:29
one of malefactors *r.* on. *Luke* 23:39

railer

keep not company with *r. 1 Cor* 5:11*

railing, *adjective*

angels bring not *r. 2 Pet* 2:11
Michael durst not bring against him a *r.* accusation. *Jude* 9

railing

cometh envy, strife, *r. 1 Tim* 6:4
not rendering *r.* for *r. 1 Pet* 3:9*

raiment

the servant gave *r.* to. *Gen* 24:53
Rebekah took goodly *r.* of. 27:15
Isaac smelled his *r.* and. 27
Lord will give me *r.* to put. 28:20
shaved, and changed his *r.* 41:14
gave to each man changes of *r.*, but to Benjamin five changes of *r.* 45:22
borrow of the Egyptians *r. Ex* 3:22
12:35
her food and *r.* shall he not. 21:10
trespass for sheep, for *r.* 22:9
thy neighbour's *r.* to pledge. 26, 27
unclean beast falls on *r. Lev* 11:32
purify all your *r.* all. *Num* 31:20
thy *r.* waxed not old. *Deut* 8:4
loveth stranger, giving him *r.* 10:18
she shall put *r.* of her captivity. 21:13
lost *r.* restore, and all lost. 22:3
that he may sleep in his *r.* 24:13
not take a widow's *r.* to pledge. 17
to your tents with much *r. Josh* 22:8
a dagger under his *r. Judg* 3:16
purple *r.* that was on kings. 8:26
and put thy *r.* upon thee. *Ruth* 3:3
himself and put on *r. 1 Sam* 28:8
with him ten changes of *r. 2 Ki* 5:5
the lepers carried thence *r.* and. 7:8
Solomon, gold, and *r. 2 Chr* 9:24
the queen sent *r.* to clothe. *Esth* 4:4
and though he prepare *r. Job* 27:16
to king in *r.* of needlework. *Ps* 45:14*
cast out as the *r.* of. *Isa* 14:19*
and I will stain all my *r.* 63:3
thy *r.* was of fine linen. *Ezek* 16:13
thee with change of *r. Zech* 3:4*
his *r.* of camels' hair. *Mat* 3:4
and the body more than *r.* 6:25
Luke 12:23
why take ye thought for *r.*? *Mat* 6:28

a man clothed in soft *r.* *Mat* 11:8; *Luke* 7:
his *r.* white as light. *Mat* 17
Mark 9:3; *Luke* 9:
put his own *r.* on him. *Mat* 27:
his *r.* was white as snow. 28
who stripped him of *r. Luke* 10:
they parted his *r.* and cast lots. 23:34; *John* 19:
Paul shook his *r.* and. *Acts* 18
I kept the *r.* of them that. 22:
having food and *r.* let us. *1 Tim* 6:
a poor man in vile *r. Jas* 2
be clothed in white *r. Rev* 3
buy white *r.* that thou mayest.
elders clothed in white *r.* 4

rain

Palestine has its rainy season a[nd] its dry season. During the latt[er] the brooks dry up, and the fi[rst] rains are very welcome. Ear[ly] rain meant the autumn ra[in] Deut 11:14, *and latter rain that [of] the Spring,* Pr 16:15.

r. was upon the earth. *Gen* 7:
r. from heaven was restrained. 8
the *r.* was not poured on. *Ex* 9:
Pharaoh saw the *r.* ceased.
I will give you *r.* in due season. *Lev* 26:4; *Deut* 11:14; 28:
land drinks water of *r. Deut* 11:
heaven that there be no *r.* *1 Ki* 8:35; *2 Chr* 6:26; 7:
make *r.* of thy land. *Deut* 28:
my doctrine shall drop as the *r.* 32
on the Lord to send *r. 1 Sam* 12:
sent thunder and *r.* that day.
no dew nor *r.* upon. *2 Sam* 1:
by clear shining after *r.* 23
give *r.* upon thy land. *1 Ki* 8:
2 Chr 6:
shall not be dew nor *r. 1 Ki* 17
because there had been no *r.*
till that day the Lord send *r.*
shew to Ahab, I will send *r.* 18
a sound of abundance of *r.*
that the *r.* stop thee not.
and there was a great *r.*
not see wind, nor see *r. 2 Ki* 3:
trembling for the great *r. Ezra* 10
and it is a time of much *r.*
giveth *r.* upon the earth. *Job* 5:
he made a decree for *r.* and. 28:
waited for me as for the *r.* 29:
clouds pour down *r.* 36:
to small *r.* and to great *r.* of. 37
hath *r.* a father? or who hath? 38:
didst send a plentiful *r. Ps* 68
down like *r.* on mown grass. 72
the *r.* also filleth the pools. 84
he gave them hail for *r.* and. 105:
he maketh lightnings for the *r.* 135
Lord, who prepareth *r.* for. 147
clouds and wind without *r. Pr* 25:
the north wind driveth away *r.*
as snow in summer, and *r.* in. 26
poor, is like a sweeping *r.* 28
if clouds be full of *r. Eccl* 11
clouds return after the *r.* 12
winter is past, *r.* is over. *S of S* 2:
a covert from storm and *r. Isa* 4
clouds they *r.* no *r.* on it. 5
then shall he give the *r.* of. 30:
as ash, and *r.* doth nourish it. 44:
as the *r.* cometh down. 55:
the Lord that giveth *r. Jer* 5:
lightnings with *r.* 10:13; 51:
for there was no *r.* 14
vanities of Gentiles can cause *r.*?
bow in cloud in day of *r. Ezek* 1:
I will *r.* an overflowing *r.* 38:2
shall make us as the *r. Hos* 6
to come down for you *r. Joel* 2:
withholden the *r.* from you. *Amos* 4
upon them shall be no *r. Zech* 14:
go not up, that have no *r.*
he sendeth *r.* on just and. *Mat* 5:
r. descended, and floods. 7:25,
did good, and gave us *r. Acts* 14:
because of the present *r.* 28
which drinketh in the *r. Heb* 6
and the heaven gave *r. Jas* 5:

see **latter**

rain, *verb*
Lord had not caused it to *r. Gen* 2:5
cause it to *r.* forty days. 7:4
I will cause it to *r.* *Ex* 9:18
I will *r.* bread from heaven. 16:4
God shall *r.* his fury. *Job* 20:23
cause it to *r.* on the earth. 38:26
wicked he shall *r.* snares. *Ps* 11:6
that they *r.* no rain on it. *Isa* 5:6
. an overflowing rain. *Ezek* 38:22
r. righteousness on you. *Hos* 10:12
I caused it to *r.* on one city. *Amos* 4:7
earnestly it might not *r.* *Jas* 5:17
that it *r.* not in days of. *Rev* 11:6

rainbow
there was a *r.* round. *Rev* 4:3
I saw an angel, and a *r.* was. 10:1

rained
Lord *r.* upon Sodom. *Gen* 19:24
the Lord *r.* hail on land. *Ex* 9:23
had *r.* down manna. *Ps* 78:24, 27
the land not *r.* upon. *Ezek* 22:24
one piece was *r.* upon; and the piece whereupon it *r.* not. *Amos* 4:7
the same day it *r.* fire. *Luke* 17:29
it *r.* not for three years. *Jas* 5:17

rainy
dropping in a *r.* day. *Pr* 27:15

raise
marry her, and *r.* up seed. *Gen* 38:8
shalt not *r.* a false report. *Ex* 23:1
God will *r.* up a prophet. *Deut* 18:15
18; *Acts* 3:22; 7:37
refuseth to *r.* up to brother a name. *Deut* 25:7
r. thereon a great heap. *Josh* 8:29
to *r.* up the name of. *Ruth* 4:5, 10
I will *r.* me up a faithful priest. *1 Sam* 2:35
I will *r.* up evil. *2 Sam* 12:11
elders went to him to *r.* him. 17
Lord shall *r.* up a king. *1 Ki* 14:14
I will *r.* up thy seed. *1 Chr* 17:11
who are ready to *r.* up their mourning. *Job* 3:8
his troops *r.* up their way. 19:12
they *r.* up against me ways of. 30:12
merciful to me, and *r.* me. *Ps* 41:10
they shall *r.* up a cry of. *Isa* 15:5
I will *r.* forts against thee. 29:3
I will *r.* up decayed places. 44:26
my servant to *r.* up tribes. 49:6
r. up foundations of many. 58:12
they shall *r.* up the former. 61:4
r. to David a righteous. *Jer* 23:5
their king, whom I will *r.* up. 30:9
I will *r.* against Babylon. 50:9
none shall *r.* him up. 32
r. a destroying wind. 51:1
I will *r.* up thy lovers. *Ezek* 23:22
I will *r.* up for them a plant. 34:29
third day he will *r.* us up. *Hos* 6:2
I will *r.* them out of the. *Joel* 3:7
there is none to *r.* her up. *Amos* 5:2
I will *r.* a nation against you. 6:14
I will *r.* up the tabernacle of David, and I will *r.* up his ruins. 9:11
we shall *r.* against him. *Mi* 5:5
there are that *r.* up strife. *Hab* 1:3
I will *r.* up the Chaldeans. 6
I will *r.* up a shepherd. *Zech* 11:16
to *r.* up children to Abraham. *Mat* 3:9; *Luke* 3:8
cleanse lepers, *r.* dead. *Mat* 10:8
marry his wife, and *r.* up seed. 22:24; *Mark* 12:19; *Luke* 20:28
in three days I will *r.* it. *John* 2:19
will *r.* it up again. 6:39, 40, 44, 54
he would *r.* up Christ to. *Acts* 2:30
incredible that God should *r.*? 26:8
will also *r.* up us by his. *1 Cor* 6:14
r. up us also by Jesus. *2 Cor* 4:14
accounting God was able to *r.* him up. *Heb* 11:19
Lord shall *r.* him up. *Jas* 5:15

raised
I *r.* thee up to shew my power. *Ex* 9:16; *Rom* 9:17
children whom he *r.* up. *Josh* 5:7
they *r.* over him a great heap. 7:26
Lord *r.* up judges. *Judg* 2:16, 18
Lord *r.* up a deliverer. 3:9, 15
man who was *r.* up. *2 Sam* 23:1
Solomon *r.* up a levy of Israel. *1 Ki* 5:13; 9:15
and *r.* it up to the towers. *2 Chr* 32:5; 33:14
whose spirit God *r.* to. *Ezra* 1:5
not awake, nor be *r.* out. *Job* 14:12
I *r.* thee up under. *S of S* 8:5
it *r.* up from their thrones. *Isa* 14:9
the Assyrian *r.* up the palaces. 23:13
who *r.* up the righteous man. 41:2
I have *r.* up one from north. 25
r. him up in righteousness. 45:13
a great nation shall be *r.* *Jer* 6:22
a great whirlwind shall be *r.* 25:32
Lord hath *r.* us up prophets. 29:15
many kings shall be *r.* from. 50:41
Lord *r.* up the spirit of kings. 51:11
a bear *r.* up itself on. *Dan* 7:5
I *r.* up of your sons for. *Amos* 2:11
is *r.* up out of his holy. *Zech* 2:13
when I have *r.* up thy sons. 9:13
Joseph being *r.* from sleep. *Mat* 1:24
the dead are *r.* up. 11:5; *Luke* 7:22
killed, and *r.* up again the third day. *Mat* 16:21; 17:23; *Luke* 9:22
hath *r.* up an horn of. *Luke* 1:69
now that the dead are *r.* 20:37
Lazarus whom he *r.* *John* 12:1, 9, 17
God hath *r.* up. *Acts* 2:24, 32; 3:15
26; 4:10; 5:30; 10:40; 13:30, 33
34; 17:31; *Rom* 10:9; *1 Cor* 6:14
2 Cor 4:14; *Gal* 1:1; *Eph* 1:20
angel *r.* up Peter. *Acts* 12:7
he *r.* up David. 13:22
God *r.* to Israel a Saviour. 23
the Jews *r.* persecution against. 50
if we believe on him that *r.* *Rom* 4:24
r. again for our justification. 25
like as Christ was *r.* from dead. 6:4
Christ being *r.* from the dead. 9
him who is *r.* from the dead. 7:4
Spirit of him that *r.* up Jesus . . . he that *r.* up Christ. 8:11
r. up Christ; whom he *r.* *1 Cor* 15:15
rise not, then is not Christ *r.* 16
if Christ be not *r.* your faith. 17
will say, How are the dead *r.*? 35
corruption, *r.* in incorruption. 42, 52
r. in glory, it is *r.* in power. 43
natural body, *r.* a spiritual body. 44
hath *r.* us up together in. *Eph* 2:6
operation of God who *r.* *Col* 2:12
his Son, whom he *r.* *1 Thes* 1:10
remember Jesus was *r.* *2 Tim* 2:8
their dead *r.* to life *Heb* 11:35
God that *r.* him up from the dead. *1 Pet* 1:21

raiser
stand up a *r.* of taxes. *Dan* 11:20

raiseth
he *r.* poor out of the dust. *1 Sam* 2:8; *Ps* 113:7
when he *r.* himself. *Job* 41:25
and *r.* stormy wind. *Ps* 107:25
he *r.* those that be bowed down. 145:14; 146:8
as Father *r.* up the dead. *John* 5:21
trust in God which *r.* *2 Cor* 1:9

raising
baker who ceaseth from *r.* *Hos* 7:4
nor found they me *r.* up. *Acts* 24:12

raisins
hundred clusters of *r.* *1 Sam* 25:18
Egyptians two clusters of *r.* 30:12
with 100 bunches of *r.* *2 Sam* 16:1
brought bunches of *r.* *1 Chr* 12:40

ram
take a *r.* of three years. *Gen* 15:9
a *r.* caught in a thicket. 22:13
take one *r.* *Ex* 29:15
thou shalt slay the *r.* 16
burn the whole *r.* 18; *Lev* 8:21
it is a *r.* of consecration. *Ex* 29:22
27, 31; *Lev* 8:22
eat the flesh of the *r.* *Ex* 29:32
take *r.* for burnt offering. *Lev* 9:2
r. for peace offering. 4
r. for trespass offering. 19:21
beside *r.* of atonement. *Num* 5:8
thus shall it be done for one *r.* 15:11
guilty, they offered a *r.* *Ezra* 10:19
shall offer a *r.* *Ezek* 43:23, 25
an ephah for a *r.* 45:24; 46:5, 7, 11
the prince shall offer a *r.* 46:4
new moon six lambs and a *r.* 6
I saw a *r.* which had two horns. *Dan* 8:3
I saw the *r.* pushing westward. 4
the goat ran to the *r.* that had. 6
come close to the *r.*: there was no power in the *r.*: none to deliver *r.* 7
the *r.* having two horns are. 20

Ram
Hezron begat *R.* and *R.* begat. *Ruth* 4:19; *1 Chr* 2:9, 10
Jerahmeel, *R.* Bunah. *1 Chr* 2:25
the sons of *R.* the firstborn. 27
Buzite of the kindred of *R.* *Job* 32:2

Ramah, Rama
R. a city of the tribe. *Josh* 18:25
Deborah dwelt between *R.* *Judg* 4:5
Elkanah came to his house in *R.* *1 Sam* 1:19; 2:11
Samuel's return was to *R.* 7:17
15:34; 16:13
all the elders came unto *R.* 8:4
David fled, and came to *R.* 19:18
Saul went to *R.* 22, 23
Saul abode in *R.* 22:6
buried in his house at *R.* 25:1; 28:3
Baasha built *R.* *1 Ki* 15:17
2 Chr 16:1
Baasha left off building of *R.* *1 Ki* 15:21; *2 Chr* 16:5
wounds the Syrians had given Joram at *R.* *2 Ki* 8:29; *2 Chr* 22:6
children of *R.* and Geba six hundred. *Ezra* 2:26; *Neh* 7:30
Benjamin dwelt at *R.* *Neh* 11:33
R. is afraid, Gibeah of. *Isa* 10:29
voice was heard in *R.* *Jer* 31:15
Mat 2:18
merchants of *R.* were. *Ezek* 27:22
blow ye the trumpet in *R.* *Hos* 5:8

Ramoth-gilead
R. in Gilead of the Gadites, a city. *Deut* 4:43; *Josh* 20:8; 21:38
Geber was officer in *R.* *1 Ki* 4:13
know ye that *R.* is ours ? 22:3
wilt thou go with me to battle to *R.*? 4; *2 Chr* 18:3
shall I go against *R.*? *1 Ki* 22:6
15; *2 Chr* 18:14
saying, Go up to *R.* and prosper. *1 Ki* 22:12; *2 Chr* 18:11
Joram went against Hazael in *R.* *2 Ki* 8:28; *2 Chr* 22:5
take this box of oil, and go to *R.* *2 Ki* 9:1
now Joram had kept *R.* 14
Gad to the Levites, *R.* *1 Chr* 6:80

rampart
he made the *r.* and the wall. *Lam* 2:8
then populous No, whose *r.* *Nah* 3:8

rams
r. which leaped. *Gen* 31:10*, 12*
the *r.* of thy flock have I not. 38
Esau 200 ewes and 20 *r.* 32:14
r. of breed of Bashan. *Deut* 32:14
hearken than fat of *r.* *1 Sam* 15:22
100,000 *r.* with wool. *2 Ki* 3:4
to the Lord 1000 *r.* *1 Chr* 29:21
Arabians brought 7700 *r.* *2 Chr* 17:11
r. for offerings of the God. *Ezra* 6:9
dedication of the house 200 *r.* 17
with this money *r.*, lambs. 7:17
offered ninety-six *r.* for a sin. 8:35
with the fat of *r.* *Ps* 66:15; *Isa* 34:6
mountains skipped like *r.* *Ps* 114:4, 6
the burnt offerings of *r.* *Isa* 1:11
is filled with fat of kidneys of *r.* 34:6
the *r.* of Nebaioth shall. 60:7
to the slaughter like *r.* *Jer* 51:40
occupied with thee in *r.* *Ezek* 27:21
I judge between the *r.* and. 34:17
ye shall drink the blood of *r.* 39:18
pleased with thousands of *r.* *Mi* 6:7
see **battering, seven**

rams' horns
bear before the ark seven trumpets of *r. horns.* *Josh* 6:4, 6, 8, 13
a long blast with the *r. horns.* 5

rams' skins
r. skins dyed red, and. *Ex* 25:5
26:14; 35:7; 36:19; 39:34

ran
Abraham *r.* to meet them. *Gen* 18:2
Abram *r.* to the herd. 7
servant *r.* to meet Rebekah. 24:17
Rebekah *r.* to the well to. 20
damsel *r.* and told her mother's. 28
r. out to the man to the well. 29
and Rachel *r.* and told her. 29:12
Laban *r.* to meet Jacob and. 13
Esau *r.* to meet him. 33:4
the fire *r.* along upon. *Ex* 9:23
r. a young man and. *Num* 11:27
Aaron *r.* into midst of the. 16:47
messenger *r.* to Aaron's. *Josh* 7:22
the ambush *r.* into Ai, and set. 8:19
all the host of Midian *r.* *Judg* 7:21
Jothan *r.* away, and fled. 9:21
Manoah's wife *r.* and shewed. 13:10
Samuel *r.* to Eli, and. *1 Sam* 3:5
a man of Benjamin *r.* out of the. 4:12
and they *r.* and fetched Saul. 10:23
David *r.* into the army and. 17:22
David *r.* and stood upon the. 51
as the lad *r.* he shot an arrow. 20:36
Cushi bowed himself to Joab and *r.*
2 Sam 18:21
Ahimaaz *r.* by the plain and. 23
servants of Shimei *r.* *1 Ki* 2:39
the water *r.* round about the. 18:35
Elijah *r.* before Ahab to Jezreel. 46
Elisha left the oxen and *r.* 19:20
the blood *r.* into the midst of. 22:35
my sore *r.* in the night. *Ps* 77:2*
waters *r.* in the dry places. 105:41
the ointment that *r.* down. 133:2
sent them, yet they *r.* *Jer* 23:21
the living creatures *r.* *Ezek* 1:14
r. out waters on the right side. 47:2
goat *r.* to the ram in fury. *Dan* 8:6
herd of swine *r.* violently. *Mat* 8:32*
Mark 5:13*; *Luke* 8:33*
one *r.* and filled a spunge.
Mat 27:48; *Mark* 15:36
many knew him, and *r.* *Mark* 6:33
r. through that whole region. 55
his father *r.* and fell on. *Luke* 15:20
Zacchaeus *r.* before and climbed. 19:4
then arose Peter and *r.* to the. 24:12
so they *r.* both together. *John* 20:4
the people *r.* together. *Acts* 3:11
they *r.* upon Stephen with. 7:57*
Philip *r.* to the chariot. 8:30
knew Peter's voice, she *r.* in. 12:14
Paul and Barnabas *r.* in. 14:14*
the people *r.* together and. 21:30
captain took soldiers and *r.* 32
they *r.* the ship aground and. 27:41
they *r.* greedily after the error of Balaam. *Jude* 11

rang
that the earth *r.* again. *1 Sam* 4:5
so that the city *r.* again. *1 Ki* 1:45

range
the *r.* of the mountains. *Job* 39:8

ranges
or *r.* for pots, they shall. *Lev* 11:35
that cometh within *r.* let. *2 Ki* 11:8*
have her forth without the *r.* 15*
2 Chr 23:14*

ranging
as a roaring lion, and a *r.* bear.
Pr 28:15

rank
ears came up upon one stalk, *r.* and good. *Gen* 41:5
devoured the seven *r.* ears. 7
forth in the second *r.* *Num* 2:16
go forward in the third *r.* 24
50,000 could keep *r.* *1 Chr* 12:33
men of war that could keep *r.* 38

ranks
against light in three *r.* *1 Ki* 7:4, 5
shall not break their *r.* *Joel* 2:7
they sat down in *r.* by. *Mark* 6:40

ransom, *substantive*
(*A price paid for freedom*)
give for the *r.* of his life. *Ex* 21:30*
every man a *r.* for his soul. 30:12
from pit, I have found a *r.* *Job* 33:24
a great *r.* cannot deliver. *Job* 36:18
give to God a *r.* for him. *Ps* 49:7
he will not regard any *r.* *Pr* 6:35
r. of a man's life are his riches. 13:8
the wicked shall be a *r.* for. 21:18
I gave Egypt for thy *r.* *Isa* 43:3
Son of man came to give his life a *r.*
Mat 20:28; *Mark* 10:45
who gave himself *r.* for all. *1 Tim* 2:6

ransom
r. them from power of. *Hos* 13:14

ransomed
r. of the Lord shall return. *Isa* 35:10
the sea a way for the *r.* to. 51:10*
redeemed Jacob and *r.* *Jer* 31:11

Rapha, and **Raphu**
Palti son of *Raphu.* *Num* 13:9
Rapha, father of Eleasah. *1 Chr* 8:37

rare
it is a *r.* thing that the king. *Dan* 2:11

rase
r. it, *r.* it, even to the. *Ps* 137:7

rash
be not *r.* with thy mouth. *Eccl* 5:2

rashly
quiet, and do nothing *r.* *Acts* 19:36

rate
gather certain *r.* every day. *Ex* 16:4
brought mules at a *r.* *1 Ki* 10:25
2 Chr 9:24
a daily *r.* for every. *2 Ki* 25:30
even after a certain *r.* *2 Chr* 8:13*

rather
if we have not *r.* done it. *Josh* 22:24
much *r.* when he saith to. *2 Ki* 5:13
chooseth death *r.* than life. *Job* 7:15
Jer 8:3
he justified himself *r.* *Job* 32:2
this hast thou chosen *r.* 36:21
and lying *r.* than to speak. *Ps* 52:3
r. be a doorkeeper in house. 84:10
receive knowledge *r.* than. *Pr* 8:10
to understanding *r.* than silver. 16:16
meet a man, *r.* than a fool. 17:12
a good name *r.* than great riches, loving favour *r.* than silver. 22:1
go *r.* to the lost sheep of. *Mat* 10:6
r. fear him that is able to. 28
r. than having two hands to. 18:8
r. than having two eyes to. 9
but go ye *r.* to them that sell. 25:9
but that *r.* tumult was made. 27:24
nothing bettered, but *r.* *Mark* 5:26
should *r.* release Barabbas. 15:11
r. rejoice, your names. *Luke* 10:20
r. blessed are they that hear. 11:28
but *r.* give alms of such things as. 41
but *r.* seek ye kingdom of God. 12:31
give peace? Nay *r.* division. 51
will not *r.* say unto him. 17:8
justified *r.* than the other. 18:14
men loved darkness *r.* than light.
John 3:19
obey God *r.* than men. *Acts* 5:29
not *r.* let us do evil, that. *Rom* 3:8
yea, *r.* that is risen again. 8:34
r. through their fall salvation. 11:11
avenge not, but *r.* give place. 12:19
another, but judge this *r.* 14:13
puffed up, and have not *r.* *1 Cor* 5:2
why do ye not *r.* take wrong? 6:7
if made free, use it *r.* 7:21
over you, are not we *r.*? 9:12
desire *r.* that ye may. 14:1, 5
had *r.* speak five words with my. 19
so that ye ought *r.* to forgive him.
2 Cor 2:7
ministration of the Spirit be *r.* 3:8
willing *r.* to be absent from. 5:8
therefore I will *r.* glory in. 12:9
God, or *r.* known of God. *Gal* 4:9
steal no more, but *r.* let. *Eph* 4:28
not named, but *r.* giving of. 5:4
with works of darkness, but *r.* 11
r. to the furtherance of. *Phil* 1:12
minister questions *r.* *1 Tim* 1:4
exercise thyself *r.* to godliness. 4:7
but *r.* do them service. 6:2
yet for love's sake I *r.* *Philem* 9
choosing *r.* to suffer. *Heb* 11:25
r. be in subjection to the. 12:9
but let it *r.* be healed. *Heb* 12:1
but I beseech you the *r.* to. 13:1
r. give diligence to. *2 Pet* 1:1

rattleth
quiver *r.* against him. *Job* 39:2

rattling
noise of the *r.* of wheels. *Nah* 3:

raven, -s
Noah sent forth a *r.* *Gen* 8:
every *r.* is unclean. *Lev* 11:1
Deut 14:1
I have commanded the *r.* *1 Ki* 17:
and the *r.* brought Elijah bread.
who provideth for the *r.* his food?
Job 38:41; *Ps* 147:
the *r.* of the valley. *Pr* 30:1
his locks bushy, and black as a *r.*
S of S 5:1
the owl and the *r.* shall. *Isa* 34:1
consider the *r.*: they. *Luke* 12:2

ravening
upon me as a *r.* lion. *Ps* 23:1
like a roaring lion *r.* *Ezek* 22:2
her princes are like wolves *r.*, the. 2
they are *r.* wolves. *Mat* 7:1
inward part is full of *r.* *Luke* 11:39

ravenous
r. beast shall go up. *Isa* 35:
calling a *r.* bird from the east. 46:1
give thee to the *r.* birds. *Ezek* 39:4

ravin
shall *r.* as a wolf. *Gen* 49:27
filled his dens with *r.* *Nah* 2:12

ravished
and be thou *r.* always. *Pr* 5:19
why wilt thou be *r.* with a strange? 20
thou hast *r.* my heart. *S of S* 4:9
the wives of Babylon shall be *r.*
Isa 13:16
r. the women in Zion. *Lam* 5:1
Jerusalem shall be *r.* *Zech* 14:2

raw
eat not of it *r.* nor sodden. *Ex* 12:9
if there be quick *r.* flesh. *Lev* 13:10
when the *r.* flesh appeareth. 14
priest see *r.* flesh, for *r.* flesh is. 15
have sodden flesh, but *r.* *1 Sam* 2:15

razor
shall no *r.* come upon his head.
Num 6:5; *Judg* 13:5; 16:17
1 Sam 1:11
thy tongue like a sharp *r.* *Ps* 52:2
shave with a *r.* hired. *Isa* 7:20
take thee a barber's *r.* *Ezek* 5:1

reach
a tower whose top may *r.* *Gen* 11:4
linen breeches shall *r.* *Ex* 28:42
your threshing shall *r.* to the vintage, and your vintage shall *r.* *Lev* 26:5
border shall *r.* to the sea. *Num* 34:11
head *r.* unto the clouds. *Job* 20:6
he shall *r.* even to the neck. *Isa* 8:8
breath shall *r.* to the midst. 30:28
thy plants *r.* to the sea. *Jer* 48:32
mountains shall *r.* to Azal. *Zech* 14:5
r. hither thy finger, and *r.* thy hand.
John 20:27
a measure to *r.* even. *2 Cor* 10:13

reached
the ladder's top *r.* to. *Gen* 28:12
he *r.* her parched corn. *Ruth* 2:14
the tree grew, and the height thereof *r.* to heaven. *Dan* 4:11, 20
as though we *r.* not to. *2 Cor* 10:14
Babylon's sins have *r.* *Rev* 18:5

reacheth
slain in a rage that *r.* up. *2 Chr* 28:9
thy faithfulness *r.* to the. *Ps* 36:5
thy truth *r.* to the clouds. 108:4
yea, she *r.* her hands to. *Pr* 31:20
sword *r.* unto the soul. *Jer* 4:10
because it *r.* to thine heart. 18
judgement *r.* to heaven. 51:9
greatness *r.* to heaven. *Dan* 4:22

reaching
r. forth to those things. *Phil* 3:13*

read
he *r.* in the audience. *Ex* 24:7
he *r.* all the words of the law.
Josh 8:34, 3

when king had *r.* letter. *2 Ki* 5:7
Hezekiah received and *r.* the. 19:14
Shaphan *r.* book of law. 22:8, 10
Josiah *r.* in their ears all the words. 23:2; *2 Chr* 34:30
curses in the book *r.* *2 Chr* 34:24
letter hath been plainly *r.* *Ezra* 4:18
king's letter was *r.* they made. 23
he *r.* the book of the law before the water gate. *Neh* 8:3, 8; 13:1
unto the last day he *r.* the law. 8:18
in their place and *r.* in the law. 9:3
book of the records was *r.* *Esth* 6:1
the letter, and *r.* it. *Isa* 37:14
Zephaniah the priest *r.* *Jer* 29:29
then *r.* Baruch the words of. 36:10
Jehudi *r.* it in ears of the king. 21
when he *r.* three or four leaves. 23
have ye not *r.*? *Mat* 12:3; 19:4
21:16; 22:31; *Mark* 2:25; 12:10
26; *Luke* 6:3
this title *r.* many of. *John* 19:20
the eunuch *r.* Esaias. *Acts* 8:28
place of scripture which he *r.* 32
prophets are *r.* every sabbath day. 13:27; 15:21
which when they had *r.* 15:31
when the governor had *r.* 23:34
our epistle, known and *r.* *2 Cor* 3:2
when Moses is *r.* the vail is upon. 15
when this epistle is *r.* *Col* 4:16
that this epistle be *r.* *1 Thes* 5:27

read

the king shall *r.* therein. *Deut* 17:19
thou shalt *r.* this law before. 31:11
r. this, I pray thee. *Isa* 29:11, 12
book of the Lord and *r.* 34:16
go and *r.* in the roll thou. *Jer* 36:6
they said, Sit down now and *r.* 15
comest to Babylon and shalt *r.* 51:61
whosoever shall *r.* writing. *Dan* 5:7
king's wise men, they could not *r.* 8
gifts be to thyself, yet I will *r.* 17
did ye never *r.* in the ? *Mat* 21:42
and stood up for to *r.* *Luke* 4:16
heard him *r.* Esaias. *Acts* 8:30
write none other things than what ye *r.* *2 Cor* 1:13
ye *r.* ye may understand. *Eph* 3:4
likewise *r.* the epistle. *Col* 4:16
worthy to *r.* the book. *Rev* 5:4

readest

written in law, how *r.*? *Luke* 10:26
Philip said, Understandest thou what thou *r.*? *Acts* 8:30

readeth

he may run that *r.* it. *Hab* 2:2
abomination, whoso *r.* let him understand. *Mat* 24:15; *Mark* 13:14
blessed is he that *r.* and. *Rev* 1:3

readiness

received the word with *r.* *Acts* 17:11
there was a *r.* to will. *2 Cor* 8:11
having a *r.* to revenge all. 10:6

reading

them to understand the *r.* *Neh* 8:8
r. in book of words of the. *Jer* 36:8
hast made an end of *r.* this. 51:63
after the *r.* of the law. *Acts* 13:15
vail untaken away in *r.* *2 Cor* 3:14
give attendance to *r.* *1 Tim* 4:13

ready

be almost *r.* to stone me. *Ex* 17:4
be *r.* against the third. 19:11, 15
be *r.* in the morning, and. 34:2
we will go *r.* armed. *Num* 32:17
r. to go up into the hill. *Deut* 1:41
a Syrian *r.* to perish was my. 26:5
the city, but be ye all *r.* *Josh* 8:4
five sheep *r.* dressed. *1 Sam* 25:18
thy servants are *r.* to. *2 Sam* 15:15
thou hast no tidings *r.*? 18:22
Ezra was a *r.* scribe in. *Ezra* 7:6
art a God *r.* to pardon. *Neh* 9:17
. against that day. *Esth* 3:14; 8:13
who are *r.* to raise up. *Job* 3:8
is *r.* to slip with his feet. 12:5
day of darkness is *r.* at hand. 15:23
prevail as a king *r.* to battle. 24
are *r.* to become heaps. 28
the graves are *r.* for me. 17:1
and destruction shall be *r.* 18:12

blessing of him *r.* to perish. *Job* 29:13
my belly is *r.* to burst like. 32:19
for I am *r.* to halt, and. *Ps* 38:17
tongue is pen of a *r.* writer. 45:1
art good, and *r.* to forgive. 86:5
I am afflicted, and *r.* to die. 88:15
to deliver those that are *r.* *Pr* 24:11
drink to him that is *r.* to. 31:6
be more *r.* to hear than. *Eccl* 5:1*
shall come who were *r.* to perish. *Isa* 27:13
shall be as a breach *r.* to fall. 30:13
stammerers be *r.* to speak. 32:4
Lord was *r.* to save me: we. 38:20
It is *r.* for the soldering. 41:7
as if he were *r.* to destroy. 51:13
now if ye be *r.* to fall. *Dan* 3:15
and all things are *r.* *Mat* 22:4
then saith he, The wedding is *r.* 8
Luke 14:17
therefore be ye also *r.* *Mat* 24:44
Luke 12:40
they that were *r.* went in. *Mat* 25:10
spirit is *r.* but the flesh. *Mark* 14:38*
servant sick, and *r.* to die. *Luke* 7:2*
Lord, I am *r.* to go with. 22:33
your time is alway *r.* *John* 7:6
to them, *r.* to depart. *Acts* 20:7*
I am *r.* not to be bound only. 21:13
come near, are *r.* to kill him. 23:15
are *r.*, looking for a promise. 21
r. to preach the gospel. *Rom* 1:15
of your *r.* mind. *2 Cor* 8:19
that Achaia was *r.* a year ago. 9:2
that, as I said, ye may be *r.* 3
same might be *r.* as a matter. 5
third time I am *r.* to come. 12:14
in good works, *r.* to. *1 Tim* 6:18
now *r.* to be offered. *2 Tim* 4:6*
put them in mind to be *r.* to. *Tit* 3:1
waxeth old, is *r.* to vanish. *Heb* 8:13*
r. to be revealed in. *1 Pet* 1:5
be *r.* always to give an answer. 3:15
account to him that is *r.* to. 4:5
not filthy lucre, but of a *r.* mind. 5:2
things that are *r.* to die. *Rev* 3:2
woman which was *r.* to be. 12:4*
see **made, make**

realm

the *r.* of Jehoshaphat. *2 Chr* 20:30
r. who are minded to go. *Ezra* 7:13
there be wrath against the *r.*? 23
better than all in his *r.* *Dan* 1:20
thought to set him over the *r.* 6:3
Darius, king over the *r.* of the. 9:1
he shall stir up all against *r.* 11:2

reap

and when ye *r.* . . . shall not wholly *r.* the. *Lev* 19:9; 23:10, 22
of itself thou shalt not *r.* 25:5
shall neither sow nor *r.* 11
eyes be on the field they *r.* *Ruth* 2:9
set your servants to *r.* *1 Sam* 8:12
in third year sow and *r.* *2 Ki* 19:29
Isa 37:30
wickedness *r.* the same. *Job* 4:8
they *r.* every one his corn. 24:6*
in tears shall *r.* in joy. *Ps* 126:5
iniquity, shall *r.* vanity. *Pr* 22:8
the clouds, shall not *r.* *Eccl* 11:4
wheat, but shall *r.* thorns. *Jer* 12:13
shall *r.* the whirlwind. *Hos* 8:7
righteousness, *r.* in mercy. 10:12
sow, but shalt not *r.* *Mi* 6:15
the fowls of the air *r.* not. *Mat* 6:26
Luke 12:24
thou knewest I *r.* where. *Mat* 25:26
r. whereon ye bestowed. *John* 4:38
if we shall *r.* your carnal. *1 Cor* 9:11
sparingly shall *r.* sparingly. . . bountifully shall *r.* bountifully. *2 Cor* 9:6
man soweth, that shall he *r.* *Gal* 6:7
of the flesh *r.* corruption . . . of the Spirit *r.* life everlasting. 8
in due season we shall *r.* if we. 9
in thy sickle, and *r.*: for the time is come for thee to *r.* *Rev* 14:15

reaped

wickedness, ye *r.* iniquity. *Hos* 10:13
labourers, which *r.* down . . . cries of them which *r.* are. *Jas* 5:4
sickle, the earth was *r.* *Rev* 14:16

reaper

the plowman shall overtake the *r.* *Amos* 9:13

reapers

Ruth gleaned after the *r.* *Ruth* 2:3
Boaz said to the *r.*, The Lord be. 4
let me glean after the *r.* 7
to his father to the *r.* *2 Ki* 4:18
to the *r.*, Gather the tares. *Mat* 13:30
enemy is devil, and *r.* are the. 39

reapest

riddance when thou *r.* *Lev* 23:22
r. that thou didst not. *Luke* 19:21

reapeth

harvestman *r.* the ears. *Isa* 17:5
r. receiveth wages, that both he that soweth and he that *r.* *John* 4:36
one soweth and another *r.* 37

reaping

of Beth-shemesh were *r.* *1 Sam* 6:13
hard man, *r.* where thou hast not. *Mat* 25:24; *Luke* 19:22

reason

[1] *That faculty whereby we judge of things,* Dan 4:36. [2] *Proof, ground, or argument,* 1 Pet 3:15. [3] *To dispute, or argue,* Mat 16:8; Mark 8:16.

this is the *r.* of the levy. *1 Ki* 9:15
that can render a *r.* *Pr* 26:16
I applied to search the *r.* *Eccl* 7:25
same time my *r.* returned. *Dan* 4:36
It is not *r.* that we should leave the word of God. *Acts* 6:2
O ye Jews, *r.* would that I. 18:14
that asketh you a *r.* of. *1 Pet* 3:15

by **reason**

plenty not known *by r.* *Gen* 41:31
land of Canaan fainted *by r.* 47:13
Israel sighed *by r.* of the. *Ex* 2:23
I heard their cry *by r.* of their. 3:7
corrupted *by r.* of the flies. 8:24
unclean *by r.* of a dead body. *Num* 9:10
hallowed things given *by r.* of. 18:8
shall bear no sin *by r.* of it. 32
afraid *by r.* of the fire. *Deut* 5:5
shoes are become old *by r.* *Josh* 9:13
for their groanings *by r.* *Judg* 2:18
Ahijah's eyes were set *by r.* of age. *1 Ki* 14:4
minister *by r.* of cloud. *2 Chr* 5:14
be not afraid *by r.* of this great. 20:15
by r. of the sickness. 21:15, 19
blackish, *by r.* of the ice. *Job* 6:16
is dim *by r.* of sorrow. 17:7
by r. of his highness I could. 31:23
by r. of oppressions . . . they cry out *by r.* of the arm. 35:9
we cannot order speech *by r.* 37:19
by r. of breakings they purify. 41:25
roared *by r.* of disquietness. *Ps* 38:8
blasphemeth *by r.* of enemy. 44:16
man that shouteth *by r.* of. 78:65
mourneth *by r.* of affliction. 88:9
if *by r.* of strength they be. 90:10
by r. of my groaning my. 102:5
not plow *by r.* of cold. *Pr* 20:4
by r. of the inhabitants. *Isa* 49:19
by r. of many waters. *Ezek* 19:10
terrors *by r.* of sword shall. 21:12*
by r. of the abundance of his. 26:10
Tyrus corrupted *by r.* of thy. 28:17
by r. of transgression. *Dan* 8:12
I cried *by r.* of my affliction. *Jonah* 2:2
noise *by r.* of multitude. *Mi* 2:12
sea arose *by r.* of a. *John* 6:18
by r. of him many believed. 12:11
by r. of him who subjected same. *Rom* 8:20
by r. of the glory that. *2 Cor* 3:10
by r. hereof he ought to. *Heb* 5:3
who *by r.* of use have senses. 14
to continue *by r.* of death. 7:23
by r. of whom the way of. *2 Pet* 2:2
by r. of the other voices. *Rev* 8:13
darkened *by r.* of the smoke. 9:2
rich *by r.* of the costliness. 18:19

reason, *verb*

that I may *r.* with you. *1 Sam* 12:7*
my words to *r.* with you. *Job* 9:14

and desire to *r.* with God. *Job* 13:3
he *r.* with unprofitable talk ? 15:3
and let us *r.* together. *Isa* 1:18
why *r.* ye among yourselves ?
Mat 16:8; *Mark* 2:8; 8:17
Pharisees began to *r.* *Luke* 5:21
Jesus said to them, What *r.* ye ? 22

reasonable

living sacrifice, which is your *r.* service. *Rom* 12:1†

reasoned

and they *r.* among. *Mat* 16:7; 21:15
Mark 8:16; 11:31; *Luke* 20:5
perceived that they so *r.* *Mark* 2:8
husbandmen *r.* among. *Luke* 20:14*
while they *r.* Jesus himself. 24:15
three sabbaths Paul *r.* *Acts* 17:2
he *r.* in the synagogue every. 18:4
Paul *r.* with Jews at Ephesus. 19
as he *r.* of righteousness and. 24:25

reasoning

hear my *r.* and hearken. *Job* 13:6
were certain scribes *r.* *Mark* 2:6
heard them *r.* together. 12:28
arose a *r.* among them. *Luke* 9:46
Jews departed, and had great *r.*
Acts 28:29

reasons

and gave ear to your *r.* *Job* 32:11
Bring forth your *r.*, saith. *Isa* 41:21

Rebekah

Bethuel begat *R.* *Gen* 22:23
R. came out. 24:15
R. is before thee. 51
they sent away *R.* 59
they blessed *R.* 60
Isaac took *R.* 67; 25:20
R. loved Jacob. 25:28
lest men kill me for *R.* 26:7
a grief of mind to *R.* 35
words of Esau were told to *R.* 27:42
that he was *R.*'s son. 29:12
R.'s nurse died. 35:8
Isaac and *R.* his wife. 49:31
R. had conceived by. *Rom* 9:10

rebel

r. not against the Lord. *Num* 14:9
doth *r.* he shall die. *Josh* 1:18
an altar that ye might *r.* 22:16
seeing that ye *r.* to-day against. 18
r. not against the Lord, nor *r.* 19
God forbid that we should *r.* 29
and not *r.* against Lord. *1 Sam* 12:14
not obey the Lord, but *r.* 15
will ye *r.* against the king ? *Neh* 2:19
thou and the Jews think to *r.* 6:6
that *r.* against the light. *Job* 24:13
if ye refuse and *r.* *Isa* 1:20
assemble for corn, and *r.* *Hos* 7:14

rebelled

thirteenth year they *r.* *Gen* 14:4
ye *r.* against my words. *Num* 20:24
27:14; *Deut* 1:26, 43; 9:23
so Israel *r.* against the house of.
1 Ki 12:19; *2 Chr* 10:19
Moab *r.* against. *2 Ki* 1:1, 3, 5, 7
Hezekiah *r.* against Assyria. 18:7
Jehoiakim *r.* against. 24:1
Zedekiah *r.* 20; *2 Chr* 36:13
Jer 52:3
Jeroboam hath *r.* *2 Chr* 13:6
were disobedient, and *r.* *Neh* 9:26
they have *r.* against thee. *Ps* 5:10
r. not against his word. 105:28
because they *r.* against the. 107:11
children, and they have *r.* *Isa* 1:2
r. and vexed his Holy Spirit. 63:10
I have *r.* *Lam* 1:18
I have grievously *r.* 20
r.: thou hast not pardoned. 3:42
to a nation that hath *r.* *Ezek* 2:3
r. in sending his ambassadors. 17:15
but they *r.* against me. 20:8, 13, 21
we have *r.* by departing. *Dan* 9:5
mercies, though we have *r.* against. 9
Samaria hath *r.* against. *Hos* 13:16

rebellest

On whom dost thou trust, that thou *r.*? *2 Ki* 18:20; *Isa* 36:5

rebellion

know thy *r.* and thy stiff. *Deut* 31:27
shall know if it be in *r.* *Josh* 22:22
r. is as the sin of. *1 Sam* 15:23
that *r.* hath been made. *Ezra* 4:19
and in their *r.* appointed. *Neh* 9:17
addeth *r.* unto his sin. *Job* 34:37
evil man seeketh only *r.* *Pr* 17:11
thou hast taught *r.* *Jer* 28:16; 29:32

rebellious

r. against Lord. *Deut* 9:7, 24; 31:27
a stubborn and *r.* son. 21:18
this our son is stubborn and *r.* 20
the perverse *r.* woman. *1 Sam* 20:30
building the *r.* and. *Ezra* 4:12, 15
let not the *r.* exalt. *Ps* 66:7
r. dwell in a dry land. 68:6
yea, for the *r.* also. 18
and a *r.* generation. 78:8
thy princes are *r.* *Isa* 1:23
woe to the *r.* children, saith. 30:1
this is a *r.* people. 9
I was not *r.* 50:5
spread out my hands to a *r.* 65:2
hath been *r.* against me. *Jer* 4:17
hath a revolting and *r.* heart. 5:23
I send thee to a *r.* nation. *Ezek* 2:3
they are a *r.* house. 5, 6, 7; 3:9, 26
27; 12:2, 3
be not thou *r.* like that *r.* house. 2:8
in the midst of a *r.* house. 12:2
say now to the *r.* house. 17:12; 44:6
parable to the *r.* house. 24:3

rebels

for a token against the *r.* *Num* 17:10
said, Hear now, ye *r.* 20:10
from among you the *r.* *Ezek* 20:38

rebuke, *substantive*

shall send on thee *r.* *Deut* 28:20
this is a day of *r.* *2 Ki* 19:3
Isa 37:3
at thy *r.*, at the blast of. *Ps* 18:15
at thy *r.* both chariot and. 76:6
they perish at the *r.* of thy. 80:16
at thy *r.* they fled, they. 104:7
scorner heareth not *r.* *Pr* 13:1
but the poor heareth not *r.* 8*
r. is better than secret love. 27:5
better to hear *r.* of. *Eccl* 7:5
the *r.* of his people shall. *Isa* 25:8
thousand shall flee at *r.* of one, at *r.* of five shall ye flee. 30:17
behold, at my *r.* I dry up the. 50:2
full of the *r.* of thy God. 51:20
to render his *r.* with flames. 66:15
for thy sake I suffered *r.* *Jer* 15:15
be desolate in the day of *r.* *Hos* 5:9
without *r.* in midst of a. *Phil* 2:15

rebuke

any wise *r.* thy neighbour. *Lev* 19:17
glean them, and *r.* her not. *Ruth* 2:16
God look thereon, and *r.* *1 Chr* 12:17
O Lord, *r.* me not. *Ps* 6:1; 38:1
r. the company of spearmen. 68:30
r. a wise man, and he. *Pr* 9:8
to them that *r.* him shall. 24:25
he shall *r.* many nations. *Isa* 2:4*
Mi 4:3*
but God shall *r.* them. *Isa* 17:13
not wroth with, nor *r.* thee. 54:9
Lord *r.* thee, even the Lord that hath chosen Jerusalem, *r.* *Zech* 3:2
I will *r.* the devourer. *Mal* 3:11
Peter began to *r.* him. *Mat* 16:22
Mark 8:32
brother trespass, *r.* him. *Luke* 17:3
said, Master, *r.* thy disciples. 19:39
r. not an elder, but. *1 Tim* 5:1
them that sin, *r.* before all. 20*
r., exhort with all long. *2 Tim* 4:2
r. them sharply. *Tit* 1:13; 2:15
said, The Lord *r.* thee. *Jude* 9
as many as I love, I *r.* *Rev* 3:19

rebuked

God hath seen and *r.* *Gen* 31:42
his father *r.* him, and said. 37:10
and I *r.* the nobles and. *Neh* 5:7*
hast *r.* the heathen, thou. *Ps* 9:5
he *r.* the Red sea also, and it. 106:9
thou hast *r.* the proud that. 119:21
he *r.* the wind. *Mat* 8:26
Mark 4:39; *Luke* 8:24
Jesus *r.* the devil; and. *Mat* 17:18
his disciples *r.* them. 19:13
Mark 10:13; *Luke* 18:15
multitude *r.* blind men. *Mat* 20:31
and Jesus *r.* him. *Mark* 1:25; 9:25
Luke 4:35; 9:42
Jesus *r.* Peter, saying. *Mark* 8:33
over her and *r.* the fever. *Luke* 4:39
turned, and *r.* James and John. 9:55
went before *r.* the blind man. 18:39
thief answering *r.* him. 23:40
when thou art *r.* of him. *Heb* 12:5
but Balaam was *r.* for. *2 Pet* 2:16

rebuker

though I have been a *r.* of. *Hos* 5:2

rebukes

when thou with *r.* dost. *Ps* 39:11
execute judgements in furious *r.*
Ezek 5:15; 25:17

rebuketh

he that *r.* a wicked man. *Pr* 9:7
he that *r.* a man, shall find. 28:23
hate him that *r.* in gate. *Amos* 5:10
r. sea, and maketh it dry. *Nah* 1:4

rebuking

foundations of world discovered at the *r.* of the Lord. *2 Sam* 22:16
r. them, suffered them. *Luke* 4:41

recall

this I *r.* to mind. *Lam* 3:21

receipt

Matthew sitting at the *r.* *Mat* 9:9*
Mark 2:14*; *Luke* 5:27*

receive

[1] *To take what is given, paid, or put into one's hands,* 2 Sam 18:12; 2 Ki 5:26. [2] *To entertain, lodge, or harbour,* Acts 28:2, 7. [3] *To bear with, or suffer,* 2 Cor 11:16. [4] *To hearken to,* Pr 2:1. [5] *To believe,* Mat 11:14; John 1:12. [6] *To admit one to be a member of the church,* Rom 14:1. [7] *To be endued with,* Acts 1:8.

thou shalt *r.* the wave. *Ex* 29:25
your tithes which you *r.* *Num* 18:28
shall *r.* of thy words. *Deut* 33:3
which thou shalt *r.* of. *1 Sam* 10:4
though I should *r.* a thousand shekels. *2 Sam* 18:12
thou shalt *r.* the cedar. *1 Ki* 5:9
shall we *r.* good of God ? *Job* 2:10
shall *r.* of the Almighty. 27:13
Lord will *r.* my prayer. *Ps* 6:9
he shall *r.* the blessing from. 24:5
my soul, for he shall *r.* me. 49:15
afterward *r.* me to glory. 73:24
I shall *r.* the congregation. 75:2
if thou wilt *r.* my words. *Pr* 2:1
the wise in heart will *r.* 10:8
I *r.* comfort in these ? *Isa* 57:6*
thou shalt *r.* sisters. *Ezek* 16:61
ye shall *r.* of me gifts. *Dan* 2:6
Ephraim shall *r.* shame. *Hos* 10:6
r. of you his standing. *Mi* 1:11*
thou wilt *r.* instruction. *Zeph* 3:7
shall *r.* a prophet's reward . . . *r.* a righteous man's. *Mat* 10:41
blind *r.* their sight, lame walk. 11:5
if ye will *r.* it, this is Elias. 14
shall *r.* one such little child. 18:5
Mark 9:37; *Luke* 9:48
said, All men cannot *r.* *Mat* 19:11
r. an hundredfold. 29; *Mark* 10:30
is right, that shall ye *r.* *Mat* 20:7
ye ask, believing, ye shall *r.* 21:22
that they might *r.* fruits of it. 34
ye shall *r.* the greater damnation.
23:14; *Mark* 12:40; *Luke* 20:47
r. the word with gladness.
Mark 4:16; *Luke* 8:13
as hear the word and *r.* *Mark* 4:20
Lord, that I might *r.* my sight. 10:51
Luke 18:41
pray, believe that ye *r.* *Mark* 11:2
might *r.* from the husbandmen. 12:
city ye enter, and they *r.* *Luke* 10:
may *r.* me into their houses. 16:
may *r.* you into everlasting.
for we *r.* the due reward of. 23:4
own name, him ye will *r.* *John* 5:4
can ye believe, which *r.* honour ? 4
on sabbath *r.* circumcision. 7:2
Spirit, which they that believe on hi
should *r.*: Holy Ghost was not. 3

I will come again, and *r.* *John* 14:3
r. of mine, and shew it to you. 16:14
ask and ye shall *r.* that your joy. 24
shall *r.* power after that. *Acts* 1:8
ye shall *r.* gift of Holy Ghost. 2:38
Jesus, whom heavens must *r.* 3:21
they might *r.* the Holy Ghost. 8:15
hands, may *r.* the Holy Ghost. 19
that he might *r.* his sight. 9:12
that thou mightest *r.* thy sight. 17
shall *r.* remission of sins. 10:43
that they may *r.* forgiveness. 26:18
r. abundance of grace. *Rom* 5:17
resist shall *r.* to themselves. 13:2
that ye *r.* her in the Lord, as. 16:2
shall *r.* his own reward. *1 Cor* 3:8
if his work abide, he shall *r.* 14
if thou didst *r.* it, why dost thou ? 4:7
the church may *r.* edifying. 14:5
that every one may *r.* *2 Cor* 5:10
touch not unclean thing, and I will *r.* 6:17
r. damage by us in nothing. 7:9
that we would *r.* the gift. 8:4
if ye *r.* another spirit ye have. 11:4
that we might *r.* promise. *Gal* 3:14
that we might *r.* the adoption. 4:5
the same shall he *r.* of. *Eph* 6:8
ye shall *r.* the reward of. *Col* 3:24
he shall *r.* for the wrong he. 25
shouldest *r.* him for ever. *Philem* 15
sons of Levi, who *r.* office. *Heb* 7:5
here men that die *r.* tithes. 8
which are called might *r.* promise. 9:15; 10:36
after *r.* for an inheritance. 11:8
think he shall *r.* any thing. *Jas* 1:7
he shall *r.* the crown of life. 12
shall *r.* greater condemnation. 3:1
until he *r.* early and latter rain. 5:7
ye shall *r.* a crown of glory. *1 Pet* 5:4
shall *r.* the reward of. *2 Pet* 2:13
we ask, we *r.* of him. *1 John* 3:22
if we *r.* the witness of men. 5:9
that we *r.* a full reward. *2 John* 8
if any man *r.* his mark in. *Rev* 14:9
but *r.* power as kings one hour. 17:12

receive, *imperatively*

then *r.* my present at. *Gen* 33:10
r. I pray thee, the law. *Job* 22:22
and *r.* my sayings. *Pr* 4:10
r. my instruction. 8:10; 19:20
let your ear *r.* the word. *Jer* 9:20
all my words *r.* in thine. *Ezek* 3:10
him, *r.* us graciously. *Hos* 14:2*
that is able, let him *r.* it. *Mat* 19:12
Jesus saith, *R.* thy sight. *Luke* 18:42 *Acts* 22:13
R. ye the Holy Ghost. *John* 20:22
Lord Jesus, *r.* my spirit. *Acts* 7:59
weak in the faith *r.* ye. *Rom* 14:1
r. ye one another, as Christ. 15:7
r. us, we have wronged. *2 Cor* 7:2
yet as a fool *r.* me. 11:16
r. him in the Lord with. *Phil* 2:29
Marcus, if he come, *r.* him. *Col* 4:10
r. him that is mine own. *Philem* 12*
if thou count me a partner, *r.* him. 17
r. with meekness the. *Jas* 1:21

receive, *negatively*

said, I will *r.* none. *2 Ki* 5:16
r. no more money of your. 12:7
shall we *r.* good, and shall we not *r.* evil ? *Job* 2:10
might not hear nor *r.* instruction. *Jer* 17:23
will ye not *r.* instruction to ? 35:13
r. no more reproach of. *Ezek* 36:30
not *r.* you nor hear. *Mat* 10:14 *Mark* 6:11; *Luke* 9:5
shall not *r.* the kingdom of God as a. *Mark* 10:15; *Luke* 18:17
not *r.* him, because his. *Luke* 9:53
and they *r.* you not, go into. 10:10
who shall not *r.* manifold. 18:30
and ye *r.* not our witness. *John* 3:11
a man can *r.* nothing, except it. 27
r. not testimony from man. 5:34
r. not honour from men. 41
in my Father's name, ye *r.* me not. 43
whom the world cannot *r.* 14:17
will not *r.* thy testimony. *Acts* 22:18
that thou didst not *r.*? *1 Cor* 4:7
that ye *r.* not the grace. *2 Cor* 6:1
against an elder *r.* not. *1 Tim* 5:19
ye ask and *r.* not, because. *Jas* 4:3
r. him not into your house. *2 John* 10
neither doth he himself *r.* *3 John* 10
ye *r.* not of her plagues. *Rev* 18:4

to **receive**

to r. brother's blood. *Gen* 4:11
to r. his pledge from woman's. 38:20
his pans *to r.* his ashes. *Ex* 27:3
gone up *to r.* the tables. *Deut* 9:9
altar before the Lord was too little *to r.* *1 Ki* 8:64; *2 Chr* 7:7
is it a time *to r.* money, *to r.* garments ? *2 Ki* 5:26
priest consented *to r.* no more. 12:8
to r. instruction of wisdom. *Pr* 1:3
refused *to r.* correction. *Jer* 5:3
not hearkened *to r.* instruction. 32:33
not room enough *to r.* it. *Mal* 3:10
to r. it, let him *r.* it. *Mat* 19:12
no room *to r.* them. *Mark* 2:2
of whom ye hope *to r.* *Luke* 6:34
nobleman went *to r.* for. 19:12
not lawful for us *to r.* *Acts* 16:21
the disciples *to r.* him. 18:27
blessed to give than *to r.* 20:35
therefore ought *to r.* such. *3 John* 8
worthy, O Lord, *to r.* glory. *Rev* 4:11
worthy is Lamb *to r.* power. 5:12
causeth *to r.* a mark in their. 13:16

received

Isaac *r.* the same year an. *Gen* 26:12
and Aaron *r.* them at. *Ex* 32:4
and they *r.* of Moses all the. 36:3
Miriam be *r.* in again. *Num* 12:14
r. commandment to bless. 23:20
two tribes and half *r.* 34:14, 15
put to the inheritance of the tribe whereunto they are *r.* 36:3, 4
the Gadites have *r.* their. *Josh* 13:8
not *r.* their inheritance. 18:2
would not have *r.* burnt offering. *Judg* 13:23
have I *r.* any bribe ? *1 Sam* 12:3*
David *r.* of Abigail that she. 23:35
merchants *r.* linen yarn at a price. *1 Ki* 10:28; *2 Chr* 1:16
Hezekiah *r.* the letter. *2 Ki* 19:14 *Isa* 37:14
then David *r.* them. *1 Chr* 12:18
Mordecai *r.* it not. *Esth* 4:4
mine ear *r.* a little thereof. *Job* 4:12
thou hast *r.* gifts for. *Ps* 68:18
it, and *r.* instruction. *Pr* 24:32
hath *r.* of the Lord's hand. *Isa* 40:2
your children, they *r.* no. *Jer* 2:30
not *r.* usury nor increase. *Ezek* 18:17
she *r.* not correction. *Zeph* 3:2
freely ye *r.*, freely give. *Mat* 10:8
which *r.* seed by the way side. 13:19
r. seed into stony. 20, 22, 23
they that *r.* tribute money. 17:24
they *r.* every man a penny. 20:9, 10
and when they had *r.* it, they. 11
immediately their eyes *r.* sight. 34
r. five talents. 25:16
r. two talents. 17
had *r.* one talent. 18
should have *r.* mine own with. 27
things which they *r.* *Mark* 7:4
he *r.* his sight. 10:52; *Luke* 18:43 *Acts* 9:18
myrrh: but he *r.* it not. *Mark* 15:23
he was *r.* up into heaven. 16:19 *Acts* 1:9
woe to rich, for ye have *r.* *Luke* 6:24
the people gladly *r.* him. 8:40
r. them and spake to them. 9:11
come, that he should be *r.* up. 51
Martha *r.* him into her house. 10:38
because he hath *r.* him safe. 15:27
Zacchaeus came down and *r.* 19:6
returned, having *r.* kingdom. 15
own, his own *r.* him not. *John* 1:11
to as many as *r.* him, to them. 12
out of fulness have all we *r.* grace. 16
he that hath *r.* testimony, hath. 3:33
Galileans *r.* him, having seen. 4:45
willingly *r.* him into the ship. 6:21
washed, and I *r.* sight. 9:11
how he had *r.* his sight. 15
that he had *r.* his sight . . . him that had *r.* his sight. *John* 9:18
this commandment I *r.* of my. 10:18
he then having *r.* the sop. 13:30
words, and they have *r.* them. 17:8
Judas having *r.* band of men. 18:3
when Jesus had *r.* vinegar. 19:30
and a cloud *r.* him out. *Acts* 1:9
and having *r.* of the Father. 2:33
they that gladly *r.* his word. 41
feet and ancle bones *r.* 3:7
who *r.* the lively oracles to. 7:38
who have *r.* law by angels, and. 53
Samaria had *r.* the word of. 8:14
them, they *r.* the Holy Ghost. 17
r. meat, he was strengthened. 9:19
the vessel was *r.* again up. 10:16
which have *r.* the Holy Ghost. 47
that Gentiles had *r.* the word. 11:1
they were *r.* of the church. 15:4
having *r.* such charge, thrust. 16:24
hither also; whom Jason hath *r.* 17:7
Bereans *r.* the word with all. 11
have ye *r.* the Holy Ghost ? 19:2
ministry which I have *r.* of. 20:24
brethren *r.* us gladly. 21:17
from which I *r.* letters to. 22:5
having *r.* authority from the. 26:10
barbarians kindled a fire and *r.* 28:2
Publius *r.* us. 7
we neither *r.* letters out of Judaea. 21
Paul *r.* all that came. 30
by whom we have *r.* grace. *Rom* 1:5
r. the sign of circumcision. 4:11
by whom we have now *r.* the. 5:11
Spirit of bondage . . . but ye have *r.* Spirit of adoption. 8:15
for God hath *r.* him. 14:3
another, as Christ also *r.* us. 15:7
have *r.* not the spirit of. *1 Cor* 2:12
as if thou hadst not *r.* it ? 4:7
I *r.* of the Lord, that which. 11:23
which also ye have *r.* 15:1
which I *r.* 3
as we have *r.* mercy. *2 Cor* 4:1
and trembling ye *r.* him. 7:15
spirit, which ye have not *r.* 11:4
five times *r.* I forty stripes. 24
gospel than that ye have *r.* *Gal* 1:9
I *r.* it not of man, neither was. 12
r. ye the Spirit by works of the ? 3:2
but *r.* me as an angel of God. 4:14
things ye have *r.* and seen. *Phil* 4:9
as ye have *r.* Christ, so. *Col* 2:6
whom, ye *r.* commandments. 4:10
ministry thou hast *r.* in Lord. 17
having *r.* the word in. *1 Thes* 1:6
r. word, ye *r.* it not as word. 2:13
as ye have *r.* of us how ye ought. 4:1
because they *r.* not the love of truth. *2 Thes* 2:10
tradition which he *r.* of us. 3:6
in world, *r.* up into glory. *1 Tim* 3:16
God hath created to be *r.* 4:3
creature is good, if it be *r.* with. 4
transgression *r.* just recompence of. *Heb* 2:2
r. tithes of Abraham and. 7:6*
under it the people *r.* the law. 11
sin wilfully after we have *r.* 10:26
faith Sarai *r.* strength to. 11:11
died, not having *r.* the promises. 13
he that *r.* promises offered up. 17
from whence also he *r.* him in. 19
had *r.* the spies. 31; *Jas* 2:25
women *r.* their dead. *Heb* 11:35
all having obtained a good report through faith, *r.* not the promise. 39
vain conversation *r.* by tradition. *1 Pet* 1:18*
as every one hath *r.* the gift. 4:10
r. from God the Father. *2 Pet* 1:17
anointing ye have *r.* *1 John* 2:27
as we have *r.* a command. *2 John* 4
even as I *r.* of my Father. *Rev* 2:27
how thou hast *r.* and heard. 3:3
who have *r.* no kingdom as yet. 17:12
had *r.* the mark of the beast. 19:20
had not *r.* the mark, reigned. 20:4

receivedst

thy lifetime *r.* thy good. *Luke* 16:25

receiver

scribe ? where is the *r.*? *Isa* 33:18*

receiveth
no man that *r.* me to. *Judg* 19:18
what *r.* he of thine hand ? *Job* 35:7
wise is instructed, he *r.* knowledge. *Pr* 21:11
r. gifts, overthroweth it. 29:4*
that *r.* not correction. *Jer* 7:28
or *r.* offering with good. *Mal* 2:13
every one that asketh, *r.* *Mat* 7:8
Luke 11:10
he that *r.* you *r.* me, and he that *r.* me *r.* him that. *Mat* 10:40; *John* 13:20
he that *r.* a prophet . . . he that *r.* a righteous man. *Mat* 10:41
heareth word, and anon *r.* it. 13:20
little child in my name, *r.* me. 18:5
whoso shall receive me, *r.* not me, but him. *Mark* 9:37; *Luke* 9:48
this man *r.* sinners. *Luke* 15:2
no man *r.* his testimony. *John* 3:32
he that reapeth *r.* wages, and. 4:36
that rejecteth me, and *r.* not. 12:48
but one *r.* the prize. *1 Cor* 9:24
for the earth *r.* blessing. *Heb* 6:7
tithes, but there he *r.* them. 7:8
Levi who *r.* tithes, payed tithes. 9
every son whom he *r.* 12:6
saving he that *r.* it. *Rev* 2:17
whosoever *r.* the mark of. 14:11

receiveth *not*
r. not the things of God. *1 Cor* 2:14
Diotrephes *r.* us *not.* *3 John* 9

receiving
spared Naaman, in not *r.* *2 Ki* 5:20
and *r.* a commandment. *Acts* 17:15
r. in themselves that. *Rom* 1:27
shall *r.* of them be but life ? 11:15
concerning giving and *r.* *Phil* 4:15
we *r.* a kingdom which. *Heb* 12:28
r. the end of your faith. *1 Pet* 1:9

Rechab
R. the son of Rimmon. *2 Sam* 4:2, 5
R. escaped. 6
on Jehonadab son of *R.* *2 Ki* 10:15
son of *R.* went into the house of. 23
father of the house of *R.* *1 Chr* 2:55
Malchiah son of *R.* *Neh* 3:14
Jonadab the son of *R.* *Jer* 35:6
see **Jonadab**

Rechabites
go to the house of the *R.* *Jer* 35:2

reckon
he shall *r.* with him that. *Lev* 25:50
shall *r.* to him the worth. 27:18, 23
by name ye shall *r.* the. *Num* 4:32*
r. to him seven days. *Ezek* 44:26
when he had begun to *r.* *Mat* 18:24
r. yourselves to be dead. *Rom* 6:11
I *r.* that the sufferings of this. 8:18

reckoned
your heave offering *r.* *Num* 18:27
people shall not be *r.* among. 23:9
for Beeroth also was *r.* to. *2 Sam* 4:2
they *r.* not with the men. *2 Ki* 12:15
genealogy is not to be *r.* by birthright. *1 Chr* 5:1
genealogy of generations was *r.* 7
all these were *r.* by genealogies. 17
7:5, 7; 9:1, 22; *2 Chr* 31:19
Ezra 2:62; 8:3; *Neh* 7:5, 64
to us cannot be *r.* up. *Ps* 40:5*
I *r.* till morning that. *Isa* 38:13*
he was *r.* amongst the. *Luke* 22:37
reward is not *r.* of grace. *Rom* 4:4
faith was *r.* to Abraham. 9
how was it then *r.*? 10

reckoneth
lord *r.* with them. *Mat* 25:19

reckoning
there was no *r.* made. *2 Ki* 22:7
they were in one *r.* *1 Chr* 23:11

recommended
whence they had been *r.* *Acts* 14:26*
being *r.* to the grace of God. 15:40*

recompence, *noun*
(*An equivalent given or received. Now spelled* recompense, *both noun and verb*)
vengeance and *r.* *Deut* 32:35
vanity shall be his *r.* *Job* 15:31
the *r.* of a man's hand. *Pr* 12:14
will come with a *r.* *Isa* 35:4
r. to his enemies, to the islands *r.* 59:18
Lord that rendereth *r.* to his. 66:6
he will render to her a *r.* *Jer* 51:6
render to them a *r.* *Lam* 3:64
days of *r.* are come. *Hos* 9:7
will ye render me a *r.*? *Joel* 3:4
I will return your *r.* on your own. 7
bid thee, and a *r.* be. *Luke* 14:12
that *r.* of their error. *Rom* 1:27
let their table be made a *r.* to. 11:9
now for a *r.* in the same. *2 Cor* 6:13
transgression received a just *r.* of. *Heb* 2:2
hath great *r.* of reward. 10:35
respect to the *r.* of reward. 11:26

recompences
year of *r.* for controversy. *Isa* 34:8
Lord God of *r.* shall surely. *Jer* 51:56

recompense, *verb*
he shall *r.* his trespass. *Num* 5:7*
if he have no kinsman to *r.* the. 8*
the Lord *r.* thy work. *Ruth* 2:12
should the king *r.* me ? *2 Sam* 19:36
he will *r.* it, whether. *Job* 34:33
I will *r.* evil. *Pr* 20:22
I will *r.* into their bosom. *Isa* 65:6
first I will *r.* their iniquity. *Jer* 16:18
will *r.* according to their deeds. 25:14; *Hos* 12:2
r. work. *Jer* 50:29
r. abominations. *Ezek* 7:3, 8
r. thy ways. 4, 9; 9:10; 11:21; 16:43
oath and my covenant I will *r.* 17:19
they shall *r.* your lewdness. 23:49
if ye *r.* me, speedily will. *Joel* 3:4
for they cannot *r.* thee. *Luke* 14:14
r. to no man evil for evil. *Rom* 12:17
to *r.* tribulation to them. *2 Thes* 1:6
that hath said, I will *r.* *Heb* 10:30

recompensed
let the trespass be *r.* to. *Num* 5:8
cleanness of my hands hath he *r.* me. *2 Sam* 22:21, 25; *Ps* 18:20, 24
the righteous shall be *r.* *Pr* 11:31
shall evil be *r.* for good ? *Jer* 18:20
their own way have I *r.* *Ezek* 22:31
be *r.* at the resurrection. *Luke* 14:14
and it shall be *r.* to him. *Rom* 11:35

recompensest
thou *r.* iniquity of fathers. *Jer* 32:18

recompensing
by *r.* his way upon his. *2 Chr* 6:23

reconcile
brought to *r.* withal. *Lev* 6:30*
should he *r.* himself ? *1 Sam* 29:4
shall ye *r.* the house. *Ezek* 45:20*
r. both to God by cross. *Eph* 2:16
by him to *r.* all things. *Col* 1:20

reconciled
first be *r.* to thy brother. *Mat* 5:24
enemies we were *r.* to. *Rom* 5:10
be *r.* to her husband. *1 Cor* 7:11
who hath *r.* us to himself. *2 Cor* 5:18
we pray you be ye *r.* to God. 20
enemies, yet now hath he *r.* *Col* 1:21

reconciliation
to make a *r.* upon it. *Lev* 8:15*
they made *r.* with their blood. *2 Chr* 29:24*
one lamb to make *r.* *Ezek* 45:15*, 17
to make *r.* for iniquity. *Dan* 9:24
to us the ministry of *r.* *2 Cor* 5:18
committed unto us the word of *r.* 19
to make *r.* for the sins. *Heb* 2:17*

reconciling
an end of *r.* holy place. *Lev* 16:20*
if casting away be *r.* *Rom* 11:15
God was in Christ, *r.* *2 Cor* 5:19

record
(Witness, *usually in Revisions*)
where I *r.* my name. *Ex* 20:24
I call heaven and earth to *r.* *Deut* 30:19; 31:28
appointed Levites to *r.* *1 Chr* 16:4*
faithful witnesses to *r.* *Isa* 8:2
I take you to *r.* this day. *Acts* 20:26

record, *substantive*
and therein was a *r.* *Ezra* 6:2
behold, my *r.* is on high. *Job* 16:1
this is the *r.* of John. *John* 1:1
John bare *r.* saying, I saw. 32, 3
r. of thyself, thy *r.* is not. 8:1
r. of myself, yet my *r.* is true.
people with him, bare *r.* 12:1
that saw bare *r.* and his *r.* is. 19:3
I bare them *r.* that. *Rom* 10:
I call God for a *r.* *2 Cor* 1:2
to their power I bear *r.*, yea. 8:
I bear you *r.*, if it had. *Gal* 4:1
God is my *r.*, how greatly. *Phil* 1:
I bear him *r.* that he. *Col* 4:1
that bear *r.* in heaven. *1 John* 5:
believeth not *r.* God gave of his So
1
this is the *r.* that God hath. 1
we bare *r.* and our *r.* is. *3 John* 1
who bare *r.* of the Word. *Rev* 1:

recorded
Levites were *r.* chief of. *Neh* 12:2

recorder
Jehoshaphat was *r.* *2 Sam* 8:1
20:24; *1 Ki* 4:3; *1 Chr* 18:1
Joah the son of Asaph the *r.* *2 Ki* 18:18; *Isa* 36:3, 2
Joah son of Joahaz *r.* to repair. *2 Chr* 34:

records
search in the book of *r.* *Ezra* 4:1
to bring the book of *r.* *Esth* 6:

recount
he shall *r.* his worthies. *Nah* 2:5

recover
why did ye not *r.* them ? *Judg* 11:2
without fail *r.* all. *1 Sam* 30:
went to *r.* his border. *2 Sam* 8:
whether I shall *r.* *2 Ki* 1:
the prophet would *r.* him of. 5:
Naaman, that thou mayest *r.*
send to me to *r.* a man.
hand over place, and *r.* the leper. 1
enquire by him, shall I *r.*? 8:8,
thou mayest *r.* 1
that shouldest surely *r.* 1
nor did Jeroboam *r.* *2 Chr* 13:2
that they could not *r.* 14:1
that I may *r.* strength. *Ps* 39:1
to *r.* the remnant of. *Isa* 11:1
so wilt thou *r.* me and. 38:1
plaister, and he shall *r.* 2
and I will *r.* my wool. *Hos* 2:9
sick, and they shall *r.* *Mark* 16:1
that they may *r.* themselves out o the snare. *2 Tim* 2:2

recovered
David *r.* all the. *1 Sam* 30:18, 1
aught of spoil we have *r.* 2
Joash beat him, and *r.* *2 Ki* 13:2
he warred, and *r.* Damascus. 14:2
Rezin king of Syria *r.* Elath. 16:
laid it on the boil, and he *r.* 20:
was sick, and was *r.* *Isa* 38:9; 39:
the health of my people *r.*? *Jer* 8:2
took the people he had *r.* 41:1

recovering
to preach *r.* of sight to. *Luke* 4:1

red
first came out *r.* all over. *Gen* 25:2
Feed me with that same *r.* 3
his eyes shall be *r.* with. 49:1
rams' skins dyed *r.* *Ex* 25:5; 26:1
35:7; 36:19; 39:3
was found *r.* skins of rams. 35:2
bring thee a *r.* heifer. *Num* 19:
saw the water *r.* as blood. *2 Ki* 3:2
on a pavement of *r.*, blue. *Esth* 1:
in hand of Lord is cup and win is *r.* 75:
look not on the wine when it is *r.* *Pr* 23:3
though your sins be *r.* *Isa* 1:1
A vineyard of *r.* wine. 27:
art thou *r.* in thine apparel ? 63:
shield of his mighty men is made *r.* *Nah* 2:
a man riding on a *r.* horse and behin him were there *r.* *Zech* 1:
in first chariot were *r.* horses. 6:
will be fair weather, for sky is *r.* *Mat* 16:2,

nother horse that was *r*. *Rev* 6:4
great *r*. dragon, seven. 12:3

Red sea

ocusts into the *R. sea*. *Ex* 10:19
y the way of the *R sea*. 13:18
rowned in the *R. sea*. 15:4
srael from the *R. sea*. 22
ounds from the *R. sea*. 23:31
ilderness by the *R. sea*. *Num* 14:25
id he in the *R. sea*.? 21:14*
ourney by the *R. sea*. *Deut* 1:40
nade the *R. sea* to overflow. 11:4
ord dried up the *R. sea*. *Josh* 2:10
our God did to the *R. sea*. 4:23
ursued after to the *R. sea*. 24:6
neir cry by the *R. sea*. *Neh* 9:9
rovoked him at the *R. sea*. *Ps* 106:7
e rebuked the *R. sea*, and it. 9
errible things by the *R. sea*. 22
ivided the *R. sea* in parts. 136:13
nd his host in the *R. sea*. 15
as heard in the *R. sea*. *Jer* 49:21
onders in the *R. sea*. *Acts* 7:36
ney passed through the *R. sea*. *Heb* 11:29

reddish

bright spot somewhat *r*. *Lev* 13:19
24:43
white *r*. sore, it is a leprosy. 13:42
lague be *r*. in garment or. 49
ith hollow strakes, *r*. 14:37

redeem

[1] *To buy again something that ad been sold, by paying back the rice to him that bought it*, Lev 25:25; 7:20. [2] *To deliver and bring ut of bondage those who were ept prisoners by their enemies*, eut 7:5; 32:6; Luke 1:68; Tim 2:6; Tit 2:14.
To redeem time, *Eph* 5:16. *To nbrace and improve every opportunity of doing good.*

will *r*. you with a stretched. *Ex* 6:6
stling of ass shall *r*. 13:13; 34:20
my children I *r*. 15; 34:20
s kin come to *r*. it. *Lev* 25:25*
he have none to *r*. it. 26
e may *r*. it. 29
e cities may the Levites *r*. 32
s brethren may *r*. him. 48
any of kin may *r*. him. 49
it if he will at all *r*. it, then. 27:13
s house will *r*. it. 15, 19, 20, 31
man shalt thou *r*. *Num* 18:15
om a month old shalt thou *r*. 16
at thou shalt not *r*. 17
ilt *r*. it, if not, I will *r*. it. *Ruth* 4:4
nnot *r*. it for myself, *r*. thou it. 6
hom God went to *r*. to himself? *2 Sam* 7:23; *1 Chr* 17:21
ir power to *r*. them. *Neh* 5:5
famine he shall *r*. thee. *Job* 5:20
r. me from the hand of. 6:23
Israel, O God, out of all. *Ps* 25:22
me and be merciful unto. 26:11
us for thy mercies' sake. 44:26
one of them can *r*. his brother. 49:7
it God will *r*. my soul from. 15
raw nigh to my soul, and *r*. it. 69:18
their soul from deceit. 72:14
e shall *r*. Israel from all his. 130:8
nortened that it cannot *r*.? *Isa* 50:2
will *r*. thee out of hand. *Jer* 15:21
ill *r*. them from death. *Hos* 13:14
ord shall *r*. thee from. *Mi* 4:10
r. them that were under. *Gal* 4:5
at he might *r*. us from. *Tit* 2:14

redeemed

e angel which *r*. me. *Gen* 48:16
eople whom thou hast *r*. *Ex* 15:13
en shall he let her be *r*. 21:8
ith a bondmaid not *r*. *Lev* 19:20
a house in a city be not *r*. 25:30
ouses of villages may be *r*. 31
a stranger may be *r*. again. 48
he be not *r*. then go out in. 54
old the field, it shall not be *r*. 27:20
n unclean beast not *r*. then. 27
o devoted thing shall be *r*. 28, 29
nd the change shall not be *r*. 33
ose be *r*. that are more. *Num* 3:46
ose that are to be *r*. from. 18:16
the Lord hath *r*. you out of the. *Deut* 7:8; 15:15; 24:18
thy people thou hast *r*. 9:26
Lord which *r*. you out of house. 13:5
Israel, whom thou hast *r*. 21:8
Lord hath *r*. my soul. *2 Sam* 4:9
1 Ki 1:29
whom thou hast *r*. out of Egypt. *1 Chr* 17:21; *Neh* 1:10; *Ps* 77:15
ability have *r*. the Jews. *Neh* 5:8
thou hast *r*. me, O Lord. *Ps* 31:5
my soul which thou hast *r*. 71:23
thine inheritance thou hast *r*. 74:2
he *r*. them from the hand of. 106:10
let the *r*. of the Lord say so, whom he hath *r*. 107:2
hath *r*. us from our enemies. 136:24
Zion shall be *r*. with. *Isa* 1:27
the Lord, who *r*. Abraham. 29:22
no lion there, but the *r*. shall. 35:9
fear not, I have *r*. thee, thou. 43:1
for I have *r*. thee. 44:22
the Lord hath *r*. Jacob. 23; 48:20
Jer 31:11
the *r*. of the Lord shall. *Isa* 51:11
ye shall be *r*. without money. 52:3
r. Jerusalem. 9
holy people *r*. of Lord. 62:12
year of my *r*. is come. 63:4
in pity he *r*. them. 9
Lord, thou hast *r*. my life. *Lam* 3:58
though I *r*. them, yet they. *Hos* 7:13
I *r*. thee out of the house. *Mi* 6:4
for them, I have *r*. them. *Zech* 10:8
visited and *r*. his people. *Luke* 1:68
he who should have *r*. Israel. 24:21
Christ *r*. us from the curse. *Gal* 3:13
ye were not *r*. with. *1 Pet* 1:18
thou hast *r*. us to God. *Rev* 5:9
the 144,000 which were *r*. 14:3*
these were *r*. from among men. 4*

redeemedst

which thou *r*. to thee. *2 Sam* 7:23

Redeemer

I know that my *R*. liveth. *Job* 19:25
my strength and my *R*. *Ps* 19:14
the high God was their *R*. 78:35
their *R*. is mighty, he. *Pr* 23:11
thy *R*. the Holy One of Israel. *Isa* 41:14; 54:5
thus saith the Lord your *R*. 43:14
thus saith the Lord, his *R*. the. 44:6
saith the Lord thy *R*. 24; 48:17
49:7; 54:8
as for our *R*., the Lord of. 47:4
I the Lord am thy *R*. 49:26; 60:16
R. shall come to Zion, to. 59:20
art our Father, our *R*. 63:16
their *R*. is strong, the. *Jer* 50:34

redeemeth

the Lord *r*. the souls. *Ps* 34:22
who *r*. life from destruction. 103:4

redeeming

the manner in Israel concerning *r*. *Ruth* 4:7
r. time, because the days are evil. *Eph* 5:16; *Col* 4:5

redemption

grant a *r*. for the land. *Lev* 25:24
give again the price of his *r*. 51, 52
Moses took the *r*. money. *Num* 3:49
r. of their soul is precious. *Ps* 49:8
he sent *r*. to his people. 111:9
with him there is plenteous *r*. 130:7
right of *r*. is thine. *Jer* 32:7, 8
to them that looked for *r*. *Luke* 2:38
look up, for your *r*. draweth. 21:28
the *r*. that is in Christ. *Rom* 3:24
to wit, the *r*. of our body. 8:23
to us sanctification and *r*. *1 Cor* 1:30
in whom we have *r*. through his blood. *Eph* 1:7; *Col* 1:14
until the *r*. of purchased. *Eph* 1:14
are sealed unto the day of *r*. 4:30
obtained eternal *r*. for us. *Heb* 9:12
for *r*. of the transgressions that. 15

redness

who hath *r*. of eyes? *Pr* 23:29

redound

that grace might *r*. to. *2 Cor* 4:15*

reed

[1] *A plant growing in fens and watery places*, Job 40:21. [2] *A staff or rod of a reed, which was put in our Saviour's hand at his passion, by way of derision, instead of a sceptre*, Mat 27:29. [3] *A Jewish measure of six cubits three inches, or three yards three inches*, Ezek 40:3.

smite Israel as a *r*. *1 Ki* 14:15
upon the staff of this bruised *r*. *2 Ki* 18:21; *Isa* 36:6
a bruised *r*. shall he not break. *Isa* 42:3; *Mat* 12:20
a staff of *r*. to Israel. *Ezek* 29:6
a man with a measuring *r*. 40:3
with measuring *r*. 42:16, 17, 18, 19
a *r*. shaken? *Mat* 11:7; *Luke* 7:24
put a *r*. in his right hand. *Mat* 27:29
smote him with a *r*. 30; *Mark* 15:19
put the spunge on a *r*. and gave. *Mat* 27:48; *Mark* 15:36
given me a *r*. like a rod. *Rev* 11:1
had a golden *r*. to measure. 21:15
he measured with the *r*. 12,000. 16

reeds

he lieth in covert of the *r*. *Job* 40:21
the *r*. and flags shall. *Isa* 19:6, 7*
of dragons shall be *r*. 35:7
the *r*. they have burnt. *Jer* 51:32
he measured east side . . . five hundred *r*. *Ezek* 42:16, 17, 18, 19
the length 25,000 *r*. 45:1

reel

they *r*. to and fro. *Ps* 107:27
earth shall *r*. to and fro. *Isa* 24:20*

refine

I will *r*. them as silver. *Zech* 13:9

refined

for the altar *r*. gold. *1 Chr* 28:18
seven thousand talents of *r*. silver. 29:4
wines on the lees well *r*. *Isa* 25:6
behold, I have *r*. thee, but not. 48:10
refine them, as silver is *r*. *Zech* 13:9

refiner

he is like a *r*.'s fire, and. *Mal* 3:2
shall sit as a *r*. and purifier. 3

reformation

until the time of *r*. *Heb* 9:10

reformed

and if ye will not be *r*. *Lev* 26:23

refrain

then Joseph could not *r*. himself. *Gen* 45:1
I will not *r*. my mouth. *Job* 7:11
my son, *r*. thy foot. *Pr* 1:15
there is a time to *r*. from. *Eccl* 3:5
I will *r*. for thee that I. *Isa* 48:9
wilt thou *r*. thyself for these? 64:12
r. voice from weeping. *Jer* 31:16
I say to you, *R*. from. *Acts* 5:38
let him *r*. his tongue. *1 Pet* 3:10

refrained

Joseph *r*. himself and. *Gen* 43:31
Haman *r*. himself. *Esth* 5:10
princes *r*. talking, and. *Job* 29:9
I have not *r*. my lips. *Ps* 40:9
I have *r*. my feet from. 119:101
still, and *r*. myself. *Isa* 42:14
they have not *r*. their feet. *Jer* 14:10

refraineth

that *r*. his lips is wise. *Pr* 10:19

refresh

with me and *r*. thyself. *1 Ki* 13:7
Julius suffered Paul to *r*. *Acts* 27:3
brother, *r*. my bowels. *Philem* 20

refreshed

stranger may be *r*. *Ex* 23:12
he rested and was *r*. 31:17
Saul was *r*. and well. *1 Sam* 16:23
r. themselves there. *2 Sam* 16:14
speak that I may be *r*. *Job* 32:20
I may with you be *r*. *Rom* 15:32
for they *r*. my spirit. *1 Cor* 16:18
spirit, was *r*. by you. *2 Cor* 7:13
Onesiphorus oft *r*. me. *2 Tim* 1:16
of the saints are *r*. by. *Philem* 7

refresheth

for he *r.* the soul of. *Pr* 25:13

refreshing

this is *r.*, yet they would. *Isa* 28:12
times of *r.* shall come. *Acts* 3:19

refuge

Cities of refuge. *In order to provide for the security of those, who unawares and without any design should kill a man, the Lord commanded Moses to appoint six cities of* refuge, *that the manslayer might retire thither, and have time to prepare for justification before the judges, so that the kinsman of the deceased might not pursue him thither and kill him. Of these cities there were three on each side Jordan: those on the west of Jordan were* Kedesh *of* Naphtali, Hebron, *and* Shechem. *Those beyond Jordan were* Bezer, Golan, *and* Ramoth-gilead, *Josh* 20:7, 8. *These cities were to be easy of access, and to have smooth and good roads to them, and bridges where there should be occasion. When there were any cross-roads, they took care to set up posts with an inscription, directing the way to the* city of refuge. *This city was to be well supplied with water and all kind of provisions. The case then came before the judges, that if possible he might clear himself. If he was found innocent, he dwelt safely in the city to which he had retired; if otherwise, he was put to death, according to the severity of the law. Though he was found innocent, he was not therefore immediately set at liberty, but he was obliged to dwell in this city, without going out of it, till the death of the high priest: And if before this time he should any where go out of the city, the avenger of blood might safely kill him,* Num 35:25, 26, **27**, etc.

shall ye have for *r.* *Num* 35:13, 15
eternal God is thy *r.* *Deut* 33:27*
your *r.* from avenger. *Josh* 20:3
high tower and my *r.* *2 Sam* 22:3
a *r.* for the oppressed, a *r.* *Ps* 9:9*
poor, because the Lord is his *r.* 14:6
God is our *r.* 46:1, 7, 11
God is known for a *r.* 48:3
thy wings I will make my *r.* 57:1
thou hast been my *r.* in the. 59:16
my *r.* is in God. 62:7
God is a *r.* for us. 8
thou art my strong *r.* 71:7; 142:5
he is my *r.* 91:2, 9
God is rock of my *r.* 94:22
high hills a *r.* for wild goats. 104:18
r. failed me. 142:4
thou art my *r.* and portion. 5
shall have a place of *r.* *Pr* 14:26
a place of *r.* *Isa* 4:6
to the needy a *r.* 25:4
we have made lies our *r.* 28:15
hail shall sweep away the *r.* 17
O Lord, my *r.* in the day. *Jer* 16:19
who have fled for *r.* to lay. *Heb* 6:18

refuse

that was vile and *r.* *1 Sam* 15:9
thou hast made us as *r.* *Lam* 3:45
sell the *r.* of wheat. *Amos* 8:6

refuse, *verb*

if thou *r.* to let them go. *Ex* 4:23
8:2; 9:2; 10:4
long wilt thou *r.* to humble? 10:3
r. ye to keep my? 16:28
if her father utterly *r.* to give. 22:17
whether thou *r.* or choose. *Job* 34:33
be wise, and *r.* it not. *Pr* 8:33
they *r.* to do judgement. 21:7
slothful, his hands *r.* to labour. 25
if ye *r.*, shall be devoured. *Isa* 1:20
may know to *r.* the evil. 7:15, 16
they *r.* to return. *Jer* 8:5
they *r.* to know me. 9:6
evil people which *r.* to. *Jer* 13:10
if they *r.* to take the cup. 25:28
if thou *r.* to go forth, this. 38:21
if I be an offender, I *r.* *Acts* 25:11
but *r.* profane and old. *1 Tim* 4:7
the younger widows *r.* 5:11
see that ye *r.* not him. *Heb* 12:25

refused

Jacob *r.* to be comforted. *Gen* 37:35
r. and said to master's wife. 39:8
Jacob *r.* to remove his hand. 48:19
Edom *r.* to give Israel. *Num* 20:21
people *r.* to obey the. *1 Sam* 8:19
look not on him for I have *r.* 16:7*
Saul *r.* and said, I will not. 28:23
Asahel *r.* to turn aside. *2 Sam* 2:23
but Amnon *r.* to eat. 13:9
man *r.* to smite him. *1 Ki* 20:35
vineyard he *r.* to give thee. 21:15
him to take it, but he *r.* *2 Ki* 5:16
and *r.* to obey. *Neh* 9:17
queen Vashti *r.* to come. *Esth* 1:12
that my soul *r.* to touch. *Job* 6:7
my soul *r.* to be comforted. *Ps* 77:2
they *r.* to walk in his law. 78:10
he *r.* tabernacle of Joseph. 67
stone which the builders *r.* 118:22*
I have called and ye *r.* *Pr* 1:24
when thou wast *r.* saith. *Isa* 54:6*
they *r.* to receive correction, they *r.* *Jer* 5:3
their fathers who *r.* to hear. 11:10
Rachel *r.* to be comforted. 31:15
all that took them *r.* to let. 50:33
for they have *r.* my. *Ezek* 5:6*
because they *r.* to return. *Hos* 11:5
but they *r.* to hearken. *Zech* 7:11
this Moses whom they *r.* *Acts* 7:35
nothing to be *r.* if it be. *1 Tim* 4:4
by faith Moses *r.* to be. *Heb* 11:24
r. him that spake on earth. 12:25

refusedst

thou *r.* to be ashamed. *Jer* 3:3

refuseth

r. to let the people go. *Ex* 7:14
Lord *r.* to give me leave. *Num* 22:13
Balaam *r.* to come with us. 14
brother *r.* to raise up name. *Deut* 25:7
but he that *r.* reproof. *Pr* 10:17*
shame shall be to him that *r.* 13:18
that *r.* instruction despiseth. 15:32
this people *r.* the waters. *Isa* 8:6
my wound which *r.* to be. *Jer* 15:18

regard, *noun*

in *r.* of the oath of God. *Eccl* 8:2
to him they had *r.* because he had. *Acts* 8:11*

regard, *verb*

[1] *To look upon with compassion,* Deut 28:50. [2] *To think of, consider, or lay to heart,* Isa 5:12. [3] *To have respect for,* 2 Ki 3:14. [4] *To hear and answer,* Ps 102:17. [5] *To observe,* Rom 14:6.

r. not your stuff. *Gen* 45:20
let them not *r.* vain. *Ex* 5:9
r. not them that have. *Lev* 19:31*
which shall not *r.* person. *Deut* 28:50
nor did she *r.* it. *1 Sam* 4:20
let not my lord *r.* this man. 25:25
r. not this, he is thy. *2 Sam* 13:20*
were it not that I *r.* *2 Ki* 3:14
that day, let not God *r.* it. *Job* 3:4
nor will the Almighty *r* it. 35:13
take heed, *r.* not iniquity. 36:21
they *r.* not the works of. *Ps* 28:5
I have hated them that *r.* 31:6
if I *r.* iniquity in my heart. 66:18
shall the God of Jacob *r.* it. 94:7*
he will *r.* the prayer of the. 102:17
thou mayest *r.* discretion. *Pr* 5:2*
will not *r.* any ransom, nor. 6:35
they *r.* not work of Lord. *Isa* 5:12
who will not *r.* silver. 13:17
will no more *r.* them. *Lam* 4:16
r. God of his fathers, nor *r.* any. *Dan* 11:37
r. the peace offering. *Amos* 5:22
behold, *r.* and wonder. *Hab* 1:5
will he *r.* your persons? *Mal* 1:9*
not God, nor *r.* man. *Luke* 18:4
to Lord he doth not *r.* it. *Rom* 14:6

regarded

he that *r.* not the word. *Ex* 9:21
voice, nor any that *r.* *1 Ki* 18:29
thou hast *r.* me as. *1 Chr* 17:1
he *r.* their affliction. *Ps* 106:4
my hand, and no man *r.* *Pr* 1:2
O king, have not *r.* thee. *Dan* 3:1
he *r.* the low estate of. *Luke* 1:48
feared not God, neither *r.* man. 18:
and I *r.* them not. *Heb* 8:

regardest

thou *r.* not princes. *2 Sam* 19:6
I stand up and thou *r.* *Job* 30:2
r. not the persons of men. *Mat* 22:16; *Mark* 12:1

regardeth

mighty and terrible, that *r.* not. *Deut* 10:1
nor *r.* the rich more. *Job* 34:1
r. the crying of the driver. 39:7
a righteous man *r.* the life. *Pr* 12:1
he that *r.* reproof shall be. 13:1
but he that *r.* reproof is. 15:
wicked *r.* not to know cause. 29:7
higher than the highest *r.* *Eccl* 5:
he that *r.* the clouds shall not. 11:
cities, he *r.* no man. *Isa* 33:
Daniel *r.* not thee, O king. *Dan* 6:1
he *r.* not the offering *Mal* 2:1
he that *r.* a day, *r.* it to. *Rom* 14:

regarding

ever without any *r.* it. *Job* 4:2
nor *r.* his life to supply. *Phil* 2:30

regeneration

Or the new birth, is the change an renovation of the soul by the Spiri and grace of God, John 3:5, 6.

in the *r.* when the Son of. *Mat* 19:2
us by the washing of *r.* *Tit* 3:

region

all the *r.* of Argob. *Deut* 3:4, 1
in all *r.* of Dor. *1 Ki* 4:11
dominion over all the *r.* 2
then went to him all the *r.* *Mat* 3:
sat in *r.* and shadow of death. 4:1
throughout all the *r.* about Galilee. *Mark* 1:28; *Luke* 4:14; 7:1
whole *r.* round about. *Mark* 6:5
Philip tetrarch of the *r.* *Luke* 3:1
published throughout *r.* *Acts* 13:4
they fled to the *r.* that lieth. 14:
gone throughout *r.* of Galatia. 16:

regions

throughout the *r.* of Judaea. *Acts* 8:1
gospel in *r.* beyond you. *2 Cor* 10:1
stop me in the *r.* of Achaia. 11:1
came into the *r.* of Syria. *Gal* 1:2

register

these sought their *r.* *Ezra* 2:6
Neh 7:6
a *r.* of the genealogy. *Neh* 7:5

rehearse

r. it in ears of Joshua. *Ex* 17:1
r. righteous acts of Lord. *Judg* 5:1

rehearsed

r. them in the ears of. *1 Sam* 8:2
they *r.* David's words. 17:3
Peter *r.* the matter from. *Acts* 11:4
they *r.* all that God had done. 14:2

Rehoboam

R. the son of Solomon reigned. *1 Ki* 11:43; 14:21; *2 Chr* 9:3
R. consulted with the old men. *1 Ki* 12:6; *2 Chr* 10:
R. reigned over them. *1 Ki* 12:1
2 Chr 10:1
to bring the kingdom again to *R.* *1 Ki* 12:21; *2 Chr* 11:
their heart shall turn again to *R.* *1 Ki* 12:2
war between *R.* and. 14:30; 15:
R. was Solomon's son. *1 Chr* 3:1
Mat 1:
they made *R.* strong. *2 Chr* 11:1
R. loved Maachah daughter of. 2
R. made Abijah the son of. 2
against *R.* when *R.* was young. 13:

Rehoboth

builded Nineveh and *R.* *Gen* 10:1
the name of the well *R.* 26:2
Saul of *R.* reigned. 36:37; *1 Chr* 1:4

Rehum

R. came with Zerubbabel. *Ezra* 2:2
Neh 12:3
R. the chancellor wrote. *Ezra* 4:8
he king sent an answer to R. and. 17
etter was read before R. 23
R. the son of Bani. *Neh* 3:17
R. of chief of the people. 10:25

reign

(*Used of temporal sovereigns; of God as spiritual ruler; and symbolically of sin or righteousness. Revisions frequently change to* rule)
Solomon's r. over Israel. *1 Ki* 6:1
n 8th year of his r. *2 Ki* 24:12
heir cities to the r. *1 Chr* 4:31
David's acts with all his r. 29:30
ill r. of the kingdom. *2 Chr* 36:20
priests recorded to r. *Neh* 12:22
king in 7th year of his r. *Esth* 2:16
year of the r. of Tiberius. *Luke* 3:1

reign, *verb*

hou indeed r. over us? *Gen* 37:8
Lord shall r. for ever. *Ex* 15:18
Ps 146:10
hat hate you shall r. *Lev* 26:17
hou shalt r. over many nations, but they shall not r. *Deut* 15:6
70 r. over you, or one r.? *Judg* 9:2
trees said, R. thou. 8, 10, 12, 14
hat I should not r. over. *1 Sam* 8:7
manner of king that shall r. 9, 11
Lord said, This same shall r. 9:17
shall Saul r. over us? 11:12
but a king shall r. over us. 12:12
hou mayest r. over all. *2 Sam* 3:21
hat Adonijah doth r.? *1 Ki* 1:11
shall r. after me. 1:13, 17, 30
Adonijah shall r. after me? 1:24
faces on me, that I should r. 2:15
take thee, and thou shalt r. 11:37
Zimri did r. seven days in. 16:15
hast made to r. in his. *2 Chr* 1:8
Behold, the king's son shall r. 23:3
hat the hypocrite r. not. *Job* 34:30
by me kings r. and princes. *Pr* 8:15
prison he cometh to r. *Eccl* 4:14
of hosts shall r. in Zion. *Isa* 24:23
behold, a king shall r. in. 32:1
shalt thou r. because? *Jer* 22:15
a king shall r. and prosper. 23:5
should not have a son to r. 33:21
he Lord shall r. over them. *Mi* 4:7
hat Archelaus did r. *Mat* 2:22
shall r. over house of. *Luke* 1:33
will not have this man to r. 19:14
would not that I should r. over. 27
shall r. in life by one. *Rom* 5:17
even so might grace r. unto life. 21
let not sin r. in your mortal. 6:12
shall rise to r. over Gentiles. 15:12
would to God ye did r. that we might r. *1 Cor* 4:8
for he must r. till he put all. 15:25
if we suffer, we shall r. *2 Tim* 2:12
and we also shall r. *Rev* 5:10
and he shall r. for ever and. 11:15
they shall r. with him 1000 years. 20:6
they shall r. for ever and ever. 22:5

see **began**

reigned

r. in Edom before any king r. over. *Gen* 36:31; *1 Chr* 1:43
when Abimelech had r. *Judg* 9:22
Saul r. one year, and when he r. *1 Sam* 13:1
Saul's son r. two years. *2 Sam* 2:10
David r. forty years over. 5:4
David r. seven years in Hebron. 5
1 Ki 2:11; *1 Chr* 3:4; 29:27
David r. over Israel. *2 Sam* 8:15
1 Chr 18:14; 29:26
Hanun his son r. in his stead.
2 Sam 10:1; *1 Chr* 19:1
whose stead thou hast r. *2 Sam* 16:8
and Solomon r. *1 Ki* 4:21; 11:42
1 Chr 29:28; *2 Chr* 9:26, 30
Rezon r. in Damascus. *1 Ki* 11:24
. over Syria. 25
Rehoboam r. 43; 12:17; *2 Chr* 9:31
10:17
Abijam his son r. *1 Ki* 14:31
2 Chr 12:16; 13:2
and Asa r. in his stead. *1 Ki* 15:8
9, 10; *2 Chr* 14:1
Jehoshaphat his son r. *1 Ki* 15:24
2 Chr 17:1; 20:31
Nadab r. *1 Ki* 15:25
Baasha r. 28, 29
Elah r. 16:6
Zimri r. in his stead. 10
Omri r. 22, 23
Omri died, and Ahab his son r. 28
Ahaziah, Ahab's son, r. 22:40, 51
2 Ki 8:24, 26; *2 Chr* 22:1, 2
Jehoshaphat r. 25 years. *1 Ki* 22:42
2 Chr 20:31
Jehoram r. *1 Ki* 22:50; *2 Ki* 3:1
8:17; *2 Chr* 21:5, 20
son that should have r. *2 Ki* 3:27
Hazael r. 8:15
Jehoahaz r. 10:35
Jehu r. 36
Jehoash r. forty years in. 12:1
Amaziah r. 21; 14:1
2 Chr 24:27; 25:1
Ben-hadad r. *2 Ki* 13:24
Jeroboam r. 14:16, 23
Zachariah r. 29
Azariah r. 15:2; *2 Chr* 26:3
and Jotham r. *2 Ki* 15:7, 33
2 Chr 26:23; 27:1, 8
Shallum r. *2 Ki* 15:10, 13
Menahem son of Gadi r. 14, 17
Pekahiah his son r. 22, 23
Pekah r. 25, 27
Hoshea r. 30
Ahaz r. 15:38; 16:2; *2 Chr* 28:1
Hezekiah r. *2 Ki* 16:20; 18:2
2 Chr 28:27; 29:1
Esarhaddon r. in his stead.
2 Ki 19:37; *Isa* 37:38
Manasseh r. *2 Ki* 20:21; 21:1
2 Chr 32:33; 33:1
Amon r. in his stead.
2 Ki 21:18, 19; *2 Chr* 33:20, 21
Josiah r. in his stead. *2 Ki* 21:26
22:1; *2 Chr* 34:1
Jehoahaz r. three months. *2 Ki* 23:31
2 Chr 36:2
Jehoiakim r. eleven years.
2 Ki 23:36; *2 Chr* 36:5
Jehoiachin his son r. *2 Ki* 24:6, 8
2 Chr 36:8, 9
Zedekiah r. *2 Ki* 24:18; *2 Chr* 36:11
Jer 37:1; 52:1
and Athaliah r. over. *2 Chr* 22:12
Ahasuerus r. from India. *Esth* 1:1
touching Shallum which r. *Jer* 22:11
death r. from Adam to. *Rom* 5:14
man's offence death r. by one. 17
r. unto death, so might grace reign. 21
ye have r. as kings. *1 Cor* 4:8
great power, and hast r. *Rev* 11:17
lived and r. with Christ. 20:4

reignest

thou r. over all, and in. *1 Chr* 29:12

reigneth

ye and the king that r. *1 Sam* 12:14
Absalom r. in Hebron. *2 Sam* 15:10
Adonijah r. *1 Ki* 1:18
the Lord r. *1 Chr* 16:31; *Ps* 96:10
97:1; 99:1
God r. over the heathen. *Ps* 47:8
Lord r., he is clothed with. 93:1
for a servant when he r. *Pr* 30:22
unto Zion, Thy God r. *Isa* 52:7
which r. over the kings. *Rev* 17:18
Lord God omnipotent r. 19:6

reigning

I have rejected him from r. over. *1 Sam* 16:1

reins

Kidneys *or* loins. *The* Hebrews *ascribe to the* reins *knowledge, joy, pain, pleasure; so in scripture it is often said, that God searcheth the hearts and the* reins, Ps 7:9; Jer 17:10; 20:12.
cleaveth my r. asunder. *Job* 16:13
though my r. be consumed. 19:27
God trieth the heart and r. *Ps* 7:9
my r. also instruct me in the. 16:7
examine me, O Lord, try my r. 26:2
thus I was pricked in my r. *Ps* 73:21
thou hast possessed my r. 139:13
yea, my r. shall rejoice. *Pr* 23:16
the girdle of his r. *Isa* 11:5
that triest the r. *Jer* 11:20
and far from their r. 12:2
I try the r. 17:10
that seest the r. 20:12
arrow to enter into my r. *Lam* 3:13
he who searcheth the r. *Rev* 2:23

reject

I will r. thee, that thou. *Hos* 4:6
he would not r. her. *Mark* 6:26
ye r. the commandment of. 7:9
and second admonition, r. *Tit* 3:13

rejected

not r. thee, but they r. *1 Sam* 8:7
ye have this day r. your God. 10:19
hast r. the word of the Lord, he hath r. thee from being king. 15:23, 26
I have r. him from being king. 16:1
they r. his statutes. *2 Ki* 17:15
Lord r. all the seed of Israel. 20
is despised and r. of men. *Isa* 53:3
for the Lord hath r. thy. *Jer* 2:37
r. my law. 6:19
because the Lord hath r. them. 30
Lord hath r. the generation of. 7:29
lo, they have r. the word of. 8:9
hast thou utterly r. Judah? 14:19
but thou hast utterly r. us. *Lam* 5:22
because thou hast r. *Hos* 4:6
stone which builders r. *Mat* 21:42
Mark 12:10; *Luke* 20:17
he shall be r. of the elders.
Mark 8:31; *Luke* 9:22
lawyers r. the counsel. *Luke* 7:30
but he must first be r. of. 17:25
ye despised not, nor r. *Gal* 4:14
thorns and briars is r. *Heb* 6:8
inherited blessing, was r. 12:17

rejecteth

that r. me, receiveth not. *John* 12:48

rejoice

ye shall r. in all. *Deut* 12:7; 14:26
thou shalt r. in thy feast. 16:14
bless thee, therefore thou shalt r. 15
thou shalt r. in every good. 26:11
Lord will r. over you. 28:63; 30:9
r. O ye nations, with his. 32:43
he said, R. Zebulun, in thy. 33:18
r. ye in Abimelech. *Judg* 9:19
Philistines gathered to r. 16:23
I r. in thy salvation. *1 Sam* 2:1
thou sawest it, and didst r. 19:5
let the heart of them r. that seek.
1 Chr 16:10; *Ps* 105:3
let the fields r. and all. *1 Chr* 16:32
and let thy saints r. *2 Chr* 6:41
made them to r. 20:27; *Neh* 12:43
and he shall not r. *Job* 20:18
they r. at the sound of the. 21:12
fear, r. with trembling. *Ps* 2:11
all that put their trust in thee r. 5:11
I will r. in thy salvation. 9:14
those that trouble me r. when. 13:4
my heart shall r. in thy salvation. 5
Jacob shall r. and Israel. 14:7
we will r. in thy salvation. 20:5*
how greatly shall he r.! 21:1
hast not made my foes to r. 30:1
for our heart shall r. in him. 33:21
my soul shall r. in his. 35:9
enemies wrongfully r. over me. 19
and let them not r. over me. 24
let them be ashamed that r. 26
lest they should r. over me. 38:16
let mount Zion r.; let Judah. 48:11
bones thou hast broken may r. 51:8
the righteous shall r. when. 58:10
in holiness, I will r. 60:6; 108:7
in shadow of thy wings will I r. 63:7
but the king shall r. in God. 11
morning and evening to r. 65:8
the little hills r. 12*
there did we r. 66:6
righteous r. yea, exceedingly r. 68:3
r. before him. 4
my lips shall greatly r. 71:23
revive us, that thy people may r. 85:6
r. the soul of thy servant. 86:4
Tabor and Hermon shall r. 89:12

in thy name shall they *r.* *Ps* 89:16
made all his enemies to *r.* 42
let the heavens *r.* 96:11
trees of the wood *r.* 12*
Lord reigneth, let the earth *r.* 97:1
make a loud noise, *r.* and sing. 98:4*
Lord shall *r.* in his works. 104:31
that I may *r.* in gladness of thy. 106:5
righteous shall see it and *r.* 107:42
ashamed, let thy servant *r.* 109:28
I *r.* at thy word, as one. 119:162
let Israel *r.* in him that. 149:2
who *r.* to do evil, and. *Pr* 2:14
r. with the wife of thy youth. 5:18
wise, mine heart shall *r.* 23:15
yea, my reins shall *r.* when. 16
righteous shall greatly *r.* 24
she that bare thee shall *r.* 25
r. not when thine enemy. 24:17
ointment and perfume *r.* the. 27:9
righteous men do *r.*, there. 28:12*
are in authority, people *r.* 29:2
righteous doth sing and *r.* 6
shall *r.* in time to come. 31:25*
a man to *r.* and do good. *Eccl* 3:12
should *r.* in his works. 22; 5:19
come after, shall not *r.* in him. 4:16
live many years, and *r.* in them. 11:8
r. O young man, in thy youth. 9
and *r.* in Rezin and. *Isa* 8:6
as men *r.* when they divide. 9:3
them that *r.* in my highness. 13:3*
yea, the fir trees *r.* at thee. 14:8
r. not thou, whole Palestina. 29
Thou shalt no more *r.* O virgin. 23:12
the noise of them that *r.* 24:8
poor among men shall *r.* in. 29:19
the desert shall *r.* 35:1
shall blossom and *r.* 2
for confusion they shall *r.* in. 61:7
as a bridegroom, so shall God *r.* 62:5
my servants shall *r.*, but ye. 65:13
I will *r.* in Jerusalem, and. 19
r. ye with Jerusalem, and. 66:10
see this, your heart shall *r.* 14
virgin *r.* in the dance, and I will make them *r.* from their. *Jer* 31:13
I will *r.* over them to do. 32:41
that they may *r.* and sleep. 51:39
thine enemy to *r.* over. *Lam* 2:17
let not the buyer *r.* nor. *Ezek* 7:12
r. at the inheritance of. 35:15
r. not, O Israel, for joy. *Hos* 9:1
ye which *r.* in a thing. *Amos* 6:13
r. not against me, O mine. *Mi* 7:8
take away them that *r.* *Zeph* 3:11
the Lord will *r.* over thee with. 17
r. O daughter of Zion. *Zech* 2:10
r. greatly, O daughter of Zion. 9:9
and their heart shall *r.* as. 10:7
and many shall *r.* at his. *Luke* 1:14
r. ye that day, and leap for. 6:23
in this *r.* not, rather *r.* because. 10:20
r. with me, for I have found. 15:6, 9
of the disciples began to *r.* 19:37
that reapeth may *r.* *John* 4:36
willing for a season to *r.* in. 5:35
if ye loved me, ye would *r.* 14:28
weep, but the world shall *r.* 16:20
you, and your heart shall *r.* 22
therefore did my heart *r.* *Acts* 2:26*
r. in hope of the glory. *Rom* 5:2
r. with them that do *r.* and. 12:15
he saith, *R.* ye Gentiles. 15:10
they that *r.* as though. *1 Cor* 7:30
all the members *r.* with it. 12:26
of whom I ought to *r.* *2 Cor* 2:3
now I *r.* not that ye were. 7:9
I *r.* that I have confidence in. 16
r. thou barren that. *Gal* 4:27
do *r.* yea, and will *r.* *Phil* 1:18
that I may *r.* in the day of. 2:16*
if I be offered, I joy and *r.* 17
same cause do ye joy and *r.* 18
see him again, ye may *r.* 28
we worship God, and *r.* in. 3:3*
now *r.* in my sufferings. *Col* 1:24
r. evermore. *1 Thes* 5:16
let the brother of low degree *r.* *Jas* 1:9*
now ye *r.* in your boastings. 4:16
wherein ye greatly *r.* *1 Pet* 1:6
r. with joy unspeakable and. 8
but *r.* in as much as ye are. 4:13
on earth shall *r.* over. *Rev* 11:10
therefore *r.* ye heavens, and. 12:12
r. over her, thou heaven. 18:20
see **glad**

rejoice *before the Lord*
shall *r. before the Lord.* *Lev* 23:40
Deut 12:12, 18; 16:11; 27:7

rejoice *in the Lord*
r. in the Lord, O ye righteous. *Ps* 33:1; 97:12
r. in the Lord, glory in. *Isa* 41:16
I will greatly *r. in the Lord.* 61:10
of Zion, *r. in the Lord.* *Joel* 2:23
yet I will *r. in the Lord.* *Hab* 3:18
heart shall *r. in the Lord.* *Zech* 10:7
brethren, *r. in the Lord.* *Phil* 3:1
r. in the Lord alway, and. 4:4

rejoiced
Jethro *r.* for all goodness. *Ex* 18:9
the Lord *r.* over you to. *Deut* 28:63
rejoice for good, as he *r.* over. 30:9
father of the damsel *r.* *Judg* 19:3
men of Beth-shemesh *r.* *1 Sam* 6:13
the men of Israel *r.* greatly. 11:15
the people *r.* so that the. *1 Ki* 1:40
Hiram *r.* greatly at Solomon's. 5:7
the people *r.* when Joash made king. *2 Ki* 11:14, 20; *2 Chr* 23:13, 21
people *r.* and David *r.* *1 Chr* 29:9
all Judah *r.* at the oath. *2 Chr* 15:15
princes and all the people *r.* 24:10
Hezekiah *r.* and all people. 29:36
of Israel and Judah *r.* 30:25
great sacrifices and *r.*: the wives also, and children *r.* *Neh* 12:43
for Judah *r.* for the priests. 44
the city of Shushan *r.* *Esth* 8:15*
if I *r.* because my wealth. *Job* 31:25
if I *r.* at the destruction of. 29
in mine adversity they *r.* *Ps* 35:15
the daughters of Judah *r.* 97:8
I have *r.* in the way of. 119:14
for my heart *r.* in all. *Eccl* 2:10
I *r.* not in the assembly. *Jer* 15:17
ye *r.* O destroyers of mine. 50:11
the Ammonites *r.* *Ezek* 25:6
the priests that *r.* on it. *Hos* 10:5
nor shouldest thou have *r.* *Ob* 12
the star, they *r.* with joy. *Mat* 2:10
my spirit hath *r.* in God. *Luke* 1:47
they *r.* with Elisabeth. 58
in that hour Jesus *r.* in spirit. 10:21
the people *r.* for the things. 13:17
your father Abraham *r.* to. *John* 8:56
r. in the works of their. *Acts* 7:41
which, when had read, they *r.* 15:31
the jailer *r.* believing in God. 16:34
as though they *r.* not. *1 Cor* 7:30
so that I *r.* the more. *2 Cor* 7:7
I *r.* in the Lord greatly. *Phil* 4:10
I *r.* greatly that I found. *2 John* 4
3 John 3

rejoiceth
My heart *r.* in the Lord. *1 Sam* 2:1
horse *r.* in his strength. *Job* 39:21
and my glory *r.* *Ps* 16:9
and *r.* as a strong man to. 19:5
therefore my heart greatly *r.* 28:7
well with righteous, city *r.* *Pr* 11:10
the light of the righteous *r.* 13:9
light of the eyes *r.* the heart. 15:30
whoso loveth wisdom *r.* his. 29:3
that *r.* shall descend into. *Isa* 5:14
as bridegroom *r.* over bride. 62:5
thou meetest him that *r.* and. 64:5
when the whole earth *r.* *Ezek* 35:14
I say to you, he *r.* more. *Mat* 18:13
bridegroom *r.* greatly. *John* 3:29
r. not in iniquity, but *r.* *1 Cor* 13:6
and mercy *r.* against. *Jas* 2:13*

rejoicest
doest evil, then thou *r.* *Jer* 11:15

rejoicing
come up from thence *r.* *1 Ki* 1:45
burnt offerings with *r.* *2 Chr* 23:18
fill thy lips with *r.* *Job* 8:21*
his statutes are right, *r.* *Ps* 19:8
r. shall they be brought to. 45:15
declare his works with *r.* 107:22*
voice of *r.* is in tabernacle. 118:15
they are the *r.* of my heart. 119:111
doubtless come again with *r.* 126:6
I was his delight, *r.* always. *Pr* 8:30
r. in the habitable part of his. 31
I create Jerusalem a *r.* *Isa* 65:18
word was to me the *r.* *Jer* 15:16
their *r.* was to devour. *Hab* 3:14
this is the *r.* city that. *Zeph* 2:15
it on his shoulders *r.* *Luke* 15:5
r. that they were counted worthy. *Acts* 5:41
eunuch went on his way *r.* 8:39
r. in hope, patient in. *Rom* 12:12
I protest by your *r.* *1 Cor* 15:31
our *r.* is this, testimony. *2 Cor* 1:12*
that we are your *r.* even as ye. 14*
as sorrowful, yet always *r.* 6:10
then shall he have *r.* *Gal* 6:4
that your *r.* may be. *Phil* 1:26*
is our crown of *r.*? *1 Thes* 2:19*
the *r.* of the hope firm. *Heb* 3:6
all such *r.* is evil. *Jas* 4:16*

release
seven years make a *r.* *Deut* 15:1
manner of the *r.*: it is the Lord's *r.* 2
the year of *r.* is at hand. 9
of the year of *r.* in feast. 31:10
he made a *r.* to provinces. *Esth* 2:18

release, *verb*
that lendeth shall *r.* it. *Deut* 15:2
with thy brother, hand shall *r.* 3
was wont to *r.* a prisoner. *Mat* 27:15
Luke 23:17; *John* 18:39
will ye that I *r.* unto you? *Mat* 27:17
21; *Mark* 15:9; *John* 18:39
that he should rather *r.* Barabbas. *Mark* 15:11; *Luke* 23:18
chastise him, and *r.* him. *Luke* 23:16
willing to *r.* Jesus, spake again. 20
I have power to *r.* thee? *John* 19:10
Pilate sought to *r.* him. 12

released
then *r.* he Barabbas to. *Mat* 27:26
Mark 15:15; *Luke* 23:25
now at that feast he *r.* *Mark* 15:6

relied
because they *r.* on the. *2 Chr* 13:18
r. on Syria, and hast not *r.* 16:7

relief
determined to send *r.* *Acts* 11:29

relieve
then thou shalt *r.* him. *Lev* 25:35*
r. the oppressed. *Isa* 1:17
things for meat to *r.* soul. *Lam* 1:11*
the comforter that should *r.* is 16*
while they sought meat to *r.* 19*
widows let them *r.* them; that it may *r.* them that are. *1 Tim* 5:16

relieved
if she have *r.* afflicted. *1 Tim* 5:10

relieveth
he *r.* the fatherless and. *Ps* 146:9*

religion
straitest sect of our *r.* *Acts* 26:5
conversation in Jews' *r.* *Gal* 1:13
profited in the Jews' *r.* above. 14
heart, this man's *r.* is vain. *Jas* 1:26
pure *r.* and undefiled before God. 27

religious
r. proselytes followed. *Acts* 13:43*
among you seem to be *r.* *Jas* 1:26

rely
because thou didst *r.* *2 Chr* 16:8

remain
r. a widow at thy. *Gen* 38:11
that the frogs *r.* in. *Ex* 8:9, 11
let nothing of it *r.* until the. 12:10
nor fat of my sacrifice *r.* 23:18
if the flesh of consecrations *r.* 29:34
if aught *r.* till third day. *Lev* 19:6
that which is sold shall *r.* 25:28
to the years that *r.* 27:18
those which ye let *r.* *Num* 33:55
all, we left none to *r.* *Deut* 2:34
nor shall any of the flesh *r.* 16:4
those which *r.* shall hear and. 19:20
she shall *r.* in thine house. 21:13
his body shall not *r.* all night on. 23
and cattle shall *r.* *Josh* 1:14*
neither did there *r.* any more. 2:11
let none of them *r.* 8:22; 10:28, 30

y lot these nations that r. Josh 23:4
mong these nations that r. 7
e cleave to these nations that r. 12
why did Dan r. in ships ? Judg 5:17
wives for them that r. 21:7, 16
halt r. by the stone. 1 Sam 20:19
ix months did Joab r. 1 Ki 11:16
ven I only, r. a prophet of. 18:22*
ve of the horses that r. 2 Ki 7:13
or we r. yet escaped. Ezra 9:15*
hall he r. in the tomb. Job 21:32*
hose that r. of him shall. 27:15
he beasts go to dens and r. 37:8
would I r. in wilderness. Ps 55:7*
erfect shall r. in the land. Pr 2:21
hall r. in congregation of. 21:16*
s yet shall he r. at Nob. Isa 10:32*
ighteousness shall r. in the. 32:16*
which r. among the graves. 65:4*
earth shall r. before me, so shall your seed and your name r. 66:22
esidue of them that r. of. Jer 8:3
nd this city shall r. for ever. 17:25
esidue of Jerusalem that r. 24:8
hose will I let r. still in. 27:11
oncerning vessels that r. 19*, 21
he palace shall r. after the. 30:18
ands of men that r. 38:4
one shall r. 42:17; 44:14; 51:62
vil, to leave you none to r. 44:7
one of them shall r. Ezek 7:11
nd they that r. shall be. 17:21
hall fowls of heaven r. 31:13*
will cause the fowls to r. 32:4*
nen to bury those that r. of. 39:14
. ten men in one house. Amos 6:9
elivered those that did r. Ob 14
lying roll shall r. in. Zech 5:4*
ll the families that r. shall. 12:14
n same house r. eating. Luke 10:7
he fragments that r. John 6:12
hat my joy might r. in you. 15:11
hat your fruit should r. 16*
hat the bodies should not r. 19:31
et her r. unmarried. 1 Cor 7:11
f whom the greater part r. 15:6
we which are alive and r. till the coming of the Lord. 1 Thes 4:15*
live and r. shall be caught up. 17*
annot be shaken may r. Heb 12:27
ave heard r. in you. 1 John 2:24*
which r ready to die. Rev 3:2

remainder

hou shalt burn the r. Ex 29:34
he r. shall Aaron and. Lev 6:16
n the morrow also the r. shall. 7:16
ut the r. on the third day shall. 17
neither name nor r. 2 Sam 14:7
he r. of wrath shalt. Ps 76:10

remained

Noah only r. alive, and. Gen 7:23*
nd they that r. fled to the. 14:10
ies, there r. not one. Ex 8:31
here r. not any green thing. 10:15
here r. not one locust in all. 19
. not so much as one chariot. 14:28
. two of the men in. Num 11:26
because he should have r. 35:28
heir inheritance r. in house. 36:12
Og, king of Bashan, r. Deut 3:11
when thou shalt have r. long. 4:25*
he rest who r. entered. Josh 10:20
n Gath there r. Anakims. 11:22
who r. of remnant of giants. 13:12
here r. of Israel seven tribes. 18:2
he Levites which r. of. 21:20, 26*
here r. with Gideon. Judg 7:3
hey which r. were scattered so that two not left. 1 Sam 11:11
David r. in a mountain. 23:14
David and his men r. in the. 24:3*
Tamar r. desolate in. 2 Sam 13:20
Sodomites which r. he. 1 Ki 22:46
Jehu slew all that r. 2 Ki 10:11, 17
nd there r. the grove also. 13:6
hat r., he set Gedaliah. 25:22*
he ark r. in Obed-edom. 1 Chr 13:14
ny wisdom r. with me. Eccl 2:9
hese defenced cities r. Jer 34:7
here r. but wounded men. 37:10
Jeremiah had r. many days in. 16
e r. in the court of the. 21; 38:13
people that r. in the city. 39:9; 52:15

away captive them that r. Jer 41:10
taste r. in him, his scent. 48:11
mighty men have r. in their. 51:30
Lord's anger none r. Lam 2:22
I r. there astonished. Ezek 3:15*
r. no strength in me. Dan 10:8, 17
and I r. there with the kings of. 13
in Sodom it would have r. Mat 11:23
fragments that r. twelve baskets. 14:20; Luke 9:17; John 6:13
beckoned, r. speechless. Luke 1:22
while it r. was it not ? Acts 5:4
forepart stuck fast, and r. 27:41

remainest

thou, O Lord, r. for ever. Lam 5:19*; Heb 1:11*

remaineth

while earth r. seed time. Gen 8:22
which r. to you from. Ex 10:5
that which r. until morning. 12:10
that which r. over lay it up. 16:23
that r. of the flesh and. Lev 8:32
take the meat offering that r. 10:12
do for the tabernacle that r. 16:16*
destroy him that r. Num 24:19*
stones that r. to this day. Josh 8:29
there r. yet much land to be. 13:1
this is land that yet r.: all Geshuri. 2
he made him that r. Judg 5:13*
which stone r. unto. 1 Sam 6:18
Jesse said, There r. yet the. 16:11
ark r. under curtains. 1 Chr 17:1*
my error r. with myself. Job 19:4
answers there r. falsehood. 21:34
in his neck r. strength. 41:22*
he that r. in Jerusalem. Isa 4:3
he that r. in this city. Jer 38:2*
Tyrus every helper that r. 47:4
he that r. and is besieged. Ezek 6:12
so my Spirit r. among. Hag 2:5*
he that r. even he shall. Zech 9:7*
therefore your sin r. John 9:41
it r. that they that have wives be. 1 Cor 7:29*
that which r. is glorious. 2 Cor 3:11
until this day r. the same vail. 14
his righteousness r. for ever. 9:9*
seeing it r. that some. Heb 4:6
there r. therefore a rest to. 9
there r. no more sacrifice for. 10:26
for his seed r. in him. 1 John 3:9*

remaining

the cloud tarried, r. on. Num 9:22*
till none was left r. to Og. Deut 3:3
he left none r. Josh 10:33, 37, 39 40; 11:8
were r. of the families of the. 21:40
be destroyed from r. in the coasts of Israel. 2 Sam 21:5
he left Ahab none r. 2 Ki 10:11
who r. in the chambers. 1 Chr 9:33*
nor shall have any r. Job 18:19
shall not be any r. of. Ob 18
shalt see the Spirit r. John 1:33*

Remaliah

fierce anger of son of R. Isa 7:4
the son of R. hath taken evil. 5
head of Samaria is R.'s son. 9
rejoice in Resin and R.'s son. 8:6

remedy

there was no r. 2 Chr 36:16
he be broken without r. Pr 6:15
be destroyed, and without r. 29:1

remember

did not butler r. Joseph. Gen 40:23
Moses said, R. this day. Ex 13:3
r. sabbath day to keep it holy. 20:8
r. Abraham, Isaac, and Israel. 32:13 Deut 9:27
we r. the fish which we. Num 11:5
r. all the commandments. 15:39
r. and do my commandments. 40
r. that thou wast a servant in the. Deut 5:15; 15:15; 16:12; 24:18, 22
thou shalt r. what the Lord. 7:18
thou shalt r. all the way the. 8:2
r. the Lord giveth thee power. 18
r. how thou provokedst the. 9:7
r. that thou wast a bondman in. 15:15; 16:12; 24:18, 22
r. the day when thou camest. 16:3

r. what the Lord thy God did. Deut 24:9
r. what Amalek did to thee. 25:17
r. the days of old, consider. 32:7
r. word which Moses. Josh 1:13
r. that I am your bone. Judg 9:2
Abigail said, Then r. 1 Sam 25:31
let the king r. the Lord. 2 Sam 14:11
neither do thou r. what thy. 19:19
r. when I and thou rode. 2 Ki 9:25
r. how I have walked before thee. 20:3; Isa 38:3
r. his marvellous works. 1 Chr 16:12; Ps 105:5
r. the mercies of David. 2 Chr 6:42
r. the word thou. Neh 1:8
r. the Lord, which is great. 4:14
r. them that have defiled. 13:29
r. who ever perished ? Job 4:7
O r. that my life is wind. 7:7
r. that thou hast made me. 10:9
r. it as waters that pass. 11:16
r. that thou magnify his work. 36:24
hand upon him, r. the battle. 41:8
r. all thy offerings and. Ps 20:3
will r. the name of the Lord. 7*
all ends of the world shall r. 22:27
r. thy mercies, they have. 25:6
r. not the sins of my youth, r. thou. 7
r. thy congregation which thou. 74:2
r. this, that the enemy hath. 18
r. how the foolish man. 22
O r. not against us former. 79:8
r. how short my time is. 89:47
r. Lord the reproach of thy. 50
and to those that r. his. 103:18
r. the word unto thy servant. 119:49
Lord, r. David, and all his. 132:1
r. O Lord, children of Edom. 137:7
let him drink, and r. his. Pr 31:7
not much r. the days. Eccl 5:20
let him r. days of darkness. 11:8
r. now thy Creator in the days. 12:1
we will r. thy love. S of S 1:4*
r. ye not the former things ? Isa 43:18; 46:9
own sake I will not r. thy sins. 43:25
r. these, O Jacob and Israel. 44:21
r. this, and shew yourselves. 46:8
neither didst r. the latter end. 47:7
shalt not r. the reproach of. 54:4
meetest those that r. thee. 64:5
not wroth, neither r. iniquity. 9
neither shall they r. it. Jer 3:16
he will now r. their iniquity. 14:10
r., break not thy covenant with. 21
their children r. their altars. 17:2
r. that I stood before thee. 18:20
I do earnestly r. him still. 31:20
did not the Lord r. them ? 44:21
escaped, r. the Lord afar off. 51:50
r. O Lord, what is come. Lam 5:1
then shalt r. thy ways. Ezek 16:61 20:43; 36:31
mayest r. and be confounded. 16:63
shalt not r. Egypt any more. 23:27
will he r. their iniquity. Hos 8:13
therefore he will r. iniquity. 9:9
r. now what Balak. Mi 6:5
in wrath r. mercy. Hab 3:2
r. the law of Moses my. Mal 4:4
neither r. the five loaves. Mat 16:9 Mark 8:18
sir, we r. that deceiver. Mat 27:63
to r. his holy covenant. Luke 1:72
r. that thou in thy lifetime. 16:25
r. Lot's wife. 17:32
r. how he spake to you. 24:6
r. the word that I said. John 15:20
time shall come ye may r. 16:4
r. that by the space of. Acts 20:31
r. words of the Lord Jesus, how. 35
would that we should r. Gal 2:10
r. that ye being in time. Eph 2:11
r. my bonds. Grace be. Col 4:18
for ye r. brethren our. 1 Thes 2:9
r. ye not that I told ? 2 Thes 2:5
r. that Jesus Christ. 2 Tim 2:8
r. them that are in bonds. Heb 13:3
r. them which have the rule over. 7
r. the words spoken of. Jude 17
r. from whence thou art fallen. Rev 2:5
r. how thou hast received. 3:3

I remember

saying, *I* do *r.* my faults. *Gen* 41:9
I r. that which Amalek. *1 Sam* 15:2*
when *I r.* I am afraid. *Job* 21:6
when *I r.* these, I pour. *Ps* 42:4
when *I r.* thee upon my bed. 63:6
if *I* do not *r.* thee, let my. 137:6
I r. the days of old, I muse. 143:5
I r. thee, the kindness of. *Jer* 2:2
consider not that *I r.* all. *Hos* 7:2

I will remember

I will r. my covenant. *Gen* 9:15, 16
Lev 26:42; *Ezek* 16:60
I will for their sakes *r.* *Lev* 26:45
therefore *will I r.* thee. *Ps* 42:6
but *I will r.* the years of the. 77:10
I will r. the works, *I will r.* thy. 11*
I will r. their sin no more. *Jer* 31:34
Heb 8:12; 10:17
I will r. his deeds which. *3 John* 10

remember me

r. me, that I may be. *Judg* 16:28
handmaid, and *r. me.* *1 Sam* 1:11
r. me, O God. *Neh* 13:14, 22, 31
a set time, and *r. me.* *Job* 14:13
r me for thy goodness'. *Ps* 25:7
r. me with the favour that. 106:4
knowest, *r. me,* and visit. *Jer* 15:15
escape of you shall *r. me.* *Ezek* 6:9
r. me in far countries. *Zech* 10:9
Lord, *r. me* when thou comest into thy kingdom. *Luke* 23:42
that ye *r. me* in all. *1 Cor* 11:2

remembered

God *r.* Noah. *Gen* 8:1
God *r.* Abraham. 19:29
God *r.* Rachel. 30:22
Joseph *r.* the dreams. 42:9
God *r.* his covenant. *Ex* 2:24; 6:5
shall be *r.* before the. *Num* 10:9
children of Israel *r.* not. *Judg* 8:34
the Lord *r.* Hannah. *1 Sam* 1:19
thus Joash *r.* not the. *2 Chr* 24:22
Ahasuerus *r.* Vashti. *Esth* 2:1
days of Purim should be *r.* 9:28
sinner shall be no more *r.* *Job* 24:20
thy name to be *r.* in all. *Ps* 45:17
I *r.* God and was troubled. 77:3
they *r.* that God was their. 78:35
for he *r.* that they were but flesh. 39
they *r.* not his hand, when he. 42
he *r.* his mercy toward the. 98:3
he hath *r.* his covenant for. 105:8
for he *r.* his holy promise. 42
they *r.* not the multitude of. 106:7
he *r.* for them his covenant, and. 45
iniquity of his fathers be *r.* 109:14
because that he *r.* not to shew. 16
wonderful works to be *r.* 111:4
I *r.* thy judgements of old. 119:52
I have *r.* thy name, O Lord. 55
who *r.* us in our low estate. 136:23
we wept, when we *r.* Zion. 137:1
yet no man *r.* that same. *Eccl* 9:15
that thou mayest be *r.* *Isa* 23:16
thou hast not *r.* me, nor laid. 57:11
then he *r.* the days of old. 63:11
heavens shall not be *r.* 65:17
name may be no more *r.* *Jer* 11:19
Jerusalem *r.* in the days. *Lam* 1:7
r. not his footstool in the day. 2:1
his righteousness shall not be *r.*
Ezek 3:20; 33:13
thou hast not *r.* the days. 16:22, 43
your iniquity to be *r.* 21:24
thou shalt be no more *r.* 32
Ammonites may not be *r.* 25:10
they shall no more be *r.* *Hos* 2:17*
Zech 13:2
and *r.* not the brotherly. *Amos* 1:9
fainted, I *r.* the Lord. *Jonah* 2:7
Peter *r.* the words of Jesus.
Mat 26:75; *Luke* 22:61
they *r.* his words, and. *Luke* 24:8
his disciples *r.* that it. *John* 2:17
risen, they *r.* that he had said. 22
was glorified, then they *r.* 12:16
then *r.* I the word of. *Acts* 11:16
hath *r.* her iniquities. *Rev* 18:5

rememberest

the slain whom thou *r.* no. *Ps* 88:5
there *r.* that thy brother. *Mat* 5:23

remembereth

maketh inquisition, he *r.* *Ps* 9:12
frame, he *r.* we are but dust. 103:14
she *r.* not her last end. *Lam* 1:9
she *r.* no more anguish. *John* 16:21
whilst he *r.* the obedience. *2 Cor* 7:15

remembering

r. mine affliction and. *Lam* 3:19
r. without ceasing your. *1 Thes* 1:3

remembrance

I will put out the *r.* *Ex* 17:14
bringing iniquity to *r.* *Num* 5:15
out the *r.* of Amalek. *Deut* 25:19
make the *r.* of them to cease. 32:26
keep my name in *r.* *2 Sam* 18:18
to call my sin to *r.*? *1 Ki* 17:18
his *r.* shall perish from. *Job* 18:17
in death is no *r.* of thee. *Ps* 6:5
give thanks at *r.* of his holiness.
30:4*; 97:12*
to cut off the *r.* of them from. 34:16
a psalm of David, to bring to *r.*
38:*title*; 70:*title*
call to *r.* my song in the night. 77:6
that Israel be no more in *r.* 83:4
thy *r.* unto all generations. 102:12*
righteous in everlasting *r.* 112:6
there is no *r.* of former. *Eccl* 1:11
no *r.* of wise more than fool. 2:16
our soul is to the *r.* of. *Isa* 26:8*
put me in *r.*, let us plead. 43:26
hast thou set up thy *r.* 57:8*
soul hath them still in *r.* *Lam* 3:20
call to *r.* the iniquity. *Ezek* 21:23
I say that ye are come to *r.* 24
calling to *r.* the days of 23:19, 21
bringeth their iniquity to *r.* 29:16
a book of *r.* was written. *Mal* 3:16
Peter calling to *r.* saith. *Mark* 11:21
he hath holpen Israel in *r.* *Luke* 1:54
this do in *r.* of me. 22:19
1 Cor 11:24
bring all things to your *r.* *John* 14:26
thine alms are had in *r.* *Acts* 10:31
who shall bring you into *r.* *1 Cor* 4:17
as oft as ye drink it, in *r.* of. 11:25
God upon every *r.* of you. *Phil* 1:3
good *r.* of us always. *1 Thes* 3:6
put the brethren in *r.* *1 Tim* 4:6*
that I have *r.* of thee. *2 Tim* 1:3
when I call to *r.* the unfeigned. 5*
I put thee in *r.* that thou stir. 6
of these things put them in *r.* 2:14
there is a *r.* of sins. *Heb* 10:3
but call to *r.* the former days. 32
to put you always in *r.* *2 Pet* 1:12
Jude 5
stir you up by putting you in *r.*
2 Pet 1:13
have these things always in *r.* 15
pure minds by way of *r.* 3:1
great Babylon came in *r.* *Rev* 16:19

remembrances

your *r.* are like to ashes. *Job* 13:12

remission

many, for the *r.* of sins. *Mat* 26:28
baptism of repentance for *r.* of sins.
Mark 1:4; *Luke* 3:3
salvation by *r.* of sins. *Luke* 1:77
that *r.* should be preached in. 24:47
baptized for *r.* of sins. *Acts* 2:38
believeth shall receive *r.* of. 10:43
for the *r.* of sins that. *Rom* 3:25*
shedding of blood is no *r.* *Heb* 9:22
where *r.* is, there no more. 10:18

remit, -ed

sins ye *r.* they are *r.* *John* 20:23*

remnant

the *r.* of meat offering. *Lev* 2:3
r. shall be the priest's as. 5:13
the *r.* of the oil that is. 14:18
only Og remained of *r.* of giants.
Deut 3:11; *Josh* 12:4; 13:12
his eye evil toward *r.* *Deut* 28:54
if ye cleave to the *r.* of. *Josh* 23:12
Gibeonites were of *r.* *2 Sam* 21:2
speak to the *r.* of the. *1 Ki* 12:23
I will take away the *r.* of. 14:10
r. of Sodomites, Jehoshaphat. 22:46
lift up thy prayer for the *r.*
2 Ki 19:4; *Isa* 37:4
the *r.* that is escaped shall yet tak
root. *2 Ki* 19:30; *Isa* 37:3
shall go forth a *r.* *2 Ki* 19:3
Isa 37:3
I will forsake the *r.* of. *2 Ki* 21:1
the *r.* did Nebuzar-adan. 25:1
he will return to the *r.* *2 Chr* 30:
the *r.* of their brethren. *Ezra* 3:
Lord to leave us a *r.* to escape. 9:
so that there should be no *r.* 1
the *r.* that are left of the. *Neh* 1:
the *r.* of them the fire. *Job* 22:2
had left us a very small *r.* *Isa* 1:
set his hand, to recover the *r.* 11:1
an highway for the *r.* of his. 1
cut off from Babylon the *r.* 14:2
and he shall slay thy *r.* 3
I will bring lions on the *r.* of. 15:
the *r.* shall be very small. 16:1
shall cease from *r.* of Syria. 17:
hearken, all the *r.* of the house. 46:
glean the *r.* of Israel. *Jer* 6:
there shall be no *r.* of them. 11:2
it shall be well with thy *r.* 15:1
will gather the *r.* of my flock. 23:
the *r.* of Ashdod did drink of. 25:2
O Lord, save thy people, the *r.* 31:
Nebuzar-adan carried away *r.* 39:
king of Babylon had left a *r.* 40:1
Jews be scattered, and *r.* of. 1
Johanan took the *r.* 41:16; 43:
the Lord, even for all this *r.* 42:
word of Lord, ye *r.* of Judah. 1
O ye *r.* of Judah, go ye not. 1
I will take the *r.* of Judah. 44:1
so that none of the *r.* of Judah. 1
the *r.* shall know whose words. 2
Lord will spoil *r.* of country of. 47:
Ashkelon is cut off, with the *r.*
the whole *r.* of thee. *Ezek* 5:1
yet will I leave a *r.* that ye. 6:
make an end of the *r.*? 11:1
therein shall be left a *r.* 14:2
and thy *r.* shall fall by the. 23:2
I will destroy the *r.* of the. 25:1
in the *r.* whom the Lord. *Joel* 2:3
the *r.* of the Philistines. *Amos* 1:
God will be gracious to the *r.* 5:1
that they may possess the *r.* of. 9:1
I will surely gather the *r.* *Mi* 2:1
make her that halted, a *r.* 4:
the *r.* of his brethren shall. 5:
the *r.* of Jacob, in the midst.
the *r.* of Jacob shall be among.
the transgression of the *r.* 7:1
the *r.* of the people shall. *Hab* 2:
and I will cut off the *r.* *Zeph* 1:
for the *r.* of house of Judah. 2:
the *r.* of my people shall possess.
the *r.* of Israel shall not do. 3:1
all the *r.* of the people. *Hag* 1:1
stirred up the spirit of the *r.* 1
marvellous in eyes of *r.* *Zech* 8:
I will cause *r.* of this people. 1
the *r.* took his servants. *Mat* 22:
Esaias also crieth, a *r.* *Rom* 9:2
at this time also there is a *r.* 11:5
the *r.* were affrighted. *Rev* 11:1
to make war with the *r.* 12:1
the *r.* were slain with the. 19:2

remove

father's hand to *r.* it. *Gen* 48:1
inheritance of Israel *r.* *Num* 36:7,
shalt not *r.* thy neighbour's land.
Deut 19:14
then ye shall *r.* from. *Josh* 3:
then would I *r.* Abimelech. *Judg* 9:2
so David would not *r.* *2 Sam* 6:1
the Lord said, I will *r.* *2 Ki* 23:2
came on Judah, to *r.* them. 24:
I any more *r.* Israel. *2 Chr* 33:
some *r.* the landmarks. *Job* 24:
I will not *r.* mine integrity. 27:5
of the wicked *r.* me. *Ps* 36:11
r. thy stroke away from me. 39:1
r. from me reproach. 119:22
r. from me the way of lying, and. 2
turn not, *r.* thy foot from. *Pr* 4:2
r. thy way far from her, and. 5:
r. not the ancient landmark. 22:2
23:1
r. from me vanity and lies. 30:
therefore *r.* sorrow. *Eccl* 11:1

he earth shall r. out of. *Isa* 13:13*
rom his place shall he not r. 46:7
hen shalt thou not r. *Jer* 4:1
rophesy a lie, to r. you far. 27:10
hat I should r. it from. 32:31
hey shall r., they shall depart. 50:3*
. out of the midst of Babylon. 8*
. by day, thou shalt r. *Ezek* 12:3
aith the Lord, R. the diadem. 21:26
. violence and spoil. 45:9
hey were like them that r. *Hos* 5:10
out I will r. the northern. *Joel* 2:20
hat ye might r. them from their. 3:6
e shall not r. your necks. *Mi* 2:3
will r. the iniquity of. *Zech* 3:9
alf the mountain shall r. 14:4
. hence, and it shall r. *Mat* 17:20
. this cup from me. *Luke* 22:42
aith, so that I could r. *1 Cor* 13:2
or else I will r. thy candlestick. *Rev* 2:5*

removed

(*In speaking of the journeying in the wilderness the Revisions have changed this word to* journeyed)
Noah r. the covering. *Gen* 8:13
Abram r. to Rehoboth. 12:8
Isaac r. from thence. 26:22
Jacob r. the he goats that. 30:35
and Joseph r. the people to. 47:21
the Lord r. the swarms. *Ex* 8:31
the angel of God r. and went. 14:19
the people saw it and r. and. 20:18*
people r. from Hazeroth. *Num* 12:16
they r. and pitched in the. 21:12, 13
Israel r. from Rameses. 33:5
they r. from Etham. 7, 9, 10
they r. from the Red sea. 11
r. from Alush. 14
r. from the desert of Sinai. 16
r. from Libnah. 21
r. from mount Shapher. 24
r. from Haradah. 25
r. from Makheloth. 26
r. from Tarah. 28
r. from Bene-jaakan. 32
r. from Jotbathah. 34
they r. from Ezion-gaber. 36
r. from Kadesh. 37
r. from Dibon-gad. 46
r. from Almon-diblathaim. 47
r. into all kingdoms. *Deut* 28:25*
they r. from Shittim. *Josh* 3:1
when the people r. to pass over. 14
hand is not r. from you. *1 Sam* 6:3
Saul r. David from him. 18:13
he r. Amasa out of. *2 Sam* 20:12*
Asa r. the idols. *1 Ki* 15:12
Maachah his mother, he r. from being queen. 13; *2 Chr* 15:16
the high places were not r. *1 Ki* 15:14*; *2 Ki* 15:4, 35
Ahaz r. the laver. *2 Ki* 16:17
Lord r. Israel out of his sight. 17:18, 23; 23:27
nations which thou hast r. 17:26*
Hezekiah r. the high places. 18:4
r. the burnt offerings. *2 Chr* 35:12
and the rock is r. out. *Job* 14:18
shall the rock be r. out? 18:4
and mine hope hath he r. 19:10*
so would he have r. thee. 36:16*
though the earth be r. *Ps* 46:2*
I r. his shoulder from. 81:6
so far hath he r. our. 103:12
it should not be r. for ever. 104:5*
Zion, which cannot be r. 125:1*
shall never be r. *Pr* 10:30
till the Lord have r. men. *Isa* 6:12
I have r. the bounds of. 10:13
Madmenah is r.: the inhabitants. 31*
in the sure place shall be r. 22:25*
the earth shall be r. like. 24:20*
thou hast r. it far to all ends. 26:15*
but have r. their heart far. 29:13
teachers be r. to a corner. 30:20*
of the stakes shall be r. 33:20*
mine age is r. from me as. 38:12*
the hills shall be r.: my kindness . . . shall not be r. saith. 54:10
I will cause them to be r. *Jer* 15:4*
I will deliver them to be r. 24:9*
29:18*; 34:17*
sinned, therefore she is r. *Lam* 1:8*
and thou hast r. my soul far. 3:17
their gold shall be r. *Ezek* 7:19*
I will give them to be r. and. 23:46*
uncleanness of a r. woman. 36:17*
banquet of them shall be r. *Amos* 6:7*
how hath he r. it from me! *Mi* 2:4
day shall the decree be far r. 7:11
if ye shall say, Be thou r. *Mat* 21:21*; *Mark* 11:23*
he r. Abraham into this land. *Acts* 7:4
when he had r. him, he raised. 13:22
are so soon r. from him. *Gal* 1:6

removeth

cursed be he that r. his neighbour's landmark. *Deut* 27:17
which r. the mountains. *Job* 9:5
he r. away the speech of the. 12:20
whoso r. stones shall be. *Eccl* 10:9*
seasons, he r. kings. *Dan* 2:21

removing

r. from thy flock all the. *Gen* 30:32
seeing I am a captive r. *Isa* 49:21*
prepare the stuff for r. *Ezek* 12:3, 4
signifieth the r. of those. *Heb* 12:27

Remphan

star of your god R. *Acts* 7:43

rend

that ephod should not r. *Ex* 39:23
neither r. your clothes. *Lev* 10:6
priest shall r. the plague out. 13:56
I will surely r. the kingdom. *1 Ki* 11:11; 12:31
howbeit, I will not r. away. *1 Ki* 11:13
I will r. the kingdom. 31; 14:8
didst r. thy clothes. *2 Chr* 34:27
a time to r. and a time. *Eccl* 3:7
oh! that thou wouldest r. *Isa* 64:1
wind shall r. it. *Ezek* 13:11, 13
thou didst break and r. all. 29:7
and I will r. the caul. *Hos* 13:8
r. your heart, and not. *Joel* 2:13
turn again and r. you. *Mat* 7:6
let us not r. it, but cast. *John* 19:24

render

every offering they r. *Num* 18:9
I will r. vengeance to. *Deut* 32:41
he will r. vengeance to his. 43
evil of men of Shechem did God r. upon their heads. *Judg* 9:57*
Lord r. to every man. *1 Sam* 26:23
r. to every man according to his. *2 Chr* 6:30
for he will r. unto man. *Job* 33:26*
of a man shall he r. to him. 34:11
r. to them their desert. *Ps* 28:4
they that r. evil for good. 38:20
I will r. praises unto thee. 56:12
and r. to our neighbour. 79:12
lift up thyself, r. a reward. 94:2
what shall I r. to the Lord? 116:12
and shall not he r. to every man? *Pr* 24:12; *Rom* 2:6
say not, I will r. to man. *Pr* 24:29
than seven men that can r. 26:16
Lord will come, to r. his. *Isa* 66:15
he will r. to Babylon. *Jer* 51:6, 24
r. to them a recompence. *Lam* 3:64
so will we r. the calves. *Hos* 14:2
will ye r. me a recompence? *Joel* 3:4
I declare, that I will r. *Zech* 9:12
r. him the fruits in. *Mat* 21:41
r. unto Caesar. 22:21; *Mark* 12:17 *Luke* 20:25
r. therefore to all their. *Rom* 13:7
let husband r. to wife. *1 Cor* 7:3
what thanks can we r.? *1 Thes* 3:9
see that none r. evil for evil. 5:15

rendered

thus God r. wickedness. *Judg* 9:56*
the king of Moab r. to. *2 Ki* 3:4
Hezekiah r. not. *2 Chr* 32:25
man's hands be r. to him. *Pr* 12:14

renderest

r. to every man according. *Ps* 62:12

rendereth

a voice of the Lord that r. *Isa* 66:6

rendering

not r. evil for evil, or. *1 Pet* 3:9

rendest

though thou r. thy face. *Jer* 4:30

rending

lest he tear my soul, r. *Ps* 7:2

renew

r. the kingdom there. *1 Sam* 11:14
and r. a right spirit. *Ps* 51:10
that wait on Lord shall r. *Isa* 40:31
the people r. their strength. 41:1
O Lord, r. our days. *Lam* 5:21
if they fall away, to r. *Heb* 6:6

renewed

Asa r. the altar. *2 Chr* 15:8
and my bow was r. *Job* 29:20
so that thy youth is r. *Ps* 103:5
inward man is r. day. *2 Cor* 4:16
and be r. in the spirit. *Eph* 4:23
the new man, which is r. *Col* 3:10

renewest

thou r. thy witnesses. *Job* 10:17
and thou r. the face. *Ps* 104:30

renewing

be transformed by the r. *Rom* 12:2
he saved us by the r. *Tit* 3:5

renounced

have r. the hidden. *2 Cor* 4:2

renown

giants of old, men of r. *Gen* 6:4
in congregation, men of r. *Num* 16:2
thy r. went forth among. *Ezek* 16:14
harlot because of thy r. 15
raise up for them a plant of r. 34:29
it shall be to them a r. 39:13
and hast gotten thee r. *Dan* 9:15

renowned

these were the r. of. *Num* 1:16*
evildoers shall never be r. *Isa* 14:20*
and great lords, and r. *Ezek* 23:23
the r. city which was strong. 26:17

rent, *substantive*

a girdle there shall be a r. *Isa* 3:24*
and the r. is made worse. *Mat* 9:16; *Mark* 2:21
the new maketh a r. *Luke* 5:36

rent, *verb*

Joseph is without doubt r. in pieces. *Gen* 37:33
ephod, that it be not r. *Ex* 28:32
bottles, old and r. *Josh* 9:4, 13
Samson r. the lion as he would have r. a kid, and he had. *Judg* 14:6
Saul r. the skirt of. *1 Sam* 15:27
Lord hath r. the kingdom. 28; 28:17
Tamar r. her garment. *2 Sam* 13:19
Hushai came with his coat r. 15:32
the earth r. with the. *1 Ki* 1:40
Ahijah r. Jeroboam's new. 11:30
the altar shall be r. 13:3
altar was r. 5
and a strong wind r. the. 19:11
he r. Israel from the. *2 Ki* 17:21
when I heard this, I r. *Ezra* 9:3
having r. my garment and my. 5
then Job arose, and r. *Job* 1:20
Job's friends r. every one. 2:12
and the cloud is not r. under. 26:8
were not afraid, nor r. *Jer* 36:24
and No shall be r. *Ezek* 30:16
veil of temple was r. in twain. *Mat* 27:51; *Mark* 15:38; *Luke* 23:45
spirit cried, and r. him. *Mark* 9:26
see **clothes**

repaid

righteous, good shall be r. *Pr* 13:21

repair

let the priests r. the breaches of the. *2 Ki* 12:5; 22:5, 6; *2 Chr* 24:4* 34:8, 10
r. ye not the breaches? *2 Ki* 12:7
neither r. the breaches of the. 8
stone to r. the breaches. 12; 22:5, 6
money to r. the house. *2 Chr* 24:5
hired carpenters to r. the house. 12*
reviving to r. the house. *Ezra* 9:9
shall r. the waste cities. *Isa* 61:4

repaired

Benjamin r. cities, and. *Judg* 21:23*
Solomon r. the breaches. *1 Ki* 11:27

Elijah r. the altar of the. *1 Ki* 18:30
the priests had not r. *2 Ki* 12:6
and r. therewith the house of. 14
and Joab r. the rest of. *1 Chr* 11:8
Hezekiah r. the doors of. *2 Chr* 29:3
Hezekiah r. Millo in the. 32:5*
Manasseh r. the altar of. 33:16*
next to them r. *Neh* 3:4, 5, 7, 8
10, 12, 19
after him r. 6, 17, 18, 20, 22, 23, 24

repairer

thou shalt be called the r. *Isa* 58:12

repairing

concerning the r. of. *2 Chr* 24:27*

repay

he will r. him to his face. *Deut* 7:10
who shall r. him that? *Job* 21:31
that I should r. him? 41:11
deeds he will r. fury, and to the islands he will r. *Isa* 59:18
again, I will r. thee. *Luke* 10:35
vengeance is mine, I will r., saith the Lord. *Rom* 12:19
written it, I will r. it. *Philem* 19

repayeth

and r. them that hate. *Deut* 7:10

repeateth

he that r. matter. *Pr* 17:9*

repent

(Repent *or* repentance *is used of regret and sorrow for having done some deed. It is not always used for godly repentance, which means such sorrow as shall cause a complete change of action. Judas repented of his betrayal of Jesus,* Mat 27:8, *but did not change his life. When the word is used in regard to God it is in a figure of speech, which speaks of him almost as if human; and since his actions are changed, attributes to him the feelings which, in a man, would cause such a change*)

lest the people r. *Ex* 13:17
turn from thy fierce wrath, and r. of this. 32:12
man, that he should r. *Num* 23:19
the Lord shall r. for his. *Deut* 32:36
will not r.: for he is not a man, that he should r. *1 Sam* 15:29
if they r. in captivity. *1 Ki* 8:47
I abhor myself, and r. *Job* 42:6
let it r. thee concerning. *Ps* 90:13
and will not r. 110:4; *Heb* 7:21
he will r. himself. *Ps* 135:14
and will not r. *Jer* 4:28
I will r. of the evil. 18:8; 26:13
if it do evil, then I will r. of. 18:10
that I may r. 26:3
for I r. of the evil. 42:10
r. and turn. *Ezek* 14:6; 18:30
spare, neither will I r. 24:14
knoweth if he will return and r.? *Joel* 2:14; *Jonah* 3:9
saying, *R.*, for the kingdom of heaven. *Mat* 3:2; 4:17
Jesus preaching, r. ye. *Mark* 1:15
preached that men should r. 6:12
except ye r. ye shall. *Luke* 13:3, 5
from the dead, they will r. 16:30
thy brother r. forgive him. 17:3, 4
r. and be baptized. *Acts* 2:38
r. ye therefore and be. 3:19
r. of this thy wickedness. 8:22
commandeth all men to r. 17:30
that they should r. and. 26:20
I do not r. though I did r. *2 Cor* 7:8
and r. . . . except thou r. *Rev* 2:5
r. or else I will come unto. 16
space to r. of her fornication. 21
except they r. of their deeds. 22
thou hast received, and r. 3:3
be zealous therefore and r. 19

repentance

r. shall be hid from mine. *Hos* 13:14
bring forth fruits meet for r. *Mat* 3:8; *Luke* 3:8
baptize with water unto r. *Mat* 3:11
to call sinners to r. 9:13; *Mark* 2:17
Luke 5:32
did preach baptism of r. *Mark* 1:4
Luke 3:3; *Acts* 13:24; 19:4
99 which need no r. *Luke* 15:7
that r. and remission of sins. 24:47
God exalted for to give r. *Acts* 5:31
Gentiles granted r. to life. 11:18
Greeks r. towards God. 20:21
and do works meet for r. 26:20
God leadeth thee to r. *Rom* 2:4
calling of God are without r. 11:29
that ye sorrowed to r. *2 Cor* 7:9
godly sorrow worketh r. to. 10
will give them r *2 Tim* 2:25
the foundation of r. *Heb* 6:1
to renew them again to r. 6
found no place of r. though. 12:17
that all should come to r. *2 Pet* 3:9

repented

it r. the Lord, that he. *Gen* 6:6
the Lord r. of the evil. *Ex* 32:14
2 Sam 24:16; *1 Chr* 21:15
Jer 26:19
it r. the Lord because. *Judg* 2:18
Israel r. for Benjamin. 21:6, 15
the Lord r. that he made Saul king. *1 Sam* 15:35
the Lord r. according to. *Ps* 106:45
no man r. him of his. *Jer* 8:6
Lord overthrew, and r. not. 20:16
that I was turned, I r. 31:19
the Lord r. for this. *Amos* 7:3, 6
God r. of the evil that. *Jonah* 3:10
punish you, and I r. not. *Zech* 8:14
because they r. not. *Mat* 11:20
they would have r. long ago. 21; *Luke* 10:13
men of Nineveh shall rise because they r. *Mat* 12:41; *Luke* 11:32
not, but afterward he r. *Mat* 21:29
ye, when ye had seen it, r. not. 32
Judas r. himself, and brought. 27:3
not to be r. of. *2 Cor* 7:10
many that have not r. of the. 12:21
repent, and she r. not. *Rev* 2:21
these plagues, yet r. not. 9:20
neither r. of their murders. 21
blasphemed and r. not. 16:9, 11

repentest

art a gracious God, and r. thee of the evil. *Jonah* 4:2

repenteth

for it r. me that I have. *Gen* 6:7
it r. me that I have set. *1 Sam* 15:11
slow to anger, and r. *Joel* 2:13
over one sinner that r. *Luke* 15:7, 10

repenting

I am weary with r. *Jer* 15:6

repentings

my heart is turned, r. are. *Hos* 11:8

repetitions

use not vain r. as heathen. *Mat* 6:7

Rephaim

Philistines spread themselves in valley of *R.* *2 Sam* 5:18, 22; 23:13
1 Chr 11:15; 14:9
ears in the valley of *R.* *Isa* 17:5

Rephaims

smote the *R.* in Ashteroth. *Gen* 14:5
have I given the land of *R.* 15:20

Rephidim

Israel pitched in *R.* *Ex* 17:1
Num 33:4
fought with Israel in *R.* *Ex* 17:8
they were departed from *R.* 19:2; *Num* 33:15

replenish

and r. the earth. *Gen* 1:28; 9:1

replenished

be r. from the east. *Isa* 2:6*
of Zidon have r. Tyre. 23:2
r. every sorrowful soul. *Jer* 31:25
r., now she is laid waste. *Ezek* 26:2
thou wast r. and made very. 27:25

repliest

O man, who art thou that r. against God? *Rom* 9:20

report

(*Of good report*, of good reputation, Acts 6:3)

to his father their evil r. *Gen* 37:2
shalt not raise a false r. *Ex* 23:1
brought up an evil r. *Num* 13:3
did bring up the evil r. died. 14:3
who shall hear r. of thee. *Deut* 2:2
It is no good r. I hear. *1 Sam* 2:2
it was a true r. I heard. *1 Ki* 10:
2 Chr 9:
matter for an evil r. *Neh* 6:1
and a good r. maketh. *Pr* 15:30
as at the r. concerning Egypt, so . . at the r. of Tyre. *Isa* 23:
vexation only to understand r. 28:19
who hath believed our r.? 53:1
John 12:38; *Rom* 10:1
Babylon hath heard the r. *Jer* 50:43
seven men of honest r. *Acts* 6:
Cornelius was of good r. 10:22
Ananias, having a good r. of. 22:1
by evil r. and good r. as. *2 Cor* 6:
things are of good r. *Phil* 4:
must have a good r. of. *1 Tim* 3:7
elders obtained a good r. *Heb* 11:2
obtained a good r. through faith. 39
Demetrius hath a good r. *3 John* 12

report, *verb*

r. say they, and we will r. it. *Jer* 20:1
he will r. that God is. *1 Cor* 14:25

reported

it is r. among heathen. *Neh* 6:6
be r. to king according to these. 7
also they r. his good deeds. 19
despise their husbands, when it shall be r. *Esth* 1:17
which had the inkhorn, r. *Ezek* 9:11
this saying is commonly r. *Mat* 28:15
r. all that chief priests. *Acts* 4:23
Timotheus was well r. of. 16:2
as we be slanderously r. *Rom* 3:8
it is r. that there is. *1 Cor* 5:1
a widow, well r. of for. *1 Tim* 5:10
that are now r. to you. *1 Pet* 1:12

reproach

[1] *Scorn or derision*, Neh 2:17; 5:9. [2] *Shame or disgrace*, Pr 6:33. [3] *Censure or blame*, Isa 51:7. [4] *Injury, either in word or deed*, 2 Cor 12:10.

rolled away r. of Egypt. *Josh* 5:9
taketh away the r. *1 Sam* 17:26
in great affliction and r. *Neh* 1:3
and turn their r. upon their. 4:4
because of the r. of heathen. 5:9
make me not the r. of the. *Ps* 39:8
save me from r. of him. 57:3
for thy sake I have borne r. 69:7
r. hath broken my heart, I am. 20
let them be covered with r. 71:13
he put them to a perpetual r. 78:66
their r. wherewith they. 79:12
remember the r. of thy servants, how I bear in my bosom the r. 89:50
remove from me r. and. 119:22
r. shall not be wiped away. *Pr* 6:33
and with ignominy cometh r. 18:3
that causeth shame and r. 19:26
strife and r. shall cease. 22:10*
to take away our r. *Isa* 4:1
fear ye not the r. of men. 51:7
not remember the r. of thy. 54:4
an everlasting r. on you. *Jer* 23:40
because I did bear the r. of. 31:19
because we have heard r. 51:51
he is filled full with r. *Lam* 3:30
thou hast heard their r. O Lord. 61
consider and behold our r. 5:1
as at the time of thy r. *Ezek* 16:57
concerning r. of Ammonites. 21:28
nor shalt thou bear r. of the. 36:15
that ye receive no more r. 30
the r. offered by him to cease, without his own r. *Dan* 11:18
and his r. shall his Lord. *Hos* 12:14
not thine heritage to r. *Joel* 2:17
shall bear r. of my people. *Mi* 6:16
I have heard the r. of Moab. *Zeph* 2:8
r. of it was a burden. 3:18
I speak as concerning r. *2 Cor* 11:21*
good report lest fall into r. *1 Tim* 3:7
both labour and suffer r. 4:10*
esteeming the r. of Christ. *Heb* 11:26
without the camp, bearing his r. 13:13

reproach, *verb*
glean, and r. her not. Ruth 2:15
whom king of Assyria hath sent to r.
2 Ki 19:4*, 16; Isa 37:4*, 17*
that they might r. me. Neh 6:13
my heart shall not r. me. Job 27:6
mine enemies r. me. Ps 42:10
the adversary r. me? 74:10
mine enemies r. me all day. 102:8
when men shall r. you. Luke 6:22

a reproach
that were a r. to us. Gen 34:14
and lay it for a r. upon. 1 Sam 11:2
that we be no more a r. Neh 2:17
he that taketh not up a r. Ps 15:3
a r. of men, and despised. 22:6
I was a r. among all mine. 31:11
thou makest us a r. to our. 44:13
a r. to our neighbours. 79:4
he is a r. to his neighbours. 89:41
I became also a r. to them. 109:25
sin is a r. to any people. Pr 14:34
people that were a r. Isa 30:5
word of Lord is to them a r. Jer 6:10
word of Lord was made a r. 20:8
to be a r. and a proverb. 24:9; 29:18
42:18; 44:8, 12
Bozrah shall become a r. and. 49:13
I will make thee a r. Ezek 5:14
Jerusalem shall be a r. and a. 15
I have made thee a r. unto. 22:4
people are become a r. Dan 9:16
no more make you a r. Joel 2:19

my reproach
hath taken away my r. Gen 30:23
the cause of my r. 1 Sam 25:39
plead against me my r. Job 19:5
heard the check of my r. 20:3
when I wept, that was my r. Ps 69:10
known my r. and my shame. 19
turn away my r. which I. 119:39
to take away my r. Luke 1:25

reproached
whom hast thou r.? 2 Ki 19:22*
Isa 37:23*
by thy messengers thou hast r. the.
2 Ki 19:23* Isa 37:24
ten times have ye r. me. Job 19:3
not an enemy that r. me. Ps 55:12
that r. thee, are fallen upon me.
69:9; Rom 15:3
that the enemy hath r. Ps 74:18
have r. thee, O Lord. 79:12
thine enemies have r. O Lord, they
have r. the footsteps. 89:51
have r. my people. Zeph 2:8
r. and magnified themselves. 10
if ye be r. for Christ. 1 Pet 4:14

reproaches
r. of them that reproached thee.
Ps 69:9; Rom 15:3
I have given Israel to r. Isa 43:28*
I take pleasure in r. 2 Cor 12:10*
made a gazingstock by r. Heb 10:33

reproachest
Master, thou r. us also. Luke 11:45

reproacheth
aught presumptuously, r. the Lord.
Num 15:30*
voice of him that r. and. Ps 44:16
how the foolish man r. thee. 74:22
to answer him that r. me. 119:42
Pr 27:11
oppresseth poor r. his Maker.
Pr 14:31; 17:5

reproachfully
smitten me on the cheek r. Job 16:10
none occasion to speak r. Tim 5:14*

reprobate
r. silver shall men call. Jer 6:30*
over them to a r. mind. Rom 1:28
r. concerning the faith. 2 Tim 3:8
to every good work r. Tit 1:16

reprobates
you, except ye be r. 2 Cor 13:5
shall know that we are not r. 6
honest, though we be as r. 7

reproof
astonished at his r. Job 26:11*
urn you at my r. Pr 1:23
ye would none of my r. Pr 1:25
despised my r. 30
my heart depised r. 5:12
but he that refuseth r. erreth. 10:17
but he that hateth r. is brutish. 12:1
he that regardeth r. shall be. 13:18
that regardeth r. is prudent. 15:5
he that hateth r. shall die. 10
heareth the r. of life, abideth. 31
he that heareth r. getteth. 32
r. entereth more into a wise. 17:10*
the rod and r. give wisdom. 29:15
is profitable for r. 2 Tim 3:16

reproofs
in whose mouth are no r. Ps 38:14
r. of instruction are way. Pr 6:23

reprove
r. the words of Rab-shakeh.
2 Ki 19:4*; Isa 37:4*
doth your arguing r.? Job 6:25
do ye imagine to r. words? 26
he will surely r. you if ye. 13:10
will he r. thee for fear of? 22:4
I will not r. thee for burnt. Ps 50:8
I will r. thee, and set them. 21
let him r. me, it shall be an. 141:5
r. not a scorner, lest he. Pr 9:8
and r. one that hath. 19:25
lest he r. thee, and thou be. 30:6
neither r. after the hearing. Isa 11:3†
and r. with equity for the meek. 4†
backslidings shall r. thee. Jer 2:19
let no man strive nor r. Hos 4:4
he will r. the world of. John 16:8*
but rather r. them. Eph 5:11
r., rebuke, exhort with. 2 Tim 4:2

reproved
she was r. Gen 20:16*
Abraham r. Abimelech. 21:25
he r. kings for their sakes.
1 Chr 16:21; Ps 105:14
often r. hardeneth his neck. Pr 29:1
not r. Jeremiah? Jer 29:27*
answer when I am r. Hab 2:1*
Herod being r. by John. Luke 3:19
lest deeds should be r. John 3:20
all things that are r. are. Eph 5:13

reprover
wise r. upon an obedient. Pr 25:12
shalt not be to them a r. Ezek 3:26

reproveth
he that r. God, let him. Job 40:2*
he that r. a scorner. Pr 9:7
scorner loveth not one that r. 15:12
snare for him that r. Isa 29:21

reputation
that is in r. for wisdom. Eccl 10:1*
Gamaliel had in r. among. Acts 5:34*
which were of r. Gal 2:2*
but made himself of no r. Phil 2:7*
therefore, hold such in r. 29*

reputed
wherefore are we r. vile? Job 18:3*
all the inhabitants are r. Dan 4:35

request, -s
desire a r. of you. Judg 8:24
king shall perform the r. 2 Sam 14:15
fulfilled the r. of his servant 22
granted him all his r. Ezra 7:6
what dost thou make r.? Neh 2:4
to make r. before him. Esth 4:8
what is thy r.? 5:3,6; 7:2; 9:12
my people at my r. 7:3
Haman stood up to make r. 7
O that I might have my r.! Job 6:8
hast not withholden r. Ps 21:2
he gave them their r. but. 106:15
r. for a prosperous. Rom 1:10
every prayer making r. Phil 1:4
let your r. be made known. 4:6

requested
earrings that he r. Judg 8:26
Elijah r. that he might. 1 Ki 19:4
Jabez what he r. 1 Chr 4:10
he r. of the prince. Dan 1:8
Daniel r. of the king. 2:49

require
your blood will I r. . . . hand of man
will I r. the life of man. Gen 9:5
of my hand didst thou r. it. 31:39
of my hand shalt thou r. him. 43:9
what doth the Lord r.? Deut 10:12
Mi 6:8
I will r. it of him. Deut 18:19
Lord will surely r. it of thee. 23:21
let Lord himself r. it. Josh 22:23
1 Sam 20:16
but one thing I r. of. 2 Sam 3:13
shall not I r. his blood? 4:11
whatsoever thou shalt r. 19:38
as the matter shall r. 1 Ki 8:59
my Lord r. this thing? 1 Chr 21:3
look on it, and r. it. 2 Chr 24:22
Ezra shall r. of you. Ezra 7:21
to r. of the king a band. 8:22
and r. nothing of them. Neh 5:12
thou wilt not r. it. Ps 10:13
but his blood will I r. at thine hand.
Ezek 3:18, 20; 33:6, 8
and there will I r. your. 20:40
and I will r. my flock at. 34:10
the Jews r. a sign. 1 Cor 1:22*
if need so r., let him do what. 7:36

required
behold, his blood is r. Gen 42:22
such things as they r. Ex 12:36*
business r. haste. 1 Sam 21:8
when he r. they set. 2 Sam 12:20
every day's work r. 1 Chr 16:37
as duty of every day r. 2 Chr 8:14
Ezra 3:4
why hast thou not r. of the? 24:6
yet r. not I the bread. Neh 5:18
she r. nothing but what. Esth 2:15
and sin offering hast thou not r.
Ps 40:6
and they that wasted us, r. 137:3
two things I have r. of thee. Pr 30:7*
who hath r. this at your? Isa 1:12
r. of this generation. Luke 11:50, 51
this night thy soul shall be r. 12:20
of him shall be much r. 48
I might have r. mine own. 19:23
that it should be as they r. 23:24*
it is r. in stewards that. 1 Cor 4:2

requirest
will do all that thou r. Ruth 3:11*

requireth
God r. that which is past. Eccl 3:15*
rare thing that the king r. Dan 2:11

requiring
r. that he might be crucified.
Luke 23:23

requite
Joseph will certainly r. Gen 50:15
do ye thus r. Lord? Deut 32:6
and I will r. you this. 2 Sam 2:6
it may be the Lord will r. me. 16:12
I will r. thee in this. 2 Ki 9:26
beholdest to r. it with. Ps 10:14*
raise me up that I may r. 41:10
God shall surely r. Jer 51:56
let them learn to r. their. 1 Tim 5:4

requited
so God hath r. me. Judg 1:7
r. me evil for good. 1 Sam 25:21*

requiting
judge thy servants by r. 2 Chr 6:23

rereward
standard of Dan was r. Num 10:25
r. came after the ark. Josh 6:9, 13
David passed on in r. 1 Sam 29:2
God will be your r. Isa 52:12
glory of Lord shall be thy r. 58:8

rescue
have none to r. them. Deut 28:31
r. my soul from their. Ps 35:17
and none shall r. him. Hos 5:14

rescued
the people r. Jonathan. 1 Sam 14:45
David r. his two wives. 30:18
came I with an army, and r. him.
Acts 23:27

rescueth
he delivereth and r. and. Dan 6:27

resemblance
this is their r. through. Zech 5:6

resemble
I r. kingdom of God? Luke 13:18*

resembled
each one r. the children. Judg 8:18

reserve
will he *r.* his anger for ever? *Jer* 3:5*
pardon them whom I *r.* 50:20*
to *r.* the unjust to the. *2 Pet* 2:9*

reserved
thou not *r.* a blessing? *Gen* 27:36
the most holy things *r.* *Num* 18:9
r. not to each his wife. *Judg* 21:22*
mother, that she had *r.* *Ruth* 2:18*
David *r.* horses for 100 chariots. *2 Sam* 8:4; *1 Chr* 18:4
wicked is *r.* to the day. *Job* 21:30
which I have *r.* against time. 38:23
but when Paul had appealed to be *r.* *Acts* 25:21*
I have *r.* to myself 7000. *Rom* 11:4*
inheritance *r.* in heaven. *1 Pet* 1:4
delivered them to be *r.* *2 Pet* 2:4
mist of darkness is *r.* for ever. 17
the heavens and earth are *r.* 3:7
r. in everlasting chains. *Jude* 6*
to whom is *r.* the blackness. 13

reserveth
he *r.* to us the weeks of. *Jer* 5:24
r. wrath for his enemies. *Nah* 1:2

residue
locusts shall eat the *r.* *Ex* 10:5
r. of the sons of Kohath. *1 Chr* 6:66
the *r.* of Israel were in. *Neh* 11:20
the *r.* of archers shall. *Isa* 21:17
Lord shall be a diadem to *r.* of. 28:5
I am deprived of the *r.* 38:10
r. thereof he maketh a god. 44:17
shall I make the *r.* thereof. 19
death chosen by all the *r.* *Jer* 8:3
r. of them will I deliver to. 15:9
and the *r.* of Jerusalem. 24:8
saith, concerning the *r.* of. 27:19
Jeremiah sent to *r.* of elders. 29:1
r. of the princes of Babylon. 39:3
Ishmael carried captive the *r.* 41:10
and the *r.* of the people that. 52:15
destroy all *r.* of Israel? *Ezek* 9:8
thy *r.* shall be devoured. 23:25
tread the *r.* of your pastures. 34:18
possession unto *r.* of heathen. 36:3
a derision to the *r.* of the heathen. 4
I spoken against *r.* of heathen. 5
the *r.* in length over against. 48:18
the *r.* shall be for the prince. 21
and stamped the *r.* *Dan* 7:7, 19
r. of my people shall. *Zeph* 2:9
speak to Joshua and the *r.* *Hag* 2:2
I will not be to the *r.* *Zech* 8:11
r. of the people shall not be. 14:2
yet had he *r.* of spirit. *Mal* 2:15
and told it to the *r.* *Mark* 16:13
that the *r.* might seek. *Acts* 15:17

resist
Satan standing at his right hand to *r.* *Zech* 3:1*
that ye *r.* not evil. *Mat* 5:39
shall not be able to *r.* *Luke* 21:15*
not able to *r.* the spirit. *Acts* 6:10*
always *r.* the Holy Ghost as. 7:51
they that *r.* shall receive. *Rom* 13:2*
these also *r.* the truth. *2 Tim* 3:8*
r. the devil and he will. *Jas* 4:7
just, and he doth not *r.* you. 5:6
whom *r.* stedfast in the. *1 Pet* 5:9*

resisted
who hath *r.* his will? *Rom* 9:19*
have not yet *r.* unto blood. *Heb* 12:4

resisteth
whosoever *r.* the power, *r.* ordinance. *Rom* 13:2*
God *r.* the proud. *Jas* 4:6; *1 Pet* 5:5

resolved
I am *r.* what to do, when. *Luke* 16:4

resort
r. ye thither to us, God. *Neh* 4:20
I may continually *r.* *Ps* 71:3
the people *r.* to him. *Mark* 10:1*
whither Jews always *r.* *John* 18:20*

resorted
and Levites *r.* to him. *2 Chr* 11:13
multitudes *r.* to him. *Mark* 2:13
and many *r.* to him. *John* 10:41*
Jesus ofttimes *r.* thither. 18:2
women who *r.* thither. *Acts* 16:13*

respect
(Respect of persons. *Favour or partiality toward the rich or powerful*)
the Lord had *r.* to Abel. *Gen* 4:4
to Cain, he had not *r.* 5
God looked, and had *r.* *Ex* 2:25*
for I will have *r.* unto. *Lev* 26:9
yet have thou *r.* unto the prayer. *1 Ki* 8:28; *2 Chr* 6:19
and the Lord had *r.* *2 Ki* 13:23
is no iniquity nor *r.* of persons with God. *2 Chr* 19:7; *Rom* 2:11 *Eph* 6:9; *Col* 3:25
have *r.* unto covenant. *Ps* 74:20
when I have *r.* to all thy. 119:6
I will have *r.* unto thy ways. 15
I will have *r.* unto thy statutes. 117
yet hath he *r.* unto the lowly. 138:6
not good to have *r.* of persons in judgement. *Pr* 24:23; 28:21
have *r.* to the Holy One. *Isa* 17:7
had *r.* to him that fashioned. 22:11
had no glory in this *r.* *2 Cor* 3:10
not that I speak in *r.* of. *Phil* 4:11
let none judge you in *r.* of. *Col* 2:16
Moses had *r.* to. *Heb* 11:26*
faith with *r.* of persons. *Jas* 2:1
ye have *r.* to him that weareth. 3*
if ye have *r.* to persons, ye. 9
without *r.* of persons. *1 Pet* 1:17

respect, *verb*
shalt not *r.* the person. *Lev* 19:15
Moses said, *R.* not thou. *Num* 16:15
ye shall not *r.* persons in judgement. *Deut* 1:17; 16:19
neither doth God *r.* any person. *2 Sam* 14:14*
nor shall *r.* that which. *Isa* 17:8

respected
they *r.* not the persons. *Lam* 4:16

respecter
God is no *r.* of persons. *Acts* 10:34

respecteth
he *r.* not any that are. *Job* 37:24*
blessed is man that *r.* not. *Ps* 40:4

respite
saw that there was *r.* *Ex* 8:15
Give us seven days' *r.* *1 Sam* 11:3

rest
(*This word includes freedom from oppression by the enemy, and peace of spirit, as well as the ordinary meanings*)
Issachar saw that *r.* was. *Gen* 49:15
to-morrow the *r.* of holy. *Ex* 16:23
the seventh is the sabbath of *r.* 31:15 35:2; *Lev* 16:31; 23:3, 32; 25:4
thee, and I will give thee *r.* *Ex* 33:14
a year of *r.* to the land. *Lev* 25:5
until the Lord have given *r.* *Deut* 3:20; *Josh* 1:13
not as yet come to the *r.* *Deut* 12:9
when he giveth you *r.* from. 10
thy God hath given thee *r.* 25:19
the sole of thy foot have *r.* 28:65
given your brethren *r.* *Josh* 1:15
the land had *r.* from war. 14:15 *Judg* 3:11; 5:31
the Lord gave them *r.* round about. *Josh* 21:44; *2 Chr* 15:15
God hath given *r.* *Josh* 22:4
Lord had given *r.* 23:1
land had *r.* eighty years. *Judg* 3:30
Lord grant you may find *r.* *Ruth* 1:9
shall I not seek *r.* for thee? 3:1
for this man will not be in *r.* till. 18
Lord had given him *r.* *2 Sam* 7:1 *1 Ki* 5:4; 8:56; *2 Chr* 14:6, 7
after that the ark had *r.* *1 Chr* 6:31
man of *r.* and I will give him *r.* 22:9
hath he not given you *r.*? 18
God of Israel hath given *r.* 23:25
to build a house of *r.* 28:2
for his God gave him *r.* *2 Chr* 20:30
but after they had *r.* they. *Neh* 9:28
the Jews had *r.* from. *Esth* 9:16
slept, then had I been at *r.* *Job* 3:13
and there the weary be at *r.* 17
not in safety, neither had I *r.* 26*
shalt take thy *r.* in safety. 11:18
r. together is in the dust. *Job* 17:1
neither is there any *r.* in. *Ps* 38:3
would I fly away and be at *r.* 55:
that thou mayest give him *r.* 94:1
should not enter into my *r.* 95:1
return to thy *r.* O my soul. 116:
arise, O Lord, into thy *r.*, thou. 132:
this is my *r.* for ever, here will. 1
son, he shall give thee *r.* *Pr* 29:1
his heart taketh not *r.* in. *Eccl* 2:2
this hath more *r.* than. 6:
and his *r.* shall be glorious. *Isa* 11:1
give thee *r.* from thy sorrow. 14:
whole earth is at *r.* 7; *Zech* 1:1
Lord said, I will take my *r.* *Isa* 18:
this is *r.* wherewith ye cause. 28:1
in returning and *r.* shall ye. 30:1
find for herself a place of *r.* 34:14
where is the place of my *r.*? 66:
find *r.* for your souls. *Jer* 6:1
return and be in *r.* 30:10*; 46:2
that he may give *r.* to land. 50:3
go to them that are at *r.* *Ezek* 38:11
Nebuchadnezzar was at *r.* *Dan* 4:
for this is not your *r.* *Mi* 2:1
Damascus shall be the *r.* *Zech* 9:
and I will give you *r.* *Mat* 11:2
ye shall find *r.* to your souls. 2
seeking *r.* and. 12:43; *Luke* 11:2
sleep on now, and take your *r.* *Mat* 26:45; *Mark* 14:4
of taking *r.* in sleep. *John* 11:1
what is place of my *r.*? *Acts* 7:4
then had the churches *r.* 9:31
who are troubled *r.* with. *2 Thes* 1:
not enter into my *r.* *Heb* 3:11, 1
being left us of entering into *r.* 4:
have believed do enter into *r.*
if they shall enter into my *r.*
for if Jesus had given them *r.*
remaineth a *r.* to the people of.
he that is entered into his *r.* hath. 1
labour to enter into that *r.* 1
see **no**

rest
Jacob fed *r.* of of Laban's. *Gen* 30:3
the names of the *r.* on. *Ex* 28:1
the *r.* of the blood shall. *Lev* 5:
the *r.* of the oil that. 14:17, 2
beside the *r.* of them. *Num* 31:
being the *r.* of the prey. 32
the *r.* of Gilead gave I. *Deut* 3:1
r. entered into fenced. *Josh* 10:2
r. bowed down to drink. *Judg* 7:
the *r.* have we utterly. *1 Sam* 15:1
the *r.* of the people he delivered to *2 Sam* 10:10; *1 Chr* 19:1
the *r.* fled to Aphek to. *1 Ki* 20:3
and thy children of the *r.* *2 Ki* 4:
Joab repaired the *r.* of. *1 Chr* 11:
Jeduthun and the *r.* chosen. 16:4
the *r.* of the money. *2 Chr* 24:1
nor told it to the *r.* that. *Neh* 2:1
r. of our enemies heard I had. 6:
r. of the people also cast lots. 11:
what have done in the *r.*? *Esth* 9:1
the *r.* to their babes. *Ps* 17:1
r. of trees of his forest. *Isa* 10:1
r. of the land shall give. *Ezek* 45:
should not perish with *r.* *Dan* 2:1
let the *r.* eat the flesh of. *Zech* 11:
r. said, Let us see if. *Mat* 27:4
ye thought for the *r.*? *Luke* 12:2
the eleven and to all the *r.* 24:
said to Peter and the *r.* *Acts* 2:3
of *r.* durst no man join. 5:1
and the *r.*, they escaped all. 27:4
election obtained it, and *r.* *Rom* 11:
r. speak I, not the Lord. *1 Cor* 7:1
r. will I set in order when I. 11:3
not live *r.* of his time to. *1 Pet* 4:
and to the *r.* in Thyatira. *Rev* 2:2
the *r.* that were not killed. 9:2
r. of the dead lived not again. 20:
see **acts**

rest, *verb*
wash your feet, and *r.* *Gen* 18:
ye make them *r.* from. *Ex* 5:
year thou shalt let it *r.* 23:1
seventh day thou shalt *r.* 12; 34:2
and in harvest thou shalt *r.* 34:2
then shall the land *r.* *Lev* 26:3
did not *r.* in your sabbaths. 3

hy maidservant may *r.* *Deut* 5:14
eet of the priests shall *r.* *Josh* 3:13
et it *r.* on the head of. *2 Sam* 3:29
ave caused thee to *r.* from. 7:11
either the birds to *r.* on them. 21:10
he spirit of Elijah doth *r.* *2 Ki* 2:15
e *r.* on thee, in thy. *2 Chr* 14:11*
here the prisoners *r.* *Job* 3:18*
hat he may *r.* till he shall. 14:6
ny flesh shall *r.* in hope. *Ps* 16:9*
Acts 2:26*
. in the Lord, and wait. *Ps* 37:7
od of wicked shall not *r.* on. 125:3
or will he *r.* content. *Pr* 6:35
hy flock to *r.* at noon. *S of S* 1:7
ll of them shall *r.* in the. *Isa* 7:19
he Spirit of the Lord shall *r.* 11:2
hall the hand of the Lord *r.* 25:10
nay cause the weary to *r.* 28:12
creech owl also shall *r.* 34:14
will make my judgement to *r.* 51:4
nter into peace, they shall *r.* 57:2
roubled sea, when it cannot *r.* 20
Jerusalem's sake I will not *r.* 62:1
he Lord caused him to *r.* 63:14
went to cause him to *r.* *Jer* 31:2
ut up into thy scabbard, *r.* 47:6
will cause my fury to *r.* *Ezek* 5:13
16:42; 21:17; 24:13
ause the blessing to *r.* 44:30
or thou shalt *r.* and. *Dan* 12:13
hat I might *r.* in the day. *Hab* 3:16
e will *r.* in love, he will. *Zeph* 3:17
lesert place, and *r.* a. *Mark* 6:31
here, your peace shall *r.* *Luke* 10:6
of Christ may *r.* on me. *2 Cor* 12:9
God did *r.* seventh day. *Heb* 4:4
hey *r.* not day and night. *Rev* 4:8
hat they should *r.* yet for a. 6:11
hat they may *r.* from their. 14:13

rested

he *r.* on seventh day. *Gen* 2:2, 3
Ex 20:11; 31:17
he ark *r.* *Gen* 8:4
ocusts *r.* in Egypt. *Ex* 10:14
he people *r.* on the seventh. 16:30
loud abode, they *r.* *Num* 9:18*, 23*
loud *r.* in the wilderness. 10:12*
when it *r.* he said, Return, O. 36
when spirit *r.* upon them. 11:25, 26
and the land *r.* from. *Josh* 11:23
he chambers *r.* on the. *1 Ki* 6:10
people *r.* on the words. *2 Chr* 32:8
lay of the same *r.* *Esth* 9:17, 18
wherein the Jews *r.* from their. 22
bowels boiled and *r.* not. *Job* 30:27
they *r.* sabbath day. *Luke* 23:56

restest

hou art a Jew, and *r.* in. *Rom* 2:17

resteth

n safety, whereon he *r.* *Job* 24:23
wisdom *r.* in heart of him. *Pr* 14:33
or anger *r.* in the bosom. *Eccl* 7:9
Spirit of God *r.* upon. *1 Pet* 4:14

resting

o search out a *r.* place. *Num* 10:33
nto thy *r.* place. *2 Chr* 6:41
spoil not his *r.* place. *Pr* 24:15
shall dwell in *r.* places *Isa* 32:18
forgotten their *r.* place. *Jer* 50:6

restitution

make full *r.* *Ex* 22:3, 5, 6, 12
his substance shall *r.* be. *Job* 20:18
until the times of the *r.* *Acts* 3:21*

restore

[1] *To give back again,* Gen 20:14; Judg 11:13. [2] *To bring back to the first state or condition,* Gen 40:13; Isa 1:26; Acts 1:6. [3] *To recover, or get again,* 2 Ki 14:25. [4] *To heal or cure,* Mat 12:13.

. the man his wife, and if thou *r.* her. *Gen* 20:7
Pharaoh will *r.* thee to thy. 40:13
o *r.* every man's money. 42:25
e shall *r.* five oxen for. *Ex* 22:1*
ound, he shall *r.* double. 4*
e shall *r.* that which he. *Lev* 6:4
e shall even *r.* it in the principal. 5
killeth a beast, he shall *r.* 24:21*
and *r.* the overplus to whom. 25:27
but if he be not able to *r.* it to. 28*
congregation shall *r.* *Num* 35:25
thou shalt *r.* again. *Deut* 22:2
therefore *r.* those lands. *Judg* 11:13
I will *r.* it. 17:3; *1 Sam* 12:3
1 Ki 20:34
I will *r.* thee all the land. *2 Sam* 9:7
he shall *r.* the lamb fourfold. 12:6
shall house of Israel *r.* me. 16:3
r. all that was hers. *2 Ki* 8:6
r. I pray you, to them. *Neh* 5:11
we will *r.* 12
and his hands shall *r.* *Job* 20:10
laboured for, shall he *r.* 18
r. to me the joy of thy. *Ps* 51:12
if he be found, he shall *r.* *Pr* 6:31
I will *r.* thy judges as. *Isa* 1:26
spoil, and none saith *r.* 42:22
to *r.* the preserved of Israel. 49:6
I will lead and *r.* comforts. 57:18
I will *r.* them to this. *Jer* 27:22
I will *r.* health to thee, and. 30:17
if the wicked *r.* pledge. *Ezek* 33:15
command to *r.* and to. *Dan* 9:25
I will *r.* to you the years. *Joel* 2:25
Elias shall come and *r.* *Mat* 17:11
have taken any thing, I *r.* *Luke* 19:8
Lord, wilt thou *r.* kingdom? *Acts* 1:6
r. such an one in the spirit. *Gal* 6:1

restored

Abimelech *r.* him Sarah. *Gen* 20:14
he *r.* the chief butler to his. 40:21
me he *r.* to mine office, him. 41:13
my money is *r.* and it is in. 42:28
shall not be *r.* to thee. *Deut* 28:31
r. 1100 shekels. *Judg* 17:3, 4
from Israel were *r.* *1 Sam* 7:14
that my hand may be *r.* to me: the king's hand was *r.* *1 Ki* 13:6
son he had *r.* to life. *2 Ki* 8:1, 5
he built and *r.* Elath to Judah. 14:22; *2 Chr* 26:2
r. coast of Israel from. *2 Ki* 14:25
the cities Huram had *r.* *2 Chr* 8:2*
brought to Babylon be *r.* *Ezra* 6:5
I *r.* that which I took not. *Ps* 69:4
but hath *r.* to the debtor. *Ezek* 18:7
violence, hath not *r.* pledge. 12
hand was *r.* whole like as the.
Mat 12:13; *Mark* 3:5; *Luke* 6:10
his sight was *r.* and he. *Mark* 8:25
that I may be *r.* to you. *Heb* 13:19

restorer

he shall be to thee a *r.* *Ruth* 4:15
shall be called *r.* of paths. *Isa* 58:12

restoreth

he *r.* my soul, he leadeth. *Ps* 23:3
Elias cometh first and *r.* *Mark* 9:12

restrain

dost thou *r.* wisdom? *Job* 15:8†
wrath shalt thou *r.* *Ps* 76:10*

restrained

rain from heaven was *r.* *Gen* 8:2
and now nothing will be *r.* 11:6*
Sarai said, Lord hath *r.* me. 16:2
were *r.* from bringing. *Ex* 36:6
sons vile, and he *r.* not. *1 Sam* 3:13
toward me, are they *r.*? *Isa* 63:15
I *r.* the floods thereof. *Ezek* 31:15
these sayings, scarce *r.* *Acts* 14:18

restrainest

thou *r.* prayer before God. *Job* 15:4

restraint

there is no *r.* to the Lord. *1 Sam* 14:6

rests

he made narrowed *r.* *1 Ki* 6:6*

resurrection

(*The rising from the dead and living again was a belief which was held by many Israelites, although it was not universal. It was a more important article of faith among the Christians, as Paul argued in* 1 Cor 15)

Sadducees, who say there is no *r.*
Mat 22:23; *Mark* 12:18
Acts 23:8; *1 Cor* 15:12
in the *r.* whose wife? *Mat* 22:28
Mark 12:23; *Luke* 20:33
in the *r.* they neither. *Mat* 22:30
as touching the *r.* have ye? 31
out of the graves after his *r.* 27:53
recompensed at the *r.* *Luke* 14:14
deny any *r.* 20:27
the children of the *r.* 36
good to the *r.* of life: evil, to the *r.* of damnation. *John* 5:29
brother shall rise in the *r.* 11:24
Jesus said, I am the *r.* and the. 25
witness with us of his *r.* *Acts* 1:22
David spake of *r.* of Christ. 2:31
preached through Jesus the *r.* 4:2
witness of the *r.* of the Lord. 33
he preached Jesus and the *r.* 17:18
heard of the *r.*, some mocked. 32
of the hope and *r.* I am called. 23:6
shall be a *r.* of the dead. 24:15
Touching *r.* of the dead. 21
declared by the *r.* from. *Rom* 1:4
in the likeness of his *r.* 6:5
but if there be no *r.* of. *1 Cor* 15:13
by man came the *r.* 21
so is the *r.* of the dead. 42
know the power of his *r.* *Phil* 3:10
if I might attain to the *r.* of. 11
that the *r.* is past. *2 Tim* 2:18
of *r.* from the dead, and. *Heb* 6:2
they might obtain a better *r.* 11:35
hope, by *r.* of Jesus. *1 Pet* 1:3
save us, by *r.* of Jesus Christ. 3:21
this is the first *r.* *Rev* 20:5
he that hath part in the first *r.* 6

retain

still *r.* thine integrity? *Job* 2:9*
he said, Let thine heart *r.* *Pr* 4:4
strong men *r.* riches. 11:16†
no man hath power to *r.* *Eccl* 8:8
she shall not *r.* the power. *Dan* 11:6
whose soever sins ye *r.* *John* 20:23
did not like to *r.* God. *Rom* 1:28*

retained

Gideon *r.* those 300. *Judg* 7:8
the damsel's father *r.* him. 19:4
and I *r.* no strength. *Dan* 10:8, 16
sins ye retain, they are *r.* *John* 20:23
whom I would have *r.* *Philem* 13

retaineth

every one that *r.* her. *Pr* 3:18
gracious woman *r.* honour. 11:16†
he *r.* not his anger for ever. *Mi* 7:18

retire

hottest battle, and *r.* *2 Sam* 11:15
toward Zion: *r.*, stay not. *Jer* 4:6*

retired

Israel *r.* in battle. *Judg* 20:39*
they *r.* from the city. *2 Sam* 20:22*

return, *substantive*

meet Abram after his *r.* *Gen* 14:17
Samuel's *r.* was to. *1 Sam* 7:17
at *r.* of year Syria. *1 Ki* 20:22, 26

return

(*Frequently means* turn again, *or* repent)

till thou *r.* to the ground: for dust thou art . . . thou *r.* *Gen* 3:19
r. to thy mistress and. 16:9
I will certainly *r.* to thee. 18:10, 14
r. to land of thy kindred. 31:3, 13
Lord, which saidst unto me, *R.* 32:9
let me *r.* to my brethren. *Ex* 4:18
Lord said unto Moses, Go *r.* 19
lest people repent, and *r.* to. 13:17
shall *r.* to his possession. *Lev* 25:10
13, 27, 28
r. unto his own family. 41
the field shall *r.* to him. 27:24
r. Lord, to the many thousands. *Num* 10:36
let us make a captain, and *r.* 14:4
the Lord said, *R.* unto Balak. 23:5
then afterward ye shall *r.* 32:22
slayer shall *r.* into the land of his. 35:28; *Josh* 20:6
r. every man to his possesssion. *Deut* 3:20; *Josh* 1:15
cause people *r.* to Egypt. *Deut* 17:16
let him *r.* to his house. 20:5, 6, 7, 8
God will *r.* and gather thee. 30:3
thou shalt *r.* and obey the voice. 8
now *r.* ye, and get you. *Josh* 22:4
saying, *R.* with much riches. 8
and afraid, let him *r.* *Judg* 7:3
when I *r.* from the children of. 11:31

she might r. from Moab. *Ruth* 1:6
Naomi said, Go, r. to her mother's. 8
surely he will r. with thee to. 10
r. thou after thy sister in law. 15
r. him trespass offering. *1 Sam* 6:3
jewels of gold which ye r. him. 8
Saul said, Come, let us r. 9:5
said Saul, *R.* my son David. 26:21
said, Make this fellow r. 29:4, 7
ere thou bid people r.? *2 Sam* 2:26
said Abner to him, Go, r. 3:16
till beards be grown, then r. 10:5
1 Chr 19:5
goest thou also with us? r.
2 Sam 15:19
I go whither I may, r. thou. 20
if thou r. to the city and say. 34
they said, *R.* thou and all thy. 19:14
see what answer I shall r. 24:13
shall r. his blood. *1 Ki* 2:32, 33
Lord shall r. thy wickedness. 44
so r. to thee with all their. 8:48
R. every man to his house. 12:24
kingdom r. to the house of David. 26
go, r. on thy way to the. 19:15
let them r. every man to his house.
22:17; *2 Chr* 11:4; 18:16
r. at all in peace. *1 Ki* 22:28
2 Chr 18:27
offended, r. from me. *2 Ki* 18:14
king of Assyria shall r. to his own land. 19:7, 33; *Isa* 37:7, 34
let the shadow r. *2 Ki* 20:10
shall r. and confess. *2 Chr* 6:24
if they r. to thee with all their. 38
that we may r. answer to. 10:9
fellow in the prison until I r. 18:26
he will r. to you. 30:6
if ye r. unto him. 9
said, When wilt thou r.? *Neh* 2:6
whence ye shall r. unto us. 4:12
r. Mordecai this answer. *Esth* 4:15
device r. upon his own head. 9:25
naked shall I r. thither. *Job* 1:21
r. yea, r. again, my. 6:29
he shall r. no more to his. 7:10
shall r. out of darkness. 15:22
as for you all, do ye r. and. 17:10
if thou r. to the Almighty. 22:23
he shall r. to the days of his. 33:25
commandeth that they r. from. 36:10
r. O Lord, deliver my soul. *Ps* 6:4
let mine enemies r. and be. 10
for their sakes therefore r. 7:7
his mischief shall r. upon his. 16
they r. at evening. 59:6
and let them r. 14
therefore his people r. hither. 73:10
let not oppressed r. ashamed. 74:21
r. we beseech thee, O God. 80:14
thou sayest, *R.* ye children. 90:3
r. O Lord, how long? 13
judgement shall r. unto. 94:15
they die, and r. to their dust. 104:29
r. to thy rest, O my soul. 116:7
none that go unto her r. *Pr* 2:19
a stone, it will r. on him. 26:27
whence rivers come, thither they r.
Eccl 1:7
naked shall he r. to go as he. 5:15
nor the clouds r. after the rain. 12:2
dust shall r. to the earth, and spirit r. to God. 7
r. r. O Shulamite, r. r. *S of S* 6:13
yet in it a tenth shall r. *Isa* 6:13
remnant shall r. to God. 10:21, 22
watchman said . . . *R.*, come. 21:12
the ransomed of the Lord shall r.
35:10; 51:11
r. unto me, for I have. 44:22
r. for thy servant's sake. 63:17
r. to her again? yet r. *Jer* 3:1
R. thou backsliding Israel. 12
r. ye backsliding children. 22
if thou wilt r., r. unto me. 4:1
I will r. and have compassion. 12:15
if thou r. let them r. unto thee, but r. not thou unto them. 15:19
r. ye every one from. 18:11; 35:15
for he shall r. no more. 22:10
that none doth r. from his. 23:14
shall r. with their whole heart. 24:7
and Jacob shall r. 30:10; 46:27
great company shall r. thither. 31:8

that ye may r., every man. *Jer* 36:3
it may be they will r. every. 7
Pharaoh's army shall r. to. 37:7
that they should r. into . . . for none shall r. but such. 44:14, 28
none shall r. in vain. 50:9
when Sodom and Samaria shall r. . . . daughters shall r. *Ezek* 16:55
wicked should r. from ways? 18:23
after it shall r. to the prince. 46:17
I r. to fight with Persia. *Dan* 10:20
and shall r. into his own land. 11:9
10, 28
the king of the north shall r. 13
time appointed he shall r. and. 29
he shall be grieved and r. 30
I will go and r. to my first. *Hos* 2:7
I will r. and take away my corn. 9
the children of Israel r. 3:5
I will go and r. to my place. 5:15
r. but not to the most High. 7:16
visit their sins they shall r. 8:13; 9:3
his reproach shall his Lord r. 12:14
dwell under his shadow shall r. 14:7
who knoweth if he will r.? *Joel* 2:14
I r. recompence on your head. 3:4, 7
thy reward shall r. upon. *Ob* 15
they shall r. to the hire. *Mi* 1:7
remnant of his brethren shall r. 5:3
Edom saith, We will r. *Mal* 1:4
R. to me, and I will r. to you, saith Lord . . . Wherein shall we r.? 3:7
shall ye r. and discern between. 18
worthy, let your peace r. *Mat* 10:13
r. into my house. 12:44; *Luke* 11:24
is in the field, r. back. *Mat* 24:18
r. to thine own house. *Luke* 8:39
when he will r. from wedding. 12:36
after this I will r. and. *Acts* 15:16
I will again r. to you, if God. 18:21

to **return**

when thou goest *to* r. *Ex* 4:21
were it not better *to* r.? *Num* 14:3
nor cause the people *to* r. *Deut* 17:16
went *to* r. unto Judah. *Ruth* 1:7
not to leave thee, or *to* r. from. 16
David rose early *to* r. *1 Sam* 29:11
to r. answer to this. *2 Chr* 10:6, 9
appointed a captain *to* r. *Neh* 9:17
they have refused *to* r. *Jer* 5:3; 8:5
Hos 11:5
to the land where they desire *to* r.
Jer 22:27; 44:14
in causing you *to* r. 29:10; 30:3
32:44; 33:7, 11, 26; 34:22; 42:12
caused the servants *to* r. 34:11, 16
cause me not *to* r. 37:20; 38:26
shall I cause it *to* r.? *Ezek* 21:30
cause them *to* r. to Pathros. 29:14
caused me *to* r. to the brink. 47:6
because they refused *to* r. *Hos* 11:5
went to receive a kingdom and *to* r.
Luke 19:12
more *to* r. to corruption. *Acts* 13:34
to r. through Macedonia. 20:3

return *unto the Lord*

and shalt r. *unto the Lord*. *Deut* 30:2
if ye r. *unto the Lord*. *1 Sam* 7:3
r. *unto the Lord*, he shall. *Isa* 19:22
let him r. *unto the Lord*, he. 55:7
let us r. *unto the Lord*, for. *Hos* 6:1
they do not r. *unto the Lord*. 7:10
O Israel, r. *unto the Lord* thy. 14:1

not **return**

will *not* r. to our houses. *Num* 32:18
Samuel said, I will *not* r. with thee.
1 Sam 15:26
he shall *not* r. to me. *2 Sam* 12:23
I may *not* r. with thee. *1 Ki* 13:16
before I go whence I shall *not* r.
Job 10:21; 16:22
forth, and r. *not* unto them. 39:4
gone out, and shall *not* r. *Isa* 45:23
it shall *not* r. to me void, but. 55:11
turn away, and *not* r.? *Jer* 8:4
destroy, since they r. *not* from. 15:7
he shall *not* r. thither. 22:11, 27
the anger of the Lord shall *not* r.
23:20; 30:24
for seller shall *not* r. . . . multitude which shall *not* r. *Ezek* 7:13
that he should *not* r. from his. 13:22
my sword *not* r. any more. 21:5

thy cities shall *not* r. and. *Ezek* 35:
he shall *not* r. by the way. 46:
they do *not* r. to the Lord. *Hos* 7:
he shall *not* r. into Egypt. 11:
I will *not* r. to destroy Ephraim.
warned they should *not* r. *Mat* 2:1
let him likewise *not* r. *Luke* 17:3

returned

waters r. from off earth. *Gen* 8:
the dove r. to him.
the dove r. not again. 1
Abraham r. unto his place. 18:3
Abraham r. to his young men. 22:1
Joseph r. again, communed. 42:2
we had r. this second time. 43:1
money that was r. in our sacks. 1
Moses r. to the Lord. *Ex* 5:22; 32:3
the sea r. to his strength. 14:27, 2
r. words of people to Lord. 19:8
she is r. to her father's. *Lev* 22:1
Balaam rose up, and r. *Num* 24:2
till pursuers be r. *Josh* 2:16, 2
that waters of Jordan r. 4:1
of Reuben and Gad r. 22:
the princes r. from Reuben. 3
judge was dead they r. *Judg* 2:1
yea, she r. answer to herself. 5:2
there r. of the people 22,000. 7:
Gideon r. from battle before. 8:1
Gideon's daughter r. to her. 11:3
the Benjamites r. to their. 21:2
so Naomi and Ruth r. *Ruth* 1:2
they r. to Ekron same. *1 Sam* 6:1
David r. from slaughter of. 17:5
the Lord hath r. the. 25:3
the sword of Saul r. *2 Sam* 1:2
Go, return, and he r. 3:1
then David r. to bless his. 6:2
Lord r. on thee all the blood of. 16:
thou seekest, is as if all r. 17:
king r. and came to Jordan. 19:1
people r. after him only to. 23:1
r. not by way that he. *1 Ki* 13:1
Jeroboam r. not from his evil way. 3
Elisha r. and walked. *2 Ki* 4:3
he r. to man of God, he and. 5:1
r. home in great anger. *2 Chr* 25:1
Sennacherib r. with shame of. 32:3
thus they r. us answer. *Ezra* 5:1
we r. all of us to the wall. *Neh* 4:1
when they r. and cried unto. 9:2
my prayer r. into mine. *Ps* 35:1
they r. and enquired early. 78:3
so sun r. ten degrees. *Isa* 38:
unto me. But she r. not. *Jer* 3:
they r. with their vessels. 14:
Jews r. out of all places. 40:1
creatures ran, and r. as. *Ezek* 1:1
they r. not when they went. 1
and have r. to provoke me to. 8:1
when I had r. behold, at the. 47:
understanding r. unto me. *Dan* 4:3
at the same time my reason r. 3
when I r. the captivity of. *Hos* 6:1
yet have ye not r. to me. *Amos* 4:
8, 9, 10, 1
they r. and said, Like as. *Zech* 1:
thus saith the Lord; I am r. to. 1
no man passed through nor r. 7:1
I am r. to Zion, and will dwell. 8:
morning as he r. into. *Mat* 21:1
when he r. he found. *Mark* 14:4
Mary r. to her own house. *Luke* 1:5
shepherds r. glorifying God. 2:2
Jesus full of the Holy Ghost r. 4:
Jesus r. in power of the Spirit. 1
into the ship and r. back again. 8:3
when Jesus r., the people gladly. 4
the apostles, when they were r. 9:1
the seventy r. again with joy. 10:1
that r. to give glory to God. 17:1
r. having received kingdom. 19:1
smote their breasts and r. 23:4
they r. and prepared spices. 5
r. from sepulchre and told. 24:
they rose same hour, and r. to. 3
they worshipped him, and r. to. 5
then r. they to Jerusalem. *Acts* 1:1
found them not, they r. 5:2
the apostles r. to Jerusalem. 8:2
Barnabas and Saul r. from. 12:2
John r. to Jerusalem. 13:1
they r. again to Lystra and. 14:2

:ook ship, and they *r.* home. *Acts* 21:6
ınd *r.* to the castle. 23:32
r. again unto Damascus. *Gal* 1:17
ɔpportunity to have *r.* *Heb* 11:15
ıow *r.* to Shepherd of. *1 Pet* 2:25

returneth

ıis breath goeth, he *r.* *Ps* 146:4
. to his vomit, so a fool *r.* *Pr* 26:11
:he wind *r.* according to. *Eccl* 1:6
ain *r.* not thither, but. *Isa* 55:10
ıim that *r.* I will cut off. *Ezek* 35:7
ɔecause of him that *r.* *Zech* 9:8

returning

n *r.* and rest shall ye. *Isa* 30:15
., found servant whole. *Luke* 7:10
. and sitting in chariot. *Acts* 8:28
net Abraham *r.* from. *Heb* 7:1

Reuben

nd called his name *R.* *Gen* 29:32
R. went in the days of wheat. 30:14
:hat *R.* went and lay with. 35:22
R., Jacob's firstborn. 23; 46:8
49:3; *Num* 26:5; *1 Chr* 5:1
R. said unto them, Shed. *Gen* 37:22
R. returned to the pit; Joseph. 29
he sons of *R.* 46:9; *Ex* 6:14
Num 16:1; 32:1, 37; *Deut* 11:6
Josh 4:12; *1 Chr* 5:3, 18
ıs *R.* and Simeon, they. *Gen* 48:5
standard of the camp of *R.*
Num 2:10; 10:18
ıumbered in the camp of *R.* 2:16
ɔrince of the children of *R.* 7:30
Moses gave to children of *R.* 32:33
Josh 13:23
nount Ebal to curse; *R.* *Deut* 27:13
et *R.* live, and not die. 33:6
o the stone of Bohan the son of *R.*
Josh 15:6; 18:17
sent to the children of *R.* 22:13
or the divisions of *R.* *Judg* 5:15, 16
ı portion for *R.* *Ezek* 48:6
ɔne gate of *R.* 31

tribe of **Reuben**

ɔf the *tribe of R.*; Elizur. *Num* 1:5
:he *tribe of R.* were numbered. 21
ɔf the *tribe of R.*, Shammua. 13:4
:he *tribe of R.* have received. 34:14
ɔut of the *tribe of R.*, Gad and.
Josh 20:8; 21:36; *1 Chr* 6:63, 78
ɔf *tribe of R.* were sealed. *Rev* 7:5

Reubenites

:he families of the *R.* *Num* 26:7
:ities gave I to the *R.* *Deut* 3:12
16; 29:8; *Josh* 12:6; 13:8
spake to the *R.* *Josh* 1:12; 22:1
Hazael smote the *R.* *2 Ki* 10:33
:he prince of the *R.* *1 Chr* 5:6
Tiglath-pilneser carried away *R.* 26
Adina a captain of the *R.* 11:42
ıis brethren over the *R.* 26:32
uler of the *R.* was Eliezer. 27:16

reveal

shall *r.* his iniquity. *Job* 20:27
will *r.* them abundance. *Jer* 33:6
couldest *r.* this secret. *Dan* 2:47
o whomsoever the Son will *r.* him.
Mat 11:27; *Luke* 10:22
grace, to *r.* his Son in me. *Gal* 1:16
God shall *r.* even this. *Phil* 3:15

revealed

ɔut things *r.* to us. *Deut* 29:29
ɔf the Lord *r.* to him. *1 Sam* 3:7
:he Lord *r.* himself to Samuel. 21
ıast *r.* to thy servant. *2 Sam* 7:27
t was *r.* in mine ears. *Isa* 22:14
rom Chittim it is *r.* to them. 23:1
glory of the Lord shall be *r.* 40:5
o whom is the arm of the Lord *r.*?
53:1; *John* 12:38
righteousness is near to be *r.*
Isa 56:1
for unto thee have I *r.* *Jer* 11:20
then was the secret *r.* to. *Dan* 2:19
this secret is not *r.* to me for. 30
a thing was *r.* to Daniel, and. 10:1
nothing covered, that shall not be *r.*
Mat 10:26; *Luke* 12:2
and *r.* them to babes. *Mat* 11:25
Luke 10:21
and blood hath not *r.* it. *Mat* 16:17
it was *r.* to Simeon by. *Luke* 2:26

of many hearts may be *r.* *Luke* 2:35
when the Son of man is *r.* 17:30
righteousness of God *r.* *Rom* 1:17
the wrath of God is *r.* from. 18
glory which shall be *r.* in us. 8:18
God hath *r.* them to us. *1 Cor* 2:10
because it shall be *r.* by fire. 3:13
if any thing be *r.* to another. 14:30
should afterwards be *r.* *Gal* 3:23
as it is now *r.* to his holy. *Eph* 3:5
Lord Jesus shall be *r.* *2 Thes* 1:7
first, and that man of sin be *r.* 2:3
he might be *r.* in his time. 6
that wicked one be *r.*, whom. 8
salvation, ready to be *r.* *1 Pet* 1:5
unto whom it was *r.* that not. 12
when his glory shall be *r.* 4:13
of the glory that shall be *r.* 5:1

revealer

your God is a God of gods, a *r.* of secrets. *Dan* 2:47

revealeth

a talebearer *r.* *Pr* 11:13; 20:19
he *r.* the deep and secret. *Dan* 2:22
God in heaven that *r.* secrets. 28
that *r.* secrets maketh known. 29
he *r.* his secrets to his. *Amos* 3:7

revelation

(*A revealing; in the Bible mainly the revealing by God of his character or deeds*)

and *r.* of the righteous. *Rom* 2:5
according to *r.* of mystery. 16:25
speak to you either by *r.* *1 Cor* 14:6
every one of you hath a *r.*, hath. 26
by the *r.* of Jesus Christ. *Gal* 1:12
and I went up by *r.* and. 2:2
Spirit of wisdom and *r.* *Eph* 1:17
how that by *r.* he made. 3:3
grace brought at the *r.* *1 Pet* 1:13
the *r.* of Jesus Christ. *Rev* 1:1

revelations

come to visions and *r.* *2 Cor* 12:1
exalted through abundance of *r.* 7

revellings

works of the flesh are *r.* *Gal* 5:21
when ye walked in lusts, *r.* *1 Pet* 4:3

revenge

(*Most frequently found where* avenge *is used in modern English. Revisions make this change*)

O Lord, *r.* me of my. *Jer* 15:15
in a readiness to *r.* all. *2 Cor* 10:6

revenge, *substantive*

and we shall take our *r.* *Jer* 20:10
Philistines have dealt by *r.*
Ezek 25:15
r. it wrought in you. *2 Cor* 7:11

revenged

because Edom *r.* *Ezek* 25:12

revenger

the *r.* shall slay the. *Num* 35:19, 21
judge between slayer and *r.* 24
slayer out of the hand of the *r.* 25
if *r.* find him without, and *r.* kill. 27
minister of God, a *r.* *Rom* 13:4

revengers

thou wouldest not suffer the *r.*
2 Sam 14:11

revenges

from the beginning of *r.* *Deut* 32:42

revengeth

the Lord *r.* and is furious. *Nah* 1:2

revenging

by the *r.* of the blood of. *Ps* 79:10

revenue

endamage the *r.* of kings. *Ezra* 4:13*
my *r.* is better than. *Pr* 8:19
harvest of the river is her *r.* *Isa* 23:3

revenues

but in the *r.* of the wicked. *Pr* 15:6
than great *r.* without right. 16:8
be ashamed of your *r.* *Jer* 12:13*

reverence

(*Where this word is used in connection with men alone it is with the old meaning of* deference, *or of an act of homage, or merely* obeisance. *When used with reference to God it means* godly fear *and* awe)

r. my sanctuary. *Lev* 19:30; 26:2
servants in gate *r.* *Esth* 3:2
They will *r.* my son. *Mat* 21:37
Mark 12:6; *Luke* 20:13
the wife see that she *r.* *Eph* 5:33

reverence, *substantive*

Mephibosheth did *r.* to. *2 Sam* 9:6*
and did *r.* to king. *1 Ki* 1:31*
nor did him *r.* *Esth* 3:2, 5
to be had in *r.* of all. *Ps* 89:7*
we gave them *r.* *Heb* 12:9
serve God with *r.* 28

reverend

holy and *r.* is his name. *Ps* 111:9

reverse

hath blessed, and I cannot *r.* it.
Num 23:20
let it be written, to *r.* *Esth* 8:5
with king's ring, may no man *r.* 8

revile

(*To use abusive language of any sort*)

thou shalt not *r.* the gods. *Ex* 22:28
ye when men shall *r.* you. *Mat* 5:11*

reviled

that passed by *r.* him. *Mat* 27:39
crucified with him *r.* *Mark* 15:32*
they *r.* him, and said. *John* 9:28
being *r.* we bless, being. *1 Cor* 4:12
when he was *r.*, *r.* not. *1 Pet* 2:23

revilers

nor *r.* shall inherit. *1 Cor* 6:10

revilest

they said, *R.* thou God's? *Acts* 23:4

revilings

neither be afraid of their *r.* *Isa* 51:7
and the *r.* of Ammon. *Zeph* 2:8

revive

(*To make to live again, or to have new life*)

will they *r.* the stones? *Neh* 4:2
wilt thou not *r.* us again? *Ps* 85:6*
thou wilt *r.* me, thou shalt. 138:7
to *r.* spirit of the humble, and to *r.* the heart of the contrite. *Isa* 57:15
after two days will he *r.* us. *Hos* 6:2
they shall *r.* as corn, and grow. 14:7
Lord, *r.* thy work in. *Hab* 3:2

revived

spirit of Jacob *r.* *Gen* 45:27
came again, and he *r.* *Judg* 15:19
soul came, and he *r.* *1 Ki* 17:22
bones of Elisha, he *r.* *2 Ki* 13:21
commandment came, sin *r.* *Rom* 7:9
both died, rose, and *r.* 14:9*

reviving

to give us a little *r.* *Ezra* 9:8, 9

revolt

speaking oppression and *r.* *Isa* 59:13

revolt, *verb*

also did Libnah *r.* *2 Chr* 21:10
ye will *r.* more and more. *Isa* 1:5

revolted

in his days Edom *r.* *2 Ki* 8:20, 22
2 Chr 21:8, 10
Libnah *r.* at the same. *2 Ki* 8:22
Israel have deeply *r.* *Isa* 31:6
this people, they are *r.* *Jer* 5:23

revolters

are all grievous *r.* *Jer* 6:28
r. are profound to make. *Hos* 5:2
all their princes are *r.* 9:15

revolting

this people hath a *r.* and. *Jer* 5:23

reward

thy exceeding great *r.* *Gen* 15:1
for it is your *r.* for. *Num* 18:31
God, who taketh not *r.* *Deut* 10:17
cursed that taketh *r.* to slay. 27:25
a full *r.* be given thee. *Ruth* 2:12
have given him a *r.* *2 Sam* 4:10
it me with such a *r.* 19:36
I will give thee a *r.* *1 Ki* 13:7
Bring to me? or Give a *r.*? *Job* 6:22*
as an hireling looketh for *r.* 7:2*

nor taketh r. against. Ps 15:5
in keeping of them is r. 19:11
desolate for a r. of their. 40:15*
there is a r. for the righteous. 58:11
let them be turned back for r. 70:3*
see the r. of the wicked. 91:8
render a r. to the proud. 94:2*
let this be the r. of mine. 109:20
the fruit of the womb is his r. 127:3
righteousness, a sure r. Pr 11:18
a r. in the bosom strong wrath. 21:14*
then there shall be a r. 24:14
there shall be no r. to the evil. 20
they have a good r. for. Eccl 4:9
neither have they any more a r. 9:5
the r. of his hands shall. Isa 3:11
justify the wicked for r. 5:23
his r. is with him, and his work before him. 40:10; 62:11
let go my captives, not for r. 45:13
captain gave Jeremiah a r. Jer 40:5
thou givest r., and no r. Ezek 16:34*
hast loved a r. upon every. Hos 9:1*
thy r. shall return upon thine. Ob 15*
heads thereof judge for r. Mi 3:11
and judge asketh for a r. 7:3
great is your r. in heaven. Mat 5:12
Luke 6:23
love you, what r. have ye? Mat 5:46
otherwise ye have no r. of your. 6:1
they have their r. 2, 5, 16
shall receive a prophet's r. . . . a righteous man's r. 10:41
he shall in no wise lose his r. 42
Mark 9:41
but do good, and your r. Luke 6:35
for we receive the due r. 23:41
field with r. of iniquity. Acts 1:18
r. not reckoned of grace. Rom 4:4
every man shall receive his own r.
1 Cor 3:8
work abide he shall receive a r. 14
thing willingly, I have a r. 9:17
what is my r. then? verily, that. 18
beguile you of your r. Col 2:18
ye shall receive the r. of the. 3:24
the labourer is worthy of his r.
1 Tim 5:18*
recompence of r. Heb 2:2
10:35; 11:26
r. of unrighteousness. 2 Pet 2:13*
that we receive a full r. 2 John 8
after error of Balaam for r. Jude 11*
thou shouldest give r. Rev 11:18
and my r. is with me. 22:12

reward, *verb*

I will r. them that hate. Deut 32:41
wherefore the Lord r. 1 Sam 24:19
the Lord shall r. the. 2 Sam 3:39
I say, how they r. us. 2 Chr 20:11
he shall r. evil to mine. Ps 54:5
the Lord shall r thee. Pr 25:22
will r. them their doings. Hos 4:9
Father himself shall r. thee openly.
Mat 6:4, 6, 18
shall r. every man according. 16:27
Lord r. him according. 2 Tim 4:14*
r. her, even as she. Rev 18:6*

rewarded

have ye r. evil for good? Gen 44:4
thou hast r. me good . . . I have r. thee evil. 1 Sam 24:17
Lord r. me according to my righteousness. 2 Sam 22:21; Ps 18:20
your work shall be r. 2 Chr 15:7
if I have r. evil to him. Ps 7:4
they r. me evil for good. 35:12
109:5
nor r. us according to our. 103:10
the commandment be r. Pr 13:13
for they have r. evil to. Isa 3:9
thy work shall be r., saith. Jer 31:16
reward her even as she r. Rev 18:6*

rewarder

r. of them that diligently. Heb 11:6

rewardeth

he r. him and he shall. Job 21:19
plentifully r proud doer. Ps 31:23
happy he that r. thee, as thou. 137:8
whoso r. evil for good. Pr 17:13
both r. the fool, and r. 26:10*

rewards

with the r. of divination. Num 22:7
followeth after r. Isa 1:23
of me gifts and r. honour. Dan 2:6
said, Give thy r. to another. 5:17
are my r. that my lovers. Hos 2:12*

Rezin

Lord began to send against Judah R. 2 Ki 15:37; 16:5; Isa 7:1
that time R. recovered. 2 Ki 16:6
took Damascus and slew R. 9
the children of R., children of Nekoda and Gazzam. Ezra 2:48; Neh 7:50
fear not the fierce anger of R. Isa 7:4
and the head of Damascus is R. 8
as the people rejoice in R. 8:6
set up the adversaries of R. 9:11

Rhegium

compass and came to R. Acts 28:13

Rhesa

who was the son of R. Luke 3:27

Rhoda

a damsel named R. Acts 12:13

Rhodes

we came unto R. Acts 21:1

rib, -s

God took one of his r. Gen 2:21
the r. which God had taken. 22
Asahel under the fifth r. 2 Sam 2:23*
Joab smote Abner and Amasa under the fifth r. 3:27*; 20:10*
smote Ish-bosheth under fifth r. 4:6*
beast had three r. in the. Dan 7:5

ribband

the borders a r. of blue. Num 15:38*

rich

Abram very r. in cattle. Gen 13:2
I have made Abram r. 14:23
r. shall not give more, nor. Ex 30:15
and if a stranger wax r. Lev 25:47
young men poor or r. Ruth 3:10
poor and maketh r. 1 Sam 2:7
men in one city, one r. 2 Sam 12:1
he shall not be r. neither. Job 15:29
nor regardeth the r. more. 34:19
the r. shall entreat. Ps 45:12
hear this, both r. and poor. 49:2
be not afraid when one is made r. 16
of the diligent maketh r. Pr 10:4
blessing of the Lord, maketh r. 22
there is that maketh himself r. 13:7
poor is hated, but the r. hath. 14:20
but the r. answereth roughly. 18:23
wine and oil shall not be r. 21:17
r. and poor meet together, Lord. 22:2
the r. ruleth over the poor, and. 7
he that giveth to the r. shall. 16
labour not to be r.: cease from. 23:4
perverse, though he be r. 28:6
he that maketh haste to be r. 20, 22
abundance of r. will not suffer.
Eccl 5:12
and the r. sit in low place. 10:6
curse not the r. in thy. 20
with the r. in his death. Isa 53:9
are great, and waxen r. Jer 5:27
in chests of r. apparel. Ezek 27:24
Yet I am become r. Hos 12:8
be the Lord, for I am r. Zech 11:5
were r., cast in much. Mark 12:41
r. he hath sent empty. Luke 1:53
but woe unto you that are r. for. 6:24
is not r. toward God. 12:21
call not thy r. neighbours. 14:12
sorrowful, for he was very r. 18:23
Zacchaeus . . . and he was r. 19:2
same Lord is r. to all. Rom 10:12
full, now ye are r. 1 Cor 4:8
yet making many r. 2 Cor 6:10
though he was r. yet he became poor, that ye might be r. 8:9
God who is r. in mercy. Eph 2:4
they that will be r. fall. 1 Tim 6:9
charge them that are r. in this. 17
that they do good, and be r. in. 18
let the r. rejoice in that. Jas 1:10
chosen the poor, r. in faith? 2:5
poverty, but thou art r. Rev 2:9
because thou sayest, I am r. 3:17
buy gold, that thou mayest be r. 18
he causeth the r. and poor to. 13:16
merchants of earth are waxed r.
Rev 18:3, 15, 19

rich *man* or *men*

r. man had exceeding. 2 Sam 12:2
a traveller to the r. man. 4
r. man shall lie down. Job 27:19
the r. man's wealth is his strong.
Pr 10:15; 18:11
the r. man is wise in his. 28:11
let not the r. man glory. Jer 9:23
the r. men thereof are full. Mi 6:12
r. man shall hardly enter. Mat 19:23
than for a r. man to enter into. 24
Mark 10:25; Luke 18:25
came a r. man of Arimathaea.
Mat 27:57
the ground of a r. man. Luke 12:16
there was a certain r. man. 16:1
a r. man was clothed in purple. 19
fell from the r. man's table. 21
the r. man also died and was. 22
and saw the r. men casting. 21:1
so also shall the r. man. Jas 1:11
do not r. men oppress you? 2:6
go to now, ye r. men, weep. 5:1
great men, and r. men. Rev 6:15

richer

the fourth shall be far r. Dan 11:2

riches

the r. God hath taken. Gen 31:16
r. were more than they might. 36:7
return with much r. to. Josh 22:8
enrich with great r. 1 Sam 17:25
neither hast asked r. 1 Ki 3:11
2 Chr 1:11
given thee both r. and. 1 Ki 3:13
Solomon exceeded all the kings of the earth for r. 10:23; 2 Chr 9:22
both r. and honour. 1 Chr 29:12
David died full of days, r. and. 28
Jehoshaphat had r. and honour.
2 Chr 17:5; 18:1
found r. with dead bodies. 20:25
Hezekiah had exceeding much r.
32:27
r. of his glorious kingdom. Esth 1:4
them of the glory of his r. 5:11
he swallowed down r. Job 20:15
will he esteem thy r.? no, not. 36:19
is better than the r. of. Ps 37:16
he heapeth up r. and knoweth. 39:6
boast themselves in their r. 49:6
trusted in the abundance of r. 52:7
if r. increase, set not your. 62:10
ungodly, they increase in r. 73:12
earth is full of thy r. 104:24
wealth and r. shall be in. 112:3
rejoiced as much as in all r. 119:14
and in her left hand r. Pr 3:16
r. and honour are with me. 8:18
r. profit not in the day of wrath. 11:4
and strong men retain r. 16
trusteth in his r. shall fall. 28
poor, yet hath great r. 13:7
of a man's life are his r. 8
crown of the wise is their r. 14:24
and r. are the inheritance of. 19:14
is rather to be chosen than r. 22:1
by the fear of the Lord are r. 4
the poor to increase his r. 16
r. certainly make themselves. 23:5
be filled with all pleasant r. 24:4
for r. are not for ever, and. 27:24
give me neither poverty nor r. 30:8
his eye satisfied with r. Eccl 4:8
even r. kept for the owners. 5:13
those r. perish by evil travail. 14
to whom God hath given r. 19; 6:2
r. to men of understanding. 9:11
the r. of Damascus shall. Isa 8:4
hand found as a nest the r. 10:14
they will carry their r. on. 30:6
I will give thee hidden r. of. 45:3
eat the r. of the Gentiles. 61:6
rich man glory in his r. Jer 9:23
so he that getteth r. and not. 17:11
because r. that he hath gotten. 48:36
make a spoil of thy r. Ezek 26:12
multitude of all kind of r. 27:12
18, 27, 33
thou hast gotten r. 28:4
increased thy r., and thine heart is lifted up because of thy r. 5

through his *r.* shall stir up. *Dan* 11:2
north shall come with much *r.* 13
them the prey, spoil and *r.* 24
return into his land with great *r.* 28
deceitfulness of *r.* choke. *Mat* 13:22
Mark 4:19; *Luke* 8:14
hardly they that have *r. Mark* 10:23
how hard is it for them that trust in *r.* to enter! 24; *Luke* 18:24
your trust the true *r.*? *Luke* 16:11
or despisest thou the *r.* of? *Rom* 2:4
he might make known the *r.* 9:23
be the *r.* of the world, and the diminishing of them the *r.* of. 11:12
O the depth of the *r.* of the. 33
abounded to the *r.* of their. *2 Cor* 8:2
redemption according to *r. Eph* 1:7
what the *r.* of the glory of his. 18
that he might shew exceeding *r.* 2:7
preach unsearchable *r.* of Christ. 3:8
grant you according to the *r.* 16
according to his *r.* in glory. *Phil* 4:19
what the *r.* of the glory. *Col* 1:27
love, and unto all the *r.* of the. 2:2
nor trust in uncertain *r. 1 Tim* 6:17
reproach of Christ greater *r.* than. *Heb* 11:26
your *r.* are corrupted. *Jas* 5:2
to receive power and *r. Rev* 5:12
in one hour so great *r.* are. 18:17

richly

of Christ dwell in you *r. Col* 3:16
living God, who giveth *r. 1 Tim* 6:17

rid

that he might *r.* him out. *Gen* 37:22
I will *r.* you out of their. *Ex* 6:6
I will *r.* evil beasts out. *Lev* 26:6*
r. them out of the hand. *Ps* 82:4*
send thine hand, *r.* me. 144:7*, 11*

riddance

thou shalt not make clean *r.* of thy. *Lev* 23:22*
he shall make even speedy *r.* of. *Zeph* 1:18*

ridden

ass, which thou hast *r.*? *Num* 22:30

riddle

put forth a *r.* to you. *Judg* 14:12
13, 14, 15, 16, 17, 18, 19
Son of man, put orth a *r. Ezek* 17:2

ride

to *r.* in the second chariot. *Gen* 41:43
he made him *r.* on high. *Deut* 32:13
ye that *r.* on white asses. *Judg* 5:10
for king's household to *r. 2 Sam* 16:2
saddle an ass that I may *r.* 19:26
cause Solomon to *r.* upon my mule. *1 Ki* 1:33, 38, 44
him to *r.* in his chariot. *2 Ki* 10:16
to *r.* upon the wind. *Job* 30:22
and in thy majesty *r. Ps* 45:4
thou hast caused men to *r.* 66:12
but ye said, We will *r. Isa* 30:16
I will cause thee to *r.* on the. 58:14
they *r.* on horses. *Jer* 6:23; 50:42
I will make Ephraim to *r. Hos* 10:11
we will not *r.* upon horses. 14:3
that thou didst *r.* upon. *Hab* 3:8
chariots, and those that *r. Hag* 2:22

rider

so that his *r.* shall fall. *Gen* 49:17
horse and *r.* thrown. *Ex* 15:1, 21
the horse and his *r. Job* 39:18
break in pieces horse and his *r.* . . . . the chariot and his *r. Jer* 51:21
I will smite his *r.* with. *Zech* 12:4

riders

if thou be able to set *r.* on. *2 Ki* 18:23; *Isa* 36:8
letters by *r.* on mules. *Esth* 8:10
the horses and their *r. Hag* 2:22
the *r.* on horses shall be. *Zech* 10:5

rideth

what saddle he *r.* on shall. *Lev* 15:9
who *r.* upon the heaven. *Deut* 33:26
horse that king *r.* upon. *Esth* 6:8
that *r.* on the heavens. *Ps* 68:4, 33
Lord *r.* on a swift cloud. *Isa* 19:1
that *r.* the horse deliver. *Amos* 2:15

ridges

waterest the *r.* thereof. *Ps* 65:10*

riding

Balaam was *r.* on his ass. *Num* 22:22
slack not thy *r.* for me. *2 Ki* 4:24
kings shall enter *r.* in chariots. *Jer* 17:25; 22:4
young men, horsemen *r.* on horses. *Ezek* 23:6, 12
great lords, all of them *r.* 23
people with thee *r.* on horses. 38:15
a man *r.* on a red horse. *Zech* 1:8
thy king cometh: *r.* upon an ass. 9:9

rie, or rye

(*Properly* spelt, *a variety of wheat*)
wheat and *r.* not smitten. *Ex* 9:32
cast in wheat, barley and *r. Isa* 28:25

rifled

houses *r.* and the women. *Zech* 14:2

right, *substantive*

shall not the Judge of all the earth do *r.*? *Gen* 18:25
of Zelophehad speak *r. Num* 27:7
r. of firstborn is his. *Deut* 21:17
redeem thou my *r.* to. *Ruth* 4:6
what *r.* have I to cry? *2 Sam* 19:28
we have also more *r.* in David. 43
no portion nor *r.* in Jerusalem. *Neh* 2:20
thou hast done *r.*, but we have. 9:33
should I lie against my *r.*? *Job* 34:6
he that hateth *r.* govern? 17
but he giveth *r.* to the poor. 36:6
maintained my *r.*: judging *r. Ps* 9:4*
hear the *r.* O Lord, attend to. 17:1
the Lord will maintain the *r.* 140:12
revenues without *r. Pr* 16:8
and they love him that speaketh *r.* 13
away the *r.* from poor. *Isa* 10:2
when the needy speaketh *r.* 32:7
the *r.* of the needy do. *Jer* 5:28
getteth riches, and not by *r.* 17:11
the *r.* of redemption is thine. 32:7, 8
to turn aside *r.* of a man. *Lam* 3:35
he come whose *r.* it is. *Ezek* 21:27
turn poor from their *r. Amos* 5:12
turn stranger from his *r. Mal* 3:5
they have no *r.* to eat. *Heb* 13:10
they may have *r.* to the tree of life. *Rev* 22:14

right, *adjective*

led me in the *r.* way. *Gen* 24:48
God of truth, just and *r. Deut* 32:4
do as seemeth good and *r. Josh* 9:25
frame to pronounce it *r. Judg* 12:6
the good and *r.* way. *1 Sam* 12:23
matters are good and *r. 2 Sam* 15:3
is thy heart *r.* as my heart? *2 Ki* 10:15
things that were not *r.* 17:9
to seek of him a *r. Ezra* 8:21*
thou gavest them *r. Neh* 9:13
and the things seem *r. Esth* 8:5
how forcible are *r.* words! *Job* 6:25*
not lay on man more than *r.* 34:23
this to be *r.* that thou saidst? 35:2*
statutes of Lord are *r. Ps* 19:8
sceptre of thy kingdom is a *r.* 45:6*
O God, renew a *r.* spirit. 51:10
led them forth by the *r.* way. 107:7*
thy judgements are *r.* 119:75*
thy precepts are *r.* 128
I have led thee in *r.* paths. *Pr* 4:11*
my lips shall be *r.* things. 8:6
they are all *r.* to them that find. 9
thoughts of the righteous are *r.* 12:5*
way which seemeth *r.* 14:12; 16:25
work be pure, and whether *r.* 20:11
lips shall speak *r.* things. 23:16
his lips that giveth a *r.* answer. 24:26
considered every *r.* work. *Eccl* 4:4*
say, Prophesy not to us *r.* things. *Isa* 30:10
declare things that are *r.* 45:19
I had planted thee wholly a *r.* seed. *Jer* 2:21
evil, and their force is not *r.* 23:10
and had done *r.* in my sight. 34:15
ways of the Lord are *r. Hos* 14:19
for they know not to do *r. Amos* 3:10
clothed, and in his *r.* mind. *Mark* 5:15; *Luke* 8:35
hast answered *r.*: this. *Luke* 10:28
r. in sight of God. *Acts* 4:19
thy heart is not *r.* in the sight. 8:21
not cease to pervert the *r. Acts* 13:10
forsaken the *r.* way. *2 Pet* 2:15

right, *adv.*

people passed over *r. Josh* 3:16
see **foot, hand**

is **right**

and do that which *is r.* in his sight. *Ex* 15:26; *1 Ki* 11:38
thou shalt do that which *is r.* *Deut* 6:18; 12:25; 21:9
whatsoever *is r.* in own eyes. 12:8
doest that which *is r.* 28; 13:18
walked to do that *is r. 1 Ki* 11:33
which *is r.* in my eyes. *2 Ki* 10:30
of me thing that *is r. Job* 42:7, 8
word of the Lord *is r. Ps* 33:4
the way of a fool *is r.* in. *Pr* 12:15
every way of man *is r.* in his. 21:2
as for the pure, his work *is r.* 8
man do that which *is r. Ezek* 18:5
done that which *is* lawful and *r.* 19
21:27; 33:14, 16, 19
whatsoever *is r.* I will. *Mat* 20:4
whatsoever *is r.* that shall ye. 7
judge ye not what *is r.*? *Luke* 12:57
in the Lord: this *is r. Eph* 6:1

was **right**

that which *was r.* in his own eyes. *Judg* 17:6; 21:25
David to do that only which *was r.* *1 Ki* 14:8; 15:5
Asa did that which *was r.* 15:11
2 Chr 14:2
Jehoshaphat doing that which *was r.* *1 Ki* 22:43; *2 Chr* 20:32
Jehoash did that which *was r.* *2 Ki* 12:2; *2 Chr* 24:2
Amaziah did that which *was r.* *2 Ki* 14:3; *2 Chr* 25:2
Azariah did that which *was r.* *2 Ki* 15:3; *2 Chr* 26:4
Jotham did that which *was r.* *2 Ki* 15:34; *2 Chr* 27:2
Ahaz did not that which *was r.* *2 Ki* 16:2
Hezekiah did that which *was r.* 18:3
2 Chr 29:2
Josiah did that which *was r.* *2 Ki* 22:2; *2 Chr* 34:2
the thing *was r.* in eyes. *1 Chr* 13:4
I have perverted that which *was r.* *Job* 33:27
their heart *was* not *r. Ps* 78:37
which came out of my lips *was r.* *Jer* 17:16*

right *cheek*

smite thee on the *r. cheek. Mat* 5:39

right *corner*

round from the *r. corner. 2 Ki* 11:11

right *early*

God shall help her, and that *r. early.* *Ps* 46:5

right *forth*

driven every man *r. forth. Jer* 49:5

right *on*

let thine eyes look *r. on. Pr* 4:25
call passengers who go *r. on.* 9:15

right *pillar*

he set up the *r. pillar. 1 Ki* 7:21

right *well*

my soul knoweth *r. well. Ps* 139:14

righteous

(*Frequently changed in the Revisions to* upright)
for thee have I seen *r. Gen* 7:1
wilt thou destroy the *r.* with? 18:23
if there be fifty *r.* wilt? 24, 26, 28
that be far from thee to slay *r.* 25
slay also a *r.* nation? 20:4
hath been more *r.* than I. 38:26
innocent and *r.* slay not. *Ex* 23:7
perverteth the words of the *r.* 8
Deut 16:19
the death of the *r. Num* 23:10
that hath judgements so *r. Deut* 4:8
they shall justify the *r.* 25:1
2 Chr 6:23
the *r.* acts of the Lord. *Judg* 5:11
1 Sam 12:7
art more *r.* than I. *1 Sam* 24:17
have slain a *r.* person. *2 Sam* 4:11

two men more *r.* than he. *1 Ki* 2:32
justifying the *r.* to give him. 8:32
Jehu said, Ye be *r.* *2 Ki* 10:9
Lord God of Israel, thou art *r.* *Ezra* 9:15; *Neh* 9:8
where were the *r.* cut off ? *Job* 4:7
whom, though I were *r.*, yet. 9:15
if I be *r.* yet will I not lift. 10:15
that he should be *r.*? 15:14
r. also shall hold on his way. 17:9
to Almighty, that thou art *r.*? 22:3
the *r.* see it, and are glad. 19
Ps 107:42
there the *r.* might dispute. *Job* 23:7
was *r.* in his own eyes. 32:1
Job hath said, I am *r.* 34:5
if thou be *r.* 35:7
withdraweth not his eyes from the *r.* 36:7; *Ps* 34:15
that thou mayest be *r.* *Job* 40:8*
the congregation of the *r.* *Ps* 1:5
Lord knoweth way of the *r.* 6
for thou wilt bless the *r.* with. 5:12
for the *r.* God trieth the hearts. 7:9
God judgeth the *r.*, God is angry. 11
what can the *r.* do ? 11:3
Lord trieth the *r.* 5
God is in the generation of the *r.* 14:5
judgements of Lord are true and *r.* 19:9; 119:7, 62, 106, 160, 164
contemptuously against the *r.* 31:18
be glad . . . and rejoice, ye *r.* 32:11
rejoice in the Lord, O ye *r.* 33:1
97:12
the *r.* cry, and the Lord. 34:17
afflictions of *r.*: Lord delivereth. 19
they that hate the *r.* shall. 21
that favour my *r.* cause. 35:27
the Lord upholdeth the *r.* 37:17
but the *r.* sheweth mercy. 21
yet have I not seen *r.* forsaken. 25
the *r.* shall inherit the land. 29
the mouth of the *r.* speaketh. 30
the wicked watcheth the *r.* 32
but the salvation of the *r.* is of. 39
the *r.* also shall see, and fear. 52:6
he shall never suffer the *r.* to. 55:22
the *r.* shall rejoice when he. 58:10
verily there is a reward for the *r.* 11
r. shall be glad in the Lord. 64:10
but let the *r.* be glad, let them. 68:3
not be written with the *r.* 69:28
in his days shall *r.* flourish. 72:7
horns of *r.* shall be exalted. 75:10
the *r.* shall flourish like the. 92:12
gather against soul of the *r.* 94:21
light is sown for *r.* and. 97:11
of compassion and *r.* 112:4; 116:5
the *r.* shall be in everlasting. 6
the tabernacles of the *r.* 118:15
this gate, into which the *r.* shall. 20
sworn that I will keep thy *r.* 119:106
r. art thou, O Lord. 137; *Jer* 12:1
thy testimonies are *r.* *Ps* 119:138
not rest upon the lot of the *r.* lest the *r.* put forth their hands. 125:3
the *r.* shall give thanks to. 140:13
let the *r.* smite me, it shall. 141:5
the *r.* shall compass me. 142:7
the Lord is *r.* in all his ways. 145:17
the Lord loveth the *r.*, he. 146:8
sound wisdom for the *r.* *Pr* 2:7
mayest keep the paths of the *r.* 20
but his secret is with the *r.* 3:32
the Lord will not suffer the *r.* 10:3
labour of the *r.* tendeth to life. 16
the lips of the *r.* feed many. 21
but the desire of the *r.* shall. 24
but the *r.* is an everlasting. 25
hope of the *r.* shall be gladness. 28
the *r.* shall never be removed. 30
the lips of the *r.* know what is. 32
r. is delivered out of trouble. 11:8
when it goeth well with the *r.* 10
but the seed of the *r.* shall be. 21
the desire of the *r.* is only good. 23
r. shall flourish as a branch. 28
the fruit of the *r.* is a tree of life. 30
behold, *r.* shall be recompensed. 31
but the root of the *r.* shall not. 12:3
thoughts of the *r.* are right, but. 5
the house of the *r.* shall stand. 7
root of the *r.* yieldeth fruit. 12
the *r.* is more excellent than his. 26
the light of the *r.* rejoiceth. *Pr* 13:9
but to the *r.* good shall be. 21
the *r.* eateth to the satisfying of. 25
among the *r.* there is favour. 14:9
bow at the gates of the *r.* 19
r. hath hope in his death. 32
in the house of the *r.* is much. 15:6
way of the *r.* is made plain. 19
the heart of the *r.* studieth to. 28
heareth the prayer of the *r.* 29
r. lips are the delight of kings. 16:13
overthrow the *r.* in judgement. 18:5
the *r.* runneth into it, and is safe. 10
shall be a ransom for the *r.* 21:18
r. giveth, and spareth not. 26
father of the *r.* shall greatly. 23:24
against the dwelling of the *r.* 24:15
to the wicked, Thou art *r.* 24
r. are bold as a lion. 28:1
whoso causeth the *r.* to go astray. 10
wicked perish, the *r.* increase. 28
when the *r.* are in authority. 29:2
the *r.* doth sing and rejoice. 6
the *r.* considereth the cause of. 7
but the *r.* shall see their fall. 16
God shall judge the *r.* *Eccl* 3:17
be not *r.* over much, neither. 7:16
according to the work of the *r.* 8:14
the *r.* and the wise are in the. 9:1
there is one event to the *r.* and. 2
say ye to the *r.*, that it shall. *Isa* 3:10
the righteousness of the *r.* 5:23
songs, even glory to the *r.* 24:16
open ye, that the *r.* nation. 26:2
that we may say, He is *r.* 41:26
my *r.* servant shall justify. 53:11
r. perisheth . . . none considering that the *r.* is taken away from. 57:1
thy people also shall be all *r.* 60:21
r. art thou, O Lord, when. *Jer* 12:1
O Lord, that triest the *r.* 20:12
raise to David a *r.* branch. 23:5
have made the *r.* sad. *Ezek* 13:22
are more *r.* than thou. 16:52
righteousness of the *r.* shall. 18:20
but when the *r.* turneth. 24; 33:18
cut off *r.* and wicked. 21:3, 4
r. shall not deliver him, nor shall the *r.* be able to live. 33:12
when I say to the *r.* he shall live. 13
they sold *r.* for silver. *Amos* 2:6
compass about the *r.* *Hab* 1:4
him that is more *r.* than he. 13
discern between the *r.* *Mal* 3:18
not come to call the *r.*, but sinners. *Mat* 9:13; *Mark* 2:17; *Luke* 5:32
then shall the *r.* shine. *Mat* 13:43
ye outwardly appear *r.* to. 23:28
garnish the sepulchres of *r.* 29
all *r.* blood shed on earth, from blood of *r.* Abel to Zacharias. 35
r. answer, Lord, when saw ? 25:37
r. shall go into life eternal. 46
and they were both *r.* *Luke* 1:6
who trusted they were *r.* and. 18:9
appearance, but judge *r.* *John* 7:24
O *r.* Father, the world hath. 17:25
and revelation of the *r.* *Rom* 2:5
it is written, There is none *r.* 3:10
of one, many be made *r.* 5:19
a manifest token of *r.* *2 Thes* 1:5
it is a *r.* thing with God to. 6
the Lord, the *r.* Judge. *2 Tim* 4:8
witness that he was *r.* *Heb* 11:4
of Lord are over the *r.* *1 Pet* 3:12
if *r.* scarcely be saved. 4:18
Lot vexed his *r.* soul. *2 Pet* 2:8
advocate, Jesus Christ the *r.* *1 John* 2:1
if ye know that he is *r.*, ye. 29
righteousness is *r.* as he is *r.* 3:7
were evil, and his brother's *r.* 12
Thou art *r.* O Lord. *Rev* 16:5
O Lord, true and *r.* are. 7; 19:2
he that is *r.* let him be *r.* 22:11

see **Lord** *is*

righteous *man*, or *men*

a little that a *r. man* hath. *Ps* 37:16
the mouth of a *r. man.* *Pr* 10:11
a *r. man* regardeth the life. 12:10
a *r. man* hateth lying, but. 13:5
a *r. man* wisely considereth. 21:12
a *r. man* falling down before. 25:26
when *r. men* do rejoice. *Pr* 28:1
who raised up the *r. man.* *Isa* 41:
when a *r. man* doth turn. *Ezek* 3:2
18:2
if thou warn the *r. man.* 3:2
and the *r. men,* they shall. 23:4
r. man in the name of a *r. man* shal receive a *r. man's.* *Mat* 10:4
many *r. men* have desired. 13:1
this was a *r. man.* *Luke* 23:4
for a *r. man* will one die. *Rom* 5:
law not made for *r. man.* *1 Tim* 1:
prayer of a *r. man* availeth. *Jas* 5:1
for that *r. man* dwelling. *2 Pet* 2:

righteously

hear causes, and judge *r.* *Deut* 1:16; *Pr* 31:
judge the people *r.* *Ps* 67:4*; 96:10
he that walketh *r.* shall. *Isa* 33:1
Lord, that judgest *r.* *Jer* 11:2
live soberly, *r.* and godly. *Tit* 2:1
to him that judgeth *r.* *1 Pet* 2:2

righteousness

(*The quality of being right or just This idea makes plain the differenc indicated by Paul between the right eousness of the law and the right eousness of God and Christ*)

and it shall be our *r.* if. *Deut* 6:2
it shall be *r.* to thee before. 24:1
shall offer sacrifices of *r.* 33:1
put on *r.*, it clothed me. *Job* 29:1
ascribe *r.* to my Maker. 36:
offer the sacrifices of *r.* *Ps* 4:
Lord loveth *r.* 11:7; 33:
he that worketh *r.* shall never. 15:
he leadeth me in paths of *r.* 23:
and *r.* from the God of his. 24:
I have preached *r.* in the. 40:
truth, and meekness, and *r.* 45:
lovest *r.* and hatest. 7; *Heb* 1:
hand, O God, is full of *r.* *Ps* 48:1
pleased with sacrifices of *r.* 51:1
lying, rather than to speak *r.* 52:
speak *r.* O congregation ? 58:
judge thy people with *r.* 72:
peace, and little hills by *r.*
r. and peace have kissed. 85:1
and *r.* shall look down from. 1
r. shall go before him, and set. 1
judgement shall return unto *r.* 94:1
judge the world with *r.* 96:13; 98:
r. is the habitation of his. 97:
executest *r.* in Jacob. 99:4; 103:
blessed is he that doeth *r.* 106:
open to me the gates of *r.*, I. 118:1
the *r.* of thy testimonies is. 119:144
all thy commandments are *r.* 172
priests be clothed with *r.*, thy. 132:
understand *r.* and judgement. *Pr* 2:
yea, durable riches and *r.* are. 8:1
I lead in the way of *r.* in midst. 20
but *r.* delivereth. 10:2; 11:4
the *r.* of the perfect shall. 11:5
r. of upright shall deliver. 6
to him that soweth *r.* shall be. 18
as *r.* tendeth to life, so he that. 19
truth, sheweth forth *r.* 12:17
in the way of *r.* is life, and. 28
r. keepeth him that is upright. 13:6
r. exalteth a nation. 14:34
that followeth after *r.* 15:9
better is a little with *r.* than. 16:8
throne is established by *r.* 12
if found in the way of *r.* 31
he that followeth after *r.* and mercy findeth life, *r.* and honour. 21:21
and the place of *r.* that. *Eccl* 3:16
r. lodged in it, but now. *Isa* 1:21
the city of *r.* 26
and her converts with *r.* 27
which take away the *r.* of the. 5:23
decreed shall overflow with *r.* 10:22
with *r.* shall he judge the poor. 11:4
r. shall be the girdle of his loins. 5
judgement, and hasting *r.* 16:5
of the world will learn *r.* 26:9
yet will he not learn *r.* 10
r. will I lay to the plummet. 28:17
and *r.* shall remain in the. 32:16
the work of *r.* shall be peace, and the effect of *r.* quietness and. 17
Zion with judgement and *r.* 33:5

and let skies pour down *r.* and let *r.* spring up together. *Isa* 45:8
I the Lord speak *r.*, I declare. 19
in the Lord have I *r.* 24*
ye that are far from *r.* 46:12
ye that follow after *r.* 51:1
ye that know *r.* 7
r. is of me, saith the Lord. 54:17
me as a nation that did *r.* 58:2
put on *r.* as a breastplate. 59:17
officers peace, thine exactors *r.* 60:17
might be called trees of *r.* 61:3
covered me with robe of *r.* 10
so Lord will cause *r.* and praise. 11
until the *r.* thereof go forth as. 62:1
that rejoiceth and worketh *r.* 64:5
the Lord which exercise *r.* *Jer* 9:24
execute ye judgement and *r.* 22:3
the Lord our *r.* 23:6; 33:16
the branch of *r.* to grow up to David, and he shall execute *r.* 33:15
hath brought forth our *r.* 51:10
own souls by their *r.* *Ezek* 14:14, 20
the *r.* of the righteous shall be. 18:20
r. of the righteous shall not. 33:12
break off thy sins by *r.* *Dan* 4:27
O Lord, *r.* belongeth unto thee. 9:7
to bring in everlasting *r.* and. 24
they that turn many to *r.* shall. 12:3
till he come and rain *r.* *Hos* 10:12
and who leave off *r.* *Amos* 5:7
let *r.* run down as a mighty. 24
ye have turned the fruit of *r.* 6:12
that ye may know the *r.* *Mi* 6:5*
seek *r.*, seek meekness. *Zeph* 2:3
shall the Sun of *r.* arise. *Mal* 4:2
becometh us to fulfil all *r.* *Mat* 3:15
that hunger and thirst after *r.* 5:6
except your *r.* exceed the *r.* 20
John came in the way of *r.* 21:32
in *r.* before him all days. *Luke* 1:75
reprove the world of sin and of *r.* *John* 16:8
of *r.*, because I go to my Father. 10
worketh *r.* is accepted. *Acts* 10:35
thou enemy of all *r.* wilt thou ? 13:10
as he reasoned of *r.* and. 24:25
therein is the *r.* of God. *Rom* 1:17
if uncircumcision keep the *r.* 2:26*
commend the *r.* of God. 3:5
the *r.* of God without the law. 21
r. of God which is by faith of. 22
to whom God imputeth *r.* 4:6
a seal of *r.* of faith, that *r.* might. 11
promise was through the *r.* 13
which receive gift of *r.* shall. 5:17
so by *r.* of one the free gift came. 18
so might grace reign through *r.* 21
instruments of *r.* to God. 6:13
death, or of obedience unto *r.* 16
ye became the servants of *r.* 18
your members servants to *r.* 19
of sin, ye were free from *r.* 20
that the *r.* of the law might be. 8:4*
but the spirit is life because of *r.* 10
who followed not after *r.*, have attained to *r.*, even the *r.* 9:30
followed after the law of *r.*, hath not attained to the law of *r.* 31*
to establish their own *r.*, have not submitted to the *r.* of God. 10:3
Moses describeth the *r.* which is. 5
the *r.* which is of faith speaketh. 6
the heart man believeth unto *r.* 10
not meat and drink, but *r.* 14:17
Christ is made unto us *r.* *1 Cor* 1:30
awake to *r.* and sin not, for. 15:34*
that we might be made the *r.* of God. *2 Cor* 3:9; 5:21
by the armour of *r.* on the right. 6:7
what fellowship hath *r.* with ? 14
increase the fruits of your *r.* 9:10
as the ministers of *r.* 11:15
if *r.* come by law, Christ. *Gal* 2:21
verily, *r* should have been. 3:21
we wait for the hope of *r.* 5:5
fruit of the Spirit is in all *r.* *Eph* 5:9
having on the breastplate of *r.* 6:14
the fruits of *r.* by Jesus. *Phil* 1:11
touching *r.* which is in the law. 3:6
r. which is of God by faith. 9
and follow after *r.* *1 Tim* 6:11
2 Tim 2:22
up for me a crown of *r.* *2 Tim* 4:8
not by works of *r.* which. *Tit* 3:5
a sceptre of *r.* is sceptre. *Heb* 1:8*
is unskilful in the word of *r.* 5:13
by interpretation, king of *r.* 7:2
and became heir of the *r.* which. 11:7
subdued kingdoms, wrought *r.* 33
peaceable fruit of *r.* 12:11
worketh not *r.* of God. *Jas* 1:20
the fruit of *r.* is sown in peace. 3:18
sin should live unto *r.* *1 Pet* 2:24
faith through *r.* of God. *2 Pet* 1:1
but saved Noah a preacher of *r.* 2:5
not to have known the way of *r.* 21
new earth, wherein dwelleth *r.* 3:13
every one that doeth *r.* *1 John* 2:29
he that doeth *r.* is righteous. 3:7
whosoever doeth not *r.* is not of. 10
for the fine linen is the *r.* *Rev* 19:8*

for righteousness

counted it to him *for r.* *Gen* 15:6
Ps 106:31; *Rom* 4:3
for thy *r.*' sake bring. *Ps* 143:11
he looked *for r.* but behold. *Isa* 5:7
which are persecuted *for r.* *Mat* 5:10
his faith is counted *for r.* *Rom* 4:5
Gal 3:6
imputed to him *for r.* *Rom* 4:22
Jas 2:23
end of the law *for r.* *Rom* 10:4
if ye suffer *for r.*' sake. *1 Pet* 3:14

his righteousness

Lord render to every man *his r.* *1 Sam* 26:23
to give according to *his r.* *1 Ki* 8:32
2 Chr 6:23
render unto man *his r.* *Job* 33:26
Lord according to *his r.* *Ps* 7:17
they shall declare *his r.* to a. 22:31
the heavens shall declare *his r.* 50:6; 97:6
his r. hath he openly shewed. 98:2
and *his r.* unto children's. 103:17
and *his r.* endureth for ever. 111:3
112:3, 9
that perisheth in *his r.* *Eccl* 7:15
pleased for *his r.* sake. *Isa* 42:21
brought salvation, and *his r.* 59:16
when a righteous man doth turn from *his r.* *Ezek* 3:20; 18:24, 26
in *his r.* that he hath done. 18:22
not be able to live for *his r.* 33:12
if he trust to *his* own *r.* and commit iniquity, *his r.* 13
and I shall behold *his r.* *Mi* 7:9
kingdom of God and *his r.* *Mat* 6:33
his r. for remission of sins. *Rom* 3:25, 26
given to the poor, *his r.* *2 Cor* 9:9

in righteousness

in r. shalt thou judge. *Lev* 19:15
before thee in truth and *in r.* *1 Ki* 3:6
judge the world *in r.* *Ps* 9:8
I will behold thy face *in r.* 17:15
by terrible things *in r.* wilt thou. 65:5
words of my mouth are *in r.* *Pr* 8:8
throne shall be established *in r.* 25:5
shall be sanctified *in r.* *Isa* 5:16
a king shall reign *in r.* and. 32:1
Lord have called thee *in r.* 42:6
have raised him *in r.* and will. 45:13
gone out of my mouth *in r.* 23
God of Israel, but not *in r.* 48:1
in r. shalt thou be established. 54:14
that speak *in r.*, mighty to. 63:1
the Lord liveth, *in r.* *Jer* 4:2
betroth thee unto me *in r.* *Hos* 2:19
sow to yourselves *in r.*, reap. 10:12
God in truth and *in r.* *Zech* 8:8
offer an offering *in r.* *Mal* 3:3
judge the world *in r.* *Acts* 17:31
and cut it short *in r.* *Rom* 9:28
new man . . . is created *in r.* *Eph* 4:24
for instruction *in r.* *2 Tim* 3:16
and *in r.* he doth judge. *Rev* 19:11

my righteousness

so *my r.* answer for me. *Gen* 30:33
saying, For *my r.* Lord. *Deut* 9:4
Lord rewarded me according to *my r.* *2 Sam* 22:21, 25; *Ps* 18:20, 24
yea, return again, *my r.* *Job* 6:29
my r. I hold fast, and will. 27:6
saidst, *my r.* is more than. 35:2
I call, O God of *my r.* *Ps* 4:1
Lord, according to *my r.* *Ps* 7:8
the right hand of *my r.* *Isa* 41:10
I bring near *my r.* 46:13
my r. is near. 51:5
my r. shall not be abolished. 6
but *my r.* shall be for ever. 8
salvation is near to come, *my r.* 56:1
not having *mine* own *r.* *Phil* 3:9

our righteousnesses

all *our r.* are as filthy. *Isa* 64:6
not for *our r.* but for. *Dan* 9:18

thy righteousness

nor for *thy r.* or. *Deut* 9:5, 6
make the habitation of *thy r.* *Job* 8:6
and *thy r.* may profit the son. 35:8
lead me, O Lo d, in *thy r.* *Ps* 5:8
deliver me in *thy r.* 31:1; 71:2
Lord, according to *thy r.* 35:24
shall speak of *thy r.* 28; 71:24
thy r. is like the great. 36:6
O continue *thy r.* to the upright. 10
he shall bring forth *thy r.* 37:6
I have not hid *thy r.* within. 40:10
shall sing aloud of *thy r.* 51:14
let them not come into *thy r.* 69:27
shew forth *thy r.* all day. 71:15
I will make mention of *thy r.* 16
thy r. O God, is very high. 19
and give *thy r.* unto the king's. 72:1
thy r. be known in land of. 88:12
and in *thy r.* shall they be. 89:16
quicken me in *thy r.* 119:40
for word of *thy r.* 123*
thy r. is an everlasting. 142
answer me, and in *thy r.* 143:1
for *thy r.*' sake, bring my soul. 11
and they shall sing of *thy r.* 145:7
had *thy r.* been as waves. *Isa* 48:18
I will declare *thy r.* and. 57:12
thy r. shall go before thee. 58:8
and the Gentiles shall see *thy r.* 62:2
according to all *thy r.* *Dan* 9:16

rightly

said, Is not he *r.* named ? *Gen* 27:36
Thou hast *r.* judged. *Luke* 7:43
know that thou teachest *r.* 20:21
r. dividing the word of. *2 Tim* 2:15*

rigour

Israel to serve with *r.* *Ex* 1:13, 14
thou shalt not rule with *r.* *Lev* 25:43
46, 53

Rimmon

Ain and *R.* cities of. *Josh* 15:32
fled towards the wilderness, to the rock *R.* *Judg* 20:45, 47; 21:13
Baanah and Rechab sons of *R.* *2 Sam* 4:2, 5, 9
goeth into the house of *R.* *2 Ki* 5:18
of Simeon were Ain, *R.* *1 Chr* 4:32
was given to Merari, *R.* 6:77
be turned as a plain to *R.* *Zech* 14:10

ring

(The signet ring of a monarch contained his seal, which was affixed to a document instead of a signature, as few people wrote in those days, and fewer still read. To give this ring to another was to give him the right to sign in place of the king. Rings of various sorts were also worn as ornaments, either by a monarch or others)

Pharaoh took off his *r.* *Gen* 41:42*
coupled unto one *r.* *Ex* 26:24; 36:29
king Ahasuerus took his *r.* *Esth* 3:10
with the king's *r.* 12; 8:8, 10
the king took off his *r.* 8:2
the father said, Put a *r.* *Luke* 15:22
a man with a gold *r.* *Jas* 2:2

ringleader

and a *r.* of the sect of. *Acts* 24:5

rings

four *r.* of gold for it. *Ex* 25:12
put staves into the *r.* 14, 15; 27:7
37:5; 38:7
their *r.* of gold. 26:29; 28:23, 26
27; 30:4; 36:34; 37:3, 13; 39:16
19, 20
upon net four brazen *r.* 27:4
the breastplate by the *r.* 28:28
jewels, bracelets, and *r.* *Num* 31:50*

fastened to silver *r.* pillars. *Esth* 1:6
his hands are as gold *r.* *S of S* 5:14
will take away the *r.* and. *Isa* 3:21
their *r.* so high that they were dreadful, their *r.* were full. *Ezek* 1:18

ringstraked

(*American Revision* ring-streaked)
he goats that were *r.* *Gen* 30:35
if he said, The *r.* shall be. 31:8
rams were *r.*, speckled. 10, 12

rinsed

pot be both scoured and *r.* *Lev* 6:28
and hath not *r.* his hands. 15:11
every vessel of wood shall be *r.* 12

riot, *substantive*

children not accused of *r.* *Tit* 1:6
to the same excess of *r.* *1 Pet* 4:4

riot

count it pleasure to *r.* *2 Pet* 2:13*

rioting

walk not in *r.* and. *Rom* 13:13*

riotous

not amongst *r.* eaters. *Pr* 23:20*
he that is a companion of *r.* 28:7*
substance with *r.* living. *Luke* 15:13

rip

wilt *r.* up their women. *2 Ki* 8:12

ripe

brought forth *r.* grapes. *Gen* 40:10
first of thy *r.* fruits. *Ex* 22:29
of the first *r.* grapes. *Num* 13:20
whatsoever is first *r.* in the. 18:13
even like the figs that are first *r.*
Jer 24:2; *Hos* 9:10; *Nah* 3:12
sickle, for the harvest is *r.* *Joel* 3:13
desired the first *r.* fruit. *Mi* 7:1
for harvest of earth is *r.* *Rev* 14:15
for her grapes are fully *r.* 18

ripening

and the sour grape is *r.* *Isa* 18:5

ripped

all the women with child he *r.* up.
2 Ki 15:16
with child shall be *r.* up. *Hos* 13:16
because they have *r.* up. *Amos* 1:13

rise

if he *r.* again and walk. *Ex* 21:19
and a sceptre shall *r.* *Num* 24:17
r. that they *r.* not again. *Deut* 33:11
shall *r.* and go through. *Josh* 18:4
R. thou and fall upon us. *Judg* 8:21
thou shalt *r.* early, and set. 9:33
that he should *r.* to lie. *1 Sam* 22:13
and suffered them not to *r.* 24:7
when child was dead, thou didst *r.*
2 Sam 12:21
all that *r.* against thee be. 18:32
upon my right hand *r.* *Job* 30:12
they were not able to *r.* *Ps* 18:38
though war should *r.* against. 27:3
down, shall not be able to *r.* 36:12
at midnight I will *r.* to give. 119:62
into deep pits, that they *r.* 140:10
calamity shall *r.* suddenly. *Pr* 24:22
when the wicked *r.* a man. 28:12, 28
I will *r.* now and go about the city.
S of S 3:2
prepare slaughter, that they do not *r.*
Isa 14:21
earth shall fall and not *r.* 24:20
deceased, they shall not *r.* 26:14
now will I *r.* saith the Lord. 33:10
down together, they shall not *r.* 43:17
every tongue that shall *r.* thou. 54:17
shall thy light *r.* in obscurity. 58:10
fall and *r.* no more. *Jer* 25:27
Babylon shall not *r.* from evil. 51:64
Israel shall no more *r.* *Amos* 5:2
I will *r.* against the house of. 7:9
he maketh sun to *r.* on. *Mat* 5:45
and third day he shall *r.* again. 20:19
Mark 9:31; 10:34; *Luke* 18:33
24:7
for nation shall *r.* against. *Mat* 24:7
Mark 13:8; *Luke* 21:10
many false prophets shall *r.*
Mat 24:11; *Mark* 13:22
r., let us be going. *Mat* 26:46
after three days I will *r.* again.
Mat 27:63; *Mark* 8:31
and should sleep, and *r.* *Mark* 4:27
be of good comfort, *r.*; he. 10:49
when they shall *r.* 12:23, 25
the dead, that they *r.* 26
trouble me not, I cannot *r.* *Luke* 11:7
though he will not *r.* because he. 8
when ye see a cloud *r.* out of. 12:54
Why sleep ye ? *r.* and pray. 22:46
to suffer and to *r.* from. 24:46
Jesus saith, *R.* take up thy. *John* 5:8
thy brother shall *r.* again. 11:23
I know he shall *r.* 24
that he must *r.* again. 20:9
r. Peter, kill and eat. *Acts* 10:13
r. and stand upon thy feet. 26:16
should be the first that should *r.* 23
he that shall *r.* to reign. *Rom* 15:12
if so be the dead *r.* not. *1 Cor* 15:15
16, 29, 32
in Christ shall *r.* first. *1 Thes* 4:16
another priest should *r.* *Heb* 7:11
r. and measure the temple. *Rev* 11:1

rise *up*

ye shall *r. up* early and go. *Gen* 19:2
that I cannot *r. up.* 31:35
r. up and stand before Pharaoh.
Ex 8:20; 9:13
r. up and get you forth from. 12:31
thou shalt *r. up* before. *Lev* 19:32
r. up, Lord, let enemies. *Num* 10:35
call thee up, *r. up* and go. 22:20
r. up, Balak, and hear, thou. 23:18
behold, the people shall *r. up.* 24
Now, *r. up*, said I, and. *Deut* 2:13
r. ye *up*, and pass over the. 24
if a man *r. up* against his. 19:11
one witness shall not *r. up:* 15
if a false witness *r. up* against. 16
thine enemies that *r. up.* 28:7
the generation that shall *r. up.* 29:22
this people will *r. up*, and. 31:16
their gods, let them *r. up.* 32:38
then ye shall *r. up* from. *Josh* 8:7
a great flame *r. up.* *Judg* 20:38, 40
wherefore *r. up* early. *1 Sam* 29:10
they said, Let us *r. up.* *Neh* 2:18
and the earth shall *r. up.* *Job* 20:27
many are they that *r. up.* *Ps* 3:1
save them from those that *r. up.* 17:7
me above those that *r. up.* 18:48
false witnesses did *r. up*, they. 35:11
he shall *r. up* no more. 41:8
them under that *r. up* against. 44:5
them that *r. up* against me. 59:1
the tumult of those that *r. up.* 74:23
desire of the wicked that *r. up.* 92:11
who will *r. up* for me against? 94:16
it is vain for you to *r. up.* 127:2
grieved with those that *r. up* ? 139:21
her children *r. up*, and call. *Pr* 31:28
the ruler *r. up* against. *Eccl* 10:4
he shall *r. up* at the voice. 12:4
unto me, *R. up*, my love. *S of S* 2:10
woe unto them that *r. up.* *Isa* 5:11
I will *r. up* against them. 14:22
Lord shall *r. up* as in mount. 28:21
r. up, ye women at ease. 32:9
should *r. up* every man. *Jer* 37:10
behold, waters *r. up* out of. 47:2
gather against her, and *r. up.* 49:14
against them that *r. up* against. 51:1
I am not able to *r. up.* *Lam* 1:14
it shall *r. up* wholly. *Amos* 8:8; 9:5
and never *r. up* again. 14
let us *r. up* against Edom. *Ob* 1
affliction shall not *r. up.* *Nah* 1:9
they not *r. up* suddenly ? *Hab* 2:7
until the day that I *r. up.* *Zeph* 3:8
his hand *r. up* against. *Zech* 14:13
children shall *r. up* against their.
Mat 10:21; *Mark* 13:12
the men of Nineveh shall *r. up.*
Mat 12:41; *Luke* 11:32
queen of the south shall *r. up.*
Mat 12:42; *Luke* 11:31
and if Satan *r. up.* *Mark* 3:26
r. up, lo, he that betrayeth me. 14:42
to say, *R. up* and walk. *Luke* 5:23
he said, *R. up* and stand forth. 6:8
in the name of Jesus *r. up.* *Acts* 3:6
I saw a beast *r. up* out. *Rev* 13:1

risen

the sun was *r.* when Lot. *Gen* 19:23
if sun be *r.* on him. *Ex* 22:3
ye are *r.* up in your. *Num* 32:14
ye are *r.* up against my. *Judg* 9:18
and when she was *r.* up. *Ruth* 2:15
a man is *r.* to pursue. *1 Sam* 25:29
whole family is *r.* up. *2 Sam* 14:7
I am *r.* up in room of David.
1 Ki 8:20; *2 Chr* 6:10
of the man of God was *r.* *2 Ki* 6:15
of Solomon is *r.* up. *2 Chr* 13:6
when Jehoram was *r.* up to. 21:4
but we are *r.* and stand. *Ps* 20:8
for false witnesses are *r.* up. 27:12
for strangers are *r.* up against. 54:3
the proud are *r.* against. 86:14
glory of the Lord is *r.* *Isa* 60:1
violence is *r.* into a rod. *Ezek* 7:11
for the waters were *r.* waters. 47:5
even of late my people is *r.* *Mi* 2:8
hath not *r.* a greater. *Mat* 11:11
is John the Baptist, he is *r.* 14:2
Mark 6:14, 16; *Luke* 9:7
until the Son of man be *r.* again.
Mat 17:9; *Mark* 9:9
after I am *r.* I will go before.
Mat 26:32; *Mark* 14:28
disciples steal him away and say he is *r.* *Mat* 27:64
he is not here: for he is *r.* as he said.
28:6; *Mark* 16:6
when Jesus was *r.* early. *Mark* 16:9
which had seen him after he was *r.*
14; *John* 21:14
that a great prophet is *r.* *Luke* 7:16
one of old prophets was *r.* 9:8, 19
master of the house is *r.* up. 13:25
the Lord is *r.* indeed, and. 24:34
when therefore he was *r.* *John* 2:22
must needs have *r.* again. *Acts* 17:3
yea rather that is *r.* again. *Rom* 8:34
then Christ is not *r.* *1 Cor* 15:13
if Christ be not *r.* 14
but now is Christ *r.* 20
in baptism ye are also *r.* *Col* 2:12
if ye be *r.* with Christ, seek. 3:1
sun is no sooner *r.* *Jas* 1:11

risest

shalt talk of them when thou *r.*
Deut 6:7; 11:19

riseth

as when a man *r.* against. *Deut* 22:26
cursed that *r.* up and. *Josh* 6:26
light when the sun *r.* *2 Sam* 23:4
the sun and it *r.* not. *Job* 9:7
man lieth down, and *r.* not. 14:12
he *r.* up, and no man is sure. 24:22
he that *r.* up against me, as. 27:7
shall I do when God *r.* up ? 31:14
just man falleth, and *r.* *Pr* 24:16
r. also while it is yet night. 31:15
know from whence it *r.* *Isa* 47:11
Egypt *r.* up like a flood. *Jer* 46:8
the daughter *r.* up against. *Mi* 7:6
Jesus *r.* from supper, and. *John* 13:4

rising, *substantive*

if in skin of his flesh a *r.* *Lev* 13:2
see if the *r.* be white. 10; 19:43
if the spot stay, it is a *r.* of. 13:28
this is the law for a *r.* and. 14:56
held spears from the *r.* *Neh* 4:21
whom there is no *r.* *Pr* 30:31
to the brightness of thy *r.* *Isa* 60:3
what the *r.* from the dead should mean. *Mark* 9:10
for the fall and *r.* of. *Luke* 2:34

***sun*-rising**

toward the *r.* of the *sun.* *Num* 2:3
before Moab, toward *sun-r.* 21:11
34:15; *Deut* 4:41, 47; *Josh* 12:1
13:5; 19:12, 27, 34
from the *r.* of the *sun.* *Ps* 50:1
from *r.* of *sun*, Lord's name. 113:3
from *r.* of *sun* shall he call. *Isa* 41:25
know from the *r.* of the *sun.* 45:6
glory from the *r.* of the *sun.* 59:19
from *r.* of *sun* my name. *Mal* 1:11
sepulchre at *r.* of the *sun.* *Mark* 16:2

rising

messengers, *r.* betimes. *2 Chr* 36:15
my leanness *r.* in me. *Job* 16:8
wild asses go forth, *r.* betimes. 24:5
murderer *r.* with the light killeth. 14

his friend, r. early. Pr 27:14
I spake unto you, r. up early.
Jer 7:13; 25:3; 35:14
the prophets to you r. up early. 7:25
25:4; 26:5; 29:19; 35:15; 44:4
r. early, and protesting. 11:7
though I taught them, r. up. 32:33
sitting down and r. up. Lam 3:63
in the morning, r. before. Mark 1:35

rites

according to all the r. Num 9:3*

river

(Frequently this word is used where the Hebrew really means a valley; *or where the stream is small and hardly deserves the name. When* the river *is referred to it usually means the* Nile. *Where the expression* river of Egypt *is used it may mean* [1] *the* Nile, *or* [2] *a small brook or desert stream which formed one of the boundaries of Egypt. The word is also used symbolically of a great abundance)*

and passed over the r. Gen 31:21
Saul of Rehoboth by the r. 36:37
1 Chr 1:48
behold, he stood by the r. Gen 41:1
ye shall cast into the r. Ex 1:22
of Pharaoh came to wash at r. 2:5
the water of the r. shall become. 4:9
the r. shall die, and r. stink. 7:18
the r. shall bring forth frogs. 8:3
may remain in the r. only. 9, 11
journey, pass over the r. Deut 2:24*
Gilead even to the r. Arnon. 3:16
the city that is in the midst of the r.
Josh 13:9*; 2 Sam 24:5*
draw to the r. Kishon. Judg 4:7
r. Kishon that ancient r. swept. 5:21
draw that city into the r. 2 Sam 17:13
reigned over from the r. 1 Ki 4:21
are on this side the r. Ezra 4:10
no portion on this side the r. 16
governor on this side the r. 5:3
to r. that runneth to Ahava. 8:15
behold he drinketh up a r. Job 40:23
make them drink of the r. Ps 36:8
a r. the streams shall make. 46:4
thou enrichest it with the r. 65:9
have dominion from the r. to. 72:8
her branches unto the r. 80:11
in the dry places like a r. 105:41
them the waters of the r. Isa 8:7
shake his hand over the r. 11:15
and the r. shall be wasted. 19:5
the harvest of the r. is her. 23:3*
pass through thy land as a r. 10*
off from channel of the r. 27:12
peace been as a r. O daughter. 48:18
extend peace to her like a r. 66:12
drink the waters of the r. Jer 2:18
out her roots by the r. 17:8
let tears run down like r. Lam 2:18
My r. is mine own. Ezek 29:3, 9
it was a r. that I could not. 47:5
live whither the r. cometh. 9
afflict you to the r. of. Amos 6:14*
from the fortress to the r. Mi 7:12
his dominion from the r. Zech 9:10
deeps of the r. shall dry up. 10:11*
were baptized in the r. Mark 1:5
we went by a r. side. Acts 16:13
pure r. of water of life. Rev 22:1
on either side of the r. was the. 2
see **bank, beyond, brink, Chebar, Euphrates**

rivers

stretch out thine hand on the r.
Ex 7:19*; 8:5*
whatsoever hath fins in r. Lev 11:9
all that have not fins in the r. 10
to Jotbath, a land of r. Deut 10:7*
r. of Damascus better? 2 Ki 5:12
I have dried up all the r. 19:24
Isa 37:25
not see the r. of honey. Job 20:17
he cutteth out the r. among. 28:10*
poureth me out r. of oil. 29:6†
planted by the r. of water. Ps 1:3*
thou driedst up mighty r. 74:15
waters to run down like r. 78:16
had turned their r. into blood. 44
set his right hand in the r. Ps 89:25
turneth r. into a wilderness. 107:33
r. of waters run down. 119:136
by the r. of Babylon there we. 137:1
and r. of waters in the. Pr 5:16†
in the hand of the Lord, as r. 21:1*
all r. run into the sea. Eccl 1:7
eyes of doves by the r. of waters.
S of S 5:12*
hiss for the fly in the r. Isa 7:18
a nation, whose land r. 18:2, 7
and they shall turn the r. far. 19:6
and on every high hill r. 30:25†
a man shall be as r. of water. 32:2†
be to us a place of broad r. 33:21
I will open r. in high places. 41:18
I will make the r. islands. 42:15
passest through the r. they. 43:2
and I will make r. in the. 19, 20
be dry, and will dry up thy r. 44:27
the thigh, pass over the r. 47:2
I make r. a wilderness, their. 50:2
them to walk by the r. Jer 31:9
are moved as the r. 46:7, 8
down with r. of waters. Lam 3:48†
Lord to the hills and r. Ezek 6:3*
that lieth in the midst of his r. 29:3
the fish of thy r. to stick to thy scales
. . . out of the midst of thy r. 4
and all the fish of thy r. 5
against thee, and against thy r. 10
I will make the r. dry, and. 30:12
him up on high with her r. 31:4
broken by the r. of the land. 12*
thou camest forth with thy r. 32:2
and the r. shall be full of thee. 6*
then will I cause their r. to run. 14
them on mountains by the r. 34:13*
in all thy r. shall they fall. 35:8*
say to the hills, to the r. and. 36:6*
whithersoever the r. shall. 47:9
for the r. of waters are. Joel 1:20*
all the r. of Judah shall flow. 3:18*
ten thousands of r. of oil. Mi 6:7
and drieth up the r. Nah 1:4
the gates of the r. shall be. 2:6
that was situate among the r. 3:8
displeased against the r.? Hab 3:8
didst cleave the earth with r. 9
flow r. of living water. John 7:38
on the third part of the r. Rev 8:10
poured out his vial on the r. 16:4

Rizpah

whose name was R. 2 Sam 3:7
two sons of R. to Gibeonites. 21:8
R. spread sackcloth for her on. 10

road

ye made a r. to-day. 1 Sam 27:10*

roar

let the sea r. 1 Chr 16:32; Ps 96:11
98:7
though waters thereof r. Ps 46:3
thine enemies r. in thy. 74:4
the young lions r. after their. 104:21
r. like young lions. Isa 5:29
in that day they shall r. against. 30
Lord shall r.; he shall prevail. 42:13*
we r. all like bears, and. 59:11
though they r. yet can. Jer 5:22
the Lord shall r. from on high. 25:30
when the waves thereof r. 31:35
their voice shall r. like the. 50:42
they shall r. together like lions. 51:38
when her waves do r. like great. 55
r. like a lion, when he shall r.
Hos 11:10
the Lord shall r. out of Zion.
Joel 3:16; Amos 1:2
will a lion r. if he hath? Amos 3:4

roared

lion r. against Samson. Judg 14:5
I have r. by reason of. Ps 38:8†
the sea, whose waves r. Isa 51:15
the young lions r. upon him. Jer 2:15
the lion hath r., who will? Amos 3:8

roareth

after it a voice r. he. Job 37:4
their voice r. like the sea. Jer 6:23
cried, as when a lion r. Rev 10:3

roaring, *substantive*

the r. of the lion. Job 4:10
from the words of my r.? Ps 22:1†
old through my r. all the. Ps 33:3†
king's wrath is as the r. Pr 19:12
the fear of a king is as the r. 20:2
their r. shall be like a lion. Isa 5:29
roar like the r. of the sea. 30
land was desolate by the noise of his
r. Ezek 19:7
a voice of the r. of young. Zech 11:3

roaring

upon me as a r. lion. Ps 22:13
as a r. lion, so is a wicked. Pr 28:15
as the young lion r. on. Isa 31:4*
conspiracy, like a r. lion. Ezek 22:25
within her are r. lions. Zeph 3:3
sea and the waves r. Luke 21:25
the devil, as a r. lion. 1 Pet 5:8

roarings

my r. are poured out. Job 3:24†

roast, -ed

flesh that night, r. with fire. Ex 12:8
but r. with fire. 9; Deut 16:7
flesh to r. for the priest. 1 Sam 2:15
they r. the passover. 2 Chr 35:13
he roasteth r., is satisfied. Isa 44:16
yea, also I have r. flesh, and. 19
king of Babylon r. in fire. Jer 29:22

roasteth

the slothful man r. not. Pr 12:27

rob

not r. thy neighbour. Lev 19:13
beasts, which shall r. you. 26:22
they r. the threshing. 1 Sam 23:1
r. not the poor, because. Pr 22:22
and that they may r. Isa 10:2*
the lot of them that r. us. 17:14
spoil, and r. those that. Ezek 39:10
will a man r. God? yet ye. Mal 3:8

robbed

and they r. all that came. Judg 9:25
in minds, as a bear r. 2 Sam 17:8
wicked have r. me. Ps 119:61*
let a bear r. of her whelps. Pr 17:12
I have r. their treasures. Isa 10:13
but this is a people r. and. 42:22
treasures, they shall be r. Jer 50:37
give again that he had r. Ezek 33:15
rob those that r. them. 39:10
r. me, wherein have we r.? Mal 3:8
with a curse, for ye have r. me. 9
I r. other churches. 2 Cor 11:8

robber

and the r. swalloweth up. Job 5:5*
and the r. shall prevail. 18:9*
beget a son that is a r. Ezek 18:10
is a thief and a r. John 10:1
Now Barabbas was a r. 18:40

robbers

tabernacles of r. prosper. Job 12:6
gave Israel to the r. Isa 42:24
house become a den of r.? Jer 7:11
the r. shall enter into it. Ezek 7:22
the r. of thy people. Dan 11:14*
troops of r. wait for a. Hos 6:9
and the troop of r. spoileth. 7:1
if r. by night, would they not? Ob 5
came before me are r. John 10:8
these men are not r. of. Acts 19:37
of waters, in perils of r. 2 Cor 11:26

robbery

and become not vain in r. Ps 62:10
the r. of the wicked shall. Pr 21:7*
I hate r. for burnt offering. Isa 61:8
have exercised r. and. Ezek 22:29
who store up r. in their. Amos 3:10
city is full of lies and r. Nah 3:1*
who thought it no r. to. Phil 2:6*

robbeth

whoso r. his father or. Pr 28:24

robe

make an ephod, and a r. Ex 28:4
shalt make the r. of the ephod. 31
on the hem of the r. 34; 39:25, 26
Aaron the coat and r. 29:5; Lev 8:7
stripped himself of his r. 1 Sam 18:4
off the skirt of Saul's r. 24:4
see the skirt of thy r. in my hand . . .
the skirt of thy r. and killed. 11
was clothed with a r. 1 Chr 15:27
judgement was as a r. Job 29:14
clothe him with thy r. Isa 22:21
hath covered me with r. of. 61:10

laid his r. from him. *Jonah* 3:6
ye pull off the r. with the garment. *Mi* 2:8
put on Jesus a scarlet r. *Mat* 27:28
after that, they took the r. off. 31
bring forth the best r. *Luke* 15:22
arrayed him in a gorgeous r. 23:11*
on Jesus a purple r. *John* 19:2*
wearing the purple r. 5*

robes

with such r. were virgins apparelled. *2 Sam* 13:18
having put on their r. *1 Ki* 22:10
put thou on thy r. 30; *2 Chr* 18:9, 29
shall lay away their r. *Ezek* 26:16
desire to walk in long r. *Luke* 20:46
and white r. were given. *Rev* 6:11
the Lamb, clothed with white r. 7:9
which are arrayed in white r.? 13
which have washed their r. 14

rock

before thee upon the r. *Ex* 17:6
thou shalt stand upon a r. 33:21
put thee in a cleft of the r. 22
speak to the r. before. *Num* 20:8
fetch you water out of this r.? 10
his rod smote the r. twice. 11
and thou puttest thy nest in a r. 24:21
thee water out of the r. *Deut* 8:15
he is the *R.*, his work is perfect. 32:4
suck honey and oil out of the r. 13
he lightly esteemed the r. of. 15
of the *R.* that begat thee thou. 18
except their *R.* had sold them. 30
for their r. is not as our *R.* 31
where is their r. in whom they? 37
and lay them upon this r. *Judg* 6:20
there rose up fire out of the r. 21
altar to the Lord on this r. 26*
they slew Oreb on the r. Oreb. 7:25
Manoah offered it on a r. to. 13:19
in the top of the r. Etam. 15:8
turned to the r. of Rimmon. 20:45
neither is there any r. *1 Sam* 2:2
a sharp r. on one side, sharp r. 14:4
David came down into a r. 23:25
sackcloth on the r. *2 Sam* 21:10
he said, Lord is my r. 22:2
Ps 18:2; 92:15
the God of my r. in him. *2 Sam* 22:3
and who is a r. save our God? 32
Ps 18:31
blessed be my r. . . . exalted be the God of r. *2 Sam* 22:47; *Ps* 18:46
God of Israel said, The r. *2 Sam* 23:3
captains went to the r. *1 Chr* 11:15
from the top of the r. *2 Chr* 25:12
water for them out of the r. for their. *Neh* 9:15; *Ps* 78:16; 105:41
the r. is removed out of. *Job* 14:18
and shall the r. be removed? 18:4
that they were graven in the r. 19:24
they embrace the r. for want of. 24:8
forth his hand upon the r. 28:9
and the r. poured out rivers. 29:6
time when wild goats of the r. 39:1
on the r. on the crag of the r. 28
set me up upon a r. *Ps* 27:5; 40:2
will I cry, O Lord, my r. 28:1
r. for an house of defence. 31:2
my r. and my fortress. 3; 71:3
I will say to God, My r. why? 42:9
lead me to the r. that is higher. 61:2
God only is my r. 62:2, 6
r. of my strength. 7
behold, he smote the r. 78:20
remembered that God was their r. 35
with honey out of the r. have. 81:16
r. of my salvation. 89:26
r. of my refuge. 94:22
make a joyful noise to the r. 95:1
which turned the r. into a. 114:8
way of a serpent upon a r. *Pr* 30:19
art in the clefts of the r. *S of S* 2:14
enter into the r. and hide. *Isa* 2:10
r. of offence to both houses. 8:14
slaughter of the r. of Oreb. 10:26
not mindful of the r. of thy. 17:10
an habitation for himself in a r. 22:16
as the shadow of a great r. 32:2
let inhabitants of the r. sing. 42:11*
caused waters to flow out of r. 48:21
look unto the r. whence ye. 51:1
faces harder than a r. *Jer* 5:3
girdle in a hole of the r. 13:4
which cometh from the r. 18:14
thee, O inhabitant of the r. 21:13
a hammer that breaketh the r. 23:29
cities, and dwell in the r. 48:28
dwellest in the clefts of the r. 49:16
it upon the top of a r. *Ezek* 24:7
blood upon the top of a r. 8
her like the top of a r. 26:4, 14
horses run upon the r.? *Amos* 6:12
in the clefts of the r. *Ob* 3
built his house upon a r. *Mat* 7:24
founded upon a r. 25; *Luke* 6:48*
upon this r. I will build. *Mat* 16:18
own new tomb, which he had hewn out in the r. 27:60; *Mark* 15:46
some fell upon a r. *Luke* 8:6
they on the r. 13
in Sion a stumbling stone, and r. of. *Rom* 9:33; *1 Pet* 2:8
spiritual r. that followed them, and that r. was Christ. *1 Cor* 10:4

rocks

for from the top of the r. *Num* 23:9
the people hid themselves in r. *1 Sam* 13:6
seek David upon the r. 24:2
brake in pieces the r. *1 Ki* 19:11
rivers among the r. *Job* 28:10
caves of the earth, and in r. 30:6
the r. in the wilderness. *Ps* 78:15
and the r. are a refuge for. 104:18
they their houses in the r. *Pr* 30:26
go into the holes of the r. *Isa* 2:19
the r. and tops of the ragged r. 21
rest in the holes of the r. 7:19
shall be the munitions of r. 33:16
under the clefts of the r. 57:5
city shall climb on the r. *Jer* 4:29
out of the holes of the r. 16:16
roll thee down from the r. 51:25
the r. are thrown down. *Nah* 1:6
quake, and the r. rent. *Mat* 27:51
have fallen upon the r. *Acts* 27:29*
in the dens and in the r. *Rev* 6:15
and said to the r., Fall on us. 16

rod

(*This word is often used to mean the* shepherd's crook)

became a r. in his hand. *Ex* 4:4
thou shalt take this r. in thine. 17
Moses took the r. of God in. 20; 17:9
to Aaron, Take thy r. 7:9, 19
down every man his r. 12
he lifted up the r. and. 20; 14:16
smite a servant with a r. 21:20
passeth under the r. *Lev* 27:32
man's name on his r. *Num* 17:2
the r. of Aaron for the house of. 8
with his r. he smote the rock. 20:11
forth the end of the r. *1 Sam* 14:27
him with the r. of men. *2 Sam* 7:14
let him take his r. away. *Job* 9:34
neither is the r. of God upon. 21:9
break them with a r. of iron. *Ps* 2:9
thy r. and thy staff they. 23:4
remember the r. of thine. 74:2*
transgression with a r. 89:32
the Lord shall send the r. of. 110:2
r. of wicked shall not rest on. 125:3*
a r. for the back of. *Pr* 10:13; 26:3
he that spareth his r. hateth. 13:24
the foolish is a r. of pride. 14:3
r. of his anger shall fail. 22:8
the r. of correction shall drive. 15
beat him with the r. 23:13, 14
the r. and reproof give. 29:15
thou hast broken the r. of. *Isa* 9:4
O Assyrian, the r. of mine. 10:5
as if the r. should shake itself. 15
he shall smite with a r. and lift. 24
as his r. was on the sea, so. 26
shall come forth a r. out of. 11:1*
shall smite the earth with the r. 4
the r. of him that smote thee. 14:29
is beaten out with a r. 28:27
which smote with a r. 30:31
and said, I see a r. of an. *Jer* 1:11
Israel the r. of his inheritance. 10:16*; 51:19*
how is the beautiful r. broken! 48:17
by the r. of his wrath. *Lam* 3:1
the r. hath blossomed. *Ezek* 7:10
violence is risen up into a r. 11
out of a r. of her branches, so that she hath no strong r. to. 19:14
pass under the r. and bring. 20:37
the r. of my son. 21:10, 13
smite Judge of Israel with a r. *Mi* 5:1
hear ye the r. and who hath. 6:9
feed thy people with thy r. 7:14
you with a r. or in love? *1 Cor* 4:21
wherein was Aaron's r. *Heb* 9:4
with a r. of iron. *Rev* 2:27; 19:15
given me a reed like to a r. 11:1
all nations with a r. of iron. 12:5

rode

Rebekah and her damsels r. on. *Gen* 24:61
thirty sons that r. on. *Judg* 10:4
nephews that r. on ass colts. 12:14
Abigail r. on the ass. *1 Sam* 25:20, 42
four hundred which r. on camels. 30:17
Absalom r. upon a mule. *2 Sam* 18:9
he r. on a cherub, and did fly. 22:11
Ps 18:10
the old prophet r. on. *1 Ki* 13:13
and Ahab r. and went to. 18:45
Jehu r. in a chariot, and. *2 Ki* 9:16
remember when I and thou r. 25
save the beast that I r. *Neh* 2:12
the posts that r. on the. *Esth* 8:14

rods

Jacob took r. of green. *Gen* 30:37
might conceive among the r. 41
Aaron's rod swallowed up their r. *Ex* 7:12
gave him twelve r. *Num* 17:6
and Moses laid up the r. before. 7
she had strong r. for the. *Ezek* 19:11
her strong r. were broken and. 12
was I beaten with r. *2 Cor* 11:25

roe, -s

as swift as the r. on. *1 Chr* 12:8
as the hind and pleasant r. *Pr* 5:19*
deliver thyself as the r. from. 6:5
I charge you by the r. and hinds. *S of S* 2:7; 3:5
is like a r. or a young hart. 9
be thou like a r. or hart. 2:17; 8:14
it shall be as the chased r. *Isa* 13:14
see **young**

wild **roe**

Asahel was as light of foot as a *wild* r. *2 Sam* 2:18

roebuck, -s

ye may eat of the r. *Deut* 12:15*, 22*
14:5*; 15:22*
besides harts and r. *1 Ki* 4:23*

roll, *verb*

we cannot, till they r. *Gen* 29:8
and Joshua said, *R.* *Josh* 10:18
r. a great stone unto me this day. *1 Sam* 14:33
and I will r. thee down. *Jer* 51:25
in Aphrah, r. thyself. *Mi* 1:10
who shall r. us away? *Mark* 16:3

roll, *substantive*

found at Achmetha a r. *Ezra* 6:2
take thee a great r. and. *Isa* 8:1*
take thee a r. of a book. *Jer* 36:2
go and read in the r. 6
till after the r. was consumed. 23
take another r. 28
saith Lord, Thou hast burnt this r. 29
an hand was sent unto me, and lo, a r. *Ezek* 2:9
eat this r. 3:1
he caused me to eat that r. 2
fill thy bowels with this r. that. 3
and behold a flying r. *Zech* 5:1, 2

rolled

they r. the stone from. *Gen* 29:3
that Jacob went near, and r. 10
I have r. away reproach of. *Josh* 5:9
in desolation they r. *Job* 30:14
with noise, and garments r. *Isa* 9:5
the heavens shall be r. together. 34:4; *Rev* 6:14
his own new tomb, he r. a great stone to door. *Mat* 27:60; *Mark* 15:46

angel came and *r*. back. *Mat* 28:2
the stone was *r*. away. 16:4
found the stone *r*. away. *Luke* 24:2

roller

bound up, to put a *r*. to. *Ezek* 30:21

rolleth

he that *r*. a stone, it will. *Pr* 26:27

rolling

nations shall flee like a *r*. thing. *Isa* 17:13*

rolls

search was made in the house of the *r*. *Ezra* 6:1*

Roman

a man that is a *R*. *Acts* 22:25, 26
tell me, Art thou a *R*.? 27
that he was a *R*. 29; 23:27

Romans

the *R*. shall come and. *John* 11:48
us to observe, being *R*. *Acts* 16:21
beaten us, being *R*. 37
heard they were *R*. 38
prisoner into hands of the *R*. 28:17

Rome

strangers of *R*. we do. *Acts* 2:10
all Jews to depart from *R*. 18:2
I must see *R*. 19:21
bear witness also at *R*. 23:11
we came to *R*., Paul dwelt. 28:16
to all that be in *R*., beloved. *Rom* 1:7
preach gospel to you that are at *R*. 15
when he was in *R*. he. *2 Tim* 1:17

roof

under the shadow of my *r*. *Gen* 19:8
a battlement for thy *r*. *Deut* 22:8
the *r*. and hid with flax which she had laid in order on *r*. *Josh* 2:6
on the *r*. were 3000. *Judg* 16:27
David walked on the *r*. . . . and from the *r*. he saw a woman. *2 Sam* 11:2
watchman went up to the *r*. 18:24
booths on the *r*. of his. *Neh* 8:16
gate from the *r*. of one. *Ezek* 40:13
that thou shouldest come under my *r*. *Mat* 8:8; *Luke* 7:6
they uncovered the *r*. *Mark* 2:4

roof with *mouth*

tongue cleaved to *r*. of their *mouth*. *Job* 29:10
cleave to *r*. of my *mouth*. *Ps* 137:6
the *r*. of thy *mouth* like. *S of S* 7:9
cleaveth to *r*. of his *mouth*. *Lam* 4:4
tongue cleave to *r*. of thy *mouth*. *Ezek* 3:26

roofs

on whose *r*. they burnt incense. *Jer* 19:13; 32:29

room

is there *r*. in thy father's? *Gen* 24:23
we have *r*. to lodge in. 25
r. for the camels. 31
Lord hath made *r*. for us. 26:22
captain in the *r*. of Joab. *2 Sam* 19:13
in Joab's *r*. and he put Zadok the priest in the *r*. of. *1 Ki* 2:35
had anointed him king in the *r*. 5:1
thy son whom I will set in thy *r*. 5
I am risen in the *r*. of David. 8:20
2 Chr 6:10
thou anoint in thy *r*. *1 Ki* 19:16
my feet in a large *r*. *Ps* 31:8*
thou preparedst *r*. before it. 80:9
a man's gift maketh *r*. *Pr* 18:16
shall not be *r*. enough. *Mal* 3:10
Archelaus reigned in the *r*. *Mat* 2:22
that there was no *r*. to. *Mark* 2:2
he will shew you a large upper *r*. 14:15; *Luke* 22:12
because there was no *r*. *Luke* 2:7
I have no *r*. to bestow my. 12:17
sit not down in the highest *r*. 14:8*
shame to take the lowest *r*. 9*
and sit down in the lowest *r*. 10*
it is done, and yet there is *r*. 22
went up to an upper *r*. *Acts* 1:13
Festus came into Felix' *r*. 24:27*
that occupieth the *r*. *1 Cor* 14:16*

rooms

r. shalt thou make in the. *Gen* 6:14
captains in their *r*. *1 Ki* 20:24
and dwelt in their *r*. *1 Chr* 4:41*

uppermost *r*. at feasts. *Mat* 23:6*
Mark 12:39*; *Luke* 20:46*
chose out the chief *r*. *Luke* 14:7*

root, *substantive*

a *r*. that beareth gall. *Deut* 29:18
out of Ephraim was a *r*. *Judg* 5:14
again take *r*. downward. *2 Ki* 19:30
the foolish taking *r*. *Job* 5:3
though the *r*. thereof wax old. 14:8
seeing the *r*. of the matter is. 19:28
my *r*. was spread out by the. 29:19
the vine to take deep *r*. *Ps* 80:9
r. of the righteous shall. *Pr* 12:3
the *r*. of the righteous yieldeth. 12
so their *r*. shall be rottenness, and. *Isa* 5:24
there shall be a *r*. of Jesse. 11:10
Rom 15:12
for out of the serpent's *r*. *Isa* 14:29
I will kill thy *r*. with famine. 30
that come of Jacob to take *r*. 27:6
37:31
their stock shall not take *r*. 40:24
as a *r*. out of a dry ground. 53:2
have taken *r*.: they grow. *Jer* 12:2
r. was by great waters. *Ezek* 31:7
out of a branch of her *r*. *Dan* 11:7
smitten, their *r*. is dried. *Hos* 9:16
neither *r*. nor branch. *Mal* 4:1
axe is laid unto the *r*. of the trees. *Mat* 3:10; *Luke* 3:9
because they had not *r*. *Mat* 13:6
21; *Mark* 4:6, 17; *Luke* 8:13
thou plucked up by the *r*. *Luke* 17:6
if the *r*. be holy, so are. *Rom* 11:16
with them partakest of the *r*. 17
thou bearest not the *r*. but the *r*. 18
love of money is the *r*. *1 Tim* 6:10
lest any *r*. of bitterness. *Heb* 12:15
r. of David hath prevailed. *Rev* 5:5
I am the *r*. and offspring of. 22:16

root

he shall *r*. up Israel. *1 Ki* 14:15
and would *r*. out all. *Job* 31:12
and *r*. thee out of the land. *Ps* 52:5
have set thee to *r*. out. *Jer* 1:10*
lest ye *r*. up the wheat. *Mat* 13:29

rooted

the Lord *r*. them out. *Deut* 29:28
confidence shall be *r*. out. *Job* 18:14
let my offspring be *r*. out. 31:8
trangressors shall be *r*. out of it. *Pr* 2:22
Ekron shall be *r*. up. *Zeph* 2:4
not planted, shall be *r*. *Mat* 15:13
being *r*. and grounded. *Eph* 3:17
r. and built up in him. *Col* 2:7

roots

them up by the *r*. *2 Chr* 7:20
his *r*. are wrapped about. *Job* 8:17
his *r*. shall be dried up. 18:16
the mountains by the *r*. 28:9
juniper *r*. for their meat. 30:4
shall grow out of his *r*. *Isa* 11:1
that spreadeth out her *r*. *Jer* 17:8
and the *r*. thereof were. *Ezek* 17:6
this vine did bend her *r*. toward. 7
not pull up the *r*. thereof? 9
the stump of his *r*. *Dan* 4:15, 23, 26
first horns plucked up by the *r*. 7:8
he shall cast forth his *r*. as. *Hos* 14:5
I destroyed his *r*. from. *Amos* 2:9
tree dried up from the *r*. *Mark* 11:20
dead, plucked up by the *r*. *Jude* 12

ropes

bind me with new *r*. *Judg* 16:11, 12
all Israel bring *r*. to. *2 Sam* 17:13
let us put *r*. on our. *1 Ki* 20:31, 32
the soldiers cut off the *r*. *Acts* 27:32

rose, *substantive*

I am the *r*. of Sharon, and. *S of S* 2:1
shall blossom as the *r*. *Isa* 35:1

rose, *verb*

Cain *r*. up against Abel. *Gen* 4:8
Lot *r*. up to meet them, and. 19:1
Abraham *r*. early, and went. 22:3
Esau did eat, and *r*. up, and. 25:34
the sun *r*. upon him as he. 32:31
his sons and daughters *r*. to. 37:35
nor *r*. any from his place. *Ex* 10:23
Pharaoh *r*. up in the night. 12:30

overthrown them that *r*. up. *Ex* 15:7
and all the people *r*. up and. 33:10
Phinehas *r*. up from. *Num* 25:7
the Lord *r*. up from Seir. *Deut* 33:2
the waters stood and *r*. *Josh* 3:16
there *r*. up fire out of. *Judg* 6:21
the men of Gibeah *r*. up. 20:5
she *r*. up before one. *Ruth* 3:14
them that *r*. up against me, hast thou. *2 Sam* 22:40; *Ps* 18:39
and the king *r*. up to. *1 Ki* 2:19
the lepers *r*. in the. *2 Ki* 7:5
the leprosy *r*. up in his. *2 Chr* 26:19
expressed by name *r*. up. 28:15
our side when men *r*. up. *Ps* 124:2
I *r*. up to open to my. *S of S* 5:5
then *r*. up certain of the. *Jer* 26:17
the lips of those that *r*. up. *Lam* 3:62
then Nebuchadnezzar *r*. *Dan* 3:24
I *r*. up and did the king's. 8:27
but Jonah *r*. up to flee. *Jonah* 1:3
they *r*. early and corrupted. *Zech* 3:7
r. up, and thrust him out. *Luke* 4:29
and he left all, *r*. up, and. 5:28
though one *r*. from the dead. 16:31
when he *r*. from prayer and. 22:45
they *r*. up the same hour, and. 24:33
Mary, that she *r*. up. *John* 11:31
then high priest *r*. up, and. *Acts* 5:17
these days *r*. up Theudas. 36
drink with him after he *r*. 10:41
king *r*. up, and the governor. 26:30
Christ both died and *r*. *Rom* 14:9*
the people did eat, and *r*. *1 Cor* 10:7
he was buried and *r*. again. 15:4
preached that he *r*. from the dead. 12
who died and *r*. again. *2 Cor* 5:15
Jesus died and *r*. again. *1 Thes* 4:14
her smoke *r*. up for ever. *Rev* 19:3

see **morning**

rot

the Lord make thy thigh to *r*. *Num* 5:21*, 22*, 27*
name of the wicked shall *r*. *Pr* 10:7
a tree that will not *r*. *Isa* 40:20

rotten

and he as a *r*. thing. *Job* 13:28
esteemeth brass as *r*. wood. 41:27
so Ebed-melech took old *r*. *Jer* 38:11
put now these *r*. rags under. 12
the seed is *r*. under their. *Joel* 1:17

rottenness

maketh ashamed, is as *r*. *Pr* 12:4
envy is the *r*. of the bones. 14:30
so their root shall be as *r*. *Isa* 5:24
to the house of Judah as *r*. *Hos* 5:12
when I heard *r*. entered. *Hab* 3:16

rough

heifer to a *r*. valley. *Deut* 21:4*
he stayeth his *r*. wind in. *Isa* 27:8
and the *r*. places shall be. 40:4
horses to come as *r*. *Jer* 51:27
the *r*. goat is the king. *Dan* 8:21
shall they wear a *r*. *Zech* 13:4*
and the *r*. ways shall be. *Luke* 3:5

roughly

Joseph spake *r*. *Gen* 42:7, 30
father answer thee *r*.? *1 Sam* 20:10
answered the people *r*. and forsook. *1 Ki* 12:13; *2 Chr* 10:13
but the rich answereth *r*. *Pr* 18:23

round, *verb*

ye shall not *r*. the corners. *Lev* 19:27

round

compassed the house *r*. *Gen* 19:4
there lay a small *r*. thing. *Ex* 16:14
shall environ us *r*. *Josh* 7:9
the molten sea was *r*. *1 Ki* 7:23
a *r*. compass. 35
top of the throne was *r*. 10:19
Bashan have beset me *r*. *Ps* 22:12
navel is like a *r*. goblet. *S of S* 7:2
take away their *r*. tires. *Isa* 3:18
shall compass thee *r*. *Luke* 19:43

round *about*

God was on cities *r*. *about*. *Gen* 35:5
digged *r*. *about* the river. *Ex* 7:24
morning dew lay *r*. *about*. 16:13
bounds to the people *r*. *about*. 19:12
house to be scraped *r*. *about*. *Lev* 14:41

Levites encamp *r. about* tabernacle. *Num* 1:50
Moses set the elders *r. about.* 11:24
all Israel, that were *r. about.* 16:34
up all that are *r. about* us. 22:4
people *r. about* you. *Deut* 6:14; 13:7
all your enemies *r. about.* 12:10
25:19; *Josh* 21:44; *2 Chr* 15:15
measure the cities *r. about* him. *Deut* 21:2
and ye shall go *r. about.* *Josh* 6:3
house *r. about.* *Judg* 19:22; 20:5
Saul compassed David *r. about.* *1 Sam* 23:26
sent into the land of Philistines *r. about.* 31:9; *1 Chr* 10:9
he made darkness pavilions *r. about* him. *2 Sam* 22:12; *Ps* 18:11
had peace on all sides *r. about.* *1 Ki* 4:24
fame was in all nations *r. about.* 31
water ran *r. about* the altar. 18:35
of fire *r. about* Elisha. *2 Ki* 6:17
they lodged *r. about.* *1 Chr* 9:27
fashioned me *r. about.* *Job* 10:8
compass me *r. about.* 16:13
his troops encamp *r. about.* 19:12
snares are *r. about* thee. 22:10
it is turned *r. about* by his. 37:12
his teeth are terrible *r. about.* 41:14
against me *r. about.* *Ps* 3:6
above mine enemies *r. about.* 27:6
r. about them that fear him. 34:7
them that are *r. about.* 44:13; 79:4
Zion, and go *r. about* her. 48:12
go *r. about* the city. 59:6, 14
let all *r. about* him bring. 76:11
they came *r. about* me daily. 88:17
faithfulness *r. about* thee. 89:8
his enemies *r. about* him. 97:3
as the mountains are *r. about.* 125:2
olive plants *r. about* thy table. 128:3
I will camp against thee *r. about.* *Isa* 29:3
set him on fire *r. about.* 42:25
up thine eyes *r. about.* 49:18; 60:4
devour all things *r. about.* *Jer* 21:14
for fear was *r. about,* saith. 46:5*
against Babylon *r. about.* 50:29
shall be against her *r. about.* 51:2
full of eyes *r. about.* *Ezek* 10:12
will make places *r. about.* 34:26
gather yourselves together *r. about.* *Joel* 3:11
judge all the heathen *r. about.* 12
even *r. about* the land. *Amos* 3:11
me *r. about,* the weeds. *Jonah* 2:5
a wall of fire *r. about.* *Zech* 2:5
the vineyard *r. about.* *Mat* 21:33
all that dwelt *r. about.* *Luke* 1:65
the Lord shone *r. about* them. 2:9
shined *r. about* him a light. *Acts* 9:3
r. about to Illyricum, I. *Rom* 15:19
was a rainbow *r. about.* *Rev* 4:3
r. about the throne were four. 4
angels *r. about* the throne. 5:11
see **camp**

rouse

lion; who shall *r.* him up? *Gen* 49:9

rovers

they helped David against the *r.* *1 Chr* 12:21

row, -s

four *r.* of stones. *Ex* 28:17; 39:10
the first *r.* 28:17; 39:10
the second *r.* 28:18; 39:11
the third *r.* 28:19; 39:12
the fourth *r.* 28:20; 39:13
cakes, six on a *r.* on the. *Lev* 24:6
pure frankincense on each *r.* 7
inner court with three *r.* *1 Ki* 6:36
four *r.* of cedar pillars. 7:2
fifteen in a *r.* 3
there were windows in three *r.* 4
round about was with three *r.* 12
two *r.* with pomegranates. 18, 42
2 Chr 4:13
two *r.* of oxen cast. *2 Chr* 4:3
a *r.* of new timber, three *r.* of. *Ezra* 6:4
thy cheeks comely with *r.* of jewels. *S of S* 1:10
boiling places under *r.* *Ezek* 46:23

rowed

men *r.* hard to bring it. *Jonah* 1:13
when they had *r.* 25 or. *John* 6:19

rowers

thy *r.* brought thee. *Ezek* 27:26

rowing

he saw them toiling in *r.* *Mark* 6:48

royal

shall yield *r.* dainties. *Gen* 49:20
as one of the *r.* cities. *Josh* 10:2
why dwell in the *r.* city? *1 Sam* 27:5
and took the *r.* city. *2 Sam* 12:26
her of his *r.* bounty. *1 Ki* 10:13
mother of Ahaziah destroyed all the seed *r.* *2 Ki* 11:1; *2 Chr* 22:10
on Solomon *r.* majesty. *1 Chr* 29:25
they gave them *r.* wine. *Esth* 1:7
the queen with the crown *r.* 11
give her *r.* estate to another that. 19
was taken into his house *r.* 2:16
so that he set the crown *r.* on. 17
Esther put on her *r.* apparel, and king sat on his *r.* throne in his *r.* 5:1
let *r.* apparel be brought, and the crown *r.* 6:8
Mordecai went in *r.* apparel. 8:15
a *r.* diadem in the hand. *Isa* 62:3
spread his *r.* pavilion. *Jer* 43:10
to establish a *r.* statute. *Dan* 6:7
Herod arrayed in *r.* *Acts* 12:21
if ye fulfil the *r.* law, ye. *Jas* 2:8
ye are a *r.* priesthood. *1 Pet* 2:9

rubbing

and did eat, *r.* them in. *Luke* 6:1

rubbish

the stones out of the *r.* *Neh* 4:2
decayed and there is much *r.* 10

rubies

price of wisdom is above *r.* *Job* 28:18; *Pr* 8:11
is more precious than *r.* *Pr* 3:15
gold, and a multitude of *r.* 20:15
for her price is far above *r.* 31:10
were more ruddy than *r.* *Lam* 4:7

rudder bands

and loosed the *r. bands.* *Acts* 27:40

ruddy

David was *r.* and beautiful. *1 Sam* 16:12; 17:42
my beloved is white and *r.* chiefest. *S of S* 5:10
Nazarites were more *r.* *Lam* 4:7

rude

though I be *r.* in speech. *2 Cor* 11:6

rudiments

you after the *r.* of the. *Col* 2:8
if dead with Christ from the *r.* 20

rue

for ye tithe mint, and *r.* *Luke* 11:42

Rufus

Simon, father of Alexander and *R.* *Mark* 15:21
salute *R.* chosen in the. *Rom* 16:13

Ruhamah

say to your sisters, *R.* *Hos* 2:1

ruin

but they were the *r.* *2 Chr* 28:23
brought his holds to *r.* *Ps* 89:40
who knoweth the *r.* of? *Pr* 24:22*
a flattering mouth worketh *r.* 26:28
and let this *r.* be under. *Isa* 3:6
land of the Chaldeans to *r.* 23:13
of a defenced city a *r.* 25:2
shall not be your *r.* *Ezek* 18:30
shall fall in the day of thy *r.* 27:27
upon his *r.* shall all the fowls. 31:13
it fell, the *r.* of that house. *Luke* 6:49

ruined

Jerusalem is *r.* and Judah. *Isa* 3:8
and the *r.* cities are. *Ezek* 36:35
I the Lord build the *r.* places. 36

ruinous

be to lay waste fenced cities into *r.* heaps. *2 Ki* 19:25; *Isa* 37:26
it shall be a *r.* heap. *Isa* 17:1

ruins

that their *r.* may be. *Ezek* 21:15*
will I raise up his *r.* *Amos* 9:11
I will build again the *r.* *Acts* 15:16

rule, *substantive*

that had *r.* over Ahab's. *1 Ki* 22:31
Jews had *r.* over them. *Esth* 9:1
shall have *r.* over a son. *Pr* 17:2
for a servant to have *r.* over. 19:10
he that hath no *r.* over his. 25:28*
yet shall he have *r.* over. *Eccl* 2:19
stretcheth out his *r.* *Isa* 44:13*
never barest *r.* over them. 63:19
have put down all *r.* *1 Cor* 15:24
to the measure of the *r.* *2 Cor* 10:13*
be enlarged according to our *r.* 15*
walk according to this *r.* *Gal* 6:16
let us walk by the same *r.* *Phil* 3:16
remember them that have *r.* over. *Heb* 13:7
obey them that have the *r.* over. 17
salute all them that have the *r.* 24
see **bare, bear**

rule

the greater light to *r.* the day, and lesser light to *r.* the. *Gen* 1:16
to *r.* over the day, and over. 18
and thy husband shall *r.* over. 3:16
desire, thou shalt *r.* over him. 4:7
not *r.* over him with rigour. *Lev* 25:43; 46:53
r. thou over us, thou. *Judg* 8:22
r. over you, nor shall my son *r.* 23
r. thou in the midst of thine enemies. *Ps* 110:2
sun to *r.* by day, for his mercy. 136:8
moon and stars to *r.* by night. 9
by me princes *r.* and. *Pr* 8:16
babes shall *r.* over them. *Isa* 3:4
as for my people, women *r.* 12
r. over their oppressors. 14:2
a fierce king shall *r.* over. 19:4
that *r.* this people that is in. 28:14
princes shall *r.* in judgement. 32:1
and his arm shall *r.* for him. 40:10
who made the righteous man *r.*? 41:2
they that *r.* over them make. 52:5
no strong rod to be a sceptre to *r.* *Ezek* 19:14
poured out, will I *r.* over you. 20:33
they shall no more *r.* over. 29:15
known that the heavens *r.* *Dan* 4:26
shall stand up, that shall *r.* 11:3
cause them to *r.* over many. 39
that the heathen should *r.* *Joel* 2:17
sit and *r.* on his throne. *Zech* 6:13
a governor that shall *r.* *Mat* 2:6*
who are accounted to *r.* *Mark* 10:42
let the peace of God *r.* *Col* 3:15
not how to *r.* his house. *1 Tim* 3:5
elders that *r.* well, worthy of. 5:17
r. with a rod. *Rev* 2:27; 12:5; 19:15

ruled

his eldest servant that *r.* *Gen* 24:2
word shall all my people be *r.* 41:40
three thousand *r.* over. *1 Ki* 5:16
have *r.* over all countries. *Ezra* 4:20
they that hated them *r.* *Ps* 106:41
he that *r.* nations in anger. *Isa* 14:6
servants have *r.* over us. *Lam* 5:8
with cruelty have ye *r.* *Ezek* 34:4
till he knew that God *r.* *Dan* 5:21

ruler

(*Revisions frequently translate this* prince, *or* governor)

Pharaoh made Joseph *r.* over all *Gen* 41:43; 45:8; *Ps* 105:21
Joseph said to the *r.* of. *Gen* 43:16*
thou shalt not curse *r.* of. *Ex* 22:28
when a *r.* hath sinned. *Lev* 4:22
every one a *r.* among. *Num* 13:2
appointed thee *r.* over. *1 Sam* 25:30
2 Sam 6:21; 7:8; *1 Chr* 11:2; 17:7
I took thee from following sheep to be *r.* *2 Sam* 7:8; *1 Chr* 17:7
appointed Solomon to be *r.* *1 Ki* 1:35
of Judah came the chief *r.* *1 Chr* 5:2
Azariah *r.* of house of God. 9:11
2 Chr 31:13
fail thee a man to be *r.* *2 Chr* 7:18
he made Abijah *r.* among. 11:22
and Hananiah the *r.* of. *Neh* 7:2
Seraiah was *r.* of the house. 11:11
Benjamin with their *r.* *Ps* 68:27
even the *r.* of the people, let. 105:20
no guide, overseer, or *r.* *Pr* 6:7

sittest to eat with a *r*. *Pr* 23:1
so is a wicked *r*. over the. 28:15
if a *r*. hearken to lies, his. 29:12
many seek *r*.'s favour, but. 26
if the spirit of the *r*. rise. *Eccl* 10:4
which proceedeth from the *r*. 5
be thou our *r* *Isa* 3:6
make me not a *r*. 7
send ye the lamb to the *r*. of. 16:1
in the land, *r*. against *r*. *Jer* 51:46
no king nor *r*. asked. *Dan* 2:10
and hath made thee *r*. over. 38, 48
shall be third *r*. in the. 5:7, 16, 29
he come that is to be *r*. *Mi* 5:2
things that have no *r*. *Hab* 1:14
there came a certain *r*. *Mat* 9:18
whom his Lord hath made *r*. 24:45
Luke 12:42
make him *r*. over all. *Mat* 24:47
I will make thee *r*. over. 25:21, 23
there came from the *r*. of the synagogue's. *Mark* 5:35; *Luke* 8:49
the *r*. of the synagogue. *Luke* 13:14
when the *r*. of the feast. *John* 2:9
a man named Nicodemus, a *r*. 3:1
who made thee a *r*.? *Acts* 7:27, 35
the same did God send to be *r*. 35
beat Sosthenes the chief *r*. 18:17
shalt not speak evil of the *r*. 23:5

rulers

then make them *r*. over. *Gen* 47:6
r. of thousands, *r*. *Ex* 18:21, 25
Moses called the *r*. of the. 34:31
the *r*. brought onyx stones to. 35:27
and I will make them *r*. *Deut* 1:13*
not the Philistines are *r*.? *Judg* 15:11
sons were chief *r*. *2 Sam* 8:18*
were *r*. of his chariots. *1 Ki* 9:22
Jehu wrote to the *r*. *2 Ki* 10:1
Jehoiada set *r*. over. 11:4*, 19*
all there were *r*. of. *1 Chr* 27:31
r. of the house of God. *2 Chr* 35:8
the hand of the *r*. chief. *Ezra* 9:2
r. were behind the house. *Neh* 4:16
I rebuked the *r*. and said, Ye. 5:7
the *r*. of the people dwelt at. 11:1
and the half of the *r*. with me. 12:40
then contended I with the *r*. 13:11
the *r*. of the provinces. *Esth* 9:3
the *r*. take counsel against. *Ps* 2:2
hear word of the Lord, ye *r*. *Isa* 1:10
broken the sceptre of the *r*. 14:5
all thy *r*. are fled together. 22:3
and your *r*. the seers hath. 29:10*
to a servant of *r*. kings shall. 49:7
any of his seed to be *r*. *Jer* 33:26
in pieces captains and *r*. 51:23*
prepare against her *r*. 28*
made drunk her *r*. 57*
were captains and *r*. *Ezek* 23:6
raise up those *r*. against thee. 23
all the *r*. were gathered. *Dan* 3:3
her *r*. with shame do love. *Hos* 4:18
cometh one of the *r*. of. *Mark* 5:22
brought before *r*. 13:9*; *Luke* 21:12
called together the *r*. *Luke* 23:13
and *r*. also with the people. 35
how our priests and *r*. 24:20
do the *r*. know that ? *John* 7:26
have any of *r*. believed on him ? 48
many among the chief *r*. 12:42
ye did it, as also did *r*. *Acts* 3:17
the *r*. were gathered against. 4:26
the *r*. of the synagogue. 13:15
and their *r*. because they knew. 27
of the Jews, with their *r*. 14:5
masters drew them to the *r*. 16:19
they troubled the people and *r*. 17:8
r. not a terror to good. *Rom* 13:3
we wrestle against the *r*. *Eph* 6:12

rulest

and *r*. not thou over ? *2 Chr* 20:6
r. the raging of the sea. *Ps* 89:9

ruleth

he that *r*. over men. *2 Sam* 23:3
let them know that God *r*. *Ps* 59:13
he *r*. by his power for ever. 66:7
and his kingdom *r*. over all. 103:19
that *r*. his spirit is better. *Pr* 16:32
rich *r*. over the poor, and. 22:7
wherein one man *r*. over. *Eccl* 8:9
more than cry of him that *r*. 9:17
the most High *r*. *Dan* 4:17, 25, 32
Judah yet *r*. with God. *Hos* 11:12
he that *r*. with diligence. *Rom* 12:8
r. well his own house. *1 Tim* 3:4

ruling

must be just, *r*. in the. *2 Sam* 23:3
sit on throne, and *r*. *Jer* 22:30
r. their children and. *1 Tim* 3:12

rumbling

at *r*. of his wheels, fathers. *Jer* 47:3

rumour, -s

(*American Revision usually translates* tidings)
and he shall hear a *r*. *2 Ki* 19:7
Isa 37:7
I have heard a *r*. from. *Jer* 49:14
r. in the land, a *r*. shall come one year, in another year a *r*. 51:46
on mischief, *r*. shall be upon *r*.
Ezek 7:26
we have heard a *r*. from. *Ob* 1
of wars and *r*. of wars. *Mat* 24:6
Mark 13:7
r. of him went forth. *Luke* 7:17*

rump

(*Revisions*, the fat tail)
ram and the fat and the *r*. *Ex* 29:22
Lev 3:9; 7:3; 8:25; 9:19

run

whose branches *r*. over. *Gen* 49:22
whether his flesh *r*. with. *Lev* 15:3
if a woman's issue *r*. beyond. 25
lest angry fellows *r*. *Judg* 18:25*
some shall *r*. before his. *1 Sam* 8:11
r. to the camp to thy brethren. 17:17*
asked me, that he might *r*. to. 20:6
r., find out now the arrows which. 36
horses, and fifty men to *r*. before.
2 Sam 15:1; *1 Ki* 1:5
let me now *r*. and bear tidings.
2 Sam 18:19, 22, 23
I have *r*. through a troop. 22:30
Ps 18:29
that I may *r*. to the man. *2 Ki* 4:22
r. now, I pray thee, to meet her. 26
as the Lord liveth, I will *r*. 5:20
eyes of Lord *r*. to and. *2 Chr* 16:9
as strong man to *r*. a race. *Ps* 19:5
them melt as waters, which *r*. 58:7
they *r*. and prepare themselves. 59:4
he caused waters to *r*. down. 78:16
the springs, which *r*. among. 104:10
I will *r*. the way of thy. 119:32
rivers of waters *r*. down mine. 136
for their feet *r*. to evil. *Pr* 1:16
Isa 59:7
rivers *r*. into the sea. *Eccl* 1:7
draw me, we will *r*. *S of S* 1:4
of locusts shall he *r*. on. *Isa* 33:4*
they shall *r*. and not be weary. 40:31
knew not thee shall *r*. to thee. 55:5
r. ye to and fro through. *Jer* 5:1
that your eyes may *r*. down. 9:18
hast *r*. with the footmen. 12:5
mine eyes shall *r*. down with tears, because the Lord's. 13:17; 14:17
lament, and *r*. to and fro. 49:3
I will make him *r*. away. 19; 50:44
post shall *r*. to meet another. 51:31
let tears *r*. down like a. *Lam* 2:18
neither shall thy tears *r*. *Ezek* 24:16
cause their rivers to *r*. like oil. 32:14
many shall *r*. to and fro. *Dan* 12:4
horsemen, so shall they *r*. *Joel* 2:4
they shall *r*. like mighty men. 7
they shall *r*. in the city, shall *r*. on. 9*
judgement *r*. down as. *Amos* 5:24*
shall horses *r*. upon the rock ? 6:12
shall *r*. to and fro to seek word. 8:12
r. like the lightnings. *Nah* 2:4
write vision, that he may *r*. *Hab* 2:2
and ye *r*. every man to his. *Hag* 1:9
R., speak to this young man. *Zech* 2:4
eyes of the Lord *r*. to and fro. 4:10
they did *r*. to bring his. *Mat* 28:8
r. in a race *r*. all, but one receiveth the prize, so *r*. that ye. *1 Cor* 9:24
I therefore so *r*. not as. 26
I should *r*. or had *r*. in. *Gal* 2:2
ye did *r*. well, who did ? 5:7
I have not *r*. in vain. *Phil* 2:16
let us *r*. with patience. *Heb* 12:1
that ye *r*. not to the same. *1 Pet* 4:4

runnest

when thou *r*. thou shalt. *Pr* 4:12

runneth

he *r*. upon him, even on. *Job* 15:26
he breaketh me, he *r*. upon me. 16:14
thou anointest my head, my cup *r*. over. *Ps* 23:5
his word *r*. very swiftly. 147:15
the righteous *r*. into it. *Pr* 18:10
mine eyes *r*. down with water.
Lam 1:16; 3:48
the bottles break, and the wine *r*.
Mat 9:17*
then she *r*. and cometh. *John* 20:2
not of him that willeth, nor of him that *r*. *Rom* 9:16

running

one bird be killed over *r*. water.
Lev 14:5, 6, 50
dip them in *r*. water, and sprinkle. 51
cleanse the house with the *r*. 52
any man hath a *r*. issue. 15:2; 22:4
shall bathe his flesh in *r*. water. 13
unclean person take *r*. *Num* 19:17
and behold, a man *r*. alone.
2 Sam 18:24, 26
the *r*. of the foremost is like *r*. 27
when Naaman saw him *r*. *2 Ki* 5:21
Athaliah heard the people *r*.
2 Chr 23:12
and *r*. waters out of thine own well.
Pr 5:15
feet that be swift in *r*. to. 6:18
the *r*. to and fro of locusts. *Isa* 33:4*
with her rivers *r*. about. *Ezek* 31:4
the people *r*. to him. *Mark* 9:15
when Jesus saw the people *r*. 25
there came one *r*. and. 10:17
good measure and *r*. over. *Luke* 6:38
and *r*. under a certain island.
Acts 27:16
as the sound of chariots *r*. *Rev* 9:9

rush, *substantive*

can the *r*. grow without mire ?
Job 8:11
Lord will cut off branch and *r*. in one.
Isa 9:14
any work which branch or *r*. 19:15

rush

nations shall *r*. like the rushing of many waters. *Isa* 17:13

rushed

Abimelech and company *r*. *Judg* 9:44
the liers in wait hasted and *r*. 20:37
they *r*. with one accord. *Acts* 19:29

rushes

where dragons lay shall be reeds and *r*. *Isa* 35:7

rusheth

every one turned, as horse *r*. *Jer* 8:6

rushing

and to the *r*. of nations, that make a *r*. like the *r*. of many. *Isa* 17:12
nations shall rush like the *r*. 13
at *r*. of chariots fathers. *Jer* 47:3
voice of a great *r*. *Ezek* 3:12, 13
as of a *r*. mighty wind. *Acts* 2:2

rust

where moth and *r*. *Mat* 6:19, 20
r. of them shall be a witness. *Jas* 5:3

Ruth

name of the other was *R*. *Ruth* 1:4
R. clave to her. 14
who art thou ? I am *R*. 3:9
thou must buy it also of *R*. the. 4:5
moreover, *R*. have I purchased. 10
Booz begat Obed of *R*. *Mat* 1:5

S

Sabaoth

A Hebrew *word meaning* Hosts *or* Armies. Jehovah Sabaoth, The Lord of hosts, Rom 9:29.

except the Lord of *S*. *Rom* 9:29
the ears of the Lord of *s*. *Jas* 5:4

sabbath

The Hebrew word means rest, *from the statement in* Gen 2:2, *that God rested and hallowed the seventh day. By the Jewish law given at Sinai the seventh day was to be a day of rest, in which no secular work was to be done, and which was to be kept holy to God. At a later period the simple Jewish law of early days was added to by the traditions of the elders, until the sabbath rules became burdensome, and, in some cases, foolish. It was against this, and not against God's law of the sabbath that Jesus set himself in his teaching and healing.*

The sabbath, *one day out of each week, was kept by the Jews on the day now called Saturday. How early this was taken to be the seventh day is not known. After the ascension of Jesus the disciples met on the first day of each week for prayer and praise. The Jewish Christians for a long time kept both the seventh and the first; but as Gentile Christians, having never kept any such day before, celebrated only the first day of the week as* the Lord's Day, *the celebration of the seventh by Christians was finally abandoned.*

Because of the rule that a long journey should not be made on the sabbath, the short distance permitted, about a mile, received the name of a sabbath day's journey.

The word sabbath *is often used in speaking of the rest of the fields from tillage, the rules for which are given in the Pentateuch.*

is rest of the holy *s.* *Ex* 16:23
eat that to-day, for to-day is a *s.* 25
Lord hath given you the *s.* 29
seventh day is the *s.* 20:10; 31:15
35:2; *Lev* 23:3; *Deut* 5:14
ye shall keep the *s.* *Ex* 31:14, 16
an atonement, it shall be a *s.* of rest.
Lev 16:31; 23:3, 32
s. priest shall wave it. 23:11
from the morrow after the *s.* 15
after the seventh *s.* shall ye. 16
1st of the month shall ye have a *s.* 24
shall ye celebrate your *s.* 32
shall be a *s.*, on the eighth a *s.* 39
every *s.* he shall set it in order. 24:8
shall the land keep a *s.* 25:2, 4, 6
burnt offering of every *s.* *Num* 28:10
neither new moon nor *s.* *2 Ki* 4:23
you that enter in on the *s.* 11:5
you that go forth on the *s.*, even they.
7, 9; *2 Chr* 23:8
covert for the *s.* turned. *2 Ki* 16:18
shewbread every *s.* *1 Chr* 9:32
desolate, she kept the *s.* *2 Chr* 36:21
known to them thy holy *s.* *Neh* 9:14
buy it of them on the *s.* 10:31
winepresses on the *s.* 13:15
brought ware, and sold on the *s.* 16
Israel, by profaning the *s.* 18
began to be dark before the *s.* 19
came they no more on the *s.* 21
man that keepeth the *s.* *Isa* 56:2, 6
the *s.*; call the *s.* a delight. 58:13
from one *s.* to another shall. 66:23
but on the *s.* it shall be. *Ezek* 46:1
saying, When will the *s.*? *Amos* 8:5
in the end of the *s.* came. *Mat* 28:1
s. was made for man, not man for
the *s.* *Mark* 2:27
is Lord of the *s.* 28; *Luke* 6:5
when the *s.* was past. *Mark* 16:1
on another *s.* 6
in the synagogue on the *s.* 13:10
doth not each on the *s.* loose? 15
and the *s.* drew on. 23:54
not only had broken the *s.* *John* 5:18
preached to them next *s.* *Acts* 13:42
on the *s.* we went out of city. 16:13
in the synagogue every *s.* 18:4
see **day, days**

sabbaths

saying, My *s.* ye shall keep.
Ex 31:13; *Lev* 19:3, 30; 26:2
seven *s.* shall be. *Lev* 23:15
beside the *s.* of the Lord. *Lev* 23:38
and thou shalt number seven *s.* 25:8
enjoy her *s.*, even then shall the land
. . . her *s.* 26:34, 43; *2 Chr* 36:21
did not rest in your *s.* *Lev* 26:35
burnt sacrifices in the *s.* *1 Chr* 23:31
2 Chr 2:4; 8:13; 31:3; *Neh* 10:33
new moons and *s.* I. *Isa* 1:13
to eunuchs that keep my *s.* 56:4
did mock at her *s.* *Lam* 1:7*
Lord caused *s.* to be forgotten. 2:6
also I gave them my *s.* *Ezek* 20:12
and my *s.* they greatly. 13, 16, 24
hast profaned my *s.* 22:8; 23:38
have hid their eyes from my *s.* 22:26
my laws and hallow my *s.* 44:24
part to give offerings for *s.* 45:17
worship at this gate in the *s.* 46:3
make to cease her *s.* *Hos* 2:11

Sabeans

the *S.* fell on the oxen. *Job* 1:15
merchandise of the *S.* *Isa* 45:14
with the men of the common sort
were brought *S.* *Ezek* 23:42*
shall sell them to the *S.* *Joel* 3:8

sack

to restore every man's money into
his *s.* *Gen* 42:25, 35; 43:21; 44:1
put my silver cup in *s.'s* mouth. 44:2
they took down every man his *s.* 11
cup was found in Benjamin's *s.* 12
or *s.* of unclean must be. *Lev* 11:32

sackbut

sound of the *s.* *Dan* 3:5, 7, 10, 15

sackcloth

(A coarse cloth made of camel's and goat's hair. It was used for making the rough garments worn by mourners. It therefore became a symbol for sorrow and mourning)

and Jacob put *s.* upon. *Gen* 37:34
said, Gird you with *s.* *2 Sam* 3:31
Rizpah took *s.* and spread it. 21:10
merciful kings, let us put *s.* on our
loins, and ropes. *1 Ki* 20:31, 32
s. on his flesh, and lay in *s.* 21:27
and he had *s.* within. *2 Ki* 6:30
Hezekiah covered himself with *s.*
19:1; *Isa* 37:1
elders of the priests covered with *s.*
2 Ki 19:2; *Isa* 37:2
David and elders were clothed with
s. *1 Chr* 21:16
clothes, and put on *s.* *Esth* 4:1
enter the gate clothed with *s.* 2
sewed *s.* upon my skin. *Job* 16:15
hast put off my *s.* and. *Ps* 30:11
sick, my clothing was *s.* 35:13
I made *s.* also my garment. 69:11
stomacher, a girding of *s.* *Isa* 3:24
gird themselves with *s.* 15:3
go, and loose the *s.* from off. 20:2
Lord call to girding with *s.* 22:12
make you bare, and gird *s.* 32:11
Jer 4:8; 6:26; 48:37; 49:3
I make *s.* the covering of the. 50:3
themselves with *s.*: virgins hang
down heads. *Lam* 2:10; *Ezek* 7:18
27:31
Lord with fasting and *s.* *Dan* 9:3
virgin girded with *s.* for. *Joel* 1:8
lie all night in *s.*, ye ministers. 13
and I will bring up *s.* *Amos* 8:10
of Nineveh put on *s.* *Jonah* 3:5
the king covered him with *s.* 6
man and beast he covered with *s.* 8
became black as *s.* of hair. *Rev* 6:12
prophesy, clothed in *s.* 11:3

sackclothes

Israel assembled with *s.* *Neh* 9:1

sacks

to fill their *s.* with corn. *Gen* 42:25*
44:1
brought again in your *s.* 43:12
who put our money in our *s.* 22
given you treasure in your *s.* 23
the Gibeonites took old *s.* *Josh* 9:4

sacrifice

An offering of any sort to a deity, with the idea of procuring favour or avoiding disaster. The idea of sacrifice is deeply rooted in the instincts of humanity; for it i[s] found among every race at th[e] earliest known period of its histor[y] as a well-established and thor[-] oughly understood custom. Th[e] sacrifices were, in general, of tw[o] sorts: [1] *the offering of the first fruits, or of incense, to show th[e] dependence of man on his deity and to thank him for his benefits* [2] *the burnt offering, to appeas[e] an angry god when displeased an[d] ready to bring distress upon him.*

Most probably the plan of sacri[-] fices arranged by Moses was a[n] adaptation of what had always bee[n] their customs, from the time o[f] Abraham. One respect in whic[h] the Jews differed from the heathe[n] nations around them was in th[e] absence of human sacrifice.

The book of Hebrews shows ho[w] Jesus Christ, in becoming a sacri[-] fice for man, made further sacri[-] fices unnecessary.

The Jews ceased offering sacri[-] fice when the Temple was de[-] stroyed, A.D. 70. The custom i[s] now found only in savage tribes.

The word is also used symboli[-] cally, as the sacrifice of one's lips.

Revisions very often translate [it] offering.

then Jacob offered *s.* *Gen* 31:5[4]
do *s.* to the Lord. *Ex* 5:17; 8:[8]
say, It is the *s.* of the Lord's. 12:2[7]
not offer blood of *s.* 23:18*; 34:2[5]
and thou eat of his *s.* 34:1[5]
nor shall *s.* of passover be left. 2[5]
then he shall offer with *s.* *Lev* 7:1[2]
leavened bread with *s.* of. 13; 22:2[9]
if *s.* be a vow, it shall be eaten. 1[6]
offereth a *s.* and bringeth. 17:[8]
which they do not offer a *s.* 27:1[1]
or make a *s.* in performing a vow.
Num 15:3, [8]
it is for a sweet savour, a *s.* 28:[6]
8, 13, 19, 24; 29:6, 13, 3[6]
from them that offer *s.* *Deut* 18:3
an altar, not for *s.* *Josh* 22:2[6]
for to offer a great *s.* *Judg* 16:23
offer the yearly *s.* *1 Sam* 1:21; 2:19
wherefore kick ye at my *s.* 2:29
Eli's house not purged with *s.* 3:14
there is a *s.* of people to-day. 9:12
because he doth bless the *s.* 13
to obey is better than *s.* 15:22
call Jesse to the *s.* and I will. 16:3, 5
yearly *s.* for all the family. 20:6, 29
if this people do *s.* at. *1 Ki* 12:27
till time of the evening *s.* 18:29
at the time of evening *s.* Elijah. 36
not offer *s.* to other gods. *2 Ki* 5:17
for I have a great *s.* to do to. 10:19
and to him shall ye do *s.* 17:36
save only to burn *s.* before. *2 Chr* 2:6
king Solomon offered a *s.* of. 7:5
myself for an house of *s.* 12
astonied until the evening *s.* *Ezra* 9:4
at the evening *s.* I arose up from. 5
s. thou didst not desire. *Ps* 40:6
51:16
made a covenant with me by *s.* 50:5
I will offer to thee the *s.* 116:17
bind the *s.* with cords to. 118:27
of my hands as evening *s.* 141:2
s. of the wicked is an. *Pr* 15:8
more acceptable than *s.* 21:3
to hear than to give the *s.* *Eccl* 5:1
the Egyptians shall do *s.* *Isa* 19:21
for the Lord hath a *s.* in Bozrah. 34:6
wentest thou to offer *s.* 57:7
that bring the *s.* of praise. *Jer* 33:11
nor want a man to do *s.* 18
for God hath a *s.* in the north. 46:10
to my *s.*, even a great *s.* *Ezek* 39:17
till ye be drunken of my *s.* 19
they shall slay the *s.* for. 44:11
where ministers boil the *s.* 46:24
daily *s.* was taken away. *Dan* 8:11
9:27; 11:31
given him against the daily *s.* 8:12
be the vision of the daily *s.*? 13
from the time daily *s.* shall. 12:11

many days without a *s*. *Hos* 3:4
I desired mercy, and not *s*. 6:6
Mat 9:13; 12:7
offer a *s*. of thanksgiving. *Amos* 4:5
then the men offered a *s*. *Jonah* 1:16
for the Lord hath prepared a *s*.
Zeph 1:7, 8
if ye offer the blind for *s*. *Mal* 1:8
every *s*. shall be salted. *Mark* 9:49
and to offer a *s*. according. *Luke* 2:24
in those days they offered *s*. to.
Acts 7:41
and would have done *s*. with. 14:13
that they had not done *s*. unto. 18
your bodies a living *s*. *Rom* 12:1
in *s*. to idols. *1 Cor* 8:4; 10:19, 28
a *s*. to God for a sweet. *Eph* 5:2
if I be offered on the *s*. *Phil* 2:17
a *s*. acceptable, wellpleasing. 4:18
needeth not daily, as those high priests, to offer up *s*. *Heb* 7:27
to put away sin by the *s*. 9:26
he saith, S. and offering. 10:5, 8
had offered one *s*. for sins, for. 12
there remaineth no more *s*. for. 26
to God a more excellent *s*. 11:4
let us offer the *s*. of praise. 13:15
see **burnt, peace offering**

sacrifice, *verb*

let us go and *s*. to the Lord our God.
Ex 3:18; 5:3, 8; 8:27; 10:25
Go ye, *s*. 8:25
shall we *s*. the abomination of? 26
in not letting the people go to *s*. 29
I *s*. to Lord all that openeth. 13:15
thou shalt *s*. thereon thy. 20:24
thou shalt not *s*. it. *Deut* 15:21; 17:1
thou shalt therefore *s*. 16:2, 6
not *s*. the passover within any. 5
yearly to *s*. to the Lord. *1 Sam* 1:3
the people spared the best to *s*. 15:15
should have been destroyed to *s*. 21
come to *s*. to the Lord. 16:2, 5
went to Gibeon to *s*. there. *1 Ki* 3:4
as yet the people did *s*. and.
2 Ki 14:4; *2 Chr* 33:17
nor shall *s*. to other gods. *2 Ki* 17:35
to Jerusalem to *s*. to. *2 Chr* 11:16
we seek your God, and do *s*. to.
Ezra 4:2
will they *s*.? will they? *Neh* 4:2
I will freely *s*. to thee. *Ps* 54:6
let them *s*. sacrifices of. 107:22
gather to my *s*. that I do *s*. for you.
Ezek 39:17
they *s*. on the tops of. *Hos* 4:13
and they *s*. with harlots. 14
they *s*., but the Lord accepteth. 8:13
are vanity, they *s*. bullocks. 12:11
men that *s*. kiss the calves. 13:2
I will *s*. to thee with. *Jonah* 2:9
therefore they *s*. unto. *Hab* 1:16
they that *s*. shall seethe. *Zech* 14:21
things Gentiles *s*., they *s*. *1 Cor* 10:20

sacrificed

calf and *s*. thereunto. *Ex* 32:8
they *s*. unto devils, not. *Deut* 32:17
they *s*. thereon peace. *Josh* 8:31
and they *s*. there unto. *Judg* 2:5
said to the man that *s*. *1 Sam* 2:15
and *s*. sacrifices the same day. 6:15
went to Gilgal and *s*. 11:15
David *s*. oxen and. *2 Sam* 6:13
only the people *s*. in the high places.
1 Ki 3:2, 3; *2 Ki* 12:3; 15:4, 35
16:4; *2 Chr* 28:4
his strange wives, and *s*. *1 Ki* 11:8
lowest priests which *s*. *2 Ki* 17:32
then he *s*. there. *1 Chr* 21:28
assembled before ark *s*. *2 Chr* 5:6
Ahaz *s*. to the gods of. 28:23
Manasseh *s*. on the altar of. 33:16
for Amon *s*. to all the carved. 22
on graves of them that had *s*. 34:4
yea, they *s*. their sons. *Ps* 106:37
daughters, they *s*. to the idols. 38
these thou *s*. to them. *Ezek* 16:20
of my sacrifice which I have *s*. 39:19
. to Baalim, and burnt. *Hos* 11:2
our Passover is *s*. for us. *1 Cor* 5:7
to eat things *s*. to idols. *Rev* 2:14, 20

sacrificedst

which thou *s*. the first day. *Deut* 16:4

sacrifices

Beer-sheba offered *s*. to. *Gen* 46:1
must give us also *s*. *Ex* 10:25
father in law, took *s*. for God. 18:12
of the *s*. of the Lord. *Lev* 10:13
the *s*. which they offer in the. 17:5
no more offer their *s*. to devils. 7
they called to the *s*. *Num* 25:2
my *s*. shall ye observe to offer. 28:2
bring your *s*. and tithes. *Deut* 12:6
which did eat the fat of their *s*. 32:38
there they shall offer the *s*. 33:19
s. of the Lord are their. *Josh* 13:14
the altar not for *s*.; but it. 22:28, 29
and sacrificed *s*. same. *1 Sam* 6:15
Lord as great delight in *s*.? 15:22
they sacrificed *s*. in. *1 Chr* 29:21
and consumed the *s*. *2 Chr* 7:1
bring *s*.: they brought in *s*. 29:31
where he offered *s*. be. *Ezra* 6:3
that they may offer *s*. to God. 10
day they offered great *s*. *Neh* 12:43
offer *s*. of righteousness. *Ps* 4:5
therefore I will offer *s*. of joy. 27:6
not reprove thee for thy *s*. 50:8
s. of God are a broken spirit. 51:17
then shalt thou be pleased with *s*. 19
Baal-peor, and eat *s*. of dead. 106:28
let them sacrifice the *s*. of. 107:22
than a house full of *s*. *Pr* 17:1
is the multitude of *s*.? *Isa* 1:11
year to year, let them kill *s*. 29:1
nor honoured me with thy *s*. 43:23
filled me with the fat of thy *s*. 24
their *s*. shall be accepted on. 56:7
nor are your *s*. sweet. *Jer* 6:20
burnt offerings to your *s*. 7:21
commanded them concerning *s*. 22
bringing *s*. of praise to house. 17:26
high hill and offered *s*. *Ezek* 20:28
be ashamed, because of their *s*.
Hos 4:19
their *s*. shall be as the bread. 9:4
and bring your *s*. every. *Amos* 4:4
have ye offered unto me *s*.? 5:25
Lord is more than all *s*. *Mark* 12:33
mingled with their *s*. *Luke* 13:1
have ye offered *s*. for? *Acts* 7:42
that eat the *s*. partakers? *1 Cor* 10:18
he may offer gifts and *s*. *Heb* 5:1
priest is ordained to offer *s*. 8:3
offered both gifts and *s*. 9:9
heavenly things with better *s*. 23
can never with those *s*. make. 10:1
but in those *s*. there is a. 3
in *s*. for sin thou hast had no. 6
offering oftentimes the same *s*. 11
for with such *s*. God is well. 13:16
to offer up spiritual *s*. *1 Pet* 2:5
see **burnt**

sacrificeth

he that *s*. to any god, save. *Ex* 22:20
s. and to him that *s*. not. *Eccl* 9:2
people that *s*. in gardens. *Isa* 65:3
he that *s*. a lamb as if he cut. 66:3
and *s*. a corrupt thing. *Mal* 1:14

sacrificing

him *s*. sheep and oxen. *1 Ki* 8:5
s. to the calves that he had. 12:32

sacrilege

dost thou commit *s*.? *Rom* 2:22*

sad

them, behold they were *s*. *Gen* 40:6
was no more *s*. *1 Sam* 1:18
why is thy spirit so *s*.? *1 Ki* 21:5
I had not been before *s*. *Neh* 2:1
Why is thy countenance *s*.? 2
should not my countenance be *s*.? 3
the heart of righteous *s*. whom I have not made *s*. *Ezek* 13:22
not as hypocrites, of a *s*. *Mat* 6:16
was *s*. at that saying. *Mark* 10:22*
as ye walk, and are *s*. *Luke* 24:17

saddle

what *s*. he rideth upon. *Lev* 15:9

saddle, *verb*

I will *s*. me an ass. *2 Sam* 19:26
s. me the ass. *1 Ki* 13:13, 27

saddled

early, and *s*. his ass. *Gen* 22:3
Balaam *s*. his ass. *Num* 22:21
the Levite two asses *s*. *Judg* 19:10
met David with a couple of asses *s*.
2 Sam 16:1
Ahithophel *s*. his ass, and gat. 17:23
Shimei *s*. and went after. *1 Ki* 2:40
so they *s*. him the ass. 13:13, 23, 27
she *s*. an ass. *2 Ki* 4:24

Sadducees

A religious party or sect among the Jews at the time of Christ. They were probably disciples of a Zadok—but authorities are uncertain who he was or when he lived. The sect was small but very wealthy, and included the higher priests. The chief distinction between these and the Pharisees was the insistence by the Sadducees that only the written law was obligatory.

The special doctrines of the Sadducees were [1] *the denial of a resurrection and a future life, with all that includes;* [2] *the denial of the existence of angels or spirits.*

when he saw the S. come. *Mat* 3:7
the S. came tempting Jesus. 16:1
beware of the leaven of the S. 6, 11
beware of the doctrine of the S. 12
came to him the S. which say. 22:23
had heard that he had put the S. 34
the priests and the S. came. *Acts* 4:1
the S. laid their hands on. 5:17
the one part were S. 23:6
dissension between the Pharisees and S. 7
for the S. say, that there is no. 8

sadly

why look ye so *s*. to-day? *Gen* 40:7

sadness

by *s*. of countenance the. *Eccl* 7:3

safe

and ye dwelled *s*. *1 Sam* 12:11*
man Absalom *s*.? *2 Sam* 18:29*, 32*
their houses are *s*. from. *Job* 21:9
up, and I shall be *s*. *Ps* 119:117
run into it, and are *s*. *Pr* 18:10
in the Lord shall be *s*. 29:25
carry the prey away *s*. *Isa* 5:29
they shall be *s*. in. *Ezek* 34:27*
had received him *s*. *Luke* 15:27
they may bring him *s*. *Acts* 23:24
they escaped all *s*. to land. 27:44
things, for you it is *s*. *Phil* 3:1

safeguard

me thou shalt be in *s*. *1 Sam* 22:23

safely

he led them on *s*. they. *Ps* 78:53
to me shall dwell *s*. *Pr* 1:33*
thou walk in thy way *s*. 3:23*
heart of her husband doth *s*. 31:11
them, and passed *s*. *Isa* 41:3
make them to lie down *s*. *Hos* 2:18
Jerusalem shall be *s*. *Zech* 14:11
and lead him away *s*. *Mark* 14:44
jailor to keep them *s*. *Acts* 16:23
see **dwell**

safety

I was not in *s*. nor had I. *Job* 3:26*
his children are far from *s*. and. 5:4
mourn may be exalted to *s*. 11
thou shalt take thy rest in *s*. 11:18
be given him to be in *s*. 24:23*
I will set him in *s*. from. *Ps* 12:5
an horse is a vain thing for *s*. 33:17
of counsellors is *s*. *Pr* 11:14; 24:6
horse is for battle, but *s*. is. 21:31*
shall lie down in *s*. *Isa* 14:30
found we shut with all *s*. *Acts* 5:23
shall say, Peace and *s*. *1 Thes* 5:3
see **dwell**

saffron

spikenard and *s*. *S of S* 4:14

said

Adam *s*. This is bone of. *Gen* 2:23
the serpent *s*. Hath God *s*. ye? 3:1
Noah *s*. Blessed be the Lord. 9:26
Sarah hath *s*. hearken to her. 21:12
had *s*. It is my master. 24:65
began to come, as Joseph *s*. 41:54
returned to the Lord and *s*. *Ex* 5:22
serve the Lord as ye have *s*. 12:31
and herds, as ye have *s*. 32

Joshua did as Moses had *s.* *Ex* 17:10
out, as Moses had *s.* *Lev* 10:5
thou hast *s.* I will give. *Num* 11:21
ye *s.* should be a prey. 14:31
Deut 1:39
did as Balaam had *s.* *Num* 23:50
sons of Joseph hath *s.* well. 36:5
God of thy fathers hath *s.* *Deut* 1:21
Hebron to Caleb, as Moses *s.*
Judg 1:20
Israel, as thou hast *s.* 6:36, 37
thee, what Samuel *s.* *1 Sam* 10:15
who is he that *s.* Shall Saul ? 11:12
to you in all ye *s.* to me. 12:1
David *s.* I shall now perish. 27:1
Lord, do as thou hast *s.* *2 Sam* 7:25
as thy servant *s.* so it is. 13:35
sweet psalmist of Israel *s.* 23:1
as my lord king hath *s.* *1 Ki* 2:38
thou hast *s.* My name shall be there.
8:29; *2 Chr* 6:20
Jeroboam *s.* Now shall. *1 Ki* 12:26
s. to her, Go, do as thou hast *s.* 17:13
s. on this matter, another *s.* 22:20
the man of God had *s.* *2 Ki* 7:17
Lord, do as thou hast *s.* *1 Chr* 17:23
hast *s.* so must we do. *Ezra* 10:12
that *s.* We are many. *Neh* 5:2, 3
do as Esther hath *s.* *Esth* 5:5
to-morrow as the king hath *s.* 8
thou hast *s.*, My doctrine. *Job* 11:4
if men of my tabernacle *s.* not. 31:31
when I *s.* Hitherto shalt thou. 38:11
who *s.* With our tongue. *Ps* 12:4
fool *s.* in his heart. 14:1; 53:1
my heart *s.* to thee, Thy face. 27:8
an impudent face, *s.* unto. *Pr* 7:13
thou hast *s.* I will ascend. *Isa* 14:13
s. We have made a covenant. 28:15
ye *s.* No, for we will flee. 30:16
thou hast *s.* None seeth me. 47:10
the priests *s.* not, Where ? *Jer* 2:8
what the prophets *s.* 23:25
Jeremiah *s.* Amen. 28:6
because ye *s.* The Lord hath. 29:15
what thou hast *s.* to the king, also what the king *s.* unto thee. 38:25
of whom we *s.* Under his. *Lam* 4:20
and I *s.* Ah, Lord God. *Ezek* 9:8
not the rebellious house *s.*? 12:9
Tyrus hath *s.* against. 26:2; 36:2
O Tyrus, thou hast *s.* I am. 27:3
hast *s.* I am a god, I sit. 28:2
which hath *s.* My river is mine. 29:3
Nebuchadnezzar *s.* Blessed be God.
Dan 3:28
another saint *s.* to that saint. 8:13
Jonah *s.* It is better for. *Jonah* 4:8
her who *s.* to me, Where ? *Mi* 7:10
city that *s.* in her heart. *Zeph* 2:15
ye have *s.* it is vain to. *Mal* 3:14
behold, a voice which *s.* This is my beloved Son. *Mat* 17:5; *Luke* 3:22
also *s.* all the disciples. *Mat* 26:35
saith unto him, Thou hast *s.* 64
that that deceiver *s.* 27:63
he *s.* to Levi, Follow me. *Mark* 2:14
the angel *s.* to him. *Luke* 1:13, 30
s., Master, thou hast well *s.* 20:39
had seen angels, who *s.* that. 24:23
even so as the women had *s.* 24
straight the way, as *s.* *John* 1:23
but *s.* also, that God was his. 5:18
as the scripture hath *s.* out. 7:38
these things *s.* Esaias, when. 12:41
even as the Father *s.* unto me. 50
then Peter *s.*, Repent and. *Acts* 2:38
all the chief priests had *s.* 4:23
this is that Moses who *s.* 7:37
your own poets have *s.* 17:28
except law had *s.* Thou. *Rom* 7:7
as we *s.* before, so say. *Gal* 1:9
by him that *s.* to him. *Heb* 7:21
we know him that hath *s.* 10:30
the four beasts *s.* Amen. *Rev* 5:14
see **Jesus**

said, *participle*
wherefore it is *s.* even. *Gen* 10:9
as it is *s.* to this day, in. 22:14
after it was *s.* Ye shall. *Ex* 5:19
it was *s.* by the word. *1 Ki* 13:17
perish, in which it was *s.* *Job* 3:3
surely it is meet to be *s.* to. 34:31
of Zion it shall be *s.* This. *Ps* 87:5
better it be *s.* to thee. *Pr* 25:7
thing whereof it may be *s.*? *Eccl* 1:10
it shall be *s.* in that day. *Isa* 25:9
it shall no more be *s.* The. *Jer* 16:14
shall it not be *s.* Where ? *Ezek* 13:12
it was *s.* to them, Ye are. *Hos* 1:10
it was *s.* by them. *Mat* 5:21, 27, 33
heard it hath been *s.* 31, 38, 43
which is *s.* in law of Lord. *Luke* 2:24
having *s.* thus, he gave up. 23:46
it was *s.* The elder shall. *Rom* 9:12
that where it was *s.* Ye are not. 26
whilst it is *s.* To-day. *Heb* 3:15; 4:7
of whom it was *s.* In Isaac. 11:18
s. to them, They should. *Rev* 6:11

answered and **said**
all the people *answered and s.*
Ex 24:3
one of the same place *answered and s.* *1 Sam* 10:12
Satan *answered and s.* Skin for skin.
Job 2:4
Lord *answered* Job *and s.* 40:1
he *answered* one of them, *and s.*, Friend, I do thee no. *Mat* 20:13
John *answered and s.* *Luke* 9:49
see **answered**

God **said**
yea, hath *God s.* ye.? *Gen* 3:1, 3
same day, as *God* had *s.* 17:23
whatsoever *God* hath *s.* 31:16
house of which *God s.* *2 Chr* 33:7
and the nation will I judge, *s. God.*
Acts 7:7
living God, as *God* hath *s.* *2 Cor* 6:16

he **said**
he s. Escape for thy life. *Gen* 19:17
s. he not unto me, She is my ? 20:5
if *he s.*, The speckled shall. 31:8
he s. Lift up thine eyes and see. 12
he s. Let me go, for the day. 32:26
he s. What is thy name ? and *he s.* 27
God, *s. he*, hath made me. 41:51
all that Jethro had *s.* *Ex* 18:24
stand before you, as *he* hath *s.*
Deut 11:25; 18:2; 29:13
Josh 13:14, 33
kept me alive, as *he s.* *Josh* 14:10
abated, when *he* had *s.* *Judg* 8:3
hide any thing *he s.* *1 Sam* 3:17
not fail thee, *s. he*, a man. *1 Ki* 2:4
do as *he* hath *s.*, and fall upon him. 31
he s. by all his servants. *2 Ki* 17:23
build the house, as *he s.* *1 Chr* 22:11
he s. Lord, look on it. *2 Chr* 24:22
to man *he s.* Behold. *Job* 28:28
he hath *s.* in his heart. *Ps* 10:6
11:13
he s. that he would destroy. 106:23
to whom *he s.* This is. *Isa* 28:12
the voice said, Cry, *he s.* What ? 40:6
for *he s.* Surely they are my. 63:8
now the Lord hath done as *he* hath *s.*
Jer 40:3
to the others *he s.* in. *Ezek* 9:5
because *he* hath *s.* The river. 29:9
of the evil *he* had *s.* *Jonah* 3:10
for *he s.* I am the Son. *Mat* 27:43
he has risen, as *he s.* 28:6
came and found as *he s.*
Mark 14:16; *Luke* 22:13
there shall ye see him, as *he s.*
Mark 16:7
not knowing what *he s.* *Luke* 9:33
when *he s.* these things. 13:17
remembered that *he s.* *John* 2:22
this *he s.* to prove him, for. 6:6
what sayest thou ? *he s.* He is. 9:17
this *he s.*, not that he cared. 12:6
this *he s.*, signifying what death. 33
as soon as *he s.* to them, I am. 18:6
he s. It is finished, and bowed. 19:30
when *he* had so *s.* he shewed. 20:20
when *he* had *s.* this, he breathed. 22
when *he* had *s.* this, he fell. *Acts* 7:60
he s. Who art thou, Lord ? 9:5
how *he s.* It is more blessed. 20:35
when *he* had so *s.* there arose. 23:7
he *s.* My grace is sufficient for thee.
2 Cor 12:9
the angels *s. he* at any ? *Heb* 1:5, 13
then *s. he*, Lo, I come to do. *Heb* 10:9
for *he* hath *s.* I will never. 13:5
he that *s.* Do not commit. *Jas* 2:11
he s. These things are. *Rev* 22:6

I **said**
I s. Lest I die for her. *Gen* 26:9
I have *s.* I will bring. *Ex* 3:17
in all things that *I* have *s.* 23:13
I s. I would scatter. *Deut* 32:26
that have I given, as *I s.* *Josh* 1:3
I s. unto you, I am the. *Judg* 6:10
I s. indeed, that thy. *1 Sam* 2:30
portion, of which *I s.* Set it by. 9:23
I s. Thou and Ziba. *2 Sam* 19:29
house of which *I s.* My. *2 Ki* 23:27
thing, therefore *I s.* it. *Job* 9:22
I s. I shall die in my nest. 29:18
I s. Days should speak, and. 32:7
in prosperity *I s.* I shall. *Ps* 30:6
I s. I will take heed to my. 39:1
then *s. I*, Lo, I come. 40:7
Heb 10:7
I s. Lord, be merciful to. *Ps* 41:4
I have *s.* Ye are gods. 82:6
I s. My foot slippeth. 94:18
I s. O my God, take me not. 102:24
I s. Thou art my refuge and. 142:5
I s. in mine heart, Go to. *Eccl* 2:1, 15
3:17, 18
s. I, Lord, how long ? *Isa* 6:11
I s. not, Seek ye me in vain. 45:19
I s. Behold me, to a nation. 65:1
I s. when thou wast in. *Ezek* 16:6
he of whom *I s.* After. *John* 1:30
marvel not that *I s.* Ye must be. 3:7
the same that *I s.* from the. 8:25
I s. I am the Son of God. 10:36
s. I not to thee, If thou. 11:40
I s. it, that they may believe. 42
ye have heard how *I s.* to you. 14:28
these things *I s.* not at the. 16:4
in secret have *I s.* nothing. 18:20
heard me, what *I* have *s.* 21
I s. Not so, Lord, for. *Acts* 11:8
I have *s.* that ye are in our hearts.
2 Cor 7:3
that as *I s.* ye may be ready. 9:3
see **Jesus**

she **said**
for God, *s. she*, hath appointed me.
Gen 4:25
she s. He is my brother. 20:5
this man ? *she s.* I will. 24:58
then *she s.* A bloody. *Ex* 4:26
to say, and *she s.* Say on. *1 Ki* 2:14
she s. Truth, Lord, yet. *Mat* 15:27
she s. No man, Lord. *John* 8:11
she had so *s.* she went her. 11:28
she had thus *s.* she turned. 20:14
she s. Yea, for so much. *Acts* 5:8

they **said**
and *they s.* All that the Lord. *Ex* 24:7
they have well *s.* all. *Deut* 5:28
s. they, He is the son of. *2 Chr* 22:9
for *they s.* He is a leper. 26:23
they have *s.* Come, let us cut them.
Ps 83:4
neither *s. they*, Where is ? *Jer* 2:6
believe ye ? *they s.* unto him, Yea.
Mat 9:28
they all *s.* Let him be crucified. 27:22
for *they s.* He is beside. *Mark* 3:21
because *they s.* He hath an. 30
amazed, nor *s. they* any thing. 16:8
they s. The Lord hath. *Luke* 19:34
s. they, It is his angel. *Acts* 12:15

saidst
why *s.* thou, She is my ? *Gen* 12:19
s. thou, She is my sister ? 26:9
the Lord, which *s.* to me. 32:9
s. I will surely do thee good. 12
s. to them, I will multiply. *Ex* 32:13
mouth wherewith thou *s.* *Judg* 9:38
thou *s.* The word I have. *1 Ki* 2:42
thou *s.* my righteousness. *Job* 35:2
s. Seek ye my face. *Ps* 27:8
thou *s.* I shall be a lady. *Isa* 47:7
and thou *s.* I will not. *Jer* 2:20
but thou *s.* There is no hope. 25
I spake, but thou *s.* I will. 22:21
I called: thou *s.* Fear not. *Lam* 3:57
because thou *s.*, Aha. *Ezek* 25:3

whom thou *s*. Give me. *Hos* 13:10
in that *s*. thou truly. *John* 4:18

sail, *substantive*

could not spread the *s*. *Isa* 33:23
thou spreadest forth to be thy *s*. *Ezek* 27:7
they strake *s*. and so. *Acts* 27:17*
and hoised up the main *s*. to. 40

sail

as he was about to *s*. *Acts* 20:3
Paul had determined to *s*. 16
we should *s*. into Italy. 27:1
all them that *s*. with thee. 24

sailed

as they *s*. he fell asleep. *Luke* 8:23
when we launched, we *s*. *Acts* 27:4
and when we had *s*. slowly. 7

sailing

finding a ship *s*. over. *Acts* 21:2*
centurion found a ship *s*. 27:6
when *s*. was now dangerous. 9*

sailors

all the company in ships, and *s*. stood afar off. *Rev* 18:17*

saint

The Revisions translate this holy one, *and the plural* holy ones, *where marked, except in* Hos 11:12, *where it is* Holy One, *and* Rev 15:3, *where the word is* ages.

then I heard one *s*. speak, another *s*. said to that *s*. which. *Dan* 8:13*
salute every *s*. in Christ. *Phil* 4:21*

saints

with ten thousands of *s*. *Deut* 33:2*
he loved the people; all his *s*. are. 3
keep the feet of his *s*. *1 Sam* 2:9*
s. rejoice in goodness. *2 Chr* 6:41
and to which of the *s*.? *Job* 5:1*
putteth no trust in his *s*. 15:15*
but to the *s*. that are in. *Ps* 16:3
sing to the Lord, O ye *s*. of. 30:4
O love the Lord, all ye his *s*. 31:23
fear the Lord, ye his *s*. 34:9
Lord forsaketh not his *s*. 37:28
gather my *s*. together to me. 50:5
for it is good before thy *s*. 52:9
the flesh of thy *s*. to beasts. 79:2
in the congregation of the *s*. 89:5*
in the assembly of the *s*. 7*
preserveth the souls of his *s*. 97:10
precious . . . is death of his *s*. 116:15
and let thy *s*. shout for joy. 132:9
her *s*. shall shout aloud for joy. 16
all thy works praise, and *s*. 145:10
the praise of all his *s*. 148:14
praise in congregation of *s*. 149:1
let *s*. be joyful in glory, let them. 5
this honour have all his *s*. Praise. 9
the way of his *s*. *Pr* 2:8
but *s*. shall take. *Dan* 7:18, 22, 27
the horn made war with the *s*. 21
and shall wear out the *s*. of the. 25
is faithful with the *s*. *Hos* 11:12*
God shall come, and all the *s*. with thee. *Zech* 14:5*
many bodies of *s*. that. *Mat* 27:52
evil he hath done to thy *s*. *Acts* 9:13
Peter came down also to the *s*. 32
called the *s*. and widows. 41
s. did I shut up in prison. 26:10
of God, called to be *s*. *Rom* 1:7
maketh intercession for the *s*. 8:27
to the necessity of the *s*. 12:13
Jerusalem to minister to the *s*. 15:25
contribution for the poor *s*. 26
may be accepted of the *s*. 31
in the Lord as becometh the *s*. 16:2
salute all the *s*. 15; *Heb* 13:24
sanctified, called to be *s*. *1 Cor* 1:2
law, and not before the *s*.? 6:1
do ye not know that the *s*. shall? 2
as in all the churches of the *s*. 14:33
the collection for the *s*. 16:1
themselves to the ministry of *s*. 15
with all the *s*. which are. *2 Cor* 1:1
upon us the ministering to the *s*. 8:4
the ministering to the *s*. 9:1
supplieth the want of the *s*. 12
the *s*. salute you. 13:13; *Phil* 4:22
to the *s*. at Ephesus, and. *Eph* 1:1
of your love to all the *s*. *Eph* 1:15
glory of his inheritance in the *s*. 18
fellow citizens with the *s*. 2:19
less than the least of all *s*. 3:8
able to comprehend with all *s*. 18
of the *s*. for the ministry. 4:12
once named, as becometh *s*. 5:3
and supplication for all *s*. 6:18
to all the *s*. in Christ. *Phil* 1:1
to all the *s*. and faithful. *Col* 1:2
of the love ye have to all the *s*. 4
inheritance of the *s*. in light. 12
now made manifest to his *s*. 26
our Lord with all his *s*. *1 Thes* 3:13
to be glorified in his *s*. *2 Thes* 1:10
washed the *s*.' feet. *1 Tim* 5:10
which thou hast to all *s*. *Philem* 5
the bowels of the *s*. are refreshed. 7
ministered to the *s*. *Heb* 6:10
once delivered to the *s*. *Jude* 3
with ten thousand of his *s*. 14*
prayers of the *s*. *Rev* 5:8; 8:3, 4
give reward to thy *s*. 11:18
to make war with the *s*. 13:7
patience and faith of the *s*. 10
here is the patience of the *s*. 14:12
thy ways, thou King of *s*. 15:3*
shed the blood of the *s*. 16:6
drunken with the blood of *s*. 17:6
found the blood of the *s*. 18:24
is the righteousness of the *s*. 19:8
the camp of the *s*. about. 20:9

saith

one *s*. This is my son that liveth, and the other *s*. Nay. *1 Ki* 3:23
thus *s*. Ben-hadad, Thy silver. 20:2
servant Ben-hadad *s*. I pray thee. 32
s. the king, Put this fellow in prison. 22:27; *2 Chr* 18:26
thus *s*. the king, Is it peace? *2 Ki* 9:18, 19
thus *s*. the great king, the. 18:19
s. king, Let not Hezekiah deceive. 29
31; *2 Chr* 32:10; *Isa* 36:14
thus *s*. Hezekiah, This day is a day of. *2 Ki* 19:3; *Isa* 37:3
thus *s*. Cyrus, king of Persia. *2 Chr* 36:23; *Ezra* 1:2
the depth *s*. and the sea *s*. *Job* 28:14
he *s*. Deliver him. 33:24
but none *s*. Where is God? 35:10
of the wicked *s*. *Ps* 36:1
understanding, she *s*. *Pr* 9:4, 16
naught, it is naught, *s*. the. 20:14
the slothful man *s*., There is a lion. 22:13; 26:13
deceiveth, and *s*. Am not I? 26:19
who is he that *s*. and? *Lam* 3:37
not every one that *s*. to me. *Mat* 7:21
to him, Master *s*. My time. 26:18
Peter *s*. to him, Thou. *Mark* 8:29
fulfilled which *s*. 15:28; *Jas* 2:23
what the unjust judge *s*. *Luke* 18:6
who it is that *s*. Give. *John* 4:10
might be fulfilled, *s*. I thirst. 19:28
dwelleth not in temples made with hands, as *s*. *Acts* 7:48
thus *s*. the Holy Ghost, So. 21:11
the law *s*. it *s*. to them. *Rom* 3:19
for what *s*. the scripture? 4:3; 10:8
for scripture *s*. to Pharaoh. 9:17
for scripture *s*. Whosoever. 10:11
for Esaias *s*. 16, 20
first Moses *s*. 19
what the scripture *s*. of Elias? 11:2
but what *s*. the answer of God? 4
for while one *s*. I am of Paul. *1 Cor* 3:4
or *s*. not the law the same also? 9:8
be under obedience, as also *s*. 14:34
what *s*. the scripture? *Gal* 4:30
1 Tim 5:18
as the Holy Ghost *s*. If. *Heb* 3:7
do ye think the scriptures *s*. *Jas* 4:5
the Spirit *s*. to the churches. *Rev* 2:7
11, 17, 29; 3:6, 13, 22
s. the First and the Last. 2:8
s. the Son of God. 18
s. the Amen. 3:14
yea, *s*. the Spirit. 14:13
she *s*. I sit a queen, and am. 18:7
s. Surely I come quickly. 22:20

God **saith**

what my *God s*. that. *2 Chr* 18:13
thus *s*. *God*, Why transgress? 24:20
to wicked *God s*. What? *Ps* 50:16
thus *s*. *God* the Lord. *Isa* 42:5
wast refused, *s*. thy *God*. 54:6
There is no peace, *s*. my *God*. 57:21
shut the womb, *s*. thy *God*. 66:9
come to pass in the last days *s*. *God*. *Acts* 2:17

he **saith**

go to Joseph, what *he s*. *Gen* 41:55
all that *he s*. cometh. *1 Sam* 9:6
likewise what *he s*. *2 Sam* 17:5
when *he s*. to thee, Wash and be. *2 Ki* 5:13
for *he s*. to the snow, Be. *Job* 37:6
Eat and drink, *s*. *he* to. *Pr* 23:7
he that *s*. to wicked, Thou. 24:24
nor *s*. *he*, For whom do? *Eccl* 4:8
he s. to every one that he is. 10:3
he s. shall come to pass, he shall have whatsoever *he s*. *Mark* 11:23
whatsoever *he s*. to you. *John* 2:5
he s.? we cannot tell what *he s*. 16:18
knoweth that *he s*. true. 19:35
he s. to Peter, Feed my. 21:15, 16
which, *s*. *he*, ye have. *Acts* 1:4
more silence, and *he s*. 22:2
to Israel *he s*. *Rom* 10:21
again *he s*. 15:10
for two, *s*. *he*, shall be. *1 Cor* 6:16
or *s*. *he* it altogether for our? 9:10
he s. I have heard thee. *2 Cor* 6:2
he s. not, And to seeds. *Gal* 3:16
See, *s*. *he*, that thou. *Heb* 8:5
in that *he s*. A new covenant. 13

see **Jesus, Lord**

sake

not curse the ground for man's *s*. *Gen* 8:21
Abram well for her *s*. 12:16
will not do it for forty's *s*. 18:29
not for twenty's *s*. 31
not for ten's *s*. 32
slay me for my wife's *s*. 20:11
thy seed for Abraham's *s*. 26:24
Egyptian's house for Joseph's *s*. 39:5
done to Egypt for Israel's *s*. *Ex* 18:8
let him go free for eye's *s*. 21:26
for his tooth's *s*. 27
enviest thou for my *s*.? *Num* 11:29
he was zealous for my *s*. 25:11
day of the plague for Peor's *s*. 18
people for his name's *s*. *1 Sam* 12:22
destroy the city for my *s*. 23:10
kingdom for Israel's *s*. *2 Sam* 5:12
for thy word's *s*. hast done all. 7:21
1 Chr 17:19
kindness for Jonathan's *s*. *2 Sam* 9:1, 7
deal gently for my *s*. with. 18:5
out of a far country for thy name's *s*. *1 Ki* 8:41; *2 Chr* 6:32
David thy father's *s*. *1 Ki* 11:12
13, 32, 34; 15:4; *2 Ki* 8:19; 19:34
20:6; *Ps* 132:10
for Jerusalem's *s*. which I have. *1 Ki* 11:13
them for great mercies' *s*. *Neh* 9:31
entreated for children's *s*. *Job* 19:17
save me for thy mercies' *s*. *Ps* 6:4
31:16
for his name's *s*. 23:3; 31:3
me for thy goodness' *s*. 25:7
for thy name's *s*. pardon mine. 11
us for thy mercies' *s*. 44:26
not be confounded for my *s*. 69:6
our sins for thy name's *s*. 79:9
saved them for his name's *s*. 106:8
me, for thy name's *s*. 109:21
for thy mercy and truth's *s*. 115:1
for thy name's *s*.: for thy righteousness' *s*. bring my soul. 143:11
own *s*. and David's *s*. *Isa* 37:35
for his righteousness' *s*. 42:21
for your *s*. I have sent to. 43:14
transgressions for mine own *s*. 25
for Jacob's *s*. I have even. 45:4
for my name's *s*. will I defer. 48:9
even for mine own *s*. will I do it. 11
for Zion's *s*., for Jerusalem's *s*. 62:1

return for thy servant's *s.* *Isa* 63:17
out for my name's *s.* said. 66:5
thou it for thy name's *s.* *Jer* 14:7
abhor us for thy name's *s.* 21
but I wrought for my name's *s.* that.
Ezek 20:9, 14, 22, 44; 36:22
sanctuary, for the Lord's *s.* *Dan* 9:17
defer not for thine own *s.* 19
for my *s.* this great. *Jonah* 1:12
shall Zion for your *s.* be. *Mi* 3:12
for righteousness' *s.* *Mat* 5:10
against you falsely for my *s.* 11
before governors and kings, for my *s.*
10:18; *Mark* 13:9; *Luke* 21:12
hated of all men, for my name's *s.*
Mat 10:22; 24:9; *Mark* 13:13
Luke 21:17
loseth his life for my *s.* *Mat* 10:39
16:25; *Mark* 8:35; *Luke* 9:24
Herod bound John for Herodias' *s.*
Mat 14:3; *Mark* 6:17
nevertheless, for the oath's *s.*
Mat 14:9; *Mark* 6:26
kingdom of heaven's *s.* *Mat* 19:12
left lands for my name's *s.* shall.
29; *Mark* 10:29; *Luke* 18:29
no flesh be saved, but for elect's *s.*
Mat 24:22; *Mark* 13:20
ariseth for the world's *s.* *Mark* 4:17
name for Son of man's *s.* *Luke* 6:22
not for Jesus' *s.* only. *John* 12:9
lay down thy life for my *s.*? 13:38
for the very works' *s.* 14:11
do to you for my name's *s.* 15:21
suffer for my name's *s.* *Acts* 9:16
for which hope's *s.* I am. 26:7
written for his *s.* alone. *Rom* 4:23
are enemies for your *s.* 11:28
be subject for conscience *s.* 13:5
for Lord's *s.* strive with. 15:30
for Christ's *s.* ye are wise. *1 Cor* 4:10
this I do for the gospel's *s.* 9:23
question for conscience *s.* 10:25, 27
eat not, for his *s.* that shewed it, and
for conscience *s.* 28
servants for Jesus' *s.* *2 Cor* 4:5
delivered to death for Jesus' *s.* 11
in distresses for Christ's *s.* 12:10
as God for Christ's *s.* *Eph* 4:32
also to suffer for his *s.* *Phil* 1:29
for his body's *s.* which. *Col* 1:24
for which thing's *s.* wrath of. 3:6
men we were for your *s.* *1 Thes* 1:5
highly for their work's *s.* 5:13
wine, for thy stomach's *s.* *1 Tim* 5:23
for filthy lucre's *s.* *Tit* 1:11
yet for love's *s.* I rather. *Philem* 9
ordinance for Lord's *s.* *1 Pet* 2:13
ye suffer for righteousness' *s.* 3:14
forgiven for name's *s.* *1 John* 2:12
for the truth's *s.* that. *2 John* 2
because for his name's *s.* *3 John* 7
and for my name's *s.* hast. *Rev* 2:3

thy **sake**

the ground for *thy s.* *Gen* 3:17
well with me for *thy s.* 12:13
hath blessed me for *thy s.* 30:27
for *thy s.* are we killed all day long.
Ps 44:22; *Rom* 8:36
because for *thy s.* I have borne.
Ps 69:7
against thee, shall fall for *thy s.*
Isa 54:15
know that for *thy s.* I have. *Jer* 15:15
down my life for *thy s.* *John* 13:37

sakes

the place for their *s.* *Gen* 18:26
I will for their *s.* remember the.
Lev 26:45
the Lord was angry with me for your
s. saying. *Deut* 1:37; 3:26; 4:21
to them for our *s.* *Judg* 21:22
me much for your *s.* *Ruth* 1:13
reproved kings for their *s.*
1 Chr 16:21; *Ps* 105:14
for their *s.* therefore. *Ps* 7:7
with Moses for their *s.* 106:32
and companions' *s.* 122:8
for my servant's *s.* *Isa* 65:8
not this for your *s.* *Ezek* 36:22, 32
but for their *s.* that. *Dan* 2:30
and I will rebuke the devourer for
your *s.*, he shall not. *Mal* 3:11
for their *s.* which sat. *Mark* 6:26
I am glad for your *s.* I. *John* 11:15
not for me, but for your *s.* 12:30
and for their *s.* I sanctify. 17:19
for their fathers' *s.* *Rom* 11:28
transferred for your *s.* *1 Cor* 4:6
our *s.*? for our *s.* no doubt. 9:10
all things are for your *s.* *2 Cor* 4:15
though rich, yet for your *s.* 8:9
your *s.* before God. *1 Thes* 3:9
things for the elect's *s.* *2 Tim* 2:10

Salathiel

S. the son of Jechoniah. *1 Chr* 3:17
Mat 1:12
which was the son of *S.* *Luke* 3:27

sale

the years of the *s.* thereof. *Lev* 25:27
price of his *s.* shall be. 50
which cometh of the *s.* *Deut* 18:8

Salem

Melchizedek king of *S.* *Gen* 14:18
in *S.* also is his tabernacle. *Ps* 76:2
Melchizedek king of *S.* who blessed.
Heb 7:1
king of *S.* is king of peace. 2

Salmon

Nahshon begat *S.* *Ruth* 4:20
S. begat Boaz. 21; *1 Chr* 2:11
Mat 1:4, 5
white as snow in *S.* *Ps* 68:14
which was the son of *S.* *Luke* 3:32

Salmone

Crete, over against *S.* *Acts* 27:7

Salome

Mary, mother of *S.* *Mark* 15:40
16:1

salt

This was even more indispensable to the Hebrews than to us, as they used it as an antidote to the effects of the heat of the climate on animal food, and it also was used in the sacrifices. They had an inexhaustible and ready supply of it on the southern shores of the Salt Sea, now called the Dead Sea.
Salt symbolized hospitality, durability and purity. To eat the salt of the king was to owe him the utmost fidelity. To eat bread and salt together was to make an unbreakable league of friendship.

became a pillar of *s.* *Gen* 19:26
offerings thou shalt offer *s.* *Lev* 2:13
whole land thereof is *s.* *Deut* 29:23
Judah had the city of *s.* *Josh* 15:62
city, and sowed it with *s.* *Judg* 9:45
in the valley of *s.* *2 Sam* 8:13
cruse, put *s.* therein. *2 Ki* 2:20
and cast the *s.* in there. 21
Edom in the valley of *s.* 10,000.
14:7; *1 Chr* 18:12; *2 Chr* 25:11
need of, wheat, *s.*, wine. *Ezra* 6:9
and *s.* without prescribing. 7:22
be eaten without *s.*? *Job* 6:6
inhabit places in a *s.* land. *Jer* 17:6
the priest shall cast *s.* *Ezek* 43:24
thereof shall be given to *s.* 47:11
Moab shall be as *s.* pits. *Zeph* 2:9
s. of the earth, but if the *s.* *Mat* 5:13
shall be salted with *s.* *Mark* 9:49
s. have lost his saltness, wherewith
will ye season it ? have *s.* 50
s. is good, but if *s.* have. *Luke* 14:34
speech be seasoned with *s.* *Col* 4:6
no fountain can yield *s.* *Jas* 3:12

see **covenant of salt**

salt sea

(*Now called the Dead Sea*)

which is the *s. sea.* *Gen* 14:3
shall be at the *s. sea.* *Num* 34:12
coast even to the *s. sea.* *Deut* 3:17
came toward the *s. sea.* *Josh* 3:16
even to *s. sea.* 12:3; 15:2, 5; 18:19

salted

thou wast not *s.* at all. *Ezek* 16:4
wherewith shall it be *s.*? *Mat* 5:13
one shall be *s.* with fire and every
sacrifice shall be *s.* *Mark* 9:49

saltness

if salt have lost his *s.* *Mark* 9:50

salutation

what manner of *s.* this. *Luke* 1:29
at *s.* of Mary, babe leaped. 41, 44
you, the *s.* of me, Paul. *1 Cor* 16:21
Col 4:18; *2 Thes* 3:17

salutations

scribes who love *s.* in. *Mark* 12:38

salute

will *s.* thee and give. *1 Sam* 10:4
that he might *s.* Samuel. 13:10
David sent to *s.* our master. 25:14
Joram his son to *s.* *2 Sam* 8:10
s. him not, if any *s.* thee. *2 Ki* 4:29
we go to *s.* the children of. 10:13
and if ye *s.* your brethren. *Mat* 5:47
come into an house, *s.* it. 10:12
and began to *s.* him. *Mark* 15:18
shoes, and *s.* no man. *Luke* 10:4
Bernice came to *s.* Festus. *Acts* 25:13
s. my wellbeloved. *Rom* 16:5
s. Andronicus. 7
s. Urbane our helper. 9
s. Apelles, *s.* them of Aristobulus'. 10
s. Herodian. 11
s. the beloved Persis. 12
s. Rufus chosen in the Lord. 13
s. with an holy kiss, churches *s.* 16
I Tertius, who wrote this, *s.* you. 22
the churches of Asia *s.* you, Aquila
and Priscilla *s.* you. *1 Cor* 16:19
all the saints *s.* you. *2 Cor* 13:13
Phil 4:22
s. every saint in Christ. *Phil* 4:21
s. the brethren in Laodicea. *Col* 4:15
s. the household of. *2 Tim* 4:19
all that are with me, *s.* thee. *Tit* 3:15
there *s.* thee Epaphras. *Philem* 23
s. them that have the rule over you;
they of Italy *s.* you. *Heb* 13:24
our friends *s.* thee, greet. *3 John* 14

saluted

the Danites came and *s.* *Judg* 18:15*
David came and *s.* *1 Sam* 17:22
to the people and *s.* them. 30:21
Jehu *s.* Jehonadab. *2 Ki* 10:15
running to Jesus, *s.* him. *Mark* 9:15
Mary entered, and *s.* *Luke* 1:40
Paul, when he had *s.* *Acts* 18:22
we came to Ptolemais, and *s.* 21:7
when Paul had *s.* James and. 19

saluteth

and Erastus *s.* you. *Rom* 16:23
my fellow-prisoner *s.* you. *Col* 4:10
servant of Christ, *s.* you. 12
is at Babylon *s.* you. *1 Pet* 5:13

salvation

[1] *Preservation from trouble or danger.* [2] *Deliverance from sin and its consequences.*

see the *s.* of the Lord. *Ex* 14:13
2 Chr 20:17
the rock of his *s.* *Deut* 32:15
the Lord wrought *s.* *1 Sam* 11:13*
hath wrought this great *s.* 14:45
the Lord wrought a great *s.* 19:5*
he is the tower of *s.* for his king.
2 Sam 22:51*
from day to day his *s.* *1 Chr* 16:23
save us, O God of our *s.* and. 35
be clothed with *s.* *2 Chr* 6:41
s. belongeth to the Lord. *Ps* 3:8
O that the *s.* of Israel. 14:7; 53:6
from the God of his *s.* 24:5
my soul shall rejoice in his *s.* 35:9
the *s.* of the righteous is of. 37:39
will I shew the *s.* of God. 50:23
answer us, O God of our *s.*? 65:5
Lord, even the God of our *s.* 68:19
our God, is the God of *s.* 20*
working *s.* in the midst of. 74:12
they trusted not in his *s.* 78:22
help us, O God of our *s.*, for. 79:9
turn us, O God of our *s.* 85:4
surely his *s.* is nigh them that. 9
joyful noise to the rock of our *s.* 95:1
forth his *s.* from day to day. 96:2
hath made known his *s.* 98:2
have seen the *s.* of our God. 3
I will take the cup of *s.* 116:13
the voice of *s.* is in. 118:15
s. is far from the wicked. 119:155
clothe her priests with *s.* 132:16

that giveth *s.* unto kings. *Ps* 144:10
beautify the meek with *s.* 149:4
water out of the wells of *s. Isa* 12:3
glad and rejoice in his *s.* 25:9
s. will God appoint for walls. 26:1
be thou our *s.* in the time of. 33:2
knowledge, and strength of *s.* 6
and let them bring forth *s.* 45:8
saved with an everlasting *s.* 17
I will place *s.* in Zion for. 46:13
in a day of *s.* have I helped. 49:8
him that publisheth *s.* 52:7
shall see the *s.* of our God. 10
we look for *s.* but it is far. 59:11
therefore his arm brought *s.* 16
he put on an helmet of *s.* upon. 17
but shalt call thy walls *s.* 60:18
me with the garments of *s.* 61:10
and the *s.* thereof as a lamp. 62:1
own arm brought *s.* to me. 63:5
is *s.* hoped for from the hills and mountains . . . *s.* of. *Jer* 3:23*
quietly wait for the *s.* *Lam* 3:26
S. is of the Lord. *Jonah* 2:9
ride on thy chariots of *s.* *Hab* 3:8
thou wentest forth for *s.* of thy people, even for *s.* with thine. 13
he is just, and having *s.* *Zech* 9:9
up an horn of *s.* for us. *Luke* 1:69
knowledge of *s.* to his people. 77
all flesh shall see the *s.* of. 3:6
Jesus said, This day is *s.* 19:9
we know what we worship, for *s.* is of the Jews. *John* 4:22
neither is there *s.* in any. *Acts* 4:12
the word of this *s.* sent. 13:26
thou shouldest be for *s.* unto the. 47
shew to us the way of *s.* 16:17
the *s.* of God is sent unto the. 28:28
the power of God unto *s.* *Rom* 1:16
confession is made unto *s.* 10:10
through their fall *s.* is come. 11:11
now is our *s.* nearer than. 13:11
comforted, it is for your *s. 2 Cor* 1:6
in the day of *s.* have I succoured thee; behold now is the day of *s.* 6:2
worketh repentance to *s.* 7:10
the gospel of your *s.* *Eph* 1:13
take the helmet of *s.* and. 6:17
an evident token of *s.* *Phil* 1:28
work out your own *s.* with. 2:12
an helmet the hope of *s. 1 Thes* 5:8
hath appointed us to obtain *s.* 9
chosen you to *s.* *2 Thes* 2:13
obtain the *s.* in Christ. *2 Tim* 2:10
able to make thee wise unto *s.* 3:15
God that bringeth *s.* *Tit* 2:11
shall be heirs of *s.* *Heb* 1:14
if we neglect so great *s.*? 2:3
the Captain of their *s.* perfect. 10
the Author of eternal *s.* 5:9
things that accompany *s.* 6:9
second time without sin unto *s.* 9:28
through faith unto *s.* *1 Pet* 1:5
receiving the end of your faith, *s.* 9
of which *s.* the prophets have. 10
the longsuffering of the Lord is *s.* *2 Pet* 3:15
to you of the common *s.* *Jude* 3
saying; *S.* to our God. *Rev* 7:10
s. and glory, unto the Lord. 19:1
now is come *s.* and strength. 12:10

my salvation

song, he is become *my s.* *Ex* 15:2
shield, the horn of *my s. 2 Sam* 22:3
the rock of *my s.* 47; *Ps* 18:46
for this is all *my s.* and. *2 Sam* 23:5
he also shall be *my s.* *Job* 13:16
art the God of *my s.* *Ps* 25:5
the Lord is my light and *my s.* 27:1
62:6; *Isa* 12:2
O God of *my s. Ps* 27:9; 51:14; 88:1
O Lord *my s.* 38:22
God, from him cometh *my s.* 62:1
he only is *my s.* 2, 6
in God is *my s.* 7
my God, rock of *my s.* 89:26
him, and shew him *my s.* 91:16
become *my s.* 118:14, 21; *Isa* 12:2
Lord, strength of *my s.* *Ps* 140:7
my s., he is become *my s.* *Isa* 12:2
far off, *my s.* shall not tarry. 46:13
thou mayest be *my s.* to end. 49:6
my s. is gone forth. *Isa* 51:5
my s. shall be for ever. 6
and *my s.* from generation to. 8
my s. is near to come, and my. 56:1
the God of *my s.* my God. *Mi* 7:7
joy in the God of *my s.* *Hab* 3:18
that this shall turn to *my s. Phil* 1:19

thy salvation

I have waited for *thy s.* *Gen* 49:18
because I rejoice in *thy s. 1 Sam* 2:1
also given me the shield of *thy s.* *2 Sam* 22:36; *Ps* 18:35
I will rejoice in *thy s.* *Ps* 9:14
my heart shall rejoice in *thy s.* 13:5
we will rejoice in *thy s.* 20:5
and in *thy s.* how greatly! 21:1
his glory is great in *thy s.* 5
say unto my soul, I am *thy s.* 35:3
thy faithfulness and *thy s.* 40:10
let such as love *thy s.* say, Lord. 16
me the joy of *thy s.* 51:12; 70:4
me in the truth of *thy s.* 69:13
I am poor, let *thy s.* set me up. 29
shall shew forth *thy s.* 71:15
O Lord, grant us *thy s.* 85:7
O visit me with *thy s.* 106:4
let *thy s.* come according. 119:41
my soul fainteth for *thy s.* 81
mine eyes fail for *thy s.* and. 123
Lord, I have hoped for *thy s.* 166
I have longed for *thy s.* O Lord. 174
forgotten the God of *thy s. Isa* 17:10
say to Zion, Behold, *thy s.* 62:11
eyes have seen *thy s.* *Luke* 2:30

Samaria

places which are in *S.* *1 Ki* 13:32
Omri bought the hill *S.* of. 16:24
besieged *S.* 20:1; *2 Ki* 6:24
if the dust of *S.* shall suffice. *1 Ki* 20:10
there are men come out of *S.* 17
sat on their throne in the entrance of the gate of *S.* 22:10; *2 Chr* 18:9
chariot in the pool of *S.* *1 Ki* 22:38
were in the midst of *S.* *2 Ki* 6:20
shekel in the gate of *S.* 7:1, 18
king of Assyria took *S.* 17:6; 18:10
have they delivered *S.* out of mine hand? 18:34; *Isa* 36:19
Jerusalem the line of *S. 2 Ki* 21:13
prophet that came out of *S.* 23:18
upon the cities; from *S. 2 Chr* 25:13
Asnapper set in the cities of *S.* *Ezra* 4:10
spake before army of *S.* *Neh* 4:2
Ephraim is *S.* and the head of *S.* is. *Isa* 7:9
and the spoil of *S.* shall be. 8:4
Ephraim and inhabitants of *S.* 9:9
is not Hamath as Arpad? *S.* 10:9
folly in the prophets of *S. Jer* 23:13
vines on the mountains of *S.* 31:5
certain from Shechem and *S.* 41:5
thine elder sister is *S.* *Ezek* 16:46
nor hath *S.* committed half. 51
S. is Aholah, and Jerusalem. 23:4
then the wickedness of *S.* *Hos* 7:1
thy calf, O *S.* hath cast thee. 8:5
but the calf of *S.* shall be broken. 6
inhabitants of *S.* shall fear. 10:5
as for *S.* her king is cut off as. 7
S. shall become desolate, she. 13:16
on mountains of *S.* *Amos* 3:9
Bashan, in mountain of *S.* 4:1
trust in the mountain of *S.* 6:1
swear by the sin of *S.* and. 8:14
possess the fields of *S.* *Ob* 19
which he saw concerning *S.* *Mi* 1:1
I will make *S.* as an heap of. 6
through the midst of *S. Luke* 17:11
must needs go through *S.* *John* 4:4
of me, who am a woman of *S.*? 9
through the regions of *S.* *Acts* 8:1
preached Christ to them of *S.* 5
the apostles heard that *S.* 14

***in* Samaria**

Omri buried *in S.* *1 Ki* 16:28
Ahab reigned *in S.* 29
was a sore famine *in S.* 18:2
as my father made *in S.* 20:34
king of Israel which is *in S.* 21:18
Ahab buried *in S.* 22:37
Ahaziah reigned *in S.* 51
Jehoram to reign *in S.* *2 Ki* 3:1
were with the prophets *in S.* 5:3
was a great famine *in S.* 6:25
Jehu slew all that remained to Ahab *in S.* 10:17
Jehoahaz reigned *in S.* 13:1
remained the grove also *in S.* 6
Jehoahaz buried *in S.* 9
Jehoash to reign *in S.* 10
Joash, buried *in S.* 13; 14:16
Jeroboam reigned *in S.* 14:23
Zechariah reigned *in S.* 15:8, 13
Menahem to reign *in S.* 17
Pekah to reign *in S.* 27
Hoshea to reign *in S.* 17:1
for Ahaziah was hid *in S. 2 Chr* 22:9
so Israel that dwell *in S. Amos* 3:12
be witnesses to me *in S.* *Acts* 1:8
had the churches rest *in S.* 9:31

***to* or *unto* Samaria**

displeased came *to S.* *1 Ki* 20:43
so king was brought *to S.* 22:37
from Carmel *to S.* *2 Ki* 2:25
but Elisha led them *to S.* 6:19
Jehu sent letters *to S.* 10:1
Jehu came *to S.* 12, 17
Jehoash took hostages, and returned *to S.* 14:14; *2 Chr* 25:24
Menahem came *to S.* *2 Ki* 15:14
king of Assyria went up *to S.* 17:5
Jehoshaphat went down *to S.* *2 Chr* 18:2
brought the spoil of Judah *to S.* 28:8
as I have done *unto S.* *Isa* 10:11

Samaritan

but a certain *S.* came. *Luke* 10:33
gave thanks, and he was a *S.* 17:16
that thou art a *S.* and. *John* 8:48

Samaritans

places the *S.* had made. *2 Ki* 17:29
into any city of the *S.* *Mat* 10:5
into a village of the *S.* *Luke* 9:52
no dealings with the *S.* *John* 4:9
many of the *S.* of that city. 39
the *S.* besought him to tarry. 40
many villages of the *S.* *Acts* 8:25

same

saying, This *s.* shall. *Gen* 5:29
the *s.* became mighty men. 6:4
Resen, the *s.* is a great city. 10:12
the *s.* is Zoar. 14:8
the *s.* is Hebron. 23:2, 19
let the *s.* be she that. 24:14, 44
appeared to Isaac the *s.* night. 26:24
spake them these *s.* words. 44:6
in the way of Ephrath, the *s.* 48:7
shall be of the *s.* *Ex* 25:31; 37:17
knops and branches shall be of the *s.* 25:36; 37:22
his horns shall be of the *s.* 27:2
37:25; 38:2
ephod shall be of the *s.* 28:8; 39:5
the *s.* goodness will we. *Num* 10:32
presumptuously, the *s.* 15:30
the Jebusite, the *s.* *Josh* 15:8
the *s.* shall go, the *s.* *Judg* 7:4
the *s.* shall reign over. *1 Sam* 9:17
Zion, the *s.* is the city. *2 Sam* 5:7
nor turn again by the *s.* way. *1 Ki* 13:9
year ye shall eat that which springeth of the *s.* *2 Ki* 19:29; *Isa* 37:30
Abram, the *s.* is. *1 Chr* 1:27
hath confirmed the *s.* to Jacob. 16:17; *Ps* 105:10
the *s.* may be a priest. *2 Chr* 13:9
s. is Micaiah the son of Imla. 18:7
hath not the *s.* Hezekiah? 32:12
Shimei, and Kelaiah, the *s.* is Kelita. *Ezra* 10:23
the thirteenth day of *s.* *Esth* 9:1
wickedness reap the *s.* *Job* 4:8
what ye know, the *s.* do I. 13:2
of thy dogs in the *s.* *Ps* 68:23*
he poureth out of the *s.* 75:8
but thou art the *s.*, and thy years shall have no. 102:27; *Heb* 1:12
to the going down of the *s.* *Ps* 113:3; *Mal* 1:11
the *s.* is the companion. *Pr* 28:24
remembered that *s.* poor. *Eccl* 9:15
prophet died the *s.* year. *Jer* 28:17
s. wicked man shall die. *Ezek* 3:18
this shall not be the *s.*: exalt. 21:26

go out by the way of the *s.* *Ezek* 44:3
the *s.* horn made war. *Dan* 7:21
go in to the *s.* maid. *Amos* 2:7
s. shall be called great. *Mat* 5:19
even the publicans the *s.*? 46
the *s.* is my brother and sister.
12:50; *Mark* 3:35
s. is become the head of the corner.
Mat 21:42; *Luke* 20:17; *1 Pet* 2:7
shall endure, *s.* shall be saved.
Mat 24:13; *Mark* 13:13
he that dippeth his hand with me . . .
the *s.* shall betray me. *Mat* 26:23
that *s.* is he, hold. 48; *Mark* 14:44
thieves also cast the *s.* *Mat* 27:44
lose his life, the *s.* shall save it.
Mark 8:35; *Luke* 9:24
desire to be first, the *s.* *Mark* 9:35
sinners also do even the *s.* *Luke* 6:33
for with the *s.* measure that ye. 38
is forgiven, the *s.* loveth little. 7:47
the *s.* shall be great. 9:48
the *s.* was accused that he. 16:1
the *s.* shall receive greater. 20:47
the *s.* had not consented to. 23:51
the *s.* was in the beginning. *John* 1:2
the *s.* came for a witness of. 7
the *s.* is he which baptizeth with. 33
the *s.* is true. 7:18
the *s.* I said to you from the. 8:25
the *s.* is a thief. 10:1
he abode two days still in the *s.* 11:6
high priest that *s.* year. 49; 18:13
the *s.* shall judge him in the. 12:48
abideth in me, the *s.* bringeth. 15:5
this *s.* Jesus shall so. *Acts* 1:11
God made that *s.* Jesus both. 2:36
the *s.* dealt subtilly with our. 7:19
the *s.* did God send to be. 35
began at the *s.* scripture and. 8:35
God hath fulfilled the *s.* to. 13:33
the *s.* heard Paul speak. 14:9
the *s.* followed Paul and us. 16:17
or else let these *s.* here say. 24:20
not only do the *s.* *Rom* 1:32
which do such, and doest the *s.* 2:3
who hath subjected the *s.* 8:20
the *s.* Lord over all is rich to. 10:12
members have not the *s.* 12:4
be of the *s.* mind one toward. 16
1 Cor 1:10; *Phil* 4:2; *1 Pet* 4:1
have praise of the *s.* *Rom* 13:3
ye all speak the *s.* thing. *1 Cor* 1:10
or saith not the law the *s.* also? 9:8
did all eat the *s.* spiritual meat. 10:3
the *s.* drink. 4
but the *s.* Spirit. 12:4; *2 Cor* 4:13
12:18
but the *s.* Lord. *1 Cor* 12:5
but it is the *s.* God. 6
all flesh is not the *s.* flesh. 15:39
but the *s.* which is made. *2 Cor* 2:2
I wrote this *s.* unto you, lest. 3
to the glory of the *s.* Lord. 8:19
s. might be ready as a matter. 9:5
the *s.* was mighty in me. *Gal* 2:8
the *s.* are the children of. 3:7
descended is the *s.* that. *Eph* 4:10
the *s.* shall he receive of Lord. 6:8
having the *s.* conflict. *Phil* 1:30
having the *s.* love, being of one. 2:2
the *s.* rule, mind the *s.* things. 3:16
and watch in the *s.* with. *Col* 4:2
the *s.* commit thou to. *2 Tim* 2:2
likewise took part of the *s.* *Heb* 2:14
the heirs with him of the *s.* 11:9
Jesus Christ, the *s.* yesterday. 13:8
if any offend not, the *s.* is. *Jas* 3:2
even so minister the *s.* *1 Pet* 4:10
of the *s.* is he brought. *2 Pet* 2:19
by the *s.* word are kept in store. 3:7
denieth the Son, *s.* hath. *1 John* 2:23
as the *s.* anointing teacheth you. 27
overcometh, the *s.* shall. *Rev* 3:5
see **day, hour**

Samson

called his name *S.* *Judg* 13:24
S. went to Timnath. 14:1
she pleased *S.* well. 7
S. made there a feast. 10
S.'s wife wept before him. 16
S. caught foxes. 15:4
to bind *S.* are we come. 10
S. is come hither. *Judg* 16:2
S. lay till midnight. 3
be upon thee, *S.* 9, 12, 14, 20
our god hath delivered *S.* into. 23
they said, Call for *S.* 25
S. called unto the Lord. 28
S. took hold of the pillars. 29
S. said, Let me die with. 30
fail me to tell of *S.* *Heb* 11:32

Samuel

son, and called him *S.* *1 Sam* 1:20
S. ministered before the Lord. 2:18
child *S.* grew before the Lord. 21
the Lord called *S.*: and he answered,
Here am I. 3:4, 6, 8, 10
and *S.* feared to shew Eli the. 15
the Lord revealed himself to *S.* 21
and the word of *S.* came to all. 4:1
S. judged the children. 7:6, 15
S. cried to the Lord for Israel. 9
Philistines all the days of *S.* 13
displeased *S.* when they said. 8:6
refused to obey the voice of *S.* 19
and *S.* heard all the words of. 21
Lord told *S.* in his ear before. 9:15
so Saul did eat with *S.* that. 24
S. called Saul to the top of the. 26
S. took a vial of oil and. 10:1
we came to *S.* 14
tell me, I pray thee, what *S.* said. 15
then *S.* told the manner of the. 25
not forth after Saul and *S.* 11:7
the Lord sent *S.* 12:11
greatly feared the Lord and *S.* 18
he tarried the set time that *S.* 13:8
it grieved *S.* 15:11
S. turned about to go away, *S.*'s. 27
S. hewed Agag in pieces. 33
nevertheless, *S.* mourned for. 35
Jesse made seven of his sons to pass
before *S.* 16:10
S. took the horn of oil and. 13
David fled and came to *S.* 19:18
said, Where are *S.* and David? 22
S. died. 25:1
Saul said, Bring me up *S.* 28:11
Saul perceived that it was *S.* 14
sons of *S.* *1 Chr* 6:28
whom David and *S.* the seer. 9:22
word of the Lord by *S.* 11:3
all that *S.* had dedicated. 26:28
like that from *S.* *2 Chr* 35:18
S. among them that call. *Ps* 99:6
Moses and *S.* stood. *Jer* 15:1
the prophets from *S.* *Acts* 3:24
judges 450 years till *S.* 13:20
would fail me to tell of *S.* *Heb* 11:32

Sanballat

when *S.* heard of it. *Neh* 2:10, 19
when *S.* heard we builded. 4:1, 7
S. sent to me. 6:2, 5
for Tobiah and *S.* had hired. 12
my God, think upon *S.* 14
Joiada was son in law to *S.* 13:28

sanctification

of God is made unto us *s.* *1 Cor* 1:30
of God, even your *s.* *1 Thes* 4:3
to possess his vessel in *s.* 4
through *s.* of the Spirit. *2 Thes* 2:13
1 Pet 1:2

sanctified

seventh day and *s.* it. *Gen* 2:3*
Moses *s.* the people. *Ex* 19:14
the tabernacle shall be *s.* for. 29:43
s. the tabernacle, and. *Lev* 8:10
s. the altar. 15
s. Aaron and his garments. 30
I will be *s.* in them that come. 10:3
if he that *s.* it will redeem. 27:15
and if he that *s.* the field will. 19
s. the tabernacle. *Num* 7:1
s. the firstborn of Israel. 8:17
because ye *s.* me not. *Deut* 32:51
s. Eleazar his son to. *1 Sam* 7:1
he *s.* Jesse and his sons to. 16:5
though it were *s.* this day in. 21:5
Levites *s.* themselves. *1 Chr* 15:14
priests present were *s.* *2 Chr* 5:11
I have chosen and *s.* 7:16*, 20*
and *s.* themselves. 29:15
they *s.* the house of the. 17
vessels have we prepared and *s.* 19
till other priests had *s.* *2 Chr* 29:34
the priests had not *s.* 30:3
sanctuary which he hath *s.* for ever. 8
were ashamed, and *s.* themselves. 15
congregation were not *s.* 17
a great number of the priests *s.* 24
in their set office they *s.* 31:18
and *s.* the sheep gate. *Neh* 3:1
they *s.* holy things to the Levites, and
the Levites *s.* them to the. 12:47
Job sent and *s.* his sons. *Job* 1:5
holy God shall be *s.* in. *Isa* 5:16
I have commanded my *s.* ones. 13:3
I *s.* thee, and ordained. *Jer* 1:5
I will be *s.* in you. *Ezek* 20:41
36:23
when I shall be *s.* in her. 28:22
I shall be *s.* in thee. 38:16
be *s.* in them in sight of. 25; 39:27
the priests that are *s.* 48:11
whom the Father *s.* *John* 10:36
that they also might be *s.* 17:19
an inheritance among them which
are *s.* *Acts* 20:32; 26:18
s. by the Holy Ghost. *Rom* 15:16
them that are *s.* in Christ. *1 Cor* 1:2
but now ye are *s.* in the name. 6:11
husband is *s.* . . . wife is *s.* 7:14
it is *s.* by the word of. *1 Tim* 4:5
shall be a vessel *s.* for. *2 Tim* 2:21
and they who are *s.* are. *Heb* 2:11
by the which will we are *s.* 10:10
perfected them that are *s.* 14
covenant wherewith he was *s.* 29
to them that are *s.* by God. *Jude* 1*

sanctifieth

temple that *s.* the gold? *Mat* 23:17
the altar that *s.* the gift? 19
both he that *s.* and they. *Heb* 2:11
if blood of bulls *s.* to the. 9:13

sanctify

[1] *To dedicate.* [2] *To set aside for holy uses.* [3] *To make holy.*

s. unto me all the firstborn. *Ex* 13:2
go and *s.* them to-day. 19:10
and let the priests also *s.* 22
about the mount, and *s.* it. 23
shalt anoint and *s.* 28:41; 29:33
40:13; *Lev* 8:12; 21:8
thou shalt *s.* the breast. *Ex* 29:27
shalt *s.* the altar. 36, 37; 40:10
I will *s.* the tabernacle and. 29:44
and thou shalt *s.* the. 30:29; 40:10
11; *Lev* 8:11
I am the Lord that doth *s.* *Ex* 31:13
Lev 20:8; 21:8; *Ezek* 20:12
ye shall *s.* yourselves. *Lev* 11:44
20:7; *Num* 11:18; *Josh* 3:5; 7:13
1 Sam 16:5
seed, I the Lord do *s.* *Lev* 21:15
I the Lord do *s.* them. 23; 22:9, 16
when a man shall *s.* his. 27:14
if a man shall *s.* his field. 16, 17
18, 22
firstling, no man shall *s.* 26
ye believed me not, to *s.* me.
Num 20:12; 27:14
keep the sabbath day to *s.* it.
Deut 5:12*; *Neh* 13:22
firstling males thou shalt *s.* 15:19
up, *s.* the people, *s.* *Josh* 7:13
s. yourselves. *1 Chr* 15:12
2 Chr 29:5; 35:6
he should *s.* the most. *1 Chr* 23:13
upright in heart to *s.* *2 Chr* 29:34
one that was not clean to *s.* 30:17
s. the Lord himself. *Isa* 8:13
they shall *s.* the Holy One. 29:23
they that *s.* themselves in. 66:17
I will *s.* my great name. *Ezek* 36:23
that I the Lord do *s.* Israel. 37:28
magnify myself, and *s.* myself. 38:23
shall not *s.* people with garments.
44:19; 46:20
s. ye a fast. *Joel* 1:14; 2:15
s. the congregation, assemble. 2:16
s. them through thy. *John* 17:17
and for their sakes I *s.* myself. 19
that he might *s.* and. *Eph* 5:26
very God of peace *s.* *1 Thes* 5:23
that he might *s.* people. *Heb* 13:12
but *s.* the Lord God in. *1 Pet* 3:15

sanctuaries
that he profane not my *s.* *Lev* 21:23
bring your *s.* to desolation. 26:31
strangers are come into *s.* *Jer* 51:51
hast defiled thy *s.* by. *Ezek* 28:18
the *s.* of Israel shall be. *Amos* 7:9

sanctuary
(*Generally a place set apart for the worship of God. Specifically the Temple at Jerusalem, most especially the Most Holy Place, or Holy of Holies. It is also used as meaning a refuge, or place of protection*)
plant them in the *s.* *Ex* 15:17
let them make me a *s.* 25:8
one after the shekel of the *s.* 30:13
shekels after the shekel of the *s.* 24
manner of work for the *s.* 36:1, 3, 4
more work for offering of the *s.* 6
the shekel of the *s.* 38:24, 25, 26
Lev 5:15; 27:3, 25; *Num* 3:47, 50
7:13, 19, 25, 31, 37; 18:16
cast the sockets of the *s.* *Ex* 28:27
before the vail of the *s.* *Lev* 4:6
brethren from before the *s.* 10:4
nor come into the *s.* till her. 12:4
atonement for the holy *s.* 16:33
shall reverence my *s.* 19:30; 26:2
go out of the *s.* nor profane the *s.* of his God. 21:12
keeping charge of the *s.* *Num* 3:28
Aaron keeping charge of the *s.* 38
they minister in the *s.* 4:12
an end of covering the *s.* 15
the service of *s.* belonging. 7:9
Israel come nigh to the *s.* 8:19
set forward, bearing the *s.* 10:21
bear the iniquity of the *s.* 18:1
not come nigh the vessels of the *s.* 3
shall keep the charge of the *s.* 5
because he hath defiled the *s.* 19:20
a great stone by the *s.* *Josh* 24:26
instruments of the *s.* *1 Chr* 9:29
arise, and build ye the *s.* of. 22:19
for the governors of the *s.* 24:5
build an house for the *s.* 28:10
built thee a *s.* therein. *2 Chr* 20:8
go out of the *s.* for thou. 26:18
for a sin offering for the *s.* and. 29:21
to Lord, and enter into his *s.* 30:8
to the purification of the *s.* 19
Babylon slew men in the *s.* 36:17
the vessels of the *s.* *Neh* 10:39
send thee help from the *s.* *Ps* 20:2
as I have seen thee in the *s.* 63:2
seen thy goings in the *s.* 68:24
till I went into the *s.* of God. 73:17
enemy hath done wickedly in *s.* 74:3
they have cast fire into thy *s.* 7
thy way, O God, is in the *s.* 77:13
to the border of his *s.* 78:54
built his *s.* like high palaces. 69
strength and beauty are in his *s.* 96:6
from the height of his *s.* 102:19
Judah was his *s.*, Israel his. 114:2
lift up your hands in the *s.* 134:2
Lord, praise God in his *s.* 150:1
hosts, he shall be for a *s.* *Isa* 8:14
that he shall come to his *s.* to. 16:12
profaned the princes of the *s.* 43:28
to beautify the place of my *s.* 60:13
trodden down thy *s.* 63:18
is the place of our *s.* *Jer* 17:12
entered into her *s.* *Lam* 1:10
the Lord hath abhorred his *s.* 2:7
prophet be slain in the *s.*? 20
stones of the *s.* are poured. 4:1
thou hast defiled my *s.* *Ezek* 5:11
will I be to them as a little *s.* 11:16
defiled my *s.* in the same day. 23:38
day into my *s.* to profane it. 39
between *s.* and the profane. 42:20*
with every going forth of the *s.* 44:5
day that he goeth into the *s.* 27
in it shall be the *s.* and most. 45:3
they issued out of the *s.* 47:12
s. shall be in the midst. 48:8, 10, 21
and the place of his *s.* *Dan* 8:11
to give the *s.* to be trodden. 13
he said to me, then shall the *s.* 14
face to shine upon thy *s.* 9:17
destroy the city and the *s.* 26
they shall pollute the *s.* 11:31
have polluted the *s.* *Zeph* 3:4
a minister of the *s.* and. *Heb* 8:2
covenant had a worldly *s.* 9:1
tabernacle which is called the *s.* 2*
blood is brought into the *s.* 13:11*

sand
(*The word is frequently used in the Bible as a symbol of uncounted multitudes, or a weight impossible to measure*)
seed as the *s.* *Gen* 22:17; 32:12
gathered corn as the *s.* of. 41:49
hid the Egyptian in the *s.* *Ex* 2:12
treasures hid in *s.* *Deut* 33:19
much people as the *s.* *Josh* 11:4
as the *s.* by the sea. *Judg* 7:12
gathered to fight as the *s.* *1 Sam* 13:5
all Israel be gathered as the *s.* *2 Sam* 17:11
are many, as the *s.* *1 Ki* 4:20
largeness of heart as the *s.* 29
be heavier than the *s.* *Job* 6:3
multiply my days as the *s.* 29:18
fowls like as the *s.* *Ps* 78:27
in number than the *s.* 139:18
a stone is heavy, and the *s.* *Pr* 27:3
Israel be as the *s.* *Isa* 10:22
thy seed also had been as *s.* 48:19
which placed the *s.* for. *Jer* 5:22
increased to me above the *s.* 15:8
as the *s.* of the sea, cannot. 33:22
shall be as the *s.* of the sea. *Hos* 1:10; *Rom* 9:27
the captivity as the *s.* *Hab* 1:9
built his house on *s.* *Mat* 7:26
of one, so many as the *s.* *Heb* 11:12
I stood upon the *s.* of the. *Rev* 13:1
the number of whom is as the *s.* 20:8

sandals
(*At first were only soles tied to the feet with strings or thongs; afterwards they were covered; and at last even shoes were called* Sandals)
but be shod with *s.* put. *Mark* 6:9
thyself, and bind thy *s.* *Acts* 12:8

sang
then *s.* Moses and Israel. *Ex* 15:1
Israel *s.* this song. *Num* 21:17
then *s.* Deborah and. *Judg* 5:1
David of whom they *s.*? *1 Sam* 29:5
the singers *s.* the. *2 Chr* 29:28
s. praises with gladness, and. 30
the singers *s.* aloud. *Neh* 12:42
when the morning stars *s.* *Job* 38:7
his word, *s.* his praise. *Ps* 106:12
Silas *s.* praises to God. *Acts* 16:25

sank
they *s.* into the bottom. *Ex* 15:5
they *s.* as lead in the mighty. 10

sap
the trees are full of *s.* *Ps* 104:16*

Saphir
thou inhabitant of *S.* *Mi* 1:11

Sapphira
Ananias, with *S.* his wife. *Acts* 5:1

sapphire
(*A precious stone of a bright blue colour. It is thought to mean lapis lazuli rather than our modern sapphire*)
paved work of *s.* stone. *Ex* 24:10
a *s.* a diamond. 28:18; 39:11
be valued with onyx or *s.* *Job* 28:16
their polishing was of *s.* *Lam* 4:7
as appearance of *s.* *Ezek* 1:26
over them as it were a *s.* 10:1
the *s.* and the emerald were. 28:13
of the wall was *s.* *Rev* 21:19

sapphires
of it are the place of *s.* *Job* 28:6
ivory overlaid with *s.* *S of S* 5:14
foundations with *s.* *Isa* 54:11

Sarah
not Sarai, but *S.* shall. *Gen* 17:15
S. thy wife shall bear. 19; 18:14
where is *S.* thy wife? 18:9
it ceased to be with *S.* after. 11
S. laughed. 12
wherefore did *S.* laugh? 13
Abraham said of *S.* She. *Gen* 20:2
Abimelech restored *S.* 14
because of *S.* 18
the Lord did unto *S.* as he. 21:1
S. should have given children. 7
in all that *S.* said to thee. 12
years of the life of *S.* 127. 23:1
S. died. 2
Abraham buried *S.* his wife. 19
into his mother *S.*'s tent. 24:67
Abraham buried, and *S.* 25:10; 49:31
daughter of Asher was *S.* *Num* 26:46
look to Abraham and to *S.* *Isa* 51:2
deadness of *S.*'s womb. *Rom* 4:19
at this time I will come, *S.* 9:9
through faith *S.* received strength. *Heb* 11:11
as *S.* obeyed Abraham. *1 Pet* 3:6

Sarai
Abraham's wife was *S.* *Gen* 11:29
but *S.* was barren, she. 30; 16:1
Pharaoh because of *S.* 12:17
when *S.* dealt hardly with. 16:6
from the face of my mistress *S.* 8
thou shalt not call her name *S.* 17:15

sardine or **sardius**
(*Probably carnelian*)
shall be a *s.* *Ex* 28:17; 39:10
the *s.* and diamond. *Ezek* 28:13
he that sat was to look upon like a *s.* stone. *Rev* 4:3
of the wall was a *s.* 21:20

Sardis
write and send it to *S.* and. *Rev* 1:11
of the church in *S.* write. 3:1
a few names in *S.* which have not. 4

sardonyx
(*A* Sardius *united to an* Onyx)
wall of the city was a *s.* *Rev* 21:20

Sarepta
save to *S.* a city of Sidon. *Luke* 4:26; *1 Ki* 17:9

Saron
and all that dwelt at *S.* *Acts* 9:35

Saruch
Nachor, the son of *S.* *Luke* 3:35

sat
Rachel had taken and *s.* *Gen* 31:34
Tamar, covered with a vail, *s.* 38:14
that *s.* on his throne. *Ex* 12:29
when we *s.* by the flesh pots. 16:3
on the morrow Moses *s.* 18:13
they wept and *s.* before. *Judg* 20:26
now Eli *s.* on a seat by. *1 Sam* 1:9
Eli *s.* on a seat by the wayside. 4:13
as soon as he *s.* on his. *1 Ki* 16:11
the children of Belial *s.* before. 21:13
the two kings *s.* each on his. 22:10
but Elisha *s.* in his house, and elders *s.* with him, and the. *2 Ki* 6:32
as David *s.* in his house. *1 Chr* 17:1
David *s.* before the Lord. 16
made booths, and *s.* *Neh* 8:17
their way, and *s.* chief. *Job* 29:25
I have not *s.* with vain. *Ps* 26:4
in the ways hast thou *s.* *Jer* 3:2
I *s.* not in the assembly of the mockers nor rejoiced; I *s.* 15:17
s. in the winterhouse. 36:22
I *s.* where they *s.* *Ezek* 3:15
as I *s.* in my house, the elders *s.* 8:1
s. women weeping for Tammuz. 14
enquire of the Lord, and *s.* 20:1
but Daniel *s.* in the gate. *Dan* 2:49
people who *s.* in darkness saw great light; to them that *s.* *Mat* 4:16
for them which *s.* with him. 14:9
Mark 6:26
I *s.* daily with you teaching in the. *Mat* 26:55
Peter *s.* with the servants, to see. 58
blind Bartimaeus *s.* by. *Mark* 10:46
Luke 18:35; *John* 9:8
and he *s.* on the right. *Mark* 16:19
he that was dead *s.* up. *Luke* 7:15
Mary *s.* at Jesus' feet, and. 10:39
a colt whereon never man *s.* 19:30
Mark 11:2
Jesus, wearied, *s.* thus. *John* 4:6
cloven tongues *s.* upon. *Acts* 2:3
he who *s.* for alms at the. 3:10

he that *s.* on the throne. *Rev* 4:3
on the cloud one *s.* like the. 14:14
he that *s.* upon him was called. 19:11
make war against him that *s.* 19

sat *down*

the people *s. down* to. *Ex* 32:6
and they *s. down* at thy. *Deut* 33:3
and *s. down* astonied. *Ezra* 9:3
they *s. down* to examine the. 10:16
I *s. down* and mourned. *Neh* 1:4
king and Haman *s. down. Esth* 3:15
Job *s. down* among ashes. *Job* 2:8
there we *s. down*, yea. *Ps* 137:1
s. down under his shadow. *S of S* 2:3
and *s. down* with him. *Mat* 9:10
he *s. down* with the twelve. 26:20
Luke 22:14
minister, and *s. down. Luke* 4:20
s. down and taught the people. 5:3
people came, he *s. down. John* 8:2
synagogue and *s. down. Acts* 13:14
we *s. down* and spake to the. 16:13
s. down on right. *Heb* 1:3; 10:12

Satan

A Hebrew *word, signifying an* adversary, *an* enemy, *an* accuser. *Most commonly* Satan *is taken for the* Devil, *or chief of the evil spirits. It is also used for those adversaries of Christianity who seemed filled with some malignant spirit in their persecution of the* Church, Mat 12:26; Rev 20:2.

S. provoked David to. *1 Chr* 21:1
and *S.* came also. *Job* 1:6; 2:1
S., Whence comest thou? 1:7; 2:2
S., Hast thou considered? 1:8; 2:3
S. went out from the presence. 1:12
S., Behold, he is in thine. 2:6
so went *S.* forth from. 2:7
and let *S.* stand at his. *Ps* 109:6*
S. standing at his right. *Zech* 3:1
S., The Lord rebuke thee, O *S.* 2
him, Get thee hence, *S.* *Mat* 4:10
if *S.* cast out *S.* 12:26; *Mark* 3:23
26; *Luke* 11:18
get thee behind me, *S.* *Mat* 16:23
Mark 8:33; *Luke* 4:8
he was tempted of *S.* *Mark* 1:13
S. cometh and taketh. 4:15
I beheld *S.* as lightning. *Luke* 10:18
whom *S.* hath bound these. 13:16
entered *S.* into Judas Iscariot. 22:3
Simon, Simon, *S.* hath desired. 31
the sop, *S.* entered. *John* 13:27
why hath *S.* filled thine? *Acts* 5:3
from the power of *S.* to God. 26:18
God shall bruise *S.* under. *Rom* 16:20
one to *S.*, that the spirit. *1 Cor* 5:5
that *S.* tempt you not for your. 7:5
lest *S.* should get an. *2 Cor* 2:11
S. himself is transformed. 11:14
given to me, the messenger of *S.* 12:7
come, but *S.* hindered. *1 Thes* 2:18
after the working of *S.* *2 Thes* 2:9
have delivered unto *S.* *1 Tim* 1:20
already turned aside after *S.* 5:15
but the synagogue of *S.* *Rev* 2:9
where Satan's seat is: where *S.* 13
not known the depths of *S.* 24
of the synagogue of *S.* 3:9
dragon was cast out, called *S.* 12:9
on the dragon, which is *S.* 20:2
S. shall be loosed out of his. 7

satest

thou *s.* in the throne. *Ps* 9:4
s. upon a stately bed. *Ezek* 23:41

satiate

I will *s.* soul of the priests. *Jer* 31:14
the sword shall be *s.* with. 46:10

satiated

I have *s.* the weary soul. *Jer* 31:25

satisfaction

shall take no *s.* for life. *Num* 35:31*
take no *s.* for him that is fled. 32*

satisfy

to *s.* the desolate and. *Job* 38:27
O *s.* us early with thy. *Ps* 90:14
with long life will I *s.* him. 91:16
I will *s.* her poor with bread. 132:15
let her breasts *s.* thee at. *Pr* 5:19
if he steal to *s.* his soul when. 6:30
if thou *s.* the afflicted. *Isa* 58:10
Lord shall guide and *s.* thy soul. 11
they shall not *s.* their. *Ezek* 7:19
whence can a man *s.*? *Mark* 8:4

satisfied

shall be *s.* upon them. *Ex* 15:9
shall eat and not be *s.* *Lev* 26:26
shall eat and be *s.* *Deut* 14:29
O Naphtali, *s.* with favour. 33:23
and why are ye not *s.*? *Job* 19:22
his offspring shall not be *s.* 27:14
of his flesh! we cannot be *s.* 31:31
I shall be *s.*, when I awake. *Ps* 17:15
the meek shall eat and be *s.* 22:26
they shall be *s.* with the. 36:8
famine they shall be *s.* 37:19
grudge if they be not *s.* 59:15
my soul shall be *s.* as with. 63:5
we shall be *s.* with the. 65:4
of rock should I have *s.* thee. 81:16
the earth is *s.* with the fruit. 104:13
he *s.* them with the bread. 105:40
his land shall be *s.* *Pr* 12:11*
a man shall be *s.* with good by. 14
and a good man shall be *s.* 14:14
a man's belly be *s.* with. 18:20*
he that hath it shall abide *s.* 19:23
eyes, and thou shalt be *s.* 20:13
things that are never *s.* 30:15
the eye is not *s.* with. *Eccl* 1:8
neither is his eye *s.* with riches. 4:8
that loveth silver, shall not be *s.* 5:10
eat and not be *s.* *Isa* 9:20; *Mi* 6:14
he roasteth roast and is *s.* *Isa* 44:16
of travail of his soul, and be *s.* 53:11
be *s.* with the breasts of her. 66:11
my people shall be *s.* *Jer* 31:14
spoil Chaldea shall be *s.* 50:10
his soul shall be *s.* on mount. 19
hand to Egyptians, to be *s.* *Lam* 5:6
couldest not be *s.* *Ezek* 16:28, 29
drink water, but were not *s.* *Amos* 4:8
death, and cannot be *s.* *Hab* 2:5

satisfiest

and thou *s.* the desire. *Ps* 145:16

satisfieth

who *s.* thy mouth with. *Ps* 103:5
for he *s.* the longing soul. 107:9
labour for that which *s.* not. *Isa* 55:2

satisfying

the righteous eateth to *s.* *Pr* 13:26
not in any honour to the *s.* *Col* 2:23*

satyr

and the *s.* shall cry to. *Isa* 34:14†

satyrs

dwell there, and *s.* dance. *Isa* 13:21†

Saul, *first king of Israel*

S. of Rehoboth reigned. *Gen* 36:37
S. died. 38
Kish had a son, whose name was *S.*
1 Sam 9:2; 14:51
Samuel a day before *S.* came. 9:15
when Samuel saw *S.* 17
S. drew near to Samuel. 18
set it before *S.*, so *S.* did eat. 24
is *S.* also among the prophets?
10:11, 12; 19:24
S. was taken. 10:21
Spirit of God came upon *S.* 11:6
cometh not forth after *S.* and. 7
shall *S.* reign over us? 12
to Gilgal, there they made *S.* 15
S. blew the trumpet. 13:3
as for *S.* he was yet in Gilgal and. 7
S. went out to meet Samuel. 10
S. numbered the people. 15
for *S.* had adjured the people. 14:24
S. built an altar. 35
S. asked counsel of God. 37
S. went up from following the. 46
when *S.* saw any strong man, he. 52
me that I have set up *S.* 15:11
Samuel turned again after *S.* 31
Samuel came no more to see *S.* 35
long wilt thou mourn for *S.*? 16:1
if *S.* hear it. 2
Spirit of Lord departed from *S.* 14
the evil spirit from God was on *S.*
23; 18:10; 19:9
and you servants to *S.*? 17:8
for an old man in the days of *S.* 12
S. and all Israel were in the. 19
and *S.* armed David with his.
1 Sam 17:38
came out to meet king *S.* 18:6
S. eyed David from that day. 9
S. afraid; Lord departed from *S.* 12
when *S.* saw that he behaved. 15, 30
S. became David's enemy. 29
spake good of David to *S.* 19:4
Jonathan brought David to *S.* 7
S. sent messengers. 11, 14, 15, 20
Abner sat by *S.*'s side. 20:25
S. cast a javelin. 33
fled that day for fear of *S.* 21:10
saying, *S.* hath slain his. 11; 29:5
that he would surely tell *S.* 22:22
will *S.* come down as thy? 23:11
shall be king, and that *S.* my. 17
S. returned from pursuing after. 28
David cut off the skirt of *S.* 24:4
them not to rise against *S.* 7
David cried after *S.* 8
David sware to *S.* 22
David understood *S.* was. 26:4
beheld the place where *S.* lay. 5
behold, *S.* lay sleeping within. 7
S. knew David's voice. 17
S. returned. 25
one day by the hand of *S.* 27:1
behold, thou knowest what *S.* 28:9
S. sware to her by the Lord. 10
for thou art *S.* 12
S. fell straightway all along. 20
not this David servant of *S.*? 29:3
Philistines followed hard upon *S.*
31:2; *1 Chr* 10:2
that *S.* and his sons were dead.
1 Sam 31:7; *1 Chr* 10:7
what the Philistines had done to *S.*
1 Sam 31:11; *1 Chr* 10:11
S. leaned on his spear. *2 Sam* 1:6
the shield of *S.* 21
of Israel, weep over *S.* 24
be ye valiant, for your master *S.* 2:7
the house of *S.* waxed weaker. 3:1
to translate the kingdom from house of *S.* and to set. 10; *1 Chr* 12:23
tidings saying, *S* is dead. *2 Sam* 4:10
when *S.* was king. 5:2; *1 Chr* 11:2
my mercy shall not depart, as I took it from *S.* *2 Sam* 7:15
any left of the house of *S.*? 9:1, 3
all the land of *S.* thy father. 7
out of the hand of *S.* 12:7; 22:1
blood of the house of *S.* 16:8
for *S.* and for his bloody. 21:1
will have no silver nor gold of *S.* 4
David took the bones of *S.* 12
in the days of *S.* they. *1 Chr* 5:10
S. died for his transgression. 10:13
himself close because of *S.* 12:1
enquired not at it in the days of *S.* 13:3
all that Samuel and *S.* had. 26:28
Gibeah of *S.* is fled. *Isa* 10:29
God gave unto them *S.* *Acts* 13:21
see **Jonathan**

Saul (Paul)

feet, whose name was *S.* *Acts* 7:58
and *S.* was consenting unto. 8:1
as for *S.* he made havoc of the. 3
S. S. why persecutest thou me?
9:4; 22:7; 26:14
enquire for one called *S.* of. 9:11
brother *S.* the Lord hath. 17; 22:13
but *S.* increased more in. 9:22
laying wait was known of *S.* 24
S. was come to Jerusalem. 26
went to Tarsus to seek *S.* 11:25
the hands of Barnabas and *S.* 30
prophets brought up with *S.* 13:1
separate me Barnabas and *S.* 2
called for Barnabas and *S.* 7
S. set his eyes on him, and said. 9

save

[1] *To preserve from danger.* [2] *To deliver from sin and its consequences.*

God sent me before you to *s.*
Gen 45:7
goeth with you to *s.* you. *Deut* 20:4
there was none to *s.* her. 22:27
and no man shall *s.* thee. 28:29
thou shalt *s.* Israel. *Judg* 6:14
O my Lord, wherewith shall I *s.*? 15

angel of his presence *s.* *Isa* 63:9
God who hath *s.* us and. *2 Tim* 1:9
how that the *Lord,* having *s.* the. *Jude* 5

shall be **saved**

ye *shall be s.* from your enemies. *Num* 10:9
I *shall be s.* from mine enemies. *2 Sam* 22:4; *Ps* 18:3
cause thy face to shine, we *shall be s.* *Ps* 80:3, 7, 19
uprightly *shall be s.* *Pr* 28:18
and rest *shall* ye *be s.* *Isa* 30:15
but Israel *shall be s.* in Lord. 45:17
continuance, and we *shall be s.* 64:5
save me, and I *shall be s.* *Jer* 17:14
Judah *shall be s.* 23:6; 33:16
Jacob's trouble; but he *shall be s.* 30:7
endureth to the end *shall be s.* *Mat* 10:22; 24:13; *Mark* 13:13
that believeth *shall be s.* *Mark* 16:16
man enter, he *shall be s.* *John* 10:9
call on name of the Lord, *shall be s.* *Acts* 2:21; *Rom* 10:13
thy house *shall be s.* *Acts* 11:14
through grace we *shall be s.* 15:11
Jesus, and thou *shalt be s.* 16:31
shall be s. from wrath. *Rom* 5:9
being reconciled, we *shall be s.* 10
sand, a remnant *shall be s.* 9:27
raised him, thou *shalt be s.* 10:9
so all Israel *shall be s.* as it is. 11:26
but he himself *shall be s.* *1 Cor* 3:15
shall be s. in childbearing, if. *1 Tim* 2:15

savest

my Saviour, thou *s.* *2 Sam* 22:3
how *s.* thou the arm that? *Job* 26:2
O thou that *s.* by thy right. *Ps* 17:7

saveth

liveth, who *s.* Israel. *1 Sam* 14:39
the Lord *s.* not with sword. 17:47
but he *s.* the poor from. *Job* 5:15
God, who *s.* the upright. *Ps* 7:10
now know I that the Lord *s.* 20:6
he *s.* such as be of a contrite. 34:18
they cry, he *s.* them out of. 107:19

saving

shewed me in *s.* my life. *Gen* 19:19
s. that every one put. *Neh* 4:23
with the *s.* strength of. *Ps* 20:6
he is the *s.* strength of his. 28:8
thy *s.* health among all nations. 67:2
s. the beholding of them. *Eccl* 5:11
s. that I will not utterly. *Amos* 9:8
s. for the cause of. *Mat* 5:32
cleansed, *s.* Naaman. *Luke* 4:27
believe to *s.* of the soul. *Heb* 10:39
Noah prepared an ark to the *s.* 11:7
no man knoweth, *s.* he. *Rev* 2:17

saviour

(*In general used for any one who saves. In the New Testament especially it refers nearly always to* our Lord and Saviour Jesus Christ)

my refuge, my *s.* *2 Sam* 22:3
Lord gave Israel a *s.* *2 Ki* 13:5
they forgat God their *s.* *Ps* 106:21
he shall send them a *s.* *Isa* 19:20
Holy One of Israel thy *s.* 43:3
beside me there is no *s.* 11
O God of Israel, the *s.* 45:15
a just God and a *s.*; there is. 21
know that I am thy *s.* 49:26
that I the Lord am thy *s.* 60:16
people, so he was their *s.* 63:8
the *s.* of Israel in time. *Jer* 14:8
for there is no *s.* beside. *Hos* 13:4
rejoiced in God my *s.* *Luke* 1:47
in the city of David a *s.* 2:11
this is Christ the *s.* of. *John* 4:42
to be a prince and *s.* *Acts* 5:31
raised unto Israel a *s.*, Jesus. 13:23
and Christ is the *s.* of the. *Eph* 5:23
whence we look for the *s.* *Phil* 3:20
by the commandment of God our *s.* *1 Tim* 1:1
in the sight of God our *s.* 2:3
God, who is the *s.* of all men. 4:10
the appearing of our *s.* *2 Tim* 1:10
to the commandment of God our *s.* *Tit* 1:3
the Lord Jesus Christ our *s.* *Tit* 1:4
the doctrine of God our *s.* 2:10
glorious appearing of our *s.* 13
after the kindness of God our *s.* 3:4
abundantly through Christ our *s.* 6
of God and our *s.* *2 Pet* 1:1
kingdom of our Lord and *s.* 11
knowledge of the Lord and *s.* 2:20
apostles of the Lord and *s.* 3:2
knowledge of our *s.* Christ. 18
sent the Son to be the *s.* *1 John* 4:14
to the only wise God our *s.* *Jude* 25

saviours

thou gavest them *s.* who. *Neh* 9:27
and *s.* shall come up on. *Ob* 21

savour

(*An odour or scent. Used frequently in a symbolic sense*)

ye have made our *s.* *Ex* 5:21
will not smell *s.* of. *Lev* 26:31
send forth a stinking *s.* *Eccl* 10:1*
because of the *s.* of thy. *S of S* 1:3
his stink and his ill *s.* *Joel* 2:20
if the salt have lost his *s.* *Mat* 5:13; *Luke* 14:34
maketh manifest the *s.* *2 Cor* 2:14
the *s.* of death unto death, *s.* of. 16

sweet **savour**

Lord smelled a *sweet s.* *Gen* 8:21
it is a *sweet s.* an offering. *Ex* 29:18
Lev 1:9, 13, 17; 2:9; 3:5; 8:21
Num 15:14; 18:17; 28:8
for a *sweet s.* an offering. *Ex* 29:25
41; *Lev* 2:12; 3:16; 4:31; 6:15
21; 8:28; 17:6; 23:13; *Num* 15:7
24; 28:2, 6, 13, 27; 29:2, 6, 8
Ezek 16:19
of *sweet s.* unto the Lord. *Lev* 23:18
Num 28:24; 29:13, 36
to make a *sweet s.* *Num* 15:3
a burnt offering of a *sweet s.* 28:13
did offer *sweet s.* to their idols. *Ezek* 6:13
they made their *sweet s.* 20:28
accept you with your *sweet s.* 41
for we are to God a *sweet s.* of. *2 Cor* 2:15
for a *sweet*-smelling *s.* *Eph* 5:2*

savourest

thou *s.* not things of God. *Mat* 16:23*; *Mark* 8:33*

sweet **savours**

sacrifices of *sweet s.* *Ezra* 6:10

savoury

make me *s.* meat. *Gen* 27:4, 7, 14
Esau had made *s.* meat, and. 31

saw

the woman *s.* the tree was. *Gen* 3:6
sons of God *s.* the daughters. 6:2
Ham *s.* the nakedness of his. 9:22
they *s.* not their father's. 23
Abraham *s.* the place afar. 22:4
they said, We *s.* the Lord. 26:28
when he *s.* that he prevailed. 32:25
for she *s.* that Shelah was. 38:14
his master *s.* that the Lord. 39:3
in that we *s.* the anguish of. 42:21
when Joseph *s.* Benjamin. 43:16
when he *s.* the wagons which. 45:27
Issachar *s.* that rest was good. 49:15
his brethren *s.* that their. 50:15
Joseph *s.* Ephraim's children of. 23
when she *s.* that he was. *Ex* 2:2
when he *s.* that there was no. 12
they *s.* not one another for. 10:23
Israel *s.* that great work the. 14:31
they *s.* the God of Israel. 24:10, 11
all the people *s.* the cloudy. 33:10
we *s.* the children of. *Num* 13:28
ass *s.* the angel of Lord. 22:23, 27
and when Phinehas *s.* it he. 25:7
when they *s.* the land, they. 32:9
heard a voice, but *s.* no. *Deut* 4:12, 15
which thine eyes *s.* 7:19
all that *s.* it said, No. *Judg* 19:30
when she *s.* she was. *Ruth* 1:18
they *s.* the ark, and. *1 Sam* 6:13
when we *s.* they were no where. 10:14
Israel, when they *s.* the man. 17:24
Saul *s.* that the Lord was. 18:28
David *s.* a woman. *2 Sam* 11:2
s. that the wisdom of. *1 Ki* 3:28
when Zimri *s.* that the city. 16:18
when Ahab *s.* Elijah, he said. 18:17
when he *s.* that, he arose and. 19:3
Elisha *s.* it, and he *s.* *2 Ki* 2:12
s. the water on the other side. 3:22
man of God *s.* her afar off. 4:25
of the young man and he *s.* 6:17
he *s.* the oppression of Israel. 13:4
Ahaz *s.* an altar that was at. 16:10
they *s.* that the Lord. *2 Chr* 15:9
and they *s.* one another in. 25:21
when princes *s.* heaps, they. 31:8
when *s.* these things they. *Neh* 6:16
the princes which *s.* the. *Esth* 1:14
he *s.* that there was evil. 7:7
they *s.* that his grief was. *Job* 2:13
as infants which never *s.* light. 3:16
eye which *s.* him, shall see. 20:9
the young men *s.* me, and. 29:8
when the eye *s.* me, it gave. 11
they *s.* it, and so they. *Ps* 48:5
waters *s.* thee, O God, the waters *s.* 77:16
your fathers proved me, and *s.* 95:9
the earth *s.* his lightnings and. 97:4
sea *s.* it and fled: Jordan. 114:3
s. ye him whom my soul loveth? *S of S* 3:3
isles *s.* it, and feared. *Isa* 41:5
sister Judah *s.* it. *Jer* 3:7
when Zedekiah *s.* them, and. 39:4
for then we were well, and *s.* 44:17
adversaries *s.* her and. *Lam* 1:7
I went in, and *s.* behold. *Ezek* 8:10
then they *s.* every high hill. 20:28
as soon as she *s.* them, she. 23:16
s. these men on whom. *Dan* 3:27
whereas the king *s.* a watcher. 4:23
the king *s.* part of the hand. 5:5
when Ephraim *s.* his sickness and Judah *s.* his wound. *Hos* 5:13
who among you *s.* this house? *Hag* 2:3
the star which they *s.* *Mat* 2:9
s. the Spirit of God descending. 3:16; *Mark* 1:10
dumb both spake and *s.* *Mat* 12:22
s. no man, save Jesus only. 17:8
husbandmen *s.* the son. 21:38
s. a man who had not on. 22:11
Lord, when *s.* we thee? 25:37, 44
when *s.* we thee a stranger? 38
when *s.* thee sick? 39
another maid *s.* him, and said. 26:71
Mark 14:69; *Luke* 22:58
Judas, when he *s.* that he. *Mat* 27:3
they *s.* him they worshipped. 28:17
when Jesus *s.* their faith. *Mark* 2:5
he asked him, if he *s.* aught. 8:23
saying, Master, we *s.* one casting out devils in thy. 9:38; *Luke* 9:49
when they *s.* what was. *Luke* 8:34
when the woman *s.* that she was. 47
when they were awake, they *s.* 9:32
his father *s.* him, and had. 15:20
one of them, when he *s.* he. 17:15
but him they *s.* not. 24:24
because ye *s.* miracles. *John* 6:26
Abraham *s.* my day, and was. 8:56
when he *s.* his glory. 12:41
he that *s.* it, bare record. 19:35
disciples were glad when they *s.* 20:20
when they *s.* the boldness. *Acts* 4:13
s. his face as it had been face. 6:15
Stephen *s.* the glory of God. 7:55
when Simon *s.* that Holy Ghost. 8:18
Philip, the eunuch *s.* him no more. 39
when his eyes were opened, he *s.* 9:8
all at Lydda *s.* him, and turned. 35
and when Tabitha *s.* Peter, she. 40
Cornelius *s.* a vision. 10:3
s. heaven opened. 11
and because he *s.* it pleased. 12:3
David *s.* corruption. 13:36
s. no corruption. 37
masters *s.* the hope of their. 16:19
he *s.* the city wholly given to. 17:16
they *s.* indeed the light and. 22:9
had looked, and *s.* no harm. 28:6
but when they *s.* that the gospel of the uncircumcision. *Gal* 2:7
conflict which ye *s.* *Phil* 1:30

your fathers s. my works. Heb 3:9
s. he was a proper child. 11:23
record of all things he s. Rev 1:2
great fear fell on them who s. 11:11
when the dragon s. that he. 12:13
cried, when they s. smoke of. 18:18

saw, *substantive*

shall the s. magnify? Isa 10:15

saw joined with *Lord* or *God*

and God s. the light that. Gen 1:4
God called the dry land earth, and God s. 10, 12, 18, 21, 25, 31
God s. that the wickedness. 6:5
when the Lord s. that Leah. 29:31
when the Lord s. that he. Ex 3:4
when the Lord s. it, he. Deut 32:19
the Lord s. the affliction. 2 Ki 14:26
when the Lord s. they. 2 Chr 12:7
the Lord s. it, and it. Isa 59:15
Lord s. that there was no man. 16
God s. their works, that. Jonah 3:10
Lord s. her, he had compassion on. Luke 7:13

***I* saw**

such as I never s. in Egypt for. Gen 41:19
one went out, and I s. him. 44:28
I s. among the spoils. Josh 7:21
I s. that he delivered. Judg 12:3
I s. the son of Jesse. 1 Sam 22:9
I s. gods ascending out of the. 28:13
I s. Absalom hanged. 2 Sam 18:10
I s. great tumult, but knew not. 29
I s. all Israel scattered. 1 Ki 22:17
I s. the Lord on his throne. 19
2 Chr 18:18
in those days s. I in Judah. Neh 13:15
I s. my help in the gate. Job 31:21
when I s. the prosperity. Ps 73:3
then I s. and considered. Pr 24:32
this also I s. from hand. Eccl 2:24
so I s. the wicked buried. 8:10
among whom I s. Jaazaniah son of. Ezek 11:1
took them away as I s. good. 16:50
then I s. that she was defiled. 23:13
I s. your fathers as the. Hos 9:10
Ephraim, as I s. Tyrus, is. 13
I s. the Spirit descending. John 1:32
under the fig tree, I s. thee. 48
I s. in the way a light. Acts 26:13
the apostles s. I none. Gal 1:19
when I s. that they walked. 2:14
when I s. him, I fell at. Rev 1:17

sawed

costly stones s. with saws. 1 Ki 7:9

sawest

what s. thou, that thou? Gen 20:10
s. it and didst rejoice. 1 Sam 19:5
afraid, for what s. thou? 28:13
behold, thou s. him. 2 Sam 18:11
when thou s. a thief. Ps 50:18
king, s. a great image. Dan 2:31
thou s. till that a stone was. 34, 45
the tree thou s. which grew. 4:20
the ram which thou s. having. 8:20
seven stars thou s.; seven candlesticks thou s. Rev 1:20
the beast that thou s. was. 17:8
the ten horns which thou s. 12, 16
waters thou s. where the whore. 17:15
the woman which thou s. is that. 18

sawn

they were s. asunder. Heb 11:37

saws

he put Ammonites under s.
2 Sam 12:31; 1 Chr 20:3

say

lest thou shouldest s. Gen 14:23
what ye shall s. to me. 34:11, 12
for I heard them s. Let us. 37:17
we will s. Some evil beast hath. 20
I have heard s. that thou. 41:15
Judah said, What shall we s.? 44:16
so shall ye s. to Joseph, Forgive, I. 50:17
thou s. unto the children of Israel, I AM hath. Ex 3:14,15; 19:3; 20:22
teach you what thou shalt s. 4:12
when your children shall s. 12:26
Pharaoh will s. of the children. 14:3
if the servant shall s. I love. 21:5
woman shall s. Amen. Num 5:22
that thou shouldest s. to me. 11:12
know what the Lord will s. 22:19
have I now any power at all to s.? 38
the Lord our God shall s. Deut 5:27
then thou shalt s. to thy son. 6:21
of whom thou hast heard s. 9:2
thou shalt s., and at even s. 28:67
so that they will s. in that. 31:17
lest they should s. Our hand. 32:27
your children may not s. Josh 22:27
when they should s. to us in time. 28
shalt hear what they s. Judg 7:11
canst thou s. I love thee? 16:15
is this ye s. to me, What? 18:24
in all they s. unto thee. 1 Sam 8:7
if they s. thus, Come up to us. 14:10
if he s. thus. 20:7
therefore thou shalt s. to my servant David. 2 Sam 7:8; 1 Chr 7:21
he s. I have no delight. 2 Sam 15:26
what you shall s. that will I. 21:4
of my lord s. so too. 1 Ki 1:36
for he will not s. thee nay. 2:17
shall s. Why hath the Lord done thus to this land? 9:8; 2 Chr 7:21
Lord did s. Eat no bread. 1 Ki 13:22
let not the king s. so. 22:8
2 Chr 18:7
if we s. We will enter. 2 Ki 7:4
so that they shall not s. this. 9:37
that thou s. nothing but truth to me. 2 Chr 18:15
they should s. to Iddo. Ezra 8:17
O our God, what shall we s.? 9:10
who will s. to him, What dost thou? Job 9:12; Eccl 8:4
they s. unto God, Depart. Job 21:14
then shalt thou s. There is. 22:29
what he would s. to me. 23:5
destruction and death s. We. 28:22
searched out what to s. 32:11
if any s. I have sinned. 33:27
teach us what we shall s. 37:19
many s. of my soul, There. Ps 3:2
there be that s. Who will shew? 4:6
let them not s. We have. 35:25
so that a man shall s. There. 58:11
for who, s. they, doth hear? 59:7
yet they s. Lord shall not see. 94:7
nor do they who go by s. 129:8
if they s. Come, let us lay. Pr 1:11
s. I have made my heart? 20:9
when thou shalt s. I have. Eccl 12:1
people shall go and s. Isa 2:3
they s. Who seeth us? and. 29:15
shall the work s. of him that made it? or the thing framed s. of? 16
who s. to the seers, See not. 30:10
the inhabitant shall not s. I. 33:24
one shall s. I am the Lord's. 44:5
surely shall one s. In the Lord. 45:24
lest thou shouldest s. My idol. 48:5
thou shouldest s. Behold, I knew. 7
Why have we fasted, s. they? 58:3
cry, and he shall s. Here I am. 9
in trouble they will s. Arise. Jer 2:27
understandest what they s. 5:15
shall ye s. to them, The gods. 10:11
Therefore thou shalt s. this. 14:17
Report, s. they, and we will. 20:10
shall no more s. The Lord. 23:7
they shall s. no more, Fathers. 31:29
do to him even as he shall s. 39:12
all that the Lord shall s. 42:20
ye s. The Lord saith it. Ezek 13:7
wilt thou yet s. before him that? 28:9
nor will we s. to the work. Hos 14:3
Ephraim shall s. What have I to? 8
prophesy ye not, s. they to. Mi 2:6
they will s. Is not the Lord? 3:11
see what he will s. to me. Hab 2:1
they that sell them s. I am. Zech 11:5
yet ye s., Wherein hast thou loved us? Mal 1:2; 2:14, 17; 3:13
think not to s. within yourselves. Mat 3:9; Luke 3:8
shall s. all manner of evil. Mat 5:11
will s. to me in that day. 7:22
have ye understood? they s. 13:51
Jesus said, Whom do men s.? 16:13
Mark 8:27; Luke 9:18
Whom s. ye that I am? Mat 16:15
Mark 8:29; Luke 9:20
s. aught to you, ye shall s. Mat 21:3
and s. to him, Hearest thou what these s.? 16
if we should s. From heaven, he will s. 25; Mark 11:31; Luke 20:5
if we shall s., Of men. Mat 21:26
Mark 11:32; Luke 20:6
do not their works, for they s. Mat 23:3
and saith, See thou s. Mark 1:44
he wist not what to s. for they. 9:6
ye will surely s. this proverb, Physician, heal thyself. Luke 4:23
Simon, I have somewhat to s. 7:40
no thought what ye shall s. 12:11
shall teach what ye ought to s. 12
ye s. That Jerusalem is. John 4:20
he speaketh, and they s. 7:26
I have many things to s. of you. 8:26; 16:12
S. we not well, that thou hast a? 8:48
ye s. that he is your God. 54
ye call me master, ye s. well. 13:13
hear in all things ye shall s. Acts 3:22
they could s. nothing against it. 4:14
we heard him s. that Jesus. 6:14
do therefore this that we s. 21:33
who hath something to s. 23:18
or else let these same here s. 24:20
things but what Moses did s. 26:22
what shall we s. Is God? Rom 3:5
as some affirm that we s. Let us. 8
what shall we then s.? 4:1; 6:1
7:7; 8:31; 9:14, 30
shall thing formed s. to him? 9:20
no man can s. that Jesus. 1 Cor 12:3
how shall he s. Amen at thy? 14:16
will they not s. that ye are mad? 23
how s. some that there is? 15:12
we, that we s. not. 2 Cor 9:4
for his letters, s. they, are. 10:10
this we s. to you by word of the. 1 Thes 4:15
neither what they s. 1 Tim 1:7
having no evil thing to s. Tit 2:8
albeit I do not s. how. Philem 19
have many things to s. Heb 5:11
as I may so s. Levi paid tithes. 7:9
that is to s. not of this building. 9:11
that is to s. his flesh. 10:20
they that s. such things. 11:14
we may boldly s. The Lord. 13:6
let no man s. when he is. Jas 1:13
go to now ye that s. To-day. 4:13
that ye ought to s. If the Lord. 15
we s. we have fellowship. 1 John 1:6
if we s. We have no sin, we. 8
if a man s. I love God, and. 4:20
I do not s. that he shall pray. 5:16
which s. they are apostles. Rev 2:2
which s. they are Jews. 9; 3:9
spirit and the bride s. Come. 22:17

see **began**

say, *imperatively*

s. I pray thee, thou art. Gen 12:13
at every place, s. of me, He. 20:13
s. unto them, Go not. Deut 1:42
s., The sword of the. Judg 7:18
they said to him, S. now. 12:6
he said to him, S. on. 1 Sam 15:16
2 Sam 14:12; 1 Ki 2:14, 16
Luke 7:40; Acts 13:15
s. not, Go and come again. Pr 3:28
s. not, I will do so to him as. 24:29
lest I deny thee, and s. Who? 30:9
s. not thou, What is the cause? Eccl 7:10
s. ye to righteous, It. Isa 3:10
s. to them that are of fearful. 35:4
s. to cities of Judah, Behold. 40:9
hear, and s. It is truth. 43:9
neither let the eunuch s. I am. 56:3
s. ye to the daughter of Zion. 62:11
s. not, I am a child, for. Jer 1:7
s. ye, Stand fast, and prepare. 46:14
ask her that escapeth, and s. 48:19
s. Babylon is taken, Bel is. 50:2
thy foot, and s. Alas. Ezek 6:11
s. I am your sign, like as. 12:11
and s. What is thy mother? 19:2
s. A sword is sharpened. 21:9
s. The sword is drawn for the. 28
s. unto him, Take away all. Hos 14:2

hall be clothed with *s.* *Dan* 5:7*
16*, 29*
aliant men are in *s.* *Nah* 2:3
ut on Jesus a *s.* robe. *Mat* 27:28
ok water, and *s.* wool. *Heb* 9:19
saw a woman sit upon a *s.* coloured
beast. *Rev* 17:3
rrayed in purple and *s.* 4
ayeth the merchandise of *s.* 18:12
as clothed with *s.* 16

scatter

ord *s.* them on earth. *Gen* 11:9
Jacob, *s.* them in Israel. 49:7
nd I will *s.* you. *Lev* 26:33
ensers, and *s.* the fire. *Num* 16:37
nd the Lord shall *s.* *Deut* 4:27
28:64; *Jer* 9:16; *Ezek* 22:15
said, I would *s.* them. *Deut* 32:26
e shall *s.* them beyond. *1 Ki* 14:15
ye transgress, I will *s.* *Neh* 1:8
them by thy power. *Ps* 59:11
thou the people that delight. 68:30
fted up his hand to *s.* 106:27
ast forth lightning, and *s.* 144:6
broad fitches, and *s.* *Isa* 28:25
hirlwind shall *s.* them. 41:16
erefore I will *s.* them. *Jer* 13:24
will *s.* them as with an. 18:17
oe to the pastors that *s.* 23:1
will *s.* into all winds them that are.
49:32, 36; *Ezek* 5:10, 12
nalt *s.* in the wind. *Ezek* 5:2
will *s.* your bones round. 6:5
l thine hand, and *s.* the. 10:2
will *s.* toward every wind. 12:14
hen I shall *s.* them among. 15
nat I would *s.* them among. 20:23
will *s.* the Egyptians. 29:12
30:23, 26
ew down the tree, and *s.* *Dan* 4:14
e shall *s.* among them the. 11:24
s. the power of the holy. 12:7*
s a whirlwind to *s.* me. *Hab* 3:14
orn over Judah to *s.* it. *Zech* 1:21

scattered

st we be *s.* abroad. *Gen* 11:4
the Lord *s.* them abroad from. 8
e people were *s.* to. *Ex* 5:12
t thine enemies be *s.* *Num* 10:35
Ps 68:1
y God hath *s.* thee. *Deut* 30:3
at remained were *s.* *1 Sam* 11:11
eople were *s.* from Saul. 13:8
ecause I saw the people were *s.* 11
e battle was *s.* over. *2 Sam* 18:8
e sent out arrows and *s.* them.
22:15; *Ps* 18:14
saw all Israel *s.* *1 Ki* 22:17
2 Chr 18:16
rmy were *s.* from him. *2 Ki* 25:5
Jer 52:8
ere is a certain people *s.* *Esth* 3:8
e stout lions' whelps are *s.*
Job 4:11
rimstone shall be *s.* on his. 18:15
ou hast *s.* us among heathen.
Ps 44:11; 60:1
od hath *s.* the bones of him. 53:5
lmighty *s.* kings in it. 68:14
ou hast *s.* thine enemies. 89:10
iniquity shall be *s.* 92:9
ur bones are *s.* at the grave's. 141:7
a nation *s.* and peeled. *Isa* 18:2
e brought of a people *s.* 7
f thyself the nations were *s.* 33:3
nd hast *s.* thy ways to. *Jer* 3:13
eir flocks shall be *s.* 10:21
e have *s.* my flock, and. 23:2
ations whither I have *s.* thee. 30:11
e that *s.* Israel will gather. 31:10
hat all Jews should be *s.*? 40:15
srael is a *s.* sheep: the lions. 50:17
hen ye shall be *s.* through. *Ezek* 6:8
hough I *s.* them, I will be. 11:16
ou out of countries where ye have
been *s.* 17; 20:34, 41; 28:25
ey that remain shall be *s.* 17:21
hither they were *s.* 29:13
because there is no shepherd, they
. . . when they were *s.* 34:5
y flock was *s.* on the face of. 6
mong his sheep that are *s.* where
they have been *s.* in the. 12

till ye have *s.* them. *Ezek* 34:21
s. them among the heathen. 36:19
that my people be not *s.* every. 46:18
people whom they have *s.* *Joel* 3:2
thy people is *s.* on the. *Nah* 3:18
mountains were *s.* *Hab* 3:6
horns which have *s.* *Zech* 1:19, 21
I *s.* them with whirlwind. 7:14
shepherd, and the sheep shall be *s.*
13:7; *Mat* 26:31; *Mark* 14:27
they were *s.* as sheep. *Mat* 9:36
he hath *s.* the proud. *Luke* 1:51
children that were *s.* *John* 11:52
now, that ye shall be *s.* 16:32
obeyed Theudas were *s.* *Acts* 5:36
were *s.* abroad through the. 8:1
were *s.* went every where. 4, 11, 19
tribes that are *s.* abroad. *Jas* 1:1
Peter to the strangers *s.* *1 Pet* 1:1*

scattereth

the thick cloud he *s.* his. *Job* 37:11
which *s.* the east wind upon. 38:24
he *s.* the hoarfrost like. *Ps* 147:16
there is that *s.* and yet. *Pr* 11:24
a king *s.* away all evil with. 20:8
a wise king *s.* the wicked. 26
the Lord *s.* the inhabitants. *Isa* 24:1
and he that gathereth not with me *s.*
Mat 12:30; *Luke* 11:23
the wolf catcheth and *s.* *John* 10:12

scattering

shew his anger with *s.* *Isa* 30:30

scent

yet through the *s.* of water. *Job* 14:9
therefore his *s.* is not. *Jer* 48:11
the *s.* thereof be the wine. *Hos* 14:7

sceptre

(*The word originally meant a rod or a staff. Thence it came to mean a shepherd's crook, and then the wand or sceptre of a ruler. The references to it, save in Esther, are all metaphorical, expressing supreme power*)

the *s.* shall not depart. *Gen* 49:10
and a *s.* shall rise out. *Num* 24:17
hold out the golden *s.* *Esth* 4:11
to Esther the golden *s.* 5:2; 8:4
the *s.* of thy kingdom is a right *s.*
Ps 45:6
Lord hath broken the *s.* *Isa* 14:5
rods for the *s.* of them. *Ezek* 19:11
no strong rod to be a *s.* to rule. 14
I will cut off him that holdeth the *s.*
Amos 1:5, 8
and the *s.* of Egypt. *Zech* 10:11
the *s.* of righteousness is the *s.* of.
Heb 1:8

Sceva

sons of one *S.* a Jew. *Acts* 19:14

schism

(*A division*)

should be no *s.* in the. *1 Cor* 12:25

scholar

they cast lots, the teacher as the *s.*
1 Chr 25:8
cut off master and the *s.* *Mal* 2:12*

school

disputing in the *s.* of one. *Acts* 19:9

schoolmaster

(*The Roman* pedagogue, *who did not teach, but was the slave whose duty it was to take the child to the school*)

the law was our *s.* to. *Gal* 3:24*
are no longer under a *s.* 25

science

wisdom, understanding *s.* *Dan* 1:4
and oppositions of *s.* *1 Tim* 6:20*

scoff

they shall *s.* at the kings. *Hab* 1:10

scoffers

in last days *s.* walking. *2 Pet* 3:3

scorch

given him to *s.* men. *Rev* 16:8

scorched

when sun was up they were *s.*
Mat 13:6; *Mark* 4:6
and men were *s.* with. *Rev* 16:9

scorn, *verb*

my friends *s.* me, mine. *Job* 16:20

scorn

he thought *s.* to lay hands. *Esth* 3:6
a reproach and *s.* *Ps* 44:13; 79:4
princes shall be a *s.* *Hab* 1:10*
see **laughed**

scorner

(*A* Scorner, *as the word is used in Scripture, is one who makes a mock of sin, and of God's threatenings and judgements against sinners; one who derides all wholesome reproofs and counsels, and scoffs at religion. Usually the revisions change to* scoffer)

reproveth a *s.* getteth. *Pr* 9:7
reprove not a *s.*, lest he hate thee. 8
but a *s.* heareth not rebuke. 13:1
a *s.* seeketh wisdom, and. 14:6
a *s.* loveth not one that. 15:12
smite a *s.* 19:25
when the *s.* is punished. 21:11
s. is his name, who dealeth in. 24
cast out the *s.* 22:10
and the *s.* is an abomination. 24:9
the *s.* is consumed, and. *Isa* 29:20

scorners

how long will *s.* delight? *Pr* 1:22
surely he scorneth the *s.* but. 3:34
judgements are prepared for *s.* and.
19:29
stretched out his hand with *s.* *Hos* 7:5

scornest

if thou *s.* thou alone. *Pr* 9:12
in that thou *s.* hire. *Ezek* 16:31

scorneth

s. the multitude of the city. *Job* 39:7
the ostrich, she *s.* the horse. 18
surely he *s.* the scorners. *Pr* 3:34
witness *s.* judgement, and. 19:28

scornful

in the seat of the *s.* *Ps* 1:1
s. men bring a city into. *Pr* 29:8
of the Lord, ye *s.* men. *Isa* 28:14

scorning

drinketh up *s.* like water? *Job* 34:7
is filled with *s.* of those. *Ps* 123:4
scorners delight in their *s.* *Pr* 1:22

scorpion

A well-known venomous insect of hot climates, shaped much like a lobster, and closely akin to the spider. It is usually about 2 *or* 3 *inches long, but in tropical climates grows much larger.*

The word used in 1 Ki 12:11 *is metaphorical.*

will he offer him a *s.*? *Luke* 11:12
as the torment of a *s.* *Rev* 9:5

scorpions

wherein were *s.* *Deut* 8:15
I will chastise you with *s.*
1 Ki 12:11, 14; *2 Chr* 10:11, 14
among *s.* be not afraid. *Ezek* 2:6
tread on serpents and *s.* *Luke* 10:19
power, as *s.* have power. *Rev* 9:3
they had tails like to *s.* and. 10

scoured

a brasen pot, it shall be *s.* *Lev* 6:28

scourge

A whip made of cords or leather thongs fastened into a handle. Usually there were three of these thongs in each scourge, and they were often reinforced with bits of metal which tore the skin and flesh. Notable scourgings mentioned in the Bible are those of Christ, in the Gospels, and of Paul, in 2 Cor 11:24. *The scourge of small cords used by Jesus in clearing the Temple, was merely a symbol of authority. Scourging differs from* beating, *which was done with rods.*

The word is also used as to-day, figuratively, for a cause of calamity of any sort.

hid from *s.* of the tongue. *Job* 5:21
if the *s.* slay suddenly, he. 9:23

shall stir up a *s.* for him. *Isa* 10:26
when the overflowing *s.* 28:15, 18
when he had made a *s.* *John* 2:15

scourge, *verb*

they will *s.* you in their. *Mat* 10:17
they shall *s.* him. 20:19
Mark 10:34; *Luke* 18:33
some of them ye shall *s.* *Mat* 23:34
for you to *s.* a Roman ? *Acts* 22:25

scourged

maid, she shall be *s.* *Lev* 19:20
they had *s.* Jesus, he. *Mat* 27:26
Mark 15:15; *John* 19:1

scourges

s. in your sides, and. *Josh* 23:13

scourgeth

the Lord *s.* every son. *Heb* 12:6

scourging

should be examined by *s.* *Acts* 22:24

scourgings

others had trial of *s.*, yea. *Heb* 11:36

scrabbled

himself mad, and *s.* *1 Sam* 21:13

scrape

dust that they *s.* off. *Lev* 14:41
Job took a potsherd to *s.* *Job* 2:8
I will also *s.* her dust. *Ezek* 26:4

scraped

house to be *s.* within. *Lev* 14:41
after he hath *s.* the house. 43

screech owl

s. also shall rest there. *Isa* 34:14*

scribe

[1] *In the Old Testament any government clerk or secretary.* [2] *The* Sopherim (plur.) *who copied, taught, and explained the law. Ezra was one of the most noted of those in Old Testament times. Before the Exile this work was done by the Levites, but later it was gradually put into the hands of a specially trained body of laymen.*
Not only did they copy the written law, but they formulated and wrote down the detailed rules made by later authorities, which made up what was called the oral law, or the traditions of the elders. They had much opportunity for the exercise of that hypocrisy for which our Lord denounced them in company with the Pharisees.

Seraiah was the *s.* *2 Sam* 8:17
Sheva was *s.* 20:25
and Shebna the *s.* *2 Ki* 18:18, 37
19:2; *Isa* 36:3, 22; 37:2
Shaphan, the *s.* *2 Ki* 22:3, 8, 9, 10
12; *2 Chr* 34:15, 18, 20; *Jer* 36:10
he took the principal *s.* of the host.
2 Ki 25:19; *Jer* 52:25
and Shemaiah the *s.* *1 Chr* 24:6
a wise man and a *s.* 27:32
Shimshai the *s.* wrote a letter.
Ezra 4:8, 9, 17, 23
was a ready *s.* in the law. 7:6, 11
12; *Neh* 8:4, 9, 13; 12:26, 36
Ezra the *s.* stood upon. *Neh* 8:4
the priest, Zadok the *s.* 13:13
where is the *s.*? where? *Isa* 33:18
sat there, even Elishama the *s.*
Jer 36:12, 20, 21
Baruch the *s.* 26, 32
Jonathan the *s.* 37:15, 20
a *s.* said, Master, I will. *Mat* 8:19
s. instructed unto the. 13:52
the *s.* said unto him. *Mark* 12:32
where is the *s.*? where ? *1 Cor* 1:20

scribes

Ahiah, sons of Shisha, *s.* *1 Ki* 4:3
the families of the *s.* *1 Chr* 2:55
of Levites there were *s.* *2 Chr* 34:13
then were the king's *s.* called.
Esth 3:12; 8:9
the pen of the *s.* is in. *Jer* 8:8
righteousness of the *s.* *Mat* 5:20
having authority, and not as the *s.*
7:29; *Mark* 1:22
many things of the *s.* *Mat* 16:21
why say *s.* Elias. 17:10; *Mark* 9:11
Son of man shall be betrayed unto the chief priests and the *s.* *Mat* 20:18
Mark 10:33
when the *s.* saw, they. *Mat* 21:15
s. and Pharisees sit in. 23:2
woe to you *s.* 13, 14, 15, 23, 25, 27
29; *Luke* 11:44
priests and *s.* and elders. *Mat* 26:3
Mark 14:53; *Luke* 22:66
went certain *s.* *Mark* 2:6
when the *s.* saw him eat with. 16
the *s.* said, he hath Beelzebub. 3:22
be rejected of *s.* 8:31; *Luke* 9:22
the *s.* questioning with. *Mark* 9:14
the *s.* and chief priests heard it, and.
11:18; *Luke* 19:47
s. say, By what authority ?
Mark 11:27
one of the *s.* asked, What is ? 12:28
How say *s.* that Christ is the ? 35
he said to them, Beware of *s.* 38
Luke 20:46
s. sought how to take. *Mark* 14:1
their *s.* and Pharisees murmured.
Luke 5:30; 15:2
s. watched him. 6:7
the *s.* began to urge him. 11:53
the *s.* came upon him. 20:1
priests and *s.* sought to lay. 19
the chief priests and *s.* sought. 22:2
s. stood and vehemently. 23:10
the *s.* brought a woman. *John* 8:3
the *s.* gathered against. *Acts* 4:5
the *s.* brought Stephen to. 6:12
the *s.* of the Pharisees' part. 23:9

scrip

(*Revisions*, wallet. *A sort of bag in which were carried a small amount of food and other necessary conveniences for a journey*)

smooth stones in a *s.* *1 Sam* 17:40
nor *s.* for your journey. *Mat* 10:10
Mark 6:8; *Luke* 9:3; 10:4
without *s.* lacked ye. *Luke* 22:35
take his purse and his *s.* 36

scripture

(*Literally from the Latin, a* writing.
The word as used in the Bible refers almost invariably to the sacred writings, which at that time consisted of the Old Testament only. It is also used of a part of it, especially when that part is quoted in a later passage)

noted in the *s.* of truth. *Dan* 10:21
read this *s.*, The stone? *Mark* 12:10
the *s.* was fulfilled, which. 15:28
said, This day is this *s.* *Luke* 4:21
they believed the *s.* and. *John* 2:22
on me, as the *s.* saith. 7:38
not the *s.* said, Christ cometh ? 42
word came, and the *s.* cannot. 10:35
again another *s.* saith, They. 19:37
this *s.* must needs have. *Acts* 1:16
the place of the *s.* which. 8:32
Philip began at the same *s.* 35
what saith the *s.*? *Rom* 4:3; 11:2
Gal 4:30
for the *s.* saith. *Rom* 9:17; 10:11
1 Tim 5:18
the *s.* foreseeing that God. *Gal* 3:8
but the *s.* hath concluded all. 22
all *s.* is given by. *2 Tim* 3:16
do ye think the *s.* saith ? *Jas* 4:5
the *s.*, Behold I lay in Sion. *1 Pet* 2:6
no prophecy of *s.* is of. *2 Pet* 1:20

scriptures

read in the *s.* the stone ? *Mat* 21:42
ye do err, not knowing the *s.* 22:29
Mark 12:24
how then shall the *s.* be ? *Mat* 26:54
but the *s.* must be. *Mark* 14:49
to them in all the *s.* *Luke* 24:27
while he opened to us the *s.*? 32
that they might understand the *s.* 45
search the *s.*; for in them. *John* 5:39
with them out of the *s.* *Acts* 17:2
and searched the *s.* daily. 11
Apollos, mighty in the *s.* 18:24
shewing by the *s.* that Jesus was. 28
prophets in the holy *s.* *Rom* 1:2
that we through comfort of *s.* 15:4
and by the *s.* made known. *Rom* 16:2
Christ died according to *s.* *1 Cor* 15:
rose according to the *s.*
hast known the holy *s.* *2 Tim* 3:1
as they do also other *s.* *2 Pet* 3:1

scroll

rolled together as a *s.* *Isa* 34:
departed as a *s.* rolled. *Rev* 6:1

scum

(*Revisions*, rust)

woe to the pot whose *s.* *Ezek* 24:
s. of it may be consumed. 1
her great *s.* went not forth of her, he
s. shall be in the fire. 1

scurvy

none shall approach that is *s.* or.
Lev 21:2
the *s.* or scabbed ye shall not. 22:2

Scythian

neither barbarian, *S.* *Col* 3:1

sea

(*The molten sea made for the Temple*)

he made a molten *s.* *1 Ki* 7:2
2 Chr 4:
were knops compassing *s.* *1 Ki* 7:2
the *s.* was set above upon oxen. 2
2 Chr 4:
set the *s.* on right side of the. 3
took down the *s.* from. *2 Ki* 16:1
the *s.* did Chaldeans break. 25:13, 1
s. was for the priests. *2 Chr* 4:
one *s.* and twelve oxen under. 1
concerning the pillars and *s.*
Jer 27:1

sea

The Hebrews knew little, an most of them nothing, about th ocean as we understand this word though the ocean is probabl referred to in Gen 1. [1] *Th largest body of water really know to them was the* Mediterranea Sea, *which is probably referred t in* Deut 11:24, *and several oth places.* [2] *The* Red Sea *w naturally a familiar name to them* Ex 15:4. [3] *The* Salt Sea, *o* Dead Sea, *and other large inlan waters are meant in such place as* Deut 3:17; Joel 2:20. [4 *Any great collections of waters, a the Nile,* Isa 19:5, *and the Eu phrates,* Jer 51:36, *are in som places called Seas.*

hand over the *s.* *Ex* 14:16, 2
s. to go back, made the *s.* dry. 2
didst blow, the *s.* covered. 15:1
Lord made the *s.* and all. 20:1
Ps 95:5; *Jonah* 1:9; *Acts* 4:2
14:1
quails from the *s.* *Num* 11:3
beyond *s.* that thou shouldest sa
Who shall go over *s.*? *Deut* 30:1
you came unto the *s.* *Josh* 24:
he brought the *s.* upon them.
at *s.* a navy of Tharshish. *1 Ki* 10:2
look toward the *s.* 18:
coast to the *s.* of plain. *2 Ki* 14:2
let the *s.* roar. *1 Chr* 16:3
Ps 96:11; 98:
against thee beyond *s.* *2 Chr* 20:
divide the *s.*, went through the *s.*
Neh 9:11; *Job* 26:12; *Ps* 74:1
78:13; *Jer* 31:3
am I a *s.* or a whale ? *Job* 7:1
is broader than the *s.* 11:
as the waters fail from *s.* 14:1
s. saith, It is not with me. 28:1
or who shut up the *s.*? 38:
he maketh the *s.* like a pot. 41:3
the *s.* into dry land. *Ps* 66:
dominion from *s.* to *s.* 72:
but the *s.* overwhelmed their. 78:5
she sent out her boughs to *s.* 80:1
so is this great and wide *s.* 104:2
down to the *s.* in ships. 107:2
the *s.* saw it and fled. 114:
O thou *s.*, that thou ?
gave to the *s.* his decree. *Pr* 8:2
as the waters cover the *s.* *Isa* 11:
Hab 2:1

stretched and gone over *s.* *Isa* 16:8
the waters shall fail from the *s.* 19:5
Zidon that pass over *s.* 23:2
be ashamed, O Zion, for the *s.* 4
stretched his hand over the *s.* 11
shall cry aloud from the *s.* 24:14
ye that go down to the *s.* 42:10
my rebuke, I dry up the *s.* 50:2
which hath dried the *s.*? 51:10
are like the troubled *s.* 57:20
their voice roareth like the *s.* *Jer* 6:23
thy plants are gone over *s.* 48:32
voice shall roar like the *s.* 50:42
I will dry up her *s.* and make. 51:36
the *s.* is come up upon. 42
breach is great like the *s.* *Lam* 2:13
as the *s.* causeth his waves to. *Ezek* 26:3
came up from the *s.* *Dan* 7:3
wander from *s.* to *s.* *Amos* 8:12
shall we do, that the *s.*? *Jonah* 1:11
that day he shall come from *s.* to *s.* *Mi* 7:12
he rebuketh the *s.* and. *Nah* 1:4
whose rampart was the *s.* 3:8
was thy wrath against *s.*? *Hab* 3:8
thou didst walk through the *s.* 15
heavens, earth, and *s.* *Hag* 2:6
shall be from *s.* to *s.* *Zech* 9:10
through the *s.* with affliction. 10:11
and rebuked the *s.* *Mat* 8:26
even winds and *s.* obey him. 8:27; *Mark* 4:39, 41
go thou to the *s.* and cast an. *Mat* 17:27
for ye compass *s.* and land. 23:15
the *s.* and the waves. *Luke* 21:25
themselves to the *s.* *Acts* 27:40
he hath escaped the *s.* 28:4
passed through the *s.* *1 Cor* 10:1
throne was a *s.* of glass. *Rev* 4:6
to hurt the earth and *s.* 7:2
Hurt not the earth nor the *s.* 3
who created the *s.* and the. 10:6
worship him that made the *s.* 14:7
I saw a *s.* of glass, mingled. 15:2
and the *s.* gave up the dead. 20:13
and there was no more *s.* 21:1
see **coast, great, red, salt**

by the **sea**

ye encamp *by the s.* *Ex* 14:2
encamping *by the s.* 9
be gathered as sand *by the s.* *2 Sam* 17:11
Israel as sand *by the s.* *1 Ki* 4:20
I will convey them *by the s.* 5:9
2 Chr 2:16
ambassadors *by the s.* *Isa* 18:2
as Carmel *by the s.* so. *Jer* 46:18
multitude was *by the s.* *Mark* 4:1
trade *by the s.* stood. *Rev* 18:17

in and *into the* **sea**

that came *into the s.* *Ex* 14:28
he thrown *into the sea.* 15:1, 21
host hath he cast *into the s.* 4
horsemen went *into the s.* 19
thy way is *in the s.* thy path. *Ps* 77:19
set his hand also *in the s.* 89:25
all rivers run *into the s.* *Eccl* 1:7
dragon that is *in the s.* *Isa* 27:1
maketh a way *in the s.* 43:16
was strong *in the s.* *Ezek* 26:17
the isles that are *in the s.* shall. 18
these waters go *into the s.* which being brought forth *into the s.* 47:8
tempest *in the s.* *Jonah* 1:4
forth the wares *into the s.* 5
cast me *into the s.* 12, 15
smite her power *into the s.* *Zech* 9:4
smite the waves *into the s.* 10:11
casting a net *into the s.* *Mat* 4:18
Mark 1:16
great tempest *in the s.* *Mat* 8:24
swine ran *into the s.* 32; *Mark* 5:13
like a net cast *into the s.* *Mat* 13:47
be thou cast *into the s.* 21:21
Mark 11:23
and he were cast *into the s.* *Mark* 9:42; *Luke* 17:2
be thou planted *in the s.* *Luke* 17:6
cast himself *into the s.* *John* 21:7
the wheat *into the s.* *Acts* 27:38
themselves first *into the s.* 43*

cloud, and *in the s.* *1 Cor* 10:2
in perils *in the s.* *2 Cor* 11:26
beast and things *in the s.* *Jas* 3:7
every creature *in the s.* *Rev* 5:13
burning was cast *into the s.* 8:8
living soul died *in the s.* 16:3
all that had ships *in the s.* 18:19
cast a millstone *into the s.* 21

of the **sea**

have dominion over fish *of the s.* *Gen* 1:26, 28; *Ps* 8:8
upon all fishes *of the s.* *Gen* 9:2
seed as the sand *of the s.* 32:12
corn as the sand *of the s.* 41:49
dwell at the haven *of the s.* 49:13
in the heart *of the s.* *Ex* 15:8
the waters *of the s.* upon them. 19
all the fish *of the s.* be? *Num* 11:22
the channels *of the s.* *2 Sam* 22:16
a cloud out *of the s.* *1 Ki* 18:44
than the sand *of the s.* *Job* 6:3
upon the waves *of the s.* 9:8
the fishes *of the s.* shall. 12:8
covered the bottom *of the s.* 36:30
into the springs *of the s.*? 38:16
waters *of the s.* together. *Ps* 33:7
people from depths *of the s.* 68:22
like as the sand *of the s.* 78:27
rulest the raging *of the s.* 89:9
than the mighty waves *of the s.* 93:4
uttermost parts *of the s.* 139:9
the roaring *of the s.* *Isa* 5:30
her by the way *of the s.* 9:1
as the sand *of the s.* yet a remnant shall. 10:22; *Hos* 1:10; *Rom* 9:27
even the strength *of the s.* *Isa* 23:4
as the waves *of the s.* 48:18
made the depths *of the s.* 51:10
abundance *of the s.* shall be. 60:5
them up out *of the s.* 63:11
for the bound *of the s.* *Jer* 5:22
neither the sand *of the s.* 33:22
the princes *of the s.* *Ezek* 26:16
situate at the entry *of the s.* 27:3
the ships *of the s.* were in thee. 9
all the pilots *of the s.* shall. 29
fishes *of the s.* shall shake. 38:20
the fishes *of the s.* shall be. *Hos* 4:3
calleth for the waters *of the s.* *Amos* 5:8; 9:6
in the bottom *of the s.* 9:3
sins into depths *of the s.* *Mi* 7:19
men as the fishes *of the s.* *Hab* 1:14
consume the fishes *of the s.* *Zeph* 1:3
by way *of the s.* beyond. *Mat* 4:15
drowned in the depth *of the s.* 18:6
is like a wave *of the s.* *Jas* 1:6
raging waves *of the s.* *Jude* 13
the third part *of the s.* *Rev* 8:8
of earth and *of the s.* 12:12
a beast rise up out *of the s.* 13:1
is as the sand *of the s.* 20:8
see **midst, sand**

on or *upon the* **sea**

afar off *upon the s.* *Ps* 65:5
there is sorrow *on the s.* *Jer* 49:23
walking *on the s.* *Mat* 14:25
Mark 6:48; *John* 6:19
disciples saw him walking *on the s.* *Mat* 14:26; *Mark* 6:49
should not blow *on the s.* *Rev* 7:1
his right foot *upon the s.* 10:2
which I saw stand *upon the s.* 5, 8
and I saw them stand *on the s.* 15:2
poured out his vial *upon the s.* 16:3

seafaring *men*

inhabited of *s. men.* *Ezek* 26:17

sea *monsters*

even the *s. monsters* draw out the. *Lam* 4:3*

sea *shore*

as sand which is upon the *s. shore.* *Gen* 22:17
saw the Egyptians dead upon *s. shore.* *Ex* 14:30
as sand upon *s. shore.* *Josh* 11:4
Asher continued on the *s. shore.* *Judg* 5:17
the Philistines as sand on the *s. shore.* *1 Sam* 13:5
heart as sand on *s. shore.* *1 Ki* 4:29
given it a charge against the *s. shore* *Jer* 47:7

sprang many, as sand by *s. shore.* *Heb* 11:12

sea *side*

the way of the *s. side.* *Deut* 1:7
as sand by the *s. side.* *Judg* 7:12
Eloth at the *s. side.* *2 Chr* 8:17
sat by the *s. side.* *Mat* 13:1
forth again by the *s. side.* *Mark* 2:13
to teach by the *s. side.* 4:1
Simon, whose house is by the *s. side.* *Acts* 10:6, 32

seal

Because of the fact that few could read or write, the use of the seal was far more common in olden times than now. Each person had his own private seal which it was a capital crime to copy. This was affixed to every sort of a document, as we now sign our names.

The word is very frequently used symbolically, as in Rom 4:11; *circumcision is said to be a* seal *of the righteousness of faith.*

letters with Ahab's *s.* *1 Ki* 21:8
as clay to the *s.* they. *Job* 38:14
shut up as with a close *s.* 41:15
s. on thy heart, as a *s.* on. *S of S* 8:6
hath set to his *s.* that God is true. *John* 3:33*
circumcision a *s.* of. *Rom* 4:11
the *s.* of mine apostleship are ye. *1 Cor* 9:2
having this *s.* the Lord *2 Tim* 2:19
he opened the second *s.* *Rev* 6:3
the third *s.* 5
the fourth *s.* 7
the fifth *s.* 9
the sixth *s.* 12
another angel, having the *s.* 7:2
opened the seventh *s.* 8:1
that have not the *s.* of God. 9:4
and shut him up, and set a *s.* 20:3

seal, *verb*

our princes and priests *s.* unto it. *Neh* 9:38; 10:1
s. the law among my. *Isa* 8:16
evidences, and *s.* them. *Jer* 32:44
seventy weeks to *s.* up. *Dan* 9:24
O Daniel, shut up the words, *s.* 12:4
s. those things the seven. *Rev* 10:4
s. not the sayings of the. 22:10

sealed

is not this *s.* up among? *Deut* 32:34
the letters were *s.* with. *1 Ki* 21:8
written and *s.* with. *Esth* 3:12; 8:8
my transgression is *s.* *Job* 14:17
my spouse; a fountain *s.* *S of S* 4:12
the words of a book *s.* *Isa* 29:11
I subscribed and *s.* the. *Jer* 32:10
both that which was *s.* and. 11, 14
s. it with his own signet. *Dan* 6:17
and *s.* till the time. 12:9
God the Father *s.* *John* 6:27
when I have *s.* to them. *Rom* 15:28
who hath *s.* us and given. *2 Cor* 1:22
ye were *s.* with that Holy. *Eph* 1:13
whereby ye are *s.* to-day. 4:30
book *s.* with seven seals. *Rev* 5:1
sea, till we have *s.* servants. 7:3
number of them which were *s.*; there were *s.* 144,000 of all the. 4
of Juda were *s.* 12,000; of Reuben; of Gad *s.* 5
of Nephthalim *s.*; of Manasses *s.* 6
of Levi; of Issachar were *s.* 7
of Joseph; of Benjamin were *s.* 8

sealest

thou *s.* up the sum full. *Ezek* 28:12

sealeth

commandeth the sun, and *s.* *Job* 9:7
he openeth their ears, and *s.* 33:16
he *s.* up hand of every man. 37:7

sealing

s. the stone and setting. *Mat* 27:66

seals

book sealed with seven *s.* *Rev* 5:1
who is worthy to loose the *s.*? 2
Juda prevailed to loose the *s.* 5
to take and open the *s.* 9
Lamb opened one of the *s.* 6:1

seam
was without s., woven. John 19:23

search
enquire and made s. Deut 13:14
that s. may be made in. Ezra 4:15
5:17
s. hath been made, and it. 4:19; 6:1
prepare thyself to the s. Job 8:8
hast thou walked in the s.? 38:16*
accomplish a diligent s. Ps 64:6
my spirit made diligent s. 77:6
not found it by secret s. Jer 2:34

search, *verb*
he shall not s. whether. Lev 27:33
to s. out a resting place. Num 10:33
that they may s. the land. 13:2
which we have gone to s. it. 32
passed through to s. it, is. 14:7
of the men that went to s. 38
men, and they shall s. Deut 1:22
before to s. you out a place. 33
men to s. the country. Josh 2:2, 3
the Danites sent men to s. Judg 18:2
land, I will s. him out. 1 Sam 23:23
servants unto thee to s. the city?
2 Sam 10:3; 1 Chr 19:3
servants, and they shall s. 1 Ki 20:6
s. that none of the servants.
2 Ki 10:23
is it good that he should s.? Job 13:9
shall not God s. this out? Ps 44:21
they s. and accomplish a. 64:6
s. me, O God, and know. 139:23
kings to s. out a matter. Pr 25:2
for men to s. their own glory. 27
I gave my heart to s. by wisdom.
Eccl 1:13; 7:25
I the Lord s. the heart. Jer 17:10
when ye shall s. for me. 29:13
let us s. our ways, and. Lam 3:40
and none did s. or seek. Ezek 34:6
neither did my shepherds s. for. 8
I will both s. my sheep, and. 11
of seven months shall they s. 39:14
I will s. and take them out. Amos 9:3
I will s. Jerusalem with. Zeph 1:12
and s. diligently for the. Mat 2:8
s. the scriptures; for in. John 5:39
s. for out of Galilee ariseth. 7:52

searched
Laban s. the tent. Gen 31:34, 35
whereas thou hast s. all my. 37
the steward s. for the cup. 44:12
so they went up, and s. Num 13:21
evil report of the land, and s. 32
Caleb s. the land. 14:6, 38
of days ye s. the land. 34
valley of Eshcol, and s. Deut 1:24
we have s. it, and know. Job 5:27
he prepared it, yea, and s. 28:27
which I knew not, I s. out. 29:16
whilst ye s. out what to say. 32:11
his years be s. out. 36:26
O Lord, thou hast s. me. Ps 139:1
foundations of the earth s. Jer 31:37
though it cannot be s. 46:23
things of Esau s. out. Ob 6
s. the scriptures daily. Acts 17:11
prophets s. diligently. 1 Pet 1:10

searchest
that thou s. after my sin. Job 10:6
if thou s. for her as for hid. Pr 2:4

searcheth
for the Lord s. all hearts. 1 Chr 28:9
and he s. out all perfection. Job 28:3
and he s. after every green. 39:8
cometh and s. him. Pr 18:17
understanding s. him out. 28:11
that s. hearts, knows. Rom 8:27*
Spirit s. all things. 1 Cor 2:10
that I am he which s. Rev 2:23

searching
they returned from s. Num 13:25
canst thou by s. find out God?
Job 11:7
s. all the inward parts. Pr 20:27
there is no s. of his. Isa 40:28
s. what time the Spirit. 1 Pet 1:11

searchings
of Reuben were great s. Judg 5:16

seared
having their conscience s. 1 Tim 4:2*

seas
gathering of the waters called he s.
Gen 1:10
and fill the waters in the s. 22
fins and scales in the s. eat. Lev 11:9
that have not fins in the s. be. 10
of abundance of the s. Deut 33:19
thou hast made the s. Neh 9:6
through paths of the s. Ps 8:8
founded it upon the s. 24:2
noise of the s., ... their waves. 65:7
let the s. praise him, and. 69:34
pleased, that did he in the s. 135:6
noise like noise of the s. Isa 17:12
increased above sand of s. Jer 15:8
thy borders in the midst of the s.
Ezek 27:4
glorious in midst of the s. 25
hath broken thee in the midst of s.
26, 27, 34
wares went forth out of the s. 33
seat of God, in midst of the s. 28:2
slain in the midst of the s. 8
art as a whale in the s. 32:2
palace between the s. Dan 11:45
me into midst of the s. Jonah 2:3
a place where two s. met. Acts 27:41

season
and they continued a s. Gen 40:4
this ordinance in his s. Ex 13:10
at the s. thou camest. Deut 16:6
unto thy land in his s. 28:12
the wilderness a long s. Josh 24:7*
about this s. thou shalt. 2 Ki 4:16
woman bare a son at that s. 17
altar was at that s. 1 Chr 21:29*
for long s. been without. 2 Chr 15:3
corn cometh in his s. Job 5:26
pierced in the night s. 30:17
Mazzaroth in his s. 38:32
bringeth forth fruit in his s. Ps 1:3
I cry in the night s. and am. 22:2
a word spoken in due s. Pr 15:23
to every thing there is a s. Eccl 3:1
to speak a word in s. Isa 50:4*
latter rain in his s. Jer 5:24
day and night in their s. 33:20
shower come down in s. Ezek 34:26
prolonged for a s. Dan 7:12
wine in the s. thereof. Hos 2:9
at the s. he sent to the. Mark 12:2
be fulfilled in their s. Luke 1:20
departed from him for a s. 4:13
were present at that s. some. 13:1
at the s. he sent a servant. 20:10
to see him of a long s. 23:8*
went down at a certain s. John 5:4
ye were willing for a s. to. 35
seeing the sun for a s. Acts 13:11
stayed in Asia for a s. 19:22*
when I have a convenient s. 24:25
though it were but for a s. 2 Cor 7:8
instant in s., out of s. 2 Tim 4:2
departed for a s. Philem 15
pleasures of sin for a s. Heb 11:25
though for a s. if need be. 1 Pet 1:6*
rest yet for a little s. Rev 6:11*
must be loosed a little s. 20:3*
see **appointed, due**

season, *verb*
shalt thou s. with salt. Lev 2:13
wherewith will ye s. it? Mark 9:50

seasoned
wherewith shall it be s.? Luke 14:34
be always with grace, s. Col 4:6

seasons
signs, and s. and days. Gen 1:14
the people at all s. Ex 18:22, 26
proclaim in their s. Lev 23:4
instruct me in the night s. Ps 16:7
he appointeth the moon for s. 104:19
the times and the s. Dan 2:21
the fruits in their s. Mat 21:41
know the times and the s. Acts 1:7
gave us rain and fruitful s. 14:17
been with you at all s. 20:18
of the s. ye have no. 1 Thes 5:1

seat
Eglon rose out of his s. Judg 3:20
Eli sat upon a s. by a post.
1 Sam 1:9; 4:13
he fell from off the s. 1 Sam 4:18
be missed, because thy s. 20:18
the king sat on his s. on a s. by. 25
the Tachmonite that sat in the s.
2 Sam 23:8*
caused a s. to be set. 1 Ki 2:19*
set Haman's s. above all. Esth 3:1
come even to his s.! Job 23:3
prepared my s. in the street. 29:7
nor sitteth in the s. of the. Ps 1:1
sitteth on a s. in the city. Pr 9:14
where was the s. of the. Ezek 8:3
I sit in the s. of God, in midst. 28:2
and cause the s. of violence to come.
Amos 6:3
Pharisees sit in Moses' s. Mat 23:2
where Satan's s. is. Rev 2:13*
see **judgement, mercy**

seated
the lawgiver was he s. Deut 33:21*

seats
moneychangers and the s. of them.
Mat 21:12; Mark 11:15
love chief s. in the synagogues.
Mat 23:6; Mark 12:39
the mighty from their s. Luke 1:52*
love the uppermost s. 11:43; 20:46
four-and-twenty s. upon. Rev 4:4*
sat before God on their s. 11:16*

Seba
the sons of Cush, S. Gen 10:7
the kings of Sheba and S. Ps 72:10
I gave Ethiopia and S. Isa 43:3

second
with s. and third stories. Gen 6:16
and so commanded he the s. 32:19
he made him to ride in the s. 41:43
the coupling of the s. Ex 26:4, 5
10; 36:11, 12, 17
the s. row shall be an. 28:18; 39:11
he shall offer the s. for. Lev 5:10
set forth in the s. rank. Num 2:16
the s. lot came forth to. Josh 19:1
the s. bullock of seven. Judg 6:25
take s. bullock and offer. 26
the s. was offered. 28
then he sent out a s. 2 Ki 9:19
brethren of s. degree. 1 Chr 15:18
him in the s. chariot. 2 Chr 35:24
silver basons of a s. sort. Ezra 1:10
to confirm this s. letter. Esth 9:29
alone, there is not a s. Eccl 4:8
with the s. child that shall. 15
the s. face was the. Ezek 10:14
behold, another beast, a s. like.
Dan 7:5
howling from the s. Zeph 1:10*
in the s. chariot were. Zech 6:2
he came to the s. and. Mat 21:30
likewise the s. had her, and. 22:26
Mark 12:21; Luke 20:30
s. commandment is like unto it.
Mat 22:39; Mark 12:31
and it came to pass on s. Luke 6:1
if he shall come in s. watch. 12:38
the s. came saying, Lord thy. 19:18
this is the s. miracle that. John 4:54
were past the s. ward. Acts 12:10
as it is written in the s. psalm. 13:33
the s. man is the Lord. 1 Cor 15:47
that ye might have a s. 2 Cor 1:15
after the first and s. Tit 3:10
have been sought for the s. Heb 8:7
and after the s. veil, the. 9:3
into the s. went the high priest. 7
that he may establish the s. 10:9
this s. epistle I now write. 2 Pet 3:1
hurt of the s. death. Rev 2:11; 20:6
the s. beast like a calf, the. 4:7
I heard the s. beast say, Come. 6:3
s. angel sounded, and as it. 8:8
the s. woe is past, the third. 11:14
the s. angel poured out his vial. 16:3
this is the s. death. 20:14; 21:8
the s. foundation of the wall. 21:19
see **day, month**

second *time*
called to Abraham the s. time.
Gen 22:15
and dreamed the s. time. 41:5
had returned this s. time. 43:10
be washed the s. time. Lev 13:58

an alarm the s. time. Num 10:6
circumcise Israel the s. time. Josh 5:2
smite him the s. time. 1 Sam 26:8
sent to Joab the s. time. 2 Sam 14:29
Solomon the s. time. 1 Ki 9:2
s. time, they did it the s. time. 18:34
again to Elijah the s. time. 19:7
a letter the s. time. 2 Ki 10:6
Solomon king s. time. 1 Chr 29:22
gathered the s. time. Esth 2:19
his hand the s. time. Isa 11:11
came to me the s. time saying, What? Jer 1:13; 13:3; 33:1
came to Jonah the s. time. Jonah 3:1
not rise up the s. time. Nah 1:9
he went again the s. time. Mat 26:42
s. time the cock crew. Mark 14:72
can he enter the s. time? John 3:4
Jesus saith to Peter the s. time. 21:16
at the s. time Joseph. Acts 7:13
to Peter again the s. time. 10:15
present the s. time. 2 Cor 13:2
he shall appear the s. time. Heb 9:28

second *year*

they came the s. year. Gen 47:18
in the s. year, the first. Ex 40:17
in the s. year after. Num 1:1
in first month of s. year. 9:1
in the s. year the cloud was. 10:11
shall eat in the s. year that which. 2 Ki 19:29; Isa 37:30
paid Jotham the s. year. 2 Chr 27:5
in the s. year of their. Ezra 3:8
it ceased to the s. year of. 4:24
in the s. year of reign. Dan 2:1
in s. year of Darius. Hag 1:1, 15
2:10; Zech 1:7

secondarily

God set s. prophets. 1 Cor 12:28

secret

not thou into their s. Gen 49:6*
heard the s. of God? Job 15:8
when the s. of God was upon. 29:4
and bind their faces in s. 40:13*
the s. of the Lord is with. Ps 25:14
in s. of his tabernacle. 27:5*; 31:20
that they may shoot in s. 64:4*
when I was made in s. 139:15
but his s. is with the. Pr 3:32
stolen waters, bread eaten in s. 9:17
a gift in s. pacifieth anger. 21:14
discover not a s. to another. 25:9
I have not spoken in s. Isa 45:19
48:16
no s. that they can hide. Ezek 28:3
God concerning this s. Dan 2:18
then was the s. revealed to. 19
the s. which the king hath. 27
this s. not revealed to me for. 30
thou couldest reveal this s. 47
because I know that no s. 4:9
he revealeth his s. to his. Amos 3:7
be in s.: and thy Father which seeth in s. shall reward. Mat 6:4, 6, 18
pray to thy Father which is in s. 6
to thy Father which is in s. 18
man doth any thing in s. John 7:4
feast as it were in s. 10
I speak openly, in s. have I. 18:20
are done of them in s. Eph 5:12

secret, *adjective*

idol in a s. place. Deut 27:15
s. things belong unto Lord. 29:29
I have a s. errand unto. Judg 3:19
my name, seeing it is s.? 13:18*
had emerods in their s. parts. 1 Sam 5:9
take heed, abide in a s. place. 19:2
wouldest keep me s. Job 14:13
is there any s. with thee? 15:11
shall be hid in his s. places. 20:26*
in s. places doth he. Ps 10:8*
lion lurking in s. places. 17:12
made darkness his s. place. 18:11*
cleanse thou me from s. faults. 19:12*
hide me from the s. counsel. 64:2
I answered thee in the s. 81:7
our s. sins in the light of thy. 90:8
that dwelleth in the s. place. Ps 91:1
Open rebuke is better than s. love. Pr 27:5*
bring into judgement every s. thing. Eccl 12:14*
art in the s. places. S of S 2:14*
discover their s. parts. Isa 3:17
hidden riches of s. places. 45:3
found it by s. search. Jer 2:34
my soul shall weep in s. 13:17
can any hide himself in s.? 23:24
have uncovered his s. places. 49:10
he was to me as a lion in s. places. Lam 3:10
pollute my s. place. Ezek 7:22
deep and s. things. Dan 2:22
I will utter things which have been kept s. Mat 13:35; Rom 16:25
he is in s. chambers, believe it not. Mat 24:26*
was anything kept s. Mark 4:22*
Luke 8:17
a candle in a s. place. Luke 11:33

secretly

thou flee away s.? Gen 31:27
if thy brother entice thee s. Deut 13:6
smiteth his neighbour s. 27:24
for want of all things s. 28:57
sent two men to spy s. Josh 2:1
commune with David s. and say. 1 Sam 18:22
David knew that Saul s. 23:9
for thou didst it s. 2 Sam 12:12
did s. those things that. 2 Ki 17:9
now a thing was s. Job 4:12
will reprove you, if you s. 13:10
hath been s. enticed. 31:27
he lieth in wait s. as. Ps 10:9*
keep them s. in a pavilion. 31:20
Zedekiah asked s. Is? Jer 37:17
Zedekiah the king sware s. 38:16
to Gedaliah in Mizpah s. 40:15
was to devour the poor s. Hab 3:14
went and called Mary her sister s. John 11:28
Joseph was a disciple, but s. 19:38

secrets

shew thee the s. of. Job 11:6
for he knoweth the s. of. Ps 44:21
a talebearer revealeth s. Pr 11:13
talebearer, revealeth s. 20:19
God that revealeth s. Dan 2:28
he that revealeth s. maketh. 29
God is the revealer of s. 47
God shall judge the s. Rom 2:16
thus are the s. of his. 1 Cor 14:25

secrets

taketh him by the s. Deut 25:11

sect

This word is generally used to mean a party in religion, differing in belief from the main body. In our old version it is frequently translated heresy, *which the Revisions change to* sect. *There were several sects among the Jews in the time of Christ, the chief being:* [1] the Pharisees *or* formalists; [2] the Sadducees *or* materialists; *and* [3] the Essenes, *a sort of monastic body. Other divisions, as the Herodians and Zealots, were mainly political.*

The religion preached by Christ and his disciples was frequently called a sect, *for it was quite a number of years before it was extended to the Gentiles, and the Jews who embraced it were faithful to the major part of their ancestral faith.*

which is the s. of the. Acts 5:17
the s. of the Pharisees. 15:5
a ringleader of the s. of the. 24:5
straitest s. of our religion. 26:5
this s. is every where spoken. 28:22

secure

the host, for it was s. Judg 8:11
manner of the Zidonians, s. 18:7
shall come to a people s. 10, 27
thou shalt be s. because. Job 11:18
they that provoke God are s. 12:6
will persuade him, and s. you. Mat 28:14*

securely

seeing he dwelleth, s. by. Pr 3:29
them that pass by s. Mi 2:8

security

when they had taken s. Acts 17:9

sedition

that they moved s. Ezra 4:15, 19
for a certain s. cast into prison. Luke 23:19*, 25*
this man a mover of s. Acts 24:5*

seditions

works of the flesh are s. Gal 5:20*

seduce

signs and wonders to s. Mark 13:22
written concerning them that s. you. 1 John 2:26*
sufferest Jezebel to s. Rev 2:20

seduced

Manasseh s. them to. 2 Ki 21:9
they have also s. Egypt. Isa 19:13*
have also s. my people. Ezek 13:10

seducers

but s. shall wax worse. 2 Tim 3:13*

seduceth

the wicked s. them. Pr 12:26*

seducing

faith, giving heed to s. 1 Tim 4:1

see

unto Adam, to s. what he. Gen 2:19
he sent a dove to s. if the. 8:8
and the Lord came down to s. 11:5
he said unto him, S. I have. 19:21
s. the smell of my son is as. 27:27
he said, I s. your father's. 31:5
Dinah went out to s. the. 34:1
but to s. the nakedness. 42:9, 12
thou saidst, You shall s. 44:23
your eyes s. and the eyes of. 45:12
he said, S. that ye fall not out. 24
s. Joseph before I die. 28
I had not thought to s. thy. 48:11
when ye s. them upon the stools. Ex 1:16
I will turn aside and s. this. 3:3, 4
s. whether my brethren be. 4:18
s. that thou do those wonders. 21
the officers did s. they were. 5:19
now shalt thou s. what I will. 6:1
that one cannot be able to s. 10:5
take heed to thyself, s. my face. 28
I will s. thy face no more. 29
when I s. the blood, I will. 12:13
repent when they s. war. 13:17
stand still and s. the. 14:13
s. for the Lord hath given. 16:29
they may s. the bread. 32
for there shall no man s. 33:20
and thou shalt s. my back parts. 23
the people shall s. the work. 34:10
priest shall s. him. Lev 13:10, 17
s. her nakedness and she s. 20:17
shall not go in to s. Num 4:20
shalt s. whether my word. 11:23
s. the land, what it is. 13:18
that provoked me s. it. 14:23
that thence he might s. the. 22:41
top of the rocks I s. him. 23:9
come to another place, whence thou mayest s. them, thou shalt s. 13
I shall s. him, but not now. 24:17
and s. the land, which I. 27:12
from Kadesh to s. land. 32:8
men that came up out of Egypt shall s. the land. 32:11; Deut 1:35
save Caleb, he shall s. Deut 1:36
I pray thee, let me s. the. 3:25
the land which thou shalt s. 28
that he s. no unclean thing. 23:14
all people shall s. that thou. 28:10
eyes which thou shalt s. 34, 67
thou shalt s. it no more again. 68
not given you eyes to s. 29:4
when they s. the plagues of. 22
s. I have set before thee life. 30:15
he said, I will s. what their. 32:20
s. now, I, even I, am he, there. 39
yet thou shalt s. land before. 52

I have caused thee to *s.* *Deut* 34:4
there a great altar to *s.* *Josh* 22:10
Samson turned aside to *s.* *Judg* 14:8
s. wherein his great strength. 16:5
shall *s.* an enemy in. *1 Sam* 2:32
ark, and rejoiced to *s.* it. 6:13
now *s.* this great thing. 12:16
ye may *s.* that your wickedness. 17
number now, and *s.* who. 14:17
and *s.* wherein this sin hath. 38
Samuel came no more to *s.* 15:35
thou mightest *s.* the battle. 17:28
and what I *s.* that I will tell. 19:3
messengers again to *s.* David. 15
me get away, I pray, and *s.* 20:29
Ye *s.* the man is mad. 21:14
know and *s.* his place, where. 23:22
my father *s.* yea, *s.* the skirt. 24:11
s. where king's spear is. 26:16
when thy father cometh to *s.* thee, let Tamar . . . may *s.* it. *2 Sam* 13:5
now therefore, let me *s.* the. 14:32
S. thy matters are good and. 15:3
my lord the king may *s.* it. 24:3
s. what answer I shall return. 13
s. to thy house, David. *1 Ki* 12:16
2 Chr 10:16
Elijah said, *S.* thy son liveth. *1 Ki* 17:23
and *s.* how this man seeketh. 20:7
mark and *s.* what thou doest, 22
thou shalt *s.* in that day. 22:25
2 Chr 18:24
if thou *s.* when I am. *2 Ki* 2:10
s. how he seeketh a. 5:7
open his eyes that he may *s.* 6:17
these men that they may *s.* 20
s. how this son of a murderer. 32
shalt *s.* it with thine eyes. 7:2, 19
let us send and *s.* 13
saying, Go and *s.* 14
went down to *s.* Joram. 8:29
9:16; *2 Chr* 22:6
the watchman said, I *s.* a. *2 Ki* 9:17
go *s.* now this cursed woman. 34
come with me, and *s.* my. 10:16
thine eyes, and *s.* 19:16; *Isa* 37:17
title is this that I *s.*? *2 Ki* 23:17
he said, I did *s.* all Israel.
2 Chr 18:16
s. the salvation of the Lord. 20:17
go, and *s.* that ye hasten the. 24:5
come, let us *s.* one another. 25:17
was not meet to *s.* the. *Ezra* 4:14
didst *s.* affliction of our. *Neh* 9:9
to *s.* if Mordecai's. *Esth* 3:4
so long as I *s.* Mordecai the. 5:13
endure to *s.* the evil that shall come upon my people ? to *s.* the. 8:6
neither let it *s.* the dawning. *Job* 3:9
mine eye shall no more *s.* 7:7
the eye that hath seen me shall *s.* 8
my days flee away, they *s.* no. 9:25
s. thou mine affliction. 10:15
as for my hope, who shall *s.*? 17:15
yet in my flesh shall I *s.* God. 19:26
whom I shall *s.* for myself. 27
the eye which saw him shall *s.* 20:9
eyes shall *s.* his destruction. 21:20
righteous *s.* it, and are glad. 22:19
know him not *s.* his days ? 24:1
saith, No eye shall *s.* me. 15
did he *s.* it, and declare it. 28:27
doth not he *s.* my ways ? 31:4
shall pray, and he will *s.* his. 33:26
his life shall *s.* the light. 28
look unto the heavens, and *s.* 35:5
every man may *s.* it. 36:25
God will never *s.* it. *Ps* 10:11
God looked to *s.* if any. 14:2; 53:2
Holy One to *s.* corruption. 16:10
Acts 2:27, 31; 13:35
all they that *s.* laughed me. *Ps* 22:7
believed to *s.* the goodness. 27:13
they that did *s.* me without. 31:11
O taste and *s.* that the Lord. 34:8
days, that he may *s.* good. 12
are cut off, thou shalt *s.* it. 37:34
many shall *s.* it and trust in. 40:3
if he come to *s.* me, he. 41:6
he shall go, they shall never *s.* 49:19
the righteous also shall *s.* and. 52:6
God shall let me *s.* my desire on my. 59:10; 92:11; 118:7

to *s.* thy power and glory. *Ps* 63:2
say, Who shall *s.* them ? 64:5
all that *s.* them shall flee away. 8
come and *s.* the works of God. 66:5
the humble shall *s.* this, and. 69:32
which hate me may *s.* it. 86:17
thou shalt *s.* the reward of. 91:8
and all the people *s.* his glory. 97:6
that I may *s.* the good of. 106:5
these *s.* the works of the. 107:24
righteous shall *s.* it and rejoice. 42
till he *s.* his desire upon his. 112:8
the wicked shall *s.* it and be. 10
glad when they *s.* me. 119:74
thou shalt *s.* the good of. 128:5
thou shalt *s.* thy children's. 6
thy eyes did *s.* my substance. 139:16
search, *s.* if there be any. 24
lest the Lord *s.* and. *Pr* 24:18
but the righteous shall *s.* 29:16
whereof it may be said, *S.* *Eccl* 1:10
till I might *s.* what was good. 2:3
men might *s.* that themselves. 3:18
bring him to *s.* what shall be. 22
there is profit to them that *s.* 7:11
to *s.* the business that is done. 8:16
O my dove, let me *s.* *S of S* 2:14
I went into the garden of nuts to *s.* the fruits, and to *s.* 6:11; 7:12
his work, that we may *s.* *Isa* 5:19
lest they *s.* with their eyes. 6:10
that *s.* thee shall narrowly. 14:16
they shall *s.* and be ashamed. 26:11
eyes of the blind shall *s.* out. 29:18
eyes shall *s.* thy teachers. 30:20
the eyes of them that *s.* shall. 32:3
thine eyes shall *s.* the king. 33:17
thine eyes shall *s.* Jerusalem. 20
they shall *s.* the glory of the. 35:2
and all flesh shall *s.* it together. 40:5
that they may *s.* and know. 41:20
s. all this. 48:6
kings shall *s.* and arise. 49:7
for they shall *s.* eye to eye. 52:8
the earth shall *s.* salvation of our. 10
been told them shall they *s.* 15
when we shall *s.* him, there is. 53:2
he shall *s.* his seed, he shall. 10
he shall *s.* of travail of his soul. 11
then thou shalt *s.*, and flow. 60:5
all that *s.* them shall. 61:9
the Gentiles shall *s.* thy. 62:2
behold, *s.* we beseech, we are. 64:9
and they shall come and *s.* 66:18
I *s.* a rod. *Jer* 1:11
s. a seething pot. 13
send to Kedar, *s.* if there be. 2:10
know and *s.* that it is an evil. 19
s. thy way in the valley, know. 23
and *s.* where thou hast not. 3:2
how long shall I *s.* the ? 4:21
s. now and know, and seek. 5:1
stand ye in the ways and *s.* 6:16
go to my place, and *s.* what. 7:12
me *s.* thy vengeance. 11:20; 20:12
out of the womb to *s.* labour. 20:18
he shall die and *s.* this land. 22:12
s. whether man doth travail ? why do I *s.* every man with his ? 30:6
and shalt *s.* and shalt read. 51:61
s. O Lord, consider, for. *Lam* 1:11
s. if there be any sorrow like. 12
thou shalt *s.* greater abominations. *Ezek* 8:6, 13, 15
that *s.* vanity. 13:9
s. visions of peace for her. 16
may *s.* all thy nakedness. 16:37
all flesh shall *s.* that I. 20:48
whiles they *s.* vanity unto. 21:29
Pharaoh shall *s.* them. 32:31
the watchman *s.* the sword. 33:6
all the heathen shall *s.* my. 39:21
why should he *s.* your ? *Dan* 1:10
I *s.* four men loose, walking. 3:25
dream dreams, your young men shall *s.* visions. *Joel* 2:23; *Acts* 2:17
Calneh and *s.*, go ye to. *Amos* 6:2
might *s.* what would. *Jonah* 4:5
the man of wisdom shall *s.* *Mi* 6:9
mine enemy shall *s.* it. 7:10
the nations shall *s.* and be. 16
I will watch to *s.* what he. *Hab* 2:1
to *s.* what is the breadth. *Zech* 2:2
shall *s.* the plummet in hand. 4:10

I *s.* a flying roll. *Zech* 5:2
lift your eyes, *s.* what is this that. 5
s. it, and fear, Geza shall *s.* it. 9:5
yea, their children shall *s.* it. 10:7
and your eyes shall *s.* *Mal* 1:5
for they shall *s.* God. *Mat* 5:8
they may *s.* your good works. 16
and then shalt thou *s.* clearly. 7:5
Luke 6:42
s. thou tell no man, shew *Mat* 8:4
9:30; *Mark* 1:44; *Acts* 23:22
things you hear and *s.* *Mat* 11:4
out into wilderness to *s.*? a reed shaken. 7, 8, 9, *Luke* 7:24, 25, 26
Master, we would *s.* a sign from. *Mat* 12:38
seeing, ye shall *s.* 13:14; *Mark* 4:12
Acts 28:26
any time they should *s.* with their eyes. *Mat* 13:15; *Acts* 28:27
your eyes, for they *s.* *Mat* 13:16
to *s.* those things which ye *s.* 17
the blind to *s.* 15:31; *Luke* 7:22
they *s.* the Son of man. *Mat* 16:28
when the king came in to *s.* 22:11
shall hear of wars, *s.* that ye. 24:6
they shall *s.* the Son of man coming. 30; *Mark* 13:26; *Luke* 21:27
Peter sat with the servants, to *s.* the end. *Mat* 26:58
they said, *S.* thou to that. 27:4
s. ye to it. 24
let us *s.* whether Elias will. 49
come *s.* the place where the. 28:6
there shall they *s.* me. 10
they went out to *s.* what. *Mark* 5:14
he looked to *s.* her that had. 32
go and *s.* 6:38
I *s.* men as trees walking. 8:24
that we may *s.* and believe. 15:32
Bethlehem and *s.* this. *Luke* 2:15
flesh shall *s.* the salvation. 3:6
enter in may *s.* light. 8:16; 11:33
desiring to *s.* thee. 8:20
he desired to *s.* him. 9:9; 23:8
not taste of death till they *s.* 27
ground, I must go and *s.* it. 14:18
when ye shall desire to *s.* 17:22
s. here, or *s.* there, go not. 23
Zacchaeus sought to *s.* Jesus. 19:3
sycamore tree to *s.* him. 4
him when they *s.* him. 20:13
myself, handle me and *s.* 24:39
on whom thou shalt *s.* the Spirit. *John* 1:33
come and *s.* 39, 46; 11:34; *Rev* 6:1
3, 5, 7
shalt *s.* greater things. *John* 1:50
s. a man who told me all. 4:29
shall never *s.* death. 8:51
rejoiced to *s.* my day. 56
I washed, and do *s.* 9:15
how then doth he now *s.*? 19
I was blind, now I *s.* 25
that they who *s.* not might *s.* and that they who *s.* might be. 39
if believe, thou shouldest *s.* 11:40
but that they might *s.* Lazarus. 12:9
Sir, we would *s.* Jesus. 21
ye have sorrow, but I will *s.* 16:22
except I *s.* in his hands. 20:25
and *s.* how they do. *Acts* 15:36
I must also *s.* Rome. 19:21
ye all shall *s.* my face. 20:25, 38
know his will, and *s.* that. 22:14
I called you, to *s.* you. 28:20
for I long to *s.* you. *Rom* 1:11
I *s.* another law in my. 7:23
spoken of, they shall *s.* 15:21
to *s.* you in my journey. 24
if any man *s.* thee that. *1 Cor* 8:10
s. that he may be with you. 16:10
s. that ye abound in. *2 Cor* 8:7
Jerusalem to *s.* Peter. *Gal* 1:18
make all men *s.* what is. *Eph* 3:9
s. that ye walk circumspectly. 5:15
the wife *s.* that she reverence. 33
whether I come and *s.* *Phil* 1:27
so soon as I *s.* how it will go. 2:23
to *s.* your face with. *1 Thes* 2:17
to *s.* us, as we also to *s.* you. 3:6
s. that none render evil for. 5:15
hath seen, nor can *s.* *1 Tim* 6:16
greatly desiring to *s.* *2 Tim* 1:4

s. thou make all according. *Heb* 8:5
no man *s.* the Lord. 12:14
s. that ye refuse not him that. 25
he come shortly, I will *s.* you. 13:23
s. that ye love one. *1 Pet* 1:22
he that will *s.* good days. 3:10
if any man *s.* his brother sin a sin not unto death. *1 John* 5:16
I shall shortly *s.* thee. *3 John* 14
every eye shall *s.* him. *Rev* 1:7
to *s.* the voice that spake. 12
eyesalve, that thou mayst *s.* 3:18
and *s.* thou hurt not the oil. 6:6
shall *s.* their dead bodies. 11:9
lest he walk naked, and they *s.* 16:15
I sit a queen, shall *s.* no sorrow. 18:7
when they shall *s.* the smoke. 9
he said to me, *S.* thou. 19:10; 22:9
and they shall *s.* his face. 22:4

see *not*, or *not* **see**

let me *not s.* the death. *Gen* 21:16
old, that he could *not s.* 27:1
ye shall *not s.* my face. 43:3, 5
for we may *not s.* the man's. 44:26
were dim, he could *not s.* 48:10
thou canst *not s.* my face. *Ex* 33:20
let me *not s.* my wretchedness. *Num* 11:15
they shall *not s.* the land. 14:23
utmost part, and shall *not s.* 23:13
thou shalt *not s.* thy. *Deut* 22:1
shalt *not s.* thy brother's ass. 4
Eli, his eyes dim, he could *not s.* *1 Sam* 3:2; 4:15
not s. my face, except. *2 Sam* 3:13
let *not* Absalom *s.* my face. 14:24
Ahijah could *not s.* *1 Ki* 14:4
not s. wind, nor shall ye *s.* *2 Ki* 3:17
thine eyes shall *not s.* all evil. 22:20
by me, and I *s.* him *not*. *Job* 9:11
he shall *not s.* the rivers of. 20:17
that thou canst *not s.* 22:11
himself that I *cannot s.* him. 23:9
that which I *s. not* teach. 34:32
sayest, thou shalt *not s.* him. 35:14
men *s. not* the bright light. 37:21
should still live, and *not s.* *Ps* 49:9
pass away, that they may *not s.* the sun. 58:8
be darkened, that they *s. not*. 69:23
we *s. not* our signs, there. 74:9
and shall *not s.* death. 89:48
the Lord shall *not s.* 94:7
the eye, shall he *not s.*? 9
eyes have they, but they *s. not*. 115:5; 135:16; *Jer* 5:21
is lifted up, they will *not s.* *Isa* 26:11
say to the seers, *S. not*. 30:10
thou shalt *not s.* a fierce. 33:19
I shall *not s.* the Lord, even. 38:11
they *s. not*, that they may be. 44:9
eyes, that they *cannot s.* 18
they said, He shall *not s.* *Jer* 12:4
prophets say, Ye shall *not s.* 14:13
like heath, he shall *not s.* 17:6
he shall *not s.* when heat. 8
that I shall *not s.* him? 23:24
cover thy face, that thou *s. not* the ground. *Ezek* 12:6, 12
yet shall he *not s.* it, though he. 13
gods of gold, which *s. not*. *Dan* 5:23
thou shalt *not s.* evil. *Zeph* 3:15
because they seeing *s. not*; and hearing they hear not. *Mat* 13:13
ye shall *not s.* me henceforth. 23:39 *Luke* 13:35
Jesus said, *S.* ye *not* all? *Mat* 24:2
having eyes *s.* ye *not*? *Mark* 8:18
not s. death, before. *Luke* 2:20
seeing, they might *not s.* 8:10
to *s.* and ye shall *not s.* it. 17:22
cannot s. the kingdom. *John* 3:3
shall *not s.* life, but wrath. 36
they who *s. not* might see. 9:39
that they should *not s.* with. 12:40
shall *not s.* me. 16:16, 17, 19
I *not s.* thee in the garden? 18:26
when I could *not s.* for. *Acts* 22:11
that they should *not s.* *Rom* 11:8
darkened that they may *not s.* 10
for I will *not s.* you. *1 Cor* 16:7
but we *s. not* yet all things. *Heb* 2:8
he should *not s.* death. 11:5

now ye *s.* him *not*, yet. *1 Pet* 1:8
he is blind, and *cannot s.* *2 Pet* 1:9

we **see**

we shall *s.* what will. *Gen* 37:20
light shall *we s.* light. *Ps* 36:9
neither shall *we s.* sword. *Jer* 5:12
where *we* shall *s.* no war. 42:14
that *we* may *s.* and believe. *Mark* 15:32; *John* 6:30
now ye say, *We s.* your. *John* 9:41
for that *we s.* not. *Rom* 8:25
now *we s.* through a. *1 Cor* 13:12
we might *s.* your face. *1 Thes* 3:10
but *we s.* Jesus, who was. *Heb* 2:9
so *we s.* that they could not. 3:19
for *we* shall *s.* him as. *1 John* 3:2

ye **see**, or **see** *ye*

ye shall *s.* them again. *Ex* 14:13
then *ye* shall *s.* the glory of. 16:7
when *ye s.* the ark of. *Josh* 3:3
s. ye him whom the? *1 Sam* 10:24
to hissing, as *ye s.* *2 Chr* 29:8
to desolation, as *ye s.* 30:7
I said, *Ye s.* the distress. *Neh* 2:17
ye s. my casting down. *Job* 6:21
what will *ye s.* in the? *S of S* 6:13
and *s. ye* indeed, but. *Isa* 6:9
s. ye, when he lifteth up an. 18:3
ye blind, that *ye* may *s.* 42:18
when *ye s.* your hearts shall. 66:14
O generation, *s. ye* the word of the. *Jer* 2:31
ye shall *s.* this place no more. 42:18
therefore *ye* shall *s.* no. *Ezek* 13:23
ye shall *s.* their way and. 14:22
they shall comfort you when *ye s.* 23
because *ye s.* the thing. *Dan* 2:8
to *s.* those things which *ye s.* and. *Mat* 13:17; *Luke* 10:23
Jesus said *S. ye* not all? *Mat* 24:2
when *ye* shall *s.* all these. 33 *Mark* 13:29; *Luke* 21:31
hereafter shall *ye s.* the Son of. *Mat* 26:64; *Mark* 14:62
I am innocent, *s. ye* to it. *Mat* 27:24; *Mark* 15:36
into Galilee; there shall *ye s.* him *Mat* 28:7; *Mark* 16:7
when *ye s.* a cloud rise. *Luke* 12:54
and when *ye s.* the south wind. 55
when *ye* shall *s.* Abraham. 13:28
when *ye* shall *s.* Jerusalem. 21:20
ye s. and know of yourselves. 30
and bones, as *ye s.* me. 24:39
ye shall *s.* heaven open. *John* 1:51
except *ye s.* signs ye will not. 4:48
what if *ye* shall *s.* the Son of. 6:62
but *ye s.* me. 14:19
and *ye s.* me no more. 16:10
while *ye* shall *s.* me. 16, 17, 19
shed this which *ye* now *s.* *Acts* 2:33
whom *ye s.* and know. 3:16
ye s. and hear, that not alone. 19:26
ye s. this man, about whom. 25:24
for *ye s.* your calling. *1 Cor* 1:26
ye s. how large a letter. *Gal* 6:11
when *ye s.* him again. *Phil* 2:28
much more, as *ye s.* day. *Heb* 10:25
ye s. how that by works. *Jas* 2:24
though now *ye s.* him not. *1 Pet* 1:8

seed

[1] *The seed of plants.* [2] *The posterity of any particular man, as the* seed of Abraham, *referring to all his descendants.*

herbs yielding *s.* *Gen* 1:11, 12, 29
give us *s.* that we may live. 47:19
lo, here is *s.* for you. 23
shall be your own for *s.* 24
was like coriander *s.* *Ex* 16:31
fall on any sowing *s.* *Lev* 11:37
water be put upon the *s.* 38
sow thy field with mingled *s.* 19:19
shall sow your *s.* in vain. 26:16
according to the *s.* an homer of barley *s.* valued at 50. 27:16
s. of the land is the Lord's. 30
it is no place of *s.* or of figs. *Num* 20:5
where thou sowedst *s.* *Deut* 11:10
all the increase of thy *s.* 14:22
thy *s.* sown be defiled *s.* 22:9*
thou shalt carry much *s.* into. 28:38

the king will take the tenth of *s.* *1 Sam* 8:15
two measures of *s.* *1 Ki* 18:32
unicorn bring home thy *s.*? *Job* 39:12
forth bearing precious *s.* *Ps* 126:6
in the morning sow thy *s.* *Eccl* 11:6
the *s.* of an homer shall. *Isa* 5:10
in the morning make thy *s.* 17:11
great waters the *s.* of Sihor. 23:3
that it may give *s.* to the. 55:10
nor shall sow *s.* nor plant. *Jer* 35:7
have we vineyard, field, nor *s.* 9
he took also of the *s.* *Ezek* 17:5
the *s.* is rotten under. *Joel* 1:17
him that soweth *s.* *Amos* 9:13
is the *s.* yet in the barn? *Hag* 2:19
s. shall be prosperous. *Zech* 8:12
I will corrupt your *s.* *Mal* 2:3
which receive *s.* by the. *Mat* 13:19
s. into stony places. 20
s. among the thorns. 22
but he that received *s.* into good. 23
a man which sowed good *s.* 24
didst not thou sow good *s.*? 27
he that soweth the good *s.* is. 37
the good *s.* are the children of. 38
if a man should cast *s.* *Mark* 4:26
and the *s.* should spring and. 27
to sow his *s.*: some fell by. *Luke* 8:5
parable is this; the *s.* is word. 11
every *s.* his own body. *1 Cor* 15:38
that ministereth *s.* to. *2 Cor* 9:10
not of corruptible *s.* *1 Pet* 1:23
for his *s.* remaineth in. *1 John* 3:9

seed for *posterity*

appointed me another *s.* *Gen* 4:25
to keep *s.* alive upon the face. 7:3
to me thou hast given no *s.* 15:3
preserve *s.* of our father. 19:32, 34
marry her, and raise up *s.* to. 38:8 *Mat* 22:24; *Mark* 12:19 *Luke* 20:28
Onan knew that the *s.* *Gen* 38:9
conceived *s.* and born. *Lev* 12:2
hath a blemish of the *s.* 21:21
what man of the *s.* of Aaron. 22:4
woman shall conceive *s.* *Num* 5:28
which is not of *s.* of Aaron. 16:40
their *s.* after them. *Deut* 1:8; 11:9
he chose their *s.* after them. 4:37 10:15
the mouths of their *s.* 31:21
s. the Lord shall give. *Ruth* 4:12
the Lord give thee *s.* *1 Sam* 2:20
thou wilt not cut off my *s.* 24:21
king's *s.* in Edom. *1 Ki* 11:14
will for this afflict the *s.* of David. 39
of Ahaziah, arose and destroyed all the *s.* *2 Ki* 11:1; *2 Chr* 22:10
the Lord rejected all the *s.* of. *2 Ki* 17:20
Ishmael of the *s.* royal came. 25:25 *Jer* 41:1
O ye *s.* of Israel his. *1 Chr* 16:13
they could not shew their *s.* *Ezra* 2:59; *Neh* 7:61
the holy *s.* have mingled. *Ezra* 9:2
the *s.* of Israel separated. *Neh* 9:2
if Mordecai be of the *s.* *Esth* 6:13
took upon them and their *s.* 9:27, 31
of them perish from their *s.* 28
their *s.* is established in. *Job* 21:8
their *s.* shalt thou destroy. *Ps* 21:10
ye the *s.* of Jacob, glorify him; and fear him, all ye the *s.* of. 22:23
a *s.* shall serve him, it shall be. 30
but the *s.* of the wicked shall. 37:28
the *s.* also of his servants. 69:36
their *s.* shall be established. 102:28
to overthrow their *s.* 106:27
the *s.* of righteous shall. *Pr* 11:21
ah, sinful nation, a *s.* of. *Isa* 1:4
the holy *s.* shall be the. 6:13
the *s.* of evildoers shall. 14:20
I said not unto *s.* of Jacob. 45:19
in the Lord shall all *s.* of Israel. 25
the *s.* of the adulterer and. 57:3
of transgression, a *s.* of falsehood. 4
their *s.* shall be known among the Gentiles; that they are *s.* 61:9
bring forth a *s.* out of Jacob. 65:9
they are the *s.* of the blessed. 23
thee wholly a right *s.* *Jer* 2:21

I will cast out the whole *s.* of. *Jer* 7:15
which led the *s.* of the house. 23:8
sow with *s.* of man and *s.* of. 31:27
then *s.* of Israel also shall cease. 36
off all the *s.* of Israel. 37; 33:26
so will I multiply the *s.* of. 33:22
taken of the king's *s.* *Ezek* 17:13
I lifted up my hand to the *s.* 20:5
that be of the *s.* of Zadok. 43:19
maidens of the *s.* of Israel. 44:22
children of the king's *s.* *Dan* 1:3
themselves with the *s.* of. 2:43
Darius of the *s.* of the Medes. 9:1
might seek a godly *s.* *Mal* 2:15
dying left no *s.* *Mark* 12:20, 21, 22
that Christ cometh of *s.* *John* 7:42
this man's *s.* hath God. *Acts* 13:23
was made of the *s.* of David.
Rom 1:3; *2 Tim* 2:8
be sure to all his *s.* *Rom* 4:16
the promise counted for *s.* 9:8
of sabaoth had left us a *s.* 29
it was added, till the *s.* *Gal* 3:19
strength to conceive *s.* *Heb* 11:11
the remnant of her *s.* *Rev* 12:17
see **Abraham**

his **seed**

with Isaac and *his s.* *Gen* 17:19
Jacob came, and all *his s.* 46:6, 7
and *his s.* shall become a. 48:19
a statute of *his s.* after him.
Ex 28:43; 30:21
giveth any of *his s.* to Molech.
Lev 20:2, 3, 4
nor shall ye profane *his s.* 21:15
servant Caleb and *his s.* *Num* 14:24
and *his s.* shall be in many. 24:7
he shall have it, and *his s.* 25:13
I multiplied *his s.* and. *Josh* 24:3
thee of Saul and *his s.* *2 Sam* 4:8
to David and *his s.* for evermore.
2 Sam 22:51; *Ps* 18:50
on head of Joab and *his s.* for ever, upon David and *his s.* *1 Ki* 2:33
covenant to give it to *his s.* *Neh* 9:8
peace to all *his s.* *Esth* 10:3
his s. shall inherit the. *Ps* 25:13
nor have I seen *his s.* begging. 37:25
he is merciful, and *his s.* is. 26
his s. also will I make to endure.
89:29, 36
his s. shall be mighty. 112:2
he shall see *his s.* *Isa* 53:10
cast out, he and *his s.*? *Jer* 22:28
for no man of *his s.* shall prosper. 30
punish Shemaiah and *his s.* 29:32
I will not take any of *his s.* 33:26
Jehoiachim and *his s.* 36:31
Esau, *his s.* is spoiled. 49:10
him and *his s.* after him. *Acts* 7:5
that *his s.* should sojourn in a. 6

thy **seed**

between *thy s.* and her *s.* *Gen* 3:15
to *thy s.* will I give this land. 12:7
13:15; 15:18; 17:8; 24:7; 26:3
28:4, 13; 35:12; 48:4; *Ex* 33:1
Deut 34:4
I will make *thy s.* as dust.
Gen 13:16; 16:10; 28:14
he said to him, So shall *thy s.* be.
15:5; *Rom* 4:18
that *thy s.* shall be a stranger in a.
Gen 15:13
between me and *thy s.* after thee; . . . to thee and *thy s.* 17:7, 10
thou and *thy s.* after thee in. 9
a stranger not of *thy s.* shall. 12
in Isaac shall *thy s.* be called. 21:12
Heb 11:18
Ishmael a nation, because he is *thy s.*
Gen 21:13
thy s. possess the gate of enemies.
22:17; 24:60
in *thy s.* all the nations of the. 22:18
26:4; 28:14; *Acts* 3:25
and multiply *thy s.* for. *Gen* 26:24
will make *thy s.* as the sand. 32:12
shewed me also *thy s.* 48:11
not any of *thy s.* pass. *Lev* 18:21
whosoever of *thy s.* hath any. 21:17
I give thee and *thy s.* *Num* 18:19
sign on *thy s.* for ever. *Deut* 28:46
Lord will make plagues of *thy s.* 59
circumcise heart of *thy s.* *Deut* 30:6
choose life, that thou and *thy s.* 19
be between my *s.* and *thy s.*
1 Sam 20:42
I will set up *thy s.* *2 Sam* 7:12
1 Chr 17:11
cleave to thee and *thy s.* *2 Ki* 5:27
thy s. shall be great. *Job* 5:25
thy s. will I establish. *Ps* 89:4
I will bring *thy s.* from. *Isa* 43:5
I will pour my spirit upon *thy s.*
44:3
thy s. also had been as the. 48:19
and *thy s.* shall inherit the. 54:3
depart out of the mouth of *thy s.* nor *thy* seed's *s.* 59:21
thy s. from the land of captivity.
Jer 30:10; 46:27
thy s. which is Christ. *Gal* 3:16

your **seed**

will I give to *your s.* *Ex* 32:13
whosoever of *your s.* goeth. *Lev* 22:3
so shall *your s.* and your. *Isa* 66:22

seeds

vineyard with divers *s.* *Deut* 22:9
when he sowed, some *s.* *Mat* 13:4
which is the least of all *s.* 32
Mark 4:31
he saith not, and to *s.* as. *Gal* 3:16

seedtime

s. and harvest shall not. *Gen* 8:22

seeing, *substantive*

or who maketh the *s.*? *Ex* 4:11

seeing

driven away, no man *s.* *Ex* 22:10
s. him not, cast it upon him, that he die. *Num* 35:23
mine eyes even *s.* it. *1 Ki* 1:48
maketh the *s.* eye. *Pr* 20:12
eye is not satified with *s.* *Eccl* 1:8
dismayed at the *s.* of it. *Isa* 21:3
shutteth his eyes from *s.* evil. 33:15
s. many things, but thou. 42:20
s. vanity, and divining. *Ezek* 22:28
because they *s.* see not. *Mat* 13:13
s. ye shall see and shall not perceive. 14; *Mark* 4:12; *Acts* 28:26
washed and came *s.* *John* 9:7
he *s.* this, spake of the. *Acts* 2:31
s. Peter and John about to go. 3:3
s. one of them suffer wrong. 7:24
the people *s.* the miracles. 8:6
speechless, hearing a voice, but *s.* 9:7
be blind, not *s.* the sun for. 13:11
he endured as *s.* him. *Heb* 11:27
in *s.* and hearing, vexed. *2 Pet* 2:8

seeing, *adverb*

what wilt thou give me, *s.* *Gen* 15:2
s. thou hast not withheld. 22:12
s. the Lord hath prospered. 24:56
come ye to me, *s.* ye hate me? 26:27
s. his life is bound up in. 44:30
s. all the congregation. *Num* 16:3
my name, *s.* it is secret. *Judg* 13:18
s. I have a Levite. 17:13
s. women are destroyed out. 21:16
s. the Lord hath testified. *Ruth* 1:21
s. I have rejected him. *1 Sam* 16:1
s. the Lord is departed from. 28:16
s. there is no wrong in. *1 Chr* 12:17
s. the root of the matter. *Job* 19:28
s. he judgeth those that are. 21:22
s. times are not hidden from. 24:1
s. thou hatest instruction. *Ps* 50:17
s. he dwelleth securely. *Pr* 3:29
s. I have lost my. *Isa* 49:21
s. the Lord hath given. *Jer* 47:7
s. thou couldest reveal. *Dan* 2:47
s. I know not a man. *Luke* 1:34
s. thou art in the same condemnation. 23:40
s. he is Lord of heaven. *Acts* 17:24
s. he giveth to all life and. 25
s. it is one God who shall. *Rom* 3:30
s. then that we have. *2 Cor* 3:12
s. that ye have put off. *Col* 3:9
s. it remaineth some must. *Heb* 4:6
s. then that we have a great. 14
hard to be uttered, *s.* ye are dull.
5:11
s. they crucify the Son of God. 6:6
s. he ever liveth to make. 7:25
s. we are compassed about. *Heb* 12:
s. ye have purified your. *1 Pet* 1:2
s. ye look for such things, be diligen
2 Pet 3:1
s. ye know these things before. 1

seek

I *s.* my brethren, tell. *Gen* 37:1
that he may *s.* occasion. 43:1
and *s.* ye the priesthood also?
Num 16:1
Balaam went not to *s.* for. 24:
if thou *s.* him with all. *Deut* 4:2
to his habitation shall ye *s.* 12:
till thy brother *s.* after it. 22:
Saul his son, Go *s.* the asses.
1 Sam 9:
ye? he said, To *s.* the asses. 10:1
to *s.* out a cunning player. 16:1
Saul come to *s.* his life. 23:15, 2
24:2; 26:
they that *s.* evil to my Lord. 25:2
is risen to pursue and *s.* thy soul. 2
Israel is come out to *s.* a flea. 26:2
Saul shall despair to *s.* me. 27:
s. me a woman that hath a. 28:
came up to *s.* David. *2 Sam* 5:1
Shimei went to *s.* his. *1 Ki* 2:4
Lord hath not sent to *s.* the. 18:1
they *s.* my life to take. 19:10, 1
let them go and *s.* thy. *2 Ki* 2:1
to the man whom ye *s.* 6:1
s. the commandments. *1 Chr* 28:
if thou *s.* him, he. 9; *2 Chr* 15:
thine heart to *s.* God. *2 Chr* 19:
that prepareth his heart to *s.* 30:1
to *s.* his God, he did it with. 31:2
Josiah began to *s.* after the. 34:
build, for we *s.* your God. *Ezra* 4:
prepared his heart to *s.* the. 7:1
to *s.* him a right way for us. 8:2
them for good that *s.* him. 2
to *s.* the welfare of. *Neh* 2:1
I would *s.* unto God. *Job* 5:
shalt *s.* me in morning, but. 7:2
if thou wouldest *s.* unto God. 8:
his children shall *s.* to please. 20:1
will ye *s.* after leasing? *Ps* 4:
forsaken them that *s.* thee. 9:1
s. out his wickedness till thou. 10:1
any that did *s.* God. 14:2; 53:
of them that *s.* him. 24:
that will I *s.* after. 27:
s. ye my face, thy face, Lord, will I s
8
s. peace, and pursue it. 34:1
1 Pet 3:1
let them be put to shame that *s.*
Ps 35:4
s. my life, they that *s.* 38:1
confounded that *s.* after my soul.
40:14; 70:2
oppressors *s.* after my soul. 54:3
God, early will I *s.* thee. 63:1
those that *s.* my soul go into the. 9
let not those that *s.* thee be. 69:6
heart shall live that *s.* God. 32
let all those that *s.* thee rejoice. 70:4
dishonour that *s.* my hurt. 71:13
unto shame that *s.* my hurt. 24
that they may *s.* thy name. 83:16
the young lions *s.* their meat. 104:21
his children *s.* their bread. 109:10
blessed, that *s.* him with. 119:2
I will walk at liberty, for I *s.* 45
as a sheep, *s.* thy servant. 176
I will *s.* thy good. 122:9
they shall *s.* me, but. *Pr* 1:28
and those that *s.* me early. 8:17
and fro of them that *s.* death. 21:6
sorrow? they that tarry long at wine, they that go to *s.* 23:30
when I shall awake, I will *s.* it. 35
upright: the just *s.* his soul. 29:10
many *s.* the ruler's favour. 26
I gave my heart to *s.* *Eccl* 1:13
I applied mine heart to *s.* out. 7:25
though a man labour to *s.* it. 8:17
I will *s.* him whom my. *S of S* 3:2
thy beloved, that we may *s.* 6:1
learn to do well, *s.* *Isa* 1:17
s. unto them that have familiar spirits; should not a people *s.*? 8:19
to it shall the Gentiles *s.* 11:10

they shall *s.* to the charmers. *Isa* 19:3
my spirit within me will I *s.* 26:9
s. ye out of book of the Lord. 34:16
thou shalt *s.* them, and not. 41:12
when the needy *s.* water, and. 17
I said not to Jacob, *S.* ye. 45:19
yet they *s.* me daily, and. 58:2
that *s.* her, in her month. *Jer* 2:24
thou thy way to *s.* love ? 33
thee, they will *s.* thy life. 4:30
the men of Anathoth, that *s.* 11:21
to fall by them that *s.* 19:7; 21:7
they that *s.* their lives shall. 9
them that *s.* thy life. 22:25; 38:16
s. the peace of the city. 29:7
ye shall *s.* me, and find me. 13
them that *s.* their life. 34:20, 21
give Pharaoh into the hand of them that *s.* his life. 44:30
Egyptians to those that *s.* 46:26
them that *s.* their life. 49:37
all her people sigh, they *s.* *Lam* 1:11
they shall *s.* peace there. *Ezek* 7:25
then shall they *s.* a vision. 26
flock was scattered, none did *s.* 34:6
I will search my sheep, and *s.* 11
as a shepherd so will I *s.* out. 12
I will *s.* that which was lost. 16
I set my face unto God, to *s.* by prayer. *Dan* 9:3
he shall *s.* them, but not. *Hos* 2:7
saith the Lord, *S.* me. *Amos* 5:4
s. him that maketh the seven. 8
s. good and not evil, that ye. 14
to *s.* the word of the Lord. 8:12
shall I *s.* comforters for ? *Nah* 3:7
thou shalt be hid, thou shalt *s.* 11
s. ye the Lord, ye meek. *Zeph* 2:3
a shepherd shall not *s.* *Zech* 11:16
in that day I will *s.* to destroy. 12:9
they should *s.* the law at. *Mal* 2:7
that he might *s.* a godly seed. 15
Herod will *s.* young child. *Mat* 2:13
things do the Gentiles *s.* 6:32
s. ye first the kingdom of God. 33
Luke 12:31
s. and ye shall find, knock.
Mat 7:7; *Luke* 11:9
for I know that ye *s.* Jesus.
Mat 28:5; *Mark* 16:6
they said to him, All men *s.*
Mark 1:37
thy mother and thy brethren *s.* 3:32
generation *s.* after a sign. 8:12; 11:29
do the nations *s.* after. *Luke* 12:30
many, I say unto you, will *s.* 13:24
doth she not *s.* diligently till ? 15:8
whosoever shall *s.* to save. 17:33
the Son of man is come to *s.* 19:10
why *s.* ye the living among ? 24:5
unto them, What *s.* ye ? *John* 1:38
ye *s.* me, not because ye saw. 6:26
he whom they *s.* to kill ? 7:25
ye shall *s.* me, and shall not. 34, 36
ye shall *s.* me, and shall die. 8:21
but ye *s.* to kill me. 37, 40
ye shall *s.* me, and whither I. 13:33
unto them, Whom *s.* ye ? 18:4, 7
if ye *s.* me, let these go their way. 8
three men *s.* thee. *Acts* 10:19
I am he whom ye *s.* 21
to Tarsus, to *s.* Saul. 11:25
to them who *s.* for glory. *Rom* 2:7
and they *s.* my life. 11:3
and the Greeks *s.* *1 Cor* 1:22
let no man *s.* his own, but. 10:24
s. that ye may excel to. 14:12
since ye *s.* a proof of. *2 Cor* 13:3
do I persuade, or *s.* to ? *Gal* 1:10
if, while we *s.* to be justified. 2:17
for all *s.* their own. *Phil* 2:21
if ye be risen, *s.* those things. *Col* 3:1
of them that *s.* him. *Heb* 11:6
they declare plainly that they *s.* 14
no city, but we *s.* one to come. 13:14
in those days shall men *s.* *Rev* 9:6
see **face, Lord**

not **seek,** or **seek** *not*
the priest shall *not s.* *Lev* 13:36
neither s. after wizards. 19:31
that ye *s. not* after. *Num* 15:39
thou shalt *not s.* their peace.
Deut 23:6; *Ezra* 9:12
daughter, shall I *not s.*? *Ruth* 3:1
the wicked will *not s.* *Ps* 10:4
they *s. not* thy statutes. 119:155
lovers, they *s.* thee *not.* *Jer* 30:14
great things ? *s.* them *not.* 45:5
but *s. not* Beth-el. *Amos* 5:5
a shepherd shall *not s.* *Zech* 11:16
s. not what ye shall eat. *Luke* 12:29
because I *s. not* mine. *John* 5:30
s. not the honour that cometh. 44
I *s. not* mine own glory. 8:50
s. not to be loosed. Art thou loosed ? *s. not* a wife. *1 Cor* 7:27
for I *s. not* yours, but. *2 Cor* 12:14

seekest
him, what *s.* thou ? *Gen* 37:15
the man whom thou *s.* *Judg* 4:22
the man thou *s.* is as. *2 Sam* 17:3
thou *s.* to destroy a mother. 20:19
that thou *s.* to go to. *1 Ki* 11:22
if thou *s.* her as silver. *Pr* 2:4
s. thou great things ? seek. *Jer* 45:5
yet no man said, What *s.*? *John* 4:27
woman, whom *s.* thou ? 20:15

seeketh
Saul my father *s.* to. *1 Sam* 19:2
that he *s.* my life ? 20:1
that *s.* my life, *s.* thy life. 22:23
Saul *s.* to destroy the city. 23:10
saying, David *s.* thy hurt ? 24:9
who came forth of my bowels *s.* my life. *2 Sam* 16:11
and see how this man *s.* *1 Ki* 20:7
see how he *s.* a quarrel. *2 Ki* 5:7
thence she *s.* the prey. *Job* 39:29
watcheth righteous, and *s.* *Ps* 37:32
he that diligently *s.* good procureth favour, but he that *s.* *Pr* 11:27
a scorner *s.* wisdom and. 14:6
he that hath understanding *s.* 15:14
a transgression, *s.* love. 17:9
an evil man *s.* only rebellion. 11
he that exalteth his gate *s.* 19
having separated himself, *s.* 18:1
ear of the wise *s.* knowledge. 15
the virtuous woman *s.* wool. 31:13
which yet my soul *s.* but. *Eccl* 7:28
he *s.* unto him a cunning. *Isa* 40:20
any that *s.* the truth, I. *Jer* 5:1
Zion, whom no man *s.* after. 30:17
this man *s.* not the welfare. 38:4
the soul that *s.* him. *Lam* 3:25
him that *s.* unto him. *Ezek* 14:10
as a shepherd *s.* out his. 34:12
and he that *s.* findeth. *Mat* 7:8
Luke 11:10
an adulterous generation *s.* a sign.
Mat 12:39; 16:4
leaveth the 99, and *s.* that. 18:12
Father *s.* such to worship him.
John 4:23
doeth in secret, and *s.* to be. 7:4
s. his own glory; *s.* the glory. 18
is one that *s.* and judgeth. 8:50
there is none that *s.* *Rom* 3:11
not obtained that which he *s.* 11:7
charity *s.* not her own. *1 Cor* 13:5

seeking
Mordecai *s.* the wealth. *Esth* 10:3
s. judgement, and hasting. *Isa* 16:5
s. rest, and findeth none.
Mat 12:43; *Luke* 11:24
like to a merchantman *s.* goodly.
Mat 13:45
s. of him a sign from. *Mark* 8:11
to Jerusalem, *s.* him. *Luke* 2:45
s. something out of his mouth. 11:54
come *s.* fruit, and find none. 13:7
and came to Capernaum, *s.* for Jesus. *John* 6:24
s. to turn away the deputy from.
Acts 13:8
went about *s.* some to lead him. 11
not *s.* mine own profit. *1 Cor* 10:33
s. whom he may devour. *1 Pet* 5:8

seem
s. to him a deceiver. *Gen* 27:12
not *s.* hard, when. *Deut* 15:18
then thy brother should *s.* vile. 25:3
if it *s.* evil unto you to. *Josh* 24:15
let not all the trouble *s.* *Neh* 9:32
if the thing *s.* right. *Esth* 8:5
the chariot shall *s.* like. *Nah* 2:4*
but if any man *s.* to. *1 Cor* 11:16
those members which *s.* to be. 12:22
I may not *s.* as if I would terrify.
2 Cor 10:9
lest any of you should *s.* *Heb* 4:1
if any among you *s.* to be religious.
Jas 1:26*
see **good**

seemed
but he *s.* as one that. *Gen* 19:14
and they *s.* unto him but a. 29:20
this wisdom *s.* great unto. *Eccl* 9:13
given earth unto whom it *s.* meet.
Jer 27:5
their words *s.* to them. *Luke* 24:11*
but these who *s.* to be. *Gal* 2:6*
James, Cephas, and John, who *s.* 9*

seemeth
it *s.* there is a plague in. *Lev* 14:35
s. it but a small thing ? *Num* 16:9
s. it light to be a king's son in law ?
1 Sam 18:23
there is a way which *s.* right.
Pr 14:12; 16:25
in his own cause *s.* just. 18:17
s. it a small thing to ? *Ezek* 34:18
taken what he *s.* to. *Luke* 8:18*
he *s.* a setter forth of. *Acts* 17:18
it *s.* unreasonable to send. 25:27
if any *s.* wise, let him. *1 Cor* 3:18*
now no chastening *s.* to. *Heb* 12:11
see **good**

seemly
delight is not *s.* for a fool. *Pr* 19:10
honour is not *s.* for a fool. 26:1

seen
God hath *s.* mine affliction and.
Gen 31:42
fathers have not *s.* *Ex* 10:6
whether he hath *s.* or known.
Lev 5:1
those men which have *s.* *Num* 14:22
nor hath he *s.* perverseness. 23:21
thou hast *s.* it, thou shalt. 27:13
we have *s.* the sons of. *Deut* 1:28
thou hast *s.* how the Lord bare. 31
thine eyes have *s.* all the Lord. 3:21
s. what the Lord did because. 4:3
the things thine eyes have *s.* 9
we have *s.* that God doth talk. 5:24
things thine eyes have *s.* 10:21
have not *s.* the chastisement. 11:2
but your eyes have *s.* all the. 7
nor have our eyes *s.* it. 21:7
temptations thine eyes have *s.* 29:3
his mother, I have not *s.* him. 33:9
eyes have *s.* what I have. *Josh* 24:7
the elders who had *s.* the. *Judg* 2:7
because we have *s.* God. 13:22
we have *s.* the land, behold it is. 18:9
five lords had *s.* it. *1 Sam* 6:16
see his place, and who hath *s.* 23:22
day thine eyes have *s.* how. 24:10
king what thou hast *s.* *2 Sam* 18:21
queen of Sheba had *s.* *1 Ki* 10:4
mine eyes had *s.* 7; *2 Chr* 9:3, 6
had *s.* what way man. *1 Ki* 13:12
hast thou *s.* all this great ? 20:13
s.? Hezekiah said, All things in mine house . . . *s.* *2 Ki* 20:15; *Isa* 39:4
when he had *s.* him. *2 Ki* 23:29
many that had *s.* the first house.
Ezra 3:12
of that which they had *s.* *Esth* 9:26
eye that hath *s.* me shall. *Job* 7:8
say, I have not *s.* thee. 8:18
died, and no eye had *s.* me. 10:18
mine eye had *s.* all this, mine. 13:1
they that have *s.* him shall. 20:7
vulture's eye hath not *s.* 28:7
s. doors of the shadow ? 38:17
or hast thou *s.* the treasures ? 22
thou hast *s.* it, for. *Ps* 10:14
our eye hath *s.* 35:21
this thou hast *s.* 22
so have we *s.* in city of Lord. 48:8
mine eye hath *s.* his desire. 54:7
have *s.* thy goings, O God. 68:24
years wherein we have *s.* evil. 90:15
ends of earth have *s.* salvation. 98:3
whom thine eyes have *s.* *Pr* 25:7

who hath not *s.* the evil. *Eccl* 4:3
not *s.* the sun, nor known. 6:5
yea, though he live, yet hath he *s.* 6
eyes have *s.* the Lord. *Isa* 6:5
walked in darkness have *s.* 9:2
nor hath eye *s.* what he hath. 64:4
who hath heard, who hath *s.*? 66:8
isles afar off that have not *s.* 19
Lord, thou hast well *s.* *Jer* 1:12
hast thou *s.* what backsliding? 3:6
thou hast *s.* me, and tried my. 12:3
because they have *s.* her. *Lam* 1:8
she hath *s.* heathen entered. 10
thy prophets have *s.* vain and foolish
things for thee, they have *s.* 2:14
have found, we have *s.* it. 16
O Lord, thou hast *s.* my wrong. 3:59
thou hast *s.* all their vengeance. 60
thou hast *s.* what the. *Ezek* 8:12
then said he, Hast thou *s.* this? 15
17; 47:6
and have *s.* nothing. 13:3
they have *s.* vanity. 6
have ye not *s.* a vain vision? 7
Gabriel whom I had *s.* *Dan* 9:21
and the diviners have *s.* a lie.
Zech 10:2
s. his star in the east. *Mat* 2:2
to see those things which ye see, and
have not *s.* 13:17; *Luke* 10:24
and ye, when ye had *s.* *Mat* 21:32
they have *s.* the kingdom. *Mark* 9:1
what things they had *s.* 9
them which had *s.* him. 16:14
that he had *s.* a vision. *Luke* 1:22
for all things they had *s.* 2:20
not see death before he had *s.* 26
mine eyes have *s.* thy salvation. 30
saying, We have *s.* strange. 5:26
things which they had *s.* 9:36
works that they had *s.* 19:37
he hoped to have *s.* some. 23:8
saying, that they had *s.* a. 24:23
that they had *s.* a spirit. 37
no man hath *s.* God at any time, the.
John 1:18; *1 John* 4:12
we testify that we have *s.* *John* 3:11
what he hath *s.* and heard. 32
the Galileans had *s.* all he did. 4:45
ye have not at any time *s.* 5:37
those men, when they had *s.* 6:14
not any man hath *s.* the Father. 46
hast thou *s.* Abraham? 8:57
which before had *s.* him. 9:8
that thou hast both *s.* and. 37
had *s.* what Jesus did. 11:45
he that hath *s.* me, hath *s.* 14:9
have *s.* and hated both me. 15:24
she had *s.* the Lord. 20:18
have *s.* the Lord. 25
because thou hast *s.* me. 29
speak things we have *s.* *Acts* 4:20
fashion that he had *s.* 7:44
he hath *s.* in a vision a man. 9:12
declared to them how he had *s.* 27
what this vision he had *s.* 10:17
how he had *s.* an angel. 11:13
when he had *s.* the grace of God. 23
after he had *s.* the vision. 16:10
they had *s.* the brethren, they. 40
they had *s.* before with him. 21:29
of what thou hast *s.* 22:15; 26:16
eye hath not *s.* nor ear. *1 Cor* 2:9
s. Jesus Christ our Lord? 9:1
things ye have heard and *s.* *Phil* 4:9
as have not *s.* my face. *Col* 2:1
those things he hath not *s.* 18
whom no man hath *s.* *1 Tim* 6:16
that which we have *s.* *1 John* 1:1
and we have *s.* it. 2
that which we have *s.* declare. 3
whosoever sinneth hath not *s.* 3:6
we have *s.* and do testify. 4:14
not his brother whom he hath *s.*, how
can he love God . . . not *s.*? 20
evil, hath not *s.* God. *3 John* 11
things which thou hast *s.* *Rev* 1:19
when I had heard and *s.* I fell. 22:8

have I **seen**

thee *have I s.* righteous. *Gen* 7:1
now *have I s.* thy people to offer.
1 Chr 29:17
yet *have I* not *s.* righteous. *Ps* 37:25
all things *have I s.* in. *Eccl* 7:15
all this *have I s.* and applied. 8:9
this wisdom *have I s.* under. 9:13
wherefore *have I s.* them? *Jer* 46:5
for now *have I s.* with. *Zech* 9:3

I have **seen**

I have s. all that Laban. *Gen* 31:12
I have s. God face to face. 32:30
for therefore *I have s.* thy face.
33:10; 46:30
I have s. the affliction. *Ex* 3:7
I have also *s.* the oppression. 9, 16
I have s. this people. 32:9
Deut 9:13
alas, for because *I have s.* an angel.
Judg 6:22
I have s. a woman in Timnah. 14:2
I have s. a son of Jesse, cunning.
1 Sam 16:18
surely *I have s.* yesterday the blood
of Naboth. *2 Ki* 9:26
I have s. thy tears. 20:5; *Isa* 38:5
as *I have s.*, they that plow. *Job* 4:8
I have s. the foolish taking. 5:3
that which *I have s.* I declare. 15:17
if *I have s.* any perish for want. 31:19
I have s. the wicked in. *Ps* 37:35
I have s. violence and strife. 55:9
glory, so as *I have s.* thee in. 63:2
I have s. an end of all. 119:96
I have s. all the works. *Eccl* 1:14
I have s. the travail which. 3:10
is a sore evil which *I have s.* 5:13
I have s. it is good to eat. 18
evil which *I have s.* 6:1; 10:5
I have s. servants upon horses. 10:7
I am warm, *I have s.* *Isa* 44:16
I have s. his ways, and will. 57:18
behold, *I have s.* it, saith. *Jer* 7:11
I have s. thine adulteries. 13:27
I have s. folly in prophets. 23:13, 14
I have s. affliction by rod. *Lam* 3:1
known unto me the dream *I have s.*
Dan 2:26
dream that *I have s.* 4:9, 18
I have s. an horrible. *Hos* 6:10
I speak that *I have s.* *John* 8:38
I have s. the affliction. *Acts* 7:34

ye have **seen**

of all that *ye have s.* *Gen* 45:13
Egyptians whom *ye have s.* *Ex* 14:13
ye have s. what I did unto. 19:4
ye have s. that I have talked. 20:22
ye have s. all that the Lord did.
Deut 29:2; *Josh* 23:3
ye have s. their abominations.
Deut 29:17
what *ye have s.* me do. *Judg* 9:48
have ye s. this man? *1 Sam* 17:25
ye yourselves *have s.* it. *Job* 27:12
ye have s. the breaches. *Isa* 22:9
ye have s. all the evil. *Jer* 44:2
ye have s. lies, therefore I am.
Ezek 13:8
what things *ye have s.* *Luke* 7:22
ye also *have s.* me, and. *John* 6:36
ye do that which *ye have s.* 8:38
ye know him, and *have s.* him. 14:7
as *ye have s.* him go. *Acts* 1:11
and *ye have s.* the end. *Jas* 5:11

seen, *passive*

tops of the mountains *s.* *Gen* 8:5
shall be *s.* in the cloud. 9:14
of the Lord it shall be *s.* 22:14
no leavened bread be *s.* *Ex* 13:7
Deut 16:4
but my face shall not be *s.* *Ex* 33:23
neither let any man be *s.* 34:3
Lord, art *s.* face to face. *Num* 14:14
a shield or spear *s.* *Judg* 5:8
no such deed done nor *s.* 19:30
they might not be *s.* *2 Sam* 17:17
he was *s.* upon the wings. 22:11
there was no stone *s.* *1 Ki* 6:18
ends of the staves were not *s.* 8:8
no such almug trees were *s.* 10:12
consumed, it cannot be *s.* *Job* 33:21
channels of water were *s.* *Ps* 18:15
s. that Moab is weary. *Isa* 16:12
thy shame shall be *s.* 47:3
and his glory shall be *s.* 60:2
and the Lord shall be *s.* *Zech* 9:14
alms to be *s.* of men. *Mat* 6:1, 5
saying, It was never so *s.* *Mat* 9:33
all their works they do to be *s.* 23:5
he had been *s.* of her. *Mark* 16:11
being *s.* of them forty days.
Acts 1:3; 13:31
things of him clearly *s.* *Rom* 1:20
but hope that is *s.* is not hope. 8:24
he was *s.* of Cephas. *1 Cor* 15:5
after that he was *s.* of above 500. 6
s. of James. 7
last of all he was *s.* of me also. 8
we look not at things *s.*, but at things
not *s.*: for things *s.* *2 Cor* 4:18
in flesh, *s.* of angels. *1 Tim* 3:16
evidence of things not *s.* *Heb* 11:1
so that things which are *s.* were. 3
warned of God of things not *s.* 7
having *s.* them afar off, were. 13
whom having not *s.* ye love. *1 Pet* 1:8
there was *s.* in his temple the ark.
Rev 11:19

seer

(*Another word for Prophet. Seer* one who sees, *inferring that he sees visions*)

s. he that is a prophet was beforetime called a *s.* *1 Sam* 9:9
is the *s.* here? 11
where the *s.*'s house is. 18
Saul, and said, I am the *s.* 19
art not thou a *s.*? *2 Sam* 15:27
word came to Gad, David's *s.*
24:11; *1 Chr* 21:9
Samuel the *s.* did ordain in their set
office. *1 Chr* 9:22
Heman the king's *s.* in the. 25:5
all that Samuel the *s.* had. 26:28
in the book of Samuel the *s.* and in
the book of Gad the *s.* 29:29
visions of Iddo the *s.* *2 Chr* 9:29
acts of . . . book of Iddo the *s.* 12:15
Hanani the *s.* came to Asa. 16:7
then Asa was wroth with the *s.* 10
Jehu son of Hanani the *s.* went. 19:2
of Gad the king's *s.* 29:25
David and Asaph the *s.* 30
Jeduthun the king's *s.* 35:15
said unto Amos, O thou *s.* flee.
Amos 7:12

seers

Israel and Judah by *s.* *2 Ki* 17:13
words of the *s.* that spake.
2 Chr 33:18
among the sayings of the *s.* 19*
your rulers, the *s.* hath. *Isa* 29:10
who say to the *s.* see not, and. 30:10
shall the *s.* be ashamed. *Mi* 3:7

seest

the land thou *s.* to thee. *Gen* 13:15
that spake, Thou God *s.* me. 16:13
Laban said, All that thou *s.* is. 31:43
that day thou *s.* my face. *Ex* 10:28
lest when thou *s.* the sun. *Deut* 4:19
every place that thou *s.* 12:13
goest to battle and *s.* horses. 20:1
and *s.* among captives a. 21:11
thou *s.* the shadow of. *Judg* 9:36
s. thou how Ahab. *1 Ki* 21:29
hast thou eyes, *s.* thou? *Job* 10:4
s. thou a man diligent? *Pr* 22:29
s. thou a man wise in his? 26:12
s. thou a man that is hasty? 29:20
if thou *s.* the oppression. *Eccl* 5:8
fasted, and thou *s.* not? *Isa* 58:3
when thou *s.* the naked, that. 7
to Jeremiah, What *s.* thou? *Jer* 1:11
13; 24:3; *Amos* 7:8; 8:2
Zech 4:2; 5:2
s. thou not what they do in cities?
Jer 7:17
O Lord, that *s.* the reins. 20:12
and behold, thou *s.* it. 32:24
son of man, *s.* thou? *Ezek* 8:6
declare all thou *s.* to the house. 40:4
and as thou *s.* deal. *Dan* 1:13
thou *s.* the multitude. *Mark* 5:31
Jesus said, *S.* thou these? 13:2
he said to Simon, *S.*? *Luke* 7:44
thou *s.* how many. *Acts* 21:20
s. thou how faith? *Jas* 2:22
what thou *s.* write in a book and.
Rev 1:11

seeth
after him that *s.* me? *Gen* 16:13
when he *s.* lad is not with us. 44:31
and when he *s.* thee he. *Ex* 4:14
and when he *s.* the blood. 12:23
priest *s.* the plague in. *Lev* 13:20
when he *s.* that their power is. *Deut* 32:36
Lord *s.* not as man *s.* *1 Sam* 16:7
pleasant, as my lord *s.* *2 Ki* 2:19
and *s.* the place of stones. *Job* 8:17
he *s.* wickedness also. 11:11
covering to him that he *s.* not. 22:14
and his eye *s.* every precious. 28:10
s. under the whole heaven. 24
his eyes are on man, he *s.* 34:21
but now mine eye *s.* thee. 42:5
for he *s.* that his day. *Ps* 37:13
he *s.* that wise men die. 49:10
shall rejoice, when he *s.* 58:10
neither day nor night *s.* *Eccl* 8:16
watchman declare what he *s.* *Isa* 21:6
looketh upon it, *s.* it. 28:4
and they say, Who *s.* us.? 29:15
none *s.* me. 47:10
Lord *s.* us not. *Ezek* 8:12; 9:9
the vision that he *s.* is for. 12:27
if he beget a son that *s.* 18:14
if when he *s.* the sword come. 33:3
when any *s.* a man's bone. 39:15
thy father who *s.* *Mat* 6:4, 6, 18
he *s.* tumult, and. *Mark* 5:38
he *s.* Abraham afar off. *Luke* 16:23
next day John *s.* Jesus. *John* 1:29
do nothing but what he *s.* 5:19
who *s.* the Son, and believeth. 6:40
by what means he now *s.* 9:21
but an hireling *s.* the wolf. 10:12
he stumbleth not, because he *s.* 11:9
s. me, *s.* him that sent me. 12:45
because it *s.* him not, nor. 14:17
a little while, and the world *s.* 19
s. the stone taken away. 20:1
Peter went in and *s.* the linen. 6
and *s.* two angels in white. 12
s. the disciple whom Jesus. 21:20
what a man *s.* why doth? *Rom* 8:24
what he *s.* me to be. *2 Cor* 12:6
s. brother have need. *1 John* 3:17

seethe
(*American Revision*, boil)
and *s.* that ye will *s.* *Ex* 16:23
thou shalt not *s.* a kid in his mother's milk. 23:19; 34:26; *Deut* 14:21
thou shalt *s.* his flesh. *Ex* 29:31
s. pottage for the sons. *2 Ki* 4:38
let them *s.* the bones. *Ezek* 24:5
come and *s.* therein. *Zech* 14:21

seething
came, while flesh was *s.* *1 Sam* 2:13
goeth smoke as out of a *s.* pot. *Job* 41:20
I said, I see a *s.* pot. *Jer* 1:13

Seir
to the land of *S.* the. *Gen* 32:3
till I come to my lord to *S.* 33:14
these are the sons of *S.* 36:20, 21 *1 Chr* 1:38
S. shall be a possession. *Num* 24:18
destroyed you in *S.* *Deut* 1:44
from Sinai and rose up from *S.* 33:2
thou wentest out of *S.* *Judg* 5:4
of the inhabitants of *S.* *2 Chr* 20:23
of children of *S.* 10,000. 25:11
gods of the children of *S.* 14
he calleth to me out of *S.* *Isa* 21:11
that Moab and *S.* do say. *Ezek* 25:8

mount **Seir**
Horites in their *mount S.* *Gen* 14:6
dwelt Esau in *mount S.* 36:8, 9
we compassed *mount S.* *Deut* 2:1
have given *mount S.* to Esau. 5 *Josh* 24:4
sons of Simeon, 500 men went to *mount S.* *1 Chr* 4:42
mount S. whom thou wouldest not let Israel invade. *2 Chr* 20:10
ambushments against *mount S.* 22
Moab stood up against *mount S.* 23
face against *mount S.* *Ezek* 35:2
say to it, Behold, O *mount S.* 3
thus will I make *mount S.* 7, 15

seize
ye shall rise up and *s.* *Josh* 8:7
night, let darkness *s.* *Job* 3:6
let death *s.* upon them. *Ps* 55:15*
let us kill him, and *s.* *Mat* 21:38

seized
feeble, fear hath *s.* on. *Jer* 49:24

selah
This Hebrew word is found seventy one times in the book of Psalms, and three times in Habakkuk. It is very probably a musical or liturgical sign.
The older view was that it indicated a pause, but it is now believed to be derived from a word signifying Up! *This may have been intended for the players, for the singers, or for the congregation, or for all of them.*
help for him in God, *s.* *Ps* 3:2
heard me out of his holy hill, *s.* 4
blessing is upon thy people, *s.* 8
forgavest iniquity of my sin, *s.* 32:5
See Ps 4:2, 4; 7:5; 9:16, 20; 20:3 21:2; 24:6, 10; 32:4, 7; 39:5, 11 44:8; 46:3, 7, 11; 47:4; 48:8 49:13, 15; 50:6; 52:3, 5; 54:3 55:7, 19; 57:3, 6; 59:5, 13; 60:4 61:4; 62:4, 8; 66:4, 7, 15; 67:1 4; 68:7, 19, 32; 75:3; 76:3, 9 77:3, 9, 15; 81:7; 82:2; 83:8 84:4, 8; 85:2; 87:3, 6; 88:7, 10 89:4, 37, 45, 48; 140:3, 5, 8; 143:6 *Hab* 3:3, 9, 13

Seleucia
they departed unto *S.* *Acts* 13:4

own **self**
swarest by thine *own s.* *Ex* 32:13
I can of mine *own s.* *John* 5:30
thou me with thine *own s.* 17:5
I judge not mine *own s.* *1 Cor* 4:3
even thine *own s.* *Philem* 19
who his *own s.* bare our. *1 Pet* 2:24

selfsame
healed the *s.* hour. *Mat* 8:13
that one and *s.* Spirit. *1 Cor* 12:11
wrought us for *s.* thing. *2 Cor* 5:5
this *s.* thing that ye. 7:11
see same **day**

selfwill
in their *s.*, they digged. *Gen* 49:6

selfwilled
bishop must not be *s.* *Tit* 1:7
presumptuous are they, *s.* *2 Pet* 2:10

sell
(*In case of extreme necessity the Hebrews were allowed to sell themselves and their children into temporary servitude. This was closely regulated, however, in the law*)
Jacob said, *S.* me this. *Gen* 25:31
come, let us *s.* him to the. 37:27
if a man *s.* his daughter. *Ex* 21:7
to *s.* her to strange nation, shall. 8
they shall *s.* the live ox and. 35
an ox, and kill it, or *s.* it. 22:1
if thou *s.* aught unto. *Lev* 25:14
if a man *s.* a dwelling house. 29
if thy brother *s.* himself unto. 47
thou shalt *s.* me meat. *Deut* 2:28
s. that which dieth of itself. 14:21
thou shalt not *s.* her at all. 21:14
s. Sisera into the hand. *Judg* 4:9
Ahab did *s.* himself to. *1 Ki* 21:25
go *s.* the oil, and pay. *2 Ki* 4:7
and will ye even *s.* your? *Neh* 5:8
on the sabbath day to *s.* 10:31
buy truth, and *s.* it not. *Pr* 23:23
s. land into the hand. *Ezek* 30:12
they shall not *s.* the firstfruits. 48:14
I will *s.* your sons and daughters into hand of Judah, they shall *s.* *Joel* 3:8
that we may *s.* corn. *Amos* 8:5
yea, and *s.* the refuse of the. 6
and they that *s.* them. *Zech* 11:5
go and *s.* that thou hast. *Mat* 19:21 *Mark* 10:21; *Luke* 12:33; 18:22
go ye rather to them that *s.* *Mat* 25:9
let him *s.* his garment. *Luke* 22:36
we will buy and *s.* and. *Jas* 4:13
no man might buy or *s.* *Rev* 13:17

seller
buyer, so with the *s.* *Isa* 24:2
rejoice, nor the *s.* mourn. *Ezek* 7:12
the *s.* shall not return to that. 13
woman named Lydia, a *s.* *Acts* 16:14

sellers
merchants and *s.* *Neh* 13:20

sellest
thou *s.* thy people for. *Ps* 44:12

selleth
a man and *s.* him, he shall surely. *Ex* 21:16; *Deut* 24:7
Naomi *s.* a part of land. *Deut* 4:3
head of him that *s.* corn. *Pr* 11:26
maketh fine linen and *s.* it. 31:24
that *s.* nations through. *Nah* 3:4
he *s.* all, and buyeth. *Mat* 13:44

selvedge
from the *s.* in the coupling. *Ex* 26:4; 36:11

selves
also of your own *s.* *Acts* 20:30
but first gave their own *s.* to the. *2 Cor* 8:5
own *s.* Know ye not your own *s.*? 13:5
lovers of their own *s.* *2 Tim* 3:2
deceiving your own *s.* *Jas* 1:22

Semei
which was the son of *S.* *Luke* 3:26

senate
they called all the *s.* *Acts* 5:21

senators
and teach his *s.* wisdom. *Ps* 105:22

send
God shall *s.* his angel. *Gen* 24:7, 40
I pray thee, *s.* me good speed. 12
he said, *S.* me away unto. 54, 56
a pledge, till thou *s.* it? 38:17
wilt *s.* our brother with us. 43:4
God did *s.* me before you, to. 45:5
s. by hand of him whom. *Ex* 4:13
that he *s.* children of Israel. 7:2*
s. therefore now, and gather. 9:19
that they might *s.* them out. 12:33
whom thou wilt *s.* with me. 33:12
s. him away by the hand. *Lev* 16:21
s. thou men to search land, of every tribe shall ye *s.* a man. *Num* 13:2
of every tribe *s.* a thousand. 31:4
we will *s.* men before us. *Deut* 1:22
thy God will *s.* the hornet. 7:20
the elders shall *s.* and fetch. 19:12
give her a bill of divorce, and *s.* 24:1
Lord shall *s.* upon thee. 28:20
Lord shall *s.* against thee. 48
thou didst *s.* come again. *Judg* 13:8
s. away the ark of God. *1 Sam* 5:11 6:8
tell us wherewith we shall *s.* it. 6:2
if ye *s.* away the ark of God, *s.* 3
saying, Up, that I may *s.* thee. 9:26
give us respite, that we may *s.* 11:3
the Lord shall *s.* thunder. 12:17
Samuel said to Jesse, *S.* 16:11
Saul sent, and said, *S.* me David. 19
young men thou didst *s.* 25:25
David sent saying, *S.* me. *2 Sam* 11:6
come hither, that I may *s.* 14:32
by them ye shall *s.* unto me. 15:36
now therefore *s.* quickly. 17:16
all thou didst *s.* for. *1 Ki* 20:9
ye shall not *s.* *2 Ki* 2:16
he said, *S.* 17
doth *s.* to me to recover a man. 5:7
that I may *s.* and fetch him. 6:13
let us *s.* and see. 7:13
s. to meet Jehu. 9:17
the Lord began to *s.* against. 15:37
let us *s.* abroad our. *1 Chr* 13:2
s. me therefore a man. *2 Chr* 2:7
s. me also cedar trees, fir trees. 8
then hear thou, and *s.* rain. 6:27
Ahaz did *s.* to king of Assyria. 28:16
Sennacherib did *s.* servants. 32:9
let king *s.* his pleasure. *Ezra* 5:17
that thou wouldest *s.* me. *Neh* 2:5
so it pleased the king to *s.* me. 6
eat, drink, and *s.* portions. 8:10, 12
s. forth their little ones. *Job* 21:11

canst thou s. lightnings ? Job 38:35
s. thee help from sanctuary. Ps 20:2
O s. out thy light and truth. 43:3
he shall s. from heaven, and . . . reproach; God shall s. forth. 57:3
God didst s. a plentiful rain. 68:9
he doth s. out his voice, a. 33*
shall s. rod of thy strength. 110:2
O Lord, I beseech thee, s. 118:25
s. thine hand from above, rid. 144:7*
sluggard to them that s. Pr 10:26
truth to them that s. to thee. 22:21
faithful messenger to them that s. him. 25:13
ointment to s. forth a. Eccl 10:1
whom shall I s.? I said, Here am I, s. Isa 6:8
Lord shall s. among his fat ones. 10:16
s. ye the lamb to the ruler of. 16:1
he shall s. them a Saviour. 19:20
that s. forth thither the feet. 32:20
didst s. thy messengers far off. 57:9
to all that I shall s. thee. Jer 1:7
s. unto Kedar. 2:10
s. for cunning women. 9:17
s. the yokes to king of Edom. 27:3
s. of them of the captivity. 29:31
for the which the Lord shall s. 42:5
the Lord, to whom we s. thee. 6
pray ye the Lord that he will s. forth labourers. Mat 9:38; Luke 10:2
that I am come to s. peace. 10:34
till he s. forth judgement. 12:20
Son of man shall s. forth his angels. 13:41; 24:31; Mark 13:27
s. her away, for she crieth. Mat 15:23
straightway he will s. them. 21:3
Mark 11:3
that he might s. them to preach. Mark 3:14; 6:7
would not s. them away out. 5:10
besought him, saying, S. us. 12
s. Lazarus. Luke 16:24
s. to my father's house. 27
whom the Father will s. John 14:26
believed that thou didst s. me. 17:8
shall s. Jesus Christ who. Acts 3:20
same did God s. to be ruler. 7:35
and now s. men to Joppa. 10:5, 32
11:13
disciples determined to s. 11:29
to s. chosen men of. 15:22, 25
that he would s. for him to. 25:3
it seemeth unreasonable to s. 27
Lord to s. Timotheus. Phil 2:19, 23
I supposed it necessary to s. 25
God shall s. delusion. 2 Thes 2:11
when I shall s. Artemas. Tit 3:12
doth fountain s. sweet? Jas 3:11
write and s. it to seven. Rev 1:11
and they shall s. gifts one. 11:10

I send

behold I s. an angel. Ex 23:20
did I not earnestly s.? Num 22:37
and I s. not to thee. 1 Sam 20:12
business whereabout I s. thee. 21:2
if I s. pestilence. 2 Chr 7:13
Ezek 14:19
say, Whom shall I s.? Isa 6:8
nations to whom I s. thee. Jer 25:15
I s. thee to the children of Israel. Ezek 2:3, 4
I s. my four sore judgements. 14:21
behold I s. you forth. Mat 10:16
behold I s. my messenger before. 11:10; Mark 1:2; Luke 7:27
behold I s. you prophets. Mat 23:34
if I s. them away fasting. Mark 8:3
I s. you forth as lambs. Luke 10:3
I s. the promise of my Father. 24:49
receiveth whom I s. John 13:20
sent me, even so s. I you. 20:21
to be kept till I s. him. Acts 25:21
unto whom now I s. thee. 26:17

I will send

I will s. and fetch thee. Gen 27:45
come, and I will s. thee unto. 37:13
he said, I will s. thee a. 38:17
I will s. thee unto Pharaoh. Ex 3:10
Acts 7:34
I will s. swarms of flies. Ex 8:21
I will s. all my plagues upon. 9:14
I will s. my fear. 23:27
I will s. hornets. Ex 23:28
I will s. an angel before thee. 33:2
I will s. wild beasts. Lev 26:22
I will s. pestilence. 25
I will s. faintness. 36
I will s. grass in thy. Deut 11:15
I will s. the teeth of beasts. 32:24
I will s. thee a man. 1 Sam 9:16
I will s. thee to Jesse the. 16:1
I will shew it thee, and s. thee. 20:13
and I will s. rain upon. 1 Ki 18:1
yet I will s. my servants. 20:6
I will s. thee away with this. 34
I will s. a blast upon him. 2 Ki 19:7
Isa 37:7
I will s. him against. Isa 10:6
I will s. those that escape. 66:19
behold I will s. serpents. Jer 8:17
I will s. a sword after them. 9:16
24:10; 25:16, 27; 29:17; 49:37
I will s. for many fishers. 16:16
I will s. and take the families. 25:9
I will s. Nebuchadnezzar my. 43:10
behold, I will s. unto him. 48:12
and I will s. unto Babylon. 51:2
I will s. famine. Ezek 5:16, 17
14:13; Amos 8:11
I will s. mine anger upon. Ezek 7:3
I will s. into her pestilence. 28:23
I will s. you corn, and. Joel 2:19
I will s. a curse. Mal 2:2
I will s. my messenger, and he. 3:1
I will s. Elijah. 4:5
I will not s. them away. Mat 15:32
I will s. them prophets. Luke 11:49
what shall I do? I will s. 20:13
the Comforter whom I will s. John 15:26; 16:7
I will s. thee far hence. Acts 22:21
approve, them I will s. 1 Cor 16:3
see **fire**

sendest

when thou s. him. Deut 15:13*, 18*
whithersoever thou s. Josh 1:16
that thou s. to enquire. 2 Ki 1:6
and s. him away. Job 14:20
thou s. thy Spirit, they. Ps 104:30

sendeth

latter husband s. her out. Deut 24:3
that the Lord s. rain. 1 Ki 17:14
and who s. waters upon. Job 5:10
he s. them out, they overturn. 12:15
he s. the springs into. Ps 104:10
he s. forth his. 147:15, 18
that s. a message by the. Pr 26:6
my spikenard s. forth. S of S 1:12
that s. ambassadors by. Isa 18:2
and s. rain on the just. Mat 5:45
he s. forth two of his disciples. Mark 11:1; 14:13
s. and desireth conditions of peace. Luke 14:32
Claudius Lysias to Felix s. Acts 23:26

sending

evil in s. me away. 2 Sam 13:16*
his s. messengers. 2 Chr 36:15
Jer 7:25; 25:4; 26:5; 29:19
35:15; 44:4
and of s. portions. Esth 9:19, 22
by s. evil angels. Ps 78:49*
it shall be for the s. Isa 7:25
rebelled in s. ambassadors unto. Ezek 17:15
God s. his own Son in the likeness of sinful flesh. Rom 8:3

Sennacherib

S. came up against Judah. 2 Ki 18:13; Isa 36:1
see and hear the words of S. 2 Ki 19:16; Isa 37:17
thou hast prayed to me against S. 2 Ki 19:20; Isa 37:21
S. departed and dwelt at Nineveh. 2 Ki 19:36; Isa 37:37
the Lord saved Hezekiah from S. 2 Chr 32:22

senses

have their s. exercised. Heb 5:14

sensual

is earthly, s., devilish. Jas 3:15
be s. having not the Spirit. Jude 19

sent

s. coat of many colours. Gen 37:22
Judah s. the kid by hand. 38:20
Tamar s. to her father in law. 25
then Pharaoh s. and called. 41:14
but Benjamin, Jacob s. not. 42:4
it was not you that s. me. 45:8
s. messengers unto Joseph. 50:16
I AM hath s. me to you. Ex 3:14
why is it that thou hast s. me? 5:22
the names of the men Moses s. Num 13:16; 14:36
Balak king of Moab hath s. 22:10
Balak s. yet again princes more. 15
hid the messengers we s. Josh 6:17
old was I when Moses s. me. 14:7
I cut her in pieces and s. Judg 20:6
s. into the land of the. 1 Sam 31:9
return to him that s. 2 Sam 24:13
my lord hath not s. 1 Ki 18:10
elders did as Jezebel had s. 21:11
return unto king that s. 2 Ki 1:6
king of Israel s. to the place. 6:10
thistle s. to the cedar in. 14:9
according as Ahaz had s. 16:11
Rab-shakeh said to them, Hath my master s. me? 18:27; Isa 36:12
his master s. to reproach. 2 Ki 19:4
Lord God of Israel, Tell the man that s. 22:15, 18; 2 Chr 34:23
copy of the letter they s. Ezra 4:11
they s. unto me four times. Neh 6:4
king s. and loosed him. Ps 105:20
his Spirit hath s. me. Isa 48:16
their nobles have s. their. Jer 14:3
I have not s. these prophets. 23:21
because thou hast s. letters. 29:25
say unto the king that s. you. 37:7
whom ye s. to present. 42:9, 20
ye have s. for men. Ezek 23:40
who hath s. his angel. Dan 3:28
Ephraim went and s. Hos 5:13
when they had s. unto. Zech 7:2
receiveth him that s. me. Mat 10:40
Mark 9:37; Luke 9:48
John 13:20
s. Jesus two disciples. Mat 21:1
Pilate's wife s. unto him. 27:19
immediately the king s. Mark 6:27
John Baptist hath s. us. Luke 7:20
Jesus s. them two and two. 10:1
he s. his servant at supper. 14:17
they s. a message after him. 19:14
mocked him, and s. him. 23:11
to them that s. us. John 1:22
do the will of him that s. me. 4:34
the Father who hath s. me. 5:23
believeth on him that s. me. 24
12:44
but the will of the Father which hath s. me. 5:30; 6:38, 39, 40
ye s. unto John, and he. 5:33
bear witness that the Father hath s. 5:36, 37; 6:57; 8:16, 18
except the Father which s. me. 6:44
but his that s. me. 7:16
seeketh his glory that s. him. 18
Pharisees and priests s. officers. 32
the works of him that s. me. 9:4
whom the Father hath s. 10:36
believe thou hast s. me. 11:42
seeth him that s. me. 12:45
Father who s. me gave me a. 49
mine, but Father's who s. me. 14:24
know not him that s. me. 15:21
go my way to him that s. me. 16:5
know Jesus whom thou hast s. 17:3
s. me into the world, so have I s. 18
believe that thou hast s. me. 21
know thou hast s. me. 23
that thou hast s. me. 25
as my Father hath s. me. 20:21
s. to the prison to have. Acts 5:21
I ask for what intent ye have s. 10:29
s. it to elders by Barnabas. 11:30
the rulers of the synagogue s. 13:15
we have therefore s. Judas. 15:27
the magistrates have s. to. 16:36
Paul's friends s. unto him. 19:31
Christ s. me not to. 1 Cor 1:17
we have s. with him. 2 Cor 8:18
in Thessalonica ye s. once. Phil 4:16
testify that the Father s. the Son. 1 John 4:14

sent *away*
Pharaoh s. away Abraham and his. Gen 12:20
s. Ishmael and Hagar away. 21:14
they s. away Rebekah their. 24:59
s. Keturah's children away. 25:6
me and have s. me away. 26:27
as we have s. thee away in peace. 29
Isaac s. away Jacob to. 28:5
blessed Jacob and s. him away. 6
I might have s. thee away. 31:27
surely thou hadst s. me away. 42
s. he his brethren away. 45:24
s. her away, may not. Deut 24:4
Rahab s. spies away. Josh 2:21
s. Reubenites and Gadites away. 22:6, 7
s. his daughter away. Judg 11:38
s. all the people away. 1 Sam 10:25
thou s. away my enemy? 19:17
David s. Abner away. 2 Sam 3:21
is it that thou hast s. him away? 24
cut garments, and s. them away. 10:4; 1 Chr 19:4
lords of Philistines s. David away. 1 Chr 12:19
s. widows away empty. Job 22:9
and beat him, and s. him away. Mark 12:3, 4; Luke 20:10, 11
he hath s. empty away. Luke 1:53
but Jesus s. him away. 8:38
them, they s. them away. Acts 13:3
s. away Paul and Silas. 17:10, 24

God **sent**
God s. me before you. Gen 45:7
God of your fathers hath s. me. Ex 3:13
the God of Jacob hath s. me. 15
God s. an evil spirit between Abimelech and. Judg 9:23
God s. an angel unto. 1 Chr 21:15
that God had not s. him. Neh 6:12
Lord their God s. him. Jer 43:1
God hath not s. to thee to say. 2
God hath s. his angel. Dan 6:22
God s. not his Son to. John 3:17
he whom God hath s. speaketh. 34
raised up his Son Jesus, s. Acts 3:26
word of God s. unto the. 10:36
God s. forth his Son. Gal 4:4
God hath s. forth the Spirit of. 6
God s. his only begotten. 1 John 4:9
God s. his Son to be a propitiation. 10
God s. his angel to shew. Rev 22:6

he **sent**
to his father he s. after. Gen 45:23
he s. Judah before him unto. 46:28
he had s. her back. Ex 18:2
hearkened not to words he s. Judg 11:28
and he s. for David. 1 Sam 17:31
he s. of the spoil unto the. 30:26
he s. to meet them. 2 Sam 10:5; 1 Chr 19:5
when he s. again, he would. 14:29
he s. from above, he took me. 22:17; Ps 18:16
for he s. unto me for my. 1 Ki 20:7
therefore he s. lions. 2 Ki 17:26
yet he s. prophets. 2 Chr 24:19
he s. unto Amaziah a prophet. 25:15
he s. and called for his. Esth 5:10
he s. them meat to the. Ps 78:25
he s. a man before them. 105:17
he s. Moses his servant and. 26
he s. darkness, and made it dark. 28
but he s. leanness into. 106:15
he s. his word and healed. 107:20
he s. redemption unto his. 111:9
he hath s. me to bind up the broken-hearted. Isa 61:1; Luke 4:18
he s. unto us in Babylon. Jer 29:28
for the which he hath s. me. 42:21
from above he s. fire. Lam 1:13
after the glory hath he s. Zech 2:8
he s. other servants. Mat 21:36
last of all he s. unto them his Son. 37; Mark 12:4
he s. forth his armies. Mat 22:7
he that s. me to baptize. John 1:33
for whom he hath s., him. 5:38
on him whom he hath s. 6:29
he that s. me is true. John 7:28; 8:26
and he hath s. me. 7:29
and he that s. me is with me. 8:29
I of myself, but he s. me. 42
wherefore he s. for Paul. Acts 24:26
he s. and signified it by. Rev 1:1

I **sent**
I have s. to tell my lord. Gen 32:5
I s. this kid, and thou hast. 38:23
token that I have s. thee. Ex 3:12
fathers when I s. them. Num 32:8
I s. Moses also and Aaron. Josh 24:5; Mi 6:4
have not I s. thee? Judg 6:14
I have s. Naaman my. 2 Ki 5:6
the law which I s. to you by. 17:13
my messenger that I s.? Isa 42:19
for your sake I have s. to Babylon. 43:14
in the thing whereto I s. it. 55:11
I s. unto you all my servants the. Jer 7:25; 26:5; 35:15; 44:4
I s. them not, nor commanded. 14:14, 15; 23:21, 32; 27:15; 29:9
I s. him not, he caused you. 29:31
surely had I s. thee. Ezek 3:6
to thee am I now s. Dan 10:11
my great army which I s. Joel 2:25
I have s. among you. Amos 4:10
I have s. forth thy prisoners out. Zech 9:11
know that I have s. this. Mal 2:4
for therefore am I s. Luke 4:43
when I s. you without. 22:35
so have I s. them into. John 17:18
for I have s. them. Acts 10:20
immediately therefore I s. to thee. 33
for this cause have I s. 1 Cor 4:17
yet have I s. brethren. 2 Cor 9:3
gain of you by any whom I s.? 12:17
desired Titus, and with him I s. 18
whom I have s. for the same purpose. Eph 6:22; Col 4:8
I s. him therefore. Phil 2:28
for this cause I s. to know. 1 Thes 3:5
whom I have s. again. Philem 12
see Lord

sent *forth*
Noah s. forth a raven. Gen 8:7
s. forth a dove. 10
hath s. forth her maidens. Pr 9:3
Herod s. forth and slew. Mat 2:16
these twelve Jesus s. forth. 10:5
and s. forth his servants to. 22:3
Herod s. forth and laid. Mark 6:17
scribes s. forth spies. Luke 20:20
the brethren s. him forth. Acts 9:30
they s. forth Barnabas as far. 11:22

sent *out*
God s. Lot out of midst. Gen 19:29
David therefore s. out. 1 Sam 26:4
and he s. out arrows. 2 Sam 22:15; Ps 18:14
who hath s. out the wild? Job 39:5
poured out, skies s. out. Ps 77:17
she s. out her boughs to sea. 80:11
whom I have s. out of this place. Jer 24:5
she hath s. out her little. Ezek 31:4
Jacob s. out our fathers. Acts 7:12
Rahab had s. them out. Jas 2:25

sent, *passive*
it is a present s. to my. Gen 32:18
I am s. to thee with. 1 Ki 14:6
forasmuch as thou art s. Ezra 7:14
shall be s. against him. Pr 17:11
an ambassador is s. unto. Jer 49:14
behold, a hand was s. Ezek 2:9
not s. to a people of a strange. 3:5
whom a messenger was s. 23:40
then was part of hand s. Dan 5:24
an ambassador is s. among. Ob 1
s. but unto lost sheep. Mat 15:24
and stonest them who are s. 23:37; Luke 13:34
I am Gabriel, and am s. Luke 1:19
angel Gabriel was s. from God. 26
of them was Elias s. save. 4:26
a man s. from God. John 1:6
John was s. to bear witness. 8*
they who were s. were of the. 24
I said, I am not Christ, but s. 3:28
which is by interpretation, S. John 9:7
is s. greater than he that s. 13:16
men that were s. had. Acts 10:17
to the men who were s. 21; 11:11
as soon as I was s. for. 10:29
so they being s. forth by. 13:4
word of this salvation s. 26
the salvation of God is s. 28:28
except they be s.? Rom 10:15
which were s. from you. Phil 4:18
spirits s. forth to minister for them. Heb 1:14
with the Holy Ghost s. 1 Pet 1:12
as them that are s. by him. 2:14
the seven spirits s. forth. Rev 5:6

sentence
shall shew thee the s. Deut 17:9
do according to the s. 10*, 11*
let my s. come forth. Ps 17:2
a divine s. is in the lips. Pr 16:10
s. is not executed speedily. Eccl 8:11
now also will I give s. Jer 4:12*
Pilate gave s. that it. Luke 23:24
s. is that we trouble. Acts 15:19*
we had the s. of death. 2 Cor 1:9

sentences
shewing of hard s. found. Dan 5:12
a king understanding dark s. 8:23

sentest
s. forth thy wrath which. Ex 15:7
land whither thou s. us. Num 13:27
the messengers thou s. us. 24:12
things thou s. to me for. 1 Ki 5:8

separate, *verb*
[1] *To part or divide*, Gen 30:40. [2] *To consecrate and set apart for some special ministry or service*, Acts 13:2. [3] *To forsake the communion of the church*, Jude 19. [4] *To excommunicate*, Luke 6:22.
Abram said, S. thyself. Gen 13:9
Jacob did s. the lambs. 30:40
shall ye s. the children. Lev 15:31
and his sons that they s. 22:2
shall s. themselves to vow a vow, to s. themselves unto. Num 6:2
the Nazarite shall s. himself. 3
thus shalt thou s. the Levites. 8:14
s. yourselves from among. 16:21
shalt s. three cities. Deut 19:2, 7
Lord shall s. him unto evil. 29:21
didst s. them to be thine. 1 Ki 8:53
s. yourselves from people of the. Ezra 10:11
Jeremiah went to s. himself thence. Jer 37:12*
he shall s. them, as a. Mat 25:32
when men shall s. you. Luke 6:22
s. me Barnabas and Saul. Acts 13:2
who shall s. us from the love of Christ? Rom 8:35
nor any other . . . able to s. us from. 39
they who s. themselves. Jude 19

separate
head of Joseph and of him that was s. Gen 49:26; Deut 33:16
the s. cities of Ephraim. Josh 16:9
was before the s. place. Ezek 41:12
the house and the s. places. 13
the breadth of the s. place. 14
chamber over against the s. place. 42:1, 10, 13
come out from among them, and be ye s. 2 Cor 6:17
undefiled, s. from sinners. Heb 7:26

separated
then Abram and Lot s. Gen 13:11
Lord said, after that Lot was s. 14
two manner of people be s. 35:23
so shall we be s. from. Ex 33:16
I am the Lord who have s. you. Lev 20:24
which I have s. from you as. 25
of Israel hath s. you. Num 16:9
the Lord s. the tribe of. Deut 10:8
when he s. sons of Adam. 32:8
there s. unto David. 1 Chr 12:8
Aaron was s. that he should. 23:13
David s. to the service of sons. 25:1
then Amaziah s. them. 2 Chr 25:10
all that had s. themselves. Ezra 6:21
then I s. twelve of the chief. 8:24

priests and Levites have not *s.* *Ezra* 9:1
who would not come, be *s.* 10:8
by their names were *s.* 16
we are *s.* upon the wall. *Neh* 4:19
Israel *s.* themselves from. 9:2
they that had *s.* clave to the. 10:28
they *s.* from Israel the mixed. 13:3
man having *s.* himself. *Pr* 18:1
but the poor is *s.* from his. 19:4
the Lord hath *s.* me from. *Isa* 56:3
iniquities have *s.* between. 59:2
for themselves are *s.* *Hos* 4:14
they went and *s.* themselves. 9:10
Paul departed and *s.* *Acts* 19:9
Paul an apostle, *s.* unto the. *Rom* 1:1
God who *s.* me from my. *Gal* 1:15
Peter withdrew and *s.* himself. 2:12

separateth

fulfilled in which he *s.* *Num* 6:5
the days he *s.* himself. 6
and a whisperer *s.* chief. *Pr* 16:28
he that repeateth a matter *s.* 17:9
of the stranger which *s.* *Ezek* 14:7

separation

the days of the *s.* for her. *Lev* 12:2
two weeks, as in her *s.* 5
out of the time of her *s.* 15:25
days of *s.* shall he eat. *Num* 6:4
all days of his *s.* no razor shall. 5
all the days of his *s.* he is holy. 8
to Lord the days of his *s.* and bring a lamb, because his *s.* was. 12
when the days of his *s.* are. 13
Nazarite shall shave the head of his *s.* and take the hair of his *s.* 18
after the hair of the Nazarite's *s.* 19
his *s.* after the law of *s.* 21
kept for a water of *s.* 19:9
the water of *s.* hath not. 13, 20
he that sprinkleth the water of *s.* . . . that toucheth water of *s.* 19:21
purified with the water of *s.* 31:23
wall round to make a *s.* *Ezek* 42:20

separating

weep in the fifth month, *s.* *Zech* 7:3

Sepharvaim

brought men from *S.* *2 Ki* 17:24
where are the gods of *S.*? 18:34
Isa 36:19
where is the king of *S.*? *2 Ki* 19:13
Isa 37:13

sepulchre

Or grave. The Hebrews have always taken great care about the burial of their dead. Most of their sepulchres were hollow places dug into rocks, as was that bought by Abraham, for the burying of Sarah, Gen 23:6, *those of the kings of Judah and Israel; and that wherein our Saviour was laid.*

Our Saviour in Mat 23:7, *compares the hypocritical Pharisees to* whited sepulchres *which appeared fine without, but inwardly were full of rottenness and corruption. It is said, that every year, on the fifteenth of February, the Jews took care to whiten their sepulchres anew.*

The Revisions usually change this to tomb.

withhold from thee his *s.* *Gen* 23:6
no man knoweth of his *s.* *Deut* 34:6
buried in his father's *s.* *Judg* 8:32
two men by Rachel's *s.* *1 Sam* 10:2
Asahel in his father's *s.* *2 Sam* 2:32
Ish-bosheth buried in Abner's *s.* 4:12
Ahithophel buried in the *s.* of. 17:23
bones of Saul in the *s.* of Kish. 21:14
shall not come to the *s.* *1 Ki* 13:22
bury me in the *s.* wherein the man. 31
Ahaziah in the *s.* with. *2 Ki* 9:28
they cast the man into the *s.* 13:21
Amon was buried in his *s.* in. 21:26
they told him, It is the *s.* of the. 23:17
Josiah buried in his own *s.* 30
2 Chr 35:24
their throat is an open *s.* *Ps* 5:9
Rom 3:13

hewed thee out a *s.* here as he that heweth out a *s.* on. *Isa* 22:16
stone to the door of *s.* *Mat* 27:60
Mary, sitting over against the *s.* 61
command that the *s.* be. 64, 66
Mary came to see the *s.* 28:1
depart quickly from the *s.* 8
and laid him in a *s.* . . . door of the *s.*
Mark 15:46; *Luke* 23:53
Acts 13:29
the *s.* at rising of sun. *Mark* 16:2
the stone from the door of the *s.* 3
entering into the *s.* 5
they fled from the *s.* 8
women also beheld the *s.* *Luke* 23:55
morning they came to the *s.* 24:1
found the stone rolled from *s.* 2
John 20:1
returned from the *s.* *Luke* 24:9
Peter ran to the *s.* 12
which were early at the *s.* 22
with us went to the *s.* 24
in the garden there was a new *s.*
John 19:41
for the *s.* was nigh at hand. 42
Mary when it was dark to the *s.* 20:1
taken away the Lord out of the *s.* 2
disciple came to the *s.* 3, 4, 8
Peter, and went into the *s.* 6
at the *s.* weeping . . . she stooped down and looked into the *s.* 11
and his *s.* is with us. *Acts* 2:29
Jacob laid in the *s.* that. 7:16

sepulchres

in the choice of our *s.* bury. *Gen* 23:6
Josiah spied the *s.* and took the bones out of the *s.* *2 Ki* 23:16
Jehoram not buried in *s.* *2 Chr* 21:20
Joash not buried in *s.* of. 24:25
Ahaz not in *s.* of kings. 28:27
buried in the chiefest of the *s.* 32:33
place of my fathers' *s.* *Neh* 2:3
me to the city of my fathers' *s.* 5
repaired to place over against *s.* 3:16
are like unto whited *s.* *Mat* 23:27
because ye garnish the *s.* of the. 29
ye build the *s.* of the prophets.
Luke 11:47, 48

Seraiah

Zadok the priest, and *S.* *2 Sam* 8:17
the captain of the guard took *S.* the chief. *2 Ki* 25:18; *Jer* 52:24
to Gedaliah, *S.* *2 Ki* 25:23
Jer 40:8
S. begat Joab. *1 Chr* 4:14
Josibiah son of *S.* 35
Azariah begat *S.* and *S.* begat. 6:14
Ezra the son of *S.* *Ezra* 7:1
S. sealed. *Neh* 10:2
S. was ruler of the house. 11:11
S. the priest went up with. 12:1
the fathers: of *S.*, Meraiah. 12
king commanded *S.* to. *Jer* 36:26
Jeremiah commanded *S.* the son of Neriah, this *S.* was a. 51:59
Jeremiah said to *S.*, When thou. 61

seraphims

above it stood the *s.* each. *Isa* 6:2
then flew one of the *s.* having. 6

sergeants

sent the *s.* saying, Let. *Acts* 16:35
the *s.* told these words unto. 38

Sergius Paulus

S. Paulus a prudent man. *Acts* 13:7

serpent

There are several words in the Bible for various sorts of serpents. It is not always certain which of the many sorts is referred to. The Hebrew word nachash *is a general term for any sort of serpent. Satan is called a serpent partly because of various qualities of the serpent which seem similar to his; partly because he assumed the form of a serpent in Eden; and partly because the serpent was a common symbol for evil.*

In the wilderness the Israelites were plagued by fiery serpents. They were probably so called from the intense burning pain of their bite. The brazen serpent was made by Moses at the command of God to heal those who were so troubled. This was preserved till the time of Hezekiah, when it was destroyed because it had become an object of worship.

the *s.* was more subtle. *Gen* 3:1
woman said, The *s.* beguiled me. 13
2 Cor 11:3
Dan shall be a *s.* by the. *Gen* 49:17
the rod became a *s.* *Ex* 4:3, 7, 9
10, 15
make thee a fiery *s.* *Num* 21:8
Moses made a *s.* of brass . . . if a *s.* had bitten any man . . . *s.* of. 9
in pieces the brasen *s.* *2 Ki* 18:4
formed the crooked *s.* *Job* 26:13
like the poison of a *s.* *Ps* 58:4
their tongues like a *s.* 140:3
at the last it biteth like a *s.* *Pr* 23:32
the way of a *s.* upon a rock. 30:19
s. shall bite him. *Eccl* 10:8
surely the *s.* will bite without. 11
s.'s root shall come forth a cockatrice; his fruit . . . flying *s.* *Isa* 14:29
punish the *s.*, that crooked *s.* 27:1
viper and fiery flying *s.* 30:6
shall be the *s.*'s meat. 65:25
thereof shall go like a *s.* *Jer* 46:22
and a *s.* bit him. *Amos* 5:19
I will command the *s.* and. 9:3
lick the dust like a *s.* *Mi* 7:17
will he give him a *s.*? *Mat* 7:10
Luke 11:11
as Moses lifted up the *s.* *John* 3:14
that old *s.* called. *Rev* 12:9; 20:2
nourished, from face of the *s.* 12:14
the *s.* cast out of his mouth. 15

serpents

rods, they became *s.* *Ex* 7:12
the Lord sent fiery *s.* *Num* 21:6
take away the *s.* from us. 7
wherein were fiery *s.* *Deut* 8:15
also send the poison of *s.* 32:24*
I will send *s.* among you. *Jer* 8:17
be ye therefore wise as *s.* *Mat* 10:16
ye *s.* how can ye escape? 23:33
they shall take up *s.* *Mark* 16:18
power to tread on *s.* *Luke* 10:19
and were destroyed of *s.* *1 Cor* 10:9
beasts and of *s.* is tamed. *Jas* 3:7
tails were like unto *s.* *Rev* 9:19

servant

This word in the Bible usually means bond-servant, *or* slave, *as there were rarely any others who acted as servants. See* **slave**. *It also means any one who serves another, as Joshua was the servant of Moses. Here the Revisions frequently change it to* minister.

Servant *is put for the subject of a prince. The servant of Pharaoh, the* servants *of* Saul *and those of* David, *are their subjects in general, and their domestics in particular,* 2 Sam 11:11; 12:19; 1 Chr 21:3. *In like manner also the* Philistines, *the* Syrians, *and several other nations, were* servants of David; *they obeyed him, they were his subjects, they paid him tribute,* 2 Sam 8:6.

Moses *is often called* the servant of the Lord, Deut 34:5, Josh 1:2.

Servant *is also taken* for a person *of a servile ignoble condition and spirit, who is altogether unfit for places of dignity,* Eccl 10:7.

Canaan, a *s.* of servants. *Gen* 9:25
I am Abraham's *s.* 24:34
became a *s.* to tribute. 49:15
if the *s.* plainly say. *Ex* 21:5
wast a *s.* in Egypt. *Deut* 5:15
thou shalt not deliver the *s.* 23:15
priest's *s.* came. *1 Sam* 2:13, 15
Samuel said, Bid the *s.* pass. 9:27
let thy handmaid be a *s.* 25:41
is not this David the *s.* of? 29:3
I am a young man *s.* to an. 30:13
s. named Ziba. *2 Sam* 9:2; 19:17

Ziba the *s.* of Mephibosheth. *2 Sam* 16:1
king's *s.* and me thy *s.* 18:29
Jeroboam Solomon's *s.* *1 Ki* 11:26
if thou wilt be a *s.* to this. 12:7
she said to her *s.*, Drive. *2 Ki* 4:24
when the *s.* of the man of. 6:15
Tobiah the *s.* the. *Neh* 2:10, 19
there; and the *s.* is free. *Job* 3:19
as a *s.* earnestly desireth the. 7:2
leviathan for a *s.* for ever ? 41:4
who was sold for a *s.* *Ps* 105:17
the fool shall be *s.* to. *Pr* 11:29
is despised and hath a *s.* 12:9
favour is toward a wise *s.* 14:35
a wise *s.* shall have rule over. 17:2
much less for a *s.* to rule. 19:10
and the borrower is *s.* to the. 22:7
a *s.* will not be corrected. 29:19
accuse not *s.* to his master. 30:10
the earth cannot bear a *s.* when. 22
as with the *s.* so with. *Isa* 24:2
to a *s.* of rulers. 49:7
is Israel a *s.*? *Jer* 2:14
s. of the living God. *Dan* 6:20
can *s.* of my lord talk? 10:17
s. honoureth his master. *Mal* 1:6
nor the *s.* above his lord. *Mat* 10:24
it is enough for the *s.* to be. 25
s. fell down and worshipped. 18:26
the lord of that *s.* was moved. 27
O thou wicked *s.* I forgave. 32
chief among you, let him be your *s.* 20:27; 23:11; *Mark* 10:44
wise *s.* whom lord. *Mat* 24:45
blessed is that *s.* whom his lord. 46 *Luke* 12:43
but if that evil *s.* shall say. *Mat* 24:48; *Luke* 12:45
the lord of that *s.* shall come. *Mat* 24:50; *Luke* 12:46
good and faithful *s.* enter thou into joy. *Mat* 25:21, 23; *Luke* 19:17
thou wicked and slothful *s.* *Mat* 25:26; *Luke* 19:22
cast the unprofitable *s.* *Mat* 25:30
Peter struck a *s.* of the high priest, and smote off his ear. 26:51 *Mark* 14:47; *John* 18:10
and he sent to the husbandmen a *s.* *Mark* 12:2
that *s.* which knew his. *Luke* 12:47
so that *s.* came and shewed. 14:21
but which of you having a *s.* 17:7
he thank that *s.*? I trow not. 9
at the season he sent a *s.* 20:10, 11
sin, is the *s.* of sin. *John* 8:34
the *s.* abideth not in the house. 35
the *s.* is not greater than his lord. 13:16; 15:20
the *s.* knoweth not what. 15:15
Paul a *s.* of Jesus Christ. *Rom* 1:1
judgest another man's *s.*? 14:4
I commend to you Phebe, our *s.* 16:1
thou called being a *s.*? *1 Cor* 7:21*
called, being a *s.* is the Lord's. 22*
yet I have made myself a *s.* 9:19*
I should not be the *s.* *Gal* 1:10
differeth nothing from a *s.* 4:1*
wherefore thou art no more a *s.* 7*
him the form of a *s.* *Phil* 2:7
Epaphras, a *s.* of Christ. *Col* 4:12
s. of Lord must not strive. *2 Tim* 2:24
as a *s.* but above a *s.* a brother. *Philem* 16
in his house as a *s.* *Heb* 3:5
Simon Peter, a *s.* of. *2 Pet* 1:1
Jude the *s.* of Jesus Christ. *Jude* 1

see **David, hired, maid**

servant, and **servants** *of God*

forgive the *s. of* the *God* of thy. *Gen* 50:17
as Moses the *s. of God.* *1 Chr* 6:49
Moses the *s. of God* said. *2 Chr* 24:9
law, which was given by Moses the *s. of God* to observe. *Neh* 10:29
he said, O Daniel, *s. of* the living *God.* *Dan* 6:20
law of Moses the *s. of God.* 9:11
a *s. of God.* *Tit* 1:1
James a *s. of God.* *Jas* 1:1
not using liberty, but as a *s. of God.* *1 Pet* 2:16
sealed the *s. of* our *God.* *Rev* 7:3
song of Moses the *s. of God.* 15:3

his **servant**

and Canaan shall be *his s.* *Gen* 9:26 27
Lord and *his s.* Moses. *Ex* 14:31
if a man smite *his s.* and die. 21:20
if he smite the eye of *his s.* that. 26
but *his s.* Joshua departed. 33:11*
saith my Lord to *his s.*? *Josh* 5:14
God commanded *his s.* Moses. 9:24
down with Phurah *his s.* *Judg* 7:11
the Levite went, having *his s.* 19:3
rose to depart, he and *his s.* 9
king sin against *his s.* *1 Sam* 19:4
impute any thing to *his s.* 22:15
the Lord hath kept *his s.* 25:39
thus pursue after *his s.*? 26:18
king hear the words of *his s.* 19
hath commanded *his s.* *2 Sam* 9:11
fulfilled the request of *his s.* 14:22
my lord come to *his s.*? 24:21
he will not slay *his s.* *1 Ki* 1:51
by the hand of Moses *his s.* 8:56
cause of *his s.* and Israel. 59
hand of *his s.* Ahijah. 14:18; 15:29
Elijah came and left *his s.* 19:3
he spake by *his s.* Elijah. *2 Ki* 9:36
he spake by *his s.* Jonah. 14:25
Hoshea became *his s.* and. 17:3
and Jehoiakim became *his s.* 24:1
seed of Israel *his s.* *1 Chr* 16:13
spake against *his s.* Hezekiah. *2 Chr* 32:16
let every one with *his s.* *Neh* 4:22
in prosperity *of his s.* *Ps* 35:27
O ye seed of Abraham *his s.* 105:6
he sent Moses *his s.* and Aaron. 26
remembered Abraham *his s.* 42
heritage unto Israel *his s.* 136:22
that delicately bringeth up *his s.* *Pr* 29:21
that confirmeth the word of *his s.* *Isa* 44:26
redeemed *his s.* Jacob. 48:20
from the womb to be *his s.* 49:5
obeyeth the voice of *his s.* 50:10
caused every man *his s.* *Jer* 34:16
his s. was healed in the. *Mat* 8:13
he hath holpen *his s.* *Luke* 1:54
would come and heal *his s.* 7:3
and sent *his s.* at supper time. 14:17
his angel unto *his s.* John. *Rev* 1:1

see **Lord**

man-**servant**

shalt not do any work, thou, nor thy *man-s.* *Ex* 20:10; *Deut* 5:14
not covet thy neighbour's *man-s.* *Ex* 20:17; *Deut* 5:21
if he smite out his *man-s.*'s tooth. *Ex* 21:27
if the ox shall push a *man-s.* 32
eat them, thou, and thy *man-s.* *Deut* 12:18
Lord, thou and thy *man-s.* 16:11
feast, thou, and thy *man-s.* 14
the cause of my *man-s.* *Job* 31:13
should let his *man-s.* go free. *Jer* 34:9, 10

my **servant**

I will multiply thy seed for *my s.*'s sake. *Gen* 26:24
he with whom it is found shall be *my s.* 44:10*, 17*
my s. Moses is not so. *Num* 12:7
why were ye not afraid to speak against *my s.*? 8
but *my s.* Caleb had another. 14:24
Moses *my s.* is dead. *Josh* 1:2
that my son had stirred up *my s.* *1 Sam* 22:8
therefore he shall be *my s.* 27:12
my lord, O king, *my s.* *2 Sam* 19:26
sent Naaman *my s.* *2 Ki* 5:6
according to the law *my s.* 21:8
considered *my s.* Job ? *Job* 1:8; 2:3
I called *my s.* and he gave. 19:16
right, as *my s.* Job hath. 42:7
go to *my s.* Job, he shall pray. 8
like as *my s.* Isaiah. *Isa* 20:3
I will call *my s.* Eliakim. 22:20
Israel, art *my s.*, fear not. *Isa* 41:8, 9
behold *my s.* whom I uphold. 42:1
blind but *my s.* that I sent ? 19
ye are witnesses, and *my s.* 43:10
hear, O Jacob, *my s.* 44:1
fear not, O Jacob, *my s.* 2
for thou art *my s.* 21; 49:3
for Jacob *my s.*'s sake, and. 45:4
thou shouldest be *my s.* 49:6
behold, *my s.* shall deal. 52:13
so will I do for *my s.*'s sake. 65:8
Nebuchadnezzar *my s.* *Jer* 25:9 27:6; 43:10
fear thou not, O *my s.* Jacob. 30:10 46:27, 28
land I have given to *my s.* Jacob. *Ezek* 28:25; 37:25
thee, O Zerubbabel *my s.* *Hag* 2:23
bring forth *my s.* the BRANCH. *Zech* 3:8
the law of Moses *my s.* *Mal* 4:4
my s. lieth at home sick. *Mat* 8:6
speak, and *my s.* shall be healed. 8 *Luke* 7:7
and to *my s.*, Do this, and he doeth it. *Mat* 8:9; *Luke* 7:8
behold, *my s.* whom I. *Mat* 12:18
there shall also *my s.* be. *John* 12:26

thy **servant**

I pray thee, from *thy s.* *Gen* 18:3
behold, *thy s.* hath found grace. 19:19; *Neh* 2:5
hast appointed for *thy s.* *Gen* 24:14
the mercies shewed to *thy s.* 32:10
shalt say, They be *thy s.* Jacob's. 18
which God hath given *thy s.* 33:5
grey hairs of *thy s.* our father. 44:31
thy s. became surety for the lad. 32
hast spoken unto *thy s.* *Ex* 4:10
for thee, and for *thy s.* *Lev* 25:6
thou afflicted *thy s.*? *Num* 11:11
hast begun to shew *thy s.* *Deut* 3:24
and he shall be *thy s.* for ever. 15:17
down with Phurah *thy s.* *Judg* 7:10
deliverance into hand of *thy s.* 15:18
speak, Lord, for *thy s.* heareth. *1 Sam* 3:9, 10
thy s. slew both the lion. 17:36
if he say thus, *thy s.* shall. 20:7
for *thy s.* knew nothing of all. 22:15
I beseech thee, tell *thy s.* 23:11
know what *thy s.* can do. 28:2
hast spoken of *thy s.*'s house. *2 Sam* 7:19
thou, Lord God, knowest *thy s.* 20
to bless the house of *thy s.* 29
answered, Behold *thy s.* 9:6
the king's sons came as *thy s.* 13:35
even there will *thy s.* be. 15:21
he hath slandered *thy s.* 19:27
away the iniquity of *thy s.* 24:10
but me, even me *thy s.* and Zadok the priest, and *thy s.* *1 Ki* 1:26
king said, so will *thy s.* do. 2:38
and *thy s.* is in the midst of. 3:8
give *thy s.* understanding heart. 9
to the prayer of *thy s.* 8:28
but I *thy s.* fear the Lord. 18:12
this day that I am *thy s.* 36
thy s. Ben-hadad saith, I pray. 20:32
as *thy s.* was busy here and there. 40
thy s. my husband is dead, and thou knowest *thy s.* did fear. *2 Ki* 4:1
pardon *thy s.* in this thing. 5:18
Gehazi said, *Thy s.* went no. 25
but what, is *thy s.* a dog ? 8:13
I am *thy s.* 16:7
prosper, I pray thee, *thy s.* this day. *Neh* 1:11
by them is *thy s.* warned. *Ps* 19:11
thy s. from presumptuous sins. 13
put not *thy s.* away in anger. 27:9
shine upon *thy s.*: save me. 31:16
hide not thy face from *thy s.* 69:17
O my God, save *thy s.* that. 86:2
give thy strength unto *thy s.* 16
void the covenant of *thy s.* 89:39
truly I am *thy s.* 116:16; 119:125 143:12
lest thou hear *thy s.* *Eccl* 7:21
hear the prayer of *thy s.* *Dan* 9:17
now lettest thou *thy s.* *Luke* 2:29

servants

Canaan, a servant of *s.* *Gen* 9:25
have I given him for *s.* 27:37
children of Israel are *s.* *Lev* 25:55
and say, We are your *s.* *Josh* 9:11
that ye be not *s.* unto. *1 Sam* 4:9
Philistine, and you *s.* to Saul ? 17:8
will we be your *s.*: but if I kill him, then shall ye be our *s.* 9
but the *s.* of the king would. 22:17
many *s.* break away from. 25:10
to wash the feet of the *s.* of. 41
became David's *s.* *2 Sam* 8:2
Edom became David's *s.* 14
fifteen sons and twenty *s.* 9:10
all in the house of Ziba *s.* 12
Hanun took David's *s.* and shaved. 10:4; *1 Chr* 19:4
the *s.* of my Lord are. *2 Sam* 11:11
two of the *s.* of Shimei. *1 Ki* 2:39
the *s.* of Amon. *2 Ki* 21:23
not all my lord's *s.*? *1 Chr* 21:3
children of Israel Solomon made no *s.* *2 Chr* 8:9
Babylon, where they were *s.* 36:20
we are the *s.* of the God. *Ezra* 5:11
their *s.* bare rule over. *Neh* 5:15
behold, we are *s.* this day, *s.* 9:36
they have slain the *s.* *Job* 1:15, 17
as the eyes of *s.* look. *Ps* 123:2
I got me *s.* and had *s.* born. *Eccl* 2:7
I have seen *s.* upon horses, and princes walking as *s.* 10:7
shall possess them for *s.* *Isa* 14:2
s. whom they had let go free, to return... subjection for *s.* *Jer* 34:11
s. have ruled over us. *Lam* 5:8
ye *s.* of the most high God. *Dan* 3:26
upon the *s.* will I pour. *Joel* 2:29
be a spoil to their *s.* *Zech* 2:9
then said the king to the *s.* *Mat* 22:13
the lord of those *s.* cometh. 25:19
the *s.* did strike Jesus. *Mark* 14:65*
blessed are those *s.* *Luke* 12:37, 38
say, We are unprofitable *s.* 17:10
I call you not *s.*, for. *John* 15:15
these men are *s.* of the. *Acts* 16:17
ye yield yourselves *s.* to obey. *Rom* 6:16
that ye were the *s.* of sin. 17
made free, ye became the *s.* 18
your members *s.* to sin. 19
s. of sin, ye were free from. 20
and become *s.* to God. 22
be not ye the *s.* of men. *1 Cor* 7:23
and ourselves your *s.* *2 Cor* 4:5
s. be obedient to your. *Eph* 6:5
Col 3:22; *Tit* 2:9; *1 Pet* 2:18
eye service, but as the *s.* of. *Eph* 6:6
Paul and Timotheus the *s.* *Phil* 1:1
masters, give unto your *s.* *Col* 4:1
let as many *s.* as are. *1 Tim* 6:1
but as the *s.* of God. *1 Pet* 2:16
they themselves are the *s.* of. *2 Pet* 2:19
till we have sealed the *s.* *Rev* 7:3
see **hired, Lord, maid, men, women**

his **servants**

feast unto all *his s.* *Gen* 40:20
Pharaoh made *his s.* *Ex* 9:20
in the night, he and *his s.* 12:30
his two *s.* with him. *Num* 22:22
repent himself for *his s.* *Deut* 32:36
the blood of *his s.* 43
and give to *his s.* *1 Sam* 8:14, 15
tenth, ye shall be *his s.* 17
Saul spake to all *his s.* to kill. 19:1
and all *his s.* were standing. 22:6
his s. came near. *2 Ki* 5:13
are not *his s.* come to ? *1 Chr* 19:3
they shall be *his s.* *2 Chr* 12:8
his s. spake yet more against. 32:16
therefore we *his s.* will. *Neh* 2:20
put no trust in *his s.* *Job* 4:18
the seed also of *his s.* *Ps* 69:36
to deal subtilly with *his s.* 105:25
himself concerning *his s.* 135:14
if hearken to lies, all *his s.* *Pr* 29:12
of the Lord, to be *his s.* *Isa* 56:6
the Lord shall call *his s.* by. 65:15
be known toward *his s.* 66:14
on horses, he and *his s.* *Jer* 22:4
punish him, his seed and *his s.* 36:31
prince give a gift to *his s.* *Ezek* 46:17
and delivered *his s.* that. *Dan* 3:28
take account of *his s.* *Mat* 18:23
he sent *his s.* to husbandmen. 21:34
he called *his* ten *s.* *Luke* 19:13
his s. ye are to whom. *Rom* 6:16
to shew *his s.* things. *Rev* 1:1; 22:6
hath avenged blood of *his s.* 19:2
praise God, all ye *his s.* and. 5
throne shall be in it, and *his s.* 22:3

my **servants**

they are *my s.* whom I brought. *Lev* 25:42, 55
I have appointed *my s.* *1 Sam* 21:2
my s. shall be with thy servants. *1 Ki* 5:6; *2 Chr* 2:8
yet I will send *my s.* *1 Ki* 20:6
let *my s.* go with thy servants. 22:49
the blood of *my s.* *2 Ki* 9:7
the half of *my s.* wrought. *Neh* 4:16
neither I nor *my s.* put off our. 23
I and *my s.* might exact of. 5:10
all *my s.* were gathered thither. 16
and some of *my s.* sat. 13:19
mine elect and *my s.* shall. *Isa* 65:9
my s. shall eat. 13
my s. shall sing for joy. 14
I have even sent to you all *my s.* *Jer* 7:25; 44:4
world, then would *my s.* fight. *John* 18:36
on *my s.* I will pour out. *Acts* 2:18
prophetess, to seduce *my s.* *Rev* 2:20
see **prophets**

thy **servants**

thy s. are no spies. *Gen* 42:11
out the iniquity of *thy s.* 44:16*
thy s. are shepherds, both we. 47:3
said, Behold, we be *thy s.* 50:18
wherefore dealest thou thus with *thy s.*? *Ex* 5:15
these *thy s.* shall bow down. 11:8
Abraham and Israel *thy s.* 32:13
Deut 9:27
thy s. will do as my lord. *Num* 32:25, 31
to Joshua, We are *thy s.* *Josh* 9:8
slack not thy hand from *thy s.* 10:6
pray for *thy s.* to the. *1 Sam* 12:19
faithful among all *thy s.*? 22:14
comfortably to *thy s.* *2 Sam* 19:7
word, return thou and all *thy s.* 14
they told Shimei, *thy s.* *1 Ki* 2:39
my servants shall be with *thy s.* 5:6
2 Chr 2:8
and mercy with *thy s.* *1 Ki* 8:23
hear thou and judge *thy s.* 32
2 Chr 6:23
happy are these *thy s.* *1 Ki* 10:8
2 Chr 9:7
they will be *thy s.* for ever. *1 Ki* 12:7; *2 Chr* 10:7
content, and go with *thy s.* *2 Ki* 6:3
now these are *thy s.* and. *Neh* 1:10
attentive to prayer of *thy s.* 11
the bodies of *thy s.* have. *Ps* 79:2
of the blood of *thy s.* shed. 10
Lord, the reproach of *thy s.* 89:50
repent thee concerning *thy s.* 90:13
let thy work appear unto *thy s.* 16
for *thy s.* take pleasure in. 102:14
children of *thy s.* shall continue. 28
this day, for all are *thy s.* 119:91
by *thy s.* hast thou. *Isa* 37:24
return, for *thy s.'* sake. 63:17
prove *thy s.* I beseech. *Dan* 1:12
as thou seest, deal with *thy s.* 13
grant unto *thy s.* that. *Acts* 4:29

serve

shall *s.* them 400 years. *Gen* 15:13
that nation whom they shall *s.* 14
elder shall *s.* the younger. 25:23
let people *s.* thee, nations. 27:29
by thy sword shalt thou live, and *s.* 40
therefore *s.* me for nought ? 29:15
I will *s.* thee seven years for. 18
thou shalt *s.* with me seven. 27
they made Israel to *s.* *Ex* 1:13
ye shall *s.* God upon this mountain. 3:12
my son go, that he may *s.* me. 4:23
let my people go, that they may *s.* 7:16; 8:1, 20; 9:1, 13; 10:3
that we may *s.* Egyptians, for it had been better for us to *s.* *Ex* 14:12
not bow down to them, nor *s.* them. 20:5; *Deut* 5:9
Hebrew servant, six years he shall *s.* *Ex* 21:2
ear, and he shall *s.* him for ever. 6
him to *s.* as bondservant. *Lev* 25:39
s. thee unto the year of jubile. 40
the family of the Gershonites to *s.* *Num* 4:24
made for them, so shall they *s.* 26
of fifty they shall *s.* no more. 8:25
Levi, for their service they *s.* 18:21
be driven to *s.* them. *Deut* 4:19
the Lord thy God, and *s.* him. 6:13
10:12, 20; 11:13; 13:4; *Josh* 22:5
24:14, 15; *1 Sam* 7:3; 12:14, 20
24
sold to thee, and *s.* six years. *Deut* 15:12
to thee, and shall *s.* thee. 20:11
shalt thou *s.* thine enemies. 28:48
this day whom ye will *s.* *Josh* 24:15
should *s.* Shechem, should *s.* Hamor. *Judg* 9:28
that we should *s.* him ? 38
occasion shall *s.* thee. *1 Sam* 10:7
with us, and we will *s.* thee. 11:1
deliver us, and we will *s.* 12:10
be our servants, and *s.* us. 17:9
whom should I *s.*? should I not *s.*? *2 Sam* 16:19
a people I knew not shall *s.* me. 22:44; *Ps* 18:43
heavy yoke lighter, and we will *s.* *1 Ki* 12:4; *2 Chr* 10:4
Jehu shall *s.* Baal. *2 Ki* 10:18
the land, and *s.* the king of. 25:24
Jer 27:11, 12, 17; 28:14; 40:9
and *s.* him with a perfect heart. *1 Chr* 28:9
chosen you to *s.* him. *2 Chr* 29:11*
Josiah made all present to *s.* 34:33
that we should *s.* him ? *Job* 21:15
if they obey and *s.* him, they. 36:11
unicorn be willing to *s.* thee ? 39:9
a seed shall *s.* him and. *Ps* 22:30
kings, all nations shall *s.* him. 72:11
all they that *s.* graven images. 97:7
perfect way, he shall *s.* me. 101:6*
wherein thou wast made to *s.* *Isa* 14:3
the Egyptians shall *s.* with. 19:23*
I have not caused thee to *s.* 43:23
but thou hast made me to *s.* 24†
themselves to the Lord, to *s.* 56:6*
the nation that will not *s.* thee. 60:12
so shall ye *s.* strangers. *Jer* 5:19
cause thee to *s.* thine enemies. 17:4
these nations shall *s.* the king. 25:11
many nations shall *s.* themselves. 14; 27:7
of field have I given to *s.* him. 27:6
the nation which will not *s.* the king. 8
that say, Ye shall not *s.* 9, 14
no more *s.* themselves of him. 30:8
that none should *s.* himself. 34:9, 10
fear not to *s.* the Chaldeans. 40:9
I will *s.* the Chaldeans. 10*
the countries to *s.* wood. *Ezek* 20:32
O house of Israel, go *s.* ye. 39
all of them in the land shall *s.* me. 40
his army *s.* a great service. 29:18
food to them that *s.* the city. 48:18*
that *s.* the city, shall *s.* it out of. 19*
God whom we *s.* is able. *Dan* 3:17
they might not *s.* any, except. 28
languages should *s.* him. 7:14
all dominions shall *s.* and obey. 27
s. him with one consent. *Zeph* 3:9
it is in vain to *s.* God. *Mal* 3:14
him only shalt thou *s.* *Mat* 4:10
Luke 4:8
no man can *s.* two masters; ye cannot *s.* God. *Mat* 6:24; *Luke* 16:13
delivered, might *s.* him. *Luke* 1:74
sister hath left me to *s.* alone. 10:40
he will come forth and *s.* them. 12:37
lo, these many years do I *s.* thee. 15:29
say, Gird thyself and *s.* me ? 17:8
is chief, as he that doth *s.* 22:26
if any man *s.* me, let him follow. *John* 12:26

word of God, and s. Acts 6:2
shall they come forth and s. 7:7
angel of God, whom I s. 27:23
whom I s. with my spirit in the gospel of his Son. Rom 1:9
we should not s. sin. 6:6
we should s. in newness of. 7:6
so then, with the mind I s. the. 25
it was said, the elder shall s. 9:12
they that are such s. not our. 16:18
but by love s. one another. Gal 5:13
for ye s. the Lord Christ. Col 3:24
turned from idols to s. 1 Thes 1:9
I thank God whom I s. 2 Tim 1:3
who s. unto the example and shadow of heavenly. Heb 8:5
purge from dead works to s.? 9:14
whereby ye may s. God. 12:28
no right to eat, which s. the. 13:10
they s. him day and night. Rev 7:15
and his servants shall s. him. 22:3
see **Lord**

serve joined with *gods*

thou shalt not s. their gods. Ex 23:24
Deut 6:14; 28:14; Josh 23:7
2 Ki 17:35; Jer 25:6; 35:15
if thou s. their gods it will. Ex 23:33
s. gods, the work of men's hands.
Deut 4:28; 28:36, 64; Jer 16:13
that they may s. other gods.
Deut 7:4; 31:20
s. other gods and worship. 8:19
11:16; 30:17; Josh 24:20
2 Chr 7:19
nations s. their gods? Deut 12:30
and s. other gods. 13:2, 6, 13
from God to s. other gods. 29:18
we should s. other gods. Josh 24:16
more than their fathers to s. other gods. Judg 2:19; Jer 11:10; 13:10
saying, Go s. other gods.
1 Sam 26:19
to anger, to s. other gods. Jer 44:3
they s. not thy gods. Dan 3:12
do ye not s. my gods? 14
we will not s. thy gods. 18

served

twelve years they s. Gen 14:4
Jacob s. seven years. 29:20, 30
children for whom I s. thee. 30:26
knowest how I have s. thee. 29
with all my power I have s. 31:6
I s. thee 14 years for thy two. 41
wherein the nations s. Deut 12:2
hath gone and s. other gods. 17:3
29:26; Josh 23:16
fathers s. other gods. Josh 24:2, 15
gods which your fathers s. 14
and Israel s. the Lord all the days of Joshua. 31; Judg 2:7
Israel s. Baalim. Judg 2:11, 13
3:7; 10:6, 10
to sons, and s. their gods. 3:6
Israel s. Chushan-rishathaim. 8
so Israel s. Eglon king of Moab. 14
Why hast thou s. us thus? 8:1
ye have forsaken me, and s. 10:13
they put away gods, s. 16; 1 Sam 7:4
peace and s. Israel. 2 Sam 10:19
s. in thy father's presence. 16:19
presents and s. Solomon. 1 Ki 4:21
because they s. other gods. 9:9
2 Chr 7:22
Ahab s. Baal. 1 Ki 16:31
Ahazian s. Baal. 22:53
Ahab s. Baal a little. 2 Ki 10:18
Hezekiah s. not the king of. 18:7
Manasseh s. host of heaven. 21:3
2 Chr 33:3
Amon s. the idols that his father s.
2 Ki 21:21; 2 Chr 33:22
Judah s. groves and. 2 Chr 24:18
they have not s. thee in. Neh 9:35
and they s. their idols. Ps 106:36
thee as thou hast s. us. 137:8
the king himself is s. Eccl 5:9
as ye have s. strange gods. Jer 5:19
and moon, whom they have s. 8:2
after other gods and s. them. 16:11
worshipped other gods and s. 22:9
he hath s. thee six years. 34:14
for the service which he had s.
Ezek 29:18, 20
the hands of those that s. Ezek 34:27
Israel s. for a wife; he. Hos 12:12
Anna s. God night and. Luke 2:37*
a supper and Martha s. John 12:2
after David had s. his. Acts 13:36
who worshipped and s. Rom 1:25
he hath s. with me in. Phil 2:22

servedst

thou s. not the Lord. Deut 28:47

servest

thy God whom thou s. Dan 6:16
is thy God whom thou s. able? 20

serveth

of Merari all that s. Num 3:36
his son that s. him Mal 3:17
s. God, and him that s. not. 18
sitteth at meat or he that s.? but I am among . . . s. Luke 22:27
he that in these things s. Christ is.
Rom 14:18
prophecy s. not them. 1 Cor 14:22*
wherefore then s. the law? Gal 3:19

service

for the s. that thou. Gen 29:27
thou knowest the s. which. 30:26
s. in field; all their s. wherein they.
Ex 1:14
come to land, ye shall keep this s.
12:25; 13:5
say, What mean ye by this s.? 12:26
all vessels in all the s. 27:19
make the clothes of the s. 31:10
35:19
more than enough for the s. 36:5
tribe of Levi to do s. Num 3:7, 8
charge of Gershonites for the s. 26
s. of sanctuary the charge. 31; 4:4
shall appoint them to the s. 4:19
in to perform the s. to do work. 23
the s. of the Gershonites. 24, 27, 28
s. of the sons of Merari. 30, 33, 43
that they may do the s. of the. 7:5
Levites may execute the s. of. 8:11
they shall go in to wait upon s. 24
shall cease waiting on the s. 25
thing to bring you to the s. 16:9
joined to thee for all the s. 18:4
given as a gift to do the s. 6
tenth in Israel for their s. 21, 31
that we might do the s. Josh 22:27
thou the grievous s. lighter. 1 Ki 12:4
David set over the s. 1 Chr 6:31
very able men for the work of the s.
9:13; 26:8
distributed them in their s. 24:3
for all the work of the s. 28:13
be with thee for all the s. 21
to consecrate his s. to the Lord.? 29:5
and gave for the s. of house. 7
of the priests to their s. 2 Chr 8:14
they may know my s. and s. 12:8
money to such as did the s. 24:12
so the s. of the house was set. 29:35
every man according to his s. 31:2
work that he began in the s. 21
encouraged them to the s. of. 35:2
so the s. of the Lord was. 10, 16
in their courses, for the s. of God.
Ezra 6:18; 7:19
part of a shekel for s. Neh 10:32
to grow for the s. Ps 104:14
useth neighbour's s. without wages.
Jer 22:13
army to serve a great s. Ezek 29:18
charge of house for all the s. 44:14
who killeth you will think he doeth s. unto God. John 16:2
pertaineth the s. of God. Rom 9:4
which is your reasonable s. 12:1
that my s. may be accepted. 15:31*
administration of this s. 2 Cor 9:12
wages of them to do you s. 11:8*
did s. to them who by nature. Gal 4:8
with good will doing s. Eph 6:7
if I be offered upon the s. Phil 2:17
supply your lack of s. toward. 30
rather do s. because they. 1 Tim 6:2
had ordinances of divine s. Heb 9:1
the priests accomplishing the s. 6
make him that did the s. perfect. 9
works, and charity, and s. Rev 2:19*

bond-**service**

Solomon did levy a tribute of bond-s.
1 Ki 9:21

eye **service**

eye s. as men pleasers. Eph 6:6

servile

ye shall do no s. work. Lev 23:7
8, 21, 25, 35, 36; Num 28:18, 25
26; 29:1, 12, 35

serving

let Israel go from s. us. Ex 14:5
hired servant in s. thee. Deut 15:18
cumbered about much s. Luke 10:40
s. the Lord with all humility.
Acts 20:19
tribes instantly s. God day. 26:7
fervent in spirit, s. Lord. Rom 12:11
foolish, s. divers lusts. Tit 3:3

servitor

s. said, Should I set this? 2 Ki 4:43*

servitude

ease somewhat grievous s. of thy.
2 Chr 10:4*
gone because of great s. Lam 1:3

set

s. the stars in firmament. Gen 1:17
Lord s. a mark upon Cain. 4:15*
door of the ark shalt s. in the. 6:16
I do s. my bow in the cloud. 9:13
Abraham s. calf before them. 18:8
the angel s. Lot without the. 19:16
s. it before my brethren and. 31:37
Pharaoh s. him over the land. 41:33
I have s. thee over all the land. 41
if I bring him not, and s. him. 43:9
Jacob s. Ephraim before. 48:20
nor did he s. his heart. Ex 7:23*
s. apart to Lord all that open. 13:12
thou shalt s. bounds. 19:12, 23
which thou shalt s. before. 21:1
I will s. thy bounds from the. 23:31
thou shalt s. on table shew. 25:30
s. the table without. 26:35
s. in order things that are to be s. in.
40:4
thou shalt s. the altar of gold. 5
s. altar of burnt offering. 6
s. the laver between. 7
he s. the staves on the ark. 20
s. the bread in order. 23
sabbath he shall s. it in. Lev 24:8
I will s. my tabernacle among. 26:11
Judah, these shall first s. forth.
Num 2:9
as the camp is to s. forward. 4:15
the priest shall s. her before. 5:16
thou shalt s. the Levites. 8:13
s. forward bearing the. 10:17
Lord said, S. the fiery serpent. 21:8
let the Lord s. a man over. 27:16*
I have s. the land before you.
Deut 1:8, 21
as all this law which I s. 4:8, 44
Lord did not s. his love on. 7:7
I s. before you a blessing. 11:26
judgements which I s. before. 32
choose to s. his name there. 14:24
Neh 1:9
shalt say, I will s. a king. Deut 17:14
in any wise shalt s. him the. 15
which they of old time have s. 19:14
s. down the basket. 26:4, 10*
the Lord thy God will s. thee. 28:1
would not s. sole of her foot. 56
I have s. before you life. 30:15, 19
he s. bounds of the people by. 32:8
s. your hearts unto all the. 46
he s. them a statute in. Josh 24:25
till I bring and s. my. Judg 6:18
that lappeth, him shalt thou s. 7:5
but newly s. the watch. 19
Lord s. every man's sword. 22
out of the dust, to s. them among princes; he hath s. 1 Sam 2:8
the Philistines s. the ark of. 5:2
as for thine asses, s. not thy. 9:20
ye have said, Nay, but s. a. 10:19
the Lord hath s. a king over. 12:13
Israel s. the battle in array. 17:2, 8
2 Sam 10:17; 1 Ki 20:12
1 Chr 19:17

they s. the ark of God. 2 Sam 6:3
s. Uriah in forefront of the. 11:15
yet didst thou s. thy servant. 19:28
that all Israel s. their. 1 Ki 2:15
son, whom I will s. on throne. 5:5
he s. the one in Beth-el, the. 12:29
and s. Naboth on high among. 21:9
thou shalt s. aside that. 2 Ki 4:4
let us s. for him there a bed. 10
s. on the great pot, and seethe. 38
what, should I s. this before an? 43
s. bread and water before. 6:22
s. thine house in order. 20:1
Isa 38:1
they s. the ark in midst. 1 Chr 16:1
s. your heart to seek. 22:19
because I s. my affection to. 29:3
s. their hearts to seek. 2 Chr 11:16
he feared, and s. himself to. 20:3
they s. the house of God. 24:13
Josiah s. the priests in their. 35:2
they s. the priests in. Ezra 6:18
pleased the king, and I s. Neh 2:6
we s. a watch against them. 4:9
increase to kings s. over us. 9:37
I gathered and s. them. 13:11
the terrors of God s. Job 6:4
thou shouldest s. thine heart. 7:17
why hast thou s. me as a mark? 20
shall s. me a time to plead? 9:19
and he hath s. darkness in. 19:8
have disdained to s. with. 30:1
they s. forward my calamity. 13
s. thy words in order before. 33:5
if he s. his heart upon man. 34:14
and s. others in their stead. 24
canst thou s. dominion? 38:33
the kings of the earth s. Ps 2:2
yet have I s. my king on my holy. 6
I will not be afraid if 10,000 s. 3:6
the Lord hath s. apart him that. 4:3
who hast s. thy glory above. 8:1
I will s. him in safety from. 12:5
I have s. the Lord always. 16:8
in them hath he s. a tabernacle. 19:4
thou hast s. my feet in a large room. 31:8
brought me up, and s. my feet. 40:2
I will s. them in order. 50:21
they have not s. God before. 54:3
if riches, s. not your heart. 62:10
surely thou didst s. them in. 73:18
thou hast s. all the borders of. 74:17
that they might s. their hope. 78:7
a generation that s. not their. 8
and shall s. us in the way. 85:13
violent men have not s. thee. 86:14
thou hast s. our iniquities. 90:8
s. his love upon me, therefore will I deliver him and s. 91:14
I will s. no wicked thing. 101:3
thou hast s. a bound that they. 104:9
s. thou a wicked man over. 109:6
that he may s. him with. 113:8
Lord answered, and s. me in. 118:5
fruit of thy body will I s. 132:11
proud have s. gins for me. 140:5
s. a watch, O Lord, before. 141:3
ye have s. at nought all. Pr 1:25
landmark which thy fathers have s. 22:28
wilt thou s. thine eyes on? 23:5
also he hath s. the world. Eccl 3:11
God hath s. the one against. 7:14
he sought out, and s. in order. 12:9
s. me as a seal upon thine heart. S of S 8:6
let us s. a king in midst of it. Isa 7:6
the Lord will s. them in their. 14:1
s. it with strange slips. 17:10
I will s. Egyptians against. 19:2
go s. a watchman, let him. 21:6
shall s. themselves in array. 22:7
who would s. briers and? 27:4
I will s. in the desert the fir. 41:19
till he have s. judgement. 42:4
who as I, shall s. it in order? 44:7
they carry him, and s. him. 46:7
mountain hast thou s. thy bed. 57:7
I have s. watchmen on thy walls. 62:6; Jer 6:17
I will s. a sign among. Isa 66:19
see, I have s. thee over. Jer 1:10
lay wait, they s. a trap. 5:26
I have s. thee for a tower. Jer 6:27
the place where I s. my. 7:12*
they s. their abominations in. 30
law which I s. before them. 9:13
I s. before you the way of life. 21:8
for I will s. mine eyes on. 24:6
to walk in my law, which I s. 26:4
his servant, whom he had s. 34:16
I s. pots of wine before sons. 35:5
my friends have s. thee on. 38:22
statutes which I s. before. 44:10
hath s. me in dark places. Lam 3:6
he hath s. me as a mark for. 12
I have s. it in the midst. Ezek 5:5
I s. it far from thee. 7:20
s. a mark on the foreheads. 9:4
for I have s. thee for a sign. 12:6
thou hast s. my oil before. 16:18, 19
off highest branch, I will s. it. 17:22
then nations s. against him on. 19:8
in thee have they s. light. 22:7
king of Babylon s. himself. 24:2
s. on a pot, s. it on, and also. 3
her blood, she s. it upon the. 7, 8
whereon they s. their minds. 25
I shall s. glory in the land. 26:20
they of Persia s. forth thy. 27:10
though thou s. thy heart. 28:2
cherub, and I have s. thee so. 14
they s. her a bed in the midst. 32:25
I will s. my sanctuary in. 37:26
I will s. my glory among. 39:21
s. thy heart upon all that I. 40:4
have s. keepers of my charge. 44:8
king thought to s. him. Dan 6:3
he s. his heart on Daniel to. 14
to walk in his laws which he s. 9:10
thou didst s. thine heart to. 10:12
lest I s. her as in the day. Hos 2:3
s. their heart on their iniquity. 4:8
Judah, he hath s. an harvest. 6:11
how shall I s. thee as Zeboim? 11:8
we may s. forth wheat. Amos 8:5
I will s. mine eyes upon them. 9:4
though thou s. thy nest. Ob 4
that he may s. his nest. Hab 2:9
I said, Let them s. a fair. Zech 3:5
it shall be s. there upon her. 5:11
make crowns, and s. them. 6:11
I s. all men, every one against. 8:10
I am come to s. a man. Mat 10:35
he shall s. the sheep on his. 25:33
and s. an hedge about it. Mark 12:1
to s. at liberty them. Luke 4:18
and s. him on his own beast. 10:34
I have nothing to s. before. 11:6
Herod with men of war s. 23:11
every man doth s. forth. John 2:10
he hath s. to his seal, that. 3:33
no, not so much as to s. Acts 7:5
then Paul s. his eyes on him. 13:9
I have s. thee to be a light to. 47
no man shall s. on thee to. 18:10
whom God s. forth to be. Rom 3:25
why dost thou s. at nought? 14:10
God hath s. forth us. 1 Cor 4:9
s. them to judge who are least. 6:4
now God hath s. the members. 12:18
God hath s. some in the church. 28
when he s. him at his own. Eph 1:20
s. your affection on things. Col 3:2
thou didst s. him over work. Heb 2:7
I have s. before thee an open door. Rev 3:8
shut him up, and s. a seal. 20:3*

set *up*

stone and s. it up for a pillar, and. Gen 28:18, 22; 31:45; 35:14
shalt s. up the tabernacle. Ex 40:2
thou shalt s. up the court. 8, 18, 21
he s. up hanging at door of tabernacle. 28*, 33
nor shall ye s. up any. Lev 26:1*
when the tabernacle is pitched, the Levites shall s. it up. Num 1:51
that Moses had fully s. up the. 7:1
and other did s. it up against. 10:21
s. up these stones. Deut 27:2, 4
Joshua s. up twelve stones. Josh 4:9
shall he s. up gates of it. 6:26
1 Ki 16:34
children of Dan s. up. Judg 18:30
they s. them up Micah's graven. 31
it repenteth me I have s. up Saul. 1 Sam 15:11
behold, Saul hath s. him up a. 12
to s. up throne of David. 2 Sam 3:10
I will s. up thy seed after thee. 7:12
to s. up his son after. 1 Ki 15:4
they s. them up images. 2 Ki 17:10
s. them up an altar in. 1 Chr 21:18*
Amaziah s. them up to. 2 Chr 25:14
Manasseh s. up groves and. 33:19
offered freely to s. up. Ezra 2:68
Jews have s. up the walls thereof. 4:12, 13, 16
a great king of Israel, s. up. 5:11*
being s. up, let him be hanged. 6:11
to give us a reviving, to s. up. 9:9
they sanctified it, and s. up. Neh 3:1, 3, 6, 13, 14, 15; 7:1
time I had not s. up the doors. 6:1
to s. up on high those. Job 5:11
hath shaken me, and s. me up. 16:12
name of God we will s. up. Ps 20:5
he shall hide me, and s. me up. 27:5
O God, s. me up on high. 69:29
s. up their ensigns for signs. 74:4
thou hast s. up right hand of. 89:42*
I was s. up from everlasting, from. Pr 8:23
Lord shall s. up the. Isa 9:11
he shall s. up an ensign for. 11:12
they s. up towers thereof. 23:13
that s. up wood of their. 45:20*
I will s. up my standard. 49:22
s. up thy remembrance. 57:8
s. up the standard toward. Jer 4:6
none to s. up my curtains. 10:20
have ye s. up altars to that. 11:13
and I will s. up shepherds. 23:4
s. thee up way marks, make. 31:21
s. up a standard, publish. 50:2
51:12, 27
s. up the watchmen, prepare. 51:12
he hath s. up horn of thy. Lam 2:17*
these men have s. up. Ezek 14:3*
the deep s. him up on high. 31:4
I will s. up one shepherd. 34:23
God of heaven shall s. up. Dan 2:44
golden image I have s. up. 3:14
whom he would he s. up and. 5:19
that maketh desolate s. up. 12:11
they have s. up kings. Hos 8:4
work wickedness are s. up. Mal 3:15
and s. up over his head. Mat 27:37
and s. up false witnesses. Acts 6:13
again the ruins, and s. it up. 15:16

set, *passive*

there was s. meat before. Gen 24:33
because the sun was s. 28:11
a ladder was s. upon earth. 12
stones s. in ephod. Ex 25:7; 28:11
35:9, 27
two tenons s. in order. 26:17
they are s. on mischief. 32:22
the rings to be s. 37:3
the lamps s. in order. 39:37
name was much s. by. 1 Sam 18:30
as thy life was much s. by. 26:24
crown was s. on David's head. 2 Sam 12:30; 1 Chr 20:2
a seat to be s. for the. 1 Ki 2:19
could not see, for his eyes were s. 14:4
that every man is s. at. 2 Ki 12:4*
appointed in their s. 1 Chr 9:22
Joab saw that battle was s. 19:10
onyx stones and stones to be s. 29:2
I am s. on the throne. 2 Chr 6:10
house of Lord was s. in. 29:35
in their s. office to give. 31:15
in their s. office they sanctified. 18
and what should be s. on. Job 36:16
eyes are privily s. against. Ps 10:8
s. thrones of judgement. 122:5
let my prayer be s. forth. 141:2
heart is fully s. in them. Eccl 8:11
folly s. in great dignity; rich. 10:6
are as the eyes of doves fitly s. S of S 5:12
his hands are as gold rings s. 14
s. upon sockets of fine gold. 15
thy belly as a heap of wheat s. 7:2
and instead of well s. hair. Isa 3:24
s. in my ward whole nights. 21:8

silver purified *s. times.* *Ps* 12:6
s. times a day do I praise. 119:164
falleth *s. times*, and riseth. *Pr* 24:16
heat the furnace one *s. times* more. *Dan* 3:19
let *s. times* pass over him. 4:16
23, 25, 32
shall I forgive ? till *s. times.* *Mat* 18:21
I say not, till *s. times*, but until seventy *times s.* 22
trespass against thee *s. times* a day, and *s. times* a day. *Luke* 17:4

seven *and twenty, see* **twenty**

seven *years*

I will serve thee *s. years.* *Gen* 29:18
served *s. years.* 20
serve *s.* other *years.* 27, 30
good kine are *s. years*, and the seven good ears are *s. years.* 41:26
kine are *s. years*, seven empty ears shall be *s. years* of famine. 27
come *s. years* of plenty. 29, 34, 47, 48
arise *s. years* of famine. 30, 36, 54
the *s. years* of plenteousness. 53
seven times *s. years.* *Lev* 25:8
was built *s. years* before Zoan. *Num* 13:22
end of every *s. years* a release. *Deut* 15:1; 31:10
Israel to Midian *s. years.* *Judg* 6:1
second bullock of *s. years* old. 25
Ibzan of Bethlehem judged Israel *s. years.* 12:9
David was king in Hebron *s. years.* *2 Sam* 2:11; 5:5; *1 Ki* 2:11
1 Chr 29:27
shall *s. years* of famine come ? *2 Sam* 24:13
Solomon was *s. years* in building. *1 Ki* 6:38
famine shall come upon land *s. years.* *2 Ki* 8:1
with the Philistines *s. years.* 2
s. years old was Jehoash when he. 11:21; *2 Chr* 24:1
at end of *s. years* let ye. *Jer* 34:14
burn weapons with fire *s. years.* *Ezek* 39:9
an husband *s. years.* *Luke* 2:36

sevenfold

shall be taken on him *s.* *Gen* 4:15
avenged *s.* Lamech 70 and *s.* 24
render *s.* into their bosom. *Ps* 79:12
found he shall restore *s.* *Pr* 6:31
of the sun shall be *s.* *Isa* 30:26

sevens

beast shalt thou take by *s.* *Gen* 7:2
air by *s.* the male and female. 3

seventeen

Joseph being *s.* years old. *Gen* 37:2
in the land of Egypt *s.* years. 47:28
reigned *s.* years in Jerusalem. *1 Ki* 14:21
son of Jehu reigned *s.* years. *2 Ki* 13:1
bought field, weighed *s.* *Jer* 32:9

seventeenth

on *s.* day the fountains. *Gen* 7:11
ark rested on the *s.* day in. 8:4
to reign the *s.* year. *1 Ki* 22:51
in *s.* year of Pekah son. *2 Ki* 16:1
the *s.* lot came to Hezir. *1 Chr* 24:15
s. lot came to Joshbekashah. 25:24

seventh

in *s.* he shall go out free. *Ex* 21:2
but in the *s.* is the sabbath. 31:15
after the *s.* sabbath. *Lev* 23:16
at the *s.* time when the. *Josh* 6:16
s. lot came out for the tribe. 19:40
at the *s.* time there arose a cloud. *1 Ki* 18:44
David was the *s.* son. *1 Chr* 2:15
s. lot came forth to Hakkoz. 24:10
Elioenai the *s.* son of. 26:3
Issachar was the *s.* son of. 5
s. captain for the *s.* month. 27:10
and the third, to the *s.* *Mat* 22:26
yesterday at *s.* hour the. *John* 4:52
Enoch the *s.* from Adam. *Jude* 14
he had opened the *s.* seal. *Rev* 8:1
of the voice of the *s.* angel. 10:7
the *s.* angel sounded, there. *Rev* 11:15
s. angel poured out his vial. 16:17
the *s.* foundation was a. 21:20
see **day**

seventh *month*

ark rested in *s. month* on. *Gen* 8:4
in *s. month* afflict your souls. *Lev* 16:29; 23:27; 25:9
in the *s. month* shall ye. 23:24
in *s. month* an holy. *Num* 29:1, 12
at feast of the *s. month.* *1 Ki* 8:2
in the *s. month* Ishmael smote Gedaliah. *2 Ki* 25:25; *Jer* 41:1
in *s. month* Solomon. *2 Chr* 7:10
the heaps in the *s. month.* 31:7
when *s. month* was come, and the. *Ezra* 3:1; *Neh* 7:73
the first day of *s. month.* *Ezra* 3:6
the *s. month* Ezra read. *Neh* 8:2
in feasts of *s. month* Israel. 14
died in the *s. month.* *Jer* 28:17
in the *s. month* shall he. *Ezek* 45:25
in the *s. month* the word. *Hag* 2:1
in fifth and *s. month.* *Zech* 7:5
the fast of the *s. month* shall. 8:19

seventh *year*

the *s. year* thou shalt let. *Ex* 23:11
in the *s. year* shall be a. *Lev* 25:4
shall we eat in the *s. year* ? 20
saying, The *s. year*, year of release. *Deut* 15:9
in the *s. year* thou shalt let. 12
in the *s. year* Jehoiada sent and. *2 Ki* 11:4; *2 Chr* 23:1
in *s. year* of Jehu. *2 Ki* 12:1
in *s. year* of Hoshea king of. 18:9
went up unto Jerusalem in the *s. year* of the king. *Ezra* 7:7, 8
leave *s. year*, and exaction. *Neh* 10:31
taken to king in *s. year.* *Esth* 2:16
away captive in *s. year.* *Jer* 52:28
the *s. year* elders came to enquire. *Ezek* 20:1

seventy

truly Lamech *s.* and sevenfold. *Gen* 4:24
and Cainan lived *s.* years. 5:12
Terah lived *s.* years and. 11:26
Abram was *s.*-five years old. 12:4
of Jacob were *s.* souls. *Ex* 1:5
and *s.* elders of Israel. 24:1, 9
the offering was *s.* talents. 38:29
was one silver bowl of *s.* shekels. *Num* 7:13, 19, 25, 31, 37, 43, 49
55, 61, 67, 73, 79
each bowl weighing *s.* shekels. 85
gather unto me *s.* men of. 11:16, 24
of the spirit unto the *s.* elders. 25
slaying his *s.* brethren. *Judg* 9:56
had *s.* sons in Samaria. *2 Ki* 10:1, 6
took king's sons, and slew *s.* 7
children of Hodaviah *s.*-four. *Ezra* 2:40; *Neh* 7:43
with Jeshaiah *s.* males. *Ezra* 8:7
Zabbud, with them *s.* males. 14
Tyre shall be forgotten *s.* years. *Isa* 23:15
after end of *s.* years, the Lord. 17
king of Babylon *s.* years. *Jer* 25:11
when *s.* years are accomplished. 12
29:10
there stood before them *s.* men. *Ezek* 8:11
accomplish *s.* years in. *Dan* 9:2
s. weeks are determined upon. 24
even those *s.* years, did. *Zech* 7:5
till seven times, but until *s.* times. *Mat* 18:22
Lord appointed other *s.* *Luke* 10:1
the *s.* returned again with joy. 17

sever

will *s.* in that day the land. *Ex* 8:22
Lord shall *s.* between cattle. 9:4
shall *s.* out men of continual employment. *Ezek* 39:14
and *s.* the wicked from. *Mat* 13:49

several

and a *s.* tenth deal of flour mingled. *Num* 28:13, 21, 29; 29:10, 15
Azariah . . . his death, and dwelt in a *s.* house. *2 Ki* 15:5†; *2 Chr* 26:21†
in every *s.* city put. *2 Chr* 11:12
in every *s.* city of Judah. *2 Chr* 28:2
sons of Aaron in every *s.* city. 31:1
according to his *s.* ability. *Mat* 25:1
every *s.* gate was one of. *Rev* 21:2

severally

dividing to every man *s.* *1 Cor* 12:1

severed

I have *s.* you from other people. *Lev* 20:26*
Moses *s.* three cities. *Deut* 4:41*
Heber had *s.* himself. *Judg* 4:1

severity

the goodness and *s.* of God: on them which fell, *s.*; but. *Rom* 11:2

sew

time to rend and a time to *s.* *Eccl* 3:
woe to the women that *s.* pillows to all armholes. *Ezek* 13:1

sewed

they *s.* fig leaves together. *Gen* 3:
I have *s.* sackcloth upon. *Job* 16:1

sewest

in a bag, and thou *s.* up mine iniquity. *Job* 14:17*

seweth

no man *s.* a piece of new cloth on. *Mark* 2:21

shade

the Lord is thy *s.* upon. *Ps* 121:5

shadow

(*This word has often the rare meaning of a shelter. It also means at times, as in* Col 2:17, *a representation, a sample which gives an idea of what the real thing is to be. In many cases the American Revision changes to* shade)

they came under the *s.* of my roof. *Gen* 19:8
put your trust in my *s.* *Judg* 9:15
seest the *s.* of the mountains. 3
s. go forward ten degrees ? *2 Ki* 20:
it is a light thing for the *s.* to go. 1
s. ten degrees backward. 1
our days on earth are as a *s.* *1 Chr* 29:15; *Job* 8:
earnestly desireth the *s.* *Job* 7:2
he fleeth also as a *s.* and. 14:2
all my members are as a *s.* 17:7
trees cover him with their *s.* 40:22
hide me under the *s.* *Ps* 17:8
their trust under the *s.* 36:7; 57:1
in the *s.* of thy wings will. 63:7
covered with the *s.* of it. 80:1
shall abide under the *s.* of the. 91:1
my days are like a *s.* that. 102:11
I am gone like a *s.* when. 109:23
man is like to vanity: his days are as a *s.* 144:4; *Eccl* 8:13
he spendeth as a *s.* *Eccl* 6:12
I sat under his *s.* with. *S of S* 2:3
a tabernacle for a *s.* in daytime. *Isa* 4:6
make thy *s.* as the night in. 16:3
thou hast been a *s.* from the. 25:4
down the heat with *s.* of a cloud.
trust in the *s.* of Egypt. 30:2
and the trust in the *s.* of Egypt.
as the *s.* of a great rock in. 32:2
and gather under her *s.* 34:15
I will bring again the *s.* of the. 38:8
in *s.* of his hand hath he hid me. 49:2; 51:1
they stood under the *s.* *Jer* 48:4
under his *s.* we shall live. *Lam* 4:2
in the *s.* thereof shall. *Ezek* 17:23
and under his *s.* dwelt all. 31:
are gone down from his *s.* 1
that dwelt under his *s.* in midst. 1
field had *s.* under it. *Dan* 4:1
under elms, because *s.* *Hos* 4:1
they that dwell under his *s.* 14:7
and sat under it in the *s.* *Jonah* 4:
might be *s.* over his head.
lodge under the *s.* of it. *Mark* 4:3
that *s.* of Peter might. *Acts* 5:1
which are a *s.* of things. *Col* 2:1
who serve unto the *s.* of. *Heb* 8:
the law having a *s.* of good. 10:
with whom is no *s.* of. *Jas* 1:1
see **death**

shadowing
roe to the land *s.* with wings. *Isa* 18:1*
edar with a *s.* shroud. *Ezek* 31:3
ver cherubims of glory *s.* the. *Heb* 9:5*

shadows
ıntil the day break, and the *s.* flee away. *S of S* 2:17; 4:6
or *s.* of the evening are. *Jer* 6:4

Shadrach, *see* **Abed-nego**

shady
e lieth under the *s.* trees. *Job* 40:21*
he *s.* trees cover him with. 22*

shaft
is *s.* and branches, his bowls and. *Ex* 25:31*; 31:17*; *Num* 8:4*
nake me a polished *s.* *Isa* 49:2

shake
will go out and *s.* myself. *Judg* 16:20
ap, and said, So God *s.* *Neh* 5:13
vhich made my bones to *s.* *Job* 4:14
e shall *s.* off his unripe grape. 15:33
ould heap up words, and *s.* 16:4
ut the lip, they *s.* head. *Ps* 22:7
hough the mountains *s.* 46:3
heir loins continually to *s.* 69:23
he fruit thereof shall *s.* like. 72:16
riseth to *s.* the earth. *Isa* 2:19, 21
s if the rod should *s.* itself. 10:15†
e shall *s.* his hand against. 32
he Lord shall *s.* his hand. 11:15†
xalt the voice unto them, *s.* 13:2*
will *s.* heavens. 13*; *Joel* 3:16 *Hag* 2:6, 21
oundations of the earth do *s.* *Isa* 24:18
Bashan and Carmel *s.* off. 33:9
. thyself from the dust, O. 52:2
s broken, all my bones *s.* *Jer* 23:9
hy walls shall *s.* at noise of. *Ezek* 26:10
ot the isles *s.* at the sound? 15
he suburbs shall *s.* at the. 27:28
made nations *s.* at the sound. 31:16
ll men of the earth shall *s.* at. 38:20
. off his leaves, and. *Dan* 4:14
intel that the posts may *s.* *Amos* 9:1
will *s.* all nations, desire. *Hag* 2:7
will *s.* my hand on them. *Zech* 2:9
. off the dust of your feet. *Mat* 10:14 *Mark* 6:11; *Luke* 9:5
ear of him the keepers did *s.* *Mat* 28:4*
ouse, and could not *s.* it. *Luke* 6:48
once more I *s.* not the earth only. *Heb* 12:26

shaked
hey looked on me, they *s.* their. *Ps* 109:25

shaken
he sound of a *s.* leaf shall chase. *Lev* 26:36*
Israel as a reed is *s.* in water. *1 Ki* 14:15
he daughter of Jerusalem hath *s.* *2 Ki* 19:21; *Isa* 37:22
even thus be he *s.* out. *Neh* 5:13
aken me by my neck, *s.* *Job* 16:12*
hat the wicked might be *s.* 38:13
of the hills were *s.* *Ps* 18:7
r trees shall be terribly *s.* *Nah* 2:3
f *s.* they fall into the mouth. 3:12
reed *s.* with the wind. *Mat* 11:7 *Luke* 7:24
nd powers of heaven shall be *s.* *Mat* 24:29; *Mark* 13:25 *Luke* 21:26
ood measure, pressed, *s.* together. *Luke* 6:38
prayed, the place was *s.* *Acts* 4:31
of the prison were *s.* 16:26
be not soon *s.* in mind. *2 Thes* 2:2
hat are *s.*, that those things which cannot be *s.* may. *Heb* 12:27
s a fig tree when *s.* of. *Rev* 6:13

shaketh
which *s.* the earth out of. *Job* 9:6
he voice of the Lord *s.* *Ps* 29:8
breaches thereof, for it *s.* 60:2
nagnify against him that *s.* it? *Isa* 10:15†
the Lord which he *s.* over it. *Isa* 19:16
that *s.* hand from holding of. 33:15

shaking
laugheth at the *s.* of. *Job* 41:29*
the *s.* of the head among. *Ps* 44:14
as the *s.* of an olive tree. *Isa* 17:6 24:13
shall fear, because of the *s.* of. 19:16
battles of *s.* shall he fight. 30:32
s. and bones came. *Ezek* 37:7*
shall be a great *s.* in Israel. 38:19

Shalim
they passed through the land of *S.* *1 Sam* 9:4

Shalisha
through the land of *S.* *1 Sam* 9:4

Shallum
S. son of Jabesh killed. *2 Ki* 15:10
Menahem slew *S.* son of Jabesh. 14
to Huldah the prophetess, the wife of *S.* 22:14; *2 Chr* 34:22
of Judah, *S.* *1 Chr* 2:40
of Simeon, *S.* 4:25
of Levi, *S.* 6:12
S. the son of Naphtali. 7:13
S. a porter. 9:17, 19
S. the Korahite. 31
Jehizkiah the son of *S.* *2 Chr* 28:12
porters, the children of *S.* *Ezra* 2:42 10:24; *Neh* 7:45; *Jer* 35:4
S. the son of Zadok, the. *Ezra* 7:2
S. and Amariah had taken. 10:42
unto him repaired *S.* *Neh* 3:12, 15
thus saith the Lord touching *S.* son of. *Jer* 22:11
Hanameel the son of *S.* thine. 32:7

Shalmanezer
S. came up against Samaria. *2 Ki* 17:3; 18:9

shambles
sold in the *s.* that eat. *1 Cor* 10:25

shame
them naked unto their *s.* *Ex* 32:25
put them to *s.* in any. *Judg* 18:7
father had done him *s.* *1 Sam* 20:34
I cause my *s.* to go? *2 Sam* 13:13
returned with *s.* of face. *2 Chr* 32:21
shall be clothed with *s.* *Job* 8:22
ye turn my glory into *s.*? *Ps* 4:2
put them to *s.* that seek after. 35:4*
let them be clothed with *s.* 26
let them be put to *s.* that wish me evil. 40:14*; 83:17
desolate for reward of their *s.* 40:15
to *s.* that hated us. 44:7; 53:5
hast cast off and put us to *s.* 44:9*
the *s.* of my face hath. 15; 69:7
known my reproach and *s.* 69:19
back for reward of their *s.* 70:3
let them be brought unto *s.* 71:24
fill their faces with *s.* O Lord. 83:16*
thou hast covered him with *s.* 89:45
mine adversaries be clothed with *s.* 109:29*
testimonies; O Lord, put me not to *s.* 119:31
enemies will I clothe with *s.* 132:18
but *s.* shall be the promotion of. *Pr* 3:35
a scorner, getteth *s.* 9:7†
is a son that causeth *s.* 10:5
pride cometh, then cometh *s.* 11:2
but a prudent man covereth *s.* 12:16
loathsome and cometh to *s.* 13:5
s. shall be to him that refuseth. 18
is against him that causeth *s.* 14:35
over a son that causeth *s.* 17:2
heareth, it is folly and *s.* to him. 18:13
mother, is a son causeth *s.* 19:26
neighbour hath put thee to *s.* 25:8
heareth it put thee to *s.* 10
himself brings his mother to *s.* 29:15
uncovered, to *s.* of Egypt. *Isa* 20:4
chariots shall be the *s.* of. 22:18
Pharaoh shall be your *s.* 30:3, 5
be uncovered, yea, thy *s.* shall. 47:3
I hid not my face from *s.* 50:6
not be put to *s.* nor confounded, for thou shalt forget *s.* of. 54:4
for your *s.* ye shall have double. 61:7
s. devoured the labour. *Jer* 3:24*
we lie down in *s.* and our. 25
I will discover, that thy *s.* *Jer* 13:26
days may be consumed with *s.* 20:18
a perpetual *s.*, which shall. 23:40
nations have heard of thy *s.* 46:12
Moab turned back with *s.*! 48:39
s. hath covered our faces, for. 51:51*
s. shall be on all faces. *Ezek* 7:18
thine own *s.* for thy sins. 16:52, 54
thy mouth because of thy *s.* 63
have they borne their *s.* 32:24, 25
bear their *s.* with them that go. 30
nor bear the *s.* of the heathen. 34:29
because ye have borne the *s.* 36:6
they shall bear their *s.* 7; 44:13
nor cause to hear in thee the *s.* 36:15
they have borne their *s.* 39:26
shall awake, some to *s.* *Dan* 12:2
change their glory into *s.* *Hos* 4:7
her rulers with *s.* do love. 18
separated themselves unto that *s.* 9:10
Ephraim shall receive *s.* 10:6
for thy violence *s.* shall. *Ob* 10
pass ye away, having thy *s.* *Mi* 1:11
prophesy, they shall not take *s.* 2:6
s. shall cover her which said. 7:10
shew the kingdoms thy *s.* *Nah* 3:5
consulted *s.* to thy house. *Hab* 2:10
thou art filled with *s.* for glory. 16
the unjust knoweth no *s.* *Zeph* 3:5
where they have been put to *s.* 19
thou begin with *s.* to take. *Luke* 14:9
were counted worthy to suffer *s.* *Acts* 5:41*
these things to *s.* you. *1 Cor* 4:14
I speak to your *s.* 6:5; 15:34
a *s.* for a woman to be shorn. 11:6
if a man have long hair, it is a *s.* 14*
church of God, and *s.* them? 22
it is a *s.* for a woman to speak. 14:35
a *s.* to speak of things. *Eph* 5:12
whose glory is in their *s.* *Phil* 3:19
and put him to an open *s.* *Heb* 6:6
the cross, despising the *s.* 12:2
foaming out their own *s.* *Jude* 13
that *s.* of thy nakedness. *Rev* 3:18
naked, and they see his *s.* 16:15

shamed
thou hast *s.* the faces. *2 Sam* 19:5
ye have *s.* the counsel. *Ps* 14:6

shamefacedness
adorn themselves with *s.* *1 Tim* 2:9*

shameful
up altars to that *s.* thing. *Jer* 11:13
and *s.* spewing be on thy glory. *Hab* 2:16*

shamefully
conceived them, hath done *s.* *Hos* 2:5
sent him away *s.* handled. *Mark* 12:4; *Luke* 20:11
and were *s.* entreated. *1 Thes* 2:2

shamelessly
vain fellows, *s.* uncovereth. *2 Sam* 6:20

shameth
of riotous men *s.* his father. *Pr* 28:7

Shamgar
after him was *S.* the son. *Judg* 3:31
the days of *S.* highways. 5:6

Shammah
the son of Reuel, *S.* *Gen* 36:13 17; *1 Chr* 1:37
S. the son of Jesse. *1 Sam* 16:9 17:13; *1 Chr* 2:13
after him was *S.* the Hararite. *2 Sam* 23:11, 33
S. the Harodite. 25
son of Zophah, *S.* *1 Chr* 7:37

Shammuah
to spy the land, *S.* son of Zacur. *Num* 13:4
S. the son of David. *2 Sam* 5:14 *1 Chr* 14:4
Abda son of *S.* dwelt at. *Neh* 11:17

shape
descended in bodily *s.* *Luke* 3:22*
his voice, nor seen his *s.* *John* 5:37*

shapen
I was *s.* in iniquity. *Ps* 51:5

shapes
s. of the locusts were like. *Rev* 9:7

Shaphan
Josiah sent *S.* the scribe to repair. *2 Ki* 22:3; *2 Chr* 34:8
Hilkiah gave the book to *S.* *2 Ki* 22:8; *2 Chr* 34:15
Ahikam the son of *S.* and *S.* the scribe. *2 Ki* 22:12
Ahikam the son of *S.* 25:22
Jer 39:14; 40:11
the hand of son of *S.* *Jer* 26:24
sent by Elasah son of *S.* 29:3
chamber of Gemariah son of *S.* 36:10
stood Jaazaniah son of *S.* *Ezek* 8:11

Shaphat
of the tribe of Simeon, *S.* *Num* 13:5
anoint Elisha son of *S.* *1 Ki* 19:16
if the head of Elisha the son of *S.* shall stand on him. *2 Ki* 6:31
Shemaiah, Neariah, *S.* *1 Chr* 3:22
of the Gadites, *S.* in Bashan. 5:12
in valleys was *S.* son of Adlai. 27:29

share
went down to sharpen every man his *s.* *1 Sam* 13:20

Sharezer
S. his son smote him. *2 Ki* 19:37
Isa 37:38

Sharon
in all the suburbs of *S.* *1 Chr* 5:16
over the herds that fed in *S.* 27:29
I am the rose of *S.* the. *S of S* 2:1
S. is like a wilderness. *Isa* 33:9
of Carmel and *S.* given thee. 35:2
S. shall be a fold of flocks. 65:10

sharp
Zipporah took a *s.* stone. *Ex* 4:25
make thee *s.* knives. *Josh* 5:2*
Joshua made *s.* knives and. 3*
between passages a *s.* *1 Sam* 14:4*
s. stones are under him, he spreadeth *s.* pointed things. *Job* 41:30*
arrows *s.* in the heart. *Ps* 45:5
thy tongue like a *s.* razor. 52:2
their tongue a *s.* sword. 57:4
s. arrows of mighty with. 120:4
her end is *s.* as a twoedged. *Pr* 5:4
bears false witness is *s.* arrow. 25:18
whose arrows are *s.* *Isa* 5:28
I will make thee a *s.* threshing. 41:15
my mouth like a *s.* sword. 49:2
take thee a *s.* knife. *Ezek* 5:1
the contention was so *s.* *Acts* 15:39
went a *s.* twoedged sword. *Rev* 1:16; 19:15
he that hath the *s.* sword. 2:12
in his hand a *s.* sickle. 14:14, 17
to him that had the *s.* sickle. 18

sharpen
went down to *s.* every. *1 Sam* 13:20
a file for axes, and to *s.* 21*

sharpened
they *s.* their tongues. *Ps* 140:3
a sword is *s.* and furbished. *Ezek* 21:9, 10, 11

sharpeneth
mine enemy *s.* his eyes. *Job* 16:9
iron *s.* iron, so a man *s.* *Pr* 27:17

sharper
the most upright is *s.* *Mi* 7:4*
the word of God is *s.* *Heb* 4:12

sharply
did chide with Gideon *s.* *Judg* 8:1
rebuke them *s.* that they. *Tit* 1:13

sharpness
present I should use *s.* *2 Cor* 13:10

Shaul
S. (sixth king of Edom). *1 Chr* 1:48

shave
but scall shall he not *s.* *Lev* 13:33
person shall *s.* off his hair. 14:8, 9
nor shall they *s.* the corner of. 21:5
shall *s.* his head in the day of his cleansing . . . shall he *s.* *Num* 6:9
Nazarite shall *s.* the head of his. 18
let them *s.* their flesh, and. 8:7*
captive shall *s.* her head. *Deut* 21:12
caused him to *s.* off seven locks. *Judg* 16:19
Lord shall *s.* with a razor. *Isa* 7:20
neither shall they *s.* *Ezek* 44:20
be at charges, that they *s.* their. *Acts* 21:24

shaved
Joseph *s.* and changed. *Gen* 41:14
s. off half their beards. *2 Sam* 10:4
1 Chr 19:4
Job rent his mantle and *s.* *Job* 1:20

shaven
be *s.* but the scall shall. *Lev* 13:33
hair of his separation is *s.* *Num* 6:19
if I be *s.* my strength. *Judg* 16:17
to grow again after he was *s.* 22
men having their beards *s.* *Jer* 41:5
all one as if she were *s.* *1 Cor* 11:5
if it be a shame to be *s.* let her. 6

sheaf
s. arose, and also stood upright . . . obeisance to my *s.* *Gen* 37:7
a *s.* of the firstfruits. *Lev* 23:10
wave the *s.* before the Lord. 11, 12
hast forgot a *s.* shalt not go to fetch it. *Deut* 24:19
they take away the *s.* *Job* 24:10
Judah like a torch in a *s.* *Zech* 12:6

Shealtiel, *see* **Zerubbabel**

shear
and Laban went to *s.* *Gen* 31:19
Judah goeth to Timnah to *s.* 38:13
nor shalt *s.* the firstling. *Deut* 15:19
Nabal did *s.* his sheep. *1 Sam* 25:4

shearer
a lamb dumb before his *s.* *Acts* 8:32

shearers
went up unto his sheep *s.* *Gen* 38:12
heard that thou hast *s.* *1 Sam* 25:7
my flesh I have killed for my *s.* 11
Absalom had *s.* in Baal-hazor. *2 Sam* 13:23, 24
sheep before her *s.* is. *Isa* 53:7

shearing
and Nabal was *s.* sheep. *1 Sam* 25:2

shearing *house*
of Ahaziah at *s. house.* *2 Ki* 10:12
slew them at the pit of *s. house.* 14

Shear-jashub
meet Ahaz, thou and *S.* *Isa* 7:3

sheath
the sword out of his *s.* *1 Sam* 17:51
with a sword fastened in the *s.* *2 Sam* 20:8
the angel put the sword into his *s.* *1 Chr* 21:27
will draw his sword out of the *s.* *Ezek* 21:3, 4, 5
cause it to return into his *s.*? will. 30
put up thy sword into *s.* *John* 18:11

sheaves
behold, we were binding *s.* *Gen* 37:7
let me glean and gather among the *s.* *Ruth* 2:7, 15
sabbath bringing in *s.* *Neh* 13:15
he shall come bringing *s.* *Ps* 126:6
that bindeth *s.* his bosom. 129:7
a cart pressed full of *s.* *Amos* 2:13
shall gather them as the *s.* *Mi* 4:12

Sheba, Shebah
son of Raamah *S.* *Gen* 10:7
S. son of Joktan. 28
Jokshan begat *S.* and Dedan. 25:3
1 Chr 1:32
Isaac called the well *S.* *Gen* 26:33
in their inheritance *S.* *Josh* 19:2
queen of *S.* heard of the fame of. *1 Ki* 10:1; *2 Chr* 9:1
the son of Raamah, *S.* *1 Chr* 1:9
son of Joktan, *S.* 22
children of Gad, *S.* and Jorai. 5:13
companies of *S.* waited. *Job* 6:19
kings of *S.* and Seba. *Ps* 72:10
to him shall be given of gold of *S.* 15; *Isa* 60:6
is incense from *S.*? *Jer* 6:20
merchants of *S.* thy merchants. *Ezek* 27:22, 23
S. shall say, Art thou come? 38:13
see **Bichri**

Shebna
to the king, there came out to them *S.* *2 Ki* 18:18, 37; *Isa* 36:
Hezekiah sent *S.* to Isaiah. *2 Ki* 19:
Isa 37:
thee to this treasurer, *S.* *Isa* 22:1

Shechem
to Salem a city of *S.* *Gen* 33:1
at the hand of Hamor, *S.'s* father. 1
S. lay with Dinah. 34:
they slew *S.* 2
under an oak that was by *S.* 35:
their father's flock in *S.* 37:1
the vale of Hebron to *S.* 1
of *S.* the family of the. *Num* 26:3
lot for the children of *S.* *Josh* 17:
S. in mount Ephraim a city of. 20:7; 21:21; *1 Chr* 6:6
the tribes of Israel to *S.* *Josh* 24:
bones of Joseph buried they in *S.* 3
Gideon's concubine in *S.* *Judg* 8:3
son of Jerubbaal went to *S.* 9:
hearken to me, ye men of *S.*
come out from the men of *S.* 2
who is *S.*? 2
Gaal and brethren come to *S.* 3
they should not dwell in *S.* 4
the evil of the men of *S.* did God. 5
Rehoboam went to *S.* *1 Ki* 12:
2 Chr 10:
Jeroboam built *S.* in mount Ephraim *1 Ki* 12:2
Shemida, Ahian and *S.* *1 Chr* 7:1
I will rejoice, I will divide *S.* *Ps* 60:6; 108:
came certain from *S.* *Jer* 41:

shed
Joab *s.* Amasa's bowels to the. *2 Sam* 20:1
is *s.* for many for the. *Mat* 26:2
promise of Holy Ghost, he hath *s.* *Acts* 2:33*
love of God is *s.* abroad in. *Rom* 5:5
he *s.* on us abundantly. *Tit* 3:6*
see **blood**

shedder
beget a son that is a *s.* *Ezek* 18:1

sheddeth
whosoever *s.* man's blood, his. *Gen* 9:
the city *s.* blood in the. *Ezek* 22:

shedding
and without *s.* of blood. *Heb* 9:22

sheep
Abel was a keeper of *s.* *Gen* 4:2
daughter cometh with the *s.* 29:6,
hand of Lord is upon the *s.* *Ex* 9:3*
ye shall take it out from the *s.* 12:5
sacrifice thereon thy *s.* and. 20:24
if a man steal a *s.* and kill it or sell. 22:1, 4,
to his neighbour a *s.* to keep. 1
with the firstling of *s.* 30; 34:1
if his offering be of the *s.* *Lev* 1:1
shall eat no manner of fat of *s.* 7:23
ye shall offer a male of the *s.* 22:1
sanctify the firstling of a *s.* 27:2
the firstling of *s.* *Num* 18:17
cities and folds for your *s.* 32:24, 3
bless the flocks of thy *s.* *Deut* 7:13*
thou shalt not sacrifice *s.* 17:1
from them that offer *s.* 18:3, 4
thy brother's *s.* go astray. 22:1
blessed shall be the flocks of thy *s.* 28:4
cursed shall be the flocks of thy *s.* 18; 31:51
butter of kine, milk of *s.* 32:14
at Jericho ox and *s.* *Josh* 6:21
Joshua took Achan's *s.* and. 7:24
left neither *s.* nor oxen. *Judg* 6:4
take tenth of your *s.* *1 Sam* 8:17*
upon the spoil and took *s.* 14:32
every man his ox and his *s.* 34
slay both ox and *s.* 15:3
Saul spread the *s.* 9
this bleating of *s.* in my ears? 14
the people took of the spoil, *s.* 21
behold, he keepeth the *s.* 16:11
my son, who is with the *s.* 19
returned to feed his father's *s.* 17:15
he rose early and left the *s.* with. 20

kept his father's s. 1 Sam 17:34
3000 s.: he was shearing his s. 25:2
Abigail hasted, and took five s. 18
David took away the s. 27:9
thee from following the s. 2 Sam 7:8
brought David butter and s. 17:29
Lo, I have sinned, but these s. what? 24:17; 1 Chr 21:17
Adonijah hath slain s. 1 Ki 1:19, 25
Solomon's provision for one day hundred s. 4:23
all the congregation sacrificing s. 8:5
Solomon offered s. 63; 2 Chr 5:6 7:5
is it a time to receive s.? 2 Ki 5:26
from Hagarites 250,000 s. 1 Chr 5:21
oxen and s. abundantly. 12:40
Asa carried from the Ethiopians s. 2 Chr 14:15
offered of the spoil 7000 s. 15:11
Ahab killed s. and oxen for. 18:2
consecrated things were 3000 s. 29:33
give 7000 s. and the princes gave to the congregation 10,000 s. 30:24
in the tithes of oxen and s. 31:6
daily one ox, six choice s. Neh 5:18
substance also was 7000 s., 3000 camels. Job 1:3
fallen, and hath burnt up the s. 16
warmed with fleece of my s. 31:20
for he had 14,000 s. and 6000. 42:12
given him all s. and oxen. Ps 8:7
thou hast given us like s. for. 44:11
like s. are laid in the grave. 49:14
anger smoke against thy s.? 74:1
own people go forth like s. 78:52
people and s. of thy pasture. 79:13
the s. of his hand. 95:7; 100:3
gone astray like a lost s. 119:176
that our s. may bring forth. 144:13
thy teeth are like a flock of s. S of S 4:2*; 6:6*
a man shall nourish two s. Isa 7:21
gladness, and killing of s. 22:13
all we like s. have gone astray. 53:6
pull them out like s. for. Jer 12:3
pastors that scatter the s. 23:1
my people hath been lost s. 50:6
Israel is a scattered s.; the lions. 17
my s. wander through. Ezek 34:6
I will search my s. and seek, 11, 12
and for a wife he kept s. Hos 12:12
the flocks of s. are made. Joel 1:18
as a young lion among the flocks of s. Mi 5:8
shepherd, and s. shall be scattered. Zech 13:7; Mat 26:31 Mark 14:27
false prophets in s.'s clothing. Mat 7:15
go rather to the lost s. of the. 10:6
if one s. fall into a pit on the. 12:11
is a man better than a s.? 12
unto the lost s. of Israel. 15:24
if a man have a 100 s. and. 18:12
he rejoiceth more of that s. 13 Luke 15:4, 6
as a shepherd divideth his s. Mat 25:32
he shall set s. on his right hand. 33
temple those that sold s. John 2:14
out of the temple, and the s. 15
by the door is shepherd of the s. 10:2
the s. hear his voice. 3, 27
the s. follow him. 4*
verily I am the door of the s. 7
were robbers, but the s. did not. 8
shepherd giveth his life for his s. 11
hireling leaveth the s. and fleeth. 12*
hireling careth not for the s. 13
good shepherd, I know my s. 14*
I lay down my life for the s. 15
other s. I have. 16
because ye are not of my s. 26
Peter, Feed my s. 21:16, 17
great Shepherd of s. Heb 13:20
none buyeth s., horses. Rev 18:13

as sheep

be not as s. which have. Num 27:17
Israel scattered on the hills as s. 1 Ki 22:17; 2 Chr 18:16
the day long; we are counted as s. Ps 44:22; Rom 8:36
it shall be as a s. that no. Isa 13:14
and as a s. before his shearers. 53:7
together as s. of Bozra. Mi 2:12
fainted and were scattered as s. Mat 9:36; Mark 6:34
I send you forth as s. Mat 10:16
led as s. to the slaughter. Acts 8:32
were as s. going astray. 1 Pet 2:25

sheepcote

took thee from the s. 2 Sam 7:8 1 Chr 17:7

sheepcotes

Saul came to the s. 1 Sam 24:3

sheepfold

he that entereth not the s. John 10:1

sheepfolds

build s. for our cattle. Num 32:16
thou among the s.? Judg 5:16
David, took him from the s. Ps 78:70

sheep gate

brethren built the s. gate. Neh 3:1
up of the corner to the s. gate. 32
they went on to the s. gate. 12:39

sheep market

Jerusalem by the s. market a pool. John 5:2

sheepmaster

Mesha king of Moab was a s. 2 Ki 3:4
see **shearers**

sheepskins

in the s. and goatskins. Heb 11:37

sheet

a vessel descending as a great s. Acts 10:11; 11:5

sheets

I will give you thirty s. Judg 14:12*
thirty s. and thirty change. 13*

shekel

(The unit of weight and of money among the Jews. It weighed about ½ ounce, and as coined in silver was worth about two shillings and ninepence, or 65 cents. In gold one or two pounds, or 4.85 to 9.69 dollars according to period)

took an earring of half a s. Gen 24:22
a s. after the s. of the sanctuary, a s. Ex 30:13; Num 3:47; Ezek 45:12
give less than half a s. Ex 30:15
the fourth part of a s. 1 Sam 9:8
of fine flour for a s. 2 Ki 7:1, 16, 18
charged yearly with the third of a s. Neh 10:32
small, and the s. great. Amos 8:5

shekels

land is worth 400 s. Gen 23:15, 16
her hands of ten s. weight. 24:22
give her master thirty s. Ex 21:32
s. of sweet cinnamon 250 s., of sweet calamus 250 s. 30:23
the estimation by s. Lev 5:15 27:3, 4, 5, 6, 7, 16
one spoon of ten s. of gold, full of incense. Num 7:14, 20, 26, 32 38, 44, 50, 56, 62, 68, 74, 80
amerce him in 100 s. Deut 22:19
to the damsel's father fifty s. 29
saw in the spoils 200 s. Josh 7:21
earrings was 1700 s. Judg 8:26
the 1100 s. of silver were taken. 17:2
had restored the s. 3
I will give thee ten s. of silver. 10
Absalom weighed his hair, 200 s. 2 Sam 14:26
I would have given thee ten s. 18:11
David bought oxen for fifty s. 24:24
six hundred s. of gold to. 1 Ki 10:16
each man fifty s. of silver. 2 Ki 15:20
gave to Ornan 600 s. 1 Chr 21:25
governors had taken 40 s. by year. Neh 5:15
I bought the field for 17 s. Jer 32:9
by weight twenty s. a day. Ezek 4:10
see **sanctuary**

Shelah

Judah's son S. Gen 38:5
gave her not to S. my son. 26
Judah, Er, Onan and S. 46:12 Num 26:20; 1 Chr 2:3; 4:21
Arphaxad begat S. and S. Eber. 1 Chr 1:18, 24

Shelemiah

lot eastward fell to S. 1 Chr 26:14
S. and Nathan had taken strange. Ezra 10:39
I made S. the priest. Neh 13:13
S. son of Cushi. Jer 36:14
S. son of Abdeel. 26

shelter

the rock for want of a s. Job 24:8
for thou hast been s. for. Ps 61:3*

Shelumiel

the prince of Simeon, S. the son of. Num 1:6; 2:12; 7:36; 10:19

Shem

Noah begat S. Gen 5:32; 6:10 10:1; 1 Chr 1:4
S. took a garment and. Gen 9:23
blessed be the Lord God of S. 26
dwell in the tents of S. 27
the children of S. 10:21, 22, 31 11:10; 1 Chr 1:17
which was the son of S. Luke 3:36

Shemaiah

word of God came to S. the man. 1 Ki 12:22; 2 Chr 11:2; 12:7
Shimri the son of S. 1 Chr 4:37
of Reuben, S. the son of Joel. 5:4
of the Levites, S. 9:14, 16; 15:8 11; 24:6; 26:4, 6, 7; 2 Chr 17:8 29:14; 31:15; 35:9; Ezra 8:16 10:21, 31
S. (the son of Adonikam). Ezra 8:13
S. keeper of the east gate. Neh 3:29
I came to the house of S. son. 6:10
S. a priest sealed. 10:8
of the Levites, S. 11:15; 12:6, 18 35, 36
S. the priest. 12:34, 42
Urijah the son of S. Jer 26:20
say to S. the Nehelamite. 29:24 31, 32
and Delaiah the son of S. 36:12

Sheminith

with harps on the S. 1 Chr 15:21

Shenir

the Amorites call S. Deut 3:9
look from the top of S. S of S 4:8

Shephatiah

S. the fifth son of David. 2 Sam 3:4 1 Chr 3:3
Meshullam son of S. 1 Chr 9:8
the Haruphite came to David. 12:5
the ruler of the Simeonites was S. 27:16
the children of S., 372. Ezra 2:4 Neh 7:9
S. heard the words of. Jer 38:1

shepherd

every s. is abomination. Gen 46:34
from thence is the s., the stone. 49:24
he put the stones into a s.'s bag. 1 Sam 17:40
the Lord is my s. I shall. Ps 23:1
give ear, O s. of Israel, thou. 80:1
words which are given from one s. Eccl 12:11
departed from me as a s. Isa 38:12
he shall feed his flock like a s. 40:11
saith of Cyrus, He is my s. 44:28
that brought them up with the s. 63:11
and keep him as a s. Jer 31:10
array himself as a s. putteth. 43:12
who is that s. that will stand? 49:19 50:44
I will also break in pieces s. 51:23
because there is no s. Ezek 34:5
prey, because there was no s. 8
as a s. seeketh out his flock. 12
s. over them, my servant David shall feed . . . be their s. 23; 37:24
s. taketh out of mouth. Amos 3:12
because there was no s. Zech 10:2
instruments of a foolish s. 11:15
raise up a s. in the land. 16
woe to the idle s. that leaveth. 17
O sword, against my s. and. 13:7
is an hireling, and not s. John 10:12
I am the good s., know my sheep. 14
shall be one fold and one s. 16

that great *s.* of the sheep. *Heb* 13:20
returned unto the *s.* *1 Pet* 2:25
when the chief *s.* shall appear. 5:4
see **sheep**

shepherds

and the men are *s.* *Gen* 46:32
thy servants are *s.* 47:3
and the *s.* came and drove. *Ex* 2:17
delivered us out of the hand of *s.* 19
thy *s.* which were with. *1 Sam* 25:7
kids beside the *s.*' tents. *S of S* 1:8
shall the *s.* make their. *Isa* 13:20
when multitude of *s.* is called. 31:4
and they are *s.* that cannot. 56:11
the *s.* with their flocks shall come. *Jer* 6:3
I will set up *s.* over them. 23:4
howl, ye *s.* and cry. 25:34
the *s.* have no way to flee. 35
a voice of the cry of the *s.* and. 36
shall be an habitation of *s.* 33:12
their *s.* have caused them to go. 56
the *s.* of Israel, woe to the *s.* of Israel . . . should not *s.* feed? *Ezek* 34:2
nor did my *s.* search for my flock, but *s.* fed themselves and fed. 8
I am against the *s.* neither shall the *s.* feed themselves any more. 10
habitations of the *s.* shall. *Amos* 1:2
raise against him seven *s.* *Mi* 5:5
thy *s.* slumber, O king of Assyria. *Nah* 3:18
shall be cottages for *s.* *Zeph* 2:6
kindled against the *s.* *Zech* 10:3
voice of the howling of the *s.* 11:3
and their own *s.* pity them not. 5
three *s.* also I cut off in one. 8
same country *s.* in field. *Luke* 2:8
were told them by the *s.* 18
the *s.* returned, glorifying and. 20

sherd

shall not be found a *s.* *Isa* 30:14

sherds

thou shalt break the *s.* *Ezek* 23:34

sheriffs

sent to gather the *s.* *Dan* 3:2
then the *s.* and rulers were. 3

Sheshach

the king of *S.* shall drink. *Jer* 25:26
how is *S.* taken! how is the! 51:41

Sheshbazzar

he numbered them to *S.* *Ezra* 1:8
did *S.* bring up from Babylon. 11
delivered to *S.* whom he had. 5:14
S. laid the foundation of the. 16

shew, *substantive*
(*In all places the American Revision uses the modern spelling* show, *when the word is retained*)

walketh in a vain *s.* *Ps* 39:6
the *s.* of their countenance. *Isa* 3:9
and for a *s.* make long. *Luke* 20:47*
to make a fair *s.* in flesh. *Gal* 6:12
spoiled powers made a *s.* *Col* 2:15
which things have a *s.* of wisdom. 23

shew

speak, saying, *S.* a miracle. *Ex* 7:9
I raised up for to *s.* in thee. 9:16
that I might *s.* my signs. 10:1
and thou shalt *s.* thy son in. 13:8*
the salvation Lord will *s.* to. 14:13*
shalt *s.* way they must walk. 18:20
Deut 1:33
it according to all that I *s.* *Ex* 25:9
s. me now thy way. 33:13
s. me thy glory. 18
I stood to *s.* you the word of the. *Deut* 5:5
no covenant, nor *s.* mercy. 7:2
Lord may *s.* thee mercy. 13:17
they shall *s.* thee the sentence. 17:9
thou shalt do as they shall *s.* 10, 11
not regard old, nor *s.* favour. 28:50
ask thy father, and he will *s.* 32:7
he would not *s.* the land. *Josh* 5:6
s. us, we pray thee, the entrance into the city, and we will *s.* *Judg* 1:24
then *s.* me a sign that thou. 6:17
Samuel feared to *s.* Eli the vision. *1 Sam* 3:15
s. them the manner of the. 8:9
man of God peradventure can *s.* *1 Sam* 9:6*
stand, that I may *s.* thee the. 27*
I will come and *s.* thee what. 10:8
come up to us, and we will *s.* 14:12
do nothing, he will *s.* it me. 20:2*
not unto thee, and *s.* it thee. 12*
he fled, and did not *s.* it. 22:17*
men, and they will *s.* thee. 25:8*
he will *s.* me, both it. *2 Sam* 15:25
if he will *s.* himself a. *1 Ki* 1:52
therefore, and *s.* thyself a man. 2:2
to Elijah, Go *s.* thyself. 18:1, 2
will ye not *s.* me which? *2 Ki* 6:11
to *s.* himself strong. *2 Chr* 16:9
s. their father's house whether they. *Ezra* 2:59; *Neh* 7:61
the pillar of fire to *s.* *Neh* 9:19
to *s.* the people and. *Esth* 1:11
Mordecai charged her not to *s.* 2:10
of the writing to *s.* Esther. 4:8
s. me wherefore thou. *Job* 10:2
he would *s.* thee the secrets of. 11:6
I was afraid, durst not *s.* you. 32:6
if a messenger to *s.* to man. 33:23
many will say, Who will *s.*? *Ps* 4:6
may *s.* forth all thy praise. 9:14
wilt *s.* me the path of life. 16:11
s. me thy ways, O Lord, teach. 25:4
the Lord will *s.* them his. 14
mouth shall *s.* forth thy praise. 51:15
my mouth shall *s.* forth thy. 71:15*
we thy people will *s.* forth. 79:13
s. us mercy, O Lord, grant. 85:7
s. me a token of good, that. 86:17
wilt thou *s.* wonders to the? 88:10
to *s.* that Lord is upright, he. 92:15
O God, to whom vengeance belongeth, *s.* thyself. 94:1*
can *s.* forth all his praise? 106:2
a man must *s.* himself. *Pr* 18:24*
formed them will *s.* no. *Isa* 27:11
the Lord shall *s.* lightning. 30:30
them forth and *s.* us what shall happen, let them *s.* the. 41:22*
s. the things that are to come. 23*
who among them can *s.* us? 43:9
people have I formed, shall *s.* 21*
coming, let them *s.* to them. 44:7*
and *s.* yourselves men. 46:8
say to them in darkness, *s.* 49:9
s. my people their transgression. 58:1
they shall *s.* forth the praises. 60:6*
thou shalt *s.* them all. *Jer* 16:10
into a land, where I will not *s.* 13
thy God may *s.* us the way we. 42:3
to *s.* the king of Babylon. 51:31
thou shalt *s.* her all her. *Ezek* 22:2*
for with their mouth they *s.* 33:31
wilt thou not *s.* us what thou? 37:18
upon all that I shall *s.* thee. 40:4
son of man, *s.* the house to. 43:10
s. them the form of the house. 11*
the sorcerers for to *s.* king his. *Dan* 2:2*
will *s.* the interpretation. 4, 7
if ye *s.* the dream and interpretation, therefore *s.* the dream and. 6
not a man that can *s.* the king's. 10
s. the king the interpretation. 16
cannot the wise men *s.* to the. 27
I thought it good to *s.* the signs. 4:2
shall *s.* me the interpretation. 5:7
and I am come to *s.* thee. 9:23*
dost thou *s.* me iniquity? *Hab* 1:3
s. thyself to the priest. *Mat* 8:4
Mark 1:44; *Luke* 5:14; 17:14
go and *s.* John these. *Mat* 11:4*
he shall *s.* judgement to the. 12:18
therefore mighty works do *s.* forth. *Mat* 14:2*; *Mark* 6:14*
desired he would *s.* a sign. *Mat* 16:1
s. me the tribute money. 22:19
Luke 20:24
came to *s.* him the buildings of the. *Mat* 24:1
arise false Christs, and shall *s.* great. *Mat* 24:24; *Mark* 13:22
s. you a large upper room furnished. *Mark* 14:15; *Luke* 22:12
I am sent to *s.* thee these glad. *Luke* 1:19*
s. how great things God hath. 8:39*
he will *s.* him greater works. *John* 5:20
if thou do these things *s.* thyself. 7:4*
where he were, he should *s.* it. 11:57
s. us the Father and it. 14:8, 9
he will *s.* you things to come. 16:13*
he shall receive of mine, and *s.* it. 14*, 15*
but I shall *s.* you plainly of the. 25*
Lord *s.* whether of these. *Acts* 1:24
the land which I shall *s.* thee. 7:3
Go, *s.* these things to James. 12:17*
the men who *s.* to us the way. 16:17*
Felix willing to *s.* the Jews. 24:27
that he should *s.* light to. 26:23*
who *s.* work of the law. *Rom* 2:15
thee, that I might *s.* my power. 9:17
willing to *s.* his wrath, endured. 22
ye do *s.* the Lord's death till he come. *1 Cor* 11:26*
yet *s.* I you a more excellent. 12:31
I *s.* you a mystery, we shall. 15:51*
s. ye to them the proof. *2 Cor* 8:24
s. the exceeding riches. *Eph* 2:7
for they themselves *s.* *1 Thes* 1:9*
that Christ might *s.* all. *1 Tim* 1:16
let them learn first to *s.* piety. 5:4
which in his times he shall *s.* 6:15
study to *s.* thyself approved unto God. *2 Tim* 2:15*
that every one of you *s.* *Heb* 6:11
God willing to *s.* to the heirs. 17
s. me thy faith without. *Jas* 2:18
let him *s.* his works out of. 3:13
ye should *s.* forth the praises of. *1 Pet* 2:9
and *s.* unto you that eternal life. *1 John* 1:2*
he sent his angel to *s.* his servants. *Rev* 1:1; 22:6

I will **shew**

a land that *I will s.* thee. *Gen* 12:1
I will be gracious, *I will s.* mercy on whom *I will s.* mercy. *Ex* 33:19
I will s. thee the man. *Judg* 4:22
I will s. thee what thou. *1 Sam* 16:3
evil, then *I will s.* it thee. 20:13*
I will surely *s.* myself. *1 Ki* 18:15
I will s. you what Syrians. *2 Ki* 7:12
I will s. thee that which. *Job* 15:17
I also *will s.* mine opinion. 32:10
17; 36:2
I will s. forth all thy marvellous. *Ps* 9:1
I will s. the salvation. 50:23; 91:16
I will s. them the back. *Jer* 18:17
I will s. thee great and mighty. 33:3
I will s. mercies unto you. 42:12*
I will s. the king the interpretation. *Dan* 2:24
I will s. thee what is noted. 10:21*
and now *I will s.* thee the truth. 11:2
I will s. wonders in heaven. *Joel* 2:30; *Acts* 2:19
I will s. to him marvellous things. *Mi* 7:15
I will s. the nations thy. *Nah* 3:5
angel said, *I will s.* thee. *Zech* 1:9
I will s. you to whom he. *Luke* 6:47
I will s. him how great things he. *Acts* 9:16
I will s. thee my faith by. *Jas* 2:18
I will s. thee things which. *Rev* 4:1
I will s. thee the judgement of. 17:1
I will s. thee the bride, the. 21:9
see **kindness**

shewbread

shall set upon a table *s.* *Ex* 25:30
make the table, and the *s.* 35:13
39:36
on table of *s.* shall. *Num* 4:7
was no bread but the *s.* *1 Sam* 21:6
table of gold whereon the *s.* was. *1 Ki* 7:48
Kohathites to prepare *s.* *1 Chr* 9:32
service both for the *s.* and. 23:29
gave gold for the tables of *s.* 28:16
house for the continual *s.* *2 Chr* 2:4
tables whereon the *s.* was set. 4:19
s. also they set in order. 13:11
have cleansed the *s.* table. 29:18
ourselves for the *s.* *Neh* 10:33

ıto the house of God, and did eat *s.* *Mat* 12:4; *Mark* 2:26; *Luke* 6:4
'herein was the *s.* *Heb* 9:2

shewed (showed)

white spot, and it be *s.* to priest. *Lev* 13:19, 49
nd *s.* them the fruit of the land. *Num* 13:26
'hich Moses *s.* in the sight of. *Deut* 34:12*
nd when he *s.* them the entrance. *Judg* 1:25
. Sisera, that Barak was gone up. 4:12*
aste, and *s.* her husband. 13:10*
ome up, for he hath *s.* me. 16:18*
hath been *s.* me all. *Ruth* 2:11
ame and *s.* to the men. *1 Sam* 11:9
›nathan *s.* him all those. 19:7
biathar *s.* David that Saul. 22:21*
hou hast *s.* this day how. 24:18*
ıessenger *s.* David. *2 Sam* 11:22
ıou hast not *s.* it to. *1 Ki* 1:27
is might that he *s.* 16:27; 22:45
'here fell it? he *s.* him. *2 Ki* 6:6
›ok an oath, and *s.* them. 11:4
nd *s.* them all the house of his. 20:13; *Isa* 39:2
ıere is nothing I have not *s.* *2 Ki* 20:15; *Isa* 39:4
riches of his glorious. *Esth* 1:4
sther had not *s.* her. 2:10, 20
r they had *s.* him the people. 3:6
ty should be *s.* from. *Job* 6:14
thy strength to this. *Ps* 71:18*
ıey *s.* his signs among them. 105:27*; *Acts* 7:36*
y complaint, I *s.* before him my. *Ps* 142:2*
is wickedness shall be *s.* *Pr* 26:26
bour, wherein I have *s.* *Eccl* 2:19
ho *s.* to him the way? *Isa* 40:14
ıey *s.* no difference. *Ezek* 22:26*
ıd *s.* to chief priests. *Mat* 28:11
evil *s.* him all kingdoms. *Luke* 4:5
e disciples of John *s.* him. 7:18
ıd he said, He that *s.* mercy. 10:37
ıat servant came and *s.* 14:21
re raised, Moses *s.* at bush. 20:37
›od works have I *s.* you. *John* 10:32
s. unto them his hands. 20:20
esus *s.* himself again. 21:1, 14* *Acts* 1:3
iracle of healing was *s.* *Acts* 4:22
Ioses *s.* himself to them. 7:26*
ıd *s.* wonders and signs. 36
hich *s.* before of the coming. 52
s. how he had seen an. 11:13
nfessed, *s.* their deeds. 19:18
ıt have *s.* and have taught. 20:20
have *s.* you all things, how. 35*
ll no man thou hast *s.* 23:22
ıt first Paul *s.* to them of. 26:20
e barbarous people *s.* no. 28:2
ne of brethren *s.* or spake. 21*
r his sake that *s.* it. *1 Cor* 10:28
ve which ye have *s.* *Heb* 6:10
ıdgement, that hath *s.* no. *Jas* 2:13
ıgel *s.* me the city of. *Rev* 21:10
s. me a pure river of water. 22:1
orship the angel who *s.* me. 8

God, or *Lord* **shewed**, *expressly, or implicitly*

y mercy *s.* to me in. *Gen* 19:19
at thou hast *s.* kindness. 24:14
ast of the mercies thou hast *s.* 32:10
e *Lord* *s.* Joseph mercy, and. 39:21
od *s.* Pharaoh what he is. 41:25*
rasmuch as *God* hath *s.* thee. 39
ıd lo, *God* hath *s.* me also. 48:11*
e *Lord* *s.* him a tree. *Ex* 15:25
ake them after the pattern *s.* 25:40 26:30; 27:8; *Heb* 8:5
the *Lord* might be *s.* *Lev* 24:12
e *Lord* had *s.* Moses. *Num* 8:4
signs I have *s.* among them. 14:11*; *Deut* 6:22
ıd upon earth he *s.* *Deut* 4:36
hold, the *Lord* our *God* *s.* 5:24
e *Lord* *s.* him all the land. 34:1
r would he have *s.* *Judg* 13:23
ıst *s.* to thy servant David my. *1 Ki* 3:6; *2 Chr* 1:8
Lord hath *s.* me, he. *2 Ki* 8:10
the *Lord* hath *s.* me that thou. 13
the *Lord* had *s.* David. *2 Chr* 7:10
s. from *Lord* our *God*. *Ezra* 9:8
he hath *s.* me his marvellous. *Ps* 31:21
thou hast *s.* thy people hard. 60:3
thou hast *s.* me great and. 71:20
wonders he had *s.* them. 78:11
his righteousness hath *s.* in. 98:2
he *s.* his people the power of. 111:6
God is the *Lord* who hath *s.* 118:27*
let favour be *s.* to wicked. *Isa* 26:20
I have *s.* when there was no. 43:12
s. them; I did them suddenly. 48:3
before it came to pass I *s.* it thee. 5
Lord *s.* me two baskets. *Jer* 24:1
the word the *Lord* hath *s.* me. 38:21
the *Lord* hath *s.* me. *Ezek* 11:25
gave statutes and *s.* them. 20:11
thus hath the *Lord* *s.* me. *Amos* 7:1 4:7; 8:1
he hath *s.* thee, O man. *Mi* 6:8
and the *Lord* *s.* me four. *Zech* 1:20
s. me Joshua standing before the angel of the *Lord*. 3:1
he hath *s.* strength with. *Luke* 1:51
heard how *Lord* had *s.* great. 58*
which *God* before had *s.* *Acts* 3:18*
God *s.* I should not call any. 10:28
God raised him third day and *s.* 40*
God hath *s.* it to them. *Rom* 1:19*
Lord Jesus hath *s.* me. *2 Pet* 1:14*

shewedst

and *s.* signs and wonders. *Neh* 9:10
I know it; then thou *s.* *Jer* 11:18

shewest

s. thyself marvellous. *Job* 10:16
thou *s.* lovingkindness. *Jer* 32:18
Jews said, What sign *s.* thou to us? *John* 2:18; 6:30*

sheweth

to do, he *s.* to Pharaoh. *Gen* 41:28
whatsoever he *s.* me. *Num* 23:3
none *s.* me that my. *1 Sam* 22:8*
he *s.* mercy to his anointed, to. *2 Sam* 22:51; *Ps* 18:50
he *s.* them their work. *Job* 36:9
noise thereof *s.* concerning it. 33*
firmament *s.* his handywork. *Ps* 19:1
night unto night *s.* knowledge. 2
good man *s.* favour, and. 112:5*
he *s.* his word unto Jacob. 147:19
he that speaketh truth, *s.* *Pr* 12:17
the tender grass *s.* itself. 27:25
yea, there is none that *s.* *Isa* 41:26
and *s.* him all kingdoms. *Mat* 4:8
Father loveth, and *s.* the. *John* 5:20

shewing, *verb*

and *s.* mercy unto thousands. *Ex* 20:6; *Deut* 5:10
s. to generation to come. *Ps* 78:4*
my beloved *s.* himself. *S of S* 2:9
thine iniquities by *s.* *Dan* 4:27
s. of hard sentences found. 5:12
s. glad tidings of kingdom. *Luke* 8:1*
and *s.* the coats which. *Acts* 9:39
s. by scripture that Jesus. 18:28
of God, *s.* himself that. *2 Thes* 2:4*
in all things *s.* thyself. *Tit* 2:7
not purloining, but *s.* all good. 10
but be gentle, *s.* all meekness. 3:2

shewing

deserts till day of his *s.* to Israel. *Luke* 1:80

Shibboleth

say now *S.* and he said. *Judg* 12:6

shield

A piece of defensive armour, commonly of wood, covered with leather, plates of gold, or brass. Sometimes shields were made all of gold, or brass. Those that Solomon *made were of beaten gold,* 1 Ki 10:17. Shishak *king of* Egypt *took these away, and* Rehoboam *made others of brass to serve in their stead,* 1 Ki 14:26, 27.

In scripture God is often called the shield *of his people,* Gen 15:1, Ps 5:12. *Faith in scripture is likewise called a shield,* Eph 6:16.

Shields *were hung up upon towers for ornaments, or as trophies of victory. The tower of* David *was adorned with a thousand* shields, S of S 4:4.

I am thy *s.*, and thy exceeding great reward. *Gen* 15:1
saved by the Lord, the *s.* of thy. *Deut* 33:29
was there a *s.* or spear seen in Israel? *Judg* 5:8
one bearing a *s.* *1 Sam* 17:7, 41
me with a spear and a *s.* 45*
s. of the mighty is vilely cast away, *s.* *2 Sam* 1:21
he is my *s.* 22:3; *Ps* 3:3; 28:7 119:114; 144:2
given me the *s.* of thy salvation. *2 Sam* 22:36; *Ps* 18:35
of gold went to one *s.* *1 Ki* 10:17
come before it with a *s.* nor cast a. *2 Ki* 19:32; *Isa* 37:33
that could handle *s.* *1 Chr* 12:8
children of Judah that bare *s.* 24
of Naphtali with *s.* and spear. 34
could handle spear and *s.* *2 Chr* 25:5
spear and *s.* rattleth. *Job* 39:23*
compass him as with a *s.* *Ps* 5:12
the Lord is our *s.* 33:20; 59:11 84:9
take hold of the *s.* and buckler. 35:2
the arrows of bow, the *s.* 76:3
the Lord God is a sun and *s.* 84:11
be thy *s.* and buckler. 91:4
help and their *s.* 115:9, 10, 11
he is a *s.* to them that. *Pr* 30:5
princes, and anoint the *s.* *Isa* 21:5
quiver, Kir uncovered the *s.* 22:6
order buckler and *s.* *Jer* 46:3
Libyans, that handle the *s.* 9
the buckler and *s.* *Ezek* 23:24
hanged the *s.* and helmet. 27:10, 11
the *s.* of his mighty men. *Nah* 2:3
taking the *s.* of faith. *Eph* 6:16

shields

David took the *s.* of gold that were on. *2 Sam* 8:7; *1 Chr* 18:7
Solomon made 300 *s.* of beaten. *1 Ki* 10:17; *2 Chr* 9:16
all, even all *s.* of gold, which Solomon. *1 Ki* 14:26; *2 Chr* 12:9
Rehoboam made in their stead brazen *s.* *1 Ki* 14:27; *2 Chr* 12:10
priest gave king David *s.* *2 Ki* 11:10 *2 Chr* 23:9
every several city put *s.* *2 Chr* 11:12
out of Benjamin that bare *s.* 14:8 17:17
Uzziah prepared for them *s.* 26:14
darts and *s.* in abundance. 32:5, 27
half of them held spears and *s.* *Neh* 4:16
the *s.* of the earth belong. *Ps* 47:9
bucklers, all *s.* of mighty men. *S of S* 4:4
the arrows, gather the *s.* *Jer* 51:11
great company with bucklers and *s.* *Ezek* 38:4, 5
they shall burn the *s.* and. 39:9

Shiggaion

(*This word is found in the title of* Ps 7. *The meaning is not certainly known. It was perhaps a* wild, mournful ode)

Shiloah

refuseth the waters of *S.* *Isa* 8:6

Shiloh

(*It has long been supposed to refer directly to* Christ, *the* Messiah; *but as there is no reference to it in the* New Testament *many are now doubtful. Some consider it as referring to the city of Shiloh*)

the sceptre shall not depart from Judah, nor a lawgiver from between his feet, until *S.* come. *Gen* 49:10

Shiloh

assembled together at *S.* *Josh* 18:1
cast lots for you in *S.* 8, 10
departed from Israel out of *S.* 22:9
house of God was in *S.* *Judg* 18:31

the young virgins to S. Judg 21:12
feast of the Lord in S. yearly. 19
if the daughters of S. come out. 21
up to worship in S. 1 Sam 1:3
to house of the Lord in S. 24
so did the priests in S. to all. 2:14
the Lord appeared again in S. 3:21
ark of the Lord out of S. 4:3
man came to S. with his clothes. 12
Ahitub the Lord's priest in S. 14:3
the house of Eli in S. 1 Ki 2:27
get thee to S. to Ahijah the. 14:2
wife arose and went to S. 4
the tabernacle of S. Ps 78:60
my place which was in S. Jer 7:12
house as I have done to S. 14
I make this house like S. 26:6, 9
there came certain from S. 41:5

Shilonite, *see* Ahijah

Shimeah

friend, Jonadab son of S. 2 Sam 13:3
32; 21:21; 1 Chr 20:7
S. was born to David in. 1 Chr 3:5
Berachiah, the son of S. 6:39

Shimei

S. son of Gera of Bahurim.
2 Sam 16:5; 19:16
S. went along on the hill's side. 16:13
thou hast with thee S. 1 Ki 2:8
that two of the servants of S. 39
S. the son of Elah, officer in. 4:18
S. son of Pedaiah. 1 Chr 3:19
S. son of Joel. 5:4
Mishma, Hamuel, Zaccur, S. 4:26
S. had sixteen sons and six. 27
S. son of Gershom. 6:17, 42, 23:7
S. son of Merari. 6:29
sons of S. 23:9, 10
the tenth lot to S. 25:17
over vineyards was S. 27:27
Heman, Jehiel and S. 2 Chr 29:14
dedicated things was S. 31:12, 13
S. had taken a strange wife.
Ezra 10:23, 33, 38
of Jair, the son of S. Esth 2:5
the family of S. shall. Zech 12:13

Shimshai

S. the scribe wrote a. Ezra 4:8, 9
the king sent an answer to S. 17

Shinar

Calneh in the land of S. Gen 10:10
a plain in the land of S. 11:2
Amraphel king of S. 14:1
recover remnant from S. Isa 11:11
into the land of S. Dan 1:2
house in the land of S. Zech 5:11

shine

Lord make his face s. Num 6:25
neither let light s. on it. Job 3:4
s. on counsel of the wicked. 10:3
thou shalt s. forth, thou. 11:17*
spark of his fire shall not s. 18:5
and the light shall s. upon. 22:28
light he commandeth not to s. 36:32*
the light of his cloud to s. 37:15
light doth s. and his eyes. 41:18*
he maketh a path to s. after him. 32
make thy face to s. Ps 31:16
face to s. upon us. 67:1; 80:3, 7, 19
between cherubims, s. forth. 80:1
oil to make his face to s. 104:15
make thy face to s. upon. 119:135
maketh his face to s. Eccl 8:1
not cause her light to s. Isa 13:10
arise, s. for thy light is come. 60:1
are waxen fat, they s. Jer 5:28
cause thy face to s. Dan 9:17
wise shall s. as the brightness. 12:3
let your light so s. Mat 5:16
shall the righteous s. forth. 13:43
his face did s. as sun, and his. 17:2
gospel of Christ should s. 2 Cor 4:4*
God who commanded light to s. 6
ye s. as lights in world. Phil 2:15
light of a candle shall s. Rev 18:23
sun nor moon to s. in it. 21:23

shined

the Lord s. forth from. Deut 33:2
when his candle s. upon. Job 29:3
if I beheld the sun when it s. 31:26
of beauty God hath s. Ps 50:2
upon them hath the light s. Isa 9:2
earth s. with his glory. Ezek 43:2
suddenly there s. about. Acts 9:3
the angel came, and a light s. 12:7
for God hath s. in our. 2 Cor 4:6

shineth

moon, and it s. not. Job 25:5*
the night s. as the day. Ps 139:12
shining light that s. more. Pr 4:18
as lightning s. even to. Mat 24:27*
and s. to other part. Luke 17:24
the light s. in darkness. John 1:5
as to a light that s. in. 2 Pet 1:19
the true light now s. 1 John 2:8
was as the sun s. Rev 1:16

shining

by clear s. after rain. 2 Sam 23:4
path of just is as the s. light. Pr 4:18
will create the s. of a. Isa 4:5
withdraw their s. Joel 2:10; 3:15
they went at the s. Hab 3:11
raiment became s. white. Mark 9:3
when the s. of a candle. Luke 11:36
two men stood by them in s. 24:4
a burning and a s. light. John 5:35
the brightness of sun s. Acts 26:13

ship

(*In the Gospels the Revisions change this word to* boat)

the way of a s. in the midst. Pr 30:19
no gallant s. shall pass. Isa 33:21
Jonah found a s. going. Jonah 1:3
a tempest, so that the s. was. 4
forth the wares into the s. 5
in a s. with Zebedee. Mat 4:21
and they left the s. and followed. 22
that the s. was covered with. 8:24
the s. was tossed with waves. 14:24
Mark 4:37
in the s. mending their. Mark 1:19
father Zebedee in the s. 20
hinder part of the s. asleep. 4:38
neither had they in the s. 8:14
immediately the s. was. John 6:21
net on right side of the s. 21:6
accompanied him to the s. Acts 20:38
finding a s. sailing over unto. 21:2
into a s. of Adramyttium. 27:2

ship *boards*

all thy s. boards of fir trees.
Ezek 27:5

shipmaster

s. said, What meanest? Jonah 1:6
every s. and sailors afar. Rev 18:17

shipmen

Hiram sent s. that had. 1 Ki 9:27
the s. were about to flee out of.
Acts 27:30*

shipping

they took s. and came. John 6:24

ships

shall be an haven for s. Gen 49:13
and s. shall come from Chittim.
Num 24:24
thee into Egypt with s. Deut 28:68
did Dan remain in s.? Judg 5:17
king Solomon made a navy of s.
1 Ki 9:26
s. of Tarshish to go to Ophir, the s.
22:48; 2 Chr 20:37
my servants go with thine in the s.
1 Ki 22:49
sent him s. and servants. 2 Chr 8:18
king's s. went to Tarshish. 9:21
passed away as the swift s. Job 9:26
thou breakest the s. of. Ps 48:7
there go the s.: there is that. 104:26
down to the sea in s. that. 107:23
merchant s. she brings. Pr 31:14
Lord on the s. of Tarshish. Isa 2:16
howl, ye s. of Tarshish, no. 23:1, 14
whose cry is in the s. 43:14
the s. of Tarshish first, to. 60:9
all s. of the sea with. Ezek 27:9
s. of Tarshish did sing of thee. 25
come down from their s. 29
go forth from me in s. 30:9
for s. of Chittim shall. Dan 11:30
north shall come with many s. 40
they filled both the s. Luke 5:7
behold also the s. though. Jas 3:4
the third part of the s. Rev 8:9
the company in s. stood. Rev 18:17*
made rich all that had s. 19

shipwreck

stoned, thrice I suffered s.
2 Cor 11:25
faith have made s. 1 Tim 1:19

Shishak

in fifth year of Rehoboam, S. king.
1 Ki 14:25; 2 Chr 12:2
together because of S. I left you in the hand of S. 2 Chr 12:5
be poured out on Jerusalem by S. 7
S. took away the treasures of. 9

shittah tree

in wilderness the s. tree. Isa 41:19

Shittim

Israel abode in S. Num 25:1
sent out of S. two men. Josh 2:1
they removed from S. and. 3:1
water the valley of S. Joel 3:18
him from S. to Gilgal. Mi 6:5

shittim wood

(Acacia, *as in Revisions*)

skins and s. wood. Ex 25:5; 35:7
shall make an ark of s. wood.
25:10; 37:1; Deut 10:3
make staves of s. wood. Ex 25:13
28; 27:6; 37:4, 15, 28; 38:6
thou shalt make a table of s. wood.
25:23; 37:10
make boards for tabernacle of s. wood. 26:15; 36:20
thou shalt make bars of s. wood.
26:26; 36:21
pillars of s. wood. 26:32, 37; 36:36
make an altar of s. wood. 27:1
30:1
with whom was found s. wood. 35:24

shivers

potter shall be broken to s. Rev 2:27

shock

like as a s. of corn cometh. Job 5:26

shocks

Samson burnt up the s. Judg 15:5

shod

captives and s. them. 2 Chr 28:15
I s. thee with badgers'. Ezek 16:10
be s. with sandals, put not on.
Mark 6:9
s. with the preparation. Eph 6:15

shoe

To take off shoe was, [1] *A sign of reverence,* Ex 3:5; [2] *Of disgrace,* Deut 25:10; [3] *Of a contract,* Ruth 4:7; [4] *Of mourning,* Ezek 24:17.

wife shall loose his s. Deut 25:9
the house of him that hath his s. 10
thy s. is not waxen old upon. 29:5
thy s. from off thy foot. Josh 5:15
man plucked off his s. Ruth 4:7
it for thee, so he drew off his s.
over Edom will I cast out my s.
Ps 60:8; 108:9
and put off thy s. Isa 20:2

shoelatchet

take from thread to a s. Gen 14:2
whose s. I am not worthy. John 1:2

shoes

put off thy s. from thy feet.
Ex 3:5; Acts 7:3
with your s. on your feet. 12:1
s. shall be iron and. Deut 33:25
old s. and clouted upon. Josh 9:
our s. are become old with. 1
put the blood in his s. 1 Ki 2:
are thy feet with s.! S of S 7:1
nor the latchet of their s. Isa 5:2
put on thy s. upon. Ezek 24:17, 2
they sold the poor for a pair of s.
Amos 2:
buy the needy for a pair of s. 8:
whose s. I am not worthy. Mat 3:1
carry neither s. nor staves. 10:1
Luke 10:
s. I am not worthy to. Mark 1:
Luke 3:16; Acts 13:2
ring on his hand, and s. Luke 15:2
you without purse and s. 22:

he shall come down as *s.* *Ps* 72:6
therefore the *s.* have been. *Jer* 3:3
can the heavens give *s.*? 14:22
shall be *s.* of blessing. *Ezek* 34:26
shall be as *s.* on grass. *Mi* 5:7
the Lord shall give them *s.* of rain. *Zech* 10:1

shrank

Israel eat not of sinew that *s.* *Gen* 32:32*

shred

came and *s.* wild gourds. *2 Ki* 4:39

shrines

made silver *s.* for Diana. *Acts* 19:24

shroud

was a cedar with a shadowing *s.* *Ezek* 31:3

shrubs

child under one of the *s.* *Gen* 21:15

Shuah

Keturah bare Ishbak, *S.* *Gen* 25:2
1 Chr 1:32
daughter of a Canaanite named *S.* *Gen* 38:2, 12; *1 Chr* 2:3

Shual

turned to the land of *S.* *1 Sam* 13:17

Shuhite, *see* **Bildad**

Shulamite

return, O *S.* What will ye see in the *S.*? *S of S* 6:13

shun

but *s.* profane and vain. *2 Tim* 2:16

Shunammite

a fair damsel Abishag a *S.* *1 Ki* 1:3
Abishag the *S.* to wife. 2:17
why dost thou ask Abishag the *S.*? 22
call this *S.* *2 Ki* 4:12, 36
yonder is that *S.* 25

shunned

I have not *s.* the whole. *Acts* 20:27*

Shushan

to pass as I was in *S.* *Neh* 1:1
were gathered to *S.* *Esth* 2:8
but the city *S.* was perplexed. 3:15
gather all the Jews in *S.* and. 4:16
the city of *S.* rejoiced and. 8:15
number slain in *S.* was brought. 9:11
Jews slew in *S.* three hundred. 15
see **palace**

shut

the Lord *s.* him in. *Gen* 7:16
wilderness hath *s.* them in. *Ex* 14:3
let her be *s.* out from camp. *Num* 12:14
Miriam was *s.* out from the camp. 15
nor *s.* thy hand from. *Deut* 15:7
s. the gate of Jericho. *Josh* 2:7
they *s.* the tower to them. *Judg* 9:51
for he is *s.* in, by entering into. *1 Sam* 23:7
gates to be *s.* till after. *Neh* 13:19
not the pit *s.* her mouth. *Ps* 69:15
s. their eyes, lest they. *Isa* 6:10
so he shall open and none shall *s.*; he shall *s.* and none shall. 22:22
for he hath *s.* their eyes. 44:18
and gates shall not be *s.* 45:1
kings shall *s.* their mouths. 52:15
thy gates shall not be *s.* day. 60:11
shall I *s.* the womb? saith. 66:9
Spirit said, Go *s.* thyself. *Ezek* 3:24
looked toward the east was *s.* 44:1
this gate shall be *s.*, it shall not be opened, God . . . it shall be *s.* 2
the gate shall be *s.* the six. 46:1
the gate shall not be *s.* till the. 2
after his going forth, one shall *s.* 12
my God hath *s.* the lions'. *Dan* 6:22
prison truly found we *s.* *Acts* 5:23
power to *s.* heaven. *Rev* 11:6
gates shall not be *s.* by day. 21:25
see **door**

shut ***up***

priest shall *s.* him *up* that hath. *Lev* 13:4, 5, 21, 26, 31, 33, 50, 54
the priest shall not *s.* him *up.* 11
priest shall *s. up* the house. 14:38
goeth in while the house is *s. up.* 46
the Lord's wrath be kindled, and he *s. up* the heaven. *Deut* 11:17
their rock the Lord had *s.* them *up.* *Deut* 32:30*
there is none *s. up* nor left. 36
Jericho was straitly *s. up.* *Josh* 6:1
Lord had *s. up* Hannah's womb. *1 Sam* 1:5
because the Lord had *s. up* her. 6
hid them and *s. up* their calves. 6:10
concubines were *s. up* to day of. *2 Sam* 20:3
when heaven is *s. up.* *1 Ki* 8:35
2 Chr 6:26; 7:13
from Jeroboam him that is *s. up* and. *1 Ki* 14:10; 21:21; *2 Ki* 9:8
was not any *s. up.* *2 Ki* 14:26
king of Assyria *s.* him *up.* 17:4
Ahaz *s. up* doors of house. *2 Chr* 28:24; 29:7
Shemaiah who was *s. up.* *Neh* 6:10
because it *s.* not *up* my. *Job* 3:10
if he cut off, and *s. up,* who? 11:10
or who hath *s. up* the sea? 38:8
his scales are *s. up* together. 41:15
hast not *s.* me *up* into. *Ps* 31:8
he in anger *s. up* his tender? 77:9
I am *s. up,* and I cannot come. 88:8
spring *s. up,* a fountain. *S of S* 4:12
every house is *s. up,* no. *Isa* 24:10
shall be *s. up* in the prison. 22
the south shall be *s. up.* *Jer* 13:19
as fire *s. up* in my bones. 20:9
the prophet was *s. up* by Zedekiah. 32:2, 3
word of Lord came, while he was *s. up.* 33:1; 39:15
I am *s. up,* I cannot go to the. 36:5
s. up the vision. *Dan* 8:26
s. up the words. 12:4
ye *s. up* kingdom of. *Mat* 23:13
he *s. up* John in prison. *Luke* 3:20
heaven was *s. up* three years. 4:25
many saints did I *s. up.* *Acts* 26:10
s. up unto the faith that. *Gal* 3:23
s. up the devil, and set. *Rev* 20:3

shutteth

he *s.* up a man, there. *Job* 12:14
he *s.* his eyes to devise. *Pr* 16:30
he that *s.* his lips. is a man. 17:28
s. his eyes from seeing. *Isa* 33:15
also when I cry, he *s.* *Lam* 3:8
and *s.* up his bowels. *1 John* 3:17
no man *s.*; and *s.*, and no man openeth. *Rev* 3:7

shutting

about time of *s.* the gate. *Josh* 2:5

shuttle

swifter than a weaver's *s.* *Job* 7:6

sick

behold thy father is *s.* *Gen* 48:1
the law of her that is *s.* *Lev* 15:33
sent, she said, He is *s.* *1 Sam* 19:14
three days ago I fell *s.* 30:13
the child, and it was *s.* *2 Sam* 12:15
vexed, he fell *s.* for Tamar. 13:2
make thyself *s.* 5
Amnon made himself *s.* 6
son of Jeroboam fell *s.* *1 Ki* 14:1
cometh to ask for son, for he is *s.* 5
son of the woman fell *s.* 17:17
down in Samaria, was *s.* *2 Ki* 1:2
the king of Syria was *s.* 8:7
went to see Joram son of Ahab, because he was *s.* 29; *2 Chr* 22:6
Elisha was fallen *s.* of. *2 Ki* 13:14
was Hezekiah *s.* unto death. 20:1
2 Chr 32:24; *Isa* 38:1
heard that Hezekiah had been *s.* *2 Ki* 20:12; *Isa* 39:1
sad, seeing thou art not *s.*? *Neh* 2:2
when they were *s.*, my clothing was sackcloth. *Ps* 35:13
maketh the heart *s.* *Pr* 13:12
stricken me, and I was not *s.* 23:35*
me with apples, I am *s.* of love. *S of S* 2:5
tell him that I am *s.* of love. 5:8
whole head is *s.* and the whole heart faint. *Isa* 1:5
shall not say, I am *s.* 33:24
when Hezekiah had been *s.* 38:9
behold them that are *s.* *Jer* 14:18
healed that which was *s.* *Ezek* 34:4
strengthen that which was *s.* 16
and was *s.* certain days. *Dan* 8:
princes made him *s.* with. *Hos* 7
will I make thee *s.* in. *Mi* 6:1
if ye offer the lame and *s.*? *Mal* 1
ye brought the lame, and the *s.*
brought to him all *s.* people. *Mat* 4:2
saw his wife's mother laid, and *s.* a fever. 8:14; *Mark* 1:
and healed all that were *s.* *Mat* 8:16; 14:
not a physician, but they that are *s.* 9:12; *Mark* 2:17; *Luke* 5:
heal the *s.*, cleanse the lepers. *Mat* 10:8; *Luke* 9:2; 10:
I was *s.* and ye visited. *Mat* 25:
saw we thee *s.*? in prison? 39,
hands on a few *s.* folk. *Mark* 6
they laid the *s.* in the streets. *Acts* 5:
lay hands on the *s.* and. *Mark* 16:
centurion's servant was *s.* *Luke* 7
whole that had been *s.*
nobleman's son was *s.* *John* 4:
Lazarus of Bethany was *s.* 11:1,
he whom thou lovest is *s.*
he had heard he was *s.* he abode.
in those days Dorcas was *s.* and. *Acts* 9:
unto the *s.* handkerchiefs. 19:
father of Publius lay *s.* of a. 28:
heard that he had been *s.* *Phil* 2:
he was *s.* nigh unto death.
have I left at Miletum *s.* *2 Tim* 4:
is any *s.* let him call elders. *Jas* 5:
prayer of faith shall save the *s.*
see **palsy**

sickle

as thou beginnest to put *s.* to. *Deut* 16:
s. unto thy neighbour's corn. 23:
cut off him that handleth *s.* *Jer* 50:
put ye in the *s.* for the. *Joel* 3:
he putteth in the *s.* *Mark* 4:
and in his hand a sharp *s.* *Rev* 14:
an angel crying, Thrust in thy *s.* 16, 18,
he also having a sharp *s.*

sickly

for this cause many are *s.* among. *1 Cor* 11:

sickness

I will take *s.* away from. *Ex* 23:
man lie with a woman having her *s.* *Lev* 20:
will take from thee all *s.* *Deut* 7:
every *s.* that is not written. 28:
whatsoever *s.* there be. *1 Ki* 8:
2 Chr 6:
his *s.* was so sore, there. *1 Ki* 17:
Elisha sick of the *s.* *2 Ki* 13:
great *s.* by disease of thy bowels, reason of the *s.* *2 Chr* 21:
by reason of his *s.* so he died.
all his bed in his *s.* *Ps* 41
and wrath with his *s.* *Eccl* 5:
was recovered of his *s.* *Isa* 38
will cut me off with pining *s.*
Ephraim saw his *s.*, and Judah sa his wound. *Hos* 5:
healing all manner of *s.* *Mat* 4:
preaching and healing every *s.* 9:
power to heal all manner of *s.* 10: *Mark* 3:
this *s.* is not unto death. *John* 11

sicknesses

the sore *s.* and of long. *Deut* 28:
when they see the *s.* Lord laid. 29:
saying, Himself bare our *s.* *Mat* 8:

side

shall set in the *s.* thereof. *Gen* 6:
walked along by river *s.* *Ex* 2
blood on the two *s.* posts. 12:7,
blood on the lintel and *s.* posts.
Moses' hands, the one on the one and the other on the other *s.* 17:
who is on Lord's *s.*? let him. 32:
sword by his *s.* go in and out. 2
he shall kill it on *s.* of. *Lev* 1:
blood shall be wrung out at the *s.*
sin offering sprinkled on *s.* of. 5
s. and a wall on that *s.* *Num* 22:

as gardens by the river's *s.* Num 24:6
inherit on yonder *s.* Jordan. 32:19
ask from one *s.* of heaven to the. Deut 4:32*
put the book of the law in the *s.* 31:26
a Levite sojourned on *s.* of Ephraim Judg 19:1, 18
fell backward by the *s.* 1 Sam 4:18
put the mice in a coffer by the *s.* 6:8
I will shoot three arrows on the *s.* 20:20
and Abner sat by Saul's *s.* 25
sword into his fellow's *s.* 2 Sam 2:16
came by way of the hill *s.* 13:34
on the hill *s.* over against. 16:13
Who is on my *s.*? who? 2 Ki 9:32
David, and on thy *s.* 1 Chr 12:18
Benjamin on his *s.* 2 Chr 11:12*
his sword girded by his *s.* Neh 4:18
shall be ready at his *s.* Job 18:12
thousand shall fall at thy *s.* Ps 91:7
the Lord is on my *s.* I will. 118:6
the Lord who was on our *s.* 124:1, 2
the *s.* of their oppressors. Eccl 4:1
shall be nursed at thy *s.* Isa 60:4*
not turn from one *s.* to another. Ezek 4:8
days that thou shalt lie upon thy *s.* 9
writer's inkhorn by his *s.* 9:2, 3, 11
I will open the *s.* of Moab. 25:9
because ye have thrust with *s.* 34:21
it raised itself on one *s.* Dan 7:5
shall not stand on his *s.* 11:17
thieves, on either *s.* one. John 19:18
soldiers with a spear pierced his *s.* 34
them his hands and his *s.* 20:20
except I thrust my hand into his *s.* 25
and thrust it into my *s.* 27
the angel smote Peter on the *s.*, and raised him up. Acts 12:7
we went out by the river *s.* 16:13
on either *s.* of river was. Rev 22:2
see **chambers, left, sea, south, way, west**

every **side**

of Abiram on *every s.* Num 16:27
the trumpets on *every s.* Judg 7:18
delivered them from their enemies on *every s.* 8:34; 1 Sam 12:11
enemies on *every s.* 1 Sam 14:47
about him on *every s.* 1 Ki 5:3
given me rest on *every s.* 4
hath he not given you rest on *every s.*? 1 Chr 22:18
he hath given us rest on *every s.* 2 Chr 14:7
Lord guided them on *every s.* 32:22
about all he hath on *every s.* Job 1:10
make him afraid on *every s.* 18:11
destroyed me on *every s.* I. 19:10
wicked walk on *every s.* Ps 12:8
fear was on *every s.* while. 31:13
little hills rejoice on *every s.* 65:12*
comfort me on *every s.* 71:21*
fear is on *every s.* Jer 6:25; 20:10 49:29
that they may come to thee on *every s.* Ezek 16:33
set against him on *every s.* 19:8
them against thee on *every s.* 23:22
sword upon her on *every s.* 28:23
swallowed you up on *every s.* 36:3
I will gather them on *every s.* 37:21
to my sacrifice on *every s.* 39:17
keep thee in on *every s.* Luke 19:43
we are troubled on *every s.* 2 Cor 4:8; 7:5

farther **side**

farther *s.* of Jordan. Mark 10:1*

on this **side**

one cherub *on this s.*, other on that side. Ex 37:8
quails a day's journey *on this s.* Num 11:31
on this s. and on that side. 22:24
inheritance *on this s.* Jordan. 32:19 32*; 34:15*
refuge *on this s.* Jordan. 35:14*
some *on this s.* of Ai, and some on that side. Josh 8:22
Israel and judges stood *on this s.* 33
arrows are *on this s.* 1 Sam 20:21
Saul went *on this s.* of the. 23:26
no portion *on this s.* the river. Ezra 4:16*
governor *on this s.* the river. 5:3* 6*, 6:13*; 8:36*
throne of the governor *on this s.* the river. Neh 3:7*
two wings, *on this s.* Ezek 1:23
two tables *on this s.* and two on that side. 40:39
on this s., four tables on that side. 41
on bank of river *on this s.* 47:12
stood other two, the one *on this s.* Dan 12:5
stealeth shall be cut off as *on this s.* ... sweareth on that side. Zech 5:3

on other **side**

your fathers dwelt *on* the *other s.* of the flood. Josh 24:2*
I and Jonathan will be *on* the *other s.* 1 Sam 14:40
saw water *on other s.* 2 Ki 3:22*
stood *on* one and *other s.* 2 Chr 9:19
stoodest *on* the *other s.* Ob 11
found him *on* the *other s.* of the sea. John 6:25

right **side**

chamber was on *right s.* 1 Ki 6:8
the *right s.* the house; set the sea on *right s.* 7:39; 2 Chr 4:10
five candlesticks on the *right s.* 1 Ki 7:49; 2 Chr 4:8
of a lion on the *right s.* Ezek 1:10
lie again on thy *right s.* and shalt. 4:6
from under *right s.* of house. 47:1, 2
on *right s.* the bowl. Zech 4:3, 11
they saw a young man sitting on *right s.* of sepulchre. Mark 16:5
angel standing on *right s.* Luke 1:11
cast the net on the *right s.* John 21:6

sides

were written on both *s.* Ex 32:15
shall be thorns in your *s.* Num 33:55; Judg 2:3
be scourges in your *s.* Josh 23:13
needlework on both *s.* Judg 5:30
David and his men in *s.* of the cave. 1 Sam 24:3*
peace on all *s.* round. 1 Ki 4:24
beautiful is Zion on the *s.* Ps 48:2
wife as a fruitful vine by *s.* 128:3*
I will sit also in the *s.* Isa 14:13*
thou shalt be brought down to *s.* 15*
ye shall be borne upon her *s.* 66:12
nation raised from *s.* of the earth. Jer 6:22*
maketh her nest in the *s.* 48:28†
their calamity from all *s.* 49:32
upon their four *s.* Ezek 1:17; 10:11
whose graves are set in the *s.* 32:23*
these are his *s.* east and west. 48:1
say unto him that is by *s.* Amos 6:10*
Jonah was gone down into the *s.* of the ship. Jonah 1:5*

Sidon, called **Zidon**, 1 Chr 1:13
Canaan begat *S.* his. Gen 10:15
Canaanites was from *S.* 19
Laish was far from *S.* Judg 18:28
done in Tyre and *S.* Mat 11:21
it shall be more tolerable for *S.* 22; Luke 10:13, 14
into the coasts of Tyre and *S.* behold, a woman. Mat 15:21; Mark 7:24
they about Tyre and *S.* came. Mark 3:8; Luke 6:17
the coasts of Tyre and *S.* Mark 7:31
sent, save to Sarepta a city of *S.* Luke 4:26
was displeased with them of *S.* Acts 12:20
next day we touched at *S.* 27:3

siege

cut to employ them in *s.* Deut 20:19
eat thy children in the *s.* 28:53
nothing left him in the *s.* 55, 57
whereon do ye trust, that ye abide in the *s.*? 2 Chr 32:10
I will lay *s.* against thee. Isa 29:3
flesh of his friend in the *s.* Jer 19:9
lay *s.* against it and build a fort. Ezek 4:2, 3
days of the *s.* are fulfilled. 5:2
he hath laid *s.* against us. Mi 5:1
waters for the *s.*, fortify. Nah 3:14
trembling, when in the *s.* Zech 12:2

sieve

sift the nations with the *s.* of vanity. Isa 30:28
I will sift, like as corn is sifted in a *s.* Amos 9:9

sift

to *s.* the nations with. Isa 30:28
I will *s.* Israel as corn is. Amos 9:9
Satan hath desired to have you, that he may. Luke 22:31

sigh

all merry-hearted do *s.* Isa 24:7
her priests *s.* Lam 1:4
all her people *s.* 11
they have heard that I *s.* 21
foreheads of men that *s.* Ezek 9:4
breaking of thy loins, and with bitterness *s.* before their eyes. 21:6

sighed

Israel *s.* by reason of. Ex 2:23
up to heaven, he *s.* Mark 7:34
s. deeply in his spirit, and. 8:12

sighest

to thee, Wherefore *s.*? Ezek 21:7

sigheth

yea, she *s.* and turneth. Lam 1:8

sighing

my *s.* cometh before I eat. Job 3:24
for the *s.* of the needy. Ps 12:5
with grief, my years with *s.* 31:10
let the *s.* of the prisoner. 79:11
all the *s.* thereof have. Isa 21:2
sorrow and *s.* shall flee away. 35:10
I fainted in my *s.* and I. Jer 45:3

sighs

for my *s.* are many. Lam 1:22

sight

(*Revisions frequently change to* eyes)

that is pleasant to the *s.* Gen 2:9
turn and see this great *s.* Ex 3:3
s. of glory of Lord was like. 24:17*
the plague in *s.* be deeper. Lev 13:3*, 20*, 25*, 30*
in *s.* be not deeper. 4*, 31*, 32*, 34
if the plague in *s.* be lower. 14:37
in our own *s.* as grasshoppers, and so we were in their *s.* Num 13:33
give him charge in their *s.* 27:19
shalt be mad for *s.* Deut 28:34, 67
them from out of your *s.* Josh 23:5
did those great signs in our *s.* 24:17
reputed vile in your *s.*? Job 18:3
I am an alien in their *s.* 19:15
seed is established in their *s.* 21:8
them in the open *s.* of others. 34:26
be cast down at the *s.* of him? 41:9
the heathen in our *s.* Ps 79:10
better is the *s.* of the eyes. Eccl 6:9
prudent in their own *s.* Isa 5:21
he shall not judge after the *s.* 11:3
evil done in Zion in your *s.* Jer 51:24
shalt bake it with dung in their *s.* Ezek 4:12
remove by day in their *s.* 12:3
dig thou through the wall in their *s.* 5
in whose *s.* I made myself. 20:9
heathen in whose *s.* I brought. 14, 22
yourselves in your own *s.* 43; 36:31
a false divination in their *s.* 21:23
thereof, and write in their *s.* 43:11
s. thereof to end of. Dan 4:11, 20
whoredoms out of her *s.* Hos 2:2*
the blind receive their *s.*, the lame. Mat 11:5; 20:34; Luke 7:21
the recovering of *s.* to the blind. Luke 4:18
that came to that *s.* smote. 23:48
he vanished out of their *s.* 24:31
washed, and I received *s.* John 9:11
cloud received him out of their *s.* Acts 1:9
saw it, he wondered at the *s.* 7:31
was three days without *s.* 9:9
he received *s.* forthwith, arose. 18
walk by faith, not by *s.* 2 Cor 5:7
so terrible was the *s.* Heb 12:21*

sight *of God*

good understanding in the *s. of God.* *Pr* 3:4
is abomination in the *s. of God.* *Luke* 16:15
right in the *s. of God* to. *Acts* 4:19
not right in the *s. of God.* 8:21
had in remembrance in the *s. of God.* 10:31
in the *s. of God* speak we. *2 Cor* 2:17
conscience in the *s. of God.* 4:2
our care for you in *s. of God.* 7:12
by the law in *s. of God.* *Gal* 3:11
remembering work of faith in *s. of God.* *1 Thes* 1:3
this is good and acceptable in the *s. of God.* *1 Tim* 2:3
thee charge in the *s. of God.* 6:13
which is in the *s. of God* of. *1 Pet* 3:4
see **Lord**

his **sight**

if thou wilt do that which is right in *his s.* *Ex* 15:26
if the plague in *his s.* be. *Lev* 13:5
scall be in *his s.* at a stay. 37
burn the heifer in *his s.* *Num* 19:5
he brought thee out in *his s.* *Deut* 4:37*
Lord departed out of *his s.* *Judg* 6:21
Lord, to do evil in *his s.*? *2 Sam* 12:9
went and made cakes in *his s.* 13:8
remove them out of *his s.* *2 Ki* 17:18, 20, 23; 24:3
do what is right in *his s.* *1 Chr* 19:13*
are not clean in *his s.* *Job* 15:15
stars are not pure in *his s.* 25:5
are far above out of *his s.* *Ps* 10:5
shall their blood be in *his s.* 72:14
to a man that is good in *his s.* *Eccl* 2:26
be not hasty to go out of *his s.* 8:3*
and we shall live in *his s.* *Hos* 6:2
immediately received *his s.* and. *Mark* 10:52; *Luke* 18:43
he had received *his s.* *John* 9:15, 18
he might receive *his s.* *Acts* 9:12
no flesh be justified in *his s.* *Rom* 3:20
present you holy in *his s.* *Col* 1:22
is manifest in *his s.* *Heb* 4:13
is well pleasing in *his s.* 13:21
things that are pleasing in *his s.* *1 John* 3:22

in the **sight**

grievous *in* Abraham's *s.* *Gen* 21:11
aught left *in the s.* of my lord. 47:18
signs *in the s.* of the people. *Ex* 4:30
he smote the waters *in the s.* 7:20
Moses sprinkled the ashes *in the s.* 9:8
great *in the s.* of Pharaoh's. 11:3
Moses did so *in the s.* of the. 17:6
come down *in the s.* of people. 19:11
fire by night *in the s.* of Israel. 40:38
shall be cut off *in the s.* *Lev* 20:17
out of Egypt *in the s.* of the. 26:45
ministered *in the s.* of Aaron. *Num* 3:4*
Eleazar went *in the s.* of. 20:27
woman *in the s.* of Moses. 25:6
went with high hand *in the s.* 33:3
is your wisdom *in the s.* of nations. *Deut* 4:6
Joshua *in the s.* of all Israel. 31:7
terror Moses shewed *in the s.* 34:12
to magnify thee *in the s.* of Israel. *Josh* 3:7; 4:14
he said, *In the s.* of Israel. 10:12
David accepted *in the s.* of the. *1 Sam* 18:5
lie with thy wives *in the s.* of this sun. *2 Sam* 12:11
in the s. of all Israel. *1 Chr* 28:8
Solomon *in the s.* of Israel. 29:25
Hezekiah magnified *in s.* of nations. *2 Chr* 32:23
in the s. of kings of Persia. *Ezra* 9:9
grant him mercy *in the s.* *Neh* 1:11
opened the book *in the s.* of all. 8:5
things did he *in the s.* of their fathers. *Ps* 78:12
he openly shewed *in the s.* of. 98:2
in vain net is spread *in the s.* *Pr* 1:17
beloved *in the s.* of my mother. *Pr* 4:3
walk *in the s.* of thine. *Eccl* 11:9
break the bottle *in the s.* *Jer* 19:10
I gave the evidence *in the s.* 32:12*
hid stones *in the s.* of the men. 43:9
execute judgements *in the s.* of the. *Ezek* 5:8
Jerusalem a reproach *in s.* of. 14
judgement on thee *in the s.* 16:41
name not polluted *in s.* of. 20:22
thee to ashes *in the s.* of all. 28:18
sanctified in them *in s.* of heathen. 25; 39:27
lay desolate *in the s.* of all. 36:34
I will discover lewdness *in s.* of. *Hos* 2:10
gave him wisdom *in the s.* *Acts* 7:10
provide things honest *in the s.* of all. *Rom* 12:17
come down *in s.* of men. *Rev* 13:13
miracles he had power to do *in s.* 14

my **sight**

bury my dead out of *my s.* *Gen* 23:4, 8
found grace in *my s.* *Ex* 33:12, 17
coming is good in *my s.* *1 Sam* 29:6
thou art good in *my s.* as an. 9
be base in *mine* own *s.* *2 Sam* 6:22
and dress the meat in *my s.* 13:5
me a couple of cakes in *my s.* 6
not fail thee a man in *my s.* *1 Ki* 8:25; *2 Chr* 6:16
hallowed for my name will I cast out of *my s.* *1 Ki* 9:7; *2 Chr* 7:20
do that is right in *my s.* *1 Ki* 11:38
which was evil in *my s.* *2 Ki* 21:15
Judah also out of *my s.* 23:27
shed much blood in *my s.* *1 Chr* 22:8
shall not tarry in *my s.* *Ps* 101:7
wast precious in *my s.* *Isa* 43:4
abominations out of *my s.* *Jer* 4:1
I will cast you of *my s.* as. 7:15
of Judah have done evil in *my s.* 30
cast them out of *my s.* and. 15:1
if it do evil in *my s.* that it. 18:10
and had done right in *my s.* 34:15
he went in *my s.* to fill. *Ezek* 10:2
up from the earth in *my s.* 19
be hid from *my s.* in the bottom. *Amos* 9:3
thee? Lord, that I might receive *my s.* *Mark* 10:51; *Luke* 18:41

thy **sight**

hath found grace in *thy s.* *Gen* 19:19
let it not be grievous in *thy s.* 21:12
If I have found grace in *thy s.* 33:10 47:29; *Ex* 33:13, 16; 34:9 *Judg* 6:17
rule with rigour in *thy s.* *Lev* 25:53
little in *thine* own *s.* *1 Sam* 15:17
cut off thine enemies out of *thy s.* *2 Sam* 7:9*
yet a small thing in *thy s.* 19
I have found grace in *thy s.* 14:22
let my life be precious in *thy s.* *2 Ki* 1:13, 14
I have done that which is good in *thy s.* 20:3; *Isa* 38:3
shall not stand in *thy s.* *Ps* 5:5
let heathen be judged in *thy s.* 9:19
heart be acceptable in *thy s.* 19:14
and done this evil in *thy s.* 51:4
who may stand in *thy s.*? 76:7
a thousand years in *thy s.* 90:4
for in *thy s.* shall no man. 143:2
been in *thy s.* O Lord. *Isa* 26:17
forgive not iniquity, neither blot out their sin from *thy s.* *Jer* 18:23
I am cast out of *thy s.* *Jonah* 2:4
so it seemed good in *thy s.* *Mat* 11:26; *Luke* 10:21
sinned against heaven and in *thy s.* *Luke* 15:21
unto him, Receive *thy s.* 18:42
that thou mightest receive *thy s.* *Acts* 9:17
Brother Saul, receive *thy s.* 22:13
see **favour, find**

sights

shall be fearful *s.* signs from. *Luke* 21:11*

sign

This word is used [1] *as we use the word sign or token,* Gen 9:12, 13. [2] *For a miracle,* Ex 4:17. [3] *The phenomena of the heavens,* Jer 10:2.

if they believe not nor hearken to voice of first *s.* they. *Ex* 4:8
to-morrow shall this *s.* be. 8:23
it shall be a *s.* to thee upon. 13:9
for it is a *s.* between me and you. 31:13, 17; *Ezek* 20:12, 20
and they shall be a *s.* *Num* 16:38
and they became a *s.* 26:10
bind them for a *s.* *Deut* 6:8; 11:18
a prophet, and giveth thee a *s.* 13:1
and *s.* come to pass whereof. 2
they shall be on thee for a *s.* 28:46
that this may be a *s.* *Josh* 4:6
shew me a *s.* that thou. *Judg* 6:17
appointed *s.* between Israel. 20:38
a *s.* to thee, in one day they shall. *1 Sam* 2:34; *2 Ki* 19:29
we will go up: and this shall be a *s.* *1 Sam* 14:10
gave a *s.* the same day, saying, This is the *s.* the Lord hath. *1 Ki* 13:3
according to the *s.* the man of. 5
shall be the *s.* that the? *2 Ki* 20:8
this *s.* shalt thou have of the Lord. 9 *Isa* 37:30; 38:7, 22
him, he gave him a *s.* *2 Chr* 32:24
ask thee a *s.* of the Lord. *Isa* 7:11
give you a *s.*; Behold a virgin shall. 14
be for a *s.* unto the Lord. 19:20
walked barefoot for a *s.* 20:3
a name, for an everlasting *s.* 55:13
I will set a *s.* among them. 66:19
set up a *s.* of fire in Beth-haccerem. *Jer* 6:1*
and this shall be a *s.* unto you. 44:29 *Luke* 2:12
this shall be a *s.* to the house of. *Ezek* 4:3
I have set thee for a *s.* to. 12:6, 11
I will make him a *s.* a proverb. 14:8
thus Ezekiel is a *s.* 24:24
thou shalt be a *s.* 27
then shall he set up a *s.* by it. 39:15
we would see a *s.* from. *Mat* 12:38 16:1; *Mark* 8:11; *Luke* 11:16
evil and adulterous generation seeketh after a *s.* *Mat* 12:39; 16:4 *Mark* 8:12; *Luke* 11:29
no *s.* be given to it, but the *s.* of the prophet Jonas. *Mat* 12:39 *Mark* 8:12; *Luke* 11:29, 30
be the *s.* of thy coming? *Mat* 24:3
shall appear the *s.* of the Son. 30
betrayed him gave them a *s.* 26:48
what *s.* when all these. *Mark* 13:4
for a *s.* which shall be. *Luke* 2:34
what *s.* shewest thou unto us? *John* 2:18; 6:30
a ship, whose *s.* was Castor and Pollux. *Acts* 28:11
s. of circumcision, a seal. *Rom* 4:11
for the Jews require a *s.*, and the Greeks seek. *1 Cor* 1:22
tongues are for a *s.*, not. 14:22
I saw another *s.* in heaven. *Rev* 15:1

sign, *verb*

decree, *s.* the writing. *Dan* 6:8

signed

king Darius *s.* the writing. *Dan* 6:9
knew that the writing was *s.* 10
hast thou not *s.* a decree? 12

signet

give me thy *s.* and. *Gen* 38:18, 25
engraver on stone, like engravings of a *s.* *Ex* 28:11, 21, 36; 39:14, 30
though Coniah were *s.* on. *Jer* 22:24
sealed it with his own *s.* *Dan* 6:17
and make thee as a *s.* *Hag* 2:23

signets

onyx stones graven as *s.* *Ex* 39:6

signification

none of them without *s.* *1 Cor* 14:10

signified

Agabus *s.* there should. *Acts* 11:28
s. it by his angel to his. *Rev* 1:1

signifieth
s. removing of those things shaken. *Heb* 12:27

signify
to s. the accomplishment of the. *Acts* 21:26*
s. thee to chief captain that. 23:15
and not to s. the crimes laid. 25:27
searching what the Spirit of Christ in them did s. *1 Pet* 1:11

signifying
said, s. by what death he should die. *John* 12:33; 18:32; 21:19
the Holy Ghost this s. *Heb* 9:8

signs
for s. and for seasons. *Gen* 1:14
not believe these two s. *Ex* 4:9
in thy hand thou shalt do s. 17
all words of Lord and all s. which he. *Ex* 4:28, 30; *Josh* 24:17
I will multiply my s. in. *Ex* 7:3
mayest tell thy son my s. 10:2
for all the s. which I. *Num* 14:11
to take him a nation by s. *Deut* 4:34
26:8
Lord shewed s. on Egypt, on. 6:22
Neh 9:10; *Ps* 78:43
the great s. which thine. *Deut* 7:19; 29:3
in all s. which the Lord sent. 34:11
when these s. are come. *1 Sam* 10:7
and all those s. came to pass. 9
set up their ensigns for s. *Ps* 74:4
we see not our s., there is no more. 9
shewed his s. among them. 105:27
I and the children are for s. *Isa* 8:18
be not dismayed at the s. *Jer* 10:2
which hast set s. and wonders. 32:20
Israel out of Egypt with s. 21
I thought it good to shew s. *Dan* 4:2
how great are his s.! how mighty! 3
he worketh s. in heaven and. 6:27
can ye not discern the s.? *Mat* 16:3
and false prophets, and shall shew great s. 24:24; *Mark* 13:22
these s. follow them. *Mark* 16:17
confirming the word with s. 20
made s. to his father. *Luke* 1:62
and great s. shall there be. 21:11
there shall be s. in the sun. 25
except ye see s. ye will. *John* 4:48
and many other s. truly did. 20:30
I will shew s. in the earth. *Acts* 2:19
a man approved of God by s. 22
many s. were done by the apostles. 43; 5:12
that s. may be done by the. 4:30
after he had shewed s. and. 7:36
beholding the s. done. 8:13
granted s. and wonders to be. 14:3
not wrought by me through mighty s. *Rom* 15:19; *2 Cor* 12:12
working of Satan, with s. *2 Thes* 2:9
bearing them witness with s. and. *Heb* 2:4

Sihon
S. would not suffer Israel to pass. *Num* 21:23; *Judg* 11:20
let the city of S. be. *Num* 21:27
gone out from the city of S. 28
do to him as thou didst to S. 34
Deut 3:2, 6
S. king of Heshbon would. *Deut* 2:30
behold, I have begun to give S. 31
S. came out against us. 32; 29:7
Judg 11:20
do to them as he did to S. *Deut* 31:4
all that he did to S. *Josh* 9:10
God delivered S. into. *Judg* 11:21
possessed the land of S. *Neh* 9:22
shall come from the midst of S. *Jer* 48:45

Sihon *king of the Amorites*
Israel sent messengers unto S. *king of the Amorites*. *Num* 21:21
Deut 2:26; *Judg* 11:19
Hesbon was a city of S. *king of Amorites*. *Num* 21:26; *Josh* 12:2
his daughters into captivity to S. *king of Amorites*. *Num* 21:29
as thou didst to S. *king of Amorites*. 34; *Deut* 3:2
slain S. *king of the Amorites* and. *Deut* 1:4; *Ps* 135:11; 136:19
cities of S. *king of Amorites*. *Josh* 13:10
kingdom of S. *king of Amorites*. 21
officer in country of S. *king of Amorites*. *1 Ki* 4:19

Sihor
from S. which is before. *Josh* 13:3
to drink the waters of S. *Jer* 2:18

Silas
sent S. chief among the brethren. *Acts* 15:22, 27
it pleased S. to abide there. 34
Paul chose S. 40
caught Paul and S. 16:19
at midnight Paul and S. prayed. 25
fell down before Paul and S. 29
consorted with Paul and S. 17:4
sent away S. by night. 10
receiving a commandment to S. 15
when S. was come. 18:5

silence
This word signifies not only the ordinary silence, or refraining from speaking; but also an entire ruin or destruction, a total subjection, Isa 15:1; Jer 8:14; *death and the grave,* Ps 94:17; 115:17.
before me, there was s. *Job* 4:16
men gave ear, and kept s. at. 29:21
lying lips be put to s. *Ps* 31:18*
I was dumb with s., I held. 39:2
my soul had almost dwelt in s. 94:17
any that go down into s. 115:17
to s.; Kir brought to s. *Isa* 15:1*
God hath put us to s. *Jer* 8:14
alone and keepeth s. *Lam* 3:28
cast them forth with s. *Amos* 8:3
had put Sadducees to s. *Mat* 22:34
was made a great s. he. *Acts* 21:40
in Hebrew, they kept more s. 22:2*
let woman learn in s. *1 Tim* 2:11*
nor to usurp authority over the man, but to be in s. 12*
put to s. the ignorance. *1 Pet* 2:15
there was s. in heaven. *Rev* 8:1
see **keep, kept**

silent
the wicked shall be s. *1 Sam* 2:9
night season, and am not s. *Ps* 22:2
s. to me, lest if thou be s. 28:1*
sing praise to thee, not be s. 30:12
wicked be s. in the grave. 31:17
sit thou s. and get thee. *Isa* 47:5
cities, let us be s. there. *Jer* 8:14
be s. O all flesh, before. *Zech* 2:13

silk
her clothing is s. and. *Pr* 31:22
I covered thee with s. *Ezek* 16:10
thy raiment was of s. and. 13
their merchandise of s. *Rev* 18:12

silly
and envy slayeth the s. *Job* 5:2
Ephraim also is like a s. *Hos* 7:11
captive s. women laden. *2 Tim* 3:6

Siloah, Siloam
the wall of pool of S. *Neh* 3:15
wash in the pool of S. *John* 9:7, 11

Silvanus
among you by me and S. *2 Cor* 1:19
Paul, S. and Timotheus to. *1 Thes* 1:1; *2 Thes* 1:1
by S. a faithful brother. *1 Pet* 5:12

silver
is worth 400 shekels of s. *Gen* 23:15
weighed 400 shekels of s. 16
make gods of s. or gold. *Ex* 20:23
sockets of s. 26:19, 21, 25, 32
36:24, 26, 30, 36
hooks shall be of s. 27:17; 38:19
they did offer an offering of s. 35:24
s. of them that were numbered of. 38:25
estimation by shekels of s. *Lev* 5:15
of male 50 shekels of s. 27:3
female three shekels of s. 6
barley seed at fifty shekels of s. 16
was one s. charger, one s. bowl of 70 shekels. *Num* 7:13, 19, 25
31, 37, 43, 49, 55, 61, 67, 73, 79
chargers of s., twelve s. *Num* 7:84
each charger of s. weighing. 85
make thee two trumpets of s. 10:2
him in 100 shekels of s. *Deut* 22:19
damsel's father 50 shekels of s. 29
I saw 200 shekels of s. *Josh* 7:21
and the s. under it. 22, 24
1100 shekels of s. that were taken from thee, behold, s. *Judg* 17:2
when he had restored the s. 3
gave s. to the founder. 4
I will give thee ten shekels of s. 10
fourth part of a shekel of s. *1 Sam* 9:8
given 10 shekels of s. *2 Sam* 18:11
receive 1000 shekels of s. 12
oxen for 50 shekels of s. 24:24
none were of s. *1 Ki* 10:21
2 Chr 9:20
s. to be in Jerusalem. *1 Ki* 10:27
shalt pay a talent of s. 20:39
I pray thee, a talent of s. *2 Ki* 5:22
each man fifty shekels of s. 15:20
Hezekiah gave him all the s. 18:15
that Hilkiah may sum the s. 22:4*
s. also for all instruments of s. *1 Chr* 28:14; 29:2, 5
for candlesticks of s. 28:15
for every bason of s. 17
brought Jehoshaphat presents of s. *2 Chr* 17:11
had taken 40 shekels of s. *Neh* 5:15
who filled houses with s. *Job* 3:15
thou shalt have plenty of s. 22:25
though he heap up s. as the. 27:16
innocent shall divide the s. 17
shall s. be weighed for price. 28:15
words are pure, as s. tried. *Ps* 12:6
O God, hast tried us, as s. 66:10
if thou seekest her as s. and. *Pr* 2:4
wisdom is better than . . . of s. 3:14
receive instruction, and not s. 8:10
and my revenue than choice s. 19
of the just is as choice s. 10:20
chosen rather than s. 16:16
fining pot is for s., and the. 17:3
away the dross from the s. 25:4
he that loveth s. shall not be satisfied with s. *Eccl* 5:10
on her a palace of s. *S of S* 8:9
thy s. is become dross. *Isa* 1:22
covering of thy images of s. 30:22
refined thee, but not with s. 48:10
for iron I will bring s. and for. 60:17
reprobate s. shall men. *Jer* 6:30
s. spread into plates is brought. 10:9
even seventeen shekels of s. 32:9
are even the dross of s. *Ezek* 22:18
as they gather s., brass, and iron. 20
as s. is melted in the midst. 22
with s. Tarshish traded in. 27:12
breast and arms were of s. *Dan* 2:32
pleasant places for s. *Hos* 9:6
molten images of their s. 13:2
sold the righteous for s. *Amos* 2:6
that we may buy poor for s. 8:6
howl, all they that bear s. *Zeph* 1:11
Tyrus heaped up s. as dust. *Zech* 9:3
refine them as s. is refined. 13:9
as a refiner and purifier of s. *Mal* 3:3
see **fillets, gold, pieces**

silver, *adjective*
put my s. cup in sack's mouth. *Gen* 44:2
covered with s. dross. *Pr* 26:23
or ever s. cord be loosed or the golden bowl be broken. *Eccl* 12:6
the goldsmith casteth s. *Isa* 40:19
chief priests took the s. *Mat* 27:6
Demetrius made s. shrines. *Acts* 19:24

talents of **silver**
for two *talents of* s. *1 Ki* 16:24
with him ten *talents of* s. *2 Ki* 5:5
and bound two *talents of* s. 23
gave Pul 1000 *talents of* s. 15:19
sent 1000 *talents of* s. *1 Chr* 19:6
thousand thousand *talents of* s. 22:14
7000 *talents of* refined s. 29:4
mighty men for 100 *talents of* s. *2 Chr* 25:6
gave Jotham 100 *talents of* s. 27:5
land in 100 *talents of* s. 36:3

decree it be done to 100 talents of s. Ezra 7:22
to their hand 650 talents of s. 8:26
ten thousand talents of s. Esth 3:9

vessels of **silver**

all the s. vessels weighed 2400 shekels. Num 7:85
with him vessels of s. 2 Sam 8:10
his present, vessels of s. 1 Ki 10:25
not made vessels of s. 2 Ki 12:13
all manner of vessels of s., gold and brass. 1 Chr 18:10; 2 Chr 24:14
hands with vessels of s. Ezra 1:6, 11
vessels of gold and s. of the. 5:14
let the golden and s. vessels. 6:5
I weighed s. vessels. 8:26
bring golden and s. vessels. Dan 5:2
precious vessels of s. and gold. 11:8
see **vessels**

silverlings

thousand vines at a thousand s. Isa 7:23

silversmith

Demetrius a s. made. Acts 19:24

Simeon

called his name S. Gen 29:33
S. and Levi took each man. 34:25
S. son of Leah. 35:23
Joseph took from them S. 42:24
S. is not. 36
and he brought S. out unto. 43:23
the sons of S. 46:10; Ex 6:15
Num 1:22; 26:12; 1 Chr 4:24, 42
12:25
Reuben and S. they shall. Gen 48:5
S. and Levi are brethren. 49:5
S. son of Israel. Ex 1:2
prince of S. was Shelumiel. Num 1:6; 2:12; 7:36
S. Levi and Judah stand to bless. Deut 27:12
lot came forth to S. Josh 19:1
S. had their inheritance within. 9
S. went with Judah. Judg 1:3
Judah with S. 17
the strangers out of S. 2 Chr 15:9
so did Josiah in the cities of S. 34:6
S. have a portion. Ezek 48:24
one gate of S. 33
whose name was S. Luke 2:25
S. blessed Joseph and Mary. 34
which was the son of S. 3:30
at Antioch, S. that was. Acts 13:1
S. hath declared how God. 15:14

tribe of **Simeon**

tribe of S. numbered. Num 1:23
the tribe of S. shall pitch. 2:12
over the host of the tribe of S. 10:19
of the tribe of S. Shaphat. 13:5
of tribe of S. Shemuel to. 34:20
second lot came out for the tribe of S. Josh 19:1
inheritance of the tribe of S. 8
Levites had out of tribe of S. 21:4
9; 1 Chr 6:65
of the tribe of S. were. Rev 7:7

similitude

the s. of the Lord shall. Num 12:8*
heard voice of words, but saw no s. Deut 4:12* 15*
lest ye make the s. of any figure. 16*
under it was s. of oxen. 2 Chr 4:3
glory into s. of an ox. Ps 106:20*
corner stones polished after s. 144:12
one like the s. of the. Dan 10:16
after the s. of Adam's. Rom 5:14*
after s. of Melchizedek ariseth. Heb 7:15*
made after the s. of God. Jas 3:9*

similitudes

I have used s. by ministry of. Hos 12:10

Simon

S. the Canaanite. Mat 10:4
Mark 3:18
his brethren James, Joses, and S. Mat 13:55; Mark 6:3
blessed art thou, S. Bar-jona. Mat 16:17
what thinkest thou, S. of ? 17:25
in the house of S. the leper. Mat 26:6
Mark 14:3
man of Cyrene, S. by. Mat 27:32
Mark 15:21; Luke 23:26
they entered into the house of S. Mark 1:29; Luke 4:38
S. sleepest thou ? Mark 14:37
the ships, which was S.'s. Luke 5:3
he said unto S. Launch out into. 4
John who were partners with S. 10
S. called Zelotes. 6:15; Acts 1:13
S. I have somewhat to. Luke 7:40
S. S. Satan hath desired to. 22:31
and hath appeared to S. 24:34
his own brother S. John 1:41
Jesus said, Thou art S. the son. 42
Judas Iscariot the son of S. 6:71
12:4; 13:2, 26
S. son of Jonas, lovest thou me ? 21:15, 16, 17
a man, S. who before. Acts 8:9
then S. himself believed also. 13
Peter tarried many days at Joppa with one S. 9:43; 10:6, 17, 32
see **Peter**

simple

[1] *Undesigning, straightforward,* Rom 16:19. [2] *Ignorant, yet sincere and willing to be taught,* Prov 9:4. [3] *Silly, foolish, credulous, easily deceived with the smooth words and fair pretences of false and deceitful men,* Pr 14:15; 22:3.

law . . . making wise the s. Ps 19:7
Lord preserveth the s.: I was. 116:6
understanding to the s. 119:130
give subtilty to s., to young. Pr 1:4
how long, ye s. ones, will ye ? 22
the turning away of the s. shall. 32
among the s. ones a young. 7:7
O ye s. understand wisdom. 8:5
whoso is s. let him turn. 9:4, 16
a foolish woman is s. and. 13
s. believeth every word. 14:15
the s. inherit folly. 18
the s. will beware. 19:25
the scorner is punished, the s. 21:11
the s. pass on and are. 22:3; 27:12
do for him that is s. Ezek 45:20
deceive the hearts of s. Rom 16:18*
have you wise unto good, and s. 19

simplicity

they went in their s. 2 Sam 15:11
simple ones, will ye love s.? Pr 1:22
let him do it with s. Rom 12:8*
in s. we had our. 2 Cor 1:12*
be corrupted from the s. that. 11:3

sin

Any thought, word, action, omission, or desire, contrary to the law of God. Sin is taken both for the guilt and punishment of sin, Ps 32:1; Mat 9:2.

doest not well, s. lieth. Gen 4:7
forgiving iniquity, transgression, and s. Ex 34:7
if priest s. according to s. Lev 4:3
when s. is known, congregation. 14
offereth it for s. 6:26; 9:15
and not suffer s. upon thy. 19:17
the s. which he hath done shall. 22
or woman shall commit s. Num 5:6
thee lay not the s. upon us. 12:11
it is a purification for s. 19:9, 17
our father died in his own s. 27:3
he cry unto the Lord . . . and it be s. unto thee. Deut 15:9; 24:15
shall not rise up for any s. 19:15
committed s. worthy of death. 21:22
there is in damsel no s. 22:26
it, and it would be s. in thee. 23:21
to vow, it shall be no s. 22
be put to death for his own s. 24:16
2 Ki 14:6; 2 Chr 25:4
for rebellion is as the s. 1 Sam 15:23
forgive s. of thy people. 1 Ki 8:34
forgive the s. of thy servants. 36
2 Chr 6:25, 27
this thing became a s. 12:30; 13:34
the s. money was not. 2 Ki 12:16
his bones are full of s. Job 20:11
blessed is he whose s. Ps 32:1
and in s. did my mother. Ps 51:5
s. of their mouth let them. 59:12
and let his prayer become s. 109:7
let not the s. of his mother. 14
the wicked tendeth to s. Pr 10:16
of words there wanteth not s. 19
fools make a mock at s. but. 14:9
s. is a reproach to any people. 34
plowing of the wicked is s. 21:4
thought of foolishness is s. 24:9
woe to them that draw s. Isa 5:18
that they may add s. to s. 30:1
your hands have made for s. 31:7
make his soul an offering for s. 53:10
he bare the s. of many, and. 12
s. of Judah written with. Jer 17:1
I will give thy high places for s. 3
their land was filled with s. 51:5
punishment of the s. of. Lam 4:6
eat up s. of my people. Hos 4:8
the s. of Israel shall be. 10:8
none iniquity in me that were s. 12:8
that swear by the s. of. Amos 8:14
she is the beginning of s. Mi 1:13
fruit of my body for s. of my. 6:7
a fountain opened for s. Zech 13:1
all manner of s. shall be. Mat 12:31
which taketh away the s. John 1:29
he that is without s. among. 8:7
committeth s. is the servant of s. 34
blind, he should have no s. 9:41
they had not had s. 15:22, 24
will reprove the world of s. 16:8
of s. because they believe not. 9
me unto thee hath greater s. 19:11
Lord, lay not this s. to. Acts 7:60
Gentiles are all under s. Rom 3:9
by the law is the knowledge of s. 20
blessed are they whose s. is. 4:7
the world, and death by s. 5:12
the law s. was in the world. 13
s. abounded, grace much more. 20
that as s. reigned unto death. 21
say ? shall we continue in s.? 6:1
how shall we that are dead to s.? 2
the body of s. might be destroyed . . . we should not serve s. 6
that is dead is freed from s. 7
that he died, he died unto s. once. 10
to be dead indeed unto s. 11
let not s. therefore reign in your. 12
members as instruments to s. 13
for s. shall not have dominion. 14
servants ye are . . . whether of s. 16
ye were the servants of s. 17
being then made free from s. 18, 22
when ye were the servants of s. 20
for wages of s. is death, but the. 23
is the law s.? God forbid. Nay, I had not known s. 7:7
s. taking occasion wrought in me . . . for without the law s. was. 8
commandment came, s. revived. 9
for s. by the commandment. 11
s., that it might appear s., that s. 13
but I am carnal, sold under s. 14
but s. that dwelleth in me. 17, 20
me into captivity to the law of s. 23
but with the flesh, the law of s. 25
and for s., condemned s. in. 8:3
body is dead because of s. 10
is not of faith, is s. 14:23
every s. a man doth is. 1 Cor 6:18
the sting of death is s. and the strength of s. is the law. 15:56
made him to be s. for us, who knew no s. 2 Cor 5:21
Christ the minister of s.? Gal 2:17
hath concluded all under s. 3:22
man of s. be revealed. 2 Thes 2:3
through the deceitfulness of s. Heb 3:13
like as we are, yet without s. 4:15
he appeared to put away s. 9:26
he shall appear without s. unto. 28
in sacrifices for s. thou hast. 10:6
offering for s. thou wouldest not. 8
is no more offering for s. 18
than to enjoy pleasures of s. 11:25
let us lay aside the s. that doth. 12:1
not yet resisted, striving against s. 4
those beasts, for s. are burned. 13:11
lust conceived, it bringeth forth s.: and s., when finished. Jas 1:15

persons, ye commit *s.* *Jas* 2:9
eth not good, to him it is *s.* 4:17
d no *s.* neither was. *1 Pet* 2:22
sh hath ceased from *s.* 4:1
nnot cease from *s.* *2 Pet* 2:14
e blood of Jesus Christ cleanseth us from all *s.* *1 John* 1:7
we say we have no *s.* we. 8
mmittteth *s.* transgresseth also the law, for *s.* is the. 3:4
d in him is no *s.* 5
mmitteth *s.* is of the devil. 8
rn of God doth not commit *s.* 9
brother *s.* a *s.* which is not to death. There is a *s.* unto. 5:16
unrighteousness is *s.* and there is a *s.* not unto death. 17
see **bear, offering**

sin, *verb*

w can I do this great wickedness and *s.* against God? *Gen* 39:9
uben said, Do not *s.* 42:22
fore you, that ye *s.* not. *Ex* 20:20
ake thee *s.* against me. 23:33
through ignorance against commandments. *Lev* 4:2
the priest *s.* 3
congregation *s.* 13
any one of the common people *s.* 27
a soul *s.* and hear the voice. 5:1
a soul commit a trespass and *s.* 15, 17; *Num* 15:27
a soul *s.* and lie unto. *Lev* 6:2
all one man *s.* and wilt thou be? *Num* 16:22
should you *s.* against Lord. *Deut* 20:18
alt not cause the land to *s.* 24:4
against another; if a man *s.* against the Lord, who shall? *1 Sam* 2:25
od forbid I should *s.* in. 12:23
hold, the people *s.* against. 14:33
y them, and *s.* not in eating. 34
not the king *s.* against. 19:4
erefore wilt thou *s.* against? 5
they *s.* against thee. *1 Ki* 8:46 *2 Chr* 6:36
ade Judah to *s.* with idols. *2 Ki* 21:11
a man *s.* against his. *2 Chr* 6:22
raid, and do so, and *s.* *Neh* 6:13
d not Solomon *s.* by these? 13:26
all this did not Job *s.* *Job* 2:10
habitation and not *s.* 5:24
I *s.*, then thou markest me. 10:14
suffered my mouth to *s.* 31:30
and in awe, and *s.* not. *Ps* 4:4
will take heed, that I *s.* not. 39:1
might not *s.* against thee. 119:11
t thy mouth to cause thy flesh to *s.* *Eccl* 5:6
cause Judah to *s.* *Jer* 32:35
hteous *s.* not, and he doth not *s.* *Ezek* 3:21
ade many altars to *s.*, altars shall be unto him to *s.* *Hos* 8:11
d now they *s.* more and. 13:2
t shall my brother *s.*? *Mat* 18:21
no more, lest a worse. *John* 5:14
I condemn thee, *s.* no. 8:11
no did *s.*, this man, or his? 9:2
all we *s.* because we are not? *Rom* 6:15
so against the brethren and wound their conscience, ye *s.* *1 Cor* 8:12
hteousness, and *s.* not. 15:34
ye angry, and *s.* not. *Eph* 4:26
em that *s.* rebuke. *1 Tim* 5:20
we *s.* wilfully after. *Heb* 10:26
at ye *s.* not, and if any man *s.* we. *1 John* 2:1
nnot *s.* because he is born of. 3:9
. . . *s.* not unto death, he shall give him life for them that *s.* 5:16
see **Israel**

great **sin**

d my kingdom *great s.* *Gen* 20:9
ought this *great s.* on them. *Ex* 32:21
id, Ye have sinned a *great s.* 30
is people have sinned a *great s.* 31
of the young men was very *great.* *1 Sam* 2:17
Jeroboam made them sin a *great s.* *2 Ki* 17:21

his **sin**

bring for *his s.* he sinned. *Lev* 4:3
or if *his s.* come to his knowledge. 23, 28
atonement for *his s.* and it shall be forgiven. 4:26, 35; 5:6, 10, 13
a kid of the goats for *his s.* 28
his trespass offering for *his s.* 5:6
Nadab walked in the way of *his s.* *1 Ki* 15:26
in the way of Jeroboam and *his s.* 34
Zimri in *his s.* which he did. 16:19
Omri walked in *his s.* 26
beside *his s.* wherewith. *2 Ki* 21:16
acts of Manasseh, and *his s.* 17
all *his s.* before he was humbled. *2 Chr* 33:19
addeth rebellion to *his s.* *Job* 34:37
fruit to take away *his s.* *Isa* 27:9
he shall die in *his s.* *Ezek* 3:20 18:24
if he turn from *his s.* and. 33:14
bound up; *his s.* is hid. *Hos* 13:12
to declare to Israel *his s.* *Mi* 3:8

my **sin**

what is *my s.* that thou hast? *Gen* 31:36
therefore forgive *my s.* *Ex* 10:17
I pray thee, pardon *my s.*, and turn again. *1 Sam* 15:25
what is *my s.* before thy father? 20:1
come to call *my s.* to? *1 Ki* 17:18
thou searchest after *my s.* *Job* 10:6
know transgression and *my s.* 13:23
thou not watch over *my s.*? 14:16
if I be cleansed from *my s.*? 35:3
my s. and iniquity to thee, and thou . . . iniquity of *my s.* *Ps* 32:5
in my bones because of *my s.* 38:3
for I will be sorry for *my s.* 18
cleanse me from *my s.* 51:2
my s. is ever before me. 3
not for *my s.* O Lord. 59:3
I am pure from *my s.*? *Pr* 20:9
I was confessing *my s.* *Dan* 9:20
see **offering**

our **sin**

our iniquity and *our s.* *Ex* 34:9
what is *our s.* we have? *Jer* 16:10

their **sin**

Lord said, Because *their s.* is very. *Gen* 18:20
forgive, I pray thee, *their s.* 50:17 *2 Chr* 7:14
if thou wilt forgive *their s.* *Ex* 32:32
when I visit, I will visit *their s.* 34
they shall confess *their s.* *Num* 5:7
look not unto the stubbornness, nor to *their s.* *Deut* 9:27
if they turn from *their s.* *1 Ki* 8:35 *2 Chr* 6:26
let not *their s.* be blotted. *Neh* 4:5
hast covered all *their s.* 85:2
declare *their s.* as Sodom. *Isa* 3:9
I will recompense *their s.* double. *Jer* 16:18
neither blot out *their s.* from. 18:23
and I will remember *their s.* 31:34
may forgive their iniquity and *their s.* 36:3
no cloke for *their s.* *John* 15:22

thy **sin**

hath put away *thy s.* *2 Sam* 12:13
is taken away, *thy s.* is purged. *Isa* 6:7

your **sin**

atonement for *your s.* *Ex* 32:30
be sure *your s.* will find you out. *Num* 32:23
I took *your s.*, the calf which ye. *Deut* 9:21
ye say, We see; therefore *your s.* remaineth. *John* 9:41
see **Israel**

Sin

into the wilderness of *S.* *Ex* 16:1
Israel journeyed from *S.* 17:1 *Num* 33:12
pour my fury upon *S.* *Ezek* 30:15
S. shall have great pain, No shall. 16

Sinai

Lord came from *S.* unto. *Deut* 33:2
melted, even that *S.* *Judg* 5:5
S. was moved at the. *Ps* 68:8
the Lord is among them as in *S.* 17
see **mount**

since

the Lord hath blessed thee *s.* my coming. *Gen* 30:30
and I saw him not *s.* 44:28
let me die, *s.* I have seen. 46:30
s. I came to Pharaoh. *Ex* 5:23
hail, such as not in Egypt *s.* the. 9:18
Egypt, *s.* it became a nation. 24
ridden ever *s.* I was thine. *Num* 22:30
arose not a prophet *s.* *Deut* 34:10
swear, *s.* I have shewed. *Josh* 2:12
Lord kept me alive, even *s.* 14:10
all that thou hast done . . . *s.* death of thy husband. *Ruth* 2:11
s. I said, I have invited. *1 Sam* 9:24
three days *s.* I came out. 21:5
I found no fault in him *s.* he. 29:3
s. the time that I brought. *2 Sam* 7:6
and *s.* I commanded judges. 11 *1 Chr* 17:10
s. the time of Solomon. *2 Chr* 30:26
s. the people began to bring. 31:10
s. the days of Esar-haddon king. *Ezra* 4:2
s. that time till now hath it. 5:16
s. days of our fathers have we. 9:7
s. man was placed upon. *Job* 20:4
commanded morning *s.* thy days? 38:12
s. thou art laid down. *Isa* 14:8
concerning Moab *s.* that time. 16:13
s. thou wast precious in my. 43:4
s. I appointed the ancient. 44:7
s. the beginning men have not. 64:4
s. they return not from. *Jer* 15:7
for *s.* I spake, I cried out, I. 20:8
but *s.* ye say, the burden of. 23:38
s. I spake against him, I. 31:20
s. we left off to burn incense. 44:18
s. thou speakest of him. 48:27
as never was *s.* there. *Dan* 12:1
s. those days were when one came. *Hag* 2:16
not *s.* the beginning. *Mat* 24:21
long is it ago *s.* this came to him? *Mark* 9:21
been *s.* the world began. *Luke* 1:70 *John* 9:32
s. the time I came in, she hath not. *Luke* 7:45
s. that time kingdom of God. 16:16
is the third day *s.* these things. 24:21
s. the world began. *Acts* 3:21 *Rom* 16:25
received the Holy Ghost *s.* ye believed? *Acts* 19:2
yet but twelve days *s.* I went. 24:11
for *s.* by man came death, by man. *1 Cor* 15:21
s. ye seek a proof of Christ in me. *2 Cor* 13:3
s. we heard of your faith. *Col* 1:4
word of oath which was *s.* the law. *Heb* 7:28
for *s.* the fathers fell asleep, all. *2 Pet* 3:4
as was not *s.* men were. *Rev* 16:18
see **day**

sincere

The Latin word, sincerus, *is derived from* sine *and* cera, *without wax, honey separated from the wax, or pure honey. In the scripture* sincere *signifies pure, or without mixture,* Phil 1:10; 1 Pet 2:1. Sincerity *is opposed to double-mindedness or deceit, when the sentiments of the heart are contrary to the language of the mouth,* 1 Cor 5:8.

ye may be *s.* till day. *Phil* 1:10
as babes, desire *s.* milk. *1 Pet* 2:2

sincerely
now if ye have done truly and *s.* *Judg* 9:16*, 19*
one preach Christ, not *s.* *Phil* 1:16*

sincerity
serve the Lord in *s.* and. *Josh* 24:14
unleavened bread of *s.* *1 Cor* 5:8
in godly *s.* we have had. *2 Cor* 1:12
but as of *s.* in the sight of God. 2:17
to prove *s.* of your love. 8:8
them that love our Lord Jesus in *s.* *Eph* 6:24
doctrine shewing gravity, *s.* *Tit* 2:7

sinew
Israel eat not of the *s.* that shrank . . . Jacob in the *s.* *Gen* 32:32*
thy neck is an iron *s.* *Isa* 48:4

sinews
hast fenced me with bones and *s.* *Job* 10:11
pierced, and my *s.* take no. 30:17*
the *s.* of his stones are. 40:17
I will lay *s.* upon you. *Ezek* 37:6
the *s.* and the flesh came up. 8

sinful
an increase of *s.* men. *Num* 32:14
ah *s.* nation, a people. *Isa* 1:4
eyes of the Lord are on the *s.* kingdom. *Amos* 9:8
be ashamed in this *s.* generation. *Mark* 8:38
for I am a *s.* man, O Lord. *Luke* 5:8
into the hands of *s.* men. 24:7
that sin might become exceeding *s.* *Rom* 7:13
Son in the likeness of *s.* flesh. 8:3

sing
s. to the Lord. *Ex* 15:21
1 Chr 16:23; *Ps* 30:4; 95:1; 96:1 2; 98:1; 147:7; 149:1; *Isa* 12:5
noise of them that *s.* *Ex* 32:18
spring up, O well, *s.* ye. *Num* 21:17
did they not *s.* one? *1 Sam* 21:11
unto him, *s.* psalms. *1 Chr* 16:9
trees of the wood *s.* out. 33
when they began to *s.* *2 Chr* 20:22
commanded the Levites to *s.* 29:30
widow's heart to *s.* for. *Job* 29:13
so will we *s.* and praise. *Ps* 21:13
praise the Lord, *s.* unto him. 33:2
s. unto him a new song. 3; *Isa* 42:10
my tongue *s.* of thy righteousness. *Ps* 51:14; 145:7
shout for joy, they also *s.* 65:13
s. forth the honour of his name. 66:2
the earth *s.* to thee, they shall *s.* 4
nations be glad and *s.* for. 67:4
s. to God, ye kingdoms of. 68:32
to thee will I *s.* with the harp. 71:22 98:5
s. aloud unto God our strength. 81:1
the fowls which *s.* among the. 104:12
s. unto him, *s.* psalms unto. 105:2
saying, *S.* us one of the songs. 137:3
how shall we *s.* Lord's song in a? 4
yea, they shall *s.* in the ways. 138:5
let the saints *s.* aloud upon. 149:5
but the righteous doth *s.* *Pr* 29:6
seventy years shall Tyre *s.* *Isa* 23:15
they shall *s.* for the majesty. 24:14
awake and *s.* ye that dwell. 26:19
in that day *s.* ye unto her. 27:2
the tongue of the dumb *s.* 35:6
therefore we will *s.* my songs. 38:20
inhabitants of the rock *s.* 42:11
s. for Lord hath done it. 44:23 49:13
voice together shall they *s.* 52:8
s. to the Lord, ye waste places. 9
s. O barren, thou that didst. 54:1
my servants shall *s.* for joy. 65:14
s. with gladness for Jacob. *Jer* 31:7
they shall come and *s.* in the. 12
all that is therein shall *s.* 51:48
ships of Tarshish did *s.* *Ezek* 27:25
shall *s.* as in the days. *Hos* 2:15
their voice shall *s.* in. *Zeph* 2:14
s. O daughter. 3:14; *Zech* 2:10
merry? let him *s.* psalms. *Jas* 5:13
they *s.* the song of Moses. *Rev* 15:3

***I will* sing**
I will s. to the Lord. *Ex* 15:1
Judg 5:3; *Ps* 13:6
my heart is fixed, *I will s.* *Ps* 57:7
I will s. unto thee among the. 9
I will s. of thy power, of. 59:16; 89:1
O my strength, *will I s.* for God. 17
I will s. of mercy and judgement. 101:1
I will s. unto the Lord as. 104:33
I will s. a new song unto. 144:9
will I s. to my wellbeloved a song. *Isa* 5:1
for this cause *will I s.* *Rom* 15:9
I will s. with the spirit, and *I will s.* with understanding. *1 Cor* 14:15

see **praise, praises**

singed
nor an hair of their head *s.* *Dan* 3:27

singer
Heman a *s.* the son. *1 Chr* 6:33
to chief *s.* on my stringed instruments. *Hab* 3:19*

singers
king made psalteries for *s.* *1 Ki* 10:12; *2 Chr* 9:11
these are the *s.*, chief of the Levites. *1 Chr* 9:33; 15:16
s. were appointed to sound. 15:19
and the *s.* had fine linen. 27
the trumpeters and *s.* *2 Chr* 5:13
Jehoshaphat appointed *s.* unto. 20:21
rejoiced and also the *s.* 23:13; 29:28
the *s.* the sons of Asaph. 35:15
the *s.* an hundred twenty. *Ezra* 2:41
s. dwelt in their. 70; *Neh* 7:73
some of the *s.* went up. *Ezra* 7:7
not lawful to impose toll upon *s.* 24
the *s.* gave their hands to. 10:24
the porters and the *s.* *Neh* 7:1
the *s.* clave to their brethren. 10:29
the *s.* were over the business. 11:22
a portion shall be for the *s.* 23 12:47; 13:5
sons of *s.* gathered themselves. 12:28
s. had builded them villages. 29
s. sang aloud. 42
s. kept ward of their God. 45
David, there were chief of *s.* 46
for the Levites and the *s.* 13:10
s. went before, players. *Ps* 68:25
as well the *s.* as the players. 87:7
the chambers of the *s.* *Ezek* 40:44

***men* singers, *women* singers**
I gat me *men s.* and *women s.* *Eccl* 2:8

singeth
so is he that *s.* songs to. *Pr* 25:20

singing
women came out of cities of Israel *s.* *1 Sam* 18:6
they ministered with *s.* *1 Chr* 6:32*
played before God with *s.* 13:8*
burnt offerings with *s.* *2 Chr* 23:18
s. with loud instruments unto. 30:21
dedication of the wall with *s.* *Neh* 12:27
his presence with *s.* *Ps* 100:2
our tongue filled with *s.* 126:2
time of the *s.* of birds. *S of S* 2:12
break forth into *s.* *Isa* 14:7
there shall be no *s.* 16:10
rejoice even with joy and *s.* 35:2
break forth into *s.* ye. 44:23
Chaldeans with a voice of *s.* 48:20
earth, and break forth into *s.* 49:13
shall come with *s.* to Zion. 51:11
break forth into *s.* O barren. 54:1
shall break forth into *s.* 55:12
will joy over thee with *s.* *Zeph* 3:17
s. in your heart to the Lord. *Eph* 5:19; *Col* 3:16

singing men, singing women
can I hear any more the voice of *s. men, s. women*? *2 Sam* 19:35
all the *s. men* spake. *2 Chr* 35:25
s. men, 200 *s. women*. *Ezra* 2:65
245 *s. men* and *s. women*. *Neh* 7:67

single
thine eye be *s.* thy whole body shall. *Mat* 6:22; *Luke* 11:34

singleness
with gladness and *s.* of heart. *Acts* 2:
servants, be obedient, in *s.* of yo heart. *Eph* 6:5; *Col* 3:

singular
shall make a *s.* vow. *Lev* 27:

sink
I *s.* in deep mire where. *Ps* 69
out of the mire, and let me not *s.*
thus shall Babylon *s.* and. *Jer* 51:
beginning to *s.* he cried. *Mat* 14:
so that they began to *s.* *Luke* 5
let these sayings *s.* down. 9:

sinned
Pharaoh *s.* yet more. *Ex* 9:
Ye have *s.* a great sin. 32:30,
whosoever hath *s.* against me, hi will I blot out of my book.
bring for the sin he hath *s.* *Lev* 4
sin the congregation have *s.*
when a ruler hath *s.* 22,
one of common people *s.*
he shall confess he hath *s.* 5
for sin which he hath *s.* shall.
atonement for the sin he hath *s.* ar 10, 11, 13; *Num* 6:
he hath *s.*, he shall restore. *Lev* 6
lay not sin on us wherein we have *Num* 12:
ye have *s.* against the Lord. 32:
and, behold, ye had *s.* against t Lord. *Deut* 9:
your sins which ye *s.* in doing.
Israel hath *s.* and transgressed. *Josh* 7:
wherefore I have not *s.* *Judg* 11:
because he hath not *s.* *1 Sam* 19
know that I have not *s.* 24:
they have *s.* against thee, and sha *1 Ki* 8:33, 35; *2 Chr* 6:24,
forgive thy people that *s.* *1 Ki* 8: *2 Chr* 6:
sins of Jeroboam which he *s.* *1 Ki* 15:30; 16:13,
What have I *s.* that thou? 18
Israel had *s.* against. *2 Ki* 17
sin that Manasseh had *s.* 21:
s. against thy judgements. *Neh* 9:
may be that my sons have *s.* *Job* 1
in all this Job *s.* not, nor charged.
if children have *s.* against him. 8
the grave those which have *s.* 24:
they *s.* yet more. *Ps* 78:17,
thy first father hath *s.* *Isa* 43:
sayest, I have not *s.* *Jer* 2:
they have *s.* against me. 33
because ye have *s.* and not obeye 40:3; 44:
because they have *s.* against the. 50:7; *Zeph* 1:
Babylon hath *s.* against. *Jer* 50:
Jerusalem hath grievously *s.* *Lam* 1
our fathers have *s.* and are not. 5
in sin that he hath *s.*, in. *Ezek* 18:
with violence, and thou hast *s.* 28:
places wherein they *s.* 37:
they increased so they *s.* *Hos* 4
O Israel, thou hast *s.* from. 10
hast *s.* against thy soul. *Hab* 2:
neither this man *s.* nor. *John* 9
for as many as have *s.* without la as have *s.* in the law. *Rom* 2:
for all have *s.* and come short. 3:23; 5:
over them that had not *s.* 5:
not as it was by one that *s.* so.
marry, thou hast not *s.* and if a v gin . . . hath not *s.* *1 Cor* 7:
bewail many that have *s.* *2 Cor* 12:
which heretofore have *s.* 13
with them that had *s.*? *Heb* 3:
spared not the angels that *s.* *2 Pet* 2
if we say we have not *s.* *1 John* 1:

***I have* sinned**
Pharaoh said, *I have s.* this time. *Ex* 9:27; 10:
Balaam said to angel of Lord, *I ha s.* *Num* 22:
indeed *I have s.* against the Lo God. *Josh* 7:

aul said, I have s. 1 Sam 15:24
30; 26:21
Nathan, I have s. 2 Sam 12:13
24:10, 17; 1 Chr 21:8, 17
oth know that I have s. 2 Sam 19:20
have s.; what shall I do? Job 7:20
any say, I have s. 33:27
eal my soul; for I have s. Ps 41:4
gainst thee, thee only have I s. 51:4
have s. against him. Mi 7:9
have s. in betraying. Mat 27:4
ather, I have s. against heaven, and
before thee. Luke 15:18, 21

we have **sinned**

ot sin on us, wherein we have s.
Num 12:11
e will go up, for we have s. 14:40
Deut 1:41
e have s., we have spoken.
Num 21:7
e have s. because we have.
Judg 10:10; 1 Sam 12:10
e have s.: do to us. Judg 10:15
at day, and said, We have s.
1 Sam 7:6
e have s. and have done perversely. 1 Ki 8:47
ying, We have s. 2 Chr 6:37
e sins which we have s. Neh 1:6
e have s. with our fathers. Ps 100:6
gainst whom we have s. Isa 42:24
t wroth, for we have s. 64:5
our shame, for we have s. Jer 3:25
s water of gall, for we have s. 8:14
acksliding are many, we have s.
14:7
ur wickedness, for we have s. 20
oe to us that we have s. Lam 5:16
e have s. and have committed.
Dan 9:5
nfusion, because we have s. 8
oured on us, because we have s. 11
Lord, we have s. we have. 15

sinner

e wicked and the s. Pr 11:31
verthroweth the s. 13:6
e wealth of the s. is laid up. 22
the s. he giveth travail. Eccl 2:26
it the s. shall be taken by her. 7:26
ough s. do evil an hundred. 8:12
s is the good, so is the s. and. 9:2
it one s. destroyeth much good. 18
being 100 years old. Isa 65:20
the city who was a s. Luke 7:37
hat woman this is: for she is a s. 39
y in heaven over one s. 15:7, 10
od be merciful to me a s. 18:13
uest with a man that is a s. 19:7
ow can a man a s. do? John 9:16
e know this man is a s. 24
hether he be a s. I know not. 25
n I also judged as a s.? Rom 3:7
that converteth a s. Jas 5:20
all the ungodly and s. appear?
1 Pet 4:18

sinners

e men of Sodom were s. Gen 13:13
e censers of these s. Num 16:38
tterly destroy the s. 1 Sam 15:18
andeth not in the way of s. Ps 1:1
or s. in the congregation of the. 5
erefore will he teach s. in. 25:8
ather not my soul with s. nor. 26:9
nd s. shall be converted. 51:13
t the s. be consumed out. 104:35
s. entice thee, consent not. Pr 1:10
vil pursueth s. but to the. 13:21
t not thine heart envy s. 23:17
e destruction of the s. Isa 1:28
e shall destroy the s. thereof. 13:9
e s. in Zion are afraid. 33:14
of my people shall die. Amos 9:10
any s. sat at meat with Jesus.
Mat 9:10; Mark 2:15
hy eateth your master with publicans and s.? Mat 9:11; Mark 2:16
Luke 5:30; 15:2
call the righteous, but s. to.
Mat 9:13; Mark 2:17; Luke 5:32
friend of publicans and s.
Mat 11:19; Luke 7:34
on of man is betrayed into the hands
of s. Mat 26:45; Mark 14:41

for s. also love those. Luke 6:32
what thank have ye? for s. also. 33
for s. also lend to s. to receive. 34
these were s. above all. 13:2, 4*
the publicans and s. for to. 15:1
that God heareth not s. John 9:31
while we were yet s., Christ. Rom 5:8
disobedience many were made s. 19
we Jews by nature, not s. Gal 2:15
we ourselves also are found s. 17
the law is made for s. 1 Tim 1:9
that Christ Jesus came to save s. 15
holy, separate from s. Heb 7:26
endured such contradiction of s. 12:3
cleanse your hands, ye s., purify.
Jas 4:8
speeches which ungodly s. Jude 15

sinnest

if thou s. what doest? Job 35:6

sinneth

make atonement for soul that s.
Num 15:28*
have one law for him that s. 29*
not rise, in any sin he s. Deut 19:15
if they sin against thee, for there is no
man that s. not. 1 Ki 8:46
2 Chr 6:36; Eccl 7:20
he that s. against me. Pr 8:36
despiseth his neighbour s. 14:21
he that hasteth with his feet s. 19:2
whoso provoketh a king, s. 20:2
when the land s. then. Ezek 14:13
the soul that s. it shall die. 18:4, 20
righteousness in the day he s. 33:12
but fornicator s. against. 1 Cor 6:18
let him do what he will, he s. not. 7:36
he is subverted, and s. Tit 3:11
whosoever abideth in him s. not,
whosoever s. hath. 1 John 3:6
is of the devil, for devil s. from. 8
whosoever is born of God s. not. 5:18

sinning

I withheld thee from s. Gen 20:6
that a man doth, s. therein. Lev 6:3

sins

He shall give Israel up, because of s.
of Jeroboam. 1 Ki 14:16
Abijam walked in the s. of. 15:3
smote Nadab because of the s. 30
s. of Baasha, and the s. of. 16:13
for his s. which Zimri sinned. 19
a light thing to walk in the s. 31
Jehoram cleaved to the s. 2 Ki 3:3
from the s. of Jeroboam Jehu. 10:29
not from the s. of Jeroboam. 13:6, 11
departed not from the s. 14:24
departed from s. 15:9, 18, 24, 28
Israel walked in all the s. 17:22
Judah for the s. of Manasseh. 24:3
not even with you s.? 2 Chr 28:10
and confess the s. of the children.
Neh 1:6
mine iniquities and s.? Job 13:23
from presumptuous s. Ps 19:13
remember not the s. of my. 25:7
holden with cords of his s. Pr 5:22
up strifes, love covereth all s. 10:12
he that covereth his s. shall. 28:13
double for all her s. Isa 40:2
made me to serve with thy s. 43:24
I will not remember thy s. 25
blotted out as a cloud thy s. 44:22
I give to spoil for all thy s. Jer 15:13
thy s. were increased. 30:14, 15
the s. of Judah sought for. 50:20
the punishment of his s. Lam 3:39
for the s. of her prophets and. 4:13
Edom, he will discover thy s. 22
neither hath Samaria committed half
thy s. Ezek 16:51
thine own shame for thy s. 52
beget son that seeth all his father's s.
18:14
will turn from all his s. 21
and he shall bear the s. of. 23:49
none of his s. that he hath. 33:16
break off thy s. by. Dan 4:27
determined to make an end of s. 9:24
the s. of the house of Israel. Mi 1:5
desolate because of thy s. 6:13
for the remission of s. Mat 26:28
of repentance for the remission of s.
Mark 1:4; Luke 3:3

that remission of s. should be.
Luke 24:47
Thou wast altogether born in s.
John 9:34
s. ye remit, whose soever s. ye. 20:23
baptized for remission of s. Acts 2:38
repentance and remission of s. 5:31
shall receive remission of s. 10:43
wash away thy s. calling on. 22:16
for the remission of s. Rom 3:25
the motions of s. did work in. 7:5
who were dead in s. Eph 2:1, 5
in putting off the body of s. Col 2:11
of other men's s. 1 Tim 5:22
some men's s. open beforehand. 24
silly women laden with s. 2 Tim 3:6
make reconciliation for s. Heb 2:17
offer gifts and sacrifices for s. 5:1
also for himself, to offer for s. 3
first for his own s. then for. 7:27
offered to bear s. of many. 9:28
no more conscience of s. 10:2
a remembrance again made of s. 3
blood of bulls not take away s. 4
can never take away s. 11
one sacrifice for s. for ever. 12
no more sacrifice for s 26
shall hide multitude of s. Jas 5:20
we being dead to s. 1 Pet 2:24
hath once suffered for s. 3:18
cover the multitude of s. 4:8
purged from his old s. 2 Pet 1:9
but also for s. of the whole world.
1 John 2:2
be not partakers of her s. Rev 18:4
s. have reached unto heaven. 5
see **forgive, forgiven**

my **sins**

hide thy face from my s. Ps 51:9
O God, my s. are not hid. 69:5
thou hast cast my s. Isa 38:17

our **sins**

for we have added to all our s. this.
1 Sam 12:19
add more to our s. 2 Chr 28:13
kings set over us because of our s.
Neh 9:37
purge away our s. for thy name's.
Ps 79:9
our secret s. in the light of. 90:8
with us according to our s. 103:10
our s. testify against us. Isa 59:12
if our s. be upon us. Ezek 33:10
because of our s. thy people are.
Dan 9:16
Christ died for our s. 1 Cor 15:3
who gave himself for our s. Gal 1:4
when he had by himself purged our s.
Heb 1:3
who his own self bare our s. in his.
1 Pet 2:24
confess our s. he is faithful and just
to forgive us our s. 1 John 1:9
propitiation for our s. 2:2; 4:10
manifested to take away our s. 3:5
washed us from our s. Rev 1:5

their **sins**

transgressions in their s. Lev 16:16
over the live goat all their s. 21
to make atonement for their s. 34
consumed in all their s. Num 16:26
they provoked him with their s.
1 Ki 14:22
me to anger with their s. 16:2
and confessed their s. Neh 9:2
house of Jacob their s. Isa 58:1
and visit their s. Jer 14:10
Hos 8:13; 9:9
cast all their s. into the. Mi 7:19
his people from their s. Mat 1:21
were baptized, confessing their s.
3:6; Mark 1:5
and their s. should be. Mark 4:12
the remission of their s. Luke 1:77
shall take away their s. Rom 11:27
to fill up their s. 1 Thes 2:16
will be merciful to their s. Heb 8:12
their s. and iniquities I will. 10:17

your **sins**

clean from all your s. Lev 16:30
seven times for your s. 26:18, 24, 28
plagues on you according to your s.
21

water, because of *your* s. *Deut* 9:18
will not forgive *your* s. *Josh* 24:19
though *your* s. be as scarlet, they shall be as white as snow. *Isa* 1:18
and *your* s. have hid his face. 59:2
your s. have withholden. *Jer* 5:25
in all your doings *your* s. appear. *Ezek* 21:24
know *your* transgressions and mighty s. *Amos* 5:12
and die in *your* s. *John* 8:21, 24
repent, that *your* s. may. *Acts* 3:19
not raised, ye are yet in *your* s. *1 Cor* 15:17
you being dead in *your* s. *Col* 2:13
your s. are forgiven. *1 John* 2:12

sir

s. we came at first time. *Gen* 43:20*
s. didst thou not sow? *Mat* 13:27
said, I go s. and went not. 21:30
s. we remember that that. 27:63
s. thou hast nothing to. *John* 4:11
s. give me this water that I. 15
s. I perceive that thou art a. 19
the nobleman saith, S. come ere. 49
s. I have no man to put me. 5:7
certain Greeks saying, S. we. 12:21
s. if thou have borne him. 20:15
I said unto him, S. thou. *Rev* 7:14*

Sirion

the Sidonians call S. *Deut* 3:9
Lebanon and S. like a. *Ps* 29:6

sirs

s. ye are brethren, why? *Acts* 7:26
crying out, S. why do ye? 14:15
he said, S. what must I do? 16:30
s. ye know that by this craft. 19:25
s. I perceive this voyage will. 27:10
Paul said, S. ye should have. 21
wherefore, s. be of good cheer. 25

Sisera

of Jabin's host was S. *Judg* 4:2
S. fled away on his feet. 17
S. lay dead. 22
the stars fought against S. 5:20
with the hammer she smote S. 26
the mother of S. looked out. 28
into the hand of S. *1 Sam* 12:9
children of S. went up. *Ezra* 2:53 *Neh* 7:55
do unto them, as to S. *Ps* 83:9

sister

This name has much the same latitude as that of brother. As Christian men were used to salute one another by the name of brothers or brethren, so they called Christian women, who professed the same faith in Christ, by the name of sisters, Jas 2:15, 16.

Rebekah their s. *Gen* 24:59
thou art our s., be thou mother. 60
heard of Jacob his s.'s son. 29:13
Rachel envied her s. and said. 30:1
defiled Dinah their s. 34:13
we cannot give our s. to one. 14
should he deal with our s. 31
his s. stood afar off to wit. *Ex* 2:4
Jochebed his father's s. to wife. 6:20
Miriam s. of Aaron took a. 15:20
not uncover the nakedness of thy s. *Lev* 18:9
she is thy s. 11
not nakedness of father's s. 12
mother's s. 13
not take a wife to her s. 18
if a man take his s. and see. 20:17
of thy father's s., mother's s. 19
for his s. a virgin; for her he. 21:3
not be defiled for his s. *Num* 6:7
he that lieth with his s. *Deut* 27:22
younger s. fairer than she? *Judg* 15:2
Absalom had a fair s. *2 Sam* 13:1
he fell sick for his s. Tamar. 2
I love my brother Absalom's s. 4
had forced his s. Tamar. 22, 32
Jehosheba s. of Ahaziah took Joash. *2 Ki* 11:2; *2 Chr* 22:11
a little s. and she hath no breasts . . . do for our s. in the? *S of S* 8:8
her treacherous s. Judah. *Jer* 3:7
her s. feared not. 8
her s. hath not turned. *Jer* 3:10
him, saying, Ah, my s. 22:18
thou art the s. of thy sisters who. *Ezek* 16:45
thy elder s. is Samaria, thy younger s. Sodom. 46
Sodom thy s. hath not done as. 48
this was the iniquity of thy s. 49
for thy s. Sodom was not. 56
in thee hath humbled his s. 22:11
elder, and Aholibah her s. 23:4
and when her s. Aholibah saw. 11
was alienated from her s. 18
walked in the way of thy s. 31
thy s.'s cup deep and large. 32, 33
for s. that hath no husband. 44:25
the same is my brother, s. *Mat* 12:50
she had a s. called Mary. *Luke* 10:39; *John* 11:1, 5
therefore his s. sent. *John* 11:3
by the cross his mother's s. 19:25
Paul's s.'s son heard of. *Acts* 23:16
commend to you Phœbe our s. a servant. *Rom* 16:1
a brother or a s. is not. *1 Cor* 7:15
power to lead about a s. a wife? 9:5*
Marcus s.'s son to Barnabas. *Col* 4:10*
if a brother or s. be naked. *Jas* 2:15
children of thy elect s. *2 John* 13

my sister

pray thee, thou art *my* s. *Gen* 12:13
why saidst, She is *my* s? 19; 20:2 5, 12; 26:7, 9
I have wrestled with *my* s. 30:8
Let *my* s. Tamar come. *2 Sam* 13:5, 6
Come lie with me, *my* s. 11
Hold now thy peace, *my* s. 20
said to the worm, Thou art *my* s. *Job* 17:14
Thou art *my* s.; and call. *Pr* 7:4
hast ravished my heart, *my* s. my. *S of S* 4:9
how fair is thy love, *my* s. my. 10
a garden inclosed is *my* s. my. 12
I am come into my garden, *my* s. 5:1
open to me, *my* s. my love, my. 2
same is my brother, *my* s. *Mark* 3:35
that *my* s. hath left me? *Luke* 10:40

sister in law

s. *in law* is gone back to her people . . . after thy s. *in law*. *Ruth* 1:15

sisters

will save alive my father, and *my* s. *Josh* 2:13
whose s. were Zeruiah. *1 Chr* 2:16
they called for their three s. *Job* 1:4
his brethren and all his s. 42:11
the sister of thy s. *Ezek* 16:45
thou hast justified thy s. in. 51, 52
when thy s. and daughters. 55
when thou shalt receive thy s. 61
unto your s. Ruhamah. *Hos* 2:1
are not his s. with us? *Mat* 13:56 *Mark* 6:3
s. or father, or mother. *Mat* 19:29 *Mark* 10:29; *Luke* 14:26
100 fold, houses, brethren, s. *Mark* 10:30
women, as s. with purity. *1 Tim* 5:2

sit

war, and shall ye s. here? *Num* 32:6
ye that s. in judgement. *Judg* 5:10
s. still, my daughter. *Ruth* 3:18
turn aside, s. down here. 4:1, 2
and make them s. in. *1 Sam* 9:22
we will not s. down till he. 16:11
I should not fail to s. with. 20:5
behold, the king doth s. *2 Sam* 19:8
Solomon shall s. *1 Ki* 1:13, 17
who hath given one to s. 48; 3:6
not fail thee a man to s. on the throne. 8:25; *2 Chr* 6:16; *Jer* 33:17
why s. we here? *2 Ki* 7:3, 4
thy sons shall s. on. 10:30; 15:12
men who s. on wall. 18:27; *Isa* 36:12
and will not s. with the. *Ps* 26:5
they that s. in the gate speak. 69:12
such as s. in darkness and. 107:10
said to my Lord, S. thou at. 110:1
princes also did s. and speak. 119:23
to rise early and s. up late. 127:2*
their children shall s. upon. 132:12
folly in dignity, and rich s. *Eccl* 10
being desolate, shall s. *Isa* 3:
I will s. upon mount of the. 14:
he shall s. upon the throne in. 16
their strength is to s. still. 30
bring them that s. in darkness. 42
s. in the dust, s. on. 47:1; 52
s. thou silent, get thee into. 47
thou that sayest, I shall not s.
nor a fire to s. before it.
why do we s. still? *Jer* 8:
that s. on David's throne. 13:
s. down now. 18; 36:
he shall have none to s. 36:
and s. in thirst. 48:
how doth city s. solitary! *Lam* 1
elders of Zion s. on ground. 2:
they shall s. upon the. *Ezek* 26:
because thou hast said, I s. in. 28
and they s. before thee as. 33:
prince shall s. in it to eat. 44:
the ancient of days did s. *Dan* 7
but the judgement shall s. they.
there will I s. to judge. *Joel* 3:
they shall s. every man. *Mi* 4:
when I s. in darkness, Lord. 7:
and thy fellows that s. *Zech* 3:
he shall s. and rule upon. 6:
s. as a refiner and purifier of silve *Mal* 3:
many shall s. down with. *Mat* 8:
s. in the throne of his glory, ye al shall s. 19:28; 25:31; *Luke* 22:
my two sons may s. on. *Mat* 20:
but to s. on my right hand. *Mark* 10:37, 4
s. thou on my right hand till I mak *Mat* 22:44; *Mark* 12: *Luke* 20:42; *Heb* 1:1
the scribes and Pharisees s. in. *Mat* 23:
s. ye here while I pray yonder. 26:36; *Mark* 14:
make them s. by fifties. *Luke* 9:
make them to s. down, and. 12:
shall s. down in the kingdom. 13:
bidden, s. not down in highest. 14:
take thy bill, s. down quickly. 16:
will say to him, Go, and s. 17:
Make the men s. down. *John* 6:
would raise up Christ to s. on. *Acts* 2:3
that he would come up and s. 8:
to see thee s. at meat in. *1 Cor* 8:
hath made us s. in heavenly. *Eph* 2:
and say, S. thou here in a. *Jas* 2:
will I grant to s. with me. *Rev* 3:
a woman s. on a scarlet beast. 17:
for she saith in her heart, I s. 18:

sith

s. thou hast not hated blood, even. *Ezek* 35:6

sittest

why s. thou thyself alone? *Ex* 18:
talk of them when thou s. in thi house. *Deut* 6:7; 11:
thou s. and speakest against thy. *Ps* 50:
thou s. to eat with a ruler. *Pr* 23:
hear, O king of Judah, that s. on. *Jer* 22:
s. thou to judge me after? *Acts* 23:

sitteth

from the firstborn that s. *Ex* 11:
every thing whereon he s. *Lev* 15:
whereon he or she s. be unclean. 6, 20, 23,
when he s. on the throne. *Deut* 17:
Solomon s. on throne of. *1 Ki* 1:
do so to Mordecai that s. *Esth* 6:
nor s. in the seat of the. *Ps* 1:
s. in the heavens shall laugh. 2:
he s. in the lurking places. 10:
s. on the flood; yea, the Lord s. ki for ever, the Lord will. 29:
God s. on the throne of his. 47:
Lord reigneth, he s. between. 99:
for she s. at the door of. *Pr* 9:
a king that s. in the throne. 20:
when he s. among the elders. 31:
while king s. at his table. *S of S* 1:
spirit of judgement to him that s. *Isa* 28:

t is he that s. on the circle. *Isa* 40:22
partridge s. on eggs. *Jer* 17:11
saith of the king that s. upon. 29:16
he s. alone and keepeth. *Lam* 3:28
behold, all the earth s. *Zech* 1:11
a woman that s. in the midst. 5:7
sweareth by him that s. *Mat* 23:22
s. not down first and. *Luke* 14:28, 31
he that s. at meat or he that serveth? is not he that s. at meat? 22:27
revealed to another that s. by. *1 Cor* 14:30
where Christ s. on the right hand. *Col* 3:1
he, as God, s. in the. *2 Thes* 2:4
power to him that s. *Rev* 5:13
from the face of him that s. 6:16
salvation to our God which s. 7:10
he that s. on throne shall dwell. 15
the whore that s. upon. 17:1, 15
mountains, on which the woman s. 9

sitting

dam s. on the young. *Deut* 22:6
s. in a summer parlour. *Judg* 3:20
seen the s. of his servants. *1 Ki* 10:5; *2 Chr* 9:4
found the man of God s. *1 Ki* 13:14
saw the Lord s. on his throne. 22:19; *2 Chr* 18:18; *Isa* 6:1
of the prophets were s. *2 Ki* 4:38
captains of the host were s. 9:5
the queen also s. by him. *Neh* 2:6
see Mordecai the Jew s. *Esth* 5:13
my down-s. and up-rising. *Ps* 139:2
kings and princes s. upon the throne of David. *Jer* 17:25; 22:4, 30
the king then s. in the gate. 38:7
behold their s. down. *Lam* 3:63
s. at receipt of. *Mat* 9:9; *Mark* 2:14 *Luke* 5:27
like children s. in the markets. *Mat* 11:16; *Luke* 7:32
behold, two blind men s. *Mat* 20:30
thy king cometh, s. on an ass. 21:5*; *John* 12:15
ye shall see the Son of man s. on the. *Mat* 26:64; *Mark* 14:62
and s. down, they watched him there. *Mat* 27:36
the other Mary s. over against. 61
that was possessed s. *Mark* 5:15
they saw a young man s. on. 16:5
found him s. in midst of. *Luke* 2:46
doctors of the law s. by. 5:17
found him s. clothed, and in. 8:35
s. in sackcloth and ashes. 10:13
changers of money s. *John* 2:14
two angels in white s. 20:12
house where they were s. *Acts* 2:2
eunuch was returning, and s. 8:28
saw twenty-four elders s. *Rev* 4:4

sitting place

each side of s. *place*. *2 Chr* 9:18*

situate

Tyrus, O thou that art s. at entry. *Ezek* 27:3*
populous No that was s. *Nah* 3:8

situation

s. of the city is pleasant. *2 Ki* 2:19
beautiful for s., the joy of. *Ps* 48:2*

Sivan

that is the month S. *Esth* 8:9

six

s. cakes on a row on the. *Lev* 24:6
s. covered waggons, and. *Num* 7:3
on every hand s. fingers, every foot s. *2 Sam* 21:20; *1 Chr* 20:6
sixteen sons and s. *1 Chr* 4:27
eastward were s. Levites. 26:17
prince shall offer to Lord, shall be s. lambs without blemish. *Ezek* 46:4
new moon shall be s. lambs. 6
see **branches, days, hundreds**

six *boards*

thou shalt make s. *boards*. *Ex* 26:22
tabernacle he made s. *boards*. 36:27

six *brethren*

moreover these s. *brethren*. *Acts* 11:12

six *cities*

shall be s. *cities* for refuge. *Num* 35:6, 13, 15

six *cubits*

Goliath's height was s. *cubits*. *1 Sam* 17:4
chamber was s. *cubits*. *1 Ki* 6:6
reed of s. *cubits* long. *Ezek* 40:5
the little chambers were s. *cubits*. 12
he measured posts s. *cubits*. 41:1
doors s. *cubits*. 3
wall of the house s. *cubits*. 5
a full reed of s. great *cubits*. 8
of the image of gold s. *cubits*. *Dan* 3:1

six *curtains*

couple s. *curtains* by themselves. *Ex* 26:9; 36:16

six *measures*

gave Ruth of barley s. *measures*. *Ruth* 3:15
she said, These s. *measures*. 17

six *men*

s. *men* came from the way. *Ezek* 9:2

six *months*

king . . . seven years, s. *months*. *2 Sam* 2:11; 5:5; *1 Chr* 3:4
s. *months* Joab remained in Edom. *1 Ki* 11:16
Zachariah reigned s. *months* over. *2 Ki* 15:8
s. *months* with oil of myrrh and s. *months* with sweet. *Esth* 2:12
heaven was shut up three years and s. *months*. *Luke* 4:25; *Jas* 5:17
at Corinth a year and s. *months*. *Acts* 18:11

six *names*

s. of their *names* on one stone, and the other s. *names* of. *Ex* 28:10

six *paces*

when the Levites had gone s. *paces* he. *2 Sam* 6:13

six *sheep*

for me daily s. choice *sheep*. *Neh* 5:18

six *sons*

me, I have borne s. *sons*. *Gen* 30:20
sons of Shechaniah, s. *1 Chr* 3:22
and Azel had s. *sons*, whose names. 8:38; 9:44

six *steps*

the throne had s. *steps*. *1 Ki* 10:19
twelve lions on the s. *steps*. 20 *2 Chr* 9:18

six *things*

these s. *things* doth. *Pr* 6:16

six *times*

smitten five or s. *times*. *2 Ki* 13:19

six *troubles*

deliver thee in s. *troubles*, in seven. *Job* 5:19

six *waterpots*

set there s. *waterpots* of stone. *John* 2:6

six *wings*

each one had s. *wings*. *Isa* 6:2
beasts had each s. *wings*. *Rev* 4:8

six *years*

I served thee s. *years*. *Gen* 31:41
s. *years* he shall serve. *Ex* 21:2 *Deut* 15:12; *Jer* 34:14
s. *years* thou shalt sow. *Ex* 23:10
s. *years* thou shalt prune. *Lev* 25:3
hired servant in serving s. *years*. *Deut* 15:18
judged Israel s. *years*. *Judg* 12:7
Omri reigned s. *years*. *1 Ki* 16:23
nurse in the house of the Lord s. *years*. *2 Ki* 11:3; *2 Chr* 22:12

sixscore

Hiram sent Solomon s. *1 Ki* 9:14

sixth

bare Jacob the s. son. *Gen* 30:19
thou shall couple s. curtain. *Ex* 26:9
my blessing on you s. year. *Lev* 25:21
the s. lot came out for. *Josh* 19:32
Ithream, David's s. son. *2 Sam* 3:5 *1 Chr* 3:3
in s. year of Hezekiah. *2 Ki* 18:10
house was finished in s. *Ezra* 6:15
drink also water by measure, the s. part of an hin. *Ezek* 4:11
in the s. year the hand of. 8:1
I will leave but the s. part of. 39:2
the oblation the s. part of an. 45:13
a meat offering the s. part. 46:14
went out about the s. *Mat* 20:5
all the land from the s. to ninth hour. 27:45; *Mark* 15:33; *Luke* 23:44
about the s. hour Jesus. *John* 4:6
it was about the s. hour. 19:14
pray about the s. hour. *Acts* 10:9
when he opened s. seal. *Rev* 6:12
s. angel sounded, and I heard. 9:13
saying to the s. angel, Loose. 14
s. angel poured out vial on. 16:12
the s. foundation of the wall. 21:20
see **day, month**

sixteen

Zilpah bare to Jacob s. *Gen* 46:18
sockets of silver, s. sockets. *Ex* 26:25; 36:30
Jehoash reigned s. years. *2 Ki* 13:10
Azariah, when s. years old. 14:21
over Judah s. years in Jerusalem. 15:33; *2 Chr* 27:1, 8; 28:1
Shimei had s. sons. *1 Chr* 4:27
among sons of Eleazar were s. 24:4
sons and s. daughters. *2 Chr* 13:21

sixteenth

s. lot came forth to. *1 Chr* 24:14
the s. lot came forth to. 25:23

sixty

Mahalaleel lived s. years. *Gen* 5:15
Enoch lived s. five years and begat. 21
the male from twenty to s. *Lev* 27:3
if it be from s. years old above. 7
s. rams, s. he goats, s. lambs. *Num* 7:88
brought forth s. fold. *Mat* 13:8, 23 *Mark* 4:8, 20

size

the curtains were all of one s. *Ex* 36:9, 15
of one measure and s. *1 Ki* 6:25*
one measure, and of one s. 7:37*
for all manner of s. David left. *1 Chr* 23:29

skies

of the s. his pavilions round about. *2 Sam* 22:12; *Ps* 18:11
the s. sent out a sound. *Ps* 77:17
and let the s. pour down. *Isa* 45:8
is lifted up even to the s. *Jer* 51:9

skilful

Reuben and Gadites s. *1 Chr* 5:18
instructed, because he was s. 15:22
with thee every willing s. man. 28:21
deliver thee into the hand of men s. to destroy. *Ezek* 21:31
children s. in all wisdom. *Dan* 1:4
such are s. of lamentation to. *Amos* 5:16

skilfully

sing a new song, play s. *Ps* 33:3

skilfulness

and guided them by s. *Ps* 78:72

skill, *verb*

not any that can s. to hew timber. *1 Ki* 5:6†; *2 Chr* 2:8
a man that can s. to grave. *2 Chr* 2:7†
that could s. of instruments. 34:12†

skill

nor yet favour to men of s. but. *Eccl* 9:11
God gave them knowledge and s. *Dan* 1:17
I am now come forth to give thee s. 9:22

skin

it is his raiment for s. *Ex* 22:27
flesh of the bullock, and his s. and dung burn. 29:14; *Lev* 4:11
Moses wist not that the s. of his face. *Ex* 34:29, 30, 35
offereth shall have the s. *Lev* 7:8
if dead fall on s. or sack it. 11:32
shall have in the s. a rising. 13:2
look on the plague in the s. of the flesh, and if deeper than the s. 3
if bright spot be white in the s. 4

if the plague spread not in the *s*. *Lev* 13:5, 6, 22, 28
if scab spread abroad in the *s*. 7, 8, 27, 35, 36
if the rising be white in the *s*. 10
it is an old leprosy in the *s*. of. 11
rend it out of garment or *s*. 56
s. wherein is seed washed. 15:17
burn heifer, her *s*. and. *Num* 19:5
s. for *s*. all that a man hath. *Job* 2:4
my *s*. is broken, and become. 7:5
thou hast clothed me with *s*. 10:11
I sewed sackcloth on my *s*. 16:15
devour the strength of his *s*. 18:13*
to my *s*. and to my flesh, and I am escaped with the *s*. of my. 19:20
after my *s*. worms destroy. 26
my *s*. is black upon me. 30:30
canst thou fill his *s*. with barbed? 41:7
my bones cleave to my *s*. *Ps* 102:5*
Ethiopian change his *s*.? *Jer* 13:23
my flesh and *s*. hath he. *Lam* 3:4
their *s*. cleaveth to their bones. 4:8
our *s*. was black like an oven. 5:10
I will cover you with *s*., and put breath in you. *Ezek* 37:6, 8
who pluck off their *s*. *Mi* 3:2
who eat flesh, and flay their *s*. 3
John had a girdle of *s*. *Mark* 1:6*

skins

Lord made coats of *s*. *Gen* 3:21
she put *s*. of kids of goats. 27:16
were found red *s*. of rams and badgers' *s*., brought them. *Ex* 35:23
law of the plague of *s*. *Lev* 13:59
shall burn in fire their *s*. 16:27
raiment, all made of *s*. *Num* 31:20
in sheep *s*. and goat *s*. *Heb* 11:37

skip

maketh them also to *s*. *Ps* 29:6

skipped

mountains *s*. like rams. *Ps* 114:4, 6

skippedst

since thou spakest of him, thou *s*. for joy. *Jer* 48:27*

skipping

behold, he cometh *s*. upon. *S of S* 2:8

skirt

(*The lower part of the long mantle worn by the Jews*)
uncover his father's *s*. *Deut* 22:30
uncovereth his father's *s*. 27:20
spread therefore thy *s*. *Ruth* 3:9
he laid hold on the *s*. *1 Sam* 15:27
David cut off the *s*. of Saul's. 24:4
because he cut off Saul's *s*. 5
my father, see the *s*. of thy robe. 11
behold, I spread my *s*. *Ezek* 16:8
if one bear holy flesh in the *s*. and with his *s*. do touch. *Hag* 2:12
shall take hold of *s*. of. *Zech* 8:23

skirts

that went down to the *s*. of. *Ps* 133:2
in *s*. is found blood of poor. *Jer* 2:34
for thy iniquity are thy *s*. 13:22
will I discover thy *s*. 26; *Nah* 3:5
her filthiness is in her *s*. *Lam* 1:9
bind a few hairs in thy *s*. *Ezek* 5:3

skull

millstone to break his *s*. *Judg* 9:53
more of Jezebel than *s*. *2 Ki* 9:35
to say, the place of a *s*. *Mat* 27:33 *Mark* 15:22; *John* 19:17

sky

in his excellency on the *s*. *Deut* 33:26
him spread out the *s*.? *Job* 37:18
it will be fair weather: for the *s*. is red. *Mat* 16:2*, 3
discern face of the *s*. *Luke* 12:56*
many as the stars of *s*. *Heb* 11:12*

slack

(*Sluggish, loosened, slowed down*)
he will not be *s*. to him. *Deut* 7:10
How long are ye *s*. to go? *Josh* 18:3
dealeth with a *s*. hand. *Pr* 10:4
said to Zion, Let not thine hands be *s*. *Zeph* 3:16
Lord is not *s*. concerning. *2 Pet* 3:9

slack, *verb*

vow a vow, thou shalt not *s*. to pay it. *Deut* 23:21
saying, *S*. not thy hand. *Josh* 10:6
s. not riding for me. *2 Ki* 4:24*

slacked

the law is *s*., and judgement. *Hab* 1:4

slackness

slack, as some men count *s*. *2 Pet* 3:9

slain, *verb*

for I have *s*. a man to. *Gen* 4:23
therefore he hath *s*. them in. *Num* 14:16
surely now I had *s*. thee. 22:33
after he had *s*. Sihon. *Deut* 1:4*
be not known who hath *s*. him. 21:1
and have *s*. his sons. *Judg* 9:18
jaw bone of an ass have I *s*. 15:16*
thought to have *s*. me. 20:5
Saul hath *s*. his. *1 Sam* 18:7; 21:11
shewed David that Saul had *s*. 22:21
saying, I have *s*. the. *2 Sam* 1:16
Abner, because he had *s*. 3:30
men have *s*. a righteous person. 4:11
hast *s*. Uriah with the sword. 12:9
Absalom hath *s*. all king's sons. 13:30
they have not *s*. all, for Amnon. 32
when the Philistines had *s*. 21:12
Ishbi-benob thought to have *s*. 16
Adonijah hath *s*. oxen. *1 Ki* 1:19, 25
Pharaoh had gone up and *s*. 9:16
lion hath torn and *s*. him. 13:26
Zimri hath *s*. the king. 16:16*
Ahab told how he had *s*. all. 19:1
for Israel have *s*. thy. 10, 14
servants who had *s*. king. *2 Ki* 14:5
hast *s*. thy brethren. *2 Chr* 21:13
for the band of men had *s*. 22:1
when they had *s*. Ahaziah, they. 9
quiet after they had *s*. 23:21
s. them in rage that reacheth. 28:9
Jews have *s*. 500 men. *Esth* 9:12
the Sabeans have *s*. *Job* 1:15, 17
men have been *s*. by her. *Pr* 7:26
destroyed and *s*. people. *Isa* 14:20
bodies of men whom I have *s*. in my anger. *Jer* 33:5
he had *s*. Gedaliah. 41:4, 9, 16, 18
hast *s*. them in day. *Lam* 2:21; 3:43
hast *s*. my children. *Ezek* 16:21
s. their children to idols. 23:39
I have *s*. them by words. *Hos* 6:5
your young men have I *s*. *Amos* 4:10
by wicked hands have *s*. *Acts* 2:23
have *s*. them that shewed. 7:52
nothing till we have *s*. Paul. 23:14

slain

Jacob came upon the *s*. *Gen* 34:27
the blood of the *s*. bird. *Lev* 14:51
and ye shall be *s*. before. 26:17*
shall the flocks and the herds be *s*.? *Num* 11:22
toucheth any *s*. 19:16, 18; 31:19
drink the blood of the *s*. 23:24
name of the Israelite that was *s*. was Zimri. 25:14
woman that was *s*. was Cozbi. 15, 18
rest of them that were *s*. 31:8
if one be found *s*. in land giveth. *Deut* 21:1*
the city next to the *s*. man. 3
thine ox shall be *s*. before. 28:31
arrows drunk with blood of *s*. 32:42
will I deliver them up all *s*. *Josh* 11:6
among them that were *s*. 13:22
the woman that was *s*. *Judg* 20:4*
Hophni and Phinehas were *s*. *1 Sam* 4:11
as Lord liveth, he shall not be *s*. 19:6
to-morrow thou shalt be *s*. 11
shall he be *s*.? what hath? 20:32
Philistines, and fell down *s*. in mount Gilboa. 31:1; *1 Chr* 10:1
when the Philistines came to strip the *s*. *1 Sam* 31:8
beauty of Israel is *s*. *2 Sam* 1:19
from the blood of *s*. from fat. 22
O Jonathan, thou wast *s*. in. 25
Israel were *s*. before David's. 18:7*
was gone to bury the *s*. *1 Ki* 11:15
the kings are surely *s*. *2 Ki* 3:23*
from among them that were *s*. 11:2
within ranges let him be *s*. *2 Ki* 11
on her, and there was she *s*.
there fell down many *s*., because th war was of God. *1 Chr* 5:2
fell *s*. of Israel 500,000. *2 Chr* 13:1
I and my people, to be *s*. *Esth* 7:
number of the *s*. in Shushan. 9:1
and where the *s*. are. *Job* 39:3
ye shall be *s*. all of you. *Ps* 62:
like the *s*. that lie in the grave. 88:
Rahab in pieces as one *s*. 89:1
man saith, I shall be *s*. *Pr* 22:1
those that are ready to be *s*. 24:1
shall fall under the *s*. *Isa* 10:
raiment of those that are *s*. 14:1
thy *s*. men were not *s*. with. 22:
shall no more cover her *s*. 26:2
s. according to slaughter, or *s*. 27:
their *s*. also shall be cast out. 34:
and the *s*. of the Lord shall. 66:1
that I might weep for *s*. *Jer* 9:
behold the *s*. with the sword. 14:1
men be *s*. by sword in battle. 18:21
s. of the Lord be from one. 25:3
filled the pit with the *s*. 41:
thus the *s*. shall fall in land. 51:
her *s*. shall fall in the midst. 4
caused *s*. of Israel to fall, so at Baby lon shall fall the *s*. of all. 4
priest and prophet be *s*. *Lam* 2:2
be *s*. with sword, are better than the that be *s*. with hunger. 4:
and the *s*. shall fall in. *Ezek* 6:
when the *s*. men shall be among. 1
and fill the courts with *s*. 9:
your *s*. in the city, ye have filled th streets with the *s*. 11:
your *s*., they are the flesh, and this.
s. it is the sword of great men *s*. 21:14
upon necks of them that are *s*. 2
daughters in field shall be *s*. 26:
deaths of them that are *s*. 28:
great pain when the *s*. shall. 30:
shall fill the land with the *s*. 1
with him unto them that be *s*. 31:1
with them *s*. with sword. 18; 32:2
fall in the midst of the *s*. 32:20, 2
lie *s*. by the sword. 21, 22, 23, 2
circumcised, *s*. by sword. 25, 26, 3
all his army *s*. by sword. 31, 3
mountains with his *s*. men. 35:
breathe upon these *s*. 37:
wise men to be *s*.; they sought Danie and his fellows to be *s*. *Dan* 2:1
was Belshazzar the king *s*. 5:3
I beheld, even till beast was *s*. 7:1
and many shall fall down *s*. 11:2
there is multitude of *s*. *Nah* 3:
ye Ethiopians shall be *s*. *Zeph* 2:1
Son of man must be *s*. *Luke* 9:2
Theudas was *s*.; and all. *Acts* 5:3
ye offered to me *s*. beasts? 7:4
Pilate that he should be *s*. 13:2
by the cross, having *s*. *Eph* 2:1
they were stoned, were *s*. *Heb* 11:3
who was *s*. among you. *Rev* 2:1
stood a Lamb, as it had been *s*. 5:
thou wast *s*.
the Lamb that was *s*. 12; 13:8
souls of them that were *s*. for. 6:9
in the earthquake were *s*. 11:1
the blood of all that were *s*. 18:24
remnant *s*. with sword of. 19:21

slander

bringing up a *s*. on land. *Num* 14:36*
for I have heard the *s*. *Ps* 31:13*
he that uttereth a *s*. *Pr* 10:18

slandered

he hath *s*. thy servant. *2 Sam* 19:27

slanderers

must be grave, not *s*. *1 Tim* 3:11

slanderest

s. thine own mother's son. *Ps* 50:20

slandereth

whoso *s*. his neighbour, him. *Ps* 101:5

slanderously

as we be *s*. reported. *Rom* 3:8

slanders

revolters walking with *s*. *Jer* 6:28
neighbour will walk with *s*. 9:4

slang

om his bag a stone and s. it. 1 Sam 17:49

slaughter

ıat first s. which. 1 Sam 14:14
ot been now much greater s.? 30
s David returned from s. of Philistine. 17:57; 18:6; 2 Sam 1:1
ı s. among people who. 2 Sam 17:9
ɑs come from the s. 2 Chr 25:14
s sheep for the s. Ps 44:22
fter her, as an ox to the s. Pr 7:22
ıe s. of Midian at Oreb. Isa 10:26
repare s. for his children. 14:21
ccording to s. of them that. 27:7
nd delivered them to s. 34:2
e is brought as a lamb to the s. 53:7
Jer 11:19
hall all bow down to the s. Isa 65:12
ophet, but valley of s. Jer 7:32
19:6
ıll them out like sheep for s., prepare them for day of s. 12:3
ɔr the days of your s. are. 25:34
oung men are gone down to s. 48:15
et them go down to the s. 50:27
hem down like lambs to the s. 51:40
nd every man a s. weapon in his. Ezek 9:2
s sharpened to make sore s. 21:10
: is wrapped up for the s. 15
ɔ open the mouth in the s. 22
ıe sword is drawn: for the s. 28
hen the s. is made in the. 26:15
re profound to make s. Hos 5:2
Esau may be cut off by s. Ob 9
ord, Feed the flock of s. Zech 11:4
will feed the flock of s. O poor. 7
e was led as a sheep to s. Acts 8:32
Saul yet breathing out s. against. 9:1
ve are accounted as sheep for the s. Rom 8:36
ıbraham returning from the s. of the kings. Heb 7:1
our hearts, as in day of s. Jas 5:5
see **great**

slave, -s

(Slavery under the Hebrews was s mild as was possible in that age. No Hebrew could become permanently the slave of another Hebrew, but must be freed when e had paid the debt for which e was sold; in the seventh year f his service whether the debt vas paid or not; and in the year of Jubilee, whatever the time he had served. Gentile slaves were mostly var captives, or purchased from egular slave-dealers. These could be freed at the will of the master, but there was no law requiring it)
s he a homeborn s.? Jer 2:14
he merchandise of s. Rev 18:13

slay

hat findeth me shall s. Gen 4:14
Lord, wilt thou s. also a? 20:4
and they will s. me for my. 11
will I s. my brother Jacob. 27:41
gather together against me and s. 34:30*
therefore and let us s. him. 37:20
What profit is it if we s. brother? 26
s. my two sons if I bring him. 42:37
bring these men home, s. 43:16
behold, I will s. thy son. Ex 4:23
the innocent and righteous s. 23:7
shalt s. ram and sprinkle. 29:16
bring them out to s. them. 32:12
s. every man his brother. 27
s. sin offering. Lev 4:29, 33
s. the lamb. 14:13
with a beast, ye shall s. beast. 20:15
one shall s. red heifer. Num 19:3
s. ye every one his men joined. 25:5
revenger of blood shall s. 35:19, 21
of blood pursue and s. Deut 19:6
Israel did s. Balaam. Josh 13:22
alive, would not s. you. Judg 8:19
his firstborn. Up and s. them. 20
s. me, that men say not. 9:54
Lord would s. them. 1 Sam 2:25
ark of God that it s. us not. 5:11
any man his ox, and s. 1 Sam 14:34
spare them not, but s. both. 15:3
up to me, that I may s. him. 19:15
if there be in me iniquity, s. 20:8
said, Turn and s. the priests. 22:17
me, stand upon me and s. 2 Sam 1:9
let king swear to me he will not s. 1 Ki 1:51
child, in no wise s. it. 3:26, 27
did Baasha s. and reigned. 15:28
find thee, he shall s. me. 18:12
shall Jehu s.: him that escapeth from sword of Jehu shall Elisha s. 19:17
art departed, a lion shall s. 20:36
young men wilt thou s. 2 Ki 8:12
go in and s. them, let none. 10:25
sent lions, and they s. them. 17:26
s. her not in the house. 2 Chr 23:14
priests too few to s. all the. 29:34
we will s. them and cause. Neh 4:11
if the scourge s. suddenly. Job 9:23
though he s. me, yet will I. 13:15
viper's tongue shall s. him. 20:16
evil shall s. wicked that. Ps 34:21
s. them not, lest my people. 59:11
they s. the widow and the. 94:6
that he might s. the broken. 109:16
thou wilt s. the wicked. 139:19
of the simple shall s. them. Pr 1:32
his lips shall he s. wicked. Isa 11:4
with famine, and he shall s. 14:30
Lord shall s. the dragon that. 27:1
for Lord God shall s. thee. 65:15
the forest shall s. them. Jer 5:6
Judah captive and s. them. 20:4
shall s. Ahab and Zedekiah. 29:21
I will s. Ishmael, son of Nathaniah; wherefore should he s.? 40:15
found that said, S. us not. 41:8
s. all her bullocks; woe unto. 50:27
s. utterly old and young. Ezek 9:6
they shall s. their sons and. 23:47
he shall s. with sword thy. 26:8
he shall s. thy people by. 11
they shall s. the burnt. 44:11
set her like a dry land and s. Hos 2:3
yet will I s. the fruit. 9:16
s. all princes thereof. Amos 2:3
I will s. the last of them with. 9:1
sword, and it shall s. them. 4
whose possessors s. them. Zech 11:5
some of them they shall s. and. Luke 11:49
bring hither, and s. them. 19:27

to slay

be far from thee to s. Gen 18:25
stretched his hand to s. his. 22:10
they conspired against him to s. him. 37:18
Pharaoh sought to s. Moses. Ex 2:15
sword in their hand to s. us. 5:21
man come on neighbour to s. 21:14
brought them out to s. Deut 9:28
cursed that taketh reward to s. 27:25
brought the ark to s. us. 1 Sam 5:10
why then sin, to s. David? 19:5
Saul went to watch him and s. 11
of his father to s. David. 20:33
the king to s. Abner. 2 Sam 3:37
Saul sought to s. them in his. 21:2
thou come to s. my son? 1 Ki 17:18
the hand of Ahab to s. me. 18:9
utterly to s. and. 2 Chr 20:23
to s. thee, in night to s. Neh 6:10
to s. the power that would assault. Esth 8:11
to s. such as be of upright. Ps 37:14
and seeketh to s. him. 32
sword to s. dogs, to tear. Jer 15:3
all their counsel to s. me. 18:23
sent Ishmael to s. thee? 40:14
to s. the souls that. Ezek 13:19
two tables to s. thereon. 40:39
gone forth to s. wise men. Dan 2:14
continually to s. nations. Hab 1:17
Jesus, and sought to s. John 5:16
they took counsel to s. Acts 5:33
but they went about to s. him. 9:29
angels prepared to s. third. Rev 9:15

slayer

refuge that the s. may flee thither. Num 35:11; Deut 4:42; 19:3, 4 Josh 20:3
shall judge between s. Num 35:24
congregation shall deliver s. 25
if the s. shall at any time come. 26
of blood find and kill the s. 27
s. shall return into the land of his. 28 Josh 20:6
of blood pursue the s. Deut 19:6
not deliver the s. up. Josh 20:5
Hebron to be a city of refuge for s. 21:13
gave Shechem for the s. 21, 27, 32
to be a city of refuge for s. 38
sword is furbished to be given to s. Ezek 21:11

slayeth

to him, whosoever s. Cain. Gen 4:15
neighbour and s. him. Deut 22:26
wrath killeth and envy s. Job 5:2
that s. thee, I am God? . . . man in hand of them that s. Ezek 28:9*

slaying

when Israel made an end of s. Josh 8:24; 10:20
rendered wickedness in s. Judg 9:56
on widow by s. her son. 1 Ki 17:20
s. oxen, killing sheep. Isa 22:13
s. the children in the valleys. 57:5
while they were s. them. Ezek 9:8*

sleep

(Sleep is used in the Bible for natural sleep; for the indolence and dullness of the soul; or figuratively for death)
God caused a deep s. to. Gen 2:21
sun going down, a deep s. 15:12
Jacob awaked out of his s. 28:16
thus I was, my s. departed. 31:40
awaked out of his s. Judg 16:14, 20
a deep s. from God. 1 Sam 26:12
when deep s. falleth on men. Job 4:13; 33:15
nor be raised out of their s. 14:12
lest I s. the s. of death. Ps 13:3
stouthearted slept their s. 76:5
horse are cast into a deep s. 6
awaked as one out of s. 78:65
them away, they are as a s. 90:5
for so he giveth his beloved s. 127:2
I will not give s. to mine eyes. 132:4
shalt lie down, and thy s. Pr 3:24
their s. is taken away, unless. 4:16
not s. to thine eyes, nor slumber. 6:4
wilt thou arise out of thy s.? 9
a little s. a little slumber. 10; 24:33
casteth into a deep s. 19:15
love not s. lest thou come. 20:13
the s. of a labouring man. Eccl 5:12
neither day nor night seeth s. 8:16
on you spirit of deep s. Isa 29:10
I awaked, and my s. Jer 31:26
sleep a perpetual s. 51:39, 57
spirit troubled, and his s. Dan 2:1
passed the night and his s. 6:18
I was in a deep s. on my. 8:18; 10:9
as a man that is wakened out of s. Zech 4:1
being raised from s. did. Mat 1:24
were heavy with s. Luke 9:32
may awake him out of s. John 11:11
spoken of taking of rest in s. 13
awaking out of his s. Acts 16:27
Eutychus being fallen into a deep s. 20:9
time to awake out of s. Rom 13:11

sleep, *verb*

down in that place to s. Gen 28:11
raiment, wherein shall he s.? Ex 22:27
thou shalt not s. with. Deut 24:12
he may s. in his own raiment. 13
thou shalt s. with thy fathers. 31:16
2 Sam 7:12
and she made him s. Judg 16:19
was laid down to s. 1 Sam 3:3
my lord the king shall s. 1 Ki 1:21
on that night could not the king s. Esth 6:1
shall I s. in the dust. Job 7:21
lay me down in peace and s. Ps 4:8
lighten mine eyes, lest I s. the. 13:3
shall neither slumber nor s. 121:4
s. not, except they have. Pr 4:16
how long wilt thou s. O? 6:9
folding of the hands to s. 10; 24:33

the *s.* of a labouring man is sweet . . .
not suffer him to *s.* *Eccl* 5:12
I *s.* but my heart waketh. *S of S* 5:2
none shall slumber nor *s.* *Isa* 5:27
s. a perpetual sleep. *Jer* 51:39, 57
and they shall *s.* in. *Ezek* 34:25
many that *s.* in the dust. *Dan* 12:2
s. on now, and take your rest.
Mat 26:45; *Mark* 14:41
and should *s.* and the seed should.
Mark 4:27
he said, Why *s.* ye ? *Luke* 22:46
Lord, if he *s.* he shall. *John* 11:12
many among you *s.* *1 Cor* 11:30
we shall not all *s.*, but we. 15:51
them who *s.* in Jesus. *1 Thes* 4:14
let us not *s.* as do others. 5:6
they that *s.* sleep in the night. 7
that whether we wake or *s.* 10

sleeper

what meanest thou, O *s.*? *Jonah* 1:6

sleepest

awake, why *s.* thou ? *Ps* 44:23
when thou *s.* it shall. *Pr* 6:22
Simon, *s.* thou ? *Mark* 14:37
awake, thou that *s.* and. *Eph* 5:14

sleepeth

Peradventure he *s.* *1 Ki* 18:27
he that *s.* in harvest is a son that
causeth shame. *Pr* 10:5
their baker *s.* all night. *Hos* 7:6
place, for the maid is not dead but *s.*
Mat 9:24; *Mark* 5:39; *Luke* 8:52
our friend Lazarus *s.* *John* 11:11

sleeping

behold, Saul lay *s.* *1 Sam* 26:7
watchmen blind: *s.* *Isa* 56:10*
suddenly he find you *s.* *Mark* 13:36
he cometh and findeth them *s.* 14:37
Peter was *s.* between. *Acts* 12:6

sleight

about by the *s.* of men. *Eph* 4:14

slept

Adam *s.* *Gen* 2:21
Pharaoh *s.* and dreamed. 41:5
Uriah *s.* at door of the. *2 Sam* 11:9
while thine handmaid *s.* *1 Ki* 3:20
as he lay and *s.* an angel. 19:5
I have been quiet and have *s.*
Job 3:13
I laid me down and *s.* *Ps* 3:5
the stouthearted have *s.* 76:5
while men *s.* his enemy. *Mat* 13:25
tarried, they slumbered and *s.* 25:5
of saints which *s.* arose. 27:52
stole him away while we *s.* 28:13
the firstfruits of them that *s.*
1 Cor 15:20
see **fathers**

slew

seed instead of Abel, whom Cain *s.*
Gen 4:25
they *s.* all the males. 34:25
they *s.* Hamor. 26
for in their anger they *s.* a man. 49:6
Moses *s.* the Egyptian. *Ex* 2:12*
the Lord *s.* all the firstborn. 13:15
he *s.* the bullock and took the blood.
Lev 8:15, 23
Aaron *s.* the calf of the. 9:8, 15
s. the burnt offering, presented. 12
they *s.* all the males. *Num* 31:7
s. kings of Midian, Balaam also they
s. 8
and *s.* the men of Ai. *Josh* 8:21
Gibeonites, they *s.* them not. 9:26
Joshua *s.* the five kings and. 10:26
they *s.* of them in Bezek. *Judg* 1:4*
they *s.* Sheshai. 10*
they *s.* the Canaanites. 17*
they *s.* of Moab 10,000 men. 3:29*
Shamgar *s.* of the Philistines. 31*
they *s.* Oreb and Zeeb the. 7:25
he *s.* men of Penuel. 8:17
men were they whom ye *s.*? 18
s. Zebah, Zalmunna. 21
Abimelech *s.* his brethren. 9:5
Samson *s.* thirty men of. 14:19*
jawbone Samson *s.* 1000. 15:15*
delivered our enemy, which *s.* 16:24
the dead which he *s.* at his. 30
Hannah *s.* a bullock. *1 Sam* 1:25
the Philistines *s.* of Israel. *1 Sam* 4:2
Israel *s.* the Ammonites. 11:11*
and his armourbearer *s.* 14:13
the people *s.* oxen and calves. 32
every man brought his ox and *s.* 34
thy servant *s.* both the lion. 17:36*
put his life in his hand, and *s.* 19:5*
Doeg *s.* 85 persons that did. 22:18
sang, Saul *s.* his thousands. 29:5
the Amalekites *s.* not any. 30:2
the Philistines *s.* Jonathan. 31:2
Abishai his brother *s.* *2 Sam* 3:30
David *s.* them and cut off. 4:12
David *s.* of the Syrians. 8:5*
David *s.* the men of 700. 10:18
for Saul, because he *s.* 21:1
he *s.* two lion-like men of Moab, he
s. lion in. 23:20; *1 Chr* 11:22
he *s.* an Egyptian, a goodly man.
2 Sam 23:21; *1 Chr* 11:23
and Amasa, whom he *s.* *1 Ki* 2:5
Zimri on the throne *s.* all. 16:11*
what I did when Jezebel *s.* 18:13
they took them, and Elijah *s.* 40
Had Zimri peace, who *s.* his ?
2 Ki 9:31
behold, I *s.* him, but who *s.*? 10:9*
he *s.* all that remained to. 17*
people *s.* Mattan the priest. 11:18
they *s.* Athaliah. 20; *2 Chr* 23:15, 17
was confirmed Amaziah *s.* servants.
2 Ki 14:5; *2 Chr* 25:3
but their children he *s.* not.
2 Ki 14:6; *2 Chr* 25:4
he *s.* of Edom in valley of salt.
2 Ki 14:7; *1 Chr* 18:12*
took Damascus and *s.* *2 Ki* 16:9
lions which *s.* some of them. 17:25
Amon conspired and *s.* him. 21:23
people of the land *s.* them. 24
2 Chr 33:25
Josiah *s.* all the priests. *2 Ki* 23:20
Nebuchadnezzar *s.* sons of Zedekiah.
25:7; *Jer* 39:6; 52:10
of Gath in that land *s.* *1 Chr* 7:21
Jehoram *s.* all his brethren with.
2 Chr 21:4
Jehu found, and *s.* the princes. 22:8
Pekah *s.* in Judah in one day. 28:6
they *s.* thy prophets. *Neh* 9:26
the Jews *s.* of their. *Esth* 9:16
God *s.* the fattest of. *Ps* 78:31
when he *s.* them, then they. 34
waters into blood, and *s.* 105:29
who *s.* great kings. 135:10
s. famous kings. 136:18
killeth an ox is as if he *s.* *Isa* 66:3
because he *s.* me not. *Jer* 20:17
Ishmael *s.* all the Jews that. 41:3
he forbare, and *s.* them not. 8
s. all that were pleasant. *Lam* 2:4
fire *s.* the men that took. *Dan* 3:22
whom he would he *s.* 5:19
Herod sent, and *s.* all the children.
Mat 2:16
took his servants and *s.* them. 22:6
ye *s.* between the temple. 23:35
tower in Siloam fell, and *s.* *Luke* 13:4
raised up Jesus, whom ye *s.* *Acts* 5:30
Jesus whom they *s.* and. 10:39
the commandment *s.* me. *Rom* 7:11
Cain who *s.* his brother. *1 John* 3:12

slew *him*

against Abel and *s. him.* *Gen* 4:8
wicked, and the Lord *s. him.* 38:7
displeased the Lord, and he *s. him.*
10
of me, A woman *s. him.* *Judg* 9:54
took and *s. him* at passages. 12:6
by beard and *s. him.* *1 Sam* 17:35
the Philistine and *s. him.* 50
so I stood upon him and *s. him.*
2 Sam 1:10
Ish-bosheth and *s. him.* 4:7
I took hold of him, and *s. him.* 10
compassed Absalom and *s. him.*
18:15
the son of Shimeah *s. him.* 21:21
he went down and *s. him.* 23:21
upon Joab and *s. him.* *1 Ki* 2:34
a lion met him by the way and *s.*
him. 13:24; 20:36
my master and *s. him.* *2 Ki* 10:9
they sent after him to Lachish, an
s. him. *2 Ki* 14:19; *2 Chr* 25:2
against him and *s. him.* *2 Ki* 15:1
smote Shallum and *s. him.* 1
against Pekah and *s. him.* 3
Pharaoh-necho *s. him* at. 23:2
therefore he *s. him.* *1 Chr* 10:1
so that Athaliah *s. him* not.
2 Chr 22:1
his own servants *s. him* on. 24:2
forth of his own bowels *s. him.* 32:2
his servants *s. him* in his. 33:2
Jehoiakim who *s. him.* *Jer* 26:2
Ishmael *s. him* whom the king. 41:
cast him out of vineyard and *s. him*
Mat 21:3
raiment of them that *s. him.*
Acts 22:2

slewest

Goliath whom thou *s.* *1 Sam* 21:

slide

their foot shall *s.* in. *Deut* 32:3
in the Lord, I shall not *s.* *Ps* 26:1
his heart, none of steps shall *s.* 37:3

slidden

this people of Jerusalem *s.* back ?
Jer 8:

slideth

Israel *s.* back as a. *Hos* 4:16

slightly

hurt of my people *s.* *Jer* 6:14; 8:1

slime

had brick for stone, *s.* *Gen* 11:3
she daubed the ark with *s.* *Ex* 2:3

slimepits

Siddim was full of *s.* *Gen* 14:1

sling, *verb*

every one could *s.* stones at an hair
breadth. *Judg* 20:16
them shall he *s.* out. *1 Sam* 25:29
I will *s.* out inhabitants. *Jer* 10:18

sling

(A common weapon among the Jews, especially among the shepherds, who could sling a stone to a long distance with great accuracy, and thus drive away wild beasts when other weapons would be useless)

his *s.* in his hand. *1 Sam* 17:40
over the Philistine with a *s.* 50
as out of the middle of a *s.* 25:29
bindeth a stone in a *s.* so is. *Pr* 26:8

slingers

the *s.* went about it. *2 Ki* 3:25

slings

Uzziah prepared *s.* to. *2 Chr* 26:14*

slingstones

s. are turned with him. *Job* 41:28

slip

that my feet did not *s.* *2 Sam* 22:37
Ps 18:36
he that is ready to *s.* *Job* 12:5
that my footsteps *s.* not. *Ps* 17:5
we should let them *s.* *Heb* 2:1

slippery

their way be dark and *s.* *Ps* 35:6
didst set them in *s.* places. 73:18
be to them as *s.* ways. *Jer* 23:12

slippeth

and the head *s.* from. *Deut* 19:5
when my foot *s.* they. *Ps* 38:16
when I said, My foot *s.*; thy. 94:18

slips

shalt set it with strange *s.* *Isa* 17:10

slipt

David *s.* out of Saul's. *1 Sam* 19:10
my steps had well nigh *s.* *Ps* 73:2

slothful

be not *s.* to go to possess. *Judg* 18:9
the *s.* shall be under. *Pr* 12:24
s. roasteth not that he took in. 27
the way of the *s.* is a hedge. 15:19*
the *s.* is brother to him that. 18:9*
s. hideth his hand in. 19:24*; 26:15*
the desire of *s.* killeth him. 21:25
the *s.* man saith. 22:13*; 26:13*
I went by field of the *s.* 24:30

Thou wicked and *s.* servant. *Mat* 25:26
not *s.* in business, fervent in spirit. *Rom* 12:11
that ye be not *s.* but followers of. *Heb* 6:12

slothfulness

s. casteth into a deep. *Pr* 19:15
by much *s.* the building. *Eccl* 10:18

slow

s. of speech, and of a *s.* tongue. *Ex* 4:10
art a God *s.* to anger. *Neh* 9:17
is *s.* to wrath, is of great. *Pr* 14:29
O fools and *s.* of heart. *Luke* 24:25
the Cretians are liars, *s.* *Tit* 1:12*
every man be *s.* to speak, *s.* *Jas* 1:19
see **anger**

slowly

when we had sailed *s.* *Acts* 27:7

sluggard

go to the ant, thou *s.* *Pr* 6:6
how long wilt thou sleep, O *s.*? 9
eyes, so is the *s.* to them. 10:26
the soul of the *s.* desireth. 13:4
s. will not plow, therefore. 20:4*
s. is wiser in his own conceit. 26:16

sluices

that make *s.* and ponds. *Isa* 19:10*

slumber, *substantive*

I will not give *s.* to mine. *Ps* 132:4
give not sleep to thine eyes, nor *s.* *Pr* 6:4
yet a little sleep, a little *s.* 10; 24:33
given them the spirit of *s.* *Rom* 11:8*

slumber

keepeth thee will not *s.* *Ps* 121:3
Israel, shall neither *s.* nor sleep. 4
none shall *s.* nor sleep. *Isa* 5:27
lying down, loving to *s.* 56:10
thy shepherds *s.* O king. *Nah* 3:18

slumbered

while the bridegroom tarried they all *s.* *Mat* 25:5

slumbereth

their damnation *s.* not. *2 Pet* 2:3

slumberings

God speaketh in *s.* upon. *Job* 33:15

small

it is a *s.* matter thou hast. *Gen* 30:15
it shall become *s.* dust in all. *Ex* 9:9
as round thing, as *s.* as the. 16:14
every *s.* matter they shall. 18:22, 26
beat some of it very *s.* 30:36
sweet incense beaten *s.* *Lev* 16:12
a *s.* thing that the God of? *Num* 16:9
is it a *s.* thing that thou hast? 13
Jair went and took the *s.* 32:41
calf *s.* even as *s.* as dust. *Deut* 9:21*
doctrine shall distil as *s.* rain. 32:2
a *s.* thing in thy sight, O Lord God. *2 Sam* 7:19; *1 Chr* 17:17
till there be not one *s.* stone found. *2 Sam* 17:13
I beat them as *s.* as the dust. 22:43 *Ps* 18:42
I desire one *s.* petition. *1 Ki* 2:20
after the fire, a still *s.* voice. 19:12
inhabitants were of *s.* power, they. *2 Ki* 19:26; *Isa* 37:27
he brought out the grove and stamped it *s.* to powder. *2 Ki* 23:6, 15
Syrians came with a *s.* *2 Chr* 24:24
passover offerings 2600 *s.* 35:8
chief of Levites gave 500 *s.* cattle. 9
though thy beginning was *s.* *Job* 8:7
are the consolations of God *s.*? 15:11
for he maketh *s.* the drops. 36:27*
I am *s.* yet do not I. *Ps* 119:141
adversity, thy strength is *s.* *Pr* 24:10
had left to us a *s.* remnant. *Isa* 1:9
it a *s.* thing for you to weary? 7:13
the remnant shall be very *s.* 16:14
him all vessels of *s.* quantity. 22:24
strangers shall be like *s.* dust. 29:5
are counted as the *s.* dust. 40:15
mountains, and beat them *s.* 41:15
brought me the *s.* cattle. 43:23
for a *s.* moment have I. 54:7
a *s.* one shall become a strong. 60:22
and they shall not be *s.* *Jer* 30:19
yet a *s.* number shall return. 44:28
I will make thee *s.* among. *Jer* 49:15
whoredoms a *s.* matter? *Ezek* 16:20
seemeth it *s.* to have eaten? 34:18
strong with a *s.* people. *Dan* 11:23
Jacob arise? he is *s.* *Amos* 7:2, 5
I have made thee *s.* among. *Ob* 2
hath despised day of *s.* things? *Zech* 4:10
they had a few *s.* fishes. *Mark* 8:7
had made a scourge of *s.* cords. *John* 2:15
barley loaves and two *s.* fishes. 6:9
there was no *s.* stir. *Acts* 12:18
Paul and Barnabas had no *s.* 15:2
there arose no *s.* stir about. 19:23
Demetrius brought no *s.* gain. 24
and no *s.* tempest lay on us. 27:20
very *s.* thing that I should. *1 Cor* 4:3
turned with a very *s.* helm. *Jas* 3:4
see **great**

smallest

Benjamite, of *s.* of tribes? *1 Sam* 9:21
to judge the *s.* matters? *1 Cor* 6:2

smart

for a stranger shall *s.* for it. *Pr* 11:15

smell

smelled the *s.* of his raiment, said, See, *s.* of my son is as *s.* *Gen* 27:27
spikenard sendeth forth the *s.* *S of S* 1:12*
tender grape give a good *s.* 2:13*
the *s.* of thy ointment better. 4:10
s. of thy garments is like the *s.* 11
s. of thy nose like apples. 7:8
mandrakes give a *s.* and at. 13*
instead of sweet *s.* there. *Isa* 3:24*
s. of the fire had passed. *Dan* 3:27
olive, his *s.* as Lebanon. *Hos* 14:6
sent an odour of sweet *s.* *Phil* 4:18

smell, *verb*

like unto that to *s.* thereto. *Ex* 30:38
I will not *s.* the savour. *Lev* 26:31
which neither see nor *s.* *Deut* 4:28
all thy garments *s.* of myrrh. *Ps* 45:8
noses have they, they *s.* not. 115:6
not *s.* in your solemn. *Amos* 5:21

smelled

Lord *s.* a sweet savour. *Gen* 8:21
Isaac *s.* smell of his raiment. 27:27

smelleth

he *s.* the battle afar off. *Job* 39:25

smelling

fingers with sweet *s.* myrrh on. *S of S* 5:5*
lilies dropping sweet *s.* myrrh. 13*
where were the *s.*? *1 Cor* 12:17
sacrifice to God for sweet *s.* *Eph* 5:2

smite

The word smite *ordinarily meaning simply* strike, *is very often used in the Bible with the meaning of killing, or putting to death,* 1 Sam 17:49; 2 Sam 6:7. To smite with the tongue *is to utter such reproaches as shall hurt as do blows the physical body,* Jer 18:18.

to one company and *s.* it. *Gen* 32:8
lest he will come and *s.* me. 11
I will *s.* upon the waters. *Ex* 7:17
say to Aaron, *S.* the dust. 8:16
suffer the destroyer to *s.* you. 12:23
behold, thou shalt *s.* the rock. 17:6
together, and one *s.* another. 21:18
if a man *s.* his servant and he. 20
if a man *s.* the eye of his servant. 26
if he *s.* out his man servant's or. 27
that we may *s.* them. *Num* 22:6
sceptre out of Israel shall *s.* 24:17
vex the Midianites and *s.* 25:17
s. him with an instrument. 35:16
and if he *s.* him with throwing. 17
with a hand weapon of wood. 18
or in enmity *s.* him with his. 21
thou shalt *s.* Canaanites. *Deut* 7:2
shalt surely *s.* inhabitants. 13:15
if any *s.* his neighbour. 19:11
thou shalt *s.* every male. 20:13
or three thousand *s.* Ai. *Josh* 7:3
help me that we may *s.* Gibeon. 10:4
pursue after, and *s.* the. 19
did Moses and Israel *s.* 12:6; 13:12
thou shalt *s.* the Midianites as one. *Judg* 6:16
then Benjamin began to *s.* 20:31, 39
go and *s.* the inhabitants of. 21:10
go and *s.* Amalek, and. *1 Sam* 15:3
I will *s.* thee, and take. 17:46
Saul said, I will *s.* David. 18:11
Saul sought to *s.* David to. 19:10
javelin at him to *s.* him. 20:33
shall I go and *s.* the Philistines? Go, *s.* Philistines. 23:2
let me *s.* him to the earth at once, I pray thee, and I will not *s.* the. 26:8
why should I *s.* thee? *2 Sam* 2:22
I say, *S.* Amnon, then kill. 13:28
lest he *s.* city with the edge. 15:14
people shall flee, and I will *s.* 17:2
Joab said, Why didst thou not *s.* him there? 18:11
s. me, I pray thee, and the men refused to *s.* him. *1 Ki* 20:35, 37
s. every fenced city. *2 Ki* 3:19
I *s.* them? shall I *s.* them? 6:21
s. them, wouldest thou *s.* those? 22
shalt *s.* the house of Ahab 9:7
Jehu, said, *S.* him also in. 27
shall *s.* Syrians, till thou. 13:17
he said to the king, *S.* upon. 18
now thou shalt *s.* Syria. 19
sun shall not *s.* thee. *Ps* 121:6
let righteous *s.* me, it shall. 141:5
s. a scorner, the simple. *Pr* 19:25
he shall *s.* thee with a rod. *Isa* 10:24
the heat nor sun *s.* them. 49:10
ye fast to *s.* with the fist of. 58:4
come, let us *s.* him with. *Jer* 18:18
king of Babylon shall *s.* Judah. 21:7
he shall *s.* the land of. 43:11; 46:13
Nebuchadrezzar shall *s.* 49:28
part of hair, and *s.* about it. *Ezek* 5:2
s. with thy hand, and stamp. 6:11
him through the city and *s.* 9:5
son of man, *s.* therefore. 21:12
prophesy, and *s.* thine hands. 14
he said, *S.* the lintel. *Amos* 9:1
shall *s.* judge of Israel. *Mi* 5:1
melteth, the knees *s.* *Nah* 2:10
and shall *s.* the waves. *Zech* 10:11
the men, and they shall *s.* 11:6
whoso shall *s.* thee on. *Mat* 5:39
to *s.* his fellow-servants. 24:49
Lord, shall we *s.* with? *Luke* 22:49
commanded to *s.* Paul. *Acts* 23:2
ye suffer, if a man *s.* *2 Cor* 11:20
witnesses have power to *s.* the earth. *Rev* 11:6

smite, *referred to* God, *expressly or implicitly*

nor will I *s.* any more. *Gen* 8:21
out my hand and *s.* Egypt. *Ex* 3:20
behold, I will *s.* all thy borders. 8:2
that I may *s.* thee and thy. 9:15
I will *s.* all the firstborn in. 12:12
when I *s.* the land of Egypt. 13, 23
I will *s.* them with the. *Num* 14:12
Lord shall *s.* with consumption. *Deut* 28:22
Lord shall *s.* with the botch. 27
s. with madness. 28
Lord shall *s.* thee in the knees. 35
s. through the loins of them. 33:11
The Lord shall *s.* him. *1 Sam* 26:10
for then shall the Lord go out to *s.* *2 Sam* 5:24; *1 Chr* 14:15
Lord shall *s.* Israel as a. *1 Ki* 14:15
Elisha said, *S.* this people with. *2 Ki* 6:18
plague will the Lord *s.* *2 Chr* 21:14
s. with a scab daughters. *Isa* 3:17
he shall *s.* the earth with rod. 11:4
s. Egypt in the seven streams. 15
19:22
I will *s.* the inhabitants of this city. *Jer* 21:6
will also *s.* mine hands. *Ezek* 21:17
I shall *s.* them that dwell in. 32:15
I will *s.* thy bow out of thy. 39:3
will *s.* the winter house. *Amos* 3:15
Lord will *s.* the great house. 6:11
the Lord will *s.* her power. *Zech* 9:4
that day I will *s.* every horse. 12:4
awake, O sword, *s.* the shepherd. 13:7 *Mat* 26:31; *Mark* 14:27

plague wherewith the Lord will s. Zech 14:12, 18
lest I come and s. the. Mal 4:6
that with it he should s. Rev 19:15

smiters

I gave my back to the s. Isa 50:6

smitest

he said, Wherefore s.? Ex 2:13
if I have spoken well, why s. thou me? John 18:23

smiteth

he that s. a man so he die. Ex 21:12
he s. father and mother, surely. 15
to deliver her husband out of the hand of him that s. him. Deut 25:11
cursed be he that s. his. 27:24
he that s. Kirjath-sepher. Josh 15:16; Judg 1:12
that s. the Jebusites. 2 Sam 5:8* 1 Chr 11:6
by understanding he s. Job 26:12
turn not to him that s. Isa 9:13
cheek to him that s. him. Lam 3:30
that I am the Lord that s. Ezek 7:9
that s. thee on one cheek. Luke 6:29

smith

there was no s. found. 1 Sam 13:19
the s. with tongs worketh. Isa 44:12
I have created the s. that. 54:16
Demetrius a silver s. Acts 19:24
Alexander the copper s. 2 Tim 4:14

smiths

away all princes, craftsmen and s. 2 Ki 24:14, 16; Jer 24:1
the s. were departed. Jer 29:2

smiting

Moses spied an Egyptian s. Ex 2:11
when he returned from s. the. 2 Sam 8:13
smote him, so that in s. 1 Ki 20:37
they went forward s. 2 Ki 3:24
make thee sick in s. thee. Mi 6:13

smitten

Lord had s. the river. Ex 7:25
flax and the barley was s. 9:31
wheat and the rye were not s. 32
if a thief be found, and be s. 22:2
go not up, that ye be not s. Num 14:42; Deut 1:42
that thou hast s. me? Num 22:28
wherefore hast thou s. thine ass? 32
their firstborn the Lord had s. 33:4
thine enemies to be s. Deut 28:7
Lord shall cause thee to be s. 25
Judah had s. Jerusalem. Judg 1:8
Benjamin said, They are s. 20:32
saw they were s. 36
surely they are s. down. 39
Israel was s. before. 1 Sam 4:2, 10
why hath Lord s. us to-day? 3
the men that died not, were s. 5:12
because the Lord had s. many. 6:19
the Philistines were s. 7:10
Saul had s. a garrison of. 13:4
Amalekites had s. Ziklag. 30:1
had s. of Abner's men. 2 Sam 2:31
Toi heard that David had s. the. 8:9, 10; 1 Chr 18:9, 10
Syrians saw that they were s. 2 Sam 10:15*, 19*
that he may be s. and die. 11:15
people Israel be s. down. 1 Ki 8:33
after he had s. every male. 11:15
and when he also had s. 2 Ki 2:14
have surely s. one another. 3:23
have s. five or six times, then hadst thou s. Syria till thou. 13:19
indeed s. Edom. 14:10; 2 Chr 25:19
mount Seir were s. 2 Chr 20:22
why shouldest thou be s.? 25:16
because the Lord hath s. him. 26:20
Edomites had come and s. 28:17
they have s. me upon. Job 16:10
save me, for thou hast s. Ps 3:7
him whom thou hast s. 69:26
my heart is s. and withered. 102:4
he hath s. my life down to. 143:3
therefore the Lord hath s. Isa 5:25
gate is s. with destruction. 24:12
hath he s. him, as he smote? 27:7
did esteem him stricken, s. 53:4
in vain have I s. your. Jer 2:30
why hast thou s. us, and? Jer 14:19
though ye had s. whole army. 37:10
I have s. my hand at. Ezek 22:13
me, saying, The city is s. 33:21
year after the city was s. 40:1
he hath s. and he will bind. Hos 6:1
Ephraim is s., their root is. 9:16
I have s. you, yet have. Amos 4:9
commandest me to be s.? Acts 23:3
part of the sun was s. Rev 8:12

smoke

Sodom, and lo, the s. of the country went up as s. of a. Gen 19:28
was altogether on a s. Ex 19:18
the s. of Ai ascended up to heaven. Josh 8:20, 21
should make s. rise. Judg 20:38
when pillar of s. began to rise. 40
a s. out of his nostrils, and fire out. 2 Sam 22:9; Ps 18:8
out of his nostrils goeth s. Job 41:20
shall consume into s. Ps 37:20
s. is driven away, so drive. 68:2
my days are consumed like s. 102:3
become like a bottle in the s. 119:83
as s. to the eyes, so is a. Pr 10:26
out of wilderness like pillars of s. S of S 3:6
her assemblies a s. by day. Isa 4:5
the house was filled with s. 6:4
mount up like the lifting up of s. 9:18
come from the north a s. 14:31
the s. thereof shall go up. 34:10
shall vanish away like s. 51:6
these are a s. in my nose, a. 65:5
they shall be as the s. out. Hos 13:3
and fire and pillars of s. Joel 2:30
burn her chariots in the s. Nah 2:13
blood, fire, and vapour of s. Acts 2:19
s. of the incense ascended. Rev 8:4
there arose a s. out of the. 9:2
there came out of the s. locusts. 3
their mouths issued fire and s. 17
of men killed by the fire and s. 18
s. of their torment ascended. 14:11
temple was filled with s. from. 15:8
lament for her when they see s. 18:9
cried when they saw the s. of. 18
and her s. rose up for ever. 19:3

smoke, *verb*

anger of Lord shall s. Deut 29:20
why doth thine anger s.? Ps 74:1
the hills, and they s. 104:32
mountains, and they shall s. 144:5

smoking

behold a s. furnace. Gen 15:7
saw the mountain s. Ex 20:18
for the two tails of these s. Isa 7:4
the s. flax shall he not quench. 42:3 Mat 12:20

smooth

man, and I am a s. man. Gen 27:11
put the skins of kids on the s. 16
chose him five s. stones. 1 Sam 17:40
speak unto us s. things. Isa 30:10
among s. stones of the stream. 57:6
the rough ways shall be made s. Luke 3:5

smoother

words of his mouth were s. Ps 55:21
her mouth is s. than oil. Pr 5:3

smootheth

he that s. with hammer. Isa 41:7

smote

they s. the men at door. Gen 19:11
s. Midian in field of Moab. 36:35 1 Chr 1:46
he lift up the rod, and s. Ex 7:20
he s. the dust. 8:17
the hail s. every herb. 9:25
who passed over, when he s. 12:27
the Lord s. all the firstborn in. 29 Num 3:13; 8:17; Ps 78:51 105:36; 135:8
Lord s. the people with. Num 11:33
came down and s. them. 14:45
Moses s. the rock. 20:11; Ps 78:20
Balaam s. the ass to turn her. Num 22:23, 25, 27
Balak s. his hands together. 24:10
the country the Lord s. is a. 32:4
Amalek s. the hindmost. Deut 25:18
Og came against us, and we s. 29:7
the men of Ai s. of them. Josh 7:5
s. them not, because princes. 9:18
they s. all the souls that. 11:11
and s. all the kings with. 12, 17
because he s. his neighbour. 20:5
Jael s. the nail into. Judg 4:21
hammer she s. Sisera, she s. 5:26
came into a tent, and s. it. 7:13
Samson s. them hip and thigh. 15:8
Lord s. Benjamin before. 20:35
these are the gods that s. 1 Sam 4:8
it is not his hand that s. us. 6:9
s. the men of Beth-shemesh, s. 19
David s. the Philistine in. 17:49
Saul s. the javelin into the. 19:10
that the Lord s. Nabal. 25:38
David s. them from twilight. 30:17
deliver him that s. his. 2 Sam 14:7
Zedekiah s. Micaiah. 1 Ki 22:24 2 Chr 18:23
Elijah s. the waters. 2 Ki 2:8
Elisha s. the waters. 14
and he s. them with blindness. 6:18
the Lord s. the king, so that he. 15:5
to Menahem, therefore he s. it. 16
angel of the Lord s. 185,000. 19:35 Isa 37:36
God s. Jeroboam. 2 Chr 13:15
the Lord s. the Ethiopians. 14:12
and cursed them, and s. Neh 13:25
and s. down the chosen. Ps 78:31
he s. his enemies in the. 66
found me, they s. me. S of S 5:7
stay on him that s. them. Isa 10:20
he who s. the people is. 14:6
because the rod of him that s. 29
be beaten down which s. 30:31
him that s. the anvil. 41:7
in my wrath I s. thee, but. 60:10
then Pashur s. Jeremiah. Jer 20:2
after I was instructed, I s. 31:19
then arose Ishmael and s. 41:2
which Nebuchadrezzar s. 46:2
a stone cut out, which s. the. Dan 2:34, 35
Belshazzar's knees s. one. 5:6
moved with choler s. the ram. 8:7
a worm s. the gourd. Jonah 4:7
I s. you with blasting. Hag 2:17
Peter drew his sword, s. Mat 26:51
prophesy, who is he that s. thee. 68 Luke 22:64
but the publican s. upon. Luke 18:13
many beholding Jesus, s. 23:48
angel s. Peter on the side. Acts 12:7

smote *him*

he that s. him be quit. Ex 21:19
he that s. him shall. Num 35:21
David's heart s. him. 1 Sam 24:5
s. him under the fifth rib. 2 Sam 2:23; 3:27; 4:6
s. him there for his error. 6:7 1 Chr 13:10
man s. him, so that he. 1 Ki 20:37
his sons s. him with sword. 2 Ki 19:37; Isa 37:38
Syria s. him, king of Israel s. him. 2 Chr 28:5
hath he smitten him as he smote those that s. him? Isa 27:7
of his covetousness I s. him. 57:17
princes were wroth with Jeremiah, and s. him. Jer 37:15
others s. him with palms. Mat 26:67
they took the reed and s. him. 27:30 Mark 15:19; Luke 22:63 John 19:3
angel of the Lord s. him. Acts 12:23

smotest

rod wherewith thou s. Ex 17:5

Smyrna

send to the church in S. Rev 1:11
the church in S. write. 2:8

snail

lizard, the s. and mole. Lev 11:30*
as a s. let every one of. Ps 58:8

snare

this man be a s. unto us? Ex 10:7
gods, it will surely be a s. unto thee. 23:33; Deut 7:16; Judg 2:3
the inhabitants of the land, lest it be a s. in the midst of thee. Ex 34:12
thing became a s. unto. Judg 8:27

her, that she may be a s. 1 Sam 18:21
wherefore then layest thou a s.? 28:9
a net, he walketh on a s. Job 18:8*
s. is laid for him in the ground. 10*
table become a s. unto them, and. Ps 69:22; Rom 11:9
shall deliver thee from s. Ps 91:3
their idols: which were a s. 106:36
wicked have laid s. for me. 119:110
escaped as a bird out of the s. of the fowlers; the s. is broken. 124:7
proud have hid a s. for me. 140:5
keep me from the s. which. 141:9
have they privily laid s. for. 142:3
as a bird hasteth to the s. Pr 7:23
a fool's lips are the s. of his. 18:7
s. to man who devoureth. 20:25
lest learn his ways, and get a s. 22:25
of an evil man is a s. 29:6
bring a city into s. but wise. 8*
the fear of man bringeth a s. 25
birds that are caught in s. Eccl 9:12
for a s. to the inhabitants. Isa 8:14
fear, and the pit, and the s. are upon. 24:17, 18; Jer 48:43, 44
that lay a s. for him. Eccl 29:21
I have laid a s. for thee. Jer 50:24
s. is come upon us. Lam 3:47*
he shall be taken in my s. Ezek 12:13; 17:20
because ye have been a s. Hos 5:1
prophet is a s. of a fowler. 9:8
a s. upon the earth where no gin is for him? . . . up a s.? Amos 3:5
for as a s. shall it come. Luke 21:35*
not that I may cast a s. 1 Cor 7:35
lest he fall into the s. 1 Tim 3:7
will be rich, fall into a s. 6:9
may recover out of the s. 2 Tim 2:26

snared

silver, lest thou be s. Deut 7:25
take heed that thou be not s. 12:30
wicked is s. in the work of. Ps 9:16
art s. with the words of thy mouth. Pr 6:2; 12:13
so are the sons of men s. Eccl 9:12
stumble and fall and be s. Isa 8:15
might fall, and be s. and. 28:13
are all of them s. in holes. 42:22

snares

shall be s. and traps. Josh 23:13
s. of death prevented me. 2 Sam 22:6; Ps 18:5
therefore s. are round. Job 22:10
nose pierceth through s. 40:24
on wicked he shall rain s. Ps 11:6
after my life lay s. for me. 38:12
commune of laying s. privily. 64:5
to depart from the s. of death. Pr 13:14; 14:27
thorns and s. are in the. 22:5
woman whose heart is s. Eccl 7:26
they lay wait as he that setteth s. Jer 5:26*
they have digged and hid s. 18:22

snatch

he shall s. on right hand. Isa 9:20

snorting

s. of his horses was heard. Jer 8:16

snout

jewel of gold in a swine's s. Pr 11:22

snow

hand was leprous as s. Ex 4:6*
leprous, white as s. Num 12:10
slew a lion in the midst of a pit, in the time of s. 2 Sam 23:30
out a leper white as s. 2 Ki 5:27
and wherein the s. is hid. Job 6:16
if I wash myself in s. water. 9:30
heat consumeth s. waters. 24:19
he saith to the s., Be thou on. 37:6
into treasures of the s.? 38:22
I shall be whiter than s. Ps 51:7
it was white as s. in Salmon. 68:14*
he giveth s. like wool. 147:16
fire, hail s. and vapour. 148:8
as the cold of s. in time. Pr 25:13
as s. in summer, so honour. 26:1
she is not afraid of the s. for. 31:21
scarlet shall be white as s. Isa 1:18
as the s. from heaven. 55:10
will a man leave the s.? Jer 18:14
her Nazarites purer than s. Lam 4:7
garment was white as s. Dan 7:9
his raiment white as s. Mat 28:3
Mark 9:3*
his hairs as white as s. Rev 1:14

snowy

lion in a pit in a s. day. 1 Chr 11:22*

snuffed

wild asses s. up the wind. Jer 14:6*
ye have s. at it, saith the. Mal 1:13

snuffdishes

s. shall be of pure gold. Ex 25:38
37:23
cloth, and cover his s. Num 4:9

snuffers

s. of pure gold. Ex 37:23; 1 Ki 7:50
2 Chr 4:22
s. made of money that. 2 Ki 12:13
pots and s. took they away. 25:14
Jer 52:18

snuffeth

a wild ass that s. up the. Jer 2:24

so

so Abraham departed. Gen 12:4
as the stars, so. 15:5; Rom 4:18
Rebekah said, If it be so. Gen 25:22
done foolishly in so doing. 31:28
if it must be so now do this. 43:11
Moses spake so to the. Ex 6:9
let Lord be so with you, as. 10:10
even so shall ye make it. 25:9
as the Lord commanded, so. 39:43
as the sin offering, so is. Lev 7:7
so I am commanded. 8:35; 10:13
as he hath done, so shall. 24:19, 20
bear all that is made, so. Num 4:26
as ye are, so shall stranger. 15:15
so the plague was stayed. 25:8
Ps 106:30
so shall the Lord do to. Deut 7:19
as nations Lord destroyeth, so. 8:20
so thou shalt put the evil away. 17:7
19:19; 21:21; 22:21, 22, 24
as when man riseth, even so. 22:26
and as thy days, so shall. 33:25
as strength then, even so. Josh 14:11
as I have done, so God hath. Judg 1:7
so let all thine enemies perish. 5:31
As thou art, so were they. 8:18
man is, so is his strength. 21
as they did to me, so have I. 15:11
then speakest thou so to me? 1 Sam 9:21
so shall it be done unto his. 11:7
so shall thy mother be childless. 15:33
hast thou deceived me so? 19:17
as his name is, so is he. 25:25
so shall his part be that. 30:24
so shalt thou say to my. 2 Sam 7:8
as thy servant said, so it is. 13:35
so let him curse. Who shall then . . . done so? 16:10; 1 Ki 1:6
so shall I be saved from mine. 2 Sam 22:4; Ps 18:3
so the Lord was entreated for. 2 Sam 24:25
even so will I certainly. 1 Ki 1:30
my lord the king say so too. 36
the king said, So shall thy. 20:40
not king say so. 22:8; 2 Chr 18:7
so it fell out to him. 2 Ki 7:20
so be established, so. 2 Chr 20:20
so kill the passover and. 35:6
so it ceased to the second year of. Ezra 4:24
so I prayed. Neh 2:4
so God shake out. 5:13
not children of Israel done so. 8:17
so didst thou get thee a name. 9:10
and so will I go in unto. Esth 4:16
so it is, hear it. Job 5:27
I know it is so of truth: but? 9:2
and if it were so, why? 21:4
so should I be delivered for. 23:7
in so doing, my Maker. 32:22
so will we sing and. Ps 21:13
let them not say, So would. 35:25
do good, so shalt thou dwell. 37:3
so panteth my soul after thee. 42:1
so shall the King desire thy. 45:11
as we have heard, so have we. 48:8
so is thy praise to the ends. Ps 48:10
thy glory, so as I have seen. 63:2
so foolish was I, and ignorant. 73:22
so he fed them. 78:72
so we thy people. 79:13
so will we not go back from. 80:18
so I gave them up. 81:12
so is thy wrath. 90:11
so the Lord pitieth them. 103:13
so let it come, so let it be. 109:17
so is every one that. 115:8; 135:18
he hath not dealt so with. 147:20
so shalt thou find favour and. Pr 3:4
so shall they be life to thy soul 22
so shall thy poverty. 6:11; 24:34
whirlwind, so is the wicked. 10:25
in his heart, so is he. 23:7
as the one dieth, so dieth. Eccl 3:19
all points as he came, so shall. 5:16
as is the good, so is the sinner. 9:2
so shall it come to pass, so. Isa 14:24
for so Lord said to me, I will. 18:4
as with the people, so with. 24:2
so have we been in thy sight. 26:17
so is Pharaoh king of Egypt to. 36:6
hast laboured, if so be thou shalt be able to profit; if so thou. 47:12
as a lamb, so he openeth not. 53:7
so shall thy sons; so shall God. 62:5
they are my people, so he was. 63:8
so will I comfort you, ye shall. 66:13
saith the Lord so shall your seed. 22
people love to have it so. Jer 5:31
that they may find it so. 10:18
so shall ye be my people, I your God. 11:4; Ezek 37:23
saith Lord, so will I break. Jer 19:11
Come, and let us go, so we. 35:11
obey the Lord, so shall it be. 38:20
so he dwelt among the people. 39:14
so shall be with all men that. 42:17
mouth in dust, if so be. Lam 3:29
as I have done, so shall. Ezek 12:11
saying, As is the mother, so is. 16:44
repent, so iniquity shall not. 18:30
covereth, I have set thee so. 28:14
so thou shalt do, so shall ye. 45:20
if it be so, our God is. Dan 3:17
shalt abide for me; so will. Hos 3:3
so were they filled. 13:6
so shall they run. Joel 2:4
so the Lord of hosts shall. Amos 5:14
so their dwelling should. Zeph 3:7
so my Spirit remaineth. Hag 2:5
so is this people, so is this. 14
to our doings, so hath. Zech 1:6
so will I save you, and ye. 8:13
so shall be plague of horse. 14:15
Suffer it to be so now. Mat 3:15
for so persecuted they. 5:12
let your light so shine. 16
shall teach men so. 19
if God so clothe the grass. 6:30
as thou hast believed, so be. 8:13
it was never so seen in. 9:33
even so, Father: for so it seemed good in thy. 11:26; Luke 10:21
so shall the Son of man be. Mat 12:40
Luke 11:30; 17:24
if case of the man be so. Mat 19:10
when cometh shall find so doing. 24:46; Luke 12:43
are ye so without? Mark 7:18
so shall it not be among you. 10:43
watch, and find them so. Luke 12:38
and so it is. 54
found it so as the women said. 24:24
God so loved the world. John 3:16
Father said to me, so I speak. 12:50
ye say well, for so I am. 13:13
even so I do. 14:31
ye bear much fruit, so shall. 15:8
as the Father hath loved me, so. 9
so have I also sent them into world. 17:18; 20:21
thou the high priest so? 18:22
this Jesus shall so come. Acts 1:11
he hath so fulfilled. 3:18
are these things so? 7:1
as a lamb dumb, so opened he. 8:32
for so hath the Lord. 13:47
they so spake, that a great. 14:1
so were the churches. 16:5
so mightily grew the word of. 19:20

for *so* had he appointed. *Acts* 20:13
so worship I the God. 24:14
so came to pass they escaped. 27:44
not as the offence, *so* also. *Rom* 5:15
so they that are in the flesh. 8:8
so then it is not of him that. 9:16
so all Israel shall be saved. 11:26
so doing shalt heap coals of. 12:20
so every one shall give. 14:12
saved, yet *so* as by fire. *1 Cor* 3:15
let man *so* account of us. 4:1
concerning him that hath *so*. 5:3
is it *so*, that there is not a wise? 6:5
so let him walk, *so* ordain I. 7:17
good for a man *so* to be. 26
but she is happier if she *so* abide. 40
when ye sin *so* against the. 8:12
even *so* hath Lord ordained. 9:14
so run. 24, 26
so let him eat that bread. 11:28
one body, *so* also is Christ. 12:12
so we preach, and *so* ye. 15:11
as he is Christ's, *so*. *2 Cor* 10:7
so will I keep myself from. 11:9
so am I; Israelites? *so* am I. 22
so, I did not burden you. 12:16
then persecuted, even *so* it is now. *Gal* 4:29
bear burdens, and *so* fulfil the. 6:2
new man, *so* making peace. *Eph* 2:15
mark them which walk *so*. *Phil* 3:17
my brethren, *so* stand fast in. 4:1
received Christ Jesus, *so*. *Col* 2:6
even *so* we speak, not. *1 Thes* 2:4
and *so* shall we ever be with. 4:17
so I sware in my wrath. *Heb* 3:11
as I may *so* say, Levi paid. 7:9
so be ye holy. *1 Pet* 1:15
so is the will of God. 2:15
if the will of God be *so*. 3:17
he ought himself *so* to walk. *1 John* 2:6
God *so* loved us, we ought. 4:11
because as he is, *so* are we. 17
even *so*, amen. *Rev* 1:7
even *so*, come, Lord Jesus. 22:20
see **did, do, great, long, much**

so *be it*

said, According to your words, *so be it*. *Josh* 2:21
I answered and said, *So be it*, O. *Jer* 11:5

***not* so**

do *not so* wickedly. *Gen* 19:7
oh *not so*, my Lord. 18
it must *not* be *so* done in. 29:26
not so, my father, this is. 48:18
not so, go ye that are. *Ex* 10:11
servant Moses is *not so*. *Num* 12:7
Lord, but they did *not so*. *Judg* 2:17
is it *not so*? 14:15
it is *not so*. *1 Sam* 20:2
the matter is *not so*. *2 Sam* 20:21
house be *not so* with God. 23:5
but it is *not so* with me. *Job* 9:35
if it be *not so*, who will? 24:25
but now because it is *not so*. 35:15
ungodly are *not so*, but are. *Ps* 1:4
the foolish doeth *not so*. *Pr* 15:7
not so, nor heart think so. *Isa* 10:7
but his lies shall *not* be *so*. 16:6
it shall *not* be *so*; his lies shall *not so* affect it. *Jer* 48:30
beginning it was *not so*. *Mat* 19:8
but it shall *not* be *so* among. 20:26
not so, lest there be not. 25:9
not so, but he shall be. *Luke* 1:60
over them, but shall *not* be *so*. 22:26
if it were *not so*, I would. *John* 14:2
Not so, Lord. *Acts* 10:14; 11:8
not only *so*, but we glory. *Rom* 5:3
not only *so*, but we also joy in. 11
ye have *not so* learned. *Eph* 4:20
things ought *not so* to be. *Jas* 3:10

so *that*

so that all that hear. *Gen* 21:6
so that I come again to my. 28:21
so that land of Egypt and. 47:13
so that he would not let Israel go. *Ex* 10:20; 11:10
smiteth a man, *so that*. 21:12
so that thou shalt be mad for. *Deut* 28:34
so that they could not. *Judg* 2:14
shouted, *so that* the. *1 Sam* 4:5
so that his name was. 18:30
so that thy children take heed. *1 Ki* 8:25; *2 Chr* 6:16
his face, *so that* he died. *2 Ki* 8:15
so that they shall not say. 9:37
so that after him was none. 18:5
so that there should be. *Ezra* 9:14
so that this man was. *Job* 1:3
set me as a mark, *so that* I am. 7:20
so that I am not able. *Ps* 40:12
so that a man shall say. 58:11
he led them safely, *so that*. 78:53
so that it went ill with. 106:32
so that he wanted nothing. *Eccl* 6:2
so that thou didst not lay. *Isa* 47:7
been forsaken, *so that* no. 60:15
so that I will not take. *Jer* 33:26
so that the Lord could no. 44:22
so that in all your doings your sins. *Ezek* 21:24
so that all the trees in Eden. 31:9
so that no beast might. *Dan* 8:4
so that no man did lift. *Zech* 1:21
answered not, *so that*. *Mark* 15:5
so that they which would pass to. *Luke* 16:26
so that they are without. *Rom* 1:20
so that from Jerusalem I. 15:19
so that contrariwise. *2 Cor* 2:7
so that I rejoiced the more. 7:7
so that ye cannot do the. *Gal* 5:17
so that ye were ensamples to all. *1 Thes* 1:7
so that we may boldly say, the Lord is my helper. *Heb* 13:6

was* so, or so *was

and it *was so*. *Gen* 1:7, 9, 11, 15, 24, 30
interpreted to us, so it *was*. 41:13
so it *was* always, cloud. *Num* 9:16
so it *was* when cloud was on. 20
so it *was* when the cloud abode. 21
fleece only, and it *was so*. *Judg* 6:38
it *was so* that all who saw it. 19:30
men of Ashdod saw that it *was so*. *1 Sam* 5:7
it *was so* that when he turned. 10:9
it *was so* from that day. 30:25
it *was so* when any came to the king. *2 Sam* 15:2
it *was so* that when any man. 5
so was all the counsel of. 16:23
so was it charged me. *1 Ki* 13:9
so it *was* that Israel. *2 Ki* 17:7
so was Israel carried away to. 23
so was the commandment of the Lord. *2 Chr* 29:25
and so it *was* that while. *Luke* 2:6
Jesus, who *was so* named of. 21
and *so was* also James and. 5:10
affirmed it *was* even *so*. *Acts* 12:15

So

he sent messengers to *S*. *2 Ki* 17:4

soaked

their land shall be *s*. with. *Isa* 34:7*

sober

whether we be *s*. it is. *2 Cor* 5:13*
but let us watch and be *s*. *1 Thes* 5:6
are of the day be *s*., putting on. 8
a bishop then must be *s*. *1 Tim* 3:2* *Tit* 1:8*
deacons' wives must be *s*. faithful. *1 Tim* 3:11*
that aged men be *s*. grave. *Tit* 2:2*
teach the young women to be *s*. 4
loins of your mind, be *s*. *1 Pet* 1:13
be ye therefore *s*. and watch. 4:7*
be *s*., be vigilant, because your. 5:8

soberly

but to think *s*. according. *Rom* 12:3
that we should live *s*. *Tit* 2:12

sober minded

exhort young men to be *s. minded*. *Tit* 2:6

soberness

the words of truth and *s*. *Acts* 26:25

sobriety

adorn themselves with *s*. *1 Tim* 2:9
in faith and holiness with *s*. 15

socket

talents, a talent for a *s*. *Ex* 38:27

sockets

make forty *s*. of silver... two *s*. under one board for two tenons, two *s*. *Ex* 26:19, 21, 25; 36:24, 26
their *s*. of silver, sixteen *s*. 26:25 36; 30:36
thou shalt cast five *s*. of brass. 26:37 36:38
their twenty *s*. shall be of brass. 27:10; 38:10, 11
pillars ten, their *s*. ten. 27:12; 38:12
one side, their *s*. three. 27:14
side shall be three *s*. 15; 38:14, 15
be four, their *s*. four. 27:16
of silver and their *s*. brass. 17, 18
make bars, pillars, *s*. of. 35:11
court, pillars, and their *s*. 17
s. of the sanctuary, *s*. of the veil, hundred *s*. 38:27
brass of the offerings he made *s*. 30
s. of the court, and the *s*. of. 31
tabernacle and fastened his *s*. 40:18
charge of the sons of Merari shall be the *s*. *Num* 3:26, 37; 4:31, 32
marble set on *s*. of gold. *S of S* 5:15

sod

(*American Revision, everywhere in the Old Testament*, boiled)
Jacob *s*. pottage, Esau. *Gen* 25:29
offerings *s*. they in pots. *2 Chr* 35:13

sodden

(*American Revision, everywhere in the Old Testament*, boiled)
eat not of it raw, nor *s*. *Ex* 12:9
wherein it is *s*. shall be broken, if it be *s*. in a brasen pot. *Lev* 6:28
priest shall take the *s*. *Num* 6:19
he will not have *s*. flesh. *1 Sam* 2:15
the women have *s*. their. *Lam* 4:10

sodering

it is ready for *s*.; he fastened. *Isa* 41:7

Sodom

destroyed *S*. and Gomorrah. *Gen* 13:10
the men of *S*. were wicked. 13
goods of *S*. and Gomorrah. 14:11
they took Lot who dwelt in *S*. 12
king of *S*. went out to meet. 17
because the cry of *S*. is great. 18:20
if I find in *S*. fifty righteous. 26
Lord rained upon *S*. fire out. 19:24
like the overthrow of *S*. *Deut* 29:23 *Isa* 13:19; *Jer* 49:18; 50:40
vine is of the vine of *S*. *Deut* 32:32
we should have been as *S*. *Isa* 1:9
word of the Lord, ye rulers of *S*. 10
declare their sin as *S*. 3:9
of them unto me as *S*. *Jer* 23:14
punishment of sin of *S*. *Lam* 4:6
thy younger sister is *S*. *Ezek* 16:46 48, 49, 55
again the captivity of *S*. 53
as God overthrew *S*. *Amos* 4:11
Moab shall be as *S*. *Zeph* 2:9
tolerable for land of *S*. *Mat* 10:15 11:24; *Mark* 6:11; *Luke* 10:12
Lot went out of *S*. *Luke* 17:29
seed, we had been as *S*. *Rom* 9:29
turning cities of *S*. and. *2 Pet* 2:6
even as *S*. and Gomorrah. *Jude* 7
city spiritually called *S*. *Rev* 11:8

sodomite

there shall be no *s*. of. *Deut* 23:17

sodomites

there were also *s*. in. *1 Ki* 14:24
Asa took away the *s*. 15:12
Jehoshaphat took the remnant of the *s*. 22:46
down the houses of the *s*. *2 Ki* 23:7

soft

God maketh my heart *s*. *Job* 23:16*
speak *s*. words unto thee? 41:3
makest it *s*. with showers. *Ps* 65:10
a *s*. answer turneth. *Pr* 15:1
and a *s*. tongue breaketh. 25:15
s. raiment; they that wear *s*. clothing. *Mat* 11:8; *Luke* 7:25

softer

words were *s*. than oil. *Ps* 55:21

softly

I will lead on s., as the children be able to endure. Gen 33:14
Jael went s. to him and. Judg 4:21
came s. and uncovered. Ruth 3:7
lay in sackcloth, went s. 1 Ki 21:27
waters of Shiloah that go s. Isa 8:6
I shall go s. all my years in. 38:15
when south wind blew s. Acts 27:13

soil

it was planted in a good s. Ezek 17:8

sojourn

down into Egypt to s. Gen 12:10
This one fellow came in to s. 19:9
s. in this land, and I will be. 26:3
they said, For to s. in the land. 47:4
will s. with thee and keep. Ex 12:48
Lev 19:33; Num 9:14; 15:14
which s. that offereth sacrifice. Lev 17:8
of strangers that s. that eateth. 10
s. among you, that hunteth. 13
of strangers that s., that giveth. 20:2
of strangers that s., of them. 25:45
a Levite went to s. Judg 17:8
said to Micah, I go to s. where. 9
Elimelech went to s. Ruth 1:1
widow with whom I s. 1 Ki 17:20
s. wheresoever thou canst s. 2 Ki 8:1
woe is me, that I s. in Meshech. Ps 120:5
carry her afar off to s. Isa 23:7
went down into Egypt to s. 52:4
faces to enter into Egypt and go to s. Jer 42:15, 17; 44:12, 14, 28
place whither ye desire to s. 42:22
shall no more s. there. Lam 4:15
them from where they s. Ezek 20:38
and strangers who s. among. 47:22
that his seed should s. Acts 7:6

sojourned

from thence Abraham s. Gen 20:1
and s. in the Philistines' land. 21:34
I s. with Laban, and stayed. 32:4
Abraham and Isaac s. 35:27
come from where he s. Deut 18:6
s. in Egypt with a few, and. 26:5
s. in Bethlehem-judah. Judg 17:7
an old man of Ephraim s. in. 19:16
she s. in the land of the. 2 Ki 8:2
Jacob s. in the land. Ps 105:23
by faith he s. in the land. Heb 11:9

sojourner

I am a s. with you, give. Gen 23:4
a s. of the priest shall not. Lev 22:10
relieve him: though he be a s. 25:35
shall be as a s. with thee. 40
s. wax rich by thee and brother sell himself to s. 47
six cities a refuge for Israel and s. Num 35:15
I am a stranger, a s., as. Ps 39:12

sojourners

strangers and s. with me. Lev 25:23
the Beerothites were s. 2 Sam 4:3
we are s. as were all. 1 Chr 29:15

sojourneth

borrow of her that s. Ex 3:22
be to him that is homeborn, and to stranger that s. 12:49; Lev 16:29
stranger that s. eat blood. Lev 17:12
that s. among you shall keep. 18:26
meat for stranger that s. 25:6
be for you and for the stranger that s. Num 15:15; 16:29; 19:10
forgiven the stranger that s. 15:26
refuge for stranger that s. Josh 20:9
in any place where he s. Ezra 1:4
every one that s. in Israel. Ezek 14:7
in whatever tribe stranger s. 47:23

sojourning

the s. of Israel in Egypt. Ex 12:40
a certain Levite s. on. Judg 19:1
pass the time of your s. 1 Pet 1:17

solace

come, let us s. ourselves. Pr 7:18

sold

Esau s. his birthright. Gen 25:33
father hath s. us, devoured. 31:15
s. Joseph to the Ishmaelites. 37:28
the Midianites s. him into. 36
Joseph s. corn unto the. Gen 41:56
was that s. to all the people. 42:6
Joseph your brother whom ye s. 45:4
angry with yourselves that ye s. 5
the Egyptians s. every man. 47:20
the priests s. not their lands. 22
nothing then shall be s. Ex 22:3
the land shall not be s. Lev 25:23
redeem that which his brother s. 25
house that was s. shall go out. 33
of the suburbs may not be s. 34
shall not be s. as bondmen. 42
no devoted thing shall be s. 27:28
and if thy brother be s. Deut 15:12
there shall ye be s. unto your. 28:68
except their Rock had s. them. 32:30
he s. them into the hands. Judg 2:14
s. them to Cushan-rishathaim. 3:8
s. to Jabin. 4:2
s. them into the hands of the. 10:7
s. them into the hand of Sisera. 1 Sam 12:9
thou hast s. thyself to. 1 Ki 21:20
ass's head was s. for 80. 2 Ki 6:25
fine flour s. for a shekel. 7:1, 16
Israel s. themselves to do. 17:17
our brethren who were s. to the . . . they be s. unto us ? Neh 5:8
in day wherein they s. victuals. 13:15
who brought ware and s. on. 16
are s. I and my people to be slain and perish; but . . . been s. Esth 7:4
Joseph who was s. for. Ps 105:17
creditors is it to whom I s. you ? for your iniquities have ye s. Isa 50:1
ye have s. yourselves for. 52:3
brother who hath been s. Jer 34:14
our wood is s. unto us. Lam 5:4
return to that which is s. Ezek 7:13
and they have s. a girl. Joel 3:3
children of Judah have ye s. 6
out of place whither ye s. them. 7
s. the righteous for silver. Amos 2:6
are not two sparrows s.? Mat 10:29
went and s. all that he had. 13:46
commanded him to be s. 18:25
s. and bought, overthrew . . . that s. 21:12; Mark 11:15; Luke 19:45
might have been s. for much and. Mat 26:9; Mark 14:5; John 12:5
are not five sparrows s.? Luke 12:6
bought, they s. they planted. 17:28
the temple those that s. John 2:14
said to them that s. doves, Take. 16
and s. their possessions and goods. Acts 2:45; 4:34
Joses having land s. it and. 4:37
Ananias s. a possession. 5:1
after it was s. was it not in thine ? 4
ye s. the land for so much ? 8
I am carnal, s. under sin. Rom 7:14
is s. in shambles, that. 1 Cor 10:25
one morsel of meat s. Heb 12:16

soldier

parts, to every s. a part. John 19:23
Cornelius called a devout s. that waited on. Acts 10:7
to dwell by himself, with a s. 28:16
hardness as a good s. 2 Tim 2:3
who hath chosen him to be a s. 4

soldiers

the s. fell upon the. 2 Chr 25:13*
to require of the king s. Ezra 8:22
the armed s. of Moab. Isa 15:4*
having s. under me. Mat 8:9
Luke 7:8
s. took Jesus, and gathered unto him the whole band of s. Mat 27:27
gave large money unto the s. 28:12
s. demanded, saying. Luke 3:14
the s. mocked him, offered. 23:36
s. platted a crown of. John 19:2
the s. took his garments, and. 23
these things the s. did. 24
s. brake the legs. 32
but one of the s. with a spear. 34
Peter to four quaternions of s. Acts 12:4
Peter was sleeping between two s. 6
no small stir among the s. 18
saw the chief captain and s. 21:32
that he was borne of the s. 35
make ready 200 s. to go to. 23:23
Paul said to the s. Except. Acts 27:31
then the s. cut off the ropes. 32
the s.' counsel was to kill. 42

sole

but the dove found no rest for the s. of her foot. Gen 8:9
a sore botch from the s. Deut 28:35
would not set the s. of her foot. 56
neither shall the s. of thy foot. 65
every place s. of your foot. Josh 1:3
from the s. of his foot to the crown of his head was no. 2 Sam 14:25
Satan smote Job from s. Job 2:7
from s. of foot to head. Isa 1:6
s. of their feet like the s. Ezek 1:7
see **feet**

solemn

in your s. days ye. Num 10:10*
sing praise with a s. sound. Ps 92:3
it is iniquity, even the s. Isa 1:13
called as in a s. day. Lam 2:22
what will ye do in s. day? Hos 9:5
see **assembly, feast, feasts**

solemnities

Zion, the city of our s. Isa 33:20
offerings in s. of Israel. Ezek 45:17*
in the s. meat offering shall. 46:11

solemnity

in the s. of the year of. Deut 31:10*
shall have song as when a holy s. is. Isa 30:29*

solemnly

the man did s. protest. Gen 43:3
yet protest s. to them. 1 Sam 8:9

solitarily

people which dwell s. in. Mi 7:14

solitary

that night be s., let no. Job 3:7*
and famine they were s. 30:3*
setteth the s. in families. Ps 68:6
in the wilderness in a s. 107:4*
wilderness and s. place. Isa 35:1
how doth city sit s. that. Lam 1:1
Jesus departed into a s. Mark 1:35*

Solomon

born to David in Jerusalem, S. 2 Sam 5:14; 1 Chr 3:5; 14:4
he called his name S. 2 Sam 12:24
S. his brother he called not. 1 Ki 1:10, 19, 26
S. thy son shall reign after. 13, 17, 30
I and my son S. shall be. 1:21
God save king S. 34, 39
David even so be he with S. 37
hath made S. king. 43
God make the name of S. 47
let S. swear to me that he will. 51
David charged S. his son. 2:1
king S. sware. 23
established in the hand of S. 46
S. made affinity with Pharaoh. 3:1
S. loved the Lord. 3
the Lord appeared to S. 5; 9:2
2 Chr 1:7; 7:12
S. had asked this thing. 1 Ki 3:10
S.'s provision for one day. 4:22
God gave S. wisdom. 29; 5:12
came to hear the wisdom of S. 4:34
Mat 12:42; Luke 11:31
Tyre sent his servants to S. 1 Ki 5:1
king S. raised a levy out of. 13
so S. built the house and. 6:14
2 Chr 7:11; Acts 7:47
the work that S. made. 1 Ki 7:51
S. assembled the elders of Israel. 8:1; 2 Chr 5:2
S. spread forth his hands. 1 Ki 8:22
when S. made an end of praying. 54; 2 Chr 7:1
S. held a feast. 1 Ki 8:65
S. made a navy of ships. 9:26
when the queen of Sheba heard of the fame of S. 10:1; 2 Chr 9:1
all the earth sought to S. 1 Ki 10:24
2 Chr 9:23
but king S. loved many. 1 Ki 11:1
S. clave to these in love. 2
when S. was old. 4
S. went after Ashtoreth and. 5
S. did evil. 6
S. built for Chemosh and Molech. 7

the Lord was angry with *S.* *1 Ki* 11:9
Edomite, an adversary to *S.* 14
S. built Millo. 27
S. made Jeroboam ruler over. 28
S. sought therefore to kill. 40
S. slept with his fathers. 43
fled from the presence of *S.* 12:2
shields of gold which *S.* made. 14:26; *2 Chr* 12:9
of which the Lord said to David and to *S.* *2 Ki* 21:7; *2 Chr* 33:7
S. my son is young. *1 Chr* 22:5
for his name shall be *S.* 9
to help *S.* 17
S. thy son, he shall build. 28:6
thou *S.* my son, know the God. 9
David gave to *S.* the pattern. 11
S. my son, whom God alone. 29:1
give to *S.* my son a perfect. 19
S. sat on the throne of the. 23
Lord magnified *S.* exceedingly. 25
S. numbered all the. *2 Chr* 2:17
are the things wherein *S.* 3:3
since time of *S.* not such joy. 30:26
children of *S.'s* servants. *Ezra* 2:55
58; *Neh* 7:57, 60; 11:3
the commandment of *S.* *Neh* 12:45
did not king *S.* sin by? 13:26
proverbs of *S.* *Pr* 1:1; 10:1; 25:1
of songs which is *S.'s.* *S of S* 1:1
but comely, as the curtains of *S.* 5
behold, his bed which is *S.'s.* 3:7
behold king *S.* 11
S. had a vineyard at. 8:11
S. must have a thousand. 12
the sea *S.* made was. *Jer* 52:20
David begat *S.* *Mat* 1:6
S. begat Roboam. 7
S. in all his glory. 6:29; *Luke* 12:27
a greater than *S.* is here. *Mat* 12:42; *Luke* 11:31
Jesus walked in *S.'s.* *John* 10:23
people ran to them to *S.'s.* *Acts* 3:11
with one accord in *S.'s* porch. 5:12

some

Lot said, lest *s.* evil. *Gen* 19:19
let me now leave with thee *s.* 33:15
cast him into *s.* pit, and we will say, *S.* evil beast hath. 37:20
took *s.* of his brethren and. 47:2
gathered *s.* more, *s.* less. *Ex* 16:17
but *s.* of them left of it till. 20
s. went out on seventh day. 27
shall put *s.* of the blood. *Lev* 4:7, 18
the priest shall dip his finger in *s.* 17
Arad took *s.* of them. *Num* 21:1
thou shalt put *s.* of thine. 27:20
because he hath found *s.* *Deut* 24:1
let fall *s.* of the handfuls. *Ruth* 2:16
s. bade me kill thee. *1 Sam* 24:10
hid in *s.* pit, or in *s.* *2 Sam* 17:9
in him there is found *s.* *1 Ki* 14:13
s. mischief will come. *2 Ki* 7:9
but I will grant *s.* deliverance. *2 Chr* 12:7
Asa oppressed *s.* of the people. 16:10
s. had wives by whom. *Ezra* 10:44
s. said, We have mortgaged our. *Neh* 5:3
saw I *s.* treading winepresses. 13:15
and *s.* of my servants set. 19
s. remove landmarks. *Job* 24:2
s. trust in chariots, *s.* *Ps* 20:7
I looked for *s.* to take pity. 69:20
unless they cause *s.* to fall. *Pr* 4:16
not leave *s.* gleaning? *Jer* 49:9
and it cast down *s.* of the. *Dan* 8:10
s. of them of understanding. 11:35
s. to everlasting life, and *s.* to. 12:2
overthrown *s.*, as God. *Amos* 4:11
they not leave *s.* grapes? *Ob* 5
s. fell by the way side. *Mat* 13:4
Mark 4:4; *Luke* 8:5
s. fell on stony places, where they had not much. *Mat* 13:5; *Mark* 4:5
and *s.* fell among thorns. *Mat* 13:7
Mark 4:7; *Luke* 8:7
S. say thou art John the Baptist, *s.* *Mat* 16:14; *Mark* 8:28; *Luke* 9:19
be *s.* standing here, which shall not. *Mat* 16:28; *Mark* 9:1; *Luke* 9:27
s. eunuchs which were so born, *s.* made. *Mat* 19:12
s. ye shall kill and crucify, *s.* *Mat* 23:34
they worshipped him, but *s.* 28:17
s. fell upon a rock, and. *Luke* 8:6
and *s.* of you shall cause to. 21:16
there are *s.* of you that. *John* 6:64
Peter overshadow *s.* of. *Acts* 5:15
giving out that himself was *s.* 8:9
how can I except *s.* man should? 31
seeking *s.* to lead him by. 13:11
s. of them believed. 17:4
hear *s.* new thing. 21
s. mocked. 32
s. cried one thing, *s.* 19:32; 21:34
I pray you take *s.* meat. 27:34
s. on boards, *s.* on broken. 44
s. believed and *s.* believed not. 28:24
that I may impart to you *s.* *Rom* 1:11
that I might have *s.* fruit. 13
for what if *s.* did not believe? 3:3
as *s.* affirm that we say, Let us. 8
for a good man *s.* would even. 5:7
any means I might save *s.* of. 11:14
and if *s.* of the branches be. 17
now *s.* are puffed up. *1 Cor* 4:18
such were *s.* of you, but ye. 6:11
for *s.* with conscience of the. 8:7
might by all means save *s.* 9:22
neither be idolaters as were *s.* 10:7
commit fornication, as *s.* of them. 8
as *s.* tempted Christ and were. 9
nor murmur ye as *s.* of them. 10
and God hath set *s.* in the. 12:28
greater part remain, but *s.* 15:6
how say *s.* that there is no? 12
for *s.* have not the knowledge. 34
I think to be bold against *s.* which think of us as if. *2 Cor* 10:2
not compare ourselves with *s.* 12
be *s.* that trouble you. *Gal* 1:7
s. prophets, *s.* evangelists. *Eph* 4:11
s. indeed preach Christ. *Phil* 1:15
there are *s.* among you. *2 Thes* 3:11
charge *s.* that they teach. *1 Tim* 1:3
from which *s.* having swerved. 6
s. having put away, have made. 19
in latter times *s.* shall depart. 4:1
s. are already turned aside. 5:15
s. men's sins open beforehand, *s.* 24
the good works of *s.* are. 25
which while *s.* coveted after. 6:10
overthrow the faith of *s.* *2 Tim* 2:18
s. vessels to honour and *s.* 20
house is builded by *s.* man. *Heb* 3:4
for *s.* when they heard, did. 16
it remaineth, that *s.* must. 4:6
as the manner of *s.* is. 10:25
having provided *s.* better. 11:40
thereby *s.* entertained angels. 13:2
Lord is not slack, as *s.* *2 Pet* 3:9
in which are *s.* things hard to be. 16
of *s.* have compassion. *Jude* 22
devil shall cast *s.* of you. *Rev* 2:10

somebody

Jesus said, *S.* hath touched me. *Luke* 8:46*
boasting himself to be *s.* *Acts* 5:36

something

for he thought, *s.* hath. *1 Sam* 20:26
that *s.* should be given. *Mark* 5:43
and seeking to catch *s.* *Luke* 11:54
should give *s.* to poor. *John* 13:29
to receive *s.* of them. *Acts* 3:5
as though ye would enquire *s.* 23:15*
man who hath *s.* to say to thee. 18
a man think himself to be *s.* *Gal* 6:3

sometime, -s

ye who were *s.* afar off. *Eph* 2:13*
for ye were *s.* darkness, but. 5:8*
you that were *s.* alienated. *Col* 1:21*
in which ye walked *s.* when. 3:7
also were *s.* foolish. *Tit* 3:3*
who *s.* were disobedient . . . in days of Noah. *1 Pet* 3:20*

somewhat

have done *s.* against commandments. *Lev* 4:13*, 27*
ruler hath done *s.* through. 22*
if the plague be *s.* dark. 13:6, 21
26, 28, 56
bright spot, and *s.* reddish. 19, 24
he said, I have *s.* to say. *1 Ki* 2:14
him, and take *s.* of him. *2 Ki* 5:2
ease *s.* grievous servitude of. *2 Chr* 10:4*
ease *s.* the yoke. 9*
make it *s.* lighter for us. 1
Simon, I have *s.* to say. *Luke* 7:4
as to enquire *s.* of him. *Acts* 23:2
that I might have *s.* to write. 25:2
if first I be *s.* filled with. *Rom* 15:24*
that you may have *s.* to. *2 Cor* 5:1
though I should boast *s.* more. 10:
those who seemed to be *s.* *Gal* 2:
necessity this man have *s.* *Heb* 8:
nevertheless, I have *s.* *Rev* 2:4

son

This word is used as now, and als for a grandson, 2 Sam 9:6, *and eve for more remote descendants,* Isa 19:11. *The word is also used for pupil, much as one uses it now, as term of affection,* 1 Tim 1:2. *I is also used in such expressions a* son of Belial, 1 Sam 25:17

I will give thee *s.* of Sarah. *Gen* 17:16, 19; 18:10, 1
Sarah bare Abraham a *s.* 21:2,
cast this bondwoman and her *s.* 1
my master's wife bare a *s.* 24:3
appointed for my master's *s.* 4
let her be thy master's *s.'s* wife. 5
therefore given me this *s.* 29:3
heard me, and given me a *s.* 30:
shall add to me another *s.* 2
shalt have this *s.* also. 35:1
because he was the *s.* of his. 37:
if it be a *s.* then ye. *Ex* 1:1
every *s.* that is born ye shall. 2
grew, and he became her *s.* 2:1
cut off the foreskin of her *s.* 4:2
have gored a *s.* or a daughter. 21:3
the *s.* of thy handmaid may. 23:1
that *s.* that is priest in stead. 29:3
her purifying for a *s.* *Lev* 12:
the *s.* of an Israelitish. 24:1
the Israelitish woman's *s.* 1
his uncle, or his uncle's *s.* may. 25:4
me, thou *s.* of Zippor. *Num* 23:1
because he hath no *s.* 27:
if a man die and have no *s.*
if *s.* of thy mother entice. *Deut* 13:
the *s.* of the beloved, firstborn, before the *s.* of the hated. 21:16, 1
a stubborn and rebellious *s.* 1
this our *s.* is stubborn and. 2
eye shall be evil towards her *s.* 28:5
in his youngest *s.* set up. *Josh* 6:2
border went by the valley of *s.* 15:
arise, Barak, lead captivity captive thou *s.* of. *Judg* 5:1
have made thee the *s.* of his. 9:1
Is not he the *s.* of Jerubbaal? 2
the *s.* of a strange woman. 11:
besides her he had neither *s.* 3
conceive and bear a *s.* 13:3, 5,
the woman bare a *s.* and called. 2
Ruth bare a *s.* *Ruth* 4:1
a *s.* born to Naomi. 1
Hannah gave her *s.* suck until. *1 Sam* 1:2
Fear not, for thou hast born a *s.* 4:2
Kish had a *s.* whose name was. 9:
that is come to *s.* of Kish? 10:1
I have seen a *s.* of Jesse. 16:1
whose *s.* is this? 17:5
whose *s.* art thou? 5
cometh not the *s.* of Jesse? 20:2
s. of the perverse rebellious. 3
as long as the *s.* of Jesse liveth. 3
will *s.* of Jesse give you fields. 22:
Doeg said, I saw the *s.* of Jesse.
Hear now, thou *s.* of Ahitub. 1
who is the *s.* of Jesse? 25:1
he is such a *s.* of Belial. 1
am the *s.* of a stranger. *2 Sam* 1:1
Jonathan hath yet a *s.* lame. 9:
given thy master's *s.* all that.
master's *s.* may have food to eat Mephibosheth thy master's *s.* 1
I will shew kindness to the *s.* 10:
where is thy master's *s.*? 16:
my hand against the king's *s.* 18:1
I have no *s.* to keep my name in. 1
tidings, because king's *s.* is dead. 2

ıheritance in the s. of Jesse.
2 Sam 20:1
ıou hast given him a s. 1 Ki 3:6
owels yearned upon her s. 26
avid a wise s. over this. 5:7
iram was a widow's s. of. 7:14
either inheritance in the s. of Jesse.
12:16; 2 Chr 10:16
.bijah the s. of Jeroboam. 1 Ki 14:1
) ask a thing of thee for her s. 5
ıe s. of the mistress of the. 17:17
n the widow, by slaying her s. 20
arry him back to Joash the king's s.
22:26; 2 Chr 18:25
eigned, because he had no s.
2 Ki 1:17
he said unto her s., Bring me. 4:6
eason thou shalt embrace a s. 16
nd the woman bare a s. at. 17
id I desire a s. of my lord ? 28
ok up her s. 37
ıy s. that we may eat him: and she
hath hid her s. 6:29
ee ye how this s. of a murderer. 32
ıe woman, whose s. he had. 8:1
er s. whom Elisha restored to. 5
thaliah saw her s. was dead. 11:1
2 Chr 22:10
ıewed them the king's s. 2 Ki 11:4
e brought forth the king's s. and. 12
de, thou s. of Jesse. 1 Chr 12:18
lso was the s. of the giant. 20:6
ehold, a s. shall be born to. 22:9
ıere was never a s. left him.
2 Chr 21:17
uried him, because he is s. of. 22:9
e said, Behold, the king's s. 23:3
abdiel their overseer, s. Neh 11:14
e shall neither have s. Job 18:19
iss the S. lest he be angry. Ps 2:12
ine own mother's s. 50:20
ghteousness unto the king's s. 72:1
e s. of thine handmaid. 86:16
or shall the s. of wickedness. 89:22
am the s. of thine. 116:16
a father the s. in whom he. Pr 3:12
was my father's s., only. 4:3
wise s. maketh a glad father. 10:1
15:20
wise s.: he that sleepeth in harvest
is a s. causeth. 10:5; 17:2; 19:26
wise s. heareth his father's. 13:1
olish s. is a grief to his. 17:25
foolish s. is the calamity. 19:13
eepeth the law, is a wise s. 28:7
hat, the s. of my womb, s. of ? 31:2
e begetteth a s., nothing. Eccl 5:14
essed land, when king is s. 10:17
ot afraid of anger of the s. Isa 7:4
t us set a king in it, even the s. 6
amaria is Remaliah's s. 9
rgin shall conceive and bear a s. 14
a child is born, unto us a s. 9:6
llen, O Lucifer, s. of. 14:12
will cut off from Babylon s. 22
am s. of the wise, the s. of. 19:11
ot have compassion on the s. 49:15
e s. of the stranger speak. 56:3
ıourning, as for an only s. Jer 6:26
ıould not have a s. to reign. 33:21
eliver neither s. nor daughter.
Ezek 14:20
so the soul of the s. is mine. 18:4
he beget s. that is a robber. 10
s. that seeth his father's sins. 14
hy, doth not s. bear iniquity of the
father ? when the s. hath done. 19
shall not bear the iniquity of the
father, nor the father of the s. 20
or s. or daughter they may. 44:25
hich bare him a s. Hos 1:3, 8
e is an unwise s. for he. 13:13
or was I a prophet's s. Amos 7:14
s mourning of an only s. 8:10
or the s. dishonoureth. Mi 7:6
s. honoureth his father. Mal 1:6
he shall bring forth a s. Mat 1:21
Luke 1:31
esus said, S. be of good cheer.
Mat 9:2; Mark 2:5
e that loveth s. or. Mat 10:37
ıe S., but the Father; nor any the
Father, save the S., and he to whom
the S. 11:27; Luke 10:22

the carpenter's s. Mat 13:55
Mark 6:3; Luke 4:22
Christ the s. of the living. Mat 16:16
S. go work to-day in my. 21:28
but when husbandmen saw the s. 38
of Christ ? whose s. is he ? 22:42
having yet one s. his. Mark 12:6
and the father betray the s. 13:12
knoweth not the s., but Father. 32
art thou the Christ, the s. of ? 14:61
Elisabeth shall bear thee a s.
Luke 1:13
be called the S. of the Highest. 32
Elisabeth conceived a s. 36
she brought forth a s. 57
mother said, S. why hast thou ? 2:48
30 years, being, as was supposed,
the s. of Joseph, who was s. 3:23
dead man carried out, only s. 7:12
if s. of peace be there, your. 10:6
if a s. shall ask bread of any. 11:11
shall be divided against the s. 12:53
the younger s. gathered all. 15:13
s. thou art ever with me, and all. 31
s. remember, that thou in. 16:25
forasmuch as he also is the s. 19:9
only begotten s. which is in the bosom
of. John 1:18
Jesus of Nazareth, s. of Joseph. 45
the Father loveth the s., and hath
given all things. 3:35; 5:20
on the s.: he that believeth not s. 3:36
nobleman whose s. was sick. 4:46
s. can do nothing of himself, what
things Father . . . the s. 5:19
even so the s. quickeneth whom. 21
committed all judgement to the s. 22
honour the s. He that honoureth not
the s. honoureth not the Father. 23
so hath he given to the s. to have. 26
every one who seeth s. and. 6:40
said, Is not this Jesus the s.? 42
but the S. abideth ever. 8:35
if s. therefore shall make you free. 36
is this your s.? 9:19
We know that this is our s. 20
Father may be glorified in s. 14:13
none of them is lost, but the s. 17:12
Simon, s. of Jonas, lovest ? 21:15
Barnabas, the s. of consolation, a
Levite. Acts 4:36
and nourished for her own s. 7:21
David the s. of Jesse, a man. 13:22
Pharisee, the s. of a Pharisee. 23:6
Paul's sister's s. heard of their. 16
Sarah shall have a s. Rom 9:9
shall s. also himself. 1 Cor 15:28
but s. and if s. then an heir. Gal 4:7
and her s.: for the s. of the bondwoman shall not be heir with s. 30
s. with father, he served. Phil 2:22
Marcus, sister's s. to. Col 4:10
man of sin, s. of perdition. 2 Thes 2:3
I commit unto thee, s. Timothy.
1 Tim 1:18
and he shall be to me a s. Heb 1:5
unto the s. he saith, Thy throne is. 8
but Christ as a s. over his. 3:6
though he were a s. yet learned. 5:8
of the oath maketh the s. 7:28
s. of Pharaoh's daughter. 11:24
and scourgeth every s. 12:6
for what s. is he whom father ? 7
of Balaam, s. of Bosor. 2 Pet 2:15
denieth Father and s. 1 John 2:22
s. the same hath not the Father, but
he that acknowledgeth the s. 23
ye also shall continue in the s. 24
sent the s. to be the Saviour. 4:14
he that hath the s. hath life, and he
that hath not the s. of God. 5:12
from Lord Jesus Christ, s. 2 John 3
hath both the Father and the s. 9
see **David**

son of God
fourth is like s. of God. Dan 3:25
if thou be the s. of God, command.
Mat 4:3; 27:40; Luke 4:3, 9
do with thee, Jesus thou s. of God ?
Mat 8:29; Luke 8:28
truth thou art s. of God. Mat 14:33
thou be Christ the s. of God. 26:63
I am the s. of God. 27:43

truly this was the s. of God.
Mat 27:54; Mark 15:39
Jesus Christ the s. of God. Mark 1:1
saying, Thou art the s. of God.
3:11; John 1:49
shall be called s. of God. Luke 1:35
son of Adam, which was the s. of
God. 3:38
crying out, thou art Christ the s. of
God. 4:41; John 6:69; 11:27
then the s. of God ? Luke 22:70
this is the s. of God. John 1:34
the only begotten s. of God. 3:18
hear the voice of the s. of God. 5:25
thou believe on the s. of God ? 9:35
I said, I am the s. of God. 10:36
s. of God might be glorified. 11:4
made himself the s. of God. 19:7
Jesus is Christ, the s. of God. 20:31
he said, I believe that Jesus Christ is
the s. of God. Acts 8:37
that he is the s. of God. 9:20
declared to be the s. of God with.
Rom 1:4
for the s. of God was not yea and
nay. 2 Cor 1:19
faith of the s. of God. Gal 2:20
of knowledge of s. of God. Eph 4:13
high priest, Jesus the s. of God.
Heb 4:14
themselves the s. of God afresh. 6:6
like to the s. of God abideth. 7:3
trodden under foot s. of God. 10:29
for this purpose the s. of God was.
1 John 3:8
confess Jesus is the s. of God. 4:15
believeth Jesus is the s. of God. 5:5
he that believeth on the s. of God. 10
believe on the name of s. of God. 13
we know that the s. of God is. 20
things saith the s. of God. Rev 2:18

his son
after name of his s. Enoch. Gen 4:17
what his younger s. had done. 9:24
grievous because of his s. 21:11
the knife to slay his s. 22:10
burnt offering instead of his s. 13
brother's daughter to his s. 24:48
sent from Isaac his s. while. 25:6
Abraham, God blessed his s. 11
Shechem his s. came to gate. 34:20
Hamor and Shechem his s. 26
Jacob mourned for his s. 37:34
betrothed her to his s. Ex 21:9
every man upon his s. 32:29
but for his s. he may. Lev 21:2
on Eleazar his s. Num 20:26, 28
as a man doth bear his s. Deut 1:31
thou shalt not give to his s. 7:3
as a man chasteneth his s. so the. 8:5
not any maketh his s. to pass. 18:10
mourned for his s. 2 Sam 13:37
serve in presence of his s.? 16:19
king was grieved for his s. 19:2
out of his s.'s hand. 1 Ki 11:35
and to his s. will I give one tribe. 36
give him a lamp, to set up his s. 15:4
for all the sins of Elah his s. 16:13
in his s.'s days will I bring. 21:29
took his eldest s., offered. 2 Ki 3:27
Ahaz made his s. to pass. 16:3
Manasseh made his s. pass. 21:6
said to David and to Solomon his s.
7; 2 Chr 33:7
no man might make his s. pass.
2 Ki 23:10
the king slew his s. 2 Chr 24:22
his rod, hateth his s. Pr 13:24
shall have him become his s. 29:21
what is his s.'s name, if thou. 30:4
all nations shall serve his s. and his
son's s. Jer 27:7
thou his s. O Belshazzar. Dan 5:22
as a man spareth his s. Mal 3:17
what man, whom if his s.? Mat 7:9
he sent unto them his s. 21:37
made a marriage for his s. 22:2
how is he then his s.? 45
Mark 12:37; Luke 20:44
gave his only begotten s. John 3:16
God sent not his s. to condemn. 17
Jacob gave to his s. Joseph. 4:5
come down and heal his s. 47

glorified *his s.* Jesus. *Acts* 3:13
God having raised up *his s.* 26
serve in the gospel of *his s. Rom* 1:9
reconciled to God by the death of *his s.* 5:10
God sending *his* own *s.* in. 8:3
to the image of *his s.* 29
he that spared not *his* own *s.* 32
fellowship of *his s.* Jesus. *1 Cor* 1:9
God to reveal *his s.* in me. *Gal* 1:16
God sent forth *his s.* made. 4:4
God sent the spirit of *his s.* into. 6
into kingdom of *his* dear *s. Col* 1:13
and to wait for *his s.* *1 Thes* 1:10
hath in these last days spoken unto us by *his s.* *Heb* 1:2
offered up *his* only begotten *s.* 11:17
offered Isaac *his s.* on altar. *Jas* 2:21
is with Father and *his s.* Jesus. *1 John* 1:3
blood of Jesus Christ *his s.* 7
on the name of *his s.* Jesus. 3:23
God sent *his* only begotten *s.* 4:9
sent *his s.* to be the propitiation. 10
which he hath testified of *his s.* 5:9
hath made him a liar; he believeth not record God gave of *his s.* 10
this life is in *his s.* 11
we are in *his s.* Jesus. 20

see **beloved**

son *in law*

any besides ? *s. in law.* *Gen* 19:12
Samson the *s. in law* of. *Judg* 15:6
father said unto his *s. in law.* 19:5
s. in law to the king. *1 Sam* 18:18, 23
shalt this day be my *s. in law.* 21
be the king's *s. in law.* 22
David well to be king's *s. in law.* 26
might be the king's *s. in law.* 27
faithful as the king's *s. in law?* 22:14
Jehoram was *s. in law.* *2 Ki* 8:27
Tobiah was *s. in law* to. *Neh* 6:18
was *s. in law* to Sanballat the. 13:28

my **son**

not be heir with *my s.* *Gen* 21:10
wilt not deal falsely with *my s.* 23
he said, Here am I, *my s.* 22:7
my s. God will provide himself. 8
wife to *my s.* of Canaanites. 24:3, 37
and take a wife unto *my s.* 4, 7, 38
that thou bring not *my s.* 6, 8
my s. obey my voice. 27:8, 43
Upon me be thy curse, *my s.* 13
here am I; who art thou, *my s.?* 18
thou be *my* very *s.* Esau or not. 21, 24
see, the smell of *my s.* is as. 27
I do now unto thee, *my s.?* 37
the soul of *my s.* longeth for. 34:8
and said, It is *my s.*'s coat. 37:33
I will go into the grave to *my s.* 35
remain, till Shelah *my s.* 38:11
I gave her not to Shelah *my s.* 26
he said, *My s.* shall not go. 42:38
God be gracious to thee, *my s.* 43:29
it is enough, Joseph *my s.* 45:28
Jacob said, I know it, *my s.* 48:19
from the prey, *my s.* thou. 49:9
Israel is *my s.* even my. *Ex* 4:22
let *my s.* go, that he may serve. 23
my s. give glory to the. *Josh* 7:19
neither shall *my s.* rule. *Judg* 8:23
Blessed be thou of Lord, *my s.* 17:2
dedicated for *my s.* to make a. 3
I called not, *my s.*; lie. *1 Sam* 3:6
What is there done, *my s* ? 4:16
What shall I do for *my s.?* 10:2
though it be in Jonathan *my s.* 14:39
and Jonathan *my s.* will be. 40
between me and Jonathan *my s.* 42
that *my s.* hath made a league with the son of Jesse, or that *my s.* 22:8
is this thy voice, *my s.* David ? 24:16; 26:17
I have sinned, return, *my s.* 26:21
Blessed be thou, *my s.* David. 25
father, he shall be *my s.* *2 Sam* 7:14
king said, Nay, *my s.* let us. 13:25
lest they destroy *my s.* 14:11
destroy me and *my s.* out of the. 16
behold *my s.* who came forth. 16:11
wherefore wilt thou run, *my s.?* 18:22
thus he said, *My s.* Absalom, *my s.* *my s.* Absalom. 33; 19:4
I and *my s.* be counted. *1 Ki* 1:21
she arose and took *my s.* 3:20
behold, it was not *my s.* which. 21
Nay; but the living is *my s.* 22
thy son is the dead, and *my s.* 23
dress it for me and *my s.* 17:12
thou come to me to slay *my s.* 18
and we will eat *my s.* *2 Ki* 6:28
my s. and did eat him: give thy s. 29
give thy daughter to *my s.* 14:9
2 Chr 25:18
shall be *my s.* *1 Chr* 17:13; 22:10
now, *my s.* Lord will be with. 22:11
I have chosen him to be *my s.* 28:6
thou, Solomon *my s.* know God. 9
Solomon *my s.* whom God. 29:1
give to Solomon *my s.* a perfect. 19
Thou art *my s.*; this day. *Ps* 2:7
Acts 13:33; *Heb* 1:5; 5:5
my s. despise not the chastening of. *Pr* 3:11; *Heb* 12:5
do this now, *my s.* and. *Pr* 6:3
my s. give me thine heart. 23:26
my s. fear thou the Lord. 24:21
my s. be wise, and make. 27:11
what, *my s.?* and what, the *s.?* 31:2
further by these, *my s.* *Eccl* 12:12
is Ephraim *my* dear *s.?* *Jer* 31:20
it contemneth the rod of *my s.*, as every tree. *Ezek* 21:10
I called *my s.* out of Egypt. *Hos* 11:1; *Mat* 2:15
This is *my* beloved *s. Mat* 3:17; 17:5
have mercy on *my s.*: for he. 17:15
they will reverence *my s.* 21:37
Mark 12:6
brought to thee *my s.* *Mark* 9:17
thee, look upon *my s.* *Luke* 9:38
for this *my s.* was dead and. 15:24
to Timothy *my* own *s.* *1 Tim* 1:2
my s. be strong in grace. *2 Tim* 2:1
to Titus *mine* own *s.* *Tit* 1:4
I beseech thee for *my s.* *Philem* 10
his God, he shall be *my s. Rev* 21:7

thy **son**

thy s. thine only *s.* Isaac. *Gen* 22:2
thou hast not withheld *thy s.* 12, 16
must I needs bring *thy s.?* 24:5
I am *thy s.* thy firstborn. 27:32
whether it be *thy s.*'s coat. 37:32
behold, *thy s.* Joseph cometh. 48:2
I will slay *thy s.* even. *Ex* 4:23
ears of *thy s.* and son's s. 10:2
thou shalt shew *thy s.* in that. 13:8
when *thy s.* asketh thee, what is this ? 14; *Deut* 6:20
not do any work, thou, nor *thy s.* *Ex* 20:10; *Deut* 5:14
shalt say unto *thy s.* *Deut* 6:21
shalt thou take unto *thy s.* 7:3
they will turn away *thy s.* from. 4
thou must eat them before the Lord, thou, and *thy s.* 12:18; 16:11, 14
if *thy s.* entice thee secretly. 13:6
bring out *thy s.* that. *Judg* 6:30
thou, *thy s.* and *thy son's s.* 8:22
send me David *thy s.* *1 Sam* 16:19
servants, and to *thy s.* David. 25:8
one hair of *thy s.* fall. *2 Sam* 14:11
and life of *thy s.* Solomon. *1 Ki* 1:12
thy s. Solomon shall reign. 13, 17, 30
the dead is *thy s.* 3:22
and *thy s.* is the dead. 23
thy s. whom I will set upon. 5:5
out of the hand of *thy s.* 11:12
I will give one tribe to *thy s.* 13
for thee and for *thy s.* 17:13
give me *thy s.* 19
Elisha said, See, *thy s.* liveth. 23
he said, Take up *thy s.* *2 Ki* 4:36
give *thy s.* that we may eat. 6:28, 29
I am thy servant, and *thy s.* 16:7
thy s. shall build my house . . . to be my s. *1 Chr* 28:6; *2 Chr* 6:9
chasten *thy s.* while. *Pr* 19:18
correct *thy s.* and he shall. 29:17
Jesus said, Bring *thy s.* *Luke* 9:41
worthy to be called *thy s.* 15:19, 21
as soon as this *thy s.* was come. 30
go thy way, *thy s.* liveth. *John* 4:50, 51, 53
glorify *thy s.* that *thy s.* also. 17:1
mother, Woman, behold *thy s.* 19:26

son *of man*

he said *S. of man,* stand. *Ezek* 2:
s. of man, I send thee to the.
and thou, *s. of man,* be not.
thou *s. of man,* hear what I say.
s. of man, eat that thou findest. 3:
s. of man, cause thy belly to eat.
s. of man, go get thee to the house.
s. of man, all the words that I. 1
s. of man, I have made thee a. 1
O *s. of man,* they shall put. 2
thou also *s. of man,* take thee. 4:
s. of man, I will break staff of. 1
thou *s. of man,* take thee a. 5:
s. of man, set thy face towar the mountains. 6:
thou *s. of man,* thus saith the. 7:
s. of man, lift up thine eyes. 8:
he said, *S. of man,* seest thou ?
S. of man, dig now in the wall.
s. of man, hast thou seen what ? 1
thou seen this, O *s. of man* ? 15, 1
s. of man, these are the men. 11:
prophesy, O *s. of man.*
s. of man, thy brethren are. 1
s. of man, thou dwellest in a. 12:
thou *s. of man,* prepare thee.
s. of man, hath not the house of ?
s. of man, eat thy bread with. 1
s. of man, what is that proverb ? 2
s. of man, behold, they of house. 2
s. of man, prophesy against th prophets. 13:
s. of man, set thy face against th people. 1
s. of man, these men have set. 14:
s. of man, when the land sinneth. 1
s. of man, What is the vine tree ? 15:
s. of man, cause Jerusalem. 16:
s. of man, put forth a riddle. 17:
s. of man, speak to the elders. 20:
s. of man, wilt thou judge them ?
therefore *s. of man,* speak to. 2
s. of man, set thy face toward th south. 4
s. of man, set thy face towar Jerusalem. 21:
sigh therefore, thou *s. of man.*
s. of man, prophesy and say, a. 9, 2
cry and howl *s. of man,* for it. 1
s. of man, prophesy and smite. 1
also thou *s. of man,* appoint. 1
s. of man, wilt thou judge ? 22:
s. of man, house of Israel is to. 1
s. of man, say to her, Thou art. 2
s. of man, there were two women o 23:
s. of man, wilt thou judge Aholah? 3
s. of man, write thee the name. 24:
s. of man, I take away the desire. 1
s. of man, shall it not be in day ? 2
s. of man, set thy face agains the Ammonites. 25:
s. of man, because that Tyrus. 26:
s. of man, take up a lamentation. 27:2; 28:1
s. of man, say unto the prince. 28:
s. of man, set thy face against Zido 2
s. of man, set thy face agains Pharaoh. 29:
s. of man, Nebuchadrezzar.
s. of man, prophesy, and say, Thu saith the Lord. 30:
s. of man, I have broken the. 2
s. of man, speak to Pharaoh. 31:
s. of man, take up a lamentation fo Pharaoh. 32:
s. of man, wail for the multitude.
s. of man, speak to children. 33:
thou, O *s. of man,* I have set.
O *s. of man,* speak to the house. 1
s. of man, say to the children. 1
s. of man, they that inhabit. 2
s. of man, thy people still are. 3
s. of man, prophesy against th shepherds. 34:
s. of man, set thy face against mou Seir. 35:
thou *s. of man,* prophesy to. 36:
s. of man, when the house of.
he said, *S. of man,* can these ? 37:
prophesy, *s. of man,* and say.
s. of man, these bones are the.

s. of man, take thee one stick. *Ezek* 37:16
s. of man, set thy face against Gog. 38:2
s. of man, prophesy and say unto Gog. 14
s. of man, prophesy against Gog. 39:1
s. of man, thus saith the Lord. 17
43:18
s. of man, behold with thine. 40:4
he said, *S. of man*, the place. 43:7
s. of man, shew the house to. 10
s. of man, mark well, behold. 44:5
he said, *S. of man*, hast thou ? 47:6

see **man**

song

We find in Scripture several songs *composed upon important occasions; for example*, Moses *made one after the passage through the Red Sea, to thank God for the deliverance of his people*, Ex 15:1, 2, etc. *David composed a song in mourning for the death of Saul and Jonathan, and another for the death of Abner*, 2 Sam 1:18, 19; 3:33. *Jeremiah wrote his* Lamentations, *which are a song, wherein he deplores the calamities and ruin of* Jerusalem; *and he made another upon the death of Josiah king of Judah*, 2 Chr 35:25. *Deborah and Barak made a triumphant hymn after the defeat of Sisera*, Judg 5:1, 2, 3, etc. *The* Canticles, *or the* Song of Songs, *and the* 45th Psalm, *are songs to celebrate weddings, and are considered by many to be allegorical. Hannah the mother of Samuel, and king* Hezekiah, *returned thanks to God in* songs, *for the favours they had received*, 1 Sam 2:1, 2, etc.; Isa 38:10, 11, etc. *The* songs *of the Virgin* Mary, Zacharias *the father of* John *the* Baptist, *and old* Simeon *are of the same nature. They are thanksgivings to God for blessings received from him*, Luke 1:46, 68; 2:29, 30.

the children of Israel sang this *s.* unto. *Ex* 15:1; *Num* 21:17
the Lord is my strength and *s.* and. *Ex* 15:2; *Ps* 118:14; *Isa* 12:2
write this *s.*: that this *s. Deut* 31:19
this *s.* shall testify. 21
Moses wrote this *s.* 22
the words of this *s.* 30; 32:44
awake, Deborah, utter a *s. Judg* 5:12
to Lord words of this *s. 2 Sam* 22:1
whom David set over the service of *s.* *1 Chr* 6:31
chief of Levites was for a *s.* 15:22, 27
under their father for *s.* in. 25:6
s. of the Lord began. *2 Chr* 29:27
now I am their *s.*, yea, I am. *Job* 30:9
and with my *s.* will I. *Ps* 28:7
unto him a new *s.* 33:3; *Isa* 42:10
and he hath put a new *s.* *Ps* 40:3
night his *s.* shall be with me. 42:8
the *s.* of the drunkards. 69:12
the name of God with a *s.* 30
remembrance my *s.* in night. 77:6
O sing a new *s.* 96:1; 98:1; 149:1
there they required of us a *s.* 137:3
how shall we sing the Lord's *s.* in ? 4
I will sing a new *s.* unto. 144:9
man to hear the *s.* of fools. *Eccl* 7:5
the *s.* of songs which is. *S of S* 1:1
I sing a *s.* of my beloved. *Isa* 5:1
not drink wine with a *s.* 24:9
in that day shall this *s.* be sung. 26:1
shall have a *s.* as in the night. 30:29
a derision and their *s.* *Lam* 3:14
them as a very lovely *s. Ezek* 33:32
they sung a new *s.*, saying, Thou art worthy. *Rev* 5:9; 14:3
learn that *s.* but the 144,000. 14:3
s. of Moses and *s.* of the Lamb. 15:3

songs

sent thee away with *s.* *Gen* 31:27
his *s.* were a thousand. *1 Ki* 4:32
were instructed in the *s. 1 Chr* 25:7*
of David there were *s.* *Neh* 12:46
maker who giveth *s.* in. *Job* 35:10
shall compass about with *s. Ps* 32:7
have been my *s.* in house. 119:54
Sing us one of the *s.* of Zion. 137:3
so is he that singeth *s.* *Pr* 25:20
the song of *s.* which is. *S of S* 1:1
sweet melody, sing *s.* *Isa* 23:16
part of earth have we heard *s.* 24:16
shall come to Zion with *s.* 35:10
will sing my *s.* to the stringed. 38:20
noise of thy *s.* to cease. *Ezek* 26:13
away from me the noise of thy *s.* *Amos* 5:23
s. of temple shall be howlings. 8:3
I will turn all your *s.* into. 10
in psalms and spiritual *s.* *Eph* 5:19
one another in hymns and spiritual *s.* *Col* 3:16

sons

(*In Revisions very frequently*, children)

the *s.* of Noah entered. *Gen* 7:13
the *s.* of Noah that went forth. 9:18
there are the three *s.* of Noah. 19
were *s.* born after the flood. 10:1
and spake to his *s.* in law. 19:14
in the presence of the *s.* of. 23:11
and let thy mother's *s.* bow. 27:29
s. of Jacob came upon slain. 34:27
lad was with the *s.* of Bilhah. 37:2
s. of Israel came to buy corn. 42:5
one man's *s.* we are no spies. 11, 32
the *s.* of Israel carried Jacob. 46:5
earrings in ears of your *s.* *Ex* 32:2
eat the flesh of your *s.* *Lev* 26:29
ye take too much upon you, ye *s.* of Levi. *Num* 16:7
of their tents, their wives and *s.* 27
in his own sin, and had no *s.* 27:3
if they be married to *s.* of. 36:3
a sodomite of the *s.* *Deut* 23:17
separated the *s.* of Adam. 32:8
Caleb drove three *s.* of Anak. *Josh* 15:14; *Judg* 1:20
they were even the *s.* *Judg* 8:19
Gideon had 70 *s.* 30
Jair had thirty *s.* 10:4
Abdon had forty *s.* and thirty. 12:14
s. of Belial beset house. 19:22
are there yet any more *s.*? *Ruth* 1:11
better to thee than ten *s.*? *1 Sam* 1:8
s. of Eli were *s.* of Belial. 2:12
will take your *s.* and appoint. 8:11
there were three *s.* of. *2 Sam* 2:18
these men *s.* of Zeruiah be too. 3:39
eat as one of the king's *s.* 9:11
invited all the king's *s.* 13:23
hath slain all the king's *s.* 30
what to do with you, ye *s.* of Zeruiah ? 16:10; 19:22
but *s.* of Belial shall be as. 23:6
all the king's *s.* *1 Ki* 1:9, 19, 25
kindness to *s.* of Barzillai. 2:7
for he was wiser than the *s.* 4:31
a certain man of the *s.* of. 20:35
set two men, *s.* of Belial. 21:10
she shut the door upon her and upon her *s.* *2 Ki* 4:5
meetest of your master's *s.* 10:3
the heads of the king's *s.* 8
stole him from the king's *s.* 11:2
2 Chr 22:11
they slew *s.* of Zedekiah before his. *2 Ki* 25:7; *Jer* 39:6; 52:10
birthright was given to *s.* *1 Chr* 5:1
Ornan and his four *s.* with. 21:20
Eleazar, who had no *s.* 24:28
among the *s.* of my fathers. 28:4
as the Lord said of the *s. 2 Chr* 23:3
for blood of the *s.* of Jehoiada. 24:25
one of the *s.* of Joiada. *Neh* 13:28
the ten *s.* of Haman. *Esth* 9:10
let Haman's ten *s.* be hanged. 13, 14
who among *s.* of mighty can? *Ps* 89:6
our *s.* may be as plants. 144:12
as apple tree so is my beloved among *s.* *S of S* 2:3
guide her among all the *s. Isa* 51:18
s. of the stranger that join. 56:6
draw near hither, ye *s.* of. 57:3
the *s.* of the stranger shall. 60:10
the *s.* of them that afflicted thee. 14
the *s.* of the alien shall be. 61:5
s. of the stranger shall not. *Isa* 62:8
the fathers and *s.* shall. *Jer* 6:21
even fathers and *s.* together. 13:14
high places to burn their *s.* 19:5
beget *s.*, take wives for your *s.* 29:6
I set before *s.* of Rechabites. 35:5
no wine, ye, nor your *s.* for ever. 6
Israel no *s.*? hath he no heir ? 49:1
precious *s.* of Zion. *Lam* 4:2
fathers shall eat the *s.*, *s.* *Ezek* 5:10
when ye make your *s.* pass. 20:31
they caused their *s.* to pass. 23:37
s. of the living God. *Hos* 1:10
I raised up of your *s.* *Amos* 2:11
he shall purify *s.* of Levi. *Mal* 3:3
therefore ye *s.* of Jacob are. 6
is, The *s.* of thunder. *Mark* 3:17
whom do your *s.* cast ? *Luke* 11:19
but as my beloved *s.* *1 Cor* 4:14
receive the adoption of *s.* *Gal* 4:5
because ye are *s.*, God hath sent. 6
bringing many *s.* to glory. *Heb* 2:10
blessed both *s.* of Joseph. 11:21
dealeth with you as with *s.* 12:7
then are ye bastards, and not *s.* 8

sons *of God*

the *s. of God* saw the. *Gen* 6:2
the *s. of God* came in to the. 4
s. of God came to present. *Job* 1:6
2:1
all the *s. of God* shouted for. 38:7
are *s. of* the living *God*. *Hos* 1:10
them power to become *s. of God*. *John* 1:12
led by the Spirit of God, they are the *s. of God*. *Rom* 8:14
the manifestation of *s. of God*. 19
be harmless, the *s. of God*. *Phil* 2:15
be called the *s. of God*. *1 John* 3:1
beloved, now are we the *s. of God*. 2

his **sons**

Noah and *his s.* went into the ark. *Gen* 7:7
Noah went forth, and *his s.* 8:18
God blessed Noah and *his s.* 9:1
his s. Isaac and Ishmael buried. 25:9
them into the hands of *his s.* 30:35
his s. Esau and Jacob buried. 35:29
end of commanding *his s.* 49:33
his s. did unto him as he. 50:12
his s. carried him into the land. 13
Jethro came with *his s.* and. *Ex* 18:5
Aaron and *his s.* to minister. 28:1
put the garments on *his s.* 41; 29:8
tip of the right ear of *his s.* 29:20
sprinkle the blood upon *his s.* 21
sanctify that which is for *his s.* 27
Lev 8:30
priest of *his s.* that is anointed. *Lev* 6:22
smote Og and *his s.* *Num* 21:35
we smote Sihon, *his s.* *Deut* 2:33
Lord hath chosen him and *his s.* 18:5
when he maketh *his s.* to. 21:16
have slain *his s.* 70 persons on. *Judg* 9:18
Micah consecrated one of *his s.* 17:5
was to him as one of *his s.* 11
his s. were priests to tribe of. 18:30
now Eli heard all that *his s.* did. *1 Sam* 2:22
his s. made themselves vile. 3:13
Samuel when old made *his s.* 8:1
his s. walked not in his ways. 3
me a king among *his s.* 16:1
grieved, every man for *his s.* 30:6
upon Saul and upon *his s.* and slew. 31:2; *1 Chr* 10:2
let seven men of *his s.* *2 Sam* 21:6
his s. came and told. *1 Ki* 13:11
his s. had seen what way the. 12
blood of Naboth and *his s. 2 Ki* 9:26
his s. smote him with the sword. 19:37; *Isa* 37:38
Jeroboam and *his s.* *2 Chr* 11:14
and *his s.* by a covenant of salt. 13:5
light to him, and to *his s.* for. 21:7
his s. save the youngest of *his s.* 17
were servants to him and *his s.* 36:20
life of the king and *his s.* *Ezra* 6:10
he and *his s.* be hanged. *Esth* 9:25
and *his s.* went and feasted. *Job* 1:4
his s. come to honour, he. 14:21

guide Arcturus with his s.? Job 38:32
Job saw his s. and his s.' sons. 42:16
Jonadab commanded his s. not to. Jer 35:14
give a gift to any of his s. Ezek 46:16
his s. shall be stirred up. Dan 11:10

my sons
his father, They are my s. Gen 48:9
nay, my s. for it is no good report I hear. 1 Sam 2:24
Samuel said, Behold, my s. 12:2
of all my s. he hath chosen. 1 Chr 28:5
Hezekiah said, My s. 2 Chr 29:11
Job said, It may be that my s. Job 1:5
to come concerning my s. Isa 45:11
but as my beloved s. I. 1 Cor 4:14
see **seven**

thy sons
into ark, thou and thy s. Gen 6:18
ark, thou, thy wife, and thy s. 8:16
ordinance to thee and thy s. Ex 12:24; Num 18:8
firstborn of thy s. shalt. Ex 22:29
make thy s. go a whoring. 34:16
all the firstborn of thy s. thou. 20
not drink wine, nor thy s. Lev 10:9
it is thy due, and thy s.' due. 14
thou and thy s. shall bear. Num 18:1
but thou and thy s. with thee. 2
thou and thy s. shall keep your. 7
holy for thee and for thy s. 9
given them to thee and to thy s. 11
teach them thy s. and thy s.' sons. Deut 4:9
and honourest thy s. 1 Sam 2:29
thou art old, and thy s. walk not. 8:5
to-morrow shalt thou and thy s. 28:19
and thy s. shall till. 2 Sam 9:10
door upon thee and thy s. 2 Ki 4:4
said to Jehu, Thy s. shall sit on. 15:12; 1 Chr 17:11
thy s. shall be eunuchs in Babylon. 2 Ki 20:18; Isa 39:7
bring thy s. in their arms. Isa 49:22
thy s. have fainted, they lie. 51:20
come to thee, thy s. shall. 60:4, 9
marrieth virgin, so shall thy s. 62:5
thy s. and daughters are. Jer 48:46
raised up thy s. O Zion, against thy s. Zech 9:13

two sons
to Eber were born two s. Gen 10:25; 1 Chr 1:19
two of the s. of Jacob. Gen 34:25
unto Joseph were born two s. 41:50
slay my two s. if I bring him. 42:37
that my wife bare me two s. 44:27
took with him his two s. 48:1, 5
Zipporah and her two s. Ex 18:3
the death of the two s. Lev 16:1
two s. Mahlon and. Ruth 1:1, 2
she was left and her two s. 3
left of her two s. 5
come upon thy two s. 1 Sam 2:34
the two s. of Eli were there. 4:4
thy two s. Hophni and Phinehas. 17
thy handmaid had two s. 2 Sam 14:6
there with them their two s. 15:36
but the king took the two s. 21:8
creditor to take two s. 2 Ki 4:1
grant that these my two s. may sit in thy kingdom. Mat 20:21
a certain man had two s. 21:28; Luke 15:11
took with him Peter and the two s. of Zebedee. Mat 26:37
Midian, where he begat two s. Acts 7:29
that Abraham had two s. Gal 4:22

soon
ye are come so s. to-day? Ex 2:18
ye shall s. utterly perish. Deut 4:26
my maker would s. take me. Job 32:22
they shall s. be cut down. Ps 37:2
shall s. stretch out her hands. 68:31
I should s. have subdued. 81:14
for it is s. cut off, and we. 90:10
they s. forgat his works. 106:13
that is s. angry dealeth. Pr 14:17
how s. is the fig tree! Mat 21:20
I marvel that ye are so s. Gal 1:6
ye be not s. shaken in. 2 Thes 2:2
not selfwilled, not s. angry. Tit 1:7

as soon as
as s. as he came nigh. Ex 32:19
ran as s. as he had stretched. Josh 8:19
as s. as they hear they shall be obedient to me. 2 Sam 22:45; Ps 18:44
they go astray as s. as. Ps 58:3
as s. as his ministration. Luke 1:23
as s. as I see how it will. Phil 2:23

sooner
be restored to you the s. Heb 13:19
sun is no s. risen, but it. Jas 1:11

soothsayer
Diviner or Magician. These were very common among Eastern nations, magicians and soothsayers being referred to at various times, from the mention in Ex 7:11 of the magicians of Pharaoh, to the time of the Apostles, when the trade was still very lucrative, Acts 8:9; 13:6; 19:19.

The law of Moses forbade the consultation of magicians and soothsayers, upon pain of death, Lev 20:6. Saul did what he could to drive them out of the country of Israel, 1 Sam 28:3. But, for all this, many were still to be found; and the Israelites were always much addicted to these sorts of superstitions. And the same king who had been so eager in driving them out of his dominions, at last went to consult one himself, 1 Sam 28:7, 8, etc.

see **divinations, exorcists**
Balaam the son of Beor the s., did Israel slay. Josh 13:22

soothsayers
people, because they are s. Isa 2:6
the secret cannot the s. Dan 2:27
to bring Chaldeans and s. 5:7
king made master of the s. 11
shalt have no more s. Mi 5:12

soothsaying
masters much gain by s. Acts 16:16

sop
I shall give a s., when he had dipped the s., he gave it to. John 13:26
after the s. Satan entered. 27, 30

sope (soap)
wash and take thee much s. Jer 2:22
who may abide his coming? for he is like fuller's s. Mal 3:2

sorcerer
found a certain s. a false. Acts 13:6
Elymas the s. withstood them. 8

sorcerers
also called wise men and s. Ex 7:11
hearken not to your s. Jer 27:9
commanded to call s. Dan 2:2
swift witness against the s. Mal 3:5
s. shall have their part. Rev 21:8
for without are dogs and s. 22:15

sorceress
hither, ye sons of the s. Isa 57:3

sorceries
come on thee for thy s. Isa 47:9
with the multitude of thy s. 12
bewitched them with s. Acts 8:11
repented they of their s. Rev 9:21
for by thy s. were all nations. 18:23

sorcery
which beforetime used s. Acts 8:9

sore
they pressed s. upon the. Gen 19:9
because thou s. longest after. 31:30
day, when they were s. 34:25
the famine waxed s. in land. 41:56
s. in all lands. 57
s. in Canaan. 43:1; 47:4, 13
they mourned with a s. 50:10
Lord shewed signs great and s. on. Deut 6:22
smite thee with a s. botch. 28:35
s. sicknesses, and of long. Deut 28:59
so that Israel was s. Judg 10:9
because she lay s. upon him. 14:17
Samson was s. athirst, and. 15:18
against Gibeah, the battle was s. 20:34; 1 Sam 31:3*; 2 Sam 2:17; 2 Ki 3:26
lifted up their voices and wept s. Judg 21:2
also provoked her s. 1 Sam 1:6
prayed to the Lord, and wept s. 10
hand is s. on us, and on Dagon. 5:7
there was s. war against the. 14:52
I am s. distressed. 28:15, 21
his servants wept s. 2 Sam 13:36
sickness so s. no breath. 1 Ki 17:17
and there was a s. famine in. 18:2
Syria was s. troubled. 2 Ki 6:11
Hezekiah wept s. 20:3; Isa 38:3
know his own s. grief. 2 Chr 6:29*
so Jehoram died of s. 21:19
Ahaz transgressed s. against. 28:19
have me away, for I am s. 35:23
people wept very s. Ezra 10:1
it grieved me s. therefore. Neh 13:8
smote Job with s. boils. Job 2:7
he maketh s. and bindeth. 5:18
and vex in his s. displeasure. Ps 2:5
soul is s. vexed, but thou, O Lord. 6:3
enemies be ashamed, and s. 10
fast, thy hand presseth me s. 38:2
I am feeble and s. broken, I. 8
thou hast s. broken us in. 44:19
my heart is s. pained within. 55:4
shewed me great and s. 71:30
thou hast thrust s. at me. 118:13
chastened me s. but not given. 18
s. travail hath God. Eccl 1:13; 4:8
there is s. evil I have seen. 5:13, 16
with s. and great sword. Isa 27:1
we roar like bears, mourn s. 59:11
be not wroth very s. O Lord. 64:9
thy peace, afflict us very s.? 12
mine eye shall weep s. Jer 13:17
weep s. for him that goeth. 22:10
famine was s. in city, there. 52:6
she weepeth s. in the. Lam 1:2
mine enemies chased me s. 3:52
when I send my four s. Ezek 14:21
it is sharpened to make a s. 21:10
king was s. displeased. Dan 6:14
destroy you even with s. Mi 2:10
the Lord hath been s. Zech 1:2, 15
for he is lunatick, and s. vexed. Mat 17:15*
Hosanna, they were s. 21:15*
they were s. amazed in. Mark 6:51
spirit cried, rent him s. and. 9:26
Jesus began to be s. amazed. 14:33
wept s. and kissed Paul. Acts 20:37
see **afraid**

sore, substantive
if a white reddish s. it. Lev 13:42*
if rising of s. be white reddish. 43*
s. or sickness there be. 2 Chr 6:28*
stand aloof from my s. Ps 38:11*
my s. ran in the night and. 77:2*
there fell a grievous s. Rev 16:2

Sorek
a woman in valley of S. Judg 16:4

sorely
archers s. grieved him. Gen 49:23
so shall they be s. pained at. Isa 23:5

sorer
how much s. punishment. Heb 10:29

sores
bruises, and putrifying s. Isa 1:6
at his gate full of s. Luke 16:20, 21
blasphemed God because of their pains and s. Rev 16:11

sorrow
I will greatly multiply thy s. and conception, in s. thou shalt. Gen 3:16
in s. shalt thou eat of it all days. 17*
ye bring down my gray hairs with s. to the grave. 42:38; 44:29, 31
s. take hold of inhabitants. Ex 15:14*
terror shall cause s. of. Lev 26:16
shall give s. of mine. Deut 28:65*
I bare him with s. 1 Chr 4:9
this is nothing else but s. Neh 2:2

was turned from s. to joy. Esth 9:22
because it hid not s. from mine eyes. Job 3:10*
I would harden myself in s. 6:10*
mine eye is dim by reason of s. 17:7
and s. is turned into joy. 41:22
having s. in my heart. Ps 13:2
and my s. is continually. 38:17
I held my peace, and my s. 39:2
mischief also and s. are in. 55:10
their strength labour and s. 90:10
brought low through s. 107:39
I found trouble and s. 116:3
that winketh eye, causeth s. Pr 10:10
rich, he addeth no s. with it. 22
but by s. of heart the spirit. 15:13
a fool, doeth it to his s. 17:21
who hath woe ? who hath s.? 23:29
he that increaseth knowledge. Eccl 1:18
he hath much s. and wrath. 5:17
s. is better than laughter, heart. 7:3
therefore remove s. from thy. 11:10
unto the land, behold s. Isa 5:30
shall give thee rest from thy s. 14:3
heap in the day of desperate s. 17:11
Ariel, and there shall be s. 29:2
s. and sighing shall flee away. 35:10
have, ye shall lie down in s. 50:11
and s. and mourning shall. 51:11
sing, but ye shall cry for s. 65:14
comfort myself against s. Jer 8:18
to see labour and s.? 20:18
why criest thou ? thy s. is. 30:15
rejoice from their s. 31:13
hath added grief to my s. 45:3
there is s. on the sea, it cannot. 49:23
any s. like unto my s. Lam 1:12
behold my s. 18
give them s. of heart. 3:65
filled with drunkenness and s. Ezek 23:33
them sleeping for s. Luke 22:45
said these things, s. filled. John 16:6
sorrowful, but your s. shall be. 20
when she is in travail, hath s. 21
therefore have s. but I will see you again, and your heart shall. 22
that I have continual s. Rom 9:2
when I came, I should have s. 2 Cor 2:3
swallowed up with overmuch s. 7
godly s. worketh repentance to salvation, but the s. of the world. 7:10
also, lest I have s. upon s. Phil 2:27
s. give her: for she saith, I . . . shall see no s. Rev 18:7
no more death, neither s. 21:4

sorrow, *verb*

and they shall not s. any. Jer 31:12
land shall tremble and s. 51:29
they shall s. a little for. Hos 8:10
that ye s. not as others. 1 Thes 4:13

sorrowed

now I rejoice that ye s. to. 2 Cor 7:9
selfsame thing, that ye s. after a. 11

sorroweth

thy father s. for you. 1 Sam 10:2

sorrowful

a woman of a s. spirit. 1 Sam 1:15
things my soul refused to touch are as my s. meat. Job 6:7
poor and s.: let salvation. Ps 69:29
laughter the heart is s. Pr 14:13
replenished every s. soul. Jer 31:25
gather them that are s. Zeph 3:18
shall see it, and be very s. Zech 9:5
he went away s. Mat 19:22
Luke 18:23, 24
they were exceeding s. Mat 26:22
Mark 14:19
and he began to be s. Mat 26:37
my soul is exceeding s. even unto death. 38; Mark 14:34
ye shall be s. but sorrow. John 16:20
as s. yet always rejoicing. 2 Cor 6:10
and I may be the less s. Phil 2:28

sorrowing

father and I sought thee s. Luke 2:48
s. they should see his face no more. Acts 20:38

sorrows

their cry, for I know their s. Ex 3:7
s. of hell compassed me about. 2 Sam 22:6; Ps 18:4, 5; 116:3
I am afraid of all my s., . . . thou wilt not hold me innocent. Job 9:28
distributeth s. in his anger. 21:17
they cast out their s. 39:3
s. shall be multiplied that. Ps 16:4
many s. shall be to wicked. 32:10
rise up, to eat the bread of s. 127:2
for all his days are s. and. Eccl 2:23
pangs and s. shall take. Isa 13:8
a man of s. and acquainted. 53:3
borne our griefs and carried our s. 4
not s. take as a woman. Jer 13:21
s. have taken her as a woman. 49:24
by vision my s. are. Dan 10:16
s. of travailing woman. Hos 13:13
these are beginning of s. Mat 24:8
Mark 13:8
they pierced themselves through with many s. 1 Tim 6:10

sorry

of you that is s. for me. 1 Sam 22:8
holy to Lord, neither be ye s. Neh 8:10
I will be s. for my sin. Ps 38:18
who shall be s. for thee ? Isa 51:19
and the king was s. Mat 14:9
Mark 6:26
they were exceeding s. Mat 17:23
if I make you s., . . . glad, but the same which is made s.? 2 Cor 2:2
you s., same epistle made you s. 7:8
ye were made s., for ye were s. 9

sort

two of every s. shalt bring into ark. Gen 6:19, 20
every bird of every s. into. 7:14
they divided one s. 1 Chr 24:5
be able to offer after this s. 29:14
silver basons of second s. Ezra 1:10
Artaxerxes king after this s. 4:8
four times after this s. Neh 6:4
men of the common s. Ezek 23:42
to ravenous birds of every s. 39:4
every oblation of every s. 44:30
than children of your s. Dan 1:10
no God can deliver after this s. 3:29
fellows of the baser s. Acts 17:5
more boldly in some s. Rom 15:15
work, of what s. it is. 1 Cor 3:13
sorrowed after a godly s. 2 Cor 7:11
of this s. are they who creep into. 2 Tim 3:6
journey after a godly s. 3 John 6

sorts

a garment of divers s. Deut 22:11
days store of all s. of wine. Neh 5:18
he sent divers s. of flies. Ps 78:45
105:31
instruments and that of all s. Eccl 2:8
merchants in all s. of things. Ezek 27:24
clothed with all s. of armour. 38:4

Sosipater

and S. my kinsmen. Rom 16:21

Sosthenes

the Greeks took S. and. Acts 18:17
Paul and S. to the church. 1 Cor 1:1

sottish

foolish, they are s. children. Jer 4:22

sought

he s. where to weep, entered his chamber. Gen 43:30
when Pharaoh heard, he s. Ex 2:15
men are dead which s. thy life. 4:19
that the Lord met him and s. 24
every one that s. the Lord went. 33:7
Moses diligently s. goat. Lev 10:16
was not his enemy, nor s. Num 35:23
because he s. to thrust. Deut 13:10
pursuers s. the spies. Josh 2:22
Samson s. occasion against. Judg 14:4
Danites s. them an inheritance. 18:1
Saul s. to smite David. 1 Sam 19:10
Saul s. no more again for him. 27:4
ye s. for David in times past to be king. 2 Sam 3:17
head of thine enemy that s. thy life. 2 Sam 4:8
Saul s. to slay them in his zeal. 21:2
they s. for a fair damsel. 1 Ki 1:3
all the earth s. to Solomon. 10:24
Solomon s. therefore to kill. 11:40
s. three days for Elijah. 2 Ki 2:17
Hebronites were s. for. 1 Chr 26:31
have s. the Lord our God. 2 Chr 14:7
disease he s. not to the Lord. 16:12
Jehoshaphat s. not unto. 17:3
s. to the Lord God of his father. 4
he s. Ahaziah, and they caught him; because Jehoshaphat s. the. 22:9
s. after gods of Edom ? 25:15, 20
he s. God in the days of Zechariah; as long as he s. the Lord. 26:5
these s. their register. Ezra 2:62
Neh 7:64
they s. the Levites out. Neh 12:27
s. to lay hand on. Esth 2:21; 6:2
wherefore Haman s. to destroy. 3:6
to lay hand on such as s. 9:2
I s. the Lord, and he heard me. Ps 34:4; 77:2
assemblies of violent men s. 86:14
s. out of all that have. 111:2
whole heart have I s. thee. 119:10
for I have s. thy precepts. 94
s. out many inventions. Eccl 7:29
preacher s. out and set in order. 12:9
the preacher s. to find. 10
shalt be called, s. out, city. Isa 62:12
s. of them that asked not for me; I am . . . s. not. 65:1; Rom 10:20
for my people that have s. me. Isa 65:10
moon, whom they have s. Jer 8:2
for the pastors have not s. 10:21
king s. to put him to death. 26:21
to Nebuchadrezzar that s. his. 44:30
iniquity of Israel shall be s. 50:20
they s. meat to relieve. Lam 1:19
and I s. for a man. Ezek 22:30
tho' s. for, yet shalt thou never. 26:21
neither have ye s. that which. 34:4
they s. Daniel and his. Dan 2:13
and my lords s. unto me. 4:36
s. occasion against Daniel. 6:4
even I, had s. for the meaning. 8:15
Esau's hidden things s. up. Ob 6
that have not s. the Lord. Zeph 1:6
bay went forth and s. to go. Zech 6:7
they are dead which s. Mat 2:20
s. to lay hands on him. 21:46
Mark 12:12; Luke 20:19
from that time he s. opportunity to betray him. Mat 26:16; Luke 22:6
they s. false witness against Jesus. Mat 26:59; Mark 14:55
s. how they might destroy him. Mark 11:18; 14:1; Luke 19:47
22:2
thy father and I s. thee. Luke 2:48
how is it that ye s. me ? wist ? 49
and they s. means to bring. 5:18
multitude s. to touch him. 6:19
others s. of him a sign from. 11:16
he s. fruit thereon, and. 13:6
Zacchaeus s. to see Jesus. 19:3
s. to slay him. John 5:16, 18; 7:1
then the Jews s. him. 7:11; 11:56
s. to take him. 7:30; 10:39
Master, the Jews of late s. 11:8
from thenceforth Pilate s. to. 19:12
and when Herod had s. Acts 12:19
they s. to bring them out to. 17:5
because s. it not by faith. Rom 9:32
nor of men s. we glory. 1 Thes 2:6
in Rome he s. me out. 2 Tim 1:17
no place should have been s. for. Heb 8:7
though he s. it carefully with. 12:17

sought *him*

he s. *him* he could not. 1 Sam 10:21
the Lord hath s. *him* a man. 13:14
Saul s. *him* every day, God. 23:14
we s. *him* not after the. 1 Chr 15:13
have s. *him*, he hath. 2 Chr 14:7
when they s. *him*, he was. 15:4
for they s. *him* with their whole. 15
I s. *him*, but he could not. Ps 37:36
slew them, then they s. *him*. 78:34

on my bed I *s. him* whom my soul loveth; I *s. him. S of S* 3:1, 2; 5:6
and they *s. him* among. *Luke* 2:44
people *s. him*, and came. 4:42

soul

(*This word is used in the Bible in much the same variety of senses as it is used to-day. The Hebrews used the word rather more generally, and the renderings of Hebrew expressions given in the margins of many editions of the Bible frequently contain the word when it does not appear in the text, but some other word, as* mind, life, *or* persons, *is used. Frequently, where the word soul is used in the Authorised or " King James " Version the revisions have changed it to* life)

man became a living *s*. *Gen* 2:7
the *s*. of my son longeth for. 34:8
as her *s*. was in departing. 35:18
if a *s*. shall sin through. *Lev* 4:2*
if a *s*. sin, and hear the voice. 5:1*
or if *s*. touch any unclean thing. 2*
if a *s*. swear. 4*
if a *s*. commit a trespass. 15
if a *s*. sin and commit any. 17*
if a *s*. lie. 6:2*
an atonement for the *s*. 17:11*
no *s*. of you shall eat blood. 12
if the priest buy any *s*. with. 22:11
whatsoever *s*. doth any work. 23:30
or if your *s*. abhor my. 26:15
because their *s*. abhorred my. 43
even the same *s*. shall. *Num* 9:13
the *s*. of the people was. 21:4
she hath bound her *s*. 30:4, 5, 6, 7, 8, 9, 10, 11, 12, 13
one *s*. of five hundred for. 31:28
serve him with all your *s*. *Deut* 11:13
lay up these my words in your *s*. 18
love the Lord God with all your *s*. 13:3; *Josh* 22:5; *1 Ki* 2:4
s. of Jonathan was knit to *s*. of. *1 Sam* 18:1
s. of my lord bound up in. 25:29
because the *s*. of all the people. 30:6
are hated of David's *s*. *2 Sam* 5:8
the *s*. of David longed to go. 13:39
to thee with all their *s*. *1 Ki* 8:48
let this child's *s*. come into. 17:21
let her alone for her *s*. is. *2 Ki* 4:27
commandments with all their *s*. 23:3
your *s*. to seek the Lord. *1 Chr* 22:19
to thee with all their *s*. *2 Chr* 6:38
Lord God with all their *s*. 15:12
given to the bitter in *s*.? *Job* 3:20
in whose hand is the *s*. of. 12:10
if your *s*. were in my *s*.'s stead. 16:4
s. of the wounded crieth out. 24:12
is perfect, converting the *s*. *Ps* 19:7
to deliver their *s*. from death. 33:19
the Lord redeemeth the *s*. of. 34:22
the redemption of their *s*. is. 49:8†
redeem their *s*. from deceit. 72:14
O deliver not the *s*. of thy. 74:19
not their *s*. from death. 78:50
rejoice the *s*. of thy servant. 86:4
they gather against the *s*. of. 94:21
sent leanness into their *s*. 106:15
thirsty, their *s*. fainted in them. 107:5
longing *s*. and filleth hungry *s*. 9
s. abhorreth all manner of meat. 18
s. is melted because of trouble. 26
suffer the *s*. of righteous. *Pr* 10:3
liberal *s*. shall be made fat. 11:25
but the *s*. of transgressors. 13:2
the *s*. of the sluggard desireth. 4
accomplished is sweet to the *s*. 19
words are sweet to the *s*. 16:24
the *s*. be without knowledge. 19:2
and an idle *s*. shall suffer hunger. 15
s. of the wicked desireth evil. 21:10
Lord will spoil *s*. of those. 22:23*
he refresheth the *s*. of his masters. 25:13
as cold waters to a thirsty *s*. so is. 25
the full *s*. loatheth an honeycomb; but to the hungry *s*. every. 27:7
woe to their *s*.! they have. *Isa* 3:9
empty the *s*. of the hungry. 32:6
s. delight itself in fatness. *Isa* 55:2
hear, and your *s*. shall live. 3
thou satisfy the afflicted *s*. 58:10
their *s*. delighteth in their. 66:3
sword reacheth to the *s*. *Jer* 4:10†
delivered the *s*. of the poor. 20:13
their *s*. shall be as a watered. 31:12
satiate the *s*. of the priests. 14
satiated the weary *s*. and I have replenished every sorrowful *s*. 25
liveth, that made us this *s*. 38:16
meat to relieve the *s*. *Lam* 1:11
when their *s*. was poured out. 2:12
the Lord is good to the *s*. that. 3:25
as *s*. of father, so *s*. of son is mine, the *s*. that sinneth. *Ezek* 18:4, 20
what your *s*. pitieth shall. 24:21
their *s*. shall not come. *Hos* 9:4*
me about, even to the *s*. *Jonah* 2:5
able to kill the *s*.: fear him that can destroy both *s*. and. *Mat* 10:28
with all the heart and *s*. *Mark* 12:33
fear came upon every *s*.: and many wonders. *Acts* 2:43
every *s*. which will not hear. 3:23
believed of one heart and *s*. 4:32
anguish on every *s*. of man that. *Rom* 2:9
let every *s*. be subject to the. 13:1
that your *s*. and body. *1 Thes* 5:23
piercing to dividing of *s*. *Heb* 4:12
we have as an anchor of the *s*. 6:19
believe to saving of the *s*. 10:39
shall save a *s*. from death. *Jas* 5:20
which war against the *s*. *1 Pet* 2:11
Lot vexed his righteous *s*. *2 Pet* 2:8
and every living *s*. died. *Rev* 16:3

see **afflicted, bitterness**

***his* soul**

his s. clave to Dinah. *Gen* 34:3
we saw anguish of *his s*. 42:21
ransom for *his s*. to Lord. *Ex* 30:12
to bind *his s*. to Lord. *Num* 30:2
his s. was grieved for. *Judg* 10:16
she urged him, so that *his s*. 16:16
Josiah who turned to the Lord with all *his s*. *2 Ki* 23:25; *2 Chr* 34:31
and *his s*. within him. *Job* 14:22
in the bitterness of *his s*. 21:25
what *his s*. desireth, even. 23:13
when God taketh away *his s*. 27:8
by wishing a curse to *his s*. 31:30*
he keepeth back *his s*. from. 33:18
his s. abhorreth dainty meat. 20
yea, *his s*. draweth near unto. 22
he will deliver *his s*. from. 28, 30
loveth violence, *his s*. hateth. *Ps* 11:5
who hath not lifted up *his s*. 24:4
his s. shall dwell at ease. 25:13
he lived he blessed *his s*. 49:18
shall he deliver *his s*. from ? 89:48
those that condemn *his s*. 109:31
if he steal to satisfy *his s*. *Pr* 6:30
eateth to satisfying of *his s*. 13:25
his way, preserveth *his s*. 16:17
lips are the snare of *his s*. 18:7
his mouth, keepeth *his s*. 21:23
that doth keep *his s*. shall be. 22:5
deliver *his s*. from hell. 23:14
but the just seek *his s*. 29:10*
that he should make *his s*. *Eccl* 2:24
wanteth nothing for *his s*. 6:2
and *his s*. be not filled with good. 3
his s. is empty; behold he is faint and *his s*. hath appetite. *Isa* 29:8
that he cannot deliver *his s*. 44:20
shalt make *his s*. an offering. 53:10
he shall see of the travail of *his s*. 11
because he poured out *his s*. 12
his s. shall be satisfied. *Jer* 50:19
deliver every man *his s*. 51:6*, 45
right, he shall save *his s*. *Ezek* 18:27
warning, shall deliver *his s*. 33:5
his s. that is lifted up, is not. *Hab* 2:4
lose *his* own *s*.? what can man . . . for *s*.? *Mat* 16:26*; *Mark* 8:37*
his s. was not left in hell. *Acts* 2:31*

***my* soul**

and *my s*. shall live. *Gen* 12:13
thither, and *my s*. shall live. 19:20
that *my s*. may bless thee. 27:4, 25
O *my s*. come not thou into. 49:6
and *my s*. shall not. *Lev* 26:11, 30
O *my s*. thou hast trodden down. *Judg* 5:21
poured out *my s*. *1 Sam* 1:15
yet thou huntest *my s*. to. 24:11†
because *my s*. was precious. 26:21*
who hath redeemed *my s*. *2 Sam* 4:9; *1 Ki* 1:29
the things *my s*. refused. *Job* 6:7
my s. chooseth strangling. 7:15
yet would I not know *my s*. 9:21*
my s. is weary of life, I will speak in bitterness of *my s*. 10:1
ye vex *my s*. with words ? 19:2
who hath vexed *my s*. 27:2
pursue *my s*. as the wind. 30:15*
and now *my s*. is poured out. 16
my s. grieved for the poor ? 25
which say of *my s*., There is. *Ps* 3:2
my s. is sore vexed. 6:3
deliver *my s*. 4; 17:13; 22:20; 116:4; 120:2
lest he tear *my s*. like a lion. 7:2
let the enemy persecute *my s*. 5
how say ye to *my s*. Flee as a ? 11:1
I take counsel in *my s*.? 13:2
not leave *my s*. in hell. 16:10; *Acts* 2:27
he restoreth *my s*. *Ps* 23:3
to thee I lift *my s*. 25:1
O keep *my s*. and deliver me. 20
gather not *my s*. with sinners. 26:9
thou hast brought up *my s*. 30:3
thou hast known *my s*. in. 31:7
yea, *my s*. and my belly are. 9
my s. shall make her boast in. 34:2
my s. I am thy salvation. 35:3
put to shame that seek after *my s*. 4
they have digged a pit for *my s*. 7
and *my s*. shall be joyful in. 9
me to the spoiling of *my s*. 12
as for me, I humbled *my s*. 13
rescue *my s*. from their. 17
let them be confounded that seek after *my s*. 40:14
heal *my s*. for I have sinned. 41:4
as the hart, so panteth *my s*. 42:1
my s. thirsteth for the. 2; 143:6
I remember, I pour out *my s*. 42:4
cast down, O *my s*.? 5, 11; 43:5
O my God, *my s*. is cast down. 42:6
God will redeem *my s*. from. 49:15
oppressors seek after *my s*. 54:3
with them that uphold *my s*. 4
hath delivered *my s*. in peace. 55:18
steps, when they wait for *my s*. 56:6
for thou hast delivered *my s*. 13
be merciful, O God: for *my s*. 57:1
my s. is among lions. 4
my s. is bowed down. 6
for lo, they lie in wait for *my s*. 59:3
truly *my s*. waiteth upon God. 62:1
my s. wait thou only upon God. 5
O God, *my s*. thirsteth for. 63:1
my s. shall be satisfied as with. 5
my s. followeth hard after thee. 8
but those that seek *my s*. to. 9
what God hath done for *my s*. 66:16
waters are come in unto *my s*. 69:1
when I wept and chastened *my s*. 10
draw nigh to *my s*. and redeem it. 18
that seek after *my s*. 70:2; 71:13
my s. shall rejoice which. 71:23
my sore ran, *my s*. refused to. 77:2
my s. longeth for the courts. 84:2
preserve *my s*. 86:2
O Lord, do I lift up *my s*. 4; 143:8
thou hast delivered *my s*. 86:13
violent men sought after *my s*. 14
my s. is full of troubles, my life. 88:3
Lord, why castest thou off *my s*.? 14
my s. had almost dwelt in. 94:17
thy comforts delight *my s*. 19
bless the Lord, O *my s*. 103:1, 2, 22; 104:1, 35
that speak against *my s*. 109:20
return unto thy rest, O *my s*. 116:7
for thou hast delivered *my s*. 8
my s. breaketh for the. 119:20
my s. cleaveth to the dust. 25
my s. melteth for heaviness. 28
my s. fainteth for thy salvation. 81
my s. is continually in my hand. 109
therefore doth *my s*. keep them. 129
my s. hath kept thy testimonies. 167

let my s. live, and it. Ps 119:175
deliver my s. O Lord, from. 120:2
my s. hath dwelt with him that. 6
I wait for the Lord, my s. 130:5, 6
my s. is even as a weaned. 131:2
me with strength in my s. 138:3
my s. knoweth right well. 139:14
leave not my s. destitute. 141:8
no man cared for my s. 142:4
bring my s. out of prison, that I. 7
enemy hath persecuted my s. 143:3
O Lord, bring my s. out of. 11
praise the Lord, O my s. 146:1
I bereave my s. of good ? Eccl 4:8
which yet my s. seeketh, but. 7:28
O thou whom my s. loveth.
S of S 1:7; 3:1, 2, 3, 4
my s. failed when he spake. 5:6
my s. made me like chariots. 6:12
and feasts my s. hateth. Isa 1:14
with my s. have I desired thee. 26:9
thou hast in love to my s. 38:17
mine elect, in whom my s. delighteth. 42:1
my s. shall be joyful in. 61:10
hast heard, O my s. Jer 4:19
my s. is wearied because of. 31
my s. be avenged ? 5:9, 29; 9:9
O Jerusalem, lest my s. depart. 6:8
beloved of my s. into the. 12:7
my s. shall weep in secret. 13:17
have digged a pit for my s. 18:20
over them with my whole s. 32:41
that should relieve my s. Lam 1:16
thou hast removed my s. far. 3:17
my s. hath them still in. 20
Lord is my portion, saith my s. 24
pleaded the causes of my s. 58
behold, my s. hath not. Ezek 4:14
my s. fainted within me. Jonah 2:7
my body for the sin of my s. Mi 6:7
my s. desired the first ripe fruit. 7:1
cut off, my s. loathed. Zech 11:8
beloved, in whom my s. Mat 12:18
my s. is exceeding sorrowful. 26:38
Mark 14:34
my s. doth magnify. Luke 1:46
I will say to my s., Soul, eat. 12:19
my s. is troubled, and. John 12:27
for a record upon my s. 2 Cor 1:23
my s. shall have no pleasure in.
Heb 10:38

***our* soul**

our s. is dried away. Num 11:6
no bread, our s. loatheth this. 21:5
our s. waiteth for Lord. Ps 33:20
for our s. is bowed down. 44:25
who holdeth our s. in life. 66:9
our s. is exceedingly filled. 123:4
gone over our s. 124:4, 5
our s. is escaped as a bird out. 7
the desire of our s. is to. Isa 26:8

***own* soul**

if a friend is as thine own s.
Deut 13:6
knit to David, and he loved him as his own s. 1 Sam 18:1, 3; 20:17
keep alive his own s. Ps 22:29
destroyeth his own s. Pr 6:32
sinneth, wrongeth his own s. 8:36
doeth good to his own s. 11:17
he that refuseth instruction despiseth his own s. 15:32
wisdom, loveth his own s. 19:8
commandments keepeth his own s. 16
king, sinneth against his own s. 20:2
with thief, hateth his own s. 29:24
gain whole world and lose his own s.?
Mat 16:26; Mark 8:36
pierce through thy own s. Luke 2:35

***that* soul**

that s. shall be cut off from his.
Gen 17:14; Ex 31:14; Lev 7:20
21, 25, 27; 19:8; Num 15:30
that s. shall be cut off from Israel.
Ex 12:15; Num 19:13
whoso eateth leavened bread, that s. shall be cut. Ex 12:19; Num 19:20
face against that s. Lev 17:10; 20:6
that s. shall be cut off. 22:3
that s. will I destroy from. 23:30
that s. shall utterly be. Num 15:31

***thy* soul**

eat, that thy s. may. Gen 27:19, 31
take heed, and keep thy s. Deut 4:9
if thou seek him with all thy s. 29
thy God with all thy s. 6:5; 30:6
Lord thy God with all thy s. 10:12
thy s. lusteth after. 12:15; 14:26
do them with all thy s. 26:16
with all thine heart and thy s. 30:2
unto the Lord with all thy s. 10
take as much as thy s. desireth.
1 Sam 2:16
whatsoever thy s. desireth, I. 20:4
to all the desire of thy s. 23:20
risen to pursue and seek thy s. 25:29
reign according to all thy s. desireth.
1 Ki 11:37
Lord shall preserve thy s. Ps 121:7
is pleasant to thy s. Pr 2:10
shall they be life to thy s. and. 3:22
and let not thy s. spare for. 19:18*
and get a snare to thy s. 22:25
he that keepeth thy s., doth ? 24:12
knowledge of wisdom be to thy s. 14
give delight to thy s. 29:17
which have said to thy s. Isa 51:23
if thou draw out thy s. to. 58:10
the Lord shall satisfy thy s. 11
hath thy s. loathed Zion ? Jer 14:19
then thy s. shall live. 38:17, 20
hast delivered thy s. Ezek 3:19; 21
33:9
sinned against thy s. Hab 2:10
heart and with all thy s. Mat 22:27
Mark 12:30; Luke 10:27
this night thy s. shall be. Luke 12:20
prosper, even as thy s. prospereth.
3 John 2
the fruits thy s. lusted. Rev 18:14
see **liveth**

souls

Abraham took s. they. Gen 12:5
the s. by Leah were thirty. 46:15
by Zilpah sixteen s. 18
by Rachel fourteen s. 22
all the s. Jacob had by Bilhah. 25
all the s. that came into Egypt. 26
Egypt, were two s.: all s. of house of Jacob were seventy s. 27; Ex 1:5
according to number of s. Ex 12:4
an atonement for your s. 30:15, 16
Lev 17:11; Num 31:50
even s. that commit. Lev 18:29
make your s. abominable. 20:25
against their own s. Num 16:38*
wherewith have bound their s. 30:9
destroyed them and all the s. that.
Josh 10:28, 30, 32; 11:11
your hearts and in all your s. 23:14
s. of thine enemies. 1 Sam 25:29
and shall save the s. of. Ps 72:13
preserveth the s. of his saints. 97:10
he that winneth s. is wise. Pr 11:30
a true witness delivereth s. 14:25
spirit should fail, and s. Isa 57:16
is found the blood of s. Jer 2:34
ye shall find rest for your s. 6:16
Mat 11:29
procure great evil against our s.
Jer 26:19
great evil against your s.? 44:7
meat to relieve their s. Lam 1:19
not satisfy their s. Ezek 7:19
to hunt s. will ye hunt s. . . . will ye save the s. alive.? 13:18, 20
to slay the s. that should not die. 19
deliver but their own s. 14:14
all s. are mine. 18:4
they have devoured s. 22:25
are like wolves to destroy s. 27
patience possess your s. Luke 21:19
added to them 3000 s. Acts 2:41
Jacob and his kindred 75 s. 7:14
confirming s. of the disciples. 14:22
troubled you, subverting your s. 15:24
in all in the ship 276 s. 27:37
imparted our own s. 1 Thes 2:8
for they watch for your s. Heb 13:17
is able to save your s. Jas 1:21
the salvation of your s. 1 Pet 1:9
purified your s. in obeying truth. 22
to the Shepherd of your s. 2:25
wherein few, that is, eight s. 3:20
keeping of their s. to him. 1 Pet 4:19
sin; beguiling unstable s. 2 Pet 2:14
I saw under the altar the s. Rev 6:9
no man buyeth slaves and s. 18:13
I saw the s. of them that were. 20:4
see **afflict**

sound, *substantive*

his s. shall be heard. Ex 28:35
the s. of a shaken leaf. Lev 26:36
as soon as ye hear the s. of the trumpet. Josh 6:5, 20
hearest the s. of a going in the tops.
2 Sam 5:24; 1 Chr 14:15
ark with shouting and the s. of the.
2 Sam 6:15; 1 Chr 15:28
when ye hear the s. say. 2 Sam 15:10
rent with the s. of them. 1 Ki 1:40
when Joab heard the s. of the. 41
when Ahijah heard the s. of. 14:6
there is a s. of abundance of. 18:41
is not the s. of his master's feet behind him ? 2 Ki 6:32
but Asaph made a s. 1 Chr 16:5
those that should make a s. 42
as one, to make one s. 2 Chr 5:13
in what place ye hear s. Neh 4:20
a dreadful s. in his ears. Job 15:21
at the s. of the organ. 21:12
hear the s. that goeth out. 37:2
nor believeth he it is the s. 39:24*
the Lord gone up with s. Ps 47:5
water, skies sent out a s. 77:17
people that know the joyful s. 89:15
the harp with a solemn s. 92:3
trumpets and s. of cornet. 98:6
praise him with the s. of. 150:3
s. of the grinding is low. Eccl 12:4
O my soul, the s. of. Jer 4:19
I hear the s. of the trumpet ? 21
Hearken to the s. of trumpet. 6:17
trembled at s. of the neighing. 8:16
I will take from them s. of. 25:10
where we shall hear no s. 42:14
s. of battle is in the land. 50:22
a s. of a cry cometh from. 51:54
s. of the cherubim's. Ezek 10:5
the s. of thy harps shall be. 26:13
shall not the isles shake at the s.? 15
suburbs shall shake at s. of. 27:28
I made nations to shake at s. 31:16
heareth the s. and taketh. 33:4
he heard s. of trumpet and took. 5
when ye hear the s. Dan 3:5, 7, 10, 15
Moab shall die with s. Amos 2:2
that chant to the s. of the viol. 6:5
his angels with a great s. Mat 24:31
hearest the s. but canst. John 3:8*
suddenly there came a s. Acts 2:2
verily their s. went into. Rom 10:18
without life giving s. 1 Cor 14:7*
trumpet give an uncertain s. 8*
ye are not come to the s. Heb 12:19
s. of many waters. Rev 1:15*
s. of their wings was as the s. 9:9
the s. of a millstone shall be. 18:22*

sound, *adjective*

let my heart be s. in. Ps 119:80*
he layeth up s. wisdom. Pr 2:7
my son, keep s. wisdom and. 3:21
counsel is mine and s. wisdom. 8:14
s. heart is the life of the flesh. 14:30
received him safe and s. Luke 15:27
contrary to s. doctrine. 1 Tim 1:10
but hath given us the spirit of a s. mind. 2 Tim 1:7*
hold fast the form of s. words. 13
will not endure s. doctrine. 4:3
may be able by s. doctrine. Tit 1:9
rebuke them, that they may be s. 13
the things which become s. 2:1
that the aged men be s. in faith. 2
s. speech that cannot be. 8

sound, *verb*

of jubile to s. in day of atonement make the trumpet s. Lev 25:9*
ye shall not s. an alarm. Num 10:7
and Asaph were appointed to s.
1 Chr 15:19
bowels shall s. for Moab. Isa 16:11
heart shall s. for Moab. Jer 48:36
and s. an alarm in my. Joel 2:1
therefore do not s. a. Mat 6:2
for the trumpet shall s. 1 Cor 15:52

angels prepared themselves to s. Rev 8:6
three angels who are yet to s. 13
seventh angel shall begin to s. 10:7

sounded

the trumpet s. long. Ex 19:19
I have s. my father. 1 Sam 20:12
priests s. trumpets. 2 Chr 7:6, 13, 14
the people rejoiced, and s. 23:13
sang and the trumpeters s. 29:28
he that s. the trumpet. Neh 4:18
as soon as voice of salutation s. Luke 1:44
from you s. out the word. 1 Thes 1:8
the first angel s. and there. Rev 8:7
the second s. 8, 10, 12
the fifth s. 9:1, 13
seventh s. 11:15

sounded *(of the sea)*

they s. and found it twenty fathoms; they s. again and. Acts 27:28

soundeth

when the trumpet s. long. Ex 19:13

sounding

instruments of music s. 1 Chr 15:16
them 120 priests s. 2 Chr 5:12
his priests with s. trumpets. 13:12*
upon the high s. cymbals. Ps 150:5
where is thy zeal, the s.? Isa 63:15*
the s. again of mountains. Ezek 7:7*
charity, I am as s. brass. 1 Cor 13:1

soundness

there is no s. in my flesh. Ps 38:3, 7
no s. in it, but wounds. Isa 1:6
this perfect s. in presence. Acts 3:16

sounds

give a distinction in the s. 1 Cor 14:7

sour

when the s. grape is. Isa 18:5*
fathers have eaten a s. grape, and. Jer 31:29; Ezek 18:2
man that eateth s. grape. Jer 31:30
their drink is s. they have. Hos 4:18

south

journeyed towards the s. Gen 12:9
Abram went up into the s. 13:1
spread abroad to north and s. 28:14
tabernacle toward the s. Ex 26:35
dwell in the land of the s. Num 13:29
possess thou west and s. Deut 33:23
smote country of the s. Josh 10:40
abide in their coast on the s. 18:5
the Canaanites in the s. Judg 1:9
out of a place toward s. 1 Sam 20:41
against the s. of Judah, s. 27:10
had invaded the s. 30:1, 14
they went out to the s. 2 Sam 24:7
three looking towards s. 1 Ki 7:25; 2 Chr 4:4
porters were toward s. 1 Chr 9:24
Philistines invaded s. 2 Chr 28:18
the chambers of the s. Job 9:9
out of s. cometh the whirlwind. 37:9
her wings toward the s. 39:26
neither from east nor s. Ps 75:6
the north and s. thou hast. 89:12
them from the north and s. 107:3
captivity as the streams in s. 126:4
goeth toward the s. Eccl 1:6
tree fall toward the s. or the. 11:3
as whirlwinds in the s. Isa 21:1
of the beasts of the s. 30:6
and I will say to the s., Keep. 43:6
the cities of the s. shall. Jer 13:19
from the s. bringing burnt. 17:26
buy fields in the cities of the s. 32:44
in the cities of the s. shall the. 33:13
toward the s. and drop thy word toward s. . . . s. field. Ezek 20:46
forest of s. . . . faces from s. to. 47
against all flesh from s. to. 21:4
as the frame of a city on s. 40:2
he brought me toward the s. 24
prospect was toward the s. 44
another door was toward the s. 41:11
by way of the s. gate; and he that entereth by the way of s. go. 46:9
waxed great toward the s. Dan 8:9
and the king of the s. shall. 11:5
king's daughter of the s. shall. 6
king of the s. shall come into his. 9
king of the s. shall be moved. 11
arms of the s. shall not. Dan 11:15
and the king of the s. shall be. 25
return, and come toward the s. 29
the king of the s. shall push at. 40
they of s. shall possess. Ob 19
shall possess the cities of the s. 20
when men inhabited the s. Zech 7:7
go with whirlwinds of the s. 9:14
mountain remove toward the s. 14:4
queen of the s. shall rise. Mat 12:42
come from s. to sit down. Luke 13:29
and go toward the s. Acts 8:26
on the s. three gates, on. Rev 21:13

south *border*

s. border the outmost coast of the salt sea. Num 34:3
the s. border of Judah. Josh 15:2

south *country*

sojourned toward the s. country. Gen 20:1
dwelt in the s. country. 24:62
Joshua took all the s. country. Josh 11:16; 12:8
go forth toward s. country. Zech 6:6

south *field*

the forest of the s. field. Ezek 20:46

south *land*

thou hast given me a s. land. Josh 15:19; Judg 1:15

south *quarter*

s. quarter from Zin by. Num 34:3
s. quarter from end of. Josh 18:15

south *side*

twenty boards on the s. side. Ex 26:18; 36:23
on s. side shall be standard of. Num 2:10
camps which lie on the s. side. 10:6
he measured the s. side. Ezek 42:18
the waters came at the s. side. 47:1
and the s. side 4500. 48:16, 33

southward

to Abraham, Look s. Gen 13:14
pitch on side of tabernacle s. Num 3:29
Get ye up this way s. 13:17
I saw the ram pushing s. Dan 8:4

south *west*

lying towards the s. west. Acts 27:12

south *wind*

earth by the s. wind. Job 37:17
he brought in the s. wind. Ps 78:26
come, thou s. wind. S of S 4:16
when see s. wind blow. Luke 12:55
the s. wind blew softly. Acts 27:13

sow

the s. washed, to her. 2 Pet 2:22

sow, *verb*

and ye shall s. the land. Gen 47:23
six years s. the land. Ex 23:10; Lev 25:3
shall not s. with mingled seed. Lev 19:19; Deut 22:9
7th year thou shalt not s. Lev 25:4, 11
we shall not s. nor gather. 20
ye shall s. the eighth year. 22
ye shall s. your seed in vain. 26:16
in the third year s. ye. 2 Ki 19:29; Isa 37:30
they that s. wickedness. Job 4:8
then let me s. and let another. 31:8
s. fields, and plant. Ps 107:37
they that s. in tears shall. 126:5
he that observeth the wind shall not s. Eccl 11:4
in the morning s. thy seed, and. 6
plow all day to s.? Isa 28:24
give rain of seed, thou shalt s. 30:23
blessed are ye that s. beside. 32:20
break fallow ground, s. not. Jer 4:3
I will s. the house of Israel. 31:27
ye build house nor s. seed. 35:7
and I will s. her unto me. Hos 2:23
s. to yourselves in righteousness. 10:12
thou shalt s. but thou. Mi 6:15
I will s. them among. Zech 10:9
fowls of the air s. not. Mat 6:26
a sower went forth to s.; and when he. 13:3; Mark 4:3; Luke 8:5
didst not thou s. good seed? Mat 13:27
ravens: they neither s. Luke 12:24
that thou didst not s. 19:21, 22

sowed

Isaac s. in that land. Gen 26:12
Abimelech s. Shechem. Judg 9:45
when he s. some fell by the way. Mat 13:4; Mark 4:4; Luke 8:5
which s. good seed. Mat 13:24
the enemy s. tares. 25, 39

sowedst

Egypt, where thou s. Deut 11:10

sower

give seed to s. and bread. Isa 55:10
cut off s. from Babylon. Jer 50:16
behold, a s. went forth to sow. Mat 13:3; Mark 4:3; Luke 8:5
the parable of the s. Mat 13:18
s. soweth the word. Mark 4:14
ministereth seed to the s. 2 Cor 9:10

sowest

that which thou s. is. 1 Cor 15:36
thou s. not that body that shall. 37

soweth

he s. discord. Pr 6:14
he that s. discord. 19
to him that s. righteousness. 11:18
a froward man s. strife. 16:28*
he that s. iniquity shall. 22:8
overtake him that s. seed. Amos 9:13
he that s. good seed is. Mat 13:37
sower s. the word. Mark 4:14
both he that s. and reapeth. John 4:36
one s. and another reapeth. 37
s. sparingly; he who s. bountifully. 2 Cor 9:6
for whatsoever a man s. Gal 6:7
that s. to his flesh, shall reap corruption; but he that s. to the. 8

sowing

fall upon any s. seed. Lev 11:37
shall reach to the s. time. 26:5

sown

fall on sowing seed to be s. Lev 11:37
valley neither eared nor s. Deut 21:4
lest the fruit of thy seed s. 22:9
that land is not s. nor beareth. 29:23
when Israel had s. the. Judg 6:3
light is s. for the righteous. Ps 97:11
every thing s. by the brooks. Isa 19:7
planted, yea, shall not be s. 40:24
garden causeth the things s. 61:11
after me in a land not s. Jer 2:2
they have s. wheat, but shall. 12:13
shall be tilled and s. Ezek 36:9
have s. the wind, shall. Hos 8:7
more of thy name be s. Nah 1:14
ye have s. much, and. Hag 1:6
catcheth away that which was s. Mat 13:19; Mark 4:15
reaping where thou hast not s. Mat 25:24
these are they which s. Mark 4:16
s. among thorns. 18
are s. in good ground. 20
which when it is s. is less than. 31
if we have s. to you. 1 Cor 9:11
it is s. in corruption. 15:42
is s. in dishonour. 43
it is s. a natural body, it is raised. 44
multiply your seed s. and increase. 2 Cor 9:10
righteousness is s. in peace. Jas 3:18

space

abode with him the s. of. Gen 29:14
and put a s. betwixt drove. 32:16
the s. of seven sabbaths. Lev 25:8*
if it be not redeemed in the s. of. 30
there shall be a s. between. Josh 3:4
s. between David's company and. 1 Sam 26:13
for a little s. grace. Ezra 9:8*
s. of two full years. Jer 28:11
s. of one hour after. Luke 22:59
about s. of three hours. Acts 5:7
the apostles forth a little s. 34*
beasts by the s. of forty years. 7:42
gave judges about the s. 13:20
God gave them Saul for the s. 21
he spake boldly the s. of three. 19:8

continued by the *s.* of two years.
Acts 19:10
all with one voice about *s.* of. 34
by the *s.* of three years I. 20:31
it rained not by the *s.* of. *Jas* 5:17*
I gave her *s.* to repent of her.
Rev 2:21*
there was silence about the *s.* 8:1
blood came by the *s.* of 1600. 14:20*
he must continue a short *s.* 17:10*

Spain

take my journey into *S.* *Rom* 15:24
I will come by you into *S.* 28

spake

(*Revisions frequently change to* said)
Lot went out, and *s.* to. *Gen* 19:14
saying, Thus *s.* the man. 24:30
while he yet *s.* with them. 29:9
it came to pass as she *s.* to. 39:10
that is it that I *s.* unto you. 42:14
for he *s.* unto them by an. 23
old man of whom ye *s.* is. 43:27
younger brother of whom ye *s.*? 29
and Joseph wept when they *s.* 50:17
Miriam and Aaron *s.* *Num* 12:1
the people *s.* against God. 21:5
so I *s.* to you, and ye. *Deut* 1:43
bring thee by way whereof I *s.* 28:68
they *s.* to the master. *Judg* 19:22
kinsman of whom Boaz *s.* *Ruth* 4:1
now Hannah *s.* in her heart.
1 Sam 1:13
On this manner *s.* David. 18:24
nevertheless Saul *s.* not any. 20:26
for the people *s.* of stoning him. 30:6
was alive, we *s.* to him. *2 Sam* 12:18
while he yet *s.*, behold. *1 Ki* 1:42
s. before king Solomon. 3:22
saying which Elisha *s.* *2 Ki* 2:22
Thus and thus *s.* he to me. 9:12
went up at saying which Gad *s.*
1 Chr 21:19
one *s.* saying after. *2 Chr* 18:19
Hezekiah *s.* comfortably to them.
30:22; 32:6
servant *s.* yet more against. 32:16
s. against the God of Jerusalem. 19
that *s.* to Manasseh in the. 33:18
children *s.* half in speech. *Neh* 13:24
to pass, when they *s.* *Esth* 3:4
they sat down, and none *s.* *Job* 2:13
and they *s.* against me. 19:18
after my words they *s.* not. 29:22
for they *s.* not, but stood still. 32:16
fire burned, then *s.* I with. *Ps* 39:3
yea, they *s.* against God. 78:19
so that he *s.* unadvisedly. 106:33
man *s.* to Ithiel and Ucal. *Pr* 30:1
my beloved *s.* and said. *S of S* 2:10
my soul failed when he *s.* 5:6
I hearkened and heard, they *s.*
Jer 8:6
for since I *s.* I cried out, I cried. 20:8
so I *s.* to the people in. *Ezek* 24:18
words which the horn *s.* *Dan* 7:11
Ephraim *s.* trembling. *Hos* 13:1
that feared Lord *s.* often. *Mal* 3:16
while he *s.* these things. *Mat* 9:18
17:5; 26:47; *Mark* 5:35; 14:43
Luke 8:49; 22:47, 60
devil was cast out, dumb *s.*
Mat 9:33; 12:22; *Luke* 11:14
they perceived that he *s.* of them.
Mat 21:45
as he *s.* to our fathers. *Luke* 1:55
not the saying which he *s.* 2:50
he *s.* unto them of the kingdom. 9:11
who *s.* of his decease which he. 31
other things blasphemously *s.* 22:65
remember how he *s.* to you. 24:6
as they *s.* Jesus stood in midst. 36
was he of whom I *s.* *John* 1:15
no man *s.* openly of him for. 7:13
Never man *s.* like this man. 46
not that he *s.* of the Father. 8:27
they were which he *s.* to them. 10:6
all things that John *s.* of this. 41
howbeit Jesus *s.* of his death. 11:13
this *s.* he not of himself. 51
others said, An angel *s.* to. 12:29
fulfilled which he *s.* 38; 18:9, 32
when he saw his glory, and *s.* 12:41
doubting of whom he *s.* *John* 13:22
who it should be of whom he *s.* 24
for what intent he *s.* this. 28
this *s.* he, signifying by what. 21:19
resist spirit by which he *s.* *Acts* 6:10
those things which Philip *s.* 8:6
while Peter yet *s.* these. 10:44
Jews *s.* against those things. 13:45
so *s.* that a great multitude. 14:1
but *s.* evil of that way before. 19:9
for the words which he *s.* 20:38
voice of him that *s.* to me. 22:9
as he thus *s.* for himself. 26:24
Well *s.* the Holy Ghost by. 28:25
child, I *s.* as child. *1 Cor* 13:11
that ye all *s.* with tongues. 14:5
the blessedness ye *s.* of ? *Gal* 4:15
of which tribe Moses *s.* *Heb* 7:14
him that *s.* on earth. 12:25
holy men of God *s.* as. *2 Pet* 1:21
voice that *s.* with me. *Rev* 1:12
another beast *s.* as a dragon. 13:11

God **spake**

Jacob called the place where *God s.* Beth-el. *Gen* 35:15
God s. all these words. *Ex* 20:1
the Lord our *God s.* to us. *Deut* 1:6
not one thing failed of good things *God s.* *Josh* 23:14
how in the bush *God s.* *Mark* 12:26
we know that *God s.* *John* 9:29
and *God s.* on this wise. *Acts* 7:6
God who *s.* in time past. *Heb* 1:1
see **Lord**

Lord or *God* **spake,** *implicitly*

who *s.* to me, and sware. *Gen* 24:7
behold the man whom I *s.* to thee of.
1 Sam 9:17
Lord hath done to him as he *s.* 28:17
s. I a word with any of ? *2 Sam* 7:7
God said, The rock of Israel *s.* 23:3
word which I *s.* unto. *1 Ki* 6:12
fulfilled that which he *s.* *2 Chr* 6:4
he *s.* to him, and gave him. 32:24
he *s.* and it was done. *Ps* 33:9
he *s.* unto them in the cloudy. 99:7
he *s.* and there came flies. 105:31
he *s.* and the locusts came. 34
when I *s.* ye did not hear. *Isa* 65:12
66:4
I *s.* to you, rising up. *Jer* 7:13
I *s.* not to your fathers, I. 22
I sent them not, neither *s.* 14:14
commanded not, nor *s.* it. 19:5
I *s.* unto thee in thy prosperity. 22:21
for since I *s.* against him. 31:20
a voice of one that *s.* *Ezek* 1:28; 2:2
he *s.* unto the man clothed. 10:2
his words which he *s.* *Dan* 9:12
in Beth-el, there he *s.* with. *Hos* 12:4
as he *s.* by mouth of his. *Luke* 1:70
words which I *s.* to you. 24:44
he *s.* in a certain place. *Heb* 4:4

spakest

art thou the man that *s.*? *Judg* 13:11
the silver thou *s.* of also. 17:2
words which thou *s.* *1 Sam* 28:21
thou *s.* also with thy mouth, and hast.
1 Ki 8:24; *2 Chr* 6:15
be verified which thou *s.* *1 Ki* 8:26
separate them, as thou *s.* by. 53
s. with them from heaven. *Neh* 9:13
then thou *s.* in vision to. *Ps* 89:19
since thou *s.* of him. *Jer* 48:27

span

a *s.* shall be the length, and a *s.* the.
Ex 28:16; 39:9
height six cubits and a *s.* *1 Sam* 17:4
out heaven with the *s.*? *Isa* 40:12
eat their children of a *s.* *Lam* 2:20*
of the altar shall be a *s.* *Ezek* 43:13

spanned

hath *s.* the heavens. *Isa* 48:13*

spare

not *s.* the place for the fifty righteous.
Gen 18:24
then I will *s.* all the place. 26
thou shalt not *s.* nor. *Deut* 13:8
Lord will not *s.* him, but. 29:20*
Amalek, *s.* them not. *1 Sam* 15:3
and *s.* me according to. *Neh* 13:22
let him not *s.*; I have not. *Job* 6:10
reins asunder, doth not *s.* *Job* 16:13
though he *s.* it and forsake. 20:13
cast upon him, and not *s.* 27:22
they *s.* not to spit in my face. 30:10
O *s.* me that I may. *Ps* 39:13
shall *s.* the poor and needy. 72:13*
he will not *s.* in the day. *Pr* 6:34
thy soul *s.* for his crying. 19:18*
no man shall *s.* his brother. *Isa* 9:19
eye shall not *s.* children. 13:18
break it, he shall not *s.* 30:14
s. not, lengthen cords. 54:2
cry aloud, *s.* not, lift up voice. 58:1
I will not *s.* them. *Jer* 13:14
Ezek 24:14
he shall not *s.* them. *Jer* 21:7
s. no arrows. 50:14
s. ye not her young men. 51:3
nor shall mine eye *s.* nor will I have.
Ezek 5:11; 7:4, 9; 8:18; 9:10
let not your eye *s.* neither. 9:5
let them say, *S.* thy people. *Joel* 2:17
should not I *s.* Nineveh ? *Jonah* 4:11*
and not *s.* continually to. *Hab* 1:17
I will *s.* them as a man. *Mal* 3:17
have bread enough to *s.* *Luke* 15:17
lest he also *s.* not thee. *Rom* 11:21
trouble, but I *s.* you. *1 Cor* 7:28
that to *s.* you I came not. *2 Cor* 1:23
come again, I will not *s.* 13:2

spared

the people *s.* Agag. *1 Sam* 15:9
for the people *s.* the best of the. 15
kill thee, but mine eye *s.* 24:10
s. to take of his own flock, and.
2 Sam 12:4
king *s.* Mephibosheth son of. 21:7
master hath *s.* Naaman. *2 Ki* 5:20
he *s.* not their soul. *Ps* 78:50
mine eye *s.* them from. *Ezek* 20:17
he that *s.* not his own Son. *Rom* 8:32
if God *s.* not the natural. 11:21
if God *s.* not the angels. *2 Pet* 2:4
and *s.* not the old world, but. 5

spareth

he that *s.* his rod. *Pr* 13:24
he that hath knowledge, *s.* 17:27
righteous giveth, and *s.* not. 21:26
them, as a man *s.* his son. *Mal* 3:17

sparing

enter in, not *s.* the flock. *Acts* 20:29

sparingly

who soweth *s.* shall reap *s.* *2 Cor* 9:6

spark

and the *s.* of his fire shall. *Job* 18:5
maker of it shall be as a *s.* *Isa* 1:31

sparkled

s. like the colour of. *Ezek* 1:7

sparks

trouble, as *s.* fly upward. *Job* 5:7
go burning lamps, *s.* of fire. 41:19
yourselves about with *s.* *Isa* 50:11*

sparrow

s. hath found an house. *Ps* 84:3
I am as a *s.* alone upon the. 102:7

sparrows

are not two *s.* sold for ? *Mat* 10:29
are of more value than many *s.* 31
Luke 12:7
are not five *s.* sold for ? *Luke* 12:6

spat

spoken, he *s.* on ground. *John* 9:6

speak

(*Revisions frequently,* say *or* talk)
on me to *s.* to God. *Gen* 18:27, 31
we cannot *s.* unto thee bad. 24:50
take heed thou *s.* not to. 31:24
s. to my lord Esau. 32:4, 19
say ? what shall we *s.*? 44:16
I know that he can *s.* well. *Ex* 4:14
since I came to *s.* to Pharaoh. 5:23
thou shalt *s.* all that I command. 7:2
shalt not *s.* in a cause to decline. 23:2
where I will meet you, to *s.* 29:42
wherefore should Egyptians *s.*? 32:12
until he went in to *s.* with. 34:35
were ye not afraid to *s.*? *Num* 12:8
the fame of thee will *s.* 14:15
why they that *s.* in proverbs. 21:27
as the Lord shall *s.* to me. 22:8
I *s.* to thee, that thou shalt *s.* 35

Balak, and thus thou shalt *s.* *Num* 23:5
must I not take heed to *s.* that? 12
of Zelophehad *s.* right. 27:7
words which he shall *s.* *Deut* 18:19
which shall presume to *s.* a word. 20
and thou shalt *s.* and say. 26:5
your children might *s.* to. *Josh* 22:24
that a man cannot *s.* to. *1 Sam* 25:17
went also to *s.* to David. *2 Sam* 3:19
Joab took him aside to *s.* with. 27
so did Nathan *s.* to David. 7:17
why *s.* ye not one word of? 19:10
near hither that I may *s.* with. 20:16
they were wont to *s.* in old time. 18
she went to *s.* to him. *1 Ki* 2:19
wilt *s.* good words to them. 12:7
2 Chr 10:7
saying, Thus shalt thou *s.* *1 Ki* 12:10
spirit from me to *s.* to thee. 22:24
2 Chr 18:23
sent me to thy master and to thee to *s.*? *2 Ki* 18:27; *Isa* 36:12
what can David *s.*? *1 Chr* 17:18
rail and *s.* against God. *2 Chr* 32:17
could not *s.* in the Jews' language.
Neh 13:24
to *s.* to the king to hang. *Esth* 6:4
wilt thou *s.* these things? *Job* 8:2
but, oh that God would *s.* 11:5
ye *s.* wickedly for God and? 13:7
and afterwards we will *s.* 18:2
my lips shall not *s.* wickedness. 27:4
I said, Days should *s.* and. 32:7
I have yet to *s.* on God's. 36:2
man *s.* he shall be swallowed. 37:20
will he *s.* soft words unto thee? 41:3
then shall he *s.* to them. *Ps* 2:5
destroy them that *s.* leasing. 5:6
they *s.* vanity, they *s.* with a. 12:2
their mouth they *s.* proudly. 17:10
which *s.* peace to their. 28:3
in his temple doth every one *s.* 29:9
s. grievous things proudly. 31:18
for they *s.* not peace, but. 35:20
my tongue shall *s.* of thy. 28
they *s.* mischievous things. 38:12
would declare and *s.* of them. 40:5
enemies *s.* evil of me, when? 41:5
my mouth shall *s.* of wisdom. 49:3
lovest lying rather than to *s.* 52:3
and lying which they *s.* 59:12
mouth of them that *s.* lies. 63:11
they that sit in the gate *s.* 69:12
for mine enemies *s.* against. 71:10
they *s.* wickedly, *s.* loftily. 73:8
what God the Lord will *s.*: for he will *s.* peace unto his people. 85:8
they utter and *s.* hard things? 94:4
reward of them that *s.* evil. 109:20
have mouths, but they *s.* not. 115:5
135:16
princes also did sit and *s.* 119:23
my tongue shall *s.* of thy word. 172
shall *s.* with the enemies. 127:5
for they *s.* against thee. 139:20
men shall *s.* of might of thy. 145:6
they shall *s.* of the glory of thy. 11
my mouth shall *s.* the praise. 21
my mouth shall *s.* truth. *Pr* 8:7
when lips *s.* right things. 23:16
silent, and a time to *s.* *Eccl* 3:7
those that are asleep to *s.* *S of S* 7:9
if they *s.* not according. *Isa* 8:20
shall *s.* and say unto thee. 14:10
five cities in Egypt shall *s.* 19:18
with another tongue shall he *s.* to this people. 28:11
shalt *s.* out of the ground. 29:4
stammerers shall *s.* plainly. 32:4
vile person will *s.* villany. 6
that I should know how to *s.* 50:4
that I am he that doth *s.* 52:6
trust in vanity, and *s.* lies. 59:4
whatsoever I command thee thou shalt *s.* *Jer* 1:7
because ye *s.* this word. 5:14
thou shalt *s.* all these words. 7:27
s. the truth, taught to *s.* lies. 9:5
as palm tree, but *s.* not. 10:5
believe not, though they *s.* fair. 12:6
shalt *s.* this word to them. 13:12
I shall *s.* about a nation. 18:7, 9
I stood before thee to *s.* good. 20

I said, I will not *s.* any more. *Jer* 20:9
s. a vision of their own heart. 23:16
s. all the words I commanded thee to *s.* 26:2, 8
the Lord hath sent me to *s.* 15
thus shalt thou also *s.* to. 29:24
and shall *s.* with him mouth. 32:4
he shall *s.* with thee mouth. 34:3
thou shalt *s.* my words. *Ezek* 2:7
words that I shall *s.* receive. 3:10
they say of me, Doth he not *s.*? 20:49
and thou shalt *s.* and be no. 24:27
mighty shall *s.* to him. 32:21
if dost not *s.* to warn wicked. 33:8
thus ye *s.* 10
and *s.* one to another. 30
children of thy people shall *s.* 37:18
prepared corrupt words to *s.* *Dan* 2:9
s. any thing amiss against the. 3:29
he shall *s.* great words. 7:25
shall *s.* lies at one table, but. 11:27
but at the end it shall *s.* *Hab* 2:3
how or what ye shall *s.* *Mat* 10:19
Mark 13:11
for it is not ye that *s.* *Mat* 10:20
Mark 13:11
how can ye being evil *s.*? *Mat* 12:34
every idle word that men shall *s.* 36
without, desiring to *s.* with. 46
why doth this man thus *s.*? *Mark* 2:7
do a miracle, that can lightly *s.* 9:39
not this man of whom ye *s.* 14:71
in my name they shall *s.* with. 16:17
I am sent to *s.* to thee. *Luke* 1:19
not able to *s.* till these shall. 20
when he came out he could not *s.* 22
suffered them not to *s.* 4:41
all men shall *s.* well of you. 6:26
and to provoke him to *s.* of. 11:53
s. a word against Son of man. 12:10
verily we *s.* that we do know, and.
John 3:11
of age, ask him, he shall *s.* 9:21
s. of himself; that shall he *s.* 16:13
when I shall no more *s.* to you in. 25
are not all these which *s.*? *Acts* 2:7
we do hear them *s.* in tongues. 11
that they *s.* to no man in this. 4:17
not to *s.* at all in the name. 18; 5:40
we cannot but *s.* 4:20
boldness they may *s.* thy word. 29
him *s.* blasphemous words. 6:11
ceaseth not to *s.* blasphemous. 13
cometh shall *s.* unto thee. 10:32
as I began to *s.* 11:15
same heard Paul *s.* 14:9
I beseech thee suffer me to *s.* 21:39
thou shalt not *s.* evil of ruler. 23:5
permitted to *s.* for thyself. 26:1
I *s.* forth the words of truth and. 25
I will not dare to *s.* of. *Rom* 15:18
that ye all *s.* same thing. *1 Cor* 1:10
things also we *s.*, not man's. 2:13
not *s.* to you as to spiritual. 3:1
do all *s.* with tongues? 12:30
if all *s.* 14:23
for women to *s.* in church. 35
and forbid not to *s.* with tongues. 39
in the sight of God *s.* we. *2 Cor* 2:17
we also believe and therefore *s.* 4:13
we *s.* before God in Christ. 12:19
it is a shame to *s.* of. *Eph* 5:12
manifest, as I ought to *s.* *Col* 4:4
so that we need not to *s.* *1 Thes* 1:8
so we *s.* not as pleasing men. 2:4
forbidding us to *s.* to Gentiles. 16
put them in mind to *s.* evil. *Tit* 3:2
to come, whereof we *s.* *Heb* 2:5
though we thus *s.* 6:9
of which we cannot *s.* 9:5
let every man be slow to *s.* *Jas* 1:19
they *s.* against you as evil doers.
1 Pet 2:12
his lips that they *s.* no guile. 3:10
whereas they *s.* evil of you, as. 16
not afraid to *s.* evil of dignities.
2 Pet 2:10
s. evil of the things that they. 12
they *s.* great swelling words. 18
of world, therefore *s.* *1 John* 4:5
these filthy dreamers *s.* evil. *Jude* 8
but these *s.* evil of those things. 10
depths of Satan, as they *s.* *Rev* 2:24
of the beast should both *s.* 13:15

speak, *imperatively*

s. thou with us, and we. *Ex* 20:19
s. ye to the rock before. *Num* 20:8
Lord said, *S.* no more to. *Deut* 3:26
s. thou unto us all that the Lord shall *s.* to thee. 5:27
s. ye that ride on white. *Judg* 5:10
consider, take advice, and *s.* 19:30
S. Lord, for thy. *1 Sam* 3:9, 10
saying? if not; *s.* thou. *2 Sam* 17:6
s. that which is good. *1 Ki* 22:13
2 Chr 18:12
s. in Syrian language. *2 Ki* 18:26
Isa 36:11
and to morrow *s.* thou. *Esth* 5:14
or *s.* to the earth, and it. *Job* 12:8
or let me *s.* and answer thou. 13:22
s. for I desire to justify thee. 33:32
s. what thou knowest. 34:33
lift not your horn: *s.* not. *Ps* 75:5
s. not in the ears of. *Pr* 23:9
s. word, it shall not stand. *Isa* 8:10
s. unto us smooth things. 30:10
s. ye comfortably to Jerusalem. 40:2
come near, then let them *s.* 41:1
son of a stranger *s.* saying. 56:3
s. to them all that I. *Jer* 1:17
hath my word, let him *s.* word. 23:28
I said, Let my lord *s.* *Dan* 10:19
s. every man the truth. *Zech* 8:16
Eph 4:25
s. word only, my servant. *Mat* 8:8
what I tell in darkness, that *s.* 10:27
shall be given you in that hour, *s.* ye.
Mark 13:11
s. to my brother that he. *Luke* 12:13
let me freely *s.* to you of. *Acts* 2:29
go, stand and *s.* in the temple. 5:20
be not afraid, but *s.*, hold not. 18:9
let him *s.* to himself. *1 Cor* 14:28
let prophets *s.* two or three. 29
s. the things that become. *Tit* 2:1
these things *s.* and exhort. 15
so *s.* ye and do, as they. *Jas* 2:12
s. not evil one of another. 4:11
let him *s.* as the oracles. *1 Pet* 4:11

I speak

people may hear when *I s.* *Ex* 19:9
shalt obey and do all that *I s.* 23:22
God putteth in my mouth that shall *I s.* *Num* 22:38
which *I s.* in your ears. *Deut* 5:1
I s. not with your children. 11:2
Lord saith, that will *I s.* *1 Ki* 22:14
if *I s.* of strength, lo, he. *Job* 9:19
would *I s.* and not fear him. 35
I would *s.* to the Almighty. 13:3
let me alone, that *I* may *s.* 13
I also could *s.* as ye do, I. 16:4
though *I s.*, my grief is not. 6
told him that *I s.*? if a man *s.* 37:20
I s. of things which I. *Ps* 45:1
troubled that *I* cannot *s.* 77:4
when *I s.* they are for war. 120:7
I the Lord *s.* righteousness. *Isa* 45:19
I that *s.* in righteousness. 63:1
ah, Lord God, *I* cannot *s.* for. *Jer* 1:6
to whom shall *I s.* and give? 6:10
hear this word that *I s.* in. 28:7
voice of the Lord which *I s.* 38:20
when *I s.* with thee, I. *Ezek* 3:27
O Daniel, understand words that *I s.*
Dan 10:11
therefore *s. I* to them. *Mat* 13:13
Jesus saith, *I* that *s.* to. *John* 4:26
the words that *I s.* to you. 6:63
of God or whether *I s.* of myself. 7:17
I s. to the world those things. 8:26
as my Father hath taught me *I s.* 28
I s. that which I have seen with. 38
gave commandment what *I* should *s.*
12:49
whatsoever *I s.* therefore, as the Father said unto me, so *I s.* 50
I s. not of all, I know whom. 13:18
the words that *I s. I s.* not. 14:10
things *I s.* in the world. 17:13
may *I s.* unto thee? *Acts* 21:37
I also *s.* freely. 26:26
unrighteous? *I s.* as a man. *Rom* 3:5
I s. after the manner of men. 6:19
Gal 3:15
I s. to them that know the. *Rom* 7:1

s. to you Gentiles, I am. Rom 11:13
s. to your shame. 1 Cor 6:5; 15:34
s. this by permission, not of. 7:6
ut to the rest s. I, not the Lord. 12
nd this I s. for your own profit. 35
s. as to wise men, judge ye. 10:15
hough I s. with tongues of men. 13:1
xcept I shall s. to you by. 14:6
s. with tongues more than you. 18
had rather s. five words with. 19
s. as to my children. 2 Cor 6:13
s. not this to condemn you. 7:3
hat which I s., I s. it not after. 11:17
s. as concerning reproach, I s. 21
re they ministers ? I s. as a fool. 23
ut I s. concerning Christ. Eph 5:32
may s. boldly, as I ought to s. 6:20
ot that I s. in respect. Phil 4:11
s. the truth in Christ, I. 1 Tim 2:7

I will **speak,** or *will I* **speak**

et not Lord be angry, and I will s. Gen 18:30, 32
nd I will s. to him in a dream. Num 12:6
vith him will I s. mouth to mouth. 8
vhat the Lord saith, that will I s. 24:13; 1 Ki 22:14; 2 Chr 18:13
) ye heavens, and I will s. Deut 32:1
Gideon said, I will s. but. Judg 6:39
' will s. to the king. 2 Sam 14:15
' will s. for thee to king. 1 Ki 2:18
' will s. in the anguish. Job 7:11
' will s. in the bitterness of. 10:1
' will s. that I may be. 32:20
old thy peace, and I will s. 33:31
beseech thee, and I will s. 42:4
) my people, and I will s. Ps 50:7
f I say, I will s. thus, I. 73:15
will s. of thy testimonies. 119:46
will s. of the honour. 145:5
ear, for I will s. of excellent things. Pr 8:6
ne to great men, and I will s. Jer 5:5
eet, and I will s. to thee. Ezek 2:1
will s. and the word I s. shall. 12:25
will allure her, and s. Hos 2:14
vith other lips will I s. 1 Cor 14:21

speaker

. be established in earth. Ps 140:11
e was the chief s. Acts 14:12

speakest

wherefore then s. thou so to me ? 1 Sam 9:21
why s. thou any more ? 2 Sam 19:29
he words thou s. in thy. 2 Ki 6:12
hou s. as one of the foolish women. Job 2:10
hou sittest and s. against. Ps 50:20
e justified when thou s. 51:4
why s. thou, O Israel, My. Isa 40:27
hou s. falsely of Ishmael. Jer 40:16
hou s. falsely, the Lord hath. 43:2
im not warning, nor s. Ezek 3:18
or thou s. lies in the name of. Zech 13:3
why s. thou to them in ? Mat 13:10
Lord, s. thou this parable to us or to ? Luke 12:41
ow s. thou plainly, and s. no. John 16:29
Pilate saith to him, S. thou ? 19:10
his whereof thou s.? Acts 17:19

speaketh

mouth that s. to you. Gen 45:12
s a man s. unto his friend. Ex 33:11
ll that the Lord s. Num 23:26
when a prophet s. in the. Deut 18:22
s. flattery to his friends. Job 17:5
for God s. once, yea, twice. 33:14
tongue that s. proud things. Ps 12:3
s. the truth in his heart. 15:2
the mouth of the righteous s. 37:30
to see me, he s. vanity. 41:6
whose mouth s. vanity. 144:8, 11
from the man that s. froward things. Pr 2:12
he s. with his feet, he teacheth. 6:13
a false witness that s. lies and. 19
the wicked s. frowardness. 10:32
he that s. truth, sheweth. 12:17
there is that s. like the piercings. 18
deceitful witness s. lies. 14:25
they love him that s. right. 16:13
that s. lies shall not escape. Pr 19:5
and he that s. lies shall perish. 9
the man that heareth s. constantly. 21:28
he s. fair, believe him not. 26:25
and every mouth s. folly. Isa 9:17
even when the needy s. right. 32:7
he that s. uprightly shall dwell. 33:15
their tongue s. deceit; one s. Jer 9:8
which the Lord s. to you. 10:1
thus s. the Lord the God of. 28:2
29:25; 30:2; Hag 1:2; Zech 6:12
7:9
voice of Almighty God when he s. Ezek 10:5
they abhor him that s. uprightly. Amos 5:10
Spirit of your Father who s. in you. Mat 10:20
whoso s. a word against the Son of man; but whosoever s. 12:32
for out of the abundance of the heart the mouth s. 34; Luke 6:45
he that is of the earth, s. John 3:31
he whom God sent, s. the words. 34
he that s. of himself, seeketh. 7:18
but lo, he s. boldly, they say. 26
s. a lie, he s. of his own. 8:44
who maketh himself a king, s. 19:12
pray, of whom s. the prophet this ? Acts 8:34
righteousness of faith s. Rom 10:6
s. in an unknown tongue; howbeit in the Spirit he s. 1 Cor 14:2
he that prophesieth, s. unto men. 3
s. in an unknown tongue edifieth. 4
prophesieth, than he that s. 5
unto him that s. a barbarian. 11
that s. in an unknown tongue. 13
now Spirit s. expressly. 1 Tim 4:1
he being dead yet s. Heb 11:4
exhortation which s. to you. 12:5
that s. better things than that. 24
refuse not him that s. . . . from him that s. from heaven. 25
he that s. evil of his brother and judgeth his brother, s. Jas 4:11
and their mouth s. great. Jude 16

speaking

done s., Rebekah came. Gen 24:15
before I had done s. in mine. 45
God s. out of the midst. Deut 5:26
s. of them when thou sittest. 11:19
then she left s. unto her. Ruth 1:18
s. peace to all his seed. Esth 10:3
yet s. another came. Job 1:16, 17, 18
can withhold himself from s.? 4:2
no more, they left off s. 32:15
thy lips from s. guile. Ps 34:13
as soon as they be born, s. lies. 58:3
away from thee s. vanity. Isa 58:9
nor s. thine own words. 13
in lying, and s. oppression. 59:13
they are yet s. I will hear. 65:24
rising up early and s. Jer 7:13
25:3; 35:14
he weakeneth the hands in s. 38:4
they left off s.; the matter was. 27
and a mouth s. great things. Dan 7:8; Rev 13:5
I heard one saint s. and. Dan 8:13
whiles I was s. praying. 9:20, 21
they abode, s. boldly. Acts 14:3
s. perverse things, to draw. 20:30
no man s. by the Spirit. 1 Cor 12:3
proof of Christ s. in me. 2 Cor 13:3
but s. the truth in love. Eph 4:15
s. to yourselves in psalms. 5:19
shall depart from faith, s. lies. 1 Tim 4:2
busybodies s. things which. 5:13
same excess of riot, s. evil of you. 1 Pet 4:4

see **end**

speaking, *substantive*

be heard for much s. Mat 6:7
let all evil s. be put away. Eph 4:31

speakings

all guile, envies, and evil s. 1 Pet 2:1

spear

Stretch out thy s. Josh 8:18*, 26*
was there a s. seen ? Judg 5:8
s. with any, but with. 1 Sam 13:22
s. was like a weaver's beam. 1 Sam 17:7; 2 Sam 21:19
1 Chr 20:5
a sword, and with a s. 1 Sam 17:45
saveth not with sword and s. 47
under thy hand s. or sword ? 21:8
and Saul's s. stuck in the. 26:7, 11
I pray thee, with the s. 8
now see where the king's s. is. 16
Saul leaned upon his s. 2 Sam 1:6
Abner with the end of the s. 2:23
with iron and staff of a s. 23:7
he lift up his s. against 800. 8
he lifted up his s. against 300 and slew them. 18; 1 Chr 11:11, 20
he slew Egyptian with his own s. 2 Sam 23:21; 1 Chr 11:23
quiver rattleth, glittering s. and. Job 39:23
s. of him that layeth at him. 41:26
laugheth at the shaking of a s. 29*
draw out also the s., stop. Ps 35:3
and cutteth s. in sunder. 46:9
lay hold on bow and s. Jer 6:23
lifteth up the sword and s. Nah 3:3
shining of the glittering s. Hab 3:11
soldier with a s. pierced. John 19:34

spearmen

rebuke the company of s. Ps 68:30*
ready two hundred s. Acts 23:23

spears

Hebrews make them swords or s. 1 Sam 13:19
to captains did priest give king David's s. 2 Ki 11:10; 2 Chr 23:9
city he put shields and s. 2 Chr 11:12
for them shields and s. 26:14
the people with their s. Neh 4:13
half of them held the s. 16, 21
whose teeth are s. and. Ps 57:4
shall beat s. into pruning hooks. Isa 2:4; Mi 4:3
furbish the s. and put on. Jer 46:4
they shall burn s. with. Ezek 39:9
pruning hooks into s. Joel 3:10

special

chosen thee to be a s. Deut 7:6*
God wrought s. miracles. Acts 19:11

see **especially**

speckled

from thence the s. cattle. Gen 30:32
the s. shall be thy wages; then the cattle bare s. 31:8
is to me as a s. bird. Jer 12:9
behind were red horses, s. Zech 1:8*

spectacle

made a s. to the world. 1 Cor 4:9

sped

have they not s.? have. Judg 5:30*

speech

hearken to my s. Gen 4:23
earth was of one s. 11:1
Lord, I am slow of s. Ex 4:10
and give occasion of s. Deut 22:14*
my s. shall distil as dew, as. 32:2
about this form of s. 2 Sam 14:20*
seeing the s. of all Israel. 19:11
s. pleased the Lord. 1 Ki 3:10
children spake half in s. of Ashdod. Neh 13:24
he removeth away the s. Job 12:20
hear diligently my s. and. 13:17
21:2; Ps 17:6; Isa 28:23; 32:9
my s. nothing worth ? Job 24:25
my s. dropped upon them. 29:22
order our s. by reason of. 37:19
day unto day uttereth s. Ps 19:2
there is no s. where their voice. 3
with her fair s. she caused. Pr 7:21
excellent s. becometh not a. 17:7
scarlet, thy s. is comely. S of S 4:3
thy s. shall be low out of the dust; thy s. shall whisper. Isa 29:4
of a deeper s. than thou canst. 33:19
shall use this s. in Judah. Jer 31:23
voice of s. as the noise. Ezek 1:24*
sent to a people of a strange s. 3:5, 6
O Lord, I have heard thy s. Hab 3:2*
art one of them, thy s. Mat 26:73
impediment in his s. Mark 7:32
art a Galilean, and thy s. 14:70
not understand my s.? John 8:43

saying in the *s.* of Lycaonia. *Acts* 14:11
continued his *s.* till midnight. 20:7
excellency of *s.* or wisdom. *1 Cor* 2:1
s. was not with enticing words. 4
and will know, not the *s.* but. 4:19
use great plainness of *s.* *2 Cor* 3:12
great is my boldness of *s.* 7:4
bodily presence weak, his *s.* 10:10
though I be rude in *s.* yet not in. 11:6
your *s.* be always with grace. *Col* 4:6
sound *s.* that cannot be. *Tit* 2:8

speeches

with him not in dark *s.* *Num* 12:8
and the *s.* of one that is. *Job* 6:26
or with *s.* wherewith he can? 15:3
I answer him with your *s.* 32:14
by fair *s.* deceive the. *Rom* 16:18
them of all their hard *s.* *Jude* 15

speechless

garment, and he was *s.* *Mat* 22:12
beckoned unto them and remained *s.* *Luke* 1:22*
journeyed with him stood *s.* *Acts* 9:7

speed

Lord, I pray thee, send me good *s.* *Gen* 24:12
a decree, let it be done with *s.* *Ezra* 6:12*
shall come with *s.* swiftly. *Isa* 5:26
come to him with all *s.* *Acts* 17:15
nor bid him God *s.* *2 John* 10*
biddeth him God *s.* is partaker. 11*
see **make, made**

speedily

that I should *s.* escape. *1 Sam* 27:1
not in plains, but *s.* *2 Sam* 17:16*
offerings divided they *s.* *2 Chr* 35:13
the king had sent, so they did *s.* *Ezra* 6:13*
that thou mayest buy *s.* with. 7:17*
shall require, it be done *s.* 21*
let judgement be executed *s.* 26*
he *s.* gave her her things. *Esth* 2:9
deliver me *s.* *Ps* 31:2
hear me *s.* 69:17; 143:7
tender mercies *s.* prevent us. 79:8
when I call, answer me *s.* 102:2
sentence is not executed *s.* *Eccl* 8:11
shall spring forth *s.* *Isa* 58:8
and if ye recompense me, *s.* *Joel* 3:4
let us go *s.* and pray. *Zech* 8:21
he will avenge them *s.* *Luke* 18:8

speedy

make even a *s.* riddance. *Zeph* 1:18*

spend

I will *s.* mine arrows. *Deut* 32:23
they *s.* their days in wealth, and. *Job* 21:13
s. their days in prosperity. 36:11
we *s.* our years as a tale. *Ps* 90:9*
why *s.* money for that which is not? *Isa* 55:2
because he would not *s.* *Acts* 20:16
I will very gladly *s.* *2 Cor* 12:15

spendest

whatsoever thou *s.* more, I will. *Luke* 10:35

spendeth

foolish man *s.* it up. *Pr* 21:20*
with harlots *s.* substance. 29:3*
which he *s.* as a shadow. *Eccl* 6:12

spent

and the water was *s.* in. *Gen* 21:15
not hide it how that our money is *s.* 47:18
strength shall be *s.* in vain. *Lev* 26:20
by Jebus, day was far *s.* *Judg* 19:11
for the bread is *s.* in. *1 Sam* 9:7
days are *s.* without hope. *Job* 7:6
for my life is *s.* with grief. *Ps* 31:10
s. my strength for naught. *Isa* 49:4
bread in the city was *s.* *Jer* 37:21
and had *s.* all that she had. *Mark* 5:26; *Luke* 8:43
when the day was now far *s.* *Mark* 6:35; *Luke* 24:29
the prodigal had *s.* all. *Luke* 15:14
s. their time to tell. *Acts* 17:21
the night is far *s.*, the day. *Rom* 13:12
spend and be *s.* for you. *2 Cor* 12:15

spewing

and shameful *s.* shall be on thy glory. *Hab* 2:16*

spice

rulers brought *s.* and oil. *Ex* 35:28
my myrrh with my *s.* *S of S* 5:1

spice

flesh and *s.* it well. *Ezek* 24:10

spice *merchants*

of the traffic of the *s.* *merchants.* *1 Ki* 10:15

spiced

thee to drink of *s.* wine. *S of S* 8:2

spicery

Ishmaelites bearing *s.* balm and. *Gen* 37:25

spices

a present, balm and *s.* *Gen* 43:11
s. for anointing oil. *Ex* 25:6; 35:8
thee principal *s.* of myrrh. 30:23, 34
the pure incense of sweet *s.* 37:29
camels that bare *s.* *1 Ki* 10:2, 10 *2 Chr* 9:1
they brought to Solomon *s.* *1 Ki* 10:25; *2 Chr* 9:24
shewed them *s.* ointment and all that was. *2 Ki* 20:13; *Isa* 39:2
appointed to oversee *s.* *1 Chr* 9:29
priests made the ointment of *s.* 30
Sheba gave Solomon *s.* *2 Chr* 9:9
divers *s.* prepared for the. 16:14
treasures for *s.* and gold. 32:27
thine ointments than all *s.* *S of S* 4:10
aloes, with all the chief *s.* 14
blow upon my garden, that *s.* 16
his cheeks are as a bed of *s.* 5:13
gone down to the beds of *s.* 6:2
hart upon the mountains of *s.* 8:14
fairs with chief of all *s.* *Ezek* 27:22
Mary had bought sweet *s.* *Mark* 16:1; *Luke* 24:1
returned and prepared *s.* *Luke* 23:56
it in linen with the *s.* *John* 19:40

spider

trust shall be a *s.*'s web. *Job* 8:14
the *s.* taketh hold with. *Pr* 30:28
eggs and weave *s.*'s web. *Isa* 59:5

spied

he *s.* an Egyptian smiting. *Ex* 2:11
s. the company of Jehu. *2 Ki* 9:17
they *s.* a band of men. 13:21
he *s.* sepulchres that were. 23:16
see **espy, espied**

spies

them, Ye are *s.* *Gen* 42:9, 14, 16
we are no *s.* 11, 31
the man took us for *s.* 30
then shall I know ye are no *s.* 34
by the way of the *s.* *Num* 21:1
men that were *s.* went in. *Josh* 6:23
the *s.* saw a man come. *Judg* 1:24
David therefore sent out *s.* and. *1 Sam* 26:4
Absalom sent *s.* throughout all the tribes of Israel. *2 Sam* 15:10
him and sent forth *s.* *Luke* 20:20
received *s.* with peace. *Heb* 11:31

spikenard

my *s.* sendeth forth. *S of S* 1:12
fruits, camphire with *s.* 4:13, 14
having an alabaster box of ointment of *s.* *Mark* 14:3; *John* 12:3

spilled

Onan *s.* it on the. *Gen* 38:9
bottles burst, and wine is *s.* *Mark* 2:22; *Luke* 5:37

spilt

we are as water *s.* on. *2 Sam* 14:14

spin

were wise hearted, did *s.* *Ex* 35:25
they toil not, neither do they *s.* *Mat* 6:28; *Luke* 12:27

spindle

her hands to the *s.* *Pr* 31:19*

spirit

In Hebrew, Ruach, *in* Greek, Pneuma, *wind, air. In scripture the word* Spirit *is taken,* [1] *For the Holy Ghost, the third person of the Trinity.* [2] *For the renewed nature, or spiritual part in man,* Mat 26:41. [3] *Signifies the soul, which continues in being even after the death of the body,* Acts 7:59. [4] *Good angels are called spirits,* Heb 1:14. [5] *The devils are often called unclean spirits, evil spirits,* Mark 5:13; *Luke* 7:21. *So in* 1 Sam 18:10. [6] *Spirit signifies an apparition or ghost,* Mat 14:26, Luke 24:37, 39. [7] *For the breath, the respiration, the animal life that is in beasts,* Eccl 3:21. [8] Spirit *is also taken for the wind,* Amos 4:13, He that createth the wind, *or* spirit. These are the four spirits of the heavens, *in* Hebrew, winds, Zech 6:5. *And in* John 3:8, The wind bloweth where it listeth, *in* Greek, pneuma, *the spirit.*

Pharaoh's *s.* was troubled. *Gen* 41:8
the *s.* of Jacob their father. 45:27
to Moses for anguish of *s.* *Ex* 6:9
every one whom his *s.* made. 35:21
I will take of the *s.* *Num* 11:17, 25
the *s.* rested upon them and. 26
that the Lord would put his *s.* 29
he had another *s.* with him. 14:24
a man in whom is the *s.* 27:18
thy God hardened his *s.* *Deut* 2:30
nor was there *s.* in them. *Josh* 5:1
when he had drunk, his *s.* *Judg* 15:19
when he had eaten, his *s.* came again to him. *1 Sam* 30:12
there was no *s.* in her. *1 Ki* 10:5 *2 Chr* 9:4
Why is thy *s.* so sad? *1 Ki* 21:5
came forth a *s.* 22:21; *2 Chr* 18:20
portion of thy *s.* be on me. *2 Ki* 2:9
s. of Elijah doth rest on Elisha. 15
the Lord stirred up the *s.* *1 Chr* 5:26
the *s.* came upon Amasai. 12:18
all that he had by the *s.* 28:12
against Jehoram *s.* of. *2 Chr* 21:16
whose *s.* God raised to go up. *Ezra* 1:5
testifiedst by the *s.* in. *Neh* 9:30
s. passed before my face. *Job* 4:15
thou turnest thy *s.* against. 15:13
s. of my understanding causeth. 20:3
whose *s.* came from thee? 26:4
by his *s.* he garnished the. 13
a *s.* in man, inspiration of. 32:8
s. within me constraineth me. 18
if he gather to himself his *s.* 34:14
in whose *s.* there is no guile. *Ps* 32:2
clean heart, renew a right *s.* 51:10
and uphold me with thy free *s.* 12
cut off the *s.* of princes. 76:12
and whose *s.* was not stedfast. 78:8
thou sendest forth thy *s.* 104:30
they provoked his *s.*, so. 106:33
whither shall I go from thy *s.*? 139:7
s. is good, lead me to land. 143:10
he that is hasty of *s.* *Pr* 14:29
therein is a breach in the *s.* 15:4
an haughty *s.* before a fall. 16:18
he that ruleth his *s.* than he that. 32
the *s.* of a man will sustain. 18:14
the *s.* of a man is the candle. 20:27
that hath no rule over his *s.* 25:28
the *s.* of man, *s.* of beast. *Eccl* 3:21
hasty in thy *s.* to be angry. 7:9
power over *s.* to retain the *s.* 8:8
s. of the ruler rise against. 10:4
not what is the way of the *s.* 11:5*
and the *s.* shall return to God. 12:7
the *s.* of Egypt shall fail. *Isa* 19:3
poured on you the *s.* of deep. 29:10
they that erred in *s.* shall come. 24
their horses flesh, and not *s.* 31:3
till the *s.* be poured upon us. 32:15
his *s.* it hath gathered them. 34:16
he that giveth *s.* to them that. 42:5
the Lord God and his *s.* hath. 48:16
forsaken and grieved in *s.* 54:6
the *s.* shall fail before me, and the souls. 57:16
the *s.* of the Lord God is upon me. 61:1; *Luke* 4:18
the garment of praise for the *s.* of. *Isa* 61:3
Lord raised the *s.* of king. *Jer* 51:11
whither *s.* was to go. *Ezek* 1:12, 20

. was in wheels. *Ezek* 1:21; 10:17
. entered into me when. 2:2; 3:24
hen the *s.* took me up. 3:12; 11:24
o *s.* lifted me up, and took me away
. . . heat of my *s.* 3:14; 8:3; 11:1
hat follow their own *s.* 13:3
very *s.* shall faint, all knees. 21:7
Nebuchadnezzar's *s.* was. *Dan* 2:1
he *s.* of the holy gods: and before
him I told. 4:8, 9, 18; 5:11, 14
xcellent *s.* . . . were found. 5:12; 6:3
f a man walking in the *s.* *Mi* 2:11
ord stirred up the *s.* of Zerubbabel.
Hag 1:14
ath sent in his *s.* by. *Zech* 7:12
ormeth *s.* of man within. 12:1
he residue of the *s.* Therefore take
heed to your *s.* *Mal* 2:15, 16
Jesus was led up of the *s.* *Mat* 4:1
Luke 4:1
were troubled; saying, It is a *s.*
Mat 14:26*; *Mark* 6:49*
ow doth David in *s.* call? *Mat* 22:43
he *s.* indeed is willing. 26:41
Mark 14:38
s. descending on him. *Mark* 1:10
John 1:32
s. driveth him into the. *Mark* 1:12
and he sighed deeply in his *s.* 8:12
straightway the *s.* tare him. 9:20
the *s.* cried and rent him. 26*
go before him in the *s.* of Elias.
Luke 1:17
child waxed strong in *s.* 80; 2:40
and he came by the *s.* into the. 2:27
n power of the *s.* into Galilee. 4:14
her *s.* came again, and she. 8:55
what manner of *s.* ye are of. 9:55
Jesus rejoiced in *s.* and said. 10:21
a woman who had a *s.* of. 13:11
that they had seen a *s.* 24:37
for a *s.* hath not flesh and. 39
shalt see *s.* descending. *John* 1:33
the *s.* by measure to him. 3:34
worship the Father in *s.* 4:23
s.: they must worship him in *s.* 24
it is the *s.* that quickeneth; words
. . . they are *s.* and they. 6:63
this spake he of the *s.* 7:39
he groaned in *s.* 11:33
troubled in *s.* and testified. 13:21
spake as the *s.* gave them. *Acts* 2:4
were not able to resist the *s.* 6:10
then the *s.* said unto Philip. 8:29
the *s.* said unto Peter. 10:19; 11:12
Agabus signified by the *s.* 11:28
assayed, but the *s.* suffered. 16:7
his *s.* was stirred within him. 17:16
Paul was pressed in *s.* 18:5*
being fervent in *s.* 25
now I go bound in the *s.* to. 20:22
said to Saul through the *s.* 21:4
that there is no angel nor *s.* 23:8
if a *s.* or an angel hath spoken. 9
Son of God according to the *s.*
Rom 1:4
is that of the heart, in the *s.* 2:29
not after the flesh, but after *s.* 8:1, 4
the law of the *s.* of life hath. 2
after the *s.* the things of the *s.* 5
in the flesh, but *s.* if so be that *s.* 9
but the *s.* is life because of. 10
s. of him that raised up Jesus from
the dead . . . bodies by his *s.* 11
but if ye through the *s.* do mortify. 13
the *s.* itself beareth witness with our
s. 16
who have firstfruits of the *s.* 23
s. also helpeth our infirmities; the
s. itself maketh intercession. 26
what is the mind of the *s.* 27
fervent in *s.* 12:11
for the love of the *s.* 15:30
but in demonstration of *s.* *1 Cor* 2:4
revealed them to us by his *s.*: for *s.*
searcheth all things, yea, the deep. 10
save the *s.* of a man which is. 11
not *s.* of the world, but the *s.* 12
absent in body, but present in *s.* 5:3
that *s.* may be saved in day of the. 5
joined to the Lord is one *s.* 6:17
God in your body and in your *s.* 20
holy both in body and *s.* 7:34
of gifts, but same *s.* 12:4, 8, 9, 11

is given by *s.* the word. *1 Cor* 12:8
s. are we all baptized into one body;
and have been all . . . into one *s.* 13
in the *s.* he speaketh. 14:2
I will sing with the *s.* 15
shalt bless with the *s.* 16
was made a quickening *s.* 15:45
new testament, not of letter but of
the *s.* . . . but the *s.* *2 Cor* 3:6
shall not ministration of the *s.*? 8
the Lord is that *s.*: where the *s.* 17
the same *s.* of faith, we. 4:13
all filthiness of the flesh and *s.* 7:1
because his *s.* was refreshed. 13
another *s.* which ye have not. 11:4
walked we not in the same *s.*? 12:18
received ye the *s.* by the? *Gal* 3:2
having begun in the *s.* 3
ministereth to you the *s.* 5
promise of the *s.* through faith. 14
sent forth the *s.* of his Son. 4:6
for we through *s.* wait for hope. 5:5
walk in the *s.* 16
lusteth against the *s.* and the *s.* 17
but if ye be led by the *s.* 18
the *s.*, let us walk in the *s.* 25
soweth to *s.* shall of the *s.* reap. 6:8
grace of our Lord be with your *s.* 18
Philem 25
the *s.* that now worketh in. *Eph* 2:2
access by one *s.* unto the Father. 18
of God through the *s.* 22
to the apostles by the *s.* 3:5
might by his *s.* in inner man. 16
to keep unity of the *s.* in the. 4:3
there is one body, and one *s.* 4
and be renewed in the *s.* of. 23
with wine, but be filled with *s.* 5:18
take sword of the *s.* which is. 6:17
with all prayer in the *s.* 18
the supply of the *s.* of. *Phil* 1:19
that ye stand fast in one *s.* 27
if any fellowship of the *s.* 2:1
which worship God in the *s.* 3:3
to us your love in the *s.* *Col* 1:8
flesh, yet am I with you in *s.* 2:5
quench not *s.*, despise. *1 Thes* 5:19
pray your *s.* soul, and body be. 23
neither by *s.* nor by word. *2 Thes* 2:2
Lord shall consume with the *s.* 8*
sanctification of the *s.* and belief. 13
justified in *s.* seen of angels.
1 Tim 3:16
now the *s.* speaketh expressly. 4:1
an example in *s.*, in faith. 12
Christ be with thy *s.* *2 Tim* 4:22
asunder of soul and *s.* *Heb* 4:12
who through the eternal *s.* 9:14
without the *s.* is dead. *Jas* 2:26
the *s.* that dwelleth in us. 4:5
through sanctification of the *s.* to.
1 Pet 1:2
in obeying truth through the *s.* 22
of a meek and quiet *s.* 3:4
death in flesh, but quickened by *s.* 18
according to God in the *s.* 4:6
by the *s.* which he hath. *1 John* 3:24
beloved, believe not every *s.* 4:1
every *s.* that confesseth Jesus. 2
every *s.* that confesseth not that. 3
because he hath given us of his *s.* 13
s. that beareth witness, *s.* 5:6
witness in earth, the *s.* the water. 8
sensual, not having the *s.* *Jude* 19
in the *s.* on the Lord's. *Rev* 1:10
hear what the *s.* saith unto the
churches. 2:7, 11, 17, 29; 3:6, 13, 22
and immediately I was in the *s.* 4:2
the *s.* of life from God. 11:11*
blessed dead: Yea, saith the *s.* 14:13
carried me away in the *s.* 17:3; 21:10
the *s.* and the bride say. 22:17
see **evil, holy, Lord, lying, vexation**

spirit *of adoption*
have received the *s. of adoption.*
Rom 8:15

spirit *of antichrist*
this is that *s. of antichrist* ye heard.
1 John 4:3

spirit *of bondage*
not received the *s. of bondage.*
Rom 8:15

born of the **spirit**
except a man be *born of the s.* he.
John 3:5
is *born of the s.* is spirit. 6
one that is *born of the s.* 8
that was *born* after *the s.* *Gal* 4:29

broken **spirit**
of God are a *broken s.* *Ps* 51:17
sorrow of the heart the *s.* is *broken.*
Pr 15:13
a *broken s.* drieth the bones. 17:22
see **contrite**

spirit *of burning*
of Jerusalem by the *s. of burning.*
Isa 4:4

spirit *of Christ*
have not the *s. of Christ.* *Rom* 8:9
what the *s. of Christ* in. *1 Pet* 1:11

spirit *of counsel*
the *s. of counsel* shall rest. *Isa* 11:2

spirit *of divination*
possessed with a *s. of divination.*
Acts 16:16

dumb **spirit**
my son, who hath a *dumb s.*
Mark 9:17
thou *dumb s.* I charge thee. 25

earnest of the **spirit**
hath given us the *earnest of the s.*
2 Cor 1:22; 5:5

spirit *of error*
the *s. of* truth and *error.* *1 John* 4:6

faithful **spirit**
he that is of *faithful s.* *Pr* 11:13
see **familiar**

spirit *of fear*
given us the *s. of fear.* *2 Tim* 1:7

foul **spirit**
he rebuked the *foul s.* *Mark* 9:25
the hold of every *foul s.* *Rev* 18:2

fruit of the **spirit**
the *fruit of the s.* is love. *Gal* 5:22
for the *fruit of the s.* is in. *Eph* 5:9*

good **spirit**
thou gavest thy *good s.* *Neh* 9:20
thy *s.* is *good,* lead me. *Ps* 143:10

spirit *of God*
s. of God moved on the. *Gen* 1:2
man in whom the *s. of God.* 41:38
filled Bezaleel with the *s. of God.*
Ex 31:3; 35:31
and the *s. of God* came. *Num* 24:2
the *s. of God* came on Saul, and.
1 Sam 10:10; 11:6; 19:23
s. of God came on the messengers.
19:20
the *s. of God* came upon Azariah.
2 Chr 15:1
s. of God is in my nostrils. *Job* 27:3
the *s. of God* hath made me. 33:4
in vision by the *s. of God* into
Chaldea. *Ezek* 11:24
s. of God descending. *Mat* 3:16
out devils by the *s. of God.* 12:28
if so be that the *s. of God.* *Rom* 8:9
as are led by the *s. of God.* 14
by the power of the *s. of God.* 15:19
man, but the *s. of God.* *1 Cor* 2:11
the things of the *s. of God.* 14
s. of God dwelleth in you. 3:16
sanctified by the *s. of* our *God.* 6:11
also that I have the *s. of God.* 7:40
by the *s. of God,* calleth. 12:3
the *s. of* the living *God.* *2 Cor* 3:3
not the holy *s. of God.* *Eph* 4:30
s. of God resteth on. *1 Pet* 4:14
know ye the *s. of God.* *1 John* 4:2

spirit *of glory*
s. of glory resteth on. *1 Pet* 4:14

spirit *of grace*
I will pour upon the house of David
the *s. of grace.* *Zech* 12:10
done despite to the *s. of grace.*
Heb 10:29

humble **spirit**
is to be of an *humble s.* *Pr* 16:19
shall uphold the *humble* in *s.* 29:23
that is of an *humble s.* *Isa* 57:15

spirit *of jealousy*
and *s. of jealousy.* *Num* 5:14, 30
spirit *of judgement*
blood of Jerusalem by *s. of judgement.* *Isa* 4:4
be for a *s. of judgement* to him. 28:6
spirit *of knowledge*
s. of knowledge shall rest. *Isa* 11:2
spirit *of meekness*
come to you in the *s. of meekness*? *1 Cor* 4:21
restore such a one in the *s. of meekness.* *Gal* 6:1
my **spirit**
my s. shall not always strive with. *Gen* 6:3
whereof drinketh up *my s.* *Job* 6:4
in the anguish of *my s.* 7:11
visitation hath preserved *my s.* 10:12
if so, why should not *my s.*? 21:4
thine hand I commit *my s.* *Ps* 31:5
I complained, and *my s.* was. 77:3
and *my s.* made diligent search. 6
my s. was overwhelmed in me. 142:3
is *my s.* overwhelmed in me. 143:4
hear me speedily, O Lord, *my s.* 7
pour out *my s.* unto you. *Pr* 1:23
yea, with *my s.* will I seek thee. *Isa* 26:9
a covering, but not of *my s.* 30:1
things is the life of *my s.* 38:16
I have put *my s.* upon him. 42:1
pour *my s.* upon thy seed. 44:3
my s. that is upon thee shall. 59:21
in the heat of *my s.* *Ezek* 3:14
and I will put *my s.* within you. 36:27; 37:14
for I have poured out *my s.* on. 39:29
my s. was troubled. *Dan* 2:3
grieved in *my s.* 7:15
I will pour out *my s.* upon all flesh. *Joel* 2:28, 29; *Acts* 2:17, 18
so *my s.* remaineth among you: fear. *Hag* 2:5
nor by power, but by *my s.* *Zech* 4:6
these have quieted *my s.* in the. 6:8
I will put *my s.* upon. *Mat* 12:18
my s. hath rejoiced in God my. *Luke* 1:47
hands I commend *my s.* 23:46
Lord Jesus, receive *my s.* *Acts* 7:59
whom I serve with *my s.* *Rom* 1:9
are gathered together and *my s.* *1 Cor* 5:4
my s. prayeth, but my. 14:14
they have refreshed *my s.* 16:18
I had no rest in *my s.* *2 Cor* 2:13
new **spirit**
I will put a *new s.* within you. *Ezek* 11:19; 36:26
a new heart and a *new s.* 18:31
newness of **spirit**
serve in *newness of* the *s.* *Rom* 7:6
patient **spirit**
patient in *s.* is better. *Eccl* 7:8
perverse **spirit**
mingled a *perverse s.* *Isa* 19:14
poor in **spirit**
blessed are the *poor in s.* *Mat* 5:3
spirit *of promise*
sealed with that holy *s. of promise.* *Eph* 1:13
spirit *of prophecy*
testimony of Jesus is the *s. of prophecy.* *Rev* 19:10
spirit *of slumber*
them the *s. of slumber.* *Rom* 11:8
sorrowful **spirit**
woman of a *sorrowful s.* *1 Sam* 1:15
spirit *of truth*
S. of truth whom world. *John* 14:17
even the *S. of truth* which. 15:26
when *S. of truth* is come. 16:13
we *S. of truth* and error. *1 John* 4:6
unclean **spirit**
I will cause *unclean s.* to pass out. *Zech* 13:2
when the *unclean s.* is gone out of a man. *Mat* 12:43; *Luke* 11:24
their synagogue a man with an *unclean s.* *Mark* 1:23
and when the *unclean s.* had. 26
said, He hath an *unclean s.* 3:30
him a man with an *unclean s.* 5:2
come out of the man, thou *unclean s.* 8; *Luke* 8:29
young daughter had an *unclean s.* *Mark* 7:25
Jesus rebuked *unclean s.* *Luke* 9:42
spirit *of understanding*
the *s. of understanding.* *Isa* 11:2
spirit *of whoredoms*
s. of whoredoms caused. *Hos* 4:12
for the *s. of whoredoms* is in. 5:4
spirit *of wisdom*
filled with *s. of wisdom.* *Ex* 28:3
full of the *s. of wisdom.* *Deut* 34:9
s. of wisdom shall rest. *Isa* 11:2
give to you *s. of wisdom.* *Eph* 1:17
wounded **spirit**
but a *wounded s.* who? *Pr* 18:14
spirits
O God, the God of *s.* of all flesh. *Num* 16:22; 27:16
who maketh his angels *s.* *Ps* 104:4* *Heb* 1:7
the Lord weigheth the *s.* *Pr* 16:2
these are the four *s.* of. *Zech* 6:5
and he cast out the *s.* *Mat* 8:16
he gave them power against unclean *s.* 10:1; *Mark* 6:7
authority commandeth he the unclean *s.* *Mark* 1:27; *Luke* 4:36
unclean *s.* fell down. *Mark* 3:11
the unclean *s.* entered into. 5:13
rejoice not that *s.* are. *Luke* 10:20
were vexed with unclean *s.* *Acts* 5:16
for unclean *s.* crying, came. 8:7
another discerning of *s.* *1 Cor* 12:10
s. of the prophets are. 14:32
depart from faith, giving heed to seducing *s.* *1 Tim* 4:1
not all ministering *s.*? *Heb* 1:14
be in subjection to Father of *s.* 12:9
s. of just men made perfect. 23
and preached to the *s.* in prison. *1 Pet* 3:19
try the *s.* whether they. *1 John* 4:1
I saw three unclean *s.* *Rev* 16:13
s. of devils, working miracles. 14
see **evil, familiar, seven**
spiritual
the prophet is a fool, the *s.* *Hos* 9:7
impart to you some *s.* *Rom* 1:11
we know that the law is *s.* 7:14
partakers of their *s.* things. 15:27
speak, comparing *s.* things with *s.* *1 Cor* 2:13
but he that is *s.* judgeth all things. 15
not speak to you as unto *s.* 3:1
sown unto you *s.* things. 9:11
all eat the same *s.* meat. 10:3
s. drink, drank of that *s.* rock. 4
now concerning *s.* gifts. 12:1
desire *s.* gifts. 14:1
ye are zealous of *s.* gifts. 12
himself to be a prophet, or *s.* 37
s. body, there is a *s.* body. 15:44
which is *s.* but that which is natural; and afterwards that which is *s.* 46
ye which are *s.* restore. *Gal* 6:1
blessed us with all *s.* *Eph* 1:3
in psalms and *s.* songs. 5:19
wrestle against *s.* wickedness. 6:12
be filled with all *s.* understanding. *Col* 1:9
another in psalms and *s.* songs. 3:16
ye are built up a *s.* house, to offer up *s.* sacrifices. *1 Pet* 2:5
spiritually
but to be *s.* minded is. *Rom* 8:6
because are *s.* discerned. *1 Cor* 2:14
which *s.* is called Sodom. *Rev* 11:8
spit
that hath the issue, *s.* on. *Lev* 15:8
if her father had but *s.* *Num* 12:14
she shall *s.* in his face. *Deut* 25:9
and they spare not to *s.* *Job* 30:10
they did *s.* in his face. *Mat* 26:67
and they *s.* upon him and. 27:30
and he *s.* and touched. *Mark* 7:33
he had *s.* on his eyes. *Mark* 8:23
they shall *s.* upon him and. 10:34
began to *s.* on him. 14:65; 15:19
spite
for thou beholdest *s.* *Ps* 10:14
spitefully
they entreated them *s.* *Mat* 22:6*
shall be *s.* entreated. *Luke* 18:32*
spitted
spitefully entreated and *s.* on. *Luke* 18:32
spitting
face from shame and *s.* *Isa* 50:6
spittle
he let his *s.* fall down. *1 Sam* 21:13
till I swallow down my *s.* *Job* 7:19
he made clay of *s.* and. *John* 9:6
spoil, *substantive*
he shall divide the *s.* *Gen* 49:27
said, I will divide the *s.* *Ex* 15:9
Israel took the *s.* *Num* 31:9, 11
brought the prey and *s.* to Moses. 12
cattle we took for prey and the *s.* *Deut* 2:35; 3:7; *Josh* 8:27; 11:14
thou shalt gather all *s.* *Deut* 13:16
s. thou shalt take. 20:14; *Josh* 8:2
necks of them that take *s.* *Judg* 5:30
thirty men and took their *s.* 14:19
freely to-day of the *s.* *1 Sam* 14:30
the people flew upon the *s.* and. 32
but didst fly upon the *s.* and. 15:19
but the people took of the *s.* 21
because the great *s.* that. 30:16
neither *s.* nor any thing. 19
and said, This is David's *s.* 20
not give them aught of the *s.* 22
s. to the elders of Judah and his friends; behold, a . . . the *s.* 26
brought in a great *s.* *2 Sam* 3:22
he brought forth of the *s.* 12:30
Moab, to the *s.* *2 Ki* 3:23
they shall become a *s.* to. 21:14
be brought much *s.* *1 Chr* 20:2
they carried away *s.* *2 Chr* 14:13, 14
Lord at same time of the *s.* 15:11
take the *s.*: they were three days in gathering the *s.* it was. 20:25
the Syrians sent *s.* to the king. 24:23
of them, and took much *s.* 25:13
took much *s.* and brought *s.* 28:8
men left the captives and the *s.* 14
with the *s.* clothed all that were. 15
been delivered to a *s.* *Ezra* 9:7
to take the *s.* of them for a prey. *Esth* 3:13; 8:11
but on the *s.* laid they not. 9:10
I plucked the *s.* out of. *Job* 29:17
at home, divided the *s.* *Ps* 68:12
word, as one findeth great *s.* 119:162
fill our houses with *s.* *Pr* 1:13
than to divide the *s.* with. 16:19
he shall have no need of *s.* 31:11
the *s.* of the poor is in. *Isa* 3:14
the *s.* of Samaria shall be. 8:4
rejoice when they divide the *s.* 9:3
him a charge to take the *s.* 10:6
your *s.* shall be gathered, like. 33:4
prey of a great *s.* divided. 23
they are for a *s.* and none. 42:22
who gave Jacob for a *s.*? 24
he shall divide the *s.* with. 53:12
violence and *s.* is heard in. *Jer* 6:7
and treasures will I give to *s.* 15:13
substance and treasures to *s.* 17:3
I cried violence and *s.* 20:8
that *s.* thee shall be a *s.* 30:16
their cattle shall be a *s.* 49:32
and Chaldea shall be a *s.* 50:10
it to the wicked for a *s.* *Ezek* 7:21
Ammonites for a *s.* 25:7
Tyrus a *s.* 26:5, 12
Nebuchadrezzar shall take *s.* 29:19
I will go up to take a *s.* and. 38:12
art thou come to take a *s.*? 13
remove violence and *s.* 45:9
he shall scatter among them the *s.* *Dan* 11:24
they shall fall by *s.* many days. 33
s. of silver, take *s.* of gold. *Nah* 2:9
the *s.* of beasts shall. *Hab* 2:17
they shall be a *s.* to their. *Zech* 2:9
thy *s.* shall be divided in the. 14:1

spoil, *verb*

ye shall *s.* the Egyptians. *Ex* 3:22
s. them until morning. *1 Sam* 14:36
returned after him only to *s.* *2 Sam* 23:10
they who hate us *s.* for. *Ps* 44:10
pass by the way *s.* him. 89:41
and let the stranger *s.* his labour. 109:11
will *s.* soul of those that. *Pr* 22:23
s. not his resting place. 24:15
take us the foxes that *s.* *S of S* 2:15
they shall *s.* them of the. *Isa* 11:14
portion of them that *s.* us. 17:14
when shalt cease to *s.* thou. 33:1
the evenings shall *s.* them. *Jer* 5:6
I will give Jerusalem to them that shall *s.* it. 20:5
they that *s.* thee shall be a *s.* 30:16
the day that cometh to *s.* the. 47:4
go up to Kedar and *s.* the men. 49:28
that *s.* her shall be satisfied. 50:10
and they *s.* it, so that it. *Ezek* 14:15
and they shall *s.* the pomp. 32:12
s. those that spoiled them. 39:10
shall break their altars, shall *s.* *Hos* 10:2
he shall *s.* the treasure of all. 13:15
of the people shall *s.* thee. *Hab* 2:8
my people shall *s.* them. *Zeph* 2:9
into a strong man's house, and *s.*? *Mat* 12:29; *Mark* 3:27
beware lest any man *s.* *Col* 2:8

spoiled

sons of Jacob came and *s.* the city. *Gen* 34:27
they *s.* all that was in Hamor's. 29
they *s.* the Egyptians. *Ex* 12:36
only oppressed and *s.* *Deut* 28:29
hand of spoilers that *s.* *Judg* 2:14
hand of those that *s.* them. 16
delivered Israel from them that *s.* *1 Sam* 14:48
they *s.* the Philistines' tents. 17:53
Israel *s.* the tents of. *2 Ki* 7:16
Asa *s.* all the cities. *2 Chr* 14:14
he leadeth counsellors away *s.* *Job* 12:17
away *s.*, overthroweth the mighty. 19
the stouthearted are *s.* *Ps* 76:5
soul of those that *s.* them. *Pr* 22:23
shall be *s.*, their wives. *Isa* 13:16
land the rivers have *s.* 18:2, 7
be utterly emptied and *s.* 24:3
spoilest, and wast not *s.* 33:1
is a people robbed and *s.* 42:22
servant ? why is he *s.*? *Jer* 2:14
woe unto us, for we are *s.* 4:13
is *s.*: suddenly are my tents *s.* 20
and when thou art *s.* what wilt ? 30
how are we *s.*! 9:19
my tabernacle is *s.* 10:20
deliver him that is *s.* 21:12; 22:3
for the Lord hath *s.* their. 25:36
Nebo is *s.* 48:1
Moab is *s.* and gone. 15, 20
howl, for Ai is *s.* 49:3
Esau, his seed is *s.* 10
the Lord hath *s.* Babylon. 51:55
and hath *s.* none by violence. *Ezek* 18:7, 16
hath *s.* by violence. 12, 18
them to be removed and *s.* 23:46
spoil those that *s.* them. 39:10
fortresses shall be *s.* *Hos* 10:14
thy palaces shall be *s.* *Amos* 3:11
strengtheneth the *s.* against. 5:9
say, We be utterly *s.* *Mi* 2:4
hast *s.* many nations. *Hab* 2:8
the nations which *s.* you. *Zech* 2:8
howl, because the mighty are *s.* 11:2
is *s.*: for the pride of Jordan is *s.* 3
and having *s.* principalities. *Col* 2:15

spoiler

covert from face of *s.* the *s.* *Isa* 16:4
s. spoileth, go up, O Elam. 21:2
for the *s.* shall suddenly. *Jer* 6:26
I have brought upon them a *s.* 15:8
the *s.* shall come upon every. 48:8
the *s.* of Moab shall come upon. 18
s. is fallen upon thy summer. 32
because the *s.* is come upon. 51:56

spoilers

delivered them into the hand of *s.* *Judg* 2:14; *2 Ki* 17:20
s. came out of camp. *1 Sam* 13:17
the garrison and the *s.* they. 14:15
the *s.* are come upon all. *Jer* 12:12
for the *s.* shall come to her. 51:48
yet from me shall *s.* come to her. 53

spoilest

woe to thee that *s.* and thou. *Isa* 33:1

spoileth

needy from him that *s.* *Ps* 35:10
the spoiler *s.* *Isa* 21:2
troop of robbers *s.* *Hos* 7:1
the cankerworm *s.* *Nah* 3:16

spoiling

me evil for good, to the *s.* *Ps* 35:12
of the *s.* of the daughter. *Isa* 22:4
a voice from Horonaim *s.* *Jer* 48:3
for *s.* and violence are. *Hab* 1:3
for ye took joyfully the *s.* *Heb* 10:34

spoils

I saw among the *s.* a goodly garment. *Josh* 7:21
out of *s.* in battle did. *1 Chr* 26:27
their pride with the *s.* *Isa* 25:11
and divideth his *s.* *Luke* 11:22
gave the tenth of the *s.* *Heb* 7:4

spoken

what he hath *s.* of him. *Gen* 18:19
have *s.* in mine ears. *Num* 14:28
we have *s.* against the Lord. 21:7
hath he *s.* and shall he not ? 23:19
words they have *s.* to thee. they have well said . . . have *s.* *Deut* 5:28
because he hath *s.* to turn. 13:5
s. that which they have *s.* 18:17
done all he hath *s.* *1 Sam* 25:30
unless thou hadst *s.*, the people had gone up. *2 Sam* 2:27
my lord the king hath *s.* 14:19
Ahithophel hath *s.* after this. 17:6
have not *s.* this word. *1 Ki* 2:23
answer this people who have *s.* to ? 12:9; *2 Chr* 10:9
people said, It is well *s.* *1 Ki* 18:24
wouldest thou be *s.* for to ? *2 Ki* 4:13
tongue hath *s.* in my. *Job* 33:2
Job hath *s.* without knowledge. 34:35
ye have not *s.* of me as. 42:7, 8
my mouth hath *s.* when. *Ps* 66:14
glorious things are *s.* of thee. 87:3
they have *s.* against me with. 109:2
a word *s.* in due season. *Pr* 15:23
a word fitly *s.* is like apples. 25:11
to all words that are *s.* *Eccl* 7:21
when she shall be *s.* for. *S of S* 8:8
for the sea hath *s.* *Isa* 23:4
he hath *s.* 38:15
defiled, your lips have *s.* lies. 59:3
hath *s.* to us in the name. *Jer* 26:16
and have *s.* lying words in. 29:23
not what this people have *s.*? 33:24
ye and your wives have *s.* 44:25
have ye not *s.* a lying ? *Ezek* 13:7
because ye have *s.* vanity, and. 8
to thee it is *s.* *Dan* 4:31
yet they have *s.* lies. *Hos* 7:13
they have *s.* words, swearing. 10:4
with you, as ye have *s.* *Amos* 5:14
nor shouldest thou have *s.* *Ob* 12
thereof have *s.* lies. *Mi* 6:12
the idols have *s.* vanity. *Zech* 10:2
what have we *s.* so ? *Mal* 3:13
he hath *s.* blasphemy. *Mat* 26:65
s. of for a memorial. *Mark* 14:9
things which were *s.* *Luke* 2:33
and for a sign which shall be *s.* 34
s. in darkness, what *s.* in ear. 12:3
they the things which were *s.* 18:34
if I had not come and *s.* *John* 15:22
as many as have *s.* *Acts* 3:24
none of these things ye have *s.* 8:24
lest that come upon you *s.* of. 13:40
the word first have been *s.* to you. 46
to the things that were *s.* 16:14
things cannot be *s.* against. 19:36
if a spirit or angel hath *s.* 23:9
things that were *s.* by Paul. 27:11
when he had thus *s.*, took bread. 35
every where it is *s.* against. 28:22
your faith is *s.* of through. *Rom* 1:8
according to that which was *s.* *Rom* 4:18
your good be evil *s.* of. 14:16
to whom he was not *s.* of. 15:21
why am I evil *s.* of for ? *1 Cor* 10:30
it be known what is *s.*? 14:9
hath in these last days *s.* *Heb* 1:2
if the word *s.* by angels was. 2:2
of those things to be *s.* after. 3:5
he would not afterward have *s.* 4:8
he of whom these things are *s.* 7:13
of things which we have *s.* 8:1
the word should not be *s.* any. 12:19
have *s.* unto you the word. 13:7
their part he is evil *s.* of. *1 Pet* 4:14
truth shall be evil *s.* of. *2 Pet* 2:2
of words which were *s.* before. 3:2
ungodly sinners have *s.* *Jude* 15
the words which were *s.* before. 17

spoken *with* God, *expressly*

of which God had *s.* to him. *Gen* 21:2
an holy people to thy God as he hath *s.* *Deut* 26:19
God hath *s.* in his. *Ps* 60:6; 108:7
God hath *s.* once; twice. 62:11
was *s.* unto you by God. *Mat* 22:31
which God hath *s.* by. *Acts* 3:21
see **Lord**

I have, or *have I* **spoken**

which *I have s.* to thee. *Gen* 28:15
this is the thing *I have s.* 41:28
all this land *I have s.* *Ex* 32:13
the place of which *I have s.* 34
out of my grief *have I s.* *1 Sam* 1:16
Eli all things which *I have s.* 3:12
the matter which *I have s.* 20:23
and after that *I have s.* *Job* 21:3
once *have I s.* but I will not. 40:5
I believed, therefore *have I s.* *Ps* 116:10; *2 Cor* 4:13
I have not *s.* in secret. *Isa* 45:19
48:16
I have s. it, I will also bring. 46:11
I, even I, *have s.*; yea, I have. 48:15
I have s. it, I have proposed it. *Jer* 4:28
I have not *s.* to them yet. 23:21
I have s. unto you, rising early and. 25:3; 35:14
words *I have s.* to thee. 30:2; 36:2
because *I have s.* but they. 35:17
word which *I have s.* *Ezek* 12:28
saith it, albeit *I have* not *s.* 13:7
for *I have s.* it, saith the. 26:5; 28:10
fire of my jealousy *have I s.* 36:5, 6
art thou he of whom *I have s.*? 38:17
fire of my wrath *have I s.* 19
is the day whereof *I have s.* 39:8
I have also *s.* by the. *Hos* 12:10
the word that *I have s.* *John* 12:48
for *I have* not *s.* of myself but. 49
these things *have I s.* 14:25; 15:11
16:1, 25, 33
the word *I have s.* to you. 15:3
if *I have s.* evil, bear witness. 18:23

had **spoken**

the word Joseph *had s.* *Gen* 44:2
did as Balaam *had s.* *Num* 23:2
words he *had s.* to king. *1 Ki* 13:11
the Jezreelite *had s.* to him. 21:4
word which Elijah *had s.* *2 Ki* 1:17
as the man of God *had s.* 7:18
because we *had s.* unto. *Ezra* 8:22
king's words that he *had s.* *Neh* 2:18
Mordecai, who *had s.* good. *Esth* 7:9
had waited till Job *had s.* *Job* 32:4
wrote words the Lord *had s.* *Jer* 36:4
and when he *had s.* this. *Dan* 10:11
when he *had s.* such words. 15
when he *had s.* unto me, I was. 19
he *had s.*, the leprosy. *Mark* 1:42
they knew that he *had s.* the parable. 12:12; *Luke* 20:19
when he *had* thus *s.* *Luke* 19:28
24:40; *John* 9:6; 11:43; 18:22
Acts 19:41; 20:36; 26:30
the man believed the word that Jesus *had s.* *John* 4:50
they thought he *had s.* of. 11:13
when he *had s.* this, he saith. 21:19
that he *had s.* unto him. *Acts* 9:27
departed, after Paul *had s.* 28:25
when Moses *had s.* every. *Heb* 9:19

spoken with *prophet*
but *prophet* hath *s.* it. *Deut* 18:22
if *prophet* be deceived when he hath *s.* *Ezek* 14:9
that which was *s.* by Jeremy the *prophet.* *Mat* 2:17; 27:9
might be fulfilled which was *s.* by the *prophet.* 2:23; 13:35; 27:35
s. of by the *prophet* Esaias. 3:3
which was *s.* by Esaias the *prophet.* 4:14; 8:17; 12:17; 21:4
of desolation *s.* of by Daniel the *prophet.* 24:15; *Mark* 13:14
believe all that the *prophets* have *s.* *Luke* 24:25
s. of by the *prophet* Joel. *Acts* 2:16
take *prophets,* who have *s. Jas* 5:10

thou hast **spoken**
this city for the which *thou hast s.* *Gen* 19:21
nor since *thou hast s.* to. *Ex* 4:10
Moses said, *Thou hast s.* well. 10:29
this thing that *thou hast s.* 33:17
be great, as *thou hast s. Num* 14:17
the thing which *thou hast s.* is good. *Deut* 1:14
thou hast s. friendly to. *Ruth* 2:13
maid servants which *thou hast s.* of. *2 Sam* 6:22
but *thou hast s.* also of thy servant's. 7:19, 25; *1 Chr* 17:17, 23
good is the word of the Lord which *thou hast s.* *2 Ki* 20:19; *Isa* 39:8
fail of all that *thou hast s. Esth* 6:10
surely *thou hast s.* in my. *Job* 33:8
behold, *thou hast s.* and done evil. *Jer* 3:5
and that which *thou hast s.* is. 32:24
the words which *thou hast s.* 44:16
O Lord, *thou hast s.* against. 51:62
I have heard all thy blasphemies which *thou hast s.* *Ezek* 35:12

spokes
their felloes and *s.* *1 Ki* 7:33

spokesman
thy *s.* unto the people. *Ex* 4:16

spoon
one *s.* of ten shekels of gold, full of. *Num* 7:14, 20, 26, 32, 38, 44, 50 56, 62

spoons
dishes thereof and *s.* *Ex* 25:29
he made his dishes and his *s.* 37:16
and put thereon the dishes and the *s.* *Num* 4:7
bowls, twelve *s.* of gold. 7:84, 86
the *s.* were of pure gold. *1 Ki* 7:50 *2 Chr* 4:22
the *s.* took he away. *2 Ki* 25:14 *Jer* 52:18, 19
of rest of the money *s. 2 Chr* 24:14

sport
make *s.* And he made *s. Judg* 16:25
beheld while Samson made *s.* 27
it is a *s.* to a fool to do. *Pr* 10:23
and saith, Am not I in *s.*? 26:19

sport
against whom do ye *s.*? *Isa* 57:4

sporting
Isaac was *s.* with. *Gen* 26:8
s. themselves with their. *2 Pet* 2:13*

spot
a red heifer without *s.* *Num* 19:2
two lambs without *s.* 28:3* 9*, 11*; 29:17*, 26*
their *s.* is not the *s.* *Deut* 32:5
lift up thy face without *s. Job* 11:15
fair, there is no *s.* in thee. *S of S* 4:7
church, not having *s.* *Eph* 5:27
keep this commandment without *s.* *1 Tim* 6:14
who offered himself without *s.* to God. *Heb* 9:14*
as of a lamb without *s.* *1 Pet* 1:19
may be found without *s.* *2 Pet* 3:14
see **bright**

spots
can leopard change his *s.*? *Jer* 13:23
s. they are and blemishes, sporting themselves with their. *2 Pet* 2:13
these are *s.* in your feasts. *Jude* 12

spotted
thence all the *s.* cattle. *Gen* 30:32
every one that is not *s.* shall be. 33
forth cattle speckled and *s.* 39
the garment *s.* by the flesh. *Jude* 23

spouse
(*Revisions,* bride)
from Lebanon, my *s.* *S of S* 4:8
my heart, my sister, my *s.* 9
fair is thy love, my sister, my *s.* 10
thy lips, O my *s.* drop as the. 11
inclosed is my sister, my *s.* 12
into my garden, my sister, my *s.* 5:1

spouses
(*Revisions,* brides)
and your *s.* shall commit. *Hos* 4:13
I will not punish your *s.* when. 14

spouts, *see* **waterspouts**

sprang
and did yield fruit that *s.* up. *Mark* 4:8*; *Luke* 8:8*
for a light and *s.* in. *Acts* 16:29
it is evident our Lord *s.* *Heb* 7:14
s. of one so many as the stars. 11:12
see **sprung**

spread
field where Jacob had *s.* his tent. *Gen* 33:19; 35:21
and the plague *s. Lev* 13:5, 6, 23, 28
if the scall *s.* not. 32, 34
but if the scall *s.* much. 35, 36
if the plague be *s.* 51; 14:39, 44
and if the plague be not *s.* 13:53 55; 14:18
shall *s.* cloth of blue. *Num* 4:7, 11
they shall *s.* a scarlet cloth. 8
s. a purple cloth. 13
they shall *s.* on it a covering of. 14
s. the cloth before the. *Deut* 22:17
they *s.* a garment. *Judg* 8:25
Philistines *s.* themselves. 15:9
came and *s.* themselves in valley of. *2 Sam* 5:18, 22; *1 Chr* 14:9*, 13*
they *s.* Absalom a tent. *2 Sam* 16:22
woman *s.* a covering on the. 17:19
Rizpah *s.* sackcloth for her. 21:10
carvings of cherubims, and *s.* gold. *1 Ki* 6:32
he arose, with his hands *s.* 8:54
Hazael *s.* a thick cloth. *2 Ki* 8:15
s. the letter before the Lord. 19:14 *Isa* 37:14
he *s.* a cloud for a. *Ps* 105:39
they have *s.* a net by the way. 140:5
in vain net is *s.* in sight. *Pr* 1:17
worm is *s.* under thee. *Isa* 14:11
they that *s.* nets on the waters. 19:8
they could not *s.* the sail. 33:23
to *s.* sackcloth and ashes. 58:5
and they shall *s.* them. *Jer* 8:2
silver *s.* into plates is brought. 10:9
he hath *s.* net for my feet. *Lam* 1:13
s. the roll before me. *Ezek* 2:10
my net also will I *s.* 12:13; 17:20
thou shalt be a place to *s.* 26:14
because ye have been a net *s.* upon Tabor. *Hos* 5:1
when they shall go, I will *s.* 7:12
branches shall *s.*, his beauty. 14:6
as the morning *s.* upon. *Joel* 2:2
their horsemen shall *s.* *Hab* 1:8
behold, I will *s.* dung upon. *Mal* 2:3
s. their garments in the. *Mat* 21:8 *Mark* 11:8; *Luke* 19:36
but that it *s.* no further. *Acts* 4:17

spread *abroad*
families of the Canaanites were *s. abroad.* *Gen* 10:18
thou shalt *s. abroad* to west. 28:14
I will *s. abroad* my hands. *Ex* 9:29
Moses *s. abroad* his hands to. 33
he *s. abroad* the tent over. 40:19
but if the scab *s.* much *abroad.* *Lev* 13:7, 22, 27
they *s. abroad* the quails round the. *Num* 11:32
they were *s. abroad* on the earth. *1 Sam* 30:16
I did stamp and *s. abroad* mine enemies. *2 Sam* 22:43
the Philistines *s.* themselves *abroad.* *1 Chr* 14:13*
Uzziah's name *s. abroad.* *2 Chr* 26:8, 15
prosperity be *s. abroad* *Zech* 1:17
I have *s.* you *abroad* as the. 2:6
departed, *s. abroad* his fame in all. *Mat* 9:31; *Mark* 1:28; 6:14
God-ward is *s. abroad.* *1 Thes* 1:8

spread *forth*
valleys are they *s. forth.* *Num* 24:6
the cherubims *s. forth.* *1 Ki* 8:7
Solomon *s. forth.* 22; *2 Chr* 6:12, 13
plague of his own heart, and *s. forth* his hands. *1 Ki* 8:38; *2 Chr* 6:29
when ye *s. forth* your hands. *Isa* 1:15
he shall *s. forth* hands, as he. 25:11
saith God, he that *s. forth* 42:5
a place to *s. forth* nets. *Ezek* 47:10

spread *over*
they shall *s. over* it a cloth. *Num* 4:6
s. therefore thy skirt *over.* *Ruth* 3:9
that is *s. over* all nations. *Isa* 25:7
s. his royal pavilion *over.* *Jer* 43:10
shall *s.* his wings *over* Moab. 48:40
s. his wings *over* Bozrah. 49:22
I *s.* my skirt *over* thee. *Ezek* 16:8
nations *s.* their net *over* him. 19:8

spread *out*
cherubims *s. out* wings. *Ex* 37:9 *1 Chr* 28:18
I *s. out* my hands to the. *Ezra* 9:5
my root was *s. out* by. *Job* 29:19
hast thou with him *s. out* the sky? 37:18
have *s. out* my hands. *Isa* 65:2
hath *s. out* his hand. *Lam* 1:10
I will therefore *s. out* my net over. *Ezek* 32:3

spreadest
fine linen which thou *s.* *Ezek* 27:7

spreadeth
if the priest see that scab *s. Lev* 13:8
as an eagle *s.* abroad. *Deut* 32:11
God who alone *s.* out. *Job* 9:8
and he *s.* his cloud upon it. 26:9
behold, he *s.* his light upon it. 36:30
he *s.* sharp pointed things. 41:30
flattereth his neighbour *s.* a net. *Pr* 29:5
as he that swimmeth *s.* *Isa* 25:11
and the goldsmith *s.* it over. 40:19
that *s.* the heavens as a tent. 22
I the Lord that *s.* abroad the. 44:24
the daughter of Zion *s.* *Jer* 4:31
a tree that *s.* out her roots. 17:8
Zion *s.* forth her hands. *Lam* 1:17

spreading
appears, it is a *s.* plague. *Lev* 13:57
the wicked *s.* himself. *Ps* 37:35
and became a *s.* vine. *Ezek* 17:6
place for the *s.* of nets. 26:5

spreadings
can any understand the *s.*? *Job* 36:29

sprigs
he shall cut off the *s.* with pruning hooks. *Isa* 18:5
a vine, and shot forth *s. Ezek* 17:6

spring, *substantive*
about *s.* of the day Samuel called. *1 Sam* 9:26
he went forth to the *s.* *2 Ki* 2:21
fountain and corrupt *s.* *Pr* 25:26
spouse, is a *s.* shut up. *S of S* 4:12
shalt be like *s.* of water. *Isa* 58:11
all the leaves of her *s.* *Ezek* 17:9*
his *s.* shall become dry. *Hos* 13:15
see **day** *spring*

spring
Israel sang, *S.* up, O. *Num* 21:17
depths that *s.* out of valleys and. *Deut* 8:7
day began to *s.* they. *Judg* 19:25
neither doth trouble *s.* *Job* 5:6
of the tender herb to *s.* forth. 38:27
truth shall *s.* out of the. *Ps* 85:11
wicked *s.* as the grass. 92:7
before they *s.* forth, I tell. *Isa* 42:9
new thing, now it shall *s.* 43:19
shall *s.* up as among the grass. 44:4
and let righteousness *s.* 45:8
and thine health shall *s.* forth. 58:8

causeth things that are sown to *s.*:
Lord will cause praise to *s.* *Isa* 61:11
for the pastures do *s.* *Joel* 2:22
the seed should *s.*, he. *Mark* 4:27

springeth

even to hyssop that *s.* *1 Ki* 4:33
the second year that which *s.* of. *2 Ki* 19:29; *Isa* 37:30
thus judgement *s.* up as. *Hos* 10:4

springing

there a well of *s.* water. *Gen* 26:19
as the tender grass *s.* *2 Sam* 23:4
thou blessedst the *s.* *Ps* 65:10
him a well of water *s.* up. *John* 4:14
any root of bitterness *s.* *Heb* 12:15

springs

to the plain under the *s.* of Pisgah. *Deut* 4:49*
all the country of the *s.* *Josh* 10:40*
in the plains and in the *s.* 12:8*
give me *s.* of water. And he gave her the upper *s.* 15:19; *Judg* 1:15
hast thou entered into the *s.* of the sea? *Job* 38:16
all my *s.* are in thee. *Ps* 87:7
s. into the valleys. 104:10
he turneth the water *s.* into. 107:33
dry ground into water *s.* 35
land become *s.* of water. *Isa* 35:7
I will make the dry land *s.* 41:18
even by the *s.* of water shall. 49:10
dry up her sea and make her *s.* dry. *Jer* 51:36

sprinkle

let Moses *s.* the ashes. *Ex* 9:8
he shall *s.* on him that. *Lev* 14:7
the priest shall *s.* of the oil. 16
priest shall *s.* of the oil with. 27
s. the house seven times. 51
shall *s.* on the mercy seat. 16:14, 15
s. water of purifying. *Num* 8:7
shall *s.* it upon the tent, and. 19:18
the clean person shall *s.* it on. 19
shall he *s.* many nations. *Isa* 52:15
will I *s.* clean water. *Ezek* 36:25

sprinkled

Moses *s.* the ashes up. *Ex* 9:10
was not *s.* on him. *Num* 19:13, 20
and *s.* dust on their heads. *Job* 2:12
he *s.* both the book and. *Heb* 9:19
having our hearts *s.* from an. 10:22
see **blood**

sprinkleth

priest's that *s.* the blood. *Lev* 7:14
he that *s.* the water. *Num* 19:21

sprinkling

the ashes of a heifer *s.* *Heb* 9:13
through faith he kept the *s.* 11:28
to Jesus, and to the blood of *s.* 12:24
and the *s.* of the blood. *1 Pet* 1:2

sprout

a tree that it will *s.* again. *Job* 14:7

sprung

seven thin ears *s.* up. *Gen* 41:6, 23
it is a leprosy *s.* up in. *Lev* 13:42
sat in shadow of death, light is *s.* up. *Mat* 4:16
forthwith they *s.* up. 13:5; *Mark* 4:5
the thorns *s.* up and choked them. *Mat* 13:7; *Luke* 8:7
but when blade was *s.* up. *Mat* 13:26
as soon as it was *s.* up. *Luke* 8:6

spue

that the land *s.* you not out also. *Lev* 18:28*; 20:22*
drink, *s.* and fall. *Jer* 25:27
so then I will *s.* thee out. *Rev* 3:16

spued

as it *s.* out nations. *Lev* 18:28*

spun

that which they had *s.* *Ex* 35:25
the women *s.* goats' hair. 26

spunge

(*Revisions*, sponge)
took a *s.* and filled it with vinegar. *Mat* 27:48; *Mark* 15:36
John 19:29

spy

men which Moses sent to *s.* land. *Num* 13:16, 17
Moses sent to *s.* out Jaazer. 21:32
Joshua sent two men to *s.* secretly. *Josh* 2:1; 6:23, 25
sent to *s.* the land. *Judg* 18:2, 14, 17
his servants to *s.* out the city. *2 Sam* 10:3; *1 Chr* 19:3
he said, Go and *s.* *2 Ki* 6:13
came in privily to *s.* out. *Gal* 2:4

square

all doors and posts were *s.* *1 Ki* 7:5
s. round about, and 50. *Ezek* 45:2
see **four-square**

squared

of the temple were *s.* *Ezek* 41:21

squares

in four *s.* thereof. *Ezek* 43:16*
fourteen broad in the four *s.* 17*

stability

knowledge shall be the *s.* *Isa* 33:6

stable, *substantive*

I will make Rabbah a *s.* *Ezek* 25:5

stable

world also shall be *s.* *1 Chr* 16:30

stablish, -ed, -eth, *see* **establish, -ed, -eth**

Stachys

salute Urbane, and *S.* *Rom* 16:9

stacks

so that the *s.* of corn. *Ex* 22:6*

stacte

(*This Greek word signifies the gum that distils from the myrrh trees.* Moses *speaks of* stacte *in the enumeration of the drugs that were to enter into the composition of the perfume, which was to be offered in the holy place upon the golden altar*)
take to thee sweet spices, *s.* and. *Ex* 30:34

staff

with my *s.* I passed. *Gen* 32:10
Thy signet and thy *s.* 38:18, 25
eat it, with your *s.* in. *Ex* 12:11
and walk abroad on his *s.* 21:19
bare one cluster of grapes between two upon a *s.* *Num* 13:23
smote the ass with a *s.* 22:27
put forth the end of his *s.* *Judg* 6:21
s. of his spear was like a weaver's. *1 Sam* 17:7; *2 Sam* 21:19
David took his *s.* in his hand, and. *1 Sam* 17:40
one that leaneth on a *s.* *2 Sam* 3:29
he must be fenced with the *s.* 23:7
to him with a *s.* 21; *1 Chr* 11:23
take my *s.*: lay my *s.* on. *2 Ki* 4:29
Gehazi laid the *s.* on the face. 31
on *s.* of this reed. 18:21; *Isa* 36:6
thy rod and thy *s.* *Ps* 23:4
take from Judah the *s.* *Isa* 3:1
for thou hast broken the *s.* 9:4
and the *s.* in their hand is. 10:5
or as if the *s.* should lift up. 15
and shall lift up his *s.* 10:24
the Lord hath broken the *s.* 14:5
are beaten out with a *s.* 28:27
where grounded *s.* shall pass. 30:32
say, How is the strong *s.*! *Jer* 48:17
have been a *s.* of reed. *Ezek* 29:6
and their *s.* declareth. *Hos* 4:12
every man with his *s.* in. *Zech* 8:4
and I took my *s.* even Beauty. 11:10
then I cut asunder my other *s.* 14
journey, save a *s.* only. *Mark* 6:8
leaning on the top of his *s.* *Heb* 11:21
see **bread**

stagger

to *s.* like a drunken man. *Job* 12:25
Ps 107:27
they *s.* but not with strong drink. *Isa* 29:9

staggered

he *s.* not at the promise of God. *Rom* 4:20*

staggereth

as a drunken man *s.* *Isa* 19:14

stain

the shadow of death *s.* it. *Job* 3:5*
Lord purposed to *s.* the pride of. *Isa* 23:9
their blood sprinkled, I will *s.* 63:3

stairs

up with winding *s.* *1 Ki* 6:8
him on the top of the *s.* *2 Ki* 9:13
stood on the *s.* Joshua. *Neh* 9:4
secret places of the *s.* *S of S* 2:14*
and his *s.* shall look. *Ezek* 43:17*
Paul stood on the *s.* *Acts* 21:40

stakes

not one of the *s.* shall. *Isa* 33:20
cords and strengthen thy *s.* 54:2

stalk

seven rank ears came up on one *s.* *Gen* 41:5, 22
it hath no *s.*: the bud. *Hos* 8:7*

stalks

and she hid them with the *s.* of flax. *Josh* 2:6

stall

eat the calves out of the midst of the *s.* *Amos* 6:4
grow up as calves of the *s.* *Mal* 4:2
loose his ox from the *s.* *Luke* 13:15

stalled

than a *s.* ox and hatred. *Pr* 15:17

stalls

Solomon had forty thousand *s.* of. *1 Ki* 4:26; *2 Chr* 9:25
Hezekiah had *s.* for all manner of beasts. *2 Chr* 32:28
shall be no herd in the *s.* *Hab* 3:17

stammerers

the tongue of the *s.* shall. *Isa* 32:4

stammering

s. lips and another tongue. *Isa* 28:11*
see a people of a *s.* tongue. 33:19*

stamp

I did *s.* them as the mire of the street. *2 Sam* 22:43
hand, *s.* with thy foot. *Ezek* 6:11

stamped

I *s.* the calf and ground. *Deut* 9:21
Josiah *s.* the grove. *2 Ki* 23:6
s. high places small to powder. 15
her idol and *s.* it. *2 Chr* 15:16*
hast *s.* with the feet. *Ezek* 25:6
fourth beast *s.* residue. *Dan* 7:7, 19
the he goat cast down and *s.* 8:7*
cast down some of stars, and *s.* 10*

stamping

at noise of *s.* of hoofs. *Jer* 47:3

stanched

her issue of blood *s.* *Luke* 8:44

stand

cloudy pillar *s.* at door. *Ex* 33:10
priest shall estimate it, so shall it *s.* *Lev* 27:14, 17
her vows shall *s.* *Num* 30:4, 5, 7, 11
her vows or her bond shall not *s.* 12
hath chosen him to *s.* *Deut* 18:5
if he *s.* to it and say, I like. 25:8
when he shall *s.* at entering gate. *Josh* 20:4
now *s.* and see this great thing. *1 Sam* 12:16
I will go out and *s.* before my. 19:3
the house, priests could *s.* to minister. *1 Ki* 8:11; *2 Chr* 5:14
as the Lord liveth, before whom I *s.* *1 Ki* 17:1; 18:15; *2 Ki* 3:14; 5:16
will come out and *s.* *2 Ki* 5:11
how then shall we *s.*? 10:4
the angel of the Lord *s.* *1 Chr* 21:16
to *s.* every morning to thank. 23:30
all present to *s.* to it. *2 Chr* 34:32
rulers of congregation *s.* *Ezra* 10:14*
see if Mordecai's matters would *s.* *Esth* 3:4
to gather themselves, and to *s.* 8:11
lean on his house, it shall not *s.* *Job* 8:15
he shall *s.* at the latter day. 19:25
and they *s.* as a garment. 38:14
and my kinsmen *s.* afar off. *Ps* 38:11
on right hand did *s.* queen. 45:9
and he made the waters to *s.* 78:13
Satan *s.* at his right hand. 109:6
he shall *s.* at the right hand. 31
our feet shall *s.* within thy. 122:2
if thou shouldest mark iniquities, O Lord, who shall *s.*? 130:3
house of righteous shall *s.* *Pr* 12:7

counsel of the Lord shall *s*. *Pr* 19:21
and *s*. not in the place of. 25:6
s. not in an evil thing. *Eccl* 8:3*
thus saith Lord God, It shall not *s*. *Isa* 7:7; 8:10
a root of Jesse, which shall *s*. 11:10
purposed, so it shall *s*. 14:24
my Lord, I *s*. continually on. 21:8
your agreement with hell shall not *s*. 28:18
liberal things shall he *s*. 32:8*
word of our God shall *s*. for. 40:8
counsel shall *s*. and I will do. 46:10
s. now with thine enchantments. 47:12
and strangers shall *s*. and feed. 61:5
s. ye in the ways and see. *Jer* 6:16
know whose word shall *s*. 44:28
did not *s*. because day was. 46:21
keeping of his covenant it might *s*. *Ezek* 17:14
their loins to be at a *s*. 29:7
and the kingdom shall *s*. *Dan* 2:44
king of the north shall not *s*. 11:6
king of the south shall not *s*. 25
nor shall he *s*. that handleth the. *Amos* 2:15
he shall *s*. and feed in. *Mi* 5:4
S., *s*., shall they cry. *Nah* 2:8
and who shall *s*. when he ? *Mal* 3:2
kingdom divided against itself shall not *s*. *Mat* 12:25, 26; *Mark* 3:24 25; *Luke* 11:18
when ye *s*. praying. *Mark* 11:25
why *s*. ye gazing up ? *Acts* 1:11
go, *s*. and speak in the temple. 5:20
Paul said, I *s*. at Caesar's. 25:10
I *s*. and am judged for hope. 26:6
this grace wherein we *s*. *Rom* 5:2
according to election might *s*. 9:11
God is able to make him *s*. 14:4
the gospel wherein ye *s*. *1 Cor* 15:1
and why *s*. we in jeopardy ? 30
joy, for by faith ye *s*. *2 Cor* 1:24
having done all to *s*. *Eph* 6:13
s. having your loins girt about. 14
grace of God wherein ye *s*. *1 Pet* 5:12
behold, I *s*. at the door. *Rev* 3:20
who shall be able to *s*.? 6:17
merchants *s*. afar off for fear. 18:15

stand *abroad*

s. *abroad*, man shall. *Deut* 24:11

stand *against*

neither shalt thou *s*. *against* the blood of thy neighbour. *Lev* 19:16
widow shall *s*. *against*. *Num* 30:9
that my words shall *s*. *against* you. *Jer* 44:29
to *s*. *against* wiles of devil. *Eph* 6:11

stand *aloof*

and my friends *s*. *aloof*. *Ps* 38:11

stand *back*

said, *S*. *back*. This fellow. *Gen* 19:9

stand *before*

rise up early, *s*. *before* Pharaoh. *Ex* 8:20; 9:13
could not *s*. *before* Moses. 9:11
I will *s*. *before* thee on the rock. 17:6
woman *s*. *before* a beast. *Lev* 18:23
no power to *s*. *before* your enemies. 26:37; *Josh* 7:12, 13; *Judg* 2:14
s. *before* the congregation to minister. *Num* 16:9
and he shall *s*. *before* Eleazar. 27:21
till he *s*. *before* congregation. 35:12 *Josh* 20:6
shall no man be able to *s*. *before* thee. *Deut* 7:24; 11:25; *Josh* 1:5 10:8; 23:9
can *s*. *before* the children ? *Deut* 9:2
tribe of Levi to *s*. *before* the. 10:8 *2 Chr* 29:11; *Ezek* 44:11, 15
the men shall *s*. *before*. *Deut* 19:17
s. this day all of you *before*. 29:10
who is able to *s*. *before* ? *1 Sam* 6:20
I pray thee, *s*. *before* me. 16:22
virgin *s*. *before* the king. *1 Ki* 1:2
happy are these thy servants who *s*. *before* thee. 10:8; *2 Chr* 9:7
s. on the mount *before*. *1 Ki* 19:11
we *s*. *before* this house. *2 Chr* 20:9
we cannot *s*. *before* thee. *Ezra* 9:15
is able to *s*. *before* me ? *Job* 41:10
can *s*. *before* his cold ? *Ps* 147:17
in business ? he shall *s*. *before* kings, he shall not *s*. *before*. *Pr* 22:29
who is able to *s*. *before* envy ? 27:4
come and *s*. *before* me. *Jer* 7:10
thou shalt *s*. *before* me. 15:19
want a man to *s*. *before* me. 35:19
appoint ? who is that shepherd that will *s*. *before* me ? 49:19; 50:44
might *s*. *before* king. *Dan* 1:5
beasts might *s*. *before* him. 8:4
in the ram, to *s*. *before* him. 7
none shall *s*. *before* him, he. 11:16
s. *before* his indignation ? *Nah* 1:6
s. *before* the Son of man. *Luke* 21:36
we shall all *s*. *before* judgement seat of Christ. *Rom* 14:10
I saw the dead, small and great, *s*. *before* God. *Rev* 20:12

stand *by*

behold I *s*. *by* the well. *Gen* 24:43
s. *by* the river's brink. *Ex* 7:15
and all the people *s*. *by* thee. 18:14
s. *by* the burnt offering. *Num* 23:3
while they *s*. *by* let them. *Neh* 7:3
who say, *S*. *by* thyself, I. *Isa* 65:5
s. *by* the way and ask. *Jer* 48:19
prince shall *s*. *by* the. *Ezek* 46:2
give places to walk among these that *s*. *by*. *Zech* 3:7
ones that *s*. *by* the Lord. 4:14
the people which *s*. *by*. *John* 11:42

stand *fast*

shall *s*. *fast* with him. *Ps* 89:28
all his commandments *s*. *fast*. 111:8*
say ye, *S*. *fast*, and. *Jer* 46:14
watch ye, *s*. *fast* in. *1 Cor* 16:13
s. *fast* therefore in liberty. *Gal* 5:1
s. *fast* in one spirit. *Phil* 1:27
so *s*. *fast* in the Lord. 4:1
live, if ye *s*. *fast* in Lord. *1 Thes* 3:8
s. *fast* and hold. *2 Thes* 2:15

stand *forth*

get up, and *s*. *forth* with. *Jer* 46:4
he saith to the man, *S*. *forth*. *Mark* 3:3; *Luke* 6:8

stand *here*

s. *here* by well of water. *Gen* 24:13
he said, *S*. *here* by the burnt offering. *Num* 23:15
thee, *s*. thou *here* by me. *Deut* 5:31
turn aside, and *s*. *here*. *2 Sam* 18:30
s. ye *here* all day idle ? *Mat* 20:6
some *s*. *here* who shall not. *Mark* 9:1
even by him doth this man *s*. *here* whole. *Acts* 4:10

stand *in*

s. *in* the door of the tent. *Judg* 4:20
s. *in* holy place according. *2 Chr* 35:5
the ungodly shall not *s*. *in*. *Ps* 1:5
s. *in* awe, sin not, commune. 4:4
foolish shall not *s*. *in* thy sight. 5:5
who shall *s*. *in* his holy place ? 24:3
of the world *s*. *in* awe. 33:8
who may *s*. *in* thy sight when ? 76:7
hast not made him to *s*. *in*. 89:43
s. *in* house of Lord. 134:1; 135:2
s. *in* gate of Lord's house. *Jer* 7:2
the wild asses did *s*. *in* the. 14:6
s. *in* the gate of the children. 17:19
s. *in* the court of the Lord's. 26:2
have not gone up to *s*. *in* the battle. *Ezek* 13:5
that should *s*. *in* gap before. 22:30
they shall *s*. *in* judgement. 44:24
had ability in them to *s*. *in*. *Dan* 1:4
s. *in* the glorious land. 11:16
shall *s*. *in* thy lot at the end. 12:13
feet *s*. *in* that day on. *Zech* 14:4
when ye see abomination *s*. *in* holy place. *Mat* 24:15
Gabriel, that *s*. *in* presence of God. *Luke* 1:19
not *s*. *in* wisdom of men. *1 Cor* 2:5
to change my voice, for I *s*. *in*. *Gal* 4:20*

stand *on*

to-morrow I will *s*. *on* top. *Ex* 17:9
of Elisha shall *s*. *on* him. *2 Ki* 6:31
shall not *s*. *on* his side. *Dan* 11:17
arms shall *s*. *on* his part, and they shall pollute. *Dan* 11:31
s. *on* sea of glass, having. *Rev* 15:2

stand *out*

eyes *s*. *out* with fatness. *Ps* 73:7

stand *perfect*

may *s*. *perfect* and complete in will. *Col* 4:12

stand *still*

Fear ye not, *s*. *still* and see the. *Ex* 14:13; *2 Chr* 20:17
s. *still*, I will hear what. *Num* 9:8*
ye shall *s*. *still* in Jordan. *Josh* 3:8
sun *s*. *still* upon Gibeon, and. 10:12
s. thou *still* a while. *1 Sam* 9:27
now *s*. *still* that I may reason. 12:7
we will *s*. *still* in our place. 14:9
s. *still* and consider the. *Job* 37:14
escaped sword *s*. not *still*. *Jer* 51:50
the chariot to *s*. *still*. *Acts* 8:38

stand *strong*

mountain to *s*. *strong*. *Ps* 30:7

stand *there*

that they may *s*. *there*. *Num* 11:16
as Levites who *s*. *there*. *Deut* 18:7
to the poor, *S*. thou *there*. *Jas* 2:3

stand *together*

let us *s*. *together*: who ? *Isa* 50:8

stand *up*

s. *up* and bless the Lord. *Neh* 9:5
I *s*. *up*, and thou regardest me not. *Job* 30:20
in order before me, *s*. *up*. 33:5
take hold of shield, *s*. *up*. *Ps* 35:2
who will *s*. *up* for me against ? 94:16
with child that shall *s*. *up*. *Eccl* 4:15
images shall not *s*. *up*. *Isa* 27:9*
let them *s*. *up* yet they shall. 44:11
prognosticators *s*. *up*. 47:13
them, they *s*. *up* together. 48:13
awake, *s*. *up*, O Jerusalem. 51:17
nor their trees *s*. *up* in. *Ezek* 31:14
four kingdoms shall *s*. *up*. *Dan* 8:22
of fierce countenance shall *s*. *up*. 23
he shall also *s*. *up* against prince. 25
there shall *s*. *up* three kings. 11:2
and a mighty king shall *s*. *up*. 3, 4
her roots shall one *s*. *up*. 7
many shall *s*. *up* against king. 14
s. *up* in his estate a raiser of taxes. 20
estate shall *s*. *up* a vile person. 21
time shall Michael *s*. *up*. 12:1
Peter said, *S*. *up*; I. *Acts* 10:26

stand *upon*

thou shalt *s*. *upon* a rock. *Ex* 33:21
s. *upon* mount Gerizim. *Deut* 27:12
these shall *s*. *upon* mount Ebal. 13
and they shall *s*. *upon*. *Josh* 3:13
Saul said, *S*. *upon* me. *2 Sam* 1:9
s. *upon* the mount. *1 Ki* 19:11
son of man, *s*. *upon* thy feet. *Ezek* 2:1; *Acts* 26:16
pilots of the sea shall *s*. *upon* the land. *Ezek* 27:29
ye *s*. *upon* sword, ye work. 33:26
fishes shall *s*. *upon* it from. 47:10
made *s*. *upon* the feet. *Dan* 7:4
I will *s*. *upon* my watch. *Hab* 2:1
while they *s*. *upon* feet. *Zech* 14:12
angel I saw *s*. *upon* sea. *Rev* 10:5

stand *upright*

risen and *s*. *upright*. *Ps* 20:8
understand words, *s*. *upright*. *Dan* 10:11
said, *S*. *upright* on thy feet. And he leaped and walked. *Acts* 14:10

stand *with*

men that shall *s*. *with* you. *Num* 1:5

stand *without*

not able to *s*. *without*. *Ezra* 10:13
s. *without*, desiring to speak. *Mat* 12:47; *Luke* 8:20
ye begin to *s*. *without*. *Luke* 13:25

standard

and every man by his own *s*. *Num* 1:52; 2:2, 17
east side shall the *s*. of Judah. 2:3
south side shall be the *s*. of. 10
west side shall be the *s*. of. 18
north side shall be the *s*. of Dan. 25
in the first place went the **s**. 10:14

I will set up my s. to the people. Isa 49:22*
Lord shall lift up a s. against. 59:19*
lift up a s. for the people. 62:10*
set up s. toward Zion. Jer 4:6
how long shall I see the s. and? 21
set ye up a s. in the land. 50:2
51:12, 27

standardbearer

they shall be as when a s. Isa 10:18

standards

hindmost with their s. Num 2:31
so they pitched by their s. and. 34

standest

come in; wherefore s. thou without? Gen 24:31
the place whereon thou s. is holy. Ex 3:5; Josh 5:15; Acts 7:33
why s. thou afar off? Ps 10:1
were broken off, thou s. by faith. Rom 11:20

standeth

and that thy cloud s. Num 14:14
son of Nun, which s. before thee. Deut 1:38
hearken to the priest that s. 17:12
but with him that s. with us. 29:15
to feel pillars whereon the house s. Judg 16:26*
Haman s. in the court. Esth 6:5
the gallows s. in the house of. 7:9
nor s. in the way of sinners. Ps 1:1
my foot s. in an even place. 26:12
the counsel of the Lord s. 33:11
God s. in the congregation. 82:1
but my heart s. in awe. 119:161
wisdom s. in the top of. Pr 8:2
behold, he s. behind. S of S 2:9
Lord s. up to plead, s. to. Isa 3:13
in his place, and he s. 46:7
justice s. afar off, truth is. 59:14
the great prince who s. for. Dan 12:1
feed that that s. still. Zech 11:16*
. one among you, whom. John 1:26
the friend of the bridegroom s. 3:29
to his own master he s. Rom 14:4
that s. stedfast in heart. 1 Cor 7:37
no flesh while the world s. 8:13
thinketh he s. take heed. 10:12
the foundation of God s. 2 Tim 2:19
every priest s. daily. Heb 10:11
behold, the judge s. Jas 5:9
angel who s. on the sea. Rev 10:8

standing, *substantive*

mire where there is no s. Ps 69:2
receive of you his s. Mi 1:11*

standing

nor rear ye up a s. image. Lev 26:1*
angel of the Lord s. Num 22:23, 31
Samuel s. as appointed. 1 Sam 19:20
servants were s. about him. 22:6
and the lion s. by. 1 Ki 13:25, 28
host of heaven s. 22:19; 2 Chr 18:18
and two lions s. by. 2 Chr 9:18
Esther the queen s. in. Esth 5:2
turneth wilderness into a s. water. Ps 107:35*
the rock into a s. water. 114:8*
saw the Lord s. upon. Amos 9:1
will cut off thy s. images. Mi 5:13*
Satan s. at his right hand. Zech 3:1
which go forth from s. before. 6:5
they love to pray s. in. Mat 6:5
be some s. here. 16:28; Luke 9:27
. idle in the market. Mat 20:3, 6
his mother s. without. Mark 3:31
the abomination s. where it. 13:14
an angel s. on the right. Luke 1:11
the publican s. afar off smote. 18:13
and woman s. in midst. John 8:9*
she turned and saw Jesus s. 20:14
but Peter s. up with. Acts 2:14
beholding the man healed s. 4:14
found the keepers s. without. 5:23
the men are s. in the temple. 25
. on the right hand of God. 7:55, 56
was s. by and consenting. 22:20
first tabernacle was yet s. Heb 9:8
earth s. out of the water. 2 Pet 3:5*
four angels s on four. Rev 7:1
two candlesticks s. before. 11:4

s. afar off for the fear of. Rev 18:10
I saw an angel s. in the sun. 19:17
see **corn**

stank

died, and the river s. Ex 7:21
frogs on heaps, and land s. 8:14
manna bred worms and s. 16:20
Ammon saw they s. 2 Sam 10:6*

star

This word included, for the Hebrew, all heavenly bodies except the sun and the moon. The stars and the grouping into constellations early attracted man's attention, and they are alluded to in the earliest-written of the books of the Bible. Among idolaters the stars soon became objects of worship. They were supposed to foretell events, and a whole science was built up around them.

Several stars spoken of especially in the New Testament have a figurative rather than a literal use.

[1] The day star *is given as a sign of Christ's coming, or as a symbol of the spirit's illumination of the heart of one who has accepted Christ,* 2 Pet 1:19.

[2] The morning star, *which precedes the coming of day, is given as a designation of Christ as bringing the day of gospel light,* Rev 2:28.

[3] The star of the wise men, *which is the subject of much discussion,* Mat 2:2.

The number of the stars was looked upon as infinite. When the scripture would express a very extraordinary increase and multiplication, it uses the symbol of the stars of heaven, or of the sand of the sea, Gen 15:5; 22:17; 26:4.

there shall come a s. out. Num 24:17
but ye have borne the s. Amos 5:26
for we have seen his s. Mat 2:2
of them what time s. appeared. 7
lo, the s. which they saw in east. 9
when they saw s. they rejoiced. 10
s. of your god Remphan. Acts 7:43
s. differeth from another s. in glory. 1 Cor 15:41
there fell a great s. Rev 8:10, 11
a s. fell from heaven unto. 9:1

day **star**

till the *day* s. arise in. 2 Pet 1:19

morning **star**

give him the *morning* s. Rev 2:28
the bright and *morning* s. 22:16

stare

may tell all my bones: they look and s. upon me. Ps 22:17

stargazers

let the s. stand up and. Isa 47:13

stars

lights, he made s. also. Gen 1:16
tell the s. if thou be able to. 15:5
sun, moon, and eleven s. made. 37:9
when thou seest s. should. Deut 4:19
the s. in their courses. Judg 5:20
the morning till the s. Neh 4:21
let the s. of the twilight. Job 3:9
sun, and sealeth up the s. 9:7
behold height of the s. how. 22:12
s. are not pure in his sight. 25:5
when the morning s. sang. 38:7
moon and s. which thou. Ps 8:3
moon and s. to rule by night. 136:9
he telleth number of the s. 147:4
sun, moon, all ye s. of light. 148:3
while the sun or s. be. Eccl 12:2
throne above s. of God. Isa 14:13
giveth the s. for a light. Jer 31:35
I will make the s. Ezek 32:7
it cast down some of the s. Dan 8:10
shall shine as the s. for ever. 12:3
s. shall withdraw. Joel 2:10; 3:15
set thy nest among the s. Ob 4
be signs in sun, moon, and s. Luke 21:25
when neither sun nor s. Acts 27:20
glory of s. for one star. 1 Cor 15:41

so many as s. of the sky. Heb 11:12
raging waves, wandering s. Jude 13
the third part of the s. Rev 8:12
head a crown of twelve s. 12:1
see **heaven, seven**

state

every man at his best s. is. Ps 39:5*
the last s. of that man is worse than. Mat 12:45; Luke 11:26
see **estate**

stately

satest upon a s. bed. Ezek 23:41

station

from thy s. and state. Isa 22:19*

stature

saw are men of great s. Num 13:32
on the height of his s. 1 Sam 16:7
s. with six fingers and with six toes. 2 Sam 21:20; 1 Chr 11:23; 20:6
this thy s. is like a palm tree and. S of S 7:7
the high ones of s. shall. Isa 10:33
men of s. shall come over. 45:14
upon head of every s. Ezek 13:18
a spreading vine of low s. 17:6
her s. was exalted among. 19:11
was a cedar of an high s. 31:3
not add one cubit to his s. Mat 6:27†; Luke 12:25
Jesus increased in wisdom and s. Luke 2:52
Zacchaeus little of s. climbed. 19:3
measure of the s. of fulness of Christ. Eph 4:13

statute

there he made a s. and. Ex 15:25
shall be theirs for perpetual s. 29:9
a perpetual s. Lev 3:17; 16:34
24:9; Num 19:21
it shall be for a s. of judgement. Num 27:11; 35:29
and he set them a s. Josh 24:25
David made it a s. for. 1 Sam 30:25
was a s. for Israel and. Ps 81:4
to establish a royal s. Dan 6:7
that no s. king establisheth may. 15

statutes

know the s. of God. Ex 18:16
teach Israel all the s. Lev 10:11
these are the s. the Lord. Num 30:16
shall hear all these s. Deut 4:6
Lord commanded us to do all these s. 6:24
shalt oberve and do these s. 16:12
to keep these s. to do them. 17:19
walking in the s. of David. 1 Ki 3:3
and walked in s. of the heathen. 2 Ki 17:8, 19
neither do they after their s. 34
the s. he wrote, ye shall. 37
take heed to do the s. 2 Chr 33:8
them s. and laws. Neh 9:14
s. of Lord are right. Ps 19:8
I gave them s. that. Ezek 20:25
walk in the s. of life. 33:15
for s. of Omri are kept. Mi 6:16
see statute for **ever**

his **statutes**

ear to his commandments and keep all *his* s. Ex 15:26; Deut 6:17
10:13; 11:1
shalt do *his* s. which I. Deut 27:10
not observe to do *his* s. 28:15
his s., I did not depart. 2 Sam 22:23
hearts be perfect to walk in *his* s. 1 Ki 8:61
they rejected *his* s. 2 Ki 17:15
made a covenant to keep *his* s. 23:3; 2 Chr 34:31
even a scribe of *his* s. Ezra 7:11
put away *his* s. from me. Ps 18:22
observe *his* s. and laws. 105:45
in his law, nor in *his* s. Jer 44:23
see **judgements**

my **statutes**

kept *my* s. and laws. Gen 26:5
ye shall therefore keep *my* s. Lev 18:5, 26; 19:19
ye shall do *my* s. 25:18
if ye walk in *my* s. 26:3
if ye despise *my* s. 15
they abhorred *my* s. 43

if thou wilt keep *my s.* *1 Ki* 3:14
will not keep *my s.* 9:6
hast not kept *my s.* 11:11
he kept *my s.* 34
keep *my s.* *2 Ki* 17:13
turn away, and forsake *my s.* *2 Chr* 7:19
to do to declare *my s.*? *Ps* 50:16
if they break *my s.*, keep not. 89:31
they walked in *my s.* *Jer* 44:10
hath changed *my s.* more. *Ezek* 5:6
ye have not walked in *my s.* 7
they may walk in *my s.* and. 11:20
son hath kept all *my s.* 18:19
cause you to walk in *my s.* 36:27
my s. did take hold of. *Zech* 1:6

thy statutes

him a perfect heart to keep *thy s.* *1 Chr* 29:19
O Lord, teach me *thy s.* *Ps* 119:12
26, 33, 64, 68, 124, 135
I will delight myself in *thy s.* 119:16
servant did meditate in *thy s.* 23
and I will meditate in *thy s.* 48
thy s. have been my songs in. 54
that I might learn *thy s.* 71
let my heart be sound in *thy s.* 80
bottle, yet do I not forget *thy s.* 83
heart to perform *thy s.* alway. 112
I will have respect to *thy s.* 117
them that err from *thy s.* 118
for the wicked seek not *thy s.* 155
when thou hast taught *thy s.* 171

staves

thou shalt make *s.* of shittim wood.
Ex 25:13, 28; 27:6; 30:5; 37:4
put *s.* into rings. 25:14, 15; 27:7
37:5; 38:7
s. of shittim wood. 37:15, 28; 38:5
he set *s.* on the ark and put. 40:20
they shall put in *s.* thereof.
Num 4:6, 8, 11, 14
people digged with their *s.* 21:18
am I a dog, that thou comest to me with *s.*? *1 Sam* 17:43
carried the ark with *s.* *1 Chr* 15:15
strike through with his *s.* *Hab* 3:14
I took unto me two *s.* I. *Zech* 11:7
nor take two coats nor *s.* *Mat* 10:10
Luke 9:3
great multitude with *s.* from chief priests. *Mat* 26:47; *Mark* 14:43
thief with sword and *s.*? *Mat* 26:55
Mark 14:48; *Luke* 22:52

stay, *substantive*

plague in his sight be at a *s.* *Lev* 13:5
scall in his sight be at a *s.* 37
but the Lord was my *s.* *2 Sam* 22:19
Ps 18:18
away the *s.* and staff, the whole *s.* of bread, and the whole *s.* *Isa* 3:1
even they that are the *s.* 19:13*

stay

neither *s.* thou in all the. *Gen* 19:17
ye shall *s.* no longer. *Ex* 9:28
if bright spot *s.* *Lev* 13:23, 28
s. not, but pursue after. *Josh* 10:19
would ye *s.* for them from. *Ruth* 1:13
s. and I will tell thee. *1 Sam* 15:16
make speed, haste, *s.* not. 20:38
s. now thine hand. *2 Sam* 24:16
1 Chr 21:15
he will not *s.* them when. *Job* 37:4
or who can *s.* the bottles of? 38:37*
let no man *s.* him. *Pr* 28:17
s. me with flagons. *S of S* 2:5
shall no more *s.* on him. *Isa* 10:20†
s. yourselves and wonder, cry. 29:9
and *s.* on oppression. 30:12†
woe to them that *s.* on horses. 31:1†
for they *s.* themselves on the. 48:2
let him trust in Lord, and *s.* 50:10†
s. not, for I will bring evil. *Jer* 4:6
forbearing, I could not *s.* 20:9
none can *s.* his hand, or. *Dan* 4:35
not *s.* in the place of. *Hos* 13:13*

stayed

and Noah *s.* yet other seven days.
Gen 8:10, 12
with Laban, and I have *s.* 32:4
flocks and herds be *s.* *Ex* 10:24
and Hur *s.* up Moses' hands. 17:12
dead and living, plague was *s.*
Num 16:48, 50; 25:8; *2 Sam* 24:25
Ps 106:30
I *s.* in mount forty days. *Deut* 10:10
still, and the moon *s.* *Josh* 10:13
hast *s.* three days. *1 Sam* 20:19
David *s.* his servants with. 24:7*
that were left behind *s.* 30:9
now Jonathan *s.* by. *2 Sam* 17:17
that the plague may be *s.* 24:21
1 Chr 21:22
king was *s.* up in his chariot, and died. *1 Ki* 22:35; *2 Chr* 18:34
a vessel more, and oil *s.* *2 Ki* 4:6
and he smote thrice, and *s.* 13:18
the king of Assyria *s.* not in. 15:20
thy proud waves be *s.* *Job* 38:11
whose mind is *s.* on thee. *Isa* 26:3
no hands *s.* on her. *Lam* 4:6*
great waters were *s.* *Ezek* 31:15
heaven is *s.*, the earth is *s.* *Hag* 1:10
came to him and *s.* him. *Luke* 4:42
but he himself *s.* in Asia. *Acts* 19:22

stayeth

he *s.* his rough wind in the day of.
Isa 27:8*

stays

were *s.* on either side throne; two lions stood beside the *s.*
1 Ki 10:19; *2 Chr* 9:18

stead

he closed up the flesh in *s.* *Gen* 2:21
me another seed in *s.* of Abel. 4:25
Abraham offered the ram in *s.* 22:13
am I in God's *s.* 30:2
abide in *s.* of the lad. 44:33
he shall be to thee in *s.* of a mouth, thou shalt be to him in *s.* *Ex* 4:16
to gather stubble in *s.* of straw. 5:12
that son that is priest in his *s.* 29:30
Lev 16:32
I have taken the Levites in *s.* of all firstborn. *Num* 3:12, 41, 45; 8:16
cattle of the Levites in *s.* 3:41, 45
in *s.* of thy husband. 5:19, 20, 29
mayest be to us in *s.* of eyes. 10:31
risen up in your father's *s.* 32:14
Esau dwelt in their *s.* *Deut* 2:12
dwelt in their *s.* 21, 22, 23
son ministered in his *s.* 10:6
whom he raised in their *s.* *Josh* 5:7
I pray, her sister in *s.* *Judg* 15:2
Saul, in whose *s.* thou. *2 Sam* 16:8
he made Amasa captain in *s.* 17:25
sit on my throne in my *s.* *1 Ki* 1:30
for he shall be king in my *s.* 35
made me king in *s.* of David. 3:7
Rehoboam made in their *s.* 14:27
placed in cities of Samaria in *s.* of Israel. *2 Ki* 17:24
queen in *s.* of Vashti. *Esth* 2:4, 17
were in my soul's *s.* *Job* 16:4
let thistles grow in *s.* of wheat, and cockle in *s.* of barley. 31:40
to thy wish in God's *s.* 33:6*
shall set others in their *s.* 34:24
in *s.* of thy fathers shall. *Ps* 45:16
wicked cometh in his *s.* *Pr* 11:8
shall stand up in his *s.* *Eccl* 4:15
in *s.* of sweet smell there shall be stink, in *s.* of. *Isa* 3:24
in *s.* of the thorn shall come up fir tree, and in *s.* of the brier. 55:13
who taketh strangers in *s.* of her.
Ezek 16:32
pray you in Christ's *s.* *2 Cor* 5:20*
in thy *s.* might have. *Philem* 13*

see **reigned**

steads

they dwelt in their *s.* till. *1 Chr* 5:22

steady

Moses' hands were *s.* *Ex* 17:12

steal

(*Theft was made the subject of one of the ten commandments. There was no penalty attached to theft of property but restitution, double or more, as the case might be. If restitution was not made it was treated as a case of debt, the property or even the person of the debt being sold to cover it. The man-stealer, who reduced his pre to slavery, was to be put to death*)
wherefore didst thou *s.*? *Gen* 31:2
how then should we *s.* silver? 44:
thou shalt not *s.* *Ex* 20:15; *Lev* 19:1
Deut 5:19; *Mat* 19:18; *Rom* 13:
if a man *s.* an ox, he shall. *Ex* 22:
as people *s.* away. *2 Sam* 19:
if he *s.* to satisfy his soul. *Pr* 6:3
or lest I be poor and *s.* and. 30:
will ye *s.*, murder, and? *Jer* 7:
prophets that *s.* my words. 23:3
and where thieves break throug and *s.* *Mat* 6:1
do not break through nor *s.* 2
come and *s.* him away. 27:6
do not kill, do not *s.* *Mark* 10:1
Luke 18:2
cometh not, but for to *s.* *John* 10:1
preachest a man should not *s.*, dos thou *s.*? *Rom* 2:2
him that stole *s.* no more. *Eph* 4:2

stealers

law was made for men-*s.* *1 Tim* 1:1

stealeth

he that *s.* a man and. *Ex* 21:1
a tempest *s.* him away in. *Job* 27:2
that *s.* shall be cut off. *Zech* 5:

stealing

if a man be found *s.* any. *Deut* 24:
by swearing and *s.* they. *Hos* 4:

stealth

the people gat them by *s.* *2 Sam* 19:

stedfast

yea, thou shalt be *s.* *Job* 11:1
whose spirit was not *s.* *Ps* 78:
neither were they *s.* in his. 37
living God, and *s.* for ever. *Dan* 6:2
he that standeth *s.* in his heart doet well. *1 Cor* 7:3
my beloved brethren, be ye *s.* 15:5
our hope of you is *s.* *2 Cor* 1:
for if the word spoken by angels wa *s.* *Heb* 2:
if we hold our confidence *s.* 3:14
have as an anchor sure and *s.* 6:1
whom resist *s.* in faith. *1 Pet* 5:

stedfastly

that she was *s.* minded. *Ruth* 1:1
settled his countenance *s.* *2 Ki* 8:1
he *s.* set his face to go. *Luke* 9:5
looked *s.*, behold, two men. *Acts* 1:1
s. in the apostles' doctrine. 2:4
they all looking *s.* on him. 6:15
up *s.* into heaven, saw glory. 7:5
who *s.* beholding him and. 14:9
Israel could not *s.* behold. *2 Cor* 3:
could not *s.* look to the end of. 1

stedfastness

beholding the *s.* of your faith i Christ. *Col* 2:
ye fall from your own *s.* *2 Pet* 3:1

steel

(*Revisions*, brass)
a bow of *s.* is broken. *2 Sam* 22:3
Ps 18:3
bow of *s.* shall strike. *Job* 20:2
iron break northern iron and *s.*?
Jer 15:1

steep

the *s.* places shall fall. *Ezek* 38:2
are poured down a *s.* place. *Mi* 1:
swine ran violently down a *s.* place.
Mat 8:32; *Mark* 5:13; *Luke* 8:3

stem

a rod out of the *s.* of. *Isa* 11:1

step

there is but a *s.* between. *1 Sam* 20:
if my *s.* hath turned out. *Job* 31:

Stephanas

the household of *S.* *1 Cor* 1:1
the house of *S.*, the firstfruits. 16:1
I am glad of the coming of *S.* 1

Stephen

they chose *S.*, a man. *Acts* 6:5,
they stoned *S.*, calling upon God. 7:5
devout men carried *S.* to his. 8:
on the persecution about *S.* 11:1
of thy martyr *S.* was shed. 22:2

stepped
whosoever first *s.* in was. *John* 5:4

steppeth
while I am coming, another *s.* down. *John* 5:7

steps
neither go up by *s.* to. *Ex* 20:26
thou hast enlarged my *s.* *2 Sam* 22:37; *Ps* 18:36
the throne had six *s.* *1 Ki* 10:19 *2 Chr* 9:18
twelve lions stood on the *s.* *1 Ki* 10:20; *2 Chr* 9:19
thou numberest my *s.* *Job* 14:16
the *s.* of his strength shall be. 18:7
my foot hath held his *s.* 23:11
I washed my *s.* with butter. 29:6
my ways and count my *s.* 31:4
to him the number of my *s.* 37
compassed us in our *s.* *Ps* 17:11
s. of a good man are ordered. 37:23*
the law in his heart, none of his *s.* 31
nor have our *s.* declined from. 44:18
mark my *s.* when they wait. 56:6
prepared a net for my *s.* 57:6
as for me, my *s.* had well. 73:2
set us in the way of his *s.* 85:13
order my *s.* in thy word. 119:133
when goest thy *s.* shall not. *Pr* 4:12
her *s.* take hold on hell. 5:5
but the Lord directeth his *s.* 16:9
the *s.* of the needy shall. *Isa* 26:6
it is not in man that walketh to direct his *s.* *Jer* 10:23
they hunt our *s.*, we cannot. *Lam* 4:18
up to it by seven *s.* *Ezek* 40:22, 26
up to it had eight *s.* 31, 34, 37
he brought me by *s.* whereby. 49
the Ethiopians shall be at his *s.* *Dan* 11:43
but walk in *s.* of that faith. *Rom* 4:12
not in the same *s.*? *2 Cor* 12:18
ye should follow his *s.* *1 Pet* 2:21

stern
four anchors out of the *s.* *Acts* 27:29

steward
and the *s.* of my house. *Gen* 15:2*
near to the *s.* of Joseph's. 43:19
drinking himself drunk in the house of his *s.* *1 Ki* 16:9
the lord saith unto his *s.* *Mat* 20:8
wife of Chuza, Herod's *s.* *Luke* 8:3
is that faithful and wise *s.* 12:42
certain rich man who had a *s.* 16:1
thou mayest be no longer *s.* 2
Lord commended the unjust *s.* 8
blameless, as the *s.* of God. *Tit* 1:7

stewards
and David assembled captains and *s.* *1 Chr* 28:1*
as ministers and *s.* of. *1 Cor* 4:1
it is required in *s.* that a man. 2
as good *s.* of manifold. *1 Pet* 4:10

stewardship
give an account of thy *s.* *Luke* 16:2
taketh away from me the *s.* 3, 4

stick, *verb*
his bones, not seen, *s.* out. *Job* 33:21
his scales are joined, they *s.* 41:17
for thine arrows *s.* fast. *Ps* 38:2
I will cause the fish to *s.* *Ezek* 29:4

stick
cut down a *s.* and cast. *2 Ki* 6:6
withered and become like a *s.* *Lam* 4:8
s. write upon it: then take another *s.* *Ezek* 37:16
one to another into one *s.* 17, 19

sticketh
there is a friend *s.* closer. *Pr* 18:24

sticks
a man that gathered *s.* *Num* 15:32
they found him gathering *s.* 33
woman was gathering *s.* *1 Ki* 17:10
gathering two *s.* to go in. 12
and the *s.* whereon. *Ezek* 37:20
gathered a bundle of *s.* *Acts* 28:3

stiff
rebellion and thy *s.* neck. *Deut* 31:27
speak not with a *s.* neck. *Ps* 75:5
but made their neck *s.* *Jer* 17:23

stiffened
he *s.* his neck and. *2 Chr* 36:13

stiffhearted
impudent children and *s.* *Ezek* 2:4

stiffnecked
people is a *s.* people. *Ex* 32:9
thou art a *s.* people. 33:3; *Deut* 9:6
Ye are a *s.* people. *Ex* 33:5
it is a *s.* people. 34:9; *Deut* 9:13
circumcise your heart, be no more *s.* *Deut* 10:16
be not *s.* as your fathers. *2 Chr* 30:8
ye *s.* ye do always resist. *Acts* 7:51

still, *adjectve*
shall be as *s.* as a stone. *Ex* 15:16
good, and are ye *s.*? *Judg* 18:9
after fire a *s.* small voice. *1 Ki* 19:12
Gilead is ours, and we be *s.* 22:3
and if we sit *s.* here. *2 Ki* 7:4
for now should I have lain *s.* *Job* 3:13
your heart and be *s.* *Ps* 4:4
beside the *s.* waters. 23:2
be *s.* and know that I am. 46:10
the earth feared, and was *s.* 76:8
peace, and be not *s.* O God. 83:1
that waves thereof are *s.* 107:29
be *s.* ye inhabitants of. *Isa* 23:2
cried, their strength is to sit *s.* 30:7
I have been *s.* and refrained. 42:14
why do we sit *s.*? *Jer* 8:14
of the Lord, rest and be *s.* 47:6
feed that that standeth *s.* *Zech* 11:16
to the sea, Peace, be *s.* *Mark* 4:39

still, *adverb*
were *s.* ill favoured, as at. *Gen* 41:21
and wilt hold them *s.* *Ex* 9:2
and if it appear *s.* in. *Lev* 13:57
and Caleb lived *s.* *Num* 14:38
Balaam blessed you *s.* *Josh* 24:10
but if ye shall *s.* do. *1 Sam* 12:25
Saul said, Thou also shalt *s.* 26:25
good to have been there *s.* *2 Sam* 14:32
and cursed *s.* as he came. 16:5
the people sacrificed *s.* and burnt. *2 Ki* 12:3; 15:4, 35; *2 Chr* 33:17
had no power to keep *s.* *2 Chr* 22:9
and *s.* he holdeth fast. *Job* 2:3
his wife said, Dost thou *s.* retain? 9
though he keep it *s.* within. 20:13
he should *s.* live for ever. *Ps* 49:9
such a one as goeth on *s.* 68:21
for all this they sinned *s.* 78:32
in thy house: they will be *s.* 84:4
they shall *s.* bring forth fruit. 92:14
when I awake, I am *s.* 139:18
he *s.* taught the people. *Eccl* 12:9
but his hand is stretched out *s.* *Isa* 5:25; 9:12, 17, 21; 10:4
they say *s.* unto them that. *Jer* 23:17
those will I let remain *s.* in. 27:11
I earnestly remember him *s.* 31:20
if ye will *s.* abide in this. 42:10
my soul hath them *s.* in. *Lam* 3:20
thy people *s.* are talking. *Ezek* 33:30
winding about *s.* upward. 41:7
when he had said these words, he abode *s.* in Galilee. *John* 7:9; 11:6
it pleased Silas to abide *s.* *Acts* 15:34; 17:14
s. in unbelief, be graffed. *Rom* 11:23
abide *s.* at Ephesus. *1 Tim* 1:3
unjust *s.*: filthy *s.*: holy *s.* *Rev* 22:11
see **stand, stood**

still, *verb*
that thou mightest *s.* enemy. *Ps* 8:2

stilled
Caleb *s.* the people. *Num* 13:30
so the Levites *s.* all. *Neh* 8:11

stillest
waves arise thou *s.* them. *Ps* 89:9

stilleth
s. the noise of the seas. *Ps* 65:7

sting
O death, where is thy *s.*? *1 Cor* 15:55
the *s.* of death is sin. 56

stingeth
it *s.* like an adder. *Pr* 23:32

stings
were *s.* in their tails. *Rev* 9:10

stink, *substantive*
smell, there shall be *s.* *Isa* 3:24*
their *s.* shall come out of. *Isa* 34:3†
s. shall come up, and ill. *Joel* 2:20†
made *s.* of your camps. *Amos* 4:10†

stink
ye have made me to *s.* *Gen* 34:30*
die, and the river shall *s.* *Ex* 7:18
that was laid up did not *s.* 16:24
my wounds *s.* and are. *Ps* 38:5

stinketh
their fish *s.* because there. *Isa* 50:2
Lord, by this time he *s.* *John* 11:39

stinking
to send forth a *s.* savour. *Eccl* 10:1†

stir, *verb*
he lay down as a lion, who shall *s.* him up? *Num* 24:9
innocent *s.* up himself. *Job* 17:8
is so fierce that dare *s.* him. 41:10
s. up thyself, and awake. *Ps* 35:23
and he did not *s.* up all his. 78:38
s. up thy strength, and come. 80:2
but grievous words *s.* *Pr* 15:1
that ye *s.* not up my love. *S of S* 2:7 3:5; 8:4
the Lord shall *s.* up a. *Isa* 10:26
behold, I will *s.* up the Medes. 13:17
he shall *s.* up jealousy like. 42:13
he shall *s.* up all against. *Dan* 11:2
shall *s.* up his power against. 25
that thou *s.* up the gift. *2 Tim* 1:6
meet to *s.* you up. *2 Pet* 1:13; 3:1

stir
was no small *s.* among the soldiers. *Acts* 12:18
small *s.* about that way. 19:23

stirred
whose heart *s.* him up. *Ex* 35:21 26; 36:2
that my son hath *s.* up. *1 Sam* 22:8
if the Lord have *s.* thee up. 26:19
Lord *s.* up an adversary. *1 Ki* 11:14
God *s.* him up another adversary. 23*
whom Jezebel his wife *s.* up. 21:25
God *s.* up the spirit. *1 Chr* 5:26
Lord *s.* up against Jehoram the *2 Chr* 21:16
Lord *s.* up the spirit of Cyrus. 36:22 *Ezra* 1:1
and my sorrow was *s.* *Ps* 39:2
but his sons shall be *s.* *Dan* 11:10*
king of the south shall be *s.* up. 25*
the Lord *s.* up the spirit. *Hag* 1:14
they *s.* up the people. *Acts* 6:12 17:13; 21:27
Jews *s.* up devout women. 13:50*
the unbelieving Jews *s.* up. 14:2
his spirit was *s.* in him. 17:16*

stirreth
an eagle *s.* up her nest. *Deut* 32:11
hatred *s.* up strifes, but. *Pr* 10:12
man *s.* up strife. 15:18; 29:22
that is of a proud heart *s.* 28:25
hell from beneath *s.* up. *Isa* 14:9
none *s.* up himself to take hold. 64:7
he *s.* up people teaching. *Luke* 23:5

stirs
full of *s.* a tumultuous city. *Isa* 22:2*

stock
or to the *s.* of the stranger's family. *Lev* 25:47
though the *s.* thereof die. *Job* 14:8
yea, their *s.* shall not take. *Isa* 40:24
down to the *s.* of a tree? 44:19
saying to a *s.*, Thou art my father. *Jer* 2:27
are brutish, the *s.* is a doctrine. 10:8
of the *s.* of Abraham. *Acts* 13:26
of the *s.* of Israel, an. *Phil* 3:5

stocks
my feet also in the *s.* *Job* 13:27
he putteth my feet in *s.* 33:11
the correction of the *s.* *Pr* 7:22
adultery with stones and *s.* *Jer* 3:9
put Jeremiah in the *s.* 20:2, 3
put him in prison and *s.* 29:26*
ask counsel at their *s.* *Hos* 4:12
their feet fast in the *s.* *Acts* 16:24

Stoics
Were a school of Grecian philosophers, who took their name from the Greek word stoa, *meaning*

portico, *because* Zeno, *the head of the Stoics, taught in a portico in the city of Athens. They held, that a wise man ought to be free from all passions; never to be moved either with joy or grief, esteeming all things to be ordered by an inevitable necessity and fate. Josephus says, that the* Pharisees *approach very near to the sentiments of the Stoics. They affected the same stiffness, patience, apathy, austerity, and insensibility. The sect of the* Stoics *was still considerable at* Athens *when* St. Paul *visited that city,* Acts 17:18.

stole

Jacob *s.* away unawares. *Gen* 31:20
so Absalom *s.* the hearts of Israel. *2 Sam* 15:6
Jehosheba *s.* Joash from among king's. *2 Ki* 11:2; *2 Chr* 22:11
his disciples *s.* him. *Mat* 28:13
let him that *s.* steal no more, but. *Eph* 4:28

stolen

that shall be counted *s.* *Gen* 30:33
Rachel had *s.* her father's images. 31:19, 32
thou hast *s.* away unawares to. 26
hast thou *s.* my gods? 30
whether *s.* by day, or *s.* by. 39
indeed I was *s.* away out. 40:15
if the stuff be *s.* out of. *Ex* 22:7
if it be *s.* from him, he shall. 12
s. and dissembled also. *Josh* 7:11
men of Judah *s.* thee? *2 Sam* 19:41
Jabesh had *s.* the bones of. 21:12
s. waters are sweet. *Pr* 9:17
would they not have *s* till? *Ob* 5

stomach

little wine for thy *s.*'s sake. *1 Tim* 5:23

stomacher

instead of a *s.* a girding. *Isa* 3:24*

stone

Precious stones *as named in the Bible are difficult to identify, as no sufficient description is given of them.*

The corner stone, *or the* head stone of the corner, Ps 118:22, *is that put as the angle of a building, whether at the foundation, or at the top of the wall, and is of fundamental importance. It is often used metaphorically. Jesus Christ is the* corner stone *rejected by the* Jews, *but become the corner stone of the* church, *and the stone that binds and unites the Jews and Gentiles in the union of the same faith,* Mat 21:42; Eph 2:20.

As Christ the Head is called the corner stone, so also his members, true believers, who are built upon, and derive spiritual life from the foundation, Christ, *are called* stones, 1 Pet 2:5. *As the law was engraven on two tables of stones, so believers have the law written in their hearts. They are* stones *for their constancy, strength, and unmovableness in all the storms of life.*

The white stone, Rev 2:17, *has been variously regarded. Some think it is an allusion to an ancient custom of delivering a* white stone *to those who were acquitted in judgement, or of giving a white stone as a reward to such as conquered in their games.*

Great heaps of stones, raised up for a witness of any memorable event, and to preserve the remembrance of some matter of great importance are the most ancient monuments among the Hebrews. Jacob and Laban raised such a monument upon mount Gilead, in memory of their covenant, Gen 31:46. Joshua *erected one at Gilgal made of stones taken out of the Jordan, to preserve the memorial of his miraculous passage over this river,* Josh 4:5, 6, 7. *The Israelites that dwelt beyond* Jordan, *also raised one upon the banks of the river, as a testimony that they constituted but one nation with their brethren on the other side,* Josh 22:10.

had brick for *s.* and slime. *Gen* 11:3
up a *s.* for a pillar. 28:18, 22; 31:45
they rolled *s.* from the well's mouth. 29:3, 8, 10
Jacob set up a pillar of *s.* 35:14
the shepherd, the *s.* of Israel. 49:24
Zipporah took a sharp *s.* *Ex* 4:25*
sank into the bottom as a *s.* 15:5
arm they shall be as still as *s.* 16
and they took a *s.* and put it. 17:12
wilt make an altar of *s.* 20:25
smite another with a *s.* 21:18
names on one *s.*, six on other *s.* 28:10
work of an engraver in *s.* 11
neither shall ye set up any image of *s.* in your land. *Lev* 26:1
with throwing a *s.* *Num* 35:17, 23
take you up every man of you a *s.* upon his shoulder. *Josh* 4:5
the border went up to the *s.* 15:6
descended to the *s.* of Bohan. 18:17
s. shall be a witness unto us. 24:27
slew seventy persons on one *s.* *Judg* 9:5, 18
which *s.* remaineth. *1 Sam* 6:18
Samuel set up a *s.* and called. 7:12
from his bag a *s.* and slang it, the *s.* sunk into the Philistine's. 17:49
over the Philistine with a *s.* 50
shalt remain by the *s.* Ezel. 20:19
died in him, he became as a *s.* 25:37
there be not one small *s.* *2 Sam* 17:13
house was built of *s.* *1 Ki* 6:7
cedar, there was no *s.* seen. 18
cast every man his *s.* *2 Ki* 3:25
with thee hewers of *s.* *1 Chr* 22:15
skilful to work in gold, silver, and *s.* *2 Chr* 2:14
thou threwest as a *s.* *Neh* 9:11
is molten out of the *s.* *Job* 28:2
waters are hid as with a *s.* 38:30
his heart is as firm as a *s.* 41:24
lest thou dash thy foot against a *s.* *Ps* 91:12; *Mat* 4:6; *Luke* 4:11
s. which builders refused . . . *s.* of. *Ps* 118:22; *Mat* 21:42; *Mark* 12:10
as he that bindeth a *s.* *Pr* 26:8
and he that rolleth a *s.* it will. 27
s. is heavy, a fool's wrath. 27:3
and to a *s.* thou hast. *Jer* 2:27
they shall not take of thee a *s.* for a corner, nor a *s.* for. 51:26
cast a *s.* upon me. *Lam* 3:53
a *s.* was cut out of the mountain. *Dan* 2:34, 45
s. was laid upon the mouth. 6:17
for the *s.* shall cry out. *Hab* 2:11
saith to the dumb *s.*, Arise. 19
s. was laid upon a *s.* in. *Hag* 2:15
s. that I have laid before Joshua, upon one *s.* shall be seven. *Zech* 3:9
shall bring forth the head *s.* 4:7
their hearts as an adamant *s.* 7:12
if his son ask bread, will he give him a *s.*? *Mat* 7:9; *Luke* 11:11
whosoever shall fall on this *s.* shall be broken. *Mat* 21:44; *Luke* 20:18
not left here one *s.* upon. *Mat* 24:2
Mark 13:2; *Luke* 19:44; 21:6
sealing the *s.* *Mat* 27:66
the angel rolled back the *s.* 28:2
saw that the *s.* was rolled away. *Mark* 16:4; *Luke* 24:2; *John* 20:1
command this *s.* that it be. *Luke* 4:3
s. which the builders rejected, 20:17; *Acts* 4:11; *1 Pet* 2:7
he was withdrawn from them about a *s.*'s cast. *Luke* 22:41
is by interpretation a *s.* *John* 1:42*
set there six waterpots of *s.* 2:6
let him first cast *s.* at her. 8:7
it was a cave, and a *s.* lay. 11:38
take ye away the *s.* 39
they took away the *s.* 41
is like to a *s.* graven. *Acts* 17:29
fell a great hail, every *s.* *Rev* 16:21
an angel took up a *s.* like a. 18:21
see **corner, great, hewed, stumbling, wall**

stone, *verb*

and will they not *s.* us? *Ex* 8:26
they be almost ready to *s.* me. 17:4
people of land shall *s.* *Lev* 20:2
shall *s.* the wizards with stones. 27
let congregation *s.* him. 24:14, 16, 23
congregation bade *s.* *Num* 14:10
s. him with stones. 15:35, 36
shalt *s.* him with stones. *Deut* 13:10
shalt *s.* idolaters. 17:5
s. rebellious son. 21:21
they shall *s.* her that playeth. 22:21
ye shall *s.* adulterers with stones. 24
carry Naboth out, *s.* him. *1 Ki* 21:10
and they shall *s.* thee. *Ezek* 16:40
the company shall *s.* them. 23:47
men, the people will *s.* us. *Luke* 20:6
stones again to *s.* him. *John* 10:31
for which works do ye *s.* me? 32
saying, For a good work we *s.* 33
Jews of late sought to *s.* thee. 11:8
assault made to *s.* them. *Acts* 14:5

burdensome **stone**

make Jerusalem a *burdensome s.* *Zech* 12:3

hewn **stone**

not build altar of *hewn s.* *Ex* 20:25
masons, to buy timber and *hewn s.* *2 Ki* 22:6; *2 Chr* 34:11
my ways with *hewn s.* *Lam* 3:9
tables were of *hewn s.* *Ezek* 40:42
built houses of *hewn s.* *Amos* 5:11
sepulchre *hewn* in *s.* *Luke* 23:53

living **stone**

to whom coming, as unto a *living s.* chosen of God. *1 Pet* 2:4

precious **stone**

a gift is a *precious s.* to him. *Pr* 17:8
I lay in Zion a *precious* corner *s.* *Isa* 28:16; *1 Pet* 2:6
every *precious s.* was. *Ezek* 28:13
decked with gold and *precious s.* *Rev* 17:4
like to a *s.* most *precious.* 21:11

tables of **stone**

I will give thee *tables of s.* *Ex* 24:12
31:18
Lord said, Hew thee two *tables of s.* 34:1; *Deut* 10:1
he hewed two *tables of s.* *Ex* 34:4
Deut 10:3
he wrote on the two *tables of s.* *Deut* 4:13; 5:22
up to receive the *tables of s.* 9:9
delivered to me two *tables of s.* 10
gave me the two *tables of s.* 11
in ark save two *tables of s.* *1 Ki* 8:9
not in *tables of s.* but in fleshly. *2 Cor* 3:3

tried **stone**

Zion a stone, a *tried s.* *Isa* 28:16

white **stone**

I will give him a *white s.* *Rev* 2:17

stone joined with *wood*

vessels of *wood* and *s.* *Ex* 7:19
gods the work of men's hands, *wood* and *s.* *Deut* 4:28; 28:36, 64
29:17; *2 Ki* 19:18; *Isa* 37:19
Ezek 20:32
praised the gods of gold, *wood*, and *s.* *Dan* 5:4, 23
not worship idols of *wood* and *s.* *Rev* 9:20

stone *of Zoheleth*

sheep by *s.* of *Zoheleth.* *1 Ki* 1:9

stoned

be *s.* or shot through. *Ex* 19:13
ox shall be surely *s.* 21:28, 29, 32
all Israel *s.* Achan. *Josh* 7:25
all Israel *s.* Adoram. *1 Ki* 12:18
2 Chr 10:18
they *s.* Naboth. *1 Ki* 21:13, 14, 15
they *s.* Zechariah in. *2 Chr* 24:21
beat one, *s.* another. *Mat* 21:35
that such should be *s.* *John* 8:5
they should have been *s.* *Acts* 5:26
they *s.* Stephen, calling. 7:58, 59
having *s.* Paul, drew him out. 14:19

beaten, once was I *s.* *2 Cor* 11:25
they were *s.* they were. *Heb* 11:37
the mount it shall be *s.* 12:20

stones

his brethren, gather *s.* *Gen* 31:46
engrave the two *s.* *Ex* 28:11, 12
settings of *s.*, even four rows of *s.* 17
the *s.* shall be with the names of. 21
s. for a memorial to Israel. 39:7
they take away the *s.* *Lev* 14:40
other *s.* in the place of those *s.* 42
down the house, the *s.* of it. 45
or hath his *s.* broken. 21:20
a land whose *s.* are iron. *Deut* 8:9
that is wounded in the *s.* 23:1
these *s.* in mount Ebal. 27:4
build an altar of *s.* 5
write on the *s.* all the words. 8
you hence twelve *s.* *Josh* 4:3, 9
What mean ye by these *s.*? 6, 21
twelve *s.* out of the midst. 8
twelve *s.* did Joshua pitch. 20
on the *s.* a copy of the law. 8:32
every one could sling *s.* at an hair-breadth. *Judg* 20:16
him five smooth *s.* *1 Sam* 17:40
Shimei cast *s.* at David and. *2 Sam* 16:6, 13
prepared timber and *s.* *1 Ki* 5:18
s. of eight and *s.* of ten cubits. 7:10
silver to be in Jerusalem as *s.* and. 10:27; *2 Chr* 1:15; 9:27
took away the *s.* of Ramah. *1 Ki* 15:22; *2 Chr* 16:6
Elijah took twelve *s.* *1 Ki* 18:31
with the *s.* he built an altar. 32
good piece of land with *s.* *2 Ki* 3:19
Kir-haraseth left they the *s.* 25
it upon a pavement of *s.* 16:17
in hurling of *s.* and. *1 Chr* 12:2
Uzziah prepared slings to cast *s.* *2 Chr* 26:14
will they revive the *s.* out of the heaps? *Neh* 4:2
in league with *s.* of field. *Job* 5:23
strength the strength of *s.*? 6:12
and seeth the place of *s.* 8:17
the waters wear the *s.* 14:19
the gold of Ophir as the *s.* of. 22:24
the *s.* of it are the place of. 28:6
the sinews of his *s.* are. 40:17*
take pleasure in her *s.* *Ps* 102:14
thy little ones against the *s.* 137:9
away *s.*, a time to gather *s.* *Eccl* 3:5
whoso removeth *s.* shall be. 10:9
and gathered out the *s.* *Isa* 5:2
down to the *s.* of the pit. 14:19
s. of the altar as chalk *s.* 27:9
behold, I will lay thy *s.* with. 54:11
thy borders of pleasant *s.* 12
smooth *s.* of the stream. 57:6
bring for *s.*, iron. 60:17
gather out the *s.* 62:10
adultery with *s.* and stocks. *Jer* 3:9
set his throne on these *s.* 43:10
the *s.* of the sanctuary. *Lam* 4:1
lay thy *s.* in the water. *Ezek* 26:12
in the midst of the *s.* of fire. 28:14
from the midst of the *s.* of fire. 16
I will pour down the *s.* *Mi* 1:6
consume it with the *s.* *Zech* 5:4
as *s.* of a crown lifted up. 9:16
of these *s.* to raise up children. *Mat* 3:9; *Luke* 3:8
these *s.* be made bread. *Mat* 4:3
cutting himself with *s.* *Mark* 5:5
and at him they cast *s.* and. 12:4
Master, see what manner of *s.* 13:1
s. would immediately. *Luke* 19:40
took up *s.* to cast. *John* 8:59; 10:31
engraven in *s.* was glorious. *2 Cor* 3:7
ye as lively *s.* are built. *1 Pet* 2:5
see **costly, great, stone,** *verb*

corner **stones**

our daughters may be as *corner s.* *Ps* 144:12

stones *of darkness*

he searcheth out the *s. of darkness.* *Job* 28:3

stones *of emptiness*

stretch out upon it *s. of emptiness.* *Isa* 34:11

glistering **stones**

I have prepared *glistering s.* for house. *1 Chr* 29:2

gravel **stones**

hath broken my teeth with *gravel s.* *Lam* 3:16

heap of **stones**

raised a great *heap of s.* *Josh* 7:26
and raise a great *heap of s.* 8:29
they laid a *heap of s.* on Absalom. *2 Sam* 18:17

hewed **stones**

they brought *hewed s.* to. *1 Ki* 5:17*
the measures of *hewed s.* 7:9, 11

hewn **stones**

will build with *hewn s.* *Isa* 9:10

marble **stones**

I have prepared *marble s.* in. *1 Chr* 29:2

precious **stones**

gold with *precious s.* *2 Sam* 12:30
queen of Sheba came with *precious s.* *1 Ki* 10:2
navy of Hiram brought *precious s.* 11; *2 Chr* 9:10
I prepared all manner of *precious s.* *1 Chr* 29:2
whom *precious s.* were found. 8
the house with *precious s.* *2 Chr* 3:6
treasuries for *precious s.* 32:27
occupied in thy fairs with *precious s.* *Ezek* 27:22
honour with *precious s.* *Dan* 11:38
build on this foundation *precious s.* *1 Cor* 3:12
no man buyeth *precious s.* *Rev* 18:12
decked with gold and *precious s.* 16
garnished with *precious s.* 21:19

whole **stones**

shalt build the altar of *whole s.* *Deut* 27:6; *Josh* 8:31

wrought **stones**

masons to hew *wrought s.* *1 Chr* 22:2

stonesquarers

builders and *s.* did hew. *1 Ki* 5:18*

stonest

s. them that are sent to thee. *Mat* 23:37; *Luke* 13:34

stoning

people spake of *s.* David. *1 Sam* 30:6

stony

overthrown in *s.* places. *Ps* 141:6*
I will take the *s.* heart. *Ezek* 11:19
36:26
some fell on *s.* places. *Mat* 13:5*, 20*
Mark 4:5*, 16*

stood

but Abraham *s.* yet. *Gen* 18:22
pillar of cloud *s.* behind. *Ex* 14:19
he *s.* between the dead. *Num* 16:48
ye came near and *s.* *Deut* 4:11
I *s.* between the Lord and you. 5:5
the waters *s.* and rose up. *Josh* 3:16
twelve stones where the priests' feet *s.* 4:3, 9
Joash said to all that *s.* *Judg* 6:31
pillars on which the house *s.* 16:29
Lord *s.* and called Samuel. *1 Sam* 3:10
when he *s.* among the people. 10:23
Goliath *s.* and cried to the. 17:8
servants that *s.* about him. 22:7
king said to footmen that *s.* 17
and all the congregation of Israel *s.* *1 Ki* 8:14; *2 Chr* 6:3; 7:6
Solomon *s.* and blessed. *1 Ki* 8:55
sons of prophets *s.* to view. *2 Ki* 2:7
the people *s.* to the covenant. 23:3
on scaffold Solomon *s.* *2 Chr* 6:13
they *s.* and confessed. *Neh* 9:2
the other Jews *s.* for. *Esth* 9:16
commanded and it *s.* fast. *Ps* 33:9
above it *s.* the seraphims. *Isa* 6:2
they *s.* not because Lord. *Jer* 46:15
they *s.* under the shadow. 48:45
those *s.*, these *s.* *Ezek* 1:21; 10:17
when they *s.* they let down. 1:24
was a voice when they *s.* 25
came near where I *s.* *Dan* 8:17
when he had spoken this, I *s.* 10:11
s. to confirm and to strengthen. 11:1
I looked, and behold, there *s.* *Dan* 12:5
s. and measured the earth. *Hab* 3:6
he *s.* among the myrtle trees. *Zech* 1:8, 10, 11
brethren *s.* without. *Mat* 12:46
withered hand *s.* forth. *Luke* 6:8
the Pharisee *s.* and prayed. 18:11
Simon Peter *s.* and. *John* 18:25
but Mary *s.* without at. 20:11
the lame man leaping up *s.* *Acts* 3:8
the men that were with him *s.* 9:7
s. a man of Macedonia and. 16:9
Paul *s.* forth in the midst. 27:21
s. only in meats, and. *Heb* 9:10

stood *above*

Lord *s. above* the ladder. *Gen* 28:13
Zechariah *s. above* the people. *2 Chr* 24:20
the waters *s. above* the. *Ps* 104:6

stood *afar*

his sister *s. afar* off, to. *Ex* 2:4
removed and *s. afar* off. 20:18, 21
lepers who *s. afar* off. *Luke* 17:12
s. afar off beholding. 23:49
trade by sea *s. afar* off. *Rev* 18:17

stood *at*

they *s. at* nether part. *Ex* 19:17
they *s.* every man *at* his tent. 33:8
the cloudy pillar *s. at* door of. 9
Naaman *s. at* door of. *2 Ki* 5:9
singers *s. at* the east. *2 Chr* 5:12
the king *s. at* his pillar, at. 23:13
cherubims *s. at* door. *Ezek* 10:19
the king *s. at* the parting. 21:21
woman *s. at* his feet. *Luke* 7:38
but Peter *s. at* the door. *John* 18:16
another angel came and *s. at* the altar. *Rev* 8:3

stood *before*

to the place where he *s. before* the Lord. *Gen* 19:27
Egypt, and *s. before* Joseph. 43:15
ashes and *s. before* Pharaoh. *Ex* 9:10
the congregation *s. before.* *Lev* 9:5
Zelophehad *s. before* Moses. *Num* 27:2
s. before the congregation. *Josh* 20:9
Phinehas *s. before* ark. *Judg* 20:28
and *s. before* Saul. *1 Sam* 16:21
Bath-sheba *s. before.* *1 Ki* 1:28
Solomon *s. before* the ark. 3:15
were harlots *s. before* him. 16
Solomon *s. before* the altar. 8:22
2 Chr 6:12
old men that *s. before* Solomon. *1 Ki* 12:6; *2 Chr* 10:6
young men that *s. before* him. *1 Ki* 12:8; *2 Chr* 10:8
spirit *s. before* the Lord. *1 Ki* 22:21
2 Chr 18:20
the Shunammite *s. before* Elisha. *2 Ki* 4:12
returned and *s. before* Elisha. 5:15
Gehazi went in and *s. before.* 25
Hazael came and *s. before.* 8:9
two kings *s.* not *before* him. 10:4
arose, and *s. before* king. *Esth* 8:4
Moses his chosen *s. before* him. *Ps* 106:23
Samuel *s. before* me. *Jer* 15:1
I *s. before* thee to speak. 18:20
s. before them seventy. *Ezek* 8:11
therefore they *s. before* the king. *Dan* 1:19; 2:2
great image *s. before* thee. 2:31
they *s. before* the image. 3:3
times ten thousand *s. before.* 7:10
s. before the river a ram. 8:3
s. before me as the appearance. 15
Joshua *s. before* the angel. *Zech* 3:3
spake to those that *s. before* him. 4
and Jesus *s. before* the. *Mat* 27:11
three men *s. before* the. *Acts* 10:17
a man *s. before* me in bright. 30
Peter *s. before* the gate. 12:14
while I *s. before* the council. 24:20
multitude *s. before* throne. *Rev* 7:9
angels which *s. before* God. 8:2
dragon *s. before* the woman. 12:4

stood *beside*

Absalom *s. beside* the. *2 Sam* 15:2
lions *s. beside* the stays. *1 Ki* 10:19

which s. beside the king. Jer 36:21
the six men s. beside. Ezek 9:2
then he went in and s. beside. 10:6

stood *by*

lo, three men s. by him. Gen 18:2
behold, he s. by the camels. 24:30
and lo, he s. by the river. 41:1
not refrain himself before all that s. by him. 45:1
the people s. by Moses. Ex 18:13
Balak s. by his. Num 23:6, 17
all that s. by him went. Judg 3:19
the men s. by the entering of. 18:16
that s. by thee, praying. 1 Sam 1:26
servants s. by with. 2 Sam 13:31
and Jeroboam s. by the. 1 Ki 13:1
ass s. by it, the lion also s. by. 24
two s. by Jordan. 2 Ki 2:7, 13
king s. by a pillar. 11:14; 23:3
they came and s. by the conduit of the upper pool. 18:17; Isa 36:2
the angel s. by the. 1 Chr 21:15
the women that s. by. Jer 44:15
and the man s. by me. Ezek 43:6
to one of them that s. by. Dan 7:16
angel of the Lord s. by. Zech 3:5
one of them that s. by. Mark 14:47
some of them that s. by. 15:35
he s. by the lake of. Luke 5:1
he said to them that s. by. 19:24
two men s. by them in shining. 24:4
an officer that s. by. John 18:22
there s. by the cross of Jesus. 19:25
two men s. by them in. Acts 1:10
and all the widows s. by him. 9:39
to the centurion that s. by. 22:25
commanded them that s. by. 23:2
they that s. by said, Revilest? 4
night following the Lord s. by him. 11
there s. by me this night the. 27:23

stood *in*

Aaron, who s. in the way. Ex 5:20
then Moses s. in the gate. 32:26
Lord s. in the door of. Num 12:5
thereon, and s. in the door. 16:18
Dathan and Abiram s. in door. 27
the angel s. in the way. 22:22, 24
angel went further and s. in a. 26
the priests s. in midst of Jordan. Josh 3:17; 4:10
Jotham s. in the top of. Judg 9:7
Gaal s. in the entering of the. 35
Abimelech s. in the entering of. 44
the priests s. in the entering. 18:17
he s. in the midst of. 2 Sam 23:12
and he s. in the entering. 1 Ki 19:13
and s. in the border. 2 Ki 3:21
the Shunammite s. in the door. 4:15
and they s. in their place. 2 Chr 30:16; 35:10
king s. in his place, and. 34:31
and all the people s. in. Neh 8:7
Esther s. in the inner court. Esth 5:1
Jeremiah s. in court of. Jer 19:14
for who hath s. in counsel. 23:18
but if they had s. in my counsel. 22
Jaazaniah s. in the midst. Ezek 8:11
neither have s. in crossway. Ob 14
Jesus himself s. in the midst of them. Luke 24:36; John 20:19, 26
then Paul s. in the. Acts 17:22
in the midst of the elders s. Rev 5:6

stood *on*

Philistines s. on a mountain on the one side, Israel s. on. 1 Sam 17:3
then David s. on the top. 26:13
Benjamin s. on the top. 2 Sam 2:25
Asaph, who s. on his. 1 Chr 6:39
sons of Merari s. on the left. 44
the cherubims s. on. 2 Chr 3:13
cherubims s. on the. Ezek 10:3
whole multitude s. on. Mat 13:2
Jesus s. on the shore. John 21:4
Paul s. on the stairs. Acts 21:40
and lo, a lamb s. on the. Rev 14:1

stood *over*

pillar of cloud s. over. Deut 31:15
man s. over against him. Josh 5:13
glory of the Lord s. over the threshold of the house. Ezek 10:4
glory of the Lord s. over cherubims. 18
star s. over where young. Mat 2:9
s. over her and rebuked. Luke 4:39

stood *round*

sheaves s. round about. Gen 37:7
disciples s. round about. Acts 14:20
Jews s. round about Paul, and. 25:7
angels s. round about the. Rev 7:11

stood *still*

the sun s. still, and. Josh 10:13*
as for cities that s. still in. 11:13
came to the place s. still. 2 Sam 2:23
trumpet and all the people s. still. 28
saw that all people s. still. 20:12
and they s. still in the. Neh 12:39
it s. still, but I could not. Job 4:16
they spake not, but s. still. 32:16
sun and moon s. still in. Hab 3:11
and Jesus s. still and. Mat 20:32
Jesus s. still and commanded him. Mark 10:49
that bare him s. still. Luke 7:14

stood *there*

and s. with him there. Ex 34:5
the field and s. there. 1 Sam 6:14
twelve lions s. there. 1 Ki 10:20
2 Chr 9:19
glory of the Lord s. there. Ezek 3:23
from the days of Gibeah there they s. Hos 10:9
some of them that s. there. Mat 27:47; Mark 11:5
and officers s. there. John 18:18

stood *up*

Abraham s. up from. Gen 23:3
Abraham s. up and bowed. 7
but Moses s. up and. Ex 2:17
the people s. up all that. Num 11:32
Satan s. up gainst Israel. 1 Chr 21:1
then David the king s. up upon. 28:2
Abijah s. up and said. 2 Chr 13:4
the Levites s. up to praise. 20:19
Ammon and Moab s. up against. 23
s. up against them that came. 28:12
till there s. up a priest with Urim and. Ezra 2:63; Neh 7:65
when he opened the book the people s. up. Neh 8:5
they s. up in their place and. 9:3
then s. up upon the stairs, of. 4
that Mordecai s. not up. Esth 5:9
Haman s. up to make request. 7:7
the hair of my flesh s. up. Job 4:15
and the aged arose and s. up. 29:8
I s. up and cried in the. 30:28
then s. up Phinehas and. Ps 106:30
they lived, and s. up. Ezek 37:10
whereas four s. up for it. Dan 8:22
Jesus s. up to read in. Luke 4:16
a certain lawyer s. up and. 10:25
in those days Peter s. up. Acts 1:15
the kings of the earth s. up. 4:26
s. up one Gamaliel, a doctor. 5:34
Agabus s. up, and signified. 11:28
Paul s. up, and beckoning. 13:16
whom when the accusers s. up. 25:18

stood *upon*

behold I s. upon the bank. Gen 41:17
David ran and s. upon. 1 Sam 17:51
so I s. upon Saul and. 2 Sam 1:10
the sea s. upon twelve oxen. 1 Ki 7:25; 2 Chr 4:4
he revived and s. upon. 2 Ki 13:21
Ezra the scribe s. upon. Neh 8:4
glory of the Lord s. upon. Ezek 11:23
the Lord s. upon a wall. Amos 7:7
the two prophets s. upon. Rev 11:11
I s. upon the sand of the sea. 13:1

stood *with*

there s. with him no man. Gen 45:1
every man s. with his. 2 Ki 11:11
the Levites s. with. 2 Chr 29:26
then Joshua s. with his. Ezra 3:9
he s. with his right hand. Lam 2:4
two men that s. with him. Luke 9:32
Judas also s. with them. John 18:5
Peter s. with them and warmed. 18
no man s. with me. 2 Tim 4:16
Lord s. with me. 17

stoodest

that thou s. in the way. Num 22:34
day that thou s. before. Deut 4:10
in the day that thou s. on. Ob 11

stool

a bed, table, and a s. 2 Ki 4:10

stools

ye see them upon the s. Ex 1:16*

stoop

the proud helpers do s. Job 9:13
maketh the heart of man s Pr 12:25
they s., they bow down. Isa 46:2
I am not worthy to s. Mark 1:7

stooped

Judah s. down, he couched. Gen 49:9
David s. to the earth. 1 Sam 24:8*
Saul s. to the ground. 28:14*
had no compassion on him that s. 2 Chr 36:17
Jesus s. down and wrote. John 8:6, 8
and as she wept, she s. down. 20:11

stoopeth

Bel boweth down, Nebo s. Isa 46:1

stooping

s. down saw the linen clothes. Luke 24:12; John 20:5

stop

that the rain s. thee not. 1 Ki 18:44
s. all wells of water. 2 Ki 3:19, 25
he took counsel to s. 2 Chr 32:3
s. the way against them. Ps 35:3
and all iniquity shall s. her. 107:42
it shall s. the noses of. Ezek 39:11
no man shall s. me of. 2 Cor 11:10

stopped

windows of heaven were s. Gen 8:2
Philistines had s. the wells. 26:15, 18
or his flesh be s. from. Lev 15:3
s. all the fountains and the brook. 2 Chr 32:4
Hezekiah s. the watercourse. 30
breaches began to be s. Neh 4:7
speaketh lies shall be s. Ps 63:11
that the passages are s. Jer 51:32*
refused, and s. their ears. Zech 7:11
they s. their ears and ran. Acts 7:57
every mouth may be s. Rom 3:19
whose mouths must be s. Tit 1:11
through faith s. the mouths of lions. Heb 11:33

stoppeth

the poor hath hope, and iniquity s. her mouth. Job 5:16
adder that s. her ear. Ps 58:4
whoso s. his ears at the. Pr 21:13
s. his ears from hearing. Isa 33:15

store

saith the Lord, who s. up violence and robbery in their. Amos 3:10

store, *substantive*

and great s. of servants. Gen 26:14*
that food shall be for s. to. 41:36
eat of the old s. Lev 25:22; 26:10
blessed shall be thy basket and thy s. Deut 28:5*, 17*
is not this laid up in s. with? 32:34
of spices very great s. 1 Ki 10:10
fathers have laid up in s. 2 Ki 20:17
all this s. cometh of. 1 Chr 29:16
he put s. of victuals. 2 Chr 11:11
is left is this great s. 31:10
s. of all sorts of wine. Neh 5:18
affording all manner of s. Ps 144:13
fathers have laid up in s. Isa 39:6
there is none end of the s. Nah 2:9
of you lay by him in s. 1 Cor 16:2
laying up in s. a good. 1 Tim 6:19
same word are kept in s. 2 Pet 3:7

store cities

cities of s. Solomon had. 1 Ki 9:19
2 Chr 8:6
and all the s. cities which he built. 2 Chr 8:4
all the s. cities of Naphtali. 16:4
Jehoshaphat built s. cities. 17:12

storehouse

the tithes into the s. Mal 3:10
neither have s. nor barn. Luke 12:24

storehouses

Joseph opened all the s. Gen 41:56
blessing on thee in thy s. Deut 28:8*
over the s. was Jehonathan. 1 Chr 27:25*
Hezekiah made s. also. 2 Chr 32:28

layeth up the depth in s. Ps 33:7
open her s., cast her up. Jer 50:26

stories

with second and third s. Gen 6:16
galleries three s. over. Ezek 41:16
against gallery in three s. 42:3*, 6
he that buildeth his s. Amos 9:6*

stork

(*A bird of the heron family, white, with black wings and bright red beak, or entirely black. Both species were found in Palestine. They are migratory birds, and very regular in their coming and going. They feed upon offal, and were therefore not permitted to be used by the Israelites as food*)

the s. thou shalt not eat. Lev 11:19
Deut 14:18
as for the s., the fir trees. Ps 104:17
s. knoweth her appointed. Jer 8:7
like the wings of a s. Zech 5:9

storm

and as chaff that the s. Job 21:18
and as s. hurleth him out of. 27:21
I would hasten my escape from the windy s. Ps 55:8
make them afraid with thy s. 83:15
he maketh the s. a calm. 107:29
and for a covert from s. Isa 4:6
hast been a refuge from the s. 25:4
which as destroying s. shall. 28:2
thou shalt be visited with s. 29:6*
ascend and come like a s. Ezek 38:9
in the whirlwind and s. Nah 1:3
there arose a great s. Mark 4:37
there came down a s. of wind. Luke 8:23

stormy

raiseth the s. wind. Ps 107:25
snow and vapour, s. wind. 148:8
s. wind shall rend. Ezek 13:11
I will rend it with a s. wind. 13

story

Abijah in the s. of Iddo. 2 Chr 13:22*
written in the s. of the book. 24:27*

stout

the s. lion's whelps are. Job 4:11*
the fruit of the s. heart. Isa 10:12
whose look was more s. Dan 7:20
your words have been s. Mal 3:13

stouthearted

s. are spoiled, they slept. Ps 76:5
hearken unto me, ye s. Isa 46:12

stoutness

that say in the pride and s. Isa 9:9

straight

shall ascend every man s. Josh 6:5
the kine took s. the way. 1 Sam 6:12
make thy way s. before. Ps 5:8
let thine eyelids look s. Pr 4:25
crooked cannot be made s. Eccl 1:15
make that s. he made crooked ? 7:13
make s. in desert a highway. Isa 40:3
the crooked shall be made s. 4
42:16; 45:2*; Luke 3:5
to walk in a s. way. Jer 31:9
and their feet were s. feet. Ezek 1:7
every one s. forward. 9, 12; 10:22
firmament were their wings s. 1:23
of Lord, make his paths s. Mat 3:3
Mark 1:3; Luke 3:4; John 1:23
made s. and glorified. Luke 13:13
street which is called S. Acts 9:11
and make s. paths for. Heb 12:13

straightway

shall s. find him before. 1 Sam 9:13
then Saul fell s. all along. 28:20
he goeth after her s. as. Pr 7:22
s. there remained no. Dan 10:17
Jesus went up s. out of water.
Mat 3:16; Mark 1:10
and they s. left their nets.
Mat 4:20; Mark 1:18
Lord hath need of them, and s. he.
Mat 21:3; Mark 11:3
s. one of them ran and. Mat 27:48
s. the fountain of her. Mark 5:29
s. they knew him. 6:54
s. desireth new. Luke 5:39
will not s. pull him out ? 14:5
God shall s. glorify him. John 13:32
then fell she down s. at. Acts 5:10
and s. he preached Christ. 9:20
was baptized, he and all his, s. 16:33
then s. they departed from. 22:29
told me, I sent s. to thee. 23:30
s. forgetteth what manner. Jas 1:24

strain

guides s. at a gnat and. Mat 23:24

strait, *substantive*

saw that they were in a s. 1 Sam 13:6
I am in a great s. 2 Sam 24:14
1 Chr 21:13
would have removed thee out of the s. Job 36:16*
for I am in a s. betwixt. Phil 1:23

strait

we dwell is too s. for us. 2 Ki 6:1
the place is too s. for. Isa 49:20
enter ye in at s. gate. Mat 7:13*
because s. is the gate and narrow is the way. 14*; Luke 13:24*

straiten

their lives, shall s. them. Jer 19:9†

straitened

his strength shall be s. Job 18:7
breadth of the waters is s. 37:10
thy steps shall not be s. Pr 4:12
therefore the building was s. more. Ezek 42:6
is the spirit of the Lord s.? Mi 2:7
how am I s. till it be accomplished! Luke 12:50
ye are not s. in us, but ye are s. in your. 2 Cor 6:12

straiteneth

enlargeth nations and s. Job 12:23*

straitest

after the most s. sect. Acts 26:5

straitly

man asked us s. of our state and. Gen 43:7
for Joseph had s. sworn. Ex 13:19
Jericho was s. shut up. Josh 6:1
thy father s. charged people with oath. 1 Sam 14:28
he s. charged them, saying, See that,
Mat 9:30*; Mark 3:12*; 5:43*
Luke 9:21*
he s. charged him and. Mark 1:43*
but let us s. threaten them. Acts 4:17
did not we s. command you ? 5:28

straitness

shalt eat flesh of thy children in s.
Deut 28:53†, 55†, 57†
place where there is no s. Job 36:16
eat flesh of his friend in the s.
Jer 19:9†

straits

sufficiency he shall be in s. Job 20:22
overtook her between the s. Lam 1:3

strake

they fearing, s. sail. Acts 27:17*
see **struck**

strakes

Jacob piled white s. in. Gen 30:37†
the walls with hollow s. Lev 14:37†

strange

but Joseph made himself s. Gen 42:7
not ashamed that ye make yourselves s. to me. Job 19:3*
my breath is s. to my wife. 17
man is froward and s. Pr 21:8*
wherein they think it s. 1 Pet 4:4
s. concerning trial, as though s. 12
see **children, god, gods**

strange *act*

pass his act, his s. act. Isa 28:21

strange *apparel*

clothed with s. apparel. Zeph 1:8*

strange *cities*

even to s. cities. Acts 26:11*

strange *country*

as in a s. country. Heb 11:9*

strange *doctrines*

be not carried about with s. doctrines. Heb 13:9

strange *fire*

Abihu offered s. fire before the.
Lev 10:1; Num 3:4; 26:61

strange *flesh*

Gomorrah, going after s. flesh. Jude 7

strange *incense*

shall offer no s. incense. Ex 30:9

strange *land*

have been a stranger in a s. land.
Ex 2:22; 18:3
shall we sing Lord's song in a s. land? Ps 137:4
his seed should sojourn in a s. land. Acts 7:6

strange *language*

a people of s. language. Ps 114:1

strange *lips*

shalt set it with s. lips. Isa 17:10

strange *nation*

to sell her to a s. nation. Ex 21:8

strange *punishment*

a s. punishment to the. Job 31:3*

strange *speech*

not sent to a people of s. speech.
Ezek 3:5, 6

strange *thing*

counted as a s. thing. Hos 8:12
as though some s. thing. 1 Pet 4:12

strange *things*

seen s. things to-day. Luke 5:26
thou bringest certain s. things to. Acts 17:20

strange *vanities*

me to anger with s. vanities? Jer 8:19

strange *vine*

plant of a s. vine. Jer 2:21

strange *waters*

and drunk s. waters. 2 Ki 19:24

strange *wives*

he for all his s. wives. 1 Ki 11:8
we have taken s. wives. Ezra 10:2
10, 14, 17, 44
yourselves from the s. wives. 11
were found to have taken s. wives. 18
in marrying s. wives. Neh 13:27

strange *woman*

the son of a s. woman. Judg 11:2
from the s. woman. Pr 2:16
the lips of a s. woman drop. 5:3
ravished with a s. woman ? 20
flattery of s. woman. 6:24*; 7:5
take a pledge of him for a s. woman.
20:16*; 27:13
and a s. woman is a narrow. 23:27

strange *women*

loved many s. women. 1 Ki 11:1
the mouth of s. women is. Pr 22:14
eyes shall behold s. women. 23:33

strange *work*

do his work, his s. work. Isa 28:21

strangely

lest adversaries should behave themselves s. Deut 32:27

stranger

[1] *One that is in a strange land,* Gen 23:4. [2] *One that is not a Jew, but of some other nation,* Isa 14:1. [3] *One who is not of the king's stock and family,* Mat 17:25, 26. [4] *A woman that is not a man's own wife,* Pr 5:20. *The Revisions usually change this word to* alien, *or* foreigner; *occasionally to* sojourner.

thy seed shall be a s. in a land. Gen 15:13
give land wherein thou art a s.
17:8; 28:4; 37:1
bought with money of any s. 17:12
bought with money of the s. 27
I am a s. with you. 23:4; Ps 39:12
119:19
I have been a s. in a. Ex 2:22
shall be cut off, whether a s. 12:19
Lev 16:29; 17:15; Num 15:30
no s. eat thereof. Ex 12:43; 29:33
when a s. will keep the passover.
12:48; Num 9:14
shall be to him that is homeborn and the s. Ex 12:49; Lev 24:22
Num 9:14; 15:15, 16, 29

nor s. that is within thy gates. Ex 20:10; Deut 5:14
vex or oppress a s. Ex 22:21
ye know heart of a s. seeing. 23:9
shalt rest, that the s. may be. 12
putteth any of it upon a s. 30:33
neither shall any s. among. Lev 17:12
thou shalt leave them for s. 19:10 23:22; 25:6
if a s. sojourn in the land ye. 19:33
the s. be as one born among you. 34; Num 15:15
there shall no s. eat. Lev 22:10, 13
if she be married to a s. she. 12
neither from a s.'s hand shall ye. 25
as well s. when blasphemeth. 24:16
yea, though he be a s. thou. 25:35
if a s. wax rich by thee, and thy poor brother sell himself to the s. 47
Levites set up tabernacle, the s. that. Num 1:51; 3:10, 38
and if a s. sojourn and will. 15:14
that no s. come near to offer. 16:40
and a s. shall not come nigh. 18:4
the s. that cometh nigh shall. 7
it shall be unto Israel and the s. 19:10
six cities of refuge for the s. 35:15 Josh 20:9
judge righteously between the s. Deut 1:16
Lord loveth the s. in giving. 10:18
love the s., for ye were strangers. 19
that dieth of itself: give to s. 14:21
not set a s. over thee who is. 17:15
thou wast a s. in his land. 23:7
unto a s. thou mayest lend. 20
not marry without to a s. 25:5
shalt rejoice, thou, and the s. 26:11
the s. shall get up above thee. 28:43
thy s. to enter into covenant. 29:11
s. that shall come from afar. 22
gather the people, and thy s. 31:12
as well the s. as he. Josh 8:33
aside to city of a s. Judg 19:12
grace, seeing I am a s.? Ruth 2:10
I am the son of a s. an Amalekite. 2 Sam 1:13
for thou art a s. and also an. 15:19
there was no s. with us. 1 Ki 3:18
moreover concerning a s. 8:41 2 Chr 6:32
do according to all that the s. calleth. 1 Ki 8:43; 2 Chr 6:33
and no s. passed among. Job 15:19
my maids count me for a s. 19:15
the s. did not lodge in street. 31:32
I am become a s. to my. Ps 69:8
they slay the widow and the s. 94:6
let the s. spoil his labour. 109:11
to deliver thee even from the s. Pr 2:16
labours be in the house of a s. 5:10
embrace the bosom of a s.? 20
stricken thine hand with a s. 6:1
they may keep thee from the s. 7:5
he that is surety for a s. shall. 11:15
and a s. doth not intermeddle. 14:10
take his garment that is surety for a s. 20:16; 27:13
let a s. praise thee, and not. 27:2
eat thereof, but a s. eateth. Eccl 6:2
neither let the son of a s. Isa 56:3
the sons of the s. that join. 6
the sons of the s. shall not. 62:8
why shouldest thou be as a s. in? Jer 14:8
every s. that setteth up. Ezek 14:7
oppression with the s. 22:7, 29
no s. uncircumcised shall enter. 44:9
what tribe the s. sojourneth. 47:23
day that he became a s. Ob 12*
and that turn aside the s. Mal 3:5
I was a s. and ye. Mat 25:35, 43
when saw we thee a s.? 38, 44
returned, save this s. Luke 17:18
art thou only a s. in Jerusalem? 24:18
s. will they not follow, but. John 10:5
Moses was a s. in land. Acts 7:29
see **fatherless, proselyte**

strangers

not counted of him s.? Gen 31:15
the land wherein they were s. 36:7 Ex 6:4
for ye were s. in the land of Egypt. Ex 22:21; 23:9; Lev 19:34; 25:23 Deut 10:19
s. that offer an. Lev 17:8; 22:18
whatsoever of the s. that. 17:10
the s. that hunteth shall pour. 13
the s. that giveth of his seed. 20:2
children of the s. shall. 25:45
not oppress a servant though of s. Deut 24:14
after gods of the s. of land. 31:16*
s. that were conversant. Josh 8:35
s. shall submit themselves unto me. 2 Sam 22:45
s. shall fade away and be afraid. 46; Ps 18:44, 45
when ye were s. in it. 1 Chr 16:19 Ps 105:12
to gather the s. in Israel. 1 Chr 22:2
for we are s. as were all. 29:15
numbered all the s. 2 Chr 2:17
all Judah and the s. 15:9
the s. of Israel and all Judah. 30:25
seed of Israel separated themselves from all s. Neh 9:2
cleansed I them from all s. 13:30
for s. are risen up against me and. Ps 54:3
the Lord preserveth the s. 146:9
lest s. be filled with thy. Pr 5:10
let them be only thine own, not s. 17
s. devour it in your presence, it is desolate as . . . by s. Isa 1:7
themselves in the children of s. 2:6
of the fat ones shall s. eat. 5:17*
and the s. shall be joined. 14:1
thou hast made a palace of s. 25:2
bring down the noise of s. 5
multitude of thy s. shall be. 29:5*
the sons of s. shall build up. 60:10
and s. shall stand and feed. 61:5
I have loved s. and after. Jer 2:25
scattered thy ways to the s. 3:13
so shall ye serve s. in a land. 5:19
s. shall no more serve. 30:8
live in the land where ye be s. 35:7
for s. are come into the. 51:51
our inheritance is turned to s. Lam 5:2
give it into hand of s. Ezek 7:21
you into the hands of s. 11:9
a wife who taketh s. instead. 16:32
therefore I will bring s. upon. 28:7
the deaths by the hand of s. 10
land waste by the hand of s. 30:12
s. have cut him off. 31:12
brought into my sanctuary s. 44:7
inheritance to you and to the s. 47:22
s. have devoured his. Hos 7:9
if so be it yield, the s. shall. 8:7
there shall no s. pass. Joel 3:17
in the day that s. carried. Ob 11
take tribute? of children or of s.? Mat 17:25
Peter saith to him, Of s. 26
to bury s. in. 27:7
know not the voice of s. John 10:5
and s. of Rome, Jews. Acts 2:10
when they dwelt as s. in the. 13:17
s. from the covenants of. Eph 2:12
no more s. but fellow-citizens. 19
if she have lodged s., if. 1 Tim 5:10
confessed they were s. Heb 11:13
be not forgetful to entertain s. 13:2
so the s. scattered through Pontus. 1 Pet 1:1
I beseech you as s. and pilgrims. 2:11
whatsoever thou dost to s. 3 John 5

strangled

the lion did tear and s. for. Nah 2:12
that they abstain from things s. Acts 15:20, 29; 21:25

strangling

so that my soul chooseth s. Job 7:15

straw

we have both s. and. Gen 24:25
he gave s. and provender for. 32
ye shall no more give s. Ex 5:7 10, 16, 18
go ye, get you s. where you. 11
yet there is both s. and. Judg 19:19
brought barley also and s. 1 Ki 4:28
he esteemeth iron as s. Job 41:27
and the lion shall eat s. like the ox. Isa 11:7; 65:25
be trodden down, even as s. 25:10

strawed

(*Revisions change to* strewed *or to* scattered)
he ground the calf, s. it. Ex 32:20
he s. upon the graves. 2 Chr 34:4
cut down branches and s. them. Mat 21:8; Mark 11:8
and gathering where thou hast not s. Mat 25:24
and gather where I have not s. 26

stream

what he did at the s. Num 21:15*
and as the s. of brooks. Job 6:15*
then the s. had gone over. Ps 124:4
beat off to the s. of Egypt. Isa 27:12
breath as an overflowing s. 30:28
like a s. of brimstone, doth. 33
among smooth stones of the s. 57:6*
the Gentiles like a flowing s. 66:12
fiery s. issued and came. Dan 7:10
and righteousness as a mighty s. Amos 5:24
s. beat vehemently. Luke 6:48, 49

streams

thine hand on their s. Ex 7:19; 8:5
s. whereof shall make glad. Ps 46:4
he brought s. also out of rock. 78:16
gushed out, the s. overflowed. 20
turn again our captivity as s. 126:4
well of living waters, s. S of S 4:15
smite it in the seven s. Isa 11:15
on every high hill shall be s. 30:25
place of broad rivers and s. 33:21
the s. thereof shall be turned. 34:9
break out, and s. in the desert. 35:6

street

we will abide in the s. Gen 19:2
shalt gather all the spoil into the midst of the s. Deut 13:16
of thy house into the s. Josh 2:19
he sat down in a s. of the city. Judg 19:15, 17
only lodge not in the s. 20
had stolen from the s. 2 Sam 21:12
them as the mire of the s. 22:43
and gathered them in the east s. 2 Chr 29:4*; 32:6*
in s. of house of God. Ezra 10:9*
people gathered as one man into the s. Neh 8:1*
he read therein before the s. 3*
so people made booths in the s. 16*
bring him on horseback through the s. Esth 6:9, 11
have no name in the s. Job 18:17
prepared my seat in the s. 29:7
stranger did not lodge in the s. 31:32
passing through the s. Pr 7:8
nor cause his voice to be heard in the s. Isa 42:2; Mat 12:19
laid thy body as the s. Isa 51:23
for truth is fallen in the s. 59:14
bread out of bakers' s. Jer 37:21
hunger in top of every s. Lam 2:19
out in the top of every s. 4:1
made thee an high place in every s. Ezek 16:24, 31
the s. shall be built again. Dan 9:25
into the s. called Straight. Acts 9:11
and passed through one s. 12:10
shall lie in the s. of city. Rev 11:8
s. of the city was pure gold. 21:21
in the midst of the s. was. 22:2

streets

not in the s. of Askelon. 2 Sam 1:20
make s. in Damascus. 1 Ki 20:34
out as dirt in the s. Ps 18:42
guile depart not from her s. 55:11
sheep may bring forth ten thousands in our s. 144:13*
no complaining in our s. 14
uttereth her voice in the s. Pr 1:20*
and rivers of water in the s. 5:16
is she without, now in the s. 7:12*
a lion without, I shall be slain in the s. 22:13
man saith, A lion is in the s. 26:13
the doors shall be shut in the s. Eccl 12:4*

mourners go about the *s.* *Eccl* 12:5
go about the city in *s.* *S of S* 3:2
carcases were torn in midst of *s.* *Isa* 5:25
down like the mire of the *s.* 10:6
in their *s.* they shall gird. 15:3*
a crying for wine in the *s.* 24:11
sons lie at the head of all the *s.* 51:20
run ye to and fro through *s.* *Jer* 5:1
seest thou not what they do in *s.*? 7:17
cease from the *s.* of Jerusalem. 34
cut off young men from the *s.* 9:21
proclaim these words in the *s.* 11:6
according to the number of the *s.* 13
people shall be cast out in *s.* 14:16
mirth shall be heard in *s.* of. 33:10
my anger was kindled in the *s.* 44:6
wickedness they have committed in *s.* of Jerusalem. 9
the incense that ye burn in *s.* 21
lamentations in the *s.* of Moab. 48:38
her young men shall fall in her *s.* 49:26; 50:30
are thrust through in her *s.* 51:4
sucklings swoon in the *s.* of the city. *Lam* 2:11, 12
the old lie on the ground in the *s.* 21
feed delicately, are desolate in *s.* 4:5
Nazarites are not known in the *s.* 8
wandered as blind men in the *s.* 14
steps, that we cannot go in our *s.* 18
cast their silver in the *s.* *Ezek* 7:19
ye have filled the *s.* thereof. 11:6
of his horses tread down thy *s.* 26:11
pestilence and blood into her *s.* 28:23
wailing be in all *s.* and. *Amos* 5:16*
down as mire of the *s.* *Mi* 7:10
rage in the *s.*, shall justle. *Nah* 2:4
in pieces at the top of the *s.* 3:10
I made their *s.* waste. *Zeph* 3:6
old women shall dwell in *s.* *Zech* 8:4
s. of the city shall be full of boys. 5
up fine gold as mire in the *s.* 9:3
down their enemies in the *s.* 10:5
a trumpet before thee in *s.* *Mat* 6:2
to pray standing in corners of *s.* 5
they laid the sick in the *s.* *Mark* 6:56*; *Acts* 5:15
go out into the *s.* of. *Luke* 10:10
Thou hast taught in our *s.* 13:26
go out quickly into the *s.* and. 14:21

strength

not henceforth yield her *s.* *Gen* 4:12
by *s.* the Lord brought you out. *Ex* 13:3, 14, 16
he hath the *s.* of an unicorn. *Num* 23:22; 24:8
thou hast trodden down *s.* *Judg* 5:21
they are girded with *s.* *1 Sam* 2:4
wicked be silent, for by *s.* shall. 9
he shall give *s.* unto his king. 10
the *s.* of Israel will not lie. 15:29
eat, that thou mayest have *s.* 28:22
girded me with *s.* to battle, hast. *2 Sam* 22:40; *Ps* 18:32, 39
I have counsel and *s.* for war. *2 Ki* 18:20; *Isa* 36:5
and there is not *s.* to bring forth. *2 Ki* 19:3; *Isa* 37:3
s. and gladness are in. *1 Chr* 16:27
give to the Lord glory and *s.* 28 *Ps* 29:1; 96:7
brethren, able men for *s.* *1 Chr* 26:8
in thine hand it is to give *s.* 29:12
neither did Jeroboam recover *s.* *2 Chr* 13:20
s. of the bearers of. *Neh* 4:10
if I speak of *s.* lo, he. *Job* 9:19
with him is wisdom and *s.* 12:13*, 16
weakened the *s.* of the mighty. 21*
devour the *s.* of his skin. 18:13*
no; but he would put *s.* in me. 23:6*
whereto might *s.* of their hands. 30:2
not esteem all the forces of *s.* 36:19
hast thou given the horse *s.*? 39:19*
in his neck remaineth *s.* 41:22
of babes hast ordained *s.* *Ps* 8:2
saving *s.* of his right hand. 20:6
the Lord is the *s.* of my life. 27:1
and he is the saving *s.* of his. 28:8*
the Lord will give *s.* to his. 29:11
not delivered by much *s.* 33:16
that I may recover *s.* 39:13
God is our refuge and *s.* *Ps* 46:1 81:1
Ephraim is the *s.* 60:7*; 108:8*
ascribe ye *s.* unto God, his *s.* 68:34
God of Israel is he that giveth *s.* 35
but God is the *s.* of my heart. 73:26
sing aloud unto God our *s.* 81:1
blessed is the man whose *s.* 84:5
they go from *s.* to *s.*, every one. 7
and if by reason of *s.* they. 90:10
is clothed with majesty and *s.* 93:1
the *s.* of the hills is his also. 95:4*
s. and beauty are in his. 96:6
king's *s.* also loveth judgement. 99:4
thou strengthenedst me with *s.* 138:3
O God the Lord, the *s.* of my. 140:7
I have *s.* *Pr* 8:14*
the way of the Lord is *s.* 10:29*
increase is by the *s.* of ox. 14:4
casteth down the *s.* thereof. 21:22
of knowledge increaseth *s.* 24:5*
she girdeth her loins with *s.* 31:17
s. and honour are her clothing. 25
Wisdom is better than *s.* *Eccl* 9:16
then must he put to more *s.* 10:10
princes eat for *s.* and not for. 17
and men of *s.* to mingle. *Isa* 5:22
by the *s.* of my hand I have. 10:13
sea hath spoken, even the *s.* 23:4*
been a *s.* to the poor, a *s.* to. 25:4*
in Jehovah is everlasting *s.* 26:4*
for *s.* to them that turn the. 28:6
the *s.* of Pharaoh shall be. 30:3
shall be stability and *s.* of. 33:6*
lift up thy voice with *s.* 40:9
no might, he increaseth *s.* 29
he hath poured on him the *s.* 42:25
he worketh it with the *s.* 44:12*
have I righteousness and *s.* 45:24
awake, awake, put on thy *s.* 51:9
moreover I will deliver all the *s.* of this city. *Jer* 20:5*
fortify the height of her *s.* 51:53
they are gone without *s.* *Lam* 1:6
pour my fury on sin, *s.* *Ezek* 30:15*
the pomp of her *s.* shall. 18*; 33:28*
given thee power, *s.* glory. *Dan* 2:37
but there shall be in it of the *s.* 41
neither shall there be any *s.* 11:15
to enter with the *s.* of his whole. 17
pollute the sanctuary of *s.* 31*
the Lord the *s.* of the. *Joel* 3:16*
horns by our own *s.*? *Amos* 6:13
Ethiopia and Egypt were her *s.* *Nah* 3:9
thou also shalt seek *s.* because. 11*
destroy *s.* of kingdoms. *Hag* 2:22
he hath shewed *s.* with. *Luke* 1:51
ancle bones received *s.* *Acts* 3:7
without *s.*, Christ died. *Rom* 5:6
the sting of death is sin; the *s.* of sin is the law. *1 Cor* 15:56*
out of measure, above *s.* *2 Cor* 1:8*
Sara herself received *s.* *Heb* 11:11
for thou hast a little *s.* *Rev* 3:8*
worthy is Lamb to receive *s.* 5:12*
Now is come salvation and *s.* 12:10*
their power and *s.* to beast. 17:13*
see **no**

his **strength**

sea returned to *his s.* *Ex* 14:27
is the beginning of *his s.* *Deut* 21:17
as the man is, so is *his s.* *Judg* 8:21
see wherein *his* great *s.* lieth. 16:5
his s. was not known. 9
his s. went from him. 19
a bow with *his* full *s.* *2 Ki* 9:24
seek the Lord and *his s.* *1 Chr* 16:11 *Ps* 105:4
the steps of *his s.* shall. *Job* 18:7
his s. shall be hunger bitten. 12
of death shall devour *his s.* 13
one dieth in *his* full *s.* being. 21:23
to the great rain of *his s.* 37:6*
trust him because *his s.* is? 39:11
rejoiceth in *his s.* 21
his s. is in his loins. 40:16
deliver any by *his* great *s.* *Ps* 33:17*
that made not God *his s.* 52:7
because of *his s.* will I wait. 59:9
who by *his s.* setteth fast the. 65:6
ascribe *s.* to God, *his s.* is. 68:34
the generation to come *his s.* 78:4
delivered *his s.* into captivity. *Ps* 78:61
hungry, and *his s.* faileth. *Isa* 44:12
sworn by the arm of *his s.* 62:8
in the greatness of *his s.* 63:1
by *his s.* shall stir up all. *Dan* 11:2*
strangers devoured *his s.* *Hos* 7:9
and by *his s.* he had power. 12:3*
was as the sun in *his s.* *Rev* 1:16

in **strength**

but his bow abode *in s.* *Gen* 49:24
went *in* the *s.* of that. *1 Ki* 19:8
he is wise in heart, and mighty *in s.* *Job* 9:4; 36:5
I will go *in* the *s.* of the. *Ps* 71:16*
his angels that excel *in s.* 103:20
he delighteth not *in* the *s.* 147:10
themselves *in s.* of Pharaoh. *Isa* 30:2
and he shall feed *in* the *s.* *Mi* 5:4
increased the more *in s.* *Acts* 9:22

my **strength**

the beginning of *my s.* *Gen* 49:3
Lord is *my s.* and song. *Ex* 15:2 *2 Sam* 22:33; *Ps* 18:2*; 28:7 118:14; *Isa* 12:2
as *my s.* was then, even so is *my s.* *Josh* 14:11
if I be shaven, *my s.* *Judg* 16:17
what is *my s.* that I should hope? *Job* 6:11
is *my s.* of stones? or is my? 12
love thee, O Lord, *my s.* *Ps* 18:1
O Lord, *my s.* 19:14*; 22:19*
my s. is dried up. 22:15
the net, for thou art *my s.* 31:4*
my s. fails because of mine iniquity. 10; 38:10; 71:9
art the God of *my s.* why go? 43:2
to thee, O *my s.* will I sing. 59:17
art rock of *my s.* 62:7
he weakened *my s.* 102:23
blessed be Lord *my s.* who. 144:1*
let him take hold of *my s.* *Isa* 27:5
I have spent *my s.* for nought. 49:4
my God shall be *my s.* 5
O Lord, *my s.* *Jer* 16:19
he made *my s.* to fall. *Lam* 1:14
I said, *My s.* and hope is. 3:18
the Lord God is *my s.* *Hab* 3:19
my s. in Lord of hosts. *Zech* 12:5
my s. is made perfect. *2 Cor* 12:9*

their **strength**

as for cities that stood still in *their s.* *Josh* 11:13*
he is *their s.* in the time. *Ps* 37:39*
their death, *their s.* is firm. 73:4
he smote the chief of *their s.* 78:51 105:36
art the glory of *their s.* 89:17
yet is *their s.* labour and. 90:10*
the glory of young men is *their s.* *Pr* 20:29
I have cried, *their s.* is. *Isa* 30:7*
on Lord shall renew *their s.* 40:31
let the people renew *their s.* 41:1
I will bring down *their s.* 63:6*
take from them *their s.* *Ezek* 24:25
and vine do yield *their s.* *Joel* 2:22

thy **strength**

guided them in *thy s.* *Ex* 15:13
days, so shall *thy s.* be. *Deut* 33:25
wherein *thy s.* lieth. *Judg* 16:6, 15
thou, and the ark of *thy s.* *2 Chr* 6:41 *Ps* 132:8
the king shall joy in *thy s.* *Ps* 21:1
O Lord, in *thine* own *s.* 13
thy name, judge me by *thy s.* 54:1
hath commanded *thy s.* 68:28
until I have shewed *thy s.* 71:18
divide the sea by *thy s.* 74:13
thou hast declared *thy s.* 77:14
stir up *thy s.* and come. 80:2*
O turn to me, give *thy s.* to. 86:16
Lord shall send rod of *thy s.* 110:2
if thou faint in day of adversity, *thy s.* *Pr* 24:10
give not *thy s.* unto women. 31:3
mindful of rock of *thy s.* *Isa* 17:10
awake, awake, put on *thy s.* 52:1
where is thy zeal and *thy s.*? 63:15
he shall bring down *thy s.* *Amos* 3:11

thy God with all thy heart and all *thy* *s.* *Mark* 12:30, 33; *Luke* 10:27

your strength

and *your s.* shall be spent in vain. *Lev* 26:20
joy of the Lord is *your s.* *Neh* 8:10
howl, ye ships, *your s.* *Isa* 23:14
in confidence will be *your s.* 30:15
excellency of *your s.* *Ezek* 24:21

strengthen

charge Joshua, and encourage him and *s.* him. *Deut* 3:28
s. me, I pray thee. *Judg* 16:28
go, *s.* thyself, and mark. *1 Ki* 20:22
to *s.* their hands in the. *Ezra* 6:22
now therefore, O God, *s.* *Neh* 6:9
but I would *s.* you with. *Job* 16:5
Lord send thee help, *s.* thee. *Ps* 20:2
wait on Lord, he shall *s.* thy heart. 27:14*; 31:24*
Lord will *s.* him upon the bed. 41:3*
s. that which thou hast. 68:28
mine arm also shall *s.* him. 89:21
s. thou me according to. 119:28
and I will *s.* him with. *Isa* 22:21
to *s.* themselves in the strength. 30:2
not well *s.* their mast. 33:23
s. ye the weak hands. 35:3
I will *s.* thee. 41:10
lengthen thy cords, and *s.* 54:2
s. also the hands of evil. *Jer* 23:14
nor shall any *s.* himself. *Ezek* 7:13
neither did she *s.* hand of poor. 16:49
I will *s.* arms of the king. 30:24, 25*
I will *s.* that which was sick. 34:16
to confirm and to *s.* him. *Dan* 11:1
strong shall not *s.* his. *Amos* 2:14
and I will *s.* the house. *Zech* 10:6
I will *s.* them in the Lord, they. 12
thou art converted, *s.* *Luke* 22:32*
you perfect, stablish, *s.* *1 Pet* 5:10
be watchful and *s.* things. *Rev* 3:2*

strengthened

Israel *s.* himself, and sat. *Gen* 48:2
the Lord *s.* Eglon against. *Judg* 3:12
shall thine hands be *s.* 7:11
and *s.* his hand in God. *1 Sam* 23:16
let your hands be *s.* *2 Sam* 2:7
who *s.* themselves. *1 Chr* 11:10
and Solomon was *s.* *2 Chr* 1:1
s. the kingdom of Judah. 11:17
when Rehoboam had *s.* himself. 12:1
have *s.* themselves against. 13:7
Jehoshaphat *s.* himself against. 17:1
Jehoram *s.* himself and slew. 21:4
Jehoiada *s.* himself and took. 23:1
house in his state, and *s.* it. 24:13
Amaziah *s.* himself, and led. 25:11*
Uzziah *s.* himself exceedingly. 26:8
and distressed Ahaz, but *s.* 28:20
Hezekiah *s.* himself, and built. 32:5*
all that were about them *s.* *Ezra* 1:6
I was *s.* as hand of my God. 7:28
they *s.* their hands for. *Neh* 2:18
hast *s.* the weak hands. *Job* 4:3
hast *s.* the feeble knees. 4*
and *s.* himself in his. *Ps* 52:7
for he hath *s.* the bars of. 147:13
when he *s.* the fountains of. *Pr* 8:28
ye have *s.* the hands of. *Ezek* 13:22
diseased have ye not *s.* nor. 34:4
one touched me, and *s.* me. *Dan* 10:18, 19
he that begat her and *s.* her. 11:6
many, but he shall not be *s.* by. 12*
though I have bound and *s.* *Hos* 7:15
Saul was *s.* *Acts* 9:19
to be *s.* with might by Spirit. *Eph* 3:16
s. with all might according. *Col* 1:11
stood with me and *s.* me. *2 Tim* 4:17

strengthenedst

s. me with strength in. *Ps* 138:3*

strengtheneth

he *s.* himself against. *Job* 15:25*
and bread which *s.* *Ps* 104:15
girdeth her loins, and *s.* *Pr* 31:17
wisdom *s.* the wise more. *Eccl* 7:19
the cypress and oak he *s.* *Isa* 44:14
s. the spoiled against. *Amos* 5:9*
I can do all things through Christ which *s.* me. *Phil* 4:13

strengthening

appeared an angel *s.* *Luke* 22:43
Paul went to Galatia, *s.* *Acts* 18:23*

stretch

s. out thy hand upon. *Ex* 7:19
s. forth thine hand over streams. 8:5
s. out thy rod and smite dust. 16
cherubims shall *s.* forth their. 25:20
s. out spear that is in. *Josh* 8:18
I will *s.* over Jerusalem. *2 Ki* 21:13
if thou *s.* thine hands. *Job* 11:13
doth the hawk *s.* her wings? 39:26
shall soon *s.* out her hands. *Ps* 68:31
that a man can *s.* himself. *Isa* 28:20
he shall *s.* upon it the line. 34:11
s. forth the curtains of thy. 54:2
there is none to *s.* forth. *Jer* 10:20
king of Babylon shall *s.* *Ezek* 30:25
and *s.* themselves upon. *Amos* 6:4
man, *S.* forth thy hand. *Mat* 12:13
thou shalt *s.* forth thy. *John* 21:18
for we *s.* not ourselves. *2 Cor* 10:14

stretched

Abraham *s.* forth hand. *Gen* 22:10
Israel *s.* out right hand, laid. 48:14
Aaron *s.* out his hand. *Ex* 8:6, 17
Moses *s.* forth his rod. 9:23; 10:13
Moses *s.* forth his hand to heaven. 10:22; 14:21, 27
and Joshua *s.* out the spear. *Josh* 8:18, 26
they ran as soon as he had *s.* 19
the cherubims *s.* forth. *1 Ki* 6:27
he *s.* himself upon the child. 17:21
2 Ki 4:34, 35
angel with a sword *s.* *1 Chr* 21:16
who hath *s.* the line upon? *Job* 38:5
or *s.* our hands to a. *Ps* 44:20
I have *s.* out my hands unto. 88:9
to him that *s.* out the earth. 136:6
because I have *s.* out. *Pr* 1:24
because they walk with *s.* *Isa* 3:16
s. forth his hand against them; his hand is *s.* 5:25; 9:12, 17, 21; 10:4
this is the hand that is *s.* out. 14:26
hand is *s.* out, and who shall? 27
her branches are *s.* out. 16:8
he *s.* out his hand over sea. 23:11
that *s.* out the heavens. 42:5; 45:12
51:13
the shadows are *s.* out. *Jer* 6:4
he *s.* out the heavens. 10:12
he *s.* out heaven by his. 51:15
Lord hath *s.* out a line. *Lam* 2:8
and their wings were *s.* *Ezek* 1:11
one cherub *s.* forth his hand. 10:7
behold, I have *s.* out my hand. 16:27
he *s.* out his hand with. *Hos* 7:5
that *s.* themselves shall. *Amos* 6:7
a line shall be *s.* forth. *Zech* 1:16
and he *s.* forth his hand. *Mat* 12:13
Mark 3:5
ye *s.* forth no hands. *Luke* 22:53
Herod *s.* forth his hands. *Acts* 12:1
all day long I have *s.* *Rom* 10:21
see **arm**

stretchedst

thou *s.* out thy right hand. *Ex* 15:12

stretchest

who *s.* out the heavens. *Ps* 104:2

stretcheth

for he *s.* out his hand. *Job* 15:25
he *s.* out the north over the. 26:7
she *s.* out her hand to. *Pr* 31:20
that *s.* out the heavens. *Isa* 40:22
the carpenter *s.* out his rule. 44:13
that *s.* forth the heavens alone. 24
Zech 12:1

stretching

s. of his wings shall fill. *Isa* 8:8
by *s.* forth thy hand. *Acts* 4:30

stricken

Abram and Sarah well *s.* in age. *Gen* 18:11; 24:1
now Joshua was *s.* in years. *Josh* 13:1; 23:1, 2
when Jael had *s.* *Judg* 5:26
old and *s.* in years. *1 Ki* 1:1
if thou hast *s.* thy hand. *Pr* 6:1
they have *s.* me and I was. 23:35
why should ye be *s.* any more? *Isa* 1:5
surely they are *s.* *Isa* 16:7
did esteem him *s.* 53:4
of my people was he *s.* 8
thou hast *s.* them, they. *Jer* 5:3
s. through for want of the. *Lam* 4:9
Elisabeth well *s.* in. *Luke* 1:7, 18

strife

there was a *s.* between. *Gen* 13:7
Abram said, Let there be no *s.* 8
ye rebelled in the *s.* of. *Num* 27:14
myself alone bear your *s.*? *Deut* 1:12
I and my people were at great *s.* with. *Judg* 12:2
all the people were at *s.* *2 Sam* 19:9
shalt keep them from *s.* *Ps* 31:20
for I have seen violence and *s.* 55:9
thou makest us a *s.* to our. 80:6
him at the waters of *s.* 106:32*
man stirreth up *s.* . . . slow to anger appeaseth *s.* *Pr* 15:18; 29:22
a froward man soweth *s.* 16:28
house full of sacrifices with *s.* 17:1
beginning of *s.* is as when one. 14
loveth transgression, that loveth *s.* 19
for a man to cease from *s.* 20:3
cast out the scorner, and *s.* 22:10
he that meddleth with *s.* 26:17
is no talebearer, the *s.* ceaseth. 20
so is a contentious man to kindle *s.* 21
a proud heart stirreth up *s.* 28:25
of wrath bringeth forth *s.* 30:33
behold, ye fast for *s.* and. *Isa* 58:4
hast borne me a man of *s.* *Jer* 15:10
even to the waters of *s.* *Ezek* 47:19*; 48:28*
there are that raise up *s.* *Hab* 1:3
there was a *s.* among. *Luke* 22:24
walk honestly, not in *s.* *Rom* 13:13
there is among you *s.* *1 Cor* 3:3
of the flesh are wrath, *s.* *Gal* 5:20*
preach Christ even of *s.* *Phil* 1:15
let nothing be done through *s.* 2:3*
whereof cometh envy, *s.* *1 Tim* 6:4
to them an end of all *s.* *Heb* 6:16*
bitter envying and *s.* *Jas* 3:14*
where *s.* is, there is confusion. 16*

strifes

hatred stirreth up *s.*: love. *Pr* 10:12
envyings, wraths, *s.* *2 Cor* 12:20*
doting about questions and *s.* of words. *1 Tim* 6:4*
that they do gender *s.* *2 Tim* 2:23

strike

and *s.* blood on the two side posts. *Ex* 12:7*, 22
shall *s.* off the heifer's. *Deut* 21:4
come and *s.* his hand. *2 Ki* 5:11*
who is he that will *s.* hands with? *Job* 17:3
and the bow of steel shall *s.* 20:24
shall *s.* through kings in. *Ps* 110:5
till a dart *s.* through. *Pr* 7:23
it is not good to *s.* princes. 17:26
one of them that *s.* hands. 22:26
thou didst *s.* through. *Hab* 3:14
s. him with palms of. *Mark* 14:65*

striker

a bishop must be sober, no *s.* *1 Tim* 3:3; *Tit* 1:7

striketh

he *s.* them as wicked men. *Job* 34:26
of understanding *s.* hands. *Pr* 17:18
scorpion, when he *s.* a man. *Rev* 9:5

string

ready their arrow upon *s.* *Ps* 11:2
s. of his tongue was loosed, he. *Mark* 7:35*

stringed

him with *s.* instruments. *Ps* 150:4
will sing my songs to *s.* *Isa* 38:20
to chief singer on my *s.* *Hab* 3:19

strings

make ready their arrows upon *s.* *Ps* 21:12*
with the psaltery, and an instrument of ten *s.* 33:2; 92:3; 144:9

strip

and *s.* Aaron of his. *Num* 20:26
Philistines came to *s.* slain. *1 Sam* 31:8; *1 Chr* 10:8
s. ye, make ye bare, gird. *Isa* 32:11

they shall *s.* thee of thy clothes. *Ezek* 16:39; 23:26
lest I *s.* her naked, and. *Hos* 2:3

stripe

wound for wound, *s.* for *s.* *Ex* 21:25

stripes

(*Strokes given by a scourge or rod. The law forbade giving more than* 40 *and the Jews stopped at* 39 *for fear of wrong count*)
forty *s.* he may give him . . . above these with many *s.* *Deut* 25:3
and with *s.* of the children of men. *2 Sam* 7:14
visit their iniquity with *s.* *Ps* 89:32
than an hundred *s.* into. *Pr* 17:10
and *s.* prepared for the back. 19:29
so do *s.* the inward parts. 20:30
with his *s.* we are healed. *Isa* 53:5
1 Pet 2:24
be beaten with many *s.* *Luke* 12:47
not, shall be beaten with few *s.* 48
had laid many *s.* upon. *Acts* 16:23
same hour and washed their *s.* 33
in *s.*, in imprisonments. *2 Cor* 6:5
s. above measure, in prisons. 11:23
received I forty *s.* save one. 24

stripling

Inquire whose son the *s.* *1 Sam* 17:56

stripped

that they *s.* Joseph out. *Gen* 37:23
Israel *s.* themselves of. *Ex* 33:6
Moses *s.* Aaron of his. *Num* 20:28
Jonathan *s.* himself of. *1 Sam* 18:4
Saul *s.* off his clothes also. 19:24
the Philistines *s.* Saul of his. 31:9
jewels which they *s.* off. *2 Chr* 20:25
he *s.* me of my glory. *Job* 19:9
for thou hast *s.* the naked of. 22:6
therefore I will go *s.* *Mi* 1:8
they *s.* Jesus, put on. *Mat* 27:28
thieves, which *s.* him. *Luke* 10:30

strive

spirit shall not always *s.* *Gen* 6:3
the herdmen of Gerar did *s.* 26:20
if men *s.* together, and. *Ex* 21:18
if man *s.* and hurt a woman with child, he shall. 22; *Deut* 25:11
with whom thou didst *s.* *Deut* 33:8
did he ever *s.* against Israel or? *Judg* 11:25
why dost thou *s.* against? *Job* 33:13
with them that *s.* with me. *Ps* 35:1
s. not with a man. *Pr* 3:30
go not forth hastily to *s.*, lest. 25:8
and they that *s.* with thee. *Isa* 41:11
potsherd *s.* with potsherds. 45:9*
let no man *s.*; thy people are as they that *s.* *Hos* 4:4
he shall not *s.*, nor cry. *Mat* 12:19
s. to enter in at the strait gate. *Luke* 13:24
s. with me in your prayers to. *Rom* 15:30
and if a man also *s.* *2 Tim* 2:5*
that they *s.* not about words. 14
of the Lord must not *s.* 24

strived

so have I *s.* to preach. *Rom* 15:20*

striven

because thou hast *s.* *Jer* 50:24

striveth

woe to him that *s.* with. *Isa* 45:9
every man that *s.* for mastery. *1 Cor* 9:25

striving

with one mind *s.* for faith. *Phil* 1:27
s. according to his working. *Col* 1:29
ye have not resisted to blood, *s.* against sin. *Heb* 12:4

strivings

delivered me from the *s.* of the people, and. *2 Sam* 22:44; *Ps* 18:43
avoid contentions and *s.* *Tit* 3:9*

stroke

hard between *s.* and *s.* *Deut* 17:8
and his hand fetcheth a *s.* 19:5
by their word shall every *s.* 21:5
their enemies with the *s.* *Esth* 9:5
my *s.* is heavier than. *Job* 23:2
take thee away with his *s.* 36:18
remove thy *s.* away from. *Ps* 39:10
people with a continual *s.* *Isa* 14:6
the Lord healeth the *s.* of. 30:26
of thine eyes with a *s.* *Ezek* 24:16

strokes

a fool's mouth calleth for *s.* *Pr* 18:6*

strong

Issachar is a *s.* ass. *Gen* 49:14
arms of his hands were made *s.* 24
with a *s.* hand shall he let them go. *Ex* 6:1; 13:9
the Lord turned a mighty *s.* 10:19
sea to go back by a *s.* east. 14:21
Edom came against him with a *s.* *Num* 20:20
children of Ammon was *s.* 21:24
Balaam said, *S.* is thy. 24:21
the *s.* wine to be poured out. 28:7
one city too *s.* for us. *Deut* 2:36*
as yet I am as *s.* this. *Josh* 14:11
were waxen *s.* 17:13; *Judg* 1:28
Lord hath driven out great nations and *s.* *Josh* 23:9
but there was a *s.* tower. *Judg* 9:51
out of the *s.* came forth. 14:14
that they were too *s.* for him. 18:26
Saul saw any *s.* man. *1 Sam* 14:52*
Abner made himself *s.* for the house of Saul. *2 Sam* 3:6
Syrians be too *s.* for me, if Ammon be too *s.* for. 10:11; *1 Chr* 19:12
make thy battle more *s.* *2 Sam* 11:25
the conspiracy was *s.* 15:12
from my *s.* enemy; . . . for they were too *s.* for me. 22:18*; *Ps* 18:17
shall hear of thy name and *s.* hand. *1 Ki* 8:42
a great and *s.* wind rent the. 19:11
cities exceeding *s.* *2 Chr* 11:12
so they made Rehoboam *s.* 17
eyes run to shew himself *s.* 16:9
when Uzziah was *s.* he. 26:16
redeemed by thy *s.* hand. *Neh* 1:10
and they took *s.* cities and. 9:25*
mouth be like a *s.* wind. *Job* 8:2*
speak of strength, lo, he is *s.* 9:19*
with thy *s.* hand thou. 30:21*
spread out the sky, which is *s.*? 37:18
bones are as *s.* pieces of. 40:18*
and rejoiceth as a *s.* man. *Ps* 19:5
Lord *s.* and mighty, the Lord. 24:8
my mountain to stand *s.* 30:7
be thou my *s.* rock, and house. 31:2
me his kindness in a *s.* city. 21
poor from him that is too *s.* 35:10
are lively and they are *s.* 38:19
bring me into *s.* city? 60:9; 108:10
thou hast been a *s.* tower from. 61:3
be my *s.* habitation. 71:3*
thou art my *s.* refuge. 7
the branch thou madest *s.* 80:15, 17
O Lord, who is a *s.* Lord? 89:8*
s. is thy hand, and high is thy. 13
with a *s.* hand, and a stretched out arm. 136:12; *Jer* 32:21
yea, many *s.* men have. *Pr* 7:26*
rich man's wealth is his *s.* city. 10:15; 18:11
s. men retain riches. 11:16*
fear of the Lord is a *s.* tower. 14:26
name of the Lord is a *s.* tower. 18:10
is harder to be won than a *s.* city. 19
the bosom pacifieth *s.* wrath. 21:14
a wise man is *s.* 24:5
ants are a people not *s.* 30:25
the battle is not to the *s.* *Eccl* 9:11
and the *s.* men shall bow. 12:3
as a seal, for love is *s.* *S of S* 8:6
the *s.* shall be as tow. *Isa* 1:31
Lord bringeth on them waters, *s.* 8:7
spake thus to me with a *s.* 11
his *s.* cities shall be as a. 17:9
therefore shall the *s.* people. 25:3
be sung: We have a *s.* city. 26:1
with his *s.* sword shall punish. 27:1
Lord hath a mighty and *s.* one. 28:2
lest your bands be made *s.* 22
horsemen, because they are *s.* 31:1
will come with a *s.* hand. 40:10*
for that he is *s.* in power, not. 26
bring forth your *s.* reasons. 41:21
divide the spoil with the *s.* 53:12
a small one shall become a *s.* 60:22
against you with a *s.* arm. *Jer* 21:5
say ye, We are mighty, *s.*? 48:14*
How is the *s.* staff broken! 17
against habitation of the *s.* 49:19
Redeemer is *s.*; the Lord of. 50:34
up to the habitation of the *s.* 44
make the watch *s.*, set up. 51:12
thy face *s.* thy forehead *s.* *Ezek* 3:8*
but the hand of the Lord was *s.* 14
the pomp of the *s.* to cease. 7:24
had *s.* rods for sceptres of. 19:11
her *s.* rods were broken. 12
so she hath no *s.* rod to be a. 14
thy *s.* garrisons shall go. 26:11*
the renowned city which wast *s.* 17
bind it, to make it *s.* to hold. 30:21
and I will break the *s.* arms. 22
s. shall speak to him out of. 32:21
destroy the fat and the *s.* 34:16
tree grew, and was *s.* *Dan* 4:11, 20
O king, art grown and become *s.* 22
the fourth beast terrible, *s.* 7:7
when he was *s.* the great horn. 8:8
he shall become *s.* with a. 11:23
nation is come up on my land, *s.* *Joel* 1:6; 2:2
as the noise of a *s.* people set. 2:5
for he is *s.* that executeth his. 11
let the weak say, I am *s.* 3:10
the Amorite was *s.* as. *Amos* 2:9
and the *s.* shall not strengthen. 14
the spoiled against the *s.* 5:9
he shall rebuke *s.* nations. *Mi* 4:3
was cast far off, *s.* nation. 7
hear, ye *s.* foundations of the. 6:2*
make thy loins *s.*, fortify. *Nah* 2:1
s. nations shall come to. *Zech* 8:22
enter into a *s.* man's house . . . the *s.* man? *Mat* 12:29; *Mark* 3:27
grew and waxed *s.* *Luke* 1:80; 2:40
when a *s.* man armed keepeth. 11:21
through faith hath made this man *s.* *Acts* 3:16
was *s.* in faith, giving. *Rom* 4:20
we that are *s.* ought to bear. 15:1
weak, but ye are *s.* *1 Cor* 4:10
am weak, then am I *s.* *2 Cor* 12:10
we are weak, and ye are *s.* 13:9
God shall send them *s.* *2 Thes* 2:11*
up prayers with *s.* crying. *Heb* 5:7
of milk, and not of *s.* meat. 12*
s. meat belongeth to them that. 14*
we might have a *s.* consolation. 6:18
weakness were made *s.* 11:34
ye are *s.*, word of God. *1 John* 2:14
I saw a *s.* angel proclaiming. *Rev* 5:2
a *s.* voice, Babylon is fallen. 18:2*
for *s.* is the Lord God who. 8

see **drink**

***be* strong**

see whether they *be s.* *Num* 13:18
the people *be s.* that dwell. 28
keep commandments, that ye may *be s.* *Deut* 11:8
drive out Canaanites, though they *be s.* *Josh* 17:18
be s. and quit yourselves. *1 Sam* 4:9
hands of all with thee shall *be s.* *2 Sam* 16:21
be thou *s.* and shew. *1 Ki* 2:2
be too *s.* for me, if Ammon *be* too *s.* for thee. *1 Chr* 19:12
Lord hath chosen thee, *be s.* 28:10
be s., your work shall. *2 Chr* 15:7
if thou wilt go, do it, *be s.* for. 25:8
that ye may *be s.* and eat. *Ezra* 9:12
that our oxen may *be s.* *Ps* 144:14*
fearful heart, *Be s.*, fear not. *Isa* 35:4
can thy hands be *s.*, in? *Ezek* 22:14
fourth kingdom shall *be s.* *Dan* 2:40
kingdom shall *be* partly *s.* 42
Peace be unto thee, *be s.*, yea, *be s.* 10:19
the south shall *be s.* and he shall *be s.* above him and have. 11:5
that know their God shall *be s.* 32
be s. O Zerubbabel, *be s.* O Joshua, *be s.* all ye people of. *Hag* 2:4
let your hands *be s.* ye that hear in these days. *Zech* 8:9
but let your hands *be s.* 13
quit you like men, *be s.* *1 Cor* 16:13
finally, brethren, *be s.* in. *Eph* 6:10

my son, be s. in grace. 2 Tim 2:1
see **courage**

strong hold and holds
tents or in s. holds. Num 13:19
them caves and s. holds. Judg 6:2
abode in wilderness in s. holds. 1 Sam 23:14
hide himself with us in s. holds? 19
and David dwelt in s. holds. 29
took the s. hold of Zion. 2 Sam 5:7
and came to the s. hold of. 24:7
their s. holds wilt thou. 2 Ki 8:12
fortified the s. holds. 2 Chr 11:11
brought his s. holds to ruin. Ps 89:40
to destroy the s. holds. Isa 23:11
over to his s. holds for fear. 31:9
destroy thy s. holds. Jer 48:18
Kerioth is taken, the s. holds. 41
down s. holds of Judah. Lam 2:2
hath destroyed his s. holds. 5
forecast his devices against the s. holds. Dan 11:24
he do in the most s. holds. 39*
the s. hold of the daughter. Mi 4:8*
Lord is a s. hold in the day. Nah 1:7
for siege, fortify thy s. holds. 3:14*
deride every s. hold. Hab 1:10
did build herself a s. hold. Zech 9:3
s. hold, ye prisoners of hope. 12
to pulling down of s. holds. 2 Cor 10:4

strong ones
poor may fall by his s. ones. Ps 10:10
the neighing of his s. ones. Jer 8:16

stronger
one people shall be s. Gen 25:23
whensoever the s. cattle did. 30:41
were Laban's, and s. Jacob's. 42
be not able, they are s. Num 13:31
the men said, What is s.? Judg 14:18
Saul and Jonathan were s. than lions. 2 Sam 1:23
but David waxed s. and s. and. 3:1
but Ammon being s. than she. 13:14
gods of hills, therefore s., surely we shall be s. than. 1 Ki 20:23, 25
hath clean hands shall be s. and s. Job 17:9
he made them s. than. Ps 105:24
deliver me, for they are s. 142:6
thou art s. than I, and. Jer 20:7
him that was s. than he. 31:11
when a s. than he shall. Luke 11:22
weakness of God is s. 1 Cor 1:25
provoke Lord ? are we s.? 10:22

strongest
a lion which is s. among. Pr 30:30*

strongly
foundation thereof be s. Ezra 6:3

strove
they s. with him. Gen 26:20, 21
well, and for that they s. not. 22
two men of the Hebrews s. Ex 2:13
and a man of Israel s. Lev 24:10
the children of Israel s. Num 20:13
Dathan, who s. against Moses. 26:9
they two s. together in. 2 Sam 14:6
four winds s. upon the. Dan 7:2*
the Jews s. among. John 6:52
himself to them as they s. Acts 7:26
and s. saying, We find no evil. 23:9

struck
he s. it into the pan or. 1 Sam 2:14
the Lord s. the child. 2 Sam 12:15
Joab s. him not again, and. 20:10
the Lord s. Jeroboam. 2 Chr 13:20
one of them s. a servant. Mat 26:51
s. Jesus on the face. Luke 22:64
John 18:22

struggled
children s. together. Gen 25:22

stubble
scattered to gather s. Ex 5:12
which consumed them as s. 15:7
thou pursue the dry s.? Job 13:25
they are as s. before the wind. 21:18
are turned with him into s. 41:28
darts are counted as s. 29
as s. before the wind. Ps 83:13
as fire devoureth the s. so. Isa 5:24
chaff and bring forth s. 33:11
take them away as s. 40:24
he gave them as driven s. 41:2
they shall be as s., the fire. Isa 47:14
will I scatter them as s. Jer 13:24
flame, that devoureth the s. Joel 2:5
house of Esau shall be for s. Ob 18
devoured as s. fully dry. Nah 1:10
wickedly and proud be s. Mal 4:1
gold, wood, hay, s. 1 Cor 3:12

stubborn
if a man have a s. Deut 21:18
say to elders, This our son is s. 20
not from their s. way. Judg 2:19
might not be as fathers, a s. Ps 78:8
she is loud and s.; her feet. Pr 7:11*

stubbornness
look not to s. of this. Deut 9:27
and s. is as iniquity. 1 Sam 15:23

stuck
spear s. in the ground. 1 Sam 26:7
I have s. unto thy. Ps 119:31
for part of the ship s. Acts 27:41*

studieth
heart of the righteous s. Pr 15:28
for their heart s. destruction. 24:2

studs
of gold with s. of silver. S of S 1:11

study
and much s. is a weariness of the. Eccl 12:12
that ye s. to be quiet. 1 Thes 4:11
s. to shew thyself approved unto. 2 Tim 2:15*

stuff
hast searched all my s. Gen 31:37
regard not your s.; the good of. 45:20
money or s. to keep. Ex 22:7
the s. they had was sufficient. 36:7
even among their own s. Josh 7:11
himself among the s. 1 Sam 10:22†
two hundred abode by the s. 25:13†
part be that tarrieth by s. 30:24†
prepare thee s. for removing and. Ezek 12:3
shalt thou bring forth thy s. 4, 7
and his s. in the house. Luke 17:31*

stumble
and thy foot not s. Pr 3:23; 4:12
know not at what they s. 4:19
none shall be weary, nor s. Isa 5:27
many among them shall s. 8:15
they err in vision, they s. 28:7
we grope, we s. at noon day. 59:10
that they should not s. 63:13
before your feet s. on dark mountains. Jer 13:16
they have caused them to s. 18:15
my persecutors shall s. 20:11
way wherein they shall not s. 31:9
they shall s. and fall toward. 46:6
and the most proud shall s. 50:32
he shall s. and fall. Dan 11:19
shall s. in their walk. Nah 2:5
multitude of slain, they s. upon. 3:3
caused many to s. at. Mal 2:8
offence to them that s. 1 Pet 2:8

stumbled
and they that s. are girt. 1 Sam 2:4
ark, for the oxen s. 1 Chr 13:9
to eat up my flesh, they s. Ps 27:2
the mighty man hath s. Jer 46:12
for they s. at that stumblingstone. Rom 9:32
I say then, Have they s. that? 11:11

stumbleth
let not thy heart be glad when he s. Pr 24:17*
walk in the day, he s. not. John 11:9
walk in the night, he s. 10
any thing whereby thy brother s. Rom 14:21

stumbling
there is none occasion of s. in him. 1 John 2:10

stumblingblock
a s. before the blind. Lev 19:14
take up the s. out of the way of my. Isa 57:14
and I lay a s. before him. Ezek 3:20
it is the s. of their iniquity. 7:19
put the s. of their iniquity. 14:3, 4, 7
table be made a trap, a s. Rom 11:9
that no man put a s. in his. 14:13
Christ crucified, to Jews a s. 1 Cor 1:23
this liberty of yours become a s. 8:9
Balak to cast a s. before. Rev 2:14

stumblingblocks
behold, I will lay s. before. Jer 6:21
I will consume the s. Zeph 1:3

stumblingstone
shall be for a stone of s. Isa 8:14
stumbled at that s. Rom 9:32*
in Sion a s. and rock of offence. 33*
a stone of s. to them. 1 Pet 2:8

stump
only the s. of Dagon. 1 Sam 5:4
s. in the earth. Dan 4:15, 23, 26

subdue
God said, Replenish the earth and s. it. Gen 1:28
s. all thine enemies. 1 Chr 17:10
he shall s. the people. Ps 47:3
have holden, to s. nations. Isa 45:1
another rise, and he shall s. three. Dan 7:24
turn again, he will s. Mi 7:19*
they shall devour and s. Zech 9:15*
able to s. all things. Phil 3:21

subdued
and the land be s. before. Num 32:22
land shall be s. before you. 29
bulwarks, until it be s. Deut 20:20*
and the land was s. Josh 18:1
so Moab was s. Judg 3:30
God s. Jabin. 4:23
thus Midian was s. 8:28
Ammon was s. 11:33
Philistines were s. 1 Sam 7:13
2 Sam 8:1; 1 Chr 18:1; 20:4
all nations which he s. 2 Sam 8:11
them that rose up against me hast thou s. under. 22:40; Ps 18:39
and the land is s. 1 Chr 22:18
I should soon have s. Ps 81:14
things shall be s. unto. 1 Cor 15:28*
who through faith s. Heb 11:33

subduedst
thou s. the inhabitants. Neh 9:24

subdueth
it is God that s. the people under me. Ps 18:47; 144:2
iron breaks and s. all. Dan 2:40

subject
and was s. to them. Luke 2:51
even the devils are s. to us. 10:17
that the spirits are s. to you. 20
is not s. to the law of. Rom 8:7
creature was made s. to vanity. 20
let every soul be s. to the. 13:1
wherefore ye must needs be s. 5
spirits of prophets are s. 1 Cor 14:32
Son also himself be s. to him. 15:28
church is s. to Christ. Eph 5:24
as though living in the world, are ye s.? Col 2:20
put them in mind to be s. Tit 3:1
lifetime s. to bondage. Heb 2:15
Elias was s. to like. Jas 5:17
servants, be s. to your. 1 Pet 2:18
and powers being made s. 3:22
all of you be s. one to another. 5:5*

subjected
of him who hath s. the. Rom 8:20

subjection
were brought into s. Ps 106:42
brought them into s. Jer 34:11, 16
bring my body into s. 1 Cor 9:27*
they glorify God for your professed s. 2 Cor 9:13*
to whom we give place by s. Gal 2:5
learn in silence with all s. 1 Tim 2:11
having his children in s. with. 3:4
put in s. the world to come. Heb 2:5
put all things in s. under his feet. 8
rather be in s. to the Father of. 12:9
wives, be in s. to your. 1 Pet 3:1, 5

submit
return, and s. thyself. Gen 16:9
strangers shall s. themselves to me. 2 Sam 22:45; Ps 18:44
enemies shall s. themselves. Ps 66:3
till every one s. himself with. 68:30
that ye s. yourselves. 1 Cor 16:16

wives, s. yourselves to your own husbands. Eph 5:22; Col 3:18
s. yourselves: for they. Heb 13:17
s. yourselves therefore to God. Jas 4:7
s. yourselves to every. 1 Pet 2:13
ye younger, s. yourselves to. 5:5

submitted

the sons of David s. 1 Chr 29:24
the Lord should have s. Ps 81:15
s. to the righteousness. Rom 10:3

submitting

s. yourselves one to another in fear. Eph 5:21

suborned

then they s. men who said. Acts 6:11

subscribe

another shall with his hand s. Isa 44:5
men shall s. evidences. Jer 32:44

subscribed

I s. the evidence, and. Jer 32:10
the witnesses that s. the book. 12

substance

destroy every living s. Gen 7:4*
every living s. was destroyed. 23*
Abram took all the s. they. 12:5
their s. was great, so that they. 13:6
shall come out with great s. 15:14
cattle and their s. be ours? 34:23
his cattle and all his s. 36:6*
how the earth swallowed them up, and all the s. Deut 11:6*
bless, Lord, his s. and accept. 33:11
Levites cities for their s. Josh 14:4
were the rulers of the s. 1 Chr 27:31
the stewards over all the s. of. 28:1
they carried away all s. 2 Chr 21:17
the king's portion of his s. 31:3
God had given Hezekiah s. 32:29
bullocks, these were of king's s. 35:7
a right way for our s. Ezra 8:21
not come, all his s. should. 10:8
Job's s. also was seven. Job 1:3
his s. is increased in the land. 10
robber swalloweth up their s. 5:5
give a reward for me of your s.? 6:22
rich, nor shall his s. continue. 15:29
according to his s. shall the. 20:18
our s. is not cut down, but. 22:20*
me up and dissolvest my s. 30:22*
their s. to their babes. Ps 17:14
Joseph ruler over all his s. 105:21
my s. was not hid from thee. 139:15*
eyes did see my s. yet being. 16
we shall find all precious s. Pr 1:13
honour the Lord with thy s. and. 3:9
he shall give all the s. of his. 6:31
those that love me inherit s. 8:21
but he casteth away the s. 10:3*
but the s. of a diligent man is. 12:27
by usury increaseth his s. 28:8
with harlots, spendeth his s. 29:3
give all his s. for love. S of S 8:7
as an oak, whose s. is in them, so the holy seed shall be s. Isa 6:13*
thy s. will I give to the spoil. Jer 15:13; 17:3
I am become rich, I have found me out s. Hos 12:8*
nor laid hands on their s. Ob 13
I will consecrate their s. Mi 4:13
to him of their s. Luke 8:3
wasted his s. with riotous. 15:13
knowing that ye have in heaven a better and enduring s. Heb 10:34*
now faith is the s. of things. 11:1*

subtil

the serpent was more s. Gen 3:1*
was a very s. man. 2 Sam 13:3*
an harlot, and s. of heart. Pr 7:10*

subtilly

that he dealeth very s. 1 Sam 23:22
to deal s. with his. Ps 105:25
the same dealt s. with. Acts 7:19

subtilty

thy brother came with s. Gen 27:35*
Jehu did it in s. that. 2 Ki 10:19
to give s. to the simple. Pr 1:4
might take Jesus by s. Mat 26:4
said, O full of all s. Acts 13:10*
beguiled Eve through s. 2 Cor 11:3

suburbs

but the field of the s. may. Lev 25:34
the s. of them shall be. Num 35:3
cities shall ye give with their s. 7
save cities with s. for their cattle. Josh 14:4; 21:2
horses by chamber in s. 2 Ki 23:11*
Levites left their s. and came to Judah. 2 Chr 11:14
the s. shall shake at the. Ezek 27:28
round about for the s. thereof. 45:2
place for dwelling and for s. 48:15
the s. of the city shall be. 17
see **cities**

subvert

to s. a man in his cause. Lam 3:36
who s. whole houses. Tit 1:11*

subverted

such is s. and sinneth. Tit 3:11*

subverting

with words, s. souls. Acts 15:24
words to no profit, but to s. of. 2 Tim 2:14

succeed

the firstborn shall s. his. Deut 25:6

succeeded

but the children of Esau s. them. Deut 2:12, 22
the Ammonites s. them, and. 21

succeedest

when thou s. them in their land. Deut 12:29*; 19:1

success

then thou shalt have good s. Josh 1:8

Succoth

to S. and made booths for his cattle, therefore it is called S. Gen 33:17
from Rameses to S. Ex 12:37
they took their journey from S. 13:20; Num 33:5, 6
Gad had in the valley, S. Josh 13:27
the men of S. give bread. Judg 8:5
answered as the men of S. 8
he taught the men of S. 16
king cast them in the clay ground between S. 1 Ki 7:46; 2 Chr 4:17
I will mete out the valley of S. Ps 60:6; 108:7

Succoth-benoth

men of Babylon made S. 2 Ki 17:30

succour

when the Syrians came to s. Hadadezer. 2 Sam 8:5
it is better that thou s. us out. 18:3
he is able to s. them. Heb 2:18

succoured

Abishai s. him, and. 2 Sam 21:17
of salvation have I s. 2 Cor 6:2

succourer

she hath been a s. of. Rom 16:2

such

Jabal was the father of s. Gen 4:20
Jubal was the father of s. as. 21
savoury meat, s. as I love. 27:4, 9, 14
wife of daughters of Heth, s. as. 46
speckled and spotted, of s. 30:32
s. as I never saw in Egypt. 41:19
wot ye not that s. a man as? 44:15
s. hail as hath not. Ex 9:18, 24
no s. locusts as they, nor shall be s. 10:14
shall be a great cry, s. as there. 11:6
thou shalt provide able men, s. 18:21
s. as have not been done in all. 34:10
s. water cometh be unclean . . . be drunk in every s. Lev 11:34
two pigeons s. as he is. 14:22, 30, 31
the soul that turneth after s. 20:6
soul that hath touched any s. 22:6
giveth of s. to the Lord, shall. 27:9
instead of s. as open. Num 8:16
hath been any s. thing. Deut 4:32
O that there were s. an heart. 5:29
shalt do no more any s. 13:11; 19:20
s. abomination is wrought. 14; 17:4
s. time as thou beginnest. 16:9
at least s. as before knew. Judg 3:2
was no s. deed done or seen. 19:30
hath not been s. a thing. 1 Sam 4:7
he is s. a son of Belial. 1 Sam 25:17
look on s. a dead dog as I. 2 Sam 9:8
with s. robes were the virgins. 13:18
hast thou thought s. a thing? 14:13
s. as faint in wilderness. 16:2
recompense me with s.? 19:36
came no more s. abundance of spices. 1 Ki 10:10
no s. almug trees. 12; 2 Chr 9:11
thou pass not s. a place. 2 Ki 6:9
windows, might s. a thing be? 7:19
bringing s. evil on Jerusalem. 21:12
surely there was not holden s. 23:22
s. as went forth to. 1 Chr 12:33, 36
the Lord bestowed on him s. 29:25
s. as none of the kings. 2 Chr 1:12
nor was any s. spice as the. 9:9
s. as set their hearts to seek. 11:16
people rejoiced, and s. taught. 23:13
gave it to s. as did the work. 24:12
done it of a long time in s. sort. 30:5
and at s. a time. Ezra 4:10, 11, 17
7:12
all s. as had separated. 6:21
all s. as know the laws of. 7:25
which hath put s. a thing in. 27
and of s. as lay in wait by. 8:31
and hast given s. deliverance. 9:13
put away the wives, and s. are. 10:3
I said, Should s. a man? Neh 6:11
except s. to whom the king shall. Esth 4:11
the kingdom for s. a time. 14
to lay hand on s. as sought. 9:2
and upon all s. as joined 27
and lettest s. words go. Job 15:13
surely s. are the dwellings. 18:21
to s. as keep his covenant. Ps 25:10
103:18
and s. as breathe out cruelty. 27:12
to slay s. as be of upright. 37:14
s. as be blessed of him shall. 22
respecteth not proud nor s. 40:4
let s. as love thy salvation. 16; 70:4
his hands against s. as be at. 55:20
God is good to s. as are of. 73:1
s. as sit in darkness, and. 107:10
as for s. as turn aside to. 125:5
s. knowledge is too. 139:6
people that is in s. a case. 144:15
but s. as are upright. Pr 11:20
but s. as keep the law contend. 28:4
in cause of s. as are appointed. 31:8
behold, the tears of s. as. Eccl 4:1
dimness shall not be s. as. Isa 9:1
s. as are escaped of the. 10:20
behold, s. is our expectation. 20:6
eat this year s. as groweth. 37:30
is it s. a fast that I have? 58:5
s. a thing? who hath seen s.? 66:8
see if there be s. a thing. Jer 2:10
my soul be avenged on s. a nation. 5:9, 29; 9:9
s. as are for death, to death, s. as are for sword, s. as are for famine, s. as are for captivity. 15:2; 43:11
I will deliver s. as are left in. 21:7
in speaking s. words unto them. 38:4
for none shall return, but s. as. 44:14
s. as had ability in them. Dan 1:4
had spoken s. words to me. 10:15
s. as do wickedly shall be. 11:32
shall be a time of trouble, s. 12:1
shall call s. as are skilful. Amos 5:16
in anger and fury, s. they. Mi 5:15
s. as are clothed with. Zeph 1:8
glorified God who had given s. power to men. Mat 9:8
receive one s. little child in my name. 18:5; Mark 9:37
suffer little children to come unto me, for of s. Mat 19:14; Mark 10:14
Luke 18:16
then shall be great tribulation, s. as. Mat 24:21; Mark 13:19
in s. an hour as ye think. Mat 24:44
he said, Go into the city to s. a man. 26:18
sown among thorns, s. as. Mark 4:18
ground, are s. as hear the word. 20
with many s. parables spake he. 33
for the Father seeketh s. John 4:23
Moses commanded that s. 8:5
is a sinner do s. miracles? 9:16

the Lord added daily *s.* as should be saved. *Acts* 2:47
s. as I have give I thee, rise. 3:6
to whom we gave no *s.* 15:24
who having received *s.* a 16:24
will be no judge of *s.* matters. 18:15
that they observe no *s.* thing. 21:25
Away with *s.* a fellow from. 22:22
I doubted of *s.* manner of. 25:20
and altogether *s.* as I am. 26:29
that are *s.* serve not. *Rom* 16:18
s. fornication as is not. *1 Cor* 5:1
and *s.* were some of you, but. 6:11
is not under bondage in *s.* cases. 7:15
s. shall have trouble in the flesh. 28
no temptation, but *s.* as is. 10:13
we have no *s.* custom. 11:16
s. are they that are earthy, *s.* 15:48
that ye submit yourselves to *s.* 16:16
acknowledge ye them that are *s.* 18
sufficient to *s.* a man is. *2 Cor* 2:6
s. trust we have through Christ. 3:4
seeing then that we have *s.* hope. 12
let *s.* an one think, *s.* as we are in word by letters, *s.* will we. 10:11
for *s.* are false apostles. 11:13
not find you *s.* as I would; and that I shall be found to you *s.* as. 12:20
meekness, against *s.* *Gal* 5:23
spot or wrinkle, or any *s.* *Eph* 5:27
receive him, and hold *s.* *Phil* 2:29
is the avenger of all *s.* *1 Thes* 4:6
now them that are *s.* *2 Thes* 3:12
corrupt men, from *s.* *1 Tim* 6:5
traitors, heady, from *s.* *2 Tim* 3:5
he that is *s.* is subverted. *Tit* 3:11
ye are become *s.* as have. *Heb* 5:12
s. an high priest became us. 7:26
have *s.* an high priest, who is. 8:1
endured *s.* contradiction of. 12:3
for with *s.* sacrifices God is. 13:16
we will go into *s.* a city. *Jas* 4:13
all *s.* rejoicing is evil. 16
came *s.* a voice to him. *2 Pet* 1:17
we ought to receive *s.* *3 John* 8
s. as are in the sea. *Rev* 5:13
s. as was not since men were. 16:18
on *s.* the second death hath. 20:6

such *like*

and doeth not *s. like.* *Ezek* 18:14
revellings and *s. like.* *Gal* 5:21

such *a one*

find *s. a one* as this is. *Gen* 41:38
ho, *s. a one*, turn aside. *Ruth* 4:1
open thine eyes on *s. a one*? *Job* 14:3
I was *s. a one* as thyself. *Ps* 50:21
hairy scalp of *s. a one* as. 68:21
to deliver *s. an one.* *1 Cor* 5:5
if a drunkard, with *s. an one.* 11
s. a one be swallowed up. *2 Cor* 2:7
let *s. an one* think this, that. 10:11
s. an one caught up to the. 12:2
of *s. an one* will I glory, yet. 5
restore *s. an one* in the. *Gal* 6:1
I beseech thee, being *s. an one* as Paul. *Philem* 9

such *and* **such**

appointed my servants to *s. and s.* place. *1 Sam* 21:2
given *s. and s.* things. *2 Sam* 12:8
in *s. and s.* a place shall. *2 Ki* 6:8

such *things*

they lent *s. things* as. *Ex* 12:36
s. things have befallen. *Lev* 10:19
they that do *s. things.* *Deut* 25:16
nor have told us *s. things* as these. *Judg* 13:23
Why do ye *s. things*? *1 Sam* 2:23
shall eat *s. things* as. *2 Ki* 19:29
the captain took *s. things* as. 25:15
there are no *s. things* done as thou. *Neh* 6:8
with *s. things* as belonged. *Esth* 2:9
yea, who knoweth not *s. things* as? *Job* 12:3
I have heard many *s. things.* 16:2
and many *s. things* are with. 23:14
who hath heard *s. things.* *Jer* 18:13
shall he escape that doth *s. things*? *Ezek* 17:15
no king asked *s. things.* *Dan* 2:10
many other *s.* like *things* ye do. *Mark* 7:8, 13
troubled, *s. things* must. *Mark* 13:7
of whom I hear *s.* things? *Luke* 9:9
remain, eating *s. things* as. 10:7, 8
but give alms of *s. things.* 11:41
because they suffered *s. things.* 13:2
the people murmured *s. things.* *John* 7:32
no accusation of *s. things.* *Acts* 25:18
they laded us with *s. things* as. 28:10
who commit *s. things* are. *Rom* 1:32
them who commit *s. things.* 2:2
judgest them which do *s. things.* 3
that do *s. things* shall not inherit. *Gal* 5:21
they that say *s. things.* *Heb* 11:14
be content with *s. things* as. 13:5
that ye look for *s. things.* *2 Pet* 3:14

suck

made him to *s.* honey. *Deut* 32:13
shall *s.* of the abundance of. 33:19
breast that I should *s.*? *Job* 3:12
he shall *s.* the poison of asps. 20:16
young ones also *s.* up blood. 39:30
shalt *s.* the milk of the Gentiles, and shalt *s.* the breast of. *Isa* 60:16
that ye may *s.* and be satisfied. 66:11
then shall ye *s.*, ye shall be borne. 12
drink it and *s.* it out. *Ezek* 23:34*
and those that *s.* breasts. *Joel* 2:16

suck, *give*

that Sarah should have given children *s.* *Gen* 21:7
Hannah abode and gave her son *s.* *1 Sam* 1:23
to give my child *s.* *1 Ki* 3:21
the sea monsters give *s.* *Lam* 4:3
and to them that give *s.* *Mat* 24:19
Mark 13:17; *Luke* 21:23
paps that never gave *s.* *Luke* 23:29

sucked

that *s.* the breasts of. *S of S* 8:1
paps that thou hast *s.* *Luke* 11:27

sucking

nursing father beareth the *s.* child. *Num* 11:12
Samuel took a *s.* lamb. *1 Sam* 7:9
s. child shall play on the. *Isa* 11:8
woman forget her *s.* child? 49:15
tongue of the *s.* child. *Lam* 4:4

suckling

the *s.* also with the man. *Deut* 32:25
slay both man and woman, infant and *s.* *1 Sam* 15:3
off from you child and *s.* *Jer* 44:7

sucklings

children and *s.* of Nob. *1 Sam* 22:19
out of the mouth of babes and *s.* *Ps* 8:2; *Mat* 21:16
s. swoon in the streets. *Lam* 2:11

sudden

s. fear troubleth thee. *Job* 22:10
be not afraid of *s.* fear. *Pr* 3:25
s. destruction cometh. *1 Thes* 5:3

suddenly

man die very *s.* by him. *Num* 6:9
the Lord spake *s.* unto Moses. 12:4
but if he thrust him *s.* without. 35:22
Lord will destroy you *s.* *Deut* 7:4*
Joshua came unto them *s.* *Josh* 10:9; 11:7
lest he overtake us *s.* *2 Sam* 15:14*
the thing was done *s.* *2 Chr* 29:36
taking root, but *s.* I cursed. *Job* 5:3
scourge slay *s.* he will laugh. 9:23
return and be ashamed *s.* *Ps* 6:10
s. do they shoot at him and. 64:4
with an arrow *s.* shall they be. 7
therefore his calamity shall come *s.*; he shall be broken *s.* *Pr* 6:15
calamity shall rise *s.* 24:22
shall *s.* be destroyed, and. 29:1
it falleth *s.* upon them. *Eccl* 9:12
it shall be at an instant *s.* *Isa* 29:5
whose breaking cometh *s.* 30:13
shall come upon thee *s.* 47:11
I did them *s.* and they came. 48:3
s. are my tents spoiled. *Jer* 4:20
spoiler shall *s.* come upon us. 6:26
caused him to fall upon it *s.* 15:8
bring a troop *s.* on them. 18:22
s. make him run away. 49:19; 50:44
Babylon is *s.* fallen and. *Jer* 51:
shall they not rise up *s.* *Hab* 2:
the Lord shall *s.* come. *Mal* 3:
s. saw no man any more. *Mark* 9:
lest coming *s.* he find you. 13:3
s. there was with angel. *Luke* 2:1
a spirit taketh him, and he *s.* 9:3
and *s.* there came a sound. *Acts* 2:
s. there shined a light. 9:3; 22:
and *s.* there was a great. 16:2
should have fallen down dead *s.* 28:
lay hands *s.* on no man. *1 Tim* 5:22

sue

if any man will *s.* thee. *Mat* 5:40

suffer

This word frequently means [1] bear, Pr 19:19; [2] bear with, Ma 17:17; [3] permit, 1 Tim 2:12.

s. the destroyer to come. *Ex* 12:2
thou shalt not *s.* a witch to. 22:1
nor shalt *s.* salt of the covenant to. *Lev* 2:1
shalt rebuke him, and not *s.* 19:1
or *s.* them to bear the iniquity. 22:16
not *s.* Israel to pass. *Num* 21:2
s. them not to enter. *Josh* 10:1
not *s.* them to come down to the valley. *Judg* 1:3
would not *s.* him to go in. 15:
Samson said, *S.* me that I. 16:2
not *s.* the revengers of blood any. *2 Sam* 14:11
that he might not *s.* *1 Ki* 15:1
king's profit to *s.* them. *Esth* 3:
he will not *s.* me to take. *Job* 9:1
s. me that I may speak, after. 21:
winepresses, and *s.* thirst. 24:1
s. me a little, and I will shew. 32:
trouble which I *s.* of them. *Ps* 9:1
neither *s.* thine Holy One to see corruption. 16:10; *Acts* 2:27; 13:3
young lions do lack and *s.* *Ps* 34:1
he will never *s.* the righteous. 55:2
while I *s.* thy terrors, I am. 88:1
nor *s.* my faithfulness to. 89:3
a proud heart will not I *s.* 101:
he will not *s.* thy foot to be. 121:
s. the soul of righteous to. *Pr* 10:
an idle soul shall *s.* hunger. 19:1
man of wrath shall *s.* punishment. 19
s. not thy mouth to cause. *Eccl* 5:
rich not *s.* him to sleep. 1
nor *s.* their locks to. *Ezek* 44:2
S. it to be so now. *Mat* 3:1
s. me first to bury my father. 8:2
Luke 9:5
s. us to go away into the swine. *Mat* 8:31; *Luke* 8:3
that he must *s.* many things of the elders. *Mat* 16:21; 17:1
Mark 8:31; 9:12; *Luke* 9:22; 17:2
how long shall I *s.* you? *Mat* 17:17
Mark 9:19*; *Luke* 9:41
s. little children to come. *Mat* 19:1
Mark 10:14; *Luke* 18:1
neither *s.* ye them that. *Mat* 23:1
ye *s.* him no more to do. *Mark* 7:1
Jesus would not *s.* any man to. 11:1
desired to eat this passover before *s.* *Luke* 22:1
s. ye thus far, and he touched his. 5
it behoved Christ to *s.* 24:4
Acts 3:18; 26:2
that Christ should *s.* *Acts* 3:1
counted worthy to *s.* shame. 5:4
seeing one of them *s.* wrong. 7:2
how great things he must *s.* for. 9:1
beseech thee, *s.* me to speak. 21:39
if so be that we *s.* with. *Rom* 8:1
if any man's work be burnt, he shall *s.* loss. *1 Cor* 3:1
bless; being persecuted, we *s.* 4:12
why not rather *s.* yourselves? 6:
not used this power but *s.* 9:12
will not *s.* you to be tempted. 10:1
one member *s.* all members *s.* 12:2
sufferings which we also *s.* *2 Cor* 1:
for ye *s.* fools gladly, seeing. 11:19
for ye *s.* if a man bring you. 20*
if I preach, why do I yet *s.*? *Gal* 5:11
lest they should *s.* persecution. 6:1
to believe and to *s.* for. *Phil* 1:2
to abound and to *s.* need. 4:12

efore, that we should s. 1 Thes 3:4
od for which ye also s. 2 Thes 1:5
s. not a woman to teach nor to.
1 Tim 2:12*
e both labour and s. 4:10*
also s. these things. 2 Tim 1:12
herein I s. trouble as an evil. 2:9
we s. we shall also reign. 12*
ll that live godly shall s. 3:12
ather to s. affliction. Heb 11:25*
emember them which s. 13:3*
. the word of exhortation. 22*
e do well, and s. for it. 1 Pet 2:20
ut if ye s. for righteousness. 3:14
t is better that ye s. for well. 17
one of you s. as a murderer. 4:15
et if any man s. as a Christian. 16
et them that s. according to the. 19
hose things thou shalt s. Rev 2:10
ot s. dead bodies to be put. 11:9

suffered

. I thee not to touch her. Gen 20:6
od s. him not to hurt me. 31:7
nd hast not s. me to kiss my. 28
nd s. thee to hunger. Deut 8:3
od hath not s. thee so to do. 18:14
. not a man to pass over. Judg 3:28
avid s. them not to rise. 1 Sam 24:7
nd s. not the birds. 2 Sam 21:10
e s. no man to do them wrong.
1 Chr 16:21; Ps 105:14
either have I s. my. Job 31:30
or thy sake I s. rebuke. Jer 15:15
to be so; then he s. him. Mat 3:15
loses s. you to put away your. 19:8
or s. his house to be broken. 24:43
Luke 12:39
have s. many things. Mat 27:19
e s. not the devils to speak.
Mark 1:34; Luke 4:41
owbeit, Jesus s. him not. Mark 5:19
. many things of many. 26
nd he s. no man to follow him. 37
loses s. to write a bill of. 10:4
e s. them to enter. Luke 8:32*
e s. no man to go in, save. 51
ere sinners, because they s. 13:2
hrist have s. these things? 24:26
bout forty years s. he. Acts 13:18†
ho s. all nations to walk in. 14:16
ut the Spirit s. them not. 16:7
hrist must needs have s. 17:3
isciples s. him not to enter. 19:30
aul was s. to dwell by. 28:16
is cause that s. wrong. 2 Cor 7:12
hrice I s. shipwreck. 11:25
. so many things in vain? Gal 3:4
or whom I have s. the loss. Phil 3:8
hat we had s. before. 1 Thes 2:2
e have s. like things of your. 14
imself hath s. being tempted.
Heb 2:18
bedience by things which he s. 5:8
hey were not s. to continue. 7:23*
or then must he often have s. 9:26
esus also s. without the gate. 13:12
hrist s. for us, leaving. 1 Pet 2:21
when he s. he threatened not. 23
or Christ hath once s. for sins. 3:18
s Christ hath s. for us in the flesh:
he that hath s. in the flesh. 4:1
fter ye have s. a while. 5:10

sufferest

s. that woman Jezebel. Rev 2:20

suffereth

bless God who s. not our. Ps 66:9
and s. not their cattle to. 107:38
of heaven s. violence. Mat 11:12
yet vengeance s. him. Acts 28:4
charity s. long and is kind, envieth
not. 1 Cor 13:4

suffering

wind not s. us, we sailed. Acts 27:7
s. of death, crowned. Heb 2:9
for an example of s. affliction, and of
patience. Jas 5:10
if a man endure grief, s. 1 Pet 2:19
an example, s. the vengeance, Jude 7

sufferings

I reckon that the s. of. Rom 8:18
for as the s. of Christ. 2 Cor 1:5
enduring the same s. which we. 6

ye are partakers of the s. 2 Cor 1:7
the fellowship of his s. Phil 3:10
who now rejoice in my s. Col 1:24
make the captain of their salvation
perfect through s. Heb 2:10
the s. of Christ, and the. 1 Pet 1:11
ye are partakers of Christ's s. 4:13
am a witness of the s. of Christ. 5:1

suffice

to s. them? or shall fish of the sea be
gathered together to s.? Num 11:22
let it s. thee; speak no. Deut 3:26
if dust of Samaria shall s. for.
1 Ki 20:10
let it s. you of all. Ezek 44:6; 45:9
may s. to have wrought. 1 Pet 4:3

sufficed

yet so they s. them not. Judg 21:14
she did eat, and was s. Ruth 2:14
she had reserved, after she was s. 18

sufficeth

us the Father and it s. us. John 14:8

sufficiency

in fulness of his s. he shall. Job 20:22
sufficient, but our s. is of. 2 Cor 3:5
s. in all things ye may abound. 9:8

sufficient

had was s. for work. Ex 36:7
thou shalt lend him s. Deut 15:8
let his hand be s. for him, thou. 33:7
honey as is s. for thee. Pr 25:16
Lebanon is not s. to burn, nor the
beasts thereof s. for. Isa 40:16
s. unto the day is the evil. Mat 6:34
whether he have s. to. Luke 14:28
200 penny-worth of bread is not s.
John 6:7
s. to such a man is this. 2 Cor 2:6
who is s. for these things? 16
not that we are s. of ourselves. 3:5
he said to me, My grace is s. 12:9

sufficiently

sanctified themselves s. 2 Chr 30:3
before the Lord to eat s. Isa 23:18

suit

give thee a s. of apparel. Judg 17:10
man who hath any s. 2 Sam 15:4
yea, many shall make s. Job 11:19

suits

changeable s. of apparel. Isa 3:22*

sum

there be laid on him a s. Ex 21:30*
takest the s. of the children of. 30:12
this is the s. of the tabernacle. 38:21
take the s. of all the. Num 1:2; 26:2
not take the s. of the Levites. 49
s. of the sons of Kohath. 4:2
the s. of the sons of Gershon. 22
s. of people from twenty years. 26:4
take the s. of the prey that. 31:26
have taken the s. of the men. 49
Joab gave up the s. unto the king.
2 Sam 24:9; 1 Chr 21:5
may s. the silver brought. 2 Ki 22:4
the s. of money that. Esth 4:7*
how great is the s. of! Ps 139:17
thou sealest up the s. full of wisdom.
Ezek 28:12
Daniel told the s. of the. Dan 7:1
Abraham bought for a s. Acts 7:16*
with a great s. obtained I. 22:28
we have spoken this is the s. Heb 8:1

summer

s. and winter, day and. Gen 8:22
turned into drought of s. Ps 32:4
hast made s. and winter. 74:17
her meat in s. Pr 6:8; 30:25
he that gathereth in s. is a. 10:5
as snow in s. and as rain in. 26:1
the fowls shall s. upon. Isa 18:6
hasty fruit before the s. 28:4
the harvest is past, the s. Jer 8:20
as the chaff of the s. Dan 2:35
in s. and in winter shall. Zech 14:8
leaves, ye know that s. is. Mat 24:32
Mark 13:28; Luke 21:30

summer *chamber*

surely he covereth his feet in his s.
chamber. Judg 3:24†

summer *fruit*

bread and s. fruit for. 2 Sam 16:2
a basket of s. fruit. Amos 8:1, 2

summer *fruits*

Ziba brought 100 bunches of s. fruits.
2 Sam 16:1
shouting for thy s. fruits. Isa 16:9
wine and s. fruits. Jer 40:10, 12
fallen on s. fruits and vintage. 48:32
have gathered s. fruits. Mi 7:1

summer *house*

I will smite winter house with s.
house. Amos 3:15

summer *parlour*

sitting in a s. parlour. Judg 3:20†

sumptuously

fared s. every day. Luke 16:19

sun

(The sun has been the object of worship and adoration to the greatest part of the people of the East. It is thought to be the sun that the Phenicians worshipped under the name of Baal, *the Moabites under the name of Chemosh, the Ammonites by that of Moloch, and the Israelites by the name of Baal and by* the king of the host of heaven. *They did not separate his worship from that of the moon, whom they called* Astarte, *and the* queen of heaven)

when the s. went down. Gen 15:17
the s. was risen when Lot. 19:23
all night, because the s. was. 28:11
passed over Penuel, s. rose. 32:31
the s. moon, and stars made. 37:9
and when the s. waxed. Ex 16:21
if s. be risen, blood shall be. 22:3
and when the s. is down, he shall.
Lev 22:7; Deut 23:11
before the Lord against the s.
Num 25:4
seest the s. and moon. Deut 4:19
worshipped either the s. or. 17:3
shall the s. go down upon it. 24:15
fruits brought forth by s. 33:14
the going down of the s. Josh 1:4
as soon as the s. was down. 8:29
S. stand thou still upon. 10:12
and the s. stood still, and the. 13
as the s. when he goeth. Judg 5:31
Gideon returned before the s. 8:13*
as soon as the s. is up, thou. 9:33
they said to him before the s. 14:18
s. went down when they were. 19:14
by time the s. be hot. 1 Sam 11:9
the s. went down, they. 2 Sam 2:24
if taste bread or aught till the s. 3:35
thy wives in sight of this s. 12:11
this thing before Israel and the s. 12
morning when the s. riseth. 23:4
they rose, and s. shone. 2 Ki 3:22
also that burn incense to s. 23:5
burnt the chariot of the s. with fire. 11
opened till the s. be hot. Neh 7:3
is green before the s. Job 8:16
which commandeth the s. 9:7
I went mourning without the s. 30:28
if I beheld s. when it shined. 31:26
he set a tabernacle for s. Ps 19:4
they may not see the s. 58:8
shall fear thee as long as s. 72:5
be continued as long as the s. 17
prepared the light and the s. 74:16
for the Lord God is a s. 84:11
throne shall endure as the s. 89:36
the s. ariseth, they gather. 104:22
s. shall not smite thee by day. 121:6
made the s. to rule by day. 136:8
praise ye him, s. and moon. 148:3
s. also ariseth, and the s. Eccl 1:5
he hath not seen the s. nor. 6:5
profit to them that see the s. 7:11
for the eyes to behold the s. 11:7
while the s. or the stars be. 12:2
s. hath looked upon me. S of S 1:6
fair as moon, clear as the s. 6:10
the s. shall be ashamed. Isa 24:23
moon shall be as the light of the s.
and the light of the s. 30:26
gone down in s. dial, so the s. 38:8

nor shall the heat, nor s. Isa 49:10
s. shall be no more thy light. 60:19
s. shall no more go down, nor. 20
spread them before the s. Jer 8:2
her s. is gone down while it. 15:9
which giveth the s. for a light. 31:35
they worshipped the s. Ezek 8:16
cover the s. with a cloud. 32:7
s. and the moon shall be darkened.
Joel 2:10; 3:15; Mat 24:29
Mark 13:24; Luke 23:45
s. shall be turned into. Joel 2:31
I will cause the s. to go. Amos 8:9
s. did arise, and the s. beat on the head of Jonah. Jonah 4:8
the s. shall go down. Mi 3:6
but when the s. ariseth. Nah 3:17
s. and moon stood still. Hab 3:11
s. of righteousness arise. Mal 4:2
he maketh his s. to rise. Mat 5:45
when s. was up they were scorched.
13:6; Mark 4:6
righteous shine as the s. Mat 13:43
his face did shine as the s. 17:2
Rev 1:16; 10:1
when the s. did set they. Mark 1:32
when the s. was setting. Luke 4:40
shall be signs in the s. and. 21:25
the s. into darkness. Acts 2:20
blind, not seeing the s. for. 13:11
above the brightness of the s. 26:13
neither s. nor stars appeared. 27:20
is one glory of the s. 1 Cor 15:41
let not the s. go down. Eph 4:26
s. is no sooner risen. Jas 1:11
the s. became black as. Rev 6:12
nor shall the s. light on them. 7:16
third part of the s. was. 8:12
s. and the air were darkened. 9:2
a woman clothed with the s. 12:1
poured out his vial on the s. 16:8
angel standing in the s.; and he. 19:17
had no need of the s. 21:23; 22:5
see **goeth, going, rising**

under the **sun**

labour which he taketh under the s.?
Eccl 1:3; 2:18, 19, 20, 22; 5:18; 9:9
no new thing under the s. 1:9
all the works done under s.; all is vanity. 14; 2:17; 4:3; 8:17; 9:3
was no profit under the s. 2:11
I saw under the s. the place. 3:16
that are done under the s. 4:1
and I saw vanity under the s. 7
a sore evil I have seen under the s.
5:13; 6:1; 10:5
shall be after him under the s. 6:12
heart to every work under the s. 8:9
hath no better thing under the s. 15
in any thing under the s. 9:6
he hath given thee under the s. 9
I saw under the s. that race. 11
wisdom have I seen also under s. 13

sunder

cutteth the spear in s. Ps 46:9
he brake their bands in s. 107:14
cut the bars of iron in s. 16
stones that are beaten in s. Isa 27:9
I will cut in s. the bars of iron. 45:2
I will burst thy bonds in s. Nah 1:13
come and cut him in s. Luke 12:46

sundered

scales stick together, they cannot be s. Job 41:17

sundry

God who at s. times. Heb 1:1*

sung

they s. together by course. Ezra 3:11
day shall this song be s. Isa 26:1
when they had s. an hymn, they went.
Mat 26:30; Mark 14:26
they s. a new song, saying. Rev 5:9
they s. as it were a new song. 14:3

sunk

that the stone s. into. 1 Sam 17:49
and Jehoram s. down. 2 Ki 9:24
heathen are s. down in. Ps 9:15
no water, but mire: so Jeremiah s.
Jer 38:6
thy feet are s. in the mire, they. 22
her gates are s. into the. Lam 2:9
Eutychus s. down with. Acts 20:9*

sup

their faces shall s. up. Hab 1:9*
ready wherewith I may s. Luke 17:8
I will s. with him, and he. Rev 3:20

superfluity

lay apart all filthiness, s. Jas 1:21*

superfluous

man hath any thing s. Lev 21:18
lamb that hath any thing s. 22:23
the ministering, it is s. 2 Cor 9:1

superscription

(It was a custom among the Romans to write on a board the crime for which any man suffered death and to carry the board before him to execution)

is this image and s.? Mat 22:20
Mark 12:16; Luke 20:24
the s. of his accusation. Mark 15:26
Luke 23:38

superstition

questions against him of their own s.
Acts 25:19*

superstitious

in all things ye are too s. Acts 17:22*

supped

cup, when he had s. 1 Cor 11:25

supper

made a s. to his lords. Mark 6:21
makest a dinner or s. Luke 14:12
a certain man made a great s. 16
and sent his servant at s. time. 17
none bidden shall taste of my s. 24
likewise also the cup after s. 22:20
there they made Jesus a s.; Martha served. John 12:2
and s. being ended. 13:2
Jesus riseth from s. 4
leaned on his breast at s. 21:20
not to eat the Lord's s. 1 Cor 11:20
taketh before other his own s. 21
called to the marriage s. Rev 19:9
come to the s. of the great God. 17

supplant

brother will utterly s. Jer 9:4

supplanted

for he hath s. me these. Gen 27:36

supple

washed in water to s. Ezek 16:4*

suppliants

my s. shall bring mine. Zeph 3:10

supplication

and I have not made s. 1 Sam 13:12*
have respect to his s. 1 Ki 8:28
2 Chr 6:19
hearken thou to the s. 1 Ki 8:30
45:49; 2 Chr 6:35
and make s. to thee. 1 Ki 8:33, 47
2 Chr 6:24
eyes may be open to s. 1 Ki 8:52
praying all this prayer and s. 54
wherewith I have made s. 59
I have heard thy s. that thou. 9:3
what s. shall be made. 2 Chr 6:29
heard Manasseh's s. then. 33:13
and should make s. to. Esth 4:8
make thy s. to the Almighty. Job 8:5
make my s. to my judge. 9:15
heard my s.; receive my. Ps 6:9
Lord I made my s. 30:8; 142:1
hide not thyself from my s. 55:1
let my s. come before thee. 119:170
they shall make s. to thee. Isa 45:14
will present their s. to Lord. Jer 36:7
O king, let my s. be accepted. 37:20
I presented my s. before the. 38:26
let our s. be accepted before. 42:2
me to present your s. before. 9
and Daniel making s. Dan 6:11
while I was presenting my s. 9:20
he wept and made s. unto. Hos 12:4
accord in prayer and s. Acts 1:14*
with all prayer and s. in spirit for.
Eph 6:18
by prayer and s. let Phil 4:6

supplications

hearken to s. of thy. 2 Chr 6:21
their prayer and their s. 39
leviathan make many s.? Job 41:3
hear voice of my s. when I cry.
Ps 28:2; 140:6
because he hath heard the voice of my s. 28:6; 31:22; 116:1
attend to the voice of my s. 86:6
be attentive to my s. 130:2; 143:1
weeping and s. of Israel. Jer 3:21
come with weeping and with s. 31:9
to seek by prayer and s. Dan 9:3
prayer of thy servant and his s. 17
we do not present our s. for. 18
at the beginning of thy s. the. 23
the Spirit of grace and s. Zech 12:10
the first of all s. be made. 1 Tim 2:1
she continueth in s. and prayers. 5:5
offered up prayers and s. Heb 5:7

supplied

your part, they have s. 1 Cor 16:17
what was lacking to me, the brethren s. 2 Cor 11:9

supplieth

not only s. the want of. 2 Cor 9:12*
that which every joint s. Eph 4:16

supply, *substantive*

a s. for their want, that their abundance be a s. for your. 2 Cor 8:14
through prayer and the s. Phil 1:19

supply, *verb*

his life to s. lack of service. Phil 2:30
but my God shall s. all your. 4:19

support

ye ought to s. the weak. Acts 20:35*
1 Thes 5:14

suppose

let not my lord s. that. 2 Sam 13:32
I s. that he to whom. Luke 7:43
s. ye that I am come to give? 12:51
s. ye that these Galileans? 13:2
I s. the world could not. John 21:25
not drunken, as ye s. Acts 2:15
I s. that this is good. 1 Cor 7:26
I s. I was not behind. 2 Cor 11:5
sorer punishment s. ye? Heb 10:29
a faithful brother, as I s. 1 Pet 5:12

supposed

they s. they should have. Mat 20:10
s. it had been a spirit. Mark 6:49
Jesus being, as was s. Luke 3:23
terrified and s. that they. 24:37
for he s. his brethren. Acts 7:25
whom they s. that Paul had. 21:29
acusation of such things as I s. 25:18
I s. it necessary to send. Phil 2:25

supposing

they s. him to have been. Luke 2:44
she s. him to be the gardener, saith.
John 20:15
who drew Paul out, s. Acts 14:19
jailor s. that the prisoners. 16:27
s. that they had obtained. 27:13
s. to add affliction to my. Phil 1:16
men of corrupt minds, s. 1 Tim 6:5

supreme

it be to the king as s. 1 Pet 2:13

sure

cave, were made s. Gen 23:17, 20
I am s. the king will. Ex 3:19
and be s. your sin. Num 32:23
only be s. that thou eat. Deut 12:23
build him a s. house. 1 Sam 2:35
s. that evil is determined by. 20
will make my Lord a s. house. 25:28
because I was s. that. 2 Sam 1:10
ordered in all things and s. 23:5
build thee a s. house. 1 Ki 11:38
we make a s. covenant. Neh 9:38
no man is s. of life. Job 24:22
testimony of the Lord is s. Ps 19:7
thy testimonies are very s. 93:5
all his commandments are s. 111:7
and make s. thy friend. Pr 6:3
that hateth suretiship, is s. 11:15
righteousness shall be s. reward. 18
as a nail in a s. place. Isa 22:23, 25
I lay in Zion for a s. 28:16
my people shall dwell in s. 32:18
given him; waters shall be s. 33:16
even the s. mercies of David. 55:3
Acts 13:34
interpretation thereof is s. Dan 2:45
thy kingdom shall be s. unto. 4:26

sepulchre be made s. *Mat* 27:64, 66
your way, make it as s. as you. 65
be s. of this, that the kingdom of God
is come nigh. *Luke* 10:11
believe and are s. that. *John* 6:69
we are s. that thou knowest. 16:30
s. that the judgement of. *Rom* 2:2
to end the promise might be s. 4:16
I am s. that when I come. 15:29
of God standeth s. *2 Tim* 2:19
hope we have as anchor s. *Heb* 6:19
to make your calling s. *2 Pet* 1:10
we have also a more s. word. 19

surely

eatest thereof, thou shalt s. die.
Gen 2:17
the woman, Ye shall not s. die. 3:4
and s. your blood of your lives. 9:5
Abraham shall s. become a. 18:18
her not, thou shalt s. die. 20:7
s. the fear of God is not in. 11
Jacob said, S. Lord is in this. 28:16
I will s. give the tenth unto. 22
Laban said, S. thou art my. 29:14
s. the Lord hath looked upon. 32
come in unto me, for s. I. 30:16
s. thou hadst sent me away. 31:42
and thou saidst, I will s. do. 32:12
s. ye are spies. 42:16
s. now we had returned this. 43:10
s. he is torn in pieces. 44:28
and I will also s. bring thee. 46:4
I die, God will s. visit you. 50:24
25; *Ex* 13:19
S. this thing is known. *Ex* 2:14
I have s. seen the affliction. 3:7, 16
she said, S. a bloody husband. 4:25
he shall s. thrust you out hence. 11:1
thou wilt s. wear away, thou. 18:18
but he shall s. be stoned. 19:13
he shall be s. punished. 21:20, 22
then the ox shall be s. stoned. 28
he shall s. pay ox for ox, dead. 36
he that kindleth fire shall s. 22:6
if it be hurt or die, he shall s. 14
if lie with her, he shall s. endow. 16
to me, I will s. hear their cry. 23
thou shalt s. bring it back to. 23:4
if thou see, thou shalt s. help. 5
if thou serve their gods, it will s. be
a snare. 33; *1 Ki* 11:2
anointing shall s. be an. *Ex* 40:15
s. it floweth with milk. *Num* 13:27
s. they shall not see the land. 14:23
I will s. do it to all this evil. 35
of man shalt thou s. redeem. 18:15
s. now I had slain thee, and. 22:33
s. there is no enchantment. 23:23
had said, They shall s. die. 26:65
s. give them a possession of. 27:7
s. none from twenty years old and.
32:11; *Deut* 1:35
s. this great nation is. *Deut* 4:6
testify this day that ye shall s. perish.
8:19; 30:18
shalt s. kill the idolater. 13:9
shalt s. smite the inhabitants. 15
shalt s. lend him sufficient. 15:8
shalt s. give thy poor brother. 10
shalt s. rejoice in the feast. 16:15
shalt s. help him to lift them. 22:4
the Lord will s. require thy. 23:21
and I will s. hide my face. 31:18
s. the land shall be thine. *Josh* 14:9
they said, S. he covereth. *Judg* 3:24
and Deborah said, I will s. go. 4:9
the Lord said to Gideon, S. I. 6:16
forth to meet me, shall s. be. 11:31
we will bind, but s. we will. 15:13
s. they are smitten down. 20:39
he saith cometh s. to. *1 Sam* 9:6
Agag said, S. the bitterness. 15:32
they said, S. to defy Israel. 17:25
for Saul thought, s. he is. 20:26
I knew it that Doeg would s. 22:22
I know well that thou shalt s. 24:20
s. in vain have I kept all. 25:21
s. there had not been left to. 34
s. thou shalt know what thy. 28:2
s. as the Lord liveth, thou. 29:6
pursue, for thou shalt s. 30:8
s. the people had gone up. *2 Sam* 2:27
I will s. shew thee kindness for. 9:7
he said, S. the men prevailed.
2 Sam 11:23
s. where the king shall be. 15:21
I will s. go forth with you. 18:2
she spake, They shall s. ask. 20:18
nay, but I will s. buy it of. 24:24
I have s. built thee house. *1 Ki* 8:13
I will s. rend the kingdom. 11:11
against the altar shall s. 13:32
I will s. shew myself unto. 18:15
s. we shall be stronger. 20:23, 25
they said, S. it is the king of. 22:32
s. were it not I regard. *2 Ki* 3:14
is blood, the kings are s. slain. 23
I thought, he will s. come out. 5:11
told me that thou shouldest s. 8:14
s. I have seen yesterday the. 9:26
the Lord will s. deliver us. 18:30
Isa 36:15
s. there was not holden. *2 Ki* 23:22
s. at command of the Lord. 24:3
not prevail, but shalt s. *Esth* 6:13
s. now he would awake for. *Job* 8:6
s. I would speak to the. 13:3
he will s. reprove you, if ye. 10
s. the mountain falling cometh. 14:18
s. such as are the dwellings. 18:21
s. he shall not feel quietness. 20:20
s. there is a vein for the silver. 28:1
s. take it upon my shoulder. 31:36
s. thou hast spoken in. 33:8
s. God will not do wickedly. 34:12
s. God will not hear vanity. 35:13
s. in the floods they. *Ps* 32:6
s. every man walketh in vain. 39:6
his beauty consumes, s. every. 11
s. thou didst set them in. 73:18
s. the wrath of man shall. 76:10
s. I will remember thy. 77:11
s. his salvation is nigh them. 85:9
s. he shall deliver thee from. 91:3
s. he shall not be moved. 112:6
s. I have behaved and quieted. 131:2
s. I will not come into my. 132:3
s. thou wilt slay the wicked. 139:19
s. the righteous shall give. 140:13
s. in vain the net is spread. *Pr* 1:17
s. he scorneth the scorners, but. 3:34
walketh uprightly, walketh s. 10:9
that giveth to the rich, shall s. 22:16
s. there is an end. 23:18
s. I am more brutish. 30:2
s. the churning of milk. 33
s. this also is vanity. *Eccl* 4:16
s. oppression maketh a wise. 7:7
s. it shall be well with them. 8:12
s. the serpent will bite. 10:11
will not believe, s. ye shall not be.
Isa 7:9
s. as I have thought so shall. 14:24
shall mourn, s. are stricken. 16:7
s. the princes of Zoan are. 19:11
s. this iniquity shall not be. 22:14
behold, the Lord will s. cover. 17
he will s. violently turn and toss. 18
s. your turning of things. 29:16
grass withereth, s. the people. 40:7
s. God is in thee, and there. 45:14
s. in Lord have I righteousness. 24
yet s. my judgement is with. 49:4
s. he hath borne our griefs. 53:4
they shall s. gather together. 54:15
s. the isles shall wait for me. 60:9
s. I will no more give thy corn. 62:8
he said S. they are my people. 63:8
s. his anger shall turn from. *Jer* 2:35
s. as a wife treacherously. 3:20
s. thou hast greatly deceived. 4:10
s. they swear falsely. 5:2
I said, S. these are poor. 4
I will s. consume them, saith. 8:13
s. our fathers have inherited. 16:19
yet s. I will make thee a. 22:6
s. thou shalt be ashamed for. 22
s. thus saith the Lord, so will. 24:8
ye shall s. bring innocent. 26:15
have s. heard Ephraim. 31:18
s. after that I was turned. 19
therefore I will s. have mercy. 20
but thou shalt s. be taken. 34:3
we will s. tell the king of all. 36:16
the Chaldeans shall s. depart. 37:9
this city shall s. be given. 38:3
I will s. deliver thee, thou. 39:18
we will perform our vows. *Jer* 44:25
my words shall s. stand against. 29
s. as Carmel by the sea, so. 46:18
unpunished, but s. drink it. 49:12
s. the least of the flock shall draw.
20; 50:45
saying, S. I will fill thee. 51:14
of recompences shall s. requite. 56
he shall s. live, because. *Ezek* 3:21
18:9, 17, 19, 21, 28; 33:13, 15, 16
s. because thou hast defiled my. 5:11
s. in the place where the king. 17:16
s. with a mighty hand will I. 20:33
he shall s. deal with him. 31:11
s. they in the wastes shall fall. 33:27
as I live, s. because my flock. 34:8
s. in the fire of my jealousy. 36:5
s. the heathen, they shall bear. 7
s. in that day there shall be a. 38:19
known that which shall s. *Hos* 5:9
s. they are vanity, they. 12:11
s. the Lord will do nothing. *Amos* 3:7
Gilgal shall s. go into captivity. 5:5
Israel shall s. be led away. 7:11, 17
s. I will never forget any of. 8:7
I will s. assemble, O Jacob, all of
thee, I will s. gather. *Mi* 2:12
because it will s. come. *Hab* 2:3
as I live, s. Moab shall. *Zeph* 2:9
s. thou wilt fear me, and. 3:7
s. thou also art one of them.
Mat 26:73; *Mark* 14:70
things which are most s. *Luke* 1:1
ye will s. say unto me this. 4:23
known s. that I came. *John* 17:8
saying, S. blessing, I will. *Heb* 6:14
S. I come quickly, even. *Rev* 22:20
see **die**

surely *be put to death*

toucheth this man, shall s. *be put to d.* *Gen* 26:11
whosoever toucheth the mount, shall
be s. put to d. *Ex* 19:12
killeth a man, shall *be s. put to d.*
21:12
smiteth his father, shall *be s. put to d.* 15
stealeth a man shall s. *be put to d.* 16
that curseth his father shall s. *be put to d.* 17; *Lev* 20:9
lieth with a beast, shall s. *be put to d.*
Ex 22:19; *Lev* 20:15, 16
defileth the sabbath shall s. *be put to d.* *Ex* 31:14, 15
to Moloch, s. *be put to d.* *Lev* 20:2
adulteress shall s. *be put to d.* 10
wife, both shall s. *be put to d.* 11
daughter in law, both shall s. *be put to d.* 12
with mankind, both s. *be put to d.* 13
blasphemeth, shall s. *be put to d.*
24:16
killeth any man, shall s. *be put to d.*
17; *Num* 35:16, 17, 18, 21, 31
redeemed, but shall s. *be put to d.*
Lev 27:29
came not up, shall s. *be put to d.*
Judg 21:5
not s. *put* me to *d.*? *Jer* 38:15

sureties

them that are s. for debts. *Pr* 22:26

suretiship

he that hateth s. is sure. *Pr* 11:15

surety

One who undertakes to pay another man's debt, in case the principal debtor, either through unfaithfulness or poverty, should prove insolent. It was an ancient custom in suretyship for the surety *to give his hand to, or strike hands with the creditor,* Job 17:3, Pr 6:1, 2.

I will be s. for him. *Gen* 43:9
for thy servant became s. for. 44:32
put me in a s. with thee. *Job* 17:3
be s. for thy servant. *Ps* 119:122
my son, if thou be s. for. *Pr* 6:1
he that is s. for a stranger. 11:15
and becometh s. in presence. 17:18
his garment that is s. for a stranger.
20:16; 27:13
Jesus made s. of a better. *Heb* 7:22

of a **surety**
know *of a s.* thy seed. *Gen* 15:13
shall I *of a s.* bear a child? 18:13
Abimelech said, Behold, *of a s.* 26:9
I know *of a s.* the Lord. *Acts* 12:11*

surfeiting
be overcharged with *s.* *Luke* 21:34

surmisings
cometh envy, strife, evil *s. 1 Tim* 6:4

surname
and *s.* himself by the name of Israel. *Isa* 44:5
Lebbaeus, whose *s.* was. *Mat* 10:3
Simon, whose *s.* is Peter. *Acts* 10:5
32; 11:13
John, whose *s.* was Mark. 12:12
25; 15:37*

surnamed
I have *s.* thee, though. *Isa* 45:4
and Simon he *s.* Peter. *Mark* 3:16
Acts 10:18
he *s.* them Boanerges. *Mark* 3:17
Satan entered into Judas, *s.* Iscariot. *Luke* 22:3*
Barsabas, who was *s.* *Acts* 1:23
Joses, who by the apostles was *s.* Barnabas. 4:36
to send Judas, *s.* Barsabas. 15:22*

surprised
sinners afraid, fearfulness *s.* *Isa* 33:14†
the strong holds are *s.* *Jer* 48:41
praise of the whole earth *s.*! 51:41

Susanna
Joanna and *S.* ministered. *Luke* 8:3

sustain
widow woman to *s.* thee. *1 Ki* 17:9
years didst thou *s.* them. *Neh* 9:21
the Lord, he shall *s.* thee. *Ps* 55:22
the spirit of a man will *s.* *Pr* 18:14

sustained
and wine have I *s.* him. *Gen* 27:37
for the Lord *s.* me. *Ps* 3:5
righteousness, it *s.* him. *Isa* 59:16

sustenance
left no *s.* for Israel. *Judg* 6:4
provided the king of *s. 2 Sam* 19:32
our fathers found no *s.* *Acts* 7:11

swaddled
those that I have *s.* hath. *Lam* 2:22*
salted at all nor *s.* at all. *Ezek* 16:4

swaddling
darkness a *s.* band for. *Job* 38:9
wrapped him in *s.* *Luke* 2:7, 12

swallow
(*The words* swallow *and* crane *are frequently interchanged in the old version of the Bible, so that the Revisions merely substitute the word* swallow *for* crane *and* crane *for* swallow *and the sense of the verse is not really changed.*
There are many varieties of this common bird found in Palestine)
the *s.* hath found a nest. *Ps* 84:3
as the *s.* by flying, so the. *Pr* 26:2
like a crane or a *s.* so. *Isa* 38:14
crane and *s.* observe. *Jer* 8:7

swallow, *verb*
earth open and *s.* them. *Num* 16:30
for they said, Lest the earth *s.* 34
why wilt thou *s.* up? *2 Sam* 20:19
far be it from me, that I should *s.* 20
let me alone till I *s.* down. *Job* 7:19
he shall restore, and not *s.* 20:18
the Lord shall *s.* them up. *Ps* 21:9
O God, man would *s.* me up. 56:1
would daily *s.* me up. 2
of him that would *s.* me up. 57:3
neither let the deep *s.* me up. 69:15
let us *s.* them up alive. *Pr* 1:12
lips of a fool will *s.* up. *Eccl* 10:12
will *s.* up death in victory. *Isa* 25:8
the strangers shall *s.* it up. *Hos* 8:7
hear this, O ye that *s.* up. *Amos* 8:4
drink, and they shall *s.* down. *Ob* 16
Lord prepared a fish to *s. Jonah* 1:17
at a gnat, and *s.* a camel. *Mat* 23:24

swallowed
but Aaron's rod *s.* up. *Ex* 7:12
right hand, the earth *s.* them. 15:12
earth opened and *s.* *Num* 16:32
26:10; *Deut* 11:6
lest the king be *s.* up. *2 Sam* 17:16
heavier than sand: therefore my words are *s.* up. *Job* 6:3*
he hath *s.* down riches, he. 20:15
surely he shall be *s.* up. 37:20
say, We have *s.* him up. *Ps* 35:25
the earth opened and *s.* up. 106:17
they had *s.* us up quick. 124:3
the priest and the prophet are *s.* up. *Isa* 28:7
they that *s.* thee up shall. 49:19
s. me up like a dragon. *Jer* 51:34
out of his mouth that which hath *s.* 44
hath *s.* up all the habitation of Jacob. *Lam* 2:2
he hath *s.* up Israel, he hath *s.* up. 5
they hiss and say, We have *s.* 16
because they have *s.* *Ezek* 36:3
Israel is *s.* up among the. *Hos* 8:8
death is *s.* up in victory. *1 Cor* 15:54
lest such one should be *s. 2 Cor* 2:7
that mortality might be *s.* up. 5:4
the earth opened and *s.* *Rev* 12:16

swalloweth
and the robber *s.* up. *Job* 5:5*
he *s.* the ground with. 39:24*

swan
the *s.*, the pelican, unclean. *Lev* 11:18*; *Deut* 14:16*

sware
(*The old form of the past tense of* swear)
Beersheba, because they *s.* both of them. *Gen* 21:31
the Lord God of heaven that *s.* 24:7
the servant *s.* to him concerning. 9
Swear to me, and he *s.* to him. 25:33
perform the oath which I *s.* 26:3
Abimelech and Isaac *s.* to one. 31
and Jacob *s.* by the fear of his. 31:53
Joseph *s.* to Jacob his father. 47:31
to this land he *s.* to Abraham. 50:24
the land which the Lord *s.* *Ex* 13:5
11; 33:1; *Num* 14:16, 30; 32:11
Deut 1:8, 35; 6:10, 18, 23; 7:13
8:1; 11:9, 21; 26:3; 28:11; 30:20
31:21, 23; 34:4; *Josh* 1:6; 5:6
21:43
anger was kindled, and he *s.* saying. *Num* 32:10; *Deut* 1:34
were wasted, as Lord *s.* *Deut* 2:14
Lord *s.* that I should not go. 4:21
not forget the covenant which he *s.* 31
which he *s.* to thy salvation. 7:12
covenant which he *s.* 8:18; 9:5
bring out Rahab, as ye *s.* *Josh* 6:22
princes of congregation *s.* to. 9:15
because of the oath which we *s.* 20
Moses *s.* on that day, saying. 14:9
rest according to all that he *s.* 21:44
brought to land which I *s.* *Judg* 2:1
Saul *s.* that David shall. *1 Sam* 19:6
David *s.* moreover to Jonathan. 20:3
David *s.* to Saul, and Saul. 24:22
Saul *s.* to her by the Lord, . . . no punishment. 28:10
David *s.* he would not eat till sun. *2 Sam* 3:35
king David *s.* to Shimei. 19:23
1 Ki 2:8
king David *s.* to. *1 Ki* 1:29, 30
Solomon *s.* that Adonijah. 2:23
Gedaliah *s.* to them. *2 Ki* 25:24
Jer 40:9
they *s.* to the Lord with. *2 Chr* 15:14
they *s.* to put away. *Ezra* 10:5
to whom I *s.* in my wrath. *Ps* 95:11
Heb 3:11
how he *s.* to Lord and vowed. 132:2
so the king *s.* secretly. *Jer* 38:16
I *s.* and entered into. *Ezek* 16:8
s. by him that liveth for ever. *Dan* 12:7; *Rev* 10:6
Herod *s.* to the daughter. *Mark* 6:23
remember oath which he *s.* to Abraham. *Luke* 1:73
to whom *s.* he that they. *Heb* 3:18
swear by no greater, he *s.* *Heb* 6:13
that said, The Lord *s.* and will. 7:21
see their **fathers**

swarest
to whom thou *s.* by thine. *Ex* 32:13
land thou *s.* to fathers. *Num* 11:12
land given us, as thou *s. Deut* 26:15
thou *s.* that Solomon. *1 Ki* 1:17
kindnesses thou *s.* to. *Ps* 89:49

swarm
there came a grievous *s.* *Ex* 8:24
a *s.* of bees and honey in. *Judg* 14:8

swarms
s. of flies upon thee, houses of the . . . be full of *s.* of flies. *Ex* 8:21
no *s.* of flies shall be in Goshen. 22
that the *s.* of flies may depart. 29
he removed the *s.* of flies from. 31

swear
In the Bible this has either the meaning of profanity, *which is forbidden, or of a solemn* asseveration, *which is allowed,* Lev 19:12; Ex 20:7; Deut 6:13; Jer 4:2.
to Abraham, *S.* to me. *Gen* 21:23
and Abraham said, I will *s.* 24
and I will make thee *s.* by. 24:3
my master made me *s.* saying. 37
Jacob said, *S.* to me, and he. 25:33
Jacob said unto Joseph, *S.* 47:31
my father made me *s.*, saying 50:5
concerning which I did *s.* *Ex* 6:8*
if a soul *s.* *Lev* 5:4
and ye shall not *s.* by my. 19:12
if man *s.* an oath to bind. *Num* 30:2
and thou shalt *s.* by his name. *Deut* 6:13; 10:20
Rahab said to spies, *S.* to me. *Josh* 2:12
which thou hast made us *s.* 17, 20
nor cause to *s.* by their gods. 23:7
s. to me that ye will. *Judg* 15:12
Jonathan caused David to *s.* again. *1 Sam* 20:17
s. that thou wilt not cut off my. 24:21
s. by God that thou wilt. 30:15
I *s.* by the Lord. *2 Sam* 19:7
didst not thou *s.* unto thine? *1 Ki* 1:13
saying, Let king Solomon *s.* 51
did I not make thee to *s.*? 2:42
an oath be laid on him to cause him to *s.* 8:31; *2 Chr* 6:22
made him *s.* by God. *2 Chr* 36:13
then Ezra made Levites and all Israel to *s.* *Ezra* 10:5
I made them *s.* by God. *Neh* 13:25
in that day shall he *s.* I. *Isa* 3:7*
five cities in Egypt shall *s.* 19:18
to me every tongue shall *s.* 45:23
which *s.* by the Lord, but not. 48:1
that sweareth, shall *s.* by. 65:16
shalt *s.*, The Lord liveth. *Jer* 4:2
Lord liveth, they *s.* falsely. 5:2
will ye *s.* falsely? 7:9
ways of my people, to *s.* by my name, as they taught people to *s.* 12:16
I *s.* by myself, saith the Lord. 22:5
them this land thou didst *s.* 32:22
up to Beth-aven nor *s.* *Hos* 4:15
they that *s.* by the sin. *Amos* 8:14
that *s.* by the Lord, that *s. Zeph* 1:5
s. not at all. *Mat* 5:34
s. not by thy head. 36
shall *s.* by the temple; *s.* by. 23:16
whoso shall *s.* by the altar. 18
shall *s.* by the altar, sweareth. 20
shall *s.* by the temple. 21
shall *s.* by heaven. 22
then began he to curse and *s.* 26:74
Mark 14:71
could *s.* by no greater, he *s. Heb* 6:13
for men verily *s.* by the greater. 16
my brethren, *s.* not. *Jas* 5:12

swearers
be a swift witness against false *s.* *Mal* 3:5

sweareth
what was lost, and *s.* *Lev* 6:3*
that *s.* to his hurt, and. *Ps* 15:4
every one that *s.* by him shall. 63:11
s. as he that feareth an oath. *Eccl* 9:2
he that *s.* shall swear by. *Isa* 65:16

and every one that *s*. shall. *Zech* 5:3
enter into the house of him *s*. 4
whosoever *s*. by the gift. *Mat* 23:18
s. by the altar. 20
s. by temple, and by him. 21
s. by throne of God, and by him. 22

swearing

and hear the voice of *s*. *Lev* 5:1*
because of *s*. the land. *Jer* 23:10
s. and lying, and stealing. *Hos* 4:2
have spoken words, *s*. falsely. 10:4

sweat

in the *s*. of thy face. *Gen* 3:19
any thing that causeth *s*. *Ezek* 44:18
his *s*. was as it were great drops of blood. *Luke* 22:44

sweep

I will *s*. it with the besom. *Isa* 14:23
the hail shall *s*. away the. 28:17
doth not *s*. the house. *Luke* 15:8

sweeping

is like a *s*. rain which. *Pr* 28:3

sweet

waters were made *s*. *Ex* 15:25
take of myrrh and *s*. 30:23
David the *s*. psalmist. *2 Sam* 23:1
eat the fat, and drink the *s*. *Neh* 8:10
wickedness be *s*. in. *Job* 20:12
valley shall be *s*. to him. 21:33
thou bind the *s*. influences ? 38:31*
took *s*. counsel together and walked. *Ps* 55:14
meditation of him shall be *s*. 104:34
how *s*. are thy words unto! 119:103
my words, for they are *s*. 141:6
and thy sleep shall be *s*. *Pr* 3:24
stolen waters are *s*., and bread. 9:17
the desire accomplished is *s*. 13:19
pleasant words are *s*. to the. 16:24
bread of deceit is *s*. to a man. 20:17
and lose thy *s*. words. 23:8
the honeycomb, which is *s*. 24:13
soul every bitter thing is *s*. 27:7
of a labouring man is *s*. *Eccl* 5:12
truly the light is *s*., and. 11:7
his fruit was *s*. *S of S* 2:3
for *s*. is thy voice. 14
dropped with *s*. smelling myrrh. 5:5*
cheeks as a bed of spices, as *s*. flowers: his lips like lilies, dropping *s*. 13*
his mouth is most *s*. yea, he is. 16
instead of *s*. smell, there. *Isa* 3:24
put bitter for *s*. and *s*. for bitter. 5:20
make *s*. melody, sing songs to. 23:16
your sacrifices *s*. unto me. *Jer* 6:20*
awaked, and my sleep was *s*. 31:26
same place *s*. water. *Jas* 3:11
thy mouth *s*. as honey. *Rev* 10:9, 10
see **incense, odours, savour**

sweet *calamus*

take of *s*. *calamus* 250. *Ex* 30:23

sweet *cane*

hast brought me no *s*. *cane* with money. *Isa* 43:24
the *s*. *cane* came from a. *Jer* 6:20

sweet *spices*

take to thee *s*. *spices*. *Ex* 30:34
pure incense of *s*. *spices*. 37:29
bought *s*. *spices* that they. *Mark* 16:1

sweet *wine*

blood as with *s*. *wine*. *Isa* 49:26
mount shall drop *s*. *wine*. *Amos* 9:13
and *s*. *wine*, but shalt not. *Mi* 6:15*

sweeter

men of city said, What is *s*. than ? *Judg* 14:18
s. also than honey. *Ps* 19:10
thy words are *s*. than honey. 119:103

sweetly

worm shall feed *s*. on him. *Job* 24:20
wine, that goeth down *s*. *S of S* 7:9*

sweetness

should I forsake my *s*.? *Judg* 9:11
of the strong came forth *s*. 14:14
s. of the lips increaseth. *Pr* 16:21
so doth *s*. of a man's friend. 27:9
roll was in my mouth as honey for *s*. *Ezek* 3:3

swell

and thy belly to *s*. *Num* 5:21, 22
her belly shall *s*. and her thigh. 27
nor did thy foot *s*. these. *Deut* 8:4

swelled

40 years their feet *s*. not. *Neh* 9:21

swelling

shake with *s*. thereof. *Ps* 46:3
as a breach *s*. out in a. *Isa* 30:13
do in the *s*. of Jordan ? *Jer* 12:5*
from the *s*. of Jordan. 49:19*; 50:44*
speak great *s*. words. *2 Pet* 2:18
speaking great *s*. words. *Jude* 16

swellings

I fear lest there be *s*. *2 Cor* 12:20

swept

the river of Kishon *s*. *Judg* 5:21
valiant men *s*. away ? *Jer* 46:15
house, when come, he findeth it empty, *s*. *Mat* 12:44; *Luke* 11:25

swerved

which some having *s*. *1 Tim* 1:6

swift

shall bring a nation as *s*. *Deut* 28:49
were as *s*. as roes on. *1 Chr* 12:8
passed away as the *s*. ships. *Job* 9:26
he is *s*. as the waters, he. 24:18
feet that be *s*. in running. *Pr* 6:18
race is not to the *s*. *Eccl* 9:11
go, ye *s*. messengers. *Isa* 18:2
Lord rideth upon a *s*. cloud. 19:1
we will ride on the *s*.: therefore shall they that pursue you be *s*. 30:16
your brethren on *s*. beasts. 66:20
s. dromedary traversing her ways. *Jer* 2:23
let not *s*. flee away, nor mighty. 46:6
flight shall perish from *s*. *Amos* 2:14
he that is *s*. of foot shall not. 15
bind the chariot to *s*. beast. *Mi* 1:13
I will be a *s*. witness. *Mal* 3:5
their feet are *s*. to shed. *Rom* 3:15
let every man be *s*. to hear. *Jas* 1:19
themselves *s*. destruction. *2 Pet* 2:1

swifter

s. than eagles, stronger. *2 Sam* 1:23
s. than a weaver's shuttle. *Job* 7:6
now my days are *s*. than a post. 9:25
horses are *s*. than eagles. *Jer* 4:13
our persecutors are *s*. *Lam* 4:19
their horses are *s*. than. *Hab* 1:8

swiftly

his word runneth very *s*. *Ps* 147:15
shall come with speed *s*. *Isa* 5:26
Gabriel being caused to fly *s*. *Dan* 9:21
if ye recompense me *s*. *Joel* 3:4

swim

stick, and the iron did *s*. *2 Ki* 6:6
make I my bed to *s*. *Ps* 6:6
spreadeth forth hands to *s*. *Isa* 25:11
risen, waters to *s*. in. *Ezek* 47:5
lest any of them should *s*. out and. *Acts* 27:42
that they who could *s*. 43

swimmest

the land wherein thou *s*. *Ezek* 32:6

swimmeth

as he that *s*. spreadeth. *Isa* 25:11

swine

the *s*. is unclean to you. *Lev* 11:7 *Deut* 14:8
as a jewel of gold in a *s*.'s. *Pr* 11:22
eat *s*.'s flesh, and broth of. *Isa* 65:4
oblation, as if he offered *s*.'s. 66:3
eating *s*.'s flesh, and abomination. 17
cast ye your pearls before *s*. *Mat* 7:6
an herd of *s*. feeding. 8:30 *Mark* 5:11; *Luke* 8:32
suffer us to go into the herd of *s*. *Mat* 8:31; *Mark* 5:12
they went into the *s*. . . . the whole herd of *s*. ran. *Mat* 8:32 *Mark* 5:13; *Luke* 8:33
they that fed the *s*. fled. *Mark* 5:14
them also concerning the *s*. 16
into his field to feed *s*. *Luke* 15:15
belly with husks the *s*. did eat. 16

swollen

when he should have *s*. *Acts* 28:6

swoon

because the children *s*. *Lam* 2:11

swooned

they *s*. as the wounded. *Lam* 2:12

sword

The sword in scripture is often used for war, Gen 27:40; Lev 26:2. *By* sword *is understood the judgements which God inflicts upon sinners,* Deut 3:41, 42; *also the instrument which God uses to execute his judgements,* Ps 17:13. Sword *is figuratively put for power and authority,* Rom 13:4. *The word of God is called the* sword of the Spirit, Eph 6:17. *Moses calls God* the sword of Israel's excellency, Deut 33:29. *He is their strength, the author of all their past or approaching victories, by whose assistance they did excel, and gloriously conquer, and triumph over their enemies.*

cherubims, and flaming *s*. *Gen* 3:24
took each man his *s*. and. 34:25
put a *s*. in their hands. *Ex* 5:21
he said, Put every man his *s*. 32:27
nor shall the *s*. go through. *Lev* 26:6
bring a *s*. upon you. 25; *Ezek* 5:17 6:3; 14:17; 29:8, 33:2
I will draw out a *s*. after. *Lev* 26:33
fall as it were before a *s*. 37
the angel's *s*. drawn. *Num* 22:23, 31
I would there were a *s*. in mine. 29
s. without, and terror. *Deut* 32:25
and who is the *s*. of thy! 33:29
stood with his *s*. drawn. *Josh* 5:13
not with thy *s*. nor with thy. 24:12
this is nothing save the *s*. *Judg* 7:14
say, The *s*. of the Lord, and. 18, 20
and the Lord set every man's *s*. 7:22; *1 Sam* 14:20
120,000 men that drew *s*. *Judg* 8:10
the youth drew not his *s*. for. 20
he said unto him, Draw thy *s*. 9:54
400,000 that drew *s*. 20:2, 17
26,000 men that drew *s*. 15
all these drew the *s*. 25
25,100 men that drew the *s*. 35
25,000 that drew the *s*. 46
neither *s*. nor spear. *1 Sam* 13:22
as thy *s*. hath made women. 15:33
his *s*. on his armour. 17:39; 25:13
but there was no *s*. in the. 17:50
David ran and took his *s*. 51
even to his *s*. and to his bow. 18:4
under thy hand a spear or *s*. 21:8
the *s*. of Goliath is here wrapt. 9
and he gave him the *s*. of. 22:10
given him bread, and a *s*. 13
Gird ye on every man his *s*. and they girded on every man his *s*. 25:13
draw thy *s*. and thrust me through therewith. . . . Saul took a *s*. and fell upon it. 31:4; *1 Chr* 10:4
armourbearer fell likewise upon his *s*. and died with him. *1 Sam* 31:5 *1 Chr* 10:5
the *s*. of Saul returned. *2 Sam* 1:22
and thrust his *s*. through. 2:16
Abner said, Shall the *s*. devour ? 26
fail one that falleth on the *s*. 3:29
the *s*. devoureth one as well. 11:25
the *s*. shall never depart from. 12:10
wood devoured more than *s*. 18:8
Amasa took no heed to the *s*. 20:10
his hand clave unto the *s*. 23:10
800,000 men that drew the *s*. 24:9
a *s*. and they brought a *s*. *1 Ki* 3:24
him that escapeth the *s*. of. 19:17
to bear buckler and *s*. *1 Chr* 5:18
men that drew *s*. and Judah was 470,000 that drew *s*. 21:5
that the *s*. of thine enemies overtake, or else three days the *s*. 12
the angel having a *s*. drawn. 16
and he put up his *s*. again into. 27
he was afraid, because of the *s*. 30
s. of judgement cometh. *2 Chr* 20:9
our kings are delivered to the *s*. *Ezra* 9:7
one had his *s*. girded. *Neh* 4:18
their enemies with the *s*. *Esth* 9:5

in war to deliver from power of the s. Job 5:20
and he is waited for of the s. 15:22
s.: for wrath bringeth the punishments of the s. 19:29
the glittering s. cometh. 20:25*
multiplied, it is for the s. 27:14
make his s. to approach. 40:19
the s. of him that layeth at. 41:26
turn not, he will whet his s. Ps 7:12
the wicked, which is thy s. 17:13
wicked have drawn out the s. 37:14
their s. shall enter into their. 15
gird thy s. on thy thigh. 45:3
and their tongue a sharp s. 57:4
who whet their tongue like a s. 64:3
brake he the shield and the s. 76:3
his people over unto the s. 78:62
twoedged s. in their hand. 149:6
is sharp as a twoedged s. Pr 5:4
like the piercings of a s. 12:18
beareth false witness is a s. 25:18
every man hath his s. upon his thigh. S of S 3:8
nation shall not lift up s. Isa 2:4
s., not of a mean man, shall. 31:8
the s. of the Lord is filled. 34:6
them as the dust to his s. 41:2
my mouth like a sharp s. 49:2
the famine and the s. are. 51:19
will I number you to the s. 65:12
by his s. will the Lord plead. 66:16
your own s. devoured. Jer 2:30
whereas the s. reacheth unto. 4:10
neither shall we see s. 5:12; 14:13
for the s. of the enemy is. 6:25
will send a s. after them. 9:16; 24:10
25:27; 29:17; 49:37
for the s. of the Lord shall. 12:12
Ye shall not see the s. 14:13
say, S. and famine shall not be. 15
in the streets because of the s. 16
are for the s., to the s. 15:2; 43:11
I will appoint the s. to slay. 15:3
them will I deliver to the s. 9
blood by the force of the s. 18:21
be mad because of the s. 25:16
I will call for a s. 29; Ezek 38:21
that are wicked to the s. Jer 25:31
the people left of the s. found. 31:2
city is given because of the s. 32:24
a liberty for you, to the s. 34:17
the s. ye feared shall overtake. 42:16
number which escape the s. 44:28
the s. shall devour and. 46:10, 14
O thou s. of the Lord, how? 47:6
O madmen, the s. shall pursue. 48:2
cursed that kepeeth back his s. 10
for fear of the oppressing s. 50:16
a s. is on the Chaldeans, saith. 35
a s. is on the liars, a s. is on. 36
a s. is on their horses, a s. on. 37
ye that have escaped the s. 51:50
by peril because of the s. Lam 5:9
I will draw out a s. Ezek 5:2, 12
I bring the s. upon thee. 17; 6:3
some that shall escape the s. 6:8
the s. is without, the pestilence. 7:15
the s. and I will bring a s. 11:8
if I bring a s. and say, S. go. 14:17
four sore judgements, the s. 21
prophesy and say, A s. a s. 21:9, 11
terrors, by reason of the s. on. 12
and what if the s. contemn? 13
s. be doubled, the s. of the great men slain, it is the s. of great men. 14
set the point of the s. against. 15
appoint two ways, that the s. 19
appoint a way, that s. may come. 20
the s. the s. is drawn for the. 28
s. shall come upon Egypt. 30:4
make it strong to hold the s. 21
I will cause the s. to fall out. 22
the s. of the king of Babylon. 32:11
if when he seeth the s. come. 33:3
if the s. come and take him. 4, 6
watchman see the s. come; if the s. come and take any person. 6
ye stand upon your s. and ye. 26
blood by the force of the s. 35:5
break the bow and the s. Hos 2:18
and the s. shall abide on. 11:6
will I command the s. Amos 9:4
nation shall not lift up s. Mi 4:3
will I give up to the s. Mi 6:14
the s. shall devour the. Nah 2:13
lifteth up both the bright s. 3:3
there the s. shall cut thee off. 15
made thee as the s. of. Zech 9:13
the s. shall be upon his arm. 11:17
O s. against my shepherd. 13:7
to send peace, but a s. Mat 10:34
one of them drew his s. and. 26:51
Mark 14:47; John 18:10
put up again thy s. Mat 26:52
John 18:11
a s. shall pierce through. Luke 2:35
he that hath no s. let him buy. 22:36
he drew his s. and. Acts 16:27
separate us? shall s.? Rom 8:35
for he beareth not the s. in. 13:4
s. of the Spirit, which is. Eph 6:17
than any twoedged s. Heb 4:12
went a twoedged s. Rev 1:16
which hath the sharp s. with. 2:12
given to him a great s. 6:4
mouth goeth a sharp s. 19:15, 21

by the **sword**

by the s. thou shalt live. Gen 27:40
shall fall before you by the s. Lev 26:7, 8
were fallen by the s. 2 Sam 1:12
have fallen by the s. 2 Chr 29:9
from perishing by the s. Job 33:18
they shall perish by the s. 36:12
got not the land by their s. Ps 44:3
their priests fell by the s. 78:64
Lord, Their young men shall die by the s. Jer 11:22; 18:21; Lam 2:21
consume them by the s. Jer 14:12
by s. and famine shall those. 15
shall be consumed by the s. 16:4
44:12, 18, 27
cause them to fall by the s. 19:7
abideth, shall die by the s. 21:9
38:2; 42:17, 22
why will ye die by the s.? 27:13
shall be delivered by the s. 32:36
are thrown down by the s. 33:4
thou shalt not die by the s. 34:4
punished Jerusalem by the s. 44:13
shall be slain by the s. Ezek 26:6
he shall slay thy people by the s. 11
be judged in her by the s. 28:23
them that be slain by the s. 31:18
32:20, 21, 22, 25, 30; 33:27
so they fell all by the s. 39:23
not save them by bow, nor by s. Hos 1:7
Jeroboam shall die by the s. Amos 7:11
people shall die by the s. 9:10
every one by the s. Hag 2:22
had the wound by a s. Rev 13:14

see **edge, fall**

from the **sword**

delivered me from the s. of. Ex 18:4
as fleeing from a s. Lev 26:36
him that escapeth from the s. of Jehu. 1 Ki 19:17
that escaped from the s. 2 Chr 36:20
saveth poor from the s. Job 5:15
turneth he back from the s. 39:22
deliver my soul from the s.; my darling from the power. Ps 22:20
David from the hurtful s. 144:10
fled from the drawn s. Isa 21:15
but he shall flee from the s. 31:8
such as are left from the s. Jer 21:7
let us go from the oppressing s. 46:16
few men of them from s. Ezek 12:16
is brought back from the s. 38:8

my **sword**

from Amorite with my s. Gen 48:22
I will draw my s. my. Ex 15:9
I whet my glittering s. Deut 32:41
and my s. shall devour flesh. 42
neither brought my s. 1 Sam 21:8
neither shall my s. save me. Ps 44:6
for my s. shall be bathed. Isa 34:5
I will draw my s. out. Ezek 21:3
therefore my s. shall go out of. 4
I the Lord have drawn my s. out. 5
I have put my s. in his. 30:24, 25
when I shall brandish my s. 32:10
shall be slain by my s. Zeph 2:12

with the **sword**

captives taken with the s. Gen 31:26
lest he fall on us with the s. Ex 5:3
I will kill you with the s. 22:24
toucheth one slain with the s. Num 19:16
out against thee with the s. 20:18
Balaam also they slew with the s. 31:8
the Lord shall smite thee with the s. Deut 28:22
whom Israel slew with the s. Josh 10:11; 13:22
king of Hazor with the s. 11:10
comest to me with a s. 1 Sam 17:45
the Lord saveth not with s. and. 47
killed Uriah with the s. 2 Sam 12:9
a girdle with a s. fastened. 20:8
being girded with a s. 21:16
will not slay his servant with the s. 1 Ki 1:51
not put thee to death with the s. 2:8
and slew them with the s. 32
slain all the prophets with the s. 19:1
slain thy prophets with the s. 10, 14
young men wilt thou slay with the s. 2 Ki 8:12
and him that followeth her, kill with the s. 11:15; 2 Chr 23:14
they slew Athaliah with the s. 2 Ki 11:20; 2 Chr 23:21
Sennacherib king of Assyria with the s. 2 Ki 19:37; 2 Chr 32:21
Isa 37:38
his brethren with the s. 2 Chr 21:4
their young men with the s. 36:17
as with a s. in my bones. Ps 42:10
be devoured with the s. Isa 1:20
slain, thrust through with a s. 14:19
men are not slain with the s. 22:2
the Lord with his strong s. 27:1
thy cities with the s. Jer 5:17
behold the slain with the s. 14:18
shall slay Judah with the s. 20:4
who slew Urijah with the s. 26:23
nation will I punish with the s. 27:8
persecute them with the s. 29:18
smote Gedaliah with the s. 41:2
that be slain with the s. Lam 4:9
shall die with the s. Ezek 7:15
slew her with the s. 23:10
daughters of Tyrus with the s. 26:8
with them that be slain with the s. 31:17; 32:28, 32; 35:8
his brother with the s. Amos 1:11
men have I slain with the s. 4:10
house of Jeroboam with the s. 7:9
slay the last of them with the s. 9:1
the land of Assyria with the s. Mi 5:6
s. shall perish with the s. Mat 26:52
we smite with the s.? Luke 22:49
killed James with the s. Acts 12:2
were tempted, were slain with the s. Heb 11:37
against them with the s. Rev 2:16
and power to kill with s. and. 6:8
with s. must be killed with s. 13:10
remnant were slain with the s. 19:21

swords

Hebrews make them s. 1 Sam 13:19
700 men that drew s. 2 Ki 3:26
the people with their s. Neh 4:13
his words were drawn s. Ps 55:21
behold, they belch out, s. are. 59:7
whose teeth are as s. Pr 30:14
they all hold, s., being. S of S 3:8
beat their s. into plowshares and their spears. Isa 2:4; Mi 4:3
they fled from the s. and. Isa 21:15
thrust thee through with their s. Ezek 16:40
dispatch them with their s. 23:47
strangers shall draw their s. 28:7
they shall draw their s. 30:11
by the s. of the mighty will. 32:12
they have laid their s. under. 27
your plowshares into s. Joel 3:10
a great multitude with s. from the chief. Mat 26:47; Mark 14:43
as against a thief with s. and staves to take me? Mat 26:55
Mark 14:48; Luke 22:52
behold, here are two s. Luke 22:38

sworn

by myself have I *s.* saith the Lord.
Gen 22:16; *Isa* 45:23; *Jer* 49:13
51:14; *Amos* 6:8
had straitly *s.* Israel. *Ex* 13:19
the Lord hath *s.* that he will. 17:16
about which he hath *s.* *Lev* 6:5
would keep the oath he had *s.*
Deut 7:8; *Jer* 11:5
multiply thee, as he hath *s.* to thy fathers. *Deut* 13:17
thy coast, as he hath *s.* 19:8
shall establish thee, as he hath *s.*
28:9; 29:13
to land Lord hath *s.* 31:7; *Neh* 9:15
because the princes had *s.* *Josh* 9:18
we have *s.* to them by the Lord. 19
2 Sam 21:2
for evil, as Lord had *s.* *Judg* 2:15
now the men of Israel had *s.* 21:1
we have *s.* not to give them. 7, 18
I have *s.* unto the house of Eli.
1 Sam 3:14
forasmuch as we have *s.* 20:42
Lord hath *s.* to David. *2 Sam* 3:9
children of Israel had *s.* to. 21:2
they had *s.* with all. *2 Chr* 15:15
many in Judah *s.* to. *Neh* 6:18
the land which thou hadst *s.* 9:15*
who hath not *s.* deceitfully. *Ps* 24:4
I have *s.* unto David my. 89:3
s. by my holiness that. 35; *Amos* 4:2
are mad against me, are *s.* *Ps* 102:8
the Lord hath *s.* and will. 110:4
I have *s.* and I will. 119:106
the Lord hath *s.* in truth to. 132:11
the Lord of hosts hath *s.* *Isa* 14:24
I have *s.* by myself, the word. 45:23
I have *s.* that waters of Noah no more go over the earth, so have I *s.* 54:9
Lord hath *s.* by his right hand. 62:8
they have *s.* by them. *Jer* 5:7
have *s.* by my great name. 44:26
them that have *s.* oaths. *Ezek* 21:23
hath *s.* by the excellency. *Amos* 8:7
the mercy thou hast *s.* *Mi* 7:20
knowing God hath *s.* by. *Acts* 2:30
drew nigh which God had *s.* 7:17*
I have *s.* in my wrath. *Heb* 4:3

sycamine

say to this *s.* tree, Be. *Luke* 17:6

sycamore, *see* **sycomore**

sycomore

This tree is not the sycamore *of England and America but an entirely different tree, the Egyptian fig tree, or* fig-mulberry. *It spreads its branches widely, making a delightful shade, for which reason it was often planted by the roadside,* Luke 19:4. *Its fruit was much like a fig, but to make it eatable it used to be thought necessary to puncture it three or four days before it was ripe,* Amos 7:14. *But this is not done now, the fruit ripening in the ordinary manner. The value of the tree was mainly in its timber.*

sycomore *fruit*

a gatherer of *s. fruit.* *Amos* 7:14

sycomore *tree*

climbed up into a *s. tree.* *Luke* 19:4

sycomore *trees*

Solomon made cedars to be as *s. trees.* *1 Ki* 10:27; *2 Chr* 1:15; 9:27
over the *s. trees* was Baal-hanan.
1 Chr 27:28
destroyed their *s. trees.* *Ps* 78:47

sycomores

the *s.* are cut down, but. *Isa* 9:10

synagogue

This word is found only once in the Old Testament in Ps 74:8, *and there is no indication that synagogues existed before the Exile, although there are some reasons to think that they were in existence centuries earlier. As to* Ps 74:8, They have burned up all the *synagogues* of God in the land; *the original is,* all the assemblies of God, *by which must be understood the places where the people assembled to worship God. But this does not infer that those places were what we now mean by synagogues. After the Maccabaean period there were synagogues in every settlement where there were enough Jews to erect one. It is said that there were in the city of Jerusalem alone no less than four hundred and sixty, or even four hundred and eighty; but this is most probably an exaggeration. Every trading fraternity had a* synagogue *of their own, and even strangers built some for those of their own nation. Hence it is, that in* Acts 6:9, *mention is made of the* synagogues of the Libertines, Cyrenians, Alexandrians, Cilicians, and Asiatics; *which were appointed for the use of such of the inhabitants of these cities, or of these nations, as should at any time be at Jerusalem. The synagogue worship became the regular worship of the people outside of Jerusalem, the temple being visited at one or more of the great feasts.*

In Palestine the synagogue was so built that the worshipper would face Jerusalem. At the upper end was the chest which contained the Book of the Law. Here were the chief seats *so desired by the Pharisees,* Mat 23:6; Jas 2:2, 3. *In later times the congregation was divided, men on one side and women on the other, with a lattice partition between.*

The word is used in the New Testament [1] *for the building,* Luke 7:5. [2] *For the* organization *which worshipped there,* Acts 6:9. *The* ruler of the synagogue *was the one who had the responsibility of maintaining order, deciding on the order of public worship, etc.,* Luke 8:41; Acts 18:8. The minister *had duties of a lower kind, more like those of a modern deacon, or of a sacristan.*

Worship was held in the synagogue every sabbath, and every feast day, the main part of the service being the reading of the law, with an exposition of what was read, Acts 15:21; 13:15.

The ordinary school for Jewish children was in the synagogue of each village. Every boy was supposed to attend, and the teaching was mostly in the Law and other Scriptures.

The organization of the synagogue, where possible, included a council of the elders; and in these cases they had a certain amount of judicial power, Mat 10:17.

The synagogue of the Libertines, or freedmen, Acts 6:9, *was, according to most interpreters, that of those Jews, who having been led away captive by Pompey and others, had afterwards recovered their liberty, and returned to Jerusalem, when Tiberias drove the Jews out of Italy.*

he went into their *s.* *Mat* 12:9
he taught them in their *s.* 13:54
Mark 6:2
and there was in their *s.* a man with.
Mark 1:23; *Luke* 4:33
when they were come out of the *s.*
Mark 1:29; *Luke* 4:38
one of the rulers of the *s.* besought.
Mark 5:22, 36, 38; *Luke* 8:41, 49
he went into the *s.* on the sabbath.
Luke 4:16
the eyes of all in the *s.* were. 20
nation and hath built us a *s.* 7:5
things said he in the *s.* *John* 6:59
he should be put out of the *s.*
John 9:22
they should be put out of *s.* 12:42
I ever taught in the *s.* and. 18:20
certain of the *s.* which is called the *s.* of the Libertines. *Acts* 6:9
the *s.* on the sabbath day. 13:14
the rulers of the *s.* sent to them. 15
the Jews were gone out of the *s.* 42
Barnabas went both into the *s.* 14:1
to Thessalonica where was a *s.* 17:1
therefore he disputed in the *s.* 17
and he reasoned in the *s.* 18:4
house joined hard to the *s.* 7
Crispus the chief ruler of the *s.* 8
Sosthenes chief ruler of the *s.* 17
to speak boldy in the *s.* 26
beat in every *s.* such. 22:19; 26:11
but are the *s.* of Satan. *Rev* 2:9
I will make them of the *s.* of. 3:9

synagogues

burned up all the *s.* of God. *Ps* 74:8
Jesus went teaching in their *s.* and.
Mat 4:23; 9:35; *Mark* 1:39
Luke 13:10
the hypocrites do in the *s.* *Mat* 6:2
love to pray standing in the *s.* 5
they will scourge you in their *s.*
10:17; 23:34
for they love the chief seats in the *s.*
23:6; *Mark* 12:39; *Luke* 11:43
20:46
and in the *s.* ye shall be. *Mark* 13:9
he taught in the *s.* being. *Luke* 4:15
and he preached in the *s.* of. 44
they bring you unto the *s.* 12:11
delivering you up to the *s.* 21:12
put you out of the *s.* *John* 16:2
of him letters to the *s.* *Acts* 9:2
he preached Christ in the *s.* 20
Barnabas preached in the *s.* 13:5
being read in the *s.* every. 15:21
up the people in the *s.* 24:12

Syria

served the gods of *S.* *Judg* 10:6
David put garrisons in *S.*
2 Sam 8:6; *1 Chr* 18:6
I abode at Geshur in *S.* *2 Sam* 15:8
for the kings of *S.* did. *1 Ki* 10:29
Rezon abhorred Israel and reigned over *S.* 11:25
anoint Hazael to be king of *S.* 19:15
2 Ki 13:3
war between *S.* and Israel. *1 Ki* 22:1
by Naaman deliverance given to *S.*
2 Ki 5:1
the bands of *S.* came no. 6:23
was no man in the camp of *S.* 7:5
that thou shalt be king of *S.* 8:13
the king of *S.* had destroyed. 13:7
arrow of deliverance from *S.* 17
but now thou shalt smite *S.* 19
S. recovered Elath to *S.* 16:6
thou shalt push *S.* *2 Chr* 18:10
the host of *S.* came up. 24:23
the gods of kings of *S.* help. 28:23
S. is confederate with. *Isa* 7:2
for head of *S.* is Damascus, and. 8
of the daughters of *S.* *Ezek* 16:57
S. was thy merchant for thy. 27:16
into the country of *S.* *Hos* 12:12
the people of *S.* shall go. *Amos* 1:5
went throughout all *S.* *Mat* 4:24
was governor of *S.* *Luke* 2:2
to the brethren in *S.* *Acts* 15:23
went through *S.* and Cilicia. 41
sailed thence into *S.* 18:18; 21:3
Gal 1:21

see **king**

Syriac

spake to the king in *S.* **Dan 2:4**

Syrian

daughter of Bethuel the *S.*, Laban the *S.* *Gen* 25:20; 28:5; 31:20, 24
a *S.* ready to perish. *Deut* 26:5
spared Naaman this *S.* *2 Ki* 5:20
speak in the *S.* language. 18:26
Isa 36:11
letter was written in the *S.* tongue and interpreted in the *S.* *Ezra* 4:7
saving Naaman the *S.* *Luke* 4:27

Syrians

S. of Damascus came to succour Hadadezer . . . of *S.* *2 Sam* 8:5
the *S.* became David's servants. 6
1 Chr 18:5, 6
from smiting of the *S.* *2 Sam* 8:13
sent and hired the *S.* 10:6
if the *S.* be too strong for me. 11
1 Chr 19:12
so the *S.* feared to help the children of. *2 Sam* 10:19; *1 Chr* 19:19
the *S.* fled and Israel. *1 Ki* 20:20
Israel's little flocks, but *S.* 27
Israel slew of the *S.* 100,000. 29
these shalt thou push the *S.* 22:11
the *S.* had taken a maid. *2 Ki* 5:2
beware, for thither the *S.* are. 6:9
fall into the host of the *S.* 7:4
the Lord made the host of the *S.* 6
we came to camp of the *S.* 10
S. wounded Joram. 8:28, 29; 9:15
2 Chr 22:5
from under the hand of *S.* *2 Ki* 13:5
for thou shalt smite the *S.* in. 17
the *S.* came to Elath and. 16:6
the *S.* before, and the. *Isa* 9:12
fear of the army of *S.* *Jer* 35:11
have not I brought the *S.*? *Amos* 9:7

Syrophenician

Greek, a *S.* by nation. *Mark* 7:26

T

Tabeal

midst of it, even the son of *T.* *Isa* 7:6

Taberah

name of the place *T.* *Num* 11:3
at *T.* he provoked the. *Deut* 9:22

tabering

the voice of doves *t.* *Nah* 2:7

tabernacle

This word literally means tent, *and is used of any sort of temporary tent or booth, as well as for the* tabernacle *erected for the worship of God. Where the word is plural, except in the expression* feast of tabernacles, *it has the meaning of* dwelling, *or* dwelling-place.

The Tabernacle *erected for worship in the wilderness was thirty cubits in length, and ten in breadth and in height. It was divided into two partitions: the first was called* The Holy Place, *which was twenty cubits long, and ten wide: here were placed the table of shewbread, the golden candlestick, and the golden altar of incense. The second was called* The most Holy Place, *whose length was ten cubits, and breadth ten cubits. Here the* ark of the covenant *was kept, which was a symbol of God's gracious presence with the Jewish church. The* most Holy *was divided from the* Holy Place *by a curtain, or veil of very rich cloth, which hung upon four pillars of shittim wood, that were covered with plates of gold,* Ex 26:1; Heb 9:2, 3. *St. Paul refers to our natural body as a tabernacle,* 2 Cor 5:1; 2 Pet 1:13.

The feast of tabernacles, *Lev* 23:34, *was so called, because the Israelites kept it under booths of branches in memory of their dwelling in tents in their passage through the wilderness. It was one of the three great yearly feasts, when all the males were obliged to present themselves before the Lord. It was celebrated after harvest, on the 15th day of the month Tisri, which answers to our month of October. The feast continued eight days; but the first day and the last were the most solemn.*

The Revised Versions most frequently use the word tent, *in place of* tabernacle.

the manner of the *t.* *Ex* 25:9
thou shalt make the *t.* with. 26:1
curtains, and it shall be one *t.*
6; 36:13
of goats' hair to be a covering upon the *t.* 26:7; 35:11; 36:14
for the *t.* of shittim wood. 26:15, 17
20, 26; 36:20, 22, 23, 28, 31, 32
make bars for the *t.* 26:26, 27
rear up the *t.* 30
vessels of *t.* of brass. 27:19; 39:40
the *t.* shall be sanctified. 29:43
all the furniture of the *t.* 31:7
Moses pitched the *t.* without. 33:7
departed not out of the *t.* 11
the pins of the *t.* 35:18; 38:20, 31
wrought the work of the *t.* 36:8
thus was the work of the *t.* 39:32
they brought the *t.* to Moses. 33
thou shalt set up the *t.* 40:2
anoint the *t.* 9
on the first day, the *t.* was reared up.
17, 18; *Num* 7:1
the tent over the *t.* *Ex* 40:19
he brought the ark into the *t.* 21
court round about the *t.* 33
glory of the Lord filled the *t.* 34, 35
cloud taken up from over the *t.* 36
Num 9:17; 10:11; 12:10
cloud was on the *t.* by day, and fire.
Ex 40:38; *Num* 9:18, 19, 22
Moses anointed the *t.* *Lev* 8:10
not when they defile my *t.* 15:31
not an offering before the *t.* 17:4
I will set my *t.* among you. 26:11
Levites over the *t.*; bear the *t.*; encamp round the *t.* *Num* 1:50, 53
the *t.* setteth forward, and when *t.* 51
keep the charge of the *t.* 53; 3:7
25; 18:3; 31:30, 47
t. to do the service of the *t.* 3:7
shall pitch behind the *t.* 23
pitch northward of the *t.* 35
those that encamp before the *t.* 38
oversight of the *t.* pertaineth. 4:16
bear the curtains of the *t.* 25
shall bear the boards of the *t.* 31
take of the dust of the *t.* 5:17
their offering before the *t.* 7:3
on the day that the *t.* was reared up, the cloud covered the *t.* 9:15
Kohathites did set up the *t.* 10:21
elders round about the *t.* 11:24
went not out unto the *t.* 26
small to do the service of the *t.* 16:9
get you up from about the *t.* 24, 27
whoso cometh near to the *t.* 17:13
Lord appeared in *t.* in. *Deut* 31:15
wherein the Lord's *t.* *Josh* 22:19
set the ark in the midst of the *t.*
2 Sam 6:17
walked in a tent and in a *t.* 7:6
Zadok took a horn of oil out of the *t.*
1 Ki 1:39
Joab fled to the *t.* of the Lord. 2:28
vessels in the *t.* were brought up.
8:4; *2 Chr* 5:5
the service of the *t.* *1 Chr* 6:48
keepers of the gates of the *t.* 9:19
oversight of the house of the *t.* 23
the priests, before *t.* of the. 16:39
but have gone from one *t.* 17:5
for the *t.* which Moses made. 21:29
no more carry the *t.* 23:26
brazen altar before the *t.* *2 Chr* 1:5
shalt know that thy *t.* *Job* 5:24
the light shall be dark in his *t.* 18:6
shall be rooted out of his *t.* 14
destruction shall dwell in his *t.* 15
encamp round about my *t.* 19:12
with him that is left in his *t.* 20:26
secret of God was upon my *t.* 29:4
if the men of my *t.* said not. 31:31
understand the noise of his *t.*?
36:29*
who shall abide in thy *t.*? *Ps* 15:1
in them hath he set a *t.* for. 19:4
in the secret of his *t.* shall. 27:5
I will offer in his *t.* sacrifices. 6
I will abide in thy *t.* for ever. 61:4
in Salem is his *t.*, his dwelling. 76:2
so that he forsook the *t.* of. 78:60
moreover he refused the *t.* 67
I will not come into the *t.* 132:3, 7
the *t.* of the upright shall. *Pr* 14:11
there shall be a *t.* for a. *Isa* 4:6*
he shall sit upon it in the *t.* 16:5
a *t.* that shall not be taken. 33:20
my *t.* is spoiled, and all my. *Jer* 10:20
were pleasant in the *t.* *Lam* 2:4
violently taken away his *t.* 6
my *t.* also shall be. *Ezek* 37:27
was the breadth of the *t.* 41:1
but ye have borne the *t.* *Amos* 5:26*
day will I raise up the *t.* of. 9:11
took up the *t.* of Moloch. *Acts* 7:43
desired to find a *t.* for the God. 46
and will build again the *t.* 15:16
if our house of this *t.* *2 Cor* 5:1
we that are in this *t.* do groan. 4
true *t.* which the Lord. *Heb* 8:2
Moses was about to make the *t.* 5
there was a *t.* made, called. 9:2
t. which is called the holiest. 3
went always into the first *t.* 6
while as the first *t.* was yet. 8
by a greater and more perfect *t.* 11
he sprinkled with blood the *t.* 21
no right to eat which serve *t.* 13:10
as long as I am in this *t.* *2 Pet* 1:13
shortly I must put off my *t.* 14
to blaspheme his name and his *t.*
Rev 13:6
behold the temple of the *t.* 15:5
see **congregation, door**

tabernacle *of witness*

laid up the rods in the *t. of witness.*
Num 17:7
Moses went into the *t. of witness.* 8
before the *t. of witness.* 18:2
bring the collection for *t. of witness.*
2 Chr 24:6
fathers had the *t. of witness.*
Acts 7:44

tabernacles

how goodly are thy *t.* O. *Num* 24:5
wickedness dwell in thy *t.* *Job* 11:14
the *t.* of robbers prosper, and. 12:6
and fire shall consume the *t.* 15:34
away iniquity far from thy *t.* 22:23
bring me unto thy *t.* *Ps* 43:3
make glad the holy place of *t.* 46:4
their strength in *t.* of Ham. 78:51
t. of Edom have consulted. 83:6
how amiable are thy *t.* O Lord. 84:1
salvation is in the *t.* of the. 118:15
we will go into his *t.* and. 132:7
he shall plant the *t.* of. *Dan* 11:45
thorns shall be in their *t.* *Hos* 9:6
make thee to dwell in *t.* 12:9
cut off the man out of the *t.* *Mal* 2:12
let us make here three *t.* *Mat* 17:4
Mark 9:5; *Luke* 9:33
Abraham dwelling in *t.* *Heb* 11:9
see **feast**

Tabitha

a disciple named *T.* *Acts* 9:36
to the body, said, *T.* arise. 40

table

shalt also make a *t.* of. *Ex* 25:23
places of staves to bear the *t.* 27, 28
37:14
thou shalt set the *t.* without. 26:35
thou shalt anoint the *t.* and. 30:27
Bezaleel shall make the *t.* 31:8
he made the *t.* 37:10
the vessels on the *t.* 16
brought the *t.* unto Moses. 39:33
thou shalt bring in the *t.* and. 40:4
put the *t.* in the tent of the. 22
on a row on the pure *t.* *Lev* 24:6
charge shall be the *t.* *Num* 3:31
their meat under my *t.* *Judg* 1:7
not to the king's *t.* *1 Sam* 20:29
Jonathan arose from the *t.* in. 34
Mephibosheth shall eat bread at my *t.* *2 Sam* 9:7, 10, 11, 13; 19:28
those that eat at thy *t.* *1 Ki* 2:7
came to king Solomon's *t.* 4:27
when the queen of Sheba saw the meat of his *t.* 10:5; *2 Chr* 9:4
as they sat at *t.* word of. *1 Ki* 13:20
which eat at Jezebel's *t.* 18:19
let us set for him a *t.* *2 Ki* 4:10
at my *t.* 150 Jews. *Neh* 5:17
should be set on thy *t.* *Job* 36:16
thou preparest a *t.* *Ps* 23:5

let their *t.* become a snare. *Ps* 69:22
can God furnish a *t.* in the? 78:19
olive plants about thy *t.* 128:3
on the *t.* of thy heart. *Pr* 3:3; 7:3
hath also furnished her *t.* 9:2
the king sitteth at his *t.* *S of S* 1:12
prepare the *t.*, watch, eat. *Isa* 21:5
write it before them in a *t.* 30:8*
prepare a *t.* for that troop. 65:11
it is graven on the *t.* of. *Jer* 17:1
and a *t.* prepared before. *Ezek* 23:41
ye shall be filled at my *t.* 39:20
this is the *t.* that is before. 41:22
shall come near to my *t.* 44:16
speak lies at one *t.* *Dan* 11:27
the *t.* of the Lord is. *Mal* 1:7
ye say, The *t.* of the Lord is. 12
crumbs which fall from their master's *t.* *Mat* 15:27; *Mark* 7:28
fell from rich man's *t.* *Luke* 16:21
the hand of him that betrayeth me is with me on the *t.* 22:21
ye may eat and drink at my *t.* 30
one of them that sat at *t.* *John* 12:2*
no man at the *t.* knew for. 13:28
their *t.* be made a snare. *Rom* 11:9
devils, ye cannot be partakers of the Lord's *t.* and of the *t.* *1 Cor* 10:21
see **shewbread**

writing **table**
Zacharias asked for a *writing t.* *Luke* 1:63

tables
Frequently meaning tablets, Ex 32:15; Isa 30:8. *To serve tables was to oversee the caring for the poor,* Acts 6:2.
the *t.* were written on. *Ex* 32:15
t. were the work of God, graven on the *t.* 16
he cast the *t.* out of his hands. 19
on these *t.* the words in first *t.* 34:1
he wrote on the *t.* *Deut* 10:4
put the *t.* in the ark. 5; *Heb* 9:4
David gave gold for *t.* *1 Chr* 28:16
Solomon also made ten *t.* *2 Chr* 4:8
the *t.* whereon the shewbread. 19
all *t.* are full of vomit. *Isa* 28:8
eight *t.* whereupon they. *Ezek* 40:41
four *t.* were of hewn stone for. 42
and make it plain on *t.* *Hab* 2:2
he overthrew the *t.* of the money changers. *Mat* 21:12; *Mark* 11:15
cups, pots, and of *t.* *Mark* 7:4
and overthrew the *t.* *John* 2:15
leave the word of God, and serve *t.* *Acts* 6:2
t. of stone, but fleshly *t.* *2 Cor* 3:3
see **stone, two**

tablets
they brought *t.*, all jewels. *Ex* 35:22*
we brought *t.* to make. *Num* 31:50*
I will take away the *t.* *Isa* 3:20*

Tabor
and draw toward mount *T.* *Judg* 4:6
Barak was gone up to mount *T.* 12
they whom ye slew at *T.*? 8:18
come to the plain of *T.* *1 Sam* 10:3
T. and Hermon shall rejoice in thy name. *Ps* 89:12
surely, as *T.* is among. *Jer* 46:18
been a net spread upon *T.* *Hos* 5:1

tabret
away with *t.* and harp. *Gen* 31:27
high place with a *t.* *1 Sam* 10:5*
aforetime I was as a *t.* *Job* 17:6*
the *t.*, pipe, and wine are. *Isa* 5:12

tabrets
to meet Saul with *t.* *1 Sam* 18:6*
the mirth of *t.* ceaseth. *Isa* 24:8
shall be with *t.* and harps. 30:32
be adorned with thy *t.* *Jer* 31:4
workmanship of thy *t.* *Ezek* 28:13

taches
(*Revisions substitute the word* clasps)
thou shalt make fifty *t.* *Ex* 26:6
make fifty *t.* of brass. 11; 35:11
hang up the vail under the *t.* 26:33
he made fifty *t.* of gold. 36:13, 18
brought his *t.*, his boards. 39:33

tackling
we cast out the *t.* of. *Acts* 27:19

tacklings
thy *t.* are loosed, could. *Isa* 33:23

Tadmor
Solomon built *T.* in the. *2 Chr* 8:4

Tahapanes, *or* **Tehaphnehes**
children of *T.* have broken. *Jer* 2:16
thus came they even to *T.* 43:7
publish in Noph and *T.* 46:14
at *T.* also the day. *Ezek* 30:18

Tahpenes
sister of *T.* the queen. *1 Ki* 11:19

tail
hand, take it by the *t.* *Ex* 4:4
head, not the *t.* *Deut* 28:13, 44
foxes and turned *t.* to *t.* *Judg* 15:4
behemoth moveth his *t.* *Job* 40:17
off from Israel head and *t.* *Isa* 9:14
teacheth lies, he is the *t.* 15
the head or *t.* may do. 19:15
his *t.* drew the third. *Rev* 12:4

tails
firebrand between two *t.* *Judg* 15:4
two *t.* of these smoking firebrands. *Isa* 7:4
t. like to scorpions, stings in their *t.* *Rev* 9:10
power in their *t.*: their *t.* were. 19

take
wilt *t.* the left hand. *Gen* 13:9
the persons, *t.* the goods to. 14:21
arise, *t.* thy wife and thy. 19:15
t. now thy son, thine only son. 22:2
thou shalt not *t.* a wife to. 24:3, 37
to *t.* my master's brother's. 48
what is thine with me, *t.* it. 31:32
if thou *t.* other wives besides. 50
t. our daughters unto you. 34:9
will *t.* your daughters to us. 16
let her *t.* it to her, lest we be. 38:23
I will *t.* you to me for a. *Ex* 6:7
for thereof must we *t.* to. 10:26
and thy rod *t.* in thine hand. 17:5
shalt not *t.* the name of the Lord thy God. 20:7; *Deut* 5:11
t. him from mine altar. *Ex* 21:14
and thou shalt *t.* no gift. 23:8
Deut 16:19
pardon and *t.* us for. *Ex* 34:9
lest thou *t.* of their daughters. 16
Deut 7:3
neither *t.* her son's. *Lev* 18:17
neither shalt thou *t.* a wife to. 18
and if a man *t.* a wife, and. 20:14
not *t.* a wife that is a whore, nor *t.* a. 21:7; *Ezek* 44:22
t. a wife in her virginity. *Lev* 21:13
t. thou no usury of him, or. 25:36
ye shall *t.* them as an inheritance. 46
t. the Levites from among. *Num* 8:6
I will *t.* of the spirit that is on. 11:17
Korah said, Ye *t.* too much. 16:3, 7
ye shall *t.* no satisfaction. 35:31, 32
t. ye wise men and. *Deut* 1:13
and *t.* him a nation, from. 4:34
then thou shalt *t.* an awl and. 15:17
elders of that city shall *t.* 22:18
shall not *t.* his father's wife. 30
may not *t.* her again to be his. 24:4
no man shall *t.* a millstone to. 6
t. a widow's raiment to pledge. 17
if he say, I like not to *t.* her. 25:8
when ye *t.* of the accursed thing. *Josh* 6:18
family which the Lord shall *t.*; household which the Lord shall *t.* 7:14
they should *t.* his carcase. 8:29
their land did Joshua *t.* at. 10:42
they shall *t.* him into the city. 20:4
t. ye possession among us. 22:19
for the necks of them that *t.* spoil. *Judg* 5:30
that thou goest to *t.* a wife. 14:3
have ye called us to *t.* that? 15*
consider, *t.* advice, and speak. 19:30
t. knowledge of me. *Ruth* 2:10
t. as much as thy soul desireth, and if not I will *t.* it by. *1 Sam* 2:16
he will *t.* your sons for himself. 8:11
he will *t.* your daughters. 13
he will *t.* your fields. 14
t. the tenth of your seed. *1 Sam* 8:15
he will *t.* your menservants. 16
how thy brethren fare, and *t.* 17:18
and *t.* thine head from thee. 46
messengers to *t.* David. 19:14, 20
if thou wilt *t.* that, *t.* it, there. 21:9
huntest my soul to *t.* it. 24:11
shall I then *t.* my bread, and? 25:11
t. now the spear that is at his. 26:11
he spared to *t.* of his. *2 Sam* 12:4
I will *t.* thy wives before thine. 11
t. it, lest I *t.* the city, and it be. 28
t. the thing to his heart. 13:33; 19:19
me go over, and *t.* off his head. 16:9
said, Yea, let him *t.* all. 19:30
Jeroboam, *T.* ten pieces. *1 Ki* 11:31
will not *t.* the whole kingdom. 34
t. with thee ten loaves. 14:3
t. the prophets of Baal. 18:40
war or peace, *t.* them alive. 20:18
arise, *t.* possession of. 21:15, 16
t. Micaiah, carry him back. 22:26
2 Chr 18:25
creditor is come to *t.* *2 Ki* 4:1
t. my staff and go. 29
t. a blessing of thy servant. 5:15
urged him to *t.* it. 16
I will *t.* somewhat. 20
be content, *t.* two talents. 23
t. a present and go. 8:8
t. this box of oil in thine. 9:1, 3
t. ye the heads of your. 10:6
he said, *T.* them alive. 14
let the priests *t.* it. 12:5
said, *T.* bow and arrows. 13:15, 18
shall yet *t.* root downward. 19:30
Isa 37:31
I will not *t.* that which. *1 Chr* 21:24
those did Cyrus *t.* *Ezra* 5:14
t. these vessels. 15
not *t.* their daughters. 9:12
Neh 10:30; 13:25
t. the apparel, and do. *Esth* 6:10
knoweth the way that I *t.* *Job* 23:10
they *t.* the widow's ox for a. 24:3
and they *t.* a pledge of the poor. 9
and my sinews *t.* no rest. 30:17
surely I would *t.* it upon. 31:36
thou *t.* him for a servant for? 41:4
therefore *t.* to you now seven. 42:8
the rulers *t.* counsel. *Ps* 2:2
persecute my soul, and *t.* it. 7:5*
I will *t.* no bullock out of thy. 50:9
shouldest *t.* my covenant in. 16
and *t.* not thy Holy Spirit. 51:11
t. him, for there is none to. 71:11
t. a psalm, and bring. 81:2
t. the houses of God. 83:12
will I not utterly *t.* from him. 89:33
and let another *t.* his office. 109:8
t. the cup of salvation, and. 116:13
t. not the word of truth. 119:43
if I *t.* the wings of the. 139:9
and thine enemies *t.* thy name. 20
his own iniquities shall *t.* *Pr* 5:22
neither let her *t.* thee with her. 6:25
can a man *t.* fire in his bosom? 27
let us *t.* our fill of love until. 7:18
t. his garment that is surety for stranger, *t.* a pledge. 20:16; 27:13
and *t.* the name of my God. 30:9*
and shall *t.* nothing of. *Eccl* 5:15
and to *t.* his portion and rejoice. 19
t. us the foxes, the. *S of S* 2:15
them of Jacob to *t.* root. *Isa* 27:6
time it goeth, it shall *t.* you. 28:19
not a sherd to *t.* fire from. 30:14
is divided, the lame *t.* the. 33:23
their stock shall not *t.* root. 40:24
will *t.* thereof and warm. 44:15
t. the millstones, and grind. 47:2
I will *t.* vengeance, I will not. 3
vanity shall *t.* them, wind. 57:13*
t. delight in approaching to. 58:2
also *t.* of them for priests. 66:21
t. thee much sope [soap]. *Jer* 2:22
I will *t.* you one of a city. 3:14
t. the girdle that thou. 13:4, 6
shall not sorrows *t.* thee as a. 21
if thou *t.* forth the precious. 15:19
thou shalt not *t.* thee a wife. 16:2
have digged a pit to *t.* me. 18:22
t. of the ancients of the people. 19:1
we shall *t.* our revenge. 20:10

I will t. all the families. Jer 25:9
I will t. from them the voice. 10
if they refuse to t. the cup at. 28
t. ye wives, and beget sons. 29:6
come to the city to t. it. 32:24
money, and t. witnesses. 25, 44
king of Babylon shall t. it. 28
t. Jeremiah, and look well to. 39:12
Gilead, and t. balm. 46:11; 51:8
t. vengeance upon her; as she. 50:15
shall not t. of thee a stone. 51:26
behold I will t. vengeance for thee. 36
what thing shall I t. to witness? Lam 2:13
t. thee a tile and lay it. Ezek 4:1
t. thou an iron pan. 3
t. unto thee wheat, barley, and. 9
t. a sharp knife, t. a razor, t. 5:1
t. fire from between the wheels. 10:6
I will t. the stony heart out. 11:19
that I may t. the house. 14:5
will men t. a pin of it to hang? 15:3
remove the diadem, t. off the. 21:26
thou shalt t. thine inheritance. 22:16*
t. the choice of the flock, and. 24:5
fury to come up to t. vengeance. 8
I t. from them their strength. 25
t. a multitude, t. her spoil, t. 29:19
if people of the land t. a man. 33:2
I will t. you from among the. 36:24
t. thee one stick, t. another. 37:16
I will t. the stick of Joseph. 19
to t. a spoil, and to t. a prey. 38:12
art thou come to t. prey, to t. a? 13
the prince not t. the people's. 46:18
but the saints shall t. the. Dan 7:18
the king shall t. the most. 11:15
to the isles, and shall t. many. 18
go t. unto thee a wife of. Hos 1:2
I was as they that t. off the. 11:4
t. with you words, and turn. 14:2
ye t. from him burdens. Amos 5:11
afflict the just, they t. a bribe. 12
shall mine hand t. them. 9:2, 3
t. I beseech thee, my life. Jonah 4:3
they covet fields and t. Mi 2:2
that they shall not t. shame. 6*
the Lord will t. vengeance. Nah 1:2
t. ye the spoil of silver, t. the. 2:9
heap dust and t. it. Hab 1:10
build the house; and I will t. Hag 1:8
I t. thee, O Zerubbabel my. 2:23
t. of them of the captivity. Zech 6:10
t. yet instruments of a foolish. 11:15
fear not to t. unto thee. Mat 1:20
and t. the young child and. 2:13
t. no thought for your life. 6:25*
28*, 31*, 34*; 10:19*; Mark 13:11*
Luke 12:11*, 22*, 26*
and the violent t. the. Mat 11:12
t. my yoke upon you, and learn. 29
It is not meet to t. the children's bread. 15:26; Mark 7:27
they had forgotten to t. bread. Mat 16:5; Mark 8:14
kings of earth t. custom. Mat 17:25
then t. with thee one or two. 18:16
t. that thine is and go thy. 20:14
on the house top not come down to t. any. 24:17; Mark 13:15
t. therefore the talent. Mat 25:28
that they might t. Jesus. 26:4
Mark 14:1, 44
took bread and said, T. Mat 26:26
Mark 14:22; 1 Cor 11:24
sleep on now, and t. your rest. Mat 26:45; Mark 14:41
they that t. sword shall. Mat 26:52
with swords and staves to t. me. 55
Mark 14:48
t. nothing for their journey. Mark 6:8; Luke 9:3
his brother should t. his wife. Mark 12:19; Luke 20:28
casting lots what every man should t. Mark 15:24
whether Elias will come to t. 36
David did t. and eat the. Luke 6:4
forbid him not to t. thy coat. 29
said, T. care of him. 10:35
soul, t. thine ease. 12:19
then begin with shame to t. the. 14:9
t. thy bill and write. 16:6, 7
t. from him the pound. 19:24
t. this and divide it. Luke 22:17
hath a purse, let him t. it. 36
Jesus said to them, T. John 2:16
of them may t. a little. 6:7
that they would come and t. him. 15
they sought to t. him. 7:30, 32
10:39; 11:57
loveth me, because I lay down my life, that I might t. it. 10:17, 18
he shall t. of mine, and shew. 16:15
thou shouldest t. them out. 17:15
t. ye him, and judge him. 18:31
Pilate saith, T. ye him, and. 19:6
bishoprick let another t. Acts 1:20
further to t. Peter also. 12:3
to t. out of them a people. 15:14
Barnabas determined to t. with. 37
Paul thought not good to t. him. 38
there intending to t. in Paul. 20:13
I t. you to record this day. 26*
them t. and purify thyself. 21:24
besought them to t. meat. 27:33, 34
why not rather t. wrong? 1 Cor 6:7
shall I then t. the members of? 15
doth God t. care for oxen? 9:9
t. upon us the ministering. 2 Cor 8:4
ye suffer, if a man t. of you. 11:20*
therefore I t. pleasure in. 12:10
t. to you the whole. Eph 6:13
and t. the helmet of salvation. 17
how shall he t. care of? 1 Tim 3:5
t. Mark, and bring him. 2 Tim 4:11
a commandment to t. tithes. Heb 7:5
t. my brethren, the prophets, for an. Jas 5:10
if ye t. it patiently, it. 1 Pet 2:20
hold fast, that no man t. Rev 3:11
thou art worthy to t. the book. 5:9
power given him to t. peace from. 6:4
t. the little book. 10:8
t. it and eat it. 9
let him t. the water of life. 22:17

see **counsel**

take *away*

wouldest thou t. away my son's mandrakes? Gen 30:15
ye will t. Benjamin away. 42:36
t. this child away, and. Ex 2:9
that he may t. away the frogs. 8:8
that he may t. away from me. 10:17
and I will t. sickness away. 23:25
Deut 7:15
I will t. away mine hand. Ex 33:23
it shall he t. away. Lev 3:4, 10, 15
4:9; 7:4
t. away all the fat thereof. 4:31, 35
that they t. away the stones. 14:40
shalt t. away the ashes. Num 4:13
thou shalt quite t. away their. 17:10
t. away the serpents from us. 21:7
until ye t. a. the accursed. Josh 7:13
shall I not t. you away? 2 Sam 4:11
except thou t. away the blind. 5:6
t. away the iniquity of thy. 24:10
mayest t. away the innocent blood. 1 Ki 2:31
t. away the remnant of the. 14:10*
t. away the posterity. 16:3*; 21:21*
now, O Lord, t. away my life. 19:4
seek my life to t. it away. 10, 14
shall my servants t. away. 20:6
t. the kings away and put. 24
the Lord will t. away. 2 Ki 2:3, 5
sent to t. away mine head. 6:32
till I come and t. you away. 18:32
Isa 36:17
I will not t. my mercy away from him. 1 Chr 17:13
to t. away his sackcloth. Esth 4:4
why dost thou not t. away? Job 7:21
t. his rod away from me. 9:34
they violently t. away flocks. 24:2
they t. away the sheaf from the. 10
my maker would soon t. me a. 32:22
lest he t. thee away with. 36:18*
devised to t. away my life. Ps 31:13
he shall t. thee away and. 52:5
he shall t. them away with. 58:9
t. me not away in the midst. 102:24
why should he t. away thy bed? Pr 22:27
t. away the dross from the. 25:4
t. away the wicked from before. 5
I will t. away all thy tin. Isa 1:25
t. away the stay and staff. 3:1
t. away bravery. 18
to t. away our reproach. 4:1
I will t. away the hedge. 5:5
t. away the righteousness of. 23
to t. away the right from. 10:2
of his people shall he t. away. 25:8
all the fruit, to t. away his sin. 27:9
thy sons shall they t. away. 39:7
whirlwind shall t. them away. 40:24
if thou t. away from the midst. 58:9
t. away the foreskins of. Jer 4:4
destroy and t. away her. 5:10
t. me not away in thy long. 15:15
shall t. away the detestable things. Ezek 11:18
they shall t. away thy nose. 23:25
t. away thy fair jewels. 26
t. away thy labour. 29
behold, I t. away the desire. 24:16
come and t. him away. 33:4, 6
and I will t. away the stony. 36:26
t. away your exactions from. 45:9
and they shall t. away. Dan 7:26
they shall t. away the daily. 11:31
utterly t. them away. Hos 1:6
and t. away my corn in the. 2:9
for I will t. away the names. 17
and new wine t. away the heart. 4:11
I will t. away and none shall. 5:14
unto him, T. away all iniquity. 14:2
that he will t. you away. Amos 4:2
t. away from me the noise of. 5:23
they covet houses, and t. them away. Mi 2:2
I will t. away out of the midst of. Zeph 3:11
t. away the filthy garments. Zech 3:4
I will t. away his blood out. 9:7
one shall t. you away. Mal 2:3
and t. away thy coat, let. Mat 5:40
t. away and cast him into. 22:13
Father, t. away this cup. Mark 14:36
to t. away my reproach. Luke 1:25
not come down to t. it away. 17:31
said, T. away the stone. John 11:39
the Romans shall t. away our. 48
when I shall t. away. Rom 11:27
blood should t. away sins. Heb 10:4
manifested to t. away. 1 John 3:5
t. away from the words of the book, God shall t. away his. Rev 22:19

take *heed*

t. heed that thou speak not to Jacob. Gen 31:24, 29
t. heed to thyself. Ex 10:28; 34:12
Deut 4:9; 12:13, 19, 30
1 Sam 19:2; 1 Tim 4:16
t. heed to yourselves. Ex 19:12
Deut 2:4; 4:15, 23; 11:16
Josh 23:11; Jer 17:21
must I not t. heed to? Num 23:12
t. heed in the plague of. Deut 24:8
t. heed and hearken, O. 27:9
t. diligent heed to do. Josh 22:5
if thy children t. heed. 1 Ki 2:4
8:25; 2 Chr 6:16
t. heed now; for the Lord. 1 Chr 28:10
t. heed what ye do, for ye judge not for man. 2 Chr 19:6
fear of the Lord be on you, t. heed. 7
so that they will t. heed to do. 33:8
Ezra 4:22
t. heed, regard not. Job 36:21
I said, I will t. heed to. Ps 39:1
t. no heed to all words. Eccl 7:21
T. heed and be quiet, for. Isa 7:4
t. heed every one of his. Jer 9:4
have left off to t. heed to. Hos 4:10
t. heed to your spirit. Mal 2:15, 16
t. heed that ye do not your alms before men. Mat 6:1
t. heed of the leaven of the Pharisees. 16:6; Mark 8:15
t. heed that ye despise. Mat 18:10
t. heed that no man deceive you. 24:4; Mark 13:5
he said to them, T. heed. Mark 4:24
t. heed to yourselves. 13:9
Luke 17:3; 21:34; Acts 5:35; 20:28
t. heed: behold, I have foretold you all things. Mark 13:23

. ye *heed*, watch, pray. *Mark* 13:33
. *heed* therefore how ye hear. *Luke* 8:18
. *heed* that the light in thee. 11:35
. *heed* and beware of. 12:15
ıe said, *T. heed* that ye be. 21:8
ːaying, *T. heed* what thou doest. *Acts* 22:26*
'. *heed* lest he also spare not thee. *Rom* 11:21*
et every man *t. heed*. *1 Cor* 3:10
. *heed* lest this liberty of. 8:9
hat standeth *t. heed* lest he. 10:12
. *heed* that ye be not consumed one of another. *Gal* 5:15
. *heed* to the ministry. *Col* 4:17
. *heed* lest an evil heart. *Heb* 3:12
'e do well that ye *t. heed*. *2 Pet* 1:19

take *hold*

ıorrow shall *t. hold* on. *Ex* 15:14
rembling shall *t. hold* upon. 15
hat the loops *t. hold* one of. 26:5*
ınd if mine hand *t. hold*. *Deut* 32:41
errors *t. hold* on him. *Job* 27:20
ustice *t. hold* on thee. 36:17
t might *t. hold* on the ends. 38:13
. *hold* of shield and. *Ps* 35:2
wrathful anger *t. hold* of. 69:24*
ıeither *t.* they *hold* of the paths of life. *Pr* 2:19*
. fast *hold* of instruction, let. 4:13
ıer steps *t. hold* on hell. 5:5
t is good that thou *t. hold* of this. *Eccl* 7:18
will *t. hold* of the boughs. *S of S* 7:8
when a man shall *t. hold* of. *Isa* 3:6
seven women shall *t. hold* of. 4:1
sorrows shall *t. hold* of them. 13:8
et him *t. hold* of my strength. 27:5
:o the eunuchs that *t. hold* of. 56:4
ıimself to *t. hold* of thee. 64:7
:hou shalt *t. hold* but. *Mi* 6:14*
lid they not *t. hold* of your fathers? *Zech* 1:6*
:en men shall *t. hold* of him. 8:23
:hat they might *t. hold*. *Luke* 20:20
:ould not *t. hold* of his words. 26

take *up*

'. *up* the fifth part of the. *Gen* 41:34
ınd the priest shall *t. up*. *Lev* 6:10
'. *up* the censers out of. *Num* 16:37
'. *up* the ark of the. *Josh* 3:6; 6:6
'. *up* every man a stone out. 4:5
:he Lord would *t. up* Elijah. *2 Ki* 2:1
ıe said, *T. up* thy son. 4:36
'. *up* the iron. 6:7
'. *up* and cast him into the. 9:25
we *t. up* corn for them. *Neh* 5:2*
ıor *t. up* their names. *Ps* 16:4
:hen the Lord will *t.* me *up*. 27:10
:hat thou shalt *t. up* this. *Isa* 14:4
'. *up* the stumblingblock out. 57:14
'. *up* a lamentation on the. *Jer* 7:29
for the mountains will I *t. up*. 9:10
'. *up* wailing for us. 18
'. *up* Jeremiah, before he die. 38:10
'. *up* a lamentation for the princes. *Ezek* 19:1
'. *up* a lamentation for Tyrus. 26:17; 27:2, 32
'. *up* a lamentation upon king of Tyrus. 28:12
'. *up* a lamentation for Pharaoh. 32:2
shall one *t. up* a snare. *Amos* 3:5*
hear his word which I *t. up*. 5:1
a man's uncle shall *t.* him *up*. 6:10
'. me *up* and cast me. *Jonah* 1:12
shall one *t. up* a parable. *Mi* 2:4
they *t. up* all of them. *Hab* 1:15
not all these *t. up* a parable? 2:6
Jesus saith, Arise, *t. up* thy bed. *Mat* 9:6; *Mark* 2:9, 11; *Luke* 5:24 *John* 5:8, 11, 12
let him *t. up* his cross and follow me. *Mat* 16:24; *Mark* 8:34; 10:21 *Luke* 9:23
and *t. up* the fish that. *Mat* 17:27
shall *t. up* serpents. *Mark* 16:18

taken

Lord God had *t.* from man. *Gen* 2:22
because she was *t.* out of man. 23
of the ground wast thou *t.* 3:19, 23
vengeance shall be *t.* on him. 4:15
the woman was *t.* into. *Gen* 12:15
so I might have *t.* her to me. 19
heard that his brother was *t.* 14:14
I have *t.* upon me to speak. 18:27
which thou hast *t.* is a wife. 20:3
is he that hath *t.* venison? 27:33
the riches God hath *t.* from. 31:16
now Rachel had *t.* the images. 34
staves shall not be *t.* *Ex* 25:15
shoulder have I *t.* of Israel. *Lev* 7:34
t. the Levites for the firstborn of. *Num* 3:12; 8:16, 18; 18:6
neither she be *t.* with the. 5:13
and the tabernacle was *t.* 10:17
I have not *t.* one ass from. 16:15
we have *t.* the sum of the. 31:49
their inheritance be *t.* from. 36:3
Lord hath *t.* you out of. *Deut* 4:20
wife, and hath not *t.* her. 20:7
when a man hath *t.* a wife. 24:1
t. a new wife, he shall be free at . . . his wife which he hath *t.* 5
they have *t.* of the. *Josh* 7:11
he that is *t.* shall be burnt. 15
and the tribe of Judah was *t.* 16
and Zabdi was *t.* 17
and Achan was *t.* 18
Lord hath *t.* vengeance. *Judg* 11:36
he told not them that he had *t.* 14:9
because he had *t.* his wife. 15:6
the 1100 shekels that were *t.* 17:2
the ark of God was *t.* *1 Sam* 4:11 17, 19, 21, 22
which the Philistines had *t.* 7:14
and Saul was *t.* 10:21
whose ox have I *t.*? 12:3
nor hast thou *t.* aught of any. 4
Saul and Jonathan were *t.* 14:41
Cast lots, and Jonathan was *t.* 42
and David's two wives were *t.* 30:5
that they had *t.* to them. 19
hast *t.* his wife to. *2 Sam* 12:9, 10
and I have *t.* the city of waters. 27
thou art *t.* in thy mischief. 16:8
because they cannot be *t.* 23:6
saw that the city was *t.* *1 Ki* 16:18
killed and also *t.* possession? 21:19
when I am *t.* from thee *2 Ki* 2:10
of Hosea, Samaria was *t.* 18:10
household being *t.* for Eleazar, and one *t.* for Ithamar. *1 Chr* 24:6
captives you have *t.* *2 Chr* 28:11
king had *t.* counsel to keep. 30:2
for they have *t.* of their. *Ezra* 9:2
and we have *t.* strange wives. 10:2* 14*, 17*, 18*
all these had *t.* strange wives. 44
had *t.* of them bread. *Neh* 5:15
who had *t.* Esther for his. *Esth* 2:15
so Esther was *t.* unto king. 16
king took off his ring he had *t.* 8:2
also *t.* me by my neck. *Job* 16:12
he hath *t.* the crown from. 19:9
thou hast *t.* a pledge from thy. 22:6
they are *t.* out of the way. 24:24
iron is *t.* out of the earth. 28:2
in net is their own foot *t.* *Ps* 9:15
let them be *t.* in the devices. 10:2
even be *t.* in their pride. 59:12
have *t.* crafty counsel against. 83:3
I *t.* as an heritage for ever. 119:111
thy foot from being *t.* *Pr* 3:26
thou art *t.* with the words of. 6:2
he hath *t.* a bag of money. 7:20
transgressors shall be *t.* in. 11:6
my labour which I had *t.* *Eccl* 2:18
nor any thing *t.* from it. 3:14
the sinner shall be *t.* by her. 7:26
as the fishes that are *t.* in. 9:12
t. evil counsel against thee. *Isa* 7:5
shall be broken, and snared, and *t.* 8:15
who hath *t.* this counsel? 23:8
shall be *t.* in the snare. 24:18 *Jer* 48:44
might be broken, snared, and *t.* *Isa* 28:13
that shall not be *t.* down. 33:20*
thou whom I have *t.* from ends. 41:9
shall the prey be *t.* from the? 49:24
I have *t.* the cup of trembling. 51:22
he was *t.* from prison and. 53:8
the wife shall be *t.* *Jer* 6:11
ashamed, dismayed, and *t.* 8:9
planted, they have *t.* root. *Jer* 12:2
shalt surely be *t.* 34:3; 38:23
day that Jerusalem was *t.* 38:28
when they had *t.* him, they. 39:5
he had *t.* him, being bound. 40:1
dwell in your cities, that ye have *t.* 10
Kiriathaim is *t.* 48:1
thy treasures, thou also shalt be *t.* 7
joy and gladness is *t.* from the. 33
Kirioth is *t.* 41
thy sons are *t.* captives. 46
hear the counsel he hath *t.* 49:20
sorrows have *t.* Damascus. 24
Nebuchadnezzar hath *t.* counsel. 30
publish and say, Babylon is *t.* 50:2 24; 51:31, 41
anointed of the Lord was *t.* *Lam* 4:20
the prince of Israel be *t.* *Ezek* 12:13
shall wood be *t.* thereof to do? 15:3
also *t.* thy fair jewels of gold. 16:17
thou hast *t.* thy sons and thy. 20
and hath *t.* the king thereof. 17:12
t. of the king's seed, hath *t.* 13
and he shall be *t.* in my snare. 20
neither hath *t.* any increase. 18:8
usury, and hath *t.* increase. 13
that hath *t.* off his hand from. 17*
he was *t.* in their pit. 19:4, 8
call to remembrance, that they may be *t.* 21:23
they *t.* gifts; thou hast *t.* usury. 22:12
have *t.* vengeance with a. 25:15
his father had *t.* out. *Dan* 5:2, 3
ye have *t.* my silver. *Joel* 3:5
if he have *t.* nothing? *Amos* 3:4, 5
so shall Israel be *t.* that dwell. 12*
have we not *t.* to us horns by? 6:13
the city shall be *t.* and. *Zech* 14:2
bridegroom shall be *t.* *Mat* 9:15
we have *t.* no bread. 16:7
the kingdom of God shall be *t.* 21:43
one shall be *t.* 24:40; *Luke* 17:34 35, 36
had *t.* counsel, they gave. *Mat* 28:12
from him *t.* even that. *Mark* 4:25
when he had *t.* the five loaves. 6:41
t. him in his arms, he said. 9:36
night, and have *t.* nothing. *Luke* 5:5
of fishes which they had *t.* 9
if I have *t.* any thing from. 19:8*
some would have *t.* him. *John* 7:44
a woman *t.* in adultery. 8:3, 4
ye have *t.* and by wicked. *Acts* 2:23
for his life is *t.* from the. 8:33
this man was *t.* of the Jews. 23:27*
fasting, having *t.* nothing. 27:33
not as though the word hath *t.* none effect. *Rom* 9:6*
no temptation *t.* you. *1 Cor* 10:13
being *t.* from you for. *1 Thes* 2:17*
will let, until he be *t.* *2 Thes* 2:7
let not a widow be *t.* *1 Tim* 5:9*
who are *t.* captive by him at his will. *2 Tim* 2:26
every high priest *t.* from. *Heb* 5:1
made to be *t.* and destroyed. *2 Pet* 2:12
when he had *t.* the book. *Rev* 5:8
hast *t.* to thee thy great. 11:17
beast was *t.* and with him. 19:20

taken *away*

servants had *t. away*. *Gen* 21:25
Jacob came and hath *t. away*. 27:35
he hath *t. away* my blessing. 36
God hath *t. away* my reproach. 30:23
Jacob hath *t. away* all that is. 31:1
thus God hath *t. away* the cattle. 9
hast thou *t.* us *away* to die? *Ex* 14:11
as the fat is *t. away* from the sacrifice. *Lev* 4:31, 35
trespass in a thing *t. away* by. 6:2
after that he hath *t. away* the. 14:43
nor *t. away* aught for. *Deut* 26:14
be violently *t. away* from. 28:31
have *t. away* my gods. *Judg* 18:24
day when it was *t. away*. *1 Sam* 21:6
the high places were not *t. away*. *1 Ki* 22:43; *2 Ki* 12:3; 14:4 *2 Chr* 15:17; 20:33
before I be *t. away* from thee. *2 Ki* 2:9
altars Hezekiah hath *t. away*. 18:22 *2 Chr* 32:12; *Isa* 36:7
t. away the groves. *2 Chr* 19:3

the Lord hath t. away. Job 1:21
hath violently t. away an. 20:19
God liveth, who hath t. away. 27:2
hath t. away my judgement. 34:5
and the mighty shall be t. away. 20
t. away all thy wrath. Ps 85:3
their sleep is t. away. Pr 4:16
thine iniquity is t. away. Isa 6:7
of Samaria shall be t. away. 8:4
the burden shall be t. away. 10:27
the gladness is t. away. 16:10
Damascus is t. away. 17:1
the mighty shall be t away. 49:25
that my people is t. away for. 52:5
t. away, righteous is t. away. 57:1
like the wind have t. us away. 64:6
I have t. away my peace. Jer 16:5
hath violently t. away. Lam 2:6
t. away in his iniquity. Ezek 33:6
their dominion t. away. Dan 7:12
by him the daily sacrifice was t. away. 8:11; 12:11
fishes shall be t. away. Hos 4:3
and I have t. away your horses. Amos 4:10
t. away my glory for ever. Mi 2:9
the Lord hath t. away thy judgements. Zeph 3:15
from him shall be t. away. Mat 13:12
25:29; Luke 8:18; 19:26
the bridegroom shall be t. away. Mark 2:20; Luke 5:35
that good part which shall not be t. away. Luke 10:42
ye have t. away the key of. 11:52
they might be t. away. John 19:31
seeth the stone t. away from. 20:1
they have t. away the Lord. 2
they have t. away my Lord. 13
judgement was t. away. Acts 8:33
should be saved was t. away. 27:20
this, might be t. away. 1 Cor 5:2
vail shall be t. away. 2 Cor 3:16

taken *hold*

and have t. hold upon. 1 Ki 9:9
days of affliction have t. hold upon. Job 30:16
iniquities have t. hold. Ps 40:12*
anguish have t. hold on me. 119:143
pangs have t. hold on me. Isa 21:3
anguish hath t. hold on us. Jer 6:24

taken *up*

cloud was t. up from. Ex 40:36
not t. up, till the day it was t. up. 37
the cloud was t. up. Num 9:17, 21
but when it was t. up. 22; 10:11
Absalom was t. up. 2 Sam 18:9
they have t. up their. Isa 10:29
shall be t. up a curse. Jer 29:22
ye are t. up in the lips. Ezek 36:3
so Daniel was t. up out. Dan 6:23
there was t. up of the. Luke 9:17
day in which he was t. up. Acts 1:2
while they beheld, he was t. up. 9
this same Jesus which is t. up. 11*
day he was t. up from us. 22
and was t. up dead. 20:9
when they had t. up they. 27:17*
had t. up the anchors. 40*

takest

the water thou t. out of the. Ex 4:9
when thou t. the sum of. 30:12
journey thou t. not be. Judg 4:9
thou t. away their breath. Ps 104:29
what is man that thou t.? 144:3
and thou t. no knowledge. Isa 58:3
t. up that thou layedst. Luke 19:21

takest *heed*

if thou t. heed to fulfil. 1 Chr 22:13*

taketh

that t. his name in vain. Ex 20:7
Deut 5:11
persons nor t. reward. Deut 10:17
t. a man's life to pledge. 24:6
putteth her hand and t. him. 25:11
cursed be he that t. reward. 27:25
as an eagle t. them, beareth. 32:11
tribe which the Lord t. Josh 7:14
smiteth Kirjath-sepher and t. it. 15:16; Judg 1:12
and t. away reproach. 1 Sam 17:26
as a man t. away dung. 1 Ki 14:10*
t. it even out of the thorns. Job 5:5
he t. the wise in their craftiness. 13
1 Cor 3:19
he t. away, who can? Job 9:12*
and t. away the understanding. 12:20
he t. away the heart of the chief. 24
what is the hope, when God t.? 27:8
he t. it with his eyes, his nose. 40:24
nor t. up reproach against. Ps 15:3
nor t. reward against the innocent. 5
Lord t. my part with them. 118:7*
happy shall he be that t. 137:9
he t. not pleasure in the legs. 147:10
the Lord t. pleasure in them. 11
for the Lord t. pleasure in his. 149:4
which t. away the life. Pr 1:19
better than he that t. a city. 16:32
a wicked man t. a gift out of. 17:23
as he that t. away a garment. 25:20
is like one that t. a dog by. 26:17
of all his labour which he t. Eccl 1:3*
heart t. not rest in the night. 2:23
sheep that no man t. up. Isa 13:14
he t. up the isles as a very. 40:15
the carpenter t. the cypress. 44:14
nor is there any that t. her by. 51:18
who t. strangers instead. Ezek 16:32
and t. not warning. 33:4
but he that t. warning. 5
as the shepherd t. out of. Amos 3:12*
the devil t. him up into. Mat 4:5
t. him up into an exceeding high. 8
t. from garment, and rent is made worse. 9:16; Mark 2:21
and t. not his cross and. Mat 10:38
he goeth, t. seven other spirits. 12:45; Luke 11:26
Jesus t. Peter, James. Mat 17:1
Mark 9:2; 14:33
Satan cometh and t. away the word. Mark 4:15; Luke 8:12
he t. the father and. Mark 5:40
he t. him, he teareth him. 9:18
that t. away thy cloak. Luke 6:29
and of him that t. thy goods. 30
spirit t. him, and he suddenly. 9:39
a stronger t. from him all his. 11:22
my lord t. away from me the. 16:3
the Lamb of God which t. John 1:29
no man t. it from me, I lay it. 10:18
beareth not fruit, he t. away. 15:2
your joy no man t. from you. 16:22
Jesus then cometh, t. bread. 21:13
is God unrighteous, who t.? Rom 3:5*
in eating every one t. 1 Cor 11:21
no man t. this honour. Heb 5:4
he t. away the first that he may. 10:9

taketh *hold*

I am afraid, and trembling t. hold on my flesh. Job 21:6
the spider t. hold with. Pr 30:28
every one that t. hold of. Isa 56:6

taking

with God there is no t. of. 2 Chr 19:7
I have seen the foolish t. root. Job 5:3
by t. heed thereto. Ps 119:9
at noise of t. of Babylon. Jer 50:46
dealt against Judah by t. Ezek 25:12
I taught Ephraim also to go, t. them by their arms. Hos 11:3
which of you by t. thought? Mat 6:27*; Luke 12:25*
Son of man is as a man t. a far. Mark 13:34*
the devil, t. him up into. Luke 4:5
t. up that I laid not down. 19:22
he had spoken of t. rest. John 11:13
sin t. occasion by the. Rom 7:8, 11
t. my leave of them, I. 2 Cor 2:13
t. wages of them to do you. 11:8
above all t. the shield of. Eph 6:16
in flaming fire t. vengeance on them. 2 Thes 1:8*
t. the oversight thereof. 1 Pet 5:2*
they went forth t. nothing. 3 John 7

tale (*quantity*)

the t. of bricks which. Ex 5:8
he deliver the t. of bricks. 18
they gave the foreskins in full t. to the king. 1 Sam 18:27
bring vessels in and out by t. 1 Chr 9:28

tale

years as a t. that is told. Ps 90:

talebearer

up and down as a t. Lev 19:
a t. revealeth. Pr 11:13; 20:
the words of a t. are. 18:8*; 26:22
where there is no t., the strife. 26:20

talent

[1] *A weight among the Jews, of 5 to 100 pounds, according to th standard in use at the time. Th value of the gold talent would be a as much as 29,000 dollars, or near £6000, that of the silver talent u to 1940 dollars, or nearly £40 In the times of the New Testame the talent was reckoned only silver, and was worth about 115 dollars, or £240. These amoun are not intended to be absolute exact, but give values in roun numbers. There is great diversi in estimates given,* Ex 25:39; 38:2 [2] *The gifts of God bestowed o men,* Mat 25:15.

of a t. of pure gold make it. Ex 25:39; 37:2
sockets, a t. for a socket. 38:2
the weight of the crown was a t. 2 Sam 12:3
pay a t. of silver. 1 Ki 20:3
give them a t. of silver. 2 Ki 5:2
a tribute of a t. of gold. 23:3
2 Chr 36:
lifted up a t. of lead. Zech 5:
hid thy t. in the earth. Mat 25:2
take therefore the t. from him. 2
about the weight of a t. Rev 16:2

talents

of the offering, was 29 t. Ex 38:2
of 100 t. of silver were cast. 2
hill of Samaria for two t. 1 Ki 16:2
Naaman took ten t. 2 Ki 5:
be content, take two t. 2
Menahem gave Pul 1000 t. 15:1
Hezekiah 300 t. and 30 of gold. 18:1
land to a tribute of 100 t. 23:3
2 Chr 36:
Ammonites sent 1000 t. 1 Chr 19:
David gave 3000 t. of gold. 29:
gold, 5000 t. and of silver 10,000 t.
we do for the 100 t.? 2 Chr 25:
of Ammon gave him 100 t. 27:
owed him 10,000 t. Mat 18:2
gave five t., to another two. 25:1

see **gold, silver**

tales

men that carry t. to. Ezek 22:9
their words seemed to them as idl t. Luke 24:11

Talitha cumi

(*An Aramaic expression meanin Damsel, arise. Used by Jesu when raising Jairus's daughter*)

he said unto her, T., damsel, arise. Mark 5:4

talk

should a man full of t.? Job 11:
reason with unprofitable t.? 15:
the t. of the lips tendeth. Pr 14:2
end of his t. is mischievous. Eccl 10:1
entangle him in his t. Mat 22:1

talk, *verb*

I will come down and t. Num 11:1
God doth t. with man. Deut 5:2
t. of them when thou sittest. 6:
t. no more so exceeding proudly. 1 Sam 2:
t. not with us in the Jews' languag 2 Ki 18:2
sing psalms, t. ye of all his won drous. 1 Chr 16:9; Ps 105:
and will ye t. deceitfully? Job 13:
they t. to the grief of. Ps 69:2
my tongue shall t. of thy. 71:2
meditate and t. of thy doings. 77:1
I t. of thy wondrous works. 119:2
kingdom and t. of thy power. 145:1
awakest it shall t. with thee. Pr 6:2
and their lips t. of mischief. 24:
let me t. with thee of. Jer 12:

arise and I will there *t*. *Ezek* 3:22
servant *t*. with my lord ? *Dan* 10:17
I will not *t*. much with. *John* 14:30

talked

brethren *t*. with him. *Gen* 45:15
ye have seen that I have *t*. with you.
Ex 20:22; *Deut* 5:4
and the Lord *t*. with Moses. *Ex* 33:9
of his face shone while he *t*. 34:29
Saul *t*. unto the priest. *1 Sam* 14:19
to pass as he *t*. with him. *2 Chr* 25:16
princes hear that I have *t*. *Jer* 38:25
t. with him two men, Moses and.
Luke 9:30
heart burn, while he *t*. with us? 24:32
marvelled that he *t*. with. *John* 4:27
Peter *t*. with Cornelius. *Acts* 10:27
and *t*. long, even till break of. 20:11
they *t*. between themselves. 26:31
he that *t*. with me had a. *Rev* 21:15

talkers

up in the lips of *t*. *Ezek* 36:3
unruly and vain *t*. *Tit* 1:10

talkest

sign that thou *t*. with me. *Judg* 6:17
yet *t*. with the king. *1 Ki* 1:14
no man said, Why *t*. thou with her?
John 4:27

talketh

tongue *t*. of judgement. *Ps* 37:30
seen him, and it is he that *t*. with.
John 9:37

talking

he left off *t*. with him. *Gen* 17:22
he is a god, he is *t*. or. *1 Ki* 18:27
they were *t*. with him. *Esth* 6:14
the princes refrained *t*. and. *Job* 29:9
thy people are still *t*. *Ezek* 33:30
Moses and Elias *t*. with him.
Mat 17:3; *Mark* 9:4
neither filthiness, nor foolish *t*.
Eph 5:4
a trumpet *t*. with me. *Rev* 4:1

tall

a people *t*. as the Anakims.
Deut 2:10, 21; 9:2
cut down the *t*. cedar trees and the choice fir. *2 Ki* 19:23; *Isa* 37:24

taller

people is greater and *t*. *Deut* 1:28

Tamar

Er, whose name was *T*. *Gen* 38:6
was told Judah, *T*. hath played. 24
house of Pharez, whom *T*. bare to.
Ruth 4:12; *1 Chr* 2:4; *Mat* 1:3
a fair sister, named *T*. *2 Sam* 13:1
Ammon fell sick for *T*. 2
he forced *T*. 22, 32
daughter, whose name was *T*. 14:27
side southward from *T*. *Ezek* 47:19

tame

nor could any man *t*. him. *Mark* 5:4
but the tongue can no man *t*.; it is an unruly evil. *Jas* 3:8

tamed

n sea, is *t*., and hath been *t*. *Jas* 3:7

Tammuz

there sat women weeping for *T*.
Ezek 8:14

tanner

Peter tarried with one Simon a *t*.
Acts 9:43
odged with one Simon a *t*. 10:6, 32

tapestry, *see* **coverings**

tare

he king arose and *t*. *2 Sam* 13:31*
wo she bears *t*. forty. *2 Ki* 2:24
straightway the spirit *t*. him.
Mark 9:20; *Luke* 9:42

tares

Darnel, *a weed of which some arieties are poisonous. It looks nuch like wheat until near harvest ime. when the two can be readily istinguished,* Mat 13:29.
is enemy sowed *t*. *Mat* 13:25
p, then appeared the *t*. also. 26
rom whence then hath it *t*.? 27
est while ye gather up the *t*. 29
eclare to us the parable of the *t*. 36

target

(*A large, heavy shield*)
Goliath had a *t*. of. *1 Sam* 17:6*
six hundred shekels of gold went to one *t*. *1 Ki* 10:16†; *2 Chr* 9:15†

targets

made two hundred *t*. *1 Ki* 10:16†
Asa had an army that bare *t*. and.
2 Chr 14:8*

tarried

Abraham's servant *t*. all. *Gen* 24:54
Jacob *t*. there all night and. 28:11
Jacob and Laban *t*. all night in. 31:54
when the cloud *t*. *Num* 9:19, 22
t. till they were ashamed. *Judg* 3:25
Ehud escaped while they *t*. and. 26
they *t*. till afternoon and did. 19:8
save that she *t*. a little. *Ruth* 2:7
t. seven days according. *1 Sam* 13:8
but David *t*. still at. *2 Sam* 11:1
the king *t*. in a place that. 15:17
Zadok and Abiathar *t*. at. 29
but he *t*. longer than the set. 20:5
they came, for he *t*. at. *2 Ki* 2:18
and she that *t*. at home. *Ps* 68:12
while the bridegroom *t*. *Mat* 25:5
marvelled that he *t*. *Luke* 1:21
the child Jesus *t*. behind in. 2:43
then he *t*. with them. *John* 3:22
Peter *t*. many days in Joppa.
Acts 9:43
Judas and Silas . . . *t*. a space. 15:33
Paul *t*. a good while at Corinth and.
18:18
these going before *t*. for us at. 20:5
finding the disciples, we *t*. 21:4
as we *t*. many days at Caesarea. 10
Festus *t*. at Jerusalem more. 25:6
fourteenth day ye have *t*. fasting.
27:33
landing at Syracuse, we *t*. 28:12

tarriest

now why *t*. thou ? arise. *Acts* 22:16

tarrieth

shall his part be that *t*. *1 Sam* 30:24
that *t*. not for a man, nor. *Mi* 5:7

tarry

[1] *To remain,* Gen 27:41. [2] *To wait for,* Ex 24:14. [3] *To delay,* Gen 45:9.

and *t*. all night, and. *Gen* 19:2
and *t*. with Laban a few days. 27:44
found favour in thine eyes, *t*. 30:27
Come down to me, *t*. not. 45:9
thrust out, and could not *t*. *Ex* 12:39
t. ye here for us till we come. 24:14
leper shall *t*. out of his tent. *Lev* 14:8
I pray you *t*. here also. *Num* 22:19
why *t*. the wheels of ? *Judg* 5:28
he said, I will *t*. until thou. 6:18
and *t*. all night. 19:6, 9
the man would not *t*. 10
would ye *t*. for them till they were grown ? *Ruth* 1:13
t. this night, and it shall be. 3:13
t. until thou have weaned him.
1 Sam 1:23
seven days shalt thou *t*. till I. 10:8
if they say, *T*. till we come. 14:9
t. at Jericho till your beards be.
2 Sam 10:5; *1 Chr* 19:5
t. here to-day. *2 Sam* 11:12
I will *t*. in the plain. 15:28
Joab said, I may not *t*. thus. 18:14
will not *t*. one with thee. 19:7
t. here. I pray thee; for the Lord hath sent me. *2 Ki* 2:2, 4, 6
the lepers said, If we *t*. till the. 7:9
open door and flee, and *t*. not. 9:3
glory of this, and *t*. at home. 14:10
a liar shall not *t*. in my. *Ps* 101:7
that *t*. long at the wine. *Pr* 23:30
my salvation shall not *t*. *Isa* 46:13
that turneth aside to *t*. *Jer* 14:8
t., wait for it; for it will not *t*. *Hab* 2:3
t. ye here and watch. *Mat* 26:38
Mark 14:34
and he went in to *t*. *Luke* 24:29
but *t*. ye in the city of Jerusalem. 49
besought that he would *t*. *John* 4:40
if I will that he *t*. till. 21:22, 23
they prayed Peter to *t*. *Acts* 10:48
desired Paul to *t*. longer. *Acts* 18:20
were desired to *t*. with them. 28:14
wherefore *t*. one for. *1 Cor* 11:33
I trust to *t*. a while with you. 16:7
but I will *t*. at Ephesus until. 8
but if I *t*. long, that. *1 Tim* 3:15
he that shall come, will come and not *t*. *Heb* 10:37

tarrying

make no *t*. O my God. *Ps* 40:17
70:5

Tarshish

the sons of Javan; Elishah, and *T*.
Gen 10:4; *1 Chr* 1:7
king had at sea a navy of *T*. with a.
1 Ki 10:22; *2 Chr* 9:21
make ships to go to *T*. *2 Chr* 20:36
broken and not able to go to *T*. 37
thou breakest ships of *T*. *Ps* 48:7
the kings of *T*. shall bring. 72:10
Lord on all the ships of *T*. *Isa* 2:16
howl, ye ships of *T*. it is. 23:1, 14
over to *T*. howl, ye inhabitants. 6
thy land, O daughter of *T*. 10
the ships of *T*. shall wait for. 60:9
send those that escape to *T*. 66:19
silver is brought from *T*. *Jer* 10:9
T. was thy merchant. *Ezek* 27:12
the ships of *T*. did sing of thee. 25
the merchants of *T*. shall say. 38:13
rose up to flee unto *T*. *Jonah* 1:3
therefore I fled before unto *T*. 4:2

Tarsus

enquire for one Saul of *T*. *Acts* 9:11
brethren sent him forth to *T*. 30
Barnabas departed to *T*. to. 11:25
I am a man who am a Jew of *T*.
21:39; 22:3

Tartak

the Avites made *T*. *2 Ki* 17:31

task, -s

your works, your daily *t*. *Ex* 5:13
why not fulfilled your *t*. in ? 14
minish from your daily *t*. 19

taskmasters

set over them *t*. to afflict. *Ex* 1:11
cry by reason of their *t*. 3:7
and Pharaoh commanded *t*. 5:6
t. told them. 10
t. hasted them. 13
officers which the *t*. had set. 14

taste

the *t*. of manna was like. *Ex* 16:31
the *t*. of it was as the *t*. of fresh oil.
Num 11:8
is there any *t*. in the white of an egg ?
Job 6:6
cannot my *t*. discern perverse ? 30
are thy words to my *t*.! *Ps* 119:103
honeycomb is sweet to *t*. *Pr* 24:13
fruit was sweet to my *t*. *S of S* 2:3
his *t*. remained in him. *Jer* 48:11

taste, *verb*

[1] *To try the relish of any thing by the tongue,* Job 34:3. [2] *Figuratively,* to prove, Ps 34:8. [3] *To eat a little,* 1 Sam 14:29, 43.

did but *t*. a little honey. *1 Sam* 14:43
if I *t*. bread or aught else. *2 Sam* 3:35
can thy servant *t*. what I eat ? 19:35
the mouth *t*. his meat ? *Job* 12:11
O *t*. and see that the Lord. *Ps* 34:8
neither herd nor flock *t*. *Jonah* 3:7
standing here which shall not *t*. of.
Mat 16:28; *Mark* 9:1; *Luke* 9:27
none bidden shall *t*. of. *Luke* 14:24
he shall never *t*. death. *John* 8:52
touch not, *t*. not, handle. *Col* 2:21
that he should *t*. death. *Heb* 2:9

tasted

so none *t*. any food. *1 Sam* 14:24
I *t*. a little of this honey. 29
Belshazzar, whiles he *t*. wine.
Dan 5:2
when he had *t*. thereof. *Mat* 27:34
the ruler had *t*. the water. *John* 2:9
t. of the heavenly gift. *Heb* 6:4
have *t*. the good word of God. 5
have *t*. that the Lord. *1 Pet* 2:3

tasteth
words as the mouth *t.* *Job* 34:3

tattlers
not only idle but *t.* and. *1 Tim* 5:13

taught
I have *t.* you statutes. *Deut* 4:5
Moses *t.* the children of Israel. 31:22
with them he *t.* the men. *Judg* 8:16
and *t.* them how to fear. *2 Ki* 17:28
thou hast *t.* them the. *2 Chr* 6:27
Levites *t.* the people in Judah. 17:9
people rejoiced, such as *t.* 23:13
that *t.* the good knowledge of. 30:22*
said to the Levites that *t.* all. 35:3
that *t.* the people said. *Neh* 8:9
O God, thou hast *t.* me. *Ps* 71:17
119:102
when thou hast *t.* me. 119:171
he *t.* me also, and said. *Pr* 4:4
t. thee in the way of wisdom. 11
prophecy that his mother *t.* him. 31:1
he still *t.* the people. *Eccl* 12:9
their fear is *t.* by the. *Isa* 29:13
counsellor hath *t.* him. 40:13, 14
all thy children shall be *t.* 54:13
hast thou *t.* the wicked. *Jer* 2:33
t. their tongues to speak lies. 9:5
which their fathers *t.* them. 14
t. my people to swear by. 12:16
for thou hast *t.* them to be. 13:21
thou hast *t.* rebellion against. 28:16
he hath *t.* rebellion against. 29:32
though I have *t.* them, rising. 32:33
women *t.* not to do after. *Ezek* 23:48
as a heifer that is *t.* *Hos* 10:11
I *t.* Ephraim to go, taking them. 11:3
man *t.* me to keep cattle. *Zech* 13:5*
he *t.* them as one having authority.
Mat 7:29; *Mark* 1:22
and did as they were *t.* *Mat* 28:15
told him all things they had done and
t. *Mark* 6:30
as he was wont he *t.* them. 10:1
while he *t.* in the temple. 12:35
Luke 19:47; 20:1; *John* 7:14, 28
teach us to pray, as John *t.* his.
Luke 11:1
thou hast *t.* in our streets. 13:26
shall be all *t.* of God. *John* 6:45
he sat down and *t.* them. 8:2
as my father hath *t.* me, I. 28
I ever *t.* in the synagogue and. 18:20
being grieved that they *t.* the people.
Acts 4:2
into the temple early and *t.* 5:21
Paul and Barnabas *t.* much people.
11:26; 14:21
certain men *t.* the brethren. 15:1
t. diligently the things of the. 18:25
I have shewed you, and *t.* 20:20
t. according to the perfect. 22:3
nor was I *t.* it but by. *Gal* 1:12
let him that is *t.* in the word. 6:6
been *t.* by him as truth. *Eph* 4:21
the faith, as ye have been *t.* *Col* 2:7
ye are *t.* of God to love. *1 Thes* 4:9
hold the traditions ye have been *t.*
2 Thes 2:15
the word, as he hath been *t.* *Tit* 1:9
anointing hath *t.* you. *1 John* 2:27
who *t.* Balak to cast a. *Rev* 2:14

taunt
will deliver them to be a *t.* *Jer* 24:9
a reproach and a *t.* *Ezek* 5:15

taunting
all these take up a *t.* proverb.
Hab 2:6

taverns
meet us as far as the three *t.*
Acts 28:15*

taxation
every one according to *t.* *2 Ki* 23:35

taxed
but Jehoiakim *t.* the. *2 Ki* 23:35
a decree that all the world should be
t. *Luke* 2:1*
all went to be *t.* 3*
Joseph went to be *t.* 5*

taxes
stand up a raiser of *t.* *Dan* 11:20

taxing
and this *t.* was first made. *Luke* 2:2*
in the days of the *t.* *Acts* 5:37*

teach
and I will *t.* you what. *Ex* 4:15
in his heart that he may *t.* 35:34
that ye may *t.* Israel. *Lev* 10:11
to *t.* when it is unclean and. 14:57
judgements which I *t.* you. *Deut* 4:1
and that they may *t.* their children. 10
Lord commanded me to *t.* 14; 6:1
t. you not to do after their. 20:18
priests the Levites shall *t.* you. 24:8
write and *t.* the children of. 31:19
shall *t.* Jacob thy judgements. 33:10
t. us what we shall do. *Judg* 13:8
I will *t.* you the good. *1 Sam* 12:23
bade them *t.* the use. *2 Sam* 1:18
to *t.* in the cities of. *2 Chr* 17:7
to *t.* in Israel statutes. *Ezra* 7:10
any *t.* God knowledge? *Job* 21:22
t. you by the hand of God. 27:11
of years should *t.* wisdom. 32:7
t. us what we shall say unto. 37:19
will *t.* sinners in the way. *Ps* 25:8
will he guide and *t.* his way. 9
him that feareth Lord shall he *t.* 12
t. you the fear of the Lord. 34:11
then will I *t.* transgressors. 51:13
so *t.* us to number our days. 90:12
and *t.* his senators wisdom. 105:22
t. a just man, and he will. *Pr* 9:9
and he will *t.* us of his ways. *Isa* 2:3
Mi 4:2
whom shall he *t.* knowledge? *Isa* 28:9
for his God doth instruct and *t.* 26
and *t.* your daughters. *Jer* 9:20
they shall *t.* no more every man his.
31:34; *Heb* 8:11
t. my people the difference between.
Ezek 44:23
whom they might *t.* learning of.
Dan 1:4
priests thereof *t.* for hire. *Mi* 3:11
stone, Arise, it shall *t.*! *Hab* 2:19
shall *t.* men so. *Mat* 5:19
t. all nations. 28:19
Lord, *t.* us to pray, as. *Luke* 11:1
Holy Ghost shall *t.* you what. 12:12
t. the Gentiles. *John* 7:35
dost thou *t.* us? 9:34
Holy Ghost shall *t.* you all. 14:26
Jesus began to do and *t.* *Acts* 1:1
speak nor *t.* in the name of Jesus.
4:18; 5:28
to *t.* and preach Jesus Christ. 5:42
t. customs which are not. 16:21
as I *t.* every where in. *1 Cor* 4:17
even nature itself *t.* you? 11:14
that by my voice I might *t.* 14:19
charge some they *t.* no. *1 Tim* 1:3
but I suffer not a woman to *t.* 2:12
bishop must be apt to *t.* 3:2
2 Tim 2:24
things command and *t.* *1 Tim* 4:11
these things *t.* and exhort. 6:2
if any man *t.* otherwise, he. 3
shall be able to *t.* others. *2 Tim* 2:2
that they *t.* young women. *Tit* 2:4
ye have need that one *t.* *Heb* 5:12
not that any man *t.* you. *1 John* 2:27
that woman Jezebel to *t.* *Rev* 2:20
see **began**

teach *me*
t. me and I will hold my. *Job* 6:24
I see not, *t.* thou *me*. 34:32
t. me thy paths. *Ps* 25:4
lead me and *t. me*. 5
t. me thy way, O Lord. 27:11; 86:11
t. me thy statutes. 119:12, 26, 33
64, 68, 124, 135
t. me good judgements. 119:66
t. me thy judgements. 108
t. me to do thy will, for. 143:10

teach *thee*
I will *t. thee* what thou. *Ex* 4:12
which they shall *t. thee*. *Deut* 17:11
shall not they *t thee*? *Job* 8:10
beasts, and they shall *t. thee*. 12:7
earth, and it shall *t. thee*. 8
I shall *t. thee* wisdom. 33:33
I will *t. thee* in the way. *Ps* 32:8
thy right hand shall *t. thee*. 45:4

teach *them*
t. them ordinances and. *Ex* 18:20
that thou mayest *t. them*. 24:12
t. them thy sons, and. *Deut* 4:9
which thou shalt *t. them*. 5:31
t. them diligently to thy. 6:7; 11:19
know to *t. them* war. *Judg* 3:2
that thou *t. them* the good way.
1 Ki 8:36
t. them the manner of. *2 Ki* 17:27
t. ye *them* that know. *Ezra* 7:25
keep my testimony that I shall *t.*
them. *Ps* 132:12
do and *t. them* shall be. *Mat* 5:19
he began to *t. them*. *Mark* 6:34
to *t. them* that the son of. 8:31

teacher
cast lots, as well the *t.* *1 Chr* 25:8
the image, a *t.* of lies. *Hab* 2:18
we know thou art a *t.* *John* 3:2
thou art a *t.* of babes. *Rom* 2:20
I am a *t.* *1 Tim* 2:7; *2 Tim* 1:11

teachers
more understanding than all my *t.*
Ps 119:99
obeyed the voice of my *t.* *Pr* 5:13
t. be removed into a corner any
more . . . shall see thy *t.* *Isa* 30:20
thy *t.* have transgressed. 43:27*
certain prophets and *t.* *Acts* 13:1
hath set prophets, *t.* *1 Cor* 12:28
are all *t.*? 29
evangelists, pastors, and *t.* *Eph* 4:11
desiring to be *t.* of law. *1 Tim* 1:7
to themselves *t.* having. *2 Tim* 4:3
that the aged women be *t.* *Tit* 2:3
time ye ought to be *t.* *Heb* 5:12
as there shall be false *t.* *2 Pet* 2:1

teachest
the man whom thou *t.* *Ps* 94:12
thou art true, and *t.* the way of God.
Mat 22:16; *Mark* 12:14; *Luke* 20:21
thou *t.* the Jews to. *Acts* 21:21
thou that *t.* another, *t.*? *Rom* 2:21

teacheth
he *t.* my hands to war. *2 Sam* 22:35
Ps 18:34
t. us more than the beasts. *Job* 35:11
God exalteth, who *t.* like? 36:22
that *t.* man knowledge. *Ps* 94:10
which *t.* my hands to war. 144:1
a wicked man *t.* with. *Pr* 6:13*
of the wise *t.* his mouth. 16:23*
the prophet that *t.* lies. *Isa* 9:15
I am thy God which *t.* thee. 48:17
the man that *t.* all men. *Acts* 21:28
or he that *t.*, on teaching. *Rom* 12:7
man's wisdom *t.* but which the Holy
Ghost *t.* *1 Cor* 2:13
let him communicate to him that *t.*
Gal 6:6
as the same anointing *t.* *1 John* 2:27

teaching
been without a *t.* priest. *2 Chr* 15:3
rising up early and *t.* them.
Jer 32:33
Jesus went about Galilee, *t.* in their.
Mat 4:23; 9:35; *Luke* 13:10
worship me, *t.* for doctrines the.
Mat 15:9; *Mark* 7:7
unto him as he was *t.* *Mat* 21:23
I sat daily with you *t.* in. 26:55
t. them to observe all things. 28:20
t. throughout all Jewry. *Luke* 23:5
the apostles *t.* the people. *Acts* 5:25
Barnabas continued in Antioch, *t.*
and preaching. 15:35
Paul *t.* the word of God at. 18:11
Paul *t.* at Rome with all. 28:31
or he that teacheth, on *t.* *Rom* 12:7
warning and *t.* every man. *Col* 1:28
t. and admonishing one another. 3:16
t. things which they. *Tit* 1:11
t. us, that denying ungodliness. 2:12

tear
then will I *t.* your flesh. *Judg* 8:7
lest he *t.* my soul like a lion. *Ps* 7:2
did *t.* me and ceased not. 35:15
lest I *t.* you in pieces. 50:22
over them the dogs to *t.* *Jer* 15:3
nor shall men *t.* themselves. 16:7*

pillows I will *t.* from. *Ezek* 13:20
kerchiefs will I *t.* and deliver. 21
I, even I, will *t.* and go. *Hos* 5:14
the wild beast shall *t.* them. 13:8
off pity, his anger did *t.* *Amos* 1:11
the lion did *t.* enough. *Nah* 2:12
the shepherd shall *t.* *Zech* 11:16

teareth

lion, and *t.* the arm. *Deut* 33:20
he *t.* me in his wrath. *Job* 16:9
he *t.* himself in his anger. 18:4
as a young lion *t.* in pieces. *Mi* 5:8
taketh him, he *t.* him and he foameth. *Mark* 9:18*; *Luke* 9:39

tears

I have seen thy *t.* *2 Ki* 20:5; *Isa* 38:5
but mine eye poureth out *t.* unto. *Job* 16:20
I water my couch with my *t.* *Ps* 6:6
hold not thy peace at my *t.* 39:12
my *t.* have been my meat day. 42:3
put thou my *t.* in thy bottle. 56:8
feedest them with the bread of *t.* and givest them *t.* to drink in. 80:5
delivered mine eyes from *t.* 116:8
that sow in *t.* shall reap in joy. 126:5
behold the *t.* of such as. *Eccl* 4:1
I will water thee with *t.* *Isa* 16:9
wipe away *t.* from all faces. 25:8
eyes were a fountain of *t.* *Jer* 9:1
our eyes may run down with *t.* 18
mine eyes shall run down with *t.* 13:17
let mine eyes run with *t.* 14:17
weeping, thine eyes from *t.* 31:16
she weepeth, and her *t.* are. *Lam* 1:2
mine eyes do fail with *t.* 2:11
let *t.* run down like a river. 18
neither shall thy *t.* *Ezek* 24:16
altar of the Lord with *t.* *Mal* 2:13
the father said with *t.* *Mark* 9:24
wash his feet with her *t.* *Luke* 7:38
she hath washed my feet with *t.* 44
serving the Lord with many *t.* *Acts* 20:19
to warn every one with *t.* 31
wrote to you with many *t.* *2 Cor* 2:4
being mindful of thy *t.* *2 Tim* 1:4
up supplications with *t.* *Heb* 5:7
sought it carefully with *t.* 12:17
shall wipe away all *t.* *Rev* 7:17; 21:4

teats

shall lament for the *t.* *Isa* 32:12*
they bruised the *t.* *Ezek* 23:3†, 21†

Tebeth

tenth month, which is *T.* *Esth* 2:16

tedious

that I be not further *t.* *Acts* 24:4

teeth

and his *t.* shall be white. *Gen* 49:12
flesh was yet between their *t.* *Num* 11:33
t. of beasts upon them. *Deut* 32:24
fleshhook of three *t.* *1 Sam* 2:13
the *t.* of the young lions. *Job* 4:10
I take my flesh in my *t.*? 13:14
with the skin of my *t.* 19:20
plucked the spoil out of his *t.* 29:17
Leviathan's *t.* are terrible. 41:14
thou hast broken the *t.* of. *Ps* 3:7
whose *t.* are spears and arrows. 57:4*
break their *t.*, O God, in. 58:6
given us as a prey to their *t.* 124:6
as vinegar to the *t.* so. *Pr* 10:26
whose *t.* are like swords, jaw-*t.* 30:14
thy *t.* are like a flock. *S of S* 4:2; 6:6
an instrument having *t.* *Isa* 41:15
children's *t.* are set on edge. *Jer* 31:29; *Ezek* 18:2
eateth sour grapes, his *t.* *Jer* 31:30
hath broken my *t.* with. *Lam* 3:16
ribs between the *t.* of it. *Dan* 7:5
beast had great iron *t.* 7, 19
hath the cheek *t.* of a lion. *Joel* 1:6
you cleanness of *t.* *Amos* 4:6
that bite with their *t.* *Mi* 3:5
from between his *t.* *Zech* 9:7
cast the same in his *t.* *Mat* 27:44*
t. were as the *t.* of lions. *Rev* 9:8

see **gnash**

tell *tree*

as a *t. tree* and as an oak. *Isa* 6:13

Tekel

written, Mene, Mene, *T.* *Dan* 5:25
T. thou art weighed in the. 27

Tekoah, *or* Tekoa

Joab sent to *T.* to fetch. *2 Sam* 14:2
when the woman of *T.* spake to. 4
Abiah bare Ashur the father of *T.* *1 Chr* 2:24
Ashur the father of *T.* had two. 4:5
built Etam and *T.* *2 Chr* 11:6
went into the wilderness of *T.* 20:20
blow the trumpet in *T.* *Jer* 6:1
was among herdmen of *T.* *Amos* 1:1

tell

[1] *To count, number, or reckon,* Gen 15:5. [2] *To declare or make known,* Gen 12:18; 21:26.

t. the stars if thou be. *Gen* 15:5
and I have sent to *t.* my Lord. 32:5
as to *t.* the man whether ye. 43:6
we cannot *t.* who put our money. 22
t. my father of all my glory. 45:13
mayest *t.* in the ears. *Ex* 10:2
t. the priest, saying, It. *Lev* 14:35
they will *t.* it to the. *Num* 14:14
t. us wherewith we shall *1 Sam* 6:2
give to the man of God, to *t.* 9:8
liveth, O king, I cannot *t.* 17:55
he would surely *t.* Saul. 22:22
I beseech thee *t.* thy servant. 23:11
should *t.* on us, saying, So. 27:11
t. it not in Gath. *2 Sam* 1:20
go *t.* my servant. 7:5; *1 Chr* 17:4
feared to *t.* him that. *2 Sam* 12:18
was alive, I said, Who can *t.*? 22
thou shalt *t.* to Zadok and. 15:35
go *t.* the king what thou hast. 18:21
that thou shouldest *t.* *1 Ki* 1:20
go, *t.* thy lord, Elijah is. 18:8, 11, 14
when I come and *t.* Ahab, he. 12
t. my lord the king, all thou. 20:9
t. him, let not him that girdeth. 11
that we may *t.* the king's. *2 Ki* 7:9
It is false; *t.* us now. 9:12
to go to *t.* it in Jezreel. 15
t. the man that sent you. 22:15; *2 Chr* 34:23
I may *t.* all my bones. *Ps* 22:17
publish and *t.* of all thy. 26:7
go round about her, *t.* the. 48:12
that ye may *t.* the generation. 13
son's name, if thou canst *t.* *Pr* 30:4
who can *t.* a man what shall be after? *Eccl* 6:12; 10:14
for who can *t.* him when it? 8:7
hath wings shall *t.* the matter. 10:20
t. him that I am sick of. *S of S* 5:8
go and *t.* this people. *Isa* 6:9
t. this. 48:20
t. such as are for death. *Jer* 15:2
dreams which they *t.* 23:27; 28:32
we will *t.* the king of all. 36:16
t. us now how thou didst write. 17
t. it in Arnon, that Moab is. 48:20
wilt thou not *t.* us what? *Ezek* 24:19
O king, *t.* thy servants the dream. *Dan* 2:4, 7, 9
t. the king the interpretation. 36
t. ye your children, and let your children *t.* their children. *Joel* 1:3
who can *t.* if God will? *Jonah* 3:9
see thou *t.* no man. *Mat* 8:4; *Mark* 8:26, 30; 9:9; *Luke* 5:14; 8:56; *Acts* 23:22
disciples that they should *t.* no man. *Mat* 16:20; *Mark* 7:36; *Luke* 9:21
t. the vision to no man. *Mat* 17:9
t. him his fault. 18:15
t. it unto the church. 17
t. ye the daughter of Sion. 21:5
t. us, when shall these things be? 24:3; *Mark* 13:4
that thou *t.* us, whether. *Mat* 26:63; *Luke* 22:67; *John* 10:24
go and *t.* his disciples that. *Mat* 28:7
as they went to *t.* his disciples. 9; *Mark* 16:7
anon they *t.* him of her. *Mark* 1:30
t. them how great things the. 5:19
said, We cannot *t.* 11:33; *Luke* 20:7
t. John what things ye. *Luke* 7:22
go ye, and *t.* that fox, I cast. 13:32
but canst not *t.* whence. *John* 3:8
when he is come, he will *t.* 4:25
but ye cannot *t.* whence I come. 8:14
we cannot *t.* what he saith. 16:18
or did other *t.* thee of me? 18:34
who shall *t.* you the. *Acts* 15:27
but either to *t.* or hear some. 17:21
certain thing to *t.* him. 23:17
the body I cannot *t.* *2 Cor* 12:2, 3
fail to *t.* of Gideon. *Heb* 11:32

tell *me*

why didst not *t. me* she? *Gen* 12:18
t. me nor heard I of it. 21:26
t. me whose daughter art? 24:23
t. me, and if not, *t. me* that I. 49
t. me what shall thy wages be? 29:15
from me, and didst not *t. me.* 31:27
t. me thy name. 32:29
t. me where they feed. 37:16
t. me now what thou hast done, hide. *Josh* 7:19
t. me wherein thy great. *Judg* 16:6
wilt not redeem it, *t. me.* *Ruth* 4:4
t. me where the seer's. *1 Sam* 9:18
t. me I pray thee what Samuel. 10:15
Saul said, *T. me* what thou. 14:43
Jonathan, who shall *t. me*? 20:10
how went the matter? *t. me,* I. *2 Sam* 1:4
lean, wilt thou not *t. me*? 13:4
that thou *t. me* nothing *1 Ki* 22:16
shall I do for thee? *t. me.* *2 Ki* 4:2
t. me the great things that. 8:4
of understanding *t. me.* *Job* 34:34
t. me, O thou whom. *S of S* 1:7
which if ye *t. me.* *Mat* 21:24
t. me which of them. *Luke* 7:42
t. me where thou hast. *John* 20:15
t. me whether ye sold the. *Acts* 5:8
t. me, art thou a Roman? 22:27
is that thou hast to *t. me*? 23:19
t. me, ye that desire to. *Gal* 4:21

tell *thee*

one of the mountains I will *t. thee* of. *Gen* 22:2
land which I will *t. thee* of. 26:2
word we did *t. thee* in. *Ex* 14:12
sheweth me, I will *t. thee.* *Num* 23:3
the judgement which they shall *t. thee.* *Deut* 17:11
elders, and they will *t. thee.* 32:7
not told it and shall I *t.* it *thee*? *Judg* 14:16
he will *t. thee* what thou. *Ruth* 3:4
I will *t. thee* all that is. *1 Sam* 9:19
I will *t. thee* what the Lord. 15:16
I see, that I will *t. thee.* 19:3
then would not I *t.* it *thee*? 20:9
t. thee what shall become of the child. *1 Ki* 14:3
did I not *t. thee* that he would prophesy no good? 22:18; *2 Chr* 18:17
I *t. thee* that the Lord. *1 Chr* 17:10
I am escaped alone to *t. thee.* *Job* 1:15, 16, 17, 19
teach thee and *t. thee.* 8:10
the air, and they shall *t. thee.* 12:7
if I were hungry I would not *t. thee.* *Ps* 50:12
let thy wise men *t. thee.* *Isa* 19:12
words that I shall *t. thee.* *Jer* 19:2
I *t. thee* thou shalt not. *Luke* 12:59
t. thee, the cock shall not. 22:34
he shall *t. thee* what thou oughtest to do. *Acts* 10:6; 11:14
I will *t. thee* the mystery. *Rev* 17:7

I* tell *you,* or tell *I you

that *I* may *t. you* what. *Gen* 49:1
I will *t. you* what I will do. *Isa* 5:5
they spring forth, *I t. you.* 42:9
I t. you in darkness. *Mat* 10:27
neither *t. I you* by what authority. 21:27; *Mark* 11:33; *Luke* 20:8
I will *t. you* by what. *Mark* 11:29
but *I t. you* of a truth. *Luke* 4:25; 9:27
I t. you that many prophets. 10:24
I t. you nay, but rather. 12:51
I t. you nay, but except. 13:3, 5
I t. you I know not whence. 27
I t. you there shall be two. 17:34

I t. you that he will avenge. *Luke* 18:8
I t. you this man went to his. 14
I t. you that if these should. 19:40
he said, If *I t. you* ye will not. 22:67
shall ye believe if *I t. you* ? *John* 3:12
because *I t. you* the truth. 8:45
Gal 4:16
I t. you before it come. *John* 13:19
I t. you the truth, it is. 16:7
of which *I t. you* before. *Gal* 5:21
of whom *I* now *t. you*. *Phil* 3:18

tellest

thou *t.* my wanderings. *Ps* 56:8

telleth

the Lord *t.* thee that he. *2 Sam* 7:11
Elisha *t.* the king of. *2 Ki* 6:12
goeth abroad he *t.* it. *Ps* 41:6
he that *t.* lies shall not tarry. 101:7
he *t.* the number of the stars. 147:4
under hands of him that *t. Jer* 33:13
Philip cometh and *t.* *John* 12:22

telling

when Gideon heard the *t. Judg* 7:15
hast made an end of *t. 2 Sam* 11:19
as he was *t.* the king how. *2 Ki* 8:5

Tema

sons of Ishmael, Hadar, *T. Gen* 25:15
1 Chr 1:30
the troops of *T.* looked. *Job* 6:19
the inhabitants of *T.* *Isa* 21:14
I made Dedan and *T.* *Jer* 25:23

Teman

Eliphaz were *T.* Omar. *Gen* 36:11
duke *T.*, duke Kenaz. 15, 42
1 Chr 1:53
is wisdom no more in *T.*? *Jer* 49:7
Lord hath purposed against *T.* 20
make it desolate from *T. Ezek* 25:13
will send a fire upon *T.* *Amos* 1:12
thy mighty men, O *T.*, shall. *Ob* 9
God came from *T.* *Hab* 3:3

Temanite, *see* **Eliphaz**

temper

an hin of oil to *t.* with. *Ezek* 46:14*

temperance

as he reasoned of *t.* *Acts* 24:25
meekness, *t.*: against such. *Gal* 5:23
to knowledge *t.* and to *t.* *2 Pet* 1:6

temperate

for the mastery, is *t.* *1 Cor* 9:25
a bishop must be *t.* *Tit* 1:8
aged men *t.* 2:2

tempered

unleavened *t.* with oil. *Ex* 29:2*
a perfume *t.* together, pure. 30:35*
but God hath *t.* the body together.
1 Cor 12:24

tempest

[1] *A most violent commotion of the air, either with or without rain, hail, or snow,* Acts 27:18, 20. [2] *Grievous, and unexpected affliction,* Job 9:17.

breaketh me with a *t.* *Job* 9:17
a *t.* stealeth him away in. 27:20
on wicked shall he rain a *t. Ps* 11:6*
from the windy storm and *t.* 55:8
so persecute them with thy *t.* 83:15
one, which as a *t.* of hail. *Isa* 28:2
visited with storm and *t.* 29:6
shall be beaten with a *t.* 30:30
shall be a covert from the *t.* 32:2
afflicted, tossed with *t.* 54:11
with a *t.* in the day of the. *Amos* 1:14
there was a mighty *t.* in. *Jonah* 1:4
for my sake this great *t.* is come. 12
there arose a great *t.* *Mat* 8:24
tossed with a *t.* *Acts* 27:18*
no small *t.* lay on us, hope was. 20
come to darkness and *t. Heb* 12:18
are carried with a *t.* *2 Pet* 2:17*

tempestuous

it shall be very *t.* round. *Ps* 50:3
wrought and was *t.* *Jonah* 1:11, 13
against it a *t.* wind. *Acts* 27:14

temple

A house or dwelling of God, a building erected and set apart for the worship of the true God. The word is used in the Bible, [1] *Of the tabernacle,* 1 Sam 1:9. [2] *Of Solomon's temple, the wonder of the whole world. This is referred to in all parts of the Bible written before the captivity, when this temple was destroyed. It is also referred to at the time of the building of the second temple, after the Return.* [3] *The temple as rebuilt in the times of Ezra and Nehemiah. This was larger than that of Solomon, but not so rich and beautiful.* [4] *All references in the New Testament to the existing temple are to Herod's temple, built by Herod the Great to win the allegiance of the Jews.* [5] *Of Christ's body or human nature, in which the fulness of the Godhead dwelt,* John 2:19, 21; Col 2:9. [6] *Of the human body,* 1 Cor 3:16.

a seat by a post of the *t. 1 Sam* 1:9
he did hear my voice out of his *t.*, and my cry. *2 Sam* 22:7; *Ps* 18:6
the *t.* before it was 40. *1 Ki* 6:17
had prepared the *t.* *2 Chr* 35:20
and put the vessels in his *t.* 36:7
that they builded the *t.* *Ezra* 4:1
out of the *t.* brought to *t.* 5:14; 6:5
the *t.*, shut doors of the *t. Neh* 6:10
and to enquire in his *t.* *Ps* 27:4
in his *t.* doth every one speak. 29:9
thy lovingkindness, O God, in the midst of thy *t.* 48:9
because of thy *t.* at Jerusalem. 68:29
and his train filled the *t.* *Isa* 6:1
and to the *t.* thy foundation. 44:28
a voice from the *t.*, a voice. 66:6
declare the vengeance of his *t.*
Jer 50:28; 51:11
he brought me to the *t.* *Ezek* 41:1
vessels taken out of the *t. Dan* 5:2, 3
the songs of the *t.* shall. *Amos* 8:3
that the *t.* might be built. *Zech* 8:9
come suddenly to his *t.* *Mal* 3:1
set him on a pinnacle of the *t.*
Mat 4:5; *Luke* 4:9
is one greater than the *t.* *Mat* 12:6
Whosoever shall swear by the *t.* or by the gold of the *t.* 23:16, 17, 21
whom ye slew between the *t.* 35*
to shew him the buildings of the *t.*
24:1; *Luke* 21:5
I am able to destroy the *t. Mat* 26:61
thou that destroyest the *t.* 27:40
Mark 15:29
behold the vail of the *t.* *Mat* 27:51
Mark 15:38; *Luke* 23:45
any vessel through the *t. Mark* 11:16
I will destroy this *t.* made. 14:58
departed not from the *t.* *Luke* 2:37
drove them all out of the *t. John* 2:15
destroy this *t.* 19
forty and six years was this *t.* 20
he spake of *t.* of his body. 21
gate of the *t.* to ask alms of them that entered the *t.* *Acts* 3:2, 10
the *t.* of goddess Diana. 19:27
and drew him out of the *t.* 21:30
gone about to profane the *t.* 24:6
neither against the *t.* nor. 25:8
that ye are the *t.* of God ? *1 Cor* 3:16
t. of God, him shall God destroy, for the *t.* of God is holy, which *t.* 17
your body is the *t.* of the Holy ? 6:19
sit at meat in an idol's *t.* 8:10
live of the things of the *t.* 9:13
hath the *t.* of God with idols ? for ye are the *t.* of the. *2 Cor* 6:16
day and night in his *t.* *Rev* 7:15
saying, Rise and measure the *t.* 11:1
t. of God was opened in heaven, and the . . . was seen in his *t.* 19
angel came out of the *t.* 14:15, 17
the *t.* of the tabernacle was. 15:5
seven angels came out of the *t.* 6
t. was filled with smoke from the. 8
a great voice out of the *t.* 16:1, 17
no *t.* therein, for the Lord God almighty and Lamb are *t.* 21:22

see **holy, Lord**

in, or *into the* **temple**

spears that were *in the t. 2 Ki* 11:10
priest's office *in the t.* *1 Chr* 6:10
head *in the t.* of Dagon. 10:10
candlesticks *in the t.* *2 Chr* 4:7, 8
these vessels *into the t.* *Ezra* 5:15
would go *into the t.* to save his life.
Neh 6:11
priests *in the t.* profane. *Mat* 12:5
into the t., cast out all them that sold and bought *in the t.* 21:12
Mark 11:15; *Luke* 19:45
blind and lame came to see him *in the t.* *Mat* 21:14
children crying *in the t.* and. 15
I sat daily teaching *in the t.* 26:55
Luke 21:37
pieces of silver *in the t. Mat* 27:5*
I was daily teaching *in the t.*
Mark 14:49; *Luke* 22:53
tarried so long *in the t.* *Luke* 1:21
he had seen a vision *in the t.* 22
by the spirit *into the t.* 2:27
they found him *in the t.* sitting. 46
two men went up *into the t.* 18:10
and were continually *in the t.* 24:53
one accord *in the t.* *Acts* 2:46
went up together *into the t.* 3:1
about to go *into the t.* 3
stand and speak *in the t.* 5:20
the men are standing *in the t.* 25
Paul entered *into the t.* 21:26
saw him *in the t.* 27
Greeks also *into the t.* 28, 29
even while I prayed *in the t.* I. 22:17
found me *in the t.* disputing. 24:12
found me purified *in the t.* 18
the Jews caught me *in the t.* 26:21
he as God sitteth *in the t.* of God.
2 Thes 2:4
will I make a pillar *in the t.* of my God. *Rev* 3:12
no man was able to enter *into t.* 15:8

temples

Maker, and buildeth *t.* *Hos* 8:14*
ye carried into your *t.* *Joel* 3:5
Most High dwelleth not in *t.* made with hands. *Acts* 7:48; 17:24

temples, *of the head*

Jael smote the nail into his *t.*
Judg 4:21, 22
she had stricken through his *t.* 5:26
thy *t.* like a piece of pomegranate.
S of S 4:3; 6:7

temporal

which are seen are *t.* *2 Cor* 4:18

tempt

[1] *When spoken of God it means to try or test, with the idea of proving man's faith and obedience, and the desire and certainty that man will not fail,* Gen 22:1. [2] *Man tempts God when he puts him to the proof simply to see if he will keep his promises,* Isa 7:12; Mat 4:7. [3] *The endeavour of the evil one or of evil men to cause a man to commit sin. It is nearly always in this sense that the word* temptation *is used.*

God did *t.* Abraham. *Gen* 22:1
do ye *t.* the Lord ? *Ex* 17:2
ye shall not *t.* the Lord. *Deut* 6:16
I will not ask, nor will I *t.* *Isa* 7:12
yea, they that *t.* God are. *Mal* 3:15
is written again, Thou shalt not *t.* the. *Mat* 4:7; *Luke* 4:12
why *t.* ye me ? *Mat* 22:18
Mark 12:15; *Luke* 20:23
together to *t.* the Spirit. *Acts* 5:9
now therefore why *t.* ye God ? 15:10
that Satan *t.* you not for. *1 Cor* 7:5
neither let us *t.* Christ as. 10:9

temptation

harden not your hearts, as in the day of *t.* *Ps* 95:8*; *Heb* 3:8
and lead us not into *t.* *Mat* 6:13
Luke 11:4
that ye enter not into *t.* *Mat* 26:41
Mark 14:38; *Luke* 22:40, 46
devil had ended all his *t. Luke* 4:13
and in time of *t.* fall away. 8:13

hath no *t.* taken you; but will with the *t.* *1 Cor* 10:13
and my *t.* in my flesh ye. *Gal* 4:14
will be rich fall into *t.* *1 Tim* 6:9
man that endureth *t.* *Jas* 1:12
also from the hour of *t.* *Rev* 3:10

temptations

out of a nation by *t.* *Deut* 4:34
great *t.* thine eyes saw. 7:19; 29:3
with me in my *t.* *Luke* 22:28
with many tears and *t.* *Acts* 20:19
when ye fall into divers *t.* *Jas* 1:2
in heaviness through manifold *t.* *1 Pet* 1:6
deliver the godly out of *t.* *2 Pet* 2:9

tempted

and because they *t.* the. *Ex* 17:7
and have *t.* me now. *Num* 14:22
not tempt God as ye *t.* *Deut* 6:16
and they *t.* God in. *Ps* 78:18, 41
yet they *t.* and provoked the. 56
when your fathers *t.* me. 95:9
Heb 3:9
but lusted, and *t.* God in. *Ps* 106:14
to be *t.* of the devil. *Mat* 4:1
Mark 1:13; *Luke* 4:2
a lawyer *t.* him, saying. *Luke* 10:25
as some of them *t.* and. *1 Cor* 10:9
who will not suffer you to be *t.* 13
lest thou also be *t.* *Gal* 6:1
means the tempter *t.* you. *1 Thes* 3:5
he hath suffered being *t.* *Heb* 2:18
but was in all points *t.* like as. 4:15
were sawn asunder, were *t.* 11:37
when he is *t.*, I am *t.* of God; for God cannot be *t.* with evil. *Jas* 1:13
but every man is *t.* when he is. 14

tempter

when the *t.* came to him. *Mat* 4:3
lest by means the *t.* have. *1 Thes* 3:5

tempteth

cannot be tempted, neither *t.* he any. *Jas* 1:13

tempting

the Pharisees *t.* Christ. *Mat* 16:1
Mark 8:11; *Luke* 11:16
also came to him, *t.* him. *Mat* 19:3
him a question, *t.* him. 22:35
put away his wife, *t.* him. *Mark* 10:2
this they said *t.* him, that. *John* 8:6

ten

Abraham dwelt *t.* years. *Gen* 16:3
t. shall be found there: he said, I will not destroy it for *t.*'s sake. 18:32
the servant took *t.* camels of. 24:10
bracelets for her hands of *t.* 22
Jacob took *t.* bulls and *t.* 32:15
Joseph's *t.* brethren went to. 42:3
Joseph's sent *t.* asses and *t.* 45:23
tabernacle with *t.* curtains. *Ex* 26:1
pillars *t.* and their sockets *t.* 27:12
wrote *t.* commandments. 34:28
Deut 4:13; 10:4
t. women shall bake. *Lev* 26:26
for the female *t.* shekels. 27:5, 7
one spoon of *t.* shekels. *Num* 7:14
20, 26
least gathered *t.* homers. 11:32
the fourth day *t.* bullocks. 29:23
there fell *t.* portions to. *Josh* 17:5
lot out of Ephraim, Manasseh, and Dan, *t.* cities. 21:5; *1 Chr* 6:61
with Phinehas *t.* princes. *Josh* 22:14
Gideon took *t.* men of. *Judg* 6:27
judged Israel *t.* years. 12:11
I will give thee *t.* shekels of. 17:10
we will take *t.* men of an. 20:10
Moab about *t.* years. *Ruth* 1:4
Boaz took *t.* men of the elders. 4:2
am not I better to thee than *t.* sons? *1 Sam* 1:8
take these *t.* loaves and run. 17:17
carry these *t.* cheeses to the. 18
David sent out *t.* young men. 25:5
David left *t.* concubines to keep. *2 Sam* 15:16
have given thee *t.* shekels. 18:11
t. young men smote Absalom. 15
they said, We have *t.* parts. 19:43
the king took his *t.* concubines. 20:3
t. fat oxen in one day. *1 Ki* 4:23
t. knots in a cubit compassing. 7:24
made *t.* bases of brass. *1 Ki* 7:27, 37
he made *t.* lavers of brass. 38, 43
2 Chr 4:6
t. pieces; I will give *t.* *1 Ki* 11:31, 35
with thee *t.* loaves to Ahijah. 14:3
t. talents, *t.* changes. *2 Ki* 5:5
fifty horsemen and *t.* chariots. 13:7
Menahem reigned *t.* years. 15:17
Ishmael came and *t.* men with him. 25:25; *Jer* 41:1, 2
he made *t.* candlesticks. *2 Chr* 4:7
t. tables. 8
and *t.* brethren were. *Ezra* 8:24
bring one of *t.* to dwell. *Neh* 11:1
the *t.* sons of Haman. *Esth* 9:10, 12
and let Haman's *t.* sons be. 13, 14
instrument of *t.* strings. *Ps* 33:2
92:3; 144:9
more than *t.* mighty men. *Eccl* 7:19
t. acres of vineyard shall. *Isa* 5:10
an homer of *t.* baths, *t.* *Ezek* 45:14
the fourth beast had *t.* horns. *Dan* 7:7, 20, 24
shall leave *t.* to the house. *Amos* 5:3
if *t.* men remain in one house. 6:9
came to an heap of twenty measures, there were but *t.* *Hag* 2:16
of the roll is *t.* cubits. *Zech* 5:2
t. men shall take hold of him. 8:23
and when the *t.* heard it. *Mat* 20:24
Mark 10:41
be likened to *t.* virgins. *Mat* 25:1
to him that hath *t.* talents. 25:28
woman having *t.* pieces. *Luke* 15:8
there met him *t.* men that. 17:12
Were there not *t.* cleansed? 17
delivered them *t.* pounds. 19:13
thy pound hath gained *t.* pounds. 16
have thou authority over *t.* cities. 17
to him that hath *t.* pounds. 24
Lord, he hath *t.* pounds. 25
a dragon having *t.* horns. *Rev* 12:3
13:1; 17:3
of seven heads and *t.* horns. 17:7
t. horns thou sawest are the *t.* 12
the *t.* horns thou sawest shall. 16
see **cubits, days, degrees, thousand, thousands**

ten *times*

and hath changed my wages *t. times.* *Gen* 31:7, 41
tempted me now these *t. times.* *Num* 14:22
they said unto us *t. times.* *Neh* 4:12
these *t. times* have ye. *Job* 19:3
he found them *t. times.* *Dan* 1:20

tend

thoughts of diligent *t.* to. *Pr* 21:5

tendeth

of the righteous *t.* to life. *Pr* 10:16
as righteousness *t.* to life, so. 11:19
is that withholdeth, but it *t.* to. 24
the talk of the lips *t.* only to. 14:23
the fear of the Lord *t.* to life. 19:23

tender

[1] *Weak and feeble,* Gen 33:13. [2] *Of a compassionate and forgiving temper,* Eph 4:32.
ran and fetched a calf *t.* and good. *Gen* 18:7
that the children are *t.* 33:13
so the man that is *t.* *Deut* 28:54
the *t.* and delicate woman. 56
the small rain on the *t.* herb. 32:2
as the *t.* grass springing. *2 Sam* 23:4
because thy heart was *t.* *2 Ki* 22:19
2 Chr 34:27
is young and *t.* *1 Chr* 22:5; 29:1
that the *t.* branch will not. *Job* 14:7
to cause the bud of the *t.* herb. 38:27
t. and beloved in sight. *Pr* 4:3
hay appears, and the *t.* grass. 27:25
the vines with *t.* grape. *S of S* 2:13
for our vines have *t.* grapes. 15*
see whether the *t.* grape. 7:12
thou shalt no more be called *t.* and. *Isa* 47:1
up before him as a *t.* plant. 53:2
I will crop off a *t.* one. *Ezek* 17:22
brought Daniel into *t.* love. *Dan* 1:9*
in earth, in the *t.* grass. 4:15, 23
when his branch is *t.* *Mat* 24:32
Mark 13:28
through the *t.* mercy. *Luke* 1:78
pitiful, and of *t.* mercy. *Jas* 5:11*
see **mercies**

tenderhearted

when Rehoboam was young and *t.* *2 Chr* 13:7
be kind and *t.* one to. *Eph* 4:32

tenderness

foot on the ground for *t.* *Deut* 28:56

tenons

two *t.* in one board. *Ex* 26:17, 19
36:22, 24

tenor

according to the *t.* of. *Gen* 43:7
after *t.* of these words. *Ex* 34:27

tens

such over them to be rulers of *t.* *Ex* 8:21, 25
heads, captains over *t.* *Deut* 1:15

tent

(*This word is often used of the tabernacle. Tents were the only homes of the early patriarchs. Their use was common through all Bible times, as it is now among the desert tribes*)
was uncovered in his *t.* *Gen* 9:21
and pitched his *t.* 12:8; 13:3
Lot pitched his *t.* towards. 13:12
Abraham removed his *t.* and. 18
he sat in *t.* door. 18:1
he hastened into the *t.* 6
thy wife? he said, In the *t.* 9
her into his mother Sarah's *t.* 24:67
and Isaac pitched his *t.* in. 26:17
built an altar, and pitched his *t.* 25
Jacob had pitched his *t.* in. 31:25
Jacob's *t.*, Leah's *t.*, Rachel's *t.* 33
Jacob pitched his *t.* before. 33:18, 19
Israel spread his *t.* beyond. 35:21
Jethro came into the *t.* *Ex* 18:7
couple the *t.* together that it. 26:11
stood every man at his *t.* door. 33:8
every man in his *t.* door. 10
make the tabernacle, his *t.* 35:11
he made taches to couple the *t.* 36:18
he made a covering for the *t.* 19
brought the *t.* to Moses. 39:33
the *t.* over the tabernacle, and put the covering of the *t.* 40:19
leper shall tarry out of his *t.* seven. *Lev* 14:8
Gershon shall be the *t.* *Num* 3:25
the cloud covered the *t.* of. 9:15
weep every man in his *t.* 11:10
a man dieth in a *t.*: all that come into the *t.* and is in the *t.* 19:14
clean person shall sprinkle the *t.* 18
the man of Israel into the *t.* 25:8
earth in the midst of my *t.* *Josh* 7:21
the *t.*; and it was hid in his *t.* 22
out of the midst of the *t.* 23
all Israel burnt his *t.* and all. 24
Sisera fled on his feet to the *t.* of. *Judg* 4:17
stand in the door of the *t.* 20
Jael took a nail of the *t.* and. 21
be above women in the *t.* 5:24
of Israel every man to his *t.* 7:8
barley bread came unto a *t.* 13
will not any of us go to his *t.* 20:8
and they fled every man into his *t.* *1 Sam* 4:10; *2 Sam* 18:17; 19:8
sent every man to his *t.* *1 Sam* 13:2
Goliath's armour into his *t.* 17:54
but I have walked in a *t.* *2 Sam* 7:6
1 Chr 17:5
spread Absalom a *t.* on. *2 Sam* 16:22
retired every man to his *t.* 20:22
went into one *t.*, another *t.* *2 Ki* 7:8
David pitched a *t.* for. *1 Chr* 15:1
they set it in midst of the *t.* 16:1
2 Chr 1:4
fled every man to his *t.* *2 Chr* 25:22
the *t.* which he placed. *Ps* 78:60
nor Arabian pitch *t.* there. *Isa* 13:20
is removed as a shepherd's *t.* 38:12
spreadeth them out as a *t.* 40:22
enlarge the place of thy *t.* 54:2
to stretch forth my *t.* *Jer* 10:20
rise up every man in his *t.* 37:10

tenth
I will surely give the *t.* *Gen* 28:22
the *t.* shall be holy. *Lev* 27:32
children of Levi the *t.* *Num* 18:21*
enter to *t.* generation. *Deut* 23:2, 3
king will take the *t.* of. *1 Sam* 8:15
he will take the *t.* of your sheep. 17
t. captain of sons of. *1 Chr* 12:13
the *t.* lot came forth to. 24:11
t. lot came forth to Shimei. 25:17
the *t.* captain for the *t.* month. 27:13
but yet in it shall be a *t.* *Isa* 6:13
in the *t.* year of Zedekiah. *Jer* 32:1
it was about the *t.* hour. *John* 1:39
t. foundation a chrysoprasus. *Rev* 21:20
see **day, deal, month, part**

tentmakers
occupation they were *t.* *Acts* 18:3

tents
father of such as dwell in *t.* *Gen* 4:20
Japheth shall dwell in the *t.* 9:27
flocks, and herds, and *t.* 13:5
plain man, dwelling in *t.* 25:27
into the maid servants' *t.* 31:33
for them that are in *t.* *Ex* 16:16
Israel shall pitch their *t.* *Num* 1:52
cloud abode, they pitched *t.* 9:17
cloud abode, they rested in their *t.* 18, 20, 22, 23
whether they dwell in *t.* or. 13:19
depart from the *t.* of these. 16:26
stood in the door of their *t.* 27
Israel abiding in his *t.* 24:2
how goodly are thy *t.* O Jacob. 5
in your *t.* and said. *Deut* 1:27
a place to pitch your *t.* in. 33
Get ye into your *t.* again. 5:30
swallowed them up and their *t.* 11:6
turn and go unto thy *t.* 16:7
rejoice, Issachar, in thy *t.* 33:18
and get you into your *t.* *Josh* 22:4, 6
with much riches unto your *t.* 8
came with their *t.* *Judg* 6:5
of them that dwelt in *t.* 8:11
the Philistines' *t.* *1 Sam* 17:53
and Judah abide in *t.* *2 Sam* 11:11
every man to his *t.* 20:1
1 Ki 12:16; *2 Chr* 10:16
Israel went to their *t.* *1 Ki* 8:66
2 Chr 7:10
Syrians left their *t.* *2 Ki* 7:7, 10
Israel spoiled the *t.* of the. 16
people fled into their *t.* 8:21; 14:12
of Israel dwelt in their *t.* 13:5
smote the *t.* of Ham. *1 Chr* 4:41
dwelt in the Hagarites' *t.* 5:10
also the *t.* of cattle. *2 Chr* 14:15
to praise in the gates of the *t.* 31:2
at Ahava we abode in *t.* *Ezra* 8:15
none dwell in their *t.* *Ps* 69:25
Israel to dwell in their *t.* 78:55
than to dwell in the *t.* of. 84:10
murmured in their *t.* and. 106:25
woe is me, that I dwell in the *t.* 120:5
but comely, as the *t.* of Kedar. *S of S* 1:5
kids beside the shepherds' *t.* 8
suddenly are my *t.* spoiled. *Jer* 4:20
they shall pitch their *t.* against. 6:3
the captivity of Jacob's *t.* 30:18
days ye shall dwell in *t.* 35:7
but we have dwelt in *t.* and. 10
their *t.* and flocks shall they. 49:29
I saw the *t.* of Cushan in. *Hab* 3:7
the Lord shall save the *t.* *Zech* 12:7
plague shall be in these *t.* 14:15

Terah
Nahor begat *T.* *Gen* 11:24
1 Chr 1:26
T. begat Abram. *Gen* 11:26, 27
Josh 24:2
T. took Abram his son. *Gen* 11:31

teraphim
made an ephod and *t.* *Judg* 17:5
in these houses is *t.* 18:14
took the *t.* 20
abide many days without *t.* *Hos* 3:4

termed
be *t.* forsaken, neither shall thy land any more be *t.* desolate. *Isa* 62:4

terraces
made of algum trees *t.* *2 Chr* 9:11

terrestrial
there are bodies *t.*: the glory of the *t.* *1 Cor* 15:40

terrible
for it is a *t.* thing. *Ex* 34:10
went through that *t.* wilderness. *Deut* 1:19; 8:15
a mighty God and *t.* 7:21; 10:17
Neh 1:5; 4:14; 9:32
hath done for thee *t.* things. *Deut* 10:21; *2 Sam* 7:23
angel of God, very *t.* *Judg* 13:6
with God is *t.* majesty. *Job* 37:22
the glory of his nostrils is *t.* 39:20
his teeth are *t.* round about. 41:14
shall teach thee *t.* things. *Ps* 45:4
for the Lord Most High is *t.* 47:2
by *t.* things in righteousness. 65:5
say unto God, How *t.* art thou ! 66:3
t. in his doing towards the children. 5
t. out of thy holy places. 68:35
t. to the kings of the earth. 76:12
praise thy great and *t.* name. 99:3
who had done *t.* things by. 106:22
of the might of thy *t.* acts. 145:6
thou art *t.* as an army. *S of S* 6:4*
lay low the haughtiness of the *t.* *Isa* 13:11
go to a people *t.* hitherto. 18:2
from a people *t.* hitherto. 7
from the desert, from a *t.* land. 21:1
the city of the *t.* nations shall. 25:3
when the blast of the *t.* ones is. 4
the branch of the *t.* ones shall be. 5
multitude of the *t.* ones shall. 29:5
for the *t.* one is brought to naught. 20
and the prey of the *t.* shall be. 49:25
when thou didst *t.* things. 64:3
out of the hand of the *t.* *Jer* 15:21
with me as a mighty *t.* one. 20:11
skin was black, because of *t.* famine. *Lam* 5:10*
colour of the *t.* crystal. *Ezek* 1:22
behold therefore I will bring the *t.* of. 28:7; 30:11; 31:12
I will cause to fall the *t.* of. 32:12
form of the image was *t.* *Dan* 2:31
fourth beast dreadful and *t.* 7:7*
day of Lord is very *t.* *Joel* 2:11
t. day of the Lord come. 31
the Chaldeans are *t.* and. *Hab* 1:7
the Lord will be *t.* unto. *Zeph* 2:11
so *t.* was the sight that. *Heb* 12:21

terribleness
Lord brought us out with great *t.* *Deut* 26:8
thee a name of greatness and *t.* *1 Chr* 17:21*
thy *t.* hath deceived thee. *Jer* 49:16

terribly
shake *t.* the earth. *Isa* 2:19*, 21*
fir trees shall be *t.* shaken. *Nah* 2:3

terrified
fear not nor be *t.* *Deut* 20:3
hear of wars, be not *t.* *Luke* 21:9
but they were *t.* and. 24:37
and in nothing *t.* by your. *Phil* 1:28

terrifiest
then thou *t.* me through. *Job* 7:14

terrify
blackness of the day *t.* it. *Job* 3:5
rod, and let not his fear *t.* 9:34
contempt of families *t.* me ? 31:34
seem as if I would *t.* *2 Cor* 10:9

terror
and the *t.* of God was. *Gen* 35:5
even appoint over you *t.* *Lev* 26:16
the sword without and *t.* *Deut* 32:25
in all the great *t.* which Moses. 34:12
and that your *t.* is fallen. *Josh* 2:9
from God was a *t.* to me. *Job* 31:23
behold, my *t.* shall not make. 33:7
not be afraid for the *t.* *Ps* 91:5
lop the bough with *t.* *Isa* 10:33
land of Judah shall be a *t.* 19:17
thine heart shall meditate *t.* 33:18
thou shalt be far from *t.* 54:14
be not a *t.* to me. *Jer* 17:17
a *t.* to thyself. 20:4
forth Israel with great *t.* *Jer* 32:2
cause *t.* to be on all. *Ezek* 26:1
I will make thee a *t.* 21; 27:3
28:1
which caused *t.* in the land. 32:2
24, 25, 26, 2
with their *t.* they are ashamed. 3
I have caused my *t.* in the land. 3
for rulers are not a *t.* *Rom* 13:
knowing therefore the *t.* *2 Cor* 5:1
be not afraid of their *t.* *1 Pet* 3:1

terrors
a nation by great *t.* *Deut* 4:3
t. of God do set themselves. *Job* 6:
t. shall make him afraid on. 18:1
bring him to the king of *t.* 1
the sword cometh, *t.* are. 20:2
are in the *t.* of the shadow. 24:1
t. take hold on him as waters. 27:2
t. are turned upon me. 30:1
the *t.* of death are fallen. *Ps* 55:
utterly consumed with *t.* 73:1
while I suffer thy *t.* I am. 88:1
wrath goeth over me, thy *t.* 1
I caused *t.* to fall upon. *Jer* 15:
thou hast called my *t.* *Lam* 2:2
t. by reason of the sword shall be. *Ezek* 21:1

Tertius
I *T.* who wrote this epistle salute. *Rom* 16:2

Tertullus
certain orator named *T.* *Acts* 24:1
T. began to accuse Paul, saying.

testament
(*The usual meaning of this word as in* Old Testament *and* New Testament, *is* covenant, *that is, the old and the new* Dispensation, *or relations between God and man. In a few cases it seems to mean the same as it does now in law, in the phrase* last will and testament, Heb 9:16, 17. *But the Revisions render the term in each case by the word* covenant)
this is my blood in new *t.* *Mat* 26:28; *Mark* 14:24
this cup is the new *t.* *Luke* 22:20
1 Cor 11:25
ministers of the new *t.* *2 Cor* 3:6
vail, in reading the old *t.* 14
a surety of a better *t.* *Heb* 7:22
of the new *t.* for the redemption of trangressions under first *t.* 9:15
where a *t.* is there must also. 16
for a *t.* is of force after men. 17
the blood of the *t.* which God. 20
the ark of his *t.* *Rev* 11:19

testator
be the death of the *t.* *Heb* 9:16*
no strength while the *t.* liveth. 17*

testified
and it hath been *t.* to his. *Ex* 21:29
hath *t.* falsely against. *Deut* 19:18
seeing the Lord hath *t.* *Ruth* 1:21
thy mouth hath *t.* *2 Sam* 1:16
yet the Lord *t.* against. *2 Ki* 17:13
his testimonies which he *t.* 15
prophets *t.* against them. *2 Chr* 24:19
Neh 9:26
I *t.* against them. *Neh* 13:15, 21
which the woman *t.* *John* 4:39
Jesus himself *t.* that a prophet. 44
13:21
when they had *t.* and. *Acts* 8:25
Paul *t.* to the Jews, that Jesus. 18:5
for as thou hast *t.* of me. 23:11
to whom he *t.* the kingdom. 28:23
are false, because we have *t.* of God. *1 Cor* 15:15
forewarned you and *t.* *1 Thes* 4:6
gave himself, to be *t.* *1 Tim* 2:6
in a certain place *t.* saying. *Heb* 2:6
when it *t.* beforehand. *1 Pet* 1:11
God hath *t.* of his Son. *1 John* 5:9
and *t.* of the truth that. *3 John* 3

testifiedst
and *t.* against them. *Neh* 9:29, 30

testifieth
the pride of Israel *t.* to. *Hos* 7:10
seen and heard, that he *t.* *John* 3:32

isciple which *t.* of these. *John* 21:24
thou art a priest for. *Heb* 7:17
which *t.* these things. *Rev* 22:20

testify

ne witness not *t.* against any. *Num* 35:30
t. against you that ye. *Deut* 8:19
a false witness *t.* against. 19:16
is song shall *t.* against. 31:21
earts to the words which I *t.* 32:46
dst *t.* against them. *Neh* 9:34
ea, thine own lips *t.* *Job* 15:6
Israel, I will *t.* against thee. *Ps* 50:7; 81:8
efore thee, and our sins *t.* *Isa* 59:12
ough our iniquities *t.* *Jer* 14:7
e pride of Israel doth *t.* *Hos* 5:5
in the house of Jacob. *Amos* 3:13
ave I done ? *t.* against me. *Mi*6:3
at he may *t.* to them. *Luke* 16:28
y should *t.* of man. *John* 2:25
d *t.* that we have seen. 3:11
ey *t.* of me. 5:39
ecause I *t.* of it. 7:7
e shall *t.* of me. 15:26
her words did he *t.* *Acts* 2:40
that it is he who was ordained. 10:42
t. the gospel of the grace. 20:24
e know they, if they would *t.* 26:5
t. to every man that. *Gal* 5:3
in the Lord, that ye. *Eph* 4:17
een, and do *t.*, that. *1 John* 4:14
ave sent my angel to *t.* *Rev* 22:16
t. to every man that heareth. 18

testifying

both to the Jews and. *Acts* 20:21
btained witness, God *t.* *Heb* 11:4
that this is the true. *1 Pet* 5:12

testimonies

ese are the *t.* which. *Deut* 4:45
e shall diligently keep the *t.* 6:17
hat mean the *t.* which God ? 20
eep his statutes and his *t.* *1 Ki* 2:3
2 Ki 23:3; *1 Chr* 29:19; *2 Chr* 34:31
ejected his *t.* and. *2 Ki* 17:15
ings hearkened to thy *t.* *Neh* 9:34
is covenant and his *t.* *Ps* 25:10
nd keep not his *t.* 78:56
y *t.* are sure. 93:5
ept his *t.* and the ordinance. 99:7
lessed are they that keep his *t.* and seek him. 119:2
ejoiced in the way of thy *t.* 14
r I have kept thy *t.* 22, 167, 168
hy *t.* are my delight. 24
stuck to thy *t.* 31
cline my heart to thy *t.*, not to. 36
will speak of thy *t.* also. 46
nd I turned my feet to thy *t.* 59
et those that have known thy *t.* 79
ut I will consider thy *t.* 95
r thy *t.* are my meditation. 99
have I taken as an heritage. 111
love thy *t.* 119
hat I may know thy *t.* 125
hy *t.* are wonderful, therefore. 129
hy *t.* are righteous and very. 138
he righteousness of thy *t.* is. 144
nd I shall keep thy *t.* 146
oncerning thy *t.*, I have known. 152
et do I not decline from thy *t.* 157
ot walked in his *t.* *Jer* 44:23

testimony

[1] *A witnessing evidence, or roof,* Acts 14:3. [2] *The whole cripture, or word of God, which eclares what is to be believed and ractised,* Ps 19:7. [3] *The two ables of stone, whereon the law, or en commandments, were written, which were witnesses of that coveant made between God and his eople,* Ex 25:16, 21; 31:18. [4] *The book of the law which testifies f God's will and man's duty,* 2 Ki 1:12. [5] *The ark in which the aw was deposited,* Ex 16:34.

f manna before the *t.* *Ex* 16:34
ut into the ark the *t.* 25:16, 21
ail which is before the *t.* 27:21
mercy seat that is over the *t.* *Ex* 30:6 *Lev* 16:13
and put it before the *t.* *Ex* 30:36
gave to Moses two tables of *t.* 31:18
the two tables of *t.* 32:15; 34:29
sum of the tabernacle of *t.* 38:21
over the tabernacle of *t.* *Num* 1:50
pitch about the tabernacle of *t.* 53
covered the tent of the *t.* 9:15
taken off the tabernacle of *t.* 10:11
up the rods before the *t.* 17:4
Aaron's rod again before the *t.* 10
shoe, and this was a *t.* in. *Ruth* 4:7
gave the king the *t.* *2 Ki* 11:12 *2 Chr* 23:11
for he established a *t.* *Ps* 78:5
ordained in Joseph for a *t.* 81:5
so shall I keep the *t.* of. 119:88
the tribes go up to the *t.* of. 122:4
children will keep my *t.* 132:12
bind up the *t.* *Isa* 8:16
to the law and to the *t.* 20
the gift Moses commanded for a *t.* *Mat* 8:4; *Mark* 1:44; *Luke* 5:14
for a *t.* against them. *Mat* 10:18 *Mark* 13:9
shake off the dust for a *t.* *Mark* 6:11; *Luke* 9:5
shall turn to you for a *t.* *Luke* 21:13
no man receiveth his *t.* *John* 3:32
he that receiveth his *t.* hath. 33
it is written, the *t.* of two men. 8:17
and we know that his *t.* is. 21:24
to whom also he gave *t.* *Acts* 13:22
who gave *t.* to the word of. 14:3
not receive thy *t.* of me. 22:18
as the *t.* of Christ was. *1 Cor* 1:6
unto you the *t.* of God. 2:1
the *t.* of our conscience. *2 Cor* 1:12
because our *t.* among. *2 Thes* 1:10
be not ashamed of the *t.* *2 Tim* 1:8
for a *t.* of those things. *Heb* 3:5
Enoch had this *t.* that he. 11:5
who bare record of the *t.* *Rev* 1:2
in the isle of Patmos for the *t.* 9
them that were slain for the *t.* 6:9
shall have finished their *t.* 11:7
by the word of their *t.* 12:11
them which have *t.* of Jesus. 17
tabernacle of the *t.* in heaven. 15:5
that have the *t.* of Jesus; for the *t.* of Jesus is the spirit of. 19:10
see **ark**

Tetrarch, *see* **Herod**

thank

that love you, what *t.* have you ? *Luke* 6:32, 33, 34

thank, *verb*

Levites to *t.* the Lord. *1 Chr* 16:4
David delivered this psalm to *t.* 7
to stand every morning to *t.* 23:30
we *t.* thee and praise thy. 29:13
I *t.* thee and praise thee. *Dan* 2:23
I *t.* thee, O Father, Lord of heaven and. *Mat* 11:25; *Luke* 10:21
doth he *t.* that servant ? *Luke* 17:9
God, I *t.* thee, that I am not. 18:11
Father, I *t.* thee, that. *John* 11:41
I *t.* my God through Jesus Christ. *Rom* 1:8; 7:25
I *t.* my God always on. *1 Cor* 1:4
I *t.* God that I baptized none. 14
I *t.* my God I speak with. 14:18
I *t.* my God on every remembrance of you. *Phil* 1:3
for this cause also *t.* *1 Thes* 2:13
we are bound to *t.* God. *2 Thes* 1:3
I *t.* Jesus Christ who hath enabled. *1 Tim* 1:12
I *t.* God, whom I serve with pure. *2 Tim* 1:3
I *t.* my God, making. *Philem* 4
see **offering**

thanked

bowed himself and *t.* *2 Sam* 14:22*
Paul *t.* God and took. *Acts* 28:15
but God be *t.* that ye were the servants. *Rom* 6:17

thankful

be *t.* to him, bless his name. *Ps* 100:4*; *Col* 3:15
him not, neither were *t.* *Rom* 1:21*

thankfulness

noble Felix, with all *t.* *Acts* 24:3

thanking

were as one in *t.* the Lord. *2 Chr* 5:13

thanks

companies that gave *t.* *Neh* 12:31
two companies that gave *t.* 40
he prayed and gave *t.* *Dan* 6:10
he took the cup and gave *t.* *Mat* 26:27; *Luke* 22:17
seven loaves and gave *t.* *Mark* 8:6
when he had given *t.* he gave. 14:23
Anna gave *t.* to the Lord. *Luke* 2:38
he took bread, and gave *t.* 22:19
when he had given *t.* *John* 6:11
after the Lord had given *t.* 23
and gave *t.* to God. *Acts* 27:35
Lord, for he giveth God *t.*; he eateth not, and giveth God *t.* *Rom* 14:6
when he had given *t.* *1 Cor* 11:24
for thou verily givest *t.* well. 14:17
t. be to God, who giveth us. 15:57
t. may be given to many. *2 Cor* 1:11
t. be to God who causeth us. 2:14
t. to God, who put the same. 8:16
t. be to God for his unspeakable gift. 9:15
giving *t.* always for all. *Eph* 5:20
what *t.* can we render ? *1 Thes* 3:9
of praise, giving *t.* *Heb* 13:15
give *t.* to him that sat. *Rev* 4:9
see **give, giving**

thanksgiving

[1] *An acknowledging and confessing with gladness, the benefits and mercies, which God bestows either upon ourselves or others,* Phil 4:6; 1 Tim 2:1. [2] *The sacrifice of* thanksgiving, Lev 7:12, 15. [3] *Psalms of* thanksgiving, Neh 12:8.

if he offer it for a *t.* *Lev* 7:12, 13 15; 22:29
principal to begin the *t.* *Neh* 11:17
which was over the *t.*, he and. 12:8
of praise and *t.* to God. 46
publish with the voice of *t.* *Ps* 26:7
offer unto God *t.* and pay thy. 50:14
I will magnify him with *t.* 69:30
come before his face with *t.* 95:2
enter into his gates with *t.* 100:4
sacrifice sacrifices of *t.* 107:22
offer to thee sacrifices of *t.* 116:17
sing unto the Lord with *t.*; sing. 147:7
t. and melody shall be. *Isa* 51:3
of them shall proceed *t.* *Jer* 30:19
offer a sacrifice of *t.* *Amos* 4:5
to thee with the voice of *t.* *Jonah* 2:9
grace might through the *t.* *2 Cor* 4:15
which causeth through us *t.* 9:11
with *t.* let your requests. *Phil* 4:6
abounding therein with *t.* *Col* 2:7
watch in the same with *t.* 4:2
to be received with *t.* *1 Tim* 4:3
good, if it be received with *t.* 4
t. and honour be to our. *Rev* 7:12

thanksgivings

the dedication with *t.* *Neh* 12:27
abundant by many *t.* to. *2 Cor* 9:12

thankworthy

this is *t.* if a man. *1 Pet* 2:19*

that

t. is it which compasseth. *Gen* 2:11
what Adam called, *t.* was the. 19
t. be far from thee, to slay. 18:25
t. shalt be accounted stolen. 30:33
shall make like unto *t.* *Ex* 30:38
when Moses heard *t.* he. *Lev* 10:20
yet for all I will not cast. 26:44
besides *t. t.* his hand. *Num* 6:21
the word which I say, *t.* 22:20
t. will I speak. 24:13; *1 Ki* 22:14
anger was abated, when he had said *t.* *Judg* 8:3
do according to *t.* which. 11:36
behold, *t.* which is left. *1 Sam* 9:24
if thou wilt take *t.* take it. 21:9
for *t.* thou hast done to me. 24:19
with *t.* which the Lord hath. 30:23
if *t.* had been too little. *2 Sam* 12:8
in *t.* thou lovest thine enemies. 19:6
offer of *t.* which doth cost. 24:24

according to *t.* which was written. *2 Ki* 14:6; *2 Chr* 35:26
t. which thou hast prayed. *2 Ki* 19:20
t. which thou hast promised. *2 Chr* 6:15, 16
t. which they have need. *Ezra* 6:9
t. do after the will of your. 7:18
t. which I was afraid of is. *Job* 3:25
t. which I have seen I will. 15:17
he shall not save of *t.* which. 20:20
what his soul desireth even *t.* 23:13
t. which I see not, teach. 34:32
t. will I seek after, that. *Ps* 27:4
then I restored *t.* which I took. 69:4
when I wept, *t.* was to my. 10
the thing hath been, it is *t.* which shall be; *t.* which is done, is *t.* *Eccl* 1:9
t. which is wanting cannot be. 15
what was *t.* good for the sons of. 2:3
what profit in *t.* wherein he ? 3:9
and God requireth *t.* which is. 15
when thou vowest, pay *t.* thou. 5:4
knowest not whether this or *t.* 11:6
t. which I have heard. *Isa* 21:10
for *t.* which had not been told them shall they see, *t.* they had. 52:15
for *t.* which Manasseh. *Jer* 15:4
t. which I have built, *t.* which. 45:4
t. Daniel regardeth not thee, O king. *Dan* 6:13
for *t. t.* is determined shall. 11:36
t. t. dieth, let it die, *t. t.* *Zech* 11:9
for *t.* which is conceived. *Mat* 1:20
whole from *t.* hour. 9:22; 15:28
for Sodom than for *t.* city. 10:15 *Mark* 6:11
taken away *t.* he hath. *Mat* 13:12 25:29; *Mark* 4:25
t. shall ye receive. *Mat* 20:7
t. observe and do. 23:3
is *t.* to us ? see thou to *t.* 27:4
t. which cometh out, *t.* *Mark* 7:20
given in *t.* hour, *t.* speak. 13:11
all will I give, for *t.* is. *Luke* 4:6
even *t.* he seemeth to have. 8:18
he *t.* made *t.* which is without make *t.* which is within also ? 11:40
not faithful in *t.* which is. 16:12
t. which is highly esteemed. 15
we have done *t.* which was. 17:10
t. which was come to pass. 24:12
he was not *t.* light. *John* 1:8
t. was the light. 9
t. which is born of flesh, *t.* born. 3:6
we speak *t.* we know, testify *t.* 11
is not thy husband, in *t.* saidst. 4:18
is *t.* saying true, one soweth. 37
what man is *t.* which said to ? 5:12
labour for *t.* meat which. 6:27
Moses gave you not *t.* bread. 32
I am *t.* bread of life. 48
this is *t.* bread. 58
I speak *t.* I have seen with my Father; ye do *t.* which ye. 8:38
t. thou doest, do quickly. 13:27
t. will I do. 14:13
what he shall hear, *t.* shall. 16:13
what is *t.* to thee, follow. 21:22, 24
went abroad, that *t.* disciple. 23
this is *t.* which was spoken. *Acts* 2:16
all glorified God for *t.* which. 4:21
heard *t.* they lifted up. 24; 5:21, 33
this is *t.* Moses which said. 7:37
t. word you know, which. 10:37
because *t.* which may be. *Rom* 1:19
according to *t.* which was. 4:18
in *t.* he died, in *t.* he liveth. 6:10
t. being dead wherein we were held, *t.* we. 7:6
was then *t.* which is good made ? 13
t. I do, I allow not. 15
t. I would not, *t.* I do. 19
put away from you *t.* *1 Cor* 5:13
nay, you defraud, and *t.* your. 6:8
t. spiritual rock, and *t.* rock. 10:4
spoken of, for *t.* which I. 30
t. which also I delivered unto. 11:23
eat of *t.* bread, and drink of *t.* cup. 28
t. which is perfect, *t.* which. 13:10
and yet for all *t.* they will not. 14:21
and *t.* which thou sowest thou sowest not *t.* body that shall be. 15:37
t. was not first which is spiritual, but *t.* which. 46
if *t.* which is done away. *2 Cor* 3:11
it is accepted according to *t.* 8:12
what I do, *t.* I will do, *t.* I may. 11:2
what a man soweth, *t.* *Gal* 6:7
that I may apprehend *t.* *Phil* 3:12
might perfect *t.* which. *1 Thes* 3:10
all things; hold fast *t.* is good. 5:21
life *t.* now is, and of *t.* *1 Tim* 4:8
keep *t.* which is committed. 6:20
if he oweth, put *t.* on. *Philem* 18
and was heard in *t.* he. *Heb* 5:7
which entereth into *t.* within. 6:19
could not endure *t.* which. 12:20
for *t.* is unprofitable for you. 13:17
shall live, and do this or *t.* *Jas* 4:15
he *t.* will harm you, if ye be followers of *t.*? *1 Pet* 3:13; *3 John* 11
t. which was from the. *1 John* 1:1
t. which we have seen. 3; 2:24
let *t.* abide in you which ye. 2:24
t. which ye have, hold. *Rev* 2:25
see **after, day, man, place, so, soul, thing, time**

theatre

with one accord into the *t.* *Acts* 19:29
not adventure himself into the *t.* 31

Thebez

went Abimelech to *T.* and took *T.* *Judg* 9:50
that he died in *T.* *2 Sam* 11:21

thee

t. have I seen righteous. *Gen* 7:1
multiply *t.* exceedingly. 17:2
in blessing I will bless *t.* 22:17
I *t.*, and the cave I give it *t.* 23:11
back any thing from me but *t.* 39:9
the stranger shall get above *t.* *Deut* 28:43
have not rejected *t.* but. *1 Sam* 8:7
arrows are beyond *t.* 20:22, 37
the king charged *t.* *2 Sam* 18:12
they have not set *t.* *Ps* 86:14
enemy to entreat *t.* well. *Jer* 15:11
I will recompense *t.* *Ezek* 7:9
I will leave *t.* and all the fish. 29:5
when saw we *t.* an hungered, and fed *t.*? *Mat* 25:37
when saw we *t.* a stranger ? 38
when saw we *t.* sick ? 39
he that bade *t.* and him. *Luke* 14:9
but the root bearest *t.* *Rom* 11:18
lest he also spare not *t.* 21
see **teach, tell**

about **thee**

thou shalt dig *about t.* *Job* 11:18
shut thy doors *about t.* *Isa* 26:20
sword devour round *about t.* *Jer* 46:14; *Ezek* 5:12
all those that be *about t.* *Jer* 49:5
among nations that are round *about t.* *Ezek* 5:14
to the nations round *about t.* 15
cast a trench *about t.* *Luke* 19:43
cast thy garment *about t.* *Acts* 12:8

after **thee**

to thy seed *after t.* *Gen* 17:7, 8, 9 10; 35:12; 48:4
with thy children *after t.* *Deut* 4:40 12:25, 28
after t. Benjamin among. *Judg* 5:14
set up thy seed *after t.* *2 Sam* 7:12
will come in *after t.* and. *1 Ki* 1:14
nor *after t.* shall any arise like thee. 3:12; *2 Chr* 1:12
panteth my soul *after t.* *Ps* 42:1
my soul followeth hard *after t.* 63:8
my soul thirsteth *after t.* 143:6
we will run *after t.* *S of S* 1:4
they shall come *after t.* *Isa* 45:14
called a multitude *after t.* *Jer* 12:6
after t. shall rise another. *Dan* 2:39
cry at Beth-aven, *after t.* *Hos* 5:8

against **thee**

that rose *against t.* *Ex* 15:7
of the field multiply *against t.* 23:29
sinned, for we have spoken *against t.* *Num* 21:7
Lord be kindled *against t.* *Deut* 6:15
and he cry to the Lord *against t.* 15:9; 24:15
they hired Balaam *against t.* 23:4
against t. one way, and flee. 28:7
the Lord shall send *against t.* *Deut* 28:48,
there for a witness *against t.* 31:
fortify the city *against t.* *Judg* 9:
we have sinned *against t.* 10: *Neh* 1:6; *Jer* 14:7,
I have not sinned *against t.* *Judg* 11:27; *1 Sam* 24:
he hath not sinned *against t.* *1 Sam* 19
hath testified *against t.* *2 Sam* 1:
I will raise up evil *against t.* 12:
that rose up *against t.* 18:31,
because they have sinned *against t* *1 Ki* 8:33, 35; *2 Chr* 6:24,
if they sin *against t.* and repent. *1 Ki* 8:46; *2 Chr* 6:
people that have sinned *against* and all their. *1 Ki* 8:50; *2 Chr* 6:
king of Syria will come up *against* *1 Ki* 20:
out to fight *against t.* *2 Ki* 19
man prevail *against t.* *2 Chr* 14:
hath spoken evil *against t.* 18:
a great multitude *against t.* 20
I come not *against t.* this day. 35:
very corruptly *against t.* *Neh* 1
they rebelled *against t.* 9:
why hast thou set me as a ma *against t.*? *Job* 7:
would open his lips *against t.* 11:
own lips testify *against t.* 15:
my wrath is kindled *against t.* 42:
have rebelled *against t.* *Ps* 5:
they intended evil *against t.* 21:
Lord, heal my soul, for I have sinne *against t.* 41:
and I will testify *against t.* 50:
against t. have I sinned, and dor this evil. 51:
that rise up *against t.* 74: 139:21; *Eccl* 10:
that I might not sin *against t.* *Ps* 119:
for they speak *against t.* 139:
evil counsel *against t.* *Isa* 7:
shall lift up his staff *against t.* 10:
fight *against t.* but they shall not pr vail *against t.* *Jer* 1:19; 15:
behold I am *against t.* 21:13; 50: 51:25; *Ezek* 5:8; 21:3; 26: 28:22; 29:3, 10; 35:3; 38: 39:1; *Nah* 2:13; 3:
thy enemies opened their mou *against t.* *Lam* 2:
still are talking *against t.* *Ezek* 33:
hath conspired *against t.* *Amos* 7:
spoken so much *against t.* *Mal* 3:
that thy brother hath aught *against* *Mat* 5:2
if thy brother trespass *against t.* 18:15; *Luke* 17:3,
which these witness *against t.*? *Mat* 26:62; *Mark* 14:60; 15:
I have somewhat *against t.* *Rev* 2:
a few things *against t.* 14, 2

at **thee**

hath shaken her head *at t.* *2 Ki* 19:2 *Isa* 37:2
fir trees rejoice at *t.* *Isa* 14:
as many were astonied *at t.* 52:1 *Ezek* 26:16; 27:35; 28:1
by clap their hands *at t.* *Lam* 2:1
shall hiss *at t.* *Ezek* 27:3
many people amazed *at t.* 32:1

before **thee**

is not whole land *before t.*? *Gen* 13:
Ishmael might live *before t.* 17:1
behold my land is *before t.* 20:1 47:
heaven shall send his angel *before* 24:7; *Ex* 23:20, 23; 32:34; 33:
Rebekah is *before t.* *Gen* 24:5
I cannot rise up *before t.* 31:3
I will go *before t.* 33:12; *Isa* 45:
set him *before t.* *Gen* 43:
will stand *before t.* there. *Ex* 17:
I will send my fear *before t.* 23:2
before t. which shall drive out th Canaanites *before t.* 28, 29, 30, 3 34:11; *Deut* 4:38; 9:4, 5; 18:1
goodness pass *before t.* and I wi proclaim . . . *before t.* *Ex* 33:1

I will cast out *before t.* *Ex* 34:24
Deut 6:19; 7:1; 9:4
hate thee flee *before t.* *Num* 10:35
no man able to stand *before t.*
Deut 7:24; *Josh* 1:5; 10:8
they shall flee *before t.* *Deut* 28:7
I have set *before t.* this day. 30:15
he shall go over *before t.* 31:3, 8
shalt see the land *before t.* 32:52
shall put incense *before t.* 33:10
Lord gone out *before t.*? *Judg* 4:14
bring forth, and set it *before t.* 6:18
1 Sam 9:24
let me set a morsel of bread *before t.* *1 Sam* 28:22
Lord go out *before t.* *2 Sam* 5:24
Saul, whom I put away *before t.* 7:15
be established for ever *before t.*
16, 26; *1 Chr* 17:24
as he walked *before t.* *1 Ki* 3:6
none like thee *before t.* 12
thy servants that walk *before t.*
8:23; *2 Chr* 6:14
which stand continually *before t.*
1 Ki 10:8; *2 Chr* 9:7
done evil above all that were *before t.* *1 Ki* 14:9
how I have walked *before t.*
2 Ki 20:3; *Isa* 38:3
for God is gone forth *before t.*
1 Chr 14:15
from him that was *before t.* 17:13
before t. in our trespasses, we cannot stand *before t.* *Ezra* 9:15
sin be blotted out *before t.* *Neh* 4:5
his heart faithful *before t.* 9:8
trouble seem little *before t.* 32
Lord, all my desire is *before t.* and.
Ps 38:9
age is as nothing *before t.* 39:5
adversaries are all *before t.* 69:19
I was as a beast *before t.* 73:22
the prisoner come *before t.* 79:11
let my prayer come *before t.*: incline thine ear unto my cry. 88:2; 141:2
hast set our iniquities *before t.* 90:8
my ways are *before t.* 119:168
let my cry come *before t.* 169
diligently what is *before t.* *Pr* 23:1
they joy *before t.* as men. *Isa* 9:3
righteousness shall go *before t.* 58:8
lips, was right *before t.* *Jer* 17:16
I stood *before t.* to turn. 18:20
the prophets that have been *before t.* of old. 28:8
all the land is *before t.*: go. 40:4
wickedness come *before t.* *Lam* 1:22
and they sit *before t.* *Ezek* 33:31
also *before t.* O king. *Dan* 6:22
I sent *before t.* Moses. *Mi* 6:4
fellows that sit *before t.* *Zech* 3:8
a trumpet *before t.* *Mat* 6:2
which shall prepare thy way *before t.*
11:10; *Mark* 1:2; *Luke* 7:27
I have sinned *before t.* *Luke* 15:18
to say *before t.* what. *Acts* 23:30
been here *before t.* to object. 24:19
before t. O king Agrippa. 25:26
set *before t.* an open door. *Rev* 3:8

behind **thee**

life, look not *behind t.* *Gen* 19:17
Amalek smote the feeble *behind t.*
Deut 25:18
castest my words *behind t.* *Ps* 50:17
hear a word *behind t.* *Isa* 30:21

beside **thee**

to redeem it *beside t.* *Ruth* 4:4
there is none *beside t.* *1 Sam* 2:2
2 Sam 7:22; *1 Chr* 17:20
that I desire *beside t.* *Ps* 73:25
other lords *beside t.* have. *Isa* 26:13
eye seen, O God, *beside t.* 64:4

between **thee**

will put enmity *between t.* *Gen* 3:15
my covenant *between* me and *t.*
17:2, 7
witness *between* me and *t.* 31:44
48:50
Lord watch *between* me and *t.* 49
the Lord be *between t.* and me for.
1 Sam 20:23, 42
set it for a wall of iron *between t.*
Ezek 4:3
been witness *between t.* *Mal* 2:14
fault *between t.* and. *Mat* 18:15

by **thee**

the people stand *by t.* *Ex* 18:14
woman that stood *by t.* *1 Sam* 1:26
I said to thee, Set it *by t.* 9:23
by t. I ran through a troop.
2 Sam 22:30; *Ps* 18:29
by t. have I been holpen. *Ps* 71:6
when thou hast it *by t.* *Pr* 3:28
dwell securely *by t.* 29
but *by t.* only will we make mention of thy name. *Isa* 26:13
when I passed *by t.* *Ezek* 16:6, 8
seeing that *by t.* we enjoy quietness.
Acts 24:2
saints are refreshed *by t.* *Philem* 7

concerning **thee**

Lord said *con. t.* and me. *Josh* 14:6
he hath spoken *con. t.* *1 Sam* 25:30
I will give charge *con. t.* *2 Sam* 14:8
spoken evil *con. t.* *1 Ki* 22:23
hath given commandment *con. t.*
Nah 1:14
angels charge *con. t.* *Mat* 4:6
neither we letters *con. t.* *Acts* 28:21

for **thee**

food *for t.* and them. *Gen* 6:21
shall pray *for t.* 20:7
but as *for t.* and thy servants, I.
Ex 9:30
sabbath shall be meat *for t.* and.
Lev 25:6
shall be most holy *for t.* *Num* 18:9
as *for t.* stand by me. *Deut* 5:31
18:14; *2 Sam* 13:13
I will try them *for t.* *Judg* 7:4
have made ready a kid *for t.* 13:15
better *for t.* to be a priest to. 18:19
shall I not seek rest *for t.*? *Ruth* 3:1
buy it *for t.* 4:8
hath it been kept *for t.* *1 Sam* 9:24
soul desireth, I will do it *for t.* 20:4
I am distressed *for t.* *2 Sam* 1:26
be too strong *for t.*, help thee. 10:11
would God I had died *for t.* 18:33
requirest, that I will do *for t.* 19:38
I will speak *for t.* unto. *1 Ki* 2:18
and after make *for t.* and. 17:13
thou shalt make streets *for t.* 20:34
what I shall do *for t.* *2 Ki* 2:9
what is to be done *for t.*? 4:13
and as *for t.* *2 Chr* 7:17; *Dan* 2:29
Zech 9:11
surely now he would awake *for t.*
Job 8:6
earth be forsaken *for t.*? 18:4
my soul thirsteth *for t.*, my. *Ps* 63:1
praise waiteth *for t.* O God. 65:1
it is time *for t.* O Lord. 119:126
fruits I have laid up *for t.* *S of S* 7:13
beneath is moved *for t.* *Isa* 14:9
have waited *for t.* 26:8; 33:2
Ethiopia and Seba *for t.* 43:3
therefore will I give men *for t.* 4
for my praise will I refrain *for t.* 48:9
who shall be sorry *for t.* 51:19
is nothing too hard *for t.* *Jer* 32:17
so shall they burn odours *for t.* 34:5
I will weep *for t.* 48:32
I laid a snare *for t.* 50:24
I take vengeance *for t.* 51:36
I take to witness *for t.* *Lam* 2:13
thy prophets have seen *for t.* 14
it watcheth *for t.*; behold. *Ezek* 7:6
be horribly afraid *for t.* 32:10
another, so will I be *for t.* *Hos* 3:3
he hath set a harvest *for t.* 6:11
I seek comfort *for t.* *Nah* 3:7
is profitable *for t.* *Mat* 5:29, 30
for Sodom than *for t.* 11:24
it is not lawful *for t.* to have her.
14:4; *Mark* 6:18
one *for t.*, and one for Moses.
Mat 17:4; *Mark* 9:5; *Luke* 9:33
better *for t.* to enter into life.
Mat 18:8, 9; *Mark* 9:43, 45
him, All men seek *for t.* *Mark* 1:37
thy brethren seek *for t.* 3:32
the Lord hath done *for t.* 5:19
but I have prayed *for t.* *Luke* 22:32
come, and calleth *for t.* *John* 11:28
hard *for t.* to kick against the pricks.
Acts 9:5; 26:14
to send *for t.* into his house. 10:22
season, I will call *for t.* 24:25
grace is sufficient *for t.* *2 Cor* 12:9

from **thee**

be far *from t.* to slay. *Gen* 18:25
anger turn away *from t.* 27:45
hath withheld *from t.* the fruit. 30:2
behold, I go out *from t.* *Ex* 8:29
put off thy ornaments *from t.* 33:5
be too far *from t.* *Deut* 12:21; 14:24
him go free *from t.* 15:12, 13, 18
I will not go away *from t.* 16
cities far *from t.* 20:15
it is not hidden *from t.* neither. 30:11
shekels taken *from t.* *Judg* 17:2
Eli said unto her, Put away thy wine *from t.* *1 Sam* 1:14
hath rent the kingdom *from t.* 15:28
1 Ki 11:11
take thine head *from t.* *1 Sam* 17:46
far be it *from t.* 20:9; *Mat* 16:22
not withhold me *from t.* *2 Sam* 13:13
before I be taken *from t.* *2 Ki* 2:9
shall issue *from t.* 20:18; *Isa* 39:7
came up *from t.* to us. *Ezra* 4:12
be withholden *from t.* *Job* 42:2
groaning is not hid *from t.* *Ps* 38:9
sins are not hid *from t.* 69:5
they that are far *from t.* shall. 73:27
so will we not go back *from t.* 80:18
darkness hideth not *from t.* 139:12
my substance was not hid *from t.* 15
wrath I hid my face *from t.* *Isa* 54:8
shall not depart *from t.* 10
my soul depart *from t.* *Jer* 6:8
I will cut off *from t.* *Ezek* 21:3, 4
those that be far *from t.* shall. 22:5
I take away *from t.* the desire. 24:16
secret that they can hide *from t.* 28:3
gone into captivity *from t.* *Mi* 1:16
iniquity to pass *from t.* *Zech* 3:4
pluck it out and cast it *from t.*
Mat 5:29, 30; 18:8, 9
I came out *from t.* *John* 17:8
for a promise *from t.* *Acts* 23:21
see **departed**

in **thee**

in t. shall all families be blessed.
Gen 12:3; 28:14
in t. shall Israel bless. 48:20
to shew *in t.* my power. *Ex* 9:16
no unclean thing *in t.* *Deut* 23:14
it would be sin *in t.* 21
shall be no sin *in t.* 22
king hath delight *in t.* *1 Sam* 18:22
evil hath not been found *in t.* 25:28
29:6
I have no delight *in t.* *2 Sam* 15:26
good things found *in t.* *2 Chr* 19:3
put trust *in t.* . . . love thy name be joyful *in t.* *Ps* 5:11; 7:1; 9:10
16:1; 17:7; 25:2, 20; 31:1, 19
55:23
rejoice *in t.* 9:2; 40:16; 70:4; 85:6
S of S 1:4
our fathers trusted *in t.* *Ps* 22:4, 5
I trusted *in t.* 31:14
hope *in t.* 33:22; 38:15; 39:7
trust *in t.* 56:3; 57:1; 84:12; 86:2
141:8; 143:8
there shall no strange god be in *t.*
81:9
man whose strength is *in t.* 84:5
all my springs are *in t.* 87:7
there is no spot *in t.* *S of S* 4:7
because he trusteth *in t.* *Isa* 26:3
surely God is *in t.*; and there. 45:14
for the Lord delighteth *in t.* 62:4
that my fear is not *in t.* *Jer* 2:19
I will do *in t.* what I. *Ezek* 5:9
will execute judgements *in t.* 10, 15
the contrary is *in t.* from. 16:34
I will kindle a fire *in t.*, and it. 20:47
were *in t.* to their power to. 22:6
in t. have they set light by father. 7
in t. are men that carry tales. 9
in t. have they taken gifts. 12
set palaces *in t.*, dwellings *in t.* 25:4
O Tyrus, that were *in t.* 27:8, 9
till iniquity was found *in t.* 28:15
be sanctified *in t.* O Gog. 38:16

spirit of the holy gods is *in t.* *Dan* 4:9, 18; 5:14
for *in t.* the fatherless. *Hos* 14:3
Israel were found *in t.* *Mi* 1:13
cry ? is there no king *in t.*? 4:9
if the light that is *in t.* *Mat* 6:23
which have been done *in t.* 11:23
my beloved Son; *in t.* I. *Luke* 3:22
the light which is *in t.* be not. 11:35
not leave *in t.* one stone. 19:44
art in me, and I *in t.* *John* 17:21
shew my power *in t.* *Rom* 9:17
in t. shall all nations. *Gal* 3:8
the gift that is *in t.* *1 Tim* 4:14
faith that is *in t.* first in Lois and Eunice, and . . . *in t.* *2 Tim* 1:5
stir up the gift of God which is *in t.* 6
of the truth that is *in t.* *3 John* 3
heard no more at all *in t.* *Rev* 18:22
shall shine no more at all *in t.* 23

into **thee**

no more *into t.* the. *Isa* 52:1

of **thee**

of t. a great nation. *Gen* 12:2
17:6; 35:11; 46:3; 48:4; *Ex* 32:10
and my soul shall live because *of t.* *Gen* 12:13
I have heard say *of t.* that. 41:15
heard the fame *of t.* *Num* 14:15
I will put the dread *of t.* and the fear *of t.* . . . because *of t.* *Deut* 2:25
Lord require *of t.* 10:12; *Mi* 6:8
take knowledge *of t.* *Ruth* 2:19
with my father *of t.* *1 Sam* 19:3
and the Lord avenge me *of t.* 24:12
I will require *of t.* *2 Sam* 3:13
but I will surely buy it *of t.* 24:24
one petition *of t.* *1 Ki* 2:16, 20
as this is done *of t.* 11:11
house as he said *of t.* *1 Chr* 22:11
and honour come *of t.* 29:12
all things come *of t.*, and of thine. 14
God exacteth *of t.* less. *Job* 11:6
for I will demand *of t.* 38:3; 40:7; 42:4
heard *of t.* by the hearing. 42:5
my praise shall be *of t.* *Ps* 22:25; 71:6
glorious things are spoken *of t.* 87:3
lest he be weary *of t.* *Pr* 25:17
two things have I required *of t.* 30:7
they that shall be *of t.* *Isa* 58:12
up himself to take hold *of t.* 64:7
I will not make a full end *of t.* *Jer* 30:11; 46:28
thus saith the Lord *of t.*, Thou. 34:4
shall not take *of t.* a stone. 51:26
man and beast out *of t.* *Ezek* 29:8
rivers shall be full *of t.* 32:6
made known what we desired *of t.* *Dan* 2:23
petition, save *of t.* O king. 6:7, 12
assemble all *of t.* *Mi* 2:12
yet out *of t.* shall come forth. 5:2
shall fear because *of t.* 7:17
come out *of t.* a wicked. *Nah* 1:11
who are *of t.* to whom. *Zeph* 3:18
for out *of t.* shall come. *Mat* 2:6
need to be baptized *of t.* 3:14
him that would borrow *of t.* 5:42
no man eat fruit *of t.* *Mark* 11:14
which shall be born *of t.* *Luke* 1:35
every man that asketh *of t.* 6:30
soul shall be required *of t.* 12:20
how is it that I hear this *of t.*? 16:2
hast given me are *of t.* *John* 17:7
and to hear words *of t.* *Acts* 10:22
nor spake any harm *of t.* 28:21
we desire to hear *of t.* what. 22
I have no need *of t.* *1 Cor* 12:21
let me have joy *of t.* *Philem* 20

see, in the **midst**

off **thee**

head from *off t.* and birds shall eat thy flesh from *off t.* *Gen* 40:19
break his yoke from *off t.* *Nah* 1:13

on or *upon* **thee**

my wrong be *upon t.* *Gen* 16:5
this breach be *upon t.* 38:29
of these diseases *upon t.* *Ex* 15:26
woollen come *upon t.* *Lev* 19:19
his face shine *upon t.* *Num* 6:25
up his countenance *upon t.* *Num* 6:26
of the spirit which is *upon t.* 11:17
all these things are come *upon t.* *Deut* 4:30; 30:1
the Lord may have compassion *upon t.* 13:17; 30:3
so blood be *upon t.* 19:10
blessings come *on t.* 28:2
all these curses shall come *upon t.* 28:15, 20, 45
the Philistines be *upon t.*, Samson. *Judg* 16:9, 12, 14, 20
is it not *upon t.* and thy. *1 Sam* 9:20
hand shall not be *upon t.* 24:12, 13
all Israel are *upon t.* *1 Ki* 1:20
upon t. shall he offer the priests, and . . . shall be burnt *upon t.* 13:2
bring evil *upon t.* and take. 21:21
shalt shut door *upon t.* *2 Ki* 4:4
Lord, for we rest *upon t.* *2 Chr* 14:11
wrath *upon t.* from the Lord. 19:2
to do: but our eyes are *upon t.* 20:12
but now it is come *upon t.* *Job* 4:5
I have called *upon t.* *Ps* 17:6
31:17; 86:5, 7; 88:9; *Lam* 3:57
I was cast *upon t.* *Ps* 22:10
wait *upon t.* 25:3, 5, 21; 59:9
meditate *on t.* 63:6
these wait *upon t.* 104:27; 145:15
that we may look *upon t.* *S of S* 6:13
I will turn my hand *upon t.* *Isa* 1:25
pit, and the snare are *upon t.* 24:17
whose mind is stayed *upon t.* 26:3
they shall come *upon t.* in. 47:9
desolation shall come *upon t.* 11, 13
and bind them *on t.* as a. 49:18
will I have mercy *on t.* 54:8, 10
my spirit that is *upon t.* 59:21
glory of Lord is risen *upon t.* 60:1, 2
will wait *upon t.* for thou. *Jer* 14:22
for who shall have pity *upon t.*? 15:5
all that prey *upon t.* will I. 30:16
they shall put bands *upon t.* *Ezek* 3:25; 4:8
and I will bring the sword *upon t.* 5:17; 29:8
when they leaned *upon t.* 29:7
as I had pity *upon t.* *Mat* 18:33
let no fruit grow *on t.* 21:19
the Holy Ghost shall come *upon t.* *Luke* 1:35
days shall come *upon t.* that. 19:43
hand of Lord is *upon t.* *Acts* 13:11
no man shall set *on t.* to. 18:10
beat them that believed *on t.* 22:19
which went before *on t.* *1 Tim* 1:18
on t. as a thief, and thou shalt not know . . . come *upon t.* *Rev* 3:3

over **thee**

and he shall rule *over t.* *Gen* 3:16
shall not reign *over t.* *Deut* 15:6
him king *over t.*: thou mayest not set a stranger *over t.* 17:15; 28:36
Lord will again rejoice *over t.* 30:9
give his angels charge *over t.* *Ps* 91:11; *Luke* 4:10
God rejoice *over t.* *Isa* 62:5
them to be chief *over t.* *Jer* 13:21
enemy to rejoice *over t.* *Lam* 2:17
I spread my skirt *over t.* *Ezek* 16:8
spread out my net *over t.* 32:3
and seven times shall pass *over t.* *Dan* 4:25, 32
shall clap the hands *over t.* *Nah* 3:19
will rejoice *over t.*, he will joy *over t.* *Zeph* 3:17

through **thee**

through t. will we push. *Ps* 44:5

to or *unto* **thee**

unto t. shall be his desire. *Gen* 4:7
to t. will I give it. 13:15, 17; 17:8
26:3; 28:4, 13; 35:12
certainly return *unto t.* 18:10, 14
to t. a covering of the eyes. 20:16
nations bow down *to t.* 27:29
which I have spoken *to t.* of. 28:15
give the tenth of all *unto t.* 22
better I give her *to t.* than to. 29:19
all that Laban doth *unto t.* 31:12
God hath said *unto t.* do. 16
thine with me, and take *to t.* 32
torn I brought not *unto t.* 39
not pass over this heap *to t.* 52
let me come in *unto t.* *Gen* 38:16
if I bring him not *to t.* 42:37; 43:9; 44:32
money we brought again *unto t.* 44:8
for they did *unto t.* evil. 50:17
shall be a token *unto t.* *Ex* 3:12
to t. instead of a mouth. 4:16
be *unto t.* for a sign. 13:9
2 Ki 19:29; *Isa* 38:7
they shall bring *unto t.* *Ex* 18:22
take *unto t.* Aaron thy brother. 28:1
unto t. principal spices. 30:23
know what to do *unto t.* 33:5
shall be holy *unto t.* for. *Lev* 21:8
that they bring *unto t.* pure. 24:2
Lord be gracious *unto t.* *Num* 6:25
word shall come to pass *unto t.* 11:23
Levi may be joined *unto t.* 18:2, 4
it is a covenant of salt *unto t.* 19
Balak, lo, I am come *unto t.* 22:38
unto t. it was shewed. *Deut* 4:35
gold of their gods *unto t.* 7:25
and it be sin *unto t.* 15:9, 24:15
Lord will raise up *unto t.* 18:15
up a prophet like *unto t.* 18
and take the young *to t.* 22:7
from his master *unto t.* 23:15
who is like *unto t.*, O people. 33:29
1 Sam 26:15; *Ps* 35:10; 71:19
will we hearken *unto t.* *Josh* 1:17
household home *unto t.* 2:18
of whom I say *unto t.* *Judg* 7:4
I will restore it *unto t.* 17:3
perform *unto t.* the part. *Ruth* 3:13
he shall be *unto t.* a restorer of thy life: for thy daughter in law, better *to t.* than seven sons. 4:15
am not I better *to t.* than ? *1 Sam* 1:8
in all that they say *unto t.* 8:7
so do they *unto t.* 8
man I speak *to t.* of shall. 9:17
we will come out *to t.* 11:3
him whom I name *unto t.* 16:3
but I come *to t.* in the name. 17:45
for there is peace *to t.* 20:21
peace be *to t.* 25:6
whom I shall name *unto t.* 28:8
no punishment happen *to t.* 10
about all Israel *unto t.* *2 Sam* 3:12
child that is born *unto t.* shall. 12:14
bring back all the people *unto t.* 17:3
that will be worse *unto t.* 19:7
his head shall be thrown *to t.* 20:21
I will give thanks *unto t.* 22:50
Ps 18:49; 30:12; 75:1; 119:62
that I may do it *unto t.* *2 Sam* 24:12
any arise like *unto t.* *1 Ki* 3:12
that they call for *unto t.* 8:52
will give ten tribes *unto t.* 11:31
and will give Israel *unto t.* 38
sent *to t.* with heavy tidings. 14:6
for what have I done *to t.*? 19:20
send my servants *unto t.* 20:6
inheritance of my fathers *unto t.* 21:3
from me to speak *unto t.*? 22:24
it shall be so *unto t.* *2 Ki* 2:10
this letter is come *unto t.* 5:6
Naaman shall cleave *unto t.* 27
take it up *to t.* 6:7
what said Elisha *to t.*? 8:14
he said, I have an errand *to t.* 9:5
came this mad fellow *to t.*? 11
from whence came they *unto t.*? 20:14; *Isa* 39:3
peace be *unto t.* and. *1 Chr* 12:18
unto t. will I give the land. 16:18
Ps 105:11
appertaineth not *unto t.* *2 Chr* 26:18
matter belongeth *unto t.* *Ezra* 10:4
them to turn them *to t.* *Neh* 9:26
the silver is given *to t.* *Esth* 3:11
what shall I do *unto t.*? *Job* 7:20
for *unto t.* will I pray. *Ps* 5:2, 3
committeth himself *unto t.* 10:14
goodness extendeth not *to t.* 16:2
they cried *unto t.* and were. 22:5
unto t., O Lord, do I lift up my soul 25:1; 86:4; 143:8
my heart said *unto t.*, Thy face. 27:8
unto t. will I cry. 28:1, 2; 30:8
31:22; 56:9; 61:2; 86:3; 88:1
130:1; 141:1
may sing praise *to t.* 30:12; 56:1
59:17; 66:4; 71:22, 2

acknowledged my sin unto t. Ps 32:5
unto t. O Lord, belongeth. 62:12
and unto t. shall the vow be. 65:1
O thou that hearest prayer, unto t. 2
my prayer is unto t. in an. 69:13
gods there is none like unto t. 86:8
a strong Lord like unto t.? 89:8
unto t. O Lord, will I. 101:1; 108:3
138:1; 144:9; Heb 2:12
let my cry come unto t. Ps 102:1
what shall be given unto t.? 120:3
unto t. will I lift up. 123:1; 141:8
light are both alike to t. 139:12
made known to t. this day, even to t. Pr 22:19
Eat and drink, saith he to t. 23:7
better it be said unto t. Come. 25:7
speak and say unto t. Isa 14:10
be very gracious unto t. 30:19
hath my master sent me to t.? 36:12
two things shall come to t. 47:9
thus shall they be unto t. with. 15
together and come to t. 49:18
two things are come unto t. 51:19
knew not thee shall run unto t. 55:5
moon give light unto t.: the Lord shall be unto t. an everlasting. 60:19
come no more unto t. Jer 2:31
come unto t. for thou art our. 3:22
as there is none like unto t. 10:6
who would not fear, for to t. doth? 7
for unto t. have I revealed my. 11:20; 20:12
let them return unto t. but. 15:19
a man child is born unto t. 20:15
unto t. in thy prosperity. 22:21
done these things unto t. 30:15
I speak unto t.: so it shall be well unto t. 38:20
I will look well unto t. 40:4
we will not hearken unto t. 44:16
but thy life will I give unto t. 45:5
Israel a derision unto t.? 48:27
I liken to t., O Jerusalem? what shall I equal to t., that I? Lam 2:13
shall pass through unto t. 4:21
turn thou us unto t. and we. 5:21
hearkened unto t. Ezek 3:6
Israel will not hearken unto t. 7
to do any of these unto t. 16:5
I said unto t. when thou wast in. 6
no reward is given unto t. 34
establish unto t. an everlasting. 60
and I will give them unto t. for. 61
shall be sure unto t. Dan 4:26
to t. it is spoken, the kingdom is. 31
righteousness belongeth unto t. 9:7
what shall I do unto t.? Hos 6:4
to t. will I cry. Joel 1:19
the beasts cry unto t. 20
thus will I do unto t.: and because I will do this unto t. Amos 4:12
shall we do unto t.? Jonah 1:11
my prayer came in unto t. 2:7
saying, I will prophesy unto t. of wine. Mi 2:11
unto t. shall it come. 4:8
what have I done unto t.? 6:3
he shall come to t. even from. 7:12
I even cry out unto t. Hab 1:2
right hand be turned unto t. 2:16
Lord hath sent me unto t. Zech 2:11
behold, thy king cometh unto t. 9:9
Mat 21:5
hast believed, so be it done unto t. Mat 8:13
hath not revealed it unto t. 16:17
and I say also unto t. that thou. 18
I will give unto t. the keys of. 19
this shall not be unto t. 22
him be unto t. as an heathen. 18:17
Jesus saith, I say not unto t. Until. 22
this last even as unto t. 20:14
thou stonest them sent unto t. 23:37
Luke 13:34
did not minister unto t.? Mat 25:44
I say unto t. Arise. Mark 5:41
Luke 5:24; 7:14
What wilt thou that I do unto t.?
Mark 10:51; Luke 18:41
I am sent to speak unto t. Luke 1:19
myself worthy to come unto t. 7:7
I have somewhat to say unto t. 40
God hath done unto t. 8:39

saith, I that speak unto t. am he. John 4:26
a worse thing come unto t. 5:14
what did he to t.? 9:26
said I not unto t.? 11:40
world, and I am come to t. 17:11, 13
have delivered him unto t. 18:30
he that delivered me unto t. 19:11
what is that to t.? follow. 21:22, 23
appeared unto t. sent me. Acts 9:17
cometh, shall speak unto t. 10:32
therefore I sent to t. 33
captain, May I speak unto t.? 21:37
for I have appeared unto t. 26:16
will I confess to t. Rom 15:9
committed unto t. keep. 2 Tim 1:14
but now profitable to t. Philem 11
but how much more to t.? 16
thou hast taken to t. thy. Rev 11:17

towards **thee**

his works have been very good towards t. 1 Sam 19:4
I would not look towards t. nor. 2 Ki 3:14
mine heart towards t. Jer 12:3
so will I make my fury towards t. to rest. Ezek 16:42
when I am pacified towards t. 63
but towards t. goodness. Rom 11:22

under **thee**

the earth that is under t. Deut 28:23
the people fall under t. Ps 45:5
take thy bed from under t.? Pr 22:27
worm is spread under t. Isa 14:11
laid a wound under t. Ob 7

with **thee**

with t. will I establish. Gen 6:18
my covenant is with t. 17:4
Ex 34:27; Deut 29:12
now will we deal worse with t. than. Gen 19:9
saying, God is with t. in all. 21:22
will send his angel with t. 24:40
I will be with t. 26:3
I am with t. 24; 28:15; 31:3; 46:4
Ex 3:12; Deut 31:23; Josh 1:5
3:7; 1 Ki 11:38; Isa 43:2
the Lord was with t. Gen 26:28
God shall be with t. Ex 18:19
I will meet with t. 25:22; 30:6, 36
my presence shall go with t. 33:14
Deut 31:6, 8; Judg 6:16
not abide with t. all night. Lev 19:13
if no man hath lien with t. be thou. Num 5:19
some man hath lien with t. 20
What men are these with t.? 22:9
God hath been with t. Deut 2:7
go well with t. 4:40; 5:16; 6:3, 18
12:25, 28; 19:13; 22:7
go because he is well with t. 15:16
the Lord thy God is with t. 20:1
Josh 1:9; Judg 6:12; 2 Sam 7:3
against the city that maketh war with t. Deut 20:20
he shall dwell with t. even. 23:16
I will surely go with t. Judg 4:9
the people that are with t. 7:2
this shall go with t. 4
peace be with t. 19:20
that it may be well with t. Ruth 3:1
for God is with t. 1 Sam 10:7
Luke 1:28
I am with t. according to. 1 Sam 14:7
the Lord be with t. 17:37; 20:13
1 Chr 22:11, 16
and no man with t.? 1 Sam 21:1
I will deliver Israel with t. 28:19
so long as I have been with t. 29:8
my hand shall be with t. 2 Sam 3:12
I was with t. 7:9; 1 Chr 17:8
Amnon been with t. 2 Sam 13:20
Why should he go with t.? 26
Lord thy God will be with t. 14:17
1 Chr 28:20
and truth be with t. 2 Sam 15:20
I may not tarry thus with t. 18:14
there will not tarry one with t. 19:7
thou hast with t. Shimei. 1 Ki 2:8
uprightness of heart with t. 3:6
perform my word with t. 6:12
I will not go in with t. 13:8, 16

what have I to do with t.? 1 Ki 17:18
2 Ki 3:13; 2 Chr 35:21; Mark 5:7
Luke 8:28; John 2:4
is it well with t.? 2 Ki 4:26
went not mine heart with t.? 5:26
ever thou and Judah with t. 14:10
2 Chr 25:19
nothing with t. to help. 2 Chr 14:11
we will be with t. 18:3; Ezra 10:4
let not the army of Israel go with t. 2 Chr 25:7
be at peace with t. Job 5:23
I know that this is with t. 10:13
me into judgement with t. 14:3
number of his months are with t. 5
of God small with t.? is there any secret thing with t.? 15:11
perfect in knowledge with t. 36:4
behemoth, which I made with t. 40:15
nor shall evil dwell with t. Ps 5:4
with t. is the fountain of life. 36:9
I am a stranger with t. and. 39:12
I am continually with t. 73:23
have fellowship with t.? 94:20
dealt bountifully with t. 116:7
it shall be well with t. 128:2
but there is forgiveness with t. 130:4
awake, I am still with t. 139:18
my commandments with t. Pr 2:1
and not strangers with t. 5:17
it shall talk with t. 6:22
his heart is not with t. 23:7
may seek him with t. S of S 6:1
outcast dwell with t. Moab. Isa 16:4
I am with t. 41:10; 43:5; Jer 1:8
19; 15:20; 30:11; 46:28
Acts 18:10
they that strive with t. Isa 41:11, 12
that contendeth with t. 49:25
I would not be wroth with t. 54:9
I will plead with t. Jer 2:35
when I plead with t. 12:1
and he shall speak with t. 34:3
with t. will I break in pieces the nations. 51:20
with t. will I break in pieces horse and rider. 21
with t. will I break in pieces old and young. 22
with t. will I break shepherd. 23
and thorns be with t. Ezek 2:6
I will there talk with t. 3:22
into a covenant with t. 16:8
I will even deal with t. as thou. 59
establish my covenant with t. 62
that I shall deal with t. 22:14
they occupied with t. in lambs. 27:21
beasts of the earth with t. 32:4
his bands and many people with t.
38:6, 9, 15; 39:4
the prophet shall fall with t. Hos 4:5
Is there yet any with t.? Amos 6:10
were at peace with t. Ob 7
all the saints with t. Zech 14:5
will he be pleased with t.? Mal 1:8
What have we to do with t.?
Mat 8:29; Mark 1:24; Luke 4:34
desiring to speak with t. Mat 12:47
then take with t. one or two. 18:16
Peter said, Though I should die with t. 26:35; Mark 14:31
I am ready to go with t. Luke 22:33
he that was with t. John 3:26
is he that talketh with t. 9:37
glory which I had with t. 17:5
him, We also go with t. 21:3
Thy money perish with t. Acts 8:20
that it may be well with t., and that thou mayest live long. Eph 6:3
grace be with t. 1 Tim 6:21
bring with t. 2 Tim 4:11, 13

within **thee**

the stranger within t. Deut 28:43
say, Peace be within t. Ps 122:8
thy children within t. 147:13
if thou keep them within t. Pr 22:18
thoughts lodge within t. Jer 4:14
thy children within t. Luke 19:44

without **thee**

without t. shall no man lift up his. Gen 41:44

theft, -s
be sold for his *t.* *Ex* 22:3
if the *t.* be certainly found in. 4
out of the heart proceed *t.*
Mat 15:19; *Mark* 7:22
repented they of their *t.* *Rev* 9:21

their's
be a stranger in a land that is not *t.'s.*
Gen 15:13
every beast of *t.'s,* be our's ? 34:23
times as much as any of *t.'s.* 43:34
priests' office shall be *t.'s.* *Ex* 29:9
for *t.'s* is thine own nakedness.
Lev 18:10
and touch nothing of *t.'s.* *Num* 16:26
t.'s, every meat offering of *t.'s.* 18:9
for *t.'s* was the first lot. *Josh* 21:10
1 Chr 6:54
let thy word be like one of *t.'s.*
2 Chr 18:12
shall stand, mine, or *t.'s.* *Jer* 44:28
remain, nor any of *t.'s.* *Ezek* 7:11
thing in Israel shall be *t.'s.* 44:29
dwelling places that are not *t.'s.*
Hab 1:6
for *t.'s* is the kingdom. *Mat* 5:3, 10
call on our Lord, both *t.'s.* *1 Cor* 1:2
manifest, as *t.'s* was. *2 Tim* 3:9

them
male, female created he *t.* *Gen* 1:27
your little ones, *t.* will. *Num* 14:31
t. will the Lord bring. *Deut* 28:61
t. that honour me, I. *1 Sam* 2:30
t. shall he sling out, as out. 25:29
t. they hold also to. *1 Ki* 13:11
t. that burnt incense. *2 Ki* 23:5
t. hath the Lord chosen. *1 Chr* 15:2
t. did Solomon make to. *2 Chr* 8:8
let *t.* shout for joy, let *t.* *Ps* 5:11
nor let *t.* wink with eye that. 35:19
let *t.* also that hate him flee. 68:1
even *t.* that contended. *Isa* 41:12
even *t.* will I bring to my. 56:7
they cast *t.* into the den. *Dan* 6:24
t. that worship the host. *Zeph* 1:5
take away *t.* that rejoice in thy. 3:11
shall gather out *t.* which. *Mat* 13:41
then let *t.* which be in Judea flee.
24:16; *Mark* 13:14; *Luke* 21:21
neither believed they *t.* *Mark* 16:13
to set at liberty *t.* that. *Luke* 4:18
and *t.* that were entering in. 11:52
cast out *t.* that sold and *t.* 19:45
and *t.* that were with *t.* 24:33
other sheep I have, *t.* *John* 10:16
that we trouble not *t.* *Acts* 15:19
t. take and purify thyself with *t.* 21:24
that I beat *t.* that believed. 22:19
t. he also called: *t.* he also justified:
and *t.* he also glorified. *Rom* 8:30
provoke to emulation *t.* which. 11:14
to judge *t.* also that. *1 Cor* 5:12
but *t.* that are without God. 13
acknowledge ye *t.* that are. 16:18
even so *t.* also that. *1 Thes* 4:14
now *t.* that are such, we. *2 Thes* 3:12
shalt save thyself and *t.* *1 Tim* 4:16
t. that sin rebuke before all. 5:20
hath perfected *t.* that. *Heb* 10:14
remember *t.* that are in bonds. 13:3
let *t.* that suffer according to will of
God. *1 Pet* 4:19
horses and *t.* that sat on *t.* *Rev* 9:17
and measure *t.* that worship. 11:1
to blaspheme *t.* that dwell in. 13:6
beast was taken, and *t.* 19:20
see **teach**

above them
proudly, he was *above t.* *Ex* 18:11
were over and *above t.* *Num* 3:49
lifted *above t.* that rose against me.
2 Sam 22:49
images that were *above t.* he cut.
2 Chr 34:4

about them
cities round *about t.* *Gen* 35:5
city was moved *about t.* *Ruth* 1:19
the heathen that were *about t.*
2 Ki 17:15
make *about t.* walls. *2 Chr* 14:7
all *about t.* strengthened. *Ezra* 1:6
eyes round *about t.* four. *Ezek* 1:18
despise them round *about t.* 28:26
great multitude *about t.* *Mark* 9:14
fear came on all that dwelt round
about t. *Luke* 1:65
of the Lord shone round *about t.* 2:9
and the cities *about t.* in. *Jude* 7

after them
seven other kine came up *after t.*
Gen 41:3, 19, 27
withered sprung up *after t.* 23
shall arise *after t.* seven years. 30
which thou begettest *after t.* 48:6
neither *after t.* shall be. *Ex* 10:14
he shall follow *after t.* and I. 14:4
go a whoring *after t.* *Lev* 20:6
and their seed *after t.* *Deut* 1:8
chose their seed *after t.* 4:37; 10:15
pursue *after t.* quickly. *Josh* 2:5
the men pursued *after t.* 7; 8:16
Judg 8:12; 20:45
generation *after t.* *Judg* 2:10
reap, go thou *after t.* *Ruth* 2:9
Philistines went *after t.* *1 Sam* 6:12
they followed hard *after t.* in. 14:22
upon their children that were left
after t. *1 Ki* 9:21; *2 Chr* 8:8
went *after t.* to Jordan. *2 Ki* 7:15
not from *after t.* to wit. 10:29
go not up *after t.* *1 Chr* 14:14
and I *after t.* *Neh* 12:33
cried *after t.* as after. *Job* 30:5
strangers, and *after t.* *Jer* 2:25
send a sword *after t.* 9:16; 49:37
Ezek 5:2, 12; 12:14
Sheshach shall drink *after t.*
Jer 25:26
iniquity of the fathers into the bosom
of their children *after t.* 32:18
good of their children *after t.* 39
army pursued *after t.* 39:5
and utterly destroy *after t.* 50:21
shall look *after t.* *Ezek* 29:16
did search or seek *after t.* 34:6
king shall rise *after t.* *Dan* 7:24
horses go forth *after t.* *Zech* 6:6
land was desolate *after t.* 7:14
see here; or, see there: go not *after*
t. *Luke* 17:23; 21:8
away disciples *after t.* *Acts* 20:30

against them
against t. by night. *Gen* 14:15
my wrath may wax hot *against t.*
Ex 32:10; *Num* 12:9; *Deut* 2:15
31:17; *Judg* 2:15
congregation *against t.* *Num* 16:19
Bashan went out *against t.* 21:33
forcing an axe *against t.* *Deut* 20:19
go out one way *against t.* 28:25
song shall testify *against t.* 31:21
and earth to record *against t.* 28
and the other issued out of the city
against t. *Josh* 8:22
intend to go up *against t.* in. 22:33
strive or fight *against t.*? *Judg* 11:25
he moved David *against t.* to say.
2 Sam 24:1
he testified *against t.* *2 Ki* 17:15
dwelt over *against t.* *1 Chr* 5:11
they were helped *against t.* for. 20
ye down *against t.* *2 Chr* 20:16, 17
prophets testified *against t.* 24:19
Neh 9:26, 29, 30, 34
stood up *against t.* that came. 28:12
hired counsellors *against t.* *Ezra* 4:5
but his wrath is *against t.* 8:22
we set a watch *against t.* *Neh* 4:9
set a great assembly *against t.* 5:7
dealt proudly *against t.* 9:10
brethren were over *against t.* 12:9
hired Balaam *against t.* 13:2
I testified *against t.* 15, 21
those that rise up *against t.* *Ps* 17:7
face of the Lord is *against t.* that do
evil. 34:16; *1 Pet* 3:12
doth witness *against t.* *Isa* 3:9
forth his hand *against t.* 5:25
stir up the Medes *against t.* 13:17
I will rise up *against t.* 14:22
he fought *against t.* 63:10
I will utter my judgements *against*
t. *Jer* 1:16
I will give sentence *against t.* 4:12
I am *against t.* 23:32
prophesy *against t.* *Jer* 25:30
Ezek 6:2; 13:17; 25:2
evil he pronounced *against t.*
Jer 26:19; 35:17; 36:31
it prevaileth *against t.* *Lam* 1:13
set my face *against t.* *Ezek* 15:7
my anger *against t.* in Egypt. 20:8
out of thy hatred *against t.* 35:11
bring thee *against t.* 38:17
horn prevailed *against t.* *Dan* 7:21
is kindled *against t.* *Hos* 8:5
shall be gathered *against t.* 10:10
for a testimony *against t.* *Mat* 10:18
Mark 6:11; 13:9; *Luke* 9:5
spoken that parable *against t.*
Mark 12:12; *Luke* 20:19
off the dust of their feet *against t.*
Acts 13:51
rose up together *against t.* 16:22
spirit was prevailed *against t.* 19:16
I gave my voice *against t.* 26:10
being mad *against t.* 11
judgement of God is *against t.* that.
Rom 2:2
and be not bitter *against t.* *Col* 3:19
accusation *against t.* *2 Pet* 2:11
shall make war *against t.* *Rev* 11:7
see **fight, over**

among or *amongst* them
men of activity *among t.* *Gen* 47:6
of Israel from *among t.* *Ex* 7:5
which I have done *amongst t.* 10:2
that I may dwell *among t.* 25:8
29:46; *Ps* 68:18
be no plague *among t.* *Ex* 30:12
defile my tabernacle that is *among t.*
Lev 15:31
not numbered *among t.* *Num* 1:47
fire of Lord burnt *among t.* 11:1, 3
the mixt multitude *among t.* 4
the Lord is *among t.* 16:3; *Ps* 68:17
Aaron shall have no part *among t.*
Num 18:20; *Josh* 14:3
shout of a king is *among t.*
Num 23:21
the hornet *among t.* *Deut* 7:20
that was born *among t.* *Josh* 8:33
were conversant *among t.* 35
that they dwelt *among t.* 9:16
that he may dwell *among t.* 20:4
that which I did *amongst t.* 24:5
the Canaanites dwelt *among t.*
Judg 1:30
strange gods from *among t.* 10:16
he wrought *among t.* *1 Sam* 6:6
Neh 9:17
chiefest place *among t.* *1 Sam* 9:22
and he prophesied *among t.* 10:10
thy servant *among t.* *2 Sam* 19:28
the Lord sent lions *among t.*
2 Ki 17:25
Levi and Benjamin not counted
among t. *1 Chr* 21:6
found mighty men *among t.* 26:31
found *among t.* abundance of spoil.
2 Chr 20:25
that were naked *among t.* 28:15
were *among t.* 200 singing men.
Ezra 2:65
midst *among t.* and slay. *Neh* 4:11
establish the Purim *among t.*
Esth 9:21
and Satan came also *among t.*
Job 1:6; 2:1
no stranger passed *among t.* 15:19
garments *among t.*, and cast lots upon.
Ps 22:18; *Mat* 27:35; *John* 19:24
seize upon them; for wickedness is
among t. *Ps* 55:15
and I lie even *among t.* that. 57:4
among t. were damsels. 68:25
sorts of flies *among t.* 78:45
sending evil angels *among t.* 49
and Samuel *among t.* that call. 99:6
shewed his signs *among t.* 105:27
out Israel from *among t.* 136:11
barren *among t.* *S of S* 4:2; 6:6
weary or stumble *among t.* *Isa* 5:27
many *among t.* shall stumble. 8:15
there was no man *among t.* 41:28
who *among t.* can declare this? 43:9
which *among t.* hath declared. 48:14
I will set a sign *among t.* 66:19

hey shall fall *among t.* that fall. *Jer* 6:15; 8:12
) congregation, what is *among t.* 18
ouse of Judah from *among t.* 12:14
nd pestilence *among t.* 24:10
word that I will send *among t.* 25:16
ut wounded men *among t.* 37:10
en men found *among t.* that. 41:8
s a menstruous woman *among t.* *Lam* 1:17
here hath been a prophet *among t.* *Ezek* 2:5; 33:33
nd remained there *among t.* 3:15
halt not go out *among t.* 25
ne man *among t.* had a writer's. 9:2
srael that are *among t.* 12:10
nd the prince that is *among t.* 12
am prophet *among t.* 22:26
sought a man *among t.* 30
prophet hath been *among t.* 33:33
)avid a prince *among t.* 34:24
nyself known *among t.* 35:11
mong t. was found none. *Dan* 1:19
ame up *among t.* another. 7:8
hall scatter *among t.* the prey. 11:24
here is none *among t.* *Hos* 7:7
hat is feeble *among t.* *Zech* 12:8
umult shall be *among t.* 14:13
say, *Among t.* that are born of. *Mat* 11:11
wo fishes divided he *among t.* *Mark* 6:41
reasoning *among t.* *Luke* 9:46
was also a strife *among t.* 22:24
Peter sat down *among t.* in. 55
was a division *among t.* *John* 9:16
f I had not done *among t.* 15:24
mong t. that lacked. *Acts* 4:34
Paul departed from *among t.* 17:33
he word of God *among t.* 18:11
nheritance *among t.* that are. 20:32
26:18
were grafted in *among t.* *Rom* 11:17
we speak wisdom *among t.* that. *1 Cor* 2:6
come out from *among t.* *2 Cor* 6:17
man dwelling *amongst t.* *2 Pet* 2:8
preeminence *among t.* *3 John* 9
hat are ungodly *among t.* *Jude* 15
n the throne shall dwell *among t.* *Rev* 7:15

at **them**

we have shot *at t.*: Heshbon is perished. *Num* 21:30
not be affrighted *at t.* *Deut* 7:21
his enemies, he puffeth *at t.* *Ps* 10:5
O Lord, shalt laugh *at t.* 59:8
but God shall shoot *at t.* 64:7
heathen are dismayed *at t.* *Jer* 10:2

before **them**

and set it *before t.* *Gen* 18:8
he passed over *before t.* 33:3
before t. there were no such locusts. *Ex* 10:14
the Lord went *before t.* by day. 13:21; *Num* 14:14
thou shalt set *before t.* *Ex* 21:1
ark of the Lord went *before t.* *Num* 10:33
to go out and in *before t.* 27:17
1 Sam 18:16
destroyed them from *before t.* *Deut* 2:12, 21, 22; *1 Chr* 5:25
Neh 9:24
shalt flee seven ways *before t.* *Deut* 28:25
armed men went *before t.* *Josh* 6:13
land was subdued *before t.* 18:1
man of their enemies *before t.* 21:44
Ehud *before t.* *Judg* 3:27
take *before t.* waters. 7:24
tabret, a pipe and harp, *before t.* *1 Sam* 10:5
and Shobach went *before t.* *2 Sam* 10:16; *1 Chr* 19:16
Amasa went *before t.* *2 Sam* 20:8
give them compassion *before t.* *1 Ki* 8:50; *2 Chr* 30:9
prophets prophesied *before t.* *1 Ki* 22:10; *2 Chr* 18:19
Moabites fled *before t.* *2 Ki* 3:24
Gehazi passed on *before t.* 4:31
so he set it *before t.* 44
bread and water *before t.* *2 Ki* 6:22
Lord carried away *before t.* 17:11
priest sounded trumpets *before t.* *2 Chr* 7:6
Ezra the scribe *before t.* *Neh* 12:36
will pay my vows *before t.* *Ps* 22:25
not set God *before t.* 54:3; 86:14
the heathen also *before t.* 78:55
he sent a man *before t.* 105:17
all that have been *before t.* *Eccl* 4:16
hatred by all that is *before t.* 9:1
now go write it *before t.* *Isa* 30:8
darkness light *before t.* 42:16
dividing the water *before t.* 63:12
lest I confound thee *before t.* *Jer* 1:17
my law which I set *before t.* 9:13
charged Baruch *before t.* 32:13
more be a nation *before t.* 33:24
to be dismayed *before t.* 49:37
before t. seventy men. *Ezek* 8:11
oil and incense *before t.* 16:18, 19
I will set judgement *before t.* 23:24
brandish my sword *before t.* 32:10
stand *before t.* to minister. 44:11
a fire devoureth *before t.* . . . garden of Eden *before t.* *Joel* 2:3
the earth shall quake *before t.* 10
the Amorite *before t.* *Amos* 2:9
breaker is come up *before t.* and their king . . . *before t.* *Mi* 2:13
angel of Lord *before t.* *Zech* 12:8
the star went *before t.* *Mat* 2:9
she danced *before t.* 14:6
and was transfigured *before t.* 17:2
Mark 9:2
but he denied *before t.* *Mat* 26:70
gave to his disciples to set *before t.* *Mark* 6:41; 8:6, 7
Jesus went *before t.* and they. 10:32
Judas went *before t.* *Luke* 22:47
he did eat *before t.* 24:43
shepherd goeth *before t.* *John* 10:4
so many miracles *before t.* 12:37
he set meat *before t.* *Acts* 16:34
set Paul *before t.* 22:30
I said to Peter *before t.* all. *Gal* 2:14

behind **them**

and stood *behind t.* *Ex* 14:19
of Ai looked *behind t.* *Josh* 8:20
the Benjamites looked *behind t.* *Judg* 20:40
a compass *behind t.* *2 Sam* 5:23
to come about *behind t.* *2 Chr* 13:13
behind t. a flame burneth, *behind t.* *Joel* 2:3

beside **them**

the asses were feeding *beside t.* *Job* 1:14
wheels turned not from *beside t.* *Ezek* 10:16, 19; 11:22
I have gained *beside t.* five talents. *Mat* 25:20, 22

between **them**

oath of the Lord shall be *between t.* *Ex* 22:11
and bells of gold *between t.* 28:33
valley *between t.* and Ai. *Josh* 8:11
a valley *between t.* and the Philistines. *1 Sam* 17:3
great space being *between t.* 26:13
Lord's oath *between t.* *2 Sam* 21:7
they divided the land *between t.* *1 Ki* 18:6
can come *between t.* *Job* 41:16
shall be *between t.* both. *Zech* 6:13
was so sharp *between t.* *Acts* 15:39

by **them**

neither seek after wizards, to be defiled *by t.* *Lev* 19:31
nor cause to swear *by t.* *Josh* 23:7
to prove Israel *by t.* *Judg* 3:1, 4
by t. ye shall send to. *2 Sam* 15:36
was perfected *by t.* *2 Chr* 24:13
for *by t.* judgeth he the. *Job* 36:31
by t. is thy servant. *Ps* 19:11
by t. beyond the river. *Isa* 7:20
and have sworn *by t.* that. *Jer* 5:7
the wheels went *by t.* *Ezek* 1:19
I be enquired of at all *by t.*? 14:3
by t. their portion is fat. *Hab* 1:16
that it was said *by t.* of old. *Mat* 5:21, 27, 33
would have passed *by t.* *Mark* 6:48
two men stood *by t.* in white. *Luke* 24:4; *Acts* 1:10
miracle has been done *by t.* *Acts* 4:16
God hath wrought *by t.* 15:12
things shall live *by t.* *Rom* 10:5
provoke you to jealousy *by t.* 19
by t. which are of the house of. *1 Cor* 1:11
thou *by t.* mightest war. *1 Tim* 1:18
confirmed to us *by t.* *Heb* 2:3
reported to you *by t.* *1 Pet* 1:12

concerning **them**

so *con. t.* Moses. *Num* 32:28
Samson said *con. t.*, Now I. *Judg* 15:3
commandment *con. t.* *Neh* 11:23
to be ignorant *con. t.* *1 Thes* 4:13
have I written *con. t.* *1 John* 2:26

for **them**

food for thee and *for t.* *Gen* 6:21
is large enough *for t.* 34:21
and they set on bread *for t.* 43:32
the Lord fighteth *for t.* *Ex* 14:25
make an atonement *for t.* *Lev* 4:20
9:7; 10:17; *Num* 8:21; 16:46
there is one law *for t.* the. *Lev* 7:7
a resting place *for t.* *Num* 10:33
for t., fishes gathered *for t.* 11:22
fail with longing *for t.* *Deut* 28:32
hand went a fiery law *for t.* 33:2
Joshua cast lots *for t.* *Josh* 18:10
Judah was too much *for t.* 19:9
Dan went out too little *for t.* 47
do for wives *for t.*? *Judg* 21:16
inheritance *for t.* escaped. 17
would ye tarry *for t.* till? *Ruth* 1:13
prayed *for t.* saying. *2 Chr* 30:18
of the Lord for me and *for t.* 34:21
God keepeth mercy *for t.* *Neh* 1:5
we take up corn *for t.* that we. 5:2
broughtest forth water *for t.* 9:15
banquet I shall prepare *for t.* *Esth* 5:8
of Sheba waited *for t.* *Job* 6:19
the Almighty do *for t.*? 22:17
wilderness yieldeth food *for t.* 24:5
laid up *for t.* that fear thee, *for t.* that trust in thee. *Ps* 31:19
thou hast founded *for t.* 104:8
and he remembered *for t.* 106:45
hath done great things *for t.* 126:2
Assyrian founded it *for t.* *Isa* 23:13
for her merchandise shall be *for t.* 18
he hath cast the lot *for t.*, and. 34:17
places shall be glad *for t.* 35:1
in the ways hast thou sat *for t.* as. *Jer* 3:2
lift up cry nor prayer *for t.* 7:16
nor shall men lament *for t.* 16:6
neither men tear themselves *for t.* 7
thee to speak good *for t.* 18:20
shalt make *for t.* yokes. 28:13
there be wailing *for t.* *Ezek* 7:11
but as *for t.* whose heart. 11:21
to pass through the fire *for t.* 16:21
a land I had espied *for t.* 20:6
flock may not be meat *for t.* 34:10
I will raise up *for t.* a plant. 29
enquired of to do *for t.* 36:37
make reconciliation *for t.* 45:15
his inheritance shall be his sons' *for t.* 46:17
for t. even for the priests. 48:10
no place was found *for t.* *Dan* 2:35
Rev 20:11
make a covenant *for t.* *Hos* 2:18
I will hiss *for t.* and. *Zech* 10:8
place shall not be found *for t.* 10
pray *for t.* which despitefully use. *Mat* 5:44; *Luke* 6:28
nor lawful *for t.* that. *Mat* 12:4
it shall be done *for t.* of my. 18:19
hard *for t.* that trust. *Mark* 10:24
there was no room *for t.* *Luke* 2:7
is not sufficient *for t.* *John* 6:7
I pray *for t.*: . . . but for them. 17:9, 20
and John prayed *for t.* *Acts* 8:15
Cornelius waited *for t.* and. 10:24
now while Paul waited *for t.* 17:16
God hath prepared *for t.* *1 Cor* 2:9
it is good *for t.* if they abide. 7:8

but prophesying serveth *for t.* 1 Cor 14:22
him which died *for t.* 2 Cor 5:15
what conflict I have *for t.* Col 2:1
hath a great zeal *for t.* that. 4:13
to minister *for t.* who shall? Heb 1:14
make intercession *for t.* 7:25
he hath prepared *for t.* a city. 11:16
it had been better *for t.* 2 Pet 2:21
give life *for t.* that sin. 1 John 5:16

from **them**

will be restrained *from t.* Gen 11:6
he took *from t.* Simeon and. 42:24
not taken one ass *from t.* Num 16:15
I have given you *from t.* 18:26
from t. that have many ye shall give many, but *from t.* that have. 35:8
and hide thyself *from t.* Deut 22:1, 4
hide my face *from t.* 31:17; 32:20
Ezek 7:22; Mi 3:4
their calves home *from t.* 1 Sam 6:7
them, turn away *from t.* 1 Chr 14:14
but they turned *from t.* 2 Chr 20:10
deliver me *from t.* that. Ps 31:15
defend me *from t.* that rise up. 59:1
will he withhold *from t.* 84:11
withhold not good *from t.* Pr 3:27
his soul shall be far *from t.* 22:5
desired I kept not *from t.* Eccl 2:10
little that I passed *from t.* S of S 3:4
given shall pass *from t.* Jer 8:13
leave my people and go *from t.* 9:2
turn away thy wrath *from t.* 18:20
I will take *from t.* the voice. 25:10
I will not turn away *from t.* 32:40
I have set it far *from t.* Ezek 7:20
mind was alienated *from t.* 23:17
the day when I take *from t.* 24:25
hid I my face *from t.* 39:23, 24
hide my face any more *from t.* 29
withdrawn himself *from t.* Hos 5:6
them, so they went *from t.* 11:2
with the garment *from t.* Mi 2:8
the bridegroom shall be taken *from t.*
Mat 9:15; Mark 2:20; Luke 5:35
and fled *from t.* naked. Mark 14:52
understood not, it was hid *from t.*
Luke 9:45; 18:34
parted *from t.* and carried. 24:51
did hide himself *from t.* John 12:36
but thrust him *from t.* Acts 7:39
delivered *from t.* that. Rom 15:31
sorrow *from t.* of whom. 2 Cor 2:3
I may cut off occasion *from t.* 11:12
is not counted *from t.* Heb 7:6
clean escaped *from t.* 2 Pet 2:18
death shall flee *from t.* Rev 9:6
see **depart, -ed**

in **them**

heaven and earth, the sea, and all that *in t.* is. Ex 20:11; Acts 4:24
and be consecrated *in t.* Ex 29:29
I will be sanctified *in t.* Lev 10:3
he shall live *in t.* 18:5; Neh 9:29
Ezek 20:11, 13, 21; Gal 3:12
was sanctified *in t.* Num 20:13
such an heart *in t.* Deut 5:29
any understanding *in t.* 32:28
nor was there spirit *in t.* Josh 5:1
built not, and ye dwell *in t.* 24:13
wash *in t.* and be clean? 2 Ki 5:12
how much less *in t.* that? Job 4:19
excellency *in t.* go away? 21
in t. hath he set a tabernacle. Ps 19:4
their soul fainteth *in t.* 107:5
so is every one that trusteth *in t.*
115:8; 135:18
pleasure *in t.* that fear. 147:11
froward or perverse *in t.* Pr 8:8
there is no good *in t.* Eccl 3:12
their heart is fully set *in t.* 8:11
I have no pleasure *in t.* 12:1
whose substance is *in t.* Isa 6:13
there is no light *in t.* 8:20
shalt not prosper *in t.* Jer 2:37
the word is not *in t.* 5:13
what wisdom is *in t.*? 8:9
cannot do evil nor is it *in t.* 10:5
there is no breath *in t.* 14; 51:17
houses, and dwell *in t.* 29:5, 28
have not walked *in t.* Ezek 5:6
accomplished my fury *in t.* 13
of the living creature was *in t.* 10:17
sin, *in t.* shall he die. Ezek 18:24, 26
be sanctified *in t.* in sight. 28:25
pine away *in t.* 33:10
was no breath *in t.* 37:8
concubines drank *in t.* Dan 5:3, 23
the just shall walk *in t.* Hos 14:9
ye shall not dwell *in t.* Amos 5:11
they shall kindle *in t.* and. Ob 18
evil, he delighteth *in t.* Mal 2:17
in t. is fulfilled the. Mat 13:14
in t. therefore come and. Luke 13:14
in t. ye think ye have. John 5:39
and I am glorified *in t.* 17:10
I *in t.*, and thou in me. 23
may be *in t.* and I *in t.* 26
God, is manifest *in t.* Rom 1:19
but have pleasure *in t.* that do. 32
in t. that are saved, *in t.* 2 Cor 2:15
will dwell *in t.* and walk *in t.* 6:16
that we should walk *in t.* Eph 2:10
the ignorance that is *in t.* 4:18
walked, when ye lived *in t.* Col 3:7
all deceivableness *in t.* 2 Thes 2:10
continue *in t.*: for in. 1 Tim 4:16
with faith *in t.* that. Heb 4:2
Christ which was *in t.* 1 Pet 1:11
speaking *in t.* of these. 2 Pet 3:16
and all that are *in t.* Rev 5:13
and ye that dwell *in t.* 12:12
for *in t.* is filled up the. 15:1
dead which were *in t.* 20:13
in t. the names of the. 21:14

into **them**

the breath came *into t.* Ezek 37:10
into the swine, that we may enter *into t.* Mark 5:12; Luke 8:32
from God entered *into t.* Rev 11:11

of **them**

the eyes *of t.* both were. Gen 3:7
cry *of t.* is waxen great. 19:13
generation *of t.* that hate me.
Ex 20:5; Deut 5:9
to thousands *of t.* that love me.
Ex 20:6; Deut 5:10
of t. that do any work. Ex 35:35
do against any *of t.* Lev 4:2
of t. ye shall not eat. 11:4
of t. eat. 22; Deut 20:19
an offering by fire *of t.* Lev 22:22
of t. buy bondmen and. 25:44, 45
land also shall be left *of t.* 26:43
were numbered *of t.* Num 1:21
23, 25; 2:4, 13; 3:22, 34
took money *of t.* that. 3:49
take it *of t.* 7:5
were *of t.* that were written. 11:26
nor shall any *of t.* that. 14:23
fled at the cry *of t.* 16:34
not a man *of t.* 26:64
which ye let remain *of t.* 33:55
neither be afraid *of t.* Deut 1:29
7:18; 20:1, 3; Josh 11:6; Neh 4:14
buy meat *of t.*, buy water *of t.* for.
Deut 2:6
loins *of t.* that rise, and *of t.* 33:11
there shall not a man *of t.* Josh 10:8
and *of t.* shall I be had. 2 Sam 6:22
nor left he any *of t.* 2 Ki 10:14
he was intreated *of t.* 1 Chr 5:20
of t. were expressed by. Ezra 8:20
would not buy it *of t.* Neh 10:31
he perceiveth it not *of t.* Job 14:21
in keeping *of t.* there is. Ps 19:11
arrows against the face *of t.* 21:12
this is the generation *of t.* 24:6
delivered him out *of t.* all. 34:19
none *of t.* that trust in him shall. 22
if I would speak *of t.* they are. 40:5
and *of t.* that are afar off. 65:5
heart are the ways *of t.* 84:5
all *of t.* shall wax old like. 102:26
tossed to and fro *of t.* that. Pr 21:6
God shall come forth *of t.* Eccl 7:18
they that are led *of t.* Isa 9:16
portion *of t.* that spoil us. 17:14
he shall be intreated *of t.* 19:22
Hezekiah was glad *of t.* and. 39:2
that when I asked *of t.* 41:28
spring forth I tell you *of t.* 42:9
spoiled, they are all *of t.* snared. 22
image, are all *of t.* vanity. 44:9
of t. that asked not for me, I am found *of t.* 65:1; Rom 10:20
those that escape *of t.* Isa 66:1
I will take *of t.* for priests. 2
because *of t.* that dwell in. Jer 8:1
be not afraid *of t.* 10:5; Ezek 2:
Luke 12:
of t. unto me as Sodom. Jer 23:1
shall serve themselves *of t.* 25:1
and *of t.* shall be taken up. 29:2
and out *of t.* shall proceed. 30:1
should serve himself *of t.* 34:9, 1
and none *of t.* shall remain. 42:1
Ezek 7:1
all *of t.* mourning every. Ezek 7:1
all *of t.* in the land shall. 20:4
all *of t.* desirable young men. 23:
12, 2
in dyed attire, all *of t.* princes. 1
of t. clothed with all sorts. 38:
and gates all *of t.* dwelling. 1
they say *of t.* Let the men. Hos 13:
all *of t.*; he that fleeth *of t.* Amos 9:
off their skin from *off t.* Mi 3:2,
land desolate because *of t.* 7:1
a goodly price that I was prized a *of t.* Zech 11:1
whether *of t.* twain did. Mat 21:3
perceived that he spake *of t.* 4
whose wife shall she be *of t.*?
Mark 12:23; Luke 20:3
of t. he chose twelve. Luke 6:1
tell me, which *of t.* will love? 7:4
which *of t.* should be greatest.
9:46; 22:2
which *of t.* it was that. 22:2
and said, Thou art also *of t.* 5
then enquired he *of t.* John 4:5
remember that I told you *of t.* 16:
of t. which thou gavest me. 18:
to take out *of t.* a people. Acts 15:1
there lie in wait *of t.* more. 23:2
if the fall *of t.* be the riches of world and diminishing *of t.* Rom 11:1
if the casting away *of t.* be the. 1
out *of t.* all the Lord. 2 Tim 3:1
are not *of t.* who draw back, but *of t*
Heb 10:3
is sown in peace *of t.* Jas 3:1
of t. which keep sayings. Rev 22:
see **both, one, some**

on or *upon* **them**

images and sat *upon t.* Gen 31:3
my name be named *on t.* 48:1
shall be satisfied *upon t.* Ex 15:
Lord break forth *upon t.* 19:22, 2
so great a sin *upon t.* 32:2
will visit their sin *upon t.* 3
their blood shall be *upon t.*
Lev 20:11, 12, 13, 16, 2
upon t. that are left will I. 26:3
of the spirit *upon t.* Num 11:17, 2
the earth closed *upon t.* and. 16:3
have no pity *upon t.* Deut 7:1
silver or gold that is *on t.* 2
on t. was written according. 9:1
not lift up any iron tool *upon t.* 27:
I will heap mischiefs *upon t.* 32:2
shall come *upon t.* make haste. 3
down great stones *upon t.* Josh 10:1
upon t. came the curse. Judg 9:5
blood gushed out *upon t.* 1 Ki 18:2
if able to set riders *upon t.*
2 Ki 18:23; Isa 36:
burnt men's bones *upon t.* 2 Ki 23:2
charge was *upon t.* 1 Chr 9:2
laid their hands *on t.* 2 Chr 29:2
Acts 6:6; 8:17; 13:3
Lord came not *upon t.* 2 Chr 32:2
Lord brought *upon t.* king. 33:1
he brought *upon t.* the king. 36:1
for fear was *upon t.* Ezra 3:3
of the Jews fell *upon t.* Esth 8:1
fear of Mordecai fell *upon t.* 9:3
Jews took *upon t.* to keep the. 2
nor is the rod of God *upon t.*
Job 21:
eye of the Lord is *upon t.* Ps 33:1
fear took hold *upon t.* there. 48:
set not your heart *upon t.* 62:1
thine indignation *upon t.* 69:2
down manna *upon t.* to eat. 78:2
he rained flesh also *upon t.* as. 2
he cast *upon t.* the fierceness. 4
he shall bring *upon t.* their. 94:2

to everlasting *upon t.* *Ps* 103:17
plague brake in *upon t.* 106:29
I see my desire *upon t.* 118:7
upon t. hath the light. *Isa* 9:2
thy chastening was *upon t.* 26:16
will not have mercy *on t.* 27:11
he that hath mercy *on t.* shall. 49:10
evil shall come *upon t.* *Jer* 2:3
I will bring *upon t.* 11:8, 11; 23:12
36:31; 49:37
have compassion *on t.* 12:15
I will set mine eyes *upon t.* 24:6
32:42
I will have mercy *upon t.* 33:26
calamity was come *upon t.* 46:21
she doted *upon t.* *Ezek* 23:16
flesh came *upon t.* 37:8
no wool shall come *upon t.* 44:17
of fire had passed *on t.* *Dan* 3:27
pour out my wrath *upon t.* *Hos* 5:10
go, I will spread my net *upon t.* 7:12
mine eyes *upon t.* for evil. *Amos* 9:4
lookest thou *upon t.* that. *Hab* 1:13
I will bring them again: for I have mercy *upon t.* *Zech* 10:6
who will not come up *upon t.* 14:17
should put his hands *upon t.*
Mat 19:13; *Mark* 10:16
and his mercy is *on t.* *Luke* 1:50
angel of the Lord came *upon t.* 2:9
this, he breathed *on t.* *John* 20:22
Sadducees came *upon t.* *Acts* 4:1
they laid hands *on t.* 3
great grace was *upon t.* 33
fear came *on* all *t.* that heard. 5:5
the Holy Ghost fell *on t.* as on us.
11:15; 19:6
took *upon t.* to call over. 19:13
and the man leapt *on t.* and. 16
men which have a vow *on t.* 21:23
on t. which fell, severity. *Rom* 11:22
peace be *on t.* and mercy *Gal* 6:16
wrath is come *upon t.* *1 Thes* 2:16
destruction cometh *upon t.* 5:3
taking vengeance *on t.* *2 Thes* 1:8
and *on t.* that are out of. *Heb* 5:2
avenge our blood *on t.* *Rev* 6:10
nor shall the sun light *on t.* 7:16
and great fear fell *upon t.* 11:11
and *upon t.* which worshipped. 16:2

over them

set *over t.* taskmasters. *Ex* 1:11
taskmasters had set *over t.* 5:14
place such *over t.* to be rulers. 18:21
were *over t.* that were numbered.
Num 7:2
thy cloud standeth *over t.* 14:14
to anoint a king *over t.* *Judg* 9:8
Jephthah captain *over t.* 11:11
rejected me that I should not reign *over t.* *1 Sam* 8:7
the manner of the king that shall reign *over t.* 9
standing as appointed *over t.* 19:20
became a captain *over t.* 22:2
anointed me king *over t.* *2 Sam* 2:7
was the ruler *over t.* *1 Chr* 9:20
over t. that did the work was. 27:26
he that made thee king *over t.*
2 Chr 2:11; 9:8
had the dominion *over t.* *Neh* 9:28
the enemies of the Jews hoped to have power *over t.* *Esth* 9:1
have dominion *over t.* *Ps* 49:14
hated them ruled *over t.* 106:41
bringeth the wheel *over t.* *Pr* 20:26
babes shall rule *over t.* *Isa* 3:4
women rule *over t.* 12
a fierce king shall rule *over t.* 19:4
they that rule *over t.* make. 52:5
I will appoint *over t.* *Jer* 15:3
I will set shepherds *over t.* 23:4
watched *over t.*, to pluck up, so will I watch *over t.* to build. 31:28
yea, I will rejoice *over t.* to. 32:41
I will watch *over t.* for evil. 44:27
there appeared *over t.* as it were a sapphire stone. *Ezek* 10:1
of Israel was *over t.* 19; 11:22
set up one shepherd *over t.* 34:23
servant shall be king *over t.* 37:24
thee ruler *over t.* all. *Dan* 2:38
heathen should rule *over t.* *Joel* 2:17
shall be dark *over t.* *Mi* 3:6
the Lord shall reign *over t.* in. 4:7
that have no ruler *over t.* *Hab* 1:14
and the Lord shall be seen *over t.*
Zech 9:14
exercise dominion *over t.* *Mat* 20:25
Mark 10:42; *Luke* 22:25
men that walk *over t.* *Luke* 11:44
I should reign *over t.* 19:27
to call *over t.* that had. *Acts* 19:13
even *over t.* that had not sinned.
Rom 5:14
triumphing *over t.* in it. *Col* 2:15
they had a king *over t.* *Rev* 9:11
earth shall rejoice *over t.* 11:10

through them

that *through t.* I may prove Israel.
Judg 2:22
none can pass *through t.* *Jer* 9:10

to or *unto* them

will send thee *unto t.* *Gen* 37:13
unto t. and spake roughly *unto t.*
42:7
provision, thus did Joseph *unto t.* 25
spake kindly *unto t.* 50:21
and God had respect *unto t.*
Ex 2:25; *2 Ki* 13:23
what shall I say *unto t.*? *Ex* 3:13
darkness *to t.* 14:20
the waters were a wall *unto t.* 22
not bow down thyself *to t.* nor serve.
20:5; *Josh* 23:7; *2 Ki* 17:35
shall be a statute for ever *to t.*
Ex 30:21; *Lev* 17:7
I have given it *unto t.* *Lev* 6:17
but thus do *unto t.* *Num* 4:19
all that appertain *unto t.* 16:30
as I thought to do *unto t.* 33:56
and *to t.* ye shall add forty. 35:6
Lord sware to give *unto t.* *Deut* 1:8
31:23
hath God so nigh *unto t.*? 4:7
this we will do *unto t.* *Josh* 9:20
so did he *unto t.* 26
bowed themselves *unto t.* *Judg* 2:17
mayest do *to t.* as thou shalt. 9:33
unto me, so have I done *unto t.* 15:11
nothing lacking *to t.* *1 Sam* 30:19
sent spoil *to t.* 27, 28, 29, 30, 31
but went not in *unto t.* *2 Sam* 20:3
speak good words *to t.* *1 Ki* 12:7
messenger came *to t.* *2 Ki* 9:18, 20
let the priests take it *to t.* 12:5
thereof pertained *to t.* *1 Chr* 9:27
spake comfortably *to t.* *2 Chr* 32:6
custom was paid *unto t.* *Ezra* 4:20
separated themselves *unto t.* 6:21
restore *to t.* this day their. *Neh* 5:11
month was turned *unto t.* *Esth* 9:22
layeth not folly *to t.* *Job* 24:12
morning is *to t.* even as the. 17
give them, render *to t.* *Ps* 28:4
for there is no want *to t.* that. 34:9
thou hadst a favour *unto t.* 44:3
do *unto t.* as to the Midianites. 83:9
them are like *unto t.* 115:8; 135:18
do good *to t.* that are upright. 125:4
a buckler *to t.* that walk. *Pr* 2:7
a tree of life *to t.* that lay. 3:18
they are right *to t.* that find. 8:9
so is the sluggard *to t.* that. 10:26
mercy and truth be *to t.* that. 14:22
so is a faithful messenger *to t.* 25:13
a shield *unto t.* that put their. 30:5
wisdom giveth life *to t.* *Eccl* 7:12
to t. that have familiar. *Isa* 19:3
the word was *unto t.* precept. 28:13
to t. that have no might he. 40:29
hath given spirit *to t.* that walk. 42:5
these things will I do *unto t.* 16
to t. that are in darkness. 49:9
Mat 4:16; *Luke* 1:79
to t. will I give in mine. *Isa* 56:5
to t. hast thou poured a. 57:6
to t. that turn from transgression in Jacob. 59:20
everlasting joy shall be *unto t.* 61:7
thus shall it be done *unto t.* *Jer* 5:13
word of the Lord is *unto t.* 6:10
but return not thou *unto t.* 15:19
evil I thought to do *unto t.* 18:8
though I was husband *unto t.* 31:32
and do *unto t.* as thou. *Lam* 1:22
the Lord is good *unto t.* that.
Lam 3:25
of heart, thy curse *unto t.* 65
I do send thee *unto t.* *Ezek* 2:4
had I sent thee *unto t.* they. 3:6
and thou shalt not be *to t.* a. 26
yet will I be *to t.* as a little. 11:16
so shall it be done *unto t.* 12:11
I made myself known *unto t.* 20:9
lo, thou art *unto t.* as a very. 33:32
shall be *to t.* a renown. 39:13
because they ministered *unto t.* before idols. 44:12
oblation shall be *unto t.* 48:12
shall be for food *unto t.* 18
the dream be *to t.* that. *Dan* 4:19
might give account *unto t.* 6:2
and keeping mercy *to t.* that. 9:4
but many shall cleave *to t.* 11:34
staff declareth *unto t.* *Hos* 4:12
destruction *unto t.* because. 7:13
I was *to t.* as they that take off. 11:4
said, he would do *unto t.* *Jonah* 3:10
say they *to t.* that prophesy, they shall not prophesy *to t.* *Mi* 2:6
be ye not like *unto t.* *Mat* 6:8
do ye so *to t.* 7:12
he spake *unto t.* of John the. 17:13
servants, they did *unto t.* 21:36
but go ye rather *to t.* that sell. 25:9
but *to t.* that are without in parables.
Mark 4:11
shall be given *to t.* for whom. 10:40
and was subject *unto t.* *Luke* 2:51
do ye also *to t.* likewise. 6:31
if ye do good *to t.* that do good. 33
if ye lend *to t.* of whom ye hope. 34
give the Holy Spirit *to t.* that. 11:13
that he may testify *unto t.* 16:28
of the vineyard do *unto t.*? 20:15
Jesus turning *unto t.* said. 23:28
their words seemed *unto t.* as. 24:11
he expounded *unto t.* in all the. 27
to t. gave he power to become the sons of God, even *to t.* *John* 1:12
we may give an answer *to t.* that. 22
not commit himself *unto t.* 2:24
spake *to t.* of the Father. 8:27
they are remitted *unto t.* 20:23
who was guide *to t.* that. *Acts* 1:16
unto t. cloven tongues, as of. 2:3
added *unto t.* about 3000 souls. 41
durst no man join himself *to t.* 5:13
whom God hath given *to t.* that. 32
not done sacrifice *unto t.* 14:18
preach the gospel *unto t.* 16:10
my necessities, and *to t.* that. 20:34
no man may deliver me *unto t.* 25:11
God hath shewed it *unto t.* *Rom* 1:19
to t. who by patient continuance. 2:7
for good *to t.* that love God. 8:28
made manifest *unto t.* that. 10:20
unto t. that are sanctified. *1 Cor* 1:2
unto t. that are called, both. 24
my answer *to t.* that do examine. 9:3
not permitted *unto t.* to speak. 14:34
if gospel hid, it is hid *to t.* *2 Cor* 4:3
to t. which were apostles. *Gal* 1:17
unto t. who are of the household of faith. 6:10
preached peace *to t.* that. *Eph* 2:17
is *to t.* an evident token. *Phil* 1:28
tribulation *to t.* that trouble you.
2 Thes 1:6
meditate, give thyself wholly *to t.*
1 Tim 4:15
but *unto* all *t.* that love. *2 Tim* 4:8
nothing be wanting *unto t.* *Tit* 3:13
not enter, but *to t.* that believed not.
Heb 3:18
preached as well as *unto t.* 4:2
I will be *to t.* a God. 8:10
yieldeth *unto t.* that are. 12:11
word should not be spoken *to t.* 19
Lord promised *to t.* that love him.
Jas 1:12; 2:5
gospel preached also *to t.* *1 Pet* 4:6
to t. that obtained like. *2 Pet* 1:1
happened *unto t.* according to. 2:22
unto t. was given power, as. *Rev* 9:3
to t. it was given that they should. 5
they sat, and judgement was given *unto t.* 20:4

see **say, woe**

toward **them**
so great is his mercy *toward t.* that fear him. *Ps* 103:11
Jesus was moved with compassion *toward t. Mat* 14:14; *Mark* 6:34
walk in wisdom *toward t.* *Col* 4:5
honestly *toward t.* that. *1 Thes* 4:12

under **them**
clave asunder that was *under t.* *Num* 16:31
and the cloud is not *under t. Job* 26:8

with **them**
deal worse with thee than *with t.* *Gen* 19:9
Hamor communed *with t.* 34:8
Joseph saw Benjamin *with t.* 43:16
established my covenant with *t. Ex* 6:4
thou shalt make no covenant *with t.* 23:32; *Deut* 7:2
shall pine away *with t.* *Lev* 26:39
to break my covenant *with t.* 44
thou shalt not go *with t. Num* 22:12
arise, go *with t.* 20
we will not inherit *with t.* on. 32:19
meddle not *with t.* *Deut* 2:5, 19
that it might be well *with t.* 5:29
neither make marriages *with t.* 7:3 *Josh* 23:12
thus shall ye deal *with t.* *Deut* 7:5
who keepeth covenant *with t.* 9
and Joshua made peace *with t.* *Josh* 9:15, 16
and the Lord was *with t.* *Judg* 1:22
and do *with t.* what seemeth. 19:24
shalt prophesy *with t.* *1 Sam* 10:6
lest I destroy you *with t.* 15:6
nor did he eat *with t.* *2 Sam* 12:17
they have there *with t.* their. 15:36
and thou be angry *with t.* *1 Ki* 8:46 *2 Chr* 6:36
they that be *with t.* *2 Ki* 6:16
with t. that should go out on the sabbath and came. 11:9; *2 Chr* 23:8
no reckoning made *with t.* *2 Ki* 22:7
brethren were to come *with t.* *1 Chr* 9:25
and *with t.* 120 priests. *2 Chr* 5:12
with many, or *with t.* that. 14:11
with t. he sent Levites, and *with t.* 17:8
book of the law of the Lord *with t.* 9
and he was *with t.* hid in the. 22:12
with t. were the prophets. *Ezra* 5:2
thou spakest *with t.* *Neh* 9:13
that they might do *with t.* as. 24
and I contended *with t.* and. 13:25
to do *with t.* as it seemeth. *Esth* 3:11
seed is established in their sight *with t.* *Job* 21:8
is perished *with t.* *Ps* 9:6
secret of the Lord is *with t.* 25:14
plead my cause *with t.* that. 35:1
with t. to the house of God. 42:4
the Lord is *with t.* that. 54:4; 118:7
I am counted *with t.* that go. 88:4
for *with t.* thou hast. 119:93
not thou in the way *with t.* *Pr* 1:15
desire to be *with t.* 24:1
keep the law contend *with t.* 28:4
it shall be well *with t.* *Eccl* 8:12
shall be joined *with t.* *Isa* 14:1
thou shalt not be joined *with t.* 20
shall come down *with t.* 34:7
and made covenant *with t.* 57:8
this is my covenant *with t.* 59:21
silver and their gold *with t.* 60:9
everlasting covenant *with t.* 61:8
and their offspring *with t.* 65:23
deal thus *with t.* in time. *Jer* 18:23
word of the Lord be *with t.* 27:18
I will gather *with t.* the blind. 31:8
an everlasting covenant *with t.* 32:40
and didst commit whoredom *with t.* *Ezek* 16:17, 28; 23:7, 43
bring thee down *with t.* that. 26:20
with t. that go down to the pit. 31:14 32:18, 24, 25, 29
I will make *with t.* covenant of peace. 34;25; 37:26
I the Lord their God am *with t.* 34:30 *Zech* 10:5
my tabernacle also shall be *with t.* *Ezek* 37:27
also shall fall *with t.* *Hos* 5:5
as long as the bridegroom is *with t.*? *Mat* 9:15; *Mark* 2:19; *Luke* 5:34
also the wheat *with t.* *Mat* 13:29
have been partakers *with t.* 23:30
and took no oil *with t.* 25:3
the Lord working *with t. Mark* 16:20
he eateth *with t.* *Luke* 15:2
though he bear *with t.* 18:7
found the eleven and them that were *with t.* 24:33
while I was *with t.* in the world. *John* 17:12
betrayed him stood *with t.* 18:5
but Thomas was not *with t.* 20:24
he was *with t.* coming. *Acts* 9:28
made while she was *with t.* 39
arise, and go *with t.* 10:20
didst eat *with t.* 11:3
spirit bade me go *with t.* 12
hand of the Lord was *with t.* 21
they took *with t.* John. 12:25
all that God had done *with t.* 14:27 15:4
not good to take him *with t.* 15:38
down and prayed *with t.* all. 20:36
be at charges *with t.* that. 21:24
and *with t.* partakest of. *Rom* 11:17
rejoice *with t.* that do rejoice, and weep *with t.* that weep. 12:15
therefore partakers *with t.* *Eph* 5:7
grace be *with t.* that love our. 6:24
shall be caught up together *with t.* *1 Thes* 4:17
peace, *with t.* that call. *2 Tim* 2:22
was it not *with t.* that had sinned? *Heb* 3:17
for finding fault *with t.* he. 8:8
covenant I will make *with t.* 10:16
Rahab perished not *with t.* 11:31
in bonds, as bound *with t.* 13:3
ye husbands, dwell *with t.* *1 Pet* 3:7
that ye run not *with t.* to the. 4:4
latter end is worse *with t.* *2 Pet* 2:20
had heads, and *with t.* *Rev* 9:19
with men, he will dwell *with t.* 21:3

without **them**
while she lieth desolate *without t.* *Lev* 26:43

themselves
they wearied *t.* to find. *Gen* 19:11
t. for the Egyptians by *t.* 43:32
go and gather straw for *t.* *Ex* 5:7
prepared for *t.* victual. 12:39
people have corrupted *t.* 32:7 *Deut* 9:12; 32:5; *Judg* 2:19 *Hos* 9:9
wash, and so make *t.* *Num* 8:7
even our enemies *t.* *Deut* 32:31
sons made *t.* vile and. *1 Sam* 3:13
both of them discovered *t.* to. 14:11
if they shall bethink *t.* *1 Ki* 8:47 *2 Chr* 6:37
choose one bullock for *t.* *1 Ki* 18:23
Edom made a king over *t.* *2 Ki* 8:20; *2 Chr* 21:8
sold *t.* to do evil in the. *2 Ki* 17:17
made to *t.* of the lowest of them. 32
eat such things as grow of *t.* 19:29
had made *t.* odious to. *1 Chr* 19:6
people shall humble *t.* *2 Chr* 7:14
princes and king humbled *t.* 12:6, 7
which they stript off for *t.* 20:25
they made ready for *t.* and. 35:14
of their daughters for *t.* *Ezra* 9:2
decreed for *t.* and seed. *Esth* 9:31
they had marked for *t.* *Job* 24:16
they rolled *t.* upon me. 30:14
they are firm in *t.* 41:23
the kings of the earth set *t.* *Ps* 2:2
the nations may know *t.* to be. 9:20
which hate us spoil for *t.* 44:10
whereof they are fallen *t.* 57:6
they joined *t.* also to Baal. 106:28
desires, lest they exalt *t.* 140:8
riches make *t.* wings. *Pr* 23:5
might see that they *t.* *Eccl* 3:18
and they please *t.* in children. *Isa* 2:6
they have rewarded evil to *t.* 3:9
but *t.* are gone into captivity. 46:2
they shall not deliver *t.* from. 47:14
call *t.* of the holy city, and. 48:2
sons of the stranger that join *t.* 56:6
seek her will not weary *t.* *Jer* 2:24
and the nations shall bless *t.* 4:2
do they not provoke *t.* to the? 7:19
they weary *t.* 9:5
they had done against *t.* 11:17
have put *t.* to pain, but shall. 12:13
nor cut *t.* nor make *t.* bald for. 16:6
great kings shall serve *t.* of. 27:7
and their nobles shall be of *t.* 30:21
that none should serve *t.* of. 34:10
lifted up, these lift up *t.* *Ezek* 10:17
their appearance and *t.* 22
shall only be delivered *t.* 14:18
of Israel that do feed *t.* 32:2
nor shall the shepherds feed *t.* 10
Levites of the house have for *t.* 45:5
for *t.* are separated with. *Hos* 4:14
they assembled *t.* for corn. 7:14
but they separated *t.* to that. 9:10
shall proceed of *t.* *Hab* 1:7
the people shall weary *t.* for. 2:13
the golden oil out of *t.* *Zech* 4:12
who slay them, and hold *t.* 11:5
mighty works do shew forth *t.* in. *Mat* 14:2; *Mark* 6:14
reasoned among *t.* *Mat* 16:7 *Mark* 8:16; *Luke* 20:14
there be eunuchs, who made *t.* *Mat* 19:12
reasoned with *t.* 21:25; *Mark* 11:31 *Luke* 20:5
but they *t.* will not move. *Mat* 23:4
have no root in *t.* *Mark* 4:17
kept that saying with *t.* 9:10
counsel of God against *t.* *Luke* 7:30
certain which trusted in *t.* 18:9
spies which should feign *t.* 20:20
were at enmity between *t.* 23:12
my joy fulfilled in *t.* *John* 17:13
they *t.* went not into the. 18:28
Judas and Silas being prophets also *t.* *Acts* 15:32
but let them come *t.* and fetch. 16:37
and when they opposed *t.* and. 18:6
that they kept *t.* from things. 21:25
certain Jews bound *t.* 23:12, 21
hope toward God which they *t.* 24:15
they agreed not among *t.* 28:25
had great reasoning among *t.* 29
professing *t.* to be wise. *Rom* 1:22
their own bodies between *t.* 24
receiving in *t.* that recompence. 27
the law, are a law unto *t.* 2:14
have not submitted *t.* to 10:3
shall receive to *t.* damnation. 13:2
nor abusers of *t.* with. *1 Cor* 6:9
not henceforth live unto *t.* *2 Cor* 5:15
power they were willing of *t.* 8:3
measuring *t.* by *t.* comparing *t.* with *t.* 10:12
t. into the apostles of Christ. 11:13
neither do they *t.* keep. *Gal* 6:13
who have given *t.* over to. *Eph* 4:19
esteem other better than *t.* *Phil* 2:3
for they *t.* shew of us. *1 Thes* 1:9
them that defile *t.* with. *1 Tim* 1:10
t. in modest apparel. 2:9; *1 Pet* 3:5
purchased to *t.* a good. *1 Tim* 3:13
laying up in store for *t.* a good. 6:19
those that oppose *t.* *2 Tim* 2:25
may recover *t.* out of the snare. 26
heap to *t.* teachers, having. 4:3
one of *t.* even a prophet. *Tit* 1:12
seeing they crucify to *t.* *Heb* 6:6
that not to *t.* but us. *1 Pet* 1:12
bring upon *t.* swift. *2 Pet* 2:1
sporting *t.* with their own. 13
they *t.* are the servants of. 19
giving *t.* over to fornication. *Jude* 7
they corrupt *t.* 10
feeding *t.* without fear. 12
who separate *t.*, sensual, having. 19
see **gather, hide, spread**

then
t. began men to call. *Gen* 4:26
the Canaanite dwelt *t.* in. 13:7
t. shall thy seed also be. 16
t. will I slay my brother. 27:41
t. shall the Lord be my God. 28:21
if our brother be with us, *t.* we. 44:26
t. defiledst thou it; he went up. 49:4
if *t.* their hearts be humbled, and they *t.* accept of the. *Lev* 26:41

t. I will remember my covenant. Lev 26:42
as my strength was t. Josh 14:11
if the Lord be with me, t. I. 12
they choose new gods, t. Judg 5:8
what meaneth t. this bleating of the sheep? 1 Sam 15:14
t. remember thine handmaid. 25:31
t. hear thou in heaven. 1 Ki 8:32, 34 36, 39, 45, 49
there was t. no king in. 22:47
t. let fire come down. 2 Ki 1:10
Jehoshaphat being t. king. 8:16
t. open the door and flee and. 9:3
and David was t. in. 1 Chr 11:16
t. Manasseh knew the. 2 Chr 33:13
t. the prophets prophesied. Ezra 5:1
t. rose up Zerubbabel to build the. 2
t. went Haman forth that. Esth 5:9
t. said Zeresh his wife, and his. 14
t. was the king's wrath. 7:10
I should have slept, t. Job 3:13
he seeth also, will he not t.? 11:11
t. shalt thou have delight in. 22:26
t. thou shalt say, There is lifting up. 29
because thou wast t. born. 38:21
t. the Lord will take me. Ps 27:10
t. will I teach transgressors. 51:13
was not an enemy, t. I could. 55:12
t. I restored that which I took not away. 69:4
t. believed they his words. 106:12
t. shall I not be ashamed. 119:6
t. shalt thou understand the fear of the Lord. Pr 2:5
t. shalt thou understand righteousness. 9
t. there shall be a reward. 24:14
t. judgement shall dwell. Isa 32:16
t. shall thy light break forth. 58:8
t. shalt thou call, and the Lord. 9
t. shalt thou not remove. Jer 4:1
when thou doest evil, t. thou. 11:15
t. thou shewedst me their doings. 18
t. they should have turned. 23:22
t. will I cast away the seed. 33:26
t. shall they know that. Ezek 39:28
t. was part of the hand. Dan 5:24
t. they that feared the Lord spake often. Mal 3:16
and t. come and offer. Mat 5:24
t. shall they fast. 9:15; Mark 2:20 Luke 5:35
t. will he spoil his house. Mat 12:29 Mark 3:27
and t. he shall reward. Mat 16:27
Jesus saith, T. are the. 17:26
saying, Who t. can be saved? 19:25 Mark 10:26; Luke 18:26
for a witness to all, t. Mat 24:14
for t. shall be great tribulation. 21
t. all the disciples forsook. 26:56
and whence is he t. his son? Mark 12:37
t. let them that be in Judaea flee to. 13:14; Luke 21:21
t. shalt thou see clearly. Luke 6:42
asked What t.? Art thou Elias? John 1:21
Why baptizest thou t.? 25
t. I go unto him that sent me. 7:33
t. shall ye know that I am he. 8:28
t. Peter said to them. Acts 2:38
t. they that gladly received his word. 41
t. hath God to the Gentiles granted. 11:18; 26:20
what fruit had ye t. in? Rom 6:21
what shall we say t.? Is the law sin? 7:7; 9:14
if children, t. heirs, heirs of. 8:17
so t. at this present time there. 11:5
t. shall every man have. 1 Cor 4:5
what say I t.? that the idol is. 10:19
but t. face to face: now I know in part; t. shall I know even. 13:12
what is it t.? 14:15
t. am I strong. 2 Cor 12:10
come by the law, t. Christ. Gal 2:21
if ye be Christ's, t. are ye. 3:29
but as t. he that was born. 4:29
t. shall he have rejoicing in. 6:4
t. sudden destruction. 1 Thes 5:3
t. shall that Wicked be. 2 Thes 2:8
first for his own sins, t. Heb 7:27
t. are ye bastards, and not. 12:8
t. have we confidence. 1 John 3:21

thence

wife to my son from t. Gen 24:7
send and fetch thee from t. 27:45
from t. is the shepherd. 49:24
cut down from t. Num 13:23, 24
Curse me them from t. 23:13, 27
if from t. thou shalt seek. Deut 4:29
the Lord brought thee out t. 5:15 6:23; 24:18
send and fetch him t. 19:12
from t. will the Lord gather thee, and from t. 30:4; Neh 1:9
from t. am I. Judg 19:18
bring from t. the ark of. 1 Sam 4:4 2 Sam 6:2; 1 Chr 13:6
go not forth from t. 1 Ki 2:36
shall not be from t. any more death. 2 Ki 2:21
went up from t. to Beth-el. 23
from t. to Carmel, and from t. to. 25
the lepers carried t. silver and. 7:8
out Uzziah from t. 2 Chr 26:20
therefore, be ye far from t. Ezra 6:6
depart, go ye out from t. Isa 52:11
no more t. an infant of days. 65:20
every one that goeth t. shall. Jer 5:6
signet, yet would I pluck thee t. 22:24
cause to cease from t. man. 36:29
forth, to separate himself t. 37:12
and he shall go forth from t. 43:12
I will bring thee down from t. 49:16
all abominations from t. Ezek 11:18
her vineyards from t. Hos 2:15
from t. go ye to Hamath. Amos 6:2
dig into hell, t. shall my hand. 9:2, 3
t. will I command the sword, it. 4
among stars, t. will I bring. Ob 4
by no means come out t. Mat 5:26
there abide, till ye go t. 10:11
when ye depart t. shake. Mark 6:11
that would come from t. Luke 16:26

thenceforth

t. it shall be accepted. Lev 22:27
was magnified from t. 2 Chr 32:23
is t. good for nothing. Mat 5:13
from t. Pilate sought. John 19:12*

Theophilus

thee, most excellent T. Luke 1:3
treatise have I made, O T. Acts 1:1

there

t. he put the man whom. Gen 2:8
if I find forty-five t. I will. 18:28
he blessed him t. 32:29
t. God appeared. 35:7
t. they buried Abraham and Sarah, t. they buried Isaac and. 49:31
no swarms of flies shall be t. Ex 8:22
t. he made a statute, t. he. 15:25
behold, I will stand before thee t. 17:6
the mount, and be t. 24:12; 34:2
and he was t. with the Lord. 34:28
t. eat it. Lev 8:31
shall leave them t. 16:23
and talk with thee t. Num 11:17
we saw the children of Anak t. 13:28 33; Deut 1:28; Josh 14:12
died t. and was buried t. Num 20:1
Aaron shall die t. 26, 28; Deut 10:6
t. ye shall serve gods, work of. Deut 4:28; 28:36, 64; Jer 16:13
and t. they be unto this day. Deut 10:5; Josh 4:9
choose to put his name t. Deut 12:5 14:23; 16:2, 11; 1 Ki 8:29; 9:3
it may be t. for a witness. Deut 31:26
where he bowed, t. he. Judg 5:27
I will try them for thee t. 7:4
inhabitants of Jabesh-gilead t. 21:9
where thou diest, t. will. Ruth 1:17
the priests of the Lord were t. 1 Sam 1:3; 4:4
worshipped the Lord t. 1:28
and renew the kingdom t. 11:14
t. they made Saul king before the Lord, t. they sacrificed, and t. 15
of the servants of Saul t. 21:7
Doeg the Edomite was t. 22:22
Joab smote Abner t. 2 Sam 3:27
God smote Uzzah t. and t. he died. 2 Sam 6:7
even t. also will thy servant. 15:21
hast thou not t. Zadok and? 35
staves, and t. they are. 1 Ki 8:8
chosen to put my name t. 11:36 2 Ki 23:27; 2 Chr 6:5, 6; 7:16 Neh 1:9
the ravens to feed thee t. 1 Ki 17:4
when they said, He is not t.; he. 18:10
and left his servant t. 19:3
and cast the salt in t. 2 Ki 2:21
he came and lay t. 4:11
and we shall die t. 7:4
come, there was no man t. 5, 10
they left their gods, t. 1 Chr 14:12
prophet of the Lord was t. 2 Chr 28:9
they slew Sennacherib t. with. 32:21
God hath caused his name to dwell t. Ezra 6:12
t. the wicked cease from troubling, and t. the weary be at. Job 3:17
t. the prisoners rest together. 18
small and great are t.; the servant. 19
t. the righteous might dispute. 23:7
t. they cry, but none giveth. 35:12
and where the slain are, t. 39:30
t. were they in great fear. Ps 14:5 53:5
daughter of Tyre shall be t. 45:12
fear took hold upon them t. 48:6
went through flood, t. did we. 66:6
cities that they may dwell t. 69:35
Tyre, this man was born t. 87:4, 6
players on instruments shall be t. 7
t. go the ships, t. is that. 104:26
t. the Lord commanded the. 133:3
behold, thou art t. 139:8
t. shall thy hand lead me. 10
I was t.: when he set. Pr 8:27
that the dead are t. 9:18
where no wood is, t. the fire. 26:20
was t., iniquity was t. Eccl 3:16
for t. is a time t. for every. 17
tree falleth, t. it shall be. 11:3
t. thy mother brought. S of S 8:5
nor shall shepherds make their fold t. Isa 13:20
beasts of the desert shall lie t. 21
t. shalt thou die, and t. the. 22:18
to Chittim, t. also shalt thou. 23:12
here a little, and t. a little. 28:10
t. glorious Lord will be a. 33:21
and an highway shall be t. 35:8
but the redeemed shall walk t. 9
from the beginning; t. am I. 48:16
my servant shall dwell t. 65:9
is t. no balm in Gilead, no physician t.? Jer 8:22
t. will I cause thee to hear. 18:2
t. thou shalt die, and shalt be buried t. 20:6
country: t. shall ye die. 22:26; 42:16
and t. shall they be till I. 27:22
he was t. when Jerusalem. 38:28
will go into Egypt, and t. will. 42:14
against Ashkelon, t. hath he. 47:7
go to the plain, I will t. Ezek 3:22
see it, though he shall die t. 12:13
I will plead with him t. for. 17:20
and they offered t. their sacrifices, t. they presented the. 20:28
and t. will I plead with you face. 35
t. will I accept them, t. 40
and I will leave you t. and. 22:20
t. were their breasts pressed, t. 23:3
and they shall be t. a base. 29:14
Ashur is t. and all her. 32:32
whereas the Lord was t. 35:10
name shall be, The Lord is t. 48:35
and she shall sing t. as. Hos 2:15
yea, grey hairs are here and t. 7:9
t. I hated them. 9:15
t. he spake with us. 12:4
I will plead with them t. Joel 3:2
one plow t. with oxen? Amos 6:12
t. eat bread and prophesy t. 7:12
t. be delivered, t. Lord shall. Mi 4:10
shall cry t. bitterly. Zeph 1:14
be thou t. till I bring. Mat 2:13
t. rememberest that thy brother. 5:23
leave t. thy gift before the altar. 24
where your treasure is, t. will. 6:21

t. shall be gnashing of teeth. Mat 8:12; 22:13; 24:51
they enter in, and dwell t. 12:45
Luke 11:26
in my name, t. am I in. Mat 18:20
lo, here is Christ, or t. 24:23
Mark 13:21
I hid thy talent, t. thou. Mat 25:25
down, they watched him t. 27:36
in Galilee, t. shall ye see him. 28:7
Mark 16:7
I may preach t. also. Mark 1:38
and he could t. do no mighty. 6:5
and if the son of peace be t. Luke 10:6
t. will I bestow all my fruits. 12:18
where I am, t. shall my. John 12:26
that where I am, t. ye may be. 14:3
that shall befall me t. Acts 20:22
t. it shall be told thee of all. 22:10
t. be called the children. Rom 9:26
for there shall be no night t. Rev 21:25; 22:5
see **abode, is, none, one, stand, stood, was**

thereabout

were much perplexed t. Luke 24:4

thereat

their hands and feet t. Ex 30:19
40:31
there be which go in t. Mat 7:13*

thereby

t. shall I know thou hast. Gen 24:14
should be defiled t. Lev 11:43
with God, t. good will. Job 22:21
whoso is deceived t. is. Pr 20:1
shall be endangered t. Eccl 10:9
gallant ships pass t. Isa 33:21
passeth t. shall be astonished. Jer 18:16; 19:8
any son of man pass t. 51:43
wall and carry on t. Ezek 12:5, 12
he shall not fall t. 33:12
he shall die t. 18*
do what is lawful, he shall live t. 19
also shall border t. Zech 9:2
God might be glorified t. John 11:4
having slain the enmity t. Eph 2:16
who are exercised t. Heb 12:11
root springing up, and t. many. 15
t. some have entertained. 13:2
word that ye may grow t. 1 Pet 2:2*

therefore

t. shall a man leave his. Gen 2:24
shall keep my covenant t. 17:9
guilty, t. is this distress. 42:21
t. God dealt well with. Ex 1:20
t. go. 4:12
they be idle, t. they cry. 5:8, 17
t. shall ye observe. 12:17; 13:10
t. he giveth you on the sixth. 16:29
ye shall keep the sabbath t. 31:14
ye shall t. sanctify yourselve, be holy; for I am holy. Lev 11:44, 45; 21:6
t. I do visit the iniquity. 18:25
ye shall t. keep my statutes and. 26
t. keep my ordinances. 30; 19:37
20:22; 22:9
ye shall not t. oppress one. 25:17
t. the Levites shall be. Num 3:12
t. the Lord thy God commanded. Deut 5:15; 15:11, 15; 24:18, 22
t. thou shalt serve thine. 28:48
t. we turn again to. Judg 11:8
t. also I have lent him. 1 Sam 1:28
t. hath the Lord done this. 28:18
t. Michal had no child. 2 Sam 6:23
be strong t. and shew. 1 Ki 2:2
t. thy life shall go for his life. 20:42
t. thou shalt not. 2 Ki 1:6, 16
t. they have destroyed them. 19:18
t. he slew Saul, and. 1 Chr 10:14
t. hath he brought all. 2 Chr 7:22
t. gave them up to desolation. 30:7
t. we his servants will arise and. Neh 2:20
t. I chased him from me. 13:28
t. they say to God. Job 21:14
judgement is before him, t. 35:14
t. take unto you seven bullocks. 42:8
t. my heart is glad. Ps 16:9
t. lead me. 31:3
t. the children of men put. Ps 36:7
t. God hath blessed thee for. 45:2
t. God hath anointed thee with oil. 7
t. shall the people praise. 17
have no changes, t. they fear. 55:19*
t. in the shadow of thy wings. 63:7
t. his people return hither. 73:10
set his love upon me, t. will I. 91:14
t. he said that he would. 106:23
t. have I spoken. 116:10; 2 Cor 4:13
t. I hate every false way. Ps 119:104
are wonderful: t. doth my soul. 129
depart from me t. ye. 139:19
t. leave off contention. Pr 17:14
God is in heaven, t. let. Eccl 5:2
t. the misery of man is great. 8:6
t. the heart of men is set in them. 11
t. the Lord will smite. Isa 3:17
t. the Lord of hosts shall. 10:16
t. hath the curse devoured. 24:6
t. he hath poured the fury of. 42:25
t. his arm brought salvation. 59:16
t. they shall fall among. Jer 6:15
ye obeyed not, t. this thing is. 40:3
Lord is my portion, t. will. Lam 3:24
t. I fled before unto. Jonah 4:2
t. I am returned to Jerusalem with. Zech 1:16
t. came a great wrath from. 7:12
t. ye sons of Jacob are. Mal 3:6
be ye t. perfect. Mat 5:48
fear ye not t. 10:31
what t. God hath joined. 19:6
what shall we have t.? 27
watch t. 24:42, 44; 25:13
Mark 13:35
go ye t. teach all nations. Mat 28:19
t. came I forth. Mark 1:38
do ye not t. err? 12:24
David t. himself calleth him Lord. 37
for t. am I sent. Luke 4:43
be ye t. merciful. 6:36
t. shall they be your judges. 11:19
t. also said the wisdom of God. 49
have married a wife, and t. I. 14:20
what t. shall the Lord of the vineyard do? 20:15; Mark 12:9
t. in the resurrection? Mat 20:33
this my joy t. is fulfilled. John 3:29
ye t. hear them not, because. 8:47
but ye say, We see; t. your sin. 9:41
t. doth my Father love me. 10:17
whatsoever I speak t., even as. 12:50
chosen you, t. the world. 15:19
repent ye t. and be converted. Acts 3:19
t. it was imputed to. Rom 4:22
t. if thine enemy hunger. 12:20
t. glorify God in your body and. 1 Cor 6:20
not the hand, is it t. not of? 12:15, 16
t. be ye stedfast, unmoveable. 15:58
t. as ye abound in every. 2 Cor 8:7
be not ye t. partakers. Eph 5:7
t. as the church is subject to. 24
be not t. ashamed of the. 2 Tim 1:8
see **now**

therefrom

that ye turn not aside t. Josh 23:6
sins of Jeroboam, he departed not t. 2 Ki 3:3; 13:2

therein

multiply t. Gen 9:7
for fifty righteous t. 18:24
the cave that is t. I give. 23:11, 17, 20
you, dwell and trade t. 34:10, 21
was there any worm t. Ex 16:24
doeth any work t. be cut. 31:14; 35:2
shalt thou put t. the ark of. 40:3
tabernacle and all t. 9; Lev 8:10
sinning t. Lev 6:3
done in trespassing t. 7
no white hairs t. 13:21
black hairs t. 37
ordinances to walk t. 18:4
Judg 2:22; Isa 42:5
shall be no blemish t. Lev 22:21
ye shall do no work t.: it is. 23:3
Deut 16:8; Num 29:7; Jer 17:24
do no servile work t. Lev 23:7, 8, 21
25, 35, 36; Num 28:18; 29:35
eat your fill and dwell t. Lev 25:19
be wood t. or not. Num 13:20
put fire t. and put incense. Num 16:7, 46
lest thou be snared t. Deut 7:25
destroy all that is t. 13:15
Josh 10:28, 39
if there be any blemish t. Deut 15:21
he shall read t. all the days. 17:19
people that is found t. shall. 20:11
nor any grass groweth t. 29:23
thou shalt meditate t. day. Josh 1:8
the city and all t. shall. 6:17, 24
my name might be t. 1 Ki 8:16
new cruse, and put salt t. 2 Ki 2:20
let the fields rejoice, and all that is t. 1 Chr 16:32; Ps 96:12
sedition been made t. Ezra 4:19
there was no breach left t. Neh 6:1
but the people were few t. 7:4
found it written t. 5, 13:1
he read t. 8:3
made the earth, the seas, and all that is t. 9:6; Ps 24:1; 69:34; 98:7
let no joyful voice come t. Job 3:7
he shall not rejoice t. 20:18
shall dwell t. for ever. Ps 37:29
love his name shall dwell t. 69:36
for wickedness of them that dwell t. 107:34; Jer 12:4
that have pleasure t. Ps 111:2
thy commandments, t. do. 119:35
made the sea and all t. is. 146:6
Acts 14:15; 17:24; Rev 10:6
shall fall t. Pr 22:14; 26:27
Jer 23:12; Hos 14:9
make a breach t. for us. Isa 7:6
the people that dwell t. shall. 33:24
though fools, shall not err t. 35:8
gladness shall be found t. 51:3
they that dwell t. shall die in. 6
whosoever goeth t. shall not. 59:8
walk t.; we will not walk t. Jer 6:16
my voice, neither walked t. 9:13
and no man dwelleth t. 44:2
48:9; 50:3, 40
and all that is t. shall sing. 51:48
behold, t. shall be left. Ezek 14:22
city, to the pot whose scum is t. 24:6
mourn that dwelleth t. Hos 4:3
Amos 8:8; 9:5
t. shall be cut off and die, but the third part shall be left t. Zech 13:8
he shall not enter t. Mark 10:15
Luke 18:17
and let no man dwell t. Acts 1:20
t. is the righteousness of God. Rom 1:17
dead to sin, live any longer t.? 6:2
wherein he is called, t. 1 Cor 7:24
that t. I may speak boldly. Eph 6:20
and I t. do rejoice, and. Phil 1:18
taught, abounding t. with. Col 2:7
that some must enter t. Heb 4:6
not, nor hadst pleasure t. 10:8
of liberty, and continueth t. Jas 1:25
the earth and works t. 2 Pet 3:10
rise and measure them that worship t. Rev 11:1
causeth them that dwell t. to. 13:12
and I saw no temple t. 21:22
see **dwelt**

thereinto

in the countries enter t. Luke 21:21

thereof

eatest t. surely die. Gen 2:17; 3:5
I will do in midst t. Ex 3:20
for t. must we take to serve. 10:26
no stranger shall eat t. 12:43
45:48; 2 Ki 7:2
then shall he eat t. Ex 12:44
I have not eaten t. in. Deut 26:14
shall eat and leave t. 2 Ki 4:43, 44
know not the ways t. Job 24:13
the humble shall hear t. Ps 34:2
the whole disposing t. Pr 16:33
not power to eat t. Eccl 6:2

thereon

shalt sacrifice t. the. Ex 20:24
cloud abode t. 40:35; Num 9:22
spread ground corn t. 2 Sam 17:19
an ass that I may ride t. 19:26
God of our fathers look t. 1 Chr 12:17
let him be hanged t. Ezra 6:11
said, Hang Haman t. Esth 7:9

perverseness, and stay t. Isa 30:12
it to hang a vessel t. Ezek 15:3
they set him t. Mat 21:7
Luke 19:35; John 12:14
and found nothing t. Mat 21:19
Mark 11:13; Luke 13:6
thought t. he wept. Mark 14:72
another buildeth t. 1 Cor 3:10
open the book or look t. Rev 5:3, 4
was given to him that sat t. 6:4
gates, and names written t. 21:12

thereout

he shall take t. his handful of flour. Lev 2:2
there came water t. Judg 15:19

thereto

unto that to smell t. Ex 30:38
add the fifth part t. Lev 5:16; 6:5
27:13, 31
before a beast to lie down t. 18:23
shall be put t. in a vessel. Num 19:17
thou shalt not add t. Deut 12:32
king of Edom would not hearken t. Judg 11:17
thou mayest add t. 1 Chr 22:14
heavy, but I will add t. 2 Chr 10:14
Jehoram compelled Judah t. 21:11*
by taking heed t. according to thy. Ps 119:9
and falleth down t. Isa 44:15
thy speech agreeth t. Mark 14:70
no man disannulleth or addeth t. Gal 3:15

thereunto

made a molten calf, and sacrificed t. Ex 32:8
all the places nigh t. Deut 1:7
and watching t. with all. Eph 6:18
that we are appointed t. 1 Thes 3:3
the comers t. perfect. Heb 10:1
ye are t. called, that ye. 1 Pet 3:9

thereupon

playedst the harlot t. Ezek 16:16
of Judah shall feed t. Zeph 2:7
heed how he buildeth t. 1 Cor 3:10
work abide which he hath built t. 14

therewith

to blind mine eyes t. 1 Sam 12:3
and cut off his head t. 17:51
and thrust me through t. 31:4
1 Chr 10:4
I have t. sent Naaman. 2 Ki 5:6
and repaired t. the house of. 12:14
treasure and trouble t. Pr 15:16
a stalled ox, and hatred t. 17
quietness t. 17:1
lest thou be filled t. and. 25:16
travail to be exercised t. Eccl 1:13
stones shall be hurt t. 10:9
prepare thy bread t. Ezek 4:15
oil, wine, ye shall be satisfied t. Joel 2:19
state, I have learned t. Phil 4:11
food and raiment, let us be t. content. 1 Tim 6:8
t. bless we God, and t. Jas 3:9
and not content t. 3 John 10

these

by t. were the isles of. Gen 10:5, 32
Jacob take a wife of such as t. 27:46
t. daughters, t. children, t. 31:43
asketh, saying, Whose are t.? 32:17
Joseph said, Bring t. men home, make ready, for t. men. 43:16
gave light by night to t. Ex 14:20
and if he do not t. three unto. 21:11
t. be thy gods, O Israel. 32:4, 8
hath sinned in one of t. Lev 5:13
t. shall ye not eat. 11:4
t. shall ye eat. 9, 21, 22; Deut 14:9
for t. ye shall be unclean. Lev 11:24
t. shall be unclean. 29
ye shall not offer t. to. 22:22, 25
unto t. the land shall. Num 26:53
but among t. there was not a. 64
t. stand on mount. Deut 27:12
and t. shall stand upon mount. 13
Lord hath not chosen t. 1 Sam 16:10
Saul, I cannot go with t. 17:39
meanest thou by t.? 2 Sam 16:2
as t. which the queen of. 1 Ki 10:10
Solomon clave to t. strange. 11:2
be dew nor rain t. years. 1 Ki 17:1
Lord, With t. shalt thou push the Syrians. 22:11; 2 Chr 18:10
Lord said, T. have no master.
1 Ki 22:17; 2 Chr 18:16
Nebuzar-adan took t. 2 Ki 25:20
t. were of the king's. 2 Chr 35:7
t. sought their register. Ezra 2:62
t. went and could not shew. Neh 7:61
now t. that sealed the covenant. 10:1
who knoweth not such things as t.? Job 12:3
t. wait all upon thee, that. Ps 104:27
days were better than t. Eccl 7:10
further, by t. my son, be. 12:12
no one of t. shall fail. Isa 34:16
what said t. men? 39:3
remember t. O Jacob. 44:21
t. shall come from far, t. from north, and from the west, and t. 49:12
begotten me t.? who that brought up t.? I was left alone; t. where? 21
I receive comfort in t.? 57:6
but t. have altogether. Jer 5:5
t. men have done evil in all. 38:9
I give thee into hand of t. 16
pomegranates were like to t. 52:22
for t. pine away, stricken. Lam 4:9
when those went, t. went, and when those stood, t. Ezek 1:21; 10:17
greater abominations than t. 8:15
t. men have set up their idols. 14:3
thee, to do any of t. to thee. 16:5
and t. hast thou sacrificed unto. 20
t. discovered her nakedness. 23:10
in t. were they thy merchants. 27:21
what thou meanest by t. 37:18
they brought t. men. Dan 3:13
t. men were bound. 21
princes saw t. men. 27
over t. Darius set three. 6:2
then t. men assembled, and. 11, 15
t. great beasts, which are four. 7:17
by a dead body touch t. Hag 2:13
I will shew thee what t. be.
Zech 1:9; 4:5, 13
I said to the angel, What be t.? 1:19
21; 4:12
what is more than t. cometh of evil. Mat 5:37
not arrayed like one of t. 6:29
Hearest thou what t. say? 21:16
on t. commandments hang. 22:40
t. ought ye to have done. 23:23
done it unto one of the least of t. 25:40
did it not to one of the least of t. 45
and t. shall go into everlasting. 46
what is it which t. witness? 26:62
Mark 14:60
no other commandment greater than t. Mark 12:31
t. shall receive greater. 40
Seest thou t. great buildings? 13:2
am sent to shew thee t. Luke 1:19
God is able of t. stones to. 3:8
let t. sayings sink down into. 9:44
see greater things than t. John 1:50
in t. lay a great multitude of. 5:3
what he doeth, t. doeth the Son. 19
shew him greater works than t. 20
shall we buy bread that t.? 6:5
he do more miracles than t.? 7:31
neither pray I for t. alone. 17:20
and t. have known that thou. 25
seek me, let t. go their way. 18:8
lovest thou me more than t.? 21:15
of t. which companied. Acts 1:21
shew whether of t. two thou. 24
others said, T. men are full of. 2:13
likewise foretold of t. days. 3:24
What shall we do to t. men? 4:16
before t. days rose up. 5:36
refrain from t. men, and let. 38
can any forbid that t. should? 10:47
t. that have turned the world. 17:6
t. were more noble than those. 11
t. having not the law, are. Rom 2:14
more shall t. be graffed. 11:24
even so have t. also now not. 31
upon t. we bestow. 1 Cor 12:23
t. three, but the greatest of t. 13:13
having t. promises, let us cleanse. 2 Cor 7:1
but of t. who seemed to. Gal 2:6
t. only are my fellow-workers to. Col 4:11
let t. also first be proved. 1 Tim 3:10
himself from t. he shall. 2 Tim 2:21
with t., but heavenly things with better sacrifices than t. Heb 9:23
now where remission of t. is. 10:18
by t. might be partakers. 2 Pet 1:4
but t. as brute beasts made. 2:12
Enoch also prophesied of t. Jude 14
t. be they who separate. 19
t. have power to shut heaven. Rev 11:6
t. were redeemed. 14:4
t. have one mind. 17:13
he said, T. sayings are faithful. 22:6
see **abominations, things, words**

these *are*, or *are* **these**

by the man whose t. are. Gen 38:25
whose t. are. 48:8
t. are that Aaron and Moses. Ex 6:26
t. are the judgements. 21:1
Lev 26:46; Deut 6:1
t. are unclean. Lev 11:31
t. are my feasts. 23:2, 4
God said, What men are t. with thee? Num 22:9
t. are tokens of her. Deut 22:17
what cities are t. thou? 1 Ki 9:13
happy are t. thy servants. 10:8
her sons are t. 1 Chr 2:18
t. are ancient things. 4:22
now t. are thy servants. Neh 1:10
t. are part of his ways. Job 26:14
behold, t. are the ungodly. Ps 73:12
who are t. that flee as a cloud, as? Isa 60:8
t. are a smoke in my nose. 65:5
surely t. are poor, they. Jer 5:4
The temple of the Lord are t. 7:4
t. are the men that. Ezek 11:2
they said, T. are the people. 36:20
visions of thy head are t. Dan 2:28
spirit straitened? are t. his doings? Mi 2:7
then said I, O my lord, what are t.?
Zech 1:9; 4:4; 6:4
and t. are they by the way side.
Mark 4:15, 16, 18, 20
famines, t. are the beginnings. 13:8
and brethren are t. which. Luke 8:21
t. are not the words of. John 10:21
but t. are in the world, and I. 17:11
but t. are written that ye. 20:31
t. are not drunken, as. Acts 2:15
t. are not the children of. Rom 9:8
t. are contrary the one to. Gal 5:17
flesh are manifest, which are t. 19
t. are wells without water. 2 Pet 2:17
t. are murmurers, walking. Jude 16
what are t. which are arrayed in? Rev 7:13
t. are they which came out of. 14
t. are they which were not defiled with women. T. are they which. 14:4
t. are the true sayings. 19:9; 22:6

Thessalonica

at T. was a synagogue. Acts 17:1
more noble than those of T. 11
one Aristarchus of T. being. 27:2
even in T. ye sent once. Phil 4:16
for Demas is departed into T. 2 Tim 4:10

Theudas

days rose up T. boasting. Acts 5:36

they

of thee a nation mightier than t. Num 14:12
t. and all theirs went down. 16:33
not come nigh, that neither t. 18:3
more honourable than t. 22:15
be stronger than t. 1 Ki 20:23, 25
are more than t. that. 2 Ki 6:16
t. that hate me, t. would. Ps 69:4
there be higher than t. Eccl 5:8
and t. together shall be against. Isa 9:21
but t. also have erred through. 28:7
therefore t. that pursue you. 30:16
t. are thy lot, to them thou. 57:6
t. that shall be of thee shall 58:12
t., their kings and priests. Jer 2:26

whom neither *t.* nor their fathers.
Jer 9:16; 19:4; 44:3
t. whose judgement was not. 49:12
t. and their fathers have. *Ezek* 2:3
wast corrupted more than *t.* in ways. 16:47
abominations more than *t.* 51, 52
know that *t.* are my people. 34:30
when an hungered, and *t.* that were.
Mat 12:3; *Mark* 2:25; *Luke* 6:3
receive this, save *t.* to. *Mat* 19:11
t. that are great exercise. 20:25
t. that are whole have no need.
Mark 2:17; *Luke* 5:31
and *t.* that had eaten were. *Mark* 8:9
hardly shall *t.* which have riches. 10:23
t. that went before and *t.* that. 11:9
and *t.* that were sent. *Luke* 7:10
t. on the rock are *t.* which. 8:13
t. which have continued. 22:28
for *t.* also went unto the feast. *John* 4:45
dead shall hear, and *t.* that. 5:25
t. that have done good, *t.* that. 29
scriptures: and *t.* are *t.* which. 39
what are *t.* amongst so many? 6:9
I am come, that *t.* which see not might see, and that *t.* which. 9:39
t. are not of the world, even. 17:16
that *t.* all may be one, as thou. 21
that *t.* may be made perfect. 23
Father, I will that *t.* whom thou hast given me be with me, that *t.* 24
t. went not in, lest *t.* 18:28
t. of circumcision contended with. *Acts* 11:2
now *t.* that were scattered. 19
t. that dwell at Jerusalem because *t.* 13:27
through grace we shall be saved even as *t.* 15:11
we and *t.* of that place. 21:12
are we better than *t.*? *Rom* 3:9
for if *t.* which are of the law. 4:14
t. that are in the flesh cannot. 8:8
not only *t.* but ourselves also. 23
t. which are the children of the. 9:8
t. also, if *t.* abide not still. 11:23
for *t.* that are such serve not. 16:18
t. that have wives, as though *t.* had none. *1 Cor* 7:29
t. that weep, *t.* that rejoice, *t.* 30
t. that use this world, as not. 31
that *t.* who run in a race run. 9:24
that *t.* which are approved. 11:19
whether it were I or *t.* so we. 15:11
then *t.* also which are fallen. 18
afterwards *t.* that are Christ's. 23
Gal 5:24
as is earthy, such are *t.* *1 Cor* 15:48
t. who seemed somewhat. *Gal* 2:6
t. gave the right hand of. 9
know ye, that *t.* which are. 3:7, 9
I would *t.* were cut off which. 5:12
t. who do such things shall not. 21
nor *t.* who are circumcised. 6:13
t. shew of us what entering in we had. *1 Thes* 1:9
for *t.* that sleep; *t.* that be. 5:7
t. that used the office. *1 Tim* 3:13
t. who labour in the word. 5:17
and *t.* that are otherwise cannot. 25
t. that will be rich fall into. 6:9
of this sort are *t.* which. *2 Tim* 3:6
that *t.* which have believed. *Tit* 3:8
more excellent name than *t.* *Heb* 1:4
seeing *t.* to whom it was first. 4:6
that *t.* without us should. 11:40
t. watch, as *t.* that must. 13:17
salute all the saints, *t.* of Italy. 24
as *t.* that shall be judged. *Jas* 2:12
t. went out that *t.* might be made manifest, that *t.* were. *1 John* 2:19
t. are of the world, *t.* speak. 4:5
these be *t.* who separate. *Jude* 19
t. who pierced him. *Rev* 1:7
for *t.* are worthy. 3:4; 16:6
whence came *t.*? 7:13
these are *t.* who came out of. 14
for *t.* are virgins. These are *t.* 14:4
here are *t.* that keep the. 12
but *t.* that are written in. 21:27

thick

art waxen fat, thou art grown *t.* *Deut* 32:15
the mule went under the *t.* boughs. *2 Sam* 18:9
he took a *t.* cloth and. *2 Ki* 8:15*
fetch branches of *t.* trees to make booths. *Neh* 8:15
runneth on the *t.* bosses. *Job* 15:26
axes on the *t.* trees. *Ps* 74:5*
be under every *t.* oak. *Ezek* 6:13
exalted among *t.* branches. 19:11
his top was among the *t.* boughs. 31:3, 10, 14
ladeth himself with *t.* clay. *Hab* 2:6
people were gathered *t.* together. *Luke* 11:29*

see **clouds, darkness**

thicker

little finger shall be *t.* than my father's loins. *1 Ki* 12:10; *2 Chr* 10:10

thicket

a ram caught in a *t.* by. *Gen* 22:13
the lion is come up from his *t.* *Jer* 4:7

thickets

themselves in *t.* in rocks. *1 Sam* 13:6
kindle in the *t.* of forest. *Isa* 9:18
he shall cut down the *t.* of. 10:34
shall flee and go into *t.* *Jer* 4:29

thickness

the *t.* of the sea was an. *2 Chr* 4:5
the *t.* of the pillars was. *Jer* 52:21
t. of the wall was five. *Ezek* 41:9
the chambers were in the *t.* 42:10

thief

(*The Revisions usually change* thief *and* thieves *to* robber *and* robbers, *as having a little more exactly the meaning*)

if a *t.* be found breaking. *Ex* 22:2, 7
if the *t.* be not found, then the. 8
then that *t.* shall die. *Deut* 24:7
in the night is as a *t.* *Job* 24:14
after them as after a *t.* 30:5
when thou sawest a *t.* *Ps* 50:18
men do not despise *t.* if. *Pr* 6:30
whoso is partner with a *t.* 29:24
as a *t.* is ashamed when. *Jer* 2:26
the *t.* cometh in, and. *Hos* 7:1
enter at windows like a *t.* *Joel* 2:9
into the house of the *t.* *Zech* 5:4
in what watch the *t.* would come.
Mat 24:43; *Luke* 12:39
ye come as against a *t.*? *Mat* 26:55
Mark 14:48; *Luke* 22:52
in heaven, where no *t.* *Luke* 12:33
door, the same is a *t.* *John* 10:1
the *t.* cometh not but to steal. 10
but because he was a *t.* and. 12:6
day of the Lord cometh as a *t.*
1 Thes 5:2; *2 Pet* 3:10
overtake you as a *t.* *1 Thes* 5:4
none of you suffer as a *t.* *1 Pet* 4:15
I will come on thee as a *t.* *Rev* 3:3
16:15

thieves

thy princes are companions of *t.* *Isa* 1:23
not Israel found among *t.*? *Jer* 48:27
if *t.* by night, they will. 49:9; *Ob* 5
and where *t.* break. *Mat* 6:19
and where *t.* do not break. 20
made it a den of *t.* 21:13
Mark 11:17; *Luke* 19:46
two *t.* crucified with him. *Mat* 27:38
Mark 15:27
t. also cast the same in. *Mat* 27:44
Jericho and fell among *t.* *Luke* 10:30
to him that fell among *t.*? 36
came before me are *t.* *John* 10:8
nor *t.*, shall inherit the kingdom of God. *1 Cor* 6:10

thigh

put thy hand under my *t.* *Gen* 24:2
9; 47:29
the hollow of Jacob's *t.* 32:25
he halted upon his *t.* 31
the Lord maketh thy *t.* to rot.
Num 5:21, 22, 27
dagger on his right *t.* *Judg* 3:16
dagger from his right *t.* 21
smote them hip and *t.* 15:8
gird thy sword on thy *t.* *Ps* 45:3
hath his sword on his *t.* *S of S* 3:8
uncover the *t.*, pass over. *Isa* 47:2*
I smote upon my *t.* *Jer* 31:19
smite therefore upon *t.* *Ezek* 21:12
gather the *t.* and shoulder. 24:4
he hath on his *t.* a name. *Rev* 19:16

thighs

breeches shall reach from loins to the *t.* *Ex* 28:42
the joints of thy *t.* are. *S of S* 7:1
his belly and his *t.* were. *Dan* 2:32

thin

and behold seven *t.* ears. *Gen* 41:6
7, 23, 24
the seven *t.* kine are seven. 27
gold into *t.* plates. *Ex* 39:3
in it a yellow *t.* hair. *Lev* 13:30
additions made of *t.* work. *1 Ki* 7:29*
Jacob shall be made *t.* *Isa* 17:4

thine

any thing that is *t.* *Gen* 14:23
thou and all that are *t.* 20:7
discern what is *t.* with me. 31:32
issue after them shall be *t.* 48:6
it shall be *t.* and thy sons. *Lev* 10:15
Num 18:9, 11, 13, 14, 15, 18
ridden ever since I was *t.* *Num* 22:30
that which is *t.* with thy. *Deut* 15:3
if any of *t.* be driven into. 30:4
mountains shall be *t.* and the outgoings of it shall be *t.* *Josh* 17:18
the man of *t.* whom I. *1 Sam* 2:33
given it to a neighbour of *t.* 15:28
t. are all that pertained to Mephibosheth. *2 Sam* 16:4
mine nor *t.* but divide. *1 Ki* 3:26
O king, I am *t.* and all that. 20:4
shall lick thy blood, even *t.* 21:19
t. are we, David, and. *1 Chr* 12:18
not take that which is *t.* 21:24
t. O Lord, is the greatness, power, and glory: the earth is *t.*, *t.* is. 29:11
righteousness even *t.* *Ps* 71:16
day is *t.*, the night also is *t.* 74:16
are *t.*, the earth also is *t.* 89:11
I am *t.*, save me; I sought. 119:94
of Egypt shall be *t.* *Isa* 45:14
we are *t.*: thou never barest. 63:19
of inheritance is *t.* *Jer* 32:8
t. is the kingdom. *Mat* 6:13
take that is *t.* 20:14
there thou hast that is *t.* 25:25
worship me, all shall be *t.* *Luke* 4:7
but *t.* eat and drink? 5:33
all I have is *t.* 15:31
my will but *t.* be done. 22:42
t. they were. *John* 17:6
for they are *t.* 9
all mine are *t.* and *t.* are mine. 10

thing

the *t.* was very grievous. *Gen* 21:11
t. proceedeth from the Lord. 24:50
which *t.* ought not to be done. 34:7
2 Sam 13:12
young man deferred not to do the *t.* *Gen* 34:19
and the *t.* which he did displeased.
38:10; *2 Sam* 11:27
because the *t.* is established by. *Gen* 41:32
not any green *t.* in the. *Ex* 10:15
in the *t.* wherein they dealt. 18:11
Jethro said, The *t.* that thou. 17
for any manner of lost *t.* 22:9
if it be an hired *t.* it came for. 15
a terrible *t.* that I will do. 34:10
a *t.* most holy of your offerings. *Lev* 2:3, 10
and the *t.* be hid from the eyes. 4:13
trespass in a *t.* taken away. 6:2
t. deceitfully gotten, or the lost *t.* 4
she shall touch no hallowed *t.* 12:4
it is a wicked *t.*; they shall be. 20:17
but if the Lord make a new *t.*, and the earth. *Num* 16:30
the *t.* which thou hast spoken is. *Deut* 1:14
what *t.* soever I command. 12:32
and the *t.* certain. 13:14; 17:4
if the *t.* follow not, nor. 18:22
it is not a vain *t.* for you; it is. 32:47

from the accursed *t.* *Josh* 6:18
the *t.* pleased the children of. 22:33
which *t.* became a snare. *Judg* 8:27
do not so vile a *t.* 19:24
finished the *t.* to-day. *Ruth* 3:18
I will do a *t.* in Israel. *1 Sam* 3:11
what is the *t.* that the Lord hath? 17
there hath not been such a *t.* 4:7
the *t.* displeased Samuel, when. 8:6
and we will shew you a *t.* 14:12
Saul, and the *t.* pleased him. 18:20
not take the *t.* to heart. *2 Sam* 13:33
hast thou thought such a *t.*? 14:13
hide not the *t.* that I shall ask. 18
what *t.* thou shalt hear, tell. 15:35
she spread corn, and the *t.* 17:19
the wife of Jeroboam cometh to ask a *t.* of thee. *1 Ki* 14:5
Thou hast asked a hard *t.* *2 Ki* 2:10
in heaven, might such a *t.* be. 7:19
that the Lord will do the *t.* 20:9
t. was right in the eyes. *1 Chr* 13:4
let the *t.* thou hast spoken. 17:23
for the *t.* was done. *2 Chr* 29:36
the *t.* pleased the king and congregation. 30:4
hath put such a *t.* in. *Ezra* 7:27
the *t.* pleased the king and he did so. *Esth* 2:4
the *t.* was known to Mordecai. 22
the *t.* pleased Haman, and he. 5:14
and if the *t.* seem right before. 8:5
the *t.* I greatly feared is. *Job* 3:25
now a *t.* was secretly brought. 4:12
God would grant me the *t.* 6:8
he as a rotten *t.* consumeth. 13:28
who can bring a clean *t.* out? 14:4
thou shalt decree a *t.*. it shall. 22:28
he performeth the *t.* that is. 23:14
plentifully declared the *t.*? 26:3
of me the *t.* that is right. 42:7, 8
people imagine a vain *t.*? *Ps* 2:1
horse is a vain *t.* for safety. 33:17
because I follow the *t.* that. 38:20
nor alter the *t.* that is gone out. 89:34
I will set no wicked *t.* before. 101:3
wisdom is the principal *t.* *Pr* 4:7
for it is a pleasant *t.* if thou. 22:18
glory of God to conceal a *t.* 25:2
t. that hath been, it is that which shall be, and there is no new *t.* *Eccl* 1:9
better is the end of a *t.* than. 7:8
the interpretation of a *t.*? 8:1
a man hath no better *t.* than to. 15
pleasant *t.* it is for the eyes to. 11:7
is it a small *t.* for you to? *Isa* 7:13
there is no green *t.* 15:6
rolling *t.* before the whirlwind. 17:13
shall the *t.* framed say of him? 29:16
that turn aside the just for a *t.* 21
the isles as a very little *t.* 40:15
and they shall be as a *t.* of. 41:12
I will do a new *t.*; now it shall. 43:19
prosper in the *t.* whereto. 55:11
who hath heard such a *t.*? 66:8
see if there be such a *t.* *Jer* 2:10
a horrible *t.* is committed. 5:30
altars to that shameful *t.* 11:13
they prophesy unto you a *t.* 14:14
Israel hath done a horrible *t.* 18:13
in the prophets a horrible *t.* 23:14
Lord hath created a new *t.* in. 31:22
king said, I will ask thee a *t.* 38:14
that God may shew us the *t.* 42:3
that whatsoever *t.* the Lord. 4
we will do what *t.* goeth out. 44:17
what *t.* shall I take to witness for thee, what *t.* shall I? *Lam* 2:13
he hath spoken a *t.* *Ezek* 14:9
as if that were a very little *t.* 16:47
the king said, The *t.* is. *Dan* 2:5, 8
and it is a rare *t.* that the king. 11
Arioch made the *t.* known to. 15
Daniel made the *t.* known to. 17
the same hour was the *t.* 4:33
could not shew the interpretation of the *t.* 5:15
the interpretation of the *t.*: Mene. 26
t. is true, according to the law. 6:12
t. was revealed to Daniel; and *t.* was true: and he understood the *t.* 10:1
I have seen an horrible *t.* *Hos* 6:10
were counted as a strange *t.* 8:12
ye which rejoice in a *t.* *Amos* 6:13

to the Lord, a corrupt *t.* *Mal* 1:14
what *t.* is this? what? *Mark* 1:27
how or what *t.* ye shall. *Luke* 12:11
sin no more, lest a worse *t.* come. *John* 5:14
Herein is a marvellous *t.* 9:30
it is unlawful *t.* for man. *Acts* 10:28
tell or hear some new *t.* 17:21
they observe no such *t.* 21:25
for he hath a certain *t.* to tell. 23:17
of whom I have no certain *t.* 25:26
why should it be thought a *t.*? 26:8
which *t.* I also did in Jerusalem. 10
shall *t.* formed say to? *Rom* 9:20
I beseech you that ye all speak the same *t.* *1 Cor* 1:10
with me it is a very small *t.* 4:3
some eat it as a *t.* offered. 8:7
wrought us for the selfsame *t.* is God. *2 Cor* 5:5
this selfsame *t.* that ye. 7:11
let us mind the same *t.* *Phil* 3:16
seeing it is a righteous *t.* *2 Thes* 1:6
covenant an unholy *t.* *Heb* 10:29
a fearful *t.* to fall into the hands. 31
as though some strange *t.* *1 Pet* 4:12
which *t.* is true in him. *1 John* 2:8
doctrine of Nicolaitanes, which *t.* I hate. *Rev* 2:15
see **accursed, great, holy, light, one, small**

any thing

I will not take *any t.* that. *Gen* 14:23
is *any t.* too hard for the? 18:14
cannot do *any t.* till thou be. 19:22
neither do thou *any t.* unto. 22:12
Thou shalt not give me *any t.* 30:31
nor hath he kept back *any t.* 39:9
he looked not to *any t.* under. 23
unto thee any likeness of *any t.* *Ex* 20:4; *Deut* 4:18, 23, 25; 5:8
nor *any t.* that is thy neighbour's. *Ex* 20:17; *Deut* 5:21
forgiven him for *any t.* *Lev* 6:7
in *any t.* made of skin. 13:48, 49, 52, 53, 57, 59
that sitteth on *any t.* 15:6, 23
who toucheth *any t.* that was. 10, 22
ye shall not eat *any t.* with. 19:26
or that hath *any t.* superfluous. 21:18, 22, 23
without doing *any t.* else. *Num* 20:19
any power at all to say *any t.*? 22:38
cast upon him *any t.* 35:22
hath been *any* such *t.* *Deut* 4:32
thou shalt not lack *any t.* in. 8:9
not eat *any* abominable *t.* 14:3
ye shall not eat *any t.* that dieth. 21
nor shall there *any t.* of the. 16:4
usury of *any t.* that is lent. 23:19
lend thy brother *any t.* 24:10
have not known *any t.* 31:13
failed not aught of *any t.* *Josh* 21:45
art thou *any t.* better? *Judg* 11:25
put them to shame in *any t.* 18:7
a place where there is no want of *any t.* 10; 19:19
thee, if thou hide *any t.* *1 Sam* 3:17
but Saul spake not *any t.* 20:26
but the lad knew not *any t.* 39
let no man know *any t.* of the. 21:2
let not the king impute *any t.* 22:15
neither missed we *any t.* 25:15
there was not lacking *any t.* 30:19
hard to do *any t.* to her. *2 Sam* 13:2
went in simplicity, they knew not *any t.* 15:11
there was not *any t.* hid. *1 Ki* 10:3
turned not aside from *any t.* 15:5
whether *any t.* would come. 20:33
hath not *any t.* save a. *2 Ki* 4:2
hath dedicated *any t.* *1 Chr* 26:28
silver was not *any t.* *2 Chr* 9:20
that none unclean in *any t.* 23:19
is there *any* secret *t.*? *Job* 15:11
if thou hast *any t.* to say. 33:32
shall not want *any* good *t.* *Ps* 34:10
my heart to *any* evil *t.* 141:4
any t. whereof it may be said. *Eccl* 1:10
nothing be put to it, nor *any t.* 3:14
heart not be hasty to utter *any t.* 5:2
dead know not *any t.* nor have. 9:5

is there *any t.* too hard? *Jer* 32:27
is not he that can do *any t.* 38:5
nor *any t.* for which he hath. 42:21
which speak *any t.* amiss. *Dan* 3:29
man nor beast taste *any t.* *Jonah* 3:7
agree touching *any t.* *Mat* 18:19
to take *any t.* out of his house. 24:17; *Mark* 13:15
nor was *any t.* kept secret. *Mark* 4:22; *Luke* 8:17
thou canst do *any t.* have. *Mark* 9:22
if haply he might find *any t.* 11:13
neither said they *any t.* to. 16:8
if I have taken *any t.* *Luke* 19:8
lacked ye *any t.*? and they. 22:35
was not *any t.* made. *John* 1:3
can there *any* good *t.* come? 46
no man that doeth *any t.* in. 7:4
if ye ask *any t.* in my name. 14:14
I have never eaten *any t.* *Acts* 10:14
as though he needed *any t.* 17:25
Caesar, have I offended *any t.* 25:8
committed *any t.* worthy of. 11
lay *any t.* to the charge? *Rom* 8:33
owe no man *any t.* but to love. 13:8
any t. whereby thy brother. 14:21
nor to know *any t.* save. *1 Cor* 2:2
neither is he that planteth *any t.* 3:7
think that he knoweth *any t.* 8:2
that the idol is *any t.* 10:19
if they will learn *any t.* let. 14:35
to whom ye forgive *any t.* I forgive, for if I forgive *any t.* *2 Cor* 2:10
not sufficient to think *any t.* as. 3:5
giving no offence in *any t.* that. 6:3
for if I have boasted *any t.* to. 7:14
neither circumcision availeth *any t.* *Gal* 5:6
wrinkle, or *any* such *t.* *Eph* 5:27
if in *any t.* ye be. *Phil* 3:15
need not to speak *any t.* *1 Thes* 1:8
if there be *any* other *t.* *1 Tim* 1:10
that he shall receive *any t.* *Jas* 1:7
if we ask *any t.* according to his will. *1 John* 5:14
not hurt *any* green *t.* *Rev* 9:4
in no wise enter *any t.* that. 21:27

every thing

every t. that is in the. *Gen* 6:17
Noah and *every* living *t.* 8:1
every moving *t.* that liveth. 9:3
every t. whereon he sitteth, unclean. *Lev* 15:4
every t. she sitteth on shall. 20
ye shall offer *every t.* upon. 23:37
every devoted *t.* is most holy. 27:28
every t. devoted in Israel shall be. *Num* 18:14; *Ezek* 44:29
every t. that openeth the matrix be. *Num* 18:15
every t. that may abide fire. 31:23
from *every* wicked *t.* *Deut* 23:9
the priests stood till *every t.* was. *Josh* 4:10
every t. that was vile. *1 Sam* 15:9
send unto me *every t.* *2 Sam* 15:36
told *every t.* that had. *Esth* 6:13
eye seeth *every* precious *t.* *Job* 28:10
searcheth after *every* green *t.* 39:8
that thou canst do *every t.* 42:2
let *every t.* that hath breath praise. *Ps* 150:6
every bitter *t.* is sweet. *Pr* 27:7
to *every t.* there is a season. *Eccl* 3:1
hath made *every t.* beautiful in. 11
judgement with *every* secret *t.* 12:14
every t. sown by the brooks. *Isa* 19:7
every t. shall live where. *Ezek* 47:9
told *every t.* and what was befallen. *Mat* 8:33
in *every t.* ye are enriched. *1 Cor* 1:5; *2 Cor* 9:11
as ye are bound in *every t.* in faith. *2 Cor* 8:7
and *every* high *t.* that exalteth. 10:5
their husbands in *every t.* *Eph* 5:24
in *every t.* by prayer and. *Phil* 4:6
in *every t.* give thanks. *1 Thes* 5:18
see **creepeth, creeping, evil, good, living**

that thing

hide from Abraham *that t.* *Gen* 18:17
and the Lord did *that t.* *Ex* 9:6

he hath sinned in *that t.* *Lev* 5:5
committed *that* wicked *t.* *Deut* 17:5
to tell no man *that t.* *Luke* 9:21
if ye be not able to do *that t.* 12:26
not himself in *that t.* *Rom* 14:22

this **thing**

thee concerning *this t.* *Gen* 19:21
thou hast done *this t.* 20:10
hath done *this t.*; neither. 21:26
done *this t.* and not withheld. 22:16
if wilt do *this t.* I will again. 30:31
we cannot do *this t.* to give. 34:14
this is the *t.* I have spoken. 41:28
should do according to *this t.* 44:7
why have ye done *this t.*? *Ex* 1:18
Moses said, Surely *this t.* 2:14
Pharaoh heard *this t.*, he sought. 15
Lord shall do *this t.* in land. 9:5
observe *this t.* for an. 12:24
this is the *t.* which the Lord. 16:16
32; 35:4; *Lev* 8:5; 9:6; 17:2
Num 30:1; 36:6; *Deut* 15:15
24:18, 22
what is *this t.* thou doest ? *Ex* 18:14
this t. is too heavy for thee. 18
if thou shalt do *this t.* and God. 23
this is the *t.* that thou shalt. 29:1
I will do *this t.* that thou. 33:17
if ye will do *this t.*, if ye. *Num* 32:20
this t. Lord doth command. 36:6
yet in *this t.* ye did not. *Deut* 1:32
for *this t.* the Lord thy God. 15:10
if *this t.* be true, and tokens. 22:20
through *this t.* ye shall prolong. 32:47
and have done *this t.* *Josh* 9:24
done it for fear of *this t.* 22:24
Who hath done *this t.*? Gideon hath done *this t.* *Judg* 6:29
let *this t.* be done for me, let. 11:37
this shall be the *t.* which we. 20:9
and *this* is the *t.* that ye. 21:11
my father hide *this t.* from me?
1 Sam 20:2
that I should do *this t.* 24:6
this t. is not good that. 26:16
happen to thee for *this t.* 28:10
Lord hath done *this t.* unto thee. 18
ye have done *this t.* *2 Sam* 2:6
liveth, I will not do *this t.* 11:11
say to Joab, Let not *this t.* 25
man that hath done *this t.* 12:5
because he did *this t.* and had. 6
but I will do *this t.* before all. 12
brother; regard not *this t.* 13:20
the king doth speak *this t.* as. 14:13
I am come to speak of *this t.* 15
thy servant Joab hath done *this t.* 20
why doth my lord the king delight in *this t.*? 24:3
is *this t.* done by my? *1 Ki* 1:27
Solomon had asked *this t.* 3:10, 11
him concerning *this t.* 11:10
return every man, for *this t.* 12:24
made two calves, and *this t.* 30
after *this t.* Jeroboam. 13:33
this t. became sin to the house. 34
tell my lord the king *this t.* 20:9
do *this t.*, take the kings away. 24
the Lord pardon in *this t.* *2 Ki* 5:18
Syria was troubled for *this t.* 6:11
windows, might *this t.* be. 7:2
this is the *t.* that ye shall do. 11:5
2 Chr 23:4
Ye shall not do *this t.* *2 Ki* 17:12
God forbid that I should do *this t.*
1 Chr 11:19
my lord require *this t.*? 21:3
was displeased with *this t.* 7
because I have done *this t.* 8
return every man, *this t.* *2 Chr* 11:4
with him, because of *this t.* 16:10
when I heard *this t.* I rent. *Ezra* 9:3
Israel concerning *this t.* 10:2
have transgressed in *this t.* 13
what is *this t.* that ye do? *Neh* 2:19
Lord will do *this t.* that. *Isa* 38:7
but *this* is the *t.* that I command.
Jer 7:23
if ye do *this t.* indeed, then. 22:4
therefore *this t.* is come upon. 40:3
Thou shalt not do *this t.* 16
oh do not *this* abominable *t.* 44:4
her that had done *this t.* *Mark* 5:32
and see *this t.* which is. *Luke* 2:15
it was that should do *this t.* 22:23
sayest thou *this t.* of? *John* 18:34
why hast thou conceived *this t.* in thine heart? *Acts* 5:4
for *this t.* was not done in a. 26:26
continually upon *this* very *t.*
Rom 13:6
if I do *this t.* willingly, I. *1 Cor* 9:17
for *this t.* I besought. *2 Cor* 12:8
being confident in *this* very *t.* that.
Phil 1:6
but *this* one *t.* I do, I press. 3:13

unclean **thing**

if a soul touch any *unclean t.*
Lev 5:2; 7:21
flesh that toucheth *unclean t.* 7:19
wife, it is an *unclean t.* 20:21
no *unclean t.* in thee. *Deut* 23:14
and eat not any *unclean t.* *Judg* 13:4
7, 14
touch no *unclean t.* *Isa* 52:11
2 Cor 6:17
we are all as an *unclean t.* *Isa* 64:6
any *t.* that is *unclean.* *Acts* 10:14

things

with the good *t.* of Egypt. *Gen* 45:23
if a soul sin through ignorance concerning *t.* *Lev* 4:2, 13, 22, 27
lest thou forget *t.* thine. *Deut* 4:9
with all lost *t.* of thy brother's. 22:3
the secret *t.* belong unto the. 29:29
t. that shall come on them. 32:35
for the chief *t.* of the ancient. 33:15
took the *t.* which Micah. *Judg* 18:27
ye go after vain *t.* *1 Sam* 12:21
people took the chief of the *t.* 15:21
I offer thee three *t.* *2 Sam* 24:12
1 Chr 21:10
Solomon brought in the *t.* *1 Ki* 7:51
Asa brought in the *t.* 15:15
2 Chr 15:18
wicked *t.* to provoke *2 Ki* 17:11
and these are ancient *t.* *1 Chr* 4:22
the office over *t.* that were. 9:31
t. of gold, silver for *t.* of silver, brass for *t.* of brass, iron for *t.* 29:2
and also in Judah *t.* *2 Chr* 12:12
let *t.* for purification. *Esth* 2:3, 12
who doth marvellous *t.* *Job* 5:9
the *t.* that my soul refuseth. 6:7
my taste discern perverse *t.*? 30
he discovereth deep *t.* out of. 12:22
only do not two *t.* to me: then. 13:20
writest bitter *t.* against me. 26
he beholdeth all high *t.* 41:34
I have uttered *t.* too wonderful. 42:3
that speaketh proud *t.* *Ps* 12:3
thine eyes behold the *t.* 17:2
speak grievous *t.* proudly. 31:18
they laid to my charge *t.* I. 35:11
hurt, speak mischievous *t.* 38:12
I speak of the *t.* which I. 45:1
hand shall teach thee terrible *t.* 4
shewed thy people hard *t.* 60:3
by terrible *t.* wilt thou answer. 65:5
who only doeth wondrous *t.* 72:18
marvellous *t.* did he in. 78:12; 98:1
and dost wondrous *t.* 86:10
glorious *t.* are spoken of thee. 87:3
utter and speak hard *t.*? 94:4
terrible *t.* by the Red sea. 106:22
himself to behold the *t.* that. 113:6
I may behold wondrous *t.* 119:18
great matters, or in *t.* too high. 131:1
that speaketh froward *t.* *Pr* 2:12
of excellent *t.* . . . shall be right *t.* 8:6
eyes to devise froward *t.* 16:30
written to thee excellent *t.* 22:20
when thy lips speak right *t.* 23:16
heart shall utter perverse *t.* 33
two *t.* have I required of thee. 30:7
there are three *t.* that are never. 15
there be three *t.* that be too. 18
for three *t.* the earth is. 21
four *t.* which are little on the. 24
there be three *t.* which go well. 29
any remembrance of *t.* *Eccl* 1:11
wisdom, and the reason of *t.* 7:25
he hath done excellent *t.* *Isa* 12:5
thou hast done wonderful *t.* 25:1
unto all people a feast of fat *t.* 6
surely your turning of *t.* 29:16
prophesy not to us right *t.* *Isa* 30:10
liberal deviseth liberal *t.* and by liberal *t.* shall he stand. 32:8
shew the *t.* that are to come. 41:23
t. come to pass, and new *t.* 42:9
I will make crooked *t.* straight. 16
the *t.* that are coming and. 44:7
of *t.* to come concerning my. 45:11
I the Lord speak, I declare *t.* 19
thee new *t.*, even hidden *t.* 48:6
the eunuchs that choose the *t.* 56:4
when thou didst terrible *t.* 64:3
and all our pleasant *t.* are laid. 11
broth of abominable *t.* is in. 65:4
walked after *t.* that do not profit.
Jer 2:8; 16:19
the *t.* I have given them shall. 8:13
shall eat them as common *t.* 31:5
Jerusalem remembered her pleasant *t.* *Lam* 1:7
they have given her pleasant *t.* 11
prophets have seen foolish *t.* 2:14
I know the *t.* that come. *Ezek* 11:5
like *t.* shall not come, neither. 16:16
at the same time shall *t.* 38:10
the deep and secret *t.* *Dan* 2:22
shall speak marvellous *t.* 11:36
your temples my goodly *t.* *Joel* 3:5
t. of Esau searched out! how are his hidden *t.* sought up! *Ob* 6
unto him marvellous *t.* *Mi* 7:15
who hath despised the day of small *t.*? *Zech* 4:10
thought for *t.* of itself. *Mat* 6:34
bringeth out of his treasure *t.* 13:52
savourest not *t.* that be of God.
16:23; *Mark* 8:33
to Caesar the *t.* that are Caesar's, and to God the *t.* that are God's.
Mat 22:21; *Mark* 12:17; *Luke* 20:25
lusts of other *t.* *Mark* 4:19
but the *t.* which come out of. 7:15
seen strange *t.* to-day. *Luke* 5:26
call me Lord, and do not the *t.* 6:46
the eyes which see the *t.* 10:23
in the abundance of the *t.* he. 12:15
and did commit *t.* worthy of. 48
the *t.* which are impossible. 18:27
hadst known the *t.* which. 19:42
for the *t.* concerning me 22:37
all people beholding the *t.* 23:48
hast not known the *t.* which. 24:18
he expounded the *t.* concerning. 27
thou shalt see greater *t.* *John* 1:50
told you earthly *t.*, heavenly *t.*? 3:12
the Spirit will shew you *t.* 16:13
speaking of *t.* pertaining. *Acts* 1:3
we cannot but speak the *t.* 4:20
the people imagine vain *t.*? 25
that aught of the *t.* he possessed. 32
preaching the *t.* concerning. 8:12
abstain from *t.* strangled. 15:20, 29
she attended to the *t.* spoken. 16:14
Apollos taught diligently the *t.* 18:25
persuading *t.* concerning the. 19:8
not knowing the *t.* that shall. 20:22
arise, speaking perverse *t.* to. 30
that they keep from *t.* offered. 21:25
neither can they prove the *t.* 24:13
saying none other *t.* than the. 26:22
some believed the *t.* that were. 28:24
invisible *t.* of him are clearly seen, being understood by *t.* *Rom* 1:20
judgest, doest the same *t.* 2:1
Gentiles do by nature *t.* contained. 14
and approvest the *t.* that are. 18
mind the *t.* of the flesh, mind *t.* 8:5
nor *t.* present, nor *t.* to come. 38
1 Cor 3:22
mind not high *t.* *Rom* 12:16
provide *t.* honest. 17
follow after *t.* that make for. 14:19
whatsoever *t.* were written. 15:4
partakers of spiritual *t.*, their duty is to minister to them in carnal *t.* 27
foolish *t.* of the world, weak *t.* to confound *t.* which are. *1 Cor* 1:27
base *t.* and *t.* despised hath. 28
the *t.* which God hath prepared. 2:9
the Spirit searcheth the deep *t.* 10
knoweth the *t.* of a man, even so the *t.* of God knoweth no man. 11
we might know the *t.* that are. 12
t. we speak, comparing spiritual *t.* 13

man receiveth not the *t.* of. *1 Cor* 2:14
will bring to light the hidden *t.* 4:5
much more *t.* shall pertain to. 6:3, 4
careth for the *t.* of the Lord. 7:32, 34
married careth for the *t.* that are. 33
as touching *t.* offered to idols. 8:1
sown spiritual *t.* if reap carnal *t.* 9:11
the *t.* which the Gentiles. 10:20
a man, I put away childish *t.* 13:11
and even *t.* without life giving. 14:7
acknowledge that the *t.* that. 37
let all your *t.* be done with. 16:14
write none other *t.* unto. *2 Cor* 1:13
or the *t.* that I purpose, do I. 17
but have renounced the hidden *t.* 4:2
the *t.* which are seen, *t.* seen are
temporal, *t.* not seen are. 18
every one may receive the *t.* 5:10
old *t.* are passed away, all *t.* are. 17
providing for honest *t.*, not only. 8:21
do ye look on *t.* after the? 10:7
we will not boast of *t.* without. 13, 15
boast in another man's line of *t.* 16
I will glory of the *t.* which. 11:30
if I build again the *t.* *Gal* 2:18
which *t.* are an allegory, for. 4:24
so that ye cannot do the *t.* 5:17
and, ye masters, do the same *t.* unto.
Eph 6:9
that ye may approve *t.* that. *Phil* 1:10
the *t.* which happened unto me. 12
look not on his own *t.*, but every man
also on the *t.* of others. 2:4
of *t.* in heaven, *t.* in earth, *t.* 10
not the *t.* which are Jesus Christ's. 21
to write the same *t.* 3:1
who mind earthly *t.* 19
whatsoever *t.* are true, honest. 4:8
having received the *t.* sent from. 18
t. in earth, or *t.* in heaven. *Col* 1:20
which are a shadow of *t.* to come.
2:17; *Heb* 10:1
t. have indeed a shew of. *Col* 2:23
affection on *t.* above, not on *t.* 3:2
for which *t.*'s sake the wrath of. 6
suffered like *t.* of your. *1 Thes* 2:14
and will do the *t.* which. *2 Thes* 3:4
speaking *t.* which they. *1 Tim* 5:13
the *t.* which thou hast. *2 Tim* 2:2
continue in *t.* which thou. 3:14
set in order the *t.* wanting. *Tit* 1:5
teaching *t.* they ought not for. 11
speak thou the *t.* which become. 2:1
give heed to the *t.* which. *Heb* 2:1
be faithful high priest in *t.* pertaining
to God. 17; 5:1
learned he obedience by the *t.* 5:8
persuaded better *t.* of you, and *t.*
that accompany salvation. 6:9
that by two immutable *t.*, in which. 18
of the *t.* we have spoken this. 8:1
shadow of heavenly *t.* 5
patterns of *t.* in the heavens be purified, but heavenly *t.* with. 9:23
now faith is the substance of *t.* hoped
for, the evidence of *t.* not. 11:1
t. seen were not made of *t.* which. 3
Noah being warned of God of *t.* 7
Esau concerning *t.* to come. 20
that speaketh better *t.* than. 12:24
and *t.* in the sea are tamed. *Jas* 3:7
minister *t.* which are now reported;
which *t.* the angels. *1 Pet* 1:12
redeemed with corruptible *t.* 18
speak evil of *t.* they. *2 Pet* 2:12
neither the *t.* that are. *1 John* 2:15
Jesus Christ to shew to his servants
t. which must shortly. *Rev* 1:1; 22:6
t. which thou hast seen, the *t.* which
are, and *t.* which shall be. 1:19
a few *t.* against thee, . . . to eat *t.*
sacrificed unto idols. 2:14, 20
strengthen the *t.* which remain. 3:2
I will shew thee *t.* which must. 4:1
who created heaven, earth, sea, and
all *t.* that therein are. 10:6
former *t.* are passed away. 21:4
take his part from *t.* written. 22:19
see **creeping, dedicate, detestable, evil, former, holy, many,
precious, such**

all **things**

herb have I given you *all t.* *Gen* 9:3
blessed Abraham in *all t.* *Gen* 24:1
the servant told Isaac *all t.* that. 66
in *all t.* I have said. *Ex* 23:13
do according to *all t.* which I. 29:35
Aaron and his sons did *all t.* *Lev* 8:36
the Levites over *all t.* *Num* 1:50
and purify *all t.* made of. 31:20
I commanded you *all t.* *Deut* 1:18
as the Lord our God is in *all t.* 4:7
ye shall not do after *all t.* that. 12:8
for the abundance of *all t.* 28:47
thine enemies in want of *all t.* 48
want of *all t.* secretly in siege. 57
we hearkened to Moses in *all t.*
Josh 1:17
the spies told him *all t.* that. 2:23
manner, to confirm *all t.* *Ruth* 4:7
perform *all t.* concerning. *1 Sam* 3:12
if thou hide any of *all t.* he said. 17
shewed David *all* those *t.* 19:7
told David *all* the *t.* *2 Sam* 11:18
to know *all t.* that are in. 14:20
covenant ordered in *all t.* 23:5
he did *all t.* as did the. *1 Ki* 21:26
captains did according to *all t.* that
Jehoiada. *2 Ki* 11:9; *2 Chr* 23:8
Amaziah, according to *all t.* that.
2 Ki 14:3
they have seen *all t.* that are. 20:15
all t. come of thee. *1 Chr* 29:14
Solomon brought *all t.* *2 Chr* 5:1
tithe of *all t.* brought they in. 31:5
the Lord made *all t.* *Neh* 9:6
Acts 14:15; 17:24, 25; *Col* 1:16
Rev 4:11
he beholdeth *all* high *t.* *Job* 41:34
thou hast put *all t.* under his feet.
Ps 8:6; *1 Cor* 15:27; *Eph* 1:22
that performeth *all t.* for me. *Ps* 57:2
precepts concerning *all t.* to. 119:128
precious than *all t.* *Pr* 3:15; 8:11
the Lord hath made *all t.* for. 16:4
great God that formed *all t.* 26:10
seek the Lord understand *all t.* 28:5
all t. are full of labour. *Eccl* 1:8
all t. have I seen in days. 7:15
all t. come alike to all, there. 9:2
this is an evil among *all t.* done. 3
but money answereth *all t.* 10:19
I am the Lord that maketh *all t.*
Isa 44:24; 66:2
for he is the former of *all t.*
Jer 10:16; 51:19
heart is deceitful above *all t.* 17:9
do not even according to *all t.* 42:5
we wanted *all t.* and have. 44:18
I spake *all t.* the Lord. *Ezek* 11:25
all creeping *t.* shall shake. 38:20
the first of *all t.* shall be. 44:30
as iron subdueth *all t.* *Dan* 2:40
I will consume *all t.* *Zeph* 1:2
all t. ye would that men. *Mat* 7:12
all t. are delivered unto me of my
Father. 11:27; *Luke* 10:22
they shall gather *all t.* *Mat* 13:41
Elias shall restore *all t.* 17:11
Mark 9:12
is impossible, but with God *all t.* are.
Mat 19:26; *Mark* 10:27; 14:36
all t. whatsoever ye shall. *Mat* 21:22
behold *all t.* are ready, come unto the
marriage. *Mat* 22:4; *Luke* 14:17
sweareth by it, and by *all t.* thereon.
Mat 23:20
teaching them to observe *all t.* 28:20
he expounded *all t.* to. *Mark* 4:34
told him *all t.*, both what they. 6:30
He hath done *all t.* well. 7:37
all t. are possible to him. 9:23
I have foretold you *all t.* 13:23
praising God for *all t.* *Luke* 2:20
performed *all t.* according to. 39
they wondered at *all t.* which. 9:43
and behold, *all t.* are clean. 11:41
all t. written concerning Son. 18:31
21:22; 24:44; *John* 19:28
all t. were made by him. *John* 1:3
and hath given *all t.* 3:35; 13:3
is come, he will tell us *all t.* 4:25
see a man who told me *all t.* 29
Father sheweth the Son *all t.* 5:20
all t. that John spake of him. 10:41
Holy Ghost, he shall teach you *all t.*,
and bring *all t.* to your. 14:26
all t. I have heard, I have. *John* 15:15
all t. that the Father hath. 16:15
sure that thou knowest *all t.* 30
that *all t.* thou hast given me. 17:7
Jesus therefore knowing *all t.*
18:4; 19:28
Lord, thou knowest *all t.* 21:17
had *all t.* common. *Acts* 2:44; 4:32
of restitution of *all t.* 3:21
him shall ye hear in *all t.* he shall. 22
to hear *all t.* commanded. 10:33
we are witnesses of *all t.* 39
are justified from *all t.* 13:39
heaven, earth, sea, and *all t.* 14:15
you *all t.* how ye ought. 20:35
it shall be told thee of *all t.* 22:10
believing *all t.* which are. 24:14
touching *all* the *t.* whereof. 26:2
and we know that *all t.* *Rom* 8:28
also freely give us *all t.*? 32
him, and to him, are *all t.* 11:36
that he may eat *all t.* 14:2
all t. indeed are pure, but it is. 20
Spirit searcheth *all t.* *1 Cor* 2:10
he that is spiritual judgeth *all t.* 15
no man glory in men, for *all t.* 3:21
are the offscouring of *all t.* 4:13
all t. are lawful unto me, but *all t.* are
. . . *all t.* are lawful. 6:12; 10:23
of whom are *all t.*; and one Lord
Jesus Christ, by whom are *all t.* 8:6
suffer *all t.* 9:12
I am made *all t.* to all men. 22
that striveth is temperate in *all t.* 25
as I please all men in *all t.* 10:33
that ye remember me in *all t.* 11:2
but *all t.* are of God. 12; *2 Cor* 5:18
charity beareth *all t.*, believeth *all t.*,
hopeth *all t.*, endureth *all t.*
1 Cor 13:7
let *all t.* be done unto edifying. 14:26
let *all t.* be done decently. 40
all t. shall be subdued, then shall the
Son be subject . . . *all t.* 15:28
ye be obedient in *all t.* *2 Cor* 2:9
for *all t.* are for your sakes. 4:15
old things are passed away; behold
all t. are. 5:17
in *all t.* approving ourselves. 6:4
nothing, yet possessing *all t.* 10
in *all t.* ye have approved. 7:11
but as we speak *all t.* to you. 14
confidence in you in *all t.* 16
all sufficiency in *all t.* 9:8
made manifest to you in *all t.* 11:6
in *all t.* I kept myself from being. 9
but we do *all t.* for your. 12:19
continueth not in *all t.* *Gal* 3:10
in one *all t.* in Christ. *Eph* 1:10
worketh *all t.* after the counsel. 11
gave him to be head over *all t.* 22
in God, who created *all t.* by. 3:9
up, that he might fill *all t.* 4:10
grow up into him in *all t.* which. 15
all t. that are reproved are. 5:13
giving thanks always for *all t.* 20
shall make known to you *all t.* 6:21
Col 4:9
do *all t.* without murmurings.
Phil 2:14
I count *all t.* but loss for knowledge
of Christ . . . loss of *all t.* 3:8
he is able even to subdue *all t.* to. 21
and in *all t.* I am instructed. 4:12
I can do *all t.* through Christ. 13
is before *all t.*, by him *all t.* *Col* 1:17
in *all t.* he might have the. 18
and by him to reconcile *all t.* 20
obey your parents in *all t.* 3:20
obey in *all t.* your masters. 22
prove *all t.*; hold fast. *1 Thes* 5:21
must be faithful in *all t.* *1 Tim* 3:11
is profitable unto *all t.* 4:8
of God who quickeneth *all t.* 6:13
who giveth us richly *all t.* to enjoy. 17
understanding in *all t.* *2 Tim* 2:7
endure *all t.* for the elect's sake. 10
but watch thou in *all t.*, endure. 4:5
unto pure *all t.* are pure. *Tit* 1:15
all t. shewing thyself a pattern. 2:7
and please them well in *all t.* 9
the doctrine of God in *all t.* 10
appointed heir of *all t.* *Heb* 1:2
upholding *all t.* by the word of. 3

put all t. in subjection under his feet;
but now we see not yet all t. Heb 2:8
are all t. and by whom are all t. 10
in all t. it behoved him to be like. 17
he that built all t. is God. 3:4
all t. are naked and opened. 4:13
make all t. according to the. 8:5
almost all t. are by the law. 9:22
in all t. willing to live. 13:18
above all t. my brethren. Jas 5:12
the end of all t. is at hand. 1 Pet 4:7
above all t. have fervent charity. 8
God in all t. may be glorified. 11
hath given us all t. that. 2 Pet 1:3
all t. continue as they were. 3:4
ye have an unction, and ye know all t. 1 John 2:20
anointing teacheth you all t. 27
heart, and knoweth all t. 3:20
I wish above all t. that. 3 John 2
who bare record of all t. Rev 1:2
thou hast created all t. and. 4:11
I make all t. new. 21:5
he shall inherit all t. 7

these **things**

them of her mother's house these t. Gen 24:28
Jacob said, All these t. are. 42:36
he shall be guilty in one of these t. Lev 5:5, 17
yourselves in any of these t. 18:24
committed all these t. 20:23
not be reformed by these t. 26:23
these t. are the burden of sons of. Num 4:15
of the country shall do these t. 15:13
these t. ye shall do to Lord. 29:39
these t. shall be for a statute. 35:29
when all these t. are. Deut 4:30
all that do these t. are an. 18:12
when all these t. are come. 30:1
as we heard these t., our. Josh 2:11
have shewed us these t. Judg 13:23
had told him these t. 1 Sam 25:37
these t. did these three mighty. 2 Sam 23:17; 1 Chr 11:19
these t. did Benaiah. 2 Sam 23:22; 1 Chr 11:24
these t. did Araunah. 2 Sam 24:23
I have done all these t. 1 Ki 18:36
proclaimed these t. 2 Ki 23:17
in these t. was Solomon. 2 Chr 3:3
Solomon sin by these t.? Neh 13:26
wilt thou speak these t.? Job 8:2
these t. hast thou hid in. 10:13
lo, all these t. worketh God. 33:29
he that doeth these t. Ps 15:5
I remember these t., I pour. 42:4
these t. hast thou done and. 50:21
these six t. doth the Lord. Pr 6:16
these t. also belong to wise. 24:23
for these t. God will bring. Eccl 11:9
O Lord, by these t. men live, and in all these t. is the life. Isa 38:16
who hath created these t.? 40:26
these t. will I do, and not. 42:16
I the Lord do all these t. 45:7
not lay these t. to heart. 47:7
these two t. shall come to thee. 9
save thee from these t. 13
them hath declared these t. 48:14
these two t. are come unto. 51:19
refrain thyself for these t.? 64:12
she had done all these t. Jer 3:7
procured these t. unto thee. 4:18
shall I not visit for these t.? 5:9; 29; 9:9
have turned away these t. 5:25
for in these t. do I delight. 9:24
come these t. on me? 13:22
thou hast made all these t. 14:22
thy sins I have done these t. 30:15
for these t. I weep, mine. Lam 1:16
our heart is faint; for these t. 5:17
seeing thou doest all these t. Ezek 16:30; 17:18
hast fretted me in all these t. 16:43
know ye not what these t.? 17:12
like to any one of these t. 18:10
I will do these t. unto thee. 23:30
thou not tell what these t.? 24:19
none that holdeth with me in these t. Dan 10:21
all these t. shall be finished. Dan 12:7
what shall be the end of these t.? 8
shall understand these t. Hos 14:9
these are the t. which ye shall do. Zech 8:16
for all these are t. that I hate. 17
he thought on these t. Mat 1:20
when Herod heard these t. 2:3
these t. do the Gentiles seek . . . all these t. 6:32; Luke 12:30
all these t. shall be added unto you. Mat 6:33; Luke 12:31
hast hid these t. from the wise. Mat 11:25; Luke 10:21
ye understood these t.? Mat 13:51
hath this man these t.? 56; Mark 6:2
these are the t. which defile a man. Mat 15:20
all these t. have I kept from. 19:20
by what authority doest thou these t.? 21:23; Mark 11:28; Luke 20:2
authority I do these t. Mat 21:24, 27; Mark 11:29, 33; Luke 20:8
all these t. shall come on. Mat 23:36
See ye not all these t.? 24:2
when shall these t. be? 3; Mark 13:4; Luke 21:7
all these t. must come to pass. Mat 24:6; Luke 21:9, 28
ye shall see all these t. Mat 24:33; Mark 13:29; Luke 21:31
till all these t. be fulfilled. Mat 24:34; Mark 13:30
till the day that these t. Luke 1:20
but Mary kept all these t. and. 2:19
not answer him to these t. 14:6
asked what these t. meant. 15:26
understood none of these t. 18:34
to escape all these t. that. 21:36
do these t. in a green tree. 23:31
is third day since these t. 24:21
Christ to have suffered these t.? 26
and ye are witnesses of these t. 48
Take these t. hence. John 2:16
seeing that thou doest these t. 18
to him, How can these t. be? 3:9
Israel, and knowest not these t.? 10
he had done these t. on the. 5:16
if thou do these t. shew thyself. 7:4
these t. understood not his disciples, they . . . these t. were. 12:16
these t. said Esaias, when he. 41
if ye know these t. happy. 13:17
all these t. will they do. 15:21; 16:3
these t. therefore the soldiers. 19:24
these t. were done, that the. 36
his witnesses of these t. Acts 5:32
are these t. so? 7:1
my hand made all these t.? 50
when they heard these t. they. 54
pray for me, that none of these t. 8:24
sirs, why do ye these t.? 14:15
Lord, who doeth all these t. 15:17
know what these t. mean. 17:20
seeing these t. cannot be. 19:36
none of these t. move me. 20:24
saying that these t. were so. 24:9
and there be judged of these t. 25:9
thee a witness of these t. 26:16
the king knoweth of these t. 26
then say to these t.? Rom 8:31
for he that in these t. serveth. 14:18
say I these t. as a man. 1 Cor 9:8
I used none of these t. nor have. 15
these t. were our examples. 10:6
sufficient for these t.? 2 Cor 2:16
because of these t. cometh. Eph 5:6
praise, think on these t. Phil 4:8
and above all these t. put. Col 3:14
in remembrance of these t. 1 Tim 4:6
these t. command. 11
meditate on these t. 15
these t. give in charge. 5:7
observe these t. 21
these t. exhort. 6:2; Tit 2:15
flee these t. 1 Tim 6:11
of these t. put them. 2 Tim 2:14
these t. I will that thou affirm constantly. These t. are good. Tit 3:8
for he of whom these t. are spoken. Heb 7:13
brethren, these t. ought not. Jas 3:10
for if these t. be in you. 2 Pet 1:8
he that lacketh these t. is. 2 Pet 1:9
for if ye do these t. ye shall. 10
in remembrance of these t. 12
to have these t. always in. 15
seeing all these t. shall be. 3:11
speaking in them of these t. 16
seeing ye know these t. before. 17
angel who shewed me these t. Rev 22:8
to testify to you these t. in the. 16
he which testifieth these t. 20

those **things**

eat those t. wherewith. Ex 29:33
in those t. which they. Lev 22:2
those t. which are revealed. Deut 29:29
did secretly those t. 2 Ki 17:9
will observe those t. Ps 107:43
for all those t. hath mine hand made, and all those t. have. Isa 66:2
approach to those t. Ezek 42:14
those t. which ye see, and hear those t. Mat 13:17; Luke 10:24
offer those t. which Moses commanded. Mark 1:44
a performance of those t. Luke 1:45
wondered at those t. told them. 2:18
then whose shall those t. be, which thou hast provided? 12:20
I do always those t. John 8:29
but those t. he hath so fulfilled. Acts 3:18
gave heed to those t. which. 8:6
spake against those t. which. 13:45
searched whether those t. 17:11
cared for none of those t. 18:17
of those t. in which I will appear. 26:16
those t. spoken by Paul. 27:11
to do those t. which are. Rom 1:28
calleth those t. which be not. 4:17
in those t. whereof ye are now ashamed, for end of those t. 6:21
the man that doeth those t. 10:5
I may glory in those t. which. 15:17
to speak of any of those t. 18
eating of those t. 1 Cor 8:4, 10
besides those t. which. 2 Cor 11:28
even to speak of those t. Eph 5:12
forgetting those t. which are behind, and reaching to those t. Phil 3:13
those t. which ye have learned. 4:9
intruding into those t. he. Col 2:18
seek those t. which are above. 3:1
for a testimony of those t. Heb 3:5
the removing of those t. which are shaken, that those t. which. 12:27
ye give not those t. which. Jas 2:16
do those t. that are pleasing in his. 1 John 3:22
we lose not those t. we. 2 John 8
but speak evil of those t. Jude 10
they that keep those t. Rev 1:3
fear none of those t. which. 2:10
those t. the seven thunders. 10:4
were judged out of those t. 20:12

unclean **things**

and they shall eat unclean t. Hos 9:3

what **things**

tell thy son what t. I have. Ex 10:2
Father knoweth what t. ye. Mat 6:8
should tell no man what t. Mark 9:9
began to tell them what t. 10:32
what t. soever ye desire. 11:24
go, tell John what t. ye. Luke 7:22
what t. they said to him. 24:19
and they told what t. were done. 35
what t. soever he doeth. John 5:19
they understood not what t. 10:6
some told them what t. Jesus. 11:46
what t. God wrought. Acts 21:19
what t. were gain to me. Phil 3:7

think

but t. on me, when it be. Gen 40:14
let them marry to whom they t. best. Num 36:6
to t. that all the king's. 2 Sam 13:33
ye t. to withstand kingdom of Lord. 2 Chr 13:8
t. on me, my God, for. Neh 5:19
thou and the Jews t. to rebel. 6:6
my God, t. thou on Tobiah and. 14
t. not thou shalt escape. Esth 4:13

why then should I *t.* upon? *Job* 31:1
t. the deep to be hoary. 41:32
wise man *t.* to know it. *Eccl* 8:17
nor doth his heart *t.* so. *Isa* 10:7
t. to cause my people. *Jer* 23:27
I know the thoughts that I *t.* 29:11
and thou shalt *t.* an evil. *Ezek* 38:10
he shall *t.* to change times. *Dan* 7:25
if so be that God will *t.* *Jonah* 1:6
if ye *t.* good, give me. *Zech* 11:12
and *t.* not to say within. *Mat* 3:9
t. not that I am come to destroy. 5:17
t. they shall be heard for much. 6:7
why *t.* ye evil in your hearts? 9:4
t. not I am come to send. 10:34
how *t.* ye? if a man have. 18:12
what *t.* ye? a certain man had. 21:28
what *t.* ye of Christ? 22:42; 26:66
Mark 14:64
in such an hour as ye *t.* not.
Mat 24:44; *Luke* 12:40
t. ye that they were sinners above.
Luke 13:4
them ye *t.* ye have eternal. *John* 5:39
do not *t.* I will accuse you to. 45
what *t.* ye, that he will not? 11:56
killeth you will *t.* that he doeth. 16:2
whom *t.* ye that I am? *Acts* 13:25
not to *t.* that the Godhead. 17:29
t. myself happy, king Agrippa. 26:2
not to *t.* of himself more highly than
he ought to *t.*, but to *t.* *Rom* 12:3
in us not to *t.* of men. *1 Cor* 4:6
I *t.* that God hath set forth us. 9
if any man *t.* that he behaveth. 7:36
I *t.* also that I have the Spirit. 40
if any man *t.* that he knoweth. 8:2
of body, which we *t.* to be less. 12:23
if any man *t.* himself to be a. 14:37
ourselves to *t.* any thing. *2 Cor* 3:5
I *t.* to be bold against some, which *t.*
of us as if we walked. 10:2
that he is Christ, let him *t.* 7, 11
I say again, Let no man *t.* me. 11:16
lest any *t.* of me above what. 12:6
if a man *t.* himself to be. *Gal* 6:3
above all that we ask or *t.* *Eph* 3:20
if there be any praise, *t.* *Phil* 4:8
let not that man *t.* he shall. *Jas* 1:7
do ye *t.* that the scripture? 4:5
wherein they *t.* strange. *1 Pet* 4:4
t. it not strange concerning the. 12
I *t.* it meet as long as I am in this.
2 Pet 1:13

thinkest

t. thou that David doth honour thy?
2 Sam 10:3; *1 Chr* 19:3
t. thou this right, that? *Job* 35:2
Jesus said, What *t.* thou?
Mat 17:25; 22:17
t. thou that I cannot pray? 26:53
which *t.* thou was neighbour to?
Luke 10:36
hear of thee what thou *t.* *Acts* 28:22
t. thou this, O man, that? *Rom* 2:3

thinketh

me *t.* the running of the. *2 Sam* 18:27
yet the Lord *t.* on me. *Ps* 40:17
for as he *t.* in his heart. *Pr* 23:7
let him that *t.* he standeth, take heed.
1 Cor 10:12
seeketh not her own, *t.* no evil. 13:5
man *t.* he hath whereof. *Phil* 3:4

thinking

t. to have brought good. *2 Sam* 4:10
t., David cannot come in hither. 5:6

third

he the second and the *t.* *Gen* 32:19
saw Ephraim's children of *t.* 50:23
to *t.* and fourth generation. *Ex* 20:5
34:7; *Num* 14:18; *Deut* 5:9
and the *t.* row a ligure, an agate.
Ex 28:19; 39:12
Ephraim in the *t.* rank. *Num* 2:24
Edomite shall enter in *t.* *Deut* 23:8
the *t.* lot came up for. *Josh* 19:10
a captain of the *t.* fifty. *2 Ki* 1:13
the *t.* lot came forth to. *1 Chr* 24:8
t. lot came forth for Zaccur. 25:10
t. captain of the host for the *t.* 27:5
shall Israel be the *t.* with. *Isa* 19:24
t. was the face of a lion. *Ezek* 10:14
and another *t.* kingdom. *Dan* 2:39
t. ruler in kingdom. *Dan* 5:7; 16:29
t. chariot white horses. *Zech* 6:3
out about the *t.* hour. *Mat* 20:3
likewise the second also, and the *t.*
22:26; *Mark* 12:21; *Luke* 20:31
it was *t.* hour, and they. *Mark* 15:25
come in the *t.* watch. *Luke* 12:38
he sent a *t.* and they. 20:12
it is but the *t.* hour of the. *Acts* 2:15
fell down from the *t.* loft. 20:9
be ready at the *t.* hour of. 23:23
up to the *t.* heaven. *2 Cor* 12:2
the *t.* beast had a face as a. *Rev* 4:7
the *t.* seal, I heard the *t.* beast. 6:5
the *t.* angel sounded, there fell. 8:10
and behold, the *t.* woe cometh. 11:14
and the *t.* angel followed them. 14:9
the *t.* angel poured out his vial. 16:4
the *t.* foundation was a. 21:19
see **day, month, part**

third *time*

Samuel the *t. time.* *1 Sam* 3:8
messengers again the *t. time.* 19:21
do it the *t. time.* And they did it
the *t. time.* *1 Ki* 18:34
be doubled the *t. time.* *Ezek* 21:14
and he prayed the *t. time.*
Mat 26:44; *Mark* 14:41
t. time Jesus shewed. *John* 21:14
t. time, Lovest thou me? Peter was
grieved . . . to him *t. time.* 17
the *t. time* I am ready to come.
2 Cor 12:14; 13:1

third *year*

t. year, which is the year. *Deut* 16:12
in *t. year* of Asa, did Baasha slay.
1 Ki 15:28, 33
Lord came to Elijah in *t. year.* 18:1
in *t. year,* Jehoshaphat came to. 22:2
in the *t. year* of Hoshea. *2 Ki* 18:1
in the *t. year* sow ye and reap.
19:29; *Isa* 37:30
in *t. year* of Jehoshaphat's reign.
2 Chr 17:7
paid the second and *t. year.* 27:5
t. year of the reign of Ahasuerus.
Esth 1:3
t. year of the reign of Jehoiakim.
Dan 1:1
t. year of the reign of Belshazzar. 8:1
t. year of Cyrus king of Persia. 10:1

thirdly

t. teachers, after that. *1 Cor* 12:28

thirst, *substantive*

our children with *t.* *Ex* 17:3
serve thine enemies in *t.* *Deut* 28:48
to add drunkenness to *t.* 29:19*
shall die for *t.* and fall. *Judg* 15:18
you to die by *t.* *2 Chr* 32:11
water for their *t.* *Neh* 9:15, 20
winepresses and suffer *t.* *Job* 24:11
in my *t.* they gave me. *Ps* 69:21
wild asses quench their *t.* 104:11
multitude dried up with *t.* *Isa* 5:13
their tongue faileth for *t.* 41:17
fish stinketh, and dieth for *t.* 50:2
thy throat from *t.* *Jer* 2:25
from thy glory, and sit in *t.* 48:18
roof of his mouth for *t.* *Lam* 4:4
naked, and slay her with *t.* *Hos* 2:3
not a *t.* for water, but of. *Amos* 8:11
young men shall faint for *t.* 13
in hunger and *t.* *2 Cor* 11:27

thirst, *verb*

they shall not hunger nor *t.* *Isa* 49:10
which hunger and *t.* after. *Mat* 5:6
this water, shall *t.* again. *John* 4:13
drinketh, shall never *t.* 14; 6:35
this water, that I *t.* not. 15
if any man *t.* let him come unto. 7:37
after this Jesus saith, I *t.* 19:28
if thine enemy *t.* give. *Rom* 12:20
this present hour we *t.* *1 Cor* 4:11
and they shall not *t.* *Rev* 7:16

thirsted

people *t.* there for water. *Ex* 17:3
they *t.* not when he led. *Isa* 48:21

thirsteth

my soul *t.* for God. *Ps* 42:2; 63:1*
143:6*
ho, every one that *t.*, come. *Isa* 55:1

thirsty

little water, for I am *t.* *Judg* 4:19
the people is *t.* in the. *2 Sam* 17:29
my flesh longeth in a *t.* land.
Ps 63:1; 143:6
hungry and *t.*, their soul. 107:5
if thine enemy be *t.* give. *Pr* 25:21
as cold water to a *t.* soul, so is. 25
water to him that was *t.* *Isa* 21:14
it shall be as when a *t.* man. 29:8
the drink of the *t.* to fail. 32:6
t. land shall become springs. 35:7
pour water upon him that is *t.* 44:3
shall drink, but ye shall be *t.* 65:13
in a dry and *t.* ground. *Ezek* 19:13
for I was *t.* and ye gave. *Mat* 25:35
when saw we thee *t.* and gave? 37
for I was *t.* and ye gave me no. 42

thirteen

Ishmael his son was *t.* *Gen* 17:25
ye shall offer *t.* young bullocks.
Num 29:13, 14
his own house *t.* years. *1 Ki* 7:1
brethren of Hosah *t.* *1 Chr* 26:11
of the gate *t.* cubits. *Ezek* 40:11

thirteenth

t. year they rebelled. *Gen* 14:4
the *t.* lot came forth. *1 Chr* 24:13
t. lot came forth to Shubael. 25:20
in the *t.* year of the reign. *Jer* 1:2
from the *t.* year of Josiah the. 25:3
see **day**

thirtieth

Shallum to reign in nine and *t.* year.
2 Ki 15:13
in the nine and *t.* year of king. 17
seven and *t.* year of the captivity of.
25:27; *Jer* 52:31
five and *t.* year of Asa. *2 Chr* 15:19
in the six and *t.* year of the. 16:1
the two and *t.* year of Artaxerxes.
Neh 5:14; 13:6

thirty

height of the ark was *t.* *Gen* 6:15
Salah lived *t.* years, and. 11:14
Peleg lived *t.* years, and. 18
Serug lived *t.* years, and. 22
shall be *t.* found, he said, I will not
do it if I find *t.* there. 18:30
t. milch camels with their. 32:15
Joseph was *t.* years old. 41:46
their master *t.* shekels. *Ex* 21:32
the length of one curtain *t.* cubits.
26:8; 36:15
thy estimation shall be *t.* *Lev* 27:4
from *t.* years old and upwards.
Num 4:3, 23, 30, 35, 39, 43, 47
1 Chr 23:3
Jair had *t.* sons, and they had *t.*
Judg 10:4
t. sons and *t.* daughters he sent
abroad, took in *t.* daughters. 12:9
forty sons and *t.* nephews. 14
they brought *t.* companions. 14:11
give you *t.* sheets, *t.* change. 12
ye shall give *t.* sheets, *t.* change. 13
Samson slew *t.* men, and took. 19
to smite about *t.* men of. 20:31, 39
them, about *t.* persons. *1 Sam* 9:22
David was *t.* years old. *2 Sam* 5:4
and three of the *t.* chief. 23:13
Benaiah was more honourable than
the *t.* 23; *1 Chr* 11:15, 25; 27:6
Asahel, brother of Joab, was one of
the *t.* *2 Sam* 23:24
provision for one day was *t.*
1 Ki 4:22
house of the Lord was *t.* cubits. 6:2
house of the forest was *t.* cubits. 7:2
of the porch was *t.* cubits. 6
a line of *t.* cubits did compass. 23
to Hezekiah *t.* talents. *2 Ki* 18:14
captain, and *t.* with him. *1 Chr* 11:42
of them was *t.* chargers. *Ezra* 1:9
t. basons of gold, silver basons. 10
take from hence *t.* men. *Jer* 38:10
t. chambers were on. *Ezek* 40:17
and the side chambers were *t.* 41:6
there were courts joined of *t.* 46:22
for my price *t.* pieces. *Zech* 11:12
and I took the *t.* pieces of silver. 13
Mat 27:9

brought some *t.* fold. *Mat* 13:8, 23
Mark 4:8, 20
with him for *t.* pieces. *Mat* 26:15
again the *t.* pieces of silver. 27:3
Jesus began to be about *t. Luke* 3:23
about 25 or *t.* furlongs. *John* 6:19
see **days, thousand**

thirty *one*

the kings Joshua subdued *t.* and *one.* *Josh* 12:24
in the *t.* and *first* year. *1 Ki* 16:23
Josiah eight years old, and reigned *t.* and *one.* *2 Ki* 22:1; *2 Chr* 34:1

thirty *two*

Reu lived *t. two* years. *Gen* 11:20
Lord's tribute was *t. two* persons. *Num* 31:40
t. two kings were with Ben-hadad. *1 Ki* 20:1, 16
king commanded his *t. two* captains. 22:31
Jehoram was *t. two* years. *2 Ki* 8:17
2 Chr 21:5, 20

thirty *three*

all the souls of sons and daughters *t. three.* *Gen* 46:15
purifying *t. three* days. *Lev* 12:4
in Jerusalem *t.* and *three. 2 Sam* 5:5
1 Ki 2:11; *1 Chr* 3:4; 29:27

thirty *four*

Eber lived *t. four* years. *Gen* 11:16

thirty *five*

lived *five* and *t.* years. *Gen* 11:12
Jehoshaphat was *t. five* years old. *1 Ki* 22:42; *2 Chr* 20:31
made two pillars *t. five.* *2 Chr* 3:15

thirty *six*

Ai smote *t. six* men. *Josh* 7:5

thirty *seven*

Hittite, *t. seven* in all. *2 Sam* 23:39
in the *t.* and *seventh.* *2 Ki* 13:10

thirty *eight*

brook Zered, *t. eight* years. *Deut* 2:14
in the *t.* and *eighth* year of Asa. *1 Ki* 16:29
the *t.* and *eighth* year of Azariah. *2 Ki* 15:8
an infirmity *t. eight* years. *John* 5:5

thirty *nine*

Asa in the *t.* and *ninth. 2 Chr* 16:12

this

t. same shall comfort us. *Gen* 5:29
T. shall not be thine heir. 15:4
and I will speak but *t.* once. 18:32
they said, *T.* one fellow came. 19:9
we will give thee *t.* also for. 29:27
but in *t.* will we consent. 34:15
sent the coat, and said, *T.* 37:32
bound a thread, saying, *T.* 38:28
is not *t.* it in which my lord? 44:5
if ye take *t.* from me, and mischief. 29
t. shall be a token that I. *Ex* 3:12
in *t.* thou shalt know that I. 7:17
neither did he set his heart to *t.* 23
t. they shall give, each half. 30:13
t. shall be thine of the most holy. *Num* 18:9; *Deut* 18:3
live when God doth *t.*? *Num* 24:23
O that they were wise, that they understood *t.* *Deut* 32:29
is not *t.* laid up in store with me? 34
t. shall go with thee, *t.* *Judg* 7:4
come up *t.* once, for he hath. 16:18
the Lord chosen *t.* *1 Sam* 16:8, 9
Let not Jonathan know *t.* 20:3
that *t.* be no grief unto thee. 25:31
t. was a small thing in. *2 Sam* 7:19
Shimei be put to death for *t.*? 19:21
is not *t.* the blood of the men? 23:17
to judge *t.* thy so great. *1 Ki* 3:9
and *t.* was the cause that he. 11:27
I will for *t.* afflict the seed of. 39
by *t.* I know that thou art a. 17:24
should I set *t.* before an. *2 Ki* 4:43
glory of *t.* and tarry at home. 14:10
commandment of Lord came *t.* 24:3
because *t.* was in thine heart, not. *2 Chr* 1:11
able to give thee more than *t.* 25:9
his pleasure concerning *t. Ezra* 5:17
be made a dunghill for *t.* *Ezra* 6:11
put such a thing as *t.* in the. 7:27
besought our God for *t.* 8:23
given us such deliverance as *t.* 9:13
stand before thee because of *t.* 15
remember me concerning *t.* *Neh* 13:14, 22
to kingdom for such a time as *t.* *Esth* 4:14
lo, *t.* we have searched it. *Job* 5:27
of the Lord hath wrought *t.* 12:9
men shall be astonied at *t.* 17:8
for *t.* I make haste. 20:2
knowest thou not *t.* of old? 4
hear and let *t.* be your. 21:2
in *t.* thou art not just, I will. 33:12
thinkest thou *t.* to be right? 35:2
t. shall be the portion. *Ps* 11:6
though war rise, in *t.* will I. 27:3
for *t.* shall every one that is. 32:6
t. thou hast seen, keep not. 35:22
by *t.* I know that thou. 41:11
shall not God search *t.* out? 44:21
for *t.* God is our God for ever. 48:14
t. their way is their folly. 49:13
now consider *t.* ye that forget. 50:22
shall turn back, *t.* I know for. 56:9
twice have I heard *t.* that. 62:11
t. also shall please the Lord. 69:31
the humble shall see *t.* and be. 32
when I thought to know *t.* it. 73:16
the Lord heard *t.* and was. 78:21, 59
for *t.* was a statute for Israel. 81:4
t. he ordained in Joseph for a. 5
neither doth a fool understand *t.* 92:6
let *t.* be the reward of mine. 109:20
t. I had, because I kept. 119:56
t. honour have all his saints. 149:9
for *t.* a man is envied of. *Eccl* 4:4
t. hath more rest than the other. 6:5
enquire wisely concerning *t.* 7:10
thou shouldest take hold of *t.*; yea also from *t.* withdraw not. 18
t. have I found. 27
lo, *t.* only have I found. 29
whether shall prosper, either *t.* 11:6
who hath required *t.*? *Isa* 1:12
and he said, Lo *t.* hath touched. 6:7
Lord of hosts will perform *t.* 9:7
surely *t.* iniquity shall not be. 22:14
by *t.* shall the iniquity of Jacob. 27:9
t. also cometh forth from. 28:29
Read *t.* I pray thee. 29:11, 12
have I cried concerning *t.* 30:7
them can declare *t.*? 43:9; 45:21
remember *t.* 46:8
hear now *t.* 47:8; 48:1, 16; 51:21
declare ye, tell *t.* 48:20
t. shall ye have of mine hand. 50:11
blessed is the man that doeth *t.* 56:2
wilt thou call *t.* a fast? 58:5
is not *t.* the fast that I have? 6
when ye see *t.* your hearts. 66:14
O ye heavens, at *t.* *Jer* 2:12
procured *t.* unto thyself? 17
for *t.* gird you with sackcloth. 4:8
for *t.* shall the earth mourn. 28
shall I pardon thee for *t.*? 5:7
shall not my soul be avenged on such a nation as *t.*? 9, 29; 9:9
that glorieth, glory in *t.* 9:24
I will *t.* once cause them to. 16:21
was not *t.* to know me? saith. 22:16
t. hath been thy manner from thy. 21
long shall *t.* be in the heart? 23:26
t. shall be the covenant that I. 31:33
I knew that *t.* was the word. 32:8
t. I call to mind, therefore I hope. *Lam* 3:21
for *t.* our heart is faint; our. 5:17
he said, Hast thou seen *t.*? *Ezek* 8:15, 17; 47:6
t. was the iniquity of thy. 16:49
in *t.* your fathers have. 20:27
saith the Lord, *t.* shall not be. 21:26
her sister Aholibah saw *t.* 23:11
t. cometh, ye shall know. 24:24
33:33
I will yet for *t.* be enquired. 36:37
t. gate shall be shut, no man. 44:2
not find occasion against *t.* Daniel. *Dan* 6:5, 28
t. shall be their derision. *Hos* 7:16
t. liketh you, O children. *Amos* 4:5
the Lord repented for *t.* *Amos* 7:3, 6
the land tremble for *t.*? 8:8
saith the Lord that doeth *t.* 9:12
was not *t.* my saying? *Jonah* 4:2
t. shall they have for their pride. *Zeph* 2:10
t. shall come to pass if ye will obey Lord. *Zech* 6:15
t. shall be the plague. 14:12, 15
t. shall be the punishment of. 19
t. hath been by your means. *Mal* 1:9
should I accept *t.* of your hands? 13
will cut off the man that doeth *t.* 2:12
known what *t.* meaneth. *Mat* 12:7
is not *t.* the carpenter's son? 13:55
Mark 6:3; *Luke* 4:22; *John* 6:42
saying, Lord, *t.* shall not. *Mat* 16:22
know *t.* that if the good man of the house. 24:43; *Luke* 12:39
shall also *t.* that *t.* woman. *Mat* 26:13
saying, Truly *t.* was the Son. 27:54
if *t.* come to the governor's. 28:14
the second is like, namely, *t.* *Mark* 12:31
I know *t.*? for I am old. *Luke* 1:18
how shall *t.* be, seeing I know? 34
manner of child shall *t.* be? 66
added yet *t.* above all, that. 3:20
have ye not read so much as *t.*? 6:3
be sure of *t.* 10:11
in *t.* rejoice not. 20
t. my son was dead and is. 15:24
take *t.* and divide it among. 22:17
t. must yet be accomplished. 37
certainly *t.* was a righteous. 23:47
saying, *T.* was he of. *John* 1:15
remembered he had said *t.* 2:22
on *t.* came his disciples. 4:27
is not *t.* the Christ? 29
marvel not at *t.* 5:28
he said *t.* to prove him, for. 6:6
is not *t.* he whom they seek? 7:25
t. did not Abraham. 8:40
believest thou *t.*? 11:26
t. spake he not of himself. 51
t. he said, not that he cared. 12:6
for what intent he spake *t.* 13:28
by *t.* shall all men know ye are. 35
love hath no man than *t.* 15:13
by *t.* we believe that thou. 16:30
t. Jesus shall so come in. *Acts* 1:11
what meaneth *t.*? 2:12
he seeing *t.* before. 31
t. Jesus hath God raised up. 32
he hath shed forth *t.* which ye. 33
when they heard *t.* they were. 37
Israel, why marvel ye at *t.*? 3:12
whereunto *t.* would grow. 5:24
that *t.* Jesus of Nazareth shall destroy *t.* place. 6:14
t. Moses whom they refused. 7:35
as for *t.* Moses, we wot not. 40
repent therefore of *t.* thy. 8:22
scripture which he read was *t.* 32
is not *t.* he that destroyed? 9:21
when the Gentiles heard *t.* 13:48
to *t.* agree the words of the. 15:15
t. did she many days, but. 16:18
when they heard *t.* they were. 19:5
but *t.* I confess to thee, that. 24:14
thinkest thou *t.* O man. *Rom* 2:3
knowing *t.* that our old man is. 6:6
not only *t.* but when Rebecca. 9:10
therefore I have performed *t.* 15:28
t. I say, every one saith. *1 Cor* 1:12
to them that examine me is *t.* 9:3
in *t.* that I declare to you. 11:17
shall I praise you in *t.*? 22
not knowledge, I speak *t.* to. 15:34
in *t.* we groan, earnestly. *2 Cor* 5:2
I speak not *t.* to condemn you. 7:3
t. they did, not as we hoped. 8:5
of himself think *t.* again. 10:7, 11
and *t.* also we wish, even your. 13:9
t. would I learn of you. *Gal* 3:2
fulfilled in one word, even in *t.* 5:14
t. I say therefore, and. *Eph* 4:17
for *t.* ye know, that no whoremonger. 5:5
t. I pray, that your love. *Phil* 1:9
I know that *t.* shall turn to my. 19
when with you, *t.* we. *2 Thes* 3:10
knowing *t.* *1 Tim* 1:9; *Jas* 1:3
2 Pet 1:20; 3:3

doing *t.* thou shalt both. *1 Tim* 4:16
but *t.* with an oath. *Heb* 7:21
t. did he once. 27
t. the children of God. *1 John* 3:10
in *t.* was manifested the love. 4:9
by *t.* we know that we love. 5:2
remembrance, though ye once knew *t.* *Jude* 5
t. thou hast, that thou hatest. *Rev* 2:6
see **after, all, book, cause, child, city, day, do, doctrine, done, evil, house, land, law, life, man, month, people, thing, word, world**

is this

the woman, What *is t.* that thou? *Gen* 3:13; 12:18; 26:10; 29:25
what man *is t.* that walketh in the? 24:65
what *is t.* that God hath? 42:28
is t. your younger brother? 43:29
what deed *is t.* that ye have? 44:15
saying, What *is t.*? *Ex* 13:14
Judg 18:24
is t. that thou hast brought? *Ex* 17:3
what trespass *is t.* ye? *Josh* 22:16
what *is t.* thou hast done? *Judg* 15:11; *2 Sam* 12:21
what wickedness *is t.*? *Judg* 20:12
what *is t.* come to the son of Kish? *1 Sam* 10:11
Saul said, *Is t.* thy voice? 24:16
is t. the manner of man? *2 Sam* 7:19
is t. thy kindness to thy friend? 16:17
what confidence *is t.*? *2 Ki* 18:19
is t. a work of one day. *Ezra* 10:13
who *is t.* that darkeneth? *Job* 38:2
who *is t.* cometh out of? *S of S* 3:6
who *is t.* that cometh up from? 8:5
is t. your joyous city? *Isa* 23:7
who *is t.* that cometh from? 63:1
who *is t.* that engaged? *Jer* 30:21
who *is t.* that cometh up as? 46:7
is t. of thy whoredoms a small matter? *Ezek* 16:20
is not *t.* a brand plucked? *Zech* 3:2
see what *is t.* that goeth forth. 5:5
manner of man *is t.* that the winds? *Mat* 8:27; *Mark* 4:41; *Luke* 8:25
said, *Is* not *t.* the son? *Mat* 12:23
who *is t.*? 21:10
what thing *is t.*? *Mark* 1:27
whence *is t.* to me, that? *Luke* 1:43
a word *is t.*! with authority he. 4:36
who *is t.* which speaketh? 5:21
who *is t.* that forgiveth sins? 7:49
but who *is t.* of whom I hear? 9:9
he said, What *is t.* then that? 20:17
of saying *is t.* he said? *John* 7:36
is t. your son, who ye say was? 9:19
what *is t.* that he saith? 16:17, 18
for our rejoicing *is t.* *2 Cor* 1:12
unto me *is t.* grace given, that I should preach. *Eph* 3:8
religion and undefiled *is t.* *Jas* 1:27

this *is*

Adam said, *T. is* now bone. *Gen* 2:23
t. is thy kindness which thou. 20:13
T. is none other but the house of God, and *t. is* the gate of. 28:17
Jacob saw them, he said, *T. is.* 32:2
Can we find such a one as *t. is*? 41:38
for *t. is* the firstborn. 48:18
t. is my name for ever. *Ex* 3:15
the magicians said, *T. is* the. 8:19
t. is that which the Lord. 16:23
t. is that the Lord spake. *Lev* 10:3
t. is it that belongeth. *Num* 8:24
and *t. is* thine, the heave. 18:11
such wickedness as *t. is.* *Deut* 13:11
and *t. is* the manner of the. 15:2
anoint him, for *t. is* he. *1 Sam* 16:12
t. is done of thee. *1 Ki* 11:11
t. is the sign which the Lord. 13:3
t. is but a light thing in. *2 Ki* 3:18
t. is not the way, neither is. 6:19
t. is the woman, and *t. is* her. 8:5
so that they shall not say, *T. is.* 9:37
t. is that king Ahaz. *2 Chr* 28:22
t. is nothing but sorrow. *Neh* 2:2
t. is thy God that brought thee. 9:18
behold, *t. is* the joy of. *Job* 8:19
I know that *t. is* with thee. *Job* 10:13
t. is the place of him that. 18:21
t. is the portion of a wicked man. 20:29; 27:13
t. is the generation of. *Ps* 24:6
t. is the hill God desireth to. 68:16
t. is my infirmity, but I will. 77:10
know that *t. is* thy hand. 109:27
t. is the Lord's. 118:23; *Mat* 21:42
t. is my comfort in mine. *Ps* 119:50
t. is my rest for ever, here. 132:14
may be said, See, *t. is* new. *Eccl* 1:10
to rejoice in labour, *t. is* the. 5:19
t. is the whole duty of man. 12:13
t. is my beloved, and *t. is.* *S of S* 5:16
sing to the Lord; *t. is* known. *Isa* 12:5
lo, *t. is* our God, we have. 25:9
t. is all the fruit, to take away. 27:9
t. is the rest, and *t. is* the. 28:12
saying, *T. is* the way, walk. 30:21
for *t. is* as the waters of Noah. 54:9
t. is the heritage of the servants. 17
as for me, *t. is* my covenant. 59:21
t. is thy wickedness, it. *Jer* 4:18
t. is a nation that obeyeth not. 7:28
t. is a grief. 10:19
t. is thy lot. 13:25
t. is the name whereby . . . The Lord our Righteousness. 23:6; 33:16
t. is Zion, whom no man. 30:17
t. is Jerusalem, I set it. *Ezek* 5:5
t. is a lamentation, and shall. 19:14
t. is Pharaoh and all his. 31:18
t. is the writing that. *Dan* 5:25
arise, depart, for *t. is* not. *Mi* 2:10
t. is the rejoicing city. *Zeph* 2:15
t. is the curse that. *Zech* 5:3
he said, *T. is* an ephah that. 6
t. is wickedness. 8
for *t. is* he that was spoken. *Mat* 3:3
t. is my beloved Son. 17; 17:5
Mark 9:7; *Luke* 9:35
for *t. is* the law and. *Mat* 7:12
t. is he of whom it is written. 10:11
Luke 7:27
t. is Elias which was for. *Mat* 11:14
t. is he which received seed. 13:19
Jesus said, With men *t. is.* 19:26
t. is the heir. 21:38; *Mark* 12:7
Luke 20:14
t. is the first commandment. *Mat* 22:38; *Mark* 12:30
Take, eat, *t. is* my body. *Mat* 26:26
t. is my blood. 28; *Mark* 14:22, 24
Luke 22:19, 20; *1 Cor* 11:24, 25
t. is one of them, and. *Mark* 14:69
manner of woman *t. is.* *Luke* 7:39
t. is your hour and the power. 22:53
t. is the record of John. *John* 1:19
t. is he of whom I said, After. 30
I bare record that *t. is* the Son. 34
t. is the condemnation, that. 3:19
that *t. is* indeed the Christ. 4:42
7:26, 41
t. is the work of God, that. 6:29
t. is the Father's will. 39, 40
t. is the bread which cometh. 50
t. is that bread which came. 58
t. is an hard saying, who can? 60
some said, *T. is* he. 9:9
we know *t. is* our son. 20
t. is my commandment, that. 15:12
t. is life eternal, that they. 17:3
t. is that which was spoken by the prophet Joel. *Acts* 2:16
t. is that Moses which said. 7:37
t. is he that was in the church. 38
Saul increased, proving that *t. is* very Christ. 9:22
t. is my covenant. *Rom* 11:27
Heb 8:10; 10:16
t. is not to eat the. *1 Cor* 11:20
obey your parents, for *t. is.* *Eph* 6:1
if I live, *t. is* the fruit. *Phil* 1:22
for *t. is* well pleasing. *Col* 3:20
for *t. is* the will of God. *1 Thes* 4:3
5:18
t. is a faithful saying. *1 Tim* 1:15
3:1; 4:9; *Tit* 3:8
for *t. is* acceptable in the. *1 Tim* 2:3
for *t. is* thankworthy, if. *1 Pet* 2:19
take it patiently, *t. is* acceptable. 20
t. is the message. *1 John* 1:5; 3:11
and *t. is* the promise, even. 2:25
t. is his commandment that we. *1 John* 3:23
t. is that spirit of antichrist. 4:3
t. is the love of God, that we. 5:3
and *t. is* the victory, even our. 4
t. is he that came by water. 6
t. is the witness of God which. 9
t. is the record, that God hath. 11
t. is the confidence that we have. 14
t. is the true God, and eternal. 20
t. is love, that we walk. *2 John* 6
t. is a deceiver and an antichrist. 7
years were finished, *t. is.* *Rev* 20:5
into lake of fire, *t. is* the second. 14

thistle

t. that was in Lebanon, a wild . . . the *t.* *2 Ki* 14:9; *2 Chr* 25:18
thorn and *t.* shall come. *Hos* 10:8

thistles

thorns and *t.* shall it. *Gen* 3:18
let *t.* grow instead of. *Job* 31:40
do men gather figs of *t.*? *Mat* 7:16

thither

near, oh let me escape *t.* *Gen* 19:20
escape *t.* till thou be come *t.* 22
bring not my son *t.* 24:6, 8
bring in *t.* the ark. *Ex* 26:33
that the slayer may flee *t.* *Num* 35:6
11, 15; *Deut* 4:42; 19:3, 4
Josh 20:3, 9
saying, Thou shalt not go in *t.* *Deut* 1:37, 38, 39
unto his habitation, *t.* thou. 12:5
t. ye shall bring your burnt. 6, 11
Israel went *t.* a whoring. *Judg* 8:27
and *t.* fled all the men and. 9:51
to Israelites that came *t.* *1 Sam* 2:14
the ark of God about *t.* 5:8
if the man should come *t.* 10:22
before it was brought *t.* *1 Ki* 6:7
waters were divided hither and *t.* *2 Ki* 2:8, 14
turned in *t.* to eat bread. 4:8, 11
t. the Syrians are come down. 6:9
saying, Carry *t.* one of the. 17:27
resort ye *t.* to us: our God. *Neh* 4:20
t. brought I again the vessels. 13:9
they came *t.* and were. *Job* 6:20
the rain returneth not *t.* *Isa* 55:10
he shall not return *t.* *Jer* 22:11
but to the land, *t.* shall they not. 27
t. was their spirit to go. *Ezek* 1:20
Israel shall come *t.* and shall. 11:18
these waters shall come *t.* 47:9
t. cause thy mighty ones. *Joel* 3:11
he was afraid to go *t.* *Mat* 2:22
t. will the eagles be. *Luke* 17:37
where I am, *t.* ye. *John* 7:34, 36
and goest thou *t.* again? 11:8
Jesus ofttimes resorted *t.* 18:2
Judas cometh *t.* with lanterns. 3
Philip ran *t.* to him, and. *Acts* 8:30
women which resorted *t.* 16:13

thitherward

t. and came to Micah's. *Judg* 18:15
Zion, with their faces *t.* *Jer* 50:5

Thomas

T. and Matthew the. *Mat* 10:3
Mark 3:18; *Luke* 6:15; *Acts* 1:13
T. said, Let us go and. *John* 11:16
T. was not with them when. 20:24
T. was with them. 26
T. Reach hither thy finger. 27
Simon Peter and *T.* 21:2

thongs

as they bound him with *t.* *Acts* 22:25

thorn

(*There are some 18 or 20 Hebrew words which point to different kinds of prickly shrubs, which are variously rendered in the Authorized Version. Probably there is no other country where so many plants of this sort exist. There are at least 200 different species of thorny plants found there*)
bore his jaw through with a *t.*? *Job* 41:2*
as a *t.* goeth into the hand. *Pr* 26:9
instead of the *t.* shall. *Isa* 55:13
no more any grieving *t.* *Ezek* 28:24
the *t.* shall come up on. *Hos* 10:8

is sharper than a *t.* hedge. *Mi* 7:4
there was given me a *t.* *2 Cor* 12:7

thorns

t. and thistles shall it. *Gen* 3:18
break out and catch in *t.* *Ex* 22:6
they shall be *t.* in your sides.
Num 33:55; *Judg* 2:3
but they shall be *t.* in your eyes.
Josh 23:13
of Belial shall be as *t.* *2 Sam* 23:6
Manasseh among the *t.* *2 Chr* 33:11*
pots can feel the *t.*, he shall. *Ps* 58:9
quenched as the fire of *t.* 118:12
man is an hedge of *t.* *Pr* 15:19
t. and snares are in the way. 22:5
was all grown over with *t.* 24:31
as the crackling of *t.* under. *Eccl* 7:6
as the lily among *t.* so is. *S of S* 2:2
they shall rest upon all *t.* *Isa* 7:19
as *t.* cut up shall they be. 33:12
and *t.* shall come up in her. 34:13
and sow not among *t.* *Jer* 4:3
sown wheat, but shall reap *t.* 12:13
hedge up thy way with *t.* *Hos* 2:6
t. shall be in their tabernacles. 9:6
be folden together as *t.* *Nah* 1:10
do men gather grapes of *t.*?
Mat 7:16; *Luke* 6:44
fell among *t.* *Mat* 13:7, 22
Mark 4:7, 18; *Luke* 8:7, 14
platted a crown of *t.* *Mat* 27:29
Mark 15:17; *John* 19:2
see **briers**

those

Esau said, Who are *t.*? *Gen* 33:5
let them be of *t.* that. *1 Ki* 2:7
upon *t.* did Solomon levy a. 9:21
t. did Cyrus king of Persia. *Ezra* 1:8
did what they would to *t.* *Esth* 9:5
to set up on high *t.* *Job* 5:11
seeing he judgeth *t.* that. 21:22
are of *t.* that rebel. 24:13
so doth the grave *t.* which. 19
t. that remain of him shall. 27:15
t. that wait on the Lord. *Ps* 37:9
t. that have made a covenant. 50:5
t. planted in house of Lord. 92:13
t. that fear thee turn unto me, and *t.*
that have known thy. 119:79
to do to *t.* that love thy name. 132
am not I grieved with *t.* that ? 139:21
t. that seek me early shall. *Pr* 8:17
with *t.* that shall come. *Eccl* 1:11
but it shall be for *t.* *Isa* 35:8
t. that remember thee in thy ways,
in those is continuance. 64:5
t. will I let remain in. *Jer* 27:11
t. that walk in pride he. *Dan* 4:37
t. that have not sought. *Zeph* 1:6
thou savourest *t.* things. *Mat* 16:23
among *t.* that are born. *Luke* 7:28
but *t.* mine enemies bring. 19:27
woman, where are *t.*? *John* 8:10
keep through thy name *t.* thou. 17:11
t. that thou gavest me I have. 12
from Samuel and *t.* that. *Acts* 3:24
there come in *t.* that. *1 Cor* 14:23
what things were gain, *t.* I. *Phil* 3:7
Saviour, especially of *t.* *1 Tim* 4:10
belongeth to *t.* who by. *Heb* 5:14
an ensample to *t.* that. *2 Pet* 2:6
allure *t.* that were clean escaped. 18
see **days, things**

thou

the woman whom *t.* gavest. *Gen* 3:12
know thou, that *t.* shalt surely die, *t.*
20:7; *1 Sam* 22:16
t. art our sister, be *t.* *Gen* 24:60
t. art now the blessed of the. 26:29
discreet and wise as *t.* art. 41:39
throne will I be greater than *t.* 40
t. shalt be near to me, *t.* and. 45:10
t. art he whom thy brethren. 49:8
t. shalt come up, *t.* and. *Ex* 19:24
t. and all the company. *Num* 16:11
be *t.* and they, and Aaron before. 16
may rest as well as *t.* *Deut* 5:14
nations mightier than *t.* 7:1; 20:1
t. hast not known, *t.* nor. 13:6; 28:64
that both *t.* and thy seed. 30:19
that is better than *t.* *1 Sam* 15:28
T. are more righteous than I. 24:17
blessed be *t.* that kept me. 25:33
Nathan said to David *T.* *2 Sam* 12:7
said, Of what city art *t.*? 15:2
T. and Ziba divide the land. 19:29
t. even *t.* knowest the. *1 Ki* 8:39
t. and thy father's house. 18:18
order the battle ? he said *T.* 20:14
that when I and *t.* rode. *2 Ki* 9:25
that *t.* shouldest fall, even *t.* and.
14:10; *2 Chr* 25:19
t. art the God, even *t.* *2 Ki* 19:15
19; *Neh* 9:6; *Isa* 37:20
but *t.* art a God, ready to. *Neh* 9:17
t. and thy father's house shall be
. . . whether *t.* art. *Esth* 4:14
which are higher than *t.* *Job* 35:5
I will fear no evil, for *t.* *Ps* 23:4
it was *t.*, a man mine equal. 55:13
t. art he that took me out of. 71:6
t. even *t.* art to be feared, and who
may stand . . . once *t.* art ? 76:7
t. whose name is Jehovah. 83:18
t. art the same, thy years. 102:27
they may know, that *t.* Lord. 109:27
t. art my God, and I will. 118:28
t. art my hiding place. 119:114
arise into thy rest, *t.* and ark. 132:8
up into heaven, *t.* art there. 139:8
tell me, O *t.* whom my. *S of S* 1:7
t. art my servant, I have. *Isa* 41:9
and saith, Deliver me, for *t.* 44:17
verily *t.* art a God that hidest. 45:15
who art *t.*, that *t.* shouldest be ? 51:12
t. art our father *t.* O Lord. 63:16
to me, I am holier than *t.* 65:5
t. shalt continue from. *Jer* 17:4
there *t.* shalt die, *t.* and all thy. 20:6
will ye die, *t.* and thy people ? 27:13
t. O Lord, remainest for. *Lam* 5:19
O *t.* that dwellest in the. *Ezek* 7:7
more righteous than *t.* 16:52
it is *t.* O king, that art. *Dan* 4:22
t. his son hast not humbled. 5:32
whence comest *t.*? of what people art
t.? *Jonah* 1:8
O *t.* that art named the. *Mi* 2:7
t. O tower of the flock, to thee. 4:8
art *t.* not from everlasting? *Hab* 1:12
art *t.* O great mountain ? *Zech* 4:7
but *t.* when *t.* prayest. *Mat* 6:6
but *t.* when *t.* fastest, anoint. 17
t. art the Christ, the Son of the. 16:16
Mark 8:29; *Luke* 4:41; *John* 11:27
not as I will, but as *t.* wilt. *Mat* 26:39
saying, *T.* also wast with Jesus. 69
Mark 14:67
hail, *t.* that art highly. *Luke* 1:28
saying, Art *t.* he that ? 7:19, 20
lest a more honourable than *t.* 14:8
owest *t.* unto my lord ? 16:5, 7
t. in thy lifetime receivedst thy
good things . . . and *t.* art. 25
if thou hadst known, even *t.* 19:42
to ask him, Who art *t.*? *John* 1:19
22; 8:25; 21:12
they asked, art *t.* Elias ? art *t.*? 1:21
t. art Simon thou shalt be called. 42
art *t.* a master in Israel ? 3:10
that *t.* being a Jew, askest. 4:9
to him, Art *t.* also of Galilee ? 7:52
but what sayest *t.*? 8:5
t. art his disciple. 9:28
t. hast seen him, and he. 37
I in them, and *t.* in me, that. 17:23
art not *t.* one of this man's ? 18:17
t. Lord, who knowest. *Acts* 1:24
t. art in the gall of bitterness. 8:23
whereby *t.* and thy house. 11:14
t. child of the devil, *t.* enemy, wilt *t.*
not cease to pervert the ? 13:10
t. art my son, this day have I. 33
art not *t.* that Egyptian which ? 21:38
tell me, art *t.* a Roman ? he. 22:27
I would, that not only *t.* but. 26:29
t. therefore which teachest another.
Rom 2:21
but be *t.* an example. *1 Tim* 4:12
t. O man of God, flee these. 6:11
be not *t.* ashamed of the. *2 Tim* 1:8
t. therefore, my son, be strong. 2:1
t. therefore receive him. *Philem* 12
t., Lord, hast laid the foundation of
the earth. *Heb* 1:10
they shall be changed, but *t.* art. 12
who art *t.* that judgest ? *Jas* 4:12
t. art worthy, O Lord, to. *Rev* 4:11
t. art worthy to take the book. 5:9
see **alone**

though

vine was as *t.* it budded. *Gen* 40:10
t. he wist it not, yet is. *Lev* 5:17
thou shalt relieve him, *t.* he be. 25:35
t. I walk in the imagination of.
Deut 29:19
drive out Canaanites, *t.* they have
iron chariots and *t.* *Josh* 17:18
t. thou detain me, I will. *Judg* 13:16
t. ye have done this, yet will. 15:7
t. I be not like one of thy hand-
maidens. *Ruth* 2:13
t. it be in Jonathan. *1 Sam* 14:39
I will shoot arrows, as *t.* I. 20:20
t. it were sanctified this day. 21:5
I am this day weak, *t.* *2 Sam* 3:39
t. I should receive a thousand. 18:12
t. there were of you cast. *Neh* 1:9
t. he slay me, yet will I. *Job* 13:15
t. wickedness be sweet in. 20:12
what the hypocrite's hope, *t.* 27:8
t. he heap up silver as the dust. 16
as *t.* he had been my friend or.
Ps 35:14
t. he fall, he shall not utterly. 37:24
t. the Lord be high, yet hath. 138:6
t. hand join in hand. *Pr* 11:21; 16:5
than he that is perverse, *t.* 28:6
t. he understand, he will not. 29:19
the wayfaring men *t.* fools. *Isa* 35:8
surnamed thee, *t.* thou hast not.
45:4, 5
he cause grief, yet will he. *Lam* 3:32
t. briers and thorns be with thee, *t.*
Ezek 2:6; 3:9; 12:3
t. these three men. 14:14, 16, 18, 20
t. thou be sought for, yet. 26:21
not humbled, *t.* thou. *Dan* 5:22
t. thou be little among. *Mi* 5:2
t. they be quiet, and. *Nah* 1:12
ye will not believe, *t.* it. *Hab* 1:5
t. it tarry, wait for it, it will. 2:3
t. I should die with thee. *Mat* 26:35
face was as *t.* he would. *Luke* 9:53
avenge his elect, *t.* he bear. 18:7
he made as *t.* he would have. 24:28
wrote on the ground, as *t.* *John* 8:6
t. ye believe not me, believe. 10:38
t. he were dead, yet shall. 11:25
as *t.* by our own power we. *Acts* 3:12
ye shall not believe, *t.* a man. 13:41
as *t.* he needed any thing. 17:25
t. he be not far from every one. 27
as *t.* ye would enquire. 23:15, 20
t. he hath escaped the sea. 28:4
things which be not, as *t.* *Rom* 4:17
no adulteress, *t.* she be married. 7:3
that have wives, be as *t.* *1 Cor* 7:29
as *t.* they wept not, as *t.* they. 30
but *t.* our outward man. *2 Cor* 4:16
t. he was rich, yet for our sakes. 8:9
for *t.* we walk in the flesh, we. 10:3
in nothing am I behind, *t.* I. 12:11
do what is honest, *t.* we be. 13:7
t. we or an angel preach. *Gal* 1:8
heir differeth nothing *t.* he be. 4:1
t. I might also have confidence in.
Phil 3:4
not as *t.* I had attained or were. 12
t. I be absent in the flesh. *Col* 2:5
why, as *t.* living, are ye subject. 20
t. he were a son, yet learned.
Heb 5:8
better things, *t.* we thus speak. 6:9
t. he sought it carefully with. 12:17
t. a man say he hath faith. *Jas* 2:14
as *t.* some strange thing. *1 Pet* 4:12
put you in remembrance, *t.* ye know.
2 Pet 1:12
put you in remembrance, *t.* ye once
knew this. *Jude* 5

thought

I *t.* the fear of God is not. *Gen* 20:11
Judah saw her, he *t.* her to. 38:15
Israel said, I had not *t.* to. 48:11
but as for you, ye *t.* evil. 50:20*
of the evil he *t.* to do. *Ex* 32:14*
I *t.* to promote thee to. *Num* 24:11
I shall do unto you, as I *t.* 33:56
ye do to him, as ye *t.* *Deut* 19:19

I verily *t.* that thou hadst hated her. *Judg* 15:2
the men of Gibeah *t.* to have. 20:5
therefore Eli *t.* she had. *1 Sam* 1:13
Saul *t.* to make David fall. 18:25
who *t.* that I would have given him a reward. *2 Sam* 4:10*
Amnon *t.* it hard to do any. 13:2
Ishbi-benob *t.* to have slain. 21:16
I *t.* he will surely come. *2 Ki* 5:11
Rehoboam *t.* to make. *2 Chr* 11:22*
Sennacherib *t.* to win them. 32:1
t. to do me mischief. *Neh* 6:2
he *t.* scorn to lay hands. *Esth* 3:6
Haman *t.* in his heart, to. 6:6*
we have *t.* of thy loving. *Ps* 48:9
when I *t.* to know this, it was 73:16
I *t.* on my ways, and turned. 119:59
if thou hast *t.* evil, lay. *Pr* 30:32
as I have *t.* so shall it. *Isa* 14:24
of the evil I *t.* to do. *Jer* 18:8
Lord of hosts *t.* to do to us. *Zech* 1:6
as I *t.* to punish you. 8:14
I *t.* to do well. 15
a book for them that *t.* *Mal* 3:16
but while he *t.* on these. *Mat* 1:20
and when he *t.* thereon. *Mark* 14:72
nor *t.* I myself worthy. *Luke* 7:7
he *t.* within himself, what. 12:17*
they *t.* the kingdom of God. 19:11*
they *t.* he had spoken. *John* 11:13
t. the gift of God may. *Acts* 8:20
while Peter *t.* on the vision. 10:19
wist not it was true, but *t.* he. 12:9
Paul *t.* not good to take him. 15:38
why should it be *t.* a thing ? 26:8*
I *t.* that I ought to do many things. 9
when I was a child, I *t.* *1 Cor* 13:11
t. it not robbery to be. *Phil* 2:6*
punishment he be *t.* *Heb* 10:29*

thought, *substantive*

that there be not a *t.* in. *Deut* 15:9
my father take *t.* for us. *1 Sam* 9:5†
is despised in the *t.* of him. *Job* 12:5
that no *t.* can be withholden. 42:2*
their *t.* is, their houses. *Ps* 49:11
the inward *t.* of every one of. 64:6
thou understandest my *t.* 139:2
t. of foolishness is sin. *Pr* 24:9
king, no not in thy *t.* *Eccl* 10:20
shalt think an evil *t.* *Ezek* 38:10*
to man what is his *t.* *Amos* 4:13
I say to you, Take no *t.* *Mat* 6:25* 31, 34*; 10:19*; *Mark* 13:11* *Luke* 12:11*, 22*
which of you by taking *t.* can add one cubit ? *Mat* 6:27*; *Luke* 12:25*
why take *ye t.* for raiment ? *Mat* 6:28*; *Luke* 12:26*
if the *t.* of thy heart. *Acts* 8:22
bringing into captivity every *t.* to the obedience of Christ. *2 Cor* 10:5

thoughtest

thou *t.* I was such a one. *Ps* 50:21

thoughts

imagination of the *t.* of his. *Gen* 6:5
for Reuben there were great *t.* of heart. *Judg* 5:15*
understandeth the *t.* *1 Chr* 28:9
the imagination of the *t.* 29:18
in *t.* from the visions. *Job* 4:13
are broken off, even my *t.* 17:11
therefore do my *t.* cause me. 20:2
I know your *t.* and devices. 21:27
God is not in all his *t.* *Ps* 10:4
and the *t.* of his heart to all. 33:11
thy *t.* cannot be reckoned. 40:5
all their *t.* are against me. 56:5
thy works! thy *t.* are very deep. 92:5
Lord knoweth the *t.* of man. 94:11
in the multitude of my *t.* 19
I hate vain *t.* but thy law. 119:113*
how precious are thy *t.* 139:17
O God, try me, and know my *t.* 23
in that very day his *t.* perish. 146:4
the *t.* of the righteous. *Pr* 12:5
the *t.* of the wicked are an. 15:26*
and thy *t.* shall be established. 16:3
the *t.* of the diligent tend to. 21:5
man forsake his *t.* *Isa* 55:7
for my *t.* are not your *t.* saith. 8
so are my *t.* higher than your *t.* 9
evil, their *t.* are *t.* of iniquity. 59:7
walketh after their own *t.* *Isa* 65:2
their works and their *t.* 66:18
vain *t.* lodge in thee ? *Jer* 4:14
even the fruit of their *t.* 6:19
till he have performed the *t.* 23:20*
I know the *t.* that I think towards you, *t.* of peace and not. 29:11
mightest know the *t.* of. *Dan* 2:30
Nebuchadnezzar's *t.* upon bed. 4:5
Daniel was astonished, and his *t.* 19
Belshazzar's *t.* troubled him. 5:6
Let not thy *t.* trouble thine. 10
but they know not the *t.* *Mi* 4:12
Jesus, knowing their *t.* said. *Mat* 9:4 12:25; *Luke* 5:22*; 6:8; 9:47 11:17
out of the heart proceed evil *t.* *Mat* 15:19; *Mark* 7:21
the *t.* of many hearts. *Luke* 2:35
and why do *t.* arise in your ? 24:38*
their *t.* accusing, or else. *Rom* 2:15
the Lord knoweth the *t.* *1 Cor* 3:20*
God is a discerner of the *t.* *Heb* 4:12
become judges of evil *t.* *Jas* 2:4

thousand

thy brother a *t.* pieces. *Gen* 20:16
of every tribe a *t.* shall ye send to the war. *Num* 31:4, 5, 6
suburbs of cities are *t.* cubits. 35:4
you a *t.* times so many. *Deut* 1:11
covenant to a *t.* generations. 7:9
how should one chase a *t.*? 32:30 *Josh* 23:10
died, about a *t.* men. *Judg* 9:49
Samson slew a *t.* men. 15:15, 16
an hundred of a *t.*, a *t.* out of. 20:10
the captain of their *t.* *1 Sam* 17:18
David his captain over a *t.* 18:13
three *t.* sheep and a *t.* goats. 25:2
from him a *t.* chariots and seven. *2 Sam* 8:4; *1 Chr* 18:4
though I should receive a *t.* 18:12
t. men of Benjamin with him. 19:17
a *t.* burnt offerings did Solomon. *1 Ki* 3:4; *2 Chr* 1:6
gave Pul a *t.* talents. *2 Ki* 15:19
craftsmen and smiths a *t.* 24:16
greatest was over a *t.* *1 Chr* 12:14
of Naphtali a *t.* captains, and. 34
word he commanded to a *t.* 16:15
Ammon sent a *t.* talents. 19:6
sacrifices unto the Lord a *t.* bullocks, a *t.* rams, and a *t.* lambs. 29:21
did give a *t.* bullocks. *2 Chr* 30:24
bring forth a *t.* chargers. *Ezra* 1:9
gold, and other vessels a *t.* 10
answer him one of a *t.* *Job* 9:3
interpreter, one of a *t.* 33:23
t. yoke of oxen, a *t.* she asses. 42:12
cattle on a *t.* hills are. *Ps* 50:10
day in courts is better than a *t.* 84:10
a *t.* years in thy sight are but. 90:4
a *t.* shall fall at thy side, and. 91:7
yea, though he live a *t.* *Eccl* 6:6
one man among a *t.* have I. 7:28
whereon there hang a *t.* *S of S* 4:4
fruit was to bring a *t.* pieces. 8:11
thou, O Solomon, must have a *t.* 12
a *t.* vines, at a *t.* silverlings. *Isa* 7:23
one *t.* shall flee at the rebuke. 30:17
a little one shall become a *t.* 60:22
measured a *t.* cubits. *Ezek* 47:3
again he measured a *t.* and. 4, 5
feast to a *t.* of his lords, and drank wine before the *t.* *Dan* 5:1
out by a *t.* shall leave. *Amos* 5:3
day is with the Lord as a *t.* years, and a *t.* years as one day. *2 Pet* 3:8
bound Satan a *t.* years. *Rev* 20:2
deceive nations no more, till *t.* 3
reigned with Christ a *t.* years. 4
and when the *t.* years are expired. 7

one **thousand** *two hundred sixty*

prophesy *one t.* 260 days. *Rev* 11:3
feed her *one t.* 260 days. 12:6

one **thousand** *two hundred ninety*

be *one t.* 290 days. *Dan* 12:11

one **thousand** *three hundred thirty-five*

to the *t.* 335 days. *Dan* 12:12

one **thousand** *six hundred*

of *one t.* 600 furlongs. *Rev* 14:20

two **thousand**

two t. cubits, on the west side *two t.*, south side *two t.* *Num* 35:5
you and the ark *two t.* *Josh* 3:4
sea contained *two t.* baths. *1 Ki* 7:26
deliver thee *two t.* horses if thou be able. *2 Ki* 18:23; *Isa* 36:8
gave *two t.* pounds of. *Neh* 7:72
about *two t.* swine were. *Mark* 5:13

two **thousand** *two hundred*

two t. 200 pounds of silver. *Neh* 7:71

two **thousand** *three hundred*

two t. 300 days, sanctuary. *Dan* 8:14

two hundred **thousand**

captive of brethren 200 *t.* *2 Chr* 28:8

two hundred eighty **thousand**

out of Benjamin *two hundred eighty t.* *2 Chr* 14:8

two hundred **thousand thousand**

of horsemen were *two hundred thousand thousand.* *Rev* 9:16*

three **thousand**

of the people *three t.* *Ex* 32:28
to Ai about *three t.* men. *Josh* 7:4
three t. went to bind. *Judg* 15:11
upon the roof *three t.* men. 16:27
Saul chose *three t.* men. *2 Sam* 13:2
took *three t.* chosen men. 24:2; 26:2
three t. sheep and a *t.* goats. 25:2
spake *three t.* proverbs. *1 Ki* 4:32
sea held *three t.* baths. *2 Chr* 4:5
his substance was *three t.* *Job* 1:3
captive *three t.* Jews. *Jer* 52:28
to them *three t.* souls. *Acts* 2:41

four **thousand**

Israel about *four t.* men. *1 Sam* 4:2
four t. porters, *four t.* *1 Chr* 23:5
Solomon had *four t.* stalls for horses. *2 Chr* 9:25
they that did eat were *four t.* *Mat* 15:38; *Mark* 8:9
seven loaves among *four t.* *Mat* 16:10; *Mark* 8:20
wilderness *four t.* men. *Acts* 21:38

four **thousand** *five hundred*

of the city *four t.* 500 measures, east side . . . *four t.* 500 measures. *Ezek* 48:16, 30, 32, 33, 34

five **thousand**

about *five t.* men. *Josh* 8:12
of them *five t.* men. *Judg* 20:45
of gold *five t.* talents. *1 Chr* 29:7
for offerings *five t.* *2 Chr* 35:9
they gave *five t.* pounds. *Ezra* 2:69
eaten were about *five t.* *Mat* 14:21
neither remember the five loaves of the *five t.* 16:9; *Mark* 6:44; 8:19 *Luke* 9:14; *John* 6:10
number that believed were about *five t.* *Acts* 4:4

five **thousand** *four hundred*

and silver *five t.* 400. *Ezra* 1:11

six **thousand**

with *six t.* horsemen. *1 Sam* 13:5
six t. pieces of gold. *2 Ki* 5:5
and *six t.* were officers. *1 Chr* 23:4
for Job had *six t.* camels. *Job* 42:12

six **thousand** *seven hunderd and twenty*

asses, *six t. seven hundred and twenty.* *Ezra* 2:67; *Neh* 7:69

seven **thousand**

seven t. in Israel who have not. *1 Ki* 19:18; *Rom* 11:4
Israel, being *seven t.* *1 Ki* 20:15
men of might, *seven t.* *2 Ki* 24:16
mighty men, *seven t.* *1 Chr* 12:25
from him *seven t.* horsemen. 18:4
the Syrians *seven t.* men. 19:18
I prepared *seven t.* talents of. 29:4
they offered *seven t.* *2 Chr* 15:11
congregation *seven t.* sheep. 30:24
also was *seven t.* sheep. *Job* 1:3
were slain *seven t.* men. *Rev* 11:13

seven **thousand** *seven hundred*

brought Jehoshaphat *seven t.* 700 rams, *seven t.* 700. *2 Chr* 17:11

ten **thousand**

an hundred shall put *ten t.* *Lev* 26:8
two put *ten t.* to flight ? *Deut* 32:30

them in Bezek *ten t.* men. *Judg* 1:4
they slew of Moab *ten t.* men. 3:29
Barak, go, and take *ten t.* men. 4:6
he went up with *ten t.* men. 10, 14
remained to Gideon *ten t.* 7:3
against Gibeah *ten t.* men. 20:34
art worth *ten t.* of us. *2 Sam* 18:3
Lebanon, *ten t.* a month. *1 Ki* 5:14
Jehoahaz *ten t.* footmen. *2 Ki* 13:7
Edom in the valley *ten t.* 14:7
away even *ten t.* captives. 24:14
children of Seir *ten t.* *2 Chr* 25:11
other *ten t.* left alive, did Judah. 12
gave Jotham the same year *ten t.*. . . *ten t.* of barley. 27:5
congregation *ten t.* sheep 30:24
I will pay *ten t.* talents. *Esth* 3:9
ten t. shall fall at thy. *Ps* 91:7
chiefest among *ten t.* *S of S* 5:10
the breadth of the land shall be *ten t.* *Ezek* 45:1, 3, 5; 48:9, 10, 13, 18
ten t. times *ten t.* stood. *Dan* 7:10
him *ten t.* talents. *Mat* 18:24
able with *ten t.* to meet. *Luke* 14:31
though ye have *ten t.* *1 Cor* 4:15
than *ten t.* words in an. 14:19
was *ten t.* times *ten t.* *Rev* 5:11

twelve **thousand**

fell of Ai were *twelve t.* *Josh* 8:25
sent *twelve t.* men to. *Judg* 21:10
Solomon had *twelve t.* *1 Ki* 4:26 10:26; *2 Chr* 1:14; 9:25
of tribe of Juda, Reuben, Gad, sealed *twelve t.* *Rev* 7:5
of Aser, Naphthalim, Manasses, sealed *twelve t.* 6
of Simeon, Levi, Issachar, were sealed *twelve t.* 7
of Zabulon, Joseph, Benjamin, sealed *twelve t.* 8
city *twelve t.* furlongs. 21:16

fourteen **thousand**

Job had *fourteen t.* sheep. *Job* 42:12

fourteen **thousand** *seven hundred*

plague *fourteen t.* 700. *Num* 16:49

sixteen **thousand**

were *sixteen t.* *Num* 31:40, 46

sixteen **thousand** *seven hundred fifty*

gold of offering *sixteen t. seven hundred* and *fifty.* *Num* 31:52

seventeen **thousand** *two hundred*

sons of Jediael *seven t. two hundred.* *1 Chr* 7:11

eighteen **thousand**

Israel *eighteen t.* men. *Judg* 20:25
of Benjamin *eighteen t.* men. 44
Manasseh *eighteen t.* *1 Chr* 12:31
of the Edomites *eighteen t.* 18:12
they gave of brass *eighteen t.* 29:7

twenty **thousand**

Hadadezer king of Zobah, *twenty t.* *2 Sam* 8:4; *1 Chr* 18:4
of Ammon hired Syrians, *twenty t.* *2 Sam* 10:6
Absalom's company *twenty t.* 18:7
Hiram *twenty t.* measures of wheat. *1 Ki* 5:11; *2 Chr* 2:10
work *twenty t.* drams. *Neh* 7:71, 72
chariots of God *twenty t.* *Ps* 68:17
cometh, with *twenty t.* *Luke* 14:31

twenty two **thousand**

Levites *twenty two t.* *Num* 3:39
males were *twenty two t.* 43
Simeonites *twenty two t.* 26:14
returned of Gideon's army *twenty two t.* *Judg* 7:3
of Israel *twenty two t.* 20:21
David slew of the Syrians *twenty two t.* *2 Sam* 8:5; *1 Chr* 18:5
Solomon offered *twenty two t.* oxen. *1 Ki* 8:63; *2 Chr* 7:5
of Tola *twenty two t.* *1 Chr* 7:2
of Bela *twenty two t.* 7

twenty three **thousand**

Levites *twenty three t.* *Num* 26:62
day *three* and *twenty t.* *1 Cor* 10:8

twenty four **thousand**

plague *twenty four t.* *Num* 25:9
twenty four t. Levites to forward. *1 Chr* 23:4
served were *twenty four t.* 27:1

twenty five **thousand**

destroyed of Benjamites *twenty five t.* *Judg* 20:35, 46
of land *twenty five t.* *Ezek* 45:1 3, 5, 6; 48:8, 9, 10, 13

twenty six **thousand**

numbered *twenty six t.* *Judg* 20:15
apt to war, *twenty six t.* *1 Chr* 7:40

twenty seven **thousand**

twenty seven t. men. *1 Ki* 20:30

twenty eight **thousand**

expert in war, *twenty eight t.* *1 Chr* 12:35

thirty **thousand**

and the asses were *thirty t.* *Num* 31:39, 45
Joshua chose *thirty t.* *Josh* 8:3
Israel *thirty t.* footmen. *1 Sam* 4:10
men of Judah were *thirty t.* 11:8
Philistines gathered *thirty t.* 13:5
David gathered *thirty t.* *2 Sam* 6:1
levy was *thirty t.* men. *1 Ki* 5:13

thirty two **thousand**

thirty two t. women. *Num* 31:35
Ammon hired *thirty two t.* chariots. *1 Chr* 19:7

thirty two **thousand** *two hundred*

number of Manasseh *thirty two t. two hundred.* *Num* 1:35; 2:21

thirty two **thousand** *five hundred*

of Ephraim were numbered *thirty two t. five hundred.* *Num* 26:37

thirty three **thousand**

gave *thirty three t.* *2 Chr* 35:7

thirty five **thousand**

of Benjamin were *thirty five t.* *Num* 1:37

thirty six **thousand**

were *thirty* and *six t.* *Num* 31:38
congregation *thirty six t.* beeves. 44
soldiers were *thirty six t.* *1 Chr* 7:4

thirty seven **thousand**

Naphtali *thirty* and *seven t.* *1 Chr* 12:34

thirty eight **thousand**

Levites from thirty years, *thirty eight t.* *1 Chr* 23:3

forty **thousand**

about *forty t.* prepared. *Josh* 4:13
was there a shield seen among *forty t.*? *Judg* 5:8
David slew *forty t.* *2 Sam* 10:18
Solomon had *forty t.* *1 Ki* 4:26
expert in war, *forty t.* *1 Chr* 12:36
slew of Assyrians *forty t.* 19:18

forty **thousand** *five hundred*

of Ephraim were *forty t. five hundred.* *Num* 1:33; 2:19
Gad were numbered *forty t.* and *five hundred.* 26:18

forty one **thousand** *five hundred*

of Asher numbered *forty one t. five hundred.* *Num* 1:41; 2:28

forty two **thousand**

Ephraimites *forty two t.* *Judg* 12:6
whole congregation *forty two t.* *Ezra* 2:64; *Neh* 7:66

forty three **thousand** *seven hundred thirty*

of Reubenites *forty three t. seven hundred thirty.* *Num* 26:7

forty four **thousand** *seven hundred sixty*

of Reubenites to war *forty four t. seven hundred sixty.* *1 Chr* 5:18

forty five **thousand** *four hundred*

of Naphtali were *forty five t. four hundred.* *Num* 26:50

forty five **thousand** *six hundred*

of Benjamin *forty five t. six hundred.* *Num* 26:41

forty five **thousand** *six hundred fifty*

numbered of Gad *forty five t. six hundred fifty.* *Num* 1:25; 2:15

forty six **thousand** *five hundred*

of Reuben *forty six t.* and *five hundred.* *Num* 1:21; 2:11

fifty **thousand**

the Lord smote *fifty t.* *1 Sam* 6:19
Hagarites' sheep *fifty t.* *1 Chr* 5:21
of Zebulun *fifty t.* could keep. 12:33
the book *fifty t.* pieces. *Acts* 19:19

fifty two **thousand** *seven hundred*

of Manasseh *fifty two t.* and *seven hundred.* *Num* 26:34

fifty three **thousand** *four hundred*

of Naphtali *fifty three t. four hundred.* *Num* 1:43; 2:30

fifty four **thousand** *four hundred*

of Issachar *fifty four t. four hundred.* *Num* 1:29; 2:6

fifty seven **thousand** *four hundred*

of Zebulun *fifty seven t. four hundred.* *Num* 1:31; 2:8

fifty nine **thousand** *three hundred*

of Simeon *fifty nine t. three hundred.* *Num* 1:23; 2:13

sixty **thousand**

sixty t. horsemen. *2 Chr* 12:3

sixty **thousand** *five hundred*

of Zebulunites, *sixty t.* and *five hundred.* *Num* 26:27

sixty one **thousand**

was *sixty one t.* asses. *Num* 31:34
they gave *sixty one t.* *Ezra* 2:69

sixty two **thousand** *seven hundred*

of tribe of Dan *sixty two t. seven hundred.* *Num* 1:39; 2:26

sixty four **thousand** *three hundred*

of Issachar *sixty four t.* and *three hundred.* *Num* 26:25

sixty four **thousand** *four hundred*

of the Shuhamites *sixty four t. four hundred.* *Num* 26:43

seventy **thousand**

the people *seventy t.* *2 Sam* 24:15
Solomon had *seventy t.* that bare. *1 Ki* 5:15; *2 Chr* 2:2, 18
fell of Israel *seventy t.* *1 Chr* 21:14

seventy two **thousand**

booty of beeves was *seventy two t.* *Num* 31:33

seventy four **thousand** *six hundred*

number of Judah *seventy four t.* and *six hundred.* *Num* 1:27; 2:4

seventy five **thousand**

seventy five t. sheep. *Num* 31:32
their foes *seventy five t.* *Esth* 9:16

seventy six **thousand** *five hundred*

numbered of Judah *seventy six t. five hundred.* *Num* 26:22

eighty **thousand**

Solomon had *eighty t.* hewers in the. *1 Ki* 5:15; *2 Chr* 2:2, 18

eighty seven **thousand**

of Issachar, reckoned *eighty seven t.* *1 Chr* 7:5

thousand thousand

of Israel were a *t. t.* *1 Chr* 21:5
have prepared a *t. t.* talents. 22:14
came with a host of a *t. t.* *2 Chr* 14:9

two hundred **thousand thousand**

army of horsemen *two hundred t. t.* *Rev* 9:16

thousands

be thou the mother of *t.* *Gen* 24:60
over them rulers of *t.* *Ex* 18:21, 25
shewing mercy to *t.* of them. 20:6 *Deut* 5:10
keeping mercy for *t.* *Ex* 34:7
heads of *t.* in Israel. *Num* 1:16 10:4; *Josh* 22:14, 21, 30
to the many *t.* of Israel. *Num* 10:36
were delivered out of the *t.* 31:5
them captains over *t.* *Deut* 1:15
the Lord came with ten *t.* of saints. 33:2; *Jude* 14
are the *t.* of Manasseh. *Deut* 33:17
him captains over *t.* *1 Sam* 8:12
yourselves by your *t.* 10:19
they have ascribed but *t.* 18:8
make you all captains of *t.*? 22:7
search him out throughout *t.* 23:23
Philistines passed on by *t.* 29:2

people came out by t. 2 Sam 18:4
thy law is better than t. Ps 119:72
lovingkindness unto t. Jer 32:18
thousand t. ministered. Dan 7:10
thou be little among the t. Mi 5:2
Lord be pleased with t. of rams ? 6:7
how many t. of Jews. Acts 21:20
number of them was t. of t. Rev 5:11
see **captains**

ten **thousands**

the *ten t.* of Ephraim. Deut 33:17
David slain his *ten t.* 1 Sam 18:7
8; 21:11; 29:5
I will not be afraid of *ten t.* Ps 3:6
sheep may bring forth *ten t.* 144:13
cast down many *ten t.* Dan 11:12
ten t. of rivers of oil. Mi 6:7

thread

take from a t. to a latchet. Gen 14:23
his hand a scarlet t. 38:28, 30
shalt bind this scarlet t. Josh 2:18
withs as a t. of tow. Judg 16:9*
ropes from his arms as a t. 12
thy lips are like a t. of. S of S 4:3

threaten, -ed

but let us straitly t. them not to.
Acts 4:17, 21
when he suffered he t. not. 1 Pet 2:23

threatening, -s

Lord, behold their t. and. Acts 4:29
Saul yet breathing out t. and. 9:1
same things unto them, forbearing t.
Eph 6:9

three

he looked, and lo, t. men. Gen 18:2
not these t. unto her. Ex 21:11
t. branches of the candlestick.
25:32; 37:18
t. bowls made like unto. 33; 37:19
altar shall be t. cubits. 27:1; 38:1
pillars t., their sockets t. 14, 15
38:14, 15
t. tenth deals of fine flour for a meat.
Lev 14:10; Num 15:9; 28:12
for the female estimation t. Lev 27:6
come out ye t. And they t. came out.
Num 12:4
t. tenth deals for a bullock. 28:20
28; 29:3, 9, 14
ye shall give t. cities on this. 35:14
Moses severed t. cities. Deut 4:41
19:2, 3, 7, 9
at the mouth of t. 17:6; 19:15
and Caleb drove thence the t. sons.
Josh 15:14; Judg 1:20
t. men for each tribe. Josh 18:4
the t. companies blew. Judg 7:20
he divided the people into t. 9:43
Hannah took with her t. 1 Sam 1:24
with fleshhook of t. teeth. 2:13
Hannah bare t. sons and two. 21
t. men, one carrying t. kids, another
carrying t. loaves of bread. 10:3
people in t. companies. 11:11
the t. eldest of Jesse's. 17:13, 14
I will shoot t. arrows on the. 20:20
Saul died, and his t. sons. 31:6
1 Chr 10:6
Saul and his t. sons. 1 Sam 31:8
there were born t. sons. 2 Sam 14:27
Joab thrust t. darts through. 18:14
Eleazar, one of the t. mighty. 23:9
1 Chr 11:12
t. of the thirty chief. 2 Sam 23:13
t. mighty brake through. 16, 17
Abishai brother of Joab chief among
t. 23:18, 19
attained not to the first t. 19, 23
Benaiah had the name among t. 22
I offer thee t. things. 24:12
1 Chr 21:10
inner court with t. rows. 1 Ki 6:36
were windows in t. rows. 7:4
t. oxen looking toward the north t. to
the west, t. to the south, t. to. 25
t. pound of gold went to one. 10:17
Alas ! that the Lord hath called
these t. kings. 2 Ki 3:10, 13
sons of Zeruiah were t. 1 Chr 2:16
sons of Neariah t. 3:23
sons of Mushi t. 23:23
fourteen sons and t. daughters. 25:5
be laid with t. rows. Ezra 6:4

to Job t. daughters. Job 1:2; 42:13
the Chaldeans made out t. 1:17
Job's t. friends heard of all. 2:11
t. things which are never. Pr 30:15
there be t. things too wonderful. 18
t. things the earth is disquieted. 21
there be t. things which go well. 29
two or t. berries in the top. Isa 17:6
though these t. men were in it.
Ezek 14:14, 16, 18
the little chambers were t. 40:10, 21
the side chambers were t. 41:6
t. gates, after names of tribes. 48:31
32, 33, 34
did not we cast t. men ? Dan 3:24
set over these t. presidents. 6:2
it had t. ribs in the mouth. 7:5
were t. of the first horns. 8, 20, 24
mourning t. full weeks. 10:2, 3
there shall stand up t. kings. 11:2
for t. transgressions. Amos 1:3, 6, 9
11, 13
t. transgressions of. 2:1, 4, 6
so two or t. cities wandered. 4:8
t. shepherds I cut off. Zech 11:8
hid in t. measures of meal.
Mat 13:33; Luke 13:21
let us make here t. tabernacles.
Mat 17:4; Mark 9:5; Luke 9:33
in the mouth of two or t. witnesses.
Mat 18:16; 2 Cor 13:1
where two or t. are gathered together
in my name. Mat 18:20
t. was neighbour to ? Luke 10:36
Friend, lend me t. loaves. 11:5
divided, t. against two, and two
against t. 12:52
t. hours after, when his. Acts 5:7
t. men seek thee. 10:19; 11:11
us as far as The t. taverns. 28:15
faith, hope, charity . . . t. 1 Cor 13:13
by two, or at most by t. and. 14:27
let the prophets speak two or t. 29
but before two or t. 1 Tim 5:19
two or t. witnesses. Heb 10:28
there are t. that bear record in heaven:
these t. are one. 1 John 5:7
t. bear witness in earth, and these t. 8
and t. measures of barley. Rev 6:6
trumpet of t. angels who are. 8:13
by these t. was the third part. 9:18
I saw t. unclean spirits like. 16:13
city was divided into t. parts. 19
on the east t. gates, on the north t.
gates, on south t. . . . west t. 21:13
see **days, hundred**

three *months*

about t. months after. Gen 38:24
she hid him t. months. Ex 2:2
in house of Obed-edom, t. months.
2 Sam 6:11; 1 Chr 13:14
wilt thou flee t. months before ?
2 Sam 24:13; 1 Chr 21:12
son of Josiah reigned t. months.
2 Ki 23:31; 2 Chr 36:2
Jehoiachin reigned t. months.
2 Ki 24:8; 2 Chr 36:9
there were yet t. months. Amos 4:7
nourished up t. months. Acts 7:20
boldly the space of t. months. 19:8
Paul abode in Greece t. months. 23
Moses was hid t. months. Heb 11:23

three *times*

t. times thou shalt keep. Ex 23:14
t. times in the year all thy males. 17
Deut 16:16
thou hast smitten me these t. times.
Num 22:28, 32
turned from me these t. times. 33
blessed them these t. times. 24:10
hast mocked me these t. times.
Judg 16:15
and bowed t. times. 1 Sam 20:41
offered t. times a year. 1 Ki 9:25
himself on the child t. times. 17:21
t. times did Joash beat. 2 Ki 13:25
offering t. times in the. 2 Chr 8:13
his knees t. times a day. Dan 6:10
his petition t. times a day. 13
this was done t. times. Acts 11:10

three *years*

heifer of t. years old, a she goat t.
years old . . . t. years. Gen 15:9

uncircumcised t. years. Lev 19:23
bring forth fruit for t. years. 25:21
at the end of t. years. Deut 14:28
had reigned t. years. Judg 9:22
in Geshur t. years. 2 Sam 13:38
in the days of David t. years. 21:1
at end of t. years Shimei's servant.
1 Ki 2:39
once in t. years came the navy.
10:22; 2 Chr 9:21
Abijam reigned t. years in Jerusalem. 1 Ki 15:2; 2 Chr 13:2
they continued t. years. 1 Ki 22:1
besieged Samaria t. years. 2 Ki 17:5
and at the end of t. years. 18:10
became his servant t. years. 24:1
either t. years' famine, or three
months to be. 1 Chr 21:12
strong t. years, t. years they walked
in way of David. 2 Chr 11:17
Abijah reigned t. years. 13:2
males, from t. years old. 31:16
an heifer of t. years old. Isa 15:5*
Jer 48:34*
within t. years, as years of. Isa 16:14
walked barefoot t. years. 20:3
nourishing them t. years. Dan 1:5
your tithes after t. years. Amos 4:4
heaven shut up t. years. Luke 4:25
Jas 5:17
t. years I come seeking. Luke 13:7
t. years I ceased not to. Acts 20:31
after t. years I went up. Gal 1:18

threefold

t. cord is not quickly. Eccl 4:12

threescore

Isaac t. years old when. Gen 25:26
took from them t. cities. Deut 3:4
Josh 13:30
so that three hundred and t. died.
2 Sam 2:31
pertained t. great cities. 1 Ki 4:13
his provision was t. measures. 22
The house . . . built for the Lord,
the length thereof was t. cubits.
6:2; 2 Chr 3:3
and he took t. men. 2 Ki 25:19
married when t. years. 1 Chr 2:21
Rehoboam took t. 2 Chr 11:21
temple t. cubits, breadth t. Ezra 6:3
t. valiant men are. S of S 3:7
there are t. queens, fourscore. 6:8
put to death t. men of the. Jer 52:25
whose height was t. cubits. Dan 3:1
from Jerusalem about t. Luke 24:13
widow be taken under t. 1 Tim 5:9
see **sixty**

threescore *and one*

Lord's tribute of asses, t. and one.
Num 31:39

threescore *and two*

able men t. and two. 1 Chr 26:8
t. and two years old. Dan 5:31
in t. and two weeks the street. 9:25
after t. and two weeks Messiah. 26

threescore *and five*

within t. and five years. Isa 7:8

threescore *and six*

souls which came with Jacob t. and
six. Gen 46:26
of her purifying t. and six days.
Lev 12:5

threescore *and seven*

t. and seven priests'. Neh 7:72

threescore *and eight*

brethren t. and eight. 1 Chr 16:38

threescore *and ten*

which came into Egypt, were t. and
ten. Gen 46:27; Deut 10:22
for Israel t. and ten days. Gen 50:3
twelve wells of water, and t. and ten
palm trees. Ex 15:27; Num 33:9
t. and ten kings, their. Judg 1:7
had t. and ten sons. 8:30; 9:2
they gave him t. and ten pieces. 9:4
he slew t. and ten persons. 5, 18, 24
rode on t. and ten ass colts. 12:14
brought t. and ten bullocks.
2 Chr 29:32
sabbath, to fulfil t. and ten. 36:21
of our years are t. and ten. Ps 90:10

thou hast had indignation these *t. and ten* years? *Zech* 1:12
t. and ten horsemen. *Acts* 23:23
see **seventy**

threescore *and twelve*
t. and twelve beeves. *Num* 31:38

threescore *and fifteen*
kindred *t. and fifteen.* *Acts* 7:14

threescore *and seventeen*
Succoth *t. and seventeen.* *Judg* 8:14

thresh
thou shalt *t.* the mountains. *Isa* 41:15
it is time to *t.* her. *Jer* 51:33*
arise, and *t.* O daughter. *Mi* 4:13
thou didst *t.* the heathen. *Hab* 3:12

threshed
Gideon *t.* wheat by the. *Judg* 6:11*
fitches not *t.* with a threshing. *Isa* 28:27
because they *t.* Gilead. *Amos* 1:3

thresheth
t. in hope, be partaker. *1 Cor* 9:10

threshing
your *t.* shall reach unto. *Lev* 26:5
here be *t.* instruments. *2 Sam* 24:22
1 Chr 21:23
like the dust by *t.* *2 Ki* 13:7
Ornan was *t.* wheat. *1 Chr* 21:20
O my *t.* and the corn of my floor. *Isa* 21:10
he will not ever be *t.* it. 28:28
will make thee a new sharp *t.* 41:15
see **floor, floors**

threshold
hands were upon the *t.* *Judg* 19:27
hands cut off upon the *t.* *1 Sam* 5:4
tread not on the *t.* of Dagon. 5
to *t.* the child died. *1 Ki* 14:17
the glory of God was gone up to the *t.* of the house. *Ezek* 9:3; 10:4
God departed from the *t.* 10:18
in their setting of their *t.* by. 43:8
prince shall worship at the *t.* 46:2
out from under the *t.* eastward. 47:1
all that leap on the *t.* *Zeph* 1:9

thresholds
keeping ward at the *t.* *Neh* 12:25*
of their threshold by my *t.* *Ezek* 43:8
desolation shall be in the *t.* *Zeph* 2:14

threw
Shimei *t.* stones at David and cast dust. *2 Sam* 16:13
they *t.* Jezebel down. *2 Ki* 9:33
and they *t.* down the. *2 Chr* 31:1*
a certain poor widow and she *t.* in two mites, which. *Mark* 12:42
the devil *t.* him down. *Luke* 9:42
as they cried, and *t.* *Acts* 22:23

threwest
their persecutors thou *t.* *Neh* 9:11

thrice
t. in the year shall. *Ex* 34:23, 24
and Joash smote *t.* *2 Ki* 13:18
thou shalt smite Syria but *t.* 19
thou shalt deny me *t.* *Mat* 26:34
75; *Mark* 14:30, 72; *Luke* 22:34
61; *John* 13:38
this was done *t.* *Acts* 10:16
t. was I beaten with rods, once was I stoned, *t.* I suffered. *2 Cor* 11:25
I besought the Lord *t.* 12:8

throat
their *t.* is an open sepulchre. *Ps* 5:9; *Rom* 3:13
crying, my *t.* is dried. *Ps* 69:3
nor speak they through their *t.* 115:7
put a knife to thy *t.* if. *Pr* 23:2
and withhold thy *t.* from. *Jer* 2:25
servant took him by the *t.* *Mat* 18:28

throne
The seat in which a king sits on ceremonial occasions. The scripture describes the throne *of Solomon as the finest and richest* throne *in the world,* 1 Ki 10:20. *It was all of ivory, and plated with pure gold. The ascent was six steps; the back was round, and two arms supported the seat. Twelve golden lions, one on each side of every step, made a principal part of its ornament.*
Throne *is also used as a symbol of sovereign power and dignity; thus Pharaoh tells Joseph,* Gen 41:40, Only in the *throne* will I be greater than thou.
Heaven is the throne *of God,* Isa 66:1. Justice and judgement are the habitation of the *throne* of the Lord, Ps 89:14. Christ Jesus is set down at the right hand of the *throne* of God, Heb 12:2.
only in the *t.* will I be. *Gen* 41:40
when he sitteth on *t.* of. *Deut* 17:18
make them inherit the *t.* *1 Sam* 2:8
to set up the *t.* of David. *2 Sam* 3:10
stablish *t.* of his kingdom. 7:13, 16
Solomon shall sit on my *t.* *1 Ki* 1:13, 17, 24, 30, 35
given one to sit on my *t.* this day. 48
not fail thee a man on the *t.* 2:4; 8:25
9:5; *2 Chr* 6:16; *Jer* 33:17
Solomon sat on *t.* of. *1 Ki* 2:12, 24
8:20; 10:9; *1 Chr* 29:23
2 Chr 6:10
the king made a great *t.* *1 Ki* 10:18
2 Chr 9:17
set him on his father's *t.* *2 Ki* 10:3
fourth generation shall sit on the *t.* 30; 15:12
Joash sat on *t.* 11:19; *2 Chr* 23:20
repaired unto the *t.* of the. *Neh* 3:7
kings are they on the *t.* *Job* 36:7
thou satest in the *t.* *Ps* 9:4
the Lord's *t.* is in heaven, his. 11:4
thy *t.* O God, is for ever. 45:6
Lam 5:19; *Heb* 1:8
God sitteth on the *t.* of. *Ps* 47:8
I will build thy *t.* to all. 89:4
judgement are habitation of thy *t.* 14
t. of iniquity have fellowship? 94:20
thy body will I set on thy *t.* 132:11
children shall sit on thy *t.* 12
a king that sitteth in the *t.* *Pr* 20:8
the Lord sitting upon a *t.* *Isa* 6:1
on *t.* of David and his kingdom. 9:7
I will exalt my *t.* above the. 14:13
shall be for a glorious *t.* 22:23
there is no *t.* O daughter. 47:1
the heaven is my *t.* and earth. 66:1
Acts 7:49
shall call Jerusalem the *t.* *Jer* 3:17
kings that sit on David's *t.* 13:13
disgrace the *t.* of thy glory. 14:21
a glorious high *t.* from the. 17:12
kings sitting on the *t.* 25; 22:4, 30
O king, that sittest upon the *t.* 22:2
29:16
none to sit on the *t.* of David. 36:30
I will set my *t.* in Elam. 49:38
was the likeness of a *t.* *Ezek* 1:26
10:1
the place of my *t.* shall Israel. 43:7
I will overthrow the *t.* of. *Hag* 2:22
by heaven, for it is God's *t.* *Mat* 5:34; 23:22
the Son of man shall sit in the *t.* 19:28; 25:31
give him the *t.* of David. *Luke* 1:32
let us come boldly to the *t.* *Heb* 4:16
right hand the *t.* of God. 8:1; 12:2
I grant to sit in my *t.* *Rev* 3:21
a *t.* was set in heaven, and one. 4:2
a rainbow round about the *t.* 3
about the *t.* were four and. 4
t. proceeded lightnings and thunderings ... seven lamps before *t.* 5
before the *t.* there was a sea of glass, in *t.* and round about the *t.* were. 6
thanks to him that sat on the *t.* 9
fall down before him that sat on the *t.* 10; 7:11
him that sat on the *t.* a book. 5:1
midst of the *t.* stood a Lamb. 6
right hand of him that sat on the *t.* 7
many angels about the *t.* 11
be unto him that sitteth upon the *t.* 13
6:16
multitude stood before the *t.* 7:9
our God which sitteth on the *t.* 10
are they before the *t.* of God and serve him: he that sitteth on *t.* 15
the Lamb in midst of the *t.* shall. *Rev* 7:17
altar which was before the *t.* 8:3
a new song before the *t.* 14:3
without fault before the *t.* of God. 5
a voice from the *t.* 16:17; 19:5
God that sat on the *t.* 19:4
I saw a great white *t.* and. 20:11
he that sat on *t.* said, Behold. 21:5
river, proceeding out of the *t.* 22:1
the *t.* of God and of the Lamb. 3

his **throne**
from firstborn of Pharaoh that sitteth on *his t.* *Ex* 11:5; 12:29
and the king and *his t.* *2 Sam* 14:9
the Lord make *his t.* greater. *1 Ki* 1:37, 47
and sat down on *his t.* 2:19
upon his seed, and on *his t.* shall. 33
Zimri sat on his *t.*, he slew. 16:11
and Jehoshaphat king of Judah, sat each on *his t.* 22:10; *2 Chr* 18:9
I saw the Lord sitting on *his t.* *1 Ki* 22:19; *2 Chr* 18:18
and Jeroboam sat upon *his t.* *2 Ki* 13:13
set *his t.* above *t.* 25:28; *Jer* 52:32
back the face of *his t.* *Job* 26:9
he hath prepared *his t.* *Ps* 9:7
his t. to endure as the days. 89:29
shall endure, and *his t.* as the sun. 36
thou hast cast *his t.* down to. 44
the habitation of *his t.* 97:2
the Lord hath prepared *his t.* 103:19
and *his t.* is upholden. *Pr* 20:28
set each *his t.* at the gates. *Jer* 1:15
should not have a son on *his t.* 33:21
and I will set *his t.* upon these. 43:10
deposed from *his* kingly *t.* *Dan* 5:20
his t. was like the fiery flame. 7:9
Nineveh rose from *his t.* *Jonah* 3:6
rule upon *his t.* and he shall be a priest on *his t.* and. *Zech* 6:13
Christ to sit on *his t.* *Acts* 2:30
from seven spirits which are before *his t.* *Rev* 1:4
sit down with my Father in *his t.* 3:21
caught up to God, to *his t.* 12:5
see **establish, established**

thrones
for there are set *t.* of. *Ps* 122:5
raised up from their *t.* *Isa* 14:9
come down from their *t.* *Ezek* 26:16
till the *t.* were cast down. *Dan* 7:9
upon twelve *t.* judging the twelve. *Mat* 19:28; *Luke* 22:30
him, whether they be *t.* *Col* 1:16
I saw *t.* and they sat upon. *Rev* 20:4

throng
lest they should *t.* him. *Mark* 3:9
the multitude *t.* thee. *Luke* 8:45*

thronged
and much people *t.* him. *Mark* 5:24
Luke 8:42

thronging
thou seest the multitude *t.* thee. *Mark* 5:31

through
thrust both of them *t.* *Num* 25:8
Ahaziah fell *t.* a lattice. *2 Ki* 1:2
yet *t.* the scent of water. *Job* 14:9
their tongue walketh *t.* *Ps* 73:9
t. idleness the house droppeth *t.* *Eccl* 10:18
shewing himself *t.* the. *S of S* 2:9
I would go *t.* them, I would burn. *Isa* 27:4
thou passest *t.* the waters, and *t.* 43:2
go *t.* go *t.* the gates, prepare. 62:10
after he brought me *t.* *Ezek* 46:19
and brought me *t.* the waters. 47:4
the third part *t.* fire. *Zech* 13:9
he walketh *t.* dry places. *Mat* 12:43
they let him down *t.* the. *Luke* 5:19
ye are clean *t.* the word I. *John* 15:3
keep *t.* thine own name those. 17:11
sanctify them *t.* thy truth, thy. 17
believing ye might have life *t.* 20:31
peace with God *t.* our Lord Jesus. *Rom* 5:1
is eternal life *t.* Jesus Christ. 6:23
if ye *t.* the spirit do mortify the. 8:13

of him, *t.* him, to him, are. *Rom* 11:36
to God be glory *t.* Jesus Christ. 16:27
t. the thanksgiving of. *2 Cor* 4:15
for I *t.* the law am dead to. *Gal* 2:19
kindness towards us *t.* Christ Jesus. *Eph* 2:7
habitation of God *t.* the Spirit. 22
is above all, and *t.* all, in you all. 4:6
t. the ignorance that is in them. 18
pierced themselves *t.* *1 Tim* 6:10
who *t.* the eternal Spirit. *Heb* 9:14
t. the vail, that is to say. 10:20
t. the blood of the everlasting. 13:20

throughly

(*American Revision changes to* thoroughly)

cause him to be *t.* healed. *Ex* 21:19
his images brake they in pieces *t.* *2 Ki* 11:18
my grief were *t.* weighed. *Job* 6:2*
wash me *t.* from mine. *Ps* 51:2
shall *t.* glean the remnant. *Jer* 6:9
if ye *t.* amend your ways and your doings, if ye *t.* execute. 7:5
he shall *t.* plead their cause. 50:34
I *t.* washed away thy. *Ezek* 16:9
he will *t.* purge his floor. *Mat* 3:12
Luke 3:17
been *t.* made manifest. *2 Cor* 11:6
man of God *t.* furnished unto all. *2 Tim* 3:17*

throughout

I led Abraham *t.* the land. *Josh* 24:3
search him *t.* thousands of Judah. *1 Sam* 23:23
Hezekiah *t.* all Judah. *2 Chr* 31:20
be preached *t.* the world. *Mark* 14:9
woven from the top *t.* *John* 19:23
is spoken of *t.* the world. *Rom* 1:8
see **generations**

throw

ye shall *t.* down their altars. *Judg* 2:2*
t. down the altar of Baal thy. 6:25
t. her down. So they. *2 Ki* 9:33
the nations to *t.* down. *Jer* 1:10
as I have watched over them, to *t.* down. 31:28
they shall *t.* down thine. *Ezek* 16:39
I will *t.* down all thy strong. *Mi* 5:11
build, but I will *t.* down. *Mal* 1:4

throwing

him with *t.* a stone. *Num* 35:17*

thrown

the horse and his rider hath he *t.* *Ex* 15:1, 21
because he hath *t.* down. *Judg* 6:32
his head be *t.* to thee. *2 Sam* 20:21
Israel have *t.* down thine altars. *1 Ki* 19:10, 14
it shall not be *t.* down. *Jer* 31:40
her walls are *t.* down. 50:15
the Lord hath *t.* down. *Lam* 2:2
he hath *t.* down, and hath not. 17
I will leave thee *t.* into. *Ezek* 29:5
mountains shall be *t.* down. 38:20
and the rocks are *t.* down. *Nah* 1:6
upon another, that shall not be *t.* *Mat* 24:2; *Mark* 13:2; *Luke* 21:6
when the devil had *t.* him. *Luke* 4:35
Babylon shall be *t.* down. *Rev* 18:21

thrust

he shall surely *t.* you. *Ex* 11:1
because they were *t.* out of. 12:39
Balaam's ass *t.* herself. *Num* 22:25
Phinehas *t.* both of them. 25:8
but if he *t.* him of hatred. 35:20
but if he *t.* him suddenly without. 22
hath spoken . . . to *t.* thee. *Deut* 13:5
because he sought to *t.* thee from. 10
the awl through his ear. 15:17
he shall *t.* out the enemy. 33:27
Ehud *t.* the dagger into. *Judg* 3:21
he *t.* the fleece together, and. 6:38
and Zebul *t.* out Gaal and. 9:41
his young men *t.* Abimelech. 54
wives' sons grew up, and they *t.* 11:2
t. out all your right eyes. *1 Sam* 11:2
t. me through therewith . . . come and *t.* me. 31:4; *1 Chr* 10:4
and *t.* his sword in his. *2 Sam* 2:16
Joab *t.* 3 darts through heart. 18:14

shall be as thorns *t.* away. *2 Sam* 23:6
Solomon *t.* out Abiathar. *1 Ki* 2:27
came near to *t.* her away. *2 Ki* 4:27
they *t.* Uzziah out. *2 Chr* 26:20
thou hast *t.* at me, that. *Ps* 118:13
found shall be *t.* through. *Isa* 13:15
of those that are *t.* through. 14:19
they that are *t.* through. *Jer* 51:4
shall *t.* thee through with swords. *Ezek* 16:40
t. with side and shoulder. 34:21
to *t.* them out of their. 46:18
neither one *t.* another. *Joel* 2:8
shall *t.* him through. *Zech* 13:3
they rose and *t.* him. *Luke* 4:29
and prayed him he would *t.* out. 5:3
shalt be *t.* down to hell. 10:15
and you yourselves *t.* out. 13:28
and *t.* my hand into his side. *John* 20:25, 27
he that did the wrong *t.* *Acts* 7:27
but our fathers *t.* him from them. 39
t. them into the inner prison. 16:24
and now do they *t.* us out privily? 37
if it were possible, to *t.* in. 27:39
stoned or *t.* through with. *Heb* 12:20
t. in thy sickle, for the. *Rev* 14:15
he sat on the cloud, *t.* in his sickle. 16
t. in thy sharp sickle and gather. 18
the angel *t.* in his sickle into. 19

thrusteth

God *t.* him down, not man. *Job* 32:13

thumb

thou put it on the *t.* of their right hand. *Ex* 29:20; *Lev* 8:23, 24
14:14, 17, 25, 28

thumbs

him and cut off his *t.* *Judg* 1:6
their *t.* and toes cut off. 7

Thummim

Urim *and* Thummim; *According to the Hebrew,* Ex 28:30, *the literal signification of these two words is,* lights *and* perfections, *or* the shining *and* the perfect. *According to St. Jerome,* doctrine *and* judgement. *According to the LXX,* declaration *or* manifestation, *and* truth. *They were worn in or attached to the breastplate of the high priest when inquiring of God.*

breastplate of judgement, the Urim and the *T.* *Ex* 28:30; *Lev* 8:8
let thy *T.* and Urim be with thy Holy One. *Deut* 33:8
stood up priest with Urim and *T.* *Ezra* 2:63; *Neh* 7:65

thunder

the Lord sent *t.* and hail. *Ex* 9:23
the *t.* shall cease, nor shall. 29
thundered with great *t.* *1 Sam* 7:10
he shall send *t.* 12:17
the Lord sent *t.* 18
the *t.* of his power who? *Job* 26:14
a way for the lightning of the *t.* 28:26; 38:25
clothed his neck with *t.*? 39:19*
smelleth the *t.* of the captains. 25
the voice of thy *t.* was in. *Ps* 77:18
in the secret place of *t.* 81:7
at the voice of thy *t.* they. 104:7
visited of the Lord with *t.* *Isa* 29:6
which is, The sons of *t.* *Mark* 3:17
as it were the noise of *t.* *Rev* 6:1
as the voice of a great *t.* 14:2

thunder, *verb*

shall he *t.* upon them. *1 Sam* 2:10
or canst thou *t.* with a voice? *Job* 40:9

thunderbolts

their flocks to hot *t.* *Ps* 78:48

thundered

the Lord *t.* with a great. *1 Sam* 7:10
the Lord *t.* from heaven. *2 Sam* 22:14; *Ps* 18:13
heard it, said that it *t.* *John* 12:29

thundereth

he *t.* with the voice of his. *Job* 37:4
God *t.* marvellously with his. 5
the God of glory *t.* *Ps* 29:3

thunderings

be no more mighty *t.* *Ex* 9:28
and all the people saw the *t.* 20:18
out of the throne proceeded *t.* *Rev* 4:5; 19:6
there were voices and *t.* 8:5; 11:19

thunders

the *t.* and hail ceased. *Ex* 9:33, 34
there were *t.* and lightnings. 19:16
Rev 16:18

see **seven**

thus

t. did Noah, according as God. *Gen* 6:22
t. she was reproved. 20:16
why am I *t.*? 25:22
dealest thou *t.* with us? *Ex* 5:15
t. shall ye eat it, with your. 12:11
hast thou dealt *t.* with us? 14:11
t. separate the children. *Lev* 15:31
t. shall Aaron come into the. 16:3
t. shalt thou separate the. *Num* 8:14
deal *t.* with me, kill me. 11:15
hath the Lord done *t.*? *Deut* 29:24
wherefore liest thou *t.* on? *Josh* 7:10
hast thou served us *t.*? *Judg* 8:1
why askest thou *t.* after my? 13:18
if they say *t.* to us, Tarry. *1 Sam* 14:9
but if they say *t.*, Come up to us. 10
if he say *t.*, It is well. 20:7
2 Sam 15:26
be more vile than *t.* *2 Sam* 6:22
I may not tarry *t.* with thee. 18:14
t. he said, O my son Absalom. 33
t. they spake before. *1 Ki* 3:22
t. the Lord saved Hezekiah. *2 Chr* 32:22
and *t.* they returned. *Ezra* 5:11
and therein was a record *t.* 6:2
even *t.* be he shaken out. *Neh* 5:13
t. shall it be done to. *Esth* 6:9, 11
why then are ye *t.*? *Job* 27:12
if I say I will speak *t.* *Ps* 73:15
t. my heart was grieved, and. 21
t. shall the man be blessed. 128:4
when *t.* it shall be in the. *Isa* 24:13
t. shall they be unto thee with. 47:15
for *t.* hath the Lord. *Jer* 4:27; 6:6
t. shall it be done unto them. 5:13
deal *t.* with them in time of. 18:23
why hath the Lord done *t.* to? 22:8
t. might we procure evil. 26:19
to whom art thou *t.* like? *Ezek* 31:18
is it not even *t.* O children of Israel? *Amos* 2:11
t. ye brought an offering. *Mal* 1:13
t. it is written of the prophet. *Mat* 2:5; *Luke* 24:46
t. it becomes us to fulfil. *Mat* 3:15
scriptures be fulfilled, that *t.* 26:54
t. hath Lord dealt with. *Luke* 1:25
hast thou *t.* dealt with us? 2:48
master, *t.* saying, thou reproachest. 11:45
t. shall it be when Son of man. 17:30
Pharisee prayed *t.*, God, I. 18:11
said, Suffer ye *t.* far. 22:51
having said *t.* he gave up. 23:46
t. spake, Jesus himself stood in. 24:36
when he had *t.* spoken, he. 40
it is written, *t.* it behoved Christ. 46
journey, sat *t.* on well. *John* 4:6
when he *t.* had spoken, he cried. 11:43
if we let him *t.* alone, all will. 48
he said, *T.* saith the Holy. *Acts* 21:11
Why hast made me *t.*? *Rom* 9:20
t. are the secrets of his heart made manifest. *1 Cor* 14:25
love of Christ constraineth us, because we *t.* judge, that if. *2 Cor* 5:14
be perfect, be *t.* minded. *Phil* 3:15
though we *t.* speak. *Heb* 6:9
t. I saw horses in vision. *Rev* 9:17
because thou hast judged *t.* 16:5
see **did, do, Lord**

thus *and* **thus**

Achan said *t.* *and* *t.* *Josh* 7:20
t. *and* *t.* dealeth Micah. *Judg* 18:4
t. *and* *t.* did Ahithophel counsel Absalom, and *t.* *and* *t.* have I. *2 Sam* 17:15
t. *and* *t.* shalt thou say to. *1 Ki* 14:5

T. and t. said the maid. *2 Ki* 5:4
he said, *T. and t.* spake he to. 9:12

Thyatira

Lydia, of the city of *T.* *Acts* 16:14
send it to *T.* *Rev* 1:11
of the church in *T.* write. 2:18
unto you and unto the rest in *T.* 24

thyine

merchandise of *t.* wood. *Rev* 18:12

thyself

separate *t.* I pray thee. *Gen* 13:9
persons, and take goods to *t.* 14:21
return, and submit *t.* under. 16:9
that thou hast unto *t.* 33:9
as yet exaltest *t.* *Ex* 9:17
wilt thou refuse to humble *t.*? 10:3
take heed to *t.*, see my face.28; 34:12
Deut 4:9; 12:13, 19, 30
1 Sam 19:2
why sittest thou *t.* alone ? *Ex* 18:14
so shall it be easier for *t.* and. 22
come and present *t.* there. 34:2
an atonement for *t.* *Lev* 9:7
neighbour's wife to defile *t.* 18:20
lie with any beast to defile *t.* 23
love thy neighbour as *t.* 19:18
Mat 19:19; 22:39; *Mark* 12:31
thou shalt love him as *t.* *Lev* 19:34
bear it not *t.* alone. *Num* 11:17
except thou make *t.* a prince. 16:13
nations greater than *t.* *Deut* 9:1
spoil shalt thou take to *t.* 20:14
wherewith thou coverest *t.* 22:12
redeem thou my right to *t.* *Ruth* 4:6
if iniquity be in me, slay me *t.*
1 Sam 20:8
thee from avenging *t.* 25:26
thou shalt bestir *t.* *2 Sam* 5:24
has confirmed to *t.* thy people. 7:24
thy bed and make *t.* sick. 13:5
feign *t.* a mourner and put. 14:2
t. wouldest have set *t.* against. 18:13
thou wilt shew *t.* merciful. 22:26
Ps 18:25
with the pure thou wilt shew *t.* pure.
2 Sam 22:27; *Ps* 18:26
and shew *t.* a man. *1 Ki* 2:2
thou hast not asked for *t.* long life.
3:11; *2 Chr* 1:11
with me and refresh *t.* *1 Ki* 13:7
pray thee, and disguise *t.* 14:2
why feignest thou *t.* to be ? 6
go shew *t.* to Ahab, and I. 18:1
strengthen *t.* and see what. 20:22
so shall thy judgement be, *t.* hast. 40
because thou hast sold *t.* to. 21:20
hast humbled *t.* *2 Ki* 22:19
2 Chr 34:27
advise with *t.* what. *1 Chr* 21:12
thou hast joined *t.* with Ahaziah.
2 Chr 20:37
thy brethren, better than *t.* 21:13
think not with *t.* that thou. *Esth* 4:13
dost restrain wisdom to *t.*? *Job* 15:8
acquaint *t.* with him, and. 22:21
thou opposest *t.* against me. 30:21
thine anger, lift up *t.* *Ps* 7:6
why hidest thou *t.* in times ? 10:1
stir up *t.* and awake to my. 35:23
delight *t.* also in the Lord. 37:4
when thou doest well to *t.* 49:18
altogether such an one as *t.* 50:21
boastest thou *t.* in mischief ? 52:1
displeased, O turn *t.* to us. 60:1
madest strong for *t.* 80:15, 17
shew *t.* 94:1
lift up *t.* thou judge. 2
do this, my son, and deliver *t.*
Pr 6:3, 5
thou shalt be wise for *t.* 9:12
fret not *t.* because of evil men. 24:19
and make it fit for *t.* in the. 27
put not forth *t.* in presence of. 25:6
boast not *t.* of to-morrow. 27:1
foolishly in lifting up *t.* 30:32
make *t.* over wise; why shouldest thou destroy *t* ? *Eccl* 7:16
that thou *t.* also hast cursed. 22
hide *t.* as for a little. *Isa* 26:20
lifting up *t.* the nations were. 33:3
art a God that hidest *t.* 45:15
shake *t.* from the dust, loose *t.* 52:2
thou hast discovered *t.* to. 57:8
thou didst debase *t.* even. *Isa* 57:9
thou delight *t.* in the Lord. 58:14
make *t.* a glorious name. 63:14
wilt thou refrain *t.* for these ? 64:12
which say, Stand by *t.*, come. 65:5
procured this unto *t.* *Jer* 2:17
clothest *t.* with crimson, in vain shalt thou make *t.* fair; thy lovers. 4:30
sackcloth, wallow *t.* in ashes. 6:26
t. shall discontinue from. 17:4
I will make thee a terror to *t.* 20:4
because thou clothest *t.* in. 22:15
redemption is thine, buy it for *t.* 32:8
seekest thou great things for *t.* 45:5
furnish *t.* to go into captivity. 46:19
how long wilt thou cut *t.*? 47:5
O sword, put up *t.* into thy. 6
give *t.* no rest, let not. *Lam* 2:18
thou hast covered *t.* with. 3:44
be drunken, make *t.* naked. 4:21
go shut *t.* within thine. *Ezek* 3:24
thou madest to *t.* images. 16:17
and thou hast defiled *t.* in. 22:4
for whom thou didst wash *t.* 23:40
hast lifted up *t.* in height. 31:10
prepare for *t.* and all thy. 38:7
said, Let thy gifts be to *t.* *Dan* 5:17
but hast lifted up *t.* against. 23
and to chasten *t.* before thy. 10:12
thou hast destroyed *t.* *Hos* 13:9
though thou exalt *t.* as the. *Ob* 4
Aphrah roll *t.* in dust. *Mi* 1:10
now gather *t.* in troops, O. 5:1
make *t.* many as the. *Nah* 3:15
deliver *t.* O Zion, that. *Zech* 2:7
If thou be the Son of God, cast *t.* down. *Mat* 4:6; *Luke* 4:9
shalt not forswear *t.* *Mat* 5:33
shew *t.* to priest. 8:4; *Mark* 1:44
Luke 5:14
save *t.* *Mat* 27:40; *Mark* 15:30
Luke 23:39
Physician, heal *t.* *Luke* 4:23
when thou *t.* beholdest not. 6:42
Lord, trouble not *t.* for I am. 7:6
love thy neighbour as *t.* 10:27
Rom 13:9; *Gal* 5:14; *Jas* 2:8
will not rather say, Make ready and gird *t.* *Luke* 17:8
what sayest thou of *t.*? *John* 1:22
if thou do these things, shew *t.* 7:4
thou bearest record of *t.* it. 8:13
whom makest thou *t.*? 53
a man, makest *t.* God. 10:33
thou wilt manifest *t.* unto us ? 14:22
sayest thou this of *t.*? or did ? 18:34
young, thou girdest *t.* 21:18
join *t.* to this chariot. *Acts* 8:29
gird *t.* 12:8
do *t.* no harm. 16:28
purify *t.* with them, that all may know that thou *t.* walkest. 21:24
t. mayest take knowledge. 24:8
permitted to speak for *t.* . . . Festus said, Paul, thou art beside *t.* 26:1
thou condemnest *t.* *Rom* 2:1
that thou *t.* art guide of the blind. 19
teachest thou not *t.*? 21
hast thou faith ? have it to *t.* 14:22
considering *t.* lest thou. *Gal* 6:1
oughtest to behave *t.* *1 Tim* 3:15
and exercise *t.* rather unto. 4:7
these things, give *t.* wholly to. 15
take heed to *t.* and to the doctrine; in doing this thou shalt save *t.* 16
other men's sins: keep *t.* pure. 5:22
minds, from such withdraw *t.* 6:5
to shew *t.* approved. *2 Tim* 2:15
shewing *t.* a pattern of. *Tit* 2:7

Tiberias

which is the sea of *T.* *John* 6:1
there came other boats from *T.* 23

Tibni

half of the people followed *T.*
1 Ki 16:21
against those that followed *T.* 22

tidings

heard these evil *t.* *Ex* 33:4
wife heard the *t.* *1 Sam* 4:19
they told the *t.* of the men of Jabesh.
11:4*, 5*
alive to bring *t.* to Gath. 27:11*
when *t.* came of Saul. *2 Sam* 4:4
t. came, saying, Absalom. 13:30
run and bear the king *t.* 18:19
shalt not bear *t.* this day. 20
thou hast no *t.* ready. 22
Cushi came, Cushi said, *T.* my. 31
then *t.* came to Joab. *1 Ki* 2:28
sent to thee with heavy *t.* 14:6
and sent to carry *t.* to. *1 Chr* 10:9
not be afraid of evil *t.* *Ps* 112:7
man that brought *t.* *Jer* 20:15
for they have heard evil *t.* 49:23
shalt answer for the *t.* *Ezek* 21:7
t. out of the east shall. *Dan* 11:44
I am sent to shew thee these glad *t.*
Luke 1:19; 2:10
shewing the glad *t.* of the. 8:1
t. of these things came. *Acts* 11:22*
we declare unto you glad *t.* 13:32
t. came to the chief captain. 21:31
that bring glad *t.* of good. *Rom* 10:15
see **good**

tie

and *t.* the kine. *1 Sam* 6:7, 10
bind on thy heart and *t.* *Pr* 6:21

tied

they *t.* to it a lace of blue. *Ex* 39:31
but horses *t.*, and asses *t.* *2 Ki* 7:10
ye shall find as ass *t.* *Mat* 21:2
Mark 11:2, 4; *Luke* 19:30

Tiglath-pileser

T. came and took Ijon. *2 Ki* 15:29
Ahaz sent messengers to *T.* 16:7
T. carried away Beerah. *1 Chr* 5:6
stirred up the spirit of *T.* 26
T. came and distressed Ahaz.
2 Chr 28:20

tile

son of man, take thee a *t.* *Ezek* 4:1

tiling

they let him down through the *t.*
Luke 5:19*

till

do any thing *t.* thou be. *Gen* 19:22
t. I know what God will. *1 Sam* 22:3
if I taste bread *t.* the. *2 Sam* 3:35
he was helped *t.* he. *2 Chr* 26:15
t. the wrath arose, *t.* there. 36:16
t. there stood up a priest. *Ezra* 2:63
Neh 7:65
be angry with us *t.* thou. *Ezra* 9:14
all the days will I wait *t.* *Job* 14:14
t. I die. 27:5
not purged, *t.* ye die. *Isa* 22:14
wickedness *t.* thou find. *Ps* 10:15
a wise man keepeth it in *t.* *Pr* 29:11*
t. I might see what was. *Eccl* 2:3
stir not up my love *t.* he please.
S of S 2:7; 3:5
that lay field to field, *t.* *Isa* 5:8
no rest, *t.* he establish, and *t.* he make Jerusalem a praise. 62:7
destroy *t.* they. *Jer* 49:9; *Ob*
t. he had cast them out. *Jer* 52:
t. the Lord look down. *Lam* 3:50
wast perfect, *t.* iniquity. *Ezek* 28:15
t. seven times pass over. *Dan* 4:2
but go thou thy way *t.* the. 12:1
t. they acknowledge their. *Hos* 5:15
t. he rain righteousness upon. 10:12
t. she had brought forth. *Mat* 1:25
t. heaven and earth pass, one. 5:18
I am straitened *t.* it be. *Luke* 12:50
doth not seek diligently *t.* she. 15:8
he said unto them, Occupy *t.* 19:13
if I will that he tarry *t.* I come.
John 21:22, 23
t. another king arose. *Acts* 7:18
not eat, *t.* they had killed Paul.
23:12, 14, 21
t. we all come in the. *Eph* 4:13
without offence, *t.* the day. *Phil* 1:10
t. I come, give attendance to reading. *1 Tim* 4:13
which ye have, hold fast *t.* I come.
Rev 2:25
t. we have sealed the servants. 7:3
t. the seven plagues were. 15:8
t. the thousand years should. 20:3
see **consumed, morning, until**

till, *verb*

was not a man to *t.* the ground.
Gen 2:5; 3:23

thy servants shall *t.* *2 Sam* 9:10
they shall *t.* it, and dwell therein. *Jer* 27:11

tillage

was over them that were for *t.* *1 Chr* 27:26
have the tithes of *t.* *Neh* 10:37
much food is in the *t.* *Pr* 13:23

tilled

ye shall be *t.* and sown. *Ezek* 36:9
the desolate land shall be *t.* 34

tiller

but Cain was a *t.* of. *Gen* 4:2

tillest

when thou *t.* ground, it. *Gen* 4:12

tilleth

he that *t.* land shall. *Pr* 12:11
he that *t.* his land shall have. 28:19

timber

break down the *t.* thereof. *Lev* 14:45
prepared *t.* and stones to build. *1 Ki* 5:18; *1 Chr* 22:14; *2 Chr* 2:9
away the *t.* of Ramah. *1 Ki* 15:22
t. is laid in the walls. *Ezra* 5:8
let *t.* be pulled down from. 6:11*
that he may give me *t.* *Neh* 2:8
they shall lay thy *t.* in. *Ezek* 26:12
the beam out of the *t.* *Hab* 2:11
consume it with the *t.* *Zech* 5:4

timbrel

and Miriam took a *t.* in. *Ex* 15:20
they take the *t.* and harp. *Job* 21:12
bring hither the *t.* *Ps* 81:2
praises to him with the *t.* 149:3
praise him with the *t.* and. 150:4

timbrels

went out after her with *t.* *Ex* 15:20
his daughter came out with *t.* *Judg* 11:34
of Israel played before the Lord on *t.* *2 Sam* 6:5; *1 Chr* 13:8
damsels playing with *t.* *Ps* 68:25

time

(*This word is frequently used with the meaning of* season)
return according to the *t.* of life. *Gen* 18:10, 14
the *t.* that women go out to. 24:11
from the *t.* he had made him. 39:5
the *t.* drew nigh that Israel. 47:29
pay for loss of his *t.* *Ex* 21:19
if beyond the *t.* of her. *Lev* 15:25
a wife besides the other in her life *t.* 18:18
the *t.* was the *t.* of first. *Num* 13:20
what *t.* the fire devoured. 26:10
t. thou put the sickle. *Deut* 16:9
at the *t.* of the going down of the sun. *Josh* 10:27; *2 Chr* 18:34
did Joshua take at one *t.* *Josh* 10:42
all the *t.* the house of. *Judg* 18:31
the *t.* I commanded *2 Sam* 7:11
at the *t.* when kings go forth. 11:1
eight hundred he slew at one *t.* 23:8
is it *t.* to receive money? *2 Ki* 5:26
were to come from *t.* to *t.* *1 Chr* 9:25
on this side the river, and at such a *t.* *Ezra* 4:10, 17; 7:12
and it is a *t.* of rain. 10:13
return? and I set him a *t.* *Neh* 2:6
what *t.* they wax warm. *Job* 6:17
who shall set me a *t.* to plead? 9:19
accomplished before his *t.* 15:32
which were cut down out of *t.* 22:16
which I reserved against the *t.* 38:23
knowest thou the *t.* they bring forth? 39:1, 2
in a *t.* when thou mayest. *Ps* 32:6
not be ashamed in the evil *t.* 37:19
the Lord will deliver him in *t.* 41:1
what *t.* I am afraid, I will. 56:3
to thee in an acceptable *t.* 69:13
their *t.* should have endured. 81:15
remember how short my *t.* is. 89:47
until the *t.* that his word. 105:19
there is a *t.* to every purpose. *Eccl* 3:1, 17; 8:6
a *t.* to be born, and a *t.* to die; a *t.* 3:2
thou die before thy *t.*? 7:17
a wise man's heart discerneth *t.* 8:5
but *t.* and chance happeneth. 9:11
of men snared in an evil *t.* *Eccl* 9:12
that draweth near the *t.* *Isa* 26:17
from the *t.* it goeth forth it. 28:19
declared this from ancient *t.*? 45:21*
from the *t.* that it was. 48:16
in an acceptable *t.* have I heard thee. 49:8; *2 Cor* 6:2
Lord will hasten it in his *t.* *Isa* 60:22
at the *t.* I visit, they shall. *Jer* 6:15
crane and swallow observe the *t.* 8:7
looked for a *t.* of health, and. 15
the Saviour thereof in *t.* 14:8
and for the *t.* of healing, and. 19
it is even the *t.* of Jacob's. 30:7
and the *t.* of their visitation. 46:21 50:27
the *t.* that I will visit him. 49:8 50:31
will appoint me the *t.*? 49:19; 50:44
floor, it is *t.* to thresh her. 51:33
from *t.* to *t.* shalt thou. *Ezek* 4:10
thy *t.* was the *t.* of love, I. 16:8
as at the *t.* of thy reproach of. 57
day is near, it shall be the *t.* 30:3
ye would gain the *t.* *Dan* 2:8
to speak before me, till the *t.* 9
that he would give him *t.* 16
at what *t.* ye hear the sound of cornet. 3:5, 15
were prolonged for a *t.* 7:12
t. came that the saints possessed. 22
t. and the dividing of *t.* 25; 12:7
at the *t.* of the end shall be. 8:17
about the *t.* of evening. 9:21
forecast his devices for a *t.* 11:24
to make them white, even to the *t.* 35
at the *t.* of the end shall the king. 40
shall be a *t.* of trouble. 12:1
even to the *t.* of the end. 4, 9
from the *t.* the daily sacrifice. 11
it is *t.* to seek the Lord. *Hos* 10:12
till the *t.* that she which travaileth. *Mi* 5:3
is it *t.* to dwell in your? *Hag* 1:4
that at evening *t.* it. *Zech* 14:7
her fruit before the *t.* *Mal* 3:11
the *t.* they were carried. *Mat* 1:11
Herod enquired what *t.* the star. 2:7
to torment us before the *t.*? 8:29
and when the *t.* of the fruit. 21:34
master saith, My *t.* is. 26:18
the *t.* is fulfilled, repent. *Mark* 1:15
and so endure but for a *t.* 4:17
this is a desert, and now the *t.* 6:35
for the *t.* of figs was not yet. 11:13
ye know not when the *t.* is. 13:33
Elisabeth's full *t.* came. *Luke* 1:57
all kingdoms in a moment of *t.* 4:5
but this woman, since the *t.* 7:45
which in *t.* of temptation fall. 8:13
ye shall not see me, till the *t.* 13:35
thou knewest not the *t.* of thy. 19:44
t. is not come, your *t.* *John* 7:6
the *t.* cometh that whosoever. 16:2
the *t.* cometh when I shall no. 25
all the *t.* the Lord went. *Acts* 1:21
but when the *t.* of the promise. 7:17
in which *t.* Moses was born. 20
spent their *t.* in nothing else. 17:21
it is high *t.* to awake. *Rom* 13:11
judge nothing before the *t.* *1 Cor* 4:5
except with consent for a *t.* 7:5
but this I say, brethren, the *t.* 29
redeeming the *t.* *Eph* 5:16 *Col* 4:5
from you for a short *t.* *1 Thes* 2:17
that he might be revealed in his *t.* *2 Thes* 2:6
t. come, when they will. *2 Tim* 4:3
and the *t.* of my departure is. 6
grace to help in *t.* of need. *Heb* 4:16
when for the *t.* ye ought to. 5:12
which was a figure for the *t.* 9:9
imposed on them till the *t.* 10
the *t.* would fail me to tell of. 11:32
appeareth a little *t.* *Jas* 4:14
what manner of *t.* the. *1 Pet* 1:11
pass the *t.* of your sojourning. 17
should live the rest of his *t.* 4:2
for the *t.* is at hand. *Rev* 1:3; 22:10
sware, that there should be *t.* 10:6
t. of the dead, that they. 11:18
that he hath but a short *t.* 12:12
she is nourished for a *t.* and times, and half a *t.* *Rev* 12:14
see **appointed, before, come, day, due, last, long, many, old, past, process, second, set, third**

***any* time**

may redeem at *any t.* *Lev* 25:32
if the slayer at *any t.* *Num* 35:26
sounded my father to-morrow at *any t.* *1 Sam* 20:12
displeased him at *any t.* *1 Ki* 1:6
bear thee up, lest at *any t.* thou dash. *Mat* 4:6; *Luke* 4:11
lest at *any t.* the adversary deliver. *Mat* 5:25
lest at *any t.* they should see. 13:15 *Mark* 4:12
transgressed I at *any t.* *Luke* 15:29
lest at *any t.* your hearts be. 21:34
hath seen God at *any t.* *John* 1:18
ye heard his voice at *any t.* 5:37
unclean hath at *any t.* entered. *Acts* 11:8
who goeth a warfare *any t.* at his own charges? *1 Cor* 9:7
nor at *any t.* used we. *1 Thes* 2:5
to which of the angels said he at *any t.*? *Heb* 1:5, 13
lest at *any t.* we should let. 2:1
hath seen God at *any t.* *1 John* 4:12

***in the* time**

came to pass *in the t.* of. *Gen* 38:27
commanded *in the t.* of. *Ex* 34:18
them deliver *in the t.* *Judg* 10:14
in the t. of wheat harvest. 15:1
in the t. of old age he. *1 Ki* 15:23
in the t. of distress. *2 Chr* 28:22
in the t. of their trouble. *Neh* 9:27
more than *in the t.* when corn. *Ps* 4:7
as a fiery oven *in the t.* of. 21:9
in the t. of trouble he shall. 27:5
he is their strength *in the t.* 37:39
cast me not off *in the t.* of. 71:9
as the cold of snow *in the t.* of harvest. *Pr* 25:13
unfaithful man *in the t.* of. 19
salvation *in the t.* of trouble. *Isa* 33:2
in the t. of trouble they. *Jer* 2:27
if they can save thee *in the t.* 28
in the t. of visitation they shall be cast down. 8:12
in the t. of visitation they shall perish. 10:15; 51:18
shall not save them at all *in the t.* of trouble. 11:12
I will not hear them *in the t.* that. 14
enemy to entreat thee well *in the t.* of evil, and *in the t.* of. 15:11
deal thus with them *in the t.* 18:23
handleth the sickle *in the t.* 50:16
in the t. when thou shalt. *Ezek* 27:34
a perpetual hatred, *in the t.* of their calamity, *in the t.* that their. 35:5
I will take away my corn *in the t.* thereof. *Hos* 2:9
ask rain *in the t.* of the. *Zech* 10:1
in the t. of harvest I. *Mat* 13:30
many lepers *in the t.* of. *Luke* 4:27

***same* time**

Lord's anger was kindled the *same t.* *Num* 32:10
for Aaron also the *same t.* *Deut* 9:20
then Libnah revolted at the *same t.* *2 Ki* 8:22; *2 Chr* 21:10
the *same t.* 700 oxen. *2 Chr* 15:11
the people at the *same t.* 16:10
at the *same t.* came to. *Ezra* 5:3
vineyards at the *same t.* *Jer* 39:10
at the *same t.* shalt thou think evil. *Ezek* 38:10
at the *same t.* my reason. *Dan* 4:36
as never was to that *same t.* 12:1
the *same t.* there arose. *Acts* 19:23

***that* time**

not recover in *that t.*? *Judg* 11:26
to-morrow by *that t.* the sun be hot. *1 Sam* 11:9
since *that t.* hath it been. *Ezra* 5:16
to pass from *that t.* forth. *Neh* 4:16; 13:21
spoken concerning Moab since *that t.* *Isa* 16:13

in *that t.* shall the present be. *Isa* 18:7
I not told thee from *that t.*? 44:8
hath told it from *that t.*? 45:21
from *that t.* that thine ear. 48:8
that t. Israel shall come. *Jer* 50:4
in *that t.* the iniquity of Israel. 20
keep silence in *that t.* *Amos* 5:13
from *that t.* Jesus began. *Mat* 4:17
from *that t.* began to shew. 16:21
from *that t.* Judas sought. 26:16
since *that t.* the kingdom of God is preached. *Luke* 16:16
that t. many disciples. *John* 6:66
about *that t.* Herod. *Acts* 12:1

at that **time**

king of Moab *at that t.* *Num* 22:4
and I spake to you *at that t.* saying. *Deut* 1:9
judges *at that t.* saying. 16
I commanded you *at that t.* 18; 3:18
Joshua *at that t.* saying. 3:21
I besought the Lord *at that t.* 23
the Lord and you *at that t.* 5:5
the Lord hearkened to me *at that t.* 9:19; 10:10
the ark was *at that t.* *1 Sam* 14:18
Israel brought under *at that t.* *2 Chr* 13:18
not keep the passover *at that t.* 30:3
kept the passover *at that t.* 35:17
at that t. they shall call. *Jer* 3:17
at that t. shall they bring out. 8:1
at that t. cause the branch of. 33:15
at that t. shall Michael. *Dan* 12:1
face from them *at that t.* *Mi* 3:4
at that t. I will search. *Zeph* 1:12
at that t. I will undo all that. 3:19
at that t. will I bring you again. 20
at Jerusalem *at that t.* *Luke* 23:7
at that t. there was a great. *Acts* 8:1
at that t. ye were without Christ. *Eph* 2:12

this **time**

this t. will my husband. *Gen* 29:34
Pharaoh hardened his heart at *this t.* *Ex* 8:32
I will at *this t.* send all my. 9:14
to-morrow about *this t.* I will. 18
said, I have sinned *this t.* 27
according to *this t.* it. *Num* 23:23
nor would as at *this t.* *Judg* 13:23
not give unto them at *this t.* 21:22
for about *this t.* ye shall find him. *1 Sam* 9:13
the counsel is not good at *this t.* *2 Sam* 17:7
I will not at *this t.* put. *1 Ki* 2:26
by to-morrow about *this t.* 19:2; 20:6
2 Ki 7:1, 18; 10:6
in all *this t.* was not I at. *Neh* 13:6
thy peace at *this t.*: art come to the kingdom . . . *t.* as *this*? *Esth* 4:14
blessed be the Lord from *this t.* forth. *Ps* 113:2
bless the Lord from *this t.* forth. 115:18
will preserve thee from *this t.* 121:8
new things from *this t.* *Isa* 48:6
wilt thou not from *this t.*? *Jer* 3:4
this is the *t.* of the Lord's. 51:6
haughtily; for *this t.* is evil. *Mi* 2:3
since the beginning of the world to *this t.* *Mat* 24:21; *Mark* 13:19
receive an hundred-fold now in *this t.* *Mark* 10:30; *Luke* 18:30
do not discern *this t.*? *Luke* 12:56
by *this t.* he stinketh. *John* 11:39
wilt thou at *this t.* restore? *Acts* 1:6
go thy way for *this t.* 24:25
to declare at *this t.* *Rom* 3:26
sufferings of *this* present *t.* 8:18
at *this t.* will I come, and Sarah. 9:9
so at *this* present *t.* there is. 11:5
not to come at *this t.* *1 Cor* 16:12
that now at *this t.* your. *2 Cor* 8:14

times

he hath supplanted me these two *t.* *Gen* 27:36
ye shall not observe *t.* *Lev* 19:26*
Deut 18:10*, 14*
hated him not in *t.* past. *Deut* 4:42
the Spirit of the Lord began to move him at *t.* *Judg* 13:25
as at other *t.* and shake. *Judg* 16:20
in array as at other *t.* 20:30
began to kill as at other *t.* 31
as at other *t.*, Samuel. *1 Sam* 3:10
with his hand as at other *t.* 18:10*
on his seat as at other *t.* 20:25
not heard of ancient *t.* that I have formed it? *2 Ki* 19:25; *Isa* 37:26
Manasseh observed *t.* *2 Ki* 21:6*
2 Chr 33:6*
understanding of the *t.* *1 Chr* 12:32
the *t.* that went over him and. 29:30
in those *t.* there was no. *2 Chr* 15:5
men which knew the *t.* *Esth* 1:13
t. are not hidden from. *Job* 24:1
Lord will be a refuge in *t.* *Ps* 9:9
thyself in *t.* of trouble? 10:1
my *t.* are in thy hand, deliver. 31:15
thou didst in the *t.* of old. 44:1
the years of ancient *t.* 77:5
be the stability of thy *t.* *Isa* 33:6
from ancient *t.* things not. 46:10
of the *t.* far off. *Ezek* 12:27
he changeth the *t.* and. *Dan* 2:21
he shall think to change *t.* 7:25
shall be built in troublous *t.* 9:25
in those *t.* there shall many. 11:14
t. and an half. 12:7; *Rev* 12:14
not discern the signs of the *t.*? *Mat* 16:3
the *t.* of the Gentiles. *Luke* 21:24
for you to know the *t.* *Acts* 1:7
when the *t.* of refreshing. 3:19
till the *t.* of restitution of all. 21
who in *t.* past suffered all. 14:16*
hath determined the *t.* 17:26*
the *t.* of this ignorance God. 30
as ye in *t.* past have not. *Rom* 11:30
of Jews five *t.* received I forty stripes. *2 Cor* 11:24
persecuted us in *t.* past. *Gal* 1:23
and months, *t.* and years. 4:10
of the fulness of *t.* *Eph* 1:10
the *t.* ye have no need. *1 Thes* 5:1
in latter *t.* some shall. *1 Tim* 4:1
in his *t.* he shall shew, who is. 6:15
perilous *t.* shall come. *2 Tim* 3:1
hath in due *t.* manifested. *Tit* 1:3
God who at sundry *t.* spake to the. *Heb* 1:1*

see **appointed, many, seven, ten, three**

all **times**

that he come not at *all t.* *Lev* 16:2
of his people at *all t.* *1 Ki* 8:59
I will bless the Lord at *all t.*: his praise. *Ps* 34:1
trust in him at *all t.* ye people. 62:8
doeth righteousness at *all t.* 106:3
to thy judgements at *all t.* 119:20
satisfy thee at *all t.* *Pr* 5:19
a friend loveth at *all t.* 17:17

Timnath

to his shearers in *T.* *Gen* 38:12
Samson went down to *T.* *Judg* 14:1

Timotheus

a certain disciple named *T.* *Acts* 16:1
T. my workfellow saluteth you. *Rom* 16:21
if *T.* come. *1 Cor* 16:10
T. our brother. *2 Cor* 1:1
was preached even by me and *T.* 19
Lord to send *T.* to you. *Phil* 2:19
we sent *T.* to establish. *1 Thes* 3:2
to *T.* my own son. *1 Tim* 1:2, 18
2 Tim 1:2
T. is set at liberty. *Heb* 13:23

tin

t. that may abide fire. *Num* 31:22
take away all thy *t.* *Isa* 1:25
brass, and *t.* and iron. *Ezek* 22:18
lead and *t.* into the furnace. 20
thy merchant in *t.* and lead. 27:12

tingle

ears of every one that heareth it shall *t.* *1 Sam* 3:11; *2 Ki* 21:12
Jer 19:3

tinkling

mincing and making a *t.* *Isa* 3:16
bravery of their *t.* ornaments. 18*
as a *t.* cymbal. *1 Cor* 13:1*

tip

may dip the *t.* of his finger in water. *Luke* 16:24
see right **ear**

tire

bind the *t.* of thy head. *Ezek* 24:17

tired

Jezebel *t.* her head. *2 Ki* 9:30

tires

Lord will take away their *t.* *Isa* 3:18*
and your *t.* shall be on. *Ezek* 24:23

Tirshatha

(*This word is not strictly a proper name, but the title of the Governor of Judaea, under the Persians. In some places it is rendered* governor)
T. said that they should not eat of the holy things. *Ezra* 2:63; *Neh* 7:65
the *T.* gave gold to the. *Neh* 7:70
sealed were Nehemiah the *T.* 10:1

Tirzah

Hoglah, Milcah, and *T.* *Num* 26:33
27:1; 36:11; *Josh* 17:3
smote the king of *T.* *Josh* 12:24
wife came to *T.* *1 Ki* 14:17
dwelt and reigned in *T.* 15:21, 33
Elah reigned in *T.* 16:8
Zimri reigned in *T.* 15
Omri besieged *T.* 17
Omri reigned in *T.* 23
smote coasts from *T.* *2 Ki* 15:16
O my love, as *T.* *S of S* 6:4

Tishbite, *see* **Elijah**

tithe

The practice of paying tithes *is very ancient; for we find,* Gen 14:20, *that Abraham gave* tithes *to Melchizedek, king of Salem, at his return from his expedition against Chedorlaomer, and the four kings in confederacy with him. Abraham gave him the* tithe *of all the booty taken from the enemy. Jacob imitated this piety of his grandfather when he vowed to the Lord the* tithe *of all the substance he might acquire in Mesopotamia,* Gen 28:22. *Under the law, Moses ordained,* Lev 27:30, 31, 32, All the *tithe* of the land, whether of the seed of the land, or of the fruit of the tree, is the Lord's; it is holy unto the Lord, etc.

There were three sorts of tithes *to be paid from the people (besides those from the Levites to the priests),* Num 28:26, 27, etc. (1) *To the Levites, for their maintenance,* Num 18:21, 24. (2) *For the Lord's feasts and sacrifices, to be eaten* in the place which the Lord should choose to put his name there; *to wit, where the ark should be, the tabernacle or temple. This tenth part was either sent to Jerusalem in kind, or, if it was too far, they sent the value in money, which was to be laid out for oxen, sheep, wine, or what else they pleased,* Deut 14:22, 23, 24, etc. (3) *Besides these two, there was to be, every third year, a* tithe *for the poor, to be eaten in their own dwellings,* Deut 14:28, 29.

In the New Testament, *neither our Saviour, nor his apostles have commanded any thing in this affair of* tithes.

all the *t.* of the land is. *Lev* 27:30
concerning the *t.* of the herd. 32
a tenth part of the *t.* *Num* 18:26
thy gates the *t.* of corn. *Deut* 12:17
eat *t.* in the place the Lord. 14:23
three years bring forth the *t.* 28
firstfruits of corn and the *t.* of all. *2 Chr* 31:5, 6, 12; *Neh* 13:12
shall bring up *t.* of tithes. *Neh* 10:38
ye pay *t.* of mint, anise. *Mat* 23:23

tithe, *verb*

t. increase of thy seed. *Deut* 14:22
for ye *t.* mint, and rue. *Luke* 11:42

tithes
Melchizedek *t.* of all. *Gen* 14:20
redeem aught of his *t.* *Lev* 27:31
the *t.* I have given to. *Num* 18:24
take of the children of Israel *t.* 26
unto the Lord of all your *t.* 28
shall bring your *t.* *Deut* 12:6, 11
made an end of tithing the *t.* 26:12
Levites might have the *t. Neh* 10:37
were appointed for the *t.* 12:44
they laid the *t.* of corn. 13:5
bring your *t.* after three years. *Amos* 4:4; *Mal* 3:10
ye have robbed me. In *t.* *Mal* 3:8
I give *t.* of all that I. *Luke* 18:12
priesthood have commandment to take *t.* *Heb* 7:5
he received *t.* of Abraham, and. 6
and here men that die receive *t.* 8
Levi who receiveth *t.* payed *t.* in. 9

tithing
hast made an end of *t.*, third year which is the year of *t. Deut* 26:12

title
he said, What *t.* is that? *2 Ki* 23:17*
Pilate wrote a *t.* and put it on the cross. *John* 19:19
t. then read many of the Jews. 20

titles
give flattering *t.* to man. *Job* 32:21
for I know not to give flattering *t.* 22

tittle
one *t.* shall in no wise pass. *Mat* 5:18
than for one *t.* of the law. *Luke* 16:17

Titus
because I found not *T.* *2 Cor* 2:13
us by the coming of *T.* 7:6
joyed we for the joy of *T.* 13
boasting which I made before *T.* 14
we desired *T.* 8:6
care into the heart of *T.* 16
whether any enquire of *T.* he is. 23
I desired *T.* Did *T.* make a? 12:18
I took *T.* with me. *Gal* 2:1
neither *T.* was compelled to. 3
T. is departed to. *2 Tim* 4:10

to *and* **fro**, *see* **fro**

Tobiah
children of *T.* not shew. *Ezra* 2:60
Sanballat and *T.* heard. *Neh* 2:10
19; 4:7; 6:1
T. had hired him. 6:12
my God, think thou upon *T.* 14
and *T.* sent letters to put me. 19
Eliashib was allied to *T.* 13:4
all the household stuff of *T.* 8

to-day, *see* **day**

toe
great *t.* of their right foot. *Ex* 29:20
Lev 8:23, 24; 14:14, 17, 25, 28

toes
thumbs and his great *t.* *Judg* 1:6
having thumbs and *t.* cut off. 7
fingers and *t.* were. *1 Chr* 20:6, 24
the *t.* part of iron. *Dan* 2:41, 42

Togarmah
sons of Gomer, Riphath, *T.* *Gen* 10:3; *1 Chr* 1:6
they of the house of *T.* *Ezek* 27:14

together
plow with ox and ass *t.* *Deut* 22:10
he divided her, *t.* with. *Judg* 19:29
died that same day *t.* *1 Sam* 31:6
we were *t.*, there was no. *1 Ki* 3:18
women, *t.* with the daughter. 11:1
when thou and I rode *t.* *2 Ki* 9:25
we ourselves *t.* will build. *Ezra* 4:3
let us take counsel *t.* *Neh* 6:7
let us meet *t.* 10
there the prisoners rest *t.* *Job* 3:18
have fashioned me *t.* round. 10:8
go down, when our rest *t.* is. 17:16
the poor hide themselves *t.* 24:4
all flesh shall perish *t.* 34:15
counsel *t.* against the Lord. *Ps* 2:2
all *t.* become filthy. 14:3; *Rom* 3:12
and let us exalt his name *t.* *Ps* 34:3
the transgressors be destroyed *t.* 37:38; *Isa* 1:28
the rich and poor meet *t.* *Pr* 22:2
and the deceitful man meet *t.* 29:13
if two lie *t.* then they. *Eccl* 4:11
t. shall be against Judah. *Isa* 9:21
t. with my dead body shall. 26:19
that we may behold it *t.* 41:23
with the voice *t.* shall they. 52:8, 9
and the lamb shall feed *t.* 65:25
the bones came *t.*, bone. *Ezek* 37:7
he and his princes *t.* *Amos* 1:15
can two walk *t.* except they? 3:3
or three are gathered *t.* *Mat* 18:20
what God hath joined *t.* 19:6
Mark 10:9
he calleth *t.* his friends. *Luke* 15:6
that believed were *t.* *Acts* 2:44
ye have agreed *t.* to tempt. 5:9
all things work *t.* for good. *Rom* 8:28
hath quickened us *t.* *Eph* 2:5
hath raised us *t.* 6
building fitly framed *t.* 21, 22
striving *t.* for the faith. *Phil* 1:27
brethren, be followers *t.* of me. 3:17
being knit *t.* in love. *Col* 2:2, 19
dead in sins, hath he quickened *t.* 13
shall be caught up *t.* *1 Thes* 4:17
we should live *t.* with him. 5:10
you by our gathering *t.* *2 Thes* 2:1
as being heirs *t.* of the. *1 Pet* 3:7
see **dwell**

toil
concerning our work and *t. Gen* 5:29
hath made me forget my *t.* 41:51

toil, *verb*
they *t.* not, neither do they spin. *Mat* 6:28; *Luke* 12:27

toiled
Master, we have *t.* all. *Luke* 5:5

toiling
and he saw them *t.* *Mark* 6:48*

token
this is the *t.* of the covenant. *Gen* 9:12, 13, 17
and it shall be a *t.* of the. 17:11
this shall be a *t.* that I. *Ex* 3:12
the blood shall be for a *t.* on. 12:13
it shall be for a *t.* upon. 13:16*
to be kept for a *t.* *Num* 17:10
and give me a true *t.* *Josh* 2:12
shew me a *t.* for good. *Ps* 86:17
given them a *t.* saying. *Mark* 14:44
is to them an evident *t.* *Phil* 1:28
a manifest *t.* of righteous. *2 Thes* 1:5
of Paul, which is the *t.* in. 3:17

tokens
being *t.* of damsel's virginity. *Deut* 22:15, 17, 20
and do ye not know their *t.*? *Job* 21:29
they are afraid at thy *t.* *Ps* 65:8
who sent *t.* in the midst of. 135:9*
that frustrateth the *t.* of. *Isa* 44:25

Tola
T. the son of Issachar. *Gen* 46:13
1 Chr 7:1
T. son of Puah arose to. *Judg* 10:1

told
who *t.* thee that thou wast naked? *Gen* 3:11
and Ham *t.* his two brethren. 9:22
till I have *t.* mine errand. 24:33
Joseph *t.* his brethren. 37:5, 9
he *t.* it to his father and his. 10
T. not I thee, All that? *Num* 23:26
it be *t.* thee, and behold. *Deut* 17:4
which our fathers *t.* of. *Judg* 6:13
was a man that *t.* a dream. 7:13
I asked not, neither *t.* he me. 13:6
nor would as at this time have *t.* 23
he came up, and *t.* his father. 14:2
but he *t.* not his father. 6, 9, 16
1 Sam 14:1
day he *t.* her, she *t.* the riddle. *Judg* 14:17
she urged him, he *t.* her. 16:17, 18
he *t.* us that the asses were found. *1 Sam* 10:16
Abigail *t.* not her husband. 25:19
and the woman sent and *t.* David. *2 Sam* 11:5
and *t.* them, they *t.* David. 17:17
t. her all her questions, not any . . . he *t.* not. *1 Ki* 10:3; *2 Chr* 9:2
the words they *t.* also to. *1 Ki* 13:11
came and *t.* it in the city where. 25
hast *t.* thou wilt build. *1 Chr* 17:25
I *t.* them what they should say to. *Ezra* 8:17
Haman *t.* of the glory of. *Esth* 5:11
for Esther had *t.* what he was. 8:1
which wise men have *t.* *Job* 15:18
fathers have *t.* us. *Ps* 44:1; 78:3
have not I *t.* thee from? *Isa* 44:8
who hath *t.* it from that time? 45:21
what had not been *t.* them. 52:15
because he had *t.* them. *Jonah* 1:10
the city and *t.* every thing. *Mat* 8:33
body, and went and *t.* Jesus. 14:12
they went and *t.* it to. *Mark* 16:13
the man *t.* the Jews it. *John* 5:15
it shall be *t.* thee what thou must do. *Acts* 9:6; 22:10
into the castle and *t.* Paul. 23:16
he *t.* us your earnest. *2 Cor* 7:7

told, *participle*
it was certainly *t.* thy. *Josh* 9:24
oxen could not be *t.* *1 Ki* 8:5
was it not *t.* my lord what? 18:13
gave money, being *t.* *2 Ki* 12:11
years as a tale that is *t.* *Ps* 90:9
it was *t.* the house of David. *Isa* 7:2
and the vision which is *t.* *Dan* 8:26
there shall this be *t.* for. *Mat* 26:13
a performance of things which were *t.* *Luke* 1:45
those things *t.* by shepherds. 2:18

told *him*
which God had *t. him.* *Gen* 22:3, 9
I have *t. him,* I will judge his. *1 Sam* 3:13
Samuel *t. him* every whit and. 18
the kingdom he *t. him* not. 10:16
she *t. him* nothing till morning. 25:36
the man of God *t. him.* *2 Ki* 6:10
be *t. him* that I speak. *Job* 37:20
but the woman *t. him.* *Mark* 5:33

told *me*
thou hast mocked me and *t. me* lies. *Judg* 16:10, 13
hast not *t. me* wherein thy. 15
for it is *t. me* that he dealeth very subtilly. *1 Sam* 23:22
when one *t. me,* saying, Saul is dead. *2 Sam* 4:10
the half was not *t. me.* *1 Ki* 10:7
2 Chr 9:6
t. me I should be king. *1 Ki* 14:2
me and hath not *t. me.* *2 Ki* 4:27
he *t. me* that thou shouldest. 8:14
see a man which *t. me* all things. *John* 4:29, 39
even as it was *t. me.* *Acts* 27:25

told *you*
hath it not been *t. you*? *Isa* 40:21
believe, though it be *t. you. Hab* 1:5
I have *t. you* before. *Mat* 24:25
see him, lo, I have *t. you.* 28:7
if I have *t. you* earthly. *John* 3:12
a man that hath *t. you* truth. 8:40
he said, I have *t. you* already. 9:27
10:25
I would have *t. you.* 14:2
now I have *t. you* before it. 29
have I *t. you,* that when time shall come . . . *t. you* of them. 16:4
Jesus said, I have *t. you* that. 18:8
I *t. you* before, and. *2 Cor* 13:2
as I have also *t. you* in. *Gal* 5:21
of whom I have *t. you.* *Phil* 3:18
we *t. you* that we should suffer. *1 Thes* 3:4
when with you, I *t. you. 2 Thes* 2:5
they *t. you* there should. *Jude* 18

tolerable
it shall be more *t.* for Sodom and. *Mat* 10:15; 11:24; *Mark* 6:11
Luke 10:12
more *t.* for Tyre and Sidon *Mat* 11:22; *Luke* 10:14

toll
then will they not pay *t.* *Ezra* 4:13*
t., tribute, and custom, was paid. 20*
lawful to impose *t.* on them. 7:24*

tomb
shall remain in the *t.* *Job* 21:32
Joseph laid the body in his own new *t.* *Mat* 27:60

disciples laid John's corpse in a *t.* *Mark* 6:29

tombs

met him two possessed with devils, coming out of the *t.* *Mat* 8:28
Mark 5:2, 3, 5; *Luke* 8:27
because ye build the *t.* *Mat* 23:29*

to-morrow, *see* **morrow**

tongs

(*American Revision changes this word to* snuffers)

shalt make thee *t.* thereof. *Ex* 25:38
they shall cover his *t.* *Num* 4:9
lamps and *t.* of gold. *1 Ki* 7:49
2 Chr 4:21
a coal which he had taken with the *t.* *Isa* 6:6
smith with the *t.* worketh. 44:12*

tongue

This word is taken in three different senses. (1) *For the material* tongue, *or organ of speech,* Jas 3:5. (2) *For the* tongue *or language* that *is spoken in any country,* Deut 28:49. (3) *For good or bad discourse,* Pr 12:18; 17:20.

To gnaw one's *tongue, is a token of fury, despair, and torment. The men that worship the beast are said* to gnaw their *tongues* for pain, Rev 16:10. The scourge of the *tongue,* Job 5:21, *is malicious scandal, calumny, insulting, and offensive speeches.*

The gift of *tongues, which God granted to the Apostles and disciples assembled at Jerusalem, on the day of Pentecost,* Acts 2:3, 4, etc., *is not fully understood. St. Paul speaks of it as still existing,* 1 Cor 12:10; 14:2.

not a dog move his *t.* *Ex* 11:7
none moved his *t.* against. *Josh* 10:21
the water with his *t.* *Judg* 7:5
from the scourge of the *t.* *Job* 5:21
and thou choosest the *t.* of. 15:5
hide wickedness under his *t.* 20:12
poison of asps, the viper's *t.* shall. 16
their *t.* cleaved to roof of. 29:10
they flatter with their *t.* *Ps* 5:9
under his *t.* is mischief and. 10:7
shall cut off the *t.* that speaketh. 12:3
who have said, With our *t.* will. 4
that backbiteth not with his *t.* 15:3
keep thy *t.* from evil. 34:13
1 Pet 3:10
and his *t.* talketh of. *Ps* 37:30
and thy *t.* frameth deceit. 50:19
thy *t.* deviseth mischiefs like. 52:2
and their *t.* is a sharp sword. 57:4
who whet their *t.* like a sword. 64:3
shall make their *t.* to fall on. 8
t. of thy dogs shall be dipped. 68:23
and their *t.* walketh through. 73:9
against me with a lying *t.* 109:2
done to thee, thou false *t.*? 120:3
our *t.* filled with singing. 126:2
a proud look, a lying *t.* *Pr* 6:17
from the flattery of the *t.* of a. 24
the *t.* of the just is as choice. 10:20
the froward *t.* shall be cut out. 31
t. of the wise is health. 12:18
but a lying *t.* is but for a. 19
t. of the wise useth knowledge. 15:2
a wholesome *t.* is a tree of life. 4
and the answer of the *t.* is. 16:1
giveth heed to a naughty *t.* 17:4
he that hath a perverse *t.* falleth. 20
life are in the power of the *t.* 18:21
treasures by a lying *t.* is vanity. 21:6
whoso keepeth his *t.* keepeth. 23
soft *t.* breaketh the bone. 25:15
angry countenance a backbiting *t.* 23
lying *t.* hateth those afflicted. 26:28
that flattereth with the *t.* 28:23
and in her *t.* is the law of. 31:26
milk are under thy *t.* *S of S* 4:11
because their *t.* is against. *Isa* 3:8
Lord shall destroy the *t.* 11:15
t. is as a devouring fire. 30:27
the *t.* of the stammerers shall. 32:4
a people of a stammering *t.* 33:19
shall the *t.* of the dumb sing. 35:6
and when their *t.* faileth for. *Isa* 41:17
that unto me every *t.* shall. 45:23
the Lord hath given me the *t.* 50:4
t. that shall rise against thee. 54:17
whom draw ye out the *t.*? 57:4
t. hath muttered perverseness. 59:3
their *t.* like their bow. *Jer* 9:3
taught their *t.* to speak lies. 5
their *t.* is as an arrow shot out. 8
let us smite him with the *t.* 18:18
the *t.* of the sucking child cleaveth. *Lam* 4:4
I will make thy *t.* cleave. *Ezek* 3:26
princes shall fall for the rage of their *t.* *Hos* 7:16
holdest thy *t.* when the wicked devoureth. *Hab* 1:13*
their *t.* shall consume. *Zech* 14:12
spit, and touched his *t.* *Mark* 7:33
and straightway his *t.* was loosed. 35; *Luke* 1:64
and bridleth not his *t.* *Jas* 1:26
so the *t.* is a little member. 3:5
the *t.* is a fire. 6
the *t.* can no man tame. 8
nor let us love in *t.* but. *1 John* 3:18
see **deceitful, hold**

my **tongue**

his word was in *my t.* *2 Sam* 23:2
sold, I had held *my t.* *Esth* 7:4
is there iniquity in *my t.*? *Job* 6:30
nor shall *my t.* utter deceit. 27:4
my t. hath spoken in my mouth. 33:2
and *my t.* cleaveth to my. *Ps* 22:15
my t. shall speak of thy righteousness. 35:28; 51:14; 71:24
that I sin not with *my t.* 39:1
was hot, then spake I with *my t.* 3
my t. is the pen of a ready. 45:1
God was extolled with *my t.* 66:17
my t. shall speak of thy. 119:172
let *my t.* cleave to the roof. 137:6
not a word in *my t.* but thou. 139:4
finger, and cool *my t.* *Luke* 16:24
rejoice, *my t.* was glad. *Acts* 2:26

tongue for *language, speech*

isles were divided every one after his *t.* *Gen* 10:5
of speech, and of a slow *t.* *Ex* 4:10
a nation whose *t.* shall. *Deut* 28:49
letter was written in the Syrian *t.* and interpreted in Syrian *t.* *Ezra* 4:7*
for with another *t.* will. *Isa* 28:11
they might teach the *t.* of. *Dan* 1:4
called in the Hebrew *t.* Bethesda. *John* 5:2
field called in their proper *t.* Aceldama. *Acts* 1:19*
every man in our own *t.*? 2:8*
in the Hebrew *t.* Saul, Saul. 26:14*
every *t.* shall confess. *Rom* 14:11
he that speaketh in an unknown *t.* *1 Cor* 14:2, 4, 13, 14, 19, 27
except ye utter by the *t.* words. 9
hath a psalm, hath a *t.* 26
that every *t.* confess that. *Phil* 2:11
hast redeemed us out of every *t.* *Rev* 5:9
in the Hebrew *t.* is Abaddon. 9:11
the gospel to preach to every *t.* 14:6
the Hebrew *t.* Armageddon. 16:16

tongued

be grave, not double-*t.* *1 Tim* 3:8

tongues

of Ham, after their *t.* *Gen* 10:20
sons of Shem, after their *t.* 31
them from the strife of *t.* *Ps* 31:20
O Lord, and divide their *t.* 55:9
lied to him with their *t.* 78:36
they sharpened their *t.* like. 140:3
gather all nations and *t.* *Isa* 66:18
that use their *t.* and say. *Jer* 23:31
shall speak with new *t.* *Mark* 16:17
there appeared to them cloven *t.* *Acts* 2:3
began to speak with other *t.* 4
we hear in our *t.* the wonderful. 11
heard them speak with *t.* 10:46
and they spake with *t.* and. 19:6
with their *t.* they have used deceit. *Rom* 3:13
to another divers kinds of *t.* *1 Cor* 12:10, 28
do all speak with *t.*? do all? 30
though I speak with the *t.* of. 13:1
there be *t.*, they shall cease. 8
I would ye all spake with *t.* 14:5
if I come to you speaking with *t.* 6
I thank God, I speak with *t.* 18
with men of other *t.* will I speak. 21
t. are for a sign. 22
if all speak with *t.* 23
forbid not to speak with *t.* 39
people and *t.* stood before. *Rev* 7:9
again before nations and *t.* 10:11
t. and nations shall see their. 11:9
power was given him over all *t.* 13:7
and they gnawed their *t.* for. 16:10
sawest are nations and *t.* 17:15

took

Enoch was not, for God *t.* him. *Gen* 5:24
his mother *t.* him a wife out. 21:21
God, which *t.* me from my. 24:7
the lord of the land *t.* us for. 42:30
Moses *t.* the redemption money. *Num* 3:49, 50
the Lord *t.* of the Spirit that. 11:25
king Arad *t.* some of them. 21:1
I *t.* thee to curse mine. 23:11
so I *t.* the chief of your. *Deut* 1:15
only the cattle we *t.* for a prey. 2:35
there was not a city we *t.* not. 3:4
I *t.* your sin, the calf which. 9:21
I *t.* this woman and found. 22:14
I coveted them, and *t.* *Josh* 7:21
the men *t.* of their victuals. 9:14
I *t.* your father Abraham. 24:3
Philistines *t.* Samson. *Judg* 16:21
silver is with me, I *t.* it. 17:2
no man *t.* them into his house. 19:15
the man *t.* his concubine, and. 25
I *t.* my concubine, and cut. 20:6
brought up, the priest *t.* *1 Sam* 2:14
Philistines *t.* the ark of God. 5:1, 2
Samuel *t.* a vial of oil and. 10:1
so Saul *t.* the kingdom over. 14:47
people *t.* of the spoil, sheep. 15:21
Samuel *t.* horn of oil and. 16:13
Saul *t.* him, would not let him. 18:2
David *t.* the spear from. 26:12
I *t.* the crown and. *2 Sam* 1:10
Uzzah *t.* hold of it for the. 6:6
I *t.* thee from the sheepcote. 7:8
not depart, as I *t.* it from Saul. 15
but *t.* the poor man's lamb. 12:4
Zadok the priest *t.* an. *1 Ki* 1:39
she arose and *t.* my son from. 3:20
the cities my father *t.* I will. 20:34
but Jehu *t.* no heed to. *2 Ki* 10:31
yet David *t.* the castle. *1 Chr* 11:5
which *t.* Manasseh among thorns. *2 Chr* 33:11
vessels which Nebuchadnezzar *t.* *Ezra* 5:14; 6:5
whom Mordecai *t.* for his. *Esth* 2:7
then *t.* Haman the apparel and. 6:11
t. upon them, that they would. 9:27
he that *t.* me out of the womb. *Ps* 22:9; 71:6
fear *t.* hold upon them there. 48:6
we *t.* sweet counsel together. 55:14
he chose David, and *t.* from. 78:70
I *t.* me faithful witnesses. *Isa* 8:2
with whom *t.* he counsel? 40:14
then *t.* I the cup at the. *Jer* 25:17
in the day I *t.* them by the hand. 31:32; *Heb* 8:9
even they *t.* Jeremiah out. *Jer* 39:14
and he *t.* me by a lock. *Ezek* 8:3
he *t.* fire from between the. 10:7
he heard the trumpet, and *t.* 33:5
the Lord *t.* me as I followed the. *Amos* 7:15
I *t.* me two staves, Beauty and Bands. *Zech* 11:7
I *t.* the thirty pieces and cast. 13
himself *t.* our infirmities. *Mat* 8:17
like leaven which a woman *t.* 13:33
Luke 13:21
the foolish virgins *t.* no oil. *Mat* 25:3
ye *t.* me in. 35
I was a stranger and ye *t.* me not. 43
the first *t.* a wife, and. *Mark* 12:20

second t. her and died. Mark 12:21
Luke 20:29, 30
n the temple teaching, and ye t. me not. Mark 14:49
hat disciple t. her to his. John 19:27
o them who t. Jesus. Acts 1:16
ut Barnabas t. him, and. 9:27
. with them John whose. 12:25
. on them to call over them. 19:13
whom we t. and would have judged according to our law. 24:6
Paul thanked God and t. 28:15
I went up, and t. Titus. Gal 2:1
and t. upon him the form. Phil 2:7
. it out of the way. Col 2:14
he also himself t. part. Heb 2:14
ye t. joyfully the spoiling of. 10:34
he t. the book. Rev 5:7
angel t. the censer. 8:5
I t. the little book out of the. 10:10

took away

he t. away my birthright. Gen 27:36
a west wind t. away the. Ex 10:19
he t. not away the pillar of. 13:22
shall restore that which he t. away. Lev 6:4
Gideon t. away their. Judg 8:21
Israel t. away my land when. 11:13
Israel t. not away the land. 15
David t. away the. 1 Sam 27:9
Shishak t. away the treasures. 1 Ki 14:26
Asa t. away the sodomites. 15:12
and they t. away the stones of. 22
Josiah t. away the horses. 2 Ki 23:11
all the vessels wherewith they ministered the Chaldeans t. away. 25:14, 15; Jer 52:18, 19
Asa t. away the altars. 2 Chr 14:3, 5
Jehoshaphat t. away the high. 17:6
Hezekiah t. away the altars. 30:14
Manasseh t. away the strange. 33:15
I restored that which I t. not away. Ps 69:4
keepers t. away my vail. S of S 5:7
I t. them away as I saw good. Ezek 16:50
and I t. the king away in my wrath. Hos 13:11
flood came and t. them all away. Mat 24:39
then they t. away the stone from. John 11:41

he took

Shechem saw her, he t. Gen 34:2
when he t. it out, his hand. Ex 4:6
he t. the book of the covenant. 24:7
and he t. the calf which they. 32:20
he t. the vail off, until he. 34:34
he t. all the fat on the inwards. Lev 8:16, 25
he t. the elders of the city. Judg 8:16
he t. men of the elders. Ruth 4:2
he t. a yoke of oxen. 1 Sam 11:7
when Saul saw any valiant man, he t. him unto him. 14:52
he t. Agag king of the. 15:8
he t. his staff in his hand. 17:40
he t. hold of her, and. 2 Sam 13:11
he t. three darts, and thrust. 18:14
above, he t. me. 22:17; Ps 18:16
he t. her son out of. 1 Ki 17:19
he t. the mantle of. 2 Ki 2:14
he t. his eldest son and. 3:27
he t. them from their hand. 5:24
he t. a thick cloth and dipped. 8:15
and he t. unto him bow and. 13:15
he t. him a potsherd to. Job 2:8
slothful roasteth not that which he t. Pr 12:27
he t. his brother by the. Hos 12:3
he t. the seven loaves. Mat 15:36
Mark 8:6
he t. the cup. Mat 26:27
Luke 22:17; 1 Cor 11:25
he t. with him Peter, James, John. Mat 26:37; Luke 9:28
he t. water and washed. Mat 27:24
and he t. the blind man. Mark 8:23
he t. a child and set him in. 9:36
he t. the five loaves. Luke 9:16
he t. out two pence and gave. 10:35
he t. bread. 22:19; 24:30 Acts 27:35
he t. them the same hour. Acts 16:33
he t. Paul's girdle and bound. 21:11
he t. not on him the. Heb 2:16
he t. the blood of calves. 9:19

they took

they t. them wives. Gen 6:2
and they t. all the goods of. 14:11
they t. Lot, Abram's brother's son. 12
and they t. every man. Num 16:18
and they t. of the fruit. Deut 1:25
people went up and they t. the city. Josh 6:20
the king of Ai they t. alive. 8:23
save Hivites, all other they t. 11:19
they t. their daughters. Judg 3:6
they t. them alive and. 2 Ki 10:14
they t. the young men. Lam 5:13
I saw that they t. both. Ezek 23:13
and they t. his glory. Dan 5:20
because they t. him for a prophet. Mat 21:46
so they t. the money, and did. 28:15
they t. him, and killed him, and cast. Mark 12:8
they t. him and led him. Luke 22:54
John 19:16
and they t. knowledge. Acts 4:13
they t. him down from the tree and laid. 13:29
they t. him, and expounded. 18:26

took up

Balaam t. up his parable. Num 23:7
18; 24:3, 15, 20, 21, 23
the priests t. up the ark. Josh 3:6
6:12; 1 Ki 8:3
then the man t. up his. Judg 19:28
cook t. up the shoulder. 1 Sam 9:24
they t. up Asahel and. 2 Sam 2:32
Mephibosheth's nurse t. him up. 4:4
prophet t. up the carcase. 1 Ki 13:29
he t. up also the mantle. 2 Ki 2:13
the Shunammite t. up her son. 4:37
and he t. him up to him into. 10:15
I t. up the wine and gave. Neh 2:1
they t. Jeremiah up out of. Jer 38:13
then the Spirit t. me up. Ezek 3:12
11:24; 43:5
flame slew men that t. up Shadrach, Meshach and Abed-nego. Dan 3:22
so they t. up Jonah. Jonah 1:15
they t. up the body of John. Mat 14:12; Mark 6:29
t. up of the fragments. Mat 14:20
15:37; Mark 6:43; 8:8, 20
many baskets ye t. up. Mat 16:9, 10
and he t. up the bed and. Mark 2:12
he t. them up in his arms. 10:16
t. him up in his arms. Luke 2:28
t. up stones to cast at him. John 8:59; 10:31
daughter t. Moses up. Acts 7:21
yea, ye t. up the tabernacle of. 43
but Peter t. him up, saying. 10:26
we t. up our carriages and. 21:15
angel t. up a stone. Rev 18:21

tookest

though thou t. vengeance. Ps 99:8
and t. thy broidered. Ezek 16:18

tool

if thou lift up thy t. upon it. Ex 20:25
fashioned it with a graving t. 32:4
lift up any iron t. on them. Deut 27:5
nor any t. of iron heard. 1 Ki 6:7

tooth

give t. for t. Ex 21:24; Lev 24:20
Deut 19:21; Mat 5:38
or his maidservant's t. he shall let him go free for his t.'s. Ex 21:27
is like a broken t., a foot. Pr 25:19

top

tower whose t. may reach. Gen 11:4
the t. of the ladder reached to. 28:12
Jacob poured oil on the t. of. 18
on the t. of the mount: and called Moses to the t. Ex 19:20; 34:2
like devouring fire on the t. 24:17
be an hole in the t. of it. 28:32*
the t. with pure gold. 30:3; 37:26
they gat up into the t. Num 14:40
Aaron died there in the t. of. 20:28
for from the t of the rocks. 23:9
the t. of Pisgah. Deut 3:27; 34:1
from sole of foot to the t. Deut 28:35*
on t. of the head of him that. 33:16*
build an altar on the t. Judg 6:26
the people gat up to the t. of. 9:51*
Samson dwelt in the t. of the. 15:8*
communed on the t. of the house. 1 Sam 9:25, 26
spread a tent on the t. of the house. 2 Sam 16:22
the t. of the throne. 1 Ki 10:19
him on the t. of the stairs. 2 Ki 9:13
from the t. of the rock. 2 Chr 25:12
the t. of the sceptre. Esth 5:2
of corn on t. of mountains. Ps 72:16
a sparrow alone on the house-t. 102:7
she standeth in the t. of. Pr 8:2
It is better to dwell in a corner of the house-t. 21:9; 25:24
lieth on the t. of a mast. 23:34
t. of Amana, from the t. S of S 4:8
Lord's house shall be established in the t. Isa 2:2; Mi 4:1
two or three berries in the t. Isa 17:6
beacon on the t. of a mountain. 30:17
let them shout from the t. of. 42:11
faint for hunger in t. of every street. Lam 2:19†
poured out in t. of every street. 4:1†
he cropped off the t. of. Ezek 17:4*
from the t. of his young twigs. 22*
she set it on the t. of a rock. 24:7*
blood on the t. of a rock. 8*
her like the t. of a rock. 26:4*, 14*
his t. was among the thick boughs. 31:3, 10, 14
law of the house: on the t. of. 43:12
her children were dashed at the t. of all the streets. Nah 3:10†
on the house-t. not come. Mat 24:17
Mark 13:15; Luke 17:31
vail rent from t. to the bottom. Mat 27:51; Mark 15:38
house-t. and let down. Luke 5:19
was woven from the t. John 19:23
leaning on t. of his staff. Heb 11:21
see **Carmel, hill**

topaz

(*A green gem of golden hue, one of the stones in the high priest's breastplate*)

the first row a sardius, a t. Ex 28:17
39:10
the t. of Ethiopia shall. Job 28:19
the sardius, the t. Ezek 28:13
beryl, the ninth a t. Rev 21:20

Tophet

Tophet, "place of burning," *was at Jerusalem, lying to the south of the city, in the valley of the children of Hinnom. There they burned the carcases and other filthiness from the city. It was in the same place that they cast away the ashes and remains of the images of false gods, when they demolished their altars, and broke down their statues. Isaiah seems to allude to this custom of burning dead carcases in* Tophet, *when speaking of the defeat of the army of Sennacherib,* Isa 30:33.

Josiah defiled T. in the. 2 Ki 23:10
for T. is ordained of old. Isa 30:33
built the high places of T. Jer 7:31
no more be called T. 32; 19:6
they shall bury in T., till. 7:32; 19:11
and even make this city as T. 19:12
Jerusalem shall be defiled as T. 13
then came Jeremiah from T. 14

tops

the t. of the mountains. Gen 8:5
sound of a going in the t. of the. 2 Sam 5:24; 1 Chr 14:15
as the grass upon the house-t. 2 Ki 19:26; Ps 129:6; Isa 37:27
and cut off as the t. of. Job 24:24
t. of the ragged rocks. Isa 2:21*
on the t. of houses every one. 15:3
wholly gone up to the house-t. 22:1
be lamentation on all house-t. Jer 48:38

their slain men shall be in all the *t.* of the mountains. Ezek 6:13
they sacrifice on the *t.* of. Hos 4:13
worship the host of heaven on house-*t.* Zeph 1:5
that preach ye upon the house-*t.* Mat 10:27
proclaimed on the house-*t.* Luke 12:3

torch

make the governors of Judah like a *t.* Zech 12:6

torches

shall be with flaming *t.* Nah 2:3*
the chariots shall seem like *t.* 4
with lanterns and *t.* John 18:3

torment

into this place of *t.* Luke 16:28
because fear hath *t.* 1 John 4:18*
their *t.* was as the *t.* of. Rev 9:5
smoke of their *t.* ascendeth. 14:11
so much *t.* and sorrow give her. 18:7
afar off for the fear of her *t.* 10, 15

torment, *verb*

art thou come to *t.* us? Mat 8:29
that thou *t.* me not. Mark 5:7
Luke 8:28

tormented

lieth grievously *t.* Mat 8:6
send Lazarus, for I am *t.* in this flame. Luke 16:24*
comforted, and thou art *t.* 25*
destitute, afflicted, *t.* Heb 11:37*
but that they should be *t.* Rev 9:5
two prophets *t.* them that. 11:10
he shall be *t.* with fire and. 14:10
and shall be *t.* day and night. 20:10

tormentors

delivered him to the *t.* Mat 18:34

torments

taken with divers diseases and *t.* Mat 4:24
in hell he lift up his eyes, being in *t.* Luke 16:23

torn

that which was *t.* of beasts I brought not. Gen 31:39
Surely he is *t.* in pieces. 44:28
if *t.* in pieces, let him bring it for witness . . . what was *t.* Ex 22:13
shall eat any flesh *t.* of beasts. 31
fat of that which is *t.* may. Lev 7:24
if any eat that which was *t.* 17:15
dieth of itself, or *t.* of beasts. 22:8
lion, which hath *t.* him. 1 Ki 13:26
not eaten carcase nor *t.* the ass. 28
carcases *t.* in the midst of. Isa 5:25*
goeth out shall be *t.* Jer 5:6
not eaten of that which is *t.* Ezek 4:14
not eat any thing that is *t.* 44:31
for he hath *t.* and he will. Hos 6:1
brought that which was *t.* Mal 1:13*
when the unclean spirit hath *t.* him. Mark 1:26

tortoise

This is probably a sort of lizard. It is numbered among the unclean animals, Lev 11:29.
the *t.* shall be unclean. Lev 11:29*

tortured

others were *t.* not accepting deliverance. Heb 11:35

toss

he will turn and *t.* thee. Isa 22:18
though the waves thereof *t.* Jer 5:22

tossed

I am *t.* up and down. Ps 109:23
is a vanity, *t.* to and fro. Pr 21:6
O thou afflicted, *t.* with. Isa 54:11
was now *t.* with waves. Mat 14:24*
t. with a tempest. Acts 27:18*
children, *t.* to and fro. Eph 4:14
wavereth is like a wave *t.* Jas 1:6

tossings

I am full of *t.* to and fro. Job 7:4

tottering

all of you as a *t.* fence. Ps 62:3

touch

not eat of it, nor shall ye *t.* Gen 3:3
suffered I thee not to *t.* her. 20:6
that ye *t.* not the border. Ex 19:12
there shall not an hand *t.* it. Ex 19:13
if a soul *t.* any unclean. Lev 5:2
or if he *t.* the uncleanness of man. 5:3; 7:21
whatsoever shall *t.* the flesh. 6:27
their carcase ye shall not *t.* 11:8
Deut 14:8
whosoever doth *t.* them when dead. Lev 11:31
he shall *t.* no hallowed thing. 12:4
they shall not *t.* any holy. Num 4:15
depart and *t.* nothing of theirs. 16:26
we may not *t.* them. Josh 9:19
they should not *t.* thee. Ruth 2:9
and he shall not *t.* thee any more. 2 Sam 14:10
t. the young man Absalom. 18:12
the man that shall *t.* them. 23:7
t. not mine anointed. 1 Chr 16:22
Ps 105:15
but *t.* all he hath and he will curse. Job 1:11
t. his bone and his flesh, he will. 2:5
there shall no evil *t.* thee. 5:19
that my soul refused to *t.* 6:7
t. the mountains and they. Ps 144:5
t. no unclean thing. Isa 52:11
2 Cor 6:17
that *t.* the inheritance of. Jer 12:14
so that men could not *t.* Lam 4:14
it is unclean, depart, *t.* not. 15
if one with his skirt do *t.* Hag 2:12
if one that is unclean *t.* any of. 13
if I may but *t.* his garment. Mat 9:21; Mark 5:28
they might *t.* the hem. Mat 14:36
Mark 5:28; 6:56; 8:22
they pressed on him to *t.* him. Mark 3:10; Luke 6:19
they besought him to *t.* the blind. Mark 8:22
ye yourselves *t.* not the. Luke 11:46
that he would *t.* them. 18:15
unto her, *T.* me not. John 20:17
a man not to *t.* a woman. 1 Cor 7:1
t. not, taste not, handle not. Col 2:21
firstborn, should *t.* them. Heb 11:28
if so much as a beast *t.* the. 12:20

touched

as we have not *t.* thee. Gen 26:29
t. the hollow of Jacob's. 32:25, 32
the soul which hath *t.* Lev 22:6
and whosoever hath *t.* Num 31:19
the angel of the Lord *t.* Judg 6:21
hearts God had *t.* 1 Sam 10:26
the wings of cherubims *t.* 1 Ki 6:27
an angel *t.* him and said. 19:5, 7
when the man *t.* the bones of Elisha. 2 Ki 13:21
so Esther *t.* the top of. Esth 5:2
the hand of God hath *t.* Job 19:21
lo, this hath *t.* thy lips. Isa 6:7
Lord *t.* my mouth. Jer 1:9
and the he goat *t.* not. Dan 8:5
but he *t.* me. 18; 9:21; 10:10, 16, 18
and Jesus *t.* him. Mat 8:3
Mark 1:41; Luke 5:13
t. her hand, and the fever. Mat 8:15
with an issue of blood *t.* the hem. 9:20; Mark 5:27; Luke 8:44
then *t.* he their eyes, saying. Mat 9:29; 20:34
as many as *t.* him were made perfectly whole. 14:36; Mark 6:56
who *t.* my clothes? Mark 5:30, 31
Luke 8:45, 47
into his ears, and he spit, and *t.* his tongue. Mark 7:33
he came and *t.* the bier. Luke 7:14
what cause she had *t.* him. 8:47
and Jesus *t.* his ear and. 22:51
next day we *t.* at Sidon. Acts 27:3
priest which cannot be *t.* Heb 4:15
mount that might be *t.* 12:18

toucheth

he that *t.* this man shall. Gen 26:11
whosoever *t.* the mount. Ex 19:12
whatsoever *t.* the altar shall. 29:37
that *t.* them, shall be holy. 30:29
Lev 6:18
the flesh that *t.* any. Lev 7:19
whosoever *t.* their carcase. 11:24
27, 36, 39
every one that *t.* them shall. Lev 11:2
whoso *t.* his bed, shall wash. 15:
t. his flesh.
t. any thing under him. 1
whomsoever he *t.* that hath the. 1
the vessel of earth that he *t.* shall. 1
whoso *t.* her. 1
whosoever *t.* her bed. 2
whosoever *t.* any thing that she. 2
if on her bed, when he *t.* it, he shall 15:23, 27; 22:4, 5; Num 19:2
he that *t.* the dead body. Num 19:1
13, 1
t. a bone. 1
t. the water of separation. 2
broken when it *t.* fire. Judg 16:
it *t.* thee and thou art. Job 4:
he *t.* the hills and they. Ps 104:3
whosoever *t.* her, shall not. Pr 6:2
when the east wind *t.* it. Ezek 17:1
out, and blood *t.* blood. Hos 4:
Lord is he that *t.* the land. Amos 9:
he that *t.* you, *t.* the apple. Zech 2:
what woman this is that *t.* him. Luke 7:3
and that wicked one *t.* 1 John 5:1

touching

Esau, as *t.* thee, doth. Gen 27:4
for him, as *t.* his sin that. Lev 5:1
thus do to the Levites *t.* Num 8:2
t. matter thou and I. 1 Sam 20:2
t. the words which thou. 2 Ki 22:1
t. the Almighty, we cannot find him. Job 37:2
I have made *t.* the king. Ps 45:
a song of my beloved, *t.* Isa 5:
utter judgements *t.* all. Jer 1:1
t. the house of the king of. 21:1
thus saith the Lord *t.* Shallum. 22:1
the vision is *t.* the whole. Ezek 7:1
as *t.* any thing that they. Mat 18:1
as *t.* the resurrection of the. 22:3
Mark 12:26; Acts 24:2
t. those things whereof. Luke 23:1
to do as *t.* these men. Acts 5:3
as *t.* the Gentiles who believe. 21:2
as *t.* the election, they. Rom 11:2
now as *t.* things offered. 1 Cor 8:
t. our brother Apollos. 16:1
as *t.* the ministering to. 2 Cor 9:
of the Hebrews, as *t.* the. Phil 3:
t. the righteousness in the law.
t. whom ye received. Col 4:1
t. brotherly love, ye. 1 Thes 4:
in the Lord *t.* you. 2 Thes 3:

tow

a thread of *t.* is broken. Judg 16:9
and the strong shall be as *t.* Isa 1:31
they are quenched as *t.* 43:17*

toward, *or* **towards**

Ephraim *t.* Israel's left hand, Manasseh *t.* Israel's right. Gen 48:13
face *t.* the wilderness. Num 24:1
his eye shall be evil *t.* Deut 28:54
shall be evil *t.* her husband. 56
heart is *t.* the governors. Judg 5:9
behold, if there be good *t.* David. 1 Sam 20:12
prayer thy servant shall make *t.* 1 Ki 8:29, 30, 35; 2 Chr 6:21
done good in Israel, both *t.* God, and *t.* his house. 2 Chr 24:16
endureth for ever *t.* Israel. Ezra 3:11
I will worship *t.* thy holy temple. Ps 5:7; 138:2
eyes are ever *t.* the Lord. 25:15
hands *t.* thy holy oracle. 28:2
favour is *t.* a wise servant. Pr 14:35
the great goodness *t.* house. Isa 63:7
my mind could not be *t.* Jer 15:1
being open *t.* Jerusalem. Dan 6:10
horn waxed great *t.* the south. 8:9
look *t.* thy holy temple. Jonah 2:4
as it began to dawn *t.* the first day. Mat 28:1
peace, good will *t.* men. Luke 2:14
treasure, and not rich *t.* God. 12:21
with us, for it is *t.* evening. 24:29
Greeks, repentance *t.* God, and faith *t.* our Lord Jesus. Acts 20:21
of offence *t.* God and *t.* men. 24:16

faith which thou hast *t.* the Lord Jesus Christ, and *t.* all. *Philem* 5
see **heaven, him, me, thee, them, us, you**

towel

he riseth, and took a *t.* *John* 13:4
wipe their feet with the *t.* 5

tower

[1] Watch-towers *or fortified posts in frontier or exposed places are mentioned in Scripture, as the tower of Edar, etc.,* Gen 35:21; Isa 21:5, 8, 11; Mi 4:8.
[2] *Besides these military towers we read of towers built in vineyards as an almost necessary addition to them,* Isa 5:2; Mat 21:33.
[3] *God is often alluded to as a tower, with the idea of protection,* Ps 61:3; Pr 18:10.

let us build us a city and *t.* *Gen* 11:4
came down to see the city and *t.* 5
tent beyond the *t.* of Edar. 35:21
I will break down this *t.* *Judg* 8:9
he beat down the *t.* of Penuel. 17
men of the *t.* of Shechem. 9:46
but there was a strong *t.* within. 51
is the *t.* of salvation. *2 Sam* 22:51*
when he came to the *t.* he. *2 Ki* 5:24*
hast been a strong *t.* *Ps* 61:3
the Lord is a strong *t.* *Pr* 18:10
like the *t.* of David. *S of S* 4:4
neck is as a *t.* of ivory, thy nose is as the *t.* of Lebanon, looking. 7:4
he built a *t.* in the midst. *Isa* 5:2
I have set thee for a *t.* *Jer* 6:27†
city shall be built from *t.* of. 31:38
Egypt desolate, from the *t.* of Syene. *Ezek* 29:10
from the *t.* of Syene shall they fall in it. 30:6
O *t.* of the flock, to thee. *Mi* 4:8
set me upon the *t.* and. *Hab* 2:1
be inhabited from *t.* of. *Zech* 14:10
built a *t.* and let it out to husbandmen. *Mat* 21:33; *Mark* 12:1
those 18 on whom the *t.* *Luke* 13:4
you intending to build a *t.* 14:28

high **tower**

God is my *high t.* *2 Sam* 22:3
Ps 18:2; 144:2
day of Lord on every *high t.* *Isa* 2:15

towers

build cities and make *t.* *2 Chr* 14:7
moreover Uzziah built *t.* in. 26:9
he built *t.* in the desert and. 10
Jotham built castles and *t.* 27:4
raised up the wall to the *t.* 32:5
Zion and tell her *t.* *Ps* 48:12
and my breasts like *t.* *S of S* 8:10
the Assyrian set up the *t.* *Isa* 23:13
hill rivers, when the *t.* fall. 30:25
the forts and *t.* shall be for. 32:14
he that counted the *t.*? 33:18
they shall break down her *t.* *Ezek* 26:4, 9
Gammadims were in thy *t.* 27:11
their *t.* are desolate. *Zeph* 3:6

to wit

to wit whether the Lord had made his journey. *Gen* 24:21
to wit what would be done. *Ex* 2:4
to wit, that God was in Christ reconciling. *2 Cor* 5:19
you *to wit* of the grace of God. 8:1

town

(*The Revised Versions frequently change this reading either to* city *or to* village *according as either is appropriate*)

house was on the *t.* wall. *Josh* 2:15
and the elders of *t.* *1 Sam* 16:4
shut in, by entering into a *t.* 23:7
give me a place in some *t.* 27:5
woe to him that builds a *t.* *Hab* 2:12
t. ye shall enter. *Mat* 10:11
blind man out of the *t.* *Mark* 8:23
nor go into the *t.* nor tell it to. 26
Christ cometh out of the *t.* of. *John* 7:42
the *t.* of Mary and her sister. 11:1
Jesus was not yet come into the *t.* 30

townclerk

the *t.* had appeased the. *Acts* 19:35

towns

dwelt in unwalled *t.* *Esth* 9:19
on all her *t.* the evil. *Jer* 19:15
Jerusalem be inhabited as *t.* without walls. *Zech* 2:4
went through the *t.* *Luke* 9:6
that they may go into the *t.* 12

trade

their *t.* hath been about cattle. *Gen* 46:32*, 34*

trade, *verb*

dwell and *t.* ye. *Gen* 34:10, 21
as many as *t.* by sea. *Rev* 18:17*

traded

Tarshish *t.* in thy fairs. *Ezek* 27:12
Javan, Tubal, Meshech, *t.* the. 13
Togarmah *t.* with horses. 14
Judah and Israel *t.* in thy market. 17
five talents, went and *t.* *Mat* 25:16

trading

how much every man had gained by *t.* *Luke* 19:15

tradition

(*Usually this word means laws and regulations handed down orally from one generation to another, and forming the Oral Law of the Jews, which Jesus frequently denounced when it was against the real law of God*)

why do thy disciples transgress the *t.* of ? *Mat* 15:2; *Mark* 7:5
transgress the commandment of God by your *t.*? *Mat* 15:3; *Mark* 7:9
commandment of God of none effect by your *t.* *Mat* 15:6; *Mark* 7:13
t. of the elders. *Mark* 7:3, 8, 9
after the *t.* of men. *Col* 2:8
not after the *t.* which he. *2 Thes* 3:6
received by *t.* from. *1 Pet* 1:18*

traditions

being zealous of the *t.* *Gal* 1:14
hold the *t.* ye have. *2 Thes* 2:15

traffick

ye shall *t.* in the land. *Gen* 42:34

traffick, *substantive*

of *t.* of merchants. *1 Ki* 10:15
it into a land of *t.* *Ezek* 17:4
by thy *t.* hast thou increased. 28:5
sanctuaries by iniquity of *t.* 18

traffickers

whose *t.* are the honourable. *Isa* 23:8

train

Jerusalem with a great *t.* *1 Ki* 10:2
his *t.* filled the temple. *Isa* 6:1

train, *verb*

t. up a child in the way. *Pr.* 22:6

trained

his *t.* servants, 318. *Gen* 14:14

traitor

Iscariot, which was the *t.* *Luke* 6:16

traitors

men shall be *t.*, heady. *2 Tim* 3:4

trample

the dragon shalt thou *t.* *Ps* 91:13
will *t.* them in my fury. *Isa* 63:3
pearls, lest they *t.* them. *Mat* 7:6

trance

vision falling into a *t.* *Num* 24:4*, 16*
he fell into a *t.* and saw. *Acts* 10:10
and in a *t.* I saw a vision. 11:5
in the temple, I was in a *t.* 22:17

tranquillity

lengthening of thy *t.* *Dan* 4:27

transferred

have in figure *t.* to myself. *1 Cor* 4:6

transfigured

(*The history of Christ's* transfiguration *is recorded in each of the first three Gospels. All three agree that this* transfiguration *was celebrated upon a mountain, which modern commentators think was Mount Hermon*)

and he was *t.* before them. *Mat* 17:2; *Mark* 9:2

transformed

but be ye *t.* by renewing. *Rom* 12:2
for Satan is *t.* into an. *2 Cor* 11:14*
if his ministers also be *t.* 15*

transforming

t. themselves into. *2 Cor* 11:13*

transgress

wherefore now do ye *t.* the commandment? *Num* 14:41; *2 Chr* 24:20
the Lord's people to *t.* *1 Sam* 2:24
if ye *t.* I will scatter you. *Neh* 1:8
shall we hearken to you to *t.*? 13:27
my mouth shall not *t.* *Ps* 17:3
let them be ashamed who *t.* 25:3
bread that man will *t.* *Pr* 28:21
thou saidst, I will not *t.* *Jer* 2:20
purge out them that *t.* *Ezek* 20:38
come to Beth-el and *t.* *Amos* 4:4
why do thy disciples *t.*? *Mat* 15:2
t. the commandment of God ? 3
who by circumcision dost *t.* the law. *Rom* 2:27

transgressed

I have not *t.* thy commandments. *Deut* 26:13
Israel hath sinned, and they have also *t.* my covenant. *Josh* 7:11, 15
t. covenant of Lord your God. 23:16
he said, Ye have *t.* *1 Sam* 14:33
I have *t.* the commandment. 15:24
wherein they have *t.* *1 Ki* 8:50
Achar, who *t.* in the. *1 Chr* 2:7*
they *t.* against the God of. 5:25*
because they *t.* against. *2 Chr* 12:2*
Uzziah *t.* against the Lord. 26:16*
and Ahaz *t.* sore against. 28:19*
the priests and the people *t.* 36:14*
ye have *t.* and taken. *Ezra* 10:10*
we are many that have *t.* in. 13
they have *t.* the laws. *Isa* 24:5
teachers have *t.* against me. 43:27
carcases of men that have *t.* 66:24
the pastors *t.* against me. *Jer* 2:8
why will ye plead ? ye all have *t.* 29
acknowledge that thou hast *t.* 3:13
iniquities whereby they *t.* 33:8
I will give the men that *t.* 34:18
we have *t.* and have rebelled. *Lam* 3:42
they and their fathers have *t.* *Ezek* 2:3
transgressions whereby ye *t.* 18:31
yea, all Israel have *t.* *Dan* 9:11
because they have *t.* *Hos* 7:13
not ashamed for doings wherein thou *t.* *Zeph* 3:11
nor *t.* I at any time thy. *Luke* 15:29
see **covenants**

transgressest

why *t.* thou the king's ? *Esth* 3:3

transgresseth

his mouth *t.* not in judgement. *Pr* 16:10
because he *t.* by wine. *Hab* 2:5*
committeth sin, *t.* law. *1 John* 3:4*
whoso *t.* and abideth not. *2 John* 9*

transgressing

wrought wickedness in *t.* *Deut* 17:2
in *t.* and lying against. *Isa* 59:13

transgression

forgiving *t.* and sin. *Ex* 34:7
Num 14:18
or if it be in *t.* against. *Josh* 22:22*
that there is no *t.* in. *1 Sam* 24:11
carried to Babylon for their *t.* *1 Chr* 9:1
so Saul died for his *t.* which. 10:13*
Ahaz cast away in *t.* *2 Chr* 29:19*
because of *t.* of those carried away. *Ezra* 9:4*
mourned because of their *t.* 10:6*
thou not pardon my *t.*? *Job* 7:21
cast them away for their *t.* 8:4
make me to know my *t.* and. 13:23
my *t.* is sealed up in a bag. 14:17
I am clean without *t.* 33:9
is incurable without *t.* 34:6
innocent from the great *t.* *Ps* 19:13
is he whose *t.* is forgiven. 32:1
the *t.* of the wicked saith. 36:1
against me; not for my *t.* 59:3
visit their *t.* with a rod. 89:32

fools because of their *t.* are. *Ps* 107:17
the wicked is snared by *t.* *Pr* 12:13
covereth a *t.* seeketh love. 17:9
he loveth *t.* that loveth strife. 19
glory to pass over a *t.* 19:11
for the *t.* of a land many are. 28:2
and saith, It is no *t.* 24
in the *t.* of an evil man there. 29:6
when the wicked are multiplied, *t.* 16
and a furious man aboundeth in *t.* 22
the *t.* thereof shall be. *Isa* 24:20
for the *t.* of my people was he. 53:8
ye not children of *t.*, a seed of ? 57:4
shew my people their *t.* 58:1
and to them that turn from *t.* 59:20
him in the day of his *t.* *Ezek* 33:12
against the daily sacrifice by reason of *t.* *Dan* 8:12
concerning sacrifice, and the *t.* 13
determined to finish the *t.* 9:24
at Gilgal multiply *t.*, bring. *Amos* 4:4
t. of Jacob is all this, and for the sins . . . what is the *t.*? *Mi* 1:5
power to declare to Jacob his *t.* 3:8
firstborn for my *t.*? 6:7
that passeth by the *t.* of the. 7:18
which Judas by *t.* fell. *Acts* 1:25*
no law is, there is no *t.* *Rom* 4:15
after similitude of Adam's *t.* 5:14
the woman being deceived was in the *t.* *1 Tim* 2:14
every *t.* received just recompence of. *Heb* 2:2
for sin is the *t.* of the. *1 John* 3:4*

transgressions

pardon your *t.* for my. *Ex* 23:21
atonement because of their *t.* *Lev* 16:16
confess over the goat all their *t.* 21
will not forgive your *t.* *Josh* 24:19
thy people all their *t.* *1 Ki* 8:50
if I covered my *t.* as Adam, by hiding. *Job* 31:33
if thy *t.* be multiplied, what ? 35:6
them their work and *t.* 36:9
in the multitude of their *t.* *Ps* 5:10
sins of my youth, nor my *t.* 25:7
I said I will confess my *t.* 32:5
deliver me from all my *t.* and. 39:8
blot out all my *t.* 51:1
for I acknowledge my *t.*: my sin. 3
as for our *t.* thou shalt purge. 65:3
so far hath he removed our *t.* 103:12
he that blotteth out thy *t.* *Isa* 43:25
out as a thick cloud thy *t.* 44:22
for your *t.* is your mother put. 50:1
but he was wounded for our *t.* 53:5
t. are multiplied before thee, and our sins testify . . . for our *t.* 59:12
because their *t.* are many. *Jer* 5:6
for the multitude of her *t.* *Lam* 1:5
the yoke of my *t.* is bound by. 14
as hast done to me for all my *t.* 22
any more with their *t.* *Ezek* 14:11
all his *t.* shall not be. 18:22
turneth away from all his *t.* 28
turn yourselves from your *t.* 30
cast away all your *t.* whereby. 31
in that your *t.* are discovered. 21:24
if our *t.* be upon us and we pine. 33:10
themselves any more with *t.* 37:23
according to their *t.* have I. 39:24
for three *t.* of Damascus. *Amos* 1:3
for three *t.* of Gaza. 6
for three *t.* of Ammon. 13
I will visit the *t.* of Israel. 3:14
I know your manifold *t.* and. 5:12
for the *t.* of Israel were. *Mi* 1:13
the law was added because of *t.*, till the seed. *Gal* 3:19
for the redemption of the *t.* *Heb* 9:15

transgressor

the *t.* shall be a ransom. *Pr* 21:18*
the words of the *t.* 22:12*
thou wast called a *t.* *Isa* 48:8
I make myself a *t.* *Gal* 2:18
kill, thou art become a *t.* *Jas* 2:11

transgressors

the *t.* shall be destroyed. *Ps* 37:38
then will I teach *t.* thy ways. 51:13
be not merciful to any wicked *t.* 59:5
t. shall be rooted out. *Pr* 2:22*
the perverseness of *t.* shall. 11:3*
t. shall be taken in their own naughtiness. 6*
but the soul of the *t.* shall eat. 13:2*
but the way of *t.* is hard. 15*
and she increaseth the *t.* 23:28*
rewardeth the fool and the *t.* 26:10*
the destruction of *t.* shall. *Isa* 1:28
bring it again to mind, O ye *t.* 46:8
numbered with the *t.* and bare the sin of many, . . . for the *t.* 53:12
when the *t.* are come to. *Dan* 8:23
but the *t.* shall fall therein. *Hos* 14:9
he was numbered with *t.* *Mark* 15:28
Luke 22:37
convinced of the law as *t.* *Jas* 2:9

translate

to *t.* the kingdom from. *2 Sam* 3:10

translated

t. us into the kingdom of. *Col* 1:13
Enoch was *t.* that he should not see death. *Heb* 11:5

translation

before his *t.* he had this. *Heb* 11:5

transparent

was as it were *t.* glass. *Rev* 21:21

trap, -s

but they shall be *t.* *Josh* 23:13
and a *t.* is laid for him. *Job* 18:10
let it become a *t.* *Ps* 69:22
they lay wait, set a *t.* *Jer* 5:26
be made a snare, a *t.* *Rom* 11:9

travail

time of her *t.* behold. *Gen* 38:27
Moses told Jethro, all the *t.* *Ex* 18:8
them as of a woman in *t.* *Ps* 48:6
Jer 6:24; 13:21; 22:23; 49:24
50:43; *Mi* 4:9, 10
this sore *t.* hath God. *Eccl* 1:13
are sorrows, his *t.* is grief. 2:23
but to the sinner he giveth *t.* 26
I have seen the *t.* God hath. 3:10
again I considered all *t.* and. 4:4
than both the hands full with *t.* 6
vanity, yea it is a sore *t.* 8
riches perish by evil *t.* 5:14
I *t.* not. *Isa* 23:4
see of the *t.* of his soul. 53:11
sing, thou that didst not *t.* 54:1
voice as of a woman in *t.* *Jer* 4:31
whether a man doth *t.*? . . . as a woman in *t.*? 30:6
compassed me with gall and *t.* *Lam* 3:5
a woman when she is in *t.* hath sorrow. *John* 16:21
my children, of whom I *t.* in birth. *Gal* 4:19
for ye remember our labour and *t.* *1 Thes* 2:9
destruction cometh, as *t.* 5:3
but wrought with *t.* night and day. *2 Thes* 3:8

travailed

Rachel *t.* *Gen* 35:16
Tamar *t.* 38:28
Phinehas' wife bowed herself, and *t.* *1 Sam* 4:19
she *t.* she brought forth. *Isa* 66:7
as soon as Zion *t.* she brought. 8

travailest

cry, thou that *t.* not. *Gal* 4:27

travaileth

behold, he *t.* with iniquity. *Ps* 7:14
they shall be in pain as a woman that *t.* *Isa* 13:8
as the pangs of a woman that *t.* 21:3
and with them her that *t.* *Jer* 31:8
till she who *t.* hath brought. *Mi* 5:3
the whole creation *t.* in pain until now. *Rom* 8:22

travailing

I cry like a *t.* woman. *Isa* 42:14
sorrows of a *t.* woman. *Hos* 13:13
a woman cried, *t.* in birth. *Rev* 12:2

travel

thou knowest the *t.* that. *Num* 20:14
Paul's companion in *t.* *Acts* 19:29
chosen of the churches to *t.* with us. *2 Cor* 8:19

travelled

t. as far as Phenice and. *Acts* 11:19

traveller

there came a *t.* to the. *2 Sam* 12:4
opened my doors to the *t.* *Job* 31:32

travellers

the *t.* walked through. *Judg* 5:6

travelleth

wicked man *t.* with pain. *Josh* 15:20
poverty come as one that *t.* *Pr* 6:11*; 24:34*

travelling

in Arabia lodge, O ye *t.* *Isa* 21:13†
who is this *t.* in the greatness ? 63:1
heaven is as a man *t.* *Mat* 25:14

traversing

thou art a swift dromedary *t.* her ways. *Jer* 2:23

treacherous

t. dealer dealeth treacherously. *Isa* 21:2; 24:16
turned not, and her *t.* sister Judah. *Jer* 3:7
her *t.* sister Judah feared not. 8
her *t.* sister Judah hath not. 10
Israel hath justified herself more than *t.* Judah. 11
be an assembly of *t.* men. 9:2
are light and *t.* persons. *Zeph* 3:4

treacherously

men of Shechem dealt *t.* *Judg* 9:23
and dealest *t.*, and they dealt not *t.* with thee. *Isa* 33:1
thou wouldest deal very *t.* 48:8
as a wife *t.* departeth. *Jer* 3:20
the house of Judah hath dealt *t.* 5:11; *Mal* 2:11
happy that deal very *t.*? *Jer* 12:1
even they have dealt *t.* with thee. 6
all her friends have dealt *t.* *Lam* 1:2
they have dealt *t.* against. *Hos* 5:7
there have they dealt *t.* against. 6:7
why do we deal *t.* every ? *Mal* 2:10
against whom thou hast dealt *t.* 14
let none deal *t.* against the wife. 15
your spirit, that ye deal not *t.* 16

treachery

Joram said, There is *t.* *2 Ki* 9:23

tread

soles of your feet *t.* *Deut* 11:24
you on all the land that ye *t.* 25
thou shalt *t.* upon their high. 33:29
none *t.* on the threshold. *1 Sam* 5:5
t. their winepresses, and. *Job* 24:11
and *t.* down the wicked in. 40:12
let him *t.* down my life. *Ps* 7:5
name will we *t.* them under. 44:5
t. down our enemies. 60:12; 108:13
thou shalt *t.* upon the lion. 91:13
who hath required this at your hand, to *t.* my courts ? *Isa* 1:12*
to *t.* them down, like the mire. 10:6
upon my mountains *t.* him. 14:25
treaders shall *t.* out no wine. 16:10
the foot shall *t.* it down. 26:6
t. them in mine anger. 63:3, 6
a shout, as they that *t.* *Jer* 25:30
wine to fail, none shall *t.* 48:33
with his hoofs shall he *t.* *Ezek* 26:11
but ye must *t.* the residue. 34:18
fourth beast shall *t.* it. *Dan* 7:23
Ephraim loveth to *t.* *Hos* 10:11
the Lord will *t.* on the. *Mi* 1:3
when the Assyrian shall *t.* 5:5
thou shalt *t.* the olives, but. 6:15
t. the mortar, make. *Nah* 3:14
as mighty men which *t.* *Zech* 10:5
and ye shall *t.* down the. *Mal* 4:3
I will give you power to *t.* on scorpions. *Luke* 10:19
holy city shall they *t.* *Rev* 11:2

treader, -s

t. shall tread out no wine. *Isa* 16:10
the *t.* of grapes shall overtake the sower. *Amos* 9:13

treadeth

not muzzle ox when he *t.* *Deut* 25:4
1 Cor 9:9; *1 Tim* 5:18
which *t.* upon the waves. *Job* 9:8
come as the potter *t.* clay. *Isa* 41:25
thy garments like him that *t.* 63:2

e that t. on the high places of the earth. Amos 4:13
nd when he t. within. Mi 5:6
f he go through, he both t. down. 8
e t. the winepress of. Rev 19:15

treading

n those days saw I some t. winepresses on the sabbath. Neh 13:15
t shall be for the t. of. Isa 7:25
of trouble and of t. down. 22:5
forasmuch as your t. Amos 5:11*

treason

acts of Zimri and his t. 1 Ki 16:20
Athaliah cried, T. T. 2 Ki 11:14
2 Chr 23:13

treasure

The word treasure, *among the Hebrews, signifies anything collected together; provisions, stores. So they say, a* treasure *of corn, of wine, of oil, of honey,* Jer 41:8. *So also* treasures *of gold, silver, brass,* Ezek 28:4; Dan 11:43. *Snow, winds, hail, rain, waters, are in the* treasuries *of God,* Job 38:22; Ps 135:7. *The wise men opened their* treasures, *that is, their boxes or bundles, to offer presents to our Saviour,* Mat 2:11.

God hath given you t. Gen 43:23
ye shall be a peculiar t. to me. Ex 19:5†; Ps 135:4
open to thee his good t. Deut 28:12
gave them to the t. of. 1 Chr 29:8
after their ability to t. of work. Ezra 2:69*
the Tirshatha gave to t. Neh 7:70*
the fathers gave to the t. of. 71*
thou fillest with hid t. Ps 17:14
Israel for his peculiar t. 135:4†
of the righteous is much t. Pr 15:6
a little, than great t. and trouble. 16
there is a t. to be desired. 21:20
I gathered the peculiar t. Eccl 2:8
fear of the Lord is his t. Isa 33:6
have taken the t. and. Ezek 22:25
he shall spoil t. of all. Hos 13:15
for where your t. is, there. Mat 6:21
Luke 12:34
t. of his heart, an evil man out of the evil t. Mat 12:35; Luke 6:45
heaven is like to a t. hid. Mat 13:44
who bringeth out of his t. things. 52
shalt have t. in heaven. 19:21
Mark 10:21; Luke 18:22
so is he that layeth up t. Luke 12:21
provide a t. in the heavens. 33
had charge of all her t. Acts 8:27
we have this t. in earthen. 2 Cor 4:7
ye have heaped t. for the. Jas 5:3

treasure *cities*

for Pharaoh t. cities. Ex 1:11

treasure *house*

let search be made in the king's t. house. Ezra 5:17
out of the king's t. house. 7:20
Levites shall bring up the tithe into the t. house. Neh 10:38
brought vessels into t. house of his god. Dan 1:2

treasured

Tyre, it shall not be t. Isa 23:18

treasurer

forth the vessels by the t. Ezra 1:8
get thee unto this t., even. Isa 22:15

treasurers

make a decree to all t. Ezra 7:21
and I made t. over the. Neh 13:13
gathered the t. Dan 3:2, 3

treasures

sealed up among my t. Deut 32:34
suck of t. hid in the sand. 33:19
he put dedicated things among the t. 1 Ki 7:51*
Shishak took away the t. of. 14:26
Asa took gold left in the t. 15:18
2 Chr 16:2
Jehoash took gold found in t. 2 Ki 12:18; 14:14
gold that was found in the t. 16:8
gave him silver found in the t. 18:15
and gold and all that was found in his t. 2 Ki 20:13, 15; Isa 39:2, 4
thence all the t. of the house of the Lord, and the t. of the king's. 2 Ki 24:13; 2 Chr 36:18
Ahijah was over t. of. 1 Chr 26:20*
Shebuel was ruler of the t. 24*
his brethren were over the t. 26
and over the king's t. was. 27:25*
concerning the t. 2 Chr 8:15
appointed for the t. Neh 12:44
it more than for hid t. Job 3:21
into the t. of the snow? or hast thou seen the t. of the hail? 38:22*
if thou searchest for her as for hid t. Pr 2:4
I will fill the t. of those that. 8:21*
t. of wickedness profit. 10:2
the getting of t. by a lying. 21:6
neither any end of their t. Isa 2:7
I have robbed their t. 10:13
their t. on bunches of camels. 30:6
and I will give thee the t. 45:3
he bringeth wind out of his t. Jer 10:13*; 51:16*
thy t. I will give to the spoil. 15:13
17:3; 20:5
slay us not: for we have t. 41:8*
thou hast trusted in thy t. 48:7
daughter, that trusted in her t. 49:4
a sword is on her t.; they shall. 50:37
many waters, abundant in t. 51:13
silver and gold into thy t. Ezek 28:4
power over the t. of gold. Dan 11:43
are there yet the t. of wickedness in the house of? Mi 6:10
they had opened their t. Mat 2:11
lay not up for yourselves t. 6:19
but lay up for yourselves t. 20
in whom are hid all the t. Col 2:3
than the t. in Egypt. Heb 11:26

treasurest

t. up wrath against the. Rom 2:5

treasuries

Levites were over the t. 1 Chr 9:26
Solomon pattern of the t. 28:11, 12
Hezekiah made t. for. 2 Chr 32:27
the tithe unto the t. Neh 13:12
I made treasurers over the t. 13
to bring it into the king's t. Esth 3:9
promised to pay to the king's t. 4:7
the wind out of his t. Ps 135:7

treasury

they shall come into the t. of the Lord. Josh 6:19, 24
the house under the t. Jer 38:11
it is not lawful to put them into the t. Mat 27:6
the t., and beheld how the people cast money into the t. Mark 12:41
rich men casting their gifts into the t. Luke 21:1
spake Jesus in the t. John 8:20

treatise

former t. have I made. Acts 1:1

tree

you every t. for meat. Gen 1:29
God made every t. to grow, the t. of life also, and the t. of. 2:9
of every t. of the garden thou. 16
but of the t. of knowledge. 17; 3:3
when the woman saw that the t. 3:6
hast thou eaten of the t.? 11, 17
the woman gave me of the t. 12
lest he take also of the t. of life. 22
keep the way of the t. of life. 24
rest yourselves under the t. 18:4
he stood by them under the t. 8
Pharaoh shall hang thee on a t. 40:19
the hail brake every t. Ex 9:25
the locusts shall eat every t. 10:5
and the Lord shewed him a t. 15:25
seed or fruit of t. is Lord's. Lev 27:30
a stroke to cut down the t. Deut 19:5
t. of the field is man's life. 20:19
and if thou hang him on a t. 21:22
not remain all night on the t. 23
bird's nest in the way in any t. 22:6
take the king of Ai down from the t. Josh 8:29
now Saul abode under a t. in Ramah. 1 Sam 22:6*
buried them under a t. at Jabesh. 1 Sam 31:13*
shall fell every good t. 2 Ki 3:19
were both hanged on a t. Esth 2:23
there is hope of a t. if it. Job 14:7
hath he removed like a t. 19:10
shall be broken as a t. 24:20
like a t. planted by the rivers. Ps 1:3
she is a t. of life to them. Pr 3:18
the fruit of the righteous is a t. 11:30
desire cometh, it is a t. of life. 13:12
tongue is a t. of life. 15:4
if the t. fall toward the south or the north; where the t. Eccl 11:3
a t. that will not rot. Isa 40:20
down to the stock of a t.? 44:19
eunuch say, I am a dry t. 56:3
as days of a t. are the days. 65:22
themselves behind one t. 66:17
for one cutteth a t. out. Jer 10:3
destroy the t. with the fruit. 11:19
he shall be as a t. planted by. 17:8
vine t. more than any t.? Ezek 15:2
the high t., exalted the low t., dried up the green t., made dry t. to. 17:24
rod of my son, as every t. 21:10
nor any t. in the garden of. 31:8
the t. of the field shall yield. 34:27
multiply the fruit of the t. 36:30
and behold a t. Dan 4:10
the t. grew. 11, 20
said thus, Hew down the t. 4:14, 23
fear not for the t. beareth. Joel 2:22
every t. that bringeth not forth good fruit. Mat 3:10; 7:19; Luke 3:9
good t. bringeth forth good fruit, but a corrupt t. Mat 7:17; Luke 6:43
good t. cannot bring forth. Mat 7:18
the t. good and his fruit good; for the t. is known. 12:33; Luke 6:44
mustard seed becometh a t. Mat 13:32; Luke 13:19
say to the sycamine t. Luke 17:6
ye slew and hanged on a t. Acts 5:30
they slew, and hanged on a t. 10:39
took him down from the t. 13:29
one that hangeth on a t. Gal 3:13
in his own body on the t. 1 Pet 2:24
I give to eat of the t. of life. Rev 2:7
should not blow on any t. 7:1
hurt any green thing, nor t. 9:4
was there the t. of life. 22:2
have right to the t. of life. 14
see **green**

trees

amongst the t. of garden. Gen 3:8
all the t. were made sure. 23:17
did eat the fruit of the t. Ex 10:15
planted all manner of t. Lev 19:23
the boughs of goodly t. 23:40
and the t. of the field shall. 26:4
neither shall the t. of the land. 20
as t. of lign aloes which the Lord ... as cedar t. beside. Num 24:6
not plant a grove of any t. Deut 16:21
not destroy t. thereof by axe. 20:19
t. thou knowest not to be t. for. 20
all thy t. and fruit shall the. 28:42
hanged them on five t. Josh 10:26
took them down off the t. 27
the t. went forth to anoint. Judg 9:8
be promoted over the t. 9, 11, 13
the t. said to the fig tree, reign. 10
t. said to the vine. 12
t. said to the bramble. 14
cut down a bough from the t. 48
spake of t. from cedar. 1 Ki 4:33
felled all the good t. 2 Ki 3:25
then shall the t. of the wood sing. 1 Chr 16:33; Ps 96:12
firstfruits of all t. Neh 10:35, 37
under the shady t. Job 40:21, 22
lifted up axes on thick t. Ps 74:5
their sycamore t. with frost. 78:47
the t. of the Lord are full of. 104:16
and brake the t. of their. 105:33
fruitful t. and cedars praise. 148:9
I planted t. of all kinds. Eccl 2:5
apple tree among the t. S of S 2:3
with all t. of frankincense. 4:14
heart was moved as the t. Isa 7:2
the rest of the t. of his forest. 10:19
strengtheneth among the t. 44:14

t. of fields shall clap their. *Isa* 55:12
called *t.* of righteousness. 61:3
Lord said, Hew down *t.* *Jer* 6:6
be poured out upon the *t.* 7:20
all the *t.* of the field. *Ezek* 17:24
they saw all the thick *t.* 20:28
was exalted above all the *t.* 31:5
so that all the *t.* of Eden. 9
many *t.* on the one side and. 47:7
by the rivers shall grow all *t.* 12
all the *t.* of the field are. *Joel* 1:12
the flame hath burnt all the *t.* 19
the axe is laid unto the root of the *t.* *Mat* 3:10; *Luke* 3:9
others cut down branches from the *t.* *Mat* 21:8; *Mark* 11:8*
I see men as *t.* walking. *Mark* 8:24
fig tree and all the *t.* *Luke* 21:29
t. whose fruit withereth. *Jude* 12
hurt not the *t.* till we have. *Rev* 7:3
and the third part of the *t.* 8:7
see **palm**

tremble

nations shall *t.* because. *Deut* 2:25
fear not and do not *t.* 20:3
of those that *t.* at the. *Ezra* 10:3
earth, the pillars thereof *t.* *Job* 9:6
the pillars of heaven *t.* and. 26:11
hast made the earth to *t.* *Ps* 60:2
Lord reigneth, let the people *t.* 99:1
t. thou earth at the presence. 114:7
of the house shall *t.* *Eccl* 12:3
hills did *t.*, their carcases. *Isa* 5:25
man that made the earth to *t.* 14:16
t. ye women that are at ease. 32:11
that the nations may *t.* at thy. 64:2
hear word of Lord, ye that *t.* 66:5
will ye not *t.* at my presence? *Jer* 5:22
at his wrath the earth shall *t.* 10:10
and they shall *t.* for all the. 33:9
the land of Babylon shall *t.* 51:29
they shall *t.* at every moment. *Ezek* 26:16; 32:10
now shall isles *t.* in the day. 26:18
men *t.* before the God. *Dan* 6:26
then the children shall *t.* *Hos* 11:10
t. as a bird out of Egypt. 11
inhabitants of the land *t.* *Joel* 2:1
quake, the heavens shall *t.* 10
shall not the land *t.* for. *Amos* 8:8
the land of Midian did *t.* *Hab* 3:7
devils also believe and *t.* *Jas* 2:19*

trembled

Isaac *t.* very exceedingly. *Gen* 27:33
that was in the camp *t.* *Ex* 19:16
earth *t.* and the heavens. *Judg* 5:4
2 Sam 22:8; *Ps* 18:7; 77:18; 97:4
Eli's heart *t.* for the. *1 Sam* 4:13
the spoilers *t.* 14:15
the elders of the town *t.* 16:4
and his heart greatly *t.* 28:5
to me every one that *t.* *Ezra* 9:4
and lo the mountains *t.* *Jer* 4:24
Hab 3:10*
whole land *t.* at neighing. *Jer* 8:16
all people and nations *t.* *Dan* 5:19
when I heard, my belly *t.* and I *t.* in. *Hab* 3:16
sepulchre, for they *t.* *Mark* 16:8
then Moses *t.* *Acts* 7:32
Felix *t.* 24:25*

trembleth

at this also my heart *t.* *Job* 37:1
looketh on earth and it *t.* *Ps* 104:32
my flesh *t.* for fear of thee. 119:120
I will look, to him that *t.* *Isa* 66:2

trembling

t. take hold on the mighty. *Ex* 15:15
shall give thee a *t.* heart. *Deut* 28:65
people followed him *t.* *1 Sam* 13:7
there was a very great *t.* 14:15
all people sat *t.* because. *Ezra* 10:9
fear came upon me and *t.* *Job* 4:14
I am afraid and *t.* taketh. 21:6*
fear and rejoice with *t.* *Ps* 2:11
fearfulness and *t.* are come. 55:5
the dregs of the cup of *t.* *Isa* 51:17*
out of thy hand the cup of *t.* 22*
have heard a voice of *t.* *Jer* 30:5
drink thy water with *t.* *Ezek* 12:18
clothe themselves with *t.* 26:16
spoken this, I stood *t.* *Dan* 10:11
when Ephraim spake *t.* *Hos* 13:1
Jerusalem a cup of *t.* *Zech* 12:2*
the woman fearing and *t.* *Mark* 5:33
Luke 8:47
Saul *t.* said, Lord, what wilt thou have me to do? *Acts* 9:6
gaoler came *t.* and fell down. 16:29
you in fear and much *t.* *1 Cor* 2:3
how with fear and *t.* ye. *2 Cor* 7:15
obedient with fear and *t.* *Eph* 6:5
salvation with fear and *t.* *Phil* 2:12

trench

David came to the *t.* *1 Sam* 17:20*
lay sleeping within the *t.* 26:5*, 7*
Elijah made a *t.* about. *1 Ki* 18:32
and he filled the *t.* also. 35, 38
enemies shall cast a *t.* *Luke* 19:43*

trespass

(*American Revision usually, and English sometimes, substitutes the word* guilt *for this word*)

what is my *t.* that thou? *Gen* 31:36
we pray thee, forgive the *t.* 50:17*
of *t.* whether for ox. *Ex* 22:9
he shall bring for his *t.* *Lev* 5:15
if they shall confess their *t.* 26:40
when any do a *t.* against. *Num* 5:6
he shall recompense his *t.* with. 7
no kinsman to recompense the *t.* 8
if she have done *t.* against her. 27
forgive the *t.* of thine. *1 Sam* 25:28
why will he be a cause of *t.* to? *1 Chr* 21:3
on Judah for their *t.* *2 Chr* 24:18
add more to our sins and *t.* 28:13
Manasseh's prayer and *t.* are. 33:19
have been chief in this *t.* *Ezra* 9:2
and our *t.* is grown up unto the. 6
we have been in a great *t.* 7, 13
wives, to increase *t.* of Israel. 10:10
a ram of the flock for their *t.* 19
with him there for his *t.* *Ezek* 17:20
in his *t.* he hath trespassed. 18:24
because of their *t.* they. *Dan* 9:7
see **commit, committed, offering**

trespass, *verb*

if any man *t.* against his. *1 Ki* 8:31
warn that they *t.* not. *2 Chr* 19:10
Ahaz did *t.* yet more against. 28:22
if brother *t.*, tell him his. *Mat* 18:15
if thy brother *t.* against. *Luke* 17:3*
if he *t.* against thee seven times. 4

trespass *money*

the *t. money* was not. *2 Ki* 12:16

trespassed

he hath certainly *t.* against. *Lev* 5:19
their trespass which they *t.* 26:40
him against whom he *t.* *Num* 5:7
because ye *t.* against me. *Deut* 32:51
go out of sanctuary, for thou hast *t.* *2 Chr* 26:18
for our fathers have *t.* and. 29:6
be not like your fathers who *t.* 30:7
but Amon *t.* more and more. 33:23
who have *t.* against our God. *Ezra* 10:2
his trespass that he *t.* *Ezek* 17:20
they *t.* against me. 39:23, 26
their trespass that they *t.* *Dan* 9:7
because they have *t.* *Hos* 8:1

trespasses

are before thee in our *t.* *Ezra* 9:15
as goeth on still in his *t.* *Ps* 68:21
they have borne their shame and *t.* *Ezek* 39:26
if ye forgive men their *t.* *Mat* 6:14
not men their *t.* neither will your Father forgive your *t.* 15; 18:35
may forgive you your *t.* *Mark* 11:25
your Father forgive your *t.* 26
not imputing their *t.* *2 Cor* 5:19
were dead in *t.* and sins. *Eph* 2:1
having forgiven you all *t.* *Col* 2:13

trespassing

that he hath done in *t.* *Lev* 6:7
sinneth against me by *t.* *Ezek* 14:13

trial

he will laugh at the *t.* of. *Job* 9:23
because it is a *t.* *Ezek* 21:13
how that in a great *t.* *2 Cor* 8:2
others had *t.* of cruel. *Heb* 11:36
that the *t.* of your faith. *1 Pet* 1:7*
strange concerning the fiery *t.* 4:12

tribe

Jacob had twelve sons, who were the heads of so many great families, which altogether formed a great nation; every one of these families was called a tribe. *But Jacob on his death bed adopted Ephraim and Manasseh, the sons of Joseph, as two* tribes *of Israel,* Gen 48:5. *Instead of twelve* tribes, *there were now thirteen, that of Joseph being divided into two. However, in the distribution of lands to the people made by Joshua, by the command of God, they counted but twelve* tribes, *and made but twelve lots. For the* tribe *of Levi, which was appointed to the service of the tabernacle of the Lord, had no share in the distribution of the land, but only some cities to dwell in, and the firstfruits, tithes and oblations of the people,* Num 35:2; Josh 13:7, 8, 14, 33.

The twelve tribes, *while they were in the desert, encamped round about the tabernacle of the covenant, every one according to its order. The Levites were distributed around the tabernacle, nearer the holy place than the other* tribes, Num 2:2, 3, *etc.*

In the marches of the army of Israel, the twelve tribes *were divided into four great bodies, as bodies of troops, each composed of three* tribes. *Between the second and third there came the Levites and priests, with the ark of the Lord, the curtain, the planks, the pillars, and all the other furniture of the tabernacle.*

The twelve tribes *continued united under one head, making but one state, one people, and one monarchy, till after the death of Solomon. Then ten of the* tribes *of Israel revolted from the house of David, and received for their king Jeroboam, the son of Nebat; and only the* tribes *of Judah and Benjamin continued under the government of Rehoboam,* 1 Ki 12:16, 20. *After a separate existence of a little over 200 years, Shalmaneser, king of Assyria, took the city of Samaria, destroyed it, took away the rest of the inhabitants of Israel, carried them beyond the Euphrates, and sent other inhabitants into the country to cultivate and possess it,* 2 Ki 17:6, 24; 18:10, 11. *This ended the kingdom of the ten* tribes *of Israel.*

As to the tribes *of Judah and Benjamin, who remained under the government of the kings of the family of David, they continued a much longer time in their own country. But at last Nebuchadnezzar took he city of Jerusalem, entirely ruined it, and burnt the temple, and took away all the inhabitants of Judah and Benjamin to Babylon, and to the other provinces of his empire. This captivity continued for seventy years, as the prophet had foretold them,* Jer 25:11, 12; 29:10.

Then came the Return under Ezra and Nehemiah, the rebuilding of Jerusalem and the temple. But the people never entirely regained their independence. There has been much discussion of the identity of the ten tribes *after the destruction of their kingdom, on the understanding that they were destroyed as a race as well as a nation. But the Jews are always*

spoken of in the New Testament as the twelve tribes, never as the two, and Ezra 6:17 *certainly indicates that they were thus considered at the time of the Return.*
shall be a man of every *t.* head of house of. *Num* 1:4; 13:2; 34:18
cut ye not off the *t.* of the. 4:18
the *t.* of thy father bring thou. 18:2
of every *t.* a thousand. 31:4, 5, 6
the *t.* of the sons of Joseph. 36:5
they shall marry only to the family of the *t.* 6, 8
neither shall the inheritance remove from one *t.* to another *t.*; but. 9
I took one of a *t.* *Deut* 1:23
Josh 3:12; 4:2, 4
family or *t.* whose heart. *Deut* 29:18
t. which the Lord taketh. *Josh* 7:14
from you three men for each *t.* 18:4
thou be a priest to a *t.* *Judg* 18:19
should be one *t.* lacking. 21:3, 6
but will give one *t.* to thy son.
1 Ki 11:13, 32, 36
of the family of that *t.* *1 Chr* 6:61
in what *t.* the stranger. *Ezek* 47:23
pertaineth to another *t.* *Heb* 7:13
of Judah; of which *t.* Moses. 14
see **Reuben, Simeon** *and the rest*

tribes

according to the twelve *t.* *Ex* 28:21
39:14
tents according to their *t.* *Num* 24:2
according to *t.* of your fathers. 33:54
to give to the nine *t.* 34:13
Josh 13:7; 14:2
the two *t.* and the half have received.
Num 34:15; *Josh* 14:3
wise men, known among your *t.*
Deut 1:13
the place which the Lord shall choose out of all your *t.* to. 12:5, 14
chosen him out of all thy *t.* 18:5
ye shall be brought according to your *t.* *Josh* 7:14
before Lord by your *t.* *1 Sam* 10:19
and I will give ten *t.* *1 Ki* 11:31
according to number of the *t.* 18:31
feeble among their *t.* *Ps* 105:37
whither the *t.* go up, the *t.* 122:4
that are the stay of *t.* *Isa* 19:13
be my servant to raise up the *t.* 49:6
return for the *t.* of thine. 63:17
according to their *t.* *Ezek* 45:8
to the oaths of the *t.* *Hab* 3:9
then shall all the *t.* of the earth.
Mat 24:30
which promise our 12 *t.* *Acts* 26:7
to the twelve *t.* which are. *Jas* 1:1
144,000 of all the *t.* *Rev* 7:4
see **Israel**

tribulation

when thou art in *t.* if thou. *Deut* 4:30
let them deliver you in the time of *t.*
Judg 10:14*
deliver me out of all *t.* *1 Sam* 26:24
when *t.* ariseth, he is. *Mat* 13:21
then shall be great *t.*, such. 24:21
immediately after the *t.* 29
Mark 13:24
ye shall have *t.*: but be. *John* 16:33
we must through much *t.* enter the kingdom. *Acts* 14:22
t. and anguish on every soul. *Rom* 2:9
knowing that *t.* worketh. 5:3
shall *t.* separate us from the ? 8:35
rejoicing in hope, patient in *t.* 12:12
comforteth us in all our *t.* *2 Cor* 1:4*
exceeding joyful in all our *t.* 7:4*
we told you, that we should suffer *t.*
1 Thes 3:4*
recompense *t.* to them. *2 Thes* 1:6*
am your companion in *t.* *Rev* 1:9
I know thy works, and *t.* and. 2:9
ye shall have *t.* ten days. 10
I will cast them into great *t.* 22
which came out of great *t.* 7:14

tribulations

you out of all your *t.* *1 Sam* 10:19*
but we glory in *t.* also. *Rom* 5:3
ye faint not at my *t.* *Eph* 3:13
for your faith in all *t.* *2 Thes* 1:4*

tributaries

found therein shall be *t.* *Deut* 20:11
the Canaanites became *t.* *Judg* 1:30
33, 35

tributary

how is she become *t.*! *Lam* 1:1

tribute

[1] *Tribute was exacted at all times from conquered nations. The Jews paid it when dependent and received it when powerful.* [2] *The tribute money mentioned in* Mat 17:24, 25 *was the half shekel paid by every Israelite toward the general expenses of the temple.* [3] *The tribute named in* Mat 22:17 *was the tax paid to Rome.*
became a servant to *t.* *Gen* 49:15*
levy a *t.* to the Lord. *Num* 31:28
the Lord's *t.* of the sheep was. 37
beeves, the Lord's *t.* was 72. 38
asses, the Lord's *t.* was 61. 39
16,000, the Lord's *t.* 32 persons. 40
with a *t.* of a freewill. *Deut* 16:10
Canaanites serve under *t.*
Josh 16:10*; 17:13*
was over the *t.* *2 Sam* 20:24
1 Ki 4:6*; 12:18*; *2 Chr* 10:18*
did Solomon levy a *t.* *1 Ki* 9:21*
put the land to a *t.* *2 Ki* 23:33
Solomon make to pay *t.* *2 Chr* 8:8*
Philistines brought *t.* silver. 17:11
then will they not pay *t.* *Ezra* 4:13
and toll, *t.* and custom was. 20
of the *t.* expences be given 6:8
not lawful to impose *t.* on. 7:24
money for king's *t.* *Neh* 5:4
slothful shall be under *t.* *Pr* 12:24*
t. money came to Peter and said, Doth not . . . pay *t.*? *Mat* 17:24*
kings of the earth take *t.*? 25
is it lawful to give *t.* to ? 22:17
Mark 12:14; *Luke* 20:22
shew me the *t.* money. *Mat* 22:19
to give *t.* to Caesar. *Luke* 23:2
cause pay ye *t.* also. *Rom* 13:6
therefore *t.* to whom *t.* is due. 7

trickleth

mine eye *t.* down. *Lam* 3:49*

tried

shall every stroke be *t.* *Deut* 21:5
the word of the Lord is *t.*
2 Sam 22:31; *Ps* 18:30
when he hath *t.* me, I. *Job* 23:10
desire is that Job may be *t.* 34:36
silver is *t.* in a furnace. *Ps* 12:6
thou hast *t.* me and shalt find. 17:3
hast *t.* us, as silver is *t.* 66:10
the word of the Lord *t.* him. 105:19
I lay in Zion a *t.* stone. *Isa* 28:16
thou hast *t.* mine heart. *Jer* 12:3
shall be purified and *t.* *Dan* 12:10*
try them as gold is *t.* *Zech* 13:9
Abraham when he was *t.* *Heb* 11:17
when *t.* he shall receive. *Jas* 1:12*
gold, though it be *t.* *1 Pet* 1:7*
hast *t.* them which say. *Rev* 2:2
into prison, that ye may be *t.* 10
thee to buy of me gold *t.* 3:18*

triest

I know that thou *t.* *1 Chr* 29:17
O Lord, that *t.* the reins. *Jer* 11:20
but, O Lord of hosts, that *t.* 20:12

trieth

ear *t.* words, as the mouth. *Job* 34:3
the righteous God *t.* the. *Ps* 7:9
the Lord *t.* the righteous. 11:5
but the Lord *t.* the hearts. *Pr* 17:3
God who *t.* our hearts. *1 Thes* 2:4*

trimmed

Mephibosheth had not *t.* his beard.
2 Sam 19:24
all those virgins arose and *t.* their lamps. *Mat* 25:7

trimmest

why *t.* thou thy way to ? *Jer* 2:33

triumph, *verb*

of the uncircumcised *t.* *2 Sam* 1:20
let not mine enemies *t.* *Ps* 25:2
enemy doth not *t.* over me. 41:11
Philistia, *t.* thou because of. *Ps* 60:8*
t. in the works of thy hands. 92:4
how long shall the wicked *t.*? 94:3
us to give thanks and *t.* 106:47
over Philistia will I *t.* 108:9*
causeth us to *t.* in Christ. *2 Cor* 2:14

triumph

with the voice of *t.* *Ps* 47:1

triumphed

hath *t.* gloriously. *Ex* 15:1, 21

triumphing

that the *t.* of the wicked. *Job* 20:5
made a show of them, *t.* *Col* 2:15

Troas

by Mysia they came to *T.* *Acts* 16:8
loosing from *T.* 11
tarried for us at *T.* 20:5
when I came to *T.* to. *2 Cor* 2:12
the cloke I left at *T.* *2 Tim* 4:13

trodden

I give the land that he hath *t.* upon.
Deut 1:36; *Josh* 14:9
O my soul, thou hast *t.* *Judg* 5:21*
which wicked men have *t.* *Job* 22:15
the lion's whelps have not *t.* it. 28:8
thou hast *t.* down all. *Ps* 119:118*
vineyard shall be *t.* down. *Isa* 5:5
art cast out, as carcase *t.* 14:19
meted out and *t.* down. 18:2, 7
t. under him as straw is *t.* 25:10
Ephraim shall be *t.* under. 28:3
then ye shall be *t.* down. 18
I have *t.* the winepress alone 63:3
our adversaries have *t.* down. 18
they have *t.* my portion. *Jer* 12:10
the Lord hath *t.* under foot the mighty men, he hath *t.* *Lam* 1:15*
my flock eat what ye have *t.* under feet. *Ezek* 34:19
sanctuary and host to be *t.* *Dan* 8:13
now shall she be *t.* as mire. *Mi* 7:10
salt unsavoury to be *t.* *Mat* 5:13
way side and was *t.* down. *Luke* 8:5
Jerusalem shall be *t.* down of. 21:24
who hath *t.* under foot. *Heb* 10:29
the winepress was *t.* *Rev* 14:20

trode

t. the grapes and cursed. *Judg* 9:27
Israel *t.* the Benjamites. 20:43
the people *t.* upon him in the gate.
2 Ki 7:17, 20
Jehu *t.* Jezebel under foot. 9:33
a beast *t.* down the thistle. 14:9
2 Chr 25:18
insomuch that they *t.* *Luke* 12:1

troop

a *t.* cometh. *Gen* 30:11
Gad, a *t.* shall overcome him. 49:19
I pursue after this *t.*? *1 Sam* 30:8
Benjamin became one *t.* *2 Sam* 2:25*
Joab came from pursuing a *t.* 3:22
by thee have I run through a *t.*
22:30; *Ps* 18:29
Philistines were gathered into a *t.*
2 Sam 23:11
the *t.* pitched in the valley of. 13
ye are they that prepare a table for that *t.* *Isa* 65:11*
when thou shalt bring a *t.* *Jer* 18:22
the *t.* of robbers spoileth. *Hos* 7:1
he hath founded his *t.* *Amos* 9:6*

troops

t. of Tema looked. *Job* 6:19*
his *t.* come together and raise. 19:12
they assembled by *t.* in *Jer* 5:7
and as *t.* of robbers wait. *Hos* 6:9
in *t.* O daughter of *t.* *Mi* 5:1
invade them with his *t.* *Heb* 3:16

trouble

in my *t.* I prepared for. *1 Chr* 22:14*
when they in their *t.* did turn unto the Lord. *2 Chr* 15:4*; *Neh* 9:27
let not all the *t.* seem. *Neh* 9:32*
I quiet, yet *t.* came. *Job* 3:26
neither doth *t.* spring out of. 5:6
yet man is born to *t.* as the sparks. 7
few days and full of *t.* 14:1
t. and anguish shall make. 15:24*
will God hear his cry when *t.*? 27:9
weep for him that was in *t.*? 30:25
quietness, who can make *t.*? 34:29*

reserved against time of *t. Job* 38:23
be a refuge in times of *t. Ps* 9:9
O Lord, consider my *t.* which. 13*
thou thyself in times of *t.*? 10:1
be not far from me, for *t.* is. 22:11
for in time of *t.* he shall hide. 27:5
thou hast considered my *t.* 31:7*
upon me, O Lord, for I am in *t.* 9*
thou shalt preserve me from *t.* 32:7
strength in the time of *t.* 37:39
deliver him in time of *t.* 41:1*
refuge, a present help in *t.* 46:1
hath delivered me out of *t.* 54:7
give us help from *t.*: for vain. 60:11*
spoken when I was in *t.* 66:14*
face from me, for I am in *t.* 69:17*
not in *t.* as other men. 73:5
years did he consume in *t.* 78:33*
upon them indignation and *t.* 49
thou calledst in *t.* and I. 81:7
I will be with him in *t.*; I will. 91:15
face from me when I am in *t.* 102:2*
they cried unto the Lord in their *t.* 107:6, 13, 19
their soul is melted because of *t.* 26
cry unto the Lord in their *t.* 28
hell gat hold on me, I found *t.* 116:3
t. and anguish have taken. 119:143
though I walk in the midst of *t.* 138:7
out my complaint before him, I shewed before him my *t.* 142:2
bring my soul out of *t.* 143:11
righteous is delivered out of *t.* *Pr* 11:8; 12:13
revenues of the wicked is *t.* 15:6
little, than great treasure and *t.* 16
unfaithful man in *t.* is like. 25:19
they are a *t.* to me. *Isa* 1:14
look to the earth and behold *t.* 8:22*
and behold, at eveningtide *t.* 17:14
Lord, in *t.* have they visited. 26:16
into the land of *t.* they will. 30:6
salvation also in time of *t.* 33:2
not save him out of his *t.* 46:7
nor bring forth for *t.* 65:23*
in time of *t.* they will say. *Jer* 2:27
save thee in the time of thy *t.* 28
for health, and behold *t.* 8:15*
save them at all in time of *t.* 11:12
they cry to me for their *t.* 14
Saviour of Israel in time of *t.* 14:8
time of healing, and behold *t.* 19*
it is the time of Jacob's *t.* 30:7
have heard of my *t.* *Lam* 1:21
be a time of *t.* such as. *Dan* 12:1
have *t.* in the flesh. *1 Cor* 7:28*
be able to comfort them which are in *t.* *2 Cor* 1:4*
not have you ignorant of our *t.* 8*
wherein I suffer *t.* as. *2 Tim* 2:9*
see **day**

trouble, *verb*
lest ye *t.* the camp. *Josh* 6:18
Joshua said, The Lord shall *t.* 7:25
one of them that *t.* me. *Judg* 11:35
they cried in the Jews' speech unto the people to *t.* them. *2 Chr* 32:18
increased that *t.* me ! *Ps* 3:1*
those that *t.* me, rejoice when. 13:4*
the foot of man *t.* them any more, nor the hoofs of beasts *t.* *Ezek* 32:13
the interpretation *t.* thee. *Dan* 4:19
let not thy thoughts *t.* thee. 5:10
out of the north shall *t.* him. 11:44
why *t.* ye the woman ? *Mat* 26:10 *Mark* 14:6
Lord, *t.* not thyself, for. *Luke* 7:6
he shall say, *T.* me not, the. 11:7
that we *t.* not Gentiles. *Acts* 15:19
these men do exceedingly *t.* 16:20
t. not yourselves, for his life. 20:10*
but there be some that *t.* *Gal* 1:7
were cut off who *t.* you. 5:12*
henceforth let no man *t.* me. 6:17
tribulation to them that *t.* you. *2 Thes* 1:6*
lest any root of bitterness *t.* you. *Heb* 12:15

troubled
ye have *t.* me, to make. *Gen* 34:30
Pharaoh's spirit was *t.* 41:8
his brethren were *t.* at his. 45:3
the Lord *t.* the host of. *Ex* 14:24*
Why hast thou *t.* us ? *Josh* 7:25
Jonathan said, My father hath *t.* the land. *1 Sam* 14:29
evil spirit from the Lord *t.* him. 16:14
saw that Saul was sore *t.* 28:21
all the Israelites were *t.* *2 Sam* 4:1
I have not *t.* Israel. *1 Ki* 18:18
Syria was sore *t.* for this. *2 Ki* 6:11
then the people *t.* them in. *Ezra* 4:4
thee and thou art *t.* *Job* 4:5
why should not my spirit be *t.*? 21:4*
am I *t.* at his presence. 23:15
shall be *t.* at midnight. 34:20*
hide thy face and I was *t.* *Ps* 30:7
I am *t.* 38:6*
waters thereof roar and be *t.* 46:3
the kings were *t.*, and hasted. 48:5*
I remembered God, and was *t.* 77:3*
I am so *t.* that I cannot speak. 4
afraid, the depths also were *t.* 16*
let them be confounded and *t.* 83:17*
by thy wrath are we *t.* 90:7
hidest thy face, they are *t.* 104:29
is as a *t.* fountain and. *Pr* 25:26
and years shall ye be *t.* *Isa* 32:10
tremble, ye women, be *t.* ye. 11
wicked are like the *t.* sea. 57:20
my bowels are *t.* for him. *Jer* 31:20†
I am in distress, my bowels are *t.* *Lam* 1:20; 2:11
of the people shall be *t.* *Ezek* 7:27
are in the sea shall be *t.* 26:18*
their kings shall be *t.* in. 27:35
Nebuchadnezzar's spirit was *t.* *Dan* 2:1, 3
and the visions of my head *t.* me. 4:5; 7:15
Daniel astonied, his thoughts *t.* 4:19
Belshazzar's thoughts *t.* him. 5:6, 9
my cogitations much *t.* me. 7:28
were *t.* because there. *Zech* 10:2*
Herod was *t.* and all Jerusalem. *Mat* 2:3
saw him on sea, they were *t.* 14:26 *Mark* 6:50
see that ye be not *t.* for all. *Mat* 24:6 *Mark* 13:7; *John* 14:1, 27
Zacharias was *t.* *Luke* 1:12
Mary was *t.* 29
Martha, thou art *t.* about. 10:41
why are ye *t.* and why do ? 24:38
down and *t.* the water. *John* 5:4
I have no man when water is *t.* 7
Jesus groaned and was *t.* 11:33 12:27; 13:21
from us have *t.* you. *Acts* 15:24
and they *t.* the people and. 17:8
we are *t.* on every side. *2 Cor* 4:8* 7:5*
and to you that are *t.* *2 Thes* 1:7*
ye be not *t.* neither by spirit. 2:2
of their terror, nor be *t.* *1 Pet* 3:14

troubledst
and thou *t.* the waters. *Ezek* 32:2

troubler
Achar, the *t.* of Israel. *1 Chr* 2:7

troubles
many evils and *t.* *Deut* 31:17, 21
he shall deliver thee in six *t.*: yea. *Job* 5:19
the *t.* of mine heart. *Ps* 25:17
O God, out of all his *t.* 22
saved him out of all his *t.* 34:6
thou hast shewed me sore *t.* 71:20
for my soul is full of *t.* 88:3
keepeth his soul from *t.* *Pr* 21:23
former *t.* are forgotten. *Isa* 65:16
shall be famine and *t.* *Mark* 13:8

troublest
why *t.* thou the Master ? *Mark* 5:35

troubleth
spirit from God *t.* *1 Sam* 16:15
Art thou he that *t.* Israel ? *1 Ki* 18:17
sudden fear *t.* thee. *Job* 22:10
my heart soft, Almighty *t.* me. 23:16
he that is cruel *t.* his. *Pr* 11:17
he that *t.* his own house shall. 29
he that is greedy of gain *t.* 15:27
I know that no secret *t.* *Dan* 4:9
because this widow *t.* me. *Luke* 18:5
he that *t.* you shall bear. *Gal* 5:10

troubling
there the wicked cease from *t.* and there the weary. *Job* 3:17
stepped in first after the *t.* *John* 5:4

troublous
be built again in *t.* times. *Dan* 9:25

trough, -s
her pitcher into the *t.* *Gen* 24:20
rods in the watering *t.* 30:38
filled the *t.* to water. *Ex* 2:16
see **kneadingtroughs**

trow
that servant ? I *t.* not. *Luke* 17:9

trucebreakers
last days men shall be *t.* *2 Tim* 3:3*

true
see comment on **truth**
we are *t.* men. *Gen* 42:11, 31
if ye be *t.* men. 19
I know that ye are *t.* men. 33, 34
if ye be *t.* and thing certain. *Deut* 17:4; 22:20
and give me a *t.* token. *Josh* 2:12
it is *t.* that I am thy. *Ruth* 3:12
God, and thy words be *t.* *2 Sam* 7:28
it was a *t.* report I heard. *1 Ki* 10:6 *2 Chr* 9:5
but that which is *t.* *1 Ki* 22:16
thou gavest them *t.* laws. *Neh* 9:13
of the Lord are *t.* *Ps* 19:9
thy word is *t.* from the. 119:160
a *t.* witness delivereth. *Pr* 14:25
the Lord be a *t.* witness. *Jer* 42:5
he that hath executed *t.* *Ezek* 18:8
is it *t.* O Shadrach, do ? *Dan* 3:14*
t. O king. 24
king said, The thing is *t.* 6:12
vision which is told is *t.* 8:26
revealed and the thing was *t.* 10:1
execute *t.* judgement and. *Zech* 7:9
we know that thou art *t.* *Mat* 22:16 *Mark* 12:14
your trust the *t.* riches. *Luke* 16:11
that was the *t.* light. *John* 1:9
when the *t.* worshippers shall. 4:23
is that saying *t.*, One soweth. 37
myself, my witness is not *t.* 5:31
he witnesseth of me is *t.* 32
giveth you the *t.* bread. 6:32
the same is *t.* 7:18
he that sent me is *t.* 28; 8:26
thy record is not *t.* 8:13
yet my record is *t.* 14
my judgement is *t.* 16
the testimony of two men is *t.* 17
John spake of this man were *t.* 10:41
I am the *t.* vine, my Father. 15:1
and his record is *t.* 19:35; 21:24
wist not that it was *t.* *Acts* 12:9
but as God is *t.*, our. *2 Cor* 1:18*
as deceivers, and yet *t.* 6:8
after God is created in *t.* holiness. *Eph* 4:24
also, *t.* yokefellow, help. *Phil* 4:3
things are *t.*, think on these. 8
this is a *t.* saying, If. *1 Tim* 3:1*
this witness is *t.* Wherefore. *Tit* 1:13
t. tabernacle which the Lord pitched. *Heb* 8:2
which are the figures of the *t.* 9:24
let us draw near with a *t.* 10:22
t. grace of God wherein. *1 Pet* 5:12
according to the *t.* proverb, The dog is. *2 Pet* 2:22
which thing is *t.* in him and in you: because . . . *t.* light. *1 John* 2:8
that we may know him that is *t.* and we are in him that is *t.*, even. 5:20
that our record is *t.* *3 John* 12
that is holy, he that is *t.* *Rev* 3:7
the faithful and *t.* witness. 14
How long, O Lord, holy and *t.*? 6:10
just and *t.* are thy ways, thou. 15:3
t. and righteous are. 16:7; 19:2
the *t.* sayings of God. 19:9; 22:6
was called Faithful and *T.* 19:11
write, for these words are *t.* 21:5

true *God*
without the *t.* God. *2 Chr* 15:3
the Lord is the *t.* *God.* *Jer* 10:10
to know the only *t.* *God.* *John* 17:3

idols to serve the t. God. 1 Thes 1:9
this is the t. God and. 1 John 5:20

truly

and now if ye will deal t. Gen 24:49; 47:29
t. his younger brother shall. 48:19
as t. as I live, saith. Num 14:21, 28
thou shalt t. tithe the. Deut 14:22
that we will deal t. and. Josh 2:14
t. the Lord hath delivered all. 24
if ye have done t. Judg 9:16, 19
t. there is but a step between me and death. 1 Sam 20:3
for t. my words shall not. Job 36:4
t. my soul waiteth upon. Ps 62:1
t. God is good to Israel, even. 73:1
t. I am thy servant, I am. 116:16
they that deal t. are his. Pr 12:22
t. the light is sweet. Eccl 11:7
t. in vain is salvation hoped for from hills, t. in the Lord. Jer 3:23
t. this is a grief and I. 10:19
known that the Lord hath t. 28:9
judgements to deal t. Ezek 18:9
but t. I am full of power. Mi 3:8
the harvest t. is plenteous. Mat 9:37; Luke 10:2
Elias t. shall first come. Mat 17:11
saying, T. this was the Son. 27:54
the spirit t. is ready. Mark 14:38
the way of God t. Luke 20:21
t. Son of man goeth, as it. 22:22
I have no husband: in that saidst thou t. John 4:18
for John t. baptized with. Acts 1:5
Moses t. said to the fathers. 3:22
the prison t. found we shut. 5:23
t. signs of an apostle. 2 Cor 12:12
and they t. were many. Heb 7:23
t. if they had been mindful. 11:15
t. our fellowship is with. 1 John 1:3

trump

at the last t.: the dead. 1 Cor 15:52
descend with the t. of God. 1 Thes 4:16

trumpet

the voice of the t. exceeding loud. Ex 19:16
heard the noise of the t. 20:18
blow but with one t. Num 10:4
and he put a t. in every. Judg 7:16
when I blow with a t. then. 18
blow up the t. in the. Ps 81:3
and when he bloweth a t. Isa 18:3
great t. shall be blown and. 27:13
lift up thy voice like a t. 58:1
blow ye the t. in the land. Jer 4:5
blow the t. in Tekoah and set. 6:1
blow the t. among the. 51:27
they have blown the t. Ezek 7:14
if he blow the t. and warn. 33:3
watchman blow not the t. 6
blow ye the t. in Ramah. Hos 5:8
set the t. to thy mouth. 8:1
blow the t. in Zion. Joel 2:1, 15
shall a t. be blown? Amos 3:6
a day of the t. against. Zeph 1:16
God shall blow the t. Zech 9:14
I heard a great voice, as of a t. Rev 1:10; 4:1
the other voices of the t. 8:13
sixth angel which had the t. 9:14
see **blew, sound,** subst. verb

trumpeters

princes and t. stood. 2 Ki 11:14
as the t. and singers. 2 Chr 5:13
the singers sang, and the t. 29:28
the voice of t. shall be. Rev 18:22

trumpets

a memorial of blowing t. Lev 23:24
Num 29:1
make two t. of silver of. Num 10:2
sons of Aaron shall blow with the t. 8
blow an alarm with the t. 9
shall blow with t. over your. 10
and with the t. to blow in his. 31:6
shall blow with the t. Josh 6:4
priests bearing the seven t. of. 8
that blew with the t. 9, 13, 16, 20
the two hundred men took t. Judg 7:8, 16
when I blow, then blow ye the t. 18
they blew the t., brake the. Judg 7:19, 20, 22
they blew with t. saying. 2 Ki 9:13
and trumpeters blew with t. 11:14
made for house of the Lord t. 12:13
cymbals and with t. 1 Chr 13:8
priests did blow with t. 15:24
16:6, 42; 2 Chr 5:12; 7:6
13:12, 14
all Israel brought up the ark with t. 1 Chr 15:28
lift up their voice with t. 2 Chr 5:13
the song began with the t. 29:27
saith among the t. Ha, ha. Job 39:25
with t. make a joyful noise. Ps 98:6
see **feast, seven**

trust

and whose t. shall be a. Job 8:14
putteth no t. in his saints. 15:15
that maketh the Lord his t. Ps 40:4
O Lord God, thou art my t. 71:5
in thee is my t.; leave not. 141:8
that thy t. may be in. Pr 22:19
that putteth his t. in the Lord. 28:25
who putteth his t. in the Lord. 29:25
the t. in Egypt shall be. Isa 30:3
that putteth t. in me shall. 57:13†
commit to your t. the. Luke 16:11
such t. have we through Christ to. 2 Cor 3:4
was committed to my t. 1 Tim 1:11
which is committed to thy t. 6:20*
see **put**

trust, verb

wings thou art come to t. Ruth 2:12
in him will I t. 2 Sam 22:3†
Ps 18:2; 91:2
a buckler to all that t. in him. 2 Sam 22:31; Ps 18:30
now on whom dost thou t.? 2 Ki 18:20
2 Chr 32:10; Isa 36:5
so is Pharaoh to all that t. in him. 2 Ki 18:21; Isa 36:6
if ye say, We t. in the Lord our God. 2 Ki 18:22; Isa 36:7
make you t. in the Lord, saying, The Lord. 2 Ki 18:30; Isa 36:15
yet will I t. in him. Job 13:15†
that is deceived t. in vanity. 15:31
judgement is before him, therefore t. in him. 35:14*
wilt thou t. him because he? 39:11
some t. in chariots, and. Ps 20:7
I t. in thee. 25:2; 31:6; 55:23
56:3; 143:8
for them that t. in thee. 31:19†
none that t. in him shall be. 34:22†
t. in the Lord. 37:3, 5; 40:3; 62:8
115:9, 10, 11; Pr 3:5; Isa 26:4
because they t. in him. Ps 37:40*
I will not t. in my bow, nor. 44:6
they that t. in their wealth. 49:6
I t. in the mercy of God for. 52:8
I will t. in the covert of. 61:4*
t. not in oppression, become. 62:10
be glad, and t. in him. 64:10†
under his wings shalt thou t. 91:4*
better to t. in the Lord. 118:8, 9
I shall have to answer, for I t. 119:42
that t. in the Lord shall be as. 125:1
shield, and he in whom I t. 144:2†
her husband doth t. in her. Pr 31:11
God my salvation, I will t. Isa 12:2
poor of his people shall t. in it. 14:32*
and to t. in the shadow of. 30:2
because ye t. in oppression and. 12
and t. in chariots, because. 31:1
be ashamed that t. in graven. 42:17
let him t. in the name of the. 50:10
and on mine arm shall they t. 51:5
they t. in vanity and speak lies. 59:4
t. ye not in lying words. Jer 7:4
ye t. in lying words that cannot. 8
by my name, wherein ye t. 14
take ye heed, and t. ye not in. 9:4
makest this people to t. in a lie. 28:15; 29:31
Pharaoh and all that t. in him. 46:25
and let thy widows t. in me. 49:11
but thou didst t. in thy beauty. Ezek 16:15
t. to his own righteousness. 33:13
because thou didst t. in. Hos 10:13
them that t. in the mountain of. Amos 6:1*
t. ye not in a friend, put. Mi 7:5
them that t. in him. Nah 1:7†
they shall t. in the name of the Lord. Zeph 3:12†
and in his name shall the Gentiles t. Mat 12:21*; Rom 15:12*
them that t. in riches. Mark 10:24
Moses, in whom ye t. John 5:45
for I t. to see you in. Rom 15:24*
but I t. to tarry a while. 1 Cor 16:7
that we should not t. in. 2 Cor 1:9
in whom we t. that he will yet. 10*
I t. ye shall acknowledge even. 13*
I t. are made manifest in. 5:11*
if any man t. to himself, that he. 10:7
I t. ye shall know we are not. 13:6*
thinketh he hath whereof to t. Phil 3:4*
because we t. in the living God. 1 Tim 4:10*
that they t. not in uncertain. 6:17*
for we t. we have a good. Heb 13:18*
but I t. to come unto you. 2 John 12*
but I t. I shall shortly see. 3 John 14

trusted

rock in whom they t.? Deut 32:37†
Sihon t. not Israel to. Judg 11:20
because they t. to the liers. 20:36
he t. in the Lord God of. 2 Ki 18:5
but I have t. in thy mercy. Ps 13:5
fathers t. in thee; they have t. 22:4, 5
he t. on the Lord that he would. 8*
I have t. also in the Lord. 26:1
28:7; 31:14
have t. in his holy name. 33:21
familiar friend in whom I t. 41:9
but t. in the abundance of his. 52:7
they t. not in his salvation. 78:22
t. in thy wickedness. Isa 47:10
thou hast t. in falsehood. Jer 13:25
thou hast t. in thy works. 48:7
daughter that t. in her treasures. 49:4
servants that t. in him. Dan 3:28
she t. not in the Lord. Zeph 3:2
he t. in God, let him. Mat 27:43
armour wherein he t. Luke 11:22
he spake to certain which t. 18:9
we t. it had been he which should have redeemed Israel. 24:21*
who first t. in Christ. Eph 1:12*
in whom ye also t. after ye heard. 13
women who t. in God. 1 Pet 3:5*

trustedst

down wherein thou t. Deut 28:52
shall impoverish thy fenced cities wherein thou t. Jer 5:17
land of peace wherein thou t. 12:5*

trustest

what confidence is this wherein thou t.? 2 Ki 18:19; Isa 36:4
thou t. on staff of this bruised reed. 2 Ki 18:21; Isa 36:6
let not thy God in whom thou t. 2 Ki 19:10; Isa 37:10

trusteth

he t. that he can draw up. Job 40:23*
for the king t. in the Lord. Ps 21:7
t. in the Lord, mercy shall. 32:10
the man that t. in him. 34:8†; 84:12
Pr 16:20; Jer 17:7
for my soul t. in thee. Ps 57:1*
save thy servant that t. 86:2
so is every one that t. in them. 115:8; 135:18
he that t. in his riches. Pr 11:28
he that t. in his own heart. 28:26
thou wilt keep him in perfect peace, because he t. in thee. Isa 26:3
cursed be the man that t. Jer 17:5
the maker of his work t. Hab 2:18
widow indeed, t. in God. 1 Tim 5:5*

trusting

his heart is fixed, t. in. Ps 112:7

trusty

removeth away the speech of the t. Job 12:20

truth

[1] *What is opposed to a falsehood, lie, or deceit,* Pr 12:17. [2]

Fidelity, sincerity, and punctuality in keeping promises. Generally to truth, *taken in this sense, if referred to God, is joined* mercy *or* kindness, *as in* Gen 24:27. [3] Truth *is put for the true doctrine of the gospel,* Gal 3:1. [4] Truth *is opposed to hypocrisy, dissimulation or formality,* Heb 10:22.
not left destitute of his *t. Gen* 24:27
of the least of all the *t.* 32:10
whether there be any *t.* in. 42:16
men of *t. Ex* 18:21
Lord abundant in *t.* 34:6
behold, if it be *t. Deut* 13:14
a God of *t.* 32:4
kindness and *t.* to you. *2 Sam* 2:6
return thou, mercy and *t.* be. 15:20
of Lord in thy mouth is *t. 1 Ki* 17:24
if peace and *t.* be in my days. *2 Ki* 20:19; *Isa* 39:8
say nothing but the *t. 2 Chr* 18:15
wrought that which was *t.* 31:20*
with words of peace and *t. Esth* 9:30
he that speaketh the *t.* in. *Ps* 15:2
of the Lord are mercy and *t.* 25:10
redeemed me, O Lord God of *t.* 31:5
prosperously, because of *t.* 45:4
desirest *t.* in the inward parts. 51:6
send forth his mercy and his *t.* 57:3
be displayed because of the *t.* 60:4
O prepare mercy and *t.*, which. 61:7
mercy and *t.* are met together. 85:10
t. shall spring out of the earth. 11
plenteous in mercy and *t.* 86:15
mercy and *t.* shall go before. 89:14
his *t.* shall be thy shield and. 91:4
judge the people with his *t.* 96:13
remembered his mercy and his *t.* 98:3*
his *t.* endureth to all. 100:5*; 117:2
I have chosen the way of *t.* 119:30*
and thy law is the *t.* 142, 151
God who keepeth *t.* for ever. 146:6
let not mercy and *t. Pr* 3:3
for my mouth shall speak *t.* 8:7
he that speaketh *t.* sheweth. 12:17
lip of *t.* shall be established. 19
mercy and *t.* be to them that. 14:22
mercy and *t.* iniquity is purged. 16:6
mercy and *t.* preserve the. 20:28
of the words of *t.*; thou mightest answer the words of *t.* 22:21
buy the *t.* and sell it not. 23:23
written were words of *t. Eccl* 12:10
are faithfulness and *t. Isa* 25:1
the nation which keepeth *t.* 26:2†
forth judgement unto *t.* 42:3
them hear, and say, It is *t.* 43:9
nor any pleadeth for *t.*: they. 59:4
for *t.* is fallen in the street and. 14
yea *t.* faileth, and he that. 15
any that seeketh the *t. Jer* 5:1
are not thine eyes upon the *t.*? 3
t. is perished and cut off from. 7:28
they are not valiant for the *t.* 9:3
and will not speak the *t.* 5
abundance of peace and *t.* 33:6
the king of heaven, all whose works are *t. Dan* 4:37
I asked him the *t.* of all. 7:16, 19
and it cast down the *t.* to the. 8:12
noted in the scripture of *t.* 10:21
now will I shew thee the *t.* 11:2
there is no *t.* nor mercy. *Hos* 4:1
thou wilt perform the *t. Mi* 7:20
be called a city of *t. Zech* 8:3
speak ye every man the *t.* 16
Eph 4:25
execute the judgement of *t.* and peace. *Zech* 8:16
love the *t.* and peace. 19
the law of *t.* was in his. *Mal* 2:6
she said, *T.* Lord, yet dogs eat the. *Mat* 15:27*
fearing told him all the *t. Mark* 5:33
Master, thou hast said the *t.* 12:32*
full of grace and *t. John* 1:14
but grace and *t.* came by Jesus. 17
he bare witness unto the *t.* 5:33
ye shall know the *t.*, the *t.* shall. 8:32
a man that told you the *t.* 40
t. because there is no *t.* in him. 44
because I tell you the *t.* ye. 45
if I say the *t.* why do ye? *John* 8:46
I am the way, and the *t.* and. 14:6
I tell you the *t.*; It is expedient. 16:7
of *t.* will guide you into all *t.* 13
sanctified through the *t.* 17:19
should bear witness to the *t.* Every one that is of the *t.* heareth. 18:37
Pilate saith unto him What is *t.*? 38
forth the words of *t. Acts* 26:25
who hold the *t.* in. *Rom* 1:18
who changed the *t.* of God into. 25
of God is according to *t.* 2:2
that do not obey the *t.* 8
which hast the form of the *t.* in. 20
for if the *t.* of God hath more. 3:7
I say the *t.* in Christ, I lie not. 9:1
circumcision for *t.* of God. 15:8
unleavened bread of *t. 1 Cor* 5:8
but by manifestation of the *t.* *2 Cor* 4:2
boasting, I made, is found a *t.* 7:14
as the *t.* of Christ is in me. 11:10
a fool, for I will say the *t.* 12:6
nothing against *t.*, but for the *t.* 13:8
the *t.* of the gospel might. *Gal* 2:5
they walked not according to *t.* 14
that ye should not obey the *t.* 3:1
5:7
because I tell you the *t.*? 4:16
but speaking the *t.* in love. *Eph* 4:15
have been taught by him as the *t.* 21
fruit of the Spirit is in all *t.* 5:9
your loins girt about with *t.* 6:14
not the love of the *t. 2 Thes* 2:10
damned who believed not the *t.* 12
salvation, through belief of the *t.* 13
knowledge of the *t. 1 Tim* 2:4
I speak the *t.* in Christ and. 7
pillar and ground of the *t.* 3:15
of them which know the *t.* 4:3
and destitute of the *t.* 6:5
who concerning the *t. 2 Tim* 2:18
to acknowledging of the *t.* 25
to the knowledge of the *t.* 3:7
so do these resist the *t.* 8
turn away their ears from the *t.* 4:4
the acknowledging of *t. Tit* 1:1
of men that turn from the *t.* 14
after we received knowledge of the *t.* *Heb* 10:26
and lie not against the *t. Jas* 3:14
if any of you err from the *t.* 5:19
your souls in obeying *t. 1 Pet* 1:22
the way of *t.* shall be evil. *2 Pet* 2:2
we lie and do not the *t. 1 John* 1:6
we deceive ourselves, the *t.* is. 8
the *t.* is not in him. 2:4
ye know not the *t.*, but because ye know it, and no lie is of the *t.* 21
is *t.* and is no lie. 27
know that we are of the *t.* 3:19
because the Spirit is *t.* 5:6
that have known the *t. 2 John* 1
for the *t.'s* sake which dwelleth in. 2
came and testified of the *t. 3 John* 3
be fellow-helpers to the *t.* 8
of all men and of the *t.* 12
see **spirit**

in truth

serve him *in t. Josh* 24:14
1 Sam 12:24
if *in t.* ye anoint me king. *Judg* 9:15
walk *in t. 1 Ki* 2:4
as he walked *in t.* 3:6
I have walked *in t. 2 Ki* 20:3
all his works are done *in t.* *Ps* 33:4*; 111:8
the Lord hath sworn *in t.* 132:11
to all that call upon him *in t.* 145:18
the Holy One of Israel *in t. Isa* 10:20
he shall sit upon it *in t.* judging. 16:5
God of Israel, but not *in t.* 48:1
I will direct their work *in t.* and. 61:8
the Lord liveth *in t. Jer* 4:2
I will be their God *in t. Zech* 8:8
teachest the way of God *in t.* *Mat* 22:16; *Mark* 12:14
shall worship the Father in spirit and *in t. John* 4:23, 24
all things to you *in t. 2 Cor* 7:14
in pretence or *in t.* Christ is. *Phil* 1:18
the grace of God *in t. Col* 1:6
but as it is *in t.* the word of God. *1 Thes* 2:13
love in tongue, but *in t. 1 John* 3:18
the Son of the Father, *in t. 2 John* 3
rejoiced that I found of thy children walking *in t.* 4; *3 John* 4

in the truth

hear me *in the t.* of. *Ps* 69:13
he was a murderer and abode not *in the t. John* 8:44
charity rejoiceth not in iniquity, but *in the t. 1 Cor* 13:6
established *in the* present *t.* *2 Pet* 1:12
elect lady, whom I love *in the t.* *2 John* 1; *3 John* 1
thou walkest *in the t. 3 John* 3

of a truth

of a t. women have been. *1 Sam* 21:5
of a t. Lord, the kings of Assyria. *2 Ki* 19:17; *Isa* 37:18
I know it is so *of a t. Job* 9:2
of a t. many houses shall. *Isa* 5:9
for *of a t.* the Lord hath. *Jer* 26:15
of a t. it is, your God. *Dan* 2:47
of a t. thou art the Son. *Mat* 14:33
I tell you *of a t. Luke* 4:25; 9:27
of a t. I say unto you. 12:44; 21:3
of a t. this fellow also was. 22:59
this is *of a t.* that prophet. *John* 6:14; 7:40
of a t. against thy holy. *Acts* 4:27
of a t. I perceive that God is. 10:34
God is in you *of a t. 1 Cor* 14:25

thy truth

lead me in *thy t.* and. *Ps* 25:5
and I have walked in *thy t.* 26:3
praise and declare *thy t.*? 30:9
and *thy t.* from the great. 40:10
let *thy t.* continually preserve. 11
send out thy light and *thy t.* 43:3
cut them off in *thy t.* 54:5
thy t. unto the clouds. 57:10; 108:4
I will praise *thy t.* 71:22
will walk in *thy t.* 86:11
swarest to David in *thy t.* 89:49*
glory for *thy t.'s* sake. 115:1; 138:2
that go into the pit cannot hope for *thy t. Isa* 38:18
children shall make known *thy t.* 19
might understand *thy t. Dan* 9:13
thy t.: thy word is truth. *John* 17:17

word of truth

take not *word of t.* out. *Ps* 119:43
approving ourselves by the *word of t.* *2 Cor* 6:7
ye heard the *word of t. Eph* 1:13
whereof ye heard before in the *word of t. Col* 1:5
dividing the *word of t. 2 Tim* 2:15
begat he us by *word of t. Jas* 1:18

try

and I will *t.* them for thee. *Judg* 7:4
God left him to *t.* him. *2 Chr* 32:31
that thou shouldest *t. Job* 7:18
doth not the ear *t.* words? 12:11
his eyelids *t.* the. *Ps* 11:4
t. my reins and my heart. 26:2
t. me. 139:23
thou mayest know and *t. Jer* 6:27
I will melt them and *t.* them. 9:7
Zech 13:9
I *t.* the reins. *Jer* 17:10
search and *t.* our ways. *Lam* 3:40
shall fall to *t.* them. *Dan* 11:35*
the fire shall *t.* every. *1 Cor* 3:13*
fiery trial which is to *t.* you. *1 Pet* 4:12*
t. the spirits whether. *1 John* 4:1*
hour of temptation to *t. Rev* 3:10

trying

the *t.* of your faith worketh. *Jas* 1:3

Tryphena, Tryphosa

salute *T.* and *T. Rom* 16:12

Tubal

sons of Japheth, Javan, *T. Gen* 10:2
1 Chr 1:5
those that escape to *T. Isa* 66:19
Javan, *T.* they were. *Ezek* 27:13
there is Meshech, *T.* and her. 32:26
the chief prince of Meshech and *T.* 38:2, 3; 39:1

tumbled

a cake of barley bread t. Judg 7:13

tumult

the noise of this t.? 1 Sam 4:14
I saw a t. but knew not. 2 Sam 18:29
rage against me and thy t. is come.
2 Ki 19:28*; Isa 37:29*
which stilleth the t. of. Ps 65:7
the t. of those that rise up. 74:23
thine enemies make a t. 83:2
at the noise of the t. the. Isa 33:3
with noise of a great t. Jer 11:16
t. rise among thy people. Hos 10:14
and Moab shall die with t. Amos 2:2
a great t. from the Lord. Zech 14:13
but rather a t. was made. Mat 27:24
he seeth the t. and them. Mark 5:38
know the certainty for t. Acts 21:34*
multitude, nor with t. 24:18

tumults

behold the great t. in the. Amos 3:9
as ministers in t. 2 Cor 6:5
whisperings, swellings, t. 12:20

tumultuous

a t. noise of the kingdoms gathered.
Isa 13:4
thou that art a t. city. 22:2
the head of the t. ones. Jer 48:45

turn

when every maid's t. was come to.
Esth 2:12
now when the t. of Esther was. 15

turn, *verb*

that I may t. to the right. Gen 24:49
make thine enemies t. Ex 23:27
t. from thy fierce wrath and. 32:12
t. ye not unto idols, nor. Lev 19:4
to-morrow t. you, get. Num 14:25
we will not t. to the right. 20:17
we will not t. into the fields. 21:22
he smote the ass to t. her. 22:23
was no way to t. to the right or. 26
t. you, and go to the mount. Deut 1:7
and t. ye, take your journey. 40
that the Lord may t. from. 13:17
then shall t. it into money. 14:25
then the Lord will t. 30:3
then will they t. to other gods. 31:20
t. not from it to the right. Josh 1:7
an altar to t. from following. 22:23, 29
then he will t. and do you hurt. 24:20
nor will any of us t. Judg 20:8
t. thee, behold, I am. 1 Sam 14:7
t. and slay the priests of. 22:17, 18
none can t. to the right. 2 Sam 14:19
the king said, Let him t. to his. 24
Lord, t. Ahithophel's counsel. 15:31
t. from their sin. 1 Ki 8:35
2 Chr 6:26, 37; 7:14
if ye shall at all t. from. 1 Ki 9:6
get hence, t. thee eastward. 17:3
he said, T. thine hand. 22:34
2 Chr 18:33
and Jehu said, T. thee behind me.
2 Ki 9:18, 19
t. ye from your evil ways. 17:13
Jer 18:8; 26:3; Zech 1:3, 4
to t. the kingdom of. 1 Chr 12:23
but Josiah would not t. his face.
2 Chr 35:22
if ye t. and keep my. Neh 1:9
Ezek 3:20; 18:21; 33:11, 14, 19
and t. their reproach on. Neh 4:4
prophets which testified to t. 9:26
of the saints wilt thou t.? Job 5:1
t. from him that he may rest. 14:6
mind, and who can t. him? 23:13
t. the needy out of the way. 24:4
how long will ye t. my glory? Ps 4:2
if he t. not, he will whet his. 7:12
thou shalt make them t. their. 21:12
t. thee unto me. 25:16; 69:16
86:16
t. us, O God of our salvation. 85:4
let those that fear thee t. 119:79
to David, he will not t. 132:11
t. you at my reproof, I. Pr 1:23
pass not by it, t. from it. 4:15
t. not to the right hand nor to. 27
all are of dust, and all t. Eccl 3:20
t. my beloved, and be. S of S 2:17
I will t. my hand on thee. Isa 1:25
they shall every man t. to his. 13:14
and they shall t. the rivers. 19:6
he will violently t. and toss. 22:18
she shall t. to her hire, and. 23:17
for strength to them that t. 28:6
when ye t. to the right hand. 30:21
t. ye to him from whom Israel. 31:6
t. from transgression. 59:20
surely his anger shall t. Jer 2:35
and I said, T. unto me. 3:7, 14
t. it into the shadow of death. 13:16
for I will t. their mourning. 31:13
t. thou me, and I shall be turned. 18
hearkened not to t. from. 44:5
they shall t. every one to. 50:16
t. us unto thee, O Lord. Lam 5:21
he t. not from his wickedness.
Ezek 3:19; 33:9
shall not t. thee from one side. 4:8
my face will I t. also from. 7:22
repent and t. yourselves from your
idols. 14:6; 18:30, 32; 33:9, 11
Hos 12:6; Joel 2:12
I will t. unto you, and ye. Ezek 36:9
to t. thine hand upon the. 38:12
that we might t. from. Dan 9:13
t. his face unto the isles, and take
many; shall cause . . . t. 11:18
then he shall t. his face toward. 19
and they that t. many to. 12:3
not frame their doings to t. Hos 5:4
therefore t. thou to thy God. 12:6
and I will t. mine hand. Amos 1:8
ye who t. judgement. 5:7
and I will t. your feasts. 8:10
let them t. every one from his evil
way. Jonah 3:8
then will I t. to people. Zeph 3:9
t. ye to the strong hold, ye. Zech 9:12
I will t. mine hand upon the. 13:7
t. the heart of fathers. Mal 4:6
on thy right cheek, t. Mat 5:39
to t. the hearts of the fathers to.
Luke 1:17
and it shall t. to you for a. 21:13
of life, lo we t. to. Acts 13:46
that ye should t. from these. 14:15
and to t. them from darkness. 26:18
that they should repent and t. 20
I know this shall t. to. Phil 1:19
commandments of men that t.
Tit 1:14
and we t. about their. Jas 3:3
to t. from the holy. 2 Pet 2:21
and have power to t. Rev 11:6

turn *again*

if the raw flesh t. again. Lev 13:16
therefore we t. again. Judg 11:8
she said, T. again, my daughters.
Ruth 1:11, 12
I pray thee, t. again with me.
1 Sam 15:25, 30
shall t. again to thee. 1 Ki 8:33
heart of this people t. again. 12:27
eat not, nor t. again by the. 13:9, 17
go t. again to the king. 2 Ki 1:6
t. again and tell Hezekiah. 20:5
t. again to the Lord. 2 Chr 30:6
if ye t. again. 9
and man shall t. again. Job 34:15
nor did I t. again till. Ps 18:37
O t. thyself to us again. 60:1
t. us again, O Lord God. 80:3, 7, 19
them not t. again to folly. 85:8
they t. not again to cover. 104:9
t. again our captivity, as. 126:4
t. ye again every one from. Jer 25:5
t. again, O virgin of Israel, t. again.
31:21
try our ways and t. again to the
Lord. Lam 3:40
t. again and thou shalt see.
Ezek 8:6, 13, 15
he will t. again, he will. Mi 7:19
children and t. again. Zech 10:9
lest they t. again and rend. Mat 7:6
shall t. to you again. Luke 10:6
times in a day t. again to thee. 17:4
how t. ye again to the weak elements? Gal 4:9

turn *aside*

I will now t. aside and. Ex 3:3
shall not t. aside to the. Deut 5:32
and ye t. aside and serve. 11:16, 28
that he t. not aside from. 17:20
my death ye will t. aside. 31:29
that ye t. not aside therefrom to the.
Josh 23:6; 1 Sam 12:20, 21
ho, such a one, t. aside. Ruth 4:1
Asahel, t. aside and. 2 Sam 2:21
howbeit he refused to t. aside. 23
the king said, T. aside and. 18:30
such as t. aside to lies. Ps 40:4
of them that t. aside. 101:3
as for such as t. aside to. 125:5
to t. aside the needy from. Isa 10:2
t. aside the just for a thing. 29:21
get out of the way, t. aside. 30:11
to t. aside the right of a. Lam 3:35
and that t. aside the way. Amos 2:7
and they t. aside the poor in. 5:12
that t. aside the stranger. Mal 3:5

turn *away*

brother's fury t. away. Gen 27:44
till thy brother's anger t. away. 45
for if ye t. away from after him.
Num 32:15; Deut 30:17
Josh 22:16; 2 Chr 7:19
they will t. away thy son. Deut 7:4
he hath spoken to t. you away. 13:5
that his heart t. not away. 17:17
no unclean thing and t. away. 23:14
surely they will t. away your heart.
1 Ki 11:2
how wilt thou t. away the face of one
captain? 2 Ki 18:24; Isa 36:9
go not up; t. away. 1 Chr 14:14
O Lord God, t. not away the face of.
2 Chr 6:42; Ps 132:10
Amaziah did t. away from following.
2 Chr 25:27
that his wrath may t. away. 29:10
30:8; Ps 106:23; Pr 24:18
Lord will not t. away his face.
2 Chr 30:9
t. away mine eyes from. Ps 119:37
t. away my reproach which I fear. 39
infamy t. not away. Pr 25:10
but wise men t. away wrath. 29:8
t. away thine eyes from. S of S 6:5
thou t. away thy foot from. Isa 58:13
who can t. her away? Jer 2:24
and thou shalt not t. away. 3:19
saith Lord, Shall he t. away? 8:4
I stood to t. away thy wrath. 18:20
I will t. away your captivity. 29:14
Zeph 2:7
I will not t. away from. Jer 32:40
to t. away captivity. Lam 2:14
t. away your faces from. Ezek 14:6
and for four I will not t. away the.
Amos 1:3, 6, 9, 11, 13; 2:1, 4, 6
God will t. away from. Jonah 3:9
and did t. many away from iniquity.
Mal 2:6
of thee, t. not thou away. Mat 5:42
seeking to t. away the. Acts 13:8
t. away ungodliness. Rom 11:26
heady, from such t. away. 2 Tim 3:5
they shall t. away their ears. 4:4
how escape, if we t. away from him?
Heb 12:25

turn *back*

t. back and cover that. Deut 23:13
a hook in thy nose and t. thee back.
2 Ki 19:28; Isa 37:29
makest us to t. back. Ps 44:10
shall mine enemies t. back. 56:9
who shall t. it back? Isa 14:27
neither will I t. back. Jer 4:28
t. back thine hand as a. 6:9
behold, I will t. back the. 21:4
flee ye, t. back, dwell deep. 49:8
I will t. thee back. Ezek 38:4; 39:2
when I t. back your. Zeph 3:20
not t. back to take up. Mark 13:16

turn *in*

now, my lords, t. in, I. Gen 19:2
t. in, my lord, t. in to. Judg 4:18
let us t. in to this city of. 19:11
of God shall t. in thither. 2 Ki 4:10
let him t. in hither. Pr 9:4, 16

turn *to the Lord*

if thou t. to the Lord thy God.
Deut 4:30; 30:10

trouble did *t. to the Lord. 2 Chr* 15:4
world shall *t. to the Lord. Ps* 22:27
let us try our ways and *t. to the Lord. Lam* 3:40
take with you words and *t. to the Lord. Hos* 14:2
heart and *t. to the Lord. Joel* 2:13
many of Israel shall he *t. to the Lord. Luke* 1:16
nevertheless, when it shall *t. to the Lord. 2 Cor* 3:16

turned

sword which *t.* every way. *Gen* 3:24
Joseph *t.* about from them. 42:24
the rod which was *t. Ex* 7:15
in the river shall be *t.* to blood. 17, 20 *Ps* 78:44; 105:29
heart of Pharaoh was *t. Ex* 14:5
when the hair is *t.* white. *Lev* 13:3 10, 17, 20, 25
they *t.* and went by way. *Num* 21:33
ass saw me and *t.* from me. 22:33
t. the curse into a blessing. *Deut* 23:5; *Neh* 13:2
in that they are *t.* unto. *Deut* 31:18
so the Lord *t.* from the fierceness of his anger. *Josh* 7:26
they *t.* quickly out of. *Judg* 2:17
Samson took firebrands and *t.* 15:4
therefore they *t.* their backs. 20:42
and thou shalt be *t.* into another man. *1 Sam* 10:6
even they also *t.* to be with. 14:21
whithersoever he *t.* himself he. 47
as Samuel *t.* about to go. 15:27
David *t.* from him towards. 17:30
Asahel *t.* not from. *2 Sam* 2:19
the victory that day was *t.* 19:2
the kingdom is *t.* about. *1 Ki* 2:15
Joab *t.* after Adonijah, though. 28
the king *t.* his face about. 8:14
because his heart was *t.* from. 11:9
so Naaman *t.* and went. *2 Ki* 5:12
Ahaz *t.* the covert from the. 16:18
t. his face to the wall, and prayed. 20:2; *Isa* 38:2
Josiah *t.* himself he spied. *2 Ki* 23:16
was no king that *t.* to the Lord. 25
Lord *t.* not from the fierceness. 26
he *t.* the kingdom unto. *1 Chr* 10:14
the wrath of the Lord *t. 2 Chr* 12:12
t. from them and destroyed. 20:10
for our fathers have *t.* their. 29:6
t. the heart of the king of. *Ezra* 6:22
wrath of our God be *t.* from. 10:14
neither *t.* they from their. *Neh* 9:35
though it was *t.* to the contrary. *Esth* 9:1
the mouth which was *t.* to them. 22
God *t.* me into the hands. *Job* 16:11
and they whom I loved are *t.* 19:19
yet his meat in his bowels is *t.* 20:14
under it is *t.* up as it were fire. 28:5
terrors are *t.* upon me. 30:15
my harp is *t.* to mourning, and. 31
if my step hath *t.* out of the. 31:7
it is *t.* as clay to the seal. 38:14
and sorrow is *t.* into joy. 41:22
and the Lord *t.* the captivity. 42:10
the wicked shall be *t. Ps* 9:17
thou hast *t.* my mourning. 30:11
he *t.* the sea into dry land. 66:6
and *t.* my hand against their. 81:14
he *t.* their heart to hate. 105:25
which *t.* the rock into a. 114:8
I *t.* my feet unto thy. 119:59
and I *t.* myself to behold. *Eccl* 2:12
night of my pleasure he *t. Isa* 21:4
Lebanon shall be *t.* into a. 29:17
the streams thereof shall be *t.* 34:9
we have *t.* every one to his. 53:6
therefore he was *t.* to be their. 63:10
how then art thou *t.* into a degenerate plant? *Jer* 2:21
they have *t.* their back to me. 27
Judah hath not *t.* to me with. 3:10
their houses shall be *t.* unto. 6:12
no man repented, every one *t.* 8:6
should have *t.* them from. 23:22
and I shall be *t.* 31:18
after that I was *t.* 19
they *t.* unto me the back. 32:33
now *t.* and had done right. 34:15
but ye *t.* and polluted my. 16
how hath Moab *t.* the? *Jer* 48:39
Lord, mine heart is *t. Lam* 1:20
surely against me is he *t.* 3:3
our inheritance is *t.* to strangers. 5:2
our dance is *t.* into mourning. 15
O Lord, and we shall be *t.* 21
they *t.* not when they went. *Ezek* 1:9, 12; 10:11
a vine, whose branches *t.* 17:6
she is *t.* unto me, I shall be. 26:2
my comeliness was *t. Dan* 10:8
vision my sorrows are *t.* upon me. 16
Ephraim is a cake not *t. Hos* 7:8
Ephraim, mine heart is *t.* 11:8
sun shall be *t.* into darkness. *Joel* 2:31; *Acts* 2:20
ye have *t.* judgement. *Amos* 6:12
they *t.* from their evil. *Jonah* 3:10
cup shall be *t.* unto thee. *Hab* 2:16
all the land shall be *t. Zech* 14:10
Jesus *t.* about in press. *Mark* 5:30
the Lord *t.* and looked. *Luke* 22:61
but your sorrow shall be *t.* into joy. *John* 16:20
God *t.* and gave them up. *Acts* 7:42
all at Lydda saw him and *t.* 9:35
believed and *t.* to the Lord. 11:21
Gentiles are *t.* to God. 15:19
t. the world upside down. 17:6
shew how ye *t.* to God. *1 Thes* 1:9
and they shall be *t.* unto. *2 Tim* 4:4
t. to flight the armies. *Heb* 11:34
lest that which is lame be *t.* 12:13
t. with a very small helm. *Jas* 3:4
let your laughter be *t.* to. 4:9
the dog is *t.* to his own. *2 Pet* 2:22

turned *again*

behold it was *t. again* as. *Ex* 4:7
Ehud *t. again* from the. *Judg* 3:19
Israel *t. again,* went a whoring. 8:33
t. again, Benjamites amazed. 20:41
Samuel *t. again* after. *1 Sam* 15:31
I *t.* not *again* till I. *2 Sam* 22:38
when the man *t. again* from his chariot. *2 Ki* 5:26
Lord *t. again* the captivity. *Ps* 126:1

turned *aside*

that he *t. aside* to see. *Ex* 3:4
they have *t. aside* quickly. 32:8 *Deut* 9:12, 16
he *t. aside* to see the. *Judg* 14:8
the kine *t.* not *aside. 1 Sam* 6:12
but *t. aside* after lucre, and. 8:3
David *t.* not *aside* from. *1 Ki* 15:5
a man *t. aside* and brought. 20:39
Josiah *t.* not *aside* to. *2 Ki* 22:2
of their way are *t. aside. Job* 6:18
they were *t. aside* like. *Ps* 78:57
is thy beloved *t. aside*? *S of S* 6:1
heart hath *t.* him *aside. Isa* 44:20
he hath *t. aside* my ways. *Lam* 3:11
have *t. aside* unto vain. *1 Tim* 1:6
for some are already *t. aside.* 5:15

turned *away*

because ye are *t. away. Num* 14:43
wherefore Israel *t. away.* 20:21
of the Lord may be *t. away.* 25:4
t. my wrath *away* from Israel. 11
wives *t. away* his heart. *1 Ki* 11:3, 4
Ahab *t. away* and would eat. 21:4
our fathers *t. away* their. *2 Chr* 29:6
which hath not *t. away. Ps* 66:20
time *t.* he his anger *away.* 78:38
his anger is not *t. away,* but his hand. *Isa* 5:25; 9:12, 17, 21; 10:4
thy anger is *t. away.* 12:1
nor *t.* I *away.* 50:5
and judgement is *t. away.* 59:14
your iniquities have *t. away* these. *Jer* 5:25
sunk, they are *t. away* back. 38:22
have seen them *t. away* back? 46:5
shepherds have *t.* them *away.* 50:6
let thy fury be *t. away. Dan* 9:16
for mine anger is *t. away. Hos* 14:4
the Lord hath *t. away* excellency of Jacob. *Nah* 2:2
this Paul hath *t. away. Acts* 19:26
Asia be *t. away* from me. *2 Tim* 1:15

turned *back*

the people *t. back* upon. *Josh* 8:20
Joshua at that time *t. back.* 11:10
Saul is *t. back* from. *1 Sam* 15:11
of Jonathan *t.* not *back. 2 Sam* 1:22
t. their heart *back. 1 Ki* 18:37
not king of Israel, they *t. back.* 22:33
when the messengers *t. back,* Why are ye now *t. back*? *2 Ki* 1:5
he *t. back* and looked on them. 2:24
so the king of Assyria *t. back.* 15:20
Ornan *t. back,* and. *1 Chr* 21:20
because they *t. back. Job* 34:27
enemies are *t. back. Ps* 9:3
let them be *t. back* that devise. 35:4; 70:2, 3
our heart is *t. back* from. 44:18
children of Ephraim *t. back* in. 78:9
yea, they *t. back* and tempted. 41, 57
and let them be *t. back* that. 129:5
they shall be *t. back* that. *Isa* 42:17
the anger of the Lord is not *t. back. Jer* 4:8
they are *t. back* to iniquities. 11:10
they also are *t. back,* and. 46:21
he hath *t.* me *back,* and. *Lam* 1:13
them that are *t. back* from the Lord. *Zeph* 1:6
t. back again to Jerusalem seeking. *Luke* 2:45
out of the lepers *t. back,* and. 17:15
she *t.* herself *back* and. *John* 20:14
in their hearts *t. back. Acts* 7:39

turned *in*

the two angels *t. in. Gen* 19:3
Judah *t. in* to Hirah the. 38:1
when Sisera had *t. in. Judg* 4:18
the Danites *t. in* thither and. 18:3
Elisha *t. in* thither to. *2 Ki* 4:8
he *t. into* the chamber and lay. 11

turnest

whithersoever thou *t. 1 Ki* 2:3
that thou *t.* thy spirit. *Job* 15:13
thou *t.* man to destruction. *Ps* 90:3

turneth

soul that *t.* after wizards. *Lev* 20:6
whose heart *t.* away this. *Deut* 29:18
shall I say, when Israel *t.*? *Josh* 7:8
the horse *t.* not back. *Job* 39:22
he *t.* rivers into a. *Ps* 107:33
he *t.* the wilderness into a. 35
the way of the wicked he *t.* 146:9
a soft answer *t.* away. *Pr* 15:1
a gift, whithersoever it *t.* 17:8
he *t.* the king's heart. 21:1
as the door *t.* upon his hinges. 26:14
that *t.* away his ear from. 28:9
a lion that *t.* not away for. 30:30
the wind *t.* about unto. *Eccl* 1:6
be as one that *t.* aside? *S of S* 1:7
the people *t.* not to him. *Isa* 9:13
the Lord *t.* the earth upside. 24:1
that *t.* wise men backward. 44:25
that *t.* aside to tarry. *Jer* 14:8
Damascus is feeble, and *t.* 49:24
yea, she sigheth and *t. Lam* 1:8
he *t.* his hand against me all. 3:3
when righteous *t.* away. *Ezek* 18:24 26; 33:18
when the wicked man *t.* away. 18:27, 28; 33:12
t. the shadow of death. *Amos* 5:8

turning

Jerusalem as a dish, *t.* it. *2 Ki* 21:13
he hardened his heart from *t.* unto the Lord. *2 Chr* 36:13
the *t.* away of the simple. *Pr* 1:32
your *t.* of things upside. *Isa* 29:16
t. away he hath divided. *Mi* 2:4
to bless you in *t.* you. *Acts* 3:26
whom is no shadow of *t. Jas* 1:17
t. Sodom and Gomorrah. *2 Pet* 2:6
t. the grace of God into. *Jude* 4

turtle, -s, turtledove, -s
(*Turtle means* turtledove)

take a *t.* and a young pigeon. *Gen* 15:9
his offering of *t. Lev* 1:14
for his trespass two *t.* or two pigeons. 5:7; 12:8; 14:22, 30; 15:14, 29
be not able to bring two *t.* 5:11
she shall bring a *t.* for. 12:6
day he shall bring two *t. Num* 6:10
O deliver not the soul of thy *t.* unto the wicked. *Ps* 74:19

the voice of the *t.* is. *S of S* 2:12
t. and crane observe the. *Jer* 8:7
to offer a sacrifice, A pair of *t.* or two young pigeons. *Luke* 2:24

tutors
the heir while a child is under *t.* and governors. *Gal* 4:2*

twain
thou shalt be my son in law in the one of the *t.* *1 Sam* 18:21*
shut the door on them *t.* and prayed. *2 Ki* 4:33
with *t.* he covered his face, with *t.* he covered his feet, with *t.* *Isa* 6:2
they cut the calf in *t.* *Jer* 34:18
both *t.* shall come out. *Ezek* 21:19
go a mile, go with him *t.* *Mat* 5:41
cleave to his wife, and they *t.* 19:5
wherefore they are no more *t.* 6 *Mark* 10:8
whether of *t.* did the ? *Mat* 21:31
whether of the *t.* will ye ? 27:21
the vail of the temple was rent in *t.* 51 *Mark* 15:38
to make in himself of *t.* *Eph* 2:15

twelfth
oxen, he with the *t.* *1 Ki* 19:19
the *t.* lot came forth to Jakim. *1 Chr* 24:12
the *t.* lot came forth to Hashabiah. 25:19
t. captain for the *t.* month. 27:15
in the *t.* year of Josiah's reign. *2 Chr* 34:3
in the *t.* year of king. *Esth* 3:7
in the *t.* year, in the *t.* *Ezek* 32:1
in the *t.* year and fifteenth day. 17
in the *t.* year of our captivity. 33:21
the *t.* foundation was an. *Rev* 21:20
see **day, month**

twelve
t. years they served. *Gen* 14:4
t. princes shall Ishmael beget. 17:20; 25:16
now the sons of Jacob were *t.* 35:22
they said, Thy servants are *t.* brethren. 42:13, 32
all these are the *t.* tribes. 49:28
they came to Elim, where were *t.* wells. *Ex* 15:27
t. pillars according to the *t.* 24:4
t. precious stones. 28:21; 39:14
thou shalt bake *t.* cakes. *Lev* 24:5
t. princes. *Num* 1:44
they brought *t.* oxen. 7:3
t. chargers, *t.* silver bowls, *t.* 84
t. bullocks, rams *t.*, lambs of the first year *t.* 87
t. rods, according to house. 17:2, 6
on second day offer *t.* young. 29:17
I took *t.* men of you. *Deut* 1:23
take ye *t.* men out of the tribes. *Josh* 3:12; 4:2
take ye *t.* stones out of Jordan. 4:3, 8, 9, 20
went over by number *t.* of Benjamin, and *t.* of the servants. *2 Sam* 2:15
Solomon had *t.* officers. *1 Ki* 4:7
the sea stood on *t.* oxen. 7:25, 44 *2 Chr* 4:15
t. lions on the one side. *1 Ki* 10:20 *2 Chr* 9:19
Jeroboam's garment in *t.* pieces. *1 Ki* 11:30
Elijah took *t.* stones and built. 18:31
found Elisha plowing with *t.* 19:19
with brethren and sons *t.* *So to the end.* *1 Chr* 25:9
for a sin offering *t.* he goats. *Ezra* 6:17; 8:35
I separated *t.* of the chief. 8:24
t. years not eaten bread. *Neh* 5:14
t. brazen bulls, Nebuzar-adan took. *Jer* 52:20
the altar shall be *t.* cubits long, *t.* broad. *Ezek* 43:16
land according to the *t.* tribes. 47:13
at end of *t.* months he. *Dan* 4:29
diseased with an issue of blood *t.* *Mat* 9:20; *Mark* 5:25; *Luke* 8:43
the names of the *t.* apostles. *Mat* 10:2; *Luke* 6:13
they took up of fragments *t.* baskets. *Mat* 14:20; *Mark* 6:43; 8:19 *Luke* 9:17; *John* 6:13
sit upon *t.* thrones, judging the *t.* tribes. *Mat* 19:28; *Luke* 22:30
he sat down with the *t.* *Mat* 26:20 *Mark* 14:17; *Luke* 22:14
yet spake, Judas one of the *t.* came. *Mat* 26:47; *Mark* 14:10, 43 *Luke* 22:47; *John* 6:71
than *t.* legions of angels. *Mat* 26:53
she was of the age of *t.* years. *Mark* 5:42; *Luke* 8:42
of the *t.*, that dippeth. *Mark* 14:20
and when Jesus was *t.* *Luke* 2:42
have I not chosen you *t.*? *John* 6:70
not *t.* hours in the day ? 11:9
Thomas one of the *t.* was. 20:24
and Jacob begat the *t.* *Acts* 7:8
all the men were about *t.* 19:7
but *t.* days since I went up. 24:11
to which promise our *t.* tribes. 26:7
of Cephas, then of the *t.* *1 Cor* 15:5
to the *t.* tribes which are. *Jas* 1:1
head a crown of *t.* stars. *Rev* 12:1
t. gates, at the gates *t.* angels. 21:12
city had *t.* foundations, and in them the names of the *t.* apostles. 14
the *t.* gates were *t.* pearls. 21
tree of life bare *t.* manner of. 22:2
see **hundred, thousand**

twenty
shall be *t.* found there. He said, I will not destroy it for *t.'s.* *Gen* 18:31
this *t.* years have I been. 31:38, 41
for Esau, *t.* he goats, *t.* rams. 32:14
and ten bulls, *t.* she asses. 15
they sold Joseph for *t.* pieces. 37:28
a shekel is *t.* gerahs. *Ex* 30:13 *Lev* 27:25; *Num* 3:47; 18:16 *Ezek* 45:12
t. years old and above. *Ex* 30:14 38:26; *Num* 1:3, 18, 20; 14:29 26:2; 32:11; *1 Chr* 23:24, 27 *2 Chr* 25:5; 31:17; *Ezra* 3:8
of the male from *t.* years. *Lev* 27:3
5 years old to *t.* years, *t.* shekels. 5
shall not eat neither ten days, nor *t.* days. *Num* 11:19
the shekel is *t.* gerahs. 18:16
oppressed Israel *t.* years. *Judg* 4:3
from Aroer even *t.* cities. 11:33
judged Israel *t.* years. 15:20; 16:31
in Kirjath-jearim *t.* years. *1 Sam* 7:2
armourbearer slew *t.* men. 14:14
to David with *t.* men. *2 Sam* 3:20
Ziba had fifteen sons and *t.* servants. 9:10; 19:17
provision daily, *t.* oxen. *1 Ki* 4:23
at the end of *t.* years, when Solomon. 9:10; *2 Chr* 8:1
Solomon gave Hiram *t.* *1 Ki* 9:11
man of God *t.* loaves. *2 Ki* 4:42
I even weighed *t.* basons. *Ezra* 8:27
weight, *t.* shekels a day. *Ezek* 4:10
of the porch was *t.* cubits. 40:49
the breadth of the door was *t.* 41:2
heap of *t.* measures, to draw out fifty vessels . . . but *t.* *Hag* 2:16
the flying roll *t.* cubits. *Zech* 5:2
and found it *t.* fathoms. *Acts* 27:28

twenty *two*
judged Israel *t. two* years. *Judg* 10:3
Jeroboam reigned *t. two* years. *1 Ki* 14:20
Ahab reigned over Israel *t. two* years. 16:29
t. and *two* years old was Ahaziah. *2 Ki* 8:26
Amon *t. two* years old when. 21:19
of his father's house *t. two* captains. *1 Chr* 12:28
but Abijah begat *t.* and *two* sons. *2 Chr* 13:21

twenty *three*
Tola judged Israel *t. three* years. *Judg* 10:2
Jehoahaz was *t. three* years old. *2 Ki* 23:31
Jair had *t. three* cities. *1 Chr* 2:22
of Josiah to *t. third* year. *Jer* 25:3
in the *t. third* year of. 52:30

twenty *four*
were *t.* and *four* bullocks. *Num* 7:88
fingers and toes *t. four.* *2 Sam* 21:20
reigned *t.* and *four* years. *1 Ki* 15:33
consider from *t. fourth* day and. *Hag* 2:18
the throne were *t. four* seats, and on the seats I saw *t. four.* *Rev* 4:4
the *t. four* elders fell down. 5:8 11:16; 19:4

twenty *five*
from *t. five* years old. *Num* 8:24
reigned *t.* and *five* years in Jerusalem. *1 Ki* 22:42; *2 Chr* 20:31
t. five years old when he began to. *2 Ki* 14:2; *2 Chr* 25:1
Jotham *t. five* years old. *2 Ki* 15:33 *2 Chr* 27:1, 8
Hezekiah *t. five* years old. *2 Ki* 18:2 *2 Chr* 29:1
Jehoiakim *t. five* years. *2 Ki* 23:36 *2 Chr* 36:5
the wall finished in *t. fifth* day. *Neh* 6:15
t. fifth day Evil-merodach lifted. *Jer* 52:31

twenty *six*
in the *t. sixth* year of Asa. *1 Ki* 16:8

twenty *seven*
t. seventh day of second month. *Gen* 8:14
27th year of Asa. *1 Ki* 16:10, 15
on *t. seventh* day of twelfth month. *2 Ki* 25:27

twenty *eight*
length of curtain *t. eight* cubits. *Ex* 26:2; 36:9
reigned *t.* and *eight* years. *2 Ki* 10:36
Rehoboam begat *t. eight* sons. *2 Chr* 11:21

twenty *nine*
Nahor lived *t. nine* years. *Gen* 11:24
Amaziah reigned *t. nine* years. *2 Ki* 14:2
Hezekiah reigned *t. nine* years. 18:2 *2 Chr* 25:1; 29:1
see **thousand**

twice
dream was doubled *t.* *Gen* 41:32
shall be *t.* as much. *Ex* 16:5, 22
rod he smote the rock *t.* *Num* 20:11
out of his presence *t.* *1 Sam* 18:11
appeared unto him *t.* *1 Ki* 11:9
there, not once nor *t.* *2 Ki* 6:10
Jerusalem once or *t.* *Neh* 13:20
speaketh once, yea *t.* *Job* 33:14
yea *t.*; but I will proceed no. 40:5
Lord gave Job *t.* as much as. 42:10
t. have I heard, power. *Ps* 62:11
a thousand years *t.* told. *Eccl* 6:6
before cock crow *t.* thou shalt deny me. *Mark* 14:30, 72
I fast *t.* in the week. *Luke* 18:12
t. dead, plucked up by. *Jude* 12

twigs
the top of his young *t.* *Ezek* 17:4
off from the top of his young *t.* 22

twilight
smote them from the *t.* *1 Sam* 30:17
the lepers rose in the *t.* to go to the. *2 Ki* 7:5
they arose and fled in the *t.* 7
let the stars of the *t.* thereof be dark. *Job* 3:9
adulterer waiteth for the *t.* 24:15
way to her house in the *t.* *Pr* 7:9
shalt carry it forth in the *t.* *Ezek* 12:6*
and brought it forth in the *t.* 7*
the prince shall bear it in the *t.* 12*

twined, *see* **fine**

twinkling
all be changed, in the *t.* *1 Cor* 15:52

twins
Rebekah had *t.* *Gen* 25:24
Tamar had *t.* 38:27
every one bear *t.* *S of S* 4:2; 6:6
like two roes that are *t.* 4:5; 7:3

two
took unto him *t.* wives. *Gen* 4:19
t. of every sort shalt thou bring. 6:19

of beasts that are not clean by t.
Gen 7:2; 9:15
t. nations are in thy womb, and t.
manner of people shall be. 25:23
he hath supplanted me these t. 27:36
and now I am become t. bands. 32:10
Issachar is an ass couching between
t. burdens. 49:14
they gathered t. omers. Ex 16:22
if he continue a day or t. 21:21
t. turtledoves or t. pigeons. Lev 5:7
12:8; 14:22; 15:14, 29; Num 6:10
not able to bring t. turtledoves.
Lev 5:11
she shall be unclean t. weeks. 12:5
Aaron shall take t. goats. 16:7
cast lots upon t. 8
shalt set the cakes in t. rows. 24:6
brought a waggon for t. Num 7:3
t. oxen. 17, 23, 29, 35, 41, 47, 53
59, 65, 71
make thee t. trumpets of silver. 10:2
his ass, Balaam's t. servants. 22:22
t. rams. 29:14, 17, 20, 23, 26, 29, 32
and divide the prey into t. 31:27
t. kings. Deut 3:8, 21; 4:47
Josh 2:10; 9:10
at the mouth of t. or three witnesses,
be put to death. Deut 17:6; 19:15
Mat 18:16; 2 Cor 13:1
if a man have t. wives. Deut 21:15
should t. put ten thousand to? 32:30
t. tribes. Josh 14:3, 4; 21:16
t. cities. 21:25
man a damsel or t. Judg 5:30
let me alone t. months, that. 11:37
be avenged for my t. eyes. 16:28
t. went till they came to. Ruth 1:19
which t. did build the house. 4:11
t. wives. 1 Sam 1:2; 27:3; 30:5
18; 2 Sam 2:2
with t. lines measured. 2 Sam 8:2
he did to the t. captains. 1 Ki 2:5
there was none save we t. in. 3:18
Hiram and Solomon, t. made. 5:12
t. months they were at home. 14
and they t. were alone in. 11:29
Jeroboam made t. calves. 12:28
2 Ki 17:16
I am gathering t. sticks. 1 Ki 17:12
how long halt ye between t.? 18:21
Israel pitched like t. little. 20:27
fire burnt up the t. 2 Ki 1:14
they t. went on. 2:6
came forth t. she bears. 24
give, I pray thee, t. changes. 5:22
be content, take t. talents, and. 23
t. measures of barley for. 7:1, 16, 18
behold, t. kings stood not. 10:4
of Tekoah, had t. wives. 1 Chr 4:5
more honourable than the t. 11:21
Jehoiada took for Joash t. wives.
2 Chr 24:3
only do not t. things unto. Job 13:20
kindled against thy t. friends. 42:7
t. things have I required. Pr 30:7
t. are better than one. Eccl 4:9
if t. lie together. 11
t. shall withstand him. 12
thy t. breasts are like t. young roes.
S of S 4:5; 7:3
it were company of t. armies. 6:13
t. or three berries in top of. Isa 17:6
but these t. things shall come. 47:9
these t. things are come unto. 51:19
have committed t. evils. Jer 2:13
I will take one of a city, and t. 3:14
son of man, appoint thee t. ways.
Ezek 21:19
were t. women, daughters of. 23:2
hast said, These t. nations. 35:10
shall be no more t. nations. 37:22
Joseph shall have t. portions. 47:13
behold, there stood other t. Dan 12:5
can t. walk together? Amos 3:3
so t. or three cities wandered. 4:8
t. olive trees by it. Zech 4:3, 11, 12
these are the t. anointed ones. 4:14
there came out t. women who. 5:9
four chariots from between t. 6:1
I took unto me t. staves and. 11:7
t. parts therein shall be cut off. 13:8
no man can serve t. masters.
Mat 6:24; Luke 16:13
than having t. hands or t. feet.
Mat 18:8; Mark 9:43
rather than having t. eyes.
Mat 18:9; Mark 9:47
with thee one or t. more. Mat 18:16
that if t. of you shall agree on. 19
where t. or three are gathered. 20
on these t. hang all the law. 22:40
then shall t. be in the field. 24:40
received t. he gained other t. 25:17
send them forth by t. and t. Mark 6:7
he sendeth t. disciples. 11:1; 14:13
Luke 19:29
she threw in t. mites. Mark 12:42
after that Jesus appeared to t. 16:12
he that hath t. coats, let. Luke 3:11
certain creditor which had t. 7:41
neither take money, nor have t. 9:3
took out t. pence and gave. 10:35
shew whether of these t. Acts 1:24
for t. shall be one flesh. 1 Cor 6:16
Eph 5:31
let it be by t. or at the. 1 Cor 14:27
let the prophets speak t. or three. 29
these are the t. covenants. Gal 4:24
a strait betwixt t., a desire. Phil 1:23
but before t. or three. 1 Tim 5:19
that by t. immutable things . . . we.
Heb 6:18
died without mercy under t. 10:28
there come t. woes more. Rev 9:12
I will give power to my t. 11:3
these are t. olive trees and t. 4
because these t. prophets. 10
woman were given t. wings. 12:14
he had t. horns like a lamb. 13:11
see **daughters, days, fifty, forty, hundred, kidneys, lambs, sons, thirty, thousand, twenty**

two *men*
t. men of the Hebrews. Ex 2:13
there remained t. men. Num 11:26
out t. men to spy secretly. Josh 2:1
Rahab hid the t. men. 4
the t. men returned. 23
find t. men by Rachel's. 1 Sam 10:2
there were t. men in one city, one
rich. 2 Sam 12:1
fell on t. men more. 1 Ki 2:32
set t. men, sons of Belial. 21:10, 13
t. blind men followed. Mat 9:27
talked with him t. men. Luke 9:30
t. men in one bed. 17:34
t. men in the field. 36
t. men went up to the temple. 18:10
perplexed, behold, t. men stood.
Luke 24:4; Acts 1:10
testimony of t. men is true.
John 8:17
they sent t. men to Peter. Acts 9:38

two *tables*
gave to Moses t. tables. Ex 31:18
the t. tables were in his hands.
32:15; 34:29
hew thee t. tables of stone. 34:1
Deut 10:1
he hewed t. tables of stone.
Ex 34:4; Deut 10:3
he wrote upon t. tables. Deut 4:13
5:22
the Lord delivered unto me t. tables.
9:10, 11
nothing in the ark save the t. tables.
1 Ki 8:9; 2 Chr 5:10
t. tables on this side. Ezek 40:39
t. tables on that. 40

two *years*
begat Arphaxad t. years. Gen 11:10
these t. years hath the famine. 45:6
when Saul had reigned t. years.
1 Sam 13:1
Ish-bosheth Saul's son reigned t.
years. 2 Sam 2:10
after t. years, Absalom had. 13:23
Absalom dwelt t. years in. 14:28
Nadab reigned over Israel t. years.
1 Ki 15:25
Elah reigned t. years. 16:8
Ahaziah reigned t. years. 22:51
2 Ki 15:23; 21:19
after t. years his bowels. 2 Chr 21:19
within t. full years will I bring again
the vessels. Jer 28:3, 11
words of Amos, t. years. Amos 1:1
slew children from t. years. Mat 2:16
t. years they in Asia. Acts 19:10
Paul dwelt t. years in his. 28:30

twofold
ye make him t. more the child of hell.
Mat 23:15

Tychicus
T. of Asia accompanied. Acts 20:4
T. shall make known to. Eph 6:21
all my state shall T. Col 4:7
and T. have I sent to. 2 Tim 4:12
when I shall send T. Tit 3:12

Tyrannus
disputing in the school of one T.
Acts 19:9

Tyre
coast turneth to the strong city T.
Josh 19:29
the strong hold of T. 2 Sam 24:7
fetched Hiram out of T. 1 Ki 7:13
his father was a man of T. 14
2 Chr 2:14
Hiram came out from T. to.
1 Ki 9:12
and drink to them of T. Ezra 3:7
there dwelt men of T. Neh 13:16
the daughter of T. shall. Ps 45:12
with the inhabitants of T. 83:7
Philistia and T. 87:4
the burden of T. Isa 23:1
pained at the report of T. 5
this counsel against T.? 8
T. shall be forgotten. 15
Lord will visit T. 17
what have ye to do with me, O
T.? Joel 3:4
if the mighty works had been done
in T. Mat 11:21; Luke 10:13
Herod was displeased with them of
T. Acts 12:20
see **king, Sidon**

Tyrus
made all the kings of T. Jer 25:22
send yokes to the kings of T. 27:3
to cut off from T. and Zidon. 47:4
because T. said against. Ezek 26:2
behold, I am against thee, O T. 3
take up a lamentation for T. 27:2
what city is like T., like the? 32
say to the prince of T. 28:2
lamentation on the king of T. 12
great service against T. 29:18
Ephraim, as I saw T. Hos 9:13
transgressions of T. Amos 1:9
a fire on the wall of T. 10
T. and Zidon, though it. Zech 9:2
T. build herself a strong hold. 3

U

Ucal
spake to Ithiel and U. Pr 30:1

unaccustomed
Ephraim, as a bullock u. Jer 31:18

unadvisedly
so that he spake u. with. Ps 106:33

unawares
Jacob stole away u. to Laban.
Gen 31:20, 26
slayer may flee thither, who killeth
any person u. Num 35:11*, 15*
Deut 4:42; Josh 20:3*, 9*
let destruction come on him at u.
Ps 35:8
day come upon you u. Luke 21:34*
because of false brethren u. Gal 2:4*
have entertained angels u. Heb 13:2
certain men crept in u. Jude 4*

unbelief
did not many mighty works there
because of their u. Mat 13:58
could not cast him out, because of
your u. 17:20*
because of their u. Mark 6:6
help thou mine u. 9:24
upbraided them with their u. 16:14
shall their u. make faith? Rom 3:3*
not at the promise through u. 4:20

purpose to keep u. Judah for. 2 Chr 28:10
name will we tread them u. Ps 44:5
should be u. my head. S of S 8:3
with idols u. every green tree. Isa 57:5; Jer 2:20
perish from the earth, and from u. Jer 10:11; Lam 3:66
get away from u. it. Dan 4:14
u. the whole heaven hath not. 9:12
gone a whoring from u. Hos 4:12
from two years old and u. Mat 2:16
u. authority, having soldiers u. 8:9
enter u. my roof. Luke 7:6
when thou wast u. the fig tree. John 1:48
have proved that they are all u. sin. Rom 3:9
not u. the law, but u. grace. 6:15
but I am carnal, sold u. sin. 7:14
brought u. power of any. 1 Cor 6:12
u. the law, as u. the law. 9:20
I keep u. my body and bring it. 27
our fathers were u. the cloud. 10:1
u. the curse. Gal 3:10
hath concluded all u. sin. 22
we were kept u. the law. 23
faith is come, we are no longer u. 25
and things u. the earth. Phil 2:10
as are u. the yoke. 1 Tim 6:1
for u. it the people. Heb 7:11
in chains u. darkness. Jude 6
see **feet, him, law, me, sun, thee, them, us**

undergirding
used helps, u. the ship. Acts 27:17

underneath
u. are the everlasting. Deut 33:27

undersetters
the four corners thereof had u. 1 Ki 7:30, 34

understand
they may not u. one. Gen 11:7
thou canst u. a dream. 41:15
ye shall u. that these. Num 16:30
tongue thou shalt not u. Deut 28:49
servants in the Syrian language, for we u. it. 2 Ki 18:26; Isa 36:11
the Lord made me u. 1 Chr 28:19
before those that could u. Neh 8:3
the people to u. the law. 7, 8, 13
cause me to u. wherein. Job 6:24
I would u. what he would say. 23:5
of his power who can u.? 26:14
nor do the aged u. judgement. 32:9
can any u. the spreadings? 36:29
if there were any that did u. Ps 14:2; 53:2
who can u. his errors? cleanse. 19:12
know not, neither will they u. 82:5
neither doth a fool u. this. 92:6
u. ye brutish among the people. 94:8
u. the lovingkindness of. 107:43
make me to u. the way of. 119:27
I u. more than the ancients. 100
then shalt thou u. the fear. Pr 2:5
then shalt thou u. righteousness. 9
u. wisdom, and, ye fools, be of. 8:5
prudent is to u. his way. 14:8
reprove one, and he will u. 19:25
how can a man then u. his? 20:24
evil men u. not judgement, but they that seek the Lord u. all. 28:5
for though he u. he will not. 29:19
Hear ye indeed, but u. not. Isa 6:9
lest they u. with their heart. 10 John 12:40
whom shall he make to u.? Isa 28:9
it shall be a vexation only to u. 19
the heart of the rash shall u. 32:4
tongue that thou canst not u. 33:19
u. together that the Lord. 41:20
that ye may know and u. 43:10
hearts, that they cannot u. 44:18
shepherds that cannot u. 56:11
who is the wise man that may u. this? Jer 9:12
words thou canst not u. Ezek 3:6
make this man to u. the. Dan 8:16
but he said unto me, U. O son. 17
and u. thy truth. 9:13
u. the matter. 23, 25
didst set thy heart to u. 10:12
I am come to make thee u. Dan 10:14
and they that u. shall instruct. 11:33
none . . . u., but the wise shall u. 12:10
people that doth not u. Hos 4:14
and he shall u. these things? 14:9
neither u. they the counsel. Mi 4:12
neither do they u. Mat 13:13
hear and not u. 14
hear and u. 15:10; Mark 7:14
do not ye yet u.? Mat 15:17; 16:9, 11 Mark 8:17, 21
whoso readeth, let him u. Mat 24:15 Mark 13:14
and not perceive, that hearing they may hear and not u. Mark 4:12 Luke 8:10; Acts 28:26
I know not nor u. I what. Mark 14:68
that they might u. the. Luke 24:45
ye not u. my speech? John 8:43
have not heard shall u. Rom 15:21
and though I u. all mysteries . . . I am nothing. 1 Cor 13:2
through faith we u. worlds. Heb 11:3
evil of things they u. not. 2 Pet 2:12*

understandest
what u. thou, which is not? Job 15:9
thou u. my thoughts. Ps 139:2
neither u. thou what they. Jer 5:15
Philip said, U. thou what? Acts 8:30

understandeth
Lord u. the imaginations. 1 Chr 28:9
God u. the way thereof. Job 28:23
is in honour and u. not. Ps 49:20
all plain to him that u. Pr 8:9
easy unto him that u. 14:6
in this, that he u. me. Jer 9:24
the word and u. it not. Mat 13:19
heareth the word and u. it. 23
there is none that u. Rom 3:11
men, for no man u. 1 Cor 14:2
say Amen, seeing he u. not what? 16

understanding
Bezaleel with wisdom and u. and in. Ex 31:3; 35:31; 36:1
wisdom and your u. Deut 4:6
neither is there any u. in. 32:28
hast asked for thyself u. 1 Ki 3:11
Solomon wisdom and u. 4:29
was filled with wisdom and u. 7:14
were men that had u. 1 Chr 12:32
give thee wisdom and u. 22:12
a wise son endued with u. 2 Chr 2:12
Zechariah had u. in the visions. 26:5
for Elnathan, men of u. Ezra 8:16*
could hear with u. Neh 8:2
knowledge and having u. 10:28
but I have u. as well as you. Job 12:3
in length of days is u. 12
he hath u. 13
away the u. of the aged. 20
hid their heart from u. 17:4
the spirit of my u. causeth me. 20:3
and by his u. he smiteth. 26:12
where is the place of u.? 28:12, 20
to depart from evil is u. 28
Almighty giveth them u. 32:8
hearken to me, ye men of u. 34:10
if now thou hast u. hear this. 16
let men of u. tell me, let a wise. 34
declare, if thou hast u. 38:4
who hath given u. to the heart? 36
he imparted to her u. 39:17
mule that hath no u. Ps 32:9
sing ye praises with u. 47:7
of my heart shall be of u. 49:3
give me u. 119:34, 73, 125, 144, 169
I have more u. 99
through thy precepts I get u. 104
thy word giveth u. 130
our Lord, his u. is infinite. 147:5
to perceive words of u. Pr 1:2
that thou apply thine heart to u. 2:2
liftest up thy voice for u. 3
cometh knowledge and u. 6
thee, u. shall keep thee. 11
and lean not unto thine own u. 3:5
happy is the man that getteth u. 13
by u. hath he established the. 19
ye children, attend to know u. 4:1
get u. 5, 7
my son, bow thine ear to my u. 5:1
committeth adultery, lacketh u. 6:32
and call u. thy kinswoman. 7:4
not u. put forth her voice? Pr 8:1
I am u. 14
as for him that wanteth u. 9:4, 16
and go in the way of u. 6
knowledge of the holy is u. 10
that hath u. wisdom is found. 10:13
slow to wrath is of great u. 14:29
in the heart of him that hath u. 33
hath u. seeketh knowledge. 15:14
heareth reproof getteth u. 32
to get u. rather to be chosen. 16:16
u. is a wellspring of life to him. 22
before him that hath u. 17:24
a fool hath no delight in u. but. 18:2
he that keepeth u. shall find. 19:8
reprove one that hath u. he will. 25
wandereth out of the way of u. 21:16
there is no u. nor counsel against. 30
and instruction, and u. 23:23
by u. an house is established. 24:3
poor that hath u. searcheth. 28:11
the prince that wanteth u. is an. 16
and have not the u. of a man. 30:2
yet riches to men of u. Eccl 9:11
the spirit of u. shall rest. Isa 11:2
make him of quick u. in the fear. 3*
for it is a people of no u. 27:11
the u. of their prudent men. 29:14
framed it, He had no u.? 16
erred in spirit shall come to u. 24
shewed to him the way of u.? 40:14
there is no searching of his u. 28
is there knowledge nor u. 44:19
which shall feed you with u. Jer 3:15
is foolish, they have no u. 4:22
people and without u. 5:21
out the heaven by his u. 51:15
with thy u. thou hast got. Ezek 28:4
u. science. Dan 1:4
Daniel had u. in visions. 17
in all matters of u. he found. 20
knowledge to them that know u. 2:21
u. returned to me, I blessed. 4:34
light and u. was found. 5:11, 12, 14
u. dark sentences. 8:23
came forth to give thee u. 9:22
had u. of the vision. 10:1
some of them of u. shall fall. 11:35
according to their own u. Hos 13:2
there is no u. in him. Ob 7
shall I not destroy u. out of the? 8
are ye also yet without u.? Mat 15:16; Mark 7:18
and to love him with all the u. Mark 12:33
to me, having had perfect u. of. Luke 1:3*
were astonished at his u. 2:47
then opened he their u. that. 24:45
without u., unmerciful. Rom 1:31
bring to nothing the u. of. 1 Cor 1:19
my spirit prayeth, but my u. is. 14:14
pray with the u., sing with the u. 15
speak five words with my u. 19
be not children in u., but in u. 20
the eyes of your u. being. Eph 1:18
having the u. darkened, being. 4:18
but u. what the will of the Lord. 5:17
God which passeth all u. Phil 4:7
filled with all spiritual u. Col 1:9
the full assurance of u. 2:2
u. neither what they say. 1 Tim 1:7
the Lord give thee u. in. 2 Tim 2:7
Son hath given us an u. 1 John 5:20
him that hath u. count. Rev 13:18
see **good**

understanding, *adjective*
take ye wise men and u. Deut 1:13
great nation is an u. people. 4:6
give thy servant an u. 1 Ki 3:9
thee a wise and an u. heart. 12
be ye of an u. heart. Pr 8:5

man of **understanding**
brought us a *man of u.* Ezra 8:18
a *man of u.* shall attain. Pr 1:5
but a *man of u.* hath wisdom. 10:23
man of u. holdeth his peace. 11:12
man of u. walketh uprightly. 15:21
a *man of u.* is of an excellent. 17:27
lips, is esteemed a *man of u.* 28*
but a *man of u.* will draw out. 20:5
but by a *man of u.* and. 28:2

void of **understanding**
young man *void of u.* *Pr* 7:7
a rod for back of him that is *void of u.* 10:13
vain persons is *void of u.* 12:11
a man *void of u.* striketh. 17:18
vineyard of the man *void of u.* 24:30

understood
not that Joseph *u.* them. *Gen* 42:23
were wise, that they *u.* *Deut* 32:29
they *u.* that ark of Lord. *1 Sam* 4:6
David *u.* that Saul was come. 26:4
people *u.* it was not of David to. *2 Sam* 3:37
they had *u.* the words. *Neh* 8:12
I *u.* of the evil Eliashib did. 13:7
ear hath heard and *u.* it. *Job* 13:1
have I uttered that I *u.* not. 42:3
went to sanctuary, then *u.* *Ps* 73:17*
a language that I *u.* not. 81:5
fathers *u.* not thy wonders. 106:7
u. from foundations of. *Isa* 40:21
not known nor *u.*: for he shut. 44:18
at the vision, but none *u.* *Dan* 8:27
I Daniel *u.* by books. 9:2
he *u.* the vision. 10:1
I heard, but I *u.* not: then. 12:8
have ye *u.* all these things? *Mat* 13:51
u. they how he bade them. 16:12
u. that he spake of John. 17:13
they *u.* not that saying. *Mark* 9:32
Luke 2:50; 9:45; *John* 8:27; 10:6
and they *u.* none of. *Luke* 18:34
these things *u.* not his. *John* 12:16
have *u.* that God by his hand would . . . but they *u.* not. *Acts* 7:25
I rescued him, having *u.* he. 23:27
I *u.* that he was of Cilicia. 34
being *u.* by the things that. *Rom* 1:20
child, I *u.* as a child. *1 Cor* 13:11
by tongue words easy to be *u.* 14:9
some things hard to be *u.* *2 Pet* 3:16

undertake
oppressed, *u.* for me. *Isa* 38:14*

undertook
Jews *u.* to do as they. *Esth* 9:23

undo
to *u.* heavy burdens. *Isa* 58:6
at that time I will *u.* all. *Zeph* 3:19*

undone
thou art *u.* O people. *Num* 21:29
Joshua left nothing *u.* *Josh* 11:15
woe is me, for I am *u.* *Isa* 6:5
not to leave the other *u.* *Mat* 23:23
Luke 11:42

undressed
grapes of thy vine *u.* *Lev* 25:5, 11

unequal
are not your ways *u.*? *Ezek* 18:25, 29

unequally
be ye not *u.* yoked with. *2 Cor* 6:14

unfaithful
confidence in an *u.* man. *Pr* 25:19

unfaithfully
they dealt *u.* like their. *Ps* 78:57*

unfeigned
Holy Ghost, by love *u.* *2 Cor* 6:6
a pure heart and faith *u.* *1 Tim* 1:5
remembrance the *u.* faith. *2 Tim* 1:5
through the Spirit unto *u.* love of the brethren. *1 Pet* 1:22

unfruitful
riches, choke word, and he becometh *u.* *Mat* 13:22; *Mark* 4:19
my understanding is *u.* *1 Cor* 14:14
no fellowship with the *u.* works. *Eph* 5:11
works, that they be not *u.* *Tit* 3:14
be barren nor *u.* in the. *2 Pet* 1:8

ungirded
the man *u.* the camels. *Gen* 24:32

ungodliness
the wrath of God revealed against all *u.* *Rom* 1:18
and he shall turn away *u.* 11:26
increase unto more *u.* *2 Tim* 2:16
that, denying *u.* and worldly. *Tit* 2:12

ungodly
death compassed me, the floods of *u.* men. *2 Sam* 22:5; *Ps* 18:4
Shouldest thou help *u.*? *2 Chr* 19:2*
delivered me to the *u.* *Job* 16:11
say to princes, Ye are *u.*? 34:18*
in the counsel of the *u.* *Ps* 1:1*
the *u.* are not so. 4*
u. not stand in judgement. 5*
but the way of the *u.* shall perish. 6*
broken the teeth of the *u.* 3:7*
cause against an *u.* nation. 43:1
these are the *u.* who prosper. 73:12*
an *u.* man diggeth up evil. *Pr* 16:27*
an *u.* witness scorneth. 19:28*
that justifieth the *u.* *Rom* 4:5
Christ died for the *u.* 5:6
the law is for the *u.* and. *1 Tim* 1:9
where shall the *u.* and sinner? *1 Pet* 4:18
flood on world of the *u.* *2 Pet* 2:5
those who after should live *u.* 6
and perdition of *u.* men. 3:7
u. men turning the grace. *Jude* 4
that are *u.* of their *u.* deeds. 15
walk after their own *u.* lusts. 18

unholy
may put difference between holy and *u.* *Lev* 10:10*
law was made for the *u.* *1 Tim* 1:9
shall be unthankful, *u.* *2 Tim* 3:2
of covenant an *u.* thing. *Heb* 10:29

unicorn
(*This animal is mythical. The word as used in the Bible probably means the wild ox, as the Revised Versions render it*)
as it were the strength of an *u.* *Num* 23:22; 24:8
will the *u.* be willing to? *Job* 39:9
canst thou bind the *u.* in the? 10
Sirion like a young *u.* *Ps* 29:6
exalt like the horn of an *u.* 92:10

unicorns
like the horns of *u.* *Deut* 33:17
from the horns of the *u.* *Ps* 22:21
and the *u.* shall come. *Isa* 34:7

unite
u. my heart to fear thy. *Ps* 86:11

united
mine honour, be not thou *u.* *Gen* 49:6

unity
to dwell together in *u.* *Ps* 133:1
endeavouring to keep the *u.* *Eph* 4:3
till we come in the *u.* of the faith. 13

unjust
deliver me from the *u.* *Ps* 43:1
and the hope of *u.* men. *Pr* 11:7*
who by *u.* gain increaseth his. 28:8
an *u.* man is an abomination. 29:27
u. knoweth no shame. *Zeph* 3:5
rain on the just and *u.* *Mat* 5:45
the Lord commended the *u.* steward. *Luke* 16:8*
he that is *u.* in the least, is *u.* 10*
hear what the *u.* judge saith. 18:6*
I am not as other men are, *u.* 11
both of the just and *u.* *Acts* 24:15
go to law before the *u.*? *1 Cor* 6:1*
the just for the *u.* *1 Pet* 3:18*
reserve the *u.* to the day of judgement. *2 Pet* 2:9*
he that is *u.* let him be *u.* still. *Rev* 22:11*

unjustly
how long will ye judge *u.*? *Ps* 82:2
in land of uprightness will he deal *u.* *Isa* 26:10*

unknown
To the *u.* God. *Acts* 17:23
that speaketh in an *u.* tongue. *1 Cor* 14:2, 4, 13, 27
if I pray in an *u.* tongue, my. 14
than ten thousand words in an *u.* 19
as *u.* and yet well known. *2 Cor* 6:9
I was *u.* by face unto the churches of Judaea which were. *Gal* 1:22

unlade
there the ship was to *u.* *Acts* 21:3

unlawful
an *u.* thing for a man. *Acts* 10:28
with their *u.* deeds. *2 Pet* 2:8*

unlearned
that they were *u.* *Acts* 4:13
occupieth the room of the *u.* *1 Cor* 14:16
come in those that are *u.* 23, 24
but foolish and *u.* questions avoid. *2 Tim* 2:23*
which they that are *u.* *2 Pet* 3:16

unleavened
they baked *u.* cakes of. *Ex* 12:39
it shall be an *u.* cake of fine flour mingled with oil, or *u.* *Lev* 2:4, 5
he shall offer *u.* cakes mingled. 7:12
and Moses took one *u.* cake. 8:26
priest shall take one *u.* cake, one *u.* wafer, and put them. *Num* 6:19
old corn of the land *u.* *Josh* 5:11
ready a kid and *u.* cakes. *Judg* 6:19
take the flesh and the *u.* cakes. 20
and *u.* cakes; fire out of the rock consumed the flesh and *u.* 21
for flour and *u.* cakes. *1 Chr* 23:29
a new lump, as ye are *u.* *1 Cor* 5:7
see **bread**

unless
unclean *u.* he wash his. *Lev* 22:6
u. she had turned from me, I had. *Num* 22:33
u. thou hadst spoken. *2 Sam* 2:27
I had fainted, *u.* I had. *Ps* 27:13
u. the Lord had been my help. 94:17
u. thy law had been my. 119:92
sleep not, *u.* they cause. *Pr* 4:16
ye are saved, *u.* ye have. *1 Cor* 15:2

unloose
not worthy to stoop down and *u.* *Mark* 1:7; *Luke* 3:16; *John* 1:27

unmarried
I say to the *u.* *1 Cor* 7:8
let her remain *u.* 11
he that is *u.* 32
the *u.* woman careth for. 34

unmerciful
implacable, *u.* *Rom* 1:31

unmindful
begat thee thou art *u.* *Deut* 32:18

unmoveable
of the ship remained *u.* *Acts* 27:41
be ye stedfast, *u.* *1 Cor* 15:58

unoccupied
Shamgar, highways were *u.* *Judg* 5:6

unperfect
substance, yet being *u.* *Ps* 139:16

unprepared
with me, and find you *u.* *2 Cor* 9:4

unprofitable
reason with *u.* talk? *Job* 15:3
cast the *u.* servant into. *Mat* 25:30
We are *u.* servants. *Luke* 17:10
altogether become *u.* *Rom* 3:12
genealogies, for they are *u.* *Tit* 3:9
time past was to thee *u.* *Philem* 11
for that is *u.* for you. *Heb* 13:17

unprofitableness
weakness and *u.* thereof. *Heb* 7:18

unpunished
wicked shall not be *u.* *Pr* 11:21
the proud shall not be *u.* 16:5
at calamities, shall not be *u.* 17:5
false witness shall not be *u.* 19:5, 9
utterly *u.*? ye shall not be *u.* *Jer* 25:29
not leave thee altogether *u.* 30:11
not leave thee wholly *u.* 46:28
go *u.*? thou shalt not go *u.* 49:12

unquenchable
garner, but burn up the chaff with *u.* fire. *Mat* 3:12; *Luke* 3:17

unreasonable
it seemeth to me *u.* to send a. *Acts* 25:27
delivered from *u.* men. *2 Thes* 3:2

unrebukeable
this commandment *u.* *1 Tim* 6:14*

unreproveable
to present you holy, *u.* in. *Col* 1:22

unrighteous
hand to be an u. witness. Ex 23:1
against me, be as the u. Job 27:7
out of the hand of the u. Ps 71:4
woe unto them that decree u. Isa 10:1
let the u. man forsake his. 55:7
not been faithful in the u. Luke 16:11
is God u. who taketh ? Rom 3:5
the u. shall not inherit. 1 Cor 6:9
for God is not u. to forget. Heb 6:10

unrighteously
all that do u. are an. Deut 25:16

unrighteousness
ye shall do no u. in judgement. Lev 19:15, 35
there is no u. in him. Ps 92:15
buildeth his house by u. Jer 22:13
the mammon of u. Luke 16:9
and no u. is in him. John 7:18
all u. of men who hold the truth in u. Rom 1:18
filled with all u., fornication. 29
them that obey u., indignation. 2:8
if our u. commend the. 3:5
members as instruments of u. 6:13
is there u. with God ? 9:14
righteousness with u.? 2 Cor 6:14
deceiveableness of u. 2 Thes 2:10
not, but had pleasure in u. 12
be merciful to their u. Heb 8:12*
receive the reward of u. 2 Pet 2:13*
who loved the wages of u. 15*
to cleanse us from all u. 1 John 1:9
all u. is sin: there is a sin not. 5:17

unripe
shake off his u. grape. Job 15:33

unruly
warn them that are u. 1 Thes 5:14
not accused of riot, or u. Tit 1:6
for there are many u. and vain. 10
the tongue is an u. evil. Jas 3:8*

unsatiable
because thou wast u. Ezek 16:28

unsavoury
can what is u. be eaten ? Job 6:6

unsearchable
great things and u. Job 5:9
Lord, his greatness is u. Ps 145:3
heart of kings is u. Pr 25:3
how u. are his judgements, and his ways! Rom 11:33
the u. riches of Christ. Eph 3:8

unseemly
working that which is u. Rom 1:27
not behave itself u. 1 Cor 13:5

unshod
thy foot from being u. Jer 2:25

unskilful
babe is u. in the word. Heb 5:13*

unspeakable
be to God for his u. gift. 2 Cor 9:15
paradise and heard u. words. 12:4
in whom ye rejoice with joy u. and full of glory. 1 Pet 1:8

unspotted
to keep himself u. from. Jas 1:27

unstable
u. as water, thou shalt. Gen 49:4†
a double minded man is u. in all. Jas 1:8
from sin, beguiling u. 2 Pet 2:14
are unlearned and u. wrest. 3:16

unstopped
ears of the deaf shall be u. Isa 35:5

untaken
the same vail u. away. 2 Cor 3:14

untempered
and lo others daubed it with u. Ezek 13:10, 11, 14, 15; 22:28

unthankful
for he is kind to the u. Luke 6:35
blasphemers, u., unholy. 2 Tim 3:2

until
u. I have done that I. Gen 28:15
and stayed there u. now. 32:4
our youth, even u. now. 46:34
nor a lawgiver depart, u. 49:10
this people u. now. Num 14:19
to Dan u. the captivity. Judg 18:30
will not eat u. he come. 1 Sam 9:13
to see Saul u. his death. 15:35
from thy youth u. now. 2 Sam 19:7
nor trimmed, u. the day he. 24
with bread and water of affliction, u. I come. 1 Ki 22:27; 2 Chr 18:26
she left the land, u. now. 2 Ki 8:6
city be not built, u. Ezra 4:21
since then u. now hath it. 5:16
u. the fierce wrath of God. 10:14
keep me secret u. thy. Job 14:13
u. his iniquity be found. Ps 36:2
u. I went into the sanctuary. 73:17
u. I find a place for the Lord. 132:5
u. the day break. S of S 2:17; 4:6
u. the spirit be poured. Isa 32:15
u. I come and take you away. 36:17
u. the righteousness thereof. 62:1
and there shall he be u. Jer 32:5
be consumed u. there be an. 44:27
overturn, u. he come. Ezek 21:27
bear indignation, u. he. Mi 7:9
be thou there u. I bring. Mat 2:13
the prophets and the law prophesied u. John. 11:13; Luke 16:16
trodden down u. the times of the Gentiles. Luke 21:24; Rom 11:25
u. ye be endued with power from on high. Luke 24:49
u. the day in which he. Acts 1:2
for u. the law, sin was. Rom 5:13
judge nothing u. the. 1 Cor 4:5
will perform it u. the day of Jesus Christ. Phil 1:6
will let, u. he be taken out. 2 Thes 2:7
u. the appearing of our Lord Jesus. 1 Tim 6:14
u. the words of God. Rev 17:17
lived not u. the 1000 years. 20:5

untimely
or as an hidden u. birth. Job 3:16
pass away like the u. birth. Ps 58:8
I say that an u. birth is. Eccl 6:3
fig tree casteth her u. figs. Rev 6:13

untoward
save yourselves from this u. Acts 2:40*

unwalled
took sixty cities, beside u. towns. Deut 3:5
dwelt in the u. towns. Esth 9:19
land of u. villages. Ezek 38:11

unwashen
but to eat with u. hands defileth not. Mat 15:20; Mark 7:2, 5*

unweighed
left all the vessels u. 1 Ki 7:47

unwise
do you thus requite the Lord, O u. people ? Deut 32:6
he is an u. son, he should not stay. Hos 13:13
to the wise and to the u. Rom 1:14*
not u. but understanding. Eph 5:17*

unwittingly
if a man eat of the holy thing u. Lev 22:14
killeth any person u. Josh 20:3*, 5*

unworthily
this cup of the Lord u. 1 Cor 11:27
and drinketh u. eateth. 29

unworthy
ourselves u. of life. Acts 13:46
are ye u. to judge the ? 1 Cor 6:2

up ! *exclamation*
Lot said, U., get you out. Gen 19:14
Joseph said, U. follow after. 44:4
u. make us gods that. Ex 32:1
u. sanctify the people. Josh 7:13
u. for this is the day in. Judg 4:14
he said to his firstborn, U., slay. 8:20
u. thou and the people that. 9:32
u. and let us be going, but. 19:28
saying, U. that I may. 1 Sam 9:26

up
rose u. early and gat them u. saying, We . . . will go u. Num 14:40
go not u. for the Lord is not. 42
they presumed to go u. unto. 44
from battle before sun u. Judg 8:13
as soon as sun is u. thou. Judg 9:33
as soon as ye be u. early, depart. 1 Sam 29:10
when David was u. 2 Sam 24:11
to die from my youth u. Ps 88:15
from the ground u. to. Ezek 41:16
when the sun was u. they were. Mat 13:6; Mark 4:6
kept from my youth u. Mat 19:20
Luke 18:21
and they filled them u. John 2:7
see **down**

upbraid
with whom ye did u. me. Judg 8:15*
then began he to u. the. Mat 11:20

upbraided
he u. them with their. Mark 16:14

upbraideth
all men liberally and u. not. Jas 1:5

Upharsin
MENE, MENE, TEKEL, U. Dan 5:25

Uphaz
gold is brought from U. Jer 10:9
girded with gold of U. Dan 10:5

upheld
salvation and my fury it u. me. Isa 63:5

uphold
and u. me with thy free. Ps 51:12
the Lord is with them that u. 54:4
u. me according to thy word. 119:116
honour shall u. the humble in spirit. Pr 29:23*
I will u. thee with the right hand. Isa 41:10
behold my servant whom I u. 42:1
that there was none to u. 63:5
they also that u. Egypt. Ezek 30:6

upholden
thy words have u. him. Job 4:4
the king's throne is u. Pr 20:28

upholdest
as for me, thou u. me in mine. Ps 41:12

upholdeth
but the Lord u. the. Ps 37:17
for the Lord u. him with his. 24
thy right hand u. me. 63:8
the Lord u. all that fall. 145:14

upholding
u. all things by the word. Heb 1:3

upper
shall strike blood on the u. Ex 12:7*
covering on his u. lip. Lev 13:45
no man take the u. millstone to. Deut 24:6
he gave her the u. springs. Josh 15:19; Judg 1:15
they stood by the conduit of the u. pool. 2 Ki 18:17; Isa 7:3; 36:2
shall lodge in u. lintels. Zeph 2:14*
he will shew you a large u. room. Mark 14:15; Luke 22:12
up into an u. room. Acts 1:13
passed through the u. coasts. 19:1
see **chamber**

uppermost
in the u. basket were all. Gen 40:17
in the top of the u. bough. Isa 17:6
cities shall be as an u. branch. 9
they love the u. rooms at. Mat 23:6*
Mark 12:39*; Luke 11:43*

upright
my sheaf arose and also stood u. Gen 37:7
yoke and made you go u. Lev 26:13
Surely as Lord liveth, thou hast been u. 1 Sam 29:6; 2 Chr 29:34
I was also u. before him. 2 Sam 22:24*; Ps 18:23*
with the u. man thou wilt shew thyself u. 2 Sam 22:26*; Ps 18:25*
were more u. in heart. 2 Chr 29:34
Job was a perfect and u. man. Job 1:1, 8; 2:3
if thou wert u. he would awake. 8:6
the just u. man is laughed. 12:4*
u. men shall be astonished. 17:8

doth behold the u. Ps 11:7
then shall I be u., I shall be. 19:13
the Lord is good and u. 25:8; 92:15
praise is comely for the u. 33:1
to slay such as be of u. 37:14
knoweth the days of the u. 18
perfect man and behold the u. 37
the u. shall have dominion. 49:14
Lord in the assembly of the u. 111:1
the generation of the u. 112:2
unto the u. there ariseth light. 4
righteous art thou, and u. are. 119:137
do good to them that are u. 125:4
the u. shall dwell in thy. 140:13
for the u. shall dwell in. Pr 2:21
of Lord is strength to the u. 10:29
integrity of the u. shall guide. 11:3
the righteousness of the u. shall. 6
by the blessings of the u. the city. 11
such as are u. in their way are. 20*
mouth of the u. shall deliver. 12:6
righteousness keepeth the u. 13:6
the tabernacle of the u. shall. 14:11
but the prayer of the u. is his. 15:8
highway of the u. is to depart. 16:17
shall be a ransom for the u. 21:18
but as for the u. he directeth. 29
the u. shall have good things. 28:10*
the bloodthirsty hate the u. 29:10*
he that is u. is an abomination to. 27
God hath made man u. Eccl 7:29
was written was u. words. 12:10*
remember thy love, the u. love. S of S 1:4*
thou most u. dost weigh. Isa 26:7
they are u. as palm tree. Jer 10:5
touched me and set me u. Dan 8:18
enter and u. ones with him. 11:17
is none u. among men. Mi 7:2
the most u. is sharper than a. 4
soul lifted up is not u. Hab 2:4
see **heart, stand, stood**

uprightly

walketh u. shall abide in. Ps 15:2
do ye judge u.? 58:1
I will judge u. 75:2
from them that walk u. 84:11
buckler to them that walk u. Pr 2:7*
he that walketh u. walketh. 10:9
of understanding walketh u. 15:21
walketh u. shall be saved. 28:18
he that speaketh u. shall. Isa 33:15
him that speaketh u. Amos 5:10
my words do good to him that walketh u. Mi 2:7
that they walked not u. Gal 2:14

uprightness

before thee in u. of heart. 1 Ki 3:6
thou hast pleasure in u. 1 Chr 29:17
is not this thy hope and the u. of thy ways? Job 4:6*
to shew unto man his u. 33:23*
minister judgement to the people in u. Ps 9:8
let integrity and u. preserve. 25:21
for ever and are done in u. 111:8
lead me into the land of u. 143:10
paths of u. to walk. Pr 2:13
he that walketh in u. feareth. 14:2
poor that walketh in his u. 28:6*
the way of the just is u. Isa 26:7
in the land of u. will he deal. 10
each one walking in his u. 57:2
see **heart**

uprising

my downsitting and u. Ps 139:2

uproar

city being in an u. 1 Ki 1:41
lest there be an u. Mat 26:5; Mark 14:2
all the city on an u. Acts 17:5
in question for this day's u. 19:40*
after the u. was ceased, Paul. 20:1
that all Jerusalem was in an u. 21:31
Egyptian who madest an u.? 38

upside *down*

Jerusalem as a man wipeth a dish, turning it u. down. 2 Ki 21:13
wicked he turneth u. down. Ps 146:9
turneth the earth u. down. Isa 24:1
turning of things u. down. 29:16
have turned the world u. down. Acts 17:6

upward

twenty years old and u. Ex 38:26
Num 1:3, 20, 22, 24, 26, 28; 14:29
1 Chr 23:24; 2 Chr 31:17; Ezra 3:8
shalt number every male from a month old and u. Num 3:15, 22
28, 34, 39, 40, 43; 26:62
u. even to fifty. 4:3, 23, 30, 35
39, 43, 47; 1 Chr 23:3
five years old and u. Num 8:24
Saul was higher from shoulders u. 1 Sam 9:2; 10:23
remnant shall bear fruit u. 2 Ki 19:30; Isa 37:31
males from three years old and u. 2 Chr 31:16
to trouble as sparks fly u. Job 5:7
spirit of man that goeth u. Eccl 3:21
king and God, and look u. Isa 8:21
mine eyes fail with looking u. 38:14
from appearance of his loins u. Ezek 1:27; 8:2
was a winding about still u. 41:7*
from this day and u. Hag 2:15, 18

Ur

before his father in U. Gen 11:28
brought thee out of U. of the Chaldees. 15:7; Neh 9:7
Eliphal the son of U. 1 Chr 11:35

urge

scribes and pharisees began to u. Luke 11:53*

urged

Jacob u. Esau, and he. Gen 33:11
Delilah u. Samson. Judg 16:16
his father in law u. him. 19:7
when they u. him till. 2 Ki 2:17
Naaman u. Elisha. 5:16
he u. Gehazi. 23

urgent

the Egyptians were u. Ex 12:33
king's commandment was u. Dan 3:22

Uri

Bezaleel the son of U. Ex 31:2
35:30; 38:22; 1 Chr 2:20
2 Chr 1:5
Geber the son of U. 1 Ki 4:19
Shallum, Telem, and U. Ezra 10:24

Uriah, *called* **Urijah**

is not this Bath-sheba the wife of U.? 2 Sam 11:3
send me U. 6
sent it by U. 14
U. is dead. 21
thou hast killed U. the Hittite. 12:9
U. one of David's worthies. 23:39
1 Chr 11:41
in the matter of U. 1 Ki 15:5
by Meremoth son of U. Ezra 8:33
next repaired Meremoth the son of U. Neh 3:4, 21
Ezra and beside him stood U. 8:4
I took faithful witnesses, U. Isa 8:2
Solomon of the wife of U. Mat 1:6

Urijah

Ahaz sent U. the fashion. 2 Ki 16:10
thus did U. as king Ahaz. 16
U. prophesied. Jer 26:20
U. fled into Egypt. 21

Urim

breastplate of judgement, the U. Ex 28:30; Lev 8:8
counsel after the judgement of U. Num 27:21
let thy U. be with thy. Deut 33:8
neither by dreams, by U. 1 Sam 28:6
stood up a priest with U. and. Ezra 2:63; Neh 7:65
see **Thummim**

us

with u. even u. who are all of u. Deut 5:3
save thyself and u. Luke 23:39
even u. whom he hath. Rom 9:24
God hath set forth u. 1 Cor 4:9
and will also raise up u. by. 6:14
acknowledged u. in part. 2 Cor 1:14
he which establisheth u. with. 21
who hath reconciled u. to. 5:18
brethren, as ye have u. Phil 3:17
let u. who are of the. 1 Thes 5:8
for God hath not appointed u. 1 Thes 5:9
of his own will begat he u. Jas 1:18

about **us**

lick up all that are round about u. Num 22:4
heathen that are about u. Neh 5:17
the heathen about u. saw. 6:16
a reproach to all about u. Dan 9:16

after **us**

will come out after u. Josh 8:6
to our generations after u. 22:27
away, for she crieth after u. Mat 15:23

against **us**

seek occasion against u. Gen 43:18
enemies and fight against u. Ex 1:10
that ye murmur against u.? 16:7
are not against u. but God. 8
Sihon came out against u. Deut 2:32; 29:7
Og came out against u. 3:1
of Ai came out against u. Josh 8:5
Amorites gathered against u. 10:6
rebel not against the Lord, nor against u. 22:19
ye come up against u.? Judg 15:10
delivered company that came against u. 1 Sam 30:23
surely the men prevailed against u. 2 Sam 11:23
man that devised against u. 21:5
wrath of Lord against u. 2 Ki 22:13
great company that cometh against u. 2 Chr 20:12
under that rise against u. Ps 44:5
remember not against u. 79:8
when men rose up against u. 124:2
wrath was kindled against u. 3
feller is come up against u. Isa 14:8
and our sins testify against u. 59:12; Jer 14:7
all this evil against u. Jer 16:10
maketh war against u. 21:2
shall come down against u.? 13
setteth thee on against u. 43:3
their mouth against u. Lam 3:46
art very wroth against u. 5:22
words he spake against u. Dan 9:12
Forbid him not. For he that is not against u. Mark 9:40; Luke 9:50
who can be against u.? Rom 8:31
blotting out the handwriting that was against u. Col 2:14
prating against u. with. 3 John 10

among or *amongst* **us**

mighty prince among u. Gen 23:6
the Lord among u. or not? Ex 17:7
I pray thee, go among u. 34:9
God is not among u. Deut 31:17
ye dwell among u. Josh 9:7, 22
take possession among u. 22:19
perceive the Lord is among u. 31
voice be heard among u. Judg 18:25
among u. it may save us. 1 Sam 4:3
not among u. any that can skill to hew. 1 Ki 5:6
his hands amongst u. Job 34:37
not among u. any that knoweth. Ps 74:9
cast in thy lot among u. Pr 1:14
who among u. shall dwell with the devouring fire? Isa 33:14
Is not the Lord among u.? Mi 3:11
a great prophet is risen up among u. Luke 7:16
Word was made flesh and dwelt among u. John 1:14
Lord Jesus went in and out among u. Acts 1:21
God made choice among u. 15:7

at **us**

if it first begin at u. 1 Pet 4:17

before **us**

make us gods which shall go before u. Ex 32:23; Acts 7:40
will send men before u. Deut 1:22
God delivered him before u. 2:33
dried up from before u. Josh 4:23
they flee before u. 8:6
drave out before u. 24:18
the Lord shall drive out before u. Judg 11:24

down *before u.* as. *Judg* 20:32, 39
king may judge us and go out *before u.* *1 Sam* 8:20
thy servant pass on *before u.* 9:27
land is yet *before u.* *2 Chr* 14:7
cause the Holy One of Israel to cease from *before u.* *Isa* 30:11
laws which he set *before u.* *Dan* 9:10
to lay hold on the hope set *before u.* *Heb* 6:18
the race that is set *before u.* 12:1

behind **us**

also he is *behind u.* *Gen* 32:18, 20

between or *betwixt* **us**

now an oath *betwixt u.* *Gen* 26:28
may judge *betwixt u.* both. 31:27
God of Abraham judge *betwixt u.* 53
Jordan a border *between u.* *Josh* 22:25
be a witness *between u.* 27, 28, 34
the Lord be witness *between u.* *Judg* 11:10; *Jer* 42:5
neither is there any daysman *betwixt u.* *Job* 9:33
between u. and you. *Luke* 16:26
put no difference *between u.* and. *Acts* 15:9
the middle wall of partition *between u.* *Eph* 2:14

by **us**

hath not the Lord spoken also *by u.*? *Num* 12:2
man of God passeth *by u.* *2 Ki* 4:9
Jesus was preached among you *by u.* *2 Cor* 1:19
to the glory of God *by u.* 20
savour of his knowledge *by u.* 2:14
of Christ, ministered *by u.* 3:3
God did beseech you *by u.* 5:20
ye might receive damage *by u.* 7:9
which is administered *by u.* 8:19, 20

concerning **us**

do according to all which is written *concerning u.* *2 Ki* 22:13

for **us**

hath made room *for u.* *Gen* 26:22
yet any inheritance *for u.*? 31:14
better *for u.* to serve. *Ex* 14:12
tarry ye here *for u.* until. 24:14
better *for u.* to return. *Num* 14:3
people, for they are bread *for u.* 9
one city too strong *for u.* *Deut* 2:36
say, Who shall go up *for u.*? 30:12
Who shall go over the sea *for u.*? 13
art thou *for u.* or for our? *Josh* 5:13
of Peor too little *for u.*? 22:17
who go up *for u.* against? *Judg* 1:1
cry unto the Lord *for u.* *1 Sam* 7:8
lest father take thought *for u.* 9:5
the Lord will work *for u.* 14:6
they will not care *for u.* *2 Sam* 18:3
neither *for u.* shalt thou kill. 21:4
hast been careful *for u.* *2 Ki* 4:13
we dwell is too strait *for u.* 6:1
as *for u.* the Lord is. *2 Chr* 13:10
him a right way *for u.* *Ezra* 8:21
our God shall fight *for u.* *Neh* 4:20
he shall choose our inheritance *for u.* *Ps* 47:4
God is a refuge *for u.* 62:8
that thou hast wrought *for u.* 68:28
hath done great things *for u.* 126:3
send, and who will go *for u.*? *Isa* 6:8
thou wilt ordain peace *for u.* 26:12
take up a wailing *for u.* *Jer* 9:18
there is no healing *for u.* 14:19
I pray thee, of the Lord *for u.* 21:2
pray to the Lord our God *for u.* 37:3
42:2, 20
as *for u.* our eyes as. *Lam* 4:17
Lord, it is good *for u.* to be here. *Mat* 17:4; *Mark* 9:5; *Luke* 9:33
there be not enough *for u.* *Mat* 25:9
there make ready *for u.* *Mark* 14:15
hast raised up an horn of salvation *for u.* *Luke* 1:69
is not against us is *for u.* 9:50
for u. to whom it shall. *Rom* 4:24
sinners, Christ died *for u.* 5:8
maketh intercession *for u.* 8:26
if God be *for u.* who can be? 31
but delivered him up *for u.* all. 32
maketh intercession *for u.* 34
Christ is sacrificed *for u.* *1 Cor* 5:7
together by prayer *for u.* *2 Cor* 1:11
light affliction worketh *for u.* 4:17
made him to be sin *for u.* 5:21
us, made a curse *for u.* *Gal* 3:13
us, and given himself *for u.* *Eph* 5:2
praying *for u.* that God. *Col* 4:3
who died *for u.*, that we should live. *1 Thes* 5:10; *1 John* 3:16
pray *for u.* *1 Thes* 5:25; *2 Thes* 3:1
Heb 13:18
who gave himself *for u.* *Tit* 2:14
the forerunner is *for u.* entered. *Heb* 6:20
eternal redemption *for u.* 9:12
in the presence of God *for u.* 24
he hath consecrated *for u.* 10:20
provided some better thing *for u.* 11:40
because Christ hath suffered *for u.* *1 Pet* 2:21; 4:1

from **us**

said to Isaac, Go *from u.* *Gen* 26:16
shall he go up *from u.*? *1 Sam* 6:20
and see who is gone *from u.* 14:17
his wrath turn *from u.* *2 Chr* 29:10
Ezra 10:14
away their cords *from u.* *Ps* 2:3
our transgressions *from u.* 103:12
judgement far *from u.* *Isa* 59:9
salvation but it is far off *from u.* 11
hast hid thy face *from u.* 64:7
the anger of the Lord is not turned *from u.* *Jer* 4:8
Nebuchadrezzar may go up *from u.* 21:2
hide it not *from u.*, we will not. 38:25
he was taken up *from u.* *Acts* 1:22
certain who went out *from u.* 15:24
nor by letter as *from u.* *2 Thes* 2:2
they went out *from u.*, but they were not of us. *1 John* 2:19

see **depart**

in **us**

if the Lord delight *in u.* *Num* 14:8
thou, which is not *in u.* *Job* 15:9
thou hast wrought all our works *in u.* *Isa* 26:12
also may be one *in u.* *John* 17:21
law might be fulfilled *in u.* *Rom* 8:4
which shall be revealed *in u.* 18
ye might learn *in u.* not. *1 Cor* 4:6
of Christ abound *in u.* *2 Cor* 1:5
so death worketh *in u.* but. 4:12
ye are not straitened *in u.* but. 6:12
power that worketh *in u.* *Eph* 3:20
by Holy Ghost which dwelleth *in u.* *2 Tim* 1:14
that dwelleth *in u.* lusteth. *Jas* 4:5
truth is not *in u.* *1 John* 1:8
his word is not *in u.* 10
we know that he abideth *in u.* 3:24
God dwelleth *in u.* 4:12, 13
for the truth's sake which dwelleth *in u.* *2 John* 2

of **us**

the man is become as one *of u.* *Gen* 3:22
lacketh not a man *of u.* *Num* 31:49
faint because *of u.* *Josh* 2:24
which slew many *of u.* *Judg* 16:24
which *of u.* shall go up first? 20:18
which *of u.* is for the king of Israel? *2 Ki* 6:11
he was entreated *of u.* *Ezra* 8:23
hath been mindful *of u.* *Ps* 115:12
laid on him the iniquity *of u.* all. *Isa* 53:6
Abraham be ignorant *of u.* 63:16
hath taken hold *of u.* *Jer* 6:24
O Lord, art in the midst *of u.* 14:9
he be not far from every one *of u.* *Acts* 17:27
who is the father *of u.* all. *Rom* 4:16
account *of u.* as ministers. *1 Cor* 4:1
advantage *of u.* for we. *2 Cor* 2:11
be of God and not *of u.* 4:7
some who think *of u.* as if we. 10:2
is the mother *of u.* all. *Gal* 4:26
but to every one *of u.* is. *Eph* 4:7
became followers *of u.* *1 Thes* 1:6
they themselves shew *of u.* what. 9
the word which ye heard *of u.* 2:13
remembrance *of u.* always. *1 Thes* 3:6
that as ye have received *of u.* 4:1
tradition he received *of u.* *2 Thes* 3:6
the commandment *of u.* *2 Pet* 3:2
of u., for if they had been *of u.* they might shew . . . *of u.* *1 John* 2:19

on **us**, or *upon* **us**

brought guiltiness *upon u.* *Gen* 26:10
this distress come *upon u.* 42:21
fall *upon u.* and take us for. 43:18
upon u. with pestilence. *Ex* 5:3
lay not the sin *upon u.* *Num* 12:11
evils come *upon u.*? *Deut* 31:17
lest wrath be *upon u.* *Josh* 9:20
Rise thou and fall *upon u.* *Judg* 8:21
his hand is sore *upon u.* *1 Sam* 5:7
heavy yoke which he put *upon u.* *1 Ki* 12:4, 9; *2 Chr* 10:4, 9
some mischief will come *upon u.* *2 Ki* 7:9
made a breach *upon u.* *1 Chr* 15:13
cometh *upon u.* as sword. *2 Chr* 20:9
the wrath poured *upon u.* 34:21
by the good hand of our God *upon u.* *Ezra* 8:18, 31
after all that is come *upon u.* 9:13
let not all the trouble seem little that hath come *upon u.* *Neh* 9:32
all that is brought *upon u.* 33
bring all this evil *upon u.*? 13:18
his hand *upon u.* both. *Job* 9:33
thy countenance *upon u.* *Ps* 4:6
mercy, O Lord, be *upon u.* 33:22
all this is come *upon u.*; yet. 44:17
cause his face to shine *upon u.* 67:1
beauty of the Lord be *upon u.* 90:17
till he have mercy *upon u.* 123:2
upon u. O Lord, have mercy *upon u.* 3
Mat 9:27; 20:30, 31; *Luke* 17:13
Spirit be poured *upon u.* *Isa* 32:15
snare is come *upon u.* *Lam* 3:47
O Lord, what is come *upon u.* 5:1
and sins be *upon u.* *Ezek* 33:10
curse is poured *upon u.* *Dan* 9:11
by bringing *upon u.* a great evil. 12, 13, 14
and to the hills, Fall *on u.* *Hos* 10:8
Luke 23:30; *Rev* 6:16
cause this evil is *on u.* *Jonah* 1:7, 8
None evil can come *upon u.* *Mi* 3:11
have compassion *upon u.* 7:19
his blood be *on u.* and. *Mat* 27:25
Peter, said, Look *on u.* *Acts* 3:4
so earnestly *on u.* as though? 12
bring this man's blood *upon u.* 5:28
Holy Ghost on them, as *on u.* 11:15
Mary, who bestowed much labour *on u.* *Rom* 16:6
shed *on u.* abundantly. *Tit* 3:6
love the Father hath bestowed *on u.* *1 John* 3:1

over **us**

indeed reign *over u.*? *Gen* 37:8
who made thee a prince and a judge *over u.*? *Ex* 2:14; *Acts* 7:27
thyself a prince *over u.* *Num* 16:13
Gideon, Rule *over u.* *Judg* 8:22
to the olive tree, Reign *over u.* 9:8
10, 12, 14
but we will have a king *over u.* *1 Sam* 8:19; 10:19
Shall Saul reign *over u.*? 11:12
Saul was king *over u.* *2 Sam* 5:2
whom we anointed *over u.* 19:10
thou hast set *over u.* *Neh* 9:37
own: who is lord *over u.*? *Ps* 12:4
had dominion *over u.* *Isa* 26:13
servants have ruled *over u.*: there is none. *Lam* 5:8
this man to reign *over u.* *Luke* 19:14

through **us**

through u. thanksgiving to God. *2 Cor* 9:11

to or *unto* **us**

a man to come in *unto u.* *Gen* 19:31
hast thou done *unto u.*? 20:9; 26:10
their daughters *to u.* for wives. 34:21
Hebrew *unto u.* to mock us. 39:14
What is this that God hath done *unto u.*? 42:28; *Jer* 5:19
thou mayest be *to u.* *Num* 10:31
Lord shall do *unto u.*, the same. 32
speak thou *unto u.* and. *Deut* 5:27

revealed belong *unto u.* *Deut* 29:29
heaven and bring it *unto u.* 30:12
the sea and bring it *unto u.* 13
seemeth good and right to thee to do *unto u.* *Josh* 9:25; *Judg* 10:15
of God come again *unto u.* *Judg* 13:8
to him, as he hath done *to u.* 15:10
with us, and be *to u.* a father. 18:19
woe *unto u.* *1 Sam* 4:8; *Jer* 4:13 6:4; *Lam* 5:16
if they say thus *unto u.* *1 Sam* 14:9
were very good *unto u.* 25:15
they were a wall *unto u.* by. 16
the ark of God *to u.* *1 Chr* 13:3
came from thee *to u.* *Ezra* 4:12
brethren be sold *unto u.*? *Neh* 5:8
let us choose *to u.* judgement. *Job* 34:4
O turn thyself *to u.* again. *Ps* 60:1
not *unto u.* O Lord, not *unto u.* 115:1
except had left *unto u.* a. *Isa* 1:9
unto u. a child is born, *unto u.* 9:6
Art thou become like *unto u.*? 14:10
shall not come *unto u.* 28:15
prophesy not *unto u.* right things, speak *unto u.* smooth. 30:10
Lord will be *unto u.* a place. 33:21
speak not *to u.* in the Jews'. 36:11
to u. the appointed weeks. *Jer* 5:24
hath spoken *to u.* in the name. 26:16
the Lord shall send thee *to u.* 42:5
thou hast spoken *unto u.* 44:16
our wood is sold *unto u.* *Lam* 5:4
unto u. is this land given. *Ezek* 11:15
what these things are *to u.*? 24:19
but *unto u.* confusion. *Dan* 9:7, 8
he shall come *unto u.* *Hos* 6:3
what should a king do *to u.*? 10:3
may be calm *unto u.* *Jonah* 1:11
Lord thought to do *unto u.* *Zech* 1:6
made them equal *unto u.* *Mat* 20:12
saying, Lord, Lord, open *to u.* 25:11 *Luke* 13:25
what is that *to u.*? see. *Mat* 27:4
delivered them *unto u.* *Luke* 1:2
hath made known *unto u.* 2:15
devils are subject *unto u.* 10:17
this parable *unto u.*? 12:41
neither can they pass *to u.* 16:26
shewest thou *unto u.*? *John* 2:18
manifest thyself *unto u.*? 14:22
that he sayeth *unto u.*? 16:17
oracles to give *unto u.* *Acts* 7:38
to u. who did eat and drink. 10:41
the like gift as *unto u.* 11:17
fulfilled the same *unto u.* 13:33
Holy Ghost which is given *unto u.* *Rom* 5:5
but *unto u.* it is the power. *1 Cor* 1:18
of God is made *unto u.* wisdom. 30
God revealed them *unto u.* 2:10
but *to u.* there is but one God. 8:6
committed *to u.* word of. *2 Cor* 5:19
gave themselves *unto u.* by. 8:5
as ye abound in your love *to u.* 7
who declared *unto u.* *Col* 1:8
that God would open *unto u.* 4:3
for *unto u.* was the gospel. *Heb* 4:2
unto u. they did minister. *1 Pet* 1:12

toward **us**

thine anger *toward u.* to cease. *Ps* 85:4
kindness is great *toward u.* 117:2
his love *toward u.* *Rom* 5:8
hath abounded *toward u.* *Eph* 1:8
in his kindness *toward u.* 2:7
love of God *toward u.* *1 John* 4:9

under **us**

subdue the people *under u.* *Ps* 47:3

with **us**

no man is *with u.* *Gen* 31:50
make ye marriages *with u.* 34:9
ye shall dwell *with u.* 10
they dwell *with u.* 23
send our brother *with u.* 43:4; 44:26
lad is not *with u.* 44:30, 31
the God of the Hebrews met *with u.* *Ex* 3:18; 5:3
hast thou dealt thus *with u.*? 14:11
speak thou *with u.*: but let not God speak *with u.* 20:19
not in that thou goest *with u.*? 33:16
come thou *with u.*, we. *Num* 10:29
it shall be, if thou go *with u.* *Num* 10:32
was well *with u.* in Egypt. 11:18
and the Lord is *with u.* 14:9
refuseth to come *with u.* 22:14
made a covenant *with u.* *Deut* 5:2, 3
standeth here *with u.*, also with him that is not here *with u.* 29:15
make a league *with u.* *Josh* 9:6, 11
if the Lord be *with u.* *Judg* 6:13
thou mayest go *with u.* 11:8
Hold thy peace and go *with u.* 18:19
the ark of God shall not abide *with u.* *1 Sam* 5:7
Amnon go *with u.* *2 Sam* 13:26
no more out *with u.* to battle. 21:17
stranger *with u.* in house. *1 Ki* 3:18
the Lord our God be *with u.* 8:57
be *with u.* are more than they that. *2 Ki* 6:16; *2 Chr* 32:7
God is *with u.* *2 Chr* 13:12; 32:8
you have nothing to do *with u.* to build. *Ezra* 4:3
be angry *with u.* till thou? 9:14
with u. are the gray-headed and. *Job* 15:10
Lord of hosts is *with us.* *Ps* 46:7, 11
wilt thou be angry *with u.* for? 85:5
he hath not dealt *with u.* 103:10
come *with u.* *Pr* 1:11
God is *with u.* *Isa* 8:10
transgressions are *with u.* 59:12
law of the Lord is *with u.* *Jer* 8:8
break not thy covenant *with u.* 14:21
that it may be well *with u.* 42:6
Bethel, there he spake *with u.* *Hos* 12:4
so hath he dealt *with u.* *Zech* 1:6
interpreted, is, God *with u.* *Mat* 1:23
his sisters are all *with u.* 13:56 *Mark* 6:3
there were *with u.* seven. *Mat* 22:25
thou thus dealt *with u.*? *Luke* 2:48
he followeth not *with u.* 9:49
abide *with u.* 24:29
while he talked *with u.* 32
numbered *with u.* and had. *Acts* 1:17
his sepulchre is *with u.* unto. 2:29
one that helpeth *with u.* *1 Cor* 16:16
chosen to travel *with u.* *2 Cor* 8:19
are troubled, rest *with u.* *2 Thes* 1:7
like precious faith *with u.* *2 Pet* 1:1
have fellowship *with u.* *1 John* 1:3
have continued *with u.* 2:19
the truth shall be *with u.* *2 John* 2

within **us**

our hearts burn *within u.* while he opened to us the? *Luke* 24:32

without **us**

reigned as kings *without u.* *1 Cor* 4:8
that they *without u.* should not be made perfect. *Heb* 11:40

use

be used in any other *u.* *Lev* 7:24
aught for any unclean *u.* *Deut* 26:14
teach Judah the *u.* of bow. *2 Sam* 1:18
according to the *u.* of. *1 Chr* 28:15
did change the natural *u.* *Rom* 1:26
the men leaving the natural *u.* 27
which is good to the *u.* *Eph* 4:29
shall be a vessel meet for the master's *u.* *2 Tim* 2:21
by *u.* have their senses. *Heb* 5:14

use, *verb*

ye *u.* enchantment. *Lev* 19:26
u. trumpets for calling. *Num* 10:2
after which ye *u.* to go a. 15:39
could *u.* both right. *1 Chr* 12:2
that *u.* their tongues, and. *Jer* 23:31
as yet they shall *u.* this speech. 31:23
in vain shalt thou *u.* many. 46:11
they shall no more *u.* it as a proverb. *Ezek* 12:23
shall *u.* this proverb against. 16:44
what mean ye, that ye *u.*? 18:2
ye shall not have occasion to *u.* 3
Babylon stood to *u.* divination. 21:21
you, pray for them that despitefully *u.* you. *Mat* 5:44; *Luke* 6:28
when ye pray, *u.* not vain. *Mat* 6:7
an assault made, to *u.* them despitefully. *Acts* 14:5
be made free, *u.* it rather. *1 Cor* 7:21
they that *u.* this world as. *1 Cor* 7:31
did I *u.* lightness? *2 Cor* 1:17
we *u.* great plainness. 3:12
lest being present, I should *u.* 13:10
u. not liberty for an occasion to the. *Gal* 5:13
the law is good if a man *u.* *1 Tim* 1:8
then let them *u.* the office of. 3:10
u. a little wine for thy. 5:23
u. hospitality one to another. *1 Pet* 4:9

used

if the ox hath *u.* to push. *Ex* 21:36*
the fat may be *u.* in any. *Lev* 7:24
for so *u.* the young. *Judg* 14:10
whom Samson had *u.* as his. 20
u. enchantments. *2 Ki* 17:17; 21:6 *2 Chr* 33:6*
a wild ass *u.* to the. *Jer* 2:24
people of land have *u.* *Ezek* 22:29
thy envy which thou hast *u.* 35:11
and *u.* similitudes by. *Hos* 12:10
the disciples of John *u.* *Mark* 2:18*
man, called Simon, which beforetime *u.* *Acts* 8:9
them which *u.* curious arts. 19:19*
tongues they *u.* deceit. *Rom* 3:13
not *u.* this power. *1 Cor* 9:12
u. none of these things. 15
nor at any time *u.* we. *1 Thes* 2:5
they that have *u.* the office of a. *1 Tim* 3:13
of them that were so *u.* *Heb* 10:33

uses

to maintain good works for necessary *u.* *Tit* 3:14

usest

as thou *u.* to those that. *Ps* 119:132

useth

any that *u.* divination. *Deut* 18:10
apparel which the king *u.* *Esth* 6:8
the tongue of the wise *u.* *Pr* 15:2*
the poor *u.* entreaties, but rich. 18:23
u. his neighbour's service. *Jer* 22:13
u. proverbs, shall use. *Ezek* 16:44
every one that *u.* milk. *Heb* 5:13*

using

to perish with the *u.* *Col* 2:22
and not *u.* your liberty. *1 Pet* 2:16

usurer

not be to him as an *u.* *Ex* 22:25*

usurp

woman to *u.* authority. *1 Tim* 2:12*

usury

By usury is generally understood in the Bible any interest on a loan, whether in money or in wheat or other commodities. Modern usage has confined the meaning of the word to an unlawful interest.

The law of God prohibits rigorous imposing of interest or exacting it, or a return of a loan without regard to the condition of the borrower; whether poverty occasioned his borrowing, or a visible prospect of gain by employing the borrowed goods.

The Hebrews were plainly commanded in Ex 22:25, etc., *not to receive interest for money from any that borrowed for necessity, as in the case in* Neh 5:5, 7.

thou lay upon him *u.* *Ex* 22:25
take thou no *u.* of him. *Lev* 25:36, 37
shalt not lend on *u.* *Deut* 23:19
thou mayest lend upon *u.* 20
ye exact *u.* *Neh* 5:7
let us leave off this *u.* 10
not his money to *u.* *Ps* 15:5
he that by *u.* increaseth. *Pr* 28:8
as with the taker of *u.*, so with the giver of *u.* *Isa* 24:2
I have neither lent on *u.* nor men have lent to me on *u.* *Jer* 15:10
not given forth on *u.* *Ezek* 18:8, 17
given forth on *u.* 13
thou hast taken *u.* 22:12
received mine own with *u.* *Mat* 25:27*; *Luke* 19:23

us-ward

thy thoughts which are to *u.* *Ps* 40:5

the greatness of his power to *u.* *Eph* 1:19
but his longsuffering to *u.* *2 Pet* 3:9

utmost, outmost
to the *u.* bound of the. *Gen* 49:26
might see the *u.* of the people. *Num* 22:41; 23:13
be driven out to *o.* parts. *Deut* 30:4
Edom and all that are in the *u.* corners. *Jer* 9:26*; 25:23*; 49:32*
she came from *u.* parts. *Luke* 11:31

utter
if he do not *u.* it, then he. *Lev* 5:1
our life if ye *u.* it not this. *Josh* 2:14
if thou *u.* it, we will quit. 20
awake, Deborah, *u.* song. *Judg* 5:12
shall not they *u.* words ? *Job* 8:10
should a wise man *u.* vain ? 15:2*
nor shall my tongue *u.* deceit. 27:4
lips shall *u.* knowledge. 33:3*
I will *u.* dark sayings. *Ps* 78:2
how long shall they *u.* hard ? 94:4*
who can *u.* the mighty acts ? 106:2
my lips shall *u.* praise. 119:171
they shall *u.* the memory. 145:7
false witness will *u.* lies. *Pr* 14:5
thine heart shall *u.* use. 23:33
of labour, man cannot *u.* it. *Eccl* 1:8
let not thine heart be hasty to *u.* 5:2
a vile person will *u.* error. *Isa* 32:6
tell this, *u.* it even to the end. 48:20
I will *u.* my judgements. *Jer* 1:16
u. his voice from his holy. 25:30
u. a parable unto the. *Ezek* 24:3
the Lord shall *u.* his voice. *Joel* 2:11
u. his voice from Jerusalem. 3:16 *Amos* 1:2
I will *u.* things kept. *Mat* 13:35
except *u.* words easy to. *1 Cor* 14:9
not lawful for a man to *u.* *2 Cor* 12:4

utter, outer
a man I appointed to *u.* *1 Ki* 20:42
heard to the *o.* court. *Ezek* 10:5
me forth into the *u.* court. 42:1*
he will make an *u.* end of. *Nah* 1:8*
there shall be no more *u.* destruction. *Zech* 14:11*

utterance
as the Spirit gave them *u.* *Acts* 2:4
enriched by him in all *u.* *1 Cor* 1:5
in *u.* and knowledge. *2 Cor* 8:7
that *u.* may be given. *Eph* 6:19
open to us a door of *u.* *Col* 4:3*

uttered
if she had a husband when she *u.* *Num* 30:6*, 8*
Jephthah *u.* all his words before the Lord. *Judg* 11:11*
the most High *u.* his voice. *2 Sam* 22:14; *Ps* 46:6
whom hast thou *u.* words ? *Job* 26:4
therefore have I *u.* that I. 42:3
which my lips *u.* when. *Ps* 66:14
deep *u.* his voice and. *Hab* 3:10
groanings which cannot be *u.* *Rom* 8:26
to say, and hard to be *u.* *Heb* 5:11*
had cried, seven thunders *u.* their voices. *Rev* 10:3
when the seven thunders had *u.* 4

uttereth
for thy mouth *u.* thine. *Job* 15:5*
day unto day *u.* speech. *Ps* 19:2
wisdom *u.* her voice in. *Pr* 1:20
in the city she *u.* her words. 21
and he that *u.* a slander is. 10:18
a fool *u.* all his mind, but a. 29:11
when he *u.* his voice. *Jer* 10:13 51:16
the great man *u.* his. *Mi* 7:3

uttering
u. from the heart words. *Isa* 59:13

utterly
u. put out remembrance. *Ex* 17:14
if her father *u.* refuse to give. 22:17
thou shalt *u.* overthrow their. 23:24
pronounce him *u.* unclean. *Lev* 13:44*
enemies I will not destroy *u.* 26:44
that soul shall *u.* be cast. *Num* 15:31
I will *u.* destroy their cities. 21:2
if her husband hath *u.* made. 30:12
u. destroying men, women. *Deut* 3:6
yourselves, ye shall *u.* perish. 4:26
thou shalt *u.* destroy the Canaanites. 7:2; 20:17
shalt *u.* detest the silver and. 7:26
ye shall *u.* destroy the. 12:2
destroying *u.* city of idolaters. 13:15
after my death ye will *u.* 31:29
that he might *u.* destroy. *Josh* 11:20
put Canaanites to tribute, but did not *u.* drive. 17:13; *Judg* 1:28
I thought thou hadst *u.* *Judg* 15:2
shall *u.* destroy every male. 21:11
smite, *u.* destroy. *1 Sam* 15:3, 18
he hath made Israel *u.* to. 27:12
valiant shall *u.* melt. *2 Sam* 17:10
the sons of Belial . . . shall be *u.* burned with fire. 23:7
Israel could not *u.* destroy. *1 Ki* 9:21
lands, by destroying them *u.* *2 Ki* 19:11; *Isa* 37:11
u. to slay them of. *2 Chr* 20:23
thou didst not *u.* consume. *Neh* 9:31
though he fall shall not *u.* *Ps* 37:24
the wicked are *u.* consumed. 73:19
my lovingkindness not *u.* 89:33
statutes, O forsake me not *u.* 119:8
take not the word of truth *u.* out. 43
substance for love, it would *u.* be. *S of S* 8:7
and the idols he shall *u.* *Isa* 2:18
answered, until the land be *u.* 6:11
Lord *u.* destroy the tongue of. 11:15
land be *u.* emptied. 24:3
earth is *u.* broken. 19
done by destroying them *u.* 37:11
young men shall *u.* fall. 40:30
Lord hath *u.* separated me. 56:3
nations shall be *u.* wasted. 60:12
for every brother will *u.* *Jer* 9:4
if they will not obey, I will *u.* 12:17
hast thou *u.* rejected Judah ? 14:19
behold, I, even I will *u.* 23:39
I will *u.* destroy them. 25:9; 50:21 26; 51:3, 58
should ye be *u.* unpunished ? 25:29
but thou hast *u.* rejected. *Lam* 5:22
slay *u.* old and young. *Ezek* 9:6
being planted, shall it not *u.*? 17:10
make themselves *u.* bald. 27:31
the land of Egypt *u.* waste. 29:10
shall go forth *u.* to make. *Dan* 11:44
but I will *u.* take them. *Hos* 1:6
the king of Israel be *u.* cut off. 10:15
I will *u.* destroy the house. *Amos* 9:8
one say, We be *u.* spoiled. *Mi* 2:4
for the wicked: . . . he is *u.* *Nah* 1:15
I will *u.* consume all. *Zeph* 1:2
right eye shall be *u.* *Zech* 11:17
now there is *u.* a fault. *1 Cor* 6:7
shall *u.* perish in their. *2 Pet* 2:12
Babylon shall be *u.* burnt. *Rev* 18:8
see **destroyed**

uttermost
when lepers came to *u.* part of camp. *2 Ki* 7:5*, 8*
you cast out to *u.* part. *Neh* 1:9
I shall give thee *u.* parts for. *Ps* 2:8
till thou hast paid the *u.* *Mat* 5:26*
she came from the *u.* parts to. 12:42*
elect from the *u.* part. *Mark* 13:27
I will know the *u.* of. *Acts* 24:22
wrath is come upon them to the *u.* *1 Thes* 2:16
able to save them to the *u.* *Heb* 7:25
see **utmost**

Uz
children of Aram; *U.*, Hul. *Gen* 10:23
children of Dishan; *U.*, Aran. 36:28 *1 Chr* 1:42
Shem; Lud, Aram, and *U.* *1 Chr* 1:17
a man in the land of *U.* *Job* 1:1
I made the king of *U.* *Jer* 25:20
daughter of Edom, in *U.* *Lam* 4:21

Uzza, Uzzah
U. and Ahio drave the cart. *2 Sam* 6:3; *1 Chr* 13:7
U. put forth his hand to the ark. *2 Sam* 6:6; *1 Chr* 13:9
because the Lord had made a breach upon *U.* *2 Sam* 6:8
buried in the garden of *U.* *2 Ki* 21:18
Amon buried in the garden of *U.* 26
sons of Merari, Mahli, *U.* *1 Chr* 6:29
removed them, and begat *U.* 8:7
the children of *U.* *Ezra* 2:49 *Neh* 7:51

Uzziah, *called* **Azariah, Ozias**
A. made king. *2 Ki* 14:21; *2 Chr* 26:1
to reign in 39th year of *U.* *2 Ki* 15:13
Jotham did all that his father *U.* 34
a son of Kohath, *U.* *1 Chr* 6:24
U. the Ashterathite, a valiant. 11:44
storehouses, was the son of *U.* 27:25
the Ammonites gave gifts to *U.* *2 Chr* 26:8
U. prepared shields and slings. 14
it pertaineth not unto thee, *U.* to. 18
U. the king was a leper to the day. 21
U. son of Harim had taken a strange wife. *Ezra* 10:21
dwelt Athaiah son of *U.* *Neh* 11:4
vision in the days of *U.* *Isa* 1:1 *Hos* 1:1 ; *Amos* 1:1
in the year *U.* died, I saw. *Isa* 6:1
earthquake in days of *U.* *Zech* 14:5
Joram begat *Ozias.* *Mat* 1:8
Ozias begat Joatham. 9

Uzziel
Kohath, Amram, Izhar, *U.* *Ex* 6:18 *Num* 3:19; *1 Chr* 6:2, 18; 23:12
sons of *U.* *Ex* 6:22; *Lev* 10:4 *Num* 3:30; *1 Chr* 15:10; 23:20 24:24
of Simeon had *U.* for. *1 Chr* 4:42
U. son of Bela. 7:7
U. the son of Heman. 25:4
Jeduthun; Shemaiah, *U.* *2 Chr* 29:14
U. of the goldsmiths. *Neh* 3:8

V

vagabond
a fugitive and *v.* shalt. *Gen* 4:12*
I shall be a fugitive and *v.* 14*
then certain *v.* Jews. *Acts* 19:13*

vagabonds
let his children be *v.* *Ps* 109:10

vail, or **veil**
The use of the vail in the East was not so general in ancient as in modern times, as much of the present custom dates from the time of Mohammed only. The vail was worn only as an article of ornamental dress; by betrothed maidens in the presence of their future husbands and at the wedding; or by loose women for purposes of concealment.

The vail of the temple *was that separating the Holy Place from the Holy of Holies. This signified separation, since none but the high priest could pass beyond into the most sacred place, and he only on the Day of Atonement. It was rent at the time of the crucifixion to show that now all men could freely come to God.*

The Apostle speaks of the vail *of ignorance, blindness, and hardness of heart, which kept the Jews from understanding the scriptures of the Old Testament, the spiritual sense and meaning of the law, and from seeing that* Christ is the end of the law for righteousness, John 9:39; 2 Cor 3:14, 15.

Rebekah took a *v.* and. *Gen* 24:65
covered herself with a *v.* 38:14
shalt make a *v.* of blue. *Ex* 26:31
Moses put a *v.* on his face. 34:33, 35
made a *v.* of blue. 36:35; *2 Chr* 3:14
cover the ark with the *v.* *Ex* 40:3
holy place within the *v.* *Lev* 16:2
bring his blood within the *v.* 15
not go unto the *v.* nor come. 21:23
without the *v.* shall Aaron. 24:3
v. that thou hast upon. *Ruth* 3:15*
keepers took away my *v.* *S of S* 5:7*
destroy the *v.* spread. *Isa* 25:7

v. of the temple was rent. *Mat* 27:51
Mark 15:38; *Luke* 23:45
Moses, which put a *v.* *2 Cor* 3:13
for until this day remaineth the same *v.* untaken away; which *v.* is. 14
even to this day the *v.* is upon. 15
v. shall be taken away. 16
into that within the *v.* *Heb* 6:19
the second *v.*, the tabernacle. 9:3
through the *v.*, that is to say. 10:20

vails

Lord will take away the *v.* *Isa* 3:23

vain

(Vain *and* vanity *are used in the Bible entirely with the idea of emptiness, fruitlessness, or worthlessness, not in the sense of conceited or conceit.* Vain *is often used of an idol, as an empty worthless substitute for God*)

not regard *v.* words. *Ex* 5:9*
for it is not a *v.* thing. *Deut* 32:47
Abimelech hired *v.* persons. *Judg* 9:4
there were gathered *v.* men. 11:3
after *v.* things, which cannot profit nor deliver . . . are *v.* *1 Sam* 12:21
as one of the *v.* fellows. *2 Sam* 6:20
became *v.* and went after heathen. *2 Ki* 17:15
but they are but *v.* words. 18:20
Isa 36:5
to Jeroboam *v.* men. *2 Chr* 13:7†
he knoweth *v.* men, he. *Job* 11:11
for *v.* man would be wise, though. 12
wise man utter *v.* knowledge? 15:2
Job said, Shall *v.* words? 16:3
are ye thus altogether *v.*? 27:12
the people imagine a *v.* thing?
Ps 2:1; *Acts* 4:25
I have not sat with *v.* *Ps* 26:4†
an horse is a *v.* thing for. 33:17
man walketh in a *v.* shew. 39:6
for *v.* is the help of man. 60:11
108:12
become not *v.* in robbery. 62:10
I hate *v.* thoughts, but. 119:113*
it is *v.* for you to rise up. 127:2
followeth *v.* persons is. *Pr* 12:11
that followeth *v.* persons shall. 28:19
deceitful and beauty is *v.* 31:30
all days of his *v.* life which. *Eccl* 6:12
bring no more *v.* oblations; incense is an abomination. *Isa* 1:13
they are but *v.* words, I have. 36:5
vanity, and are become *v.* *Jer* 2:5
how long thy *v.* thoughts? 4:14*
customs of the people are *v.* 10:3
the prophets make you *v.* 23:16
have seen *v.* things. *Lam* 2:14
our eyes failed for our *v.* help. 4:17
no more any *v.* vision. *Ezek* 12:24
have ye not seen a *v.* vision? 13:7
ye have said, It is *v.* *Mal* 3:14
when ye pray, use not *v.* *Mat* 6:7
but became *v.* in their. *Rom* 1:21
thoughts of wise are *v.* *1 Cor* 3:20
then is our preaching *v.* and your faith is also *v.* 15:14, 17
let no man deceive you with *v.* words. *Eph* 5:6*
lest any spoil you through philosophy and *v.* deceit. *Col* 2:8
have turned aside to *v.* *1 Tim* 1:6
avoiding profane and *v.* babblings.
6:20; *2 Tim* 2:16
unruly and *v.* talkers. *Tit* 1:10
for they are unprofitable and *v.* 3:9
this man's religion is *v.* *Jas* 1:26
wilt thou know, O *v.* man? 2:20
your *v.* conversation. *1 Pet* 1:18

in vain

not take the name of the Lord *in v.*
Ex 20:7; *Deut* 5:11
sow your seed *in v.* *Lev* 26:16
strength shall be spent *in v.* 20
in v. have I kept all. *1 Sam* 25:21
why then labour I *in v.*? *Job* 9:29
comfort ye me *in v.* seeing? 21:34
Job open his mouth *in v.* 35:16
her labour is *in v.* without. 39:16
the hope of him is *in v.* 41:9
they are disquieted *in v.* *Ps* 39:6
cleansed my heart *in v.* 73:13
thou made all men *in v.*? *Ps* 89:47
in v.: watchman waketh *in v.* 127:1
enemies take thy name *in v.* 139:20
surely *in v.* the net is. *Pr* 1:17
the name of my God *in v.* 30:9*
Egyptians shall help *in v.* *Isa* 30:7
it not *in v.*, he formed it. 45:18*
seed of Jacob, Seek ye me *in v.* 19
have laboured *in v.*, I have spent my strength for nought and *in v.* 49:4
they shall not labour *in v.* 65:23
in v. have I smitten your. *Jer* 2:30
in v. is salvation hoped for. 3:23
in v. shalt thou make thyself. 4:30
the founder melteth *in v.* 6:29
lo, certainly *in v.* made he it, the pen of the scribes is *in v.* 8:8*
in v. shalt thou use many. 46:11
arrows, none shall return *in v.* 50:9
people shall labour *in v.* 51:58
that I have not said *in v.* *Ezek* 6:10
diviners comfort *in v.* *Zech* 10:2
but *in v.* they do worship me.
Mat 15:9; *Mark* 7:7
for he beareth not the sword *in v.*
Rom 13:4
ye have believed *in v.* *1 Cor* 15:2
his grace bestowed upon me was not *in v.* 10
your labour is not *in v.* in the Lord. 58
the grace of God *in v.* *2 Cor* 6:1
boasting of you should be *in v.* 9:3*
means I should run *in v.* *Gal* 2:2
law, then Christ is dead *in v.* 21
have ye suffered so many things *in v.*? if it be yet *in v.* 3:4
bestowed on you labour *in v.* 4:11
that I may rejoice that I have not run *in v.* nor laboured *in v.* *Phil* 2:16
that it was not *in v.* *1 Thes* 2:1
and our labour be *in v.* 3:5
the scripture saith *in v.*? *Jas* 4:5

vainglory

not be desirous of *v.* *Gal* 5:26
nothing be done through *v.* *Phil* 2:3

vainly

v. puffed up by his fleshly. *Col* 2:18

vale

kings were joined in the *v.* of Siddim.
Gen 14:3, 8
the *v.* of Siddim was full of. 10
out of the *v.* of Hebron. 37:14
in the hills and in the *v.* *Deut* 1:7*
the country of the *v.* *Josh* 10:40*
and cedars as sycamore trees in the *v.* *1 Ki* 10:27*; *2 Chr* 1:15*
in the cities of the *v.* *Jer* 33:13*

valiant

when Saul saw any *v.* *1 Sam* 14:52
son of Jesse, a mighty *v.* man. 16:18
be *v.* for me, and fight the. 18:17
Art not thou a *v.* man? 26:15
all the *v.* men took the body. 31:12
ye be *v.* *2 Sam* 2:7; 13:28
he knew that *v.* men were. 11:16
he that is *v.* 17:10
of Jehoiada, the son of a *v.* man of Kabzeel. 23:20; *1 Chr* 11:22
for thou art a *v.* man. *1 Ki* 1:42*
of Tola were *v.* men. *1 Chr* 7:2
the *v.* men of the armies. 11:26*
eighty priests, *v.* men. *2 Chr* 26:17
Solomon's; threescore *v.* men are about it, of the *v.* of. *S of S* 3:7*
inhabitants like a *v.* man. *Isa* 10:13
v. ones shall cry without. 33:7
are not *v.* for the truth. *Jer* 9:3*
are thy *v.* men swept away? 46:15*
the *v.* men are in scarlet. *Nah* 2:3
waxed *v.* in fight. *Heb* 11:34*

valiantest

12,000 men of the *v.* *Judg* 21:10

valiantly

Edom a possession, Israel shall do *v.*
Num 24:18
behave ourselves *v.* *1 Chr* 19:13*
through God we shall do *v.*
Ps 60:12; 108:13
the right hand of the Lord doeth *v.*
118:15, 16

valley

Sometimes meaning gorge *or* ravine.

The valleys most referred to in Scripture, or best known in Jewish history, are:

[1] The vale of Siddim, *or the slime pits, in which were the cities of Sodom and Gomorrah,* Gen 14:3.
[2] The valley of Eshcol, *where were famous vineyards,* Num 32:9.
[3] The valley of Achor, *where Achan was punished,* Josh 7:24.
[4] The valley of Elah, *where David killed Goliath,* 1 Sam 17:2, 19.
[5] The valley of Jezreel, *the city where Ahab's palace was built, and where Naboth's vineyard was,* Josh 19:18; 1 Ki 21:1, 23.
[6] The valley of Jehoshaphat, *which Joel prophesied should be the place of final judgement,* Joel 3:2. *It is not certain where this was, as the name was applied to the ravine between Jerusalem and the Mt. of Olives only in the middle of the fourth century.*
[7] The valley of Hinnom, *or Gehenna, near Jerusalem. See* **Tophet.**

of Sodom met him at *v.* *Gen* 14:17
they went up to *v.* of. *Num* 32:9
they came to *v.* of Eshcol. *Deut* 1:24
heifer to a rough *v.* and strike off the heifer's neck in the *v.* 21:4
the plain of *v.* of Jericho, a. 34:3
he buried Moses in a *v.* in the. 6
brought them to the *v.* of. *Josh* 7:24
moon, in the *v.* of Ajalon. 10:12
which is at the end of the *v.* 15:8
out inhabitants of the *v.* *Judg* 1:19
was sent on foot into the *v.* 5:15
Midian was beneath in the *v.* 7:8, 12
a woman in the *v.* of Sorek. 16:4
wheat harvest in the *v.* *1 Sam* 6:13
slewest in the *v.* of Elah. 21:9
spread themselves in the *v.* of Rephaim. *2 Sam* 5:18, 22; 23:13
the Syrians in the *v.* of salt. 8:13
cast him into some *v.* *2 Ki* 2:16
make this *v.* full of ditches. 3:16
he slew of Edom in the *v.* of salt ten thousand. 14:7; *1 Chr* 18:12
in *v.* of Berachah. *2 Chr* 20:26
in the *v.* of Hinnom. 28:3
to fight in *v.* of Megiddo. 35:22
the clods of the *v.* shall. *Job* 21:33
he paweth in the *v.* and. 39:21
through the *v.* of death. *Ps* 23:4
out the *v.* of Succoth. 60:6; 108:7
who passing through *v.* of Baca. 84:6
the ravens of the *v.* shall. *Pr* 30:17
see the fruits of the *v.* *S of S* 6:11
ears in the *v.* of Rephaim. *Isa* 17:5
the burden of the *v.* of vision. 22:1
trouble in the *v.* of vision. 5
is on the head of the fat *v.* 28:4
wroth as in the *v.* of Gibeon. 21
every *v.* shall be exalted. 40:4
v. of Achor a place for herds. 65:10
see thy way in the *v.* *Jer* 2:23
v. of Hinnom, but *v.* 7:32; 19:6
thee, O inhabitant of the *v.* 21:13
the *v.* also shall perish, and. 48:8
thou in thy flowing *v.*? 49:4
in the *v.* which was full. *Ezek* 37:1
break the bow of Israel in the *v.* of.
Hos 1:5
give the *v.* of Achor for a. 2:15
bring them into the *v.* of. *Joel* 3:2
multitudes, multitudes in the *v.* 14
shall water the *v.* of Shittim. 18
as the mourning in the *v.* *Zech* 12:11
and there shall be a great *v.* 14:4
flee to the *v.* of the mountains. 5
every *v.* be filled every. *Luke* 3:5
see **gate**

valleys

as the *v.* are they spread. *Num* 24:6
depths that spring out of the *v.* and.
Deut 8:7
land is a land of hills and *v.* 11:11

but he is not God of the *v.* *1 Ki* 20:28
clifts of *v.* in caves of earth. *Job* 30:6
or will he harrow the *v.* after? 39:10
the *v.* are covered over. *Ps* 65:13
they go down by the *v.* unto. 104:8
he sendeth the springs into the *v.* 10
the lily of the *v.* *S of S* 2:1
thy choicest *v.* shall be full. *Isa* 22:7
are on the head of the fat *v.* 28:1
fountains in midst of the *v.* 41:18
slaying the children in the *v.* 57:5
gloriest thou in the *v.*? *Jer* 49:4
Lord to the *v.* *Ezek* 6:3; 36:4, 6
mountains like doves of the *v.* 7:16

valour

Moab 10,000 men of *v.* *Judg* 3:29
thou mighty man of *v.* 6:12
Gileadite, a mighty man of *v.* 11:1
was a mighty man of *v.* *1 Ki* 11:28
Naaman, a mighty man in *v.* *2 Ki* 5:1
Zadok, man of *v.* *1 Chr* 12:28
a mighty man of *v.* *2 Chr* 17:17
see mighty **men**

value

lies, ye are all physicians of no *v.* *Job* 13:4
ye are of more *v.* than many sparrows. *Mat* 10:31; *Luke* 12:7

value, *verb*

the priest shall *v.* him. *Lev* 27:8
priest shall *v.* it, whether it be. 12
children of Israel did *v.* *Mat* 27:9*

valued

of barley seed *v.* at 50. *Lev* 27:16
wisdom cannot be *v.* with. *Job* 28:16
neither shall it be *v.* with pure. 19
price of him that was *v.* *Mat* 27:9*

valuest

as thou *v.* it who art the priest, so shall it be. *Lev* 27:12

vanish

wax warm, they *v.* *Job* 6:17
the heavens shall *v.* away. *Isa* 51:6
knowledge, it shall *v.* *1 Cor* 13:8*
old, is ready to *v.* away. *Heb* 8:13

vanished

hosts; is their wisdom *v.*? *Jer* 49:7
he *v.* out of their sight. *Luke* 24:31

vanisheth

consumed and *v.* away. *Job* 7:9
a vapour that *v.* away. *Jas* 4:14

vanities

me to anger with their *v.* *Deut* 32:21
1 Ki 16:13, 26; *Jer* 8:19
them that regard lying *v.* *Ps* 31:6
vanity of *v.* saith the preacher. *Eccl* 1:2; 12:8
of dreams there are also *v.* 5:7
the stock is a doctrine of *v.* *Jer* 10:8*
are there any among the *v.* of the Gentiles that can cause rain? 14:22
they that observe lying *v.* *Jonah* 2:8
turn from these *v.* *Acts* 14:15*

vanity

see meaning of **vain**

they followed *v.* and. *2 Ki* 17:15
so am I made to possess months of *v.* *Job* 7:3
let me alone, for my days are *v.* 16
let not him that is deceived trust in *v.*, for *v.* shall be his. 15:31
mischief and bring forth *v.* 35*
if I have walked with *v.* or. 31:5
surely God will not hear *v.* 35:13
how long will ye love *v.*? *Ps* 4:2
his tongue is mischief and *v.* 10:7*
they speak *v.* every one to his. 12:2†
not lifted up his soul unto *v.* 24:4
his best estate is altogether *v.* 39:5
every man is *v.* 11
come to see me, he speaketh *v.* 41:6†; 144:8†. 11†
low degree are *v.*, lighter than *v.* 62:9
days did he consume in *v.* 78:33
thoughts of man, they are *v.* 94:11
mine eyes from beholding *v.* 119:37
man is like to *v.*: his days are. 144:4
wealth gotten by *v.* shall. *Pr* 13:11
by a lying tongue is *v.* 21:6
soweth iniquity shall reap *v.* 22:8*
remove from me *v.* and lies. 30:8

v. of vanities, saith the preacher, all is *v.* *Eccl* 1:2, 14; 3:19; 11:8
12:8
this is also *v.* 2:1, 15, 19, 21, 23
4:8, 16; 5:10; 6:2, 9; 7:6; 8:10, 14
behold, all was *v.* and vexation.
2:11, 17, 26; 4:4
I saw *v.* 4:7
for he cometh in with *v.* 6:4
many things that increase *v.* 11
I seen in the days of my *v.* 7:15
there is a *v.* that is done on. 8:14
with wife all the days of thy *v.* 9:9
childhood and youth are *v.* 11:10
that draw iniquity with cords of *v.* *Isa* 5:18
nations with the sieve of *v.* 30:28
to him are counted *v.* 40:17
the judges of the earth as *v.* 23
behold, they are all *v.* 41:29; 44:9
v. shall take them: but he that. 57:13
if thou take away, speaking *v.* 58:9
they trust in *v.* 59:4
they have walked after *v.* *Jer* 2:5
they are *v.* and the work of errors. 10:15; 51:18
fathers have inherited *v.* 16:19
have burnt incense to *v.* 18:15
they have seen *v.* and divination. *Ezek* 13:6; 22:28
because ye have spoken *v.* 13:8
prophets see *v.* 9; 21:29
shall see no more *v.* 13:23
surely they are *v.* *Hos* 12:11
people shall weary themselves for very *v.* *Hab* 2:13
the idols have spoken *v.* *Zech* 10:2
was made subject to *v.* *Rom* 8:20
not as Gentiles walk in *v.* *Eph* 4:17
they speak great swelling words of *v.* *2 Pet* 2:18

vapour

pour down rain according to the *v.* *Job* 36:27
cattle also concerning the *v.* 33
and *v.* fulfilling his word. *Ps* 148:8
shew signs in the earth, *v.* of smoke. *Acts* 2:19
your life? it is even a *v.* *Jas* 4:14

vapours

v. to ascend from the ends of the. *Ps* 135:7; *Jer* 10:13; 51:16

variableness

lights, with whom is no *v.* *Jas* 1:17

variance

set a man at *v.* against. *Mat* 10:35
of the flesh are hatred, *v.* *Gal* 5:20*

Vashti

V. the queen made a feast. *Esth* 1:9
queen *V.* refused to come at. 12
that *V.* come no more before. 19
Esther queen instead of *V.* 2:17

vaunt

lest Israel *v.* themselves. *Judg* 7:2

vaunteth

charity *v.* not itself. *1 Cor* 13:4

vehement

fire that hath a *v.* flame. *S of S* 8:6*
prepared a *v.* east wind. *Jonah* 4:8*
what *v.* desire it wrought in you! *2 Cor* 7:11

vehemently

he spake the more *v.* *Mark* 14:31
the stream beat *v.* on that house. *Luke* 6:48*, 49*
began to urge him *v.* 11:53
stood and *v.* accused him. 23:10

veil, *see* **vail**

vein

there is a *v.* for the silver. *Job* 28:1*

vengeance

v. shall be taken on him. *Gen* 4:15
to me belongeth *v.* and recompence. *Deut* 32:35; *Ps* 94:1; *Heb* 10:30
I will render *v.* to mine enemies. *Deut* 32:41
for he will render *v.* to his. 43
the Lord hath taken *v.* *Judg* 11:36
when he seeth the *v.* *Ps* 58:10
tookest *v.* of their inventions. 99:8
to execute *v.* upon the heathen. 149:7

not spare in the day of *v.* *Pr* 6:34
it is the day of the Lord's *v.* and. *Isa* 34:8; 61:2; *Jer* 51:6
God will come with *v.* *Isa* 35:4
I will take *v.* 47:3; *Jer* 51:36
garments of *v.* for clothing. *Isa* 59:17
day of *v.* is in mine heart. 63:4
let me see thy *v.* on them. *Jer* 11:20
20:12
a day of *v.* 46:10
the *v.* of the Lord, take *v.* 50:15, 28
the *v.* of Lord, the *v.* of his temple. 28; 51:11
thou hast seen all their *v.* *Lam* 3:60
fury come up to take *v.* *Ezek* 24:8
Edom by taking *v.* hath. 25:12
I will lay my *v.* on Edom. 14
Philistines have taken *v.* 15
when I shall lay my *v.* on the. 17
I will execute great *v.* *Ezek* 25:17
Mi 5:15
Lord will take *v.* on his. *Nah* 1:2
these be the days of *v.* *Luke* 21:22
whom *v.* suffereth not to live. *Acts* 28:4*
unrighteous who taketh *v.*? *Rom* 3:5
v. is mine, I will repay, saith. 12:19
flaming fire, taking *v.* *2 Thes* 1:8
an example, suffering the *v.* *Jude* 7*

venison

because he did eat of his *v.* *Gen* 25:28
field and take me some *v.* 27:3, 7
thee, and eat of my *v.* 19, 31
I will eat of my son's *v.* 25
where is he that hath taken *v.*? 35

venom

is the cruel *v.* of asps. *Deut* 32:33

venomous

saw the *v.* beast hang. *Acts* 28:4

vent

wine which hath no *v.* *Job* 32:19

venture

drew a bow at a *v.* and smote the king. *1 Ki* 22:34; *2 Chr* 18:33

verified

so shall your words be *v.* *Gen* 42:20
let thy word be *v.* *1 Ki* 8:26
2 Chr 6:17

verily

are *v.* guilty concerning. *Gen* 42:21
saying, *V.* my sabbaths. *Ex* 31:13
I *v.* thought thou hadst hated her. *Judg* 15:2
v. our Lord hath made. *1 Ki* 1:43
v. she hath no child, her. *2 Ki* 4:14
I will *v.* buy it for the. *1 Chr* 21:24
my acquaintance are *v.* *Job* 19:13
do good, and *v.* thou. *Ps* 37:3
v. every man at his best state. 39:5
v. there is a reward for the righteous, *v.* he is a God that. 58:11
but *v.* God hath heard me. 66:19
v. I have cleansed my heart. 73:13
v. thou art a God that hidest thyself. *Isa* 45:15
v. it shall be well with thy remnant, *v.* I will cause the. *Jer* 15:11
v. I say unto you. *Mat* 5:18; 6:2, 5
16; 8:10; 10:15, 23, 42; 11:11
13:17; 16:28; 17:20; 18:3, 13, 18
19:23, 28; 21:21, 31; 23:36; 24:2
34, 47; 25:12, 40, 45; 26:13
Mark 3:28; 6:11; 8:12; 9:1, 41
10:15, 29; 11:23; 12:43; 13:30
14:9, 18, 25; *Luke* 4:24; 11:51
12:37; 13:35; 18:17, 29; 21:32
v. I say unto thee. *Mat* 5:26; 26:34
Mark 14:30; *Luke* 23:43
Elias *v.* cometh first. *Mark* 9:12
nay *v.* let them come. *Acts* 16:37
John *v.* baptized with baptism. 19:4
am *v.* a man which am a Jew. 22:3
I *v.* thought I ought to do. 26:9
for circumcision *v.* profiteth if thou. *Rom* 2:25
v. their sound went into all. 10:18
pleased them *v.*; debtors they. 15:27
I *v.* as absent in body. *1 Cor* 5:3
v. righteousness had been. *Gal* 3:21
for *v.* he took not on him the nature of angels. *Heb* 2:16
for men *v.* swear by the greater. 6:16

for they *v.* for a few days. *Heb* 12:10
who *v.* was foreordained. *1 Pet* 1:20
in him *v.* is the love of. *1 John* 2:5

verily, verily

v. v. I say unto you. *John* 1:51
5:19, 24, 25; 6:26, 32, 47, 53
8:34, 51, 58; 10:1, 7; 12:24
13:16, 20, 21; 14:12; 16:20, 23
v. v. I say unto thee. 3:3, 11
13:38; 21:18

verity

works of his hands are *v. Ps* 111:7*
Gentiles in faith and *v. 1 Tim* 2:7*

vermilion

cedar and painted with *v. Jer* 22:14
pourtrayed with *v. Ezek* 23:14

very

thou be my *v.* son Esau. *Gen* 27:21
in *v.* deed for this I. *Ex* 9:16
Moses was *v.* meek. *Num* 12:3
but the word is *v.* nigh. *Deut* 30:14
in *v.* deed except thou. *1 Sam* 25:34
Saul was come in *v.* deed. 26:4
have done *v.* foolishly. *2 Sam* 24:10
king Ahaziah did *v. 2 Chr* 20:35
we have dealt *v.* corruptly. *Neh* 1:7
inward part is *v.* wickedness. *Ps* 5:9
into that *v.* destruction let. 35:8
also, O God, is *v.* high. 71:19
establish in the *v.* heavens. 89:2
thy thoughts are *v.* deep. 92:5
thy testimonies are *v.* sure. 93:5
testimonies are *v.* faithful. 119:138
thy word is *v.* pure, therefore. 140
in that *v.* day his thoughts. 146:4
word runneth *v.* swiftly. 147:15
he separateth *v.* friends. *Pr* 17:9
for yet a *v.* little while. *Isa* 10:25
29:17
the land that is *v.* far off. 33:17
he taketh up the isles as a *v.* 40:15
be ye *v.* desolate, saith. *Jer* 2:12
I am pained at my *v.* heart. 4:19
transgressed to this *v.* day. *Ezek* 2:3
that were a *v.* little thing. 16:47
labour in the *v.* fire, and the people weary themselves for *v. Hab* 2:13
the *v.* hairs of your head. *Mat* 10:30
shall deceive the *v.* elect. 24:24
that this is the *v.* Christ. *John* 7:26
Acts 9:22
taken in adultery, in *v.* act. *John* 8:4
me for the *v.* works' sake. 14:11
the *v.* God of peace. *1 Thes* 5:23
and not the *v.* image of. *Heb* 10:1
the Lord is *v.* pitiful, of. *Jas* 5:11
see **great, much**

vessel

not put any in thy *v. Deut* 23:24
though sanctified this day in the *v.*
1 Sam 21:5
a little water in a *v. 1 Ki* 17:10
v. There is not a *v.* more. *2 Ki* 4:6
pieces like a potter's *v. Ps* 2:9
I am like a broken *v.* 31:12
forth a *v.* for the finer. *Pr* 25:4
an offering in a clean *v. Isa* 66:20
the *v.* was marred in the hand of the potter. *Jer* 18:4
v. wherein is no pleasure? 22:28
shall fall like a pleasant *v.* 25:34
been emptied from *v.* to *v.* 48:11
have broken Moab like a *v.* 38
hath made me an empty *v.* 51:34
put them in one *v.* and. *Ezek* 4:9
a pin of it to hang any *v.*? 15:3
shall be as a *v.* wherein is. *Hos* 8:8
carry any *v.* through the temple.
Mark 11:16
no man covereth a candle with a *v.*
Luke 8:16
for he is a chosen *v. Acts* 9:15
Peter saw a certain *v.* 10:11; 11:5
hath power to make one *v. Rom* 9:21
know to possess his *v.* in. *1 Thes* 4:4
he shall be a *v.* to honour. *2 Tim* 2:21
giving honour unto the wife as unto the weaker *v. 1 Pet* 3:7

vessels

best fruits in your *v. Gen* 43:11
anoint the altar and *v. Ex* 40:10
Lev 8:11
Levites not come nigh *v. Num* 18:3
bread is spent in our *v. 1 Sam* 9:7
and the *v.* of the young men. 21:5
borrow thee *v.* abroad of all thy neighbours, even empty *v. 2 Ki* 4:3
the *v.* king Ahaz did. *2 Chr* 29:19
king brought forth the *v. Ezra* 1:7
take these *v.* 5:15
v. are given to thee. 7:19
he weighed the silver and the *v.*
8:25, 33
thither brought I again the *v.* of the house of God. *Neh* 13:9
even in *v.* of bulrushes. *Isa* 18:2
v. of small quantity, the *v.* 22:24
be ye clean that bear the *v.* 52:11
abominable things is in their *v.* 65:4
returned with their *v. Jer* 14:3
v. of the Lord's house. 27:16; 28:3
they have brought the *v. Dan* 5:23
he shall spoil treasure of all pleasant *v. Hos* 13:15
to draw out fifty *v.* out. *Hag* 2:16
gathered the good into *v. Mat* 13:48
the wise took oil in their *v.* 25:4
the *v.* of wrath. *Rom* 9:22
the *v.* of mercy. 23
as *v.* of a potter shall. *Rev* 2:27
see **brass, earthen, gold, silver**

vestments

bring forth *v.* for the. *2 Ki* 10:22

vestry

him that was over the *v. 2 Ki* 10:22

vesture, -s

Joseph in *v.* of fine linen. *Gen* 41:42
the quarters of thy *v. Deut* 22:12
they cast lots upon my *v. Ps* 22:18
Mat 27:35; *John* 19:24
as a *v.* shalt thou change. *Ps* 102:26
and as a *v.* shalt thou fold. *Heb* 1:12*
he was clothed with a *v.* dipped in blood. *Rev* 19:13*
his *v.* and on his thigh a name. 16*

vex

thou shalt not *v.* a stranger.
Ex 22:21*; *Lev* 19:33*
not take a wife to her sister to *v.*
Lev 18:18*
v. the Midianites and. *Num* 25:17
for they *v.* you with their wiles. 18
ye let remain shall *v.* you. 33:55
how will he *v.* himself? *2 Sam* 12:18
God did *v.* them with. *2 Chr* 15:6
how long will ye *v.* my soul?
Job 19:2
and *v.* them in his sore. *Ps* 2:5
let us go up against Judah and *v.* it.
Isa 7:6
Judah shall not *v.* Ephraim. 11:13
I will *v.* the hearts of. *Ezek* 32:9
shall they not awake that shall *v.* thee? *Hab* 2:7
Herod did *v.* certain of. *Acts* 12:1*

vexation

(*Where this word occurs in Ecclesiastes the Revised Versions change it to* striving)

shall send on thee *v. Deut* 28:20*
is vanity and *v.* of spirit. *Eccl* 1:14
2:11, 17
this also is *v.* of spirit. 1:17; 2:26
4:4, 16; 6:9
man of the *v.* of his heart? 2:22
both the hands full with *v.* 4:6
such as was in her *v. Isa* 9:1*
be a *v.* only to understand. 28:19*
shall howl for *v.* of spirit. 65:14

vexations

great *v.* were on all the. *2 Chr* 15:5

vexed

the Egyptians *v.* us. *Num* 20:15*
reason of them that *v. Judg* 2:18
the Ammonites *v.* Israel. 10:8
so that his soul was *v.* unto. 16:16
Saul *v.* his enemies on. *1 Sam* 14:47†
Amnon was so *v.* that. *2 Sam* 13:2
alone, for her soul is *v. 2 Ki* 4:27
to enemies who *v.* them. *Neh* 9:27*
the Almighty, who hath *v. Job* 27:2
my bones are *v. Ps* 6:2
my soul is sore *v.* 3
be ashamed and sore *v.* 10
they rebelled and *v.* his. *Isa* 63:10*
infamous and much *v. Ezek* 22:5*
in thee they *v.* the fatherless. 7*
v. the poor. 29
my daughter is grievously *v.* with a devil. *Mat* 15:22
he is lunatic and sore *v.* 17:15*
they that were *v.* with unclean spirits.
Luke 6:18*; *Acts* 5:16
delivered just Lot, *v. 2 Pet* 2:7*
v. his righteous soul from day. 8

vial

(*Where this word or the plural occurs in Revelation the Revised Versions change it to* bowl)

Samuel took a *v.* of oil. *1 Sam* 10:1
first angel poured his *v. Rev* 16:2
second *v.* upon the sea. 3
third *v.* upon the rivers. 4
fourth *v.* upon the sun. 8
fifth *v.* upon the seat of the beast. 10
sixth *v.* upon the Euphrates. 12
seventh *v.* into the air. 17

vials

golden *v.* full of odours. *Rev* 5:8
seven angels seven golden *v.* 15:7
pour out the *v.* of the wrath. 16:1
angels which had seven *v.* 17:1; 21:9

victory

v. that day was turned. *2 Sam* 19:2
the Lord wrought a great *v.* that day.
23:10, 12
thine, O Lord, is the *v. 1 Chr* 29:11
hath gotten him the *v. Ps* 98:1*
swallow up death in *v.* and wipe away tears. *Isa* 25:8*; *1 Cor* 15:54
forth judgement unto *v. Mat* 12:20
O grave, where is thy *v.*? *1 Cor* 15:55
to God, who giveth us the *v.* 57
and this is the *v.*, even. *1 John* 5:4
the *v.* over the beast. *Rev* 15:2

victual, -s

goods of Sodom, and *v. Gen* 14:11
they prepared any *v. Ex* 12:39
him thy *v.* for increase. *Lev* 25:37
usury of *v.* of any thing. *Deut* 23:19
prepare *v. Josh* 1:11
take *v.* with you. 9:11*
the men took of their *v.* and. 14*
suit of apparel and *v. Judg* 17:10
he gave him *v.* and sword of Goliath.
1 Sam 22:10
which provided *v.* for the king.
1 Ki 4:7, 27
Pharaoh appointed him *v.* 11:18
if the people bring *v. Neh* 10:31
in the day they sold *v.* 13:15
so captain gave Jeremiah *v. Jer* 40:5
for then had we plenty of *v.* 44:17
went into villages to buy *v.*
Mat 14:15*; *Luke* 9:12†

view

go *v.* the land. *Josh* 2:1
v. the country. 7:2*
of prophets stood to *v. 2 Ki* 2:7*, 15

viewed

the men *v.* Ai. *Josh* 7:2
I *v.* the people. *Ezra* 8:15
and I *v.* the walls of. *Neh* 2:13, 15

vigilant

a bishop must be *v. 1 Tim* 3:2*
be sober, be *v.* because. *1 Pet* 5:8

vile

lest thy brother should seem *v.* to thee. *Deut* 25:3
man do not so *v.* a thing. *Judg* 19:24*
because his sons made themselves *v. 1 Sam* 3:13*
every thing that was *v.* they destroyed. 15:9
yet be more *v.* than. *2 Sam* 6:22
why are we reputed *v.* in? *Job* 18:3*
I am *v.*; what shall I answer? 40:4*
in whose eyes a *v.* person. *Ps* 15:4*
the *v.* person be no more. *Isa* 32:5†
for the *v.* person will speak. 6†
the precious from the *v. Jer* 15:19
make them like *v.* figs. 29:17
Lord, for I am become *v. Lam* 1:11
in his estate shall stand up a *v.* person. *Dan* 11:21

image, and will make thy grave, for thou art *v.* *Nah* 1:14
filth on thee and make thee *v.* 3:6
God gave them up to *v.* *Rom* 1:26
change our *v.* body. *Phil* 3:21*
come in a poor man in *v.* raiment. *Jas* 2:2

vilely

mighty is *v.* cast away. *2 Sam* 1:21

viler

of base men, they were *v.* *Job* 30:8*

vilest

wicked when the *v.* men. *Ps* 12:8

village

go into the *v.* over against. *Mat* 21:2
Mark 11:2; *Luke* 19:30
two of them went that same day to a *v.* *Luke* 24:13
they drew nigh unto the *v.* 28

villages

frogs died out of the *v.* *Ex* 8:13*
houses of the *v.* counted. *Lev* 25:31
the inhabitants of the *v.* *Judg* 5:7*
together in one of the *v.* *Neh* 6:2
Jews of *v.* made the 14th day of. *Esth* 9:19
let us lodge in the *v.* *S of S* 7:11
I will go up to the land of unwalled *v.* *Ezek* 38:11
strike the head of his *v.* *Hab* 3:14*
they may go into the *v.* and buy. *Mat* 14:15; *Mark* 6:36
see **cities**

villany

vile person will speak *v.* *Isa* 32:6*
they have committed *v.* *Jer* 29:23*

vine

God compares his people to a vine, *which he had brought out of Egypt, and planted in Palestine, as a good soil, but which, instead of bringing forth good fruit, brought forth only bitter fruit, and wild grapes,* Ps 80:8; Isa 5:1, *etc. In* John 15:1, *Christ says,* I am the true vine, and my Father is the husbandman.

The *vine* of Sodom, Deut 32:32, *is probably what is known as the* apples of Sodom, *which appear as edible fruit, but on being plucked turn at once to dust, like a puffball. The phrase is perhaps figurative, no real fruit being intended.*

Noah planted the vine *after the deluge, and was the first that cultivated it,* Gen 9:20. *Many are of opinion, that* wine *was not unknown before the deluge, and that this Patriarch only continued to cultivate the* vine *after this great catastrophe, as he had done before. But others think that he knew not the force of* wine, *having never used it before, nor having ever seen any one use it. He is supposed to be the first that pressed out the juice of the grape, and to have reduced it to a liquor. Before him, men only ate the grapes, like other fruit.*

in my dream, behold, a *v.* *Gen* 40:9
v. were three branches. 10
binding his foal to the *v.* and his ass's colt to the choice *v.* 49:11
nor gather grapes of thy *v.* undressed. *Lev* 25:5, 11
nothing made of the *v.* tree. *Num* 6:4
for their *v.* is of the *v.* *Deut* 32:32
said to *v.*, Reign over us. *Judg* 9:12
thing that cometh of the *v.* 13:14
every man under his *v.* *1 Ki* 4:25
found a wild *v.* and. *2 Ki* 4:39
eat ye every man of his own *v.* 18:31; *Isa* 36:16
his unripe grape as the *v.* *Job* 15:33
thou hast brought a *v.* *Ps* 80:8
behold, and visit this *v.* 14
thy wife shall be as a fruitful *v.* 128:3
to see whether the *v.* flourished. *S of S* 6:11; 7:12
shall be as clusters of the *v.* 7:8
it with the choicest *v.* *Isa* 5:2
for the *v.* of Sibmah. 16:8
I will bewail the *v.* of Sibmah. 9
Jer 48:32
the *v.* languisheth. *Isa* 24:7
lament for the fruitful *v.* 32:12
falleth off from the *v.* as a fig. 34:4
a noble *v.*: how then turned into degenerate plant of . . . *v.*? *Jer* 2:21
the remnant of Israel as a *v.* 6:9
grapes on the *v.* nor figs. 8:13
what is the *v.* tree more? *Ezek* 15:2
as the *v.* tree which I have given. 6
spreading *v.* of low stature. 17:6
this *v.* did bend her roots. 7
thy mother is like a *v.* in. 19:10
Israel is an empty *v.* *Hos* 10:1
revive as corn, grow as the *v.* 14:7
he laid my *v.* waste. *Joel* 1:7
the *v.* is dried up, the fig tree. 12
the fig tree and the *v.* yield. 2:22
every man under his *v.* *Mi* 4:4
as yet the *v.* hath not brought forth. *Hag* 2:19
every man under the *v.* *Zech* 3:10
the *v.* shall give her fruit. 8:12
neither shall your *v.* cast. *Mal* 3:11
v., until in my Father's. *Mat* 26:29
Mark 14:25; *Luke* 22:18
true *v.*, my Father is. *John* 15:1, 5
bear fruit, except it abide in *v.* 4
can a *v.* bear figs? *Jas* 3:12
gather clusters of the *v.* *Rev* 14:18
the angel gathered the *v.* of. 19*

vinedressers

captain of guard left the poor of the land to be *v.* *2 Ki* 25:12; *Jer* 52:16
had husbandmen and *v.* *2 Chr* 26:10
of alien shall be your *v.* *Isa* 61:5
howl, O ye *v.* *Joel* 1:11

vinegar

(*The Hebrew word translated* vinegar *was applied to a beverage turned sour, or made artificially so. It was not pleasant to take but was used by labourers. The vinegar of the Romans was much the same, and was probably that given to Jesus while on the cross*)

shall drink no *v.* of wine. *Num* 6:3
dip thy morsel in the *v.* *Ruth* 2:14
gall for my meat, in my thirst they gave me *v.* *Ps* 69:21; *Mat* 27:34*
as *v.* to the teeth, so is. *Pr* 10:26
as *v.* upon nitre, so is he. 25:20
they took a spunge and filled it with *v.* *Mat* 27:48; *Mark* 15:36
Luke 23:36; *John* 19:29, 30

vines

of *v.* or pomegranates. *Num* 20:5
a land of wheat, and barley, and *v.* *Deut* 8:8
their *v.* with hail. *Ps* 78:47
their *v.* also and fig trees. 105:33
v. give a good smell. *S of S* 2:13
little foxes, that spoil the *v.*; for our *v.* have tender grapes. 15*
were a thousand *v.* *Isa* 7:23
they shall eat up thy *v.* *Jer* 5:17
thou shalt yet plant *v.* on. 31:5*
I will destroy her *v.* and. *Hos* 2:12
nor shall fruit be in the *v.* *Hab* 3:17

vineyard

Noah planted a *v.* and. *Gen* 9:20
if a man shall cause a *v.* *Ex* 22:5
thou shalt deal with thy *v.* 23:11
shalt not glean thy *v.* *Lev* 19:10
thou shalt prune thy *v.* 25:3
thy field, nor prune thy *v.* 4
he that hath planted a *v.*? *Deut* 20:6
not sow thy *v.* with divers seeds, lest the fruit of thy seed and *v.* 22:9
into thy neighbour's *v.* 23:24
gatherest the grapes of thy *v.* 24:21
thou shalt plant a *v.* and not. 28:30
Naboth had a *v.* hard by. *1 Ki* 21:1
v., I will give thee a better *v.* 2, 6
eat bread, I will give thee the *v.* 7
the *v.* thy right hand. *Ps* 80:15*
I went by the *v.* of the man void of. *Pr* 24:30
of her hand she planted a *v.* 31:16
mine own *v.* have I not. *S of S* 1:6
Solomon had a *v.*; he let the *v.* 8:11
my *v.* which is mine. 12
daughter of Zion is left as a cottage in a *v.* *Isa* 1:8
for ye have eaten up the *v.* 3:14
my beloved touching his *v.* 5:1
for the *v.* of the Lord of hosts is. 7
yea, ten acres of *v.* shall yield. 10
sing ye to her, A *v.* of red wine. 27:2
have destroyed my *v.* *Jer* 12:10
Rechabites shall not plant *v.* 35:7, 9
I will make Samaria as plantings of a *v.* *Mi* 1:6
hire labourers into his *v.* *Mat* 20:1
them, Go ye also into the *v.* 4, 7
go work to-day in my *v.* 21:28
a certain householder planted a *v.* 33; *Mark* 12:1; *Luke* 20:9
fig tree planted in his *v.* *Luke* 13:6
to the dresser of the *v.*, Behold. 7
who planteth a *v.* and? *1 Cor* 9:7

vineyards

given us inheritance of *v.* *Num* 16:14
not pass through the *v.* 20:17; 21:22
Lord stood in a path of the *v.* 22:24
give thee *v.* and olive trees which thou plantedst not. *Deut* 6:11
Josh 24:13; *Neh* 9:25
thou shalt plant *v.* and. *Deut* 28:39
burnt up the corn, with *v.* *Judg* 15:5
Go and lie in wait in the *v.* 21:20
your fields and your *v.* *1 Sam* 8:14
give every one of you *v.*? 22:7
to receive *v.* and sheep? *2 Ki* 5:26
to a land of bread and *v.* 18:32
in the third year . . . plant *v.* 19:29
over the *v.* was Shimei, over the increase of the *v.* for. *1 Chr* 27:27
we have mortgaged our *v.* *Neh* 5:3
restore to them their *v.* and. 11
not the way of the *v.* *Job* 24:18
and plant *v.* to yield. *Ps* 107:37
houses, I planted me *v.* *Eccl* 2:4
me the keeper of the *v.* *S of S* 1:6
as a cluster of camphire in the *v.* 14
let us get up early to the *v.* 7:12
in the *v.* there shall be no singing. *Isa* 16:10
houses and inhabit; shall plant *v.* and eat the fruit. 65:21; *Amos* 9:14
houses and *v.* shall be. *Jer* 32:15
gave the poor *v.* and fields. 39:10
build houses and plant *v.* *Ezek* 28:26
I will give her her *v.* *Hos* 2:15
worm devoured your *v.* *Amos* 4:9
ye have planted *v.* but ye shall. 5:11
and in all *v.* shall be wailing. 17
they shall plant *v.* but not. *Zeph* 1:13

vintage

shall reach to the *v.* and the *v.* shall reach to the. *Lev* 26:5
than the *v.* of Abiezer? *Judg* 8:2
the *v.* of the wicked. *Job* 24:6
I have made their *v.* shouting to cease. *Isa* 16:10
grapes when *v.* is done. 24:13
the *v.* shall fail, gathering. 32:10
the spoiler is fallen upon thy *v.* *Jer* 48:32
grapegleanings of the *v.* *Mi* 7:1
the forest of the *v.* is. *Zech* 11:2*

viol

harp and *v.* and wine. *Isa* 5:12*
that chant to the sound of the *v.* *Amos* 6:5

violated

her priests have *v.* my. *Ezek* 22:26

violence

earth was filled with *v.* *Gen* 6:11, 12
thing taken away by *v.* *Lev* 6:2*
thou savest me from *v.* *2 Sam* 22:3
him that loveth *v.* his. *Ps* 11:5
v. and strife in the city. 55:9
weigh the *v.* of your hands. 58:2
redeem their soul from *v.* 72:14
therefore *v.* covereth them as. 73:6
they drink the wine of *v.* *Pr* 4:17
v. covereth the mouth of. 10:6, 11
transgressors shall eat *v.* 13:2
a man that doeth *v.* to the. 28:17*
done no *v.* nor was deceit. *Isa* 53:9
and the act of *v.* is in their. 59:6

v. shall no more be heard. *Isa* 60:18
v. and spoil is heard in. *Jer* 6:7
I cried *v.* and spoil. 20:8
do no *v.* to the stranger. 22:3
thine eyes, thine heart are for *v.* 17
v. done to me and my flesh. 51:35
a rumour, *v.* in the land. 46
v. is risen up into a rod. *Ezek* 7:11
for the city is full of *v.* 23
filled the land with *v.* 8:17; 28:16
because of the *v.* of them. 12:19
hath spoiled none by *v.* 18:7, 16
spoiled and oppressed by *v.* 12, 18
O princes of Israel, remove *v.* 45:9
be a wilderness, for the *v.* *Joel* 3:19
who store up *v.* in their. *Amos* 3:10
ye that cause the seat of *v.* to. 6:3
for thy *v.* shame shall. *Ob* 10
every one from the *v.* *Jonah* 3:8
fields, and take them by *v.* *Mi* 2:2*
rich men thereof are full of *v.* 6:12
how long shall I cry unto thee of *v.*! *Hab* 1:2
v. is before me. 3
they shall come all for *v.* 9
and for the *v.* of the land. 2:8
v. of Lebanon cover thee, *v.* of. 17
houses with *v.* and deceit. *Zeph* 1:9
have done *v.* to the law. 3:4
for one covereth *v.* with. *Mal* 2:16
of heaven suffereth *v.* *Mat* 11:12
do *v.* to no man, nor accuse any. *Luke* 3:14
captain brought them without *v.* *Acts* 5:26
Paul borne of soldiers for *v.* 21:35
hinder part was broken with *v.* 27:41
quenched the *v.* of fire. *Heb* 11:34*
with *v.* shall Babylon. *Rev* 18:21*

violent

thou hast delivered me from the *v.* man. *2 Sam* 22:49; *Ps* 18:48
his *v.* dealing come on his. *Ps* 7:16
the assemblies of *v.* men. 86:14
preserve me from the *v.* 140:1, 4
evil shall hunt the *v.* man to. 11
a *v.* man enticeth his. *Pr* 16:29
if thou seest *v.* perverting. *Eccl* 5:8
the *v.* take it by force. *Mat* 11:12

violently

servants had *v.* taken. *Gen* 21:25
shall restore that which he took *v.* *Lev* 6:4*
thine ass shall be *v.* *Deut* 28:31
he hath *v.* taken away. *Job* 20:19
they *v.* take away flocks, and. 24:2
he will surely *v.* turn. *Isa* 22:18
he hath *v.* taken away. *Lam* 2:6
swine ran *v.* into the sea. *Mat* 8:32* *Mark* 5:13*; *Luke* 8:33*

viols

the noise of thy *v.* is. *Isa* 14:11
hear the melody of thy *v.* *Amos* 5:23

viper

(*The* viper *is one of the most poisonous serpents, but the word is used in the New Testament for any poisonous serpent*)
of asps, the *v.*'s tongue. *Job* 20:16
from whence come the *v.* *Isa* 30:6
crushed breaketh out into a *v.* 59:5
came a *v.* and fastened. *Acts* 28:3

vipers

O generation of *v.* *Mat* 3:7; 12:34 23:33; *Luke* 3:7

virgin

In Greek, parthenos; *in Hebrew,* almah. *These words properly signify an unmarried young woman, who has preserved the purity of her body. But sometimes* virgin *is made use of to express a young woman whether she has kept her virginity or no,* Joel 1:8.
fair to look upon, a *v.* *Gen* 24:16
when the *v.* cometh forth to. 43
for his sister, a *v.* he. *Lev* 21:3
take a *v.* of his own people. 14
an evil name upon a *v.* *Deut* 22:19
a *v.* betrothed. 23
a *v.* not betrothed. 28
the young man and the *v.* **32:25**
fell sick for Tamar; for she was a *v.* *2 Sam* 13:2
sought for king a young *v.* *1 Ki* 1:2
the *v.* daughter of Zion hath despised thee. *2 Ki* 19:21; *Isa* 37:22
behold a *v.* shall conceive. *Isa* 7:14 *Mat* 1:23
O thou oppressed *v.* *Isa* 23:12
in the dust, O *v.* of Babylon. 47:1
marrieth a *v.* so thy sons. 62:5
the *v.* daughter of my. *Jer* 14:17
v. of Israel hath done a. 18:13
be built, O *v.* of Israel. 31:4
the *v.* rejoice in the dance. 13
turn again, O *v.* of Israel, to. 21
take balm, O *v.* the daughter. 46:11
trodden the *v.* daughter of. *Lam* 1:15
thee, O *v.* daughter of Zion. 2:13
lament like a *v.* girded. *Joel* 1:8
the *v.* of Israel is fallen. *Amos* 5:2
sent from God to a *v.* *Luke* 1:27
if a *v.* marry, she hath. *1 Cor* 7:28
between a wife and a *v.* 34
decreed that he will keep his *v.* 37
I may present you as a chaste *v.* *2 Cor* 11:2

virginity

take a wife in her *v.* *Lev* 21:13
tokens of her *v.* *Deut* 22:15, 17, 20
bewail my *v.* *Judg* 11:37, 38
the teats of their *v.* *Ezek* 23:3, 8
Anna lived seven years from her *v.* *Luke* 2:36

virgins

pay according to the dowry of *v.* *Ex* 22:17
daughters that were *v.* *2 Sam* 13:18
favour above all the *v.* *Esth* 2:17
the *v.* her companions. *Ps* 45:14
as ointment, therefore do the *v.* love thee. *S of S* 1:3
threescore queens and *v.* 6:8
nor do I bring up *v.* *Isa* 23:4
her priests sigh, her *v.* *Lam* 1:4
my *v.* and young men are gone. 18
the *v.* of Jerusalem hang. 2:10
v. and young men are fallen. 21
shall the fair *v.* faint. *Amos* 8:13
heaven be likened to ten *v.* *Mat* 25:1
Philip had four daughters, *v.* *Acts* 21:9
concerning *v.* I have no. *1 Cor* 7:25
not defiled, for they are *v.* *Rev* 14:4

young **virgins**

Jabesh-gilead were four hundred *young v.* *Judg* 21:12
there be fair *young v.* sought for king. *Esth* 2:2
together all the fair *young v.* 3

virtue

v. had gone out of him. *Mark* 5:30 *Luke* 6:19*; 8:46*
if there be any *v.* think. *Phil* 4:8
hath called us to glory and *v.* *2 Pet* 1:3
add to your faith *v.* and to *v.* 5

virtuous

thou art a *v.* woman. *Ruth* 3:11†
a *v.* woman is a crown. *Pr* 12:4†
who can find a *v.* woman? 31:10†

virtuously

have done *v.* but thou. *Pr* 31:29†

visage

his *v.* was marred more. *Isa* 52:14
their *v.* is blacker than. *Lam* 4:8
and the form of his *v.* *Dan* 3:19

visible

were all things created, *v.* and invisible. *Col* 1:16

vision

the *v.* of the Almighty. *Num* 24:4, 16
there was no open *v.* *1 Sam* 3:1
feared to shew Eli the *v.* 15
according to all these words and this *v.* *2 Sam* 7:17; *1 Chr* 17:15
they are written in the *v.* *2 Chr* 32:32
as a *v.* of the night. *Job* 20:8
thou spakest in *v.* to thy. *Ps* 89:19
no *v.* the people perish. *Pr* 29:18
the *v.* of Isaiah. *Isa* 1:1
a grievous *v.* is declared. **21:2**
burden of the valley of *v.* *Isa* 22:1, 5
they err in *v.*, they stumble. 28:7
as a dream of a night *v.* 29:7
the *v.* is become as a book. 11
unto you a false *v.* *Jer* 14:14
they speak a *v.* of their own. 23:16
prophets find no *v.* from. *Lam* 2:9
v. is touching the whole. *Ezek* 7:13
then shall they seek a *v.* of. 26
according to the *v.* that I saw. 8:4 11:24; 43:3
prolonged and every *v.* 12:22
say to them, the effect of every *v.* 23
no more any vain *v.* nor. 24
the *v.* that he seeth is for many. 27
have ye not seen a vain *v.*? 13:7
to Daniel in a night *v.* *Dan* 2:19
I saw in my *v.* by night, the. 7:2
a *v.* appeared unto me, even. 8:1
how long shall be the *v.* concerning sacrifice? 13
man to understand the *v.* 16
time of the end shall be the *v.* 17
shut up the *v.* 26
I was astonished at the *v.* 27
whom I had seen in the *v.* at. 9:21
consider the *v.* 23
and to seal up the *v.* 24
had understanding of the *v.* 10:1
the *v.*: men with me saw not *v.* 7, 8
for yet the *v.* is for many days. 14
by *v.* my sorrows are turned. 16
themselves to establish the *v.* 11:14
v. of Obadiah. *Ob* 1
that ye shall not have a *v.* *Mi* 3:6
the book of the *v.* of. *Nah* 1:1
write the *v.* and make it. *Hab* 2:2
for the *v.* is yet for an appointed. 3
the prophets shall be ashamed every one of his *v.* *Zech* 13:4
charged, saying, Tell the *v.* to no man. *Mat* 17:9
that he had seen a *v.* *Luke* 1:22
they had seen a *v.* of angels. 24:23
doubted of the *v.* *Acts* 10:17, 19
in a trance I saw a *v.*, A vessel. 11:5
true, but thought he saw a *v.* 12:9
a *v.* appeared to Paul. 16:9; 18:9
disobedient to the heavenly *v.* 26:19
I saw the horses in the *v.* *Rev* 9:17
see **oracle, prophet, Thummim**

in a **vision**

came to Abram *in a v.* *Gen* 15:1
make myself known to him *in a v.* *Num* 12:6
brought me *in a v.* by. *Ezek* 11:24
I saw *in a v.* and I was. *Dan* 8:2
said the Lord *in a v.* *Acts* 9:10
Saul hath seen *in a v.* a man. 12
Cornelius saw *in a v.* an angel. 10:3

visions

God spake to Israel in *v.* *Gen* 46:2
written in the *v.* of Iddo. *2 Chr* 9:29
understanding in *v.* of God. 26:5
in thoughts from the *v.* *Job* 4:13
terrifiest me through *v.* 7:14
and I saw the *v.* of God. *Ezek* 1:1
he brought me in the *v.* of God. 8:3
see *v.* of peace for her. 13:16
in *v.* he brought me to the land. 40:2
understanding in all *v.* *Dan* 1:17
the *v.* of thy head on thy bed. 2:28
and the *v.* of my head troubled. 4:5
Daniel had *v.* of his head. 7:1
I saw in the night *v.* and. 7, 13
v. of my head troubled me. 15
I have multiplied *v.* *Hos* 12:10
your young men shall see *v.* *Joel* 2:28; *Acts* 2:17
I will come to *v.* and. *2 Cor* 12:1

visit

(*To come with a special purpose, either of blessing or punishment*)
God will surely *v.* you. *Gen* 50:24 25; *Ex* 13:19
when I *v.* I will *v.* their. *Ex* 32:34
I do *v.* the iniquity. *Lev* 18:25
thou shalt *v.* thy habitation and not sin. *Job* 5:24
v. him every morning. 7:18
O Lord, awake to *v.* all. *Ps* 59:5
from heaven and *v.* this vine. 80:14
I *v.* their transgression with. **89:32**

remember me, O v. me with. Ps 106:4
the Lord will v. Tyre. Isa 23:17
neither shall they v. the ark of the. Jer 3:16
v. for these things ? 5:9, 29; 9:9
at time I v. them, they shall. 6:15
will remember iniquity and v. 14:10
knowest, remember and v. 15:15
I will v. on you the evil of. 23:2
shall they be till I v. them. 27:22
I will v. you and perform. 29:10
there shall he be till I v. him. 32:5
the time I will v. Esau. 49:8
v. Babylon. 50:31
he will v. thine iniquity. Lam 4:22
I will v. on her the days. Hos 2:13
now will he v. their sins. 8:13; 9:9
I will also v. the altars. Amos 3:14
Lord shall v. and turn. Zeph 2:7
which shall not v. those. Zech 11:16
it came into his heart to v. Acts 7:23
hath declared how God did v. 15:14
go again and v. our brethren in. 36
is this, to v. the fatherless. Jas 1:27

visitation

after the v. of all men. Num 16:29
thy v. hath preserved. Job 10:12
ye do in the day of v.? Isa 10:3
in the time of their v. shall. Jer 8:12
in the time of v. they shall perish. 10:15; 51:18
of Anathoth, even in the year of their v. 11:23; 23:12; 48:44
the time of their v. 46:21; 50:27
the days of v. are come. Hos 9:7
thy v. cometh, now shall be. Mi 7:4
not the time of thy v. Luke 19:44
they may glorify God in the day of v. 1 Pet 2:12

visited

and the Lord v. Sarah as. Gen 21:1
I have surely v. you. Ex 3:16
that the Lord had v. Israel. 4:31
if they be v. after visitation of all men. Num 16:29
that Samson v. his wife. Judg 15:1
she heard how the Lord had v. his. Ruth 1:6
the Lord v. Hannah. 1 Sam 2:21
now it is not so, he hath v. in his anger. Job 35:15
thou hast v. me, thou. Ps 17:3
he shall not be v. with evil. Pr 19:23
days shall they be v. Isa 24:22
therefore hast thou v. and. 26:14
Lord, in trouble have they v. 26
thou shalt be v. of the Lord. 29:6
Jerusalem is the city to be v. Jer 6:6
flock and have not v. them. 23:2
days thou shalt be v. Ezek 38:8
the Lord of hosts hath v. Zech 10:3
I was sick, and ye v. me. Mat 25:36
ye v. me not. 43
he hath v. and redeemed. Luke 1:68
dayspring from on high hath v. us. 78
saying, That God hath v. his. 7:16

visitest

and the son of man, that thou v. him? Ps 8:4; Heb 2:6
thou v. the earth and waterest it. Ps 65:9

visiteth

when he v. what shall I? Job 31:14

visiting

v. the iniquity of the fathers. Ex 20:5
34:7; Num 14:18; Deut 5:9

vocation

ye walk worthy of the v. Eph 4:1*

voice

By this word is not only understood the voice *of a man or beast, but all other sorts of sounds, noises, or cries. And even thunder is also called the* voice of God. *To hear or* to hearken *to any one's voice is to obey him,* Ex 15:26.

the v. of thy brother's. Gen 4:10
v. is Jacob's v. but the hands. 27:22
and Jacob lifted up his v. and. 29:11
heard that I lifted up my v. 39:15
believe the v. of latter sign. Ex 4:8
God answered him by a v. 19:19
beware of him, obey his v. Ex 23:21
people answered with one v. 24:3
it is not the v. of them that. 32:18
if a soul hear the v. of. Lev 5:1
the congregation lifted up their v. Num 14:1
be obedient to his v. Deut 4:30
not be obedient to his v. 8:20
any noise with your v. Josh 6:10
they knew the v. of the. Judg 18:3
is this thy v. my son David? 1 Sam 24:16; 26:17
and the most High uttered his v. 2 Sam 22:14
was no v. nor any that answered. 1 Ki 18:26, 29
after the fire a still small v. 19:12
there was neither v. nor. 2 Ki 4:31
there was no v. of man, but. 7:10
hast thou exalted thy v. and lifted up thine eyes? 19:22; Isa 37:23
by lifting up the v. with. 1 Chr 15:16
Job's friends lifted up their v. and. Job 2:12
to be solitary, let no joyful v. 3:7
my organ into the v. of them. 30:31
a v. roareth, he thundereth with the v. 37:4
marvellously with his v. 5
thunder with a v. like him? 40:9
the Highest gave his v. Ps 18:13
I may publish with the v. of. 26:7
thou heardest the v. of my. 31:22
house of God with the v. of. 42:4
for the v. of him that. 44:16
he uttered his v., the earth. 46:6
shout unto God with the v. 47:1
he hath attended to the v. of. 66:19
his v. and that a mighty v. 68:33
forget not the v. of thine. 74:23
I cried unto the Lord with my v. 77:1; 142:1
the v. of thy thunder was in. 77:18
attend to the v. of my. 86:6
floods have lifted up their v. 93:3
sing unto the Lord with the v. 98:5
by reason of the v. of my. 102:5
hearkening to the v. of his. 103:20
at v. of thy thunder they. 104:7
v. of rejoicing in tabernacles. 118:15
give ear to my v. when I cry. 141:1
her v. in the streets. Pr 1:20
if thou liftest up thy v. 2:3
I have not obeyed the v. of. 5:13
understanding put forth her v.? 8:1
to you, O men, I call, my v. is. 4
a fool's v. is known by. Eccl 5:3
God be angry at thy v.? 6
bird of the air shall carry the v. 10:20
he shall rise up at the v. of. 12:4
the v. of my beloved. S of S 2:8
the v. of the turtle is heard in. 12
it is the v. of my beloved. 5:2
posts moved at the v. of. Isa 6:4
exalt the v. unto them, shake. 13:2
thy v. be as one that hath a. 29:4
be gracious to thee at the v. 30:19
will not be afraid of their v. 31:4
the v. of him that crieth in. 40:3
Mat 3:3; Mark 1:3; Luke 3:4
v. said, Cry. Isa 40:6
with the v. of singing. 48:20
that obeyeth the v. of his. 50:10
joy, thanksgiving, and the v. 51:3
with the v. together shall they. 52:8
v. of weeping shall be no more heard in her, nor v. of crying. 65:19
a v. of noise, a v. from temple, a v. 66:6
a v. declareth from Dan. Jer 4:15
give out their v. against the cities. 16
their v. roareth like the sea. 6:23
50:42
v. of mirth, v. of gladness, v. of the bridegroom, v. of bride. 7:34
16:9; 25:10; 33:11
v. of the cry of the daughter. 8:19
uttereth his v., there is a multitude of waters. 10:13; 51:16
a v. of the cry of shepherds. 25:36
and the v. of them that make. 30:19
a v. was heard in Ramah. 31:15
saith the Lord, refrain thy v. 16
the v. thereof shall go like. 46:22*
a v. of crying shall be from. Jer 48:3*
the v. of them that flee. 50:28
hath destroyed out of her the great v. 51:55
I heard as the v. of the Almighty. Ezek 1:24*
as the v. of the Almighty God. 10:5
and a v. of a multitude. 23:42
of one that hath a pleasant v. 33:32
his v. was like a noise of many waters. 43:2; Rev 1:15; 19:6
fell a v. from heaven. Dan 4:31
lamentable v. to Daniel. 6:20
v. of his words like the v. of. 10:6
Lord shall utter his v. Joel 2:11
shall utter his v. from Jerusalem. 3:16; Amos 1:2
I will sacrifice with v. Jonah 2:9
as with the v. of doves. Nah 2:7
a v. from heaven, This is my beloved Son, in. Mat 3:17; Mark 1:11
Luke 3:22
a v. out of the cloud, This is. Mat 17:5; Mark 9:7; Luke 9:35, 36
as soon as the v. of thy. Luke 1:44
the v. of one crying in. John 1:23
of the bridegroom's v. 3:29
him, for they know his v. 10:4
for they know not the v. of. 5
a v. saying, I have glorified it. 12:28
this v. came not because of me. 30
is of the truth heareth my v. 18:37
hearing a v., but seeing no. Acts 9:7
came a v. saying, Rise, Peter. 10:13
and the v. spake unto him. 15; 11:9
when she knew Peter's v. she. 12:14
it is the v. of a god, and not. 22
all with one v. cried, Great is. 19:34
except it be for this one v. 24:21
I gave my v. against them. 26:10*
the meaning of the v. 1 Cor 14:11
that by my v. I might teach. 19
now to change my v. Gal 4:20
with v. of the archangel. 1 Thes 4:16
v. then shook the earth. Heb 12:26
came a v. from the excellent glory. 2 Pet 1:17
ass speaking with man's v. 2:16
I turned to see the v. Rev 1:12
there came a great v. saying. 16:17

voice joined with *hear*

hear my v. ye wives of. Gen 4:23
did ever people *hear* v.? Deut 4:33
he made thee to *hear* his v. 36
if we *hear* the v. of God. 5:25
he said, *Hear*, Lord, the v. 33:7
can I *hear* the v. of? 2 Sam 19:35
and he did *hear* my v. out of. 22:7
they *hear* not the v. of the. Job 3:18
hear attentively the noise of his v. 37:2
my v. shalt thou *hear* in. Ps 5:3
hear, O Lord, when I cry with my v. 27:7; 28:2; 64:1; 119:149; 130:2
140:6
hear me, because of the v. of. 55:3
aloud and he shall *hear* my v. 17
to-day if ye will *hear* his v., harden not. 95:7; Heb 3:7, 15; 4:7
hear thy v., for sweet is thy v. S of S 2:14
hear my v. ye careless. Isa 32:9
nor can men *hear* the v. Jer 9:10
any man *hear* his v. Mat 12:19
the dead shall *hear* the v. of the Son of God. John 5:25, 28
and sheep *hear* his v. 10:3, 16, 27
and shouldest *hear* the v. Acts 22:14
if any man *hear* my v. Rev 3:20
see **heard, lift, Lord, loud, obey, obeyed**

voice with *hearken, hearkened*

because thou hast *hearkened* unto the v. of thy wife. Gen 3:17
Abram *hearkened* to the v. 16:2
hath said *hearken* to her v. 21:12
shall *hearken* to thy v. Ex 3:18
will not *hearken* unto my v. 4:1
nor *hearken* to the v. of the first. 8
neither *hearken* unto thy v. 9
if diligently *hearken* to the v. 15:26
hearken unto my v., I will give. 18:19
hearkened to the v. of Jethro. 24

and not *hearkened* to my *v.*
Num 14:22; *Deut* 9:23; 28:45
Lord *hearkened* to the *v. Num* 21:3
the Lord would not *hearken* to your *v.* *Deut* 1:45
hearken to the *v.* of the Lord. 13:18
only if thou carefully *hearken* to the *v.* 15:5; 26:17; 28:1, 2; 30:10
not *hearken* to the *v.* of Lord. 28:15
hearkened to the *v.* of a man. *Josh* 10:14
this people have not *hearkened* to my *v.* *Judg* 2:20
and God *hearkened* to the *v.* 13:9
not *hearken* to the *v.* of Israel. 20:13
they *hearkened* not unto the *v.* of their father. *1 Sam* 2:25
hearken to the *v.* of the people. 8:7
9:22
I have *hearkened* to your *v.* 12:1
Saul *hearkened* to the *v.* 19:6
I have *hearkened* to thy *v.* 25:35
hearken thou to the *v.* of thy. 28:22
he would not *hearken* to our *v.* *2 Sam* 12:18
not *hearken* to her *v.* 13:14
Ben-hadad *hearkened* to their *v.* *1 Ki* 20:25
will *hearken* to my *v.* *2 Ki* 10:6
not believe he had *hearkened* to my *v.* *Job* 9:16
hearken to *v.* of my words. 34:16
hearken to the *v.* of my cry. *Ps* 5:2
will not *hearken* to the *v.* of. 58:5
would not *hearken* to my *v.* 81:11
the companions *hearken* to thy *v.* *S of S* 8:13
hearken to the *v.* of them. *Jer* 18:19

voices

lepers lifted up their *v.* *Luke* 17:13
instant with loud *v.* that he might be crucified, the *v.* of them. 23:23
knew him not nor the *v.* *Acts* 13:27
they lift up their *v.* and said. 22:22
so many *v.* in the world. *1 Cor* 14:10
out of the throne proceeded *v.* *Rev* 4:5; 16:18
into the earth: and there were *v.* 8:5
woe, by reason of the other *v.* 13
thunders uttered their *v.* 10:3, 4
there were great *v.* in heaven. 11:15
was opened, and there were *v.* 19

void

the earth was without form and *v.* *Gen* 1:2; *Jer* 4:23
but if her husband made them *v.* *Num* 30:12, 15
they are a people *v.* of. *Deut* 32:28
kings sat in a *v.* place. *1 Ki* 22:10*
2 Chr 18:9*
made *v.* the covenant of. *Ps* 89:39*
have made *v.* thy law. 119:126
v. of wisdom despiseth. *Pr* 11:12
my word shall not return to me *v.* *Isa* 55:11
I will make *v.* the counsel. *Jer* 19:7
Nineveh is empty, *v.* *Nah* 2:10
conscience *v.* of offence. *Acts* 24:16
then make *v.* the law? *Rom* 3:31*
law be heirs, faith is made *v.* 4:14
make my glorying *v.* *1 Cor* 9:15
see **understanding**

volume

Lo, I come: in the *v.* of the book it is written. *Ps* 40:7*; *Heb* 10:7*

voluntarily

prepare offerings *v.* to. *Ezek* 46:12*

voluntary

it of his own *v.* will. *Lev* 1:3*
a *v.* offering shall be eaten. 7:16*
princes shall prepare a *v.* burnt. *Ezek* 46:12*
in a *v.* humility and. *Col* 2:18

vomit

riches and shall *v.* them. *Job* 20:15
eaten shalt thou *v.* up. *Pr* 23:8
filled with honey and *v.* it. 25:16

vomit, *substantive*

dog returneth to his *v.* *Pr* 26:11
man staggereth in his *v.* *Isa* 19:14
for all tables are full of *v.* 28:8

shall wallow in his *v.* *Jer* 48:26
turned to his own *v.* *2 Pet* 2:22

vomited

the fish *v.* out Jonah on dry land. *Jonah* 2:10

vomiteth

the land *v.* out her inhabitants. *Lev* 18:25

vow

Is a promise made to God, of doing some good thing hereafter. The use of vows was common in Bible times. When Jacob went into Mesopotamia he vowed to God the tenth of his estate, and promised to offer it at Beth-el to the honour and service of God, Gen 28:20, 22. *There are several laws for the regulation and due execution of* vows. *A man might devote himself, or his children, to the Lord. Samuel was vowed and consecrated to the service of the Lord, and was offered to him, to serve in the tabernacle,* 1 Sam 1:22, 28. *If a man or woman vowed themselves, or their children to the Lord, they were obliged to adhere strictly to his service, according to the conditions of the vow; if not, they were to be redeemed. The price for redeeming persons of such and such an age is particularly limited,* Lev 27:2, 3, *etc. Only if the person was poor, and could not procure the sum limited, the priest imposed a ransom upon him according to his abilities.*

If any one had vowed an animal that was clean, he had not the liberty of redeeming it, or of exchanging it, but was obliged to sacrifice it to the Lord, or give it to the priest, according to the manner of his vow. *If it was an unclean animal, and such as was not allowed to be sacrificed, the priest made valuation of it; and if the proprietor would redeem it, he added a fifth part to the value, by way of forfeit. The same was done in proportion, when the thing vowed was a house or a field. See* Lev 27:9, 10, *etc. They could not devote the firstlings of beasts, because they belonged to the Lord,* Lev 27:26. *Whatsoever was solemnly devoted to the Lord could not be redeemed, of whatever nature or quality it was,* Lev 27:28. *Concerning the vows of the* Nazarites, *see* **Nazarite.**

The vows *and promises of children were void, except they were ratified, either by the express or tacit consent of their parents. And it was the same with the* vows *of married women; they were of no validity, unless they were confirmed by the express or tacit consent of their husbands,* Num 30:1, 2, 3, *etc.*

Under the New Testament, a vow *is either general to all Christians, as that which is made at baptism; or particular and special, as when we bind ourselves to a greater endeavour, to leave some sin, or perform some duty. A* vow, *as one observes, must be made deliberately and devoutly, for a sudden passion makes not a* vow; *and we ought to* vow *nothing but what is in our power to perform. Some vows are of evil things to an evil end; such vows ought neither to be made nor kept; of this kind was the* vow *or curse which the* Jews *bound themselves under, who conspired to murder* Paul, Acts 23:12.

The performance of solemn vows *is strictly enjoined upon us in scripture,* Eccl 5:4.

Jacob vowed a *v.* *Gen* 28:20; 31:13
if the sacrifice be a *v.* *Lev* 7:16
22:18, 21
but for a *v.* it shall not. 22:23
shall make a singular *v.* 27:2
vow a *v.* of a Nazarite. *Num* 6:2
the days of the *v.* 5
according to the *v.* 21
sacrifice in performing a *v.* 15:3, 8
Israel vowed a *v.* to the Lord. 21:2
if a man vow a *v.* 30:2
if a woman vow a *v.* 3
and her father hear her *v.* and. 4
every *v.* of a widow shall stand. 9
every *v.* her husband may. 13
price of a dog for a *v.* *Deut* 23:18
when thou shalt vow a *v.* unto. 21
Jephthah vowed a *v.* *Judg* 11:30
with her according to his *v.* 39
Hannah vowed a *v.* and. *1 Sam* 1:11
up to offer to the Lord his *v.* 21
let me go and pay my *v.* *2 Sam* 15:7
servant vowed a *v.* at Geshur. 8
to thee shall the *v.* be. *Ps* 65:1
when thou vowest a *v.* *Eccl* 5:4
they shall vow a *v.* unto. *Isa* 19:21
head, for he had a *v.* *Acts* 18:18
men which have a *v.* on them. 21:23

vow, *verb*

themselves to *v.* a vow. *Num* 6:2
if forbear to *v.*, it shall. *Deut* 23:22
and *v.* and pay to the Lord your God. *Ps* 76:11
that thou shouldest not *v.* *Eccl* 5:5

vowed

Jacob *v.* a vow. *Gen* 28:20; 31:13
ability that *v.* shall priest. *Lev* 27:8
Nazarites who hath *v.* *Num* 6:21
Israel *v.* a vow to the Lord. 21:2
if all an husband when she *v.* 30:6
and if she *v.* in her husband's. 10
shalt keep according as thou hast *v.* *Deut* 23:23
Jephthah *v.* a vow unto. *Judg* 11:30
and *v.* to the mighty God. *Ps* 132:2
pay that which thou hast *v.* *Eccl* 5:4
pay that that I have *v.* *Jonah* 2:9

vowest

when thou *v.* a vow, defer. *Eccl* 5:4

voweth

who *v.* to the Lord a. *Mal* 1:14

vows

his oblation for all his *v.* *Lev* 22:18
gifts and beside all your *v.* 23:38
shall do beside your *v.* *Num* 29:39
then all her *v.* shall stand. 30:4
7, 9, 11
not any of her *v.* or bonds. 5, 8, 12
then he established all her *v.* 14
thither bring your *v.* *Deut* 12:6, 11
17, 26
thou shalt pay thy *v.* *Job* 22:27
I will pay my *v.* unto the Lord. *Ps* 22:25; 66:13; 116:14, 18
pay thy *v.* 50:14
thy *v.* are upon me, O God. 56:12
O God, hast heard my *v.* 61:5
I may daily perform my *v.* 8
this day have I paid my *v.* *Pr* 7:14
it is a snare after *v.* to make. 20:25
and what, the son of my *v.*? 31:2
surely perform our *v.* *Jer* 44:25
feared the Lord and made *v.* *Jonah* 1:16
O Judah, keep thy solemn feasts, perform thy *v.* *Nah* 1:15

voyage

I perceive this *v.* will be. *Acts* 27:10

vulture

(*A bird of prey, which was declared unclean,* Lev 11:14. *Probably the word means the* kite *as the Revised Versions give it usually, or the* falcon *as in Job*)
v. and the kite after his kind shall. *Lev* 11:14; *Deut* 14:13
a path which the *v.* eye. *Job* 28:7*
there shall the *v.* also be. *Isa* 34:15

W

wafer

one *w.* out of the basket of the unleavened. *Ex* 29:23; *Lev* 8:26
one cake, one *w.* on. *Num* 6:19

wafers

taste of it was like *w.* *Ex* 16:31
and *w.* unleavened anointed. 29:2
w. anointed with oil. *Lev* 2:4; 7:12
Num 6:15

wag

passeth by shall *w.* his. *Jer* 18:16*
w. their heads at daughter. *Lam* 2:15
passeth shall *w.* his hand. *Zeph* 2:15

wages

what shall thy *w.* be ? *Gen* 29:15
appoint me thy *w.* and I will. 30:28
changed my *w.* ten times. 31:7, 41
the speckled shall be thy *w.* 8
this child, I will give thee *w.* *Ex* 2:9
w. of hired not abide. *Lev* 19:13
service without *w.* *Jer* 22:13
yet had he no *w.* nor. *Ezek* 29:18
her spoil shall be the *w.* for. 19
earneth *w.* to put into a. *Hag* 1:6
the hireling in his *w.* *Mal* 3:5
be content with your *w.* *Luke* 3:14
reapeth receiveth *w.* *John* 4:36
for the *w.* of sin is death. *Rom* 6:23
taking *w.* of them to do. *2 Cor* 11:8
Balaam loved the *w.* *2 Pet* 2:15

wagging

passed by reviled him, *w.* their heads. *Mat* 27:39; *Mark* 15:29

waggon

brought a *w.* for two of the princes. *Num* 7:3

waggons

w. out of Egypt. *Gen* 45:19, 21
when Jacob saw the *w.* Joseph. 27
two *w.*, four oxen to sons. *Num* 7:7
four *w.* and eight oxen to the. 8
against thee with *w.* *Ezek* 23:34

wail

w. for the multitude of. *Ezek* 32:18
I will *w.* and howl. *Mi* 1:8
earth shall *w.* for him. *Rev* 1:7*

wailed

them that wept and *w.* greatly. *Mark* 5:38

wailing

decree came there was *w.* *Esth* 4:3
for the mountains will I take up *w.* *Jer* 9:10
let them take up a *w.* for us. 18
for a voice of *w.* is heard out of. 19
teach your daughters *w.* 20
neither shall there be *w.* *Ezek* 7:11
weep for thee with bitter *w.* 27:31*
w. shall be in all streets and they shall say . . . to *w.* *Amos* 5:16
and in all vineyards shall be *w.* 17
I will make a *w.* like the. *Mi* 1:8
there shall be *w.* and gnashing of teeth. *Mat* 13:42*, 50*
the merchants stand afar off, *w.* *Rev* 18:15*, 19*

wait

him by laying of *w.* *Num* 35:20
any thing without laying *w.* 22
in his heart he layeth his *w.* *Jer* 9:8*
see **laid, lay**

wait

Aaron and sons shall *w.* on their priest's office. *Num* 3:10; 8:24
1 Chr 23:28; *2 Chr* 5:11; 13:10
should I *w.* for the Lord ? *2 Ki* 6:33
of my time I will *w.* till. *Job* 14:14
if I *w.* the grave is my house. 17:13
let none that *w.* on thee be ashamed. *Ps* 25:3; 69:6
God of salvation, on thee do I *w.* 25:5
preserve me, for I *w.* on thee. 21
w. on the Lord. 27:14; 37:34
Pr 20:22
w. patiently for him. *Ps* 37:7
that *w.* on the Lord shall inherit. 9
Lord, what *w.* I for ? 39:7
I will *w.* on thy name. 52:9
mark my steps when they *w.* *Ps* 56:6
because of his strength will I *w.* 59:9
w. only on God. 62:5
mine eyes fail while I *w.* for. 69:3
these all *w.* upon thee. 104:27
145:15
so our eyes *w.* on the Lord. 123:2
I *w.* for the Lord, my soul doth *w.* 130:5
I will *w.* upon the Lord. *Isa* 8:17
Lord *w.* to be gracious to you, blessed are all they that *w.* 30:18
but they that *w.* on the Lord shall renew their strength. 40:31
the isles shall *w.* for his law. 42:4
shall not be ashamed that *w.* 49:23
isles shall *w.* upon me. 51:5
we *w.* for light, but behold. 59:9
the isles shall *w.* for me. 60:9
we will *w.* upon thee. *Jer* 14:22
Lord is good to them that *w.* for him. *Lam* 3:25
a man hope and quietly *w.* 26
as troops of robbers *w.* *Hos* 6:9
keep mercy and *w.* on thy God. 12:6
I will *w.* for the God of. *Mi* 7:7
though vision tarry, *w.* for. *Hab* 2:3
therefore *w.* ye upon me. *Zeph* 3:8
ship should *w.* on him. *Mark* 3:9
like unto men that *w.* *Luke* 12:36
but *w.* for the promise. *Acts* 1:4
with patience *w.* for it. *Rom* 8:25
or ministry, let us *w.* on. 12:7*
which *w.* at the altar. *1 Cor* 9:13
we through the Spirit *w.* *Gal* 5:5
and to *w.* for his Son. *1 Thes* 1:10
see **liars**

waited

w. for thy salvation. *Gen* 49:18
the prophet *w.* for king. *1 Ki* 20:38
w. on Naaman's wife. *2 Ki* 5:2
and then they *w.* on their office. *1 Chr* 6:32, 33
porters that *w.* in king's gate. 9:18
2 Chr 35:15
and the priests *w.* on. *2 Chr* 7:6
and Levites that *w.* *Neh* 12:44
the companies of Sheba *w.* *Job* 6:19
he is *w.* for of the sword. 15:22
to me men gave ear, *w.* and. 29:21
w. for me as for the rain. 23
when I *w.* for light, there came. 30:26
now Elihu had *w.* till Job had. 32:4
I *w.* patiently for the Lord. *Ps* 40:1
they *w.* not for counsel. 106:13
wicked have *w.* for me to. 119:95
God, we have *w.* for him. *Isa* 25:9
judgements have we *w.* for. 26:8
us, we have *w.* for thee. 33:2
she saw that she had *w.* *Ezek* 19:5
of Maroth *w.* carefully. *Mi* 1:12
flock that *w.* upon me. *Zech* 11:11
Joseph of Arimathaea, who also *w.* *Mark* 15:43; *Luke* 23:51
the people *w.* for Zacharias. *Luke* 1:21
a soldier that *w.* on him. *Acts* 10:7
Cornelius *w.* for Peter and. 24
Paul *w.* for them, his spirit. 17:16
longsuffering of God *w.* in days of Noah. *1 Pet* 3:20

waiteth

eye of the adulterer *w.* *Job* 24:15
our soul *w.* for the Lord. *Ps* 33:20
truly my soul *w.* upon. 62:1; 130:6
praise *w.* for thee, O God. 65:1
he that *w.* on his master. *Pr* 27:18
prepared for him that *w.* *Isa* 64:4
blessed is he that *w.* and cometh to the 1335 days. *Dan* 12:12
as showers that *w.* not. *Mi* 5:7
w. for the manifestation of. *Rom* 8:19
the husbandman *w.* for. *Jas* 5:7

waiting

from the age of 50 years they shall cease *w.* upon the. *Num* 8:25
w. at the posts of my doors. *Pr* 8:34
Simeon *w.* for the consolation of. *Luke* 2:25
folk *w.* for the moving. *John* 5:3
groan, *w.* for the adoption. *Rom* 8:23
w. for the coming of our Lord Jesus Christ. *1 Cor* 1:7
into the patient *w.* for Christ. *2 Thes* 3:5

wake, awake

when I *a.*, I am still with. *Ps* 139:18
perpetual sleep and not *w.* *Jer* 51:39
prepare war, *w.* up the mighty men. *Joel* 3:9*
whether we *w.* or sleep. *1 Thes* 5:10

waked

angel came again and *w.* *Zech* 4:1

wakened

let heathen be *w.* and. *Joel* 3:12*
as a man that is *w.* out. *Zech* 4:1

wakeneth

he *w.* morning by morning, he *w.* mine ear. *Isa* 50:4

waketh

city, watchman *w.* in vain. *Ps* 127:1
I sleep but my heart *w.* *S of S* 5:2

waking

thou holdest mine eyes *w.* *Ps* 77:4

walk

the Lord, before whom I *w.* *Gen* 24:40
my fathers did *w.* bless. 48:15
whether they will *w.* in. *Exod* 16:4
way wherein they must *w.* 18:20
if he *w.* abroad, he that smote. 21:19
neither shall ye *w.* in their ordinances. *Lev* 18:3; 20:23
if ye *w.* in my statutes and. 26:3
1 Ki 6:12; *Ezek* 33:15; *Zech* 3:7
I will *w.* among you. *Lev* 26:12
if ye *w.* contrary to me. 21, 23, 27
then will I *w.* contrary to you. 24, 28
shall *w.* in all the ways. *Deut* 5:33
13:4; 28:9; *Ezek* 37:24
if ye *w.* after other gods. *Deut* 8:19
though I *w.* in the imagination. 29:19
take diligent heed to *w.* *Josh* 22:5
speak, ye that *w.* by the. *Judg* 5:10
thy house should *w.* before me for ever. *1 Sam* 2:30
he shall *w.* before mine anointed. 35
thou art old, thy sons *w.* not in. 8:5
w. to keep my commandments as . . . David did *w.* *1 Ki* 3:14; 8:25
9:4; 11:38; *2 Chr* 7:17
with thy servants that *w.* before thee with all. *1 Ki* 8:23; *2 Chr* 6:14
the good way wherein they should *w.* *1 Ki* 8:36; *2 Chr* 6:27
the wicked *w.* on every. *Ps* 12:8
though I *w.* through the valley. 23:4
but as for me, I will *w.* in mine. 26:11
that I may *w.* before God in. 56:13
they know not; they *w.* on in. 82:5
from them that *w.* uprightly. 84:11
teach me, O Lord, I will *w.* 86:11
shall *w.* in the light of thy. 89:15
if his children *w.* not in my. 30
I will *w.* in my house with a. 101:2
have they, but they *w.* not. 115:7
I will *w.* before the Lord in. 116:9
they do no iniquity, they *w.* 119:3
I will *w.* at liberty, for I seek. 45
I *w.* in the midst of trouble. 138:7
way wherein I should *w.* 143:8
he is a buckler to them that *w.* uprightly. *Pr* 2:7
that thou mayest *w.* in the way. 20
then shalt thou *w.* in thy way. 3:23
we will *w.* in his paths. *Isa* 2:3
Mi 4:2
Jacob, let us *w.* in the light. *Isa* 2:5
they *w.* with stretched forth. 3:16
that I should not *w.* in the way. 8:11
redeemed shall *w.* there. 35:9
they that wait on Lord shall *w.* 40:31
spirit to them that *w.* therein. 42:5
for they would not *w.* in his ways. 24
wait for brightness, but we *w.* 59:9
nor *w.* after imagination. *Jer* 3:17
the house of Judah shall *w.* with. 18
but they said, We will not *w.* 6:16
if ye *w.* not after other gods to. 7:6
will ye *w.* after other gods whom? 9
every neighbour will *w.* with. 9:4
w. in imagination of their heart, and *w.* after. 13:10; 16:12; 18:12
adultery, and *w.* in lies. 23:14
way wherein we may *w.* 42:3

the foxes w. upon it. Lam 5:18
w. in my statutes. Ezek 11:20
shall w. in my judgements. 37:24
those that w. in pride. Dan 4:37
they shall w. after the Lord: he shall roar like a. Hos 11:10
the just shall w. in them. 14:9
they shall w. every one. Joel 2:8
two w. together except? Amos 3:3
w. every one in name of his god, and we will w. in the name. Mi 4:5
and ye w. in the counsels of. 6:16
thou didst w. through the sea. Hab 3:15*
that they shall w. like blind men. Zeph 1:17
they might w. to and fro through the earth. Zech 6:7
they shall w. up and down. 10:12
the lame w., the lepers are cleansed. Mat 11:5; Luke 7:22
why w. not thy disciples? Mark 7:5
men that w. over them. Luke 11:44
I must w. to-day and. 13:33
communications as ye w.? 24:17
for Jesus would not w. John 7:1
shall not w. in darkness but. 8:12
if any man w. in the day. 11:9
if a man w. in the night, he. 10
who also w. in the steps of that faith of. Rom 4:12
so we should w. in newness of. 6:4
who w. not after flesh, but. 8:1, 4
for we w. by faith, not. 2 Cor 5:7
I will dwell in them and w. 6:16
we w. in the flesh, not war. 10:3
as many as w. according. Gal 6:16
ordained we should w. Eph 2:10
ye w. worthy of the vocation. 4:1
that ye w. not as other Gentiles. 17
then that ye w. circumspectly. 5:15
mark them which w. so. Phil 3:17
many w. of whom I told you. 18
that ye might w. worthy of the Lord. Col 1:10; 1 Thes 2:12
ye may w. honestly. 1 Thes 4:12
some which w. among you disorderly. 2 Thes 3:11
but chiefly them that w. 2 Pet 2:10
have fellowship, and w. in darkness. 1 John 1:6
but if we w. in the light as he. 7
w. after his commandments, as ye . . . ye should w. 2 John 6
to hear that my children w. 3 John 4
mockers should w. after. Jude 18
shall w. with me in white. Rev 3:4
see, nor hear, nor w. 9:20
watcheth, lest he w. naked. 16:15
the nations shall w. in the light. 21:24

walk, *imperatively*

arise, w. through the land. Gen 13:17; Josh 18:8
Almighty God, w. before me. Gen 17:1
w. about Zion and go. Ps 48:12
my son, w. not in the way. Pr 1:15
w. in the ways of thy heart and eyes. Eccl 11:9
O Jacob, let us w. in the. Isa 2:5
This is the way, w. ye in it. 30:21
w. in the light of your fire and. 50:11
the good way, w. therein. Jer 6:16
go not forth into fields, nor w. 25
w. ye in all the ways I. 7:23
w. ye not in statutes. Ezek 20:18
they might w. to and fro. Zech 6:7
or to say, Arise and w. Mat 9:5
Mark 2:9; Luke 5:23; John 5:8
11, 12; Acts 3:6
w. while ye have the light, lest darkness. John 12:35
let us w. honestly as in the day. Rom 13:13
as the Lord hath called every one, so let him w. 1 Cor 7:17
w. in the Spirit, and not fulfil the lusts. Gal 5:16, 25
w. in love. Eph 5:2
w. as children of light. 8
let us w. by the same rule. Phil 3:16
Christ, so w. ye in him. Col 2:6
w. in wisdom toward them. 4:5

to **walk**

to w. in my ordinances. Lev 18:4
to w. in his ways, and fear him. Deut 8:6; 10:12; 11:22; 13:5
19:9; 26:17; 30:16; Josh 22:5
Judg 2:22; 1 Ki 2:3; 8:58
2 Chr 6:31
take heed to w. before. 1 Ki 2:4
heart perfect, to w. in his statutes. 8:61; Ezek 36:27
a light thing to w. in sins. 1 Ki 16:31
Jehu took no heed to w. 2 Ki 10:31
Josiah made a covenant to w. after. 23:3; 2 Chr 34:31
take heed to w. in my law. 2 Chr 6:16
ought ye not to w. in the fear of God? Neh 5:9
they entered into an oath to w. 10:29
they refused to w. in his. Ps 78:10
leave right to w. in ways. Pr 2:13
poor that knoweth to w. Eccl 6:8
to w. in paths, in a way. Jer 18:15
if ye will not hearken to w. 26:4
I will cause them to w. in a. 31:9
I will cause men to w. Ezek 36:12
nor have we obeyed to w. Dan 9:10
to w. humbly with thy God. Mi 6:8
he will make me to w. Hab 3:19
whom Lord hath sent to w. Zech 1:10
will give places to w. among. 3:7
they saw the lame to w. Mat 15:31
the scribes desire to w. Luke 20:46
had made this man to w. Acts 3:12
suffered all nations to w. 14:16
to circumcise, nor to w. after. 21:21
how ye ought to w. and. 1 Thes 4:1
ought himself so to w. 1 John 2:6

walked

Enoch w. with God. Gen 5:22, 24
Noah was a just man, and w. 6:9
Israel w. upon the dry. Ex 14:29
that also they have w. Lev 26:40
Israel w. forty years in. Josh 5:6
of the way their fathers w. in. Judg 2:17
travellers w. through byways. 5:6
when Israel w. through the. 11:16
Samuel's sons w. not. 1 Sam 8:3
Abner and his men w. 2 Sam 2:29
David w. on the roof of the. 11:2
that they walk before me as thou hast w. 1 Ki 8:25
as David thy father w. 9:4
2 Chr 6:16; 7:17
have not w. in my ways. 1 Ki 11:33
Ezek 5:6, 7; 11:12; 20:13, 16, 21
he w. in the way of his father. 1 Ki 15:26; 22:52
in the sight of the Lord and w. in. 15:34; 16:2; 2 Ki 13:6; 17:22
returned, and w. in house. 2 Ki 4:35
Hoshea w. in the statutes of. 17:8
Judah kept not commandments of the Lord, but w. in. 19; 2 Chr 21:13
forsook the Lord, and w. not in the way of the Lord. 2 Ki 21:22
Jer 9:13; 32:23; 44:10, 23
Josiah w. in the ways of David. 2 Ki 22:2; 2 Chr 34:2
for three years they w. in the way of David. 2 Chr 11:17
Jehoshaphat w. in God's. 17:4
hast not w. in the ways of. 21:12
when by his light I w. Job 29:3
if mine heart w. after mine. 31:7
we w. to the house of. Ps 55:14
to hearts' lust: they w. in. 81:12
O that Israel had w. in my ways! 13
in the way I w. have they. 142:3
people that w. in darkness. Isa 9:2
as my servant Isaiah hath w. 20:3
that they have w. after vanity. Jer 2:5, 8
but w. in counsels of their evil heart. 7:24; 11:8
after whom they have w. 8:2; 9:14
16:11
yet hast not thou w. Ezek 16:47
hath w. in my statutes and. 18:9, 17
thou hast w. in the way of. 23:31
hast w. in the midst of the. 28:14
way which their fathers w. Amos 2:4
even the old lion, w. Nah 2:11

we have w. to and fro through the earth. Zech 1:11; 6:7
what profit that we have w. mournfully? Mal 3:14
damsel arose and w. Mark 5:42
to two of them as they w. 16:12
many disciples w. no more with him. John 6:66
Jesus w. no more openly. 11:54
and he leaping up, stood and w. Acts 3:8; 14:10
a cripple, who never had w. 14:8
who think as if we w. 2 Cor 10:2
gain of you? w. we not in the same spirit? w. we not in? 12:18
but when I saw they w. not. Gal 2:14
wherein in time past ye w. Eph 2:2
Col 3:7
w. in lasciviousness. 1 Pet 4:3

he **walked**

to David, as he w. before. 1 Ki 3:6
Abijam w. in all the sins of his father. 15:3; 2 Ki 21:21
for he w. in all the ways. 1 Ki 16:26
he w. in all the ways of Asa. 22:43
2 Chr 20:32
and he w. in the way of the kings of. 2 Ki 8:18, 27; 16:3; 2 Chr 21:6
22:3, 5; 28:2
he w. in the first ways. 2 Chr 17:3
Nebuchadnezzar w. in the palace of. Dan 4:29
he willingly w. after the. Hos 5:11
he w. with me in peace. Mal 2:6
Peter w. on the water. Mat 14:29
to walk even as he w. 1 John 2:6

I have **walked**

and that I have w. Lev 26:41
I have w. before you from childhood. 1 Sam 12:2
I have w. in a tent and tabernacle. 2 Sam 7:6
in all places wherein I have w. 7
remember how I have w. 2 Ki 20:3
if I have w. with vanity. Job 31:5
judge me, for I have w. Ps 26:1
I have w. in thy truth. 3; Isa 38:3

walkedst

when young, w. whither. John 21:18

walkest

shalt talk of them when thou w. Deut 6:7; 11:19
day thou w. abroad. 1 Ki 2:42
thou w. through the fire. Isa 43:2
thou thyself w. orderly. Acts 21:24
brother grieved, now w. Rom 14:15
truth in thee even as thou w. 3 John 3

walketh

what man is this that w.? Gen 24:65
thy God w. in midst of. Deut 23:14
behold, the king w. 1 Sam 12:2
he is cast into a net, and he w. Job 18:8
he w. in the circuit of heaven. 22:14
goeth in company, and w. with. 34:8
blessed the man that w. not in. Ps 1:1
he that w. uprightly shall dwell. 15:2
man w. in a vain shew. 39:6
and their tongue w. through. 73:9
nor for the pestilence that w. 91:6
he that w. in a perfect way. 101:6
who w. upon the wings of. 104:3
blessed is every one that w. 128:1
a wicked man w. with a. Pr 6:12
w. uprightly w. surely. 10:9; 28:18
he that w. with wise men. 13:20
he that w. in uprightness. 14:2
a man of understanding w. 15:21*
better is the poor that w. 19:1; 28:6
just man w. in his integrity. 20:7
whoso w. wisely, he shall. 28:26
the fool w. in darkness. Eccl 2:14
when he that is a fool w. by. 10:3
he that w. righteously. Isa 33:15
that w. in darkness and hath. 50:10
which w. in a way that was. 65:2
it is not in man that w. Jer 10:23
that w. after the imagination. 23:17
whose heart w. after the heart of their detestable things. Ezek 11:21
my words do good to him that w. uprightly. Mi 2:7

spirit is gone out, he *w.* through dry. *Mat* 12:43; *Luke* 11:24
he that *w.* in darkness. *John* 12:35
from brother that *w.* *2 Thes* 3:6
devil *w.* about seeking. *1 Pet* 5:8
hateth his brother, *w.* *1 John* 2:11
w. in midst of the seven. *Rev* 2:1

walking

voice of Lord *w.* in garden. *Gen* 3:8
Lord knoweth thy *w.* through this great wilderness. *Deut* 2:7
Solomon, *w.* as David. *1 Ki* 3:3
Zimri *w.* in the way of. 16:19
from *w.* up and down in the earth. *Job* 1:7; 2:2
or beheld the moon *w.* in. 31:26
I have seen princes *w.* *Eccl* 10:7
haughty, *w.* and mincing. *Isa* 3:16
and he did so, *w.* naked. 20:2
each one *w.* in his uprightness. 57:2
all grievous revolters, *w.* *Jer* 6:28
I see four men loose, *w.* *Dan* 3:25
if a man *w.* in the spirit and. *Mi* 2:11
Jesus went to them *w.* *Mat* 14:25
saw him *w.* on the sea, they were troubled. 26; *Mark* 6:48
I see men as trees *w.* *Mark* 8:24
w. in all the commandments blameless. *Luke* 1:6
lame man *w.* and leaping. *Acts* 3:8, 9
were edified, *w.* in the fear. 9:31
not *w.* in craftiness, nor. *2 Cor* 4:2
scoffers, *w.* after their own lusts. *2 Pet* 3:3; *Jude* 16
thy children *w.* in truth. *2 John* 4

wall

in their selfwill they digged down a *w.* *Gen* 49:6*
branches run over the *w.* 22
waters were a *w.* to them. *Ex* 14:22
sight lower than the *w.* *Lev* 14:37
a *w.* being on this side, a *w.* on. *Num* 22:24*
Balaam's foot against the *w.* 25
house upon the town *w.* *Josh* 2:15
the *w.* of the city shall fall down flat. 6:5, 20
I will smite David to the *w.* *1 Sam* 18:11; 19:10
sat upon his seat by the *w.* 20:25
they were a *w.* to us both. 25:16
morning light any that pisseth against the *w.* 22*; 34*; *1 Ki* 14:10* 16:11*; 21:21*; *2 Ki* 9:8*
they fastened Saul's body to the *w.* *1 Sam* 31:10
knew ye not that they would shoot from the *w.*? *2 Sam* 11:20
the *w.*, why went ye nigh the *w.*? 21
the people battered the *w.* 20:15
head shall be thrown over the *w.* 21
by my God have I leaped over a *w.* 22:30; *Ps* 18:29
that springs out of the *w.* *1 Ki* 4:33
a *w.* fell upon 27,000 of the. 20:30
dogs shall eat Jezebel by *w.* 21:23*
a burnt offering upon the *w.* *2 Ki* 3:27
a little chamber on the *w.* 4:10
king was passing by upon the *w.* 6:26
was sprinkled on the *w.* 9:33
language in the ears of the people that are on the *w.* 18:26; *Isa* 36:11
then Hezekiah turned his face to the *w.* *2 Ki* 20:2; *Isa* 38:2
Joash brake down the *w.* of Jerusalem. *2 Chr* 25:23
Nebuchadnezzar brake down the *w.* 36:19
who hath commanded you to make this *w.*? *Ezra* 5:3
to give us a *w.* in Judah. 9:9
the *w.* of Jerusalem is. *Neh* 1:3
I viewed the *w.* 2:15
let us build the *w.* 17
break down their stone *w.* 4:3
so built we the *w.*; all the *w.* was. 6
all of us to the *w.*, every one. 15
thou buildest the *w.*, that thou. 6:6
so the *w.* was finished in the. 15
at the dedication of the *w.* of. 12:27
Why lodge ye about the *w.*? 13:21
as a bowing *w.* shall ye be. *Ps* 62:3
as an high *w.* in his. *Pr* 18:11
the stone *w.* thereof was. *Pr* 24:31
standeth behind our *w.* *S of S* 2:9
if she be a *w.*, we will build. 8:9
I am a *w.* 10
of Lord on every fenced *w.* *Isa* 2:15
I will break down the *w.* of. 5:5*
is as a storm against the *w.* 25:4
swelling out in an high *w.* 30:13
we grope for the *w.* like the. 59:10
thee a fenced brasen *w.* *Jer* 15:20
I will kindle a fire in the *w.* of. 49:27
yea, the *w.* of Babylon shall. 51:44
to destroy the *w.* of the. *Lam* 2:8
their heart cried, O *w.* of the. 18
for a *w.* of iron between. *Ezek* 4:3
a hole in the *w.* 8:7
dig in the *w.* 8; 12:5
Israel pourtrayed upon the *w.* 8:10
lo, when the *w.* is fallen. 13:12, 15
accomplish my wrath upon the *w.* 15
every *w.* shall fall. 38:20
after he measured the *w.* of. 41:5
in setting the *w.* between me. 43:8
on the plaster of the *w.* *Dan* 5:5
street shall be built, and the *w.* 9:25*
I will make a *w.* that she shall not find. *Hos* 2:6*
they shall climb the *w.* *Joel* 2:7
they shall run upon the *w.* and. 9
a fire on the *w.* of Gaza. *Amos* 1:7
on the *w.* of Tyrus. 10
in the *w.* of Rabbah. 14
hand on the *w.*, a serpent bit. 5:19
behold, the Lord stood upon a *w.* 7:7
haste to the *w.* thereof. *Nah* 2:5
shall cry out of the *w.* *Hab* 2:11
disciples by night let him down by the *w.* *Acts* 9:25; *2 Cor* 11:33
smite thee, thou whited *w.* *Acts* 23:3
broken down the middle *w.* *Eph* 2:14
the *w.* of the city had twelve foundations. *Rev* 21:14
the building of the *w.* of it was. 18
see **built**

walled

if a man sell a dwelling house in a *w.* city. *Lev* 25:29
the house in the *w.* city shall. 30
the cities *w.* and very great. *Num* 13:28*; *Deut* 1:28*

wallow

gird thee with sackcloth, *w.* *Jer* 6:26
cry, *w.* yourselves in ashes. 25:34
Moab shall *w.* in his vomit. 48:26
they shall *w.* themselves. *Ezek* 27:30

wallowed

Amasa *w.* in blood in. *2 Sam* 20:12
fell on the ground and *w.* *Mark* 9:20

wallowing

and the sow washed to *w.* *2 Pet* 2:22

walls

if plague be in the *w.* *Lev* 14:37, 39
having no *w.* counted as fields. 25:31
were fenced with high *w.* *Deut* 3:5
till thy high fenced *w.* come. 28:52
men fled between two *w.* *2 Ki* 25:4
Chaldees brake down the *w.* of Jerusalem round. 10; *Jer* 39:8
if this city be built and *w.* set up. *Ezra* 4:13, 16
timber is laid in the *w.* 5:8
heard that the *w.* of Jerusalem. *Neh* 4:7
oil within their *w.* *Job* 24:11
build thou the *w.* of. *Ps* 51:18
they go about it on *w.* thereof. 55:10
peace be within thy *w.* 122:7
broken down, without *w.* *Pr* 25:28
keepers of the *w.* took. *S of S* 5:7
of breaking down the *w.* *Isa* 22:5
the fortress of thy *w.* shall. 25:12
salvation will God appoint for *w.* and bulwarks. 26:1
w. are continually before me. 49:16
w. a place and a name better. 56:5
strangers shall build up thy *w.* 60:10
thou shalt call thy *w.* salvation. 18
I have set watchmen on thy *w.* 62:6
against the *w.* of Jerusalem. *Jer* 1:15
go ye up upon her *w.* and. 5:10
Babylon's *w.* are. 50:15; 51:58
they shall destroy the *w.* of Tyrus. *Ezek* 26:4, 12
of Arvad were upon thy *w.* 27:11
talking against thee by the *w.* 33:30
dwelling without *w.* or gates. 38:11
in the day that thy *w.* *Mi* 7:11
as towns without *w.* *Zech* 2:4
by faith the *w.* of Jericho fell down. *Heb* 11:30

wander

caused me to *w.* from. *Gen* 20:13
children shall *w.* in the wilderness. *Num* 14:33; 32:13; *Ps* 107:40
that causeth blind to *w.* *Deut* 27:18
he causeth them to *w.* in. *Job* 12:24
when his young ravens *w.* for. 38:41
then would I *w.* far off. *Ps* 55:7
let them *w.* up and down. 59:15
O let me not *w.* from thy. 119:10
they shall *w.* every one. *Isa* 47:15
Thus have they loved to *w.* *Jer* 14:10
that shall cause him to *w.* 48:12
shall *w.* from sea to sea. *Amos* 8:12

wandered

Hagar *w.* in the wilderness of Beersheba. *Gen* 21:14
they *w.* in the wilderness. *Ps* 107:4 *Isa* 16:8
have *w.* as blind men. *Lam* 4:14
my sheep *w.* through. *Ezek* 34:6
two or three cities *w.* to. *Amos* 4:8
w. about in sheepskins. *Heb* 11:37
they *w.* in deserts, in mountains. 38

wanderers

I will send to him *w.* *Jer* 48:12
they shall be *w.* among. *Hos* 9:17

wanderest

every green tree thou *w.* *Jer* 2:20

wandereth

he *w.* abroad for bread. *Job* 15:23
that *w.* out of the way. *Pr* 21:16
as a bird that *w.* from her nest, so is a man that *w.* from his. 27:8
bewray not him that *w.* *Isa* 16:3
none shall gather up him that *w.* *Jer* 49:5

wandering

was *w.* in the field. *Gen* 37:15
bird by *w.*, as the swallow. *Pr* 26:2
sight of the eyes than the *w.* *Eccl* 6:9
it shall be as a *w.* bird. *Isa* 16:2
to be idle, *w.* about. *1 Tim* 5:13
w. stars to whom is reserved darkness. *Jude* 13

wanderings

thou tellest my *w.* *Ps* 56:8

want

serve thy enemies in *w.* *Deut* 28:48
she shall eat them for *w.* of all. 57
a place where is no *w.* *Judg* 18:10 19:19
they embrace the rock for *w.* of. *Job* 24:8
for *w.* and famine they were. 30:3
if I have seen any perish for *w.* 31:19
there is no *w.* to them. *Ps* 34:9
and thy *w.* as an armed man. *Pr* 6:11; 24:34
fools die for *w.* of wisdom. 10:21*
there is that is destroyed for *w.* of judgement. 13:23*
in *w.* of people is destruction. 14:28
that is hasty only to *w.* 21:5
to rich shall surely come to *w.* 22:16
stricken through for *w.* of. *Lam* 4:9
I have given you *w.* of bread in. *Amos* 4:6
she of her *w.* cast in. *Mark* 12:44
he began to be in *w.* *Luke* 15:14
be a supply for their *w.* *2 Cor* 8:14
not only supplieth the *w.* of. 9:12
not speak in respect of *w.* *Phil* 4:11

want, *verb*

my shepherd, I shall not *w.* *Ps* 23:1
Lord shall not *w.* any good. 34:10
of the wicked shall *w.* *Pr* 13:25
none shall *w.* her mate. *Isa* 34:16
David not *w.* a man to sit. *Jer* 33:17
Levites not *w.* a man. 18
Jonadab shall not *w.* a man. 35:19
that they may *w.* bread. *Ezek* 4:17

wanted
we have *w.* all things. *Jer* 44:18
when they *w.* wine. *John* 2:3*
I *w.* I was chargeable. *2 Cor* 11:9

wanteth
shall lend him for his need in that he *w.* *Deut* 15:8
that *w.* understanding. *Pr* 9:4, 16
in multitude of words there *w.* 10:19
prince that *w.* understanding. 28:16
so that he *w.* nothing for his soul. *Eccl* 6:2
goblet that *w.* not liquor. *S of S* 7:2

wanting
and all his priests, let none be *w.*: whoso be *w.* shall not. *2 Ki* 10:19
words, yet they are *w.* to. *Pr* 19:7*
that which is *w.* cannot. *Eccl* 1:15
thou art weighed in the balances, and art found *w.* *Dan* 5:27
the things that are *w.* *Tit* 1:5
that nothing be *w.* unto them. 3:13
ye may be perfect and entire, *w.* nothing. *Jas* 1:4*

wanton
Zion walk with *w.* eyes. *Isa* 3:16
to wax *w.* against Christ. *1 Tim* 5:11
ye have lived in pleasure and been *w.* *Jas* 5:5*

wantonness
walk honestly, not in chambering and *w.* *Rom* 13:13
they allure through lusts and much *w.* *2 Pet* 2:18*

wants
let all thy *w.* lie on me. *Judg* 19:20
that ministered to my *w.* *Phil* 2:25*

war
We may distinguish two kinds of wars among the Hebrews. Some were of obligation as being expressly commanded by the Lord; but others were free and voluntary. The first were such as God commanded them to undertake. For example, against the Amalekites and the Canaanites, which were nations devoted to destruction for their sins. The others were undertaken by the captains of the people, to revenge some injuries offered to the nation, to punish some insults or offences. Such was that which the Hebrews made against the city of Gibeah, and against the tribe of Benjamin, which would uphold them in their fault, Judg 20:8. *And such was that which David made against the Ammonites, whose king had affronted his ambassadors,* 2 Sam 10:1–14. *Or to maintain and defend their allies; as that of Joshua against the kings of the Canaanites, to protect the Gibeonites,* Josh 10:6–11.

The common meaning of war, in scripture, is a state of hostility between nations, states, provinces, or parties, as in 1 Ki 14:30; Luke 14:31, *and many other places: but it is taken in a spiritual sense in* 2 Cor 10:3, *where the apostle says,* We do not *war* after the flesh.

when there is *w.* they join. *Ex* 1:10
repent when they see *w.* 13:17
will have *w.* with Amalek. 17:16
a noise of *w.* in the camp. 32:17
all that are able to go forth to *w.* *Num* 1:3; 20:22; 26:2; *Deut* 3:18
ye go to *w.* ye shall blow. *Num* 10:9
Arm some of yourselves to *w.* 31:3
1000 shall ye send to *w.* 4
shall your brethren go to *w.*? 32:6
armed before the Lord to *w.* 20, 27
hath God assayed to take him a nation by *w.*? *Deut* 4:34
but will make *w.* against thee. 20:12, 19, 20
when thou goest forth to *w.* 21:10*
taken a wife, he shall not go to *w.*24:5
and the land rested from *w.* *Josh* 11:23; 14:15
so is my strength now, for *w.* 14:11
that Israel might know to teach them *w.* *Judg* 3:2
chose new gods, then was *w.* in. 5:8
not to each his wife in the *w.* 21:22
was sore *w.* against Philistines. *1 Sam* 14:52; 19:8
for the Philistines make *w.* 28:15
long *w.* between the house of Saul and the house of David. *2 Sam* 3:1
David demanded how the *w.* 11:7
shed the blood of *w.* in peace, and put the blood of *w.* *1 Ki* 2:5
w. between Rehoboam and Jeroboam. 14:30; 15:6
there was *w.* between Abijam. 15:7
there was *w.* between Asa and. 16, 32
or be come out for *w.*, take. 20:18
three years without *w.* 22:1
counsel and strength for *w.* *2 Ki* 18:20
they made *w.* with the Hagarites. *1 Chr* 5:10, 19
many slain, because the *w.* was. 22
if thy people go to *w.* *2 Chr* 6:34*
no *w.* to the 35th year. 15:19
house wherewith I have *w.* 35:21
redeem in *w.* from power. *Job* 5:20
changes and *w.* are against. 10:17*
reserved against the day of *w.* 38:23
though *w.* should rise. *Ps* 27:3
words smooth, but *w.* was in. 55:21
the people that delight in *w.* 68:30
I speak, they are for *w.* 120:7
are gathered together for *w.* 140:2
good advice make *w.* *Pr* 20:18
counsel thou shalt make thy *w.* 24:6
a time of *w.*, and a time. *Eccl* 3:8
there is no discharge in that *w.* 8:8
nor shall they learn *w.* any more. *Isa* 2:4; *Mi* 4:3
thy mighty shall fall in *w.* *Isa* 3:25
from the grievousness of *w.* 21:15
counsel and strength for *w.* 36:5
hast heard the alarm of *w.* *Jer* 4:19
prepare ye *w.* against her, arise. 6:4
in array as men for *w.* against. 23*
Nebuchadnezzar maketh *w.* 21:2
where we shall see no *w.* 42:14
We are mighty men for *w.*? 48:14
an alarm of *w.* to be heard in. 49:2
nor Pharaoh make for him in *w.* *Ezek* 17:17
the same horn made *w.* *Dan* 7:21
to the end of the *w.* are. 9:26
prepare *w.*, wake up the. *Joel* 3:9
as men averse from *w.* *Mi* 2:8
they even prepare *w.* against. 3:5
king going to make *w.*? *Luke* 14:31
the beast shall make *w.* *Rev* 11:7
there was *w.* in heaven against. 12:7
to make *w.* with the remnant of. 17
who is able to make *w.* with? 13:4
to make *w.* with saints. 7; 17:14
righteousness doth he make *w.* 19:11
kings gathered to make *w.* 19
see **expert, man, men**

war, *verb*
doest me wrong to *w.* *Judg* 11:27
he teacheth my hands to *w.* *2 Sam* 22:35; *Ps* 18:34; 144:1
Rezin and Pekah came up to Jerusalem to *w.* *2 Ki* 16:5; *Isa* 7:1
they that *w.* against thee. *Isa* 41:12
walk in flesh, we do not *w.* *2 Cor* 10:3
that thou mightest *w.* a. *1 Tim* 1:18
of your lusts that *w.* in. *Jas* 4:1
ye fight and *w.* yet ye have not. 2
from lusts which *w.* *1 Pet* 2:11

weapons of **war**
girded on *weapons of w.* *Deut* 1:41
six hundred with *weapons of w.* *Judg* 18:11, 16, 17
how are the *weapons of w.* perished! *2 Sam* 1:27
better than *weapons of w.* *Eccl* 9:18
back the *weapons of w.* *Jer* 21:4
battle axe and *weapons of w.* 51:20
hell with *weapons of w.* *Ezek* 32:27

ward
put them in *w.* *Gen* 40:3, 4, 7
wroth and put me in *w.* 41:10
Joseph put his brethren in *w.* 42:17
the blasphemer in *w.* *Lev* 24:12
gatherer of sticks in *w.* *Num* 15:34
ten concubines in *w.* *2 Sam* 20:3
had kept the *w.* of the house of Saul. *1 Chr* 12:29*
they cast lots, *w.* against *w.* 25:8*
lot came by causeway of going up, *w.* against *w.* 26:16
to give thanks *w.* over against *w.* *Neh* 12:24
were porters keeping the *w.* at. 25
kept *w.* of their God and *w.* of. 45
set in my *w.* whole nights. *Isa* 21:8
Irijah a captain of the *w.* *Jer* 37:13
they put Zedekiah in *w.* *Ezek* 19:9*
they were past first and second *w.* *Acts* 12:10

wardrobe
the wife of Shallum, the keeper of the *w.* *2 Ki* 22:14; *2 Chr* 34:22

wards
of the tabernacle by *w.* *1 Chr* 9:23
having *w.* one against another to minister. 26:12*
I appointed the *w.* of. *Neh* 13:30

ware
w. no clothes nor abode. *Luke* 8:27

ware
Lord shall come in an hour he is not *w.* of. *Mat* 24:50
they were *w.* of it and fled to Lystra. *Acts* 14:6
coppersmith be thou *w.* *2 Tim* 4:15

ware, *substantive*
if people bring *w.* on. *Neh* 10:31
brought all manner of *w.* 13:16
sellers of all kind of *w.* lodged. 20

wares
gather up thy *w.* out of. *Jer* 10:17
by reason of the multitude of *w.* *Ezek* 27:16*, 18*, 33
the mariners cast forth *w.* *Jonah* 1:5

warfare
gathered armies for *w.* *1 Sam* 28:1
cry to her that her *w.* is. *Isa* 40:2
goeth a *w.* any time at? *1 Cor* 9:7*
the weapons of our *w.* *2 Cor* 10:4
mightest war a good *w.* *1 Tim* 1:18

warm
and the flesh of the child waxed *w.* *2 Ki* 4:34
what time they wax *w.* *Job* 6:17
how thy garments are *w.* 37:17
how can one be *w.* alone? *Eccl* 4:11
he will take thereof and *w.* *Isa* 44:15
and saith, Aha, I am *w.* 16
not be a coal to *w.* at nor fire. 47:14
ye clothe you, but there is none *w.* *Hag* 1:6

warmed
he were not *w.* with fleece. *Job* 31:20
Peter *w.* himself. *Mark* 14:54 *John* 18:18, 25
depart in peace, be ye *w.* *Jas* 2:16

warmeth
ostrich that *w.* her eggs. *Job* 39:14
w. himself and saith, Aha. *Isa* 44:16

warming
when she saw Peter *w.* *Mark* 14:67

warn
shall *w.* them that they trespass not. *2 Chr* 19:10
nor speakest to *w.* *Ezek* 3:18; 33:8
yet if thou *w.* wicked. 3:19; 33:9
if thou *w.* the righteous. 3:21
w. the people 33:3, 7
I ceased not to *w.* every. *Acts* 20:31
beloved sons I *w.* you. *1 Cor* 4:14
w. them that are unruly. *1 Thes* 5:14

warned
place man of God *w.* him. *2 Ki* 6:10
by them is thy servant *w.* *Ps* 19:11
live, because he is *w.* *Ezek* 3:21
see and the people be not *w.* 33:6
Joseph being *w.* of God departed. *Mat* 2:12, 22
of vipers, who hath *w.* you to flee from the wrath? 3:7; *Luke* 3:7
Cornelius *w.* from God. *Acts* 10:22
by faith Noah being *w.* *Heb* 11:7

warning

I speak and give *w.*? *Jer* 6:10
word and give them *w.* *Ezek* 3:17
thou givest him not *w.* nor. 18, 20
taketh not *w.* 33:4
he heard and took not *w.* 5
w. every man, and teaching. *Col* 1:28

warp

plague in the *w.* or woof. *Lev* 13:48
49, 51, 57, 59
burn *w.* 52
rend *w.* 56
wash the *w.* 58

warred

and they *w.* against the Midianites. *Num* 31:7
Balak king of Moab *w.* *Josh* 24:9*
Jeroboam, how he *w.* *1 Ki* 14:19
acts of Jehoshaphat, how he *w.* 22:45
the king of Syria *w.* *2 Ki* 6:8
Uzziah *w.* against the. *2 Chr* 26:6

warreth

no man that *w.* entangleth. *2 Tim* 2:4*

warring

found the king of Assyria *w.* against. *2 Ki* 19:8; *Isa* 37:8
law in my members *w.* *Rom* 7:23

warrior, -s

chosen men who were *w.* *1 Ki* 12:21
2 Chr 11:1
battle of the *w.* is with. *Isa* 9:5*

wars

it is said in the book of the *w.* of the. *Num* 21:14
had not known all the *w.* of Canaan. *Judg* 3:1
David, for Hadadezer had *w.* with Toi. *2 Sam* 8:10; *1 Chr* 18:10
hast made great *w.* *1 Chr* 22:8
thou shalt have *w.* *2 Chr* 16:9
he maketh *w.* to cease. *Ps* 46:9
ye shall hear of *w.* and rumours of *w.* *Mat* 24:6; *Mark* 13:7; *Luke* 21:9
from whence come *w.*? *Jas* 4:1

was

with God and *w.* not. *Gen* 5:24
God *w.* with the lad, he grew. 21:20
that the Lord *w.* with thee. 26:28
Jacob told Rachel, he *w.* her. 29:12
thus I *w.* in the day, drought. 31:40
and behold, Joseph *w.* not. 37:29
Lord *w.* with Joseph, he. 39:2, 22
drew near where God *w.* *Ex* 20:21
w. not in the company. *Num* 27:3
as I *w.* with Moses, so I. *Josh* 1:5
God be with thee as he *w.* 17
the Lord *w.* with Joshua, and. 6:27
as yet I am as strong as I *w.* 14:11
how *w.* this wickedness? *Judg* 20:3
they went where the man of God *w.* *1 Sam* 9:10
the ewe lamb *w.* unto. *2 Sam* 12:3
the counsel of Ahithophel *w.* 16:23
whose the living child *w.* *1 Ki* 3:26
God be with us as he *w.* with. 8:57
the Lord *w.* not in the wind, the Lord *w.* not in the earthquake. 19:11
w. not in the fire. 12
king discerned him that he *w.* 20:41
to Ahab all that *w.* in my. *2 Ki* 10:30
told what he *w.* to her. *Esth* 8:1
I *w.* not in safety, neither. *Job* 3:26
as I *w.* in the days of my youth. 29:4
away and lo he *w.* not. *Ps* 37:36
I *w.* as a man that heareth not. 38:14
fear, where no fear *w.* 53:5
not be such as *w.* in her. *Isa* 9:1
people *w.* not till Assyrian. 23:13
w. not Israel a derision unto thee? *w.* he found among? *Jer* 48:27
I *w.* no prophet, neither *w.* I a prophet's son, but I *w.* *Amos* 7:14
I pray thee, Lord, *w.* not? *Jonah* 4:2
w. not Esau Jacob's brother? *Mal* 1:2
such as *w.* not since the beginning of. *Mat* 24:21; *Mark* 13:19
the roof where he *w.* *Mark* 2:4
always night and day he *w.* 5:5
baptism of John, *w.* it from heaven, or of men? 11:30; *Luke* 20:4
and the Word *w.* with God, and the Word *w.* God. *John* 1:1
w. the true light, that lighteth. 9
saying, He *w.* before me. 15, 30
he that *w.* with thee beyond. 3:26
ascend up where he *w.* before. 6:62
before Abraham *w.*, I am. 8:58
I am glad for your sakes I *w.* 11:15
I said, because I *w.* with you. 16:4
with thee before the world *w.* 17:5
one of twelve *w.* not with them. 20:24
full of fishes, yet *w.* not the. 21:11
after sold, *w.* it not in thy? *Acts* 5:4
sold Joseph, but God *w.* with him. 7:9
what *w.* I that I could withstand God? 11:17
near, demanded who he *w.* 21:33
our word *w.* not yea. *2 Cor* 1:18, 19
I *w.* not a whit behind chiefest. 11:5
our entrance unto you *w.* *1 Thes* 2:1
our exhortation *w.* not in deceit. 3
manifest as theirs also *w.* *2 Tim* 3:9
how great this man *w.* *Heb* 7:4
the world *w.* not worthy. 11:38
what manner of man he *w.* *Jas* 1:24
from him which is and which *w.* *Rev* 1:4, 8; 4:8
the beast thou sawest *w.* 17:8, 11
see **so**

it **was**

came to pass as he interpreted, so *it w.* *Gen* 41:13
he *it w.* sold to all the people. 42:6
now *it w.* not you that sent me. 45:8
they wist not what *it w.* *Ex* 16:15
it w. of the Lord to harden their hearts. *Josh* 11:20
I brought Moses word as *it w.* 14:7
so *it w.* when Israel had sown. *Judg* 6:3
it w. not of the king to. *2 Sam* 3:37
but I knew not what *it w.* 18:29
is my brother's: for *it w.* *1 Ki* 2:15
his hand became as *it w.* 13:6
perceived that *it w.* not the. 22:33
left the camp as *it w.* *2 Ki* 7:7
command to Mordecai to know what *it w.* and why *it w.* *Esth* 4:5
return to earth as *it w.* *Eccl* 12:7
it w. but a little that I. *S of S* 3:4
as *it w.* to Israel in the. *Isa* 11:16
from the time that *it w.* 48:16
his *it w.* *Ezek* 16:15
thus *it w.* saith the Lord. 19
went to see what *it w.* *Mark* 5:14
not tell whence *it w.* *Luke* 20:7
enquire which of them *it w.* 22:23
knew not whence *it w.* *John* 2:9
was healed wist not who *it w.* 5:13
and knew not that *it w.* Jesus. 20:14
21:4
knowing that *it w.* the Lord. 21:12
not as *it w.* by one that. *Rom* 5:16

behold it **was**

God saw every thing, *behold it w.* *Gen* 1:31
looked on earth, *behold it w.* 6:12
morning, *behold, it w.* Leah. 29:25
behold it w. not toward Jacob. 31:2
Pharaoh awoke and *behold it w.* 41:7
for *behold it w.* in the sack's. 42:27
and *behold it w.* burnt. *Lev* 10:16
1 Sam 30:3
behold it w. dead, *behold it w.* my. *1 Ki* 3:21

there **was**

light, and *there w.* light. *Gen* 1:3
and *there w.* not a man to till. 2:5
there w. not found an help meet. 20
there w. a great cry in Egypt, for *there w.* not . . . *there w.* *Ex* 12:30
there w. not a man. *Num* 26:64
there w. not one city too strong. *Deut* 2:36; 3:4
there w. no strange god with. 32:12
there w. not a man left. *Josh* 8:17
there w. not a word Joshua read. 35
there w. not any left to. 11:11
there w. not a city that made. 19
host of Sisera fell; *there w.* not a man left. *Judg* 4:16
for *there w.* his house, there he judged. *1 Sam* 7:17
there w. not a man that came not. *2 Ki* 10:21
and *there w.* she slain. 11:16
there w. not one of them left. *Ps* 106:11
and *there w.* the hiding. *Hab* 3:4
there w. a readiness. *2 Cor* 8:11
see **none**

behold there **was**

behold there w. not one of cattle. *Ex* 9:7
behold there w. a man told a dream. *Judg* 7:13
behold there w. a swarm of. 14:8
behold there w. an image in the bed. *1 Sam* 19:16
behold there w. a cake. *1 Ki* 19:6
behold there w. no man there. *2 Ki* 7:5, 10
behold there w. lifted up a talent of. *Zech* 5:7
behold there w. a great earthquake. *Mat* 28:2

wash

Since the common foot-coverings of the East were sandals, and the roads were hot and dusty during the dry season and muddy during the rains, it was a necessary custom to see that the feet were washed on entering a house. The common utensils made it hard to wash one's own feet, and as a rule it was the task of a menial, but when one wished to honour his visitor extremely, or to indicate his own humility, he would himself perform the service.

At the Lord's Supper the feet of the Apostles had to be washed; no disciple would acknowledge himself the lowest among them; and it was our Saviour himself who, to give them an example of humility, washed their feet, John 13:5.

Ceremonial washing, *as distinct from washing for cleanliness, was one of the traditions of the Jews,* Heb 9:10. To wash one's feet in butter, *etc.*, Job 29:6; Ps 58:10, *was a figurative expression to indicate a great quantity of these things.* To wash one's hands *was a sign of innocence,* Mat 27:4.

I pray you *w.* your feet. *Gen* 18:4
19:2; 24:32
Pharaoh came to *w.* *Ex* 2:5
sons thou shalt bring and *w.* them. 29:4; 30:19, 20, 21; 40:12
shalt *w.* that whereon it. *Lev* 6:27
w. the thing wherein the plague is. 13:54
of skin it be, which thou shalt *w.* 58
shave and *w.* himself in water. 14:8
Deut 23:11
w. his flesh in water. *Lev* 14:9; 15:16
16:4, 24; 22:6
if he *w.* not, he shall bear. 17:16
shall *w.* their hands. *Deut* 21:6
w. thyself therefore and anoint. *Ruth* 3:3
let thy handmaid be a servant to *w.* feet. *1 Sam* 25:41
Go down and *w.* thy feet. *2 Sam* 11:8
Elisha said, Go *w.* in Jordan seven. *2 Ki* 5:10
may I not *w.* in them and be? 12
when he saith to thee, *W.* and? 13
lavers to *w.* in, sea for priests to *w.* in. *2 Chr* 4:6
if I *w.* myself with snow water. *Job* 9:30
I will *w.* my hands in. *Ps* 26:6
w. me throughly from mine. 51:2
w. me and I shall be whiter. 7
shall *w.* his feet in the blood. 58:10
w. you, make you clean. *Isa* 1:16
w. thee with nitre and. *Jer* 2:22
O Jerusalem, *w.* thy heart. 4:14
for whom thou didst *w.* *Ezek* 23:40
but when thou fastest, *w.* *Mat* 6:17
they *w.* not their hands when. 15:2

except they *w.* oft they. *Mark* 7:3, 4
a woman began to *w.* his feet with tears. *Luke* 7:38
Jesus said, Go *w.* in the. *John* 9:7, 11
began to *w.* the disciples' feet. 13:5
Lord, dost thou *w.* my feet? 6
never *w.* my feet. If I *w.* thee not. 8
ye also ought to *w.* one another's. 14
be baptized, and *w.* away thy sins. *Acts* 22:16
see **clothes, feet**

washed

gave them water, they *w. Gen* 43:24
Joseph *w.* his face and went out. 31
Judah *w.* his garments in. 49:11
w. as the Lord commanded Moses. *Ex* 40:32
on plague after it is *w. Lev* 13:55
be *w.* the second time and. 58
concubine *w.* their feet. *Judg* 19:21
arose and *w.* himself. *2 Sam* 12:20
w. the chariot in pool. *1 Ki* 22:38
I *w.* my steps with butter. *Job* 29:6
I have *w.* my hands in. *Ps* 73:13
a generation not *w. Pr* 30:12
I have *w.* my feet, how? *S of S* 5:3
his eyes are *w.* with milk and. 12
w. away the filth of the. *Isa* 4:4
nor wast *w.* in water to. *Ezek* 16:4
I throughly *w.* away thy blood. 9
Pilate took water and *w. Mat* 27:24
she hath *w.* my feet. *Luke* 7:44*
marvelled he had not first *w.* 11:38
he went and *w.* and came seeing. *John* 9:7, 11, 15
is *w.* needeth not save to. 13:10
Lord and Master have *w.* 14
whom when they had *w. Acts* 9:37
took them, *w.* their stripes. 16:33
but ye are *w.*, but ye are sanctified. *1 Cor* 6:11
have *w.* the saints' feet. *1 Tim* 5:10
having our bodies *w. Heb* 10:22
sow that was *w.* to her wallowing. *2 Pet* 2:22
that *w.* us from our sins. *Rev* 1:5*
have *w.* their robes and made. 7:14
see **clothes**

washest

thou *w.* away the things. *Job* 14:19

washing

David saw a woman *w. 2 Sam* 11:2
but the fisherman were *w. Luke* 5:2

washing, -s

somewhat dark after *w. Lev* 13:56
that every one put them off for *w. Neh* 4:23*
like sheep which came up from the *w. S of S* 4:2; 6:6
as the *w.* of cups, pots. *Mark* 7:4, 8
cleanse it with *w.* of water. *Eph* 5:26
he saved us, by the *w.* of. *Tit* 3:5
in meats and divers *w. Heb* 9:10

washpot

Moab is my *w. Ps* 60:8; 108:9

wast

thou *w.* a servant in land. *Deut* 5:15
thou *w.* a bondman in the land of Egypt. 15:15; 16:12; 24:18, 22
because thou *w.* a stranger. 23:7
thou *w.* he that leddest. *2 Sam* 5:2
where *w.* thou when I laid the foundations of the earth? *Job* 38:4
thou art taken and *w.* not. *Jer* 50:24
I said to thee, when thou *w.* in thy blood. *Ezek* 16:6
even thou *w.* as one of them. *Ob* 11
Peter, saying, Thou also *w.* with Jesus. *Mat* 26:69; *Mark* 14:67
when thou *w.* under the fig tree, I saw thee. *John* 1:48
which art, and *w.* and art to come. *Rev* 11:17; 16:5

waste, *adjective*

the desolate *w.* ground and. *Job* 38:27
young lions yelled and made his land *w. Jer* 2:15
for Noph shall be *w.* and. 46:19*
Bozrah shall become a *w.* 49:13
will make Jerusalem *w. Ezek* 5:14*
the land of Egypt shall be *w.* 29:9
10; 30:12
which have been always *w. Ezek* 38:8
empty, and void and *w. Nah* 2:10
have made their streets *w. Zeph* 3:6
mine house that is *w. Hag* 1:9
see **cities, lay, laid, places**

waste, *substantive*

he found him in the *w. Deut* 32:10
solitary, fleeing into the *w. Job* 30:3
Lord maketh the earth *w. Isa* 24:1
I will make *w.* mountains. 42:15
they that made the *w.* shall. 49:17
to what purpose is this *w.*? *Mat* 26:8; *Mark* 14:4

waste, *verb*

meal shall not *w. 1 Ki* 17:14
of wickedness *w.* them. *1 Chr* 17:9
of the wood doth *w.* it. *Ps* 80:13*
w. inhabitants of Pekod. *Jer* 50:21*
shall *w.* the land of Assyria. *Mi* 5:6

wasted

till your carcases be *w. Num* 14:33*
the Kenite shall be *w.* 24:22
of men of war were *w. Deut* 2:14*
barrel of meal *w.* not. *1 Ki* 17:16
Joab *w.* the country of. *1 Chr* 20:1
that *w.* us required of us. *Ps* 137:3
till the cities be *w. Isa* 6:11
and the river shall be *w.* and. 19:5
nations shall be utterly *w.* 60:12
are *w.* and desolate as. *Jer* 44:6
field is *w.*, the corn is *w. Joel* 1:10
the younger son *w.* his. *Luke* 15:13
was accused that he had *w.* his. 16:1
the church and *w.* it. *Gal* 1:13*

wasteness

a day of *w.*, desolation. *Zeph* 1:15

waster

him that is a great *w. Pr* 18:9*
I have created the *w. Isa* 54:16

wastes

they shall build the old *w. Isa* 61:4
cities shall be perpetual *w. Jer* 49:13
that inhabit those *w.* of. *Ezek* 33:24
surely they in the *w.* shall fall. 27
the Lord to the desolate *w.* 36:4
and the *w.* shall be builded. 10, 33

wasteth

man dieth and *w.* away. *Job* 14:10†
nor for destruction that *w. Ps* 91:6
he that *w.* father and. *Pr* 19:26*

wasting

w. and destruction are in. *Isa* 59:7
not heard *w.* nor destruction. 60:18*

watch

Watch *is used in three senses:* [1] *to watch in order to guard,* [2] *to watch, meaning to look for,* [3] *a watch in the night. The night was divided, not into hours, but into* watches. *In the Old Testament, three are named: the* First Watch, *till midnight; the* Middle Watch, *till* 3 *a.m.; and the* Morning Watch, *till* 6 *a.m. In the New Testament there were four watches of three hours each, from* 6 *p.m. to* 6 *a.m. See* **watches.**

morning *w.* Lord looked. *Ex* 14:24
middle *w.*; and they had but newly set the *w. Judg* 7:19
Saul came in the morning *w. 1 Sam* 11:11
so shall ye keep the *w.* of the house. *2 Ki* 11:6, 7; *2 Chr* 23:6
prayed to God and set a *w. Neh* 4:9
one in his *w.* and over against. 7:3
that thou settest a *w.*? *Job* 7:12
a thousand years as a *w. Ps* 90:4
set a *w.* O Lord, before my. 141:3
the *w.* strong, set up. *Jer* 51:12
I will stand upon my *w. Hab* 2:1
in the fourth *w.* of the night Jesus. *Mat* 14:25; *Mark* 6:48
had known what *w.* the thief would. *Mat* 24:43
ye have a *w.* 27:65
sealing the stone, setting a *w.* 66
behold, some of the *w.* came. 28:11
the shepherds keeping *w. Luke* 2:8
in the second *w.* or third. 12:38

watch, *verb*

the Lord *w.* between me. *Gen* 31:49
Saul sent to *w.* David. *1 Sam* 19:11
w. ye, keep the vessels. *Ezra* 8:29
thou not *w.* over my sin? *Job* 14:16
I *w.* and am as a sparrow. *Ps* 102:7
more than they that *w.* for. 130:6
w. in the watchtower. *Isa* 21:5
and all that *w.* for iniquity. 29:20
a leopard shall *w.* over. *Jer* 5:6
will I *w.* over them to build. 31:28
I will *w.* over them for evil. 44:27
the munition, *w.* the way. *Nah* 2:1
I will *w.* to see what he. *Hab* 2:1
w. therefore, ye know not the hour. *Mat* 24:42; 25:13; *Mark* 13:35
Luke 21:36; *Acts* 20:31
Jesus said, Tarry ye here, and *w.* with me. *Mat* 26:38
could ye not *w.* with me? 40
Mark 14:34, 37
w. and pray. *Mat* 26:41
Mark 13:33; 14:38; *Col* 4:2
who commanded the porter to *w. Mark* 13:34
unto you, I say unto all, *W.* 37
w. ye, stand fast in faith. *1 Cor* 16:13
let us *w.* and be sober. *1 Thes* 5:6
1 Pet 4:7
w. thou in all things. *2 Tim* 4:5
obey them, for they *w. Heb* 13:17

watched

all my familiars *w.* for. *Jer* 20:10
like as I have *w.* over them. 31:28
w. for a nation that could. *Lam* 4:17
Lord *w.* upon evil, and. *Dan* 9:14
good man would have *w. Mat* 24:43
Luke 12:39
and sitting down they *w. Mat* 27:36
they *w.* him whether he would heal. *Mark* 3:2; *Luke* 6:7; 14:1
they *w.* him and sent forth spies. *Luke* 20:20
w. the gates day and. *Acts* 9:24

watcher, -s

published that *w.* come. *Jer* 4:16
a *w.* and an holy one. *Dan* 4:13
by decree of the *w.* 17
the king saw a *w.* 23

watches

brethren over against them in *w. Neh* 12:9
on thee in the night *w. Ps* 63:6
eyes prevent the night *w.* 119:148
in beginning of the *w.* pour. *Lam* 2:19

watcheth

wicked *w.* the righteous. *Ps* 37:32
end is come, it *w.* for thee. *Ezek* 7:6
blessed is he that *w.* and. *Rev* 16:15

watchful

be *w.*, strengthen the things. *Rev* 3:2

watching

Eli sat on a seat by the wayside *w. 1 Sam* 4:13
blessed heareth me, *w.* daily. *Pr* 8:34
our *w.* we have watched. *Lam* 4:17
centurion *w.* Jesus, saw. *Mat* 27:54
the lord when he cometh shall find *w. Luke* 12:37
praying and *w.* with all. *Eph* 6:18

watchings

in tumults, in labours, in *w.* in fastings. *2 Cor* 6:5
in *w.* often, in hunger, thirst. 11:27

watchman

the *w.* cried and told. *2 Sam* 18:25
the *w.* saw another man running. 26
the *w.* told, he cometh not again. *2 Ki* 9:18, 20
keepeth city, *w.* waketh. *Ps* 127:1
go set a *w. Isa* 21:6
w., what of the night? 11
set up the *w.*, prepare the ambushes. *Jer* 51:12
Son of man, I have made thee a *w. Ezek* 3:17; 33:7
set him up for their *w.* 33:2
the *w.* of Ephraim was. *Hos* 9:8

watchmen

w. that go about the city found me. *S of S* 3:3; 5:7
w. shall lift up the voice. *Isa* 52:8

his w. are blind, they are. Isa 56:10
I have set w. on thy walls. 62:6
also I set w. over you. Jer 6:17
w. on mount Ephraim shall. 31:6
the day of thy w. and. Mi 7:4

watch tower

when Judah came toward the w. tower. 2 Chr 20:24
watch in the w. tower. Isa 21:5
I stand continually on the w. tower. 8

water

Hagar by a fountain of w. Gen 16:7
let a little w. I pray you, be. 18:4
Abraham took a bottle of w. 21:14
Laban gave the man w. to. 24:32
I pray thee, a little w. to drink. 43
the w. is ours. 26:20
we have found w. 32
Joseph's house gave them w. 43:24
unstable as w., thou shalt not. 49:4
raw, nor sodden with w. Ex 12:9
shall come w. out of the rock. 17:6
any likeness that is in the w. 20:4
bless thy bread and thy w. 23:25
sons shall wash them with w. 29:4
30:20; 40:12; Lev 8:6; 16:4, 24
strawed it on the w. Ex 32:20
shall be scoured and rinsed in w. Lev 6:28; 15:12
vessel, it must be put into w. 11:32
but if any w. be upon the seed. 38
w. that causeth the curse. Num 5:22
sprinkle w. of purification upon. 8:7
for a w. of separation. 19:9, 13, 20
21; 31:23
thou shalt bring forth to them w. out of the rock. 20:8, 10, 11; Neh 9:15
Ps 114:8
this is the w. of Meribah. Num 20:13
24; 27:14
nor is there any w. 21:5
people, and I will give them w. 16
he shall pour the w. out of. 24:7
shall make go through the w. 31:23
to a land of brooks of w. Deut 8:7
the land drinketh w. of rain. 11:11
shalt pour it on earth as w. 12:16
24; 15:23
met you not with w. in way. 23:4
Neh 13:2
melted and became as w. Josh 7:5
he asked w. and she gave. Judg 5:25
bring them down to the w. 7:4, 5
w. came out of the jaw and. 15:19
to Mizpeh and drew w. 1 Sam 7:6
take my bread and my w.? 25:11
take now the cruse of w. 26:11
nor drunk any w. three days. 30:12
we are as w. spilt on. 2 Sam 14:14
pass quickly over the w. 17:21
till w. dropped on them out. 21:10
bread and drank w. 1 Ki 13:19
hast eaten bread and drunk w. 22
as a reed is shaken in the w. 14:15
I pray thee, a little w. 17:10
them with bread and w. 18:4, 13
w. ran about the altar, filled trench with w. 35
fire of the Lord . . . licked up the w. 38
feed him with bread and w. of affliction till I. 22:27; 2 Chr 18:26
the w. is naught, and. 2 Ki 2:19
Elisha, who poured w. on. 3:11
valley shall be filled with w. 17
and the sun shone on the w. 22
the axe head fell into the w. 6:5
set bread and w. before them. 22
he dipped a thick cloth in w.,and. 8:15
made a conduit, brought w. 20:20
of Assyria find much w. 2 Chr 32:4
can flag grow without w.? Job 8:11
the scent of w. it will bud. 14:9
drinketh iniquity like w. 15:16
thou hast not given w. to the. 22:7
who drinketh scorning like w. 34:7
I am poured out like w. Ps 22:14
river of God that is full of w. 65:9
through fire and through w. 66:12
have they shed like w. 79:3
round about me daily like w. 88:17
into his bowels like w. 109:18
as when one letteth out w. Pr 17:14
heart of man is like deep w. 20:5
in w. face answereth to face. Pr 27:19
earth that is not filled with w. 30:16
thy wine mixed with w. Isa 1:22
take away the whole stay of w. 3:1
land of Tema brought w. to him that was thirsty. 21:14
not found a sherd to take w. 30:14
though the Lord gave you the w. 20
when the poor seek w. and. 41:17
I will pour w. on him that is. 44:3
dividing the w. before them. 63:12
girdle and put it not in w. Jer 13:1
them drink the w. of gall. 23:15
mine eyes run down with w. Lam 1:16; 3:48
pour out thy heart like w. 2:19
we have drunken our w. for. 5:4
may want bread and w. Ezek 4:17
all knees shall be weak as w. 7:17
21:7
nor wast thou washed in w. to. 16:4
then washed I thee with w. and. 9
then will I sprinkle clean w. 36:25
lovers that give me my w. Hos 2:5
my wrath upon them like w. 5:10
king is cut off as foam upon w. 10:7
of bread nor thirst for w. Amos 8:11
but Nineveh is of old like a pool of w. Nah 2:8
the overflowing of the w. Hab 3:10
with w. unto repentance. Mat 3:11
Mark 1:8; Luke 3:16; John 1:26
Jesus went up out of the w. Mat 3:16; Mark 1:10
whoso giveth a cup of cold w. Mat 10:42; Mark 9:41
bid me come unto thee on the w. Mat 14:28
oft into the fire and w. 17:15
Pilate took w. and washed. 27:24
a man bearing a pitcher of w.: follow. Mark 14:13; Luke 22:10
ship was filled with w. Luke 8:23
rebuked the w. 24
the w. obeyed him. 25
dip the tip of his finger in w. 16:24
Fill the waterpots with w. John 2:7
except a man be born of w. and. 3:5
because there was much w. there. 23
given thee living w. 4:10, 11
give me this w. 15
again where he made w. wine. 46
waiting for the moving of the w. 5:3
down and troubled the w. 4
of his belly shall flow living w. 7:38
after that he poureth w. into a. 13:5
came thereout blood and w. 19:34
for John truly baptized with w. Acts 1:5; 11:16
here is w. 8:36
they went down both into the w. 38
can any forbid w., these be ? 10:47
it with the washing of w. Eph 5:26
blood of calves with w. Heb 9:19
bodies washed with pure w. 10:22
yield salt w. and fresh. Jas 3:12
eight souls were saved by w. 1 Pet 3:20
are wells without w. 2 Pet 2:17
overflowed with w., perished. 3:6
he that came by w. and. 1 John 5:6
witness, Spirit, w. and blood. 8
clouds they are without w. Jude 12
cast out of his mouth w. Rev 12:15
Euphrates, and w. dried up. 16:12
of the fountain of the w. of life. 21:6
me a pure river of w. of life. 22:1
let him take the w. of life freely. 17
see **bathe, bitter, draw, drew, drink, well**

water, verb

a river went out of Eden to w. the garden. Gen 2:10
w. ye the sheep and go and. 29:7, 8
I w. my couch with my. Ps 6:6
come down as showers that w. 72:6
pools of water to w. the. Eccl 2:6
w. thee with my tears. Isa 16:9
I will w. it every moment, lest. 27:3
he might w. it by furrows. Ezek 17:7
I will w. with my blood the land. 32:6
a fountain shall w. the valley of Shittim. Joel 3:18

no water

there was no w. in it. Gen 37:24
they went three days and found no w. Ex 15:22; 17:1; Num 20:2
33:14; Deut 8:15
Lord said, Eat no bread and drink no w. 1 Ki 13:22
was no w. for the host, and. 2 Ki 3:9
thirsty land where no w. is. Ps 63:1
as a garden that hath no w. Isa 1:30
the smith drinketh no w. 44:12
fish stinketh because there is no w. 50:2
cisterns that can hold no w. Jer 2:13
to the pits and found no w. 14:3
there was no w. but mire. 38:6
sent prisoners out of pit wherein is no w. Zech 9:11
thou gavest me no w. for my feet. Luke 7:44

waterbrooks

the hart panteth after the w. Ps 42:1

watercourse

stopped the upper w. 2 Chr 32:30
who hath divided a w.? Job 38:25

watercourses

they shall spring as willows by the w. Isa 44:4

watered

a mist that w. the face. Gen 2:6
Jordan, that it was well w. 13:10
of that well they w. flocks. 29:2, 3
Jacob w. the flock of Laban. 10
Moses helped and w. their flocks. Ex 2:17, 19
he that watereth shall be w. himself. Pr 11:25
shalt be like a w. garden. Isa 58:11
shall be as a w. garden. Jer 31:12
I have planted, Apollos w. 1 Cor 3:6

wateredst

w. it with thy foot as a. Deut 11:10

waterest

the earth and w. it. Ps 65:9
thou w. the ridges thereof. 10

watereth

he w. the hills from his. Ps 104:13
that w. shall be watered. Pr 11:25
rain returneth not, but w. Isa 55:10
neither he that planteth any thing, nor he that w. 1 Cor 3:7, 8

waterflood

let not the w. overflow me. Ps 69:15

watering

rods in the w. troughs. Gen 30:38
by w. he wearieth the thick cloud. Job 37:11*
doth not each of you lead his ass to w.? Luke 13:15

waterpot, -s

set there six w. of stone. John 2:6
Jesus saith, Fill the w. with water. 7
the woman then left her w. 4:28

waters

God moved upon face of w. Gen 1:2
divide the w. from the w. 6, 7
let the w. be gathered. 9
w. bring forth. 20
do bring a flood of w. on earth. 6:17
w. increased. 7:17
w. prevailed. 18, 19, 20, 24
w. decreased. 8:1, 3, 5
w. were dried up. 13
not be cut off any more by w. 9:11
behold, I will smite the w. Ex 7:17
w. were turned to blood. 20
out his hand over the w. 8:6
by a strong east wind the w. 14:21
w. were a wall. 22, 29
w. returned. 28; 15:19
the w. were gathered together. 15:8
they could not drink of the w. of. 23
they encamped there by the w. 27
as cedar trees beside w. Num 24:6
to Jotbath, land of rivers of w. Deut 10:7
ye trespassed at the w. of. 32:51
strive at the w. of Meribah. 33:8
the w. which came down. Josh 3:16
the w. of Jordan were cut off. 4:7
dried up the w. of Jordan. 23; 5:1
pitched at the w. of Merom. 11:5

Canaan by *w.* of Megiddo. *Judg* 5:19
and take the *w.* before them. 7:24
Lord hath broken forth as a breach of *w.* *2 Sam* 5:20; *1 Chr* 14:11
Joab said, I have taken the city of *w.* *2 Sam* 12:27
Elijah smote the *w.* *2 Ki* 2:8, 14
the spring of the *w.*, thus saith the Lord, I have healed these *w.* 21
are not ... rivers of Damascus, better than all the *w.* of Israel? 5:12
counsel to stop the *w.* *2 Chr* 32:3
are poured out like the *w.* *Job* 3:24
sendeth *w.* upon the fields. 5:10
remember thy misery as *w.* 11:16
he withholdeth the *w.* and. 12:15
as the *w.* fail from the sea. 14:11
the *w.* wear the stones: thou. 19
and abundance of *w.* cover thee. 22:11; 38:34
he is swift as the *w.*; their. 24:18
formed from under the *w.* 26:5
he bindeth up the *w.* in his thick. 8
he hath compassed the *w.* with. 10
terrors take hold on him as *w.* 27:20
the *w.* forgotten of the foot. 28:4
weighed the *w.* by measure. 25
was spread out by the *w.* 29:19
as a wide breaking in of *w.* 30:14
and the breadth of the *w.* is. 37:10
the *w.* are hid as with a stone. 38:30
he leadeth me beside the still *w.* *Ps* 23:2
gathered the *w.* of the seas. 33:7
though the *w.* thereof roar. 46:3
let them melt away as *w.* 58:7
for the *w.* are come in unto. 69:1
w. of a full cup are wrung. 73:10
w. saw thee, O God, the *w.* 77:16
he made the *w.* to stand as. 78:13
and caused *w.* to run down like. 16
he smote the rock, that the *w.* gushed out. 20; 105:41; 114:8; *Isa* 48:21
I proved thee at the *w.* of Meribah. *Ps* 81:7; 106:32
w. stood above the mountains. 104:6
turned their *w.* into blood. 105:29
the *w.* covered their enemies. 106:11
rivers of *w.* run down. 119:136
the *w.* had overwhelmed us. 124:4
then the proud *w.* had gone. 5
him that stretched the earth above the *w.* 136:6
wind to blow and *w.* flow. 147:18
ye *w.* above the heavens. 148:4
drink *w.* out of thine own. *Pr* 5:15
let rivers of *w.* be dispersed. 16
that the *w.* should not pass. 8:29
stolen *w.* are sweet, and bread. 9:17
as cold *w.* to a thirsty soul. 25:25
who hath bound the *w.* in a? 30:4
cast thy bread upon the *w.* *Eccl* 11:1
a well of living *w.* and. *S of S* 4:15
people refuseth the *w.* of. *Isa* 8:6
the Lord bringeth on them *w.* 7
as the *w.* cover the seas. 11:9
Hab 2:14
for the *w.* of Nimrim. *Isa* 15:6
for the *w.* of Dimon shall be. 9
like the rushing of mighty *w.* 17:12
and the *w.* shall fail from. 19:5
and ye gathered the *w.* of the. 22:9
w. shall overflow the hiding. 28:17
ye that sow beside all *w.* 32:20
bread be given him, his *w.* 33:16
for in the wilderness shall *w.* 35:6
who hath measured the *w.* in. 40:12
when thou passest through *w.* I. 43:2
a path in the mighty *w.* 16
I give *w.* in the wilderness and. 20
forth out of the *w.* of Judah. 48:1
he caused the *w.* to flow out. 21
which hath dried the *w.* of. 51:10
is as *w.* of Noah unto me, *w.* 54:9
thirsteth, come ye to the *w.* 55:1
like the sea, whose *w.* cast up. 57:20
of water, whose *w.* fail not. 58:11
me the fountain of living *w.* *Jer* 2:13
to drink the *w.* of Sihor? 18
as a fountain casteth out her *w.* 6:7
God hath given us *w.* of gall. 8:14
O that my head were *w.* and. 9:1
eyelids gush out with *w.* 18
is a multitude of *w.* in the heavens. *Jer* 10:13; 51:16
nobles sent little ones to the *w.* 14:3
as a liar, and as *w.* that fail? 15:18
as a tree planted by the *w.* 17:8
the Lord, fountain of living *w.* 13
shall the cold flowing *w.* be? 18:14
whose *w.* are moved as the rivers. 46:7, 8
behold, *w.* rise up out of the. 47:2
for the *w.* of Nimrim shall. 48:34
a drought is upon her *w.* and. 50:38
w. flowed over mine head. *Lam* 3:54
is like a vine by the *w.* *Ezek* 19:10
w. made him great, the deep. 31:4
that none of the trees by *w.* exalt. 14
and troublest the *w.* with thy. 32:2
behold, *w.* issued from under. 47:1
brought me through *w.*; the *w.* 3, 4
for the *w.* were risen, *w.* to. 5
these *w.* issue out toward the. 8, 12
even to the *w.* of strife. 19; 48:28
to the man upon the *w.* *Dan* 12:6, 7
calleth for *w.* of sea. *Amos* 5:8; 9:6
let judgement run down as *w.* 5:24
w. compassed me about. *Jonah* 2:5
as *w.* that are poured down. *Mi* 1:4
No, that had the *w.* round? *Nah* 3:8
draw the *w.* for the siege. 14
living *w.* shall go from. *Zech* 14:8
in perils of *w.*, in perils of. *2 Cor* 11:26
lead them unto living fountains of *w.* *Rev* 7:17
the *w.* became wormwood, and many died of the *w.* because. 8:11
have power over *w.* to turn. 11:6
made the fountain of *w.* 14:7
angel poured his vial on the *w.* 16:4
I heard the angel of the *w.* say. 5
the *w.* where the whore sits. 17:15

see **deep, great**

in, or *into* **waters**

as lead *in* the mighty *w.* *Ex* 15:10
a tree, which when cast *into* the *w.* 25
ye eat of all that are *in* the *w.*: whatsoever hath fins and scales *in* the *w.* *Lev* 11:9: 10:46; *Deut* 14:9
hath no fins nor scales *in* the *w.* unclean. *Lev* 11:12
the likeness of any fish *in* the *w.* *Deut* 4:18; 5:8
of priests rest *in* the *w.* *Josh* 3:13
stone *into* the mighty *w.* *Neh* 9:11
heads of dragons *in w.* *Ps* 74:13
beams of his chambers *in w.* 104:3
and perished *in* the *w.* *Mat* 8:32
him into fire and *into w.* *Mark* 9:22

many **waters**

seed shall be in *many w.* *Num* 24:7
he drew me out of *many w.* *2 Sam* 22:17; *Ps* 18:16
the Lord is upon *many w.* *Ps* 29:3
than the noise of *many w.* 93:4
many w. cannot quench love, neither can floods. *S of S* 8:7
the rushing of *many w.* *Isa* 17:13
dwellest upon *many w.* *Jer* 51:13
by reason of *many w.* *Ezek* 19:10
like a noise of *many w.*: and the earth shined. 43:2; *Rev* 1:15; 14:2; 19:6
that sitteth on *many w.* *Rev* 17:1

waterspouts

deep at noise of thy *w.* *Ps* 42:7

watersprings

he turneth the *w.* into. *Ps* 107:33
turneth dry ground into *w.* 35

wave

is like a *w.* of the sea. *Jas* 1:6*

wave, *verb*

shalt *w.* them for a wave offering. *Ex* 29:24; *Lev* 23:20; *Num* 6:20
thou shalt *w.* the breast. *Ex* 29:26
w. the shoulder. 27; *Lev* 7:30
8:29; 9:21; 10:15
he shall *w.* the sheaf. *Lev* 23:11, 12
the priest shall *w.* the. *Num* 5:25

waved

w. them for a wave. *Lev* 8:27, 29
take one lamb to be *w.* 14:21

see **breast, loaves, offering**

wavereth

he that *w.* is like a wave. *Jas* 1:6*

wavering

hold fast profession of faith without *w.* *Heb* 10:23
ask in faith, nothing *w.* *Jas* 1:6*

waves

all thy *w.* are gone over me. *Ps* 42:7; *Jonah* 2:3
stilleth the noise of their *w.* *Ps* 65:7
89:9; 107:29
afflicted me with all thy *w.* 88:7
voice, floods lift up their *w.* 93:3
is mightier than mighty *w.* 4*
wind which lifteth up the *w.* 107:25
righteousness as the *w.* *Isa* 48:18
I am the Lord, that divided the sea, whose *w.* roared. 51:15; *Jer* 31:35
though the *w.* toss, yet can. *Jer* 5:22
with the multitude of the *w.* 51:42
when her *w.* do roar like great. 55
as the sea causeth his *w.* *Ezek* 26:3
and shall smite the *w.* *Zech* 10:11
was covered with the *w.* *Mat* 8:24
but the ship was tossed with *w.* 14:24; *Mark* 4:37
signs, the sea and *w.* *Luke* 21:25*
was broken with the *w.* *Acts* 27:41
raging *w.* of sea, foaming. *Jude* 13

wax, *substantive*

my heart is like *w.* *Ps* 22:14
as *w.* melteth, so the wicked. 68:2
the hills melted like *w.* at the. 97:5
the valleys cleft as *w.* *Mi* 1:4

wax

my wrath shall *w.* hot. *Ex* 22:24
32:10
Lord, why doth thy wrath *w.*? 32:11
the anger of my lord *w.* hot. 22
or a stranger *w.* rich by thee, and thy brother by him *w.* *Lev* 25:47
his eyes began to *w.* dim. *1 Sam* 3:2
what time they *w.* warm. *Job* 6:17
though the root thereof *w.* old. 14:8
all of them shall *w.* old. *Ps* 102:26
Isa 50:9; 51:6; *Heb* 1:11
his flesh shall *w.* lean. *Isa* 17:4
shall his face now *w.* pale. 29:22
our hands *w.* feeble, anguish hath. *Jer* 6:24
the love of many shall *w.* cold. *Mat* 24:12
provide bags which *w.* *Luke* 12:33
began to *w.* wanton. *1 Tim* 5:11
seducers shall *w.* worse. *2 Tim* 3:13

waxed

(*grew, increased*)

Isaac *w.* great. *Gen* 26:13
famine *w.* sore. 41:56
Israel *w.* exceeding. *Ex* 1:7, 20
and when the sun *w.* hot. 16:21
when the trumpet *w.* louder. 19:19
Moses' anger *w.* hot, and he. 32:19
is the Lord's hand *w.*? *Num* 11:23
raiment *w.* not old. *Deut* 8:4; 29:5
Neh 9:21
w. fat, and kicked. *Deut* 32:15
that Joshua *w.* old and. *Josh* 23:1
she that hath many children is *w.* feeble. *1 Sam* 2:5
but David *w.* stronger. *2 Sam* 3:1
1 Chr 11:9
and David went down, fought, and *w.* faint. *2 Sam* 21:15
of the child *w.* warm. *2 Ki* 4:34
Abijah *w.* mighty and. *2 Chr* 13:21
Jehoshaphat *w.* great. 17:12
Jehoiada *w.* old. 24:15
Mordecai *w.* greater. *Esth* 9:4
silence, my bones *w.* old. *Ps* 32:3
Damascus is *w.* feeble. *Jer* 49:24
Babylon's hands *w.* feeble. 50:43
the he goat *w.* great *Dan* 8:8, 9, 10
this people's heart is *w.* gross. *Mat* 13:15; *Acts* 28:27
the child *w.* strong in spirit. *Luke* 1:80; 2:40
a grain of mustard seed *w.* 13:19*
Paul and Barnabas *w.* *Acts* 13:46
w. valiant in fight. *Heb* 11:34
of the earth are *w.* rich. *Rev* 18:3

waxen, waxed

after I am *w.* old shall? *Gen* 18:12
cry of Sodom was *w.* great. 19:13
brother be *w.* poor. *Lev* 25:25, 35, 39

w. fat, then will they turn to other gods. Deut 31:20
of Israel were w. strong. Josh 17:13
become great and w. rich. Jer 5:27
they are w. fat, they shine, they. 28
increased and w. great. Ezek 16:7

waxeth

mine eye w. old because. Ps 6:7
what w. old, is ready. Heb 8:13

waxing

brethren w. confident by. Phil 1:14

way

Is taken in a moral sense, [1] *For* conduct, Ps 1:6. [2] Ways *are put for the laws of the Lord,* Gen 18:19; Ps 18:21. [3] Way *is put for custom, manners, and* way *of life,* Gen 6:12; Jer 10:2. [4] The *method of salvation, or doctrine of the gospel,* Acts 19:9.

To go the *way* of all the earth, *means* dying *and the* grave, Josh 23:14.

Jesus Christ is called the way, John 14:6, *because it is by him alone that believers obtain eternal life.*

if thou do prosper my w. Gen 24:42
to give them provision for the w. 42:25; 45:21
led not through the w. of. Ex 13:17
led the people through the w. 18
of cloud to lead them the w. 21
shew them the w. 18:20; Neh 9:19
Ps 107:4
discouraged because of w. Num 21:4
there was no w. to turn to. 22:26
by what w. we must go. Deut 1:22
Josh 3:4
remember the w. which. Deut 8:2
if the w. be too long for thee. 14:24
return no more that w. 17:16
thou shalt prepare thee a w. 19:3
the w. is long. 6
thou shalt go out one w. 28:25
ye will turn aside from the w. 31:29
behold I am going w. of. Josh 23:14
Lord preserved us in all the w. 24:17
from their stubborn w. Judg 2:19
all that came along that w. 9:25
whether our w. which we go. 18:5
before the Lord is your w. 6
get you early on your w. 19:9
kine took straight w. 1 Sam 6:12
can shew us our w. to go. 9:6*
the man of God to tell us our w. 8
the good and the right w. 12:23
I have gone the w. the Lord. 15:20
thy servant will go a little w. over Jordan. 2 Sam 19:36
I go the w. of all the earth. 1 Ki 2:2
them the good w. to walk. 8:36
nor turn again by the same w. 13:9
he went another w. 10
what w. went he ? 12
one w., Obadiah another w. 18:6
which w. went the Spirit of the Lord from me ? 22:24; 2 Chr 18:23
which w. shall we go ? w. 2 Ki 3:8
departed from him a little w. 5:19
all the w. full of garments. 7:15
taught them the good w. 2 Chr 6:27
to seek of him a right w. Ezra 8:21
to a man whose w. is hid. Job 3:23
to wander where there is no w. 12:24; Ps 107:40
I shall go the w. whence. Job 16:22
hast thou marked the old w.? 22:15
but he knoweth the w. 23:10
God understandeth the w. 28:23
where is the w. where light ? 38:19
Lord knoweth the w. of. Ps 1:6
lest ye perish from the w. 2:12
he setteth himself in a w. 36:4
he made a w. to his anger. 78:50
wisely in a perfect w. 101:2, 6
make me understand the w. 119:27
remove from me the w. of lying. 29
I have chosen the w. of truth. 30
I will run the w. of thy. 32
teach me, O Lord, the w. 33; 143:8
I hate every false w. 119:104, 128
be any wicked w. in me. Ps 139:24
the w. of the wicked he turneth. 146:9
he preserveth the w. of. Pr 2:8
to deliver thee from the w. 12
the w. of the wicked is as. 4:19
reproofs of instruction are the w. of life. 6:23; 15:24; Jer 21:8
her corner, he went the w. Pr 7:8
her house is the w. to hell, going. 27
the w. of a fool is right in. 12:15
the w. of the wicked seduceth. 26
but the w. of transgressors. 13:15
there is a w. which seemeth right. 14:12; 16:25
the w. of the wicked is an. 15:9
to him that forsaketh the w. 10
the w. of the slothful man is as an hedge of thorns, but the w. 19
leadeth him into the w. that. 16:29
the w. of man is froward and. 21:8
w. of an eagle, of a serpent. 30:19
such is the w. of an adulterous. 20
knowest not what is the w. of the Spirit. Eccl 11:5
to err and destroy the w. Isa 3:12
w. of the just is uprightness. 26:7
an highway and a w., called w. 35:8
who shewed him the w. of ? 40:14
maketh a w. in the sea. 43:16; 51:10
I will even make a w. in the. 43:19
all my mountains a w. 49:11
prepare a w. 57:14
the w. of peace they know not. 59:8; Rom 3:17
cast up the high w. Isa 62:10
where is the good w. Jer 6:16
learn not the w. of heathen. 10:2
I know that the w. of man is not. 23
wherefore doth the w. of the ? 12:1
to walk in paths, in a w. not. 18:15
them one heart and one w. 32:39
thy God may shew us the w. 42:3
they shall ask the w. to Zion. 50:5
appoint a w. that the sword may come. Ezek 21:20
saw that they took both one w. 23:13
glory of God came from the w. 43:2
and turn aside the w. Amos 2:7
munition, watch the w. Nah 2:1
he shall prepare the w. Mal 3:1
broad is the w. that leadeth. Mat 7:13
narrow is the w. which leadeth. 14
no man might pass by that w. 8:28
not into the w. of the Gentiles. 10:5
art true, and teachest the w. of God. 22:16; Mark 12:14; Luke 20:21
by what w. they might. Luke 5:19
a certain priest that w. 10:31
he was yet a great w. off. 15:20
for he was to pass that w. 19:4
some other w. is a thief. John 10:1
the w. ye know. 14:4
Lord, how can we know the w.? 5
I am the w., the truth, and the life. 6
which shew to us the w. Acts 16:17
expounded to him w. of God. 18:26
but spake evil of that w. 19:9
no small stir about that w. 23
after the w. which they call. 24:14
to fall in brother's w. Rom 14:13
with the temptation also make a w. to escape. 1 Cor 10:13
unto you a more excellent w. 12:31
our Lord Jesus direct our w. unto. 1 Thes 3:11
the w. into the holiest not. Heb 9:8
by a living w. which he hath. 10:20
she had sent them out another w. Jas 2:25
the w. of truth shall be. 2 Pet 2:2
forsaken the right w. and are gone astray, following the w. of. 15
known the w. of righteousness. 21
that the w. of kings of the. Rev 16:12

***by the* way**

befall him by the w. ye go. Gen 42:38
Joseph said, See that ye fall not out by the w. 45:24
a serpent by the w., an adder. 49:17
by the w. in the inn, the. Ex 4:24
you into the wilderness, by the w. of the Red sea. Num 14:25; 21:4
Deut 1:2, 40; 2:1
talk of them, when thou walkest by the w. Deut 6:7; 11:19
Amalek did to thee by the w. 25:17
met thee by the w. 18; 1 Sam 15:2
bring thee by the w. I spake. 28:68
men of war died by the w. Josh 5:4
not circumcised them by the w. 7
nor turn again by the same w. that thou camest. 1 Ki 13:9, 17
a lion met him by the w. and. 24
waited for the king by the w. 20:38
water by the w. of Edom. 2 Ki 3:20
bridle in lips, I will turn thee back by the w. 19:28; Isa 37:29, 34
as lay in wait by the w. Ezra 8:31
have ye not asked them that go by the w.? Job 21:29
pass by the w. plucked her. Ps 80:12
all that pass by the w. spoil. 89:41
when fools walk by the w. Eccl 10:3
bring blind by the w. they. Isa 42:16
that leadeth thee by the w. 48:17
forsaken God when he led thee by the w. Jer 2:17
walk not by the w. for the sword of the enemy. 6:25
came by the w. of gate. Ezek 43:4
prince shall enter by the w. of porch. 44:3; 46:2, 8
he that entereth by the w. 46:9
as a leopard by the w. Hos 13:7
if I send them away fasting, they will faint by the w. Mark 8:3
by the w. he asked his disciples. 27
ye disputed by the w.? 9:33, 34
salute no man by the w. Luke 10:4
he talked with us by the w. 24:32
for I will not see you now by the w. 1 Cor 16:7

***every* way**

a flaming sword which turned every w. Gen 3:24
refrained my feet from every evil w. Ps 119:101
I hate every false w. 104, 128
every w. of man right in. Pr 21:2
buildest thine eminent place in the head of every w. Ezek 16:31
much every w. because to. Rom 3:2
every w., whether in. Phil 1:18
see **evil**

***his* way**

all flesh had corrupted his w. on earth. Gen 6:12
as for God, his w. is perfect. 2 Sam 22:31; Ps 18:30
condemning the wicked, to bring his w. 1 Ki 8:32; 2 Chr 6:23
this is the joy of his w. Job 8:19
also shall hold on his w. 17:9
who shall declare his w. to ? 21:31
his w. have I kept and not. 23:11
hath enjoined him his w.? 36:23
meek will he teach his w. Ps 25:9
who prospereth in his w. 37:7
and he delighteth in his w. 23
wait on the Lord and keep his w. 34
a young man cleanse his w.? 119:9
me in beginning of his w. Pr 8:22
righteousness of the perfect direct his w. 11:5
prudent is to understand his w. 14:8
a man's heart deviseth his w. 16:9
he that keepeth his w. preserveth. 17
of man perverteth his w. 19:3
when he is gone his w., then. 20:14
upright, he directeth his w. 21:29
make his w. prosperous. Isa 48:15
let the wicked forsake his w. 55:7
the destroyer of the Gentiles is on his w. Jer 4:7
to warn the wicked from his wicked w. Ezek 3:18
and he turn not from his wicked w. 3:19; 33:8, 9
not return from his wicked w. 13:22
the Lord hath his w. in. Nah 1:3
himself and goeth his w. Jas 1:24
sinner from the error of his w. 5:20
see **went**

***in the* way**

I being in the w. the Lord. Gen 24:27
Lord who led me in the right w. 48

Lord was with me *in the w.* *Gen* 35:3
Rachel buried *in the w.* 19; 48:7
Aaron stood *in the w.* *Ex* 5:20
send angel before thee to keep thee *in the w.* 23:20
who went *in the w.* *Deut* 1:33
you not with bread *in the w.* 23:4
Jeroboam *in the w.* *1 Ki* 11:29
his carcase was cast *in the w.* 13:24
25, 28
he walked *in the w.* of his father. 15:26; 22:52
and walked *in the w.* of Jeroboam. 15:34; 16:2, 19, 26; 22:52
as Obadiah was *in the w.* 18:7
he walked *in the w.* of the kings of. *2 Ki* 8:18; 16:3; *2 Chr* 21:6, 13
he walked *in the w.* of the house of Ahab. *2 Ki* 8:27
and walked not *in the w.* 21:22
three years they walked *in the w.* of David. *2 Chr* 11:17
he walked *in the w.* of Asa. 20:32
help us against the enemy *in the w.* *Ezra* 8:22
to give them light *in the w.* *Neh* 9:12
by day to lead *in the w.* 19
a trap for him *in the w.* *Job* 18:10
nor standeth *in the w.* *Ps* 1:1
will he teach sinners *in the w.* 25:8
shall he teach *in the w.* 12; 32:8
and shalt set us *in the w.* 85:13
my strength *in the w.* 102:23
drink of the brook *in the w.* 110:7
the undefiled *in the w.* 119:1
I have rejoiced *in the w.* 14
and lead me *in the w.* 139:24
in the w. have they privily. 142:3
walk not thou *in the w.* *Pr* 1:15
that thou mayest walk *in the w.* 2:20
I have taught thee *in the w.* 4:11
go not *in the w.* of evil men. 14
lead *in the w.* of righteousness. 8:20
go *in the w.* of understanding. 9:6
he is *in the w.* of life that. 10:17
in the w. of righteousness is. 12:28
him that is upright *in the w.* 13:6
if it be found *in the w.* of righteousness. 16:31
thorns and snares are *in the w.* 22:5
train up a child *in the w.* he. 6
guide thy heart *in the w.* 23:19
saith, There is a lion *in the w.* 26:13
upright *in the w.* is. 29:27
fears shall be *in the w.* *Eccl* 12:5
should not walk *in the w.* *Isa* 8:11
in the w. of thy judgements. 26:8
went on frowardly *in the w.* 57:17
which walked *in the w.* that. 65:2
to do *in the w.* of Egypt? or what hast thou to do *in the w.*? *Jer* 2:18
in the w. of thy sister. *Ezek* 23:31
so priests murder *in the w.* *Hos* 6:9
agree quickly whiles thou art *in the w.* *Mat* 5:25
garments *in the w.*; others strewed branches *in the w.* 21:8
Mark 11:8; *Luke* 19:36
John came *in the w.* of. *Mat* 21:32
to guide our feet *into the w.* of peace. *Luke* 1:79
as thou art *in the w.* give. 12:58
appeared to thee *in the w.* *Acts* 9:17
he had seen the Lord *in the w.* 27
they have gone *in the w.* *Jude* 11

see **Lord**

my **way**

the Lord hath prospered *my w.* *Gen* 24:56
he maketh *my w.* perfect. *2 Sam* 22:33; *Ps* 18:32
fenced up *my w.* that I. *Job* 19:8
why sayest thou, *My w.*? *Isa* 40:27
hear, O Israel, is not *my w.* equal? *Ezek* 18:25
I go *my w.* *John* 8:21
brought on *my w.* *Rom* 15:24
to be brought on *my w.* *2 Cor* 1:16*

out of the **way**

turned aside quickly *out of the w.* I commanded them. *Ex* 32:8
Deut 9:12, 16; *Judg* 2:17
the ass turned aside *out of the w.* *Num* 22:23
turn aside *out of the w.* *Deut* 11:28
thrust thee *out of the w.* 13:5
blind to wander *out of the w.* 27:18
the needy *out of the w.* *Job* 24:4
they are taken *out of the w.* 24
step hath turned *out of the w.* 31:7
wandereth *out of the w.* *Pr* 21:16
and through strong drink are *out of the w.* *Isa* 28:7*
get you *out of the w.* 30:11
stumblingblock *out of the w.* 57:14
are departed *out of the w.* *Mal* 2:8
are all gone *out of the w.* *Rom* 3:12
he took the handwriting *out of the w.* *Col* 2:14
he be taken *out of the w.* *2 Thes* 2:7
compassion on them that are *out of the w.* *Heb* 5:2*
is lame be turned *out of the w.* 12:13

own **way**

the fruit of their *own w.* *Pr* 1:31
a man understand his *own w.*? 20:24
every one to his *own w.* *Isa* 53:6
they all look to their *own w.* 56:11
their *own w.* have I. *Ezek* 22:31
they defiled Israel by their *own w.* 36:17

their **way**

take heed to *their w.* to walk before. *1 Ki* 2:4; 8:25; *2 Chr* 6:16
the paths of *their w.* are. *Job* 6:18
his troops raise up *their w.* 19:12
I chose out *their w.*, sat chief. 29:25
let *their w.* be dark. *Ps* 35:6
this *their w.* is their folly. 49:13
perverted *their w.* and. *Jer* 3:21
know and try *their w.* 6:27
their w. shall be to them as. 23:12
do to them after *their w.* and judge. *Ezek* 7:27; 9:10; 11:21
ye shall see *their w.* and. 14:22
as for them *their w.* is not. 33:17
their w. was before me as. 36:17
according to *their w.* and doings. 19
being brought on *their w.* *Acts* 15:3

see **went**

this **way**

me in *this w.* that I go. *Gen* 28:20
Moses looked *this w.* and. *Ex* 2:12
to flee *this w.* or that. *Josh* 8:20
Elisha said, *This* is not the *w.*; follow me. *2 Ki* 6:19
saying, *This* is the *w.*, walk ye in it. *Isa* 30:21
if he found any of *this w.* *Acts* 9:2
I persecuted *this w.* unto the. 22:4

thy **way**

Lord will prosper *thy w.* *Gen* 24:40
I pray, shew me *thy w.* *Ex* 33:13
thy w. is perverse. *Num* 22:32
make *thy w.* prosperous. *Josh* 1:8
return on *thy w.* to the wilderness. *1 Ki* 19:15
make *thy w.* straight. *Ps* 5:8
teach me *thy w.* O Lord, lead me. 27:11; 86:11
commit *thy w.* unto the Lord. 37:5
our steps declined from *thy w.* 44:18
that *thy w.* may be known. 67:2
thy w. O God, is in the. 77:13
thy w. is in the sea, thy path in. 19
quicken thou me in *thy w.* 119:37
thou walk in *thy w.* safely. *Pr* 3:23
remove *thy w.* far from her. 5:8
in the greatness of *thy w.* *Isa* 57:10
see *thy w.* in the valley. *Jer* 2:23
why trimmest thou *thy w.* to? 33
thou about to change *thy w.*? 36
thy w. have procured these. 4:18
will recompense *thy w.* *Ezek* 16:43
I will hedge up *thy w.* *Hos* 2:6
thou didst trust in *thy w.* 10:13
messenger, who shall prepare *thy w.* *Mat* 11:10; *Mark* 1:2; *Luke* 7:27

wayfaring

he saw a *w.* man in the. *Judg* 19:17
his own flock, to dress for the *w.* man. *2 Sam* 12:4
highways lie waste, the *w.* *Isa* 33:8
w. men, though fools, shall. 35:8
a lodging place of *w.* men. *Jer* 9:2
thou be as a *w.* man? 14:8

waymarks

set thee up *w.*, make thee. *Jer* 31:21

ways

shall rise early and go on your *w.* *Gen* 19:2
walk in all the *w.* Lord. *Deut* 5:33
walked in the *w.* of Asa. *1 Ki* 22:43
he walked in all the *w.* of Manasseh. *2 Ki* 21:21
he walked in all the *w.* of David. 22:2
2 Chr 17:3; 34:2
not walked in the *w.* of. *2 Chr* 21:12
walked in the *w.* of the house. 22:3
he walked in the *w.* of the kings. 28:2
they know not the *w.* of. *Job* 24:13
they raise up the *w.* of their. 30:12
eyes are upon the *w.* of men. 34:21
the chief of the *w.* of God. 40:19
heart are the *w.* of them. *Ps* 84:5
so are the *w.* of every one greedy. *Pr* 1:19
to walk in the *w.* of darkness. 2:13
whose *w.* are crooked, and they. 15
wisdom's *w.* are *w.* of. 3:17
paths . . . her *w.* are moveable. 5:6
w. of man are before the eyes. 21
go to the ant, consider her *w.* 6:6
heart decline to her *w.* 7:25
the end thereof are the *w.* of death. 14:12; 16:25
the *w.* of man are clean in his. 16:2
when a man's *w.* please the Lord. 7
taketh a gift to pervert the *w.* 17:23
she looketh well to the *w.* of. 31:27
O young man, walk in the *w.* of thy heart. *Eccl* 11:9
they shall feed in the *w.* *Isa* 49:9
traversing her *w.* *Jer* 2:23
in the *w.* hast thou sat for. 3:2
stand in the *w.* and see, ask. 6:16
amend your *w.* and your doings. 7:3, 5; 26:13
walk in all the *w.* I have. 7:23
if they diligently learn the *w.* 12:16
make your *w.* and your doings. 18:11
thine eyes are open on the *w.* of. 32:19
the *w.* of Zion do mourn. *Lam* 1:4
let us search and try our *w.* 3:40
are not your *w.* unequal? *Ezek* 18:25, 29
shall ye remember your *w.* 20:43
your wicked *w.* or doings. 44
son of man, appoint thee two *w.*, that the sword may. 21:19
stood at head of the two *w.* to use. 21
consider your *w.* *Hag* 1:5, 7
do to us according to our *w.* and. *Zech* 1:6
and the rough *w.* shall. *Luke* 3:5
known to me the *w.* of life. *Acts* 2:28

see **by-ways, evil, high, seven**

any **ways**

do *any w.* hide their eyes. *Lev* 20:4
if ye shall *any w.* make. *Num* 30:15
any w. able to deliver. *2 Chr* 32:13

his **ways**

of Lord, to walk in *his w.* and fear him. *Deut* 8:6; 26:17; 28:9
30:16; *1 Ki* 2:3
to walk in all *his w.* *Deut* 10:12
11:22; *Josh* 22:5; *1 Ki* 8:58
and walk ever in *his w.* *Deut* 19:9
all *his w.* are judgement. 32:4
Dan 4:37
walked not in *his w.* *1 Sam* 8:3
David behaved wisely in *his w.* 18:14
and give to every man according to *his w.* *1 Ki* 8:39; *2 Chr* 6:30
and *his w.* are written. *2 Chr* 13:22
Jotham prepared *his w.* before. 27:6
his w. are written in book. 7; 28:26
these are parts of *his w.* *Job* 26:14
man find according to *his w.* 34:11
not consider any of *his w.* 27
his w. are always grievous. *Ps* 10:5
he made known *his w.* unto Moses. 103:7
iniquity, they walk in *his w.* 119:3
one that walketh in *his w.* 128:1
is righteous in all *his w.* **145:17**

choose none of his w. Pr 3:31
he that perverteth his w. 10:9
he that is perverse in his w. 14:2
he that despiseth his w. shall. 19:16
lest thou learn his w. and. 22:25
that is perverse in his w. 28:6
he that is perverse in his w. shall. 18
he will teach us of his w. Isa 2:3
Mi 4:2
they would not walk in his w. Isa 42:24
I will direct all his w. saith. 45:13
seen his w. and will heal. 57:18
give every man according to his w.
Jer 17:10; 32:19
that he should return from his w.
Ezek 18:23
I will judge Israel according to his
w. 30; 33:20
of a fowler in all his w. Hos 9:8
punish Jacob according to his w. 12:2
march on every one in his w. Joel 2:7
the hills did bow, his w. Hab 3:6
thou shalt go before the Lord to prepare his w. Luke 1:76
his w. are past finding. Rom 11:33
man is unstable in all his w. Jas 1:8
rich man fade away in his w. 11
see **Lord**

my ways

if thou wilt walk in my w. as thy
father. 1 Ki 3:14; 11:38; Zech 3:7
and not walked in my w. 1 Ki 11:33
doth not he see my w.? Job 31:4
I will take heed to my w. Ps 39:1
Israel had walked in my w. 81:13
they have not known my w. 95:10
Heb 3:10
O that my w. were directed. Ps 119:5
I have declared my w. and thou. 26
I thought on my w. and turned. 59
all my w. are before thee. 168
acquainted with all my w. 139:3
blessed are they that keep my w.
Pr 8:32
let thine eyes observe my w. 23:26
neither are your ways my w. Isa 55:8
so are my w. higher than your. 9
and delight to know my w. 58:2
he hath inclosed my w. Lam 3:9
he turned aside my w. and. 11
my w. equal, your w.? Ezek 18:29
if thou wilt walk in my w. Zech 3:7
ye have not kept my w. Mal 2:9
remembrance of my w. 1 Cor 4:17

own ways

I will maintain my own w. Job 13:15
be filled with his own w. Pr 14:14
not doing thine own w. Isa 58:13
have chosen their own w. 66:3
then remember your own evil w.
Ezek 36:31
be ashamed for your own w. 32
nations to walk in own w. Acts 14:16

their ways

pray and turn from their wicked w.
2 Chr 7:14
eyes are upon their w. Job 24:23
turn to their crooked w. Ps 125:5
who go right on their w. Pr 9:15
return not from their w. Jer 15:7
mine eyes are upon all their w. 16:17
them to stumble in their w. 18:15
comfort you when ye see their w.
Ezek 14:23
not walked after their w. 16:47
punish them for their w. Hos 4:9
misery are in their w. Rom 3:16
follow their pernicious w. 2 Pet 2:2

thy ways

not prosper in thy w. Deut 28:29
sons walk not in thy w. 1 Sam 8:5
may fear thee to walk in thy w.
2 Chr 6:31
uprightness of thy w. Job 4:6
the knowledge of thy w. 21:14
thou makest thy w. perfect? 22:3
light shall shine upon thy w. 28
shew me thy w. O Lord. Ps 25:4
I teach transgressors thy w. 51:13
to keep thee in all thy w. 91:11
have respect unto thy w. 119:15
in all thy w. acknowledge him. Pr 3:6
let thy w. be established. Pr 4:26
nor thy w. to that which destroyeth
kings. 31:3
made us err from thy w. Isa 63:17
remember thee in thy w. 64:5
taught the wicked thy w. Jer 2:33
thou hast scattered thy w. 3:13
judge thee according to thy w.
Ezek 7:3, 4, 8, 9
corrupted more than they in all thy
w. 16:47
then remember thy w. and be. 61
according to thy w. shall they. 24:14
thou wast perfect in thy w. 28:15
whose hand are all thy w. Dan 5:23
just and true are thy w. Rev 15:3

way side

where is harlot that was by the w.
side? Gen 38:21
Eli sat on a seat by the w. side
watching. 1 Sam 4:13
the proud have spread a net by the
w. side. Ps 140:5
seeds fell by the w. side. Mat 13:4
19; Mark 4:4, 15; Luke 8:5, 12
two blind men sitting by the w. side.
Mat 20:30
blind Bartimaeus sat by the high w.
side. Mark 10:46; Luke 18:35

we

been about cattle, w. and. Gen 46:34
the men said, We be not able; for they
are stronger than w. Num 13:31
greater and taller than w. Deut 1:28
that w. may be like all. 1 Sam 8:20
w. will be with thee, be. Ezra 10:4
w. his servants will arise. Neh 2:20
w., our sons and our daughters. 5:2
w. after our ability have. 8
w. are but of yesterday. Job 8:9
w. are his people, sheep. Ps 100:3
become weak as w. are? Isa 14:10
w. are thine. 63:19
for w. are many. Mark 5:9
why could not w. cast him out? 9:28
that w. being delivered. Luke 1:74
w. be Abraham's seed. John 8:33
thou art his disciple, w. are. 9:28
are w. blind also? 40
they may be one as w. 17:11, 22
and w. are his witnesses. Acts 5:32
10:39
the Holy Ghost as well as w. 10:47
w. are men of like passions. 14:15
w., or ever he come, are ready. 23:15
w., being many, are one body in
Christ. Rom 12:5
w. that are strong ought to bear. 15:1
w. are labourers together. 1 Cor 3:9
w. are fools, but ye are wise, w. 4:10
w. bless, persecuted, w. suffer it. 12
w. in him; one Lord and w. by. 8:6
are not w. rather? 9:12
w. being many are one bread. 10:17
do w. provoke Lord, are w.? 22
w. are your rejoicing. 2 Cor 1:14
w., that w. say not, ye, should. 9:4
Christ's, so are w. Christ's. 10:7
they may be found even as w. 11:12
though w. or an angel. Gal 1:8
so w., when w. were children. 4:3
now w., as Isaac, are the children. 28
w. are his workmanship. Eph 2:10
w. which are alive shall be caught in
. . . so shall w. ever. 1 Thes 4:17
w. are not of the night nor of. 5:5
whose house are w. if w. hold fast.
Heb 3:6
w. are not of them who draw. 10:39
w. are of God. Hereby w. 1 John 4:6
w. know that w. are of God. 5:19

weak

they be strong or w. Num 13:18
then shall I be w. as other men.
Judg 16:7, 11, 17
I am this day w. though. 2 Sam 3:39
let not your hands be w. 2 Chr 15:7*
strengthened the w. hands. Job 4:3
I am w. Ps 6:2*
my knees are w. 109:24
also become w. as we? Isa 14:10
strengthen ye the w. hands. 35:3
shall be w. as water. Ezek 7:17; 21:7
how w. is thy heart? Ezek 16:30
the w. say, I am strong. Joel 3:10
but the flesh is w. Mat 26:41
Mark 14:38
ought to support the w. Acts 20:35
being not w. in faith, he. Rom 4:19
for the law was w. through the. 8:3
him that is w. in the faith. 14:1
another who is w. eateth herbs. 2
brother stumbleth or is made w. 21
bear the infirmities of the w. 15:1
w. things to confound the. 1 Cor 1:27
we are w. 4:10
conscience being w. 8:7, 10
wound their w. conscience. 12
to the w. became I as w., that I might
gain the w.: I am made. 9:22
for this cause many are w. 11:30
bodily presence is w. 2 Cor 10:10
I speak as though we had been w.
11:21
who is w. and I am not w.? 29
for when I am w. then am I. 12:10
which to you-ward is not w. but. 13:3
for we are w. in him, but shall live. 4
are glad when we are w. 9
how turn ye again to the w.? Gal 4:9
support the w., be patient toward
all. 1 Thes 5:14

weaken

which didst w. nations. Isa 14:12*

weakened

of the land w. Judah. Ezra 4:4
their hands shall be w. Neh 6:9
he w. my strength in. Ps 102:23

weakeneth

he w. the strength of. Job 12:21*
he w. the hands of the men of war.
Jer 38:4

weaker

Saul's house w. and w. 2 Sam 3:1
to the wife as the w. vessel. 1 Pet 3:7

weak handed

while he is w. handed. 2 Sam 17:2

weakness

the w. of God is stronger. 1 Cor 1:25
I was with you in w. and. 2:3
it is sown in w.; it is raised. 15:43
made perfect in w. 2 Cor 12:9
though crucified through w. 13:4
going before for the w. Heb 7:18
out of w. were made strong. 11:34

wealth

of Jacob took all their w. Gen 34:29
my hand got me this w. Deut 8:17
giveth thee power to get w. 18
kinsman, a man of w. Ruth 2:1
thou shalt see an enemy in all the w.
1 Sam 2:32
Menahem exacted money of men of
w. 2 Ki 15:20
thou hast not asked w. 2 Chr 1:11
I will give thee riches, and w. 12
nor seek their peace or w. for ever.
Ezra 9:12*
Mordecai seeking the w. Esth 10:3*
spend their days in w. Job 21:13*
if I rejoiced because my w. was
great. 31:25
and dost not increase w. Ps 44:12
they that trust in w. and boast. 49:6
die and leave their w. to others. 10
w. and riches shall be in his. 112:3
lest strangers be filled with thy w.
Pr 5:10*
rich man's w. is his. 10:15; 18:11
w. gotten by vanity shall be. 13:11
the w. of the sinner is laid up. 22
w. maketh many friends, the. 19:4
God hath given w. Eccl 5:19; 6:2
w. of all the heathen shall be.
Zech 14:14
this craft we have w. Acts 19:25
but seek every man another's w.
1 Cor 10:24*

common wealth

being aliens from the common w. of
Israel. Eph 2:12

wealthy

us out into a w. place. Ps 66:12
up into the w. nation. Jer 49:31*

weaned
Isaac grew and was *w.* *Gen* 21:8
not go till the child be *w.* *1 Sam* 1:22
whom Tahpenes *w.* in. *1 Ki* 11:20
as a child that is *w.* of his mother, my soul is as a *w.* child. *Ps* 131:2
the *w.* child put his hand. *Isa* 11:8
that are *w.* from the milk. 28:9
when she *w.* Lo-ruhama. *Hos* 1:8

weapon
a paddle upon thy *w.* *Deut* 23:13
other hand held a *w.* *Neh* 4:17
flee from the iron *w.* *Job* 20:24
no *w.* formed against thee. *Isa* 54:17
with his destroying *w.* *Ezek* 9:1, 2

weapons
take, I pray thee, thy *w.* *Gen* 27:3
neither my sword nor *w.* *1 Sam* 21:8
round about, every man with his *w.* in. *2 Ki* 11:8, 11; *2 Chr* 23:7, 10
even the Lord and the *w.* of his indignation. *Isa* 13:5; *Jer* 50:25
every one with his *w.* *Jer* 22:7
on fire and burn *w.* *Ezek* 39:9, 10
with lanterns and *w.* *John* 18:3
the *w.* of our warfare. *2 Cor* 10:4
see **war**

wear
thou wilt surely *w.* away. *Ex* 18:18
woman not *w.* what. *Deut* 22:5
thou shalt not *w.* garment of. 11
to burn incense, to *w.* an. *1 Sam* 2:28
85 persons that did *w.* an. 22:18
royal apparel the king useth to *w.* *Esth* 6:8
the waters *w.* the stones. *Job* 14:19
we eat our own bread and *w* *Isa* 4:1
shall *w.* out the saints of. *Dan* 7:25
nor shall they *w.* a rough garment. *Zech* 13:4
that *w.* soft clothing are. *Mat* 11:8
day began to *w.* away. *Luke* 9:12

weareth
ye respect him that *w.* the. *Jas* 2:3

wearied
they *w.* themselves to. *Gen* 19:11
nor have I *w.* thee with. *Isa* 43:23
thou hast *w.* me with thine. 24
thou art *w.* in the multitude of. 47:13
thou art *w.* in the greatness of. 57:10
my soul is *w.* because of. *Jer* 4:31*
w. thee? If in land of peace, wherein thou trustedst, they *w.* thee. 12:5
she hath *w.* herself with lies. *Ezek* 24:12
wherein have I *w.* thee? *Mi* 6:3
w. the Lord. Yet ye say, Wherein have we *w.* him? *Mal* 2:17
Jesus being *w.* sat thus. *John* 4:6
lest ye be *w.* and faint in. *Heb* 12:3

wearieth
by watering he *w.* the. *Job* 37:11*
labour of the foolish *w.* *Eccl* 10:15

weariness
much study is a *w.* of. *Eccl* 12:12
he said, What a *w.* is it! *Mal* 1:13
in *w.* and painfulness. *2 Cor* 11:27*

wearing
in Shiloh *w.* an ephod. *1 Sam* 14:3
Jesus came forth *w.* the. *John* 19:5
let it not be *w.* of gold. *1 Pet* 3:3

wearisome
and *w.* nights are appointed. *Job* 7:3

weary
Rebekah said, I am *w.* *Gen* 27:46
Amalek smote thee, when thou wast *w.* *Deut* 25:18
Sisera was fast asleep and *w.* *Judg* 4:21*
bread unto thy men that are *w.*? 8:15
all the people came *w.* *2 Sam* 16:14
upon him while he is *w.* 17:2
Philistines till his hand was *w.* 23:10
wicked cease, and the *w.* *Job* 3:17
my soul is *w.* of my life, leave. 10:1
now he hath made me *w.* 16:7
not given water to *w.* to drink. 22:7
I am *w.* with my groaning, I. *Ps* 6:6
confirm thy inheritance when *w.* 68:9
w. of my crying, my throat. 69:3
my son, be not *w.* of Lord's. *Pr* 3:11
lest he be *w.* of thee, and so. 25:17
feasts are trouble, I am *w.* *Isa* 1:14
none shall be *w.* nor stumble. 5:27
to *w.* men, but will ye *w.*? 7:13
it is seen that Moab is *w.* in. 16:12
ye may cause the *w.* to rest. 28:12
of a great rock in a *w.* land. 32:2
fainteth not, neither is *w.* 40:28
the youths shall faint and be *w.* 30
they shall run, and not be *w.* 31
but thou hast been *w.* of me. 43:22
a burden to the *w.* beast. 46:1
in season to him that is *w.* 50:4
all that seek her will not *w.* *Jer* 2:24
I am *w.* with holding in, I will. 6:11
they *w.* themselves to commit. 9:5
will destroy thee, I am *w.* 15:6
I was *w.* with forbearing, I. 20:9
I have satiated the *w.* soul. 31:25
labour in the fire and be *w.* 51:58
Babylon sink: and they shall be *w.* 64
w. themselves for vanity. *Hab* 2:13
lest by her continual coming she *w.* me. *Luke* 18:5*
let us not be *w.* in well doing. *Gal* 6:9; *2 Thes* 3:13

weasel
the *w.* and the mouse. *Lev* 11:29

weather
fair *w.* cometh out of. *Job* 37:22*
a garment in cold *w.* *Pr* 25:20
it will be fair *w.*: for the. *Mat* 16:2
it will be foul *w.* to day. 3

weave
they that *w.* networks. *Isa* 19:9
cockatrice' eggs and *w.* spider's. 59:5

weaver
to work the work of *w.* *Ex* 35:35
Goliath's spear was like a *w.*'s beam. *1 Sam* 17:7; *2 Sam* 21:19; *1 Chr* 11:23; 20:5
swifter than a *w.*'s shuttle. *Job* 7:6
I have cut off like a *w.* *Isa* 38:12

weavest
if thou *w.* seven locks. *Judg* 16:13

web
seven locks with the *w.* *Judg* 16:13
with pin of beam and the *w.* 14
trust shall be a spider's *w.* *Job* 8:14
weave the spider's *w.* *Isa* 59:5

webs
their *w.* shall not become. *Isa* 59:6

wedding
that were bidden to *w.* *Mat* 22:3*
the *w.* is ready. 8
the *w.* is furnished. 10
that had not on a *w.* garment. 11
will return from the *w.* *Luke* 12:36*
bidden of any man to a *w.* 14:8*

wedge
Achan saw a *w.* of gold. *Josh* 7:21
Joshua took Achan and the *w.* 24
precious than golden *w.* *Isa* 13:12*

wedlock
as women that break *w.* *Ezek* 16:38

weeds
the *w.* were wrapped. *Jonah* 2:5

week
The Hebrews had three sorts of weeks. [1] Weeks of days, *which were reckoned from one sabbath to another.* [2] Weeks *of years, which were reckoned from one sabbatical year to another, and which consisted of seven years.* [3] Weeks *of seven times seven years, or* of forty nine years, *which are reckoned from one* jubilee *to another.*
fulfil her *w.* *Gen* 29:27
and fulfilled her *w.* 28
covenant with many for one *w.*: and in the midst of the *w.* *Dan* 9:27
to dawn toward the first day of the *w.* *Mat* 28:1; *Mark* 16:2, 9; *Luke* 24:1; *John* 20:1, 19
I fast twice in the *w.* *Luke* 18:12
the first day of the *w.* Paul preached. *Acts* 20:7
on the first day of the *w.* *1 Cor* 16:2

weeks
shall be unclean two *w.* *Lev* 12:5
bring a meat offering after your *w.* *Num* 28:26
appointed *w.* of harvest. *Jer* 5:24
seventy *w.* are determined on thy people. *Dan* 9:24
threescore and two *w.* 25, 26
mourning three full *w.* 10:2
till three *w.* were fulfilled. 3
see **feast, seven**

weep
(Weeping and other open expressions of emotion, whether of joy or sorrow, were common among the people of the East, contrary to the repression common in the West. The louder the wail the greater the grief. For that reason men and women were hired to weep and wail at funerals)
mourn and *w.* for Sarah. *Gen* 23:2
did yearn, sought where to *w.* 43:30
Moses heard the people *w.* throughout their families. *Num* 11:10
they *w.* unto me, saying, Give. 13
what aileth the people that they *w.*? *1 Sam* 11:5
they had no more power to *w.* 34
Israel, *w.* over Saul. *2 Sam* 1:24
thou didst *w.* for the child. 12:21
and didst rend thy clothes, and *w.* *2 Chr* 34:27
mourn not, nor *w.* *Neh* 8:9
widows shall not *w.* *Job* 27:15*
did not I *w.* for him that? 30:25
into the voice of them that *w.* 31
a time to *w.* and a time. *Eccl* 3:4
to the high places to *w.* *Isa* 15:2
I will *w.* bitterly, labour not to. 22:4
thou shalt *w.* no more, he will. 30:19
of peace shall *w.* bitterly. 33:7
that I might *w.* day and. *Jer* 9:1
not hear it, my soul shall *w.* in secret places . . . shall *w.* sore. 13:17
w. ye not for the dead, nor bemoan him: but *w.* sore for him that. 22:10
Sibmah, I will *w.* for thee. 48:32
for these things I *w.* *Lam* 1:16
nor shalt thou mourn nor *w.* *Ezek* 24:16, 23
w. for thee with bitterness. 27:31
awake, ye drunkards, *w.* *Joel* 1:5
let the priests *w.* between the. 2:17
declare it not in Gath, *w.* *Mi* 1:10
should I *w.* in fifth month. *Zech* 7:3
ye this ado, and *w.*? *Mark* 5:39
blessed are ye that *w.* *Luke* 6:21
to you that laugh now, ye shall *w.* 25
Lord saw her and said, *W.* not. 7:13; 8:52; *Rev* 5:5
w. not for me, but *w.* for. *Luke* 23:28
the grave to *w.* there. *John* 11:31
ye shall *w.* and lament, but. 16:20
what mean ye to *w.* and break my heart? *Acts* 21:13
w. with them that *w.* *Rom* 12:15
they that *w.* as though they wept not. *1 Cor* 7:30
and mourn, and *w.* *Jas* 4:9
go to now, ye rich men, *w.* and. 5:1
merchants of earth shall *w.* and. *Rev* 18:11

weepest
Hannah, why *w.* thou? *1 Sam* 1:8
and they say unto her, Woman, why *w.* thou? *John* 20:13, 15

weepeth
Joab, behold the king *w.* *2 Sam* 19:1
Hazael said, Why *w.*? *2 Ki* 8:12
he that goeth forth and *w.* *Ps* 126:6
she *w.* sore in night, her. *Lam* 1:2

weeping
w. before the door of. *Num* 25:6
days of *w.* for Moses. *Deut* 34:8
her husband went along with her *w.* *2 Sam* 3:16
they went up, *w.* as they. 15:30
noise of joy from *w.* *Ezra* 3:13

prayed and confessed, w. Ezra 10:1
province was fasting and w. Esth 4:3
my face is foul with w. Job 16:16
heard the voice of my w. Ps 6:8
w. may endure for a night. 30:5
mingled my drink with w. 102:9
in their streets howl, w. Isa 15:3
bewail with the w. of Jazer the vine of Sibmah. 16:9; Jer 48:32
Lord of hosts call to w. Isa 22:12
the voice of w. shall be no. 65:19
the w. of Israel heard. Jer 3:21
mountains will I take up a w. 9:10
they shall come with w. and. 31:9
lamentation and bitter w.; Rachel w. for her children. 15; Mat 2:18
restrain thy voice from w. Jer 31:16
went forth to meet them w. 41:6
continual w. shall go up, a cry. 48:5
Judah going and w. to seek. 50:4
there sat women w. for. Ezek 8:14
with fasting and with w. Joel 2:12
altar of the Lord with w. Mal 2:13
there shall be w. and. Mat 8:12
22:13; 24:51; 25:30; Luke 13:28
at his feet behind him w. Luke 7:38
when Jesus saw her w. and the Jews also w. which came. John 11:33
without at the sepulchre, w. 20:11
widows stood by him w. Acts 9:39
often, now tell you even w. Phil 3:18
shall stand afar off w. Rev 18:15
shipmaster and sailors cried, w. 19

weigh

crown to w. a talent. 1 Chr 20:2
keep them until ye w. Ezra 8:29
ye w. the violence of your. Ps 58:2
thou dost w. the path of. Isa 26:7

weighed

Abraham w. to Ephraim. Gen 23:16
by the Lord actions are w. 1 Sam 2:3
his spear's head w. 600 shekels. 17:7; 2 Sam 21:16
Absalom w. the hair of. 2 Sam 14:26
priests w. to them the silver and gold. Ezra 8:25
w. into their hands the silver. 26, 33
my grief were throughly w.! Job 6:2
nor shall silver be w. for the. 28:15
let me be w. in an even balance. 31:6
hath w. the mountains. Isa 40:12
Jeremiah w. him the money. Jer 32:9
Tekel, thou art w. in. Dan 5:27
so they w. for my price. Zech 11:12

weigheth

and he w. the waters. Job 28:25
but the Lord w. the spirits. Pr 16:2

weighing

each charger w. Num 7:85
golden spoons w. 86

weight

As the Hebrews had not the use of coined money, which was of a certain determined weight, *they* weighed *all the gold and silver they used in trade. The shekel, the half shekel, and the talents, are not only denominations of money of a certain value, of gold and silver, but also of a certain* weight. *When Moses named the drugs which were to compose the perfume to be burnt upon the golden altar, he says, that they were to take* five hundred shekels of myrrh, *etc.*, Ex 30:23. *And in* 2 Sam 14:26, *it is said, that* Absalom's hair *weighed* two hundred shekels.

The shekel *of the* sanctuary, *according to several interpreters, was double the common shekel: but others think it was the same as the common shekel, and the words* of the sanctuary, *are added, to express a just and exact* weight, *according to the standards that were kept in the temple, or tabernacle.*

mouth of sack, in full w. Gen 43:21
shall there be a like w. Ex 30:34
unrighteousness in w. Lev 19:35
you your bread by w. 26:26
a perfect and just w. Deut 25:15
w. of golden earrings. Judg 8:26
w. of king's crown a. 2 Sam 12:30
neither was the w. of the brass found out. 1 Ki 7:47; 2 Ki 25:16
gave gold by w. for things of gold, silver also by w. 1 Chr 28:14
the w. for the winds. Job 28:25
just w. is his delight. Pr 11:1
a just w. and balance are. 16:11
thy meat shall be by w. Ezek 4:10
and they shall eat bread by w. 16
he cast the w. of lead. Zech 5:8
us a more exceeding w. 2 Cor 4:17
let us lay aside every w. Heb 12:1
every stone of hail the w. of a talent. Rev 16:21

weightier

ye have omitted the w. Mat 23:23

weights

just w. shall ye have. Lev 19:36
in thy bag divers w. Deut 25:13
all the w. of the bag. Pr 16:11
divers w. and measures. 20:10, 23
the bag of deceitful w. Mi 6:11

weighty

heavy and the sand w. Pr 27:3
for his letters, say they, are w. 2 Cor 10:10

welfare

of their w. and said. Gen 43:27
each other of their w. Ex 18:7
Tou sent to David to enquire of his w. 1 Chr 18:10
was come a man to seek the w. of Neh 2:10
and my w. passeth away. Job 30:15
have been for their w. Ps 69:22
this man seeketh not the w. of his people. Jer 38:4

well, *substantive*

she saw a w. of water. Gen 21:19
witness I have digged this w. 30
here by w. of water. 24:13, 43
a fruitful bough by a w. 49:22
is the w. whereof the. Num 21:16
spring up, O w. 17
princes digged the w. 18
man that had a w. in. 2 Sam 17:18
drink of the water of the w. of Bethlehem. 23:15; 1 Chr 11:17, 18
who passing ... make it a w. Ps 84:6
drink waters out of thine own w. Pr 5:15
righteous man is a w. of life. 10:11
a w. of living waters. S of S 4:15
w. was there. Jesus being wearied ... sat thus on the w. John 4:6
the w. is deep. 11
Jacob gave us the w. 12
shall be in him a w. of water. 14

well, *adverb*

if thou doest not w., sin. Gen 4:7
that it may be w. with me. 12:13
he entreated Abram w. for her. 16
Jordan was w. watered. 13:10
Abraham and Sarah w. stricken in age. 18:11; 24:1
Jacob said, Is he w.? and they said, He is w. 29:6
when it shall be w. with thee. 40:14
father w.? is he yet alive? 43:27
dealt w. with the midwives. Ex 1:20
I know that he can speak w. 4:14
for it was w. with us. Num 11:18
Caleb said, We are w. able. 13:30
of sons of Joseph hath said w. 36:5
saying pleased me w. Deut 1:23
brethren, as w. as you. 3:20
that it may go w. with thee. 4:40
5:16; 6:3, 18; 12:25, 28; 19:13
22:7; Ruth 3:1; Eph 6:3
may rest as w. as thou. Deut 5:14
I heard the words of this people: they have w. said. 28; 18:17
that it might be w. with them. 5:29
that it may be w. with you. 33
Jer 7:23
but shalt w. remember. Deut 7:18
because he is w. with thee. 15:16
if thou hast dealt w. with. Judg 9:16
me, for she pleaseth me w. 14:3, 7
as w. men of every city. Judg 20:48
w. let him do the kinsman's part. Ruth 3:13
he shall play and thou shalt be w. 1 Sam 16:16
if he say thus, It is w. 20:7
I know w. thou shalt surely. 24:20
he dealt bread as w. 2 Sam 6:19
called, and said, All is w. 18:28
David, Thou didst w. that it was in thine heart to. 1 Ki 8:18; 2 Chr 6:8
answered, It is w. spoken. 1 Ki 18:24
Is it w. with thee? is it w. with thy husband? is it w. with the child? It is w. 2 Ki 4:26
Is all w.? 5:21; 9:11
we do not w. 7:9
of Babylon; and it shall be w. with. 25:24; Ps 128:2; Jer 40:9
Judah things went w. 2 Chr 12:12
thou doest w. to thyself. Ps 49:18
thou hast dealt w. with thy. 119:65
when it goeth w. with. Pr 11:10
the prudent man looketh w. 14:15
I saw and considered it w. 24:32
things which go w., yea, four. 30:29
she looketh w. to the ways of. 31:27
it shall be w. with them. Eccl 8:12
but it shall not be w. with the. 13
it shall be w. with him. Isa 3:10
me, Thou hast w. seen. Jer 1:12
Lord said, It shall be w. with. 15:11
It was w. with him, he. 22:15, 16
take him, look w. to him, do. 39:12
come, and I will look w. to. 40:4
that it may be w. with us. 42:6
for then we were w. and. 44:17
make it boil w. and seethe. Ezek 24:5
spice it w. 10
mark w., behold, and hear. 44:5
of one that can play w. on. 33:32
said the Lord, Doest thou w. to be angry? Jonah 4:4
I do w. to be angry, even unto. 9
hypocrites, w. did Esaias prophesy. Mat 15:7; Mark 7:6; Acts 28:25
w. done, thou good and faithful servant. Mat 25:21, 23; Luke 19:17
he hath done all things w. Mark 7:37
he had answered them w. 12:28
Zacharias and Elisabeth w. Luke 1:7
when all men speak w. of you. 6:26
if it bear fruit, w.; and if not. 13:9
Master, thou hast w. said. 20:39
John 4:17
say we not w. thou hast a devil. John 8:48
ye call me Lord, ye say w. 13:13
if w. why smitest thou me? 18:23
keep his virgin, doeth w. 1 Cor 7:37
giveth her in marriage, doeth w. 38
affect you, but not w. Gal 4:17
run w.; who did hinder you? 5:7
ye have w. done, ye did. Phil 4:14
one that ruleth w. his. 1 Tim 3:4
let the elders that rule w. be. 5:17
and to please them w. Tit 2:9
is one God; thou doest w. Jas 2:19
see **as, do, doing, favoured pleased**

very **well**

as thou *very* w. knowest. Acts 25:10
he ministered to me, thou knowest *very* w. 2 Tim 1:18

wellbeloved

myrrh is my w. unto. S of S 1:13
now will I sing to my w. Isa 5:1
he sent his w. son. Mark 12:6
salute w. Epenetus. Rom 16:5
the elder to the w. Gaius. 3 John 1

well *nigh*

as for me, my steps had w. *nigh* slipped. Ps 73:2

wells

w. Abraham's servants. Gen 26:15
and Isaac digged again the w. 18
where were twelve w. Ex 15:27
drink of the water of w. Num 20:17
and w. digged which thou. Deut 6:11
and ye shall stop all w. 2 Ki 3:19
they stopped all the w. of water. 25
towers and digged w. 2 Chr 26:10
shall draw water out of w. Isa 12:3

these are *w.* without water, clouds that are. *2 Pet* 2:17

wellspring

understanding is a *w.* of. *Pr* 16:22
the *w.* of wisdom as a. 18:4

wen

maimed, or having a *w.* *Lev* 22:22

wench

a *w.* told Jonathan. *2 Sam* 17:17*

went

with me in the way I *w.* *Gen* 35:3
in the first place *w.* standard of Judah. *Num* 10:14
into the land whereto he *w.* 14:24
kindled because Balaam *w.* 22:22
Balaam *w.* not to seek for. 24:1
Phinehas *w.* after the man. 25:8
in all the way ye *w.* *Deut* 1:31
he preserved us in all the way we *w.* *Josh* 24:17
so Simeon *w.* with Judah. *Judg* 1:3
and Judah *w.* with Simeon. 17
strength *w.* from him. 16:19
said, Whither *w.* ye? *1 Sam* 10:14
there *w.* with Saul a band. 26
the man *w.* for an old man. 17:12
but David *w.* to feed his father's. 15
David and his men *w.* wherever they could go. 23:13
because they *w.* not with us. 30:22
how *w.* the matter? *2 Sam* 1:4
as he *w.* to recover his border. 8:3; *1 Chr* 18:3
Lord preserved David whithersoever he *w.* *2 Sam* 8:6, 14; *1 Chr* 18:6, 13
w. in their simplicity. *2 Sam* 15:11
as he *w.*, thus he said, O my. 18:33
Solomon *w.* not fully. *1 Ki* 11:6
said, What way *w.* he? 13:12
he *w.* after the man of God. 14
he said, Which way *w.* the Spirit of the Lord? 22:24; *2 Chr* 18:23
but they *w.* not. *1 Ki* 22:48
they two *w.* on. *2 Ki* 2:6
he said, *W.* not my heart with thee? 5:26
for he *w.* with them, and they. 6:4
when he *w.* in to his wife. *1 Chr* 7:23
when they *w.* from nation to nation. 16:20; *Ps* 105:13
so all Israel *w.* to their. *2 Chr* 10:16
in Judah things *w.* well. 12:12
people *w.* to house of Baal. 23:17
knew not whither I *w.* *Neh* 2:16
in the evening she *w.*, and on the morrow returned. *Esth* 2:14
I *w.* with them to the house of God. *Ps* 42:4
it *w.* ill with Moses for their. 106:32
a young man *w.* the way to. *Pr* 7:8
he *w.* on frowardly in the way of his heart. *Isa* 57:17
they *w.* every one straight forward. *Ezek* 1:9
turned not when they *w.* 12; 10:11
they *w.* on their four sides. 1:17
when those *w.*, these *w.* 21
for their heart *w.* after their. 20:16
she *w.* after her lovers. *Hos* 2:13
then *w.* Ephraim to the. 5:13
they *w.* to Baal-peor and. 9:10
as they called them, so they *w.* 11:2
before him *w.* the pestilence, burning coals. *Hab* 3:5
of thine arrows, they *w.* 11
he repented and *w.* *Mat* 21:29
said, I go, sir, but *w.* not. 30
while they *w.* to buy, the. 25:10
they left their father and *w.* after. *Mark* 1:20
all *w* to be taxed, every. *Luke* 2:3
one *w.* to them from the dead. 16:30
as they *w.* they were cleansed. 17:14
Joseph *w.* to Pilate and. 23:52
the Galileans also *w.* to. *John* 4:45
every man *w.* to his own house. 7:53
I *w.* and washed and I. 9:11
from God and *w.* to God. 13:3
they *w.* backward and fell to. 18:6
then *w.* this saying abroad. 21:23
they *w.* every where preaching the. *Acts* 8:4
Saul . . . threatenings *w.* unto the. 9:1
as they *w.* on their journey, Peter *w.* to pray. *Acts* 10:9
they *w.* both into synagogue. 14:1
w. not with them to the work. 15:38
as we *w.* to prayer, a damsel. 16:16
as I *w.* to Damascus with. 26:12
he *w.* and preached to. *1 Pet* 3:19
see **along**

went *about*

the people *w. about.* *Num* 11:8
the slingers *w. about* it. *2 Ki* 3:25
they *w. about* and taught. *2 Chr* 17:9
I *w. about* to cause my. *Eccl* 2:20
the watchmen that *w. about* found me. *S of S* 5:7
Jesus *w. about* teaching. *Mat* 4:23
9:35; *Mark* 6:6
they *w. about* to slay him. *Acts* 9:29; 21:31; 26:21
Jesus *w. about* doing good. 10:38
he *w. about* seeking some to. 13:11
see **arose**

went *aside*

Jesus took them and *w. aside* privately. *Luke* 9:10
chief captain *w. aside.* *Acts* 23:19

went *astray*

afflicted I *w. astray.* *Ps* 119:67
when Israel *w. astray* after idols. *Ezek* 44:10, 15
priests which *w.* not *astray* when Israel *w. astray* as Levites *w. astray.* 48:11
than of the ninety and nine which *w.* not *astray.* *Mat* 18:13

went *away*

Samson *w. away* with doors of the gates. *Judg* 16:3
and *w. away* with the pin of. 14
and his concubine *w. away.* 19:2
the mule that was under him *w. away.* *2 Sam* 18:9
was wroth, and *w. away.* *2 Ki* 5:11
queen of Sheba *w. away.* *2 Chr* 9:12
he *w. away* sorrowful. *Mat* 19:22
Mark 10:22
he *w. away* second time. *Mat* 26:42
he *w. away* the third time. 44
Mark 14:39
of him many *w. away.* *John* 12:11
the disciples *w. away* to their. 20:10
morrow Peter *w. away.* *Acts* 10:23

went *back*

so he *w. back* and did. *1 Ki* 13:19
king Joram *w. back* to. *2 Ki* 8:29
many disciples *w. back.* *John* 6:66

went *before*

the Lord *w. before.* *Ex* 13:21
the angel of God which *w. before* the camp. 14:19
the ark of the covenant *w. before* them. *Num* 10:33; *Josh* 3:6
the armed men *w. before* the priests. *Josh* 6:9, 13
one bearing a shield *w. before* him. *1 Sam* 17:7, 41
Ahio *w. before* the ark. *2 Sam* 6:4
and Shobach *w. before* them. 10:16
1 Chr 19:16
Amasa *w. before* them. *2 Sam* 20:8
they that *w. before* were affrighted. *Job* 18:20
the singers *w. before.* *Ps* 68:25
they saw *w. before* them. *Mat* 2:9
multitudes that *w. before* them cried. 21:9; *Mark* 11:9
they which *w. before* rebuked him. *Luke* 18:39
he *w. before*, to Jerusalem. 19:28
Judas *w. before*, drew near. 22:47
prophecies which *w. before.* *1 Tim* 1:18

went *behind*

the angel removed and *w. behind.* *Ex* 14:19

went *down*

Abram *w. down* into Egypt to sojourn. *Gen* 12:10
sun *w. down*, a smoking furnace and. 15:17; *Judg* 19:14; *2 Sam* 2:24
Joseph's brethren *w. down.* *Gen* 42:3
Benjamin *w. down.* 43:15
Moses *w. down* from the mount to the people. *Ex* 19:14, 25; 32:15
w. down alive into pit. *Num* 16:33
how our fathers *w. down* into. 20:15
Deut 10:22; 26:5; *Josh* 24:4
Israel *w. down* after. *Judg* 3:27, 28
Barak *w. down* from mount. 4:14
Gideon *w. down* with Phurah. 7:11
Samson *w. down* to Timnath and saw a woman. 14:1, 5, 7
him before the sun *w. down.* 18
Samson *w. down* to Ashkelon. 19
Ruth *w. down* unto the. *Ruth* 3:6
the Israelites *w. down.* *1 Sam* 13:20
his father's house *w. down* to him. 22:1
David heard, and *w. down* to the hold. *2 Sam* 5:17
but Uriah *w.* not *down.* 11:9, 10, 13
court, whither they *w. down.* 17:18
David *w. down* against the. 21:15
three of the thirty chief *w. down* and. 23:13; *1 Chr* 11:5
Benaiah *w. down* and slew a lion in. *2 Sam* 23:20
Benaiah *w. down* to the Egyptian, and slew. 21; *1 Chr* 11:22, 23
Elijah *w. down* with him. *2 Ki* 1:15
Elijah and Elisha *w. down.* 2:2
Naaman *w. down* and dipped. 5:14
Ahaziah *w. down* to see Joram. 8:29; *2 Chr* 22:6
Jehoshaphat *w. down.* *2 Chr* 18:2
ointment that *w. down.* *Ps* 133:2
w. down into the garden. *S of S* 6:11
people *w. down* aforetime. *Isa* 52:4
I *w. down* to the potter's. *Jer* 18:3
in the day when he *w. down* to the grave. *Ezek* 31:15
they also *w. down* to hell. 17
Jonah *w. down* to Joppa. *Jonah* 1:3
I *w. down* to the bottoms of. 2:6
man *w. down* justified. *Luke* 18:14
angel *w. down* and troubled the water. *John* 5:4
Jacob *w. down* into. *Acts* 7:15
Philip *w. down* to Samaria. 8:5
and they both *w. down* into the. 38
then Peter *w. down* to the. 10:21
Herod *w. down* from Judaea. 12:19
Paul *w. down* and embracing. 20:10

went *forth*

a raven *w. forth.* *Gen* 8:7
w. forth from Ur. 11:31
Noah *w. forth*, his sons and. 18, 19
out of that land *w. forth.* 10:11
they *w. forth* to go into land. 12:5
there *w. forth* a wind. *Num* 11:31
the princes *w. forth* to. 31:13; 33:1
trees *w. forth* to anoint. *Judg* 9:8
as he *w. forth* it fell out. *2 Sam* 20:8
Elisha *w. forth* unto the spring of the waters. *2 Ki* 2:21
whithersoever he *w. forth.* 18:7
then *w.* Haman *forth.* *Esth* 5:9
Satan *w. forth* from. *Job* 1:12; 2:7
angel of the Lord *w. forth.* *Isa* 37:36
the former things *w. forth*, I. 48:3
Shallum who *w. forth.* *Jer* 22:11
thy renown *w. forth* among the heathen. *Ezek* 16:14
her great scum *w.* not *forth.* 24:12
that which *w. forth* by an. *Amos* 5:3
burning coals *w. forth.* *Hab* 3:5
behold, a sower *w. forth.* *Mat* 13:3
ten virgins *w. forth* to meet. 25:1
took up bed and *w. forth.* *Mark* 2:12
name's sake they *w. forth.* *3 John* 7
he *w. forth* conquering. *Rev* 6:2

went *her way*

woman *w. her way.* *1 Sam* 1:18
the woman *w. her way.* *John* 4:28
so said, she *w. her way.* 11:28

went *his way*

and the Lord *w. his way.* *Gen* 18:33
Rebekah and *w. his way.* 24:61
and drink and *w. his way.* 25:34
Jethro *w. his way* into. *Ex* 18:27
Saul *w. his way.* *1 Sam* 24:7
David *w.* on *his way.* 26:25
of Adonijah *w. his way.* *1 Ki* 1:49
so Mordecai *w. his way.* *Esth* 4:17
Jeremiah *w. his way.* *Jer* 28:11

his enemy sowed tares and *w. his way.* *Mat* 13:25
he passing through midst of them, *w. his way.* *Luke* 4:30
he *w. his way* and published. 8:39
Judas *w. his way* and communed with priests. 22:4
man believed, and *w. his way.* *John* 4:50
eunuch *w.* on *his way.* *Acts* 8:39
Ananias *w. his way* and. 9:17

see **Jesus, went**

went *in,* or *into*

Noah *w. into* the ark and. *Gen* 7:7
w. in two and two. 9
w. in male and female. 16
Joseph *w. into* the house to. 39:11
Moses and Aaron *w. in* to Pharaoh. *Ex* 5:1; 7:10
Israel *w. into* the midst of the. 14:22
the Egyptians *w. in.* 23; 15:19
until Moses *w. in* to speak. 34:35
when Aaron *w. into* the. *Lev* 16:23
that were spies *w. in.* *Josh* 6:23
the haft also *w. in* after. *Judg* 3:22
so the Levite *w. in* and dwelt. 17:10
when the Levite *w. in* to lodge. 19:15
Saul *w. in* to cover. *1 Sam* 24:3
then *w.* David *in* before. *2 Sam* 7:18
Bath-sheba *w. in* unto. *1 Ki* 1:15
disguised *w. into* the battle. 22:30
Elisha *w. in,* shut the. *2 Ki* 4:33
then she *w. in,* fell at his feet. 37
and one *w. in* and told his lord. 5:4
Gehazi *w. in* and stood before. 25
when they *w. in* to offer. 10:24
Uzziah *w. into* the temple of the Lord. *2 Chr* 26:16
Azariah the priest *w. in* after. 17
so the children *w. in.* *Neh* 9:24
the king *w. into* the palace garden. *Esth* 7:7
until I *w. into* the sanctuary of God. *Ps* 73:17
Urijah fled and *w. into.* *Jer* 26:21
so I *w. in.* *Ezek* 8:10
six men *w. in.* 9:2
clothed with linen *w. in.* 10:2, 3, 6
when they *w. into* captivity. 25:3
Israel *w. into* captivity for. 39:23
Daniel *w. in* and desired of the king. *Dan* 2:16
w. in unto Arioch. 24
he *w. into* his house to pray. 6:10
the devils *w. into* the herd of swine. *Mat* 8:32
certain householder *w. into.* 21:33
Mark 12:1; *Luke* 19:12; 20:9
they that were ready *w. in* to the marriage. *Mat* 25:10
w. into the holy city, and. 27:53
how David *w. into* the house of God. *Mark* 2:26; *Luke* 6:4
Joseph *w. in* boldly to Pilate. *Mark* 15:43
burn incense when he *w. in. Luke* 1:9
Mary *w. into* the hill country. 39
and he *w. in* to tarry with. 24:29
that disciple *w. in* with. *John* 18:15
clothes lying, yet *w.* he not *in.* 20:5
then *w. in* also that other disciple. 8
all the time the Lord *w. in. Acts* 1:21
as Peter talked he *w. in* and. 10:27
he departed and *w. into.* 12:17
they *w. into* the synagogue on. 13:14
Paul *w. into* the synagogue. 17:2
10; 19:8
their sound *w. into* all. *Rom* 10:18

went *in,* as to a woman

Abram *w. in* unto Hagar. *Gen* 16:4
the firstborn *w. in* and lay. 19:33
Leah; and he *w. in* unto her. 29:23
he *w. in* also unto Rachel. 30
Jacob *w. in* unto Bilhah. 30:4
saw Shuah and *w. in* to her. 38:2
Onan *w. in* to his brother's wife. 9
harlot and *w. in* unto her. *Judg* 16:1
Boaz *w. in* unto Ruth. *Ruth* 4:13
David comforted Bath-sheba his wife, and *w. in.* *2 Sam* 12:24
Absalom *w. in* to his father's. 16:22
Ithra *w. in* to Abigail the daughter of Nahash. 17:25

David *w.* not *in* to them. *2 Sam* 20:3
Hezron *w. in* to. *1 Chr* 2:21
when Ephraim *w. in* to his wife. 7:23
yet they *w. in* unto her. *Ezek* 23:44

went *over*

there arose and *w. over. 2 Sam* 2:15
and they *w. over* Jordan. 19:17
Barzillai *w. over* Jordan with. 31
so they two *w. over* on. *2 Ki* 2:8
smote the waters and *w. over.* 14
these *w. over* Jordan. *1 Chr* 12:15
and times that *w. over* him. 29:30
other company *w. over.* *Neh* 12:38
street, to them that *w. over. Isa* 51:23

went *out*

Cain *w. out* from the presence of the Lord. *Gen* 4:16
Isaac *w. out* to meditate in. 24:63
Dinah *w. out* to see the daughters of the land. 34:1
washed his face and *w. out.* 43:31
and the one *w. out* from me. 44:28
Moses *w. out* to his brethren. *Ex* 2:11, 13
Aaron *w. out* from Pharaoh. 8:12, 30
9:33
hosts of the Lord *w. out.* 12:41; 14:8
all the women *w. out* after. 15:20
there *w. out* some people on. 16:27
Moses *w. out* to meet his. 18:7
every one *w. out* unto the. 33:7
there *w. out* fire from. *Lev* 10:2
them when they *w. out.* *Num* 10:34
two men *w. out* into the. 11:26
Sihon *w. out* against Israel. 21:23
Og, the king of Bashan, *w. out.* 33
behold, I *w. out* to withstand. 22:32
none *w. out,* and none. *Josh* 6:1
the men of Ai *w. out.* 8:14, 17
the Canaanite *w. out* and all. 11:4
they *w. out,* the Lord was. *Judg* 2:15
all that stood by him *w. out.* 3:19
master of the house *w. out.* 19:23
I *w. out* full, and came. *Ruth* 1:21
ere the lamp of God *w. out* in the temple. *1 Sam* 3:3
I *w. out* after the bear, and. 17:35
David *w. out* where Saul sent him. 18:5, 13, 16; 19:8
even he *w. out* to lie on. *2 Sam* 11:13
they *w. out* every man from. 13:9
the day the king *w. out* of. 19:19
they *w. out* at noon. *1 Ki* 20:16
w. out first. 17
the king of Israel *w. out* and. 21
the child *w. out* to his father to the reapers. *2 Ki* 4:18
took up her son, and *w. out.* 37
Gehazi *w. out* from his presence a leper. 5:27
they *w. out* each in his chariot. 9:21
arrow *w. out* of Jehoram's. 24
David *w. out* to meet. *1 Chr* 12:17
David heard of it, and *w. out.* 14:8
Azariah *w. out* to meet. *2 Chr* 15:2
was no peace to him that *w. out.* 5
Jehu *w. out* to meet. 19:2
to praise as they *w. out.* 20:21
Josiah *w. out* against Pharaoh-necho. 35:20
as the word *w. out* of the king's mouth. *Esth* 7:8
when I *w. out* to the gate through the city. *Job* 29:7
that I *w.* not *out* of the door? 31:34
when he *w. out* through the land of Egypt. *Ps* 81:5
Jeremiah came in and *w. out* among people. *Jer* 37:4
the cherub and *w. out.* *Ezek* 10:7
the city that *w. out* by. *Amos* 5:3
neither any peace to him that *w. out.* *Zech* 8:10
Jesus said, What *w.* ye *out* into the?
Mat 11:7, 8, 9; *Luke* 7:24, 25, 26
a man who *w. out* early to. *Mat* 20:1
he *w. out* about third hour. 3, 5, 6
those servants *w. out* into. 22:10
his friends *w. out* to lay hold on him: He is beside himself. *Mark* 3:21
unclean spirits *w. out* and entered.
5:13; *Luke* 8:33; *Acts* 19:12

they *w. out* to see what it was that was done. *Mark* 5:14; *Luke* 8:35
for there *w.* virtue *out.* *Luke* 6:19
Peter *w. out* and wept. 22:62
they which heard it, *w. out. John* 8:9
Jesus hid himself and *w. out.* 59
rose up hastily, and *w. out.* 11:31
received the sop *w. out.* 13:30
w. out that other disciple. 18:16
the Lord *w.* in and *out.* *Acts* 1:21
certain *w. out* from us have. 15:24
Abraham *w. out,* not. *Heb* 11:8
they *w. out* from us, but were not of us, they *w. out.* *1 John* 2:19

went *their way*

of Dan *w. their way.* *Judg* 18:26
Amalekites burnt Ziklag and *w. their way.* *1 Sam* 30:2
all the people *w. their way* to eat. *Neh* 8:12
w. their way as a flock. *Zech* 10:2
that kept swine fled and *w. their way.* *Mat* 8:33
whatsoever is right I will give you. And they *w. their way.* 20:4
light of it and *w. their ways.* 22:5
these words, they *w. their way.* 22
w. their way and found the colt.
Mark 11:4; *Luke* 19:32
but some *w. their ways. John* 11:46
as they *w.* on *their way.* *Acts* 8:36

went *through*

thou didst divide the sea, they *w. through.* *Neh* 9:11; *Ps* 66:6
we *w. through* fire and. *Ps* 66:12
forsaken, so that no man *w. through* thee. *Isa* 60:15
he *w. through* the corn fields on the.
Mark 2:23; *Luke* 6:1

went *up*

God *w. up* from Abraham. *Gen* 17:22
God *w. up* from Jacob in. 35:13
w. up to father's bed, he *w. up.* 49:4
Moses, Aaron and Hur *w. up.* *Ex* 17:10
Moses *w. up* unto God. 19:3, 20
24:13, 15; 34:4; *Deut* 10:3
w. up, and searched the. *Num* 13:21
but the men that *w. up* with. 31
they *w. up* into mount Hor. 20:27
33:38
w. presumptuously *up.* *Deut* 1:43
so that the people *w. up.* *Josh* 6:20
brethren that *w. up* with me. 14:8
Judah *w. up* and the Lord. *Judg* 1:4
the house of Joseph also *w. up.* 22
Barak and Deborah *w. up* with. 4:10
Gideon *w. up* thence to. 8:8, 11
Elkanah *w. up* out of his city.
1 Sam 1:3, 7, 21
Hannah *w.* not *up;* until child. 22
the cry of the city *w. up* to. 5:12
as he *w. up* barefoot. *2 Sam* 15:30
David, according to the saying of Gad, *w. up.* 24:19; *1 Chr* 21:19
Elijah *w. up* by a whirlwind to heaven. *2 Ki* 2:11
Elisha *w. up* and lay upon. 4:34, 35
Hezekiah *w. up.* 19:14; *Isa* 37:14
Josiah *w. up* into the house of the Lord. *2 Ki* 23:2; *2 Chr* 34:30
Joab *w. up* first and was. *1 Chr* 11:6
children of the province that *w. up.*
Ezra 2:1, 59; *Neh* 7:6, 61
they *w. up* in haste to Jerusalem to the Jews. *Ezra* 4:23
Ezra *w. up.* 7:6
genealogy of them that *w. up.* 8:1
the priest that *w. up.* *Neh* 12:1
it *w. up* and down among. *Ezek* 1:13
cloud of incense *w. up.* 8:11
the glory of the Lord *w. up.* 10:4
11:23, 24
he *w. up* and down among the lions. 19:6
Jesus *w. up* straightway. *Mat* 3:16
and seeing the multitudes he *w. up.*
5:1; 14:23; 15:29; *Luke* 9:28
two men *w. up* into the. *Luke* 18:10
then *w.* he also *up* unto. *John* 7:10
as he *w. up,* two men. *Acts* 1:10
Peter and John *w. up* into the. 3:1
Peter *w. up* upon the housetop. 10:9

Paul *w. up* to Jerusalem. *Acts* 24:11
Gal 1:18; 2:1, 2
w. I *up* to Jerusalem. *Gal* 1:17
they *w. up* on the breadth. *Rev* 20:9

went *a whoring*

Israel *w. a whoring* after other gods.
Judg 2:17; 8:33
w. a whoring with her. *Ps* 106:39

wentest

Reuben, thou *w.* up to. *Gen* 49:4
Lord, when thou *w.* out of. *Judg* 5:4
whithersoever thou *w.* *2 Sam* 7:9
w. thou not with thy friend ? 16:17
w. thou not with me ? 19:25
O God, when thou *w.* *Ps* 68:7
even thither *w.* thou up. *Isa* 57:7
thou *w.* to the king with ointment. 9
when thou *w.* after me in. *Jer* 2:2
heart toward the way thou *w.* 31:21
thou *w.* forth for salvation. *Hab* 3:13
thou *w.* in to men uncircumcised.
Acts 11:3

wept

Hagar sat and *w.* *Gen* 21:16
Esau *w.* 27:38
Jacob *w.* 29:11; 33:4; 37:35
Hos 12:4
from his brethren and *w.* *Gen* 42:24
43:30; 45:2, 14, 15; 46:29; 50:1, 17
and, behold, the babe *w.* *Ex* 2:6
and the children of Israel also *w.*
Num 11:4, 18, 20; 14:1; *Deut* 1:45
34:8; *Judg* 2:4; 20:23, 26; 21:2
Samson's wife *w.* before. *Judg* 14:16
daughters and *w.* *Ruth* 1:9, 14
Hannah *w.* and did. *1 Sam* 1:7, 10
all people *w.* 11:4; *2 Sam* 3:32, 34
Jonathan and David *w.* *1 Sam* 20:41
Saul *w.* 24:16
David *w.* 30:4; *2 Sam* 1:12
David *w.* at the grave. *2 Sam* 3:32
was yet alive I fasted and *w.* 12:22
the king and servants *w.* sore. 13:36
all the country *w.* 15:23
w. as he went. 30
king was much moved and *w.* 18:33
the man of God *w.* *2 Ki* 8:11
Joash *w.* over Elisha and. 13:14
remember how I have walked.
Hezekiah *w.* sore. 20:3; *Isa* 38:3
king of Judah hath *w.* *2 Ki* 22:19
seen the first house *w.* *Ezra* 3:12
people *w.* very sore. 10:1; *Neh* 8:9
I heard these words, I *w.* *Neh* 1:4
lifted up their voice and *w.* *Job* 2:12
when I *w.* and chastened. *Ps* 69:10
Babylon, we sat down and *w.* 137:1
Peter *w.* *Mat* 26:75; *Mark* 14:72
Luke 22:62
he seeth them that *w.* *Mark* 5:38
Luke 8:52
as they mourned and *w.* *Mark* 16:10
you, and ye have not *w.* *Luke* 7:32
he beheld the city and *w.* 19:41
Jesus *w.* *John* 11:35
at the sepulchre: as she *w.* 20:11
they *w.* sore and fell on. *Acts* 20:37
as though they *w.* not. *1 Cor* 7:30
I *w.* because no man. *Rev* 5:4

were

cannot do this, for that *w.* *Gen* 34:14
third day when they *w.* sore. 25
Jacob said to all that *w.* with. 35:2
gave all the strange gods that *w.* 4
Israel saw they *w.* in evil. *Ex* 5:19
since day they *w.* upon earth. 10:6
w. ye not afraid to speak ? *Num* 12:8
we *w.* in our own sight as grasshoppers, and so we *w.* in. 13:33
w. it not better for us to ? 14:3
O that there *w.* such an. *Deut* 5:29
for ye *w.* strangers in the. 10:19
whereas ye *w.* as the stars. 28:62
w. it not that I feared the. 32:27
O that they *w.* wise, that they. 29
I wist not whence they *w.* *Josh* 2:4
thou seest mountains as if they *w.*
men. *Judg* 9:36
and there they *w.* not. *1 Sam* 9:4
that valiant men *w.* *2 Sam* 11:16
we *w.* together; there. *1 Ki* 3:18
place where the officers *w.* 4:28
did evil above all that *w.* 16:30, 33

w. it not that I regard. *2 Ki* 3:14
and the tents as they *w.* 7:10
as many as *w.* of a free heart.
2 Chr 29:31
though there *w.* of you cast. *Neh* 1:9
for there *w.* that said, We. 5:2, 3, 4
seed, whether they *w.* *Job* 7:61
Oh that I *w.* as in months. 29:2
a sojourner, as all my fathers *w.*
Ps 39:12
whose captives they *w.* *Isa* 14:2
they *w.* no gods, but work of. 37:19
because they *w.* not. *Jer* 31:15
though Noah, Daniel, and Job *w.* in.
Ezek 14:14, 16, 18, 20
heathen among whom they *w.* 20:9
there *w.* but ten, there *w.* *Hag* 2:16
persecuted prophets which *w.* before.
Mat 5:12
David did and they that *w.*? 12:3, 4
Mark 2:25, 26; *Luke* 6:3, 4
whether he *w.* the Christ. *Luke* 3:15
this man, if he *w.* a prophet. 7:39
w. not ten cleansed ? where ? 17:17
if this man *w.* not of God. *John* 9:33
if any man knew where he *w.* 11:57
if ye *w.* of the world, world. 15:19
thine they *w.*, and thou gavest. 17:6
they said, If he *w.* not a. 18:30
w. not a little comforted. *Acts* 20:12
saying that these things *w.* so. 24:9
calleth things that be not as though
they *w.* *Rom* 4:17
them my people that *w.* not. 9:25
if whole body *w.* an eye, where *w.*
hearing? if whole *w.* hearing, where
w. smelling ? *1 Cor* 12:17
whatsoever they *w.* maketh. *Gal* 2:6
w. by nature children of. *Eph* 2:3
for even when we *w.* *2 Thes* 3:10
things continue as they *w.* *2 Pet* 3:4
until their brethren, be killed as they
w., should be fulfilled. *Rev* 6:11

as it **were**

it seemeth, there is *as it w.* a plague.
Lev 14:35
as it w. the company. *S of S* 6:13
that draw sin *as it w.* *Isa* 5:18
as if staff lift up itself *as it w.* 10:15
hide thyself *as it w.* for a. 26:20
and we hid *as it w.* our faces. 53:3
his sweat *as it w.* great. *Luke* 22:44
up not openly, but *as it w.* *John* 7:10
sought it *as it w.* by works. *Rom* 9:32
apostles, *as it w.* to death. *1 Cor* 4:9
and his face was *as it w.* *Rev* 10:1
I saw one of his heads *as it w.* 13:3
they sung *as it w.* a new song. 14:3
I saw *as it w.* a sea of glass. 15:2

if it **were**

if it w. so, why should not my spirit
be troubled ? *Job* 21:4
if it w. possible to deceive the very
elect. *Mat* 24:24
they might touch *if it w.* the border.
Mark 6:56
if it w. not so, I would. *John* 14:2
if it w. a matter of wrong. *Acts* 18:14

wert

O that thou *w.* as my. *S of S* 8:1
I would thou *w.* cold or. *Rev* 3:15

west

spread abroad to the *w.* *Gen* 28:14
the *w.* and the south. *Deut* 33:23
looking toward the *w.* *1 Ki* 7:25
on quarters were porters, toward the
east, *w.* *1 Chr* 9:24; *2 Chr* 4:4
they put to flight them toward east
and *w.* *1 Chr* 12:15
cometh not from the *w.* *Ps* 75:6
as east is from the *w.*, so far. 103:12
them from the east and *w.* 107:3
Philistines toward the *w.* *Isa* 11:14
and gather thee from the *w.* 43:5
they may know from the *w.* 45:6
come from the north and *w.* 49:12
fear the Lord from the *w.* 59:19
are his sides east and *w.* *Ezek* 48:1
he goat came from the *w.* *Dan* 8:5
tremble from the *w.* *Hos* 11:10
I will save my people from the *w.*
Zech 8:7
of Olives shall cleave toward *w.* 14:4

from east and *w.* and sit down with.
Mat 8:11; *Luke* 13:29
east and shineth to *w.* *Mat* 24:27
cloud rise out of the *w.* *Luke* 12:54
on south three gates, and *w.* three
gates. *Rev* 21:13

west *border*

great sea for border, this shall be
w. border. *Num* 34:6
w. border was to the great sea.
Josh 15:12
w. border a portion. *Ezek* 45:7

west *quarter*

this was the *w. quarter.* *Josh* 18:14

west *side*

on *w. side* hanging 50 cubits.
Ex 27:12; 38:12
the *w. side* the standard. *Num* 2:18
measure on the *w. side* of the. 35:5
even to the *w. side* a portion.
Ezek 48:3, 4, 5, 6, 7, 8, 23, 24

western

as for the *w.* border. *Num* 34:6

westward

looked eastward and *w.* *Gen* 13:14
behind the tabernacle *w.* *Num* 3:23
lift up thine eyes *w.* *Deut* 3:27
shall be 10,000 *w.* *Ezek* 48:18
I saw the ram pushing *w.* *Dan* 8:4

west *wind*

a strong *w. wind* took. *Ex* 10:19

wet

they are *w.* with showers. *Job* 24:8
let it be *w.* with the dew of heaven.
Dan 4:15, 23, 25, 33; 5:21

whale

(*The word sometimes translated* whale *in the Old Testament is at other times translated* dragon, serpent, *or* sea-monster. *The* whale of Jonah *is called in that book merely* a great fish. *In the New Testament the word used in the original may mean almost any large sea-animal, whale, seal, shark, or tunny*)

am I a sea, or a *w.* that ? *Job* 7:12*
Pharaoh, thou art as a *w.* in the.
Ezek 32:2*
days in the *w.*'s belly. *Mat* 12:40

whales

God created great *w.* *Gen* 1:21*

what

w. shall I do now to ? *Gen* 27:37
my master wotteth not *w.* is. 39:8
w. shall we say to my lord ? *w.* shall
we speak ? 44:16
know not with *w.* we. *Ex* 10:26
when son asketh, *W.* is this ? 13:14
w. are we ? 16:7
for they wist not *w.* it was. 15
say, *W.* shall we eat ? *Lev* 25:20
and see the land *w.* it. *Num* 13:18
w. the land is, and *w.* cities. 19, 20
it was not declared *w.* 15:34
w. is Aaron ? 16:11
w. hath the Lord spoken ? 23:17
but *w.* the Lord saith, that. 24:13
1 Ki 22:14; *2 Chr* 18:13
w. the Lord did because. *Deut* 4:3
w. Lord did to Pharaoh. 7:18; 11:6
Israel, *w.* doth the Lord require of
thee ? 10:12; *Mi* 6:8
w. man is there ? *Deut* 20:5, 6, 7, 8
O Lord, *w.* shall I say ? *Josh* 7:8
and Caleb said to her, *W.*? 15:18
Judg 1:14; *1 Ki* 1:16; *Mat* 20:21
w. have ye to do with the Lord God
of Israel ? *Josh* 22:24
thou shalt hear *w.* they. *Judg* 7:11
w. hast thou to do with me ? 11:12
w. say ye ? 18:8
the priest said, *W.* do ye ? 18
w. have I more ? *w.* is this ? *w.* aileth
thee ? 24
and he will tell thee *w.* thou shalt.
Ruth 3:4; *1 Sam* 10:8
w. is the thing the Lord ? *1 Sam* 3:17
and he said, *W.* is there done ? 4:16
w. have I to do with you ?
2 Sam 16:10; 19:22
let us hear likewise *w.* he saith. 17:5

a tumult, but I knew not *w.* *2 Sam* 18:29
their father said, *W.*? *1 Ki* 13:12
cut off house of Jeroboam *w.*? 14:14
w. have I to do with thee ? 17:18
2 Ki 3:13; *2 Chr* 35:21; *John* 2:4
said, Ask *w.* I shall do for thee ? *2 Ki* 2:9; 4:2
Jehu said, *W.* hast thou ? 9:18, 19
w. said these men, and from whence ? 20:14; *Isa* 39:3
w. have they seen in thine house ? *2 Ki* 20:15; *Isa* 39:4
Jehoshaphat said, Take heed *w.* ye do. *2 Chr* 19:6
nor know *w.* to do, but our. 20:12
w. shall we do for the hundred ? 25:9
w. shall we say after this ? *Ezra* 9:10; *Job* 37:19
king said, For *w.* dost ? *Neh* 2:4
W. thing is this ye do ? 19; 13:17
to know *w.* it was, and why. *Esth* 4:5
w. wilt thou, queen Esther ? *w.* is thy request ? 5:3, 6; 7:2; 9:12
w. is man, that thou ? *Job* 7:17
15:14; *Ps* 8:4; 144:3; *Heb* 2:6
w. shall I do unto thee ? *Job* 7:20
who will say unto him, *W.*? 9:12
Eccl 8:4; *Ezek* 12:9; *Dan* 4:35
let come on me *w.* will. *Job* 13:13
w. then shall I do ? *w.* shall ? 31:14
Luke 10:25; 12:17; 16:3
let us know *w.* is good. *Job* 34:4
Mi 6:8
w. doest thou against him ? *w.* doest to him ? *Job* 35:6
if thou be righteous, *w.* givest ? 7
w. man is he that feareth the Lord ? *Ps* 25:12; 34:12; 89:48
I will hear *w.* God the Lord. 85:8
w. shall be given unto thee? *w.*? 120:3
consider diligently *w.* is. *Pr* 23:1
lest thou know not *w.* to do. 25:8
w. is his name ? *w.* is his ? 30:4
w. my son ? and *w.* the son ? 31:2
I said of mirth, *W.* doeth ? *Eccl* 2:2
Watchman, *w.* of the night ? *Isa* 21:11
w. hast thou here ? 22:16
w. shall I say ? 38:15; *John* 12:27
therefore *w.* have I here ? *Isa* 52:5
w. wilt thou do ? *Jer* 4:30
saying, *W.* have I done ? 8:6
w. wilt thou say ? 13:21
and say, *W.* is done ? 48:19
O Ephraim, *w.* shall I ? *Hos* 6:4
give them, O Lord; *w.* wilt.? 9:14
w. have I do any more with idols ? 14:8
yea, and *w.* have ye to do with me ? *Joel* 3:4
and declare unto man *w.* *Amos* 4:13
O my Lord, *w.* are these ? *Zech* 1:9
4:4; 6:4
I said, *W.* be these ? 1:19; 4:5, 13
w. is it ? 5:6
w. do ye more than ? *Mat* 5:47
no thought *w.* ye shall eat, or *w.* 6:25, 31; *Luke* 12:22, 29
w. have we to do with thee, Jesus ? *Mat* 8:29; *Mark* 1:24; 5:7
Luke 4:34; 8:28
have ye not read *w.* David did ? *Mat* 12:3; *Mark* 2:25; *Luke* 6:3
have forsaken all; *w.*? *Mat* 19:27
they said, *W.* is that to us ? 27:4
told *w.* they had done, and *w.* they. *Mark* 6:30
for he wist not *w.* to say. 9:6
this cup, not *w.* I will, but *w.* 14:36
people asked, *W.* shall we do then ? *Luke* 3:10; 12:17
the Lord said, to *w.* are they ? 7:31
w. will I, if it be already ? 12:49
they know not *w.* they do. 23:34
w. then ? *John* 1:21
w. did he to thee ? 9:26
w. I should say, and *w.* I. 12:49
w. is this that he saith ? 16:18
w. is that to thee ? follow. 21:22, 23
w. shall we do ? *Acts* 2:37; 4:16
Lord, *W.* wilt thou have me to do ? 9:6; 22:10
w. is it, Lord ? 10:4
w. was I, that I could ? *Acts* 11:17
w. must I do ? 16:30
Unto *w.* then were ye baptized ? 19:3
w. is it therefore ? 21:22
w. shall we say ? *Rom* 3:5; 4:1
6:1; 7:7
w. then ? 3:9; 6:15; 8:31; 9:14, 30
11:7; *1 Cor* 10:19; 14:15
Phil 1:18
w. I would that do I not, but *w.* I hate, that do I. *Rom* 7:15
w. will ye ? shall I come ? *1 Cor* 4:21
w. I do, that I will do. *2 Cor* 11:12
yet *w.* I shall choose I. *Phil* 1:22
understanding neither *w.* *1 Tim* 1:7
consider *w.* I say; and the Lord give thee. *2 Tim* 2:7
w. shall I more say ? *Heb* 11:32
ye know not *w.* shall be on the morrow. For *w.* is your life ? *Jas* 4:14
searching *w.* or *w.* manner. *1 Pet* 1:11
it doth not yet appear *w.* *1 John* 3:2
see **things**

whatsoever

now *w.* God hath said. *Gen* 31:16
even of *w.* passeth under. *Lev* 27:32
I will do *w.* thou sayest. *Num* 22:17
nor *w.* the Lord our God. *Deut* 2:37
w. I command you, observe. 12:32
do thou to us *w.* *Judg* 10:15
1 Sam 14:36
w. plague, *w.* sickness. *1 Ki* 8:37
w. supplication be made. 38
2 Chr 6:28
w. is under the whole. *Job* 41:11
leaf not wither; *w.* he doeth. *Ps* 1:3
w. passeth through the paths. 8:8
God is in the heavens, he hath done *w.* he. 115:3. 135:6; *Eccl* 8:3
w. God doeth, it shall. *Eccl* 3:14
w. I command thee, thou. *Jer* 1:7
we will do *w.* goeth out of. 44:17
w. is more than these. *Mat* 5:37
w. ye would that men should. 7:12
Herod promised with an oath to give her *w.* she. 14:7; *Mark* 6:22
have done unto him *w.* they listed. *Mat* 17:12; *Mark* 9:13
and *w.* is right I will give you. *Mat* 20:4, 7
all things *w.* ye shall ask in prayer, believing, ye shall. 21:22
Mark 11:23, 24; *John* 14:13
w. they bid you observe. *Mat* 23:3
observe all things *w.* I have. 28:20
his mother saith, *W.* he saith to you. *John* 2:5
ye are my friends, if ye do *w.* 15:14
w. ye shall ask in my name. 16
16:23
him hear in all things *w.* *Acts* 3:22
for *w.* is not of faith. *Rom* 14:23
w. is sold in the shambles, that eat. *1 Cor* 10:25
w. is set before you, eat. 27
or *w.* ye do, do all to the glory. 31
w. they were, it maketh. *Gal* 2:6
w. a man soweth, that shall. 6:7
w. things are true, *w.* *Phil* 4:8
I have learned in *w.* state I am. 11
w. ye do in word . . . do all in the name of the Lord Jesus. *Col* 3:17
w. ye do, do it heartily as to. 23
w. we ask we receive of him. *1 John* 3:22; 5:15
thou doest faithfully *w.* *3 John* 5

wheat

Reuben found mandrakes in *w.* *Gen* 30:14
but the *w.* and rye were. *Ex* 9:32
the firstfruits of *w.* harvest. 34:22
Num 18:12
goats, with the fat of kidneys of *w.* *Deut* 32:14
and Gideon threshed *w.* *Judg* 6:11
time of *w.* harvest, Samson. 15:1
to glean unto the end of *w.* harvest. *Ruth* 2:23
they of Beth-shemesh reaping *w.* *1 Sam* 6:13
is it not *w.* harvest day ? 12:17
would have fetched *w.* *2 Sam* 4:6
Solomon gave Hiram *w.* *1 Ki* 5:11
I give the *w.* for the meat offering. *1 Chr* 21:23
have need of, *w.* salt, wine. *Ezra* 6:9
to an hundred measures of *w.* 7:22
let thistles grow instead of *w.* *Job* 31:40
fed them with finest of *w.* *Ps* 81:16
thee with the finest of *w.* 147:14
fool in a mortar among *w.* *Pr* 27:22
thy belly is like a heap of *w.* set. *S of S* 7:2
they have sown *w.* but. *Jer* 12:13
what is the chaff to the *w.*? 23:28
flow together, for *w.*, for wine. 31:12
Judah traded in *w.* of. *Ezek* 27:17
floors shall be full of *w.* *Joel* 2:24
from him burdens of *w.* *Amos* 5:11
that we may set forth *w.* 8:5
poor, and sell refuse of *w.* 6
gather his *w.* into the garner. *Mat* 3:12; *Luke* 3:17
sowed tares among the *w.* *Mat* 13:25
lest ye root up also the *w.* 29
to burn them, but gather the *w.* 30
said 100 measures of *w.* *Luke* 16:7
that he may sift you as *w.* 22:31
except a corn of *w.* fall. *John* 12:24
and cast out the *w.* *Acts* 27:38
it may chance of *w.* or. *1 Cor* 15:37
I heard a voice, a measure of *w.* *Rev* 6:6
merchandise of *w.* is departed. 18:13
see **barley**

wheaten

cakes and wafers; of *w.* flour shalt thou make them. *Ex* 29:2*

wheel

make them like a *w.* *Ps* 83:13
a wise king bringeth the *w.* *Pr* 20:26*
w. broken at the cistern. *Eccl* 12:6
nor break it with the *w.* *Isa* 28:28
one *w.* upon the earth. *Ezek* 1:15
w. in the midst of a *w.* 16; 10:10
wheels, in my hearing, O *w.* 10:13

wheels

took off their chariot *w.* *Ex* 14:25
why tarry the *w.* of his ? *Judg* 5:28
their *w.* like a whirlwind. *Isa* 5:28
a work on the *w.* *Jer* 18:3
the rumbling of his *w.* 47:3
the appearance of the *w.* *Ezek* 1:16
of *w.* over against them. 3:13
the *w.* also were beside them. 10:19; 11:22
come against thee with *w.* 23:24
at the noise of the *w.* 26:10
and his *w.* a burning fire. *Dan* 7:9
of the rattling of the *w.* *Nah* 3:2

whelp, -s

a bear robbed of her *w.* *2 Sam* 17:8
let a bear robbed of her *w.* *Pr* 17:12
she nourished her *w.* *Ezek* 19:2
one of her *w.* . . . a young lion. 3
she took another of her *w.* and. 5
bear bereaved of her *w.* *Hos* 13:8
the lion did tear enough for his *w.* *Nah* 2:12
see **lions**

when

w. it is unclean and *w.* *Lev* 14:57
w. thou sittest and *w.* thou walkest, *w.* thou liest down, and *w.* thou risest up. *Deut* 6:7; 11:19
w. I begin, I will also. *1 Sam* 3:12
hear thou in heaven thy dwelling place: *w.* thou hearest. *1 Ki* 8:30
the king said, *W.* wilt ? *Neh* 2:6
ye fools, *w.* will ye be wise ? *Ps* 94:8
for who can tell him *w.*? *Eccl* 8:7
clean ? *w.* shall it once be ? *Jer* 13:27
w. ye fasted. *Zech* 7:5
w. ye did eat, and *w.* ye did drink. 6
w. shall these things be ? and what ? *Mat* 24:3; *Mark* 13:4; *Luke* 21:7
w. he is come, he will tell us all things. *John* 4:25; 16:8
w. he had so said, he shewed. 20:20
w. they heard this, they. *Acts* 2:37
w. we were with you. *2 Thes* 3:10
w. he shall appear, we. *1 John* 2:28

whence
the angel said, Hagar, *w.* camest thou? *Gen* 16:8
Joseph said to them, *W.* come ye? 42:7; *Josh* 9:8
is not like Egypt, from *w.* ye came out. *Deut* 11:10
I wist not *w.* they were. *Josh* 2:4
I asked him not *w.* he. *Judg* 13:6
Micah said, *W.* comest thou? 17:9
19:17; *2 Sam* 1:3; *2 Ki* 5:25
Job 1:7; 2:2; *Jonah* 1:8
men? from *w.* came these men unto thee? *2 Ki* 20:14; *Isa* 39:3
before I go *w.* I shall not return. *Job* 10:21; 16:22
not know from *w.* it riseth. *Isa* 47:11
look to the rock *w.* ye are. 51:1
I will return to my house, *w.* I came. *Mat* 12:44; *Luke* 11:24
w. hath this man this wisdom? *Mat* 13:54
w. hath this man all these things? 56; *Mark* 6:2
calleth him Lord, *w.* is? *Mark* 12:37
w. is this to me, that the mother of my Lord? *Luke* 1:43
I know you not *w.* ye are. 13:25, 27
W. knowest thou me? *John* 1:48
and ye know *w.* I am. 7:28
ye cannot tell *w.* I come. 8:14
we know not from *w.* he is. 9:29, 30
from *w.* we look for the. *Phil* 3:20
from *w.* he received him. *Heb* 11:19
w. come wars and fightings? *Jas* 4:1
remember from *w.* thou. *Rev* 2:5
in white robes? *w.* came they? 7:13

whensoever
w. ye will ye may do. *Mark* 14:7

where
w. art thou? *Gen* 3:9
w. is he? *Ex* 2:20; *2 Sam* 9:4
Job 14:10
in all places *w.* I record. *Ex* 20:24
w. I will meet you to speak. 29:42
30:6, 36
shall say, *W.* are their gods? *Deut* 32:37
if not, *w.* and who is he? *Job* 9:24
W. is God my maker who? 35:10
w. wast thou? 38:4
to me, *W.* is thy God? *Ps* 42:3, 10
wherefore should heathen say, *W.* is their God? 79:10; 115:2; *Joel* 2:17
these, *w.* had they been? *Isa* 49:21
said they, *W.* is the Lord? *Jer* 2:6, 8
let no man know *w.* ye be. 36:19
w. it was said to them. *Hos* 1:10
fathers, *w.* are they? *Zech* 1:5
they said, *W.* Lord? *Luke* 17:37
Jews said, *W.* is he? *John* 7:11
9:12
w. I am. 7:34; 12:26; 14:3; 17:24

whereabout
know *w.* I send thee. *1 Sam* 21:2

whereas
w. I rewarded thee evil. *1 Sam* 24:17
w. it was in thine heart. *1 Ki* 8:18
w. ye say, The Lord. *Ezek* 13:7
will possess it, *w.* the Lord. 35:10
w. ye know not what will. *Jas* 4:14

whereby
iniquity *w.* they have sinned. *Jer* 33:8
transgressions *w.* ye have transgressed. *Ezek* 18:31
trespasses *w.* they have trespassed. 39:26
w. shall I know this? *Luke* 1:18
no other name *w.* we must. *Acts* 4:12
the Spirit, *w.* we cry. *Rom* 8:15
w. ye are sealed to the day. *Eph* 4:30

wherefore
w. should I fast? can I bring him? *2 Sam* 12:23
who shall then say, *W.* hast? 16:10
w. one? That he might seek a godly seed. *Mal* 2:15
O thou of little faith, *w.*? *Mat* 14:31
Jesus said, Friend, *w.* art? 26:50
what is the cause *w.* ye? *Acts* 10:21

whereto
in the thing *w.* I sent it. *Isa* 55:11

w. we have already attained, let us walk. *Phil* 3:16

wherewith
O my Lord, *w.* shall I? *Judg* 6:15
the Lord said to him, *W.*? *1 Ki* 22:22; *2 Chr* 18:20
but against the house *w.* I have war. *2 Chr* 35:21
so shall I have *w.* to. *Ps* 119:42
w. shall I come before? *Mi* 6:6
if salt lose its savour, *w.* shall it be? *Mat* 5:13; *Mark* 9:5; *Luke* 14:34
the love *w.* thou hast. *John* 17:26
for this great love *w.* he. *Eph* 2:4

wherewithal
what shall we eat? or *w.*? *Mat* 6:31

whet
if I *w.* my glittering sword I will reward. *Deut* 32:41
if he turn not, he will *w.* *Ps* 7:12
who *w.* their tongue like a. 64:3
iron blunt and he do not *w.* *Eccl* 10:10

whether
w. they be for peace, or *w.* *1 Ki* 20:18
w. they were of Israel. *Ezra* 2:59
Neh 7:61
w. they will hear or forbear. *Ezek* 2:5, 7; 3:11
w. of them twain did the will of his father? *Mat* 21:31
w. is greater, the gold or? 23:17
doctrine, *w.* it be of God. *John* 7:17
w. we live or die, we are. *Rom* 14:8
w. it were I or they, so. *1 Cor* 15:11
w. in the body, or *w.* out of the body. *2 Cor* 12:2, 3
but try the spirits *w.* *1 John* 4:1

which
of the tree *w.* I commanded thee, saying. *Gen* 3:17
in *w.* there shall be neither. 45:6
a heifer upon *w.* never. *Num* 19:2
in *w.* there shall not be. *Luke* 21:6
w. of you convinceth me? *John* 8:46
for *w.* of those works do ye? 10:32
in the *w.* I will appear. *Acts* 26:16
in the *w.* ye also walked. *Col* 3:7
a better hope; by *w.* we. *Heb* 7:19
of *w.* we cannot now speak. 9:5
follow peace with all men, and holiness, without *w.* no man. 12:14
that worthy name, by *w.* *Jas* 2:7
by *w.* he preached to. *1 Pet* 3:19

while, whiles
w. I am yet alive with. *Deut* 31:27
thou shalt not only *w.* yet I live shew me the kindness. *1 Sam* 20:14
w. the child was yet alive. *2 Sam* 12:18, 21, 22
Lord is with you *w.* ye. *2 Chr* 15:2
w. Josiah was yet young, he. 34:3
God shall rain it on him *w.* *Job* 20:23
tear my soul, *w.* there is none. *Ps* 7:2
though *w.* he lived he blessed. 49:18
thus will I bless thee *w.* I live. 63:4; 146:2
will praise God *w.* I have my being. 104:33; 146:2
w. he may be found. *Isa* 55:6
her sun is gone down *w.* it was yet day. *Jer* 15:9
w. he was not yet gone back. 40:5
agree *w.* thou art in the. *Mat* 5:25
that deceiver said, *w.* he. 27:63
of bride-chamber fast *w.* the bridegroom? *Mark* 2:19; *Luke* 5:34
I spake *w.* I was yet. *Luke* 24:44
do work of him that sent me *w.* it is day. *John* 9:4
that liveth in pleasure is dead *w.* she liveth. *1 Tim* 5:6
w. it is said, To-day if. *Heb* 3:15
see **little**

***a* while**
Joseph wept on his neck *a* good *w.* *Gen* 46:29
Samuel said to Saul, Stand thou still *a w.* *1 Sam* 9:27
spoken for *a* great *w.* *2 Sam* 7:19
root, but dureth for *a w.* *Mat* 13:21
which for *a w.* believe, and in time of temptation fall away. *Luke* 8:13
he would not for *a w.*: but. *Luke* 18:4
after have suffered *a w.* *1 Pet* 5:10

***all the* while**
all the w. David was in. *1 Sam* 22:4
none missing *all the w.* they were in Carmel. 25:7, 16
will be his manner *all the w.* 27:11
all the w. my breath is in me and Spirit of God. *Job* 27:3

***long* while**
had talked a *long w.* even till break of day. *Acts* 20:11

whip
a *w.* for the horse, a rod. *Pr* 26:3
the noise of a *w.*, the noise. *Nah* 3:2

whips
father chastised you with *w.*, I will. *1 Ki* 12:11, 14; *2 Chr* 10:11, 14

whirleth
wind *w.* continually and. *Eccl* 1:6*

whirlwind
Lord would take up Elijah by a *w.* *2 Ki* 2:1, 11
cometh the *w.* and cold. *Job* 37:9*
the Lord answered Job out of the *w.* 38:1; 40:6
as with a *w.*, both living and. *Ps* 58:9
Pr 10:25; *Hos* 13:3
destruction cometh as a *w.* *Pr* 1:27
counted it like flint and their wheels like a *w.* *Isa* 5:28
a rolling thing before the *w.* 17:13*
the *w.* shall take them away. 40:24
shalt fan them, the *w.* shall. 41:16
Lord come with chariots like a *w.* 66:15; *Jer* 4:13
a *w.* of the Lord is gone. *Jer* 23:19*
a great *w.* shall be raised up. 25:32*
a continuing *w.* shall fall on. 30:23*
behold, a *w.* came out of. *Ezek* 1:4*
king shall come against him like a *w.* *Dan* 11:40
they shall reap the *w.* *Hos* 8:7
devour palaces in the day of the *w.* *Amos* 1:14
the Lord hath his way in the *w.* *Nah* 1:3
out as a *w.* to scatter. *Hab* 3:14
but I scattered them with a *w.* *Zech* 7:14

whirlwinds
as *w.* in the south pass. *Isa* 21:1
Lord shall go forth with *w.* *Zech* 9:14

whisper
all that hate me *w.* together. *Ps* 41:7
thy speech shall *w.* out. *Isa* 29:4

whispered
when David saw that his servants *w.* *2 Sam* 12:19

whisperer
a *w.* separateth chief. *Pr* 16:28

whisperers
full of envy, murder, debate, deceit, *w.* *Rom* 1:29

whisperings
be *w.* swellings, tumults. *2 Cor* 12:20

whit
Samuel told Eli every *w.* *1 Sam* 3:18
a man every *w.* whole. *John* 7:23
feet, but is clean every *w.* 13:10
I was not a *w.* behind. *2 Cor* 11:5

white
Jacob made the *w.* appear in the rods. *Gen* 30:37
and his teeth shall be *w.* 49:12
like coriander seed, *w.* *Ex* 16:31
if the hair be turned *w.* *Lev* 13:3
4, 20, 25
if the bright spot be *w.* 4, 19, 24*
rising be *w.* in the skin. 10, 19, 43*
be no *w.* hairs therein. 21, 26
Miriam became leprous, *w.* as snow. *Num* 12:10
ye that ride on *w.* asses. *Judg* 5:10
Gehazi went out a leper *w.* as snow. *2 Ki* 5:27
the Levites being arrayed in *w.* linen. *2 Chr* 5:12*
Mordecai went out in *w.* apparel. *Esth* 8:15
taste in the *w.* of an egg? *Job* 6:6

w. as snow in Salmon. *Ps* 68:14*
garments be always *w.* *Eccl* 9:8
my beloved is *w.* and ruddy, the.
S of S 5:10
be as scarlet, they shall be as *w.* as snow. *Isa* 1:18
Damascus traded in *w.* wool.
Ezek 27:18
garment was *w.* as snow. *Dan* 7:9
shall fall to make them *w.* 11:35
be purified and made *w.* 12:10
thereof are made *w.* *Joel* 1:7
horses, speckled and *w.* *Zech* 1:8
not make one hair *w.* or black.
Mat 5:36
his raiment was *w.* as the light.
17:2; *Luke* 9:29
the angel's raiment was *w.*
Mat 28:3; *Acts* 1:10
a man clothed in a long *w.* garment.
Mark 16:5
fields are *w.* already. *John* 4:35
and his hairs were *w.* *Rev* 1:14
will give him a *w.* stone and. 2:17
they shall walk with me in *w.* 3:4
shall be clothed in *w.* raiment. 5
4:4; 7:9, 13; 15:6; 19:8, 14
buy *w.* raiment, that thou. 3:18
behold a *w.* horse. 6:2; 19:11
made them *w.* in the blood. 7:14
a *w.* cloud. 14:14
I saw a *w.* throne. 20:11

white, *verb*
no fuller on earth can *w.* *Mark* 9:3

whited
like to *w.* sepulchres. *Mat* 23:27
smite thee, thou *w.* wall. *Acts* 23:3

whiter
I shall be *w.* than snow. *Ps* 51:7
her Nazarites are *w.* than milk.
Lam 4:7

whither
maid, *w.* wilt thou go? *Gen* 16:8
keep thee in all places *w.* 28:15
Saul's uncle said, *W.* went ye?
1 Sam 10:14
Thy servant went no *w.* *2 Ki* 5:25
w. is thy beloved gone? *S of S* 6:1
I said, *W.* do these bear the ephah?
Zech 5:10
went, not knowing *w.* *Heb* 11:8
see **go, goest, goeth**

whithersoever
the Lord preserved David *w.* he.
2 Sam 8:6, 14; *2 Ki* 18:7
1 Chr 18:6, 13
w. it turneth it prospereth. *Pr* 17:8
he turneth the king's heart *w.* 21:1
I will follow thee *w.* thou goest.
Mat 8:19; *Luke* 9:57
these follow the Lamb *w.* *Rev* 14:4

who
w. art thou, my son? *Gen* 27:18, 32
Ruth 3:9, 16; *John* 1:19, 22
8:25; 21:12
Esau said, *W.* are those? *Gen* 33:5
48:8
w. am I? *Ex* 3:11; *1 Sam* 18:18
2 Sam 7:18
w. is the Lord? *Ex* 5:2; *Pr* 30:9
John 9:36
w. is like thee, O Lord, among the gods? *Ex* 15:11; *Deut* 33:29
1 Sam 26:15; *Ps* 35:10
Moses stood and said, *W.*? *Ex* 32:26
w. is David? and *w.* is? *1 Sam* 25:10
w. is on my side, *w.*? *2 Ki* 9:32
but *w.* slew all these? 10:9
Jehu said, *W.* are ye? 13
w. would go into the temple to save his life? *Neh* 6:11
w. is he? and where is he?
Esth 7:5; *Job* 17:3; 42:3; *Jer* 9:12
W. will shew us any good? *Ps* 4:6
for *w.*, say they, doth hear? 59:7
w. hath woe? *w.* hath sorrow? *w.* hath . . . ? *w.* hath? *Pr.* 23:29
w. will go for us? *Isa* 6:8
W. seeth us? 29:15
w. shall come down? *Jer* 21:13
saying, *W.* shall come unto? 49:4
w. is like me? *w.* will? 19; 50:44

of Zion: *w.* can heal thee? *Lam* 2:13
w. is he that saith, and it? 3:37
saying, *W.* is this? *Mat* 21:10
Luke 5:21; 7:49; 9:9
W. is he that smote thee? *Mat* 26:68
to see Jesus *w.* he was. *Luke* 19:3
healed, wist not *w.* it. *John* 5:13
Lord, *w.* is it? 13:25
he said, *W.* art thou, Lord?
Acts 9:5; 22:8; 26:15
but *w.* are ye? 19:15
captain demanded *w.* he was. 21:33
w. then is Paul? and *w.*? *1 Cor* 3:5
and *w.* is sufficient? *2 Cor* 2:16
w. is weak? *w.* is offended? 11:29
w. art thou that judgest? *Jas* 4:12
w. is a liar, but he that? *1 John* 2:22
w. shall be able to stand? *Rev* 6:17
saying, *W.* is like unto the beast? *w.* is able to? 13:4
w. shall not fear thee, O Lord? 15:4

whole
shalt burn *w.* ram on altar.
Ex 29:18; *Lev* 8:21
even the *w.* bullock shall. *Lev* 4:12
w. house of Israel bewail. 10:6
Joshua took the *w.* land. *Josh* 11:23
because my life is yet *w.* *2 Sam* 1:9
him with their *w.* desire. *2 Chr* 15:15
shalt be pleased with *w.* *Ps* 51:19
them up alive, and *w.* *Pr* 1:12
the *w.* disposing thereof is. 16:33
for this is the *w.* duty. *Eccl* 12:13
thy Redeemer, the Holy One, the God of *w.* earth shall he be called.
Isa 54:5; *Mi* 4:13; *Zech* 4:14
a vessel that cannot be made *w.*
Jer 19:11
pluck up, even this *w.* land. 45:4
when *w.* it was meet. *Ezek* 15:5
ye have robbed me, even this *w.* nation. *Mal* 3:9
not that thy *w.* body. *Mat* 5:29, 30
the *w.* herd of swine ran. 8:32
till the *w.* was leavened. 13:33
Luke 13:21
profited if he shall gain the *w.* world and lose his own soul? *Mat* 16:26
Mark 8:36; *Luke* 9:25
w. multitude of them arose and led him. *Luke* 23:1
and himself believed, and his *w.* house. *John* 4:53
expedient that the *w.* nation. 11:50
came almost the *w.* city. *Acts* 13:44
if *w.* body were an eye. *1 Cor* 12:17
I pray your *w.* spirit. *1 Thes* 5:23
shall keep the *w.* law. *Jas* 2:10
end of the *w.* world. *1 John* 2:2
and the *w.* world lieth in. 5:19
see **congregation, heart**

whole for *sound*
they abode in the camp till they were *w.* *Josh* 5:8
and his hands make *w.* *Job* 5:18
w. need not a physician. *Mat* 9:12
Mark 2:17; *Luke* 5:31
touch his garment, I shall be *w.*
Mat 9:21; *Mark* 5:28
woman was made *w.* *Mat* 9:22
his hand was made *w.* 12:13
Mark 3:5; *Luke* 6:10
daughter was made *w.* *Mat* 15:28
saw the maimed to be *w.* 31
thee *w.*; go in peace and be *w.* of.
Mark 5:34; *Luke* 8:48; 17:19
found the servant *w.* *Luke* 7:10
Wilt thou be made *w.*? *John* 5:6
thou art made *w.*: sin no more. 14
made a man every whit *w.* 7:23
what means he is made *w.* *Acts* 4:9
Jesus Christ maketh thee *w.* 9:34

wholesome
a *w.* tongue is a tree of. *Pr* 15:4
consent not to *w.* words. *1 Tim* 6:3*

wholly
it shall be *w.* burnt. *Lev* 6:22, 23
thou shalt not *w.* reap corners. 19:9
for they are *w.* given to. *Num* 3:9
a cloth *w.* of blue. 4:6
are *w.* given me. 8:16
because they have not *w.* 32:11

give the land, because he hath *w.*
Deut 1:36; *Josh* 14:8, 9, 14
I had *w.* dedicated the. *Judg* 17:3
a sucking lamb *w.* *1 Sam* 7:9
all the people *w.* at thy. *1 Chr* 28:21
one dieth, being *w.* at ease. *Job* 21:23
thou art *w.* gone up to the. *Isa* 22:1
planted thee *w.* a right seed. *Jer* 2:21
she is *w.* oppression in the. 6:6
Judah shall be *w.* carried. 13:19
if ye *w.* set your faces to. 42:15
yet will I not leave thee *w.* 46:28
Babylon not be inhabited, but *w.* desolate. 50:13
of Israel *w.*, are they. *Ezek* 11:15
and it shall rise up *w.* as a flood.
Amos 8:8; 9:5
he saw the city *w.* given. *Acts* 17:16
of peace sanctify you *w.* *1 Thes* 5:23
give thyself *w.* to them. *1 Tim* 4:15

whom
take thy only son Isaac *w.* *Gen* 22:2
wives, for *w.* I served thee. 30:26
the old man of *w.* ye spake, is he alive? 43:27, 29
will be gracious to *w.* I. *Ex* 33:19
after *w.* they have gone. *Lev* 17:7
people, amongst *w.* I am. *Num* 11:21
they are children in *w.* *Deut* 32:20
where their gods? their rock in *w.* 37
choose you this day *w.* *Josh* 24:15
that of *w.* I say, this shall. *Judg* 7:4
and to *w.* shall he go up from us?
1 Sam 6:20
and on *w.* is all the desire of? 9:20
David, of *w.* they sang one. 29:5
David said unto him, To *w.*? 30:13
and again, *w.* should I serve?
2 Sam 16:19
Ahab said, By *w.*? *1 Ki* 20:14; 22:8
Ezra 10:44; *Rom* 1:5; 5:2, 11
Gal 6:14
thy God in *w.* thou trustest.
2 Ki 19:10; *Isa* 37:10
but to the saints, in *w.* *Ps* 16:3
my God, my strength, in *w.* I. 18:2
w. have I in heaven but thee? 73:25
not trust in son of man, in *w.* 146:3
as a father the son, in *w.* *Pr* 3:12
good from them to *w.* it is due. 27
a king against *w.* there is no. 30:31
he, For *w.* do I labour? *Eccl* 4:8
w. my soul loveth. *S of S* 3:1, 2, 3
I heard a voice saying, *W.* shall I send? *Isa* 6:8
in day of visitation? to *w.* will? 10:3
what hast thou here? *w.*? 22:16
turn to him from *w.* Israel. 31:6
to *w.* then will ye liken God?
40:18, 25; 46:5
behold mine elect, in *w.* my. 42:1
art my servant, O Israel, in *w.* 49:3
famine and sword; by *w.* shall? 51:19
against *w.* do ye sport? 57:4
of *w.* hast thou been afraid? 11
w. they have loved, *w.* they have served, after *w.* they have walked, and *w.* they sought. *Jer* 8:2
from *w.* I am not able to rise up.
Lam 1:14
w. we said, Under his shadow. 4:20
Son of man, speak unto Pharaoh, . . . *W.* art thou like? *Ezek* 31:2
to *w.* art thou like in glory? 18
w. he would he slew, *w.* he . . . and *w.* he would he. *Dan* 5:19
O Lord, by *w.* shall Jacob arise?
Amos 7:2, 5
on *w.* hath not thy wickedness passed? *Nah* 3:19
in *w.* I am well pleased. *Mat* 3:17
17:5; *Mark* 1:11; *2 Pet* 2:17
this is he of *w.* it is written.
Mat 11:10; *John* 1:15, 30
w. say ye that I am? *Mat* 16:15
Mark 8:29; *Luke* 9:20
quickeneth *w.* he will. *John* 5:21
Moses, in *w.* ye trust. 45
Lord, to *w.* shall we go? 6:68
w. thou hast sent. 17:3
of *w.* speaketh the? *Acts* 8:34
whose I am, and *w.* I serve. 27:23
to *w.* he was not spoken. *Rom* 15:21

w. fall into their own nets. *Ps* 141:10
all the *w.* will he destroy. 145:20
he casteth the *w.* down to. 147:6
the *w.* shall be cut off. *Pr* 2:22
iniquities shall take the *w.* 5:22
a heart that deviseth *w.* 6:18
but the *w.* shall not inhabit. 10:30
the *w.* shall fall by his own. 11:5
when a *w.* man dieth, his. 7
righteous delivered, the *w.* cometh. 8
and when the *w.* perish there. 10
w. worketh a deceitful work. 18
w. shall not be unpunished. 21, 31
but a man of *w.* devices. 12:2
the *w.* are overthrown. 7; 21:12
the *w.* desireth the net of evil. 12:12
w. is snared by the transgression. 13
but the *w.* shall be filled with. 21
a *w.* messenger falleth into. 13:17
and a man of *w.* devices is. 14:17
the *w.* bow at the gates of the. 19
the *w.* is driven away in his. 32
the Lord is far from the *w.* 15:29
yea, even the *w.* for the day. 16:4
a *w.* doer giveth heed to. 17:4
he that justifieth the *w.* and he. 15
when the *w.* cometh, then. 18:3
a wise king scattereth the *w.* 20:26
the *w.* shall be ransom for. 21:18
when he bringeth it with a *w.* mind. 27
but the *w.* shall fall into. 24:16
neither be thou envious at the *w.* 19
take away the *w.* from before. 25:5
man falling down before the *w.* 26
a *w.* heart is like a potsherd. 26:23
the *w.* flee when no man. 28:1
forsake the law praise the *w.* 4
when the *w.* rise. 12, 28
so is a *w.* ruler. 15
when the *w.* beareth rule. 29:2
w. regardeth not to know it. 7
his servants are *w.* 12
the *w.* are multiplied. 16
judge the righteous and *w.* *Eccl* 3:17
be not overmuch *w.* neither. 7:17
I saw the *w.* buried, they. 8:10
not be well with the *w.* 13
which justify the *w.* for. *Isa* 5:23
of his lips shall he slay the *w.* 11:4
I will punish the *w.* for. 13:11
he deviseth *w.* devices to. 32:7
he made his grave with the *w.* 53:9
let the *w.* forsake his way. 55:7
w. are like the troubled sea. 57:20
thou hast taught the *w.* *Jer* 2:33
for the *w.* are not plucked. 6:29
deceitful and desperately *w.* 17:9*
he will give the *w.* to the. 25:31
to warn the *w.* *Ezek* 3:18, 19; 33:8, 9
behold the *w.* abominations. 8:9
these men give *w.* counsel in. 11:2
I any pleasure that the *w.*? 18:23
not according to your *w.* 20:44
the righteous and the *w.* 21:3, 4
profane *w.* prince of Israel whose. 25
if the *w.* restore the pledge. 33:15
but the *w.* shall do. *Dan* 12:10
pure with *w.* balances? *Mi* 6:11
not at all acquit the *w.* *Nah* 1:3
out of thee a *w.* counsellor. 11
for the *w.* shall no more pass. 15
w. doth compass about the righteous. *Hab* 1:4
the *w.* devoureth the man. 13
stumblingblocks with the *w.* *Zeph* 1:3
between righteous and *w.* *Mal* 3:18
and ye shall tread down the *w.* 4:3
w. than himself. Even so shall it be to this *w.* *Mat* 12:45; *Luke* 11:26
angels shall sever the *w.* *Mat* 13:49
a *w.* generation seeketh after. 16:4
thou *w.* servant. 18:32; 25:26 *Luke* 19:22
and by *w.* hands have. *Acts* 2:23*
were a matter of *w.* lewdness. 18:14
put away that *w.* person. *1 Cor* 5:13
in your mind by *w.* works. *Col* 1:21
and then shall that *w.* be. *2 Thes* 2:8*
see **man, men**

of the **wicked**

the place *of the w.* shall come to naught. *Job* 8:22
given into the hand *of the w.* 9:24
shine upon the counsel *of w.* *Job* 10:3
but the eye *of the w.* shall. 11:20
me into the hands *of the w.* 16:11
the light *of the w.* shall be. 18:5
are the dwellings *of the w.* 21
the triumphing *of the w.* 20:5
every hand *of the w.* shall. 22*
the counsel *of the w.* is far from me. 21:16; 22:18
how oft is candle *of the w.* put out? 21:17; *Pr* 13:9; 24:20
dwelling places *of the w.*? *Job* 21:28
gathered the vintage *of the w.* 24:6
and I brake the jaws *of the w.* 29:17
preserveth not the life *of the w.* 36:6
fulfilled the judgement *of the w.* 17
let the wickedness *of the w.* *Ps* 7:9
the arm *of the w.* man. 10:15
the assembly *of the w.* have. 22:16
the transgression *of the w.* 36:1
let not the hand *of the w.* 11
the arms *of the w.* shall be. 37:17
but the seed *of the w.* shall be. 28
end *of the w.* shall be cut off. 38
of the oppression *of the w.* 55:3
his feet in the blood *of the w.* 58:10
me from the counsel *of the w.* 64:2
deliver me out of the hand *of the w.* 71:4; 74:19; 82:4; 97:10
saw the prosperity *of the w.* 73:3
all the horns *of the w.* also. 75:10
ye accept the persons *of the w.*? 82:2
and see the reward *of the w.* 91:8
shall hear my desire *of the w.* 92:11
the mouth *of the w.* is opened. 109:2
desire *of the w.* shall perish. 112:10 *Pr* 10:28
because *of the w.* that forsake thy law. *Ps* 119:53
the hands *of the w.* have robbed. 61
the rod *of the w.* shall not. 125:3
asunder the cords *of the w.* 129:4
Lord, from the hands *of the w.* 140:4
O Lord, the desires *of the w.* 8
the way *of the w.* he turneth. 146:9
in frowardness *of the w.* *Pr* 2:14
of the desolation *of the w.* 3:25
curse is in the house *of the w.* 33
not into the path *of the w.* 4:14
the way *of the w.* is as darkness. 19
away the substance *of the w.* 10:3
covereth the mouth *of the w.* 6, 11
but the name *of the w.* 10:7
fruit *of the w.* tendeth to sin. 16
heart *of the w.* is little worth. 20
the fear *of the w.* it shall come. 24
but the years *of the w.* shall be. 27
the mouth *of the w.* speaketh. 32
overthrown by mouth *of the w.* 11:11
expectation *of the w.* is wrath. 23
but the counsels *of the w.* 12:5
the words *of the w.* are to lie in. 6
but the tender mercies *of the w.* 10
but the way *of the w.* seduceth. 26
belly *of the w.* shall want. 13:25
the house *of the w.* shall be. 14:11
but in the revenues *of the w.* 15:6
sacrifice *of the w.* is an abomination. 8; 21:27
the way *of the w.* is an abomination to the Lord. 15:9
the thoughts *of the w.* are an. 26
the mouth *of the w.* poureth out. 28
to accept the person *of the w.* 18:5
mouth *of the w.* devoureth. 19:28
plowing *of the w.* is sin. 21:4
robbery *of the w.* shall destroy. 7
the soul *of the w.* desireth evil. 10
considereth the house *of the w.* 12
broken the staff *of the w.* *Isa* 14:5
the deeds *of the w.* *Jer* 5:28
the way *of the w.* prosper? 12:1
thee out of the hand *of the w.* 15:21
whirlwind shall fall upon the head *of the w.* 23:19; 30:23
have strengthened the hands *of the w.* *Ezek* 13:22
wickedness *of the w.* shall. 18:20
upon the necks *of the w.* 21:29
land into the hand *of the w.* 30:12
I have no pleasure in the death *of the w.* 33:11
as for the wickedness *of the w.* 12
none *of the w.* shall *Dan* 12:10
treasures of wickedness in house *of the w.* *Mi* 6:10
woundedst the head out of the house *of the w.* *Hab* 3:13
able to quench all the fiery darts *of the w.* *Eph* 6:16
conversation *of the w.* *2 Pet* 2:7
away with the error *of the w.* 3:17
see **one**

to or *unto the* **wicked**

destruction *to the w.*? *Job* 31:3
shall be *to the w.* *Ps* 32:10
unto the w. God saith, What? 50:16
he that saith *unto the w.* *Pr* 24:24
is abomination *to the w.* 29:27
the righteous and *to the w.* *Eccl* 9:2
woe *unto the w.*! it shall be. *Isa* 3:11
let favour be shewed *to w.* 26:10
no peace, saith the Lord, *unto the w.* 48:22; 57:21
when I say *unto the w.* *Ezek* 3:18 33:8, 14
give it *to the w.* of the earth. 7:21

wickedly

Lot said, Do not so *w.* *Gen* 19:7 *Judg* 19:23
ye sinned in doing *w.* *Deut* 9:18
but if ye shall still do *w.* *1 Sam* 12:25
kept the ways of the Lord and have not *w.* *2 Sam* 22:22; *Ps* 18:21
I have sinned and have done *w.* *2 Sam* 24:17*
Manasseh hath done *w.* *2 Ki* 21:11
have done amiss, dealt *w.* *2 Chr* 6:37 *Neh* 9:33; *Ps* 106:6; *Dan* 9:5, 15
of Israel, did very *w.* *2 Chr* 20:35
his counsellor to do *w.* 22:3
you speak *w.* for God? *Job* 13:7
surely God will not do *w.* 34:12
they speak *w.* concerning. *Ps* 73:8
the enemy hath done *w.* in. 74:3
they speak against thee *w.* 139:20
such as do *w.* against. *Dan* 11:32
but the wicked shall do *w.* 12:10
all that do *w.* shall be. *Mal* 4:1

wickedness

God saw that the *w.* of. *Gen* 6:5
how can I do this great *w.*? 39:9
it is *w.* *Lev* 18:17; 20:14
land full of *w.* 19:29
be no *w.* among you. 20:14
w. of these nations. *Deut* 9:4, 5
shall do no more any such *w.* 13:11
be any that hath wrought *w.* 17:2
of the *w.* of thy doings. 28:20
thus God rendered the *w.* *Judg* 9:56
Tell us, how was this *w.*? 20:3
what *w.* is this that is done? 12
you may see that your *w.* is great. *1 Sam* 12:17
ye have done all this *w.*: yet. 20
w. proceedeth from the. 24:13
returned the *w.* of Nabal on. 25:39
evil according to his *w.* *2 Sam* 3:39
neither shall the children of *w.* afflict them any. 7:10; *Ps* 89:22
but if *w.* be found in. *1 Ki* 1:52
knowest all the *w.* thy heart. 2:44
We have committed *w.* 8:47
Ahab sold himself to work *w.* 21:25
Manasseh wrought much *w.* *2 Ki* 21:6
nor the children of *w.* *1 Chr* 17:9
sow *w.*, reap the same. *Job* 4:8*
he seeth *w.* 11:11
not *w.* dwell in thy tabernacles. 14
w. be sweet in his mouth. 20:12
w. shall be broken. 24:20
my lips shall not speak *w.* 27:4
God that he should do *w.* 34:10
not God hath pleasure in *w.* *Ps* 5:4
their inward part is very *w.* 9
let the *w.* of the wicked come. 7:9
seek out his *w.* 10:15
according to the *w.* of their. 28:4
thou hatest *w.* 45:7
strengthened himself in his *w.* 52:7
w. is in the midst thereof. 55:11
w. is in their dwellings and. 15
ye work *w.*; ye weigh violence. 58:2
dwell in the tents of *w.* 84:10
fruitful land into barrenness for the *w.* of them. 107:34; *Jer* 12:4
eat the bread of *w.* *Pr* 4:17

and w. is an abomination to. Pr 8:7
treasures of w. profit nothing. 10:2
wicked shall fall by his own w. 11:5
not be established by w. 12:3
w. overthroweth the sinner. 13:6
driven away in his w. 14:32
to kings to commit w. 16:12
the wicked for their w. 21:12
his w. shall be shewed before. 26:26
saith, I have done no w. 30:20
place of judgement, that w. Eccl 3:16
prolongeth his life in w. 7:15
heart to know the w. of folly. 25
nor shall w. deliver those that. 8:8
for w. burneth as the fire. Isa 9:18
ye smite with the fist of w. 58:4
chosen, to loose the bands of w. 6
thine own w. shall correct. Jer 2:19
wash thine heart from w. 4:14
so she casteth out her w. 6:7
see what I did for the w. of. 7:12
no man repented of his w. 8:6
we acknowledge, O Lord, our w. and iniquity. 14:20
doth return from his w. 23:14
city whose w. I hid my face. 33:5
w. of your kings, their wives, your own w. and the w. of? 44:9
if he turn not from his w. Ezek 3:19
changed my judgement into w. 5:6
is risen up into a rod of w. 7:11
the w. of the wicked shall. 18:20
turneth from the w. he hath. 27
driven him out for his w. 31:11
he turneth from his w. 33:12, 19
the w. of Samaria was. Hos 7:1
for the w. of their doings I. 9:15
ye have plowed w. and. 10:13
do to you because of your w. 15
fats overflow; for their w. is great. Joel 3:13
are there treasures of w. in the house of the wicked? Mi 6:10
and he said, This is w. And he cast it into the. Zech 5:8
them the border of w. Mal 1:4
yea, they that work w. are. 3:15
out of the heart proceedeth w., deceit. Mark 7:22
inward part is full of w. Luke 11:39
this man, if any w. in him. Acts 25:5
being filled with all w. Rom 1:29
leaven of malice and w. 1 Cor 5:8
against spiritual w. in. Eph 6:12
whole world lieth in w. 1 John 5:19

their wickedness

look not to their w. Deut 9:27
them off in their own w. Ps 94:23
the wicked for their w. Pr 21:12
touching all their w. Jer 1:16
for I will pour their w. upon. 14:16
house have I found their w. 23:11
desolation, because of their w. 44:3
their ear to turn from their w. 5
let all their w. come before. Lam 1:22
consider not that I remember all their w. Hos 7:2
they make king glad with their w. 3
all their w. is in Gilgal, there. 9:15
Nineveh, for their w. is come up. Jonah 1:2
but Jesus perceived their w. and said. Mat 22:18

thy wickedness

Lord shall return thy w. 1 Ki 2:44
is not thy w. great? Job 22:5
thy w. may hurt a man as. 35:8
hast trusted in thy w. Isa 47:10
polluted the land with thy w. Jer 3:2
this is thy w. for it is bitter. 4:18
confounded for all thy w. 22:22
to pass after all thy w. Ezek 16:23
before thy w. was discovered. 57
upon whom hath not thy w.? Nah 3:19
therefore of this thy w. Acts 8:22

wide

but thou shalt open thy hand w. Deut 15:8*; 11*
the land was w. 1 Chr 4:40
opened their mouth w. as for rain. Job 29:23
came on me as a w. breaking. 30:14
opened their mouth w. against me. Ps 35:21
open thy mouth w. and I. 81:10
so is this great and w. sea. 104:25
he that openeth w. his lips shall have destruction. Pr 13:3
than to dwell with a brawling woman in a w. house. 21:9; 25:24
make ye a w. mouth? Isa 57:4
will build me a w. house. Jer 22:14
thy gates be set w. open. Nah 3:13
w. is the gate that leadeth. Mat 7:13

wideness

between chambers the w. of 20 cubits. Ezek 41:10*

widow

Among the Hebrews, even before the law, a widow who had no children by her husband, was allowed to marry the brother of her deceased husband, in order to raise up children who might enjoy his inheritance, and perpetuate his name and family, Gen 38:6, 8, 9, 11. *The law that appoints these marriages is delivered in* Deut 25:5, 6, *etc.*

It was looked upon as a great unhappiness for a man to die without an heir, and to see his inheritance pass into another family. This law was not confined to brothers in law only, but was extended to more distant relatives of the same line, as may be seen in the example of Ruth, who married Boaz, after she had been refused by a nearer kinsman. Widowhood, as well as barrenness, was a kind of shame and reproach in Israel, Isa 54:4. *It was presumed, that a woman of merit and reputation might have found a husband, either in the family of her deceased husband, if he died without children or in some other family, if he had left children.*

God frequently recommends to his people to be very careful in affording relief to the widow and orphan, Ex 22:22; Deut 10:18. *St. Paul would have us* honour *widows* that are *widows* indeed, *and desolate, that is, destitute of such as ought to help and relieve them, such as their husbands and children,* 1 Tim 5:3, 4, 5. *There were* widows *in the Christian church, who, because of their poverty, were maintained at the charge of the faithful, and who were to attend upon the poor and sick.*

remain a w. in thy. Gen 38:11
she put her w.'s garments off. 14
ye shall not afflict any w. Ex 22:22
a w. or an harlot shall. Lev 21:14
if the priest's daughter be a w. 22:13
every vow of a w. shall. Num 30:9
execute the judgement of a w. Deut 10:18
the stranger, fatherless, and w. 14:29; 16:11, 14; 26:12
a w.'s raiment to pledge. 24:17
shall be for the stranger, for the fatherless and w. 19, 20, 21; 26:13
the judgement of the w. 27:19
I am a w. woman. 2 Sam 14:5
he was a w.'s son of tribe. 1 Ki 7:14
Zeruah was a w. woman. 11:26
I have commanded a w. to. 17:9
they take the w.'s ox for. Job 24:3
and doeth not good to the w. 21
I caused the w.'s heart to sing. 29:13
caused the eyes of the w. to. 31:16
they slay the w. and the. Ps 94:6
be fatherless, his wife a w. 109:9
the fatherless and the w. 146:9
the border of the w. Pr 15:25
plead for the w. Isa 1:17
neither doth the cause of the w. 23
I shall not sit as a w. nor. 47:8
if ye oppress not the w. Jer 7:6; 22:3; Zech 7:10
how is she become as a w.! Lam 1:1
they vexed the w. Ezek 22:7
but take a w. that had a. 44:22
those that oppress the w. Mal 3:5
certain poor w. threw. Mark 12:42
w. cast in more than all. 43; Luke 21:3
Anna was a w. about. Luke 2:37
his mother, and she was a w. 7:12
there was a w. in that city. 18:3
because this w. troubleth me, I. 5
if any w. have children. 1 Tim 5:4
she that is a w. indeed trusteth. 5
let not a w. be taken into the. 9
as queen, and am no w. Rev 18:7

widowhood

the garments of her w. Gen 38:19
David's concubines shut up, living in w. 2 Sam 20:3
loss of children, and w. Isa 47:9
the reproach of thy w. 54:4

widows

wives shall be w. Ex 22:24
thou hast sent w. away. Job 22:9
be buried in death, and w. 27:15
and a judge of the w., is God. Ps 68:5
w. made no lamentation. 78:64
he have mercy on their w. Isa 9:17
w. may be their prey, that. 10:2
their w. are increased. Jer 15:8
let their wives be w. and. 18:21
leave thy children, let thy w. 49:11
our mothers are as w. Lam 5:3
have made her many w. Ezek 22:25
ye devour w.' houses, for pretence make long prayers. Mat 23:14; Mark 12:40; Luke 20:47
were many w. in Israel. Luke 4:25
murmuring because their w. were neglected. Acts 6:1
all the w. stood by him. 9:39
called the saints and w. 41
I said to the w., It is good. 1 Cor 7:8
honour w. that are w. 1 Tim 5:3
but the younger w. refuse, they. 11
if any have w., let them relieve. 16
pure religion is to visit the fatherless and w. in affliction. Jas 1:27

wife

Abraham's w. was Sarai. Gen 11:29, 31; 12:17, 20; 20:18; 24:36
hast taken is a man's w. 20:3
Hagar took a w. for Ishmael. 21:21
a w. to my son Isaac. 24:4, 38
Abraham took a w., her name. 25:1
Jacob take a w. of the daughters of Heth, what good? 27:46; 28:1, 6
Judah took a w. for Er his. 38:6
go in unto thy brother's w. and. 8
his master's w. cast her eyes. 39:7
covet thy neighbour's w. nor any thing. Ex 20:17; Deut 5:21
if his master have given him a w. Ex 21:4
if he take him another w. her food. 10
nakedness of thy father's w. shalt. Lev 18:8; 20:11; Deut 27:20
of thy son's w. Lev 18:15
thy brother's w. 16, 20, 21
neither shalt thou take a w. 18
lie with thy neighbour's w. 20; 20:10
if a man take a w. and her. 20:14
if a man lie with his uncle's w. 20
priests shall not take a w. 21:7*
the high priest shall take a w. 13
if any man's w. go aside. Num 5:12, 29
be a w. to one of the family. 36:8
or if the w. of thy bosom. Deut 13:6
what man hath betrothed a w.? 20:7
if any man take a w. and. 22:13
humbleth his neighbour's w. 24
not take his father's w. 30
a man hath taken a w. and. 24:1
and be another man's w. 2
hath taken a new w. he shall not. 5
w. of the dead shall not marry. 25:5
like not to take his brother's w. 7
then shall his brother's w. come. 9
the w. of the one draweth near. 11
betroth a w. and another lie. 28:30
his eye be evil toward the w. 54
Deborah, w. of Lapidoth. Judg 4:4

Jael the w. of Heber the Kenite.
Judg 4:17, 21; 5:24
thou goest to take a w. of the. 14:3
Samson's w. wept before him. 16
but his w. was given to his. 20
cursed be he that giveth a w. 21:18
buy it of Ruth, the w. of. Ruth 4:5
thou hast taken the w. 2 Sam 12:10
be not known to be the w. 1 Ki 14:2
Ahijah said, Come in, thou w. 6
waited on Naaman's w. 2 Ki 5:2
w. of Jehoiada hid him. 2 Chr 22:11
with the w. of thy youth. Pr 5:18
in to his neighbour's w. 6:29
whoso findeth a w. findeth. 18:22
contentions of a w. a. 19:13
and a prudent w. is from the. 14
live joyfully with the w. Eccl 9:9
children of the married w. Isa 54:1
hath called thee as a w. of youth. 6
surely as a w. treacherously departeth. Jer 3:20
neighed after his neighbour's w. 5:8
the husband and the w. shall. 6:11
shalt not take thee a w. in. 16:2
as a w. that committeth. Ezek 16:32
nor hath defiled his neighbour's w.
18:6, 15
and defiled his neighbour's w. 11
22:11; 33:26
take unto thee a w. of. Hos 1:2
Israel served for a w. and. 12:12
between thee and the w. of thy youth, the w. of thy. Mal 2:14
treacherously against his w. 15
of her that had been the w. Mat 1:6
for sake of Philip's w. 14:3
hath forsaken w. or children for my.
19:29; Mark 10:29; Luke 18:29
the first, when he had married a w., deceased. Mat 22:25
Mark 12:20; Luke 20:29
I have married a w. Luke 14:20
remember Lot's w. 17:32
should have his father's w. 1 Cor 5:1
render to the w. due benevolence, and likewise also the w. 7:3
the w. hath not power over her. 4
let not the w. depart from her. 10
if any brother hath a w. that. 12
unbelieving w. is sanctified by. 14
what knowest thou, O w.? 16
loosed from a w.? seek not a w. 27
between a w. and a virgin. 34
the w. is bound as long as her. 39
is the head of the w. Eph 5:23
his w. even as himself, and the w. see that she reverence her. 33
the husband of one w. 1 Tim 3:2
12; Tit 1:6
a widow, having been the w. of one man. 1 Tim 5:9
giving honour to w. as. 1 Pet 3:7*
the bride, the Lamb's w. Rev 21:9

his wife

mother, and shall cleave unto his w.
Gen 2:24; Mat 19:5; Mark 10:7
naked, the man and his w. Gen 2:25
they shall say, This is his w. 12:12
hold on the hand of his w. 19:16
but his w. looked back from. 26
restore the man his w. 20:7
became his w. 24:67; 1 Sam 25:42
the Lord for his w. Gen 25:21
place asked him of his w. 26:7
toucheth this man or his w. shall. 11
because thou art his w. 39:9
then his w. shall go out. Ex 21:3
endow her to be his w. 22:16
not approach to his w. Lev 18:14
he be jealous of his w. Num 5:14, 30
the man shall bring his w. 15
between a man and his w. 30:16
she shall be his w. Deut 22:19, 29
he shall cheer up his w. that. 24:5
Manoah arose and went after his w.
Judg 13:11
Samson visited his w. with. 15:1
catch you every man his w. 21:21
save to every man his w. and children. 1 Sam 30:22
thou hast taken his w. 2 Sam 12:9
whom Jezebel his w. 1 Ki 21:25
of Ahab was his w. 2 Ki 8:18
called his friends and his w.
Esth 5:10
and let his w. be a widow. Ps 109:9
if a man put away his w. Jer 3:1
Mat 5:31, 32; 19:9; Mark 10:11
Luke 16:18
he saw his w.'s mother sick of a fever. Mat 8:14
Is it lawful for a man to put away his w.? 19:3; Mark 10:2
of a man be so with his w. Mat 19:10
seven brethren, the first deceased, and left his w. to. 22:25
Mark 12:19; Luke 20:28
and hate not his w. Luke 14:26
his w. also being privy to it. Acts 5:2
his w. not knowing what was. 7
Paul found Aquila with his w. 18:2
came with his w. Drusilla. 24:24
man have his own w. 1 Cor 7:2
the husband put away his w. 11
how he may please his w. 33
he that loveth his w. Eph 5:28
shall be joined to his w. 31
so love his w. 33
and his w. hath made. Rev 19:7

my wife

slay me for my w.'s sake. Gen 20:11
she became my w. 12
she is my w. 26:7
give me my w. 29:21
I love my w. Ex 21:5
I will go in to my w. Judg 15:1
saying, Deliver me my w. Michal.
2 Sam 3:14
my house to lie with my w.? 11:11
is strange to my w. Job 19:17
then let my w. grind unto. 31:10
so I spake, and at even my w. died.
Ezek 24:18
she is not my w. nor. Hos 2:2
my w. is well stricken. Luke 1:18

thy wife

to the voice of thy w. Gen 3:17
not tell me she was thy w. 12:18
behold thy w., take her, and go. 19
Sarah, thy w. shall bear thee a son.
17:19; 18:10
arise, take thy w. and thy. 19:15
Of a surety she is thy w. 26:9
might lightly have lien with thy w. 10
unto thee, and thy w. Ex 18:6
wouldest have her to thy w.
Deut 21:11
to her, and she shall be thy w. 13
taken the wife of Uriah to be thy w.
2 Sam 12:10
thy w. shall be as a. Ps 128:3
thy w. shall be an harlot. Amos 7:17
thou shalt save thy w. 1 Cor 7:16

to wife

taken her to me to w. Gen 12:19
Get me this damsel to w. 34:4
give him her to w. 8, 12
not given to Shelah to w. 38:14
gave Joseph to w. Asenath. 41:45
of his own people to w. Lev 21:14
I gave my daughter to this man to w. Deut 22:16
will I give Achsah my daughter to w.
Josh 15:16, 17; Judg 1:12, 13
get her for me to w. Judg 14:2
Merab, her will I give thee to w.
1 Sam 18:17
the Shunammite, to w. 1 Ki 2:17
cedar, give thy daughter to my son to w. 2 Ki 14:9; 2 Chr 25:18
daughter of Ahab to w. 2 Chr 21:6
the seven had her to w. Mark 12:23
Luke 20:33
the second took her to w. and died.
Luke 20:30

wild

Ishmael will be a w. man. Gen 16:12*
which is w. by nature. Rom 11:24
see **ass, beast, beasts**

wilderness

A wilderness, or desert place, in the Bible means simply a place that is not inhabited and usually not cultivated. Much could be used as pasture.

The desert of Arabia, wherein the Israelites sojourned forty years after the Exodus, is called wilderness, Neh 9:19, 21; Ps 78:40, 52, 107:4; Jer 2:2.

The *wilderness* of Shur *lies towards the Red Sea. This was the place of Hagar's wandering,* Gen 16:7; *and the Israelites passed through it after the Exodus,* Ex 15:22.

The *wilderness* of Paran *was in Arabia Petrea. Ishmael, the son of Abraham, dwelt in the borders of this* wilderness, Gen 21:21. *It was from hence that Moses sent out spies to bring intelligence concerning the land of promise,* Num 13:3.

The *wilderness* of Sin, *between Elim and Sinai,* Ex 16:1.

The desert of Sinai, *is that which lies about, and is adjacent to, mount* Sinai. *The people encamped there a long time, and received the greater part of those laws which are written in the books of Moses,* Ex 19:2.

are entangled, the w. Ex 14:3
we had died in this w. Num 14:2
shall fall in this w. 29, 32, 35
went through all that terrible w.
Deut 1:19; 8:15
in the waste howling w. 32:10
way to w. of Damascus. 1 Ki 19:15
the w. yieldeth food for. Job 24:5
through the depths as through the w.
Ps 106:9; 136:16; Amos 2:10
he turneth the w. into. Ps 107:35
cometh out of w.? S of S 3:6; 8:5
that made world as a w.? Isa 14:17
w. and solitary place shall be. 35:1
I will make the w. a pool. 41:18
let the w. and cities lift up. 42:11
I make the cities a w. 50:2
and he will make her w. like. 51:3
cities are a w., Zion is a w. 64:10
a w. unto Israel? Jer 2:31
lo, the fruitful place was a w. 4:26
pleasant portion a desolate w. 12:10
will make thee a w. 22:6; Hos 2:3
more desolate than the w.
Ezek 6:14
behind them a desolate w. Joel 2:3
shall be a desolate w. 3:19
Nineveh dry like a w. Zeph 2:13

in the wilderness

which I did in the w. Num 14:22
leave them in the w. and ye shall.
32:15; Ezek 29:5
Lord led thee forty years in the w.
Deut 8:2; 29:5; Josh 5:6; 14:10
who fed thee in the w. Deut 8:16
thou sustain them in w. Neh 9:21
of temptation in the w. Ps 95:8
better dwell in the w. Pr 21:19
shall dwell in the w. Isa 32:16
for in the w. shall waters. 35:6
the voice of him that crieth in the w.
40:3; Mat 3:3; Mark 1:3
Luke 3:4; John 1:23
I will plant in the w. the. Isa 41:19
make a way in the w. 43:19
wentest after me in the w. Jer 2:2
in the w. a lodging place. 9:2
left found grace in the w. 31:2
like the heath in the w. 48:6
laid wait for us in the w. Lam 4:19
she is planted in the w. Ezek 19:13
Israel rebelled against me in the w.
20:13
hand to them in the w. 15, 23
shall dwell safely in the w. 34:25
like grapes in the w. Hos 9:10
in the w. in the dry land. 13:5
John came preaching in the w. of Judaea. Mat 3:1
we have so much bread in the w., as to fill? Mat 15:33; Mark 8:4
ninety and nine in the w. Luke 15:4
an angel appeared to him in the w.
Acts 7:30, 38
in perils in the w. 2 Cor 11:26

into the **wilderness**
by a fit man *into the w.* *Lev* 16:21
let go the goat *into the w.* 22
brought them *into the w.* *Ezek* 20:10
I will bring you *into the w.* 35
and bring her *into the w.* *Hos* 2:14
what went ye out *into the w.* to see? a reed? *Mat* 11:7; *Luke* 7:24
of the devil *into the w.* *Luke* 8:29
which leddest *into the w.* *Acts* 21:38
woman fled *into the w.* *Rev* 12:6, 14
me in the spirit *into the w.* 17:3

wiles
vex you with their *w.* *Num* 25:18
against the *w.* of the devil. *Eph* 6:11

wilfully
if we sin *w.* after we have. *Heb* 10:26

wilily
work *w.* and took old sacks. *Josh* 9:4

will
for good *w.* of him that. *Deut* 33:16
deliver me not to *w.* of. *Ps* 27:12
wilt not deliver him to *w.* of. 41:2
delivered thee to *w.* of. *Ezek* 16:27
or receiveth it with good *w.* at your hand. *Mal* 2:13
that doeth the *w.* of my Father. *Mat* 7:21; 12:50
it is not the *w.* of your Father. 18:14
whether of them did the *w.* of? 21:31
on earth peace, good *w.* *Luke* 2:14
delivered Jesus to their *w.* 23:25
were born, not of the *w.* *John* 1:13
meat is to do the *w.* of him that. 4:34
I seek the *w.* of my Father. 5:30
and this is the Father's *w.* 6:39, 40
saying, The *w.* of the Lord be done. *Acts* 21:14
understanding what the *w.* *Eph* 5:17
with good *w.* doing service, as. 6:7
some also preach Christ of good *w.* *Phil* 1:15
by the which *w.* we are. *Heb* 10:10
have wrought the *w.* of. *1 Pet* 4:3
came not by the *w.* of. *2 Pet* 1:21
see **self**

will
(*The word will as a verb is sometimes the future auxiliary, but it often means* to wish, to exercise will, to be willing)
her go whither she *w.* *Deut* 21:14
let come on me what *w.* *Job* 13:13
king's heart whither he *w.* *Pr* 21:1
and giveth it to whomsoever he *w.* *Dan* 4:17, 25, 32; 5:21
I *w.*, be thou clean. *Mat* 8:3
Mark 1:41; *Luke* 5:13
what I *w.* with mine? *Mat* 20:15
what *w.* ye that I shall do? 32
not as I *w.* but as thou wilt. 26:39
Mark 14:36
whom *w.* ye that I? *Mat* 27:17, 21
Mark 15:9; *John* 18:39
I *w.* that thou give me. *Mark* 6:25
whensoever ye *w.* ye may do. 14:7
what *w.* ye then that I should? 15:12
to whomsoever I *w.* I. *Luke* 4:6
and what *w.* I, if it be? 12:49
even so the Son quickeneth whom he *w.* *John* 5:21
wherefore hear it again? *w.* ye? 9:27
what ye *w.* it shall be done. 15:7
I *w.* that they be with me. 17:24
if I *w.* that he tarry till. 21:22, 23
I *w.* return again to you. *Acts* 18:21
to *w.* is present with me. *Rom* 7:18
hath he mercy on whom he *w.* have mercy, and whom he *w.* he. 9:18
shortly, if the Lord *w.* *1 Cor* 4:19
what *w.* ye? shall I come to you? 21
let him do what he *w.* 7:36
be married to whom she *w.* 39
every man severally as he *w.* 12:11
was a readiness to *w.* *2 Cor* 8:11
worketh in you, both to *w.* *Phil* 2:13
I *w.* that men pray. *1 Tim* 2:8
I *w.* that the younger women. 5:14
these things I *w.* that thou. *Tit* 3:8
if the Lord *w.* we shall do. *Jas* 4:15
as often as they *w.* *Rev* 11:6
whosoever *w.* let him take. 22:17

his **will**
doeth according to *his w.* *Dan* 4:35
he did according to *his w.* 8:4
do *his w.* 11:3, 16, 36
neither did according to *his w.* *Luke* 12:47
if any man will do *his w.* *John* 7:17
shouldest know *his w.* *Acts* 22:14
knowest *his w.* *Rom* 2:18
who hath resisted *his w.*? 9:19
power over *his* own *w.* *1 Cor* 7:37
his w. was not at all to come. 16:12
good pleasure of *his w.* *Eph* 1:5
known to us the mystery of *his w.* 9
with knowledge of *his w.* *Col* 1:9
captive by him at *his w.* *2 Tim* 2:26
good work to do *his w.* *Heb* 13:21
according to *his w.* he hears. *1 John* 5:14
hearts to fulfil *his w.* *Rev* 17:17

my **will**
nevertheless, not *my w.* *Luke* 22:42
who shall fulfil all *my w.* *Acts* 13:22
this thing against *my w.* *1 Cor* 9:17

will *not*
so *w. not* we go back. *Ps* 80:18
I *w. not* be enquired. *Ezek* 20:3
I *w. not* again pass by them any more. *Amos* 7:8; 8:2
and said, I *w. not.* *Mat* 21:29
yet *w.* I *not* deny thee. 26:35
though all shall be offended, yet *w. not* I. *Mark* 14:29
ye *w. not* come to me that ye may have life. *John* 5:40

will *of God*
after the *w. of* your *God.* *Ezra* 7:18
who shall do the *w. of God* is my brother. *Mark* 3:35
w. of man, but *of God.* *John* 1:13
generation by *w. of God.* *Acts* 13:36
journey by *w. of God.* *Rom* 1:10
maketh intercession according to the *w. of God.* 8:27
and perfect *w. of God.* 12:2
with joy, by the *w. of God.* 15:32
an apostle of Jesus Christ by the *w. of God.* *1 Cor* 1:1; *2 Cor* 1:1
Eph 1:1; *Col* 1:1; *2 Tim* 1:1
to us by the *w. of God.* *2 Cor* 8:5
according to the *w. of God.* *Gal* 1:4
doing the *w. of God* from. *Eph* 6:6
may stand complete in all the *w. of God.* *Col* 4:12
for this is the *w. of God.* *1 Thes* 4:3
5:18
done the *w. of God.* *Heb* 10:36
so is the *w. of God* that. *1 Pet* 2:15
if the *w. of God* be so. 3:17
lusts of men, but to *w. of God.* 4:2
suffer according to the *w. of God.* 19
he that doeth the *w. of God* abideth. *1 John* 2:17

own **will**
it of his *own* voluntary *w.* *Lev* 1:3
ye shall offer it as your *own w.* 19:5; 22:19, 29
according to his *own w.* *Dan* 11:16
I seek not mine *own w.* *John* 5:30
not to do mine *own w.* 6:38
after counsel of his *own w.* *Eph* 1:11
gifts of Holy Ghost, according to his *own w.* *Heb* 2:4
of his *own w.* begat he us. *Jas* 1:18

thy **will**
I delight to do *thy w.* *Ps* 40:8
teach me to do *thy w.*; thou. 143:10
thy w. be done in earth. *Mat* 6:10
Luke 11:2
not pass, *thy w.* be done. *Mat* 26:42
lo, I come to do *thy w.* *Heb* 10:7, 9

willeth
so then it is not of him that *w.* nor of him that runneth. *Rom* 9:16

willing
the woman will not be *w.* *Gen* 24:5
if the woman will not be *w.* 8
whosoever is of a *w.* heart. *Ex* 35:5
21, 22, 29*
God with a *w.* mind. *1 Chr* 28:9
who is *w.* to consecrate his? 29:5
will the unicorn be *w.*? *Job* 39:9*
thy people shall be *w.* in. *Ps* 110:3
if ye be *w.* ye shall eat good. *Isa* 1:19
not *w.* to make her public. *Mat* 1:19
the spirit is *w.* but the flesh. 26:41
Pilate *w.* to content. *Mark* 15:15*
but he, *w.* to justify. *Luke* 10:29*
if thou be *w.* remove this. 22:42
Pilate therefore *w.* to. 23:20*
ye were *w.* for a season. *John* 5:35
Felix *w.* to shew the Jews a pleasure. *Acts* 24:27*
but Festus *w.* to do the Jews. 25:9*
but the centurion, *w.* to save. 27:43*
what if God, *w.* to shew? *Rom* 9:22
w. rather to be absent. *2 Cor* 5:8
they were *w.* of themselves. 8:3*
if there be first a *w.* mind. 12*
w. to have imparted. *1 Thes* 2:8*
ready to distribute, *w.* *1 Tim* 6:18
God, *w.* to shew to the heirs of. *Heb* 6:17*
w. to live honestly in all. 13:18*
not *w.* that any should perish, but. *2 Pet* 3:9*

willingly
every man that giveth *w.* *Ex* 25:2
the people *w.* offered. *Judg* 5:2, 9
we will *w.* give the earrings. 8:25
and rulers offered *w.* *1 Chr* 29:6, 9
14, 17; *2 Chr* 35:8; *Ezra* 1:6; 3:5
Amasiah *w.* offered. *2 Chr* 17:16
blessed the men that *w.* *Neh* 11:2
she worketh *w.* with. *Pr* 31:13
he doth not afflict *w.* *Lam* 3:33
Ephraim *w.* walked. *Hos* 5:11
they *w.* received him. *John* 6:21
the creature made subject to vanity not *w.* *Rom* 8:20
if I do this thing *w.* *1 Cor* 9:17
not as of necessity, but *w.* *Philem* 14; *1 Pet* 5:2
for this they *w.* are. *2 Pet* 3:5

willows
ye shall take *w.* of the. *Lev* 23:40
the *w.* of the brook compass him. *Job* 40:22
our harps upon the *w.* *Ps* 137:2
away to the brook of *w.* *Isa* 15:7
they shall spring up as *w.* by. 44:4

willow *tree*
he set it as a *w. tree.* *Ezek* 17:5

will *worship*
of wisdom in *w. worship.* *Col* 2:23

wilt
Caleb said to her, What *w.* thou? *Judg* 1:14; *Esth* 5:3; *Mat* 20:21
Mark 10:51; *Luke* 18:41
if thou *w.* look on thine. *1 Sam* 1:11
w. not thou, O God? *Ps* 60:10
108:11
w. thou be angry with us? 85:5
w. thou not revive us again to? 6
why *w.* thou, my son, be ravished? *Pr* 5:20
w. thou not from this time cry unto me? *Jer* 3:4
O Jerusalem, *w.* thou not be? 13:27
w. thou judge them, son of man? *Ezek* 20:4; 22:2
w. thou not tell us what? 24:19
w. thou yet say before him? 28:9
Lord, if thou *w.* thou canst make. *Mat* 8:2; *Mark* 1:40; *Luke* 5:12
w. thou then that we go and gather them up? *Mat* 13:28
unto thee even as thou *w.* 15:28
if thou *w.* let us make three. 17:4
the disciples said, Where *w.* thou? 26:17; *Mark* 14:12; *Luke* 22:9
not as I will, but as thou *w.* *Mat* 26:39; *Mark* 14:36
king said, Ask of me whatsoever thou *w.* *Mark* 6:22
w. thou that we command fire to? *Luke* 9:54
Jesus said, *W.* thou be made whole? *John* 5:6
w. thou at this time restore the kingdom? *Acts* 1:6

wimples
away mantles and *w.* *Isa* 3:22*

win

he thought to *w.* them. *2 Chr* 32:1
that I may *w.* Christ. *Phil* 3:8

wind

The powerful operations of God's Spirit, quickening or reviving the heart toward God, are compared to the blowing of the wind, John 3:8. *For as with the* wind, *man perceives, by the effects of it, that there is such a thing, and that it does blow, yet his power cannot restrain it, neither can his reason reach to know whence it rises, or from how far it comes, or how far it reaches; so is the spiritual change wrought in the soul, freely, where, in whom, when, and in what measure the Spirit pleases; and also powerfully, so as to make an evident sensible change, though the manner thereof be incomprehensible.*

God made a *w.* to pass. *Gen* 8:1
blow with thy *w.* *Ex* 15:10
the *w.* brought quails. *Num* 11:31
he was seen upon the wings of the *w.* *2 Sam* 22:11; *Ps* 18:10; 104:3
black with cloud and *w.* *1 Ki* 18:45
strong *w.* rent the mountains, but the Lord was not in the *w.* 19:11
ye shall not see *w.* nor. *2 Ki* 3:17
there came a *w.* from. *Job* 1:19
speeches which are as *w.* 6:26
O remember that my life is *w.* 7:7†
mouth be like a strong *w.* 8:2
as stubble before the *w.* 21:18
pursue my soul as the *w.* 30:15
thou liftest me up to the *w.* 22
not light in the clouds, but the *w.* 37:21; *Ps* 103:16
like chaff which the *w.* *Ps* 1:4
w. that passeth away and. 78:39
he bringeth the *w.* out of. 135:7
he causeth his *w.* to blow. 147:18
he shall inherit the *w.* *Pr* 11:29
clouds and *w.* without rain. 25:14
north *w.* driveth away rain. 23
hideth her, hideth the *w.* 27:16
gathered the *w.* in his fists. 30:4
w. goeth toward the south, and turneth . . . and the *w.* *Eccl* 1:6
he that hath laboured for the *w.*? 5:16
he that observeth the *w.* 11:4
awake, O north *w.* come. *S of S* 4:16
trees are moved with the *w.* *Isa* 7:2
with his *w.* shake his hand. 11:15
as it were brought forth *w.* 26:18
rough *w.* in day of his east *w.* 27:8*
as a hiding place from the *w.* 32:2
the *w.* shall carry them away. 41:16
57:13
their molten images are *w.* 41:29
our iniquities, like the *w.* have. 64:6
a full *w.* from those places. *Jer* 4:12
prophets shall become *w.* 5:13
brings the *w.* out of his treasuries. 10:13; 51:16
the *w.* shall eat up all thy. 22:22
thou shalt scatter in the *w.* *Ezek* 5:2
I will scatter toward every *w.* 12:14
w. son of man, say to the *w.* 37:9
and the *w.* carried them. *Dan* 2:35
the *w.* hath bound her up. *Hos* 4:19
they have sown *w.* and shall reap. 8:7
on *w.* and followeth the east *w.* 12:1
he that createth the *w.* *Amos* 4:13
Lord sent out a great *w.* *Jonah* 1:4
and the *w.* was in their. *Zech* 5:9
a reed shaken with the *w.*? *Mat* 11:7
Luke 7:24
w. was contrary. *Mat* 14:24
Mark 6:48; *Acts* 27:4
the *w.* ceased. *Mat* 14:32
Mark 4:39; 6:51
w. bloweth where it. *John* 3:8
sound as of a mighty *w.* *Acts* 2:2
carried about with every *w.* *Eph* 4:14
like a wave driven with the *w.* and. *Jas* 1:6
shaken of a mighty *w.* *Rev* 6:13
that the *w.* should not blow. 7:1

window

a *w.* shalt thou make. *Gen* 6:16*
Noah opened the *w.* of the ark. 8:6
Gerar looked out at a *w.* 26:8
spies down through a *w.* *Josh* 2:15
bound the scarlet line in the *w.* 21
Sisera's mother looked out at a *w.* *Judg* 5:28
Michal looked through a *w.*, and saw David. *2 Sam* 6:16
Jezebel painted her face, and looked out at a *w.* *2 Ki* 9:30
Open the *w.* eastward. 13:17
at the *w.* of my house. *Pr* 7:6
there sat in a *w.* a certain young man. *Acts* 20:9
through a *w.* was I let. *2 Cor* 11:33

windows

and the *w.* of heaven. *Gen* 7:11
w. of heaven were stopped. 8:2
if the Lord make *w.* in heaven. *2 Ki* 7:2, 19
those that look out of the *w.* be darkened. *Eccl* 12:3
looked forth at the *w.* *S of S* 2:9
w. from on high are. *Isa* 24:18
I will make thy *w.* of agates. 54:12*
flee as the doves to their *w.* 60:8
come up into our *w.* *Jer* 9:21
that cutteth him out *w.* 22:14
his *w.* being open in his. *Dan* 6:10
they shall enter in at the *w.* like a thief. *Joel* 2:9
shall sing in the *w.* *Zeph* 2:14
if I will not open the *w.* *Mal* 3:10

winds

weight for the *w.* *Job* 28:25
come from the four *w.* *Ezek* 37:9
the *w.* blew, and beat. *Mat* 7:25, 27
rebuked the *w.* 8:26; *Luke* 8:24
even the *w.* and the sea obey him? *Mat* 8:27; *Mark* 4:41; *Luke* 8:25
are driven of fierce *w.* *Jas* 3:4
clouds carried about of *w.* *Jude* 12
see **east, four, scatter, stormy**

windy

hasten from the *w.* storm. *Ps* 55:8

wine

There were many excellent vineyards in Palestine, and wine was made for common use. Water was scanty, especially at some seasons, and likely to be infected. Wine and milk were therefore the common beverages. The use of wine *was forbidden to the priests during all the time they were in the tabernacle, and employed in the service of the altar,* Lev 10:9. *This liquor was also forbidden to the Nazarites* Num 6:3.

In Gen 27:28, 37, corn and wine *denote all sorts of temporal good things. In the style of the sacred writers,* the wine, *or* the cup, *often represents the anger of God,* Ps 60:3; Jer 25:15. *There were certain charitable women at Jerusalem, as they tell us, who used to mix certain drugs with* wine, *to make it stronger, and more capable of easing pain. Some think it was such a mixture that was offered to our Saviour to drink, before he was fastened to the cross,* Mark 15:23.

Noah awoke from his *w.* *Gen* 9:24
brought forth bread and *w.* 14:18
garments in *w.* and clothes in. 49:11
his eyes were red with *w.* 12
part of an hin of *w.* for a drink. *Ex* 29:40; *Lev* 23:13; *Num* 15:5
separate himself from *w.* *Num* 6:3
half an hin of *w.* 15:10; 28:14
shalt cause the strong *w.* 28:7*
their *w.* is the poison. *Deut* 32:33
leave *w.* which cheereth. *Judg* 9:13
there is also bread and *w.* for. 19:19
away thy *w.* from thee. *1 Sam* 1:14
when the *w.* was gone out of. 25:37
piece of flesh, and a flagon of *w.* *2 Sam* 6:19*; *1 Chr* 16:3*
when Amnon's heart is merry with *w.* *2 Sam* 13:28
the *w.* that such as be faint. 16:2
w. was before him, I took up the *w.* *Neh* 2:1
had taken bread and *w.* 5:15
ten days store of all sorts of *w.* 18
lading asses with *w.* and. 13:15
they gave them royal *w.* *Esth* 1:7
king was merry with *w.* 10
Esther at the banquet of *w.* 5:6; 7:2
from the banquet of *w.* 7:7
drinking *w.* in eldest brother's house. *Job* 1:13, 18
behold, my belly is as *w.* that. 32:19
the *w.* is red, it is full of. *Ps* 75:8
shouteth by reason of *w.* 78:65
w. that maketh glad the. 104:15
she hath mingled her *w.* *Pr* 9:2
w. is a mocker, strong drink. 20:1
sorrow? they that tarry long at the *w.*; they that go to seek mixt *w.* 23:30
look not thou upon the *w.* when. 31
give *w.* to those that be of. 31:6
heart to give myself to *w.* *Eccl* 2:3
w. maketh merry, but money. 10:19
for thy love is better than *w.* *S of S* 1:2; 4:10
I have drunk my *w.* with my. 5:1
of thy mouth like the best *w.* 7:9
thy silver dross, thy *w.* *Isa* 1:22
that continue till night, till *w.* 5:11
pipe and *w.* are in their feasts. 12
eating flesh and drinking *w.* 22:13
there is a crying for *w.* in the. 24:11
a vineyard of red *w.* 27:2
that are overcome with *w.*! 28:1
w., and through strong drink are out of the way; they are . . . of *w.* 7
drunken, but not with *w.* 29:9; 51:21
yea, come, buy *w.* and milk. 55:1
say they, I will fetch *w* 56:12
whom *w.* hath overcome. *Jer* 23:9
take the *w.* cup of this fury. 25:15
pots full of *w.* 35:5
Jews gathered *w.* 40:12
I have caused *w.* to fail from. 48:33
drunken of her *w* are mad. 51:7
Damascus merchant in *w.* *Ezek* 27:18
the king gave of the *w.* *Dan* 1:5
not to defile himself with the *w.* 8
Belshazzar drank *w.* before. 5:1, 4
whiles he tasted *w.* 2
concubines drunk *w.* 23
neither came *w.* nor flesh. 10:3
take away my *w.* in the. *Hos* 2:9
gods and love flagons of *w.* 3:1*
the scent shall be as the *w.* 14:7
all ye drinkers of *w.* *Joel* 1:5
prophesy to thee of *w.* *Mi* 2:11
he transgresseth by *w.* *Hab* 2:5
make a noise, as through *w.* *Zech* 9:15
shall rejoice, as through *w.* 10:7
neither drinking *w.* *Luke* 7:33
wanted *w.*, the mother of Jesus saith unto him, They have no *w.* *John* 2:3
water that was made *w.* 9; 4:46
doth set forth good *w.*, but thou hast kept good *w.* till now. 2:10
be not drunk with *w.* *Eph* 5:18
not given to *w.* *1 Tim* 3:3*, 8
Tit 1:7*; 2:3
use a little *w.* for thy stomach's sake. *1 Tim* 5:23
walked in excess of *w.* *1 Pet* 4:3*
give her the cup of the *w.* *Rev* 16:19
made drunk with the *w.* of her fornication. 17:2; 18:3
see **bottle, corn, drink, new, offerings, oil, sweet**

winebibber, -s

be not among *w.* *Pr* 23:20
behold a man gluttonous, and a *w.* *Mat* 11:19; *Luke* 7:34

wine *bottles*

Gibeonites took *w. bottles* old and rent. *Josh* 9:4*
bottles of *w.* which we filled. 13*

wine *cellars*

over the *w. cellars* was. *1 Chr* 27:27

winefat

him that treadeth in the *w.*? *Isa* 63:2†
a place for the *w.* *Mark* 12:1*

winepress
fulness of the *w.* *Num* 18:27, 30
furnish him out of thy *w.* *Deut* 15:14
wheat by the *w.* *Judg* 6:11
slew at the *w.* of Zeeb. 7:25
help thee out of the *w.*? *2 Ki* 6:27
he also made a *w.* therein. *Isa* 5:2
I have trodden the *w.* alone. 63:3
of Judah as in a *w.* *Lam* 1:15
the floor and *w.* shall not. *Hos* 9:2
digged a *w.* in it, and. *Mat* 21:33
the angel cast it into the great *w.* *Rev* 14:19
the *w.* was trodden without the city, blood came out of the *w.* 20
he treadeth the *w.* of the wrath. 19:15

winepresses
treading *w.* on sabbath. *Neh* 13:15
tread their *w.* and. *Job* 24:11
wine to fail from the *w.* *Jer* 48:33
upon the king's *w.* *Zech* 14:10

wines
a feast, of *w.* on the lees. *Isa* 25:6

wing
w. of the cherub, five cubits the other *w.* *1 Ki* 6:24, 27; *2 Chr* 3:11, 12
none that moved the *w.* *Isa* 10:14
dwell fowl of every *w.* *Ezek* 17:23

winged
God created every *w.* *Gen* 1:21
likeness of any *w.* fowl. *Deut* 4:17
eagle with great wings, long-*w.* of divers colours, full of. *Ezek* 17:3

wings
I bare you on eagles' *w.* *Ex* 19:4
w. covering the mercy seat with their *w.* 25:20; 37:9; *1 Ki* 8:7
cleave it with *w.* thereof. *Lev* 1:17
abroad her *w.*, taketh them, beareth them on her *w.* *Deut* 32:11*
under whose *w.* thou art. *Ruth* 2:12
was seen upon the *w.* *2 Sam* 22:11
goodly *w.* to the peacock? or *w.* and feathers to the ostrich? *Job* 39:13*
the shadow of thy *w.* *Ps* 17:8
fly on the *w.* of the wind. 18:10
104:3
their trust under the shadow of thy *w.* 36:7; 57:1; 61:4; 91:4
Oh that I had *w.* like a dove! 55:6
in the shadow of thy *w.* will. 63:7
yet shall ye be as the *w.* 68:13
take the *w.* of the morning. 139:9
riches make themselves *w.* *Pr* 23:5
that which hath *w.* shall. *Eccl* 10:20
stood the seraphims: each one had six *w.* *Isa* 6:2
the stretching out of his *w.* 8:8
the land shadowing with *w.* 18:1
mount up with *w.* as eagles. 40:31
give *w.* to Moab, it may fly. *Jer* 48:9
spread his *w.* over Moab. 40
spread his *w.* over Bozrah. 49:22
four faces and four *w.* *Ezek* 1:6
their *w.* were joined. 9
I heard the noise of their *w.* . . . let down their *w.* 24, 25; 3:13; 10:5
w. full of eyes. 10:12
a great eagle with great *w.* 17:3
another great eagle with great *w.* 7
lion and had eagle's *w.*: I beheld till the *w.* thereof were. *Dan* 7:4
upon the back of it four *w.* of a fowl. 6
bound her up in her *w.* *Hos* 4:19
the wind was in their *w.* *Zech* 5:9
arise with healing in his *w.* *Mal* 4:2
as a hen gathereth her chickens under her *w.* *Mat* 23:37; *Luke* 13:34
the sound of their *w.* as of. *Rev* 9:9
to the woman were given two *w.* 12:14

wink
what do thy eyes *w.* at? *Job* 15:12†
nor let them *w.* with the eye. *Ps* 35:19

winked
this ignorance God *w.* at. *Acts* 17:30*

winketh
a wicked man *w.* with. *Pr* 6:13
he that *w.* with the eye. 10:10

winneth
he that *w.* souls is wise. *Pr* 11:30

winnowed
which hath been *w.* with. *Isa* 30:24

winnoweth
behold, Boaz *w.* barley. *Ruth* 3:2

winter
summer and *w.* shall not. *Gen* 8:22
made summer and *w.* *Ps* 74:17
for lo, the *w.* is past, the. *S of S* 2:11
in summer and in *w.* *Zech* 14:8
flight be not in the *w.* nor on the. *Mat* 24:20; *Mark* 13:18
dedication was in *w.* *John* 10:22
do thy diligence to come before *w.* *2 Tim* 4:21

winter, *verb*
beasts shall *w.* on them. *Isa* 18:6
haven was not commodious to *w.* in, the more . . . to *w.* *Acts* 27:12
abide and *w.* with you. *1 Cor* 16:6
determined there to *w.* *Tit* 3:12

wintered
in a ship which had *w.* *Acts* 28:11

winterhouse
king sat in the *w.* *Jer* 36:22
I will smite the *w.* with the summer house. *Amos* 3:15

wipe
I will *w.* Jerusalem as. *2 Ki* 21:13
w. not out my good deeds I have done. *Neh* 13:14
swallow up death in victory; Lord will *w.* *Isa* 25:8; *Rev* 7:17; 21:4
a woman did *w.* them with hairs of. *Luke* 7:38, 44; *John* 11:2; 12:3
he began to *w.* them. *John* 13:5

wiped
shall not be *w.* away. *Pr* 6:33

wipeth
as a man *w.* a dish. *2 Ki* 21:13
she eateth, *w.* her mouth. *Pr* 30:20

wiping
w. it, and turning it. *2 Ki* 21:13

wires
they cut gold plates into *w.* to work it. *Ex* 39:3

wisdom
(*This word is used in the Scriptures not only for learning, but for skill in the arts; the instinct of birds or beasts; discretion; and spiritual insight*)
filled him with the Spirit of God in *w.* *Ex* 31:3, 6; 35:31, 35
whose heart stirred them up in *w.* 35:26; 36:1, 2
for this is your *w.* and. *Deut* 4:6
according to the *w.* of an angel of God. *2 Sam* 14:20
to all the people in her *w.* 20:22
saw that the *w.* of God. *1 Ki* 3:28
God gave Solomon *w.* 4:29; 5:12
2 Chr 1:12
Solomon's *w.* excelled *w.* of Egypt. *1 Ki* 4:30, 34; 7:14; 10:4, 23, 24
2 Chr 9:3, 22, 23
only Lord give thee *w.* *1 Chr* 22:12*
give me *w.* *2 Chr* 1:10
but hast asked *w.* 11
thou Ezra, after the *w.* *Ezra* 7:25
they die, even without *w.* *Job* 4:21
the people, *w.* shall die with you. 12:2
and it should be your *w.* 13:5
dost thou restrain *w.* to thyself? 15:8
counselled him that hath no *w.*? 26:3
but where shall *w.* be found? 28:12
cometh *w.* and where place? 20
of years should teach *w.* 32:7
say, We have found out *w.* 13
me and I shall teach thee *w.* 33:33
Job's words were without *w.* 34:35
mighty in strength and *w.* 36:5*
number the clouds in *w.*? 38:37
hath deprived her of *w.* 39:17
of the righteous speaketh *w.* *Ps* 37:30
shalt make me to know *w.* 51:6
apply our hearts unto *w.* 90:12
in *w.* hast thou made all. 104:24
and teach his senators *w.* 105:22
to him that by *w.* made. 136:5*
to know *w.* *Pr* 1:2
fools despise *w.* and instruction. 7
w. crieth. *Pr* 1:20; 8:1
incline thine ear unto *w.* 2:2
the Lord giveth *w.* 6
he layeth up sound *w.* for the. 7
w. entereth into thine heart. 10
happy is the man that findeth *w.* 3:13
the Lord by *w.* hath founded. 19
keep sound *w.* 21
get *w.* 4:5, 7
my son, attend unto my *w.* 5:1
say to *w.*, Thou art my sister. 7:4
understand *w.* 8:5*
I *w.* dwell with prudence, and. 12
counsel is mine, and sound *w.* 14
w. builded her house. 9:1
man of understanding hath *w.* 10:23
the just bringeth forth *w.* 31
commended according to his *w.* 12:8
a scorner seeketh *w.* and. 14:6
the *w.* of the prudent is to. 8
w. resteth in heart of him that. 33
better is it to get *w.* than gold! 16:16
in hand of a fool to get *w.*? 17:16
man intermeddleth with all *w.* 18:1
he that getteth *w.* loveth 19:8
is no *w.* against the Lord. 21:30
cease from thine own *w.* 23:4
for a fool will despise the *w.* 9
buy *w.* 23
through *w.* is an house built. 24:3
whoso loveth *w.* rejoiceth his. 29:3
the rod and reproof give *w.* 15
I neither learned *w.* nor have. 30:3
openeth her mouth with *w.* 31:26
heart to search out by *w.* *Eccl* 1:13
I have gotten more *w.* than all. 16
I gave my heart to know *w.* and. 17
for in much *w.* is much grief. 18
acquainting mine heart with *w.* 2:3
so I was great, and my *w.* 9
I turned myself to behold *w.* 12
w. excelleth folly. 13
whose labour is in *w.* 21
God giveth to a man *w.* 26
w. giveth life. 7:12
w. strengtheneth the wise. 19
all this have I proved by *w.* 23
heart to know and seek out *w.* 25
a man's *w.* maketh his face. 8:1
applied my heart to know *w.* 16
there is no *w.* in the grave. 9:10
this *w.* have I seen also under. 13
a poor man by his *w.* delivered. 15
that is in reputation for *w.* 10:1
his *w.* faileth him, and he saith he. 3*
by my *w.* I have done it. *Isa* 10:13
for the *w.* of their wise men. 29:14
w. shall be the stability of. 33:6
wise man glory in his *w.* *Jer* 9:23
the world by his *w.* 10:12; 51:15
were skilful in all *w.* *Dan* 1:4, 17
with counsel and *w.* 2:14*
for *w.* and might are his. 20
he giveth *w.* to the wise, and. 21
O God, who hast given me *w.* 23
not revealed for any *w.* I have. 30
w. like the *w.* of the gods was. 5:11
came from utmost parts to hear the *w.* of. *Mat* 12:42; *Luke* 11:31
hath this man this *w.*? *Mat* 13:54
turn the disobedient to the *w.* of. *Luke* 1:17
Jesus filled with *w.* 2:40
increased in *w.* 52
said the *w.* of God, I will send. 11:49
give you a mouth and *w.* 21:15
look out seven men full of the Holy Ghost and *w.* *Acts* 6:3
were not able to resist the *w.* 10
gave Joseph *w.* in the sight of. 7:10
was learned in all the *w.* of the. 22
to preach the gospel: not with *w.* of words. *1 Cor* 1:17
I will destroy the *w.* of the wise. 19
foolish the *w.* of this world. 20
after that in the *w.* of God the world by *w.* knew not God. 21
sign, and Greeks seek after *w.* 22
power of God and the *w.* of. 24
who of God is made unto us *w.* 30
not with words of man's *w.* 2:4
not stand in the *w.* of men. 5
we speak *w.* 6
but we speak the *w.* of God 7

which man's *w.* teacheth. *1 Cor* 2:13
w. of this world is foolishness. 3:19
not with fleshly *w.* *2 Cor* 1:12
toward us in all *w.* *Eph* 1:8
known the manifold *w.* of God. 3:10
might be filled with all *w.* *Col* 1:9
teaching every man in all *w.* 28
words dwell in you in all *w.* 3:16
walk in *w.* toward them that are. 4:5
if any lack *w.* let him ask. *Jas* 1:5
this *w.* descendeth not from. 3:15
according to the *w.* given. *2 Pet* 3:15
the Lamb to receive *w.* *Rev* 5:12
blessing, and glory, and *w.* 7:12
the mind which hath *w.* 17:9

wisdom, joined with *is*

and *is w.* driven quite ? *Job* 6:13
with the ancient *is w.* 12:12, 13, 16
the price of *w. is* above rubies. 28:18; *Pr* 8:11
fear of the Lord that *is w. Job* 28:28
w. is the principal thing, get *w. Pr* 4:7
understanding *w. is* found. 10:13
but with the lowly *is w.* 11:2
but with the well advised *is w.* 13:10
w. of prudent *is* to understand. 14:8
w. is before him that hath. 17:24
w. is too high for a fool, he. 24:7
for in much *w. is* much grief. *Eccl* 1:18
w. is good with an inheritance. 7:11
for *w. is* a defence, and money. 12
w. is better than strength; nevertheless, the poor man's *w. is.* 9:16
w. is better than weapons of. 18
but *w. is* profitable to direct. 10:10
word what *w. is* in them ? *Jer* 8:9
Is w. no more in Teman ? *is* their *w.* vanished ? 49:7
that excellent *w. is* found. *Dan* 5:14
sinners, but *w. is* justified of her children. *Mat* 11:19; *Luke* 7:35
what *w. is* this which is given to him ? *Mark* 6:2
the *w.* that *is* from above. *Jas* 3:17
here *is w.* Let him that. *Rev* 13:18

of **wisdom**

shew thee the secrets *of w. Job* 11:6
price *of w.* is above rubies. 28:18
my mouth shall speak *of w. Ps* 49:3
the fear of the Lord is the beginning *of w.* 111:10; *Pr* 9:10
to receive the instruction *of w. Pr* 1:3
taught thee in the way *of w.* 4:11
but fools die for want *of w.* 10:21*
that is void *of w.* despiseth. 11:12
to him that is destitute *of w.* 15:21
of the Lord is the instruction *of w.* 33
the wellspring *of w.* as a. 18:4
so shall the knowledge *of w.* 24:14
great experience *of w.* *Eccl* 1:16
thou sealest up the sum, full *of w.* *Ezek* 28:12
in all matters *of w.* he found them better. *Dan* 1:20
the man *of w.* shall see. *Mi* 6:9
O the depth *of* the *w.* of God! *Rom* 11:33
of speech or *of w.* *1 Cor* 2:1
by the Spirit the word *of w.* 12:8
hid all the treasures *of w.* *Col* 2:3
have indeed a shew *of w.* 23
works with meekness *of w. Jas* 3:13

see **spirit**

thy **wisdom**

according to *thy w.* *1 Ki* 2:6
report that I heard of *thy w.* 10:6
thy w. and prosperity exceedeth. 7
that stand before thee continually and hear *thy w.* 8; *2 Chr* 9:5, 7
the half of *thy w.* was. *2 Chr* 9:6
the hawk fly by *thy w.*? *Job* 39:26
thy w., it hath perverted. *Isa* 47:10
with *thy w.* hast gotten. *Ezek* 28:4, 5
thou hast corrupted *thy w.* by. 17

wise

be desired to make one *w. Gen* 3:6
is none so discreet and *w.* 41:39
the gift blindeth the *w.* *Ex* 23:8; *Deut* 16:19
great nation is a *w.* people. *Deut* 4:6
O that they were *w.*, that they. 32:29
her *w.* ladies answered. *Judg* 5:29
my lord is *w.* according. *2 Sam* 14:20
I have given thee a *w.* *1 Ki* 3:12
given David a *w.* son over this great people. 5:7; *2 Chr* 2:12
for Zachariah his son, a *w.* counsellor. *1 Chr* 26:14*
he taketh the *w.* in their own craftiness. *Job* 5:13
he is *w.* in heart and mighty. 9:4
for vain man would be *w.* 11:12*
he that is *w.* may be profitable. 22:2
great men are not always *w.* 32:9
not any that are *w.* of heart. 37:24
be *w.* now, O ye kings. *Ps* 2:10
is sure, making *w.* the simple. 19:7
he hath left off to be *w.* and. 36:3
fools, when will ye be *w.*? 94:8
whoso is *w.* and will observe. 107:43
a *w.* man shall attain to *w.* *Pr* 1:5*
to understand the words of the *w.* 6
be not *w.* in thine own eyes. 3:7
the *w.* shall inherit glory: but. 35
be *w.* 6:6; 8:33; 23:19; 27:11
if thou be *w.* thou shalt be *w.* 9:12
a *w.* son maketh a glad father. 10:1; 15:20
gathereth in summer is a *w.* son. 10:5
the *w.* in heart will receive. 8
he that refraineth his lips is *w.* 19
servant to the *w.* in heart. 11:29
he that winneth souls is *w.* 30
hearkeneth to counsel is *w.* 12:15
tongue of the *w.* is health. 18
a *w.* son heareth his father's. 13:1
the law of the *w.* is a fountain. 14
with *w.* men shall be *w.* 20
but the lips of the *w.* shall. 14:3
crown of the *w.* is their riches. 24
is toward a wise servant. 35
tongue of *w.* useth knowledge. 15:2
the lips of the *w.* disperse. 7
a scorner will not go to the *w.* 12
the way of life is above to the *w.* 24
reproof abideth among the *w.* 31
the *w.* in heart shall be called prudent. 16:21
the heart of the *w.* teacheth his. 23
a *w.* servant shall have rule. 17:2
holdeth his peace is counted *w.* 28
the ear of the *w.* seeketh. 18:15
that thou mayest be *w.* in thy latter end. 19:20
is deceived thereby, is not *w.* 20:1
a *w.* king scattereth the wicked. 26
simple is made *w.*: when the *w.* is instructed he receiveth. 21:11
oil in the dwelling of the *w.* 20
ear, hear the words of the *w.* 22:17
thy heart be *w.* my heart shall. 23:15
he that begetteth a *w.* son shall. 24
for by *w.* counsel thou shalt. 24:6
also belong to the *w.* 23
so is a *w.* reprover upon an. 25:12
answer a fool lest he be *w.* 26:5
seest thou a man *w.* in his own. 12
keepeth the law is a *w.* son. 28:7
rich man is *w.* in his own conceit. 11
four things that are exceeding *w.* 30:24
and why was I more *w.*? *Eccl* 2:15
no remembrance of the *w.* 16
I have shewed myself *w.* 19
better is a *w.* child than a. 4:13
for what hath the *w.* more than ? 6:8
heart of the *w.* is in the house. 7:4
hear the rebuke of the *w.* 5
neither make thyself over *w.* 16
wisdom strengtheneth *w.* more. 19
I said, I will be *w.* but it was. 23
the *w.* and their works are in the. 9:1
I saw that bread is not to the *w.* 11
preacher was *w.*, he taught. 12:9
the words of the *w.* are as goads. 11
woe to them that are *w.* *Isa* 5:21
I am the son of the *w.*? 19:11
is *w.* and will bring evil. 31:2
they are *w.* to do evil. *Jer* 4:22
We are *w.*, and the law of. 8:8
counsel perish from the *w.* 18:18
God giveth wisdom to *w. Dan* 2:21
they that be *w.* shall shine as. 12:3
none of the wicked; but the *w.* 10
the *w.* shall understand. *Hos* 14:9
and Zidon be very *w.* *Zech* 9:2
therefore *w.* as serpents. *Mat* 10:16
hast hid these things from *w.* and prudent, and. 11:25; *Luke* 10:21
then is a faithful and *w.*? *Mat* 24:45
five virgins were *w.* and. 25:2
the *w.* took oil in their vessels. 4
faithful and *w.* steward ? *Luke* 12:42
I am debtor to the *w.* *Rom* 1:14
professing themselves *w.*, they. 22
lest ye should be *w.* in your. 11:25
be not *w.* in your own. 12:16
I would have you *w.* to. 16:19
to God only *w.*, be glory. 27; *1 Tim* 1:17; *Jude* 25
I will destroy the wisdom of the *w.* *1 Cor* 1:19
where is the *w.*? 20
to confound the *w.* 27
as a *w.* masterbuilder, I. 3:10
to be *w.* in this world, let him become a fool, that he may be *w.* 18
he taketh the *w.* in their own. 19
knoweth the thoughts of the *w.* 20
but ye are *w.* in Christ. 4:10
themselves, are not *w. 2 Cor* 10:12*
seeing ye yourselves are *w.* 11:19
not as fools, but as *w.* *Eph* 5:15
are able to make thee *w. 2 Tim* 3:15

see **man, men**

any **wise**

afflict them in *any w.* *Ex* 22:23
shall in *any w.* rebuke. *Lev* 19:17*
if he will in *any w.* redeem. 27:19*
in *any w.* set him king. *Deut* 17:15†
thou shalt in *any w.* bury. 21:23*
shalt in *any w.* let the dam. 22:7†
in *any w.* keep from the. *Josh* 6:18
if ye do in *any w.* go back. 23:12
in *any w.* send a trespass. *1 Sam* 6:3
let me go in *any w.* *1 Ki* 11:22
fret not thyself in *any w.* *Ps* 37:8*
not deny thee in *any w. Mark* 14:31

in no **wise**

the fat of beasts torn, *in no w.* eat of it. *Lev* 7:24
give the child, and *in no w.* slay it. *1 Ki* 3:26, 27
one tittle shall *in no w.* pass from the law. *Mat* 5:18
he shall *in no w.* lose his. 10:42
a woman could *in no w.* *Luke* 13:11
shall *in no w.* enter therein. 18:17; *Rev* 21:27
I will *in no w.* cast out. *John* 6:37
ye shall *in no w.* believe. *Acts* 13:41
than they ? no, *in no w.* *Rom* 3:9

on this **wise**

on this w. ye shall bless. *Num* 6:23
the birth of Jesus Christ was *on this w.* *Mat* 1:18
and *on this w.* shewed. *John* 21:1
God spake *on this w.* *Acts* 7:6
he said *on this w.*, I will give. 13:34
speaketh *on this w.* *Rom* 10:6
the seventh day *on this w. Heb* 4:4

wise *hearted*

to all that are *w. hearted.* *Ex* 28:3
I have put wisdom in all that are *w. hearted.* 31:6
every *w. hearted* among you. 35:10
that were *w. hearted* did spin. 25
wrought every *w. hearted* man. 36:1
Aholiab and every *w. hearted* man. 2
every *w. hearted* man made ten. 8

wise *men*

all the magicians of Egypt, and all the *w. men.* *Gen* 41:8; *Ex* 7:11

wise *woman*

and Joab fetched thence a *w. woman.* *2 Sam* 14:2
then cried a *w. woman* out. 20:16
every *w. woman* buildeth. *Pr* 14:1

wisely

come on, let us deal *w.* *Ex* 1:10
David behaved himself *w.* *1 Sam* 18:5, 14, 15, 30
Rehoboam dealt *w.* *2 Chr* 11:23
charming never so *w.* *Ps* 58:5
for they shall *w.* consider of. 64:9
I will behave myself *w.* in a. 101:2
handleth a matter *w.* *Pr* 16:20
w. considereth the house. 21:12

whoso walketh *w.* shall be. *Pr* 28:26
thou dost not enquire *w.* *Eccl* 7:10
because he had done *w.* *Luke* 16:8

wiser

for Solomon was *w.* *1 Ki* 4:31
who maketh us *w.* than the fowls of heaven? *Job* 35:11
thou hast made me *w.* *Ps* 119:98
and he will be yet *w.* *Pr* 9:9
the sluggard is *w.* in his own. 26:16
behold, thou art *w.* than. *Ezek* 28:3
are in their generation *w.* *Luke* 16:8
foolishness of God is *w.* *1 Cor* 1:25

wish

I am according to thy *w.* *Job* 33:6*
put to shame that *w.* evil. *Ps* 40:14*
more than heart could *w.* 73:7
I could *w.* myself accursed. *Rom* 9:3
this also we *w.*, even. *2 Cor* 13:9*
I *w.* above all things. *3 John* 2*

wished

Jonah fainted, and *w.* *Jonah* 4:8*
they cast anchor, and *w.* *Acts* 27:29

wishing

my mouth to sin, by *w.* *Job* 31:30*

wist

(*American Revision substitutes the more modern word* knew)
it is manna: for they *w.* not. *Ex* 16:15
Moses *w.* not that his face. 34:29
though he *w.* not, yet is he guilty. *Lev* 5:17, 18
but I *w.* not whence. *Josh* 2:4
w. not that there were liers. 8:14
he *w.* not that the Lord. *Judg* 16:20
he *w.* not what to say. *Mark* 9:6
neither *w.* they what to. 14:40
w. ye not I must be about? *Luke* 2:49
he that was healed *w.* not. *John* 5:13
w. not that it was true. *Acts* 12:9
said Paul, I *w.* not he was. 23:5

witch

not suffer a *w.* to live. *Ex* 22:18*
not be among you a *w.* *Deut* 18:10*

witchcraft

is as the sin of *w.* *1 Sam* 15:23
Manasseh used *w.* and. *2 Chr* 33:6*
the works of the flesh are idolatry, *w.* *Gal* 5:20*

witchcrafts

so long as Jezebel's *w.* *2 Ki* 9:22
I will cut off *w.* out of. *Mi* 5:12
w. that selleth nations through her . . . through her *w.* *Nah* 3:4

withal

w. how Elijah had slain. *1 Ki* 19:1
whilst that I *w.* escape. *Ps* 141:10
and not *w.* to signify. *Acts* 25:27

withdraw

priest, *W.* thine hand. *1 Sam* 14:19
will not *w.* his anger. *Job* 9:13
w. thine hand far from me: let. 13:21
that he may *w.* man from. 33:17
w. thy foot from thy neighbour's house. *Pr* 25:17*
from this *w.* not thine hand. *Eccl* 7:18
shall thy moon *w.* itself. *Isa* 60:20
the stars shall *w.* their shining. *Joel* 2:10; 3:15
w. yourselves from every brother. *2 Thes* 3:6
corrupt minds *w.* thyself. *1 Tim* 6:5

withdrawest

why *w.* thou thy right? *Ps* 74:11*

withdraweth

he *w.* not his eyes from. *Job* 36:7

withdrawn

have *w.* the inhabitants. *Deut* 13:13
but my beloved had *w.* *S of S* 5:6
he hath not *w.* his hand. *Lam* 2:8
that hath *w.* his hand. *Ezek* 18:8
the Lord hath *w.* himself. *Hos* 5:6
w. from them about a. *Luke* 22:41*

withdrew

they *w.* the shoulder and. *Neh* 9:29
I *w.* mine hand. *Ezek* 20:22
knew it, he *w.* himself. *Mat* 12:15
Jesus *w.* himself from thence. *Mark* 3:7; *Luke* 5:16

but when they were come, he *w.* *Gal* 2:12*

wither

his leaf also shall not *w.* *Ps* 1:3
and they shall *w.* as the green. 37:2
reeds and flags shall *w.* *Isa* 19:6
by the brooks shall *w.* 7*
upon them, and they shall *w.* 40:24
the herbs of the field *w.*? *Jer* 12:4
cut off the fruit thereof that it *w.*? it shall *w.* in all the. *Ezek* 17:9
utterly *w.*? it shall *w.* in furrows. 10
top of Carmel shall *w.* *Amos* 1:2

withered

behold seven ears *w.* thin. *Gen* 41:23
my heart is smitten and *w.* *Ps* 102:4
I am *w.* 11
hay is *w.* away, the grass. *Isa* 15:6
thereof are *w.*, be broken off. 27:11
the Nazarite's skin is *w.* *Lam* 4:8
her strong rods were *w.* *Ezek* 19:12
of the field are *w.*: joy is *w.* *Joel* 1:12
broken down, for the corn is *w.* 17
whereupon it rained not *w.* *Amos* 4:7
the gourd that it *w.* *Jonah* 4:7
and behold there was a man which had his hand *w.* *Mat* 12:10
Mark 3:1, 3; *Luke* 6:6, 8
were scorched, because having no root, they *w.* *Mat* 13:6; *Mark* 4:6
presently the fig tree *w.* *Mat* 21:19
20; *Mark* 11:21
it *w.* away because it. *Luke* 8:6
of *w.* folk, waiting for. *John* 5:3
forth as a branch and is *w.* 15:6

withereth

the flag *w.* before any. *Job* 8:12
it is cut down and *w.* *Ps* 90:6
as the grass which *w.* before it. 129:6
the grass *w.*, the flower fadeth. *Isa* 40:7, 8; *1 Pet* 1:24
risen, but it *w.* the grass. *Jas* 1:11
trees whose fruit *w.* without fruit. *Jude* 12*

withheld

for I *w.* thee from sinning. *Gen* 20:6
seeing thou hast not *w.* thy. 22:12
who *w.* from thee the fruit? 30:2
if I have *w.* the poor. *Job* 31:16
I *w.* not my heart from. *Eccl* 2:10

withheldest

w. not thy manna from. *Neh* 9:20

withhold

none of us shall *w.* from. *Gen* 23:6
for he will not *w.* me. *2 Sam* 13:13
but who can *w.* himself? *Job* 4:2
w. not thy tender mercies. *Ps* 40:11
no good thing will he *w.* from. 84:11
w. not good from them to. *Pr* 3:27
w. not correction from the. 23:13
in the evening *w.* not thy. *Eccl* 11:6
w. thy foot from being unshod. *Jer* 2:25

withholden

Lord hath *w.* thee from. *1 Sam* 25:26
thou hast *w.* bread from. *Job* 22:7
from the wicked their light is *w.* 38:15
that no thought can be *w.* 42:2*
hast not *w.* the request. *Ps* 21:2
showers have been *w.* *Jer* 3:3
your sins have *w.* good things. 5:25
hath not *w.* the pledge. *Ezek* 18:16*
the drink offering is *w.* *Joel* 1:13
also I have *w.* the rain. *Amos* 4:7

withholdeth

behold, he *w.* the waters. *Job* 12:15
there is that *w.* more. *Pr* 11:24
he that *w.* corn, the people. 26
and now ye know what *w.* that he might be revealed. *2 Thes* 2:6*

within

none of men was *w.* *Gen* 39:11
w. a full year he may. *Lev* 25:29*
of Simeon was *w.* Judah. *Josh* 19:1*
why not recover them *w.* that time? *Judg* 11:26
thou camest not *w.* the. *1 Sam* 13:11
w. the oracle he made. *1 Ki* 6:23
to the king's house *w.* *2 Ki* 7:11
whoso would not come *w.* *Ezra* 10:8
daughter is all glorious *w.* *Ps* 45:13*
will walk *w.* my house with a. 101:2

little city, few men *w.* it. *Eccl* 9:14
shut thyself *w.* thy house. *Ezek* 3:24
any vain vision *w.* Israel. 12:24
minister in the gates and *w.* 44:17
her princes *w.* are roaring. *Zeph* 3:3*
think not to say *w.* yourselves. *Mat* 3:9; *Luke* 3:8
w. herself, If I but touch. *Mat* 9:21
w. they are full of extortion. 23:25
cleanse first what is *w.* the cup. 26
are *w.* full of dead men's bones. 27
w. ye are full of hypocrisy. 28
for from *w.* proceed. *Mark* 7:21
all these evil things come from *w.* 23
from *w.* shall answer. *Luke* 11:7
he thought *w.* himself. 12:17 16:3
18:4
his disciples were *w.* *John* 20:26
we found no man *w.* *Acts* 5:23
judge them that are *w.*? *1 Cor* 5:12
fightings, *w.* were fears. *2 Cor* 7:5
full of eyes *w.*: rest not. *Rev* 4:8*
a book written *w.* and on the back. 5:1
see **gates, him, me, thee, them, us, without, you**

without

wherefore standest thou *w.*? *Gen* 24:31
the wife of the dead shall not marry *w.* unto a stranger. *Deut* 25:5
appointed eighty men *w.* *2 Ki* 10:24
Have her forth *w.* the ranges. 11:15*
I now come up *w.* the Lord against this place? 18:25; *Isa* 36:10
Israel hath been long *w.* *2 Chr* 15:3
Jehoram departed *w.* 21:20
they that did see me *w.* *Ps* 31:11
wisdom crieth *w.*; she. *Pr* 1:20*
now she is *w.* 7:12*
there is a lion *w.* 22:13
prepare thy work *w.*, and. 24:27
valiant ones shall cry *w.* *Isa* 33:7
be redeemed *w.* money. 52:3
milk *w.* money and *w.* price. 55:1
cut off the children from *w.* *Jer* 9:21
w. man, *w.* beast, and *w.* 33:10, 12
w. a king, *w.* a prince, *w.* a sacrifice, *w.* an image, *w.* an ephod, and *w.* a teraphim. *Hos* 3:4
not fall *w.* your father. *Mat* 10:29
to them that are *w.* all. *Mark* 4:11
whatsoever from *w.* entereth. 7:18
whole multitude were praying *w.* *Luke* 1:10
to judge them that are *w.* *1 Cor* 5:12
them that are *w.* God judgeth. 13
having no hope, and *w.* *Eph* 2:12
walk in wisdom toward them that are *w.* *Col* 4:5
walk honestly toward them that are *w.* *1 Thes* 4:12
report of them that are *w.* *1 Tim* 3:7
w. father, *w.* mother, *w.* *Heb* 7:3
also suffered *w.* the gate. 13:12
that they also may *w.* *1 Pet* 3:1
w. are dogs and sorcerers. *Rev* 22:15

without, joined with *within*

pitch the ark *within* and *w.* *Gen* 6:14
overlay the ark *within* and *w.* *Ex* 25:11; 37:2
be bare *within* or *w.* *Lev* 13:55
the sword *w.* and terror *within*. *Deut* 32:25
written *within* and *w.* *Ezek* 2:10
is *w.* and famine *within*. 7:15
made that which is *w.* make that which is *within* also? *Luke* 11:40
w. were fightings, *within*. *2 Cor* 7:5
see **blemish, camp, cause, city, fail, fear, him, knowledge, law, me, stand, stood, us, you**

withs

(*withes*)
if they bind me with seven green *w.* *Judg* 16:7
the lords brought *w.* 8
he brake the *w.* 9

withstand

went out to *w.* Balaam. *Num* 22:32*
young, could not *w.* them. *2 Chr* 13:7
now ye think to *w.* the kingdom. 8
none is able to *w.* thee. 20:6
no man could *w.* the Jews. *Esth* 9:2

prevail, two shall *w.* him. *Eccl* 4:12
arms of the south shall not *w.*, neither any strength to *w.* *Dan* 11:15
I that I could *w.* God? *Acts* 11:17
able to *w.* in the evil day. *Eph* 6:13

withstood

they *w.* Uzziah the king. *2 Chr* 26:18
prince of Persia *w.* me. *Dan* 10:13
Elymas the sorcerer *w.* *Acts* 13:8
at Antioch I *w.* Peter. *Gal* 2:11*
and Jambres *w.* Moses. *2 Tim* 3:8
hath greatly *w.* our words. 4:15

witness

Since there was little writing among most of the people in olden times the evidence of a transaction was most often given by some tangible memorial, as in Gen 21:30; Josh 22:10, *or some significant ceremony.*

Witness *in Greek is* Martūs, *or* Martūr, *and signifies one that gives testimony to the truth at the expense of his life. It is in this sense that the word is mainly used in the New Testament, and our word* martyr *has come from this also.*

The law appoints, that in case of a capital charge one witness *only was not sufficient,* Deut 17:6. *When any one was condemned to die the* witnesses *were the first that began the execution. They threw the first stone, for example, if the party was to be stoned,* Deut 17:7. *The law condemned a false* witness *to the same punishment that he would have subjected his neighbour to,* Deut 19:16, 17, 18, 19. *On the whole the law was very careful to provide evidence in all cases, and to punish both false swearing and one who kept back a part of the truth.*

The disciples who had been with Jesus, were to be witnesses for him, Luke 24:48, *and when they chose another apostle in place of Judas, they thought fit to appoint one who had been a* witness *of the resurrection along with them,* Acts 1:22.

The apostle Paul, in Rom 8:16 *says, that* the Spirit itself beareth *witness* with our spirit, that we are the children of God.

they may be a *w.* that I digged this well. *Gen* 21:30
let this covenant be a *w.* 31:44
this heap is a *w.*; this pillar. 48, 52
God is *w.* between me and thee. 50
1 Thes 2:5
let him bring it for a *w.* *Ex* 22:13
hand to be an unrighteous *w.* 23:1
if a soul sin, and is a *w.* *Lev* 5:1
be no *w.* against her. *Num* 5:13
one *w.* shall not testify against. 35:30
Deut 17:6; 19:15
that this song may be a *w.* for me against. *Deut* 31:19, 21, 26
the altar is a *w.* between us.
Josh 22:27, 28, 34
this stone shall be a *w.* to us. 24:27
Lord be *w.* between us. *Judg* 11:10
Jer 42:5
the Lord is *w.* against you this day.
1 Sam 12:5
wrinkles, which is a *w.* *Job* 16:8
behold, my *w.* is in heaven, my. 19
when the eye saw me, it gave *w.* to me. 29:11
established as a faithful *w.* *Ps* 89:37
a faithful *w.* will not lie, but a false *w.*
Pr 14:5
a true *w.* delivereth souls, but a deceitful *w.* 25*
an ungodly *w.* scorneth. 19:28
not *w.* against thy neighbour. 24:28
it shall be for a *w.* to the Lord of hosts. *Isa* 19:20
I have given him for a *w.* to. 55:4
I know, and am a *w.* *Jer* 29:23
Lord be a true and faithful *w.* 42:5
let the Lord God be *w.* *Mi* 1:2
Lord be *w.* between thee. *Mal* 2:14
I will be a swift *w.* against the. 3:5
be preached for a *w.* to. *Mat* 24:14*
the council sought for *w.* *Mark* 14:55
w. agreed not together. 56, 59
need we further *w.*? *Luke* 22:71
for a *w.* to bear *w.* *John* 1:7
and ye receive not our *w.* 3:11
to whom thou bearest *w.* 26
if I bear *w.* of myself, my *w.* 5:31
I know the *w.* he witnesseth of. 32
but I have greater *w.* than. 36
sent me hath borne *w.* of me. 37
ordained to be a *w.* with us. *Acts* 1:22
gave *w.* of the resurrection. 4:33
to him give all the prophets *w.* 10:43
he left not himself without *w.* 14:17
for thou shalt be his *w.* to all. 22:15
a minister and a *w.* of these. 26:16
God is my *w.* whom I serve. *Rom* 1:9
conscience also bearing *w.* 2:15; 9:1
this *w.* is true. Rebuke. *Tit* 1:13*
God also bearing them *w.* *Heb* 2:4
the Holy Ghost is a *w.* to us. 10:15
by which Abel obtained *w.* 11:4
shall be *w.* against you. *Jas* 5:3*
Peter a *w.* of the sufferings of Christ.
1 Pet 5:1
w. of men, the *w.* of God is greater, for this is the *w.* of. *1 John* 5:9
he that believeth hath the *w.* 10
borne *w.* of thy charity. *3 John* 6
who is the faithful *w.* *Rev* 1:5
these things saith the true *w.* 3:14
were beheaded for the *w.* 20:4*
see **bare, bear, beareth, false, tabernacle**

witness, *verb*

I call heaven and earth to *w.* against.
Deut 4:26
behold, here I am, *w.* *1 Sam* 12:3
their countenance doth *w.* *Isa* 3:9
I take to *w.* for thee? *Lam* 2:13*
what is it which these *w.* against?
Mat 26:62; *Mark* 14:60
thou not how many things they *w.* against? *Mat* 27:13; *Mark* 15:4*

witnessed

the men of Belial *w.* against Naboth.
1 Ki 21:13
being *w.* by the law and. *Rom* 3:21
who before Pontius Pilate *w.* a good confession. *1 Tim* 6:13
it is *w.* that he liveth. *Heb* 7:8

witnesses

to death by mouth of *w.* *Num* 35:30
at the mouth of two or three *w.*
Deut 17:6; 19:15; *2 Cor* 13:1
the hands of the *w.* shall be first upon him. *Deut* 17:7
are *w.* against yourselves that ye . . . We are *w.* *Josh* 24:22
ye are *w.* that I have bought.
Ruth 4:9, 10
and the elders said, We are *w.* 11
thou renewest thy *w.* *Job* 10:17
I took to me faithful *w.* *Isa* 8:2
nations bring forth their *w.* 43:9
ye are my *w.* saith the Lord. 10, 12
44:8
they are their own *w.*; they see. 44:9
evidence and took *w.* *Jer* 32:10, 12
field for money, and take *w.* 25, 44
mouth of two or three *w.* *Mat* 18:16
be *w.* to yourselves that ye. 23:31
what further need of *w.*? 26:65
Mark 14:63
and ye are *w.* of these. *Luke* 24:48
ye shall be *w.* to me in. *Acts* 1:8
this Jesus hath God raised up, whereof we all are *w.* 2:32; 3:15
we are his *w.* of these things. 5:32
10:39
w. laid down their clothes at. 7:58
but unto *w.* chosen before of. 10:41
his *w.* unto the people. 13:31
ye are *w.* and God also. *1 Thes* 2:10
receive no accusation but before two or three *w.* *1 Tim* 5:19
good profession before many *w.* 6:12
things heard of me among many *w.*
2 Tim 2:2
died without mercy under two or three *w.* *Heb* 10:28
with so great a cloud of *w.* 12:1
give power to my two *w.* *Rev* 11:3
see **false**

witnesseth

the witness that he *w.* *John* 5:32
save that Holy Ghost *w.* *Acts* 20:23*

witnessing

w. both to small and. *Acts* 26:22*

wits'

and are at their *w.* end. *Ps* 107:27

wittingly

guided his hands *w.* for. *Gen* 48:14

witty

I find out knowledge of *w.* inventions.
Pr 8:12*

wives

took unto him two *w.* *Gen* 4:19
they took them *w.* of all which. 6:2
give me my *w.* and children. 30:26
if thou take other *w.* besides. 31:50
that our *w.* and children. *Num* 14:3
nor shall he multiply *w.* *Deut* 17:17
if a man have two *w.*, one. 21:15
sons: for he had many *w.* *Judg* 8:30
how shall we do for *w.*? 21:7, 16
we may not give them *w.* of. 18
Elkanah. He had two *w.*; Hannah and Peninnah. *1 Sam* 1:2
also both of them David's *w.* 25:43
David took more *w.* out. *2 Sam* 5:13
I gave thee thy master's *w.* 12:8
Solomon had 700 *w.* *1 Ki* 11:3
his *w.* turned away his heart. 4
he sent unto me for my *w.* 20:7
Ashur had two *w.* *1 Chr* 4:5
the sons of Uzzi had many *w.* 7:4
Shaharaim had two *w.* 8:8
Rehoboam loved Maachah above all his *w.* *2 Chr* 11:21
and he desired many *w.* 23
Jehoiada took for him two *w.* 24:3
and our *w.* are in captivity for. 29:9
to put away all the *w.* *Ezra* 10:3, 44
the *w.* also and children. *Neh* 12:43*
I saw Jews that had married *w.* 13:23
the *w.* shall give to husbands honour.
Esth 1:20
take ye *w.*, and take *w.* *Jer* 29:6
wine, we, nor our *w.* nor sons. 35:8
his *w.* and concubines. *Dan* 5:2, 3
drank, they married *w.* *Luke* 17:27
us on our way, with *w.* *Acts* 21:5
they that have *w.* be as though they had none. *1 Cor* 7:29
w. submit yourselves to. *Eph* 5:22
Col 3:18; *1 Pet* 3:1
so let the *w.* be to their. *Eph* 5:24
refuse profane and old *w.'* *1 Tim* 4:7
by the conversation of *w.* *1 Pet* 3:1
see **strange**

their **wives**

little ones, and *their w.* took they.
Gen 34:29; *1 Sam* 30:3
they took their daughters to be *their w.* *Judg* 3:6
all Judah with *their w.* *2 Chr* 20:13
would put away *their w.* *Ezra* 10:19
a great cry of the people and of *their w.* *Neh* 5:1
their w. and daughters entered into an oath. 10:28
and *their w.* ravished. *Isa* 13:16
houses shall be turned to others, with *their* fields and *w.* *Jer* 6:12; 8:10
have none to bury *their w.* 14:16
let *their w.* be bereaved of. 18:21
the wickedness of *their w.* 44:9
men who knew *their w.* had. 15
nor take for *their w.* a. *Ezek* 44:22
cast them and *their w.* *Dan* 6:24
their w. shall mourn apart.
Zech 12:12, 13, 14
to love *their w.* as their. *Eph* 5:28
even so must *their w.* be grave, sober. *1 Tim* 3:11*

thy **wives**

I will take *thy w.* before thine eyes, . . . lie with *thy w.* *2 Sam* 12:11

saved the lives of *thy w.* *2 Sam* 19:5
gold is mine, and *thy w.* *1 Ki* 20:3
deliver me *thy w.* and children. 5
Lord will smite thy people and *thy w.* *2 Chr* 21:14
bring *thy w.* and children. *Jer* 38:23
thy w. and concubines. *Dan* 5:23

your **wives**

take waggons for *your w.* *Gen* 45:19
come not at *your w.* *Ex* 19:15*
your w. shall be widows. 22:24
golden earrings of *your w.* 32:2
your w. and your little ones and your cattle. *Deut* 3:19; *Josh* 1:14
your w.: shouldest enter into covenant with the Lord. *Deut* 29:11
fight for *your w.* and. *Neh* 4:14
wickedness of *your w.* *Jer* 44:9
Lord, saying; Ye and *your w.* 25
you to put away *your w.* *Mat* 19:8
husbands, love *your w.* *Eph* 5:25
Col 3:19

wizard

a *w.* shall surely be put. *Lev* 20:27
be found among you a *w.* *Deut* 18:11

wizards

nor seek after *w.* to be. *Lev* 19:31
the soul that turneth after *w.* 20:6
Saul had put *w.* out of the land. *1 Sam* 28:3, 9
Manasseh dealt with *w.* *2 Ki* 21:6
2 Chr 33:6
Josiah put the *w.* and. *2 Ki* 23:24
Seek unto *w.* that peep. *Isa* 8:19
shall seek to idols and *w.* 19:3

woe

w. to thee, Moab ! *Num* 21:29
Jer 48:46
w. unto us, for there hath. *1 Sam* 4:7
8; *Jer* 4:13; 6:4; *Lam* 5:16
who hath *w.*? who hath ? *Pr* 23:29
w. to him that is alone. *Eccl* 4:10
w. to thee, O land, when. 10:16
w. to their soul, for they. *Isa* 3:9
w. unto the wicked! it shall be. 11
w. to the multitude of. 17:12
w. to the land shadowing. 18:1
w. to the crown of pride, to. 28:1
w. to Ariel. 29:1
w. to the rebellious children. 30:1
w. to thee that spoilest. 33:1
w. to him that striveth with. 45:9
w. to him that saith to fatherless. 10
w. unto thee, O Jerusalem. *Jer* 13:27
w. to him that buildeth by. 22:13
w. to the pastors that destroy. 23:1
w. to Nebo. 48:1
written, mourning and *w.* *Ezek* 2:10
w. to foolish prophets, that. 13:3
w. to women that sew pillows. 18
w. w. to thee. 16:23
w. to bloody city. 24:6, 9; *Nah* 3:1
Howl, *W.* worth the day! *Ezek* 30:2
w. be to the shepherds that. 34:2
w. to you that desire the. *Amos* 5:18
w. to him that increaseth. *Hab* 2:6
w. to him that coveteth an evil. 9
w. to him that buildeth a town. 12
w. to him that giveth his. 15
w. to him that saith to the wood. 19
w. to the inhabitants of. *Zeph* 2:5
w. to her that is filthy. 3:1
w. to the idol shepherd. *Zech* 11:17
w. unto thee, Chorazin! *w.* unto thee. *Mat* 11:21; *Luke* 10:13
w. unto the world because of offences, *w.* *Mat* 18:7; *Luke* 17:1
w. unto you scribes and. *Mat* 23:13
14, 15 23, 25, 27, 29; *Luke* 11:44
w. unto you, ye blind guides, which say. *Mat* 23:16
but *w.* unto that man by. 26:24
Mark 14:21; *Luke* 22:22
w. unto you that are rich. *Luke* 6:24
w. to you that are full, *w.* to you. 25
w. unto you when all men speak. 26
but *w.* unto you Pharisees. 11:42, 43
he said, *W.* to you also. 46, 47, 52
I heard an angel flying, saying, *W. w. w.* *Rev* 8:13; 12:12
one *w.* is past. 9:12
the second *w.* is past. 11:14

woe *is me*

w. is me, that I sojourn. *Ps* 120:5
w. is me! for I am undone. *Isa* 6:5
w. is me now, for my soul. *Jer* 4:31
w. is me for my hurt. 10:19
w. is me, my mother. 15:10
w. is me, for the Lord hath. 45:3
w. is me! for I am as when. *Mi* 7:1

woe *unto me*

if I be wicked, *w. unto me.* *Job* 10:15
My leanness, *w. unto me.* *Isa* 24:16
w. unto me if I preach. *1 Cor* 9:16

woe *to them*

w. to them that join house to house. *Isa* 5:8
w. to them that rise up early in. 11
w. to them that draw iniquity. 18
w. to them that call evil good. 20
w. to them that are wise in their. 21
w. to them that are mighty to. 22
w. to them that decree. 10:1
w. to them that seek deep to. 29:15
w. to them that go down into. 31:1
w. to them, for their day. *Jer* 50:27
w. to them, for they have. *Hos* 7:13
w. to them when I depart from. 9:12
w. to them that are at. *Amos* 6:1
w. to them that devise. *Mi* 2:1
w. to them which are with child, and to them that give. *Mat* 24:19
Mark 13:17; *Luke* 21:23
w. unto them! for they have gone in the way of Cain. *Jude* 11

woeful

neither I desired the *w.* day. *Jer* 17:16

woes

behold, there come two *w.* *Rev* 9:12

wolf

In a country where a large part of wealth consisted of flocks of sheep the habits of wolves became thoroughly well known, and were often used as symbols of such habits and actions of mankind as might bear a resemblance to them, as Gen 49:27.

Isaiah describing the tranquillity of the reign of the Messiah, *says,* The *wolf* shall dwell with the lamb, and the leopard shall lie down with the kid, *etc.*, Isa 11:6. *Persecutors are elsewhere compared to wolves,* Mat 10:16, Behold, I send you forth as sheep in the midst of *wolves.*

shall ravin as a *w.* *Gen* 49:27
the *w.* shall dwell with. *Isa* 11:6
the *w.* and the lamb shall. 65:25
a *w.* of the evenings shall. *Jer* 5:6
but he that is an hireling, seeth the *w.* coming: and the *w.* *John* 10:12

wolves

her princes are like *w.* *Ezek* 22:27
fiercer than evening *w.* *Hab* 1:8
her judges evening *w.* *Zeph* 3:3
they are ravening *w.* *Mat* 7:15
as sheep in the midst of *w.* 10:16
as lambs among *w.* *Luke* 10:3
grievous *w.* shall enter in. *Acts* 20:29

woman

Woman *was created to be a companion and helper to man. She was equal to him in that authority and jurisdiction that God gave them over all other animals. But after the fall, God made her subject to the government of man,* Gen 3:16.

Weak and ineffectual men are sometimes spoken of as women, Isa 3:12; 19:16.

and the rib, taken from man, made he a *w.* *Gen* 2:22
she shall be called *W.*, she was. 23
between thee and the *w.* 3:15
the *w.* will not come. 24:5, 39
let the same be the *w.* the Lord. 44
and hurt a *w.* with child. *Ex* 21:22
nor shall a *w.* stand. *Lev* 18:23
with mankind as with a *w.* 20:13*
he shall set the *w.* *Num* 5:18, 30
the *w.* shall be a curse among. 27
brought a Midianitish *w.* in. 25:6
Phinehas thrust the *w.* through. 8
if a *w.* vow a vow unto the Lord. 30:3
now kill every *w.* that hath. 31:17
I took this *w.* and found. *Deut* 22:14
the *w.* took the two men. *Josh* 2:4
bring out thence the *w.* 6:22
Sisera into the hand of a *w.* *Judg* 4:9
a certain *w.* cast a piece of a millstone. 9:53; *2 Sam* 11:21
men say not of me, a *w.* *Judg* 9:54
man that spakest to the *w.*? 13:11
is there never a *w.* among ? 14:3
Samson loved a *w.* in the. 16:4
the *w.* in the dawning of the. 19:26
the *w.* was left of her sons. *Ruth* 1:5
know thou art a virtuous *w.* 3:11
w. like Rachel and Leah. 4:11
Hannah said, I am a *w.* of a sorrowful spirit. *1 Sam* 1:15
I am the *w.* that stood by thee. 26
Lord give thee seed of this *w.* 2:20
seek me a *w.* that hath a. 28:7
me concerning this *w.* *2 Sam* 3:8
from the roof David saw a *w.* 11:2
put now this *w.* out from me. 13:17
the *w.* spread a covering over. 17:19
then *w.* went unto all people. 20:22
I and this *w.* dwell in. *1 Ki* 3:17
herself to be another *w.* 14:5
the son of the *w.* fell sick. 17:17
where was a great *w.* *2 Ki* 4:8
there cried a *w.* saying, Help. 6:26
this is the *w.* 8:5
see this cursed *w.* 9:34
Athaliah that wicked *w.* *2 Chr* 24:7
if my heart have been deceived by a *w.* *Job* 31:9
pain as of a *w.* in travail. *Ps* 48:6
Isa 13:8; 21:3; 26:17; *Jer* 4:31
6:24; 13:21; 22:23; 30:6; 31:8
48:41; 49:22, 24; 50:43
thee from the evil *w.* *Pr* 6:24
met him a *w.* subtle of heart. 7:10
a foolish *w.* is clamorous. 9:13
a virtuous *w.* is a crown. 12:4; 31:10
every wise *w.* buildeth her. 14:1
than with a brawling *w.* in. 21:9, 19
who can find a virtuous *w.*? 31:10
a *w.* that feareth the Lord shall. 30
the *w.* whose heart is snares and nets. *Eccl* 7:26
but a *w.* among all those have I. 28
cry like a travailing *w.* *Isa* 42:14
or to the *w.*, What hast thou ? 45:10
can a *w.* forget her sucking ? 49:15
Lord hath called thee as a *w.* 54:6*
of Zion to a delicate *w.* *Jer* 6:2
created a new thing, a *w.* 31:22
Jerusalem is a menstruous *w.* *Lam* 1:17
imperious whorish *w.* *Ezek* 16:30†
unto her, as they go in to a *w.* 23:44
uncleanness of a removed *w.* 36:17
go yet, love a *w.* beloved. *Hos* 3:1
the sorrows of a travailing *w.* shall come upon. 13:13; *Mi* 4:9, 10
this is a *w.* that sitteth in. *Zech* 5:7
whoso looketh on a *w.* to lust after her. *Mat* 5:28
a *w.* which was diseased with an issue. 9:20; *Mark* 5:25; *Luke* 8:43
leaven, which a *w.* took. *Mat* 13:33
O *w.*, great is thy faith, be it. 15:28
and last of all the *w.* died also. 22:27
Mark 12:22; *Luke* 20:32
Why trouble ye the *w.*? *Mat* 26:10
this that this *w.* hath done shall. 13
if a *w.* shall put away. *Mark* 10:12
manner of *w.* this is ? *Luke* 7:39
Simon, Seest thou this *w.*? 44
ought not this *w.*, being a daughter of Abraham ? 13:16
w. what have I to do with thee ? *John* 2:4
askest drink of me who am a *w.*? 4:9
on him for the saying of the *w.* 39
brought to him a *w.* taken in. 8:3, 4
when Jesus saw none but the *w.* 10
he saith to his mother, *W.* 19:26
Dorcas: this *w.* was full. *Acts* 9:36
and a *w.* named Damaris. 17:34

the natural use of the *w.* *Rom* 1:27
the *w.* which hath an husband is. 7:2
for a man not to touch a *w.* *1 Cor* 7:1
every *w.* have her own husband. 2
but every *w.* that prayeth. 11:5
if the *w.* be not covered, let her. 6
the *w.* is the glory of the man. 7
man is not of the *w.*; but the *w.* 8
neither man for the *w.*; but the *w.* 9
the *w.* ought to have power on. 10
nevertheless, neither is the man without the *w.*, nor the *w.* 11
as the *w.* is of the man, even so is the man also by the *w.* 12
comely that a *w.* pray uncovered? 13
if a *w.* have long hair, it is a glory. 15
forth his Son, made of a *w.* *Gal* 4:4
then destruction cometh as travail on a *w.* *1 Thes* 5:3
I suffer not a *w.* to teach. *1 Tim* 2:12
the *w.* being deceived, was in the. 14
sufferest that *w.* Jezebel. *Rev* 2:20
there appeared *w.* clothed with. 12:1
the *w.* fled. 6
the earth helped the *w.* 16
dragon was wroth with the *w.* 17
I saw a *w.* sit on a scarlet. 17:3
a *w.* drunken. 6
I will tell the mystery of the *w.* 7
see **born, man, strange**

young **woman**

the seed which Lord shall give thee of this *young w.* *Ruth* 4:12

womankind

with mankind as with *w.* *Lev* 18:22

womb

two nations are in thy *w.* *Gen* 25:23
there were twins in her *w.* 24; 38:27
Lord opened Leah's *w.* 29:31
God opened Rachel's *w.* 30:22
of breasts, and of *w.* 49:25
openeth the *w.* is mine. *Ex* 13:2
are given me, instead of such as open every *w.*, even. *Num* 8:16
bless the fruit of thy *w.* *Deut* 7:13
Nazarite from the *w.* *Judg* 13:5, 7
any more sons in my *w.*? *Ruth* 1:11
had shut up her *w.* *1 Sam* 1:5, 6
why died I not from the *w.*? *Job* 3:11
brought me forth of the *w.*? 10:18
the *w.* shall forget him, he. 24:20
that made me in the *w.* make him? fashion us in the *w.*? 31:15
if it had issued out of the *w.* 38:8
out of whose *w.* came the ice? 29
who took me out of the *w.* *Ps* 22:9
I was cast upon thee from the *w.* 10
are estranged from the *w.* 58:3
I been holden up from the *w.* 71:6
from the *w.* of the morning. 110:3
the barren *w.* saith not, It. *Pr* 30:16
what, the son of my *w.*? 31:2
nor how bones grow in *w.* *Eccl* 11:5
Lord formed thee from the *w.* *Isa* 44:2, 24; 49:5
which are carried from the *w.* 46:3
a transgressor from the *w.* 48:8
called me from the *w.* 49:1
compassion on the son of her *w.*? 15
bring forth, and shut the *w.*? 66:9
camest forth out of the *w.* *Jer* 1:5
because he slew me not from the *w.*; or my mother's *w.* to be. 20:17
why came I forth of the *w.*? 18
pass through the fire all that openeth the *w.* *Ezek* 20:26
their glory shall fly away from the birth and *w.* *Hos* 9:11*
give them a miscarrying *w.* 14
brother by the heel in the *w.* 12:3
shalt conceive in thy *w.* *Luke* 1:31
leaped in her *w.* for joy. 41, 44
he was conceived in the *w.* 2:21
every male that openeth the *w.* 23
see **fruit, mother**

wombs

fast closed up all the *w.* *Gen* 20:18
blessed are the *w.* that. *Luke* 23:29

women

the time that *w.* go out to. *Gen* 24:11
all the *w.* went out after. *Ex* 15:20
w. that were wise hearted. 35:25
all the *w.* whose heart stirred. 26
ten *w.* shall bake your bread in one oven. *Lev* 26:26
Moses said, Have ye saved all the *w.* alive? *Num* 31:15
the *w.* and little ones. *Deut* 20:14
the law before the *w.* *Josh* 8:35
blessed above *w.* shall Jael wife of. *Judg* 5:24
they saved alive of the *w.* of. 21:14
they lay with the *w.* *1 Sam* 2:22
as thy sword hath made *w.* 15:33
the *w.* came out of the cities. 18:6
the *w.* answered one another as. 7
kept themselves from *w.* 21:4
of a truth *w.* have been kept. 5
Amalekites had taken the *w.* 30:2
passing the love of *w.* *2 Sam* 1:26
the king left ten *w.* to keep. 15:16
then came two *w.* that. *1 Ki* 3:16
and rip up their *w.* with child. *2 Ki* 8:12, 15, 16
where the *w.* wove hangings. 23:7
even him did outlandish *w.* cause to sin. *Neh* 13:26
made a feast for the *w.* *Esth* 1:9
loved Esther above all the *w.* 2:17
little children and *w.* 3:13; 8:11
no *w.* found so fair as. *Job* 42:15
among thy honourable *w.* *Ps* 45:9
give not thy strength to *w.* *Pr* 31:3
O thou fairest among *w.* *S of S* 1:8
5:9; 6:1
as for my people, *w.* rule. *Isa* 3:12
in that day seven *w.* shall take. 4:1
day Egypt shall be like to *w.* 19:16
the *w.* come, and set them. 27:11
rise up, ye *w.* that are at ease. 32:9
careless *w.* 10
tremble, ye *w.* that are at ease. 11
the *w.* knead their dough. *Jer* 7:18
mourning and cunning *w.* 9:17
word of the Lord, O ye *w.* 20
w. left, shall be brought to. 38:22
Jeremiah said to all the *w.* 44:24
they shall become as *w.* and. 50:37
men of Babylon became as *w.* 51:30
shall the *w.* eat children? *Lam* 2:20
the pitiful *w.* have sodden. 4:10
they ravished *w.* in Zion, and. 5:11
there sat *w.* weeping. *Ezek* 8:14
maids, little children, and *w.* 9:6
woe to *w.* that sew pillows to. 13:18
is in thee from other *w.* 16:34
I will judge thee as *w.* that. 38
there were two *w.*, daughters. 23:2
judge after the manner of *w.* 45
w. may be taught not to do after. 48
he shall give him the daughter of *w.* *Dan* 11:17
nor shall regard the desire of *w.* 37
their *w.* with child shall. *Hos* 13:16
because they have ripped up *w.* with child. *Amos* 1:13
the *w.* of my people have. *Mi* 2:9
in the midst of thee are *w.* *Nah* 3:13
two *w.* and had wings. *Zech* 5:9
old *w.* shall dwell in the streets. 8:4
the houses rifled, the *w.* shall. 14:2
that are born of *w.* there hath not risen a greater. *Mat* 11:11; *Luke* 7:28
they that had eaten were 5000 men, besides *w.* *Mat* 14:21; 15:38
two *w.* grinding at the mill. 24:41
Luke 17:35
and many *w.* were then. *Mat* 27:55
blessed art thou among *w.* *Luke* 1:28, 42
certain *w.* also made us. 24:22
and found it even so as the *w.* 24
in prayer with the *w.* *Acts* 1:14
stirred up the devout *w.* 13:50
we spake to the *w.* which. 16:13
of the chief *w.* not a few. 17:4, 12
their *w.* did change the. *Rom* 1:26
let your *w.* keep silence. *1 Cor* 14:34
shame for *w.* to speak in churches. 35
help those *w.* which laboured with me. *Phil* 4:3
w. adorn themselves in. *1 Tim* 2:9
which becometh *w.* professing. 10
let the *w.* learn in silence with. 11
intreat the elder *w.* as mothers. 5:2
that the younger *w.* marry. 14*
captive silly *w.* laden. *2 Tim* 3:6
aged *w.* behave as becometh. *Tit* 2:3
they may teach the younger *w.* 4
w. received their dead. *Heb* 11:35
the holy *w.* adorned. *1 Pet* 3:5
they had hair as hair of *w.* *Rev* 9:8
that are not defiled with *w.* 14:4
see **children, men, singing, strange**

womenservants

gave *w.* to Abraham. *Gen* 20:14
had menservants and *w.* 32:5*

won

out of the spoils *w.* in. *1 Chr* 26:27
a brother offended is harder to be *w.* *Pr* 18:19
w. by the conversation. *1 Pet* 3:1*

wonder

give thee a sign or a *w.* *Deut* 13:1
and the sign or the *w.* come. 2
upon thee for a sign and a *w.* 28:46
him to enquire of the *w.* *2 Chr* 32:31
I am as a *w.* to many. *Ps* 71:7
walked barefoot for a *w.* *Isa* 20:3
marvellous work and a *w.* 29:14
they were filled with *w.* *Acts* 3:10
a great *w.* in heaven. *Rev* 12:1*, 3*

wonder, *verb*

stay yourselves, and *w.*; cry. *Isa* 29:9
the prophets shall *w.* *Jer* 4:9
behold ye, regard and *w.* *Hab* 1:5
behold, ye despisers, *w.* *Acts* 13:41
dwell on the earth shall *w.* *Rev* 17:8

wondered

he *w.* there was no. *Isa* 59:16
I *w.* that there was none. 63:5
for they are men *w.* at. *Zech* 3:8*
all they that heard it *w.* *Luke* 2:18
they all *w.* at the gracious. 4:22
believed not for joy, and *w.* 24:41
Moses *w.* *Acts* 7:31
Simon [Magus] *w.* 8:13*
all the world *w.* after. *Rev* 13:3
I saw her, I *w.* with great. 17:6

wonderful

make thy plagues *w.* *Deut* 28:59
thy love to me was *w.* *2 Sam* 1:26
house . . . shall be *w.* great. *2 Chr* 2:9
things too *w.* for me. *Job* 42:3
thy testimonies are *w.* *Ps* 119:129
knowledge is too *w.* for me. 139:6
there be three things that are too *w.* *Pr* 30:18
his name shall be called *W.* *Isa* 9:6
for thou hast done *w.* things. 25:1
of hosts who is *w.* in counsel. 28:29
a *w.* thing is committed. *Jer* 5:30
when they saw the *w.* *Mat* 21:15
see **works**

wonderfully

when he had wrought *w.* *1 Sam* 6:6
thee for I am *w.* made. *Ps* 139:14
Jerusalem came down *w.* *Lam* 1:9
he shall destroy *w.* and. *Dan* 8:24

wondering

the man *w.* at her, held. *Gen* 24:21*
Peter *w.* at that which was come to pass. *Luke* 24:12
ran together greatly *w.* *Acts* 3:11

wonderously, wondrously

angel did *w.*: Manoah. *Judg* 13:19*
the Lord hath dealt *w.* *Joel* 2:26

wonders

my hand and smite Egypt with all my *w.* *Ex* 3:20; 7:3; 11:9
Deut 6:22; 7:19; 26:8; 34:11
see thou do those *w.* *Ex* 4:21
did these *w.* 11:10
fearful in praises, doing *w.*? 15:11
hath God assayed to go and take a nation by *w.*? *Deut* 4:34
to-morrow the Lord will do *w.* among you. *Josh* 3:5
remember his *w.* *1 Chr* 16:12
Ps 105:5
thou shewedst *w.* upon. *Neh* 9:10
nor were mindful of thy *w.* 17
Ps 78:11, 43
doeth *w.* without number. *Job* 9:10
remember thy *w.* of old. *Ps* 77:11
thou art the God that doest *w.* 14
shew *w.* to the dead? 88:10

shall thy *w.* be known in the? *Ps* 88:12
shall praise thy *w.* O Lord. 89:5
his *w.* among all people. 96:3*
they shewed his *w.* in the. 105:27
our fathers understood not thy *w.* in Egypt. 106:7
see his works and his *w.* 107:24
who sent *w.* into the midst of. 135:9
who alone doeth great *w.* 136:4
I and the children are for *w.* in Israel. *Isa* 8:18
who hath set signs and *w. Jer* 32:20
brought forth thy people with *w.* 21
to shew the signs and *w. Dan* 4:2
signs! how mighty his *w.*! 3
he worketh *w.* in heaven. 6:27
it be to the end of these *w.*? 12:6
I will shew *w.* in heaven. *Joel* 2:30 *Acts* 2:19
false prophets, and shall shew great *w. Mat* 24:24; *Mark* 13:22
Except ye see signs and *w. John* 4:48
approved of God by *w. Acts* 2:22
fear on every soul, many signs and *w.* were. 43; 5:12; 14:3; 15:12
that *w.* may be done by the. 4:30
Stephen did great *w.* among. 6:8
after he had shewed *w.* in the land of Egypt. 7:36
obedient through *w. Rom* 15:19
an apostle wrought in *w. 2 Cor* 12:12
is with signs and lying *w. 2 Thes* 2:9
witness with signs and *w. Heb* 2:4
he doeth great *w.*, so that he maketh fire come down. *Rev* 13:13*

wondrous

sing psalms, talk ye of all his *w.* *1 Chr* 16:9; *Ps* 26:7; 105:2 119:27; 145:5
consider the *w.* works. *Job* 37:14
dost thou know the *w.* works? 16
I declared thy *w.* works. *Ps* 71:17
the God of Israel, who only doeth *w.* things. 72:18; 86:10
that thy name is near, thy *w.* 75:1
they believed not for his *w.* 78:32
who had done *w.* works in. 106:22
that I may behold *w.* things. 119:18
according to his *w.* works. *Jer* 21:2

wont

if the ox were *w.* to push. *Ex* 21:29
was I ever *w.* to do so to thee? *Num* 22:30
where David and his men were *w.* to haunt. *1 Sam* 30:31
were *w.* to speak in. *2 Sam* 20:18
seven times more than *w. Dan* 3:19
the governor was *w.* to. *Mat* 27:15
as he was *w.*, he taught. *Mark* 10:1
he went as he was *w.* to. *Luke* 22:39*
where prayer was *w.* to. *Acts* 16:13

wood

Abraham took *w.* and put. *Gen* 22:6
Behold the fire and the *w.* 7
whether there be *w. Num* 13:20
things that are made of *w.* 31:20
make thee an ark of *w. Deut* 10:1
goeth into a *w.* to hew *w.* 19:5*
from the hewer of thy *w.* 29:11 *Josh* 9:21, 23, 27; *Jer* 46:22
the mountain is a *w. Josh* 17:18*
and they clave the *w. 1 Sam* 6:14
they of the land came to a *w.* 14:25
went to David into the *w.* 23:16
the *w.* devoured more. *2 Sam* 18:8*
lay the bullock on *w. 1 Ki* 18:23
she bears out of the *w. 2 Ki* 2:24
I have prepared *w.* for things of *w.* *1 Chr* 29:2
the boar out of the *w. Ps* 80:13
it in the fields of the *w.* 132:6
as when one cleaveth *w.* 141:7
where no *w.* is, there the. *Pr* 26:20
as *w.* to fire, so is a contentious. 21
he that cleaveth *w.* shall. *Eccl* 10:9
itself as if it were no *w. Isa* 10:15
thereof is fire and much *w.* 30:33
they that set up the *w.* of. 45:20
will bring silver, for *w.* brass. 60:17
I will make my words fire, this people *w. Jer* 5:14
the children gather *w.*, the. 7:18
the yokes of *w.* but shalt. 28:13
shall *w.* be taken thereof to do any work? *Ezek* 15:3
heap on *w.* 24:10
no *w.* out of the field. 39:10
dwell solitary in the *w. Mi* 7:14*
that saith to the *w.* Awake. *Hab* 2:19
go up, bring *w.* and build. *Hag* 1:8
hearth of fire among the *w. Zech* 12:6
on this foundation, *w.*, hay. *1 Cor* 3:12
but also vessels of *w. 2 Tim* 2:20
see **offering, stone**

woods

sleep safely in the *w. Ezek* 34:25

woof

be in the warp or *w. Lev* 13:48
be spread in the warp or the *w.* 51
whether warp or *w.* 52
be not spread, wash the *w.* 53, 58
rend it out of the warp or *w.* 56
of leprosy in the warp or *w.* 59

wool

I will put a fleece of *w. Judg* 6:37
100,000 rams with *w. 2 Ki* 3:4
giveth snow like *w. Ps* 147:16
she seeketh *w.* and flax. *Pr* 31:13
like crimson, shall be as *w. Isa* 1:18
like *w.*: but my righteousness. 51:8
was thy merchant in *w. Ezek* 27:18
ye clothe you with the *w.* 34:3
and no *w.* shall come upon. 44:17
the hair of his head like *w. Dan* 7:9 *Rev* 1:14
lovers that give me my *w. Hos* 2:5
I will recover my *w.* and my flax. 9

woollen

whether *w.* or linen. *Lev* 13:47, 59
the warp or woof of *w.* 48, 52
mingled of linen and *w.* come upon thee. 19:19*; *Deut* 22:11

word

(Word, *the Greek* logos, *is sometimes used of Jesus Christ,* John 1. The word of God *is a name often given to the scriptures, and the law of God*)

go and bring me *w.* again. *Gen* 37:14 *Mat* 2:8
O my lord, let me speak a *w.* *Gen* 44:18; *2 Sam* 14:12
according to *w.* of Moses. *Ex* 8:13
Israel did according to the *w.* 12:35
Levi did according to the *w.* 32:28 *Lev* 10:7
they brought back *w. Num* 13:26
lodge here, I will bring you *w.* 22:8 *Deut* 1:22
yet the *w.* I shall say to. *Num* 22:20
the *w.* I shall speak. 35
the *w.* God putteth. 38
the Lord put a *w.* in Balaam's. 23:5
they brought us *w.* again. *Deut* 1:25
ye shall not add unto the *w.* I. 4:2
but by every *w.* that proceedeth out. 8:3*; *Mat* 4:4
presume to speak a *w. Deut* 18:20
how shall we know the *w.*? 21 *Jer* 28:9
by their *w.* shall every controversy be tried. *Deut* 21:5
the *w.* is nigh thee. 30:14; *Rom* 10:8
remember the *w.* Moses. *Josh* 1:13
not a *w.* which Joshua read not. 8:35
I brought him *w.* 14:7
brought them *w.* 22:32
the *w.* of Samuel came. *1 Sam* 4:1
not answer Abner a *w. 2 Sam* 3:11
in all places spake I a *w.* 7:7 *1 Chr* 17:6
the *w.* thou hast spoken concerning thy servant. *2 Sam* 7:25
till there come *w.* from you. 15:28
speak ye not a *w.* of bringing. 19:10
the king's *w.* prevailed. 24:4 *1 Chr* 21:4
brought the king *w.* again. *1 Ki* 2:30 *2 Ki* 22:9, 20; *2 Chr* 34:16, 28
w. that I have heard is good. *1 Ki* 2:42*
hath not failed one *w.* of all. 8:56
the people answered not a *w.* 18:21 *Isa* 36:21
he smote according to the *w.* of Elisha. *2 Ki* 6:18
hear the *w.* of the great king. 18:28
mindful of the *w.* which he commanded. *1 Chr* 16:15; *Ps* 105:8
advise what *w.* I shall. *1 Chr* 21:12*
remember, the *w.* that thou. *Neh* 1:8
he did according to the *w. Esth* 1:21
as the *w.* went out of the king's. 7:8
none spake a *w.* to Job. *Job* 2:13
by the *w.* of thy lips, I have. *Ps* 17:4
the Lord gave the *w.* 68:11
remember the *w.* unto thy. 119:49
mine eyes fail for the *w.* of thy. 123
not a *w.* in my tongue. 139:4
a good *w.* maketh the. *Pr* 12:25
whoso despiseth the *w.* shall. 13:13
simple believe the *w.* but. 14:15
w. spoken in due season, how! 15:23
a *w.* fitly spoken is like apples. 25:11
where the *w.* of a king is. *Eccl* 8:4
despised *w.* of the Holy. *Isa* 5:24
speak *w.* and it shall not stand. 8:10
the Lord sent a *w.* to Jacob, it. 9:8
man an offender for a *w.* 29:21
thine ears shall hear a *w.* 30:21
counsellor could answer a *w.* 41:28
that confirmeth the *w.* of. 44:26
w. is gone out of my mouth. 45:23
should know how to speak a *w.* 50:4
become wind, and the *w. Jer* 5:13
let your ear receive *w.* 9:20; 10:1
nor shall the *w.* perish from. 18:18
for every man's *w.* shall be. 23:36
them, diminish not a *w.* 26:2
for I have pronounced the *w.* 34:5
king said, Is there any *w.*? 37:17
for the *w.* thou hast spoken. 44:16
therefore hear the *w.* at my mouth. *Ezek* 3:17; 33:7
the *w.* that I shall speak. 12:25
the *w.* that I have spoken shall. 28
would confirm the *w.* 13:6
hear what is *w.* that cometh. 33:30
changed the king's *w. Dan* 3:28
the demand is by the *w.* of. 4:17
while the *w.* was in the king's. 31
for *w.* came to the king. *Jonah* 3:6
to the *w.* I covenanted. *Hag* 2:5
speak the *w.* only, he shall. *Mat* 8:8
whoso speaketh a *w.* against the Son of man. 12:32; *Luke* 12:10
every idle *w.* men. *Mat* 12:36
when any one heareth the *w.* of the kingdom. 13:19, 20, 22, 23 *Mark* 4:16, 18, 20; *Luke* 8:15
or persecution ariseth because of the *w.*, he. *Mat* 13:21; *Mark* 4:17
he answered her not a *w.* *Mat* 15:23
that every *w.* may be established. 18:16; *2 Cor* 13:1
able to answer him a *w. Mat* 22:46
he answered him to never a *w.* 27:14
to bring his disciples *w.* 28:8
sower soweth the *w. Mark* 4:14
Peter called to mind the *w.* 14:72
the Lord confirming the *w.* 16:20
saying, What a *w.* is this! *Luke* 4:36
say in a *w.* and my servant shall. 7:7
Jesus, a prophet mighty in *w.* 24:19
the *W.* and the *W.* was with God, and the *W.* was God. *John* 1:1
the *W.* was made flesh, and. 14
they believed the *w.* that Jesus said. 2:22; 4:50
w. I have spoken shall judge. 12:48
w. which ye hear is not mine. 14:24
ye are clean through the *w.* I. 15:3
remember the *w.* that I said. 20
that *w.* might be fulfilled, written. 25
believe on me through their *w.* 17:20
the *w.* which God sent to. *Acts* 10:36
if ye have any *w.* of exhortation, say on. 13:15
to you is the *w.* of this salvation. 26
by my mouth, should hear *w.* 15:7
they received the *w.* with all. 17:11
I commend you to the *w.* of. 20:32
Paul had spoken one *w.* 28:25
that is, the *w.* of faith. *Rom* 10:8
make Gentiles obedient by *w.* 15:18
kingdom of God is not in *w.* *1 Cor* 4:20

w. of wisdom, to another the *w.* of knowledge. *1 Cor* 12:8
w. toward you was not. *2 Cor* 1:18
God committed to us the *w.* of. 5:19
such as we are in *w.* by letters. 10:11
law is fulfilled in one *w.* *Gal* 5:14
let him that is taught in the *w.* 6:6
washing of water by the *w.* *Eph* 5:26
are bold to speak the *w.* *Phil* 1:14
holding forth the *w.* of life to. 2:16
heard in the *w.* of the truth. *Col* 1:5
let the *w.* of Christ dwell in. 3:16
whatsoever ye do in *w.* or deed. 17
our gospel came not to you in *w.* only. *1 Thes* 1:5
having received the *w.* in much. 6
w. . . , ye receive it not as *w.* of men, but as it is in truth, *w.* of God. 2:13
not by Spirit, nor by *w.* *2 Thes* 2:2
have been taught, whether by *w.* 15
and stablish you in every good *w.* 17
if any man obey not our *w.* by. 3:14
be thou an example of believers in *w.* *1 Tim* 4:12
they who labour in the *w.* 5:17
their *w.* will eat as doth. *2 Tim* 2:17
preach *w.*; be instant in season. 4:2
holding fast the faithful *w.* *Tit* 1:9
upholding all things by the *w.* of his power. *Heb* 1:3
if the *w.* spoken by angels was. 2:2
but the *w.* preached did not. 4:2
is unskilful in the *w.* of. 5:13
but the *w.* of the oath, which. 7:28
intreated *w.* should not be. 12:19
brethren, suffer the *w.* of. 13:22
meekness the ingrafted *w.* *Jas* 1:21
be ye doers of the *w.* and not. 22
if any be a hearer of the *w.* and. 23
if any man offend not in *w.*, the. 3:2
the sincere milk of the *w.* *1 Pet* 2:2
who stumble at the *w.* being. 8
not the *w.*, may without the *w.* 3:1
we have a more sure *w.* of prophecy. *2 Pet* 1:19
the heavens by the same *w.* are. 3:7
handled, of the *w.* of life. *1 John* 1:1
let us not love in *w.* but in. 3:18
the Father, the *W.* and. 5:7
because thou hast kept *w.* *Rev* 3:10
they overcame by the *w.* of. 12:11

word *of God*

that I may shew thee the *w. of God.* *1 Sam* 9:27
the *w. of God* came to Shemaiah, *1 Ki* 12:22
the *w. of God* came to Nathan. *1 Chr* 17:3
every *w. of God* is pure. *Pr* 30:5
the *w. of* our *God* shall. *Isa* 40:8
making the *w. of God.* *Mark* 7:13
w. of God came unto John. *Luke* 3:2
alone, but by every *w. of God.* 4:4
on him to hear the *w. of God.* 5:1
the seed is the *w. of God.* 8:11
these that hear the *w. of God.* 21
they that hear the *w. of God.* 11:28
gods to whom *w. of God.* *John* 10:35
they spake the *w. of God.* *Acts* 4:31
should leave the *w. of God.* 6:2
the *w. of God* increased. 7; 12:24
Samaria had received the *w. of God.* 8:14
Gentiles had received the *w. of God.* 11:1
desired to hear the *w. of God.* 13:7
city came to hear the *w. of God.* 44
w. of God should have been first. 46
mightily grew the *w. of God.* 19:20
not as though the *w. of God* hath taken none effect. *Rom* 9:6
hearing by the *w. of God.* 10:17
came the *w. of God* out from you? *1 Cor* 14:36
corrupt the *w. of God.* *2 Cor* 2:17
not handling the *w. of God.* 4:2
and the sword of the Spirit, which is the *w. of God.* *Eph* 6:17
which is given me to fulfil the *w. of God.* *Col* 1:25
received the *w. of God.* *1 Thes* 2:13
it is sanctified by the *w. of God* and prayer. *1 Tim* 4:5
but the *w. of God* is not bound. *2 Tim* 2:9
the *w. of God* be not blasphemed. *Tit* 2:5
the *w. of God* is quick. *Heb* 4:12
tasted the good *w. of God.* 6:5
framed by the *w. of God.* 11:3
spoken to you the *w. of God.* 13:7
being born again by the *w. of God.* *1 Pet* 1:23
by the *w. of God* the heavens were of old. *2 Pet* 3:5
are strong, and the *w. of God* abideth in you. *1 John* 2:14
record of the *w. of God.* *Rev* 1:2
isle of Patmos, for the *w. of God.* 9
that were slain for *w. of God.* 6:9
name is called the *w. of God.* 19:13
beheaded for the *w. of God.* 20:4

see **heard**

his **word**

at *his w.* shall they go out, and at *his w.* they shall come. *Num* 27:21
he shall not break *his w.* 30:2
the Lord stablish *his w.* *1 Sam* 1:23
his w. was in my tongue. *2 Sam* 23:2
may continue *his w.* *1 Ki* 2:4
the Lord hath performed *his w.* that he spake. 8:20; *2 Chr* 6:10
to enquire of *his w.* *2 Ki* 1:16
might perform *his w.* *2 Chr* 10:15
in God I will praise *his w.*, in God I have put my trust. *Ps* 56:4, 10
unto the voice of *his w.* 103:20
the time that *his w.* came. 105:19
rebelled not against *his w.* 28
they believed not *his w.* but. 106:24
he sent *his w.* and healed. 107:20
I wait for the Lord and in *his w.* do I hope. 130:5
his w. runneth very swiftly. 147:15
sendeth out *his w.* and melteth. 18
he sheweth *his w.* unto Jacob. 19
wind fulfilling *his w.* 148:8
that tremble at *his w.* *Isa* 66:5
but *his w.* was in my heart as a fire. *Jer* 20:9
he hath fulfilled *his w.* *Lam* 2:17
that executeth *his w.* *Joel* 2:11
out the spirits with *his w.* *Mat* 8:16
for *his w.* was with power. *Luke* 4:32
many believed because of *his* own *w.* *John* 4:41
ye have not *his w.* abiding. 5:38
gladly received *his w.* *Acts* 2:41
but hath in due times manifested *his w.* *Tit* 1:3
whoso keepeth *his w.* *1 John* 2:5

see **Lord**

my **word**

whether *my w.* shall come to pass. *Num* 11:23
ye rebelled against *my w.* 20:24
will I perform *my w.* *1 Ki* 6:12
rain, but according to *my w.* 17:1
so shall *my w.* be that goeth forth out of my mouth. *Isa* 55:11
him that trembleth at *my w.* 66:2
hasten *my w.* to perform. *Jer* 1:12
my w., let him speak *my w.* 23:28
is not *my w.* like as a fire? 29
the prophets that steal *my w.* 30
I will perform *my* good *w.* 29:10
but *my w.* shall not pass. *Mat* 24:35
he that heareth *my w.* *John* 5:24
continue in *my w.*, then are ye. 8:31
kill me because *my w.* hath. 37
ye cannot hear *my w.* 43
thou hast kept *my w.*, and hast not denied my name. *Rev* 3:8

this **word**

is not *this* the *w.* that? *Ex* 14:12
since the Lord spake *this w.* to Moses. *Josh* 14:10
they sent *this w.* to the king. *2 Sam* 19:14*
hast not spoken *this w.* *1 Ki* 2:23
this is the *w.* that the Lord hath spoken of him. *2 Ki* 19:21
Isa 16:13; 24:3; 37:22
shall alter *this w.* *Ezra* 6:11
should do according to *this w.* 10:5
not according to *this w.* *Isa* 8:20
because ye despise *this w.* *Isa* 30:12
ye speak *this w.* *Jer* 5:14; 23:38
proclaim there *this w.* and say. 7:2
speak unto them *this w.* 13:12
thou say *this w.* to them. 14:17
down, and speak there *this w.* 22:1
in the reign of Jehoiakim *this w.* came. 26:1; 27:1; 34:8; 36:1
hear now *this w.* 28:7; *Amos* 3:1; 4:1; 5:1
spoken *this w.* to me. *Dan* 10:11
this is the *w.* of the Lord. *Zech* 4:6
him audience to *this w.* *Acts* 22:22
for *this* is *w.* of promise. *Rom* 9:9
this w., Yet once more. *Heb* 12:27
this is the *w.* which is. *1 Pet* 1:25

thy **word**

be according to *thy w.* *Gen* 30:34
according to *thy w.* shall my. 41:40
Be it according to *thy w.* *Ex* 8:10
I have pardoned, according to *thy w.* *Num* 14:20
have observed *thy w.* *Deut* 33:9
done according to *thy w.* *1 Ki* 3:12
let *thy w.* I pray thee, be. 8:26
done all these things at *thy w.* 18:36
let *thy w.* I pray thee, be like the word of one of. 22:13; *2 Chr* 18:12
heed according to *thy w.* *Ps* 119:9
thy w. have I hid in mine heart. 11
statutes, I will not forget *thy w* 16
live, and keep *thy w.* 17, 101
quicken me according to *thy w.* 25, 107, 154
strengthen thou me according to *thy w.* 28, 116
stablish *thy w.* 38
salvation according to *thy w.* 41
I trust in *thy w.* 42
comfort in affliction, for *thy w.* 50
be merciful to me according to *thy w.* 58, 65, 76
but now have I kept *thy w.* 67
I have hoped in *thy w.* 74, 147
I hope in *thy w.* 81, 114
mine eyes fail for *thy w.* 82
ever, O Lord, *thy w.* is settled. 89
thy w. is a lamp. 105
order my steps in *thy w.*, let not. 133
thy w. is pure. 140
that I might meditate in *thy w.* 148
because they kept not *thy w.* 158
thy w. is true. 160
standeth in awe of *thy w.* 161
I rejoice at *thy w.* 162
give me understanding according to *thy w.* 169
deliver me according to *thy w.* 170
my tongue shall speak of *thy w.* 172
thou hast magnified *thy w.* 138:2
thy w. was to me the joy. *Jer* 15:16
drop *thy w.* toward the south. *Ezek* 20:46
drop *thy w.* toward the holy. 21:2
drop not *thy w.* against. *Amos* 7:16
made naked, even *thy w.* *Hab* 3:9
according to *thy w.* *Luke* 1:38
in peace, according to *thy w.* 2:29
nevertheless at *thy w.* I will let. 5:5
and they have kept *thy w.* *John* 17:6
I have given them *thy w.* 14
thy w. is truth. 17
with all boldness they may speak *thy w.* *Acts* 4:29

see **truth**

words

shalt put *w.* in his mouth. *Ex* 4:15
let them not regard vain *w.* 5:9
returned the *w.* of the people. 19:8
the gift perverteth the *w.* of the righteous. 23:8; *Deut* 16:19
the *w.* which were in the first tables. *Ex* 34:1
Moses wrote the *w.* of the covenant. 28; *Deut* 10:2
I sent to Sihon with *w.* *Deut* 2:26
go aside from any of the *w.* 28:14
keep the *w.* of his covenant. 29:9
2 Ki 23:3, 24; *2 Chr* 34:31
hear, O earth, the *w.* of. *Deut* 32:1
Ps 54:2; 78:1; *Pr* 7:24
Saul was afraid of the *w.* of Samuel. *1 Sam* 28:20

the *w.* of men of Judah were fiercer. *2 Sam* 19:43
w. of prophets declare good to the king. *1 Ki* 22:13; *2 Chr* 18:12
Elisha telleth the *w.* *2 Ki* 6:12
but they are but vain *w.* 18:20
Isa 36:5
sing praises with the *w.* *2 Chr* 29:30
the people rested on the *w.* 32:8
he sent letters with *w.* of peace and truth. *Esth* 9:30
ye imagine to reprove *w.*? *Job* 6:26
shall *w.* of thy mouth be like ? 8:2
not the ear try *w.*? 12:11; 34:3
thou lettest such *w.* go out. 15:13
shall vain *w.* have an end ? 16:3
I could heap up *w.* against you. 4
ere ye make an end of *w.*? 18:2
ye break me in pieces with *w.*? 19:2
I would know the *w.* he would. 23:5
I have esteemed the *w.* of his. 12
he multiplieth *w.* without. 35:16
darkeneth counsel by *w.*? 38:2
let the *w.* of my mouth. *Ps* 19:14
why so far from the *w.* of ? 22:1
the *w.* of his mouth are iniquity. 36:3
thou lovest all devouring *w.* 52:4
w. of his mouth were smoother than butter. 55:21
for *w.* of their lips, let them. 59:12
to understand the *w.* of. *Pr* 1:6
decline not from the *w.* 4:5; 5:7
thou art snared with the *w.* of. 6:2
in multitude of *w.* there wanteth not sin. 10:19
w. of the wicked are to lie in wait for blood. 12:6
w. of the pure are pleasant *w.* 15:26
the *w.* of a man's mouth are as. 18:4
w. of a talebearer are as wounds. 8; 26:22
he pursueth them with *w.* 19:7
he causeth thee to err from *w.* 27
he overthroweth the *w.* of the. 22:12
bow down thine ear, hear the *w.* 17
certainty of the *w.* of truth; that thou mightest answer the *w.* of. 21
thou shalt lose thy sweet *w.* 23:8
will not be corrected by *w.* 29:19
a fool's voice is known by multitude of *w.* *Eccl* 5:3; 10:14
the *w.* of a wise man's mouth. 10:12
find out acceptable *w.*: that which was written, even *w.* of truth. 12:10
the *w.* of the wise are as goads. 11
become as the *w.* of a book sealed. *Isa* 29:11
it may be God will hear the *w.* 37:4
uttering from the heart *w.* of. 59:13
w. of this covenant. *Jer* 11:2, 6
because of the Lord, and the *w.* 23:9
w. of Jonadab son of Rechab. 35:14
remnant shall know whose *w.* 44:28
whose *w.* thou canst not. *Ezek* 3:6
shall speak great *w.* against most High. *Dan* 7:25
shut up the *w.* 12:4
the *w.* are closed up. 9
I have slain them by the *w.* of my mouth. *Hos* 6:5
take with you *w.* and turn to. 14:2
good and comfortable *w.* *Zech* 1:13
should ye not hear the *w.*? 7:7
saying the same *w.* *Mat* 26:44
Mark 14:39
wondered at gracious *w.* *Luke* 4:22
the *w.* that I speak unto you, they are spirit. *John* 6:63
to whom we go ? thou hast the *w.* 68
I have given to them the *w.* 17:8
with many other *w.* did. *Acts* 2:40
Moses was mighty in *w.* and. 7:22
was warned to hear *w.* of thee. 10:22
Peter, who shall tell thee *w.* 11:14
to this agree the *w.* of the prophets. 15:15
have troubled you with *w.* 24
but if it be a question of *w.* 18:15
to remember the *w.* of the. 20:35
most of all for the *w.* he spake. 38
but I speak forth *w.* of truth. 26:25
by good *w.* deceive hearts of the simple. *Rom* 16:18*
not with wisdom of *w.* *1 Cor* 1:17
2:4, 13
except ye utter *w.* easy to. 14:9*
I had rather speak five *w.* with. 19
deceive you with vain *w.* *Eph* 5:6
nourished up in *w.* of faith and doctrine. *1 Tim* 4:6
that they strive not about *w.* to no profit. *2 Tim* 2:14
greatly withstood our *w.* 4:15
be mindful of the *w.* spoken by prophets. *2 Pet* 3:2
hear the *w.* of this prophecy. *Rev* 1:3; 22:18
take away from the *w.* of this. 22:19

all the words

all the w. of Joseph. *Gen* 45:27
Moses told Aaron *all the w.* of the Lord. *Ex* 4:28
Moses told the people *all the w.* 24:3; *Num* 11:24
Moses wrote *all the w.* of the Lord. *Ex* 24:4
on the tables were written *all the w.* *Deut* 9:10
keep *all the w.* 17:19
write on stones *all the w.* 27:3, 8
that confirmeth not *all the w.* 26
not observe to do *all the w.* 28:58
may do *all the w.* of this law. 29:29
and observe to do *all the w.* 31:12
Moses spake *all the w.* of. 32:44
set your hearts to *all the w.* 46
he read *all the w.* of the law, the blessings and. *Josh* 8:34
Samuel told *all the w.* of the Lord. *1 Sam* 8:10
Lord will hear *all the w.* of Rabshakeh. *2 Ki* 19:4; *Isa* 37:17
Josiah read *all the w.* of the covenant. *2 Ki* 23:2; *2 Chr* 34:30
all the w. of my mouth. *Pr* 8:8
unto *all the w.* spoken. *Eccl* 7:21
bring on them *all the w.* *Jer* 11:8
speak *all the w.* that I command thee. 26:2
to *all the w.* of Jeremiah. 20
write *all the w.* I have spoken. 30:2; 36:2
Baruch wrote *all the w.* of the Lord. 36:4, 32
had ended *all the w.* of Lord. 43:1
speak to the people *all the w.* of this life. *Acts* 5:20

words *of God*

hath said, which heard the *w. of God.* *Num* 24:4, 16
Heman the king's seer in the *w. of God.* *1 Chr* 25:5
every one that trembleth at the *w. of God.* *Ezra* 9:4
they rebelled against the *w. of God.* *Ps* 107:11
he whom God sent, speaketh *w. of God.* *John* 3:34
of God, heareth the *w. of God.* 8:47
until the *w. of God* be fulfilled. *Rev* 17:17

see **heard**

his words

they hated him yet the more for *his w.* *Gen* 37:8
thou heardest *his w.* out of the fire. *Deut* 4:36
Jephthah uttered all *his w.* before the Lord. *Judg* 11:11
he let none of *his w.* fall to the ground. *1 Sam* 3:19
but they despised *his w.* *2 Chr* 36:16
and lay up *his w.* in thine. *Job* 22:22
he hath not directed *his w.* 32:14
his w. were without wisdom. 34:35
for he multiplieth *his w.* against. 37
his w. softer than oil. *Ps* 55:21
then believed they *his w.* 106:12
knowledge spareth *his w.* *Pr* 17:27
seest thou a man that is hasty in *his w.*? 29:20
add thou not unto *his w.*, lest. 30:6
will not call back *his w.* *Isa* 31:2
heed to any of *his w.* *Jer* 18:18
he hath confirmed *his w.* *Dan* 9:12
the land is not able to bear all *his w.* *Amos* 7:10
the disciples were astonished at *his w.* *Mark* 10:24
to catch him in *his w.* 12:13
Luke 20:20
not take hold of *his w.* *Luke* 20:26*
they remembered *his w.* 24:8

see **lord**

my words

he said, Hear now *my w.* *Num* 12:6
Job 34:2
make them hear *my w.* *Deut* 4:10
therefore lay up *my w.* in. 11:18
and I will put *my w.* in his. 18:18
whosoever will not hearken to *my w.* 19; *Jer* 29:19; 35:13
and they uttered *my w.* *Neh* 6:19
therefore *my w.* are swallowed up. *Job* 6:3
Oh that *my w.* were now written! 19:23
after *my w.* they spake not. 29:22
hearken to all *my w.* 33:1; 34:16
Acts 2:14
my w. shall be of the uprightness of my heart. *Job* 33:3; 36:4
give ear to *my w.* O Lord. *Ps* 5:1
seeing thou castest *my w.* 50:17
every day they wrest *my w.* 56:5
they shall hear *my w.*: for they. 141:6
known *my w.* unto you. *Pr* 1:23
if thou wilt receive *my w.* 2:1
let thine heart retain *my w.* 4:4
attend to *my w.* 4:20
keep *my w.* 7:1
I have put *my w.* in thy mouth, and say unto Zion. *Isa* 51:16; *Jer* 1:9
my w. which I have put. *Isa* 59:21
I will make *my w.* in thy mouth fire. *Jer* 5:14
have not hearkened to *my w.* 6:19
refused to hear *my w.* 11:10; 13:10
will cause thee to hear *my w.* 18:2
they might not hear *my w.* 19:15
my people to hear *my w.* 23:22
ye have not heard *my w.* 25:8
bring upon that land all *my w.* 13
I will bring *my w.* on this city. 39:16
you may know *my w.* shall. 44:29
thou shalt speak *my w.* unto them *Ezek* 2:7; 3:4, 10
there shall none of *my w.* 12:28
do not *my w.* do good to ? *Mi* 2:7
my w. did they not take hold of your fathers ? *Zech* 1:6
whosoever shall be ashamed of me and *my w.* *Mark* 8:38; *Luke* 9:26
but *my w.* shall not pass away. *Mark* 13:31; *Luke* 21:33
thou believest not *my w.* *Luke* 1:20
shall ye believe *my w.*? *John* 5:47
if any man hear *my w.* and. 12:47
he that receiveth not *my w.* 48
will keep *my w.* 14:23
my w. abide in you. 15:7

their words

their w. pleased Hamor. *Gen* 34:18
I believed not *their w.* *2 Chr* 9:6
through all the earth, *their w.* to end of the world. *Ps* 19:4; *Rom* 10:18
be not afraid of *their w.* *Ezek* 2:6
their w. seemed to them as idle tales. *Luke* 24:11

these words

according to *these w.* *Gen* 39:17
to the tenor of *these w.* 43:7
these are the *w.* thou shalt speak. *Ex* 19:6, 7
God spake all *these w.* 20:1
Deut 5:22
Lord said, Write thou *these w.* *Ex* 34:27; *Jer* 36:17
these are the *w.* which the Lord. *Ex* 35:1; *Deut* 6:6; 29:1
as he had made an end of speaking all *these w.* *Num* 16:31
Deut 32:45; *1 Sam* 24:16
observe, hear all *these w.* *Deut* 12:28; *Zech* 8:9
David laid up *these w.* *1 Sam* 21:12
his servants with *these w.* 24:7

to all *these w.*, and this vision, so did. *2 Sam* 7:17; *1 Chr* 17:15
thy master and to thee to speak *these w.*? *2 Ki* 18:27; *Isa* 36:12
the man of God proclaimed *these w.* *2 Ki* 23:16
go proclaim *these w.* *Jer* 3:12
speak all *these w.* unto. 7:27; 26:15
all *these w.* 16:10
ye will not hear *these w.* 22:5
prophesy thou all *these w.* 25:30
Let no man know of *these w.* 38:24
when he had written *these w.* 45:1
51:60
thou shalt read all *these w.* 51:61
these are the *w.* I spake. *Luke* 24:44
these w. spake his parents, because they feared Jews. *John* 9:22
these are not *w.* of him that. 10:21*
hear *these w.*; Jesus of. *Acts* 2:22
while Peter yet spake *these w.* 10:44
besought *these w.* might be preached to them. 13:42
when he had said *these w.* 28:29
comfort one another with *these w.* *1 Thes* 4:18
for *these w.* are true. *Rev* 21:5

thy **words**

shall receive of *thy w.* *Deut* 33:3
will not hearken to *thy w.* *Josh* 1:18
do not according to *thy w.* *Judg* 11:10
Manoah said, Now let *thy w.* 13:12
transgressed *thy w.* *1 Sam* 15:24
hearkened to *thy w.* 28:21
thy w.' sake hast thou done all these great things. *2 Sam* 7:21
that God, and *thy w.* be true. 28
in and confirm *thy w.* *1 Ki* 1:14
hast performed *thy w.* *Neh* 9:8
thy w. upheld him that was falling. *Job* 4:4
said I would keep *thy w.* *Ps* 119:57
how sweet are *thy w.* to my! 103
entrance of *thy w.* giveth light. 130
enemies have forgotten *thy w.* 139
shalt lose *thy* sweet *w.* *Pr* 23:8
despise the wisdom of *thy w.* 9
therefore let *thy w.* be few. *Eccl* 5:2
thy w. were found, and I did eat them. *Jer* 15:16
hear *thy w.* but do them not. *Ezek* 33:31, 32
the first day *thy w.* were heard, and I am come for *thy w.* *Dan* 10:12
for by *thy w.* thou shalt be justified, and by *thy w.* thou. *Mat* 12:37

your **words**

that *your w.* be proved. *Gen* 42:16
bring Benjamin, so shall *your w.* 20
let it be according unto *your w.* 44:10; *Josh* 2:21
the voice of *your w.* *Deut* 1:34; 5:28
I waited for *your w.*; I gave ear. *Job* 32:11
that heareth *your w.* *Isa* 41:26
to God according to *your w.* *Jer* 42:4
multiplied *your w.* against me. *Ezek* 35:13
ye have wearied the Lord with *your w.* *Mal* 2:17
your w. have been stout. 3:13
you nor hear *your w.* *Mat* 10:14

work

Is taken, [1] *For such business as is proper to every man's calling, which may be done in six days.* Ex 20:9, Six days shalt thou labour and do all thy *work.* [2] *For any thought, word, or outward action, whether good or evil,* Eccl 12:14, God shall bring every *work* into judgement. [3] Work *is put for miracle,* John 7:21.

The *works* of God, denote, [1] *His* work *of creation.* [2] *His* works *of providence in preserving and governing the world.* [3] *His* work *of redemption, and particularly the faith of true believers is called* the work of God.

By good works are to be understood all manner of duties inward and outward, thoughts as well as words and actions, toward God or man, which are commanded in the law of God, and proceed from a pure heart and faith unfeigned.

let there more *w.* be laid on the men. *Ex* 5:9
no manner of *w.* shall be done. 12:16; 20:10; *Lev* 16:29; 23:3, 28, 31; *Num* 29:7
shew them *w.* that they. *Ex* 18:20
whoso doeth any *w.* therein shall be cut off. 31:14, 15; *Lev* 23:30
six days shall *w.* be. *Ex* 35:2; 20:9
sufficient for all the *w.* and. 36:7
convocation, ye shall do no servile *w.* *Lev* 23:7, 8, 21, 25, 35, 36 *Num* 28:18, 25, 26; 29:1, 12, 35
the *w.* of men's hands. *Deut* 4:28 27:15; *2 Ki* 19:18; *2 Chr* 32:19 *Ps* 115:4; 135:15
in it thou shalt not do any *w.* *Deut* 5:14; 16:8; *Jer* 17:22, 24
that the Lord may bless thee in all *w.* *Deut* 14:29; 24:19; 28:12; 30:9
do no *w.* with the firstling of. 15:19
anger through the *w.* of your hands. 31:29; *1 Ki* 16:7; *Jer* 32:30
accept the *w* of his hands. *Deut* 33:11
officers which were over the *w.* *1 Ki* 5:16; 9:23; *1 Chr* 29:6 *2 Chr* 2:18
another court of the like *w.* *1 Ki* 7:8
into the hands of them that did the *w.* *2 Ki* 12:11; 22:5*, 9
employed in that *w.* day. *1 Chr* 9:33
to minister as every day's *w.* 16:37
Solomon young, and the *w.* is great. 29:1; *Neh* 4:19
every *w.* that he began. *2 Chr* 31:21
the men did the *w.* faithfully. 34:12
then ceased the *w.* of. *Ezra* 4:24
this *w.* goeth fast on, prospereth. 5:8
let the *w.* of this house of God. 6:7
hands in the *w.* of house of God. 22
neither is it a *w.* of one day. 10:13
put not their necks to *w.* *Neh* 3:5
slay them, and cause the *w.* 4:11
why should the *w.* cease whilst? 6:3
they perceived this *w.* was. 16
fathers gave to the *w.* 7:70
thou hast blessed the *w.* *Job* 1:10
thou shouldest despise the *w.* 10:3
thou wilt have a desire to *w.* 14:15
go they forth to their *w.* 24:5
for the *w.* of a man shall he render unto him. 34:11; *1 Pet* 1:17
are all the *w.* of his hands. *Job* 34:19
he sheweth them their *w.* and. 36:9
when I consider the *w.* of thy fingers. *Ps* 8:3, 6
the wicked is snared in the *w.* 9:16
firmament sheweth his handy *w.* 19:1
after the *w.* of their hands. 28:4
we heard what *w.* thou didst. 44:1
establish thou the *w.* of our. 90:17
proved me and saw my *w.* 95:9
I hate the *w.* of them that. 101:3
the heavens are the *w.* of thy. 102:25
on the *w.* of thy hands. 143:5
worketh a deceitful *w.* *Pr* 11:18
time there for every *w.* *Eccl* 3:17
why should God destroy the *w.*? 5:6
I applied my heart to every *w.* 8:9
according to *w.* of the wicked, according to the *w.* of the. 14
there is no *w.* in the grave. 9:10
God will bring every *w.* into. 12:14
w. of the hands of a cunning workman. *S of S* 7:1
they worship the *w.* of their own hands. *Isa* 2:8; 37:19; *Jer* 1:16 10:3, 9, 15; 51:18
he shall not look to the *w.* *Isa* 17:8
neither shall there be any *w.* 19:15
blessed be Assyria the *w.* of. 25
do his *w.*, his strange *w.* 28:21
shall the *w.* say of him that? 29:16*
he seeth his children, and the *w.* 23
the *w.* of righteousness shall. 32:17
concerning the *w.* of my hands command me. 45:11
my *w.* is with my God. 49:4*
they shall inherit the *w* of my. 60:21
will direct their *w.* in truth. 61:8*
all are the *w.* of thy hands. *Isa* 64:8
mine elect shall long enjoy *w.* 65:22
great in counsel and mighty in *w.* *Jer* 32:19
recompense her according to her *w.* 50:29; *Lam* 3:64
be taken to do any *w.*? *Ezek* 15:3
is it meet for any *w.*? 4
it was meet for no *w.* 5
w. of an imperious whorish. 16:30
w. of the craftsman. *Hos* 13:2
we will say no more to the *w.* 14:3
shalt no more worship *w.* *Mi* 5:13
for I will work a *w.* in. *Hab* 1:5
and so is every *w.* of. *Hag* 2:14
there do no mighty *w.* *Mark* 6:5
I have done one *w.* and. *John* 7:21
finished the *w.* thou gavest me. 17:4
if this *w.* be of men it will. *Acts* 5:38
for the *w.* whereunto I have. 13:2
wonder, for I work a *w.* in your days, a *w.* which ye will not believe. 41
the *w.* which they fulfilled. 14:26
not with them to the *w.* 15:38
which shew *w.* of the law. *Rom* 2:15
a short *w.* will the Lord make. 9:28
otherwise *w.* is no more *w.* 11:6*
every man's *w.* shall be. *1 Cor* 3:13
if any man's *w.* abide. 14
if *w.* be burnt. 15
are not ye my *w.* in the Lord? 9:1
he gave some for the *w.* *Eph* 4:12
for the *w.* of Christ he. *Phil* 2:30
that God may fulfil the *w.* of faith. *2 Thes* 1:11
every good word and *w.* 2:17
do the *w.* of an evangelist. *2 Tim* 4:5
patience have her perfect *w.* *Jas* 1:4
but a doer of the *w.* shall be. 25

see **evil, needle**

work, *verb*

go and *w.* *Ex* 5:18
six days thou shalt *w.* 34:21
whoso doeth *w.* therein shall. 35:2
they did *w.* wilily and went. *Josh* 9:4
the Lord will *w.* for us. *1 Sam* 14:6
sold thyself to *w.* evil. *1 Ki* 21:20, 25
people had a mind to *w.* *Neh* 4:6
left hand, where he doth *w.* *Job* 23:9
in heart ye *w.* wickedness. *Ps* 58:2
time for thee, Lord, to *w.* 119:126
w. a deceitful work. *Pr* 11:18
they that *w.* in flax, shall. *Isa* 19:9
I will *w.* and who shall let it? 43:13
ye *w.* abomination and. *Ezek* 33:26
he shall *w.* deceitfully. *Dan* 11:23
woe to them that *w.* evil. *Mi* 2:1
I will *w.* a work in your days, which. *Hab* 1:5; *Acts* 13:41
w. for I am with you. *Hag* 2:4
they that *w.* wickedness. *Mal* 3:15
son, go *w.* to-day in. *Mat* 21:28
six days in which men ought to *w.* *Luke* 13:14
my Father worketh hitherto, and I *w.* *John* 5:17
that we might *w.* the works? 6:28
What dost thou *w.*? 30
w. the works of him that sent me . . . cometh when no man can *w.* 9:4
sin by the law did *w.* in. *Rom* 7:5
we know that all things *w.* 8:28
to *w.* all uncleanness. *Eph* 4:19
w. out your own salvation. *Phil* 2:12
study to *w.* with your own hands. *1 Thes* 4:11
of iniquity doth *w.* *2 Thes* 2:7
if any would not *w.*, neither. 3:10
that with quietness they *w.* 12

see **iniquity**

work *of God,* **works** *of God*

tables were the *w. of God.* *Ex* 32:16
wondrous *w. of God.* *Job* 37:14
declare the *w. of God.* *Ps* 64:9
come and see the *w. of God.* 66:5
not forget the *w. of God.* 78:7
consider the *w. of God.* *Eccl* 7:13
beheld all the *w. of God.* 8:17
knowest not the *w. of God.* 11:5
work the *w. of God.* *John* 6:28
this is the *w. of God* that ye. 29
the *w. of God* should be made manifest in him. 9:3

speak the *w. of God.* *Acts* 2:11
destroy not *w. of God.* *Rom* 14:20
see **good, great**

his **work**

God ended *his w.* *Gen* 2:2
rested from *his w.* 3
every man from *his w.* *Ex* 36:4
he is the rock, *his w.* *Deut* 32:4
an old man came from *his w.* at even. *Judg* 19:16
asses and put to *his w.* *1 Sam* 8:16
and wrought all *his w.* *1 Ki* 7:14
with the king for *his w.* *1 Chr* 4:23
of Israel he made no servants for *his w.* *2 Chr* 8:9
Baasha let *his w.* cease, he. 16:5
every man to *his w.* *Neh* 4:15
for the reward of *his w.* *Job* 7:2*
that thou magnify *his w.* 36:24
that all men may know *his w.* 37:7
renderest to every man according to *his w.* *Ps* 62:12; *Pr* 24:29
man goeth forth to *his w.* *Ps* 104:23
his w. is honourable and. 111:3
all the weights of the bag are *his w.* *Pr* 16:11
whether *his w.* be pure or. 20:11
but as for the pure *his w.* is. 21:8
let him hasten *his w.* that. *Isa* 5:19
performed *his* whole *w.* 10:12
may do *his w.*, *his* strange *w.* 28:21
behold, *his w.* is before him. 40:10* 62:11*
an instrument for *his w.* 54:16
giveth him not for *his w.* *Jer* 22:13*
the maker of *his w.* *Hab* 2:18
to every man *his w.* *Mark* 13:34
my meat is to finish *his w.* *John* 4:34
every man prove *his* own *w.* *Gal* 6:4
give every man as *his w.* *Rev* 22:12
see **Lord**

our **work**

this shall comfort us concerning *our w.* *Gen* 5:29

thy **work**

six days do all *thy w.* *Ex* 20:9; 23:12; *Deut* 5:13
Lord recompense *thy w.* *Ruth* 2:12
meditate also of all *thy w.* *Ps* 77:12
let *thy w.* appear unto thy. 90:16
made me glad through *thy w.* 92:4
prepare *thy w.* without. *Pr* 24:27
or *thy w.*, He hath no hands? *Isa* 45:9
for *thy w.* shall be rewarded, saith the Lord. *Jer* 31:16
revive *thy w.* in the midst. *Hab* 3:2

your **work**

not aught of *your w.* *Ex* 5:11
for *your w.* shall be rewarded. *2 Chr* 15:7
ye are of nothing, *your w.* is of nought. *Isa* 41:24
remembering *your w.* of faith, and labour of love. *1 Thes* 1:3
God is not unrighteous to forget *your w.* *Heb* 6:10

worker

was a *w.* in brass. *1 Ki* 7:14

workers

w. with familiar spirits. *2 Ki* 23:24
we then as *w.* together. *2 Cor* 6:1
false apostles, deceitful *w.* 11:13
beware of evil *w.* *Phil* 3:2
see **iniquity**

worketh

lo, all these things *w.* God. *Job* 33:29
he that walketh uprightly, and *w.* righteousness. *Ps* 15:2
he that *w.* deceit shall not. 101:7
w. a deceitful work. *Pr* 11:18*
a flattering mouth *w.* ruin. 26:28
w. willingly with her hands. 31:13
what profit hath he that *w.*? *Eccl* 3:9
the smith with his tongs *w.* in the coals, and he *w.* it. *Isa* 44:12
thou meetest him that *w.* 64:5
he *w.* signs and wonders. *Dan* 6:27
my Father *w.* hitherto. *John* 5:17
he that *w.* righteousness. *Acts* 10:35
glory and peace to every one that *w.* good. *Rom* 2:10
to him that *w.* is the reward. *Rom* 4:4
to him that *w.* not, but believeth. 5
because the law *w.* wrath, for. 15
knowing that tribulation *w.* 5:3
love *w.* no ill to his neighbour. 13:10
God that *w.* all in all. *1 Cor* 12:6
all these *w.* that one and the. 11
for he *w.* the work of the. 16:10
so then death *w.* in us. *2 Cor* 4:12
w. for us a more exceeding. 17
w. repentance to salvation, but the sorrow of the world *w.* death. 7:10
w. miracles among you. *Gal* 3:5
but faith, which *w.* by love. 5:6
who *w.* all things after. *Eph* 1:11
the spirit that now *w.* in the. 2:2
the power that *w.* in us. 3:20
for it is God that *w.* in you. *Phil* 2:13
his working, which *w.* in. *Col* 1:29
effectually *w.* in you. *1 Thes* 2:13
of your faith *w.* patience. *Jas* 1:3
the wrath of man *w.* not. 20
nor whatsoever *w.* abomination. *Rev* 21:27

workfellow

Timothy my *w.* saluteth. *Rom* 16:21*

working

like a sharp razor, *w.* *Ps* 52:2
w. salvation in the midst of. 74:12
who is excellent in *w.* *Isa* 28:29*
be shut the six *w.* days. *Ezek* 46:1
the Lord *w.* with them. *Mark* 16:20
men with men *w.* that. *Rom* 1:27
sin *w.* death in me by that. 7:13
and labour, *w.* with our. *1 Cor* 4:12
not we power to forbear *w.*? 9:6
to another the *w.* of miracles. 12:10
according to the *w.* of. *Eph* 1:19
given me by the effectual *w.* 3:7
according to the effectual *w.* 4:16
w. with his hands the. 28
according to the *w.* whereby he is able. *Phil* 3:21
his *w.* which worketh in. *Col* 1:29
is after the *w.* of Satan. *2 Thes* 2:9
w. not at all, but are. 3:11
w. in you that which is. *Heb* 13:21
spirits of devils *w.* miracles. *Rev* 16:14

workman

wisdom to work all manner of work of the cunning *w.* *Ex* 35:35; 38:23
the work of a cunning *w.* *S of S* 7:1
the *w.* melteth a graven. *Isa* 40:19
he seeketh to him a cunning *w.* 20
work of the *w.* with the axe. *Jer* 10:3
the *w.* made it therefore. *Hos* 8:6
w. is worthy of his meat. *Mat* 10:10*
a *w.* that needeth not be. *2 Tim* 2:15

workmanship

and in all manner of *w.* *Ex* 31:3, 5 35:31
to all the *w.* thereof. *2 Ki* 16:10
the *w.* of tabrets was. *Ezek* 28:13
for we are his *w.* created in Christ Jesus. *Eph* 2:10

workmen

they gave that to the *w.* to repair. *2 Ki* 12:14, 15; *2 Chr* 34:10, 17
there are *w.* with thee. *1 Chr* 22:15
number of *w.* 25:1
w. wrought. *2 Chr* 24:13
to set forward the *w.* in. *Ezra* 3:9
the *w.*, they are of men. *Isa* 44:11
called with the *w.* of like occupation. *Acts* 19:25

works

fulfil your *w.* and your. *Ex* 5:13
the Lord hath sent me to do all these *w.* *Num* 16:28
the Lord blessed thee in all the *w.* *Deut* 2:7; 16:15
which knew not the *w.* *Judg* 2:10
according to all the *w.* they have done. *1 Sam* 8:8
w. the man of God did. *1 Ki* 13:11
me to anger with all the *w.* of their hands. *2 Ki* 22:17; *2 Chr* 34:25
from their wicked *w.* *Neh* 9:35
have done abominable *w.* *Ps* 14:1
concerning the *w.* of men, by the word of thy lips. 17:4
I will triumph in the *w.* of. 92:4
the *w.* of the Lord are great. *Ps* 111:2
the *w.* of his hands are verity. 7
forsake not the *w.* of. 138:8
to practise wicked *w.* with. 141:4
let her own *w.* praise her. *Pr* 31:31
I have seen the *w.* *Eccl* 1:14; 2:11
wrought all our *w.* in us. *Isa* 26:12
have done all these *w.* *Jer* 7:13
to anger with the *w.* of your hands to. 25:6, 7; 44:8
according to their deeds and the *w.* 25:14; *Rev* 2:23
w. may be abolished. *Ezek* 6:6
honour him whose *w.* *Dan* 4:37
the *w.* of the house of. *Mi* 6:16
John heard in prison the *w.* *Mat* 11:2
shew him greater *w.* *John* 5:20
the *w.* which the Father hath given me, the same *w.* that I do. 36
thy disciples may see the *w.* 7:3
because I testify that the *w.* 7
if children, ye would do the *w.* 8:39
I must work the *w.* of him. 9:4
w. that I do in my Father's. 10:25
of these *w.* do ye stone me? 32
if I do not the *w.* 37
believe the *w.* 38
he doeth the *w.* 14:10
believe me for the very *w.*' 11
the *w.* that I do, shall he do; ... *w.* 12
not done among them the *w.* 15:24
they rejoiced in the *w.* *Acts* 7:41
Gentiles should do *w.* meet. 26:20
by what law? of *w.*? *Rom* 3:27
if Abraham were justified by *w.* 4:2
imputeth righteousness without *w.* 6
not of *w.* but of him that. 9:11
but as it were by the *w.* of. 32
is it no more of *w.*: . . . but if it be of *w.*, is it no more of grace. 11:6
let us therefore cast off the *w.* 13:12
is not justified by the *w.* of the law, for by the *w.* of the law. *Gal* 2:16
Spirit by the *w.* of the law? 3:2
doeth he it by the *w.* of the law? 5
as many as are of *w.* of the law. 10
the *w.* of the flesh are manifest. 5:19
not of *w.* lest any man. *Eph* 2:9
unfruitful *w.* of darkness. 5:11
in your mind by wicked *w.* *Col* 1:21
to esteem them in love for their *w.*'s sake. *1 Thes* 5:13
saved us, not according to our *w.* *2 Tim* 1:9; *Tit* 3:5
but in *w.* they deny God. *Tit* 1:16
the heavens are the *w.* *Heb* 1:10
thou didst set him over the *w.* 2:7
your fathers . . . saw my *w.* forty. 3:9
although the *w.* were finished. 4:3
of repentance from dead *w.* 6:1
purge conscience from dead *w.* 9:14
if he have not *w.* can? *Jas* 2:14
faith without *w.* is dead. 17, 20, 26
w.: shew me thy faith without *w.* 18
Abraham justified by *w.*? 2:21
by *w.* was faith made perfect. 22
ye see then that by *w.* a man. 24
was not the harlot justified by *w.*? 25
the earth and the *w.* *2 Pet* 3:10
that he might destroy *w.* *1 John* 3:8
keepeth my *w.* to the end. *Rev* 2:26
yet repented not of the *w.* of. 9:20
double according to her *w.* 18:6
see **evil, good, work** *of God*

his **works**

his w. have been to thee very good. *1 Sam* 19:4
Hezekiah prospered in all *his w.* *2 Chr* 32:30
and all *his w.* are done. *Ps* 33:4
forgat *his w.* and his wonders. 78:11; 106:13
bless the Lord, all *his w.* 103:22
Lord shall rejoice in *his w.* 104:31
let them declare *his w.* with. 107:22
people the power of *his w.* 111:6
mercies are over all *his w.* 145:9
the Lord is holy in all *his w.* 17
possessed me before *his w.* *Pr* 8:22
to every man according to *his w.*? 24:12; *Mat* 16:27; *2 Tim* 4:14
rejoice in *his* own *w.* *Eccl* 3:22
righteous in all *his w.* *Dan* 9:14

to God are all *his w.* *Acts* 15:18
seventh day from all *his w. Heb* 4:4
ceased from *his* own *w.*? 10
faith wrought with *his w.*? *Jas* 2:22
of a good conversation *his w.* 3:13
see **Lord, marvellous, mighty**

their **works**
let the people from *their w.*? *Ex* 5:4
shalt not do after *their w.* 23:24
according to these *their w. Neh* 6:14
he knoweth *their w.* *Job* 34:25
considereth all *their w.* *Ps* 33:15
and they learned *their w.* 106:35
defiled with *their* own *w.* 39
and *their w.* are in the hand of God. *Eccl* 9:1
their w. are in the dark. *Isa* 29:15
they are vanity, *their w.* 41:29
nor shall they cover themselves with *their w.*: *their w.* are works. 59:6
their w. and their thoughts. 66:18
forget any of *their w.* *Amos* 8:7
God saw *their w.* that. *Jonah* 3:10
not ye after *their w.* *Mat* 23:3
all *their w.* they do to be seen. 5
be according to *their w. 2 Cor* 11:15
and *their w.* do follow. *Rev* 14:13
the dead judged according to *their w.* 20:12, 13

thy **works**
according to *thy w.*? *Deut* 3:24
bless thee in all *thy w.* 15:10
Lord hath broken *thy w. 2 Chr* 20:37
tell of all *thy* wondrous *w.* *Ps* 26:7
145:4
How terrible art thou in *thy w.*! 66:3
that I may declare all *thy w.* 73:28
nor any works like unto *thy w.* 86:8
O Lord, how great are *thy w.*! 92:5
satisfied with fruit of *thy w.* 104:13
how manifold are *thy w.*! 24
I meditate on all *thy w.* 143:5
all *thy w.* shall praise thee. 145:10
commit *thy w.* unto the. *Pr* 16:3
now God accepteth *thy w.* *Eccl* 9:7
I will declare *thy w.* *Isa* 57:12
hast trusted in *thy w.* *Jer* 48:7
faith without *thy w.* *Jas* 2:18
I know *thy w.* *Rev* 2:2, 9, 13, 19
3:1, 8, 15
I have not found *thy w.* perfect. 3:2

wonderful **works**
Lord, are thy *wonderful w.* *Ps* 40:5
his *wonderful w.* that he. 78:4
Lord for his *wonderful w.* to the children of men! 107:8, 15, 21, 31
made his *wonderful w.* to be. 111:4
in thy name have done many *wonderful w.* *Mat* 7:22
do hear them speak in our tongues the *wonderful w.* of. *Acts* 2:11
see **wondrous**

world
To the Eastern people of earliest times the world *was very small, including little except Mesopotamia, Canaan, Arabia, and parts of Egypt. During Old Testament times it remained much the same, extending a little to the East, as the nations there grew to power; and other parts of Asia and Africa became somewhat known to the adventurous. Few knew more than rumours of Italy and even Greece. In the time of Christ* the world *really meant the Roman Empire, with parts of Asia and Africa which were more or less under its sway. All outside of this was vague. In Bible language* world *is frequently used for the inhabitants of the world, and, in the New Testament, of mortal existence in distinction from spiritual life.*
The Revised Versions often substitute the word earth.
he hath set the *w.* *1 Sam* 2:8
the foundations of the *w.* were discovered. *2 Sam* 22:16; *Ps* 18:15
the *w.* also shall not. *1 Chr* 16:30
chased out of the *w.* *Job* 18:18
disposed the whole *w.*? *Job* 34:13
do on the face of the *w.* 37:12
he shall judge the *w.* in righteousness. *Ps* 9:8; 96:13; 98:9
soul from the men of the *w.* 17:14
their words to end of the *w.* 19:4
Rom 10:18
all the ends of the *w.* *Ps* 22:27
the earth and the *w.* is the Lord's. 24:1; 98:7; *Nah* 1:5
let the inhabitants of the *w. Ps* 33:8
all ye inhabitants of the *w.* 49:1
for the *w.* is mine. 50:12
the lightnings lightened the *w.* 77:18
97:4
thou hast founded the *w.* 89:11
formed the earth and the *w.* 90:2
the *w.* also is established, it. 93:1
w. also shall be established. 96:10
not made the dust of the *w. Pr* 8:26
also he hath set the *w.* *Eccl* 3:11†
I will punish the *w.* for. *Isa* 13:11
is this he that made the *w.*? 14:17
the face of the *w.* with cities. 21
w. languisheth and fadeth. 24:4
the face of the *w.* with fruit. 27:6
let the *w.* hear, and all that. 34:1
ye shall not be confounded, *w.* 45:17
the devil sheweth him all the kingdoms of *w.* *Mat* 4:8; *Luke* 4:5
ye are the light of the *w.* *Mat* 5:14
the field is the *w.*; good seed. 13:38
it be in the end of this *w.* 40, 49
gain the whole *w.* and lose his own? 16:26; *Mark* 8:36; *Luke* 9:25
woe to the *w.* because of. *Mat* 18:7
gospel of kingdom shall be preached in all the *w.* 24:14; *Mark* 14:9
which have been since the *w.* began. *Luke* 1:70†; *Acts* 3:21†
a decree that all the *w.* *Luke* 2:1
worthy to obtain that *w.* 20:35
in the *w.*, the *w.* was made by him, and *w.* *John* 1:10; *Acts* 17:24
taketh away the sin of *w. John* 1:29
God so loved the *w.* that he. 3:16
that the *w.* through him might. 17
Christ, the Saviour of the *w.* 4:42; *1 John* 4:14
that giveth life unto the *w. John* 6:33
I give for the life of the *w.* 51
things, shew thyself to the *w.* 7:4
the *w.* cannot hate you, but me. 7
I am the light of the *w.* 8:12; 9:5
the *w.* is gone after him. 12:19
not to judge, but to save the *w.* 47
the Spirit, whom the *w.* 14:17
a little while and the *w.* seeth. 19
thou wilt manifest thyself unto us and not unto the *w.*? 22
I give, not as the *w.* giveth. 27
that the *w.* may know I love. 14:31
if *w.* hate you. 15:18; *1 John* 3:13
if ye were of the *w.*, the *w. John* 15:19
but the *w.* shall rejoice. 16:20
the *w.* and go to the Father. 28
I have overcome the *w.* 33
with thee before the *w.* was. 17:5
men thou gavest me out of the *w.* 6
I pray not for the *w.* but for them. 9
w. hated them, because they are not of the *w.* 14
not take them out of the *w.* 15
the *w.*, even as I am not of *w.* 16
that the *w.* may believe thou. 21, 23
O Father, the *w.* hath not known. 25
I spake openly to the *w.* 18:20
suppose *w.* could not contain. 21:25
turned the *w.* upside down. *Acts* 17:6
Diana, whom Asia and the *w.* worshippeth. 19:27
a mover of sedition among all the Jews throughout the *w.* 24:5
your faith is spoken of through the whole *w.* *Rom* 1:8
how shall God judge the *w.*? 3:6
that all the *w.* may become guilty. 19
should be heir of the *w.* 4:13
of them be the riches of the *w.* 11:12
of them be the reconciling of *w.* 15
the *w.* by wisdom knew. *1 Cor* 1:21
God ordained before the *w.* 2:7
received not the spirit of the *w.* 12
or the *w.*, or life, or death. 3:22
are made a spectacle to *w. 1 Cor* 4:9
we are made as the filth of *w.* 13
must ye needs go out of the *w.* 5:10
saints shall judge the *w.*? 6:2
things that are in the *w.* 7:33, 34
I will eat no flesh while the *w.* 8:13*
not be condemned with the *w.* 11:32
God reconciling the *w.* *2 Cor* 5:19
Jesus, by whom the *w.* is crucified to me, and I to the *w.* *Gal* 6:14
in Christ before the *w.* began. *2 Tim* 1:9*; *Tit* 1:2*
subjection the *w.* to come. *Heb* 2:5
have tasted the powers of the *w.* 6:5*
the *w.* was not worthy. 11:38
unspotted from the *w.* *Jas* 1:27
the tongue is a fire, a *w.* of. 3:6
the friendship of the *w.* is enmity with God? A friend of the *w.* is. 4:4
spared not the old *w.*, bringing in the flood upon the *w.* *2 Pet* 2:5
whereby the *w.* that then was. 3:6
propitiation for sins of *w. 1 John* 2:2
love not the *w.* 15
but is of the *w.* 16
the *w.* passeth away, and the. 17
the *w.* knoweth us not, because. 3:1
w.: therefore speak they of the *w.* 4:5
of God, overcometh the *w.* 5:4, 5
we are of God, and whole *w.* lieth. 19
shall come upon all the *w. Rev* 3:10
deceiveth the whole *w.* 12:9
and all the *w.* wondered after. 13:3
see **foundation**

in, or *into the* **world**
who prosper *in the w.* *Ps* 73:12*
preached *in the* whole *w. Mat* 26:13
hundred-fold, and *in the w.* to come eternal. *Mark* 10:30; *Luke* 18:30
lighteth every man that cometh *into the w.* *John* 1:9
he was *in the w.* and the world. 10
God sent not his Son *into the w.* to condemn the world. 3:17
light is come *into the w.* and men. 19
prophet that should come *into the w.* 6:14; 11:27
in the w., I am the light of world. 9:5
I am come a light *into the w.* 12:46
in w. ye shall have tribulation. 16:33
I am no more *in the w.*, but these are *in the w.* 17:11
while I was with them *in the w.* 12
cause came I *into the w.* 18:37
as by one man sin entered *into the w.* *Rom* 5:12
until the law, sin was *in the w.* 13
an idol is nothing *in the w. 1 Cor* 8:4
having no hope, without God *in the w.* *Eph* 2:12
gospel is come to you as it is *in* all *the w.* *Col* 1:6
Christ Jesus came *into the w.* to save sinners. *1 Tim* 1:15
and believed on *in the w.* 3:16
he cometh *into the w.* *Heb* 10:5
afflictions that are *in the w. 1 Pet* 5:9
things that are *in the w. 1 John* 2:15
false prophets are gone out *into the w.* 4:1
even now already is it *in the w.* 3
greater than he that is *in the w.* 4
Son *into the w.* that we might live. 9
many deceivers are entered *into the w.* *2 John* 7

this **world**
forgiven him in *this w.* *Mat* 12:32
the care of *this w.* choke the word. 13:22; *Mark* 4:19
for the children of *this w.* are wiser than. *Luke* 16:8
The children of *this w.* marry. 20:34
ye are of *this w.*; I am not of *this w.* *John* 8:23
I am come into *this w.* 9:39
he that hateth life in *this w.* 12:25
is the judgement of *this w.*; now shall the prince of *this w.* be cast. 31
he should depart out of *this w* 13:1
for prince of *this w.* cometh. 14:30
because the prince of *this w.* 16:11
My kingdom is not of *this w.*: if my kingdom were of *this w.* 18:36

be not conformed to *this w.*: but be ye. *Rom* 12:2
of *this w.*? hath not God made foolish the wisdom of *this w.*? *1 Cor* 1:20
not the wisdom of *this w.* 2:6
seemeth to be wise in *this w.* 3:18
wisdom of *this w.* is foolishness. 19
the fornicators of *this w.* 5:10
they that use *this w.* as not. 7:31
the god of *this w.* hath blinded the minds. *2 Cor* 4:4
he might deliver us from *this* present evil *w.* *Gal* 1:4
not only in *this w.*, but in. *Eph* 1:21
to the course of *this w.* 2:2
the rulers of the darkness of *this w.* 6:12
nothing into *this w.* *1 Tim* 6:7
that are rich in *this w.* 17
loved *this* present *w.* *2 Tim* 4:10
godly in *this* present *w.* *Tit* 2:12
chosen the poor of *this w.* *Jas* 2:5
but whoso hath *this w.*'s. *1 John* 3:17
is, so are we in *this w.* 4:17

worldly

denying ungodliness and *w.* *Tit* 2:12
the first covenant had a *w.* *Heb* 9:1

worlds

by whom also he made the *w.* *Heb* 1:2
the *w.* were framed by the. 11:3

worm

was there any *w.* therein. *Ex* 16:24
I have said to the *w.*, Thou. *Job* 17:14
the *w.* shall feed sweetly on. 24:20
much less man that is a *w.* 25:6
but I am a *w.* and no man. *Ps* 22:6
the *w.* is spread under. *Isa* 14:11
fear not, thou *w.* Jacob, and. 41:14
w. shall eat them like wool. 51:8
for their *w.* shall not die, nor their fire. 66:24; *Mark* 9:44, 46, 48
God prepared a *w.*, it smote the gourd. *Jonah* 4:7

worms

their manna bred *w.* *Ex* 16:20
grapes, for the *w.* shall. *Deut* 28:39
my flesh is clothed with *w.* *Job* 7:5
though *w.* destroy this body. 19:26
they shall lie down, and *w.* 21:26
worm under thee, and the *w.* cover. *Isa* 14:11
out of their holes like *w.* *Mi* 7:17
Herod was eaten of *w.* *Acts* 12:23

wormwood

a root that beareth *w.* *Deut* 29:18
her end is bitter as *w.*, sharp as a sword. *Pr* 5:4
I will feed them with *w.* *Jer* 9:15
23:15
made me drunken with *w.* *Lam* 3:15
remembering my misery, the *w.* 19
who turn judgement to *w.* *Amos* 5:7
star is called *w.* and the third part of the waters became *w.* *Rev* 8:11

worse

we will deal *w.* with thee. *Gen* 19:9
be *w.* than all that befell. *2 Sam* 19:7
Omri did *w.* than all. *1 Ki* 16:25*
Judah was put to the *w.* before. *2 Ki* 14:12; *2 Chr* 25:22
the Syrians were put to the *w.* *1 Chr* 19:16, 19
people be put to the *w.* *2 Chr* 6:24*
Manasseh made Jerusalem do *w.* 33:9*
they did *w.* than their fathers. *Jer* 7:26; 16:12
see your faces *w.* liking? *Dan* 1:10
the rent is made *w.* *Mat* 9:16
Mark 2:21
the last state of that man is *w.* than first. *Mat* 12:45; *Luke* 11:26
last error shall be *w.* *Mat* 27:64
bettered, but grew *w.* *Mark* 5:26
then that which is *w.* *John* 2:10
sin no more, lest a *w.* thing. 5:14
eat not, are we the *w.* *1 Cor* 8:8
for the better, but for the *w.* 11:17
denied the faith, and is *w.* *1 Tim* 5:8
shall wax *w.* and *w.* *2 Tim* 3:13
the latter end is *w.* *2 Pet* 2:20

worship

lad will go yonder and *w.* *Gen* 22:5
to Lord, and *w.* ye afar off. *Ex* 24:1
for thou shalt *w.* no other god. 34:14
be driven to *w.* them. *Deut* 4:19
if thou *w.* other gods. 8:19; 11:16
30:17
before Lord, and *w.* before the Lord. 26:10; *Ps* 22:27, 29; 86:9
man went up early to *w.* *1 Sam* 1:3
turn again, that I may *w.* 15:25, 30
the people went to *w.* *1 Ki* 12:30
to *w.* in house of Rimmon. *2 Ki* 5:18
ye fear, and him shall ye *w.* 17:36*
hath said to Judah, Ye shall *w.* 18:22
2 Chr 32:12; *Isa* 36:7
w. the Lord in the beauty of holiness. *1 Chr* 16:29; *Ps* 29:2; 66:4; 96:9
Mat 4:10; *Luke* 4:8
I will *w.* toward thy holy temple. *Ps* 5:7; 138:2
he is thy Lord, and *w.* thou. 45:11
neither shalt thou *w.* any. 81:9
O come let us *w.* and bow. 95:6
w. him, all ye gods. 97:7
w. at his footstool, for. 99:5; 132:7
exalt the Lord, and *w.* at his. 99:9
they *w.* the work of their hands. *Isa* 2:8, 20; 46:6
w. the Lord in the holy mount. 27:13
princes also shall *w.* because. 49:7
all flesh shall come to *w.* 66:23
that enter in at these gates to *w.* *Jer* 7:2; 26:2
they that *w.* other gods, be. 13:10
go not after other gods to *w.* 25:6
we *w.* her without our men? 44:19
he shall *w.* at threshold. *Ezek* 46:2
the people of the land shall *w.* 3
he that entereth to *w.* by the. 9
w. the golden image. *Dan* 3:5, 10, 15
not *w.* the image. 12, 18, 28
do not ye *w.* the golden image? 3:14
if ye *w.* 15
no more *w.* the work of. *Mi* 5:13
them that *w.* the host. *Zeph* 1:5
men shall *w.* him, every one. 2:11
to *w.* the King the Lord of hosts. *Zech* 14:16, 17
star, and come to *w.* him. *Mat* 2:2
that I may come and *w.* him also. 8
if thou wilt fall down and *w.* me. 4:9; *Luke* 4:7
in vain do they *w.* me. *Mat* 15:9
Mark 7:7
Jerusalem is the place where men ought to *w.* *John* 4:20
ye *w.* ye know not what: we know what we *w.*: for salvation. 4:22
they shall *w.* the Father in. 23, 24
certain Greeks came up to *w.* 12:20
God gave up to *w.* *Acts* 7:42*, 43
came to Jerusalem to *w.* 8:27
whom ye ignorantly *w.* 17:23
persuaded men to *w.* God. 18:13
to Jerusalem to *w.* God. 24:11
they call heresy, so *w.* I the. 14*
down, he will *w.* God. *1 Cor* 14:25
which *w.* God in spirit. *Phil* 3:3
the angels of God *w.* him. *Heb* 1:6
make them come and *w.* *Rev* 3:9
and *w.* him that liveth for ever. 4:10
that they should not *w.* devils. 9:20
of God, and them *w.* therein. 11:1
all on the earth shall *w.* 13:8, 12
they that would not *w.* the image. 15
w. him that made heaven, earth. 14:7
if any man *w.* the beast and. 9
who *w.* the beast, have no rest. 11
all nations shall come and *w.* 15:4
I fell at his feet to *w.* 19:10; 22:8
w. God. 22:9

worshipped

Abraham bowed and *w.* the Lord. *Gen* 24:26, 48
Abraham's servant *w.* the Lord. 52
Israel bowed and *w.* *Ex* 4:31
12:27; 33:10
a calf, and *w.* it. 32:8; *Ps* 106:19
Moses *w.* *Ex* 34:8
other gods, and *w.* *Deut* 17:3; 29:26
1 Ki 9:9; *2 Ki* 21:21; *2 Chr* 7:22
Jer 1:16; 8:2; 16:11; 22:9
Gideon *w.* *Judg* 7:15
Hannah *w.* before Lord. *1 Sam* 1:19
Samuel *w.* 28
Saul *w.* the Lord. 15:31
then David arose and *w.* *2 Sam* 12:20; 15:32
and *w.* Ashtaroth. *1 Ki* 11:33
Baal and *w.* him. 16:31; 22:53
w. all the host of heaven and served. *2 Ki* 17:16; 21:3; *2 Chr* 33:3
congregation bowed down and *w.* the Lord. *1 Chr* 29:20; *2 Chr* 7:3
29:28, 29, 30
all people *w.* the Lord. *Neh* 8:6; 9:3
Job *w.* *Job* 1:20
w. the sun. *Ezek* 8:16
king *w.* Daniel. *Dan* 2:46
w. the golden image. 3:7
fell down and *w.* Christ. *Mat* 2:11
a leper came and *w.* him. 8:2
a certain ruler *w.* him. 9:18
were in the ship *w.* him. 14:33
woman came and *w.* him. 15:25
fell down and *w.* his lord. 18:26
by the feet and *w.* him. 28:9
his disciples *w.* him. 17; *Luke* 24:52
out of the tombs and *w.* *Mark* 5:6
and bowing knees, *w.* him. 15:19
our fathers *w.* in this. *John* 4:20
blind man believed, and *w.* him. 9:38
fell down and *w.* Peter. *Acts* 10:25
Lydia *w.* God. 16:14
neither is *w.* with men's. 17:25*
Justus *w.* God. 18:7
w. the creature more. *Rom* 1:25
above all that is *w.* *2 Thes* 2:4
Jacob *w.* *Heb* 11:21
the twenty-four elders *w.* *Rev* 5:14
11:16; 19:4
the angels *w.* God. 7:11
they *w.* the dragon, they *w.* 13:4
a sore fell on them which *w.* 16:2
them that *w.* his image. 19:20
souls that had not *w.* the beast. 20:4

worshipper

if any man be a *w.* of God. *John* 9:31
the city of Ephesus is a *w.* of Diana. *Acts* 19:35*

worshippers

destroy the *w.* of Baal. *2 Ki* 10:19
all the *w.* of Baal came. 21
that there be none but the *w.* 23
then the true *w.* shall. *John* 4:23
the *w.* once purged. *Heb* 10:2

worshippeth

host of heaven *w.* thee. *Neh* 9:6
yea, he maketh a god, and *w.* it. *Isa* 44:15, 17
falleth not down and *w.* *Dan* 3:6, 11
Asia and the world *w.* *Acts* 19:27

worshipping

as he was *w.* in the house of Nisroch. *2 Ki* 19:37; *Isa* 37:38
fell before the Lord, *w.* *2 Chr* 20:18
mother of Zebedee's children came *w.* *Mat* 20:20
beguile you in *w.* of angels. *Col* 2:18

worst

I will bring the *w.* of the. *Ezek* 7:24

worth

as much money as it is *w.* *Gen* 23:9
the land is *w.* four hundred. 15
priest shall reckon the *w.* *Lev* 27:23
hath been *w.* a double. *Deut* 15:18
but thou art *w.* ten thousand of us. *2 Sam* 18:3
give the *w.* of thy vineyard. *1 Ki* 21:2
thy speech nothing *w.* *Job* 24:25
heart of wicked is little *w.* *Pr* 10:20
howl ye, Woe *w.* the day! *Ezek* 30:2

worthies

he shall recount his *w.* *Nah* 2:5

worthily

do thou *w.* in Ephratah. *Ruth* 4:11

worthy

I am not *w.* of the least. *Gen* 32:10
if the wicked man be *w.* *Deut* 25:2
he gave a *w.* portion. *1 Sam* 1:5*
Lord liveth, ye are *w.* to die. 26:16
who is *w.* to be praised. *2 Sam* 22:4
Ps 18:3

shew himself a *w.* man. *1 Ki* 1:52
this man is *w.* to die. *Jer* 26:11
he is not *w.* 16
whose shoes I am not *w.* *Mat* 3:11
Lord, I am not *w.* that thou shouldest come under. 8:8; *Luke* 7:6
for the workman is *w.* of his meat. *Mat* 10:10
enquire who in it is *w.* and. 11
be *w.* . . . but if it be not *w.* 13
me, he is not *w.* of me. 37, 38
which were bidden were not *w.* 22:8
I am not *w.* to unloose. *Mark* 1:7
Luke 3:16; *John* 1:27; *Acts* 13:25
bring forth fruits *w.* of. *Luke* 3:8
that he was *w.* for whom. 7:4
nor thought I myself *w.* to come. 7
for the labourer is *w.* of his. 10:7
commit things *w.* of stripes. 12:48
I am no more *w.* to be. 15:19, 21
shall be accounted *w.* to. 20:35
be accounted *w.* to escape. 21:36*
very *w.* deeds are done. *Acts* 24:2
are not *w.* to be compared with the glory. *Rom* 8:18
that ye walk *w.* of the. *Eph* 4:1
that ye might walk *w.* of. *Col* 1:10
would walk *w.* of God. *1 Thes* 2:12
w. of all acceptation. *1 Tim* 1:15; 4:9
the labourer is *w.* of his reward. 5:18
sorer punishment, suppose ye, shall he be thought *w.*? *Heb* 10:29
of whom the world was not *w.* 11:38
blaspheme that *w.* name? *Jas* 2:7*
in white, for they are *w.* *Rev* 3:4
thou art *w.* to receive glory. 4:11
5:12
Who is *w.* to open the book? 5:2
found *w.* to open the book. 4
thou art *w.* to take the book and. 9
to drink, for they are *w.* 16:6
see **count, counted, death**

wot, -teth

(*The American Revision everywhere, and the English Revision usually, put here the modern word* know, *which has the same meaning*)
I *w.* not who hath done. *Gen* 21:26
my master *w.* not what is with. 39:8
w. ye not that such a man? 44:15
as for this Moses, we *w.* *Ex* 32:1
23; *Acts* 7:40
I *w.* he whom thou blessest is blessed. *Num* 22:6
the men went I *w.* not. *Josh* 2:5
I *w.* that through ignorance ye did it. *Acts* 3:17
w. ye not what the scripture saith? *Rom* 11:2
I shall choose I *w.* not. *Phil* 1:22

would

I *w.* it might be according. *Gen* 30:34
I *w.* there were a sword. *Num* 22:29
whosoever *w.*, he consecrated him *1 Ki* 13:33
do with them as they *w.* *Neh* 9:24
Jews did what they *w.* to. *Esth* 9:5
not hearken, and Israel *w.* *Ps* 81:11
but ye *w.* none of my. *Pr* 1:25
they *w.* none of my counsel. 30
whom he *w.* he slew, and whom he *w.* he kept alive, and whom he *w.* he set up, and *w.* *Dan* 5:19
whatsoever ye *w.* that men should. *Mat* 7:12; *Luke* 6:31
to release a prisoner whom they *w.* *Mat* 27:15
calleth to him whom he *w.*, and they came unto him. *Mark* 3:13
we *w.* thou shouldest do for us. 10:35
what *w.* ye that I should do? 36
fishes as much as they *w.* *John* 6:11
reason *w.* that I should. *Acts* 18:14
what I *w.* that I do not. *Rom* 7:15
for the good that I *w.* I do not. 19
I *w.* that all men were. *1 Cor* 7:7
I *w.* that ye all spake with. 14:5
not find you such as I *w.* *2 Cor* 12:20
w. that we should remember. *Gal* 2:10
I *w.* they were cut off which. 5:12
do the things that ye *w.* 17
I *w.* ye knew what great. *Col* 2:1
forbiddeth them that *w.* *3 John* 10
I know thy works, I *w.* *Rev* 3:15

would *God*

w. God we had died in Egypt, when. *Ex* 16:3; *Num* 14:2
w. God that all the Lord's people were prophets! *Num* 11:29
w. God we had died when our. 20:3
w. God it were even, *w. God* it were morning! *Deut* 28:67
w. to *God* we had dwelt on the other side Jordan! *Josh* 7:7
w. God this people were. *Judg* 9:29
w. God I had died for. *2 Sam* 18:33
w. God my lord were. *2 Ki* 5:3
w. God that all were such as I am. *Acts* 26:29
I *w.* to *God* ye did reign. *1 Cor* 4:8
w. to *God* ye could bear with me. *2 Cor* 11:1

would *not*

if I knew, then *w. not* I tell it thee? *1 Sam* 20:9
his armourbearer *w. not.* 31:4
1 Chr 10:4
he *w. not,* nor did he eat with them. *2 Sam* 12:17
but Amnon *w. not* hearken. 13:16
howbeit David *w. not* go, but. 25
but Joab *w. not* come to. 14:29
but Jehoshaphat *w. not.* *1 Ki* 22:49
which Lord *w. not* pardon. *2 Ki* 24:4
yet *w.* they *not* give ear. *Neh* 9:30
yet *w.* I *not* believe he. *Job* 9:16
and ye *w. not.* *Isa* 30:15
Mat 23:37; *Luke* 13:34
besought him to have patience, he *w. not.* *Mat* 18:30
were bidden: they *w. not* come. 22:3
we *w. not* have been partakers with them. 23:30
w. not have suffered his house. 24:43
tasted, he *w. not* drink. 27:34
he *w. not* that any man. *Mark* 9:30
angry, and *w. not* go in. *Luke* 15:28
he *w. not* for a while, but. 18:4
he *w. not* lift so much as his. 13
who *w. not* that I should reign. 19:27
he *w. not* walk in Jewry. *John* 7:1
that he *w. not* delay to. *Acts* 9:38
when he *w. not* be persuaded. 21:14
I do that which I *w. not.* *Rom* 7:16
I *w. not,* brethren, that ye should be. 11:25; *1 Cor* 10:1
I *w. not* ye should have fellowship. *1 Cor* 10:20
you, such as ye *w. not.* *2 Cor* 12:20
because we *w. not* be chargeable to you. *1 Thes* 2:9
then *w.* he *not* afterward. *Heb* 4:8

wouldest

Caleb said, What *w.* thou? *Josh* 15:18; *1 Ki* 1:16
walkedst whither thou *w.* *John* 21:18

wouldest *not*

whither thou *w. not.* *John* 21:18
offering thou *w. not.* *Heb* 10:5, 8

wound, *substantive*

give *w.* for *w.*, stripe for. *Ex* 21:25
blood ran out of the *w.* *1 Ki* 22:35
my *w.* is incurable without transgression. *Job* 34:6
a *w.* and dishonour. *Pr* 6:33
the blueness of a *w.* cleanseth. 20:30
the stroke of their *w.* *Isa* 30:26
woe is me, for my *w.* is. *Jer* 10:19
and why is my *w.* incurable? 15:18
w. is grievous. 30:12; *Nah* 3:19
thee with *w.* of an enemy. *Jer* 30:14
Judah saw his *w.* . . . yet could he not cure your *w.* *Hos* 5:13
they that eat have laid a *w.* *Ob* 7*
her *w.* is incurable, it is. *Mi* 1:9
and his deadly *w.* was healed. *Rev* 13:3*, 12*, 14*

wound

alive; I *w.* and I heal. *Deut* 32:39
God shall *w.* the head. *Ps* 68:21*
he shall *w.* the heads over. 110:6*
when ye *w.* their weak. *1 Cor* 8:12

wound, *verb*

they *w.* body of Jesus. *John* 19:40*
young men *w.* up Ananias. *Acts* 5:6*

wounded

is *w.* in the stones. *Deut* 23:1
w. of the Philistines. *1 Sam* 17:52
Saul was *w.* of the archers. 31:3*
1 Chr 10:3*
I have *w.* mine enemies. *2 Sam* 22:39*; *Ps* 18:38*
in smiting he *w.* him. *1 Ki* 20:37
carry me out, for I am *w.* 22:34
2 Chr 18:33
the Syrians *w.* Joram. *2 Ki* 8:28
for I am sore *w.* *2 Chr* 35:23
soul of the *w.* crieth out. *Job* 24:12
suddenly shall they be *w.* *Ps* 64:7
of those whom thou hast *w.* 69:26
my heart is *w.* within me. 109:22
cast down many *w.* *Pr* 7:26
a *w.* spirit who can bear? 18:14*
found me, they *w.* me. *S of S* 5:7
art thou not it that *w.*? *Isa* 51:9*
but he was *w.* for our. 53:5
I *w.* thee with the wound. *Jer* 30:14
but *w.* men among them. 37:10
through all the land the *w.* 51:52
when they swooned as *w.* *Lam* 2:12
when the *w.* cry, shall? *Ezek* 26:15
the *w.* shall be judged in the. 28:23
groanings of a deadly *w.* 30:24
when they fall on the sword, shall not be *w.* *Joel* 2:8*
I was *w.* in the house. *Zech* 13:6
cast stones and they *w.* him in the head. *Mark* 12:4; *Luke* 20:12
thieves, which *w.* him. *Luke* 10:30
they fled out of that house naked and *w.* *Acts* 19:16
heads, as it were *w.* *Rev* 13:3*

woundedst

thou *w.* the head out of. *Hab* 3:13

woundeth

he *w.*, and his hands make. *Job* 5:18

wounding

slain a man to my *w.* *Gen* 4:23

wounds, *substantive*

went back to be healed of the *w.* *2 Ki* 8:29; 9:15; *2 Chr* 22:6
he multiplied my *w.* *Job* 9:17
my *w.* stink, are corrupt. *Ps* 38:5
and bindeth up their *w.* 147:3
words of a talebearer are as *w.* *Pr* 18:8*; 26:22*
who hath woe? who hath *w.*? 23:29
faithful are *w.* of friend, but. 27:6
in it, but *w.*, bruises, and. *Isa* 1:6
continually is grief and *w.* *Jer* 6:7
I will heal thee of thy *w.* saith. 30:17
what are these *w.* in thy hands? *Zech* 13:6
bound up his *w.* *Luke* 10:34

wove

the women *w.* hangings. *2 Ki* 23:7

woven

ephod have binding of *w.* work. *Ex* 28:32; 39:22
made coats of fine linen *w.* 39:27
the coat was without seam, *w.* *John* 19:23

wrap

he can *w.* himself in it. *Isa* 28:20
a reward; so they *w.* it up. *Mi* 7:3*

wrapped

Tamar *w.* herself and sat. *Gen* 38:14
Goliath's sword is *w.* *1 Sam* 21:9
Elijah *w.* his face in. *1 Ki* 19:13
mantle and *w.* it together. *2 Ki* 2:8
roots are *w.* about the heap. *Job* 8:17
sinews of his stones are *w.* 40:17*
the sword is *w.* up for. *Ezek* 21:15*
the weeds were *w.* about. *Jonah* 2:5
Joseph *w.* the body in a clean linen cloth. *Mat* 27:59; *Mark* 15:46*
Luke 23:53
Mary *w.* him in swaddling clothes. *Luke* 2:7
babe *w.* in swaddling clothes. 12
napkin *w.* together in a. *John* 20:7*

wrath

(Generally the Revised Versions use the more modern terms anger, vexation, indignation, fury)

cursed be their *w.* for it. *Gen* 49:7
lest *w.* come upon all. *Lev* 10:6
that no *w.* be on the congregation. *Num* 1:53; 18:5
for there is *w.* gone out from. 16:46
remember, how thou provokedst the Lord thy God to *w.* *Deut* 9:7, 22
the Lord rooted them out in anger and *w.* 29:28
were it not I feared the *w.* 32:27
let them live, lest *w.* *Josh* 9:20
and *w.* fell on all the. 22:20
if the king's *w.* arise. *2 Sam* 11:20
turned not from great *w.* *2 Ki* 23:26
because there fell *w.* *1 Chr* 27:24
therefore is *w.* upon thee. *2 Chr* 19:2
they trespass not, and so *w.* 10
w. came upon Judah for. 24:18
and there is fierce *w.* 28:13
that his fierce *w.* may turn. 29:10
therefore there was *w.* upon. 32:25
provoked God to *w.* *Ezra* 5:12
should there be *w.* against? 7:23
yet ye bring more *w.* *Neh* 13:18
shall arise too much *w.* *Esth* 1:18
when the *w.* of the king was. 2:1
not, then Haman full of *w.* 3:5
was the king's *w.* pacified. 7:10
for *w.* killeth the foolish man. *Job* 5:2
w. bringeth the punishments. 19:29
he shall drink of the *w.* of. 21:20
hypocrites in heart heap up *w.* 36:13
because there is *w.*, beware. 18
forsake *w.* *Ps* 37:8
in *w.* they hate me. 55:3
surely the *w.* of man shall praise thee, the remainder of *w.* 76:10
stretch thy hand against *w.* of. 138:7
of the wicked is *w.* *Pr* 11:23
a fool's *w.* presently known. 12:16
that is slow to *w.* is of great. 14:29
a soft answer turneth away *w.* 15:1
w. of a king is as messengers. 16:14
king's *w.* is as the roaring. 19:12
a man of great *w.* shall suffer. 19
bosom pacifieth strong *w.* 21:14
who dealeth in proud *w.* 24
but a fool's *w.* is heavier. 27:3
w. is cruel, and anger is. 4
but wise men turn away *w.* 29:8
forcing of *w.* bringeth forth. 30:33
much *w.* with his sickness. *Eccl* 5:17
day of Lord cometh with *w.* *Isa* 13:9
he who smote the people in *w.* 14:6
in a little *w.* I hid my face. 54:8
fight against you in *w.* *Jer* 21:5
driven them in great *w.* 32:37
in that ye provoke me to *w.* 44:8
w. is on all the multitude. *Ezek* 7:12
and he reserveth *w.* for. *Nah* 1:2
O Lord, in *w.* remember. *Hab* 3:2
not deliver in day of *w.* *Zeph* 1:18
therefore came a great *w.* *Zech* 7:12
fathers provoked me to *w.* 8:14
to flee from *w.* to come. *Mat* 3:7
Luke 3:7
they were filled with *w.* *Luke* 4:28
Acts 19:28
be *w.* on this people. *Luke* 21:23
but treasurest up *w.* against the day of *w.* *Rom* 2:5
that obey unrighteousness, *w.* 8
because the law worketh *w.* 4:15
we shall be saved from *w.* 5:9
endured the vessels of *w.* fitted. 9:22
but rather give place unto *w.* 12:19
minister of God to execute *w.* 13:4
be subject, not only for *w.* 5
works of flesh are *w.*, strife. *Gal* 5:20
by nature the children of *w.* *Eph* 2:3
not sun go down upon your *w.* 4:26
let all *w.*, anger, and clamour. 31
provoke not your children to *w.* 6:4
put off all these; *w.*, malice. *Col* 3:8
who delivered us from the *w.* to come. *1 Thes* 1:10
for *w.* is come on them to. 2:16
hath not appointed us to *w.* 5:9
holy hands, without *w.* *1 Tim* 2:8
Moses not fearing the *w.* of the king. *Heb* 11:27
slow to speak, slow to *w.* *Jas* 1:19
w. of man worketh not. 20
and hide us from the *w.* *Rev* 6:16
come down, having great *w.* 12:12
she made all nations drink wine of *w.* 14:8; 18:3

day of **wrath**

his goods flow away in the *day of* his *w.* *Job* 20:28
the wicked brought forth to the *day of w.* 21:30
Lord strike through kings in *day of* his *w.* *Ps* 110:5
profit not in the *day of w.* *Pr* 11:4
that day is a *day of w.* *Zeph* 1:15
w. against the *day of w.* *Rom* 2:5
the great *day of* his *w.* is. *Rev* 6:17

wrath *of God*

the fierce *w. of God* is. *2 Chr* 28:11
till the *w. of God* be turned from us. *Ezra* 10:14
the *w. of God* came. *Ps* 78:31
but the *w. of God* abideth. *John* 3:36
the *w. of God* is revealed. *Rom* 1:18
things, *w. of God* cometh on the children. *Eph* 5:6; *Col* 3:6
shall drink of the wine of the *w. of God.* *Rev* 14:10
into winepress of the *w. of God.* 19
is filled up the *w. of God.* 15:1
golden vials full of the *w. of God.* 7
vials of the *w. of God* on earth. 16:1
winepress of the *w. of God.* 19:15

his **wrath**

Lord overthrew in *his w.* *Deut* 29:23
nor executedst *his w.* *1 Sam* 28:18
turned not from *his w.* *2 Ki* 23:26
his fierce *w.* may turn away. *2 Chr* 29:10; 30:8
his w. is against them. *Ezra* 8:22
from the banquet in *his w.* *Esth* 7:7
he teareth me in *his w.* *Job* 16:9
the fury of *his w.* on him. 20:23
he speak to them in *his w.* *Ps* 2:5
swallow them up in *his w.* 21:9
take them away in *his w.* 58:9
did not stir up all *his w.* 78:38
the fierceness of *his w.* 49
stood to turn away *his w.* 106:23
his w. against him that. *Pr* 14:35
turn away *his w.* from him. 24:18
Moab's pride and *his w.* *Isa* 16:6
the Lord hath forsaken the generation of *his w.* *Jer* 7:29
at *his w.* the earth shall. 10:10
I know *his w.*, saith the Lord. 48:30
hath thrown down in *his w.* *Lam* 2:2
affliction by the rod of *his w.* 3:1
because he kept *his w.* *Amos* 1:11
God willing to shew *his w.* *Rom* 9:22
of fierceness of *his w.* *Rev* 16:19

see **kindled,** *wrath of the* **Lord**

my **wrath**

my w. shall wax hot. *Ex* 22:24
let me alone, that *my w.* 32:10
hath turned *my w.* away. *Num* 25:11
my w. shall not be poured out on Jerusalem. *2 Chr* 12:7
to whom I sware in *my w.* *Ps* 95:11
against the people of *my w.* *Isa* 10:6
for in *my w.* I smote thee. 60:10
for *my w.* is on all the multitude. *Ezek* 7:14
thus will I accomplish *my w.* 13:15
thee in fire of *my w.* 21:31; 22:21
them with the fire of *my w.* 22:31
of *my w.* have I spoken. 38:19
I will pour out *my w.* on. *Hos* 5:10
I took him away in *my w.* 13:11
so sware in *my w.* they. *Heb* 3:11
as I have sworn in *my w.*, if they. 4:3

thy **wrath**

thou sentest *thy w.* which. *Ex* 15:7
doth *thy w.* wax hot against? 32:11
turn from *thy* fierce *w.* and. 12
keep me secret until *thy w.* be past. *Job* 14:13
cast abroad the rage of *thy w.* 40:11
rebuke me not in *thy w.* *Ps* 38:1
pour out *thy w.* on the heathen. 79:6
taken away all *thy w.* *Ps* 85:3
thy w. lieth hard on me. 88:7
thy fierce *w.* goeth over me. 16
how long shall *thy w.* burn? 89:46
and by *thy w.* are we troubled. 90:7
days are passed away in *thy w.* 9
according to thy fear, so is *thy w.* 11
thine indignation and *thy w.* 102:10
I stood to turn away *thy w.* *Jer* 18:20
was *thy w.* against the sea. *Hab* 3:8
thy w. is come, and time. *Rev* 11:18

wrathful

let thy *w.* anger take. *Ps* 69:24
a *w.* man stirreth up. *Pr* 15:18

wraths

be envyings, *w.*, strifes. *2 Cor* 12:20

wreath

two rows of pomegranates on each *w.* *2 Chr* 4:13*

wreathed

my transgressions are *w.* *Lam* 1:14*

wreathen

two chains at the ends, of *w.* work. *Ex* 28:14, 22, 24, 25; 39:15, 17, 18
pillar of *w.* work he carried away. *2 Ki* 25:17*

wreaths

w. of chain work for. *1 Ki* 7:17
two *w.* to cover the. *2 Chr* 4:12*
pomegranates on the two *w.* 13*

wrest

many, to *w.* judgement. *Ex* 23:2
thou shalt not *w.* the judgement of thy poor. 6
thou shalt not *w.* judgement; neither take a gift. *Deut* 16:19
day they *w.* my words. *Ps* 56:5
they that are unstable *w.* *2 Pet* 3:16

wrestle

we *w.* not against flesh. *Eph* 6:12

wrestled

wrestlings have I *w.* with. *Gen* 30:8
there *w.* a man with him. 32:24
thigh was out of joint as he *w.* 25

wrestlings

with great *w.* have I wrestled with my sister. *Gen* 30:8

wretched

O *w.* man that I am! *Rom* 7:24
knowest not thou art *w.* *Rev* 3:17

wretchedness

let me not see my *w.* *Num* 11:15

wring

the priest shall *w.* off his head. *Lev* 1:15; 5:8
all the wicked shall *w.* *Ps* 75:8†

wringed

Gideon *w.* the dew out. *Judg* 6:38

wringing

the *w.* of the nose bringeth forth blood. *Pr* 30:33

wrinkle

a glorious church not having spot or *w.* *Eph* 5:27

wrinkles

hast filled me with *w.* *Job* 16:8*

write

I will *w.* on these tables. *Ex* 34:1
Deut 10:2
W. thou these words. *Ex* 34:27
w. thou every man's. *Num* 17:2
thou shalt *w.* Aaron's name on. 3
w. them on posts. *Deut* 6:9; 11:20
then let him *w.* her a bill of divorcement, and. 24:1, 3; *Mark* 10:4
w. on the stones the. *Deut* 27:3, 8
now therefore *w.* ye this. 31:19
Uzziah did Isaiah *w.* *2 Chr* 26:22
we might *w.* the names. *Ezra* 5:10
sure covenant and *w.* it. *Neh* 9:38
w. ye also for the Jews. *Esth* 8:8
w. them on the table. *Pr* 3:3; 7:3
w. in the great roll with. *Isa* 8:1
that *w.* grievousness which. 10:1
few, that a child may *w.* them. 19
now go, *w.* it before them. 30:8
saith the Lord, *W.* ye. *Jer* 22:30
w. the words I have spoken. 30:2
36:2, 17, 28

I will *w*. it in their hearts. *Jer* 31:33
Heb 8:10
son of man, *w*. the name. *Ezek* 24:2
w. upon the sticks for. 37:16
w. it in their sight, that they. 43:11
w. the vision and make it. *Hab* 2:2
it seemed good to me to *w*. to thee in order. *Luke* 1:3
take thy bill and *w*. fifty. 16:6
w. fourscore. 7
and the prophets did *w*. *John* 1:45
w. not, King of the Jews, but. 19:21
that we *w*. to them that. *Acts* 15:20
thing to *w*. unto my lord, that I might have somewhat to *w*. 25:26
I *w*. not these things to. *1 Cor* 4:14
things I *w*. are the. 14:37
for we *w*. none other things to you.
2 Cor 1:13
to this end also did I *w*., that. 2:9
it is superfluous for me to *w*. to. 9:1
I *w*. to them which heretofore. 13:2
therefore I *w*. these things, being. 10
now the things I *w*. unto. *Gal* 1:20
to *w*. the same things. *Phil* 3:1
not that I *w*. to you. *1 Thes* 4:9; 5:1
so I *w*. *2 Thes* 3:17
these things I *w*. *1 Tim* 3:14
minds will I *w*. them. *Heb* 10:16
I now *w*. unto you. *2 Pet* 3:1
1 John 2:1
these things *w*. we to. *1 John* 1:4
brethren, I *w*. no new. 2:7
again, a new commandment I *w*. 8
I *w*. to you, little children. 12, 13
I *w*. to you, fathers, I *w*. to you. 13
having many things to *w*. *2 John* 12
ink and pen *w*. to you. *3 John* 13
diligence to *w*. of common salvation, it was needful for me to *w*. *Jude* 3
what thou seest, *w*. *Rev* 1:11, 19
unto the angel of the church of . . . *w*.
2:1, 8, 12, 18; 3:1, 7, 14
I will *w*. on him the name of my God . . . I will *w*. upon him my new. 3:12
to *w*.: a voice saying, *w*. not. 10:4
W., Blessed are the dead which. 14:13
W., Blessed are they which. 19:9
w.: for these words are true. 21:5
see **book**

writer

handle the pen of the *w*. *Judg* 5:14*
the pen of a ready *w*. *Ps* 45:1
a man with a *w*.'s inkhorn by his side. *Ezek* 9:2, 3

writest

for thou *w*. bitter things. *Job* 13:26
sticks whereon thou *w*. *Ezek* 37:20

writeth

count, when he *w*. up. *Ps* 87:6

writing

and the *w*. was the *w*. of. *Ex* 32:16
plate of the holy crown a *w*. 39:30
according to the first *w*. *Deut* 10:4
made an end of *w*. the law. 31:24
the Lord made me understand in *w*.
1 Chr 28:19
Huram answered in *w*. *2 Chr* 2:11
came a *w*. from Jehoram. 21:12
prepare according to the *w*. of. 35:4
Cyrus put the proclamation in *w*.
36:22; *Ezra* 1:1
the *w*. of the letter was in. *Ezra* 4:7
unto all provinces according to the *w*.
Esth 1:22; 3:12; 8:9; 9:27
copy of the *w*. was published. 3:14
to Hatach a copy of the *w*. 4:8
the *w*. in the king's name may. 8:8
the *w*. of Hezekiah, when. *Isa* 38:9
not written in the *w*. of. *Ezek* 13:9
whosoever shall read this *w*. *Dan* 5:7
could not read the *w*. 8
should read this *w*. 15
if thou canst read the *w*. thou. 16
yet I will read the *w*. to the king. 17
this is the *w*. that was. 24, 25
sign the *w*. 6:8
king Darius signed the *w*. 9
when Daniel knew that the *w*. 10
give her a *w*. of divorcement.
Mat 5:31; 19:7
the *w*. was, Jesus of. *John* 19:19

hand-**writing**

blotting out the *hand-w*. *Col* 2:14

writings

if ye believe not his *w*. *John* 5:47

writing table

asked for a *w*. *table*. *Luke* 1:63

written

w. with the finger of God. *Ex* 31:18
Deut 9:10
elders did as it was *w*. *1 Ki* 21:11
these *w*. by name smote. *1 Chr* 4:41
the passover as it was *w*. *2 Chr* 30:5
a letter wherein was *w*. *Ezra* 5:7
therein was a record thus *w*. 6:2
weight of the vessels was *w*. 8:34
sent an open letter, wherein was *w*.
Neh 6:6
they found *w*. in the law. 8:14
and therein was found *w*. 13:1
it be *w*. among the laws. *Esth* 1:19
let it be *w*. that they may be. 3:9
of king Ahasuerus was it *w*. 12
found *w*. that Mordecai told of. 6:2
let it be *w*. to reverse Haman's. 8:5
let them not be *w*. with. *Ps* 69:28
be *w*. for the generation to. 102:18
on them the judgement *w*. 149:9
have not I *w*. to thee excellent things? *Pr* 22:20
that which was *w*. was. *Eccl* 12:10
shall be *w*. in the earth. *Jer* 17:13
hast *w*., saying, The king? 36:29
the roll was *w*. within. *Ezek* 2:10
nor *w*. in the writing of house. 13:9
writing that was *w*. *Dan* 5:24, 25
set up his accusation *w*. *Mat* 27:37
is it not *w*., My house? *Mark* 11:17
of his accusation was *w*. 15:26
Luke 23:38; *John* 19:20
place where it was *w*. *Luke* 4:17
rejoice that your names are *w*. 10:20
all things *w*. shall be accomplished.
18:31; 21:22
disciples remembered that it was *w*.
John 2:17
Is it not *w*. in your law, I said? 10:34
but these are *w*. that ye might. 20:31
w. every one, the world could not contain the books . . . be *w*. 21:25
fulfilled all that was *w*. *Acts* 13:29
the Gentiles, we have *w*. 21:25
the work of the law *w*. *Rom* 2:15
now it was not *w*. for his sake. 4:23
they are *w*. for our admonition.
1 Cor 10:11
ye are our epistle *w*. in our. *2 Cor* 3:2
w. not with ink, but with the. 3
if the ministration of death *w*. in. 7
I Paul have *w*. with. *Philem* 19
firstborn *w*. in heaven. *Heb* 12:23*
things which are *w*. therein. *Rev* 1:3
and in the stone a new name *w*. 2:17
not *w*. in the book of life. 13:8
having his Father's name *w*. 14:1
upon her head was a name *w*. 17:5
name *w*. on his thigh. 19:12, 16
names of the twelve tribes *w*. 21:12

is **written**

observe to do all that *is w*. *Josh* 1:8
that which *is w*. concerning us.
2 Ki 22:13
for writing which *is w*. in. *Esth* 8:8
every one that *is w*. among. *Isa* 4:3
sin of Judah *is w*. with. *Jer* 17:1
oath that *is w*. in the law. *Dan* 9:11
what *is w*. in the law? *Luke* 10:26
What is this then that *is w*.? 20:17
this that *is w*. must be. 22:37
be fulfilled that *is w*. *John* 15:25
to think of men above that which *is w*. *1 Cor* 4:6
for our sakes, no doubt, this *is w*. 9:10
the saying that *is w*., Death. 15:54

it is **written**

as *it is w*. in the law of. *Josh* 8:31
1 Ki 2:3; *2 Chr* 23:18; 25:4; 31:3
35:12; *Ezra* 3:2, 4; 6:18
Neh 8:15; 10:34, 36; *Dan* 9:13
it is w. of me. *Ps* 40:7; *Heb* 10:7
it is w. before me. *Isa* 65:6
thus *it is w*. by the prophet.
Mat 2:5; *Luke* 24:46
this is he of whom *it is w*.
Mat 11:10; *Luke* 7:27
as *it is w*. of him. *Mat* 26:24
Mark 9:13; 14:21
it is w. *Mat* 26:31; *Mark* 14:27
Luke 4:8; *Acts* 23:5
and how *it is w*. of the. *Mark* 9:12
as *it is w*. in the law. *Luke* 2:23
according as *it is w*. *Rom* 11:8
1 Cor 1:31; *2 Cor* 4:13
for *it is w*. *Rom* 12:19; 14:11
Gal 3:10
not himself, but as *it is w*. *Rom* 15:3
so *it is w*., The first man. *1 Cor* 15:45
because *it is w*., Be ye holy; for I am holy. *1 Pet* 1:16

I have, or *have I* **written**

commandment, *I have w*. *Ex* 24:12
I have w. to him great. *Hos* 8:12
Pilate said, What *I have w*. *I have w*. *John* 19:22
I have w. to you fathers. *1 John* 2:14
these things *have I w*. 26; 5:13

were **written**

of them that *were w*. *Num* 11:26
words *were* now *w*. *Job* 19:23
fulfilled which *were w*. *Luke* 24:44
things *were w*. of him. *John* 12:16
were w. aforetime *were w*. for our learning. *Rom* 15:4
see **book, chronicle**

wrong

Sarai said, My *w*. be. *Gen* 16:5
to him that did the *w*. *Ex* 2:13
against him what is *w*. *Deut* 19:16
thou doest me *w*. to war. *Judg* 11:27
seeing there is no *w*. in. *1 Chr* 12:17
no man to do them *w*.: yea, he reproved kings for. 16:21; *Ps* 105:14
not done *w*. to the king. *Esth* 1:16
behold, I cry out of *w*. *Job* 19:7
do no *w*., do no violence. *Jer* 22:3
buildeth his chambers by *w*. 13*
seen my *w*.: judge thou. *Lam* 3:59
therefore *w*. judgement. *Hab* 1:4*
Friend, I do thee no *w*. *Mat* 20:13
one of them suffer *w*. *Acts* 7:24
why do ye *w*. one to another? 26
neighbour *w*. thrust him away. 27
if it were a matter of *w*. 18:14
the Jews have I done no *w*. 25:10
do ye not rather take *w*.? *1 Cor* 6:7
nay, ye do *w*. and defraud your. 8
that had done the *w*. nor for his cause that suffered *w*. *2 Cor* 7:12
I was not burdensome to you? forgive me this *w*. 12:13
w. shall receive for the *w*. *Col* 3:25

wronged

receive us, we have *w*. *2 Cor* 7:2
if he hath *w*. thee, or. *Philem* 18

wrongeth

he that sinneth against me *w*. his own soul. *Pr* 8:36

wrongfully

the devices ye *w*. *Job* 21:27
let not mine enemies *w*. *Ps* 35:19
they that hate me *w*. are. 38:19
being mine enemies *w*. 69:4
me *w*., help thou me. 119:86
they have oppressed the stranger *w*.
Ezek 22:29
endure grief, suffering *w*. *1 Pet* 2:19

wrote

Moses *w*. all the words of the Lord and rose. *Ex* 24:4; *Deut* 31:9
Lord *w*. upon the tables words of.
Ex 34:28; *Deut* 4:13; 5:22; 10:4
and Moses *w*. their. *Num* 33:2
Moses *w*. this song the. *Deut* 31:22
Joshua *w*. upon the. *Josh* 8:32
Samuel *w*. the manner of the kingdom. *1 Sam* 10:25
David *w*. a letter to Joab.
2 Sam 11:14, 15
Jezebel *w*. letters in. *1 Ki* 21:8, 9
Jehu *w*. *2 Ki* 10:1, 6
Shemaiah *w*. *1 Chr* 24:6
Hezekiah *w*. letters to. *2 Chr* 30:1
Sennacherib *w*. to rail on the. 32:17
they *w*. an accusation. *Ezra* 4:6
Rehum *w*. 8, 9

letters which Haman *w.* *Esth* 8:5
Mordecai *w.* letters. 10; 9:20, 29
Baruch *w.* from Jeremiah. *Jer* 36:4
18, 27, 32
so Jeremiah *w.* in a book. 51:60
fingers of a man's hand *w. Dan* 5:5
then king Darius *w.* unto all. 6:25
Daniel had a dream; then he *w.* 7:1
your hardness Moses *w. Mark* 10:5
Master, Moses *w.* to us. 12:19
Luke 20:28
Zacharias *w.* saying. *Luke* 1:63
for Moses *w.* of me. *John* 5:46
Jesus with his finger *w.* 8:6, 8
Pilate *w.* a title and put. 19:19
John *w.* and testified of. 21:24
the apostles *w.* letters. *Acts* 15:23
the brethren *w.* exhorting. 18:27
Lysias *w.* a letter after. 23:25
who *w.* this epistle. *Rom* 16:22
I *w.* unto you. *1 Cor* 5:9; *2 Cor* 2:3, 4
7:12; *Eph* 3:3; *Philem* 21
things whereof ye *w.* to me. *1 Cor* 7:1
not as though I *w.* a new. *2 John* 5
I *w.* to the church. *3 John* 9

wroth

Cain was very *w.* *Gen* 4:5
why art thou *w.*? 6
Jacob was *w.* 31:36
Jacob's sons were *w.* 34:7
w. with two officers. 40:2; 41:10
Moses was *w.* *Ex* 16:20
Num 16:15; 31:14
wilt thou be *w.* with all? *Num* 16:22
your words and was *w.* *Deut* 1:34
3:26; 9:19; *2 Sam* 22:8; *2 Chr* 28:9
Ps 18:7; 78:21, 59, 62
Saul was very *w. 1 Sam* 18:8; 20:7
Philistines were *w.* with him. 29:4
Abner was *w.* *2 Sam* 3:8
David was *w.* 13:21
but Naaman was *w.* *2 Ki* 5:11
and the man of God was *w.* 13:19
Asa was *w.* *2 Chr* 16:10
Uzziah was *w.* 26:19
Sanballat was *w.* *Neh* 4:1, 7
Ahasuerus was very *w.* *Esth* 1:12
Bigthan and Teresh were *w.* 2:21
thou hast been *w.* with. *Ps* 89:38
shall be *w.* as in the. *Isa* 28:21
I was *w.* with my people. 47:6
I would not be *w.* with thee. 54:9
nor will I be always *w.* 57:16
of his covetousness was I *w.* and
smote him: I hid me . . . was *w.* 17
behold, thou art *w.*; for we. 64:5
be not *w.* very sore, O Lord; we. 9
princes were *w.* *Jer* 37:15
rejected us, thou art very *w.* against
us. *Lam* 5:22
Herod was *w.* *Mat* 2:16
his lord was *w.*, and. 18:34
king was *w.* 22:7
dragon was *w.* *Rev* 12:17

wrought

Shechem had *w.* folly in. *Gen* 34:7
what things I have *w.* in. *Ex* 10:2
then *w.* Bezaleel and Aholiab. 36:1
all the wise men *w.* the. 4, 8; 39:6
they have *w.* confusion. *Lev* 20:12
What hath God *w.*? *Num* 23:23
of them all *w.* jewels. 31:51
that such abomination is *w.*
Deut 13:14; 17:4
that hath *w.* wickedness. 17:2
heifer which hath not been *w.* 21:3
w. folly in Israel. 22:21; *Josh* 7:15
Judg 20:10
for the evils which they shall have *w.*
Deut 31:18
she had *w.*, The man's name with
whom I *w.* to-day. *Ruth* 2:19
Lord had *w.* wonderfully. *1 Sam* 6:6
w. salvation in Israel. 11:13; 19:5
for Jonathan hath *w.* with. 14:45
otherwise I should have *w.* falsehood. *2 Sam* 18:13
the Lord *w.* a great victory. 23:10, 12
who ruled over the people that *w.*
1 Ki 5:16; 9:23
of the sea was *w.* like. 7:26
and the treason he *w.* 16:20
but Omri *w.* evil in the eyes. 25
Jehoram *w.* evil. *2 Ki* 3:2; *2 Chr* 21:6
Israel *w.* wicked things. *2 Ki* 17:11
Neh 9:18
Manasseh *w.* much wickedness.
2 Ki 21:6; *2 Chr* 33:6
families that *w.* fine. *1 Chr* 4:21
masons to hew *w.* stones. 22:2
and he *w.* cherubims. *2 Chr* 3:14
they hired such as *w.* iron. 24:12
so the workman *w.* 13; 34:10, 13
half of my servants *w.* *Neh* 4:16
every one with one of his hands *w.* 17
this work was *w.* of our. 6:16
the Lord hath *w.* this. *Job* 12:9
thou hast *w.* iniquity? 36:23
hast *w.* for them that trust. *Ps* 31:19
clothing is of *w.* gold. 45:13
which thou hast *w.* for us. 68:28
how he had *w.* his signs in. 78:43
made in secret, curiously *w.* 139:15
all works my hands had *w. Eccl* 2:11
works *w.* under the sun. 17
for thou hast *w.* all our works in us.
Isa 26:12
we have not *w.* any deliverance. 18
who hath *w.* and done it? 41:4
she hath *w.* lewdness. *Jer* 11:15
and behold, he *w.* a work. 18:3
I *w.* for my name's sake. *Ezek* 20:9
14, 22, 44
because they *w.* for me. 29:20
wonders that God hath *w.* *Dan* 4:2
the sea *w.* and was. *Jonah* 1:11, 13
meek of earth who have *w. Zeph* 2:3
these last have *w.* but. *Mat* 20:12*
she hath *w.* a good work on me.
26:10; *Mark* 14:6
that they are *w.* of God. *John* 3:21
wonders were *w.* among. *Acts* 5:12
God hath *w.* 15:12; 21:19
abode with Aquila and *w.* 18:3
God *w.* special miracles by. 19:11
w. in me all manner of. *Rom* 7:8
Christ hath not *w.* by me. 15:18
he that hath *w.* us for. *2 Cor* 5:5
what carefulness it *w.* in you? 7:11
the signs of an apostle were *w.*
12:12
for he that *w.* effectually. *Gal* 2:8
which he *w.* in Christ. *Eph* 1:20
but we *w.* with labour. *2 Thes* 3:8
who, through faith, *w.* *Heb* 11:33
seest thou how faith *w.*? *Jas* 2:22
to have *w.* the will of. *1 Pet* 4:3
lose not those things which we have
w. *2 John* 8
the false prophet that *w.* *Rev* 19:20

wroughtest

to her, Where *w.* thou? *Ruth* 2:19

wrung

the blood shall be *w.* out. *Lev* 1:15*
5:9*
waters are *w.* to them. *Ps* 73:10†
thou hast *w.* out of the dregs of the
cup. *Isa* 51:17*

Y

yarn

y. out of Egypt, the king's merchants
. . . *y.* *1 Ki* 10:28*; *2 Chr* 1:16*

ye

ye shall be as gods. *Gen* 3:5
but *ye* have no portion in. *Neh* 2:20
ye are they which justify. *Luke* 16:15
but *ye* are washed, *ye* are sanctified,
ye are justified in. *1 Cor* 6:11
ye are bought with a price. 20
ye also helping by prayer. *2 Cor* 1:11
ye are our epistle, written. 3:2
ye are not straitened in us. 6:12
not that other men be eased, *ye*. 8:13
as I am, for I am as *ye* are. *Gal* 4:12
ye which are spiritual, restore. 6:1
ye who sometimes were. *Eph* 2:13
in whom *ye* also are builded. 22
joy, are not even *ye*? *1 Thes* 2:19
ye are our glory. 20
if *ye* stand fast in the Lord. 3:8
but *ye*, brethren, are not in. 5:4
ye are all children of light and. 5
but *ye*, brethren, be. *2 Thes* 3:13
but *ye* are a chosen. *1 Pet* 2:9

yea

y., hath God said, Ye. *Gen* 3:1
but let your communication be *Y.*, *y.*;
Nay, nay. *Mat* 5:37; *Jas* 5:12
said unto him, *Y. Mat* 9:28; 13:51
Sapphira said, *Y.* for so. *Acts* 5:8
thou a Roman? he said, *Y.* 22:27
y. y. and nay, nay. *2 Cor* 1:17
toward you was not *y.* and nay. 18
Son of God was not *y.* and nay. 19
God in him are *y.* and amen. 20
I do rejoice, *y.* and will. *Phil* 1:18
y. and I count all things but loss. 3:8
y. and all that live godly. *2 Tim* 3:12
y. brother, let me have. *Philem* 20

year

shall bear the next *y.* *Gen* 17:21
Isaac received the same *y.* 26:12
with bread that *y.* 47:17
first month of the *y.* *Ex* 12:2
keep it a feast unto the Lord in the
y. 23:14; *Lev* 23:41
three times in the *y.* all thy males.
Ex 23:17; 34:23, 24; *Deut* 16:16
out from thee in one *y.* *Ex* 23:29
ingathering at the *y.*'s end. 34:22
atonement once a *y.* *Lev* 16:34
it is a *y.* of rest. 25:5
redeem it within a *y.* 29
if it were a *y.* that the. *Num* 9:22
each day for a *y.* shall ye. 14:34
saying, The *y.* of release. *Deut* 15:9
the third *y.*, which is the *y.* of. 26:12
fruit of Canaan that *y.* *Josh* 5:12
that *y.* the Ammonites. *Judg* 10:8
to lament four days in a *y.* 11:40
thee ten shekels by the *y.* 17:10
David dwelt a *y.* and. *1 Sam* 27:7
that after the *y.* was. *2 Sam* 11:1
it was at every *y.*'s end that. 14:26
three times in a *y.* did. *1 Ki* 9:25
gold that came to Solomon in one *y.*
10:14; *2 Chr* 9:13
this *y.* such things as grow of themselves in second and third *y.*
2 Ki 19:29; *Isa* 37:30
gave him the same *y.* *2 Chr* 27:5
keep two days every *y.* *Esth* 9:27
thou crownest the *y.* with. *Ps* 65:11
in the *y.* that king Uzziah. *Isa* 6:1
in the *y.* that king Ahaz died. 14:28
in a *y.* all the glory of Kedar. 21:16
to proclaim the acceptable *y.* of the
Lord, and the. 61:2; *Luke* 4:19
and the *y.* of my redeemed. *Isa* 63:4
bring evil on the men of Anathoth,
even the *y. Jer* 11:23; 23:12; 48:44
shall not be careful in the *y.* 17:8
thus saith the Lord; this *y.* 28:16
prophet died the same *y.* 17
shall both come in one *y.* 51:46
each day for a *y.* *Ezek* 4:6
it shall be his to the *y.* of. 46:17
with calves of a *y.* old? *Mi* 6:6
his parents went to Jerusalem every
y. *Luke* 2:41
let it alone this *y.* also. 13:8
high priest that same *y.*, said, Ye
know. *John* 11:49, 51; 18:13
whole *y.* they assembled. *Acts* 11:26
Paul continued a *y.* at Corinth. 18:11
to be forward a *y.* ago. *2 Cor* 8:10
was ready a *y.* ago; your zeal. 9:2
went in once a *y.* *Heb* 9:7, 25
made of sins every *y.* 10:3
continue there a *y.* and buy. *Jas* 4:13
who were prepared for a month and
a *y.* *Rev* 9:15
see **first, second, third, fifth, seventh**

year *after* year

there was a famine three years *y.*
after y. *2 Sam* 21:1

year *by* year

increase of thy seed that the field
bringeth forth *y. by y. Deut* 14:22
eat it before the Lord *y. by y.* 15:20
as he did so *y. by y.*, so. *1 Sam* 1:7
gave to Hiram *y. by y.* *1 Ki* 5:11

they brought a rate *y.* *by* *y.* *1 Ki* 10:25; *2 Chr* 9:24
as he had done *y.* *by* *y.* *2 Ki* 17:4
wood offering *y.* *by* *y.* *Neh* 10:34
firstfruits of all trees *y.* *by* *y.* 35
which they offered *y.* *by* *y.* *Heb* 10:1

year *to* year

ordinance from *y.* *to* *y.* *Ex* 13:10
coat to him from *y.* *to* *y.* *1 Sam* 2:19
Samuel went from *y.* *to* *y.* in. 7:16
your God from *y.* *to* *y.* *2 Chr* 24:5
add ye *y.* *to* *y.*; let them. *Isa* 29:1
from *y.* *to* *y.* to worship. *Zech* 14:16

yearly

as a *y.* hired servant. *Lev* 25:53
daughters of Israel went *y.* to lament. *Judg* 11:40
of the Lord in Shiloh *y.* 21:19
Elkanah went up *y.* to. *1 Sam* 1:3
to offer the *y.* sacrifice. 21; 2:19
there is a *y.* sacrifice there. 20:6
keep 14th day of month Adar, and fifteenth of same *y.* *Esth* 9:21

yearn

for his bowels did *y.* *Gen* 43:30

yearned

for her bowels *y.* upon. *1 Ki* 3:26

years

for seasons, days, and *y.* *Gen* 1:14
these are the days of the *y.* 25:7
an old man and full of *y.* 8
an hundred thirty seven *y.* 17
few and evil have the *y.* of. 47:9
according to the number of *y.* *Lev* 25:15, 16, 50, 52
the money according to the *y.* 27:18
consider the *y.* of many. *Deut* 32:7
Joshua was old and stricken in *y.* *Josh* 13:1
been with me these *y.* *1 Sam* 29:3
David was old and stricken in *y.* *1 Ki* 1:1
not be dew nor rain these *y.* 17:1
Asa had no war in those *y.* *2 Chr* 14:6
after certain *y.* he went down. 18:2
are thy *y.* as man's days? *Job* 10:5
the number of *y.* is hidden to. 15:20
when a few *y.* are come, I. 16:22
and multitude of *y.* should. 32:7
they shall spend their *y.* in. 36:11
nor can number of his *y.* be. 26
and my *y.* are spent. *Ps* 31:10
wilt prolong his *y.* as many. 61:6
I considered the *y.* of ancient. 77:5
I will remember the *y.* of the. 10
their *y.* did he consume in. 78:33
for a thousand *y.* in thy sight are but. 90:4; *2 Pet* 3:8
we spend our *y.* as a tale. *Ps* 90:9
our *y.* are threescore *y.* and ten. 10
according to the *y.* wherein we. 15
thy *y.* are throughout all. 102:24
thou art the same, thy *y.* shall. 27
the *y.* of thy life shall be many. *Pr* 4:10; 9:11
lest thou give thy *y.* unto. 5:9
the *y.* of the wicked shall be. 10:27
evil days come not, nor *y.* *Eccl* 12:1
the *y.* of an hireling. *Isa* 21:16
of the residue of my *y.* 38:10
I shall go softly all my *y.* 15
I have laid on thee the *y.* *Ezek* 4:5
art come even unto thy *y.* 22:4
in latter *y.* thou shalt come. 38:8
by books the number of the *y.* *Dan* 9:2
in the end of *y.* they shall join. 11:6
continue more *y.* than the king. 8
shall come after certain *y.* 13
even to the *y.* of many. *Joel* 2:2
I will restore the *y.* the locusts. 25
in the midst of the *y.* *Hab* 3:2
the offering be pleasant as in the former *y.* *Mal* 3:4
well stricken in *y.* *Luke* 1:7, 18
days and months, and *y.* *Gal* 4:10
thy *y.* shall not fail. *Heb* 1:12
by faith Moses, when he was come to *y.*, refused. 11:24
bound Satan a thousand *y.* *Rev* 20:2
till the thousand *y.* should be. 3
reigned with Christ a thousand *y.* 4
when the thousand *y.* are expired. 7

see numeral words in their places, as **hundred, two, three.** *Also* **many, old, sin**

yell

like lions, they shall *y.* *Jer* 51:38*

yelled

roared and *y.* on him. *Jer* 2:15

yellow

behold, if there be in it a *y.* thin hair. *Lev* 13:30
if there be in it no *y.* hair. 32
priests shall not seek for *y.* hair. 36
covered with *y.* gold. *Ps* 68:13

yesterday

fulfilled your task *y.*? *Ex* 5:14
why came not the son of Jesse to meat *y.*? *1 Sam* 20:27
thou camest but *y.* *2 Sam* 15:20
I have seen *y.* the blood. *2 Ki* 9:26
we are but of *y.* and know. *Job* 8:9
a thousand years in thy sight are but as *y.* *Ps* 90:4
y. at the seventh hour. *John* 4:52
didst the Egyptian *y.*? *Acts* 7:28
Jesus Christ, the same *y.* *Heb* 13:8

yesternight

behold, I lay *y.* with my. *Gen* 19:34
your fathers spake to me *y.* 31:29
affliction, and rebuked thee *y.* 42

yet

y. did not the butler. *Gen* 40:23
as *y.* exaltest thyself. *Ex* 9:17
knowest thou not *y.* that Egypt? 10:7
if ye will not *y.* hearken. *Lev* 26:18
y. for all that, when they be. 44
y. in this thing ye did. *Deut* 1:32
y. they are thy people and. 9:29
ye are not as *y.* come to the. 12:9
y. the Lord hath not given you. 29:4
as *y.* I am as strong. *Josh* 14:11
Lord said, The people are *y.* too many. *Judg* 7:4
y. ye have forsaken me and. 10:13
y. honour me now before the elders. *1 Sam* 15:30
y. he hath made with me an everlasting covenant. *2 Sam* 23:5
y. hast not been as my. *1 Ki* 14:8
y. I have left me 7000. 19:18
there is *y.* one by whom we. 22:8
as *y.* the people did sacrifice. 43
2 Ki 14:4
y. the Lord would not destroy Judah. *2 Ki* 8:19
them from his presence as *y.* 13:23
as *y.* the people had not prepared. *2 Chr* 20:33
people did *y.* corruptly. 27:2
not cleansed, *y.* did they eat. 30:18
temple was not *y.* laid. *Ezra* 3:6
y. our God hath not forsaken us. 9:9; *Neh* 9:19
y. required not I bread. *Neh* 5:18
y. ye bring more wrath upon. 13:18
y. all this availeth me. *Esth* 5:13
while he was *y.* *Job* 1:16, 17, 18
then should I *y.* have comfort. 6:10
though he slay me, *y.* will I. 13:15
y. he shall perish for ever. 20:7
when the Almighty was *y.* 29:5
y. he knoweth it not in great. 35:15
y. have I set my king on my. *Ps* 2:6
y. have I not seen the righteous forsaken. 37:25
I shall *y.* praise him. 42:5, 11
43:5; 71:14
this is come, *y.* have we. 44:17
y. have I not declined. 119:51, 157
y. do I not forget thy statutes. 83
109, 141
y. will not his foolishness. *Pr* 27:22
y. is not washed from their. 30:12
better is he which hath not *y.* been. *Eccl* 4:3
kiss thee, *y.* I should. *S of S* 8:1
y. a remnant of them. *Isa* 10:22
for the Lord will *y.* choose. 14:1
y. gleaning grapes shall be. 17:6
while it is *y.* in his hand, he. 28:4
this is the rest, *y.* they would. 12
y. he also is wise, and will. 31:2
Israel be not gathered, *y.* shall. 49:5
they may forget, *y.* will I not. *Isa* 49:15
he was oppressed, *y.* he. 53:7
I will *y.* plead with you. *Jer* 2:9
y. return to me. 3:1
y. they prosper. 5:28
y. my mind could not be. 15:1
prophets, *y.* they ran: *y.* they. 23:21
y. they were not afraid, nor. 36:24
though they cry, *y.* will. *Ezek* 8:18
y. will I be to them as a little. 11:16
said, I am a god, *y.* thou art a. 28:2
I will *y.* for this be enquired. 36:37
y. made we not our prayer before God. *Dan* 9:13
because it is *y.* for a time. 11:35
y. he shall come to his end. 45
grey hairs are upon him, *y.* *Hos* 7:9
y. I am the Lord thy God from. 13:4
given you want of bread, *y.* have ye not returned to me. *Amos* 4:6
8, 9, 10, 11; *Hag* 2:17
he shall say, Is there *y.*? *Amos* 6:10
y. I will look toward thy. *Jonah* 2:4
y. forty days and Nineveh. 3:4
was my saying, when I was *y.* 4:2
are there *y.* the treasures? *Mi* 6:10
y. was she carried away. *Nah* 3:10
y. I will rejoice in the Lord, I will joy. *Hab* 3:18
y. is she thy companion. *Mal* 2:14
do not ye *y.* understand, that? *Mat* 15:17; 16:9; *Mark* 8:17
I kept, what lack I *y.*? *Mat* 19:20
but the end is not *y.* 24:6
Mark 13:7
time of figs was not *y.* *Mark* 11:13
words I spake while *y.* *Luke* 24:44
unto her, Mine hour is not *y.* come. *John* 2:4; 7:6, 30; 8:20
for the Holy Ghost was not *y.* 7:39
though he were dead *y.* shall. 11:25
for as *y.* they knew not the. 20:9
as *y.* the Holy Ghost was fallen upon none of them. *Acts* 8:16
he had *y.* being uncircumcised. *Rom* 4:11, 12
we were *y.* without strength. 5:6
while we were *y.* sinners. 8
why doth he *y.* hope for? 8:24
Why doth he *y.* find fault? 9:19
ye are *y.* carnal. *1 Cor* 3:3
y. so as by fire. 15
to the married I command, *y.* not I, but the Lord. 7:10
y. for all that will they not. 14:21
y. not I, but the grace of God. 15:10
your faith is vain, ye are *y.* 17
that he will *y.* deliver. *2 Cor* 1:10
to spare you I came not as *y.* 23
y. true, as unknown, *y.* known. 6:8
y. not I, but Christ. *Gal* 2:20
in vain? if it be *y.* in vain. 3:4
I, brethren, if I *y.* preach. 5:11
when I was *y.* with you. *2 Thes* 2:5
y. is he not crowned. *2 Tim* 2:5
we see not *y.* all things. *Heb* 2:8
like as we are, *y.* without sin. 4:15
for he was *y.* in the loins of. 7:10
and by it he being dead *y.* 11:4
warned of things not seen as *y.* 7
keep the whole law, *y.* *Jas* 2:10
y. if thou kill. 11
y. ye have not. 4:2
it doth not *y.* appear. *1 John* 3:2
and is not, and *y.* is. *Rev* 17:8
and the other is not *y.* come. 10
received no kingdom as *y.* 12

see **alive**

yield

the ground, it shall not henceforth *y.* her strength. *Gen* 4:12
fat, shall *y.* royal dainties. 49:20
that it may *y.* to you the increase. *Lev* 19:25
y. her increase, trees *y.* fruit. 26:4
for your land shall not *y.* her. 20
but *y.* yourselves to the Lord. *2 Chr* 30:8
the land shall *y.* her increase. *Ps* 67:6; 85:12
plant vineyards, which may *y.* 107:37
speech she caused him to *y.* *Pr* 7:21

vineyard shall *y.* one bath, and the seed of an homer shall *y.* *Isa* 5:10
the bud shall *y.* no meal: if so be it *y.* the stranger shall. *Hos* 8:7
the fig tree and vine *y.* *Joel* 2:22
fields shall *y.* no meat. *Hab* 3:17
but do not thou *y.* unto. *Acts* 23:21
nor *y.* ye your members as instruments of . . . sin, *y.* *Rom* 6:13*
that to whom ye *y.* yourselves servants. 16*
y. your members servants to. 19*
no fountain *y.* salt water. *Jas* 3:12

yielded

his sons, *y.* up the ghost. *Gen* 49:33
rod of Aaron *y.* almonds. *Num* 17:8
y. their bodies that they. *Dan* 3:28
Jesus cried again, and *y.* *Mat* 27:50
then Sapphira *y.* up the. *Acts* 5:10
ye have *y.* your members. *Rom* 6:19

yieldeth

it *y.* much increase. *Neh* 9:37
wilderness *y.* food for. *Job* 24:5
y. the peaceable fruit of. *Heb* 12:11

yielding

bring forth herb *y.* seed, tree *y.* fruit. *Gen* 1:11, 12
given you every tree *y.* seed. 29
for *y.* pacifieth great. *Eccl* 10:4
see **fruit**

yoke

This term is used both literally and figuratively in the Bible. Figuratively it is used [1] *Of the yoke of bondage, or slavery,* Lev 26:13; *Deut* 28:48. [2] *Of the yoke of afflictions and crosses,* Lam 3:27. [3] *Of the yoke of punishment for sin,* Lam 1:14. [4] *Of the yoke of Christ's service,* Mat 11:29, 30.

that thou shalt break his *y.* *Gen* 27:40; *Jer* 30:8
I have broken the bands of your *y.* *Lev* 26:13; *Ezek* 34:27
a red heifer without blemish, on which never came *y.* *Num* 19:2
Deut 21:3; *1 Sam* 6:7
he shall put a *y.* of iron upon thy neck. *Deut* 28:48; *Jer* 28:14
Saul took a *y.* of oxen. *1 Sam* 11:7
an half acre, which a *y.* of. 14:14
y. grievous, make his heavy *y.* *1 Ki* 12:4, 10, 11, 14; *2 Chr* 10:4
with twelve *y.* of oxen. *1 Ki* 19:19
he took a *y.* of oxen, and slew. 21
Job had five hundred *y.* *Job* 1:3
he had a thousand *y.* of oxen. 42:12
thou hast broken the *y.* of his burden. *Isa* 9:4; 10:27; 14:25
hast very heavily laid thy *y.* 47:6
and that ye break every *y.* 58:6
I have broken thy *y.* *Jer* 2:20
altogether broken the *y.* 5:5
not put their neck under the *y.* 27:8
bring their neck under the *y.* 11, 12
broken the *y.* of the king. 28:2; 4, 11
Hananiah had broken the *y.* 12*
unaccustomed to the *y.* 31:18
husbandman and his *y.* 51:23
the *y.* of my transgressions. *Lam* 1:14
good for a man to bear the *y.* 3:27
they that take off the *y.* *Hos* 11:4
now will I break his *y.* *Nah* 1:13
take my *y.* upon you. *Mat* 11:29
my *y.* is easy. 30
bought five *y.* of oxen. *Luke* 14:19
to put a *y.* on the disciples' neck. *Acts* 15:10
be not entangled with the *y.* *Gal* 5:1
as are under the *y.* *1 Tim* 6:1

yoked

be not unequally *y.* with. *2 Cor* 6:14

yokefellow

I intreat thee also, true *y.* *Phil* 4:3

yokes

make thee bonds and *y.* *Jer* 27:2*
y. of wood; but make *y.* of iron. 28:13
break the *y.* of Egypt. *Ezek* 30:18

yonder

I and the lad will go *y.* *Gen* 22:5
scatter thou the fire *y.* *Num* 16:37
while I meet the Lord *y.* 23:15
y. is that Shunammite. *2 Ki* 4:25
Remove hence to *y.* place. *Mat* 17:20
here, while I go and pray *y.* 26:36

you

a space between *y.* and ark. *Josh* 3:4
and shake my head at *y.* *Job* 16:4
your iniquities have separated between *y.* and your God. *Isa* 59:2
and I will put a new spirit within *y.* *Ezek* 11:19; 36:26, 27
are about *y.*, bear shame. 36:7, 36
I am pressed under *y.* *Amos* 2:13
y. only have I known of all. 3:2
he that heareth *y.* heareth me; and he that despiseth *y.* *Luke* 10:16
and *y.* yourselves thrust out. 13:28
the name of God is blasphemed through *y.* *Rom* 2:24
lest they come and find *y.* unprepared. *2 Cor* 9:4
gospel in the regions beyond *y.* 10:16
for I seek not yours but *y.* 12:14
y. hath he quickened. *Eph* 2:1
y. that were sometime alienated and enemies. *Col* 1:21
y., being dead in your sins, hath he quickened. 2:13
see **tell**

after **you**

with you, and seed *after y.* *Gen* 9:9
inheritance for your children *after y.* *Lev* 25:46; *1 Chr* 28:8
draw out a sword *after y.* *Lev* 26:33
as they pursued *after y.* *Deut* 11:4
that shall rise up *after y.* 29:22
behold, I come *after y.* *1 Sam* 25:19
shall follow close *after y.* *Jer* 42:16
which long *after y.* *2 Cor* 9:14
Phil 1:8
longed *after y.* *Phil* 2:26

against **you**

I have sinned *against y.* *Ex* 10:16
I will set my face *against y.* *Lev* 26:17; *Jer* 44:11
they murmur *against y.* *Num* 17:5
came out *against y.* *Deut* 1:44
earth to witness *against y.* this day, that ye shall soon. 4:26; 30:19
I testify *against y.* that ye. 8:19
the Lord was wroth *against y.* 9:19
11:17; *Josh* 23:16
Jericho fought *against y.* *Josh* 24:11
the Lord is witness *against y.* *1 Sam* 12:5; *Mi* 1:2
Ammonites came *against y.* *1 Sam* 12:12
hand of Lord shall be *against y.* 15
counselled *against y.* *2 Sam* 17:21
to cry alarm *against y.* *2 Chr* 13:12
heap up words *against y.* *Job* 16:4
I devise a device *against y.* *Jer* 18:11
will fight *against y.* in anger. 21:5
of evil pronounced *against y.* 26:13
Chaldeans that fight *against y.* 37:10
the king of Babylon shall not come *against y.* 19
cannot do any thing *against y.* 38:5
words shall stand *against y.* 44:29
conceived a purpose *against y.* 49:30
I am *against y.* *Ezek* 13:8
enemy said *against y.* 36:2
Lord hath spoken *against y.* *Amos* 3:1; 5:1; *Zeph* 2:5
I will raise up *against y.* a nation. *Amos* 6:14
take up a parable *against y.* *Mi* 2:4
manner of evil *against y.* *Mat* 5:11
go into the village over against *y.* 21:2; *Mark* 11:2; *Luke* 19:30
the very dust of your city we do wipe off *against y.* *Luke* 10:11
be a witness *against y.* *Jas* 5:3
whereas they speak *against y.* as evil doers. *1 Pet* 2:12

among or *amongst* **you**

strange gods that are *among y.* *Gen* 35:2; *Josh* 24:23; *1 Sam* 7:3
tabernacle *amongst y.* *Lev* 26:11
I will walk *among y.* and will. 12
I will send wild beasts *among y.* 22
I will send pestilence *among y.* 25
despised the Lord who is *among y.* *Num* 11:20; 14:42; *Deut* 6:15
7:21; *Josh* 3:10
who is there *among y.*? *2 Chr* 36:23
Ezra 1:3
who *among y.* will give? *Isa* 42:23
who is *among y.* that feareth? 50:10
purge out from *among y.* *Ezek* 20:38
who is left *among y.* that? *Hag* 2:3
who is there *among y.*? *Mal* 1:10
it shall not be so *among y.* *Mat* 20:26; *Mark* 10:43
among y. let him be your servant. *Mat* 20:27; 23:11; *Luke* 22:26
he that is least *among y.* *Luke* 9:48
but I am *among y.* as he. 22:27
standeth one *among y.* *John* 1:26
he that is without sin *among y.* 8:7
brethren, look ye out *among y.* seven men. *Acts* 6:3
and whosoever *among y.* 13:26
let them who *among y.* are. 25:5
some fruit *among y.* *Rom* 1:13
every man that is *among y.* 12:3
no divisions *among y.* *1 Cor* 1:10
contentions *among y.* 11; 11:18
to know any thing *among y.* 2:2
is *among y.* envying, strife. 3:3
if any man *among y.* seemeth. 18
there is fornication *among y.* 5:1
taken away from *among y.* 2
how say some *among y.* that? 15:12
Christ who was preached *among y.* *2 Cor* 1:19
in presence am base *among y.* 10:1
will humble me *among y.* 12:21
not be once named *among y.* *Eph* 5:3
what manner of men were *among y.* *1 Thes* 1:5
if any man *among y.* *Jas* 1:26
is any *among y.* afflicted? 5:13
is any sick *among y.*? 14
feed the flock of God which is *among y.* *1 Pet* 5:2
false teachers *among y.* *2 Pet* 2:1
who was slain *among y.* *Rev* 2:13
see **sojourneth**

before **you**

the land shall be *before y.* *Gen* 34:10
God did send me *before y.* 45:5, 7
for evil is *before y.* *Ex* 10:10
these the nations are defiled which I cast out *before y.* *Lev* 18:24
20:23; *Num* 33:52, 55; *Deut* 11:23
Josh 3:10; 9:24; 23:5, 9; 24:8
12; *Judg* 6:9
men of the land done which were *before y.* *Lev* 18:27, 28, 30
shall fall *before y.* 26:7, 8
are there *before y.* *Num* 14:43
shall be subdued *before y.* 32:29
set the land *before y.* *Deut* 1:8
Lord who goeth *before y.* shall. 30
set *before y.* this day. 4:8; 11:32
I set *before y.* a blessing and a curse. 11:26; 30:19
dried up Jordan *before y.* *Josh* 4:23
I sent the hornet *before y.* 24:12
behold, he is *before y.* *1 Sam* 9:12
the king walketh *before y.* 12:2
my statutes which I have set *before y.* *2 Chr* 7:19; *Jer* 26:4; 44:10
Lord will go *before y.* *Isa* 52:12
behold, I set *before y.* the. *Jer* 21:8
so persecuted they the prophets which were *before y.* *Mat* 5:12
kingdom of God *before y.* 21:31
risen again, I will go *before y.* 26:32
28:7; *Mark* 14:28; 16:7
eat such things as are set *before y.* *Luke* 10:8; *1 Cor* 10:27
doth this man stand here *before y.* whole. *Acts* 4:10

by **you**

I will not be enquired of *by y.* *Ezek* 20:3, 31
I trust to be brought on my way *by y.* *Rom* 15:24
if the world shall be judged *by y.* *1 Cor* 6:2

was refreshed *by y.* all. *2 Cor* 7:13
shall be enlarged *by y.* 10:15

concerning **you**

what Lord will command *concerning y.* *Num* 9:8
which the Lord spake *concerning y.* *Josh* 23:14
hath said *concerning y.* *Jer* 42:19
this is the will of God *concerning y.* *1 Thes* 5:18

for **you**

as *for y.* *Gen* 44:17; 50:20
Num 14:32; *Deut* 1:40; *Josh* 23:9
Job 17:10
one ordinance shall be *for y.* *Num* 15:15, 16
all that he did *for y.* *Deut* 1:30
4:34; *1 Sam* 12:24
as *for y.* O house of Israel. *Ezek* 20:39; 34:17
behold I am *for y.* and I will. 36:9
but one decree *for y.* *Dan* 2:9
to what end is it *for y.*? *Amos* 5:18
is it not *for y.* to know judgement? *Mi* 3:1
is it time *for y.*, to dwell? *Hag* 1:4
commandment is *for y.* *Mal* 2:1
more tolerable for Tyre and Sidon, than *for y.* *Mat* 11:22; *Luke* 10:14
kingdom prepared *for y.* *Mat* 25:34
that I should do *for y.* *Mark* 10:36
this is my body which is given *for y.* *Luke* 22:19
blood shed *for y.* 20; *1 Cor* 11:24
prepare a place *for y.* *John* 14:2, 3
I will pray the Father *for y.* 16:26
is not *for y.* to know the times or the seasons. *Acts* 1:7
therefore have I called *for y.* 28:20
God through Christ *for y.* *Rom* 1:8
was Paul crucified *for y.*? *1 Cor* 1:13
care *for y.* appear. *2 Cor* 7:12; 8:16
by their prayer *for y.* 9:14; *Phil* 1:4
Col 1:3, 9; 4:12; *2 Thes* 1:11
and be spent *for y.* *2 Cor* 12:15
I cease not to give thanks *for y.* *Eph* 1:16; *1 Thes* 1:2; 3:9
2 Thes 1:3; 2:13
at my tribulations *for y.* *Eph* 3:13
Col 1:24
is not grievous, but *for y.* *Phil* 3:1
which is laid up *for y.* *Col* 1:5
which is given to me *for y.* 25
great conflict I have *for y.* 2:1
that he hath a great zeal *for y.* 4:13
is unprofitable *for y.* *Heb* 13:17
reserved in heaven *for y.* *1 Pet* 1:4
on him, for he careth *for y.* 5:7

from **you**

sent me away *from y.* *Gen* 26:27
we are very far *from y.* *Josh* 9:22
not removed *from y.* *1 Sam* 6:3
come word *from y.* *2 Sam* 15:28
wrath turn away *from y.* *2 Chr* 30:8
turn away his face *from y.* 9
will hide mine eyes *from y.* *Isa* 1:15
have hid his face *from y.* 59:2
good things *from y.* *Jer* 5:25
which are gone *from y.* 34:21
keep nothing back *from y.* 42:4
cast away *from y.* your. *Ezek* 18:31
remove far *from y.* the. *Joel* 2:20
I have withholden the rain *from y.* *Amos* 4:7
kingdom of God shall be taken *from y.* *Mat* 21:43
no man taketh *from y.* *John* 16:22
who is taken up *from y.* *Acts* 1:11
but seeing ye put it *from y.* 13:46
word of God out *from y.* *1 Cor* 14:36
of commendation *from y.* *2 Cor* 3:1
let evil speaking be put away *from y.* *Eph* 4:31
for *from y.* sounded out. *1 Thes* 1:8
but we being taken *from y.* 2:17
and he will flee *from y.* *Jas* 4:7

in **you**

be any truth *in y.* *Gen* 42:16
let him also rejoice *in y.* *Judg* 9:19
sanctified *in y.* *Ezek* 20:41; 36:23
will put breath *in y.* 37:6, 14
I have no pleasure *in y.* saith the Lord. *Mal* 1:10
but the Spirit which speaketh *in y.* *Mat* 10:20
works which were done *in y.* 11:21
not his word abiding *in y.* *John* 5:38
not the love of God *in y.* 42
the flesh, ye have no life *in y.* 6:53
he shall be *in y.* 14:17
and I *in y.* 20; 15:4
if my words abide *in y.* 15:7
1 John 2:14, 24
the Spirit dwelleth *in y.* *Rom* 8:9
1 John 2:27
and if Christ be *in y.* *Rom* 8:10
as much as lieth *in y.*, live. 12:18
Christ is confirmed *in y.* *1 Cor* 1:6
Holy Ghost which is *in y.* 6:19
God is *in y.* of a truth. 14:25
having confidence *in y.* all. *2 Cor* 2:3
7:16; 8:22; *Gal* 5:10
but life *in y.* *2 Cor* 4:12
he was comforted *in y.* 7:7
he would finish *in y.* the same. 8:6
exceeding grace of God *in y.* 9:14
is not weak, but mighty *in y.* 13:3
that Jesus Christ is *in y.*? 5
I travail, till Christ be formed *in y.* *Gal* 4:19
one God . . . who is above all, and through all, and *in y.* all. *Eph* 4:6
let this mind be *in y.* which. *Phil* 2:5
it is God which worketh *in y.* 13
which bringeth forth fruit, as it doth also *in y.* *Col* 1:6
which is Christ *in y.*, the hope. 27
Christ dwell *in y.* richly. 3:16
worketh *in y.* *1 Thes* 2:13
so that we glory *in y.* *2 Thes* 1:4
Christ may be glorified *in y.* 12
every good thing *in y.* *Philem* 6
working *in y.* that which is well-pleasing. *Heb* 13:21
the hope that is *in y.* *1 Pet* 3:15
if these things be *in y.* *2 Pet* 1:8
which thing is true in him and *in y.* *1 John* 2:8
greater is he that is *in y.* than. 4:4

of **you**

why should I be deprived *of y.* both? *Gen* 27:45
may be done *of y.* *Ex* 12:16
unto me every one *of y.* *Deut* 1:22
faint because *of y.* *Josh* 2:9
to these nations because *of y.* 23:3
that all *of y.* have conspired against me. *1 Sam* 22:8
O people, every one *of y.* *1 Ki* 22:28
what Ezra requires *of y.* *Ezra* 7:21
though there were *of y.* cast out unto uttermost part of heaven. *Neh* 1:9
ye shall be slain all *of y.* *Ps* 62:3
that escape *of y.* shall. *Ezek* 6:9
he shall receive *of y.* *Mi* 1:11
which *of y.* by taking thought can add one cubit? *Mat* 6:27; *Luke* 12:25
doth not each one *of y.*? *Luke* 13:15
of y. convinceth me of? *John* 8:46
I speak not *of y.* all, I know. 13:18
which God did by him in the midst *of y.* *Acts* 2:22
in turning every one *of y.* 3:26
which was set at nought *of y.* 4:11
faith both *of y.* and me. *Rom* 1:12
declared to me *of y.* *1 Cor* 1:11
such were some *of y.* but ye. 6:11
the feet, I have no need *of y.* 12:21
every one *of y.* hath a psalm. 14:26
let every one *of y.* lay by him. 16:2
and our hope *of y.* is. *2 Cor* 1:7
boasted any thing to him *of y.* 7:14
suffer, if a man take *of y.* 11:20
did I make a gain *of y.*? 12:17
Did Titus make a gain *of y.*? 18
this only would I learn *of y.* *Gal* 3:2
for as many *of y.* as have been. 27
voice, for I stand in doubt *of y.* 4:20
brother, who is one *of y.* *Col* 4:9, 12
neither *of y.* sought we. *1 Thes* 2:6
every one *of y.* should know. 4:4
no evil thing to say *of y.* *Tit* 2:8
the hire which is *of y.* kept. *Jas* 5:4
they speak evil *of y.* *1 Pet* 3:16; 4:4

on, or *upon* **you**

plague shall not be *upon y.* *Ex* 12:13
bestow *upon y.* a blessing. *Ex* 32:29
oil of the Lord is *upon y.* *Lev* 10:7
they said, Ye take too much *upon y.* *Num* 16:3, 7
not set his love *upon y.* *Deut* 7:7
things are come *upon y.* *Josh* 23:15
they will be *upon y.* *Neh* 4:12
of the Lord be *upon y.* *Ps* 129:8
upon y. the spirit of sleep. *Isa* 29:10
he may have mercy *upon y.* 30:18
Jer 42:12
I will visit *upon y.* the. *Jer* 23:2
this thing is come *upon y.* 40:3
I will blow *upon y.* in. *Ezek* 22:21
days shall come *upon y.* *Amos* 4:2
before the fierce anger of the Lord come *upon y.* *Zeph* 2:2
upon y. may come the. *Mat* 23:35
of God is come *upon y.* *Luke* 11:20
and so that day come *upon y.* 21:34
I send the promise of my Father *upon y.* 24:49
darkness come *upon y.* *John* 12:35
Holy Ghost is come *upon y.* *Acts* 1:8
not cast a snare *upon y.* *1 Cor* 7:35
upon y. labour in vain. *Gal* 4:11
howl for your miseries that shall come *upon y.* *Jas* 5:1
of God resteth *upon y.* *1 Pet* 4:14
I will put *upon y.* none. *Rev* 2:24

over **you**

I will even appoint *over y.* *Lev* 26:16
hate you shall reign *over y.* 17
rejoiced *over y.* to do you good, he will rejoice *over y.* *Deut* 28:63
rule *over y.* nor my son rule *over y.*: Lord shall rule *over y.* *Judg* 8:23
seventy reign *over y.* or one? 9:2
ye anoint me king *over y.* 15
that shall reign *over y.* *1 Sam* 8:11
I have made a king *over y.* 12:1
the Lord hath set a king *over y.* 13
David to be king *over y.* *2 Sam* 3:17
chief priest is *over y.* *2 Chr* 19:11
watchmen *over y.* saying. *Jer* 6:17
fury poured out will I rule *over y.* *Ezek* 20:33
heaven *over y.* is stayed. *Hag* 1:10
me a divider *over y.*? *Luke* 12:14
not have dominion *over y.* *Rom* 6:14
of this power *over y.* *1 Cor* 9:12
over y. with godly zeal. *2 Cor* 11:2
we were comforted *over y.* in affliction. *1 Thes* 3:7
know them which are *over y.* 5:12
remember them which have the rule *over y.* *Heb* 13:7
obey them that have the rule *over y.* 17
salute them that have the rule *over y.* 24

to or *unto* **you**

every herb *to y.* it shall. *Gen* 1:29
and take our daughters *unto y.* 34:9
and will be *to y.* a God. *Ex* 6:7
children shall say *unto y.* 12:26
not make *unto y.* gods of gold. 20:23
it shall be *unto y.* most holy. 30:36
I will also do this *unto y.* *Lev* 26:16
they shall be *to y.* for an. *Num* 10:8
be *to y.* a memorial. 10
unto y. for a fringe. 15:39
I shall do *unto y.* as I thought. 33:56
to them, and they *to y.* *Josh* 23:12
as they have been *to y.* *1 Sam* 4:9
unto y. O men, I call. *Pr* 8:4
this iniquity shall be *to y.* *Isa* 30:13
to y. it is commanded. *Dan* 3:4
unto y. that fear my name. *Mal* 4:2
that men should do *to y.* *Mat* 7:12
Luke 6:31
to your faith be it *unto y.* *Mat* 9:29
because it is given *unto y.* to know. 13:11; *Mark* 4:11; *Luke* 8:10
unto y. that hear shall. *Mark* 4:24
unto y. is born this day a Saviour. *Luke* 2:11
to them which do good *to y.* 6:33
I appoint *unto y.* a kingdom. 22:29
for the promise is *unto y.* *Acts* 2:39
unto y. first, God having raised. 3:26
therefore came I *unto y.* 10:29
to y. is the word of this. 13:26

doubtless I am *to y.* 1 Cor 9:2
word of God *unto y.* only ? 14:36
to reach even *unto y.* 2 Cor 10:13
we are come as far as *to y.* 14
but *to y.* of salvation. Phil 1:28
unto y. it is given not only to. 29
our gospel came not *unto y.* in word. 1 Thes 1:5
to y. who are troubled. 2 Thes 1:7
unto y. that believe. 1 Pet 2:7
but *unto y.* I say, and. Rev 2:24
see **say, told**

toward **you**
good work *toward y.* Jer 29:10
thoughts I think *toward y.* 11
judgement is *toward y.* Hos 5:1
our word *toward y.* was. 2 Cor 1:18
is more abundant *toward y.* 7:15
all grace abound *toward y.* 9:8
being absent am bold *toward y.* 10:1
by the power of God *toward y.* 13:4
abound in love one toward another, as we do *toward y.* 1 Thes 3:12

with **you**
then we will dwell *with y.* Gen 34:16
but God shall be *with y.* 48:21
my bones hence *with y.* Ex 13:19
that I have talked *with y.* 20:22
Aaron and Hur are *with y.* 24:14
with y. shall be a man. Num 1:4
where I will meet *with y.* 17:4
it may be well *with y.* Deut 5:33
no part *with y.* 12:12
God goeth *with y.* 20:4
nor *with y.* only do I make. 29:14
neither will I be *with y.* Josh 7:12
said, The Lord be *with y.* Ruth 2:4
and mother be *with y.* 1 Sam 22:3
me, and I will go *with y.* 23:23
what have I to do *with y.*? 2 Sam 16:10; 19:22
go forth *with y.* myself. 18:2
master's sons are *with y.* 2 Ki 10:2
see there be *with y.* none of. 23
and it shall be well *with y.* 25:24
Jer 40:9
Lord your God *with y.*? 1 Chr 22:18
there are *with y.* golden calves. 2 Chr 13:8
the Lord is *with y.* while ye. 15:2
for the Lord, who is *with y.* in. 19:6
the Lord will be *with y.* 20:17
with y., even *with y.*, sins ? 28:10
let us build *with y.*: for we. Ezra 4:2
lest I deal *with y.* after. Job 42:8
do *with y.* as this potter ? Jer 18:6
I am *with y.* 42:11; Hag 1:13; 2:4
will I plead *with y.* Ezek 20:35, 36
when I have wrought *with y.* 44
the Lord shall be *with y.* Amos 5:14
with y., for God is *with y.* Zech 8:23
how long shall I be *with y.*? Mat 17:17
Mark 9:19; Luke 9:41
the poor always *with y.*, but me ye. Mat 26:11; John 12:8
I drink it new *with y.* in. Mat 26:29
I am *with y.* alway, unto the. 28:20
you, while I was *with y.* Luke 24:44
yet a little while am I *with y.*, then I go to. John 7:33; 12:35; 13:33
Have I been so long *with y.*? 14:9
that he may abide *with y.* 16
he dwelleth *with y.* 17
being present *with y.* 25
peace I leave *with y.* 27
because I was *with y.* 16:4
I should bear *with y.* Acts 18:14
I have been *with y.* at all. 20:18
comforted together *with y.* Rom 1:12
I may *with y.* be refreshed. 15:32
now the God of peace be *with y.* all. 33; 2 Cor 13:11; Phil 4:9
the grace of our Lord Jesus Christ be *with y.* Rom 16:20, 24
1 Cor 16:23; Phil 4:23; Col 4:18
1 Thes 5:28; 2 Thes 3:18
2 Tim 1:2; 4:22; Tit 3:15
Heb 13:25; 2 John 3; Rev 22:21
was *with y.* in weakness. 1 Cor 2:3
that we also might reign *with y.* 4:8
see that he may be *with y.* 16:10
my love be *with y.* all in Christ. 24
establisheth us *with y.* 2 Cor 1:21
and present us *with y.* 2 Cor 4:14
hearts to die and live *with y.* 7:3
when I was present *with y.* 11:9
Gal 4:18, 20
I joy and rejoice *with y.* Phil 2:17
am I *with y.* in the spirit. Col 2:5
glorified, as it is *with y.* 2 Thes 3:1
the Lord be *with y.* all. 16
God dealeth *with y.* as. Heb 12:7
peace be *with y.* all. 1 Pet 5:14
spots and blemishes, while they feast *with y.* 2 Pet 2:13

young
have not cast their *y.* Gen 31:38
the flocks and herds with *y.* 33:13
nothing cast their *y.* Ex 23:26
not kill it and her *y.* Lev 22:28
take the dam with the *y.* Deut 22:6
let the dam go and take the *y.* 7
shew favour to the *y.* 28:50
eagle fluttereth over her *y.* 32:11
had a *y.* son Micha. 2 Sam 9:12
my son is *y.* 1 Chr 22:5; 29:1
when Rehoboam was *y.* 2 Chr 13:7
Josiah, while he was yet *y.* 34:3
ewes great with *y.* Ps 78:71
where she may lay her *y.* 84:3
those that are with *y.* Isa 40:11
for the *y.* of the flock. Jer 31:12
cropped off the top of his *y.* twigs. Ezek 17:4, 22
whose *y.* daughter had. Mark 7:25*
when *y.* thou girdedst. John 21:18
see **child, children, man, men, old**

young *ass,* or *asses*
the shoulders of *y. asses.* Isa 30:6
the *y. asses* shall eat clean. 24
he found a *y. ass,* sat. John 12:14
see **bullock**

young *bullocks*
shall offer two *y. bullocks.* Num 28:11, 19, 27
need, both *y. bullocks.* Ezra 6:9

young *calf*
take thee a *y. calf* for. Lev 9:2*

young *cow*
man shall nourish a *y. cow.* Isa 7:21

young *dromedaries*
he sent letters by riders on *y. dromedaries.* Esth 8:10*

young *eagles*
y. eagles shall eat it. Pr 30:17

young *hart*
my beloved is like a *y. hart.* S of S 2:9, 17; 8:14
see **lion, lions**

young *one*
her eye shall be evil toward her *y. one.* Deut 28:57
neither shall seek the *y. one,* nor heal. Zech 11:16*

young *ones*
whether they be *y. ones.* Deut 22:6
when his *y. ones* cry to. Job 38:41
bring forth their *y. ones.* 39:3
their *y. ones* are in good liking. 4
is hardened against her *y. ones.* 16
the eagles' *y. ones* also suck. 30
their *y. ones* shall lie. Isa 11:7
give suck to their *y. ones.* Lam 4:3

young *pigeon*
dove, and a *y. pigeon.* Gen 15:9
bring a *y. pigeon* for a. Lev 12:6

young *pigeons*
offering of *y. pigeons.* Lev 1:14
a lamb, he shall bring two *y. pigeons.* 5:7; 12:8; 14:22, 30; 15:14, 29
Num 6:10; Luke 2:24
if he be not able to bring two *y. pigeons.* Lev 5:11

young *ravens*
food to *y. ravens* which cry. Ps 147:9

young *roes*
thy breasts are like two *y. roes.* S of S 4:5; 7:3

young *unicorn*
Sirion like a *y. unicorn.* Ps 29:6

young *virgin*
for my lord a *y. virgin.* 1 Ki 1:2

young *virgins*
found 400 *y. virgins.* Judg 21:12
let fair *y. virgins* be sought. Esth 2:2
together all the *y. virgins.* 3

young *woman*
thee of this *y. woman.* Ruth 4:12

young *women*
they may teach *y. women.* Tit 2:4

younger
Noah knew what his *y.* son. Gen 9:24*
firstborn said to the *y.* 19:31, 34
and the *y.* she also bare a son. 38
the elder shall serve the *y.* 25:23
Rom 9:12
on Jacob her *y.* son. Gen 27:15
called Jacob her *y.* son. 42
the name of the *y.* daughter. 29:16
seven years for the *y.* 18
to give the *y.* before firstborn. 26
is this your *y.* brother ? 43:29*
his right hand on the *y.* 48:14
his *y.* brother shall be greater. 19
Caleb's *y.* brother. Judg 1:13; 3:9
is not her *y.* sister fairer ? 15:2
Saul's *y.* daughter. 1 Sam 14:49
cast lots over against their *y.* brethren. 1 Chr 24:31
that are *y.* than I, have me in derision. Job 30:1
y. sister is Sodom. Ezek 16:46
sisters, thine elder and *y.* 61
y. said, Father, give me. Luke 15:12
the *y.* son gathered all, and took. 13
let him be as the *y.* 22:26
intreat the *y.* men as. 1 Tim 5:1
the *y.* women as sisters, with all. 2
the *y.* widows refuse, for when. 11
that the *y.* women marry. 14
likewise, ye *y.* submit. 1 Pet 5:5

youngest
the *y.* is this day with our father. Gen 42:13, 32
except your *y.* brother come. 15, 20
34; 44:23, 26
they sat, the *y.* according. 43:33
in the sack's mouth of the *y.* 44:2
eldest, and left off at the *y.* 12
in his *y.* son shall he set up gates of it. Josh 6:26; 1 Ki 16:34
yet Jotham the *y.* son. Judg 9:5
remaineth yet the *y.* 1 Sam 16:11
David was the *y.*: the eldest. 17:14
save Jehoahaz the *y.* 2 Chr 21:17
his *y.* son king in his stead. 22:1

yours
the land of Egypt is *y.* Gen 45:20
feet tread shall be *y.* Deut 11:24
answered, Our life for *y.* Josh 2:14
the battle is not *y.* but. 2 Chr 20:15
in land that is not *y.* Jer 5:19
y. is the kingdom of God. Luke 6:20
they will keep *y.* also. John 15:20
for all things are *y.* 1 Cor 3:21, 22
lest this liberty of *y.* become. 8:9
refreshed my spirit and *y.* 16:18
for I seek not *y.* but you. 2 Cor 12:14

yourselves
wash, and rest *y.* under. Gen 18:4
be not angry with *y.* that ye. 45:5
gather *y.* together. 49:1, 2; Jer 6:1
Ezek 39:17; Joel 3:11; Zeph 2:1
Rev 19:17
take heed unto *y.* Ex 19:12
Deut 2:4; 4:15, 23; 11:16
Josh 23:11; Jer 17:21
as for the perfume, ye shall not make to *y.* Ex 30:37
consecrate *y.* to-day to the. 32:29
ye shall not make *y.* abominable, neither shall ye make *y.* Lev 11:43
sanctify *y.* 11:44; 20:7; Num 11:18
Josh 3:5; 7:13; 1 Sam 16:5
1 Chr 15:12; 2 Chr 29:5; 35:6
ye defile *y.* Lev 11:44; 18:24, 30
nor make to *y.* molten gods. 19:4
lift you up *y.*? Num 16:3
separate *y.* from this. 21
Moses saying, Arm some of *y.* 31:3
women-children keep for *y.* 18
purify both *y.* and your. 19

lest ye corrupt *y.* *Deut* 4:16, 25
mightier nations than *y.* 11:23
not cut *y.* for the dead. 14:1
present *y.* in the tabernacle. 31:14
ye will utterly corrupt *y.* 29
hide *y.* there three days. *Josh* 2:16
keep *y.* from the accursed thing, lest
ye make *y.* accursed. 6:18
take for a prey unto *y.* 8:2
nor serve them, nor bow *y.* unto. 23:7
and bowed *y.* to them. 16
ye are witnesses against *y.* that ye
have chosen. 24:22
not fall upon me *y.* *Judg* 15:12
quit *y.* like men, O ye. *1 Sam* 4:9
present *y.* before the Lord. 10:19
Saul said, Disperse *y.* 14:34
you one bullock for *y.* *1 Ki* 18:25
set *y.* in array, and they set. 20:12
2 Chr 20:17; *Jer* 50:14
have consecrated *y.* *2 Chr* 29:31
but yield *y.* unto the Lord. 30:8
to give over *y.* to die by. 32:11
prepare *y.* by the houses of. 35:4
separate *y.* from the. *Ezra* 10:11
their daughters for *y.* *Neh* 13:25
that ye make *y.* strange. *Job* 19:3
if ye will indeed magnify *y.* 5
all ye *y.* have seen it. 27:12
and offer up for *y.* a burnt. 42:8
associate *y.*, O ye people: gird *y.*
Isa 8:9; *Joel* 1:13
stay *y.* *Isa* 29:9
shew *y.* men. 46:8
are in darkness, shew *y.* 49:9
for iniquities have ye sold *y.* 50:1
that compass *y.* about with. 11
ye have sold *y.* for nought. 52:3
against whom do ye sport *y.* 57:4
by inflaming *y.* with idols under. 5
in their glory shall ye boast *y.* 61:6
circumcise *y.* to the Lord. *Jer* 4:4
humble *y.* 13:18; *Jas* 4:10; *1 Pet* 5:6
wallow *y.* in ashes, ye. *Jer* 25:34
innocent blood upon *y.* 26:15
saith the Lord, deceive not *y.* 37:9
that ye might cut *y.* off and. 44:8
repent and turn *y.* *Ezek* 14:6
18:30, 32
defile not *y.* with the idols. 20:7, 18
ye pollute *y.* with all your idols. 31
then shall ye lothe *y.* 43; 36:31
keepers of my charge for *y.* 44:8
to *y.* in righteousness. *Hos* 10:12
your God ye made to *y.* *Amos* 5:26
eat for *y.* and drink for *y.* *Zech* 7:6
think not to say within *y.* *Mat* 3:9
Luke 3:8
lay not up for *y.* *Mat* 6:19
lay up for *y.* 20
Why reason ye among *y.*? 16:8
neither go in *y.* 23:13; *Luke* 11:52
child of hell than *y.* *Mat* 23:15
ye be witnesses unto *y.* 31
go ye rather, and buy for *y.* 25:9
come ye *y.* apart into. *Mark* 6:31
that ye disputed among *y.*? 9:33
have salt in *y.* and peace one. 50
but take heed to *y.*: they shall deliver
you up. 13:9; *Luke* 17:3; 21:34
Acts 5:35; 20:28
ye *y.* touch not the. *Luke* 11:46
provide *y.* bags which wax. 12:33
ye *y.* like unto men that wait for. 36
why even of *y.* judge ye not? 57
kingdom, ye *y.* thrust out. 13:28
make to *y.* friends of the. 16:9
ye are they which justify *y.* 15
he said, Go shew *y.* unto the. 17:14
know of *y.* that summer is. 21:30
and divide it among *y.* 22:17
but weep for *y.* and for. 23:28
ye *y.* bear me witness. *John* 3:28
said, Murmur not among *y.* 6:43
do ye enquire among *y.* of? 16:19
signs God did, as you *y.* *Acts* 2:22
save *y.* from this untoward. 40
seeing ye judge *y.* unworthy. 13:46
from which if ye keep *y.* ye. 15:29
trouble not *y.* for his life. 20:10
you *y.* know, that these hands. 34
reckon ye also *y.* to be. *Rom* 6:11
but yield *y.* unto God, as those. 13
whom ye yield *y.* servants to. 16
dearly beloved, avenge not *y.*, but
rather give place. *Rom* 12:19
put from *y.* that wicked. *1 Cor* 5:13
ye not rather suffer *y.* to be? 6:7
ye may give *y.* to fasting and. 7:5
judge in *y.*: is it comely that? 11:13
I beseech, that ye submit *y.* 16:16
yea, what clearing of *y.*, in all things
ye have approved *y.* *2 Cor* 7:11
seeing ye *y.* are wise. 11:19
examine *y.* whether ye be in. 13:5
faith, and that not of *y.* *Eph* 2:8
speaking to *y.* in psalms. 5:19
submitting *y.* one to another. 21
wives, submit *y.* unto your. *Col* 3:18
y., brethren, know our entrance in
unto you. *1 Thes* 2:1
y. know that we are appointed. 3:3
ye *y.* are taught of God, to. 4:9
y. know that the day of the Lord. 5:2
wherefore comfort *y.* together. 11
and be at peace among *y.* 13, 15
that ye withdraw *y.* *2 Thes* 3:6
y. know how ye ought to follow us. 7
knowing in *y.* ye have. *Heb* 10:34
remember, as being *y.* also. 13:3
and submit *y.*: for they watch for. 17
ye not then partial in *y.*? *Jas* 2:4
submit *y.* to God. 4:7
not fashioning *y.* to. *1 Pet* 1:14
submit *y.* to every ordinance. 2:13
arm *y.* likewise with the same. 4:1
fervent charity among *y.* 8
ye younger, submit *y.* unto. 5:5
keep *y.* from idols. *1 John* 5:21
look to *y.* that we lose not. *2 John* 8
building up *y.* on your most. *Jude* 20
keep *y.* in the love of God, looking. 21

youth

is evil from his *y.* *Gen* 8:21
youngest according to his *y.* 43:33
about cattle, from our *y.* 46:34
father's house, as in her *y.* *Lev* 22:13
being in her father's house in her *y.*
Num 30:3, 16
the *y.* drew not a sword, because yet
a *y.* *Judg* 8:20
thou art but a *y.*, and he a man of
war from his *y.* *1 Sam* 17:33
for he was but a *y.* 42
whose son is this *y.*? 55
befell thee from thy *y.* *2 Sam* 19:7
fear the Lord from my *y.* *1 Ki* 18:12
the iniquities of my *y.* *Job* 13:26
are full of the sin of his *y.* 20:11
as I was in the days of my *y.* 29:4*
on my right hand rise the *y.* 30:12*
from my *y.* he was brought up. 31:18
return to the days of his *y.* 33:25
hypocrites die in *y.* and. 36:14
not the sins of my *y.* *Ps* 25:7
thou art my trust from my *y.* 71:5
hast taught me from my *y.* 17
and ready to die from my *y.* 88:15
the days of his *y.* hast thou. 89:45
so that thy *y.* is renewed. 103:5
thou hast the dew of thy *y.* 110:3
so are the children of thy *y.* 127:4
afflicted me from my *y.* 129:1
as plants grown up in *y.* 144:12
the guide of her *y.* *Pr* 2:17
with the wife of thy *y.* 5:18
O young man in thy *y.* *Eccl* 11:9
for childhood and *y.* are vanity. 10*
Creator in the days of thy *y.* 12:1
hast laboured from thy *y.* *Isa* 47:12
thy merchants from thy *y.* 15
forget the shame of thy *y.* 54:4
hath called thee as a wife of *y.* 6
the kindness of thy *y.* *Jer* 2:2
thou art the guide of my *y.* 3:4
of our fathers from our *y.* 24
we and our fathers from our *y.* 25
been thy manner from thy *y.* 22:21
bear the reproach of my *y.* 31:19
evil before me from their *y.* 32:30
been at ease from his *y.* 48:11
bear the yoke in his *y.* *Lam* 3:27
been polluted from my *y.* *Ezek* 4:14
remembered days of thy *y.* 16:22, 43
my covenant in days of thy *y.* 60
whoredoms in their *y.* 23:3
her *y.* they lay with her and. 8
the days of her *y.* *Ezek* 23:19, 21
as in the days of her *y.* *Hos* 2:15
for the husband of her *y.* *Joel* 1:8
to keep cattle from my *y.* *Zech* 13:5
and the wife of thy *y.* *Mal* 2:14
let none deal treacherously against
the wife of his *y.* 15
all these have I kept from my *y.*
up; what lack I yet? *Mat* 19:20
Mark 10:20; *Luke* 18:21
life from my *y.* know all. *Acts* 26:4
let no man despise thy *y.* *1 Tim* 4:12

youthful

flee also *y.* lusts, but. *2 Tim* 2:22

youths

I discerned among the *y.* *Pr* 7:7
even the *y.* shall faint. *Isa* 40:30

you-ward

which to *y.-ward* is not. *2 Cor* 13:3
grace given me to *y.-ward.* *Eph* 3:2

Z

Zacchaeus

Z. make haste and. *Luke* 19:5

Zachariah, Zechariah

Z. son of Jeroboam reigned.
2 Ki 14:29; 15:8, 11
Abi daughter of *Z.* 18:2; *2 Chr* 29:1
chief of the Reubenites; Jeiel, *Z.*
1 Chr 5:7
Z. porter of the door. 9:21; 15:18
20, 24; 26:2
Geder, Ahio, *Z.* and Mickloth. 9:37
next to Asaph, *Z.* 16:5
Z. son of Isshiah. 24:25
Z. the fourth son of Hosah. 26:11
Z. the son of Shelemiah, a wise. 14
was Iddo the son of *Z.* 27:21
Jehoshaphat sent to *Z.* *2 Chr* 17:7
on Jahaziel son of *Z.* 20:14
Jehiel and *Z.* the sons of. 21:2
Spirit of God came upon *Z.* 24:20
sought God in the days of *Z.* 26:5
of the sons of Asaph, *Z.* 29:13
Z. of the Kohathites was. 34:12
Hilkiah, *Z.* rulers of the house. 35:8
Z. the son of Iddo prophesied to.
Ezra 5:1; 6:14; *Neh* 12:16
sons of Pharosh, *Z.* *Ezra* 8:3
Z. the son of Bebai. 11
Elam, *Z.* 10:26
on Ezra's left hand stood *Z.* *Neh* 8:4
Z. the son of Amariah. 11:4
Z. the son of Shiloni. 5
Z., the son of Pashur. 12
Z. the son of Jonathan. 12:35
Z. with trumpets. 41
Z. the son of Jeberechiah. *Isa* 8:2
Z. the son of Barachiah. *Zech* 1:1
7:1; *Mat* 23:35; *Luke* 11:51
see also Zacharias, p. 783

Zadok

Z. and Abimelech. *2 Sam* 8:17
Z. and Abiathar carried the. 15:29
hast thou not with thee *Z.* and? 35
Z. and Abiathar were priests. 20:25
1 Ki 4:4
but *Z.* was not with Adonijah.
1 Ki 1:8, 26
Z. and Nathan have anointed. 45
and *Z.* the priest. 2:35; *1 Chr* 29:22
Azariah the son of *Z.* *1 Ki* 4:2
Jerusha the daughter of *Z.* was.
2 Ki 15:33; *2 Chr* 27:1
Ahitub begat *Z.* *1 Chr* 6:8; 12:53
9:11; 18:16
Z. a young man, mighty man. 12:28
both *Z.* of the sons of Eleazar. 24:3
of the Aaronites, *Z.* was. 27:17
priest of the house of *Z.* *2 Chr* 31:10
Shallum, the son of *Z.* *Ezra* 7:2
Z. repaired. *Neh* 3:4, 29
Z. sealed. 10:21
of the priests, the son of *Z.* 11:11
made *Z.* the scribe treasurer. 13:13

these are the sons of *Z*. *Ezek* 40:46
43:19; 44:15
priests sanctified of sons of *Z*. 48:11

Zalmunna

after Zebah and *Z*. *Judg* 8:5
Zebah and *Z*. in thy hand. 6, 15
arose and slew Zebah and *Z*. 21
princes as Zebah and *Z*. *Ps* 83:11

Zarah, *see also* **Zerah**

Judah's son was called *Z*.
Gen 38:30; 46:12
Tamar bare Pharez and *Z*.
1 Chr 2:4; *Mat* 1:3
the sons of *Z*., Zimri, and. *1 Chr* 2:6

Zarephath

get thee to *Z*. *1 Ki* 17:9
he went to *Z*. 10
Israel shall possess to *Z*. *Ob* 20

zeal

to slay them in his *z*. *2 Sam* 21:2
come and see my *z*. for. *2 Ki* 10:16
the *z*. of the Lord shall do this. 19:31
Isa 37:32
the *z*. of thy house hath eaten me up and. *Ps* 69:9; *John* 2:17
my *z*. hath consumed. *Ps* 119:139
the *z*. of the Lord will. *Isa* 9:7
and he was clad with *z*. as. 59:17
where is thy *z*. and thy? 63:15
have spoken it in my *z*. *Ezek* 5:13
that they have *z*. of God. *Rom* 10:2
yea, what *z*.! *2 Cor* 7:11
your *z*. provoked many. 9:2
concerning *z*., persecuting. *Phil* 3:6
hath a great *z*. for you. *Col* 4:13*

zealous

was *z*. for my sake. *Num* 25:11*
he was *z*. for his God and made. 13*
are all *z*. of the law. *Acts* 21:20
Paul was *z*. towards God. 22:3
Gal 1:14
are *z*. of spiritual gifts. *1 Cor* 14:2
purify a peculiar people, *z*. *Tit* 2:14
I rebuke and chasten: be *z*. *Rev* 3:19

zealously

they *z*. affect you, but. *Gal* 4:17
it is good to be *z*. affected in a. 18

Zebah, *see* **Zalmunna**

Zebedee

ship with *Z*. their father. *Mat* 4:21
apostles, James and John the sons of *Z*. 10:2; 26:37; *Mark* 1:19; 3:17
10:35; *Luke* 5:10; *John* 21:2
mother of *Z*.'s children. *Mat* 20:20
27:56
they left their father *Z*. *Mark* 1:20

Zeboim

king of *Z*. *Gen* 14:2
overthrow of *Z*. *Deut* 29:23
the valley of *Z*. to the. *1 Sam* 13:18
Benjamin dwelt at *Z*. *Neh* 11:34
how shall I set thee at *Z*.? *Hos* 11:8

Zebul

the son of Jerubbaal, and *Z*. his officer. *Judg* 9:28
Z. thrust out Gaal and his. 41

Zebulun

Leah called his name *Z*. *Gen* 30:20
Reuben, Simeon, Judah, *Z*. 35:23
the sons of *Z*. 46:14; *Num* 1:30
26:26
Z. shall dwell at the. *Gen* 49:13
of *Z*.: Eliab the son of Helon.
Num 1:9; 2:7; 7:24; 10:16
mount Ebal to curse; Reuben, Gad, Asher, *Z*. *Deut* 27:13
of *Z*. he said, Rejoice, *Z*. in. 33:18
third lot came up for *Z*. *Josh* 19:10
nor did *Z*. drive out the. *Judg* 1:30
Barak called *Z*. and Naphtali. 4:10
out of *Z*. they that handle. 5:14
Z. and Naphtali were a people that jeoparded their lives. 18
he sent messengers to *Z*. 6:35
buried in the country of *Z*. 12:12
of *Z*. Ishmaiah was the. *1 Chr* 27:19
divers of *Z*. humbled. *2 Chr* 30:11
the princes of *Z*. and. *Ps* 68:27
afflicted the land of *Z*. *Isa* 9:1
Z. a portion. *Ezek* 48:26
one gate of *Z*. 33
in the borders of *Z*. *Mat* 4:13
the land of *Z*. and Nephthalim. 15

tribe of **Zebulun**

the *tribe of Z*. 57,400. *Num* 1:31
then the *tribe of Z*.: Eliab. 2:7; 10:16
tribe of Z., Gaddiel to spy. 13:10
prince of the *tribe of Z*. to. 34:25
out of the *tribe of Z*. twelve cities.
Josh 21:7, 34; *1 Chr* 6:63, 77
of the *tribe of Z*. were sealed 12,000.
Rev 7:8

Zedekiah

Z. made horns of iron. *1 Ki* 22:11
2 Chr 18:10
Z. smote Micaiah on the cheek.
1 Ki 22:24; *2 Chr* 18:23
changed his name to *Z*. *2 Ki* 24:17
sons of *Z*. and put out the eyes of *Z*.
25:7; *Jer* 39:6, 7; 52:10, 11
son of Josiah, *Z*. *1 Chr* 3:15
sons of Jehoiakim: *Z*. 16
Z. his brother king. *2 Chr* 36:10
I will deliver *Z*. and his. *Jer* 21:7
Lord make thee like *Z*. and. 29:22
Z. shall not escape from the. 32:4
he shall lead *Z*. to Babylon. 5
the army overtook *Z*. 39:5; 52:8

Zeeb, *see* **Oreb**

Zelophehad

Z. had no sons, but daughters.
Num 26:33; *Josh* 17:3
the daughters of *Z*. speak. *Num* 27:7
daughters of *Z*. were married. 36:11

Zelotes, *see* **Simon**

Zelzah

Rachel's sepulchre at *Z*. *1 Sam* 10:2

Zenas

bring *Z*. the lawyer and. *Tit* 3:13

Zephaniah

the captain took *Z*. second priest.
2 Ki 25:18; *Jer* 52:24
Z. of the sons of the. *1 Chr* 6:36
Zedekiah sent *Z*. to. *Jer* 21:1
letters in thy name to *Z*. 29:25
Z. read this letter in the ears. 29
Z. the son of Maaseiah. 37:3
the word came to *Z*. *Zeph* 1:1
house of Josiah son of *Z*. *Zech* 6:10
be to Hen the son of *Z*. 14

Zerah, *see also* **Zarah**

the son of Reuel, *Z*. *Gen* 36:13, 17
1 Chr 1:37
Jobab the son of *Z*. reigned.
Gen 36:33; *1 Chr* 1:44
of *Z*. the family. *Num* 26:13, 20
of Zabdi, the son of *Z*. *Josh* 7:1
did not Achan the son of *Z*.? 22:20
sons of Simeon were *Z*. *1 Chr* 4:24
Z. son of Iddo. 6:21
Ethni the son of *Z*. 41
of the sons of *Z*. Jeuel dwelt in. 9:6
Z. the Ethiopian came. *2 Chr* 14:9
of the children of *Z*. *Neh* 11:24

Zeresh

Haman called for *Z*. his. *Esth* 5:10

Zerubbabel

of Pedaiah, *Z*., sons of *Z*. *1 Chr* 3:19
which came up with *Z*. *Ezra* 2:2
Neh 12:1
Z. the son of. *Ezra* 3:2, 8; 5:2
Israel in the days of *Z*. *Neh* 12:47
Lord by Haggai to *Z*. *Hag* 1:1
then *Z*. obeyed the voice of. 12
stirred up the spirit of *Z*. 14
yet now be strong, O *Z*. 2:4
speak to *Z*. of Judah. 21
word of the Lord unto *Z*. *Zech* 4:6
before *Z*. thou shalt become. 7
the hands of *Z*. have laid. 9

Zeruiah

three sons of *Z*. there. *2 Sam* 2:18
the sons of *Z*. be too hard. 3:39
Joab son of *Z*. 8:16; *1 Chr* 18:15
What have I do with you, ye sons of *Z*.? *2 Sam* 16:10; 19:22
whose sisters were *Z*. *1 Chr* 2:16

Ziba

art thou *Z*.? *2 Sam* 9:2
Z. had fifteen sons. 10
the king said to *Z*., Thine are. 16:4
I said, Thou and *Z*. divide. 19:29

Zibeon

Anah the daughter of *Z*. the Hivite.
Gen 36:2, 14
these are the children of *Z*. 24
1 Chr 1:40
duke *Z*. *Gen* 36:29

Zidon

border shall be to *Z*. *Gen* 49:13
chased them to great *Z*. *Josh* 11:8
Kanah, even unto great *Z*. 19:28
and served the gods of *Z*. *Judg* 10:6
because it was far from *Z*. 18:28
which belongeth to *Z*. *1 Ki* 17:9
drink unto them of *Z*. *Ezra* 3:7
whom the merchants of *Z*. *Isa* 23:2
be thou ashamed, O *Z*.: the sea. 4
O thou virgin, daughter of *Z*. 12
all the kings of *Z*. *Jer* 25:22
yokes to the king of *Z*. 27:3
to cut off from Tyre and *Z*. 47:4
the inhabitants of *Z*. *Ezek* 27:8
set thy face against *Z*. and. 28:21
I am against thee, O *Z*. 22
what have ye to do with me, O Tyre, and *Z*.? *Joel* 3:4
Z. though it be very wise. *Zech* 9:2

Zidonians

Z. and Amalekites did. *Judg* 10:12
after the manner of the *Z*. 18:7
but king Solomon loved women of *Z*.
1 Ki 11:1
Ashtoreth, goddess of the *Z*. 33
Z. that are gone down. *Ezek* 32:30

Zif

the month of *Z*. which is. *1 Ki* 6:1
was laid in the month *Z*. 37

Ziklag

Achish gave *Z*. to. *1 Sam* 27:6
we burnt *Z*. 30:14
abode two days in *Z*. *2 Sam* 1:1
I slew them in *Z*. 4:10
they dwelt at *Z*. *1 Chr* 4:30
Neh 11:28
came to David to *Z*. 12:1, 20

Zilpah

Laban gave to Leah, *Z*. *Gen* 29:24
Leah gave *Z*. her maid. 30:9
Z. Leah's maid bare Jacob. 10, 12
the sons of *Z*., Gad. 35:26; 46:18
was with the sons of *Z*. 37:2

Zimri

that was slain was *Z*. *Num* 25:14
Z. conspired against. *1 Ki* 16:9, 16
Z. reigned seven days in Tirzah. 15
had *Z*. peace, who slew? *2 Ki* 9:31
the sons of Zorah, *Z*. *1 Chr* 2:6
Z. the son of Jehoadah. 8:36
Jarah begat *Z*. 9:42
I made all the kings of *Z*. *Jer* 25:25

Zin

from wilderness of *Z*. *Num* 13:21
to the desert of *Z*. 20:1; 33:36
ye rebelled in the desert of *Z*.
27:14; *Deut* 32:51

Zion, Sion

David took strong hold of *Z*. the.
2 Sam 5:7; *1 Chr* 11:5
the city of David, which is *Z*.
1 Ki 8:1; *2 Chr* 5:2
king on my holy hill of *Z*. *Ps* 2:6
walk about *Z*. and go round. 48:12
thy good pleasure unto *Z*. 51:18
for God will save *Z*. and. 69:35
the Lord loveth the gates of *Z*. 87:2
he said of *Z*., This and that man. 5
Z. heard and was glad. 97:8
arise and have mercy on *Z*. 102:13
Lord shall build up *Z*. 16
turned the captivity of *Z*. 126:1
turned back that hate *Z*. 129:5
the Lord hath chosen *Z*. 132:13
dew on the mountains of *Z*. 133:3
when we remembered *Z*. 137:1
Sing us one of the songs of *Z*. 3
reign, even thy God, O *Z*. 146:10
praise the Lord, O Jerusalem, praise thy God, O *Z*. 147:12
let the children of *Z*. be. 149:2
Z. shall be redeemed. *Isa* 1:27
shout, thou inhabitant of *Z*. 12:6
that the Lord hath founded *Z*. 14:32
the Lord hath filled *Z*. with. 33:5

APPENDIX

A List of Proper Names, seldom mentioned in Scripture, and not included in the body of the Concordance

ABDIEL. *1 Chr* 5:15
Abelshittim. *Num* 33:49
Abez. *Josh* 19:20
Abi. *2 Ki* 18:2
Abiasaph. *Ex* 6:24
Abida. *Gen* 25:4; *1 Chr* 1:33
Abiel. (1) *1 Sam* 9:1; 14:51. (2) *1 Chr* 11:32
Abihud. *1 Chr* 8:3
Abilene. *Luke* 3:1
Abimael. *Gen* 10:26-28; *1 Chr* 1:20-22
Abishalom. *1 Ki* 15:2, 10
Abishua. (1) *1 Chr* 6:4, 5, 50; *Ezra* 7:5. (2) *1 Chr* 8:4
Abishur. *1 Chr* 2:28, 29
Abital. *2 Sam* 3:4; *1 Chr* 3:3
Abitub. *1 Chr* 8:11
Accad. *Gen* 10:10
Achaz (Ahaz). *Mat* 1:9
Achbor. (1) *Gen* 36:38, 39; *1 Chr* 1:49. (2) *2 Ki* 22:12, 14. (3) *Jer* 26:22; 36:12
Adadah. *Josh* 15:21, 22
Adah. (1) *Gen* 4:19, 20, 23. (2) *Gen* 36:2, 4, 10, 12, 16
Adaiah. (1) *2 Ki* 22:1. (2) *1 Chr* 6:41. (3) *1 Chr* 8:12-21. (4) *1 Chr* 9:10-12; *Neh* 11:12. (5) *2 Chr* 23:1. (6) *Ezra* 10:29. (7) *Ezra* 10:34-39. (8) *Neh* 11:5
Adalia. *Esth* 9:8
Adamah. *Josh* 19:35, 36
Adami. *Josh* 19:33
Adbeel. *Gen* 25:13; *1 Chr* 1:29
Addan (Addon). *Ezra* 2:59; *Neh* 7:61
Addar. (1) *Josh* 15:3. (2) *1 Chr* 8:3
Ader. *1 Chr* 8:15
Adiel. (1) *1 Chr* 4:36. (2) *1 Chr* 9:12. (3) *1 Chr* 27:25
Adin. (1) *Ezra* 2:15; *Neh* 7:20. (2) *Ezra* 8:6. (3) *Neh* 10:14-16
Adina. *1 Chr* 11:42
Adino. *2 Sam* 23:8
Adithaim. *Josh* 15:33-36
Adlai. *1 Chr* 27:29
Admatha. *Esth* 1:14
Adna. (1) *Ezra* 10:30. (2) *Neh* 12:12-15
Adnah. (1) *1 Chr* 12:20. (2) *2 Chr* 17:14
Adoniram. *1 Ki* 4:6; 5:14
Adonizedek. *Josh* 10:1, 3
Adoraim. *2 Chr* 11:5-9
Adoram. (1) *2 Sam* 20:24. (2) *1 Ki* 12:18
Aeneas. *Acts* 9:33, 34
Aenon. *John* 3:23
Aharah. *1 Chr* 8:1
Aharhel. *1 Chr* 4:8
Ahasai. *Neh* 11:13
Ahasbai. *2 Sam* 23:34
Ahban. *1 Chr* 2:29
Aher. *1 Chr* 7:12
Ahi. (1) *1 Chr* 5:15. (2) *1 Chr* 7:34
Ahiam. *2 Sam* 23:33; *1 Chr* 11:35
Ahian. *1 Chr* 7:19
Ahiezer. (1) *Num* 1:12; 2:25; 7:66, 71; 10:25. (2) *1 Chr* 12:3
Ahihud. (1) *Num* 34:27. (2) *1 Chr* 8:7
Ahilud. *2 Sam* 8:16; 20:24; *1 Ki* 4:3, 12; *1 Chr* 18:15
Ahimoth. *1 Chr* 6:25
Ahinadab. *1 Ki* 4:14
Ahira. *Num* 1:15; 2:29; 7:78, 83; 10:27
Ahiram. *Num* 26:38
Ahishahar. *1 Chr* 7:10
Ahishar. *1 Ki* 4:6
Ahlab. *Judg* 1:31
Ahlai. (1) *1 Chr* 2:31. (2) *1 Chr* 11:41
Ahoah. *1 Chr* 8:4
Ahumai. *1 Chr* 4:2
Ahuzam. *1 Chr* 4:6
Ahuzzath. *Gen* 26:26
Aiah, Ajah. (1) *Gen* 36:24; *1 Chr* 1:40. (2) *2 Sam* 3:7; 21:8, 10, 11
Aija. *Neh* 11:31
Aijalon, Ajalon. (1) *Josh* 19:42; 21:24; *Judg* 1:35. (2) *Judg* 12:12. (3) *1 Sam* 14:31; *1 Chr* 8:13; *2 Chr* 11:10; 28:18. (4) *1 Chr* 6:69
Aijeleth Shahar. *Ps* 22 title
Akan (Jakan). *Gen* 36:27; *1 Chr* 1:42
Akkub. (1) *1 Chr* 3:24. (2) *1 Chr* 9:17; *Neh* 11:19; 12:25. (3) *Ezra* 2:42; *Neh* 7:45. (4) *Ezra* 2:45. (5) *Neh* 8:7
Akrabbim. *Num* 34:4; *Josh* 15:3
Alameth. *1 Chr* 7:8
Alammelech. *Josh* 19:26
Alamoth. *1 Chr* 15:20; *Ps* 46 title
Alemeth. (1) *1 Chr* 6:60. (2) *1 Chr* 8:36; 9:42
Aliah (Alva). *Gen* 36:40; *1 Chr* 1:51
Alian (Alvan). *Gen* 36:23; *1 Chr* 1:40
Allon. (1) *Josh* 19:33. (2) *1 Chr* 4:37
Allon Bachuth. *Gen* 35:8
Almodad. *Gen* 10:26; *1 Chr* 1:20
Almon. *Josh* 21:18
Almon-Diblathaim. *Num* 33:46, 47
Aloth. *1 Ki* 4:16
Altaschith. *Ps* 57 title; 58 title; 59 title; 75 title
Alvan. *See* Alian
Amad. *Josh* 19:26
Amal. *1 Chr* 7:35
Amam. *Josh* 15:26
Amariah. (1) *1 Chr* 6:7, 52; *Ezra* 7:3. (2) *1 Chr* 6:11. (3) *1 Chr* 23:19; 24:23. (4) *2 Chr* 19:11. (5) *2 Chr* 31:15. (6) *Ezra* 10:42 (7) *Neh* 10:3; 12:2, 13. (8) *Neh* 11:4. (9) *Zeph* 1:1
Amasai. (1) *1 Chr* 6:25, 35; *2 Chr* 29:12. (2) *1 Chr* 12:18. (3) *1 Chr* 15:24
Amashai. *Neh* 11:13
Amasiah. *2 Chr* 17:16
Ami. *Ezra* 2:57
Amittai. *2 Ki* 14:25; *Jonah* 1:1
Ammiel. (1) *Num* 13:12. (2) *2 Sam* 9:4, 5; 17:27. (3) *1 Chr* 3:5. (4) *1 Chr* 26:5
Ammihud. (1) *Num* 1:10; 2:18; 7:48, 53; 10:22; *1 Chr* 7:26. (2) *Num* 34:20. (3) *Num* 34:28. (4) *2 Sam* 13:37. (5) *1 Chr* 9:4
Ammihur. *2 Sam* 13:37
Ammishaddai. *Num* 1:12; 2:25; 7:66, 71; 10:25
Ammizabad. *1 Chr* 27:6
Amok. *Neh* 12:7, 20
Amraphel. *Gen* 14:1, 9
Amzi. (1) *1 Chr* 6:46. (2) *Neh* 11:12
Anab. *Josh* 11:21; 15:50
Anaharath. *Josh* 19:19
Anaiah. (1) *Neh* 8:4. (2) *Neh* 10:22
Anamim. *Gen* 10:13; *1 Chr* 1:11
Anan. *Neh* 10:26
Anani. *1 Chr* 3:24
Ananiah. *Neh* 3:23
Anath. *Judg* 3:31; 5:6
Anem. *1 Chr* 6:73
Aniam. *1 Chr* 7:19
Anim. *Josh* 15:50
Antothijah. *1 Chr* 8:24
Anub. *1 Chr* 4:8
Aphekah. *Josh* 15:53
Aphiah. *1 Sam* 9:1
Aphik. *Josh* 13:4; 19:30; *Judg* 1:31
Aphrah. *Mi* 1:10
Aphses. *1 Chr* 24:15
Appaim. *1 Chr* 2:30, 31
Apphia. *Philem* 2
Ara. *1 Chr* 7:38
Arabah. *Josh* 18:18
Arad. (1) *Num* 21:1; 33:40. (2) *1 Chr* 8:15. (3) *Josh* 12:14. *Judg* 1:16
Arah. (1) *1 Chr* 7:39. (2) *Ezra* 2:5; *Neh* 7:10. (3) *Neh* 6:18
Aramnaharaim. *Ps* 60 title
Aramzobah. *Ps* 60 title
Aran. *Gen* 36:28; *1 Chr* 1:42
Archi. *Josh* 16:2
Ard. (1) *Gen* 46:21. (2) *Num* 26:40
Ardon. *1 Chr* 2:18
Areli. *Gen* 46:16; *Num* 26:17
Aridai. *Esth* 9:9
Aridatha. *Esth* 9:8
Arieh. *2 Ki* 15:25
Arisai. *Esth* 9:9
Armoni. *2 Sam* 21:8
Arnan. *1 Chr* 3:21
Arod. *Num* 26:17
Arodi. *Gen* 46:16
Aruboth. *1 Ki* 4:10
Arumah. *Judg* 9:41
Arvad. *Ezek* 27:8, 11
Arza. *1 Ki* 16:9
Asareel. *1 Chr* 4:16
Asarelah. *1 Chr* 25:2
Aser. *Luke* 2:36; *Rev* 7:6

Ashan. *Josh* 15:42; 19:7; *1 Chr* 4:32; 6:59
Ashbea. *1 Chr* 4:21
Ashbel. *Gen* 46:21; *Num* 26:38; *1 Chr* 8:1
Ashdoth Pisgah. *Deut* 3:17; 4:49; *Josh* 12:3; 13:20
Ashima. *2 Ki* 17:30
Ashkenaz. (1) *Gen* 10:3; *1 Chr* 1:6. (2) *Jer* 51:27
Ashnah. (1) *Josh* 15:33. (2) *Josh* 15:43
Ashpenaz. *Dan* 1:3
Ashteroth Karnaim. *Gen* 14:5
Ashvath. *1 Chr* 7:33
Asiel. *1 Chr* 4:35
Asnah. *Ezra* 2:50
Aspatha. *Esth* 9:7
Asriel. (1) *Num* 26:31; *Josh* 17:2. (2) *1 Chr* 7:14
Asshurim. *Gen* 25:3
Assir. (1) *Ex* 6:24; *1 Chr* 6:22. (2) *1 Chr* 6:23, 37. (3) *1 Chr* 3:17
Assos. *Acts* 20:13, 14
Asuppim. *1 Chr* 26:15, 17
Atarah. *1 Chr* 2:26
Ataroth. (1) *Num* 32:3, 34. (2) *Josh* 16:5. (3) *Josh* 16:2, 7. (4) *1 Chr* 2:54. (5) *Num* 32:35
Ater. (1) *Ezra* 2:16; *Neh* 7:21. (2) *Ezra* 2:42; *Neh* 7:45. (3) *Neh* 10:17
Athaiah. *Neh* 11:4
Athlai. *Ezra* 10:28
Attai. (1) *1 Chr* 2:35, 36. (2) *1 Chr* 12:11. (3) *2 Chr* 11:20
Ava. *2 Ki* 17:24
Avim. (1) *Deut* 2:23; *Josh* 13:3. (2) *Josh* 18:23
Avith. *Gen* 36:35; *1 Chr* 1:46
Azal. *Zech* 14:5
Azaliah. *2 Ki* 22:3; *2 Chr* 34:8
Azaniah. *Neh* 10:9
Azareel. (1) *1 Chr* 12:6. (2) *1 Chr* 25:18. (3) *1 Chr* 27:22. (4) *Ezra* 10:41. (5) *Neh* 11:13; 12:36
Azaz. *1 Chr* 5:8
Azaziah. (1) *1 Chr* 15:21. (2) *1 Chr* 27:20. (3) *2 Chr* 31:13
Azbuk. *Neh* 3:16
Azel. *1 Chr* 8:37, 38; 9:43, 44
Azem. *Josh* 15:29; 19:3; *1 Chr* 4:29
Azgad. (1) *Ezra* 2:12; *Neh* 7:17. (2) *Ezra* 8:12. (3) *Neh* 10:15
Aziel. *1 Chr* 15:20
Aziza. *Ezra* 10:27
Azmaveth. (1) *2 Sam* 23:31; *1 Chr* 11:33. (2) *1 Chr* 8:36; 9:42. (3) *1 Chr* 12:3. (4) *Ezra* 2:24; *Neh* 12:29. (5) *1 Chr* 27:25
Azmon. *Num* 34:4, 5; *Josh* 15:4
Aznoth Tabor. *Josh* 19:34
Azor. *Mat* 1:13, 14
Azotus. *Acts* 8:40
Azriel. (1) *1 Chr* 5:24. (2) *1 Chr* 27:19. (3) *Jer* 36:26
Azrikam. (1) *1 Chr* 3:23. (2) *1 Chr* 8:38; 9:44. (3) *1 Chr* 9:14; *Neh* 11:15. (4) *2 Chr* 28:7
Azubah. (1) *1 Ki* 22:42; *2 Chr* 20:31. (2) *1 Chr* 2:18, 19
Azur (Azzur). (1) *Neh* 10:17. (2) *Jer* 28:1. (3) *Ezek* 11:1
Azzah. *Deut* 2:23; *1 Ki* 4:24; *Jer* 25:20
Azzan. *Num* 34:26

BAALAH. *Josh* 15:9
Baalath. *Josh* 19:44; *1 Ki* 9:18; *2 Chr* 8:6
Baalath-beer. *Josh* 19:8
Baale. *2 Sam* 6:2
Baal-gad. *Josh* 11:17; 12:7; 13:5
Baal-hanan. (1) *Gen* 36:38, 39; *1 Chr* 1:49, 50. (2) *1 Chr* 27:28
Baal-hazor. *2 Sam* 13:23
Baal-hermon. *Judg* 3:3; *1 Chr* 5:23
Baara. *1 Chr* 8:8
Baaseiah. *1 Chr* 6:40
Bakbakkar. *1 Chr* 9:15
Bakbuk. *Ezra* 2:51; *Neh* 7:53
Bakbukiah. *Neh* 11:17; 12:9, 25
Bamoth. *Num* 21:19, 20
Bamoth-baal. *Josh* 13:17
Bani. (1) *2 Sam* 23:36. (2) *1 Chr* 6:46. (3) *1 Chr* 9:4. (4) *Ezra* 2:10; 10:29. (5) *Ezra* 10:34. (6) *Ezra* 10:38. (7) *Neh* 3:17; 8:7; 9:4, 5. (8) *Neh* 9:4; 10:13. (9) *Neh* 10:14. (10) *Neh* 11:22
Barachiah. *Zech* 1:1, 7
Bariah. *1 Chr* 3:22
Barkos. *Ezra* 2:53; *Neh* 7:55
Bashan-havoth-jair. *Deut* 3:14
Basmath. *1 Ki* 4:15
Bath-rabbim. *S of S* 7:4
Bathshua. *1 Chr* 3:5
Bavai. *Neh* 3:18
Bazlith. *Ezra* 2:52; *Neh* 7:54
Bealiah. *1 Chr* 12:5
Bealoth. *Josh* 15:24
Bebai. (1) *Ezra* 2:11; *Neh* 7:16. (2) *Ezra* 8:11; 10:28. (3) *Neh* 10:15
Bechorath. *1 Sam* 9:1
Bedad. *Gen* 36:35; *1 Chr* 1:46
Bedeiah. *Ezra* 10:35
Beeliada. *1 Chr* 14:7
Beer. (1) *Num* 21:16. (2) *Judg* 9:21
Beera. *1 Chr* 7:37
Beerah. *1 Chr* 5:6
Beer-elim. *Isa* 15:8
Beeri. (1) *Gen* 26:34. (2) *Hos* 1:1
Beer-lahai-roi. *Gen* 16:14; 24:62; 25:11
Beeroth. (1) *Deut* 10:6. (2) *Josh* 9:17; 18:25; *2 Sam* 4:2; *Ezra* 2:25; *Neh* 7:29
Beeshterah. *Josh* 21:27
Bela. (1) *Gen* 14:2, 8. (2) *Gen* 36:32, 33; *1 Chr* 1:43, 44. (3) *Gen* 46:21; *Num* 26:38, 40; *1 Chr* 7:6, 7; 8:1, 3. (4) *1 Chr* 5:8
Ben. *1 Chr* 15:18
Beneberak. *Josh* 19:45
Benejaakan. *Num* 33:31, 32
Benhail. *2 Chr* 17:7
Benhanan. *1 Chr* 4:20
Beninu. *Neh* 10:13
Beno. *1 Chr* 24:26, 27
Benzoheth. *1 Chr* 4:20
Beon. *Num* 32:3
Bera. *Gen* 14:2
Beraiah. *1 Chr* 8:21
Berechiah. (1) *1 Chr* 3:20. (2) *1 Chr* 6:39; 15:17. (3) *1 Chr* 9:16. (4) *1 Chr* 15:23. (5) *2 Chr* 28:12. (6) *Neh* 3:4, 30; 6:18
Bered. (1) *Gen* 16:14. (2) *1 Chr* 7:20
Beri. *1 Chr* 7:36
Beriah. (1) *Gen* 46:17; *Num* 26:44, 45; *1 Chr* 7:30, 31. (2) *1 Chr* 7:23. (3) *1 Chr* 8:13, 16. (4) *1 Chr* 23:10, 11
Berodach-baladan. *See* Merodach-baladan
Berothah. *Ezek* 47:16
Besai. *Ezra* 2:49; *Neh* 7:52
Besodeiah. *Neh* 3:6
Betah. *2 Sam* 8:8
Beten. *Josh* 19:25
Bethanath. *Josh* 19:38; *Judg* 1:33
Bethanoth. *Josh* 15:59
Betharabah. *Josh* 15:6, 61; 18:22
Betharam. *Josh* 13:27
Betharbel. *Hos* 10:14
Bethazmaveth. *Neh* 7:28
Bethbaalmeon. *Josh* 13:17
Bethbarah. *Judg* 7:24
Bethbirei. *1 Chr* 4:31
Bethcar. *1 Sam* 7:11
Bethdagon. (1) *Josh* 15:41. (2) *Josh* 19:27
Bethemek. *Josh* 19:27
Bethgader. *1 Chr* 2:51
Bethharan. *Num* 32:36
Bethhoglah. *Josh* 15:6; 18:19, 21
Bethjeshimoth. *Num* 33:49; *Josh* 12:3; 13:20; *Ezek* 25:9
Bethlebaoth. *Josh* 19:6
Bethmaachah. *2 Sam* 20:14, 15, 18; *2 Ki* 15:29
Bethmarcaboth. *Josh* 19:5; *1 Chr* 4:31
Bethmeon. *Jer* 48:23
Bethnimrah. *Num* 32:36; *Josh* 13:27
Bethpalet. *Josh* 15:27; *Neh* 11:26
Bethpazzez. *Josh* 19:21
Bethrapha. *1 Chr* 4:12
Bethrehob. *Judg* 18:28; *2 Sam* 10:6
Bethshean. *Josh* 17:11, 16; *Judg* 1:27; *1 Ki* 4:12; *1 Chr* 7:29
Bethshittah. *Judg* 7:22
Bethtappuah. *Josh* 15:53
Bethul. *Josh* 19:4
Bethzur. (1) *Josh* 15:58; *2 Chr* 11:7; *Neh* 3:16. (2) *1 Chr* 2:45
Betonim. *Josh* 13:26
Bezai. (1) *Ezra* 2:17; *Neh* 7:23. (2) *Neh* 10:18
Bezer. (1) *Deut* 4:43; *Josh* 20:8; 21:36; *1 Chr* 6:78. (2) *1 Chr* 7:37
Bigtha. *Esth* 1:10
Bigvai. (1) *Ezra* 2:2; *Neh* 7:7. (2) *Ezra* 2:14; *Neh* 7:19. (3) *Ezra* 8:14. (4) *Neh* 10:16
Bileam. *1 Chr* 6:70
Bilgah. (1) *1 Chr* 24:14. (2) *Neh* 12:5, 18
Bilgai. *Neh* 10:8
Bilhan. (1) *Gen* 36:27; *1 Chr* 1:42. (2) *1 Chr* 7:10
Bilshan. *Ezra* 2:2; *Neh* 7:7
Bimhal. *1 Chr* 7:33
Binea. *1 Chr* 8:37; 9:43
Binnui. (1) *Ezra* 8:33. (2) *Ezra* 10:30. (3) *Ezra* 10:38. (4) *Neh* 3:24; 10:9. (5) *Neh* 7:15. (6) *Neh* 12:8
Birsha. *Gen* 14:2
Birzavith. *1 Chr* 7:31
Bishlam. *Ezra* 4:7
Bithiah. *1 Chr* 4:18
Bithron. *2 Sam* 2:29
Bizjothjah. *Josh* 15:28
Biztha. *Esth* 1:10
Bocheru. *1 Chr* 8:38; 9:44
Bohan. *Josh* 15:6; 18:17
Bozez. *1 Sam* 14:4
Bozkath. *Josh* 15:39; *2 Ki* 22:1
Bunah. *1 Chr* 2:25
Bunni. (1) *Neh* 9:4. (2) *Neh* 11:15. (3) *Neh* 10:15

CALAH. *Gen* 10:11, 12
Calcol. *1 Chr* 2:6
Canneh. *Ezek* 27:23
Caphtorim. *Gen* 10:14; *Deut* 2:23; *1 Chr* 1:12
Carcas. *Esth* 1:10
Careah. *2 Ki* 25:23
Carshena. *Esth* 1:14
Casluhim. *Gen* 10:14; *1 Chr* 1:12
Chanaan (*see* Canaan). *Acts* 7:11; 13:19
Chedorlaomer. *Gen* 14:1, 4, 5, 9, 17
Chelal. *Ezra* 10:30
Chellub. (1) *1 Chr* 4:11. (2) *1 Chr* 27:26
Chelluh. *Ezra* 10:35
Chelubai. *1 Chr* 2:9
Chenaanah. (1) *1 Ki* 22:11, 24; *2 Chr.* 18:10, 23. (2) *1 Chr* 7:10
Chenani. *Neh* 9:4
Chephar-haammonia. *Josh* 18:24
Chephirah. *Josh* 9:17; 18:26; *Ezra* 2:25; *Neh* 7:29
Cheran. *Gen* 36:26; *1 Chr* 1:41
Chesalon. *Josh* 15:10
Chesed. *Gen* 22:22
Chesil. *Josh* 15:30
Chesulloth. *Josh* 19:18
Chezib. *Gen* 38:5
Chidon. *1 Chr* 13:9
Chinnereth. *Num* 34:11; *Deut* 3:17; *Josh* 11:2; 12:3; 13:27; 19:35; *1 Ki* 15:20
Chislon. *Num* 34:21
Chisloth-tabor. *Josh* 19:12
Chorashan. *1 Sam* 30:30
Chozeba. *1 Chr* 4:22
Chub. *Ezek* 30:5
Chun. *1 Chr* 18:8

Hanan. (1) 1 Chr 8:23. (2) 1 Chr 8:38; 9:44. (3) 1 Chr 11:43. (4) Ezra 2:46; Neh 7:49. (5) Neh 8:7. (6) Neh 10:10; 13:13. (7) Neh 10:22. (8) Neh 10:26. (9) Jer 35:4
Hanes. Isa 30:4
Hannathon. Josh 19:14
Hanniel. (1) Num 34:23. (2) 1 Chr 7:39
Haphraim. Josh 19:19
Haradah. Num 33:24, 25
Hareph. 1 Chr 2:51
Hareth. 1 Sam 22:5
Harhaiah. Neh 3:8
Harhas. 2 Ki 22:14
Harhur. Ezra 2:51; Neh 7:53
Harim. (1) 1 Chr 24:8; Ezra 2:39; 10:21; Neh 3:11; 7:42. (2) Ezra 2:32; Neh 7:35. (3) Ezra 10:31. (4) Neh 10:5. (5) Neh 10:27. (6) Neh 12:15
Hariph. (1) Neh 7:24. (2) Neh 10:19
Harnepher. 1 Chr 7:36
Haroeh. 1 Chr 2:52
Harsha. Ezra 2:52; Neh 7:54
Harum. 1 Chr 4:8
Harumaph. Neh 3:10
Haruz. 2 Ki 21:19
Hasadiah. 1 Chr 3:20
Hasenuah. 1 Chr 9:7
Hashabiah. (1) 1 Chr 6:45. (2) 1 Chr 9:14. (3) 1 Chr 25:3. (4) 1 Chr 26:30. (5) 1 Chr 27:17. (6) 2 Chr 35:9. (7) Ezra 8:19. (8) Ezra 8:24. (9) Neh 3:17. (10) Neh 10:11. (11) Neh 11:15. (12) Neh 11:22. (13) Neh 12:21. (14) Neh 12:24
Hashbadana. Neh 8:4
Hashem. 1 Chr 11:34
Hashmonah. Num 33:29, 30
Hashub. (1) 1 Chr 9:14; Neh 11:15. (2) Neh 3:11. (3) Neh 3:23. (4) Neh 10:23
Hashubah. 1 Chr 3:20
Hashum. (1) Ezra 2:19; 10:33; Neh 7:22. (2) Neh 8:4. (3) Neh 10:18
Hasrah. 2 Chr 34:22
Hassenaah. Neh 3:3
Hasupha. Ezra 2:43; Neh 7:46
Hatach. Esth 4:5, 6, 9, 10
Hathath. 1 Chr 4:13
Hatipha. Ezra 2:54; Neh 7:56
Hatita. Ezra 2:42; Neh 7:45
Hattil. Ezra 2:57; Neh 7:59
Hattush. (1) 1 Chr 3:22. (2) Ezra 8:2; Neh 3:10; 10:4. (3) Neh 12:2
Hauran. Ezek 47:16, 18
Havilah. (1) Gen 10:7; 1 Chr 1:9. (2) Gen 10:29; 1 Chr 1:23. (3) Gen 2:11. (4) Gen 25:18; 1 Sam 15:7
Havoth-jair. Num 32:41; Deut 3:14; Judg 10:4
Hazaiah. Neh 11:5
Hazar-addar. Num 34:4
Hazar-enan. Num 34:9, 10; Ezek 47:17; 48:1
Hazar-gaddah. Josh 15:27
Hazar-hatticon. Ezek 47:16
Hazarmaveth. Gen 10:26; 1 Chr 1:20
Hazarshual. Josh 15:28; 19:3; 1 Chr 4:28; Neh 11:27
Hazarsusah. Josh 19:5
Hazerim. Deut 2:23
Hazezon-tamar. Gen 14:7; 2 Chr 20:2
Haziel. 1 Chr 23:9
Hazo. Gen 22:22
Heber. (1) 1 Chr 4:18. (2) 1 Chr 5:13. (3) 1 Chr 8:17. (4) 1 Chr 8:22. (See also p. 296)
Helah. 1 Chr 4:5, 7
Helbah. Judg 1:31
Heleb. 2 Sam 23:29
Heled. 1 Chr 11:30
Helek. Num 26:30; Josh 17:2
Helem. (1) 1 Chr 7:35. (2) Zech 6:14
Heleph. Josh 19:33
Helez. (1) 2 Sam 23:26; 1 Chr 11:27; 27:10. (2) 1 Chr 2:39
Helkai. Neh 12:15
Helkath. Josh 19:25; 21:31
Helon. Num 1:9; 2:7; 7:24, 29; 10:16
Hemam (Homam). Gen 36:22; 1 Chr 1:39
Hemath. (1) Amos 6:14. (2) 1 Chr 2:55
Hemdan. Gen 36:26
Hena. 2 Ki 18:34; 19:13; Isa 37:13
Henadad. Ezra 3:9; Neh 3:18, 24; 10:9
Hepher. (1) Num 26:32; 27:1; Josh 17:2, 3. (2) 1 Chr 4:6. (3) 1 Chr 11:36. (4) Josh 12:17; 1 Ki 4:10
Heres. Judg 1:35
Heresh. 1 Chr 9:15
Hesed. 1 Ki 4:10
Heshmon. Josh 15:27
Hethlon. Ezek 47:15; 48:
Hezeki. 1 Chr 8:17
Hezion. 1 Ki 15:18
Hezir. (1) 1 Chr 24:15. (2) Neh 10:20
Hezrai. 2 Sam 23:35
Hezro. 1 Chr 11:37
Hiddai. 2 Sam 23:30
Hierapolis. Col. 4:13
Hilen. 1 Chr 6:58
Hillel. Judg 12:13, 15
Hirah. Gen 38:1, 12
Hizkiah. Zeph 1:1
Hizkijah. Neh 10:17
Hobah. Gen 14:15
Hod. 1 Chr 7:37
Hodaiah. 1 Chr 3:24
Hodaviah. (1) 1 Chr 5:24. (2) 1 Chr 9:7. (3) Ezra 2:40
Hodesh. 1 Chr 8:9
Hodevah. Neh 7:43
Hodiah. (1) 1 Chr 4:19. (2) Neh 8:7; 9:5; 10:10, 13. (3) Neh 10:18
Hoglah. Num 26:33; 27:1; 36:11; Josh 17:3
Hoham. Josh 10:3
Holon. (1) Josh 15:51; 21:15 (2) Jer 48:21
Homam. 1 Chr 1:39
Horam. Josh 10:33
Horem. Josh 19:38
Hori. (1) Gen 36:22, 30; 1 Chr 1:39. (2) Num 13:5
Horim. Gen 14:6; 36:20, 21, 29; Deut 2:12, 22
Hosah. (1) Josh 19:29. (2) 1 Chr 16:38; 26:10, 11, 16
Hoshaiah. (1) Neh 12:32. (2) Jer 42:1; 43:2
Hoshama. 1 Chr 3:18
Hotham. (1) 1 Chr 7:32. (2) 1 Chr 11:44
Hothir. 1 Chr 25:4, 28
Hukkok. Josh 19:34
Hukok. 1 Chr 6:75
Hul. Gen 10:23; 1 Chr 1:17
Huldah. 2 Ki 22:14; 2 Chr 34:22
Humtah. Josh 15:54
Hupham. Num 26:39
Huppah. 1 Chr 24:13
Huppim. Gen 46:21; 1 Chr 7:12, 15
Huram. (1) 1 Chr 8:5. (2) 2 Chr 2:3, 11, 12. (3) 2 Chr 4:11, 16
Hushah. 1 Chr 4:4
Husham. Gen 36:34, 35; 1 Chr 1:45, 46
Hushim. (1) Gen 46:23. (2) 1 Chr 7:12. (3) 1 Chr 8:8, 11
Huz. Gen 22:21

IBLEAM. Josh 17:11; Judg 1:27; 2 Ki 9:27
Ibneiah. 1 Chr 9:8
Ibnijah. 1 Chr 9:8
Ibri. 1 Chr 24:27
Ibzan. Judg 12:8, 10
Idalah. Josh 19:15
Idbash. 1 Chr 4:3
Igal. (1) Num 13:7. (2) 2 Sam 23:36
Igeal. 1 Chr 3:22
Iim. (1) Num 33:45. (2) Josh 15:29
Ijeabarim. Num 21:11; 33:44
Ijon. 1 Ki 15:20; 2 Ki 15:29; 2 Chr 16:4
Ikkesh. 2 Sam 23:26; 1 Chr 11:28; 27:9
Ilai. 1 Chr 11:29
Imla. 1 Ki 22:8, 9; 2 Chr 18:7, 8
Immer. (1) 1 Chr 9:12; Ezra 2:37; 10:20; Neh 7:40; 11:13. (2) 1 Chr 24:14. (3) Ezra 2:59; Neh 7:61. (4) Neh 3:29. (5) Jer 20:1
Imna. 1 Chr 7:35
Imnah. (1) 1 Chr 7:30. (2) 2 Chr 31:14
Imrah. 1 Chr 7:36
Imri. (1) 1 Chr 9:4. (2) Neh 3:2
Ir. 1 Chr 7:12
Iram. Gen 36:43; 1 Chr 1:54
Iri. 1 Chr 7:7
Irnahash. 1 Chr 4:12
Irpeel. Josh 18:27
Irshemesh. Josh 19:41
Iru. 1 Chr 4:15
Iscah. Gen 11:29
Ishbah. 1 Chr 4:17
Ishbak. Gen 25:2; 1 Chr 1:32
Ishbibenoh. 2 Sam 21:16
Ishi. (1) 1 Chr 2:31. (2) 1 Chr 4:20. (3) 1 Chr 4:42. (4) 1 Chr 5:24. (5) Hos 2:16
Ishiah. (1) 1 Chr 7:3. (2) 1 Chr 24:21. (3) 1 Chr 24:25. (4) Ezra 10:31
Ishma. 1 Chr 4:3
Ishmaiah. 1 Chr 27:19
Ishmerai. 1 Chr 8:18
Ishod. 1 Chr 7:18
Ishpan. 1 Chr 8:22
Ishtob. 2 Sam 10:6, 8
Ishuah. Gen 46:17; 1 Chr 7:30
Ishui. (1) Gen 46:17; Num 26:44; 1 Chr 7:30. (2) 1 Sam 14:49
Ismachiah. 2 Chr 31:13
Ismaiah. 1 Chr 12:4
Ispah. 1 Chr 8:16
Ithai. 1 Chr 11:31
Ithmah. 1 Chr 11:46
Ithnan. Josh 15:23
Ithra. 2 Sam 17:25
Ithran. (1) Gen 36:26; 1 Chr 1:41. (2) 1 Chr 7:37
Ithream. 2 Sam 3:5; 1 Chr 3:3
Ittah-kazin. Josh 19:13
Ittai. 2 Sam 15:19, 21, 22; 18:2, 5, 12
Izhar. Ex 6:18. 21; Num 3:19; 16:1; 1 Chr 6:2, 18, 38; 23:12, 18
Izrahiah. 1 Chr 7:3
Izri. 1 Chr 25:11

JAAKAN. Deut 10:6; 1 Chr 1:42
Jaakobah. 1 Chr 4:36
Jaala. Ezra 2:56; Neh 7:58
Jaanai. 1 Chr 5:12
Jaareoregim. 2 Sam 21:19
Jaasau. Ezra 10:37
Jaasiel. (1) 1 Chr 11:47. (2) 1 Chr 27:21
Jaazer. Num 21:32; 32:35; Josh 13:25; 21:39; 2 Sam 24:5; 1 Chr 6:81; 26:31; Jer 48:32
Jaaziah. 1 Chr 24:26, 27
Jaaziel. 1 Chr 15:18
Jabneel. (1) Josh 15:11. (2) Josh 19:33
Jabneh. 2 Chr 26:6
Jachan. 1 Chr 5:13
Jada. 1 Chr 2:28, 32
Jadau. Ezra 10:43
Jaddua. (1) Neh 10:21. (2) Neh 12:11, 22
Jadon. Neh 3:7
Jagur. Josh 15:21
Jahath. (1) 1 Chr 4:2. (2) 1 Chr 6:20, 43. (3) 1 Chr 23:10, 11. (4) 1 Chr 24:22. (5) 2 Chr 32:12
Jahaziah. Ezra 10:15
Jahaziel. (1) 1 Chr 12:4. (2) 1 Chr 16:6. (3) 1 Chr 23:19; 24:23. (4) 2 Chr 20:14. (5) Ezra 8:5
Jahdai. 1 Chr 2:47

LAADAH. *1 Chr* 4:21
Laadan. (1) *1 Chr* 7:26. (2) *1 Chr* 23:7, 8, 9; 26:21
Lael. *Num* 3:24
Lahad. *1 Chr* 4:2
Lahairoi. *Gen* 24:62; 25:11
Lahmam. *Josh* 15:40
Lahmi. *1 Chr* 20:5
Lakum. *Josh* 19:33
Lapidoth. *Judg* 4:4
Lasea. *Acts* 27:8
Lasha. *Gen* 10:19
Lasharon. *Josh* 12:18
Lebanah. *Ezra* 2:45; *Neh* 7:48
Lebaoth. *Josh* 15:32
Lebonah. *Judg* 21:19
Lecah. *1 Chr* 4:21
Lehabim. *Gen* 10:13; *1 Chr* 1:11
Lehi. *Judg* 15:9, 14, 19
Leshem. *Josh* 19:47
Letushim. *Gen* 25:3
Leummim. *Gen* 25:3
Libni. (1) *Ex* 6:17; *Num* 3:18; *1 Chr* 6:17, 20. (2) *1 Chr* 6:29.
Likhi. *1 Chr* 7:19
Linus. *2 Tim* 4:21
Lod. *1 Chr* 8:12; *Ezra* 2:33; *Neh* 7:37; 11:35
Lodebar. *2 Sam* 9:4, 5; 17:27
Lotan. *Gen* 36:20, 22, 29; *1 Chr* 1:38, 39
Lubims. *2 Chr* 12:3; 16:8; *Nah* 3:9
Lud. (1) *Gen* 10:22; *1 Chr* 1:17. (2) *Isa* 66:19; *Ezek* 27:10
Ludim. *Gen* 10:13; *1 Chr* 1:11
Luhith. *Isa* 15:5; *Jer* 48:5
Lycia. *Acts* 27:5

MAADAI. *Ezra* 10:34
Maadiah. *Neh* 12:5
Maai. *Neh* 12:36
Maaleh-acrabbim. *Josh* 15:3
Maarath. *Josh* 15:59
Maasiai. *1 Chr* 9:12
Maaz. *1 Chr* 2:27
Maaziah. (1) *1 Chr* 24:18. (2) *Neh* 10:8
Machbanai. *1 Chr* 12:13
Machbenah. *1 Chr* 2:49
Machi. *Num* 13:15
Machnadebai. *Ezra* 10:40
Madai. *Gen* 10:2; *1 Chr* 1:5
Madmannah. (1) *Josh* 15:31. (2) *1 Chr* 2:49
Madmenah. *Isa* 10:31
Madon. *Josh* 11:1; 12:19
Magbish. *Ezra* 2:30
Magdalene. *Mat* 27:56, 61; 28:1; *Mark* 15:40, 47; 16:1, 9; *Luke* 8:2; 24:10; *John* 19:25; 20:1, 18
Magdiel. *Gen* 36:43; *1 Chr* 1:54
Magor-missabib. *Jer* 20:3
Magpiash. *Neh* 10:20
Mahalah. *1 Chr* 7:18
Mahalath. (1) *Gen* 28:9. (2) *2 Chr* 11:8. (3) *Ps* 53 title; *Ps* 88 title
Mahanehdan. *Judg* 18:12
Maharai. *2 Sam* 23:28; *1 Chr* 11:30; 27:13
Mahath. (1) *1 Chr* 6:35; *2 Chr* 29:12. (2) *2 Chr* 31:13
Mahazioth. *1 Chr* 25:4, 30
Mahlah. *Num* 26:33; 27:1; 36:11; *Josh* 17:3
Mahli. (1) *Ex* 6:19; *Num* 3:20; *1 Chr* 6:19, 29; 23:21; 24:26, 28; *Ezra* 8:18. (2) *1 Chr* 6:47; 23:23; 24:30
Mahol. *1 Ki* 4:31
Makaz. *1 Ki* 4:9
Makheloth. *Num* 33:25, 26
Makkedah. *Josh* 10:10, 16, 17, 21, 28, 29; 12:16; 15:41
Maktesh. *Zeph* 1:11
Malachi. *Mal* 1:1
Malchiah. (1) *1 Chr* 6:40. (2) *1 Chr* 9:12; *Neh* 11:12. (3) *1 Chr* 24:9. (4) *Ezra* 10:25. (5) *Ezra* 10:25. (6) *Ezra* 10:31. (7) *Neh* 3:11. (8) *Neh* 3:14. (9) *Neh* 3:31. (10) *Neh* 8:4. (11) *Neh* 10:3; 12:42. (12) *Jer* 21:1; 38:1
Malchiel. *Gen* 46:17; *Num* 26:45; *1 Chr* 7:31
Malchiram. *1 Chr* 3:18
Maleleel. *Luke* 3:37
Malothi. *1 Chr* 25:4, 26
Malluch. (1) *1 Chr* 6:44. (2) *Ezra* 10:29. (3) *Ezra* 10:32. (4) *Neh* 10:4; 12:2. (5) *Neh* 10:27
Manahath. (1) *Gen* 36:23; *1 Chr* 1:40. (2) *1 Chr* 8:6
Maoch. *1 Sam* 27:2
Maon. (1) *Josh* 15:55; *1 Sam* 25:2. (2) *1 Chr* 2:45
Maralah. *Josh* 19:11
Mareshah. (1) *Josh* 15:44; *2 Chr* 11:8; 14:9, 10; 20:37; *Mi* 1:15. (2) *1 Chr* 2:42. (3) *1 Chr* 4:21
Maroth. *Mi* 1:12
Marsena. *Esth* 1:14
Maschil. *Ps* 32 title, and 42, 44, 45, 52, 53, 54, 55, 74, 78, 88, 89, 142
Mash. *Gen* 10:23
Mashal. *1 Chr* 6:74
Masrekah. *Gen* 36:36; *1 Chr* 1:47
Massa. *Gen* 25:14; *1 Chr* 1:30
Matred. *Gen* 36:39; *1 Chr* 1:50
Matri. *1 Sam* 10:21
Mattanah. *Num* 21:18, 19
Mattaniah. (1) *2 Ki* 24:17. (2) *1 Chr* 9:15; *2 Chr* 20:14; *Neh* 11:17, 22; 12:8, 25, 35. (3) *1 Chr* 25:4, 16. (4) *2 Chr* 29:13. (5) *Ezra* 10:26. (6) *Ezra* 10:27. (7) *Ezra* 10:30. (8) *Ezra* 10:37. (9) *Neh* 13:13
Mattatha. *Luke* 3:31
Mattathah. *Ezra* 10:33
Mattenai. (1) *Ezra* 10:33. (2) *Ezra* 10:37. (3) *Neh* 12:19
Matthan. *Mat* 1:15.
Matthat. (1) *Luke* 3:24. (2) *Luke* 3:29
Mattithiah. (1) *1 Chr* 9:31. (2) *1 Chr* 15:18, 21; 16:5. (3) *1 Chr* 25:3, 21. (4) *Ezra* 10:43. (5) *Neh* 8:4
Meah. *Neh* 3:1; 12:39
Mearah. *Josh* 13:4
Mebunnai. *2 Sam* 23:27
Medan. *Gen* 25:2; *1 Chr* 1:32
Medeba. *Num* 21:30; *Josh* 13:9, 16; *1 Chr* 19:7; *Isa* 15:2
Mehetabel. (1) *Gen* 36:39; *1 Chr* 1:50. (2) *Neh* 6:10
Mehida. *Ezra* 2:52; *Neh* 7:54
Mehir. *1 Chr* 4:11
Mehujael. *Gen* 4:18
Mehuman. *Esth* 1:10
Mehunim. *Ezra* 2:50; *Neh* 7:52
Mejarkon. *Josh* 19:46
Mekonah. *Neh* 11:28
Melatiah. *Neh* 3:7
Melchishua. *1 Sam* 14:49; 31:2; *1 Chr* 8:33; 9:39; 10:2
Melea. *Luke* 3:31
Melech. *1 Chr* 8:35; 9:41
Melicu. *Neh* 12:14
Melita. *Acts* 28:1
Melzar. *Dan* 1:11, 16
Menan. *Luke* 3:31
Meonenim. *Judg* 9:37
Meonothai. *1 Chr* 4:14
Mephaath. *Josh* 13:18; 21:37; *1 Chr* 6:79; *Jer* 48:21
Meraiah. *Neh* 12:12
Meraioth. (1) *1 Chr* 6:6, 7, 52; *Ezra* 7:3. (2) *1 Chr* 9:11; *Neh* 11:11. (3) *Neh* 12:15
Merathaim. *Jer* 50:21
Mered. *1 Chr* 4:17, 18
Meremoth. (1) *Ezra* 8:33; *Neh* 3:4, 21. (2) *Ezra* 10:36. (3) *Neh* 10:5; 12:3
Meres. *Esth* 1:14
Meribbaal. *1 Chr* 8:34; 9:40
Merodath-baladan. *2 Ki* 20:12; *Isa* 39:1
Mesha. (1) *Gen* 10:30. (2) *2 Ki* 3:4. (3) *1 Chr* 2:42. (4) *1 Chr* 8:9
Meshelemiah. *1 Chr* 9:21; 26:1, 2, 9
Meshezabeel. (1) *Neh* 3:4. (2) *Neh* 10:21; 11:24
Meshillemith. *1 Chr* 9:12
Meshillemoth. (1) *2 Chr* 28:12. (2) *Neh* 11:13
Meshobab. *1 Chr* 4:34
Meshullam. (1) *2 Ki* 22:3. (2) *1 Chr* 3:19. (3) *1 Chr* 5:13. (4) *1 Chr* 8:17. (5) *1 Chr* 9:7. (6) *1 Chr* 9:8. (7) *1 Chr* 9:11; *Neh* 11:11. (8) *1 Chr* 9:12. (9) *2 Chr* 34:12. (10) *Ezra* 8:16. (11) *Ezra* 10:15. (12) *Ezra* 10:29. (13) *Neh* 3:4, 30; 6:18. (14) *Neh* 3:6. (15) *Neh* 8:4. (16) *Neh* 10:7. (17) *Neh* 10:20. (18) *Neh* 11:7. (19) *Neh* 12:13, 33. (20) *Neh* 12:16. (21) *Neh* 12:25
Meshullemeth. *2 Ki* 21:19
Mezahab. *Gen* 36:39; *1 Chr* 1:50
Miamin. (1) *Ezra* 10:25. (2) *Neh* 12:5
Mibhar. *1 Chr* 11:38
Mibsam. (1) *Gen* 25:13; *1 Chr* 1:29. (2) *1 Chr* 4:25
Mibzar. *Gen* 36:42; *1 Chr* 1:53
Micha. (1) *2 Sam* 9:12. (2) *Neh* 10:11. (3) *Neh* 11:17, 22
Michmas. *Ezra* 2:27; *Neh* 7:31
Michmash. *1 Sam* 13:2, 5, 11, 16, 23; 14:5, 31; *Neh* 11:31; *Isa* 10:28
Michmethah. *Josh* 16:6; 17:7
Michri. *1 Chr* 9:8
Michtam. *Ps* 16 title, and 56, 57, 58, 59, 60
Middin. *Josh* 15:61
Migdalel. *Josh* 19:38
Migdalgad. *Josh* 15:37
Migdol. (1) *Ex* 14:2; *Num* 33:7. (2) *Jer* 44:1; 46:14
Migron. *1 Sam* 14:2; *Isa* 10:28
Mijamin. (1) *1 Chr* 24:9. (2) *Neh* 10:7
Mikloth. (1) *1 Chr* 8:32; 9:37, 38. (2) *1 Chr* 27:4
Mikneiah. *1 Chr* 15:18, 21
Milalai. *Neh* 12:36
Miniamin. (1) *2 Chr* 31:15. (2) *Neh* 12:17, 41
Minni. *Jer* 51:27
Minnith. *Judg* 11:33; *Ezek* 27:17
Miphkad. *Neh* 3:31
Mirma. *1 Chr* 8:10
Misgab. *Jer* 48:1
Misham. *1 Chr* 8:12
Misheal. *Josh* 19:26; 21:30
Mishma. *Gen* 25:14; *1 Chr* 1:30; 4:25, 26
Mishmannah. *1 Chr* 12:10
Mispereth. *Neh* 7:7
Misrephothmaim. *Josh* 11:8; 13:6
Mithcah. *Num* 33:28, 29
Mithredath. (1) *Ezra* 1:8. (2) *Ezra* 4:7
Mitylene. *Acts* 20:14
Mizpar. *Ezra* 2:2
Mizraim. *Gen* 10:6, 13; *1 Chr* 1:8, 11
Mizzah. *Gen* 36:13, 17; *1 Chr* 1:37
Moadiah. *Neh* 12:17
Moladah. *Josh* 15:26; 19:2; *1 Chr* 4:28; *Neh* 11:26
Molid. *1 Chr* 2:29
Moreh. (1) *Gen* 12:6; *Deut* 11:30. (2) *Judg* 7:1
Moreshethgath. *Mi* 1:14
Mosera. *Deut* 10:6
Moseroth. *Num* 33:30, 31
Moza. (1) *1 Chr* 2:46. (2) *1 Chr* 8:36, 37; 9:42, 43
Mozah. *Josh* 18:26
Muppim. *Gen* 46:21
Mushi. *Ex* 6:19; *Num* 3:20; *1 Chr* 6:19, 47; 23:21, 23; 24:26, 30
Muthlabben. *Ps* 9 title

NAAM. *1 Chr* 4:15
Naamah. (1) *Gen* 4:22. (2) *1 Ki* 14:21, 31; *2 Chr* 12:13. (3) *Josh* 15:41
Naarah. *1 Chr* 4:5, 6
Naarai. *1 Chr* 11:37
Naaran. *1 Chr* 7:28
Naarath. *Josh* 16:7
Nachon. *2 Sam* 6:6
Nachor. *Luke* 3:34
Nahaliel. *Num* 21:19
Nahallal. *Josh* 19:15; 21:35; *Judg* 1:30

Serug. Gen 11:20, 21, 22, 23; 1 Chr 1:26
Sethur. Num 13:13
Shaalabbin. Josh 19:42
Shaalbim. Judg 1:35; 1 Ki 4:9
Shaaph. (1) 1 Chr 2:47. (2) 1 Chr 2:49
Shaaraim. Josh 15:36; 1 Sam 17:52; 1 Chr 4:31
Shaashgaz. Esth 2:14
Shabbethai. (1) Ezra 10:15. (2) Neh 8:7. (3) Neh 11:16
Shachia. 1 Chr 8:10
Shaharaim. 1 Chr 8:8
Shahazimah. Josh 19:22
Shalem. Gen 33:18
Shallecheth. 1 Chr 26:16
Shalmai. Ezra 2:46; Neh 7:48
Shalman. Hos 10:14
Shama. 1 Chr 11:44
Shamer. (1) 1 Chr 6:46. (2) 1 Chr 7:32, 34
Shamhuth. 1 Chr 27:8
Shamir. (1) Josh 15:48. (2) Judg 10:1, 2. (3) 1 Chr 24:24
Shammai. 1 Chr 2:28, 32. (2) 1 Chr 2:44, 45. (3) 1 Chr 4:17
Shammoth. 1 Chr 11:27
Shamsherai. 1 Chr 8:26
Shapham. 1 Chr 5:12
Shapher. Num 33:23, 24
Sharai. Ezra 10:40
Sharar. 2 Sam 23:33
Sharuhen. Josh 19:6
Shashai. Ezra 10:40
Shashak. 1 Chr 8:14, 25
Shaul. (1) Gen 46:10; Ex 6:15; Num 26:13; 1 Chr 4:24. (2) 1 Chr 6:24
Shaveh. Gen 14:17
Shavehkiriathaim. Gen 14:5
Shavsha. 1 Chr 18:16
Sheal. Ezra 10:29
Sheariah. 1 Chr 8:38; 9:44
Shebam. Num 32:3
Shebaniah. (1) 1 Chr 15:24. (2) Neh 9:4, 5; 10:10. (3) Neh 10:4; 12:14. (4) Neh 10:12
Shebarim. Josh 7:5
Sheber. 1 Chr 2:48
Shebna. (1) 2 Ki 18:18, 26, 37; 19:2; Isa 36:3, 11, 22; 37:2. (2) Isa 22:15
Shebuel. (1) 1 Chr 23:16; 26:24. (2) 1 Chr 25:4
Shecaniah. (1) 1 Chr 24:11. (2) 2 Chr 31:15
Shechaniah. (1) 1 Chr 3:21, 22. (2) Ezra 8:3. (3) Ezra 8:5. (4) Ezra 10:2. (5) Neh 3:29. (6) Neh 6:18. (7) Neh 12:3
Shedeur. Num 1:5; 2:10; 7:30, 35; 10:18
Shehariah. 1 Chr 8:26
Sheleph. Gen 10:26; 1 Chr 1:20
Shelesh. 1 Chr 7:35
Shelomi. Num 34:27
Shelomith. (1) Lev 24:11. (2) 1 Chr 3:19. (3) 1 Chr 23:9. (4) 1 Chr 23:18. (5) 1 Chr 26:25, 26, 28. (6) 2 Chr 11:20. (7) Ezra 8:10
Shelomoth 1 Chr 24:22
Shema. (1) Josh 15:26. (2) 1 Chr 2:43, 44. (3) 1 Chr 5:8. (4) 1 Chr 8:13. (5) Neh 8:4
Shemaah. 1 Chr 12:3
Shemariah. (1) 1 Chr 12:5. (2) 2 Chr 11:19. (3) Ezra 10:32. (4) Ezra 10:41
Shemeber. Gen 14:2
Shemer. 1 Ki 16:24
Shemidah. Num 26:32; Josh 17:2; 1 Chr 7:19
Shemiramoth. (1) 1 Chr 15:18, 20; 16:5. (2) 2 Chr 17:8
Shemuel. (1) Num 34:20. (2) 1 Chr 6:33. (3) 1 Chr 7:2
Shen. 1 Sam 7:12
Shenazar. 1 Chr 3:18
Shepham. Num 34:10, 11
Shepho. Gen 36:23; 1 Chr 1:40
Shephuphan. 1 Chr 8:5
Sherah. 1 Chr 7:24
Sherebiah. (1) Ezra 8:18, 24; Neh 8:7; 9:4, 5. (2) Neh 10:12; 12:8, 24
Sheresh. 1 Chr 7:16
Sheshai. Num 13:22; Josh 15:14; Judg 1:10
Sheshan. 1 Chr 2:31, 34, 35
Sheth. Num 24:17
Shethar. Esth 1:14
Shethar-boznai. Ezra 5:3, 6; 6:6, 13
Sheva. (1) 2 Sam 20:25. (2) 1 Chr 2:49
Shibmah. Num 32:38
Shicron. Josh 15:11
Shihon. Josh 19:19
Shihorlibnath. Josh 19:26
Shilhi. 1 Ki 22:42; 2 Chr 20:31
Shilhim. Josh 15:32
Shillem. Gen 46:24; Num 26:49
Shiloni (Shilonite). Neh 11:5
Shilshah. 1 Chr 7:37
Shimea. (1) 1 Chr 20:7. (2) 1 Chr 3:5. (3) 1 Chr 6:30. (4) 1 Chr 6:39
Shimeam. 1 Chr 9:38
Shimeath. 2 Ki 12:21; 2 Chr 24:26
Shimeon. Ezra 10:31
Shimma. 1 Chr 2:13
Shimon. 1 Chr 4:20
Shimrath. 1 Chr 8:21
Shimri. (1) 1 Chr 4:37. (2) 1 Chr 11:45. (3) 1 Chr 26:10. (4) 2 Chr 29:13
Shimrith. 2 Chr 24:26
Shimron. (1) Gen 46:13; Num 26:24; 1 Chr 7:1. (2) Josh 11:1; 19:15
Shimron-meron. Josh 12:20
Shinab. Gen 14:2
Shiphi. 1 Chr 4:37
Shiphrah. Ex 1:15
Shiphtan. Num 34:24
Shisha. 1 Ki 4:3
Shitrai. 1 Chr 27:29
Shiza. 1 Chr 11:42
Shoa. Ezek 23:23
Shobab. (1) 2 Sam 5:14; 1 Chr 3:5; 14:4. (2) 1 Chr 2:18
Shobach. 2 Sam 10:16 18
Shobai. Ezra 2:42; Neh 7:45
Shobal. (1) Gen 36:20, 23, 29; 1 Chr 1:38, 40. (2) 1 Chr 2:50, 52. (3) 1 Chr 4:1, 2
Shobek. Neh 10:24
Shobi. 2 Sam 17:27
Shoham. 1 Chr 24:27
Shomer. (1) 2 Ki 12:21. (2) 1 Chr 7:32
Shophach. 1 Chr 19:16, 18
Shophan. Num 32:35
Shoshannim. Ps 45 title; 69 title; 80 title
Shua. 1 Chr 7:32
Shual. 1 Chr 7:36
Shubael. (1) 1 Chr 24:20. (2) 1 Chr 25:20
Shuham. Num 26:42
Shunem. Josh 19:18; 1 Sam 28:4; 2 Ki 4:8
Shuni. Gen 46:16; Num 26:15
Shupham. Num 26:39
Shuppim. (1) 1 Chr 7:12, 15. (2) 1 Chr 26:16
Shur. Gen 16:7; 20:1; 25:18; Ex 15:22; 1 Sam 15:7; 27:8
Shushaneduth. Ps 60 title
Shuthelah. (1) Num 26:35 36; 1 Chr 7:20. (2) 1 Chr 7:21
Siaha. Ezra 2:44; Neh 7:47
Sibbechai. 2 Sam 21:18; 1 Chr 11:29; 20:4; 27:11
Sibmah. Josh 13:19; Isa 16:8, 9; Jer 48:32
Sibraim. Ezek 47:16
Sichem (Shechem). Gen 12:6
Siddim. Gen 14:3, 8, 10
Silla. 2 Ki 12:20
Sinim. Isa 49:12
Siphmoth. 1 Sam 30:28
Sippai. 1 Chr 20:4
Sirah. 2 Sam 3:26
Sisamai. 1 Chr 2:40
Sitnah. Gen 26:21
Socho. (1) 1 Chr 4:18. (2) 2 Chr 11:7; 28:18
Socoh. (1) Josh 15:35; 1 Sam 17:1; 1 Ki 4:10. (2) Josh 15:48
Sodi. Num 13:10
Sopater. Acts 20:4
Sophereth. Ezra 2:55; Neh 7:57
Sotai. Ezra 2:55; Neh 7:57
Suah. 1 Chr 7:36
Sur. 2 Ki 11:6
Susi. Num 13:11
Sychar. John 4:5
Sychem. See Shechem
Syene. Ezek 29:10; 30:6
Syntyche. Phil 4:2
Syracuse. Acts 28:12

TAANACH. Josh 12:21; 17:11; 21:25; Judg 1:27; 5:19; 1 Ki 4:12; 1 Chr 7:29
Taanath. Josh 16:6
Tabbaoth. Ezra 2:43; Neh 7:46
Tabbath. Judg 7:22
Tabeel. Ezra 4:7
Tabrimon. 1 Ki 15:18
Tahan. (1) Num 26:35. (2) 1 Chr 7:25
Tahath. (1) Num 33:26, 27. (2) 1 Chr 6:24, 37. (3) 1 Chr 7:20. (4) 1 Chr 7:20
Tahrea. 1 Chr 9:41
Tahtimhodshi. 2 Sam 24:6
Talmai. (1) Num 13:22; Josh 15:14; Judg 1:10. (2) 2 Sam 3:3; 13:37; 1 Chr 3:2
Talmon. 1 Chr 9:17; Ezra 2:42; Neh 7:45; 11:19; 12:25
Tanhumeth. 2 Ki 25:23; Jer 40:8
Taphath. 1 Ki 4:11
Tappuah. (1) Josh 12:17; 15:34. (2) Josh 16:8; 17:8. (3) 1 Chr 2:43
Tarah. Num 33:27, 28
Taralah. Josh 18:27
Tarea. 1 Chr 8:35
Tartan. 2 Ki 18:17; Isa 20:1
Tatnai. Ezra 5:3, 6; 6:6, 13
Tebah. Gen 22:24
Tebaliah. 1 Chr 26:11
Tehaphnehes. Ezek 30:18
Tehinnah. 1 Chr 4:12
Tel-abib. Ezek 3:15
Telah. 1 Chr 7:25
Telaim. 1 Sam 15:4
Telem. (1) Josh 15:24. (2) Ezra 10:24
Tel-melah. Ezra 2:59; Neh 7:61
Temeni. 1 Chr 4:6
Teresh. Esth 2:21; 6:2
Thaddaeus. Mat 10:3; Mark 3:18
Thahash. Gen 22:24
Thamah. Ezra 2:53; Neh 7:55
Thamar. Mat 1:3
Thara. Luke 3:34
Thelasar. 2 Ki 19:12; Isa 37:12
Tiberius Caesar. Luke 3:1
Tibhath. 1 Chr 18:8
Tidal. Gen 14:1, 9
Tikvah. (1) 2 Ki 22:14; 2 Chr 34:22. (2) Ezra 10:15
Tilon. 1 Chr 4:20
Timaeus. Mark 10:46
Timna. (1) Gen 36:12. (2) Gen 36:22; 1 Chr 1:39. (3) 1 Chr 1:36
Timnah, Thimnathah. (1) Gen 36:40; 1 Chr 1:51. (2) Josh 15:10, 57; 19:43; 2 Chr 28:18
Timnath-heres. Judg 2:9
Timnath-serah. Josh 19:50; 24:30
Timon. Acts 6:5
Tiphsah. (1) 1 Ki 4:24. (2) 1 Ki 15:16
Tiras. Gen 10:2; 1 Chr 1:5
Tirhakah. 2 Ki 19:9; Isa 37:9
Tirhanah. 1 Chr 2:48
Tiria. 1 Chr 4:16
Toah. 1 Chr 6:34
Tob. Judg 11:3, 5
Tobadonijah. 2 Chr 17:8
Tochen. 1 Chr 4:32
Tohu. 1 Sam 1:1
Toi. 2 Sam 8:9, 10; 1 Chr 18:9, 10
Tolad. 1 Chr 4:29

A LIST OF

THE PROPER NAMES

IN THE

OLD AND NEW TESTAMENTS

With the Meaning or Signification of the Words in Their Original Languages

BY REV. ALFRED JONES, M.A.

Author of "The Proper Names of the Old Testament Scriptures, Expounded and Illustrated," etc., etc.

NOTE—Some few PROPER NAMES which rarely occur in Scripture appear in this List only, and not in the following part of the Concordance; to these the Scripture References are here annexed.

A LIST OF

THE PROPER NAMES

IN THE

OLD AND NEW TESTAMENTS

AARON, *signifies* mountain of strength to the Jewish people, even as Christ is everlasting strength to His Church; *or*, a teacher, *or* teaching. *The first high priest of the Jews, the son of Amram, brother to Moses. He was, with his sons, anointed and consecrated to the priest's office*, Lev. 8.

AARONITES.

ABADDON, the destroyer, total destruction.

ABAGTHA, father of the wine-press, given by fortune.

ABANA, stone, *or* a building.

ABARIM, passages, *or* passengers, plur. of the appell. *ébher*, beyond.

ABDA, a servant, *or* servitude.

ABDI, servant of the Lord.

ABDIEL, the servant of God.

ABDON, servile.

ABED-NEGO, servant of the sun, *Dan*. 3. 23.

ABEL, vanity, *or* breath, *or* transitoriness; *second son of Adam*, Gen. 4. 4.

ABEL, *a city*.

ABEL-BETH-MAACHAH, mourning to the house of Maachah.

ABEL K'RAMIVM, plain of the vineyards. (*See* Judg. 11. 33.)

ABEL-MAIM, the mourning of the waters; *or*, the valley of waters.

ABEL-MEHOLAH, meadow of dancing.

ABEL-MIZRAIM, the mourning of the Egyptians, *Gen*. 50. 11.

ABEL-SHITTIM, meadows of acacias. *It was a city near the river Jordan in the wilderness*, Num. 33. 49.

ABEZ, white, perhaps tin was found there. *A city in the tribe of Issachar*, Josh. 19. 20.

ABI, my father. *The mother of Hezekiah*, 2 Kings 18. 2.

ABIA. *See* ABIAH.

ABIAH, the Lord is my father, *or* the father of the Lord.

ABI-ALBON, father of strength.

ABIASAPH, father of gathering, *Ex*. 6. 24.

ABIATHAR, father of plenty, *or* father of him that survived, 1 *Sam*. 22. 20.

ABIB, green fruits, *or* ears of corn.

ABIDAH, the father of knowledge, *or* the knowledge of the father. *One of the sons of Midian*, Gen. 25. 4.

ABIDAN, father of judgment, *or* my father is judge.

ABIEL, father of strength. *He was the father of Kish*, 1 Sam. 9. 1.

ABIEZER, father of help, *or* help of the father, *or* my father is my help.

ABI-EZRITE.

ABIGAIL, father of joy, or the joy of the father, 1 *Sam*. 25. 3.

ABIHAIL, father of strength, *or* father of firmness.

ABIHU, [whose] father is He, *i.e.*, God.

ABIHUD, father of praise, *or* glory of my father; the same as Hodaiah.

ABIJAH, the will of the Lord, *or* the Lord is my father.

ABIJAM, father of the sea, a maritime person.

ABILENE, grassy place, near the city Abila. *A province between Libanus and Antilibanus, whereof Lysanias was tetrarch*, Luke 3. 1.

ABIMAEL, a father sent from God, *or* my father comes from God. *He was the son of Joktan*, Gen. 10. 28.

ABIMELECH, father of the king, *or* my father the king.

ABINADAB, father of willingness; *or*, my father is a prince.

ABINOAM, father of pleasantness, the father of Barak.

ABIRAM, father of loftiness, *or* one who lifts up himself. A son of Eliab.

ABISHAG, father of error.

ABISHAI, father of gifts, or father of the present.

ABISHALOM, the father of peace, *or* the peace of the father; *or*, the recompence of the father. 1 *Kings* 15. 2.

ABISHUA, father of salvation, *or* of magnificence, *or* the salvation of my father, 1 *Chron*. 6. 4.

ABISHUR, the father of a wall, *or* of uprightness; *or*, my father is upright, 1 *Chron*. 2. 28.

ABITAL, the father of dew. *One of David's wives*, 2 Sam. 3. 4.

ABITUB, father of goodness, or my father is good, 1 *Chron*. 8. 11.

ABNER, father of light, *or* the lamp of the father, or the son of the father.

ABRAM, a high father; father of a multitude.

ABRAHAM, father of a multitude. *A son of Terah, and founder through the promise of God of the Jewish nation. He was an inhabitant of the city of Ur, whose people were ignicolists, or worshippers of fire; there are reasons for concluding that Abraham was at one time an idolater as well as his father and brethren.* (Josh. 24. 3.) *These descendants of Shem were examples of the proneness of man to wander: "all we like sheep have gone astray;" for they were all on forbidden ground—among the rebellious sons of Ham — united under the idolatrous and tyrannical Nimrod; instead of being in their own country, and among their own kin. The* Messiah *was promised to be of his family*, Gen. 12. 3; Acts 3. 25; Gal. 3. 8. *The spiritual children of faithful Abraham, are those that believe in Jesus Christ, and do the works of Abraham*, John 8. 39; Rom. 4. 16; 9. 7; Gal. 3. 7, 29.

ABSALOM, father of peace, *or* the peace of the father.

ACCAD, band or chain. *The city where Nimrod reigned*, Gen. 10. 10.

ACCHO, sand made warm by heat of the sun.

ACELDAMA, the field of blood, *Acts* 1. 19.

ACHAIA, grief, *or* trouble.

ACHAICUS, a native of Achaia, gracious.

ACHAN, *or* ACHAR, he that troubles and bruises.

ACHBOR, a mouse. *He was father of Baal-hanan, the seventh king of Edom*, Gen. 36. 38.

ACHIM, He (*i.e.*, God) will establish.

ACHISH, fear.

ACHMETHA, *a city*.

ACHOR, trouble.

ACHSAH, anklet or adorned.

ACHSHAPH, enchantment tricks; *or*, o that breaks: or the lip or brim of a thing.

ACHZIB, lying; deceptive as a fishi hook.

ADADAH, ornament. *The name of a ci* Josh. 15. 22.

ADAH, an ornament. *The wife of Lame* Gen. 4. 19. *Also the wife of Esau*, Gen. 36

ADAIAH, ornament of the Lord. T *father of Jedidah, mother of Josiah*, 2 Ki 22. 1.

ADALIAH, strong mind. *One of Hama sons*, Esth. 9. 8.

ADAM, red earth. *He was called ADA not because he would return to dust; because he was created out of the grou and probably with a prophetic referenc the fact that he would return to the dust at any time he transgressed. He was called Enosh, miserable, for he was per and happy; nor Ish, husband, because had no female and was solitary, for t term was not used till Ishah was taken ou Ish, wife out of her husband. He was ca Adam with reference to his origin, the ea Also he was called Ish, husband, when a ciated with his wife in the garden of Ed and Enosh, miserable, after his fall. name of the first man, who was made a the image of God, in a holy and happy est but by his fall and disobedience broke c nant with God, and thereby brought him and all his posterity into an estate of sin misery*, Rom. 5. 12. *But our Lord J Christ, the second Adam, is the Saviour Redeemer of all that truly believe in H* Mark 16. 16; Acts 4. 12; 16. 31.

ADAMAH, red earth. *A city*, Josh. 19.

ADAMI, my man, red, earthy, human. *city*, Josh. 19. 33.

ADAR, wide.

ADBEEL, sorrow of God: *otherwise* vexer of God. *One of Ishmael's s* Gen. 25. 13.

ADDI, my witness, adorned, passage, pr

ADDON, basis, foundation, the Lord. *name of a place*, Neh. 7. 61.

ADIEL, ornament of the Lord, 1 *Chron*. 4.

ADIN, soft, adorned, *or* voluptuous, dai *Ezra* 8. 6.

ADINA, pliant, 1 *Chron*. 11. 42.

ADINO, whose pleasure is the sp 2 *Sam*. 23. 8.

ADITHAIM, two-fold ornament, *Josh*. 15

ADLAI, justice of the Lord, 1 *Chron*. 27.

ADMAH, earthy, red earth.

ADMATHA, a cloud of death, a mo vapour, *Esth*. 1. 14.

ADNAH, rest, *or* testimony eternal. 1 *Ch* 12. 20.

ADONI-BEZEK the lightning of the Lo or the Lord of lightning; *or*, the Lor Bezek; *for he was king of this city*.

ADONIJAH, the Lord is my Lord.

ADONIKAM, the Lord of enemies.

ADONIRAM, my Lord is most high; *or* the Lord of might and elevation, 1 *Kings* 4. 6.
ADONI-ZEDEK, justice of the Lord, *or* the Lord of justice. *He was king of Jerusalem*, Josh. 10. 1.
ADORAIM, twofold habitation, 2 *Chron*. 11. 9.
ADORAM, *vide* Adoniram. 2 *Sam*. 20. 24.
ADRAMMELECH, the cloke, glory, grandeur, *or* power of the king.
ADRAMMYTTIUM, *ensign of elevation*, now called Adrampt.
ADRIA, restless, *the Adriatic sea, now the gulf of Venice*.
ADRIEL, flock of God, 1 *Sam*. 18. 19.
ADULLAM, the justice of the people.
ÆNON, fountain of the sun, *John* 3. 23.
AGABUS, a locust.
AGAG, fire.
AGAGITE, *of the race of* Agag.
AGAR, *see* HAGAR.
AGRIPPA, *this word is Latin, and signifies* one who at his birth causes great pain. who is born with his feet foremost, *ægre partus*, Acts 12. 1.
AGUR, *or* gathering, *or* gathered together.
AHAB, the brother of the father, uncle, *or* father of the brother.
AHARAH, after a brother, 1 *Chron*. 8. 1.
AHARHEL, behind the breastwork, 1 *Chron*. 4. 8.
AHASAI, possessor of God, *Neh*. 11. 13.
AHASBAI, I flee to the Lord, 2 *Sam*. 23. 34.
AHASUERUS, prince, head, *or* chief.
AHAVA, essence, *or* generation.
AHAZ, one that takes and possesses.
AHAZIAH, possession of the Lord.
AHBAN, brother of the prudent, 1 *Chron*. 2. 29.
AHER, coming slowly, 1 *Chron*. 7. 12.
AHI, brother, 1 *Chron*. 5. 15; 7. 34.
AHIAH, brother of the Lord.
AHIAM, brother's mother, 2 *Sam*. 23. 33; 1 *Chron*. 11. 35.
AHIAN, brotherly.
AHIEZER, brother of assistance. *A prince of the tribe of Dan*, Num. 1. 12.
AHIHUD, brother of praise. *The prince of the tribe of Asher*, Num. 34. 27.
AHIJAH, brother of the Lord.
AHIJAH, *the same as* AHIAH.
AHIKAM, brother of rising up.
AHIKAM, a brother that raises up.
AHILUD, a brother born. *He was secretary to David*, 2 Sam. 8. 16.
AHIMAAZ, brother of anger. Three bore this name.
AHIMAN, who is my brother?
AHIMELECH, my brother is a king, *or* the brother of my king. Three bore this name.
AHIMOTH, brother of death, *or* my brother is dead, 1 *Chron*. 6. 25.
AHINADAB, brother of nobility, 1 *Kings* 4. 14.
AHINOAM, the beauty and comeliness of the brother, *or* brother of grace.
AHIO, brotherly.
AHIRA, brother of iniquity; *otherwise* brother *or* companion of the shepherd. *He was chief of the tribe of Naphtali*, Num. 1. 15.
AHIRAM, brother of height, *Num*. 6. 38.
AHISAMACH, brother of strength *or* support, *or* my brother supports me.
AHISHAR, *or* AHISHAHAR, brother of the dawn, *or* brother of a song. *He was steward of Solomon's household*, 1 Kings 4. 6; 1 Chron. 7. 10.
AHITHOPHEL, brother of folly.
AHITUB, brother of goodness, *or* my brother is good.
AHLAB, which is of milk, *or* which is fat; *otherwise*, brother of the heart. *The name of a city*, Judg. 1. 31.
AHOLAH, she has her own tent.
AHOLIAB, the tent, *or* tabernacle of the father.
AHOLIBAH, my tent and my tabernacle in her.
AHOLIBAMAH, my tabernacle is exalted.
AHUMAI, brother of waters, 1 *Chron*. 4. 2.
AHUZAM, their possession, 1 *Chron*. 4. 6.
AHUZZATH, a passion, *Gen*. 26. 26.
AI, *or* HAI, mass *or* heap of ruins.
AIATH, *the same as* AI.
AIN, a fountain, *Num*. 34. 11; *Josh*. 15. 32; 19. 7; 21. 16; 1 *Chron*. 4. 32.
AJALON, a large stag.
AKAN, *or* JAKAN, to twist, *Gen*. 36. 27; 1 *Chron*. 1. 42.
AKKUB, insidious, 1 *Chron*. 3. 24; 9. 17; *Ezra* 2. 42, 45; *Neh*. 7. 45; 8. 7; 11. 19; 12. 25.
ALAMETH, covering, 1 *Chron*. 7. 8.
ALAMMELECH, oak of the king. *A city*, Josh. 19. 26.
ALEMETH, a hiding-place, 1 *Chron*. 6. 60; 8. 36; 9. 42.
ALEXANDER, defender of men.
ALEXANDER, *a Greek word, and signifies* one that assists men, *or* one that helps stoutly; *or*, one that turns away evil.
ALEXANDRIA, *a city in Egypt*.
ALLON, an oak, *or* strong, 1 *Chron*. 4. 37.
ALLON-BACHUTH, the oak of weeping. *The place where Rebekah's nurse was buried*, Gen. 35. 8.
ALMODAD, measure of God, *Gen*. 10. 26.
ALMODAD, immeasurable.
ALMON, hidden.
ALMON DIBLATHAIM, Almon towards Diblathaim, *Num*. 33. 46, 47.
ALPHA, *the first letter of the Greek alphabet, marked* A. Rev. 1. 8, 11; 21. 6; 22. 13.
ALPHEUS, first, *or* chief, *or* an ox.
ALUSH, a crowd of men, *Num*. 33. 13, 14.
ALVAH, iniquity, *Gen*. 36. 40; 1 *Chron*. 1. 51.
ALVAN, unrighteous, *Gen*. 36. 23; 1 *Chron*. 1. 40.
AMAD, eternal people, *Josh*. 19. 26.
AMAL, troublesome, 1 *Chron*. 7. 35.
AMALEK, a people that licks up, *or* that takes away all; *otherwise*, a people that strikes, *or* that uses ill.
AMALEKITES, *people descended from Amalek*
AMAM, people, *Josh*. 15. 26.
AMANA, a confirmation; integrity and truth.
AMARIAH, promised of the Lord, 1 *Chron*. 6. 7, 11, 52; 23. 19; 24. 23; 2 *Chron*. 19. 11; 31. 15; *Ezra* 7. 3; 10. 42; *Neh*. 10. 3; 11. 4; 12. 2, 13; *Zeph*. 1. 1.
AMASA, burden of the people.
AMASAI, burden of the Lord, 1 *Chron*. 6. 25, 35; 12. 18; 15. 24; 2 *Chron*. 29. 12.
AMASIAH, carried of the Lord, 2 *Chron*. 17. 16.
AMAZIAH, the strength of the Lord.
AMITTAI, truth of the Lord, 2 *Kings* 14. 25; *Jon*. 1. 1.
AMMAH, beginning.
AMMI, *the same with* AMMAH.
AMMIEL, one of the people of God, *Num*. 13. 12; 2 *Sam*. 9. 4, 5; 17. 27; 1 *Chron*. 3. 5; 26. 5.
AMMIHUD, people of praise, *or* praise is with me. *Num*. 1. 10.
AMMINADAB, people of liberality.
AMMI-NADIB, my people is liberal, *or* prince of the people, *or* a people that vows.
AMMISHADDAI, the people of the Almighty, *or* the Almighty is with me, *Num*. 1. 12.
AMMIZABAD, people of the bountiful giver, 1 *Chron*. 27. 6.
AMMON, great people.
AMMONITES. *A people that descended of* Ben-ammi, *son of Lot by his youngest daughter*.
AMNON, a nourisher, faithful and true; *otherwise*, foster-father, *or* tutor; *or*, son of the mother.
AMOK, deep. *Neh*. 12. 7.
AMON, faithful, true.
AMORITE, bitter, a rebel; *otherwise*, a babbler, a mountaineer, or prater.
AMOS, weighty, burden.
AMOZ, strong, robust.
AMPHIPOLIS, a city encompassed by the sea on both sides of the city, *or* a double-sided city.
AMPLIAS, enlargement. *A Latin word*.
AMRAM, an exalted people; *or*, their sheaves, *or* handfuls of corn.
AMRAPHEL, one that speaks of hidden things; one that speaks of judgment, *or* ruin, *Gen*. 14. 1, 9.
AMZI, strong, 1 *Chron*. 6. 46; *Neh*. 11. 12.
ANAH, one who answers, *or* who sings; *otherwise* poor *or* afflicted.
ANAK, a collar, *or* ornament.
ANAKIMS.
ANAMIM, responding waters, *Gen*. 10. 13; 1 *Chron*. 1. 11.
ANAMMELECH, answer, *or* song of the king.
ANAN, a cloud.
ANANI, a cloud of the Lord, 1 *Chron*. 3. 24.
ANANIAH, cloud of the Lord, *Neh*. 3. 23.
ANANIAS, graciously given of the Lor
ANATH, answer to prayer, *Judg*. 3. 31;
ANATHOTH, answer to prayers.
ANDREW, a stout and strong man. *G*
ANDRONICUS, victor of men. *Greek*.
ANEM, two fountains, 1 *Chron*. 6. 73.
ANER, exile.
ANNA, gracious, merciful.
ANNAS, graciously given. *A high pr who sent Christ bound to Caiaphas his fat in-law*.
ANTICHRIST, an adversary to Christ.
ANTIOCH, resistance. *A Greek word. city on the Orontes, one hundred miles no of Jerusalem*, Acts 11. 19.
ANTIPAS, likeness of his father. *One of martyrs slain by the people of Pergam* Rev. 2. 13.
ANTIPATRIS, likeness of his father.
APELLES, *a Greek word, from the* ἀπελλω, I exclude, I separate.
APHEK, a stream, a rapid torrent; strength, vigour.
APOLLONIA, perdition, destruction.
APOLLOS, one that destroys and la waste.
APOLLYON, one that exterminates *or* d stroys.
APPHIA, that produces, *or* is fruitf *Philem*. 2.
APPII-FORUM, *a town so called fro* Appius Claudius, *whose statue was erect there*.
APPII-FORUM, *market of Appius*.
AQUILA, an eagle. *Latin*.
AR, city.
ARABIA, sterile, *or* a place wild and desert *or*, hostages, ravens; *and also*, mixtures *because this country was inhabited by diffe ent kinds of people*.
ARABIAN.
ARAD, wild ass, *Num*. 21. 1; 33. 40; *Josh* 12. 14; *Judg*. 1. 16; 1 *Chron*. 8. 15.
ARAH, wandering, 1 *Chron*. 7. 39; *Ezr* 2. 5; *Neh*. 6. 18; 7. 10.
ARAM, highness, magnificence; *otherwise* one that deceives, or their curse. ARAM *signifies* Syria *in* Gen. 22. 21, *and elsewhere*.
ARARAT, mount of descent.
ARAUNAH, a large ash.
ARBA, quadrangular.
ARCHELAUS, prince of the people. *Greek*
ARCHIPPUS, a governor of horses, *or* master of the horse. *Greek*.
ARCTURUS, a gathering together.
ARD, fugitive. *A son of Benjamin*, Gen. 46. 21.
ARELI, lion of God. *Gen*. 46. 16.
AREOPAGITE, belonging to the council called *Areopagus*.
AREOPAGUS, the hill of Mars; *a place where the magistrates of Athens held their supreme council; from* ἀρειος, *Mars; and* παγος, a hill.
ARETAS, one that is agreeable, that pleases, that is virtuous.
ARGOB, a turf of earth, a heap of stones, *or* curse of the well.
ARIDAI, donum Ario, *Esther* 9. 9.
ARIDATHA, great birth, *Esther* 9. 8.
ARIEH, lion, 2 *Kings* 15. 25.
ARIEL, the altar, light, *or* lion of God.
ARIMATHEA, a lion dead to the Lord; *or*, the light of the death of the Lord; *or simply*, Ramath, *or* Ramah, *a city where Samuel dwelt*, 1 Sam. 1. 19.
ARIOCH, "the mighty lion."
ARISTARCHUS, a good prince, the best prince. *Greek*.
ARISTOBULUS, a good counsellor, good advice. *Greek*.
ARMAGEDDON, the mountain of *Megiddo*, *or* the mountain of the gospel; *otherwise*, the mountain of fruits, *or* of apples.
ARMENIA, *a province which is supposed to take its name from Aram*.
ARNON, rejoicing, *or* leaping for joy.
AROER, heath, tamarisk; *or*, the nakedness of the skin; *or*, nakedness of the watch, *or* of the enemy.
ARPAD, prop.; *or*, that lie down, that makes his bed.
ARPHAXAD, boundary of the Chaldeans; *or*, one that releases.
ARTAXERXES, *in Hebrew*, Artachsasta, the silence of light, *or* light that imposes silence; *otherwise*, joy that is in haste. *A Persian name*.
ARTEMAS, gift of Diana.
ARUBOTH, flood-gates, 1 *Kings* 4. 10.

FOREWORD

THE STUDY of the Word of God can best be facilitated by a wise and constant use of this Concordance. Here you will find almost every word of the whole Bible arranged alphabetically, so that at any time the student may find the location of any passage that he may desire. By this means also, the student will discover that many statements are incorrectly quoted from the Bible. Sometimes quotations are made which are not found in the Bible in any form. This may be discovered by consulting your Concordance and looking for any of the prominent words used in that quotation.

By means of this Concordance the student may study any subject desired. For instance, you might wish to study the subject of trees. Find the word "tree" in the Concordance, and then notice every place where the word occurs, and what is the subject under consideration. You will find that the "oak tree" is usually mentioned in connection with death. The "fig tree" is usually connected with political Israel, etc.

If you wish to study the subject of "grace," or "horses," or of the "blood," or of the "coming of Christ," or of the "judgments," or any other subject, just find that word in your Concordance and look up the various Scriptures in which that word occurs. By this means you will become well acquainted with your Bible, and with God's Truth.

If you hear a verse of Scripture quoted, and you do not know where it is found, seek the prominent word in the Concordance, follow down the Scriptures that are listed there, and you will find the verse that you desire to locate.

This Concordance is a library of instruction. It is a lexicon of explanation. It is a source of inspiration and knowledge which is indispensable to the Bible student. Permit me to encourage every student of the Word of God to own a copy of this wonderful and valuable book.

WALTER L. WILSON, M.D., L.H.D.

Kansas City, Missouri

ARUMAH, elevated, *Judg.* 9. 41.
ARVAD, place of future, *Ezek.* 27. 8, 11.
ARZA, earth, 1 *Kings* 16. 9.
ASA, physician, *or* cure.
ASAHEL, the work, *or* creature of God.
ASAHEL, made of God.
ASAHIAH, made of Jehovah, 2 *Kings* 22. 12, 14.
ASAIAH, the Lord hath wrought; *or*, a creature of the Lord.
ASAPH, one that assembles together; *or*, one that finishes and completes.
ASAREEL, bound of God, 1 *Chron.* 4. 16.
ASARELAH, upright of God, 1 *Chron.* 25. 2.
ASENATH, who belongs to Nuth.
ASHAN, smoke, *Josh.* 15. 42; 19. 7; 1 *Chron.* 43. 2; 6. 59.
ASHBEA, I adjure, 1 *Chron.* 4. 21.
ASHBEL, fire of Bel, *Gen.* 46. 21; *Num.* 26. 38; 1 Chron. 8. 1.
ASHDOD, inclination, leaning; *or*, a wild open place; *or*, pillage, theft.
ASHER, blessedness, *or* happiness.
ASHIMA, crime; *or*, position; *or*, fire of the sea. *The name of an idol*, 2 Kings 17. 30.
ASHKENAZ, a fire that distils or spreads. *One of the sons of Gomer*, Gen. 10. 3.
ASHNAH, strong, *Josh.* 15. 33, 43.
ASHPENAZ, horse's nose, *Dan.* 1. 3.
ASHTAROTH, Astartes, *i.e.*, statue of Astarte, *Deut.* 1. 4; *Josh.* 9. 10; 12. 4; 13. 12, 31; *Judg.* 2. 13; 10. 6; 1 *Sam.* 7. 3, 4; 12. 10; 31. 10; 1 *Chron.* 6. 71.
ASHTEROTH KARNAIM, Ashtaroth of horns, *i.e.*, the crescent moons, *Gen.* 14. 5.
ASHTORETH, Queen of Heaven, *i.e.*, the new moon, 1 *Kings* 11. 5, 33; 2 *Kings* 23. 13.
ASHUR, blackness, one that is happy, that walks on prosperously.
ASIA, land of fire.
ASKELON, migration.
ASNAPPER, bull *or* calf; *or*, fruitfulness, *or* increase of danger.
ASSIR, prisoner, fettered, 1 *Chron.* 3. 17.
ASSOS, approaching, coming near to, *Acts* 20. 13.
ASSYRIA.
ASSYRIAN.
ASYNCRITUS, incomparable.
ATAD, a thorn.
ATHALIAH, taken away of the Lord.
ATHENIANS, *inhabitants of* Athens.
ATHENS, *so called from* Athene; *or* Athenaia, Minerva. Fountain of fire, *i.e*, the sun. *It was called from Athene. The discoveries of Schliemann on the site of Ilium, or Troy, have thrown light on Biblical archæology. The tutelary goddess of Troy, whom Homer calls θέα γλαυκῶπις Ἀθήνη, "the goddess Athens with the owl's face," does not express the true meaning or idea of the goddess, for there can be no reasonable doubt that the sun was the object of worship under this name, and which was always with cruel rites.*
ATTALIA, mild, *Acts* 14. 25.
AVEN, vanity.
AUGUSTUS, increased, augmented; *or*, royal, majestic.
AZARIAH, assistance, *or* help of the Lord; *or*, he that hears the Lord, *or* whom the Lord hears.
AZEKAH, strength of walls.
AZGAD, strong in fortune; a strong army, *or* the strength of a troop; *otherwise*, a gang of robbers, *or* a troop of soldiers. *Ezra* 2. 12.
AZIEL, comforted of God, 1 *Chron.* 15. 20.
AZIZA, strong, *Ezra* 10. 27.
AZMAVETH, strong in death, 2 *Sam.* 23. 31; 1 *Chron.* 8. 36; 9. 42; 11, 33; 12. 3; 27. 25; *Ezra* 2. 24; *Neh.* 12. 29.
AZMON, strong, *Num.* 34. 4, 5; *Josh.* 15. 4.
AZNOTH-TABOR, the ears of *Tabor*; *or*, the ears of choice, purity, contrition, *Josh.* 19. 34.
AZOTUS, *the same as* ASHDOD, pillage, theft, *Acts* 8. 40.
AZRIEL, help of God, 1 *Chron.* 5. 24; 27. 19; *Jer.* 36. 26.
AZRIKAM, help against an enemy, 1 *Chron.* 3. 23; 8. 38; 9. 14, 44; 2 *Chron.* 28. 7; *Neh.* 11. 15.
AZUBAH, deserted, 1 *Kings* 22. 42; 1 *Chron.* 2. 18, 19; 2 *Chron.* 20. 31.
AZUR, helper, *Ezek.* 11. 1; *Jer.* 28. 1.
AZZAH, strong, *Deut.* 2. 23; 1 *Kings* 4. 24; *Jer.* 25. 20.
AZZAN, very strong, *Num.* 34, 26.
AZZUR, he that assists, *or* he that is assisted, *Neh.* 10. 17.

B.

BAAL, lord, *i.e.*, possessor of anything. *The sun was chiefly called by this name.*
BAALAH, her lord; *or*, she that is governed or subdued, a spouse. *A city*, Josh. 15. 9.
BAALATH BEER, lady of the well, *Josh.* 19. 8.
BAAL-BERITH, lord of the covenant; *or*, he that possesses, *or* subdues the covenant.
BAAL-GAD, the lord of the troop, of the army, *or* of felicity; *otherwise*, the Lord is master of the troop, *Josh.* 11. 17.
BAAL-HAMON, one that possesses *or* rules a multitude, a populous place.
BAAL-HERMON, the possessor of destruction; *or*, of a thing cursed, devoted, *or* consecrated to God. *It is a mountain*, Judg. 3. 3.
BAALI, lord, master, *or* lord over me.
BAALIM, masters, false gods.
BAALIM, idols of Baal.
BAALIS, son of consolation.
BAALIS, a rejoicing, *or* proud lord.
BAAL-MEON, the master of the house.
BAAL-PEOR, lord of the opening.
BAAL-PERAZIM, lord of divisions; *or*, he that possesses and enjoys divisions and dissipations.
BAAL SHALISHA, lord over three, the third idol, the third husband; *or*, that governs or presides over three.
BAAL-TAMAR, lord of the palm-tree.
BAAL ZEBUB, lord of flies.
BAAL-ZEPHON, lord of the north; *or*, hidden, secret.
BAANAH, in the answer, in affliction.
BAASHAH, evil.
BABEL, confusion.
BABYLON, *the same with* BABEL.
BABYLONIANS.
BABYLONISH.
BACA, weeping.
BAHURIM, village of choice youths.
BAJITH, a house, *or* temple.
BAKBAKKAR, diligent, searching, 1 *Chron.* 9. 15.
BAKBUK, emptied, *Ezra* 2. 51; *Neh.* 7. 53.
BAKBUKIAH, emptied of the Lord, *Neh.* 11. 17; 12. 9, 25.
BALAAM, destruction of the people. He was probably one of the *Moshelim* of the ancient Asiatics, who added to his poetic gift of sorcery and divination.
BALAK, who lays waste and destroys; *or*, who licks and laps.
BAMAH, an eminence, *or* high place.
BAMOTH, high places, *Num.* 21. 19, 20.
BAMOTH BAAL, high place of Baal, *Josh.* 13. 17.
BANI, built, 2 *Sam.* 23. 36; 1 *Chron.* 6. 46; 9. 4; *Ezra* 2. 10; 10. 29, 34, 38; *Neh.* 3. 17; 8. 7; 9. 4, 5; 10. 13, 14; 11. 22.
BARABBAS, son of the father, *or* of the master, *or* the son of confusion and shame.
BARACHEL, who blesses God, who bends the knee before God. *The father of Elihu*, Job 32. 2.
BARACHIAS, *the same with* BARACHEL.
BARAK, thunder, *or* in vain.
BARIAH, fugitive, 1 *Chron.* 3. 22.
BAR-JESUS, son of *Jesus*, or *Joshua*.
BAR-JONA, the son of *Jona*, or of a dove.
BARKOS, son of his father, *Ezra* 2. 53; *Neh.* 7. 55.
BARNABAS, the son of consolation.
BARSABAS, promised with an oath, *or* son of swearing.
BARTHOLOMEW, a son of *Tholmai*.
BARTIMEUS, the son of *Timeus*.
BARUCH, who is blessed, who bends the knee.
BARZILLAI, made of iron, most firm and true.
BASHAN, soft, sandy soil.
BASHEMATH, perfumed.
BATHRABBIM, daughter of many, *Cant.* 7. 4.
BATH-SHEBA, the seventh daughter, *or* the daughter of an oath.
BATHSHUA, daughter of an oath, 1 *Chron.* 3. 5.
BAVAI, by the mercy of the Lord, *Neh.* 3. 18.
BEDAD, alone, solitary; *or*, in friendship, in the bosom, *or* the nipple. *He was father of Hadad*, Gen. 36. 35.
BEDAD, separation.
BEDAN, fat.
BEEL-ZEBUB, *the same with* BAAL-ZEBUB.
BEER, a well. *The name of a city*, Num. 21. 16.
BEER-ELIM, well of the mighty ones, *Isa.* 15. 8.
BEER-LAHAI-ROI, the well of him that liveth and seeth me, *Gen.* 16. 14.
BEEROTH, wells, *Deut.* 10. 6; *Josh.* 9. 17; 18. 25; 2 *Sam.* 4. 2; *Ezra* 2. 25; *Neh.* 7. 29.
BEER-SHEBA, the fountain of an oath; *otherwise*, the seventh well, *or* the well of satiety.
BEKAH, *half a shekel.*
BEL, Lord.
BELIAL, wicked, worthless.
BELSHAZZAR, master of the treasure, *or* who lays up treasures in secret.
BELTESHAZZAR, who lays up treasures in secret; *or*, he that secretly endures pain and pressure.
BENAIAH built up of the Lord.
BENAIAH, son of the Lord; *or*, the understanding of the Lord; *or*, the Lord's building.
BEN-AMMI, the son of my people.
BENEBERAK, sons of thunder, *Josh.* 19. 45.
BEN-HADAD, the son of *Hadad*, son of most high.
BENJAMIN, the son of the right hand.
BENJAMITE.
BENONI, son of my sorrow.
BEN-ZOHETH, son of most violent transportation, 1 *Chron.* 4. 20.
BEOR, burning; *otherwise*, torch.
BERA, son of evil, *Gen.* 14. 2.
BERACHAH, blessing, *or* bending of knee.
BEREA, heavy, weighty; *from* βάρος, weight.
BEREA, weighty, important.
BERIAH, in calamity, *Gen.* 46. 17; *Num.* 26. 44, 45; 1 *Chron.* 7. 23, 30, 31; 8. 13, 16; 23. 10, 11.
BERITH, covenant.
BERNICE, one that brings victory.
BESOR, glad news, *or* incarnation.
BETAH, confidence. *A city*, 2 Sam. 8. 8.
BETHABARA, the house of passage, *or* house of the ferry boat.
BETHANY, the house of palms; of the grace of the Lord.
BETH-AVEN, the house of vanity, of iniquity, of trouble, of strength.
BETH-BARAH, place of the ford, *Judg.* 7. 24.
BETH-BIREI, the house of my Creator; *or*, the temple of my Creator, 1 *Chron.* 4. 31.
BETH-CAR, the house of the battering rams. *A city*, 1 Sam. 7. 11.
BETH-DAGON, the house of corn; *or*, the habitation of the fish; *or*, the temple of the god *Dagon*. Josh. 15. 41; 19. 27.
BETH-DIBLATHAIM, the house of two cakes of figs.
BETHEL, the house of God.
BETHELITE.
BETHER, division; *otherwise*, in the turtle, *or* in the trial, *or* perquisition.
BETHESDA, the house of effusion; *or*, the house of pity, *or* mercy.
BETH-EZEL, a neighbour's house.
BETH-GAMUL, the house of recompence, *or*, of the weaned; *or*, the house of the camel.
BETH-HACCEREM, house of the vineyard.
BETH-HORON, house of wrath; *or*, house of the hole, *or* of the cave, *or* of liberty.
BETH-LEHEM, the house of bread.
BETH-LEHEM-EPHRAIM, house of bread of fruitfulness.
BETH-LEHEM-JUDAH, house of bread of praise.
BETH-LEHEMITE.
BETH-PEOR, the house of opening.
BETH-PHAGE, the house of figs.
BETHSAIDA, the house of fishing, *or* of hunters, *or* of snares.
BETH-SHAN, the house of rest; *or*, the dwelling of sleep.
BETH-SHEMESH, the house of the sun; *or*, the house of service, *or* of ministry.
BETHUEL, virgin of God.
BEULAH, married.
BEZALEEL, in the shadow of God.
BEZEK, lightning: *or*, in chains *or* fetters.
BICHRI, first-born, *or* first-fruits; *otherwise*, in the ram, *or* the sheep.
BIDKAR, son of thrusting through.
BIGTHA, given by fortune, *Esther* 1. 10.
BIGTHANA, given by fortune, *Esther* 6. 2.

BIGTHAN, gift of fortune, *i.e.*, the sun. *Esth.* 2. 21, called also Bigthana, chap. 6. 2.
BIGVAI, happy, *Ezra* 2. 2, 14; 8. 14; *Neh.* 7. 7, 19; 10. 16.
BILDAD, son of contrition.
BILGAH, consolation, 1 *Chron.* 24. 14; *Neh.* 12. 5, 18.
BILGAI, consolation of the Lord, *Neh.* 10. 8.
BILHAH, who is old, troubled, *or* confused; *or*, which spreads itself.
BILSHAN, son of tongue, *i.e.*, eloquent, *Ezra* 2. 2; *Neh.* 7. 7. The Hebrews called a talkative man, *Ish shepayim*, a man of lips.
BIMHAL, son of corruption, 1 *Chron.* 7. 33.
BINEA, gushing forth, 1 *Chron.* 8. 37; 9. 43.
BIRSHA, son of wickedness. *Gen.* 14. 2.
BITHIAH, daughter of the Lord, 1 *Chron.* 4. 18.
BITHRON, division; *or*, in his examination; *or*, daughter of the song; *or*, the habitation of the song, *or* of anger, *or* of liberty, 2 *Sam.* 2. 29.
BITHYNIA, violent precipitation; *from the Greek word* βία, violence, *and the verb* θύνω, I make haste.
BIZTHA, eunuch, *Esther* 1. 10.
BLASTUS, one that sprouts and brings forth.
BOANERGES, the sons of thunder, James and John, the sons of Zebedee.
BOAZ or BOOZ, in a strength, *or* in the goat.
BOCHIM, the place of weeping, *or* of mourners, *or* of mulberry trees.
BOZEZ, mud, bog; *or*, in him the flower. *The name of a rock*, 1 Sam. 14. 4.
BOZRAH, fortification.
BUL, changeable, perishing. *The name of a month.*
BUZ, despised, *or* plundered.
BUZI, my contempt.
BUZITE, *a descendant from* Buz.

C.

CABBON, cake, *Josh.* 15. 40.
CABUL, fetter.
CAIAPHAS, a searcher; *or*, he that seeks with diligence.
CAIN, possession, *or* possessed.
CAINAN, possessor, *or* purchaser; *or*, one that laments; *or*, the builder of a nest.
CALAH, old age, completion. *A city*, Gen. 10. 12.
CALEB, a dog, *or* crow, *or* a basket; *or*, as the heart.
CALEB-EPHRATAH, *a place so called by a conjunction of the names of* Caleb *and his wife* Ephratah. *See* EPHRATAH.
CALNEH, fortified dwellings.
CALNO, fortified dwellings.
CALVARY, the place of a skull. *So called because it was a place of executions, where criminals expiated their crimes, and so rolled away their sin from the nation; but it was chiefly in reference to the death of Christ, who there rolled away the sins of the world.*
CAMON, his resurrection.
CANA, "place of reeds," *i.e.*, full of reeds.
CANAAN, a merchant, a trader. *He was the son of Ham, and gave name to the land of* Canaan. *The* Canaanites *were a wicked people, for they descended from a wicked father*, Gen. 13. 7.
CANAANITE.
CANDACE, queen or ruler of children.
CAPERNAUM, village of consolation. It was on the western side of the Lake of Gennesereth.
CAPHTOR, a sphere, a crown, a palm.
CAPPADOCIA, *in Hebrew*, CAPHTOR, *which see.*
CARCAS, eagle, *Esther* 1. 10.
CARCHEMISH, fortress of Chemosh.
CARMEL, fruitful field, the same as the Hebrew appellation.
CARMELITE.
CARMI, vine-dresser.
CARPUS, fruit, *or* fruitful. *Greek.*
CASIPHIA, silver of the Lord, *or* covetousness.
CASTOR *and* POLLUX, sons of Zeus, *Acts* 28. 11.
CEDRON, black, *or* sad; turbid.
CENCHREA, millet, small pulse.
CEPHAS, a rock, *or* stone.
CESAR, *a Latin name, from the word* cædo, cut, *because he was cut out of his mother's womb; or from the word* Cæsaries, a head of hair, *which he is said to have been born with.*
CESAREA, a bush of hair.
CHALCOL, who nourishes, consumes, and sustains the whole.
CHALDEA, as it were demons, *or* fields.
CHALDEAN.
CHALDEES.
CHANAAN, merchant, low, *Acts* 7. 11; 13. 19.
CHARASHIM, craftsman, 1 *Chron.* 4. 14; *Neh.* 11. 35.
CHARRAN, very dry, parched.
CHEBAR, abundant, *Ezek.* 10. 15, 20.
CHEDORLAOMER, handful of sheaves; *otherwise*, the roughness of the sheaf, *Gen.* 14. 4.
CHELAL, completion, *Ezra* 10. 30.
CHELUB, binding together, 1 *Chron.* 4. 11; 27. 26.
CHELUBAI, binding together of the Lord, 1 *Chron.* 2. 9.
CHEMARIMS, *the name of Baal's priests.*
CHEMOSH, of the swift, *i.e.*, the sun.
CHENANIA, preparation, *or* disposition, *or* strength, *or* rectitude of the Lord.
CHERETHIMS, who cuts, who tears away and exterminates.
CHERETHITES, *see* CHERETHIMS.
CHERITH, cutting, piercing, slaying.
CHESED, increase, *Gen.* 22. 22.
CHESIL, orion, constellations, *Josh.* 15. 30.
CHESULLOTH, confidences, *Josh.* 19. 18.
CHIDON, great distinction, 1 *Chron.* 13. 9.
CHILEAB, totality of the father, *or* the perfection of the father, 2 *Sam.* 3. 3.
CHILION, pining, consuming.
CHILMAD, as teaching or learning.
CHIMHAM, great desire.
CHINNERETH, harp, *Num.* 34. 11; *Deut.* 3. 17; *Josh.* 13. 27; 19. 35.
CHINNEROTH, harps, *Josh.* 11. 2; 12. 3; 1 *Kings* 15. 20.
CHIOS, snow.
CHISLEU, rashness, confidence, the flanks.
CHITTIM, those that bruise; *or*, gold; *or*, staining or dyeing.
CHIUN, *an Egyptian god, supposed to be the wife of* Saturn.
CHLOE, green herb.
CHORAZIN, proclamations.
CHUN, firm, 1 *Chron.* 18. 8.
CHUSHAN-RISHATHAIM, Ethiopian; *or*, blackness of iniquities.
CHUZA, the seer, *or* prophet; *or* Ethiopian. *The husband of Joanna.*
CILICIA, rough.
CIS, snaring, *Acts* 13. 21.
CLAUDA, a broken voice, a lamentable voice. *It is an island*, Acts 27. 16.
CLAUDIA, lame, 2 *Tim.* 4. 21.
CLEMENT, mild, good, modest, merciful, *Phil.* 4. 3.
CLEOPHAS, the whole glory; *or*, glory altogether.
CNIDUS, nettle or desire, *Acts* 27. 7.
COLOSSE, punishment, correction; *from the word* κολάζω, I punish.
CONIAH, the strength or stability of the Lord.
CONIAH, established of the Lord.
CONONIAH, established of the Lord.
COOS, woolly fleece, *Acts* 21. 1.
CORINTH, horn, *i.e.*, strong.
CORINTHIANS.
CORNELIUS, of a horn. *Or* κορήλιος, *as if it were* κέρας τοῦ ἡλίς, the beam of the sun.
COSAM, most abundant, snaring of birds, *Luke* 3. 28.
COZ, a thorn, 1 *Chron.* 4. 8.
COZBI, lying.
COZBI, a liar; *or*, as sliding away.
CRESCENS, growing, increasing.
CRETE, belonging to the sun, *denominated from the Curetes, the ancient priests of the Isle, who were sun worshippers.*
CRETES.
CRETIANS.
CRISPUS, curled.
CUSH, Ethiopians, *or* black.
CUSHAN, Ethiopia, black, blackness, heat.
CUSHI, *the same.*
CYPRUS, fair, *or* fairness.
CYRENE, κυρήνη, the fountain of the sun, a corrup. of *kure*, Ceres, the God of fire, and called by the Cnidians, *kura*, *i.e.*, the sun; and the Heb. *en*, fountain.
CYRENIANS, *people of Cyrene.*
CYRENIUS, who governs.
CYRUS, *the sun.* *Ctesius says, He was denominated Cyrus from the sun, which was so called.*

D.

DABAREH, a sheep walk.
DABBASHETH, "bunch" of acorns.
DABERATH, word, thing; *or*, a bee; *or*, submissive and obedient.
DAGON, corn; *or*, a fish.
DALMANUTHA, widowhood, exhaustion, leanness, branch. *A country*, Mark 8. 10.
DALMATIA, deceitful lamps, *or* vain brightness.
DAMARIS, a little wife.
DAMASCUS, 1. activity; 2. silent habitation; 3. blood drawn out; 4. blood mingled, *i.e.*, a place made up of different races of men; *or*, 5. pearl of possession. *The derivation of this word is very uncertain, as it is differently spelt in the original in various places of Scripture; but the above are literal interpretations of the name according to the five Hebrew forms of the name.*
DAN, judgment, or he that judges.
DANIEL, judgment of God; *or*, God is my judge. *A prophet descended from the royal family of David, who was carried captive to Babylon when he was very young. He was favoured with the vision of the four beasts, and of the ram and he-goat; Galriel informed him of the* seventy weeks, *which is a famous prophecy of the time of the coming of the* Messiah.
DANJAAN, judge of woodland.
DANNAH, low branch.
DARA, of the companion; *or*, race of wickedness, 1 *Chron.* 2. 6.
DARDA, pearl of wisdom.
DARIUS, a restrainer. *The king of the Medes*, Dan. 5. 31.
DARKON, thrusting through.
DATHAN, belonging to a fountain.
DAVID, beloved, dear. *The son of Jesse, the king of Judah and Israel, who was a great type of the* Messiah, *the King and spiritual head of his church. It is taken for Christ himself, who was descended of the family of David*, Jer. 30. 9; Ezek. 34. 23; 37. 24, 25.
DEBIR, an oracle.
DEBORAH, eloquent, *or* a bee.
DECAPOLIS, *a Greek word compounded of two others, of* δεκᾶ, ten, *and* πόλις, a city, *because this country contained ten cities.*
DEDAN, leading forward.
DEDANIM, *the descendants of* Dedan.
DELILAH, drawn up of the Lord.
DELILAH, delicate.
DEMAS, popular, ruler of people.
DEMETRIUS, belonging to Ceres, *or* to corn.
DERBE, juniper. *The name of a city*, Acts 14. 6.
DEUEL, invocation of God, *Num.* 1. 14.
DIANA, *or* Artemis, 1. the moon; 2. great mother; 3. nourisher. *The Latin word may signify* luminous; *the Greek word* ἄρτεμις *signifies* perfect.
DIBON, weeping.
DIBON-GAD, abundance of sons, happy and powerful; *or*, happy, *or* great understanding, *or* edifice.
DIBRI, promise of the Lord.
DIDYMUS, a twin.
DIKLAH, a palm tree.
DIMON, where it is red, *or* dunghill.
DINAH, judgment, *or* who judges.
DINHABAH, his judgment in her, *or* she gives judgment; *or*, who gives judgment, *Gen.* 36. 32.
DIONYSIUS, the bright god, *i.e.*, the sun.
DIONYSIUS, divinely touched, *from* διος, divine, *and* νύω, I strike.
DIOTREPHES, nourished by Jupiter, *or* Jupiter's foster-child; *from* διός, of Jupiter, *and* τρεφος, a foster-child.
DODAI, beloved of the Lord.
DODANIM, leaders.
DODAVAH, love of the Lord.
DOEG, who acts with uneasiness, *or* fearful.
DOPHKAH, knocking.
DOR, generation, *or* habitation.
DORCAS, the female of a roebuck. *Greek.*
DOTHAN, two customs.
DRUSILLA, watered by the dew, *from* δροσός, the dew.
DUMAH, silence, *or* resemblance.
DURAH, generation, *or* habitation.

E.

EASTER, the passover, *a feast of the Jews. This word is not properly translated, for in the original,* Acts 12. 4, *it is* το πάχα, *which signifies* the pass-over ; *which was a yearly feast among the Jews, established in commemoration of the coming forth out of Egypt, and of the angel's passing by and sparing the houses of the Israelites sprinkled with blood, when the first-born of the Egyptians were slain.* Easter *was a goddess of the Saxons, in honour of whom sacrifices were offered about that time of the year. The word* Easter *seems not to have been properly used in the English Bible or English Liturgy.*
EBAL, stone, heap of barrenness.
EBED, servant, *i.e.*, of God.
EBED-MELECH, servant of the king.
EBENEZER, stone of help.
EBER, he who passed over.
EBIASAPH, father of increase, 1 *Chron.* 6. 23, 37; 9. 19.
EBRONAH, passage of the sea, *Num.* 33. 34, 35.
ED, witness.
EDAR, EDER, flock, *Gen.* 35. 21; *Josh.* 15. 21; 1 *Chron.* 23. 23; 24. 30.
EDÆN, Paradise, a place of delight.
EDEN, pleasure, *or* delight.
EDOM, red.
EDOMITE.
EDREI, strong arm. *The city of Og,* Num. 21. 33; Deut. 1. 4; 3. 1, 10; Josh. 12. 4; 13. 12, 31.
EGLAH, a girl, heifer, chariot, round.
EGLAIM, drops of the sea.
EGLON, *the same as* EGLAH.
EGYPT, *in Hebrew,* Mizraim, land of Egypt, or Koft or Coft: and may be interpreted hollow land, or land of depression, or hidden land. The Copts called it Elkibit, inundated land; and this idea is in all the kindred roots. It was also called Mizraim, two-fold depression, and also the land of Ham, and Khemi, black land.
EGYPTIAN.
EHUD, joining togethe
EKRON, barrenness, tore away.
EKRONITES.
ELAH, an oak, a curse, oath, imprecation.
ELAM, a virgin; *or,* hidden.
ELAMITES.
ELATH, a hind, *or* strength, *or* an oak.
ELBETHEL, the God of Bethel.
ELDAD, loved of God, *or* favoured of God.
ELEALEH, ascension of God, *or* burnt-offering of God.
ELEAZAR, the help of God, *or* court of God.
EL-ELOHE, Israel, God the God of Israel.
ELHANAN, grace, gift *or* mercy of God.
ELI, ELI, my God, my God.
ELI, a foster son.
ELIAB, God my father, *or* my God father.
ELIADA, whom God knows.
ELIAKIM, God will set up.
ELIAM, the people of God, *or* the God of the people.
ELIAS. *See* ELIJAH. God Lord, or strength of the Lord.
ELIASHIB, whom God will bring back.
ELIATHAH, thou art my God; *or,* my God comes. *The son of Haman,* 1 Chron. 25. 4, 27.
ELIENAI, God of my eyes, 1 *Chron.* 8. 20.
ELIEZER, God of help.
ELIHOREPH, the God of reward, *i.e.*, gathering fruits.
ELIHU, he is my God himself.
ELIHUD, God is my praise, *or* the praise of my God.
ELIJAH, God the Lord; *or* the strong Lord.
ELIKA, God of the congregation, 2 *Sam.* 23. 25.
ELIM, strong oaks, perhaps a grove of oaks was there.
ELIMELECH, my God is king.
ELIOENAI, God the Lord of my eyes, to whom my eyes are directed. 1 *Chron.* 3. 23, 24; 4. 36; 7. 8; 26. 3; *Ezra* 8. 4; 10. 22, 27; *Neh.* 12. 41.
ELIPHALET, the God of deliverance; *or,* my God who puts to flight.
ELIPHAZ, my God is gold.
ELISABETH, God is the oath of her, *i.e.*, she worships the Lord God; God hath sworn the oath of God, *or* the fulness of God.
ELISHA, God the Saviour, salvation of God, *or* God that saves. *The name of a prophet whom Elijah anointed in his room,* 1 Kings 19. 16.
ELISHAH, God the Saviour, *son of Javan,* Gen. 10. 4. *Or the isles of* Elishah, *Ezek.* 27. 7.
ELISHAMAH, God hearing, *or* my God will hear.
ELISHAPHAT, God the judge.
ELISHEBA. *See* ELISABETH.
ELISHEBA, God of the seven, *or* oath of my God.
ELISHUA, God the rich.
ELIZUR, God is my strength, my rock; *or,* stone, *or* rock of God. *Num.* 1. 5; 2. 10; 7. 30, 35; 10. 18.
ELKANAH, God has redeemed.
ELMODAM, the God of measure; *or,* Immeasurable.
ELNAAM, God of pleasantness, 1 *Chron.* 11. 46.
ELNATHAN, God has given, *or* the gift of God.
ELON, oak, *or* grove, *or* strong.
ELPAAL, God the maker, 1 *Chron.* 8. 11, 12, 18.
ELTEKEH, God-fearing, *Josh.* 19. 44; 21. 23.
ELTEKON, God the foundation, *Josh.* 15. 59.
ELUL, cry, outcry. *The sixth month of the Hebrew year.*
ELUZAI, God of my congregation, *i.e.*, of my family, 1 *Chron.* 12. 5.
ELYMAS, *this name in Arabic signifies* a magician.
ELZABAD, God gave, 1 *Chron.* 12. 12; 26. 7.
EMIMS, fears of terrors; *or,* formidable, *or* people.
EMMANUEL, God with us, a mysterious name of our blessed Lord.
EMMAUS, people despised, *or* obscure.
EMMOR, an ass.
ENDOR, fountain of habitation.
ENEAS, laudable, *from the Greek verb* αἰνέω, I praise.
EN-EGLAIM, the fountain of the two calves.
EN-GANNIM, fountain of the gardens, *Josh.* 15. 34; 19. 21; 21. 29.
EN-GEDI, fountain of the goat, *or* of happiness.
EN-HADDAH, fountain of celerity, *i.e.*, flowing quickly, *Josh.* 19. 21.
EN-HAKKORE, fountain of calling, *or* of prayer, *Judg.* 15. 19.
EN-HAZOR, fountain of Hazor, *Josh.* 19. 37.
EN-MISHPAT, fountain of judgment, *Gen.* 14. 7.
ENOCH, dedicated, *or* disciplined and well regulated.
ENON, cloud *or* mass of darkness; *or,* his fountain; *or,* his eye.
ENOS, frail, fallen man, subject to all kind of evil in soul and body.
EN-RIMMON, fountain of the pomegranate, *Neh.* 11. 29.
EN-ROGEL, fountain of the fuller.
EN-SHEMESH, fountain of the sun, *or* sacred to the sun, *Josh.* 15. 7; 18. 17.
EN-TAPPUAH, fountain of the apple tree, *Josh.* 17. 7.
EPAPHRAS, favoured by Venus, *i.e.*, handsome, syncopated form of Epaphroditus.
EPAPHRODITUS, agreeable, handsome. *One whom Paul sent to the Philippians.*
EPENETUS, laudable, worthy of praise. *One of the first who embraced the gospel in Asia.*
EPHAH, darkness.
EPHER, a young hart, *Gen.* 25. 4; 1 *Chron.* 1. 33; 4. 17; 5. 24.
EPHES-DAMMIN, the portion *or* effusion of blood, *or* drop of blood, *or* grapes.
EPHESIANS, *the people of Ephesus.*
EPHESUS, city of the moon, *i.e.*, sacred to Artemis, *or* the moon. *The derivation is obscure, but it is most probably the true meaning, from the fact that it was sacred to the moon, and, moreover, its modern Turkish name,* Asalook, *has that meaning.*
EPHPHATHA, be opened.
EPHRAIM, twofold increase, *or* that brings fruit, *or* that grows.
EPHRAIMITE.
EPHRATAH, abundance, *or* bearing fruit, *or* increasing. *It is believed that the city* Ephratah, *otherwise called* Beth-lehem, *took its name from* Ephratah, *Caleb's wife.*
EPHRATH, *see* EPHRATAH.
EPHRATHITE, *an inhabitant of* Ephratah, *or a descendant from* Ephraim.
EPHRON, a great and choice fawn.
EPICUREANS, who give assistance; *from the Greek word* ἐπικουρέω, I help, I assist. *A sect of heathen philosophers. This sect of philosophers was founded by Epicurus, a most voluminous writer. Diogenes Laertes says he left three hundred volumes of writings, but they are almost all lost. St. Paul, while at Athens, encountered the followers of this absurd egotist, and in his sublime, wonderful, and unanswerable speech, he overturned all the schools of Gentile ethics, and more especially that of the Epicureans and Stoics, because they were most opposed to Christianity, and whose ethical systems Tertullian sums up in two words, "Zenois vigor et Zenonis stupor."*
ER, watcher, watch, *or* enemy.
ERAN, watchful, *Num.* 26. 36.
ERASTUS, lovely, *or* amiable.
ERECH, length, *or* which lengthens: *otherwise,* health, physic. *A city,* Gen. 10. 10.
ESAIAS, salvation of the Lord. ISAIAH.
ESAR-HADDON, gift of fire.
ESAU, covered with hair, hairy.
ESEK, contention.
ESH-BAAL, the fire of the Baal, 1 *Chron.* 8. 33.
ESHBAN, very red, *Gen.* 36. 26; 1 *Chron.* 1. 41.
ESHCOL, a bunch of grapes.
ESHEAN, support, *Josh.* 15. 52.
ESHEK, oppression, 1 *Chron.* 8. 39.
ESHTAOL, stout, strong woman. *Josh.* 15. 33; 19. 41; *Judg.* 13. 25; 16. 31; 18. 2, 8, 11.
ESHTEMOA, woman of fame. *Josh.* 15. 50; 21. 14; 1 *Sam.* 30. 28; 1 *Chron.* 4. 17, 19; 6. 57.
ESHTON, womanly, 1 *Chron.* 4. 11, 12.
ESLI, near me; *otherwise,* he that separates.
ESROM, the dart of joy; *or,* division of the song.
ESTHER, a star, a Jewish maiden. *When King Ahasuerus divorced his queen, he caused all the beautiful women in his dominions to be brought before him, among whom was the Jewish maiden, Hodassah, who being so beautiful, he made her his queen, and called her Sitarah, a star, which in the Greek is Aster, and Heb.* Ester.
ETAM, ravenous bird. 1 *Chron.* 4. 3.
ETHAM, boundary of the sea, an Egyptian name.
ETHAN, strong; *or,* the gift of the island
ETHANIM, strong, *or* valiant. *The seventh month of the ecclesiastical year of the Hebrews.*
ETHBAAL, with Baal; *or,* he that rules and possesses. 1 *Kings* 16. 31.
ETHER, abundance, *Josh.* 15. 42; 19. 7.
ETHIOPIA, *in Hebrew* Cush, blackness; *in Greek it signifies* heat, burning: *from* αιθω, I burn, *and* οψις, face.
ETHIOPIAN, ETHIOPIANS.
ETHNAN, gift, 1 *Chron.* 4. 7.
EUBULUS, a prudent and good counsellor. *Greek.*
EUNICE, good victory.
EUODIAS, sweet scent, *or* that smells sweet.
EUPHRATES, fertilizing, fruitful.
EUROCLYDON, a tempestuous wind, *Acts* 27. 14.
EUTYCHUS, happy, fortunate; *from* ευ, good, *and* τύχη, fortune.
EVE, life.
EVIL MERODACH, the fool of Merodach.
EZBAI, spoils, 1 *Chron.* 11. 37.
EZBON, great beauty, *Gen.* 46. 16; 1 *Chron.* 7. 7.
EZEKIAS, strength of the Lord, *Matt.* 1. 9, 10.
EZEKIEL, the strength of God, *or* supported of God, *or* God is my strength.
EZEL, going abroad.
EZION-GEBER, the backbone of a man, *or* of the strong; *or,* counsel of the man. *A city,* 1 Kings 9. 26.
EZRA, a helper. *He wrote the book of Ezra, wherein we have the history of the return from Babylon to Jerusalem, after the seventy years' captivity. Zerubbabel restored the temple;* Ezra, *the worship of God;* Nehemiah, *the city of Jerusalem.*

F.

FAIR-HAVENS, good ports. *The Greek name is* Καλοὶ λιμένες, *Acts* 27. 8.

FELIX, happy, *or* prosperous.
FESTUS, festival, *or* joyful.
FORTUNATUS, fortunate, prosperous.

G.

GAAL, loathing.
GAASH, shaking, earthquake, commotion, tumult, *or* overthrow. *A mountain*, Josh. 24. 30; Judg. 2. 9; 2 Sam. 23. 30; 1 Chron. 11. 32.
GABA, hill, *Josh.* 18. 24; *Ezra* 2. 26; *Neh.* 7. 30.
GABBAI, an exactor of tribute. *Syrian word*, Neh. 11. 8.
GABBATHA, pavement. *In Greek lithostrotus*, paved with stones; *from* λίθος, a stone, *and* στρωτός, paved.
GABRIEL, man of God, *or* strength of God, or my strong God.
GAD, a band, *or* happy, *or* armed and prepared.
GADARENES, surrounded, walled.
GADDI, troop of God; *otherwise*, a kid. *The son of Susi*, Num. 13. 11.
GADDIEL, troop of God; *or*, the Lord is my happiness, *or* my army. *Num.* 13. 10.
GADITES.
GAIUS, joy, gladness.
GALATIA, Gallo Græcia.
GALATIANS.
GALBANUM, *a sort of gum or sweet spice.*
GALEED, the heap of witness.
GALILEE, wheel, revolution, *or* revolution of the wheel.
GALILEANS.
GALLIM, who heap up, who cover, who roll.
GALLIO, revel; an imitator of the Galli or priests of Cybele.
GAMALIEL, recompence of God, *or* camel of God, *or* weaned of God.
GAMMADIMS, *soldiers placed in the towers of Turus. The word in Hebrew signifies* a cubit, *whence some call them* pigmies, *or* dwarfs. *Others think that the word is Syriac, and signifies* bold and courageous men. *Others say they were men who came from* Gammade, *a town of Phenicia.*
GATAM, great fatigue; *or*, their touch; *or*, the lowing of the perfect. *Grandson of Esau*, Gen. 36. 11, 16; 1 Chron. 1. 36.
GATH, wine-press.
GATH-RIMMON, wine-press of the pomegranate.
GAZA, strong, fortified. *It was also called* Azzah, heat, fire, *i.e.*, the sun, *and its people were sun worshippers.*
GAZEZ, shearer, 1 *Chron.* 2. 46.
GAZZAM, violently torn off, *Ezra* 2. 48; *Neh.* 7. 51.
GEBA, a hill, *or* cup.
GEBAL, bound, *or* limit.
GEBIM, pits, *Isa.* 10. 31.
GEDALIAH, God is my greatness; *or*, magnified of the Lord.
GEDER, a wall, *Josh.* 12. 13.
GEDEROTH, fortifications, folds, *Josh.* 15. 41; 2 *Chron.* 28. 18.
GEHAZI, valley of sight.
GEMALLI, camel possessor, *Num.* 13. 12.
GEMARIAH, completion, *or* accomplishment of the Lord.
GENNESARET, harp, *or* the garden of the prince; *otherwise*, protection of the prince, or of him that governs.
GENUBATH, theft, robbery; *or*, garden, or, protection of the daughter, 1 *Kings* 11. 20.
GERA, termination.
GERAH, *the twentieth part of a shekel.*
GERAR. *See* GERA.
GERGESENES, those who come from pilgrimage, *or* from fight. *A people beyond Galilee.*
GERIZIM, cutters-down.
GERSHOM, a stranger there; *or*, a traveller of reputation.
GERSHON, his banishment; *or*, the change of pilgrimage.
GESHUR, exile, expulsion.
GESHURITES.
GETHER, fear, the vale of trial; *or* of searching; *or*, the press of inquiry, *or* of contemplation. *The son of Aram*, Gen. 10. 23; 1 Chron. 1. 17.
GETHSEMANE, a very fat valley; *or*, the valley of oil.
GIAH, to guide, draw out, produce; breaking forth, ..., of a fountain.
GIBBAR, hero, *Ezra* 2. 20.
GIBBETHON, a lofty place, *Josh.* 19. 44; 21. 23; 1 *Kings* 15. 27; 16. 15, 17.
GIBEAH, a hill.
GIBEONITES, *people of* Gibeon.
GIDDALTI, I have trained up, 1 *Chron.* 25. 4, 29.
GIDEON, he that bruises and breaks; *or*, cutting off iniquity.
GIDEONI. *See* GIDEON.
GIHON, great eruption of waters, valley of grace; *or*, breast, *or* impetuous.
GILBOA, bubbling water of a fountain.
GILEAD, perpetual fountain.
GILEADITES.
GILGAL, rolling away, *so called from the circumcision of the Israelites, for it was the rolling away of the reproach of Egypt from off them; from* galál, to call away.
GILOH, exodus of a great multitude; that overturns, that passes, that reveals, *or* discovers. *A city, Josh.* 15. 51; 2 *Sam.* 15. 12.
GILONITE.
GIMZO, sycamores, 2 *Chron.* 28. 18.
GINATH, similitude, 1 *Kings* 16. 21, 22.
GINNETHON, gardener, *Neh.* 10. 6; 12. 4, 16.
GIRGASHITE, who arrives from pilgrimage, dwellers on a clayey soil.
GISPA, soothing, *Neh.* 11. 21.
GITTAIM, two wine-presses, 2 *Sam.* 4. 3; *Neh.* 11. 33.
GITTITE, a wine-press.
GIZONITE, stone quarrier, 1 *Chron.* 11. 34.
GOB, snare, pit.
GOG, roof, covering, extension.
GOLAN, passage, *or* revolution, great exodus.
GOLGOTHA, place of skulls, *as it was the spot where criminals were executed, and where they expiated their crimes, and so rolled away their sin from the nation.*
GOLIATH, exile. *A giant slain by David.*
GOMER, complete, accomplish; *otherwise*, consuming, a consumer.
GOMORRAH, a rebellious people; *or*, the people that fear.
GOSHEN, the place or temple of the sun, for Gozan; drawing near.
GOZAN, fleece, *or* pasture; *or*, who nourishes the body; cut through.
GRECIA, *the country of the Greeks.*
GRECIANS.
GREECE, beyond.
GREEK.
GREEKS.
GUNI, my garden, *Gen.* 46. 24; *Num.* 26. 48; 1 *Chron.* 5. 15; 7. 13.
GUR, sojourning, dwelling, assembly, *or* fear.

H.

HABAIAH, hidden of the Lord, *Ezra* 2. 61; *Neh.* 7. 63.
HABAKKUK, he that embraces, *or* a wrestler, *Hab.* 1. 1; 3. 1.
HABOR, uniting together, 2 *Kings* 17. 6; 18. 11; 1 *Chron.* 5. 26.
HACHALIAH, dark-flashing of the Lord, *Neh.* 1. 1; 10. 1.
HACHILAH, my hope is in her; *or*, hook in her.
HACHMONI, very wise, 1 *Chron.* 27. 32.
HADAD, chief, most eminent, *a title of the kings of Syria. The god of Rimmon was styled* Adad. *It was originally a title of the sun. It signified* THE FIRST. *Gen.* 36. 35, 36; 1 *Kings* 11. 14, 17, 19, 21, 25; 1 *Chron.* 1. 30, 46, 47, 50. 51.
HADADEZER, whose help is Hadad.
HADADRIMMON, bursting of the pomegranate. Rimmon *was a god of the Syrians;* the invocation of the god *Rimmon.*
HADAR, ornament; chamberer, *Gen.* 25. 15; 36. 39.
HADAREZER, majesty of help.
HADASSAH, a myrtle, *or* joy.
HADORAM, their beauty, their noble generation, their power, their cloke; *or*, praise, *or* a cry lifted up.
HADRACH, point, spherical.
HAGAB, grasshopper, *Ezra* 2. 46.
HAGABAH, grasshopper, *Ezra* 2. 45; *Neh.* 7. 48.
HAGAR, a stranger, *or*, that fears; flight.
HAGARENES, *of the family of* Hagar.
HAGARITES, *the same.*
HAGGAI, festival of the Lord.
HAGGITH, rejoicing.
HALLELUIAH, praise the Lord *or* praise to the Lord.
HAM, hot, heat, *or* black.
HAMAN, noise, tumult; *or*, he that prepares.
HAMATH, a wall, *or* a defence.
HAMMATH, warm baths, *Josh.* 19. 35.
HAMMEDATHA, twin.
HAMMOLEKETH, queen, 1 *Chron.* 7. 18.
HAMON-GOG, the multitude of *Gog.*
HAMOR, an ass, *or* clay, *or* wine.
HAMUEL, heat of God, 1 *Chron.* 4. 26.
HAMUTAL, akin to the dew, 2 *Kings* 23. 31; 24. 18; *Jer.* 52. 1.
HANAMEEL, gift of God.
HANANEEL, grace, mercy, gift of God.
HANANI, graciously given of the Lord.
HANANIAH, grace, *or* gift of the Lord.
HANNAH, gracious, merciful; *or*, taking rests. *The wife of Elkanah, and mother of Samuel.*
HANOCH, dedicated, initiated.
HANUM, gracious, merciful; *or*, he that rests.
HARA, mountainous, 1 *Chron.* 5. 26.
HARADAH, fear (of an host), *Num.* 33. 24, 25.
HARAN, mountaineer, *or* mountainous country. *The son of Terah.*
HARAN, *a place. See* CHARRAN.
HARARITE, mountaineer, 2 *Sam.* 23. 11, 33; 1 *Chron.* 11 34, 35.
HARBONAH, his destruction, *or* his sword, or his dryness; *or*, the anger of him that builds, *or* that understands.
HAREPH, maturity, *i.e.*, the flower of life, 1 *Chron.* 2. 51.
HARETH, a cutting, 1 *Sam.* 22. 5.
HAROD, astonishment, fear, trembling.
HAROEH, a seer, 1 *Chron.* 2. 52.
HAROSHETH, manufactures, *i.e.*, cutting and carving. *Or*, vessel of earth, *or* forest.
HARSHA, enchanter, *Ezra* 2. 52; *Neh.* 7. 54.
HARUM, high, *i.e.*, illustrious, 1 *Chron.* 4. 8.
HARUMAPH, flat-nosed, *Neh.* 3. 10.
HARUPHITE, matured, 1 *Chron.* 12. 5.
HASADIAH, love of the Lord, 1 *Chron.* 3. 20.
HASHABIAH, esteemed of the Lord, 1 *Chron.* 6. 45; 9. 14; 25. 3; 26. 30; 27. 17; 2 *Chron.* 35. 9; *Ezra* 8. 19, 24; *Neh.* 3. 17; 10. 11; 11. 15, 22; 12. 21, 24.
HASHABNIAH, esteemed of the Lord, *Neh.* 3. 10; 9. 5.
HASHBADANA, reason, thought, *Neh.* 8. 4.
HASHEM, dull, 1 *Chron.* 11. 34.
HASHMONAH, very fat, *Num.* 33. 29.
HASHUM, great, wealthy, *Ezra* 2. 19; 10. 33; *Neh.* 7. 22; 8. 4; 10. 18.
HATACH, gift, *Esther* 4. 5, 6, 9, 10.
HATATH, terror.
HATIPHA, seized, *Ezra* 2. 54; *Neh.* 7. 56.
HATITA, digging, exploring, *Ezra* 2. 42; *Neh.* 7. 45.
HATTIL, ingratitude, *Ezra* 2. 57; *Neh.* 7. 59.
HAURAN, very white, *Ezek.* 47. 16, 18.
HAVILAH, that suffers pain; that brings forth; *or*, that speaks, *or* declares to her, *Gen.* 2. 11; 10. 7, 29; 25. 18; 1 *Sam.* 15. 7; 1 *Chron.* 1. 9, 23.
HAVOTH-JAIR, the villages that enlighten, or that show forth light, *Num.* 32. 41; *Deut.* 3. 14; *Judg.* 10. 4.
HAZAEL, he who sees God.
HAZAIAH, sun of the Lord, *Neh.* 11. 5.
HAZAR ADDAR, villages of greatness, *Num.* 34. 4.
HAZAR ENAN, villages of fountains, *Num.* 34. 9, 10; *Ezek.* 47. 17; 48. 1.
HAZAR GADDAH, village of fortune, *Josh.* 15. 27.
HAZARMAVETH, court, *or* dwelling of death. *The son of Joktan.* Gen. 10. 26; 1 Chron. 1. 20.
HAZAR SHUAL, village of the fox, *Josh.* 15. 28; 19. 3; 1 *Chron.* 4. 28; *Neh.* 11. 27.
HAZELELPONI, the shadow looking at me, shade, and sorrow of countenance; *or* submersion of the face.
HAZEROTH, villages, hamlets; court, *or* porch.
HAZIEL, vision of God, 1 *Chron.* 23. 9.
HAZOR, court, *or* fence.
HAZOR HADATTAH, new castle, *Josh.* 15. 25.
HEBER, fellowship.
HEBREWS, *descended from* Eber.
HEBRON, society, confederation.

HEGAI, *or* HEGE, venerable, *Esth.* 2. 3, 8, 15.
HELAH, scum, 1 *Chron.* 4. 5, 7.
HELAM an army.
HELBON, milk, *or* fatness.
HELDAI, life.
HELEB, fat, *i.e.*, fertile, 2 *Sam.* 23. 29.
HELED, life, duration, 1 *Chron.* 11. 30.
HELEG, justice.
HELEM, robust, *Zech.* 6 14.
HELEPH, exchange, *Josh.* 19. 33.
HELEZ, liberation, 2 *Sam.* 23. 26; 1 *Chron.* 2. 39; 11. 27; 27. 10.
HELI, ascending, *or* climbing up.
HELI, strength of the Lord, *Luke* 3. 23.
HELKAI, portion of the Lord, *Neh.* 12. 15.
HELKATH, field of swords, *Josh.* 19. 25; 21. 31.
HELKATH-HAZZURIM, the field of strong men, of swords.
HEMAM, faithful, *son of Lotan*, *Gen.* 36. 22.
HEMDAN, desire, delight, *Gen.* 36. 26.
HEN, grace; *or* quiet, *or* rest.
HENA, a city of Mesopotamia; *derivation unknown*, 2 *Kings* 18. 34; 19. 13; *Isa.* 37. 13.
HENADAD, the favour of Hadad, *Ezra* 3. 9; *Neh.* 3. 18, 24; 10. 9.
HEPHER, a well, *or* pit, *Num.* 26. 32; 27. 1; *Josh.* 17. 2, 3; 1 *Chron.* 4. 6.
HEPHZI-BAH, my pleasure, *or* delight in her.
HERMAS, Mercury, *a Greek name for* Ἑρμῆς, Mercurius, *in the N. T.*, *Rom.* 16. 14.
HERMES, Mercury, *or* grain, *or* the projector, *as probably derived from the Heb. root* haram, *from the root* ramah, to throw, to deceive, to beguile.
HERMOGENES, begotten of Mercury, *or* generation of lucre. *Greek.*
HERMON, anathema, destruction.
HERMONITES.
HEROD, a hero, *or* like a hero.
HERODIANS.
HERODIAS, *the wife of* Herod.
HERODION, song of Juno; *from* Ἥρα, Juno, *and* ᾠδὴ, a song; *or*, the conqueror of heroes.
HESED, mercy, 1 *Kings* 4. 10.
HESHBON, reason, device.
HESHMON, very fat, *Josh.* 15. 27.
HETH, trembling, *or* fear.
HETHLON, hidden place, to wrap up. *The name of a city*, *Ezek.* 47. 15; 48. 1.
HEZEKI, strength, 1 *Chron.* 8. 17.
HEZEKIAH, strong in the Lord; *or*, taken and supported by the Lord.
HEZION, vision, 1 *Kings* 15. 18.
HEZIR, swine, 1 *Chron.* 24. 15; *Neh.* 10. 20.
HEZRAI, bulwark of the Lord, 2 *Sam.* 23. 35.
HEZRON, the dart of joy, *or* division of the song.
HIDDEKEL, sharp voice, *or* sound. *Swift.*
HIEL, God lives, *or* the life of God.
HIERAPOLIS, holy city; *from* ἱερὸν, holy, *and* πόλις, a city. *Col.* 4. 13.
HIGGAION, meditation, consideration.
HILKIAH, God is my portion; *according to others*, the Lord's gentleness.
HILLEL, he that praises. *The father of Abdon*, Judg. 12. 13, 15.
HINNOM, lamentation.
HIRAH, nobility, *Gen.* 38. 1, 12.
HIRAM, exaltation of life; *or*, their whiteness, *or* their liberty; *or*, he that destroys, *or* anathematizes.
HITTITES, who is broken, *or* fears. *Descendants of* Heth, *the son of Canaan*, Gen. 10. 15.
HIVITES, wicked, bad, *or* wickedness, *Gen.* 10. 17; 34. 2; 36. 2; *Exod.* 3. 8; 13. 5; 23. 23, 28; 33. 2; 34. 11; *Deut.* 7. 1; 20. 17; *Josh.* 3. 10; 9. 1, 7; 11. 3, 19; 12. 8; 24. 11; *Judg.* 3. 3, 5; 2 *Sam.* 24. 7; 1 *Kings* 9. 20; 1 *Chron.* 1. 15; 2 *Chron.* 8. 7.
HOBAB, beloved, *Num.* 10. 29; *Judg.* 4. 11.
HOBAH, hiding-place, secrecy, *Gen.* 14. 15.
HOD, glory, 1 *Chron.* 7. 37.
HODAIAH, praise the Lord, 1 *Chron.* 3. 24
HODAVIAH, praise the Lord, 1 *Chron.* 5. 24; 9. 7; *Ezra* 2. 40.
HODESH, the new moon, *i.e.*, beautiful as the new moon, 1 *Chron.* 8. 9.
HODIJAH, praise of the Lord, 1 *Chron.* 4. 19; *Neh.* 8. 7; 9. 5; 10. 10, 13, 18.
HOGLAH, partridge, boxer, *Num.* 26. 33; 27. 1; 36. 11; *Josh.* 17. 3.
HOHAM, a multitude of a multitude, *Josh.* 10. 3.
HOLAN, sandy.
HOPHNI, he that covers; *or*, my fist.
HOR, mountain, *Num.* 20. 22, 23, 25, 27; 21. 4; *Deut.* 32. 50.
HOREB, desert, solitude, destruction, dryness.
HOR-HAGIDGAD, the hill of thunder.
HORMAH, devoted *or* consecrated to God; utter destruction; anathema.
HORONAIM, two caverns.
HORONITE, anger, fury, *or* liberty.
HOSAH, a place of refuge, *Josh.* 19. 29; 1 *Chron.* 16. 38; 26. 10, 11, 16.
HOSEA *and* HOSHEA, saviour, *or* salvation.
HOSHAIAH, set free of the Lord, *Neh.* 12. 32; *Jer.* 42. 1; 43. 2.
HOTHAM, signet ring, 1 *Chron.* 7. 32; 11. 44.
HOTHIR, whom God let remain, 1 *Chron.* 25. 4, 28.
HUKKUK, appointed portion.
HULDAH, weasel, 2 *Kings* 22. 14; 2 *Chron.* 34. 22.
HUL, pain, infirmity, bringing forth children, sand, *or* expectation. *The son of Aram*, Gen. 10. 23; 1 Chron. 1. 17.
HUMTAH, a place of lizards, *Josh.* 15. 54.
HUR, hole, cavern.
HURAM, most noble, 1 *Chron.* 8. 5; 2 *Chron.* 2. 3, 12; 4. 11, 16.
HUSHAI, hasting of the Lord.
HUZZAB, molten.
HYMENEUS, nuptial, *or* marriage.

I.

IBHAR, whom He (*scil.* God) elects, 2 *Sam.* 5. 15; 1 *Chron.* 3. 6; 14. 5
IBLEAM, devouring the people, *Josh.* 17. 11; *Judg.* 1. 27; 2 *Kings* 9. 27.
IBNEIAH, he will be built up of the Lord, 1 *Chron.* 9. 8.
IBRI, beyond the river, 1 *Chron.* 24. 27.
IBZAN, great fatigue, *Judg.* 12. 8, 10.
ICHABOD, inglorious, *or* the glory is departed.
IDALAH, place of execution, *Josh.* 19. 15.
IDBASH, he will be as agreeable as honey, 1 *Chron.* 4. 3.
IDDO, great calamity, 1 *Kings* 4. 14; 1 *Chron.* 6. 21; 27. 21; 2 *Chron.* 9. 29; 12. 15; 13. 22; *Ezra* 5. 1; 6. 14; 8. 17; *Neh.* 12. 4, 16; *Zech.* 1. 1. 7.
IGDALIAH, the Lord will make great, *Jer.* 35. 4.
IGEAL, he will redeem, 1 *Chron.* 3 22
IIM, ruinous heaps, *Num.* 33. 45; *Josh.* 15. 29.
IJE-ABARIM, ruins of Abarim, *Num.* 21. 11; 33. 44.
IJON, a great heap, 1 *Kings* 15. 20; 2 *Kings* 15. 29; 2 *Chron.* 16. 4.
IKKESH, perverse, 2 *Sam.* 23. 26; 1 *Chron.* 11. 28; 27. 9.
IMLA, he will fill up, 1 *Kings* 22. 8, 9; 2 *Chron.* 18. 7, 8.
IMMANUEL, God with us, *Isa.* 7. 14; 8. 8.
IMMER, He promised, *i.e.*, the Lord, 1 *Chron.* 9. 12; 24. 14; *Ezra* 2. 37, 59; 10. 20; *Neh.* 3. 29; 7. 40, 61; 11. 13; *Jer.* 20. 1.
IMNAH, prosperity, 1 *Chron.* 7. 30; 2 *Chron.* 31. 14.
IMNA, God will restrain, 1 *Chron.* 7. 35.
IMRAH, he will extol himself, 1 *Chron.* 7. 36.
IPHEDEIAH, the Lord will redeem, 1 *Chron.* 8. 25.
IR, citizen, 1 *Chron.* 7. 12.
IR-NAHASH, city of serpents, 1 *Chron.* 4. 12.
IR-SHEMESH, city of the sun, *Josh.* 19. 41.
IRA, watchful, 2 *Sam.* 20. 26; 23. 26, 38; 1 *Chron.* 11. 28, 40; 27. 9.
IRAD, city of witness, *Gen.* 4. 18.
IRAM, belonging to a city, *Gen.* 36. 43; 1 *Chron.* 1. 54.
IRIJAH, he will see the Lord, *Jer.* 37. 13, 14.
IRON, pious, *Josh.* 19. 38.
IRPEEL, God will restore, *Josh.* 18. 27.
IRU, belonging to a city, 1 *Chron.* 4. 15.
ISAAC, he will laugh.
ISAIAH, salvation of the Lord.
ISCAH, she will look out, *Gen.* 11. 29.
ISHBAH, he will praise, 1 *Chron.* 4. 17.
ISHBAK, he will remain, *Gen.* 25. 2; 1 *Chron.* 1. 32.
ISHBI BENOB, his seat is in the high place, 2 *Sam.* 21. 16.
ISH-BOSHETH, man of shame, 2 *Sam.* 2. 8, 10, 12, 15; 3. 8, 14, 15; 4. 5, 8, 12.
ISHI, salvation, 1 *Chron.* 2. 31; 4. 20, 42; 5. 24.
ISHIAH, ISSHIAH, ISHIJAH, gift of the Lord, 1 *Chron.* 7. 3; 24. 21, 25; *Ezra* 10. 31.
ISHMA, desolateness, *i.e.*, unfortunate, 1 *Chron.* 4. 3.
ISHMAEL, he will hear God.
ISHMAIAH, he will hear the Lord, 1 *Chron.* 27. 19.
ISHMERAI, he will be kept of the Lord, 1 *Chron.* 8. 18.
ISHOD, man of beauty, 1 *Chron.* 7. 18.
ISHPAN, he will hide, 1 *Chron.* 8. 22.
ISHTOB, man of Tob, 2 *Sam.* 10. 6, 8.
ISHUAH, he will be equal, *Gen.* 46. 17; 1 *Chron.* 7. 30.
ISHUI, JESUI, ISHUAI, ISUI, equal, *Gen.* 46. 17; *Num.* 26. 44; 1 *Sam.* 14. 49; 1 *Chron.* 7. 30.
ISMACHIAH, supported of the Lord, 2 *Chron.* 31. 13.
ISPAH, he will be eminent, 1 *Chron.* 8. 16.
ISRAEL, he will be prince with God.
ISSACHAR, he is wages.
ITHAMAR, land of palm.
ITHIEL, God is with me, *Neh.* 11. 7; *Prov.* 30. 1.
ITHMAH, bereavedness, 1 *Chron.* 11. 46.
ITHNAN, stable, *Josh.* 15. 23.
ITHRAN, exalted, *Gen.* 36. 26; 1 *Chron.* 1. 41; 7. 37.
ITHREAM, exalted of the people, 2 *Sam.* 3. 5; 1 *Chron.* 3. 3.
ITTAH KAZIN, time of the judge, *Josh.* 19. 13.
ITTAI, nearness of the Lord, 2 *Sam.* 15. 19, 21, 22; 18. 2, 5, 12; 23. 29.
IVAH, overturned, 2 *Kings* 18. 34; 19. 13; *Isa.* 37. 13.
IZHAR, anointed, oil, *Exod.* 6. 18, 21; *Num.* 3. 19; 16. 1; 1 *Chron.* 6. 2, 18, 38; 23. 12, 18.
IZRAHIAH, brought to light of the Lord, 1 *Chron.* 7. 3.
IZRAHITE, he will be bright, 1 *Chron.* 27. 8.

J.

JAAKAN, twister, *Deut.* 10. 6; 1 *Chron.* 1. 42.
JAAKOBAH, a heeler, a supplanter, 1 *Chron.* 4. 36.
JAALAM, he will be hid, *or* he will hide, *Gen.* 36. 5, 14, 18; 1 *Chron.* 1. 35.
JAANAI, the Lord hears, 1 *Chron.* 5. 12.
JAARE-OREGIM, tapestry of the weavers, 2 *Sam.* 21. 19.
JAASAU, made of the Lord, *Ezra* 10. 37
JAASIEL, made of God, 1 *Chron.* 11 47; 27. 21.
JAAZANIAH, he will be heard of the Lord.
JAAZER, JAZER, whom the Lord helps, *Num.* 21. 32; 32. 1, 3, 35; *Josh.* 13. 25; 21. 39; 2 *Sam.* 24. 5; 1 *Chron.* 6. 81; 26. 31; *Isa.* 16. 8, 9; *Jer.* 48. 32.
JAAZIAH, he is comforted of the Lord, 1 *Chron.* 24. 26, 27.
JAAZIEL, he is comforted of God, 1 *Chron.* 15. 18.
JABAL, leading, flowing.
JABBOK, emptying, pouring out.
JABESH, dry, arid.
JABEZ, he will cause pain, *i.e.*, to his mother.
JABIN, he will understand.
JABNEEL, caused to be built of God, *Josh.* 15. 11; 19. 33.
JABNEH, will be built, *i.e.*, he will be prospered, 2 *Chron.* 26. 6.
JACHAN, he will stir up, 1 *Chron.* 5. 13.
JACHIN, he will establish.
JACOB, he will trip up the heels; one who supplants; *or* trip up the heels as racers do; *and as Jacob was named a supplanter, he fulfilled the prophecy in his nomination, for although he was the younger, yet he obtained the birthright, and from him descended He, in whom all the nations of the earth are blessed.*
JADA, he knows, 1 *Chron.* 2. 28, 32.
JADDUA, celebrated, known, *Neh.* 10. 21; 12. 11, 22.
JADON, whom God will judge, *Neh.* 3. 7.
JAEL, ibex, *or* chamois.
JAGUR, lodging.
JAHATH, he will carry away.
JAHAZ, a round depressed place.
JAHAZIAH, he will see the Lord, *Ezra* 10. 15.

JAHAZIEL, he will be seen of God, 1 *Chron.* 12. 4; 16. 6; 23. 19; 24. 23; 2 *Chron.* 20. 14; *Ezra* 8. 5.
JAHDAI, he will be directed of the Lord, 1 *Chron.* 2. 47.
JAHDIEL, he will be made glad of God, 1 *Chron.* 5. 24.
JAHDO, his union, 1 *Chron.* 14. 5.
JAHLEEL, hope of God, *Gen.* 46. 14; *Num.* 26. 26.
JAHMAI, he will be guarded of the Lord, 1 *Chron.* 7. 2.
JAHZEEL, he will allot of God, *Gen.* 46. 24; *Num.* 26. 48; 1 *Chron.* 7. 13.
JAHZERAH, he will cause to return, 1 *Chron.* 9. 12.
JAIR (1), he will enlighten.
JAIR (2), he will embroider.
JAIRUS, he will enlighten, *or* he will diffuse light.
JAKEH, pious, fearing God, *Prov.* 30. 1.
JAKIM, He (*i.e.*, God) will set him up, 1 *Chron.* 8. 19; 24. 12.
JALON, abiding, 1 *Chron.* 4. 17.
JAMBRES, magician.
JAMES, supplanter, *from the Greek form of the Hebrew name* Jacob. *There were three persons in the New Testament who bore this name.*
JAMIN, right hand, *Gen.* 46. 10; *Ex.* 6. 15; *Num.* 26. 12; 1 *Chron.* 2. 27; 4. 24; *Neh.* 8. 7.
JAMLECH, He (*i.e.*, God) will be made to reign, 1 *Chron.* 4. 34.
JANNA, he will answer.
JANNES, full of pleasure, *or* full of favour, 2 *Tim.* 3. 8.
JANOAH, rest, 2 *Kings* 15. 29.
JANUM, sleep, *Josh.* 15. 53.
JAPHETH, enlargement.
JAPHIA, illustrious, *Josh.* 10. 3; 19. 12; 2 *Sam.* 5. 15; 1 *Chron.* 3. 7; 14. 6.
JAPHLET, whom God will free, 1 *Chron.* 7. 32, 33.
JAPHLETI, will be liberated of the Lord, *Josh.* 16. 3.
JAPHO, beautiful city, *Josh.* 19. 46.
JAREB, he will plead.
JARED, descent.
JARESIAH, he will be nourished of the Lord, 1 *Chron.* 8. 27.
JARHA, increasing moon, 1 *Chron.* 2. 34, 35.
JARIB, he will plead the cause, *Ezra* 8. 16; 10. 18; *called* Jachin, *Gen.* 46. 10, and *Ex.* 6. 15.
JARMUTH, high, *Josh.* 10. 3, 5, 23; 12. 11; 15. 35; 21. 29; *Neh.* 11. 29.
JAROAH, moon, 1 *Chron.* 5. 14.
JASHEN, sleeping, 2 *Sam.* 23. 32.
JASHER, *vid.* JESHER.
JASIEL, made of God; *same as* Jaasiel.
JASHOBEAM, he will return among the people, 1 *Chron.* 11. 11; 12. 6; 27. 2.
JASHUB, he will return, *Num.* 26. 24; 1 *Chron.* 7. 1; *Ezra* 10. 29.
JASHUBI-LEHEM, he is restored by bread.
JASON, healed.
JATHNIEL, he will be given of God, 1 *Chron.* 26. 2.
JATTIR, pre-eminent, lofty, *Josh.* 15. 48; 21. 14; 1 *Sam.* 30. 27; 1 *Chron.* 6. 57.
JAVAN, supple, clay, *Gen.* 10. 2, 4; 1 *Chron.* 1. 7; *Isa.* 66. 19; *Ezek.* 27. 13, 19
JAZIZ, he will bring abundance, 1 *Chron.* 27. 31.
JEARIM, forests.
JEATERAI, he will abound of the Lord, 1 *Chron.* 6. 21.
JEBERECHIAH, he will be blessed of the Lord, *Isa.* 8. 2.
JEBUS, treading down, *or* a place trodden down, *Josh.* 18. 16, 28; *Judg.* 19. 10, 11; 1 *Chron.* 11. 4, 5.
JECHOLIAH, made strong of the Lord, 2 *Kings* 15. 2; 2 *Chron.* 26. 3.
JECONIAH, he will be established of the Lord.
JEDAIAH (1), praise of the Lord; (2), known of the Lord, 1 *Chron.* 4. 37; 9. 10; 24. 7; *Ezra* 2. 36; *Neh.* 3. 10; 7. 39; 11. 10; 12. 6, 7, 19, 21; *Zech.* 6. 10, 14.
JEDIAEL, known of God, 1 *Chron.* 7. 6, 10, 11; 11. 45; 12. 20; 26. 2.
JEDIDAH, beloved, 2 *Kings* 22. 1.
JEDIDIAH, beloved of the Lord.
JEDUTHUN, praising, celebrating.
JEGAR SAHADUTHA, the heap of witness. *The Syrian name which Laban gave to the heap of stones, which Jacob called* Galeed, *or hill of witness.*
JEHALELEEL, he will praise God, 1 *Chron.* 4. 16; 2 *Chron.* 29. 12.
JEHDEIAH, he will be gladdened of the Lord, 1 *Chron.* 24. 20; 27. 30.
JEHIAH, he lives of the Lord, *i.e.*, by the mercy of the Lord, 1 *Chron.* 15. 24.
JEHIEL, he lives of God, *i.e.*, by the mercy of God he lives, 1 *Chron.* 15. 18, 20; 16. 5; 23. 8; 27. 32; 29. 8; 2 *Chron.* 21. 2; 29. 14; 31. 13; 35. 8; *Ezra* 8. 9; 10. 2; 21. 26.
JEHOADAH, the Lord will adorn him, 1 *Chron.* 8. 36.
JEHOADDAN, Lord of pleasure, 2 *Kings* 14. 2; 2 *Chron.* 25. 1.
JEHOAHAZ, whom the Lord holds fast.
JEHOASH, the Lord gave.
JEHOHANAN, the Lord graciously gave, 1 *Chron.* 26. 3; 2 *Chron.* 17. 15; 23. 1; *Ezra* 10. 28; *Neh.* 12. 13, 42.
JEHOIACHIN, the Lord will establish.
JEHOIADA, the Lord knows.
JEHOIAKIM, the Lord will set up.
JEHOIARIB, the Lord will contend, *i.e.*, will defend him.
JEHONADAB, the Lord gave spontaneously, *i.e.*, gave him freely to his parents.
JEHORAM, the Lord exalts, *i.e.*, he is lifted up, and made magnificent of the Lord.
JEHOSHAPHAT, the Lord judges, *i.e.*, he will plead for him.
JEHOSHEBA, the Lord's oath, the Lord (is her) oath, *i.e.*, she is a worshipper of the Lord, 2 *Kings* 11. 2.
JEHOVAH, He will be, *i.e.*, the Eternal, who always is. *From the words in which God revealed His nature and nomination,* I am that I am; I will be that I will be; and Jehovah Elohim.
JEHOVAH-JIREH, the Lord will see, the Lord will provide, *i.e.*, will give a means of deliverance.
JEHOVAH-NISSI, the Lord is my ensign. *The name which Moses gave the altar he erected on Mount Horeb.*
JEHOVAH-SHALOM, the Lord is peace, the peace of the Lord.
JEHOZABAD, whom the Lord gave, 2 *Kings* 12. 21; 1 *Chron.* 26. 4; 2 *Chron.* 17. 18; 24. 26.
JEHOZADAK, the Lord has made just.
JEHU, the Lord (is) He. *Several persons bore this name, but the son of Nimshi was the most eminent of them.*
JEHUBBAH, he will be hidden, 1 *Chron.* 7. 34.
JEHUCAL, he will be made able, *i.e.*, strengthened of the Lord, *Jer.* 37. 3; 38. 1.
JEHUD, praise, a city of Dan, *Josh.* 19. 45.
JEHUDI, praise the Lord, *Jer.* 36. 14, 21, 23.
JEHUDIJAH, Jewish, 1 *Chron.* 4. 18.
JEHUSH, he will gather together, 1 *Chron.* 8. 39.
JEIEL, hidden of God, 1 *Chron.* 5. 7; 9. 35; 11. 44; 15. 18, 21; 16. 5; 2 *Chron.* 20. 14; 26. 11; 29. 13; 35. 9; *Ezra* 8. 13; 10. 43.
JEKABZEEL, God will assemble together, *i.e.*, the people, *Neh.* 11. 25.
JEKAMEAM, he will gather together the people, a camp, 1 *Chron.* 23. 19; 24. 23.
JEKAMIAH, he will be gathered of the Lord, 1 *Chron.* 2. 41.
JEKUTHIEL, the fear of God; *a son of Ezra*, 1 Chron. 4. 18.
JEMIMA, dove. *But it is a word of doubtful meaning, both in Hebrew and Arabic.* Job 42. 14.
JEMUEL, the day of God, *Gen.* 46. 10; *Ex.* 6. 15.
JEPHTHAH, he will open, *i.e.*, he will liberate.
JEPHUNNEH, he will be beheld, *i.e.*, cared for of God.
JERAH, the moon, *Gen.* 10. 26; 1 *Chron.* 1. 20.
JERAHMEEL, he will obtain mercy.
JEREMAI, he will be exalted of the Lord, *Ezra* 10. 33.
JEREMIAH, elevated of the Lord, or exalted of the Lord. *He was called to the extraordinary office of a prophet in his younger years, and continued in that office for at least forty years together. In his time iniquity did exceedingly abound in the land of Judah. He earnestly and frequently calls the people to repentance, both by his reproofs and threatenings for their sins. He denounced the captivity of the people by the Babylonians, for which he was put in prison; he lived to see this prophecy fulfilled. But for the comfort and support of the faithful, he foretells their return after* seventy years, *and the enlargement of the church by Christ. His style is generally the most plain of any of the prophets.*
JEREMOTH, high places. *Eleven persons bore this name in the Hebrew Bible, but no place was so named.* 1 Chron. 8. 14; Ezra 10. 26, 27.
JEREMY, elevated of the Lord. *Shortened form for* Jeremiah.
JERIAH, fear of the Lord, 1 *Chron.* 23. 19; 24. 23; 26. 31.
JERIBAI, he will contend, 1 *Chron.* 11. 46.
JERICHO, the moon, *i.e.*, city of the moon. *Jericho is situated about eighteen miles east of Jerusalem, and about five miles from the Jordan. It was called the City of the Moon by the Canaanites, who, together with all Eastern nations, worshipped that planet from the first ages after the flood. Job knew how much this idolatrous worship prevailed among his own people when he declared himself innocent of it.* (Job 31. 26.)
JERIEL, founded of God, 1 *Chron.* 7. 2.
JERIOTH, curtains, 1 *Chron.* 2. 18.
JEROBOAM, whose people are countless. *But although he is so denominated, yet he will be for ever known as* he who made Israel to sin.
JERUBBAAL, he will contend with Baal; *a cognomen of Gideon.*
JERUEL, founded of God, *vid.* JERIEL, 2 *Chron.* 20. 16.
JERUSALEM, foundations of peace, *or* He will provide peace, *or* He will pour peace on thee in floods; *i.e.*, God shall flood thee with prosperity. (1) *A composition of the Heb.* y'ru, *from the root* yarah, to lay foundations, *and* Shalaim, peace; *and it was so called with prophetic reference to the sacrifice of Jesus Christ, whose voluntary death is the only* foundation of peace between heaven and earth, God and man; *or we may regard it as a composition of the Hebrew words,* Yiréh, he will provide, or he will see, *and* Shalém, peace. *The capital of the kingdom of Judah; mean geographical position, Lat.* 31° 46′ 43″ *N. and Long.* 35° 13′ *E. from Greenwich. The ancients believed that it stood in the centre of the earth, and in the maps of mediæval times it is so represented. This idea arose, probably from the literal interpretation of the Psalmist,* "For God is my king of old, working salvation in the midst of the earth." *But it is worthy of remark that the ancient opinion is not far from the truth, both geographically and ethnologically.* (2) *The Church of Christ on earth is called by* St. Paul, *in his allegory in the Epistle to the Galatians,* "Jerusalem which is above." *He had been speaking of the earthly Jerusalem under the law, which is Hagar, and is in bondage with her children; that is to say, she was not delivered from the law, sin, and death.* (3) *The new Jerusalem of the Church triumphant, which our blessed Lord calls in* Rev. iii. 12, "the city of my God."
JERUSHA, possessed, named by her husband, 2 *Kings* 15. 33; 2 *Chron.* 27. 1.
JESHANAH, old, ancient, 2 *Chron.* 13. 19.
JESHARELAH, upright towards God, 1 *Chron.* 25. 14.
JESHEDEAR, habitation of the father.
JESHER, upright, just. *A son of Caleb. There was a book called by this name, on account of its subject,* "the book of the upright." *Josh.* 10. 13; 2 *Sam.* 1. 18; 1 *Chron.* 2. 18.
JESHISHAI, ancient of the Lord, *i.e.*, a good old man, 1 *Chron.* 5. 14.
JESHOHAIAH, depression of the Lord, 1 *Chron.* 4. 36.
JESHUA, salvation of the Lord.
JESHURUN, upright.
JESIMIEL, made of God, *i.e.*, created, 1 *Chron.* 4. 36.
JESSE, wealth of the Lord.
JESUI, salvation of the Lord, *vid.* JESHUA, *Num.* 26. 44.
JESUS (CHRIST), the Lord will save, the Lord of salvation, the Lord the saviour; *a Greek form of the Hebrew name* Y'hoshúa, *which is a compound of the Hebrew* Y' *for* Yah, the Lord, *and the Hebrew* shua, to

be freed, *or* y'shua, salvation, aid, deliverance. (*See* Matt. i. 21.) *The name of the eternal Son of God, of one substance and equal with the Father, the mediator of the covenant of grace, who in the fulness of time became man, and so was and continues to be God and man in two distinct natures and one person for ever. The word* Jesus *is taken for the doctrine of* Jesus, *Acts* 8. 35, *and for Joshua, who brought God's people into the land of Canaan, and was therein an eminent type of our Lord* Jesus.
JETHER, excellence, *Judg.* 8. 20; 1 *Kings* 2. 5, 32; 1 *Chron.* 2. 17, 32; 4. 17; 7. 38.
JETHETH, strengthener, a nail, *Gen.* 36. 40; 1 *Chron.* 1. 51.
JETHLAH, He (*i.e.*, God) will exalt, *Josh.* 19. 42.
JETHRO, the same as JETHER.
JETUR, defence, *or* enclosure, *Gen.* 25. 15; 1 *Chron.* 1. 31; 5. 19.
JEUZ, counsellor, 1 *Chron.* 8. 10.
JEW, confessor, *or* one who praises the Lord.
JEZEBEL, without cohabitation, *or* isle of the dunghill. *The wife of Ahab, whose carcase became as the dung upon the face of the field, because of her wickedness.*
JEZER, frame, form, *i.e.*, of his parents, *Gen.* 46. 24; *Num.* 26, 49; 1 *Chron.* 7. 13.
JEZIAH, he will be sprinkled of the Lord, *i.e.*, purified, *or* forgiven of the Lord, *Ezra* 10. 25.
JEZIEL, assembly of God, 1 *Chron.* 12. 3.
JEZLIAH, he will be drawn out of the Lord, *i.e.*, preserved, 1 *Chron.* 8. 18.
JEZREEL, he will be sown of God, *i.e.*, have a numerous progeny.
JIBSAM, he will smell sweetly, 1 *Chron.* 7. 2.
JIDLAPH, he will weep, *Gen.* 22. 22.
JIPHTHAH-EL, he will be opened of God, *Josh.* 19. 14, 27.
JOAB, Lord, father, *or* whose father is the Lord.
JOAH, Lord brother, 2 *Kings* 18. 18, 26; 1 *Chron.* 6. 21; 26. 4; 2 *Chron.* 29. 12; 34. 8; *Isa.* 36. 3, 11, 22.
JOANNA, the Lord is grace, *or* the Lord gives graciously.
JOATHAN, lord of integrity, *or* the Lord is upright, *Matt.* 1. 9.
JOB, the persecuted, *or* he will not cry out.
JOBAB, crying out, *i.e.*, a desert, *Gen.* 10. 29; 36. 33, 34; *Josh.* 11. 1; 1 *Chron.* 1. 23, 44, 45; 8. 9, 18.
JOCHEBED, Lord of glory, *or* glory of the Lord, *Ex.* 6. 20; *Num.* 26. 59.
JOED, Lord of witness, *Neh.* 11. 7.
JOEL, Lord of God, *or* the Lord (is) God.
JOELAH, removing of oaks, 1 *Chron.* 12. 7.
JOEZER, Lord of help, *or* help of the Lord, 1 *Chron.* 12. 6.
JOGBEHAH, exalted, *Num.* 32. 35; *Judg.* 8. 11.
JOGLI, led into exile, *Num.* 34. 22.
JOHA, haste, 1 *Chron.* 8. 16; 11. 45.
JOHN, Lord of grace, *or* whom the Lord graciously gave; *or it may be interpreted,* the Lord hath begun to speak.
JOKDEAM, possessed of the people, *Josh.* 15. 56.
JOKMEAM, gathered of the people, 1 *Chron.* 6. 68.
JOKSHAN, sportsman, *Gen.* 25. 2, 3; 1 *Chron.* 1. 32.
JOKTAN, he will be small, *Gen.* 10. 25, 26, 29; 1 *Chron.* 1. 19, 20, 23.
JOKTHEEL, subdued of God, *Josh.* 15. 38; 2 *Kings* 14. 7.
JONADAB, *vid.* JEHONADAB.
JONAH, dove.
JONAN, the Lord of grace, *Luke* 3. 30.
JONAS, dove.
JONATHAN, the Lord gave.
JOPPA, beautiful city.
JORAH, autumnal rain, *Ezra* 2. 18.
JORAI, he will be built up of the Lord, 1 *Chron.* 5. 13.
JORAM, the Lord exalts.
JORDAN, descending; a river; *so called from* descending, flowing down.
JORIM, the Lord will exalt.
JORKOAM, paleness of the people, 1 *Chron.* 2. 44.
JOSAPHAT, the Lord judges, *i.e.*, pleads for him, *Matt.* 1. 8.
JOSE, *vid.* JOSES, *Luke* 3. 29.
JOSEPH, he shall add. *There were seven persons in the Bible who bore this name.*
JOSES, aid.
JOSHAH, aid, 1 *Chron.* 4. 34.
JOSHAVIAH, sit upright of the Lord, 1 *Chron.* 11. 46.
JOSHBEKASHAH, a seat in a hard place, 1 *Chron.* 25. 4, 24.
JOSHIAH, given of the Lord.
JOSHUA, the Lord will save.
JOSIAS, given of the Lord; *a Greek form of* JOSIAH.
JOSIBIAH, he will be made to sit down of the Lord, *i.e.*, to live in tranquillity and peace, 1 *Chron.* 4. 35.
JOSIPHIAH, added of the Lord, *Ezra* 8. 10
JOTBAH, pleasant, 2 *Kings* 21. 19.
JOTBATHAH, goodness, *Num.* 33. 33, 34; *Deut.* 10. 7.
JOTHAM, the Lord is upright, *or* Lord of integrity.
JOZACHAR, the Lord is remembered, *or* Lord of remembrance, 2 *Kings* 12. 21.
JUBAL, jubilee, music, a son of Lamech, and probably the inventor of music, of the harp and organ, *Gen.* 4. 21.
JUDA, praised; *a Greek form of the Hebrew name. There were seven persons who bore this name.*
JUDÆA, the land of Judah. It was the most important of all the portions into which Palestine was divided in the time of our blessed Lord.
JUDAH, praised.
JUDAS, a man of the city of Kerioth, *and therefore called* Ish-Kerioth, *or* Iscariot.
JUDITH, praised, *Gen.* 26. 34.
JULIA, having curly hair, *Rom.* 16. 15.
JULIUS, curly-headed, *as from the Greek,* having curly hair, *Acts* 27. 1, 3.
JUNIA, belonging to Juno; *a contraction of* Juvino, *fem. of* Jove. *It originally signified* the goddess. *Rom.* 16. 7.
JUPITER, zeus, God. *It is the same as* θεός, deus, *i.e.*, the sun; *and is cognate with the Persian* Deev *or* Dew (bright, shining, *hence* heaven), *and the Sanscrit* Deva *and* Deveta. *Perhaps it is akin to* dies, day (*as in* Diespiter, *i.e*, Dies Pater, *or* Father Day), *and hence* Zeus *is the* Heaven, the god who gives light from heaven, and fertility to the earth.
JUSTUS, just. *There were three men who bore this name.*
JUTTAH, it will be stretched out, *Josh* 15. 55; 21. 16.

K.

KADESH BARNEA, sacred desert of wandering.
KADMIEL, going before God, *i.e.*, walking religiously, *Ezra* 2. 40; 3. 9; *Neh.* 7. 43; 9. 4, 5; 10. 9; 12. 8, 24.
KADMONITES, Orientals, Easterlings, ancients, *Gen.* 15. 19.
KALLAI, lightly esteemed of God, *Neh.* 12. 20.
KANAH, place of reeds, *i.e.*, full of reeds, *Josh.* 16. 8; 17. 9; 19. 28.
KARKAA, the ground, *i.e.*, pavement, *Josh.* 15. 3.
KARKOR, soft and level ground, *from Arabic* Zebah *and* Zalmunna *encamped here when attacked by* Gideon, *Judg.* 8. 10.
KARTAH, city, *Josh.* 21. 34.
KARTAN, two cities, *Josh.* 21. 32.
KATTATH, very small; a city; *also called* Kitron, *Josh.* 19. 15.
KEDAR, dark-skinned man.
KEDEMAH, eastward, *Gen.* 25. 15; 1 *Chron.* 1. 31.
KEDEMOTH, beginnings, *Deut.* 2. 26; *Josh.* 13. 18; 21. 37; 1 *Chron.* 6. 79.
KEDESH, sanctuary; a Levitical city of refuge in Galilee, *Josh.* 15. 23; 20. 7; 21. 32; *Judg.* 4. 6, 9, 10, 11; 2 *Kings* 15. 29; 1 *Chron.* 6. 72, 76.
KEHELATHAH, towards the place of assembly, and it was the nineteenth station of the Israelites in the desert, *Num.* 33. 22, 23.
KEILAH, fortress, refuge; a fortified town of Judah.
KELEIAH, congregation of the Lord.
KEMUEL, congregation of God, *Gen.* 22. 21; *Num.* 34. 24; 1 *Chron.* 27. 17.
KENATH, possession, *Num.* 32. 42; 1 *Chron.* 2. 23.
KENAZ, hunting.
KENITE, a nest.
KEREN-HAPPUCH, splendour of colour. *Job* 42. 14.
KERIOTH, cities.
KEROS, a tack, a hook, *Ezra* 2. 44; *Neh.* 7. 47.
KETURAH, incense, perfume; *the name of the second wife of Abraham, and many Jews regard her as the same as* Hagar, *as also the* Targums of Jerusalem and Jonathan Ben Uzziel.
KEZIA, Cassia, *i.e.*, equally as precious. *A daughter of Job.* Job 42. 14.
KEZIZ, cuttings off, *Josh.* 18. 21.
KIBROTH-HATTAAVAH, graves of lust, *i.e.*, the graves of the people who lusted, *Num.* 11. 34, 35; 33. 16, 17; *Deut.* 9. 22.
KIBZAIM, two heaps, *Josh.* 21. 22.
KIDRON, very black, *or* full of darkness. *A torrent which flowed between Jerusalem and Mount Olivet; from the steep sides of the heights on each side, and the thickness of the trees, the valley had a black appearance.*
KINAH, lamentation, *Josh.* 15. 22.
KIR, a wall, a fortress.
KIRIATHAIM, *vid.* KIRJATHAIM.
KIRIOTH, cities.
KIRJATH ARBA, city of Arba.
KIRJATH-HUZOTH, a city of streets, *Num.* 22. 39.
KIRJATH-JEARIM, a city of woods, *Josh.* 9. 17; 15. 9, 60; 18. 14, 15; *Judg.* 18. 12; 1 *Sam.* 6. 21; 7. 1, 2; 1 *Chron.* 2. 50, 52, 53; 13. 5, 6; 2 *Chron.* 1. 4; *Neh.* 7. 29; *Jer.* 26. 20.
KIRJATH-SANNAH, a city of learning, *i.e.*, a university, *Josh.* 15. 49.
KIRJATH-SEPHER, a city of books; perhaps it was a university, or city of learning, among the early settlers after the deluge, and where were kept their ancient records, *Josh.* 15. 15, 16; *Judg.* 1. 11, 12.
KIRJATHAIM, double city, *or* twofold.
KISH, snaring, bird-catching.
KISHI, snaring of the Lord, 1 *Chron.* 6. 44.
KISHION, very hard, *Josh.* 19. 20.
KISHON, tortuous, winding about; a river which rises in Mount Tabor, and flows into the Mediterranean Sea, *Josh.* 21. 28; *Judg.* 4. 7, 13; 5. 21; 1 *Kings* 18. 40; *Ps* 83. 9.
KITHLISH, wall of man, *Josh.* 15. 40.
KITRON, knotty, *Judg.* 1. 30.
KOHATH, congregation.
KOHATHITES.
KOLAIAH, the voice of the Lord, *Neh.* 11, 7; *Jer.* 29. 21.
KORAH, ice, hail.
KORE, partridge, 1 *Chron.* 9. 19; 26. 1, 19; 2 *Chron.* 31. 14.

L.

LAADAH, order, 1 *Chron.* 4. 21.
LAADAN, put into order, 1 *Chron.* 7, 26; 23. 7, 8, 9; 26. 21.
LABAN, white. *Son of Bethuel, and brother of Rebekah; and uncle of Jacob and Esau.*
LACHISH, obstinate.
LAEL, by God, *i.e.*, he swears or worships God, *Num.* 3. 24.
LAHAD, in triumph *or* joy, 1 *Chron.* 4. 2.
LAHMAM, because of violence, *Josh.* 15. 40.
LAHMI, a warrior, 1 *Chron.* 20. 5.
LAISH, lion. *The Greeks and Romans also named their children after the king of the forest.*
LAKUM, stopping up the way, *Josh.* 19. 33.
LAMECH, powerful.
LAODICEA, just people. *The capital of Phrygia, situated about forty miles from Ephesus. It is now called* Esky-Hissa.
LAPIDOTH, torches, *Judg.* 4. 4.
LASEA, rough, hairy; *from the Greek* λασιος, hairy. *A city on the southern coast of Crete, and about five miles east of the Fair Havens.* Acts 27. 8.
LASHA, fissure; *a city of Sodom,* Gen. 10. 19.
LAZARUS, helpless, destitute of help: *This name is a contraction of* Ἐλεάζαρος, *and the same as the Heb.* Elazar, whom God helps.
LEAH, married.
LEBANAH, moon, *Ezra* 2. 45; *Neh.* 7. 48.
LEBANON, very white. *The name of a mountain consisting of two ridges, on the borders of Syria and Palestine, and so called because the eastern ridge was covered with perpetual snow.*

LEBONAH, frankincense, *Judg.* 21. 19.
LECAH, progress, 1 *Chron.* 4. 21.
LEHABIM, flames, scorching heat. *Descendants of Mizraim, and called* Lehabæi, *Gen.* 10. 13; 1 *Chron.* 1. 11.
LEHI, jawbone; a place on the borders of the land of the Philistines, so called because Samson made there a slaughter of the Philistines with the jawbone of an ass, *Judg.* 15. 9, 14, 19.
LEMUEL, by God. *It is probable that this is a name of* Solomon.
LESHEM, precious stone. *A town, which was also called* Laish *and* Dan, *Josh.* 19. 47.
LETUSHIM, artificers, hammerers, whetter. *Tubal-Cain was the first of this craft. He is said to be father, but, literally, the* whetter, *the* sharpener, *Gen.* 25. 3.
LEUMMIM, peoples, nations, *Gen.* 25. 3.
LEVI, adhesive, joined. *A third son of Jacob by Leah.*
LIBNAH, whiteness; seventeenth station of the Israelites in the wilderness.
LIBNI, white, *Ex.* 6. 17; *Num.* 3. 18; 1 *Chron.* 6. 17, 20, 29.
LIBYA, heat, *i.e.*, of the sun; hence said to be so called from a daughter of Jove. *A region in Africa, going along the Mediterranean Sea, to the west of Egypt.*
LIKHI, learned, 1 *Chron.* 7. 19.
LO-AMMI, not of my people; a mystical name of a son of the Prophet Hosea.
LO-DEBAR, without pasture; a city of Gilead, 2 *Sam.* 9. 4, 5; 17. 27.
LO-RUHAMAH, without mercy; a mystical name of a daughter of Hosea.
LOD, contention; the name of a town of Judea, the same as Lydda of the New Testament, on the Mediterranean Sea, 1 *Chron.* 8. 12; *Ezra* 2. 33; *Neh.* 7. 37; 11. 35.
LOIS, better; the grandmother of Timothy, 2 *Tim.* 1. 5.
LOT, covering; a son of Haran.
LOTAN, covering up, *Gen.* 36. 20, 22, 29; 1 *Chron.* 1. 38, 39.
LUBIM, dwellers in a thirsty land, 2 *Chron.* 12. 3; 16. 8; *Nah.* 3. 9.
LUCIUS, light, *i.e.*, of the sun; *from* lux, light.
LUD, bending, *Gen.* 10. 22; 1 *Chron.* 1. 17; *Isa.* 66. 19; *Ezek.* 27. 10.
LUHITH, tables, slabs of stone; a town of Moab, *Isa.* 15. 5; *Jer.* 48. 5.
LUKE, light, *i.e.*, of the sun.
LUZ, an almond tree, and the name of a town in the tribe of Benjamin.
LYCAONIA, a country sacred to the sun, or country of the god of light, *i.e.*, the sun.
LYCIA, light, *i.e.*, of the sun.
LYDDA, perverted, binding; a city of the tribe of Benjamin, and anciently called Lod.
LYDIA, bending.
LYSANIAS, set free; a tetrach of Abilene.
LYSIAS, he who has the power to set free; a Roman tribune commanding in Jerusalem.
LYSTRA, unbinding; a city of the province of Lycaonia.

M.

MAACHAH, oppression. *Eleven persons bore this name.*
MAADAI, ornament of the Lord, *Ezra* 10. 34.
MAAI, compassion, *Neh.* 12. 36.
MAALEH-ACRABBIM, the going up of scorpions, *Josh.* 15. 3.
MAARATH, a place naked of trees, *Josh.* 15. 59.
MAASEIAH (1) refuge of the Lord; (2) work of the Lord. *There were twenty persons who bore this name in the Old Testament.*
MAASIAI, a contraction of the preceding name.
MAAZ, anger, 1 *Chron.* 2. 27.
MAAZIAH, consolation of the Lord, 1 *Chron.* 24. 18; *Neh.* 10. 8.
MACEDONIA, mother of the Cetims or Ketims, *or* mother-land of Juno *or* the Moon, *being a composition of the Greek* Ma *and* kc, *for* ma *and* ga, mother-earth or land; *and* Diona, *for* dia *and* Iona, Juno the moon, *to which it was consecrated. The name of a province of Greece.*
MACHBANAI, bond of the Lord, 1 *Chron.* 12. 13.
MACHBENAH, bond, 1 *Chron.* 2. 49.
MACHI, decrease, *Num.* 13. 15.
MACHIR, sold.
MACHNADEBAI, what is like the liberality of the Lord? A son of Bani, who married contrary to the law, *Ezra* 10. 40.
MACHPELAH, double, a double cave; *or* a cave within a cave, wherein Abraham buried his dead.
MADAI, extended of the Lord, *Gen.* 10. 2; 1 *Chron.* 1. 5.
MADIAN, strip; a region on the coast of the Red Sea, *Acts* 7. 29.
MADMEN, dunghill, *Jer* 48. 2.
MADON, contention, strife; a Canaanitish city subdued by Joshua, *Josh.* 11. 1; 12 19.
MAGBISH, congregation, *Ezra* 2. 30.
MAGDALA, tower, castle; a country on the east coast of the Red Sea.
MAGDIEL, prince of God, *Gen.* 36. 43; 1 *Chron.* 1. 54.
MAGOG, place of Gog *or* expansion, *i.e.*, increase of family, *Gen.* 10. 2; 1 *Chron.* 1. 5; *Ezek.* 38 2; 39. 6; *Rev.* 20. 8.
MAGOR-MISSABIB, fear round about, *Jer.* 20. 3.
MAGPIASH, killer of moths, *Neh.* 10. 20.
MAHALALEEL, praise of God, *Gen.* 5. 12, 13, 15, 16; 17; 1 *Chron.* 1. 2; *Neh.* 11. 4.
MAHALATH, harp, wind instrument, *Gen.* 28. 9; 2 *Chron.* 11. 18; *Ps.* 53, *title.*
MAHALI, infirmity.
MAHANAIM, two hosts, two camps.
MAHANEH-DAN, camp of Dan, *Judg.* 18. 12.
MAHARAI, impetuosity of the Lord, 2 *Sam.* 23. 28; 1 *Chron.* 11. 30; 27. 13.
MAHATH, seizing, 1 *Chron.* 6. 35; 2 *Chron.* 29. 12; 31. 13.
MAHAVITE, places of assembly, 1 *Chron.* 11. 46.
MAHAZIOTH, visions, 1 *Chron.* 25. 4, 30.
MAHER-SHALAL-HASH-BAZ, haste to the spoil! quick to the prey! *This name was given to a son of the prophet Isaiah, at the command of God.*
MAHLAH, disease, *Num.* 26. 33; 27. 1; 36. 11; *Josh.* 17. 3.
MAHLON, great infirmity.
MAHOL, exultation, 1 *Kings* 4. 31.
MAKAZ, end, extremity, 1 *Kings* 4. 9.
MAKHELOTH, congregations; one of the stations of the Israelites in the wilderness, *Num.* 33. 25, 26.
MAKKEDAH, a place of shepherds; a place in the plains of the tribe of Judah, *Josh.* 10. 10, 16, 21, 28, 29; 12. 16; 15. 41.
MAKTESH, mortar, a hollow place; a place near Jerusalem like a mortar, *Zeph.* 1. 11.
MALACHI, angel of the Lord. *The last of the Old Testament prophets.* Mal. 1. 1.
MALCHAM, most high king.
MALCHI-SHUA, king of help; one of Saul's sons, who was slain on Mount Gilboa.
MALCHIAH, MALCHIJAH, king of the Lord. *There were nine of this name in the Old Testament.* 1 Chron. 6. 40; 9. 12; 24. 9; Neh. 3. 11, 14, 31; 8. 4; 10. 3; 11. 12; 12. 42; Ezra 10. 25, 31; Jer. 21. 1; 38. 1.
MALCHIEL, king of God.
MALCHIRAM, king of height, 1 *Chron.* 3. 18.
MALCHUS, king; *the same as the Chaldean and Syriac. A servant of the High Priest, leader of the band of men which came to take Jesus.*
MALELEEL, praise of God, *Luke* 3. 37.
MALLOTHI, I speak, 1 *Chron.* 25. 4, 26.
MALLUCH, reigning, 1 *Chron* 6. 44; *Ezra* 10. 29, 32; *Neh* 10. 4, 27; 12. 2.
MAMRE, from seeing, from the vision.
MANAHATH, gift, *Gen.* 36. 23; 1 *Chron.* 1. 40; 8. 6.
MANASSES, forgetfulness; the firstborn of Joseph, *Matt.* 1. 10; *Rev.* 7. 6.
MANOAH, rest, *i.e.*, recreation, consolation.
MAON, place of habitation, *Josh.* 15. 55; 1 *Sam.* 25. 2; 1 *Chron.* 2. 45.
MARA, MARAH, bitterness.
MARALAH, place of concussions, *i.e.*, a place subject to earthquakes, *Josh.* 19. 11.
MARESHAH, that which is at the head, *Josh.* 15. 44; 1 *Chron.* 2. 42; 4. 21; 2 *Chron.* 11. 8; 14. 9, 10; 20. 37; *Micah* 1. 15.
MARK, indolent; *the same as the Latin* Marcus, *from* marceo, to be languid, to be lazy. *He was the son of Mary, the sister of Barnabas, and one of the four Evangelists. He founded the Church of Alexandria.*
MAROTH, bitterness, bitter fountains, *Micah* 1. 12.
MARSEANA, lofty.
MARSENA, lofty; a Persian prince, *Esth.* 1. 14.
MARTHA, lady, mistress.
MARY, exalted of the Lord. *A compound of the Heb. words* Mara, to lift up oneself, *and* Yah, *the abbreviated form of the name of Jehovah.*
MASH, drawn out. *The LXX. translate it* Meshech, *and the Samaritan Pentateuch has* Mosok. *Gen.* 10. 23.
MASREKAH, vineyards. *A city of Edom,* Gen. 36. 36; 1 Chron. 1. 47.
MASSA, bearing patiently. *A son of Ishmael.* Gen. 25. 14; 1 Chron. 1. 30.
MASSAH, temptation.
MATHUSALA, when he is dead it shall be sent, *i.e.*, the deluge of waters, *Luke* 3. 37.
MATRED, thrusting forward, *Gen.* 36. 39; 1 *Chron.* 1. 50.
MATRI, rainy, 1 *Sam.* 10. 21.
MATTAN, gift.
MATTANAH, gift, *Num.* 21. 18, 19.
MATTANIAH, gift of the Lord. *Nine persons bore this name in the Old Testament.* 2 Kings 24. 17; 1 Chron. 9. 15; 25. 4, 16; 2 Chron. 20. 14; 29. 13; Neh. 11. 17, 22; 12. 8, 25, 35; 13. 13; Ezra 10. 26, 27, 30, 37.
MATTATHA, gift, *Luke* 3. 31.
MATTHIAS, gift of the Lord.
MATTHAN, gift, *Matt.* 1. 15.
MATTHAT, gift, *Luke* 3. 24, 29.
MATTHEW, gift of the Lord.
MATTENAI, gift of the Lord, *Ezra* 10. 33, 37; *Neh.* 12. 19.
MATHIAS, gift of the Lord.
MATTITHIAH, gift of the Lord, 1 *Chron.* 9. 31; 15. 18, 21; 16. 5; 25. 3, 21; *Ezra* 10. 43; *Neh.* 8. 4.
MEAH, a hundred, *Neh.* 3. 1; 12. 39.
MEARAH, a cave, *Josh.* 13. 4.
MEBUNNAI, building of the Lord, 2 *Sam.* 23. 27.
MECHERATHITE, Swordite, *i.e.*, a soldier, and a proper name for a soldier. *He was one of the heroes of David.* 1 Chron. 11. 36.
MEDAD, love; one of the two elders included in seventy elders who remained in the camp *Num.* 11. 26, 27.
MEDAN, strife, *Gen* 25. 2; 1 *Chron.* 1. 32.
MEDE, a Median.
MEDEBA, water of rest, *Num.* 21. 30; *Josh.* 13. 9, 16; 1 *Chron.* 19. 7; *Isa.* 15. 2.
MEGIDDO, place of multitudes; and it has been the scene of many battles.
MEHETABEL, benefited of God, *Gen.* 36. 39; 1 *Chron.* 1. 50; *Neh.* 6. 10.
MEHIDA, a joining together, *Ezra* 2. 52; *Neh.* 7. 54.
MEHIR, price, wages, 1 *Chron.* 4. 11.
MEHUJAEL, destroyed of God, *Gen.* 4. 18.
MEHUMAN, faithful, *Esth.* 1. 10.
ME-JARKON, water of great greenness, *Josh.* 19. 46.
MEKONAH, base, *i.e.*, foundation, *Neh.* 11. 28.
MELATIAH, delivered of the Lord, *Neh.* 3. 7.
MELCHIZEDEK, king of righteousness. *The name of a king of Salem. He was also priest of the Most High God; and all true Christians are dignified like Him, for they are, as St. Peter says, a royal priesthood,* 1 Pet. 2. 9. *The Jews generally say he was the same as Shem.*
MELEA, fulness; father of Eliakim, *Luke* 3. 31.
MELECH, king, 1 *Chron.* 8. 35; 9. 41.
MELITA, goddess, goddess of generation, refuge. *It was called by the Arabians* Alitta, *and the Assyrians* Mylitta, *and by the Romans* Venus. Acts 28. 1.
MEMPHIS, haven of good men, gate of the blessed.
MEMUCAN, dignity, *Esth.* 1. 14, 16, 21.
MENAHEM, consoling, comforter.
MEONOTHAI, habitation of the Lord, 1 *Chron.* 4. 14.
MEPHAATH, beauty, *Josh.* 13. 18; 21. 37; 1 *Chron.* 6. 79; *Jer.* 48. 21.
MEPHIBOSHETH, exterminating the idol.

MERAB, multiplication.
MERAIAH, lifted up of the Lord. *Neh.* 12. 12.
MERAIOTH, rebellious, 1 *Chron.* 6. 7, 52; 9. 11; *Ezra* 7. 3; *Neh.* 11. 11; 12. 15.
MERARI, bitterness.
MERATHAIM, two-fold rebellion, *Jer.* 50. 21.
MERCURIUS, Hermes, interpreter.
MERED, rebellion, 1 *Chron.* 4. 17, 18.
MEREMOTH, elevation, *Ezra* 8. 33; 10. 36; *Neh.* 3. 4, 21; 10. 5; 12. 3.
MERES, lofty, *Esth.* 1. 14.
MERIB-BAAL, contender against Baal, 1 *Chron.* 8. 34; 9. 40.
MERIBAH, chiding.
MERODACH, the great lord, the illuminator of the gods; *and may be the same with* Nimrod.
MERODACH-BALADAN, the great lord is lord. Merodach *is the same god as* Marduk, *which is* Jupiter, the most brilliant, *Isa.* 39. 1.
MEROM, a high place.
MEROZ, refuge.
MESHA (1) retreat; (2) salvation, *Gen.* 10. 30; 1 *Chron.* 8. 9.
MESHACH, agile, expeditious.
MESHECH, drawing out.
MESHELEMIAH, whom the Lord repays, 1 *Chron.* 9. 21; 26. 1, 2, 9.
MESHEZABEEL, liberated of God, *Neh.* 3. 4; 10. 21; 11. 24.
MESHILLEMOTH, MESHILLEMITH, those who repay, 1 *Chron.* 9. 12; 2 *Chron.* 28. 12; *Neh.* 11. 13.
MESHOBAB, returning, 1 *Chron.* 4. 34.
MESHULLAM, repaying. *The name of sixteen persons in the Bible.* 2 Kings 22. 3; 1 Chron. 3. 19; 5. 13; 8. 17; 9. 7, 8, 11, 12; 2 Chron. 34. 12; Ezra 8. 16; 10. 15, 29; Neh. 3. 4, 6, 30; 6. 18; 8. 4; 10. 7, 20; 11. 7, 11; 12. 13, 16, 25, 33.
MESHULLEMETH, repaying, 2 *Kings* 21. 19.
MESOBAITE, congregation of the Lord, 1 *Chron.* 11. 47.
MESOPOTAMIA, region between the two rivers, and the Greek name for Aram Naharaim, or Syria of the two rivers.
METHEG-AMMAH, the bridle of the Metropolis. *A city of Gath.*
METHUSAEL, man of God, *Gen* 4. 18.
METHUSELAH, when he is dead it shall be sent, *i.e.*, the deluge.
MEZAHAB, waters of gold, *Gen.* 36. 39; 1 *Chron.* 1. 50.
MIAMIN, from the right hand, *Ezra* 10 25; *Neh.* 12. 5.
MIBHAR, most choice, *i.e.*, the best, 1 *Chron.* 11. 38.
MIBSAM, sweet smell, delight, *Gen.* 25. 13; 1 *Chron.* 1. 29: 4. 25.
MIBZAR, defence, fortress, *Gen.* 36. 42; 1 *Chron.* 1. 53.
MICAH, who is like unto the Lord!
MICAIAH, who is like unto the Lord!
MICHA, who is like unto the Lord!
MICHAEL, who is like unto God! *or* who is as God!
MICHAL, a little stream of water.
MICHMAS, treasure, treasury, a place where treasures are kept, *Ezra* 2. 27; *Neh.* 7. 31.
MICHMETHAH, a hiding place, *Josh.* 16. 6; 17. 7.
MICHRI, bought of the Lord, 1 *Chron.* 9. 8.
MIDDIN, strife, *Josh.* 15. 61.
MIGDAL-EL, tower of God, *i.e.*, a very high tower, *Josh.* 19. 38.
MIGDAL-GAD, tower of fortune, *i.e.*, a tower erected in honour of Gad. *Josh.* 15. 37.
MIGDOL, tower, a castle, *Ex.* 14. 2; *Num.* 33. 7; *Jer.* 44. 1; 46. 14.
MIGRON, place of great conflict, 1 *Sam.* 14. 2; *Isa.* 10. 28.
MIKLOTH, staves, 1 *Chron.* 8. 32; 9. 37, 38; 27. 4.
MIKNEIAH, possession of the Lord, 1 *Chron.* 15. 18, 21.
MILALAI, eloquent, *i.e.*, the promise of the Lord, *Neh.* 12. 36.
MILCAH, queen.
MILCOM, high king. *Idol of the Ammonites.*
MILETUS, refuge.
MILLO, rampart, a mound.
MINNI, part, *Jer.* 51. 27.
MINNITH, small, *Judg.* 11. 33; *Ezek.* 27. 17.
MIRIAM, their rebellion, *or* star of the sea.
MIRMA, deceit, 1 *Chron.* 8. 10.
MISGAB, refuge, *Jer.* 48. 1
MISHAEL, who (is) that which God is?
MISHAL, prayer, *Josh.* 19. 26; 21. 30.
MISHAM, their cleansing; one of the sons of Elpaal, 1 *Chron.* 8. 12.
MISHMA, hearing, *Gen.* 25. 14; 1 *Chron.* 1. 30; 4. 25, 26.
MISHMANNAH, fatness: the name of a Gadite soldier, 1 *Chron.* 12. 10.
MISHRAITES, a slippery place.
MISPAR, number, *i.e.*, few.
MISREPHOTH-MAIM, the burnings of waters, *Josh* 11. 8; 13. 6.
MITHCAH, sweetness; and probably there may have been a fountain of a pleasant water which was so denominated, *Num.* 33. 28, 29.
MITHNITE, strength, 1 *Chron.* 11. 43.
MITHREDATH, given by the sun-god, Mithras (*or* fire), the idol of the Persians, and others, and worshipped in caverns, *Ezra* 1. 8: 4. 7.
MITYLENE, last; *but the derivation is very obscure.* Acts 20. 14.
MIZPAH, watch-tower.
MIZRAIM, two-fold Egypt, *i.e.*, upper and lower Egypt, *Gen.* 10. 6. 13; 1 *Chron.* 1. 8. 11.
MNASON, remembrance.
MOAB, water of a father, *i.e.*, progeny.
MOLADAH, birthplace, *Josh.* 15. 26; 19. 2; 1 *Chron.* 4. 28; *Neh.* 11. 26.
MOLECH, the king. *The word is always written with the article,* "The King." *It was the national god of the Ammonites, Canaanites, Phœnicians, and Carthagenians, and was known by the following names:* Moloch, Molech, Malcom, and Milcom: *his worship was always with cruel rites, and Milton makes him* "*king of hell*" *in his* "*Paradise Lost.*"
MOLID, begetting, 1 *Chron.* 2. 29.
MORDECAI, a little man.
MOREH, teacher, illustrious, *Gen.* 12. 6; *Deut.* 11. 30; *Judg.* 7. 1.
MORESHETH-GATH, possession of Gath, *Micah* 1. 14.
MORIAH, visible of the Lord; a hill of Jerusalem on which the Temple was built.
MOSERA, bonds, *Deut.* 10. 6.
MOSES, taken out of the water.
MOZA, fountain, 1 *Chron.* 2. 46; 8. 36, 37; 9. 42, 43.
MUPPIM, anxieties, *Gen.* 46. 21.
MUSHI, proved of the Lord, *Ex.* 6. 19; *Num.* 3. 20; 1 *Chron.* 6. 19, 47; 23. 21, 23; 24. 26, 30.
MYRA, bad waters, *Acts* 27. 5.
MYSIA, marsh, *or* swamp. *The* Mysians *are said to have emigrated from the marshy countries about the lower Danube, called* Moesia, *whence* Mysia.

N.

NAAM, pleasantness, 1 *Chron.* 4. 15.
NAAMAH, pleasant, *Gen.* 4. 22; 1 *Kings* 14 21; 2 *Chron.* 12. 13; *Josh.* 15. 41.
NAAMAN, pleasantness. *A general of the king of Syria, who came to Elisha the prophet to be cleansed of his leprosy.*
NAAMATHITE, pleasantness.
NAARAI, child of the Lord, 1 *Chron.* 11. 37.
NAARAN, handmaid, 1 *Chron.* 7. 28.
NAASHON, enchanter, *or* serpent of the sun.
NABAL, fool, *i.e.*, impious.
NABOTH, fruits, produce.
NACHON, smitten, 2 *Sam.* 6. 6.
NACHOR, burning, *or* noble. *A son of* Serug, *whom Jewish tradition affirms was the founder of the idolatry of worshipping the dead, and probably he denominated this son in honour of the sun or fire.* Luke 3. 34.
NADAB, volunteer.
NAGGE, shining, splendour, *i.e.*, of the sun.
NAHALIEL, torrents of God; *and so called by the Israelites when they passed over them, and called* torrents of God, *because seasonable and salutary,* Num. 21. 19.
NAHALOL, NAHALLAL, NAHALAL, pasture, *i.e.*, a sheep walk, or when sheep are led out, as the shepherds in the East always go before their sheep, *Josh.* 19. 15; 21. 35; *Judg.* 1. 30.
NAHAM, consolation, *i.e.*, to his parents 1 *Chron.* 4. 19.
NAHAMANI, repenting, *Neh.* 7. 7.
NAHARAI, snorter, 2 *Sam.* 23. 37; 1 *Chron.* 11. 30.
NAHASH, serpent. *The serpent was an emblem of the sun, and the name may have been given in honour of the sun.*
NAHATH, letting down, *Gen.* 36. 13, 17; 1 *Chron.* 1. 37; 6. 26; 2 *Chron.* 31. 13.
NAHBI, hidden of the Lord, *Num.* 13. 14.
NAHOR, breathing hard.
NAHUM, consolation, *Nah.* 1. 1.
NAIN, pleasantness, pleasant to the senses.
NAIOTH, habitation, 1 *Sam.* 19. 18, 19, 22; 20. 1.
NAOMI, pleasantness, *i.e.*, of the Lord.
NAPHISH, refreshment, *Gen.* 25. 15; 1 *Chron.* 1. 31; 5. 19.
NAPHTALI, my wrestling, *or* my twisting.
NAPHTUHIM, openings; an Egyptian people who lived on the shores of the Mediterranean, *Gen.* 10. 13; 1 *Chron.* 1. 11.
NARCISSUS, daffodil, *or* narcissus, *Rom.* 16. 11.
NATHAN, given, of God.
NATHAN-MELECH, placed *or* constituted of the king, 2 *Kings* 23. 11.
NATHANAEL, given of God, *John* 1. 45, 46, 47, 48, 49; 21. 2.
NAUM, consolation.
NAZARETH, diadem, *or* consecration.
NEAH, wandering, *Josh.* 19 13.
NEAPOLIS, new city. *It was the sea-port of Philippi.*
NEBAI, fruit of the Lord, *Neh.* 10. 19.
NEBAJOTH, high places, *Gen.* 25. 13; 28. 9; 36. 3; 1 *Chron.* 1. 29; *Isa.* 60. 7.
NEBALLAT, folly in secret, *Neh.* 11. 34.
NEBAT, aspect.
NEBO, Mercury, foreteller, *i.e.*, of events, as commonly interpreted; but it is more properly the Eastern sun in the height of heaven, as identified with the Aryan *Mitra.*
NEBUCHADNEZZAR, Nebo is the god of fire.
NEBUSHASHBAN, Nebo will deliver, *and in* Dan. 6. 16, *the verb occurs,* "Thy God whom thou servest continually, he will deliver thee." *Jer.* 39. 13.
NEBUZARADAN, Mercury's lord *or* leader.
NECHO, the lame. *He was lame, and the Targum mentions this fact. He was a successful general in the early part of his reign, but his power declined before Nebuchadnezzar, and Egypt became a province of Babylon.* 2 Chron. 35. 20, 22; 36. 4.
NEDABIAH, spontaneous gift of the Lord, 1 *Chron.* 3. 18.
NEHELAMITE, made fat.
NEHEMIAH, comfort of the Lord. *He was one of the leaders in the return of the Jews out of captivity in Babylon.*
NEHUM, merciful, *Neh.* 7. 7.
NEHUSHTA, brass, 2 *Kings* 24. 8.
NEHUSHTAN, a little brazen serpent.
NEIEL, shaken of God, *Josh.* 19. 27.
NEKEB, cavern, *Josh.* 19. 33.
NEKODAH, distinguished, *Ezra* 2. 48, 60; *Neh.* 7. 50, 62.
NEMUEL, circumcision of God, *Num.* 26. 9, 12; 1 *Chron.* 4. 24.
NEPHEG, short, bud, *Ex.* 6. 21; 2 *Sam.* 5. 15; 1 *Chron.* 3. 7; 14. 6.
NEPHTOAH, opening. *The name of a fountain near Jerusalem.* Josh. 15. 9: 18. 15.
NEPHTHALIM, wrestlings, *Matt.* 4. 13, 15; *Rev.* 7. 6.
NEPHUSIM, expansions, *Ezra* 2. 50.
NER, lamp.
NEREUS, fluid, *or* flowing.
NERGAL, light rolling, *or* flashing, *or* rushing with noise.
NERGAL-SHAREZER. Nergal is the prince of fire, *or* Nergal is the brightness of light, 2 *Kings* 17 30; *Jer.* 39. 3, 13.
NERI, light of the Lord, *Luke* 3. 27.
NERIAH, light of the Lord.
NETHANEEL, given of God.
NETHANIAH, given of the Lord.
NETOPHAH, a dropping, *Ezra* 2. 22; *Neh.* 7. 26.
NEZIAH, overseer, *Ezra* 2. 54; *Neh.* 7. 50.
NEZIB, garrison, *Josh.* 15. 43.
NIBHAZ, lord of darkness, *i.e.*, an evil demon. *An idol of the Avites, and supposed by some to be the same as the Anubis of Egypt.* 2 Kings 17. 31.
NIBSHAN, level and soft soil, *Josh.*

NICANOR, conqueror of men. *Greek.*
NICODEMUS, conqueror of people.
NICOLAS, conqueror of people, *Acts* 6. 5.
NICOPOLIS, city of victory. *A city of* Epirus, *on the gulf of* Ambacia, *and opposite to* Actium, *Titus* 3. 12.
NIMROD, rebellious, the first rebel on earth in audacity and idolatrous wickedness. *Many Assyrian scholars consider him to be the same as Merodach.*
NIMSHI, selected, drawn out.
NINEVEH, habitation of Ninus. *It is probably the oldest city of the world, and was founded by Nimrod.*
NISDOCH, eagle, *i.e.*, the sun under the emblem of an eagle; and he was one of the chief idols of the Assyrians.
NO, temple, portion. *The city of* Diospolis, *or city of* Jupiter *in* Egypt.
NOADIAH, met with the Lord, *i.e.*, to whom the Lord manifested Himself.
NOAH, (1) rest, comfort; (2), motion, wandering. *The son of Lamech, of the line of Seth.*
NOB, high place.
NOBAH, a barking, a loud noise, *Num.* 32. 42; *Judg.* 8. 11.
NOD, wandering, *i.e.*, going to and fro, *Gen.* 4. 16.
NODAB, nobility, 1 *Chron.* 5. 19.
NOGAH, shining splendour, 1 *Chron.* 3. 7; 14. 16.
NOPHAH, a blast, *Num.* 21. 30.
NUN, fish.
NYMPHAS, bride. *Greek. Col.* 4. 15.

O.

OBADIAH, servant of the Lord. *Twelve persons bore this name.*
OBAL, stripped of braces, *Gen.* 10. 28.
OBED, servant, *i.e.*, of God.
OBED-EDOM, serving Edom.
OBIL, overseer of camels, 1 *Chron.* 27. 30.
OBOTH, pythones, oracular serpents, soothsayers, *Num.* 21. 10, 11; 33. 43, 44.
OCRAN, troubled.
ODED, setting up.
OG, a furrow; a king of Bashan, and of the race of the giants.
OHAD, joining together, *Gen.* 46. 10; *Ex.* 6. 15.
OHEL, tabernacle, 1 *Chron.* 3. 20.
OLYMPAS, gift of Olympus, being a contraction for *Olympodorus.*
OMAR, uppermost, *Gen.* 36. 11, 15; 1 *Chron.* 1. 36.
OMRI, servant of the Lord.
ON, sun, *i.e.*, city of the sun, and called in Greek *Heliopolis.*
ONAM, weariness, wickedness, *Gen.* 38. 4, 8, 9; 46. 12.
ONAN, iniquity.
ONESIMUS, profitable.
ONESIPHORUS, profit bearing.
ONO, strength, 1 *Chron.* 8. 12; *Ezra* 2. 33; *Neh.* 6. 2; 7. 37; 11. 35.
OPHEL, hill, activity.
OPHIR, abundance, *i.e.*, of gold.
OPHNI, mouldy (?), *Josh.* 18. 24.
OPHRAH, fawn, *Josh.* 18. 23; *Judg.* 6. 11, 24; 8. 27, 32; 9. 5; 1 *Sam.* 13. 17; 1 *Chron.* 4. 14.
OREB, raven, black
OREN, pine, *i.e.*, tall and strong, 1 *Chron.* 2. 25.
ORNAN, large pine, *i.e.*, as tall as a great pine.
ORPAH, mane, *i.e.*, neck of an animal.
OSEE, salvation, *Rom.* 9. 25.
OTHNIEL, lion of God, *i.e.*, most powerful.
OZEM, strong.
OZIAS, strength of the Lord.
OZNI, hearing, *Num.* 26. 16.

P.

PADAN-ARAM, the plain of Aram: a province between the Tigris and Euphrates.
PADON, redemption, *Ezra* 2. 44; *Neh.* 7. 47.
PAGIEL, prayer of God.
PAHATH-MOAB, governor of Moab, *Ezra* 2. 6; 8. 4; 10. 30; *Neh.* 3. 11; 7. 11; 10. 14.
PALAL, judge, *Neh.* 3. 25.
PALESTINE, the land of wanderers, *Ex.* 15. 14; *Isa.* 14. 29, 31; *Joel* 3. 4.
PALLU, separated, *Gen.* 46. 9; *Ex.* 6. 14; *Num.* 26. 5, 8; 1 *Chron.* 5. 3.
PALTI, deliverance of the Lord, *Num.* 13. 9.
PALTIEL, deliverance of God, *Num.* 34. 26; 2 *Sam.* 3. 15.
PAMPHILIA, land of every people, *or* region of mixed races.
PAPHOS, gate, cavity. *A city of Cyprus, which is said to have been founded by Cinyras, the father of Adonis, and a chief of the Accadians after the siege of Troy. The remains of an enormous temple to Venus are still discernible there.* Acts 13. 6, 13.
PARAH, village of heifers, *Josh.* 18. 23.
PARAN, abounding in foliage.
PARMASHTA, strong-fisted, *Esth.* 9. 9.
PARMENAS.
PARNACH, very nimble, *Num.* 34. 25.
PAROSH, a flea, *Ezra* 2. 3; 8. 3; 10. 25; *Neh.* 3. 25; 7. 8; 10. 14.
PARSHANDATHA, of noble birth, *Esth.* 9. 7.
PARTHIANS, horsemen. *Originally they were a people of Asia Minor.*
PARUAH, flourishing, 1 *Kings* 4. 17.
PARVAIM, oriental regions, 2 *Chron.* 3. 6.
PASACH, torn asunder, 1 *Chron.* 7. 33.
PAS-DAMMIN, extremity of Dammin, 1 *Chron.* 11. 13.
PASEAH, lame, 1 *Chron.* 4. 12; *Ezra* 2. 49; *Neh.* 3, 6; 7. 51.
PASHUR, most noble.
PATARA, interpretation, *or* oracular response. *A maritime and commercial city of Lycia.* Acts 21. 1.
PATHROS, southern region, *i.e.*, Egypt, *Isa.* 11. 11; *Jer.* 44. 1, 15; *Ezek.* 30. 14.
PATMOS, terebinth, *or* oak.
PATROBAS, life of the father, *Rom.* 16. 14.
PAU, bleating, crying out, *Gen.* 36. 39; 1 *Chron.* 1. 50.
PAUL, little, small. *He was also called* Saul.
PEDAHEL, redeemed of God, *Num.* 34. 28.
PEDAHZUR, redemption of strength, *i.e.*, God, *Num.* 1. 10; 2. 20; 7. 54, 59; 10. 23.
PEDAIAH, redemption of the Lord, 2 *Kings* 23. 36; 1 *Chron.* 3. 18, 19; 27. 20; *Neh.* 3. 25; 8. 4; 11. 7; 13. 13.
PEKAH, open-eyed.
PEKAHIAH, opening of the Lord, *i.e.*, deliverance.
PEKOD, visitation, *i.e.*, punishment, *Jer.* 50. 21; *Ezek.* 23. 23.
PELAIAH, distinguished of the Lord.
PELALIAH, judge of the Lord, *Neh.* 11. 12.
PELATIAH, deliverance.
PELEG, division, *Gen.* 10. 25; 11. 16, 17, 18, 19; 1 *Chron.* 1. 19, 25.
PELET, deliverance, 1 *Chron.* 2. 47; 12. 3.
PELETH, swiftness, *Num.* 16. 1; 1 *Chr.* 2. 33.
PELONITE, such an one, 1 *Chron.* 11. 27, 36; 27. 10.
PENINNAH, coral, 1 *Sam.* 1. 2, 4.
PENUEL, face of God.
PEOR, opening; an idol of the Moabites.
PERESH, excrement, 1 *Chron.* 7. 16.
PEREZ, breach, 1 *Chron.* 27. 33.
PEREZ-UZZAH, breach of Uzzah, 2 *Sam.* 6. 8; 1 *Chron.* 13. 11.
PERGAMOS, height, most high. *Pergamum was celebrated for its Temple of Æsculapius, whose emblem the serpent was, and who is represented on the coins of Pergamum, and is called* Pergameus Deus. (*Bishop of Lincoln's New Test.*) Rev. 2. 12.
PERGE, *valde terrestris* (Mintrat.), the metropolis of Pamphlias, and celebrated for its Temple of Diana.
PERIZITES, villagers.
PERSIA, a tract of country from Media to the Persian Gulf, embracing Susiana and Elymais.
PERSIANS, horsemen. *The founder of this race was Persis. The Persian religion consisted in the worship of the sun, moon, earth, fire, water, and the winds.*
PERSIS, one who takes by storm.
PERUDA, distinguished, *Ezra* 2. 55.
PETER, rock, or rock-like.
PETHAHIAH, loosed of the Lord, 1 *Chron.* 24. 16; *Ezra* 10. 23; *Neh.* 9. 5; 11. 24.
PETHOR, interpretation of dreams. *A city of Mesopotamia,* Num. 22. 5; Deut. 23. 4.
PETHUEL, ingeniousness of God, *Joel* 1. 1.
PEULTHAI, wages of the Lord, 1 *Chron.* 26. 5.
PHARAOH, the great house.
PHARAOH-HOPHRA, Pharaoh the priest of the sun.
PHARAOH-NECHOH, Pharaoh the lame.
PHARES, *vid.* Perez.
PHARPAR, most swift.
PHEBE, radiant as the moon.
PHENICE, palm, *i.e.*, abundant in palms.
PHICHOL, mouth of all, *Gen.* 21. 22, 32; 26. 26.
PHILADELPHIA, brotherly love.
PHILEMON, loving, friendship, *Philem.* 1.
PHINEHAS, mouth of brass.
PHILETUS, lovingly, *or* loving one's self.
PHILIP, loving.
PHILIPPI, loving horses, lover of horses.
PHILOLOGUS, lover of literature.
PHLEGON, having flaming eyes.
PHRYGIA, cold.
PHURAH, branch.
PHUVAH, mouth.
PHYGELLUS, he who flees from chains.
PI-BESETH, portion of the spouse.
PI-HAHIROTH, mouth of caverns.
PILDASH, lamp of fire, *Gen.* 22. 22.
PILEHA, servitude, *Neh.* 10. 24.
PIRAM, like a wild ass, *Josh.* 10. 3.
PIRATHON, just revenge, *Judg.* 12. 15.
PISGAH, divided rock, *or* fragment of hewn rock.
PISIDIA, damp region.
PISON, great effusion, *i.e.*, of waters.
PISPAH, dispersion, 1 *Chron.* 7. 38.
PITHOM, an enclosed place, *Ex.* 1. 11.
PITHON, great enlargement, 1 *Chron.* 8. 35; 9. 41.
POCHERETH OF ZEBAIM, retarding gazelles, *Ezra* 2. 57; *Neh.* 7. 59.
PONTIUS PILATE, *Procurator of Judea.*
PORATHA, ornament, *Esth.* 9. 8.
POTIPHAR, priest of the bull.
POTIPHERAH, priest of the sun, *in the temple of the sun, in the city of On or Heliopolis.*
PRISCA, *a shortened form for* Priscilla, 2 *Tim.* 4. 19.
PRISCILLA, ancient, old-fashioned simplicity.
PROCHORUS, leader of the choir; *one of the seven deacons,* Acts 6. 5.
PTOLEMAIS, fond of war, warlike, *Acts* 21. 7.
PUAH, splendid, light; *perhaps* joy of parents.
PUBLIUS, pertaining to the people.
PUDENS, bashful, modest.
PUHITES, a name from *Heb.* beautiful, 1 *Chron.* 2. 53.
PUL, elephant.
PUNITES, same as PHUVAH, *Num.* 26. 23.
PUNON, distraction, *Num.* 33. 42, 43.
PUT, extension.
PUTEOLI, for, pertaining to.
PUTIEL, afflicted of God, *Ex.* 6. 25.

Q.

QUARTUS, fourth, *i.e.*, child.

R

RAAMAH, thundering, *Gen.* 10. 7; 1 *Chron.* 1. 9; *Ezek.* 27. 22.
RAAMIAH, thunder of the Lord, *Neh.* 7. 7.
RAAMSES, son of the sun, (*vid.* Rameses), city of the sun, *Ex.* 1. 11.
RABBAH, great city, *i.e.*, metropolis.
RABBITH, great multitude, *Josh.* 19. 20.
RABSHAKEH, chief of the cup-bearers; an Assyrian general under Sennacherib.
RACHAL, traffic, 1 *Sam.* 30. 29.
RACHEL, an ewe; the youngest daughter of Laban, and beloved wife of Jacob.
RADDAI, subduing, 1 *Chron.* 2. 14.
RAGAU, companion, friend.
RAGUEL, friend of God, *i.e.*, a servant of God.
RAHAB, (1) insolence, fierceness; (2) spacious, *i.e.*, wide.
RAHAM, merciful, 1 *Chron.* 2. 44.
RAHEL, an ewe.
RAKKATH, a shore, *Josh.* 19. 35.
RAKKON, extreme shore, *Josh.* 19. 46.
RAM, high part.
RAMAH, lofty place.
RAMESES, son of the sun; *a city of Egypt.* *Gen.* 47. 11; *Ex.* 12. 37; *Num.* 33. 3, 5.
RAMIAH, placed of the Lord, *Ezra* 10. 25.
RAMOTH, heights, eminences.

RAPHA, giant, *whose descendants were called* Rephaim. *Some suppose they were the Titans.*
RAPHU, healed, *Num.* 13. 9.
REAIA, vision, 1 *Chron.* 5. 5.
REAIAH, vision of the Lord, *i.e.*, one who has seen the Lord, by faith, 1 *Chron.* 4. 2; *Ezra* 2. 47; *Neh.* 7. 50.
REBA, fourth, *Num.* 31. 8; *Josh.* 13. 21.
REBAIAH, fourth, *i.e.*, fourth son of the Lord.
REBEKAH, a rope with a noose.
RECHAB, horseman.
RECHAH, spacious, 1 *Chron.* 4. 12.
RED (SEA), the weed, *or* weedy sea, *Ex.* 10. 19.
REELAIAH, trembling of the Lord, *Ezra* 2. 2.
REGEM, friend, *i.e.*, of God, as from the Arabic, 1 *Chron.* 2. 47.
REGEM-MELEK, the friend of the king, *similar to the Arabic name*, Chalel Beg, friend of the king, *Zech.* 7. 2.
REHABIAH, enlarging of the Lord, 1 *Chron.* 23. 17; 24. 21; 26. 25.
REHOB, open space, *i.e.*, a street *or* road, *Num.* 13. 21; *Josh.* 19. 28, 30; 21. 31; *Judg.* 1. 31; 2 *Sam.* 8. 3, 12; 10. 8; 1 *Chron.* 6. 75; *Neh.* 10. 11.
REHOBOAM, enlarges the people, *i.e.*, sets at liberty.
REHOBOTH, streets, wide spaces; *one of the cities built by Nimrod.*
REHUM, merciful.
REI, friend of God, 1 *Kings* 1. 8.
REKEM, variegated, embroidered, *Num.* 31. 8; *Josh.* 13. 21; 18. 27; 1 *Chron.* 2. 43, 44.
REMALIAH, adorned of the Lord.
REMMON, pomegranate, *Josh.* 19. 7.
REPHAEL, healed of God, 1 *Chron.* 26. 7.
REPHAH, riches, 1 *Chron.* 7. 25.
REPHAIAH, healed of the Lord, 1 *Chron.* 3. 21; 4. 42; 7. 2; 9. 43; *Neh.* 3. 9.
REPHIDIM, props, supports.
RESEN, bridle, curb, *Gen.* 10. 12.
RESHEPH, sun-god, *whom the Hittites worshipped*, 1 Chron. 7. 25.
REU, associate, *i.e.*, of the Lord, *Gen.* 11. 18, 19, 20, 21; 1 *Chron.* 1. 25.
REUBEN, behold a son!
REUEL, friend of God, *Gen.* 36. 4, 10, 13, 17; *Ex.* 2. 18; *Num.* 2. 14; 1 *Chr.* 1. 35, 37; 9. 8.
REUMAH, exalted, *Gen.* 22. 24.
REZEPH, baking stone, 2 *Kings* 19. 12; *Isa.* 37. 12.
REZIA, delight, 1 *Chron.* 7. 39.
REZIN, firm, a king of Damascus.
REZON, prince, 1 *Kings* 11. 23.
RHEGIUM, a bursting forth.
RHESA, head first.
RHODA, a rose, *i.e., beautiful, and probably sacred to the sun.*
RHODES, *the same, famous for its Colossus.*
RIBAI, judgment of the Lord, 2 *Sam.* 23. 29; 1 *Chron.* 11. 31.
RIBLAH, multitude of people, *Num.* 34. 11; 2 *Kings* 23. 33; 25. 6, 20; *Jer.* 39. 5, 6; 52. 9, 10, 26, 27.
RIMMON, pomegranate; an Assyrian god worshipped at Damascus.
RIMMON-PAREZ, pomegranate of the breach, *Num.* 33. 19, 20.
RINNAH, a joyful cry, 1 *Chron.* 4. 20.
RIPHATH, a crusher, *i.e.*, of enemies, *Gen.* 10. 3; 1 *Chron.* 1. 6.
RISSAH, dew, *Num.* 33. 21, 22.
RITHMAH, broom, *Num.* 33. 18, 19.
RIZPAH, a baking stone.
ROGELIM, fountain of the fuller, 2 *Sam.* 17. 27; 19. 31.
ROHGAH, copious rain, 1 *Chron.* 7. 34.
ROMAMTI-EZER, I have lifted up help, 1 *Chron.* 25. 4, 31.
ROME, strong, firm.
ROSH, head, chief, *Gen.* 46. 21.
RUFUS, red.
RUMAH, high, 2 *Kings* 23. 36.
RUTH, beauty.

S.

SABTAH, breaking through, *Gen.* 10. 7; 1 *Chron.* 1. 9.
SABTECHAH, beating, *Gen.* 10. 7; 1 *Chr.* 1. 9.
SACAR, wages, 1 *Chron.* 11. 35; 26. 4.
SALAMIS, deadly serpents. *A place in the isle of Cyprus, famous for the worship of Aphrodite*, Acts 13. 5.
SALCAH, firm, binding together, *Deut.* 3. 10; *Josh.* 12. 5; 13. 11; 1 *Chron.* 5. 11.
SALEM, at peace.
SALLAI, lifted up of the Lord, *Neh.* 11. 8; 12. 20.
SALMA, garment, 1 *Chron.* 2. 51, 54.
SALMON, SALMONE, shady.
SALOME, very shady.
SALU, lifted up, *Num.* 25. 14.
SAMARIA, vigilant guardian.
SAMGAR-NEBO, sword of Nebo, *Jer.* 39. 3.
SAMLAH, garment, *Gen.* 36. 36, 37; 1 *Chron.* 1. 47, 48.
SAMOS, lofty, very high; so called because it was situated very high. *An island in the Ionian Sea*, Acts 20. 15.
SAMOTHRACIA, Upper Thracia. *An island in the Ægean Sea*, Acts 16. 11.
SAMSON, splendid sun, *i.e.*, sun-like.
SAMUEL, heard of God.
SANBALLAT, hate in disguise.
SANSANNAH, palm branch, *Josh.* 15. 31.
SAPH, tall, 2 *Sam.* 28. 18.
SAPHIR, SAPPHIRA, beautiful.
SARAH, princess.
SARAI, my princess.
SARAPH, serpent, 1 *Chron.* 4. 22.
SARDIS, things which remain, Rev. 1. 11.
SAREPTA, purified, *i.e.*, in the fire, refined.
SARGON, prince of the sun. *He was king of Assyria*, B.C. 722. *He conquered Samaria, Hamuth, Arabia, Armenia, and many other places; and the late Mr. G. Smith discovered his royal seal, with his name and date, among the ruins of Konyunjik*, Isa. 20. 1.
SARID, survivor, escaped, *Josh.* 19. 10, 12.
SARON, *vid.* SHARON.
SARSECHIM, chief of the eunuchs, *Jer.* 39. 3.
SARUCH, branch. *The same as* Serug.
SATAN, the adversary, the lier in wait, the devil, who seduces men.
SAUL, asked for.
SCEVA, expectation, *or* hope of his parents.
SEBA, eminent.
SEBAT, breaking through. *The same as* Sabtah, *Zech.* 1. 7.
SECACAH, enclosure, *Josh.* 15. 61.
SECHU, watch-tower, 1 *Sam.* 19. 22.
SECUNDUS, second, *Acts* 20. 4.
SEGUB, elevated, 1 *Kings* 16. 34; 1 *Chron.* 2. 21, 22.
SEIR, rough, bristly.
SELA, rock, 2 *Kings* 14. 7.
SELA-HAMMAHLEKOTH, rock of division, 1 Sam. 23. 28.
SELAH, rock, 2 *Kings* 14. 7; *Isa.* 16. 1.
SELED, exultation, 1 *Chron.* 2. 30.
SELEUCIA, *a city of Syria.*
SEMACHIAH, sustained of the Lord, 1 *Chron.* 26. 7.
SEMEI, heard of the Lord.
SENAAH, elevated, *Ezra* 2. 35; *Neh.* 7. 38.
SENEH, high. *A sharp rock over against Gibeah*, 1 Sam. 14. 4.
SENIR, coat of mail, 1 *Chron.* 5. 23; *Ezek.* 27. 5.
SENNACHERIB, sin has multiplied her brothers. *A son of Sargon, king of Assyria, who assumed the same title also as his predecessors*, Ebidu Malki, *subduer of kings. He was, like most of the Assyrian kings, a cruel tyrant.*
SENUAH, light.
SEORIM, barley.
SEPHAR, numbering. *A mountain in Arabia.*
SEPHARAD, *a place unknown.*
SEPHARVAIM, *a city in Mesopotamia.*
SERAH, SERAIAH, soldier of the Lord.
SERED, fear. *A son of Zebulon.*
SERGIUS PAULUS.
SERUG, branch.
SETH, appointed. *Third son of Adam.*
SETHER, hidden, mysterious. *This name contains the number of the Apocalyptic beast* (Rev. 13. 18) *in Hebrew letters.*
SHAALABBIN, place of foxes. *A Danite city.*
SHAAPH, balsam.
SHAARAIM, two gates.
SHAASHGAZ, servant of the beautiful, *if from the* Persic, *Esth.* 2. 14.
SHABBETHAI, rest of the Lord. *A Levite*, Ezra 10 15; Neh. 8, 7; 11. 16.
SHACHIA, captive of the Lord, 1 *Chron.* 8. 10.
SHADRACH, rejoicing in the way. *A companion of Daniel. Vid.* ABEDNEGO.
SHAGE, wandering; one of David's heroes, 1 *Chron.* 11. 34.
SHAHARAIM, two dawns, 1 *Chron.* 8. 8.
SHAHAZIMAH, lofty places. *A town of Issachar*, Josh. 19. 22.
SHALEM, peace, *Gen.* 33. 18.
SHALISHA, triangular; *a region near Mount Ephraim.*
SHALLECHETH, casting down; *a gate in the temple*, 1 Chron. 26. 16.
SHALLUM, SHALLUN, retribution.
SHALMAI, peace-offering of the Lord, *Ezra* 2. 46; *Neh.* 7. 48.
SHALMANESER, Shalman protects or helps, *or* likeness of Ann, *i.e.*, likeness of Noah; *or* worshippers of fire, *i.e.*, the sun.
SHAMA, hearing. *One of David's men of war.*
SHAMGAR, *one of the judges of Israel.*
SHAMIR, a sharp point; a guard, *Josh.* 15. 48; *Judg.* 10. 1, 2; 1 *Chron.* 24. 24.
SHAMMAH, astonishment, desolation.
SHAMMAI, astonishment of the Lord, 1 *Chron.* 2. 28, 32, 44, 45; 4. 17
SHAMMUA, hearing of the Lord.
SHAMSHERAI, brave, 1 *Chron.* 8. 26.
SHAPHAM, bare, 1 *Chron.* 5. 12.
SHAPHAN, cony, *i.e.*, cunning.
SHAPHAT, judge.
SHAPHER, beauty; *a place near where the Israelites pitched their twentieth camp in the wilderness*, Num. 33. 23, 24.
SHARAI, liberated of the Lord. *He was afterwards a captive to self-will.* Ezra 10. 40.
SHARAR, hand, stay, *i.e*, of the family, 2 *Sam.* 23. 33.
SHAREZER, prince of fire; *or* splendour of the sun; a son of Sennacherib, who was so called in honour of the sun. *He was one of the murderers of his father, and his name does not occur in the Assyrian inscriptions.*
SHARON, a great plain, *or* plain country, running along the coast of the Mediterranean Sea from Joppa to Cæsarea; *and was famous for its roses, which were so beautiful that the Son of God could say of Himself, "I am the Rose of Sharon."*
SHARUHEN, a pleasant dwelling-place, *Josh.* 19. 6.
SHASHAI, habitation of the Lord, *i.e.*, he was a faithful servant of God, *Ezra* 10. 40.
SHASHAK, vehement desire, 1 *Chron.* 8. 14, 25.
SHAVEH, plain, *Gen.* 14. 17.
SHAVEH-KIRIATHAIM, plain of the double city, *Gen.* 14. 5.
SHABSHA, habitation, *i.e.*, of the Lord.
SHEAL, petition; a son of Bani, who was given in answer to prayer, *Ezra* 10. 29.
SHEALTIEL, I asked for from God.
SHEAR-JASHUB, a remnant shall return, *i.e.*, from captivity. *A prophetic name of a son of Isaiah.*
SHEARIAH, estimated of the Lord; a son of Azel, 1 *Chron.* 8. 38; 9. 44.
SHEBA, (1) man; (2) oath, *or* seven. *Number seven and an oath are often interchangeable among the Chaldeans.*
SHEBAM, sweet smell. *The same as* SIBMAH, *Num.* 32. 3.
SHEBANIAH, caused to grow up of the Lord, 1 *Chron.* 15. 24; *Neh.* 9. 4, 5; 10. 4, 10, 12; 12. 14.
SHEBARIM, fractures terrors, *Josh.* 7. 5.
SHEBER, breach, *singular of the preceding*, 1 Chron. 2. 48.
SHEBNA, youth, grown up.
SHEBUEL, captive of God, 1 *Chron.* 23. 16; 25. 4; 26. 24.
SHECHANIAH, inhabited of the Lord, *i.e.*, one of the Lord's people, 1 *Chron.* 3. 21. 22; 24. 11; *Ezra* 8. 3, 5; 10 2; *Neh.* 3. 29; 6. 18; 12. 3.
SHECHEM, back; a city of Samaria. *It is now called* Nablous, *and contains about* 13,000 *inhabitants.*
SHEDEUR, casting forth of fire, *i.e.*, lightning, *Num.* 1. 5; 2. 10; 7. 30, 35; 10. 18.
SHEHARIAH, sought of the Lord, 1 *Chron.* 8. 26.
SHELAH, (1) prayer, request; (2) sent, shooting forth.
SHELEMIAH, repaid of the Lord.
SHELEPH, drawn out, *i.e.*, selected, *Gen.* 10. 26; 1 *Chron.* 1. 20.
SHELESH, triad, 1 *Chron.* 7. 35.
SHELOMI, my peace, *Num.* 34. 27.
SHELOMITH, retribution, *i.e.*, love of peace, *Lev.* 24. 11; 1 *Chron.* 3. 19; 23. 9, 18; 26. 25, 26, 28; 2 *Chron.* 11. 20; *Ezra* 8. 10.
SHELOMOTH, retribution, 1 *Chron.* 24. 22.
SHELUMIEL, friend of God.

SHEM, name; *i.e.*, distinguished.
SHEMA, hearing, fame, *Josh.* 15. 26; 1 *Chron.* 2. 43, 44; 5. 8; 8. 13; *Neh.* 8. 4.
SHEMAAH, hearing, fame. 1 *Chron.* 12. 3.
SHEMAIAH, heard of the Lord.
SHEMARIAH, guarded of the Lord, 1 *Chr.* 12. 5; 2 *Chr.* 11.19; *Ezra* 10. 32, 41.
SHEMEBER, name of wing, *i.e*, of great celebrity, *Gen.* 14. 2.
SHEMER, custody, who is in the keeping of the Lord, 1 *Kings* 16. 24.
SHEMIDA, name of knowledge, *i.e.*, famous, *Num.* 26. 32; *Josh.* 17. 2; 1 *Chron.* 7. 19.
SHEMIRAMOTH, most exalted name, 1 *Chron.* 15. 18, 20; 16. 5; 2 *Chron.* 17. 8.
SHEMUEL, asked for of God. *The same as* Samuel, *Num.* 34. 20; 1 *Chron.* 6. 33; 7. 2.
SHEN, tooth. *It was a sharp rock in shape of a tooth.* 1 Sam. 7. 12.
SHENAZAR, light of splendour, 1 *Chr.* 3.18.
SHENIR, coat of mail.
SHEPHAM, coney, *Num.* 34. 10, 11.
SHEPHATIAH, judge of the Lord.
SHEPHI, high, *i.e.*, illustrious.
SHEPHO, high, *Gen.* 36. 23; 1 *Chron.* 1. 40.
SHEPHUPHAN, a serpent, 1 *Chron.* 8. 5.
SHERAH, consanguinity, *i.e.*, a female relation by blood, 1 *Chron.* 7. 24.
SHEREBIAH, deliverance of the Lord, *i.e.*, from captivity, *Ezra* 8. 18, 24; *Neh.* 8. 7; 9. 4, 5; 10. 12; 12. 8, 24.
SHERESH, root, *i.e.*, of a family, 1 *Chron.* 7. 16.
SHESHACH, confusion, *Jer.* 25. 26; 51. 41.
SHESHAI, whitish, *Num.* 13. 22; *Josh.* 15. 14; *Judg.* 1. 10.
SHESHAN, city, *as perhaps for* Shushan, 1 *Chron.* 2. 31, 34, 35.
SHESHBAZZAR, worshipper of fire, *i.e.*, the sun.
SHETHAR, star. *Persic.* Esth. 1. 14.
SHETHAR-BOZNAI, star of splendour, *Ezra* 5. 3, 6; 6. 6, 13.
SHEVA, habitation, 2 *Sam.* 20. 25; 1 *Chron.* 2. 49.
SHIBMAH, sweet smell, *Num.* 32. 38.
SHICRON, drunkenness, *Josh.* 15. 11.
SHIHON, overturning, *Josh.* 19. 19.
SHIHOR, very black, turbid; the river Nile.
SHIHOR-LIBNATH, river of glass, *Josh.* 19. 26.
SHILHI, armed, *i.e.*, of the Lord, 1 *Kings* 22. 42; 2 *Chron.* 20. 31.
SHILHIM, armed men, *i.e.*, a fortress, *Josh.* 15. 32.
SHILOAH, sent. *So called from the sending forth of the water from one source into the two pools of Bethesda and Siloam.*
SHILOH, Pacificator, the Peace-maker, Jesus Christ.
SHILONI, SHILONITE, sent, *Neh.* 11. 5.
SHILSHAH, triad, *i.e.*, third son, 1 *Chron.* 7. 37.
SHIMEA, hearing, rumour, 1 *Chron.* 8. 32.
SHIMEAH, hearing.
SHIMEAM, astonishment, 1 *Chron.* 9. 38.
SHIMEATH, hearing, fame. *An Ammonitess.* 2 Kings 12. 21; 2 Chron. 24. 26.
SHIMEATHITES, responsers, 1 *Chr.* 2. 55.
SHIMEI, famous of the Lord.
SHIMON, great desert, 1 *Chron.* 4. 20.
SHIMRATH, ward, *i.e.*, one in the hands of the Divine guardian of men, 1 *Chr.* 8. 21.
SHIMRI, ward of the Lord, 1 *Chron.* 4. 37; 11. 45; 26. 10; 2 *Chron.* 29. 13.
SHIMRITH, guarded, *i.e.*, of the Lord, 2 *Chron.* 24. 26.
SHIMRON, vigilant, guardian, *Gen.* 46. 13; *Num.* 26. 24, 1 *Chr.* 7. 1; *Josh.* 11. 1; 19. 15.
SHIMSHAI, sun of the Lord.
SHINAB, tooth of the father, *Gen.* 14. 2.
SHINAR, a casting out, *or* a scattering every way; *but the derivation is very uncertain.*
SHIPHI, eminent, 1 *Chron.* 4. 37.
SHIPHRAH, beauty, brightness.
SHIPHTAN, most just judge, *Num.* 34. 24.
SHISHAK, *derivation obscure.*
SHITRAI, scribe of the Lord, 1 *Chr.* 27. 29.
SHIZA, raising up, 1 *Chron.* 11. 42.
SHOBAB, backsliding, 2 *Sam.* 5. 14; 1 *Chron.* 2. 18; 3. 5; 14. 4.
SHOBACH, poured out, 2 *Sam.* 10. 16. 18.
SHOBAI, recompence of the Lord, *Ezra* 2. 42; *Neh.* 7. 45.
SHOBI, *the same*, 2 Sam. 17. 27.
SHOCHO, hedge, defence, *i.e.*, fortification, 2 *Chron.* 28. 18.
SHOCHOH, *and* **SHOCO**, idea, 2 *Chr.* 11. 7.
SHOMER, guarded of the Lord, 2 *Kings* 12, 21: 1 *Chron.* 7. 32.
SHUA, wealth, 1 *Chron.* 7. 32.
SHUAH, prostration.
SHUAL, fox.
SHUHAM, pit-digger, *Num.* 26. 42.
SHULAMITE, complete.
SHUNEM, two resting places, *Josh.* 19. 18; 1 *Sam.* 28. 4; 2 *Kings* 4. 8.
SHUNI, tranquillity, quietness, *Gen.* 46. 16; *Num.* 26. 15.
SHUPHAM, serpent, *Num.* 26. 39.
SHUPPIM, serpents, 1 *Chron.* 7. 12, 15; 26. 16.
SHUR, fort, *i.e.*, a fortified place, *Gen.* 16. 7; 20. 1; 25. 18; *Ex.* 15. 22; 1 *Sam.* 15. 7; 27. 8.
SHUSHAN, lily.
SHUTHELAH, crashing and rending, *Num.* 26. 35, 36; 1 *Chron.* 7. 20, 21.
SIA, council, *Neh.* 7. 47.
SIBBECHAI, thicket of the Lord, *or* interwoven very thickly, 2 *Sam.* 21. 18; 1 *Chron.* 11. 29; 20. 4; 27. 11.
SIBRAIM, two-fold hope.
SIDDIM, plains, *Gen.* 14. 3, 8, 10.
SIDON, fishing, plenty of fish.
SIHON, sweeping away, *i.e.*, a general who drives everything before him.
SILAS, a shortened form of **SILVANUS**.
SILOAH, SILOAM, sent.
SILVANUS, born in the wood. *See* **SILAS**.
SIMEON, hearing with acceptance.
SIMON, *the same.*
SIMRI, song of the Lord. *Same as* Zimri.
SIN, clay, bush. *It was called* Pelusium. *There was a moon-god among the Babylonians of this name.*
SINAI, bush of the Lord. *A very desolate region, in the midst of which rose up the Mount of Terror.*
SINIM. Pelusiots, according to Simonis, *Isa.* 49. 12.
SINITE, *the same*, Gen. 10. 17; 1 Chr. 1. 15.
SION, lifted up, *Deut.* 4. 48; *Matt.* 21. 5; *John* 12. 15; *Rom.* 9. 33; 11. 26; *Heb.* 12. 22; 1 *Pet.* 2. 6; *Rev.* 14. 1.
SIRION, breastplate. *The Sidonian name of* Hermon, *Deut.* 3. 9; *Ps.* 29. 6.
SISAMAI, the sun, 1 *Chron.* 2. 40.
SISERA, a field of battle.
SITNAH, accusation, hatred, *Gen.* 26. 21.
SMYRNA, *derivation obscure. This city was situated about eight miles north of Ephesus.*
SO, lifted up.
SODI, acquaintance of God.
SODOM, flaming, burning.
SOLOMON, peaceable, *or* great peace.
SOPATER, a contracted form of the following name, *Acts* 20. 4.
SOPHERETH, female scribe, *Ezra* 2. 55; *Neh.* 7. 57.
SOREK, choice vine.
SOSIPATER, wealth of the father, *or* servant of the father, *Rom.* 16. 21. *Vid.* **SOPATER**
SOSTHENES.
SOTAI, drawn back of the Lord, *Ezra* 2. 55; *Neh.* 7. 57.
SPAIN, *derivation and interpretation uncertain.*
STACHYS, ear of corn, which among the ancients was an emblem of fertility and fruitfulness.
STEPHANUS, crown. *The name of a person baptized by Paul.*
STEPHEN, crown.
SUAH, sweeping. *A son of Zopah*, 1 Chron. 7. 36.
SUCCOTH, booths.
SUCCOTH-BENOB, tabernacles of daughters, *i.e.*, sacristes of Venus.
SUCHATHITES, dwellers in booths. *Place unknown*, 1 Chron. 2. 55.
SUKKIIMS, dwellers in tents, 2 *Chron.* 12. 3.
SUR, go back, 2 *Kings* 11. 6.
SUSANCHITES, inhabitants of Susa, *Ezra* 4. 9.
SUSANNA, lily.
SUSI, horseman, *Num.* 13. 11.
SYCHAR, folly, *John* 4. 5.
SYENE, opening, key, *i.e.*, of Egypt, *Ezek.* 29. 10; 30. 6.
SYNTYCHE, good fortune, good luck, *Phil.* 4. 2.
SYRACUSE, a city of Sicily, *Acts* 28. 12.
SYRIA, *vid.* **ARAM**.

T.

TAANACH, wandering through, *Josh.* 12. 21; 17. 11; 21. 25; *Judg.* 1. 27; 5. 19. 1 *Kings* 4. 12; 1 *Chron.* 7. 29.
TAANATH-SHILOH, entrance to Shiloh, *Josh.* 16. 6.
TABBAOTH, rings, *Ezra* 2. 43; *Neh.* 7. 46.
TABBATH, renowned, celebrated, *Judg.* 7. 22.
TABEEL, goodness of God, *Ezra* 4. 7.
TABERAH, consuming, burning, *Num.* 11. 3.
TABITHA, gazelle, called in the Greek Testament *Dorcas*, a gazelle, *Acts* 9. 36, 40.
TABOR, stone quarry.
TABRIMON, goodness of Rimmon, 1 *Kings* 15 18.
TACHMONITE, wisdom, 2 *Sam.* 23. 8.
TADMOR, Palmyrene, *or* admiration.
TAHAN, supplication, *i.e.*, of parents, 1 *Chron.* 7. 25.
TAHATH, depression, 1 *Chron.* 6. 24, 37; 7. 20.
TAHPENES, head of the age.
TAHTIM-HODSHI, under the new moon, 2 *Sam.* 24. 6.
TALMAI, abounding in furrows, *Num.* 13. 22; *Josh.* 15. 14; *Judg.* 1. 10; 2 *Sam.* 3. 3; 13. 37; 1 *Chron.* 3. 2.
TALMON, injurious, oppression, 1 *Chron.* 9. 17; *Ezra* 2. 42; *Neh.* 7. 45; 11. 19; 12. 25.
TAMAR, palm.
TAMMUZ, the sun of life.
TANACH, wandering through.
TANHUMETH, consolation, 2 *Kings* 25. 23; *Jer.* 40. 8.
TAPHATH, drop of myrrh, *or* stacti, *i.e.*, myrrh flowing spontaneously, 1 *Kings* 4. 11.
TAPUAH, apple, fruitful in apples, *Josh.* 12. 17; 15. 34; 16. 8; 17. 8; 1 *Chron.* 2. 43.
TARAH, delay, *Num.* 33. 27, 28.
TARALAH, reeling. *A town in the land of Benjamin*, Josh. 18. 27.
TAREA, delaying cries, 1 *Chron.* 8. 35.
TARSHISH, subjection of enemies.
TARSUS, dove.
TARTAK, the moon.
TARTAN, great increase, 2 *Kings* 18. 17; *Isa.* 20. 1.
TATNAI, gift, *Ezra* 5. 3, 6; 6. 6, 13.
TEBAH, confidence, *i.e.*, of parents, *Gen.* 22. 24.
TEBALIAH, baptized of the Lord, 1 *Chron.* 26. 11.
TEHAPHNEHES, the beginning of the age; *or*, the beginning of the world *or* earth.
TEHINNAH, grace, prayer, 1 *Chron.* 4. 12.
TEKOA, pitching, *i.e.*, of tents.
TEL-ABIB, hill of ears of corn, *Ezek.* 3. 15.
TEL-HARESHA, TEL-HARSA, hill of ploughing, *Ezra* 2. 59; *Neh.* 7. 61.
TEL-MELA, hill of salt, *Ezra* 2. 59; *Neh.* 7. 61.
TELAH, fracture 1 *Chron.* 7. 25.
TELAIM, young lambs, 1 *Sam.* 15. 4.
TELASSAR, hill of Assur.
TELEM, oppression. *A Levite porter*, Josh. 15. 24; Ezra 10. 24.
TEMA, desert. *A son of Ishmael.*
TEMAN, southern quarter.
TERAH, delay. *A son of Nahor.*
TERESH, severe, austere, *Esth.* 2. 21; 6. 2.
TERTIUS, third, *i.e.*, son.
TERTULLUS, third, diminutive.
THADDÆUS, praise of God. *The same as* Judah, *Matt.* 10. 3; *Mark* 3. 18.
THAHASH, badger. *The skin of this animal was used to cover the tabernacle, and it is rather uncertain whether it referred to the seal or badger.* Gen. 22. 24.
THAMAH, TAMAH, laughing, *i.e.*, joy of parents, *Ezra* 2. 53; *Neh.* 7. 55.
THARSHISH, *vid.* **TARSHISH**.
THEBEZ, brightness. *A town of Shechem.*
THELASAR, giver of treasure, 2 *Kings* 19. 12; *Isa.* 37. 12.
THEOPHILUS, lover of God.
THESSALONICA, victory of Thessalos.
THEUDAS, praise. *Some suppose it a contraction of the Greek name Theodorus*, the gift of God (*Acts* 5. 36).
THOMAS twin, in the Hebrew, and also called *Didymus* in the Greek, which is of the same signification.
THYATIRA.
TIBERIAS, a city built by Herod in honour of Tiberius Cæsar.
TIBERIUS, an Emperor of Rome, *Luke* 3. 1.
TIBHATH, security, *i.e.*, dwelling in safety, 1 *Chron.* 18. 8.
TIBNI, building of the Lord.
TIDAL, fear, reverence, *Gen* 14. 1, 9.
TIGLATH-PILESER, mother of the gods.

	insulin (regular)	isoproterenol	lactated Ringer's	lidocaine	methylprednisolone sodium succinate	mezlocillin	midazolam	morphine sulfate	nafcillin	norepinephrine	normal saline solution	ondansetron	oxacillin	oxytocin	penicillin G potassium	phenylephrine	phenytoin	phytonadione	piperacillin	potassium chloride	procainamide	ranitidine	sodium bicarbonate	ticarcillin	tobramycin	vancomycin	verapamil
acyclovir			4		4			4	4				4		4				4	4		4	4	4	4	4	
albumin																											
amikacin			24				24	4		24	24	4	8		8			24		4		24	24			24	24
aminophylline			24	24	?				24		24									4		24	24				
amiodarone	24	24		24			24	24		24	24				4	24				24	24				4	4	24
ampicillin	2							4			8							3		4		?	?			?	
calcium gluconate			24	24			24				24									4					1		48
cefazolin	2		24				24	4			24	4										?				?	24
cefoxitin	24		24					4			24	4											24		24		24
ceftazidime								4			24	4										?	6				
cimetidine	24	24		24	24		24				48	4			24			24		24						24	24
ciprofloxacin			48	24			24												24	24		24			24		24
clindamycin			24		24		24	4			24	4			24				48	24		?	24		48		24
dexamethasone sodium phosphate								4				4								4		24	4				24
dextrose 5% in water (D_5W)		24		24	?	24			24	24		48	6	6	24				24	24	24	48	24	24	24	24	24
D_5W in lactated Ringer's		24		24									24		24					24							24
D_5W in normal saline solution		24		24	?				24			48	?		24				24	24			24		48		24
diazepam																						?					24
diphenhydramine							4	¼				4			24					4		1					
dobutamine		24	24	24			4	4		24	24					24				?	24	48					24
dopamine			48	24	18		4	4			48		24							24		48					24
epinephrine			24				4	4		4	24							3		4		24					24
erythromycin lactobionate			18				24	4			22											24	24				24
esmolol			24				24	8	24	24	24				24		24		24	24		24			24	24	24
gentamicin	2		24				24	1			24	4			1							24					24
heparin sodium	2	24		24	?		24	1				4	4	4	?			4	6	24	4	24	24	6			24
hydrocortisone sodium succinate	4	4	24		?			4			24	4	4					4	24		4		24				24
insulin (regular)				24			24	1						2						4		24	3	2	2	2	48
isoproterenol			24								24											24					24
lactated Ringer's		24		24	?	72			24				24		24				24	24				24	24		24
lidocaine	24		24					4	48		24										24	24	24				48
methylprednisolone sodium succinate			?				24	4			?				24					?		48	2				24
mezlocillin			72								48																
midazolam	24				24			24		24		24							24	24					24	24	
morphine sulfate	1			4	4		24		4	4		4	4	1	4				4	4		1	3	4	1	4	24
nafcillin			24	48				4			24									24			24				
norepinephrine							24	4			24											4					24
normal saline solution		24		24	?	48			24	24		48	24		24				24	24	24	48	24	24	48	24	24
ondansetron							24	4			48									4		4		4		4	
oxacillin			24					4			24																
oxytocin	2							1												4			24				24
penicillin G potassium			24		24			4			24											24					24
phenylephrine																				24			24				
phenytoin																							24				48
phytonadione																				4			24				
piperacillin			24				24	4			24									24		4					24
potassium chloride	4		24		?		24	4	24		24	4		4		24		4	24		4	48	24				24
procainamide				24							24									4		24					48
ranitidine	24	24		24	48			1		4	48	4			24				4	48	24			24	24	24	
sodium bicarbonate	3			24	2			3	24		24			24		24	24	24		24							
ticarcillin	2		24								24	4										24					24
tobramycin	2		24				24	1			48											24					24
vancomycin	2						24	4			24	4										24					24
verapamil	48	24	24	48	24			24		24	24			24	24		48		24	24	48			24	24	24	

Springhouse Nurse's Drug Guide 2008

NINTH EDITION

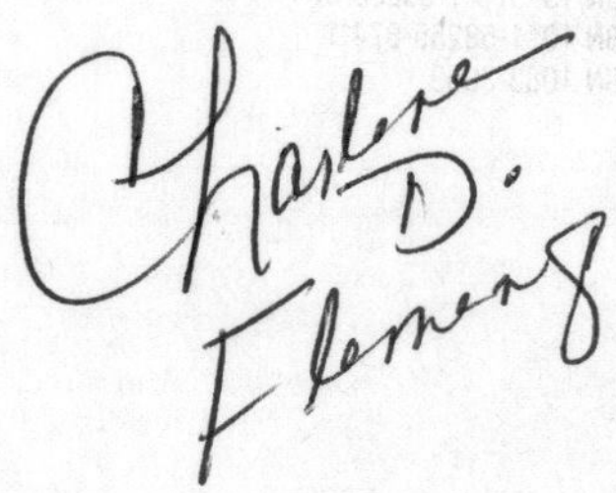

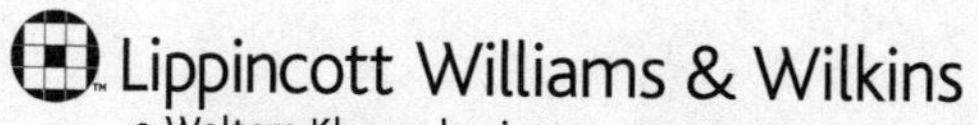

Philadelphia • Baltimore • New York • London
Buenos Aires • Hong Kong • Sydney • Tokyo

Staff

The clinical procedures described and recommended in this publication are based on research and consultation with nursing, medical, pharmaceutical, and legal authorities. To the best of our knowledge, these procedures reflect currently accepted practice; nevertheless, they can't be considered absolute and universal recommendations. For individual application, all recommendations must be considered in light of the patient's clinical condition and, before the administration of new or infrequently used drugs, in light of the latest package-insert information. The authors and publisher disclaim responsibility for adverse effects resulting directly or indirectly from the suggested procedures, from undetected errors, or from the reader's misunderstanding of the text.

Visit our Web site at eDrugInfo.com

SNDG08010607
ISBN 13: 978-1-58255-674-1
ISBN 10: 1-58255-674-1
ISSN 1088-8063

Contents

Contributors and consultants

At the time of publication, the contributors and consultants held the following positions.

Lawrence Carey, PharmD
Assistant Professor, Academic Coordinator
Philadelphia University

Cathy Conner, ADN
Practical Nurse Instructor
Concorde Career Institute
Jacksonville, Fla.

Margaret Marie Dean, RN, MSN, CS, GNP
Instructor
West Texas A&M University
Canyon, Tex.

MaryAnn Edelman, MS, CNS, RN
Assistant Professor, Department of Nursing
Kingsborough Community College
Brooklyn, N.Y.

Tatyana Gurvich, PharmD
Clinical Pharmacologist
Glendale (Calif.) Adventist Family Practice Residency Program

Debra A. Henn, PharmD
Clinical Pharmacist
Crozier-Chester Medical Center
Upland, Pa.

Catherine A. Heyneman, PharmD, MS, CGP, ANP, FASCP
Associate Professor of Pharmacy Practice
Idaho State University College of Pharmacy
Pocatello

Suzanne Igbokwe, PharmD
Drug Information Specialist, Clinical Pharmacist
AstraZeneca
Wilmington, Del.

Fiona Johnson, RN, MSN, CCRN
Clinical Education Specialist, Clinical Education and Per Diem CCU/CVICU
Memorial Health University Medical Center
Savannah, Ga.

Michelle Kosich, PharmD
Clinical Pharmacist
Mercy Fitzgerald Hospital
Darby, Pa.

Christine K. O'Neil, PharmD, BCPS, CGP
Associate Professor
Duquesne University
Mylan School of Pharmacy
Pittsburgh

Priti N. Patel, PharmD, BCPS
Assistant Clinical Professor
Director, St. John's University Drug Information Center
Queens, N.Y.

Dawn Pollitt, PharmD
Pharmacist
Medco Health Solutions
Willingboro, N.J.

Susan W. Sard, PharmD
Clinical Coordinator
Anne Arundel Medical Center
Annapolis, Md.

Karen Zulkowski, DNS, RN, CWS
Associate Professor
Montana State University-Bozeman
Billings

Foreword

As a nurse practitioner and nursing professor teaching pharmacology, I understand the daunting task of delivering safe, effective care to patients receiving drug therapy. Drug administration isn't as easy as handing the patient a pill, drawing up intramuscular or subcutaneous injections, or hanging the I.V. piggyback correctly. Psychomotor skills are just the beginning. Every nurse has the responsibility to assess drug effects, help patients understand and manage their drug therapy, and identify possible adverse effects as quickly and accurately as possible.

How do you remember this enormous volume of information? Simply put, it's impossible. Does that relieve you of your responsibility? Of course not! That's why you need a great drug reference, a reference that's reliable, concise, comprehensive, nursing-focused—and easy to use and understand. I believe that *Springhouse Nurse's Drug Guide 2008* is just such a reference. Whether you're a student nurse, a new graduate, or an experienced practicing nurse, this book will help you deliver safe, effective nursing care to patients receiving drug therapy.

In this 2008 edition, you'll find new classifications in the drug classifications chapter, 18 new drug monographs, and dozens of new indications and warnings. Drug monographs have been updated to present new off-label uses, dosing parameters, adverse effects, and nursing implications.

The book starts with a section of helpful hints for making the most of this book's special features. Next is a list of the abbreviations used throughout the book. And then you'll find a set of four chapters that concisely reviews drug therapy and the nursing process, essential dosage calculations, routes of administration, and safety tips to help you avoid medication errors.

The next section describes 45 classes of drugs with examples, a prototype for each class, and administration information that applies to the entire class. Individual drug monographs are listed alphabetically by generic name. Each monograph describes the drug's indications and dosages; I.V. administration and incompatibilities, if applicable; contraindications and cautions; lifespan considerations; adverse reactions; interactions with drugs, herbs, foods, and lifestyle; effects on lab test results; pharmacokinetics; onset, peak, and duration; the drug's chemical and therapeutic action; and its available forms. In addition, each monograph uses the nursing process to review assessment, nursing diagnoses, planning and implementation, patient teaching, and evaluation. It's also one of the few drug guides that presents the onset and duration of action of a particular drug. I use that information to determine when the patient should have an effect from the drug and to anticipate when the next dose may be needed. Make sure to look for the handy color logos that highlight dosage adjustment, lifespan, and incompatibility information. An "alert" logo calls attention to especially important nursing practice information.

The photoguide to tablets and capsules provides pictures of common drugs in their actual size and color. In my experience, many patients remember the name of their medication but not the dose. Using this convenient photoguide can help you identify a drug with certainty.

The excellent section on herbal medicines offers key information to help you counsel patients about the risks and effects of these products. It includes reported uses, preparations and amounts, cautions, potential adverse reactions, action and components, common forms, nursing considerations, and patient teaching.

The appendices offer an abundance of useful information including a new appendix on dietary teaching for drug therapy. The section also includes a glossary, pregnancy risk categories, controlled substance schedules, and appendices reviewing combination drug products, toxic drug–drug interactions, common miscommunications in drug orders, dialyzable drugs, herb–drug interactions, dietary teaching for drug therapy, equivalents and conversions, drugs that shouldn't be crushed, normal laboratory test values, adverse reactions misinterpreted as age-related changes, and an English-to-Spanish drug phrase translator.

In addition to this great text, *Springhouse Nurse's Drug Guide 2008* includes the mini-CD *PharmDisk 2008* that contains review questions for an NCLEX-style test. This is the book for you. Whether you're a novice or expert, you'll find exactly what you need.

Samantha Venable, RN, MS, FNP

How to use Springhouse Nurse's Drug Guide 2008

Springhouse Nurse's Drug Guide 2008 is the premier drug reference for all nursing students—beginning to advanced. Tightly organized entries offer consistent, practical drug information for more than 750 common generic drugs, presented in a clear writing style that beginning students can understand. The book is also a must-have for advanced students: it includes comprehensive pharmacokinetic and pharmacodynamic information and route-onset-peak-duration tables that give a clear understanding of drug actions. Because each entry also follows the nursing process, the book even helps students formulate accurate care plans. Students of all levels will find that *Springhouse Nurse's Drug Guide 2008* offers a comprehensive and convenient resource.

The book begins with introductory material crucial to safe, accurate drug administration. Chapter 1 discusses drug therapy as it relates to the nursing process. Chapter 2 explains how to calculate dosages and provides examples for each step in the calculations. Chapter 3 discusses how to give drugs by common routes and includes illustrations to guide students through the steps of each procedure. Chapter 4 focuses on common medication errors and explains how to avoid them.

Drug classifications

Springhouse Nurse's Drug Guide 2008 provides complete overviews of 40 pharmacologic and therapeutic drug classifications, from alkylating drugs to xanthine derivatives. After each class name is an alphabetical list of drugs in that class; the drug highlighted in color represents the prototype drug for the class. Each class entry has specific information on indications, actions, adverse reactions, contraindications, and precautions. Look for the special Lifespan logo (☗) for contraindications and cautions for specific populations, such as children, pregnant and breast-feeding women, and elderly patients.

Alphabetical listing of drugs

Drug entries appear alphabetically by generic name for quick reference. The generic name is followed by a pronunciation guide and an alphabetical list of brand (trade) names. Brands that don't need a prescription are designated with a dagger (†); those available only in Canada with a closed diamond (♦); those available only in Australia with an open diamond (◊); and those that contain alcohol with an asterisk (*). A trade name may also have a capsule (💊), meaning that the drug appears in the full-color photoguide. The mention of a brand name in no way implies endorsement of that product or guarantees its legality.

Each entry then identifies the drug's pharmacologic (chemical category) and therapeutic (main use) classes. Seeing both classes helps you grasp the multiple, varying, and sometimes overlapping uses of drugs within a single pharmacologic class and among different classes. Each entry then lists the drug's pregnancy risk category and, if appropriate, its controlled substance schedule.

Indications and dosages

The next section lists the drug's indications and provides dosage information for adults, children, and elderly patients. Off-label indications (uses not approved by the FDA) are designated with a double dagger (‡). Because the double dagger now appears in color, off-label indications are easier than ever to find. Dosage instructions reflect current trends in therapeutics but can't be considered absolute or universal. For your patient, dosage instructions must be considered in light of his condition.

When giving a drug to a patient who needs special dosage considerations, look for the Adjust-a-Dose label and logo (⍂) at the end of the indication.

I.V. administration

This section, only found in drugs that can be given I.V., addresses preparation, administration, and storage information, as well as cautions and other information about the safe use of I.V. drugs. A special section highlighted with a logo (⊗) lists incompatibilities in I.V. administration.

Contraindications and cautions

This section specifies situations in which the drug shouldn't be used and details recommendations for cautious use. The Lifespan logo (☀) draws your attention to contraindications and cautions for special populations, such as children, pregnant or breast-feeding women, and elderly patients.

Adverse reactions

This section lists adverse reactions by body system. The most common adverse reactions (those experienced by at least 10% of people taking the drug in clinical trials) are in *italic* type; less common reactions are in roman type; life-threatening reactions are in ***bold italic*** type; and reactions that are common *and* life-threatening are in BOLD CAPITAL letters.

Interactions

This section lists confirmed, significant interactions with other drugs (added, increased, or decreased effects), herbs, foods, and lifestyle behaviors (such as alcohol use and smoking).

Drug interactions are listed under the drug that is adversely affected. For example, antacids that contain magnesium may decrease absorption of tetracycline so this interaction is listed under tetracycline. To determine the possible effects of using two or more drugs simultaneously, check the interactions section for each of the drugs in question.

Drugs that cause interactions that arise quickly and require immediate attention, called rapid-onset interactions, are shown in color.

Effects on lab test results

This section lists increased and decreased levels, counts, false results, and other laboratory test results that may be affected by the drug.

Pharmacokinetics

This section describes absorption, distribution, metabolism, and excretion, along with the drug's half-life. It also provides a quick reference table highlighting onset, peak, and duration for each route of administration. Values for half-life, onset, peak, and duration are for patients with normal renal function, unless specified otherwise.

Action

This section explains the drug's chemical and therapeutic actions. For example, although all antihypertensives lower blood pressure, they don't all do so in the same way.

Available forms

This section lists all available preparations for each drug (for example, tablets, capsules, solutions for injection) and all available dosage forms and strengths. As with the brand names discussed above, over-the-counter dosage forms and strengths are marked with a dagger (†); those available only in Canada with a closed diamond (♦); those available only in Australia with an open diamond (◊); and those that contain alcohol with an asterisk (*).

Nursing process

This section uses the nursing process as its organizational framework. It also contains an Alert logo (⚠) to call your attention to vital, need-to-know information or to warn you about a common drug error.

- *Assessment* focuses on observation and monitoring of key patient data, such as vital signs, weight, intake and output, and laboratory values.
- *Nursing diagnoses* represent those most commonly applied to drug therapy. In actual use, nursing diagnoses must be relevant to an individual patient so they may not include the listed examples and may include others not listed.
- *Planning and implementation* offers detailed recommendations for drug administration, including full coverage of P.O., I.M., subcutaneous, and other routes.
- *Patient teaching* focuses on explaining the drug's purpose, promoting compliance, and ensuring proper use and storage of the drug. It also includes instructions for preventing or minimizing adverse reactions.

• *Evaluation* identifies the expected patient outcomes for the listed nursing diagnoses.

Because nursing considerations in this text emphasize drug-specific recommendations, they don't include standard recommendations that apply to all drugs, such as "assess the six rights of drug therapy before administration" or "teach the patient the name, dose, frequency, route, and strength of the prescribed drug."

Photoguide to tablets and capsules

To make drug identification easier and to enhance patient safety, *Springhouse Nurse's Drug Guide 2008* offers a full-color photoguide to the most commonly prescribed tablets and capsules. Shown in their actual sizes, the drugs are arranged alphabetically by generic names. Trade names and the most common dosage strengths are included. Page references appear under each drug name so you can turn quickly to information about the drug.

Herbal medicines

Herbal medicine entries appear alphabetically by name, followed by a phonetic spelling.

Reported uses

This section lists reported uses of herbal medicines. Some of these uses are based on anecdotal claims; other uses have been studied. A listing in this section should not be considered a recommendation; herbal medicines aren't regulated by the FDA.

Preparations and amounts

This section lists the preparation and amounts for each form of the herb according to its reported use. This information has been gathered from the herbal literature, anecdotal reports, and available clinical data. Not all uses have specific information; often, no consensus exists. Amounts shown reflect current trends and shouldn't be considered as recommendations by the publisher.

Cautions

This section lists any condition, especially a disease, in which use of the herbal remedy is undesirable. It also provides recommendations for cautious use, as appropriate.

Adverse reactions

This section lists undesirable effects that may follow use of an herbal supplement. Some of these effects haven't been reported but are theoretically possible, given the chemical composition or action of the herb.

Interactions

This section lists each herb's clinically significant interactions, actual or potential, with other herbs, drugs, foods, and lifestyle choices. Each statement describes the effect of the interaction and then offers a specific suggestion for avoiding the interaction. As with adverse reactions, some interactions have not been proven but are theoretically possible.

Actions and components

This section describes the herb's chemical and therapeutic actions and active components.

Common forms

This section lists the available preparations for each herbal medicine as well as forms and strengths.

Nursing considerations

This section offers helpful information, such as monitoring techniques and methods for the prevention and treatment of adverse reactions. Patient teaching tips that focus on educating the patient about the herb's purpose, preparation, administration, and storage are also included, as are suggestions for promoting patient compliance with the therapeutic regimen and steps the patient can take to prevent or minimize the risk or severity of adverse reactions.

Appendices and index

New to this edition are an appendix on dietary teaching for drug therapy and information on preventing miscommunication in drug orders. The appendices also include a glossary explaining unfamiliar medical words and phrases; a list of combination drug products with dosage forms and strengths, indications, and dosages; a list of toxic drug–drug interactions; a list of dialyzable drugs; a list of herb-drug interactions; a table of equivalents and conversions; a table of adverse reactions that can be misinterpreted as normal changes of aging; a list of drugs that shouldn't be crushed; a list of normal laboratory test values; and an English-to-Spanish translator of common drug-related phrases.

The comprehensive index lists drug classifications, generic drugs, brand names, indications, and herbal medicines included in this book. Drugs that appear in the photoguide are listed in the index with the photoguide page number in **bold**.

PharmDisk 2008

New to *PharmDisk 2008,* is a pharmacology self-test with NCLEX®-style questions, including alternate-format. *PharmDisk 2008* also provides a link to eDrugInfo.com.

eDrugInfo.com

This Web site keeps *Springhouse Nurse's Drug Guide 2008* current by providing the following features:

- updates on new drugs, indications, and warnings
- patient teaching aids on new drugs
- news summaries of pertinent drug information.

The Web site also gives you:

- two QuikTools, *Construct-a-card,* which lets you create custom drug information cards, and *Construct-a-calendar,* which lets you create individualized drug regimen calendars for your patients.
- information on herbs
- links to pharmaceutical companies, government agencies, and other drug information sites
- a bookstore full of nursing books, PDAs, software, and more.

Plus, registering with eDrugInfo.com entitles you to e-mail notifications when new drug updates are posted.

Guide to abbreviations

ACE	angiotensin-converting enzyme
ACT	activated clotting time
ADH	antidiuretic hormone
AIDS	acquired immunodeficiency syndrome
ALT	alanine transaminase
AST	aspartate transaminase
AV	atrioventricular
b.i.d.	twice daily
BPH	benign prostatic hyperplasia
BUN	blood urea nitrogen
C	celsius
cAMP	cyclic adenosine monophosphate
CBC	complete blood count
CK	creatine kinase
CMV	cytomegalovirus
CNS	central nervous system
COMT	catechol-O-methyltransferase
COPD	chronic obstructive pulmonary disease
CPK	creatine phosphokinase
CSF	cerebrospinal fluid
CV	cardiovascular
CYP	cytochrome P-450
DIC	disseminated intravascular coagulation
D_5W	dextrose 5% in water
dl	deciliter
DNA	deoxyribonucleic acid
ECG	electrocardiogram
EEG	electroencephalogram
EENT	eyes, ears, nose, throat
F	Fahrenheit
FDA	Food and Drug Administration
g	gram
G	gauge
GABA	gamma-aminobutyric acid
GFR	glomerular filtration rate
GGT	gamma-glutamyltransferase
GI	gastrointestinal
gtt	drops
GU	genitourinary
G6PD	glucose-6-phosphate dehydrogenase
H_1, H_2	histamine$_1$, histamine$_2$
HDL	high-density lipoprotein
HIV	human immunodeficiency virus
HMG-CoA	3-hydroxy-3-methylglutaryl coenzyme A
hr	hour
ICU	intensive care unit
I.D.	intradermal
I.M.	intramuscular
INR	international normalized ratio
IPPB	intermittent positive-pressure breathing
I.V.	intravenous
kg	kilogram
L	liter
lb	pound
LDH	lactate dehydrogenase
LDL	low-density lipoprotein
M	molar, moles

m^2	square meter
MAO	monoamine oxidase
mcg	microgram
mEq	milliequivalent
mg	milligram
MI	myocardial infarction
min	minute
ml	milliliter
mm^3	cubic millimeter
Na	sodium
NG	nasogastric
NSAID	nonsteroidal anti-inflammatory drug
OTC	over-the-counter
oz	ounce
PABA	para-aminobenzoic acid
$Paco_2$	partial carbon dioxide pressure
Pao_2	partial oxygen pressure
PCA	patient-controlled analgesia
P.O.	by mouth
P.R.	by rectum
p.r.n.	as needed
PT	prothrombin time
PTT	partial thromboplastin time
PVC	premature ventricular contraction
q	every
q.i.d.	four times daily
RBC	red blood cell
RDA	recommended daily allowance
REM	rapid eye movement
RNA	ribonucleic acid
RSV	respiratory syncytial virus
SA	sinoatrial
SubQ	subcutaneous
SIADH	syndrome of inappropriate antidiuretic hormone
S.L.	sublingual
SSRI	selective serotonin reuptake inhibitor
T_3	triiodothyronine
T_4	thyroxine
tbs	tablespoon
t.i.d.	three times daily
tsp	teaspoon
USP	United States Pharmacopeia
UTI	urinary tract infection
WBC	white blood cell
wk	week

1

Drug therapy and the nursing process

Springhouse Nurse's Drug Guide 2008 uses the nursing process as its organizing principle for good reason. The nursing process guides the way that nurses give drugs, ensuring patient safety and medical and legal standards. The process has four parts:

- assessment
- nursing diagnoses
- planning and implementation
- evaluation.

Assessment

Assessment begins with the patient history. After taking the patient's history, perform a thorough physical examination. Also, assess the patient's knowledge and understanding of the drug therapy he's about to receive.

History

When taking a history, investigate the patient's allergies, use of drugs and herbs, medical history, lifestyle and beliefs, and socioeconomic status.

Allergies

Specify drugs and foods to which the patient is allergic. Describe the reaction he has; its situation, time, and setting; and other contributing causes, such as a significant change in eating habits or the use of stimulants, tobacco, alcohol, or illegal drugs. Don't forget to place an allergy label conspicuously on the front of the patient's chart and place an allergy band on the patient.

Drugs and herbs

Take a complete drug history that includes both prescription and over-the-counter drugs. Also find out which herbs the patient takes. Ask the patient why he uses this drug or herb and how much he knows about its purpose. Explore the patient's thoughts and attitudes about drug use to find out if he may have trouble complying with his drug therapy. Note any special procedures the patient will need to perform himself, such as monitoring glucose level or checking heart rate; make sure he can perform them correctly.

After the patient starts taking the drug, discuss with him the effects of therapy to determine whether new symptoms or adverse drug reactions have developed. Also talk about measures the patient has taken to recognize, minimize, or avoid adverse drug reactions or accidental overdose. Ask the patient where medication is stored and what system he uses to help remember to take it as prescribed.

Medical history

Note any chronic disorders the patient has, and record the date of diagnosis, the prescribed treatment, and the name of the prescriber. Careful attention during this part of the history can uncover one of the most important problems with drug therapy: incompatible drug regimens.

Lifestyle and beliefs

Ask about the patient's support systems, marital and childbearing circumstances, attitudes toward health and health care, and daily patterns of activity. These influences all affect patient compliance and, consequently, the patient's care plan.

Also ask about the patient's diet. Certain foods can influence the effectiveness of many drugs. Don't forget to inquire about the patient's use of alcohol, tobacco, caffeine, and illegal drugs, such as marijuana, cocaine, and heroin. Note any substance used and the amount and frequency of use.

Socioeconomic status

Note the patient's age, educational level, occupation, and insurance coverage. These characteristics help determine the plan of care, the likelihood of compliance, and the possible need for financial assistance, counseling, or other social services.

Physical examination

Examine the patient closely for expected drug effects and for adverse reactions. Every drug has a desired effect on one body system, but it also may have one or more undesired effects on that or another body system. For example, chemotherapeutic drugs destroy cancer cells but also affect normal cells. These drugs typically cause hair loss, diarrhea, and nausea. Besides looking for adverse drug effects, investigate whether the patient has any sensory impairments or changes in mental state.

Sensory impairment

Assess the patient for sensory impairments that could influence his care plan. For example, impaired vision or paralysis can hinder the patient's ability to give a subcutaneous injection, break a scored tablet, or open a drug vial. Impaired hearing can prevent a patient from finding out from you all that he needs to know about the drug.

Mental state

Note whether the patient is alert, oriented, and able to interact appropriately. Assess whether he can think clearly and talk properly. Check the patient's short-term and long-term memory, which are both needed to follow the prescribed regimen correctly. Also, determine whether the patient can read and, if he can, at what level.

Understanding drug therapy

A patient is more likely to comply if he understands the reason for drug therapy. During your assessment, evaluate your patient's understanding of the therapy and the reason for it. Pay particular attention to his emotional acceptance of the need for drug therapy. For instance, a young patient being prescribed an antihypertensive may need more education than an older patient to ensure compliance.

Nursing diagnosis

Using the information you gathered during assessment, define drug-related problems by formulating each problem into a relevant nursing diagnosis. The most common problem statements related to drug therapy are "Deficient knowledge," "Ineffective health maintenance," and "Noncompliance." Nursing diagnoses provide the framework for planning interventions and outcome criteria, also known as patient goals.

Planning and implementation

Make sure that your patient goals state the desired patient behaviors or responses that should result from nursing care. Such criteria should be:

- measurable
- objective
- concise
- realistic for the patient
- attainable by nursing interventions.

Express patient behavior in terms of expectations, and specify a time frame. An example of a good outcome statement is "Before discharge, the patient verbalizes major adverse effects related to his chemotherapy."

After developing outcome criteria, determine the interventions needed to help the patient reach the desired goals. Appropriate interventions may include administration procedures and techniques, legal and ethical concerns, patient teaching, and special actions for pregnant, breast-feeding, pediatric, or geriatric patients. Interventions also may be independent nursing actions, such as turning a bedridden patient every 2 hours.

Evaluation

The final piece of the nursing process is a formal and systematic determination of your nursing care's effectiveness. This evaluation lets you determine whether outcome criteria were met so you can make informed decisions about subsequent interventions. If you stated the outcome criteria in measurable terms, you can easily evaluate whether the criteria were met.

For example, if a patient experiences relief from headache pain within 1 hour after receiving an analgesic, the outcome criterion was met. If the headache was the same or worse, the outcome criterion wasn't met. In that case, you need to reassess the patient, which may produce new data that might go against the original nursing diagnosis, new nursing interventions that are more specific or more appropriate for the patient, or a new care plan. This reassessment could lead to a higher dosage, a different analgesic, or the discovery of the underlying cause of the headache pain.

2

Essentials of dosage calculations

Because nurses frequently perform drug and intravenous (I.V.) fluid calculations, it's important to understand how drugs are weighed and measured, how to convert between systems and measures, how to compute drug dosages, and how to make adjustments for children.

Systems of drug weights and measures

Several systems of measurement can be used to determine the proper drug dosage. They include the metric, household, apothecary, and avoirdupois systems.

The metric and household systems are so widely used that most brands of medication cups for liquid measurements are standardized in both systems. The apothecary system isn't widely used but is still encountered in practice. A fourth system, the avoirdupois system, is rarely used. This system uses solid units of measure, such as the ounce and the pound. Also, some special systems of measurement—such as units, international units, and milliequivalents—have been developed by international scientists for standardization and only pertain to particular drugs or biological agents.

Metric system

The metric system is the international system of measurement, the most widely used system, and the system used by the U.S. Pharmacopoeia. This system has units for both liquid and solid measures. Among its many advantages, the metric system enables accuracy in calculating small drug dosages. The metric system uses Arabic numerals, which are commonly used by health care professionals worldwide. And most manufacturers standardize newly developed drugs in the metric system.

Liquid measures

In the metric system, one liter (L) is equal to about 1 quart in the apothecary system. Liters are often used when ordering and administering I.V. solutions. Milliliters are frequently used for parenteral and some oral drugs. One milliliter (ml) equals $\frac{1}{1,000}$ of a liter.

Solid measures

The gram (g) is the basis for solid measures or units of weight in the metric system. One milligram (mg) equals $\frac{1}{1,000}$ of a gram. Drugs are frequently ordered in grams, milligrams, or an even smaller unit, the microgram (mcg), depending on the drug. One microgram equals $\frac{1}{1,000}$ of a milligram. Body weight is usually recorded in kilograms (kg). One kilogram equals 1,000 g.

The following are examples of drug orders using the metric system:

- 30 ml Milk of Magnesia P.O. at bedtime
- 1 g Ancef I.V. q 6 hours
- 0.125 mg Lanoxin P.O. daily.

Household system

Most foods, recipes, over-the-counter drugs, and home remedies use the household system. Health care professionals seldom use this system for drug administration; however, knowledge of household measures may be useful in some home care and patient teaching situations.

Liquid measures

Liquid measurements in the household system include teaspoons (tsp) and tablespoons (tbs). For medical use, these measurements have been standardized to 5 milliliters and 15 milliliters, respectively. Using these standardized amounts, 3 teaspoons equal 1 tablespoon, 6 teaspoons equal 1 ounce, and so forth. Patients who need to measure doses by teaspoon or tablespoon should do so using standardized medical devices to make sure they receive exactly the prescribed amount. Advise patients not to use an ordinary spoon to measure a teaspoonful of a drug because the amount will most likely be inaccurate. Teaspoon sizes vary from 4 to 6 milliliters or more.

The following are examples of drug orders using the household system:

- 2 tsp Bactrim P.O. twice daily

• 2 tbs Riopan P.O. 1 hour before meals and at bedtime.

Apothecary system

Two unique features distinguish the apothecary system from other systems: the use of Roman numerals and the placement of the unit of measurement before the Roman numeral. For example, a measurement of 5 grains would be written as *grains V.*

In the apothecary system, equivalents among the various units of measure are close approximations of one another. By contrast, equivalents in the metric system are exact. When using apothecary equivalents for calculations and conversions, the calculations won't be precise but still must fall within acceptable standards. (See *Imprecision of dosage computations,* page 9.)

The apothecary system is the only system of measurement that uses both symbols and abbreviations to represent units of measure. Although the apothecary system isn't used frequently in health care today, you must still be able to read dosages that have been written in the apothecary system and convert them to the metric system.

Liquid measures

The smallest unit of liquid measurement in the apothecary system is the minim (♏), which is about the size of a drop of water; 15 to 16 minims equal about 1 ml.

Solid measures

The grain (gr) is the smallest solid measure or unit of weight in the apothecary system. It equals about 60 milligrams; 1 dram equals about 60 grains.

The following are examples of drug orders using the apothecary system:

• Robitussin fʒ (fluidrams) IV P.O. every 6 hours

• Mylanta f℥ (fluidounce) I P.O. 1 hour after meals

• Tylenol gr X P.O. every 4 hours as needed for headache.

Units, international units, and milliequivalents

For some drugs, you'll need to use a measuring system developed by drug companies. Three of the most common special systems of measurement are units, international units, and milliequivalents.

Units

Insulin is one of the drugs measured in units. Although many types of insulin exist, all are measured in units. The international standard of U-100 insulin means that 1 ml of insulin solution contains 100 units of insulin, regardless of type. Heparin, an anticoagulant, is also measured in units, as are several antibiotics available in liquid, solid, and powder forms for oral or parenteral use. Each drug company provides specific information about the measurement of its drugs that are measured in units.

The following are examples of drug orders using units:

• Inject 14 units NPH insulin subcutaneously this a.m.

• Heparin 5,000 units subcutaneously q 12 hours

• Nystatin 200,000 units P.O. q 12 hours.

The unit is not a standard measure. Different drugs, although all measured in units, may have no relationship to one another in quality or activity.

Units should never be abbreviated as "U" because of the potential for confusing a "U" with a "0."

International units

International units are used to measure biologicals, such as vitamins, enzymes, and hormones. For instance, the activity of calcitonin, a synthetic hormone used in calcium regulation, is expressed in international units.

The following are examples of drug orders using international units:

• 100 international units calcitonin (salmon) subcutaneously daily

• 8 international units somatropin subcutaneously three times a week.

Milliequivalents

Electrolytes may be measured in milliequivalents (mEq). Drug companies provide information about the number of metric units needed to provide a prescribed number of milliequivalents. Potassium chloride (KCl), for example, is usually ordered in milliequivalents.

The following are examples of drug orders using milliequivalents:

• 30 mEq KCl P.O. b.i.d.

• 1 L dextrose 5% in normal saline solution with 40 mEq KCl to be run at 125 ml/hour.

Conversions between measurement systems

You may need to convert from one measurement system to another, particularly when a drug is ordered in one system but only available in another. To perform conversion calculations, you need to know the equivalent measurements for the different systems. One of the most commonly used methods for converting drug measurements is the fraction method.

Fraction method

The fraction method for converting between measurement systems involves an equation consisting of two fractions. Set up the first fraction by placing the ordered dosage over an unknown number of units of the available dosage.

For example, say a prescriber orders 7.5 ml of acetaminophen elixir to be given by mouth. To find the equivalent in teaspoons, first set up a fraction in which the top of the fraction (numerator) represents the ordered dosage in milliliters and the bottom of the fraction (denominator) represents the unknown (x) number of teaspoons:

$$\frac{7.5 \text{ ml}}{x \text{ tsp}}$$

Then, set up the second fraction, which appears on the right side of the equation. This fraction consists of the standard equivalents between the ordered (ml) and the available (tsp) measures. Because milliliters must be converted to teaspoons, the right side of the equation appears as follows:

$$\frac{5 \text{ ml}}{1 \text{ tsp}}$$

The same unit of measure should appear in the numerator of both fractions. Likewise, the same unit of measure should appear in both denominators. The entire equation should appear as:

$$\frac{7.5 \text{ ml}}{x \text{ tsp}} = \frac{5 \text{ ml}}{1 \text{ tsp}}$$

To solve for x, cross multiply:

$$x \text{ tsp} \times 5 \text{ ml} = 7.5 \text{ ml} \times 1 \text{ tsp}$$

$$x \text{ tsp} = \frac{7.5 \text{ ml} \times 1 \text{ tsp}}{5 \cancel{\text{ml}}}$$

$$x \text{ tsp} = \frac{7.5 \times 1 \text{ tsp}}{5}$$

$$x \text{ tsp} = 1.5 \text{ tsp}$$

The patient should receive 1.5 teaspoons of acetaminophen elixir.

Computing drug dosages

Computing drug dosages is a two-step process that you complete after verifying the drug order. Determine whether the ordered drug is available in units in the same system of measurement in which the order was written. If not, convert the measurement for the ordered drug to the system used for the available drug.

If the ordered units of measurement are available, calculate how much of the available dosage form should be given. For example, if the prescribed dose is 250 mg, determine the quantity of tablets, powder, or liquid that would equal 250 mg. To determine that quantity, use one of the methods described below.

Fraction method

When using the fraction method to compute a drug dosage, write an equation consisting of two fractions. First, set up a fraction showing the number of units to be given over x, which represents the quantity of the dosage form you are trying to find. In this case, this dosage form is tablets (tab).

For example, if the number of units to be administered equals 250 mg, the first fraction in the equation would appear as:

$$\frac{250 \text{ mg}}{x \text{ tab}}$$

On the other side of the equation, set up a fraction showing the number of units of the drug in its dosage form over the quantity of dosage forms that supply that number of units. The number of units and the quantity of dosage forms are specific for each drug. In most cases, the stated quantity equals 1. You can find all of the information for the second fraction on the drug label.

The drug label states that each tablet contains 125 mg, so the second fraction would appear as:

$$\frac{125 \text{ mg}}{1 \text{ tab}}$$

Note that in the two equations, the numerator units are the same (mg) and the denominator units are the same (tab).

The entire equation would appear as:

$$\frac{250 \text{ mg}}{x \text{ tab}} = \frac{125 \text{ mg}}{1 \text{ tab}}$$

Solving for x by cross-multiplying determines the quantity of the dosage form—2 tablets, in this example.

Ratio method

To use the ratio method, write the amount of the drug to be given and the x quantity of the dosage form as a ratio. Using the example above, you would write:

$$250 \text{ mg} : x \text{ tab}$$

Next, complete the equation by forming a second ratio from the number of units in each tablet. The drug label provides this information. The entire equation is:

$$250 \text{ mg} : x \text{ tab} :: 125 \text{ mg} : 1 \text{ tab}$$

Solve for x by multiplying the inner portions (means) and outer portions (extremes) of the equation. The patient should receive 2 tablets.

Desired-available method

You can also use the desired-available method, also known as the dose-over-on hand (D/H) method. This method converts ordered units into available units and computes the drug dosage all in one step. The desired-available equation appears as:

$$\begin{array}{c} x \\ \text{quantity} \\ \text{to give} \end{array} = \frac{\begin{array}{c}\text{ordered} \\ \text{units}\end{array}}{1} \times \begin{array}{c}\text{conversion} \\ \text{fraction}\end{array} \times \frac{\begin{array}{c}\text{quantity} \\ \text{of dosage} \\ \text{form}\end{array}}{\begin{array}{c}\text{stated} \\ \text{quantity of} \\ \text{drug within} \\ \text{each dosage} \\ \text{form}\end{array}}$$

For example, say you receive an order for grains (gr) X of a drug. The drug is available only in 300-mg tablets. To determine what number of tablets to give the patient, substitute gr X (the ordered number of units) for the first element of the equation. Then use the conversion fraction as the second portion of the formula. The conversion factor is:

$$\frac{60 \text{ mg}}{\text{gr I}}$$

The measure in the denominator must be the same as the measure in the ordered units. In this case, the order specified gr X. As a result, grains will appear in the denominator of the conversion fraction.

The third element of the equation shows the dosage form over the stated drug quantity for that dosage form. Because the drug is available in 300-mg tablets, the fraction appears as:

$$\frac{1 \text{ tab}}{300 \text{ mg}}$$

The dosage form should always appear in the numerator, and the quantity of drug in each dosage form should always appear in the denominator. The completed equation is:

$$x \text{ tab} = \text{gr X} \times \frac{60 \text{ mg}}{\text{gr I}} \times \frac{1 \text{ tab}}{300 \text{ mg}}$$

Solving for x shows that the patient should receive 2 tablets.

The desired-available method has the advantage of using only one equation. However, you need to memorize an equation more elaborate than the one used in the fraction method or the ratio method. Relying on your memorization of a more complicated equation may increase the chance of error.

Dimensional analysis

A variation of the ratio method, dimensional analysis (also known as factor analysis or factor labeling) eliminates the need to memorize formulas and requires only one equation. To compare the two methods at a glance, read the following problem and solutions, and then read the paragraphs that follow for a detailed explanation.

Say the prescriber orders 0.25 g of streptomycin sulfate I.M. The vial reads 2 ml = 1 g. How many milliliters should you give?

Dimensional analysis

$$\frac{0.25 \text{ g}}{1} \times \frac{2 \text{ ml}}{1 \text{ g}} = 0.5 \text{ ml}$$

Ratio method

$$1 \text{ g} : 2 \text{ ml} :: 0.25 \text{ g} : x \text{ ml}$$

$$x = 2 \times 0.25$$

$$x = 0.5 \text{ ml}$$

Explanation

When using dimensional analysis you arrange a series of ratios, called factors, in a single (although sometimes lengthy) fractional equation. Each factor, written as a fraction, consists of two quantities and their related units of measurement. For instance, if 1,000 ml of a drug should be given over 8 hours, the relationship between the dose and time is expressed by the fraction:

$$\frac{1{,}000\text{ ml}}{8\text{ hr}}$$

When a problem includes a quantity or a unit of measurement that doesn't have an equivalent in the problem, these numbers appear in the numerator of the fraction, and 1 becomes the denominator. In the problem and solutions above, 0.25 g is such a number.

Some mathematical problems contain all the information you need to identify the factors, set up the equation, and find the solution. Other problems require you to use a conversion factor. Conversion factors are equivalents (for example, 1 g = 1,000 mg) that you can memorize or get from a conversion chart. Because the two quantities and units of measurement are equivalent, they can serve as the numerator or the denominator; thus, the conversion factor 1 g = 1,000 mg can be written in fraction form as:

$$\frac{1{,}000\text{ mg}}{1\text{ g}} \text{ or } \frac{1\text{ g}}{1{,}000\text{ mg}}$$

The factors given in the problem, plus any conversion factors needed to solve the problem, are called *knowns*. The quantity of the answer, of course, is the *unknown*. When setting up an equation in dimensional analysis, work backward, beginning with the unit of measurement of the answer. After plotting all the knowns, find the solution by following this sequence:

- Cancel similar quantities and units of measurement.
- Multiply the numerators.
- Multiply the denominators.
- Divide the numerator by the denominator.

Mastering dimensional analysis can take practice, but it will be well worth it. To understand more fully how dimensional analysis works, review the following problem and the steps taken to solve it.

A prescriber orders grains X of a drug. The pharmacy supplies the drug in 300-mg tablets (tab). How many tablets should you administer?

- Write down the unit of measurement of the answer, followed by an "equal to" symbol:

$$\text{tab} =$$

- Search the problem for the quantity with the same unit of measurement (if one doesn't exist, use a conversion factor); place this in the numerator and its related quantity and unit of measurement in the denominator:

$$\text{tab} = \frac{1\text{ tab}}{300\text{ mg}}$$

- Separate the first factor from the next with a multiplication symbol:

$$\text{tab} = \frac{1\text{ tab}}{300\text{ mg}} \times$$

- Place the unit of measurement of the first factor's denominator in the second factor's numerator. Then search the problem for the quantity with the same unit of measurement (if one doesn't exist, as in this example, use a conversion factor); place this in the numerator and its related quantity and unit of measurement in the denominator, and follow the fraction with a multiplication symbol. Repeat this step until all known factors are included in the equation:

$$\text{tab} = \frac{1\text{ tab}}{300\text{ mg}} \times \frac{60\text{ mg}}{\text{gr I}} \times \frac{\text{gr X}}{1}$$

- Treat the equation as a large fraction. First, cancel similar units of measurement in the numerator and the denominator. What remains should be what you began with: the unit of measurement of the answer. If not, check your equation to find and correct the error. Next, multiply the numerators and then the denominators. Finally, divide the numerator by the denominator:

$$\text{tab} = \frac{1\text{ tab}}{300\text{ }\cancel{\text{mg}}} \times \frac{60\text{ }\cancel{\text{mg}}}{\cancel{\text{gr}}\text{ I}} \times \frac{\cancel{\text{gr}}\text{ X}}{1}$$

$$= \frac{60 \times 10\text{ tab}}{300}$$

$$= \frac{600\text{ tab}}{300}$$

$$= 2\text{ tab}$$

For more practice, study the following examples, which use dimensional analysis to solve various mathematical problems common to dosage calculations and drug administration.

1. A patient weighs 140 lb. What is his weight in kilograms (kg)?

$$\text{1st factor (conversion factor): } \frac{1 \text{ kg}}{2.2 \text{ lb}}$$

$$\text{2nd factor: } \frac{140 \text{ lb}}{1}$$

$$\text{kg} = \frac{1 \text{ kg}}{2.2 \cancel{\text{lb}}} \times 140 \cancel{\text{lb}}$$

$$= \frac{140}{2.2}$$

$$= 63.6 \text{ kg}$$

2. A physician prescribes 75 mg of a drug. The pharmacy stocks a multidose vial containing 100 mg/ml. How many milliliters should you give?

$$\text{1st factor: } \frac{1 \text{ ml}}{100 \text{ mg}}$$

$$\text{2nd factor: } \frac{75 \text{ mg}}{1}$$

$$\text{ml} = \frac{1 \text{ ml}}{100 \cancel{\text{mg}}} \times \frac{75 \cancel{\text{mg}}}{1}$$

$$= 0.75 \text{ ml}$$

3. A nurse practitioner prescribes 1 tsp of a cough elixir. The pharmacist sends up a bottle whose label reads 1 ml = 50 mg. How many milligrams should you give?

$$\text{1st factor: } \frac{50 \text{ mg}}{1 \text{ ml}}$$

$$\text{2nd factor (conversion factor): } \frac{5 \text{ ml}}{1 \text{ tsp}}$$

$$\text{3rd factor: } \frac{1 \text{ tsp}}{1}$$

$$\text{mg} = \frac{50 \text{ mg}}{1 \text{ ml}} \times \frac{5 \cancel{\text{ml}}}{1 \cancel{\text{tsp}}} \times \frac{1 \cancel{\text{tsp}}}{1}$$

$$= 50 \text{ mg} \times 5$$

$$= 250 \text{ mg}$$

4. A physician prescribes 1,000 ml of an I.V. solution to be given over 8 hours. The I.V. tubing delivers 15 drops (gtt)/ml/minute. What is the infusion rate in gtt/minute?

$$\text{1st factor: } \frac{15 \text{ gtt}}{1 \text{ ml}}$$

$$\text{2nd factor: } \frac{1{,}000 \text{ ml}}{8 \text{ hr}}$$

$$\text{3rd factor (conversion factor): } \frac{1 \text{ hr}}{60 \text{ min}}$$

$$\text{gtt/minute} = \frac{15 \text{ gtt}}{1 \cancel{\text{ml}}} \times \frac{1{,}000 \cancel{\text{ml}}}{8 \cancel{\text{hr}}} \times \frac{1 \cancel{\text{hr}}}{60 \text{ min}}$$

$$= \frac{15 \text{ gtt} \times 1{,}000 \times 1}{8 \times 60 \text{ min}}$$

$$= \frac{15{,}000 \text{ gtt}}{480 \text{ min}}$$

$$= 31.3 \text{ or } 31 \text{ gtt/min}$$

5. A physician prescribes 10,000 units of heparin added to 500 ml of 5% dextrose and water at 1,200 units/hour. How many drops per minute should you give if the I.V. tubing delivers 10 gtt/ml?

$$\text{1st factor: } \frac{10 \text{ gtt}}{1 \text{ ml}}$$

$$\text{2nd factor: } \frac{500 \text{ ml}}{10{,}000 \text{ units}}$$

$$\text{3rd factor: } \frac{1{,}200 \text{ units}}{1 \text{ hr}}$$

$$\text{4th factor (conversion factor): } \frac{1 \text{ hr}}{60 \text{ min}}$$

$$\frac{\text{gtt/}}{\text{minute}} = \frac{10 \text{ gtt}}{1 \cancel{\text{ml}}} \times \frac{500 \cancel{\text{ml}}}{10{,}000 \cancel{\text{units}}} \times \frac{1{,}200 \cancel{\text{units}}}{1 \cancel{\text{hr}}} \times \frac{1 \cancel{\text{hr}}}{60 \text{ min}}$$

$$= \frac{10 \times 500 \times 1{,}200 \text{ gtt}}{10{,}000 \times 60 \text{ min}}$$

$$= \frac{6{,}000{,}000 \text{ gtt}}{600{,}000 \text{ min}}$$

$$= 10 \text{ gtt/min}$$

Special computations

The fraction, ratio, and desired-available methods, as well as dimensional analysis, can be used to compute drug dosages when the ordered drug and the available form of the drug occur in the same units of measure. These methods can also be used when the availability of a particular dosage form differs from the units in which the dosage form is given.

For example, if a patient is to receive 1,000 mg of a drug available in liquid form and measured in milligrams, with 100 mg contained in 6 ml, how many milliliters should the patient receive? Because the ordered and the available dosages are in milligrams, no initial conversions are needed. The fraction method would be used to determine the number of milliliters the patient should receive, in this case, 60 ml.

Because the drug will be given in ounces (oz), the number of ounces should be determined using a conversion method. For the fraction method of conversion, the equation would appear as:

$$\frac{60\text{ ml}}{x\text{ oz}} = \frac{30\text{ ml}}{1\text{ oz}}$$

Solving for x shows that the patient should receive 2 oz of the drug.

To use the desired-available method, change the order of the elements in the equation to correspond with the situation. The revised equation should appear as:

$$x\text{ quantity to give} = \frac{\text{ordered units}}{1} \times \frac{\text{quantity of dosage form}}{\text{stated quantity of drug within each dosage form}} \times \text{conversion fraction}$$

Placing the given information into the equation results in:

$$x\text{ oz} = \frac{1{,}000\text{ mg}}{1} \times \frac{6\text{ ml}}{100\text{ mg}} \times \frac{1\text{ oz}}{30\text{ ml}}$$

Solving for x shows that the patient should receive 2 oz of the drug.

Imprecision of dosage computations

Converting drug measurements from one system to another and then determining the amount of a dosage to give can easily produce inexact dosages. A rounding error made during computation or discrepancies in the dosage may occur, depending on the conversion standard used in calculation. Or, you may determine a precise amount to be given, only to find that giving that amount is impossible. For example, precise computations may indicate that a patient should receive 0.97 tablets. Giving such an amount is impossible.

The following rule helps avoid calculation errors and discrepancies between theoretical and real dosages: No more than a 10% variation should exist between the dosage ordered and the dosage to be given. For example, if you determine that a patient should receive 0.97 tablets, you can safely give 1 tablet. If your calculations don't give you a clear answer, notify the prescriber and request an equivalent dosage in the form you have available.

Computing parenteral dosages

The methods for computing drug dosages can be used not just for oral but also for parenteral routes. The following example shows how to determine a parenteral drug dosage. Say a prescriber orders 75 mg of Demerol. The package label reads: meperidine (Demerol), 100 mg/ml. By using the fraction method to determine the number of milliliters the patient should receive, your equation should look like this:

$$\frac{75\text{ mg}}{x\text{ ml}} = \frac{100\text{ mg}}{1\text{ ml}}$$

To solve for x, cross multiply:

$$x\text{ ml} \times 100\text{ mg} = 75\text{ mg} \times 1\text{ ml}$$

$$x\text{ ml} = \frac{75\ \cancel{\text{mg}} \times 1\text{ ml}}{100\ \cancel{\text{mg}}}$$

$$x\text{ ml} = \frac{75\text{ ml}}{100}$$

$$x\text{ ml} = 0.75\text{ ml}$$

The patient should receive 0.75 ml.

Reconstituting powders for injection

Although a pharmacist usually reconstitutes powders for parenteral use, nurses sometimes perform this function by following the directions on the drug label. The label gives the total quantity of drug in the vial or ampule, the amount and type of diluent to be added to the powder, and the strength and expiration date of the resulting solution.

When you add diluent to a powder, the powder increases the fluid volume. That's why the label calls for less diluent than the total volume of the prepared solution. For example, a label may tell you to add 1.7 ml of diluent to a vial of powdered drug to obtain a 2-ml total volume of prepared solution.

To determine the amount of solution to give, use the manufacturer's information about the concentration of the solution. For example, if you want to give 500 mg of a drug and the concentration of the prepared solution is 1 g (1,000 mg)/10 ml, use the following equation:

$$\frac{500 \text{ mg}}{x \text{ ml}} = \frac{1{,}000 \text{ mg}}{10 \text{ ml}}$$

The patient would receive 5 ml of the prepared solution.

Intravenous drip rates and flow rates

Make sure you know the difference between I.V. drip and flow rates and also how to calculate each rate. I.V. drip rate refers to the number of drops of solution to be infused per minute. Flow rate refers to the number of milliliters of fluid to be infused over 1 hour.

To calculate an I.V. drip rate, first set up a fraction showing the volume of solution to be delivered over the number of minutes in which that volume should be infused. For example, if a patient should receive 100 ml of solution in 1 hour, the fraction would be written as:

$$\frac{100 \text{ ml}}{60 \text{ min}}$$

Multiply the fraction by the drip factor (the number of drops contained in 1 ml) to determine the number of drops per minute to be infused, or the drip rate. The drip factor varies among different I.V. sets and should appear on the package that contains the I.V. tubing administration set.

Following the manufacturer's directions for drip factor is a crucial step. Standard administration sets have drip factors of 10, 15, or 20 gtt/ml. A microdrip, or minidrip, set has a drip factor of 60 gtt/ml.

Use the following equation to determine the drip rate of an I.V. solution:

$$\text{gtt/min} = \frac{\text{total no. of ml}}{\text{total no. of min}} \times \text{drip factor}$$

The equation applies to I.V. solutions that infuse over many hours or to small-volume infusions such as those used for antibiotics usually given in less than an hour. For example, if an order requires 1,000 ml of 5% dextrose in normal saline solution to infuse over 12 hours and the administration set delivers 15 gtt/ml, what should the drip rate be?

$$x \text{ gtt/min} = \frac{1{,}000 \text{ ml}}{720 \text{ min}} \times 15 \text{ gtt/ml}$$

$$x \text{ gtt/min} = 20.83 \text{ gtt/min}$$

The drip rate would be rounded to 21 gtt per minute.

You'll use flow-rate calculations when working with I.V. infusion pumps to set the number of milliliters to be delivered in an hour. To perform this calculation, you should know the total volume in milliliters to be infused and the amount of time for the infusion. Use the following equation:

$$\text{flow rate} = \frac{\text{total volume ordered}}{\text{number of hours}}$$

Quick methods for calculating drip rates

To give an I.V. solution through a microdrip set, adjust the flow rate (number of milliliters per hour) to equal the drip rate (gtt per minute).

Using this method, the flow rate is divided by 60 minutes and then multiplied by the drip factor, also 60. Because the flow rate and the drip factor are equal, the two arithmetic operations cancel each other out. For example, if 125 ml/hour represented the ordered flow rate, the equation is:

$$\text{drip rate (125)} = \frac{125 \text{ ml}}{60 \text{ min}} \times 60$$

Rather than spending time calculating the equation, you can use the number assigned to the flow rate as the drip rate.

For I.V. administration sets that deliver 15 gtt/ml, the flow rate divided by 4 equals the drip rate. For sets with a drip factor of 10, the flow rate divided by 6 equals the drip rate.

Critical care calculations

Many drugs given on the critical care unit are used to treat life-threatening disorders. You must be able to perform calculations swiftly and accurately, prepare the drug for infusion, give the drug, and then observe the patient closely to evaluate the drug's effectiveness.

Three calculations must be performed before giving critical care drugs:

- Calculate the concentration of the drug in the I.V. solution.

- Figure the flow rate needed to deliver the desired dose.
- Determine the needed dosage.

Calculating concentration

To calculate the drug's concentration, use the following formula:

concentration in mg/ml = mg of drug/ml of fluid

To express the concentration in mcg/ml, multiply the answer by 1,000.

Figuring flow rate

To determine the I.V. flow rate per minute, use the following formula:

$$\frac{\text{dose/min}}{x \text{ ml/min}} = \frac{\text{concentration of solution}}{\text{1 ml of fluid}}$$

To calculate the hourly flow rate, first multiply the ordered dose, given in milligrams or micrograms per minute, by 60 minutes to determine the hourly dose. Then use the following equation to compute the hourly flow rate:

$$\frac{\text{hourly dose}}{x \text{ ml/hr}} = \frac{\text{concentration of solution}}{\text{1 ml of fluid}}$$

Determining dosage

To determine the dosage in mg/kg of body weight/minute, first determine the concentration of the solution in milligrams per milliliter. (If a drug is ordered in micrograms, convert milligrams to micrograms by multiplying by 1,000.) To determine the dose in milligrams per hour, multiply the hourly flow rate by the concentration using the following formula:

$$\begin{array}{c}\text{dose in}\\ \text{mg/hr}\end{array} = \begin{array}{c}\text{hourly}\\ \text{flow rate}\end{array} \times \text{concentration}$$

Then calculate the dose in milligrams per minute. Divide the hourly dose by 60 minutes.

$$\text{dose in mg/min} = \frac{\text{dose in mg/hr}}{\text{60 min}}$$

Divide the dose per minute by the patient's weight, using the following formula:

$$\text{mg/kg/min} = \frac{\text{mg/min}}{\text{patient's weight in kg}}$$

Finally, make sure that the drug is being given within a safe and therapeutic range. Compare the amount in milligrams per kilogram per minute to the safe range shown in this book.

The following examples show how to calculate an I.V. flow rate using the different formulas.

Example 1

A patient has frequent runs of ventricular tachycardia that subside after 10 to 12 beats. The prescriber orders 2 g (2,000 mg) of lidocaine in 500 ml of D_5W to infuse at 2 mg/minute. What's the rate in milliliters per minute? Milliliters per hour?

First, find the concentration of the solution by setting up a proportion with the unknown concentration in one fraction and the ordered dose in the other fraction:

$$\frac{x \text{ mg}}{\text{1 ml}} = \frac{\text{2,000 mg}}{\text{500 ml}}$$

Cross multiply the fractions:

$$x \text{ mg} \times \text{500 ml} = \text{2,000 mg} \times \text{1 ml}$$

Solve for x by dividing each side of the equation by 500 ml and canceling units that appear in both the numerator and denominator:

$$\frac{x \text{ mg} \times \cancel{\text{500 ml}}}{\cancel{\text{500 ml}}} = \frac{\text{2,000 mg} \times 1 \cancel{\text{ml}}}{500 \cancel{\text{ml}}}$$

$$x = \frac{\text{2,000 mg}}{500}$$

$$x = \text{4 mg}$$

The concentration of the solution is 4 mg/ml. Next, calculate the flow rate per minute needed to deliver the ordered dose of 2 mg/minute. To do this, set up a proportion with the unknown flow rate per minute in one fraction and the concentration of the solution in the other fraction:

$$\frac{\text{2 mg}}{x \text{ ml}} = \frac{\text{4 mg}}{\text{1 ml}}$$

Cross multiply the fractions:

$$x \text{ ml} \times \text{4 mg} = \text{1 ml} \times \text{2 mg}$$

Solve for x by dividing each side of the equation by 4 mg and canceling units that appear in both the numerator and denominator:

$$\frac{x \text{ ml} \times \cancel{\text{4 mg}}}{\cancel{\text{4 mg}}} = \frac{\text{1 ml} \times 2 \cancel{\text{mg}}}{4 \cancel{\text{mg}}}$$

$$x = \frac{\text{2 ml}}{4}$$

$$x = \text{0.5 ml}$$

The patient should receive 0.5 ml/minute of lidocaine. Because lidocaine must be given with an infusion pump, compute the hourly flow rate. Set up a proportion with the unknown flow rate per hour in one fraction and the drip rate per minute in the other fraction:

$$\frac{x \text{ ml}}{60 \text{ min}} = \frac{0.5 \text{ ml}}{1 \text{ min}}$$

Cross multiply the fractions:

$$x \text{ ml} \times 1 \text{ min} = 0.5 \text{ ml} \times 60 \text{ min}$$

Solve for x by dividing each side of the equation by 1 minute and canceling units that appear in both the numerator and denominator:

$$\frac{x \text{ ml} \times 1 \cancel{\text{min}}}{1 \cancel{\text{min}}} = \frac{0.5 \text{ ml} \times 60 \cancel{\text{min}}}{1 \cancel{\text{min}}}$$

$$x = 30 \text{ ml}$$

Set the infusion pump to deliver 30 ml/hour.

Example 2

A 200-lb patient is scheduled to receive an I.V. infusion of dobutamine at 10 mcg/kg/minute. The package insert says to dilute 250 mg of the drug in 50 ml of dextrose 5% in water (D_5W). Because the drug vial contains 20 ml of solution, the total to be infused is 70 ml (50 ml of D_5W plus 20 ml of solution). How many micrograms of the drug should the patient receive each minute? Each hour?

First, compute the patient's weight in kilograms. To do this, set up a proportion with the weight in pounds and the unknown weight in kilograms in one fraction and the number of pounds per kilogram in the other fraction:

$$\frac{200 \text{ lb}}{x \text{ kg}} = \frac{2.2 \text{ lb}}{1 \text{ kg}}$$

Cross multiply the fractions:

$$x \text{ kg} \times 2.2 \text{ lb} = 1 \text{ kg} \times 200 \text{ lb}$$

Solve for x by dividing each side of the equation by 2.2 lb and canceling units that appear in both the numerator and denominator:

$$\frac{x \text{ kg} \times \cancel{2.2 \text{ lb}}}{\cancel{2.2 \text{ lb}}} = \frac{1 \text{ kg} \times 200 \cancel{\text{lb}}}{2.2 \cancel{\text{lb}}}$$

$$x = \frac{200 \text{ kg}}{2.2}$$

$$x = 90.9 \text{ kg}$$

The patient weighs 90.9 kg. Next, determine the dose in micrograms per minute by setting up a proportion with the patient's weight in kilograms and the unknown dose in micrograms per minute in one fraction and the known dose in micrograms per kilogram per minute in the other fraction:

$$\frac{90.9 \text{ kg}}{x \text{ mcg/min}} = \frac{1 \text{ kg}}{10 \text{ mcg/min}}$$

Cross multiply the fractions:

$$x \text{ mcg/min} \times 1 \text{ kg} = 10 \text{ mcg/min} \times 90.9 \text{ kg}$$

Solve for x by dividing each side of the equation by 1 kg and canceling units that appear in both the numerator and denominator:

$$\frac{x \text{ mcg/min} \times 1 \cancel{\text{kg}}}{1 \cancel{\text{kg}}} = \frac{10 \text{ mcg/min} \times 90.9 \cancel{\text{kg}}}{1 \cancel{\text{kg}}}$$

$$x = 909 \text{ mcg/min}$$

The patient should receive 909 mcg of dobutamine every minute. Finally, determine the hourly dose by multiplying the dose per minute by 60:

$$909 \text{ mcg/min} \times 60 \text{ min/hr} = 54{,}540 \text{ mcg/hr}$$

The patient should receive 54,540 mcg of dobutamine every hour.

Pediatric dosages

To determine the correct pediatric dosage of a drug, prescribers, pharmacists, and nurses use one of two computational methods. One is based on a child's weight in kilograms; the other is based on the child's body surface area. Other methods are less accurate and not recommended.

Dose range per kilogram of body weight

Many drug companies provide information on the safe dosage ranges for drugs given to children. The companies usually provide the dose ranges in milligrams per kilogram of body weight and, in many cases, give similar information for adult dose ranges. The following example and explanation show how to calculate the safe pediatric dosage range for a drug, using the company's suggested safe dose range provided in milligrams per kilogram.

For a child, a prescriber orders a drug with a suggested dosage range of 10 to 12 mg/kg of body weight/day. The child weighs 12 kg. What is the safe daily dose range for the child?

You must calculate the lower and upper limits of the dose range provided by the manufacturer. First, calculate the dose based on 10 mg/kg of body weight. Then, calculate the dose based on 12 mg/kg of body weight. The answers represent the lower and upper limits of the daily dose range, expressed in mg/kg of the child's weight.

Body surface area

A second method for calculating safe pediatric doses uses the child's body surface area. This method may provide a more accurate calculation because the child's body surface area is thought to parallel the child's organ growth and maturation and metabolic rate.

You can determine the body surface area of a child by using a three-column chart called a nomogram. Mark the child's height in the first column and weight in the third column. Then draw a line between the two marks. The point at which the line intersects the vertical scale in the second column is the child's estimated body surface area in square meters. To calculate the child's approximate dose, use the body surface area measurement in the following equation:

$$\frac{\text{body surface area of child}}{\text{average adult body surface area } (1.73\ \text{m}^2)} \times \text{average adult dose} = \text{child's dose}$$

The following example illustrates the use of the equation. The nomogram shows that a 25-lb (11.3-kg) child who is 33 inches (84-cm) tall has a body surface area of 0.52 m^2. To determine the child's dose of a drug with an average adult dose of 100 mg, the equation would appear as:

$$\frac{0.52\ \text{m}^2}{1.73\ \text{m}^2} \times 100\ \text{mg} = \begin{matrix}30.06\ \text{mg} \\ \text{(child's dose)}\end{matrix}$$

The child should receive 30 mg of the drug. Many facilities have guidelines that determine acceptable calculation methods for pediatric doses. If you work with children, familiarize yourself with your facility's policies about pediatric doses.

3

Drug administration routes

You will give drugs by many routes, including oral (P.O.), intravenous (I.V.), intramuscular (I.M.), subcutaneous, topical, ophthalmic, rectal (P.R.), buccal and sublingual (S.L.), inhalation, nasogastric (NG), otic, and vaginal. No matter which route you use, you need to follow the established procedure to make sure you give the right drug, in the right dose, to the right patient, at the right time, and by the right route. Immediately after giving the drug, you need to provide the right documentation. This procedure includes:

- checking the order, medication record, and label
- confirming the patient's identity
- following standard drug safety procedures
- addressing all of the patient's questions
- correctly documenting the drug administration in the patient's medical record.

Check the order

Make sure you have a written order for every drug given. Use verbal orders only in emergencies; write them out and get the prescriber to sign them within the time period specified by your facility.

If your facility has a computerized order system, it may allow prescribers to order drugs electronically from the pharmacy. The computer may indicate whether the pharmacy has the drug and trigger the pharmacy staff to fill the prescription. A computerized order also may generate a patient record, either paper or electronic, on which you can document medication administration.

Computer systems offer several advantages over paper systems. Drugs often arrive on the unit or floor more quickly. Documentation is quicker and easier. Prescribers can see at a glance which drugs have been given. Errors can't result from poor handwriting (although typing mistakes may occur). Finally, computerized records are easier to store than paper records.

Check the medication record

Check the order on the patient's medication record against the prescriber's order.

Check the label

Before giving a drug, check its label three times to make sure you're giving the prescribed drug and the prescribed dose. First, check the label when you take the container from the shelf or drawer. Next, check the label right before pouring the drug into the medication cup or drawing it into the syringe. Finally, check the label again before returning the container to the shelf or drawer. If you're giving a unit-dose drug, open the container at the patient's bedside. Check the label for the third time immediately after pouring the drug and again before discarding the wrapper.

Don't give a drug from a poorly labeled or unlabeled container. Also, don't attempt to label a drug or to reinforce a label that is falling off or improperly placed. Instead, return the drug to the pharmacist for verification and proper relabeling.

Confirm the patient's identity

Before giving the drug, ask the patient his full name and confirm his identity by comparing two patient identifiers, such as the medical record number and the patient's birthdate, against the medication administration record. Don't rely on information that can vary during a hospital stay, such as a room or bed number. In nonacute settings, identify the patient by picture or other specific information.

Check again that you have the correct drug, and make sure the patient isn't allergic to it. If the patient has any drug allergies, check to make sure the chart and medication administration record are labeled accordingly and that the patient is wearing an allergy wristband that identifies the allergen.

Follow safety procedures

Whenever you give a drug, follow these safety procedures:

- Never give a drug poured or prepared by someone else.
- Never allow the medication cart or tray out of your sight once you've prepared a dose.
- Never leave a drug at a patient's bedside.
- Always observe the patient during drug administration; make sure he swallows oral drugs or uses an inhaler appropriately. If the patient is giving the drug to himself, make sure his technique is correct.
- Never return unwrapped or prepared drugs to stock containers; instead, dispose of them and notify the pharmacy.
- Keep the medication cart locked at all times.
- Follow your facility's standard precautions.

Respond to questions

If the patient questions you about his drug or dosage, check his medication record again. If the drug you're giving is correct, reassure the patient and explain the reason for the drug. Explain any changes to his drug regimen or drug dosage. Instruct him, as appropriate, about possible adverse reactions, and ask him to report anything that he feels may be an adverse reaction.

Oral administration

Because oral drug administration is usually the safest, most convenient, and least expensive method, most drugs are given this way. Drugs for oral administration are available in many forms: tablets, enteric-coated tablets, capsules, syrups, elixirs, oils, liquids, suspensions, powders, and granules. Some require special preparation before administration, such as mixing with juice to make them more palatable.

Oral drugs are sometimes prescribed in higher dosages than their parenteral equivalents because after the drugs are absorbed through the gastrointestinal (GI) system, the liver breaks them down before they reach the systemic circulation.

Equipment and preparation

- Check the chart and the medication administration record.
- Gather the drug and medication cup.
- If the patient is a child or an elderly person, you may need to gather a mortar and pestle for crushing pills and an appropriate buffer, such as jelly or applesauce for crushed pills or juice, water, or milk for liquid drugs.

Implementation

- Wash your hands.
- Confirm the patient's identity using two patient identifiers.
- Make sure the patient isn't allergic to the drug or any of its components.
- Assess the patient's condition, including level of consciousness and vital signs. Changes in the patient's condition may call for withholding the drug.
- Give the patient the drug. If needed and verified safe, crush the drug to facilitate swallowing or mix it with a soft food or liquid to aid swallowing, minimize adverse effects, or promote absorption.
- Stay with the patient until he has swallowed the drug. If he seems confused or disoriented, check his mouth to make sure he has indeed swallowed the drug. Return and reassess the patient's response within one hour of giving the drug.

Nursing considerations

- To avoid damaging or staining the patient's teeth, give acid or iron preparations through a straw. An unpleasant-tasting liquid usually can be made more palatable if taken through a straw because the liquid contacts fewer taste buds.
- If the patient can't swallow a whole tablet or capsule, ask the pharmacist if the drug is available in liquid form or if it can be given by another route. If not, ask the pharmacist if the tablet can be crushed or if capsules can be opened and mixed with food.
- Don't crush sustained-action, buccal, S.L., or enteric-coated drugs because this may counteract the safety or effectiveness of these drugs.

Intravenous bolus administration

In this method, rapid I.V. administration allows the drug level to quickly peak in the bloodstream. This method also may be used for drugs that can't be given I.M. because they're toxic or because the patient can't absorb them well. It may also be used for drugs that can't be diluted. Bolus doses may be injected directly into a vein or through an existing I.V. line.

Equipment and preparation

- Check the chart and the medication administration record. Gather the prescribed drug, 20G needle and syringe, diluent (if needed), tourniquet, alcohol sponge, sterile 2″ × 2″ gauze pad, gloves, adhesive bandage, and tape. Other materials may include a winged device primed with normal saline solution and a second syringe (and needle) filled with normal saline solution.
- Draw the drug into the syringe and dilute if needed.

Implementation

- Confirm the patient's identity using two patient identifiers.
- Make sure the patient isn't allergic to the drug or any of its components.

To give a direct injection

- Wash your hands and put on gloves.
- Select the largest vein suitable to dilute the drug and minimize irritation.
- Apply a tourniquet above the site to distend the vein, and clean the site with an alcohol sponge, working outward in a circle.
- If you're using the needle of the drug syringe, insert it at a 30-degree angle with the bevel up. The bevel should reach ¼″ (0.6 cm) into the vein. Insert a winged device bevel-up at a 10- to 25-degree angle. Lower the angle once you enter the vein. Advance the needle into the vein. Tape the wings in place when you see blood return, and attach the syringe containing the drug.
- Check for blood backflow.
- Remove the tourniquet, and inject the drug at the ordered rate.
- Check for blood backflow to ensure that the needle remained in place and the entire amount of injected drug entered the vein.
- For a winged device, flush the line with normal saline solution from the second syringe to ensure complete delivery.
- Withdraw the needle and discard it in a biohazard container. Apply pressure to the site with the sterile gauze pad for at least 3 minutes to prevent hematoma.
- Apply an adhesive bandage when the bleeding stops.
- Remove and discard your gloves in a designated biohazard container. Wash your hands.

To inject through an existing line

- Wash your hands and put on gloves.
- Check the drug's compatibility with the I.V. solution.
- If the drug isn't compatible with the I.V. solution, flush the line with normal saline solution before and after the injection.
- Close the flow clamp, wipe the injection port with an alcohol sponge, and inject the drug as you would a direct injection
- Open the flow clamp and readjust the flow rate.
- Remove and discard your gloves in a designated biohazard container. Wash your hands.

Nursing considerations

- If the existing I.V. line is capped, making it an intermittent infusion device, verify patency and placement of the device before injecting the drug. Then flush the device with normal saline solution, give the drug, and follow with the appropriate flush.
- Immediately report signs of acute allergic reaction or anaphylaxis. If extravasation occurs, stop the injection, estimate the amount of infiltration, and notify the prescriber.
- When giving diazepam or chlordiazepoxide hydrochloride through a steel needle winged device or an I.V. line, flush device with bacteriostatic water before and after use to prevent precipitation.

Intravenous administration through a secondary line

A secondary I.V. line is a complete I.V. set connected to the lower Y-port (secondary port) of a primary line instead of to the I.V. catheter or needle. It features an I.V. container, long tubing, and either a microdrip or a macrodrip system, and this line can be used for continuous or intermittent drug infusion. When used continuously, it permits drug infusion and titration while the primary line maintains a constant total infusion rate.

A secondary I.V. line used only for intermittent drug administration is called a piggyback set. In this case, the primary line maintains venous access between drug doses. A piggyback set includes a small I.V. container, short tubing, and usually a macrodrip system, and it connects to the primary line's upper Y-port (piggyback port).

Equipment and preparation

- Check the chart and the medication administration record.
- Make sure the patient isn't allergic to the drug or any of its components.
- Gather the prescribed I.V. drug, diluent (if needed), prescribed I.V. solution, administration set with secondary injection port, 22G 1″ needle or a needleless system, gloves, alcohol sponges, 1″ (2.5 cm) adhesive tape, time tape, labels, infusion pump, extension hook, and solution for intermittent piggyback infusion.
- Wash your hands and put on gloves.
- Inspect the I.V. container for cracks, leaks, or contamination.
- Check the expiration date.
- Check compatibility with the primary solution.
- Determine whether the primary line has a secondary injection port.
- If needed, add the drug to the secondary I.V. solution (usually 50- to 100-ml of normal saline solution or D_5W). To do so, remove the seals from the secondary container and wipe the main port with an alcohol sponge.
- Inject the prescribed drug and agitate the solution to mix the drug.
- Label the I.V. mixture.
- Insert the administration set spike, and attach the needle or needleless system.
- Open the flow clamp and prime the line. Then close the flow clamp.
- Some drugs come in vials that can hang directly on the I.V. pole. In this case, inject diluent directly into the drug vial. Then spike the vial, prime the tubing, and hang the set.

Implementation

- If the drug is incompatible with the primary I.V. solution, replace the primary solution with a fluid that's compatible with both solutions, and flush the line before starting the drug infusion.
- Confirm the patient's identity using two patient identifiers.
- Hang the container of the secondary set and wipe the injection port of the primary line with an alcohol sponge.
- Insert the needle or needleless system from the secondary line into the injection port, and tape it securely to the primary line.
- To run the container of the secondary set by itself, lower the primary set's container with an extension hook. To run both containers simultaneously, place them at the same height.
- Open the clamp and adjust the drip rate.
- For continuous infusion, set the secondary solution to the desired drip rate; then adjust the primary solution to the desired total infusion rate.
- For intermittent infusion, wait until the secondary solution has completely infused; then adjust the primary drip rate, as needed.
- If the secondary solution tubing is being reused, close the clamp on the tubing and follow your facility's policy: Remove the needle or needleless system and replace it with a new one, or leave it taped to the injection port, and label it with the time it was first used.
- Leave the empty container in place until you replace it with a new dose of drug at the prescribed time. If the tubing won't be reused, discard it appropriately with the I.V. container.

Nursing considerations

- If institutional policy allows, use a pump for drug infusion. Place a time tape on the secondary container to help prevent an inaccurate administration rate.
- When reusing secondary tubing, change it when your facility's policy requires, usually every two or three days. Inspect the injection port for leakage with each use; change it more often, if needed.
- Except for lipids, don't piggyback a secondary I.V. line to a total parenteral nutrition line because this risks contamination.

Intramuscular administration

You'll use intramuscular (I.M.) injections to deposit up to 5 ml of drug deep into well-vascularized muscle for rapid systemic action and absorption.

Equipment and preparation

- Check the chart and the medication administration record.
- Make sure the patient isn't allergic to the drug or any of its components.

• Gather the prescribed drug, diluent, or filter needle (if needed), 3- to 5-ml syringe, 20G to 25G 1″ to 3″ needle, gloves, alcohol sponges, and a nonsterile cotton ball or 2″ × 2″ gauze pad.
• The prescribed drug must be sterile. The needle may be packaged separately or already attached to the syringe. Needles used for I.M. injections are longer than those used for subcutaneous injections because they must reach deep into the muscle. Needle length also depends on the injection site, the patient's size, and the amount of subcutaneous fat covering the muscle. A larger needle gauge can accommodate viscous solutions and suspensions.
• Check the drug for abnormal changes in color and clarity. If in doubt, ask the pharmacist.
• Wipe the stopper that tops the drug vial with alcohol, and draw up the prescribed amount of drug.
• Provide privacy and explain the procedure to the patient.
• Position the patient and drape him appropriately, making sure that the site is well lit and exposed.

Implementation

• Wash your hands.
• Confirm the patient's identity using two patient identifiers.
• Make sure the patient isn't allergic to the drug or any of its components.
• Select an appropriate injection site. Avoid any site that looks inflamed, edematous, or irritated. Also, avoid using injection sites that contain moles, birthmarks, scar tissue, or other lesions. The dorsogluteal and ventrogluteal muscles are used most commonly for I.M. injections.

Dorsogluteal muscle

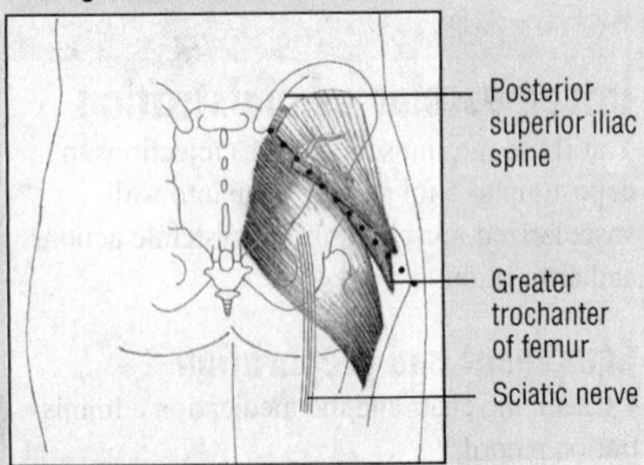

Ventrogluteal muscle

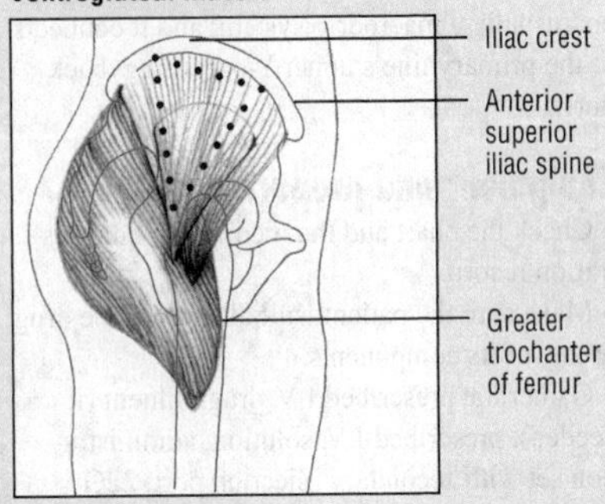

• The deltoid muscle may be used for injections of 2 ml or less.

Deltoid muscle

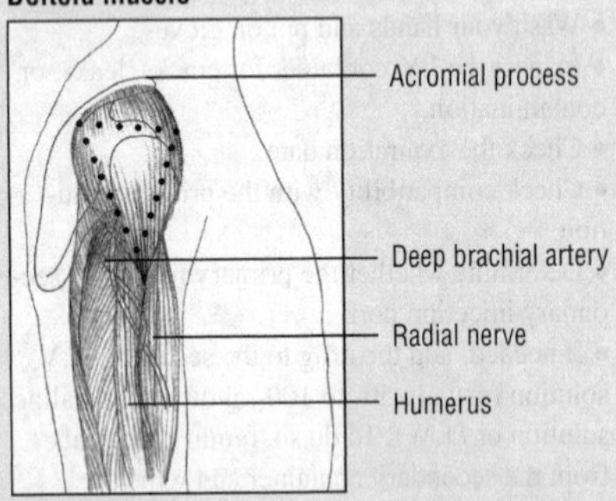

• The vastus lateralis muscle is used most often in children; the rectus femoris may be used in infants.

Vastus lateralis and rectus femoris muscles

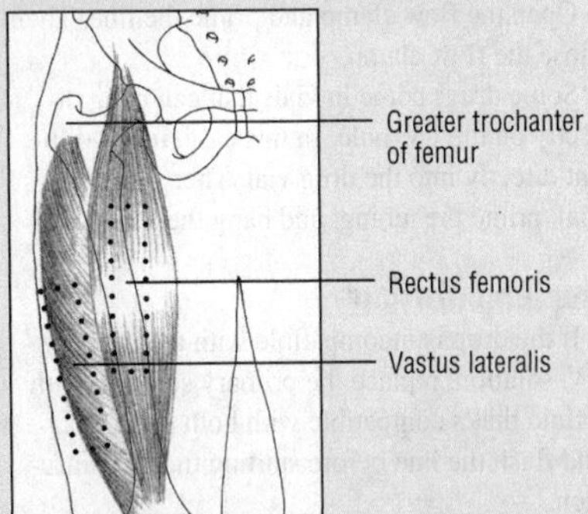

• Loosen, but don't remove, the needle sheath.
• Gently tap the site to stimulate nerve endings and minimize pain.

• Clean the site with an alcohol sponge, starting at the site and moving outward in expanding circles to about 2″ (5 cm). Allow the skin to dry because wet alcohol stings in the puncture.
• Put on gloves.
• With the thumb and index finger of your nondominant hand, gently stretch the skin.
• With the syringe in your dominant hand, remove the needle sheath with the free fingers of the other hand.
• Position the syringe perpendicular to the skin surface and a couple of inches from the skin. Tell the patient that he'll feel a prick. Then quickly and firmly thrust the needle into the muscle.
• Pull back slightly on the plunger to aspirate for blood. If blood appears, the needle is in a blood vessel. Withdraw the needle, prepare a fresh syringe, and inject another site. If no blood appears, inject the drug slowly and steadily to let the muscle distend gradually. You should feel little or no resistance. Gently but quickly remove the needle at a 90-degree angle.
• Using a gloved hand, apply gentle pressure to the site with the cotton ball or 2″ × 2″ gauze. Massage the relaxed muscle, unless contraindicated, to distribute the drug and promote absorption.
• Inspect the site for bleeding or bruising. Apply pressure as needed.
• Discard all equipment properly. Don't recap needles; put them in an appropriate biohazard container to avoid needle-stick injuries.
• Remove and discard your gloves in a biohazard container. Wash your hands.

Nursing considerations

• To slow absorption, some drugs are dissolved in oil. Mix them well before use.
ALERT: If you must inject more than 5 ml, divide the solution and inject it at two different sites.
• Rotate injection sites for patients who need repeated injections.
• Urge the patient to relax the muscle to reduce pain and bleeding.
ALERT: Never inject into the gluteal muscles of a child who has been walking for less than one year.
• Keep in mind that I.M. injections can damage local muscle cells and elevate CK levels, which can be confused with elevated levels caused by MI. Diagnostic tests can be used to differentiate between them.

Subcutaneous administration

A subcutaneous injection allows slower, more sustained administration than an I.M. injection. Drugs and solutions delivered subcutaneously are injected through a relatively short needle using sterile technique.

Equipment and preparation

• Check the chart and the medication administration record.
• Make sure the patient isn't allergic to the drug or any of its components.
• Gather drug, needle of appropriate gauge and length, 1- to 3-ml syringe, gloves, alcohol sponges, and nonsterile cotton ball or 2″ × 2″ gauze pad. Other materials may include antiseptic cleanser, filter needle, insulin syringe, and insulin pump.
• Inspect the drug to make sure it's the right color and consistency and is free of precipitates.
• Wash your hands.

For single-dose ampules

• Wrap the neck of the ampule in an alcohol sponge and snap off the top, directing it away from you.
• If desired, attach a filter needle to the needle, slightly tip the ampule, and withdraw the desired amount of the drug.
• Tap the syringe to disperse air bubbles.
• Cover the needle with the attached safety sheath by placing the needle sheath on the counter or medication cart and sliding the needle into the sheath.
• Before discarding the ampule, check the label against the patient's medication record.
• Discard the filter needle and the ampule in a biohazard container.
• Attach the appropriate-sized needle to the syringe.

For single-dose and multidose vials

• Reconstitute powdered drugs according to the instructions on the label.
• Clean the rubber stopper on the vial with an alcohol sponge for at least 15 seconds.
• Pull the syringe plunger back until the volume of air in the syringe equals the volume of drug to be withdrawn from the vial.
• Insert the needle into the vial.

• Inject the air, invert the vial, and keep the bevel tip of the needle below the level of the solution as you withdraw the prescribed amount of drug.
• Tap the syringe to disperse air bubbles.
• Cover the needle with the attached safety sheath by placing the needle sheath on the counter or medication cart and sliding the needle into the sheath.
• Check the drug label against the patient's medication record before returning the multidose vial to the shelf or drawer or before discarding the single-dose vial.
• Attach the appropriate-sized needle to the syringe.

Implementation

• Confirm the patient's identity using two patient identifiers.
• Make sure the patient isn't allergic to the drug or any of its components.
• Select the injection site from those shown below, and tell the patient where you'll be giving the injection.

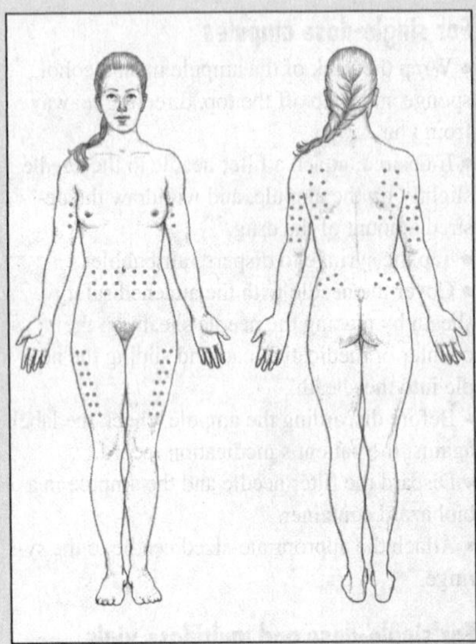

• Wash your hands and put on gloves. Position and drape the patient.
• Clean the injection site with an alcohol sponge. Loosen the protective needle sheath.
• With your nondominant hand, pinch the skin around the injection site firmly to elevate the subcutaneous tissue, forming a 1″ (2.5 cm) fat fold, as shown below.

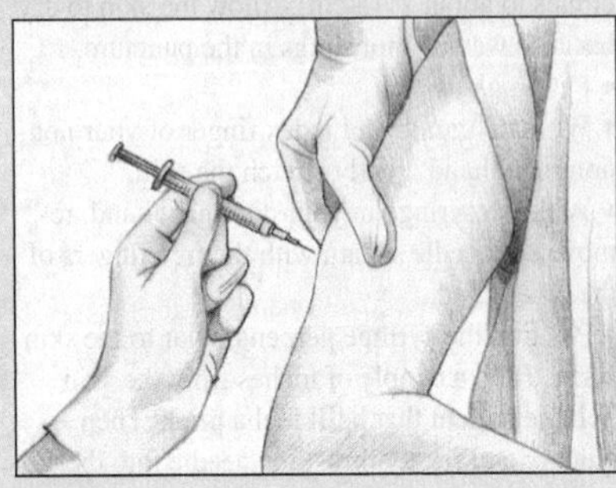

• Holding the syringe in your dominant hand, grip the needle sheath between the fourth and fifth fingers of your nondominant hand while continuing to pinch the skin around the injection site with the index finger and thumb of your nondominant hand. Pull the sheath back to uncover the needle. Don't touch the needle.
• Position the needle with its bevel up.
• Tell the patient he'll feel a prick as you insert the needle. Do so quickly, in one motion, at a 45-degree or 90-degree angle, as shown below. The needle length and the angle you use depend on the amount of subcutaneous tissue at the site. Some drugs, such as heparin, should always be injected at a 90-degree angle.

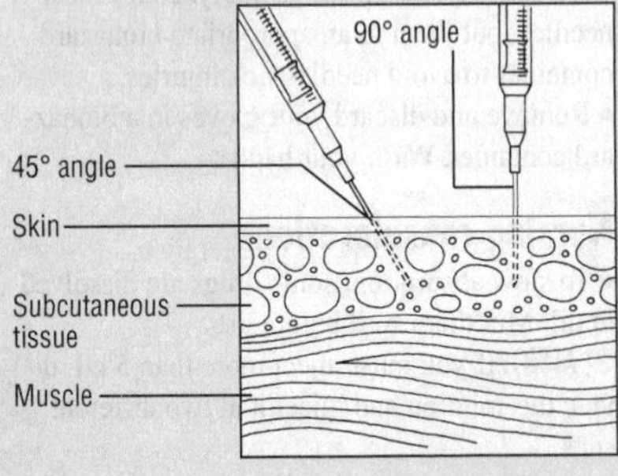

• Release the skin to avoid injecting the drug into compressed tissue and irritating the nerves. Except for insulin and heparin, pull the plunger back slightly to check for blood return. If blood appears, withdraw the needle, prepare another syringe, and repeat the procedure. If no blood appears, slowly inject the drug.
• After injection, remove the needle at the same angle you used to insert it. Using a gloved hand, apply gentle pressure to the site with the

cotton ball or 2″ × 2″ gauze pad. Massage the site gently, unless contraindicated, to distribute the drug and promote absorption.

• Inspect the injection site for bleeding or bruising.

• Discard all equipment properly. Don't recap needles; put them in a biohazard container to avoid needle-stick injuries.

• Remove and discard your gloves in a biohazard container. Wash your hands.

Nursing considerations

ALERT: Don't aspirate for blood return when giving insulin or heparin. It isn't necessary with insulin and may cause a hematoma with heparin.

• Don't massage the site after giving heparin.

ALERT: Repeated injections in the same site can cause lipodystrophy, a natural immune response. Rotating injection sites can minimize this complication.

Topical administration

Topical drugs, such as patches, lotions, and ointments, are applied directly to the skin. They're commonly used for local rather than systemic effects. Certain types of topical drugs—known as transdermal drugs—are meant to enter the patient's bloodstream and to have a systemic effect after you apply them.

Equipment and preparation

• Check the chart and the drug administration record.

• Make sure the patient isn't allergic to the drug or any of its components.

• Gather the prescribed drug, sterile tongue blades, gloves, sterile gloves for open lesions, sterile 4″ × 4″ gauze pads, transparent semipermeable dressing, adhesive tape, normal saline solution, cotton-tipped applicators, gloves, and linen savers, if needed.

Implementation

• Confirm the patient's identity using two patient identifiers.

• Make sure the patient isn't allergic to the drug or any of its components.

• Explain the procedure to the patient because, after discharge, he may have to apply the drug himself.

• If the procedure is uncomfortable, premedicate the patient with an analgesic. Give it time to take effect.

• Wash your hands to reduce the risk of cross-contamination, and glove your dominant hand.

• Help the patient to a comfortable position, and expose the area to be treated. Make sure the skin or mucous membrane is intact (unless the drug is for a skin lesion). Applying the drug to broken or abraded skin may cause unwanted systemic absorption and further irritation.

• If needed, clean debris from the skin. You may have to change your gloves if they become soiled.

To apply paste, cream, or ointment

• Open the container. Place the cap upside down to avoid contaminating its inner surface.

• Remove a tongue blade from its sterile wrapper, and cover one end of the blade with drug from the tube or jar. Then transfer the drug from the blade to your gloved hand.

• Apply the drug to the affected area with long, smooth strokes that follow the direction of hair growth. This technique avoids forcing the drug into hair follicles, which can cause irritation and folliculitis. Don't press too hard because it could abrade the skin and cause discomfort.

• When applying a drug to the patient's face, use cotton-tipped applicators for small areas, such as under the eyes. For larger areas, use a sterile gauze pad.

• To avoid contaminating the drug, use a new sterile tongue blade each time you remove the drug from its container.

• Remove and discard your gloves and wash your hands.

To apply transdermal ointment

• Choose the application site—usually a dry, hairless spot on the patient's chest or upper arm.

• To help absorption, wash the site with soap and warm water and dry thoroughly.

• Wash your hands and put on gloves.

• If the patient has a previously applied medication strip at another site, remove it and swab or wash this area to clear away the drug residue.

• If the area you choose is hairy, clip excess hair rather than shaving it. Shaving causes irritation, which the drug may worsen.

• Squeeze the prescribed amount of ointment onto the application strip or measuring paper. Don't get the ointment on your skin.

• Apply the strip, drug side down, directly to the patient's skin.
• Maneuver the strip slightly to spread a thin layer of the ointment over a 3″ (8-cm) area, but don't rub the ointment into the skin.
• Secure the application strip to the patient's skin by covering it with a semipermeable dressing or plastic wrap.
• Tape the covering securely in place.
• Label the strip with the date, time, and your initials, if required by your facility.
• Remove your gloves and wash your hands.

To apply a transdermal patch

• Remove the old patch and swab or wash the site to remove any residual drug or adhesive.
• Choose a dry, hairless application site.
• Clip (don't shave) hair from the chosen site. Wash the area with warm water and soap, and dry it thoroughly.
• Wash your hands and put on gloves.
• Without touching the adhesive surface, remove the clear plastic backing.
• Apply the patch to the site without touching the adhesive.
• If required by your facility's policy, label the patch with the date, time, and your initials.
• Remove your gloves and wash your hands.

To remove ointment

• Wash your hands and put on gloves.
• Gently swab ointment from the patient's skin using a sterile 4″ × 4″ gauze pad saturated with normal saline solution.
• Don't wipe too hard because you could irritate the skin.
• Remove and discard your gloves and wash your hands.

Nursing considerations

• To prevent skin irritation, always remove previous drug applications by swabbing or washing; then select a new site.
• Always wear gloves to protect your skin.
• Never apply ointment to the eyelids or ear canal. The ointment may congeal and occlude the tear duct or ear canal.
• Inspect the treated area frequently for allergic or other adverse reactions.
• Don't apply a topical drug to scarred or callused skin because this may slow absorption.
• Don't place a defibrillator paddle on a transdermal patch. The aluminum on the patch can cause electrical arcing during defibrillation, resulting in smoke and thermal burns. If a patient has a patch on a standard paddle site, remove the patch and swab the skin quickly before applying the paddle, or use another site, if possible.

Ophthalmic administration

Ophthalmic drugs—drops or ointments—serve both diagnostic and therapeutic purposes. During an ophthalmic examination, drugs can be used to anesthetize the eye, dilate the pupil, and stain the cornea to identify anomalies. Therapeutic uses include eye lubrication and treatment of glaucoma and infections.

Equipment and preparation

• Check the chart and the medication administration record.
• Make sure the patient isn't allergic to the drug or any of its components.
• Gather the prescribed ophthalmic drug, sterile cotton balls, gloves, warm water or normal saline solution, sterile gauze pads, and facial tissue. An ocular dressing also may be used.
• Make sure the drug is labeled for ophthalmic use. Check the expiration date. Remember to date the container after first use. If in doubt, consult the pharmacist.
• Inspect ocular solutions for cloudiness, discoloration, and precipitation, keeping in mind that some drugs are suspensions that normally appear cloudy.

Implementation

• Make sure you know which eye you are treating because different drugs or doses may be ordered for each eye.
• Confirm the patient's identity using two patient identifiers.
• Make sure the patient isn't allergic to the drug or any of its components.
• Wash your hands and put on gloves.
• If the patient has an eye dressing, remove it by pulling it down and away from his forehead, being careful not to contaminate your hands. (If you do, remove the contaminated gloves, wash your hands, and put on new gloves.) Don't apply pressure to the area around the eyes.
• To remove exudates or meibomian gland secretions, clean around the eye with sterile cotton balls or sterile gauze pads that have been

moistened with warm water or normal saline solution. Have the patient close his eyes; then gently wipe the eyelids from the inner to the outer canthus. Use a fresh cotton ball or gauze pad for each stroke, and use a different cotton ball or pad for each eye.

- Have the patient sit or lie on his back. Tell him to tilt his head back and toward his affected eye so that any excess drug can flow away from the tear duct, minimizing systemic absorption through the nasal mucosa.
- Remove the dropper cap from the drug container, and draw the drug into the dropper. Or, if the bottle has a dropper tip, remove the cap and hold or place it upside down to prevent contamination.
- Before instilling eyedrops, tell the patient to look up and away. This moves the cornea away from the lower lid and minimizes the risk of touching the lid with the dropper.

To instill eyedrops

- Steady the hand that's holding the dropper by resting it gently against the patient's forehead. With your other hand, gently pull down the lower lid of the affected eye, and instill the drops in the conjunctival sac. Never instill eyedrops directly onto the eyeball.
- After instilling the eyedrops, tell the patient to close his eyes gently without squeezing the lids shut and not to blink.
- Instruct the patient to place a finger in the corner of the eye between the bridge of the nose and the eyelid and to apply gentle pressure for 2 to 3 minutes to prevent systemic absorption of drops through the lacrimal sac. Then have the patient wipe away any excess drops or tears with a clean tissue before opening the eyes. Use a fresh tissue for each eye.
- Remove and discard your gloves and wash your hands.
- An elderly patient may have difficulty feeling the drops in his eye. When teaching an elderly patient how to instill drops himself, suggest that he chill the drug slightly in the refrigerator because cold drops are easier to feel.

To apply eye ointment

- Squeeze a small ribbon of drug on the edge of the conjunctival sac from the inner to the outer canthus, as shown at the top of the next column. Cut off the ribbon by turning the tube. Don't touch the eye with the tip of the tube.

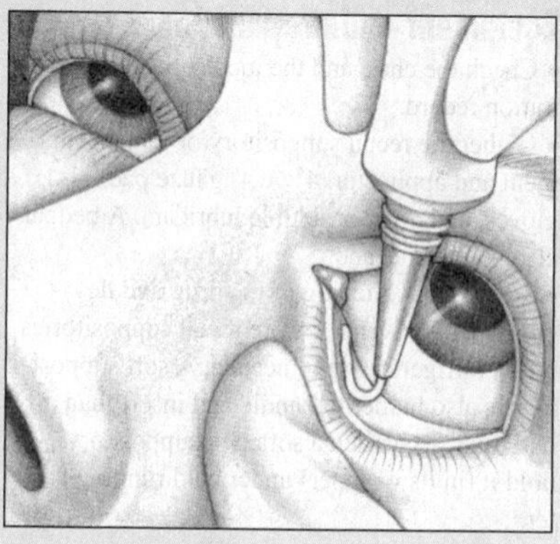

- After applying ointment, tell the patient to close his eye gently without squeezing the lid shut and to roll his eye behind a closed lid to help distribute the drug over the eyeball. Have the patient sit with the eye closed for 2 to 3 minutes to facilitate absorption and avoid "clouding" of the vision from the ointment.
- Use a tissue to remove any excess drug that leaks from the eye. Use a fresh tissue for each eye to prevent cross-contamination.
- Apply a new eye dressing, if needed.
- Remove and discard your gloves and wash your hands.

Nursing considerations

- Urge the patient not to rub his eye or blink immediately after eyedrops.
- To maintain the drug container's sterility, don't put the cap down after opening the container, and never touch the eye area with the tip of the dropper or bottle. Discard any solution remaining in the dropper before returning it to the bottle. If the dropper or bottle tip is contaminated, discard it and use another sterile dropper. Never share eyedrops between patients.

Rectal administration

A rectal suppository is a small, solid drug mass, usually cone shaped, with a cocoa butter or glycerin base. It may be inserted to stimulate peristalsis and defecation or to relieve pain, vomiting, and local irritation. An ointment is a semisolid drug used to produce local effects. It may be applied externally to the anus or internally to the rectum.

Equipment and preparation

- Check the chart and the medication administration record.
- Gather the rectal suppository or tube of ointment and applicator, 4″ × 4″ gauze pads, gloves, and a water-soluble lubricant. A bedpan also may be needed.
- To prevent softening of the drug and decreased effectiveness, store rectal suppositories in the refrigerator until needed. A soft suppository is also harder to handle and insert than a hard one. To harden a softened suppository, hold it (in its wrapper) under cold running water.

Implementation

- Confirm the patient's identity using two patient identifiers.
- Make sure the patient isn't allergic to the drug or any of its components.
- Wash your hands.

To insert a rectal suppository

- Place the patient on his left side in Sims' position. Drape him with the bedcovers, exposing only his buttocks.
- Put on gloves. Unwrap the suppository and lubricate it with water-soluble lubricant.
- Lift the patient's right buttock with your nondominant hand to expose the anus.
- Instruct the patient to take several deep breaths through his mouth to relax the anal sphincter and to reduce anxiety and discomfort during drug insertion.
- Using the index finger of your dominant hand, insert the suppository—tapered end first—about 3″ (8 cm) until you feel it pass the internal anal sphincter, as shown below.

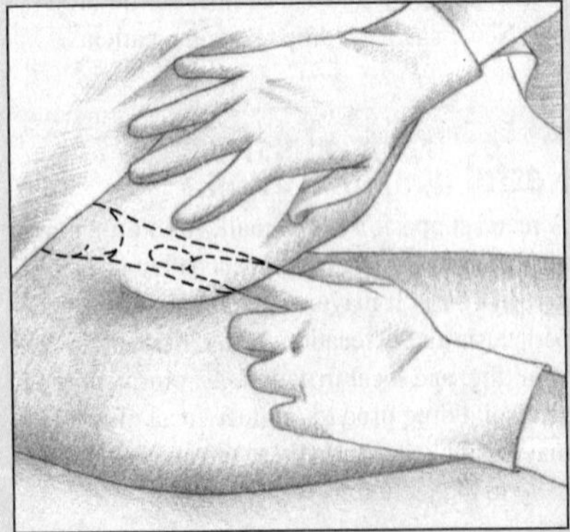

- Direct the tapered end of the suppository toward the side of the rectum so the drug contacts the membranes.
- Encourage the patient to lie quietly and, if possible, to contract his anal sphincter and buttocks together to retain the suppository for the correct length of time. Press on the patient's anus with a gauze pad, if needed, until the urge to defecate passes.
- Discard the used equipment and gloves. Wash your hands thoroughly.

To apply an ointment

- For external application, put on gloves and use a gauze pad to spread the drug over the anal area. For internal application, attach the end of the applicator to the tube of ointment, and coat the applicator with water-soluble lubricant.
- Use about 1″ (2.5 cm) of ointment. To gauge how much pressure to use during application, try squeezing a small amount from the tube before you attach the applicator.
- Place the patient on his left side in Sims' position. Drape him with the bedcovers, exposing only his buttocks.
- Lift the patient's right buttock with your nondominant hand to expose the anus.
- Tell the patient to take several deep breaths through his mouth to relax the anal sphincter and reduce anxiety and discomfort during insertion. Gently insert the applicator, directing it toward the umbilicus.
- Squeeze the tube to eject drug.
- Remove the applicator and place a folded 4″ × 4″ gauze pad between the patient's buttocks to absorb excess ointment.
- Disassemble the tube and applicator and recap the tube. Clean the applicator with soap and warm water and store or discard it. Remove and discard your gloves, and wash your hands thoroughly.

Nursing considerations

- Because eating and drinking stimulates peristalsis, a suppository for relieving constipation should be inserted about 30 minutes before mealtime to help soften the stool and facilitate defecation. A medicated retention suppository should be inserted between meals.
- Tell the patient to try to retain the suppository. If this is difficult, place the patient on a bedpan.

• Make sure that the patient's call button is handy, and watch for his signal because he may be unable to suppress the urge to defecate.
• Inform the patient that the suppository may discolor his next bowel movement.

Buccal and sublingual administration

Certain drugs are given buccally (between the cheek and teeth) or S.L. (under the tongue) to bypass the digestive tract and speed absorption into the bloodstream. When using either method, observe the patient carefully to make sure he doesn't swallow the drug or develop mucosal irritation.

Equipment and preparation

• Check the chart and the medication administration record.
• Gather the prescribed drug, medication cup, and gloves.

Implementation

• Wash your hands. If you'll be placing the drug into the patient's mouth, put on gloves.
• Confirm the patient's identity using two patient identifiers.
• Make sure the patient isn't allergic to the drug or any of its components.
• For buccal administration, place the tablet in the patient's buccal pouch, between the cheek and teeth, as shown below.

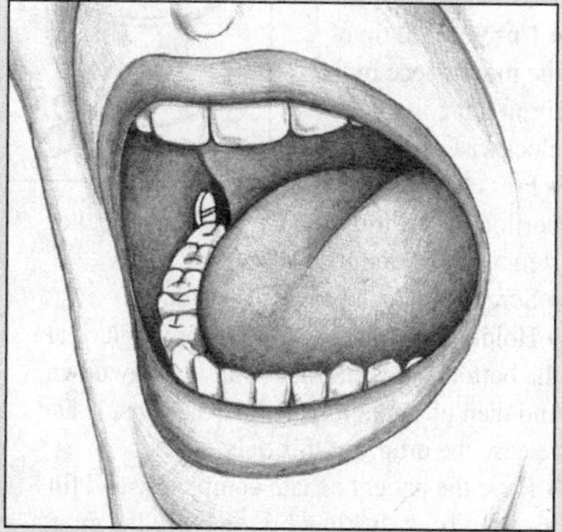

• For S.L. administration, place the tablet under the patient's tongue, as shown below.

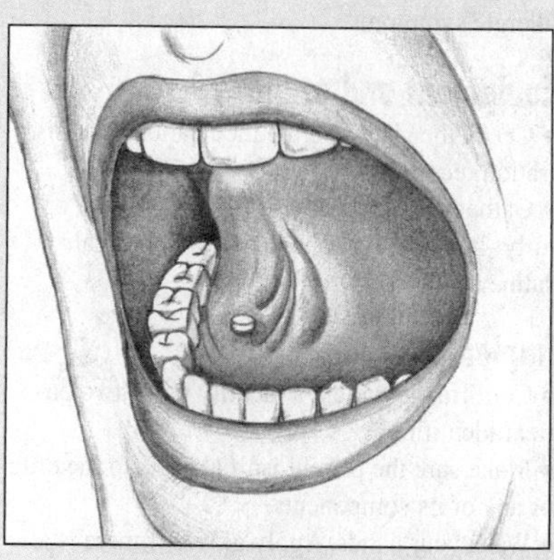

• Remove and discard gloves and wash your hands.
• Instruct the patient to keep the drug in place until it dissolves completely to ensure absorption. Caution the patient against chewing the tablet or touching it with his tongue to prevent accidental swallowing.
• Tell the patient not to smoke before the drug has dissolved because nicotine constricts blood vessels and slows drug absorption.

Nursing considerations

• Don't give liquids until a buccal tablet is absorbed; in some cases, this make take up to an hour.
• If the patient has angina, tell him to wet the nitroglycerin tablet with saliva and keep it under his tongue until it's fully absorbed.
• Make sure a patient with angina knows how to take nitroglycerin, how many doses to take, and when to call for emergency help.

Inhalation administration

Hand-held oropharyngeal inhalers include the metered-dose inhaler, dry-powder multidose inhaler, nasal inhaler, and turbo-inhaler. These devices deliver topical drugs to the respiratory tract, producing local and systemic effects. The mucosal lining of the respiratory tract absorbs the inhalant almost immediately. Examples of oral inhalants are bronchodilators, which improve airway patency and facilitate mucous drainage, and mucolytics, which liquefy tenacious bronchial secretions. Examples of nasal inhalants include corticosteroids, which reduce allergic symptoms.

Equipment and preparation

- Check the chart and the medication administration record.
- Gather the metered-dose inhaler, diskus, or turbo-inhaler, prescribed drug, and normal saline solution.

Implementation

- Confirm the patient's identity using two patient identifiers.
- Make sure the patient isn't allergic to the drug or any of its components.
- Wash your hands. Apply gloves if there is a risk of aerosol or secretion exposure.

To use a metered-dose inhaler

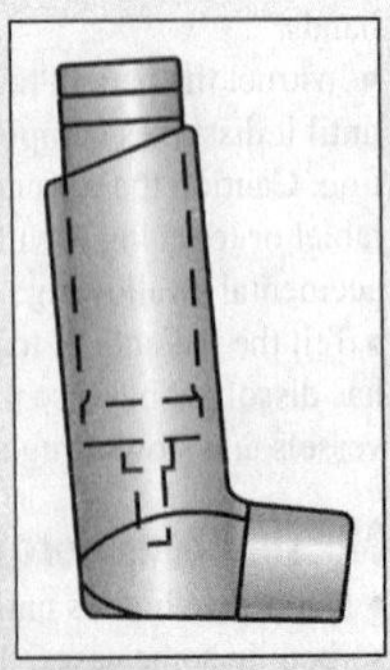

- Shake the inhaler bottle. Remove the cap and insert the stem into the small hole on the flattened portion of the mouthpiece, as shown.
- Place the inhaler about 1″ (2.5 cm) in front of the patient's open mouth.
- Tell the patient to exhale.
- If using a spacer, which can make the inhaler more effective, tell the patient to place the spacer mouthpiece in his mouth and to press his lips firmly around the mouthpiece.
- As you push the bottle down against the mouthpiece, tell the patient to inhale slowly through his mouth and to continue inhaling until his lungs feel full. Compress the bottle against the mouthpiece only once.
- Remove the inhaler and tell the patient to hold his breath for several seconds. Then instruct him to exhale slowly through pursed lips to keep distal bronchioles open and allow increased absorption and diffusion of the drug.
- Have the patient gargle with normal saline solution or water to remove the drug from his mouth and the back of his throat and to help prevent oral fungal infections. Warn the patient not to swallow after gargling, but rather to spit out the liquid.

To use a dry-powder multidose inhaler

- Hold the dry-powder multidose inhaler in one hand and put the thumb of your other hand on the thumbgrip. Push your thumb away from you as far as it will go, until the mouthpiece appears and snaps into position.
- Hold the dry-powder multidose inhaler level horizontally with the mouthpiece toward the patient. Slide the lever away from the patient as far as it will go until it clicks.
- Instruct the patient to exhale fully (not into the mouthpiece of the dry-powder multidose inhaler).
- Instruct the patient to breathe in quickly and deeply through the dry-powder multidose inhaler's mouthpiece, then hold the breath for 10 or more seconds. Then have the patient breathe out slowly.
- Wipe off the mouthpiece with a clean tissue, if needed, and close. (It will automatically reset for the next dose.)
- Tell the patient to rinse his mouth with water, without swallowing, after each dose.
- Never take a dry-powder multidose inhaler apart or wash any part of it. Check counter on top of dry-powder multidose inhaler to be sure dose is available and reorder five inhalations from end.

To use a turbo-inhaler

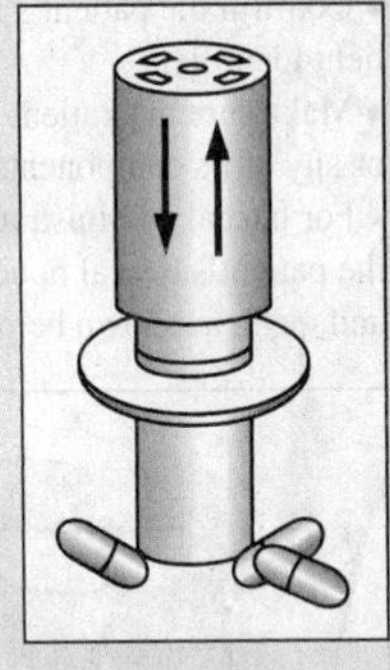

- Hold the mouthpiece in one hand. With the other hand, slide the sleeve away from the mouthpiece as far as possible, as shown.
- Unscrew the tip of the mouthpiece by turning it counterclockwise.
- Press the colored portion of the drug capsule into the propeller stem of the mouthpiece.
- Screw the inhaler together again.
- Holding the inhaler with the mouthpiece at the bottom, slide the sleeve all the way down and then up again to puncture the capsule and release the drug. Do this only once.
- Have the patient exhale completely and tilt his head back. Instruct him to place the mouthpiece in his mouth, close his lips around it, and inhale once. Tell him to hold his breath for several seconds.

• Remove the inhaler from the patient's mouth, and tell him to exhale as much air as possible.
• Repeat the procedure until the entire amount of drug in the device is inhaled.
• Have the patient gargle and spit with normal saline solution or water, if desired, to remove the drug from his mouth and the back of his throat.

To use a nasal inhaler

• Instruct patient to clear his nasal passages before administration.
• Shake the container to ensure even distribution of contents.
• Wipe the tip of the container with a clean tissue, if needed.
• Tell patient to place a finger against the nostril not being treated to block air entrance. Instruct the patient to exhale fully through the mouth.
• Place tip of nasal container into appropriate nostril without directing it onto nasal mucosa. Instruct patient to inhale quickly and deeply through this nostril, with mouth closed, while squeezing the nasal inhaler to release spray along with inhalation.
• Remove the inhaler and have the patient gently press closed the medicated nostril, breathing through his mouth for several seconds. Treat the opposite nostril, if indicated, or give two inhalations to each nostril, if indicated, spaced 3 to 5 seconds apart.

Nursing considerations

• Teach the patient how to use the inhaler so he can continue treatments after discharge, if needed. Explain that overdose can cause the drug to lose its effectiveness. Tell him to record the date and time of each inhalation and his response.
• Some inhalants may cause restlessness, palpitations, nervousness, and other systemic effects. They also may cause hypersensitivity reactions, such as a rash, urticaria, rhinitis, nasal bleeding, or bronchospasms.
• Give oral inhalants cautiously to patients with heart disease because these drugs may lead to coronary insufficiency, cardiac arrhythmias, or hypertension. If paradoxical bronchospasm occurs, stop the drug and use a different drug.
• If the patient is prescribed a bronchodilator and a corticosteroid, give the bronchodilator first so the air passages can open fully before the patient uses the corticosteroid.
• Instruct the patient to keep an extra inhaler handy.
• Instruct the patient to discard the inhaler after taking the prescribed number of doses and to start a new inhaler.
• Urge the patient to notify his prescriber if he notices an increased use of or need for an inhaler, or if symptoms are not relieved with the prescribed regimen.

Nasogastric administration

Besides providing another way to feed patients who can't eat normally, an NG tube allows for the instillation of drugs directly into the GI system.

Equipment and preparation

• Check the chart and the medication administration record.
• Gather equipment for use at the bedside, including prescribed drug, towel or linen-saver pad, 50- or 60-ml piston-type catheter-tip syringe, feeding tubing, two 4″ × 4″ gauze pads, stethoscope, gloves, diluent (juice, water, or a nutritional supplement), cup for mixing drug and fluid, spoon, 50-ml cup of water, and rubber band. You may also need pill-crushing equipment and a clamp, if it's not already attached to the tube.
• Make sure that liquids are at room temperature to avoid abdominal cramping and that the cup, syringe, spoon, and gauze are clean.

Implementation

• Wash your hands and put on gloves.
• Confirm the patient's identity using two patient identifiers.
• Make sure the patient isn't allergic to the drug or any of its components.
• Unpin the tube from the patient's gown. To avoid soiling the sheets during the procedure, fold back the bed linens and drape the patient's chest with a towel or linen-saver pad.
• Help the patient into Fowler position, if possible.
• After unclamping the tube, auscultate the patient's abdomen about 3″ (8 cm) below the sternum as you gently insert 10 ml of air into the tube with the 50- or 60-ml syringe. You

should hear the air bubble entering the stomach. Gently draw back on the piston of the syringe. The appearance of gastric contents indicates that the tube is patent and is properly placed in the stomach.

• If no gastric contents appear or if you meet resistance, the tube may be lying against the gastric mucosa. Withdraw the tube slightly or turn the patient to free it.

• Clamp the tube, detach the syringe, and lay the end of the tube on the 4″ × 4″ gauze pad.

• If the drug is a tablet, crush it before mixing it with the diluent. Make sure the particles are small enough to pass through the eyes at the distal end of the tube. Some drugs (extended release, enteric-coated, or S.L. drugs, for example) shouldn't be crushed. If you aren't sure, ask the pharmacist. Also, check to see if the drug comes as a liquid form or if a capsule may be opened and the contents poured into a diluent. Pour liquid drugs into the diluent and stir well.

• Reattach the syringe, without the piston, to the end of the tube. Holding the tube upright at a level slightly above the patient's nose, open the clamp and pour the drug in slowly and steadily, as shown below.

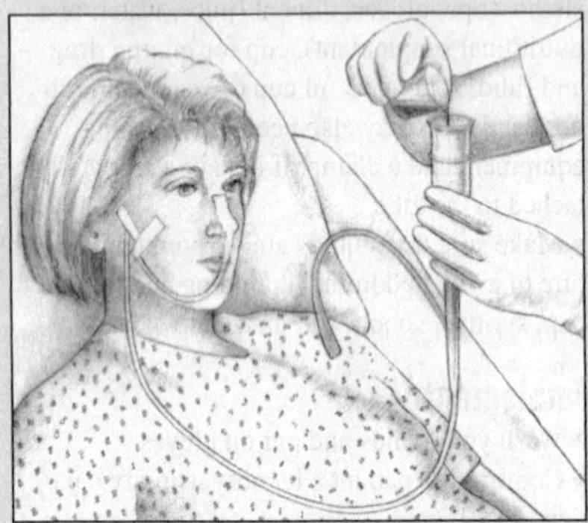

• To keep air from entering the patient's stomach, hold the tube at a slight angle and add more drug before the syringe empties. If the drug flows smoothly, slowly give the entire dose. If it doesn't flow, it may be too thick. If so, dilute it with water. If you suspect that tube placement is inhibiting flow, stop the procedure and reevaluate the placement.

• Watch the patient's reaction. If you see signs of discomfort, stop immediately.

• As the last of the drug flows out of the syringe, start to irrigate the tube by adding 30 to 50 ml of water (15 to 30 ml for a child). Irrigating clears drug from the tube and reduces the risk of clogging.

• When the water stops flowing, clamp the tube. Detach the syringe, and discard it properly.

• Fasten the tube to the patient's gown, and make the patient comfortable.

• Leave the patient in Fowler position or on his right side with his head partially elevated for at least 30 minutes to ease flow and prevent esophageal reflux.

• Remove and discard your gloves and wash your hands.

Nursing considerations

• If you must give a tube feeding and a drug, give the drug first to make sure the patient receives the entire drug.

• Certain drugs—such as phenytoin (Dilantin)—bind with tube feedings, decreasing the availability of the drug. Stop the tube feeding for 2 hours before and after the dose, according to your facility's policy.

• If residual stomach contents exceed 150 ml, withhold the drug and feeding, and notify the prescriber. Excessive stomach contents may indicate intestinal obstruction or paralytic ileus.

• Never crush enteric-coated, buccal, S.L., or sustained-release drugs.

• If suction is on, turn it off for 20 to 30 minutes after giving a drug.

Otic administration

Eardrops may be instilled to treat infection and inflammation, to soften cerumen for removal, to produce local anesthesia, or to remove an insect trapped in the ear.

Equipment and preparation

• Check the chart and the medication administration record.

• Gather the eardrops, gloves, a light, and facial tissue or cotton-tipped applicators. Cotton balls and a bowl of warm water may be needed.

• First, warm the drug to body temperature in the bowl of warm water, or carry the drug in your pocket for 30 minutes before giving. Test the temperature of the drug by placing a drop on your wrist. If the drug is too hot, it may burn the patient's eardrum.

• To avoid injuring the ear canal, check the dropper before use to make sure it's not chipped or cracked.

Implementation

• Wash your hands and put on gloves.

• Confirm the patient's identity using two patient identifiers.

• Make sure the patient isn't allergic to the drug or any of its components.

• Have the patient lie on the side opposite the affected ear.

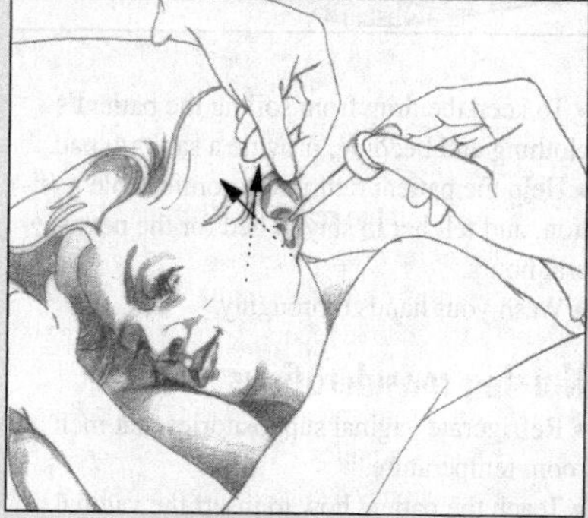

• Straighten the patient's ear canal. For an adult, pull the auricle up and back, as shown above. For a child younger than age 3, pull the auricle down and back, as shown below, because the ear canal is straighter at this age.

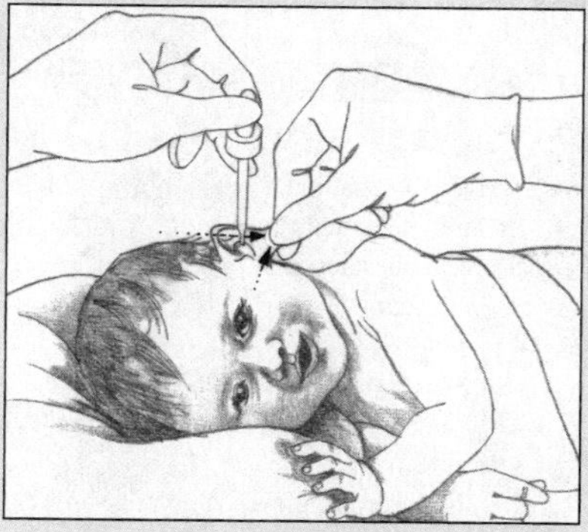

• Using a light, examine the ear canal for drainage. If you see drainage, gently clean the canal with the tissue or cotton-tipped applicators because drainage can reduce the effectiveness of the drug. Never insert an applicator past the point where you can see it.

• Compare the label on the eardrops to the order on the patient's medication record. Check the label again while drawing the drug into the dropper. Check the label for the final time before giving the eardrops.

• Straighten the patient's ear canal once again, and instill the proper number of drops. For the patient's comfort, aim the dropper so that the drops fall against the sides of the ear canal, not on the eardrum. Hold the ear canal in position until you see the drug disappear down the canal. Then release the ear.

• To avoid damaging the ear canal with the dropper, especially with a struggling child, it may be necessary to gently rest the hand that is holding the dropper against the patient's head to secure a safe position before giving the drug.

• Instruct the patient to remain on his side for 5 to 10 minutes to allow the drug to run down into the ear canal.

• Tuck a cotton ball with a small amount of petroleum jelly on it loosely into the opening of the ear canal to prevent the drug from leaking out. Don't insert the cotton too deeply into the canal because this may prevent secretions from draining and may increase pressure on the eardrum.

• Clean and dry the outer ear.

• If needed, repeat the procedure in the other ear after 5 to 10 minutes.

• Help the patient into a comfortable position.

• Remove your gloves and wash your hands.

Nursing considerations

• Some conditions make the normally tender ear canal even more sensitive, so be especially gentle.

• To prevent injury to the eardrum, never insert a cotton-tipped applicator into the ear canal past the point where you can see the tip.

• After instilling eardrops to soften cerumen, irrigate the ear to remove.

• If the patient has vertigo, keep the side rails of his bed up and assist him as needed during the procedure. Also, move slowly to avoid worsening his vertigo.

• Teach the patient to instill the eardrops himself so that he can continue treatment at home. Have him try it himself while you observe.

Vaginal administration

Vaginal drugs can be inserted as topical treatment for infection, particularly *Trichomonas vaginalis* and vaginal candidiasis or inflammation. Suppositories melt when they contact the vaginal mucosa, and the drug diffuses topically.

Vaginal drugs usually come with a disposable applicator that enables placement of drug in the anterior and posterior fornices. Vaginal administration is most effective when the patient can remain lying down afterward to retain the drug.

Equipment and preparation

- Check the chart and the medication administration record.
- Gather the prescribed drug and applicator, gloves, water-soluble lubricant, and a small sanitary pad.

Implementation

- If possible, give vaginal drugs at bedtime when the patient is lying down.
- Confirm the patient's identity using two patient identifiers.
- Make sure the patient isn't allergic to the drug or any of its components.
- Wash your hands, explain the procedure to the patient, and provide privacy.
- Ask the patient to void.
- Ask the patient if she would prefer to insert the drug herself and give instruction.
- Help the patient into the lithotomy position. Drape her, exposing only the perineum.
- Remove the suppository from the wrapper and lubricate it with water-soluble lubricant.
- Put on gloves and expose the vagina by spreading the labia. If you see discharge, wash the area with several cotton balls soaked in warm, soapy water. Clean each side of the perineum and then the center, using a fresh cotton ball for each stroke. Rinse well with clean, warm water. While the labia are still separated, insert the suppository or vaginal applicator about 3″ to 4″ (7.6 to 10 cm) into the vagina, as shown at the top of the next column.
- After insertion, wash the applicator with soap and warm water, and store or discard it. Label it so it will be used only for this patient.
- Remove and discard gloves.

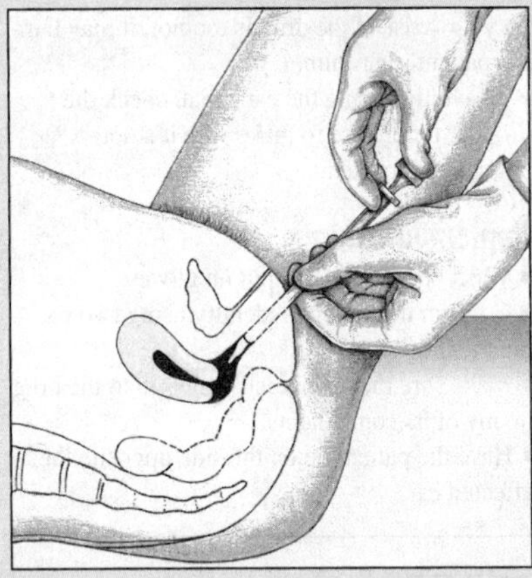

- To keep the drug from soiling the patient's clothing and bedding, provide a sanitary pad.
- Help the patient return to a comfortable position, and tell her to stay in bed for the next several hours.
- Wash your hands thoroughly.

Nursing considerations

- Refrigerate vaginal suppositories that melt at room temperature.
- Teach the patient how to insert the vaginal drug because she may have to insert it herself after she is discharged. Give her instructions in writing, if possible.
- Instruct the patient not to insert a tampon after inserting a vaginal drug because the tampon will absorb the drug and decrease its effectiveness.

4

Drug administration safety

Nurses carry a great deal of responsibility for administering drugs safely and correctly, for making sure the right patient gets the right drug, in the right dose, at the right time, and by the right route. By staying aware of potential trouble areas, you can minimize your risk of making medication errors and maximize the therapeutic effects of your patients' drug regimens.

Name game

Drugs with similar-sounding names can be easily confused. Even different-sounding names can look similar when written rapidly by hand on a prescription form. An example is Soriatane and Loxitane, which are both capsules. If the patient's drug order doesn't seem right for his diagnosis, call the prescriber to clarify the order.

Allergy alert

Once you've verified your patient's full name, check to see if he's wearing an allergy bracelet. If he is, the allergy bracelet should conspicuously display the name of the allergen. The allergy information also should be labeled on the front of the patient's chart and on his medication record. Whether the patient is wearing an allergy bracelet or not, take the time to double-check and ask the patient whether he has any allergies—even if he's in distress.

A patient who's severely allergic to peanuts could have an anaphylactic reaction to ipratropium bromide (Atrovent) aerosol given by metered-dose inhaler. Ask your patient or his parents whether he's allergic to peanuts before you give this drug. If you find that he is allergic, you'll need to use the nasal spray and inhalation solution form of the drug. Because it doesn't contain soy lecithin, it's safe for patients allergic to peanuts.

Compound errors

Many medication errors occur because of a compound problem—a mistake or group of mistakes that could have been caught at any of several steps along the way. For a drug to be given correctly, each member of the health care team must fill the appropriate role:

- The prescriber must write the order correctly and legibly.
- The pharmacist must evaluate whether the order is appropriate and fill it correctly.
- The nurse must evaluate whether the order is appropriate and give it correctly.

A breakdown anywhere along this chain of events can lead to a medication error. That's why it's so important for members of the health care team to act as a real team so that they can check each other and catch any problems that might arise before those problems affect the patient's health. Encourage an environment in which professionals double-check each other.

Route trouble

Many drug errors happen, at least in part, from problems related to the route of administration. The risk of error increases when a patient has several I.V. lines running for different purposes.

Risky abbreviations

Abbreviating drug names is risky. Abbreviations may not be commonly known and, in some cases, the same abbreviation may be used for different drugs or compounds. For example, epoetin alfa is commonly abbreviated EPO; however, some use the abbreviation EPO to stand for "evening primrose oil." Ask all prescribers to spell out drug names.

Unclear orders

A patient was supposed to receive one dose of the antineoplastic lomustine to treat brain cancer. (Lomustine typically is given as a single oral dose once every 6 weeks.) The doctor's order read, "Administer h.s." Because a nurse misinterpreted the order to mean every night, the patient received nine daily doses, developed severe thrombocytopenia and leukopenia, and died.

If you're unfamiliar with a drug, check a drug book before giving it. If a prescriber uses "h.s." and doesn't specify the frequency of administration, ask him to clarify the order. When documenting orders, note "at bedtime nightly" or "at bedtime one dose today."

Color changes

If a familiar drug seems to have an unfamiliar appearance, investigate the cause. If the pharmacist cites a manufacturing change, ask him to double-check whether he has received verification from the manufacturer. Always document the appearance discrepancy, your actions, and the pharmacist's response in the patient record.

Stress levels

Committing a serious error can cause enormous stress and cloud your judgment. If you're involved in a drug error, ask another professional to give the antidote.

Drug Classifications

Alkylating drugs

altretamine
busulfan
carboplatin
carmustine
chlorambucil
cisplatin
cyclophosphamide
dacarbazine
ifosfamide
lomustine
mechlorethamine hydrochloride
melphalan
procarbazine hydrochloride
thiotepa

Indications

▶ Various tumors, especially those with large volume and slow cell-turnover rate.

Contraindications and cautions

- Contraindicated in patients hypersensitive to these drugs.
- Use cautiously in patients receiving other cell-destroying drugs or radiation therapy.

Lifespan: In pregnant women, use only when potential benefits to the mother outweigh known risks to the fetus. Breast-feeding women should stop breast-feeding during therapy because drugs are found in breast milk. In children, safety and effectiveness of many alkylating drugs haven't been established. Elderly patients have an increased risk of adverse reactions; monitor these patients closely.

Adverse reactions

The most common adverse reactions are anxiety, bone marrow depression, chills, diarrhea, fever, flank pain, hair loss, leukopenia, nausea, redness or pain at the injection site, sore throat, swelling of the feet or lower legs, thrombocytopenia, and vomiting.

Action

Alkylating drugs appear to act independently of a specific cell-cycle phase. They are polyfunctional compounds that can be divided chemically into five groups: nitrogen mustards, ethyleneimines, alkyl sulfonates, triazines, and nitrosoureas. These drugs are highly reactive; they primarily target nucleic acids and form links with the nuclei of different molecules. This allows the drugs to cross-link double-stranded DNA and to prevent strands from separating for replication, which may contribute to these drugs' ability to destroy cells.

NURSING PROCESS

Assessment

- Perform a complete assessment before therapy begins.
- Monitor patient for adverse reactions throughout therapy.
- Monitor platelet and total and differential leukocyte counts, hematocrit, and BUN, ALT, AST, LDH, bilirubin, creatinine, uric acid, and other levels as needed.
- Monitor vital signs and patency of catheter or I.V. line throughout administration.

Key nursing diagnoses

- Ineffective protection related to thrombocytopenia
- Risk for infection related to immunosuppression
- Risk for deficient fluid volume related to adverse GI effects

Planning and implementation

- Give under the supervision of a physician experienced in the use of antineoplastics.
- Follow established procedures for safe and proper handling, administration, and disposal of chemotherapeutic drugs.
- Treat extravasation promptly.
- While giving carboplatin or cisplatin, keep epinephrine, corticosteroids, and antihistamines available. Anaphylactoid reactions may occur.
- Give ifosfamide with mesna to prevent hemorrhagic cystitis.
- Give lomustine 2 to 4 hours after meals. Nausea and vomiting usually last less than 24 hours, although loss of appetite may last for several days.
- Maintain adequate hydration before and for 24 hours after cisplatin treatment.
- Allopurinol may be prescribed to prevent drug-induced hyperuricemia.

Patient teaching

- Tell patient to avoid people with bacterial or viral infections because chemotherapy can in-

Prototype drug

crease susceptibility. Urge him to report signs of infection promptly.
- Review proper oral hygiene, including cautious use of toothbrush, dental floss, and toothpicks.
- Advise patient to complete dental work before therapy begins or to delay it until blood counts are normal.
- Warn patient that he may bruise easily because of drug's effect on blood count.

Evaluation
- Patient develops no serious bleeding complications.
- Patient remains free from infection.
- Patient maintains adequate hydration.

Alpha blockers (peripherally acting)

alfuzosin hydrochloride (selective)
doxazosin mesylate (nonselective)
prazosin hydrochloride (nonselective)
tamsulosin hydrochloride (selective)
terazosin hydrochloride (nonselective)

Indications

▶ Hypertension, or mild to moderate urinary obstruction in men with BPH.

Contraindications and cautions

- Contraindicated in patients with MI, coronary insufficiency, or angina or with hypersensitivity to these drugs or any of their components. Also contraindicated in combination therapy with phosphodiesterase type 5 inhibitors (sildenafil, tadalafil, vardenafil), although tadalafil may be taken with tamsulosin 0.4 mg daily.

Lifespan: In pregnant or breast-feeding women, use cautiously. In children, the safety and effectiveness of many alpha blockers haven't been established; use cautiously. In elderly patients, hypotensive effects may be more pronounced.

Adverse reactions

Alpha blockers may cause severe orthostatic hypotension and syncope, especially with the first few doses, an effect commonly called the "first-dose effect." The most common adverse effects of $alpha_1$ blockade are dizziness, headache, drowsiness, somnolence, and malaise. These drugs also may cause tachycardia, palpitations, fluid retention (from excess renin secretion), nasal and ocular congestion, and aggravation of respiratory tract infection.

Action

Selective alpha blockers decrease vascular resistance and increase vein capacity, thereby lowering blood pressure and causing nasal and scleroconjunctival congestion, ptosis, orthostatic and exercise hypotension, mild to moderate miosis, interference with ejaculation, and pink, warm skin. They also relax nonvascular smooth muscle, especially in the prostate capsule, which reduces urinary problems in men with BPH. Because $alpha_1$ blockers don't block $alpha_2$ receptors, they don't cause transmitter overflow.

Nonselective alpha blockers antagonize both $alpha_1$ and $alpha_2$ receptors. Generally, alpha blockade results in tachycardia, palpitations, and increased renin secretion because of abnormally large amounts of norepinephrine (from transmitter overflow) released from adrenergic nerve endings as a result of the blockade of $alpha_1$ and $alpha_2$ receptors. Norepinephrine's effects are counterproductive to the major uses of nonselective alpha blockers.

NURSING PROCESS

Assessment
- Monitor vital signs, especially blood pressure.
- Monitor patient closely for adverse reactions.

Key nursing diagnoses
- Decreased cardiac output related to hypotension
- Acute pain related to headache
- Excessive fluid volume related to fluid retention

Planning and implementation
- Give at bedtime to minimize dizziness or light-headedness.
- Begin therapy with a small dose to avoid first-dose syncope.

Patient teaching
- Warn patient not to rise suddenly from a lying or sitting position.

• Urge patient to avoid hazardous tasks that require mental alertness until the drug's full effects are known.
• Advise patient that alcohol, excessive exercise, prolonged standing, and heat exposure will intensify adverse effects.
• Tell patient to report promptly dizziness or irregular heartbeat.
• Caution patient to speak to his prescriber before taking a drug for erectile dysfunction.

Evaluation
• Patient maintains adequate cardiac output.
• Patient's headache is relieved.
• Patient has no edema.

Aminoglycosides

amikacin sulfate
gentamicin sulfate
neomycin sulfate
streptomycin sulfate
tobramycin sulfate

Indications

▶ Septicemia; postoperative, pulmonary, intra-abdominal, and urinary tract infections; skin, soft tissue, bone, and joint infections; aerobic gram-negative bacillary meningitis not susceptible to other antibiotics; serious staphylococcal, *Pseudomonas aeruginosa,* and *Klebsiella* infections; enterococcal infections; nosocomial pneumonia; anaerobic infections involving *Bacteroides fragilis;* tuberculosis; initial empiric therapy in febrile, leukopenic patients.

Contraindications and cautions

• Contraindicated in patients hypersensitive to these drugs.
• Use cautiously in patients with a neuromuscular disorder and in those taking neuromuscular blockades.
• Use at lower dosages in patients with renal impairment.
Lifespan: In pregnant women, use cautiously. In breast-feeding women, safety hasn't been established. In neonates and premature infants, the half-life of aminoglycosides is prolonged because of immature renal systems. In infants and children, dosage adjustment may be needed. Elderly patients have an increased risk of nephrotoxicity and commonly need a lower dose and longer intervals; they're also susceptible to ototoxicity and superinfection.

Adverse reactions

Ototoxicity and nephrotoxicity are the most serious complications. Neuromuscular blockade also may occur. Oral forms most commonly cause diarrhea, nausea, and vomiting. Parenteral drugs may cause vein irritation, phlebitis, and sterile abscess.

Action

Aminoglycosides are bactericidal. They bind directly and irreversibly to 30S ribosomal subunits, inhibiting bacterial protein synthesis. They're active against many aerobic gram-negative and some aerobic gram-positive organisms.

NURSING PROCESS

Assessment
• Obtain patient's history of allergies.
• Monitor patient for adverse reactions.
• Obtain results of culture and sensitivity tests before first dose, and check tests periodically to assess drug effectiveness.
• Monitor vital signs and electrolyte levels. Conduct hearing ability and renal function studies before and during therapy.
• Draw blood for peak level 1 hour after I.M. injection and 30 minutes to 1 hour after I.V. infusion; for trough level, draw sample just before next dose. Time and date all blood samples. Don't use heparinized tube to collect blood samples because it interferes with results.

Key nursing diagnoses
• Risk for injury related to nephrotoxicity and ototoxicity
• Risk for infection related to drug-induced superinfection
• Risk for deficient fluid volume related to adverse GI reactions

Planning and implementation
• Keep patient hydrated to minimize chemical irritation of renal tubules.
• Don't add or mix other drugs with I.V. infusions, particularly penicillins, which inactivate

aminoglycosides. If other drugs must be given I.V., temporarily stop infusion of primary drug.
• Follow manufacturer's instructions for reconstitution, dilution, and storage of drugs; check expiration dates.
• Shake oral suspension well before giving it.
• Give I.M. dose deep into the gluteal muscle mass or midlateral thigh; rotate injection sites to minimize tissue injury. Apply ice to injection site to relieve pain.
• Giving I.V. dose too rapidly may cause neuromuscular blockade. Infuse I.V. dose continuously or intermittently over 30 to 60 minutes for adults, 1 to 2 hours for infants; dilution volume for children is determined individually.

Patient teaching

• Teach signs and symptoms of hypersensitivity and other adverse reactions. Urge patient to report unusual effects promptly.
• Emphasize importance of adequate fluid intake.

Evaluation

• Patient maintains pretreatment renal and hearing functions.
• Patient is free from infection.
• Patient maintains adequate hydration.

Angiotensin-converting enzyme inhibitors

benazepril hydrochloride
captopril
enalapril maleate
enalaprilat
fosinopril sodium
lisinopril
moexipril hydrochloride
perindopril erbumine
quinapril hydrochloride
ramipril
trandolapril

Indications

▶ Hypertension, heart failure, left ventricular dysfunction (LVD), MI (with ramipril and lisinopril), and diabetic nephropathy (with captopril).

Contraindications and cautions

• Contraindicated in patients hypersensitive to these drugs.
• Use cautiously in patients with impaired renal function or serious autoimmune disease and in those taking other drugs known to decrease WBC count or immune response.

Lifespan: Women of childbearing age taking ACE inhibitors should report suspected pregnancy immediately to prescriber. High risks of fetal morbidity and mortality are linked to ACE inhibitors, especially in the second and third trimesters. Some ACE inhibitors appear in breast milk. To avoid adverse effects in infants, instruct patient to stop breast-feeding during therapy. In children, safety and effectiveness haven't been established; give drug only if potential benefits outweighs risks. Elderly patients may need lower doses because of impaired drug clearance.

Adverse reactions

The most common adverse effects of therapeutic doses are angioedema of the face and limbs, dry cough, dysgeusia, fatigue, headache, hyperkalemia, hypotension, proteinuria, rash, and tachycardia. Severe hypotension may occur at toxic drug levels.

Action

ACE inhibitors prevent conversion of angiotensin I to angiotensin II, a potent vasoconstrictor. Besides decreasing vasoconstriction and thus reducing peripheral arterial resistance, inhibiting angiotensin II decreases adrenocortical secretion of aldosterone. This reduces sodium and water retention and extracellular fluid volume. ACE inhibition also causes increased levels of bradykinin, which results in vasodilation. This decreases heart rate and systemic vascular resistance.

NURSING PROCESS

Assessment

• Observe patient for adverse reactions.
• Monitor vital signs regularly, and monitor WBC count and electrolyte level periodically.

Key nursing diagnoses

• Risk for trauma related to orthostatic hypotension

- Ineffective protection related to hyperkalemia
- Acute pain related to headache

Planning and implementation

- To reduce risk of hypotension, stop diuretic 2 to 3 days before starting ACE inhibitor. If drug doesn't adequately control blood pressure, diuretics may be restarted.
- If patient has impaired renal function, give a reduced dosage.
- Give potassium supplements and potassium-sparing diuretics cautiously because ACE inhibitors may cause potassium retention.
- If patient becomes pregnant, stop ACE inhibitors. These drugs can cause birth defects or fetal death in the second and third trimesters.
- Give captopril and moexipril 1 hour before meals.

Patient teaching

- Tell patient that drugs may cause a dry, persistent, tickling cough that stops when therapy stops.
- Urge patient to report light-headedness, especially in the first few days of therapy so that the dosage can be adjusted. Tell him to report signs of infection, such as sore throat and fever, because these drugs may decrease WBC count; facial swelling or difficulty breathing, because these drugs may cause angioedema; and loss of taste, for which therapy may stop.
- Advise patient to avoid sudden position changes to minimize orthostatic hypotension.
- Warn patient to seek medical approval before taking self-prescribed cold preparations.
- Tell women to report pregnancy at once.
- Warn patient to use salt substitutes containing potassium cautiously because ACE inhibitors may cause potassium retention.

Evaluation

- Patient sustains no injury from orthostatic hypotension.
- Patient's WBC count remains normal throughout therapy.
- Patient's headache is relieved by mild analgesic.

Antacids

aluminum hydroxide
calcium carbonate
magaldrate
magnesium hydroxide
magnesium oxide
sodium bicarbonate

Indications

▶ Hyperacidity; hyperphosphatemia (aluminum hydroxide); hypomagnesemia (magnesium oxide); postmenopausal hypocalcemia (calcium carbonate).

Contraindications and cautions

- Calcium carbonate, magaldrate, and magnesium oxide are contraindicated in patients with severe renal disease. Sodium bicarbonate is contraindicated in patients with hypertension, renal disease, or edema; patients who are vomiting; patients receiving diuretics or continuous GI suction; and patients on sodium-restricted diets.
- In patients with mild renal impairment, give magnesium oxide cautiously.
- Give aluminum preparations, calcium carbonate, and magaldrate cautiously in elderly patients; in those receiving antidiarrheals, antispasmodics, or anticholinergics; and in those with dehydration, fluid restriction, chronic renal disease, or suspected intestinal absorption problems.

Lifespan: Pregnant women should consult their prescriber before using antacids. Breastfeeding women may take antacids. In infants, serious adverse effects are more likely from changes in fluid and electrolyte balance; monitor them closely. Elderly patients have an increased risk of adverse reactions; monitor them closely; also, give these patients aluminum preparations, calcium carbonate, magaldrate, and magnesium oxide cautiously.

Adverse reactions

Antacids containing aluminum may cause aluminum intoxication, constipation, hypophosphatemia, intestinal obstruction, and osteomalacia. Antacids containing magnesium may cause diarrhea or hypermagnesemia (in renal failure). Calcium carbonate, magaldrate, magnesium oxide, and sodium bicarbonate may cause constipation, milk-alkali syndrome, or rebound hyperacidity.

Action

Antacids reduce the total acid load in the GI tract and elevate gastric pH to reduce pepsin activity. They also strengthen the gastric mucosal barrier and increase esophageal sphincter tone.

NURSING PROCESS

Assessment

- Assess patient's condition before therapy and regularly thereafter.
- Record number and consistency of stools.
- Observe patient for adverse reactions.
- Monitor patient receiving long-term, high-dose aluminum carbonate and hydroxide for fluid and electrolyte imbalance, especially if patient is on a sodium-restricted diet.
- Monitor phosphate level in a patient taking aluminum carbonate or hydroxide.
- Watch for signs of hypercalcemia in a patient taking calcium carbonate.
- Monitor magnesium level in a patient with mild renal impairment who takes magaldrate.

Key nursing diagnoses

- Constipation related to adverse effects of aluminum-containing antacid
- Diarrhea related to adverse effects of magnesium-containing antacid
- Ineffective protection related to drug-induced electrolyte imbalance

Planning and implementation

- Manage constipation with laxatives or stool softeners, or switch patient to a magnesium preparation.
- If patient suffers from diarrhea, give an antidiarrheal, and switch patient to an antacid containing aluminum.
- Shake container well, and give with small amount of water or juice to facilitate passage. When giving through an NG tube, make sure the tube is patent and placed correctly. After instilling the drug, flush the tube with water to ensure passage to the stomach and to clear the tube.

Patient teaching

- Warn patient not to take antacids randomly or to switch antacids without prescriber's consent.
- Tell patient not to take calcium carbonate with milk or other foods high in vitamin D.
- Warn patient not to take sodium bicarbonate with milk because doing so could cause hypercalcemia.

Evaluation

- Patient regains normal bowel pattern.
- Patient states that diarrhea is relieved.
- Patient maintains normal electrolyte balance.

Antianginals

Beta blockers

acebutolol
atenolol
bisoprolol fumarate
esmolol hydrochloride
metoprolol
nadolol
propranolol hydrochloride

Calcium channel blockers

amlodipine besylate
diltiazem hydrochloride
nicardipine hydrochloride
nifedipine
verapamil hydrochloride

Nitrates

isosorbide dinitrate
isosorbide mononitrate
nitroglycerin

Indications

▶ Moderate to severe angina (beta blockers); classic, effort-induced angina and Prinzmetal angina (calcium channel blockers); recurrent angina (long-acting nitrates and topical, transdermal, transmucosal, and oral extended-release nitroglycerin); acute angina (S.L. nitroglycerin and S.L. or chewable isosorbide dinitrate); unstable angina (I.V. nitroglycerin).

Contraindications and cautions

- Beta blockers are contraindicated in patients hypersensitive to them and in patients with cardiogenic shock, sinus bradycardia, heart block greater than first degree, or bronchial asthma. Calcium channel blockers are contraindicated in patients with severe hypotension or heart block greater than first degree (except with functioning pacemaker). Nitrates are contraindicated in patients with severe anemia, cerebral hemorrhage, head trauma, glaucoma, or hyperthyroidism or in patients using phosphodiesterase type 5 inhibitors (sildenafil, tadalafil, vardenafil).

• Use beta blockers cautiously in patients with nonallergic bronchospastic disorders, diabetes mellitus, or impaired hepatic or renal function. Use calcium channel blockers cautiously in patients with hepatic or renal impairment, bradycardia, heart failure, or cardiogenic shock. Use nitrates cautiously in patients with hypotension or recent MI.

Lifespan: In pregnant women, use beta blockers cautiously. Recommendations for breast-feeding vary by drug; use beta blockers and calcium channel blockers cautiously. In children, safety and effectiveness haven't been established. Check with prescriber before giving these drugs to children. Elderly patients have an increased risk of adverse reactions; use cautiously.

Adverse reactions

Beta blockers may cause bradycardia, cough, diarrhea, disturbing dreams, dizziness, dyspnea, fatigue, fever, heart failure, hypotension, lethargy, nausea, peripheral edema, and wheezing. Calcium channel blockers may cause bradycardia, confusion, constipation, depression, diarrhea, dizziness, dyspepsia, edema, elevated liver enzyme levels (transient), fatigue, flushing, headache, hypotension, insomnia, nervousness, and rash. Nitrates may cause alcohol intoxication (from I.V. preparations containing alcohol), flushing, headache, orthostatic hypotension, reflex tachycardia, rash, syncope, and vomiting.

Action

Beta blockers decrease catecholamine-induced increases in heart rate, blood pressure, and myocardial contraction. Calcium channel blockers inhibit the flow of calcium through muscle cells, which dilates coronary arteries and decreases systemic vascular resistance, known as afterload. Nitrates decrease afterload and left ventricular end-diastolic pressure, or preload, and increase blood flow through collateral coronary vessels.

NURSING PROCESS

Assessment

• Monitor vital signs. With I.V. nitroglycerin, monitor blood pressure and pulse rate every 5 to 15 minutes while adjusting dosage and every hour thereafter.
• Monitor the drug's effectiveness.
• Observe patient for adverse reactions.

Key nursing diagnoses

• Risk for injury related to adverse reactions
• Excessive fluid volume related to adverse CV effects of beta blockers or calcium channel blockers
• Acute pain related to headache

Planning and implementation

• Have patient sit or lie down when receiving the first nitrate dose; take his pulse and blood pressure before giving dose and when drug action starts.
• Don't give a beta blocker or calcium channel blocker to relieve acute angina.
• Withhold the dose and notify prescriber if patient's heart rate is slower than 60 beats/minute or systolic blood pressure is lower than 90 mm Hg.

Patient teaching

• Warn patient not to stop drug abruptly without prescriber's approval.
• Teach patient to take his pulse before taking a beta blocker or calcium channel blocker. Tell him to withhold the dose and alert the prescriber if his pulse rate is slower than 60 beats/minute.
• Instruct patient taking nitroglycerin S.L. to go to the emergency department if 3 tablets taken 5 minutes apart don't relieve angina.
• Caution patient about the dangers of using nitrates with certain erectile dysfunction drugs.
• Tell patient to report serious or persistent adverse reactions.

Evaluation

• Patient sustains no injury from adverse reactions.
• Patient maintains normal fluid balance.
• Patient's headache is relieved with mild analgesic.

Antiarrhythmics

adenosine
Class IA
disopyramide
moricizine hydrochloride
procainamide hydrochloride
quinidine bisulfate
quinidine gluconate
quinidine sulfate
Class IB
lidocaine hydrochloride
mexiletine hydrochloride
phenytoin sodium
Class IC
flecainide acetate
propafenone hydrochloride
Class II (beta blockers)
acebutolol hydrochloride
esmolol hydrochloride
propranolol hydrochloride
Class III
amiodarone hydrochloride
bretylium tosylate
dofetilide
ibutilide fumarate
sotalol hydrochloride
Class IV (calcium channel blocker)
verapamil hydrochloride

Indications

▶ Atrial and ventricular arrhythmias.

Contraindications and cautions

- Contraindicated in patients hypersensitive to these drugs.
- Many antiarrhythmics are contraindicated or require cautious use in patients with cardiogenic shock, digitalis toxicity, and second- or third-degree heart block (unless patient has a pacemaker).

Lifespan: In pregnant women, use only if potential benefits to the mother outweigh risks to the fetus. In breast-feeding women, use cautiously; many antiarrhythmics appear in breast milk. In children, monitor closely because they have an increased risk of adverse reactions. In elderly patients, use these drugs cautiously because these patients may exhibit physiologic alterations in CV system.

Adverse reactions

Most antiarrhythmics can aggravate existing arrhythmias or cause new ones. They also may produce CNS disturbances, such as dizziness or fatigue, GI problems, such as nausea, vomiting, or altered bowel elimination; hypersensitivity reactions; and hypotension. Some antiarrhythmics may worsen heart failure. Class II drugs may cause bronchoconstriction.

Action

Class I drugs reduce the inward current carried by sodium ions, which stabilizes neuronal cardiac membranes. Class IA drugs depress phase 0, prolong the action potential, and stabilize cardiac membranes. Class IB drugs depress phase 0, shorten the action potential, and stabilize cardiac membranes. Class IC drugs block the transport of sodium ions, which decreases conduction velocity but not repolarization rate. Moricizine is a class I drug that possesses characteristics of the IA, B, and C classes. Class II drugs decrease the heart rate, myocardial contractility, blood pressure, and AV node conduction. Class III drugs prolong the action potential and refractory period. Class IV drugs decrease myocardial contractility and oxygen demand by inhibiting calcium ion influx; they also dilate coronary arteries and arterioles.

NURSING PROCESS

Assessment

- Monitor ECG continuously when therapy starts and when dosage is adjusted.
- Monitor patient's vital signs frequently, and assess for signs of toxicity and adverse reactions.
- Measure apical pulse rate before giving drug.
- Monitor drug level as indicated.

Key nursing diagnoses

- Decreased cardiac output related to arrhythmias or myocardial depression
- Ineffective protection related to adverse reactions
- Noncompliance related to long-term therapy

Planning and implementation

- Don't crush sustained-release tablets.
- Take safety precautions if adverse CNS reactions occur.
- Notify prescriber about adverse reactions.

Patient teaching

- Stress the importance of taking drug exactly as prescribed.
- Teach patient to take his pulse before each dose. Tell him to notify prescriber if his pulse is irregular or slower than 60 beats/minute.
- Instruct patient to avoid hazardous activities that require mental alertness if adverse CNS reactions occur.
- Tell patient to limit fluid and salt intake if his prescribed drug causes fluid retention.

Evaluation

- Patient maintains adequate cardiac output, as shown by normal vital signs and adequate tissue perfusion.
- Patient has no serious adverse reactions.
- Patient states importance of compliance with therapy.

Antibiotic antineoplastics

bleomycin sulfate
daunorubicin hydrochloride
doxorubicin hydrochloride
epirubicin hydrochloride
idarubicin hydrochloride
mitomycin
mitoxantrone hydrochloride

Indications

▶ Various tumors.

Contraindications and cautions

- Contraindicated in patients hypersensitive to these drugs.

Lifespan: In pregnant women, avoid antineoplastics. Breast-feeding during therapy isn't recommended. In children, safety and effectiveness of some drugs haven't been established; use cautiously. In elderly patients, use cautiously because of their increased risk of adverse reactions.

Adverse reactions

The most common adverse reactions include anxiety, bone marrow depression, chills, confusion, diarrhea, fever, flank or joint pain, hair loss, leukopenia, nausea, redness or pain at the injection site, sore throat, swelling of the feet or lower legs, and vomiting.

Action

Although classified as antibiotics, these drugs destroy cells, thus ruling out their use as antimicrobials alone. They interfere with proliferation of malignant cells in several ways. Their action may be specific to cell-cycle phase, not specific to cell-cycle phase, or both. Some of these drugs act like alkylating drugs or antimetabolites. By binding to or creating complexes with DNA, antibiotic antineoplastics directly or indirectly inhibit DNA, RNA, and protein synthesis.

NURSING PROCESS

Assessment

- Perform a complete assessment before therapy begins.
- Monitor patient for adverse reactions.
- Monitor vital signs and patency of catheter or I.V. line.
- Monitor platelet and total and differential leukocyte counts, and monitor ALT, AST, LDH, bilirubin, creatinine, uric acid, BUN, and hemoglobin levels and hematocrit.
- Monitor pulmonary function tests in a patient receiving bleomycin. Assess lung function regularly.
- Monitor ECG before and during treatment with daunorubicin and doxorubicin.

Key nursing diagnoses

- Ineffective protection related to thrombocytopenia
- Risk for infection related to immunosuppression
- Risk for deficient fluid volume related to adverse GI effects

Planning and implementation

- Follow established procedures for safe and proper handling, administration, and disposal of chemotherapeutic drugs.
- Try to ease anxiety in patient and family before treatment.
- Keep epinephrine, corticosteroids, and antihistamines available during bleomycin therapy. Anaphylactoid reaction may occur.
- Treat extravasation promptly.

• Ensure adequate hydration during idarubicin therapy.
• Stop procarbazine and notify prescriber if patient becomes confused or neuropathies develop.

Patient teaching

• Advise patient to avoid exposure to people with bacterial or viral infections because chemotherapy increases susceptibility. Urge him to report signs of infection immediately.
• Review proper oral hygiene, including cautious use of toothbrush, dental floss, and toothpicks. Chemotherapy can increase the risk of microbial infection, delayed healing, and bleeding gums.
• Urge patient to complete dental work before therapy begins or to delay it until blood counts are normal.
• Warn patient that he may bruise easily.
• Tell patient to report redness, pain, or swelling at injection site immediately. Local tissue injury and scarring may result if I.V. infiltration occurs.
• Advise patient taking daunorubicin, doxorubicin, or idarubicin that his urine may turn orange or red for 1 to 2 days after therapy begins.

Evaluation

• No serious bleeding complications develop.
• Patient remains free from infection.
• Patient maintains adequate hydration.

Anticholinergics

atropine sulfate
benztropine mesylate
dicyclomine hydrochloride
scopolamine
scopolamine hydrobromide

Indications

▶ Prevention of motion sickness, preoperative reduction of secretions and blockage of cardiac reflexes, adjunct treatment of peptic ulcers and other GI disorders, blockage of cholinomimetic effects of cholinesterase inhibitors or other drugs, and (for benztropine) various spastic conditions, including acute dystonic reactions, muscle rigidity, parkinsonism, and extrapyramidal disorders.

Contraindications and cautions

• Contraindicated in patients hypersensitive to these drugs and in those with angle-closure glaucoma, renal or GI obstructive disease, reflux esophagitis, or myasthenia gravis.
• Use cautiously in patients with heart disease, GI infection, open-angle glaucoma, prostatic hypertrophy, hypertension, hyperthyroidism, ulcerative colitis, autonomic neuropathy, or hiatal hernia with reflux esophagitis.

Lifespan: In pregnant women, safe use hasn't been established. In breast-feeding women, avoid anticholinergics because they may decrease milk production; some may appear in breast milk and cause infant toxicity. In children, safety and effectiveness haven't been established. Patients older than age 40 may be more sensitive to these drugs. In elderly patients, use cautiously and give a reduced dosage, as indicated.

Adverse reactions

Therapeutic doses commonly cause blurred vision, constipation, cycloplegia, decreased sweating or anhidrosis, dry mouth, headache, mydriasis, palpitations, tachycardia, and urinary hesitancy and retention. These reactions usually disappear when therapy stops. Toxicity can cause signs and symptoms resembling psychosis (disorientation, confusion, hallucinations, delusions, anxiety, agitation, and restlessness); dilated, nonreactive pupils; blurred vision; hot, dry, flushed skin; dry mucous membranes; dysphagia; decreased or absent bowel sounds; urine retention; hyperthermia; tachycardia; hypertension; and increased respirations.

Action

Anticholinergics competitively antagonize the actions of acetylcholine and other cholinergic agonists at muscarinic receptors.

NURSING PROCESS

Assessment

• Monitor patient regularly for adverse reactions.
• Check vital signs at least every 4 hours.
• Measure urine output; check for urine retention.

• Assess patient for changes in vision and for signs of impending toxicity.

Key nursing diagnoses
• Urinary retention related to adverse effect on bladder
• Constipation related to adverse effect on GI tract
• Acute pain related to headache

Planning and implementation
• Provide ice chips, cool drinks, or hard candy to relieve dry mouth.
• Relieve constipation with stool softeners or bulk laxatives.
• Give a mild analgesic for headache.
• Notify prescriber about urine retention, and be prepared to catheterize patient, if needed.

Patient teaching
• Teach patient how and when to take the drug and caution him not to take other drugs unless prescribed.
• Warn patient to avoid hazardous tasks if he experiences dizziness, drowsiness, or blurred vision. Inform him that the drug may increase his sensitivity to or intolerance of high temperatures, resulting in dizziness.
• Advise patient to avoid alcohol because it may cause additive CNS effects.
• Urge patient to drink plenty of fluids and to eat a high-fiber diet to prevent constipation.
• Tell patient to notify prescriber promptly if he experiences confusion, rapid or pounding heartbeat, dry mouth, blurred vision, rash, eye pain, significant change in urine volume, or pain or difficulty on urination.
• Advise women to report planned or known pregnancy.

Evaluation
• Patient maintains normal voiding pattern.
• Patient regains normal bowel patterns.
• Patient is free from pain.

Anticoagulants

Coumarin derivative
warfarin sodium
Heparin derivative
heparin sodium
Low-molecular-weight heparins
dalteparin sodium
enoxaparin sodium
tinzaparin sodium
Selective factor Xa inhibitor
fondaparinux sodium
Thrombin inhibitors
argatroban
bivalirudin

Indications

▶ Pulmonary emboli, deep vein thrombosis, thrombus, blood clotting, DIC, unstable angina, MI, atrial fibrillation.

Contraindications and cautions

• Contraindicated in patients hypersensitive to these drugs or any of their components; in patients with aneurysm, active bleeding, CV hemorrhage, hemorrhagic blood dyscrasias, hemophilia, severe hypertension, pericardial effusions, or pericarditis; and in patients undergoing major surgery, neurosurgery, or ophthalmic surgery.
• Use cautiously in patients with severe diabetes, renal impairment, severe trauma, ulcerations, or vasculitis.

Lifespan: Most anticoagulants (except warfarin) may be used in pregnancy only if clearly necessary. In pregnant women and those who have just had a threatened or complete spontaneous abortion, warfarin is contraindicated. Women should avoid breast-feeding during therapy. Infants, especially neonates, may be more susceptible to anticoagulants because of vitamin K deficiency. Elderly patients are at greater risk for hemorrhage because of altered hemostatic mechanisms or age-related deterioration of hepatic and renal functions.

Adverse reactions

Anticoagulants commonly cause bleeding and may cause hypersensitivity reactions. Warfarin may cause agranulocytosis, alopecia (long-term use), anorexia, dermatitis, fever, nausea, tissue necrosis or gangrene, urticaria, and vomiting. Heparin derivatives may cause thrombocytopenia and may increase liver enzyme levels. Nonhemorrhagic adverse reactions associated with thrombin inhibitors may include back pain, bradycardia, and hypotension.

Action

Heparin derivatives accelerate formation of an antithrombin III-thrombin complex. It inactivates thrombin and prevents conversion of fibrinogen to fibrin. The coumarin derivative warfarin inhibits vitamin K–dependent activation of clotting factors II, VII, IX, and X, which are formed in the liver. Thrombin inhibitors directly bind to thrombin and inhibit its action. Selective factor Xa inhibitors bind to antithrombin III, which in turn initiates the neutralization of factor Xa.

NURSING PROCESS

Assessment

- Monitor patient closely for bleeding and other adverse reactions.
- Check PT, INR, or PTT.
- Monitor vital signs, hemoglobin, and hematocrit.
- Assess patient's urine, stools, and emesis for blood.

Key nursing diagnoses

- Ineffective protection related to drug's effects on body's normal clotting and bleeding mechanisms
- Risk for deficient fluid volume related to bleeding
- Noncompliance related to long-term warfarin therapy

Planning and implementation

- Don't give heparin I.M., and avoid I.M. injections of any anticoagulant if possible.
- Keep protamine sulfate available to treat severe bleeding caused by heparin. Keep vitamin K available to treat frank bleeding caused by warfarin.
- Notify prescriber about serious or persistent adverse reactions.
- Maintain bleeding precautions throughout therapy.

Patient teaching

- Urge patient to take drug exactly as prescribed. If he's taking warfarin, tell him to take it at night and to have blood drawn for PT or INR in the morning for accurate results.
- Advise patient to consult his prescriber before taking any other drug, including OTC medications and herbal remedies.
- Review bleeding-prevention precautions to take in everyday living. Urge patient to remove safety hazards and make home repairs to reduce risk of injury.
- Advise patient not to increase his intake of green, leafy vegetables because vitamin K may antagonize anticoagulant effects.
- Instruct patient to report bleeding or other adverse reactions promptly.
- Encourage patient to keep appointments for blood tests and follow-up examinations.
- Advise woman to report planned or known pregnancy.

Evaluation

- Patient has no adverse change in health status.
- Patient has no evidence of bleeding or hemorrhaging.
- Patient demonstrates compliance with therapy, as shown by normal bleeding and clotting values.

Anticonvulsants

carbamazepine
clonazepam
clorazepate dipotassium
diazepam
divalproex sodium
fosphenytoin sodium
gabapentin
lamotrigine
levetiracetam
magnesium sulfate
oxcarbazepine
phenobarbital
phenobarbital sodium
phenytoin sodium
phenytoin sodium (extended)
primidone
tiagabine hydrochloride
topiramate

valproate sodium
valproic acid
zonisamide

Indications

▶ Seizure disorders; acute, isolated seizures not caused by seizure disorders; status epilepticus; prevention of seizures after trauma or craniotomy; neuropathic pain.

Contraindications and cautions

- Contraindicated in patients hypersensitive to these drugs.
- Carbamazepine is contraindicated within 14 days of MAO inhibitor use.
- Use cautiously in patients with blood dyscrasias. Also, use barbiturates cautiously in patients with suicidal ideation.

Lifespan: In pregnant women, therapy usually continues despite the fetal risks caused by some anticonvulsants (barbiturates, phenytoin). In breast-feeding women, the safety of many anticonvulsants hasn't been established. Children, especially young ones, are sensitive to the CNS depression of some anticonvulsants; use cautiously. Elderly patients are sensitive to CNS effects and may require lower doses. Also, some anticonvulsants may take longer to be eliminated because of decreased renal function, and parenteral use is more likely to cause apnea, hypotension, bradycardia, and cardiac arrest.

Adverse reactions

Anticonvulsants can cause adverse CNS effects, such as ataxia, confusion, somnolence, and tremor. Many anticonvulsants also cause CV disorders, such as arrhythmias and hypotension; GI effects, such as vomiting; and hematologic disorders, such as agranulocytosis, bone marrow depression, leukopenia, and thrombocytopenia. Stevens-Johnson syndrome, other severe rashes, and abnormal liver function test results may occur with certain anticonvulsants.

Action

Anticonvulsants include six classes of drugs: selected hydantoin derivatives, barbiturates, benzodiazepines, succinimides, iminostilbene derivatives (carbamazepine), and carboxylic acid derivatives. Magnesium sulfate is a miscellaneous anticonvulsant. Some hydantoin derivatives and carbamazepine inhibit the spread of seizure activity in the motor cortex. Some barbiturates and succinimides limit seizure activity by increasing the threshold for motor cortex stimuli. Selected benzodiazepines and carboxylic acid derivatives may increase inhibition of GABA in brain neurons. Magnesium sulfate interferes with the release of acetylcholine at the myoneural junction.

NURSING PROCESS

Assessment

- Monitor drug level and patient's response as indicated.
- Monitor patient for adverse reactions.
- Assess patient's compliance with therapy at each follow-up visit.

Key nursing diagnoses

- Risk for trauma related to adverse reactions
- Impaired physical mobility related to sedation
- Noncompliance related to long-term therapy

Planning and implementation

- Give oral forms with food to reduce GI irritation.
- Phenytoin binds with tube feedings, thus decreasing absorption of drug. Turn off tube feedings for 2 hours before and after giving phenytoin, according to your facility's policy.
- Adjust dosage according to patient's response.
- Take safety precautions if patient has adverse CNS reactions.

Patient teaching

- Instruct patient to take drug exactly as prescribed and not to stop drug without medical supervision.
- Urge patient to avoid hazardous activities that require mental alertness if adverse CNS reactions occur.
- Advise patient to wear or carry medical identification at all times.

Evaluation

- Patient sustains no trauma from adverse reactions.
- Patient maintains physical mobility.
- Patient complies with therapy and has no seizures.

Antidepressants, tricyclic

amitriptyline hydrochloride
amoxapine
clomipramine hydrochloride
desipramine hydrochloride
doxepin hydrochloride
imipramine hydrochloride
imipramine pamoate
nortriptyline hydrochloride

Indications

▶ Depression, anxiety (doxepin hydrochloride), obsessive-compulsive disorder (clomipramine), enuresis in children older than age 6 (imipramine).

Contraindications and cautions

- Contraindicated in patients hypersensitive to these drugs and in patients with urine retention or angle-closure glaucoma.
- Tricyclic antidepressants are contraindicated within 2 weeks of MAO inhibitor therapy.
- Use cautiously in patients with suicidal tendencies, schizophrenia, paranoia, seizure disorders, CV disease, or impaired hepatic function.

Lifespan: In pregnant and breast-feeding women, safety hasn't been established; use cautiously. In children younger than age 12, tricyclic antidepressants aren't recommended. Elderly patients are more sensitive to therapeutic and adverse effects; they need lower dosages.

Adverse reactions

Adverse reactions include anticholinergic effects, orthostatic hypotension, and sedation. The tertiary amines (amitriptyline, doxepin, and imipramine) exert the strongest sedative effects; tolerance usually develops in a few weeks. Amoxapine is most likely to cause seizures, especially with overdose. Tricyclic antidepressants may cause cardiovascular effects such as T-wave abnormalities, conduction disturbances, and arrhythmias.

Action

Tricyclic antidepressants may inhibit reuptake of norepinephrine and serotonin in CNS nerve terminals (presynaptic neurons), thus enhancing the concentration and activity of neurotransmitters in the synaptic cleft. Tricyclic antidepressants also exert antihistaminic, sedative, anticholinergic, vasodilatory, and quinidine-like effects.

NURSING PROCESS

Assessment

- Observe patient for mood changes to monitor drug effectiveness; benefits may not appear for 3 to 6 weeks.
- Check vital signs regularly for tachycardia or decreased blood pressure; observe patient carefully for other adverse reactions and report changes. Check ECG in patients older than age 40 before starting therapy.
- Monitor patient for anticholinergic adverse reactions, such as urine retention or constipation, which may require dosage reduction.

Key nursing diagnoses

- Disturbed thought processes related to adverse effects
- Risk for injury related to sedation and orthostatic hypotension
- Noncompliance related to long-term therapy

Planning and implementation

- Make sure patient swallows each dose; a depressed patient may hoard pills for suicide attempt, especially when symptoms begin to improve.
- Don't withdraw drug abruptly; instead, gradually reduce dosage over several weeks to avoid rebound effect or other adverse reactions.

Patient teaching

- Explain to patient the rationale for therapy and its anticipated risks and benefits. Inform patient that full therapeutic effect may not occur for several weeks.
- Teach patient how and when to take the drug. Warn him not to increase dosage, stop taking the drug, or take any other drug, including OTC medicines and herbal remedies, without medical approval.
- Because overdose with tricyclic antidepressants is commonly fatal, entrust a reliable family member with the drug, and warn him to store drug safely away from children.
- Advise patient not to take drug with milk or food to minimize GI distress. Suggest taking full dose at bedtime if daytime sedation is a problem.
- Tell patient to avoid alcohol.

• Advise patient to avoid hazardous tasks that require mental alertness until full effects of drug are known.
• Warn patient that excessive exposure to sunlight, heat lamps, or tanning beds may cause burns and abnormal hyperpigmentation.
• Urge diabetic patient to monitor his glucose level carefully because drug may alter it.
• Recommend sugarless gum or hard candy, artificial saliva, or ice chips to relieve dry mouth.
• Advise patient to report adverse reactions promptly.

Evaluation

• Patient regains normal thought processes.
• Patient sustains no injury from adverse reactions.
• Patient complies with therapy, and his depression is alleviated.

Antidiabetics

acarbose
glimepiride
glipizide
glyburide
metformin hydrochloride
miglitol
nateglinide
pioglitazone hydrochloride
repaglinide
rosiglitazone maleate

Indications

▶ Mild to moderately severe, stable, nonketotic, type 2 diabetes mellitus that can't be controlled by diet alone.

Contraindications and cautions

• Contraindicated in patients hypersensitive to these drugs and in patients with diabetic ketoacidosis with or without coma. Metformin is also contraindicated in patients with renal disease or metabolic acidosis and generally should be avoided in patients with hepatic disease.
• Use sulfonylureas cautiously in patients with renal or hepatic disease. Use metformin cautiously in patients with adrenal or pituitary insufficiency and in debilitated and malnourished patients. Alpha-glucosidase inhibitors should be used cautiously in patients with mild to moderate renal insufficiency. Thiazolidinediones aren't recommended in patients with edema, heart failure, or liver disease.

Lifespan: In pregnant or breast-feeding women, use is contraindicated. Oral antidiabetics appear in small amounts in breast milk and may cause hypoglycemia in the infant. In children, oral antidiabetics aren't effective in type 1 diabetes mellitus. Elderly patients may be more sensitive to these drugs, usually need lower dosages, and are more likely to develop neurologic symptoms of hypoglycemia; monitor these patients closely. In elderly patients, avoid chlorpropamide use because of its long duration of action.

Adverse reactions

Sulfonylureas cause dose-related reactions that usually respond to decreased dosage: anorexia, headache, heartburn, nausea, paresthesia, vomiting, and weakness. Hypoglycemia may follow excessive dosage, increased exercise, decreased food intake, or alcohol use.

The most serious adverse reaction linked to metformin is lactic acidosis. It's rare and most likely to occur in patients with renal dysfunction. Other reactions to metformin include dermatitis, GI upset, megaloblastic anemia, rash, and unpleasant or metallic taste.

Thiazolidinediones may cause fluid retention leading to or exacerbating heart failure. Alpha-glucosidase inhibitors can cause abdominal pain, diarrhea, and flatulence.

Action

Oral antidiabetics come in several types. Sulfonylureas are sulfonamide derivatives that aren't antibacterial. They lower glucose levels by stimulating insulin release from the pancreas. These drugs work only in the presence of functioning beta cells in the islet tissue of the pancreas. After prolonged administration, they produce hypoglycemia by acting outside of the pancreas, including reduced glucose production by the liver and enhanced peripheral sensitivity to insulin. The latter may result from an increased number of insulin receptors or from changes after insulin binding. Sulfonylureas are divided into first-generation drugs, such as chlorpropamide, and second-generation drugs, such as glyburide, glimepiride, and glipizide. Although their mechanisms of action are similar, the second-generation drugs carry a more lipophilic side chain, are more potent, and cause fewer adverse reactions. Their most important difference is their duration of action.

Meglitinides, such as nateglinide and repaglinide, are nonsulfonylurea antidiabetics that stimulate the release of insulin from the pancreas.

Metformin decreases hepatic glucose production, reduces intestinal glucose absorption, and improves insulin sensitivity by increasing peripheral glucose uptake and utilization. With metformin therapy, insulin secretion remains unchanged, and fasting insulin levels and all-day insulin response may decrease.

Alpha-glucosidase inhibitors, such as acarbose and miglitol, delay digestion of carbohydrates, resulting in a smaller rise in glucose levels.

Rosiglitazone and pioglitazone are thiazolidinediones, which lower glucose levels by improving insulin sensitivity. These drugs are potent and highly selective agonists for receptors found in insulin-sensitive tissues, such as adipose, skeletal muscle, and liver.

NURSING PROCESS

Assessment

- Monitor patient's glucose level regularly. Increase monitoring during periods of increased stress, such as infection, fever, surgery, or trauma.
- Monitor patient for adverse reactions.
- Assess patient's compliance with drug therapy and other aspects of diabetic treatment.

Key nursing diagnoses

- Risk for injury related to hypoglycemia
- Risk for deficient fluid volume related to adverse GI effects
- Noncompliance related to long-term therapy

Planning and implementation

- Give sulfonylurea 30 minutes before morning meal for once-daily regimen or 30 minutes before morning and evening meals for twice-daily regimen. Give metformin with morning and evening meals. Alpha-glucosidase inhibitors should be taken with the first bite of each main meal three times daily.
- Patients who take a thiazolidinedione should have liver enzyme levels measured at the start of therapy, every 2 months for the first year of therapy, and periodically thereafter.
- Keep in mind that a patient transferring from one oral antidiabetic to another (except chlorpropamide) usually needs no transition period.
- Anticipate patient's need for insulin during periods of increased stress.

Patient teaching

- Emphasize importance of following the prescribed regimen. Urge patient to adhere to diet, weight reduction, exercise, and personal hygiene recommendations.
- Explain that therapy relieves symptoms but doesn't cure the disease.
- Teach patient how to recognize and treat hypoglycemia.

Evaluation

- Patient sustains no injury.
- Patient maintains adequate hydration.
- Patient complies with therapy, as shown by normal or near-normal glucose level.

Antidiarrheals

bismuth subgallate
bismuth subsalicylate
calcium polycarbophil
diphenoxylate hydrochloride and atropine sulfate
kaolin and pectin mixtures
loperamide hydrochloride
octreotide acetate
opium tincture
opium tincture, camphorated

Indications

▶ Mild, acute, or chronic diarrhea. Octreotide acetate is only indicated for diarrhea caused by tumors.

Contraindications and cautions

- Contraindicated in patients hypersensitive to these drugs.

Lifespan: Some antidiarrheals may appear in breast milk; check individual drugs for specific recommendations. For infants younger than age 2, don't give kaolin and pectin mixtures. For children or teenagers recovering from flu or chickenpox, consult prescriber before giving bismuth subsalicylate. For elderly patients, use caution when giving antidiarrheal drugs, especially opium preparations.

Adverse reactions

Bismuth preparations may cause salicylism (with high doses) or temporary darkening of tongue and stools. Kaolin and pectin mixtures may cause constipation and fecal impaction or ulceration. Opium preparations may cause dizziness, light-headedness, nausea, physical dependence (with long-term use), and vomiting.

Action

Bismuth preparations may have a mild water-binding capacity, may absorb toxins, and provide a protective coating for the intestinal mucosa. Kaolin and pectin mixtures decrease fluid in the stool by absorbing bacteria and toxins that cause diarrhea. Opium preparations increase smooth muscle tone in the GI tract, inhibit motility and propulsion, and decrease digestive secretions.

NURSING PROCESS

Assessment

- Assess patient's condition before therapy and regularly thereafter.
- Monitor fluid and electrolyte balance.
- Observe patient for adverse reactions.

Key nursing diagnoses

- Constipation related to adverse effect of bismuth preparations on GI tract
- Risk for injury related to adverse CNS reactions
- Risk for deficient fluid volume related to GI upset

Planning and implementation

- Take safety precautions if patient has adverse CNS reactions.
- Don't substitute opium tincture for paregoric.
- Notify prescriber about serious or persistent adverse reactions.

Patient teaching

- Instruct patient to take drug exactly as prescribed; warn that excessive use of opium preparations can lead to dependence.
- Instruct patient to notify prescriber if diarrhea lasts longer than 2 days and to report adverse reactions.
- Warn patient to avoid hazardous activities that require alertness if CNS depression occurs.

Evaluation

- Patient doesn't develop constipation.
- Patient isn't injured during therapy.
- Patient maintains adequate hydration.

Antihistamines

azelastine hydrochloride
brompheniramine maleate
cyproheptadine hydrochloride
desloratadine
diphenhydramine hydrochloride
fexofenadine hydrochloride
hydroxyzine embonate
hydroxyzine hydrochloride
hydroxyzine pamoate
loratadine
meclizine hydrochloride
promethazine hydrochloride

Indications

▶ Allergic rhinitis, urticaria, pruritus, vertigo, motion sickness, nausea and vomiting, sedation, dyskinesia, parkinsonism.

Contraindications and cautions

- Contraindicated in patients hypersensitive to these drugs and in those with angle-closure glaucoma, stenosing peptic ulcer, pyloroduodenal obstruction, or bladder neck obstruction. Also contraindicated in those taking MAO inhibitors.

Lifespan: In pregnant women, safe use hasn't been established. During breast-feeding, antihistamines shouldn't be used because many of these drugs appear in breast milk and may cause unusual excitability in the infant. Neonates, especially premature infants, may experience seizures. Children, especially those younger than age 6, may experience paradoxical hyperexcitability with restlessness, insomnia, nervousness, euphoria, tremors, and seizures; give cautiously. Elderly patients usually are more sensitive to the adverse effects of antihistamines, especially dizziness, sedation, hypotension, and urine retention; use cautiously and monitor these patients closely.

Adverse reactions

Most antihistamines cause drowsiness and impaired motor function early in therapy. They also can cause blurred vision, constipation, and dry mouth and throat. Some antihistamines, such as promethazine, may cause cholestatic jaundice, which may be a hypersensitivity reaction, and may predispose patients to photosensitivity. Promethazine may also cause extrapyramidal reactions with high doses.

Action

Antihistamines are structurally related chemicals that compete with histamine for histamine H_1-receptor sites on smooth muscle of bronchi, GI tract, and large blood vessels, binding to cellular receptors and preventing access to and subsequent activity of histamine. They don't directly alter histamine or prevent its release.

NURSING PROCESS

Assessment
- Monitor patient for adverse reactions.
- Monitor blood counts during long-term therapy; watch for signs of blood dyscrasia.

Key nursing diagnoses
- Risk for injury related to sedation
- Impaired oral mucous membrane related to dry mouth
- Constipation related to anticholinergic effect of antihistamines

Planning and implementation
- Reduce GI distress by giving antihistamines with food.
- Provide sugarless gum, hard candy, or ice chips to relieve dry mouth.
- Increase fluid intake or humidify air to decrease adverse effect of thickened secretions.

Patient teaching
- Advise patient to take drug with meals or snacks to prevent GI upset.
- Suggest that patient use warm water rinses, artificial saliva, ice chips, or sugarless gum or candy to relieve dry mouth. Tell him to avoid overusing mouthwash, which may worsen dryness and destroy normal flora.
- Warn patient to avoid hazardous activities until full CNS effects of drug are known.
- Tell patient to seek medical approval before using alcohol, tranquilizers, sedatives, pain relievers, or sleeping medications.
- For accurate diagnostic skin test results, advise patient to stop taking antihistamines 4 days before test.

Evaluation
- Patient sustains no injury from sedation.
- Patient maintains normal mucous membranes by using preventive measures throughout therapy.
- Patient maintains normal bowel function.

Antihypertensives

Angiotensin-converting enzyme inhibitors
benazepril hydrochloride
captopril
enalapril maleate
enalaprilat
fosinopril sodium
lisinopril
moexipril hydrochloride
perindopril erbumine
quinapril hydrochloride
ramipril
trandolapril

Angiotensin II receptor blockers
candesartan cilexetil
eprosartan mesylate
irbesartan
losartan potassium
olmesartan medoxomil
telmisartan
valsartan

Beta blockers
acebutolol hydrochloride
atenolol
bisoprolol fumarate
carvedilol
labetalol hydrochloride
metoprolol tartrate
nadolol
pindolol
propranolol hydrochloride
timolol maleate

Calcium channel blockers
amlodipine besylate
diltiazem hydrochloride
felodipine
nicardipine hydrochloride
nifedipine
nisoldipine
verapamil hydrochloride
Centrally acting alpha blockers (sympatholytics)
clonidine hydrochloride
guanfacine hydrochloride
methyldopa
Peripherally acting alpha blockers
doxazosin mesylate
prazosin hydrochloride
terazosin hydrochloride
Vasodilators
diazoxide
hydralazine hydrochloride
minoxidil
nitroprusside sodium

Indications

▶ Essential and secondary hypertension.

Contraindications and cautions

• Contraindicated in patients hypersensitive to these drugs and in those with hypotension.
• Use cautiously in patients with hepatic or renal dysfunction.
Lifespan: In pregnant women, use cautiously when potential benefits to the mother outweigh risks to the fetus. Check each drug because some are safe only in the first trimester. In breast-feeding women, use cautiously; some antihypertensives appear in breast milk. In children, safety and effectiveness of many antihypertensives haven't been established; give these drugs cautiously and monitor children closely. Elderly patients are more susceptible to adverse reactions and may need lower maintenance doses; monitor these patients closely.

Adverse reactions

Antihypertensives commonly cause orthostatic changes in heart rate, headache, hypotension, nausea, and vomiting. Other reactions vary greatly among different drug types. Centrally acting sympatholytics may cause constipation, depression, dizziness, drowsiness, dry mouth, headache, palpitations, severe rebound hypertension, and sexual dysfunction; methyldopa also may cause aplastic anemia and thrombocytopenia. Rauwolfia alkaloids may cause anxiety, depression, drowsiness, dry mouth, hyperacidity, impotence, nasal stuffiness, and weight gain. Vasodilators may cause ECG changes, diarrhea, dizziness, heart failure, palpitations, pruritus, and rash.

Action

For information on the action of ACE inhibitors, alpha blockers, angiotensin II receptor blockers, beta blockers, calcium channel blockers, and diuretics, see their individual drug class entries. Centrally acting sympatholytics stimulate central alpha-adrenergic receptors, reducing cerebral sympathetic outflow, thereby decreasing peripheral vascular resistance and blood pressure. Rauwolfia alkaloids bind to and gradually destroy the norepinephrine-containing storage vesicles in central and peripheral adrenergic neurons. Vasodilators act directly on smooth muscle to reduce blood pressure.

NURSING PROCESS

Assessment

• Obtain baseline blood pressure and pulse rate and rhythm; recheck regularly.
• Monitor patient for adverse reactions.
• Monitor patient's weight and fluid and electrolyte status.
• Monitor patient's compliance with treatment.

Key nursing diagnoses

• Risk for trauma related to orthostatic hypotension
• Risk for deficient fluid volume related to GI upset
• Noncompliance related to long-term therapy or adverse reactions

Planning and implementation

• Give drug with food or at bedtime, as indicated.
• When mixing and giving parenteral drugs, follow manufacturer's guidelines.
• Take steps to prevent or minimize orthostatic hypotension.
• Maintain patient's nondrug therapy, such as sodium restriction, calorie reduction, stress management, and exercise program.

Patient teaching

- Instruct patient to take drug exactly as prescribed. Warn against stopping drug abruptly.
- Review adverse reactions caused by drug, and urge patient to notify prescriber of serious or persistent reactions.
- To prevent dizziness, light-headedness, or fainting, advise patient to avoid sudden changes in position.
- Warn patient to avoid hazardous activities until full effects of drug are known. Also, warn patient to avoid physical exertion, especially in hot weather.
- Advise patient to consult prescriber before taking any OTC medications or herbal remedies; serious drug interactions can occur.
- Encourage patient to comply with therapy.

Evaluation

- Patient doesn't experience trauma from orthostatic hypotension.
- Patient maintains adequate hydration.
- Patient complies with therapy, as shown by normal blood pressure.

Antilipemics

atorvastatin calcium
cholestyramine
colesevelam hydrochloride
ezetimibe
fenofibrate
fluvastatin sodium
gemfibrozil
lovastatin
pravastatin sodium
rosuvastatin calcium
simvastatin

Indications

▶ Hyperlipidemia, hypercholesterolemia.

Contraindications and cautions

- Contraindicated in patients hypersensitive to these drugs. Also, bile-sequestering drugs are contraindicated in patients with complete biliary obstruction. Fibric acid derivatives are contraindicated in patients with primary biliary cirrhosis or significant hepatic or renal dysfunction. HMG-CoA reductase inhibitors and cholesterol absorption inhibitors are contraindicated in patients with active liver disease or persistently elevated transaminase levels.
- Use bile-sequestering drugs cautiously in constipated patients. Use fibric acid derivatives cautiously in patients with peptic ulcer. Use HMG-CoA inhibitors cautiously in patients who consume large amounts of alcohol or who have a history of liver or renal disease.

Lifespan: In pregnant women, use bile-sequestering drugs and fibric acid derivatives cautiously and avoid using HMG-CoA inhibitors. In breast-feeding women, avoid using fibric acid derivatives and HMG-CoA inhibitors; give bile-sequestering drugs cautiously. In children ages 10 to 17, certain antilipemics have been approved to treat heterozygous familial hypercholesterolemia. Elderly patients have an increased risk of severe constipation; use bile-sequestering drugs cautiously and monitor patients closely.

Adverse reactions

Antilipemics commonly cause GI upset. Bile-sequestering drugs may cause bloating, cholelithiasis, constipation, and steatorrhea. Fibric acid derivatives may cause cholelithiasis and have other GI or CNS effects. Use of gemfibrozil with lovastatin may cause myopathy. HMG-CoA reductase inhibitors may affect liver function or cause rash, pruritus, increased CK levels, rhabdomyolysis, and myopathy.

Action

Antilipemics lower elevated lipid levels. Bile-sequestering drugs (cholestyramine and colesevelam) lower LDL level by forming insoluble complexes with bile salts, thus triggering cholesterol to leave the bloodstream and other storage areas to make new bile acids. Fibric acid derivatives (gemfibrozil) reduce cholesterol formation, increase sterol excretion, and decrease lipoprotein and triglyceride synthesis. HMG-CoA reductase inhibitors (atorvastatin, fluvastatin, lovastatin, pravastatin, rosuvastatin, simvastatin) interfere with the activity of enzymes that generate cholesterol in the liver. Selective cholesterol absorption inhibitors (ezetimibe) inhibit cholesterol absorption by the small intestine, reducing hepatic cholesterol stores and increasing cholesterol clearance from the blood.

NURSING PROCESS

Assessment

- Monitor cholesterol and lipid levels before and periodically during therapy.
- Monitor CK level when therapy begins and every 6 months thereafter. Also, check CK level in a patient who complains of muscle pain.
- Monitor patient for adverse reactions.

Key nursing diagnoses

- Risk for deficient fluid volume related to adverse GI reactions
- Constipation related to adverse effect on bowel
- Noncompliance related to long-term therapy

Planning and implementation

- Mix powder form of bile-sequestering drugs with 120 to 180 ml of liquid. Never give dry powder alone because patient may inhale it accidentally.
- Give lovastatin with evening meal, simvastatin in the evening, and fluvastatin and pravastatin at bedtime.

Patient teaching

- Instruct patient to take drug exactly as prescribed. If he takes a bile-sequestering drug, warn him never to take the dry form.
- Stress importance of diet in controlling lipid levels.
- Advise patient to drink 2 to 3 L of fluid daily and to report persistent or severe constipation.

Evaluation

- Patient maintains adequate fluid volume.
- Patient doesn't experience severe or persistent constipation.
- Patient complies with therapy, as shown by normal lipid and cholesterol levels.

Antimetabolite antineoplastics

capecitabine
cytarabine
cytarabine liposomal
fludarabine phosphate
fluorouracil
hydroxyurea
mercaptopurine
methotrexate
pentostatin
thioguanine

Indications

▶ Various tumors.

Contraindications and cautions

- Contraindicated in patients hypersensitive to these drugs.

Lifespan: Pregnant women should be informed of the risks to the fetus. Breast-feeding isn't recommended for women taking these drugs. In children, safety and effectiveness of some drugs haven't been established; use cautiously. Elderly patients have an increased risk of adverse reactions; monitor them closely.

Adverse reactions

The most common adverse effects include anemia, anxiety, bone marrow depression, chills, diarrhea, fever, flank or joint pain, hair loss, leukopenia, nausea, redness or pain at injection site, thrombocytopenia, swelling of the feet or lower legs, and vomiting.

Action

Antimetabolites are structurally similar to naturally occurring metabolites and can be divided into three subcategories: purine, pyrimidine, and folinic acid analogues. Most of these drugs interrupt cell reproduction at a specific phase of the cell cycle. Purine analogues are incorporated into DNA and RNA, interfering with nucleic acid synthesis (by miscoding) and replication. They also may inhibit synthesis of purine bases through pseudofeedback mechanisms. Pyrimidine analogues inhibit enzymes in metabolic pathways that interfere with biosynthesis of uridine and thymine. Folic acid antagonists prevent conversion of folic acid to tetrahydrofolate by inhibiting the enzyme dihydrofolic acid reductase.

NURSING PROCESS

Assessment

- Perform a complete assessment before therapy begins.
- Monitor patient for adverse reactions.
- Monitor vital signs and patency of catheter or I.V. line throughout administration.

• Monitor platelet and total and differential leukocyte counts, hematocrit, and ALT, AST, LDH, bilirubin, creatinine, uric acid, and BUN levels.

Key nursing diagnoses
• Ineffective protection related to thrombocytopenia
• Risk for infection related to immunosuppression
• Risk for deficient fluid volume related to adverse GI effects

Planning and implementation
• Follow established procedures for safe and proper handling, administration, and disposal of drugs.
• Try to ease patient's and family's anxiety before treatment.
• Give an antiemetic to reduce nausea before giving drug.
• Give cytarabine with allopurinol to decrease the risk of hyperuricemia. Encourage patient to drink plenty of fluids.
• Provide diligent mouth care to prevent stomatitis with cytarabine, fluorouracil, or methotrexate therapy.
• Anticipate the need for leucovorin rescue with high-dose methotrexate therapy.
• Treat extravasation promptly.
• Anticipate diarrhea, possibly severe, with prolonged fluorouracil therapy.

Patient teaching
• Teach patient proper oral hygiene, including cautious use of toothbrush, dental floss, and toothpicks. Chemotherapy can increase the incidence of microbial infection, delayed healing, and bleeding gums.
• Advise patient to complete dental work before therapy begins or to delay it until blood counts are normal.
• Tell patient to defer immunizations if possible until hematologic stability is confirmed.
• Warn patient that he may bruise easily because of drug's effect on platelets.
• Advise patient to avoid close contact with people who have taken oral poliovirus vaccine or who have been exposed to people with bacterial or viral infection because chemotherapy may increase susceptibility. Urge patient to notify prescriber promptly if he develops signs or symptoms of infection.
• Instruct patient to report redness, pain, or swelling at injection site. Local tissue injury and scarring may result from tissue infiltration at infusion site.

Evaluation
• Patient doesn't have serious bleeding complications.
• Patient doesn't have an infection.
• Patient maintains adequate hydration.

Antiparkinsonians
amantadine hydrochloride
apomorphine hydrochloride
benztropine mesylate
bromocriptine mesylate
diphenhydramine hydrochloride
entacapone
levodopa
levodopa and carbidopa
levodopa, carbidopa, and entacapone
pergolide mesylate
pramipexole dihydrochloride
ropinirole hydrochloride
selegiline hydrochloride
tolcapone
trihexyphenidyl hydrochloride

Indications
Signs and symptoms of Parkinson disease and drug-induced extrapyramidal reactions.

Contraindications and cautions
• Contraindicated in patients hypersensitive to these drugs.
• Use cautiously in patients with prostatic hyperplasia or tardive dyskinesia and in debilitated patients.
• Neuroleptic malignant–like syndrome involving muscle rigidity, increased body temperature, and mental status changes may occur with abrupt withdrawal of antiparkinsonians.

Lifespan: In pregnant women, safe use hasn't been established. Antiparkinsonians may appear in breast milk; a decision should be made to stop the drug or stop breast-feeding, taking into account the importance of the drug to the mother. In children, safety and effectiveness haven't been established. Elderly patients have an increased risk for adverse reactions; monitor them closely.

Adverse reactions

Anticholinergics may cause blurred vision, cycloplegia, constipation, decreased sweating or anhidrosis, dry mouth, headache, mydriasis, palpitations, tachycardia, and urinary hesitancy and urine retention. Dopaminergics may cause arrhythmias, confusion, disturbing dreams, dystonias, hallucinations, headache, muscle cramps, nausea, orthostatic hypotension, and vomiting. Amantadine also causes irritability, insomnia, and livedo reticularis (with prolonged use).

Action

Antiparkinsonians include synthetic anticholinergics, dopaminergics, and the antiviral amantadine. Anticholinergics probably prolong the action of dopamine by blocking its reuptake into presynaptic neurons and by suppressing central cholinergic activity. Dopaminergics act in the brain by increasing dopamine availability, thus improving motor function. Entacapone is a reversible inhibitor of peripheral catechol-*O*-methyltransferase (commonly known as COMT), which is responsible for elimination of various catecholamines, including dopamine. Blocking this pathway when giving levodopa and carbidopa should result in higher levels of levodopa, thereby allowing greater dopaminergic stimulation in the CNS and leading to a greater effect in treating parkinsonian symptoms. Amantadine is thought to increase dopamine release in the substantia nigra.

NURSING PROCESS

Assessment
- Obtain baseline assessment of patient's impairment, and reassess regularly to monitor the drug's effectiveness.
- Monitor patient for adverse reactions.
- Monitor vital signs, especially during dosage adjustments.

Key nursing diagnoses
- Risk for injury related to adverse CNS effects
- Urinary retention related to anticholinergic effect on bladder
- Sleep disturbance related to amantadine-induced insomnia

Planning and implementation
- Give drug with food to prevent GI irritation.
- Adjust dosage according to patient's response and tolerance.
- Never withdraw drug abruptly.
- Institute safety precautions.
- Provide ice chips, drinks, or sugarless hard candy or gum to relieve dry mouth. Increase fluid and fiber intake to prevent constipation, as appropriate.
- Notify prescriber about urine retention, and be prepared to catheterize patient, if needed.

Patient teaching
- Instruct patient to take drug exactly as prescribed, and warn him not to suddenly stop taking the drug.
- Advise patient to take drug with food to prevent GI upset.
- Teach patient how to manage anticholinergic effects.
- Instruct patient to avoid hazardous tasks if adverse CNS effects occur. Tell him to avoid alcohol during therapy.
- Encourage patient to report severe or persistent adverse reactions.

Evaluation
- Patient remains free from injury.
- Patient's voiding pattern doesn't change.
- Patient's sleep pattern isn't altered by amantadine.

Barbiturates

amobarbital sodium
pentobarbital sodium
phenobarbital
phenobarbital sodium
primidone
secobarbital sodium

Indications

▶ Sedation, preanesthetic, short-term treatment of insomnia, seizure disorders.

Contraindications and cautions

- Contraindicated in patients hypersensitive to these drugs and in those with bronchopneumonia, other severe pulmonary insufficiency, or liver dysfunction.

Prototype drug

• Use cautiously in patients with blood pressure alterations, pulmonary disease, and CV dysfunction. Use cautiously, if at all, in patients who are depressed or have suicidal tendencies.

Lifespan: Barbiturates can cause fetal abnormalities; avoid use in pregnant women. Barbiturates appear in breast milk and may result in infant CNS depression; use cautiously. Premature infants are more susceptible to depressant effects of barbiturates because of their immature hepatic metabolism. Children may experience hyperactivity, excitement, or hyperalgesia; use cautiously and monitor closely. Elderly patients may experience hyperactivity, excitement, or hyperalgesia; use cautiously.

Adverse reactions

CNS depression, drowsiness, headache, lethargy, and vertigo are common with barbiturates. After hypnotic doses, a hangover effect, subtle distortion of mood, and impaired judgment and motor skills may continue for many hours. After dosage reduction or discontinuation, rebound insomnia or increased dreaming or nightmares may occur. Barbiturates cause hyperalgesia in subhypnotic doses. They can also cause paradoxical excitement at low doses, confusion in elderly patients, and hyperactivity in children. High fever, severe headache, stomatitis, conjunctivitis, or rhinitis may precede potentially fatal skin eruptions. Withdrawal symptoms may occur after as little as 2 weeks of uninterrupted therapy.

Action

Barbiturates act throughout the CNS, especially in the mesencephalic reticular activating system, which controls the CNS arousal mechanism. The main anticonvulsant actions are reduced nerve transmission and decreased excitability of the nerve cell. Barbiturates decrease presynaptic and postsynaptic membrane excitability by promoting the actions of GABA. They also depress respiration and GI motility and raise the seizure threshold.

NURSING PROCESS

Assessment

• To evaluate the drug's effectiveness, assess patient's level of consciousness and sleeping patterns before and during therapy. Monitor neurologic status for alteration or deterioration.
• Assess vital signs often, especially during I.V. use.
• Monitor seizure character, frequency, and duration for changes.
• Observe patient to prevent hoarding and taking extra doses, especially if patient is depressed, suicidal, or drug dependent.

Key nursing diagnoses

• Risk for injury related to sedation
• Disturbed thought processes related to confusion
• Risk-prone health behavior related to drug dependence

Planning and implementation

• When giving parenteral drug, inject I.V. or deep I.M., to avoid extravasation, which may cause local tissue damage and tissue necrosis. To avoid tissue damage, don't exceed 5 ml for any I.M. injection site.
• Keep resuscitative measures available. Giving I.V. drug too rapidly may cause respiratory depression, apnea, laryngospasm, or hypotension.
• Take seizure precautions as needed.
• Take precautions to prevent falls and injury. Raise side rails, help patient out of bed, and keep call light within easy reach.
• Stop drug slowly. Stopping drug abruptly may cause withdrawal symptoms.

Patient teaching

• Explain that barbiturates can cause physical or psychological dependence.
• Instruct patient to take drug exactly as prescribed. Warn him not to change the dosage or take other drugs, including OTC medications or herbal remedies, without prescriber's approval.
• Reassure patient that a morning hangover is common after therapeutic use of barbiturates.
• Advise patient to avoid hazardous tasks, driving a motor vehicle, or operating machinery while taking the drug, and to review other safety measures to prevent injury.
• Instruct patient to report skin eruptions or other significant adverse effects.

Evaluation

• Patient sustains no injury from sedation.
• Patient maintains normal thought processes.
• Patient doesn't develop physical or psychological dependence.

Benzodiazepines

alprazolam
chlordiazepoxide hydrochloride
clonazepam
clorazepate dipotassium
diazepam
estazolam
flurazepam hydrochloride
lorazepam
midazolam hydrochloride
oxazepam
quazepam
temazepam
triazolam

Indications

▶ Seizure disorders (clonazepam, clorazepate, diazepam, midazolam, parenteral lorazepam); anxiety, tension, and insomnia (chlordiazepoxide, clorazepate, diazepam, estazolam, flurazepam, lorazepam, oxazepam, quazepam, temazepam, triazolam); conscious sedation or amnesia in surgery (diazepam, lorazepam, midazolam); skeletal muscle spasm and tremor (oral forms of chlordiazepoxide and diazepam); delirium.

Contraindications and cautions

- Contraindicated in patients hypersensitive to these drugs, in those with acute angle-closure glaucoma, and in those with depressive neuroses or psychotic reactions in which anxiety isn't prominent.
- Avoid use in patients with suicidal tendencies and patients with a history of drug abuse.
- Use cautiously in patients with chronic pulmonary insufficiency or sleep apnea and in those with hepatic or renal insufficiency.

Lifespan: In pregnant patients, benzodiazepines increase the risk of congenital malformation if taken in the first trimester. Use during labor may cause neonatal flaccidity. A neonate whose mother took a benzodiazepine during pregnancy may have withdrawal symptoms. In breast-feeding mothers, benzodiazepines may cause sedation, feeding difficulties, and weight loss in the infant. In children, use caution; they're especially sensitive to CNS depressant effects. In elderly patients, benzodiazepine elimination may be prolonged; consider a lower dosage.

Adverse reactions

Therapeutic dose may cause drowsiness, impaired motor function, constipation, diarrhea, vomiting, altered appetite, urinary changes, visual disturbances, and CV irregularities. Toxic dose may cause continuing problems with short-term memory, confusion, severe depression, shakiness, vertigo, slurred speech, staggering, bradycardia, shortness of breath, difficulty breathing, or severe weakness. Prolonged or frequent use of benzodiazepines can cause physical dependency and withdrawal syndrome when drug is stopped.

Action

Benzodiazepines act selectively on polysynaptic neuronal pathways throughout the CNS. Precise sites and mechanisms of action aren't fully known. However, benzodiazepines enhance or facilitate the action of GABA, an inhibitory neurotransmitter in the CNS. These drugs appear to act at the limbic, thalamic, and hypothalamic levels of the CNS to produce anxiolytic, sedative, hypnotic, skeletal muscle relaxant, and anticonvulsant effects.

NURSING PROCESS

Assessment

- Assess level of consciousness and neurologic status before therapy and often during therapy. Monitor patient for paradoxical reactions, especially early in therapy.
- Observe sleep patterns and quality, and watch for changes in seizure character, frequency, or duration.
- Assess vital signs often during therapy. Significant changes in blood pressure and heart rate may indicate impending toxicity.

Key nursing diagnoses

- Anxiety related to underlying condition
- Risk for injury related to drug-induced CNS effects
- Decreased cardiac output related to hypotension

Planning and implementation

- Don't use benzodiazepines in patients with chronic pulmonary insufficiency, sleep apnea, depressive neuroses or psychotic reactions without predominant anxiety, or acute alcohol intoxication.

- Give dose with milk or just after a meal to prevent GI upset. Give antacid, if needed, at least 1 hour before or after dose to prevent interaction and ensure maximum drug absorption and effectiveness.
- Periodically monitor renal and hepatic function to ensure adequate drug removal and prevent cumulative effects.
- Institute safety measures—raised side rails and ambulatory assistance—to prevent injury. Anticipate possible rebound excitement.
- After prolonged use, stopping drug abruptly may cause withdrawal symptoms; instead, stop gradually.

Patient teaching

- To prevent additive depressant effects, caution patient to avoid use of alcohol or other CNS depressants, such as antihistamines, analgesics, MAO inhibitors, antidepressants, and barbiturates.
- Caution patient to take drug as prescribed and not to give drug to others. Tell him not to change the dose or frequency and to call before taking OTC cold or allergy medicines because they may worsen CNS depressant effects.
- Warn patient to avoid activities requiring alertness and good psychomotor coordination until the CNS response to the drug is determined. Instruct him in safety measures to prevent injury.
- Tell patient to avoid using antacids, which may delay drug absorption, unless prescribed.
- Make sure patient understands that benzodiazepines may cause physical and psychological dependence with prolonged use.
- Warn patient not to stop taking the drug abruptly to prevent withdrawal symptoms after prolonged therapy.
- Tell patient that smoking decreases drug effectiveness. Encourage patient to stop smoking during therapy.
- Tell patient to report adverse reactions. These are often dose-related and can be relieved by dosage adjustments.
- Inform a woman of childbearing age to contact prescriber if she suspects pregnancy or intends to become pregnant during therapy.

Evaluation

- Patient is less anxious.
- Patient sustains no injury from drug-induced CNS reactions.
- Patient's blood pressure stays within normal limits.

Beta blockers

Beta$_1$ blockers

acebutolol hydrochloride
atenolol
bisoprolol fumarate
esmolol hydrochloride
metoprolol tartrate

Beta$_1$ and beta$_2$ blockers

carvedilol
labetalol hydrochloride
nadolol
pindolol
propranolol hydrochloride
sotalol hydrochloride
timolol maleate

Indications

▶ Hypertension (most drugs), angina pectoris (atenolol, metoprolol, nadolol, and propranolol), arrhythmias (acebutolol hydrochloride, esmolol, propranolol, and sotalol), glaucoma (betaxolol and timolol), prevention of MI (atenolol, metoprolol, propranolol, and timolol), prevention of recurrent migraine and other vascular headaches (propranolol and timolol), pheochromocytomas or essential tremors (selected drugs), heart failure (atenolol, bisoprolol, carvedilol, metoprolol).

Contraindications and cautions

- Contraindicated in patients hypersensitive to these drugs and in patients with cardiogenic shock, sinus bradycardia, heart block greater than first degree, bronchial asthma, and heart failure unless failure is caused by tachyarrhythmia treatable with propranolol.
- Use cautiously in patients with nonallergic bronchospastic disorders, diabetes mellitus, or impaired hepatic or renal function.

Lifespan: In pregnant women, use cautiously. Drugs appear in breast milk. In children, safety and effectiveness haven't been established; use only if the benefits outweigh the risks. In elderly patients, use cautiously; these patients may need reduced maintenance doses because of increased bioavailability, delayed metabolism, and increased adverse effects.

Adverse reactions

Therapeutic dose may cause bradycardia, dizziness, and fatigue; some may cause other CNS disturbances, such as depression, hallucinations, memory loss, and nightmares. Toxic dose can produce severe hypotension, bradycardia, heart failure, or bronchospasm.

Action

Beta blockers compete with beta agonists for available beta receptors; individual drugs differ in their ability to affect beta receptors. Some drugs are nonselective: they block $beta_1$ receptors in cardiac muscle and $beta_2$ receptors in bronchial and vascular smooth muscle. Several drugs are cardioselective and, in lower doses, inhibit mainly $beta_1$ receptors. Some beta blockers have intrinsic sympathomimetic activity and stimulate and block beta receptors, thereby decreasing cardiac output. Others stabilize cardiac membranes, which affects cardiac action potential.

NURSING PROCESS

Assessment

- Check apical pulse rate daily; alert prescriber about extremes, such as a pulse rate lower than 60 beats/minute.
- Monitor blood pressure, ECG, and heart rate and rhythm frequently; be alert for progression of AV block or bradycardia.
- If patient has heart failure, weigh him regularly; watch for weight gain of more than 2.25 kg (5 lb) per week.
- Observe diabetic patients for sweating, fatigue, and hunger. Signs of hypoglycemic shock may be masked.

Key nursing diagnoses

- Risk for injury related to adverse CNS effects
- Excessive fluid volume related to edema
- Decreased cardiac output related to bradycardia or hypotension

Planning and implementation

- Stop beta blockers before surgery for pheochromocytoma. Before any surgical procedure, notify anesthesiologist that patient is taking a beta blocker.
- Keep glucagon nearby to reverse beta blocker overdose.

Patient teaching

- Teach patient to take drug exactly as prescribed, even when he feels better.
- Warn patient not to stop taking the drug suddenly. Stopping suddenly can worsen angina or precipitate MI.
- Tell patient not to take OTC medications or herbal remedies without prescriber's approval.
- Explain potential adverse reactions, and stress importance of reporting unusual effects.

Evaluation

- Patient remains free from injury.
- Patient has no signs of edema.
- Patient maintains normal blood pressure and heart rate.

Calcium channel blockers

amlodipine besylate
diltiazem hydrochloride
felodipine
nicardipine hydrochloride
nifedipine
nisoldipine
verapamil hydrochloride

Indications

▶ Prinzmetal variant angina, chronic stable angina, unstable angina, mild-to-moderate hypertension, arrhythmias.

Contraindications and cautions

- Contraindicated in patients hypersensitive to these drugs and in those with second- or third-degree heart block (except those with a pacemaker) and cardiogenic shock. Use diltiazem and verapamil cautiously in patients with heart failure.

Lifespan: In pregnant women, use cautiously. Calcium channel blockers may appear in breast milk; instruct patient to stop breastfeeding during therapy. In neonates and infants, adverse hemodynamic effects of parenteral verapamil are possible, but safety and effectiveness of other calcium channel blockers haven't been established; avoid use, if possible. In elderly patients, the half-life of calcium channel blockers may be increased as a result of decreased clearance; use cautiously.

Adverse reactions

Verapamil may cause bradycardia, hypotension, various degrees of heart block, and worsening of heart failure after rapid I.V. delivery. Prolonged oral verapamil therapy may cause constipation. Nifedipine may cause flushing, headache, heartburn, hypotension, light-headedness, and peripheral edema. The most common adverse reactions with diltiazem are anorexia and nausea; it also may induce bradycardia, heart failure, peripheral edema, and various degrees of heart block.

Action

The main physiologic action of calcium channel blockers is to inhibit calcium influx across the slow channels of myocardial and vascular smooth muscle cells. By inhibiting calcium flow into these cells, calcium channel blockers reduce intracellular calcium levels. This, in turn, dilates coronary arteries, peripheral arteries, and arterioles and slows cardiac conduction.

When used to treat Prinzmetal variant angina, calcium channel blockers inhibit coronary spasm, which then increases oxygen delivery to the heart. Peripheral artery dilation reduces afterload, which decreases myocardial oxygen use. Inhibiting calcium flow into specialized cardiac conduction cells in the SA and AV nodes slows conduction through the heart. Verapamil and diltiazem have the greatest effect on the AV node, which slows the ventricular rate in atrial fibrillation or flutter and converts supraventricular tachycardia to a normal sinus rhythm.

NURSING PROCESS

Assessment

- Monitor cardiac rate and rhythm and blood pressure carefully when therapy starts or dosage increases.
- Monitor fluids and electrolytes.
- Monitor patient for adverse reactions.

Key nursing diagnoses

- Decreased cardiac output related to adverse CV reactions
- Constipation related to oral verapamil therapy
- Noncompliance related to long-term therapy

Planning and implementation

- Don't give calcium supplements while patient is taking a calcium channel blocker; they may decrease the drug's effectiveness.
- Expect to decrease dosage gradually; don't stop calcium channel blockers abruptly.

Patient teaching

- Teach patient to take drug exactly as prescribed, even if he feels better.
- Instruct patient to take a missed dose as soon as possible, unless it's almost time for his next dose. Warn him never to take a double dose.
- Warn patient not to stop drug suddenly; abrupt discontinuation can produce serious adverse effects.
- Urge patient to report irregular heartbeat, shortness of breath, swelling of hands and feet, pronounced dizziness, constipation, nausea, or hypotension.

Evaluation

- Patient maintains adequate cardiac output throughout therapy, as shown by normal blood pressure and pulse rate.
- Patient regains normal bowel pattern.
- Patient complies with therapy, as shown by absence of symptoms related to disorder.

Cephalosporins

First generation

cefadroxil monohydrate
cefazolin sodium
cephalexin monohydrate

Second generation

cefaclor
cefoxitin sodium
cefprozil
cefuroxime axetil
cefuroxime sodium
loracarbef

Third generation

cefdinir
cefditoren pivoxil

cefixime
cefoperazone sodium
cefotaxime sodium
cefpodoxime proxetil
ceftazidime
ceftibuten
ceftizoxime sodium
ceftriaxone sodium

Indications

▶ Infections of the lungs, skin, soft tissue, bones, joints, urinary and respiratory tracts, blood, abdomen, and heart; CNS infections caused by susceptible strains of *Neisseria meningitidis, Haemophilus influenzae,* and *Streptococcus pneumoniae;* meningitis caused by *Escherichia coli* or *Klebsiella;* infections that develop after surgical procedures classified as contaminated or potentially contaminated; penicillinase-producing *N. gonorrhoeae;* otitis media and ampicillin-resistant middle ear infection caused by *H. influenzae.*

Contraindications and cautions

• Contraindicated in patients hypersensitive to these drugs.
• Use cautiously in patients with renal or hepatic impairment, history of GI disease, or allergy to penicillins.
Lifespan: In pregnant women, use cautiously; safety hasn't been definitively established. In breast-feeding women, use cautiously because drugs appear in breast milk. In neonates and infants, half-life is prolonged; use cautiously. Elderly patients are susceptible to superinfection and coagulopathies, commonly have renal impairment, and may need a lower dosage; use cautiously.

Adverse reactions

Many cephalosporins have similar adverse effects. Hypersensitivity reactions range from mild rashes, fever, and eosinophilia to fatal anaphylaxis and are more common in patients with penicillin allergy. Adverse GI reactions include abdominal pain, diarrhea, dyspepsia, glossitis, nausea, tenesmus, and vomiting. Hematologic reactions include positive direct and indirect antiglobulin in Coombs' test, thrombocytopenia or thrombocythemia, transient neutropenia, and reversible leukopenia. Minimal elevation of liver function test results occurs occasionally. Adverse renal effects may occur with any cephalosporin; they are most common in older patients, those with decreased renal function, and those taking other nephrotoxic drugs.

Local venous pain and irritation are common after I.M. injection; these reactions occur more often with higher doses and long-term therapy. Disulfiram-type reactions occur when cefoperazone is given within 3 days of alcohol use. Bacterial and fungal superinfections may result from suppression of normal flora.

Action

Cephalosporins are chemically and pharmacologically similar to penicillin; they act by inhibiting bacterial cell wall synthesis, causing rapid cell destruction. Their sites of action are enzymes known as penicillin-binding proteins. The affinity of certain cephalosporins for these proteins in various microorganisms helps explain the differing actions of these drugs. They are bactericidal: they act against many aerobic gram-positive and gram-negative bacteria and some anaerobic bacteria but don't kill fungi or viruses.

First-generation cephalosporins act against many gram-positive cocci, including penicillinase-producing *Staphylococcus aureus* and *Staphylococcus epidermidis, S. pneumoniae,* group B streptococci, and group A beta-hemolytic streptococci. Susceptible gram-negative organisms include *Klebsiella pneumoniae, E. coli, Proteus mirabilis,* and *Shigella.*

Second-generation cephalosporins are effective against all organisms attacked by first-generation drugs and have additional activity against *Moraxella catarrhalis, H. influenzae, Enterobacter, Citrobacter, Providencia, Acinetobacter, Serratia,* and *Neisseria. Bacteroides fragilis* are susceptible to cefoxitin.

Third-generation cephalosporins are less active than first- and second-generation drugs against gram-positive bacteria but are more active against gram-negative organisms, including those resistant to first- and second-generation drugs. They have the greatest stability against beta-lactamases produced by gram-negative bacteria. Susceptible gram-negative organisms include *E. coli, Klebsiella, Enterobacter, Providencia, Acinetobacter, Serratia, Proteus, Morganella,* and *Neisseria.* Some third-generation drugs are active against *B. fragilis* and *Pseudomonas.*

NURSING PROCESS

Assessment

- Review patient's history of allergies. Try to determine whether any previous reactions were true hypersensitivity reactions or adverse effects (such as GI distress) that patient interpreted as allergy.
- Monitor patient continuously for possible hypersensitivity reactions or other adverse effects.
- Obtain culture and sensitivity specimen before giving first dose; check test results periodically to assess drug's effectiveness.
- Monitor renal function study; dosage of certain cephalosporins must be lowered in a patient with severe renal impairment. In patient with decreased renal function, monitor BUN and creatinine levels and urine output for significant changes.
- Monitor PT and platelet count, and assess patient for signs of hypoprothrombinemia, which may occur, with or without bleeding, during therapy with cefoperazone or ceftriaxone. It usually occurs in elderly, debilitated, malnourished, or immunocompromised patients and in patients with renal impairment or impaired vitamin K synthesis.
- Monitor patient receiving long-term therapy for possible bacterial and fungal superinfection; this is especially problematic in elderly or debilitated patients and in those receiving immunosuppressants or radiation therapy.
- Monitor at-risk patients for fluid retention while they are taking sodium salts of cephalosporins.

Key nursing diagnoses

- Ineffective protection related to hypersensitivity
- Risk for infection related to superinfection
- Risk for deficient fluid volume related to adverse GI reactions

Planning and implementation

- Give these drugs at least 1 hour before bacteriostatic antibiotics, such as tetracyclines, erythromycin, and chloramphenicol; the antibiotics keep bacteria from growing by decreasing cephalosporin uptake by bacterial cell walls.
- Refrigerate oral suspensions, which are stable for 14 days; to ensure correct dosage, shake well before giving.
- Give I.M. dose deep into gluteal muscle mass or midlateral thigh; rotate injection sites to minimize tissue injury.
- Don't add or mix other drugs with I.V. infusions, particularly aminoglycosides, which will be inactivated if mixed with cephalosporins. If other drugs must be given I.V., temporarily stop infusion of primary drug.
- Ensure adequate dilution of I.V. infusion and rotate site every 48 hours to help minimize local vein irritation; using a small-gauge needle in a larger available vein may be helpful.

Patient teaching

- Make sure patient understands how and when to take drug. Urge him to comply with instructions for around-the-clock dosage and to complete the prescribed regimen.
- Advise patient to take oral drug with food if GI irritation occurs.
- Review proper storage and disposal of drug, and remind him to check expiration date.
- Teach signs and symptoms of hypersensitivity and other adverse reactions, and emphasize importance of reporting unusual effects.
- Teach signs and symptoms of bacterial and fungal superinfection, especially if patient is elderly or debilitated or has low resistance from immunosuppressants or irradiation. Emphasize importance of promptly reporting signs or symptoms.
- Warn patient not to ingest alcohol in any form within 3 days of treatment with cefoperazone.
- Advise patient to add yogurt or buttermilk to diet to prevent intestinal superinfection resulting from suppression of normal intestinal flora.
- Advise diabetic patient to monitor glucose level with Diastix, not Clinitest.
- Urge patient to keep follow-up appointments.

Evaluation

- Patient has no evidence of hypersensitivity.
- Patient is free from infection.
- Patient maintains adequate hydration.

Corticosteroids

betamethasone
betamethasone sodium phosphate
cortisone acetate
dexamethasone
dexamethasone acetate
dexamethasone sodium phosphate
fludrocortisone acetate
hydrocortisone
hydrocortisone acetate
hydrocortisone cypionate
hydrocortisone sodium phosphate
hydrocortisone sodium succinate
methylprednisolone
methylprednisolone acetate
methylprednisolone sodium succinate
prednisolone
prednisolone acetate
prednisolone sodium phosphate
prednisolone tebutate
prednisone
triamcinolone

Indications

▶ Hypersensitivity; inflammation, particularly of eye, nose, and respiratory tract; to initiate immunosuppression; replacement therapy in adrenocortical insufficiency, dermatologic diseases, respiratory disorders, rheumatic disorders.

Contraindications and cautions

• Contraindicated in patients hypersensitive to these drugs or any of their components and in those with systemic fungal infection.
• Use cautiously in patients with GI ulceration, renal disease, hypertension, osteoporosis, varicella, vaccinia, exanthema, diabetes mellitus, hypothyroidism, thromboembolic disorder, seizures, myasthenia gravis, heart failure, tuberculosis, ocular herpes simplex, hypoalbuminemia, emotional instability, or psychosis.
Lifespan: In pregnant women, avoid use, if possible, because of risk to the fetus. Women should stop breast-feeding because these drugs appear in breast milk and could cause serious adverse effects in infants. In children, long-term use should be avoided whenever possible because stunted growth may result. Elderly patients may have an increased risk of adverse reactions; monitor them closely.

Adverse reactions

Systemic corticosteroid therapy may suppress the hypothalamic-pituitary-adrenal (HPA) axis. Excessive use may cause cushingoid symptoms and various systemic disorders, such as diabetes and osteoporosis. Other effects may include dermatologic disorders, edema, euphoria, fluid and electrolyte imbalances, hypertension, immunosuppression, increased appetite, insomnia, peptic ulcer, psychosis, and weight gain.

Action

Corticosteroids suppress cell-mediated and humoral immunity by reducing levels of leukocytes, monocytes, and eosinophils; by decreasing immunoglobulin binding to cell-surface receptors; and by inhibiting interleukin synthesis. They reduce inflammation by preventing hydrolytic enzyme release into the cells, preventing plasma exudation, suppressing polymorphonuclear leukocyte migration, and disrupting other inflammatory processes.

NURSING PROCESS

Assessment

• Establish baseline blood pressure, fluid and electrolyte status, and weight; reassess regularly.
• Monitor patient closely for adverse reactions.
• Evaluate drug effectiveness at regular intervals.

Key nursing diagnoses

• Ineffective protection related to suppression of HPA axis with long-term therapy
• Risk for injury related to severe adverse reactions
• Risk for infection related to immunosuppression

Planning and implementation

• Give drug early in the day to mimic circadian rhythm.
• Give drug with food to prevent GI irritation.
• Take precautions to avoid exposing patient to infection.
• Don't stop drug abruptly.
• Notify prescriber of severe or persistent adverse reactions.

• Avoid prolonged use of corticosteroids, especially in children.

Patient teaching

• Teach patient to take drug exactly as prescribed, and warn him never to stop it abruptly.
• Tell patient to notify prescriber if stress level increases; dosage may need to be temporarily increased.
• Instruct patient to take oral drug with food.
• Urge patient to report black tarry stools, bleeding, bruising, blurred vision, emotional changes, or other concerns.
• Encourage patient to wear or carry medical identification at all times.

Evaluation

• Patient has no evidence of adrenal insufficiency.
• Patient remains free from injury.
• Patient is free from infection.

Diuretics, loop

bumetanide
ethacrynate sodium
ethacrynic acid
furosemide
torsemide

Indications

▶ Edema from heart failure, hepatic cirrhosis, or nephrotic syndrome; mild-to-moderate hypertension; adjunct treatment in acute pulmonary edema or hypertensive crisis.

Contraindications and cautions

• Contraindicated in patients hypersensitive to these drugs and in patients with anuria, hepatic coma, or severe electrolyte depletion.
• Use cautiously in patients with severe renal disease. Also use cautiously in patients with severe hypersensitivity to sulfonamides because allergic reaction may occur.

Lifespan: In pregnant women, use cautiously. In breast-feeding women, don't use. In neonates, use cautiously; the usual pediatric dose can be used, but dosage intervals should be extended. In elderly patients, use a lower dose, if needed, and monitor patient closely; these patients are more susceptible to drug-induced diuresis.

Adverse reactions

Therapeutic dose commonly causes metabolic and electrolyte disturbances, particularly potassium depletion. It also may cause hyperglycemia, hyperuricemia, hypochloremic alkalosis, and hypomagnesemia. Rapid parenteral administration may cause hearing loss (including deafness) and tinnitus. High doses can produce profound diuresis, leading to hypovolemia and CV collapse. Photosensitivity also may occur.

Action

Loop diuretics inhibit sodium and chloride reabsorption in the ascending loop of Henle, thus increasing excretion of sodium, chloride, and water. Like thiazide diuretics, loop diuretics increase excretion of potassium. Loop diuretics produce more diuresis and electrolyte loss than thiazide diuretics.

NURSING PROCESS

Assessment

• Monitor blood pressure and pulse rate, especially during rapid diuresis. Establish baseline values before therapy begins and watch for significant changes.
• Establish baseline CBC (including WBC count), liver function test results, and electrolyte, carbon dioxide, magnesium, BUN, and creatinine levels. Review periodically.
• Assess patient for evidence of excessive diuresis: hypotension, tachycardia, poor skin turgor, excessive thirst, or dry and cracked mucous membranes.
• Monitor patient for edema and ascites. Observe the legs of ambulatory patients and the sacral area of patients on bed rest.
• Weigh patient each morning immediately after he voids and before breakfast, in the same type of clothing, and on the same scale. Weight provides a reliable indicator of patient's response to diuretic therapy.
• Monitor and record patient's intake and output daily.

Key nursing diagnoses

• Risk for deficient fluid volume related to excessive diuresis

• Impaired urinary elimination related to change in diuresis pattern
• Ineffective protection related to electrolyte imbalance

Planning and implementation

• Give diuretics in morning to ensure that major diuresis occurs before bedtime. To prevent nocturia, give diuretics before 6 p.m.
• Reduce dosage for patient with hepatic dysfunction, and increase dosage for patient with renal impairment, oliguria, or decreased diuresis. Inadequate urine output may result in circulatory overload, which causes water intoxication, pulmonary edema, and heart failure. Increase dosage of insulin or oral hypoglycemic in diabetic patient, and reduce dosage of other antihypertensives.
• Take safety measures for all ambulatory patients until response to diuretic is known.
• Consult dietitian about need for potassium supplements.
• Keep urinal or commode readily available to patient.

Patient teaching

• Explain rationale for therapy and importance of following prescribed regimen.
• Review adverse effects, and urge patient to report symptoms promptly, especially chest, back, or leg pain; shortness of breath; dyspnea; increased edema or weight; and excess diuresis shown by weight loss of more than 0.9 kg (2 lb) daily.
• Advise patient to eat potassium-rich foods and to avoid high-sodium foods, such as lunch meat, smoked meats, and processed cheeses. Instruct him not to add table salt to foods.
• Encourage patient to keep follow-up appointments to monitor effectiveness of therapy.

Evaluation

• Patient maintains adequate hydration.
• Patient states importance of taking diuretic early in the day to prevent nocturia.
• Patient complies with therapy, as shown by improvement in underlying condition.

Diuretics, potassium-sparing

amiloride hydrochloride
spironolactone
triamterene

Indications

▶ Edema from hepatic cirrhosis, nephrotic syndrome, and heart failure; mild or moderate hypertension; diagnosis of primary hyperaldosteronism; metabolic alkalosis produced by thiazide and other kaliuretic diuretics; recurrent calcium nephrolithiasis; lithium-induced polyuria secondary to lithium-induced nephrogenic diabetes insipidus; aid in the treatment of hypokalemia; prophylaxis of hypokalemia in patients taking cardiac glycosides; precocious puberty and female hirsutism; adjunct to treatment of myasthenia gravis and familial periodic paralysis.

Contraindications and cautions

• Contraindicated in patients hypersensitive to drug, those with a potassium level above 5.5 mEq/L, those taking other potassium-sparing diuretics or potassium supplements, and those with anuria, acute or chronic renal insufficiency, or diabetic nephropathy.
• Use cautiously in patients with severe hepatic insufficiency, because electrolyte imbalance may lead to hepatic encephalopathy, and in patients with diabetes, who are at increased risk for hyperkalemia.

Lifespan: In pregnant women, no controlled studies exist. Women who wish to breast-feed should consult prescriber because drug may appear in breast milk. In children, use cautiously; they're more susceptible to hyperkalemia. In elderly and debilitated patients, observe closely and reduce dosage, if needed; they're more susceptible to drug-induced diuresis and hyperkalemia.

Adverse reactions

Hyperkalemia is the most important adverse reaction; it may occur with all drugs in this class and could lead to arrhythmias. Other adverse reactions include nausea, vomiting, headache, weakness, fatigue, bowel disturbances, cough, and dyspnea.

Action

Amiloride and triamterene act directly on the distal renal tubules, inhibiting sodium reabsorption and potassium excretion, thereby reducing potassium loss. Spironolactone competitively inhibits aldosterone at the distal renal tubules, also promoting sodium excretion and potassium retention.

NURSING PROCESS

Assessment

- Patients with hepatic dysfunction and those taking other antihypertensives may need a decreased dosage. Patients with renal impairment may need increased dosage. Diabetic patients may need changes in insulin dosage.
- Monitor vital signs, intake and output, weight, and blood pressure daily; also, check patient for edema, oliguria, or lack of diuresis, which may indicate drug tolerance.
- Monitor patient with hepatic disease, for whom mild drug-induced acidosis may be hazardous; watch for mental confusion, lethargy, or stupor. Patients with hepatic disease are especially susceptible to diuretic-induced electrolyte imbalance; in extreme cases, coma and death can result.
- Watch for other signs of toxicity.

Key nursing diagnoses

- Risk for deficient fluid volume related to excessive diuresis
- Impaired urinary elimination related to change in diuresis pattern
- Ineffective protection related to electrolyte imbalance

Planning and implementation

- Establish safety measures for ambulatory patients until response is known; diuretics may cause orthostatic hypotension, weakness, ataxia, and confusion.
- Give diuretics in the morning to ensure that major diuresis occurs before bedtime. To reduce the likelihood of nocturia, advise patient not to take diuretics after 6 p.m.
- Measure potassium and other electrolyte levels often to avoid imbalances that could cause arrhythmias. At baseline and periodically, monitor CBC with WBC count; carbon dioxide, BUN, and creatinine levels; and especially liver function test values.

Patient teaching

- Explain possible adverse effects and the importance of reporting unusual changes.
- Tell patient to weigh himself each morning after voiding and before dressing and eating, using the same scale. Urge him to report weight gain or loss of more than 2 lb (0.9 kg) per day.
- Teach patient how to minimize dizziness from orthostatic hypotension by avoiding sudden position changes.
- Advise patient to avoid potassium-rich food and potassium-containing salt substitutes or supplements, which increase the hazard of hyperkalemia.
- Tell patient to take drug at same time each morning to avoid interrupted sleep from nighttime diuresis.
- Advise patient to take drug with or after meals to minimize GI distress.
- Caution patient to avoid hazardous activities, such as driving or operating machinery, until response to drug is known.
- Tell patient to seek medical approval before taking OTC drugs; many contain sodium and potassium and can cause electrolyte imbalance.

Evaluation

- Patient maintains adequate hydration.
- Patient states importance of taking diuretic early in the day to prevent nocturia.
- Patient complies with therapy, as shown by improvement in underlying condition.

Diuretics, thiazide and thiazide-like

Thiazide
chlorothiazide
hydrochlorothiazide
Thiazide-like
indapamide
metolazone

Indications

▶ Edema from right-sided heart failure, mild-to-moderate left-sided heart failure, or nephrotic syndrome; edema and ascites caused by hepatic cirrhosis; hypertension; diabetes insipidus, particularly nephrogenic diabetes insipidus.

Contraindications and cautions

• Contraindicated in patients hypersensitive to these drugs and in those with anuria.
• Use cautiously in patients with severe renal disease, impaired hepatic function, or progressive liver disease.
Lifespan: In pregnant women, use cautiously. In breast-feeding women, thiazides are contraindicated because they appear in breast milk. In children, safety and effectiveness haven't been established. In elderly patients, reduce dosage, if needed, and monitor patient closely; these patients are more susceptible to drug-induced diuresis.

Adverse reactions

Therapeutic dose causes electrolyte and metabolic disturbances, most commonly potassium depletion. Other abnormalities include elevated cholesterol levels, hypercalcemia, hyperglycemia, hyperuricemia, hypochloremic alkalosis, hypomagnesemia, and hyponatremia. Photosensitivity also may occur.

Action

Thiazide and thiazide-like diuretics interfere with sodium transport across the tubules of the cortical diluting segment in the nephron, thereby increasing renal excretion of sodium, chloride, water, potassium, and calcium.

Thiazide diuretics also exert an antihypertensive effect. Although the exact mechanism is unknown, direct arteriolar dilation may be partially responsible. In diabetes insipidus, thiazides cause a paradoxical decrease in urine volume and an increase in renal concentration of urine, possibly because of sodium depletion and decreased plasma volume. This increases water and sodium reabsorption in the kidneys.

NURSING PROCESS

Assessment

• Monitor patient's intake, output, and electrolyte level regularly.
• Weigh patient each morning immediately after he voids and before breakfast, in the same type of clothing, and on the same scale. Weight provides a reliable indicator of patient's response to diuretic therapy.
• Monitor diabetic patient's glucose level. Diuretics may cause hyperglycemia.
• Monitor creatinine and BUN levels regularly. Drug isn't as effective if these levels are more than twice normal. Also, monitor uric acid level.

Key nursing diagnoses

• Risk for deficient fluid volume related to excessive diuresis
• Impaired urinary elimination related to change in diuresis pattern
• Ineffective protection related to electrolyte imbalance

Planning and implementation

• Give drug in the morning to prevent nocturia.
• Provide a high-potassium diet.
• Give potassium supplements to maintain acceptable potassium level.
• Keep urinal or commode readily available to patient.

Patient teaching

• Explain the rationale for therapy and the importance of following the prescribed regimen.
• Tell patient to take drug at the same time each day to prevent nocturia. Suggest taking drug with food to minimize GI irritation.
• Urge patient to seek prescriber's approval before taking any other drug, including OTC medications and herbal remedies.
• Advise patient to record his weight each morning after voiding and before breakfast, in the same type of clothing, and on the same scale.
• Review adverse effects, and urge the patient to promptly report symptoms, especially chest, back, or leg pain; shortness of breath; dyspnea; increased edema or weight; or excess diuresis shown by weight loss of more than 0.9 kg (2 lb) daily. Warn him about photosensitivity reactions that usually occur 10 to 14 days after initial sun exposure.
• Advise patient to eat potassium-rich foods and to avoid high-sodium foods, such as lunch meat, smoked meats, processed cheeses. Instruct him not to add table salt to foods.
• Encourage patient to keep follow-up appointments to monitor effectiveness of therapy.

Evaluation

• Patient maintains adequate hydration.
• Patient states importance of taking diuretic early in the day to prevent nocturia.

• Patient complies with therapy, as shown by improvement in underlying condition.

Estrogens

esterified estrogens
estradiol
estradiol cypionate
estradiol valerate
estrogenic substances, conjugated
estrone
estropipate

Indications

▶ Prevention of moderate to severe vasomotor symptoms linked to menopause, such as hot flushes and dizziness; stimulation of vaginal tissue development, cornification, and secretory activity; inhibition of hormone-sensitive cancer growth; female hypogonadism; female castration; primary ovulation failure; ovulation control; prevention of conception.

Contraindications and cautions

• Contraindicated in women with thrombophlebitis or thromboembolic disorders, unexplained abnormal genital bleeding, or estrogen-dependent neoplasia.
• Use cautiously in patients with hypertension; metabolic bone disease; migraines; seizures; asthma; cardiac, renal, or hepatic impairment; blood dyscrasia; diabetes; family history of breast cancer; or fibrocystic disease.

Lifespan: In pregnant or breast-feeding women, use is contraindicated. In adolescents whose bone growth isn't complete, use cautiously because of effects on epiphyseal closure. Postmenopausal women with a history of long-term estrogen use have an increased risk of endometrial cancer and stroke. Postmenopausal women also have increased risk for breast cancer, MI, stroke, and blood clots with long-term use of estrogen plus progestin.

Adverse reactions

Acute adverse reactions include abdominal cramps; bloating caused by fluid and electrolyte retention; breast swelling and tenderness; changes in menstrual bleeding patterns, such as spotting and prolongation or absence of bleeding; headache; loss of appetite; loss of libido; nausea; photosensitivity; swollen feet or ankles; and weight gain.

Long-term effects include benign hepatomas, cholestatic jaundice, elevated blood pressure (sometimes into the hypertensive range), endometrial carcinoma (rare), and thromboembolic disease (risk increases greatly with cigarette smoking, especially in women older than age 35).

Action

Estrogens promote the development and maintenance of the female reproductive system and secondary sexual characteristics. They inhibit the release of pituitary gonadotropins and have various metabolic effects, including retention of fluid and electrolytes, retention and deposition in bone of calcium and phosphorus, and mild anabolic activity. Of the six naturally occurring estrogens in humans, estradiol, estrone, and estriol are present in significant quantities.

Estrogens and estrogenic substances given as drugs have effects related to endogenous estrogen's mechanism of action. They can mimic the action of endogenous estrogen when used as replacement therapy and can inhibit ovulation or the growth of certain hormone-sensitive cancers. Conjugated estrogens and estrogenic substances are normally obtained from the urine of pregnant mares. Other estrogens are manufactured synthetically.

NURSING PROCESS

Assessment

• Monitor patient regularly to detect improvement or worsening of symptoms; observe patient for adverse reactions.
• If patient has diabetes mellitus, watch closely for loss of diabetes control.
• Monitor PT of patient receiving warfarin-type anticoagulant. Adjust anticoagulant dosage.

Key nursing diagnoses

• Excessive fluid volume related to drug-induced fluid retention
• Risk of injury related to adverse effects
• Noncompliance related to long-term therapy

Planning and implementation

• Notify pathologist of patient's estrogen therapy when sending specimens for evaluation.

• Give drug once daily for 3 weeks, followed by 1 week without drugs; repeat as needed.

Patient teaching

• Urge patient to read the package insert describing adverse reactions. Follow this with a verbal explanation. Tell patient to keep the package insert for later reference.
• Advise patient to take drug with meals or at bedtime to relieve nausea. Reassure patient that nausea usually disappears with continued therapy.
• Teach patient how to apply estrogen ointments or transdermal estrogen. Review symptoms that accompany a systemic reaction to ointments.
• Teach patient how to insert intravaginal estrogen suppository. Advise her to use sanitary pads instead of tampons when using suppository.
• Teach patient how to perform routine monthly breast self-examination.
• Tell patient to stop taking drug immediately if she becomes pregnant because estrogens can harm fetus.
• Remind patient not to breast-feed during estrogen therapy.
• If patient is receiving cyclic therapy for postmenopausal symptoms, explain that withdrawal bleeding may occur during the week off, but that fertility hasn't been restored and ovulation won't occur.
• Explain that medical supervision is essential during prolonged therapy.
• Tell man on long-term therapy about possible temporary gynecomastia and impotence, which will disappear when therapy ends.
• Instruct patient to notify prescriber immediately if patient experiences abdominal pain; pain, numbness, or stiffness in legs or buttocks; pressure or pain in chest; shortness of breath; severe headaches; visual disturbances, such as blind spots, flashing lights, or blurriness; vaginal bleeding or discharge; breast lumps; swelling of hands or feet; yellow skin and sclera; dark urine; or light-colored stools.
• Urge diabetic patient to report symptoms of hyperglycemia or glycosuria.

Evaluation

• Patient experiences only minimal fluid retention.
• Patient doesn't develop serious complications of estrogen therapy.
• Patient complies with therapy, as shown by improvement in condition or absence of pregnancy.

Fluoroquinolones

ciprofloxacin
gemifloxacin
levofloxacin
lomefloxacin hydrochloride
moxifloxacin
norfloxacin
ofloxacin
sparfloxacin

Indications

▶ Bone and joint infection, bacterial bronchitis, endocervical and urethral chlamydial infection, bacterial gastroenteritis, endocervical and urethral gonorrhea, intra-abdominal infection, empiric therapy for febrile neutropenia, pelvic inflammatory disease, bacterial pneumonia, bacterial prostatitis, acute sinusitis, skin and soft tissue infection, typhoid fever, bacterial UTI (prevention and treatment), chancroid, meningococcal carriers, and bacterial septicemia caused by susceptible organisms.

Contraindications and cautions

• Contraindicated in patients hypersensitive to fluoroquinolones because serious, possibly fatal, reactions can occur.
• Use cautiously in patients with known or suspected CNS disorders that predispose them to seizures or lower seizure threshold, cerebral ischemia, severe hepatic dysfunction, or renal insufficiency.
Lifespan: In pregnant women, these drugs cross the placental barrier and may cause arthropathies. Breast-feeding isn't recommended because these drugs may cause arthropathies in newborns and infants, although it isn't known if all fluoroquinolones appear in breast milk. In children, fluoroquinolones aren't recommended because they can cause joint problems. In elderly patients, reduce dosage, if needed, because these patients are more likely to have reduced renal function.

Adverse reactions

Adverse reactions that are rare but need medical attention include CNS stimulation (acute psychosis, agitation, hallucinations, tremors), hepatotoxicity, hypersensitivity reactions, interstitial nephritis, phlebitis, pseudomembranous colitis, and tendinitis or tendon rupture. Adverse reactions that need no medical attention unless they persist or become intolerable include CNS effects (dizziness, headache, nervousness, drowsiness, insomnia), GI reactions, and photosensitivity.

Action

Fluoroquinolones produce a bactericidal effect by inhibiting intracellular DNA topoisomerase II (DNA gyrase) or topoisomerase IV. These enzymes are essential catalysts in the duplication, transcription, and repair of bacterial DNA.

Fluoroquinolones are broad-spectrum, systemic antibacterial drugs active against a wide range of aerobic gram-positive and gram-negative organisms. Gram-positive aerobic bacteria include *Staphylococcus aureus, Staphylococcus epidermis, Staphylococcus hemolyticus, Staphylococcus saprophyticus;* penicillinase- and non–penicillinase-producing staphylococci and some methicillin-resistant strains*; Streptococcus pneumoniae;* group A (beta) hemolytic streptococci *(S. pyogenes);* group B streptococci *(S. agalactiae);* viridans streptococci; groups C, F, and G streptococci and nonenterococcal group D streptococci; *Enterococcus faecalis.* These drugs are active against gram-positive aerobic bacilli including *Corynebacterium* species, *Listeria monocytogenes,* and *Nocardia asteroides.*

Fluoroquinolones are also effective against gram-negative aerobic bacteria including, but not limited to, *Neisseria meningitidis* and most strains of penicillinase- and non–penicillinase-producing *Haemophilus ducreyi, Haemophilus influenzae, Haemophilus parainfluenzae, Moraxella catarrhalis, Neisseria gonorrhoeae,* and most clinically important Enterobacteriaceae, *Pseudomonas aeruginosa, Vibrio cholerae,* and *Vibrio parahaemolyticus.* Certain fluoroquinolones are active against *Chlamydia trachomatis, Legionella pneumophila, Mycobacterium avium-intracellulare, Mycoplasma hominis,* and *Mycoplasma pneumoniae.*

NURSING PROCESS

Assessment

- Obtain specimen for culture and sensitivity tests before starting therapy and as needed to detect bacterial resistance. Therapy may begin pending results.
- Obtain history of seizure disorders or other CNS diseases, such as cerebral arteriosclerosis, before starting therapy.
- Monitor renal and liver function test values in patients with impaired renal or hepatic function.
- Achilles and other tendon ruptures have occurred with fluoroquinolone use. Stop drug if patient experiences pain, inflammation, or rupture of a tendon.

Key nursing diagnoses

- Ineffective protection related to presence of bacteria
- Risk for deficient fluid volume related to drug-induced adverse GI reactions
- Risk for unstable blood glucose

Planning and implementation

- Treat acute hypersensitivity reactions with epinephrine, oxygen, I.V. fluids, antihistamines, corticosteroids, pressor amines, and airway management.
- Notify prescriber if patient has symptoms of excessive CNS stimulation (restlessness, tremor, confusion, hallucination). Take seizure precautions.
- If patient develops severe diarrhea or diarrhea unresponsive to treatment suspect pseudomembranous colitis and notify prescriber.

Patient teaching

- Instruct patient to take drug as prescribed and to finish the full course of therapy.
- Tell patient to take drug with an 8-oz (240-ml) glass of water.
- Caution patient that norfloxacin should be taken on an empty stomach.
- Instruct patient that, if a dose is missed, the next dose should be taken as soon as possible; advise patient not to double the dose.
- Advise patient to avoid concurrent use of antacids or sucralfate and oral fluoroquinolones. If coadministration can't be avoided, tell patient to separate doses by at least 2 hours.

• Tell patient fluoroquinolones may cause dizziness so avoid engaging in activities that require mental alertness until CNS effects on him are known.
• Caution patient not to take other drugs without medical approval.

Evaluation

• Patient is free from infection.
• Patient maintains adequate hydration throughout drug therapy.
• Patient's blood sugar level remains within normal limits.

Histamine$_2$-receptor antagonists

cimetidine
famotidine
nizatidine
ranitidine hydrochloride

Indications

▶ Acute duodenal or gastric ulcer, Zollinger-Ellison syndrome, gastroesophageal reflux.

Contraindications and cautions

• Contraindicated in patients hypersensitive to these drugs.
• Use cautiously in patients with impaired renal or hepatic function.

Lifespan: In pregnant women, use cautiously. In breast-feeding women, histamine$_2$ (H_2)-receptor antagonists are contraindicated because they may appear in breast milk. In children, safety and effectiveness haven't been established. Elderly patients have increased risk of adverse reactions, particularly those affecting the CNS; use cautiously.

Adverse reactions

H_2-receptor antagonists rarely cause adverse reactions. Cardiac arrhythmias, dizziness, fatigue, gynecomastia, headache, mild and transient diarrhea, and thrombocytopenia are possible.

Action

All H_2-receptor antagonists inhibit the action of H_2-receptors in gastric parietal cells, reducing gastric acid output and concentration, regardless of stimulants, such as histamine, food, insulin, and caffeine, or basal conditions.

NURSING PROCESS

Assessment

• Monitor patient for adverse reactions, especially hypotension and arrhythmias.
• Periodically monitor laboratory tests, such as CBC and renal and hepatic studies.

Key nursing diagnoses

• Risk for infection related to drug-induced neutropenia
• Decreased cardiac output related to adverse CV effects (cimetidine)
• Fatigue related to drug's CNS effects

Planning and implementation

• Give once-daily dose at bedtime, twice-daily doses in morning and evening, and multiple doses with meals and at bedtime. A once-daily dose at bedtime promotes compliance.
• Don't exceed recommended infusion rates when giving drugs I.V.; doing so increases risk of adverse CV effects. Continuous I.V. infusion may suppress acid secretion more effectively.
• Give antacids at least 1 hour before or after H_2-receptor antagonists. Antacids can decrease drug absorption.
• Adjust dosage for patient with renal disease.
• Don't abruptly stop the drug.

Patient teaching

• Teach patient how and when to take drug, and warn him not to abruptly stop taking it.
• Review possible adverse reactions, and urge patient to report unusual effects.
• Caution patient to avoid smoking during therapy; smoking stimulates gastric acid secretion and worsens the disease.

Evaluation

• Patient is free from infection.
• Patient maintains a normal heart rhythm.
• Patient states appropriate management plan for combating fatigue.

Laxatives

Bulk-forming

calcium polycarbophil
methylcellulose
psyllium

Emollient

docusate calcium
docusate potassium
docusate sodium

Hyperosmolar

glycerin
lactulose
lubiprostone
magnesium citrate
magnesium hydroxide
magnesium sulfate
sodium phosphates

Stimulant

bisacodyl
senna

Indications

▶ Constipation, irritable bowel syndrome, diverticulosis.

Contraindications and cautions

- Contraindicated in patients with GI obstruction or perforation, toxic colitis, megacolon, nausea and vomiting, or acute surgical abdomen.
- Use cautiously in patients with rectal or anal conditions such as rectal bleeding or large hemorrhoids.

Lifespan: For pregnant women and breast-feeding women, recommendations vary for individual drugs. Infants and children have an increased risk of fluid and electrolyte disturbances; use cautiously. In elderly patients, dependence is more likely to develop because of age-related changes in GI function. Monitor these patients closely.

Adverse reactions

All laxatives may cause flatulence, diarrhea, abdominal discomfort, weakness, and dependence. Bulk-forming laxatives may cause intestinal obstruction, impaction, or (rarely) esophageal obstruction. Emollient laxatives may cause a bitter taste or throat irritation. Hyperosmolar laxatives may cause fluid and electrolyte imbalances. Stimulant laxatives may cause urine discoloration, malabsorption, and weight loss.

Action

Laxatives promote movement of intestinal contents through the colon and rectum in several ways: bulk-forming, emollient, hyperosmolar, and stimulant.

NURSING PROCESS

Assessment

- Obtain baseline assessment of patient's bowel patterns and GI history before giving.
- Monitor patient for adverse reactions.
- Monitor bowel pattern throughout therapy. Assess bowel sounds and color and consistency of stools.
- Monitor patient's fluid and electrolyte status during administration.

Key nursing diagnoses

- Diarrhea related to adverse GI effects
- Acute pain related to abdominal discomfort
- Ineffective health maintenance related to laxative dependence

Planning and implementation

- Don't crush enteric-coated tablets.
- Time administration so that bowel evacuation doesn't interfere with sleep.
- Make sure patient has easy access to bedpan or bathroom.
- Take precautions to prevent constipation.

Patient teaching

- Advise patient that therapy should be short-term. Point out that abuse or prolonged use can cause nutritional imbalances.
- Tell patient that stool softeners and bulk-forming laxatives may take several days to achieve results.
- Encourage patient to remain active and to drink plenty of fluids if he takes a bulk-forming laxative.
- Explain that stimulant laxatives may cause harmless urine discoloration.
- Teach patient about including foods high in fiber into diet.

Evaluation

- Patient regains normal bowel pattern.

Prototype drug

• Patient states that pain is relieved with stool evacuation.
• Patient discusses dangers of laxative abuse and importance of limiting laxative use.

Nonsteroidal anti-inflammatory drugs

celecoxib
diclofenac potassium
diclofenac sodium
diflunisal
etodolac
ibuprofen
indomethacin
indomethacin sodium trihydrate
ketoprofen
ketorolac tromethamine
meloxicam
nabumetone
naproxen
naproxen sodium
oxaprozin
piroxicam
sulindac

Indications

▶ Mild to moderate pain, inflammation, stiffness, swelling, or tenderness caused by headache, arthralgia, myalgia, neuralgia, dysmenorrhea, rheumatoid arthritis, juvenile arthritis, osteoarthritis, or dental or surgical procedures.

Contraindications and cautions

• Contraindicated in patients with GI lesions or GI bleeding and in patients hypersensitive to these drugs.
• Use cautiously in patients with cardiac decompensation, hypertension, risk of MI, fluid retention, or coagulation defects.
Lifespan: In pregnant women, use cautiously in the first and second trimesters; don't use in the third trimester. For breast-feeding women, NSAIDs aren't recommended. In children younger than age 14, safety of long-term therapy hasn't been established. Patients older than age 60 may be more susceptible to toxic effects of NSAIDs because of decreased renal function.

Adverse reactions

Adverse reactions chiefly involve the GI tract, particularly erosion of the gastric mucosa. The most common symptoms are abdominal pain, dyspepsia, epigastric distress, heartburn, and nausea. CNS and skin reactions also may occur. Flank pain with other evidence of nephrotoxicity occurs occasionally. Fluid retention may aggravate hypertension or heart failure.

Action

The analgesic effect of NSAIDs may result from interference with the prostaglandins involved in pain. Prostaglandins appear to sensitize pain receptors to mechanical stimulation or to other chemical mediators. NSAIDs inhibit synthesis of prostaglandins peripherally and possibly centrally.

Like salicylates, NSAIDs exert an anti-inflammatory effect that may result in part from inhibition of prostaglandin synthesis and release during inflammation. The exact mechanism isn't clear.

NURSING PROCESS

Assessment

• Assess patient's level of pain and inflammation before therapy begins, and evaluate drug effectiveness.
• Monitor patient for evidence of bleeding. If patient needs surgery, assess bleeding time.
• Monitor ophthalmic and auditory function before and periodically during therapy to detect toxicity.
• Monitor CBC, platelet count, PT, and hepatic and renal function studies periodically to detect abnormalities.
• Watch for bronchospasm in patients with aspirin hypersensitivity, rhinitis or nasal polyps, and asthma.

Key nursing diagnoses

• Risk for injury related to adverse reactions
• Excessive fluid volume related to fluid retention
• Disturbed sensory perception (visual and auditory) related to toxicity

Planning and implementation

• Give oral NSAIDs with 8 oz (240 ml) of water to ensure adequate passage into the stomach. Have patient sit up for 15 to 30 minutes after

Prototype drug

taking drug to prevent it from lodging in esophagus.

- Crush tablets or mix with food or fluid to aid swallowing. Give with antacids to minimize GI upset.

Patient teaching

- Encourage patient to take drug as directed to achieve desired effect. Explain that he may not notice benefits of drug for 2 to 4 weeks.
- Review methods to prevent or minimize GI upset.
- Work with patient on long-term therapy to arrange for monitoring of laboratory values, especially BUN and creatinine levels, liver function test results, and CBC.
- Instruct patient to notify prescriber about severe or persistent adverse reactions.

Evaluation

- Patient remains free from injury.
- Patient shows no signs of edema.
- Patient maintains normal visual and auditory function.

Nucleoside reverse transcriptase inhibitors

abacavir sulfate
didanosine
emtricitabine
lamivudine
stavudine
tenofovir disoproxil fumarate
zidovudine

Indications

▶ HIV infection, AIDS, prevention of maternal-fetal HIV transmission, prevention of HIV infection after occupational exposure (as by needle stick) or nonoccupational exposure to blood, genital secretions, or other potentially infectious body fluids of an HIV-infected person when there's substantial risk of transmission.

Contraindications and cautions

- Contraindicated in patients hypersensitive to these drugs and patients with moderate to severe hepatic impairment (abacavir) or pancreatitis (didanosine).
- Use cautiously in patients with mild hepatic impairment or risk factors for liver impairment, risk for pancreatitis (didanosine), or compromised bone marrow function (zidovudine).

Lifespan: In pregnant women, use drug only if benefits outweigh risks. HIV-infected mothers shouldn't breast-feed to reduce the risk of transmitting the virus. It isn't known if NRTIs appear in breast milk. The pharmacokinetic and safety profile of NRTIs is similar in children and adults. NRTIs may be used in children age 3 months and older, but the half-life may be prolonged in neonates. In elderly patients, elimination half-life may be prolonged.

Adverse reactions

Because of the complexity of HIV infection, it's often difficult to distinguish between disease-related symptoms and adverse drug reactions. The most frequently reported adverse effects of NRTIs are anemia, leukopenia, and neutropenia. Thrombocytopenia is less common. Rare adverse effects of NRTIs are hepatotoxicity, myopathy, and neurotoxicity. Any of these adverse effects requires prompt medical attention.

Adverse effects that don't need medical attention unless they persist or are bothersome include headache, severe insomnia, myalgias, nausea, or hyperpigmentation of nails.

Action

NRTIs suppress HIV replication by inhibiting HIV DNA polymerase. Competitive inhibition of nucleoside reverse transcriptase inhibits DNA viral replication by chain termination, competitive inhibition of reverse transcriptase, or both.

NURSING PROCESS

Assessment

- Obtain baseline assessment of patient's infection, and reassess regularly to monitor drug effectiveness.
- Monitor hepatic function CBC, and platelet count regularly.
- Assess patient for risk factors for liver disease. Lactic acidosis and severe hepatomegaly with steatosis may occur, especially in women or patients who are obese or have prolonged exposure to nucleosides. If patient has symptoms of lactic acidosis or pronounced hepatotoxicity,

stop treatment. Symptoms may include hepatomegaly and steatosis, even without elevated transaminase levels.

Key nursing diagnoses

- Disturbed body image related to redistribution of body fat from antiretroviral therapy
- Diarrhea related to drug-induced adverse effect on bowel
- Ineffective coping related to HIV infection

Planning and implementation

- Combination therapy should include three or more antiretrovirals, usually two NRTIs and a protease inhibitor or nonnucleoside reverse transcriptase inhibitor.
- Give didanosine on an empty stomach, at lease 30 minutes before or 2 hours after meals.
- Redistribution or accumulation of body fat, including central obesity, dorsocervical fat enlargement (buffalo hump), peripheral wasting, facial wasting, breast enlargement, and cushingoid appearance, may occur.
- Patients with renal impairment may need dosage adjustment.
- Notify prescriber about persistent GI adverse effects.

Patient teaching

- Tell patient to take drug as prescribed, no more and no less, and to finish the full course of therapy.
- Instruct patient not to miss a dose but, if a dose is missed, to take the next dose as soon as possible; caution against doubling the dose.
- Advise patient to keep scheduled appointments because important blood tests are needed to evaluate the response to this drug.
- Tell patient not to take other drugs without medical approval.
- Tell patient to practice safe sex.

Evaluation

- Patient doesn't experience altered body image.
- Patient regains normal bowel pattern.
- Patient demonstrates adequate coping mechanisms.

Opioids

alfentanil hydrochloride
codeine phosphate
codeine sulfate
difenoxin hydrochloride
diphenoxylate hydrochloride
fentanyl citrate
hydrocodone bitartrate
hydromorphone hydrochloride
meperidine hydrochloride
methadone hydrochloride
morphine sulfate
oxycodone hydrochloride
oxymorphone hydrochloride
propoxyphene hydrochloride
propoxyphene napsylate
sufentanil citrate

Indications

Moderate to severe pain from acute and some chronic disorders; diarrhea; dry, nonproductive cough; management of opioid dependence; anesthesia support; sedation.

Contraindications and cautions

- Contraindicated in patients hypersensitive to these drugs and in those who have recently taken an MAO inhibitor. Also contraindicated in those with acute or severe bronchial asthma or respiratory depression.
- Use cautiously in patients with head injury, increased intracranial or intraocular pressure, hepatic or renal dysfunction, mental illness, emotional disturbances, or drug-seeking behaviors.

Lifespan: In pregnant or breast-feeding women, use cautiously; codeine, meperidine, methadone, morphine, and propoxyphene appear in breast milk. Breast-feeding infants of women taking methadone may develop physical dependence. In children, safety and effectiveness of some opioids haven't been established; use cautiously. Elderly patients may be more sensitive to opioids, and lower doses are usually given.

Adverse reactions

Respiratory and circulatory depression (including orthostatic hypotension) are the major hazards of opioids. Other adverse CNS effects include agitation, coma, depression, dizziness, dysphoria, euphoria, faintness, mental clouding, nervousness, restlessness, sedation, seizures, and visual disturbances, and weakness. Adverse GI effects include biliary colic, constipation, nausea, and vomiting. Urine retention or hypersensitivity also may occur. Tolerance to the drug and psychological or physical dependence may follow prolonged therapy.

Action

Opioids act as agonists at specific opiate-receptor binding sites in the CNS and other tissues, altering the patient's perception of and emotional response to pain.

NURSING PROCESS

Assessment

- Obtain baseline assessment of patient's pain, and reassess frequently to determine the drug's effectiveness.
- Evaluate patient's respiratory status before each dose; watch for respiratory rate below patient's baseline level and for restlessness, which may be compensatory signs of hypoxia. Respiratory depression may last longer than the analgesic effect.
- Monitor patient for other adverse reactions.
- Monitor patient for tolerance and dependence. The first sign of tolerance to opioids is usually a shortened duration of effect.

Key nursing diagnoses

- Ineffective breathing pattern related to respiratory depression
- Risk for injury related to orthostatic hypotension
- Ineffective coping related to drug dependence

Planning and implementation

- Keep resuscitative equipment and an opioid antagonist, such as naloxone, available.
- Give I.V. drug by slow injection, preferably in diluted solution. Rapid I.V. injection increases the risk of adverse effects.
- Give drug I.M. or subcutaneously, cautiously, to a patient with decreased platelet count and to a patient who is chilled, hypovolemic, or in shock; decreased perfusion may lead to drug accumulation and toxicity. Rotate injection sites to avoid induration.
- Carefully note the strength of solution when measuring a dose. Oral solutions of varying concentrations are available.
- For maximum effectiveness, give on a regular dosage schedule rather than p.r.n.
- Institute safety precautions.
- Encourage postoperative patient to turn, cough, and breathe deeply every 2 hours to avoid atelectasis.
- If GI irritation occurs, give oral forms with food.
- Withdrawal symptoms—including tremors, agitation, nausea, and vomiting—may occur if drug is stopped abruptly. Monitor patient with these symptoms carefully and provide supportive therapy.

Patient teaching

- Teach patient to take drug exactly as prescribed. Urge him to call prescriber if he isn't experiencing desired effect or if he is experiencing significant adverse reactions.
- Warn patient to avoid hazardous activities until drug's effects are known.
- Advise patient to avoid alcohol while taking opioid; alcohol will cause additive CNS depression.
- Suggest measures to prevent constipation, such as increasing fiber in diet and using a stool softener.
- Instruct patient to breathe deeply, cough, and change position every 2 hours to avoid respiratory complications.

Evaluation

- Patient maintains adequate ventilation, as shown by normal respiratory rate and rhythm and pink color.
- Patient remains free from injury.
- Patient doesn't become tolerant to drug.

Penicillins

Natural penicillins

penicillin G benzathine
penicillin G potassium
penicillin G procaine
penicillin G sodium
penicillin V potassium

Aminopenicillins
amoxicillin and clavulanate potassium
amoxicillin trihydrate
ampicillin
ampicillin sodium and sulbactam sodium
ampicillin trihydrate
Extended-spectrum penicillins
carbenicillin indanyl sodium
piperacillin sodium and tazobactam sodium
ticarcillin disodium
ticarcillin disodium and clavulanate potassium
Penicillinase-resistant penicillins
dicloxacillin sodium
nafcillin sodium
oxacillin sodium

Indications

▶ Streptococcal pneumonia; enterococcal and nonenterococcal group D endocarditis; diphtheria; anthrax; meningitis; tetanus; botulism; actinomycosis; syphilis; relapsing fever; Lyme disease; pneumococcal infections; rheumatic fever; bacterial endocarditis; neonatal group B streptococcal disease; septicemia; gynecologic infections; infections of urinary, respiratory, and GI tracts; infections of skin, soft tissue, bones, and joints.

Contraindications and cautions

• Contraindicated in patients hypersensitive to these drugs.
• Use cautiously in patients with history of asthma or drug allergy, mononucleosis, renal impairment, CV diseases, hemorrhagic condition, or electrolyte imbalance.
Lifespan: In pregnant women, use cautiously. For breast-feeding patients, recommendations vary depending on the drug. For children, dosage recommendations have been established for most penicillins. Elderly patients are susceptible to superinfection and renal impairment, which decreases excretion of penicillins; use cautiously and at a lower dosage.

Adverse reactions

With all penicillins, hypersensitivity reactions range from mild rash, fever, and eosinophilia to fatal anaphylaxis. Hematologic reactions include hemolytic anemia, leukopenia, thrombocytopenia, and transient neutropenia.

Certain adverse reactions are more common with specific classes. For example, bleeding episodes are usually seen with high doses of extended-spectrum penicillins, whereas GI adverse effects are most common with ampicillin. In patients with renal disease, high doses, especially of penicillin G, irritate the CNS by causing confusion, twitching, lethargy, dysphagia, seizures, and coma. Hepatotoxicity may occur with penicillinase-resistant penicillins, and hyperkalemia and hypernatremia have been reported with extended-spectrum penicillins.

Local irritation from parenteral therapy may be severe enough to warrant administration by subclavian or centrally placed catheter or stopping therapy.

Action

Penicillins are generally bactericidal. They inhibit synthesis of the bacterial cell wall, causing rapid cell destruction. They're most effective against fast-growing susceptible bacteria. Their sites of action are enzymes known as penicillin-binding proteins (PBPs). The affinity of certain penicillins for PBPs in various microorganisms helps explain the different activities of these drugs.

Susceptible aerobic gram-positive cocci include *Staphylococcus aureus;* nonenterococcal group D streptococci; groups A, B, D, G, H, K, L, and M streptococci; *Streptococcus viridans;* and *Enterococcus* (usually with an aminoglycoside). Susceptible aerobic gram-negative cocci include *Neisseria meningitidis* and non–penicillinase-producing *N. gonorrhoeae.*

Susceptible aerobic gram-positive bacilli include *Corynebacterium, Listeria,* and *Bacillus anthracis*. Susceptible anaerobes include *Peptococcus, Peptostreptococcus, Actinomyces, Clostridium, Fusobacterium, Veillonella,* and non–beta-lactamase–producing strains of *Streptococcus pneumoniae*. Susceptible spirochetes include *Treponema pallidum, T. pertenue, Leptospira, Borrelia recurrentis,* and, possibly, *B. burgdorferi*.

Aminopenicillins have uses against more organisms, including many gram-negative organisms. Like natural penicillins, aminopenicillins are vulnerable to inactivation by penicillinase. Susceptible organisms include *Escherichia coli, Proteus mirabilis, Shigella, Salmonella, S.*

pneumoniae, N. gonorrhoeae, Haemophilus influenzae, S. aureus, S. epidermidis (non–penicillinase-producing *Staphylococcus*), and *Listeria monocytogenes.*

Penicillinase-resistant penicillins are semisynthetic penicillins designed to remain stable against hydrolysis by most staphylococcal penicillinases and thus are the drugs of choice against susceptible penicillinase-producing staphylococci. They also act against most organisms susceptible to natural penicillins.

Extended-spectrum penicillins offer a wider range of bactericidal action than the other three classes and usually are given in combination with aminoglycosides. Susceptible strains include *Enterobacter, Klebsiella, Citrobacter, Serratia, Bacteroides fragilis, Pseudomonas aeruginosa, Proteus vulgaris, Providencia rettgeri,* and *Morganella morganii.* These penicillins are also vulnerable to beta-lactamase and penicillinases.

NURSING PROCESS

Assessment

- Assess patient's history of allergies. Try to find out whether any previous reactions were true hypersensitivity reactions or adverse reactions (such as GI distress) that patient interpreted as allergy.
- Keep in mind that a patient who has never had a penicillin hypersensitivity reaction may still have future allergic reactions; monitor patient continuously for possible allergic reactions or other adverse effects.
- Obtain culture and sensitivity tests before giving first dose; repeat tests periodically to assess drug's effectiveness.
- Monitor vital signs, electrolytes, and renal function studies.
- Assess patient's consciousness and neurologic status when giving high doses; CNS toxicity can occur.
- Coagulation abnormalities, even frank bleeding, can follow high doses, especially of extended-spectrum penicillins. Monitor PT, INR, and platelet counts. Assess patient for signs of occult or frank bleeding.
- Monitor patients, especially elderly patients, debilitated patients, and patients receiving immunosuppressants or radiation, receiving long-term therapy for possible superinfection.

Key nursing diagnoses

- Ineffective protection related to hypersensitivity
- Risk for infection related to superinfection
- Risk for deficient fluid volume related to adverse GI reactions

Planning and implementation

- Give penicillin at least 1 hour before bacteriostatic antibiotics, such as tetracyclines, erythromycin, and chloramphenicol; these drugs inhibit bacterial cell growth and decrease rate of penicillin uptake by bacterial cell walls.
- To enhance GI absorption, give oral penicillin at least 1 hour before or 2 hours after meals.
- Refrigerate oral suspensions, which will be stable for 14 days; to ensure correct dosage, shake suspension well before giving it.
- To minimize tissue injury, give I.M. dose deep into gluteal muscle mass or midlateral thigh, and rotate injection sites. To relieve pain, apply ice to injection site. Don't inject more than 2 g of drug per injection site.
- With I.V. infusions, don't add or mix another drug, especially an aminoglycoside, which will become inactive if mixed with a penicillin. If other drugs must be given I.V., temporarily stop infusion of primary drug.
- Infuse I.V. drug continuously or intermittently over 30 minutes. Rotate infusion site every 48 hours. Intermittent I.V. infusion may be diluted in 50 to 100 ml sterile water, normal saline solution, D_5W, D_5W and half-normal saline solution, or lactated Ringer solution.

Patient teaching

- Make sure patient understands how and when to take drug. Urge him to complete the prescribed regimen, comply with instructions for around-the-clock scheduling, and keep follow-up appointments.
- Teach patient signs and symptoms of hypersensitivity and other adverse reactions. Urge him to report unusual reactions.
- Tell patient to check drug's expiration date and to discard unused drug. Warn him not to share drug with family or friends.

Evaluation

- Patient shows no signs of hypersensitivity.
- Patient is free from infection.
- Patient maintains adequate hydration.

Phenothiazines

chlorpromazine hydrochloride
fluphenazine
mesoridazine besylate
perphenazine
prochlorperazine
promazine hydrochloride
promethazine
thioridazine hydrochloride
thiothixene
trifluoperazine hydrochloride

Indications

▶ Agitated psychotic states, hallucinations, manic-depressive illness, excessive motor and autonomic activity, nausea and vomiting, moderate anxiety, behavioral problems caused by chronic organic mental syndrome, tetanus, acute intermittent porphyria, intractable hiccups, itching, symptomatic rhinitis.

Contraindications and cautions

- Contraindicated in patients with CNS depression, bone marrow suppression, heart failure, circulatory collapse, coronary artery or cerebrovascular disorders, subcortical damage, or coma. Also contraindicated in patients receiving spinal and epidural anesthetics and adrenergic blockers.
- Use cautiously in debilitated patients and in those with hepatic, renal, or CV disease; respiratory disorders; hypocalcemia; seizure disorders; suspected brain tumor or intestinal obstruction; glaucoma; and prostatic hyperplasia.

Lifespan: In pregnant women, use only if clearly necessary; safety hasn't been established. Women shouldn't breast-feed during therapy because most phenothiazines appear in breast milk and directly affect prolactin levels. For children younger than age 12, phenothiazines aren't recommended unless otherwise specified; use cautiously for nausea and vomiting. Acutely ill children, such as those with chickenpox, measles, CNS infections, or dehydration have a greatly increased risk of dystonic reactions. Elderly patients are more sensitive to therapeutic and adverse effects, especially cardiac toxicity, tardive dyskinesia, and other extrapyramidal effects; use cautiously and give reduced doses, adjusting dosage to patient response.

Adverse reactions

Phenothiazines may produce extrapyramidal symptoms, such as dystonic movements, torticollis, oculogyric crises, and parkinsonian symptoms ranging from akathisia during early treatment to tardive dyskinesia after long-term use. A neuroleptic malignant syndrome resembling severe parkinsonism may occur, most often in young men taking fluphenazine. The progression of elevated liver enzyme levels to obstructive jaundice usually indicates an allergic reaction.

Other adverse reactions include abdominal pain, agitation, anorexia, arrhythmias, confusion, constipation, dizziness, dry mouth, endocrine effects, fainting, hallucinations, hematologic disorders, local gastric irritation, nausea, orthostatic hypotension with reflex tachycardia, photosensitivity, seizures, skin eruptions, urine retention, visual disturbances, and vomiting.

Action

Phenothiazines are believed to function as dopamine antagonists by blocking postsynaptic dopamine receptors in various parts of the CNS. Their antiemetic effects result from blockage of the chemoreceptor trigger zone. They also produce varying degrees of anticholinergic effects and alpha-adrenergic–receptor blocking.

NURSING PROCESS

Assessment

- Check vital signs regularly for decreased blood pressure, especially before and after parenteral therapy, or tachycardia; observe patient carefully for other adverse reactions.
- Check intake and output for urine retention or constipation, which may require dosage reduction.
- Monitor bilirubin level weekly for the first 4 weeks. Establish baseline CBC, ECG (for quinidine-like effects), liver and renal function test results, electrolyte level (especially potassium), and eye examination findings. Monitor these findings periodically thereafter, especially in patients receiving long-term therapy.
- Observe patient for mood changes and monitor progress.
- Monitor patient for involuntary movements. Check patient receiving prolonged treatment at least once every 6 months.

Key nursing diagnoses
- Risk for injury related to adverse reactions
- Impaired physical mobility related to extrapyramidal symptoms
- Noncompliance related to long-term therapy

Planning and implementation
- Don't stop drug abruptly. Although physical dependence doesn't occur with antipsychotic drugs, rebound worsening of psychotic symptoms may occur, and many drug effects may persist.
- Follow manufacturer's guidelines for reconstitution, dilution, administration, and storage of drugs. Slightly discolored liquids may or may not be acceptable for use. Check with pharmacist.

Patient teaching
- Teach patient how and when to take drug. Tell him not to increase the dosage or stop taking the drug without prescriber's approval. Suggest taking the full dose at bedtime if daytime sedation occurs.
- Explain that full therapeutic effect may not occur for several weeks.
- Teach signs and symptoms of adverse reactions, and urge patient to report unusual effects, especially involuntary movements.
- Instruct patient to avoid beverages and drugs containing alcohol, and warn him not to take other drugs, including OTC or herbal products, without prescriber's approval.
- Advise patient to avoid hazardous tasks until full effects of drug are established. Explain that sedative effects will lessen after several weeks.
- Inform patient that excessive exposure to sunlight, heat lamps, or tanning beds may cause photosensitivity reactions. Advise him to avoid exposure to extreme heat or cold.
- Explain that phenothiazines may cause pink or brown discoloration of urine.

Evaluation
- Patient remains free from injury.
- Patient doesn't develop extrapyramidal symptoms.
- Patient complies with therapy, as shown by improved thought processes.

Protease inhibitors

amprenavir
atazanavir sulfate
fosamprenavir calcium
indinavir sulfate
lopinavir
nelfinavir mesylate
ritonavir
saquinavir
saquinavir mesylate
tipranavir

Indications

▶ HIV infection and AIDS.

Contraindications and cautions

- Contraindicated in patients hypersensitive to drug or its components, patients taking a drug highly dependent on CYP3A4 for metabolism, and patients with renal failure (amprenavir oral solution).
- Use cautiously in patients with impaired hepatic or renal function and those with diabetes mellitus or hemophilia.

Lifespan: In pregnant women, use drug only if benefits outweigh risks. Contact the pregnancy registry at 1-800-258-4263 or www.apregistry.com to report pregnant women on therapy. HIV-infected mothers shouldn't breast-feed to reduce the risk of transmitting HIV to the infant.

Adverse reactions

The most common adverse effects, which require immediate medical attention, include kidney stones, pancreatitis, diabetes or hyperglycemia, ketoacidosis, and paresthesia.

Common adverse effects that don't need medical attention unless they persist or are bothersome include generalized weakness, GI disturbances, headache, insomnia, and taste disturbance. Less common adverse effects include dizziness and somnolence.

Action

Protease inhibitors bind to the protease active site and inhibit HIV protease activity. This enzyme is required for the proteolysis of viral polyprotein precursors into individual functional proteins found in infectious HIV. The net effect is formation of noninfectious, immature viral particles.

NURSING PROCESS

Assessment
- If patient has hepatic dysfunction, consider the risks and potential benefits of therapy with protease inhibitors.
- Monitor patient for opportunistic infections and drug resistance.
- Observe patients with hemophilia closely for spontaneous bleeding.

Key nursing diagnoses
- Risk for disturbed body image related to redistribution of body fat from antiretroviral therapy
- Diarrhea related to drug-induced adverse effect on bowel
- Ineffective individual coping related to HIV infection

Planning and implementation
- Protease inhibitors are used with other antiretrovirals. Combination therapy should include three or more antiretrovirals, including a protease inhibitor.
- Protease inhibitors have many interactions. Be aware of what drugs you shouldn't give with a protease inhibitor.
- Check blood glucose levels in patients with diabetes. Drug may cause hyperglycemia, new-onset diabetes, or worsened existing diabetes.
- Indinavir may cause nephrolithiasis. Advise increasing fluid intake.
- Redistribution or accumulation of body fat, including central obesity, dorsocervical fat enlargement (buffalo hump), peripheral wasting, facial wasting, breast enlargement, and cushingoid appearance, may occur.

Patient teaching
- Instruct patient to take drug as prescribed and to finish the full course of therapy.
- Tell patient to take the next dose as soon as possible after a missed dose but not to double the dose.
- Advise patient that drug should be taken with plenty of water 1 or 2 hours before meals and that he should drink about 48 oz of water daily.
- Instruct patient not to take other drugs without medical approval.

Evaluation
- Patient doesn't experience altered body image.
- Patient regains normal bowel pattern.
- Patient demonstrates adequate coping mechanisms.

Selective serotonin reuptake inhibitors

citalopram hydrobromide
escitalopram oxalate
fluoxetine hydrochloride
fluvoxamine maleate
paroxetine hydrochloride
sertraline hydrochloride

Indications

▶ Major depression, obsessive-compulsive disorder, bulimia nervosa, premenstrual dysphoric disorders, panic disorders, post-traumatic stress disorder (sertraline).

Contraindications and cautions

- Contraindicated in patients hypersensitive to drug or its components.
- Use cautiously in patients with hepatic, renal, or cardiac insufficiency.

Lifespan: In pregnant women, use drug only if benefits outweigh risks; use of certain SSRIs in the first trimester may cause birth defects. Neonates born to women who took an SSRI during the third trimester may develop complications that warrant prolonged hospitalization, respiratory support, and tube feeding. In breast-feeeding women, use isn't recommended. SSRIs appear in breast milk and may cause diarrhea and sleep disturbance in neonates. However, risks and benefits to both the woman and infant must be considered. Children and adolescents may be more susceptible to increased suicidal tendencies when taking SSRIs or other antidepressants. Elderly patients may be more sensitive to the insomniac effects of SSRIs.

Adverse reactions

Common adverse effects include headache, tremor, dizziness, sleep disturbances, GI disturbances, and sexual dysfunction. Less common adverse effects include bleeding (ecchymoses, epistaxis), akathisia, breast tenderness or en-

Prototype drug

largement, extrapyramidal effects, dystonia, fever, hyponatremia, mania or hypomania, palpitations, serotonin syndrome, weight gain or loss, rash, urticaria, or pruritus.

Action

SSRIs selectively inhibit the reuptake of serotonin with little or no effects on other neurotransmitters such as norepinephrine or dopamine, in the CNS.

NURSING PROCESS

Assessment

- Obtain a detailed mental health history, including a family history of suicide, bipolar disorder, or depression, before therapy starts.
- Monitor patient closely for increased suicidal tendencies.
- Hyponatremia usually results from inappropriate secretion of antidiuretic hormone. This problem is most often seen in elderly patients and those treated with diuretics.
- Diarrhea, fever, palpitations, mood swings, behavior changes, restlessness, shaking, and shivering characterize serotonin syndrome. Hypertension and seizures may occur as well. Risk of this syndrome is highest within days after dosage increases and if patient takes another serotonergic drug.

Key nursing diagnoses

- Disturbed thought processes related to presence of depression
- Risk for injury related to drug-induced adverse CNS reaction
- Deficient knowledge related to drug therapy

Planning and implementation

- Don't use an SSRI within 14 days of an MAO inhibitor.
- Don't stop therapy abruptly. Taper gradually over several weeks, and monitor the patient carefully for serotonin syndrome.
- Notify prescriber immediately if patient's depression worsens or if he's having thoughts of suicide.

Patient teaching

- Tell patient that drug may take 4 to 5 weeks to produce its full benefit. Advise patient to take drug as prescribed and not to double the next dose if a dose is missed.
- Instruct patient to stop drug and call as soon as possible if a rash or hives develops.
- Caution family members or caregivers to monitor closely for suicidal behaviors or increased agitation.
- Caution patient to avoid alcohol, drugs, or substances that have serotonergic activity.
- Tell patient to use caution when driving or performing tasks requiring alertness because these drugs may cause drowsiness or impair judgment or motor skills.

Evaluation

- Patient's thought process remains clear.
- Patient's safety is maintained.
- Patient and family state understanding of drug therapy.

Skeletal muscle relaxants

baclofen
carisoprodol
chlorzoxazone
cyclobenzaprine hydrochloride
methocarbamol

Indications

▶ Painful musculoskeletal disorders, spasticity caused by multiple sclerosis.

Contraindications and cautions

- Contraindicated in patients hypersensitive to these drugs.
- Use cautiously in patients with impaired renal or hepatic function.

Lifespan: In pregnant women and breastfeeding women, use only when potential benefits to the patient outweigh risks to the fetus or infant. In children, recommendations vary. Elderly patients have an increased risk of adverse reactions; monitor them carefully.

Adverse reactions

Skeletal muscle relaxants may cause ataxia, confusion, depressed mood, dizziness, drowsiness, dry mouth, hallucinations, headache, hypotension, nervousness, tachycardia, tremor, and vertigo. Baclofen also may cause seizures.

Action

All skeletal muscle relaxants, except baclofen, reduce impulse transmission from the spinal cord to skeletal muscle. Baclofen's mechanism of action is unclear.

NURSING PROCESS

Assessment

- Monitor patient for hypersensitivity reactions.
- Assess degree of relief obtained to determine when dosage can be reduced.
- Watch for increased seizures in epileptic patient receiving baclofen.
- Monitor CBC results closely.
- In patient receiving cyclobenzaprine, monitor platelet counts.
- In patient receiving methocarbamol, watch for orthostatic hypotension.
- In patient receiving long-term baclofen or chlorzoxazone therapy, monitor hepatic function and urinalysis results.
- In patient receiving long-term therapy, assess compliance.

Key nursing diagnoses

- Risk for trauma related to baclofen-induced seizures
- Disturbed thought processes related to confusion
- Noncompliance related to long-term therapy

Planning and implementation

- Avoid withdrawal symptoms, such as insomnia, headache, nausea, and abdominal pain, by not abruptly stopping baclofen or carisoprodol after long-term therapy, unless patient has severe adverse reactions.
- Institute safety precautions as needed.
- Prevent GI distress by giving oral forms of drug with meals or milk.
- Obtain an order for a mild analgesic to relieve drug-induced headache.

Patient teaching

- Tell patient to take drug exactly as prescribed. Teach him to avoid withdrawal symptoms by not stopping baclofen or carisoprodol abruptly after long-term therapy.
- Instruct patient to avoid hazardous activities that require mental alertness until CNS effects of drug are known.
- Advise patient to avoid alcohol use during therapy.
- Advise patient to follow prescriber's advice regarding rest and physical therapy.
- Instruct patient receiving cyclobenzaprine or baclofen to report urinary hesitancy.
- Inform patient taking methocarbamol or chlorzoxazone that urine may be discolored.

Evaluation

- Patient remains free from seizures.
- Patient exhibits normal thought processes.
- Patient complies with therapy, as shown by pain relief or improvement of spasticity.

Sulfonamides

co-trimoxazole (trimethoprim and sulfamethoxazole)
sulfasalazine

Indications

▶ Bacterial infections, nocardiosis, toxoplasmosis, chloroquine-resistant *Plasmodium falciparum* malaria.

Contraindications and cautions

- Contraindicated in patients hypersensitive to these drugs.
- Use cautiously in patients with renal or hepatic impairment, bronchial asthma, severe allergy, or G6PD deficiency.

Lifespan: In pregnant women at term and in breast-feeding women, use is contraindicated; sulfonamides appear in breast milk. In infants younger than age 2 months, sulfonamides are contraindicated unless there's no therapeutic alternative. In children with fragile X chromosome and mental retardation, use cautiously. Elderly patients are susceptible to bacterial and fungal superinfection and have an increased risk of folate deficiency anemia and adverse renal and hematologic effects.

Adverse reactions

Many adverse reactions stem from hypersensitivity, including bronchospasm, conjunctivitis, erythema multiforme, erythema nodosum, exfoliative dermatitis, fever, joint pain, pruritus, leukopenia, Lyell syndrome, photosensitivity, rash, Stevens-Johnson syndrome, and toxic epidermal necrolysis. GI reactions include anorexia, diarrhea, folic acid malabsorption, nausea, pancreatitis, stomatitis, and vomiting. Hematologic reactions include agranulocytosis, granulocytopenia, hypoprothrombinemia thrombocytopenia, and, in G6PD deficiency, hemolytic anemia. Renal effects usually result from crystalluria caused by precipitation of sulfonamide in renal system.

Action

Sulfonamides are bacteriostatic. They inhibit biosynthesis of tetrahydrofolic acid, which is needed for bacterial cell growth. They're active against some strains of staphylococci, streptococci, *Nocardia asteroides* and *brasiliensis, Clostridium tetani* and *perfringens, Bacillus anthracis, Escherichia coli,* and *Neisseria gonorrhoeae* and *meningitidis.* Sulfonamides are also active against organisms that cause UTIs, such as *E. coli, Proteus mirabilis* and *vulgaris, Klebsiella, Enterobacter,* and *Staphylococcus aureus,* and genital lesions caused by *Haemophilus ducreyi* (chancroid).

NURSING PROCESS

Assessment

- Assess patient's history of allergies, especially to sulfonamides or to any drug containing sulfur, such as thiazides, furosemide, and oral sulfonylureas.
- Monitor patient for adverse reactions; patients with AIDS have a much higher risk of adverse reactions.
- Obtain culture and sensitivity tests before first dose; check test results periodically to assess the drug's effectiveness.
- Monitor urine cultures, CBC, and urinalysis before and during therapy.
- During long-term therapy, monitor patient for possible superinfection.

Key nursing diagnoses

- Ineffective protection related to hypersensitivity
- Risk for infection related to superinfection
- Risk for deficient fluid volume related to adverse GI reactions

Planning and implementation

- Give oral dose with 8 oz (240 ml) of water. Give 3 to 4 L of fluids daily, depending on drug; patient's urine output should be at least 1,500 ml daily.
- Follow manufacturer's directions for reconstituting, diluting, and storing drugs; check expiration dates.
- Shake oral suspensions well before giving to ensure correct dosage.

Patient teaching

- Urge patient to take drug exactly as prescribed, to complete the prescribed regimen, and to keep follow-up appointments.
- Advise patient to take oral drug with full glass of water and to drink plenty of fluids; explain that tablet may be crushed and swallowed with water to ensure maximal absorption.
- Teach signs and symptoms of hypersensitivity and other adverse reactions. Urge patient to report bloody urine, difficulty breathing, rash, fever, chills, or severe fatigue.
- Advise patient to avoid direct sun exposure and to use a sunscreen to help prevent photosensitivity reactions.
- Tell diabetic patient that sulfonamides may increase effects of oral hypoglycemics. Tell him not to use Clinitest to monitor glucose level.
- Inform patient taking sulfasalazine that it may cause an orange-yellow discoloration of urine or skin and may permanently stain soft contact lenses yellow.

Evaluation

- Patient exhibits no signs of hypersensitivity.
- Patient is free from infection.
- Patient maintains adequate hydration.

Tetracyclines

doxycycline
doxycycline hyclate
minocycline hydrochloride
oxytetracycline hydrochloride
tetracycline hydrochloride

Indications

▶ Bacterial, protozoal, rickettsial, and fungal infections.

Contraindications and cautions

- Contraindicated in patients hypersensitive to these drugs.

• Use cautiously in patients with renal or hepatic impairment.

Lifespan: In pregnant or breast-feeding women, use is contraindicated; tetracyclines appear in breast milk. Children younger than age 8 shouldn't take tetracyclines; these drugs can cause permanent tooth discoloration, enamel hypoplasia, and a reversible decrease in bone calcification. Elderly patients may have decreased esophageal motility; use these drugs cautiously, and monitor patients for local irritation from slow passage of oral forms. Elderly patients also are more susceptible to superinfection.

Adverse reactions

The most common adverse effects involve the GI tract and are dose related; they include abdominal discomfort; anorexia; bulky, loose stools; epigastric burning; flatulence; nausea; and vomiting. Superinfections also are common. Photosensitivity reactions may be severe. Renal failure may be caused by Fanconi syndrome after use of outdated tetracycline. Permanent discoloration of teeth occurs if drug is given during tooth formation in children younger than age 8.

Action

Tetracyclines are bacteriostatic but may be bactericidal against certain organisms. They bind reversibly to 30S and 50S ribosomal subunits, which inhibits bacterial protein synthesis.

Susceptible gram-positive organisms include *Bacillus anthracis, Actinomyces israelii, Clostridium perfringens* and *tetani, Listeria monocytogenes,* and *Nocardia.*

Susceptible gram-negative organisms include *Neisseria meningitidis, Pasteurella multocida, Legionella pneumophila, Brucella, Vibrio cholerae, Yersinia enterocolitica, Yersinia pestis, Bordetella pertussis, Haemophilus influenzae, Haemophilus ducreyi, Campylobacter fetus, Shigella,* and many other common pathogens.

Other susceptible organisms include *Rickettsia akari, typhi, prowazekii,* and *tsutsugamushi; Coxiella burnetii; Chlamydia trachomatis* and *psittaci; Mycoplasma pneumoniae* and *hominis; Leptospira; Treponema pallidum* and *pertenue;* and *Borrelia recurrentis.*

NURSING PROCESS

Assessment

• Assess patient's allergic history.
• Monitor patient for adverse reactions.
• Obtain culture and sensitivity tests before first dose; check cultures periodically to assess drug effectiveness.
• Check expiration dates before giving. Outdated tetracyclines may cause nephrotoxicity.
• Monitor patient for bacterial and fungal superinfection, especially if patient is elderly, debilitated, or receiving immunosuppressants or radiation therapy; watch especially for oral candidiasis.

Key nursing diagnoses

• Ineffective protection related to hypersensitivity
• Risk for infection related to superinfection
• Risk for deficient fluid volume related to adverse GI reactions

Planning and implementation

• For maximum absorption, give all oral tetracyclines except doxycycline and minocycline 1 hour before or 2 hours after meals. Don't give drug with food, milk or other dairy products, sodium bicarbonate, iron compounds, or antacids, which may impair absorption.
• Give water with and after oral drug to help it pass to the stomach because incomplete swallowing can cause severe esophageal irritation. To prevent esophageal reflux, don't give drug within 1 hour of bedtime.
• Monitor I.V. injection sites and rotate routinely to minimize local irritation. I.V. administration may cause severe phlebitis.

Patient teaching

• Urge patient to take drug exactly as prescribed, to complete the prescribed regimen, and to keep follow-up appointments.
• Warn patient not to take drug with food, milk or other dairy products, sodium bicarbonate, or iron compounds because they may interfere with absorption. Advise him to wait 3 hours after taking tetracycline before taking an antacid.
• Instruct patient to check expiration dates and to discard any expired drug.
• Teach signs and symptoms of adverse reactions, and urge patient to report them promptly.

• Advise patient to avoid direct exposure to sunlight and to use a sunscreen to help prevent photosensitivity reactions.

Evaluation

• Patient shows no signs of hypersensitivity.
• Patient is free from infection.
• Patient maintains adequate hydration.

Xanthine derivatives

aminophylline
theophylline

Indications

▶ Asthma and bronchospasm from emphysema and chronic bronchitis.

Contraindications and cautions

• Contraindicated in patients hypersensitive to these drugs.
• Use cautiously in patients with arrhythmias, cardiac or circulatory impairment, cor pulmonale, hepatic or renal disease, active peptic ulcers, hyperthyroidism, or diabetes mellitus.
Lifespan: In pregnant women, use cautiously. In breast-feeding women, avoid these drugs because they appear in breast milk, and infants may have serious adverse reactions. Small children may have excessive CNS stimulation; monitor them closely. In elderly patients, use cautiously.

Adverse reactions

Adverse effects, except for hypersensitivity, are dose related and can be controlled by dosage adjustment. Common reactions include arrhythmias, headache, hypotension, irritability, nausea, palpitations, restlessness, urine retention, and vomiting.

Action

Xanthine derivatives are structurally related; they directly relax smooth muscle, stimulate the CNS, induce diuresis, increase gastric acid secretion, inhibit uterine contractions, and exert weak inotropic and chronotropic effects on the heart. Of these drugs, theophylline exerts the greatest effect on smooth muscle.

The action of xanthine derivatives isn't completely caused by inhibition of phosphodiesterase. Current data suggest that inhibition of adenosine receptors or unidentified mechanisms may be responsible for therapeutic effects. By relaxing smooth muscle of the respiratory tract, they increase airflow and vital capacity. They also slow onset of diaphragmatic fatigue and stimulate the respiratory center in the CNS.

NURSING PROCESS

Assessment

• Monitor theophylline level closely because therapeutic level ranges from 10 to 20 mcg/ml.
• Monitor patient closely for adverse reactions, especially toxicity.
• Monitor vital signs.

Key nursing diagnoses

• Insomnia related to CNS effects
• Urinary retention related to adverse effects on bladder
• Noncompliance related to long-term therapy

Planning and implementation

• Don't crush or allow patient to chew timed-release forms.
• Calculate dosage from lean body weight because theophylline doesn't distribute into fatty tissue.
• Adjust daily dosage in elderly patients and in those with heart failure or hepatic disease.
• Provide patient with nondrug sleep aids, such as a back rub or milk-based beverage.

Patient teaching

• Tell patient to take drug exactly as prescribed.
• Advise patient to check with prescriber before using any other drug, including OTC medications or herbal remedies, and before switching brands.
• If patient smokes, tell him that doing so may decrease theophylline level. Urge him to notify prescriber if he quits smoking because the dosage will need adjustment to avoid toxicity.

Evaluation

• Patient sleeps usual number of hours without interruption.
• Patient's voiding pattern doesn't change.
• Patient complies with therapy, as shown by maintenance of therapeutic level.

Alphabetical Listing of Drugs

abacavir sulfate
(uh-BACK-uh-veer SULL-fayt)
Ziagen

Pharmacologic class: nucleoside analogue reverse transcriptase inhibitor (NRTI)
Therapeutic class: antiretroviral
Pregnancy risk category: C

Indications and dosages

▶ **HIV-1 infection.** *Adults:* 300 mg P.O. b.i.d. with other antiretrovirals.
Children ages 3 months to 16 years: 8 mg/kg (up to 300 mg) P.O. b.i.d. with other antiretrovirals.
Adjust-a-dose: For patients with mild hepatic impairment, reduce dosage to 200 mg P.O. b.i.d.

Contraindications and cautions

- Contraindicated in patients hypersensitive to the drug or any of its components, and in patients with moderate to severe hepatic impairment.
- Use cautiously in patients at high risk for liver disease. Lactic acidosis and severe hepatomegaly with steatosis may occur, most commonly in women, obese patients, or those with prolonged NRTI exposure.

Lifespan: In pregnant women, use only if potential benefits outweigh risks to the fetus. In elderly patients, use cautiously as they may have decreased renal or hepatic function.

Adverse reactions

CNS: fever, headache, insomnia, sleep disorders.
GI: anorexia, diarrhea, loss of appetite, *nausea, vomiting.*
Hepatic: ***hepatotoxicity.***
Metabolic: ***lactic acidosis.***
Skin: rash.
Other: ***fatal hypersensitivity reaction.***

Interactions

Drug-drug. *Methadone:* May increase methadone clearance. Methadone dosage may need to be increased.
Drug-lifestyle. *Alcohol use:* May decrease drug elimination, increasing exposure. Discourage use together.

Effects on lab test results

- May increase liver enzymes, creatinine, glucose, and triglyceride levels.

Pharmacokinetics

Absorption: Rapid and extensive. Oral solution and tablet forms may be used interchangeably.
Distribution: In extravascular space. About 50% bound to plasma proteins.
Metabolism: In the liver, alcohol dehydrogenase and glucuronyl transferase metabolize the drug to form two inactive metabolites.
Excretion: Mainly in urine; about 16% in feces. *Half-life:* 1 to 2 hours.

Route	Onset	Peak	Duration
P.O.	Unknown	Unknown	Unknown

Action

Chemical effect: Inhibits the activity of HIV-1 reverse transcriptase, stopping viral DNA growth.
Therapeutic effect: Treats HIV-1 infection.

Available forms

Oral solution: 20 mg/ml
Tablets: 300 mg

NURSING PROCESS

Assessment

- Assess patient's condition before therapy and regularly thereafter.
- Watch for hypersensitivity reaction.
- Monitor glucose level during therapy.
- Assess patient for risk factors of liver disease. Lactic acidosis and severe hepatomegaly with steatosis may occur, especially in women or patients who are obese or have prolonged exposure to nucleosides. If patient has symptoms of lactic acidosis or pronounced hepatotoxicity, stop treatment. Symptoms may include hepatomegaly and steatosis, even without an elevated transaminase level.
- Assess patient's and family's knowledge of drug therapy.

Nursing diagnoses
- Risk for infection secondary to presence of HIV
- Ineffective coping related to HIV infection
- Deficient knowledge related to drug therapy

Planning and implementation
- Always give drug with other antiretrovirals, never alone.
- Register pregnant woman with the Antiretroviral Pregnancy Registry at 1-800-258-4263.

ALERT: Drug may cause fatal hypersensitivity reactions. If a patient develops fever, rash, fatigue, nausea, vomiting, diarrhea, or abdominal pain, stop the drug and immediately notify the prescriber.
- Don't restart the drug after a hypersensitivity reaction because more severe signs and symptoms, including life-threatening hypotension, may recur within hours. To report hypersensitivity reactions, register patient with the Abacavir Hypersensitivity Registry at 1-800-270-0425.

ALERT: Don't use triple NRTI (abacavir, lamivudine, and tenofovir) as a new treatment because of the high rate of early viral resistance and virologic failure.

Patient teaching
- Give written information about the drug with each new prescription and refill. Also give the patient, and instruct him to carry, a warning card summarizing a hypersensitivity reaction.
- Tell patient to take the drug exactly as prescribed.
- Inform patient that the drug can be taken with or without food.
- Inform patient that the drug can cause a life-threatening hypersensitivity reaction. Tell patient to stop the drug and immediately seek medical attention if he develops symptoms of hypersensitivity, such as fever, rash, severe fatigue, achiness, nausea, vomiting, diarrhea, stomach pain, or a generally ill feeling.
- Explain that the drug neither cures HIV nor reduces the risk of transmitting HIV to others and that its long-term effects are unknown.

Evaluation
- Patient has reduced signs and symptoms of infection.
- Patient shows adequate coping mechanisms.
- Patient and family state understanding of drug therapy.

abatacept
(uh-BAY-tah-sept)
Orencia

Pharmacologic class: immunomodulator
Therapeutic class: antirheumatic
Pregnancy risk category: C

Indications and dosages
▶ **To reduce signs and symptoms and structural damage and improve physical function in patients with moderate to severe rheumatoid arthritis whose response to one or more disease-modifying drugs has been inadequate. Used alone or with other disease-modifying drugs (except tumor necrosis factor [TNF] antagonists and anakinra).** *Adults weighing more than 100 kg (220 lb):* 1 g I.V. over 30 minutes. Repeat 2 and 4 weeks after initial infusion, and then every 4 weeks thereafter.
Adults weighing 60 to 100 kg (132 to 220 lb): 750 mg I.V. over 30 minutes. Repeat 2 and 4 weeks after initial infusion, and then every 4 weeks thereafter.
Adults weighing less than 60 kg: 500 mg I.V. over 30 minutes. Repeat 2 and 4 weeks after initial infusion, and then every 4 weeks thereafter.

I.V. administration
- Reconstitute vial with 10 ml of sterile water for injection, using only the silicone-free disposable syringe provided, to yield 25 mg/ml.
- Gently swirl contents until completely dissolved. Avoid vigorous shaking.
- Vent the vial with a needle to dissipate any foam.
- Solution should be clear and colorless to pale yellow.
- Further dilute to 100 ml with normal saline solution. Infuse over 30 minutes using an infusion set and a sterile, nonpyrogenic, low–protein-binding filter.
- Store diluted solution at room temperature or refrigerate at 36° to 46° F (2° to 8° C). Infusion must be completed within 24 hours of reconstitution.

⊗ **Incompatibilities**
Don't infuse in the same line with other I.V. drugs.

A

Contraindications and cautions

• Contraindicated in patients hypersensitive to abatacept or any component of the drug. Don't use in patients taking a TNF antagonist or anakinra.

• Use cautiously in patients with active infection, history of chronic infections, scheduled elective surgery, or COPD. Patients who test positive for tuberculosis should be treated before receiving abatacept.

Lifespan: In pregnant women, use drug only if clearly needed. It isn't known if drug appears in breast milk; drug could cause serious adverse reactions in a breast-fed infant and may affect the developing immune system. In elderly patients, use drug cautiously because older adults may have a higher risk of infection and malignancy.

Adverse reactions

CNS: dizziness, *headache.*
CV: hypertension.
EENT: *nasopharyngitis,* rhinitis, sinusitis.
GI: diverticulitis, dyspepsia, *nausea.*
GU: acute pyelonephritis, UTI.
Musculoskeletal: back pain, limb pain.
Respiratory: bronchitis, cough, pneumonia, *upper respiratory tract infection.*
Skin: cellulitis, rash.
Other: herpes simplex, *infections,* influenza, infusion reactions, ***malignancies.***

Interactions

Drug-drug. *Anakinra, TNF antagonists:* May increase risk of infection. Avoid use together.
Live-virus vaccines: May decrease effectiveness of vaccine. Avoid giving vaccines during abatacept treatment or within 3 months after stopping.

Effects on lab test results

None reported.

Pharmacokinetics

Absorption: Given I.V.
Distribution: Not reported.
Metabolism: Not reported.
Excretion: Not reported. *Half-life:* 13 days.

Route	Onset	Peak	Duration
I.V.	Unknown	Unknown	Unknown

Action

Chemical effect: Inhibits T-cell activation, decreases T-cell proliferation, and inhibits production of TNF-alpha, interferon-gamma, and interleukin-2.
Therapeutic effect: Reduces pain and inflammation and improves physical function in patients with rheumatoid arthritis.

Available forms

Lyophilized powder for injection: 250 mg/15-ml single-use vial

NURSING PROCESS

Assessment

• Screen patient for tuberculosis before giving abatacept.

• Assess patient's condition before starting therapy and regularly thereafter to monitor drug's effectiveness.

• Monitor patient carefully for infections and malignancies.

• Assess patient and family's knowledge of drug therapy.

Nursing diagnoses

• Ineffective health maintenance related to underlying disease

• Risk for infection related to abatacept therapy

• Deficient knowledge related to drug therapy

Planning and implementation

• Don't give abatacept with TNF antagonists (Enbrel, Remicade, Humira) or anakinra.

• Notify prescriber if patient develops a severe infection; therapy may need to be stopped.

• If patient has COPD, monitor patient for worsening of symptoms during drug therapy.

Patient teaching

• Urge patient to have tuberculosis screening before starting abatacept treatment.

• Tell patient to continue taking prescribed arthritis drugs. Caution against taking TNF antagonists (Enbrel, Remicade, Humira) or anakinra.

• Tell patient to avoid exposure to infections during treatment.

• Tell patient to immediately report signs and symptoms of infection, swollen face or tongue, and difficulty breathing.

• Tell patient with COPD to report worsening signs and symptoms.

• Advise patient to avoid live-virus vaccines during abatacept treatment and for up to 3 months after it's stopped.

• Advise patient to consult prescriber if she becomes pregnant or plans to breast-feed.
• Advise patient to contact prescriber before taking any other drugs or herbal supplements.
• Remind patient to contact prescriber before being scheduled for surgery.

Evaluation
• Patient's rheumatoid arthritis symptoms and level of physical function improve.
• Patient is free from infection during drug therapy.
• Patient and family state understanding of drug therapy.

abciximab
(ab-SICKS-ih-mahb)
ReoPro

Pharmacologic class: glycoprotein IIb/IIIa receptor blocker
Therapeutic class: platelet-aggregation inhibitor
Pregnancy risk category: C

Indications and dosages
▶ **Adjunct for percutaneous coronary intervention (PCI) to prevent acute cardiac ischemic complications in patients at high risk for abrupt closure of treated coronary vessel.**
Adults: 0.25 mg/kg as I.V. bolus 10 to 60 minutes before PCI, followed by continuous I.V. infusion of 0.125 mcg/kg/minute (maximum, 10 mcg/minute) for 12 hours.
▶ **Patients with unstable angina not responding to conventional medical therapy who will undergo PCI within 24 hours.**
Adults: 0.25 mg/kg as I.V. bolus; then an 18- to 24-hour infusion of 10 mcg/minute, concluding 1 hour after PCI.

I.V. administration
• Intended for use with heparin and aspirin.
• Anticipate hypersensitivity reactions. Have epinephrine, dopamine, theophylline, antihistamine, and corticosteroid available for immediate use.
• If solution contains opaque particles, discard it and obtain a new vial.
• For I.V. bolus, withdraw needed amount of drug into syringe; then inject through a sterile 0.2- to 5-micron syringe filter.
• For I.V. infusion, withdraw needed amount of drug through a 0.2- to 5-micron syringe filter; then inject drug into normal saline solution or D_5W, and infuse via continuous infusion pump equipped with 0.2- or 0.22-micron in-line filter.
• Discard any unused portion of vials or mixed drug.

⊗ **Incompatibilities**
• Give drug in a separate I.V. line; don't add another drug to infusion solution.

Contraindications and cautions
• Contraindicated in patients hypersensitive to a drug component or to murine proteins and in patients with active internal bleeding; bleeding diathesis; platelet count less than 100,000/mm³; intracranial neoplasm, arteriovenous malformation, or aneurysm; severe uncontrolled hypertension; a history of stroke within 2 years or with significant residual neurologic deficit; or a history of vasculitis. Also contraindicated within 6 weeks of major surgery, trauma, or GI or GU bleeding; when oral anticoagulants have been given within 7 days unless PT is 1.2 times control or less; and when I.V. dextran is used before or during PCI.
• Use cautiously in patients who weigh less than 75 kg (165 lb), have a history of GI disease, or are receiving thrombolytics because these patients are at increased risk for bleeding. Conditions that increase risk of bleeding include PCI within 12 hours of onset of symptoms of acute MI, PCI lasting longer than 70 minutes, failed PCI, and use of heparin.
Lifespan: In pregnant or breast-feeding women, use cautiously. In children, safety and effectiveness of drug haven't been established. In patients older than age 65, use cautiously.

Adverse reactions
CNS: hypoesthesia, confusion, headache, pain.
CV: hypotension, chest pain, ***bradycardia***, peripheral edema.
EENT: abnormal vision.
GI: nausea, vomiting, abdominal pain.
Hematologic: ***bleeding, thrombocytopenia***, anemia, leukocytosis.
Musculoskeletal: *back pain.*
Respiratory: pleural effusion, pleurisy, pneumonia.

A

Interactions

Drug-drug. *Antiplatelets, heparin, NSAIDs, other anticoagulants, thrombolytics:* May increase risk of bleeding. Monitor patient closely.

Effects on lab test results

- May decrease hemoglobin level and hematocrit.
- May decrease platelet counts. May increase WBC count.

Pharmacokinetics

Absorption: Given I.V.
Distribution: Rapidly binds to platelet receptors.
Metabolism: Unknown.
Excretion: Unknown. *Half-life:* Initially, less than 10 minutes; second phase, about 30 minutes.

Route	Onset	Peak	Duration
I.V.	Immediate	Immediate	24 hr

Action

Chemical effect: Prevents binding of fibrinogen, von Willebrand factor, and other adhesive molecules to receptor sites on activated platelets.
Therapeutic effect: Inhibits platelet aggregation.

Available forms

Injection: 2 mg/ml

NURSING PROCESS

Assessment

- PCI patients at risk for abrupt closure include those with unstable angina, non–Q-wave MI, acute Q-wave MI within 12 hours of symptom onset, two type B lesions in the artery to be dilated, one type B lesion in the artery to be dilated in a patient with diabetes or a woman older than age 65, one type C lesion in the artery to be dilated, or angioplasty of an infarct-related lesion within 7 days of MI.
- Assess vital signs and evaluate bleeding studies before therapy.
- Monitor patient closely for bleeding, particularly bleeding at the arterial access site for cardiac catheterization and internal bleeding involving the GI or GU tract or retroperitoneal sites.
- Look for adverse reactions and drug interactions.
- Assess patient's and family's knowledge of drug therapy.

Nursing diagnoses

- Ineffective cerebral or cardiopulmonary tissue perfusion related to patient's underlying condition
- Risk for deficient fluid volume related to drug-induced bleeding
- Deficient knowledge related to drug therapy

Planning and implementation

- Institute bleeding precautions. Keep patient on bed rest for 6 to 8 hours after removing sheath or stopping infusion, whichever is later.
- Drug is intended for use with aspirin and heparin.

ALERT: Keep epinephrine, dopamine, theophylline, antihistamines, and corticosteroids available in case of anaphylaxis.

Patient teaching

- Teach patient about his disease and therapy.
- Stress the importance of reporting adverse reactions.

Evaluation

- Patient maintains adequate tissue perfusion.
- Patient maintains adequate hydration.
- Patient and family state understanding of drug therapy.

acamprosate calcium
(ay-CAM-proh-sate KAL-see-um)
Campral

Pharmacologic class: GABA and glutamate agonist
Therapeutic class: alcohol deterrent
Pregnancy risk category: C

Indications and dosages

▶ **Maintenance of alcohol abstinence as part of a comprehensive treatment program.** *Adults:* 666 mg P.O. t.i.d.
Adjust-a-dose: If patient's creatinine clearance is 30 to 50 ml/minute, give 333 mg t.i.d.

Contraindications and cautions

- Contraindicated in patients allergic to drug or its components and in those whose creatinine clearance is 30 ml/minute or less.
- Use cautiously in patients with moderate renal impairment or a history of depression with suicidal thoughts or attempts.

Lifespan: Use cautiously in women who are pregnant or breast-feeding and in elderly patients. Safety and effectiveness haven't been evaluated in children. In elderly patients, drug levels are likely to be increased because these patients commonly have reduced renal function; consider a reduced dosage, and monitor renal function.

Adverse reactions

CNS: abnormal thinking, amnesia, anxiety, asthenia, depression, dizziness, headache, insomnia, paresthesia, somnolence, ***suicidal ideation,*** syncope, tremor.
CV: hypertension, palpitations, peripheral edema, vasodilation.
EENT: abnormal vision, pharyngitis, rhinitis.
GI: abdominal pain, anorexia, constipation, *diarrhea,* dry mouth, dyspepsia, flatulence, increased appetite, nausea, taste disturbance, vomiting.
GU: impotence.
Metabolic: weight gain.
Musculoskeletal: arthralgia, back pain, chest pain, myalgia.
Respiratory: bronchitis, dyspnea, increased cough.
Skin: increased sweating, pruritus, rash.
Other: accidental injury, chills, flulike symptoms, infection, pain.

Interactions

None significant.

Effects on lab test results

- May increase ALT, AST, and bilirubin levels. May decrease hemoglobin level and hematocrit.
- May decrease platelet count.

Pharmacokinetics

Absorption: Absolute bioavailability is about 11%.
Distribution: Into plasma. Negligibly protein-bound.
Metabolism: Not metabolized.
Excretion: By the kidneys as unchanged drug. *Half-life:* 20 to 33 hours.

Route	Onset	Peak	Duration
P.O.	Unknown	3–8 hr	Unknown

Action

Chemical effect: Restores the balance of neuronal excitation and inhibition, probably by interacting with glutamate and gamma aminobutyric acid neurotransmitter systems, thus reducing alcohol dependence.
Therapeutic effect: Aids maintenance of alcohol abstinence.

Available forms

Tablets (delayed-release): 333 mg

NURSING PROCESS

Assessment

- Obtain a history of the patient's alcohol use before therapy.
- Assess the patient's support system and his involvement in a comprehensive treatment program.
- Monitor the patient for adverse reactions to drug therapy.
- Monitor the patient for development of depression or suicidal thoughts.
- Assess the patient's and family's knowledge of drug therapy.

Nursing diagnoses

- Ineffective health maintenance related to alcoholism
- Risk for injury related to alcoholism and drug-induced adverse CNS effects
- Deficient knowledge related to drug therapy

Planning and implementation

- Use drug only after the patient has successfully achieved abstinence.
- Drug doesn't eliminate or reduce withdrawal symptoms.
- Drug doesn't cause alcohol aversion or a disulfiram-like reaction if used with alcohol.

Patient teaching

- Tell patient to continue the alcohol abstinence program, including counseling and support.
- Advise patient to notify his prescriber if he develops depression, anxiety, thoughts of suicide, or severe diarrhea.
- Caution patient's family or caregiver to watch for signs of depression or suicidal ideation.
- Tell patient that drug may be taken without regard to meals, but that taking it with meals may help him remember to take it.
- Tell patient not to crush, break, or chew the tablets but to swallow them whole.
- Advise women to use effective contraception while taking this drug. Tell the patient to contact

her prescriber if she becomes pregnant or plans to become pregnant.

• Explain that this drug may impair judgment, thinking, or motor skills. Urge patient to use caution when driving or performing hazardous activities until drug's effects are known.

• Tell patient to continue taking acamprosate and to contact his prescriber if he resumes drinking.

Evaluation

• Patient abstains from alcohol consumption.

• Patient abstains from alcohol and doesn't experience injury.

• Patient and family state understanding of drug therapy.

acarbose

(ay-KAR-bohs)

Precose

Pharmacologic class: alpha-glucosidase inhibitor

Therapeutic class: antidiabetic

Pregnancy risk category: B

Indications and dosages

▶ **To lower glucose level in patients with type 2 diabetes mellitus, along with diet, exercise, and possibly a sulfonylurea, metformin, or insulin.** *Adults:* Initially, 25 mg P.O. t.i.d. with the first bite of each main meal. Adjust dosage q 4 to 8 weeks based on glucose level and tolerance 1 hour after a meal. Maximum dosage is 50 mg P.O. t.i.d. for patients weighing 60 kg (132 lb) or less and 100 mg P.O. t.i.d. for patients weighing more than 60 kg.

Contraindications and cautions

• Contraindicated in patients hypersensitive to drug and in patients with diabetic ketoacidosis, cirrhosis, inflammatory bowel disease, colonic ulceration, partial intestinal obstruction, predisposition to intestinal obstruction, chronic intestinal disease with disorder of digestion or absorption, or conditions that may deteriorate because of increased intestinal gas formation.

• Drug isn't recommended in patients with severe renal impairment.

• Use cautiously in patients receiving insulin or a sulfonylurea. Drug may increase the hypoglycemic potential of a sulfonylurea.

Lifespan: In pregnant or breast-feeding women, drug isn't recommended. In children, safety and effectiveness haven't been established.

Adverse reactions

GI: *abdominal pain, diarrhea, flatulence.*

Interactions

Drug-drug. *Calcium channel blockers, corticosteroids, estrogens, hormonal contraceptives, isoniazid, nicotinic acid, phenothiazines, phenytoin, sympathomimetics, thiazides and other diuretics, thyroid products:* May cause hyperglycemia and loss of glucose control during use or hypoglycemia when withdrawn. Monitor glucose level.

Digestive enzyme preparations containing carbohydrate-splitting enzymes (such as amylase, Beano enzyme, pancreatin), intestinal adsorbents (such as activated charcoal): May reduce effect of acarbose. Don't give together.

Digoxin: May decrease digoxin level. Monitor digoxin level.

Drug-herb. *Aloe, bilberry leaf, bitter melon, burdock, dandelion, fenugreek, garlic, ginseng:* May improve glucose control and allow reduced antidiabetic dosage. Urge patient to discuss herbal products with prescriber before use.

Effects on lab test results

• May increase ALT and AST levels. May decrease hemoglobin level and hematocrit.

Pharmacokinetics

Absorption: Minimal.

Distribution: Acts locally in GI tract.

Metabolism: Exclusively in the GI tract, mainly by intestinal bacteria and partly by digestive enzymes.

Excretion: Almost completely excreted by the kidneys. *Half-life:* 2 hours.

Route	Onset	Peak	Duration
P.O.	Unknown	1 hr	2–4 hr

Action

Chemical effect: Delays carbohydrate digestion and glucose absorption. Inhibits the metabolism of sucrose to glucose and fructose.

Therapeutic effect: Lessens postprandial hyperglycemia.

Available forms

Tablets: 25 mg, 50 mg, 100 mg

NURSING PROCESS

Assessment
- Obtain baseline creatinine level. Drug isn't recommended in patient with a creatinine level greater than 2 mg/dl.
- Monitor glucose level 1 hour after a meal to determine effectiveness and to identify appropriate dose. Report hypoglycemia or hyperglycemia to prescriber.
- Measure glycosylated hemoglobin level every 3 months.
- In a patient receiving 50 mg t.i.d. or more, monitor transaminase level every 3 months in first year of therapy and periodically thereafter. Report abnormalities to prescriber.
- Assess patient's and family's knowledge of drug therapy.

Nursing diagnoses
- Risk for imbalanced fluid volume related to adverse GI effect
- Imbalanced nutrition: less than body requirements related to patient's underlying condition
- Deficient knowledge related to drug therapy

Planning and implementation
- If dosage exceeds 50 mg t.i.d., watch for high transaminase and bilirubin levels and low calcium and vitamin B_6 levels.
- Drug may increase hypoglycemic potential of sulfonylureas. Closely monitor any patient receiving both drugs. If hypoglycemia occurs, treat with dextrose, I.V. glucose infusion, or glucagon. Report hypoglycemia to prescriber.
- Insulin may be needed during increased stress, such as during infection, fever, surgery, or trauma.

Patient teaching
- Tell patient to take drug daily with first bite of each of three main meals.
- Explain that therapy relieves symptoms but doesn't cure the disease.
- Stress the importance of adhering to specific diet, weight reduction, exercise, and hygiene programs. Show patient how to monitor glucose level and how to recognize and treat hyperglycemia.
- Teach patient to recognize hypoglycemia and to treat symptoms with a form of dextrose rather than with a product containing table sugar.
- Instruct patient to check with the prescriber before using any OTC natural or herbal products, such as Beano.
- Urge patient to wear or carry medical identification at all times.

Evaluation
- Patient maintains adequate fluid volume balance.
- Patient doesn't experience hypoglycemia.
- Patient and family state understanding of drug therapy.

acebutolol
(as-ih-BYOO-tuh-lol)
Sectral

Pharmacologic class: beta blocker
Therapeutic class: antihypertensive, antiarrhythmic
Pregnancy risk category: B

Indications and dosages
▶ **Hypertension.** *Adults:* 400 mg P.O. as single daily dosage or in divided doses b.i.d. Maximum, 1,200 mg daily.

▶ **Suppression of PVCs.** *Adults:* 400 mg P.O. in divided doses b.i.d. Increase dosage to attain adequate response. Usual dosage is 600 to 1,200 mg daily.

▶ **Stable angina‡.** *Adults:* Initially, 200 mg P.O. b.i.d. Increase dosage up to 800 mg daily until angina is controlled. Patients with severe stable angina may require higher doses.

Adjust-a-dose: For patients with renal impairment, if creatinine clearance is less than 50 ml/minute, decrease dosage by 50%; if creatinine clearance is less than 25 ml/minute, decrease dosage by 75%. In elderly patients, don't exceed 800 mg daily.

Contraindications and cautions
- Contraindicated in patients with persistently severe bradycardia, second- or third-degree heart block, overt heart failure, or cardiogenic shock.
- Use cautiously in patients with heart failure, peripheral vascular disease, bronchospastic disease, diabetes, or hepatic impairment. Avoid abrupt withdrawal.

Lifespan: In pregnant women, use cautiously and only if benefits to mother outweigh risks to fetus. In breast-feeding women, use is contraindicated. In children, safety of drug hasn't been established. In elderly patients, use cautiously and at a reduced dose.

Adverse reactions

CNS: abnormal dreams, depression, dizziness, *fatigue,* fever, headache, insomnia.
CV: ***bradycardia,*** chest pain, edema, ***heart failure,*** hypotension.
EENT: abnormal vision, dry eye, eye pain, rhinitis.
GI: constipation, diarrhea, dyspepsia, flatulence, ***mesenteric arterial thrombosis,*** nausea, vomiting.
GU: impotence.
Metabolic: hyperglycemia, ***hypoglycemia,*** unstable diabetes mellitus.
Musculoskeletal: arthralgia, myalgia.
Respiratory: ***bronchospasm,*** cough, dyspnea.
Skin: rash.

Interactions

Drug-drug. *Alpha-adrenergic stimulants:* May increase hypertensive response. Use together cautiously.
Digoxin, diltiazem: May cause excessive bradycardia and increase myocardial depression. Use together cautiously.
Insulin, oral antidiabetics: May alter dosage requirements in previously stabilized diabetic patient. Observe patient carefully.
NSAIDs: May decrease antihypertensive effect. Monitor blood pressure and adjust dosage.
Prazosin: May increase the risk of orthostatic hypotension early in use together. Help patient to stand slowly until effects are known.
Reserpine: May have an additive effect. Monitor patient closely.
Verapamil: May increase the effects of both drugs. Monitor cardiac function closely, and decrease dosages as needed.

Effects on lab test results

- May cause false-positive antinuclear antibody test result. May cause false results with glucose or insulin tolerance tests.

Pharmacokinetics

Absorption: Well absorbed after oral use.
Distribution: About 25% protein-bound. Minimal quantities detected in CSF.
Metabolism: Undergoes extensive first-pass metabolism in liver.
Excretion: 30% to 40% of dose is excreted in urine, the rest in feces and bile. *Half-life:* 3 to 4 hours.

Route	Onset	Peak	Duration
P.O.	1–1½ hr	2½ hr	< 24 hr

Action

Chemical effect: May reduce cardiac output and inhibit renin release. May decrease myocardial contractility and heart rate.
Therapeutic effect: Lowers blood pressure and heart rate and restores normal sinus rhythm.

Available forms

Capsules: 200 mg, 400 mg

NURSING PROCESS

Assessment

- Assess blood pressure and heart rate and rhythm before and during therapy.
- Monitor energy level.
- Be alert for adverse reactions and drug interactions.
- Assess patient's and family's knowledge of drug therapy.

Nursing diagnoses

- Risk for injury related to patient's underlying condition
- Fatigue related to drug-induced CNS adverse reactions
- Deficient knowledge related to drug therapy

Planning and implementation

- Drug may be removed by hemodialysis.
- Check apical pulse before giving drug; if it's slower than 60 beats/minute, withhold drug and call prescriber.

ALERT: Don't stop drug abruptly. Doing so may worsen angina or cause an MI or rebound hypertension.
- Before surgery, notify anesthesiologist about patient's drug therapy.

ALERT: Don't confuse Sectral with Factrel or Septra.

Patient teaching

- Teach patient how to take his pulse, if it's lower than 60 beats/minute, instruct him to skip the dose and notify his prescriber.

• Warn patient that drug may cause dizziness. Instruct him to avoid sudden position changes and to sit down immediately if he feels dizzy.
• Explain the importance of taking the drug as prescribed, even when feeling well.
• Tell a diabetic patient to monitor glucose level closely because this drug may mask the symptoms of hypoglycemia.

☑ Evaluation
• Patient's blood pressure and heart rate and rhythm are normal.
• Patient effectively combats fatigue.
• Patient and family state understanding of drug therapy.

acetaminophen (APAP, paracetamol)

(as-ee-tuh-MIH-nuh-fin)

Abenol ◆ †, Acephen†, Aceta†, Aceta Elixir*†, Acetaminophen Uniserts†, Anacin†, Anacin Maximum Strength Aspirin Free†, Apacet†, Apo-Acetaminophen ◆ †, Arthritis Pain Formula Aspirin Free†, Atasol Caplets ◆ †, Atasol Drops ◆ †, Atasol Elixir*†, Atasol Tablets ◆ †, Dymadon ◇ †, FeverAll Children's ◆ †, FeverAll Infants†, FeverAll Junior Strength†, Genapap†, Genapap Children's Chewable Tablets†, Genapap Children's Elixir†, Genapap Extra Strength†, Genapap Infants' Drops†, Genebs†, Genebs Extra Strength†, Liquiprin Infants' Drops†, Mapap†, Meda-Cap†, Meda Tab†, Neopap†, Oraphen-PD†, Panadol†, Panadol Children's†, Redutemp†, Silapap Children's, Silapap Infants' Drops, St. Joseph Aspirin-Free Fever Reducer for Children†, Tapanol Extra Strength†, Tempra†, Tempra Infants'†, Tylenol†, Tylenol Arthritis Pain Extended Relief, Tylenol Children's Chewable Tablets†, Tylenol Children's Elixir†, Tylenol Concentrated Infant's' Drops†, Tylenol Extended Relief†, Tylenol Extra Strength†, Tylenol Infants' Drops†, Tylenol Junior Strength†

Pharmacologic class: para-aminophenol derivative
Therapeutic class: nonopioid analgesic, antipyretic
Pregnancy risk category: B

Indications and dosages

▶ **Mild pain or fever.** *Adults and children older than age 12:* Give 325 to 650 mg P.O. or P.R. q 4 hours, p.r.n. Or 1 g P.O. t.i.d. or q.i.d., p.r.n. Or two extended-release caplets P.O. q 8 hours. Maximum daily dose, 4 g. Maximum dosage for chronic alcoholics is 2 g daily.
Children ages 11 to 12: Give 480 mg P.O. or P.R. q 4 to 6 hours p.r.n.
Children ages 9 to 10: Give 400 mg P.O. or P.R. q 4 to 6 hours p.r.n.
Children ages 6 to 8: Give 320 mg P.O. or P.R. q 4 to 6 hours p.r.n.
Children ages 4 to 5: Give 240 mg P.O. or P.R. q 4 to 6 hours p.r.n.
Children ages 2 to 3: Give 160 mg P.O. or P.R. q 4 to 6 hours p.r.n.
Children ages 12 to 23 months: Give 120 mg P.O. q 4 to 6 hours p.r.n.
Infants ages 4 to 11 months: Give 80 mg P.O. q 4 to 6 hours p.r.n.
Infants age 3 months or younger: Give 40 mg P.O. q 4 to 6 hours p.r.n.
▶ **Osteoarthritis.** *Adults:* Up to 1 g P.O. q.i.d.

Contraindications and cautions

• Contraindicated in patients hypersensitive to drug.
• Use cautiously in patients with a history of chronic alcohol abuse because hepatotoxicity may occur after therapeutic doses.
Lifespan: In pregnant or breast-feeding women, use cautiously.

Adverse reactions

Hematologic: hemolytic anemia, ***leukopenia, neutropenia, pancytopenia, thrombocytopenia.***
Hepatic: ***liver damage*** (with toxic doses), jaundice.
Metabolic: ***hypoglycemia.***
Skin: rash, urticaria.

Interactions

Drug-drug. *Barbiturates, carbamazepine, hydantoins, isoniazid, rifampin, sulfinpyrazone:* May reduce therapeutic effects and enhance hepatotoxic effects of acetaminophen with high doses or long-term use of these drugs. Avoid use together.

A

Warfarin: May increase hypoprothrombinemic effect with long-term use of high doses of acetaminophen. Monitor PT and INR closely.
Zidovudine: May increase risk of bone marrow suppression because of impaired zidovudine metabolism. Monitor patient closely.
Drug-food. *Caffeine:* May enhance analgesic effects. Monitor patient for effect.
Drug-lifestyle. *Alcohol use:* May increase risk of liver damage. Discourage use together.

Effects on lab test results

- May decrease hemoglobin level and hematocrit.
- May decrease neutrophil, WBC, RBC, and platelet counts.
- May produce false-positive results for urinary 5-hydroxyindoleacetic acid.

Pharmacokinetics

Absorption: Rapid and complete.
Distribution: 25% protein-bound. Level isn't connected strongly with analgesic effect but is with toxicity.
Metabolism: 90% to 95% metabolized in liver.
Excretion: In urine. *Half-life:* 1 to 4 hours.

Route	Onset	Peak	Duration
P.O., P.R.	Unknown	10–60 min	4–6 hr

Action

Chemical effect: Blocks pain impulses, probably by inhibiting prostaglandin or pain receptor sensitizers. May relieve fever by acting in hypothalamic heat-regulating center.
Therapeutic effect: Relieves pain and reduces fever.

Available forms

Caplets: 165 mg†, 500 mg†, 650 mg†
Caplets (extended-release): 650 mg†
Capsules: 500 mg†
Elixir: 80 mg/2.5 ml†, 80 mg/5 ml†,120 mg/5 ml†,160 mg/5 ml*†
Gelcaps: 500 mg†
Geltab: 500 mg†
Geltab (extended-release): 500 mg†, 650 mg†
Infant drops: 80 mg/0.8 ml†, 100 mg/ml†
Liquid: 160 mg/5 ml† 500 mg/15 ml†
Solution: 80 mg/1.66 ml†, 100 mg/ml†
Sprinkles: 80 mg/capsule†, 160 mg/capsule†
Suppositories: 80 mg†,120 mg†, 125 mg†, 300 mg†, 325 mg†, 650 mg†
Tablets: 160 mg†, 325 mg†, 500 mg†, 650 mg†
Tablets (chewable): 80 mg†, 160 mg†
Tablets (disintegrating): 80 mg†, 160 mg†

NURSING PROCESS

Assessment

- Assess patient's pain or temperature before and during therapy.
- Assess patient's drug history, and calculate total daily dosage accordingly. Many OTC products and combination prescription pain products contain acetaminophen.
- Be alert for adverse reactions and drug interactions.
- Assess patient's and family's knowledge of drug therapy.

Nursing diagnoses

- Acute pain related to patient's underlying condition
- Risk for injury related to drug-induced liver damage with toxic doses
- Deficient knowledge related to drug therapy

Planning and implementation

- Give liquid form to children and other patients who have trouble swallowing.

ALERT: When giving liquid form, use caution because drops and elixir have different concentrations.

- Use P.R. in young children and patients for whom oral forms aren't practical.

Patient teaching

ALERT: Tell patient not to use drug for fever that's higher than 103.1° F (39.5° C), lasts longer than 3 days, or recurs.

ALERT: Tell patient that drug is for short-term use. Explain the need to contact the prescriber if a child takes the drug for longer than 5 days or an adult takes it for longer than 10 days.

- Warn patient that high doses or unsupervised long-term use can cause liver damage. Excessive alcohol use may increase risk of hepatotoxicity.
- Tell patient to keep track of daily acetaminophen intake, including OTC and prescription medications. Warn patient not to exceed total recommended dose of acetaminophen per day because of risk of hepatotoxicity.
- Tell breast-feeding woman that drug appears in breast milk in levels less than 1% of dose.

She may use the recommended dose safely for short-term therapy.

Evaluation

- Patient reports pain relief with drug.
- Patient's liver function test results remain normal.
- Patient and family state understanding of drug therapy.

acetazolamide

(ah-see-tuh-ZOH-luh-mighd)

Apo-Acetazolamide ♦, Diamox, Diamox Sequels

acetazolamide sodium

Diamox

Pharmacologic class: carbonic anhydrase inhibitor
Therapeutic class: anticonvulsant, diuretic
Pregnancy risk category: C

Indications and dosages

▶ **Secondary glaucoma; preoperative management of acute angle-closure glaucoma.** *Adults:* 250 mg P.O. q 4 hours, or 250 mg P.O. or I.V. b.i.d. for short-term therapy. For some acute glaucomas, 500 mg P.O.; then 125 to 250 mg P.O. q 4 hours.

▶ **Edema in heart failure.** *Adults:* 250 to 375 mg (5 mg/kg) P.O. daily in a.m.

▶ **Chronic open-angle glaucoma.** *Adults:* 250 mg to 1 g P.O. daily in divided doses q.i.d., or 500 mg extended-release P.O. b.i.d.

▶ **Prevention or amelioration of acute mountain sickness.** *Adults:* 500 mg to 1 g P.O. daily in divided doses q 8 to 12 hours, or 500 mg extended-release P.O. q 12 hours. Start therapy 24 to 48 hours before ascent and continue for 48 hours while at high altitude.

▶ **Adjunct treatment of myoclonic, refractory generalized tonic-clonic, absence, or mixed seizures.** *Adults and children:* 8 to 30 mg/kg P.O. daily in divided doses. Optimum dosage, 375 mg to 1 g daily. When given with other anticonvulsants, the initial dosage is 250 mg daily.

▶ **Drug-induced edema.** *Adults:*250 to 375 mg (5 mg/kg) P.O. as a single dose for 1 or 2 days alternating with one drug-free day.

▶ **Periodic paralysis.** *Adults:* 250 mg P.O. b.i.d. or t.i.d., not to exceed 1.5 g daily.

I.V. administration

- Reconstitute 500-mg vial with at least 5 ml of sterile water for injection.
- Inject 100 to 500 mg/minute into large vein using 21G or 23G needle.
- Intermittent or continuous infusion isn't recommended.
- Use within 24 hours.

⊗ **Incompatibilities**
Multivitamins.

Contraindications and cautions

- Contraindicated in patients hypersensitive to drug, patients undergoing long-term therapy for chronic noncongestive angle-closure glaucoma, and patients with hyponatremia, hypokalemia, renal or hepatic impairment, adrenal gland failure, or hyperchloremic acidosis.
- Use cautiously in patients receiving other diuretics and in patients with respiratory acidosis, emphysema, or COPD.

Lifespan: In pregnant women, use cautiously. In breast-feeding women, drug is contraindicated. In children, safety and effectiveness of drug haven't been established, and cases of growth retardation have been reported.

Adverse reactions

CNS: confusion, drowsiness, paresthesia.
EENT: transient myopia.
GI: altered taste, anorexia, nausea, vomiting.
GU: crystalluria, hematuria, renal calculi.
Hematologic: ***aplastic anemia,*** hemolytic anemia, ***leukopenia.***
Metabolic: asymptomatic hyperuricemia, ***hyperchloremic acidosis,*** hypokalemia.
Skin: rash.
Other: *pain at injection site,* sterile abscesses.

Interactions

Drug-drug. *Amphetamines, anticholinergics, mecamylamine, procainamide, quinidine, tricyclic antidepressants:* May decrease renal clearance of these drugs, increasing toxicity. Monitor patient closely.
Cyclosporine: May increase cyclosporine level, causing toxicity. Use cautiously together.
Lithium: May increase lithium secretion. Monitor patient.

Methenamine: May reduce acetazolamide effectiveness. Avoid use together.
Salicylates: May cause acetazolamide accumulation and toxicity, including CNS depression and metabolic acidosis. Monitor patient closely.
Phenytoin: May increase risk of osteomalacia with long-term use. Use cautiously together.
Primidone: May decrease primidone absorption, reducing anticonvulsant effect. Use cautiously together.

Effects on lab test results

- May increase uric acid level. May decrease potassium and hemoglobin levels and hematocrit. May increase or decrease glucose and theophylline levels.
- May decrease WBC count and thyroid iodine uptake.
- May cause false-positive urine protein test results.

Pharmacokinetics

Absorption: Well absorbed from GI tract.
Distribution: Throughout body tissues.
Metabolism: None.
Excretion: Mainly in urine. *Half-life:* 10 to 15 hours.

Route	Onset	Peak	Duration
P.O.			
capsules	2 hr	8–12 hr	18–24 hr
tablets	1–1½ hr	2–4 hr	8–12 hr
I.V.	2 min	15 min	4–5 hr

Action

Chemical effect: Blocks action of carbonic anhydrase, promoting urine excretion of sodium, potassium, bicarbonate, and water. Decreases secretion of aqueous humor in eye. May decrease abnormal paroxysmal or excessive neuronal discharge. Produces respiratory and metabolic acidosis that may encourage ventilation, increase cerebral blood flow, and help release oxygen from hemoglobin.
Therapeutic effect: Lowers intraocular pressure (IOP), controls seizure activity, and may improve respiratory function.

Available forms

Capsules (extended-release): 500 mg
Injection: 500 mg/vial
Tablets: 125 mg, 250 mg

NURSING PROCESS

Assessment

- In patients with glaucoma, assess eye discomfort and IOP before and during therapy; in those with heart failure, assess edema; in those with seizures, assess neurologic condition.
- Closely monitor intake and output.
- Be alert for adverse reactions and drug interactions.
- Assess patient's and family's knowledge of drug therapy.

Nursing diagnoses

- Excessive fluid volume related to patient's underlying condition
- Impaired urinary elimination related to diuretic action of drug
- Deficient knowledge related to drug therapy

Planning and implementation

- Give oral form early in the morning and the second dose early in the afternoon to avoid nocturia.
- If patient can't swallow oral form, ask pharmacist to make a suspension using crushed tablets in flavored syrup. Although concentrations up to 500 mg/5 ml are possible, concentrations of 250 mg/5 ml are more palatable. Refrigeration improves palatability but doesn't improve stability. Suspensions are stable for 1 week.
- Diuretic effect decreases with acidosis but is restored by stopping drug for several days and then restarting it, or by giving drug intermittently.

ALERT: Don't confuse acetazolamide with acetohexamide. Also don't confuse acetazolamide sodium (Diamox) with acyclovir sodium (Zovirax); these vials may appear similar.

- If hypersensitivity or adverse reactions occur, withhold drug and notify prescriber.

Patient teaching

- Advise patient to take drug early in the day to avoid sleep interruption caused by nocturia.
- Teach patient to monitor fluid volume by measuring weight, intake, and output daily.
- Encourage patient to avoid high-sodium foods and to choose high-potassium foods.
- Teach patient to recognize and report signs and symptoms of fluid and electrolyte imbalance.

Evaluation

- Patient is free from edema.
- Patient adjusts lifestyle to accommodate altered patterns of urine elimination.
- Patient and family state understanding of drug therapy.

acetylcysteine

(as-ee-til-SIS-teen)

Acetadote, Mucomyst, Mucomyst-10, Mucosil-10, Mucosil-20

Pharmacologic class: amino acid (L-cysteine) derivative

Therapeutic class: mucolytic, antidote for acetaminophen overdose

Pregnancy risk category: B

Indications and dosages

▶ **Pneumonia, bronchitis, tuberculosis, cystic fibrosis, emphysema, atelectasis (adjunct), complications of thoracic and CV surgery.** *Adults and children:* 1 to 2 ml of 10% or 20% solution by direct instillation into trachea as often as hourly; or 3 to 5 ml of 20% solution or 6 to 10 ml of 10% solution by nebulization q 2 to 3 hours p.r.n.

▶ **Acetaminophen toxicity.** *Adults and children:* Initially, 140 mg/kg P.O., followed by 70 mg/kg P.O. q 4 hours for 17 doses. Or give 150 mg/kg as loading dose I.V. over 60 minutes. Then begin maintenance doses of 50 mg/kg I.V. over 4 hours, followed by 100 mg/kg I.V. over 16 hours. Adjust total volume given for patients who weigh less than 40 kg or are fluid restricted.

I.V. administration

- If patient weighs 40 kg (88 lb) or more, dilute loading dose in 200 ml, second dose in 500 ml, and third dose in 1,000 ml of D_5W.
- If patient weighs 25 to 40 kg (55 to 88 lb), dilute loading dose in 100 ml, second dose in 250 ml, and third dose in 500 ml of D_5W.
- If patient weighs 20 kg (44 lb), dilute loading dose in 60 ml, second dose in 140 ml, and third dose in 280 ml of D_5W.
- If patient weighs 15 kg (33 lb), dilute loading dose in 45 ml, second dose in 105 ml, and third dose in 210 ml of D_5W.
- If patient weighs 10 kg (22 lb), dilute loading dose in 30 ml, second dose in 70 ml, and third dose in 140 ml of D_5W.
- Store unopened vials at controlled room temperature of 68° to 77° F (20° to 25° C). Reconstituted solution is stable for 24 hours.
- Once the stopper is punctured, drug may turn from colorless to slightly pink or purple. This change doesn't affect potency.

⊗ **Incompatibilities**

Rubber and metals, particularly iron, copper, and nickel.

Contraindications and cautions

- Contraindicated in patients hypersensitive to drug.
- Use cautiously in debilitated patients with severe respiratory insufficiency. In patients with asthma or a history of bronchospasm, use I.V. form cautiously.

Lifespan: In pregnant and breast-feeding women and in elderly patients with severe respiratory insufficiency, use cautiously.

Adverse reactions

EENT: hemoptysis, rhinorrhea.

GI: nausea, stomatitis, vomiting.

Respiratory: BRONCHOSPASM.

Interactions

Drug-drug. *Activated charcoal:* May limit acetylcysteine's effectiveness. Avoid use together in treating drug toxicity.

Effects on lab test results

None reported.

Pharmacokinetics

Absorption: Most inhaled acetylcysteine acts directly on mucus in lungs; remainder is absorbed by pulmonary epithelium. After oral administration, drug is absorbed from GI tract.

Distribution: 50% protein-bound.

Metabolism: In liver.

Excretion: The mean elimination terminal half-life is longer in newborns (11 hours) than in adults (5½ hours). *Half-life:* 6¼ hours.

Route	Onset	Peak	Duration
P.O., I.V., inhalation	Unknown	Unknown	Unknown

A

Action

Chemical effect: Increases respiratory tract fluids to help liquefy tenacious secretions. Restores glutathione in liver to treat acetaminophen toxicity.

Therapeutic effect: Thins respiratory secretions and reverses toxic effects of acetaminophen.

Available forms

I.V. injection: 200 mg/ml

Oral or inhalation solution: 10%, 20%

NURSING PROCESS

Assessment

- Assess patient's respiratory secretions before and often during therapy.
- Be alert for adverse reactions and drug interactions.
- Assess patient's and family's knowledge of drug therapy.

Nursing diagnoses

- Ineffective airway clearance related to patient's underlying condition
- Impaired oral mucous membrane related to drug-induced stomatitis
- Deficient knowledge related to drug therapy

Planning and implementation

- Dilute oral doses with cola, fruit juice, or water to treat acetaminophen overdose. Dilute 20% solution to 5% by adding 3 ml of diluent to each ml of acetylcysteine. If patient vomits within 1 hour of initial or maintenance dose, repeat dose.

ALERT: If the time of ingestion is unknown or the acetaminophen level isn't available or can't be interpreted within 8 hours of ingestion, immediately give drug I.V.

ALERT: Don't confuse acetylcysteine with acetylcholine.

- Use plastic, glass, stainless steel, or another nonreactive metal when giving by nebulization. Drug isn't compatible with rubber or metals, especially iron, copper, and nickel.
- Hand-bulb nebulizers aren't recommended because output is too small and particle size is too large.
- Before aerosol administration, have patient clear airway by coughing.

ALERT: Drug is incompatible with tetracyclines, erythromycin lactobionate, amphotericin B, and ampicillin sodium. If given by aerosol inhalation, these drugs should be nebulized separately. Iodized oil, trypsin, and hydrogen peroxide are incompatible with drug. Don't add these drugs to nebulizer.

- Have suction equipment available in case patient can't effectively clear his air passages.
- Alert prescriber if patient's respiratory secretions thicken or become purulent or if bronchospasm occurs.
- After opening, store in refrigerator, and use within 4 days.
- The vial stopper contains no natural rubber latex, dry natural rubber, or blends of natural rubber.

Patient teaching

- Instruct patient to follow directions on drug label exactly. Explain importance of using drug as directed.
- If patient's condition doesn't improve within 10 days, tell him to notify prescriber. Drug shouldn't be used for prolonged period without direct medical supervision.
- Teach patient how to use and clean nebulizer.
- Inform patient that drug may have a foul taste or smell.
- Instruct patient to clear his airway by coughing before aerosol use to achieve maximum effect.
- Instruct patient to rinse mouth with water after nebulizer treatment because it may leave a sticky coating.

Evaluation

- Patient has clear lung sounds, decreased respiratory secretions, and reduced frequency and severity of cough.
- Patient's oral mucous membranes remain unchanged.
- Patient and family state understanding of drug therapy.

activated charcoal

(AK-tih-vay-ted CHAR-kohl)

Actidose†, Actidose-Aqua†, CharcoAid†, CharcoCaps†, Insta-Char Pediatric†, Liqui-Char†, SuperChar†

Pharmacologic class: adsorbent
Therapeutic class: antidote
Pregnancy risk category: C

Indications and dosages

▶ **Poisoning.** *Adults:* Initially, 1 g/kg (30 to 100 g) P.O. or 5 to 10 times amount of poison ingested as suspension in 180 to 240 ml of water.

Children: Five to 10 times estimated weight of poison ingested, with minimum dose being 30 g P.O. in 240 ml of water to make a slurry, preferably within 30 minutes of poisoning. If patient has food in his stomach, a larger dose is needed.

▶ **Flatulence, dyspepsia.** *Adults:* 600 mg to 5 g P.O. t.i.d. after meals.

Contraindications and cautions

None reported.

Adverse reactions

GI: black stool, constipation, nausea.

Interactions

Drug-drug. *Acetylcysteine, ipecac:* May render charcoal ineffective. Don't use together, and don't perform gastric lavage until all charcoal is removed.

Drug-food. *Milk, ice cream, sherbet:* May decrease effectiveness of activated charcoal.

Effects on lab test results

None reported.

Pharmacokinetics

Absorption: None.
Distribution: None.
Metabolism: None.
Excretion: In feces.

Route	Onset	Peak	Duration
P.O.	Immediate	Unknown	Unknown

Action

Chemical effect: Adheres to many drugs and chemicals, inhibiting their absorption.
Therapeutic effect: Used as antidote for selected poisons and overdoses.

Available forms

Liquid: 208 mg/ml
Oral suspension: 15 g†, 30 g†
Powder: 15 g†, 30 g†, 40 g†, 50 g†, 120 g†, 240 g†
Tablets: 200 mg ◊ †, 300 mg ◊ †

NURSING PROCESS

Assessment

- Find out what substance was ingested and when it was ingested. Drug isn't effective for all drugs and toxic substances.
- Be alert for adverse reactions and drug interactions.
- Assess patient's and family's knowledge of drug therapy.

Nursing diagnoses

- Risk for injury related to ingestion of toxic substance or overdose
- Risk for deficient fluid volume related to drug-induced vomiting
- Deficient knowledge related to drug therapy

Planning and implementation

- Drug is commonly used for treating poisoning or overdose of acetaminophen, aspirin, atropine, barbiturates, cardiac glycosides, oxalic acid, parathion, phenol, phenytoin, poisonous mushrooms, propantheline, propoxyphene, strychnine, or tricyclic antidepressants. Check with poison control center for use in other types of poisonings or overdoses.
- Give after emesis because drug absorbs and inactivates syrup of ipecac.

ALERT: Don't give to a semiconscious or unconscious patient unless airway is protected and NG tube is in place for instillation.

- Mix powder form (most effective) with tap water to form consistency of thick syrup. Add small amount of fruit juice or flavoring to make mix more palatable.
- Give by NG tube after lavage, if needed.
- Don't give in ice cream, milk, or sherbet, which may reduce absorption.

A

• If patient vomits shortly after administration, repeat dose.
• Keep airway, oxygen, and suction equipment nearby.
• Follow treatment with stool softener or laxative to prevent constipation.
ALERT: Don't confuse Actidose with Actos.

Patient teaching
• Warn patient that feces will be black.
• Instruct patient to report respiratory difficulty immediately.

Evaluation
• Patient sustains no injury from ingesting toxic substance or from overdose.
• Patient has no signs of deficient fluid volume.
• Patient and family state understanding of drug therapy.

acyclovir sodium
(ay-SIGH-kloh-veer SOH-dee-um)
Aciclovir ◇, Acihexal ◇, Avirax ♦, Zovirax†

Pharmacologic class: synthetic purine nucleoside
Therapeutic class: antiviral
Pregnancy risk category: B

Indications and dosages
▶ **Chickenpox.** *Adults and children weighing more than 40 kg (88 lb):* 800 mg P.O. q.i.d. for 5 days.
Children age 2 and older weighing less than 40 kg: 20 mg/kg P.O. q.i.d. for 5 days.
▶ **Acute herpes zoster.** *Adults:* 800 mg P.O. q 4 hours, five times daily for 7 to 10 days. Give within 48 hours of rash onset.
▶ **Initial genital herpes.** *Adults:* 200 mg P.O. q 4 hours during waking hours (total of five capsules daily) for 10 days.
▶ **Intermittent therapy for recurrent genital herpes.** *Adults:* 200 mg P.O. q 4 hours during waking hours (total of five capsules daily) for 5 days. Start therapy at first sign of recurrence.
▶ **Long-term suppressive therapy for recurrent genital herpes.** *Adults:* 400 mg P.O. b.i.d. for up to 12 months.
Adjust-a-dose: In patients with renal impairment, if usual dosage is 800 mg five times daily and creatinine clearance is 10 to 25 ml/minute, decrease dosage to 800 mg q 8 hours. If creatinine clearance is 10 ml/minute or less, decrease the 200- to 400-mg dosage to 200 mg q 12 hours, or the 800-mg dosage to 800 mg q 12 hours.
▶ **Initial and recurrent episodes of mucocutaneous herpes simplex virus (HSV-1 and HSV-2) infections in immunocompromised patients; severe initial episodes of herpes genitalis in immunocompetent patients.** *Adults and children age 12 and older:* 5 mg/kg I.V. at constant rate over 1 hour q 8 hours for 7 days (5 days for herpes genitalis).
Children younger than age 12: Give 10 mg/kg I.V. at constant rate over 1 hour q 8 hours for 7 days (5 days for herpes genitalis).
▶ **Herpes simplex encephalitis.** *Adults:* 10 mg/kg I.V. infused at a constant rate over 1 hour, q 8 hours for 10 days.
Children ages 3 months to 12 years: 20 mg/kg I.V. at a constant rate over at least 1 hour, q 8 hours for 10 days.
▶ **Neonatal herpes simplex virus infections.** *Children from birth to age 3 months:* 10 mg/kg I.V. at a constant rate for over 1 hour, every 8 hours for 10 days.
▶ **Varicella zoster in immunocompromised patients.** *Adults and children age 12 and older:* 10 mg/kg I.V. infused at a constant rate over 1 hour, q 8 hours for 7 days. Give obese patients 10 mg/kg (ideal body weight). Don't exceed maximum dose equivalent to 500 mg/m^2 q 8 hours.
Children younger than age 12: Give 20 mg/kg I.V. q 8 hours for 7 days, or 500 mg/m^2 at a constant rate over at least 1 hour, q 8 hours for 7 days.
Adjust-a-dose: In patients with renal impairment, if creatinine clearance exceeds 50 ml/minute, give 100% of the I.V. dose q 8 hours; if it's 25 to 50 ml/minute, 100% of the dose q 12 hours; if it's 10 to 25 ml/minute, 100% of the dose q 24 hours; and if it's less than 10 ml/minute, 50% of the dose q 24 hours.
▶ **Recurrent herpes labialis (cold sores).** *Adults and children age 12 and older:* Apply cream five times daily for 4 days. Start therapy as early as possible following onset of signs and symptoms.
▶ **Genital herpes in immunocompromised patients‡.** *Adults:* 400 mg P.O. three to five times daily.
▶ **Long-term suppressive or maintenance therapy for recurrent HSV infections in pa-**

tients with HIV‡. *Adults and children older than age 12:* Give 200 mg P.O. t.i.d. or 400 mg P.O. b.i.d.
Children age 12 and younger: 600 to 1,000 mg P.O. daily in three to five divided doses.

▶ **Acute herpes zoster ophthalmicus‡.** *Adults:* 600 mg P.O. q 4 hours five times daily for 10 days, preferably within 3 days of rash onset, but no longer than 7 days.

▶ **Rectal herpes infection‡.** *Adults:* 400 mg P.O. five times daily for 10 days or until resolved. Or, give 800 mg P.O. q 8 hours for 7 to 10 days.

▶ **Disseminated herpes zoster‡.** *Adults:* 5 to 10 mg/kg I.V. q 8 hours for 7 to 10 days. Infuse over at least 1 hour.

Adjust-a-dose: In patients with renal impairment, if creatinine clearance exceeds 50 ml/minute, give 100% of the I.V. dose q 8 hours; if it's 25 to 50 ml/minute, 100% of the dose q 12 hours; if it's 10 to 25 ml/minute, 100% of the dose q 24 hours; and if it's less than 10 ml/minute, 50% of the dose q 24 hours.

I.V. administration

- Dissolve the contents of 500-mg vial in 10 ml (or 1,000-mg vial in 20 ml) of sterile water for injection to yield 50 mg/ml. Then dilute further in appropriate I.V. solution to 7 mg/ml or less. Concentrated solutions (10 mg/ml or more) increase the risk of phlebitis.
- Don't use bacteriostatic water containing benzyl alcohol or parabens.
- Give I.V. infusion over at least 1 hour to prevent renal tubular damage. Don't give by bolus injection.
- Don't exceed a maximum dose equivalent of 20 mg/kg every 8 hours.
- Make sure I.V. infusion is accompanied by adequate hydration. Monitor intake and output closely during administration.

⊗ **Incompatibilities**
Biological or colloidal solutions, idarubicin hydrochloride, parabens.

Contraindications and cautions

- Contraindicated in patients hypersensitive to drug, its components, or valacyclovir.
- Use cautiously in patients receiving other nephrotoxic drugs and those with underlying neurologic problems, renal disease, or dehydration.

Lifespan: In pregnant or breast-feeding women, use cautiously. In children younger than age 2, safety and effectiveness of drug haven't been established.

Adverse reactions

CNS: *encephalopathic changes* with I.V. use (including agitation, confusion, ***coma,*** hallucinations, headache, lethargy, obtundation, ***seizures,*** tremor), ataxia, aggressive behavior, fatigue, fever, pain.
CV: hypotension, peripheral edema.
GI: abdominal pain, diarrhea, nausea, vomiting.
GU: hematuria.
Hematologic: ***DIC, hemolysis, leukopenia.***
Hepatic: ***hepatitis,*** hyperbilirubinemia, jaundice.
Musculoskeletal: myalgia.
Skin: itching, rash, *vesicular eruptions.*
Other: ***anaphylaxis, angioedema,*** inflammation, phlebitis at injection site.

Interactions

Drug-drug. *Phenytoin, valproic acid:* May decrease levels of these drugs. Monitor patient closely.
Probenecid: May increase acyclovir level. Monitor patient for toxicity.

Effects on lab test results

- May increase BUN, creatinine, liver enzyme, and bilirubin levels. May decrease hemoglobin level and hematocrit.
- May increase or decrease platelet, neutrophil, and WBC counts.

Pharmacokinetics

Absorption: Slow, and only 15% to 30% is absorbed. Not affected by food.
Distribution: Widely to organ tissues and body fluids. CSF levels equal about 50% of serum levels, and 9% to 33% binds to plasma proteins.
Metabolism: Mainly inside viral cell to its active form.
Excretion: Up to 92% of systemically absorbed acyclovir is excreted unchanged by kidneys. *Half-life:* 2 to 3½ hours with normal renal function; up to 19 hours with renal impairment.

Route	Onset	Peak	Duration
P.O.	Unknown	Unknown	Unknown
I.V.	Immediate	Immediate	Unknown

Action

Chemical effect: Becomes incorporated into viral DNA and inhibits viral multiplication.
Therapeutic effect: Kills susceptible viruses.

Available forms

Capsules: 200 mg
Injection: 500 mg/vial, 1 g/vial
Suspension: 200 mg/5 ml
Tablets: 400 mg, 800 mg

NURSING PROCESS

Assessment

- Assess infection before and regularly during therapy.
- Monitor patient for renal toxicity. Dehydration, renal disease, and use of other nephrotoxic drugs increase risk.
- Monitor patient's mental condition when giving I.V. drug. Encephalopathic changes are more likely in patients with neurologic disorders and in those who have had neurologic reactions to cytotoxic drugs.
- If adverse GI reactions occur with oral use, monitor hydration.
- Assess patient's and family's knowledge of drug therapy.

Nursing diagnoses

- Risk for infection related to presence of virus
- Risk for deficient fluid volume related to adverse GI reactions to oral drug
- Deficient knowledge related to drug therapy

Planning and implementation

ALERT: Don't give I.M., subcutaneously, or by bolus injection.
ALERT: Don't confuse Zovirax with Zyvox. Also, don't confuse acyclovir sodium with acetazolamide sodium. The vials may look alike.

Patient teaching

- Explain that drug manages herpes infection but doesn't eliminate or cure it.
- Warn patient that drug won't prevent spread of infection to others.
- Help patient recognize early symptoms of herpes infection (tingling, itching, pain) so he can take drug before infection fully develops.
- Tell patient to report pain or discomfort at I.V. injection site.

Evaluation

- Patient's infection is eradicated.
- Patient maintains adequate hydration.
- Patient and family state understanding of drug therapy.

adalimumab

(ay-da-LIM-yoo-mab)
Humira

Pharmacologic class: tumor necrosis factor (TNF)-alpha blocker
Therapeutic class: antirheumatic
Pregnancy risk category: B

Indications and dosages

▶ **Rheumatoid arthritis; psoriatic arthritis; ankylosing spondylitis.** *Adults:* 40 mg subcutaneously q other week. Patient may continue to take methotrexate, steroids, NSAIDs, salicylates, analgesics, or other disease-modifying antirheumatic drugs during therapy. Patients with rheumatoid arthritis who aren't also taking methotrexate may have the dose increased to 40 mg weekly, if needed.

Contraindications and cautions

- Contraindicated in patients hypersensitive to drug or any of its components. Don't start drug if patient is immunosuppressed or has a chronic or localized active infection.
- Use cautiously in patients with a history of recurrent infection, those with underlying conditions that predispose them to infections, and those who have lived in areas where tuberculosis and histoplasmosis are common. Use cautiously in patients with CNS-demyelinating disorders.

Lifespan: In pregnant women, give only if benefits outweigh risks to the fetus. Breast-feeding women should either stop nursing or stop taking the drug because of the risk of serious adverse reactions. It's unknown whether drug appears in breast milk or would be absorbed by a breast-feeding infant. In children, safety and effectiveness of drug haven't been established. In elderly patients, use cautiously because serious infections and malignancies are more common in these patients.

Adverse reactions

CNS: headache.
CV: hypertension.
EENT: sinusitis.
GI: abdominal pain, nausea.
GU: hematuria, UTI.
Hematologic: ***leukopenia, pancytopenia, thrombocytopenia.***
Metabolic: hypercholesterolemia, hyperlipidemia.
Musculoskeletal: back pain.
Respiratory: bronchitis, upper respiratory tract infection.
Skin: rash.
Other: *accidental injury,* allergic reactions, ***anaphylaxis,*** flu syndrome, injection site reactions (erythema, hemorrhage, itching, pain, swelling), ***malignancy, sepsis, serious infections.***

Interactions

Drug-drug. *Anakinra:* May cause serious infections. Avoid use together.
Live-virus vaccines: May cause immunosuppression and susceptibility to disease. Avoid use together.

Effects on lab test results

- May increase alkaline phosphatase and cholesterol levels.

Pharmacokinetics

Absorption: Average absolute bioavailability is 64%.
Distribution: Levels in synovial fluid are 31% to 96% of those in serum.
Metabolism: Clearance may be higher if anti-adalimumab antibodies are present and lower in patients age 40 or older.
Excretion: Unknown. *Half-life:* Ranges from 10 to 20 days.

Route	Onset	Peak	Duration
SubQ	Variable	Variable	Unknown

Action

Chemical effect: Blocks human TNF-alpha that aids normal inflammatory and immune responses and the inflammation and joint destruction of rheumatoid arthritis.
Therapeutic effect: Reduces signs and symptoms of rheumatoid arthritis.

Available forms

Injection: 40 mg/0.8 ml in prefilled syringe or prefilled pen

NURSING PROCESS

Assessment

- Assess patient for immunosuppression or active infection before therapy and regularly thereafter.
- Monitor patient for hypersensitivity reaction.

Nursing diagnoses

- Impaired physical mobility related to rheumatoid arthritis
- Deficient knowledge related to signs and symptoms of immunosuppression or infection
- Deficient knowledge related to drug therapy

Planning and implementation

- Drug can be given alone or with methotrexate or other disease-modifying antirheumatics.
- Give first dose under supervision of experienced health care provider.
- Evaluate patient for latent tuberculosis and, if present, start treatment before giving drug.
- Serious infections and sepsis, including tuberculosis and invasive opportunistic fungal infections, may occur. If patient develops new infection during treatment, monitor him closely.

ALERT: The needle cover contains latex and shouldn't be handled by those with latex sensitivity.

- Stop drug if patient develops a severe infection, anaphylaxis, other serious allergic reaction, or evidence of a lupuslike syndrome.

Patient teaching

- Tell patient to report evidence of tuberculosis.
- If appropriate, teach patient or caregiver how to give drug.
- Tell patient to rotate injection sites and to avoid tender, bruised, red, or hard skin.
- Teach patient to dispose of used vials, needles, and syringes safely.
- Tell patient to refrigerate drug in its original container before use.

ALERT: Warn patient to seek immediate medical attention for symptoms of blood dyscrasias or infection, including fever, bruising, bleeding, and pallor.

A

Evaluation

- Patient experiences reduced signs and symptoms of rheumatoid arthritis.
- Patient remains free from infection during therapy.
- Patient and family state understanding of drug therapy.

adefovir dipivoxil

(uh-DEPH-uh-veer dih-pih-VOCKS-ul)

Hepsera

Pharmacologic class: acyclic nucleotide analogue
Therapeutic class: antiviral
Pregnancy risk category: C

Indications and dosages

▶ **Chronic hepatitis B infection.** *Adults:* 10 mg P.O. daily.

Adjust-a-dose: In patients with renal impairment, if creatinine clearance is 20 to 49 ml/minute, give 10 mg P.O. q 2 days. If creatinine clearance is 10 to 19 ml/minute, give 10 mg P.O. q 3 days. In patients receiving hemodialysis, give 10 mg P.O. q 7 days, after dialysis session.

Contraindications and cautions

- Contraindicated in patients hypersensitive to drug or its components.
- Use cautiously and at a reduced dosage in patients with renal impairment and in those receiving nephrotoxic drugs.

Lifespan: In pregnant women, use drug only if benefits to mother outweigh risks to fetus. Women should avoid breast-feeding. It's unknown if drug appears in breast milk. In children, safety and effectiveness of drug haven't been established. In elderly patients, use cautiously because of increased risk of renal or CV dysfunction.

Adverse reactions

CNS: *asthenia,* headache, fever.
EENT: pharyngitis, sinusitis.
GI: abdominal pain, diarrhea, dyspepsia, flatulence, nausea, vomiting.
GU: glycosuria, hematuria, ***renal failure,*** renal insufficiency.
Hepatic: ***hepatic failure, hepatomegaly with steatosis.***
Metabolic: ***lactic acidosis.***
Respiratory: cough.
Skin: pruritus, rash.

Interactions

Drug-drug. *Ibuprofen:* May increase adefovir bioavailability. Monitor patient closely.
Nephrotoxic drugs, such as aminoglycosides, cyclosporine, NSAIDs, tacrolimus, vancomycin: May increase risk of nephrotoxicity. Use together cautiously.

Effects on lab test results

- May increase ALT, amylase, AST, CK, creatinine, and lactic acid levels.

Pharmacokinetics

Absorption: Readily from the GI tract with a bioavailability of 59%.
Distribution: Up to 4% bound to plasma and serum proteins.
Metabolism: Rapidly converted to adefovir diphosphate, an active metabolite.
Excretion: Undergoes renal elimination. *Half-life:* Unknown.

Route	Onset	Peak	Duration
P.O.	Unknown	1–4 hr	7½ hr

Action

Chemical effect: Inhibits hepatitis B virus reverse transcriptase, which breaks the viral DNA chain.
Therapeutic effect: Reduces symptoms of hepatitis B.

Available forms

Tablets: 10 mg

NURSING PROCESS

Assessment

- Assess patient's condition before therapy and regularly thereafter.
- Watch for hypersensitivity reaction.
- Monitor renal function, especially in patients with renal dysfunction and in those taking nephrotoxic drugs.
- Monitor hepatic function.

Nursing diagnoses

- Risk for injury secondary to adverse drug effects
- Deficient knowledge related to drug therapy

Planning and implementation

- The ideal length of treatment hasn't been established.
- Offer HIV antibody testing because drug may promote resistance to antiretrovirals in patients with unrecognized or untreated HIV infection.

ALERT: Patients may develop lactic acidosis and severe hepatomegaly with steatosis during treatment. Risk is higher in women, obese patients, and those taking other antiretrovirals.

- Monitor hepatic function. If patient develops evidence of lactic acidosis and severe hepatomegaly with steatosis, notify prescriber, who will stop drug.

ALERT: Stopping drug may cause severe worsening of hepatitis. Monitor hepatic function closely in patients who stop taking drug.

- Overdose causes GI adverse effects. Treating overdose includes monitoring patient for evidence of toxicity and giving supportive therapy. Dialysis may be helpful.
- Enroll pregnant women in the Antiretroviral Pregnancy Registry, which monitors fetal outcomes, by calling 1-800-258-4263.

Patient teaching

- Inform patient that drug may be taken with or without food.
- Tell patient to immediately report weakness, muscle pain, trouble breathing, stomach pain with nausea and vomiting, dizziness, lightheadedness, fast or irregular heartbeat, or feeling cold in the arms and legs.
- Warn patient not to stop taking drug unless directed because hepatitis could worsen.
- Instruct women to tell their prescriber if they become pregnant or are breast-feeding. Advise breast-feeding women to either stop breast-feeding or stop taking the drug.

Evaluation

- Patient remains free from injury during therapy.
- Patient and family state understanding of drug therapy.

adenosine

(uh-DEN-oh-seen)

Adenocard

Pharmacologic class: nucleoside
Therapeutic class: antiarrhythmic
Pregnancy risk category: C

Indications and dosages

▶ **To convert paroxysmal supraventricular tachycardia (PSVT) to sinus rhythm.** *Adults:* 6 mg I.V. by rapid bolus injection over 1 to 2 seconds. If PSVT isn't eliminated in 1 to 2 minutes, give 12 mg by rapid I.V. bolus and repeat, if needed.

I.V. administration

- If solution is cold, check it for crystals. If they appear, gently warm solution to room temperature. Don't use cloudy solution.
- Give by rapid I.V. injection over 1 to 2 seconds, directly into vein if possible. If I.V. line is used, inject drug into the most proximal port.
- Drug has a very short half-life. Follow with rapid saline flush to ensure that drug reaches systemic circulation quickly.
- Don't give single dose that's larger than 12 mg.
- Discard unused drug. It doesn't contain preservatives.

⊗ **Incompatibilities**

Other I.V. drugs.

Contraindications and cautions

- Contraindicated in patients hypersensitive to drug and in those with second- or third-degree heart block or sick-sinus syndrome unless artificial pacemaker is present. Don't repeat dose in patients who develop significant heart block from drug.
- Use cautiously in patients with asthma because bronchoconstriction may occur.

Lifespan: In pregnant and breast-feeding women and in children, safety of drug hasn't been established.

Adverse reactions

CNS: apprehension, burning sensation, *dizziness, headache,* heaviness in arms, *lightheadedness,* numbness, tingling in arms.

CV: ***atrial fibrillation,*** *chest pressure, chest pain, facial flushing,* hypotension, palpitations, ***ventricular fibrillation, ventricular tachycardia.***
EENT: blurred vision, metallic taste, tightness in throat.
GI: nausea.
Musculoskeletal: back pain, neck pain.
Respiratory: *dyspnea,* hyperventilation.
Skin: diaphoresis.

Interactions

Drug-drug. *Carbamazepine:* May cause higher degree of heart block. Monitor patient.
Digoxin, verapamil: In rare cases, may cause ventricular fibrillation. Use together cautiously.
Dipyridamole: May potentiate adenosine's effects. A smaller dose may be needed.
Methylxanthines: May antagonize adenosine's effects. A patient taking theophylline or caffeine may need a higher dose or may not respond to therapy.
Drug-herb. *Guarana:* May decrease therapeutic response. Discourage use together.
Drug-food. *Caffeine:* May antagonize adenosine's effects. Give higher dose.

Effects on lab test results

None reported.

Pharmacokinetics

Absorption: Given I.V.
Distribution: Rapidly taken up by erythrocytes and vascular endothelial cells.
Metabolism: Within tissues to inosine and adenosine monophosphate.
Excretion: Unknown. *Half-life:* Less than 10 seconds.

Route	Onset	Peak	Duration
I.V.	Immediate	Immediate	Seconds

Action

Chemical effect: Acts on AV node to slow conduction and inhibit reentry pathways.
Therapeutic effect: Restores normal sinus rhythm.

Available forms

Injection: 3 mg/ml

NURSING PROCESS

Assessment

- Monitor patient's heart rate and rhythm before and during therapy.
- Be alert for adverse reactions and drug interactions.
- Assess patient's and family's knowledge of drug therapy.

Nursing diagnoses

- Decreased cardiac output related to arrhythmias
- Ineffective protection related to drug-induced proarrhythmias
- Deficient knowledge related to drug therapy

Planning and implementation

- If ECG disturbances occur, withhold drug, obtain rhythm strip, and notify prescriber immediately.

ALERT: Have emergency equipment and drugs on hand to treat new arrhythmias.

Patient teaching

- Teach patient and family about the disease and therapy.
- Stress importance of alerting health care provider about chest pain or dyspnea.
- Advise patient to avoid caffeine.

Evaluation

- Patient's arrhythmias are corrected and his heart maintains normal sinus rhythm.
- Patient doesn't experience proarrhythmias.
- Patient and family state understanding of drug therapy.

albumin 5%

(al-BYOO-min)

Albuminar-5, Albutein 5%, Plasbumin-5

albumin 25%

Albuminar-25, Albutein 25%, Plasbumin-25

Pharmacologic class: blood derivative
Therapeutic class: plasma volume expander
Pregnancy risk category: C

Indications and dosages

▶ **Hypovolemic shock.** *Adults:* Initially, 500 ml of 5% solution by I.V. infusion; repeat, if needed. Dosage varies with patient's condition and response. Maximum, 250 g in 48 hours. *Children:* 10 to 20 ml/kg of 5% solution by I.V. infusion, repeated in 15 to 30 minutes if response isn't adequate. Or, 2.5 to 5 ml/kg of 25% solution I.V.; repeat after 10 to 30 minutes, if needed.

▶ **Hypoproteinemia.** *Adults:* 1,000 to 1,500 ml of 5% solution by I.V. infusion daily, with maximum rate of 5 to 10 ml/minute; or 200 to 300 ml 25% solution by I.V. infusion daily, with maximum rate of 3 ml/minute. Dosage varies with patient's condition and response.

▶ **Hyperbilirubinemia.** *Infants:* 1 g albumin (4 ml of 25% solution)/kg I.V. 1 to 2 hours before transfusion.

I.V. administration

- Albumin can be given undiluted or diluted with normal saline solution or D_5W. Use within 4 hours of opening the vial, and discard unused solution because it has no preservatives. Don't use cloudy solutions or those containing sediment. Solution should be clear amber.
- Avoid infusing 10 ml/minute or faster. Infusion rate is individualized according to patient's age, condition, and diagnosis. Albumin 5% is infused undiluted; albumin 25% may be undiluted or diluted with normal saline or D_5W injection.
- Follow storage instructions on bottle. Freezing may cause bottle to break.
- Don't give more than 250 g in 48 hours.

⊗ **Incompatibilities**
Verapamil hydrochloride.

Contraindications and cautions

- Contraindicated in patients hypersensitive to drug. The 5% solution is contraindicated in patients who have severe anemia or cardiac failure with normal or increased intravascular volume. The 25% solution is contraindicated in patients at risk for circulatory overload.
- Use cautiously in patients with cardiac disease, severe pulmonary infection, renal insufficiency, or hypoalbuminemia with peripheral edema.

Lifespan: In pregnant women, use drug cautiously.

Adverse reactions

CNS: fever.
CV: altered pulse rate, hypotension, ***vascular overload.***
GI: increased salivation, nausea, vomiting.
Respiratory: altered respiration, ***pulmonary edema.***
Skin: rash, urticaria.
Other: chills.

Interactions

None significant.

Effects on lab test results

- May increase albumin level.

Pharmacokinetics

Absorption: Given I.V.
Distribution: Albumin accounts for about 50% of plasma proteins. It's distributed into the intravascular space and extravascular sites, including skin, muscle, and lungs.
Metabolism: Unknown.
Excretion: Unknown. *Half-life:* 15 to 20 days.

Route	Onset	Peak	Duration
I.V.	Immediate	15 min	Up to several hr

Action

Chemical effect: Albumin 5% supplies colloid to blood and increases plasma volume. Albumin 25% causes fluid to shift from interstitial spaces to circulation, slightly increasing protein level and providing hemodilution.
Therapeutic effect: Relieves shock by increasing plasma volume and corrects plasma protein deficiency.

Available forms

albumin 5% injection: 50-ml, 250-ml, 500-ml, and 1,000-ml vials
albumin 25% injection: 20-ml, 50-ml, and 100-ml vials

NURSING PROCESS

Assessment

- Assess patient's underlying condition.
- Be alert for adverse reactions.
- Monitor fluid intake and output; protein, electrolyte, and hemoglobin levels; and hematocrit.
- Monitor patient's blood pressure often during therapy.
- Assess patient's and family's knowledge of drug therapy.

A

Nursing diagnoses
- Deficient fluid volume related to patient's underlying condition
- Excessive fluid volume related to adverse effects of drug
- Deficient knowledge related to drug therapy

Planning and implementation
- One volume of albumin 25% is equivalent to five volumes of albumin 5% in producing hemodilution and relative anemia.
- In patient with cerebral edema, withhold fluids for 8 hours after infusion to avoid fluid overload.
- If hypotension occurs, slow or stop infusion. Use vasopressor, if needed.

Patient teaching
- Explain how and why albumin is given.
- Tell patient to report chills, fever, dyspnea, nausea, or rash immediately.

Evaluation
- Patient's deficient fluid volume is resolved.
- Patient doesn't develop fluid overload.
- Patient and family state understanding of drug therapy.

albuterol sulfate (salbutamol sulfate)
(al-BYOO-ter-oll SULL-fayt)

AccuNeb, Airomir ◊, Asmol CFC-free ◊, Proventil, Proventil HFA, Proventil Repetabs, Ventolin, Ventolin CFC-free ◊, Ventolin HFA, Ventolin Rotacaps ◊, VoSpire ER

Pharmacologic class: adrenergic
Therapeutic class: bronchodilator
Pregnancy risk category: C

Indications and dosages
▶ **To prevent exercise-induced bronchospasm.** *Adults and children age 4 and older:* Two aerosol inhalations 15 to 30 minutes before exercise.

▶ **To prevent or treat bronchospasm in patients with reversible obstructive airway disease.** ***Aerosol.*** *Adults and children age 4 and older:* One or two inhalations q 4 to 6 hours. More frequent use and more inhalations aren't recommended. Proventil isn't indicated for use in children younger than age 12.

Solution for inhalation. *Adults and children age 12 and older:* 2.5-mg solution for inhalation by nebulizer t.i.d. or q.i.d. To prepare solution, use 0.5 ml of 0.5% solution diluted with 2.5 ml normal saline solution. Or, use 3 ml of 0.083% solution.

Children ages 2 to 11: Initially, 0.1 to 0.15 mg/kg of solution for inhalation by nebulizer, adjusted to response. Don't exceed 2.5 mg t.i.d. or q.i.d. by nebulization.

Tablets. *Adults and children older than age 12:* Give 2- to 4-mg tablets P.O. t.i.d. or q.i.d. Maximum, 8 mg q.i.d.

Children ages 6 to 12: Give 2-mg tablets P.O. t.i.d. or q.i.d. Maximum dose is 6 mg q.i.d. Or, 4- to 8-mg extended-release tablets P.O. q 12 hours. Maximum, 12 to 16 mg b.i.d.

Syrup. *Adults and children age 15 and older:* 2 to 4 mg (5 to 10 ml) syrup P.O. t.i.d. or q.i.d. Maximum, 8 mg P.O. q.i.d.

Children ages 6 to 14: Give 2 mg (5 ml) syrup P.O. t.i.d. or q.i.d. Maximum, 24 mg daily in divided doses.

Children ages 2 to 5: Initially, 0.1 mg/kg syrup P.O. t.i.d. Starting dose shouldn't exceed 2 mg (5 ml) t.i.d. Maximum, 4 mg (10 ml) t.i.d.

Adjust-a-dose: For elderly patients and patients sensitive to beta-adrenergic stimulators, 2-mg tablets P.O. t.i.d. or q.i.d. tablets or syrup. Maximum, 8 mg t.i.d. or q.i.d.

Contraindications and cautions
- Contraindicated in patients hypersensitive to drug or its components.
- Use cautiously in patients with CV disorders (including coronary insufficiency, cardiac arrhythmias, and hypertension), hyperthyroidism, or diabetes mellitus and in those unusually responsive to adrenergics.
- Use extended-release tablets cautiously in patients with GI narrowing.

Lifespan: In pregnant women, use cautiously. Breast-feeding women shouldn't take drug. In children, safety of drug hasn't been established in those younger than age 6 for tablets and Repetabs, younger than age 4 for aerosol, and younger than age 2 for inhalation solution and syrup. In elderly patients, use cautiously.

Adverse reactions

CNS: dizziness, headache, insomnia, *nervousness, tremor.*
CV: hypertension, palpitations, tachycardia.
EENT: drying and irritation of nose and throat.
GI: heartburn, nausea, vomiting.
Metabolic: hypokalemia, weight loss.
Musculoskeletal: muscle cramps.
Respiratory: ***bronchospasm.***

Interactions

Drug-drug. *CNS stimulants:* May increase CNS stimulation. Avoid use together.
Levodopa: May increase risk of arrhythmias. Monitor patient closely.
MAO inhibitors, tricyclic antidepressants: May increase adverse CV effects. Monitor patient closely.
Propranolol, other beta blockers: May antagonize each other. Monitor patient carefully.
Drug-herb. *Herbs containing caffeine:* May have additive adverse effects. Discourage use together.
Drug-food. *Caffeine:* May increase CNS stimulation. Discourage use together.

Effects on lab test results

- May decrease potassium level.

Pharmacokinetics

Absorption: After inhalation, most of dose is swallowed and absorbed through GI tract.
Distribution: Doesn't cross blood–brain barrier.
Metabolism: Extensively in liver to inactive compounds.
Excretion: Rapidly in urine and feces. *Half-life:* About 4 hours for inhalation, 5 to 6 hours for oral form.

Route	Onset	Peak	Duration
P.O.	15–30 min	2–3 hr	4–6 hr
Inhalation	5–15 min	1–1½ hr	3–4 hr

Action

Chemical effect: Relaxes bronchial and uterine smooth muscle by acting on beta$_2$-adrenergic receptors.
Therapeutic effect: Improves ventilation.

Available forms

Aerosol inhaler: 90 mcg/metered spray, 100 mcg/metered spray
Solution for inhalation: 0.083%, 0.5%, 0.63 mg/3 ml, 1.25 mg/3 ml
Syrup: 2 mg/5 ml
Tablets: 2 mg, 4 mg
Tablets (extended-release): 4 mg, 8 mg

NURSING PROCESS

Assessment

- Obtain baseline assessment of patient's respiratory status, and assess patient often during therapy.
- Be alert for adverse reactions and drug interactions.
- Assess patient's and family's knowledge of drug therapy.

Nursing diagnoses

- Impaired gas exchange related to underlying respiratory condition
- Risk for injury related to drug-induced adverse reactions
- Deficient knowledge related to drug therapy

Planning and implementation

- Pleasant-tasting syrup may be taken by children as young as age 2. Syrup contains no alcohol or sugar.
- If more than one dose is ordered, wait at least 2 minutes between nebulized doses. If corticosteroid inhaler also is used, first have patient use bronchodilator, wait 5 minutes, and then have patient use corticosteroid inhaler. This permits bronchodilator to open air passages for maximum effectiveness.
- Aerosol form may be prescribed for use 15 minutes before exercise to prevent exercise-induced bronchospasm.
- Patients may use tablets and aerosol together.

ALERT: Don't confuse albuterol with atenolol or Albutein.

Patient teaching

- Warn patient to stop drug immediately if paradoxical bronchospasm occurs.
- Give these instructions for using metered-dose inhaler: Clear nasal passages and throat. Breathe out, expelling as much air from lungs as possible. Place mouthpiece well into mouth, and inhale deeply as dose is released. Hold breath for several seconds, remove mouthpiece, and exhale slowly.

A

• Advise patient to wait at least 2 minutes before repeating procedure if more than one inhalation is ordered.
• Warn patient to avoid accidentally spraying inhalant into eyes, which may cause temporary blurred vision.
• Tell patient to reduce intake of foods and herbs containing caffeine, such as coffee, cola, and chocolate, when using a bronchodilator.
• Show patient how to take his pulse. Instruct him to check pulse before and after using bronchodilator and to call prescriber if pulse rate increases more than 20 to 30 beats/minute.

Evaluation

• Patient's respiratory signs and symptoms improve.
• Patient has no injury from adverse drug reactions.
• Patient and family state understanding of drug therapy.

alefacept

(ALE-fuh-sept)
Amevive

Pharmacologic class: immunosuppressive
Therapeutic class: antipsoriatic
Pregnancy risk category: B

Indications and dosages

▶ **Moderate to severe chronic plaque psoriasis in candidates for systemic therapy or phototherapy.** *Adults:* 15 mg I.M. once weekly for 12 weeks. Another 12-week course may be given if CD4+ T lymphocyte count is normal and at least 12 weeks have passed since the previous treatment.

Adjust-a-dose: If CD4+ T lymphocyte count is below 250 cells/mm^3, withhold dose. Stop drug if CD4+ count remains below 250 cells/mm^3 for 1 month.

Contraindications and cautions

• Contraindicated in patients hypersensitive to drug or its components, patients with a history of systemic malignancy or clinically important infection, and patients with HIV infection.
• Use cautiously in patients at high risk for malignancy and in those with chronic or recurrent infections.

Lifespan: In pregnant women, use only if clearly needed because effects on fetus aren't known. Breast-feeding women should either stop nursing or stop the drug because it isn't known whether drug appears in breast milk. In children, safety and effectiveness of drug haven't been established. In elderly patients, give drug cautiously because of their increased rate of infection and malignancies.

Adverse reactions

CNS: dizziness.
CV: ***coronary artery disorder, MI.***
EENT: pharyngitis.
GI: nausea.
Hematologic: ***lymphopenia.***
Musculoskeletal: myalgia.
Respiratory: cough.
Skin: pruritus.
Other: antibody formation; chills; hypersensitivity reaction; infection; *injection site* bleeding, edema, *inflammation,* mass, or *pain;* ***malignancy.***

Interactions

Drug-drug. *Immunosuppressants, phototherapy:* May increase risk of excessive immunosuppression. Avoid using together.

Effects on lab test results

• May decrease CD4+ and CD8+ T lymphocyte counts.

Pharmacokinetics

Absorption: Unknown.
Distribution: 63% bioavailable after I.M. injection.
Metabolism: Unknown.
Excretion: Unknown. *Half-life:* 270 hours.

Route	Onset	Peak	Duration
I.M.	Unknown	Unknown	Unknown

Action

Chemical effect: Interferes with lymphocyte activation and reduces CD4+ and CD8+ T lymphocyte counts.
Therapeutic effect: Reduces symptoms of psoriasis.

Available forms

Powder for injection: 15-mg single-dose vial

NURSING PROCESS

Assessment

- Make sure patient has a normal CD4+ T lymphocyte count before therapy starts, and monitor it weekly for the 12-week course.
- Monitor patient carefully for evidence of infection or malignancy, and stop drug if it appears.

Nursing diagnoses

- Impaired skin integrity related to psoriasis
- Risk for infection related to immunosuppressive drug therapy
- Deficient knowledge related to drug therapy

Planning and implementation

ALERT: Rotate I.M. injection sites to give new injection at least 1" from the old site. Avoid areas that are bruised, tender, or hard.

- Overdose may cause chills, headache, arthralgia, and sinusitis. Provide supportive care, and closely monitor total lymphocyte and CD4+ T lymphocyte counts.
- Enroll pregnant women receiving drug into the Biogen Pregnancy Registry by calling 1-866-263-8483 so that drug effects can be studied.

Patient teaching

- Warn patient about potential adverse reactions.
- Urge patient to report evidence of infection immediately.
- Inform patient that blood tests will be done regularly to monitor WBC count.
- Tell patient to notify prescriber if she is or could be pregnant within 8 weeks of receiving drug.

Evaluation

- Patient's psoriasis improves.
- Patient remains free from infection.
- Patient and family state understanding of drug therapy.

alemtuzumab

(ah-lem-TOO-zeh-mab)

Campath

Pharmacologic class: monoclonal antibody
Therapeutic class: antineoplastic
Pregnancy risk category: C

Indications and dosages

▶ **B-cell chronic lymphocytic leukemia in patients treated with alkylating drugs and for whom fludarabine therapy has failed.** *Adults:* Initially, 3 mg I.V. infusion over 2 hours daily; if tolerated, increase to 10 mg daily; then increase to 30 mg daily. Dosage usually can be increased to 30 mg in 3 to 7 days. As maintenance, give 30 mg I.V. three times weekly on nonconsecutive days (such as Monday, Wednesday, Friday) for up to 12 weeks. Don't give a single dose greater than 30 mg or a weekly dose greater than 90 mg.

Adjust-a-dose: The first time absolute neutrophil count (ANC) is 250/mm^3 or less or platelet count is 25,000/mm^3 or less, stop therapy; resume at same dose when ANC is 500/mm^3 or more or platelet count is 50,000/mm^3 or more. If interruption is 7 days or longer, start with 3 mg and increase to 10 mg and then 30 mg as tolerated. The second time ANC is 250/mm^3 or less or platelet count is 25,000/mm^3 or less, stop therapy; when ANC returns to 500/mm^3 or more or platelet count to 50,000/mm^3 or more, resume at 10 mg; if interruption is 7 days or longer, start with 3 mg and increase only to 10 mg. The third time ANC is 250/mm^3 or less or platelet count is 25,000/mm^3 or less, stop therapy. If ANC or platelet count decreases to 50% or less of baseline in patients starting therapy with a baseline ANC of 500/mm^3 or less or a baseline platelet count 25,000/mm^3 or less, stop therapy; when ANC or platelet count returns to baseline, resume therapy. If interruption is 7 days or longer, start with 3 mg and increase to 10 mg and then 30 mg, as tolerated.

I.V. administration

- Don't use solution if it's discolored or contains precipitate. Don't shake ampule before use. Filter with a sterile, low–protein-binding, 5-micron filter before dilution. Add to 100 ml normal saline solution or D_5W. Gently invert bag to mix solution.
- Premedicate with 50 mg diphenhydramine and 650 mg acetaminophen 30 minutes before initial infusion and before each dose increase. If prescribed, give 200 mg hydrocortisone to decrease severe infusion-related adverse events.
- Give anti-infective prophylaxis, such as trimethoprim-sulfamethoxazole double strength b.i.d. three times weekly and 250 mg famciclovir (or equivalent) b.i.d. Continue prophylax-

is for 2 months or until CD4+ count is 200/mm³ or more, whichever occurs later.

- Don't give as I.V. push or bolus.
- Infuse over 2 hours.
- Protect solution from light.
- Use within 8 hours of dilution.

⊗ **Incompatibilities**

Other I.V. drugs.

Contraindications and cautions

- Contraindicated in patients with active systemic infection, underlying immunodeficiency (such as HIV), or type I hypersensitivity or anaphylactic reactions to drug or any of its components.

Lifespan: In pregnant women, benefits of drug should be weighed against risks to the fetus. Breast-feeding women should stop breast-feeding during treatment and for at least 3 months after taking last dose of drug. In children, safety and effectiveness of drug haven't been established.

Adverse reactions

CNS: asthenia, depression, dizziness, dysthenias, fatigue, fever, headache, insomnia, malaise, somnolence, syncope, tremor.
CV: edema, hypertension, hypotension, peripheral edema, SUPRAVENTRICULAR TACHYCARDIA, tachycardia.
EENT: epistaxis, *pharyngitis,* rhinitis.
GI: abdominal pain, anorexia, constipation, diarrhea, dyspepsia, mucositis, nausea, stomatitis, ulcerative stomatitis, vomiting.
Hematologic: *anemia,* NEUTROPENIA, ***pancytopenia,*** purpura, THROMBOCYTOPENIA.
Musculoskeletal: back pain, myalgias, pain, skeletal pain.
Respiratory: ***acute respiratory distress syndrome,*** bronchitis, ***bronchospasm,*** cough, dyspnea, ***pneumonia,*** pneumonitis.
Skin: increased sweating, pruritus, rash, urticaria.
Other: candidiasis, chills, herpes simplex, infection, rigors, SEPSIS.

Interactions

None reported.

Effects on lab test results

- May decrease hemoglobin level and hematocrit.
- May decrease CD4+, lymphocyte, neutrophil, WBC, RBC, and platelet counts.
- May interfere with diagnostic tests that use antibodies.

Pharmacokinetics

Absorption: Given I.V.
Distribution: Binds to various tissues.
Metabolism: Unknown.
Excretion: Unknown. *Half-life:* 12 hours to 6 days.

Route	Onset	Peak	Duration
I.V.	Unknown	Unknown	Unknown

Action

Chemical effect: Binds to CD52 and causes antibody-dependent destruction of leukemic cells following cell-surface binding.
Therapeutic effect: Destroys leukemic cells.

Available forms

Ampules: 10 mg/ml, in 3-ml ampules

NURSING PROCESS

Assessment

- Assess patient before therapy for evidence of active infection or compromised immune function.
- Obtain baseline CBC and platelet count before starting therapy.
- Monitor blood pressure, and watch for hypotension during administration.

ALERT: Monitor hematologic studies during therapy. Even with normal doses, patients may develop hematologic toxicity, including myelosuppression, bone marrow dysplasia, and thrombocytopenia. Initial doses greater than 3 mg aren't well tolerated. Extremely high doses cause acute bronchospasm, cough, shortness of breath, and anuria and may be fatal. Stop drug and provide supportive treatment.

- Monitor CBC and platelet counts weekly during therapy and more often if anemia, neutropenia, or thrombocytopenia worsens.
- After treatment, monitor CD4+ count until it reaches 200 cells/mm³.

Nursing diagnoses

- Risk for infection related to immunocompromised state
- Fatigue caused by drug therapy

• Deficient knowledge related to alemtuzumab therapy

Planning and implementation

• If transfusions are needed, irradiate blood to protect against graft-versus-host disease.
• Don't immunize with live-virus vaccines.
• If therapy is stopped for longer than 7 days, restart with gradual dose increase.
ALERT: Don't confuse alemtuzumab with trastuzumab.

Patient teaching

• Tell patient to immediately report infusion reaction, such as rigors, chills, fever, nausea, or vomiting.
• Advise patient to report signs or symptoms of infection immediately.
• Inform patient that blood tests will be done often during therapy to observe for adverse effects.
• Tell women of childbearing age and men to use effective contraception during therapy and for at least 6 months afterward.

Evaluation

• Patient remains free from infection.
• Patient has no harmful drug-induced adverse reactions.
• Patient and family state understanding of drug therapy.

alendronate sodium

(ah-LEN-droh-nayt SOH-dee-um)
Fosamax, Fosamax Plus D

Pharmacologic class: inhibitor of osteoclast-mediated bone resorption
Therapeutic class: antiosteoporotic
Pregnancy risk category: C

Indications and dosages

▶ **Osteoporosis in postmenopausal women; to increase bone mass in men with osteoporosis.** *Adults:* 10 mg P.O. daily or 70-mg tablet, one bottle of 70-mg oral solution, or one 70 mg/2,800 international units vitamin D_3 tablet, P.O. once weekly with water at least 30 minutes before first food, beverage, or medication of the day.

▶ **Prevention of osteoporosis in postmenopausal women.** *Women:* 5 mg P.O. daily or 35-mg tablet P.O. once weekly taken with water at least 30 minutes before first food, beverage, or medication of the day.

▶ **Corticosteroid-induced osteoporosis, given with calcium and vitamin D supplements.** *Adults:* 5 mg P.O. daily.
Postmenopausal women not receiving estrogen replacement therapy: 10 mg P.O. daily.

▶ **Paget disease of bone.** *Adults:* 40 mg P.O. daily for 6 months taken with water at least 30 minutes before first food, beverage, or drug of the day.

Contraindications and cautions

• Contraindicated in patients with hypocalcemia; severe renal insufficiency; inability to stand or sit upright for at least 30 minutes; abnormalities of the esophagus that delay esophageal emptying, such as stricture or achalasia; increased risk of aspiration (oral solution); or hypersensitivity to drug or its components.
• Use cautiously in patients with dysphagia, esophageal diseases, gastritis, duodenitis, ulcers, or mild to moderate renal insufficiency.
Lifespan: In pregnant women, use only if benefits outweigh risks to the fetus. In breast-feeding women and in children, safety of drug hasn't been established.

Adverse reactions

CNS: headache.
GI: abdominal distention, abdominal pain, acid regurgitation, constipation, diarrhea, dyspepsia, dysphagia, esophageal ulcer, flatulence, gastritis, nausea, taste perversion, vomiting.
Musculoskeletal: musculoskeletal pain.

Interactions

Drug-drug. *Antacids, calcium supplements, and many other oral medications:* May interfere with alendronate absorption. Give 30 minutes after alendronate dose.
Aspirin, NSAIDs: May increase risk of upper GI reactions with alendronate doses greater than 10 mg daily. Monitor patient closely.
Drug-food. *Any food:* May decrease drug absorption. Don't give drug with food.

Effects on lab test results

• May mildly decrease calcium and phosphate levels.

A

Pharmacokinetics

Absorption: Food or beverages can significantly decrease bioavailability.
Distribution: Initially to soft tissues, but rapidly redistributed to bone or excreted in urine. About 78% protein-bound.
Metabolism: None.
Excretion: In urine. *Half-life:* More than 10 years.

Route	Onset	Peak	Duration
P.O.	1 mo	3–6 mo	3 wk after therapy

Action

Chemical effect: Suppresses osteoclast activity on newly formed resorption surfaces, reducing bone turnover.
Therapeutic effect: Increases bone mass.

Available forms

Oral solution: 70 mg/75 ml
Tablets: 5 mg, 10 mg, 35 mg, 40 mg, 70 mg, 70-mg tablet also containing 2,800 international units vitamin D_3

NURSING PROCESS

Assessment

- Obtain history of patient's underlying disorder before therapy.
- Monitor calcium and phosphate levels throughout therapy.
- Be alert for adverse reactions and drug interactions.
- Assess patient's and family's knowledge of drug therapy.

Nursing diagnoses

- Risk for injury related to decreased bone mass
- Risk for deficient fluid volume related to drug-induced GI upset
- Deficient knowledge related to drug therapy

Planning and implementation

- Correct hypocalcemia and other disturbances of mineral metabolism (such as vitamin D deficiency) before therapy begins.
- Give drug in the morning at least 30 minutes before first meal, fluid, or other oral drugs.

ALERT: Don't confuse Fosamax with Flomax.

- The recommended daily intake of vitamin D is 400 to 800 international units. Fosamax Plus D provides 400 international units daily in the once-weekly formulation. Patients at risk for vitamin D deficiency, such as those who are chronically ill, have a GI malabsorption syndrome, or are older than age 70, may need additional amounts.

Patient teaching

- Advise patient to take tablets when he awakes with 6 to 8 oz of water; tell him to take oral solution with at least 2 oz of water.

ALERT: Warn patient not to lie down for at least 30 minutes after taking drug and until after the first food of the day to aid passage to stomach and reduce risk of esophageal irritation.

- Tell patient to take calcium and vitamin D supplements if daily dietary intake is inadequate.
- Show patient how to perform weight-bearing exercises, which help increase bone mass.
- Urge patient to limit or restrict smoking and alcohol use, if appropriate.

Evaluation

- Patient remains free from bone fracture.
- Patient maintains adequate hydration.
- Patient and family state understanding of drug therapy.

alfuzosin hydrochloride

(al-FYOO-zoe-sin high-droh-KLOR-ighd)
Uroxatral, Xatral ♦

Pharmacologic class: selective postsynaptic alpha$_1$-adrenergic antagonist
Therapeutic class: benign prostatic hypertrophy (BPH) drug
Pregnancy risk category: B

Indications and dosages

▶ **BPH.** *Men:* 10 mg P.O. after the same meal daily.

Contraindications and cautions

- Contraindicated in patients hypersensitive to drug or any of its components, in those with moderate or severe hepatic insufficiency (Child–Pugh categories B and C), and those being treated with potent inhibitors of CYP3A4.
- Use cautiously in patients who develop hypotension with other drugs and patients with severe renal insufficiency, congenital or acquired

prolonged QT interval, or symptomatic hypotension.

Lifespan: In women and children, drug is contraindicated.

Adverse reactions

CNS: dizziness, fatigue, headache, pain.
CV: angina, chest pain, orthostatic hypotension, tachycardia.
EENT: pharyngitis, sinusitis.
GI: abdominal pain, constipation, dyspepsia, nausea.
GU: impotence, priapism.
Respiratory: bronchitis, upper respiratory tract infection.
Skin: rash.

Interactions

Drug-drug. *Alpha blockers:* May interact, although use not studied. Don't use together.
Antihypertensives: May cause hypotension. Monitor blood pressure, and use together cautiously.
Atenolol: May decrease blood pressure and heart rate. Monitor blood pressure and heart rate.
Cimetidine: May increase alfuzosin level. Use together cautiously.
CYP3A4 inhibitors (itraconazole, ketoconazole, and ritonavir): May increase alfuzosin level. Don't use together.
Drug-food. *Any food:* May increase absorption by 50%. Give with food.

Effects on lab test results

None significant.

Pharmacokinetics

Absorption: When taken with food, bioavailability is 49% and levels peak in 8 hours.
Distribution: 82% to 90% bound to plasma proteins.
Metabolism: Extensive, mainly by CYP3A4.
Excretion: 11% unchanged in urine. *Half-life:* 10 hours.

Route	Onset	Peak	Duration
P.O.	Unknown	8 hr	Unknown

Action

Chemical effect: Blocks $alpha_1$-adrenergic receptors in the lower urinary tract, causing smooth muscle in the bladder, neck, and prostate to relax.
Therapeutic effect: Improves urine flow and reduces symptoms of BPH.

Available forms

Tablets (extended-release): 10 mg

NURSING PROCESS

Assessment

- Assess patient's condition before therapy and regularly thereafter.
- Monitor patient for adverse reactions.
- Assess patient's and family's knowledge of drug therapy.

Nursing diagnoses

- Risk for injury related to adverse reactions from drug therapy
- Deficient knowledge related to drug therapy

Planning and implementation

- Prostate cancer and BPH may cause similar symptoms. Make sure prostate cancer is ruled out before starting therapy.
- Orthostatic hypotension may occur within a few hours after therapy. Take safety precautions.
- If angina appears or worsens, stop drug.
- Current or previous alpha blocker therapy may predispose the patient to floppy iris syndrome during cataract surgery.

ALERT: If overdose leads to hypotension, provide CV support by restoring blood pressure and heart rate. Have patient lie down, and give I.V. fluids and vasopressors, if needed.

ALERT: Don't use alfuzosin to treat hypertension.

Patient teaching

- Tell patient to take drug with food and with the same meal each day.
- Advise patient to rise slowly to prevent orthostatic hypotension.
- Warn patient that he may be dizzy, and caution him to avoid hazardous tasks until drug effects are known.
- Advise patient not to crush or chew tablets.
- If patient plans cataract surgery, urge him to tell the ophthalmologist that he takes or has taken an alpha blocker.

Evaluation

- Patient remains free from any adverse effects.

• Patient and family state understanding of drug therapy.

allopurinol

(al-oh-PYOOR-ih-nol)

Allorin ◇, Apo-Allopurinol ♦, Capurate ◇, Novo-Purol ♦, Zyloprim

allopurinol sodium

Aloprim

Pharmacologic class: xanthine oxidase inhibitor

Therapeutic class: antigout drug

Pregnancy risk category: C

Indications and dosages

▶ **Gout.** *Adults:* For mild gout, 200 to 300 mg P.O. daily. For severe gout with large tophi, 400 to 600 mg P.O. daily. May be given as single dose or divided; divide doses larger than 300 mg. Maximum, 800 mg daily.

▶ **To prevent acute gouty attacks.** *Adults:* 100 mg P.O. daily; increase at weekly intervals by 100 mg to a maximum recommended dose of 800 mg daily or until uric acid level falls to 6 mg/dl or less.

▶ **Hyperuricemia secondary to malignancies.** *Adults and children older than age 10:* Give 200 to 400 mg/m^2/day I.V. 1 to 2 days before chemotherapy as a single infusion or in equally divided doses q 6, 8, or 12 hours. Maximum, 600 mg daily.

Children age 10 and younger: Initially, 200 mg/m^2/day I.V. as a single infusion or in equally divided doses q 6, 8, or 12 hours. Then, titrate according to uric acid level. For children ages 6 to 10, 300 mg P.O. daily or divided t.i.d. For children younger than age 6, 150 mg P.O. daily.

▶ **To prevent uric acid nephropathy during chemotherapy.** *Adults:* 600 to 800 mg P.O. daily for 2 to 3 days, with high fluid intake.

▶ **Recurrent calcium oxalate calculi.** *Adults:* 200 to 300 mg P.O. daily in single or divided doses.

Adjust-a-dose: In patients with renal impairment, if creatinine clearance is 10 to 20 ml/minute, give 200 mg P.O. or I.V. daily; if clearance is less than 10 ml/minute, give 100 mg P.O. or I.V. daily; if it's less than 3 ml/minute, give 100 mg P.O. or I.V. at extended intervals.

I.V. administration

• Dissolve contents of vial in 25 ml sterile water for injection. Dilute solution to desired concentration (no more than 6 mg/ml) with normal saline solution for injection or D_5W. Don't use solution that contains sodium bicarbonate.

• Store solution at 68° to 77° F (20° to 25° C) and use within 10 hours. Don't use if solution has particulates or is discolored.

⊗ **Incompatibilities**

Amikacin, amphotericin B, carmustine, cefotaxime, chlorpromazine, cimetidine, clindamycin phosphate, cytarabine, dacarbazine, daunorubicin, diphenhydramine, doxorubicin, doxycycline hyclate, droperidol, floxuridine, gentamicin, haloperidol lactate, hydroxyzine, idarubicin, imipenem and cilastatin sodium, mechlorethamine, meperidine, methylprednisolone sodium succinate, metoclopramide, minocycline, nalbuphine, netilmicin, ondansetron, prochlorperazine edisylate, promethazine, sodium bicarbonate, streptozocin, tobramycin sulfate, vinorelbine.

Contraindications and cautions

• Contraindicated in patients hypersensitive to drug and in those with idiopathic hemochromatosis.

Lifespan: In pregnant or breast-feeding women, use cautiously.

Adverse reactions

CNS: drowsiness, headache.

EENT: cataracts, retinopathy.

GI: abdominal pain, diarrhea, nausea, vomiting.

GU: ***renal failure,*** uremia.

Hematologic: ***agranulocytosis,*** anemia, ***aplastic anemia, thrombocytopenia.***

Hepatic: ***hepatitis.***

Skin: ***erythema multiforme; exfoliative lesions;*** ichthyosis; rash, usually maculopapular; ***toxic epidermal necrolysis,*** urticarial and purpuric lesions.

Other: severe furunculosis of nose.

Interactions

Drug-drug. *ACE inhibitors:* May increase risk of hypersensitivity reaction. Monitor patient closely.

Amoxicillin, ampicillin, bacampicillin: May increase risk of rash. Avoid use together.

Anticoagulants, dicumarol: May potentiate anticoagulant effect. Adjust dosage, if needed.

Antineoplastics: May increase risk of bone marrow suppression. Monitor patient carefully.
Azathioprine, mercaptopurine: May increase levels of these drugs. Adjust dosage, if needed.
Chlorpropamide: May increase hypoglycemic effect. Avoid use together.
Cyclosporine: May increase cyclosporine level. Monitor and adjust cyclosporine dose as needed.
Diazoxide, diuretics, mecamylamine, pyrazinamide: May increase uric acid level. Adjust allopurinol dosage, if needed.
Ethacrynic acid, thiazide diuretics: May increase risk of allopurinol toxicity. Reduce allopurinol dosage, and closely monitor renal function.
Uricosurics: May have an additive effect. Use to therapeutic advantage.
Urine-acidifying drugs: May increase possibility of kidney stone formation. Monitor patient carefully.
Xanthines: May increase theophylline level. Adjust theophylline dosage.
Drug-lifestyle. *Alcohol use:* May increase uric acid level. Discourage use together.

Effects on lab test results

- May increase alkaline phosphatase, AST, ALT, BUN, and creatinine levels. May decrease hemoglobin level and hematocrit.
- May decrease granulocyte and platelet counts.

Pharmacokinetics

Absorption: 80% to 90%.
Distribution: Widely throughout body except brain, where levels are 50% of those found elsewhere.
Metabolism: To oxypurinol by xanthine oxidase.
Excretion: Mainly in urine; minute amount in feces. *Half-life:* Allopurinol, 1 to 2 hours; oxypurinol, about 15 hours.

Route	Onset	Peak	Duration
P.O.	2–3 days	½–2 hr	1–2 wk
I.V.	Unknown	½ hr	Unknown

Action

Chemical effect: Reduces uric acid production by inhibiting needed biochemical reactions.
Therapeutic effect: Relieves gout symptoms and treats hyperuricemia secondary to malignancy.

Available forms

allopurinol
Capsules: 100 mg ◇, 300 mg ◇
Tablets (scored): 100 mg, 200 mg ◇ ♦, 300 mg
allopurinol sodium
Injection: 500 mg/30-ml vial

NURSING PROCESS

Assessment

- Assess patient's history. Gout may be secondary to diseases such as acute or chronic leukemia, polycythemia vera, multiple myeloma, or psoriasis.
- Assess patient's uric acid level, joint stiffness, and pain before and during therapy. Optimal benefits may take 2 to 6 weeks of therapy.
- Monitor fluid intake and output. Daily urine output of at least 2 L and urine that's neutral or slightly alkaline urine are desirable.
- Monitor CBC and hepatic and renal function at the start and periodically during therapy.
- Be alert for adverse reactions and drug interactions.
- Assess patient's and family's knowledge of drug therapy.

Nursing diagnoses

- Acute pain (joint) related to patient's underlying condition
- Risk for infection related to drug-induced agranulocytosis
- Deficient knowledge related to drug therapy

Planning and implementation

- Give drug with or just after meals to minimize adverse GI reactions.
- Have patient drink plenty of fluids while taking drug, unless contraindicated.
- Notify prescriber if renal insufficiency occurs during treatment; this usually warrants dosage reduction.

ALERT: Don't confuse Zyloprim with ZORprin.

- Give colchicine with allopurinol at the start of treatment to reduce the risk of acute gout attacks that may occur in first 6 weeks of therapy.

Patient teaching

- Advise patient not to drive or perform hazardous tasks requiring mental alertness until CNS effects of drug are known.
- Advise patient taking allopurinol for recurrent calcium oxalate stones to reduce intake of ani-

mal protein, sodium, refined sugars, oxalate-rich foods, and calcium.

- Tell patient to stop drug at first sign of rash, which may precede severe hypersensitivity or other adverse reaction. Rash is more common in patients taking diuretics and in those with renal disorders. Tell patient to report all adverse reactions immediately.
- Advise patient not to use alcohol during drug therapy.

Evaluation

- Patient expresses relief from joint pain.
- Patient is free from infection.
- Patient and family state understanding of drug therapy.

almotriptan malate

(AL-moh-trip-tan MAH-layt)

Axert

Pharmacologic class: serotonin 5-HT_1 receptor agonist
Therapeutic class: antimigraine drug
Pregnancy risk category: C

Indications and dosages

▶ **Acute migraine with or without aura.** *Adults:* 6.25-mg or 12.5-mg tablet P.O., with one additional dose after 2 hours if headache is unresolved or recurs. Maximum, two doses in 24 hours.

Adjust-a-dose: For patients with hepatic or renal impairment, initially, 6.25 mg P.O. daily. Maximum, 12.5 mg daily.

Contraindications and cautions

- Contraindicated in patients hypersensitive to drug or its components and in those with angina pectoris, a history of MI, silent ischemia, uncontrolled hypertension, other CV disease, hemiplegic or basilar migraine, or coronary artery vasospasm, such as Prinzmetal variant angina.
- Don't give within 24 hours after other serotonin agonists or ergotamine drugs.
- Use cautiously in patients with renal or hepatic impairment and in those with cataracts because of the risk of corneal opacities.
- Also use cautiously in patients with risk factors for coronary artery disease (CAD), such as obesity, diabetes, and a family history of CAD.

Lifespan: In pregnant women, use only if potential benefits outweigh risks to the fetus. In breast-feeding women, use cautiously because it isn't known whether drug appears in breast milk. In children, safety and effectiveness of drug haven't been established.

Adverse reactions

CNS: dizziness, headache, paresthesia, somnolence.
CV: ***coronary artery vasospasm, MI, transient myocardial ischemia, ventricular fibrillation, ventricular tachycardia.***
GI: dry mouth, nausea.

Interactions

Drug-drug. *MAO inhibitors, verapamil:* May increase almotriptan level. No dosage adjustment is needed.
CYP3A4 inhibitors, such as ketoconazole: May increase almotriptan level. Monitor patient for adverse reactions. Reduce dosage, if needed.
Ergot-containing drugs, serotonin 5-$HT_{1B/1D}$ agonists: May cause additive effects. Avoid using within 24 hours of almotriptan.
SSRIs: May cause additive serotonin effects, resulting in weakness, hyperreflexia, or incoordination. If given together, monitor patient closely.

Effects on lab test results

None reported.

Pharmacokinetics

Absorption: Rapid and extensive; peaks in 1 to 3 hours. Food doesn't affect absorption.
Distribution: High. Minimally protein-bound.
Metabolism: Mainly by MAO-A, CYP3A4, and CYP2D6.
Excretion: 75% through renal excretion. *Half-life:* 3 to 4 hours.

Route	Onset	Peak	Duration
P.O.	1–3 hr	1–3 hr	3–4 hr

Action

Chemical effect: Binds selectively to various serotonin receptors, mainly serotonin 5-$HT_{1B/1D}$ receptors, resulting in cranial vessel constriction, which inhibits migraine.

Therapeutic effect: Blocks neuropeptide release to the pain pathways to prevent migraines.

Available forms

Tablets: 6.25 mg, 12.5 mg

NURSING PROCESS

Assessment

- Assess patient's condition before and during drug therapy.
- Obtain list of patient's drug intake within 24 hours to prevent interactions. Use caution when giving drug to patient who takes an MAO inhibitor or a CYP3A4 or CYP2D6 inhibitor. Don't give drug with other serotonin agonist or ergotamine derivatives.
- Be alert for adverse reactions.
- Monitor ECG in patients with risk factors for CAD or with symptoms similar to those of CAD, such as chest or throat tightness, pain, and heaviness.
- Assess patient's and family's knowledge of drug therapy.

Nursing diagnoses

- Acute pain related to presence of acute migraine attack
- Risk for injury related to drug-induced interactions
- Deficient knowledge related to almotriptan therapy

Planning and implementation

- Give dose as soon as patient complains of migraine symptoms.
- Repeat dose after 2 hours if needed.
- Don't give more than two doses in 24 hours.

ALERT: Don't confuse Axert with Antivert.

Patient teaching

- Advise patient to take drug only when having a migraine.
- Teach patient to avoid possible migraine triggers, such as cheese, chocolate, citrus fruits, caffeine, and alcohol.
- Tell patient to repeat dose only once in 24 hours and no sooner than 2 hours after the first dose.
- Inform patient that other common migraine drugs may interact with this drug.
- Tell patient to immediately report any chest, throat, jaw, or neck tightness, pain, or heaviness, and to stop using the drug.
- Advise patient to use caution while driving or operating machinery.

Evaluation

- Patient's symptoms are alleviated, and patient is free from pain.
- Serious complications from drug interactions don't develop.
- Patient and family state understanding of drug therapy.

alosetron hydrochloride

(a-LOE-se-tron high-droh-KLOR-ighd)
Lotronex

Pharmacologic class: selective 5-HT_3 receptor antagonist
Therapeutic class: GI drug
Pregnancy risk category: B

Indications and dosages

▶ **Irritable bowel syndrome (IBS) in women with severe diarrhea who haven't responded adequately to conventional therapy.** *Women:* 0.5 mg P.O. b.i.d. with or without food. If, after 4 weeks, the drug is well tolerated but doesn't adequately control IBS symptoms, increase to 1 mg b.i.d. If symptoms aren't controlled after 4 weeks at this dosage, stop drug.

Contraindications and cautions

- Contraindicated in women hypersensitive to the drug or its components; those with Crohn disease, ulcerative colitis, diverticulitis, or a history of chronic or severe constipation; those with sequelae from constipation, intestinal obstruction, stricture, toxic megacolon, GI perforation, GI adhesions, ischemic colitis, impaired intestinal circulation, thrombophlebitis, or hypercoagulation; and those taking fluvoxamine.
- Women shouldn't take drug if they're constipated or the chief bowel symptom is constipation.

Lifespan: In pregnant women, use only if clearly needed. In breast-feeding women, use cautiously because it's unknown whether drug or its metabolites appear in breast milk. In children, drug isn't recommended because it hasn't been studied. In elderly women, use cautiously because they may be at greater risk for complications of constipation.

Adverse reactions

CNS: abnormal dreams, anxiety, depressive disorders, headache, sedation, sleep disorders.
CV: ***arrhythmias, hypertension.***
EENT: *allergic rhinitis; bacterial ear, nose, and throat infections; photophobia; throat and tonsil discomfort and pain.*
GI: abdominal discomfort and pain, abdominal distention, *constipation,* dyspeptic symptoms, gaseous symptoms, GI discomfort and pain, hemorrhoids, ***ileus,*** impaction, ***ischemic colitis,*** nausea, ***obstruction, perforation,*** proctitis, ***small-bowel mesenteric ischemia,*** viral GI infections.

Interactions

Drug-drug. *CYP1A2 inhibitors (cimetidine, quinolones), ketoconazole:* May increase alosetron level. Avoid use together.
Fluvoxamine: May severely increase alosetron level. Use together is contraindicated.
Hydralazine, isoniazid, procainamide: May slow metabolism and increase level of these drugs because of N-acetyltransferase inhibition. Monitor patient for toxicity.

Effects on lab test results

- May increase ALT, AST, alkaline phosphatase, and bilirubin levels.

Pharmacokinetics

Absorption: Rapid. Mean absolute bioavailability is 50% to 60%. Food decreases rate by 25%.
Distribution: 82% bound to plasma proteins.
Metabolism: Extensive, by cytochrome P-450 enzymes (CYP2C9, CYP3A4, CYP1A2).
Excretion: 7% unchanged in urine. Radiolabeled dose 73% in urine and 24% in feces. *Half-life:* 1½ hour.

Route	Onset	Peak	Duration
P.O.	Unknown	1 hr	Variable

Action

Chemical effect: Selectively inhibits 5-HT_3 receptors on enteric neurons in the GI tract. Blocks neuronal depolarization, which decreases visceral pain, colonic transit, and GI secretions.
Therapeutic effect: Relieves pain and decreases frequency of loose stools caused by IBS.

Available forms

Tablets: 0.5 mg, 1 mg

NURSING PROCESS

Assessment

ALERT: Effectiveness in men hasn't been established.

- Only physicians enrolled in the prescribing program can prescribe this drug. Call 1-888-825-5249 or visit www.lotronex.com to enroll or report adverse reactions.
- Don't use in patient whose main symptom is constipation.
- Assess patient before and during drug therapy.

Nursing diagnoses

- Diarrhea related to underlying IBS condition
- Acute pain related to underlying IBS condition
- Deficient knowledge related to drug therapy

Planning and implementation

- If patient develops constipation, therapy should be stopped and laxatives and fiber should be used until the constipation resolves.

ALERT: Death may occur in patients who develop ischemic colitis and serious complications of constipation. If patient complains of rectal bleeding or sudden worsening of abdominal pain, stop therapy and rule out acute ischemic colitis.

- Acute symptoms of toxicity include labored breathing, ataxia, subdued behavior, tremors, and seizures. No antidote exists for overdose. Treatment for overdose includes supportive care.

Patient teaching

ALERT: Explain to patient that she must be enrolled in the prescribing program. Counsel patient about the drug's risks and benefits, give instructions, answer questions, and provide information about the drug. The patient must review and sign a patient–physician agreement. A special program sticker must be affixed to all written prescriptions; no telephone, facsimile, or computerized prescriptions are permitted.

- Instruct patient not to start drug if she is constipated.

ALERT: Tell patient to stop drug and consult prescriber immediately if she becomes constipated or has signs and symptoms of ischemic

colitis, such as rectal bleeding, bloody diarrhea, or worsened abdominal pain or cramping.
• Explain that this drug doesn't cure but may alleviate some IBS symptoms. If it doesn't adequately control symptoms after twice-daily therapy, advise patient to stop taking drug and contact prescriber.
• Inform patient that most women notice symptoms improving after about 1 week, but some may take up to 4 weeks to experience relief. Symptoms usually return within 1 week of stopping therapy.

Evaluation

• Patient's symptoms related to IBS, including pain and frequency of loose stools, are relieved.
• Patient and family state understanding of drug therapy.

alprazolam

(al-PRAH-zoh-lam)

Apo-Alpraz ♦, Niravam, Novo-Alprazol ♦, Nu-Alpraz ♦, Xanax, Xanax XR

Pharmacologic class: benzodiazepine
Therapeutic class: anxiolytic
Pregnancy risk category: D
Controlled substance schedule: IV

Indications and dosages

▶ **Anxiety.** *Adults:* Usual initial dose, 0.25 to 0.5 mg P.O. t.i.d. Maximum, 4 mg daily in divided doses.
Adjust-a-dose: For elderly or debilitated patients or those with advanced liver disease, usual initial dose is 0.25 mg P.O. b.i.d. or t.i.d. Maximum, 4 mg daily in divided doses.
▶ **Panic disorders.** *Adults:* 0.5 mg P.O. t.i.d., increased q 3 to 4 days in increments of no more than 1 mg. Maximum, 10 mg daily in divided doses. Or initially 0.5 to 1 mg extended-release P.O. daily, increased q 3 to 4 days by no more than 1 mg daily. Usual dosage is 3 to 6 mg P.O. once daily, preferably in the morning. Individualize dosage as needed. Maximum, 10 mg daily. If dosage reduction is needed, decrease by no more than 0.5 mg q 3 days.
▶ **Social phobias‡.** *Adults:* 2 to 8 mg P.O. daily.

Contraindications and cautions

• Contraindicated in patients hypersensitive to drug or other benzodiazepines, those with acute angle-closure glaucoma, and those taking azole antifungals.
• Use cautiously in patients with hepatic, renal, or pulmonary disease and in patients with cardiac disease because hypotension may occur.
Lifespan: In pregnant women, drug may cause congenital abnormalities and fetal harm. Avoid use, especially during the first trimester. In breast-feeding women, drug isn't recommended. In children, safety of drug hasn't been established. In elderly patients, use cautiously because they may be more sensitive to sedation and ataxia.

Adverse reactions

CNS: agitation, akathisia, *anxiety,* ataxia, *confusion, depression, difficulty speaking, dizziness, drowsiness,* dyskinesia, emergence of anxiety between doses, *fatigue, headache,* hypoesthesia, *impaired coordination, insomnia, irritability,* lethargy, *light-headedness,* malaise, mania, *memory impairment,* mental impairment, nervousness, nightmares, paresthesia, restlessness, *sedation, somnolence,* ***suicidal thoughts,*** syncope, tremor, vertigo.
CV: chest pain, hypotension, palpitations.
EENT: allergic rhinitis, blurred vision, nasal congestion, sore throat.
GI: abdominal pain, anorexia, *constipation, diarrhea, dry mouth,* dyspepsia, increased or decreased appetite, nausea, vomiting.
GU: difficulty urinating, dysmenorrhea, premenstrual syndrome.
Metabolic: increased or decreased weight.
Musculoskeletal: arthralgia; limb and back pain; muscle rigidity, cramps, or twitching; myalgia.
Respiratory: dyspnea, hyperventilation, upper respiratory tract infection.
Skin: dermatitis, increased sweating, pruritus.
Other: decreased or increased libido, dependence, hot flushes, influenza, injury, sexual dysfunction.

Interactions

Drug-drug. *Anticonvulsants, antidepressants, antihistamines, barbiturates, benzodiazepines, general anesthetics, opioids, phenothiazines:* May increase CNS depressant effects. Avoid use together.

Carbamazepine, propoxyphene: May decrease alprazolam level. Use together cautiously.
Cimetidine, fluoxetine, fluvoxamine, hormonal contraceptives, nefazodone: May increase alprazolam level. Use together cautiously, and consider reducing alprazolam dosage.
Digoxin: May increase digoxin level. Monitor it closely.
Fluconazole, itraconazole, ketoconazole, miconazole: May increase and prolong drug levels, CNS depression, and psychomotor impairment. Use together is contraindicated.
Tricyclic antidepressants: May increase levels of these drugs. Monitor patient closely.
Drug-herb. *Calendula, hops, lemon balm, skullcap, valerian:* May increase sedative effects. Discourage use together.
Kava: May increase CNS sedation. Discourage use together.
Drug-food. *Grapefruit:* May increase alprazolam level. Use cautiously together.
Drug-lifestyle. *Alcohol use:* May cause additive CNS effects. Strongly discourage use together.
Smoking: May decrease effectiveness of drug. Help patient quit smoking.

Effects on lab test results

- May increase ALT and AST levels.

Pharmacokinetics

Absorption: Well absorbed.
Distribution: Wide. 80% of dose is bound to plasma proteins.
Metabolism: In liver by CYP3A4 pathway, equally to alpha-hydroxyalprazolam and inactive metabolites.
Excretion: In urine. *Half-life:* Immediate-release, 12 to 15 hours; extended-release, 11 to 16 hours.

Route	Onset	Peak	Duration
P.O.	Unknown	1–2 hr	Unknown
P.O. extended	Unknown	Unknown	Unknown

Action

Chemical effect: May potentiate effects of GABA, an inhibitory neurotransmitter, and depress CNS at limbic and subcortical levels of brain.
Therapeutic effect: Decreases anxiety.

Available forms

Oral solution: 0.5 mg/5 ml, 1 mg/ml (concentrate)
Tablets: 0.25 mg, 0.5 mg, 1 mg, 2 mg
Tablets (extended-release): 0.5 mg, 1 mg, 2 mg, 3 mg
Tablets (orally disintegrating): 0.25 mg, 0.5 mg, 1 mg, 2 mg

NURSING PROCESS

Assessment

- Assess patient's anxiety before and often after therapy.
- In patient receiving repeated or prolonged therapy, monitor liver, renal, and hematopoietic function test results periodically.
- Be alert for adverse reactions and drug interactions.
- Assess patient's and family's knowledge of drug therapy.

Nursing diagnoses

- Anxiety related to patient's underlying condition
- Risk for injury related to drug-induced CNS reactions
- Deficient knowledge related to drug therapy

Planning and implementation

- Drug shouldn't be given for everyday stress or for longer than 4 months.
- Make sure patient has swallowed tablets after you give them.

ALERT: Paradoxic excitation, hostility, mania, hypomania, and insomnia may occur.
ALERT: Don't stop drug abruptly after long-term use because withdrawal symptoms may occur. Abuse or addiction is possible.

- Withdrawal symptoms include seizures, status epilepticus, impaired concentration, muscle cramps or twitch, diarrhea, blurred vision, decreased appetite, and weight loss.

ALERT: Don't confuse alprazolam with alprostadil. Don't confuse Xanax with Zantac or Tenex.

- To switch patient from immediate-release to extended-release tablets, calculate the total daily dose of immediate-release tablets and give the same dose of extended-release tablets once daily.

Patient teaching

- Warn patient to avoid hazardous activities that require alertness and psychomotor coordination until CNS effects of drug are known.
- Tell patient to avoid alcohol and smoking while taking drug.
- Advise patient to take drug as prescribed and not to stop without prescriber's approval. Explain the risk of dependence if taken longer than directed.
- Instruct patient to swallow extended-release tablets whole and not to chew or crush them.
- Tell patient taking orally disintegrating tablets to remove tablet from bottle using dry hands and immediately place on his tongue, where the tablet will dissolve and can be swallowed with saliva.
- Tell patient taking half of a scored orally disintegrating tablet to destroy the unused portion.
- Advise patient to discard any cotton from the bottle of orally disintegrating tablets and to keep it tightly sealed to prevent moisture from entering the bottle and dissolving the tablets.
- Teach patient how to manage or avoid adverse reactions, such as constipation and drowsiness.

Evaluation

- Patient is less anxious.
- Patient sustains no injury from adverse CNS reactions.
- Patient and family state understanding of drug therapy.

alprostadil

(al-PROS-tuh-dil)
Prostin VR Pediatric

Pharmacologic class: prostaglandin
Therapeutic class: ductus arteriosus patency adjunct
Pregnancy risk category: NR

Indications and dosages

▶ **Temporary maintenance of patent ductus arteriosus until surgery can be performed.** *Infants:* 0.05 to 0.1 mcg/kg/minute by I.V. infusion. When therapeutic response occurs, reduce rate to lowest effective dosage. Maximum, 0.4 mcg/kg/minute. Or, drug may be given through umbilical artery catheter placed at ductal opening.

I.V. administration

- Keep respiratory and emergency equipment available.
- Before giving, dilute 500 mcg of drug with sodium chloride or dextrose injection. Dilute to appropriate volume for pump delivery system.
- Drug isn't recommended for direct injection or intermittent infusion. Give by continuous infusion using constant-rate pump. Infuse through large peripheral or central vein or through umbilical artery catheter placed at level of ductus arteriosus. If flushing occurs as a result of peripheral vasodilation, reposition catheter.
- If fever or significant hypotension develops in an infant, reduce the infusion rate.
- If apnea and bradycardia develop, stop infusion immediately. This may be a sign of drug overdose.
- In prolonged infusions, infant may develop gastric outlet obstruction, morphologic changes in pulmonary arteries, and proliferation of long bones.
- Discard solution after 24 hours.

⊗ Incompatibilities

Diluents that contain benzyl alcohol; fatal toxic syndrome may occur.

Contraindications and cautions

Lifespan: In neonates with bleeding tendencies, use cautiously because drug inhibits platelet aggregation. In neonates with respiratory distress syndrome or in premature infants with a patent ductus arteriosus, drug is contraindicated. Infants on long-term infusions may experience cortical growth of long bones.

Adverse reactions

CNS: fever, *seizures.*
CV: ***bradycardia, cardiac arrest,*** flushing, hypotension, tachycardia.
GI: diarrhea.
Hematologic: ***DIC.***
Respiratory: **APNEA.**
Other: *sepsis.*

Interactions

None significant.

Effects on lab test results

- May decrease potassium level.

Pharmacokinetics

Absorption: Given I.V.

Distribution: Rapid.
Metabolism: About 68% of dose is metabolized in one pass through lung, mainly by oxidation; 100% is metabolized within 24 hours.
Excretion: All metabolites are excreted in urine within 24 hours. *Half-life:* About 5 to 10 minutes.

Route	Onset	Peak	Duration
I.V.	5–10 min	20 min	1–3 hr

Action

Chemical effect: Relaxes smooth muscle of ductus arteriosus.
Therapeutic effect: Improves cardiac circulation.

Available forms

Injection: 500 mcg/ml

NURSING PROCESS

Assessment

- Obtain baseline assessment of infant's cardiopulmonary status before therapy.
- Measure drug's effectiveness by monitoring blood oxygenation of infants with restricted pulmonary blood flow and by systemic blood pressure and blood pH of infants with restricted systemic blood flow.
- Be alert for adverse reactions throughout therapy.
- Evaluate parent's knowledge of drug therapy.

Nursing diagnoses

- Ineffective cardiopulmonary tissue perfusion related to underlying condition
- Risk for injury related to drug-induced adverse reactions
- Deficient knowledge related to drug therapy

Planning and implementation

- Before drug is given, a differential diagnosis should be made between respiratory distress syndrome and cyanotic heart disease. Don't use drug in neonates with respiratory distress syndrome.

ALERT: Don't confuse alprostadil with alprazolam.

Patient teaching

- Keep parents informed of infant's status.
- Explain that parents will be allowed as much time and physical contact with infant as possible.

Evaluation

- Patient is stable with a working cardiopulmonary system.
- Patient isn't injured by adverse drug reactions.
- Parents state understanding of drug therapy.

alteplase (tissue plasminogen activator, recombinant; tPA)

(AL-teh-plays)

Actilyse ◇, Activase, Cathflo Activase

Pharmacologic class: enzyme
Therapeutic class: thrombolytic enzyme
Pregnancy risk category: C

Indications and dosages

▶ **Lysis of thrombi obstructing coronary arteries in acute MI.** *Adults:* 100 mg I.V. infusion over 3 hours as follows: 60 mg in first hour, with 6 to 10 mg given as bolus over first 1 to 2 minutes. Then, 20 mg/hour infusion for 2 hours. Adults weighing less than 65 kg (143 lb) receive 1.25 mg/kg using the same method (60% in first hour with 10% as bolus, then 20% of total dose per hour for 2 hours). Don't exceed 100-mg dose. Higher doses may increase risk of intracranial bleeding.

▶ **Acute massive pulmonary embolism.** *Adults:* 100 mg I.V. infusion over 2 hours. Begin heparin at end of infusion when PTT or PT returns to twice normal or less. Don't exceed 100-mg dose. Higher doses may increase risk of intracranial bleeding. ‡Also, may infuse 30 or 50 mg via intrapulmonary artery over 1½ or 2 hours, respectively, with heparin therapy.

▶ **Acute ischemic stroke.** *Adults:* 0.9 mg/kg (maximum 90 mg) I.V. over 60 minutes with 10% of the total dose given as initial bolus over 1 minute.

▶ **To restore function to central venous access devices as assessed by the ability to withdraw blood.** *Adults and children older than age 2:* For patients weighing 30 kg (66 lb) or more, instill 2 mg Cathflo Activase in 2 ml sterile water into catheter. For patients weighing 10 to 30 kg (22 to 66 lb), instill 110% of the internal lumen volume of the catheter, not to exceed 2 mg. After 30 minutes of dwell time, assess catheter function by aspirating blood. If function is restored, aspirate 4 to 5 ml of blood to remove Cathflo Activase and residual clot, and gently irrigate the catheter with normal saline solution. If catheter function isn't restored after 120 minutes, instill a second dose.

▶ **To prevent reocclusion after thrombolysis for acute MI‡.** *Adults:* 3.3 mcg/kg/minute by I.V. infusion for 4 hours with heparin immediately following initial thrombolytic infusion.

▶ **Lysis of arterial occlusion in a peripheral vessel or bypass graft.** *Adults:* 0.05 to 0.1 mg/kg/hour infused via the intrapulmonary artery for 1 to 8 hours.

I.V. administration

• Reconstitute alteplase immediately before use in sterile water for injection, without preservatives. Check label for specific information.

• Don't use vial if vacuum seal isn't present. Reconstitute with large-bore (18G) needle, directing stream of sterile water at lyophilized cake. Don't shake, but make sure that drug dissolves completely. Slight foaming is common. Solution should be clear or pale yellow.

• Drug may be given as reconstituted (1 mg/ml) or diluted with equal volume of normal saline solution or D_5W to make 0.5-mg/ml solution.

• Drug and may be stored temporarily at 35° to 86° F (2° to 30° C), but it's stable for only 8 hours at room temperature. Discard unused solution.

To restore function of a central venous catheter

• Reconstitute Cathflo Activase with 2.2 ml sterile water; dissolve completely into a colorless to pale yellow solution of 1 mg/ml. Solution is stable up to 8 hours at room temperature.

• Assess the cause of catheter dysfunction before using Cathflo Activase. Causes of occlusion may include incorrect catheter position, mechanical failure, constriction by a suture, and lipid deposits or drug precipitates in the catheter lumen. Don't try to suction because of the risk of damage to the vascular wall or collapse of soft-walled catheters.

• Don't use excessive pressure while instilling Cathflo Activase into the catheter because it could cause catheter rupture or expulsion of the clot into circulation.

⊗ **Incompatibilities**

None reported, but don't mix with other drugs.

Contraindications and cautions

• Contraindicated in patients with active internal bleeding, intracranial neoplasm, arteriovenous malformation, aneurysm, severe uncontrolled hypertension, history of stroke, known bleeding diathesis, or intraspinal or intracranial trauma or surgery within past 2 months.

• Use cautiously in patients who had major surgery within 10 days; those receiving anticoagulants; those with organ biopsy, trauma (including cardiopulmonary resuscitation), GI or GU bleeding, cerebrovascular disease, hypertension, acute pericarditis, subacute bacterial endocarditis, septic thrombophlebitis, or diabetic hemorrhagic retinopathy; and those with mitral stenosis, atrial fibrillation, or other conditions that may lead to left-sided heart thrombus.

Lifespan: During pregnancy, the first 10 days postpartum, and lactation, use cautiously. In children, safety of drug hasn't been established. In patients age 75 and older, use cautiously.

Adverse reactions

CNS: ***cerebral hemorrhage,*** fever.
CV: ***arrhythmias,*** edema, hypotension.
GI: ***bleeding,*** nausea, vomiting.
GU: bleeding.
Hematologic: ***severe, spontaneous bleeding.***
Musculoskeletal: arthralgia.
Skin: urticaria.
Other: ***anaphylaxis, angioedema,*** bleeding at puncture sites, hypersensitivity reactions.

Interactions

Drug-drug. *Abciximab, aspirin, coumarin anticoagulants, dipyridamole, heparin:* May increase risk of bleeding. Monitor patient carefully.

Nitroglycerin: May decrease tPA antigen level. Avoid use together. If unavoidable, use the lowest effective nitroglycerin dose.

Drug-herb. *Dong quai, garlic, ginkgo:* May increase risk of bleeding. Discourage use together.

Effects on lab test results

None reported.

Pharmacokinetics

Absorption: Given I.V.

A

Distribution: Rapidly cleared from plasma by liver (about 80% cleared within 10 minutes after infusion stops).
Metabolism: Mainly hepatic.
Excretion: Over 85% in urine, 5% in feces.
Half-life: Less than 10 minutes.

Route	Onset	Peak	Duration
I.V.	Immediate	45 min	4 hr

Action

Chemical effect: Binds to fibrin in thrombus and locally converts plasminogen to plasmin, which initiates local fibrinolysis.
Therapeutic effect: Dissolves blood clots in coronary arteries and lungs.

Available forms

Injection: 50-mg (29 million international units), 100-mg (58 million international units) vials
Solution for intracatheter clearance: 2-mg single-use vials

NURSING PROCESS

Assessment

- Assess patient's cardiopulmonary status (including ECG, vital signs, and coagulation studies) before and during therapy.
- Be alert for adverse reactions and drug interactions.
- Monitor patient for internal bleeding, and check puncture site often.
- Assess patient's and family's knowledge of drug therapy.

Nursing diagnoses

- Ineffective cardiopulmonary tissue perfusion related to patient's underlying condition
- Risk for injury related to adverse effects of drug therapy
- Deficient knowledge related to drug therapy

Planning and implementation

- Recanalization of occluded coronary arteries and improvement of heart function require starting drug as soon as possible after onset of symptoms.
- Heparin is given often after alteplase to reduce risk of rethrombosis.
- For arterial puncture, select site on arm and apply pressure for 30 minutes afterward. Also use pressure dressings, sand bags, or ice packs on recent puncture sites to prevent bleeding.
- Notify prescriber about severe bleeding that doesn't stop with intervention; alteplase and heparin infusions will need to be stopped.

ALERT: Have antiarrhythmics available. Coronary thrombolysis is linked to arrhythmias induced by reperfusion of ischemic myocardium.

- Avoid invasive procedures during thrombolytic therapy.

Patient teaching

- Tell patient to immediately report chest pain, dyspnea, changes in heart rate or rhythm, nausea, and bleeding.

Evaluation

- Patient's cardiopulmonary assessment findings show improved perfusion.
- Patient has no serious adverse drug reactions.
- Patient and family state understanding of drug therapy.

amantadine hydrochloride

(uh-MAN-tah-deen high-droh-KLOR-ighd)
Symmetrel

Pharmacologic class: synthetic cyclic primary amine
Therapeutic class: antiviral, antiparkinsonian
Pregnancy risk category: C

Indications and dosages

▶ **Prevention or treatment of influenza type A virus; respiratory tract illness in elderly or debilitated patients.** *Adults age 65 and older:* 100 mg P.O. once daily. Continue for 24 to 48 hours after symptoms resolve. Start prophylaxis as soon as possible after exposure, and continue for at least 10 days. When inactivated influenza A vaccine is unavailable, may continue preventive use as long as influenza A is present in community. If used with influenza vaccine, drug is continued for 2 to 4 weeks until protection develops from vaccine.
Adults age 65 and younger and children age 13 and older: 200 mg P.O. daily in single dose or divided b.i.d.
Children ages 9 to 12: Give 100 mg P.O. b.i.d.
Children ages 1 to 8: Give 4.4 to 8.8 mg/kg P.O. daily in single dose or divided b.i.d. Maximum, 150 mg daily.

▶ **Drug-induced extrapyramidal reactions.** *Adults:* 100 mg P.O. b.i.d. Occasionally, patients whose responses aren't optimal may benefit from an increase to 300 mg P.O. daily in divided doses.

▶ **Idiopathic parkinsonism, parkinsonian syndrome.** *Adults:* 100 mg P.O. b.i.d. In patients who are seriously ill or taking other antiparkinsonians, 100 mg daily for at least 1 week; then 100 mg b.i.d., p.r.n. Maximum, 400 mg daily.

Adjust-a-dose: For patients with creatinine clearance of 30 to 50 ml/minute, give 200 mg the first day and 100 mg daily thereafter; for clearance of 15 to 29 ml/minute, give 200 mg the first day and then 100 mg q other day; for clearance of less than 15 ml/minute, give 200 mg once weekly.

Contraindications and cautions

- Contraindicated in patients hypersensitive to drug.
- Use cautiously in patients with seizure disorders, heart failure, peripheral edema, hepatic disease, mental illness, eczematoid rash, renal impairment, orthostatic hypotension, or CV disease. Adjust dosage in patients with renal impairment.

Lifespan: In pregnant and breast-feeding women, use cautiously. In children younger than age 1, safety of drug hasn't been established. In elderly patients, use cautiously.

Adverse reactions

CNS: anxiety, ataxia, confusion, depression, difficulty concentrating, dizziness, fatigue, hallucinations, headache, insomnia, irritability, light-headedness, ***neuroleptic malignant syndrome,*** psychosis, weakness.
CV: ***heart failure,*** orthostatic hypotension, peripheral edema.
GI: anorexia, constipation, diarrhea, dry mouth, nausea, vomiting.
GU: urine retention.
Skin: livedo reticularis.

Interactions

Drug-drug. *Anticholinergics:* May increase adverse anticholinergic effects. Use together cautiously.
CNS stimulants: May cause additive CNS stimulation. Use together cautiously.
Hydrochlorothiazide, sulfamethoxazole, triamterene, trimethoprim: May increase amantadine level. Use together cautiously.
Quinidine, quinine: May reduce renal clearance of amantadine. Use together cautiously.
Thioridazine: May worsen tremor in elderly patients. Monitor these patients closely.
Drug-herb. *Jimsonweed:* May adversely affect CV function. Discourage use together.

Effects on lab test results

None reported.

Pharmacokinetics

Absorption: Well absorbed from the GI tract.
Distribution: Widely throughout the body; crosses the blood–brain barrier.
Metabolism: About 10% of drug is metabolized.
Excretion: About 90% unchanged in urine, mainly by tubular secretion. Some drug may appear in breast milk. Excretion rate depends on urine pH. *Half-life:* About 24 hours; with renal dysfunction, may be prolonged to 10 days.

Route	Onset	Peak	Duration
P.O.	Unknown	2–4 hr	Unknown

Action

Chemical effect: May interfere with influenza A virus penetration into susceptible cells. In parkinsonism, action is unknown.
Therapeutic effect: Protects against and reduces symptoms of influenza A viral infection and extrapyramidal symptoms.

Available forms

Capsules: 100 mg
Syrup: 50 mg/5 ml
Tablets: 100 mg

NURSING PROCESS

Assessment

- Obtain baseline assessment of patient's exposure to influenza A virus or history of Parkinson disease.
- Watch for adverse reactions and drug interactions.
- If adverse GI reactions occur, monitor patient's hydration status.
- Assess patient's and family's knowledge of drug therapy.

Nursing diagnoses

- Ineffective health maintenance related to patient's underlying condition
- Risk for deficient fluid volume related to adverse GI reactions
- Deficient knowledge related to drug therapy

Planning and implementation

- Elderly patients are more susceptible to neurologic adverse effects. Giving drug in two daily doses rather than as single dose may reduce these effects.
- For best absorption, give drug after meals.

ALERT: Don't confuse amantadine with rimantadine.

Patient teaching

- To prevent insomnia, advise patient to take drug several hours before bedtime.
- To prevent orthostatic hypotension, advise patient not to stand or change positions too quickly.
- Instruct patient to report adverse reactions, especially dizziness, depression, anxiety, nausea, and urine retention.
- Warn patient with parkinsonism not to stop drug abruptly because doing so could cause a parkinsonian crisis.

Evaluation

- Patient shows improved health.
- Patient maintains adequate hydration.
- Patient and family state understanding of drug therapy.

amikacin sulfate

(am-eh-KAY-sin SULL-fayt)
Amikin

Pharmacologic class: aminoglycoside
Therapeutic class: antibiotic
Pregnancy risk category: D

Indications and dosages

▶ **Serious infections caused by sensitive strains of *Pseudomonas aeruginosa, Escherichia coli, Proteus, Klebsiella, Serratia, Enterobacter, Acinetobacter, Providencia, Citrobacter, Staphylococcus;* meningitis.** *Adults and children:* 15 mg/kg daily divided q 8 to 12 hours I.M. or I.V. infusion.

Neonates: Initially, loading dose of 10 mg/kg I.V., followed by 7.5 mg/kg q 12 hours.

Adjust-a-dose: For patients with renal impairment, initially, 7.5 mg/kg I.M. or I.V. Later doses and interval determined by drug level and renal function test results.

▶ **Uncomplicated UTI.** *Adults:* 250 mg I.M. or I.V. b.i.d.

▶ ***Mycobacterium avium* complex, with other drugs‡.** *Adults:* 15 mg/kg I.V. daily, in divided doses q 8 to 12 hours.

Adjust-a-dose: For patients with renal impairment, initially, 7.5 mg/kg I.M or I.V. Later doses and interval determined by drug level. Keep peak level between 15 and 35 mcg/ml. Trough level shouldn't exceed 10 mcg/ml.

I.V. administration

- For adults, dilute in 100 to 200 ml of D_5W or normal saline solution. Volume for children depends on dose.
- For adults, infuse over 30 to 60 minutes. Infants should receive a 1- to 2-hour infusion.
- After I.V. infusion, flush line with normal saline solution or D_5W.

⊗ Incompatibilities

Amphotericin B, bacitracin, cephapirin, cisplatin, heparin sodium, other I.V. drugs, phenytoin, thiopental, vancomycin, vitamin B complex with C.

Contraindications and cautions

- Contraindicated in patients hypersensitive to drug or other aminoglycosides.
- Use cautiously in patients with impaired renal function or neuromuscular disorders.

Lifespan: In pregnant women, use cautiously and only if benefit outweighs risk to the fetus. In breast-feeding women, don't give drug. In neonates and infants, use cautiously. In elderly patients, use cautiously because they have a higher risk of ototoxicity.

Adverse reactions

CNS: headache, lethargy, *neuromuscular blockade.*
EENT: ototoxicity.
GU: nephrotoxicity.
Hepatic: *hepatic necrosis.*
Other: *anaphylaxis,* hypersensitivity reactions.

Interactions

Drug-drug. *Acyclovir, amphotericin B, cephalothin, cisplatin, methoxyflurane, other aminoglycosides, vancomycin:* May increase nephrotoxicity. Use together cautiously.
Atracurium, pancuronium, rocuronium, vecuronium: May increase the effects of nondepolarizing neuromuscular blockade, including prolonged respiratory depression. Dose of nondepolarizing muscle relaxant may need to be reduced.
Dimenhydrinate: May mask symptoms of ototoxicity. Use cautiously.
Indomethacin: May increase trough and peak levels of amikacin. Monitor amikacin level closely.
I.V. loop diuretics (such as furosemide): May increase ototoxicity. Use together cautiously.
Parenteral penicillins (such as ticarcillin): May cause amikacin inactivation in vitro. Don't mix.

Effects on lab test results

- May increase BUN, creatinine, nonprotein nitrogen, and urine urea levels.

Pharmacokinetics

Absorption: Rapidly after I.M. use.
Distribution: Wide. Minimally protein-bound. Drug crosses the placenta.
Metabolism: None.
Excretion: Mainly in urine by glomerular filtration. *Half-life:* 2 to 3 hours (adults); 30 to 86 hours (patients with severe renal damage).

Route	Onset	Peak	Duration
I.V.	Immediate	Immediate	8–12 hr
I.M.	Unknown	1 hr	8–12 hr

Action

Chemical effect: Inhibits protein synthesis by binding directly to 30S ribosomal subunit. Generally bactericidal.
Therapeutic effect: Kills susceptible bacteria and many aerobic gram-negative organisms (including most strains of *P. aeruginosa*) and some aerobic gram-positive organisms. Ineffective against anaerobes.

Available forms

Injection: 50 mg/ml, 250 mg/ml

NURSING PROCESS

Assessment

- Assess patient's infection, hearing, weight, and renal function test values before therapy and regularly thereafter.
- Watch for signs of ototoxicity, including tinnitus, vertigo, and hearing loss.
- Monitor amikacin level. Obtain blood for peak amikacin level 1 hour after I.M. injection and 30 minutes to 1 hour after infusion ends; for trough level, draw blood just before next dose. Don't collect blood in heparinized tube because heparin is incompatible with aminoglycosides. Peak level higher than 35 mcg/ml and trough level higher than 10 mcg/ml may raise the risk of toxicity.
- Be alert for signs of nephrotoxicity, including cells or casts in urine, oliguria, proteinuria, decreased creatinine clearance, and increased BUN and creatinine levels.
- Assess patient's and family's knowledge of drug therapy.

Nursing diagnoses

- Risk for infection related to bacteria
- Impaired urinary elimination related to amikacin-induced nephrotoxicity
- Deficient knowledge related to drug therapy

Planning and implementation

- Obtain specimen for culture and sensitivity tests before first dose. Therapy may begin before receiving results.
- Therapy usually lasts 7 to 10 days.
- Drug potency isn't affected if solution turns light yellow.
- Patient should be well hydrated while taking drug to minimize renal tubule irritation.
- If no response occurs after 5 days, therapy may be stopped and new specimens obtained for culture and sensitivity testing.

ALERT: Don't confuse Amikin with Amicar or amikacin with anakinra.

Patient teaching

- Tell patient to immediately report changes in hearing or in urine appearance or elimination pattern. Teach patient how to measure intake and output.
- Emphasize importance of drinking 2 L of fluid daily, unless contraindicated.
- Teach patient to watch for and promptly report signs of superinfection, such as continued

fever and other signs of new infections, especially of upper respiratory tract.

Evaluation

- Patient's infection is eradicated.
- Patient's renal function test values remain unchanged.
- Patient and family state understanding of drug therapy.

amiodarone hydrochloride

(am-ee-OH-dah-rohn high-droh-KLOR-ighd)
Cordarone, Pacerone

Pharmacologic class: benzofuran derivative
Therapeutic class: ventricular antiarrhythmic
Pregnancy risk category: D

Indications and dosages

▶ **Recurrent ventricular fibrillation, unstable ventricular tachycardia, atrial fibrillation‡, angina‡, and hypertrophic cardiomyopathy‡.** *Adults:* 800 to 1,600 mg P.O. daily for 1 to 3 weeks as loading dose until initial response occurs; then 650 to 800 mg P.O. daily for 1 month; then 200 to 600 mg P.O. daily as maintenance dosage. Or, for first 24 hours, 150 mg I.V. over 10 minutes (mix in 100 ml D_5W); then 360 mg I.V. over 6 hours (mix 900 mg in 500 ml D_5W); then maintenance dose of 540 mg I.V. over 18 hours at 0.50 mg/minute. After first 24 hours, continue a maintenance infusion of 0.5 mg/minute in a concentration of 1 to 6 mg/ml. For infusions longer than 1 hour, don't exceed 2 mg/ml unless you use a central venous catheter. Don't use for longer than 3 weeks.

▶ **Conversion from I.V. to P.O. route.** *Adults:* After daily dose of 720 mg I.V. (assuming rate of 0.5 mg/minute) for less than 1 week, start 800 to 1,600 mg P.O. daily; for 1 to 3 weeks, give 600 to 800 mg P.O. daily; and for longer than 3 weeks, give 400 mg P.O. daily.

▶ **Supraventricular arrhythmias‡.** *Adults:* 600 to 800 mg P.O. for 1 to 4 weeks or until supraventricular tachycardia is controlled. Maintenance dose is 100 to 400 mg P.O. daily.

I.V. administration

- Drug may be given I.V. if close monitoring of cardiac function and resuscitation is available. Initial dose of 5 mg/kg should be mixed in 250 ml of D_5W.
- Repeat doses should be given through central venous catheter. Patient should receive maximum of 1.2 g in up to 500 ml D_5W daily.
- Maintain ECG monitoring when therapy starts and dosage changes. Notify prescriber of significant change in ECG.
- Because of significant risk of life-threatening adverse reactions, drug is used after other antiarrhythmics have been ineffective.

⊗ **Incompatibilities**
Aminophylline, cefazolin sodium, heparin sodium, sodium bicarbonate.

Contraindications and cautions

- Contraindicated in patients hypersensitive to drug and in those with severe sinus node disease, bradycardia, second- or third-degree AV block (unless artificial pacemaker is present), or bradycardia-induced syncope.
- Use cautiously in patients receiving other antiarrhythmics and in patients with pulmonary or thyroid disease because use may result in fatal toxicity.

ALERT: Some I.V. Cordarone preparations contain benzyl alcohol, which may cause gasping syndrome in neonates younger than age 1 month. Monitor patient for symptoms of sudden onset of gasping respiration, hypotension, bradycardia, and CV collapse.

Lifespan: In pregnant women, use only when benefits outweigh risks to patient and fetus. In breast-feeding women, drug is contraindicated. In children, safety of drug hasn't been established. I.V. Cordarone leaches plasticizers from administration tubing, which can adversely affect male reproductive tract development in a fetus, infant, or toddler.

Adverse reactions

CNS: abnormal gait, ataxia, dizziness, extrapyramidal symptoms, fatigue, headache, malaise, paresthesias, peripheral neuropathy.
CV: ***arrhythmias, bradycardia, heart block, heart failure,*** *hypotension,* ***sinus arrest.***
EENT: *corneal microdeposits,* vision disturbances.
GI: anorexia, constipation, *nausea, vomiting.*
Hepatic: ***hepatic dysfunction.***
Metabolic: hyperthyroidism, hypothyroidism.
Musculoskeletal: muscle weakness.

Respiratory: SEVERE PULMONARY TOXICITY (ALVEOLITIS, PNEUMONITIS).
Skin: blue-gray skin, *photosensitivity.*
Other: gynecomastia.

Interactions

Drug-drug. *Antiarrhythmics:* May reduce hepatic or renal clearance of certain antiarrhythmics (especially flecainide and procainamide), and may induce torsades de pointes with other antiarrhythmics (especially disopyramide, mexiletine, procainamide, and propafenone). Monitor ECG closely.
Antihypertensives: May increase hypotensive effect. Use together cautiously.
Beta blockers, calcium channel blockers: May increase cardiac depressant effects and potentiate slowing of sinus node and AV conduction. Use together cautiously.
Cholestyramine, rifampin: May decrease amiodarone level. Use together cautiously.
Cimetidine, protease inhibitors: May increase amiodarone level. Avoid use together.
Cyclosporine: May increase cyclosporine level. Monitor patient for cyclosporine toxicity.
Digoxin: May increase digoxin level by 70% to 100%. Monitor digoxin level closely.
Phenytoin: May decrease phenytoin metabolism. Monitor phenytoin level.
Quinidine: May increase quinidine level, producing potentially fatal cardiac arrhythmias. If drugs must be used together, monitor quinidine level closely, and adjust dosage as needed.
Theophylline: May increase theophylline level and lead to toxicity. Monitor theophylline level.
Warfarin: May increase INR by 100% within 1 to 4 weeks of therapy. Decrease warfarin dosage 33% to 50% when amiodarone starts. Monitor patient closely.
Drug-herb. *Pennyroyal:* May change the rate at which toxic metabolites of pennyroyal form. Discourage use together.
St. John's wort: May decrease amiodarone levels. Discourage use together.
Drug-food. *Grapefruit juice:* May increase amiodarone levels. Discourage use together.
Drug-lifestyle. *Sun exposure:* May cause photosensitivity reaction. Advise against prolonged or unprotected sun exposure.

Effects on lab test results

- May increase ALT, AST, alkaline phosphatase, and GGT levels.
- May increase PT and INR. May alter thyroid function test results.

Pharmacokinetics

Absorption: Slow and variable.
Distribution: Wide, accumulating in adipose tissue and in organs with marked perfusion, such as lungs, liver, and spleen. Drug is 96% protein-bound.
Metabolism: Extensive in liver to active metabolite, desethyl amiodarone.
Excretion: Mainly hepatic through biliary tree. *Half-life:* 25 to 110 days (usually 40 to 50 days).

Route	Onset	Peak	Duration
P.O.	2–21 days	3–7 hr	Varies
I.V.	Unknown	Unknown	Unknown

Action

Chemical effect: Unknown; thought to prolong refractory period and duration of action potential and decrease repolarization.
Therapeutic effect: Abolishes ventricular arrhythmia.

Available forms

Injection: 50 mg/ml
Tablets: 100 mg, 200 mg, 400 mg

NURSING PROCESS

Assessment

- Assess CV status before therapy.
- Review pulmonary, liver, and thyroid function test results before and regularly during therapy.
- Continuously monitor cardiac status of patient receiving I.V. amiodarone to evaluate its effectiveness.
- Watch for adverse reactions and drug interactions.
- Monitor patient carefully for pulmonary toxicity, which can be fatal. Risk increases in patients receiving more than 400 mg daily.
- Monitor electrolytes, particularly potassium and magnesium levels, and PT and INR if on warfarin.
- Assess patient's and family's knowledge of drug therapy.

Nursing diagnoses

- Decreased cardiac output related to ventricular arrhythmia

• Risk for injury related to drug-induced adverse reactions
• Deficient knowledge related to drug therapy

Planning and implementation

• Adverse reactions commonly limit drug's use.
ALERT: Drug may pose life-threatening risks for patients already at risk for sudden death. It may cause fatal toxicities, including hepatic and pulmonary toxicity and should be used only in patients with life-threatening, recurrent ventricular arrhythmias unresponsive to other antiarrhythmics or when other drugs can't be tolerated.
• Divide oral loading dose into three equal doses and give with meals to decrease GI intolerance. If GI intolerance occurs, maintenance dosage may be given once daily or divided into two doses taken with meals.
• Instillation of methylcellulose ophthalmic solution during amiodarone therapy is recommended to minimize corneal microdeposits.
ALERT: Don't confuse amiodarone with amiloride.

Patient teaching

• Stress importance of taking drug exactly as prescribed.
• Emphasize importance of close follow-up and regular diagnostic studies to monitor drug action and detect adverse reactions.
• Warn patient that drug may cause blue-gray skin pigmentation.
• Advise patient to use sunscreen to prevent photosensitivity reaction (burning or tingling skin followed by erythema and possible blistering).
• Inform patient that adverse effects are more prevalent at high doses but are generally reversible when therapy stops. Resolution of adverse reactions may take up to 4 months.

Evaluation

• Patient's arrhythmia is corrected.
• Patient has no injury from adverse reactions.
• Patient and family state understanding of drug therapy.

amitriptyline hydrochloride

(am-ih-TRIP-tuh-leen high-droh-KLOR-ighd)

Apo-Amitriptyline ♦, Endep ◇, Tryptanol ◇

Pharmacologic class: tricyclic antidepressant
Therapeutic class: antidepressant
Pregnancy risk category: C

Indications and dosages

▶ **Depression.** *Adults:* 50 to 100 mg P.O. at bedtime, gradually increasing to 150 mg daily; maximum dosage for a hospitalized patient is 300 mg daily, if needed.
Elderly patients and adolescents: 10 mg P.O. t.i.d. and 20 mg at bedtime daily.
▶ **Anorexia or bulimia related to depression; adjunctive therapy for neurogenic pain ‡.** *Adults:* If outpatient, initially 75 to 100 mg P.O. in divided doses daily. If inpatient, 100 to 300 mg P.O. in divided doses daily. After maximum effect is achieved, gradually decrease to maintenance dose of 50 to 100 mg or less P.O. daily for a minimum of 3 months.

Contraindications and cautions

• Contraindicated during acute recovery phase of MI, in patients hypersensitive to drug, and within 14 days of MAO inhibitor therapy.
• Use cautiously in patients with history of seizures, urine retention, prostatic hypertrophy, angle-closure glaucoma, or increased intraocular pressure; in those with hyperthyroidism, CV disease, diabetes, or impaired liver function; and in those taking thyroid medications.
Lifespan: In pregnant women, use cautiously. In breast-feeding women, drug is contraindicated. In children younger than age 12, don't use drug. In elderly patients, who may experience increased falls and increased anticholinergic effects while taking this drug, use cautiously.

Adverse reactions

CNS: confusion, *drowsiness,* dizziness, EEG alterations, excitation, extrapyramidal reactions, headache, nervousness, ***seizures, stroke,*** tremors, weakness.
CV: ***arrhythmias,*** ECG changes, hypertension, ***MI,*** *orthostatic hypotension,* tachycardia.
EENT: blurred vision, mydriasis, tinnitus.

GI: anorexia, *constipation, dry mouth,* nausea, paralytic ileus, vomiting.
GU: *urine retention.*
Hematologic: ***agranulocytosis, thrombocytopenia.***
Skin: diaphoresis, photosensitivity reaction, rash, urticaria.
Other: hypersensitivity reactions.

Interactions

Drug-drug. *Barbiturates, CNS depressants:* May increase CNS depression. Avoid use together.
Cimetidine, methylphenidate: May increase tricyclic antidepressant level. Monitor patient for increased antidepressant effect.
Clonidine: May cause loss of blood pressure control and potentially life-threatening increase in blood pressure. Don't use together.
Epinephrine, norepinephrine: May increase hypertensive effect. Use together cautiously.
Guanethidine: May antagonize antihypertensive action of guanethidine. Monitor patient.
MAO inhibitors: May cause severe excitation, hyperpyrexia, or seizures, especially at high dosage. Avoid using within 14 days of each other.
Drug-herb. *SAMe, St. John's wort, yohimbe:* May cause serotonin level to become too high. Discourage use together.
Drug-lifestyle. *Alcohol use:* May increase CNS depression. Discourage use together.
Smoking: May lower drug level. Monitor patient for lack of effect.
Sun exposure: May increase risk of photosensitivity reactions. Advise against prolonged or unprotected sun exposure.

Effects on lab test results

- May increase or decrease glucose level.
- May increase eosinophil count and liver function test values. May decrease granulocyte, platelet, and WBC counts.

Pharmacokinetics

Absorption: Rapid.
Distribution: Widely into body, including CNS and breast milk. Drug is 96% protein-bound.
Metabolism: By liver to active metabolite nortriptyline; significant first-pass effect may account for variable levels in different patients taking same dosage.
Excretion: Mainly in urine. *Half-life:* Varies widely.

Route	Onset	Peak	Duration
P.O., I.M.	Unknown	2–12 hr	Unknown

Action

Chemical effect: Unknown, but tricyclic antidepressant increases levels of norepinephrine, serotonin, or both in CNS by blocking their reuptake by presynaptic neurons.
Therapeutic effect: Relieves depression.

Available forms

Tablets: 10 mg, 25 mg, 50 mg, 75 mg, 100 mg, 150 mg

NURSING PROCESS

Assessment

- Assess patient's depression before therapy.
- Be alert for adverse reactions and drug interactions.
- Assess patient's and family's knowledge of drug therapy.

Nursing diagnoses

- Ineffective coping related to depression
- Risk for injury related to adverse CNS reactions
- Deficient knowledge related to drug therapy

Planning and implementation

- Oral therapy should replace injection as soon as possible.
- Give full dose at bedtime when possible.
- Don't withdraw drug abruptly.
- If signs of psychosis occur or increase, reduce dosage. Give patient minimum supply of drug.
- Because hypertensive episodes may occur during surgery in patients receiving tricyclic antidepressants, drug should be gradually stopped several days before surgery.

ALERT: Don't confuse amitriptyline with nortriptyline or aminophylline, or Endep with Depen.

Patient teaching

- Advise patient to take full dose at bedtime, and warn of possible morning orthostatic hypotension.
- Tell patient to avoid alcohol and smoking while taking drug.

- Warn patient to avoid hazardous activities until full CNS effects of drug are known. Drowsiness and dizziness usually subside after a few weeks.
- Advise patient to consult prescriber before taking other prescription drugs, OTC medications, or herbal remedies.
- Teach patient to relieve dry mouth with sugarless hard candy or gum. Saliva substitutes may be needed.
- Advise patient to use sunblock, wear protective clothing, and avoid prolonged exposure to strong sunlight.
- Warn patient not to stop therapy abruptly. After abrupt withdrawal of long-term therapy, patient may have nausea, headache, and malaise. These symptoms don't indicate addiction.
- Tell patient to watch for urine retention and constipation. Instruct him to increase fluids, and suggest a stool softener or high-fiber diet, as needed.
- Advise patient that effects of drug may not be apparent for 2 to 3 weeks.

Evaluation

- Patient's behavior and communication indicate improvement of depression.
- Patient sustains no injury from CNS adverse reactions.
- Patient and family state understanding of drug therapy.

amlodipine besylate

(am-LOW-dih-peen BEH-sih-layt)
Norvasc

Pharmacologic class: calcium channel blocker
Therapeutic class: antianginal, antihypertensive
Pregnancy risk category: C

Indications and dosages

▶ **Chronic stable angina; vasospastic angina (Prinzmetal [variant] angina).** *Adults:* Initially, 10 mg P.O. daily.
Adjust-a-dose: For small, frail, or elderly patients or patients with hepatic insufficiency, start with 5 mg daily. Most patients need 10 mg daily for adequate results.
▶ **Hypertension.** *Adults:* Initially, 5 mg P.O. daily. Maximum, 10 mg daily.
Adjust-a-dose: For small, frail, or elderly patients, patients receiving other antihypertensives, and patients with hepatic insufficiency, start with 2.5 mg daily and adjust based on patient response and tolerance. Maximum, 10 mg daily.

Contraindications and cautions

- Contraindicated in patients hypersensitive to drug.
- Use cautiously in patients taking other peripheral vasodilators (especially those with severe aortic stenosis) and in those with heart failure.
- In patients with severe hepatic disease, use cautiously and in reduced dosage because drug is metabolized by liver.

Lifespan: In pregnant women, use cautiously. In breast-feeding women, drug is contraindicated. In children, safety of drug hasn't been established.

Adverse reactions

CNS: fatigue, headache, somnolence.
CV: dizziness, *edema,* flushing, palpitations.
GI: abdominal pain, dyspepsia, nausea.

Interactions

Drug-food. *Grapefruit juice:* May increase drug level and adverse effects. Tell patient not to take drug with grapefruit juice. However, if he has been stabilized on the drug while routinely drinking grapefruit juice, caution him not to abruptly stop doing so.

Effects on lab test results

None reported.

Pharmacokinetics

Absorption: Absolute bioavailability from 64% to 90%.
Distribution: About 93% of circulating drug is bound to plasma proteins.
Metabolism: About 90% of drug is converted to inactive metabolites in liver.
Excretion: Mainly in urine. *Half-life:* 30 to 50 hours.

Route	Onset	Peak	Duration
P.O.	Unknown	6–9 hr	24 hr

Action

Chemical effect: Inhibits calcium ion influx across cardiac and smooth-muscle cells, thus

decreasing myocardial contractility and oxygen demand. Also dilates coronary arteries and arterioles.
Therapeutic effect: Reduces blood pressure and prevents angina.

Available forms

Tablets: 2.5 mg, 5 mg, 10 mg

NURSING PROCESS

Assessment

- Assess patient's blood pressure or angina before therapy and regularly thereafter.
- Monitor patient carefully for pain. In some patients, especially those with severe obstructive coronary artery disease, increased frequency, duration, or severity of angina or even acute MI has developed after starting a calcium channel blocker or increasing dosage.
- Be alert for adverse reactions.
- Assess patient's and family's knowledge of drug therapy.

Nursing diagnoses

- Acute pain related to increased oxygen demand in cardiac tissue
- Risk for injury related to hypertension
- Deficient knowledge related to drug therapy

Planning and implementation

- Adjust dosage based on patient response and tolerance.
- Give S.L. nitroglycerin as needed for acute angina.

ALERT: Don't confuse amlodipine with amiloride.

Patient teaching

- Tell patient that S.L. nitroglycerin may be taken as needed for acute angina. If patient continues nitrate therapy during adjustment of amlodipine dosage, urge continued compliance.
- Advise patient to continue taking drug even when feeling better.

Evaluation

- Patient's blood pressure is normal.
- Patient states anginal pain occurs with less frequency and severity.
- Patient and family state understanding of drug therapy.

amoxicillin and clavulanate potassium

(uh-moks-uh-SIL-in and KLAV-yoo-lan-ayt poh-TAH-see-um)

Amoclan, Augmentin, Augmentin ES-600, Augmentin XR, Clavulin ♦

Pharmacologic class: aminopenicillin, beta-lactamase inhibitor
Therapeutic class: antibiotic
Pregnancy risk category: B

Indications and dosages

▶ **Lower respiratory tract infections, otitis media, sinusitis, skin and skin-structure infections, and UTI caused by susceptible strains of gram-positive and gram-negative organisms.** *Adults:* 250 mg (based on amoxicillin component) P.O. q 8 hours. For more severe infections, 500 mg q 8 hours or 875 mg P.O. q 12 hours.
Children: 20 to 40 mg/kg (based on amoxicillin component) P.O. daily in divided doses q 8 hours.
Neonates and infants younger than age 12 weeks: 30 mg/kg (based on amoxicillin component) P.O. daily in divided doses q 12 hours.

▶ **Recurrent or persistent acute otitis media caused by *Streptococcus pneumoniae, Haemophilus influenzae,* or *Moraxella catarrhalis.*** *Infants and children at least 3 months old, exposed to antibiotics during the previous 3 months, who are either age 2 or younger or attend daycare:* 90 mg/kg daily Augmentin ES 600 (based on amoxicillin component) P.O. q 12 hours for 10 days. Information about this drug in patients weighing 40 kg (88 lb) or more is unavailable.

▶ **Community-acquired pneumonia or acute bacterial sinusitis from confirmed, or suspected beta-lactamase–producing pathogens (*H. influenzae, M. catarrhalis, Haemophilus parainfluenzae, Klebsiella pneumoniae,* or methicillin-susceptible *Staphylococcus aureus*) and *S. pneumoniae* with reduced susceptibility to penicillin.** *Adults and children age 16 and older:* 2,000 mg/125 mg Augmentin XR q 12 hours for 7 to 10 days for pneumonia, or 10 days for sinusitis. Taken with meals.

Contraindications and cautions

- Contraindicated in patients hypersensitive to drug or other penicillins and in those with a history of amoxicillin-related cholestatic jaundice or hepatic dysfunction.
- Augmentin XR is contraindicated in hemodialysis patients and patients with creatinine clearance less than 30 ml/minute.
- Use cautiously in patients with other drug allergies, especially to cephalosporins (possible cross-sensitivity), and those with mononucleosis (high risk of maculopapular rash) or hepatic impairment.

Lifespan: In pregnant and breast-feeding women, use cautiously. In children younger than age 16, safety and effectiveness of Augmentin XR haven't been established.

Adverse reactions

CNS: agitation, anxiety, behavioral changes, confusion, dizziness, insomnia.
GI: abdominal pain, black "hairy" tongue, *diarrhea,* enterocolitis, gastritis, glossitis, indigestion, mucocutaneous candidiasis, nausea, ***pseudomembranous colitis,*** stomatitis, vomiting.
GU: vaginal candidiasis, vaginitis.
Hematologic: ***agranulocytosis,*** anemia, eosinophilia, ***leukopenia, thrombocytopenia, thrombocytopenic purpura.***
Other: hypersensitivity reactions (***anaphylaxis, angioedema,*** pruritus, ***rash,*** urticaria), overgrowth of nonsusceptible organisms, serum sickness–like reactions (urticaria or rash accompanied by arthralgia, arthritis, myalgia, and commonly fever).

Interactions

Drug-drug. *Allopurinol:* May cause rash. Monitor patient.
Probenecid: May increase level of amoxicillin and other penicillins. Probenecid may be used for this purpose.

Effects on lab test results

- May decrease hemoglobin level and hematocrit.
- May increase eosinophil count. May decrease granulocyte, platelet, and WBC counts.
- May cause false-positive urine glucose determinations with copper sulfate tests, such as Benedict solution and Clinitest.

Pharmacokinetics

Absorption: Well absorbed.
Distribution: Both drugs are distributed into pleural fluid, lungs, and peritoneal fluid, with high urine levels. Amoxicillin also appears in synovial fluid, liver, prostate, muscle, gallbladder, middle ear effusions, maxillary sinus secretions, tonsils, sputum, and bronchial secretions. Both drugs are minimally protein-bound.
Metabolism: Amoxicillin is metabolized partially; clavulanate potassium, extensively.
Excretion: Amoxicillin mainly in urine; clavulanate potassium by glomerular filtration. *Half-life:* 1 to 1½ hours (in severe renal impairment, 7½ hours for amoxicillin and 4½ hours for clavulanate).

Route	Onset	Peak	Duration
P.O.			
Augmentin	Unknown	1–2½ hr	6–8 hr
Augmentin ES-600	Unknown	1–4 hr	Unknown
Augmentin XR	Unknown	1–6 hr	Unknown

Action

Chemical effect: Prevents bacterial cell-wall synthesis during replication. Clavulanic acid increases amoxicillin's effectiveness by inactivating beta lactamases, which destroy amoxicillin.
Therapeutic effect: Kills susceptible bacteria.

Available forms

Oral suspension: 125 mg amoxicillin trihydrate and 31.25 mg clavulanic acid/5 ml (after reconstitution); 200 mg amoxicillin trihydrate and 28.5 mg clavulanic acid/5 ml (after reconstitution); 250 mg amoxicillin trihydrate and 62.5 mg clavulanic acid/5 ml (after reconstitution); 400 mg amoxicillin trihydrate and 57 mg clavulanic acid/5 ml (after reconstitution); 600 mg amoxicillin trihydrate and 42.9 mg clavulanic acid/5 ml (after reconstitution)
Tablets: 875 mg amoxicillin trihydrate, 125 mg clavulanic acid
Tablets (chewable): 125 mg amoxicillin trihydrate, 31.25 mg clavulanic acid; 200 mg amoxicillin trihydrate, 28.5 mg clavulanic acid; 250 mg amoxicillin trihydrate, 62.5 mg clavulanic acid; 400 mg amoxicillin trihydrate, 57 mg clavulanic acid
Tablets (extended-release): 1,000 mg amoxicillin trihydrate, 62.5 mg clavulanic acid

Tablets (film-coated): 250 mg amoxicillin trihydrate, 125 mg clavulanic acid; 500 mg amoxicillin trihydrate, 125 mg clavulanic acid

NURSING PROCESS

Assessment

- Before therapy begins, assess patient's infection, ask about past allergic reactions to penicillin (although negative history is no guarantee against allergic reaction), and obtain specimen for culture and sensitivity tests. Therapy may begin pending results.
- Be alert for adverse reactions and drug interactions.
- Monitor hydration status if adverse GI reactions occur.
- Assess patient's and family's knowledge of drug therapy.

Nursing diagnoses

- Ineffective protection related to presence of susceptible bacteria
- Risk for deficient fluid volume related to drug-induced adverse GI reactions
- Deficient knowledge related to drug therapy

Planning and implementation

- Give drug with food to prevent GI distress. Adverse effects for this combination drug, especially diarrhea, are more common than with amoxicillin alone.
- Give drug at least 1 hour before bacteriostatic antibiotics.

ALERT: Tablets and suspension contain varying amounts of clavulanic acid. Don't assume that two 250-mg (amoxicillin) tablets replace one 500-mg tablet because amount of clavulanic acid may not change in same proportion.

ALERT: Augmentin (250 mg or 500 mg amoxicillin) and Augmentin XR extended-release tablets aren't interchangeable because of the different amounts of clavulanic acid in each and because Augmentin XR is an extended-release formulation.

ALERT: Augmentin ES-600 is intended only for children.

- This drug combination is particularly useful with amoxicillin-resistant organisms.
- After reconstitution, refrigerate oral suspension and discard after 10 days.

ALERT: Don't confuse amoxicillin with amoxapine.

Patient teaching

- Tell patient to take entire quantity of drug exactly as prescribed, even after he feels better.
- Tell patient to call prescriber if rash develops (sign of allergic reaction).
- Instruct patient to take drug with food to prevent GI distress.

Evaluation

- Patient is free from infection.
- Patient maintains adequate hydration.
- Patient and family state understanding of drug therapy.

amoxicillin trihydrate (amoxycillin trihydrate ◇)

(uh-moks-uh-SIL-in trigh-HIGH-drayt)

Alphamox ◇, Amoxil, Apo-Amoxil, Cilamox ◇, DisperMox, Maxamox ◇, Moxacin ◇, Novamoxin ♦, Nu-Amoxi ♦, Trimox

Pharmacologic class: aminopenicillin
Therapeutic class: antibiotic
Pregnancy risk category: B

Indications and dosages

▶ **Mild to moderate infections of the ear, nose and throat, skin and skin structure, or GU tract.** *Adults and children weighing 40 kg (88 lb) or more:* 500 mg P.O. q 12 hours or 250 mg P.O. q 8 hours.

Children older than 3 months weighing less than 40 kg: 25 mg/kg/day P.O. divided q 12 hours or 20 mg/kg/day P.O. divided q 8 hours.

Neonates and infants younger than age 3 months: Up to 30 mg/kg/day P.O. divided q 12 hours.

▶ **Mild to severe infections of the lower respiratory tract and severe infections of the ear, nose and throat, skin and skin structure, or GU tract.** *Adults and children weighing 40 kg or more:* 875 mg P.O. q 12 hours or 500 mg P.O. q 8 hours.

Children older than 3 months who weigh less than 40 kg: 45 mg/kg/day P.O. divided q 12 hours or 40 mg/kg/day P.O. divided q 8 hours.

A

▶ ***Helicobacter pylori* eradication to reduce the risk of duodenal ulcer, given with other drugs.** *Dual therapy. Adults:* Amoxicillin 1 g P.O. and lansoprazole 30 mg P.O., each q 8 hours for 14 days.
Triple therapy. Adults: Amoxicillin 1 g P.O., clarithromycin 500 mg P.O., and lansoprazole 30 mg P.O., each q 12 hours for 14 days.
▶ **Uncomplicated gonorrhea.** *Adults:* 3 g P.O. as a single dose.
Children older than age 2: Give 50 mg/kg with 25 mg/kg probenecid as a single dose.
▶ **Chlamydial and mycoplasmal infections during pregnancy.** *Adults:* 500 mg P.O. t.i.d. for 7 to 10 days.
Adjust-a-dose: Patients with renal failure who need repeated doses may need an increased dose interval. If creatinine clearance is 10 to 30 ml/minute, increase to q 12 hours; if it's less than 10 ml/minute, give drug q 24 hours. Supplemental doses may be needed after hemodialysis. Don't give 875-mg tablet if creatinine clearance is less than 30 ml/minute.
▶ **Oral prophylaxis of bacterial endocarditis.** Consult current American Heart Association recommendations before giving drug. *Adults:* 2 g 1 hour before procedure.
Children: 50 mg/kg (maximum, 2 g) 1 hour before procedure.
▶ **Postexposure prophylaxis for penicillin-susceptible anthrax.** *Adults and children age 9 and older:* 500 mg P.O. t.i.d. for 60 days.
Children younger than age 9: Give 80 mg/kg/day P.O., divided t.i.d. for 60 days.
▶ **Lyme disease‡.** *Adults:* 250 to 500 mg P.O. t.i.d. or q.i.d. for 10 to 30 days.
Children: 25 to 50 mg/kg daily (maximum, 1 to 2 g daily) P.O. in three divided doses for 10 to 30 days.
▶ **Acute complicated UTI in nonpregnant women‡.** *Adults:* 3 g P.O. as a single dose.

Contraindications and cautions

- Contraindicated in patients hypersensitive to drug or other penicillins.
- Use cautiously in patients with other drug allergies, especially to cephalosporins (possible cross-sensitivity), and in those with mononucleosis (high risk of maculopapular rash), or renal impairment.

Lifespan: In pregnant or breast-feeding women, use cautiously.

Adverse reactions

CNS: ***seizures.***
GI: diarrhea, nausea, vomiting.
Hematologic: ***agranulocytosis,*** anemia, eosinophilia, ***leukopenia, thrombocytopenia, thrombocytopenic purpura.***
Other: hypersensitivity reactions (***anaphylaxis,*** erythematous maculopapular rash, urticaria), overgrowth of nonsusceptible organisms.

Interactions

Drug-drug. *Allopurinol:* May increase risk of rash. Monitor patient.
Probenecid: May increase level of amoxicillin and other penicillins. Probenecid may be used for this purpose.

Effects on lab test results

- May decrease hemoglobin level and hematocrit.
- May increase eosinophil count. May decrease granulocyte, platelet, and WBC counts.
- May cause false-positive urine glucose determinations with copper sulfate tests (such as Benedict solution and Clinitest).

Pharmacokinetics

Absorption: About 80%.
Distribution: Appears in pleural, peritoneal, and synovial fluids; lungs; prostate; muscle; liver; gallbladder; middle ear; maxillary sinus and bronchial secretions; tonsils; and sputum. Amoxicillin readily crosses placenta and is 17% to 20% protein-bound.
Metabolism: Partial.
Excretion: Mainly in urine by renal tubular secretion and glomerular filtration; also in breast milk. *Half-life:* 1 to 1½ hours (7½ hours in severe renal impairment).

Route	Onset	Peak	Duration
P.O.	Unknown	1–2 hr	6–8 hr

Action

Chemical effect: Inhibits cell-wall synthesis during bacterial multiplication.
Therapeutic effect: Kills susceptible bacteria.

Available forms

Capsules: 250 mg, 500 mg
Suspension: 50 mg/ml (pediatric drops), 125 mg/5 ml, 200 mg/5 ml, 250 mg/5 ml, 400 mg/5 ml

Tablets (chewable): 200 mg, 400 mg
Tablets (film-coated): 500 mg, 875 mg
Tablets (for oral suspension): 200 mg, 400 mg, 600 mg

NURSING PROCESS

Assessment

- Before therapy, assess patient's infection, ask about allergic reactions to drug or other forms of penicillin (although negative history doesn't guarantee against future reaction), and obtain specimen for culture and sensitivity tests. Therapy may begin pending test results.
- Be alert for adverse reactions and drug interactions.
- If adverse GI reactions occur, monitor patient's hydration status.
- Assess patient's and family's knowledge of drug therapy.

Nursing diagnoses

- Ineffective protection related to presence of susceptible bacteria
- Risk for deficient fluid volume related to drug-induced adverse GI reactions
- Deficient knowledge related to drug therapy

Planning and implementation

- Give amoxicillin at least 1 hour before bacteriostatic antibiotics.
- May be taken with or without food.
- Trimox oral suspension may be stored at room temperature for up to 2 weeks. Check individual product labels for storage information.
- For DisperMox, mix 1 tablet in 10 ml of water and have patient drink mixture. Rinse container with a small amount of water to make sure the entire tablet is taken. Don't let the patient chew or swallow tablet or let it dissolve in mouth.

ALERT: Don't confuse amoxicillin with amoxapine.

Patient teaching

- If drug allergy develops, advise patient to wear or carry medical identification stating penicillin allergy.
- Tell patient to take entire quantity of drug exactly as prescribed, even after feeling better.
- Tell patient to call prescriber if rash (most common), fever, or chills develop.
- Tell patient to take drug with or without food.
- Warn patient never to use leftover amoxicillin for a new illness or to share it with others.
- For DisperMox, give patient these instructions: Mix tablet in 10 ml of water (only water) and drink. Rinse the container with a small amount of water and drink again to get entire dose. Don't chew or swallow tablets or let them dissolve in mouth.

Evaluation

- Patient is free from infection.
- Patient maintains adequate hydration.
- Patient and family state understanding of drug therapy.

amphotericin B desoxycholate

(am-foh-TER-ah-sin bee dess-ox-ee-KOH-layt)

Amphocin, Fungizone

Pharmacologic class: polyene macrolide
Therapeutic class: antifungal
Pregnancy risk category: B

Indications and dosages

▶ **Systemic, potentially fatal fungal infections caused by susceptible organisms; fungal endocarditis; fungal septicemia.** *Adults and children:* Some clinicians recommend an initial dose of 1 mg I.V. in 20 ml D_5W infused over 20 minutes. If test dose is tolerated, then give daily doses of 0.25 to 0.3 mg/kg, gradually increasing by 5 to 10 mg daily until dosage is 0.5 to 0.7 mg/kg daily, up to 1 mg/kg daily or 1.5 mg/kg q alternate day. Duration of therapy depends on the severity and nature of infection.

▶ **Sporotrichosis.** *Adults and children:* 0.4 to 0.5 mg/kg daily I.V. for up to 9 months. Total I.V. dosage of 2.5 g over 9 months.

▶ **Aspergillosis.** *Adults and children:* 0.5 to 1.5 mg/kg daily initially and a total I.V. dose of 1.5 to 4 g over 11 months.

▶ **Disseminated or invasive candidal infections.** *Adults and children:* 0.4 to 0.6 mg/kg I.V. daily. Higher doses of up to 1.5 mg/kg have been used in rapidly progressing or potentially fatal infections. Therapy may last 7 to 14 days to more than 6 weeks depending on severity.

▶ **Coccidioidomycosis.** *Adults:* 0.5 to 1 mg/kg I.V. daily. Therapy usually lasts 4 to 12 weeks.

▶ **Cryptococcosis.** *Adults:* 0.3 to 1 mg/kg I.V. daily. Therapy may last 2 weeks to several months. Drug may be given with flucytosine P.O.

A

▶ **Cryptococcal meningitis in HIV-infected patients.** *Adults:* 0.7 mg/kg I.V. daily for 4 weeks followed by 0.7 mg/kg I.V. every other day for another 4 weeks.

▶ **Mucocutaneous leishmaniasis.** *Adults and children:* 0.25 to 0.5 mg/kg/day I.V., increased gradually to 0.5 to 1 mg/kg/day. Then give on alternate days. Treat for 3 to 12 weeks.

▶ **Visceral leishmaniasis.** *Adults and children:* 0.5 to 1 mg/kg/day I.V. on alternate days for 14 to 20 doses.

▶ **Paracoccidioidomycosis‡.** *Adults:* 0.4 to 0.5 mg/kg I.V. daily for 4 to 12 weeks.

▶ **Empiric therapy of presumed fungal infections in febrile, neutropenic patients, including those with cancer or bone marrow transplant‡.** *Adults:* 0.1 mg/kg daily.

I.V. administration

- Reconstitute only with 10 ml sterile water. To avoid precipitation, don't mix with solutions containing sodium chloride, other electrolytes, or bacteriostatic drugs (such as benzyl alcohol).
- Don't use if solution contains precipitate or foreign matter.
- Amphotericin B appears to be compatible with limited amounts of heparin sodium, hydrocortisone sodium succinate, and methylprednisolone sodium succinate.
- Give drug parenterally only in hospitalized patients, under close supervision, after diagnosis of potentially fatal fungal infection is confirmed.
- Be prepared to give an initial test dose, for which 1 mg is added to 20 ml of D_5W and infused over 20 to 30 minutes.
- Use an infusion pump and in-line filter with a mean pore diameter larger than 1 micron. Infuse over 2 to 6 hours because rapid infusion may cause CV collapse.
- Use I.V. sites in distal veins. If thrombosis occurs, alternate sites.
- If patient has severe adverse infusion reactions to first dose, stop infusion, notify prescriber, and give antipyretics, antihistamines, antiemetics, or small doses of corticosteroids. To prevent reactions during subsequent infusions, premedicate with these drugs or give amphotericin B on an alternate-day schedule.
- Reconstituted solution is stable for 1 week in refrigerator, 24 hours at room temperature, and 8 hours in room light.
- Store dry form at 36° to 46° F (2° to 8° C). Protect from light.

⊗ **Incompatibilities**

Amikacin, calcium chloride, chlorpromazine, cimetidine, diphenhydramine, edetate calcium disodium, gentamicin, kanamycin, lactated Ringer's injection, melphalan, methyldopate, normal saline solution, paclitaxel, penicillin G potassium, penicillin G sodium, polymyxin B, potassium chloride, prochlorperazine mesylate, streptomycin, verapamil. Give antibiotics separately; don't mix or piggyback with amphotericin B.

Contraindications and cautions

- Contraindicated in patients hypersensitive to drug or its components.
- Use cautiously in patients with impaired renal function.

Lifespan: In pregnant women, use cautiously. Breast-feeding women must stop breastfeeding or stop the drug. In children, safety and dosage haven't been fully established, but therapy may be successful.

Adverse reactions

CNS: encephalopathy, fever, headache, malaise, paresthesia, peripheral nerve pain, peripheral neuropathy, ***seizures.***
CV: ***arrhythmias, asystole,*** hypertension, hypotension, phlebitis, thrombophlebitis.
EENT: hearing loss, tinnitus, vertigo, visual impairment.
GI: anorexia, diarrhea, dyspepsia, epigastric cramps, ***hemorrhagic gastroenteritis,*** nausea, vomiting, weight loss.
GU: abnormal renal function with hypokalemia, anuria, azotemia, hypomagnesemia, hyposthenuria, nephrocalcinosis, oliguria, ***permanent renal impairment,*** renal tubular acidosis.
Hematologic: ***agranulocytosis,*** eosinophilia, normochromic normocytic anemia, ***thrombocytopenia.***
Hepatic: ***acute liver failure, hepatitis.***
Metabolic: hypokalemia, hypomagnesemia.
Musculoskeletal: arthralgia, myalgia.
Respiratory: dyspnea, hypersensitivity pneumonitis, pulmonary edema.
Skin: burning, irritation, pain at injection site, pruritus, rash, stinging, tissue damage with extravasation.
Other: ***anaphylactoid reactions,*** chills, generalized pain.

Interactions

Drug-drug. *Azole antifungals (fluconazole, ketoconazole):* May induce fungal resistance. Use with caution.
Corticosteroids, corticotropin: May cause potassium depletion. Monitor potassium level.
Digoxin: May increase risk of digitalis toxicity in potassium-depleted patients. Monitor patient closely.
Flucytosine: May increase flucytosine toxicity. Monitor patient closely.
Nephrotoxic drugs (such as antibiotics and antineoplastics): May increase risk of nephrotoxicity. Use together cautiously.
Skeletal muscle relaxants: May increase effects of muscle relaxants. Monitor patient for increased effects.

Effects on lab test results

- May increase urine urea, uric acid, BUN, creatinine, alkaline phosphatase, ALT, AST, GGT, LDH, and bilirubin levels. May decrease phosphate, magnesium, and hemoglobin levels and hematocrit. May increase or decrease glucose, potassium, and calcium levels.
- May decrease platelet and granulocyte counts. May increase or decrease WBC and eosinophil counts.

Pharmacokinetics

Absorption: Poor.
Distribution: Well into pleural cavities and joints; less so into aqueous humor, bronchial secretions, pancreas, bone, muscle, and parotid gland. Drug is 90% to 95% bound to plasma proteins.
Metabolism: Not well defined.
Excretion: Up to 5% unchanged in urine.
Half-life: Adults and children older than age 9, 24 hours; children age 9 and younger, 18 hours.

Route	Onset	Peak	Duration
I.V.	Immediate	Immediate	Unknown

Action

Chemical effect: May bind to sterol in fungal cell membrane and alter cell permeability, allowing leakage of intracellular components.
Therapeutic effect: Decreases activity of or kills susceptible fungi.

Available forms

Powder for injection: 50-mg lyophilized cake

NURSING PROCESS

Assessment

- Obtain history of fungal infection and samples for culture and sensitivity tests before first dose. Reevaluate condition during therapy.
- Be alert for adverse reactions and drug interactions.
- Monitor patient's pulse, respiratory rate, temperature, and blood pressure every 30 minutes for at least 4 hours after giving drug I.V.; fever, shaking chills, anorexia, nausea, vomiting, headache, tachypnea, and hypotension may appear 1 to 3 hours after start of I.V. infusion. Symptoms are usually more severe with initial dose.
- Monitor BUN, creatinine level or clearance, electrolyte levels, CBC, and liver function test results at least weekly.
- Drug is linked to rhinocerebral phycomycosis, especially in patients with uncontrolled diabetes. Leukoencephalopathy also may occur. Monitor pulmonary function. Acute reactions are characterized by dyspnea, hypoxemia, and infiltrates.
- Assess patient's and family's knowledge of drug therapy.

Nursing diagnoses

- Ineffective protection related to presence of susceptible fungal species
- Risk for injury related to drug-induced adverse reactions
- Deficient knowledge related to drug therapy

Planning and implementation

ALERT: Different amphotericin B preparations aren't interchangeable, and dosages vary.
- If BUN level exceeds 40 mg/dl, or if creatinine level exceeds 3 mg/dl, prescriber may reduce or stop drug until renal function improves. Drug may be stopped if alkaline phosphatase or bilirubin level increases.

Patient teaching

- Teach patient signs and symptoms of hypersensitivity, and stress importance of reporting them immediately.
- Warn patient that therapy may take several months; teach personal hygiene and other measures to prevent spread and recurrence of lesions.

- Urge patient to comply with prescribed regimen and recommended follow-up.
- Warn patient that discomfort at injection site and adverse reactions may occur during therapy, which may last several months.

Evaluation

- Patient is free from fungal infection.
- Patient sustains no injury from drug-induced adverse reactions.
- Patient and family state understanding of drug therapy.

amphotericin B lipid complex

(am-foe-TER-ah-sin bee LIP-id KOM-pleks)

Abelcet

Pharmacologic class: polyene antibiotic
Therapeutic class: antifungal
Pregnancy risk category: B

Indications and dosages

▶ **Invasive fungal infections, including those caused by *Aspergillus fumigatus; Candida albicans, guilliermondii, stellatoidea,* and *tropicalis; Coccidioidomycosis* sp.; *Cryptococcus* sp.; *Histoplasma* sp.; and *Blastomyces* sp. in patients refractory to or intolerant of conventional amphotericin B therapy.** *Adults and children:* 5 mg/kg daily as a single I.V. infusion. Give by continuous I.V. infusion at 2.5 mg/kg/hour.

I.V. administration

- To prepare, shake the vial gently until you see no yellow sediment. Using aseptic technique, draw the calculated dose into one or more 20-ml syringes, using an 18G needle. You'll need more than one vial.
- Attach a 5-micron filter needle to the syringe and inject the dose into an I.V. bag of D_5W. One filter needle can be used for up to four vials of drug. The volume of D_5W should be sufficient to yield a final concentration of 1 mg/ml.
- For children and patients with CV disease, the recommended final concentration is 2 mg/ml.
- Shake the bag, and check the contents for foreign matter.
- Don't use an in-line filter.
- If infusing through an existing I.V. line, flush first with D_5W.
- Solutions are stable for up to 48 hours when refrigerated at 36° to 46° F (2° to 8° C) and for up to 6 hours at room temperature.
- Refrigerate and protect from light. Don't freeze.
- Discard unused drug; it contains no preservatives.
- Slowing the infusion rate also may decrease the risk of infusion-related reactions.
- For infusions lasting longer than 2 hours, shake the I.V. bag every 2 hours to ensure an even suspension.

Incompatibilities

Electrolytes, other I.V. drugs, saline solutions.

Contraindications and cautions

- Contraindicated in patients hypersensitive to amphotericin B or its components.
- Use cautiously in patients with renal impairment.

Lifespan: In pregnant women, safety hasn't been established. Use only if benefits outweigh risks to the fetus. Breast-feeding women must stop breast-feeding or stop drug. In infants younger than 1 month, safety and effectiveness haven't been established.

Adverse reactions

CNS: fever, headache, pain.
CV: ***cardiac arrest,*** chest pain, hypertension, hypotension.
GI: abdominal pain, diarrhea, ***GI hemorrhage,*** nausea, vomiting.
GU: ***renal failure.***
Hematologic: anemia, ***leukopenia, thrombocytopenia.***
Hepatic: bilirubinemia.
Metabolic: hypokalemia.
Respiratory: dyspnea, respiratory disorder, ***respiratory failure.***
Skin: rash.
Other: chills, infection, **MULTIPLE ORGAN FAILURE,** ***sepsis.***

Interactions

Drug-drug. *Antineoplastics:* May increase risk of renal toxicity, bronchospasm, and hypotension. Use cautiously.
Azole antifungals (fluconazole, ketoconazole): May induce fungal resistance. Use with caution.
Digoxin: May increase risk of digoxin toxicity and induce hypokalemia. Monitor potassium level closely.

Corticosteroids, corticotropin: May enhance hypokalemia, which may lead to cardiac dysfunction. Monitor electrolytes and cardiac function.
Cyclosporin A: May increase renal toxicity. Monitor patient closely.
Flucytosine: May increase risk of flucytosine toxicity from increased cellular uptake or impaired renal excretion. Use together cautiously.
Imidazoles (clotrimazole, fluconazole, itraconazole, ketoconazole, miconazole): May decrease effectiveness of amphotericin B because of inhibition of ergosterol synthesis. Clinical significance is unknown.
Leukocyte transfusions: May cause acute pulmonary toxicity. Avoid use together.
Nephrotoxic drugs (aminoglycosides, pentamidine): May increase risk of renal toxicity. Use together cautiously. Monitor renal function closely.
Skeletal muscle relaxants: May enhance effects of skeletal muscle relaxants because of drug-induced hypokalemia. Monitor potassium level closely.
Zidovudine: May increase myelotoxicity and nephrotoxicity. Monitor renal and hematologic function.

Effects on lab test results

- May increase BUN, creatinine, alkaline phosphatase, ALT, AST, bilirubin, GGT, and LDH levels. May decrease potassium and hemoglobin levels and hematocrit.
- May decrease WBC and platelet counts.

Pharmacokinetics

Absorption: Given I.V.
Distribution: Well distributed. Volume increases with dose. Amphotericin B lipid complex yields measurable amphotericin B levels in spleen, lung, liver, lymph nodes, kidney, heart, and brain.
Metabolism: Unknown.
Excretion: Rapidly cleared from blood. *Terminal half-life:* About a week, probably because of slow elimination from tissues.

Route	Onset	Peak	Duration
I.V.	Unknown	Unknown	Unknown

Action

Chemical effect: Binds to sterols in fungal cell membranes, increasing cellular permeability and cell damage. It has fungistatic or fungicidal effects, depending on fungal susceptibility.
Therapeutic effect: Decreases activity of or kills susceptible fungi.

Available forms

Suspension for injection: 50 mg/10-ml vial; 100 mg/20-ml vial

NURSING PROCESS

Assessment

- Obtain history of fungal infection and samples for culture and sensitivity tests before therapy. Reevaluate condition during therapy.
- Be alert for adverse reactions and drug interactions.
- Assess renal function before therapy starts.
- Monitor liver function, creatinine and electrolyte levels (especially magnesium and potassium), and CBC during therapy.
- Assess patient's and family's knowledge of drug therapy.

Nursing diagnoses

- Risk for infection related to presence of susceptible fungal infection
- Risk for injury related to drug-induced adverse reactions
- Deficient knowledge related to drug therapy

Planning and implementation

- If severe respiratory distress develops, stop the infusion, provide supportive therapy for anaphylaxis, and notify prescriber. Don't resume the infusion.

ALERT: Different amphotericin B preparations aren't interchangeable, and dosages vary.

- Premedicate patient with acetaminophen, antihistamines, and corticosteroids to prevent or lessen the severity of infusion-related reactions, such as fever, chills, nausea, and vomiting, which occur 1 to 2 hours after the start of infusion.

Patient teaching

- Inform patient that fever, chills, nausea, and vomiting may occur during the infusion and that these reactions usually subside with later doses.
- Instruct patient to report redness or pain at the infusion site.
- Teach patient to recognize and report symptoms of acute hypersensitivity, such as respiratory distress.

• Tell patient to expect frequent laboratory testing to monitor kidney and liver function.

☑ Evaluation

• Patient is free from fungal infection.
• Patient has no injury from adverse drug reactions.
• Patient and family state understanding of drug therapy.

amphotericin B liposomal

(am-foh-TER-ah-sin bee lye-poh-SOW-mul)
AmBisome

Pharmacologic class: polyene antibiotic
Therapeutic class: antifungal
Pregnancy risk category: B

Indications and dosages

▶ **Empirical therapy for presumed fungal infection in febrile, neutropenic patients.** *Adults and children:* 3 mg/kg I.V. infusion daily.
▶ **Systemic fungal infections caused by *Aspergillus*, *Candida*, or *Cryptococcus* sp. refractory to amphotericin B deoxycholate or in patients with renal impairment or unacceptable toxicity that precludes the use of amphotericin B deoxycholate.** *Adults and children:* 3 to 5 mg/kg I.V. infusion daily.
▶ **Visceral leishmaniasis in immunocompetent patients.** *Adults and children:* 3 mg/kg I.V. infusion daily on days 1 to 5, 14, and 21. A repeat course may be beneficial if initial treatment fails to clear parasites.
▶ **Visceral leishmaniasis in immunocompromised patients.** *Adults and children:* 4 mg/kg I.V. infusion daily on days 1 to 5, 10, 17, 24, 31, and 38. Expert advice regarding further treatment is recommended if initial therapy fails or relapse occurs.
▶ **Cryptococcal meningitis in HIV-infected patients.** *Adults and children:* 6 mg/kg daily I.V. infusion over 2 hours. Infusion time may be decreased to 1 hour if well tolerated or increased if discomfort occurs.

I.V. administration

• Reconstitute each 50-mg vial of amphotericin B liposomal with 12 ml of sterile water for injection to yield 4 mg amphotericin B per milliliter.
• After reconstitution, shake vial vigorously for 30 seconds or until particulate matter disappears. Withdraw calculated amount of reconstituted solution into a sterile syringe and inject through a 5-micron filter into the appropriate amount of D_5W to a final concentration of 1 to 2 mg/ml. Lower concentrations (0.2 to 0.5 mg/ml) may be appropriate for children to provide sufficient volume for infusion.
• Flush existing I.V. line with D_5W before infusing drug. If this isn't feasible, give drug through a separate line.
• Use a controlled infusion device and an in-line filter with a mean pore diameter larger than 1 micron. Initially, infuse drug over at least 2 hours. Infusion time may be reduced to 1 hour if the treatment is well tolerated. If the patient has discomfort, infusion time may be increased.
• Observe patient closely for adverse reactions during infusion. If anaphylaxis occurs, stop the infusion immediately, provide supportive therapy, and notify the prescriber.
• Refrigerate unopened drug at 36° to 46° F (2° to 8° C). Once reconstituted, the product may be stored for up to 24 hours at 36° to 46° F. Don't freeze.

⊗ Incompatibilities
Other I.V. drugs, saline solutions, bacteriostatic water for injection and bacteriostatic drugs.

Contraindications and cautions

• Contraindicated in patients hypersensitive to drug or its components.
• Use cautiously in patients with renal impairment.
Lifespan: In pregnant women, safety hasn't been established. Use only if benefits outweigh risks to the fetus. Breast-feeding women must stop breast-feeding or stop drug. In infants younger than 1 month, safety and effectiveness haven't been established.

Adverse reactions

CNS: *anxiety, asthenia, confusion,* fever, *headache, insomnia, pain.*
CV: *chest pain, edema,* hypertension, *hypotension,* phlebitis, *tachycardia,* vasodilation.
EENT: *epistaxis, rhinitis.*
GI: *abdominal pain,* anorexia, *diarrhea, **GI hemorrhage,*** nausea, vomiting.
GU: *hematuria.*
Hepatic: hepatomegaly.

Metabolic: *hyperglycemia,* hypernatremia, *hypocalcemia,* ***hypokalemia, hypomagnesemia.***
Musculoskeletal: *back pain.*
Respiratory: *cough, dyspnea,* hyperventilation, hypoxia, *lung disorder, pleural effusion.*
Skin: *pruritus, rash,* sweating.
Other: ***anaphylaxis, blood product infusion reaction,*** *chills,* infection, ***sepsis.***

Interactions

Drug-drug. *Antineoplastics:* May increase risk of renal toxicity, bronchospasm, and hypotension. Use cautiously.
Azole antifungals (fluconazole, ketoconazole): May induce fungal resistance. Use with caution.
Corticosteroids, corticotropin: May potentiate hypokalemia, which could result in cardiac dysfunction. Monitor potassium level and cardiac function.
Digoxin: May increase risk of digoxin toxicity in potassium-depleted patients. Monitor potassium level closely.
Flucytosine: May increase flucytosine toxicity by increasing cellular uptake or impairing renal excretion of flucytosine. Monitor renal function closely.
Imidazole antifungals (clotrimazole, ketoconazole, miconazole): May induce fungal resistance to amphotericin B. Use together cautiously
Leukocyte transfusions: May increase risk of acute pulmonary toxicity. Avoid use together.
Other nephrotoxic drugs (antibiotics, antineoplastics): May increase risk of nephrotoxicity. Use together cautiously. Monitor renal function closely.
Skeletal muscle relaxants: May increase effects of skeletal muscle relaxants because of amphotericin-induced hypokalemia. Monitor potassium level.

Effects on lab test results

- May increase BUN, creatinine, glucose, sodium, alkaline phosphatase, ALT, AST, bilirubin, GGT, and LDH levels. May decrease potassium, calcium, and magnesium levels.

Pharmacokinetics

Absorption: Given I.V.
Distribution: Unknown.
Metabolism: Unknown.
Excretion: Unknown. *Initial half-life:* 7 to 10 hours with 24-hour dosing. *Terminal elimination half-life:* About 4 to 6 days.

Route	Onset	Peak	Duration
I.V.	Unknown	Unknown	Unknown

Action

Chemical effect: Binds to the sterol component of a fungal cell membrane, altering cell permeability and cell death.
Therapeutic effect: Decreases activity of or kills susceptible fungi. Treats visceral protozoal infections.

Available forms

Injection: 50-mg vial

NURSING PROCESS

Assessment

- Obtain history of fungal infection and samples for culture and sensitivity tests before therapy. Reevaluate condition during therapy.
- Carefully assess patients who are also receiving chemotherapy or bone marrow transplantation because of their increased risk of additional adverse reactions, including seizures, arrhythmias, thrombocytopenia, and respiratory failure.
- Monitor CBC, liver function test results, and creatinine, BUN, and electrolyte levels, particularly magnesium and potassium.
- Monitor patient for signs of hypokalemia, such as ECG changes, muscle weakness, cramping, and drowsiness.
- Watch for adverse reactions. Patients who receive drug may have fewer chills, decreased BUN level, a lower risk of hypokalemia, and less vomiting than patients who receive regular amphotericin B.
- Assess patient's and family's knowledge of drug therapy.

Nursing diagnoses

- Risk for infection related to presence of susceptible fungal or parasite infections
- Risk for injury related to drug-induced adverse reactions
- Deficient knowledge related to drug therapy

Planning and implementation

ALERT: Amphotericin B preparations aren't interchangeable, and dosages vary.
- To lessen the risk or severity of adverse reactions, premedicate patient with antipyretics, antihistamines, antiemetics, or corticosteroids.
- Therapy may take several weeks to months.

Patient teaching

- Teach patient signs and symptoms of hypersensitivity, and stress importance of reporting them immediately.
- Warn patient that therapy may take several months; teach personal hygiene and other measures to prevent spread and recurrence of lesions.
- Instruct patient to report adverse reactions.
- Instruct patient to watch for and report signs of hypokalemia, such as muscle weakness, cramping, and drowsiness.
- Advise patient that frequent laboratory testing will be performed.

Evaluation

- Patient is free from fungal or parasitic infection.
- Patient sustains no injury from drug-induced adverse reactions.
- Patient and family state understanding of drug therapy.

ampicillin

(am-pih-SIL-in)

Apo-Ampi ♦, Novo-Ampicillin ♦, Nu-Ampi ♦, Principen

ampicillin sodium

Ampicin ♦, Ampicyn Injection ◇, Penbritin ♦

ampicillin trihydrate

Ampicyn Oral ◇, D-Amp, Penbritin ◇, Totacillin

Pharmacologic class: aminopenicillin
Therapeutic class: antibiotic
Pregnancy risk category: B

Indications and dosages

▶ **Respiratory tract or skin and skin-structure infection.** *Adults and children weighing 40 kg (88 lb) or more:* 250 to 500 mg P.O. q 6 hours.

Children weighing less than 40 kg: 25 to 50 mg/kg/day P.O. in equally divided doses q 6 hours. Pediatric dosages shouldn't exceed recommended adult dosages.

▶ **GI infection, UTI.** *Adults and children weighing 40 kg (88 lb) or more:* 500 mg P.O. q 6 hours. For severe infections, larger doses may be needed.

Children weighing less than 40 kg: 50 to 100 mg/kg/day P.O. in equally divided doses q 6 hours.

▶ **Bacterial meningitis or septicemia.** *Adults:* 150 to 200 mg/kg/day I.V. in divided doses q 3 to 4 hours. May be given I.M. after 3 days of I.V. therapy. Maximum, 14 g daily.

Children: 100 to 200 mg/kg I.V. daily in divided doses q 3 to 4 hours. Give I.V. for 3 days; then give I.M.

▶ **Uncomplicated gonorrhea.** *Adults and children weighing more than 45 kg (99 lb):* 3.5 g P.O. with 1 g probenecid given as a single dose.

▶ **To prevent endocarditis in patients having dental procedures.** *Adults:* 2 g I.M. or I.V. within 30 minutes before procedure.

Children: 50 mg/kg I.M. or I.V. within 30 minutes before procedure.

Adjust-a-dose: In patients with severe renal impairment, increase drug interval to 12 hours. Use same dose.

I.V. administration

- Don't give I.V. unless infection is severe or patient can't take oral dose.
- For direct injection, reconstitute with bacteriostatic water for injection. Use 5 ml for 125-mg, 250-mg, or 500-mg vials; 7.4 ml for 1-g vials; and 14.8 ml for 2-g vials. Use initial dilution within 1 hour.
- Give direct I.V. injections over 3 to 5 minutes for doses of 500 mg or less; over 10 to 15 minutes for larger doses. Don't exceed 100 mg/minute.
- For an intermittent infusion, dilute in 50 to 100 ml of normal saline solution and give over 15 to 30 minutes. Follow manufacturer's directions for stability data when ampicillin is further diluted for I.V. infusion.
- Give intermittently to prevent vein irritation. Change site every 48 hours.

⊗ **Incompatibilities**

Amikacin, amino acid solutions, chlorpromazine, dextran solutions, dopamine, erythromycin lactobionate, 10% fat emulsions, fructose, gentamicin, heparin sodium, hetastarch, hydrocortisone sodium succinate, hydromorphone, kanamycin, lidocaine, lincomycin, polymyxin B, prochlorperazine edisylate, sodium bicarbonate, streptomycin, tobramycin.

Contraindications and cautions

• Contraindicated in patients hypersensitive to drug or other penicillins.
• Use cautiously in patients with other drug allergies, especially to cephalosporins (possible cross-sensitivity), and in those with mononucleosis (high risk of maculopapular rash).
Lifespan: In pregnant or breast-feeding women, use cautiously.

Adverse reactions

CNS: *seizures.*
CV: thrombophlebitis, vein irritation.
GI: nausea, vomiting, diarrhea, glossitis, stomatitis.
Hematologic: ***agranulocytosis,*** anemia, eosinophilia, ***leukopenia, thrombocytopenia, thrombocytopenic purpura.***
Other: hypersensitivity reactions (***anaphylaxis,*** maculopapular rash, urticaria), overgrowth of nonsusceptible organisms, pain at injection site.

Interactions

Drug-drug. *Allopurinol:* May increase risk of rash. Monitor patient.
Probenecid: May increase level of ampicillin and other penicillins. Probenecid may be used for this purpose.

Effects on lab test results

• May decrease hemoglobin level and hematocrit.
• May increase eosinophil count. May decrease platelet, WBC, and granulocyte counts.
• May cause false-positive urine glucose determinations with copper sulfate tests (Clinitest).

Pharmacokinetics

Absorption: About 42% after P.O. use; unknown after I.M. use.
Distribution: Into pleural, peritoneal, and synovial fluids; lungs; prostate; liver; gallbladder; middle ear effusions; maxillary sinus and bronchial secretions; tonsils; and sputum. Ampicillin is minimally protein-bound at 15% to 25%.
Metabolism: Only partial.
Excretion: In urine by renal tubular secretion and glomerular filtration. *Half-life:* About 1 to 1½ hours (10 to 24 hours in severe renal impairment).

Route	Onset	Peak	Duration
P.O.	Unknown	2 hr	6–8 hr
I.V.	Immediate	Immediate	Unknown
I.M.	Unknown	1 hr	Unknown

Action

Chemical effect: Inhibits cell-wall synthesis during microorganism multiplication.
Therapeutic effect: Kills susceptible bacteria, including non-penicillinase–producing gram-positive bacteria and many gram-negative organisms.

Available forms

Capsules: 250 mg, 500 mg
Infusion: 500 mg, 1 g, 2 g
Injection: 125 mg, 250 mg, 500 mg, 1 g, 2 g
Oral suspension: 125 mg/5 ml, 250 mg/5 ml (after reconstitution)

NURSING PROCESS

Assessment

• Obtain history of patient's infection before therapy, and observe throughout therapy to assess improvement.
• Ask patient about previous allergic reaction to penicillin. A negative history of penicillin allergy doesn't rule out future reaction.
• Obtain specimen for culture and sensitivity tests before giving first dose.
• Be alert for adverse reactions and drug interactions.
• If adverse GI reactions occur, monitor patient's hydration status.
• Assess patient's and family's knowledge of drug therapy.

Nursing diagnoses

• Risk for infection related to presence of susceptible bacterial infection
• Risk for deficient fluid volume related to drug-induced adverse GI reactions
• Deficient knowledge related to drug therapy

Planning and implementation

• Give orally either 1 hour before or 2 hours after meals. Food may interfere with absorption.
• Don't give I.M. unless infection is severe or patient can't take oral dose.
• Give at least 1 hour before bacteriostatic antibiotics.

• In children with meningitis, give with parenteral chloramphenicol for 24 hours pending culture results.
• If anaphylaxis occurs, stop drug immediately. Notify prescriber, and prepare to give immediate treatment, such as epinephrine, corticosteroids, antihistamines, and other resuscitative measures.

Patient teaching

• Tell patient to take entire quantity of drug exactly as prescribed, even after feeling better.
• Tell patient to call prescriber if a rash (most common), fever, or chills develop.
• Warn patient never to use leftover ampicillin for a new illness or to share it with others.
• Advise patient to take oral ampicillin 1 hour before or 2 hours after meals for best absorption.

Evaluation

• Patient is free from infection.
• Patient maintains adequate hydration.
• Patient and family state understanding of drug therapy.

ampicillin sodium and sulbactam sodium

(am-pih-SIL-in SOH-dee-um and sul-BAC-tam SOH-dee-um)

Unasyn

Pharmacologic class: aminopenicillin and beta-lactamase inhibitor
Therapeutic class: antibiotic
Pregnancy risk category: B

Indications and dosages

▶ **Intra-abdominal, gynecologic, and skin and skin-structure infections caused by susceptible gram-positive, gram-negative, and beta-lactamase–producing strains.** *Adults:* Dosage expressed as total drug (each 1.5-g vial contains 1 g ampicillin sodium and 0.5 g sulbactam sodium). 1.5 to 3 g I.M. or I.V. q 6 hours. Maximum, 4 g sulbactam (12 g of combined drugs) daily.
▶ **Skin and skin-structure infections caused by susceptible organisms.** *Children older than age 1:* Give 300 mg/kg I.V. daily in equally divided doses q 6 hours. Give children a maximum of 14 days of therapy. Children weighing 40 kg (88 lb) or more may receive the usual adult dosage shown above.
▶ **Pelvic inflammatory disease.** *Adults and children:* 3 g (2 g ampicillin and 1 g sulbactam) I.V. or I.M. q 6 hours, given with doxycycline 100 mg P.O. q 12 hours. Continue parenteral therapy for 24 hours after clinical improvement. Continue with oral doxycycline 100 mg P.O. b.i.d. to complete the 14-day cycle.

I.V. administration

• When preparing injection, reconstitute powder with any of the following diluents: normal saline solution, D_5W, lactated Ringer's solution, 1/6 M sodium lactate, dextrose 5% in half-normal saline solution for injection, or 10% invert sugar. Stability varies with diluent, temperature, and concentration of solution.
• After reconstitution, let vials stand for a few minutes to let foam to dissipate and permit visual inspection of contents for particles.
• Give dose by injection over 10 to 15 minutes, or dilute in 50 to 100 ml of a compatible diluent and infuse over 15 to 30 minutes. If permitted, give intermittently to prevent vein irritation. Change site every 48 hours.

⊗ **Incompatibilities**

Amikacin, amino acid solutions, chlorpromazine, dextran solutions, dopamine, erythromycin lactobionate, 10% fat emulsions, fructose, gentamicin, heparin sodium, hetastarch, hydrocortisone sodium succinate, kanamycin, lidocaine, lincomycin, netilmicin, polymyxin B, prochlorperazine edisylate, sodium bicarbonate, streptomycin, tobramycin. Don't add or mix with other drugs because they might be physically or chemically incompatible.

Contraindications and cautions

• Contraindicated in patients hypersensitive to drug or other penicillins.
• Use cautiously in patients with other drug allergies, especially to cephalosporins (possible cross-sensitivity), and in those with mononucleosis (high risk of maculopapular rash).
Lifespan: In pregnant and breast-feeding women, use cautiously. In children younger than age 1, safety of drug hasn't been established. In children age 1 and older, drug can be used I.V. for skin and skin-structure infections. Children shouldn't receive the drug I.M.

Adverse reactions

CV: thrombophlebitis, vein irritation.
GI: *diarrhea,* glossitis, nausea, stomatitis, vomiting.
Hematologic: ***agranulocytosis,*** anemia, eosinophilia, ***leukopenia, thrombocytopenia, thrombocytopenic purpura.***
Other: hypersensitivity reactions (***anaphylaxis,*** erythematous maculopapular rash, urticaria), overgrowth of nonsusceptible organisms, pain at injection site.

Interactions

Drug-drug. *Allopurinol:* May increase risk of rash. Monitor patient.
Hormonal contraceptives: May decrease effectiveness of hormonal contraceptives. Advise patient to use barrier contraception until therapy is complete.
Probenecid: May increase ampicillin level. Probenecid may be used for this purpose.

Effects on lab test results

- May increase BUN, creatinine, ALT, AST, alkaline phosphatase, bilirubin, LDH, CK, and GGT levels. May decrease hemoglobin level and hematocrit.
- May increase eosinophil count. May decrease platelet, WBC, and granulocyte counts.
- May cause false-positive urine glucose determinations with copper sulfate tests (Clinitest).

Pharmacokinetics

Absorption: Given I.V.
Distribution: Both drugs into pleural, peritoneal, and synovial fluids; lungs; prostate; liver; gallbladder; middle ear effusions; maxillary sinus and bronchial secretions; tonsils; and sputum. Ampicillin is minimally protein-bound at 15% to 25%; sulbactam is about 38% protein-bound.
Metabolism: Both drugs only partially.
Excretion: Both drugs in urine by renal tubular secretion and glomerular filtration. *Half-life:* 1 to 1½ hours (10 to 24 hours in severe renal impairment).

Route	Onset	Peak	Duration
I.V.	Immediate	Immediate	Unknown
I.M.	Unknown	Unknown	Unknown

Action

Chemical effect: Ampicillin inhibits cell-wall synthesis during microorganism multiplication; sulbactam inactivates bacterial beta-lactamase, the enzyme that inactivates ampicillin and provides bacterial resistance to it.
Therapeutic effect: Kills susceptible bacteria.

Available forms

Injection: Vials and piggyback vials containing 1.5 g (1 g ampicillin sodium with 0.5 g sulbactam sodium); 3 g (2 g ampicillin sodium with 1 g sulbactam sodium)

NURSING PROCESS

Assessment

- Obtain history of patient's infection before therapy, and observe throughout therapy to determine improvement.
- Ask patient about previous allergic reaction to penicillin. A negative history of penicillin allergy doesn't rule out future reaction.
- Obtain specimen for culture and sensitivity tests before giving first dose.
- Be alert for adverse reactions and drug interactions.
- Monitor patient's hydration status if adverse GI reactions occur.
- Assess patient's and family's knowledge of drug therapy.

Nursing diagnoses

- Risk for infection related to presence of susceptible bacterial infection
- Risk for deficient fluid volume related to drug-induced adverse GI reactions
- Deficient knowledge related to drug therapy

Planning and implementation

- When giving drug I.M., reconstitute with sterile water for injection or with 0.5% or 2% lidocaine hydrochloride. Add 3.2 ml to a 1.5-g vial (or 6.4 ml to a 3-g vial) to yield 375 mg/ml. Give deep into muscle.
- In patients with renal impairment, dosage should be reduced.
- Give drug at least 1 hour before bacteriostatic antibiotics.
- Stop drug immediately if anaphylaxis occurs. Notify prescriber and give immediate treatment, such as epinephrine, corticosteroids, antihistamines; and other resuscitative measures.

A

Patient teaching

• Tell patient to call prescriber if rash (most common), fever, or chills develop.
• Advise women taking hormonal contraceptives to use a barrier form of contraception during drug therapy.

Evaluation

• Patient is free from infection.
• Patient maintains adequate hydration.
• Patient and family state understanding of drug therapy.

amprenavir
(am-PREH-nah-veer)
Agenerase

Pharmacologic class: protease inhibitor
Therapeutic class: antiretroviral
Pregnancy risk category: C

Indications and dosages

▶ **HIV-1 infection, with other antiretrovirals.** *Adults and children ages 13 to 16 weighing 50 kg (110 lb) or more:* 1,200 mg (capsules) P.O. b.i.d. or 1,400 mg oral solution b.i.d. with other antiretrovirals. Capsules and oral solution aren't interchangeable on a milligram-per-milligram basis.
Children ages 4 to 12 or 13 to 16 weighing less than 50 kg (110 lb): Give 20 mg/kg P.O. capsules b.i.d. or 15 mg/kg P.O. t.i.d. (maximum, 2,400 mg daily) with other antiretrovirals. Or, give 22.5 mg/kg (1.5 ml/kg) oral solution P.O. b.i.d. or 17 mg/kg (1.1 ml/kg) P.O. t.i.d. (maximum, 2,800 mg daily) with other antiretrovirals. Capsules and oral solution aren't interchangeable on a milligram-per-milligram basis.
Adjust-a-dose: For patients with hepatic impairment and a Child-Pugh score of 5 to 8, reduce dosage to 450-mg capsules P.O. b.i.d. Or 513 mg (34 ml) oral solution P.O. b.i.d.

For patients with hepatic impairment and a Child-Pugh score of 9 to 12, reduce dosage to 300-mg capsules P.O. b.i.d. or 342 mg (23 ml) oral solution P.O. b.i.d.

Contraindications and cautions

• Contraindicated in patients hypersensitive to drug or its components and in patients taking disulfiram, metronidazole (oral solution), ergot derivatives, cisapride, pimozide, midazolam, triazolam, or drugs dependent on the CYP3A4 enzyme pathway.
• Use cautiously in patients with moderate or severe hepatic impairment, diabetes mellitus, sulfonamide allergy, or hemophilia A or B.
• Drug can cause severe or life-threatening rash, including Stevens-Johnson syndrome. Stop therapy if patient develops a severe or life-threatening rash or a moderate rash with systemic signs and symptoms.
Lifespan: In pregnant women, use only if potential benefits outweigh risks; no adequate studies exist. In children age 4 and younger, drug is contraindicated because of risk of toxicity.

Adverse reactions

CNS: depressive or mood disorders, headache, *paresthesia.*
GI: diarrhea or loose stools, nausea, taste disorders, vomiting.
Hepatic: hypercholesterolemia, hypertriglyceridemia.
Metabolic: hyperglycemia.
Skin: rash, ***Stevens-Johnson syndrome.***

Interactions

Drug-drug. *Antacids:* May interfere with absorption. Separate doses by at least 1 hour.
Antiarrhythmics (amiodarone, systemic lidocaine, quinidine), anticoagulants (warfarin), cyclosporine, tacrolimus, tricyclic antidepressants: May affect levels of these drugs. Monitor patient closely.
Calcium channel blockers, dihydroergotamine, midazolam, rifampin, triazolam: May cause serious or life-threatening interactions. Avoid use together.
Cimetidine, indinavir, nelfinavir, ritonavir: May increase amprenavir level. Monitor patient closely for increased adverse effects.
Efavirenz: May decrease availability of amprenavir. Increase dose accordingly.
Ethinyl estradiol and norethindrone: May cause loss of virologic response and possible resistance to amprenavir. Tell patient to use alternative method of birth control.
HMG-CoA reductase inhibitors (atorvastatin, lovastatin, simvastatin): May increase levels of these drugs and increase risk of myopathy, including rhabdomyolysis. Avoid use together.

Indinavir, nelfinavir, ritonavir: May increase amprenavir level. Monitor patient closely.
Itraconazole, ketoconazole: May increase levels of both drugs. Monitor patient closely for adverse reactions.
Macrolides: May increase amprenavir level. No adjustment needed.
Methadone: May decrease amprenavir level. Alternative antiretroviral or pain therapy should be considered. Methadone dosage may need to be increased.
Psychotherapeutic drugs: May increase CNS effects. Monitor patient closely.
Rifabutin: May decrease exposure of amprenavir to the body and increase rifabutin level by 200%. Decrease rifabutin dosage to 150 mg daily or 300 mg two to three times weekly.
Saquinavir: May decrease exposure of amprenavir to the body. Monitor patient closely.
Sildenafil, tadalafil, vardenafil: May increase levels of these drugs, increasing risk of adverse effects, including hypotension and priapism. Don't exceed recommended dose restrictions.
Drug-herb. *St. John's wort:* May decrease amprenavir level. Avoid use together.
Drug-food. *Grapefruit juice:* May affect blood levels of amprenavir. Monitor patient closely.
High-fat meals: May reduce drug absorption. Discourage taking drug with a high-fat meal.

Effects on lab test results

- May increase glucose, triglyceride, AST, ALT, and cholesterol levels.

Pharmacokinetics

Absorption: Rapid.
Distribution: Apparent volume of distribution is about 430 L. In vitro, about 90% of drug binds to plasma proteins.
Metabolism: By CYP3A4 enzymes in the liver.
Excretion: Minimal, in urine and feces. *Elimination half-life:* 7 to 10½ hours.

Route	Onset	Peak	Duration
P.O.	Unknown	1–2 hr	Unknown

Action

Chemical effect: Inhibits HIV-1 protease by binding to the active site of HIV-1 protease, which causes immature noninfectious viral particles to form.
Therapeutic effect: Reduces symptoms of HIV-1 infection.

Available forms

Capsules: 50 mg
Oral solution: 15 mg/ml

NURSING PROCESS

Assessment

- Assess patient for appropriateness of drug therapy.
- Because drug may interact with other drugs, obtain patient's complete drug history.
- Patients with moderate or severe hepatic impairment, diabetes mellitus, sulfonamide allergy, or hemophilia A or B must be monitored very closely while taking this drug.
- Determine whether patient is pregnant or plans to become pregnant.
- Assess patient's and family's knowledge about drug therapy.

Nursing diagnoses

- Risk for infection secondary to presence of HIV
- Ineffective coping related to HIV infection
- Deficient knowledge related to drug therapy

Planning and implementation

- Don't give patient high-fat foods because high-fat foods may decrease absorption of oral drug.

ALERT: Amprenavir capsules aren't interchangeable with amprenavir oral solution on a milligram-per-milligram basis.

- Monitor coagulation studies. Drug provides high daily doses of vitamin E.
- Protease inhibitors cause spontaneous bleeding in some patients with hemophilia A or B. In some patients, additional factor VIII may be required. Treatment with protease inhibitors can then continue.

Patient teaching

- Inform patient that drug doesn't cure HIV infection and that opportunistic infections and other complications may develop. Also explain that drug doesn't reduce the risk of transmitting HIV to others.
- Tell patient that drug can be taken with or without food but shouldn't be taken with a high-fat meal because doing so may decrease drug absorption.
- Urge patient to report adverse reactions, especially rash.

• Warn patient that drug may cause a redistribution of body fat, including central obesity, dorsocervical fat enlargement (buffalo hump), peripheral wasting, breast enlargement, and cushingoid appearance.
• Advise patient to take drug every day as prescribed, always with other antiretrovirals. Warn against changing the dosage or stopping the drug without prescriber's approval.
• If patient takes an antacid or didanosine, tell him to do so 1 hour before or after amprenavir to avoid interfering with amprenavir absorption.
• If patient misses a dose by more than 4 hours, tell him to wait and take the next dose at the regularly scheduled time. If he misses a dose by less than 4 hours, tell him to take the dose as soon as possible and then take the next dose at the regularly scheduled time. Caution against doubling the dose.
• Advise patient not to take supplemental vitamin E because high levels of this vitamin may worsen the blood coagulation defect of vitamin K deficiency caused by anticoagulant therapy or malabsorption.
• If patient uses a hormonal contraceptive, warn her to use another contraceptive during amprenavir therapy.
• Urge patient to notify prescriber about planned, suspected, or known pregnancy during therapy.
• Advise patient taking sildenafil, tadalafil, or vardenafil of the increased risk of adverse affects, including hypotension, visual changes, and priapism. Tell patient not to exceed 25 mg of sildenafil in a 48-hour period and to promptly report symptoms to the prescriber.

☑ Evaluation

• Patient exhibits reduced signs and symptoms of infection.
• Patient demonstrates adequate coping mechanisms.
• Patient and family state understanding of drug therapy.

anakinra

(ann-uh-KIN-ruh)
Kineret

Pharmacologic class: recombinant human interleukin-1 receptor antagonist
Therapeutic class: disease-modifying antirheumatic drug (DMARD)
Pregnancy risk category: B

Indications and dosages

▶ **Reduction in signs and symptoms and slowing of structural damage in moderate-to-severe active rheumatoid arthritis (RA) after one failure with DMARDs, used alone or combined with DMARDs other than tumor necrosis factor (TNF) blockers.** *Adults:* 100 mg subcutaneously daily.

Contraindications and cautions

• Contraindicated in patients hypersensitive to *Escherichia coli*–derived proteins or components of the product. Don't use in immunosuppressed patients or in those with chronic or active infection.
• Use caution with TNF blockers because of the increased risk of neutropenia.
Lifespan: In pregnant women, use only if necessary because no adequate, well-controlled studies exist. In breast-feeding women, use cautiously because it's unknown whether drug appears in breast milk. In patients with juvenile RA, safety and effectiveness of drug haven't been established. In elderly patients, use drug cautiously because they have a greater risk of infection and are more likely to have renal impairment.

Adverse reactions

CNS: headache.
EENT: sinusitis.
GI: abdominal pain, diarrhea, nausea.
Hematologic: ***neutropenia.***
Respiratory: upper respiratory tract infection.
Other: infection (bone and joint, cellulitis, pneumonia), flulike symptoms, injection site reactions (ecchymosis, erythema, inflammation, pain).

Interactions

Drug-drug. *Etanercept, other TNF blockers:* May increase risk of severe infection. Use together cautiously.
Vaccines: May decrease effectiveness of vaccines or increase risk of secondary transmission of infection with live vaccines. Avoid use together.

Effects on lab test results

• May increase differential percentage of eosinophils. May decrease neutrophil, WBC, and platelet counts.

Pharmacokinetics

Absorption: Absolute bioavailability is 95% after a 70-mg subcutaneous injection.
Distribution: In plasma.
Metabolism: Unknown.
Excretion: Renal. Clearance increases with increasing creatinine clearance and body weight. Mean plasma clearance decreases 70% to 75% in patients with creatinine clearance less than 30 ml/minute. *Half-life:* 4 to 6 hours.

Route	Onset	Peak	Duration
SubQ	Unknown	3–7 hr	Unknown

Action

Chemical effect: A recombinant, nonglycosylated form of the human interleukin-1 receptor antagonist (IL-1Ra). The level of naturally occurring IL-1Ra in synovium and synovial fluid from patients with RA isn't enough to compete with the elevated level of locally produced IL-1. Drug blocks the activity of IL-1 by competitively inhibiting IL-1 from binding to the interleukin-1–type receptors.
Therapeutic effect: Decreases inflammation and cartilage degradation.

Available forms

Injection: 100 mg/ml in prefilled glass syringe

NURSING PROCESS

Assessment

• Assess patient before therapy for signs and symptoms of chronic or active infection. If patient has active infection, don't start treatment.
• Obtain neutrophil count before treatment, monthly for the first 3 months of treatment, and then quarterly for up to 1 year.
• Monitor patient for infections and injection site reactions.

Nursing diagnoses

• Risk for infection related to anakinra therapy
• Chronic pain from underlying rheumatoid arthritis
• Risk for impaired skin integrity from injection site reaction

Planning and implementation

• Inject the entire contents of the prefilled syringe subcutaneously.
• Stop drug if patient develops a serious infection.
ALERT: Don't confuse anakinra with amikacin.

Patient teaching

• Tell patient to store drug in refrigerator and not to freeze or expose to excessive heat. Tell patient to allow drug to come to room temperature before injecting.
• Teach patient proper technique for administration and disposal of syringes in a puncture-resistant container. Also, warn patient not to reuse needles.
• Urge patient to rotate injection sites.
• Review with patient the signs and symptoms of allergic and other adverse reactions and the symptoms of infection. Urge patient to contact prescriber immediately if they arise. Inform patient that injection site reactions are common, are usually mild, and typically last 14 to 28 days.
• Tell patient to avoid live-virus vaccines while taking anakinra.

Evaluation

• Patient is free from infection or adverse reactions during drug therapy.
• Patient's symptoms of RA are relieved.
• Patient and family state understanding of drug therapy and give drug properly.

anastrozole

(uh-NASS-truh-zohl)
Arimidex

Pharmacologic class: nonsteroidal aromatase inhibitor
Therapeutic class: antineoplastic
Pregnancy risk category: D

Indications and dosages

▶ **First-line therapy for hormone-receptor–positive or hormone-receptor–unknown locally advanced or metastatic breast cancer; advanced breast cancer with disease progression following tamoxifen; adjuvant therapy for hormone-receptor–positive early breast cancer.** *Postmenopausal women:* 1 mg P.O. daily.

Contraindications and cautions

• Contraindicated in patients hypersensitive to the drug or its components.

• Use cautiously in patients with hepatic impairment.

Lifespan: In pregnant women, drug isn't recommended because it may cause fetal harm. In breast-feeding women, use cautiously. In children, safety of drug hasn't been established.

Adverse reactions

CNS: anxiety, asthenia, depression, dizziness, headache, insomnia, pain, paresthesia.
CV: chest pain, edema, hypertension, peripheral edema, ***thromboembolic disease,*** *vasodilation.*
EENT: cataracts, pharyngitis.
GI: abdominal pain, anorexia, constipation, diarrhea, dry mouth, nausea, vomiting.
GU: pelvic pain, vaginal dryness, ***vaginal hemorrhage.***
Metabolic: increased appetite, weight gain.
Musculoskeletal: arthralgia, back pain, bone pain.
Respiratory: dyspnea, increased cough.
Skin: rash, sweating.
Other: *hot flushes.*

Interactions

Drug-drug. *Estrogen-containing therapies, tamoxifen:* May decrease anastrazole's effect. Avoid use together.

Effects on lab test results

• May increase liver enzyme and cholesterol levels.

Pharmacokinetics

Absorption: Food doesn't affect extent of absorption.
Distribution: 40% bound to plasma proteins.
Metabolism: In liver.
Excretion: In urine. *Half-life:* About 50 hours.

Route	Onset	Peak	Duration
P.O.	Unknown	Unknown	Unknown

Action

Chemical effect: Lowers estradiol level.
Therapeutic effect: Hinders cancer cell growth.

Available forms

Tablets: 1 mg

NURSING PROCESS

Assessment

• Obtain history of patient's neoplastic disease before therapy.

• Be alert for adverse reactions.

• Assess patient's and family's knowledge of drug therapy.

Nursing diagnoses

• Ineffective health maintenance related to neoplastic disease

• Risk for deficient fluid volume related to drug-induced adverse GI reactions

• Deficient knowledge related to drug therapy

Planning and implementation

• Rule out pregnancy before treatment begins.

• Give drug under supervision of a prescriber experienced in using antineoplastics.

• Patients with hormone-receptor–negative disease and those who didn't respond to previous tamoxifen therapy, rarely respond to anastrozole.

• Patients with advanced breast cancer should continue therapy until tumor progresses.

Patient teaching

• Instruct patient to report adverse reactions.

• Stress importance of follow-up care.

Evaluation

• Patient has positive response to therapy.

• Patient maintains adequate hydration.

• Patient and family state understanding of drug therapy.

anidulafungin

(uh-nigh-doo-lah-FUN-jin)
Eraxis

Pharmacologic class: echinocandin
Therapeutic class: antifungal
Pregnancy risk category: C

Indications and dosages

▶ **Candidemia and other *Candida* infections (intra-abdominal abscess, peritonitis).** *Adults:* A single 200-mg loading dose given by I.V. infusion at no more than 1.1 mg/minute on day 1; then 100 mg daily for at least 14 days after last positive culture.

▶ **Esophageal candidiasis.** *Adults:* A single 100-mg loading dose given by I.V. infusion at no more than 1.1 mg/minute on day 1; then 50 mg daily for at least 14 days and for at least 7 more days after symptoms resolve.

I.V. administration

• Reconstitute each vial with 15 ml of supplied diluent.
• Further dilute with D_5W or normal saline solution to a final concentration of 0.5 mg/ml.
• For 50-mg dose, add to 85 ml for final infusion volume of 100 ml. For 100-mg dose, add to 170 ml for final infusion volume of 200 ml. For 200-mg dose, add to 340 ml for final infusion volume of 400 ml.
• Don't infuse at more than 1.1 mg/minute.
• Store at room temperature; don't freeze. Use reconstituted solution within 24 hours of preparation.

⊗ **Incompatibilities**
Unknown. Use only supplied diluent to reconstitute and D_5W or normal saline solution to further dilute.

Contraindications and cautions

• Contraindicated in patients hypersensitive to anidulafungin, other echinocandins, or any component of the drug.
• Use cautiously in patients with liver impairment.
Lifespan: In pregnant or breast-feeding women, use cautiously. In children, safety and effectiveness haven't been established.

Adverse reactions

CNS: headache.
CV: deep vein thrombosis, hypotension.
GI: abdominal pain, dyspepsia, nausea, vomiting.
Hematologic: ***leukopenia, neutropenia.***
Metabolic: hypokalemia.
Skin: flushing, pruritus, rash, urticaria.

Interactions

None reported.

Effects on lab test results

• May increase AST, ALT, alkaline phosphatase, GGT, hepatic enzyme, amylase, lipase, bilirubin, CK, creatinine, urea, calcium, glucose, potassium, and sodium levels. May decrease potassium and magnesium levels.
• May increase PT. May decrease neutrophil and WBC counts. May increase or decrease platelet count.

Pharmacokinetics

Absorption: Given I.V.
Distribution: Short distribution half-life; 84% bound to plasma proteins.
Metabolism: No observable hepatic metabolism.
Excretion: About 30% in feces; less than 1% in urine.

Route	Onset	Peak	Duration
I.V.	< 24 hr	Unknown	Unknown

Action

Chemical effect: Inhibits glucan synthase, which in turn inhibits formation of 1,3-β-D-glucan, an essential component of fungal cell walls.
Therapeutic effect: Kills susceptible fungi.

Available forms

Powder for injection: 50 mg/vial with companion diluent

NURSING PROCESS

Assessment

• Obtain specimens for culture and sensitivity tests and baseline laboratory tests before therapy begins.
• Monitor patient closely for changes in liver function and blood cell counts during therapy.
• Assess patient for signs or symptoms of liver toxicity, such as dark urine, jaundice, abdominal pain, and fatigue; notify prescriber.
• Assess patient and family's knowledge of drug therapy.

Nursing diagnoses

• Risk for infection related to presence of fungal infection and drug-induced leukopenia and neutropenia
• Risk for injury related to drug-induced liver toxicity
• Deficient knowledge related to drug therapy

Planning and implementation

• Use only the supplied diluent to reconstitute powder.

• To avoid histamine-mediated symptoms, such as rash, urticaria, flushing, itching, dyspnea, and hypotension, don't infuse more than 1.1 mg/minute.
• Patients with esophageal candidiasis who are HIV-positive may need suppressive antifungal therapy after anidulafungin treatment to prevent relapse.
• In case of overdose, monitor laboratory tests, especially liver function tests; drug isn't dialyzable.

Patient teaching
• Tell patient to report a rash, itching, trouble breathing, or other adverse effects during infusion.
• Explain that blood tests will be needed to monitor the drug's effects.

Evaluation
• Patient is free from infection.
• Patient does not experience symptoms of liver toxicity.
• Patient and family state understanding of drug therapy.

apomorphine hydrochloride
(ah-poe-MORE-feen high-droh-KLOR-ighd)
Apokyn

Pharmacologic class: dopamine agonist
Therapeutic class: antiparkinsonian drug
Pregnancy risk category: C

Indications and dosages

▶ **Intermittent hypomobility, "off" episodes caused by advanced Parkinson disease (with an antiemetic).** *Adults:* Initially, give a 0.2-ml test dose subcutaneously. Measure supine and standing blood pressure q 20 minutes for the first hour. If patient tolerates and responds to drug, start with 0.2 ml subcutaneously p.r.n. (outpatient). Separate doses by at least 2 hours. Increase by 0.1 ml every few days, as needed.

If initial 0.2-ml dose is ineffective but tolerated, give 0.4 ml at next "off" period, measuring supine and standing blood pressure q 20 minutes for the first hour. If drug is tolerated, start with 0.3 ml (outpatient). If needed, increase by 0.1 ml every few days.

If patient doesn't tolerate 0.4-ml dose, give 0.3 ml as a test dose at the next "off" period, measuring supine and standing blood pressure as before. If drug is tolerated, give 0.2 ml (outpatient). Increase by 0.1 ml every few days, p.r.n., but doses higher than 0.4 ml usually aren't tolerated if 0.2 ml is the starting dose.

Maximum recommended dose is usually 0.6 ml p.r.n. Most patients take drug about three times daily. Experience is limited at more than five times daily or more than 2 ml daily.

Adjust-a-dose: In patients with mild to moderate renal impairment, the test and starting doses should be 0.1 ml, given subcutaneously.

Contraindications and cautions

• Contraindicated in patients allergic to apomorphine or its ingredients, including sulfites, and in patients who take 5-HT_3 antagonists.
• Use cautiously in patients at risk for prolonged QTc interval, such as those with hypokalemia, hypomagnesemia, bradycardia, or genetic predisposition. Also use cautiously in patients with cardiovascular or cerebrovascular disease and in those with renal or hepatic impairment.

Lifespan: In pregnant and breast-feeding women, drug effects are unknown. Give drug only if clearly needed. In children, safety and effectiveness haven't been established.

Adverse reactions

CNS: aggravated Parkinson disease, anxiety, *confusion,* depression, *dizziness, drowsiness,* fatigue, *hallucinations,* headache, insomnia, *somnolence,* syncope, weakness.
CV: *angina,* ***cardiac arrest,*** *chest pain, chest pressure, edema, flushing,* ***heart failure,*** *hypotension, orthostatic hypotension,* ***MI.***
EENT: *rhinorrhea.*
GI: constipation, diarrhea, *nausea, vomiting.*
GU: UTI.
Metabolic: dehydration.
Musculoskeletal: arthralgia, back pain, *dyskinesias,* limb pain.
Respiratory: dyspnea, pneumonia.
Skin: bruising, injection site reaction, pallor, sweating.
Other: *falls, yawning.*

Interactions

Drug-drug. *Antihypertensives, vasodilators:* May increase risk of hypotension, MI, pneumonia, falls, and joint injury. Use together cautiously.

Dopamine antagonists, metoclopramide: May reduce apomorphine effectiveness. Use together cautiously.
Drugs that prolong the QTc interval: May prolong the QTc interval. Give cautiously with other drugs that prolong QTc interval.
5-HT$_3$ antagonists (alosetron, dolasetron, granisetron, ondansetron, palonosetron): May cause serious hypotension and loss of consciousness. Use together is contraindicated.
Drug-lifestyle. *Alcohol use:* May increase risk of sedation and hypotension. Discourage use together.

Effects on lab test results

None known.

Pharmacokinetics

Absorption: Rapid. Patients with hepatic or renal impairment may have higher serum level.
Distribution: Large, but CSF penetration is poor.
Metabolism: Unknown.
Excretion: Unknown. *Elimination half-life:* About 30 to 60 minutes in patients with normal or impaired renal function.

Route	Onset	Peak	Duration
SubQ	20 min	10–60 min	2 hr

Action

Chemical effect: Improves motor function by stimulating dopamine D2 receptors in the caudate-putamen area of the brain.
Therapeutic effect: Relieves signs and symptoms of parkinsonism.

Available forms

Solution for injection: 10 mg/ml (contains benzyl alcohol)

NURSING PROCESS

Assessment

- Monitor supine and standing blood pressure every 20 minutes for the first hour after therapy starts or dosage changes.

ALERT: Monitor patient for drowsiness or sleepiness, which may occur well after treatment starts. Stop drug if patient develops significant daytime sleepiness that interferes with activities of daily living.

- Watch for evidence of coronary or cerebral ischemia, and stop drug if they occur.
- Assess elderly patients carefully because adverse effects are more likely in elderly patients, particularly hallucinations, falls, CV events, respiratory problems, and GI effects.
- Assess patient's and family's knowledge of drug therapy.

Nursing diagnoses

- Impaired physical mobility related to presence of parkinsonism
- Risk for deficient fluid volume related to drug-induced nausea and vomiting
- Deficient knowledge related to drug therapy

Planning and implementation

ALERT: Drug is for subcutaneous injection only. Avoid I.V. use.

- Give with an antiemetic to avoid severe nausea and vomiting. Start with trimethobenzamide 300 mg P.O. t.i.d. 3 days before starting apomorphine, and continue antiemetic at least 2 months.

ALERT: The prescribed dose should always be specified in milliliters rather than milligrams to avoid confusion. The dosing pen is marked in milliliters.

- When programming the dosing pen, it's possible to select the appropriate dose even though insufficient drug remains in the pen. To avoid insufficient dosing, track the amount of drug received at each dose and change the cartridge before drug runs out.
- Give test dose in a medically supervised setting to determine tolerability and effect.

Patient teaching

- Tell patient to avoid sudden position changes, especially rising too quickly from lying down. A sudden drop in blood pressure, dizziness, or fainting can occur.
- Urge patient to keep taking the prescribed antiemetic because nausea and vomiting are likely.
- Instruct patient or caregiver to document each dose to make sure enough drug remains in the cartridge to provide a full next dose.
- Tell patient or caregiver to wait at least 2 hours between doses.
- Show patient or caregiver how to read the dosing pen, and make sure he understands that it's marked in milliliters and not milligrams.
- Tell patient or caregiver to rotate injection sites and to wash hands before each injection.

Applying ice to the site before and after the injection may reduce soreness, redness, pain, itching, swelling, or bruising at the site.

- Explain that hallucinations (either visual or auditory) may occur, and urge patient or caregiver to report them immediately.
- Explain that headaches may occur, and urge patient or caregiver to notify the prescriber if they become severe or don't go away.
- Advise patient to avoid hazardous activities that require alertness until drug effects are known.
- Caution patient to avoid consuming alcohol.

Evaluation

- Patient has improved physical mobility.
- Patient doesn't experience nausea and vomiting.
- Patient and family state understanding of drug therapy.

aprepitant

(uh-pre-PIH-tant)
Emend

Pharmacologic class: substance P and neurokinin-1 receptor antagonist
Therapeutic class: centrally acting antiemetic
Pregnancy risk category: B

Indications and dosages

▶ **To prevent nausea and vomiting after moderately or highly emetogenic chemotherapy (including cisplatin); given with a 5-HT_3 antagonist and a corticosteroid.** *Adults:* 125 mg P.O. on day 1 of treatment (1 hour before chemotherapy); then 80 mg P.O. q a.m. on days 2 and 3. Single doses up to 600 mg of aprepitant have been well tolerated.

▶ **Prevention of postoperative nausea and vomiting.** *Adults:* 40 mg P.O. within 3 hours before induction of anesthesia.

Contraindications and cautions

- Contraindicated in patients hypersensitive to drug or its components and in those taking cisapride or pimozide because drug may increase pimozide level, causing life-threatening reactions such as ventricular arrhythmias.
- Administration beyond 3 days per cycle of chemotherapy isn't recommended because of the potential for CYP3A4- and CYP2C9-related drug interactions.

Lifespan: In pregnant women, use with caution; drug hasn't been well studied. In breastfeeding women, use cautiously because it's unknown whether drug appears in breast milk. In children, safety and effectiveness haven't been established.

Adverse reactions

CNS: dizziness, *fatigue,* headache, insomnia.
CV: ***bradycardia,*** hypertension, hypotension.
EENT: tinnitus.
GI: abdominal pain, *anorexia, constipation, diarrhea,* gastritis, *nausea,* vomiting.
GU: proteinuria, UTI.
Hematologic: anemia, ***febrile neutropenia, neutropenia.***
Respiratory: *hiccups.*
Skin: drug-induced rash with urticaria, pruritus, ***Stevens-Johnson syndrome.***
Other: ***angioedema.***

Interactions

Drug-drug. *Benzodiazepines, such as alprazolam and midazolam:* May increase levels of these drugs. Monitor patient for increased sedation and other CNS effects. Decrease benzodiazepine dose by 50% if use together is necessary.
Chemotherapy metabolized by CYP3A4, such as etoposide, ifosfamide, irinotecan, taxanes, and vinca alkaloids: May increase levels of these drugs, leading to increased toxicity. Avoid using together if possible.
Corticosteroids: May increase levels of these drugs, leading to increased toxicity. Decrease the dose of corticosteroids by 50% if use together is necessary.
CYP3A4 inducers (carbamazepine, phenytoin, rifampin): May decrease aprepitant level and decrease antiemetic effect. Avoid use together if possible.
CYP3A4 inhibitors (azole antifungals, diltiazem, erythromycin, nelfinavir, ritonavir): May increase aprepitant level, leading to increased toxicity. Avoid use together if possible.
Diltiazem: May increase diltiazem level. Monitor heart rate and blood pressure. Avoid use together if possible.
Hormonal contraceptives: May decrease the effectiveness of these drugs. If drugs must be used

together, tell woman to use an additional form of birth control.
Phenytoin: May decrease phenytoin level. Avoid use together if possible. Monitor phenytoin level carefully; increase dose if needed.
SSRIs: May decrease the effectiveness of these drugs. Avoid use together if possible.
Tolbutamide: May decrease tolbutamide effectiveness. Monitor glucose level carefully.
Warfarin: May decrease warfarin effectiveness. Monitor INR carefully in the 2 weeks after each treatment, especially days 7 to 10. Avoid use together if possible.
Drug-herb. *St. John's wort:* May decrease antiemetic effects. Discourage use together.
Drug-food. *Grapefruit juice:* May increase drug level and toxicity. Discourage use together.

Effects on lab test results

- May increase creatinine, AST, and ALT levels.
- May decrease neutrophil counts.

Pharmacokinetics

Absorption: Well absorbed, with an average bioavailability of 60% to 65%. Food doesn't appear to have an effect. Level peaks about 4 hours after a dose.
Distribution: 95% protein-bound. May cross the placenta and blood–brain barrier.
Metabolism: Extensively in the liver by CYP3A4 and to a lesser degree by CYP1A2 and CYP2C19.
Excretion: In the urine and in the feces. *Half-life:* 9 to 13 hours.

Route	Onset	Peak	Duration
P.O.	Unknown	4 hr	9–13 hr

Action

Chemical effect: Selectively antagonizes substance P and neurokinin-1 receptors in the brain.
Therapeutic effect: Inhibits emesis caused by cytotoxic chemotherapy.

Available forms

Capsules: 40 mg, 80 mg, 125 mg

NURSING PROCESS

Assessment

- Monitor patient thoroughly for drug and herb interactions before giving.
- Assess patient's condition before therapy and regularly thereafter.
- Watch for hypersensitivity reactions.
- Monitor therapy with other drugs for potential interactions, particularly drugs metabolized by the liver.

Nursing diagnoses

- Imbalanced nutrition: less than body requirements related to chemotherapy-induced nausea and vomiting
- Ineffective individual coping related to effects of chemotherapy
- Deficient knowledge related to drug therapy

Planning and implementation

- Give the first dose of drug 1 hour before chemotherapy.
- Give drug with other antiemetics, usually a 5-HT_3 antagonist and a corticosteroid.
- Don't give for longer than 3 days per chemotherapy cycle.
- Don't give for established nausea and vomiting. Make sure patient has other antiemetics to treat breakthrough emesis.
- Higher doses may lead to drowsiness and headache. Provide supportive treatment for overdose; because of the drug's mechanism of action, antiemetics may not be effective. Drug isn't removed by hemodialysis.
- Monitor CBC, liver function tests, and creatinine periodically during drug therapy.

Patient teaching

- Advise patient that drug is given with other antiemetics and shouldn't be taken alone to prevent chemotherapy-induced nausea and vomiting.
- Tell patient that you will give the first dose 1 hour before each chemotherapy cycle, and that he should take the second and third doses in the morning on days 2 and 3 of the treatment cycle. It may be taken with or without food.
- Instruct patient to treat breakthrough emesis with other antiemetics.
- Advise patient to tell his oncologist if he starts or stops any other drugs or herbal supplements during therapy because of the many drug and herb interactions.
- Advise women of childbearing age who are taking hormonal contraceptives to use an additional form of birth control during therapy.

Evaluation

- Patient has no chemotherapy-induced nausea or vomiting.
- Patient maintains adequate nutrition and hydration during chemotherapy treatments.
- Patient and family state understanding of drug therapy.

argatroban

(ahr-GAH-troh-ban)

Pharmacologic class: direct thrombin inhibitor
Therapeutic class: anticoagulant
Pregnancy risk category: B

Indications and dosages

▶ **Prevention or treatment of thrombosis in patients with heparin-induced thrombocytopenia.** *Adults:* 2 mcg/kg/minute, given as a continuous I.V. infusion; adjust dosage until steady state PTT is 1½ to 3 times the initial baseline value, not to exceed 100 seconds; maximum dose is 10 mcg/kg/minute.

The standard infusion rates for 2 mcg/kg/minute are shown below.

Body weight (kg)	Infusion rate (ml/hour)
50	6
60	7
70	8
80	10
90	11
100	12
110	13
120	14
130	16
140	17

Adjust-a-dose: For patients with moderate hepatic impairment, reduce initial dose to 0.5 mcg/kg/minute and give as a continuous infusion. Monitor PTT closely, and adjust dosage as needed.

▶ **Anticoagulation in patients with or at risk for heparin-induced thrombocytopenia during percutaneous coronary interventions (PCI).** *Adults:* 350 mcg/kg I.V. bolus over 3 to 5 minutes. Start a continuous I.V. infusion at 25 mcg/kg/minute. Check activated clotting time (ACT) 5 to 10 minutes after giving the bolus dose and every 5 to 10 minutes during the infusion until it stabilizes at 300 seconds or longer.

Adjust-a-dose: See table below.

Activated clotting time	Additional I.V. bolus	Continuous I.V. infusion
< 300 sec	150 mcg/kg	30 mcg/kg/min***
300–450 sec	None needed	25 mcg/kg/min
> 450 sec	None needed	15 mcg/kg/min***

***Check ACT again after 5 to 10 minutes.

In case of dissection, impending abrupt closure, thrombus formation during the procedure, or inability to achieve or maintain an ACT longer than 300 seconds, give an additional bolus of 150 mcg/kg and increase infusion rate to 40 mcg/kg/minute. Check ACT again after 5 to 10 minutes.

ALERT: Check ACT every 20 to 30 minutes during a prolonged PCI.

I.V. administration

- Dilute in normal saline solution, D_5W, or lactated Ringer's injection to 1 mg/ml.
- Dilute each 2.5-ml vial to 1:100 by mixing it with 250 ml of diluent.
- Mix the constituted solution by repeatedly turning over the diluent bag for 1 minute.
- Prepared solutions are stable for up to 24 hours at 77° F (25° C).

Incompatibilities

Other I.V. drugs.

Contraindications and cautions

- Contraindicated in patients hypersensitive to drug or its components and in patients with active bleeding.
- Use cautiously in patients with hepatic disease; diseases that increase the risk of hemorrhage, such as severe hypertension; very recent lumbar puncture, spinal anesthesia, or major surgery, especially involving the brain, spinal cord, or eye; and hematologic conditions linked to increased bleeding tendencies, such as congenital or acquired bleeding disorders and GI lesions and ulcerations.

Lifespan: In pregnant women, use only if clearly needed. Breast-feeding women should either stop drug or stop breast-feeding based on importance of the drug to the mother. In children, safety and effectiveness haven't been established.

Adverse reactions

CNS: fever, pain.
CV: atrial fibrillation, ***cardiac arrest, cerebrovascular disorder, hemorrhage,*** hypotension, vasodilation, ***ventricular tachycardia.***
GI: abdominal pain, diarrhea, ***GI bleeding,*** hemoptysis, nausea, vomiting.
GU: abnormal renal function, groin bleeding, *hematuria,* UTI.
Hematologic: anemia.
Respiratory: cough, dyspnea, pneumonia.
Skin: bullous eruptions, rash.
Other: *allergic reactions (in patients also receiving thrombolytic therapy for acute MI),* brachial bleeding, infection, ***sepsis.***

Interactions

Drug-drug. *Oral anticoagulants, antiplatelet drugs:* May prolong PT and INR and increase risk of bleeding. Avoid use together.
Thrombolytics: May increase risk of intracranial bleeding. Avoid use together.

Effects on lab test results

- May decrease hemoglobin level and hematocrit.
- May increase WBC and platelet counts, PTT, ACT, and INR.

Pharmacokinetics

Absorption: Given I.V.
Distribution: Mainly in the extracellular fluid. Drug is 54% protein-bound, of which 34% is bound to alpha$_1$-acid glycoprotein and 20% to albumin.
Metabolism: Mainly in the liver by hydroxylation. Formation of four metabolites is catalyzed in the liver by CYP3A4 and CYP3A5. Primary metabolite is 20% weaker than parent drug. Other metabolites appear in low levels in urine.
Excretion: Mainly in feces, presumably through the biliary tract. *Half-life:* 39 to 51 minutes.

Route	Onset	Peak	Duration
I.V.	Rapid	1–3 hr	Until infusion stops

Action

Chemical effect: Reversibly binds to the thrombin active site and inhibits reactions catalyzed or induced by thrombin, including fibrin formation; activation of coagulation factors V, VIII, and XIII and protein C; and platelet aggregation. Inhibits the action of both free and clot-related thrombin.
Therapeutic effect: Prevents clot formation.

Available forms

Injection: 100 mg/ml

NURSING PROCESS

Assessment

- Assess patient for increased risk of bleeding or overt bleeding before starting therapy.
- Obtain baseline coagulation tests, platelet counts, hemoglobin level, and hematocrit before therapy. Check PTT and ACT. Note abnormalities, and notify prescriber.
- Stop all parenteral anticoagulants before giving drug.
- Assess patient's and family's knowledge of drug therapy.

Nursing diagnoses

- Ineffective tissue perfusion related to presence of blood clots
- Risk for injury related to increased PTT and increased risk of bleeding from drug therapy
- Deficient knowledge related to argatroban therapy and anticoagulant safety precautions

Planning and implementation

- If patient has unexplained drop in hematocrit or blood pressure or another unexplained symptom, suspect a hemorrhage and notify prescriber.

ALERT: Excessive anticoagulation, with or without bleeding, may occur with overdose. Symptoms of acute toxicity include loss of reflex, tremors, clonic seizures, limb paralysis, and coma. No specific antidote is available. Stop drug immediately and monitor PTT and other coagulation tests. Provide symptomatic and supportive therapy.

- To convert to oral anticoagulant therapy, give warfarin with argatroban at up to 2 mcg/kg/minute until INR is higher than 4. After stopping argatroban, repeat INR in 4 to 6 hours. If the repeat INR is below the desired therapeutic range, resume argatroban. Repeat daily until the desired therapeutic range is reached on warfarin alone.

ALERT: Don't confuse argatroban with Aggrastat.

Patient teaching

• Advise patient that drug can cause bleeding, and urge him to immediately report any unusual bruising, bleeding (nosebleeds, bleeding gums, ecchymosis, or hematuria), or tarry or bloody stools.

• Advise patient to avoid activities that carry a risk of injury or cuts, and instruct him to use a soft toothbrush and electric razor while taking argatroban.

• Tell patient to notify prescriber if she's pregnant, breast-feeding, or recently gave birth.

• Tell patient to notify prescriber if he has stomach ulcers or liver disease; if he's had recent surgery, radiation treatments, falls, or other injury; or if he develops wheezing, difficulty breathing, or rash.

Evaluation

• Patient doesn't develop blood clots while on drug.

• Patient has no unnecessary bruising or bleeding.

• Patient and family state understanding of drug therapy.

aripiprazole

(air-uh-PIP-rah-zol)

Abilify, Abilify Discmelt

Pharmacologic class: psychotropic
Therapeutic class: atypical antipsychotic
Pregnancy risk category: C

Indications and dosages

▶ **Schizophrenia.** *Adults:* Initially, 10 to 15 mg P.O. daily, increasing to a maximum of 30 mg daily if needed, after at least 2 weeks. Maintenance doses of 15 mg P.O. daily may be effective.

▶ **Manic and mixed episodes associated with bipolar disorder.** *Adults:* Initially, 30 mg P.O. once daily. May decrease to 15 mg daily based on patient response.

Adjust-a-dose: Give half the dose when giving with CYP3A4 or CYP2D6 inhibitors, particularly ketoconazole, quinidine, fluoxetine, or paroxetine. Double the dose when giving with CYP3A4 inducers, such as carbamazepine. Give original dose once other drugs are stopped.

▶ **Agitation in schizophrenia or in mixed or manic bipolar 1 disorder.** *Adults:* 5.25 to 15 mg by deep I.M. injection. Recommended dose is 9.75 mg. If needed, may give a second dose after 2 hours. Safety of giving more often than q 2 hours or more than 30 mg daily isn't known. Switch to P.O. route as soon as possible.

Contraindications and cautions

• Contraindicated in patients hypersensitive to drug.

• Use cautiously in patients with CV disease, cerebrovascular disease, or conditions that could predispose the patient to hypotension, such as dehydration or hypovolemia. Also use cautiously in patients with a history of seizures or with conditions that lower the seizure threshold and in those at risk for aspiration pneumonia, such as those with Alzheimer disease. Use caution in patients who engage in strenuous exercise, are exposed to extreme heat, take anticholinergic drugs, or are susceptible to dehydration.

Lifespan: In pregnant women, use only if benefits outweigh risks. In breast-feeding women, use cautiously because it's unknown whether drug appears in breast milk. In children, safety and effectiveness of drug haven't been established. In elderly patients, use cautiously because they may be more sensitive to drug.

Adverse reactions

CNS: abnormal gait, *akathisia, anxiety,* asthenia, cognitive and motor impairment, cogwheel rigidity, confusion, depression, dizziness, fatigue, fever, *headache,* hostility, *insomnia, lightheadedness,* manic behavior, nervousness, ***neuroleptic malignant syndrome, seizures,*** *somnolence,* ***suicidal thoughts,*** tardive dyskinesia, tremor.

CV: ***bradycardia,*** chest pain, hypertension, orthostatic hypotension, peripheral edema, tachycardia.

EENT: blurred vision, conjunctivitis, ear pain, increased salivation, rhinitis.

GI: abdominal pain, anorexia, *constipation,* diarrhea, dry mouth, dyspepsia, esophageal dysmotility, *nausea, vomiting.*

GU: urinary incontinence.

Hematologic: anemia.
Metabolic: ***hyperglycemia,*** weight gain, weight loss.
Musculoskeletal: muscle cramps, neck pain, neck stiffness.
Respiratory: cough, dyspnea, pneumonia.
Skin: dry skin, ecchymosis, pruritus, rash, sweating, ulcer.
Other: flulike syndrome, inability to regulate body temperature.

Interactions

Drug-drug. *Antihypertensives:* May increase antihypertensive and orthostatic hypotensive effects. Monitor blood pressure.
Carbamazepine and other CYP3A4 inducers: May decrease level and effectiveness of aripiprazole. Double the usual aripiprazole dose, and monitor patient closely.
Fluoxetine, paroxetine, quinidine, and other CYP2D6 inhibitors; ketoconazole and other CYP3A4 inhibitors: May increase level and toxicity of aripiprazole. Halve the usual aripiprazole dose, and monitor patient closely.
Drug-food. *Grapefruit juice:* May increase drug level. Advise patient to avoid grapefruit juice during treatment.
Drug-lifestyle. *Alcohol use:* May increase CNS effects. Discourage use together.

Effects on lab test results

- May increase glucose and CK levels.

Pharmacokinetics

Absorption: Good. Absolute bioavailability is 87% and isn't affected by food.
Distribution: Extensive. Drug and major metabolites are 99% protein-bound, mainly to albumin.
Metabolism: Extensively through the CYP3A4 and CYP2D6 systems, with one active metabolite.
Excretion: In urine and feces. *Elimination half-life:* About 75 hours in patients with normal metabolism and about 146 hours in those unable to metabolize the drug through CYP2D6.

Route	Onset	Peak	Duration
P.O.	Unknown	3–5 hr	Unknown
I.M.	Unknown	1–3 hr	Unknown

Action

Chemical effect: May exert antipsychotic effects through partial agonist activity at D2 and serotonin 5-HT_{1A} receptors and antagonist activity at serotonin 5-HT_{2A} receptors.
Therapeutic effect: Decreases psychotic behaviors.

Available forms

Injection: 9.75 mg/1.3-ml (7.5 mg/ml) single-dose vial
Oral solution: 1 mg/ml
Tablets: 5 mg, 10 mg, 15 mg, 20 mg, 30 mg
Tablets (orally disintegrating): 10 mg, 15 mg, 20 mg, 30 mg

NURSING PROCESS

Assessment

- Assess patient's condition before and after therapy.
- Watch for possible compliance issues.
- Be alert for adverse reactions and drug interactions.
- Assess patient and family's knowledge of drug therapy.

Nursing diagnoses

- Disturbed thought processes related to underlying disease process
- Noncompliance related to medication regimen
- Deficient knowledge related to drug therapy

Planning and implementation

ALERT: Neuroleptic malignant syndrome may occur. Monitor patient for hyperpyrexia, muscle rigidity, altered mental status, irregular pulse or blood pressure, tachycardia, diaphoresis, and cardiac arrhythmias. If signs and symptoms of neuroleptic malignant syndrome occur, stop drug immediately.
- Monitor patient for evidence of tardive dyskinesia. Elderly patients, especially elderly women, are at higher risk. If it occurs, stop drug.

ALERT: Monitor patients with diabetes regularly, because hyperglycemia may occur. Patients with risk factors for diabetes should have fasting blood glucose level tested at baseline and periodically. Monitor patient for symptoms of hyperglycemia, including polydipsia, polyuria, polyphagia, and weakness. If symptoms develop, obtain fasting blood glucose test. In some cases, hyperglycemia is reversible by stopping drug.

- Give the smallest effective dose for the shortest time. Periodically reassess need for treatment.
- To reduce risk of an overdose, make sure only a small quantity of tablets is available at any time.
- The oral solution can be substituted on a milligram-per-milligram basis in place of the 5-, 10-, 15-, or 20-mg tablets up to 25 mg. Patients taking 30-mg tablets should receive 25 mg of solution.
- Overdose may cause somnolence and vomiting. Give activated charcoal during the first hour of overdose because 50% of a 15-mg dose is absorbed within the first hour. Dialysis isn't helpful because drug is highly protein-bound.

Patient teaching

- Tell patient to use caution when driving or operating hazardous machinery because psychoactive drugs may impair judgment, thinking, or motor skills.
- Tell patient that drug may be taken without regard to meals.
- Advise patient to avoid taking drug with grapefruit juice.
- Inform patient that symptoms should improve gradually over several weeks rather than immediately.
- Explain to patient that periodic blood work will be needed.
- Tell patient to avoid alcohol use while taking drug.
- Advise patient to limit strenuous activity while taking drug to avoid dehydration and becoming overheated.
- Tell patient to keep orally disintegrating tablet in blister package until ready to use. Then, with dry hands, carefully peel open the foil backing and place tablet on the tongue. It will dissolve rapidly in saliva, making liquid unnecessary. Tell patient not to split tablet.
- Tell patient to store oral solution in refrigerator and that it can be used up to 6 months after opening.

☑ Evaluation

- Patient has reduced symptoms of underlying disease process.
- Patient is compliant with drug regimen.
- Patient and family state understanding of drug therapy.

aspirin (acetylsalicylic acid)

(ASS-prinn)

Ancasal ♦ †, Arthrinol ♦ †, Artria S.R.†, ASA†, ASA Enseals†, Aspergum†, Aspro Preparations ◇, Astrin ♦ †, Bayer Aspirin†, Bex Powders ◇, Coryphen ♦ †, Easprin†, Ecotrin†, Empirin†, Entrophen ♦ †, Halfprin, Measurin ♦ †, Norwich Extra Strength†, Novasen†, Riphen-10 ♦ †, Sal-Adult ♦ †, Sal-Infant ♦ †, Solprin ◇, Supasa ♦ †, Triaphen-10 ♦ †, Vincent's Powders ◇, ZORprin†

Pharmacologic class: salicylate
Therapeutic class: nonopioid analgesic, antipyretic, anti-inflammatory, antiplatelet drug
Pregnancy risk category: C (D in third trimester)

Indications and dosages

▶ **Arthritis.** *Adults:* Initially, 2.4 to 3.6 g P.O. daily in divided doses. Maintenance dosage is 3.6 to 5.4 g P.O. daily in divided doses.
Children: 60 to 130 mg/kg P.O. daily in divided doses.

▶ **Mild pain or fever.** *Adults:* 325 to 650 mg P.O. or P.R. q 4 hours, p.r.n.
Children: For mild pain only, 65 mg/kg P.O. or P.R. daily in four to six divided doses.

▶ **Prevention of thrombosis.** *Adults:* 1.3 g P.O. daily in two to four divided doses.

▶ **Reduction of MI risk in patients with previous MI or unstable angina.** *Adults:* 160 to 325 mg P.O. daily. Give dose immediately when acute coronary syndrome is suspected.

▶ **Kawasaki syndrome (mucocutaneous lymph node syndrome).** *Children:* 80 to 100 mg/kg P.O. daily in four divided doses during febrile phase. Some patients may need up to 120 mg/kg. When fever subsides, decrease dosage to 3 to 8 mg/kg once daily, adjusted according to salicylate level.

▶ **Prophylaxis for transient ischemic attack (TIA).** *Adults:* 50 to 325 mg P.O. daily.

▶ **TIA.** *Adults:* 160 to 325 mg P.O. immediately within 48 hours of onset of stroke.

▶ **Prevention of reocclusion in coronary revascularization procedures.** *Adults:* 325 mg P.O. q 6 hours after surgery and for 1 year.

▶ **Rheumatic fever‡.** *Adults:* 4.9 to 7.8 g P.O. daily in divided doses q 4 to 6 hours for 1 to 2 weeks. Decrease to 60 to 70 mg/kg daily for 1 to 6 weeks; then gradually withdraw over 1 to 2 weeks.

Children: 90 to 130 mg/kg P.O. daily in divided doses q 4 to 6 hours.

▶ **Pericarditis after acute MI‡.** *Adults:* 160 to 325 mg P.O. daily.

▶ **Stent implantation‡.** *Adults:* 80 to 325 mg P.O. 2 hours before stent placement and 160 to 325 mg P.O. daily thereafter.

Contraindications and cautions

- Contraindicated in patients hypersensitive to drug and those with G6PD deficiency; bleeding disorders such as hemophilia, von Willebrand disease, and telangiectasia; or NSAID-induced sensitivity reactions.
- Use cautiously in patients with GI lesions, impaired renal function, hypoprothrombinemia, vitamin K deficiency, thrombocytopenia, thrombotic thrombocytopenic purpura, or severe hepatic impairment.

Lifespan: In pregnant women, use cautiously. In breast-feeding women, safety hasn't been established.

ALERT: Because of the risk of Reye syndrome, the Centers for Disease Control and Prevention recommends not giving salicylates to children or teenagers who have or are recovering from chickenpox or flulike illness or who have acute febrile illnesses. In elderly patients, use cautiously because GI and renal adverse effects may be exacerbated.

Adverse reactions

EENT: *hearing loss, tinnitus.*

GI: dyspepsia, ***GI bleeding,*** *GI distress, nausea, occult bleeding, vomiting.*

GU: transient renal insufficiency.

Hematologic: *prolonged bleeding time,* ***thrombocytopenia.***

Hepatic: ***hepatitis.***

Skin: bruising, *rash,* urticaria.

Other: ***angioedema,*** hypersensitivity reactions (***anaphylaxis,*** asthma), ***Reye syndrome.***

Interactions

Drug-drug. *Ammonium chloride, other urine acidifiers:* May increase levels of aspirin products. Watch for aspirin toxicity.

Antacids in high doses (and other urine alkalinizers): May decrease levels of aspirin products. Watch for decreased aspirin effect.

Beta blockers: May decrease antihypertensive effect. Avoid long-term aspirin use if patient is taking antihypertensives.

Corticosteroids: May enhance salicylate elimination. Watch for decreased salicylate effect.

Heparin: May increase risk of bleeding. Monitor patient and coagulation studies closely if used together.

Ibuprofen: May negate antiplatelet effect of low-dose aspirin therapy with regular use. Avoid use together.

Methotrexate: May increase risk of methotrexate toxicity. Monitor patient closely.

NSAIDs: May alter pharmacokinetics of these drugs, leading to lower levels and decreased effectiveness. Avoid use together. May also increase risk of GI bleeding. Monitor patient closely.

Oral anticoagulants: May increase risk of bleeding. Monitor patient for signs of bleeding.

Oral antidiabetics: May increase hypoglycemic effect. Monitor patient closely.

Probenecid, sulfinpyrazone: May decrease uricosuric effect. Avoid aspirin during therapy with these drugs.

Steroids: May increase risk of GI bleeding. Monitor patient closely.

Drug-herb. *Dong quai, feverfew, garlic, ginger, horse chestnut, red clover:* May increase risk of bleeding. Monitor patient for increased effects, and discourage use together.

Drug-food. *Caffeine:* May increase the absorption of aspirin. Monitor patient for increased effects.

Drug-lifestyle. *Alcohol use:* May increase risk of GI bleeding. Discourage use together.

Effects on lab test results

- May increase liver enzyme levels.
- May decrease WBC and platelet counts.

Pharmacokinetics

Absorption: Rapid and complete.

Distribution: Wide. Protein-binding to albumin is concentration-dependent. It ranges from 75% to 90% and decreases as level increases.

Metabolism: Hydrolyzed partially in GI tract to salicylic acid, but almost completely in liver.
Excretion: In urine as salicylate and its metabolites. *Half-life:* 15 to 20 minutes.

Route	Onset	Peak	Duration
P.O.			
buffered	5–30 min	1–2 hr	1–4 hr
enteric-coated	5–30 min	4–8 hr	1–4 hr
extended-release	5–30 min	1–2 hr	4–8 hr
regular	5–30 min	25–40 min	1–4 hr
solution	5–30 min	15–60 min	1–4 hr
P.R.	5–30 min	3–4 hr	1–4 hr

Action

Chemical effect: Produces analgesia by blocking prostaglandin synthesis (peripheral action), which may prevent lowering of pain threshold that occurs when prostaglandins sensitize pain receptors to stimulation. Exerts anti-inflammatory effects by inhibiting prostaglandins and other mediators of inflammatory response. Relieves fever by acting on hypothalamic heat-regulating center to cause peripheral vasodilation, which increases peripheral blood supply and promotes sweating, heat loss, and to cooling by evaporation. In low doses, aspirin also appears to impede clotting by blocking prostaglandin synthesis, which prevents formation of platelet-aggregating substance thromboxane A2.
Therapeutic effect: Relieves pain, reduces fever and inflammation, and decreases risk of transient ischemic attacks and MI.

Available forms

Capsules: 325 mg†, 500 mg†
Chewing gum: 227.5 mg†
Suppositories: 60 mg†, 65 mg†, 120 mg†, 125 mg†, 130 mg†, 195 mg†, 200 mg†, 300 mg†, 325 mg†, 600 mg† 650 mg†
Tablets: 325 mg†, 500 mg†, 600 mg†, 650 mg†
Tablets (chewable): 81 mg†
Tablets (enteric-coated): 81 mg†, 165 mg†, 325 mg†, 500 mg†, 650 mg†, 975 mg
Tablets (extended-release): 800 mg
Tablets (timed-release): 650 mg†

NURSING PROCESS

Assessment

- Obtain history of patient's pain or fever before therapy, and monitor patient throughout therapy.
- Be alert for adverse reactions and drug interactions.
- During long-term therapy, monitor salicylate level. Therapeutic level in arthritis is 10 to 30 mg/dl. With long-term therapy, mild toxicity may occur at levels of 20 mg/dl. Tinnitus may occur at levels of 30 mg/dl and above but doesn't reliably indicate toxicity, especially in very young patients and those older than age 60.
- Assess patient's and family's knowledge of drug therapy.

Nursing diagnoses

- Acute pain related to underlying condition
- Risk for injury related to drug-induced adverse GI reactions
- Deficient knowledge related to drug therapy

Planning and implementation

- Give aspirin with food, milk, antacid, or large glass of water to reduce adverse GI reactions.
- If patient has trouble swallowing, crush aspirin, combine it with soft food, or dissolve it in liquid. Give immediately after mixing with liquid because drug doesn't stay in solution. Don't crush enteric-coated aspirin.
- Enteric-coated products are absorbed slowly and not suitable for acute effects. These products cause less GI bleeding and may be more suited for long-term therapy, such as for arthritis.
- Give P.R. after a bowel movement or at night to maximize absorption.
- Hold dose and notify prescriber if bleeding, salicylism (tinnitus, hearing loss), or adverse GI reactions develop.
- Stop aspirin 5 to 7 days before elective surgery.

ALERT: Don't confuse aspirin with Asendin or Afrin.

Patient teaching

- Encourage patient to retain suppository for as long as possible, preferably at least 10 hours to maximize absorption.
- Advise patient receiving high-dose prolonged treatment to watch for petechiae, bleeding gums, and signs of GI bleeding and to maintain

adequate fluid intake. Encourage use of a soft toothbrush.

- Because of many possible drug interactions involving aspirin, warn patient who takes prescription form to check with prescriber or pharmacist before taking herbal preparations or OTC combinations containing aspirin.
- Explain that various OTC preparations contain aspirin. Warn patient to read labels carefully to avoid overdose.
- Advise patient to avoid alcohol use during drug therapy.
- Advise patient to restrict intake of caffeine during drug therapy.
- Instruct patient to take aspirin with food or milk.
- Instruct patient not to chew enteric-coated products.
- Aspirin is a leading cause of poisoning in children. Emphasize safe storage of drugs in the home. Teach patient to keep aspirin and other drugs out of children's reach. Encourage use of child-resistant containers, even if children only visit occasionally.

Evaluation

- Patient states that aspirin has relieved pain.
- Patient remains free from adverse GI effects throughout drug therapy.
- Patient and family state understanding of drug therapy.

atazanavir sulfate

(att-uh-ZAH-nuh-veer SULL-fayt)

Reyataz

Pharmacologic class: protease inhibitor
Therapeutic class: antiretroviral
Pregnancy risk category: B

Indications and dosages

▶ **HIV-1 infection, with other antiretrovirals.** *Adults:* In antiretroviral-experienced patients, give 300 mg (as one 300-mg capsule or two 150-mg capsules) once daily plus 100 mg ritonavir once daily taken with food. For antiretroviral-naive patients, 400 mg (as two 200-mg capsules) P.O. once daily with food. When giving with efavirenz in antiretroviral-naive patients, give 300 mg atazanavir and 100 mg ritonavir with 600 mg efavirenz, all as a single daily dose with food. Recommendations for efavirenz and atazanavir in treatment-experienced patients haven't been established.

Adjust-a-dose: For patients with Child-Pugh class B hepatic insufficiency, reduce dosage to 300 mg P.O. once daily.

Contraindications and cautions

- Contraindicated in patients hypersensitive to drug or its components and in patients taking drugs highly dependent on CYP3A4 for clearance and for which elevated levels are linked to life-threatening effects, such as cisapride, dihydroergotamine, ergonovine, ergotamine, methylergonovine, midazolam, pimozide, triazolam.
- Use cautiously in patients with conduction system disease or hepatic impairment.

Lifespan: In pregnant women, drug should be used only if potential benefits outweigh risk. To help monitor maternal-fetal outcomes of pregnant women, register pregnant women in the Antiretroviral Pregnancy Registry by calling 1-800-258-4263. In breast-feeding women, use cautiously because it's unknown whether drug appears in breast milk. In children, an optimal regimen hasn't been established. In children younger than age 3, drug shouldn't be used because of a risk for kernicterus. In elderly patients, use cautiously because they may retain more of the drug.

Adverse reactions

CNS: depression, dizziness, fatigue, fever, *headache,* insomnia, pain, peripheral neurology symptoms.
CV: first-degree heart block.
GI: *abdominal pain,* diarrhea, *nausea,* vomiting.
Hepatic: ***hepatitis,*** jaundice, scleral icterus.
Metabolic: ***lactic acidosis,*** lipodystrophy, lipohypertrophy.
Musculoskeletal: arthralgia, back pain.
Respiratory: increased cough.
Skin: *rash.*

Interactions

Drug-drug. *Amiodarone, lidocaine (systemic), quinidine:* May increase levels of these drugs. Monitor levels.
Antacids and buffered drugs: May decrease atazanavir level. Give atazanavir 2 hours before or 1 hour after these drugs.

Atorvastatin, lovastatin, simvastatin: May increase statin level and the risk of myopathy and rhabdomyolysis. Use atorvastatin cautiously; don't use lovastatin or simvastatin.
Clarithromycin: May increase clarithromycin and atazanavir levels and decrease 14-OH clarithromycin levels. Reduce clarithromycin dose by 50% when giving with atazanavir. Because levels of the active metabolite 14-OH clarithromycin are significantly reduced, consider alternative therapy for indications other than infections caused by *Mycobacterium avium* complex.
Cyclosporine, sirolimus, tacrolimus: May increase immunosuppressant levels. Monitor immunosuppressant levels.
Didanosine buffered forms: May decrease atazanavir level. Give atazanavir 2 hours before or 1 hour after didanosine buffered forms.
Dihydroergotamine, ergonovine, ergotamine, methylergonovine: May cause life-threatening reactions, such as acute ergot toxicity characterized by peripheral vasospasm and ischemia of the limbs and other tissues. Don't use together.
Diltiazem: May increase diltiazem and desacetyl-diltiazem levels. Use cautiously. Reduce dose of diltiazem by 50%. Monitor ECG.
Efavirenz: May decrease atazanavir level. If used together, give 300 mg atazanavir with 100 mg ritonavir and 600 mg efavirenz all as a single daily dose with food. This combination provides atazanavir exposure similar to that of 400 mg of atazanavir alone. Don't give atazanavir with efavirenz unless also given with ritonavir.
Ethinyl estradiol and norethindrone: May increase ethinyl estradiol and norethindrone levels. Use cautiously at the lowest effective dose of each contraceptive component.
Felodipine, nicardipine, nifedipine, verapamil: May increase calcium channel blocker level. Use cautiously. Adjust calcium channel blocker dosage, and monitor ECG.
Fluticasone: May significantly increase fluticasone exposure, causing decreased serum cortisol level, leading to systemic corticosteroid effects (including Cushing syndrome). Don't use together, if possible.
H_2-receptor antagonists: May decrease atazanavir level. Give 12 hours apart.
Indinavir: May increase risk of hyperbilirubinemia. Use together isn't recommended.
Irinotecan: May interfere with irinotecan metabolism, resulting in increased irinotecan toxicities. Don't use together.
Itraconazole, ketoconazole: May interact with ritonavir-boosted atazanavir. Use together cautiously.
Midazolam, triazolam: May cause life-threatening reactions, such as prolonged or increased sedation or respiratory depression. Don't use together.
Nevirapine: May decrease atazanavir level. Use together isn't recommended.
Pimozide: May cause life-threatening reactions, such as cardiac arrhythmias. Don't use together.
Proton pump inhibitors: May substantially decrease atazanavir level and therapeutic effect. Use together isn't recommended.
Rifabutin: May increase rifabutin level. Reduce rifabutin dose by up to 75%.
Rifampin: May decrease level of most protease inhibitors, resulting in loss of therapeutic effect and development of resistance. Don't use together.
Ritonavir: May increase atazanavir level. Give 300 mg atazanavir once daily with 100 mg ritonavir once daily, with food.
Saquinavir (soft gelatin capsules): May increase saquinavir level. Appropriate dose for this combination hasn't been established.
Sildenafil, tadalafil, vardenafil: May increase levels of these drugs and adverse events, including hypotension, visual changes, and priapism. Tell patient to use caution and reduced doses: sildenafil at 25 mg every 48 hours, tadalafil at 10 mg every 72 hours, and vardenafil at 2.5 mg every 72 hours. Monitor patient for adverse events.
Tenofovir: May decrease atazanavir level, causing resistance. Give both drugs with ritonavir.
Trazodone: May increase trazodone level, causing nausea, dizziness, hypotension, and syncope. Avoid use together, or use cautiously with a lower trazodone dose.
Tricyclic antidepressants: May increase tricyclic antidepressant level. Monitor level.
Voriconazole: May interact. Monitor patient for toxicity. Avoid use with ritonavir-boosted atazanavir.
Warfarin: May increase warfarin level. Monitor INR.
Drug-herb. *St. John's wort:* May reduce atazanavir level, resulting in loss of therapeutic

effect and development of resistance. Discourage use together.

Effects on lab test results

- May increase AST, ALT, total bilirubin, amylase, and lipase levels. May decrease hemoglobin level and hematocrit.
- May decrease neutrophil count.

Pharmacokinetics

Absorption: Rapid. Level peaks about 2½ hours. Food enhances bioavailability.
Distribution: 86% protein-bound and binds to alpha$_1$-acid glycoprotein and albumin to a similar extent.
Metabolism: Extensively, mainly by the liver.
Excretion: In urine and feces. About 7% excreted unchanged in urine. *Elimination half-life:* About 7 hours.

Route	Onset	Peak	Duration
P.O.	Unknown	2 hr	Unknown

Action

Chemical effect: Prevents the formation of mature virions within HIV-1 infected cells.
Therapeutic effect: Treatment of HIV infection.

Available forms

Capsules: 100 mg, 150 mg, 200 mg, 300 mg

NURSING PROCESS

Assessment

- Monitor cardiac status during therapy.
- Test women for pregnancy before starting therapy.
- Monitor liver function tests periodically during therapy.
- Assess patient's and family's knowledge of drug therapy.

Nursing diagnoses

- Ineffective protection related to underlying HIV infection
- Risk for injury related to adverse reactions
- Deficient knowledge related to drug therapy

Planning and implementation

- Drug may prolong PR interval.
- Most patients develop asymptomatic increase in indirect bilirubin, which may cause yellowing of skin or sclerae. Hyperbilirubinemia is reversible when drug is stopped.
- Various degrees of cross-resistance among protease inhibitors may occur. Resistance to this drug doesn't preclude later use of other protease inhibitors. Give drug with other antiretrovirals.
- Patient should remain under the care of a physician while taking drug.
- At high doses, jaundice is caused by indirect (unconjugated) hyperbilirubinemia (without liver function test changes), or prolonged PR interval may occur.
- Treat overdose with general supportive measures, including monitoring of vital signs and ECG. Induce vomiting or use gastric lavage to eliminate unabsorbed drug. Also give activated charcoal to aid removal of unabsorbed drug. Because drug is highly metabolized by the liver and is highly protein-bound, dialysis probably won't help.

Patient teaching

- Tell patient that sustained decreases in HIV RNA have been linked to a reduced risk of progression to AIDS and death.
- Tell patient to remain in a physician's care while taking drug.
- Tell patient to take drug with food every day and to take other antiretrovirals as prescribed.
- Inform patient that drug doesn't cure HIV and that he may develop opportunistic infections and other complications of HIV disease. Also explain that drug doesn't reduce the risk of transmitting HIV to others.
- Tell patient not to alter dose or stop therapy without consulting the prescriber.
- If a dose is delayed, advise patient to take it as soon as possible and then return to the normal schedule. If a dose is skipped, tell patient not to double the next dose.
- Tell patient to consult prescriber about dizziness or light-headedness.
- Tell patient that elevations in indirect bilirubin may occur and to report yellowing of the skin or the whites of the eyes.
- Inform patient that drug may cause redistribution or accumulation of body fat.
- To prevent postnatal transmission of HIV, tell HIV-infected mothers to avoid breast-feeding.

Evaluation

- Patient remains free from infection.
- Patient sustains no injury from adverse reactions.

• Patient and family state understanding of drug therapy.

atenolol

(uh-TEN-uh-lol)

Apo-Atenol ♦, Noten ◊, Nu-Atenol ♦, Tenormin

Pharmacologic class: beta blocker
Therapeutic class: antihypertensive, antianginal
Pregnancy risk category: D

Indications and dosages

▶ **Hypertension.** *Adults:* Initially, 50 mg P.O. once daily. Increase to 100 mg once daily after 7 to 14 days. Doses higher than 100 mg aren't likely to produce further benefit.

Adjust-a-dose: *Elderly patients:* Initially, 25 mg P.O. daily, increased slowly until desired response. Also reduce dosage in patients with renal impairment. If creatinine clearance is 15 to 35 ml/minute, maximum dose is 50 mg daily. If clearance is less than 15 ml/minute, maximum dose is 25 mg daily.

▶ **Angina pectoris.** *Adults:* 50 mg P.O. once daily. Increase as needed to 100 mg daily after 7 days for optimal effect. Maximum dosage is 200 mg daily.

▶ **To reduce CV mortality rate and risk of reinfarction in patients with acute MI.** *Adults:* 5 mg I.V. over 5 minutes, followed by another 5 mg 10 minutes later. After another 10 minutes, 50 mg P.O., followed by 50 mg P.O. in 12 hours. Thereafter, 100 mg P.O. daily (as a single dose or 50 mg b.i.d.) for at least 7 days.

▶ **To slow rapid ventricular response to atrial tachyarrhythmias after acute MI without left ventricular dysfunction and AV block‡.** *Adults:* 2.5 to 5 mg I.V. over 2 to 5 minutes, p.r.n., to control rate. Maximum, 10 mg over a 10- to 15-minute period.

I.V. administration

• Mix doses with D_5W, normal saline solution, or dextrose and sodium chloride solutions.
• Give by slow injection, not to exceed 1 mg/minute.
• Solution is stable for 48 hours after mixing.

⊗ **Incompatibilities**
Other I.V. drugs.

Contraindications and cautions

• Contraindicated in patients with sinus bradycardia, greater than first-degree heart block, overt cardiac failure, or cardiogenic shock, or in those hypersensitive to atenolol or its components.
• Use cautiously in patients at risk for heart failure and in those with bronchospastic disease, diabetes, and hyperthyroidism.

Lifespan: In pregnant women, don't use unless absolutely necessary because fetal harm can occur. In breast-feeding women, use cautiously. In children, safety of drug hasn't been established.

Adverse reactions

CNS: fatigue, fever, hallucinations, headache, lethargy.
CV: BRADYCARDIA, intermittent claudication, PROFOUND HYPOTENSION, ***second- or third-degree AV block.***
EENT: visual disturbances.
GI: diarrhea, dry mouth, nausea, vomiting.
GU: impotence, Peyronie disease.
Respiratory: ***bronchospasm,*** dyspnea.
Skin: rash, reversible alopecia.

Interactions

Drug-drug. *Antihypertensives:* May increase hypotensive effect. Use together cautiously.
Digoxin, diltiazem: May cause excessive bradycardia and increase depressant effect on myocardium. Use together cautiously.
Insulin, oral antidiabetics: May alter dosage requirements in previously stabilized patient with diabetes. Observe patient carefully.
I.V. lidocaine: May reduce hepatic metabolism of lidocaine, increasing the risk of toxicity. Give bolus doses of lidocaine at a slower rate, and monitor lidocaine levels closely.
Prazosin: May increase the risk of orthostatic hypotension early in use together. Help patient to stand slowly until effects are known.
Reserpine: May cause hypotension. Use together cautiously.
Verapamil: May increase the effects of both drugs. Monitor cardiac function closely, and decrease dosages as needed.

Effects on lab test results

• May increase BUN, creatinine, potassium, uric acid, transaminase, alkaline phosphatase,

triglyceride, and LDH levels. May increase or decrease glucose level.
• May increase platelet count.

Pharmacokinetics

Absorption: About 50% to 60%.
Distribution: Into most tissues and fluids except brain and CSF. About 5% to 15% protein-bound.
Metabolism: Minimal.
Excretion: From 40% to 50% of dose is excreted unchanged in urine; remainder is excreted as unchanged drug and metabolites in feces. *Half-life:* 6 to 7 hours.

Route	Onset	Peak	Duration
P.O.	1 hr	2–4 hr	24 hr
I.V.	5 min	5 min	12 hr

Action

Chemical effect: Selectively blocks $beta_1$ receptors; decreases cardiac output, peripheral resistance, and cardiac oxygen consumption; and depresses renin secretion.
Therapeutic effect: Decreases blood pressure, relieves angina, and reduces CV mortality rate and risk of reinfarction after acute MI.

Available forms

Injection: 5 mg/10 ml
Tablets: 25 mg, 50 mg, 100 mg

NURSING PROCESS

Assessment

• Obtain history of patient's underlying condition.
• If prescribed for hypertension, monitor drug's effectiveness by checking patient's blood pressure often. Full antihypertensive effect may not occur for 1 to 2 weeks. For angina pectoris, monitor frequency and severity of anginal pain. For reducing CV mortality rate and risk of reinfarction after acute MI, monitor signs of reinfarction.
• Be alert for adverse reactions and drug interactions.
• Assess patient's and family's knowledge of drug therapy.

Nursing diagnoses

• Risk for injury related to underlying condition
• Decreased cardiac output related to drug-induced adverse CV reactions
• Deficient knowledge related to drug therapy

Planning and implementation

• Adjust dosage in patients with renal insufficiency and those receiving hemodialysis.
• Check patient's apical pulse before giving drug; if slower than 60 beats/minute, withhold drug and call prescriber.
• Give as a single daily dose.
• Be prepared to treat shock or hypoglycemia because this drug masks common signs of these conditions.
• Notify prescriber immediately if patient shows signs of decreased cardiac output.
ALERT: Withdraw drug gradually over 1 to 2 weeks to avoid serious adverse reactions.
ALERT: Don't confuse atenolol with timolol or albuterol.

Patient teaching

• Teach patient how to take his pulse. Tell him not to take the drug and to call his prescriber if pulse rate is slower than 60 beats/minute.
• Warn patient that stopping drug abruptly can worsen angina and MI. Drug should be withdrawn gradually over 2 weeks.
• Counsel patient to take drug at same time every day.
• Tell patient to notify prescriber of excessive fatigue.
• Tell woman to notify prescriber if she becomes pregnant because drug must be stopped.

Evaluation

• Patient's underlying condition improves with drug therapy.
• Patient's cardiac output remains unchanged throughout drug therapy.
• Patient and family state understanding of drug therapy.

atomoxetine hydrochloride

(ATT-oh-mocks-uh-teen high-droh-KLOR-ighd)
Strattera

Pharmacologic class: selective norepinephrine reuptake inhibitor
Therapeutic class: attention deficit hyperactivity disorder (ADHD) drug
Pregnancy risk category: C

A

Indications and dosages

▶**Adjunct therapy for ADHD.** *Adults and children weighing more than 70 kg (154 lb):* Initially, 40 mg P.O. daily; increase after at least 3 days to a target total daily dose of 80 mg P.O. as a single dose in the morning or two evenly divided doses in the morning and late afternoon or early evening. After 2 to 4 weeks, increase total dosage to a maximum of 100 mg, if needed. *Children weighing 70 kg or less:* Initially, 0.5 mg/kg P.O. daily; increase after at least 3 days to a target total daily dose of 1.2 mg/kg P.O. as a single dose in the morning or two evenly divided doses in the morning and late afternoon or early evening. Don't exceed 1.4 mg/kg or 100 mg daily, whichever is less.

Adjust-a-dose: For patients with moderate hepatic impairment, give 50% of the normal dose; in those with severe hepatic impairment, give 25% of the normal dose.

Contraindications and cautions

- Contraindicated in patients hypersensitive to drug or its components, those who took an MAO inhibitor within the past 14 days, those who have jaundice or laboratory evidence of liver injury, and those with narrow-angle glaucoma.
- Use cautiously in patients with hypertension, tachycardia, moderate to severe hepatic insufficiency, or CV or cerebrovascular disease.

Lifespan: In pregnant and breast-feeding women, use cautiously. In children younger than age 6, safety and effectiveness of drug haven't been established. In the elderly, safety and effectiveness haven't been established.

Adverse reactions

CNS: abnormal dreams, crying, depression, dizziness, early morning awakening, fatigue, *headache, insomnia,* irritability, mood swings, paresthesia, pyrexia, sedation, sleep disorder, somnolence, ***suicidal thoughts,*** tremor.
CV: hypertension, orthostatic hypotension, palpitations, tachycardia.
EENT: ear infection, nasal congestion, mydriasis, nasopharyngitis, rhinorrhea, sinus congestion, sinusitis, sore throat.
GI: abdominal pain, constipation, decreased appetite, dry mouth, dyspepsia, flatulence, gastroenteritis, nausea, vomiting.
GU: delayed menses, difficulty in micturition, dysmenorrhea, ejaculatory problems, erectile disturbance, impotence, menstrual disorder, prostatitis, urinary hesitation, urine retention.
Metabolic: weight loss.
Musculoskeletal: arthralgia, myalgia.
Respiratory: *cough,* upper respiratory tract infection.
Skin: dermatitis, increased sweating, pruritus.
Other: decreased libido, hot flashes, influenza, rigors.

Interactions

Drug-drug. *Albuterol:* May increase CV effects. Use together cautiously.
MAO inhibitors: May cause hyperthermia, rigidity, myoclonus, autonomic instability with possibly rapid fluctuations of vital signs, and mental status changes. Separate atomoxetine and MAO inhibitor doses by 14 days.
Pressor agents: May increase blood pressure. Use together cautiously.
Strong CYP2D6 inhibitors (fluoxetine, paroxetine, quinidine): May increase atomoxetine level. Monitor patient closely.

Effects on lab test results

- May increase liver enzyme levels.

Pharmacokinetics

Absorption: Rapid.
Distribution: Mainly into total body water. 98% bound to plasma proteins, mainly albumin.
Metabolism: Mainly through CYP2D6. Absolute bioavailability is about 63% in patients with extensive metabolism and 94% in those with poor metabolism.
Excretion: More than 80% of the dose in urine, and less than 17% of the dose via feces. *Half-life:* 2½ hours.

Route	Onset	Peak	Duration
P.O.	Rapid	1–2 hr	Unknown

Action

Chemical effect: Unknown. May relate to selective inhibition of presynaptic norepinephrine transporter.
Therapeutic effect: Decreases symptoms of ADHD.

Available forms

Capsules: 10 mg, 18 mg, 25 mg, 40 mg, 60 mg, 80 mg, 100 mg

NURSING PROCESS

Assessment

- Assess patient's condition before therapy and regularly thereafter.
- Watch for hypersensitivity reaction and evidence of liver injury (nausea, anorexia, pruritus, jaundice, right upper quadrant pain, flulike symptoms).
- Assess patient's and family's knowledge of disease and drug therapy.

Nursing diagnoses

- Disturbed thought processes related to underlying disease
- Imbalanced nutrition: less than the body requires, related to adverse effect of medication
- Deficient knowledge related to drug therapy

Planning and implementation

- Use drug as part of a total treatment program for ADHD, with psychological, educational, and social intervention.
- Periodically reevaluate patients taking drug for extended periods to determine drug's usefulness.

ALERT: Monitor children and adolescents closely for agitation, irritability, and suicidal thinking or behaviors.

- Monitor growth during treatment. If growth or weight gain is unsatisfactory, consider stopping therapy.
- Monitor blood pressure and pulse at baseline, after each dose increase, and periodically during treatment.
- Monitor patient for urinary hesitancy, urine retention, and sexual dysfunction.

ALERT: If patient becomes jaundiced or has abnormal liver function test results, stop drug.

- The patient can stop drug without tapering.
- In case of overdose, monitor patient closely and provide supportive care. Perform gastric lavage and give activated charcoal to prevent absorption.

Patient teaching

- Advise parents to call prescriber immediately if their child develops unusual behaviors or suicidal thoughts.
- Tell pregnant women, women planning to become pregnant, and breast-feeding women to consult prescriber before taking drug.
- Tell patient to use caution when operating a vehicle or machinery until drug effects are known.
- Tell patient to report itching, yellow skin, yellow sclera, nausea or decreased appetite, abdominal pain, or flulike symptoms to prescriber immediately.

Evaluation

- Patient has reduced signs and symptoms of underlying disease.
- Patient maintains adequate nutritional status.
- Patient and family state understanding of drug therapy.

atorvastatin calcium

(uh-TOR-vah-stah-tin KAL-see-um)

Lipitor

Pharmacologic class: HMG-CoA reductase inhibitor
Therapeutic class: antilipemic
Pregnancy risk category: X

Indications and dosages

▶ **Adjunct to diet to reduce elevated LDL, total cholesterol, apo B, and triglyceride levels and to increase HDL level in patients with primary hypercholesterolemia (heterozygous familial and nonfamilial) and mixed dyslipidemia (Fredrickson Types IIa and IIb).** *Adults:* Initially, 10 or 20 mg P.O. once daily. Start dosage at 40 mg once daily for patients who require a reduction in LDL cholesterol level of more than 45%. Increase dose, as needed, to maximum of 80 mg daily as single dose. Base dosage on lipid levels drawn within 4 to 6 weeks after starting therapy.

▶ **Alone or as an adjunct to lipid-lowering treatments such as LDL apheresis to reduce total cholesterol and LDL levels in patients with homozygous familial hypercholesterolemia.** *Adults:* 10 to 80 mg P.O. daily.

▶ **Heterozygous familial hypercholesterolemia.** *Children ages 10 to 17:* Give 10 mg P.O. once daily. Adjust dosage after 4 weeks to 20 mg daily.

▶ **To reduce the risk of MI, stroke, angina, and revascularization procedures in patients with no evidence of CAD but with multiple risk factors.** *Adults:* 10 mg P.O. daily.

A

Contraindications and cautions

- Contraindicated in patients hypersensitive to drug and in those with active liver disease or conditions linked with unexplained persistent increases in transaminase levels. Also contraindicated in patients with serious, acute conditions that suggest myopathy and in those at risk for renal failure caused by rhabdomyolysis from trauma; major surgery; severe metabolic, endocrine, and electrolyte disorders; severe acute infection; hypotension; or uncontrolled seizures.
- Adolescent girls must be at least 1 year postmenarche.

Lifespan: In pregnant or breast-feeding women and in women who may become pregnant, drug is contraindicated.

Adverse reactions

CNS: asthenia, fever, *headache,* malaise.
CV: chest pain.
EENT: pharyngitis, sinusitis.
GI: abdominal pain, constipation, diarrhea, dyspepsia, flatulence.
Musculoskeletal: arthralgia, back pain, myalgia, ***rhabdomyolysis.***
Skin: rash, ***erythema multiforme, Stevens-Johnson syndrome, toxic epidermal necrolysis.***
Other: accidental injury, ***anaphylaxis, angioedema,*** flulike syndrome, hypersensitivity reaction, infection.

Interactions

Drug-drug. *Antacids:* May decrease bioavailability. Give separately.
Azole antifungals, cyclosporine, erythromycin, fibric acid derivatives, niacin: May increase risk of myopathy. Avoid use together.
Bile-acid sequestrants, such as colestipol: May decrease atorvastatin level; however, these drugs may be used together for therapeutic effect. Monitor patient.
Digoxin: May increase digoxin level. Monitor digoxin level.
Erythromycin: May increase drug level. Monitor patient.
Fluconazole, itraconazole, ketoconazole: May increase level and adverse effects of atorvastatin. Avoid this combination. If they must be given together, reduce atorvastatin dose.
Hormonal contraceptives: May increase hormone levels. Consider when selecting a hormonal contraceptive.
Warfarin: May increase anticoagulant effect. Monitor INR and patient for bleeding.
Drug-food. *Grapefruit juice:* Large quantities may increase atorvastatin level, increasing the risk of myopathy. Advise patient to avoid consuming large amounts of grapefruit juice.

Effects on lab test results

- May increase ALT and AST levels.

Pharmacokinetics

Absorption: Rapid.
Distribution: 98% bound to plasma proteins.
Metabolism: By liver.
Excretion: In bile. *Half life:* 14 hours.

Route	Onset	Peak	Duration
P.O.	Unknown	1–2 hr	20–30 hr

Action

Chemical effect: Selectively inhibits HMG-CoA reductase, which converts HMG-CoA to mevalonate, a precursor of sterols.
Therapeutic effect: Lowers cholesterol and lipoprotein levels.

Available forms

Tablets: 10 mg, 20 mg, 40 mg, 80 mg

NURSING PROCESS

Assessment

- Monitor patient's lipid and liver function levels at baseline and periodically thereafter.
- Monitor patient for signs of rhabdomyolysis, especially if taking more than one class of lipid-lowering drugs.
- Assess patient's and family's knowledge of drug therapy.

Nursing diagnoses

- Risk for injury related to elevated cholesterol levels
- Deficient knowledge related to drug therapy

Planning and implementation

- Use drug only after diet and other nondrug treatments prove ineffective. Patient should follow a low-cholesterol diet before and during therapy.
- Drug can be given as a single dose at any time of the day, with or without food.

• Obtain liver function test results and lipid levels before therapy, after 6 and 12 weeks, after a dosage increase, and periodically thereafter.
• Check CK level if patient complains of muscle pain, tenderness, or weakness.
ALERT: Don't confuse Lipitor with Levatol.

Patient teaching

• Teach patient about proper diet, weight control, and exercise, and explain their role in controlling elevated lipid levels.
• Warn patient to avoid alcohol.
• Tell patient to inform prescriber of adverse reactions, such as muscle pain, tenderness, or weakness, especially if accompanied by fever or malaise.
• Urge woman to notify prescriber immediately if pregnancy is suspected.

Evaluation

• Patient's cholesterol level is within normal limits.
• Patient and family state understanding of drug therapy.

atovaquone

(uh-TOH-vuh-kwohn)
Mepron

Pharmacologic class: ubiquinone analogue
Therapeutic class: antiprotozoal
Pregnancy risk category: C

Indications and dosages

▶ **Prevention of *Pneumocystis jiroveci (carinii)* pneumonia in patients who can't tolerate co-trimoxazole, including those infected with HIV.** *Adults and children age 13 and older:* 1,500 mg (10 ml) P.O. daily with food.
Infants ages 1 to 3 months and children older than 24 months‡: 30 mg/kg P.O. once daily.
Infants ages 4 to 24 months‡: 45 mg/kg P.O. daily.

▶ **Mild to moderate *P. jiroveci (carinii)* pneumonia in patients who can't tolerate co-trimoxazole.** *Adults and children age 13 and older:* 750 mg P.O. b.i.d. for 21 days.

▶ **Prevention of toxoplasmosis in HIV-infected patients‡.** *Adults and children age 13 and older:* 1,500 mg P.O. daily.

Contraindications and cautions

• Contraindicated in patients hypersensitive to drug.
• Use cautiously with other highly protein-bound drugs because drug is almost completely protein-bound. Also use cautiously in those with liver disease.
Lifespan: In pregnant and breast-feeding women, use cautiously. In children, safety of drug hasn't been established. In elderly patients, use cautiously.

Adverse reactions

CNS: asthenia, depression, dizziness, dreams, fever, *headache,* insomnia.
EENT: visual difficulties.
GI: *abdominal pain,* anorexia, diarrhea, dyspepsia, gastritis, *nausea,* oral ulcers, *vomiting.*
Musculoskeletal: myalgia.
Respiratory: cough, rhinitis, sinusitis.
Skin: pruritus, rash, sweating.
Other: flulike syndrome.

Interactions

Drug-drug. *Highly protein-bound drugs:* May compete for receptor sites affecting drug levels. Use together cautiously.
Rifabutin, rifampin: May decrease atovaquone's steady-state level. Avoid use together.

Effects on lab test results

• May increase alkaline phosphatase, ALT, and AST levels. May decrease hemoglobin level and hematocrit.
• May decrease WBC count.

Pharmacokinetics

Absorption: Limited. Bioavailability is doubled when given with meals. Fat enhances absorption significantly.
Distribution: 99.9% bound to plasma proteins.
Metabolism: Not metabolized.
Excretion: Undergoes enterohepatic cycling and is excreted mainly in feces. *Half-life:* 2 to 3 days.

Route	Onset	Peak	Duration
P.O.	Unknown	1–8 hr	Unknown

Action

Chemical effect: Unknown; may interfere with electron transport in protozoal mitochondria, in-

hibiting enzymes needed for synthesis of nucleic acids and adenosine triphosphate.
Therapeutic effect: Kills *P. jiroveci (carinii)* protozoa.

Available forms

Suspension: 750 mg/5 ml
Tablet: 250 mg

NURSING PROCESS

Assessment

- Obtain history of patient's protozoal respiratory infection, and reassess regularly.
- Be alert for adverse reactions.
- Monitor patient's hydration if adverse GI reactions occur.
- Assess patient's and family's knowledge of drug therapy.

Nursing diagnoses

- Ineffective protection related to presence of susceptible protozoal organisms
- Risk for deficient fluid volume related to drug-induced adverse GI reactions
- Deficient knowledge related to drug therapy

Planning and implementation

- Give drug with food to improve bioavailability.

Patient teaching

- Instruct patient to take drug with meals because food significantly enhances absorption.
- Warn patient not to perform hazardous activities if dizziness occurs.
- Emphasize importance of taking drug as prescribed, even if patient is feeling better.
- Tell patient to notify prescriber if serious adverse reactions occur.

Evaluation

- Patient's infection is eradicated.
- Patient remains adequately hydrated throughout therapy.
- Patient and family state understanding of drug therapy.

atracurium besylate

(at-truh-KYOO-ree-um BESS-eh-layt)
Tracrium

Pharmacologic class: nondepolarizing neuromuscular blocker
Therapeutic class: skeletal muscle relaxant
Pregnancy risk category: C

Indications and dosages

▶ **Adjunct to general anesthesia to facilitate endotracheal intubation and cause skeletal muscle relaxation during surgery or mechanical ventilation.** *Adults and children older than age 2:* Initially 0.4 to 0.5 mg/kg by I.V. bolus. During prolonged surgery, give maintenance dose of 0.08 to 0.1 mg/kg within 20 to 45 minutes of initial dose. Maintenance doses may be given q 15 to 25 minutes in patients receiving balanced anesthesia. During prolonged surgery, a constant infusion of 5 to 9 mcg/kg/minute may be used after initial bolus.
Children ages 1 month to 2 years: Initial dose, 0.3 to 0.4 mg/kg. Frequent maintenance doses may be needed.

I.V. administration

- Drug usually is given by rapid I.V. bolus injection but may be given by intermittent or continuous infusion.
- At 0.2 to 0.5 mg/ml, drug is compatible for 24 hours in D_5W, normal saline solution injection, or dextrose 5% in normal saline solution injection.

⊗ **Incompatibilities**
Acidic and alkaline solutions, lactated Ringer's solution.

Contraindications and cautions

- Contraindicated in patients hypersensitive to drug.
- Use cautiously in debilitated patients and patients with CV disease; severe electrolyte disorders; bronchogenic carcinoma; hepatic, renal, or pulmonary impairment; neuromuscular diseases; or myasthenia gravis.

Lifespan: In pregnant women, breast-feeding women, and elderly patients, use cautiously.

Adverse reactions

CV: ***bradycardia,*** *flushing,* hypotension, increased heart rate.
Respiratory: increased bronchial secretions, ***prolonged dose-related apnea,*** wheezing.
Skin: erythema, pruritus, urticaria.
Other: ***anaphylaxis.***

Interactions

Drug-drug. *Amikacin, gentamicin, neomycin, streptomycin, tobramycin:* May increase nondepolarizing muscle relaxant effects, including prolonged respiratory depression. Use together only when necessary, and reduce dose of nondepolarizing muscle relaxant.
Carbamazepine, phenytoin, theophylline: May decrease atracurium effects. Increase atracurium dose.
Clindamycin, general anesthetics (such as enflurane, halothane, isoflurane), kanamycin, polymyxin antibiotics (colistin, polymyxin B sulfate), quinidine: May potentiate neuromuscular blockade, leading to increased skeletal muscle relaxation and prolonged effect. Use cautiously during surgical and postoperative periods.
Lithium, magnesium salts, opioid analgesics: May potentiate neuromuscular blockade, which may lead to increased skeletal muscle relaxation and, possibly, respiratory paralysis. Reduce atracurium dose.

Effects on lab test results

None reported.

Pharmacokinetics

Absorption: Given I.V.
Distribution: Into extracellular space. About 82% protein-bound.
Metabolism: Rapidly by Hofmann elimination and by nonspecific enzymatic ester hydrolysis. The liver doesn't appear to play a major role.
Excretion: Drug and metabolites are excreted in urine and feces. *Half-life:* 20 minutes.

Route	Onset	Peak	Duration
I.V.	2 min	3–5 min	35–70 min

Action

Chemical effect: Prevents acetylcholine from binding to receptors on muscle end plate, thus blocking depolarization and resulting in skeletal muscle paralysis.
Therapeutic effect: Relaxes skeletal muscles.

Available forms

Injection: 10 mg/ml

NURSING PROCESS

Assessment

- Obtain history of patient's neuromuscular status before therapy, and reassess regularly.
- Be alert for adverse reactions and interactions.
- Monitor respirations closely until patient fully recovers from neuromuscular blockade, as shown by tests of muscle strength (hand grip, head lift, and ability to cough).
- A nerve stimulator and train-of-four monitoring are recommended to confirm antagonism of neuromuscular blockade and recovery of muscle strength. Before attempting reversal with neostigmine, patient should show some evidence of spontaneous recovery.
- Assess patient's and family's knowledge of drug therapy.

Nursing diagnoses

- Risk for injury related to underlying condition
- Impaired spontaneous ventilation related to drug-induced respiratory paralysis
- Deficient knowledge related to drug therapy

Planning and implementation

- Give sedatives or general anesthetics before neuromuscular blockers. Neuromuscular blockers don't decrease consciousness or alter pain threshold.

ALERT: Use this drug only under direct medical supervision by personnel skilled in use of neuromuscular blockers and techniques for maintaining a patent airway. Don't use unless facilities and equipment for mechanical ventilation, oxygen therapy, and intubation as well as an antagonist are immediately available.

- Don't give by I.M. injection.
- Prior use of succinylcholine doesn't prolong duration of action but quickens onset and may deepen neuromuscular blockade.
- Explain all events to patient because he can still hear.
- Give analgesics for pain. Patient may have pain but be unable to express it.
- Keep airway clear. Have emergency equipment and drugs available.
- After spontaneous recovery starts, reverse atracurium-induced neuromuscular blockade with an anticholinesterase (such as neostigmine

or edrophonium). These drugs usually are given with an anticholinergic (such as atropine).

Patient teaching

- Instruct patient and family about drug therapy.
- Reassure patient and family that patient will be monitored at all times and that respiratory life support will be used during paralysis.
- Reassure patient that pain medication will be given as needed.

Evaluation

- Patient's underlying condition is resolved without causing injury.
- Patient sustains spontaneous ventilation after effects of atracurium besylate wear off.
- Patient and family state understanding of drug therapy.

atropine sulfate

(AT-truh-peen SULL-fayt)

AtroPen Auto-Injector, Sal-Tropine

Pharmacologic class: anticholinergic, belladonna alkaloid
Therapeutic class: antiarrhythmic, vagolytic
Pregnancy risk category: C

Indications and dosages

▶ **Symptomatic bradycardia, bradyarrhythmia (junctional or escape rhythm).** *Adults:* Usually 0.5 to 1 mg I.V. push; repeat q 3 to 5 minutes to maximum of 2 mg, as needed. Lower doses (less than 0.5 mg) can cause bradycardia.
Children: 0.02 mg/kg I.V. to a maximum of 1 mg; or 0.3 mg/m^2; may repeat q 5 minutes.
▶ **Anticholinesterase insecticide poisoning.** *Adults and children:* 1 to 2 mg I.M. or I.V. repeated q 20 to 30 minutes until muscarinic symptoms disappear or signs of atropine toxicity appear. Patient with severe poisoning may require up to 6 mg q hour.
▶ **Preoperatively for decreasing secretions and blocking cardiac vagal reflexes.** *Adults and children weighing 20 kg (44 lb) or more:* 0.4 mg I.M. or subcutaneously 30 to 60 minutes before anesthesia.
Children weighing less than 20 kg: 0.1 mg I.M. for 3 kg, 0.2 mg I.M. for 4 to 9 kg, 0.3 mg I.M. for 10 to 20 kg, given 30 to 60 minutes before anesthesia.
▶ **Adjunct in peptic ulcer disease; functional GI disorders such as irritable bowel syndrome.** *Adults:* 0.4 to 0.6 mg P.O. q 4 to 6 hours.
Children: 0.01 mg/kg or 0.3 mg/m^2 (not to exceed 0.4 mg) q 4 to 6 hours.

I.V. administration

- Give by direct injection into a large vein or I.V. tubing over 1 to 2 minutes.

⊗ Incompatibilities

Alkalies, bromides, iodides, isoproterenol, methohexital, norepinephrine, pentobarbital sodium, sodium bicarbonate.

Contraindications and cautions

- Contraindicated in patients hypersensitive to drug and those with acute angle-closure glaucoma, obstructive uropathy, obstructive disease of GI tract, paralytic ileus, toxic megacolon, intestinal atony, unstable CV status in acute hemorrhage, asthma, or myasthenia gravis.
- Use cautiously in patients with Down syndrome.

Lifespan: In pregnant women, use cautiously. Use in breast-feeding women isn't recommended. In children and elderly patients, use cautiously because they may have increased adverse effects.

Adverse reactions

CNS: agitation, ataxia, ***coma***, confusion, delirium, disorientation, *dizziness*, excitement, hallucinations, *headache, insomnia, restlessness.*
CV: *angina*, ***arrhythmias***, flushing, *palpitations, tachycardia.*
EENT: *blurred vision, mydriasis*, photophobia.
GI: *constipation, dry mouth*, nausea, thirst, vomiting.
GU: urine retention.
Hematologic: leukocytosis.
Other: ***anaphylaxis.***

Interactions

Drug-drug. *Antacids:* May decrease anticholinergic absorption. Give at least 1 hour apart.
Anticholinergics, drugs with anticholinergic effects (such as amantadine, antiarrhythmics, antiparkinsonians, glutethimide, meperidine, phenothiazines, tricyclic antidepressants): May cause additive anticholinergic effects. Use together cautiously.

Ketoconazole, levodopa: May decrease absorption. Avoid use together.
Methotrimeprazine: May produce extrapyramidal symptoms. Monitor patient carefully.
Potassium chloride wax matrix tablets: May increase risk of mucosal lesions. Use together cautiously.

Effects on lab test results

• May increase WBC count.

Pharmacokinetics

Absorption: Well absorbed after P.O. and I.M. use; unknown for subcutaneous use.
Distribution: Throughout the body, including CNS. 18% bound to plasma proteins.
Metabolism: In liver to several metabolites.
Excretion: Mainly through kidneys; small amount in feces and expired air. *Half-life:* Initial, 2 hours; second phase, 12½ hours.

Route	Onset	Peak	Duration
P.O.	½ hr	2 hr	4 hr
I.V.	Immediate	2–4 min	4 hr
I.M.	30 min	1–1½ hr	4 hr
SubQ	Unknown	Unknown	4 hr

Action

Chemical effect: Inhibits acetylcholine at parasympathetic neuroeffector junction, blocking vagal effects on SA node, enhancing conduction through AV node, and speeding heart rate.
Therapeutic effect: Increases heart rate, decreases secretions, and slows GI motility. Antidote for anticholinesterase insecticide poisoning.

Available forms

Injection: 0.05 mg/ml, 0.1 mg/ml, 0.3 mg/ml, 0.4 mg/ml, 0.5 mg/ml, 0.8 mg/ml, 1 mg/ml
Tablets: 0.4 mg

NURSING PROCESS

Assessment

• Obtain history of patient's underlying condition, and reassess regularly.
• Be alert for adverse reactions and drug interactions.
• Monitor patients, especially those receiving doses of 0.4 to 0.6 mg, for paradoxical initial bradycardia, which is caused by a drug effect in CNS and usually disappears within 2 minutes.
ALERT: Watch for tachycardia in cardiac patients because it may cause ventricular fibrillation.
• Assess patient's and family's knowledge of drug therapy.

Nursing diagnoses

• Ineffective health maintenance related to underlying condition
• Risk for injury related to drug-induced adverse reactions
• Deficient knowledge related to drug therapy

Planning and implementation

• Give with or without food.
• If ECG disturbances occur, withhold drug, obtain a rhythm strip, and notify prescriber immediately.
• Have emergency equipment and drugs on hand to treat new arrhythmias. Other anticholinergics may increase vagal blockage.
• Use physostigmine salicylate as antidote for atropine overdose.

Patient teaching

• Teach patient about atropine sulfate therapy.
• Instruct patient to ask for assistance with activities if adverse CNS reactions occur.
• Teach patient how to handle distressing anticholinergic effects.

Evaluation

• Patient's underlying condition improves.
• Patient has no injury as a result of therapy.
• Patient and family state understanding of drug therapy.

azacitidine

(az-uh-SIT-uh-deen)
Vidaza

Pharmacologic class: pyrimidine nucleoside analogue
Therapeutic class: antineoplastic
Pregnancy risk category: D

Indications and dosages

▶ **Myelodysplastic syndrome, including refractory anemia, refractory anemia with ringed sideroblasts (if patient has neutrope-**

nia or thrombocytopenia or needs transfusions), refractory anemia with excess blasts, refractory anemia with excess blasts in transformation, or chronic myelomonocytic leukemia. *Adults:* Initially, 75 mg/m² subcutaneously daily for 7 days, repeating cycle q 4 weeks. May increase to 100 mg/m² if no response after two treatment cycles and nausea and vomiting are the only toxic reactions. At least four treatment cycles are recommended.

Adjust-a-dose: If bicarbonate level is less than 20 mEq/L, reduce next dose by 50%. If BUN or creatinine level rises during treatment, delay the next cycle until they're normal, and then give 50% of previous dose.

Make further adjustments based on hematologic and renal toxicities.

Contraindications and cautions

- Contraindicated in patients hypersensitive to azacitidine or mannitol and in patients with advanced malignant hepatic tumors.
- Use cautiously in patients with hepatic and renal disease.

Lifespan: In pregnant patients, avoid use. In breast-feeding women, avoid use because drug may cause cancer in fetus. In children, safety and effectiveness haven't been established.

Adverse reactions

CNS: *anxiety, depression, dizziness, fatigue, headache,* hypoesthesia, *insomnia,* lethargy, *malaise,* pain, syncope, *weakness.*
CV: *cardiac murmur, chest pain, edema,* hypotension, peripheral swelling, tachycardia.
EENT: *epistaxis,* nasal congestion, *nasopharyngitis, pharyngitis,* postnasal drip, *rhinorrhea,* sinusitis.
GI: abdominal distension, *abdominal pain and tenderness, anorexia, constipation, decreased appetite, diarrhea,* dyspepsia, dysphagia, gingival bleeding, hemorrhoids, loose stools, mouth hemorrhage, *nausea,* oral mucosal petechiae, stomatitis, tongue ulceration, *vomiting.*
GU: dysuria, UTI.
Hematologic: *anemia,* FEBRILE NEUTROPENIA, hematoma, LEUKOPENIA, NEUTROPENIA, postprocedural hemorrhage, THROMBOCYTOPENIA.
Metabolic: *weight loss.*
Musculoskeletal: *arthralgia, back pain, limb pain,* muscle cramps, *myalgia.*
Respiratory: *atelectasis, cough, crackles, dyspnea,* pleural effusion, *rales, rhonchi, pneumonia, upper respiratory tract infection,* wheezing.
Skin: *bruising,* dry skin, granuloma, *pain,* pigmentation, pruritus, or swelling at injection site; cellulitis; *contusion; ecchymosis; erythema; increased sweating; injection site reaction;* night sweats; *pallor; petechiae; pitting edema; rash; skin lesion;* skin nodules; urticaria.
Other: herpes simplex, lymphadenopathy, *pyrexia, rigors.*

Interactions

None reported.

Effects on lab test results

- May increase creatinine and BUN levels. May decrease bicarbonate, potassium, and hemoglobin levels and hematocrit.
- May decrease WBC, neutrophil, and platelet counts.

Pharmacokinetics

Absorption: Rapid.
Distribution: Mean volume isn't known.
Metabolism: By the liver.
Excretion: Mainly in urine, with less than 1% in feces. *Half-life:* About 40 minutes.

Route	Onset	Peak	Duration
SubQ	Unknown	30 min	Unknown

Action

Chemical effect: Causes demethylation or hypomethylation of DNA and is toxic to abnormal hematopoietic cells in bone marrow. Hypomethylation may restore normal function to genes needed for proliferation and differentiation. Drug has little effect on nonproliferating cells.
Therapeutic effect: Restores normal bone marrow function.

Available forms

Powder for injection: 100-mg vials

NURSING PROCESS

Assessment

- Assess patient's condition before therapy and regularly thereafter.
- Check liver function test results and bicarbonate and creatinine levels before therapy starts.

• Obtain CBC before each cycle or more often.
• If patient has renal impairment, monitor him closely; check metabolic panel to assess electrolytes and renal function.
• Assess patient's and family's knowledge of drug therapy.

Nursing diagnoses

• Ineffective health maintenance related to presence of underlying disease
• Ineffective protection related to both underlying disease and drug-induced adverse hematologic reactions
• Deficient knowledge related to drug therapy

Planning and implementation

• Give antiemetic before therapy.
• Dilute using aseptic and hazardous substances techniques. Reconstitute with 4 ml sterile water for injection. Invert vial two to three times and gently rotate until a uniform suspension forms. The resulting cloudy suspension will be 25 mg/ml. Draw up suspension into syringes for injection (no more than 4 ml per syringe).
• Just before giving drug, resuspend it by inverting the syringe two to three times and gently rolling between palms for 30 seconds. Divide doses larger than 4 ml into two syringes and inject into two separate sites. Give new injection at least 1″ from previous site and never into tender, bruised, red, or hardened skin.
• Store unreconstituted vials at room temperature (59° to 86° F [15° to 30° C]).
• Reconstituted drug is stable 1 hour at room temperature and 8 hours refrigerated (36° to 46° F [2° to 8° C]). After refrigeration, suspension may be allowed to equilibrate for 30 minutes at room temperature.
ALERT: Don't confuse azacitidine with gemcitabine.

Patient teaching

• Inform patient about potential decrease in blood counts with febrile neutropenia, thrombocytopenia, and anemia.
• Advise men and women to use birth control during azacitidine therapy.

Evaluation

• Patient responds well to the drug.
• Patient doesn't develop serious complications from adverse hematologic reactions.
• Patient and family state understanding of drug therapy.

azathioprine

(ay-zuh-THIGH-oh-preen)
Azasan, Imuran, Thioprine ◊

Pharmacologic class: purine antagonist
Therapeutic class: immunosuppressant
Pregnancy risk category: D

Indications and dosages

▶ **Immunosuppression in kidney transplantation.** *Adults and children:* Initially, 3 to 5 mg/kg P.O. or I.V. daily, usually starting on day of transplantation. Maintain at 1 to 3 mg/kg daily depending on patient response.
▶ **Severe, refractory rheumatoid arthritis.** *Adults:* Initially, 1 mg/kg (about 50 mg to 100 mg) P.O. daily as single dose or as two doses. If patient response isn't satisfactory after 6 to 8 weeks, increase dosage by 0.5 mg/kg daily (up to maximum of 2.5 mg/kg daily) at 4-week intervals.

I.V. administration

• Reconstitute 100-mg vial with 10 ml of sterile water for injection. Inspect for particles before infusing or injecting.
• Drug may be given by direct I.V. injection or further diluted in normal saline solution or D_5W and infused over 30 to 60 minutes.
• Use only for patient who can't tolerate P.O. drugs.
⊗ **Incompatibilities**
None reported.

Contraindications and cautions

• Contraindicated in patients hypersensitive to drug.
• Use cautiously in patients with hepatic or renal dysfunction.
Lifespan: In pregnant women, don't use for rheumatoid arthritis. In breast-feeding women, drug isn't recommended.

Adverse reactions

GI: anorexia, esophagitis, mouth ulceration, nausea, ***pancreatitis,*** steatorrhea, vomiting.
Hematologic: anemia, ***bone marrow suppression,*** LEUKOPENIA, ***pancytopenia,*** THROMBOCYTOPENIA.
Hepatic: ***hepatotoxicity,*** jaundice.
Musculoskeletal: arthralgia, muscle wasting.

Skin: alopecia, pruritus, rash.
Other: ***immunosuppression,*** infections, ***neoplasia.***

Interactions

Drug-drug. *ACE inhibitors:* May cause severe leukopenia. Monitor patient closely.
Allopurinol: May impair inactivation of azathioprine. Decrease azathioprine dose to one-fourth or one-third normal dose.
Co-trimoxazole and other drugs that interfere with myelopoiesis: May cause severe leukopenia, especially in renal transplant patients. Use together cautiously.
Cyclosporine: May decrease cyclosporine level. Monitor level.
Methotrexate: May increase 6-MP metabolite level. Monitor patient for increased adverse effects.
Nondepolarizing neuromuscular blockers: May decrease or reverse effects of these drugs. Monitor patient for clinical effects.
Vaccines: May decrease immune response. Postpone routine immunization.
Warfarin: May inhibit anticoagulant effect of warfarin. Monitor PT and INR.

Effects on lab test results

- May increase AST, ALT, alkaline phosphatase, and bilirubin levels. May decrease uric acid and hemoglobin levels and hematocrit.
- May decrease WBC, RBC, and platelet counts.

Pharmacokinetics

Absorption: Good.
Distribution: Throughout body. I.V. and P.O. forms are 30% protein-bound.
Metabolism: Mainly to mercaptopurine; tissue levels of thiopurine nucleotide produce clinical effects.
Excretion: Small amounts of azathioprine and mercaptopurine intact in urine; most of given dose is excreted in urine as secondary metabolites. *Half-life:* About 5 hours.

Route	Onset	Peak	Duration
P.O., I.V.	Unknown	1–2 hr	Unknown

Action

Chemical effect: Unknown.
Therapeutic effect: Suppresses immune system activity.

Available forms

Injection: 100 mg
Tablets: 25 mg, 50 mg, 75 mg, 100 mg

NURSING PROCESS

Assessment

- Obtain history of patient's immune status before therapy.
- Monitor effectiveness by observing patient for signs of organ rejection. Therapeutic response usually occurs within 8 weeks.
- Be alert for adverse reactions and drug interactions.
- Monitor hemoglobin level, hematocrit, and WBC and platelet counts at least once monthly—more often at start of treatment.
- Assess patient's and family's knowledge of drug therapy.

Nursing diagnoses

- Ineffective protection related to threat of organ rejection
- Risk for infection related to drug-induced immunosuppression
- Deficient knowledge related to drug therapy

Planning and implementation

- Give in divided doses or after meals to minimize adverse GI effects.
- Benefits must be weighed against risks with systemic viral infections, such as chickenpox and herpes zoster.
- Patients with rheumatoid arthritis previously treated with alkylating drugs, such as cyclophosphamide, chlorambucil, and melphalan, may have prohibitive risk of neoplasia if treated with azathioprine.
- To prevent irreversible bone marrow suppression, stop drug immediately when WBC count is less than 3,000/mm³. Notify prescriber.
- To prevent bleeding, avoid I.M. injections when platelet count is lower than 100,000/mm³.

ALERT: Don't confuse azathioprine with azidothymidine, Azulfidine, or azatadine. Don't confuse Imuran with Inderal.

Patient teaching

- Warn patient to report even mild infections (colds, fever, sore throat, and malaise) because drug is a potent immunosuppressant.
- Instruct woman to avoid conception during therapy and for 4 months after stopping.
- Warn patient that thinning of hair is possible.

• Tell patient taking this drug for refractory rheumatoid arthritis that it may take up to 12 weeks to be effective.

Evaluation

• Patient has no signs of organ rejection.

• Patient has no signs and symptoms of infection.

• Patient and family state understanding of drug therapy.

azelastine hydrochloride

(ah-zuh-LAST-een high-droh-KLOR-ighd)
Astelin, Optivar

Pharmacologic class: H_1-receptor antagonist
Therapeutic class: antihistamine
Pregnancy risk category: C

Indications and dosages

▶ **Seasonal allergic rhinitis, such as rhinorrhea, sneezing, and nasal pruritus.** *Adults and children age 12 and older:* 2 sprays (274 mcg/2 sprays) per nostril b.i.d.
Children ages 5 to 11 years: 1 spray (137 mcg/spray) per nostril b.i.d.

▶ **Vasomotor rhinitis, such as rhinorrhea, nasal congestion, and postnasal drip.** *Adults and children age 12 and older:* 2 sprays (274 mcg/2 sprays) per nostril b.i.d.

▶ **Allergic conjunctivitis.** *Adults and children older than age 3:* Give 1 drop into affected eye b.i.d.

Contraindications and cautions

• Contraindicated in patients hypersensitive to drug.

• Use cautiously in patients with pulmonary conditions because drug can cause thickened secretions.

Lifespan: In pregnant women, drug should be used only if benefit justifies risk to fetus. Breast-feeding women shouldn't take drug. In children younger than age 5, safety and effectiveness haven't been established for treating seasonal allergic rhinitis. In children younger than age 12, don't use drug for vasomotor rhinitis.

Adverse reactions

CNS: dizziness, dysesthesia, fatigue, *headaches, somnolence.*
EENT: conjunctivitis, epistaxis, eye pain, nasal burning, paroxysmal sneezing, pharyngitis, rhinitis, sinusitis, stinging, transient eye burning, temporary eye blurring.
GI: *bitter taste,* dry mouth, nausea.
Metabolic: weight increase.
Respiratory: ***asthma,*** dyspnea.
Skin: pruritus.
Other: flulike symptoms.

Interactions

Drug-drug. *Cimetidine:* May increase azelastine level. Avoid use together.
CNS depressants: May reduce alertness and impair CNS performance. Avoid use together.
Drug-lifestyle. *Alcohol use:* May reduce alertness and cause CNS impairment if using the nasal spray. Discourage use together.

Effects on lab test results

None reported.

Pharmacokinetics

Absorption: Ophthalmic solution has low absorption.
Distribution: Systemic bioavailability is 40%.
Metabolism: After reaching steady state, level ranges from 20% to 50%.
Excretion: Oral drug is 75% excreted in feces. Less than 10% remains unchanged. *Half-life:* 22 hours.

Route	Onset	Peak	Duration
Nasal	Unknown	2–3 hr	12 hr
Ophthalmic	3 min	Unknown	8 hr

Action

Chemical effect: Exerts H_1-receptor antagonist activity.
Therapeutic effect: Relieves seasonal allergic rhinitis and conjunctivitis.

Available forms

Nasal solution: 1 mg/ml (137 mcg/spray)
Ophthalmic solution: 0.05%

NURSING PROCESS

Assessment

• Obtain history of patient's allergy condition before therapy begins, and reassess regularly thereafter.

• Be alert for adverse reactions and drug interactions.
• Assess patient's and family's knowledge of drug therapy.

Nursing diagnoses
• Ineffective health maintenance related to underlying allergic condition
• Deficient knowledge related to drug therapy

Planning and implementation
• Don't contaminate eye dropper tip or solution.
• Make sure patient removes contact lenses before giving eyedrops. Tell patient to wait at least 10 minutes before reinserting them.
• When using nasal spray, avoid spraying into patient's eyes.

Patient teaching
• Warn patient not to drive or perform hazardous activities if somnolence occurs.
• Advise patient not to use alcohol, CNS depressants, or other antihistamines while taking drug.
• Teach patient proper use of nasal spray: Replace child-resistant screw top on bottle with pump unit. Prime delivery system with four sprays or until a fine mist appears. If 3 or more days have elapsed since last use, reprime system with 2 sprays or until a fine mist appears. Store bottle upright at room temperature with pump closed tightly. Keep unit away from children.
• Tell patient to avoid getting nasal spray in eyes.

Evaluation
• Patient's allergic symptoms are relieved with drug therapy.
• Patient and family state understanding of drug therapy.

azithromycin
(uh-zith-roh-MIGH-sin)
Zithromax, Zmax

Pharmacologic class: azalide macrolide
Therapeutic class: antibiotic
Pregnancy risk category: B

Indications and dosages
▶ **Acute bacterial exacerbations of chronic obstructive pulmonary disease caused by *Haemophilus influenzae, Moraxella catarrhalis,* or *Streptococcus pneumoniae;* uncomplicated skin and skin-structure infections caused by *Staphylococcus aureus, Streptococcus pyogenes,* or *Streptococcus agalactiae;* and second-line therapy for pharyngitis or tonsillitis caused by *S. pyogenes.*** *Adults and children age 16 and older:* Initially, 500 mg P.O. as a single dose on day 1, followed by 250 mg daily on days 2 through 5. Total cumulative dose is 1.5 g. Or for COPD exacerbations, 500 mg P.O. daily for 3 days.
▶ **Community-acquired pneumonia caused by *Chlamydia pneumoniae, H. influenzae, Mycoplasma pneumoniae, S. pneumoniae;* I.V. form is also used for *Legionella pneumophila, M. catarrhalis,* and *S. aureus.*** *Adults and children age 16 and older:* 500 mg P.O. as a single dose on day 1, followed by 250 mg P.O. daily on days 2 through 5. Total dosage is 1.5 g. For patients who need initial I.V. therapy, 500 mg I.V. as a single daily dose for 2 days, followed by 500 mg P.O. as a single daily dose to complete a 7- to 10-day course. Switch from I.V. to P.O. route at prescriber's discretion and based on patient's response.
Children age 6 months and older: 10 mg/kg (maximum 500 mg) P.O. as a single dose on day 1, followed by 5 mg/kg (maximum 250 mg) daily on days 2 through 5.
▶ **Single-dose treatment for mild to moderate acute bacterial sinusitis caused by *H. influenzae, M. catarrhalis,* or *S. pneumoniae;* community-acquired pneumonia caused by *Chlamydophila pneumoniae, H. influenzae, Mycoplasma pneumoniae,* or *S. pneumoniae.*** *Adults:* 2 g P.O. (Zmax) as a single dose 1 hour before or 2 hours after a meal.
▶ **Nongonococcal urethritis or cervicitis caused by *Chlamydia trachomatis.*** *Adults and children age 16 and older:* 1 g P.O. as a single dose.
▶ **Prevention of disseminated *Mycobacterium avium* complex (MAC) disease in patients with advanced HIV infection.** *Adults:* 1,200 mg P.O. once weekly, as indicated.
Infants and children‡: 20 mg/kg P.O. (maximum, 1.2 g) weekly or 5 mg/kg (maximum, 250 mg) can be given P.O. daily. Children age 6 and older may also receive rifabutin 300 mg P.O. daily.
▶ **Disseminated MAC in patients with advanced HIV infection.** *Adults:* 600 mg P.O. daily with ethambutol 15 mg/kg daily.

▶ **Urethritis and cervicitis caused by *Neisseria gonorrhoeae.*** *Adults:* 2 g P.O. as a single dose.

▶ **Pelvic inflammatory disease caused by *C. trachomatis, N. gonorrhoeae,* or *Mycoplasma hominis* in patients who need initial I.V. therapy.** *Adults and adolescents age 16 and older:* 500 mg I.V. as a single daily dose for 1 to 2 days, followed by 250 mg P.O. daily to complete a 7-day course. Switch from I.V. to P.O. route at prescriber's discretion and based on patient's response.

▶ **Genital ulcer disease caused by *Haemophilus ducreyi* (chancroid) in men, women‡, and children‡.** *Adults:* 1 g P.O. as a single dose.
Children and infants‡: 20 mg/kg (maximum, 1 g) P.O. as a single dose.

▶ **Acute otitis media.** *Children older than age 6 months:* 30 mg/kg P.O. as a single dose. Or, 10 mg/kg P.O. once daily for 3 days. Or 10 mg/kg P.O. on day 1; then 5 mg/kg once daily on days 2 to 5.

▶ **Pharyngitis, tonsillitis caused by *S. pyogenes.*** *Children age 2 and older:* 12 mg/kg (maximum, 500 mg) P.O. daily for 5 days.

▶ **Prophylaxis for sexual assault victims‡.** *Adults:* 1 g P.O. as a single dose (conventional, immediate-release tablets) with metronidazole and ceftriaxone.

▶ **Prophylaxis of bacterial endocarditis in penicillin-allergic patients at moderate to high risk‡.** *Adults:* 500 mg P.O. 1 hour before the procedure.
Children: 15 mg/kg P.O. 1 hour before the procedure. Don't exceed adult dose.

▶ ***Chlamydial ophthalmia* neonatorum ◇.** *Infants:* 20 mg/kg once daily P.O. for 3 days.

I.V. administration

- Reconstitute drug by adding 4.8 ml sterile water for injection to 500-mg vial and shaking until all the drug is dissolved. Further dilute in 250 to 500 ml D_5W, normal saline solution, or other compatible solution.
- Infuse over 1 to 3 hours.
- Reconstituted solution is stable for 7 days if stored in refrigerator (41° F [5° C]).
- Don't give by I.V. injection or bolus.

⊗ **Incompatibilities**
Amikacin, aztreonam, cefotaxime, ceftazidime, ceftriaxone, cefuroxime, ciprofloxacin, clindamycin, famotidine, fentanyl, furosemide, gentamicin, imipenem and cilastatin, ketorolac, levofloxacin, morphine, ondansetron, piperacillin and tazobactam sodium potassium chloride, ticarcillin disodium and clavulanate potassium, tobramycin.

Contraindications and cautions

- Contraindicated in patients hypersensitive to erythromycin or other macrolides.
- Use cautiously in patients with impaired hepatic function.

Lifespan: In pregnant or breast-feeding women, use cautiously.

Adverse reactions

CNS: aggressive reaction, anxiety, dizziness, fatigue, headache, ***seizures,*** somnolence, vertigo.
CV: chest pain, palpitations, ***QT-interval prolongation, torsades de pointes.***
EENT: hearing loss, taste perversion, tinnitus.
GI: *abdominal pain,* cholestatic jaundice, *diarrhea,* dyspepsia, flatulence, melena, *nausea,* ***pseudomembranous colitis,*** *vomiting.*
GU: candidiasis, nephritis, vaginitis.
Hematologic: mild neutropenia, ***thrombocytopenia.***
Hepatic: cholestatic jaundice, ***hepatic failure, hepatic necrosis,*** hepatitis.
Skin: photosensitivity, rash, ***Stevens-Johnson syndrome, toxic epidermal necrolysis,*** urticaria.
Other: ***anaphylaxis, angioedema.***

Interactions

Drug-drug. *Antacids containing aluminum and magnesium:* May lower peak azithromycin level. Separate doses by at least 2 hours.
Digoxin: May elevate digoxin level. Monitor patient closely.
Dihydroergotamine, ergotamine: May cause acute ergot toxicity. Avoid use together.
Drugs metabolized by cytochrome P-450 system: May elevate carbamazepine, cyclosporine, hexobarbital, and phenytoin levels. Monitor patient closely.
Theophylline: May increase theophylline level with other macrolides; effect of azithromycin is unknown. Monitor theophylline level carefully.
Triazolam: May increase pharmacologic effect of triazolam. Use together cautiously.
Warfarin: May increase PT with other macrolides; effect of azithromycin is unknown. Monitor PT and INR carefully.

A

Drug-food. *Any food:* May decrease rate of absorption, but not effectiveness of drug.
Drug-lifestyle. *Sun exposure:* May cause photosensitivity reactions. Advise against prolonged or unprotected sun exposure.

Effects on lab test results

None reported.

Pharmacokinetics

Absorption: Rapid. Food decreases both maximum level and amount of drug absorbed.
Distribution: Rapid throughout body and readily penetrates cells; drug doesn't readily enter CNS. Drug concentrates in fibroblasts and phagocytes. Significantly higher levels are reached in tissues compared with plasma.
Metabolism: None.
Excretion: Mostly in feces after excretion into bile. Less than 10% in urine. *Terminal elimination half-life:* 68 hours.

Route	Onset	Peak	Duration
P.O.	Unknown	2½–4½ hr	Unknown
I.V.	Unknown	Unknown	Unknown

Action

Chemical effect: Binds to 50S subunit of bacterial ribosomes, blocking protein synthesis; bacteriostatic or bactericidal, depending on concentration.
Therapeutic effect: Hinders or kills susceptible bacteria, including many gram-positive and gram-negative aerobic and anaerobic bacteria.

Available forms

Injection: 500 mg
Powder for oral suspension: 100 mg/5 ml, 200 mg/5 ml; 1,000 mg/packet
Powder for oral suspension (extended-release): 2 g
Tablets: 250 mg, 500 mg, 600 mg

NURSING PROCESS

Assessment

- Obtain history of patient's infection before therapy, and reassess the patient regularly thereafter.
- Obtain specimen for culture and sensitivity tests before first dose. Therapy may begin pending test results.
- Be alert for adverse reactions and drug interactions.
- Assess patient's and family's knowledge of drug therapy.

Nursing diagnoses

- Ineffective protection related to drug-induced superinfection
- Deficient knowledge related to drug therapy

Planning and implementation

ALERT: Don't give drug I.M. or by I.V. bolus injection.
- If patient vomits within 5 minutes of drinking extended-release solution, consider additional antibiotic treatment. If patient vomits 5 to 60 minutes after drinking it, consider alternative treatment. If patient vomits more than 60 minutes after drinking, no further treatment is needed.
- Don't give with antacids.

Patient teaching
- Tell patient that tablets or oral suspension may be taken with or without food, but that taking with food may decrease risk of nausea.
- Tell patient to take all medication as prescribed, even after he feels better.
- Instruct patient to use sunblock and avoid prolonged exposure to the sun to decrease risk of photosensitivity reactions.

Evaluation

- Patient doesn't experience superinfection during therapy.
- Patient and family state understanding of drug therapy.

aztreonam

(az-TREE-oh-nam)
Azactam

Pharmacologic class: monobactam
Therapeutic class: antibiotic
Pregnancy risk category: B

Indications and dosages

▶ **UTI, lower respiratory tract infection, septicemia, skin and skin-structure infections, intra-abdominal infection, surgical infection, gynecologic infection caused by various aerobic organisms; or as adjunct therapy to**

pelvic inflammatory disease‡ or gonorrhea‡. *Adults:* 500 mg to 2 g I.V. or I.M. q 8 to 12 hours. For severe systemic or life-threatening infection, 2 g q 6 to 8 hours. Maximum, 8 g daily.

▶ **Infections of the respiratory or GU tract, bone, skin, or soft tissues caused by susceptible organisms‡.** *Neonates ages 1 to 4 weeks weighing more than 2 kg (4.4 lb):* 30 mg/kg I.V. q 6 hours.

Neonates ages 1 to 4 weeks weighing 2 kg or less: 30 mg/kg I.V. q 8 hours.

Neonates younger than 7 days weighing more than 2 kg: 30 mg/kg I.V. q 8 hours.

Neonates younger than 7 days weighing 2 kg or less: 30 mg/kg I.V. q 12 hours.

I.V. administration

- Inject bolus dose drug over 3 to 5 minutes directly into vein or I.V. tubing.
- Give infusion over 20 minutes to 1 hour.

⊗ **Incompatibilities**

Acyclovir, amphotericin B, ampicillin sodium, azithromycin, cephradine, chlorpromazine, daunorubicin, ganciclovir, lorazepam, metronidazole, mitomycin, mitoxantrone, nafcillin, other I.V. drugs, prochlorperazine, streptozocin, vancomycin.

Contraindications and cautions

- Contraindicated in patients hypersensitive to drug.
- Use cautiously in patients with impaired renal function. Dosage adjustment may be needed.

Lifespan: In breast-feeding women, drug isn't recommended. In children, safety of drug hasn't been established. In elderly patients, use cautiously because dosage adjustment may be needed.

Adverse reactions

CNS: confusion, headache, insomnia, ***seizures.***
CV: hypotension.
EENT: altered taste, halitosis.
GI: diarrhea, nausea, vomiting.
Hematologic: anemia, ***neutropenia, pancytopenia, thrombocytopenia.***
Other: discomfort or swelling at I.M. injection site, hypersensitivity reactions (***anaphylaxis,*** rash), rash or thrombophlebitis at I.V. site.

Interactions

Drug-drug. *Aminoglycosides, beta-lactam antibiotics, other anti-infectives:* May have synergistic effect and increase risk of ototoxicity, nephrotoxicity. Monitor patient closely.
Cefoxitin, imipenem: May have antagonistic effect. Avoid use together.
Furosemide, probenecid: May increase aztreonam level. Avoid use together.

Effects on lab test results

- May increase BUN, creatinine, ALT, AST, and LDH levels. May decrease hemoglobin level and hematocrit.
- May increase PT, PTT, and INR. May decrease neutrophil and RBC counts. May increase or decrease WBC and platelet counts.

Pharmacokinetics

Absorption: Rapid and complete.
Distribution: Rapid and wide to all body fluids and tissues, including bile, breast milk, and CSF.
Metabolism: From 6% to 16% metabolized to inactive metabolites by nonspecific hydrolysis of beta-lactam ring; 56% to 60% protein-bound, less if renal impairment is present.
Excretion: Mainly unchanged in urine by glomerular filtration and tubular secretion; 1.5% to 3.5% unchanged in feces. *Half-life:* Average 2 hours.

Route	Onset	Peak	Duration
I.V.	Immediate	Immediate	Unknown
I.M.	Unknown	½–1¼ hr	Unknown

Action

Chemical effect: Inhibits bacterial cell-wall synthesis, ultimately causing cell-wall destruction.
Therapeutic effect: Kills susceptible bacteria.

Available forms

Injection: 500-mg, 1-g, 2-g vials

NURSING PROCESS

Assessment

- Obtain history of patient's infection before therapy, and reassess regularly thereafter.
- Obtain urine specimen for culture and sensitivity tests before giving first dose. Therapy may begin pending test results.
- Be aware of adverse reactions and drug interactions.

• Patients who are allergic to penicillins or cephalosporins may not be allergic to this drug. However, closely monitor patients who have had an immediate hypersensitivity reaction to these antibiotics.

• Assess patient's and family's knowledge of drug therapy.

Nursing diagnoses

• Ineffective protection related to drug-induced superinfection

• Deficient knowledge related to drug therapy

Planning and implementation

• Give I.M. injection deep into large muscle mass, such as the upper outer quadrant of gluteus maximus or the outer thigh. Give doses larger than 1 g by I.V. route.

• Report diarrhea to the prescriber. Pseudomembranous colitis may need to be ruled out.

• Monitor renal and hepatic function.

Patient teaching

• Tell patient to report pain or discomfort at I.V. site.

• Warn patient receiving drug I.M. that pain and swelling may develop at injection site.

• Instruct patient to report signs or symptoms that suggest superinfection.

Evaluation

• Patient doesn't develop superinfection as a result of therapy.

• Patient and family state understanding of drug therapy.

B

baclofen

(BAH-kloh-fen)

Clofen ◊, Kemstro, Lioresal, Lioresal Intrathecal

Pharmacologic class: chlorophenyl derivative (GABA derivative)

Therapeutic class: skeletal muscle relaxant

Pregnancy risk category: C

Indications and dosages

▶ **Spasticity in multiple sclerosis, spinal cord injury.** *Adults:* Initially, 5 mg P.O. t.i.d. for 3 days. Based on response, increase dosage at 3-day intervals by 15 mg (5 mg/dose) daily to maximum of 80 mg daily (20 mg q.i.d.).

▶ **Severe spasticity in patients who don't respond to or can't tolerate oral baclofen therapy.** *Adults (screening phase):* Give test dose of 50 mcg in 1-ml dilution into intrathecal space by barbotage over 1 minute or longer. After test dose, give drug by implantable infusion pump. Muscle tone should be reduced or muscle spasm significantly decreased in severity or frequency in 4 to 8 hours. If response is inadequate, give a second test dose of 75 mcg/1.5 ml 24 hours after the first. If response is still inadequate, give a final test dose of 100 mcg/2 ml 24 hours later. Patients unresponsive to 100-mcg dose aren't candidates for implantable pump.

Adults (maintenance therapy): Adjust initial dose based on screening dose that elicits an adequate response. This effective dose is doubled and given over 24 hours. If screening-dose effectiveness is maintained for 8 hours or longer, dosage isn't doubled. After first 24 hours, increase dose slowly, as needed and tolerated, by 10% to 30% daily until desired effects occur. Dose may be decreased by 10% to 20% if intolerable adverse effects occur.

Children younger than age 12: Testing dose is the same as for adults (50 mcg); but for very small children, an initial dose of 25 mcg may be given.

Contraindications and cautions

• Contraindicated in patients hypersensitive to drug. Orally disintegrating tablets are contraindicated in patients hypersensitive to aspartame.

• Use cautiously in patients with impaired renal function or seizure disorder or when spasticity is used to maintain motor function.

Lifespan: In pregnant or breast-feeding women, use cautiously. In children younger than age 12, safety of oral dosage form hasn't been established. In children younger than age 4, safety of intrathecal dosage form hasn't been established.

Adverse reactions

CNS: *confusion,* dizziness, drowsiness, fatigue, *headache,* ***high fever,*** *hypotonia,* paresthesias, **SEIZURES,** somnolence, weakness.
CV: ankle edema, hypotension.
EENT: blurred vision, nasal congestion.
GI: constipation, nausea, vomiting.
GU: impotence, sexual dysfunction, urinary frequency, urinary incontinence.
Metabolic: hyperglycemia, weight gain.
Musculoskeletal: dysarthria, *muscle rigidity or spasticity,* ***rhabdomyolysis.***
Respiratory: dyspnea.
Skin: excessive perspiration, pruritus, rash.
Other: ***multiple organ-system failure.***

Interactions

Drug-drug. *CNS depressants:* May increase CNS depression. Avoid use together.
MAO inhibitors, tricyclic antidepressants: May cause CNS and respiratory depression and hypotension. Avoid use together.
Drug-lifestyle. *Alcohol use:* May increase CNS depression. Discourage use together.

Effects on lab test results

- May increase AST, alkaline phosphatase, and glucose levels.

Pharmacokinetics

Absorption: Rapid and extensive with P.O. use; may vary.
Distribution: Widely distributed throughout body, with small amounts crossing blood–brain barrier. About 30% protein-bound.
Metabolism: About 15% metabolized in liver by deamination.
Excretion: 70% to 80% in urine unchanged or as metabolites; remainder in feces. *Half-life:* 2½ to 4 hours.

Route	Onset	Peak	Duration
P.O.	Rapid	2–3 hr	8 hr
P.O. orally disintegrating	Rapid	1½ hr	8 hr
Intrathecal	½–1 hr	4 hr	4–8 hr

Action

Chemical effect: Unknown; appears to reduce transmission of impulses from spinal cord to skeletal muscle.
Therapeutic effect: Relieves muscle spasms.

Available forms

Intrathecal injection: 50 mcg/ml, 500 mcg/ml, 2,000 mcg/ml, 5,000 mcg/ml
Orally disintegrating tablets: 10 mg, 20 mg
Tablets: 10 mg, 20 mg, 25 mg

NURSING PROCESS

Assessment

- Obtain history of patient's pain and muscle spasms from underlying condition before therapy, and reassess regularly thereafter.
- Be alert for adverse reactions and drug interactions.
- Watch for increased seizures in patients with seizure disorder. Seizures have been reported during overdose and withdrawal of intrathecal baclofen, as well as in patients maintained on therapeutic doses. Monitor patient carefully, and institute seizure precautions.
- Assess patient's and family's understanding of drug therapy.

Nursing diagnoses

- Acute pain related to spasticity
- Risk for injury related to drug-induced adverse CNS reactions
- Deficient knowledge related to drug therapy

Planning and implementation

- Give with meals or milk to prevent GI distress.
- Don't give orally to treat muscle spasm caused by rheumatic disorders, cerebral palsy, Parkinson disease, or stroke because effectiveness hasn't been established.
- Treatment for oral overdose is supportive; don't induce emesis or use respiratory stimulant in an unconscious patient.
- Implantable pump or catheter failure can render intrathecal baclofen suddenly ineffective.

ALERT: Don't give intrathecal injection form by I.V., I.M., subcutaneous, or epidural routes.
- The amount of relief determines whether dose (and drowsiness) can be reduced.
- Don't stop intrathecal baclofen abruptly. Early symptoms of baclofen withdrawal may include return of baseline spasticity, pruritus, hypotension, and paresthesias. Symptoms may include high fever, altered mental status, exaggerated rebound spasticity, and muscle rigidity, which could advance to rhabdomyolysis, multiple organ-system failure, and death. To treat with-

drawal, resume intrathecal baclofen at or near the previous dosage. If delayed, treat with P.O. or enteral baclofen or with P.O., enteral, or I.V. benzodiazepines to prevent life-threatening withdrawal. Don't rely on P.O. or enteral baclofen alone to halt withdrawal from intrathecal baclofen.
- About 10% of patients may develop tolerance to drug. In some cases, this may be treated by hospitalizing patient and by slowly withdrawing drug over a 2-week period.

Patient teaching
- Tell patient to avoid activities that require alertness until drug's CNS effects are known. Drowsiness usually is transient.
- Inform patient with phenylketonuria that orally disintegrating tablets contain phenylalanine (3.9 mg/10-mg tablet and 7.9 mg/20-mg tablet).
- Instruct patient to remove orally disintegrating tablet from blister pack and immediately place on tongue to dissolve, then swallow with or without water.
- Tell patient to avoid alcohol while taking drug.
- Advise patient to follow prescriber's orders about rest and physical therapy.
- Advise patient to take drug with food or milk to prevent GI distress.

☑ Evaluation
- Patient reports that pain and muscle spasms have ceased with drug therapy.
- Patient doesn't experience injury as a result of drug-induced drowsiness.
- Patient and family state understanding of drug therapy.

balsalazide disodium
(bal-SAL-uh-zighd digh-SOH-dee-um)
Colazal

Pharmacologic class: GI drug
Therapeutic class: anti-inflammatory
Pregnancy risk category: B

Indications and dosages
▶**Ulcerative colitis.** *Adults:* 2.25 g (three 750-mg capsules) P.O. t.i.d. for a total of 6.75 g daily for 8 to 12 weeks.
▶**Mild to moderately active ulcerative colitis.** *Children age 5 and older:* Three 750-mg capsules P.O. t.i.d. (6.75 g/day) for 8 weeks. Or one 750-mg capsule P.O. t.i.d. (2.25 g/day) for 8 weeks.

Contraindications and cautions
- Contraindicated in patients hypersensitive to salicylates or balsalazide metabolites.
- Use cautiously in patients with history of renal disease or renal dysfunction.
- Use judiciously in patients with pyloric stenosis because of prolonged retention of drug. Safety and effectiveness beyond 12 weeks of treatment haven't been established.

Lifespan: In breast-feeding women, use cautiously because it's unknown whether drug appears in breast milk. In children, safety and effectiveness haven't been established.

Adverse reactions
CNS: dizziness, fatigue, fever, headache, insomnia.
EENT: pharyngitis, rhinitis, sinusitis.
GI: abdominal pain, anorexia, constipation, cramps, diarrhea, dry mouth, dyspepsia, flatulence, frequent stools, nausea, rectal bleeding, vomiting.
GU: UTI.
Hepatic: ***hepatotoxicity.***
Musculoskeletal: arthralgia, back pain, myalgia.
Respiratory: cough, respiratory infection.
Other: flulike symptoms.

Interactions
Drug-drug. *Azathioprine, 6-mercaptopurine:* May interfere with metabolism of these drugs. Use with caution.
Oral antibiotics and anti-infectives: May interfere with release of mesalamine in the colon. Monitor patient for worsening of symptoms.

Effects on lab test results
- May increase AST, ALT, LDH, alkaline phosphatase, and bilirubin levels.

Pharmacokinetics
Absorption: Very low and variable in healthy patients; 60 times greater in patients with ulcerative colitis.
Distribution: 99% or more protein-bound.
Metabolism: Metabolized to mesalamine (5-aminosalicylic acid), the active component of the drug.

Excretion: By the kidneys. Less than 1% recovered in urine. *Half-life:* Unknown.

Route	Onset	Peak	Duration
P.O.	Unknown	Unknown	Unknown

Action

Chemical effect: Probably blocks colonic production of arachidonic acid metabolites, which are increased in patients with chronic inflammatory bowel disease. Balsalazide is converted in the colon to mesalamine, which is then converted to 5-aminosalicylic acid. The mechanism of action is unknown, but it appears to be local rather than systemic.
Therapeutic effect: Decreases inflammation in the colon.

Available forms

Capsules: 750 mg

NURSING PROCESS

Assessment

- Assess patient's underlying condition and note frequency of bowel movements before starting therapy.
- Hepatotoxicity, including elevated liver function test results, jaundice, cirrhosis, liver necrosis, and liver failure, has occurred with other products containing or metabolized to mesalamine. Although no signs of hepatotoxicity have been reported with balsalazide disodium, monitor patient closely for evidence of hepatic dysfunction.
- Assess patient's and family's knowledge of drug therapy and ulcerative colitis.

Nursing diagnoses

- Diarrhea related to underlying disease process
- Imbalanced nutrition: less than body requirements related to frequent bowel movements from ulcerative colitis
- Deficient knowledge related to balsalazide disodium therapy

Planning and implementation

- Notify prescriber if drug has been given for 8 to 12 weeks or longer.

Patient teaching

- Advise patient not to take drug if he's allergic to aspirin or salicylate derivatives.
- Advise patient to promptly report adverse reactions to prescriber.

Evaluation

- Patient states that diarrhea has improved.
- Because of decreasing symptoms of ulcerative colitis, patient is able to tolerate and absorb a balanced diet.
- Patient and family state understanding of balsalazide disodium therapy.

basiliximab

(ba-sil-IK-si-mab)
Simulect

Pharmacologic class: recombinant chimeric human monoclonal antibody IgG_{1k}
Therapeutic class: immunosuppressant
Pregnancy risk category: B

Indications and dosages

▶ **To prevent acute organ rejection in renal transplant patients when used as part of immunosuppressive regimen including cyclosporine and corticosteroids.** *Adults and children weighing 35 kg (77 lb) or more:* 20 mg I.V. given within 2 hours before transplant surgery and 20 mg I.V. given 4 days after transplantation.
Children weighing less than 35 kg: 10 mg I.V. given within 2 hours before transplant and 10 mg I.V. given 4 days post-transplantation.

I.V. administration

- Reconstitute 10-mg vial with 2.5 ml sterile water for injection or 20-mg vial with 5 ml sterile water for injection. Shake vial gently to dissolve powder.
- Give by I.V. infusion or I.V. bolus.
- If giving by I.V. infusion, dilute reconstituted solution to volume of 25 ml normal saline solution or D_5W for 10-mg vial or 50 ml with normal saline solution or D_5W for infusion for the 20-mg vial. When mixing solution, gently invert bag to avoid foaming. Don't shake.
- Infuse over 20 to 30 minutes by a central or peripheral vein.
- Use reconstituted solution immediately; it may be refrigerated at 36° to 46° F (2° and 8° C) for up to 24 hours or kept at room temperature for 4 hours.

B

⊗ **Incompatibilities**
Other I.V. drugs.

Contraindications and cautions

• Contraindicated in patients hypersensitive to drug or its components.

Lifespan: In pregnant women, use only if potential benefits outweigh risks to the fetus. Breast-feeding women should stop nursing or stop taking the drug because of potential for adverse effects. It's unknown whether drug appears in breast milk. In elderly patients, use cautiously.

Adverse reactions

CNS: agitation, anxiety, asthenia, depression, *dizziness,* fatigue, *fever, headache,* hypoesthesia, *insomnia,* neuropathy, paresthesia, *tremor.*
CV: abnormal heart sounds, ***aggravated hypertension,*** angina pectoris, ***arrhythmias,*** atrial fibrillation, chest pain, general edema, ***heart failure, hemorrhage,*** *hypertension,* hypotension, *leg or peripheral edema,* tachycardia.
EENT: abnormal vision, cataract, conjunctivitis, *pharyngitis, rhinitis,* sinusitis.
GI: *abdominal pain, candidiasis, constipation, diarrhea, dyspepsia,* esophagitis, enlarged abdomen, flatulence, gastroenteritis, GI disorder, ***GI hemorrhage,*** gum hyperplasia, melena, *nausea,* ulcerative stomatitis, *vomiting.*
GU: abnormal renal function, albuminuria, bladder disorder, *dysuria,* frequent micturition, genital edema, hematuria, impotence, *increased nonprotein nitrogen,* oliguria, ***renal tubular necrosis,*** ureteral disorder, urine retention, *UTI.*
Hematologic: ***anemia,*** hematoma, *polycythemia,* ***purpura, thrombocytopenia, thrombosis.***
Metabolic: ***acidosis,*** dehydration, ***diabetes mellitus,*** fluid overload, hypercalcemia, *hypercholesterolemia, hyperglycemia,* **HYPERKALEMIA,** hyperlipemia, *hyperuricemia, hypocalcemia, hypokalemia,* hypomagnesemia, hypophosphatemia, hypoproteinemia, *weight gain.*
Musculoskeletal: arthralgia, arthropathy, *back pain,* bone fracture, cramps, hernia, *leg pain,* myalgia.
Respiratory: abnormal chest sounds, bronchitis, ***bronchospasm,*** *cough, dyspnea,* pneumonia, pulmonary disorder, ***pulmonary edema,*** *upper respiratory tract infection.*
Skin: *acne,* cyst, herpes simplex, herpes zoster, hypertrichosis, pruritus, rash, skin disorder or ulceration.
Other: accidental trauma, infection, ***sepsis,*** *surgical wound complications, viral infection.*

Interactions

None significant.

Effects on lab test results

• May increase calcium, cholesterol, glucose, lipid, and uric acid levels. May decrease magnesium, phosphorus, protein, and hemoglobin levels and hematocrit. May increase or decrease potassium level.
• May increase RBC count. May decrease platelet count.

Pharmacokinetics

Absorption: Given I.V.
Distribution: Unknown.
Metabolism: Unknown.
Excretion: Unknown. *Half-life:* About 7¼ days in adults, 9½ days in children, 9 days in adolescents.

Route	Onset	Peak	Duration
I.V.	Unknown	Immediate	Unknown

Action

Chemical effect: Binds to and blocks the interleukin (IL)-2 receptor alpha chain on the surface of activated T lymphocytes, inhibiting IL-2–mediated activation of lymphocytes, a critical pathway in the cellular immune response involved in allograft rejection.
Therapeutic effect: Prevents organ rejection.

Available forms

Injection: 10-mg and 20-mg vials

NURSING PROCESS

Assessment

• Monitor patient for anaphylactoid reactions. Be sure that drugs for treating severe hypersensitivity reactions are available for immediate use.
• Check for electrolyte imbalances and acidosis.
• Monitor patient's intake and output, vital signs, hemoglobin level, and hematocrit.
• Be alert for signs and symptoms of opportunistic infections.
• Assess patient's and family's knowledge of drug therapy.

Nursing diagnoses
- Risk for injury related to potential for organ rejection
- Ineffective protection related to drug-induced immunosuppression
- Deficient knowledge related to drug therapy

Planning and implementation
- Use drug only under supervision of prescriber experienced in this type of therapy and management of organ transplantation.
- Patients who have a severe hypersensitivity reaction shouldn't receive the drug again.

Patient teaching
- Inform patient of potential benefits and risks of therapy, including decreased risk of graft loss or acute rejection. Advise patient that therapy increases risk of lymphoproliferative disorders and opportunistic infections. Tell him to report signs and symptoms of infection immediately.
- Tell women of childbearing age to use effective contraception before, during, and for 4 months after therapy ends.
- Instruct patient to immediately report adverse effects to prescriber.
- Explain that drug is used with cyclosporine and corticosteroids.

Evaluation
- Patient doesn't have organ rejection while taking this drug.
- Patient is free from infection and serious bleeding episodes during therapy.
- Patient and family state understanding of drug therapy.

beclomethasone dipropionate
(bek-loh-METH-eh-sohn digh-proh-PIGH-uh-nayt)
QVAR

Pharmacologic class: synthetic corticosteroid
Therapeutic class: antiasthmatic
Pregnancy risk category: C

Indications and dosages
▶ **Chronic asthma.** *Adults and children age 12 and older:* Starting dose, 40 to 80 mcg b.i.d. by aerosol inhalation when used with bronchodilators alone, or 40 to 160 mcg b.i.d. when used with other inhaled corticosteroids. Maximum, 320 mcg b.i.d.

Children ages 5 to 11: Give 40 mcg b.i.d., up to 80 mcg b.i.d. by aerosol inhalation when used with bronchodilators alone or with inhaled corticosteroids.

Contraindications and cautions
- Contraindicated in patients hypersensitive to drug or its components, and in those with status asthmaticus, nonasthmatic bronchial diseases, or asthma controlled by bronchodilators or other noncorticosteroids alone.
- Use with extreme caution, if at all, in patients with tuberculosis, fungal or bacterial infections, ocular herpes simplex, or systemic viral infections.
- Use with caution in patients receiving systemic corticosteroid therapy.

Lifespan: In pregnant or breast-feeding women, use cautiously. In children younger than age 5, safety and effectiveness haven't been established.

Adverse reactions
EENT: *fungal infection of throat, hoarseness, throat irritation.*
GI: dry mouth, *fungal infection of mouth.*
Metabolic: adrenal insufficiency, ***suppression of hypothalamic-pituitary-adrenal function.***
Respiratory: ***bronchospasm,*** cough, wheezing.
Other: ***angioedema,*** facial edema, hypersensitivity reactions.

Interactions
None significant.

Effects on lab test results
None reported.

Pharmacokinetics
Absorption: Rapid from lungs and GI tract.
Distribution: No evidence of tissue storage of beclomethasone or its metabolites.
Metabolism: Mostly in liver.
Excretion: Unknown, although when drug is given systemically, its metabolites are excreted mainly in feces and, to a lesser extent, in urine. *Half-life:* 15 hours.

Route	Onset	Peak	Duration
Inhalation	1–4 wk	Unknown	Unknown

Action

Chemical effect: Decreases inflammation, mainly by stabilizing leukocyte lysosomal membranes.
Therapeutic effect: Helps alleviate asthma symptoms.

Available forms

Oral inhalation aerosol: 40 mcg/metered spray, 80 mcg/metered spray

NURSING PROCESS

Assessment

- Obtain history of patient's asthma before therapy, and reassess regularly thereafter.
- Be alert for adverse reactions.
- Monitor patient closely during times of stress (trauma, surgery, or infection) because systemic corticosteroids may be needed to prevent adrenal insufficiency in previously steroid-dependent patients.
- Periodic measurement of growth and development may be needed during high-dose or prolonged therapy in children.
- Assess patient's and family's understanding of drug therapy.

Nursing diagnoses

- Impaired gas exchange related to asthma
- Impaired oral mucous membranes related to drug-induced fungal infections
- Deficient knowledge related to drug therapy

Planning and implementation

ALERT: Never give drug to relieve an emergency asthma attack because onset of action is too slow.

- Give prescribed bronchodilators several minutes before beclomethasone.
- Have patient hold breath for a few seconds after each puff and rest 1 minute between puffs to enhance drug action.
- Use of a spacer device isn't needed.

ALERT: Taper oral corticosteroid therapy slowly. Acute adrenal insufficiency and death have occurred in patients with asthma who changed abruptly from oral corticosteroids to beclomethasone.

- Notify prescriber if decreased response is noted after giving drug.
- Have patient gargle and rinse mouth with water after inhalations to help prevent oral fungal infections.

Patient teaching

- Tell patient to prime the inhaler before first use and after 10 days of not using it by depressing canister twice into the air.
- Inform patient that drug doesn't relieve acute asthma attacks.
- Tell patient who needs a bronchodilator to use it several minutes before beclomethasone.
- Instruct patient to carry or wear medical identification indicating his need for supplemental systemic corticosteroids during stress.
- Advise patient to allow 1 minute to elapse between inhalations of drug and to hold his breath for a few seconds to enhance drug action.
- Tell patient it may take up to 4 weeks to feel the full benefit of the drug.
- Tell patient to keep inhaler clean by wiping it weekly with a dry tissue or cloth; don't get it wet.
- Advise patient to prevent oral fungal infections by gargling or rinsing his mouth with water after each use. Caution him not to swallow the water.
- Tell patient to report evidence of corticosteroid withdrawal, including fatigue, weakness, arthralgia, orthostatic hypotension, and dyspnea.
- Instruct patient to store drug at 77° F (25° C), and advise patient to use at room temperature.

Evaluation

- Patient's lungs are clear, and breathing and skin color are normal.
- Patient doesn't develop an oral fungal infection during therapy.
- Patient and family state understanding of drug therapy.

beclomethasone dipropionate monohydrate

(bek-loh-METH-eh-sohn digh-proh-PIGH-uh-nayt mon-oh-HIGH-drayt)
Beconase AQ

Pharmacologic class: corticosteroid
Therapeutic class: anti-inflammatory
Pregnancy risk category: C

Indications and dosages

▶ **Symptoms of allergic rhinitis; prevention of recurrence of nasal polyps after surgical**

removal. *Adults and children age 12 and older:* 1 to 2 inhalations or sprays in each nostril b.i.d. Maximum, 336 mcg daily, given in each nostril as 168 mcg (4 sprays) once daily.
Children ages 6 to 11: Give 1 inhalation or spray in each nostril b.i.d. Those with more severe symptoms may need 2 inhalations in each nostril b.i.d.

Contraindications and cautions

- Contraindicated in patients hypersensitive to drug and in those experiencing status asthmaticus or other acute episodes of asthma.
- Use cautiously, if at all, in patients with active or quiescent respiratory tract tubercular infections or untreated fungal, bacterial, systemic viral, or ocular herpes simplex infections. Also use cautiously in patients who've recently had nasal septal ulcers, nasal surgery, or trauma.

Lifespan: In pregnant or breast-feeding women, use cautiously. In children younger than age 6, safety and effectiveness of drug haven't been established.

Adverse reactions

CNS: headache.
EENT: epistaxis; irritation of nasal mucosa; *mild, transient, nasal burning* and stinging; nasal congestion; nasopharyngeal fungal infections; sneezing; watery eyes.
GI: nausea, vomiting.

Interactions

None significant.

Effects on lab test results

None reported.

Pharmacokinetics

Absorption: Mainly through nasal mucosa, with minimal systemic absorption.
Distribution: Unknown.
Metabolism: Most of drug in liver.
Excretion: Unknown. *Half-life:* 15 hours.

Route	Onset	Peak	Duration
Inhalation	5–7 days	≤ 3 wk	Unknown

Action

Chemical effect: Decreases nasal inflammation, mainly by stabilizing leukocyte lysosomal membranes.
Therapeutic effect: Helps relieve nasal allergy symptoms.

Available forms

Nasal spray: 42 mcg/metered spray

NURSING PROCESS

Assessment

- Obtain history of patient's allergy symptoms and nasal congestion before therapy, and reassess regularly thereafter.
- Be alert for adverse reactions.
- Monitor patient's hydration status if adverse GI reactions occur.
- Check for irritation of nasal mucosa.
- Assess patient's and family's understanding of drug therapy.

Nursing diagnoses

- Ineffective health maintenance related to allergy-induced nasal congestion
- Risk for deficient fluid volume related to drug-induced adverse GI reactions
- Deficient knowledge related to drug therapy

Planning and implementation

- Drug isn't effective for acute rhinitis. Decongestants or antihistamines may be needed.
- Shake container and invert. Have patient clear his nasal passages and then tilt his head backward. Insert nozzle (pointed away from septum) into nostril, holding other nostril closed. Deliver spray while patient inhales. Shake container and repeat in other nostril.
- Notify prescriber if relief isn't obtained or signs of infection appear.

Patient teaching

- Teach patient how to give himself nasal spray.
- Advise patient to pump new nasal spray three or four times before first use and once or twice before first use each day thereafter. Also tell patient to clean cap and nosepiece of activator in warm water every day and air-dry them.
- Advise patient to use drug regularly, as prescribed, because its effectiveness depends on regular use.
- Explain that drug's therapeutic effects, unlike those of decongestants, aren't immediate. Most patients achieve benefit within a few days, but some may need 2 to 3 weeks.

• Warn patient not to exceed recommended doses because of risk of hypothalamic-pituitary-adrenal function suppression.
• Tell patient to notify prescriber if symptoms don't improve within 3 weeks or if nasal irritation persists.
• Teach patient good nasal and oral hygiene.

Evaluation
• Patient's nasal congestion subsides with therapy.
• Patient maintains adequate hydration throughout therapy.
• Patient and family state understanding of drug therapy.

benazepril hydrochloride
(ben-AY-zuh-pril high-droh-KLOR-ighd)
Lotensin

Pharmacologic class: ACE inhibitor
Therapeutic class: antihypertensive
Pregnancy risk category: C (D in second and third trimesters)

Indications and dosages

▶ **Hypertension.** *Adults not taking diuretics:* Initially, 10 mg P.O. daily. Adjust dosage as needed and tolerated, usually to 20 to 40 mg daily, equally divided into one or two doses. Maximum, 80 mg daily.
Adults taking diuretics: Stop diuretic 2 to 3 days before starting benazepril hydrochloride to minimize hypotension. If unable to stop diuretic, start dose at 5 mg daily.
Adjust-a-dose: For adults with renal impairment, if creatinine clearance is less than 30 ml/minute, start dose at 5 mg daily. Don't exceed 40 mg P.O. daily.
Children age 6 and older with creatinine clearance greater than 30 ml/minute: 0.2 mg/kg P.O. daily. Doses exceeding 0.6 mg/kg (or in excess of 40 mg/day) haven't been studied.

Contraindications and cautions

• Contraindicated in patients hypersensitive to ACE inhibitors.
• Use cautiously in patients with impaired hepatic or renal function.
Lifespan: In pregnant women, stop drug as soon as possible; it can cause injury and death to the fetus during the second and third trimesters. With breast-feeding women, use cautiously. In children younger than age 6 years and those with a glomerular filtration rate less than 30 ml/minute, safety of drug hasn't been established.

Adverse reactions

CNS: amnesia, anxiety, asthenia, depression, dizziness, headache, insomnia, light-headedness, nervousness, neuralgia, neuropathy, paresthesia, somnolence, syncope.
CV: angina, ***arrhythmias,*** edema, palpitations, ***symptomatic hypotension.***
GI: abdominal pain, constipation, dyspepsia, dysphagia, gastritis, increased salivation, nausea, vomiting.
GU: impotence.
Metabolic: ***hyperkalemia,*** weight gain.
Musculoskeletal: arthralgia, arthritis, myalgia.
Respiratory: dry, persistent, tickling, nonproductive cough; dyspnea.
Skin: dermatitis, increased diaphoresis, photosensitivity, pruritus, purpura, rash.
Other: ***angioedema,*** hypersensitivity reactions.

Interactions

Drug-drug. *ACE inhibitors, diuretics, other antihypertensives:* May cause excessive hypotension. Stop diuretic or lower dose of benazepril, if needed.
Digoxin: May increase digoxin level. Monitor patient for toxicity.
Indomethacin, aspirin: May reduce hypotensive effects. Monitor blood pressure.
Lithium: May increase lithium level and toxicity. Avoid use together.
Potassium-sparing diuretics, potassium supplements: May cause hyperkalemia. Monitor patient closely.
Drug-herb. *Capsicum:* May aggravate or cause ACE inhibitor–induced cough. Discourage use together.
Licorice: May cause sodium retention, thus decreasing ACE inhibitor effects. Discourage use together.
Sodium substitutes containing potassium: May cause hyperkalemia. Monitor patient closely.

Effects on lab test results

• May increase BUN, creatinine, uric acid, glucose, bilirubin, liver enzymes, and potassium levels.

Pharmacokinetics

Absorption: At least 37%.
Distribution: Extensively protein-bound.
Metabolism: Almost completely in liver to benazeprilat, which has much greater ACE inhibitory activity than benazepril.
Excretion: Mainly in urine. *Half-life:* Benazepril, about ½ hour; benazeprilat, 10 to 12 hours.

Route	Onset	Peak	Duration
P.O.	≤ 1 hr	2–6 hr	24 hr

Action

Chemical effect: Inhibits ACE, preventing conversion of angiotensin I to angiotensin II, a potent vasoconstrictor. Reduced formation of angiotensin II decreases peripheral arterial resistance, thus decreasing aldosterone secretion. This reduces sodium and water retention and lowers blood pressure. Benazepril also has antihypertensive activity in patients with low-renin hypertension.
Therapeutic effect: Lowers blood pressure.

Available forms

Tablets: 5 mg, 10 mg, 20 mg, 40 mg

NURSING PROCESS

Assessment

- Obtain history of patient's blood pressure before therapy, and reassess regularly thereafter. Measure blood pressure when drug level is at peak (2 to 6 hours after dose) and trough (just before dose) to verify adequate blood pressure control.
- Be alert for adverse reactions and drug interactions.
- Monitor patient's ECG.
- Monitor renal and hepatic function periodically. Also monitor potassium levels.
- Monitor patient's CBC with differential every 2 weeks for first 3 months of therapy and periodically thereafter. Other ACE inhibitors have been linked to agranulocytosis and neutropenia.
- Assess patient's and family's understanding of drug therapy.

Nursing diagnoses

- Risk for injury related to hypertension
- Decreased cardiac output related to drug-induced arrhythmias
- Deficient knowledge related to drug therapy

Planning and implementation

- If patient takes a diuretic, benazepril dose should be reduced; excessive hypotension can occur when given with diuretics.
- For children who can't swallow pills, an oral suspension can be made from the tablet.
- Give drug at about the same time every day to maintain consistent effect on blood pressure.
- Give drug when patient's stomach is empty.

Patient teaching

- Instruct patient to take drug on an empty stomach; meals, particularly those high in fat, can impair absorption.
- Tell patient to avoid sodium substitutes because such products may contain potassium, which can cause hyperkalemia in patients taking drug.
- Tell patient to rise slowly to minimize risk of dizziness, which may occur during first few weeks of therapy. Advise patient to stop taking drug and to call prescriber immediately if dizziness occurs.
- Tell patient to use caution in hot weather and during exercise. Inadequate fluid intake, vomiting, diarrhea, and excessive perspiration can lead to light-headedness and syncope.
- Urge patient to report signs of infection, such as fever and sore throat. Also tell him to call prescriber if any of the following occurs: easy bruising or bleeding; swelling of tongue, lips, face, eyes, mucous membranes, or limbs; difficulty swallowing or breathing; or hoarseness.
- Tell woman to notify prescriber if pregnancy occurs. Drug will need to be stopped.

Evaluation

- Patient's blood pressure is normal.
- Patient has adequate cardiac output during drug therapy.
- Patient and family state understanding of drug therapy.

benztropine mesylate

(BENZ-troh-peen MESS-ih-layt)
Apo-Benztropine ♦, Cogentin

Pharmacologic class: anticholinergic
Therapeutic class: antiparkinsonian
Pregnancy risk category: C

Indications and dosages

▶ **Drug-induced extrapyramidal disorders (except tardive dyskinesia).** *Adults:* 1 to 4 mg P.O. or I.M. once or twice daily.
▶ **Acute dystonic reaction.** *Adults:* 1 to 2 mg I.V. or I.M., followed by 1 to 2 mg P.O. b.i.d. to prevent recurrence.
▶ **Parkinsonism.** *Adults:* 0.5 to 6 mg P.O. daily. Initial dose is 0.5 to 1 mg. I.M. or P.O. Because of cumulative action, start at a low dose and increase by 0.5 mg q 5 to 6 days. Adjust to meet individual requirements. Maximum, 6 mg daily.

I.V. administration

- Drug is seldom used I.V. because of small difference in onset compared with I.M. route.

⊗ **Incompatibilities**
None reported.

Contraindications and cautions

- Contraindicated in patients hypersensitive to drug or its components and in those with acute angle-closure glaucoma.
- Use cautiously in patients exposed to hot weather, those with mental disorders, and those with prostatic hyperplasia, arrhythmias, seizure disorder, obstructive disease of the GI or GU tract, or a tendency toward urine retention.

Lifespan: In pregnant women, use cautiously. In breast-feeding women and children younger than age 3, drug is contraindicated. In children age 3 and older and patients older than age 60, use cautiously.

Adverse reactions

CNS: confusion, depression, disorientation, hallucinations, headache, incoherence, irritability, nervousness, restlessness, sedation.
CV: flushing, palpitations, ***paradoxical bradycardia,*** tachycardia.
EENT: blurred vision, difficulty swallowing, dilated pupils, photophobia.
GI: *constipation,* dry mouth, epigastric distress, nausea, vomiting.
GU: urinary hesitancy, urine retention.
Musculoskeletal: muscle weakness.

Interactions

Drug-drug. *Amantadine, phenothiazines, tricyclic antidepressants:* May cause additive anticholinergic adverse reactions, such as hyperthermia or heat intolerance. Notify prescriber immediately about adverse GI effects, fever, or heat intolerance.
Anticholinergics and other antiparkinsonians: May increase anticholinergic effects and may be fatal. Use cautiously.
Cholinesterase inhibitors: May decrease effectiveness of cholinesterase inhibitors.

Effects on lab test results

None reported.

Pharmacokinetics

Absorption: Unknown.
Distribution: Largely unknown; however, drug crosses blood–brain barrier.
Metabolism: Unknown.
Excretion: In urine as unchanged drug and metabolites. *Half-life:* Unknown.

Route	Onset	Peak	Duration
P.O.	1–2 hr	Unknown	24 hr
I.V., I.M.	≤ 15 min	Unknown	24 hr

Action

Chemical effect: Unknown; thought to block central cholinergic receptors, helping to balance cholinergic activity in basal ganglia.
Therapeutic effect: Improves capability for voluntary movement.

Available forms

Injection: 1 mg/ml in 2-ml ampules
Tablets: 0.5 mg, 1 mg, 2 mg

NURSING PROCESS

Assessment

- Obtain history of patient's dyskinetic movements and underlying condition before therapy.
- Monitor effectiveness by regularly checking body movements for signs of improvement. Full effect of drug may take 2 to 3 days.
- Be alert for adverse reactions and drug interactions. Some adverse reactions may result from atropine-like toxicity and are dose related.
- Assess patient's and family's understanding of drug therapy.

Nursing diagnoses

- Impaired physical mobility related to dyskinetic movements

- Risk for injury related to drug-induced adverse CNS reactions
- Deficient knowledge related to drug therapy

Planning and implementation

ALERT: Never stop drug abruptly. Reduce dose gradually.

- Give drug after meals to help prevent GI distress.
- The I.M. route is preferred for parenteral administration.
- Give drug at bedtime if patient is to receive single daily dose.

Patient teaching

- Warn patient to avoid activities requiring alertness until CNS effects of drug are known.
- If patient will receive single daily dose, tell him to take it at bedtime.
- If patient will receive drug orally, tell him to take it after meals.
- Advise patient to report signs of urinary hesitancy or urine retention.
- Tell patient to relieve dry mouth with cool drinks, ice chips, sugarless gum, or hard candy.
- Advise patient to limit activities during hot weather because drug-induced anhidrosis may result in hyperthermia.

Evaluation

- Patient has improved mobility with reduced muscle rigidity, akinesia, and tremors.
- Patient sustains no injury as a result of drug-induced adverse CNS reactions.
- Patient and family state understanding of drug therapy.

bevacizumab

(beh-vah-SIZZ-yoo-mab)

Avastin

Pharmacologic class: monoclonal antibody
Therapeutic class: antineoplastic
Pregnancy risk category: C

Indications and dosages

▶ **Metastatic colon or rectal cancer, given with fluorouracil-based chemotherapy as first- or second-line treatment.** *Adults:* If used with bolus IFL regimen (irinotecan, 5-fluorouracil, leucovorin), give 5 mg/kg I.V. q 14 days until disease progresses. If used with FOLFOX4 regimen (5-fluorouracil, oxaliplatin, leucovorin), give 10 mg/kg I.V. q 14 days until disease progresses. Don't start therapy for at least 28 days after major surgery. Make sure incision is fully healed before therapy starts.

▶ **Unresectable, locally advanced, recurrent or metastatic nonsquamous non–small-cell lung cancer, given with carboplatin and paclitaxel as first-line treatment.** *Adults:* 15 mg/kg by I.V. infusion once q 3 weeks.

I.V. administration

- Dilute using aseptic technique. Don't freeze or shake the vials. Withdraw proper dose and mix into I.V. bag in a total volume of 100 ml normal saline solution.
- Give the first infusion over 90 minutes and, if tolerated, the second infusion over 60 minutes. Later infusions can be given over 30 minutes if patient tolerated previous infusions.
- Don't give by I.V. push or bolus.
- Drug is stable for 8 hours if refrigerated at 36° to 46° F (2° to 8° C) and protected from light.

⊗ Incompatibilities

Dextrose solutions.

Contraindications and cautions

- Contraindicated in patients with recent hemoptysis or within 28 days after major surgery.
- Use with extreme caution if patient has significant CV disease or history of arterial thromboembolism.
- Use cautiously in patients hypersensitive to drug or its components. Also use cautiously in patients who need surgery.

Lifespan: In pregnant women, use during pregnancy only if potential benefits to the mother outweigh risks to the fetus. Breast-feeding women should stop nursing during therapy and for 60 days after it stops because of the drug's long half-life. In children, safety and effectiveness haven't been established. In patients age 65 or older, increased risk of serious to fatal arterial thromboembolic events.

Adverse reactions

CNS: abnormal gait, *asthenia,* confusion, *dizziness, headache,* pain, syncope.

CV: deep vein thrombosis, heart failure, *hypertension,* hypotension, **INTRA-ABDOMINAL THROMBOSIS,** ***thromboembolism.***
EENT: *epistaxis,* excess lacrimation, gum bleeding, nasal septum perforation, taste disorder, voice alteration.
GI: abdominal pain, *anorexia,* colitis, *constipation, diarrhea,* dry mouth, *dyspepsia, flatulence,* ***GI hemorrhage,*** nausea, *stomatitis, vomiting.*
GU: proteinuria, urinary urgency, ***vaginal hemorrhage.***
Hematologic: ***leukopenia, neutropenia, thrombocytopenia.***
Metabolic: bilirubinemia, *hypokalemia, weight loss.*
Musculoskeletal: *myalgia.*
Respiratory: *dyspnea,* **HEMOPTYSIS,** *upper respiratory tract infection.*
Skin: *alopecia, dermatitis, discoloration, dry skin, exfoliative dermatitis,* nail disorder, skin ulcer.
Other: decreased wound healing, hypersensitivity.

Interactions

Drug-drug. *Irinotecan:* May increase level of irinotecan metabolite (SN-38). Monitor patient.

Effects on lab test results

- May increase bilirubin and urine protein levels. May decrease potassium level.
- May decrease WBC, neutrophil, and platelet counts.

Pharmacokinetics

Absorption: Given I.V.
Distribution: Unknown.
Metabolism: Degraded to basic peptides via phagocytosis by the reticuloendothelial system.
Excretion: Via the reticuloendothelial system. *Half-life:* 11 to 50 days.

Route	Onset	Peak	Duration
I.V.	Unknown	Unknown	Unknown

Action

Chemical effect: Inhibits actions between proteins and cell surface receptors that would normally allow proliferation of endothelial cells and new blood vessel growth.
Therapeutic effect: Inhibits metastatic colon or rectal tumor growth.

Available forms

Solution: 25 mg/ml in 4-ml and 16-ml vials

NURSING PROCESS

Assessment

- Assess patient's condition before therapy and regularly thereafter.
- Monitor CBC, platelet count, and serum electrolytes before and during therapy.
- Monitor patient for hypersensitivity reactions, which can occur during infusions.
- Monitor urinalysis for presence or worsening of proteinuria. Patients with 2+ or greater urine dipstick test should have 24-hour urine collection.
- Monitor patient for reversible posterior leukoencephalopathy syndrome (RLPS), a rare brain-capillary leak syndrome. Signs and symptoms include hypertension, fluid retention, headache, visual disturbances, altered mental state, and seizures.
- Check patient's blood pressure every 2 to 3 weeks.
- Assess patient's and family's knowledge of drug therapy.

Nursing diagnoses

- Ineffective health maintenance related to presence of neoplastic disease
- Delayed surgical recovery related to decreased wound healing effects of drug
- Deficient knowledge related to bevacizumab therapy

Planning and implementation

- Monitor patient for serious adverse effects during therapy. Stop drug if patient develops nephrotic syndrome, severe hypertension, hypertensive crisis, serious hemorrhage, GI perforation, or wound dehiscence that needs intervention.
- Stop drug before elective surgery, taking into account drug's half-life of about 20 days. Don't resume therapy until surgical incision is fully healed.

ALERT: Drug may increase the risk of serious or fatal arterial thromboembolic events, including MI, transient ischemic attack, stroke, and angina. Those at highest risk include patients age 65 or older, those with a history of arterial thromboembolism, and those previously treated

with bevacizumab. If patient has an arterial thrombotic event, stop therapy.
• Treat symptoms and provide supportive care if overdose occurs. Large doses may cause headache, and the maximum tolerated dose is unknown.

Patient teaching

• Inform patient about potential adverse reactions.
• Tell patient to immediately report adverse reactions, especially abdominal pain, constipation, or vomiting.
• Advise patient that blood pressure and urinalysis will be monitored during treatment.
• Caution women of childbearing age to avoid pregnancy during treatment.
• Urge patient to alert other health care providers about treatment and to avoid elective surgery during treatment.

Evaluation

• Patient responds to drug therapy.
• Drug is stopped prior to surgery. Drug therapy isn't started until surgical incision is fully healed.
• Patient and family state understanding of drug therapy.

bimatoprost

(by-MATT-oh-prost)
Lumigan

Pharmacologic class: prostaglandin analogue
Therapeutic class: antiglaucoma drug, ocular antihypertensive
Pregnancy risk category: C

Indications and dosages

▶ **Elevated intraocular pressure (IOP), first- or second-line treatment in patients with open-angle glaucoma or ocular hypertension.** *Adults:* Instill 1 drop in the conjunctival sac of the affected eye or eyes once daily in the evening.

Contraindications and cautions

• Contraindicated in patients hypersensitive to bimatoprost, benzalkonium chloride, or the drug's components. Also contraindicated in patients with angle-closure glaucoma, inflammatory glaucoma, or neovascular glaucoma.
• Use cautiously in patients with renal or hepatic impairment, active intraocular inflammation (iritis or uveitis), aphakic patients, pseudophakic patients with a torn posterior lens capsule, or patients at risk for macular edema.

Lifespan: In pregnant women, drug isn't recommended. In breast-feeding women, use cautiously because it's unknown whether drug appears in breast milk. In children, safety and effectiveness of drug haven't been established.

Adverse reactions

CNS: asthenia, headache.
EENT: allergic conjunctivitis, asthenopia, blepharitis, cataract, conjunctival edema, *conjunctival hyperemia,* eye discharge, eye pain, eyelash darkening, eyelid erythema, foreign body sensation, gradual change in eye color, *growth of eyelashes,* increased iris pigmentation, ocular burning, ocular dryness, ocular irritation, *ocular pruritus,* photophobia, pigmentation of the periocular skin, superficial punctate keratitis, tearing, visual disturbance.
Respiratory: *upper respiratory tract infection.*
Skin: hirsutism.
Other: *infection.*

Interactions

None significant.

Effects on lab test results

• May cause abnormal liver function test values.

Pharmacokinetics

Absorption: Through the cornea.
Distribution: Moderately into tissues. About 12% remains unbound.
Metabolism: Mainly by oxidation.
Excretion: Metabolites are 67% eliminated in urine; 25% are eliminated in feces. *Half life:* 45 minutes.

Route	Onset	Peak	Duration
Ophthalmic	4 hr	10 min	1½ hr

Action

Chemical effect: May increase the outflow of aqueous humor through the trabecular meshwork and uveoscleral routes.
Therapeutic effect: Reduces IOP.

Available forms

Ophthalmic solution: 0.03%

B

NURSING PROCESS

Assessment

ALERT: Obtain complete medication history. If more than one ophthalmic drug is being used, give drugs at least 5 minutes apart.
- Assess patient's underlying condition and eyes before giving eyedrops.
- Monitor patient for excessive ocular irritation, and evaluate the success of treatment.
- Assess patient's and family's knowledge of drug therapy and administration.

Nursing diagnoses

- Risk for injury related to improper administration of drug
- Disturbed sensory perception (visual) related to underlying condition
- Deficient knowledge related to bimatoprost therapy

Planning and implementation

ALERT: Contact lenses must be removed before using solution. Lenses may be reinserted 15 minutes after administration.
- Don't touch the tip of the dropper to the eye. Avoid contaminating the dropper.
- Apply light pressure on lacrimal sac for 1 minute after instillation to minimize systemic absorption of the drug.
- Store drug in original container at 59° to 77° F (15° to 25° C).
- Pigmentation of the iris, eyelid, and eyelashes may increase, and eyelashes may grow.

Patient teaching

- Explain to patients receiving treatment in only one eye the possibility for increased brown pigmentation of iris, eyelid skin darkening, and increased length, thickness, pigmentation, or number of lashes in the treated eye.
- Teach patient to instill drops properly, and advise him to wash his hands before and after instilling solution. Warn him not to touch the dropper tip to the eye or surrounding tissue.
- If eye trauma or infection occurs or if eye surgery is needed, tell patient to seek immediate medical advice before continuing to use multidose container.
- Urge patient to immediately report conjunctivitis or lid reactions to prescriber.

Evaluation

- Patient demonstrates proper instillation of the drug, and no injury occurs.
- Patient's underlying eye condition responds positively to drug.
- Patient and family state understanding of drug therapy.

bisacodyl

(bigh-suh-KOH-dil)

Bisac-Evac†, Bisacodyl Uniserts†, Bisacolax ♦ †, Bisalax ◇, Carter's Little Pills†, Correctol†, Dulcolax†, Durolax ◇, Feen-a-Mint†, Fleet Bisacodyl†, Fleet Laxative†, Fleet Prep Kit†, Laxit ♦ †, Modane†, Theralax†

Pharmacologic class: diphenylmethane derivative
Therapeutic class: stimulant laxative
Pregnancy risk category: NR

Indications and dosages

▶ **Chronic constipation; preparation for childbirth, surgery, or rectal or bowel examination.** *Adults and children age 12 and older:* 10 to 15 mg P.O. in evening or before breakfast. Maximum, 30 mg P.O. For evacuation before examination or surgery, 10 mg P.R.
Children ages 6 to 12: Give 5 mg P.O. or P.R. at bedtime or before breakfast.

Contraindications and cautions

- Contraindicated in patients hypersensitive to drug and in those with rectal bleeding, gastroenteritis, intestinal obstruction, or symptoms of appendicitis or acute surgical abdomen, such as abdominal pain, nausea, or vomiting.

Lifespan: In pregnant women and children younger than age 10, safety hasn't been established.

Adverse reactions

GI: *abdominal cramps, burning sensation in rectum* (with suppositories), diarrhea (with high doses), laxative dependence (with long-term or excessive use), *nausea,* protein-losing enteropathy (with excessive use), *vomiting.*
Metabolic: ***alkalosis,*** fluid and electrolyte imbalance, hypokalemia.

Musculoskeletal: muscle weakness (with excessive use), tetany.

Interactions

Drug-drug. *Antacids:* May cause gastric irritation or dyspepsia from premature dissolution of enteric coating. Avoid use together.
Drug-food. *Milk:* May cause gastric irritation or dyspepsia from premature dissolution of enteric coating. Avoid use together.

Effects on lab test results

- May increase phosphate and sodium levels. May decrease calcium, magnesium, and potassium levels.

Pharmacokinetics

Absorption: Minimal.
Distribution: Locally.
Metabolism: Up to 15% of P.O. dose may enter enterohepatic circulation.
Excretion: Mainly in feces; some in urine. *Half-life:* Unknown.

Route	Onset	Peak	Duration
P.O.	6–12 hr	Variable	Variable
P.R.	15–60 min	Variable	Variable

Action

Chemical effect: Increases peristalsis, probably by acting directly on smooth muscle of intestine. May irritate musculature, stimulate colonic intramural plexus, and promote fluid accumulation in colon and small intestine.
Therapeutic effect: Relieves constipation.

Available forms

Enema: 0.33 mg/dl†, 10 mg/5 ml (microenema) ◊, 10 mg/30 ml
Powder for rectal solution (*bisacodyl tannex*): 1.5 mg bisacodyl and 2.5 g tannic acid
Suppositories: 10 mg†
Tablets (enteric-coated): 5 mg†

NURSING PROCESS

Assessment

- Obtain history of bowel disorder, GI status, fluid intake, nutritional status, exercise habits, and normal patterns of elimination.
- Monitor effectiveness by checking frequency and characteristics of stools.
- Be alert for adverse reactions and drug interactions.
- Auscultate bowel sounds at least once per shift. Check for pain and cramping.
- Assess patient's and family's understanding of drug therapy.

Nursing diagnoses

- Constipation related to interruption of normal pattern of elimination
- Acute pain related to drug-induced abdominal cramps
- Deficient knowledge related to drug therapy

Planning and implementation

- Don't give tablets within 60 minutes of milk or antacid.
- Insert suppository as high as possible into rectum, and try to position suppository against rectal wall. Avoid embedding within fecal material because this may delay onset of action.
- Time administration of drug so as not to interfere with scheduled activities or sleep. Soft, formed stool usually is produced 15 to 60 minutes after P.R. administration.
- Tablets and suppositories are used together to clean colon before and after surgery and before barium enema.
- Store tablets and suppositories below 86° F (30° C).

Patient teaching

- Advise patient to swallow enteric-coated tablet whole to avoid GI irritation. Tell him not to take tablet within 1 hour of milk or antacid.
- Advise patient to report adverse effects to prescriber.
- Teach patient about dietary sources of fiber, including bran and other cereals, fresh fruit, and vegetables.
- Warn patient against excessive use of drug.

Evaluation

- Patient reports return of normal bowel pattern of elimination.
- Patient is free from abdominal pain and cramping.
- Patient and family state understanding of drug therapy.

B

bismuth subgallate
(BIS-muth sub-GAL-ayt)
Devrom

bismuth subsalicylate
Children's Kaopectate†, Extra Strength Kaopectate†, Kaopectate (Regular)†, Maximum Strength Pepto-Bismol†, Pepto-Bismol†

Pharmacologic class: adsorbent
Therapeutic class: antidiarrheal
Pregnancy risk category: NR

Indications and dosages

▶ **To control fecal odors in colostomy, ileostomy, or incontinence.** *Adults:* 1 to 2 tablets subgallate P.O. t.i.d. with meals. Tablet can be chewed or swallowed whole.

▶ **Mild, nonspecific diarrhea.** *Adults and children age 12 and older:* 30 ml or 2 tablets subsalicylate P.O. q 30 minutes to 1 hour up to a maximum of eight doses in 24 hours and for no longer than 2 days.
Children ages 9 to 12: Give 15 ml or 1 tablet subsalicylate P.O. q 30 minutes to 1 hour up to a maximum of eight doses in 24 hours and for no longer than 2 days.
Children ages 6 to 9: Give 10 ml or ⅔ tablet subsalicylate P.O. q 30 minutes to 1 hour up to a maximum of eight doses in 24 hours and for no longer than 2 days.
Children ages 3 to 6: Give 5 ml or ½ tablet subsalicylate P.O. q 30 minutes to 1 hour up to a maximum of eight doses in 24 hours and for no longer than 2 days.

Contraindications and cautions

- Contraindicated in patients hypersensitive to salicylates.
- Use cautiously in patients already taking aspirin.

Lifespan: In pregnant or breast-feeding women, use cautiously.

Adverse reactions

GI: temporary darkening of tongue and stools.
Other: salicylism (with high doses).

Interactions

Drug-drug. *Aspirin, other salicylates:* May increase risk of salicylate toxicity. Monitor patient closely.
Oral anticoagulants, oral antidiabetics: Theoretical risk of increased effects of these drugs after high doses of bismuth subsalicylate. Monitor patient closely.
Probenecid: May decrease uricosuric effects after high doses of bismuth subsalicylate. Monitor patient closely.
Tetracycline: May decrease tetracycline absorption. Give drugs at least 2 hours apart.

Effects on lab test results

- May increase lipid levels.

Pharmacokinetics

Absorption: Poor; significant salicylate absorption may occur after taking bismuth subsalicylate.
Distribution: Locally in gut.
Metabolism: Minimal.
Excretion: Bismuth subsalicylate is excreted in urine. *Half life:* Unknown.

Route	Onset	Peak	Duration
P.O.	1 hr	Unknown	Unknown

Action

Chemical effect: May adsorb toxins and provide protective coating for mucosa.
Therapeutic effect: Relieves diarrhea.

Available forms

bismuth subgallate
Tablets (chewable): 200 mg†
bismuth subsalicylate
Caplet: 262 mg
Liquid (Children's): 87 mg/5 ml
Liquid (Extra Strength): 175 mg/5 ml
Liquid (Regular): 87.3 mg/ml
Oral suspension: 130 mg/15 ml, 262 mg/15 ml†, 524 mg/15 ml†
Tablets (chewable): 262.5 mg†

NURSING PROCESS

Assessment

- Obtain history of patient's bowel disorder, GI status, and frequency of loose stools.
- Monitor drug's effectiveness by checking frequency and characteristics of stools.

- Be alert for adverse reactions and drug interactions.
- Check patient's hearing if he takes drug in large doses.
- Assess patient's and family's understanding of drug therapy.

Nursing diagnoses

- Diarrhea related to underlying GI condition
- Disturbed sensory perception (auditory) related to drug-induced salicylism
- Deficient knowledge related to drug therapy

Planning and implementation

- Avoid use before GI radiologic procedures because bismuth is radiopaque and may interfere with X-rays.
- Read label carefully because dosage varies with form of drug.
- If tinnitus occurs, stop drug and notify prescriber.

Patient teaching

ALERT: Oral OTC drug products containing bismuth subsalicylate or kaolin are the only ones generally recognized as safe and effective for use as antidiarrheal agents. (This doesn't affect the availability of loperamide products.)

- Advise patient that drug contains large amount of salicylate. Each tablet contains 102 mg; regular-strength liquid contains 130 mg/15 ml, and extra-strength liquid contains 230 mg/15 ml.
- Instruct patient to chew tablets well or to shake liquid before measuring dose.
- Tell patient to report diarrhea that persists for longer than 2 days or is accompanied by high fever.
- Tell patient to consult with prescriber before giving bismuth subsalicylate to children or teenagers who have or are recovering from flu or chickenpox because of risk of Reye syndrome.
- Inform patient that both liquid and tablet forms of Pepto-Bismol are effective against traveler's diarrhea. Tablets may be more convenient to carry.
- Tell patient that any darkening of stool or the tongue is temporary.

Evaluation

- Patient reports decrease or absence of loose stools.
- Patient remains free from signs and symptoms of salicylism.
- Patient and family state understanding of drug therapy.

bisoprolol fumarate

(bis-OP-roh-lol FYOO-muh-rayt)

Zebeta

Pharmacologic class: beta blocker
Therapeutic class: antihypertensive
Pregnancy risk category: C

Indications and dosages

▶ **Hypertension.** *Adults:* Initially, 5 mg P.O. once daily. If response is inadequate, increase to 10 mg or 20 mg P.O. daily. Maximum, 20 mg.

Adjust-a-dose: For patients with renal impairment, a creatinine clearance of less than 40 ml/minute, hepatic dysfunction, cirrhosis, or hepatitis, start with 2.5 mg P.O. daily. Adjust dose cautiously.

▶ **Heart failure‡.** *Adults:* 1.25 mg P.O. daily for 2 to 4 weeks. This low-dose strength isn't available in the United States. If dose is tolerated, increase dose to 2.5 mg daily for 2 to 4 weeks. Subsequent doses can be doubled q 2 to 4 weeks, if tolerated.

Contraindications and cautions

- Contraindicated in patients hypersensitive to drug and in those with cardiogenic shock, overt cardiac failure, marked sinus bradycardia, or second- or third-degree AV block.
- Use cautiously in patients with bronchospastic disease. These patients should avoid beta blockers because blockade of $beta_1$ receptors isn't absolute and blockade of pulmonary $beta_2$ receptors may worsen symptoms. If avoiding beta blockers is impossible, have a bronchodilator available. Also use cautiously in patients with diabetes, peripheral vascular disease, thyroid disease, or a history of heart failure.

Lifespan: In pregnant or breast-feeding women, use cautiously. In children, safety and effectiveness of drug haven't been established.

Adverse reactions

CNS: asthenia, depression, dizziness, fatigue, headache, hypoesthesia, insomnia, vivid dreams.

CV: ***bradycardia,*** chest pain, ***heart failure,*** peripheral edema.
EENT: pharyngitis, rhinitis, sinusitis.
GI: diarrhea, dry mouth, nausea, vomiting.
Musculoskeletal: arthralgia.
Respiratory: cough, dyspnea.
Skin: sweating.

Interactions

Drug-drug. *Beta blockers:* May cause extreme hypotension. Don't use together.
Calcium channel blockers: May cause myocardial depression and AV conductive inhibition. Monitor ECG closely.
Guanethidine, reserpine: Can cause hypotension. Monitor patient closely.
NSAIDs: May decrease antihypertensive effect. Monitor blood pressure, and adjust dosage.
Rifampin: May increase metabolic clearance of bisoprolol. Monitor patient.

Effects on lab test results

None reported.

Pharmacokinetics

Absorption: Bioavailability after 10-mg dose is about 80%.
Distribution: About 30% protein-bound.
Metabolism: First-pass metabolism of drug is about 20%.
Excretion: Equally by renal and nonrenal pathways, with about 50% of dose appearing unchanged in urine and remainder appearing as inactive metabolites. Less than 2% of dose is excreted in feces. *Half-life:* 9 to 12 hours.

Route	Onset	Peak	Duration
P.O.	Unknown	2–4 hr	24 hr

Action

Chemical effect: May decrease myocardial contractility, heart rate, and cardiac output; lowers blood pressure; and reduces myocardial oxygen consumption.
Therapeutic effect: Decreases blood pressure.

Available forms

Tablets: 5 mg, 10 mg

NURSING PROCESS

Assessment

- Obtain history of patient's hypertensive status before therapy, and check blood pressure regularly throughout therapy.
- Be alert for adverse reactions and drug interactions.
- Monitor patient's hydration status if adverse GI reactions occur.
- Monitor glucose level closely in patient with diabetes. Beta blockers may mask some evidence of hypoglycemia, such as tachycardia.
- Assess patient's and family's understanding of drug therapy.

Nursing diagnoses

- Risk for injury related to presence of hypertension
- Risk for deficient fluid volume related to drug-induced adverse GI reactions
- Deficient knowledge related to drug therapy

Planning and implementation

- Have a $beta_2$ agonist (bronchodilator) available for patients with bronchospastic disease.

ALERT: Don't stop drug abruptly; angina may occur in patients with unrecognized coronary artery disease.

ALERT: Don't confuse Zebeta with Zestril, Zetia, or Zyrtec.

Patient teaching

- Tell patient to take drug as prescribed, even when he's feeling better. Warn him that stopping drug abruptly can worsen angina and precipitate MI. Explain that drug must be withdrawn gradually over 1 to 2 weeks.
- Instruct patient to call prescriber if adverse reactions occur.
- Tell patient with diabetes to closely monitor glucose levels.
- Tell patient to check with prescriber or pharmacist before taking OTC medications or herbal remedies.

Evaluation

- Patient's blood pressure is normal.
- Patient maintains adequate fluid balance throughout therapy.
- Patient and family state understanding of drug therapy.

bivalirudin

(bye-VAL-ih-roo-din)
Angiomax

Pharmacologic class: direct thrombin inhibitor
Therapeutic class: anticoagulant
Pregnancy risk category: B

Indications and dosages

▶ **Anticoagulation in patients with unstable angina undergoing percutaneous transluminal coronary angioplasty (PTCA); anticoagulation in patients with unstable angina undergoing percutaneous coronary intervention (PCI), with provisional use of a glycoprotein IIb/IIIa platelet inhibitor (GPI).** *Adults:* 0.75 mg/kg I.V. bolus followed by a continuous infusion of 1.75 mg/kg/hour for the duration of the procedure. Check activated clotting time 5 minutes after bolus dose. May give additional 0.3-mg/kg bolus dose if needed. Infusion may continue for up to 4 hours after procedure. After 4-hour infusion, may give an additional infusion of 0.2 mg/kg/hour for up to 20 hours, if needed. Use with 300 to 325 mg aspirin.

Adjust-a-dose: For patients with creatinine clearance of 30 ml/minute or less, decrease infusion rate to 1 mg/kg/hour. For patients on hemodialysis, reduce infusion rate to 0.25 mg/kg/hour. No reduction of bolus dose is needed.

▶ **Patients with or at risk for heparin-induced thrombocytopenia (HIT) or heparin-induced thrombocytopenia and thrombosis syndrome (HITTS) undergoing PCI.** *Adults:* 0.75 mg/kg I.V. bolus followed by continuous infusion of 1.75 mg/kg/hour for the duration of the procedure. The prescriber may continue the infusion after PCI.

I.V. administration

- Reconstitute each 250-mg vial with 5 ml of sterile water for injection. Further dilute each reconstituted vial in 50 ml D_5W or normal saline solution to yield 5 mg/ml.
- To prepare low-rate infusion, further dilute each reconstituted vial in 500 ml D_5W or normal saline solution to yield 0.5 mg/ml.
- The prepared solution is stable and may be stored for up to 24 hours at 36° to 46° F (2° to 8° C).

⊗ **Incompatibilities**

Alteplase, amiodarone, amphotericin B, chlorpromazine, diazepam, prochlorperazine edisylate, reteplase, streptokinase, vancomycin, all I.V. drugs.

Contraindications and cautions

- Contraindicated in patients hypersensitive to the drug or its components and in patients with active major bleeding. Don't use drug in patients with unstable angina who aren't undergoing PTCA or PCI, in patients with other acute coronary conditions, or in patients who aren't taking aspirin.
- Use cautiously in patients with HIT or HITTS and in patients with an increased risk of bleeding.

Lifespan: In pregnant women, use only if clearly needed because of the risk of maternal bleeding. In breast-feeding women, use cautiously because it isn't known whether drug appears in breast milk. In children, safety and effectiveness of drug haven't been established. In elderly patients, use with caution because they're more likely to have puncture site hemorrhage and catheterization site hematoma.

Adverse reactions

CNS: anxiety, ***cerebral ischemia,*** confusion, fever, *headache,* insomnia, nervousness, *pain.*
CV: ***bradycardia,*** hypertension, hypotension, syncope, vascular anomaly, ***ventricular fibrillation.***
GI: abdominal pain, dyspepsia, *nausea,* vomiting.
GU: oliguria, ***renal failure,*** urine retention.
Hematologic: ***arterial site hemorrhage; severe, spontaneous bleeding (cerebral, GI, GU, retroperitoneal).***
Musculoskeletal: *back pain,* pelvic pain, facial paralysis.
Respiratory: ***pulmonary edema.***
Other: infection, pain at injection site, ***sepsis.***

Interactions

Drug-drug. *GPIIb/IIIa inhibitors:* Safety and effectiveness haven't been established. Avoid use together.
Heparin, warfarin, other oral anticoagulants: May increase risk of bleeding. Use together cautiously. If using low–molecular-weight heparin, stop it at least 8 hours before giving bivalirudin.

Effects on lab test results

- May increase activated clotting time, PTT, thrombin time, and PT.

Pharmacokinetics

Absorption: Given I.V.
Distribution: Binds rapidly to thrombin and has a rapid onset of action.
Metabolism: Rapidly cleared by a combination of renal mechanisms and proteolytic cleavage.
Excretion: Renal. Total body clearance is similar in patients with normal renal function and mild renal impairment. Clearance is reduced about 20% in patients with moderate and severe renal impairment and is reduced about 80% in dialysis-dependent patients. Bivalirudin is hemodialyzable. *Half-life:* 25 minutes in patients with normal renal function.

Route	Onset	Peak	Duration
I.V.	Rapid	Immediate	Duration of infusion

Action

Chemical effect: Directly inhibits both clot-bound and circulating thrombin, preventing generation of fibrin and further activation of the clotting cascade. Inhibits thrombin-induced platelet activation, granule release, and aggregation.
Therapeutic effect: Prevents blood clots.

Available forms

Injection: 250-mg vial

NURSING PROCESS

Assessment

- Obtain and monitor baseline coagulation tests and hemoglobin level and hematocrit before and throughout therapy.
- Monitor effectiveness by measuring APTT, PT, and thrombin time values regularly.
- Monitor venipuncture sites for bleeding, hematoma, or inflammation.
- Be alert for adverse reactions.

ALERT: If the patient has an unexplained drop in hematocrit, blood pressure, or other unexplained symptom, consider the possibility of hemorrhage.

- Assess access site regularly for bleeding.
- Assess patient's and family's knowledge of drug therapy.

Nursing diagnoses

- Risk for injury related to potential acute ischemic event caused by impaired CV status
- Ineffective protection related to increased risk of bleeding from anticoagulant therapy
- Deficient knowledge related to drug therapy

Planning and implementation

- Patients with renal failure require reduced dosage.
- Don't give I.M.

Patient teaching

- Advise patient that drug can cause bleeding. Urge patient to report immediately any unusual bruising or bleeding (nosebleeds, bleeding gums, petechiae, and hematuria), or tarry or bloody stools.
- Warn patient to avoid other aspirin-containing drugs and drugs used to treat swelling or pain (such as Motrin, Naprosyn, Aleve).
- Advise patient to avoid activities that carry a risk of injury, and instruct patient to use a soft toothbrush and electric razor while taking drug.

Evaluation

- Patient doesn't have an acute ischemic event after PTCA or PCI.
- Patient doesn't have drug-induced adverse reactions or bleeding.
- Patient and family state understanding of drug therapy.

bleomycin sulfate

(blee-oh-MIGH-sin SULL-fayt)
Blenoxane

Pharmacologic class: antibiotic
Therapeutic class: antineoplastic
Pregnancy risk category: D

Indications and dosages

▶ **Hodgkin lymphoma, squamous cell carcinoma, non-Hodgkin lymphoma, testicular cancer.** *Adults:* 10 to 20 units/m^2 (0.25 to 0.5 units/kg) I.V., I.M., or subcutaneously once or twice weekly. After 50% response in patients with Hodgkin lymphoma, maintenance dosage is 1 unit I.V. or I.M. daily or 5 units I.V. or I.M. weekly.

▶ **Malignant pleural effusion, prevention of recurrent pleural effusions or to manage**

pneumothorax related to AIDS or *Pneumocystis jiroveci (carinii)* pneumonia. *Adults:* Give 60 units as a single-dose bolus in 50 to 100 ml of normal saline solution by intrapleural injection through a thoracostomy tube. Leave in for 4 hours, then drain and resume suction. Maximum dose is 1 unit/kg.
Elderly patients receiving intrapleural injection: Don't exceed 40 units/m².
▶ **AIDS-related Kaposi sarcoma‡.** *Adults:* 20 units/m² daily I.V. continuously over 72 hours q 3 weeks.

I.V. administration

• Follow facility policy for giving drug to reduce risks. Preparation and administration of parenteral form of this drug carry carcinogenic, mutagenic, and teratogenic risks.
• For I.V. use, dissolve contents of 15 or 30-unit vial with 5 or 10 ml, respectively, of normal saline for injection. Give slowly over 10 minutes.
⊗ **Incompatibilities**
Amino acids; aminophylline; ascorbic acid injection; cefazolin; diazepam; drugs containing sulfhydryl groups; fluids containing dextrose; furosemide; hydrocortisone; methotrexate; mitomycin; nafcillin; penicillin G; riboflavin; solutions containing divalent and trivalent cations, especially calcium salts and copper; terbutaline sulfate.

Contraindications and cautions

• Contraindicated in patients hypersensitive to drug.
• Use cautiously in patients with renal or pulmonary impairment.
Lifespan: In pregnant or breast-feeding women and in children, safety of drug hasn't been established.

Adverse reactions

CNS: fever, headache, hyperesthesia of scalp and fingers.
GI: diarrhea, nausea, *prolonged anorexia, stomatitis,* vomiting.
Hematologic: leukocytosis.
Musculoskeletal: swelling of interphalangeal joints.
Respiratory: *dyspnea, fine crackles, nonproductive cough,* PNEUMONITIS, ***pulmonary fibrosis.***
Skin: *acne;* desquamation of hands, feet, and pressure areas; *erythema; hardening and discoloration of palmar and plantar skin; hyperpigmentation; reversible alopecia; vesiculation.*
Other: ***anaphylaxis, hypersensitivity reactions (fever up to 106° F [41.1° C] with chills after injection).***

Interactions

Drug-drug. *Digoxin:* May decrease digoxin level. Monitor patient closely for loss of therapeutic effect.
Oxygen: Give supplemental oxygen, if ordered after treatment, at a fraction of inspired oxygen no higher than 25% to avoid potential lung damage.
Phenytoin: May decrease phenytoin level. Monitor patient closely.

Effects on lab test results

• May increase uric acid level.
• May increase WBC count.

Pharmacokinetics

Absorption: I.M. use yields lower levels than those produced by equivalent I.V. doses.
Distribution: Widely into total body water, mainly in skin, lungs, kidneys, peritoneum, and lymphatic tissue.
Metabolism: Unknown; however, extensive tissue inactivation occurs in liver and kidneys, with much less in skin and lungs.
Excretion: Drug and its metabolites excreted primarily in urine. *Half-life:* 2 hours.

Route	Onset	Peak	Duration
I.V., I.M., SubQ, intrapleural	Unknown	Unknown	Unknown

Action

Chemical effect: May inhibit DNA synthesis and cause scission of single- and double-stranded DNA.
Therapeutic effect: Kills selected types of cancer cells.

Available forms

Injection: 15- and 30-unit vials (1 unit = 1 mg)

B

NURSING PROCESS

Assessment

• Obtain history of patient's overall physical status (especially respiratory status, CBC, and pulmonary and renal function tests) before therapy and reassess regularly thereafter.
• Be alert for adverse reactions and drug interactions. Adverse pulmonary reactions are common in patients older than age 70.
ALERT: Fatal pulmonary fibrosis occurs in 1% of patients, especially when cumulative dose exceeds 400 units.
• Monitor patient for bleomycin-induced fever, which is common and usually occurs within 3 to 6 hours after giving drug.
• Watch for hypersensitivity reactions, which may be delayed for several hours, especially in patients with lymphoma.
• Assess patient for development of fine crackles and dyspnea.
• Assess patient's and family's understanding of drug therapy.

Nursing diagnoses

• Risk for injury related to underlying neoplastic condition
• Impaired gas exchange related to drug-induced adverse pulmonary reactions
• Deficient knowledge related to drug therapy

Planning and implementation

• Follow facility policy for giving drug to reduce risks. Preparation and administration of parenteral form of this drug carry carcinogenic, mutagenic, and teratogenic risks.
• For I.M. or subcutaneous routes, reconstitute 15-unit vial with 1 to 5 ml or the 30-unit vial with 2 to 10 ml of sterile water for injection, normal saline solution for injection, or bacteriostatic water for injection.
• Follow manufacturer's guidelines for giving bleomycin subcutaneously.
• For intrapleural use, dissolve drug in 50 to 100 ml normal saline solution for injection. Give through a thoracotomy tube after excess intrapleural fluid has been drained and complete lung expansion has been confirmed.
• Refrigerate unopened vials containing dry powder.
• Reconstituted solution for injection is stable for 4 weeks refrigerated or 2 weeks at room temperature; however, manufacturer recommends use within 24 hours of preparation and disposal of unused portion.
• Stop drug if pulmonary function test shows a marked decline.
• Don't use adhesive dressings on skin. This helps prevent linear streaking from drug concentrating in keratin of squamous epithelium.
• Give acetaminophen before treatment and for 24 hours after treatment in patients susceptible to post-treatment fever.

Patient teaching

• Explain the risks of drug therapy, especially the danger of serious pulmonary reactions in high-risk patients.
• Explain the need for monitoring and the type of monitoring to be done.
• Tell patient that alopecia may occur, but that it's usually reversible.

Evaluation

• Patient exhibits positive response to therapy, as shown by follow-up diagnostic test results.
• Patient's gas exchange remains normal throughout therapy.
• Patient and family state understanding of drug therapy.

bortezomib

(bore-TEHZ-uh-mihb)
Velcade

Pharmacologic class: proteasome inhibitor
Therapeutic class: antineoplastic
Pregnancy risk category: D

Indications and dosages

▶ **Multiple myeloma and mantle cell lymphoma that's progressing after at least one previous therapy.** *Adults:* 1.3 mg/m² by I.V. bolus twice weekly for 2 weeks (days 1, 4, 8, and 11) followed by a 10-day rest period (days 12 to 21). This 3-week period is a treatment cycle. For extended therapy of longer than 8 weeks, may adjust dosage schedule to once weekly for 4 weeks (days 1, 8, 15, and 22) followed by a 13-day rest period (days 23 to 35). Separate consecutive doses of drug by at least 72 hours.
Adjust-a-dose: If patient develops a grade 3 nonhematologic or a grade 4 hematologic toxicity (excluding neuropathy), withhold drug. When toxicity resolves, restart at a 25% reduced

dose. If patient has neuropathic pain, peripheral neuropathy, or both, use the following table.

Severity of neuropathy	Dosage adjustment
Grade 1 (paresthesias, loss of reflexes, or both without pain or loss of function)	No change.
Grade 1 with pain or grade 2 (function altered but not activities of daily living)	Reduce to 1 mg/m².
Grade 2 with pain or grade 3 (interference with activities of daily living)	Hold drug until toxicity resolves; then start at 0.7 mg/m² once weekly.
Grade 4 (permanent sensory loss that interferes with function)	Stop drug.

I.V. administration

- Reconstitute with 3.5 ml of normal saline solution. Use caution and aseptic technique when preparing and handling drug. Wear gloves and protective clothing to prevent skin contact.
- Give by I.V. bolus within 8 hours of reconstitution.
- Drug may be stored up to 3 hours in a syringe, but total storage time for reconstituted solution mustn't exceed 8 hours when exposed to normal indoor lighting.
- Store unopened vials at a controlled room temperature, in original packaging, and protect from light.

⊗ Incompatibilities
None reported.

Contraindications and cautions

- Contraindicated in patients hypersensitive to bortezomib, boron, or mannitol.
- Use cautiously if patient is dehydrated, is receiving other drugs known to cause hypotension, or has a history of syncope. In patients with severe neuropathy, use cautiously and only after careful assessment of risks and benefits.

Lifespan: In pregnant or breast-feeding women, avoid use. Women should avoid breast-feeding or becoming pregnant during drug therapy. In children, safety and effectiveness of drug haven't been established.

Adverse reactions

CNS: anxiety, *asthenia,* dizziness, dysesthesia, *fever,* headache, insomnia, paresthesia, *peripheral neuropathy,* rigors.
CV: edema, orthostatic and postural hypotension.
EENT: blurred vision.
GI: abdominal pain, *constipation, decreased appetite, diarrhea,* dysgeusia, dyspepsia, *nausea, vomiting.*
GU: dehydration.
Hematologic: *anemia,* NEUTROPENIA, THROMBOCYTOPENIA.
Musculoskeletal: arthralgia, back pain, bone pain, limb pain, muscle cramps, myalgia.
Respiratory: cough, dyspnea, pneumonia, upper respiratory tract infection.
Skin: rash, pruritus.
Other: herpes zoster.

Interactions

Drug-drug. *Antihypertensives:* May cause hypotension. Monitor patient's blood pressure closely.
Drugs linked to peripheral neuropathy, such as amiodarone, antivirals, isoniazid, nitrofurantoin, statins: May worsen neuropathy. Use together cautiously.
Inhibitors or inducers of CYP3A4: Monitor patient closely for either toxicity or reduced effects.
Oral antidiabetics: May cause hypoglycemia or hyperglycemia. Monitor glucose levels closely.

Effects on lab test results

- May decrease hemoglobin level and hematocrit.
- May decrease neutrophil and platelet counts.

Pharmacokinetics

Absorption: Given I.V.
Distribution: 83% protein-bound.
Metabolism: Mainly in the liver by cytochrome P-450 enzymes.
Excretion: Unknown. *Half-life:* 9 to 15 hours.

Route	Onset	Peak	Duration
I.V.	Unknown	Unknown	Unknown

Action

Chemical effect: Disrupts intracellular homeostatic mechanisms by inhibiting the 26S proteasome, which regulates intracellular levels of certain proteins and causes cells to die.
Therapeutic effect: Destroys cancer cells.

Available forms

Injection: 3.5 mg

NURSING PROCESS

Assessment

- Assess patient's condition before therapy and regularly thereafter.
- Assess patient's nutrition and hydration status before and during therapy.
- Assess patient's and family's knowledge of drug therapy.

Nursing diagnoses

- Risk for injury related to potential neuropathy as an adverse effect
- Deficient fluid volume related to dehydration
- Risk for imbalanced nutrition: less than body requires related to underlying disease and drug adverse effects

Planning and implementation

- Monitor patient's reaction. An antiemetic, an antidiarrheal, or both may be needed because drug may cause nausea, vomiting, diarrhea, or constipation.
- Adjust antihypertensive dosage, maintain hydration status, and give mineralocorticoids to manage orthostatic hypotension.
- Watch for evidence of neuropathy, such as a burning sensation, hyperesthesia, hypoesthesia, paresthesia, discomfort, or neuropathic pain.
- Change dose and schedule if patient develops new or worsening peripheral neuropathy.

Patient teaching

- Tell patient to notify prescriber about new or worsening peripheral neuropathy.
- Urge women to use effective contraception during treatment.
- Teach patient how to avoid dehydration, and stress the need to tell prescriber about dizziness, light-headedness, or fainting spells.
- Tell patient to use caution when driving or performing potentially hazardous activities because drug may cause fatigue, dizziness, faintness, light-headedness, and vision problems.

Evaluation

- Patient has no serious drug reactions.
- Patient maintains adequate hydration status.
- Patient maintains adequate nutritional status.
- Patient and family state understanding of drug therapy.

B

bosentan

(bow-SEN-tan)

Tracleer

Pharmacologic class: endothelin receptor antagonist
Therapeutic class: vasodilator
Pregnancy risk category: X

Indications and dosages

▶ **Pulmonary arterial hypertension in patients with World Health Organization class III or IV symptoms to improve exercise ability and decrease clinical worsening.** *Adults:* 62.5 mg P.O. b.i.d. for 4 weeks. Increase to maintenance dose of 125 mg P.O. b.i.d. In patients older than age 12 who weigh less than 40 kg (88 lb), the initial and maintenance dose is 62.5 mg b.i.d. Adjust dose based on ALT and AST levels.

Contraindications and cautions

- Contraindicated in patients hypersensitive to drug. Don't use in patients with moderate-to-severe liver impairment or in those with aminotransferase (ALT/AST) levels more than three times upper limit of normal.
- Use cautiously in patients with mild liver impairment.

Lifespan: In pregnant women, drug is contraindicated. In breast-feeding women, drug isn't recommended because it's unknown whether drug appears in breast milk. In children age 12 or younger, safety and effectiveness of drug haven't been established. In elderly patients, select dose cautiously because of greater likelihood of decreased organ function.

Adverse reactions

CNS: fatigue, *headache.*
CV: edema, flushing, hypotension, lower leg edema, palpitations.
EENT: *nasopharyngitis.*
GI: dyspepsia.
Hematologic: anemia.
Hepatic: ***liver failure.***
Skin: pruritus.

Interactions

Drug-drug. *Cyclosporin A:* May increase bosentan level and decrease cyclosporine level. Avoid use together.
Glyburide: May increase risk of elevated liver enzyme levels and decrease levels of both drugs. Avoid use together.
Hormonal contraceptives: May cause contraceptive failure. Advise use of a barrier method of birth control.
Ketoconazole: May increase bosentan level. Monitor patient for increased effects of bosentan.
Simvastatin, other statins: May decrease levels of these drugs. Monitor cholesterol levels to assess need for statin dosage adjustment.

Effects on lab test results

- May increase liver aminotransferase (such as AST, ALT, and bilirubin) levels. May decrease hemoglobin level and hematocrit.

Pharmacokinetics

Absorption: 50% bioavailability after oral use.
Distribution: More than 98% protein-bound, mainly albumin.
Metabolism: Hepatically into three metabolites. Bosentan induces CYP2C9 and CYP3A4, and possibly CYP2C19.
Excretion: By biliary excretion. Less than 3% of oral dose is recovered in urine. *Half life:* About 5 hours.

Route	Onset	Peak	Duration
P.O.	Unknown	3–5 hr	Unknown

Action

Chemical effect: Antagonizes endothelin-1, which is elevated in patients with pulmonary arterial hypertension.
Therapeutic effect: Increases exercise capacity and cardiac index. Decreases blood pressure, pulmonary arterial pressure, vascular resistance, and mean right arterial pressure.

Available forms

Tablets: 62.5 mg, 125 mg

NURSING PROCESS

Assessment

- Assess patient's underlying condition before therapy, and reassess regularly thereafter.
- Make sure patient isn't pregnant. Obtain monthly pregnancy tests.
- Serious liver injury may occur. Measure aminotransferase levels before treatment and monthly thereafter, and adjust dosage accordingly.
- This drug may cause hematologic changes. Monitor hemoglobin level after 1 and 3 months of therapy and then every 3 months thereafter.
- Be alert for adverse events.
- Assess patient's and family's knowledge of drug therapy.

Nursing diagnoses

- Risk for injury related to drug-induced liver enzyme elevations
- Ineffective tissue perfusion (cardiopulmonary) related to underlying condition
- Deficient knowledge related to drug therapy

Planning and implementation

- To decrease the possibility of serious liver injury and limit the chance of fetal exposure, Tracleer may be prescribed only through the Tracleer access program at 1-866-228-3546. Adverse effects also may be reported through this number.
- For patients who develop aminotransferase abnormalities, the dosage may need to be decreased or therapy stopped until aminotransferase levels return to normal. If liver function abnormalities are accompanied by symptoms of liver injury, such as nausea, vomiting, fever, abdominal pain, jaundice, or unusual lethargy or fatigue, or if bilirubin level is greater than or equal to two times upper limit of normal, stop treatment and don't restart.
- Overdose may cause headache, nausea and vomiting, mildly decreased blood pressure, and increased heart rate. Massive overdose may cause severe hypotension requiring CV support. Treat symptoms, and provide supportive care.
- To avoid the potential for deterioration, gradually reduce the dosage when stopping drug.

Patient teaching

- Advise patient to take drug only as prescribed.
- Warn patient to avoid becoming pregnant while taking this drug because major birth defects may result. Reliable contraception must be used and a monthly pregnancy test performed.
- Advise patient to have liver tests and blood counts performed regularly.

• Tell patient not to use hormonal contraceptives, including oral, implantable, and injectable, as her only means of contraception because failure may occur.

Evaluation

• Patient has no adverse reactions or liver damage from drug therapy.
• Patient's pulmonary artery pressure decreases, and patient reaches pulmonary hemodynamic stability.
• Patient and family state understanding of drug therapy.

bromfenac ophthalmic solution

(BROM-fehn-ack off-THAL-mick suh-LOO-shun)
Xibrom

Pharmacologic classification: nonsteroidal anti-inflammatory drug
Therapeutic classification: anti-inflammatory, ophthalmic
Pregnancy risk category: C

Indications and dosages

▶ **Postoperative inflammation and pain after cataract surgery.** *Adults:* 1 drop in affected eye b.i.d. starting 24 hours after surgery and continuing for 2 weeks.

Contraindications and cautions

• Contraindicated in patients hypersensitive to any ingredient in the product. Bromfenac ophthalmic solution contains sulfite, which may cause allergic-type reactions, including anaphylaxis and life-threatening or less severe asthmatic episodes in patients sensitive to sulfites.
• Use cautiously in patients with bleeding tendencies, patients taking anticoagulants, and patients sensitive to acetylsalicylic acid, phenylacetic acid derivatives, and other NSAIDs because of the risk of cross-sensitivity reactions. Also use cautiously in patients with complicated ocular surgeries, corneal denervation, corneal epithelial defects, diabetes mellitus, ocular surface diseases (such as dry eye syndrome), rheumatoid arthritis, or recent repeat ocular surgeries because the risk of corneal adverse effects, which may be sight-threatening, is increased.

Lifespan: In pregnant women, use only if potential benefit justifies the risk. Avoid giving drug late in pregnancy because NSAIDs may cause premature closure of the ductus arteriosus, a necessary structure of fetal circulation. In breast-feeding women, use cautiously. In children, safety and effectiveness haven't been established.

Adverse reactions

CNS: headache.
EENT: abnormal sensation in the eye, burning, conjunctival hyperemia, eye irritation, eye pain, eye pruritus, eye redness, iritis, keratitis, stinging.
Other: *anaphylaxis,* hypersensitivity reactions.

Interactions

Drug-drug. *Drugs that affect coagulation:* May further increase bleeding tendency or prolong bleeding time. Avoid use together, if possible, or monitor bleeding closely.
Topical corticosteroids: May disrupt healing. Avoid use together, if possible, or monitor healing closely.

Effects on lab test results

None reported.

Pharmacokinetics

Absorption: Unknown.
Distribution: Intraocular.
Metabolism: Unknown.
Excretion: Unknown. *Half-life:* Unknown.

Route	Onset	Peak	Duration
Ophthalmic	Unknown	Unknown	Unknown

Action

Chemical effect: Blocks prostaglandin synthesis by inhibiting cyclooxygenase 1 and 2.
Therapeutic effect: Reduces postoperative inflammation after cataract surgery.

Available forms

Ophthalmic solution: 0.09%

NURSING PROCESS

Assessment

• Assess patient's risk for allergic reaction; ask patient before treatment if he is sensitive to sulfites, aspirin, or other NSAIDs.

• If patient takes an anticoagulant, watch closely for increased bleeding.
• Monitor PT and INR if appropriate.
• Assess patient's and family's knowledge of drug therapy.

Nursing diagnoses
• Disturbed visual sensory perception related to cataract surgery and potential adverse effects of medication
• Risk for activity intolerance related to decreased visual acuity
• Deficient knowledge related to drug therapy

Planning and implementation
• Patients with asthma have an increased likelihood of sulfite sensitivity.
• Begin treatment at least 24 hours after surgery, and continue for 2 weeks.
• Giving drug less than 24 hours after surgery or more than 14 days after surgery increases risk of adverse ocular effects.
• If overdose or significant adverse ocular effect occurs, stop drug and monitor ocular health closely.

Patient teaching
• Advise patient not to use drops while wearing contact lenses.
• Teach patient how to instill the drops.
• Instruct patient to start using drops 24 hours after surgery and to continue for 14 days.
• Tell him not to use drops for longer than 2 weeks after surgery or to save unused drops for other conditions.
• Review the signs and symptoms of adverse effects. If bothersome or serious adverse effects occur, inform the patient to stop the drops and contact his prescriber.
• Tell patient to store drops at room temperature.

Evaluation
• Patient has no adverse effects.
• Patient's activity level improves.
• Patient and family state understanding of drug therapy.

bromocriptine mesylate
(broh-moh-KRIP-teen MESS-ih-layt)
Parlodel, Parlodel SnapTabs

Pharmacologic class: dopamine receptor agonist
Therapeutic class: antiparkinsonian, inhibitor of prolactin and growth hormone release
Pregnancy risk category: B

Indications and dosages
▶ **Parkinson disease.** *Adults:* 1.25 to 2.5 mg P.O. b.i.d. with meals. Increase dosage q 14 to 28 days, up to 100 mg daily, as needed. Usual dosage, 10 to 40 mg daily.
▶ **Acromegaly.** *Adults:* 1.25 to 2.5 mg P.O. at bedtime with snack for 3 days. An additional 1.25 to 2.5 mg may be added q 3 to 7 days until patient receives therapeutic benefit. Usual therapeutic dose is 20 to 30 mg daily. Maximum dosage, 100 mg daily.
▶ **Amenorrhea and galactorrhea related to hyperprolactinemia; infertility or hypogonadism in women.** *Adults:* 1.25 to 2.5 mg P.O. daily. Increase by 2.5 mg daily at 3- to 7-day intervals until desired effect is achieved. Maintenance dosage is usually 5 to 7.5 mg daily, but may be 2.5 to 15 mg daily.
▶ **Premenstrual syndrome‡.** *Adults:* 2.5 to 7.5 mg P.O. b.i.d. from day 10 of menstrual cycle until onset of menstruation.
▶ **Cushing syndrome‡.** *Adults:* 1.25 to 2.5 mg P.O. b.i.d. to q.i.d.
▶ **Hepatic encephalopathy‡.** *Adults:* 1.25 mg P.O. daily, increase by 1.25 mg q 3 days until 15 mg is reached.
▶ **Neuroleptic malignant syndrome related to neuroleptic drug therapy‡.** *Adults:* 2.5 to 5 mg P.O. 2 to 6 times daily.

Contraindications and cautions
• Contraindicated in patients hypersensitive to ergot derivatives and in those with uncontrolled hypertension, severe ischemic heart disease or peripheral vascular disease, or toxemia of pregnancy.
• Use cautiously in patients with renal or hepatic impairment or history of MI with residual arrhythmias.
Lifespan: In pregnant women, use only if benefits outweigh risks to fetus. In breast-

feeding women, avoid use because it inhibits lactation. In children younger than age 15, safety and effectiveness of drug haven't been established.

Adverse reactions

CNS: confusion, delusions, depression, *dizziness,* fatigue, hallucinations, *headache,* insomnia, mania, nervousness, ***seizures, stroke, syncope,*** uncontrolled body movements.
CV: ***acute MI,*** hypertension, *hypotension,* orthostatic hypotension.
EENT: blurred vision, nasal congestion, tinnitus.
GI: *abdominal cramps,* constipation, diarrhea, *nausea,* vomiting.
GU: urinary frequency, urine retention.
Skin: coolness and pallor of fingers and toes.

Interactions

Drug-drug. *Antihypertensives:* May increase hypotensive effects. Antihypertensive dosage may need adjustment.
Ergot alkaloids, estrogens, hormonal contraceptives, progestins: May interfere with bromocriptine effects. Don't use together.
Erythromycin: May increase bromocriptine level. Bromocriptine dosage may need adjustment.
Haloperidol, loxapine, MAO inhibitors, methyldopa, metoclopramide, phenothiazines, reserpine: May interfere with bromocriptine effects. Bromocriptine dosage may need to be increased.
Levodopa: May have additive effects. Levodopa dosage may need adjustment.
Drug-lifestyle. *Alcohol use:* May cause disulfiram-like reaction. Discourage use together.

Effects on lab test results

• May increase BUN, alkaline phosphatase, uric acid, AST, ALT, and CK levels.

Pharmacokinetics

Absorption: 28% absorbed.
Distribution: 90% to 96% bound to albumin.
Metabolism: First-pass metabolism occurs with more than 90% of absorbed dose. Drug is metabolized completely in liver.
Excretion: Major route is through bile. Only 2.5% to 5.5% of dose excreted in urine. *Half-life:* 15 hours.

Route	Onset	Peak	Duration
P.O.	½–2 hr	1–3 hr	12–24 hr

Action

Chemical effect: Inhibits secretion of prolactin and acts as a dopamine-receptor agonist by activating postsynaptic dopamine receptors.
Therapeutic effect: Reverses amenorrhea and galactorrhea caused by hyperprolactinemia, increases fertility in women, improves voluntary movement, and inhibits prolactin and growth hormone release.

Available forms

Capsules: 5 mg
Tablets: 2.5 mg

NURSING PROCESS

Assessment

• Obtain history of patient's underlying condition before therapy, and reassess regularly thereafter.

• Before treatment, assess patient for evidence of dementia. Monitor patient for mental changes during therapy.

• Perform baseline and periodic evaluations of cardiac, hepatic, renal, and hematopoietic functions during prolonged therapy.

• Be alert for adverse reactions and drug interactions. Risk of adverse reactions is high, particularly at start of therapy and with doses greater than 20 mg. Adverse reactions are more common when drug is used for Parkinson disease.

• Assess patient's and family's knowledge of drug therapy.

Nursing diagnoses

• Ineffective health maintenance related to underlying condition
• Risk for injury related to drug-induced adverse CNS or CV reactions
• Deficient knowledge related to drug therapy

Planning and implementation

• Give drug with meals.
• Gradually adjust dose to effective level to minimize adverse reactions.
• Patients with impaired renal function may need dosage adjustment.

• For Parkinson disease, bromocriptine is usually given with either levodopa or levodopa and carbidopa.

Patient teaching

• Advise patient to use methods other than hormonal contraceptives during treatment.
• Advise patient to rise slowly to an upright position and avoid sudden position changes to avoid dizziness and fainting.
• Advise patient that resumption of menses and suppression of galactorrhea may take 6 weeks or longer.
• Warn patient to avoid hazardous activities that require alertness until CNS and CV effects of drug are known.
• Tell patient to take drug with meals to minimize GI distress.

Evaluation

• Patient shows improvement in underlying condition.
• Patient sustains no injury from drug-induced adverse reactions.
• Patient and family state understanding of drug therapy.

budesonide (inhalation)

(byoo-DESS-oh-nighd)

Pulmicort Respules, Pulmicort Turbuhaler, Rhinocort Aqua

Pharmacologic class: glucocorticoid
Therapeutic class: anti-inflammatory
Pregnancy risk category: B

Indications and dosages

▶ **Symptoms of seasonal or perennial allergic rhinitis and nonallergic perennial rhinitis.** *Adults and children age 6 and older:* 1 spray in each nostril once daily. In adults and children age 12 and older, may increase to 4 sprays in each nostril once daily; in children younger than age 12, may increase to 2 sprays in each nostril once daily. Maintenance dosage is fewest number of sprays needed to control symptoms.

▶ **Chronic asthma.** *Adults:* 200 to 400 mcg oral inhalation via Turbuhaler b.i.d. when patient previously used bronchodilators alone or inhaled corticosteroids; 400 to 800 mcg oral inhalation b.i.d. when patient previously used oral corticosteroids. Maximum dosage 800 mcg b.i.d.
Children age 6 and older: Initially, 200 mcg oral inhalation via Turbuhaler b.i.d. Maximum dosage is 400 mcg b.i.d.
Children ages 1 to 8: Give 0.5 mg once daily or 0.25 mg b.i.d. in child not receiving systemic or inhaled corticosteroids or 1 mg daily or 0.5 mg b.i.d. if child is receiving oral corticosteroids. Alternatively, in children unresponsive to nonsteroidal therapy, 0.25 mg Pulmicort Respules by jet nebulizer with compressor once daily.

Contraindications and cautions

• Contraindicated in patients hypersensitive to the drug or its components and in those who have had recent septal ulcers, nasal surgery, or nasal trauma, until total healing has occurred. Pulmicort Turbuhaler and Pulmicort Respules are contraindicated for primary treatment of status asthmaticus.
• Use cautiously in patients with tuberculous infections, ocular herpes simplex, or untreated fungal, bacterial, or systemic viral infections.
Lifespan: In pregnant or breast-feeding women, use cautiously. In children younger than age 1, don't use Pulmicort Respules via jet nebulizer. In children younger than age 6, safety of oral inhalation via Turbuhaler hasn't been established.

Adverse reactions

CNS: *headache,* nervousness.
CV: facial edema.
EENT: epistaxis, hoarseness, nasal irritation, nasal pain, pharyngitis, reduced sense of smell, sinusitis.
GI: bad taste, dry mouth, dyspepsia, nausea, vomiting.
Metabolic: weight gain.
Musculoskeletal: myalgia.
Respiratory: candidiasis, cough, dyspnea, wheezing.
Skin: contact dermatitis, pruritus, rash.
Other: hypersensitivity reactions.

Interactions

Drug-drug. *Alternate-day prednisone therapy, inhaled corticosteroids:* May increase risk of hypothalamic-pituitary-adrenal suppression. Monitor patient closely.
Ketoconazole: May increase budesonide level. Use together cautiously.

B

Effects on lab test results

None reported.

Pharmacokinetics

Absorption: Amount of intranasal dose that reaches systemic circulation is typically about 20%.
Distribution: 88% protein-bound.
Metabolism: Rapidly and extensively in liver.
Excretion: About 67% in urine and 33% in feces. *Half-life:* About 2 hours.

Route	Onset	Peak	Duration
Nasal inhalation	Unknown	45 min	8–10 hr
Oral inhalation	5–15 min	30 min	Unknown

Action

Chemical effect: Decreases nasal and pulmonary inflammation, mainly by inhibiting activities of specific cells and mediators involved in allergic response.
Therapeutic effect: Decreases nasal and pulmonary congestion.

Available forms

Inhalation suspension: 0.25 mg/2 ml, 0.5 mg/2 ml
Nasal spray: 32 mcg/metered spray (7-g canister)
Oral inhalation powder: 200 mcg/dose

NURSING PROCESS

Assessment

- Obtain history of patient's condition before therapy, and reassess regularly thereafter.
- Be alert for adverse reactions.
- Assess patient's and family's knowledge of drug therapy.

Nursing diagnoses

- Ineffective health maintenance related to allergy-induced nasal congestion
- Impaired gas exchange related to drug-induced wheezing
- Deficient knowledge related to drug therapy

Planning and implementation

- Before using nasal inhaler, shake container. Have patient clear his nasal passages. Insert nozzle (pointed away from septum) into nostril, holding other nostril closed. Have patient tilt head slightly forward so spray is directed up nasal passage. Deliver spray while patient inhales. Have patient tilt head back for a few seconds. Repeat in other nostril. Wipe off tip of inhaler before capping.
- Notify prescriber if relief isn't obtained or signs of infection appear.
- Obtain specimen for culture if signs of nasal infection occur.

Patient teaching

- Teach patient how to use nasal inhaler, as described above.
- Instruct patient to hold the inhaler upright while orally inhaling the dose. When loading Pulmicort Turbuhaler, tell him not to blow or exhale into the inhaler and not to shake it while loaded. Tell him to place the mouthpiece between his lips and inhale forcefully and deeply. Have him rinse mouth after use to decrease risk of fungal growth.
- Pulmicort Respules can be given only by jet nebulizer connected to an air compressor with minimum airflow of 5.5 L/minute. System should be equipped with a mouthpiece or face mask. Have patient rinse mouth after administration. When using face mask, teach him to wash face after use to decrease risk of contact dermatitis or rash.
- Inform patient that use of an oral inhaler results in improvement in asthma control in 10 to 24 hours, with maximum benefit at 1 to 2 weeks, or possibly longer.
- Advise parent that antihistamines can cause paradoxical excitement in small children.

ALERT: Advise patient that Pulmicort Turbuhaler and Pulmicort Respules aren't intended to relieve acute asthma attacks.

- Tell patient that product should be used by only one person to prevent spread of infection.
- Advise patient not to break or incinerate canister or store it in extreme heat. Contents are under pressure.
- Warn patient not to exceed prescribed dose or use for long periods because of risk of hypothalamic-pituitary-adrenal axis suppression.
- Tell patient to report worsened condition or symptoms that don't improve in 3 weeks.
- Teach patient good nasal and oral hygiene.

Evaluation

- Patient's nasal congestion subsides.

• Patient has adequate gas exchange.
• Patient and family state understanding of drug therapy.

budesonide (oral)

(byoo-DESS-uh-nighd)
Entocort EC

Pharmacologic class: corticosteroid
Therapeutic class: anti-inflammatory
Pregnancy risk category: B

Indications and dosages

▶ **Mild to moderate active Crohn disease involving the ileum or the ascending colon.** *Adults:* 9 mg P.O. once daily in the morning for up to 8 weeks. For recurrent episodes of active Crohn disease, a repeat 8-week course may be given.

▶ **To maintain remission of mild to moderate Crohn disease involving the ileum or ascending colon.** *Adults:* 6 mg P.O. daily for up to 3 months. If symptoms are controlled at 3 months, taper drug to complete stop. Maintenance treatment beyond 3 months doesn't provide additional benefit.

Contraindications and cautions

• Contraindicated in patients hypersensitive to drug.
• Use cautiously in patients with tuberculosis, hypertension, diabetes mellitus, osteoporosis, peptic ulcer disease, glaucoma, or cataracts. Also use cautiously in patients with a family history of diabetes or glaucoma and those with any other condition in which glucocorticosteroids may have unwanted effects.

Lifespan: In pregnant women, use only if potential benefit justifies risks. In breast-feeding women, the decision to breast-feed should be based on importance of drug to the mother; glucocorticoids appear in breast milk and infants may have adverse reactions. In children, safety and effectiveness of drug haven't been established. In elderly patients, give drug cautiously, starting at the lower end of the dosage range.

Adverse reactions

CNS: agitation, asthenia, confusion, dizziness, fatigue, fever, *headache,* hyperkinesia, insomnia, malaise, migraine, nervousness, pain, paresthesia, sleep disorder, somnolence, syncope, tremor, vertigo.
CV: chest pain, dependent edema, facial edema, flushing, hypertension, palpitations, tachycardia.
EENT: abnormal vision, ear infection, eye abnormality, neck pain, *pharyngitis,* sinusitis, voice alteration.
GI: abdominal pain, aggravated Crohn disease, anus disorder, *diarrhea,* dry mouth, dyspepsia, epigastric pain, fistula, flatulence, gastroenteritis, glossitis, hemorrhoids, increased appetite, intestinal obstruction, *nausea,* oral candidiasis, taste perversion, tongue edema, tooth disorder, vomiting.
GU: dysuria, intermenstrual bleeding, menstrual disorder, micturition frequency, nocturia.
Hematologic: anemia, leukocytosis.
Metabolic: ADRENAL INSUFFICIENCY, *hypercorticism,* hypokalemia, weight gain.
Musculoskeletal: aggravated arthritis, arthralgia, back pain, cramps, hypotonia, myalgia.
Respiratory: bronchitis, cough, dyspnea, *respiratory tract infection.*
Skin: acne, alopecia, dermatitis, ecchymosis, eczema, increased sweating, skin disorder.
Other: flulike syndrome, infection, viral infection.

Interactions

Drug-drug. *CYP3A4 inhibitors (erythromycin, indinavir, itraconazole, ketoconazole, ritonavir, saquinavir):* May increase budesonide effects. If drugs must be given together, watch for signs of hypercorticism and consider reducing budesonide dosage.
Drug-food. *Grapefruit or grapefruit juice:* May increase drug effects. Discourage use together.

Effects on lab test results

• May increase alkaline phosphatase and C-reactive protein levels. May decrease hemoglobin level and hematocrit. May increase or decrease potassium level.
• May increase erythrocyte sedimentation rate and atypical neutrophil and WBC counts.

Pharmacokinetics

Absorption: Complete.
Distribution: 85% to 90% protein-bound.
Metabolism: Extensive first-pass metabolism and rapid, extensive biotransformation by CYP3A4 to two major metabolites that have little glucocorticoid activity.

Excretion: In urine and feces as metabolites, excreted mainly renally. *Half-life:* Unknown.

Route	Onset	Peak	Duration
P.O.	Unknown	½–10 hr	Unknown

Action

Chemical effect: Has high affinity for glucocorticoid receptors.

Therapeutic effect: Alleviates symptoms of Crohn disease.

Available forms

Capsules: 3 mg

NURSING PROCESS

Assessment

- Assess patient's underlying condition before starting therapy, and reassess regularly thereafter.
- Monitor patient's laboratory values regularly. Monitor patient for adverse effects.
- Be alert for signs and symptoms of hypercorticism.
- Assess patient's and family's knowledge of drug therapy.

Nursing diagnoses

- Diarrhea caused by underlying Crohn disease
- Imbalanced nutrition: less than body requirements related to underlying Crohn disease
- Deficient knowledge related to drug therapy

Planning and implementation

- Patients undergoing surgery or another stressful situation may need systemic glucocorticoid supplementation in addition to budesonide therapy.
- When a patient is transferred from systemic glucocorticoid therapy to budesonide, watch carefully for evidence of steroid withdrawal. Taper glucocorticoid when budesonide treatment starts.
- Watch for immunosuppression, especially in a patient who hasn't had diseases such as chickenpox or measles, because these diseases can be fatal in a patient who is immunosuppressed or receiving glucocorticoids. Monitor adrenocortical function carefully, and reduce dosage cautiously.
- Prevent exposure to chickenpox or measles. If patient is exposed to measles, consider therapy with pooled intravenous immunoglobulin. If patient develops chickenpox, antiviral treatment and varicella zoster immune globulin may be considered.
- Acute toxicity after overdose is rare.
- Prolonged use of drug may cause hypercorticism (symptoms include swelling of the face and neck, acne, bruising, hirsutism, buffalo hump, and skin striae) and adrenal suppression. Treat with immediate gastric lavage or emesis, followed by treatment of symptoms and supportive therapy. For chronic overdose in serious disease requiring continuous steroid therapy, dosage may be reduced temporarily. Dosage may need to be reduced in patients with moderate to severe liver disease if they have increased signs or symptoms of hypercorticism.

Patient teaching

- Tell patient to swallow capsules whole and not to chew or break them.
- Advise patient not to drink grapefruit juice while taking drug.
- Tell patient to notify prescriber immediately if exposed to chickenpox or measles.

Evaluation

- Patient's symptoms of Crohn disease, including diarrhea and abdominal pain, are relieved.
- Patient's nutrition improves as symptoms improve.
- Patient and family state understanding of drug therapy.

bumetanide

(byoo-MEH-tuh-nighd)

Bumex, Burinex ◇

Pharmacologic class: loop diuretic
Therapeutic class: diuretic
Pregnancy risk category: C

Indications and dosages

▶ **Hypertension.** *Adults:* 0.5 mg P.O. daily. Oral maintenance dosage is 1 to 4 mg daily, not to exceed 5 mg P.O. daily.

▶ **Heart failure.** *Children:* 0.015 mg/kg every other day to 0.1 mg/kg daily. Use with extreme caution in neonates.

▶ **Heart failure, hepatic or renal disease, postoperative edema‡, premenstrual syndrome‡, disseminated cancer‡.** *Adults:* 0.5 to

2 mg P.O. once daily. If diuretic response isn't adequate, give second or third dose at 4- to 5-hour intervals. Maximum, 10 mg daily. Give parenterally if P.O. use isn't feasible. Usual initial dose is 0.5 to 1 mg given I.V. over 1 to 2 minutes or I.M. If response isn't adequate, give second or third dose at 2- to 3-hour intervals. Maximum, 10 mg daily.

Adjust-a-dose: For patients with severe chronic renal insufficiency, a continuous infusion of 12 mg over 12 hours may be more effective and less toxic than intermittent bolus therapy.

I.V. administration

- For direct injection, use 21G or 23G needle and give drug over 1 to 2 minutes.
- For intermittent infusion, give diluted drug through an intermittent infusion device or piggyback into an I.V. line containing free-flowing compatible solution. Infuse at ordered rate.
- Continuous infusion not recommended.

⊗ **Incompatibilities**

Dobutamine, midazolam.

Contraindications and cautions

- Contraindicated in patients hypersensitive to drug or sulfonamides (possible cross-sensitivity), in those with anuria or hepatic coma, and in those with severe electrolyte depletion.
- Use cautiously in patients with depressed renal function or hepatic cirrhosis or ascites.

Lifespan: In pregnant women, use cautiously. In breast-feeding women, drug is contraindicated. In children, safety and effectiveness of drug haven't been established.

Adverse reactions

CNS: dizziness, headache.
CV: ECG changes, orthostatic hypotension, volume depletion and dehydration.
EENT: transient deafness.
GI: nausea.
GU: azotemia, frequent urination, nocturia, oliguria, polyuria, ***renal failure.***
Hematologic: ***thrombocytopenia.***
Metabolic: asymptomatic hyperuricemia; fluid and electrolyte imbalances, including dilutional hyponatremia, hypocalcemia, and hypomagnesemia; hyperglycemia; hypochloremic alkalosis; hypokalemia; impaired glucose tolerance.
Musculoskeletal: muscle pain and tenderness.
Skin: rash.

Interactions

Drug-drug. *Aminoglycoside antibiotics:* May potentiate ototoxicity. Use together cautiously.
Antihypertensives: May increase risk of hypotension. Use together cautiously.
Chlorothiazide, chlorthalidone, hydrochlorothiazide, indapamide, metolazone: May cause excessive diuretic response, resulting in serious electrolyte abnormalities or dehydration. Adjust dosages carefully while monitoring patient for excessive diuretic responses.
Digoxin: May increase risk of digitalis toxicity from bumetanide-induced hypokalemia. Monitor potassium and digoxin levels.
Indomethacin, NSAIDs, probenecid: May inhibit diuretic response. Use together cautiously.
Lithium: May decrease lithium clearance, increasing risk of lithium toxicity. Monitor lithium level.
Other potassium-wasting drugs: May increase risk of hypokalemia. Use together cautiously.
Drug-herb. *Licorice:* May contribute to excessive potassium loss. Discourage use together.

Effects on lab test results

- May increase creatinine, urine urea, glucose, and cholesterol levels. May decrease potassium, magnesium, sodium, and calcium levels.
- May decrease platelet count.

Pharmacokinetics

Absorption: After P.O. use, 85% to 95%; food delays absorption. Complete after I.M. use.
Distribution: About 92% to 96% protein-bound. It isn't known if drug enters CSF.
Metabolism: By liver to at least five metabolites.
Excretion: In urine (80%) and feces (10% to 20%). *Half-life:* 1 to 1½ hours.

Route	Onset	Peak	Duration
P.O.	30–60 min	1–2 hr	4–6 hr
I.V.	3 min	15–30 min	½–4 hr
I.M.	40 min	Unknown	Unknown

Action

Chemical effect: Inhibits sodium and chloride reabsorption at ascending portion of loop of Henle.
Therapeutic effect: Promotes sodium and water excretion.

B

Available forms

Injection: 0.25 mg/ml
Tablets: 0.5 mg, 1 mg, 2 mg

NURSING PROCESS

Assessment

- Obtain history of patient's urine output, vital signs, electrolyte levels, breath sounds, peripheral edema, and weight before therapy, and reassess regularly thereafter.
- Be alert for adverse reactions and drug interactions.
- Assess patient's and family's knowledge of drug therapy.

Nursing diagnoses

- Excess fluid volume related to underlying condition
- Impaired urinary elimination related to therapeutic effect of drug therapy
- Deficient knowledge related to drug therapy

Planning and implementation

- Give P.O. dose with food to prevent GI upset.
- To prevent nocturia, give in morning. If second dose is needed, give in early afternoon.
- The safest and most effective dosage schedule for control of edema is intermittent dosage either given on alternate days or given for 3 to 4 days with 1- or 2-day rest periods.
- Drug can be used safely in patients allergic to furosemide: 1 mg of bumetanide equals 40 mg of furosemide. Bumetanide may be less ototoxic than furosemide.
- If oliguria or azotemia develops or increases, anticipate that prescriber may stop drug.
- Notify prescriber if drug-related hearing changes occur.

ALERT: Don't confuse bumetanide with budesonide.

Patient teaching

- Advise patient to stand up slowly to prevent dizziness; also tell him to limit alcohol intake and strenuous exercise in hot weather to avoid worsening orthostatic hypotension.
- Teach patient to monitor fluid volume by measuring weight daily.
- Advise patient to take drug early in day to avoid sleep interruption caused by nocturia.
- Tell patient with diabetes to monitor glucose levels closely.

Evaluation

- Patient is free from edema.
- Patient demonstrates adjustment of lifestyle to deal with altered patterns of urinary elimination.
- Patient and family state understanding of drug therapy.

buprenorphine hydrochloride

(byoo-preh-NOR-feen high-droh-KLOR-ighd)
Buprenex, Subutex

buprenorphine hydrochloride and naloxone hydrochloride dihydrate

Suboxone

Pharmacologic class: opioid agonist-antagonist, opioid partial agonist
Therapeutic class: analgesic
Pregnancy risk category: C
Controlled substance schedule: III

Indications and dosages

▶ **Moderate to severe pain.** *Adults and children age 13 and older:* 0.3 mg I.M. or slow I.V. q 6 hours, p.r.n., or around-the-clock. May repeat 0.3 mg or increase to 0.6 mg, if needed, 30 to 60 minutes after initial dose.
Children ages 2 to 12: Give 2 to 6 mcg/kg I.V. or I.M. q 4 to 6 hours.

▶ **Opioid dependence.** *Adults:* 12 to 16 mg Suboxone or Subutex S.L. daily. Maintenance therapy with Suboxone is preferred; target dose is 16 mg/day. Increase or decrease in increments of 2 mg or 4 mg according to withdrawal effects, usual range is 4 to 24 mg.

▶ **Postoperative pain ‡.** *Adults:* 25 to 250 mcg/hour I.V. infusion over 48 hours.

▶ **Pain ‡.** *Adults:* 60 mcg epidural injection, as a single dose. Maximum, 180 mcg in 48 hours.

▶ **Circumcision ‡.** *Children ages 9 months to 9 years:* 3 mcg/kg I.M. with surgical anesthesia.

I.V. administration

- Give by direct I.V. injection into vein or through tubing of free-flowing compatible I.V. solution over at least 2 minutes.

⊗ Incompatibilities

Diazepam, furosemide, lorazepam.

Contraindications and cautions

- Contraindicated in patients hypersensitive to drug.
- Use cautiously in debilitated patients and patients with head injury, intracranial lesions, increased intracranial pressure, or severe respiratory, liver, or kidney impairment. Also use cautiously in patients with CNS depression or coma, thyroid irregularities, adrenal insufficiency, prostatic hyperplasia, urethral stricture, acute alcoholism, alcohol withdrawal syndrome, or kyphoscoliosis.

Lifespan: In pregnant and breast-feeding women and in elderly patients, use cautiously.

Adverse reactions

CNS: confusion, depression, *dizziness,* dreaming, euphoria, fatigue, headache, ***increased intracranial pressure,*** nervousness, paresthesia, psychosis, *sedation,* slurred speech, *vertigo,* weakness.
CV: ***bradycardia, cyanosis,*** flushing, hypertension, *hypotension,* tachycardia, Wenckebach block.
EENT: blurred vision, conjunctivitis, diplopia, *miosis,* tinnitus, visual abnormalities.
GI: constipation, dry mouth, *nausea,* vomiting.
GU: urine retention.
Respiratory: dyspnea, hypoventilation, ***respiratory depression.***
Skin: *diaphoresis, pruritus.*
Other: chills, *injection site reactions,* withdrawal syndrome.

Interactions

Drug-drug. *CNS depressants, MAO inhibitors:* May have additive effects. Monitor patient.
Opioid analgesics: May decrease analgesic effect. Avoid use together.
Drug-lifestyle. *Alcohol use:* May have additive effects. Discourage use together.

Effects on lab test results

- May decrease alkaline phosphatase and hemoglobin levels and hematocrit.
- May decrease erythrocyte count and sedimentation rate.

Pharmacokinetics

Absorption: Rapid.
Distribution: About 96% protein-bound.
Metabolism: In liver.
Excretion: Mainly in feces. *Half-life:* 1 to 7 hours. *Combination drug half-life:* Buprenorphine, 37 hours; naloxone, 1 hour.

Route	Onset	Peak	Duration
I.V., I.M.	15 min	1 hr	6 hr
S.L.	Unknown	Unknown	2–8 hr

Action

Chemical effect: Binds with opiate receptors in CNS, altering perception of and emotional response to pain.
Therapeutic effect: Relieves pain.

Available forms

Injection: 0.324 mg (0.3 mg base/ml)
Sublingual: 2 mg, 8 mg
Sublingual (combination): 2 mg buprenorphine and 0.5 mg naloxone, 8 mg buprenorphine and 2 mg naloxone

NURSING PROCESS

Assessment

- Obtain history of patient's pain.
- Monitor respiratory status frequently for at least 1 hour after administration. Notify prescriber if respiratory depression occurs.
- Cytolytic hepatitis and hepatitis with jaundice can occur in an opioid-dependent patient. Monitor closely.
- Assess patient's and family's knowledge of drug therapy.

Nursing diagnoses

- Acute pain related to underlying condition
- Ineffective breathing pattern related to drug-induced respiratory depression
- Deficient knowledge related to drug therapy

Planning and implementation

- Data are insufficient to give single I.M. doses greater than 0.6 mg for long-term use.
- Analgesic potency of 0.3 mg buprenorphine is equal to that of 10 mg morphine and 75 mg meperidine, but buprenorphine has a longer duration of action.
- Notify prescriber if pain isn't relieved.
- If patient's respiratory rate falls below 8 breaths per minute, withhold dose, rouse patient to stimulate breathing, and notify prescriber.

• Naloxone won't completely reverse respiratory depression caused by buprenorphine overdose; mechanical ventilation may be needed. Doxapram and larger-than-usual doses of naloxone also may be ordered.
• Drug may precipitate withdrawal syndrome in opioid-dependent patients.
• If dependence occurs, withdrawal symptoms may appear up to 14 days after drug is stopped.

Patient teaching

• Warn ambulatory patient about getting out of bed slowly and walking cautiously because of risk of dizziness or hypotension.
• When drug is used postoperatively, encourage patient to turn, cough, and deep-breathe to prevent atelectasis.
• Teach patient to avoid activities that require full alertness until CNS effects are known.
• Instruct patient to avoid alcohol and other CNS depressants.
• For Suboxone, tell patient to take all tablets sublingually at once; if he can't fit more than two doses comfortably, tell him to take dose two tablets at a time.

☑ Evaluation

• Patient reports pain relief.
• Patient's respiratory status is within normal limits.
• Patient and family state understanding of drug therapy.

bupropion hydrochloride

(byoo-PROH-pee-on high-droh-KLOR-ighd)
Wellbutrin, Wellbutrin SR✐, Wellbutrin XL, Zyban

Pharmacologic class: aminoketone
Therapeutic class: antidepressant, aid to smoking cessation
Pregnancy risk category: B

Indications and dosages

▶ **Depression.** *Adults:* Initially, 100 mg immediate-release Wellbutrin P.O. b.i.d., increased after 3 days to 100 mg P.O. t.i.d. if needed. If no response occurs after several weeks of therapy, increase to 150 mg t.i.d. Don't exceed 150 mg for a single dose. Allow at least 6 hours between successive doses. Maximum, 450 mg daily. Or, initially, 150 mg sustained-release Wellbutrin P.O. q morning; increase to target dose of 150 mg P.O. b.i.d. as tolerated as early as day 4 of therapy. Allow at least 8 hours between successive doses. Maximum, 400 mg daily. Or, initially, 150 mg extended-release Wellbutrin P.O. q morning; increase to target dose of 300 mg P.O. daily as tolerated as early as day 4 of therapy. Allow at least 24 hours between successive doses. Maximum, 450 mg daily.

Adjust-a-dose: For patients with mild to moderate hepatic cirrhosis or renal impairment, reduce dosage. For patients with severe hepatic cirrhosis, don't exceed 75 mg immediate-release P.O. daily; 100 mg sustained-release P.O. daily; 150 mg sustained-release P.O. q other day; or 150 mg extended-release P.O. q other day.

▶ **Seasonal affective disorder.** *Adults:* Start therapy in autumn before symptoms of depression start. Initially, 150 mg P.O. (Wellbutrin XL) once daily in the morning. After 1 week, increase to 300 mg once daily if tolerated. Continue through autumn and winter; then taper to 150 mg daily for 2 weeks before stopping therapy in early spring.

▶ **Aid to smoking cessation.** *Adults:* 150 mg Zyban P.O. daily for 3 days; increase to maximum dosage of 150 mg P.O. b.i.d. at least 8 hours apart. Start therapy 1 to 2 weeks before patient stops smoking.

▶ **Attention deficit hyperactivity disorder‡.** *Adults:* 150 mg Wellbutrin P.O. daily with regular-release tablets. Adjust dosage to a maximum of 450 mg P.O. daily.

Contraindications and cautions

• Contraindicated in patients hypersensitive to drug, those who have taken MAO inhibitors during the previous 14 days, and those with seizure disorders or a history of bulimia or anorexia nervosa because of a higher risk of seizures. Also contraindicated in patients abruptly stopping alcohol or sedatives (including benzodiazepines). Don't use Wellbutrin with Zyban or other drugs containing bupropion that are used for smoking cessation.
• Use cautiously in patients with renal or hepatic impairment and in patients with recent MI or unstable heart disease.
• In adults and children with major depressive disorders, depression may worsen and suicidal ideation and behavior emerge even while taking an antidepressant. Carefully monitor patients for

worsening depression or suicidal ideation, especially when therapy starts or dosage changes. These drugs haven't been approved for use in children.

Lifespan: In pregnant women, use cautiously. If drug must be given to breast-feeding woman, breast-feeding should be stopped. In children, safety and effectiveness of drug haven't been established.

Adverse reactions

CNS: *agitation,* akathisia, anxiety, *confusion,* delusions, euphoria, fever, *headache,* hostility, impaired sleep quality, insomnia, sedation, ***seizures,*** sensory disturbance, syncope, tremor.
CV: ***arrhythmias,*** hypertension, hypotension, palpitations, tachycardia.
EENT: auditory disturbance, blurred vision.
GI: anorexia, constipation, dry mouth, dyspepsia, increased appetite, nausea, taste disturbance, vomiting.
GU: impotence, menstrual complaints, urinary frequency.
Metabolic: hyperglycemia, weight gain or loss.
Musculoskeletal: arthritis.
Skin: cutaneous temperature disturbance, diaphoresis, pruritus, rash.
Other: chills, decreased libido.

Interactions

Drug-drug. *Amantadine, levodopa, MAO inhibitors, phenothiazines, recent and rapid withdrawal of benzodiazepines, tricyclic antidepressants:* May increase risk of adverse reactions, including seizures. Monitor patient closely.
Antiarrhythmics (type 1C), antipsychotics, beta blockers, SSRIs: May inhibit metabolism by CYP2D6. If used together, consider reducing dosage.
Carbamazepine: May decrease bupropion level. Monitor patient for loss of therapeutic effect.
Nicotine replacement drugs: May cause hypertension. Monitor blood pressure.
Ritonavir: May increase bupropion level and risk of toxicity. Monitor patient closely.
Warfarin: May alter PT and INR. Monitor patient for bleeding or clotting.
Drug-lifestyle. *Alcohol use:* May alter seizure threshold. Discourage use together.
Sun exposure: Photosensitivity reactions may occur. Advise patient to wear protective clothing and sunblock and to avoid sun exposure.

Effects on lab test results

- May decrease hemoglobin level and hematocrit. May increase or decrease glucose level.
- May decrease platelet count. May increase or decrease WBC count, PT, and INR.

Pharmacokinetics

Absorption: Unknown.
Distribution: About 80% protein-bound.
Metabolism: Probably in liver; several active metabolites have been identified.
Excretion: Mainly in urine. *Half-life:* 8 to 24 hours.

Route	Onset	Peak	Duration
P.O.	1–3 wk	2 hr	Unknown
Wellbutrin SR	Unknown	3 hr	Unknown
Wellbutrin XL	Unknown	5 hr	Unknown

Action

Chemical effect: Unknown. May work through noradrenergic, dopaminergic, or both mechanisms.
Therapeutic effect: Relieves depression; smoking deterrent.

Available forms

Tablets (extended-release): 150 mg, 300 mg
Tablets (immediate-release): 75 mg, 100 mg
Tablets (sustained-release): 100 mg, 150 mg, 200 mg

NURSING PROCESS

Assessment

- Obtain history of patient's condition before therapy, and reassess regularly thereafter.
- Be alert for adverse reactions and drug interactions.
- Closely monitor a patient with history of bipolar disorder. Antidepressants can cause manic episodes during depressed phase of bipolar disorder.
- Assess patient's and family's knowledge of drug therapy.

Nursing diagnoses

- Ineffective coping related to underlying condition
- Risk for injury related to drug-induced adverse CNS reactions
- Deficient knowledge related to drug therapy

Planning and implementation

ALERT: Risk of seizure may be minimized by not exceeding 450 mg/day (immediate-release) and by giving drug daily in three equally divided doses. Dosage increases shouldn't exceed 100 mg/day in a 3-day period. For sustained-release form, don't exceed 400 mg/day, and give drug daily in two equally divided doses. Dosage increases shouldn't exceed 200 mg/day in a 3-day period. Patients who experience seizures often have predisposing factors, including history of head trauma, prior seizures, or CNS tumors, or they may be taking a drug that lowers seizure threshold.

ALERT: Don't confuse bupropion with buspirone.

- Make sure patient has swallowed dose.
- Patient may experience period of increased restlessness, agitation, insomnia, and anxiety, especially at start of therapy.
- Reassess patient taking warfarin regularly for changes in PT and INR, risk for bleeding, and clotting.
- For smoking cessation, begin therapy while patient is still smoking because about 1 week is needed to achieve steady state levels of drug. Treatment course is usually 7 to 12 weeks.

Patient teaching

- Advise patient to take drug as scheduled and to take each day's dose in three divided doses (immediate-release) or two divided doses (sustained-release) to minimize risk of seizures.
- Tell patient to avoid alcohol while taking drug because alcohol may contribute to development of seizures.
- Advise patient to avoid hazardous activities that require alertness and good psychomotor coordination until CNS effects of drug are known.

ALERT: Advise patient not to take Wellbutrin with Zyban and to seek medical advice before taking other prescription drugs, OTC medications, or herbal remedies.

- Tell patient not to crush, chew, or divide sustained-release tablets.

Evaluation

- Patient's behavior and communication indicate improvement of depression.
- Patient sustains no injury from drug-induced adverse CNS reactions.
- Patient and family state understanding of drug therapy.

buspirone hydrochloride

(byoo-SPEER-ohn high-droh-KLOR-ighd)
BuSpar

Pharmacologic class: miscellaneous anxioselective derivative
Therapeutic class: anxiolytic
Pregnancy risk category: B

Indications and dosages

▶ **Anxiety disorders, short-term relief of anxiety.** *Adults:* Initially, 7.5 mg P.O. b.i.d. Increase by 5 mg daily at 2- to 3-day intervals. Usual maintenance dosage is 20 to 30 mg daily in divided doses. Don't exceed 60 mg daily.

Adjust-a-dose: When given with a CYP3A4 inhibitor, lower initial dosage to 2.5 mg P.O. b.i.d. Subsequent dosage adjustment of either drug also may be needed.

Contraindications and cautions

- Contraindicated in patients hypersensitive to drug and in those who have taken an MAO inhibitor within 14 days.
- Use cautiously in patients with hepatic or renal failure.

Lifespan: In pregnant women, use cautiously. In breast-feeding women, don't use. In children, safety and effectiveness of drug haven't been established.

Adverse reactions

CNS: *dizziness, drowsiness,* excitement, fatigue, headache, insomnia, nervousness.
GI: diarrhea, dry mouth, nausea.

Interactions

Drug-drug. *CNS depressants:* May increase CNS depression. Avoid use together.
Erythromycin: May increase buspirone level. Consider initial dose of 2.5 mg b.i.d.
Itraconazole: May increase buspirone level. Consider initial dose of 2.5 mg once daily.
MAO inhibitors: May elevate blood pressure. Avoid use together.
Drug-food. *Grapefruit juice:* May increase buspirone level. Don't use together.
Drug-lifestyle. *Alcohol use:* May increase CNS depression. Discourage use together.

Effects on lab test results

- May increase aminotransferase level.
- May decrease WBC and platelet counts.

Pharmacokinetics

Absorption: Rapidly and completely, but extensive first-pass metabolism limits absolute bioavailability to between 1% and 13% of P.O. dose. Food slows absorption but increases amount of unchanged drug in systemic circulation.
Distribution: 95% protein-bound; doesn't displace other highly protein-bound medications.
Metabolism: In liver.
Excretion: 29% to 63% in urine in 24 hours, mainly as metabolites; 18% to 38% in feces. *Half-life:* 2 to 3 hours.

Route	Onset	Peak	Duration
P.O.	Unknown	40–90 min	Unknown

Action

Chemical effect: May inhibit neuronal firing and reduce serotonin turnover in cortical, amygdaloid, and septohippocampal tissue.
Therapeutic effect: Relieves anxiety.

Available forms

Tablets: 5 mg, 7.5 mg, 10 mg, 15 mg, 30 mg

NURSING PROCESS

Assessment

- Obtain history of patient's anxiety before therapy, and reassess regularly thereafter.
- Signs of improvement usually appear within 7 to 10 days; optimal results occur after 3 to 4 weeks of therapy.
- Be alert for adverse reactions and drug interactions.
- Assess patient's and family's knowledge of drug therapy.

Nursing diagnoses

- Anxiety related to underlying condition
- Fatigue related to drug-induced adverse reactions
- Deficient knowledge related to drug therapy

Planning and implementation

- Although drug has shown no potential for abuse and hasn't been classified as a controlled substance, it isn't recommended for relief from everyday stress.
- Before starting therapy in patient already being treated with a benzodiazepine, make sure he doesn't stop benzodiazepine abruptly because withdrawal reaction may occur.
- Give drug with food or milk but not grapefruit juice.
- Dosage may be increased in 2- to 4-day intervals.

Patient teaching

- Tell patient to take drug with food but avoid grapefruit juice.
- Warn patient to avoid hazardous activities that require alertness and psychomotor coordination until the drug's CNS effects are known.
- Review energy-saving measures with patient and family.
- If patient is already being treated with a benzodiazepine, warn him not to abruptly stop it because withdrawal reaction can occur. Teach him how and when benzodiazepine can be withdrawn safely.

Evaluation

- Patient's anxiety is reduced.
- Patient states that energy-saving measures help combat fatigue caused by therapy.
- Patient and family state understanding of drug therapy.

busulfan

(byoo-SUL-fan)
Busulfex, Myleran

Pharmacologic class: alkylating drug
Therapeutic class: antineoplastic
Pregnancy risk category: D

Indications and dosages

▶ **Palliative treatment of chronic myelocytic (granulocytic) leukemia (CML).** *Adults:* For remission induction, 4 to 8 mg P.O. daily (0.06 mg/kg or 1.8 mg/m^2). For maintenance therapy, 1 to 3 mg P.O. daily. Dosages may vary. *Children:* 0.06 mg/kg or 1.8 mg/m^2 P.O. daily. Dosages may vary.

▶ **With cyclophosphamide as a conditioning regimen before allogeneic hematopoietic progenitor cell transplantation for CML.** *Adults:* 0.8 mg/kg of ideal body weight or actual body weight (whichever is lower) I.V. by central venous catheter as a 2-hour infusion q 6 hours for

4 consecutive days for a total of 16 doses. Give phenytoin for seizure prophylaxis. Dosages may vary.

▶ **Myelofibrosis‡.** *Adults:* Initially, give 2 to 4 mg P.O. daily, then followed by the same dose two to three times weekly. Dosages may vary.

I.V. administration

- Use aseptic technique when preparing and handling drug. Wear gloves and other protective clothing to prevent skin contact.
- Dilute with normal saline solution or D_5W to a final concentration of at least 0.5 mg/ml.
- Flush catheter with diluent before and after infusion.
- Give by infusion pump over 2 hours.
- If solution is kept at room temperature, use within 8 hours of preparing; if refrigerated, within 12 hours.
- Refrigerate unopened ampules.

⊗ **Incompatibilities**
Other I.V. drugs.

Contraindications and cautions

- Contraindicated in patients with drug-resistant CML.
- Use cautiously in patients recently given other myelosuppressive drugs or radiation therapy and in those with depressed neutrophil or platelet count. Because high-dose therapy has been linked to seizures, use such therapy cautiously in patients with history of head trauma or seizures and in patients receiving other drugs that lower seizure threshold.

Lifespan: In pregnant women, use cautiously, if at all. In breast-feeding women, drug is contraindicated.

Adverse reactions

CNS: agitation, *anxiety, asthenia,* confusion, delirium, *depression, dizziness,* ***encephalopathy,*** *fever,* hallucinations, *headache, insomnia,* lethargy, *pain,* ***seizures,*** somnolence.
CV: cardiomegaly, *chest pain,* ***ECG abnormalities,*** *edema,* ***heart failure,*** *heart rhythm abnormalities, hypertension, hypotension,* ***pericardial effusion,*** *tachycardia,* ***thrombosis,*** *vasodilation.*
EENT: cataracts, ear disorder, *epistaxis, pharyngitis, rhinitis,* sinusitis.
GI: *abdominal pain and enlargement, anorexia, cheilosis (P.O.), constipation, diarrhea, dry mouth, dyspepsia, mucositis, nausea,* ***pancreatitis,*** *rectal disorder, stomatitis, vomiting.*
GU: dysuria, hematuria, hemorrhagic cystitis, *oliguria.*
Hematologic: anemia, ***granulocytopenia, leukopenia, thrombocytopenia.***
Hepatic: ***hepatic necrosis,*** hepatomegaly, *jaundice.*
Metabolic: *hyperglycemia, hypervolemia, hypocalcemia, hypokalemia, hypomagnesemia,* hyponatremia, *hypophosphatemia, weight gain.*
Musculoskeletal: *arthralgia, back pain, myalgia.*
Respiratory: ***alveolar hemorrhage, asthma,*** atelectasis, *cough, dyspnea,* hemoptysis, hypoxia, ***irreversible pulmonary fibrosis,*** *lung disorder,* pleural effusion.
Skin: acne, *alopecia,* anhidrosis, erythema nodosum, exfoliative dermatitis, *hyperpigmentation, pruritus, rash,* skin discoloration.
Other: Addison-like wasting syndrome, gynecomastia, inflammation at injection site (P.O.); *allergic reaction, chills,* ***graft-versus-host disease,*** hiccups, ***infection.***

Interactions

Drug-drug. *Acetaminophen within 72 hours:* May decrease busulfan clearance. Use together cautiously.
Anticoagulants, aspirin: May increase risk of bleeding. Avoid use together.
Cyclophosphamide: May increase risk of cardiac tamponade in patients with thalassemia. Monitor patient.
Cytotoxic drugs that cause pulmonary injury: May cause additive pulmonary toxicity. Avoid use together.
Itraconazole: May decrease busulfan clearance. Use together cautiously.
Myelosuppressives: May increase myelosuppression. Monitor patient.
Phenytoin: May decrease busulfan level. Monitor busulfan level.
Thioguanine: May cause hepatotoxicity, esophageal varices, or portal hypertension. Use together cautiously.

Effects on lab test results

- May increase serum glucose, ALT, bilirubin, alkaline phosphatase, uric acid, creatinine, and BUN levels. May decrease magnesium, calcium, potassium, phosphorus, sodium, and hemoglobin levels and hematocrit.
- May decrease WBC, and platelet counts.

Pharmacokinetics

Absorption: Well absorbed from GI tract.
Distribution: Unknown.
Metabolism: In liver.
Excretion: Cleared rapidly and excreted in urine. *Half-life:* About 2½ hours.

Route	Onset	Peak	Duration
P.O.	1–2 wk	Unknown	Unknown
I.V.	Unknown	Unknown	Unknown

Action

Chemical effect: Unknown; thought to cross-link strands of cellular DNA and interfere with RNA transcription, causing an imbalance of growth that leads to cell death.
Therapeutic effect: Kills selected type of cancer cell.

Available forms

Injection: 6 mg/ml
Tablets: 2 mg

NURSING PROCESS

Assessment

- Obtain history of patient's underlying neoplastic disease.
- Monitor WBC and platelet counts weekly while patient is receiving drug. WBC count falls about 10 days after the start of therapy and continues to fall for 2 weeks after stopping drug.
- Monitor uric acid, liver and kidney function, and glucose levels.

ALERT: Be alert for adverse reactions and drug interactions. Pulmonary fibrosis may occur as late as 4 to 6 months after treatment.

- Assess patient's and family's knowledge of drug therapy.

Nursing diagnoses

- Ineffective health maintenance related to presence of neoplastic disease
- Risk for infection related to drug-induced immunosuppression
- Deficient knowledge related to drug therapy

Planning and implementation

- Premedicate patient with phenytoin to decrease risk of seizures that can occur with I.V. infusion.
- Follow facility policy regarding preparation and handling of drug. Label as hazardous drug.
- Give drug at same time each day.
- Make sure patient is adequately hydrated.
- Adjust dosage based on patient's weekly WBC counts and temporarily stop drug therapy if severe leukocytopenia develops. Therapeutic effects are often accompanied by toxicity.
- Give with allopurinol in addition to adequate hydration to prevent hyperuricemia with resulting uric acid nephropathy.

Patient teaching

- Warn patient to watch for signs of infection, such as fever, sore throat, and fatigue, and for symptoms of bleeding, such as easy bruising, nosebleeds, bleeding gums, and melena. Advise patient to take his temperature daily.

ALERT: Instruct patient to report symptoms of toxicity so dosage adjustments can be made. Symptoms include persistent cough and progressive dyspnea with alveolar exudate, suggestive of pneumonia.

- Instruct patient to avoid OTC products that contain aspirin.
- Advise woman of childbearing age to avoid becoming pregnant during therapy. Recommend that patient consult with prescriber before becoming pregnant.
- Advise breast-feeding woman to stop breast-feeding because of possible risk of toxicity in infant.

Evaluation

- Patient has positive response to drug therapy.
- Patient remains free from infection.
- Patient and family state understanding of drug therapy.

butorphanol tartrate

(byoo-TOR-fah-nohl TAR-trayt)
Stadol, Stadol NS

Pharmacologic class: opioid agonist-antagonist
Therapeutic class: analgesic, adjunct to anesthesia
Pregnancy risk category: C

Indications and dosages

▶ **Moderate to severe pain.** *Adults:* 0.5 to 2 mg I.V. q 3 to 4 hours, p.r.n., or around-the-clock. Or 1 to 4 mg I.M. q 3 to 4 hours, p.r.n., or around-the-clock. Maximum, 4 mg per dose. Or, 1 mg by nasal spray q 3 to 4 hours (1 spray in one nostril); repeat in 60 to 90 minutes if pain relief is inadequate.

▶ **Labor for pregnant women at full term and in early labor.** *Adults:* 1 to 2 mg I.V. or I.M., repeated after 4 hours, p.r.n.

▶ **Preoperative anesthesia or preanesthesia.** *Adults:* 2 mg I.M. 60 to 90 minutes before surgery.

▶ **Adjunct to balanced anesthesia.** *Adults:* 2 mg I.V. shortly before induction or 0.5 to 1 mg I.V. in increments during anesthesia.

Adjust-a-dose: For patients with hepatic or renal impairment and elderly patients, reduce dosage to 50% of the usual parenteral adult dose at 6-hour intervals p.r.n. For nasal spray, the initial dose (1 spray in one nostril) is the same, but repeat dose is in 90 to 120 minutes, if needed. Repeat doses thereafter q 6 hours, p.r.n.

I.V. administration

- Give drug by direct I.V. injection into vein or into I.V. line containing free-flowing compatible solution.

⊗ **Incompatibilities**

Dimenhydrinate, pentobarbital sodium.

Contraindications and cautions

- Contraindicated in patients with opioid addiction; may precipitate withdrawal syndrome. Also contraindicated in patients hypersensitive to drug or to preservative (benzethonium chloride).
- Use cautiously in patients with head injury, increased intracranial pressure, acute MI, ventricular dysfunction, coronary insufficiency, respiratory disease or depression, or renal or hepatic dysfunction. Also use cautiously in patients who have recently received repeated doses of an opioid analgesic.

Lifespan: In pregnant women, use only when benefits outweigh risks to fetus. In breast-feeding women, drug is contraindicated. In children, safety and effectiveness haven't been established. In the elderly, mean half-life of the drug is extended; use cautiously because adverse reactions may increase.

Adverse reactions

CNS: agitation, *confusion,* euphoria, *floating sensation,* flushing, hallucinations, *headache,* ***increased intracranial pressure,*** lethargy, nervousness, *sedation,* unusual dreams, *vertigo.*
CV: fluctuation in blood pressure, palpitations.
EENT: blurred vision, diplopia, *nasal congestion* (with nasal spray).
GI: constipation, *dry mouth,* nausea, vomiting.
Respiratory: ***respiratory depression.***
Skin: clamminess, excessive sweating, rash, urticaria.

Interactions

Drug-drug. *CNS depressants:* May have additive effects. Use together cautiously.
Opioid analgesics: May decrease analgesic effect. Avoid use together.
Drug-lifestyle. *Alcohol use:* May have additive depressant effects. Discourage use together.

Effects on lab test results

None reported.

Pharmacokinetics

Absorption: Good after I.M. use.
Distribution: 80% protein-bound. Drug rapidly crosses placenta, and neonatal levels are 0.4 to 1.4 times maternal levels.
Metabolism: Extensive, in liver to inactive metabolites.
Excretion: In inactive form, mainly by kidneys. About 11% to 14% of parenteral dose in feces. *Half-life:* About 2 to 9¼ hours.

Route	Onset	Peak	Duration
I.V.	2–3 min	½–1 hr	2–4 hr
I.M.	10–30 min	½–1 hr	3–4 hr
Intranasal	≤ 15 min	1–2 hr	4–5 hr

Action

Chemical effect: Binds with opiate receptors in CNS, altering both perception of and emotional response to pain through unknown mechanism.
Therapeutic effect: Relieves pain and enhances anesthesia.

Available forms

Injection: 1 mg/ml, 2 mg/ml
Nasal spray: 10 mg/ml

NURSING PROCESS

Assessment

- Obtain history of patient's pain before therapy, and reassess during therapy.
- Be alert for adverse reactions and drug interactions.

- Periodically monitor postoperative vital signs and bladder function. Drug decreases both rate and depth of respirations, and monitoring arterial oxygen saturation may aid in assessing respiratory depression.
- Assess patient's and family's knowledge of drug therapy.

Nursing diagnoses

- Acute pain related to underlying condition
- Risk for injury related to drug-induced adverse CNS reactions
- Deficient knowledge related to drug therapy

Planning and implementation

- For intranasal use, have patient clear nasal passages before giving drug. Shake container. Tilt patient's head slightly backward; insert nozzle into nostril, pointing away from septum. Have patient hold other nostril closed, and spray while patient inhales gently.
- Subcutaneous route isn't recommended.
- Monitor patient for psychological and physical addiction, which may occur.
- Notify prescriber and discuss increasing dose or frequency if pain persists.
- Keep opioid antagonist (naloxone) and resuscitative equipment available.

Patient teaching

- Caution ambulatory patient to get out of bed slowly and walk carefully until CNS effects are known.
- Warn outpatient to refrain from driving and performing other activities that require mental alertness until drug's CNS effects are known.
- Warn patient that drug can cause physical and psychological dependence. Tell him to use drug only as directed and that abrupt withdrawal after prolonged use produces intense withdrawal symptoms.

Evaluation

- Patient reports relief from pain.
- Patient doesn't experience injury as a result of therapy.
- Patient and family state understanding of drug therapy.

calcitonin (salmon)

(kal-sih-TOH-nin)

Calcimar, Fortical, Miacalcin

Pharmacologic class: thyroid hormone, calcium and bone metabolism regulator
Therapeutic class: hypocalcemic, bone resorption inhibitor
Pregnancy risk category: C

Indications and dosages

▶ **Osteoporosis.** *Postmenopausal women:* 100 international units I.M. or subcutaneously q other day. Or, 200 international units (one activation) daily intranasally, alternating nostrils daily.

▶ **Paget disease of bone (osteitis deformans).** *Adults:* Initially, 100 international units daily I.M. or subcutaneously; maintenance dosage is 50 to 100 international units daily or q other day.

▶ **Hypercalcemia.** *Adults:* 4 international units/kg q 12 hours I.M. or subcutaneously. If response is inadequate after 1 or 2 days, increase dosage to 8 international units/kg I.M. q 12 hours. If response remains unsatisfactory after 2 more days, increase dosage to maximum of 8 international units/kg q 6 hours.

▶ **Osteogenesis imperfecta‡.** *Adults:* 2 international units/kg subcutaneously or I.M. three times weekly with daily calcium supplementation.

Contraindications and cautions

- Contraindicated in patients hypersensitive to drug.

Lifespan: In pregnant women, use cautiously. In breast-feeding women, don't use because drug may inhibit lactation. In children, safety and effectiveness haven't been established.

Adverse reactions

CNS: dizziness, headache, paresthesia, weakness.
CV: facial flushing, hypertension.
EENT: epistaxis, nasal symptoms (irritation, redness, sores) with intranasal use, *rhinitis.*

C

GI: anorexia, diarrhea, *nausea,* unusual taste, *vomiting.*
GU: nocturia, urinary frequency.
Metabolic: goiter, hyperglycemia, hyperthyroidism, hypocalcemia.
Musculoskeletal: arthralgia, back pain.
Skin: facial and hand flushing, rash.
Other: ***anaphylaxis;*** hand swelling, tingling, and tenderness; hypersensitivity reactions; *inflammation at injection site.*

Interactions

None significant.

Effects on lab test results

• May increase glucose, T_3, and T_4 levels. May decrease serum calcium and thyroid-stimulating hormone levels.

Pharmacokinetics

Absorption: Rapid with intranasal use.
Distribution: Unknown; however, calcitonin doesn't cross the placenta.
Metabolism: Rapidly in kidneys; additional activity in blood and peripheral tissues.
Excretion: In urine as inactive metabolites.
Half-life: Calcitonin human, 60 minutes; calcitonin salmon, 43 to 60 minutes.

Route	Onset	Peak	Duration
I.M., SubQ	≤ 15 min	≤ 4 hr	8–24 hr
Intranasal	Rapid	30 min	1 hr

Action

Chemical effect: Decreases osteoclastic activity by inhibiting osteocytic lysis; decreases mineral release and matrix or collagen breakdown in bone.
Therapeutic effect: Prohibits bone and kidney (tubular) resorption of calcium.

Available forms

Injection: 200 international units/ml, 2-ml ampules or vials
Nasal spray: 200 international units/activation in 2-ml bottle (0.09 ml/dose)

NURSING PROCESS

Assessment

ALERT: Assess postmenopausal woman's history. Drug is given only if patient can't take estrogen. Patient requires continued vitamin D and calcium supplements in addition to drug.
• Assess patient's calcium level before therapy and regularly thereafter.
• If using nasal spray, assess nasal passages before therapy and periodically thereafter.
• For Paget disease, monitor alkaline phosphatase and 24-hour urine hydroxyproline levels to evaluate the drug's effectiveness.
• Monitor glucose level and thyroid studies before and periodically during treatment. Repeat DEXA bone scan to assess effectiveness of therapy at least yearly.
• Examine urine sediment periodically for casts, particularly in immobilized patients.
• Look for adverse reactions.
• Assess patient's and family's knowledge of drug therapy.

Nursing diagnoses

• Risk for injury related to patient's underlying bone condition
• Ineffective protection related to potential for drug-induced anaphylaxis
• Deficient knowledge related to drug therapy

Planning and implementation

• Perform skin test before therapy.
• Give drug at bedtime to minimize nausea and vomiting; remind patient that these symptoms usually resolve after 1 to 2 months of treatment.
• If dose is larger than 2 ml, give it I.M.
• When using nasal spray, alternate nostrils daily.
• Keep parenteral calcium available during first doses in case hypocalcemic tetany occurs.
• Refrigerate calcitonin salmon at 36° to 46° F (2° to 8° C). Store open nasal spray at room temperature.
• In patient who relapses after a positive initial response, evaluate for antibody response to hormone protein.
• Systemic allergic reactions may occur because hormone is a protein; keep epinephrine handy.
• If symptoms have been relieved after 6 months, stop drug until symptoms or radiologic signs recur.
ALERT: Don't confuse calcitonin with calciferol or calcitriol.

Patient teaching

• For outpatient therapy for Paget disease, teach patient how to give drug subcutaneously.

• Teach patient to activate nasal spray before first use by holding bottle upright and depressing side arms six times until a faint mist appears, signifying pump is primed and ready for use. Patient doesn't need to reprime the pump before each use.
• Instruct patient to report signs of nasal irritation from spray.
• Tell patient to handle missed doses as follows: With daily use, take as soon as possible, but don't double the dose. With alternate-day use, take missed dose as soon as possible, and then resume alternate-day schedule from that point.
• Remind patient with postmenopausal osteoporosis to take adequate calcium and vitamin D supplements.

Evaluation

• Patient's calcium level is normal.
• Patient doesn't experience anaphylaxis.
• Patient and family state understanding of drug therapy.

calcitriol (1,25-dihydroxycholecalciferol)

(kal-SIH-try-ohl)
Calcijex, Rocaltrol

Pharmacologic class: vitamin D analogue
Therapeutic class: antihypocalcemic
Pregnancy risk category: C

Indications and dosages

▶ **Hypocalcemia in patients undergoing long-term dialysis.** *Adults:* Initially, 0.25 mcg P.O. daily. Increase by 0.25 mcg daily at 4- to 8-week intervals. Maintenance dosage is 0.25 mcg q other day up to 1 mcg daily or 1 to 2 mcg I.V. three times weekly. Dosages from 0.5 to 4 mcg three times weekly may be used initially. If response to initial dose is inadequate, increase by 0.5 to 1 mcg at 2- to 4-week intervals. Maintenance dosage is 0.5 to 3 mcg I.V. three times weekly.
▶ **Hypoparathyroidism and pseudohypoparathyroidism.** *Adults and children age 6 and older:* Initially, 0.25 mcg P.O. daily. Increase dosage at 2- to 4-week intervals. Maintenance dosage is 0.25 to 2 mcg daily.
▶ **Hypoparathyroidism.** *Children and infants ages 1 to 5:* Give 0.25 to 0.75 mcg P.O. daily.
▶ **To manage secondary hyperparathyroidism and resulting metabolic bone disease in predialysis patients (moderate-to-severe chronic renal impairment with creatinine clearance of 15 to 55 ml/minute).** *Adults and children age 3 and older:* Initially, 0.25 mcg P.O. daily. Increase dosage to 0.5 mcg daily, if needed.
Children younger than age 3: Initially, 0.01 to 0.015 mcg/kg P.O. daily.

I.V. administration

• For hypocalcemic patients with chronic renal impairment who are undergoing hemodialysis, give I.V. dose by rapid injection via dialysis catheter after treatment.
• Discard unused portions because drug contains no preservatives.
• Store injection at room temperature; avoid excessive heat or freezing. Protect from light.
⊗ **Incompatibilities**
None reported.

Contraindications and cautions

• Contraindicated in patients with hypercalcemia or vitamin D toxicity.
Lifespan: In pregnant or breast-feeding women, use cautiously.

Adverse reactions

CNS: headache, somnolence.
EENT: conjunctivitis, photophobia, rhinorrhea.
GI: anorexia, constipation, dry mouth, metallic taste, nausea, vomiting.
GU: polyuria.
Musculoskeletal: bone and muscle pain, weakness.

Interactions

Drug-drug. *Antacids containing magnesium:* May induce hypermagnesemia, especially in patients with chronic renal impairment. Avoid use together.
Cholestyramine, colestipol, excessive use of mineral oil: May decrease absorption of orally given vitamin D analogues. Avoid use together.
Corticosteroids: Counteracts vitamin D analogue effects. Avoid use together.
Digoxin: May increase risk of arrhythmias. Avoid use together.

Ketoconazole: May decrease endogenous calcitriol level. Monitor patient.
Phenytoin, phenobarbital: May reduce calcitriol level. Higher doses of calcitriol may be needed.
Thiazides: May induce hypercalcemia. Monitor calcium level and patient closely.
Verapamil: May cause atrial fibrillation because of increased risk of hypercalcemia. Monitor calcium level and patient closely.

Effects on lab test results

- May increase BUN, ALT, AST, albumin, and cholesterol levels.

Pharmacokinetics

Absorption: Readily.
Distribution: Wide; protein-bound.
Metabolism: In liver and kidneys.
Excretion: Mainly in feces. *Half-life:* 3 to 6 hours.

Route	Onset	Peak	Duration
P.O.	2–6 hr	3–6 hr	3–5 days
I.V.	Immediate	Unknown	3–5 days

Action

Chemical effect: Stimulates calcium absorption from GI tract; promotes calcium secretion from bone to blood.
Therapeutic effect: Raises calcium level.

Available forms

Capsules: 0.25 mcg, 0.5 mcg
Injection: 1 mcg/ml, 2 mcg/ml
Oral solution: 1 mcg/ml

NURSING PROCESS

Assessment

- Assess patient's calcium and phosphate levels before therapy and regularly thereafter to monitor drug effectiveness; make sure calcium level times phosphate level doesn't exceed 70. During dosage adjustment, determine calcium level twice weekly.
- Monitor patient for vitamin D intoxication, which may cause anorexia, arrhythmias, bone and muscle pain, conjunctivitis, constipation, decreased libido, dry mouth, headache, hypertension, hyperthermia, irritability, metallic taste, nausea, nephrocalcinosis, nocturia, pancreatitis, photophobia, polydipsia, pruritus, rhinorrhea, somnolence, vomiting, weakness, polyuria, and weight loss.
- Look for adverse reactions and drug interactions.
- Assess patient's and family's knowledge of drug therapy.

Nursing diagnoses

- Risk for injury related to patient's underlying condition
- Ineffective protection related to potential for drug-induced vitamin D intoxication
- Deficient knowledge related to drug therapy

Planning and implementation

- Keep drug away from heat, light, and moisture.
- Give drug at same time each day.
- If hypercalcemia occurs, stop drug and notify prescriber; resume drug after calcium level returns to normal. Make sure patient receives adequate daily calcium intake.

ALERT: Don't confuse calcitriol with calciferol or calcitonin.

Patient teaching

- Tell patient to immediately report early symptoms of vitamin D intoxication, such as weakness, nausea, vomiting, dry mouth, constipation, muscle or bone pain, or metallic taste.
- Instruct patient to adhere to diet and calcium supplements and to avoid OTC drugs and antacids containing magnesium.
- Warn patient that drug is the most potent form of vitamin D available and that severe toxicity can occur if ingested by anyone for whom it isn't prescribed.
- Tell patient to protect drug from light, moisture, and heat.

Evaluation

- Patient's calcium level is normal.
- Patient sustains no injury from drug-induced vitamin D toxicity.
- Patient and family state understanding of drug therapy.

calcium acetate
(KAL-see-um AS-ih-tayt)
Phos-Lo

calcium carbonate
Alka-Mints†, Amitone†, Chooz†, Equilet†, Maalox†, Mallamint†, Tums†, Tums E-X†, Tums Extra Strength†

calcium chloride†
Calciject ♦ †

calcium citrate†
Citracal†, Citracal Liquitabs ♦ †

calcium glubionate†
Calcium-Sandoz ♦ †

calcium gluconate

calcium lactate†

calcium phosphate, dibasic†

calcium phosphate, tribasic
Posture†

Pharmacologic class: mineral, electrolyte
Therapeutic class: calcium supplement, antiarrhythmic
Pregnancy risk category: NR; C (PhosLo)

Indications and dosages

▶ **Hypocalcemic emergency.** *Adults:* 7 to 14 mEq calcium I.V. May be given as 10% calcium gluconate solution or 2% to 10% calcium chloride solution.
Children: 1 to 7 mEq calcium I.V.
Infants: Up to 1 mEq calcium I.V.

▶ **Hypocalcemic tetany.** *Adults:* 4.5 to 16 mEq calcium I.V. Repeat until tetany is controlled.
Children: 0.5 to 0.7 mEq/kg calcium I.V. t.i.d. or q.i.d. until tetany is controlled.
Neonates: 2.4 mEq/kg I.V. daily in divided doses.

▶ **Adjunct in cardiac arrest.** *Adults:* 500 mg to 1 g calcium chloride I.V. Don't exceed 1 ml/minute. Determine calcium level before giving further doses.

▶ **Adjunct in magnesium intoxication.** *Adults:* Initially, 7 mEq I.V. Base later doses on patient's response.

▶ **During exchange transfusions.** *Adults:* 1.35 mEq I.V. with each 100 ml citrated blood.
Neonates: 0.45 mEq I.V. with each 100 ml citrated blood.

▶ **Hyperphosphatemia in end-stage renal failure.** *Adults:* 2 to 4 tablets calcium acetate P.O. with each meal.

▶ **Gastric hyperacidity, calcium supplement.** *Adults:* 0.5 to 1.5 g p.r.n.

I.V. administration

- Calcium salts aren't interchangeable. Verify preparation before use.
- Give calcium chloride and calcium gluconate only I.V.
- When adding calcium chloride to parenteral solutions that contain other additives (especially phosphorus or phosphate), inspect solution closely for precipitate. Use in-line filter.
- Monitor ECG when giving calcium I.V. If patient complains of discomfort, stop and notify prescriber. After injection, make sure patient remains recumbent for 15 minutes.
- Severe necrosis and tissue sloughing can occur after extravasation. Calcium gluconate is less irritating to veins and tissues than calcium chloride.

Direct injection

- Warm solution to body temperature before giving it.
- Give direct injection slowly through small needle into large vein or through I.V. line containing free-flowing, compatible solution at no more than 1 ml/minute (1.5 mEq/minute) for calcium chloride or 0.5 to 2 ml/minute for calcium gluconate. Don't use scalp veins in children.
- Rapid injection may cause syncope, vasodilation, bradycardia, arrhythmias, or cardiac arrest.

Intermittent infusion

- When giving intermittent infusion, infuse diluted solution through I.V. line containing compatible solution. Maximum, 200 mg/minute for calcium gluconate.
- Precipitate will form if drug is given I.V. with sodium bicarbonate or other alkaline drugs. Use an in-line filter.

⊗ **Incompatibilities**
Calcium chloride: amphotericin B, chlorpheniramine, dobutamine.

Calcium gluconate: amphotericin B, cefamandole, dobutamine, fluconazole, indomethacin sodium trihydrate, methylprednisolone sodium succinate, prochlorperazine edisylate.

Contraindications and cautions

• Contraindicated in patients with ventricular fibrillation, hypercalcemia, hypophosphatemia, or renal calculi.
• Use all calcium products cautiously in patients taking digitalis and in patients with sarcoidosis and renal or cardiac disease.
• Use calcium chloride cautiously in patients with cor pulmonale, respiratory acidosis, or respiratory impairment.
Lifespan: In children, use I.V. drug cautiously; safety and effectiveness haven't been established.

Adverse reactions

CNS: pain, sense of oppression or heat waves, syncope, tingling.
CV: ***arrhythmias, bradycardia, cardiac arrest,*** mild decrease in blood pressure, vasodilation.
GI: chalky taste; constipation, ***hemorrhage,*** or irritation with oral use; nausea; thirst; vomiting.
GU: polyuria, renal calculi.
Metabolic: hypercalcemia.
Skin: burning, cellulitis, necrosis, soft-tissue calcification, and tissue sloughing with I.M. use; irritation with subcutaneous injection.
Other: *vein irritation with I.V. use.*

Interactions

Drug-drug. *Atenolol, fluoroquinolones, tetracyclines:* May decrease bioavailability of these drugs and calcium when oral forms are taken together. Give drugs at different times.
Calcium channel blockers: May decrease calcium effectiveness. Avoid use together.
Ciprofloxacin, levofloxacin, lomefloxacin, moxifloxacin, norfloxacin, ofloxacin: May decrease effects of quinolone. Give antacid at least 6 hours before or 2 hours after the quinolone.
Digoxin: May increase digitalis toxicity. Use together cautiously (if at all).
Enteric-coated drugs: May cause premature release of enteric-coated drug in the stomach. Don't give within 1 hour of each other.
Sodium bicarbonate: May cause milk-alkali syndrome (confusion, headache, hypercalcemia, hypercalciuria, hypophosphatemia, metabolic alkalosis, vomiting, weakness). Discourage use together.
Sodium polystyrene sulfonate: May increase risk of metabolic acidosis in patients with renal disease. Avoid use together in patients with renal disease.
Thiazide diuretics: May increase risk of hypercalcemia. Avoid use together.
Thyroid hormone: May inhibit the absorption of thyroid drugs. Give drugs at least 2 hours apart.
Drug-food. *Foods containing oxalic acid (rhubarb, spinach), phytic acid (bran, whole cereals), or phosphorus (hard cheese, nuts, dried fruits, sardines):* May interfere with calcium absorption. Tell patient to avoid these foods.

Effects on lab test results

• May increase calcium and 11-hydroxycorticosteroid levels.
• May produce false-negative values for serum and urinary magnesium as measured by the Titan yellow method.

Pharmacokinetics

Absorption: Pregnancy and reduced calcium intake may enhance absorption. Vitamin D in active form is required for absorption.
Distribution: Enters extracellular fluid and is incorporated rapidly into skeletal tissue. Bone contains 99% of total calcium; 1% is distributed equally between intracellular and extracellular fluids. Level in CSF is about half that in blood.
Metabolism: Insignificant.
Excretion: Mainly in feces, minimally in urine. *Half-life:* Unknown.

Route	Onset	Peak	Duration
P.O.	Unknown	Unknown	Unknown
I.V.	Immediate	Immediate	½–2 hr

Action

Chemical effect: Replaces and maintains calcium. Reduces total acid load in GI tract, elevates gastric pH to reduce pepsin activity, strengthens gastric mucosal barrier and increases esophageal sphincter tone.
Therapeutic effect: Raises calcium level and relieves mild gastric discomfort.

Available forms

calcium acetate
Contains 253 mg or 12.7 mEq of elemental calcium/g

Tablets: 250 mg†, 500 mg†, 667 mg, 668 mg†, 1,000 mg†

calcium carbonate

Contains 40% calcium; 20 mEq calcium/g

Chewing gum: 500 mg/piece

Oral suspension: 400 mg/5 ml, 1.25 g/5 ml†

Tablets: 500 mg†, 600 mg†, 650 mg†, 1,250 mg†

Tablets (chewable): 350 mg†, 420 mg†, 500 mg†, 750 mg, 850 mg, 1,000 mg, 1,250 mg ◊

calcium chloride

Contains 270 mg or 13.5 mEq of elemental calcium/g

Injection: 10% solution in 10-ml ampules, vials, and syringes

calcium citrate

Contains 211 mg or 10.6 mEq of elemental calcium/g

Effervescent tablets: 2,376 mg†

Tablets: 950 mg†

calcium glubionate

Contains 64 mg or 3.2 mEq of elemental calcium/g

Syrup: 1.8 g/5 ml

calcium gluconate

Contains 90 mg or 4.5 mEq of elemental calcium/g

Injection: 10% solution in 10-ml ampules and vials, 10-ml or 50-ml vials

Tablets: 500 mg†, 650 mg†, 975 mg†, 1 g†

calcium lactate

Contains 130 mg or 6.5 mEq of elemental calcium/g

Tablets: 325 mg, 650 mg

calcium phosphate, dibasic

Contains 230 mg or 11.5 mEq of elemental calcium/g

Tablets: 468 mg†

calcium phosphate, tribasic

Contains 400 mg or 20 mEq of elemental calcium/g

Tablets: 600 mg†

NURSING PROCESS

Assessment

- Assess patient's calcium level before therapy and frequently thereafter to monitor the drug's effectiveness. Hypercalcemia may result after large doses in patients with chronic renal impairment.
- Look for adverse reactions and drug interactions.
- Assess patient's and family's knowledge of drug therapy.

Nursing diagnoses

- Ineffective protection related to calcium deficiency
- Risk for injury related to drug-induced adverse reactions
- Deficient knowledge related to drug therapy

Planning and implementation

- If hypercalcemia occurs, stop drug and notify prescriber. Provide emergency supportive care until calcium level returns to normal.
- Signs and symptoms of severe hypercalcemia may include stupor, confusion, delirium, and coma. Signs and symptoms of mild hypercalcemia may include anorexia, nausea, and vomiting.

ALERT: Make sure prescriber specifies which calcium form to use because code carts usually contain both calcium gluconate and calcium chloride.

Patient teaching

- Tell patient to take oral calcium 1 to 1½ hours after meals if GI upset occurs.

ALERT: Warn patient to avoid foods containing oxalic acid, phytic acid, and phosphorus because interactions may interfere with calcium absorption.

- Teach patient to recognize and report signs and symptoms of hypercalcemia.
- Stress importance of follow-up care and regular blood samples to monitor calcium level.
- Advise patient not to take drug indiscriminately and not to switch antacids without consulting prescriber.
- Tell patient to take calcium carbonate 1 hour after meals and at bedtime, p.r.n.

Evaluation

- Patient's calcium level is normal.
- Patient doesn't experience injury from calcium-induced adverse reactions.
- Patient and family state understanding of drug therapy.

calfactant
(kal-FAK-tant)
Infasurf

Pharmacologic class: surfactant
Therapeutic class: respiratory distress syndrome (RDS) drug
Pregnancy risk category: NR

Indications and dosages

▶ **Confirmed RDS in neonates younger than 72 hours old who need endotracheal intubation.** *Neonates:* 3 ml/kg birth weight, intratracheally, given in 2 aliquots of 1.5 ml/kg. Repeat doses of 3 ml/kg of birth weight, given in 2 aliquots of 1.5 ml/kg, up to a total of three doses given 12 hours apart.

▶ **Prevention of RDS in premature infants younger than 29 weeks' gestational age at high risk for RDS.** 3 ml/kg birth weight, given intratracheally within 30 minutes of birth, in 2 aliquots of 1.5 ml/kg each.

Contraindications and cautions

None reported.

Lifespan: Indicated for premature infants only.

Adverse reactions

CV: BRADYCARDIA, *cyanosis.*
Respiratory: AIRWAY OBSTRUCTION, APNEA, ***dislodgment of endotracheal tube,*** *hypoventilation,* ***reflux of drug into endotracheal tube.***

Interactions

None significant.

Effects on lab test results

None reported.

Pharmacokinetics

Absorption: Unknown.
Distribution: Unknown.
Metabolism: Unknown.
Excretion: Unknown. *Half-life:* Unknown.

Route	Onset	Peak	Duration
Intratracheal	24–48 hr	Unknown	Unknown

Action

Chemical effect: Modifies alveolar surface tension, thereby stabilizing the alveoli.
Therapeutic effect: Prevents or treats RDS in premature neonates with specific characteristics.

Available forms

Intratracheal suspension: 35 mg phospholipids and 0.65 mg proteins/ml; 6-ml vial

NURSING PROCESS

Assessment

- Assess patient's underlying condition before therapy and regularly thereafter.
- Monitor patient for reflux of drug into endotracheal tube, cyanosis, bradycardia, or airway obstruction. If these occur, stop the drug and stabilize infant. After infant is stable, give remainder of the dose, with appropriate monitoring.
- After giving drug, carefully monitor infant so oxygen therapy and ventilation can be adjusted for improved oxygenation and lung compliance.
- Evaluate parents' knowledge of drug therapy.

Nursing diagnoses

- Risk for injury related to potential for RDS
- Impaired gas exchange related to presence of RDS
- Deficient knowledge related to drug therapy

Planning and implementation

- Give drug under supervision of a prescriber experienced in acute care of neonates with respiratory impairment who need intubation.
- Drug is intended only for intratracheal use; to prevent RDS, give immediately after birth, preferably within 30 minutes.
- Suspension settles during storage. Gently swirl or agitate the vial to redisperse, but don't shake. Visible flecks in the suspension and foaming at the surface are normal.
- Withdraw dose into a syringe from single-use vial using a 20G or larger needle; avoid excessive foaming.
- Use each single-use vial only once; discard unused material.
- Give through a side-port adapter into the endotracheal tube. Two health care providers should be present. Give dose in 2 aliquots of 1.5 ml/kg each. Continue ventilation over 20 to 30 breaths for each aliquot, with small bursts

timed to occur during inspiration. Between aliquots, evaluate respiration and reposition infant.
- Store drug at 36° to 46° F (2° to 8° C). Don't warm drug before use; it's not needed. Unopened, unused vials that have warmed to room temperature can be returned to refrigerated storage within 24 hours for future use. Avoid repeated warming to room temperature.

Patient teaching
- Explain to parents the reason for using drug to prevent or treat RDS.
- Notify parents that although the infant may improve rapidly after therapy, he may still need intubation and mechanical ventilation.
- Notify parents about adverse effects of the drug, including bradycardia, reflux into endotracheal tube, airway obstruction, cyanosis, dislodgment of the endotracheal tube, and hypoventilation.
- Reassure parents that infant will be carefully monitored.

✓ Evaluation
- Premature infant doesn't develop RDS.
- Patient's gas exchange improves because of oxygenation and increased lung compliance.
- Parents state understanding of drug therapy.

candesartan cilexetil
(kan-dih-SAR-ten se-LEKS-ih-til)
Atacand

Pharmacologic class: angiotensin II receptor antagonist
Therapeutic class: antihypertensive
Pregnancy risk category: C (D in second and third trimesters)

Indications and dosages
▶ **Heart failure.** *Adults:* Initially, 4 mg P.O. once daily. Double the dose approximately every 2 weeks as tolerated, to a target dose of 32 mg once daily.
▶ **Hypertension (alone or with other antihypertensives).** *Adults:* Initially, 16 mg P.O. once daily when used as monotherapy; usual dosage is 8 to 32 mg P.O. daily as single dose or divided b.i.d.

Adjust-a-dose: In patients with volume depletion or moderate hepatic impairment, consider giving lower initial dose.

Contraindications and cautions
- Contraindicated in patients hypersensitive to drug or its components.
- Use cautiously in patients whose renal function depends on the renin-angiotensin-aldosterone system (such as patients with heart failure) because of risk of oliguria and progressive azotemia resulting in acute renal impairment. Also use cautiously in patients who are volume- or salt-depleted because of risk of symptomatic hypotension.

Lifespan: In pregnant women, don't use because drug acts directly on the renin-angiotensin system and may harm the fetus or neonate. If drug is absolutely needed, limit to first trimester. If pregnancy is suspected, stop the drug. In breast-feeding women, use cautiously because the effects on the infant are unknown.

Adverse reactions
CNS: dizziness, fatigue, headache.
CV: chest pain, peripheral edema.
EENT: pharyngitis, rhinitis, sinusitis.
GI: abdominal pain, diarrhea, nausea, vomiting.
GU: albuminuria.
Musculoskeletal: arthralgia, back pain.
Respiratory: bronchitis, cough, upper respiratory tract infection.

Interactions
Drug-drug. *Lithium:* May increase lithium level. Carefully monitor lithium level for toxicity.

Effects on lab test results
- May increase bilirubin, lithium, BUN, creatinine, potassium, and uric acid levels. May decrease hemoglobin level and hematocrit.
- May increase liver function test results.

Pharmacokinetics
Absorption: Absolute bioavailability is about 15%.
Distribution: More than 99% protein-bound; doesn't penetrate RBCs.
Metabolism: Rapid and complete.
Excretion: About 33% is in urine (26% unchanged) and 67% in feces. *Half-life:* 9 hours.

Route	Onset	Peak	Duration
P.O.	Unknown	3–4 hr	24 hr

Action

Chemical effect: Blocks the angiotensin II receptor on the surface of vascular smooth muscle and other tissue cells.

Therapeutic effect: Dilates blood vessels and decreases blood pressure.

Available forms

Tablets: 4 mg, 8 mg, 16 mg, 32 mg

NURSING PROCESS

Assessment

- Monitor patient's electrolytes, and assess patient for volume or sodium depletion (as from vigorous diuretic use) before starting therapy.
- Carefully monitor therapeutic response and adverse reactions, especially in elderly patients and patients with renal or moderate liver impairment
- Assess patient's and family's knowledge of drug therapy.

Nursing diagnoses

- Decreased cardiac output related to risk for symptomatic hypotension in volume- or sodium-depleted patients
- Risk for imbalanced fluid volume in patients with impaired renal function related to drug-induced oliguria
- Deficient knowledge related to drug therapy

Planning and implementation

- Make sure patient is adequately hydrated before starting therapy.
- Assess patient for hypotension. If it occurs after a dose, place patient in supine position and, if needed, give an I.V. infusion of normal saline solution.
- Most of antihypertensive effect occurs within 2 weeks. Maximal antihypertensive effect is obtained within 4 to 6 weeks. If blood pressure isn't controlled by drug alone, add diuretic.
- Drug can't be removed by hemodialysis.

Patient teaching

- Advise woman of childbearing age about risk of second- and third-trimester exposure to drug. If pregnancy is suspected, tell her to notify prescriber immediately.
- Tell patient to report adverse reactions promptly.
- Instruct patient to take drug exactly as directed.
- Tell patient that drug may be taken with or without food.

Evaluation

- Patient's volume or sodium depletion is corrected so that symptomatic hypotension doesn't occur.
- Patient maintains fluid balance.
- Patient and family state understanding of drug therapy.

capecitabine

(kayp-SITE-a-been)

Xeloda

Pharmacologic class: fluoropyrimidine carbamate

Therapeutic class: antineoplastic

Pregnancy risk category: D

Indications and dosages

▶ **First-line therapy for metastatic colorectal cancer; Dukes C colon cancer after complete resection of primary tumor when fluoropyrimidine monotherapy is preferred; metastatic breast cancer resistant to combined paclitaxel and anthracycline therapy, or to paclitaxel after anthracycline therapy, or with docetaxel after anthracycline failure.** *Adults:* 1,250 mg/m² P.O. within 30 minutes after morning and evening meals for 2 weeks; followed by a 1-week rest period. Continue as a q-3-week cycle; adjust for toxicity and individual needs. Adjuvant treatment in patients with Dukes C colon cancer is recommended for a total of 6 months.

Adjust-a-dose: For patients with renal impairment, if creatinine clearance is 30 to 50 ml/minute, reduce initial dose by 75% (from 1,250 mg/m² to 950 mg/m² twice daily).

Contraindications and cautions

- Contraindicated in patients hypersensitive to 5-fluorouracil (5-FU) and in patients with a creatinine clearance less than 30 ml/minute.

Lifespan: In pregnant women, use only in life-threatening situations or severe disease for which safer drugs can't be used or are ineffective. Breast-feeding should be stopped during therapy. In children, safety and effectiveness haven't been established. In patients older than age 80, use cautiously because they may have a greater risk of GI adverse effects.

Adverse reactions

CNS: dizziness, *fatigue, fever, headache,* insomnia, mood alteration, *pain, paresthesia, peripheral neuropathy,* tremor.
CV: dysrhythmias, *edema,* ***venous thrombosis.***
EENT: *eye irritation, increased lacrimation,* rhinorrhea, sore throat.
GI: *abdominal pain, anorexia, constipation, diarrhea,* dyspepsia, *nausea, stomatitis,* taste disturbance, *vomiting.*
Hematologic: anemia, ***leukopenia, lymphopenia, neutropenia, thrombocytopenia.***
Hepatic: *hyperbilirubinemia.*
Musculoskeletal: *back pain,* limb pain, myalgia.
Respiratory: cough, *dyspnea,* pharyngeal disorder.
Skin: alopecia, *dermatitis, hand-foot syndrome,* nail disorder.
Other: dehydration.

Interactions

Drug-drug. *Leucovorin:* May increase 5-FU level and toxicity. Monitor patient carefully.
Phenytoin: May increase phenytoin level. Monitor level carefully. Consider decreased phenytoin dose.
Warfarin: May increase risk of bleeding and death. Avoid this combination, or monitor PT and INR often and adjust warfarin dose, if needed.
Drug-food. *Any food:* May decrease rate and extent of absorption. Give drug 30 minutes after a meal to decrease GI adverse events, but avoid excessive drug inactivation.

Effects on lab test results

- May increase bilirubin, AST, ALT, alkaline phosphatase, and hemoglobin levels and hematocrit.
- May increase PT and INR. May decrease platelet, lymphocyte, and neutrophil counts.

Pharmacokinetics

Absorption: Good.
Distribution: About 60% protein-bound.
Metabolism: Extensively in the liver and tumor cells.
Excretion: 70% in urine. *Half-life:* About 45 minutes.

Route	Onset	Peak	Duration
P.O.	Unknown	1½–2 hr	Unknown

Action

Chemical effect: Interferes with DNA synthesis to inhibit cell division and with RNA processing and protein synthesis.
Therapeutic effect: Inhibits cell growth of selected cancers.

Available forms

Tablets: 150 mg, 500 mg

NURSING PROCESS

Assessment

- Assess patient's underlying condition before therapy and regularly thereafter.
- Assess patient for coronary artery disease, mild to moderate hepatic impairment caused by liver metastases, hyperbilirubinemia, and renal insufficiency.
- Monitor PT and INR in patients also taking warfarin because of increased risk of bleeding. Patients older than age 60 are also at risk for coagulopathies, even if they aren't taking warfarin.
- Monitor patient for severe diarrhea; if it occurs, notify prescriber.
- Monitor patient for hand-foot syndrome (numbness, paresthesia, tingling, painless or painful swelling, erythema, desquamation, blistering, and severe pain of hands or feet), hyperbilirubinemia, and severe nausea. If these reactions occur, adjust therapy immediately.
- Assess patient's and family's knowledge of drug therapy.

Nursing diagnoses

- Risk for infection related to adverse effects of drug
- Risk for impaired skin integrity related to potential for hand-foot syndrome
- Deficient knowledge related to drug therapy

Planning and implementation

- If diarrhea occurs and patient becomes dehydrated, give fluid and electrolyte replacement.

Stop the drug immediately until diarrhea diminishes or resolves.

- If hyperbilirubinemia occurs, stop the drug.
- Monitor patient for toxicity. To manage toxicity, treat symptoms, stop the drug temporarily, and reduce the dosage.

Patient teaching

- Inform patient and family of expected adverse drug effects, especially nausea, vomiting, diarrhea, and hand-foot syndrome. Explain that dose will be adjusted.

ALERT: Instruct patient to stop taking the drug and to contact prescriber immediately if he develops diarrhea (more than four bowel movements daily or diarrhea at night), vomiting (two to five episodes in 24 hours), nausea, appetite loss or decrease in amount of food taken each day, stomatitis (pain, redness, swelling or sores in mouth), hand-foot syndrome, fever of 100.5° F (38° C) or more, or other evidence of infection.

- Tell patient that most adverse effects improve within 2 or 3 days after stopping drug and that if they don't, he should contact prescriber.
- Tell patient how to take drug. Dosage cycle is usually to take drug for 14 days followed by 7-day rest period. Inform him how many cycles he should take.
- Instruct patient to take drug with water within 30 minutes after breakfast and after dinner.
- If a combination of tablets is prescribed, teach patient importance of correctly identifying the tablets.
- For missed doses, instruct patient not to take the missed dose and not to double the next one. Instead, he should continue with regular schedule and check with prescriber.
- Instruct patient to inform prescriber if he's taking folic acid.

Evaluation

- Patient doesn't develop infection.
- Patient doesn't develop hand-foot syndrome.
- Patient and family state understanding of drug therapy.

captopril

(KAP-toh-pril)

Capoten

Pharmacologic class: ACE inhibitor
Therapeutic class: antihypertensive, adjunct treatment of heart failure and diabetic nephropathy
Pregnancy risk category: C (D in second and third trimesters)

Indications and dosages

▶ **Hypertension.** *Adults:* Initially, 25 mg P.O. b.i.d. or t.i.d. If blood pressure isn't controlled in 1 to 2 weeks, increase dosage to 50 mg b.i.d. or t.i.d. If not controlled after another 1 to 2 weeks, add thiazide diuretic. If blood pressure needs to be reduced further, raise dosage as high as 150 mg t.i.d. while continuing diuretic. Maximum daily dose, 450 mg.

▶ **Heart failure.** *Adults:* 6.25 to 12.5 mg P.O. t.i.d. initially. Gradually increase to 50 to 100 mg t.i.d. as needed. Maximum daily dose, 450 mg.

▶ **Diabetic nephropathy.** *Adults:* 25 mg P.O. t.i.d.

▶ **Left ventricular dysfunction after MI.** *Adults:* 6.25 mg P.O. as a single dose 3 days after MI; then 12.5 mg t.i.d., increasing dosage to 25 mg t.i.d. Target dosage is 50 mg t.i.d.

Contraindications and cautions

- Contraindicated in patients hypersensitive to drug or other ACE inhibitors.
- Use cautiously in patients with renal impairment or serious autoimmune disease (particularly systemic lupus erythematosus), and in patients exposed to other drugs known to affect WBC counts or immune response.

Lifespan: In pregnant women, use cautiously. If patient becomes pregnant, drug usually is stopped. In breast-feeding women, use cautiously. In children, safety and effectiveness haven't been established.

Adverse reactions

CNS: dizziness, fainting, fever.
CV: angina pectoris, ***heart failure, hypotension,*** pericarditis, tachycardia.
GI: anorexia, dysgeusia.

GU: membranous glomerulopathy, nephrotic syndrome, proteinuria, ***renal impairment*** (in patients with renal disease or those receiving high dosages), urinary frequency.
Hematologic: ***agranulocytosis, leukopenia, pancytopenia, thrombocytopenia.***
Hepatic: cholestatic jaundice, elevated liver enzyme levels.
Metabolic: ***hyperkalemia.***
Respiratory: cough.
Skin: maculopapular rash, pruritus, urticaria.
Other: ***angioedema.***

Interactions

Drug-drug. *Antacids:* May decrease captopril effect. Separate doses.
Digoxin: May increase digoxin level by 15% to 30%. Monitor patient for digitalis toxicity.
Diuretics, other antihypertensives: May increase risk of excessive hypotension. Stop diuretic or lower captopril dosage.
Insulin, oral antidiabetics: May increase risk of hypoglycemia when captopril therapy starts. Monitor patient closely.
Lithium: May increase lithium level and cause lithium toxicity. Monitor patient closely.
NSAIDs: May reduce antihypertensive effect. Monitor blood pressure.
Potassium supplements, potassium-sparing diuretics: May increase risk of hyperkalemia. Avoid these drugs unless hypokalemic level is confirmed.
Probenecid: May increase captopril level. Avoid use together.
Drug-food. *Any food:* May reduce absorption of drug. Give drug 1 hour before meals.
Drug-herb. *Black catechu:* May have additional hypotensive effects of catechu. Discourage use together.
Capsaicin: May worsen captopril-related cough. Discourage herb use.
Licorice: May cause sodium retention, which counteracts ACE effects. Monitor blood pressure.

Effects on lab test results

- May increase alkaline phosphatase, bilirubin, and potassium levels and may cause a transient increase in hepatic enzyme levels. May decrease hemoglobin level and hematocrit.
- May decrease WBC, granulocyte, RBC, and platelet counts.

Pharmacokinetics

Absorption: Through GI tract; food may reduce absorption by up to 40%.
Distribution: Into most body tissues except CNS. 25% to 30% protein-bound.
Metabolism: About 50% in liver.
Excretion: Mainly in urine, minimally in feces. *Half-life:* Less than 2 hours.

Route	Onset	Peak	Duration
P.O.	15–60 min	30–90 min	6–12 hr

Action

Chemical effect: Thought to inhibit ACE, preventing conversion of angiotensin I to angiotensin II. Reduced formation of angiotensin II decreases peripheral arterial resistance, thus decreasing aldosterone secretion.
Therapeutic effect: Reduces sodium and water retention, lowers blood pressure, and helps improve renal function adversely affected by diabetes.

Available forms

Tablets: 12.5 mg, 25 mg, 50 mg, 100 mg

NURSING PROCESS

Assessment

- Assess patient's underlying condition before therapy and regularly thereafter.
- Monitor blood pressure and pulse rate often.
- Monitor WBC and differential counts before therapy, every 2 weeks for first 3 months, and periodically thereafter.
- Monitor potassium level and renal function (BUN and creatinine clearance levels, urinalysis).
- Be alert for adverse reactions and drug interactions.
- Assess patient's and family's knowledge of drug therapy.

Nursing diagnoses

- Risk for injury related to patient's underlying condition
- Ineffective protection related to drug-induced blood disorder
- Deficient knowledge related to drug therapy

Planning and implementation

- If patient has persistent dry, tickling, nonproductive cough, watch closely for adverse reaction and respiratory impairment.
- Because antacids decrease drug's effect, separate doses.
- If patient develops fever, sore throat, leukopenia, hypotension, or tachycardia, withhold dose and notify prescriber.
- Notify prescriber about abnormal laboratory studies.

ALERT: Don't confuse captopril with carvedilol.

Patient teaching

- Instruct patient to take drug 1 hour before meals because food decreases drug absorption.
- Inform patient that light-headedness may occur, especially during the first few days of therapy. Tell patient to rise slowly to minimize this effect and to report symptoms to prescriber. Tell patient with syncope to stop taking drug and call prescriber immediately.
- Tell patient to use caution in hot weather and during exercise. Inadequate fluid intake, vomiting, diarrhea, and excessive perspiration can lead to light-headedness and syncope.
- Advise patient to report signs of infection, such as fever and sore throat.
- Tell woman to notify prescriber if she becomes pregnant because drug will be stopped.
- Tell patient to notify prescriber if cough interferes with sleep or required activities so that drug can be changed.

Evaluation

- Patient's underlying condition improves.
- Patient's WBC and differential counts are normal.
- Patient and family state understanding of drug therapy.

carbamazepine

(kar-buh-MAH-zuh-peen)

Apo-Carbamazepine ♦, Carbatrol, Epitol, Equetro, Novo-Carbamaz ♦, Tegretol, Tegretol CR ♦, Tegretol-XR

Pharmacologic class: iminostilbene derivative
Therapeutic class: anticonvulsant, analgesic
Pregnancy risk category: D

Indications and dosages

▶ **Generalized tonic-clonic and complex partial seizures, mixed seizure patterns.** *Adults and children older than age 12:* Initially, 200 mg P.O. b.i.d. for tablets or 100 mg of suspension P.O. q.i.d. Increase at weekly intervals by 200 mg P.O. daily, in divided doses at 6- to 8-hour intervals. Adjust to minimum effective level when control is achieved. Maximum daily dosage, 1 g in children ages 12 to 15, or 1.2 g in patients older than age 15.
Children ages 6 to 12: Initially, 100 mg P.O. b.i.d., or 50 mg of suspension P.O. q.i.d. Increase at weekly intervals by 100 mg P.O. daily. Maximum daily dose is 1 g.
Children younger than age 6: Initially, 10 to 20 mg/kg P.O. daily in two to three divided doses (tablets) or four divided doses (suspension). Increase weekly to achieve optimal response. Maximum, 35 mg/kg/day.

▶ **Trigeminal neuralgia.** *Adults:* Initially, 100 mg P.O. b.i.d. or 50 mg of suspension P.O. q.i.d. with meals. Increase by 100 mg q 12 hours for tablets or 50 mg of suspension q.i.d. until pain is relieved. Maintenance dosage is 200 to 1,200 mg P.O. daily. Maximum daily dosage is 1,200 mg. Decrease dose to minimum effective level, or stop drug at least once q 3 months.

▶ **Restless leg syndrome‡.** *Adults:* 100 to 300 mg P.O. at bedtime.

▶ **Chorea‡.** *Children:* 15 to 25 mg/kg P.O. daily.

▶ **Acute manic and mixed episodes in bipolar 1 disorder (Equetro).** *Adults:* Initially, 200 mg P.O. b.i.d. Increase by 200 mg daily to achieve therapeutic response. Doses higher than 1,600 mg daily haven't been studied.

Contraindications and cautions

- Contraindicated in patients hypersensitive to drug or tricyclic antidepressants, in patients with previous bone marrow suppression, and within 14 days of MAO inhibitor therapy.
- Use cautiously in patients with mixed seizure disorders because drugs may increase risk of seizures, usually atypical absence or generalized.

Lifespan: In pregnant women, use cautiously. If breast-feeding woman must take drug, breast-feeding should be stopped.

Adverse reactions

CNS: ataxia, dizziness, drowsiness, fatigue, fever, vertigo, ***worsening of seizures*** (usually in patients with mixed seizure disorders, including atypical absence seizures).
CV: aggravation of coronary artery disease, ***heart failure,*** hypertension, hypotension.
EENT: blurred vision, conjunctivitis, diplopia, dry mouth and pharynx, nystagmus.
GI: abdominal pain, anorexia, diarrhea, glossitis, nausea, stomatitis, vomiting.
GU: albuminuria, glycosuria, impotence, urinary frequency, urine retention.
Hematologic: ***agranulocytosis, aplastic anemia,*** eosinophilia, leukocytosis, ***thrombocytopenia.***
Hepatic: ***hepatitis.***
Respiratory: pulmonary hypersensitivity.
Skin: ***erythema multiforme,*** excessive sweating, rash, ***Stevens-Johnson syndrome,*** urticaria.
Other: chills, ***water intoxication.***

Interactions

Drug-drug. *Atracurium, cisatracurium, pancuronium, rocuronium, vecuronium:* May decrease the effects of nondepolarizing muscle relaxant, causing it to be less effective. May need to increase the dose of the nondepolarizing muscle relaxant.
Charcoal: May decrease GI absorption of carbamazepine. Use only in cases of overdose to promote drug clearance.
Cimetidine, danazol, diltiazem, macrolides, isoniazid, propoxyphene, valproic acid, verapamil: May increase carbamazepine level. Use together cautiously.
Clarithromycin, erythromycin, troleandomycin: May inhibit carbamazepine metabolism, increasing the level and risk of toxicity. Avoid use together.
Doxycycline, haloperidol, hormonal contraceptives, phenytoin, tiagabine, theophylline, topiramate, valproate, warfarin: May decrease levels of these drugs. Monitor patient for decreased effect.
Lithium: May increase risk of CNS toxicity of lithium. Avoid use together.
MAO inhibitors: May increase depressant and anticholinergic effects. Don't use together.
Phenobarbital, phenytoin, primidone: May decrease carbamazepine level. Monitor patient for decreased effect.
Drug-herb. *Plantains:* Psyllium seeds may inhibit GI absorption. Discourage use together.

Effects on lab test results

- May increase BUN level. May decrease hemoglobin level and hematocrit.
- May increase eosinophil count. May decrease granulocyte, WBC, and platelet counts and thyroid and liver function test values.

Pharmacokinetics

Absorption: Slow.
Distribution: Widely throughout body; about 75% protein-bound.
Metabolism: By liver to active metabolite; may also induce its own metabolism.
Excretion: 70% in urine and 30% in feces.
Half-life: 25 to 65 hours with single dose; 8 to 29 hours with long-term use.

Route	Onset	Peak	Duration
P.O.			
extended-release	Unknown	4–8 hr	Unknown
suspension	1 hr	1½ hr	Unknown
tablets	1 hr	4–12 hr	Unknown

Action

Chemical effect: May stabilize neuronal membranes and limit seizure activity by increasing efflux or decreasing influx of sodium ions across cell membranes in motor cortex during generation of nerve impulses.
Therapeutic effect: Prevents seizure activity; eliminates pain caused by trigeminal neuralgia.

Available forms

Capsules (extended-release): 100 mg, 200 mg, 300 mg
Oral suspension: 100 mg/5 ml
Tablets: 200 mg
Tablets (chewable): 100 mg
Tablets (extended-release): 100 mg, 200 mg, 400 mg

NURSING PROCESS

Assessment

- Assess patient's seizure disorder or trigeminal neuralgia before therapy and regularly thereafter.
- Obtain baseline determinations of urinalysis, BUN level, liver function, CBC, platelet and

reticulocyte counts, and iron level. Reassess regularly.
- Monitor drug level and effects closely. Therapeutic level is 4 to 12 mcg/ml.
- Be alert for adverse reactions and drug interactions.
- Assess patient's and family's knowledge of drug therapy.

Nursing diagnoses
- Risk for injury related to seizure disorder
- Acute pain related to trigeminal neuralgia
- Deficient knowledge related to drug therapy

Planning and implementation
ALERT: Don't confuse Tegretol or Tegretol-XR with Topamax or Toprol-XL.
- Give drug in divided doses to maintain consistent level.
- Give drug with food to minimize GI distress.
- Shake oral suspension well before measuring dose.
- Extended-release capsules may be opened and contents sprinkled over food, such as a teaspoon of applesauce.
- When giving by NG tube, mix dose with equal volume of water, normal saline solution, or D_5W. Flush tube with 100 ml of diluent after giving dose.

ALERT: When treating seizures or status epilepticus, never abruptly stop giving the drug. If adverse reactions occur, notify prescriber immediately. Increase dosage gradually to minimize adverse reactions.

Patient teaching
- Tell patient to take drug with food to minimize GI distress.
- Tell patient to keep tablets in original container, tightly closed, and away from moisture. Some formulations may harden when exposed to excess moisture, resulting in decreased bioavailability and loss of seizure control.
- Inform patient with trigeminal neuralgia that prescriber may try to decrease dosage or withdraw drug every 3 months.

ALERT: Tell patient to notify prescriber immediately about fever, sore throat, mouth ulcers, or easy bruising or bleeding.
- Warn patient that drug may cause mild-to-moderate dizziness and drowsiness at first. Advise patient to avoid hazardous activities until effects disappear (usually within 3 to 4 days).
- Advise patient to have periodic eye examinations.
- Tell patient not to crush or chew capsules or their contents.

Evaluation
- Patient remains free from seizures.
- Patient reports pain relief.
- Patient and family state understanding of drug therapy.

carboplatin
(KAR-boh-plat-in)
Paraplatin, Paraplatin-AQ ♦

Pharmacologic class: alkylating drug
Therapeutic class: antineoplastic
Pregnancy risk category: D

Indications and dosages
▶ **Palliative therapy for ovarian cancer.** *Adults:* 360 mg/m[2] I.V. on day 1 q 4 weeks; don't repeat until platelet count exceeds 100,000/mm[3] and neutrophil count exceeds 2,000/mm[3]. Base later doses on blood counts.

Adjust-a-dose: For patients with renal impairment, if creatinine clearance is 41 to 59 ml/minute, starting dose is 250 mg/m[2] I.V. If creatinine clearance is 16 to 40 ml/minute, it's 200 mg/m[2]. Recommended dosage adjustments aren't available for patients with creatinine clearance of 15 ml/minute or less.

▶ **Initial therapy for advanced ovarian cancer, with cyclophosphamide.** *Adults:* Initial dose is 300 mg/m[2] I.V. on day 1 q 4 weeks for six cycles. Don't repeat cycles until neutrophil count is 2,000/mm[3] or more and platelet count is 100,000/mm[3] or more.

I.V. administration
- Have epinephrine, corticosteroids, and antihistamines available when giving drug because anaphylactoid reactions may occur within minutes of administration.
- Preparing and giving I.V. form is linked to mutagenic, teratogenic, and carcinogenic risks. Follow facility policy to reduce risks.
- Reconstitute powder for injection with D_5W, normal saline solution, or sterile water for injection to make 10 mg/ml. Add 5 ml of diluent to 50-mg vial, 15 ml of diluent to 150-mg vial, or

45 ml of diluent to 450-mg vial. Then, further dilute reconstituted powder or aqueous solution for injection with normal saline solution or D_5W before infusion. Concentrations as low as 0.5 mg/ml can be prepared.
- Give drug by continuous or intermittent infusion over at least 15 minutes.
- Don't give carboplatin with needles or I.V. administration sets that contain aluminum because drug may precipitate or lose potency.
- Store unopened vials at room temperature. Once reconstituted and diluted, drug is stable at room temperature for 8 hours. Discard unused drug at this time.

⊗ **Incompatibilities**
Amphotericin B cholesteryl sulfate complex, fluorouracil, mesna, sodium bicarbonate.

Contraindications and cautions

- Contraindicated in patients hypersensitive to cisplatin, platinum-containing compounds, or mannitol. Also contraindicated in patients with severe bone marrow suppression or bleeding.

Lifespan: In pregnant women, drug is contraindicated. In breast-feeding women and in children, safety and effectiveness haven't been established. In patients older than age 65, use cautiously because of greater risk for neurotoxicity.

Adverse reactions

CNS: CENTRAL NEUROTOXICITY, confusion, dizziness, *peripheral neuropathy,* ***stroke.***
EENT: *ototoxicity.*
CV: ***embolism, heart failure.***
GI: constipation, diarrhea, *nausea, vomiting.*
Hematologic: *anemia,* ***bone marrow suppression, leukopenia, neutropenia, thrombocytopenia.***
Hepatic: ***hepatotoxicity.***
Skin: alopecia.
Other: hypersensitivity reactions.

Interactions

Drug-drug. *Bone marrow depressants, including radiation therapy:* May increase hematologic toxicity. Monitor hematologic studies.
Nephrotoxic drugs: May enhance nephrotoxicity of carboplatin. Monitor renal function tests.

Effects on lab test results

- May increase BUN, creatinine, bilirubin, AST, and alkaline phosphatase levels. May decrease magnesium, calcium, potassium, sodium, and hemoglobin levels and hematocrit.
- May decrease neutrophil, WBC, RBC, and platelet counts.

Pharmacokinetics

Absorption: Given I.V.
Distribution: Volume distributed is about equal to that of total body water; no significant protein binding occurs.
Metabolism: Hydrolyzed to form hydroxylated and aquated types.
Excretion: 65% by kidneys within 12 hours, 71% within 24 hours. *Half-life:* 5 hours.

Route	Onset	Peak	Duration
I.V.	Unknown	Unknown	Unknown

Action

Chemical effect: Probably produces cross-linking of DNA strands.
Therapeutic effect: Impairs ovarian cancer cell replication.

Available forms

Powder for injection: 50-mg, 150-mg, 450-mg vials
Solution for injection: 50 mg/5 ml, 150 mg/15 ml, 450 mg/45 ml

NURSING PROCESS

Assessment

- Assess patient's condition before therapy and regularly thereafter.
- Determine electrolyte, creatinine, and BUN levels; creatinine clearance; CBC; and platelet count before first infusion and before each course of therapy. Lowest WBC and platelet counts usually occur by day 21. They usually return to baseline by day 28.
- Be alert for adverse reactions and drug interactions.
- Assess patient's and family's knowledge of drug therapy.

Nursing diagnoses

- Ineffective health maintenance related to ovarian cancer

- Ineffective protection related to drug-induced adverse reactions
- Deficient knowledge related to drug therapy

Planning and implementation

- Check dose carefully against laboratory test results. Only increase dose once. Don't exceed 125% of starting dose in subsequent doses.
- Bone marrow suppression may be more severe in patients with creatinine clearance below 60 ml/minute. Adjust dosage in these patients.

ALERT: Don't repeat dose unless platelet count exceeds 100,000/mm³.

- Provide antiemetic therapy. Carboplatin can produce severe vomiting.

ALERT: Don't confuse carboplatin with cisplatin.

Patient teaching

- Warn patient to watch for evidence of infection (fever, sore throat, fatigue) and bleeding (easy bruising, nosebleed, bleeding gums, melena). Tell patient to take his temperature daily.
- Instruct patient to avoid OTC products that contain aspirin.
- Advise woman of childbearing age to avoid pregnancy during therapy and to consult prescriber before becoming pregnant.
- Advise breast-feeding patient to stop breast-feeding because of risk of toxicity to infant.

Evaluation

- Patient has positive response to carboplatin as shown by follow-up diagnostic tests.
- Patient doesn't experience injury from drug therapy.
- Patient and family state understanding of drug therapy.

carisoprodol

(kar-ih-soh-PROH-dol)

Soma

Pharmacologic class: carbamate derivative
Therapeutic class: skeletal muscle relaxant
Pregnancy risk category: NR

Indications and dosages

▶ **Adjunct in acute, painful musculoskeletal conditions.** *Adults:* 350 mg P.O. t.i.d. and at bedtime.

Contraindications and cautions

- Contraindicated in patients hypersensitive to related compounds (such as meprobamate) and in patients with intermittent porphyria.
- Use cautiously in patients with hepatic or renal impairment. Prolonged use may lead to dependence; use cautiously in addiction-prone patients.

Lifespan: In pregnant or breast-feeding women and in children younger than age 12, safety and effectiveness haven't been established.

Adverse reactions

CNS: agitation, ataxia, depressive reactions, *dizziness, drowsiness,* fever, headache, insomnia, irritability, tremor, vertigo.
CV: facial flushing, orthostatic hypotension, tachycardia.
GI: epigastric distress, increased bowel activity, nausea, vomiting.
Hematologic: eosinophilia.
Respiratory: ***asthmatic episodes,*** hiccups.
Skin: ***erythema multiforme,*** pruritus, rash.
Other: ***anaphylaxis, angioedema.***

Interactions

Drug-drug. *CNS depressants:* May increase CNS depression. Avoid use together.
Drug-lifestyle. *Alcohol use:* May increase CNS depression. Discourage use together.

Effects on lab test results

- May increase eosinophil count.

Pharmacokinetics

Absorption: Unknown.
Distribution: Widely throughout body.
Metabolism: In liver.
Excretion: In urine mainly as metabolites; less than 1% excreted unchanged. *Half-life:* 8 hours.

Route	Onset	Peak	Duration
P.O.	≤ 30 min	≤ 4 hr	4–6 hr

Action

Chemical effect: Appears to modify central perception of pain without modifying pain reflexes. Blocks interneuronal activity in descending reticular activating system and in spinal cord.

Therapeutic effect: Relieves musculoskeletal pain.

Available forms

Tablets: 350 mg

NURSING PROCESS

Assessment

- Assess patient's pain before and after giving drug.
- Monitor the drug's effectiveness by regularly assessing severity and frequency of muscle spasms.
- Be alert for adverse reactions and drug interactions.

ALERT: Watch for idiosyncratic reactions after first to fourth doses (weakness, ataxia, visual and speech difficulties, fever, skin eruptions, and mental changes) and for severe reactions (bronchospasm, hypotension, and anaphylaxis).

- Assess patient for history of drug addiction. Prolonged use of drug may lead to dependence.
- Assess patient's and family's knowledge of drug therapy.

Nursing diagnoses

- Acute pain related to patient's underlying condition
- Risk for injury related to drug-induced drowsiness
- Deficient knowledge related to drug therapy

Planning and implementation

- Give drug with meals or milk to prevent GI distress.
- Once pain is adequately relieved, reduce dose.
- Stop giving the drug and notify prescriber immediately if unusual reactions occur.
- Don't stop drug abruptly because mild withdrawal effects, such as insomnia, headache, nausea, and abdominal cramps, may result.

Patient teaching

- Warn patient to avoid activities that require alertness or physical dexterity, such as operating machinery or a motor vehicle, until drug's CNS effects are known.
- Advise patient not to consume alcohol or other CNS depressants.
- Advise patient to follow prescriber's orders about rest and physical therapy.
- Tell patient to take drug with meals or milk to prevent GI distress.

Evaluation

- Patient reports pain has ceased.
- Patient doesn't experience injury from drug-induced CNS adverse reactions.
- Patient and family state understanding of drug.

carmustine (BCNU)

(kar-MUHS-teen)

BiCNU, Gliadel

Pharmacologic class: alkylating drug
Therapeutic class: antineoplastic
Pregnancy risk category: D

Indications and dosages

▶ **Hodgkin lymphoma, non-Hodgkin lymphoma, and multiple myeloma.** *Adults:* 150 to 200 mg/m² I.V. by slow infusion as single dose, repeat q 6 weeks; or 75 to 100 mg/m² I.V. by slow infusion daily for 2 days; repeat q 6 weeks. Don't repeat dose until platelet count is above 100,000/mm³ and WBC count is above 4,000/mm³.

Adjust-a-dose: Reduce dosage by 30% when WBC count is 2,000 to 3,000/mm³ and platelet count is 25,000 to 75,000/mm³. Reduce dosage by 50% when WBC count is less than 2,000/mm³ and platelet count is less than 25,000/mm³.

▶ **Recurrent glioblastoma multiforme (adjunct to surgery); newly diagnosed high-grade malignant glioma patients (adjunct to surgery and radiation).** *Adults:* 8 wafers implanted into resection cavity as size of cavity allows.

▶ **Brain‡, breast‡, GI tract‡, lung‡, and hepatic cancer‡; malignant melanomas‡.** *Adults:* 75 to 100 mg/m² I.V. by slow infusion daily for 2 days; repeat q 6 weeks if platelet count is above 100,000/mm³ and WBC count is above 4,000/mm³.

I.V. administration

- To reconstitute, dissolve 100 mg of drug in 3 ml of absolute alcohol provided by manufacturer. Dilute solution with 27 ml of sterile water for injection. Resulting solution contains 3.3 mg of drug/ml in 10% alcohol. Dilute in normal saline solution or D_5W for I.V. infusion.

• If powder liquefies or appears oily, discard drug because decomposition has occurred.
• Give only in glass containers. Solution is unstable in plastic I.V. bags.
• Give at least 250 ml over 1 to 2 hours. To reduce pain of infusion, dilute further or slow infusion rate.
• Avoid contact with skin because drug will cause brown stain. If drug contacts skin, wash it off thoroughly.
• Store unopened vials of the dry powder in refrigerator. After reconstitution, drug is stable for 8 hours at room temperature. Protect from light. May decompose at temperatures above 80° F (27° C).

⊗ **Incompatibilities**
Sodium bicarbonate. Don't mix with other drugs.

Contraindications and cautions

• Contraindicated in patients hypersensitive to drug.
Lifespan: In pregnant or breast-feeding women, drug is contraindicated. In children, safety and effectiveness haven't been established.

Adverse reactions

CNS: ataxia, ***brain edema,*** drowsiness, ***seizures.***
CV: facial flushing.
EENT: ocular toxicities.
GI: anorexia, diarrhea, dysphagia, esophagitis, nausea, vomiting.
GU: ***nephrotoxicity,*** renal impairment.
Hematologic: ***acute leukemia or bone marrow dysplasia*** (may occur after long-term use), ***cumulative bone marrow suppression*** (delayed 4 to 6 weeks, lasting 1 to 2 weeks), ***leukopenia, thrombocytopenia.***
Hepatic: ***hepatotoxicity.***
Metabolic: hyperuricemia (in lymphoma patients with rapid cell lysis).
Respiratory: ***pulmonary fibrosis.***
Skin: hyperpigmentation (if drug contacts skin).
Other: *intense pain* (at infusion site from venous spasm).

Interactions

Drug-drug. *Anticoagulants, aspirin, NSAIDs:* May increase risk of bleeding. Avoid use together.
Cimetidine: May increase carmustine's bone marrow toxicity. Avoid use together.
Digoxin, phenytoin: May reduce levels of these drugs. Use together cautiously; monitor levels.
Mitomycin: May increase corneal and conjunctival damage with high doses. Monitor patient.
Myelosuppressives: May increase risk of myelosuppression. Monitor patient's CBC periodically.

Effects on lab test results

• May increase urine urea, AST, bilirubin, and alkaline phosphatase levels. May decrease hemoglobin level and hematocrit.
• May decrease WBC and platelet counts.

Pharmacokinetics

Absorption: Given I.V.
Distribution: Rapidly into CSF.
Metabolism: Extensively in liver.
Excretion: 60% to 70% in urine within 96 hours, 6% to 10% as carbon dioxide by lungs, and 1% in feces. *Half-life:* 15 to 30 minutes.

Route	Onset	Peak	Duration
I.V., wafer	Unknown	Unknown	Unknown

Action

Chemical effect: Inhibits enzymatic reactions involved with DNA synthesis, cross-links strands of cellular DNA, and interferes with RNA transcription, causing growth imbalance that leads to cell death.
Therapeutic effect: Kills selected cancer cells.

Available forms

Injection: 100-mg vial (lyophilized), with 3-ml vial of absolute alcohol supplied as diluent
Wafer: 7.7 mg

NURSING PROCESS

Assessment

• Assess patient's neoplastic disorder before therapy and regularly thereafter.
• Obtain baseline pulmonary function tests before starting therapy because pulmonary toxicity appears to be dose related. Evaluate results of liver, renal, and pulmonary function tests periodically thereafter.
• Monitor CBC and uric acid levels.

• Be alert for adverse reactions and drug interactions.
• Assess patient's and family's knowledge of drug therapy.

Nursing diagnoses
• Ineffective health maintenance related to neoplastic disease
• Risk for injury related to drug-induced adverse reactions
• Deficient knowledge related to drug therapy

Planning and implementation
• Preparing and giving drug has carcinogenic, mutagenic, and teratogenic risks. Follow facility policy to reduce risks.
• To reduce nausea, give antiemetic before giving drug.
• Unopened foil packs containing wafers are stable at room temperature for 6 hours. Store below –4° F (–20° C).
• If handling wafer in operating room, use double gloves.
• Allopurinol may be used with adequate hydration to prevent hyperuricemia and uric acid nephropathy.

Patient teaching
• Warn patient to watch for signs of infection (fever, sore throat, fatigue) and bleeding (easy bruising, nosebleed, bleeding gums, melena). Tell patient to take temperature daily.
• Instruct patient to avoid OTC products containing aspirin.
• Advise breast-feeding women to stop breastfeeding because of toxicity to infant.
• Advise women of childbearing age to avoid pregnancy during therapy and to consult prescriber before becoming pregnant.

Evaluation
• Patient shows positive response to drug therapy as shown by follow-up diagnostic studies.
• Patient doesn't experience injury from drug-induced adverse reactions.
• Patient and family state understanding of drug therapy.

carvedilol
(kar-VAY-deh-lol)
Coreg

Pharmacologic class: alpha$_1$ and beta blocker
Therapeutic class: antihypertensive, adjunct treatment for heart failure
Pregnancy risk category: C

Indications and dosages
▶ **Hypertension.** *Adults:* Dosage highly individualized. Initially, 6.25 mg P.O. b.i.d. with food. Obtain a standing blood pressure 1 hour after initial dose. If tolerated, continue dosage for 7 to 14 days. May increase to 12.5 mg P.O. b.i.d. for 7 to 14 days, monitor blood pressure as above. Maximum dosage, 25 mg P.O. b.i.d. as tolerated.

▶ **Mild to severe heart failure.** *Adults:* Individualize and adjust dosage carefully. Initially, 3.125 mg P.O. b.i.d. with food for 2 weeks; if tolerated, increase to 6.25 mg P.O. b.i.d. Double dose q 2 weeks as tolerated. At start of new dose, observe patient for dizziness or lightheadedness for 1 hour. Maximum dosage for patients weighing less than 85 kg (187 lb) is 25 mg P.O. b.i.d.; for those weighing more than 85 kg, maximum dosage is 50 mg P.O. b.i.d.

▶ **Left ventricular dysfunction after MI.** *Adults:* Individualize dosage. Start therapy after patient is hemodynamically stable and fluid retention has been minimized. Initially, 6.25 mg P.O. b.i.d. with food. Increase after 3 to 10 days to 12.5 mg b.i.d., then again to a target dose of 25 mg b.i.d. Or, start with 3.25 mg b.i.d. May adjust dosage more slowly. Monitor blood pressure; observe patient for light-headedness with each dosage change.

Adjust-a-dose: In patients with pulse rate below 55 beats/minute, reduce dosage.

Contraindications and cautions
• Contraindicated in patients hypersensitive to drug and in those with New York Heart Association class IV decompensated heart failure requiring I.V. inotropic therapy, bronchial asthma or related bronchospastic conditions, second- or third-degree AV block, sick sinus syndrome (unless a permanent pacemaker is in place), cardiogenic shock, or severe bradycardia.

• Drug isn't recommended for patients with symptomatic hepatic impairment.
• Use cautiously in hypertensive patients with left ventricular failure, perioperative patients who receive anesthetics that depress myocardial function, patients with diabetes who receive insulin or oral antidiabetics, and patients subject to spontaneous hypoglycemia. Also use cautiously in patients with thyroid disease, pheochromocytoma, Prinzmetal variant angina, bronchospastic disease, or peripheral vascular disease.

Lifespan: In pregnant women, use only if benefits outweigh risks to the fetus. Women should stop breast-feeding during therapy. In children, safety and effectiveness haven't been established. In elderly patients, drug levels are about 50% higher than in other adults. Monitor these patients closely.

Adverse reactions

CNS: asthenia, depression, *dizziness,* fatigue, fever, headache, hypesthesia, insomnia, pain, paresthesia, somnolence, ***stroke,*** syncope, vertigo.
CV: angina pectoris, ***AV block, bradycardia,*** edema, fluid overload, hypertension, ***hypotension,*** hypovolemia, orthostatic hypotension, palpitations, peripheral edema, peripheral vascular disorder.
EENT: abnormal vision, blurred vision, pharyngitis, rhinitis, sinusitis.
GI: abdominal pain, *diarrhea,* dyspepsia, melena, nausea, periodontitis, vomiting.
GU: abnormal renal function, albuminuria, hematuria, impotence, UTI.
Hematologic: anemia, purpura, ***thrombocytopenia.***
Metabolic: diabetes mellitus, glycosuria, gout, hypercholesterolemia, *hyperglycemia,* ***hyperkalemia,*** hypertriglyceridemia, hyperuricemia, hypervolemia, ***hypoglycemia,*** hyponatremia, *weight gain,* weight loss.
Musculoskeletal: arthralgia, arthritis, back pain, hypotonia, muscle cramps.
Respiratory: bronchitis, cough, crackles, dyspnea, ***lung edema,*** *upper respiratory tract infection.*
Other: flulike syndrome, hypersensitivity reactions, infection, injury, viral infection.

Interactions

Drug-drug. *Calcium channel blockers:* May cause isolated conduction disturbances. Monitor patient's heart rhythm and blood pressure.
Catecholamine-depleting drugs (such as MAO inhibitors, reserpine): May cause bradycardia or severe hypotension. Monitor patient closely.
Cimetidine: May increase bioavailability of carvedilol. Monitor vital signs carefully.
Clonidine: May increase blood pressure and heart rate-lowering effects. Monitor vital signs closely.
Digoxin: May increase digoxin level by about 15% during therapy. Monitor digoxin level and vital signs carefully.
Fluoxetine, paroxetine, propafenone, quinidine: May increase level of R (+) enantiomer of carvedilol. Monitor patient for hypotension and dizziness.
Insulin, oral antidiabetics: May enhance hypoglycemic properties. Monitor glucose level.
Rifampin: May reduce level of carvedilol by 70%. Monitor vital signs closely.
Drug-food. *Any food:* Delays carvedilol absorption but doesn't alter extent of bioavailability. Advise patient to take drug with food to minimize orthostatic effects.

Effects on lab test results

• May increase creatinine, BUN, ALT, AST, GGT, cholesterol, triglyceride, alkaline phosphatase, sodium, uric acid, potassium, and nonprotein nitrogen levels. May increase or decrease glucose level.
• May decrease PT, INR, and platelet counts.

Pharmacokinetics

Absorption: Rapidly and extensively with absolute bioavailability of 25% to 35% because of significant first-pass metabolism.
Distribution: Extensively into extravascular tissues. About 98% protein-bound.
Metabolism: Mainly by aromatic ring oxidation and glucuronidation.
Excretion: Metabolites are excreted mainly via bile in feces. Less than 2% excreted unchanged in urine. *Half-life:* 7 to 10 hours.

Route	Onset	Peak	Duration
P.O.	Unknown	1–2 hr	7–10 hr

Action

Chemical effect: Causes significant reductions in systemic blood pressure, pulmonary arterial pressure, pulmonary capillary wedge pressure, and heart rate.
Therapeutic effect: Lowers blood pressure and heart rate.

Available forms

Tablets: 3.125 mg, 6.25 mg, 12.5 mg, 25 mg

NURSING PROCESS

Assessment

- Monitor patient for decreased PT and increased alkaline phosphatase, BUN, ALT, and AST levels.
- Assess patient with heart failure for worsened condition, renal impairment, or fluid retention; add or increase diuretics p.r.n.
- Monitor patient with diabetes closely because drug may mask signs of hypoglycemia or worsen hyperglycemia.
- Monitor elderly patients carefully because drug level is about 50% higher in elderly patients than in younger patients.
- Observe patient for dizziness or lightheadedness for 1 hour after each dosage change.
- Assess patient's and family's knowledge of drug therapy.

Nursing diagnoses

- Ineffective health maintenance related to underlying disorder
- Ineffective cerebral tissue perfusion secondary to therapeutic action of drug
- Deficient knowledge related to drug therapy

Planning and implementation

- Before therapy begins, stabilize dose of digoxin, diuretics, and ACE inhibitors.

ALERT: Patient taking a beta blocker who has a history of anaphylactic reaction to several allergens may be more reactive to repeated challenges (accidental, diagnostic, or therapeutic). Such a patient may be unresponsive to the doses of epinephrine typically used to treat allergic reactions.

- Give drug with food to reduce risk of orthostatic hypotension.
- If pulse drops below 55 beats/minute, notify prescriber and reduce the dose.

ALERT: Don't confuse carvedilol with captopril or carteolol.

Patient teaching

- Tell patient not to interrupt or stop taking the drug without medical approval. Drug should be withdrawn gradually over 1 to 2 weeks.
- Advise patient with heart failure to call prescriber about weight gain or shortness of breath.
- Inform patient that he may develop low blood pressure when standing. If he's dizzy or faint, advise him to sit or lie down.
- Warn patient not to drive or perform hazardous tasks until the drug's CNS effects are known.
- Tell patient to notify prescriber about dizziness or faintness. Dose may need to be adjusted.
- Advise patient with diabetes to promptly report changes in glucose level.
- Inform patient who wears contact lenses that decreased lacrimation may occur.

Evaluation

- Patient responds well to therapy.
- Patient doesn't experience dizziness or lightheadedness.
- Patient and family state understanding of drug therapy.

caspofungin acetate

(kas-poh-FUN-jin AS-ih-tayt)
Cancidas

Pharmacologic class: echinocandin
Therapeutic class: antifungal
Pregnancy risk category: C

Indications and dosages

▶ **Invasive aspergillosis in patients refractory to or intolerant of other drugs, such as amphotericin B, lipid formulations of amphotericin B, itraconazole.** *Adults:* A single 70-mg loading dose I.V. on day 1, followed by 50 mg daily. Duration of therapy based on severity of patient's underlying disease, recovery from immunosuppression, and response.

▶ **Candidemia and *Candida* infections including intra-abdominal abscesses, peritonitis, and pleural space infections.** *Adults:* Give a single 70-mg loading dose I.V. on day 1, followed by 50 mg daily thereafter. Duration of therapy is based on response. In general, continue antifungal therapy for at least 14 days after the last positive culture. Patients with persistent neutropenia may warrant a longer course of therapy while neutropenia resolves.

▶ **Esophageal candidiasis.** *Adults:* 50 mg I.V. daily. Because of the risk of relapse of oropharyngeal candidiasis in patients with HIV infections, suppressive oral therapy could be considered.

▶ **Empirical therapy for presumed fungal infections in febrile, neutropenic patients.** *Adults:* A single 70-mg loading dose I.V. on day 1, followed by 50 mg daily thereafter. Duration of therapy based on response. Continue empirical therapy until neutropenia resolves. Treat patients found to have a fungal infection for a minimum of 14 days; continue treatment for at least 7 days after both neutropenia and clinical symptoms are resolved. If the 50-mg dose is well tolerated but doesn't provide an adequate response, increase the daily dose to 70 mg.

Adjust-a-dose: For patients with moderate hepatic impairment and a Child-Pugh score of 7 to 9, give 35 mg daily after initial 70-mg loading dose.

I.V. administration

- Let refrigerated vial warm to room temperature before diluting.
- Dilute all doses (70 mg, 50 mg, 35 mg) in 250 ml of normal saline solution. In patients with fluid restrictions, dilute the 50-mg and 35-mg doses in 100 ml of normal saline solution.
- Give by slow I.V. infusion over about 1 hour; don't give by I.V. bolus injection.
- Use reconstituted vials within 1 hour or discard.
- Diluted solutions may be stored at 77° F (25° C) for up to 24 hours, or at 36° F to 46° F (2° C to 8° C) for 48 hours.

⊗ **Incompatibilities**

Dextrose solutions, other I.V. drugs.

Contraindications and cautions

- Contraindicated in patients hypersensitive to the drug or any of its components.

Lifespan: In pregnant women, use only when potential benefits to the mother outweigh risks to the fetus. In breast-feeding women, use cautiously because it isn't known whether drug appears in breast milk. In children, safety and effectiveness haven't been established.

Adverse reactions

CNS: *chills, fever, headache,* paresthesia.
CV: peripheral edema, *phlebitis,* swelling, ***tachycardia,*** *thrombophlebitis.*
GI: abdominal pain, anorexia, diarrhea, nausea, vomiting.
GU: hematuria, proteinuria.
Hematologic: anemia, eosinophilia.
Hepatic: hepatic dysfunction.
Metabolic: hypercalcemia.
Musculoskeletal: myalgia, pain.
Respiratory: *tachypnea.*
Skin: ***anaphylaxis,*** histamine-mediated symptoms (rash, facial swelling, phlebitis, pruritus, sensation of warmth, erythema, sweating), *infusion site complication.*

Interactions

Drug-drug. *Carbamazepine, dexamethasone, efavirenz, nelfinavir, nevirapine, phenytoin, rifampin:* May decrease caspofungin level. Consider increasing caspofungin dosage to 70 mg daily if patient doesn't respond to lower dosage.
Cyclosporine: May significantly increase AST and ALT levels and bioavailability of caspofungin. Avoid using together unless potential benefit outweighs risk.
Tacrolimus: May decrease tacrolimus level. Monitor tacrolimus level, and adjust dosage accordingly.

Effects on lab test results

- May increase ALT, AST, alkaline phosphatase, and urine protein levels. May decrease potassium and hemoglobin levels and hematocrit.
- May increase eosinophil and urine RBC counts.

Pharmacokinetics

Absorption: Rapid into plasma; slower into tissue.
Distribution: 97% bound to albumin.
Metabolism: Slowly in the tissues and liver.
Excretion: 35% of drug and metabolites in feces and 41% in urine. *Half-life:* 9 to 11 hours.

Route	Onset	Peak	Duration
I.V.	Immediate	Unknown	36–48 hr

Action

Chemical effect: Inhibits synthesis of beta (1, 3)-D-glucan, an integral component of the

cell walls of susceptible filamentous fungi that isn't found in mammal cells.
Therapeutic effect: Prevents fungi formation.

Available forms

Lyophilized powder for injection: 50-mg, 70-mg single-use vials

NURSING PROCESS

Assessment

- Assess patient's hepatic function before starting therapy.
- Observe patient for histamine-mediated reactions (rash, facial swelling, pruritus, sensation of warmth, sweating).
- Monitor I.V. site carefully for phlebitis.
- Monitor patient's liver function test results carefully during therapy.
- Assess patient's and family's knowledge of drug therapy.

Nursing diagnoses

- Risk for infection and impaired skin integrity related to adverse effects of I.V. drug administration
- Ineffective health maintenance related to underlying disease process and immunocompromised state
- Deficient knowledge related to drug therapy

Planning and implementation

- An increase in dose to 70 mg daily hasn't been studied but may be well tolerated.
- A long course of therapy hasn't been studied but may be well tolerated.
- Adjust dose in a patient with moderate hepatic insufficiency.

Patient teaching

- Instruct patient to report signs and symptoms of phlebitis.
- Tell patient to report any adverse events during drug therapy.

Evaluation

- Patient has no adverse reactions during drug therapy.
- Patient responds positively to antifungal drug therapy.
- Patient and family state understanding of drug therapy.

cefadroxil monohydrate

(seh-fuh-DROKS-il mon-oh-HIGH-drayt)
Duricef

Pharmacologic class: first-generation cephalosporin
Therapeutic class: antibiotic
Pregnancy risk category: B

Indications and dosages

▶ **UTI caused by *Escherichia coli, Proteus mirabilis,* and *Klebsiella;* skin and soft-tissue infections; and streptococcal pharyngitis.**
Adults: 1 to 2 g P.O. daily, depending on infection treated, usually as a single dose or in two divided doses.
Children: 30 mg/kg P.O. daily in two divided doses. Course of therapy is usually at least 10 days.
Adjust-a-dose: For adults with renal impairment, give initial dosage of 1 g P.O. daily. Reduce maintenance dosage as follows: If creatinine clearance is 25 to 50 ml/minute, give 500 mg q 12 hours. If creatinine clearance is 10 to 25 ml/minute, give 500 mg q 24 hours. If creatinine clearance is less than 10 ml/minute, give 500 mg q 36 hours.

Contraindications and cautions

- Contraindicated in patients hypersensitive to drug or other cephalosporins.
- Use cautiously in patients with renal impairment or a history of sensitivity to penicillin.

Lifespan: In pregnant or breast-feeding women, use cautiously.

Adverse reactions

CNS: dizziness, headache, malaise, paresthesia, ***seizures.***
GI: abdominal cramps, anal pruritus, anorexia, diarrhea, dyspepsia, glossitis, oral candidiasis, ***pseudomembranous colitis,*** nausea, tenesmus, vomiting.
GU: candidiasis, genital pruritus.
Hematologic: ***agranulocytosis,*** anemia, eosinophilia, ***leukopenia, thrombocytopenia, transient neutropenia.***
Respiratory: dyspnea.
Skin: erythematous and maculopapular rashes.
Other: hypersensitivity reactions (serum sickness, ***anaphylaxis***).

C

Interactions

Drug-drug. *Probenecid:* May inhibit excretion and increase level of cefadroxil. Monitor patient.

Effects on lab test results

• May increase ALT, AST, alkaline phosphatase, bilirubin, GGT, and LDH levels. May decrease hemoglobin level and hematocrit.
• May increase eosinophil count. May decrease neutrophil, WBC, granulocyte, and platelet counts.
• About 40% to 75% of patients receiving cephalosporins show false-positive direct Coombs' tests.
• May cause false-positive urine glucose determinations with copper sulfate tests (Clinitest).

Pharmacokinetics

Absorption: Rapid and complete.
Distribution: Wide. CSF penetration is poor. 20% protein-bound.
Metabolism: None.
Excretion: Mainly unchanged in urine. *Half-life:* About 1 to 2 hours.

Route	Onset	Peak	Duration
P.O.	Unknown	1–2 hr	6–9 hr

Action

Chemical effect: Inhibits cell-wall synthesis, promoting osmotic instability; usually bactericidal.
Therapeutic effect: Hinders or kills susceptible bacteria.

Available forms

Capsules: 500 mg
Oral suspension: 125 mg/5 ml, 250 mg/5 ml, 500 mg/5 ml
Tablets: 1 g

NURSING PROCESS

Assessment

• Assess patient's infection before therapy and regularly thereafter.
• Before giving first dose, obtain specimen for culture and sensitivity tests. Begin therapy pending test results.
• Be alert for adverse reactions and drug interactions.
• If adverse GI reactions occur, monitor patient's hydration.
• Assess patient's and family's knowledge of drug therapy.

Nursing diagnoses

• Ineffective protection related to bacteria susceptible to drug
• Risk for deficient fluid volume related to drug-induced adverse GI reactions
• Deficient knowledge related to drug therapy

Planning and implementation

• Drug's half-life permits once- or twice-daily use.
• If creatinine clearance is less than 50 ml/minute, expect prescriber to lengthen dosage interval to prevent drug accumulation.
• Store reconstituted suspension in refrigerator. Keep container tightly closed and shake well before using.
ALERT: Don't confuse with other cephalosporins with similar-sounding names.

Patient teaching

• Tell patient to take drug exactly as prescribed, even after he feels better.
• Advise patient to take drug with food or milk to lessen GI discomfort.
• Tell patient to call prescriber if rash develops.
• Inform patient using oral suspension to shake it well before using and to refrigerate mixture in tightly closed container.

Evaluation

• Patient is free from infection.
• Patient maintains adequate hydration.
• Patient and family state understanding of drug therapy.

cefazolin sodium

(sef-EH-zoh-lin SOH-dee-um)
Ancef

Pharmacologic class: first-generation cephalosporin
Therapeutic class: antibiotic
Pregnancy risk category: B

Indications and dosages

▶ **Serious infections of respiratory, biliary, and GU tracts; skin, soft-tissue, bone, and**

joint infections; septicemia; endocarditis caused by *Escherichia coli, Enterobacteriaceae gonococci, Haemophilus influenzae, Klebsiella, Proteus mirabilis, Staphylococcus aureus, Streptococcus pneumoniae,* and group A beta-hemolytic streptococci. *Adults:* 250 mg I.V. or I.M. q 8 hours to 1 g q 6 hours. Maximum, 12 g daily in life-threatening situations. *Children and infants older than 1 month:* 25 to 100 mg/kg daily I.V. or I.M. in three or four divided doses.

▶ **Perioperative prophylaxis in contaminated surgery.** *Adults:* 1 g I.V. or I.M. 30 to 60 minutes before surgery; then 0.5 to 1 g I.V. or I.M. q 6 to 8 hours for 24 hours. In operations lasting more than 2 hours, another 0.5- to 1-g dose may be given intraoperatively. In cases where infection would be devastating, prophylaxis may continue for 3 to 5 days.

Adjust-a-dose: For patients with renal impairment, after initial dose, adjust dosage as follows. If creatinine clearance is 35 to 54 ml/minute, give full dose q 8 hours; if clearance is 11 to 34 ml/minute, give 50% of usual dose q 12 hours; if clearance is less than 10 ml/minute, give 50% of usual dose q 18 to 24 hours.

I.V. administration

- Reconstitute with sterile water, bacteriostatic water, or normal saline solution as follows: 2 ml to 500-mg vial to yield 225 mg/ml; or 2.5 ml to 1-g vial to yield 330 mg/ml. Shake well until dissolved.
- For direct injection, further dilute with 5 ml of sterile water. Inject into large vein or into tubing of free-flowing I.V. solution over 3 to 5 minutes. For intermittent infusion, add reconstituted drug to 50 to 100 ml of compatible solution or use premixed solution. Give premixed frozen solutions of drug in D_5W only by intermittent or continuous I.V. infusion.
- If I.V. therapy lasts longer than 3 days, alternate injection sites. Use of small I.V. needles in larger veins may be preferable.
- Reconstituted drug is stable for 24 hours at room temperature and 96 hours if refrigerated.

⊗ **Incompatibilities**

Aminoglycosides, amiodarone, amobarbital, ascorbic acid injection, bleomycin, calcium gluconate, cimetidine, colistimethate, hydrocortisone, idarubicin, lidocaine, norepinephrine, oxytetracycline, pentobarbital sodium, polymyxin B, ranitidine, tetracycline, theophylline, vitamin B complex with C.

Contraindications and cautions

- Contraindicated in patients hypersensitive to other cephalosporins.
- Use cautiously in patients with a history of sensitivity to penicillin because of cross-allergic reaction, and in patients with renal impairment.

Lifespan: In pregnant and breast-feeding women, use cautiously.

Adverse reactions

CNS: dizziness, headache, malaise, paresthesia.
GI: abdominal cramps, anal pruritus, anorexia, *diarrhea,* dyspepsia, glossitis, nausea, oral candidiasis, ***pseudomembranous colitis,*** vomiting, tenesmus.
GU: genital pruritus and candidiasis, vaginitis.
Hematologic: anemia, eosinophilia, ***leukopenia, thrombocytopenia, transient neutropenia.***
Respiratory: dyspnea.
Skin: injection site reactions (pain, induration, abscess, tissue sloughing), *maculopapular and erythematous rashes,* **Stevens-Johnson syndrome,** *urticaria.*
Other: hypersensitivity reactions (***anaphylaxis,*** serum sickness).

Interactions

Drug-drug. *Probenecid:* May inhibit excretion and increase level of cefazolin. Monitor patient.

Effects on lab test results

- May increase ALT, AST, alkaline phosphatase, bilirubin, GGT, and LDH levels.
- May increase eosinophil count. May decrease neutrophil, WBC, and platelet counts.
- May cause false-positive urine glucose determinations with copper sulfate tests (Clinitest).

Pharmacokinetics

Absorption: Unknown after I.M. use.
Distribution: Wide. CSF penetration is poor. 74% to 86% protein-bound.
Metabolism: None.
Excretion: Mainly in urine. *Half-life:* About 1 to 2 hours.

Route	Onset	Peak	Duration
I.V.	Immediate	Immediate	Unknown
I.M.	Unknown	1–2 hr	Unknown

Action

Chemical effect: Inhibits cell-wall synthesis, promoting osmotic instability; usually bactericidal.

Therapeutic effect: Hinders or kills susceptible bacteria.

Available forms

Infusion: 500 mg/50 ml, 1 g/50 ml
Powder for injection: 500 mg, 1 g

NURSING PROCESS

Assessment

- Assess patient's infection before therapy and regularly thereafter.
- Before giving first dose, obtain specimen for culture and sensitivity tests. Begin therapy pending test results.
- Before giving first dose, ask patient about previous reactions to cephalosporins or penicillin.
- If adverse GI reactions occur, monitor patient's hydration.
- Assess patient's and family's knowledge of drug therapy.

Nursing diagnoses

- Ineffective protection related to bacteria susceptible to drug
- Risk for deficient fluid volume related to drug-induced adverse GI reactions
- Deficient knowledge related to drug therapy

Planning and implementation

- Because of long duration of effect, most infections can be treated with q-8-hour use.
- After reconstitution, inject I.M. drug without further dilution (not as painful as other cephalosporins). Inject deep into large muscle mass, such as gluteus maximus or lateral aspect of thigh.

ALERT: Don't confuse with other cephalosporins with similar-sounding names.

Patient teaching

- Tell patient to report adverse reactions.

Evaluation

- Patient is free from infection.
- Patient maintains adequate hydration.
- Patient and family state understanding of drug therapy.

cefdinir

(SEF-dih-neer)

Omnicef

Pharmacologic class: third-generation cephalosporin
Therapeutic class: antibiotic
Pregnancy risk category: B

Indications and dosages

▶ **Mild to moderate infections caused by susceptible strains of microorganisms for conditions of community-acquired pneumonia and uncomplicated skin and skin-structure infections.** *Adults and children older than age 12:* Give 300 mg P.O. q 12 hours for 10 days.
Children ages 6 months to 12 years: For uncomplicated skin and skin-structure infections, 7 mg/kg P.O. q 12 hours for 10 days; maximum daily dosage, 600 mg.

▶ **Acute exacerbations of chronic bronchitis; acute bacterial otitis media; acute maxillary sinusitis.** *Adults and children older than age 12:* Give 300 mg P.O. q 12 hours for 10 days or 600 mg P.O. q 24 hours for 10 days.
Children ages 6 months to 12 years: 7 mg/kg P.O. q 12 hours for 10 days or 14 mg/kg P.O. q 24 hours for 10 days, up to a maximum dose of 600 mg daily.

▶ **Pharyngitis, tonsillitis.** *Adults and children older than age 12:* Give 300 mg P.O. q 12 hours for 5 to 10 days or 600 mg P.O. q 24 hours for 10 days.
Children ages 6 months to 12 years: 7 mg/kg P.O. q 12 hours for 5 to 10 days or 14 mg/kg P.O. q 24 hours for 10 days, up to a maximum dosage of 600 mg daily.

Adjust-a-dose: For patients with renal impairment, if creatinine clearance is less than 30 ml/minute, reduce adult dosage to 300 mg P.O. once daily; for children, reduce to 7 mg/kg up to 300 mg P.O. once daily. In patients receiving long-term hemodialysis, dosage is 300 mg or 7 mg/kg P.O. at end of each dialysis session and subsequently q other day.

Contraindications and cautions

- Contraindicated in patients hypersensitive to cephalosporins.
- Use cautiously in patients hypersensitive to penicillin because of risk of cross-sensitivity

with other beta-lactam antibiotics. Also use cautiously in patients with history of colitis or renal impairment.

Lifespan: In breast-feeding women, use cautiously. In children younger than age 6 months, safety and effectiveness haven't been established.

Adverse reactions

CNS: headache.
GI: abdominal pain, *diarrhea,* nausea, vomiting.
GU: vaginal candidiasis, vaginitis.
Skin: rash.

Interactions

Drug-drug. *Antacids containing aluminum or magnesium, iron supplements, multivitamins containing iron:* May decrease cefdinir's absorption and bioavailability. Give such preparations 2 hours before or after cefdinir dose.
Probenecid: May inhibit the renal excretion of cefdinir. Monitor patient.

Effects on lab test results

- May increase GGT, alkaline phosphatase, and urine protein levels.
- May increase RBC count.

Pharmacokinetics

Absorption: Bioavailability of drug is about 21% after 300-mg capsule dose, 16% after 600-mg capsule dose, and 25% for suspension.
Distribution: 60% to 70% protein-bound.
Metabolism: Not appreciably metabolized; activity results mainly from parent drug.
Excretion: Mainly by renal excretion. *Half-life:* 1¾ hours.

Route	Onset	Peak	Duration
P.O.	Unknown	2–4 hr	Unknown

Action

Chemical effect: Kills bacteria by inhibiting cell-wall synthesis.
Therapeutic effect: Is stable in the presence of some beta-lactamase enzymes, causing some microorganisms resistant to penicillins and cephalosporins to be susceptible to this drug.

Available forms

Capsules: 300 mg
Suspension: 125 mg/5 ml, 250 mg/5 ml

NURSING PROCESS

Assessment

- Before giving first dose, obtain specimen for culture and sensitivity tests. Begin therapy pending test results.
- Before giving first dose, ask patient about previous reactions to cephalosporins or penicillin.
- Monitor patient for symptoms of superinfection.
- Assess patient with diarrhea carefully because pseudomembranous colitis has been reported with drug.
- Assess patient's and family's knowledge of drug therapy.

Nursing diagnoses

- Ineffective protection related to susceptible bacteria
- Risk for deficient fluid volume related to drug-induced adverse GI reactions
- Deficient knowledge related to drug therapy

Planning and implementation

- If allergic reaction is suspected, notify prescriber; stop drug and give emergency care.

ALERT: Don't confuse with other cephalosporins with similar-sounding names.

Patient teaching

- If patient takes an antacid or iron supplement, instruct him to take it 2 hours before or after cefdinir.
- Inform patient with diabetes that each teaspoon of suspension contains 2.86 g of sucrose.
- Tell patient that drug may be taken with or without food.
- Advise patient to report severe diarrhea or diarrhea accompanied by abdominal pain.
- Tell patient to promptly report adverse reactions or symptoms of superinfection.

Evaluation

- Patient is free from infection.
- Patient maintains adequate hydration.
- Patient and family state understanding of drug therapy.

C

cefditoren pivoxil

(sef-da-TOR-en pa-VOX-ill)
Spectracef

Pharmacologic class: semisynthetic third-generation cephalosporin
Therapeutic class: antibiotic
Pregnancy risk category: B

Indications and dosages

▶ **Acute bacterial exacerbation of chronic bronchitis caused by *Haemophilus influenzae, Haemophilus parainfluenzae, Streptococcus pneumoniae* (penicillin-susceptible strains only), or *Moraxella catarrhalis.*** *Adults and children age 12 and older:* 400 mg P.O. b.i.d. with meals for 10 days.

▶ **Pharyngitis, tonsillitis, and uncomplicated skin and skin-structure infections caused by *Streptococcus pyogenes.*** *Adults and children age 12 and older:* 200 mg P.O. b.i.d. with meals for 10 days.

Adjust-a-dose: For patients with renal impairment, if creatinine clearance is 30 to 49 ml/minute, don't give more than 200 mg b.i.d. If creatinine clearance is less than 30 ml/minute, give 200 mg daily.

Contraindications and cautions

- Contraindicated in patients hypersensitive to drug, other cephalosporins, and penicillins. Also contraindicated in patients with carnitine deficiency or inborn errors of metabolism that may result in significant carnitine deficiency. Because tablets contain sodium caseinate, a milk protein, don't give them to patients hypersensitive to milk protein (distinct from those with lactose intolerance).
- Use cautiously in patients with renal impairment. Drug is dialyzable.
- Not recommended for prolonged antibiotic therapy.

Lifespan: In breast-feeding women, use cautiously because cephalosporins appear in breast milk. In children younger than age 12, safety and effectiveness haven't been established.

Adverse reactions

CNS: headache.
GI: abdominal pain, *colitis, diarrhea,* dyspepsia, hepatic dysfunction (including cholestasis), nausea, vomiting.
GU: hematuria, ***nephrotoxicity,*** vaginal candidiasis.
Hematologic: anemia.
Metabolic: hyperglycemia.
Skin: ***Stevens-Johnson syndrome, toxic epidermal necrolysis.***
Other: *hypersensitivity reactions* (including serum sickness, rash, fever, ***anaphylaxis***).

Interactions

Drug-drug. *Aluminum antacids, H_2-receptor antagonists, magnesium:* May reduce cefditoren absorption. Avoid use together. If used together, separate doses.
Oral anticoagulants: May increase bleeding time. Monitor PT and patient closely for unusual bleeding or bruising.
Probenecid: May increases cefditoren level. Avoid use together.
Drug-food. *Moderate- to high-fat meals:* May increase drug bioavailability. Advise patient to take drug with meals.

Effects on lab test results

- May increase liver enzyme levels. May decrease carnitine and hemoglobin levels and hematocrit.
- May decrease PT.
- May cause a false-positive direct Coombs test result and false-positive reaction for glucose in urine using copper reduction tests (those involving Benedict solution, Fehling solution, or Clinitest tablets).

Pharmacokinetics

Absorption: From the GI tract and hydrolyzed by esterases to cefditoren.
Distribution: Wide based on volume of distribution. CSF penetration is unknown. About 88% protein-bound.
Metabolism: Not appreciably metabolized.
Excretion: Unchanged mainly in urine by glomerular filtration and tubular secretion. *Half-life:* 1½ to 2 hours in patients with normal renal function.

Route	Onset	Peak	Duration
P.O.	Unknown	1½–3 hr	Unknown

Action

Chemical effect: Mainly bactericidal. Drug acts by adhering to bacterial penicillin-binding proteins, thereby inhibiting cell-wall synthesis. Active against many gram-positive and gram-negative organisms.

Therapeutic effects: Kills susceptible bacteria.

Available forms

Tablets: 200 mg

NURSING PROCESS

Assessment

- Assess patient's history for hypersensitivity to cefditoren, cephalosporins, penicillins, or other contraindications for drug therapy.
- Monitor patient for overgrowth or recurrence of resistant organisms with prolonged or repeated drug therapy.
- Because cefditoren has been linked to *Clostridium difficile*–related colitis, monitor patient for diarrhea during therapy.
- Monitor patient for hypersensitivity reactions during therapy, as well as for any unusual bleeding or bruising.
- Assess patient's and family's knowledge of drug therapy.

Nursing diagnoses

- Noncompliance related to completion of 10-day antibiotic regimen
- Risk for infection with nonsusceptible bacteria or fungi related to prolonged or repeated drug therapy
- Deficient knowledge related to cephalosporin therapy

Planning and implementation

- Give drug with a meal to increase its bioavailability.
- If patient develops diarrhea after receiving cefditoren, keep in mind that this drug may cause pseudomembranous colitis. Notify prescriber immediately because colitis may be fatal.
- Don't use this drug if patient needs prolonged therapy.
- Signs and symptoms of overdose may include nausea, vomiting, epigastric distress, diarrhea, and seizures. Treat symptoms and provide supportive therapy.
- If hypersensitivity or allergic reaction occurs, stop drug and provide emergency care.

ALERT: Don't confuse drug with other cephalosporins with similar-sounding names.

Patient teaching

- Instruct patient to take drug with food to increase its absorption.
- Caution patient not to take drug with an H_2 antagonist or an antacid because it may reduce cefditoren absorption. If an H_2 antagonist or antacid must be used, instruct the patient to take it 2 hours before or after cefditoren.
- Explain to patient the importance of taking drug for the prescribed duration, despite feeling better, to prevent any future drug resistance.
- Instruct patient to immediately stop taking drug and call prescriber if any adverse reactions develop, such as rash, hives, difficulty breathing, unusual bleeding or bruising, or diarrhea.
- Encourage patient to contact prescriber if signs and symptoms of infection don't improve after several days of therapy.
- Urge patient not to miss any doses. However, if patient misses a dose, instruct him to take the missed dose as soon as he remembers and to wait 12 hours before taking the next dose. Tell him not to double the dose.

Evaluation

- Patient completes prescribed 10-day therapy.
- Patient doesn't experience any adverse reactions during drug therapy.
- Patient and family state understanding of drug therapy and importance of completing entire drug regimen as prescribed.

cefixime

(sef-IKS-eem)

Suprax

Pharmacologic class: third-generation cephalosporin

Therapeutic class: antibiotic

Pregnancy risk category: B

Indications and dosages

▶ **Uncomplicated UTIs caused by *Escherichia coli* and *Proteus mirabilis;* otitis media caused by *Haemophilus influenzae* (beta-lactamase–positive and –negative strains), *Moraxella catarrhalis,* and *Streptococcus pyo-***

***genes;* pharyngitis and tonsillitis caused by *S. pyogenes;* acute bronchitis and acute exacerbations of chronic bronchitis caused by *Streptococcus pneumoniae* and *H. influenzae* (beta-lactamase–positive and –negative strains).**
Adults and children older than age 12 weighing more than 50 kg (110 lb): 400 mg P.O. daily or 200 mg q 12 hours.
Children age 6 months to 12 years: 8 mg/kg P.O. daily in one or two divided doses. For otitis media, use suspension only.

▶ **Uncomplicated gonorrhea caused by *Neisseria gonorrhoeae.*** *Adults:* 400 mg P.O. as single dose.

▶ **Disseminated gonococcal infections.** *Adults:* 400 mg P.O. b.i.d. after initial therapy with I.M. or I.V. antibiotics for a total of 7 days of therapy.

Adjust-a dose: For patients with creatinine clearance of 21 to 60 ml/minute or who are receiving hemodialysis, give 75% of standard dose. For patients with creatinine clearance of 20 ml/minute or less, or who are receiving continuous ambulatory peritoneal dialysis, give 50% of standard dose.

Contraindications and cautions

- Contraindicated in patients hypersensitive to drug, other cephalosporins, or beta-lactam antibiotics.
- Use cautiously in patients with renal dysfunction or history of sensitivity to penicillin.

Lifespan: Use cautiously in pregnant or breast-feeding women.

Adverse reactions

CNS: dizziness, fatigue, headache, insomnia, malaise, nervousness, somnolence.
GI: abdominal pain, *diarrhea,* dyspepsia, flatulence, loose stools, nausea, ***pseudomembranous colitis,*** vomiting.
GU: genital candidiasis, genital pruritus, vaginitis.
Hematologic: eosinophilia, ***leukopenia, thrombocytopenia.***
Hepatic: ***hepatitis,*** jaundice.
Skin: pruritus, rash, ***Stevens-Johnson syndrome,*** urticaria.
Other: drug fever, *hypersensitivity reactions* (serum sickness, ***anaphylaxis***).

Interactions

Drug-drug. *Nifedipine:* May increase cefixime level. Avoid use together.
Probenecid: May inhibit excretion and increase level of cefixime. Monitor patient.
Salicylates: May displace cefixime from protein-binding sites. Significance is unknown.

Effects on lab test results

- May increase BUN, creatinine, ALT, AST, alkaline phosphatase, bilirubin, GGT, and LDH levels.
- May increase eosinophil count. May decrease platelet and WBC counts.
- May cause false-positive results in urine glucose tests that use copper sulfate (Clinitest).

Pharmacokinetics

Absorption: Good.
Distribution: Wide. Enters CSF in patients with inflamed meninges. 65% protein-bound.
Metabolism: 50% of drug.
Excretion: Mainly in urine. *Half-life:* 3 to 4 hours.

Route	Onset	Peak	Duration
P.O.	Unknown	2–6 hr	Unknown

Action

Chemical effect: Inhibits cell-wall synthesis, promoting osmotic instability; usually bactericidal.
Therapeutic effect: Hinders or kills bacteria, including *H. influenzae, M. catarrhalis, S. pyogenes, S. pneumoniae, E. coli,* and *P. mirabilis.*

Available forms

Oral suspension: 100 mg/5 ml (after reconstitution)
Tablets: 400 mg

NURSING PROCESS

Assessment

- Assess patient's infection before therapy and regularly thereafter.
- Before giving first dose, obtain specimen for culture and sensitivity tests. Begin therapy pending test results.
- Before giving first dose, ask patient about previous reactions to cephalosporins or penicillin.
- Be alert for adverse reactions and drug interactions.

• If adverse GI reactions occur, monitor patient's hydration.
• Assess patient's and family's knowledge of drug therapy.

Nursing diagnoses
• Ineffective protection related to bacteria susceptible to drug
• Risk for deficient fluid volume related to drug-induced adverse GI reactions
• Deficient knowledge related to drug therapy

Planning and implementation
• To prepare oral suspension, add required amount of water to powder in two portions. Shake well after each addition. After mixing, suspension is stable for 14 days (no need to refrigerate). Keep tightly closed. Shake well before using.
ALERT: Don't confuse with other cephalosporins with similar-sounding names.

Patient teaching
• Tell patient to take drug exactly as prescribed, even after he feels better.
• Tell patient to call prescriber if rash develops.
• Teach patient how to store drug.

Evaluation
• Patient is free from infection.
• Patient maintains adequate hydration.
• Patient and family state understanding of drug therapy.

cefotaxime sodium
(sef-oh-TAKS-eem SOH-dee-um)
Claforan

Pharmacologic class: third-generation cephalosporin
Therapeutic class: antibiotic
Pregnancy risk category: B

Indications and dosages
▶ **Perioperative prophylaxis in contaminated surgery.** *Adults:* 1 g I.V. or I.M. 30 to 90 minutes before surgery. In patients undergoing cesarean birth, give dose as soon as umbilical cord is clamped, followed by 1 g I.V. or I.M. 6 and 12 hours later.
▶ **Serious infections of lower respiratory and urinary tracts, CNS, skin, bone, and joints; gynecologic and intra-abdominal infections; bacteremia; and septicemia. Susceptible microorganisms include streptococci (including *Streptococcus pneumoniae* and *Streptococcus pyogenes*), *Staphylococcus aureus* (penicillinase- and non–penicillinase-producing), *Staphylococcus epidermidis, Escherichia coli, Klebsiella, Haemophilus influenzae, Enterobacter, Proteus,* and *Peptostreptococcus.* Pelvic inflammatory disease‡.** *Adults:* Usual dosage is 1 g I.V. or I.M. q 6 to 12 hours. Up to 12 g daily can be given in life-threatening infections.
Children weighing at least 50 kg (110 lb): Usual adult dose but don't exceed 12 g daily.
Children ages 1 month to 12 years weighing less than 50 kg: Give 50 to 180 mg/kg I.V. or I.M. daily in four to six divided doses.
Neonates ages 1 to 4 weeks: Give 50 mg/kg I.V. q 8 hours.
Neonates up to age 1 week: Give 50 mg/kg I.V. q 12 hours.
▶ **Disseminated gonococcal infection‡.** *Adults:* 1 g I.V. q 8 hours.
Neonates and infants: 25 to 50 mg/kg I.V. q 8 to 12 hours for 7 days, or 50 to 100 mg/kg I.M or I.V. q 12 hours for 7 days.
▶ **Gonococcal ophthalmia‡.** *Adults:* 500 mg I.V. q.i.d.
Neonates: 100 mg I.V. or I.M. for one dose; may continue until ocular cultures are negative at 48 to 72 hours.
▶ **Gonorrheal meningitis or arthritis‡.** *Neonates and infants:* 25 to 50 mg/kg I.V. q 8 to 12 hours for 10 to 14 days. Or 50 to 100 mg/kg I.M. or I.V. q 12 hours for 10 to 14 days.
Adjust-a-dose: For patients with renal impairment, if creatinine clearance is less than 20 ml/minute, give half the usual dose at the usual interval.

I.V. administration
• Reconstitute infusion vials with 50 to 100 ml D_5W or normal saline solution.
• For direct injection, reconstitute 500-mg, 1-g, or 2-g vials with 10-ml sterile water for injection. Solutions containing 1 g/14 ml are isotonic.
• Inject drug into large vein or into tubing of free-flowing I.V. solution over 3 to 5 minutes.
• Infuse drug over 20 to 30 minutes. Interrupt flow of primary I.V. solution during infusion.

C

⊗ **Incompatibilities**
Allopurinol, aminoglycosides, aminophylline, azithromycin, doxapram, filgrastim, fluconazole, hetastarch, pentamidine isethionate, sodium bicarbonate injection, vancomycin.

Contraindications and cautions

- Contraindicated in patients hypersensitive to drug or other cephalosporins.
- Use cautiously in patients with history of sensitivity to penicillin and in patients with renal impairment.

Lifespan: In pregnant or breast-feeding women, use cautiously.

Adverse reactions

CNS: dizziness, fever, headache, malaise, paresthesia.
GI: abdominal cramps, anal pruritus, anorexia, *diarrhea,* dyspepsia, glossitis, nausea, oral candidiasis, ***pseudomembranous colitis,*** tenesmus, vomiting.
GU: candidiasis, pruritus.
Hematologic: ***agranulocytosis,*** eosinophilia, hemolytic anemia, ***thrombocytopenia, transient neutropenia.***
Respiratory: dyspnea.
Skin: maculopapular and erythematous rashes, urticaria.
Other: hypersensitivity reactions (serum sickness, ***anaphylaxis***); pain, induration, sterile abscesses, warmth, tissue sloughing at injection site; phlebitis, thrombophlebitis with I.V. injection.

Interactions

Drug-drug. *Aminoglycosides:* May increase risk of nephrotoxicity. Monitor renal function closely.
Probenecid: May inhibit excretion and increase level of cefotaxime. Use together cautiously.

Effects on lab test results

- May increase ALT, AST, alkaline phosphatase, bilirubin, GGT, and LDH levels. May decrease hemoglobin level and hematocrit.
- May increase eosinophil count. May decrease neutrophil, platelet, and granulocyte counts.
- May cause false-positive urine glucose determinations with copper sulfate tests (Clinitest).

Pharmacokinetics

Absorption: Unknown after I.M. use.
Distribution: Wide. Adequate CSF penetration when meninges are inflamed. 13% to 38% protein-bound.
Metabolism: Partially to active metabolite.
Excretion: Mainly in urine. *Half-life:* 1 to 2 hours.

Route	Onset	Peak	Duration
I.V.	Immediate	Immediate	8–12 hr
I.M.	Unknown	30 min	8–12 hr

Action

Chemical effect: Inhibits cell-wall synthesis, promoting osmotic instability; usually bactericidal.
Therapeutic effect: Hinders or kills susceptible bacteria.

Available forms

Infusion: 1 g, 2 g
Injection: 500 mg, 1 g, 2 g

NURSING PROCESS

Assessment

- Assess patient's infection before therapy and regularly thereafter.
- Before giving first dose, obtain specimen for culture and sensitivity tests. Begin therapy pending test results.
- Before giving first dose, ask patient about previous reactions to cephalosporins or penicillin.
- Be alert for adverse reactions and drug interactions.
- If adverse GI reactions occur, monitor patient's hydration.
- Assess patient's and family's knowledge of drug therapy.

Nursing diagnoses

- Ineffective protection related to bacteria susceptible to drug
- Risk for deficient fluid volume related to drug-induced adverse GI reactions
- Deficient knowledge related to drug therapy

Planning and implementation

- For I.M. use, inject deep into large muscle mass, such as gluteus maximus or lateral aspect of thigh.

ALERT: Don't confuse with other cephalosporins with similar-sounding names.

Patient teaching

- Tell patient to report adverse reactions.
- Teach patient to report decrease in urinary output. May have to decrease total daily dose.

Evaluation

- Patient is free from infection.
- Patient maintains adequate hydration.
- Patient and family state understanding of drug therapy.

cefoxitin sodium

(sef-OKS-ih-tin SOH-dee-um)
Mefoxin

Pharmacologic class: second-generation cephalosporin
Therapeutic class: antibiotic
Pregnancy risk category: B

Indications and dosages

▶ **Serious infections of respiratory and GU tracts; skin, soft-tissue, bone, and joint infections; bloodstream and intra-abdominal infections caused by susceptible *Escherichia coli* and other coliform bacteria, *Staphylococcus aureus* (penicillinase- and non–penicillinase-producing), *Staphylococcus epidermidis*, streptococci, *Klebsiella, Haemophilus influenzae*, and *Bacteroides*, including *B. fragilis;* and perioperative prophylaxis.** *Adults:* 1 to 2 g I.V. q 6 to 8 hours for uncomplicated forms of infection. In life-threatening infections, up to 12 g daily.
Children and infants age 3 months and older: 80 to 160 mg/kg I.V. daily in four to six equally divided doses. Maximum daily dose is 12 g.
▶ **Prophylactic use in surgery.** *Adults:* 2 g I.V. 30 to 60 minutes before surgery; then 2 g I.V. q 6 hours for 24 hours. If used in cesarean birth give 2 g I.V. as soon as cord is clamped. Or, if a three-dose regimen is used, give 2 g I.V. as soon as cord is clamped, then 2 g I.V. 4 and 8 hours after first dose.
Children older than age 3 months: 30 to 40 mg/kg I.V. 30 to 60 minutes before surgery; then 30 to 40 mg/kg q 6 hours for 24 hours.
Adjust-a-dose: For patients with renal impairment, if creatinine clearance is 30 to 50 ml/minute, give 1 to 2 g q 8 to 12 hours; if clearance is 10 to 29 ml/minute, give 1 to 2 g q 12 to 24 hours; and if clearance is 5 to 10 ml/minute, give 500 mg to 1 g q 12 to 24 hours. If clearance is less than 5 ml/minute, give 500 mg to 1 g q 24 to 48 hours. For hemodialysis patients, give loading dose of 1 to 2 g after each session, and maintenance dose as indicated above.

I.V. administration

- Reconstitute 1 g with at least 10 ml of sterile water for injection and 2 g with 10 to 20 ml of sterile water for injection. Solutions of D_5W and normal saline solution for injection also can be used.
- For direct injection, inject reconstituted drug into large vein or into tubing of free-flowing I.V. solution over 3 to 5 minutes.
- For intermittent infusion, add reconstituted drug to 50 or 100 ml D_5W, $D_{10}W$, or normal saline solution for injection. Interrupt flow of primary I.V. solution during infusion.
- Assess I.V. site often for thrombophlebitis.
- After reconstitution, drug may be stored for 24 hours at room temperature or refrigerated for 1 week.

⊗ **Incompatibilities**
Aminoglycosides, filgrastim, hetastarch, pentamidine isethionate, ranitidine.

Contraindications and cautions

- Contraindicated in patients hypersensitive to drug or other cephalosporins.
- Use cautiously in patients with history of sensitivity to penicillin and in patients with renal impairment.

Lifespan: In pregnant or breast-feeding women, use cautiously.

Adverse reactions

CNS: fever.
CV: hypotension, *phlebitis, thrombophlebitis* with I.V. injection.
GI: *diarrhea,* ***pseudomembranous colitis.***
GU: ***acute renal failure.***
Hematologic: eosinophilia, hemolytic anemia, ***thrombocytopenia, transient neutropenia.***
Respiratory: dyspnea.
Skin: *erythematous and maculopapular rashes, urticaria.*
Other: hypersensitivity reactions (***anaphylaxis,*** serum sickness).

Interactions

Drug-drug. *Nephrotoxic drugs:* May increase risk of nephrotoxicity. Monitor renal function closely.
Probenecid: May inhibit excretion and increase level of cefoxitin. Sometimes used for this effect.

Effects on lab test results

- May increase ALT, AST, alkaline phosphatase, bilirubin, and LDH levels. May decrease hemoglobin level and hematocrit.
- May increase eosinophil count. May decrease neutrophil and platelet counts.
- May cause false-positive urine glucose determinations with copper sulfate tests (Clinitest).

Pharmacokinetics

Absorption: Unknown.
Distribution: Wide. CSF penetration is poor. 50% to 80% protein-bound.
Metabolism: Insignificant (about 2%).
Excretion: Mainly in urine. *Half-life:* About ½ to 1 hour.

Route	Onset	Peak	Duration
I.V.	Immediate	Immediate	Unknown

Action

Chemical effect: Inhibits cell-wall synthesis, promoting osmotic instability; usually bactericidal.
Therapeutic effect: Hinders or kills susceptible bacteria.

Available forms

Infusion: 1 g, 2 g
Injection: 1 g, 2 g

NURSING PROCESS

Assessment

- Assess patient's infection before therapy and regularly thereafter.
- Before giving first dose, obtain specimen for culture and sensitivity tests. Begin therapy pending test results.
- Before giving first dose, ask patient about previous reactions to cephalosporins or penicillin.
- Be alert for adverse reactions and drug interactions.
- If adverse GI reactions occur, monitor patient's hydration.
- Assess patient's and family's knowledge of drug therapy.

Nursing diagnoses

- Ineffective protection related to bacteria susceptible to drug
- Risk for deficient fluid volume related to drug-induced adverse GI reactions
- Deficient knowledge related to drug therapy

Planning and implementation

- Patients with renal impairment need dosage adjustment.

ALERT: Don't confuse with other cephalosporins with similar-sounding names.

Patient teaching

- Tell patient to report adverse reactions and signs and symptoms of superinfection promptly.
- Instruct patient to notify prescriber if he has loose stools or diarrhea.

Evaluation

- Patient is free from infection.
- Patient maintains adequate hydration.
- Patient and family state understanding of drug therapy.

cefpodoxime proxetil

(sef-poh-DOKS-eem PROKS-eh-til)
Vantin

Pharmacologic class: third-generation cephalosporin
Therapeutic class: antibiotic
Pregnancy risk category: B

Indications and dosages

▶ **Acute, community-acquired pneumonia caused by non–beta-lactamase–producing strains of *Haemophilus influenzae* or *Streptococcus pneumoniae*.** *Adults and children age 12 and older:* 200 mg P.O. q 12 hours for 14 days.

▶ **Acute bacterial exacerbation of chronic bronchitis caused by *S. pneumoniae, H. influenzae* (non–beta-lactamase–producing strains), or *Moraxella catarrhalis*.** *Adults and children age 12 and older:* 200 mg P.O. q 12 hours for 10 days.

▶ **Uncomplicated gonorrhea in men and women; rectal gonococcal infections in**

women. *Adults and children age 12 and older:* 200 mg P.O. as single dose. Follow with doxycycline 100 mg P.O. b.i.d. for 7 days.

▶ **Uncomplicated skin and skin-structure infections caused by *Staphylococcus aureus* or *Streptococcus pyogenes*.** *Adults and children age 12 and older:* 400 mg P.O. q 12 hours for 7 to 14 days.

▶ **Acute otitis media caused by *S. pneumoniae, H. influenzae,* or *M. catarrhalis*.** *Children ages 2 months to 12 years:* 5 mg/kg (not to exceed 200 mg) P.O. q 12 hours for 5 days.

▶ **Pharyngitis or tonsillitis caused by *S. pyogenes*.** *Adults and children age 12 and older:* 100 mg P.O. q 12 hours for 5 to 10 days. *Children ages 2 months to 12 years:* 5 mg/kg (not to exceed 100 mg) P.O. q 12 hours for 10 days.

▶ **Uncomplicated UTIs caused by *Escherichia coli, Klebsiella pneumoniae, Proteus mirabilis,* or *Staphylococcus saprophyticus*.** *Adults and children age 12 and older:* 100 mg P.O. q 12 hours for 7 days.

▶ **Mild to moderate acute maxillary sinusitis caused by *H. influenzae, S. pneumoniae,* or *M. catarrhalis*.** *Adults and children age 12 and older:* 200 mg P.O. q 12 hours for 10 days. *Children ages 2 months to 12 years:* 5 mg/kg P.O. q 12 hours for 10 days; maximum dosage is 200 mg.

Adjust-a-dose: For patients with renal impairment, if creatinine clearance is less than 30 ml/minute, increase dosage interval to q 24 hours. For patients undergoing dialysis, give dose three times weekly, after dialysis.

Contraindications and cautions

- Contraindicated in patients hypersensitive to drug or other cephalosporins.
- Use cautiously in patients with history of hypersensitivity to penicillin (risk of cross-sensitivity) and in patients receiving nephrotoxic drugs (other cephalosporins have had nephrotoxic potential).

Lifespan: In pregnant or breast-feeding women, use cautiously.

Adverse reactions

CNS: headache.
GI: abdominal pain, *diarrhea,* nausea, vomiting.
GU: vaginal fungal infections.
Skin: rash.
Other: hypersensitivity reactions ***(anaphylaxis)***.

Interactions

Drug-drug. *Antacids, H_2-receptor antagonists:* May decrease cefpodoxime absorption. Avoid use together.
Probenecid: May decrease cefpodoxime excretion. Monitor patient for toxicity.
Drug-food. *Any food:* May increase absorption of tablets. Give tablet form with food. Oral suspension isn't affected by food.

Effects on lab test results

- May increase BUN, creatinine, AST, ALT, GGT, alkaline phosphatase, bilirubin, and LDH levels. May decrease albumin, potassium, sodium, and hemoglobin levels and hematocrit. May increase or decrease glucose level.
- May increase eosinophil, WBC, granulocyte, lymphocyte, basophil, and platelet counts. May prolong PT and PTT.
- May cause false-positive urine glucose determinations with copper sulfate tests (Clinitest). May cause positive Coombs' test.

Pharmacokinetics

Absorption: From GI tract.
Distribution: Widely into most body tissues and fluids except CSF.
Metabolism: Drug is de-esterified to its active metabolite, cefpodoxime. **Excretion:** Mainly in urine. *Half-life:* 2 to 3 hours.

Route	Onset	Peak	Duration
P.O.	Unknown	2–3 hr	Unknown

Action

Chemical effect: Inhibits cell-wall synthesis, promoting osmotic instability; usually bactericidal.
Therapeutic effect: Hinders or kills susceptible bacteria.

Available forms

Oral suspension: 50 mg/5 ml, 100 mg/5 ml in 100-ml bottles
Tablets (film-coated): 100 mg, 200 mg

NURSING PROCESS

Assessment

- Assess patient's infection before therapy and regularly thereafter.

• Before giving first dose, obtain specimen for culture and sensitivity tests. Begin therapy pending test results.
• Before giving first dose, ask patient about previous reactions to cephalosporins or penicillin.
• Be alert for adverse reactions and drug interactions.
• If adverse GI reactions occur, monitor patient's hydration.
• Assess patient's and family's knowledge of drug therapy.

Nursing diagnoses

• Ineffective protection related to bacteria susceptible to drug
• Risk for deficient fluid volume related to drug-induced adverse GI reactions
• Deficient knowledge related to drug therapy

Planning and implementation

• Give tablets with food to minimize adverse GI reactions and increase absorption.
• Oral suspension may be given without regard to food; shake well before using.
• Store suspension in refrigerator (36° to 46° F [2° to 8° C]). Discard unused portion after 14 days.
ALERT: Don't confuse with other cephalosporins with similar-sounding names.

Patient teaching

• Advise patient to take tablets with meals to minimize GI adverse effects. Tell patient that oral suspension may be given without regard to food.
• Tell patient to take drug exactly as prescribed, even after he feels better.
• Instruct patient to notify prescriber if rash develops.
• Teach patient how to store drug.
• Instruct patient to notify prescriber about a reduction in urinary output, especially if patient takes a diuretic.

Evaluation

• Patient is free from infection.
• Patient maintains adequate hydration.
• Patient and family state understanding of drug therapy.

C

cefprozil

(SEF-pruh-zil)
Cefzil

Pharmacologic class: second-generation cephalosporin
Therapeutic class: antibiotic
Pregnancy risk category: B

Indications and dosages

▶ **Pharyngitis or tonsillitis caused by *Streptococcus pyogenes*.** *Adults and children older than age 12:* Give 500 mg P.O. daily for 10 days.
Children ages 2 to 12: Give 7.5 mg/kg P.O. q 12 hours for 10 days.
▶ **Otitis media caused by *Streptococcus pneumoniae, Haemophilus influenzae,* or *Moraxella catarrhalis*.** *Infants and children ages 6 months to 12 years:* 15 mg/kg P.O. q 12 hours for 10 days.
▶ **Secondary bacterial infections of acute bronchitis and acute bacterial exacerbation of chronic bronchitis caused by *S. pneumoniae, H. influenzae,* and *M. catarrhalis*.** *Adults and children older than age 12:* Give 500 mg P.O. q 12 hours for 10 days.
▶ **Uncomplicated skin and skin-structure infections caused by *Staphylococcus aureus* or *S. pyogenes*.** *Adults and children older than age 12:* Give 250 mg P.O. b.i.d., or 500 mg daily to b.i.d. for 10 days.
Children ages 2 to 12: Give 20 mg/kg P.O. q 24 hours for 10 days. Maximum dose is 1 g P.O. daily.
▶ **Acute sinusitis caused by *S. pneumoniae, H. influenzae,* and *M. catarrhalis*.** *Adults and children older than age 12:* Give 250 mg or 500 mg P.O. q 12 hours for 10 days.
Children ages 6 months to 12 years: 7.5 mg/kg P.O. q 12 hours or 15 mg/kg P.O. daily for 10 days.
Adjust-a-dose: For patients with renal impairment, if creatinine clearance is less than 30 ml/minute, give 50% of usual dose.

Contraindications and cautions

• Contraindicated in patients hypersensitive to drug or other cephalosporins.

• Use cautiously in patients with history of sensitivity to penicillin and patients with hepatic or renal impairment.

Lifespan: In pregnant and breast-feeding women, use cautiously. Don't give children more than the recommended adult dose.

Adverse reactions

CNS: dizziness, headache, hyperactivity, insomnia, nervousness.
GI: abdominal pain, diarrhea, *nausea*, vomiting.
GU: genital pruritus, vaginitis.
Hematologic: eosinophilia.
Skin: rash, urticaria.
Other: *hypersensitivity reactions* (***anaphylaxis,*** serum sickness), superinfection.

Interactions

Drug-drug. *Aminoglycosides:* May increase risk of nephrotoxicity. Monitor patient closely. *Probenecid:* May inhibit excretion and increase level of cefprozil. Monitor patient.

Effects on lab test results

• May increase BUN, creatinine, ALT, AST, alkaline phosphatase, bilirubin, and LDH levels.
• May increase eosinophil count. May decrease WBC, leukocyte, and platelet counts.
• May cause false-positive results in urine glucose tests that use copper sulfate (Clinitest).

Pharmacokinetics

Absorption: About 95% from GI tract.
Distribution: About 35% protein-bound. Distributed into various body tissues and fluids.
Metabolism: Probably by the liver.
Excretion: Mainly in urine. *Half-life:* 1¼ hours in patients with normal renal function; 2 hours in patients with impaired hepatic function; and 5¼ to 6 hours in patients with end-stage renal disease.

Route	Onset	Peak	Duration
P.O.	Unknown	Unknown	Unknown

Action

Chemical effect: Inhibits cell-wall synthesis, promoting osmotic instability; usually bactericidal.
Therapeutic effect: Hinders or kills susceptible bacteria.

Available forms

Oral suspension: 125 mg/5 ml, 250 mg/5 ml
Tablets: 250 mg, 500 mg

NURSING PROCESS

Assessment

• Assess patient's infection before therapy and regularly thereafter.
• Before giving first dose, obtain specimen for culture and sensitivity tests. Begin therapy pending test results.
• Before giving first dose, ask patient about previous reactions to cephalosporins or penicillin.
• Be alert for adverse reactions and drug interactions.
• If adverse GI reactions occur, monitor patient's hydration.
• Monitor patient's renal function.
• Assess patient's and family's knowledge of drug therapy.

Nursing diagnoses

• Ineffective protection related to bacteria susceptible to drug
• Risk for deficient fluid volume related to drug-induced adverse GI reactions
• Deficient knowledge related to drug therapy

Planning and implementation

• Give drug after hemodialysis is completed because procedure removes drug.
• Refrigerate reconstituted suspension (stable for 14 days). Keep tightly closed, and shake well before using.
ALERT: Don't confuse with other cephalosporins with similar-sounding names.

Patient teaching

• Tell patient to shake suspension well before measuring dose.
• Advise patient to take drug as prescribed, even after he feels better.
• Inform patient that oral suspensions are bubble-gum flavor to improve palatability and promote compliance in children. Tell him to refrigerate reconstituted suspension and to discard any unused portion after 14 days.
• Advise elderly patients also receiving diuretic therapy to notify prescriber of decreased urine output.

Evaluation

- Patient is free from infection.
- Patient maintains adequate hydration.
- Patient and family state understanding of drug therapy.

ceftazidime

(sef-TAZ-ih-deem)

Ceptaz, Fortaz, Tazicef, Tazidime

Pharmacologic class: third-generation cephalosporin

Therapeutic class: antibiotic

Pregnancy risk category: B

Indications and dosages

▶ **Serious infections of lower respiratory and urinary tracts; gynecologic, intra-abdominal, CNS, and skin infections; bacteremia; and septicemia. Among susceptible microorganisms are streptococci (including *Streptococcus pneumoniae* and *Streptococcus pyogenes*), *Staphylococcus aureus, Escherichia coli, Klebsiella, Proteus, Enterobacter, Haemophilus influenzae, Pseudomonas,* and some strains of *Bacteroides.*** *Adults and children older than age 12:* Give 1 g I.V. or I.M. q 8 to 12 hours; maximum 6 g daily for life-threatening infections. *Children ages 1 month to 12 years:* 25 to 50 mg/kg I.V. q 8 hours. Maximum 6 g daily. *Neonates age 4 weeks or younger:* 30 mg/kg I.V. q 12 hours.

▶ **Uncomplicated UTI.** *Adults:* 250 mg I.V. or I.M. q 12 hours.

▶ **Complicated UTI.** *Adults:* 500 mg I.V. or I.M. q 8 to 12 hours.

▶ **Uncomplicated pneumonia or mild skin and skin-structure infection.** *Adults:* 0.5 to 1 g I.V. or I.M. q 8 hours.

▶ **Bone and joint infection.** *Adults:* 2 g I.V. q 12 hours.

▶ **Empiric therapy in febrile neutropenic patients‡.** *Adults:* 100 mg/kg I.V. daily in three divided doses; or 2 g I.V. q 8 hours either alone or with an aminoglycoside, such as amikacin.

Adjust-a-dose: For patients with renal impairment, if creatinine clearance is 31 to 50 ml/minute, give 1 g q 12 hours; if clearance is 16 to 30 ml/minute, give 1 g q 24 hours; if clearance is 6 to 15 ml/minute, give 500 mg q 24 hours; if clearance is less than 5 ml/minute, give 500 mg q 48 hours. Drug is removed by hemodialysis; give a supplemental dose of drug after each dialysis session.

I.V. administration

- Reconstitute solutions containing sodium carbonate with sterile water for injection. Add 5 ml to 500-mg vial or 10 ml to 1- or 2-g vial. Shake well to dissolve drug.
- Carbon dioxide is released during dissolution, and positive pressure will develop in vial. Don't add air to the vial when removing dose.
- Reconstitute solutions containing arginine with 10 ml sterile water for injection; this formulation won't release gas bubbles.
- Infuse drug over 15 to 30 minutes.

⊗ **Incompatibilities**

Aminoglycosides, aminophylline, amiodarone, amphotericin B cholesteryl sulfate complex, azithromycin, clarithromycin, fluconazole, idarubicin, midazolam, pentamidine isethionate, ranitidine hydrochloride, sargramostim, sodium bicarbonate solutions, vancomycin.

Contraindications and cautions

- Contraindicated in patients hypersensitive to drug or other cephalosporins.
- Use cautiously in patients with history of sensitivity to penicillin and in patients with renal impairment.

Lifespan: In pregnant and breast-feeding women, use cautiously. In children age 12 and younger, safety and effectiveness haven't been established.

Adverse reactions

CNS: dizziness, fever, headache, ***seizures.***

GI: abdominal cramps, diarrhea, dysgeusia, nausea, ***pseudomembranous colitis,*** vomiting.

GU: candidiasis, genital pruritus.

Hematologic: ***agranulocytosis,*** eosinophilia, ***leukopenia, thrombocytosis.***

Respiratory: dyspnea.

Skin: *maculopapular and erythematous rashes, urticaria.*

Other: hypersensitivity reactions (serum sickness, ***anaphylaxis***); *pain, induration, sterile abscesses, tissue sloughing at injection site; phlebitis, thrombophlebitis with I.V. injection.*

Interactions

Drug-drug. *Chloramphenicol:* May have an antagonistic effect. Avoid use together.

Effects on lab test results

- May increase ALT, AST, alkaline phosphatase, bilirubin, and LDH levels. May decrease hemoglobin level and hematocrit.
- May increase eosinophil count. May decrease WBC and granulocyte counts. May increase or decrease platelet count.
- May cause false-positive urine glucose determinations with copper sulfate tests (Clinitest).

Pharmacokinetics

Absorption: Unknown with I.M. use.
Distribution: Wide, including CSF (unlike most other cephalosporins). 5% to 24% protein-bound.
Metabolism: None.
Excretion: Mainly in urine. *Half-life:* About 1½ to 2 hours.

Route	Onset	Peak	Duration
I.V.	Immediate	Immediate	Unknown
I.M.	Unknown	≤ 1 hr	Unknown

Action

Chemical effect: Inhibits cell-wall synthesis, promoting osmotic instability; usually bactericidal.
Therapeutic effect: Hinders or kills susceptible bacteria.

Available forms

Infusion: 1 g, 2 g in 50-ml and 100-ml vials (premixed)
Injection (with arginine): 1 g, 2 g, 6 g
Injection (with sodium carbonate): 500 mg, 1 g, 2 g

NURSING PROCESS

Assessment

- Assess patient's infection before therapy and regularly thereafter.
- Before giving first dose, obtain specimen for culture and sensitivity tests. Begin therapy pending test results.
- Before giving first dose, ask patient about previous reactions to cephalosporins or penicillin.
- Be alert for adverse reactions and drug interactions.
- If adverse GI reactions occur, monitor patient's hydration.
- Assess patient's and family's knowledge of drug therapy.

Nursing diagnoses

- Ineffective protection related to bacteria susceptible to drug
- Risk for deficient fluid volume related to drug-induced adverse GI reactions
- Deficient knowledge related to drug therapy

Planning and implementation

- Inject deep into large muscle mass, such as gluteus maximus or lateral aspect of thigh.

ALERT: Commercially available forms contain either sodium carbonate (Fortaz, Tazicef, Tazidime) or arginine (Ceptaz) to facilitate dissolution of drug.

ALERT: Don't confuse with other cephalosporins with similar-sounding names.

Patient teaching

- Tell patient to report adverse reactions.
- Instruct patient to immediately report to prescriber any change in urinary output. Dose may need to be reduced to compensate for decreased excretion.

Evaluation

- Patient is free from infection.
- Patient maintains adequate hydration.
- Patient and family state understanding of drug therapy.

ceftibuten

(sef-tih-BYOO-tin)
Cedax

Pharmacologic class: third-generation cephalosporin
Therapeutic class: antibiotic
Pregnancy risk category: B

Indications and dosages

▶ **Acute bacterial exacerbation of chronic bronchitis caused by *Haemophilus influenzae, Moraxella catarrhalis,* or penicillin-susceptible strains of *Streptococcus pneumoniae.*** *Adults and children age 12 and older:* 400 mg P.O. daily for 10 days.

▶ **Pharyngitis and tonsillitis caused by *Streptococcus pyogenes,* acute bacterial otitis media caused by *H. influenzae, M. catarrhalis,* or *S. pyogenes.*** *Adults and children age 12 and older:* 400 mg capsules P.O. daily for 10 days.

C

Children younger than age 12: Give 9 mg/kg capsules P.O. daily for 10 days. Maximum daily dose is 400 mg.
Children weighing more than 45 kg (99 lb): Give 400 mg oral suspension P.O. daily for 10 days.
Children older than age 6 months and weighing 45 kg or less: 9 mg/kg oral suspension P.O. daily for 10 days. Maximum daily dose is 400 mg.
Adjust-a-dose: For patients with renal impairment, if creatinine clearance is 30 to 49 ml/minute, give 4.5 mg/kg or 200 mg P.O. q 24 hours; if creatinine clearance is 5 to 29 ml/minute, give 2.25 mg/kg or 100 mg P.O. q 24 hours. For patients undergoing hemodialysis, give 400 mg P.O. as a single dose at the end of each dialysis session.

Contraindications and cautions

- Contraindicated in patients hypersensitive to cephalosporins.
- Use cautiously in patients with history of hypersensitivity to penicillin and in patients with GI disease or renal impairment.

Lifespan: In pregnant women, use cautiously. In breast-feeding women, use cautiously; it isn't known whether drug appears in breast milk. In elderly patients, use cautiously. Monitor their renal function, and adjust dosage p.r.n.

Adverse reactions

CNS: aphasia, dizziness, headache, psychosis.
GI: abdominal pain, diarrhea, dyspepsia, loose stools, nausea, ***pseudomembranous colitis,*** vomiting.
GU: renal dysfunction, ***toxic nephropathy.***
Hematologic: ***agranulocytosis, aplastic anemia, hemolytic anemia, hemorrhage, neutropenia, pancytopenia.***
Hepatic: hepatic cholestasis.
Skin: ***Stevens-Johnson syndrome.***
Other: allergic reaction, ***anaphylaxis,*** drug fever.

Interactions

Drug-food. *Any food:* May decrease bioavailability of drug. Give drug 2 hours before or 1 hour after a meal.

Effects on lab test results

- May increase ALT, AST, alkaline phosphatase, bilirubin, and BUN and creatinine levels. May decrease hemoglobin level and hematocrit.
- May increase eosinophil count. May decrease leukocyte count. May increase or decrease platelet count.

Pharmacokinetics

Absorption: Rapid.
Distribution: 65% protein-bound.
Metabolism: By the kidneys.
Excretion: Mainly in urine. *Half-life:* 2 to 2½ hours.

Route	Onset	Peak	Duration
P.O.	Unknown	2–4 hr	Unknown

Action

Chemical effect: Exerts bacterial action by binding to essential target proteins of the bacterial cell wall, thus inhibiting cell-wall synthesis.
Therapeutic effect: Hinders or kills susceptible bacteria.

Available forms

Capsules: 400 mg
Oral suspension: 90 mg/5 ml, 180 mg/5 ml

NURSING PROCESS

Assessment

- Before giving first dose, obtain specimen for culture and sensitivity tests. Begin therapy pending test results.
- Monitor patient for superinfection.
- Obtain specimen for *Clostridium difficile* in patient who develops diarrhea after therapy.
- Assess patient's and family's knowledge of drug therapy.

Nursing diagnoses

- Ineffective protection related to bacteria susceptible to drug
- Deficient knowledge related to drug therapy

Planning and implementation

- To prepare oral suspension, tap bottle to loosen powder. Follow chart supplied by manufacturer for mixing instructions. Suspension is stable for 14 days if refrigerated.
- Shake suspension well before use.
- Stop giving the drug and notify prescriber if allergic reaction occurs.

ALERT: Don't confuse with other cephalosporins with similar-sounding names.

Patient teaching
- Instruct patient to take drug as prescribed, even if he feels better.
- Instruct patient using oral suspension to shake bottle before use and to take it at least 2 hours before or 1 hour after a meal.
- Instruct patient to store oral suspension in the refrigerator, with lid tightly closed, and to discard unused drug after 14 days.
- Warn breast-feeding woman that it's unclear whether drug appears in breast milk.
- Tell patient with diabetes that suspension has 1 g sucrose per teaspoon.

Evaluation
- Patient is free from infection.
- Patient and family state understanding of drug therapy.

ceftizoxime sodium
(sef-tih-ZOKS-eem SOH-dee-um)
Cefizox

Pharmacologic class: third-generation cephalosporin
Therapeutic class: antibiotic
Pregnancy risk category: B

Indications and dosages
▶ **Serious infections of lower respiratory and urinary tracts, gynecologic infections, bacteremia, septicemia, meningitis, intra-abdominal infections, bone and joint infections, and skin infections. Among susceptible microorganisms are *Streptococcus pneumoniae, Streptococcus pyogenes, Staphylococcus aureus* (penicillinase- and non–penicillinase-producing), *Staphylococcus epidermidis, Escherichia coli, Klebsiella, Haemophilus influenzae, Enterobacter, Proteus,* some *Pseudomonas,* and *Peptostreptococcus.***
Adults: 1 to 2 g I.V. or I.M. q 8 to 12 hours. In life-threatening infections, 3 to 4 g I.V. q 8 hours.
Children older than age 6 months: 50 mg/kg I.V. q 6 to 8 hours. For serious infections, up to 200 mg/kg daily in divided doses may be used. Maximum, 12 g daily.
Adjust-a-dose: For patients with renal impairment, if creatinine clearance is 50 to 79 ml/minute, give 500 mg q 8 hours for less severe infections or 750 mg to 1.5 g q 8 hours for life-threatening infections. If clearance is 5 to 49 ml/minute, give 250 to 500 mg q 12 hours for less severe infections or 500 mg to 1 g q 12 hours for life-threatening infections. If clearance is less than 5 ml/minute or patient undergoes hemodialysis, give 500 mg q 48 hours or 250 q 24 hours for less severe infections or 500 mg to 1 g q 48 hours or 500 mg q 24 hours for life-threatening infections.

I.V. administration
- To reconstitute powder, add 5 ml sterile water to 500-mg vial, 10 ml to 1-g vial, or 20 ml to 2-g vial. Reconstitute piggyback vials with 50 to 100 ml of normal saline solution or D_5W. Shake vial well.
- Inject directly into vein over 3 to 5 minutes or slowly into I.V. tubing with free-flowing compatible solution.
- Give intermittent infusion over 15 to 30 minutes.
- After reconstitution or dilution, solutions are stable for 1 day at room temperature and 4 days if refrigerated.

⊗ **Incompatibilities**
Aminoglycosides.

Contraindications and cautions
- Contraindicated in patients hypersensitive to drug or other cephalosporins.
- Use cautiously in patients with history of sensitivity to penicillin and in patients with renal impairment.

Lifespan: In pregnant and breast-feeding women, use cautiously. In infants younger than age 6 months, safety and effectiveness haven't been established.

Adverse reactions
CNS: dizziness, fever, headache, malaise, paresthesia.
GI: abdominal cramps, anal pruritus, anorexia, diarrhea, dyspepsia, glossitis, nausea, ***pseudomembranous colitis,*** tenesmus, vomiting.
GU: candidiasis, pruritus.
Hematologic: eosinophilia, hemolytic anemia, ***thrombocytopenia, transient neutropenia.***
Respiratory: dyspnea.
Skin: *erythematous and maculopapular rashes, urticaria.*
Other: hypersensitivity reactions (***anaphylaxis,*** serum sickness); induration, sterile abscesses,

tissue sloughing at injection site; phlebitis, thrombophlebitis with I.V. injection.

Interactions

Drug-drug. *Probenecid:* May inhibit excretion and increase level of ceftizoxime. Sometimes used for this effect.

Effects on lab test results

• May increase BUN, creatinine, ALT, AST, alkaline phosphatase, bilirubin, GGT, and LDH levels. May decrease albumin, protein, and hemoglobin levels and hematocrit.
• May increase eosinophil count. May decrease PT and RBC, WBC, platelet, granulocyte, and neutrophil counts.
• May cause false-positive urine glucose determinations with copper sulfate tests (Clinitest).

Pharmacokinetics

Absorption: Unknown with I.M. use.
Distribution: Wide. Unlike many other cephalosporins, ceftizoxime has good CSF penetration and achieves adequate level in inflamed meninges. 28% to 31% protein-bound.
Metabolism: None.
Excretion: Mainly in urine. *Half-life:* About 1½ to 2 hours.

Route	Onset	Peak	Duration
I.V.	Immediate	Immediate	Unknown
I.M.	Unknown	½–1½ hr	Unknown

Action

Chemical effect: Inhibits cell-wall synthesis, promoting osmotic instability; usually bactericidal.
Therapeutic effect: Hinders or kills susceptible bacteria.

Available forms

Infusion: 1 g, 2 g in 100-mg vials or in 50 ml of D_5W
Injection: 500 mg, 1 g, 2 g

NURSING PROCESS

Assessment

• Assess patient's infection before therapy and regularly thereafter.
• Before giving first dose, obtain specimen for culture and sensitivity tests. Begin therapy pending test results.
• Before giving first dose, ask patient about previous reactions to cephalosporins or penicillin.
• Be alert for adverse reactions and drug interactions.
• If adverse GI reactions occur, monitor patient's hydration.
• Assess patient's and family's knowledge of drug therapy.

Nursing diagnoses

• Ineffective protection related to bacteria susceptible to drug
• Risk for deficient fluid volume related to drug-induced adverse GI reactions
• Deficient knowledge related to drug therapy

Planning and implementation

• Inject I.M. dose deep into large muscle mass, such as gluteus maximus or lateral aspect of thigh. Divide doses of 2 g or more, and give divided doses at two different sites.
ALERT: Don't confuse drug with other cephalosporins that have similar-sounding names.

Patient teaching

• Tell patient to report adverse reactions and signs and symptoms of superinfection promptly.
• Instruct patient to report discomfort at the I.V. site.
• Tell patient to notify prescriber if loose stools or diarrhea occur.

Evaluation

• Patient is free from infection.
• Patient maintains adequate hydration.
• Patient and family state understanding of drug therapy.

ceftriaxone sodium

(sef-trigh-AKS-ohn SOH-dee-um)
Rocephin

Pharmacologic class: third-generation cephalosporin
Therapeutic class: antibiotic
Pregnancy risk category: B

Indications and dosages

▶ **Uncomplicated gonococcal vulvovaginitis.** *Adults and children older than age 12 or weighing more than 45 kg (99 lb):* 125 to 250 mg I.M. as single dose, followed by either 100 mg of

doxycycline P.O. q 12 hours for 7 days, or a single oral dose of azithromycin 1 g.
Children younger than age 12 or weighing less than 45 kg: 125 mg I.M. as a single dose.

▶ **Serious infections of lower respiratory and urinary tracts; gynecologic, bone, joint, intra-abdominal, and skin infections; bacteremia; and septicemia caused by susceptible microorganisms such as *Streptococcus pneumoniae, Streptococcus pyogenes, Staphylococcus aureus, Staphylococcus epidermidis, Escherichia coli, Klebsiella, Haemophilus influenzae, Neisseria meningitides, Neisseria gonorrhoeae, Enterobacter, Proteus, Pseudomonas, Peptostreptococcus,* and *Serratia marcescens.*** *Adults and children older than age 12:* Give 1 to 2 g I.V. or I.M. daily or in equally divided doses; maximum 4 g daily for 4 to 14 days depending on severity of infection.
Children age 12 and younger: 50 to 75 mg/kg, maximum 2 g daily, given in divided doses q 12 hours.

▶ **Meningitis.** *Adults and children:* Initially, 100 mg/kg I.M. or I.V. (maximum 4 g); thereafter, 100 mg/kg I.M. or I.V. given once daily or in divided doses q 12 hours. Maximum, 4 g, for 7 to 14 days.

▶ **Preoperative prophylaxis.** *Adults:* 1 g I.V. as single dose 30 minutes to 2 hours before surgery.

▶ **Acute bacterial otitis media.** *Children:* 50 mg/kg I.M. as a single dose; maximum I.M. dose is 1 g.

▶ **Persisting or relapsing otitis media in children‡.** *Children and infants age 3 months and older:* 50 mg/kg I.M daily for 3 days.

▶ **Sexually transmitted epididymitis, pelvic inflammatory disease‡.** *Adults:* 250 mg I.M. as a single dose; follow up with other antibiotics.

▶ **Anti-infectives for sexual assault victims‡.** *Adults:* 125 mg I.M. as a single dose given with other antibiotics.

▶ **Lyme disease‡.** *Adults:* 2 g I.V. daily for 14 to 28 days.

I.V. administration

- Reconstitute with sterile water for injection, normal saline solution for injection, D_5W or $D_{10}W$ injection, or combination of saline solution and dextrose injection and other compatible solutions.
- Reconstitute by adding 2.4 ml of diluent to 250-mg vial, 4.8 ml to 500-mg vial, 9.6 ml to 1-g vial, and 19.2 ml to 2-g vial. All reconstituted solutions yield concentration that averages 100 mg/ml.
- After reconstitution, dilute further to desired concentration for intermittent infusion.
- Dilutions are stable for 24 hours at room temperature.

⊗ **Incompatibilities**
Aminoglycosides, aminophylline, azithromycin, clindamycin phosphate, filgrastim, fluconazole, labetalol, lidocaine hydrochloride, pentamidine isethionate, theophylline, vancomycin, vinorelbine tartrate.

Contraindications and cautions

- Contraindicated in patients hypersensitive to drug or other cephalosporins.
- Use cautiously in patients with history of sensitivity to penicillin.

Lifespan: In pregnant and breast-feeding women, use cautiously.

Adverse reactions

CNS: dizziness, fever, headache.
GI: diarrhea, dysgeusia, nausea, ***pseudomembranous colitis,*** vomiting.
GU: genital pruritus and candidiasis.
Hematologic: eosinophilia, ***leukopenia, thrombocytosis.***
Skin: pain, induration, and tenderness at injection site; phlebitis; *rash.*
Other: hypersensitivity reactions (serum sickness, ***anaphylaxis***).

Interactions

Drug-drug. *Aminoglycosides:* May have additive effect. Monitor drug level and adjust dosage as needed.
Probenecid: May shorten half-life of ceftriaxone in large doses. Avoid use together.
Quinolones: May have synergistic effect against *S. pneumoniae.* Use together against this organism is recommended.
Drug-lifestyle. *Alcohol use:* May cause disulfiram-like reaction. Discourage use together.

Effects on lab test results

- May increase BUN, ALT, AST, alkaline phosphatase, bilirubin, and LDH levels.
- May increase eosinophil and platelet counts. May decrease WBC count.

• May cause false-positive urine glucose determinations with copper sulfate tests (Clinitest).

Pharmacokinetics

Absorption: Unknown.
Distribution: Wide. Unlike many other cephalosporins, ceftriaxone has good CSF penetration. 58% to 96% protein-bound.
Metabolism: Partial.
Excretion: Mainly in urine, minimally in bile. *Half-life:* About 5½ to 11 hours.

Route	Onset	Peak	Duration
I.V.	Immediate	Immediate	Unknown
I.M.	Unknown	1½–4 hr	Unknown

Action

Chemical effect: Inhibits cell-wall synthesis, promoting osmotic instability; usually bactericidal.
Therapeutic effect: Hinders or kills susceptible bacteria.

Available forms

Infusion: 1 g, 2 g
Injection: 250 mg, 500 mg, 1 g, 2 g

NURSING PROCESS

Assessment

• Assess patient's infection before therapy and regularly thereafter.
• Before giving first dose, obtain specimen for culture and sensitivity tests. Begin therapy pending test results.
• Before giving first dose, ask patient about previous reactions to cephalosporins or penicillin.
• Be alert for adverse reactions and drug interactions.
• If adverse GI reactions occur, monitor patient's hydration.
• Assess patient's and family's knowledge of drug therapy.

Nursing diagnoses

• Ineffective protection related to bacteria susceptible to drug
• Risk for deficient fluid volume related to drug-induced adverse GI reactions
• Deficient knowledge related to drug therapy

Planning and implementation

• Inject deep into large muscle mass, such as gluteus maximus or lateral aspect of thigh. As needed, use lidocaine 1% without epinephrine to dilute for I.M. use.
ALERT: Don't confuse with other cephalosporins with similar-sounding names.

Patient teaching

• Tell patient to promptly report adverse reactions and signs and symptoms of superinfection.
• Instruct patient to report pain at the I.V. site.
• Tell patient to notify prescriber if loose stools or diarrhea occur.

Evaluation

• Patient is free from infection.
• Patient maintains adequate hydration.
• Patient and family state understanding of drug therapy.

cefuroxime axetil

(sef-yoor-OKS-eem AKS-eh-til)
Ceftin

cefuroxime sodium

Zinacef

Pharmacologic class: second-generation cephalosporin
Therapeutic class: antibiotic
Pregnancy risk category: B

Indications and dosages

▶ **Serious lower respiratory tract infection, UTI, skin or skin-structure infections, bone or joint infection, septicemia, meningitis, and gonorrhea.** *Adults and children age 13 and older:* 750 mg to 1.5 g cefuroxime sodium I.M. or I.V. q 8 hours for 5 to 10 days. For life-threatening infections and infections caused by less susceptible organisms, 1.5 g I.M. or I.V. q 6 hours; for bacterial meningitis, up to 3 g I.V. q 8 hours.
Children ages 3 months to 12 years: 50 to 100 mg/kg/day cefuroxime sodium I.M. or I.V. in equally divided doses q 6 to 8 hours. For more severe or serious infections, use 100 mg/kg/day, not to exceed maximum adult dosage. For bacterial meningitis, 200 to 240 mg/kg cefuroxime sodium I.V. in divided doses q 6 to 8 hours.

▶ **Perioperative prevention.** *Adults:* 1.5 g I.V. 30 to 60 minutes before surgery; in lengthy operations, 750 mg I.V. or I.M. q 8 hours. For open-heart surgery, 1.5 g I.V. at induction of anesthesia and then q 12 hours for a total dose of 6 g.

▶ **Bacterial exacerbations of chronic bronchitis or secondary bacterial infection of acute bronchitis.** *Adults:* 250 or 500 mg P.O. b.i.d. for 10 days (chronic bronchitis) or 5 to 10 days (acute bronchitis).

▶ **Acute bacterial maxillary sinusitis.** *Adults and children age 13 and older:* 250 mg P.O. b.i.d. for 10 days.

Children ages 3 months to 12 years: 30 mg/kg/day oral suspension divided b.i.d. for 10 days.

▶ **Pharyngitis and tonsillitis.** *Adults and children age 13 and older:* 250 mg P.O. b.i.d. for 10 days.

Children ages 3 months to 12 years: 125 mg P.O. b.i.d. for 10 days. For children who can't swallow tablets whole, give 20 mg/kg daily of oral suspension divided b.i.d. for 10 days. Maximum daily dose for suspension is 500 mg.

▶ **Otitis media.** *Children ages 3 months to 12 years:* 250 mg P.O. b.i.d. for 10 days. For children who can't swallow tablets whole, give 30 mg/kg/day of oral suspension divided b.i.d. for 10 days. Maximum daily dose for suspension is 1,000 mg.

▶ **Uncomplicated skin and skin-structure infection.** *Adults and children age 13 and older:* 250 mg or 500 mg P.O. b.i.d. for 10 days.

▶ **Uncomplicated UTI.** *Adults:* 125 or 250 mg P.O. b.i.d. for 7 to 10 days.

▶ **Uncomplicated gonorrhea.** *Adults:* 1.5 g I.M. with 1 g probenecid P.O. for one dose. Or, 1 g P.O. as a single dose.

▶ **Early Lyme disease.** *Adults and children age 13 and older:* 500 mg P.O. b.i.d. for 20 days.

▶ **Impetigo.** *Children ages 3 months to 12 years:* 30 mg/kg/day of oral suspension divided b.i.d. for 10 days. Maximum daily dose, 1,000 mg.

Adjust-a-dose: In adults with creatinine clearance of 10 to 20 ml/minute, give 750 mg I.M. or I.V. q 12 hours; if creatinine clearance is less than 10 ml/minute, give 750 mg I.M. or I.V. q 24 hours.

I.V. administration

- For each 750-mg vial of Zinacef, reconstitute with 8 ml sterile water for injection; for each 1.5-g vial, reconstitute with 16 ml. In each case, withdraw entire contents of vial for dose.
- For direct injection, inject into large vein or into tubing of free-flowing I.V. solution over 3 to 5 minutes.
- For intermittent infusion, add reconstituted drug to 100 ml D_5W, normal saline solution for injection, or other compatible I.V. solution. Infuse over 15 to 60 minutes.

⊗ **Incompatibilities**

Aminoglycosides, ciprofloxacin, clarithromycin, filgrastim, fluconazole, midazolam, ranitidine, sodium bicarbonate injection, vinorelbine tartrate.

Contraindications and cautions

- Contraindicated in patients hypersensitive to drug or other cephalosporins.
- Use cautiously in patients with history of sensitivity to penicillin and in patients with renal impairment.

Lifespan: In pregnant and breast-feeding women, use cautiously. In infants younger than age 3 months, safety and effectiveness haven't been established.

Adverse reactions

CNS: dizziness, headache, malaise, paresthesia.
GI: abdominal cramps, anal pruritus, anorexia, diarrhea, dyspepsia, glossitis, nausea, ***pseudomembranous colitis,*** tenesmus, vomiting.
GU: candidiasis, pruritus.
Hematologic: eosinophilia, hemolytic anemia, ***thrombocytopenia, transient neutropenia.***
Respiratory: dyspnea.
Skin: *erythematous and maculopapular rashes, urticaria.*
Other: hypersensitivity reactions (***anaphylaxis,*** serum sickness); pain, induration, sterile abscesses, warmth, tissue sloughing at injection site; phlebitis, thrombophlebitis with I.V. injection.

Interactions

Drug-drug. *Diuretics:* May increase risk of adverse renal reactions. Monitor renal function closely.
Probenecid: May inhibit excretion and increase level of cefuroxime. Sometimes used for this effect.

Drug-food. *Any food:* May increase drug absorption and bioavailability of suspension. Give suspension with food. Tablets may be given without regard to food.

Effects on lab test results

- May increase ALT, AST, alkaline phosphatase, bilirubin, and LDH levels. May decrease hemoglobin level and hematocrit.
- May increase eosinophil count, PT, and INR. May decrease neutrophil and platelet counts.
- May cause false-positive urine glucose determinations with copper sulfate tests (Clinitest).

Pharmacokinetics

Absorption: 37% to 52% of oral cefuroxime axetil reaches systemic circulation. Food appears to enhance absorption. Cefuroxime sodium isn't well absorbed from GI tract; absorption after I.M. use is unknown.
Distribution: Wide. CSF penetration is greater than that of most first- and second-generation cephalosporins and achieves adequate therapeutic level in inflamed meninges. 33% to 50% protein-bound.
Metabolism: None.
Excretion: Mainly in urine. *Half-life:* 1 to 2 hours.

Route	Onset	Peak	Duration
P.O.	Unknown	2–3 hr	Unknown
I.V.	Unknown	Immediate	Unknown
I.M.	Unknown	15–60 min	Unknown

Action

Chemical effect: Inhibits cell-wall synthesis, promoting osmotic instability; usually bactericidal.
Therapeutic effect: Hinders or kills susceptible bacteria, including many gram-positive organisms and enteric gram-negative bacilli.

Available forms

cefuroxime axetil
Suspension: 125 mg/5 ml, 250 mg/5 ml
Tablets: 125 mg, 250 mg, 500 mg
cefuroxime sodium
Infusion: 750 mg, 1.5 g premixed, frozen solution
Injection: 750 mg, 1.5 g

NURSING PROCESS

Assessment

- Assess patient's infection before therapy and regularly thereafter.
- Before giving first dose, obtain specimen for culture and sensitivity tests. Begin therapy pending test results.
- Before giving first dose, ask patient about previous reactions to cephalosporins or penicillin.
- Be alert for adverse reactions and drug interactions.
- If adverse GI reactions occur, monitor patient's hydration.
- Assess patient's and family's knowledge of drug therapy.

Nursing diagnoses

- Ineffective protection related to bacteria susceptible to drug
- Risk for deficient fluid volume related to drug-induced adverse GI reactions
- Deficient knowledge related to drug therapy

Planning and implementation

- Food enhances absorption of cefuroxime axetil.
- Cefuroxime axetil is available only in tablet form, which may be crushed for patients who can't swallow tablets. Tablets may be dissolved in small amounts of apple, orange, or grape juice or chocolate milk. However, drug has bitter taste that's difficult to mask, even with food.

ALERT: Cefuroxime tablets and oral suspensions aren't bioequivalent and can't be substituted on a milligram-for-milligram basis.

- Inject deep into large muscle mass, such as gluteus maximus or lateral aspect of thigh. Before I.M. injection, aspirate to avoid injection into a blood vessel.
- Cefuroxime isn't considered the drug of choice for meningitis or gonorrhea infections.

ALERT: Don't confuse with other cephalosporins with similar-sounding names.

Patient teaching

- Instruct patient to take drug exactly as prescribed, even after he feels better.
- Advise patient to take oral drug with food to enhance absorption. Explain that tablets may be crushed, but drug has bitter taste that's difficult to mask, even with food.
- Tell patient to report adverse reactions.

Evaluation

- Patient is free from infection.
- Patient maintains adequate hydration.
- Patient and family state understanding of drug therapy.

celecoxib

(seh-leh-COKS-ib)

Celebrex

Pharmacologic class: cyclooxygenase-2 (COX-2) inhibitor
Therapeutic class: anti-inflammatory
Pregnancy risk category: C (D in third trimester)

Indications and dosages

▶ **Relief of signs and symptoms of osteoarthritis.** *Adults:* 200 mg P.O. daily as a single dose or divided equally b.i.d.

▶ **Relief of signs and symptoms of rheumatoid arthritis.** *Adults:* 100 to 200 mg P.O. b.i.d.

▶ **Relief of signs and symptoms of juvenile rheumatoid arthritis.** *Children age 2 and older weighing 10 to 25 kg (22 to 55 lb):* 50-mg capsule P.O. b.i.d.

Children age 2 and older weighing more than 25 kg: 100-mg capsule P.O. b.i.d.

▶ **Relief of signs and symptoms of ankylosing spondylitis.** *Adults:* 200 mg P.O. once daily or divided b.i.d. If no response after 6 weeks, may increase to 400 mg daily. If no response after 6 more weeks, consider different treatment.

▶ **Adjunct to familial adenomatous polyposis to reduce the number of adenomatous colorectal polyps.** *Adults:* 400 mg P.O. b.i.d. with food for up to 6 months.

▶ **Acute pain and primary dysmenorrhea.** *Adults:* Initially, give 400 mg P.O., followed by an additional 200-mg dose on the first day, if needed. On subsequent days, 200 mg P.O. b.i.d. p.r.n.

Adjust-a-dose: For patients with moderate hepatic impairment, reduce dose by 50%; don't use in patients with severe hepatic impairment. For elderly patients who weigh less than 50 kg (110 lb), use the lowest recommended dose.

Contraindications and cautions

- Contraindicated in patients hypersensitive to drug, sulfonamides, aspirin or other NSAIDs; patients with severe hepatic or renal impairment; and patients with perioperative pain after coronary artery bypass graft surgery.
- Use cautiously in patients with known or suspected history of poor CYP2C9 metabolism and in patients with history of ulcers, GI bleeding, dehydration, anemia, symptomatic liver disease, hypertension, edema, heart failure, or asthma. Also use cautiously in patients who smoke or drink alcohol frequently, take oral corticosteroids or anticoagulants, or are at a high risk for CV complications, such as those who have recently had heart surgery.

Lifespan: In women in third trimester of pregnancy, avoid use. In elderly and debilitated patients, use cautiously because of increased risk of GI bleeding and acute renal impairment.

Adverse reactions

CNS: dizziness, *headache,* insomnia, ***stroke.***
CV: hypertension, ***MI,*** peripheral edema.
EENT: pharyngitis, rhinitis, sinusitis.
GI: *abdominal pain,* diarrhea, *dyspepsia,* flatulence, *nausea,* ***GI bleeding.***
Metabolic: hyperchloremia, hypophosphatemia.
Musculoskeletal: back pain.
Respiratory: upper respiratory tract infection.
Skin: ***erythema multiforme, exfoliative dermatitis,*** rash, ***Stevens-Johnson syndrome, toxic epidermal necrolysis.***
Other: accidental injury.

Interactions

Drug-drug. *ACE inhibitors:* May decrease antihypertensive effects. Monitor patient's blood pressure.
Aluminum- and magnesium-containing antacids: May decrease celecoxib level. Separate doses.
Aspirin: May increase risk of ulcers; low aspirin dosages can be used safely to prevent CV events. Monitor patient for GI bleeding.
Diuretics: May decrease sodium excretion of diuretics, leading to sodium retention. Monitor patient for swelling and increased blood pressure.
Fluconazole: May increase celecoxib level. Use lowest effective dose.
Lithium: May increase lithium level. Monitor lithium level.
Warfarin: May increase PT. Monitor PT and INR, and check for bleeding.

C

Drug-herb. *Dong quai, feverfew, garlic, ginger, ginkgo, horse chestnut, red clover:* May increase the risk of bleeding. Discourage use together.

Drug-lifestyle. *Chronic alcohol use, smoking:* May increase risk of GI irritation or bleeding. Check for evidence of bleeding, and discourage use together.

Effects on lab test results

• May increase BUN, ALT, AST, and chloride levels. May decrease phosphate level.

Pharmacokinetics

Absorption: Level peaks in about 3 hours. If patient receives multiple doses, expect steady-state level within 5 days. Elderly patients have higher level than younger adults.

Distribution: Extensive. Highly protein-bound, mainly to albumin.

Metabolism: By CYP2C9. No active metabolites have been identified.

Excretion: Mainly through hepatic metabolism, with less than 3% as unchanged drug in urine and feces. *Half-life:* 11 hours.

Route	Onset	Peak	Duration
P.O.	Unknown	3 hr	Unknown

Action

Chemical effect: May selectively inhibit COX-2, decreasing prostaglandin synthesis.

Therapeutic effect: Relieves pain and inflammation in joints and smooth muscle tissue.

Available forms

Capsules: 100 mg, 200 mg, 400 mg

NURSING PROCESS

Assessment

• Assess patient for appropriateness of therapy. Drug must be used cautiously in patients with history of ulcers or GI bleeding, advanced renal disease, dehydration, anemia, symptomatic liver disease, hypertension, edema, heart failure, or asthma.

ALERT: Obtain accurate list of patient's allergies. Patients may be allergic to celecoxib if they're allergic and have had anaphylactic reactions to sulfonamides, aspirin, or other NSAIDs.

• Assess patient for risk factors for GI bleeding, including corticosteroid or anticoagulant therapy, long-term NSAID therapy, smoking, alcoholism, older age, and poor overall health. Patients with a history of ulcers or GI bleeding are at higher risk for GI bleeding while taking NSAIDs such as celecoxib.

• Monitor patient for evidence of overt and occult bleeding.

ALERT: Assess patient's CV status, CV risk factors, and history, particularly for recent heart surgery, MI, or stroke, before starting therapy. NSAIDs may increase the risk of serious thrombotic events; the risk increases with duration of use and may be higher in patients with CV disease or risk factors for it.

• Monitor patient for signs and symptoms of liver toxicity. Celecoxib may be hepatotoxic.

• Assess patient's and family's knowledge of drug therapy.

Nursing diagnoses

• Acute pain related to underlying condition
• Risk for injury related to drug-induced adverse reactions
• Deficient knowledge related to drug therapy

Planning and implementation

ALERT: Use cautiously in patients at a high risk for CV complications and in those taking the drug long term because such use may increase risk of MI and stroke.

• Although drug can be given with or without food, food may decrease GI upset.

• Before therapy, rehydrate patient.

• Although celecoxib may be used with low-dose aspirin, the combination may increase the risk of GI bleeding.

• NSAIDs such as celecoxib can cause fluid retention. Closely monitor patient who has hypertension, edema, or heart failure while taking this drug.

ALERT: Don't confuse Celebrex with Cerebyx or Celexa.

Patient teaching

• Instruct patient to immediately report to prescriber signs of GI bleeding (such as bloody vomitus, blood in urine or stool, and black, tarry stools).

ALERT: Advise patient to immediately report rash, unexplained weight gain, or edema to prescriber.

• Tell woman to notify prescriber if she becomes pregnant or is planning to become pregnant while taking this drug.
• Instruct patient to take drug with food if stomach upset occurs.
• Advise patient that all NSAIDs, including celecoxib, may adversely affect the liver. Signs and symptoms of liver toxicity include nausea, fatigue, lethargy, itching, jaundice, right upper quadrant tenderness, and flulike syndrome. Advise patient to stop therapy and seek immediate medical advice if he has any of these signs or symptoms.
• Inform patient that it may take several days before he feels consistent pain relief.

Evaluation

• Patient is free from pain.
• Patient doesn't experience injury as a result of drug-induced adverse reactions.
• Patient and family state understanding of drug therapy.

cephalexin

(sef-uh-LEK-sin)

Apo-Cephalex ♦, Biocef, Keflex, Novo-Lexin ♦, Nu-Cephalex ◇

Pharmacologic class: first-generation cephalosporin
Therapeutic class: antibiotic
Pregnancy risk category: B

Indications and dosages

▶ **Respiratory tract, GI tract, skin, soft-tissue, bone, and joint infections and otitis media caused by *Escherichia coli* and other coliform bacteria, group A beta-hemolytic streptococci, *Haemophilus influenzae, Klebsiella, Moraxella catarrhalis, Proteus mirabilis, Streptococcus pneumoniae,* and staphylococci.** *Adults:* 250 mg to 1 g P.O. q 6 hours or 500 mg q 12 hours; maximum, 4 g daily.
Children: 6 to 12 mg/kg P.O. q 6 hours (monohydrate only); maximum, 25 mg/kg q 6 hours or 4 g daily.
Adjust-a-dose: For patients with renal impairment, if creatinine clearance is 11 to 40 ml/minute, give 500 mg q 8 to 12 hours; if clearance is 5 to 10 ml/minute, give 250 mg q 12 hours; if clearance is less than 5 ml/minute, give 250 mg q 12 to 24 hours.

Contraindications and cautions

• Contraindicated in patients hypersensitive to cephalosporins.
• Use cautiously in patients hypersensitive to penicillin and in patients with renal impairment.
Lifespan: In pregnant and breast-feeding women, use cautiously.

Adverse reactions

CNS: dizziness, headache, malaise, paresthesia.
GI: abdominal cramps, anal pruritus, *anorexia, diarrhea,* dyspepsia, glossitis, *nausea,* oral candidiasis, ***pseudomembranous colitis,*** tenesmus, vomiting.
GU: candidiasis, genital pruritus, vaginitis.
Hematologic: anemia, eosinophilia, ***thrombocytopenia, transient neutropenia.***
Respiratory: dyspnea.
Skin: maculopapular and erythematous rashes, urticaria.
Other: hypersensitivity reactions (***anaphylaxis,*** serum sickness).

Interactions

Drug-drug. *Probenecid:* May increase cephalosporin level. Sometimes used for this effect.

Effects on lab test results

• May increase ALT, AST, alkaline phosphatase, bilirubin, and LDH levels. May decrease hemoglobin level and hematocrit.
• May increase eosinophil count. May decrease neutrophil and platelet counts.
• May cause false-positive urine glucose determinations with copper sulfate tests (Clinitest).

Pharmacokinetics

Absorption: Rapid and complete. Food delays but doesn't prevent complete absorption.
Distribution: Wide; CSF penetration is poor. 6% to 15% protein-bound.
Metabolism: None.
Excretion: Mainly unchanged in urine. *Half-life:* 30 minutes to 1 hour.

Route	Onset	Peak	Duration
P.O.	Unknown	≤ 1 hr	Unknown

Action

Chemical effect: Inhibits cell-wall synthesis, promoting osmotic instability; usually bactericidal.
Therapeutic effect: Hinders or kills susceptible bacteria.

Available forms

Capsules: 250 mg, 500 mg
Oral suspension: 125 mg/5 ml, 250 mg/5 ml
Tablets: 250 mg, 500 mg, 1 g

NURSING PROCESS

Assessment

- Assess patient's infection before therapy and regularly thereafter.
- Before giving first dose, obtain specimen for culture and sensitivity tests. Begin therapy pending test results.
- Before giving first dose, ask patient about previous reactions to cephalosporins or penicillin.
- Be alert for adverse reactions and drug interactions.
- If adverse GI reactions occur, monitor patient's hydration.
- Assess patient's and family's knowledge of drug therapy.

Nursing diagnoses

- Ineffective protection related to bacteria susceptible to drug
- Risk for deficient fluid volume related to drug-induced adverse GI reactions
- Deficient knowledge related to drug therapy

Planning and implementation

- To prepare oral suspension, first add required amount of water to powder in two portions. Shake well after each addition. After mixing, store in refrigerator (stable for 14 days without significant loss of potency). Keep tightly closed, and shake well before using.
- To minimize adverse GI reactions, give drug with food or milk.
- Treat group A beta-hemolytic streptococcal infections for at least 10 days.
- If giving more than 4 g daily, give initial treatment with a parenteral cephalosporin; switch to oral form when patient is stable.

ALERT: Don't confuse with other cephalosporins with similar-sounding names.

Patient teaching

- Inform patient that drug may be taken with meals.
- Instruct patient to take drug exactly as prescribed, even after he feels better.
- Tell patient to call prescriber if rash develops.
- Teach patient how to store drug.

Evaluation

- Patient is free from infection.
- Patient maintains adequate hydration.
- Patient and family state understanding of drug therapy.

cetuximab

(seh-TUX-eh-mab)
Erbitux

Pharmacologic class: recombinant monoclonal antibody
Therapeutic class: epidermal growth factor receptor (EGFR) antagonist
Pregnancy risk category: C

Indications and dosages

▶ **Epidermal growth factor–expressing metastatic colorectal cancer, as monotherapy in patients intolerant of irinotecan-based chemotherapy or with irinotecan in patients refractory to irinotecan therapy alone.** *Adults:* Initial loading dose, 400 mg/m^2 I.V. over 2 hours (maximum, 5 ml/minute), alone or with irinotecan. Maintenance dosage, 250 mg/m^2 I.V. weekly over 1 hour (maximum, 5 ml/minute). Premedicate with an H_1 antagonist (such as 50 mg of diphenhydramine I.V.).

▶ **Squamous cell carcinoma of the head and neck.** *Adults:* Premedicate with an H_1 antagonist. Then loading dose of 400 mg/m^2 I.V. over 2 hours (maximum rate, 5 ml/minute) followed by weekly maintenance dose of 250 mg/m^2 I.V. over 1 hour. If used with radiation therapy, begin cetuximab 1 week before radiation starts and continue throughout radiation therapy (6 to 7 weeks). If used as monotherapy for recurrent or metastatic disease after failure of platinum-based therapy, continue treatment until disease progresses or unacceptable toxicity occurs.

Adjust-a-dose: If patient develops a grade 1 or 2 infusion reaction, permanently reduce infusion rate by 50%. If patient develops a grade 3 or 4 reaction, stop drug immediately and permanently.

I.V. administration

- Solution should be clear and colorless and may contain a small amount of particulates.
- Don't shake or dilute.
- Give by infusion pump or syringe pump. Piggyback into the patient's infusion line.
- Don't give drug by I.V. push or bolus.
- Give drug through a low–protein-binding 0.22-micrometer in-line filter.
- Flush line with normal saline solution at the end of the infusion.
- Monitor patient for 1 hour after the infusion.
- If patient develops a severe acneiform rash, follow these guidelines: The first time, delay infusion 1 to 2 weeks. If the patient improves, continue at 250 mg/m². If the patient doesn't improve, stop the drug. The second time, delay infusion 1 to 2 weeks. If the patient improves, reduce dose to 200 mg/m². If the patient doesn't improve, stop the drug. The third time, delay infusion 1 to 2 weeks. If the patient improves, reduce dose to 150 mg/m². If the patient doesn't improve, stop the drug. The fourth time, stop the drug permanently.
- Store vials at 36° to 46° F (2° to 8° C). Don't freeze. Solution in infusion container is stable up to 12 hours in refrigerator and up to 8 hours at room temperature (68° to 77° F [20° to 25° C]).

⊗ **Incompatibilities**

- Don't dilute cetuximab with other solutions.

Contraindications and cautions

- Use cautiously in patients hypersensitive to drug, its components, or murine proteins. Also, use cautiously in combination therapy with radiation in patients with a history of coronary artery disease, arrhythmias, or heart failure.

Lifespan: It isn't known whether drug can harm fetus, so give drug to a pregnant woman only if potential benefits justify risks to fetus. Before therapy starts, caution mother about risks to fetus. Urge women to stop breast-feeding while receiving drug and for 60 days after the last dose. In children, safety and effectiveness haven't been established.

Adverse reactions

CNS: *asthenia, fever,* depression, headache, insomnia, *pain.*
CV: ***cardiopulmonary arrest,*** edema.
EENT: conjunctivitis.
GI: *abdominal pain,* anorexia, *constipation, diarrhea,* dyspepsia, *dysphagia, mucositis, nausea,* stomatitis, *vomiting, xerostomia.*
GU: ***acute renal failure.***
Hematologic: *anemia,* LEUKOPENIA.
Metabolic: dehydration, *weight loss.*
Musculoskeletal: *back pain.*
Respiratory: ***bronchospasm,*** cough, dyspnea, hoarseness, ***pulmonary embolus,*** stridor.
Skin: *acneiform rash,* alopecia, maculopapular rash, nail disorder, pruritus, *radiation dermatitis.*
Other: infection, ***infusion reaction, sepsis.***

Interactions

Drug-lifestyle. *Sun exposure:* May worsen skin reactions. Urge patient to take precautions.

Effects on lab test results

None reported.

Pharmacokinetics

Absorption: Given I.V.
Distribution: Binds to EGFR, which is expressed in many normal epithelial tissues, such as skin and hair follicles, and in many cancers.
Metabolism: Unknown.
Excretion: Unknown. *Half-life:* 5 days.

Route	Onset	Peak	Duration
I.V.	Unknown	Unknown	Unknown

Action

Chemical effect: Binds to the EGFR on normal and tumor cells, keeping epidermal growth factor from binding, which inhibits cell growth, causes cell death, and decreases growth factor production.
Therapeutic effect: Inhibits tumor cells that overexpress EGFR in colorectal cancer patients.

Available forms

Injection: 2 mg/ml in 50-ml vial

NURSING PROCESS

Assessment

ALERT: Assess patient for signs and symptoms of severe infusion reactions, including acute airway obstruction, urticaria, and hypotension, usually with the first infusion and despite pre-

medication. If a severe infusion reaction occurs, immediately stop giving the drug and treat symptoms. Treat mild to moderate infusion reactions by cutting infusion rate in half and continuing antihistamines.
- Monitor patient for infusion reactions for 1 hour after the infusion.
- Assess patient for acute onset or worsening of pulmonary symptoms. If interstitial lung disease is confirmed, stop the drug.
- Monitor patient for skin toxicity, which starts most often during the first 2 weeks of therapy. Give topical and oral antibiotics.
- Assess hematologic and renal function studies before therapy and periodically thereafter.
- Patients receiving cetuximab with radiation therapy need close monitoring of their electrolytes—particularly magnesium, potassium, and calcium—during and after therapy.
- Assess patient's and family's knowledge of drug therapy.

Nursing diagnoses
- Risk for injury related to drug infusion reaction
- Impaired skin integrity related to dermatologic toxicity
- Deficient knowledge related to cetuximab therapy

Planning and implementation
- To reduce risk of pulmonary drug reactions, premedicate with 50 mg diphenhydramine I.V.
- Keep epinephrine, corticosteroids, I.V. antihistamines, bronchodilators, and oxygen available to treat severe infusion reactions.

Patient teaching
- Tell patient to promptly report adverse reactions.
- Inform patient that skin reactions may occur, typically during the first 2 weeks.
- Advise patient to avoid prolonged or unprotected sun exposure, which can worsen adverse skin reactions.

Evaluation
- Patient doesn't experience a drug infusion reaction.
- Patient doesn't develop dermatologic toxicity.
- Patient and family state understanding of drug therapy.

C

chloral hydrate
(KLOR-ul HIGH-drayt)
Aquachloral Supprettes, PMS-Chloral Hydrate ♦, Somnote

Pharmacologic class: general CNS depressant
Therapeutic class: sedative-hypnotic
Pregnancy risk category: C
Controlled substance schedule: IV

Indications and dosages
▶ **Sedation.** *Adults:* 250 mg P.O. or P.R. t.i.d. after meals. Maximum dose, 2 g.
Children: 8 mg/kg P.O. or P.R. t.i.d.; maximum 500 mg per dose daily; doses may be divided.
▶ **Insomnia.** *Adults:* 500 mg to 1 g P.O. or P.R. 15 to 30 minutes before bedtime.
Children: 50 mg/kg P.O. or P.R. 15 to 30 minutes before bedtime; maximum single dose, 1 g.
▶ **Preoperative use.** *Adults:* 500 mg to 1 g P.O. or P.R. 30 minutes before surgery.
▶ **Premedication for EEG.** *Children:* 20 to 25 mg/kg P.O. or P.R.
▶ **Alcohol withdrawal.** *Adults:* 500 mg to 1 g P.O. or P.R.; repeat at 6-hour intervals, p.r.n. Maximum, 2 g daily.

Contraindications and cautions
- Contraindicated in patients hypersensitive to drug and in those with hepatic or renal impairment. Oral administration contraindicated in patients with gastric disorders.
- Use cautiously in patients with severe cardiac disease and in patients with mental depression, suicidal tendencies, or history of drug abuse.

Lifespan: In breast-feeding women, avoid use because small amounts of drug appear in breast milk and may cause drowsiness in infants.

Adverse reactions
CNS: ataxia, dizziness, drowsiness, hangover, nightmares, paradoxical excitement.
GI: diarrhea, flatulence, nausea, vomiting.
Hematologic: eosinophilia, ***leukopenia.***
Other: hypersensitivity reactions.

Interactions
Drug-drug. *Alkaline solutions:* May be incompatible with aqueous solutions of chloral hydrate. Don't mix together.

CNS depressants, including opioid analgesics: May cause excessive CNS depression or vasodilation reaction. Use together cautiously.
Furosemide I.V.: May cause sweating, flushing, variable blood pressure, and uneasiness. Use together cautiously or use different hypnotic drug.
Oral anticoagulants: May increase risk of bleeding. Monitor patient closely.
Phenytoin: May decrease phenytoin level. Monitor level closely.
Drug-lifestyle. *Alcohol use:* May react synergistically, increasing CNS depression, or may cause a disulfiram-like reaction (rarely). Strongly discourage alcohol use.

Effects on lab test results

- May increase BUN level.
- May increase eosinophil count. May decrease WBC count.
- May interfere with fluorometric tests for urine catecholamines and Reddy-Jenkins-Thorn test for urine 17-hydroxycorticosteroids. May cause false-positive tests for urine glucose in copper sulfate tests (Clinitest).

Pharmacokinetics

Absorption: Good.
Distribution: Throughout body tissue and fluids; trichloroethanol (the active metabolite) is 35% to 41% protein-bound.
Metabolism: Rapid and nearly complete in liver and erythrocytes to trichloroethanol; then again in liver and kidneys to trichloroacetic acid and other inactive metabolites.
Excretion: Inactive metabolites mainly in urine, minimally in bile. *Half-life:* 8 to 10 hours for trichloroethanol.

Route	Onset	Peak	Duration
P.O.	≤ 30 min	Unknown	4–8 hr
P.R.	Unknown	Unknown	4–8 hr

Action

Chemical effect: Unknown; sedative effects may be caused by trichloroethanol.
Therapeutic effect: Promotes sleep and calmness.

Available forms

Capsules: 500 mg
Suppositories: 324 mg, 500 mg, 648 mg
Syrup: 250 mg/5 ml, 500 mg/5 ml

NURSING PROCESS

Assessment

- Assess patient's underlying condition.
- Evaluate drug's effectiveness.
- Be alert for adverse reactions and drug interactions.
- Assess patient's and family's knowledge of drug therapy.

Nursing diagnoses

- Insomnia related to patient's underlying condition
- Risk for trauma related to adverse CNS reactions
- Deficient knowledge related to drug therapy

Planning and implementation

ALERT: Oral liquid form comes in two strengths; double-check dose, especially when giving to children. Fatal overdose may occur.
- To minimize unpleasant taste and stomach irritation, dilute or give drug with liquid and after meals.
- Store rectal suppositories in refrigerator.
- Don't use for long-term therapy because drug loses its effectiveness in promoting sleep after 14 days of continued use. Long-term use may also cause drug dependence, and patient may experience withdrawal symptoms if drug is suddenly stopped.

ALERT: Some products may contain tartrazine, which may cause hypersensitivity reactions in susceptible people.

Patient teaching
- Warn patient about performing activities that require mental alertness or physical coordination. For inpatients, particularly elderly patients, supervise walking and raise bed rails.
- Tell patient to store capsules or syrup in dark container and to store suppositories in refrigerator.
- Explain that drug may cause morning hangover. Encourage patient to report severe hangover or feelings of oversedation so that prescriber can adjust the dose or change drug.

Evaluation

- Patient states drug effectively induced sleep.
- Patient's safety is maintained.
- Patient and family state understanding of drug therapy.

C

chlorambucil

(klor-AM-byoo-sil)
Leukeran

Pharmacologic class: alkylating drug
Therapeutic class: antineoplastic
Pregnancy risk category: D

Indications and dosages

▶ **Chronic lymphocytic leukemia; malignant lymphomas, including lymphosarcoma, giant follicular lymphoma, non-Hodgkin lymphoma, Hodgkin lymphoma, autoimmune hemolytic anemia‡, nephrotic syndrome‡, polycythemia vera‡, and ovarian neoplasms‡.** *Adults:* 0.1 to 0.2 mg/kg P.O. daily for 3 to 6 weeks; then adjust for maintenance (usually 4 to 10 mg daily).
Children: 0.1 to 0.2 mg/kg or 3 to 6 mg/m² P.O. as a single daily dose. Reduce initial dose if given within 4 weeks after a full course of radiation therapy or myelosuppressive drugs or if pretreatment leukocyte or platelet counts are depressed from bone marrow disease.

▶ **Macroglobulinemia‡.** *Adults:* 2 to 10 mg P.O. daily. Or 8 mg/m² for 10 days with prednisone 30 mg/m² daily; repeat cycle q 6 to 8 weeks as needed.

▶ **Metastatic trophoblastic neoplasia‡.** *Adults:* 6 to 10 mg P.O. daily for 5 days; repeat q 1 to 2 weeks.

▶ **Idiopathic uveitis‡.** *Adults:* 6 to 12 mg P.O. daily for 1 year.

▶ **Rheumatoid arthritis‡.** *Adults:* 0.1 to 0.3 mg/kg P.O. daily.

Contraindications and cautions

• Contraindicated in patients hypersensitive or resistant to previous therapy (those hypersensitive to other alkylating drugs also may be hypersensitive to chlorambucil).
• Use cautiously in patients with history of head trauma or seizures and in patients receiving other drugs that lower seizure threshold.
Lifespan: In pregnant women, use cautiously, if at all, because drug may harm fetus. In breast-feeding women, drug is contraindicated. In children, safety and effectiveness haven't been established, and potential benefits must be weighed against risks.

Adverse reactions

CNS: *seizures.*
GI: *nausea, stomatitis, vomiting.*
GU: *azoospermia, infertility.*
Hematologic: ***anemia, myelosuppression*** (usually moderate, gradual, and rapidly reversible), ***neutropenia*** (delayed up to 3 weeks, lasting up to 10 days after last dose), ***thrombocytopenia.***
Hepatic: ***hepatotoxicity.***
Metabolic: hyperuricemia.
Respiratory: interstitial pneumonitis, ***pulmonary fibrosis.***
Skin: exfoliative dermatitis, rash, ***Stevens-Johnson syndrome.***
Other: *allergic febrile reaction.*

Interactions

Drug-drug. *Anticoagulants, aspirin:* May increase risk of bleeding. Avoid use together. If drugs must be used together, monitor patient's coagulation studies.

Effects on lab test results

• May increase AST, ALT, alkaline phosphatase, and blood and urine uric acid levels. May decrease hemoglobin level and hematocrit.
• May decrease neutrophil, platelet, WBC, granulocyte, and RBC counts.

Pharmacokinetics

Absorption: Good.
Distribution: Highly bound to proteins.
Metabolism: Main metabolite, phenylacetic acid mustard, also has cytotoxic activity.
Excretion: In urine. *Half-life:* 2 hours for parent compound; 2½ hours for phenylacetic acid metabolite.

Route	Onset	Peak	Duration
P.O.	3–4 wk	1 hr	Unknown

Action

Chemical effect: Cross-links strands of cellular DNA and interferes with RNA transcription, causing growth imbalance that leads to cell death.
Therapeutic effect: Kills selected cancer cells.

Available forms

Tablets: 2 mg

NURSING PROCESS

Assessment

• Assess patient's underlying neoplastic disorder before and regularly during therapy.
• Monitor CBC and uric acid level.
• Be alert for adverse reactions and drug interactions.
• Assess patient's and family's knowledge of drug therapy.

Nursing diagnoses

• Ineffective health maintenance related to presence of neoplastic disease
• Ineffective protection related to drug-induced hematologic adverse reactions
• Deficient knowledge related to drug therapy

Planning and implementation

• Dosage is based on patient's response.
• Give drug 1 hour before breakfast and at least 2 hours after evening meal.
• Drug-related nausea and vomiting usually can be controlled with antiemetics.
• Allopurinol may be used with adequate hydration to prevent hyperuricemia with resulting uric acid nephropathy.
• Follow institutional policy for infection control in immunocompromised patients if WBC count falls below 2,000/mm³ or granulocyte count falls below 1,000/mm³. Severe neutropenia is reversible up to cumulative dosage of 6.5 mg/kg in single course.

Patient teaching

• Warn patient to watch for signs of infection (fever, sore throat, fatigue) and bleeding (easy bruising, nosebleed, bleeding gums, melena). Tell him to take temperature daily.
• Instruct patient to avoid OTC products that contain aspirin.
• Tell patient to take drug 1 hour before breakfast and 2 hours after evening meal if bothered by nausea and vomiting.
• Instruct patient to maintain fluid intake of 2,400 to 3,000 ml daily, if not contraindicated.
• Tell patient to use contraceptive measures while using this drug.

Evaluation

• Patient shows improvement in underlying neoplastic condition on follow-up diagnostic tests.
• Patient remains infection free and doesn't bleed abnormally.
• Patient and family state understanding of drug therapy.

chlordiazepoxide hydrochloride

(klor-digh-eh-zuh-POKS-ighd high-droh-KLOR-ighd)

Apo-Chlordiazepoxide ♦, Librium

Pharmacologic class: benzodiazepine
Therapeutic class: anxiolytic, sedative-hypnotic
Pregnancy risk category: D
Controlled substance schedule: IV

Indications and dosages

▶ **Mild to moderate anxiety.** *Adults:* 5 to 10 mg P.O. t.i.d. or q.i.d.
Children age 6 and older: 5 mg P.O. b.i.d. to q.i.d. Maximum dosage, 10 mg P.O. b.i.d. or t.i.d.

▶ **Severe anxiety.** *Adults:* 20 to 25 mg P.O. t.i.d. or q.i.d. Or 50 to 100 mg I.V. or I.M. initially, followed by 25 to 50 mg I.V. 3 or 4 times daily p.r.n.
Elderly patients: 5 mg P.O. b.i.d. to q.i.d.

▶ **Withdrawal symptoms of acute alcoholism.** *Adults:* 50 to 100 mg P.O., I.V., or I.M. Repeat in 2 to 4 hours, p.r.n. Maximum dosage is 300 mg daily.

▶ **Preoperative apprehension and anxiety.** *Adults:* 5 to 10 mg P.O. t.i.d. or q.i.d. on day preceding surgery. Or 50 to 100 mg I.M. 1 hour before surgery.

I.V. administration

• Make sure equipment and staff needed for emergency airway management are available.
• Don't give packaged diluent I.V. because air bubbles may form.
• Use 5 ml normal saline solution or sterile water for injection as diluent for an ampule containing 100 mg of drug. Give slowly over 1 minute.
• Monitor respirations every 5 to 15 minutes after use and before each repeated dose.

⊗ Incompatibilities

Other I.V. drugs.

Contraindications and cautions

• Contraindicated in patients hypersensitive to drug.

• Use cautiously in patients with mental depression, porphyria, or hepatic or renal disease. In debilitated patients, use cautiously and at a reduced dosage.

Lifespan: In pregnant women, drug is contraindicated. Breast-feeding women shouldn't use drug because of risk of adverse effects in infant. In children younger than age 6, safety and effectiveness haven't been established. In children younger than age 12, parenteral use isn't recommended. In elderly patients, use smallest effective dose to avoid ataxia and oversedation.

Adverse reactions

CNS: confusion, drowsiness, fainting, hangover, lethargy, psychosis, restlessness, ***suicidal tendencies.***
CV: *thrombophlebitis,* transient hypotension.
EENT: visual disturbances.
GI: abdominal discomfort, constipation, nausea, vomiting.
GU: incontinence, menstrual irregularities, urine retention.
Hematologic: ***agranulocytosis.***
Skin: pain at injection site, swelling.

Interactions

Drug-drug. *Cimetidine:* May increase sedation. Monitor patient carefully.
CNS depressants: May increase CNS depression. Avoid use together.
Digoxin: May increase digoxin level and risk of toxicity. Monitor patient closely; monitor level.
Fluconazole, itraconazole, ketoconazole, miconazole: May increase and prolong levels, CNS depression, and psychomotor impairment. Avoid use together.
Drug-herb. *Kava:* May lead to excessive sedation. Discourage use together.
Drug-lifestyle. *Alcohol use:* May cause additive CNS effects. Strongly discourage alcohol use.
Smoking: May increase clearance of drug. Monitor patient for lack of effectiveness.

Effects on lab test results

• May increase liver function test values. May decrease granulocyte count.
• May cause false-positive reaction in Gravindex pregnancy test. May interfere with certain tests for urine 17-ketosteroids.

Pharmacokinetics

Absorption: Good with P.O. use.
Distribution: Wide. 80% to 90% protein-bound.
Metabolism: In liver to several active metabolites.
Excretion: Most metabolites in urine. *Half-life:* 5 to 30 hours.

Route	Onset	Peak	Duration
P.O., I.V.	Unknown	½–4 hr	Unknown
I.M.	¼–½ hr	½–4 hr	Unknown

Action

Chemical effect: May potentiate the effects of GABA in brain and suppress the spread of seizure activity produced by epileptogenic foci in the cortex, thalamus, and limbic structures.
Therapeutic effect: Relieves anxiety and promotes sleep and calmness.

Available forms

Capsules: 5 mg, 10 mg, 25 mg
Powder for injection: 100 mg/ampule

NURSING PROCESS

Assessment

• Assess patient's underlying condition before and regularly during therapy.
• Monitor liver, renal, and hematopoietic function studies periodically in patients receiving repeated or prolonged therapy.
• Monitor patient for abuse and addiction.
• Be alert for adverse reactions and drug interactions.
• Assess patient's and family's knowledge of drug therapy.

Nursing diagnoses

• Anxiety related to patient's underlying condition
• Risk for injury related to drug-induced CNS reactions
• Deficient knowledge related to drug therapy

Planning and implementation

• Don't give drug regularly for everyday stress.
• Make sure patient has swallowed tablets before you leave the bedside.
ALERT: The 5-mg and 25-mg unit-dose capsules may appear similar in color when viewed through the package. Verify contents, and read label carefully.

• When using I.M., add 2 ml of diluent to powder and agitate gently until clear. Use immediately. I.M. form may be erratically absorbed.
• Recommended for I.M. use only, but may be given I.V.
• Injectable form comes in two types of ampules: as diluent and as powdered drug. Read directions carefully.
• Don't mix injectable form with any other parenteral drug.
• Refrigerate powder and keep away from light; mix just before use and discard remainder.
• Don't stop drug abruptly after long-term use because withdrawal symptoms may occur.

Patient teaching
• Warn patient to avoid hazardous activities that require alertness and good psychomotor coordination until CNS effects of drug are known.
• Tell patient to avoid alcohol while taking drug.
• Warn patient to take this drug only as directed and not to stop taking it without prescriber's approval. Inform patient of drug's potential for dependence if taken longer than directed.

Evaluation
• Patient says he's less anxious.
• Patient's safety is maintained.
• Patient and family state understanding of drug therapy.

chloroquine phosphate

(KLOR-oh-kwin FOS-fayt)
Chlorquin ◇, Aralen Phosphate

Pharmacologic class: 4-amino-quinoline
Therapeutic class: antimalarial, amebicide
Pregnancy risk category: C

Indications and dosages

▶ **Acute malarial attacks caused by *Plasmodium vivax, P. malariae, P. ovale,* and susceptible strains of *P. falciparum.*** *Adults:* 1 g (600-mg base) P.O. followed by 500 mg (300-mg base) P.O. after 6 to 8 hours; for next 2 days, a single dose of 500 mg (300-mg base) P.O. *Children:* Initially, 10 mg (base)/kg P.O.; then 5 mg (base)/kg at 6, 24, and 48 hours (don't exceed adult dosage).

▶ **Malaria prophylaxis.** *Adults:* 500 mg (300-mg base) P.O. on the same day once weekly, beginning 2 weeks before exposure. Continue for 4 weeks after leaving endemic area. *Children:* 5 mg (base)/kg P.O. on the same day once weekly (not to exceed adult dosage), beginning 2 weeks before exposure.

▶ **Extraintestinal amebiasis.** *Adults:* 1 g (600-mg base) P.O. daily for 2 days; then 500 mg (300-mg base) daily for at least 2 to 3 weeks. Therapy usually is combined with intestinal amebicide.

▶ **Rheumatoid arthritis‡.** *Adults:* 250 mg P.O. with evening meal.

▶ **Lupus erythematosus‡.** *Adults:* 250 mg P.O. daily with evening meal; reduce dosage gradually over several months when lesions regress.

Contraindications and cautions

• Contraindicated in patients hypersensitive to drug and in patients with retinal changes, visual field changes, or porphyria.
• Use cautiously in patients with severe GI, neurologic, or blood disorders. Also use cautiously in patients with hepatic disease or alcoholism (drug concentrates in liver), and in those with G6PD deficiency or psoriasis (drug may exacerbate these conditions).

Lifespan: In pregnant women, don't use except in women who may have been exposed to active malaria because fetal risks of malaria outweigh risks of drug. Warn pregnant women or those planning to become pregnant to avoid exposure to malaria. Breast-feeding women should stop breast-feeding or stop the drug.

Adverse reactions

CNS: dizziness, fatigue, irritability, mild and transient headache, neuromyopathy, nightmares, psychic stimulation, ***seizures.***
CV: ECG changes, hypotension.
EENT: ototoxicity (with prolonged high doses), *visual disturbances* (blurred vision; trouble focusing; reversible corneal changes; typically irreversible, sometimes progressive or delayed retinal changes, such as narrowing of arterioles; macular lesions; pallor of optic disk; optic atrophy; patchy retinal pigmentation, typically leading to blindness).
GI: abdominal cramps, anorexia, diarrhea, nausea, stomatitis, vomiting.
Hematologic: ***agranulocytosis, aplastic anemia, hemolytic anemia, thrombocytopenia.***

Skin: lichen planus eruptions, pleomorphic skin eruptions, pruritus, skin and mucosal pigment changes.

Interactions

Drug-drug. *Aluminum salts, kaolin, magnesium:* May decrease GI absorption. Separate doses.
Cimetidine: May decrease hepatic metabolism of chloroquine. Monitor patient for toxicity.
Drug-lifestyle. *Sun exposure:* May worsen drug-induced dermatoses. Tell patient to avoid excessive sun exposure and to wear protective clothing and sunblock.

Effects on lab test results

- May decrease hemoglobin level and hematocrit.
- May decrease granulocyte and platelet counts.

Pharmacokinetics

Absorption: Quick and almost complete.
Distribution: In liver, spleen, kidneys, heart, and brain and is strongly bound in melanin-containing cells.
Metabolism: 30%.
Excretion: 70% unchanged in urine; unabsorbed drug in feces. Small amounts of drug may be present in urine for months after drug is stopped. Renal excretion is enhanced by urine acidification. *Half-life:* 1 to 2 months.

Route	Onset	Peak	Duration
P.O.	Unknown	1–3 hr	Unknown

Action

Chemical effect: May bind to and alter properties of DNA in susceptible parasites.
Therapeutic effect: Prevents or eradicates malarial infections; eradicates amebiasis.

Available forms

Tablets: 250 mg (150-mg base), 500 mg (300-mg base)

NURSING PROCESS

Assessment

- Assess patient's infection before and regularly during therapy.
- Make sure baseline and periodic ophthalmic examinations are performed. After long-term use, check periodically for ocular muscle weakness.
- Assist patient with obtaining audiometric examinations before, during, and after therapy, especially long-term therapy.
- Monitor CBC and liver function studies periodically during long-term therapy.
- Be alert for adverse reactions and drug interactions.
- Assess patient for potential overdose, which can quickly lead to toxic symptoms: headache, drowsiness, visual disturbances, CV collapse, and seizures, followed by cardiopulmonary arrest. Children are highly susceptible to toxicity.
- Assess patient's and family's knowledge of drug therapy.

Nursing diagnoses

- Ineffective protection related to presence of organisms susceptible to drug
- Disturbed sensory perception (visual or auditory) related to adverse reactions to drug
- Deficient knowledge related to drug therapy

Planning and implementation

- Give drug at same time of same day each week.

ALERT: Give missed doses as soon as possible. To avoid doubling doses in regimens requiring more than one dose per day, give missed dose within 1 hour of scheduled time or omit dose altogether.

- Give drug with milk or meals to minimize GI distress. Tablets may be crushed and mixed with food or chocolate syrup for patients who have trouble swallowing; however, drug has bitter taste and patients may find mixture unpleasant. Crushed tablets may be placed inside empty gelatin capsules, which are easier to swallow.
- Store drug in amber-colored containers to protect from light.
- Begin prophylactic antimalarial therapy 2 weeks before exposure and continue for 4 weeks after patient leaves endemic area.
- Monitor patient's weight for significant changes because dose is based on weight.
- If patient develops severe blood disorder not attributable to disease, notify prescriber and stop drug.

Patient teaching

- Tell patient to take drug with food at same time on same day each week.

• Instruct patient to avoid excessive sun exposure to avoid worsening drug-induced dermatoses.
• Tell patient to report blurred vision, increased sensitivity to light, trouble hearing, ringing in the ears, and muscle weakness.
• Warn patient to avoid alcohol while taking drug.
• Teach patient how to take missed doses.

Evaluation
• Patient is free from infection.
• Patient maintains normal visual and auditory function.
• Patient and family state understanding of drug therapy.

chlorothiazide
(klor-oh-THIGH-uh-zighd)
Chlotride ◇, Diurigen, Diuril

chlorothiazide sodium
Diuril Sodium Intravenous

Pharmacologic class: diuretic
Therapeutic class: thiazide diuretic, antihypertensive
Pregnancy risk category: C

Indications and dosages
▶ **Edema, hypertension.** *Adults:* 500 mg to 1 g P.O. or I.V. daily or in divided doses.
▶ **Diuresis, hypertension.** *Children and infants age 6 months and older:* 10 to 20 mg/kg P.O. daily in divided doses, not to exceed 375 mg daily. *Infants age 6 months and younger:* May require 30 mg/kg P.O. daily in two divided doses.

I.V. administration
• Reconstitute 500 mg with 18 ml sterile water for injection.
• Inject reconstituted drug directly into vein; through I.V. line containing free-flowing, compatible solution; or through intermittent infusion device. Compatible solutions include dextrose and saline.
• Monitor the patient for signs and symptoms of I.V. infiltration.
• Avoid simultaneous administration with whole blood and its derivatives.
• If hypersensitivity reactions occur, stop drug and notify prescriber.
• Store reconstituted solutions at room temperature up to 24 hours.

⊗ Incompatibilities
Amikacin; chlorpromazine; codeine; hydralazine; insulin (regular); Ionosol B, D, or K and invert sugar 10%; Ionosol B or D-CM and dextrose 5%; Ionosol PSL; levorphanol; methadone; morphine; norepinephrine; Normosol-M (900 calories); Normosol-M in dextrose 5%; Normosol-R in dextrose 5%; polymyxin B; procaine; prochlorperazine; promazine; promethazine hydrochloride; streptomycin; triflupromazine; vancomycin; vitamin B complex with C; whole blood and its derivatives.

Contraindications and cautions
• Contraindicated in patients hypersensitive to other thiazides or other sulfonamide-derived drugs and in patients with anuria.
• Use cautiously in patients with severe renal disease or impaired hepatic function.
Lifespan: In pregnant or breast-feeding women, safety and effectiveness haven't been established. In children, I.V. use isn't recommended.

Adverse reactions
CV: orthostatic hypotension.
GI: anorexia, nausea, ***pancreatitis.***
GU: frequent urination, impotence, nocturia, polyuria, ***renal impairment.***
Hematologic: ***agranulocytosis, aplastic anemia, leukopenia, thrombocytopenia.***
Hepatic: ***hepatic encephalopathy.***
Metabolic: asymptomatic hyperuricemia; fluid and electrolyte imbalances, including hyperkalemia, dilutional hypochloremia and hyponatremia, and metabolic alkalosis; gout; hyperglycemia; hypokalemia; and impaired glucose tolerance.
Skin: dermatitis, photosensitivity, rash.
Other: hypersensitivity reaction.

Interactions
Drug-drug. *Barbiturates, opioids:* May increase risk of orthostatic hypotension. Monitor blood pressure closely.
Chlorthalidone, ethacrynic acid, furosemide, hydrochlorothiazide, indapamide, metolazone, bumetanide, torsemide: May cause excessive diuretic response and serious electrolyte abnor-

malities or dehydration. Adjust doses carefully while monitoring the patient closely.
Cholestyramine, colestipol: May decrease intestinal absorption of thiazides. Separate doses.
Diazoxide: May increase antihypertensive, hyperglycemic, and hyperuricemic effects. Use together cautiously.
Digoxin: May increase risk of digitalis toxicity from chlorothiazide-induced hypokalemia. Monitor potassium and digitalis levels.
Lithium: May decrease lithium clearance, increasing risk of lithium toxicity. Monitor lithium level.
NSAIDs: May increase risk of NSAID-induced renal impairment. Monitor patient for this reaction.
Drug-herb. *Licorice root:* May worsen the potassium depletion caused by thiazides. Avoid use together.
Drug-lifestyle. *Alcohol use:* May increase orthostatic hypotension. Monitor patient closely and place patient on fall precautions.

Effects on lab test results

- May increase uric acid, glucose, and calcium levels. May decrease potassium, sodium, chloride, and hemoglobin levels and hematocrit.
- May decrease granulocyte, WBC, and platelet counts.

Pharmacokinetics

Absorption: Incomplete and variable.
Distribution: Unknown.
Metabolism: None.
Excretion: Unchanged in urine. *Half-life:* 1 to 2 hours.

Route	Onset	Peak	Duration
P.O.	≤ 2 hr	4 hr	6–12 hr
I.V.	≤ 15 min	30 min	6–12 hr

Action

Chemical effect: Increases sodium and water excretion by inhibiting sodium reabsorption in nephron's cortical diluting site.
Therapeutic effect: Promotes sodium and water excretion.

Available forms

Injection: 500-mg vial
Oral suspension: 250 mg/5 ml
Tablets: 250 mg, 500 mg

NURSING PROCESS

Assessment

- Assess patient's underlying condition before therapy and regularly thereafter.
- Monitor the drug's effectiveness by regularly checking blood pressure, fluid intake, urine output, blood pressure, and weight.
- Expect therapeutic response to be delayed several days in patients with hypertension.
- Monitor electrolyte and glucose levels.
- Monitor creatinine and BUN levels regularly. If they're more than twice normal, drug isn't as effective.
- Monitor blood uric acid level, especially in patients with history of gout.
- Be alert for adverse reactions and drug interactions.
- Assess patient's and family's knowledge of drug therapy.

Nursing diagnoses

- Excessive fluid volume related to patient's underlying condition
- Impaired urinary elimination related to drug therapy
- Deficient knowledge related to drug therapy

Planning and implementation

- To prevent nocturia, give drug in the morning.
- Many patients with edema respond to intermittent therapy. Intermittent use reduces the risk of excessive response and electrolyte imbalances.

ALERT: Never inject I.M. or subcutaneously.

- Drug may be used with potassium-sparing diuretic to prevent potassium loss.
- Stop thiazides and thiazide-like diuretics before parathyroid function tests are performed.

Patient teaching

- Teach patient and family to identify and report signs of hypersensitivity and hypokalemia.
- Teach patient to monitor fluid intake and output and daily weight.
- Instruct patient to avoid high-sodium foods and to choose high-potassium foods.
- Tell patient to take drug in the morning to avoid nocturia.
- Advise patient to avoid sudden posture changes and to rise slowly to avoid orthostatic hypotension.
- Advise patient to use sunblock in order to prevent photosensitivity reactions.

• Teach patient the importance of periodic laboratory tests to detect electrolyte imbalances.

Evaluation
• Patient is free from edema.
• Patient adjusts lifestyle to cope with altered patterns of urine elimination.
• Patient and family state understanding of drug therapy.

chlorpromazine hydrochloride
(klor-PROH-meh-zeen high-droh-KLOR-ighd)
Chlorpromanyl-20 ♦, Chlorpromanyl-40 ♦, Largactil ♦ ◇, Novo-Chlorpromazine ♦, Thorazine

Pharmacologic class: aliphatic phenothiazine
Therapeutic class: antipsychotic, antiemetic
Pregnancy risk category: C

Indications and dosages
▶ **Psychosis.** *Adults:* Initially, 30 to 75 mg P.O. daily in two to four divided doses. Increase dosage by 20 to 50 mg twice weekly until symptoms are controlled. Some patients may need up to 800 mg daily. Or, for prompt control of severe symptoms, 25 mg I.M., followed by 25 to 50 mg I.M. in 1 hour if needed, then gradually increase dosage q 4 to 6 hours to maximum of 400 mg/dose. Switch to P.O. use as soon as symptoms are controlled.
Children age 6 months and older: 0.55 mg/kg P.O. q 4 to 6 hours or I.M. q 6 to 8 hours. Or 1.1 mg/kg P.R. q 6 to 8 hours. Maximum I.M. dose in children younger than age 5 or weighing less than 22.7 kg (50 lb) is 40 mg. Maximum I.M. dose in children ages 5 to 12 or weighing 22.7 to 45.5 kg (100 lb) is 75 mg.
▶ **Nausea and vomiting.** *Adults:* 10 to 25 mg P.O. q 4 to 6 hours, p.r.n. Or 50 to 100 mg P.R. q 6 to 8 hours, p.r.n. Or, 25 mg I.M. If no hypotension occurs, give 25 to 50 mg I.M. q 3 to 4 hours p.r.n. until vomiting stops.
Children and infants age 6 months and older: 0.55 mg/kg P.O. q 4 to 6 hours or I.M. q 6 to 8 hours. Or 1.1 mg/kg P.R. q 6 to 8 hours. Maximum I.M. dose in children younger than age 5 or weighing less than 22.7 kg is 40 mg. Maximum I.M. dose in children ages 5 to 12 or weighing 22.7 to 45.5 kg is 75 mg.
▶ **Intractable hiccups, acute intermittent porphyria.** *Adults:* 25 to 50 mg P.O. t.i.d. or q.i.d. If symptoms persist for 2 to 3 days, 25 to 50 mg I.M. If symptoms still persist, 25 to 50 mg diluted in 500 to 1,000 ml normal saline solution and infused slowly.
▶ **Adjunct treatment of tetanus.** *Adults:* 25 to 50 mg I.V. or I.M. t.i.d. or q.i.d., usually with barbiturates.
Children and infants age 6 months and older: 0.55 mg/kg I.M. or I.V. q 6 to 8 hours. Maximum parenteral dosage in children weighing less than 22.7 kg is 40 mg daily; in children weighing 22.7 to 45.5 kg, 75 mg daily, except in severe cases.
▶ **To relieve apprehension and nervousness before surgery and to control acute nausea and vomiting during surgery.** *Adults:* Preoperatively, 25 to 50 mg P.O. 2 to 3 hours before surgery or 12.5 to 25 mg I.M. 1 to 2 hours before surgery. To control acute nausea and vomiting during surgery, 12.5 mg I.M.; repeat after 30 minutes if needed or fractional 2-mg doses I.V. at 2-minute intervals; maximum dose, 25 mg. Postoperatively, 10 to 25 mg P.O. q 4 to 6 hours or 12.5 mg to 25 mg I.M.; repeat in 1 hour if needed.
Children and infants age 6 months and older: Preoperatively, 0.55 mg/kg P.O. 2 to 3 hours before surgery or I.M. 1 to 2 hours before surgery. To control acute nausea and vomiting during surgery, 0.275 mg/kg I.M. repeated after 30 minutes, if needed or fractional 1-mg doses I.V. at 2-minute intervals, maximum dose, 0.275 mg/kg. May repeat fractional I.V. regimen in 30 minutes, if needed; postoperatively, 0.55 mg/kg P.O. q 4 to 6 hours or 0.55 mg/kg I.M.; repeat in 1 hour if needed and hypotension doesn't occur.

I.V. administration
• Drug is compatible with most common I.V. solutions, including D_5W, Ringer's injection, lactated Ringer's injection, and normal saline solution for injection.
• For direct injection, drug may be diluted with normal saline solution for injection and injected into large vein or through tubing of free-flowing I.V. solution.
• Don't exceed 1 mg/minute for adults or 0.5 mg/minute for children.
• For I.V. infusion, dilute with 500 or 1,000 ml normal saline solution and infuse slowly.

⊗ **Incompatibilities**
Aminophylline, amphotericin B, ampicillin, chloramphenicol sodium succinate, chlorothiazide, cimetidine, dimenhydrinate, furosemide, heparin sodium, linezolid, melphalan, methohexital, paclitaxel, penicillin, pentobarbital, phenobarbital, solutions having a pH of 4 to 5, thiopental.

Contraindications and cautions

• Contraindicated in patients hypersensitive to drug and in patients with CNS depression, bone marrow suppression, subcortical damage, and coma.
• Use cautiously in debilitated patients and in those with hepatic or renal disease, severe CV disease (may cause sudden drop in blood pressure); exposure to extreme heat or cold (including antipyretic therapy); exposure to organophosphate insecticides, respiratory disorders, hypocalcemia, seizure disorders; severe reactions to insulin or electroconvulsive therapy; glaucoma; or prostatic hyperplasia.
Lifespan: In pregnant or breast-feeding women, drug isn't recommended. In acutely ill or dehydrated children, use cautiously. In elderly patients, use cautiously.

Adverse reactions

CNS: dizziness, extrapyramidal reactions, ***neuroleptic malignant syndrome,*** pseudoparkinsonism, sedation, ***seizures,*** tardive dyskinesia.
CV: ECG changes, *orthostatic hypotension,* tachycardia.
EENT: blurred vision, ocular changes.
GI: constipation, dry mouth.
GU: *erectile dysfunction,* inhibited ejaculation, menstrual irregularities, urine retention.
Hematologic: ***agranulocytosis, aplastic anemia,*** *hyperprolactinemia,* ***thrombocytopenia, transient leukopenia.***
Hepatic: cholestatic jaundice.
Skin: mild photosensitivity.
Other: allergic reactions, gynecomastia, I.M. injection site pain, sterile abscess.

Interactions

Drug-drug. *Antacids:* May inhibit absorption of oral phenothiazines. Separate antacid and phenothiazine doses by at least 2 hours.
Anticholinergics, including antidepressants and antiparkinsonians: May increase anticholinergic activity and aggravate parkinsonian symptoms. Use with caution.
Barbiturates, lithium: May decrease phenothiazine effect. Observe patient.
Centrally acting antihypertensives: May decrease antihypertensive effect. Monitor patient's blood pressure carefully.
CNS depressants: May increase CNS depression. Avoid use together.
Meperidine: May cause excessive sedation and hypotension. Don't use together.
Propranolol: May increase propranolol and chlorpromazine levels. Monitor patient.
Warfarin: May decrease effect of oral anticoagulants. Monitor PT and INR.
Drug-herb. *Dong quai, St. John's wort:* May increase risk of photosensitivity. Discourage prolonged or unprotected exposure to sunlight.
Kava: May increase the risk or severity of dystonic reactions. Discourage use together.
Yohimbe: May increase risk of toxicity. Discourage use together.
Drug-lifestyle. *Alcohol use:* May increase CNS depression, particularly psychomotor skills. Strongly discourage alcohol use.
Sun exposure: May increase photosensitivity. Discourage prolonged or unprotected exposure to sun.

Effects on lab test results

• May increase CK, GGT, and prolactin levels. May decrease hemoglobin level and hematocrit.
• May increase eosinophil count. May decrease WBC, granulocyte, and platelet counts.

Pharmacokinetics

Absorption: Erratic and variable with oral use; rapid with I.M. use.
Distribution: Wide; level usually is higher in CNS than plasma. 91% to 99% protein-bound.
Metabolism: Extensive. Forms 10 to 12 metabolites, and some are pharmacologically active.
Excretion: Most of drug as metabolites in urine; some in feces. Drug may undergo enterohepatic circulation. *Half-life:* 20 to 24 hours.

Route	Onset	Peak	Duration
P.O.	30–60 min	1–4 hr	4–6 hr
P.O. controlled-release	30–60 min	1–4 hr	10–12 hr
I.V., I.M.	Unknown	Unknown	Unknown
P.R.	> 1 hr	1–4 hr	3–4 hr

Action

Chemical effect: May block postsynaptic dopamine receptors in brain and inhibit medullary chemoreceptor trigger zone.
Therapeutic effect: Relieves nausea and vomiting, hiccups, signs and symptoms of psychosis, acute intermittent porphyria, and tetanus. Produces calmness and sleep preoperatively.

Available forms

Capsules (controlled-release): 30 mg, 75 mg, 150 mg
Injection: 25 mg/ml
Oral concentrate: 30 mg/ml, 100 mg/ml
Suppositories: 25 mg, 100 mg
Syrup: 10 mg/5 ml
Tablets: 10 mg, 25 mg, 50 mg, 100 mg, 200 mg

NURSING PROCESS

Assessment

- Assess patient's underlying condition before therapy and regularly thereafter.
- Be alert for adverse reactions and drug interactions.
- Monitor blood pressure regularly. Watch for orthostatic hypotension, especially with parenteral use. Monitor blood pressure before and after I.M. use.
- Monitor patient for tardive dyskinesia, which may occur after prolonged use. It may not appear until months or years later and may disappear spontaneously or persist for life despite stopping drug.
- Watch for symptoms of neuroleptic malignant syndrome. It's rare, but commonly fatal. It isn't necessarily related to length of drug use or type of neuroleptic, but more than 60% of affected patients are men.
- Monitor therapy with weekly bilirubin tests during the first month, periodic blood tests (CBC and liver function), and ophthalmic tests (long-term use).
- Assess patient's and family's knowledge of drug therapy.

Nursing diagnoses

- Ineffective health maintenance related to patient's underlying condition
- Impaired physical mobility related to drug-induced extrapyramidal reactions
- Deficient knowledge related to drug therapy

Planning and implementation

ALERT: Wear gloves when preparing solutions, and prevent contact with skin and clothing. Oral liquid and parenteral forms can cause contact dermatitis.

- Slight yellowing of injection or concentrate is common; potency isn't affected. Discard very discolored solutions.
- Protect liquid concentrate from light.
- Dilute liquid forms with fruit juice, milk, or semisolid food just before giving.
- Don't give chlorpromazine oral solution and carbamazepine oral solutions together. Mixing causes orange, rubbery precipitate with unknown effect on bioavailability of either drug.
- Shake syrup before giving.
- Don't crush controlled-release form.
- Give deep I.M. only in upper outer quadrant of buttocks. Massage slowly afterward to prevent sterile abscess. Injection stings.
- Store suppositories in cool place.
- Keep patient supine for 1 hour after parenteral delivery, and advise him to get up slowly.
- Don't stop drug abruptly unless required by severe adverse reactions. After abruptly stopping long-term therapy, the patient may experience gastritis, nausea, vomiting, dizziness, and tremors.
- Don't give a dose, and notify prescriber, if patient develops jaundice; symptoms of blood dyscrasia (fever, sore throat, infection, cellulitis, weakness); extrapyramidal reactions that last longer than a few hours or any extrapyramidal reaction in pregnant patients or in children.
- Dystonic reactions may often be treated with diphenhydramine or an antiparkinsonian drug.

ALERT: Don't confuse chlorpromazine with chlorpropamide or clomipramine.

Patient teaching

- Warn patient to avoid activities that require alertness or good psychomotor coordination until CNS effects of drug are known. Drowsiness and dizziness usually subside after first few weeks.
- Instruct patient to avoid alcohol while taking drug.
- Tell patient to notify prescriber about urine retention or constipation.
- Urge patient to use sunblock and wear protective clothing to avoid photosensitivity reactions. Chlorpromazine causes higher risk of photosensitivity than other drugs in its class.

• Instruct patient to use sugarless gum or hard candy to relieve dry mouth.
• Caution patient not to stop taking drug suddenly but to take it exactly as prescribed and not to double doses to compensate for missed ones.
• Tell patient which fluids are appropriate for diluting concentrate, and show dropper technique for measuring dose. Warn patient to avoid spilling liquid on skin because it may cause rash and irritation.
• Advise patient that injection stings.

Evaluation

• Patient has fewer signs and symptoms.
• Patient maintains physical mobility throughout drug therapy.
• Patient and family state understanding of drug therapy.

cholestyramine

(koh-leh-STIGH-ruh-meen)

LoCHOLEST, Prevalite, Questran, Questran Light, Questran Lite ◇

Pharmacologic class: anion exchange resin
Therapeutic class: antilipemic, bile acid sequestrant
Pregnancy risk category: C

Indications and dosages

▶ **Primary hyperlipidemia or pruritus caused by partial bile obstruction; adjunct for reduction of elevated cholesterol level in patients with primary hypercholesterolemia.** *Adults:* 4 g P.O. t.i.d. before meals. Maintenance dosage is 4 g t.i.d. before meals or q.i.d. before meals and at bedtime. Maximum, 24 g daily. *Children:* 240 mg/kg daily in two or three divided doses. Maximum, 8 g daily.

Contraindications and cautions

• Contraindicated in patients hypersensitive to bile-acid sequestering resins and in patients with complete biliary obstruction.
• Use cautiously in patients at risk for constipation and those with conditions aggravated by constipation, such as severe, symptomatic coronary artery disease.

Lifespan: In pregnant and breast-feeding women, use cautiously because of interference with fat-soluble vitamin absorption.

Adverse reactions

GI: *abdominal discomfort, constipation,* fecal impaction, flatulence, hemorrhoids, *nausea,* steatorrhea, vomiting.
Metabolic: folic acid deficiency; ***hyperchloremic acidosis*** (with long-term use or very high dosage); vitamin A, D, E, and K deficiency.
Skin: irritation of skin, tongue, and perianal area; rash.

Interactions

Drug-drug. *Acetaminophen, beta blockers, digoxin, corticosteroids, fat-soluble vitamins (A, D, E, and K), iron preparations, thiazide diuretics, thyroid hormones, warfarin and other coumarin derivatives:* May reduce absorption of these drugs. Give at least 1 hour before or 4 to 6 hours after cholestyramine.

Effects on lab test results

• May increase alkaline phosphatase and chloride levels. May decrease cholesterol; vitamins A, D, E, and K; folic acid; and hemoglobin levels and hematocrit.

Pharmacokinetics

Absorption: Not absorbed.
Distribution: None.
Metabolism: None.
Excretion: Insoluble drug with bile acid complex in feces. *Half-life:* Unknown.

Route	Onset	Peak	Duration
P.O.	1–2 wk	Unknown	2–4 wk

Action

Chemical effect: Combines with bile acid to form insoluble compound that's excreted. The liver must synthesize new bile acid from cholesterol, which reduces LDL cholesterol levels. Excretion of excess bile acids may decrease pruritus associated with partial cholestasis.
Therapeutic effect: Reduces cholesterol level and pruritus.

Available forms

Powder: 210-, 231-, 239-, 378-g cans; 5-, 5.7-, 9-g single-dose packets (4 g of cholestyramine resin in each scoop of powder or single-dose packet)

NURSING PROCESS

Assessment

- Assess patient's cholesterol level and pruritus before therapy.
- Monitor drug effectiveness by checking cholesterol and triglyceride levels in 4 weeks and every 3 to 6 months thereafter; also, ask patient whether pruritus has diminished or abated.
- Be alert for adverse reactions and drug interactions.
- Monitor patient for fat-soluble vitamin deficiency because long-term use may be linked to deficiency of vitamins A, D, E, and K and folic acid.
- Assess patient's and family's knowledge of drug therapy.

Nursing diagnoses

- Risk for injury related to elevated cholesterol level
- Constipation related to drug-induced adverse GI reactions
- Deficient knowledge related to drug therapy

Planning and implementation

- To mix powder, sprinkle on surface of preferred beverage or wet food (soup, applesauce, crushed pineapple). Let stand a few minutes; then stir to obtain uniform suspension. Mixing with carbonated beverages may cause excess foaming. Use large glass, and mix slowly.
- Give drug before meals and at bedtime.
- If therapy is stopped, lower the dose of digoxin to avoid toxicity.
- If severe constipation develops, lower the dose, add stool softener, increase fiber, and give a laxative if needed; or stop drug.
- Give all other drugs at least 1 hour before or 4 to 6 hours after cholestyramine to avoid blocking their absorption.
- Cholestyramine light contains 28.1 mg of phenylalanine per 6.4-g dose.

Patient teaching

- Instruct patient never to take drug in its dry form; esophageal irritation or severe constipation may result. Tell the patient to sprinkle powder on surface of preferred beverage in a large glass; to let mixture stand a few minutes; then to stir thoroughly. The best diluents are water, milk, and juice (especially pulpy fruit juice). Tell him that mixing with carbonated beverages could cause excess foaming. Tell him to swirl small additional amount of liquid in same glass and then to drink it all to make sure he took the whole dose.
- Advise patient to take all other drugs at least 1 hour before or 4 to 6 hours after cholestyramine to avoid blocking their absorption.
- Teach patient about proper dietary management of serum lipids (restricting total fat and cholesterol intake), as well as measures to control other cardiac disease risk factors.
- When appropriate, recommend weight control, exercise, and smoking-cessation programs.

Evaluation

- Patient's cholesterol level is normal with drug therapy.
- Patient maintains normal bowel patterns throughout drug therapy.
- Patient and family state understanding of drug therapy.

cidofovir

(sigh-doh-FOH-veer)

Vistide

Pharmacologic class: inhibitor of viral DNA synthesis
Therapeutic class: antiviral
Pregnancy risk category: C

Indications and dosages

▶ **CMV retinitis in patients with AIDS.** *Adults:* 5 mg/kg I.V. infused over 1 hour once weekly for 2 consecutive weeks, followed by maintenance dosage of 5 mg/kg I.V. infused over 1 hour once q 2 weeks. Probenecid and prehydration with normal saline solution I.V. must be given at the same time and may reduce risk of nephrotoxicity.

Adjust-a-dose: For patients with renal impairment, if creatinine level increases 0.3 to 0.4 mg/dl above baseline, reduce dose to 3 mg/kg at same rate and frequency. If creatinine level increases 0.5 mg/dl or more above baseline, or if patient develops 3+ proteinuria, stop drug.

I.V. administration

- Because of the mutagenic properties of drug, prepare in a class II laminar flow biological safety cabinet. Wear surgical gloves and a closed front surgical gown with knit cuffs.
- If drug contacts skin or membranes, wash and flush thoroughly with water. Place excess drug and all other materials used in the admixture preparation and administration in a leak-proof, puncture-proof container. Dispose of by high temperature.
- To prepare drug for infusion, remove it from vial using syringe, and transfer dose to an infusion bag containing 100 ml normal saline solution.
- Compatibility with Ringer's solution, lactated Ringer's solution, or bacteriostatic infusion fluids hasn't been evaluated.
- Infuse entire volume I.V. at constant rate over 1 hour. Use a standard infusion pump. Because of the risk of increased nephrotoxicity, don't exceed recommended dose, frequency, or rate of administration.
- Give admixtures for infusion within 24 hours of preparation.
- If admixtures aren't used immediately, they may be refrigerated at 36° to 46° F (2° to 8° C) for longer than 24 hours. Let drug reach room temperature before use.

⊗ **Incompatibilities**

Don't add other drugs or supplements to admixture.

Contraindications and cautions

- Contraindicated in patients hypersensitive to drug and in those with history of severe hypersensitivity to probenecid or other sulfa-containing drugs.
- Use cautiously in patients with renal impairment.

Lifespan: In pregnancy, use only if potential benefits to mother outweigh risks to fetus. In women who are breast-feeding, use cautiously. It isn't known whether drug appears in breast milk. In children, safety and effectiveness haven't been studied.

Adverse reactions

CNS: abnormal gait, amnesia, anxiety, *asthenia,* confusion, depression, dizziness, *fever,* hallucinations, *headache,* insomnia, malaise, neuropathy, paresthesia, ***seizures,*** somnolence, syncope.
CV: facial edema, hypotension, orthostatic hypotension, pallor, tachycardia, vasodilation.
EENT: abnormal vision, amblyopia, conjunctivitis, eye disorders, iritis, *ocular hypotony,* pharyngitis, retinal detachment, rhinitis, sinusitis, uveitis.
GI: *abdominal pain, anorexia,* aphthous stomatitis, colitis, constipation, *diarrhea,* dry mouth, dyspepsia, dysphagia, flatulence, gastritis, melena, mouth ulcerations, *nausea,* oral candidiasis, taste disturbance, tongue discoloration, rectal disorders, stomatitis, *vomiting.*
GU: glycosuria, hematuria, ***nephrotoxicity,*** *proteinuria,* urinary incontinence, UTI.
Hematologic: *anemia,* ***neutropenia, thrombocytopenia.***
Hepatic: hepatomegaly.
Metabolic: decreased bicarbonate level, fluid imbalance, hyperglycemia, hyperlipidemia, hyperkalemia, hypocalcemia, hypokalemia, weight loss.
Musculoskeletal: arthralgia; myalgia; myasthenia; pain in back, chest, or neck.
Respiratory: ***asthma,*** bronchitis, cough, *dyspnea,* hiccups, increased sputum, lung disorders, pneumonia.
Skin: acne, *alopecia,* dry skin, pruritus, *rash,* skin discoloration, sweating, urticaria.
Other: allergic reactions, *chills,* herpes simplex, *infections,* ***sarcoma, sepsis.***

Interactions

Drug-drug. *Nephrotoxic drugs (such as aminoglycosides, amphotericin B, foscarnet, I.V. pentamidine):* May increase nephrotoxicity. Use together is contraindicated.
Probenecid: Interacts with metabolism or renal tubular excretion of many drugs. May be used with drug to decrease nephrotoxicity.

Effects on lab test results

- May increase BUN, creatinine, urine glucose, protein, alkaline phosphatase, ALT, AST, and LDH levels. May decrease calcium, bicarbonate, and hemoglobin levels and hematocrit. May increase or decrease potassium level.
- May decrease neutrophil and platelet counts.

Pharmacokinetics

Absorption: Given I.V.
Distribution: Less than 6% protein-bound.
Metabolism: Mainly by kidneys.

Excretion: By renal tubular secretion. *Half-life:* Unknown.

Route	Onset	Peak	Duration
I.V.	Unknown	Unknown	Unknown

Action

Chemical effect: Selective inhibition of CMV DNA polymerase; inhibits DNA viral synthesis.
Therapeutic effect: Reduces CMV replication.

Available forms

Injection: 75 mg/ml in 5-ml ampule

NURSING PROCESS

Assessment

- Before each dose, check WBC and neutrophil counts, with differential, and renal function.
- Monitor intraocular pressure, visual acuity, and ocular symptoms periodically.

ALERT: Don't use drug in patients with baseline creatinine level above 1.5 mg/dl or calculated creatinine clearance of 55 ml/minute or less unless potential benefits outweigh risks. Monitor creatinine and urine protein within 48 hours before each dose and adjust dose according to renal function.

- Assess patient's and family's knowledge of drug therapy.

Nursing diagnoses

- Ineffective protection related to presence of virus
- Deficient knowledge related to drug therapy

Planning and implementation

- Give 1 L normal saline solution, usually over 1- to 2-hour period, immediately before each cidofovir infusion.
- Give probenecid with each cidofovir infusion.

Patient teaching

- Inform patient that drug doesn't cure CMV retinitis and that regular ophthalmologic follow-up examinations are needed.
- Explain that close monitoring of renal function is critical.
- Tell patient to take probenecid with food to reduce drug-related nausea and vomiting.
- Advise men to use barrier contraception during and for 3 months after drug therapy.

Evaluation

- Patient's infection is eradicated.
- Patient and family state understanding of drug therapy.

cilostazol

(sil-OS-tah-zol)

Pletal

Pharmacologic class: phosphodiesterase III inhibitor
Therapeutic class: antiplatelet, arterial vasodilator
Pregnancy risk category: C

Indications and dosages

▶ **To reduce symptoms of intermittent claudication.** *Adults:* 100 mg P.O. b.i.d. taken at least 30 minutes before or 2 hours after breakfast and dinner.

Adjust-a-dose: If used with CYP3A4- or CYP2C19-inhibiting drugs, decrease dosage to 50 mg P.O. b.i.d. because cilostazol level may be increased.

Contraindications and cautions

- Contraindicated in patients hypersensitive to drug or its components and in those with heart failure.
- Use cautiously in patients with severe underlying heart disease and with other drugs that have antiplatelet activity.

Lifespan: In breast-feeding women, avoid use. In children, safety and effectiveness haven't been established.

Adverse reactions

CNS: *dizziness, headache,* vertigo.
CV: *palpitations,* peripheral edema, tachycardia.
EENT: *pharyngitis, rhinitis.*
GI: abdominal pain, *abnormal stools, diarrhea,* dyspepsia, flatulence, nausea.
Musculoskeletal: back pain, myalgia.
Respiratory: increased cough.
Other: *infection.*

Interactions

Drug-drug. *Diltiazem:* May increase cilostazol level. Reduce cilostazol dosage to 50 mg b.i.d.

Erythromycin, other macrolides: May increase levels of cilostazol and one of the metabolites. Reduce cilostazol dosage to 50 mg b.i.d.
Omeprazole: May increase level of active cilostazol metabolite. Reduce cilostazol dosage to 50 mg b.i.d.
Strong inhibitors of CYP3A4, such as fluconazole, fluoxetine, fluvoxamine, itraconazole, ketoconazole, miconazole, nefazodone, sertraline: May increase levels of cilostazol and its metabolites. Reduce cilostazol dosage to 50 mg b.i.d.
Drug-food. *Grapefruit juice:* May increase cilostazol level. Tell patient to avoid grapefruit juice during therapy.
Drug-lifestyle. *Smoking:* May decrease cilostazol exposure by about 20%. Monitor patient closely and discourage patient from smoking.

Effects on lab test results

- May increase HDL level. May decrease triglyceride level.

Pharmacokinetics

Absorption: Increases by 90% when given with a high-fat meal. Absolute bioavailability is unknown.
Distribution: Highly protein-bound, mainly to albumin.
Metabolism: Extensive, mainly by CYP3A4. There are two active metabolites, one of which accounts for at least 50% of activity.
Excretion: 74% through urine. 20% in feces. *Half-life:* 11 to 13 hours.

Route	Onset	Peak	Duration
P.O.	Unknown	2–4 hr	Unknown

Action

Chemical effect: Drug is thought to inhibit the enzyme phosphodiesterase III, causing an increase of cAMP in platelets and blood vessels, thus inhibiting platelet aggregation. Drug also has a vasodilating effect that's greatest in the femoral vascular beds.
Therapeutic effect: Reduces symptoms of intermittent claudication.

Available forms

Tablets: 50 mg, 100 mg

NURSING PROCESS

Assessment

- Assess patient's underlying condition and pain level before therapy and regularly thereafter.
- Before therapy starts, make sure patient has a thorough physical examination for signs and symptoms of heart failure.
- Be alert for adverse reactions and drug interactions.
- Assess patient's and family's knowledge of drug therapy.

Nursing diagnoses

- Acute pain related to underlying disease
- Ineffective peripheral tissue perfusion secondary to underlying disease
- Deficient knowledge related to drug therapy

Planning and implementation

- Beneficial effects may not appear for up to 12 weeks.
- Dose can be reduced or drug stopped without rebound effects, such as platelet hyperaggregability. Notify prescriber of coagulation study results.
- Monitor heart rate and CV condition regularly for evidence of heart failure or tachyarrhythmias.

Patient teaching

- Advise patient to read the patient package insert carefully before starting therapy.
- Instruct patient to take cilostazol on an empty stomach, at least 30 minutes before or 2 hours after breakfast and dinner.
- Tell patient that the beneficial effect of drug on intermittent claudication isn't likely to be noticed for 2 to 4 weeks and that it may take as long as 12 weeks.
- Instruct patient not to drink grapefruit juice while taking drug.
- Inform patient that CV risk is unknown in patients who use the drug on a long-term basis and in patients who have severe underlying heart disease.
- Tell patient that drug may cause dizziness. Warn patient not to drive or perform other activities that require alertness until response to drug is known.

Evaluation

- Patient experiences a decrease in pain.
- Patient has adequate tissue perfusion.

• Patient and family state understanding of drug therapy.

cimetidine

(sih-MEH-tih-deen)

Tagamet, Tagamet HB†

Pharmacologic class: H_2-receptor antagonist
Therapeutic class: antiulcerative
Pregnancy risk category: B

Indications and dosages

▶ **Duodenal ulcer (short-term therapy).** *Adults and children age 16 and older:* 800 mg P.O. at bedtime. Or 400 mg P.O. b.i.d. or 300 mg q.i.d., with meals and at bedtime. Therapy continues for 4 to 6 weeks unless endoscopy shows healing. For maintenance therapy, 400 mg at bedtime.

▶ **Active benign gastric ulceration.** *Adults:* 800 mg P.O. at bedtime, or 300 mg P.O. q.i.d., with meals and at bedtime, for up to 8 weeks.

▶ **Pathologic hypersecretory conditions (such as Zollinger-Ellison syndrome, systemic mastocytosis, and multiple endocrine adenomas).** *Adults and children age 16 and older:* 300 mg P.O. q.i.d. with meals and at bedtime; adjust to patient's needs. Maximum oral daily dosage is 2,400 mg.

▶ **Gastroesophageal reflux disease.** *Adults:* 800 mg P.O. b.i.d. or 400 mg q.i.d. before meals and at bedtime for up to 12 weeks.

▶ **Heartburn.** *Adults:* 200 mg Tagamet HB† P.O. with water as symptoms occur, or as directed, up to b.i.d. Maximum, 400 mg daily. Don't give daily for more than 2 weeks.

▶ **To prevent upper GI bleeding in critically ill patients.** *Adults:* 50 mg/hour by continuous I.V. infusion for up to 7 days.

Adjust-a-dose: For patients with renal impairment, if creatinine clearance is less than 30 ml/minute, give 25 mg/hour by continuous I.V. infusion.

▶ **Hospitalized patients with intractable ulcers or hypersecretory conditions or patients who can't take oral drugs.** *Adults:* 300 mg I.M. q 6 to 8 hours. Or 300 mg diluted to 20 ml with normal saline solution or other compatible solution by I.V. push over 5 minutes q 6 to 8 hours. Or 300 mg diluted in 50 ml D_5W or other compatible solution by I.V. infusion over 15 to 20 minutes q 6 to 8 hours. To increase dosage, give 300-mg doses more frequently to maximum daily dosage of 2,400 mg. Or, 37.5 mg/hour (900 mg/day) I.V. continuous infusion diluted in 100 to 1,000 ml of compatible solution.

▶ **Active upper GI bleeding, peptic esophagitis, stress ulcers‡.** *Adults:* 1 to 2 g I.V. or P.O. daily in four divided doses.

Adjust-a-dose: For patients with creatinine clearance less than 30 ml/minute, decrease dosage to 300 mg P.O. or I.V. q 12 hours. If patient also has liver impairment, may need to further reduce dosage. May increase cautiously to q 8 hours based on patient response.

I.V. administration

• Dilute I.V. solutions with normal saline solution, D_5W, dextrose 10% in water, combinations of them, lactated Ringer's solution, or 5% sodium bicarbonate injection. Don't dilute with sterile water for injection. Cimetidine may be added to total parenteral nutrition solutions with or without fat emulsion.
• Direct injection requires dilution of drug in 20 ml of compatible solution. Give direct injection over at least 5 minutes. Rapid I.V. injection may result in arrhythmias and hypotension.
• Infuse drug over at least 30 minutes to minimize risk of adverse cardiac effects. If giving continuous I.V. infusion, use infusion pump if giving a total volume of 250 ml over 24 hours or less.
• In children younger than age 16, dosages of 20 to 40 mg/kg are seldom used.

⊗ **Incompatibilities**

Allopurinol, amphotericin B, barbiturates, cefepime, chlorpromazine, combination atropine sulfate and pentobarbital sodium, indomethacin sodium trihydrate, pentobarbital sodium, warfarin.

Contraindications and cautions

• Contraindicated in patients hypersensitive to drug.
• Use cautiously in debilitated patients because they may be more susceptible to drug-induced confusion.

Lifespan: In pregnant women, use cautiously. In breast-feeding women, drug is contraindicated. In patients younger than age 16, experience with drug is limited, and drug should only be used when anticipated benefits outweigh the risks. In elderly patients, use cautiously.

Adverse reactions

CNS: confusion, dizziness, headaches, peripheral neuropathy.
CV: ***bradycardia.***
GI: mild and transient diarrhea.
Hematologic: ***agranulocytosis, aplastic anemia, neutropenia, thrombocytopenia.***
Hepatic: jaundice.
Musculoskeletal: muscle pain.
Skin: acnelike rash, urticaria.
Other: hypersensitivity reactions, mild gynecomastia (if taken longer than 1 month).

Interactions

Drug-drug. *Antacids:* May interfere with cimetidine absorption. Separate administration by at least 1 hour.
Calcium channel blockers, carbamazepine, labetalol, pentoxifylline, phenytoin, some benzodiazepines, sulfonylureas, tacrine, theophylline, valproic acid, warfarin: May inhibit hepatic microsomal enzyme metabolism of these drugs. Monitor levels of these drugs.
Lidocaine (I.V.): May decrease clearance of lidocaine, increasing the risk of toxicity. Consider using a different H_2 antagonist. Monitor lidocaine level closely.
Metoprolol, propranolol, timolol: May increase the pharmacologic effects of beta blocker. Consider using another H_2 antagonist or decrease the dose of beta blocker.
Procainamide: May increase procainamide level. Use cautiously. Monitor procainamide level closely, and adjust the dose as needed.
Drug-herb. *Pennyroyal:* May change the rate at which toxic metabolites of pennyroyal form. Discourage use together.
Yerba maté: May decrease clearance of yerba maté methylxanthines and cause toxicity. Tell patient to use together cautiously.

Effects on lab test results

- May increase creatinine, alkaline phosphatase, AST, and ALT levels. May decrease hemoglobin level and hematocrit.
- May decrease neutrophil, granulocyte, leukocyte, and platelet counts.

Pharmacokinetics

Absorption: 60% to 75% of oral amount. Rate, but not extent, may be affected by food. Unknown after I.M. use.
Distribution: To many body tissues. 15% to 20% protein-bound.
Metabolism: 30% to 40%.
Excretion: Mainly in urine (48% of oral dose, 75% of parenteral dose); 10% of oral dose in feces. *Half-life:* 2 hours.

Route	Onset	Peak	Duration
P.O.	Unknown	45–90 min	4–5 hr
I.V.	Unknown	Immediate	Unknown
I.M.	Unknown	Unknown	Unknown

Action

Chemical effect: Competitively inhibits action of H_2 at receptor sites of parietal cells, decreasing gastric acid secretion.
Therapeutic effect: Lessens upper GI irritation caused by increased gastric acid secretion.

Available forms

Injection: 150 mg/ml; 300 mg in 50 ml normal saline solution for injection
Oral liquid: 300 mg/5 ml
Tablets: 200 mg†, 300 mg, 400 mg, 800 mg

NURSING PROCESS

Assessment

- Assess patient's underlying upper GI condition before and regularly throughout therapy.
- Be alert for adverse reactions and drug interactions.
- Identify tablet strength when obtaining drug history.
- Monitor patient's CV condition during I.V. use because drug can cause profound bradycardia and other cardiotoxic effects when given too rapidly.
- Assess patient's and family's knowledge of drug therapy.

Nursing diagnoses

- Impaired tissue integrity related to patient's underlying condition
- Diarrhea related to drug-induced adverse reaction
- Deficient knowledge related to drug therapy

Planning and implementation
- Give tablets with meals to ensure more consistent therapeutic effect.
- I.M. administration may be painful.
- Hemodialysis reduces level of drug. Schedule dose at end of hemodialysis. Lower dose in patients with renal impairment.
- Cimetidine shouldn't be used for self-medication (Tagamet HB†) in children younger than age 12 unless directed by a physician.

ALERT: Don't confuse cimetidine with simethicone.

Patient teaching
- Remind patient taking drug once daily to take it at bedtime for best results.
- Instruct patient to take drug as directed and to continue taking it even after pain subsides, to allow for adequate healing.
- Remind patient not to take antacid within 1 hour of taking drug.
- Because of high potential for drug interactions, advise patient to tell prescriber if he's taking other drugs.
- Urge patient to avoid cigarette smoking because it may increase gastric acid secretion and worsen disease.
- Instruct patient to immediately report black tarry stools, diarrhea, confusion, or rash.

Evaluation
- Patient experiences decrease in or relief of upper GI symptoms with drug therapy.
- Patient maintains normal bowel habits throughout drug therapy.
- Patient and family state understanding of drug therapy.

cinacalcet hydrochloride
(sin-uh-KAL-seht high-droh-KLOR-ighd)
Sensipar

Pharmacologic class: calcimimetic
Therapeutic class: hyperparathyroidism drug
Pregnancy risk category: C

Indications and dosages
▶ **Secondary hyperparathyroidism in patients with chronic kidney disease on dialysis.** *Adults:* Initially, 30 mg P.O. once daily; adjust no more than q 2 to 4 weeks through sequential doses of 60 mg, 90 mg, 120 mg, and 180 mg P.O. once daily, to reach target range of 150 to 300 picograms (pg)/ml of intact parathyroid hormone (iPTH).

▶ **Hypercalcemia in patients with parathyroid carcinoma.** *Adults:* Initially, 30 mg P.O. b.i.d.; adjust q 2 to 4 weeks through sequential doses of 60 mg, and 90 mg P.O. b.i.d., and 90 mg P.O. t.i.d. or q.i.d. daily p.r.n. to normalize calcium level.

Contraindications and cautions
- Contraindicated in patients hypersensitive to drug or any of its components and in patients with calcium level below 8.4 mg/dl.
- Use cautiously in patients with a history of a seizure disorder and patients with moderate to severe hepatic impairment.

Lifespan: In women who are breast-feeding, use cautiously. It's not known if drug appears in breast milk. In children, safety and effectiveness haven't been established.

Adverse reactions
CNS: asthenia, *dizziness.*
CV: chest pain, hypertension.
GI: anorexia, diarrhea, nausea, vomiting.
Musculoskeletal: *myalgia.*
Other: dialysis venous access site infection.

Interactions
Drug-drug. *Drugs metabolized mainly by CYP2D6 with a narrow therapeutic index (such as flecainide, thioridazine, most tricyclic antidepressants, vinblastine):* May strongly inhibit CYP2D6. Adjust dosages of these drugs as needed.
Drugs that strongly inhibit CYP3A4 (such as erythromycin, itraconazole, ketoconazole): May increase cinacalcet level. Monitor parathyroid hormone (PTH) and calcium level closely, and adjust cinacalcet dosage as needed if patient starts or stops therapy with one of these drugs.
Drug-food. *Food:* Improved concentrations of drug. Give with food or shortly after a meal.

Effects on lab test results
- May decrease calcium, phosphorous, and testosterone levels.

Pharmacokinetics
Absorption: Increases when drug is given with meals. Level peaks in about 2 to 6 hours.

Distribution: High volume. Drug reaches steady-state drug level within 7 days. 93 to 97% protein-bound.
Metabolism: Mainly by CYP3A4, CYP2D6, and CYP1A2.
Excretion: 80% in urine, 15% in feces. *Half-life:* 30 to 40 hours.

Route	Onset	Peak	Duration
P.O.	Unknown	2–6 hr	Unknown

Action

Chemical effect: Increases the sensitivity of calcium-sensing receptor to extracellular calcium.
Therapeutic effect: Decreases iPTH and calcium levels.

Available forms

Tablet: 30 mg, 60 mg, 90 mg

NURSING PROCESS

Assessment

ALERT: Monitor calcium level closely, especially if patient has a history of seizures, because a decreased calcium level lowers the threshold for seizures.
- Measure calcium level within 1 week of starting therapy or adjusting dose. Once the maintenance dosage has been established, measure calcium level monthly in patients with chronic kidney disease on dialysis and every 2 months in patients with parathyroid carcinoma.
- Watch carefully for evidence of hypocalcemia, such as paresthesias, myalgias, cramping, tetany, and seizures.
- Measure iPTH 1 to 4 weeks after therapy starts or dosage is changed. Once the maintenance dosage is established, monitor PTH every 1 to 3 months. Keep level at 150 to 300 pg/ml in patients with chronic kidney disease on dialysis.
- Assess patient's and family's knowledge of drug therapy.

Nursing diagnoses

- Risk for injury related to drug-induced hypocalcemia
- Noncompliance related to GI adverse effects of drug
- Deficient knowledge related to drug therapy

Planning and implementation

- In patient with moderate to severe hepatic impairment, adjust dose based on PTH and calcium level. Monitor patient closely.
- Give drug alone or with vitamin D sterols, phosphate binders, or both.
- If calcium level is 7.5 to 8.4 mg/dl or patient develops symptoms of hypocalcemia, give phosphate binders containing calcium, vitamin D sterols, or both to raise level. If level is below 7.5 mg/dl or hypocalcemia symptoms persist, and the vitamin D dose has reached the maximum, withhold drug until level reaches 8 mg/dl, hypocalcemia symptoms resolve, or both. Resume with the next lowest dose.
- A dynamic bone disease may develop if iPTH levels are suppressed below 100 pg/ml. If this occurs, reduce the dosage of drug or vitamin D sterols, or stop therapy.

ALERT: Drug isn't approved for patients with chronic kidney disease who aren't on dialysis because they have an increased risk of hypocalcemia.

Patient teaching
- Tell patient to take tablets whole, with food or shortly after a meal.
- Advise patient to report adverse reactions and signs of hypocalcemia, which include paresthesias, muscle weakness, muscle cramping, and muscle spasm.

Evaluation

- Patient doesn't develop hypocalcemia.
- Patient doesn't experience GI adverse effects.
- Patient and family state understanding of drug therapy.

ciprofloxacin

(sih-proh-FLOKS-uh-sin)
Cipro, Cipro I.V., Ciproxin ◇, Cipro XR

Pharmacologic class: fluoroquinolone
Therapeutic class: antibiotic
Pregnancy risk category: C

Indications and dosages

▶ **Mild to moderate UTI.** *Adults:* 250 mg P.O. or 200 mg I.V., q 12 hours.
▶ **Severe or complicated UTI; mild to moderate bone and joint infections; mild to moderate respiratory tract infections; mild to**

moderate skin and skin-structure infections; infectious diarrhea; intra-abdominal infection. *Adults:* 500 mg P.O. or 400 mg I.V., q 12 hours.

▶ **Severe or complicated bone or joint infections; severe respiratory tract infections; severe skin and skin-structure infections.** *Adults:* 750 mg P.O. q 12 hours. Or 400 mg I.V. q 8 hours.

▶ **Mild to moderate acute sinusitis caused by *Haemophilus influenzae, Streptococcus pneumoniae,* or *Moraxella catarrhalis;* mild to moderate chronic bacterial prostatitis caused by *Escherichia coli* or *Proteus mirabilis.*** *Adults:* 500 mg P.O. q 12 hours or 400 mg I.V. infusion q 12 hours.

▶ **Febrile neutropenia.** *Adults:* 400 mg I.V. q 8 hours for 7 to 14 days given in conjunction with piperacillin sodium (50 mg/kg I.V. q 4 hours, not to exceed 24 g daily).

▶ **Inhalation anthrax (postexposure).** *Adults:* 400 mg I.V. q 12 hours initially until susceptibility tests are known, then switch to 500 mg P.O. b.i.d. when patient's condition improves.
Children: 10 mg/kg I.V. q 12 hours, then switch to 15 mg/kg P.O. q 12 hours when patient's condition improves. Don't exceed 800 mg I.V. daily or 1 g P.O. daily.
For all patients: Also use one or two additional antimicrobials. Treat for a total of 60 days (I.V. and P.O. combined).

▶ **Acute uncomplicated cystitis.** *Women:* 100 or 250 mg P.O. q 12 hours for 3 days.

▶ **Cutaneous anthrax‡.** *Adults:* 500 mg P.O. b.i.d. for 60 days.
Children: 10 to 15 mg/kg q 12 hours, not to exceed 1 g daily, for 60 days.

▶ **Uncomplicated urethral, endocervical, rectal‡, or pharyngeal‡ gonorrhea.** *Adults:* 500 mg P.O. as a single dose with other anti-infectives if chlamydial infection isn't ruled out.

▶ ***Neisseria meningitidis* in nasal passages‡.** *Adults:* 500 to 750 mg P.O. as a single dose, or 250 mg P.O. b.i.d. for 2 days, or 500 mg P.O. b.i.d. for 5 days.

Adjust-a-dose: In patients with renal impairment, for all indications above, if creatinine clearance is 30 to 50 ml/minute, give 250 to 500 mg P.O. q 12 hours or the usual I.V. dose; if creatinine clearance is 5 to 29 ml/minute, give 250 to 500 mg q 18 hours or 200 to 400 mg I.V. q 18 to 24 hours. If patient is on hemodialysis, give 250 to 500 mg P.O. q 24 hours after dialysis.

▶ **UTI.** *Adults:* If uncomplicated, 500 mg (extended-release) P.O. once daily for 3 days. If complicated, 1 g (extended-release) P.O. once daily for 3 days.

Adjust-a-dose: For patients with renal impairment, if creatinine clearance is less than 30 ml/minute, give 500 mg (extended-release) P.O. daily. For dialysis patients, give dose after dialysis session.

I.V. administration

- Dilute drug using D_5W or normal saline solution for injection to final concentration of 1 to 2 mg/ml. Infuse over 1 hour into large vein.
- If giving drug through a Y-type set, stop the other I.V. solution during infusion.

⊗ **Incompatibilities**

Aminophylline, ampicillin-sulbactam, azithromycin, cefepime, clindamycin phosphate, dexamethasone sodium phosphate, furosemide, heparin sodium, methylprednisolone sodium succinate, phenytoin sodium.

Contraindications and cautions

- Contraindicated in patients hypersensitive to fluoroquinolones.
- Use cautiously in patients with CNS disorders, such as severe cerebral arteriosclerosis or seizure disorders, and in those at increased risk for seizures. May cause CNS stimulation.
- Immunocompromised patients may receive the usual dose and regimen for anthrax.

Lifespan: In pregnant women, use cautiously. Pregnant women may receive the usual dose and regimen for anthrax. In breast-feeding women, drug is contraindicated because it appears in breast milk. In children, safety and effectiveness for indications other than anthrax haven't been established. In children younger than age 18, avoid use of Cipro XR because its safety and effectiveness haven't been established.

Adverse reactions

CNS: confusion, hallucinations, headache, light-headedness, paresthesia, restlessness, ***seizures,*** tremor.
CV: thrombophlebitis.
GI: abdominal pain or discomfort, *diarrhea, nausea,* oral candidiasis, vomiting.
GU: crystalluria, interstitial nephritis.

Hematologic: eosinophilia, ***leukopenia, neutropenia, thrombocytopenia.***
Musculoskeletal: achiness, arthralgia, joint inflammation, joint or back pain, joint stiffness, neck or chest pain.
Skin: photosensitivity, rash, ***Stevens-Johnson syndrome.***
Other: burning, erythema, pruritus, swelling with I.V. use.

Interactions

Drug-drug. *Aluminum hydroxide, aluminum-magnesium hydroxide, calcium carbonate, magnesium hydroxide:* May decrease effects of ciprofloxacin. Give antacid at least 6 hours before or 2 hours after ciprofloxacin.
Iron salts: May decrease absorption of ciprofloxacin, reducing anti-infective response. Give at least 2 hours apart.
Probenecid: May elevate level of ciprofloxacin. Monitor patient for toxicity.
Sucralfate: May decrease absorption of ciprofloxacin, reducing anti-infective response. Give at least 6 hours apart.
Theophylline: May increase theophylline level and prolong theophylline half-life. Monitor level of theophylline and observe patient for adverse effects.
Tizanidine: May increase plasma level of tizanidine and cause low blood pressure, somnolence, dizziness, and slowed psychomotor skills. Avoid use together.
Warfarin: May enhance anticoagulant effects. Monitor PT closely.
Drug-herb. *Yerba maté:* May decrease clearance of yerba maté methylxanthines and cause toxicity. Discourage use together.
Drug-food. *Orange juice fortified with calcium:* May decrease absorption of drug, reducing effects. Advise patient to avoid taking drug with calcium-fortified orange juice.
Drug-lifestyle. *Caffeine:* May increase effects of caffeine. Monitor patient.

Effects on lab test results

- May increase BUN, creatinine, ALT, AST, alkaline phosphatase, bilirubin, LDH, and GGT levels.
- May increase eosinophil count. May decrease WBC, neutrophil, and platelet counts.

Pharmacokinetics

Absorption: About 70%. Food delays rate but not extent; 35% of Cipro XR is an immediate-release form, whereas 65% is a slow-release matrix.
Distribution: 20% to 40% protein-bound. CSF level is only 10% of this level.
Metabolism: May be hepatic. Four metabolites have been identified; each has less antimicrobial activity than parent compound.
Excretion: Mainly renal. *Half-life:* 4 hours. *Half-life of Cipro XR:* 6 hours in adults with normal renal function.

Route	Onset	Peak	Duration
P.O.	Unknown	1–2 hr	Unknown
P.O. extended-release	Unknown	1–4 hr	Unknown
I.V.	Immediate	Immediate	Unknown

Action

Chemical effect: Unknown. Bactericidal effects may result from inhibition of bacterial DNA gyrase and prevention of replication in susceptible bacteria.
Therapeutic effect: Kills susceptible bacteria.

Available forms

Infusion (premixed): 200 mg in 100 ml D_5W, 400 mg in 200 ml D_5W
Injection: 200 mg, 400 mg
Oral suspension: 250 mg/5 ml; 500 mg/5 ml
Tablets: 100 mg, 250 mg, 500 mg, 750 mg
Tablets (extended-release, film-coated): 500 mg, 1,000 mg

NURSING PROCESS

Assessment

- Assess patient's infection before therapy and regularly throughout.
- Before giving first dose, obtain specimen for culture and sensitivity tests. Begin therapy pending results.
- Be alert for adverse reactions and drug interactions.
- If adverse GI reactions occur, monitor patient's hydration.
- Assess patient's and family's knowledge of drug therapy.

Nursing diagnoses
- Ineffective protection related to presence of bacteria
- Risk for deficient fluid volume related to drug-induced adverse GI reactions
- Deficient knowledge related to drug therapy

Planning and implementation
- Give oral form 2 hours after meal or 2 hours before or 6 hours after taking antacids, sucralfate, or products that contain iron (such as vitamins with mineral supplements). Food doesn't affect absorption but may delay peak level.
- Reduce dose in patients with renal impairment.
- Have patient drink plenty of fluids to reduce risk of crystalluria.
- Additional antimicrobials for anthrax multidrug regimen can include rifampin, vancomycin, penicillin, ampicillin, chloramphenicol, imipenem, clindamycin, and clarithromycin.
- Steroids may be considered as adjunctive therapy for anthrax patients with severe edema and for meningitis, based on experience with bacterial meningitis of other etiologies.
- Ciprofloxacin and doxycycline are first-line therapy for anthrax. Amoxicillin 500 mg P.O. t.i.d. for adults and 80 mg/kg daily divided q 8 hours for children is an option for completion of therapy after improvement.
- Follow current Centers for Disease Control and Prevention recommendations for anthrax.

Patient teaching
- Tell patient to take drug 2 hours after meal and to take prescribed antacids at least 2 hours after taking drug.
- Advise patient not to crush, split, or chew the extended-release tablets, but to swallow them whole.
- Advise patient to drink plenty of fluids to reduce risk of crystalluria.
- Warn patient to avoid hazardous tasks that require alertness, such as driving, until CNS effects of drug are known.
- Advise patient to avoid caffeine while taking drug because of potential for cumulative caffeine effects.
- Advise patient that hypersensitivity reactions may occur even after first dose. If he notices rash or other allergic reaction, tell him to stop taking the drug and notify prescriber immediately.
- Instruct patient either to stop breast-feeding or request a different drug.

Evaluation
- Patient is free from infection.
- Patient maintains adequate hydration throughout drug therapy.
- Patient and family state understanding of drug therapy.

cisplatin (cis-platinum)
(sis-PLAH-tin)
Platinol-AQ

Pharmacologic class: alkylating drug
Therapeutic class: antineoplastic
Pregnancy risk category: D

Indications and dosages
▶ **Adjunct therapy in metastatic testicular cancer.** *Adults:* 20 mg/m² I.V. daily for 5 days. Repeat q 3 weeks for three cycles or longer.

▶ **Adjunct therapy in metastatic ovarian cancer.** *Adults:* 100 mg/m² I.V.; repeat q 4 weeks. Or 75 to 100 mg/m² I.V. once q 4 weeks with cyclophosphamide.

▶ **Advanced bladder cancer.** *Adults:* 50 to 70 mg/m² I.V. q 3 to 4 weeks. Give 50 mg/m² q 4 weeks to patients who have received other antineoplastics or radiation therapy.

▶ **Head and neck cancer‡.** *Adults:* 80 to 120 mg/m² I.V. once q 3 weeks.

▶ **Metastatic or recurrent cervical cancer‡.** *Adults:* 50 mg/m² I.V. once q 3 weeks.

▶ **Invasive cervical cancer‡.** *Adults:* 40 to 75 mg/m² I.V. weekly or daily with radiation therapy.

▶ **Non–small-cell lung cancer‡.** *Adults:* 75 to 100 mg/m² I.V. q 3 to 4 weeks with other drugs.

▶ **Brain tumor‡.** *Children:* 60 mg/m² I.V. for 2 days q 3 to 4 weeks.

▶ **Osteogenic sarcoma or neuroblastoma‡.** *Children:* 90 mg/m² I.V. q 3 weeks.

▶ **Advanced esophageal cancer‡.** *Adults:* 50 to 120 mg/m² I.V. q 3 to 4 weeks when used alone, or 75 to 100 mg/m² I.V. q 3 to 4 weeks when used with other chemotherapy.

I.V. administration

- Preparing and giving drug are linked to carcinogenic, mutagenic, and teratogenic risks. Follow facility policy to reduce risks.
- Reconstitute powder using sterile water for injection. Add 10 ml to 10-mg vial or 50 ml to 50-mg vial to make a solution containing 1 mg/ml. Further dilute with D_5W in one-third normal saline solution for injection or dextrose 5% in half-normal saline solution for injection. Solutions are stable for 20 hours at room temperature. Don't refrigerate.
- Infusions are most stable in chloride-containing solutions (such as normal, half-normal, and quarter-normal saline solution). Don't use D_5W alone.
- To prevent hypokalemia, potassium chloride (10 to 20 mEq/L) is commonly added to I.V. fluids before and after therapy. Magnesium sulfate may be added to prevent hypomagnesemia.
- Hydrate patient with normal saline solution before giving drug. Maintain urine output of at least 100 ml/hour for 4 consecutive hours before therapy and for 24 hours after therapy. Prehydration and diuresis may reduce renal toxicity and ototoxicity significantly.
- Give mannitol or furosemide boluses or infusions before and with infusion to maintain diureses of 100 to 400 ml/hour during and for 24 hours after therapy. I.V. infusion in 2 L dextrose 5% in half-normal saline solution or dextrose 5% in 0.33% sodium chloride solution with 37.5 g mannitol over 6 to 8 hours is recommended.

⊗ **Incompatibilities**
Amifostine, cefepime, D_5W, fluorouracil, mesna, 0.1% sodium chloride solution, piperacillin sodium with tazobactam sodium, sodium bicarbonate, sodium bisulfate, sodium thiosulfate, solutions with a chloride content less than 2%, thiotepa. Don't use needles or I.V. administration sets that contain aluminum because it will displace platinum, causing loss of potency and formation of black precipitate.

Contraindications and cautions

- Contraindicated in patients hypersensitive to drug or other platinum-containing compounds. Also contraindicated in patients with severe renal disease, hearing impairment, or myelosuppression.

Lifespan: In pregnant women, use cautiously and only when absolutely needed because fetal harm may occur. In breast-feeding women, drug isn't recommended. In children, safety and effectiveness haven't been established.

Adverse reactions

CNS: *peripheral neuritis,* ***seizures.***
EENT: *hearing loss, tinnitus.*
GI: diarrhea, loss of taste, metallic taste, *nausea and vomiting beginning 1 to 4 hours after dose and lasting 24 hours.*
GU: NEPHROTOXICITY.
Hematologic: ***anemia, leukopenia,*** **MILD MYELOSUPPRESSION,** nadirs in circulating platelet and WBC counts on days 18 to 23 with recovery by day 39, ***thrombocytopenia.***
Metabolic: hypocalcemia, hypokalemia, hypomagnesemia.
Other: ***anaphylactoid reaction.***

Interactions

Drug-drug. *Aminoglycoside antibiotics:* May cause additive nephrotoxicity. Monitor renal function studies carefully.
Bumetanide, furosemide: May cause additive ototoxicity. Avoid use together.
Phenytoin: May decrease phenytoin level. Monitor level.

Effects on lab test results

- May increase uric acid, liver enzyme, and bilirubin levels. May decrease magnesium, potassium, calcium, sodium, phosphate, and hemoglobin levels and hematocrit.
- May decrease WBC, RBC, and platelet counts.

Pharmacokinetics

Absorption: Given I.V.
Distribution: Wide, with highest level in kidneys, liver, and prostate. Doesn't readily cross blood–brain barrier. Extensively and irreversibly bound to plasma and tissue proteins.
Metabolism: Unknown.
Excretion: Mainly unchanged in urine. *Half-life:* Initial phase, 25 to 79 minutes; terminal phase, 58 to 78 hours.

Route	Onset	Peak	Duration
I.V.	Unknown	Immediate	Several days

Action

Chemical effect: Probably cross-links strands of cellular DNA and interferes with RNA tran-

scription, causing imbalance of growth that leads to cell death.
Therapeutic effect: Kills selected cancer cells.

Available forms

Injection: 1 mg/ml

NURSING PROCESS

Assessment

- Assess patient's underlying neoplastic disease before and regularly throughout therapy.
- Monitor CBC, electrolyte levels (especially potassium and magnesium), platelet count, and renal function studies before initial and subsequent dosages.
- To detect permanent hearing loss, obtain audiometry test results before initial dose and subsequent courses.
- Be alert for adverse reactions and drug interactions.
- Assess patient's and family's knowledge of drug therapy.

Nursing diagnoses

- Ineffective health maintenance related to presence of neoplastic disease
- Ineffective protection related to drug-induced adverse reactions
- Deficient knowledge related to drug therapy

Planning and implementation

- Renal toxicity is cumulative. Renal function must return to normal before next dose can be given.
- Don't repeat dose unless platelet count exceeds $100,000/mm^3$, WBC count exceeds $4,000/mm^3$, creatinine level is less than 1.5 mg/dl, or BUN level is less than 25 mg/dl.
- I.V. sodium thiosulfate may be used to minimize toxicity. Check current protocol.
- Nausea and vomiting may be severe and protracted (up to 24 hours). Provide I.V. hydration until patient can tolerate adequate oral intake.
- Antiemetics, such as ondansetron, granisetron, and high-dose metoclopramide, may be used to prevent and treat nausea and vomiting. Metoclopramide may be combined with dexamethasone and antihistamines, or ondansetron or granisetron with dexamethasone.
- Delayed-onset vomiting (3 to 5 days after therapy) may occur. Patients may need prolonged antiemetic treatment.
- Immediately give epinephrine, corticosteroids, or antihistamines for anaphylactoid reactions.

ALERT: Don't confuse cisplatin with carboplatin.

Patient teaching

- Warn patient to watch for signs of infection (fever, sore throat, fatigue) and bleeding (easy bruising, nosebleeds, bleeding gums, melena). Tell him to take his temperature daily.
- Tell patient to immediately report tinnitus.
- Instruct patient to avoid OTC products that contain aspirin.
- Teach patient to record intake and output on daily basis and to report edema or decrease in urine output.
- Encourage patient to notify prescriber if any concerns arise during therapy.

Evaluation

- Patient has positive response to cisplatin therapy according to follow-up diagnostic studies.
- Patient doesn't have permanent injury from drug-induced adverse reactions.
- Patient and family state understanding of drug therapy.

citalopram hydrobromide

(sih-TAL-oh-pram high-droh-BROH-mighd)

Celexa

Pharmacologic class: SSRI
Therapeutic class: antidepressant
Pregnancy risk category: C

Indications and dosages

▶ **Depression.** *Adults:* Initially, 20 mg P.O. once daily, increasing to maximum dosage of 40 mg daily after no less than 1 week.

▶ **Panic disorder‡.** *Adults:* 20 to 30 mg P.O. once daily.

Adjust-a-dose: For elderly patients and patients with hepatic impairment, give 20 mg P.O. once daily. Increase to 40 mg daily only for patients not responding to therapy.

Contraindications and cautions

- Contraindicated within 14 days of MAO inhibitor therapy. Also contraindicated in patients hypersensitive to drug, any of its components, or escitalopram. Contraindicated in patients taking pimozide.
- Use cautiously in patients with history of mania, seizures, suicidal ideation, hepatic impairment, or renal impairment.

Lifespan: In breast-feeding women, avoid drug because it appears in breast milk and may cause serious adverse reactions in infants. Drug isn't approved for pediatric use and shouldn't be used in children and adolescents younger than age 18 for major depressive disorder because of possible increased risk of suicidal behavior. In elderly patients, reduce dosage.

Adverse reactions

CNS: agitation, amnesia, anxiety, apathy, confusion, depression, dizziness, fatigue, fever, impaired concentration, insomnia, migraine, paresthesia, *somnolence, **suicide attempt,*** tremor.
CV: hypotension, orthostatic hypotension, tachycardia.
EENT: abnormal accommodation, rhinitis, sinusitis.
GI: abdominal pain, anorexia, diarrhea, dry mouth, dyspepsia, flatulence, increased appetite, increased saliva, nausea, taste disturbance, vomiting, weight changes.
GU: amenorrhea, dysmenorrhea, ejaculation disorder, impotence, polyuria.
Musculoskeletal: arthralgia, myalgia.
Respiratory: cough, upper respiratory tract infection.
Skin: increased sweating, pruritus, rash.
Other: decreased libido, yawning.

Interactions

Drug-drug. *Carbamazepine:* May increase citalopram clearance. Monitor patient for effects.
CNS drugs: May increase CNS effects. Use together cautiously.
Drugs that inhibit CYP3A4 (such as fluconazole) and CYP2C19 (such as omeprazole): May decrease citalopram clearance. Monitor patient for toxicity.
Imipramine, other tricyclic antidepressants: May increase level of imipramine metabolite desipramine by about 50%. Use together cautiously.
Lithium: May enhance serotonergic effect of citalopram. Use cautiously and monitor lithium level.
Phenelzine, selegiline, tranylcypromine: May cause serotonin syndrome, including CNS irritability, shivering, and altered consciousness. Don't give together. Wait at least 2 weeks after stopping an MAO inhibitor before giving any SSRI.
Sumatriptan: May cause weakness, hyperreflexia, and incoordination. Monitor patient closely.
Warfarin: PT increases by 5%. Monitor patient carefully; monitor PT and INR.
Drug-herb. *St. John's wort:* May raise serotonin level, causing serotonin syndrome. Discourage use together.
Drug-lifestyle. *Alcohol use:* May increase CNS effects. Discourage use together.

Effects on lab test results

- May increase liver function test values.

Pharmacokinetics

Absorption: Absolute bioavailability is 80%.
Distribution: Wide. About 80% protein-bound.
Metabolism: Mainly by the liver.
Excretion: 10% is recovered in urine. *Half-life:* 35 hours.

Route	Onset	Peak	Duration
P.O.	Unknown	4 hr	Unknown

Action

Chemical effect: May enhance serotonergic activity in CNS by inhibiting neuronal reuptake of serotonin.
Therapeutic effect: Relieves depression.

Available forms

Oral solution: 10 mg/5 ml
Tablets: 10 mg, 20 mg, 40 mg
Tablets (orally disintegrating): 10 mg, 20 mg, 40 mg

NURSING PROCESS

Assessment

- Assess patient's underlying condition before therapy and regularly thereafter.

- Check vital signs regularly for decreased blood pressure or tachycardia.
- Closely supervise high-risk patients at start of drug therapy.
- Assess patient's and family's knowledge of drug therapy.

Nursing diagnoses

- Risk for injury related to patient's underlying condition
- Ineffective coping related to patient's underlying condition
- Deficient knowledge related to drug therapy

Planning and implementation

ALERT: Don't start citalopram therapy within 14 days of MAO inhibitor therapy.
- For patient with hepatic impairment, reduce dosage.
- May increase risk of suicide in adolescents.
- Don't stop drug abruptly.

ALERT: Don't confuse Celexa with Celebrex, Cerebyx, or Concerta.

Patient teaching

- Urge patient to continue therapy as prescribed even if he improves within 1 to 4 weeks.
- Instruct patient to exercise caution when operating hazardous machinery, including automobiles, because psychoactive drugs can impair judgment, thinking, and motor skills.
- Warn patient that drug may cause photosensitivity; advise patient to take protective measures until tolerance is determined.
- Advise patient to consult prescriber before taking other prescription drugs, OTC medicines, or herbal remedies.
- Tell patient to let orally disintegrating tablet dissolve on the tongue and then swallow, with or without water. Urge patient not to cut, crush, or chew orally disintegrating tablets.

ALERT: If patient wishes to switch from an SSRI to St. John's wort, tell him to wait a few weeks for the SSRI to leave his system before he starts the herb. Urge him to ask his prescriber for advice.
- Warn patient not to consume alcohol during therapy.
- Instruct woman of childbearing age to use birth control during therapy and to notify prescriber immediately if she suspects pregnancy.

Evaluation

- Patient's safety is maintained.
- Patient's condition is improved with drug.
- Patient and family state understanding of drug therapy.

clarithromycin

(klah-rith-roh-MIGH-sin)
Biaxin, Biaxin XL

Pharmacologic class: macrolide
Therapeutic class: antibiotic
Pregnancy risk category: C

Indications and dosages

▶ **Pharyngitis or tonsillitis caused by *Streptococcus pyogenes*.** *Adults:* 250 mg P.O. q 12 hours for 10 days.
Children: 7.5 mg/kg P.O., q 12 hours for 10 days.

▶ **Acute maxillary sinusitis caused by *Streptococcus pneumoniae, Haemophilus influenzae,* or *Moraxella catarrhalis*.** *Adults:* 500 mg P.O. q 12 hours for 14 days. Or, two 500-mg extended-release tablets P.O. daily for 14 days.
Children: 7.5 mg/kg P.O. daily q 12 hours for 10 days.

▶ **Acute exacerbation of chronic bronchitis caused by *M. catarrhalis, S. pneumoniae, H. influenzae,* or *Haemophilus parainfluenzae*.** *Adults:* 250 mg P.O. q 12 hours for 7 to 14 days (for *M. catarrhalis* and *S. pneumoniae*), or 500 mg P.O. q 12 hours for 7 days for *H. parainfluenzae* (up to 14 days for *H. influenzae*). Or two 500-mg extended-release tablets P.O. daily for 7 days.

▶ **Uncomplicated skin and skin-structure infections caused by *Staphylococcus aureus* or *S. pyogenes*.** *Adults:* 250 mg P.O. q 12 hours for 7 to 14 days.

▶ **Prophylaxis and treatment of disseminated infection from *Mycobacterium avium* complex.** *Adults:* 500 mg P.O. b.i.d.
Children: 7.5 mg/kg, up to 500 mg, P.O. b.i.d.

▶ **Acute otitis media caused by *H. influenzae, M. catarrhalis,* or *S. pneumoniae*.** *Children:* 7.5 mg/kg, up to 500 mg, P.O. q 12 hours,

▶ ***Helicobacter pylori* eradication to reduce risk of duodenal ulcer recurrence.** *Adults:* For triple therapy, 500 mg clarithromycin with 30 mg lansoprazole and 1 g amoxicillin, all given P.O. q 12 hours for 10 to 14 days; or 500 mg clarithromycin with 20 mg omeprazole and 1 g amoxicillin, all given P.O. q 12 hours for 10 days; or clarithromycin 500 mg with 20 mg rabeprazole and 1 g amoxicillin, all given P.O. q 12 hours for 7 days. For dual therapy, 500 mg clarithromycin q 8 hours and 40 mg omeprazole once daily P.O. for 14 days.

▶ **Community-acquired pneumonia from *Chlamydia pneumoniae, Mycoplasma pneumoniae, S. pneumoniae, H. influenzae, H. parainfluenzae, M. catarrhalis.*** *Adults:* 250 mg P.O. q 12 hours for 7 to 14 days (for *H. influenzae,* 7 days). Or two 500-mg extended-release tablets P.O. daily for 7 days for all listed organisms. Don't use conventional tablets to treat pneumonia caused by *H. parainfluenzae* or *M. catarrhalis.*

Children: 7.5 mg/kg P.O. q 12 hours for 10 days (for *C. pneumoniae, M. pneumoniae,* or *S. pneumoniae* only).

▶ **Lyme disease‡.** *Adults:* 500 mg P.O. b.i.d. for 14 to 21 days.

Children: 7.5 mg/kg P.O., up to 500 mg, b.i.d. for 14 to 21 days

Adjust-a-dose: For patients with renal impairment, if creatinine clearance is less than 30 ml/minute, reduce dose by 50% or double frequency interval.

Contraindications and cautions

• Contraindicated in patients hypersensitive to drug and other macrolides. Use with pimozide, cisapride, or other drugs that prolong QT interval or may cause ventricular arrhythmias is contraindicated.

• Use cautiously in patients with hepatic or renal impairment.

Lifespan: In pregnant or breast-feeding women, use cautiously. In infants younger than age 6 months, safety and effectiveness haven't been established.

Adverse reactions

CNS: headache.

CV: ***ventricular arrhythmias.***

GI: abdominal pain or discomfort, abnormal taste, diarrhea, dyspepsia, nausea, ***pseudomembranous colitis,*** vomiting (pediatric).

Hematologic: coagulation abnormalities, ***leukopenia.***

Skin: rash (pediatric), ***Stevens-Johnson syndrome, toxic epidermal necrolysis.***

Interactions

Drug-drug. *Alprazolam, midazolam, triazolam:* May increase adverse CNS effects. Assess patient carefully.

Carbamazepine: May inhibit metabolism of carbamazepine and increase level and risk of toxicity. Avoid use together.

Digoxin, theophylline: May increase levels of these drugs; dosage may be reduced at start of clarithromycin therapy. Monitor patient for toxicity.

Dihydroergotamine, ergotamine: May increase risk of acute ergot toxicity with severe peripheral vasospasm and dysesthesia. Monitor patient closely.

Drugs metabolized by the CYP3A system (alfentanil, bromocriptine, cilostazol, cyclosporine, disopyramide, hexobarbital, HMG-CoA reductase inhibitors, methylprednisolone, phenytoin, quinidine, rifabutin, rifampin, sildenafil, tacrolimus, valproate): May decrease clearance of these drugs, increasing risk of toxicity. Monitor drug levels and effects closely.

Fluconazole: May increase clarithromycin level. Monitor patient.

Ritonavir: May prolong absorption of clarithromycin. Don't adjust dosage in patients with normal renal function; if creatinine clearance is 30 to 60 ml/minute, give 50% of clarithromycin dose; if less than 30 ml/minute, give 25% of clarithromycin dose.

Warfarin: May increase bleeding times. Monitor PT and INR.

Zidovudine: May alter zidovudine level. Monitor patient closely for effectiveness of both drugs.

Effects on lab test results

• May increase AST, ALT, GGT, alkaline phosphatase, LDH, total bilirubin, creatinine, and BUN levels.

• May increase PT and INR. May decrease WBC counts.

Pharmacokinetics

Absorption: Rapid.

Distribution: Wide. 40% to 70% protein-bound.

Metabolism: Extensive. Major metabolite has significant antimicrobial activity.

Excretion: In urine and feces. *Half-life:* 5 to 6 hours with 250 mg q 12 hours; 7 hours with 500 mg q 12 hours.

Route	Onset	Peak	Duration
P.O.	Unknown	2–3 hr	Unknown
P.O. extended-release	Unknown	5–6 hr	Unknown

Action

Chemical effect: Binds to 50S subunit of bacterial ribosomes, blocking protein synthesis; bacteriostatic or bactericidal, depending on concentration.
Therapeutic effect: Hinders or kills susceptible bacteria.

Available forms

Suspension: 125 mg/5 ml, 250 mg/5 ml
Tablets: 250 mg, 500 mg
Tablets (extended-release): 500 mg

NURSING PROCESS

Assessment

- Assess patient's infection before and regularly throughout therapy.
- Obtain urine specimen for culture and sensitivity tests before giving the first dose. Begin therapy pending results.
- Be alert for adverse reactions and drug interactions.
- If adverse GI reactions occur, monitor patient's hydration.
- Assess patient's and family's knowledge of drug therapy.

Nursing diagnoses

- Ineffective protection related to presence of bacteria susceptible to drug
- Risk for deficient fluid volume related to drug-induced adverse GI reactions
- Deficient knowledge related to drug therapy

Planning and implementation

- Give drug with or without food. It may be taken with milk.
- Don't refrigerate oral suspension after reconstitution. Discard unused portion after 14 days.

ALERT: Don't confuse or interchange Biaxin XL (extended-release) with Biaxin (immediate release).

Patient teaching

- Tell patient to complete therapy as prescribed, even after he feels better.
- Urge patient to notify prescriber about all prescription and OTC medications taken, and to immediately report any adverse reactions.
- Instruct patient to report persistent diarrhea to prescriber, even if it occurs a month after antibiotic therapy has ended.
- Tell patient not to chew or crush extended-release tablets.

Evaluation

- Patient is free from infection.
- Patient maintains adequate hydration throughout drug therapy.
- Patient and family state understanding of drug therapy.

clindamycin hydrochloride

(klin-duh-MIGH-sin high-droh-KLOR-ighd)
Cleocin, Dalacin C ♦ ◇

clindamycin palmitate hydrochloride

Cleocin Pediatric

clindamycin phosphate

Clindesse, Cleocin T, Clindagel, ClindaMax, Clindets, ClindaMax Lotion, Evoclin Foam

Pharmacologic class: lincomycin derivative
Therapeutic class: antibiotic
Pregnancy risk category: B

Indications and dosages

▶ **Infections caused by sensitive staphylococci, streptococci, pneumococci, *Bacteroides, Fusobacterium, Clostridium perfringens,* and other sensitive aerobic and anaerobic organisms.** *Adults:* 150 to 450 mg P.O. q 6 hours. Or 600 to 2,700 mg I.M. or I.V. daily divided into two to four doses. Don't exceed 600 mg in one I.M. dose. Don't give more than 1.2 g I.V. in a 1-hour period. Maximum adult I.V. dosage is 4.8 g daily. *Children ages 1 month to 16 years:* 8 to 25 mg/kg P.O. daily in three or four equally divided doses. Or 20 to 40 mg/kg I.M. or I.V. daily, in three or four equally divided doses, or 350 to 450 mg/m² daily.

Neonates younger than age 1 month: 15 to 20 mg/kg I.V. daily in three or four equally divided doses.

▶ **Endocarditis prophylaxis for dental procedures in patients allergic to penicillin.** *Adults:* 600 mg P.O. 1 hour before procedure or 600 mg I.V. 30 minutes before procedure.
Children ages 1 month to 16 years: 20 mg/kg P.O. 1 hour before procedure or 20 mg/kg I.V. 30 minutes before procedure (not to exceed adult dosage).

▶ **Acne vulgaris.** *Adults:* Apply a thin film of topical suspension, gel, or lotion to affected areas b.i.d. Or apply foam to skin once daily after washing with mild soap and water. Cover affected areas completely and massage in until foam disappears. Or, 150 mg P.O. b.i.d.‡

▶ **Bacterial vaginosis.** *Adults:* One applicatorful intravaginally at bedtime daily for 3 to 7 days per prescriber instructions. Or, 1 suppository intravaginally at bedtime daily for 3 days.

▶ ***Pneumocystis jiroveci (carinii)* pneumonia‡.** *Adults:* 600 mg I.V. q 6 hours. Or 300 to 450 mg P.O. q.i.d. With primaquine, give 30 mg P.O. daily for 21 days.

▶ **Toxoplasmosis (cerebral or ocular) in immunocompromised patients‡.** *Adults:* 300 to 450 mg P.O. q 6 to 8 hours with pyrimethamine (25 to 75 mg once daily) and leucovorin (10 to 25 mg once daily).
Infants and children age 16 and younger: 20 to 30 mg/kg P.O. daily in four divided doses with oral pyrimethamine (1 mg/kg daily) and oral leucovorin (5 mg once q 3 days).

I.V. administration

• For I.V. infusion, dilute each 300 mg in 50 ml solution.
• Give no faster than 30 mg/minute (over 10 to 60 minutes). Never give undiluted as bolus.
• Check I.V. site daily for phlebitis and irritation.

⊗ Incompatibilities
Allopurinol; aminophylline; ampicillin; azithromycin; barbiturates; calcium gluconate; ceftriaxone; ciprofloxacin hydrochloride; filgrastim; fluconazole; idarubicin; magnesium sulfate; phenytoin sodium; rubber closures, such as those on I.V. tubing; tobramycin sulfate.

Contraindications and cautions

• Contraindicated in patients hypersensitive to drug or lincomycin.
• Use cautiously in patients with renal or hepatic disease, asthma, history of GI disease, or significant allergies.
Lifespan: Breast-feeding women should stop breast-feeding. In neonates, use cautiously.

Adverse reactions

CV: thrombophlebitis.
EENT: pharyngitis.
GI: abdominal pain, anorexia, *bloody or tarry stools,* constipation, *diarrhea, dysphagia,* esophagitis, flatulence, *nausea,* ***pseudomembranous colitis,*** unpleasant or bitter taste, vomiting.
GU: UTI, vaginal discharge.
Hematologic: eosinophilia, ***thrombocytopenia, transient leukopenia.***
Skin: maculopapular rash, urticaria.
Other: ***anaphylaxis;*** erythema, pain (I.V. use); *induration, pain, sterile abscess* (I.M. use).

Interactions

Drug-drug. *Erythromycin:* May block clindamycin site of action. Avoid use together.
Kaolin: May decrease absorption of oral clindamycin. Separate doses.
Neuromuscular blockers: May potentiate neuromuscular blockade. Monitor patient closely.

Effects on lab test results

• May increase bilirubin, AST, alkaline phosphatase, and CK levels.
• May increase eosinophil count. May decrease WBC and platelet counts.

Pharmacokinetics

Absorption: Rapid and almost complete when given P.O. Good after I.M. administration. Minimal vaginal absorption.
Distribution: Widely to most body tissues and fluids (except CSF). Drug is about 93% protein-bound.
Metabolism: Partially, to inactive metabolites.
Excretion: 10% unchanged in urine; rest as inactive metabolites. *Half-life:* 2½ to 3 hours; 1½ to 2½ hours for cream.

Route	Onset	Peak	Duration
P.O.	Unknown	45–60 min	Unknown
I.V.	Immediate	Immediate	Unknown
I.M.	Unknown	3 hr	Unknown
Topical	Unknown	Unknown	Unknown
Vaginal	Unknown	10–14 hr	20–24 hr

Action

Chemical effect: Inhibits bacterial protein synthesis by binding to 50S subunit of ribosome.
Therapeutic effect: Hinders or kills susceptible bacteria.

Available forms

clindamycin hydrochloride
Capsules: 75 mg, 150 mg, 300 mg
clindamycin palmitate hydrochloride
Oral solution: 75 mg/5 ml
clindamycin phosphate
Foam, topical: 1%
Gel, lotion, topical suspension: 1%
Injection: 150 mg/ml
Vaginal cream: 2%
Vaginal suppository: 100 mg

NURSING PROCESS

Assessment

- Assess patient's infection before and regularly throughout therapy.
- Before giving first dose, obtain specimen for culture and sensitivity tests. Begin therapy pending results.
- Monitor renal, hepatic, and hematopoietic functions during prolonged therapy.
- Be alert for adverse reactions and drug interactions.
- If adverse GI reactions occur, monitor patient's hydration.
- Assess patient's and family's knowledge of drug therapy.

Nursing diagnoses

- Ineffective protection related to presence of bacteria susceptible to drug
- Risk for deficient fluid volume related to drug-induced adverse GI reactions
- Deficient knowledge related to drug therapy

Planning and implementation

- Don't refrigerate reconstituted oral solution because it will thicken. Drug is stable for 2 weeks at room temperature.
- Give capsule form with full glass of water to prevent dysphagia.
- For I.M. injection, inject deeply. Rotate sites. Warn patient that I.M. injection may be painful. Doses over 600 mg per injection aren't recommended.
- I.M. injection may raise CK in response to muscle irritation.

ALERT: Don't give opioid antidiarrheals to treat drug-induced diarrhea; they may prolong and worsen diarrhea.

ALERT: Because of a link to severe and even fatal colitis, give clindamycin only for serious infections.

Patient teaching

- Teach patient how to store oral solution.
- Tell patient to take entire amount prescribed even after he feels better.
- Warn patient that I.M. injection may be painful.

ALERT: Inform patient that vaginal cream contains mineral oil, which may weaken the rubber latex of condoms or contraceptive diaphragms. Tell patient not to rely on such products while taking drug and for 5 days afterward. Contraceptive and sexually transmitted disease protection may be impaired.

- Instruct patient to report diarrhea and to avoid self-treatment because of the risk of life-threatening pseudomembranous colitis.
- Tell patient receiving drug I.V. to report discomfort at infusion site.

Evaluation

- Patient is free from infection after drug therapy.
- Patient maintains adequate hydration during drug therapy.
- Patient and family state understanding of drug therapy.

clobetasol propionate

(kloh-BAY-tah-sol PRO-pee-uh-nayt)
Cormax, Dermovate*, Embeline E, Temovate, Temovate Emollient, Olux

Pharmacologic class: topical corticosteroid
Therapeutic class: anti-inflammatory
Pregnancy risk category: C

Indications and dosages

▶ **Inflammation and pruritus from moderate to severe corticosteroid-responsive dermatoses.** *Adults:* Apply a thin layer to affected skin areas b.i.d., once in the morning and once at night. Limit therapy to 14 days, with no more than 50 g cream or ointment or 50 ml lotion (25 mg total) weekly.

▶ **Inflammation and pruritus from moderate to severe corticosteroid-responsive dermatoses of the scalp; short-term topical therapy for mild to moderate plaque-type psoriasis of nonscalp regions, excluding the face and intertriginous areas.** *Adults:* Apply a small amount of Olux foam, up to a maximum of a golf ball–sized dollop, to affected skin b.i.d., once in the morning and once at night. Limit therapy to 14 days, with no more than 50 g of foam weekly.

Contraindications and cautions

- Contraindicated in patients hypersensitive to corticosteroids. Also contraindicated for acne, rosacea, perioral dermatitis, or as monotherapy for widespread plaque psoriasis.
- Use caution when applying drug to face, groin, or axillae because these areas are at an increased risk for atrophic changes.
- Use cautiously in patients with glaucoma and diabetes.

Lifespan: In pregnant women, avoid use because of possibility of teratogenic effects. In breast-feeding women, use cautiously and avoid applying to breasts because it's unknown whether drug appears in breast milk. In patients younger than age 12, drug isn't recommended. In elderly patients, begin at the low end of the dosage range and adjust carefully.

Adverse reactions

GU: glucosuria.
Metabolic: hyperglycemia.
Skin: burning and stinging sensation, pruritus, irritation, dryness and cracking, erythema, folliculitis, perioral dermatitis, allergic contact dermatitis, hypopigmentation, hypertrichosis, acneiform eruptions, skin atrophy, telangiectasia (dilatation of capillaries), striae.
Other: ***hypothalamic-pituitary-adrenal axis suppression,*** Cushing syndrome, numbness of fingers.

Interactions

None reported.

Effects on lab test results

- May increase glucose level.
- May cause false-positive results with adrenocorticotropic hormone (ACTH) stimulation, a.m. cortisol, and urine-free cortisol tests.

Pharmacokinetics

Absorption: Variable, mainly by skin. Increases in areas of skin damage, inflammation, or occlusion. Small amount is systemic.
Distribution: Throughout the local skin. Any drug absorbed systemically is rapidly removed from the blood and goes to muscle, liver, skin, intestines, and kidneys.
Metabolism: Mainly in skin. Small amount in liver to inactive compounds.
Excretion: Drug and active metabolites, in the liver and bile. Inactive metabolites, by the kidneys, mainly as glucuronides and sulfates but also as unconjugated products. Small amounts of the metabolites are also in urine and feces. *Half-life:* Unknown.

Route	Onset	Peak	Duration
Topical	Unknown	Unknown	Unknown

Action

Chemical effect: Unknown. Drug is a high-potency group I fluorinated corticosteroid usually reserved for severe dermatoses that haven't responded to a less potent formulation.
Therapeutic effect: Decreases inflammation and itching.

Available forms

Cream: 0.05%
Foam: 0.05%
Gel: 0.05%
Ointment: 0.05%
Solution: 0.05%

NURSING PROCESS

Assessment

- Assess patient before and during therapy. Topical corticosteroid therapy may adversely affect and worsen symptoms in patients with diabetes or glaucoma.
- Monitor patient for adverse effects of corticosteroid therapy.
- If applied to face, groin, or axillae, observe often for skin atrophy.
- During long-term use, obtain ACTH stimulation, a.m. cortisol, and urine-free cortisol tests

to monitor patient for hypothalamic-pituitary-adrenal (HPA) axis suppression.
- Assess patient's and family's knowledge of drug therapy.

Nursing diagnoses
- Risk for infection related to prolonged and very potent corticosteroid therapy.
- Impaired skin integrity related to underlying skin disease process
- Situational low self-esteem from underlying skin disease process
- Deficient knowledge related to topical corticosteroid therapy

Planning and implementation
- When applying foam to the scalp, move hair away from the affected area so that the foam can be applied to each affected area.
- Don't use longer than 2 weeks.
- Drug is for external use only. Avoid rubbing eyes during and after application. If drug gets into the eyes, flush affected eye with copious amounts of water.
- Don't dispense directly onto hand because cream and foam will begin to melt immediately upon contact with warm skin. When using foam, invert can and dispense foam into can cap or directly onto the lesion.
- Apply sparingly in light film; then massage into skin gently until foam disappears.
- Don't use occlusive dressings or bandages. Don't cover or wrap treated area unless instructed by prescriber.
- If skin infection develops, give antifungal or antibacterial drugs. If infection doesn't respond promptly, stop drug until infection is under control.
- If irritation, skin infection, striae, or atrophy occurs, stop drug and notify prescriber.
- Drug can suppress HPA axis at doses as low as 2 g daily. If HPA axis suppression occurs, stop giving the drug, reduce the dosage, or substitute a less potent steroid.
- If no improvement occurs within 2 weeks, reassess diagnoses.
- Don't refrigerate. Store drug at room temperature.

Patient teaching
- Advise patient that drug is for external use only and to avoid contact with eyes.
- Instruct patient to use medication only as prescribed.
- Teach patient proper application of the topical steroid to affected area. Explain that occlusive dressings aren't recommended and may increase absorption and skin atrophy.
- Inform patient of potential adverse reactions and of signs and symptoms of infection and impaired healing. Urge patient to immediately notify prescriber if any occur.
- Warn patient not to use drug for longer than 14 days.
- Caution patient that foam formulation is flammable and to avoid flames or smoking during and immediately after application.
- Instruct patients using Olux foam that the contents are under pressure and container shouldn't be punctured or incinerated. Also, tell patient not to expose to heat or store at temperatures above 120° F (49° C).

Evaluation
- Patient doesn't suffer from any infection caused by drug therapy.
- Patient is relieved of symptoms and remains free from any adverse effects of drug therapy.
- Patient's self-esteem increases as patient's skin improves.
- Patient and family state understanding of drug therapy.

clofarabine
kloh-FAR-uh-been

Clolar

Pharmacologic classification: purine nucleoside antimetabolite
Therapeutic classification: antineoplastic
Pregnancy risk category: D

Indications and dosages
▶ **Relapsed or refractory acute lymphoblastic leukemia after at least two previous regimens.** *Children ages 1 to 21:* Give 52 mg/m² by I.V. infusion over 2 hours daily for 5 consecutive days. Repeat about every 2 to 6 weeks based on recovery or return to baseline of organ function. May also administer hydrocortisone 100 mg/m² I.V. on days 1 to 3 of cycle to help prevent capillary leak syndrome.

I.V. administration

- Draw up the calculated dose through a 0.2-micron syringe filter and further dilute with D_5W or normal saline solution before infusion.
- Infuse drug within 24 hours of preparing it.
- Give over 2 hours with I.V. fluids.
- Store undiluted vials and resulting infusion solution at room temperature.

⊗ **Incompatibilities**

Don't give drug with other drugs through the same I.V. line.

Contraindications and cautions

- There are no known contraindications.
- Use very cautiously in patients with hepatic or renal dysfunction.

Lifespan: In pregnant women, drug may cause fetal harm. Women of childbearing potential should avoid becoming pregnant while receiving this drug. It isn't known whether drug appears in breast milk. Women shouldn't breastfeed while receiving drug.

Adverse reactions

CNS: *anxiety, depression, dizziness, fatigue, headache, irritability, lethargy, pain, somnolence, tremor.*
CV: *edema, flushing, hypertension, hypotension, left ventricular systolic dysfunction, pericardial effusion, tachycardia.*
EENT: *epistaxis, mucosal inflammation, sore throat.*
GI: *abdominal pain, anorexia, constipation, decreased appetite, decreased weight, diarrhea, gingival bleeding, oral candidiasis, nausea, vomiting.*
GU: *hematuria.*
Hematologic: ***bone marrow suppression,*** **FEBRILE NEUTROPENIA, NEUTROPENIA.**
Hepatic: *hepatomegaly, jaundice.*
Musculoskeletal: *arthralgia, back pain, limb pain, myalgia.*
Respiratory: *pneumonia, cough, dyspnea, pleural effusion,* **RESPIRATORY DISTRESS.**
Skin: *contusion, dermatitis, dry skin, erythema, hand-foot syndrome, petechiae, pruritus.*
Other: **BACTEREMIA,** ***capillary leak syndrome,*** *cellulitis, herpes simplex, injection site pain, pyrexia, rigors,* **SEPSIS,** *staphylococcal infections,* ***systemic inflammatory response syndrome,*** *transfusion reaction.*

Interactions

Drug-drug. *Blood pressure or cardiac drugs:* May increase the risk of adverse effects. Monitor patient closely.
Hepatotoxic drugs: May increase the risk of hepatic toxicity. Avoid use together.
Nephrotoxic drugs: May decrease excretion of clofarabine. Avoid use during the 5 days of clofarabine treatment.

Effects on lab test results

- May increase ALT, AST, bilirubin, creatinine, and hemoglobin levels and hematocrit.
- May decrease WBC counts and platelet counts.

Pharmacokinetics

Absorption: Given I.V.
Distribution: 47% bound to plasma proteins, mainly albumin.
Metabolism: Limited hepatic metabolism.
Excretion: 49% to 60% in urine unchanged. *Elimination half-life:* about 5¼ hours.

Route	Onset	Peak	Duration
I.V.	Unknown	Unknown	Unknown

Action

Chemical effect: Inhibits DNA synthesis and repair and disrupts integrity of mitochondrial membranes, leading to programmed cell death.
Therapeutic effect: Kills selected cancer cells.

Available forms

Injection: 1 mg/ml in 20-ml vials

NURSING PROCESS

Assessment

- Assess patient's underlying condition before therapy and regularly throughout therapy.
- Assess patient for signs and symptoms of tumor lysis syndrome, cytokine release (tachypnea, tachycardia, hypotension, pulmonary edema) that could develop into systemic inflammatory response syndrome, capillary leak syndrome, and organ dysfunction.
- Monitor patient's respiratory status and blood pressure closely during treatment.
- Obtain CBC and platelet counts, and monitor hepatic and renal function regularly during treatment.

• Assess patient's and family's knowledge of drug therapy.

Nursing diagnoses

• Ineffective health maintenance related to underlying condition
• Risk for injury related to drug-induced adverse hematologic reactions
• Deficient knowledge related to drug therapy

Planning and implementation

• Monitor the patient for dehydration. Give I.V. fluids continuously during the 5-day treatment period.
• If you suspect hyperuricemia, give allopurinol.
• If the patient has signs and symptoms of systemic inflammatory response syndrome or capillary leak syndrome, stop drug immediately.
• If hypotension develops, stop the drug. If it resolves without treatment, restart clofarabine at a lower dose.

Patient teaching

• Tell patient and caregiver that adverse effects are common. The patient will need close monitoring during treatment.
• Tell patient and caregiver to report dizziness, light-headedness, fainting, decreased urine output, bruising, flulike symptoms, and infection immediately.
• Urge patient and caregiver to report yellowing of skin or eyes, darkened urine, or abdominal pain.
• Tell a patient of childbearing potential to avoid pregnancy and breast-feeding during therapy.

Evaluation

• Patient demonstrates positive response to drug therapy.
• Patient doesn't experience injury as a result of drug therapy.
• Patient and family state understanding of drug therapy.

clomiphene citrate
(KLOH-meh-feen SIGH-trayt)
Clomid, Milophene, Serophene

Pharmacologic class: chlorotrianisene derivative
Therapeutic class: ovulation stimulant
Pregnancy risk category: X

Indications and dosages

▶ **To induce ovulation.** *Women:* 50 mg P.O. daily for 5 days starting on day 5 of menstrual cycle if bleeding occurs (first day of menstrual flow is day 1), or at any time if woman hasn't had recent uterine bleeding. If ovulation doesn't occur, may increase dosage to 100 mg P.O. daily for 5 days as soon as 30 days after previous course. Repeat until conception occurs or until three courses of therapy are completed.
▶ **Infertility‡.** *Men:* 50 to 400 mg P.O. daily for 2 to 12 months.

Contraindications and cautions

• Contraindicated in patients with undiagnosed abnormal genital bleeding, ovarian cyst not caused by polycystic ovarian syndrome, hepatic disease or dysfunction, uncontrolled thyroid or adrenal dysfunction, or organic intracranial lesion (such as pituitary tumor).
Lifespan: In pregnant women, drug is contraindicated.

Adverse reactions

CNS: depression, dizziness, fatigue, headache, insomnia, light-headedness, restlessness, tension, *vasomotor flushes.*
CV: hypertension.
EENT: blurred vision, diplopia, photophobia, scotoma.
GI: bloating, distention, nausea, vomiting.
GU: *ovarian enlargement and cyst formation,* which regress spontaneously when drug is stopped; urinary frequency and polyuria.
Metabolic: *hyperglycemia,* increased appetite, weight gain.
Skin: dermatitis, rash, reversible alopecia, urticaria.
Other: breast discomfort.

Interactions

None significant.

Effects on lab test results

- May increase blood glucose level.

Pharmacokinetics

Absorption: Good.
Distribution: May undergo enterohepatic recirculation or may be stored in fat.
Metabolism: By liver.
Excretion: Mainly in feces via biliary elimination. *Half-life:* 5 days.

Route	Onset	Peak	Duration
P.O.	Unknown	Unknown	Unknown

Action

Chemical effect: May stimulate release of pituitary gonadotropins, follicle-stimulating hormone, and luteinizing hormone, resulting in maturation of ovarian follicle, ovulation, and development of corpus luteum.
Therapeutic effect: Induces ovulation.

Available forms

Tablets: 50 mg

NURSING PROCESS

Assessment

- Assess patient's underlying condition before therapy and regularly thereafter.
- Monitor drug's effectiveness by assessing ovulation through biphasic body temperature measurement, postovulatory pregnanediol level in urine, estrogen excretion, and changes in endometrial tissues.
- Be alert for adverse reactions.
- Assess patient's and family's knowledge of drug therapy.

Nursing diagnoses

- Excess fluid volume related to drug-induced fluid retention
- Sexual dysfunction related to underlying condition
- Deficient knowledge related to drug therapy

Planning and implementation

- Prepare administration instructions for patient: Begin daily dose on fifth day of menstrual flow and take for 5 consecutive days.
- Don't give more than three courses of therapy to attempt conception.

Patient teaching

- Tell patient about risk of multiple births and that risk increases with larger doses.
- Teach patient how to take and chart basal body temperature and to ascertain whether ovulation has occurred.
- Reassure woman that ovulation typically occurs after first course of therapy. If pregnancy doesn't occur, course of therapy may be repeated twice.

ALERT: Advise woman to stop taking drug and to contact prescriber immediately if pregnancy is suspected, because drug may have teratogenic effect on fetus.

- Advise woman to stop taking drug and to contact prescriber immediately if abdominal symptoms or pain occur; they may indicate ovarian enlargement or ovarian cyst.
- Tell patient to immediately report signs of impending visual toxicity, such as blurred vision, diplopia, scotoma, or photophobia.
- Warn patient to avoid hazardous activities until the drug's CNS effects are known; drug may cause dizziness or visual disturbances.

Evaluation

- Patient is free from fluid retention at end of therapy.
- Woman ovulates with drug therapy.
- Patient and family state understanding of drug therapy.

clomipramine hydrochloride

(kloh-MIH-pruh-meen high-droh-KLOR-ighd)
Anafranil

Pharmacologic class: tricyclic antidepressant (TCA)
Therapeutic class: obsessive-compulsive disorder (OCD) drug
Pregnancy risk category: C

Indications and dosages

▶ **OCD.** *Adults:* Initially, 25 mg P.O. daily in divided doses with meals, gradually increase to 100 mg daily during first 2 weeks. Then increase, if needed, to maximum dosage of 250 mg daily in divided doses with meals. After adjusting dosage, give total daily dosage at bedtime.

Children ages 10 to 18: Initially, 12.5 mg P.O. b.i.d. with meals, gradually increase to daily maximum of 3 mg/kg or 100 mg P.O., whichever is smaller. After adjusting dosage, give total daily dosage at bedtime. Reassess and adjust periodically.

▶ **Panic disorder‡.** *Adults:* 12.5 to 150 mg (maximum, 200 mg) daily.

Contraindications and cautions

- Contraindicated in patients hypersensitive to drug or other TCAs, in patients in acute recovery period after MI, and within 14 days of MAO inhibitor therapy.
- Use cautiously in patients with history of seizure disorders or with brain damage; in those receiving other seizure-threshold–lowering drugs; in patients at risk for suicide; in patients with history of urine retention or angle-closure glaucoma, increased intraocular pressure, CV disease, impaired hepatic or renal function, or hyperthyroidism; in patients with tumors of the adrenal medulla; in patients receiving thyroid drug or electroconvulsive therapy; and in those undergoing elective surgery.

Lifespan: In pregnant and breast-feeding women, use cautiously.

Adverse reactions

CNS: aggressiveness, asthenia, dizziness, EEG changes, extrapyramidal reactions, fatigue, headache, insomnia, nervousness, myoclonus, ***seizures,*** somnolence, tremors.
CV: orthostatic hypotension, palpitations, tachycardia.
EENT: abnormal vision, laryngitis, otitis media in children, pharyngitis, rhinitis.
GI: abdominal pain, anorexia, constipation, diarrhea, dry mouth, dyspepsia, eructation, *nausea.*
GU: dysmenorrhea, impaired ejaculation, impotence, urinary hesitancy, UTI.
Hematologic: anemia, bone marrow suppression.
Metabolic: increased appetite, *weight gain.*
Musculoskeletal: *myalgia.*
Skin: *diaphoresis,* dry skin, photosensitivity, pruritus, rash.
Other: altered libido.

Interactions

Drug-drug. *Barbiturates:* May decrease TCA level. Monitor patient for decreased antidepressant effect.
Cimetidine, methylphenidate: May increase TCA level. Monitor patient for increased antidepressant effect.
Clonidine: May cause loss of blood pressure control and potentially life-threatening elevations in blood pressure. Avoid use together.
CNS depressants: May enhance CNS depression. Avoid use together.
Epinephrine, norepinephrine: May increase hypertensive effect. Use with caution, and monitor blood pressure.
MAO inhibitors: May cause hyperpyretic crisis, seizures, coma, or death. Don't use together or within 14 days of each other.
Drug-herb. *St. John's wort:* May raise serotonin level, causing serotonin syndrome. Discourage use together.
Drug-lifestyle. *Alcohol use:* May increase CNS depression. Discourage use together.
Smoking: May increase metabolism and decrease effectiveness. Discourage smoking.
Sun exposure: May cause photosensitivity. Urge patient to avoid sun exposure and to wear protective clothing and sunblock.

Effects on lab test results

- May decrease hemoglobin level and hematocrit.

Pharmacokinetics

Absorption: Good, but extensive first-pass metabolism limits bioavailability to about 50%.
Distribution: Into lipophilic tissues. About 98% protein-bound.
Metabolism: Mainly hepatic with several metabolites.
Excretion: 66% in urine; remainder in feces. *Half-life:* Parent compound, 32 hours; active metabolite, 69 hours.

Route	Onset	Peak	Duration
P.O.	≥ 2 wk	Unknown	Unknown

Action

Chemical effect: Selectively inhibits serotonin reuptake.
Therapeutic effect: Reduces OCD behaviors.

Available forms

Capsules: 25 mg, 50 mg, 75 mg

NURSING PROCESS

Assessment

• Assess patient's underlying condition before therapy and regularly thereafter.

• Assess patient's and family's knowledge of drug therapy.

Nursing diagnoses

• Ineffective coping related to patient's underlying condition

• Risk for injury related to drug-induced adverse reactions

• Deficient knowledge related to drug therapy

Planning and implementation

• During dosage adjustment, divide dose and give with meals to minimize GI effects. After dosage adjustment, give total daily dosage at bedtime.

• Don't abruptly stop giving the drug.

• Because hypertensive episodes may occur during surgery, taper off drug several days before surgery.

ALERT: Don't confuse clomipramine with chlorpromazine or clomiphene; don't confuse Anafranil with enalapril, nafarelin, or alfentanil.

Patient teaching

• Warn patient to avoid hazardous activities requiring alertness and good psychomotor coordination, especially during dosage adjustment. Daytime sedation and dizziness may occur.

• Tell patient to avoid alcohol while taking drug.

• Warn patient not to abruptly stop taking the drug.

• Advise patient to use sunblock, wear protective clothing, and avoid prolonged exposure to strong sunlight.

Evaluation

• Patient's behavior and communication indicate improvement of obsessive-compulsive pattern.

• Patient doesn't experience injury from drug-induced adverse CNS reactions.

• Patient and family state understanding of drug therapy.

clonazepam

(kloh-NEH-zuh-pam)

Klonopin, Rivotril ♦ ◇

Pharmacologic class: benzodiazepine
Therapeutic class: anticonvulsant, antianxiety drug
Pregnancy risk category: D
Controlled substance schedule: IV

Indications and dosages

▶ **Lennox-Gastaut syndrome; atypical absence seizures; akinetic and myoclonic seizures.** *Adults:* Initially, not to exceed 1.5 mg P.O. t.i.d. May increase by 0.5 to 1 mg q 3 days until seizures are controlled. If given in unequal doses, give largest dose at bedtime. Maximum daily dose is 20 mg.
Children age 10 and younger or weighing 30 kg (66 lb) or less: Initially, 0.01 to 0.03 mg/kg P.O. daily (maximum, 0.05 mg/kg daily) in two or three divided doses. Increase by 0.25 to 0.5 mg q third day to maximum maintenance dosage of 0.1 to 0.2 mg/kg daily as needed.

▶ **Panic disorder.** *Adults:* Initially, 0.25 mg P.O. b.i.d.; increase to target dose of 1 mg daily after 3 days. Some patients may benefit from doses up to maximum of 4 mg daily. To achieve 4 mg daily, increase dosage in increments of 0.125 to 0.25 mg b.i.d. q 3 days as tolerated until panic disorder is controlled. Stop drug gradually by decreases of 0.125 mg b.i.d. q 3 days until stopped.

▶ **Restless legs syndrome; adjunct in schizophrenia‡.** *Adults:* 0.5 to 2 mg P.O. at bedtime.

▶ **Parkinsonian dysarthria‡.** *Adults:* 0.25 to 0.5 mg P.O. daily.

▶ **Acute manic episodes‡.** *Adults:* 0.75 to 16 mg P.O. daily.

▶ **Multifocal tic disorders‡.** *Adults:* 1.5 to 12 mg P.O. daily.

▶ **Neuralgia‡.** *Adults:* 2 to 4 mg P.O. daily.

Contraindications and cautions

• Contraindicated in patients hypersensitive to benzodiazepines and in those with acute angle-closure glaucoma or significant hepatic disease.

• Use cautiously in patients with mixed type of seizure because drug may precipitate generalized tonic-clonic seizures. Also, use cautiously in patients with chronic respiratory disease, or open-angle glaucoma not well controlled.

Lifespan: In pregnant women, use only when benefits to mother outweigh risks to fetus. Breast-feeding women should stop breast-feeding because drug appears in breast milk. In children, use cautiously. In elderly patients, use cautiously and start with low doses because of possible reduced hepatic and renal function.

Adverse reactions

CNS: agitation, *ataxia, behavioral disturbances* (especially in children), confusion, *drowsiness,* migraine, nightmares, psychosis, sleep disorders, slurred speech, ***suicidal ideation,*** tremor, vertigo.
EENT: abnormal eye movements, diplopia, earache, *increased salivation,* nystagmus, otitis, rhinitis, sinusitis, sore gums.
CV: chest pain, facial and ankle edema, palpitations, postural hypotension, thrombophlebitis.
GI: abnormal thirst, appetite changes, constipation, diarrhea, gastritis, nausea.
GU: dysuria, enuresis, nocturia, urine retention.
Hematologic: eosinophilia, ***leukopenia, thrombocytopenia.***
Metabolic: change in appetite.
Musculoskeletal: muscle weakness, pain.
Respiratory: ***respiratory depression,*** upper respiratory tract infection.
Skin: acne flare, alopecia, contact dermatitis, flushing, rash.

Interactions

Drug-drug. *CNS depressants:* May increase CNS depression. Monitor patient closely.
Fluconazole, ketoconazole, itraconazole, miconazole: May increase and prolong levels, CNS depression, and psychomotor impairment. Don't use together.
Drug-herb. *Catnip, kava, lady's slipper, lemon balm, passion flower, sassafras, skullcap, valerian:* May enhance sedative effects of clonazepam. Discourage use together.
Drug-lifestyle. *Alcohol use:* May cause additive CNS effects. Strongly discourage alcohol use.

Effects on lab test results

- May increase liver function test values and eosinophil count. May decrease WBC and platelet counts.

Pharmacokinetics

Absorption: Good.
Distribution: Wide. 85% protein-bound.
Metabolism: By liver to several metabolites.
Excretion: In urine. *Half-life:* 18 to 50 hours.

Route	Onset	Peak	Duration
P.O.	Unknown	1–2 hr	Unknown

Action

Chemical effect: May act by facilitating effects of inhibitory neurotransmitter GABA.
Therapeutic effect: Prevents or stops seizure activity.

Available forms

Orally disintegrating tablets: 0.125 mg, 0.25 mg, 0.5 mg, 1 mg, 2 mg
Tablets: 0.5 mg, 1 mg, 2 mg

NURSING PROCESS

Assessment

- Assess patient's seizure condition before therapy and regularly thereafter.
- Monitor clonazepam level. Therapeutic level for anticonvulsant effects has been reported to be 20 to 80 nanograms/ml.
- Monitor CBC and liver function tests.
- Be alert for adverse reactions and drug interactions.
- Assess patient's and family's knowledge of drug therapy.

Nursing diagnoses

- Risk for injury related to potential for seizure activity
- Activity intolerance related to drug-induced sedation
- Deficient knowledge related to drug therapy

Planning and implementation

- Increase dose gradually.

ALERT: Never stop drug abruptly because seizures may worsen. Follow weaning protocol for safety.

- Withdrawal symptoms are similar to those of barbiturates (insomnia, dysphoria; then abdominal and muscle cramps, tremor, behavioral disorder; progressing to hallucinations, psychosis, convulsions).
- If adverse reactions develop, immediately call prescriber.

• Maintain seizure precautions.

ALERT: Don't confuse Klonopin or clonazepam with clonidine, clozapine, or clomiphene.

Patient teaching

• Advise patient to avoid driving or other potentially hazardous activities until drug's CNS effects are known.

• Instruct parents to monitor child's school performance because drug may interfere with attentiveness.

• For orally disintegrating tablets, instruct patient to peel back the foil blister pouch using dry hands and to place tablet in mouth immediately. The tablet disintegrates rapidly in saliva.

• Instruct patient or family to notify prescriber if oversedation or other adverse reaction develops or questions arise about therapy.

• Advise patients with panic disorder to continue psychotherapeutic interventions in addition to drug therapy.

Evaluation

• Patient is free from seizure activity during drug therapy.

• Patient is able to meet daily activity needs.

• Patient and family state understanding of drug therapy.

clonidine hydrochloride

(KLON-uh-deen high-droh-KLOR-ighd)

Catapres, Catapres-TTS, Dixarit ♦ ◇, Duraclon

Pharmacologic class: centrally acting sympatholytic

Therapeutic class: antihypertensive

Pregnancy risk category: C

Indications and dosages

▶ **Essential, renal, and malignant hypertension.** *Adults:* Initially, 0.1 mg P.O. b.i.d. Then, increase by 0.1 to 0.2 mg daily q week. Usual dosage range is 0.1 to 0.3 mg b.i.d.; infrequently, dosages as high as 2.4 mg daily are used. Or transdermal patch applied to nonhairy area of intact skin on upper arm or torso q 7 days. Start with 0.1-mg system and adjust after 1 to 2 weeks with another 0.1-mg system or larger system if increases are needed to maintain normal blood pressure.

▶ **Severe pain.** *Adults:* Starting dosage for continuous epidural infusion is 30 mcg/hour. Adjust according to patient's response.

▶ **Prophylaxis for vascular headache‡.** *Adults:* 0.025 mg P.O. b.i.d. to q.i.d., up to 0.15 mg P.O. daily in divided doses.

▶ **Adjunctive therapy for nicotine withdrawal‡.** *Adults:* Initially, 0.1 mg P.O. b.i.d., then gradually increase dose by 0.1 mg daily q week, up to 0.75 mg P.O. daily, as tolerated. Alternatively, apply transdermal patch (0.1 to 0.2 mg/24 hours) and replace weekly for the first 2 or 3 weeks after smoking cessation.

▶ **Adjunct in opioid withdrawal‡.** *Adults:* 5 to 17 mcg/kg P.O. daily in divided doses for up to 10 days. Adjust dosage to avoid hypotension and excessive sedation, and slowly withdraw drug.

▶ **Adjunct in menopausal symptoms‡.** *Adults:* 0.025 to 0.2 mg P.O. b.i.d. Or apply transdermal patch (0.1 mg/24 hours) and replace weekly.

▶ **Dysmenorrhea‡.** *Adults:* 0.025 mg P.O. b.i.d. for 14 days before onset of menses and during menses.

▶ **Ulcerative colitis‡.** *Adults:* 0.3 mg P.O. t.i.d.

▶ **Diabetic diarrhea‡.** *Adults:* 0.15 to 1.2 mg P.O. daily. Or 1 to 2 patches q week (0.3 mg/24 hours).

▶ **Attention deficit hyperactivity disorder‡.** *Children:* Initially, 0.05 mg P.O. at bedtime. Increase cautiously over 2 to 4 weeks to reach maintenance dosage of 0.05 to 0.4 mg daily depending on the patient's weight and tolerance.

Contraindications and cautions

• Contraindicated in patients hypersensitive to drug. Transdermal form is contraindicated in patients hypersensitive to any component of adhesive layer. Injectable form is contraindicated in patients receiving anticoagulation therapy and patients with a bleeding diathesis or injection-site infection.

• Use cautiously in patient with severe coronary insufficiency, recent MI, cerebrovascular disease, and chronic renal or hepatic impairment.

Lifespan: In pregnant women, safety and effectiveness haven't been established. In breast-feeding women, use cautiously. In children, safety and effectiveness haven't been established. In children with severe intractable pain from malignancy that is unresponsive to epidural or spinal opioids or other conventional analgesic techniques, injectable form is restricted.

Adverse reactions

CNS: *anxiety, confusion, dizziness, drowsiness,* fatigue, headache, nervousness, sedation, *somnolence,* vivid dreams.
CV: ***bradycardia,*** *hypotension,* orthostatic hypotension, ***severe rebound hypertension.***
GI: *constipation, dry mouth, nausea, vomiting.*
GU: urine retention, impotence, UTI.
Metabolic: transient glucose intolerance.
Skin: *pruritus and dermatitis* with transdermal patch.

Interactions

Drug-drug. *Amitriptyline, amoxapine, clomipramine, desipramine, doxepin, imipramine, nortriptyline, protriptyline, trimipramine:* May cause loss of blood pressure control with potentially life-threatening elevations in blood pressure. Don't use together.
Beta blockers, such as propranolol: May cause severe rebound hypertension. Monitor patient carefully.
CNS depressants: May enhance CNS depression. Use together cautiously.
MAO inhibitors: May decrease antihypertensive effect. Use together cautiously.
Drug-herb. *Capsicum, yohimbe:* May reduce antihypertensive effectiveness. Discourage use together.

Effects on lab test results

- May increase glucose and CK levels.

Pharmacokinetics

Absorption: Good.
Distribution: Wide.
Metabolism: Nearly 50% is transformed to inactive metabolites.
Excretion: 65% in urine; 20% in feces. *Half-life:* 6 to 20 hours.

Route	Onset	Peak	Duration
P.O.	15–30 min	1½–2½ hr	6–8 hr
Epidural	Immediate	19 min	Unknown
Transdermal	2–3 days	2–3 days	Several days

Action

Chemical effect: May inhibit central vasomotor centers, decreasing sympathetic outflow to heart, kidneys, and peripheral vasculature, resulting in decreased peripheral vascular resistance, decreased systolic and diastolic blood pressure, and decreased heart rate. Produces analgesia by mimicking the activation of descending pain-suppressing pathways arising from supraspinal control centers. Also inhibits the release of substance P, an inflammatory neuropeptide.
Therapeutic effect: Lowers blood pressure and decreases neurogenic pain.

Available forms

Injectable: 100 mcg/ml, 500 mcg/ml
Tablets: 0.025 mg, 0.1 mg, 0.2 mg, 0.3 mg
Transdermal: TTS-1 (releases 0.1 mg/24 hours), TTS-2 (releases 0.2 mg/24 hours), TTS-3 (releases 0.3 mg/24 hours)

NURSING PROCESS

Assessment

- Assess patient's blood pressure before therapy and regularly thereafter.
- Antihypertensive effects of transdermal clonidine may take 2 to 3 days to become apparent. Oral antihypertensive therapy may have to be continued in interim.
- Be alert for adverse reactions and drug interactions.
- Observe patient for tolerance to drug's therapeutic effects; increase dosage if needed.
- Periodic eye examinations are recommended.
- Monitor site of transdermal patch for dermatitis. Ask patient about pruritus.
- Assess patient's and family's knowledge of drug therapy.

Nursing diagnoses

- Risk for injury related to presence of hypertension
- Ineffective protection related to severe rebound hypertension caused by abrupt cessation of drug
- Deficient knowledge related to drug therapy

Planning and implementation

- Drug may be given to lower blood pressure rapidly in some hypertensive emergency situations.
- Adjust dosage to patient's blood pressure and tolerance.
- Give last dose of day at bedtime.

• Epidural clonidine is more likely to be effective in patients with neuropathic pain than somatic or visceral pain.
ALERT: Injection form is for epidural use only. The 500-mcg/ml dose must be diluted in normal saline for injection to provide a final concentration of 100 mcg/ml.
• When giving by epidural route, carefully monitor infusion pump and inspect catheter tubing for obstruction or dislodgement. Monitor access site for signs of infection or inflammation.
• Monitor patient closely, especially during the first few days of therapy. Respiratory depression or deep sedation may occur.
• To improve adherence of patch, apply adhesive overlay. Place patch at different site each week.
• Remove transdermal patch before defibrillation to prevent arcing.
• When stopping therapy in patients receiving both clonidine and beta blocker, gradually withdraw beta blocker first to minimize adverse reactions.
• Don't stop giving clonidine before surgery.
ALERT: Don't confuse clonidine with quinidine, clozapine, Klonopin, clonazepam, or clomiphene; or Catapres with Cetapred or Combipres.

Patient teaching

• Advise patient not to stop drug abruptly because doing so may cause severe rebound hypertension. Explain that dose must be reduced gradually over 2 to 4 days.
• Tell patient to take the last daily dose immediately before bedtime.
• Reassure patient that transdermal patch usually adheres despite showering and other routine daily activities. Teach him how to use adhesive overlay to improve skin adherence. Also tell patient to place patch at different site each week.
• Caution patient that drug can cause drowsiness, but that he will develop tolerance to this adverse effect.
• Urge patient to rise slowly and avoid sudden position changes to reduce orthostatic hypotension.

Evaluation

• Patient's blood pressure is normal with drug therapy.
• Patient understands not to stop drug abruptly.
• Patient and family state understanding of drug therapy.

C

clopidogrel bisulfate

(kloh-PIH-doh-grel bigh-SUL-fayt)
Plavix

Pharmacologic class: inhibitor of adenosine diphosphate (ADP)–induced platelet aggregation
Therapeutic class: antiplatelet
Pregnancy risk category: B

Indications and dosages

▶ **Reduce atherosclerotic events in patients with atherosclerosis documented by recent stroke, MI, or peripheral arterial disease.** *Adults:* 75 mg P.O. daily.

▶ **Reduce atherosclerotic events in patients with acute coronary syndrome (unstable angina, non–ST-segment elevation MI), including those managed medically and those who are to be managed with percutaneous coronary intervention (with or without stent) or coronary artery bypass graft.** *Adults:* Start with a single 300-mg P.O. loading dose, then continue at 75 mg P.O. once daily. Also, give 75 to 325 mg aspirin once daily during therapy.

▶ **ST-segment elevation acute MI.** *Adults:* 75 mg P.O. once daily with aspirin, with or without thrombolytics. An optional 300-mg loading dose may be given.

Contraindications and cautions

• Contraindicated in patients hypersensitive to drug or any of its components, and in those with pathologic bleeding, such as peptic ulcer or intracranial hemorrhage.
• Use cautiously in patients with hepatic impairment and in those at risk for increased bleeding from trauma, surgery, or other conditions.
Lifespan: In breast-feeding women, drug is contraindicated. In children, safety and effectiveness haven't been established.

Adverse reactions

CNS: depression, dizziness, fatigue, headache, pain.
CV: chest pain, edema, hypertension.
EENT: epistaxis, rhinitis.

GI: abdominal pain, constipation, diarrhea, dyspepsia, gastritis, ***hemorrhage,*** ulcers.
GU: UTI.
Hematologic: purpura.
Musculoskeletal: arthralgia, back pain.
Respiratory: bronchitis, cough, dyspnea, upper respiratory tract infection.
Skin: rash, pruritus.
Other: flulike symptoms.

Interactions

Drug-drug. *Aspirin, NSAIDs:* May increase risk of GI bleeding. Monitor patient for signs of GI bleeding, such as abdominal pain or blood in vomitus or stool.
Heparin, warfarin: Safety hasn't been established. Use together cautiously, and monitor patient for bleeding.
Drug-herb. *Dong quai, feverfew, garlic, ginger, horse chestnut, red clover:* May increase risk of bleeding. Monitor patient closely.

Effects on lab test results

- May decrease platelet count.

Pharmacokinetics

Absorption: At least 50% and rapid.
Distribution: 94% to 98% protein-bound.
Metabolism: Extensive.
Excretion: 50% in urine and 46% in feces.
Half-life: 8 hours.

Route	Onset	Peak	Duration
P.O.	2 hr	Unknown	5 days

Action

Chemical effect: Inhibits binding of ADP to its platelet receptor, which inhibits ADP-mediated activation and subsequent platelet aggregation. Because drug acts by irreversibly modifying the platelet ADP receptor, platelets exposed to drug are affected for their lifespan.
Therapeutic effect: Prevents clot formation.

Available forms

Tablets: 75 mg

NURSING PROCESS

Assessment

- Assess current use of OTC drugs, such as aspirin or NSAIDs, and herbal remedies.
- Assess patient for increased bleeding or bruising tendencies before and during drug therapy.
- Assess patient's and family's knowledge of drug therapy.

Nursing diagnoses

- Risk for injury related to potential for atherosclerotic events from underlying condition
- Ineffective protection related to increased risk of bleeding
- Deficient knowledge related to drug therapy

Planning and implementation

- Five days after stopping drug, expect platelet aggregation to return to normal.
- Don't give drug to a patient with hepatic impairment or an increased risk of bleeding from trauma, surgery, or other pathologic conditions.

ALERT: Don't confuse Plavix with Paxil.

Patient teaching

- Tell patient it may take longer than usual to stop bleeding. Urge him to refrain from activities that increase the risk of trauma and bleeding.
- Instruct patient to notify prescriber about unusual bleeding or bruising.
- Tell patient to inform prescriber or dentist that he's taking drug before having surgery or starting new drug therapy.
- Inform patient that drug may be taken with or without food.

Evaluation

- Patient has less risk of stroke, MI, and vascular death.
- Patient states appropriate bleeding precautions to take.
- Patient and family state understanding of drug therapy.

clozapine

(KLOH-zuh-peen)
Clozaril, FazaClo

Pharmacologic class: tricyclic dibenzodiazepine derivative
Therapeutic class: antipsychotic
Pregnancy risk category: B

Indications and dosages

▶ **Schizophrenia in severely ill patients unresponsive to other therapies; reduction in risk**

of recurrent suicidal behavior in schizophrenia or schizoaffective disorder. *Adults:* Initially, 12.5 mg P.O. once daily or b.i.d.; increase by 25 to 50 mg daily (if tolerated) to 300 to 450 mg daily by end of 2 weeks. Base dosage on response, patient tolerance, and adverse reactions. Don't increase subsequent doses more than once or twice weekly, and don't exceed 100 mg. Many patients respond to 300 to 600 mg daily, but some may need as much as 900 mg daily. Maximum, 900 mg daily.

Adjust-a-dose: In elderly patients, use lowest recommended dose when starting therapy.

Contraindications and cautions

- Contraindicated in patients taking drugs that suppress bone marrow function and in those with paralytic ileus, uncontrolled epilepsy, history of drug-induced agranulocytosis, myelosuppressive disorders, severe CNS depression or coma, paralytic ileus, or WBC count less than $3{,}500/mm^3$.
- Use cautiously in patients with prostatic hyperplasia, urinary retention, or angle-closure glaucoma because clozapine has potent anticholinergic effects. Also use cautiously in patients receiving general anesthesia and in those with hepatic, renal, or cardiac disease.

Lifespan: In pregnant women, use cautiously. In breast-feeding women, drug is contraindicated. In children younger than age 12, safety and effectiveness haven't been established. In elderly patients, use cautiously and at lowest recommended dose.

Adverse reactions

CNS: agitation, akathisia, anxiety, ataxia, confusion, depression, disturbed sleep or nightmares, *dizziness, drowsiness,* fatigue, fever, headache, hyperkinesia, hypokinesia or akinesia, insomnia, myoclonus, rigidity, *sedation,* ***seizures,*** slurred speech, *syncope,* tremor, *vertigo,* weakness.
CV: ***cardiomyopathy,*** chest pain, ECG changes, hypertension, hypotension, orthostatic hypotension, tachycardia.
GI: constipation, dry mouth, *excessive salivation,* heartburn, nausea, vomiting.
GU: abnormal ejaculation, incontinence, urinary frequency, urinary urgency, urine retention.
Hematologic: ***agranulocytosis, leukopenia.***
Metabolic: hypercholesterolemia, hypertriglyceridemia, ***severe hyperglycemia,*** weight gain.
Musculoskeletal: muscle pain or spasm, muscle weakness.
Skin: rash.

Interactions

Drug-drug. *Anticholinergics:* May increase anticholinergic effects of clozapine. Avoid use together.
Antihypertensives: May increase hypotensive effects. Monitor blood pressure.
Bone marrow suppressants: May increase bone marrow toxicity. Don't use together.
Citalopram: May significantly increase clozapine level and adverse effects. Avoid use together.
Digoxin, warfarin, other highly protein-bound drugs: May increase levels of these drugs. Monitor patient closely for adverse reactions.
Psychoactive drugs: May produce additive effects. Use together cautiously.
Drug-herb. *St. John's wort:* May reduce drug level, causing a loss of symptom control in patients taking an antipsychotic. Discourage use together.
Drug-food. *Caffeine:* May increase clozapine level. Large fluctuations in caffeine consumption may affect therapeutic response to drug. Advise patient to limit caffeine.
Drug-lifestyle. *Alcohol use:* May increase CNS depression. Discourage use together.
Smoking: May increase metabolism of drug and decrease its effectiveness. Discourage smoking.

Effects on lab test results

- May increase ALT, AST, LDH, and alkaline phosphatase levels. May increase or decrease glucose level.
- May decrease WBC and granulocyte counts.

Pharmacokinetics

Absorption: Rapid.
Distribution: 95% protein-bound.
Metabolism: Extensive.
Excretion: 50% of drug appears in urine and 30% in feces, mostly as metabolites. *Half-life:* Appears proportional to dose and may range from 8 to 12 hours.

Route	Onset	Peak	Duration
P.O.	Unknown	2½ hr	4–12 hr
P.O. orally disintegrating	Unknown	2½ hr	Unknown

Action

Chemical effect: Unknown. Binds to dopaminergic receptors (both D1 and D2) within limbic system of CNS and may interfere with adrenergic, cholinergic, histaminergic, and serotoninergic receptors.
Therapeutic effect: Relieves psychotic signs and symptoms.

Available forms

Orally disintegrating tablets: 25 mg, 100 mg
Tablets: 12.5 mg, 25 mg, 100 mg

NURSING PROCESS

Assessment

- Assess patient's psychotic condition before therapy and regularly thereafter.
- Monitor patient's baseline WBC and differential counts before therapy and weekly thereafter.
- Be alert for adverse reactions and drug interactions.
- Assess patient for risk factors of diabetes, and obtain baseline fasting blood glucose level. Routinely reassess patient for signs and symptoms of hyperglycemia, and obtain repeat laboratory work.
- After stopping drug, monitor WBC counts weekly for at least 4 weeks, and monitor patient closely for recurrence of psychotic symptoms.
- Assess patient's and family's knowledge of drug therapy.

Nursing diagnoses

- Disturbed thought processes related to patient's underlying condition
- Risk for infection related to potential for drug-induced agranulocytosis
- Deficient knowledge related to drug therapy

Planning and implementation

- Drug carries significant risk of agranulocytosis. If possible, give at least two trials of a standard antipsychotic before giving this drug.
- Before starting treatment, patient must have a baseline WBC count of at least 3,500/mm^3 and baseline ANC of at least 2,000/mm^3. During the first 6 months of therapy, monitor patient weekly. If WBC count and ANC remain acceptable (WBC count at least 3,500/mm^3 and ANC at least 2,000/mm^3) for the first 6 months of continuous therapy, reduce monitoring to every other week. After 6 more months of continuous therapy, monitoring may be reduced to monthly. If therapy stops, return to weekly monitoring of WBC count and ANC for at least 4 weeks.

ALERT: Watch for signs and symptoms of cardiomyopathy, including exertional dyspnea, fatigue, orthopnea, paroxysmal nocturnal dyspnea, and peripheral edema, and report them immediately.

ALERT: Drug may increase risk of fatal myocarditis, especially during, but not limited to, the first month of therapy. In patients in whom myocarditis is suspected (unexplained fatigue, dyspnea, tachypnea, chest pain, tachycardia, fever, palpitations, and other signs of heart failure or ECG abnormalities, such as ST-segment and T-wave abnormalities or arrhythmias), stop therapy immediately and don't rechallenge.

ALERT: If drug must be stopped, withdraw gradually over a 1- to 2-week period. However, changes in patient's medical condition (including development of leukopenia) may require abruptly stopping the drug. Abruptly stopping long-term therapy may cause a sudden recurrence of psychotic symptoms.

- If therapy is restarted, follow usual guidelines for dosage increase. Reexposure to drug may increase the risk and severity of adverse reactions. If therapy was stopped for WBC counts below 2,000/mm^3 or granulocyte counts below 1,000/mm^3, don't restart therapy.

ALERT: If dose has been set for a patient already taking St. John's wort, stopping the herb could increase drug level and cause dangerous toxic symptoms.

- Severe hypoglycemia may occur in a patient without a history of hypoglycemia. Drug may also cause hyperglycemia. Monitor diabetic patient regularly.
- Give patient no more than a 1-week supply of the drug.
- Orally disintegrating tablets contain phenylalanine.

Patient teaching

- Warn patient about risk of agranulocytosis. Tell him drug is available only through special monitoring program that requires weekly blood tests to check for agranulocytosis. Advise patient to report flulike symptoms, fever, sore throat, lethargy, malaise, or other signs of infection.
- Explain that patient should avoid activities that require alertness and good psychomotor coordination during therapy.

• Tell patient to rise slowly to avoid orthostatic hypotension.
• Advise patient to check with prescriber before taking OTC medicines, herbal remedies, or alcohol.
• Teach patient signs and symptoms of hyperglycemia (increased thirst and urination, increased appetite, weakness) and risks of diabetes, which may not resolve when drug is stopped.
• Recommend ice chips or sugarless candy or gum to help relieve dry mouth.
• Tell patient to store orally disintegrating tablets in blister pack, to immediately place in his mouth after opening pack, and to let tablet dissolve and then swallow it. There's no need for water.

Evaluation

• Patient demonstrates reduction in psychotic symptoms with drug therapy.
• Patient doesn't develop infection throughout drug therapy.
• Patient and family state understanding of drug therapy.

codeine phosphate
(KOH-deen FOS-fayt)
Paveral ♦

codeine sulfate

Pharmacologic class: opioid
Therapeutic class: analgesic, antitussive
Controlled substance schedule: II
Pregnancy risk category: C

Indications and dosages

▶ **Mild-to-moderate pain.** *Adults:* 15 to 60 mg P.O. or 15 to 60 mg codeine phosphate by subcutaneous, I.M., or I.V. route q 4 to 6 hours, p.r.n.
Children older than age 1: Give 0.5 mg/kg P.O., I.M., or subcutaneously q 4 hours, p.r.n.
▶ **Nonproductive cough.** *Adults:* 10 to 20 mg P.O. q 4 to 6 hours. Maximum daily dosage is 120 mg.
Children ages 6 to 12: Give 5 to 10 mg P.O. q 4 to 6 hours. Maximum daily dosage is 60 mg.
Children ages 2 to 6: Give 2.5 to 5 mg P.O. q 4 to 6 hours. Maximum daily dosage is 30 mg.

I.V. administration

• Keep opioid antagonist (naloxone) and resuscitative equipment available.
• Give drug very slowly by direct injection into large vein.
• Don't give drug to children by I.V. route.

⊗ **Incompatibilities**
Aminophylline, ammonium chloride, amobarbital, bromides, chlorothiazide, heparin, iodides, pentobarbital, phenobarbital, phenytoin, salts of heavy metals, sodium bicarbonate, sodium iodide, thiopental. Don't mix with other drugs.

Contraindications and cautions

• Contraindicated in patients hypersensitive to drug.
• Use cautiously in debilitated patients and in patients with head injury, increased intracranial pressure, increased CSF pressure, hepatic or renal disease, hypothyroidism, Addison disease, acute alcoholism or other drug dependencies, seizures, severe CNS depression, bronchial asthma, COPD, respiratory depression, and shock.
Lifespan: In pregnant and breast-feeding women, use cautiously. In children, use cautiously. In elderly patients, use cautiously.

Adverse reactions

CNS: *clouded sensorium, dizziness, euphoria, sedation, **seizures.***
CV: ***bradycardia,*** flushing, ***hypotension.***
GI: *constipation, dry mouth,* ileus, *nausea, vomiting.*
GU: urine retention.
Respiratory: ***respiratory depression.***
Skin: pruritus.
Other: physical dependence.

Interactions

Drug-drug. *CNS depressants, general anesthetics, hypnotics, MAO inhibitors, other opioid analgesics, sedatives, tranquilizers, tricyclic antidepressants:* May have additive effects. Use together cautiously. Monitor patient response.
Drug-lifestyle. *Alcohol use:* May have additive effects. Discourage use together.

Effects on lab test results

• May increase amylase and lipase levels.

Pharmacokinetics

Absorption: Good. Two-thirds as potent orally as parenterally.

Distribution: Wide.
Metabolism: Mainly in liver.
Excretion: Mainly in urine. *Half-life:* 2½ to 4 hours.

Route	Onset	Peak	Duration
P.O.	10–30 min	1–2 hr	4–6 hr
I.V.	Immediate	Immediate	4–6 hr
I.M.	10–30 min	½–2 hr	4–6 hr
SubQ	10–30 min	Unknown	4–6 hr

Action

Chemical effect: Binds with opiate receptors in CNS, altering perception of and emotional response to pain through unknown mechanism. Also suppresses cough reflex by direct action on cough center in medulla.
Therapeutic effect: Relieves pain and cough.

Available forms

codeine phosphate
Injection: 15 mg/ml, 30 mg/ml, 60 mg/ml
Oral solution: 15 mg/5 ml, 10 mg/ml
Soluble tablets: 30 mg, 60 mg
codeine sulfate
Tablets: 15 mg, 30 mg, 60 mg

NURSING PROCESS

Assessment

- Assess patient's pain or cough before and after drug therapy.
- Be alert for adverse reactions and drug interactions.
- Assess patient's and family's knowledge of drug therapy.

Nursing diagnoses

- Acute pain related to patient's underlying condition
- Fatigue related to presence of cough
- Deficient knowledge related to drug therapy

Planning and implementation

- For full analgesic effect, give drug before patient has intense pain.

ALERT: Codeine is metabolized to morphine by CYP2D6; this gene may be absent in up to 7% of the population who experience reduced analgesic effect.

- Don't use drug when cough is valuable diagnostic sign or is beneficial (as after thoracic surgery).
- Give drug with food or milk to minimize adverse GI reactions.
- Don't inject discolored solution.
- Codeine is often prescribed with aspirin or acetaminophen to increase pain relief.
- Abuse potential is much lower for codeine than for morphine.
- If pain or cough isn't relieved, notify prescriber.

ALERT: Don't confuse codeine with Cardene, Lodine, or Cordran.

Patient teaching

- Instruct patient to monitor bowel movements while increasing dietary fiber, fruit, and fluids if possible. Begin stimulant laxative promptly if stool hardens. Patient should notify prescriber of first missed bowel movement and secure instructions for laxative use.
- Advise patient to take oral drug with milk or meals to minimize GI distress.
- Urge patient to ask for or take drug (if at home) before pain becomes severe.
- Warn ambulatory patient that he may feel dizzy when getting out of bed or walking. Tell outpatient to avoid driving and other hazardous activities until drug's CNS effects are known.
- Tell patient to report adverse drug reactions.

Evaluation

- Patient is free of pain after drug administration.
- Patient's cough is suppressed after drug administration.
- Patient and family state understanding of drug therapy.

colchicine

(KOHL-chih-seen)

Colgout ◇

Pharmacologic class: *Colchicum autumnale* alkaloid
Therapeutic class: antigout drug
Pregnancy risk category: C (P.O.), D (I.V.)

Indications and dosages

▶ **To prevent acute gout attacks as prophylactic or maintenance therapy.** *Adults:* 0.6 mg P.O. daily. Give drug 3 to 4 days per week to patients who normally have one attack per year or fewer; give drug daily to patients who have more than one attack per year. In severe cases, 1.2 to 1.8 mg daily.

▶ **To prevent gout attacks in patients undergoing surgery.** *Adults:* 0.6 mg P.O. t.i.d. 3 days before and 3 days after surgery.

▶ **Acute gout, acute gouty arthritis.** *Adults:* Initially, 1.2 mg P.O.; then 0.6 mg q 1 to 2 hours until pain is relieved; nausea, vomiting, or diarrhea ensues; or a maximum dose of 8 mg is reached. Or 2 mg I.V. followed by 0.5 mg I.V. q 6 hours if needed. Or an initial dose of 1 mg I.V. followed by 0.5 mg once or twice daily if needed. Some prescribers prefer to give a single injection of 3 mg I.V. Don't give more than 4 mg for total I.V. dosage over 24 hours (one course). Don't give any further drug (I.V. or P.O.) for 7 days or more.

▶ **Familial Mediterranean fever‡.** *Adults:* 1 to 2 mg P.O. daily in divided doses.

▶ **Hepatic cirrhosis‡.** *Adults:* 1 mg P.O. 5 days weekly.

▶ **Primary biliary cirrhosis‡.** *Adults:* 0.6 mg P.O. b.i.d.

▶ **Behçet disease‡.** *Adults:* 0.5 to 1.5 mg P.O. daily.

▶ **Scleroderma‡.** *Adults:* 1 mg P.O. daily

▶ **Sweet syndrome‡.** *Adults:* 0.5 mg P.O. once daily to t.i.d.

Adjust-a-dose: For patients with hepatic impairment or creatinine clearance of 10 to 50 ml/minute, decrease dosage by 50%.

I.V. administration

- Don't dilute injection with D_5W injection or other fluids that might change pH of solution. If lower concentration is needed, dilute with normal saline solution or sterile water for injection.
- Preferably, inject into tubing of free-flowing I.V. solution. If diluted solution becomes turbid, don't inject.
- Give drug by slow I.V. push over 2 to 5 minutes. Monitor patient for signs of extravasation.

⊗ **Incompatibilities**

Dextrose 5% injection, bacteriostatic normal saline injection.

Contraindications and cautions

- Contraindicated in patients with serious cardiac disease, renal disease, or GI disorders.
- Use cautiously in debilitated patients, and in patients with early evidence of cardiac, renal, or GI disease.

Lifespan: In pregnant women, use cautiously if at all because fetal harm may occur. In breast-feeding women and in children, safety and effectiveness haven't been established. In elderly patients, use cautiously.

Adverse reactions

CNS: peripheral neuritis.
GI: *abdominal pain, diarrhea, nausea, vomiting.*
Hematologic: ***agranulocytosis*** (with prolonged use), ***aplastic anemia,*** nonthrombocytopenic purpura, ***thrombocytopenia.***
Hepatic: ***hepatic necrosis.***
Skin: alopecia, dermatitis, urticaria.
Other: ***anaphylaxis,*** hypersensitivity reactions, severe local irritation (if extravasation occurs).

Interactions

Drug-drug. *Loop diuretics:* May decrease effectiveness of colchicine prophylaxis. Avoid use together.
Phenylbutazone: May increase risk of leukopenia or thrombocytopenia. Don't use together.
Vitamin B_{12}: May impair absorption of vitamin B_{12}. Avoid use together.
Drug-lifestyle. *Alcohol use:* May impair effectiveness of drug prophylaxis. Discourage use together.

Effects on lab test results

- May increase alkaline phosphatase, AST, and ALT levels. May decrease carotene, cholesterol, and hemoglobin levels and hematocrit.
- May decrease platelet and granulocyte counts.
- May cause false-positive results in urine tests for hemoglobin and erythrocytes. May interfere with urinary determinations of 17-hydroxycorticosteroids using the Reddy-Jenkins-Thorn test.

Pharmacokinetics

Absorption: Rapid. Unchanged drug may be reabsorbed from intestine by biliary processes.
Distribution: Rapid. Concentrated in leukocytes and distributed into kidneys, liver, spleen, and intestinal tract, but absent in heart, skeletal muscle, and brain.
Metabolism: Partially in liver and also slowly in other tissues.

Excretion: Mainly in feces, with lesser amounts in urine. *Half-life:* 1 to 10½ hours.

Route	Onset	Peak	Duration
P.O.	≤ 12 hr	½–2 hr	Unknown
I.V.	6–12 hr	½–2 hr	Unknown

Action

Chemical effect: May decrease WBC motility, phagocytosis, and lactic acid production, decreasing urate crystal deposits and reducing inflammation. As antiosteolytic drug, apparently inhibits mitosis of osteoprogenitor cells and decreases osteoclast activity.
Therapeutic effect: Relieves gout signs and symptoms.

Available forms

Injection: 0.5 mg/ml
Tablets: 0.6 mg (1/100 grain) as sugar-coated granules

NURSING PROCESS

Assessment

- Assess patient's underlying condition before therapy and regularly thereafter.
- Before therapy, obtain baseline laboratory studies, including CBC and uric acid level. Repeat regularly.
- Be alert for adverse reactions and drug interactions.
- Assess patient's and family's knowledge of drug therapy.

Nursing diagnoses

- Acute pain related to presence of gout
- Ineffective protection related to drug-induced hematologic adverse reactions
- Deficient knowledge related to drug therapy

Planning and implementation

- Give oral form of drug with meals to reduce GI effects. May be used with uricosurics.

ALERT: After a full course of 4 mg I.V., don't give drug by any other route for at least 7 days. Drug is toxic and death can result from overdose.

- Don't give I.M. or subcutaneously because severe local irritation occurs.
- Store drug in tightly closed, light-resistant container.
- Stop drug as soon as gout pain is relieved or at first sign of GI symptoms.
- Force fluids to maintain output at 2,000 ml daily.

Patient teaching

- Teach patient how to take drug.
- Advise patient to report rash, sore throat, fever, unusual bleeding, bruising, fatigue, weakness, numbness, or tingling.
- Tell patient when to stop drug.
- Urge patient not to drink alcohol during drug therapy because it may inhibit drug action.
- Advise patient to avoid all aspirin-containing drugs because they may precipitate gout.

Evaluation

- Patient becomes pain free after drug therapy.
- Patient's CBC and platelet counts remain normal throughout drug therapy.
- Patient and family state understanding of drug therapy.

colesevelam hydrochloride

(koh-leh-SEV-eh-lam high-droh-KLOR-ighd)
WelChol

Pharmacologic class: polymeric bile acid sequestrant
Therapeutic class: antilipemic
Pregnancy risk category: B

Indications and dosages

▶ **Reduction of elevated LDL cholesterol level in patients with primary hypercholesterolemia (Frederickson Type IIa). May be given either alone or with an HMG-CoA reductase inhibitor.** *Adults:* If given alone, give 3 tablets (1,875 mg) P.O. twice daily with meals and liquid or 6 tablets (3,750 mg) once daily with a meal and liquid. Maximum dose is 7 tablets (4,375 mg). If given with an HMG-CoA reductase inhibitor (atorvastatin, fluvastatin, lovastatin, pravastatin, simvastatin), recommended dose is 4 to 6 tablets P.O. daily.

Contraindications and cautions

- Contraindicated in patients hypersensitive to drug or any of its components and in patients with bowel obstruction.
- Use cautiously in patients susceptible to vitamin K deficiency or deficiencies of fat-soluble

vitamins. Also use cautiously in patients with dysphagia, swallowing disorders, severe GI motility disorders, and major GI tract surgery. Use cautiously in patients with triglyceride levels above 300 mg/dl because effects aren't known.
Lifespan: In pregnant women, use only if clearly needed for risk of fat-soluble vitamin deficiency. In breast-feeding women, use cautiously; drug probably doesn't appear in breast milk because of lack of systemic absorption. In children, safety and effectiveness haven't been established.

Adverse reactions

CNS: asthenia, headache, pain.
EENT: pharyngitis, rhinitis, sinusitis.
GI: abdominal pain, *constipation,* diarrhea, *dyspepsia, flatulence,* nausea.
Musculoskeletal: back pain, myalgia.
Respiratory: increased cough.
Other: accidental injury, flulike syndrome, *infection.*

Interactions

None reported.

Effects on lab test results

- May increase HDL cholesterol and triglyceride levels. May decrease total cholesterol, LDL cholesterol, and apolipoprotein B levels.

Pharmacokinetics

Absorption: Not absorbed.
Distribution: None.
Metabolism: None.
Excretion: Mainly in feces as a complex bound to bile acids. Less than 0.05% of drug in urine.

Route	Onset	Peak	Duration
P.O.	Unknown	2 wk	Unknown

Action

Chemical effect: Binds to bile acids in the intestines and forms a nonabsorbable complex that's eliminated in feces. Partial removal of bile acids from the enterohepatic circulation results in an increased conversion of cholesterol to bile acids in the liver in an attempt to restore the depleted bile acids. The resulting increase in cholesterol causes systemic clearance of circulating LDL level.

Therapeutic effect: Lowers LDL and total cholesterol levels.

Available forms

Tablets: 625 mg

NURSING PROCESS

Assessment

- Rule out secondary causes of hypercholesterolemia before starting drug, such as poorly controlled diabetes, hypothyroidism, nephrotic syndrome, dysproteinemias, obstructive liver disease, other drug therapy, and alcoholism.
- Monitor total cholesterol, LDL, and triglyceride levels before and periodically during therapy.
- Monitor patient's bowel habits. If severe constipation develops, lower the dose and add a stool softener, or stop giving the drug.
- Assess patient's compliance with restricted diet and exercise program adjunctive to antilipemic therapy.
- Evaluate patient's and family's knowledge of drug therapy and importance of diet and exercise regimen.

Nursing diagnoses

- Imbalanced nutrition: more than body requirements of saturated fat and cholesterol related to dietary intake and lack of exercise program
- Risk for constipation related to drug-induced adverse gastrointestinal reactions
- Risk for injury related to presence of elevated LDL cholesterol level
- Deficient knowledge related to antilipemic drug therapy

Planning and implementation

- Give drug with a meal and a liquid.
- If given with an HMG-CoA reductase inhibitor, separate HMG-CoA reductase inhibitor and colesevelam.
- Store drug at room temperature but protect from moisture.

Patient teaching

- Instruct patient to take drug with a meal and a liquid.
- Teach patient to monitor bowel habits. Encourage a diet high in fiber and fluids. Instruct patient to notify prescriber promptly if severe constipation develops.

• Urge patient to follow prescribed diet that's restricted in saturated fat and cholesterol and high in vegetables and fiber. Also discuss and encourage an appropriate exercise program.
• Discuss with patient the importance of regularly monitoring lipid levels.
• Tell patient to notify prescriber if she's pregnant or breast-feeding.

Evaluation

• Patient begins a balanced diet and exercise regimen that's approved by prescriber.
• Patient doesn't suffer adverse GI effect from drug therapy.
• Patient's LDL cholesterol and total cholesterol levels are within normal limits.
• Patient and family state understanding of drug therapy.

conivaptan hydrochloride

(kahn-nih-VAPP-tan high-droh-KLOR-ighd)
Vaprisol

Pharmacologic class: arginine vasopressin receptor antagonist
Therapeutic class: hyponatremic drug
Pregnancy risk category: C

Indications and dosages

▶ **Euvolemic hyponatremia (as from SIADH, hypothyroidism, adrenal insufficiency, pulmonary disorders) in hospitalized patients.** *Adults:* Loading dose of 20 mg I.V. over 30 minutes; then 20 mg I.V. by continuous infusion over 24 hours for 1 to 3 days. If sodium level doesn't rise at desired rate, increase to 40 mg/day by continuous infusion. Don't exceed 4 days of treatment after loading dose.
Adjust-a-dose: If serum sodium level rises more than 12 mEq/L in 24 hours, stop infusion. If hyponatremia persists or recurs and the patient has had no adverse neurologic effects from the rapid rise in sodium level, restart infusion at a reduced dose.

If patient develops hypotension or hypovolemia, stop infusion. Monitor vital signs and volume status often. If hyponatremia persists once the patient is no longer hypotensive and volume status returns to normal, restart infusion at a reduced dose.

I.V. administration

• Dilute only with D_5W.
• For the loading dose, add 20 mg to 100 ml of D_5W. Gently invert bag to ensure complete mixing. Infuse over 30 minutes.
• For continuous infusion, add 40 mg to 250 ml of D_5W. Gently invert bag to ensure complete mixing. Infuse over 24 hours.
• Give via a large vein, and change infusion site q 24 hours.
• Solution is stable for 24 hours at room temperature.

⊗ **Incompatibilities**
Lactated Ringer's solution, normal saline solution. Don't mix or infuse with other I.V. drugs.

Contraindications and cautions

• Contraindicated in patients with hypovolemic hyponatremia, patients hypersensitive to drug or its components, and patients taking potent CYP3A4 inhibitors, such as clarithromycin, indinavir, itraconazole, ketoconazole, or ritonavir.
• Use cautiously in hyponatremic patients with underlying heart failure and patients with hepatic or renal impairment.
Lifespan: In pregnant women, safety hasn't been established; use only if benefit to mother outweighs risk to fetus. Patient shouldn't breast-feed during therapy. In children, safety hasn't been established.

Adverse reactions

CNS: confusion, fever, *headache*, insomnia.
CV: atrial fibrillation, hypertension, hypotension, orthostatic hypotension.
GI: constipation, diarrhea, dry mouth, nausea, oral candidiasis, *vomiting*.
GU: hematuria, pollakiuria, polyuria, UTI.
Hematologic: anemia.
Metabolic: dehydration, hyperglycemia, ***hypoglycemia, hypokalemia,*** hypomagnesemia, hyponatremia.
Respiratory: pneumonia.
Skin: erythema.
Other: *infusion site reactions, thirst.*

Interactions

Drug-drug. *Amlodipine*: May increase amlodipine level and half-life. Monitor blood pressure.
Digoxin: May increase digoxin level. Monitor patient, and adjust digoxin dose as needed.

Midazolam: May increase midazolam level. Monitor patient for respiratory depression and hypotension.

Potent CYP3A4 inhibitors (clarithromycin, indinavir, itraconazole, ketoconazole, ritonavir): May cause serious increases in serum levels and toxic effects. This combination is contraindicated.

Simvastatin: May increase simvastatin level. Monitor patient for evidence of rhabdomyolysis, including muscle pain, weakness, and tenderness.

Effects on lab test results

- May decrease potassium, magnesium, sodium, and hemoglobin levels and hematocrit. May increase or decrease blood glucose level.

Pharmacokinetics

Absorption: Given I.V.
Distribution: 99% protein-bound.
Metabolism: Mainly via CYP3A4 to four metabolites.
Excretion: 83% in feces; 12% in urine. *Half-life:* 5 hours.

Route	Onset	Peak	Duration
I.V.	Unknown	2–4 hr	12 hr

Action

Chemical effect: Increases the amount of free water eliminated by the kidneys by antagonizing V_{1A} and V_2 receptors in renal collecting ducts, inhibiting inappropriate or excessive arginine vasopressin (antidiuretic hormone) secretion.
Therapeutic effect: Increased net fluid loss, increased urine output, and decreased urine osmolality causing normalization of serum sodium levels.

Available forms

Injection: 20 mg/4 ml

NURSING PROCESS

Assessment

- Check serum sodium level and neurologic status regularly during therapy.
- Assess patient for infusion site reactions.
- Monitor patient for orthostatic hypotension during drug therapy.
- Assess patient and family's knowledge of drug therapy.

Nursing diagnoses

- Risk for deficient fluid volume related to excessive diuresis
- Risk for injury related to drug-induced orthostatic hypotension
- Deficient knowledge related to drug therapy

Planning and implementation

- Drug may cause significant infusion site reactions, even with proper dilution and administration. Rotate infusion site every 24 hours to reduce risk of reaction.

ALERT: Rapid correction of serum sodium level may cause osmotic demyelination syndrome. Monitor patient's serum sodium level and volume status.

- Adverse effects, including hypotension and thirst, are more common at higher doses. Monitor vital signs, and treat symptomatically if overdose occurs.

Patient teaching

- Inform patient that the infusion will be given for a maximum of 4 days after the loading dose.
- Inform patient that low blood pressure may cause him to feel dizzy or faint when rising from a sitting or lying position. Advise him to change positions slowly and to sit or lie down if needed.
- Advise patient to promptly report signs and symptoms of hypoglycemia, such as feeling shaky, nervous, tired, sweaty, cold, hungry, confused, or irritable.
- Emphasize the importance of reporting an unusually fast heartbeat or weakness.
- Tell patient that analgesics and moist heating pads can be used to treat pain and inflammation at the infusion site.

Evaluation

- Patient maintains adequate fluid volume.
- Patient maintains safety during drug therapy.
- Patient and family state understanding of drug therapy.

co-trimoxazole (sulfamethoxazole and trimethoprim)

(koh-trigh-MOX-uh-zohl)

Apo-Sulfatrim ♦, Apo-Sulfatrim DS ♦, Bactrim*, Bactrim DS, Bactrim I.V., Cotrim, Cotrim DS, Novo-Trimel ♦, Novo-Trimel D.S. ♦, Resprim ◇, Roubac ♦, Septra*, Septra DS, Septra-I.V., Septrin ◇, SMZ-TMP

Pharmacologic class: sulfonamide and folate antagonist
Therapeutic class: antibiotic
Pregnancy risk category: C (X at term)

Indications and dosages

▶ **UTI, shigellosis.** *Adults:* 160 mg trimethoprim and 800 mg sulfamethoxazole (double-strength tablet) P.O. q 12 hours for 10 to 14 days in UTIs and for 5 days in shigellosis. If indicated, I.V. infusion is given at 8 to 10 mg/kg daily (based on trimethoprim component) in two to four divided doses q 6, 8, or 12 hours for up to 14 days. Maximum trimethoprim dosage is 960 mg daily.
Children age 2 months and older: 8 mg/kg trimethoprim and 40 mg/kg sulfamethoxazole P.O. daily, in two divided doses q 12 hours (10 days for UTI; 5 days for shigellosis). If indicated, I.V. infusion is given at 8 to 10 mg/kg daily (based on trimethoprim component) in two to four divided doses q 6, 8, or 12 hours. Don't exceed adult dose.
Adjust-a-dose: In patients with impaired renal function, if creatinine clearance is 15 to 30 ml/minute, reduce dosage by 50%. Don't use if creatinine clearance is less than 15 ml/minute.

▶ **Otitis media in patients with penicillin allergy or penicillin-resistant infection.** *Children and infants age 2 months and older:* 8 mg/kg daily (based on trimethoprim component) P.O., in two divided doses q 12 hours for 10 days.

▶ ***Pneumocystis jiroveci (carinii)* pneumonia.** *Adults, children, and infants age 2 months and older:* 20 mg/kg trimethoprim and 100 mg/kg sulfamethoxazole P.O. daily, in equally divided doses q 6 hours for 14 days. If indicated, I.V. infusion may be given 15 to 20 mg/kg daily (based on trimethoprim component) in three or four divided doses q 6 to 8 hours for up to 14 days.

▶ **Chronic bronchitis.** *Adults:* 160 mg trimethoprim and 800 mg sulfamethoxazole P.O. q 12 hours for 10 to 14 days.

▶ **Traveler's diarrhea.** *Adults:* 160 mg trimethoprim and 800 mg sulfamethoxazole P.O. b.i.d. for 3 to 5 days. Some patients may require 2 days of therapy or less.

▶ **UTI in men with prostatitis‡.** *Adults:* 160 mg trimethoprim and 800 mg sulfamethoxazole P.O. b.i.d. for 3 to 6 months.

▶ **Prophylaxis of chronic UTI‡.** *Adults:* 40 mg trimethoprim and 200 mg sulfamethoxazole or 80 mg trimethoprim and 400 mg sulfamethoxazole P.O. daily or three times weekly for 3 to 6 months.

▶ **Septic agranulocytosis‡.** *Adults:* 2.5 mg/kg I.V. q.i.d.; for prophylaxis, 80 to 160 mg b.i.d.

▶ **Nocardia infection‡.** *Adults:* 640 mg P.O. (as trimethoprim component) daily for 7 months.

▶ **Pharyngeal gonococcal infection‡.** *Adults:* 720 mg P.O. (as trimethoprim component) daily for 5 days.

▶ **Chancroid‡.** *Adults:* 160 mg P.O. b.i.d. (as trimethoprim component) for 7 days.

▶ **Pertussis‡.** *Adults:* 320 mg P.O. daily (as trimethoprim component) in two divided doses. *Children:* 40 mg/kg P.O. daily in two divided doses.

▶ **Cholera‡.** *Adults:* 160 mg P.O. b.i.d. (as trimethoprim component) for 3 days.
Adjust-a-dose: For patients with renal impairment, if creatinine clearance is 15 to 30 ml/minute, reduce daily dose by 50%. Don't use if creatinine clearance is less than 15 ml/minute.

I.V. administration

- Dilute contents of 5-ml ampule of drug in 125 ml D_5W before giving. If patient is on a fluid restriction, dilute 5 ml of drug in 75 ml D_5W.
- Infuse slowly over 60 to 90 minutes. Don't give by rapid infusion or bolus injection.
- Don't refrigerate. Use within 6 hours if diluted in 125 ml and within 2 hours if diluted in 75 ml. If cloudiness or evidence of crystallization is noted after mixing, discard solution.

⊗ **Incompatibilities**
All I.V. solutions except D_5W, other I.V. drugs.

C

Contraindications and cautions

• Contraindicated in patients with megaloblastic anemia caused by folate deficiency, porphyria, severe renal impairment (creatinine clearance less than 15 ml/minute), or hypersensitivity to trimethoprim or sulfonamides.
• Use cautiously and reduce dose in patient with hepatic impairment, a creatinine clearance of 15 to 30 ml/minute, severe allergy or bronchial asthma, G6PD deficiency, or blood dyscrasia.
Lifespan: In pregnant women at term and in breast-feeding women, drug is contraindicated. In infants younger than age 2 months, safety and effectiveness haven't been established.

Adverse reactions

CNS: ataxia, fatigue, hallucinations, headache, insomnia, mental depression, nervousness, ***seizures,*** vertigo.
CV: thrombophlebitis.
GI: abdominal pain, anorexia, *diarrhea, nausea, stomatitis, vomiting.*
GU: crystalluria, hematuria, ***toxic nephrosis with oliguria and anuria.***
Hematologic: ***agranulocytosis, aplastic anemia,*** hemolytic anemia, ***leukopenia,*** megaloblastic anemia, ***thrombocytopenia.***
Hepatic: ***hepatic necrosis,*** jaundice.
Musculoskeletal: muscle weakness.
Skin: ***epidermal necrolysis, erythema multiforme,*** exfoliative dermatitis, generalized skin eruption, photosensitivity, pruritus, ***Stevens-Johnson syndrome,*** urticaria.
Other: *hypersensitivity reactions* (***anaphylaxis,*** drug fever, serum sickness).

Interactions

Drug-drug. *Hormonal contraceptives:* May decrease contraceptive effectiveness and increase risk of breakthrough bleeding. Suggest nonhormonal contraception.
Oral anticoagulants: May increase anticoagulant effect. Monitor patient for bleeding.
Oral antidiabetics: May increase hypoglycemic effect. Monitor glucose level.
Phenytoin: May inhibit hepatic metabolism of phenytoin. Monitor phenytoin level.
Drug-herb. *Dong quai, St. John's wort:* May increase risk of photosensitivity. Advise patient to avoid unprotected exposure to sunlight.
Drug-lifestyle. *Sun exposure:* May cause photosensitivity reactions. Urge patient to avoid sun exposure and wear protective clothing and sunblock.

Effects on lab test results

• May increase BUN, creatinine, aminotransferase, and bilirubin levels. May decrease hemoglobin level and hematocrit.
• May decrease granulocyte, platelet, and WBC counts.

Pharmacokinetics

Absorption: Good.
Distribution: Wide (including middle ear fluid, prostatic fluid, bile, aqueous humor, and CSF). Protein binding is 44% for trimethoprim, 70% for sulfamethoxazole.
Metabolism: By liver.
Excretion: Mainly in urine. *Half-life:* Trimethoprim, 8 to 11 hours; sulfamethoxazole, 10 to 13 hours.

Route	Onset	Peak	Duration
P.O.	Unknown	1–4 hr	Unknown
I.V.	Immediate	Immediate	Unknown

Action

Chemical effect: Sulfamethoxazole inhibits formation of dihydrofolic acid from PABA; trimethoprim inhibits dihydrofolate reductase. Both decrease bacterial folic acid synthesis.
Therapeutic effect: Inhibits susceptible bacteria.

Available forms

Injection: 16 mg trimethoprim and 80 mg/ml sulfamethoxazole (5 ml/ampule)
Oral suspension: trimethoprim 40 mg and sulfamethoxazole 200 mg/5 ml
Tablets: 80 mg trimethoprim and 400 mg sulfamethoxazole; 160 mg trimethoprim and 800 mg sulfamethoxazole

NURSING PROCESS

Assessment

• Assess patient's infection before therapy and regularly thereafter.
• Before giving first dose, obtain specimen for culture and sensitivity tests. Begin therapy pending results.
• Be alert for adverse reactions and drug interactions.

• If adverse GI reaction occurs, monitor patient's hydration.
• Monitor intake and output. Make sure urine output is at least 1,500 ml daily to ensure proper hydration. Inadequate urine output can lead to crystalluria or tubular deposits of drug.
• Assess patient's and family's knowledge of drug therapy.

Nursing diagnoses
• Ineffective protection related to presence of bacteria susceptible to drug
• Risk for deficient fluid volume related to drug-induced adverse GI reactions
• Deficient knowledge related to drug therapy

Planning and implementation
• For maximum absorption, give drug with full glass of water at least 1 hour before or 2 hours after meals. Shake oral suspension thoroughly before giving.
• Never give I.M.
ALERT: Double-check dosage, which may be written as trimethoprim component.
• Note that DS in product name means double strength.
ALERT: Adverse reactions, especially hypersensitivity reactions, rash, and fever, occur more frequently in patients with AIDS.
Patient teaching
• Tell patient to take entire amount of drug exactly as prescribed, even if he feels better.
• Tell patient to take drug with full glass of water and to drink at least 3 to 4 L of water daily.
• Advise patient to avoid exposure to direct sunlight because of risk of photosensitivity reaction.
• Tell patient to report signs of rash, sore throat, fever, or mouth sores because drug may need to be stopped.

Evaluation
• Patient is free from infection after drug therapy.
• Patient maintains adequate hydration after drug therapy.
• Patient and family state understanding of drug therapy.

cyanocobalamin (vitamin B_{12})
(sigh-an-oh-koh-BAH-luh-meen)
Anacobin ♦, Bedoz ♦, Big Shot B-12, Crystamine, Crysti 1000, Cyanoject, Cyomin, Nascobal

hydroxocobalamin (vitamin B_{12})
Hydro-Cobex, LA-12

Pharmacologic class: water-soluble vitamin
Therapeutic class: vitamin, nutrition supplement
Pregnancy risk category: A (C if used in doses above RDA)

Indications and dosages
▶ **RDA for cyanocobalamin.** *Adults and children ages 11 and older:* Give 2 mcg.
Pregnant women: Give 2.2 mcg.
Breast-feeding women: Give 2.6 mcg.
Children ages 7 to 10: Give 1.4 mcg.
Children ages 4 to 6: Give 1 mcg.
Children ages 1 to 3: Give 0.7 mcg.
Infants ages 6 months to 1 year: Give 0.5 mcg.
Neonates and infants younger than age 6 months: Give 0.3 mcg.
▶ **Vitamin B_{12} deficiency caused by inadequate diet, subtotal gastrectomy, or any other condition, disorder, or disease except malabsorption related to pernicious anemia or other GI disease.** *Adults:* 30 mcg hydroxocobalamin I.M. daily for 5 to 10 days, depending on severity of deficiency. Maintenance dosage is 100 to 200 mcg I.M. once monthly. Or 500 mcg intranasally once weekly. For subsequent prophylaxis, advise adequate nutrition and daily RDA vitamin B_{12} supplements.
Children: 1 to 5 mg hydroxocobalamin spread over 2 or more weeks in doses of 100 mcg I.M., depending on severity of deficiency. Maintenance dosage is 30 to 50 mcg I.M. monthly. For subsequent prophylaxis, advise adequate nutrition and daily RDA vitamin B_{12} supplements.
▶ **Pernicious anemia or vitamin B_{12} malabsorption.** *Adults:* Initially, 100 mcg cyanocobalamin I.M. or subcutaneously daily for 6 to 7 days; then 100 mcg I.M. or subcutaneously once monthly.
Children: 30 to 50 mcg I.M. or subcutaneously daily over 2 or more weeks; then 100 mcg I.M. or subcutaneously monthly for life.

C

▶ **Maintenance treatment for remission of pernicious anemia following I.M. vitamin B_{12} therapy in patients with no nervous system involvement; dietary deficiency, malabsorption disorders, inadequate secretion of intrinsic factor.** *Adults:* Initially, 1 spray in one nostril once weekly. Give at least 1 hour before or 1 hour after ingestion of hot foods or liquids.
▶ **Methylmalonic aciduria.** *Neonates:* 1,000 mcg cyanocobalamin I.M. daily.
▶ **Schilling test flushing dose.** *Adults and children:* 1,000 mcg hydroxocobalamin I.M. as a single dose.

Contraindications and cautions

- Contraindicated in patients with early Leber disease or hypersensitivity to vitamin B_{12} or cobalt.
- Use cautiously in anemic patients with cardiac, pulmonary, or hypertensive disease and in those with severe vitamin B_{12}–dependent deficiencies.

Lifespan: In premature infants, use cautiously because some products contain benzyl alcohol, which may cause gasping syndrome.

Adverse reactions

CV: ***heart failure,*** peripheral vascular thrombosis.
GI: transient diarrhea.
Respiratory: ***pulmonary edema.***
Skin: itching, transitory exanthema, urticaria.
Other: ***anaphylactoid reactions, anaphylaxis*** (with parenteral use); burning, pain (at subcutaneous or I.M. injection sites).

Interactions

Drug-drug. *Aminoglycosides, chloramphenicol, colchicine, para-aminosalicylic acid and salts:* May cause malabsorption of vitamin B_{12}. Don't use together.
Drug-lifestyle. *Alcohol use:* May cause malabsorption of vitamin B_{12}. Discourage use together.

Effects on lab test results

- May decrease potassium level.
- May cause false-positive results for intrinsic factor antibody test.

Pharmacokinetics

Absorption: After oral use, irregular and dependent on sufficient intrinsic factor and calcium. After intranasal, I.M., and subcutaneous use, rapid. Vitamin B_{12} is protein-bound.
Distribution: Into liver, bone marrow, and other tissues.
Metabolism: In liver.
Excretion: Amount of vitamin B_{12} needed by body is reabsorbed; excess in urine. *Half-life:* 6 days.

Route	Onset	Peak	Duration
P.O.	Unknown	8–12 hr	Unknown
I.M.	Unknown	60 min	Unknown
SubQ	Unknown	Unknown	Unknown
Intranasal	Unknown	1–2 hr	Unknown

Action

Chemical effect: Acts as a coenzyme that stimulates metabolic functions. Needed for cell replication, hematopoiesis, and nucleoprotein and myelin synthesis.
Therapeutic effect: Increases vitamin B_{12} level.

Available forms

cyanocobalamin
Injection: 100 mcg/ml, 1,000 mcg/ml
Intranasal: 500 mcg/0.1 ml
Tablets: 25 mcg†, 50 mcg†, 100 mcg†, 250 mcg†, 500 mcg†, 1,000 mcg†
hydroxocobalamin
Injection: 1,000 mcg/ml

NURSING PROCESS

Assessment

- Assess patient's vitamin B_{12} deficiency before therapy.
- Determine reticulocyte count, hematocrit, and B_{12}, iron, and folate levels before therapy starts.
- Monitor drug's effectiveness by assessing patient for improvement in signs and symptoms of vitamin B_{12} deficiency. Also, monitor reticulocyte count, hematocrit, and B_{12}, iron, and folate levels between fifth and seventh day of therapy and periodically thereafter.
- Infection, tumors, and renal, hepatic, or other debilitating diseases may reduce therapeutic response.
- Closely monitor potassium level for first 48 hours. Be alert for adverse reactions and drug interactions.
- Assess patient's and family's knowledge of drug therapy.

Nursing diagnoses

- Ineffective health maintenance related to underlying vitamin B_{12} deficiency
- Risk for injury related to parenteral administration and drug-induced hypersensitivity reactions
- Deficient knowledge related to drug therapy

Planning and implementation

- Don't mix parenteral liquids in same syringe with other drugs.
- Drug is physically incompatible with dextrose solutions, alkaline or strongly acidic solutions, oxidizing or reducing drugs, heavy metals, chlorpromazine, phytonadione, prochlorperazine, and many other drugs.
- Hydroxocobalamin is approved for I.M. or deep subcutaneous use only. Its only advantage over cyanocobalamin is its longer duration.
- Don't give large oral doses of vitamin B routinely because drug is lost through excretion.
- Protect vitamin from light. Don't refrigerate or freeze.
- Give potassium supplement, if needed.
- For intranasal form, prime the nasal device before first use. Repriming between doses isn't needed if the unit is upright.
- Give intranasal spray to one nostril weekly, at least 1 hour before or 1 hour after ingestion of hot foods or liquids.

Patient teaching

- Stress need for patient with pernicious anemia to return for monthly injections. Although total body stores may last 3 to 6 years, anemia will recur without monthly therapy.
- Emphasize importance of well-balanced diet.
- Tell patient to store oral tablets in tightly closed container at room temperature.

Evaluation

- Patient's vitamin B_{12} deficiency is resolved with drug therapy.
- Patient doesn't experience hypersensitivity reactions following parenteral administration of drug.
- Patient and family state understanding of drug therapy.

cyclobenzaprine hydrochloride

(sigh-kloh-BEN-zah-preen high-droh-KLOR-ighd)

Flexeril

Pharmacologic class: tricyclic antidepressant derivative
Therapeutic class: skeletal muscle relaxant
Pregnancy risk category: B

Indications and dosages

▶ **Adjunct to rest and physical therapy for relief of muscle spasm associated with acute, painful musculoskeletal conditions.** *Adults and children 15 and older:* 5 mg P.O. t.i.d. May increase to 10 mg P.O. t.i.d. Usual daily dose range is 20 to 40 mg, to a maximum of 60 mg. Use of cyclobenzaprine for periods longer than 3 weeks isn't recommended.

Adjust-a-dose: In elderly patients and in patients with mild hepatic impairment, start with 5 mg and increase slowly. In patients with moderate to severe hepatic impairment, drug isn't recommended.

▶ **Fibrositis‡.** *Adults:* 10 to 40 mg P.O. daily.

Contraindications and cautions

- Contraindicated in patients hypersensitive to drug; in patients in the acute recovery phase of MI; in patients with hyperthyroidism, heart block, arrhythmias, conduction disturbances, or heart failure. Also contraindicated within 14 days of MAO inhibitor therapy.
- Use cautiously in debilitated patients and in patients with history of urine retention, acute angle-closure glaucoma, or increased intraocular pressure. Also use cautiously in patients taking anticholinergics.

Lifespan: In pregnant and breast-feeding women, and in children younger than age 15, safety and effectiveness haven't been established. In elderly patients, use cautiously.

Adverse reactions

CNS: depression, *dizziness, drowsiness,* euphoria, headache, insomnia, nightmares, paresthesia, ***seizures,*** visual disturbances, weakness.
CV: ***arrhythmias,*** tachycardia.
EENT: blurred vision.
GI: abdominal pain, abnormal taste, constipation, *dry mouth,* dyspepsia.

GU: urine retention.
Skin: pruritus, rash, urticaria.

Interactions

Drug-drug. *Anticholinergics:* May have additive anticholinergic effects. Avoid use together.
CNS depressants: May cause additive CNS depression. Avoid use together.
MAO inhibitors: May worsen CNS depression or anticholinergic effects. Don't give within 14 days after stopping an MAO inhibitor.
Drug-lifestyle. *Alcohol use:* May cause additive CNS depression. Discourage use together.

Effects on lab test results

None reported.

Pharmacokinetics

Absorption: Almost complete.
Distribution: 93% protein-bound.
Metabolism: During first pass, drug and metabolites undergo enterohepatic recycling.
Excretion: Mainly in urine as conjugated metabolites; also in feces via bile as unchanged drug. *Half-life:* 1 to 3 days.

Route	Onset	Peak	Duration
P.O.	≤ 1 hr	3–8 hr	12–24 hr

Action

Chemical effect: Unknown.
Therapeutic effect: Relieves muscle spasms.

Available forms

Tablets: 5 mg, 10 mg

NURSING PROCESS

Assessment

- Assess patient's underlying condition before therapy.
- Monitor the drug's effectiveness by assessing severity and frequency of the patient's muscle spasms.
- If drug is stopped abruptly after long-term use, watch for nausea, headache, and malaise.
- Assess patient's and family's knowledge of drug therapy.

Nursing diagnoses

- Acute pain related to presence of muscle spasms
- Risk for injury related to potential for drug-induced CNS adverse reactions
- Deficient knowledge related to drug therapy

Planning and implementation

ALERT: Watch for symptoms of overdose, including cardiac toxicity. If you suspect toxicity, keep physostigmine available, and notify prescriber immediately.

- Don't give drug with other CNS depressants.
- With high doses, watch for adverse reactions similar to those of other TCAs.

ALERT: Don't confuse cyclobenzaprine with cyproheptadine.

Patient teaching

- Advise patient to report urinary hesitancy or urine retention. If constipation occurs, tell patient to increase fluid intake and suggest use of a stool softener.
- Caution patient not to split generic 10-mg tablets because the active ingredient may not split evenly.
- Warn patient to avoid activities that require alertness until drug's CNS effects are known.
- Warn patient to avoid using alcohol or other CNS depressants.
- Suggest sugarless chewing gum or hard candy to relieve dry mouth.

Evaluation

- Patient is free from pain with drug therapy.
- Patient doesn't experience injury as a result of drug-induced adverse CNS reactions.
- Patient and family state understanding of drug therapy.

cyclophosphamide

(sigh-kloh-FOS-fuh-mighd)
Cycloblastin ◇, Cytoxan, Cytoxan Lyophilized, Endoxan-Asta ◇, Neosar, Procytox ♦

Pharmacologic class: alkylating drug
Therapeutic class: antineoplastic
Pregnancy risk category: D

Indications and dosages

▶ **Breast, head, neck, prostate, lung, and ovarian cancers; Hodgkin lymphoma; chronic lymphocytic leukemia; chronic myelocytic leukemia; acute lymphoblastic leukemia;**

acute myelocytic leukemia; neuroblastoma; retinoblastoma; malignant lymphoma; multiple myeloma; mycosis fungoides; sarcoma.
Adults and children: Initially, 40 to 50 mg/kg I.V. in divided doses over 2 to 5 days. Or 10 to 15 mg/kg I.V. q 7 to 10 days, 3 to 5 mg/kg I.V. twice weekly, or 1 to 5 mg/kg P.O. daily, based on patient tolerance. Adjust dosage according to evidence of antitumor activity or leukopenia.

▶ **"Minimal change" nephrotic syndrome.** *Children:* 2.5 to 3 mg/kg P.O. daily for 60 to 90 days.

▶ **Polymyositis ‡.** *Adults:* 500 mg I.V. over 1 hour every 1 to 3 weeks, alone or with corticosteroids.

▶ **Rheumatoid arthritis‡.** *Adults:* 1.5 to 3 mg/kg P.O. daily.

▶ **Wegener granulomatosis‡.** *Adults:* 1 to 2 mg/kg P.O. daily (usually given with prednisone).

I.V. administration

• Preparing and giving I.V. form of drug cause carcinogenic, mutagenic, and teratogenic risks. Follow facility policy to reduce risks.
• Reconstitute powder using sterile water for injection or bacteriostatic water for injection that contains only parabens. For nonlyophilized product, add 5 ml to 100-mg vial, 10 ml to 200-mg vial, 25 ml to 500-mg vial, 50 ml to 1-g vial, or 100 ml to 2-g vial to produce solution containing 20 mg/ml. Shake to dissolve. Shaking may take up to 6 minutes because it may be difficult to completely dissolve drug. Lyophilized preparation is much easier to reconstitute. Check package insert for quantity of diluent needed to reconstitute drug.
• Check reconstituted solution for small particles. Filter solution if needed.
• Give by direct I.V. injection or infusion. For I.V. infusion, further dilute with D_5W, dextrose 5% in normal saline solution, dextrose 5% in Ringer's injection, lactated Ringer's injection, sodium lactate injection, or half-normal saline solution for injection.
• Reconstituted solution is stable for 6 days refrigerated or 24 hours at room temperature. However, use stored solutions cautiously because drug contains no preservatives.

⊗ **Incompatibilities**
None known.

Contraindications and cautions

• Contraindicated in patients with severe bone marrow depression.
• Use cautiously in patients who have recently undergone radiation therapy or chemotherapy and in patients with leukopenia, thrombocytopenia, malignant cell infiltration of bone marrow, or hepatic or renal disease.
Lifespan: In pregnant women, use cautiously, if at all, because fetal harm may occur. In breast-feeding women, drug is contraindicated.

Adverse reactions

CV: *cardiotoxicity* (with very high doses and with doxorubicin).
GI: anorexia, mucositis, nausea and vomiting beginning within 6 hours, stomatitis.
GU: bladder fibrosis, gonadal suppression (may be irreversible), STERILE HEMORRHAGIC CYSTITIS.
Hematologic: *anemia; **leukopenia,*** nadir between days 8 and 15, recovery in 17 to 28 days; ***thrombocytopenia.***
Metabolic: hyperuricemia.
Respiratory: ***pulmonary fibrosis*** (with high doses).
Skin: reversible alopecia in 50% of patients, especially with high doses.
Other: ***anaphylaxis, secondary malignancies,*** SIADH (with high doses), sterility.

Interactions

Drug-drug. *Barbiturates:* May increase drug effect and cyclophosphamide toxicity by inducing hepatic enzymes. Avoid use together.
Cardiotoxic drugs: May cause additive adverse cardiac effects. Avoid use together.
Chloramphenicol, corticosteroids: May reduce activity of cyclophosphamide. Use cautiously and monitor patient.
Digoxin: May decrease digoxin level. Monitor level closely and adjust dosage as needed.
Succinylcholine: May prolong neuromuscular blockade. Avoid use together.

Effects on lab test results

• May increase uric acid level. May decrease pseudocholinesterase and hemoglobin levels and hematocrit.
• May decrease WBC, RBC, and platelet counts.

Pharmacokinetics

Absorption: Almost complete with doses of 100 mg or less. Higher doses are 75% absorbed.
Distribution: Throughout body, with minimal amounts in saliva, sweat, and synovial fluid. Active metabolites are about 50% protein-bound.
Metabolism: Metabolized to its active form by hepatic microsomal enzymes.
Excretion: Mainly in urine, with 5% to 30% as unchanged drug. *Half-life:* 3 to 12 hours.

Route	Onset	Peak	Duration
P.O., I.V.	Unknown	1 hr	Unknown

Action

Chemical effect: Cross-links strands of cellular DNA and interferes with RNA transcription, causing imbalance of growth that leads to cell death.
Therapeutic effect: Kills specific types of cancer cells; improves renal function in mild nephrotic syndrome in children.

Available forms

Injection: 100-mg, 200-mg, 500-mg, 1-g, 2-g vials
Tablets: 25 mg, 50 mg

NURSING PROCESS

Assessment

- Assess patient's underlying condition before and regularly during therapy.
- Monitor CBC, uric acid level, and renal and liver function tests.
- If corticosteroid therapy is stopped, monitor patient for cyclophosphamide toxicity.
- Be alert for adverse reactions and drug interactions.
- Assess patient's and family's knowledge of drug therapy.

Nursing diagnoses

- Ineffective health maintenance related to underlying condition
- Risk for injury related to drug-induced adverse reactions
- Deficient knowledge related to drug therapy

Planning and implementation

- Tablets are used for children with "minimal change" nephrotic syndrome, not to treat neoplastic disease.
- To prevent hyperuricemia with resulting uric acid nephropathy, allopurinol may be used with adequate hydration.

Patient teaching

- Warn patient that alopecia is likely to occur but is reversible.
- Warn patient to watch for evidence of infection (fever, sore throat, fatigue) and bleeding (easy bruising, nosebleeds, bleeding gums, melena) and to take temperature daily.
- Instruct patient to avoid OTC products that contain aspirin.
- Encourage patient to void every 1 to 2 hours while awake and to drink at least 3 L of fluid daily to minimize risk of hemorrhagic cystitis. Tell patient not to take drug at bedtime because infrequent urination during night may increase possibility of cystitis. If cystitis occurs, tell patient to stop drug and notify prescriber. Cystitis can occur months after therapy ends. Mesna may be given to lower risk and severity of bladder toxicity.
- Advise both men and women to practice contraception while taking drug and for 4 months after because drug is potentially teratogenic.
- Advise women of childbearing age to avoid becoming pregnant during therapy. Also recommend consulting with prescriber before becoming pregnant.

Evaluation

- Patient shows positive response to drug therapy.
- Patient doesn't experience injury as a result of drug-induced adverse reactions.
- Patient and family state understanding of drug therapy.

cycloserine

(sigh-kloh-SER-een)
Seromycin

Pharmacologic class: isoxazoline, D-alanine analogue
Therapeutic class: antituberculotic
Pregnancy risk category: C

Indications and dosages

▶ **Adjunct in pulmonary or extrapulmonary tuberculosis.** *Adults:* Initially, 250 mg P.O. q 12 hours for 2 weeks; then, if level is below

25 to 30 mcg/ml and no toxicity has developed, 250 mg q 8 hours for 2 weeks. If optimum blood level isn't achieved and no toxicity has developed, increase to 250 mg q 6 hours. Maximum, 1 g daily. If CNS toxicity occurs, stop drug for 1 week and then resume at 250 mg daily for 2 weeks. If no serious toxic effects occur, increase by 250-mg increments q 10 days until level is 25 to 30 mcg/ml.

Contraindications and cautions

- Contraindicated in patients hypersensitive to drug, patients who consume excessive amounts of alcohol, and patients with seizure disorders, depression, severe anxiety, psychosis, or severe renal insufficiency.
- Use cautiously in patients with renal impairment, and reduce dosage.

Lifespan: In pregnant and breast-feeding women, use cautiously. In children, safety and effectiveness haven't been established.

Adverse reactions

CNS: *coma,* confusion, *depression,* drowsiness, dysarthria, *hallucinations,* headache, hyperirritability, hyperreflexia, memory loss, *nervousness,* paresis, paresthesia, ***seizures, suicidal tendencies*** and other psychotic symptoms, tremor, vertigo.
Other: hypersensitivity reactions (allergic dermatitis).

Interactions

Drug-drug. *Ethionamide, isoniazid:* May increase risk of CNS toxicity (seizures, dizziness, or drowsiness). Monitor patient closely.
Phenytoin: May increase phenytoin level. Adjust phenytoin dosage p.r.n.
Drug-lifestyle. *Alcohol use:* May increase risk of CNS toxicity. Advise patient to refrain from alcohol consumption during therapy.

Effects on lab test results

- May increase transaminase level.

Pharmacokinetics

Absorption: About 80%.
Distribution: Widely into body tissues and fluids, including CSF. Doesn't bind to proteins.
Metabolism: Possibly partial.
Excretion: Mainly in urine. *Half-life:* 10 hours.

Route	Onset	Peak	Duration
P.O.	Unknown	3–4 hr	Unknown

Action

Chemical effect: Inhibits cell-wall biosynthesis by interfering with bacterial use of amino acids (bacteriostatic).
Therapeutic effect: Aids in eradicating tuberculosis.

Available forms

Capsules: 250 mg

NURSING PROCESS

Assessment

- Assess patient's underlying condition before therapy.
- Obtain specimen for culture and sensitivity tests before therapy begins and periodically thereafter to detect resistance.
- Monitor drug's effectiveness by evaluating culture and sensitivity results; watch for improvement in patient's underlying condition.
- Monitor cycloserine level periodically, especially in patients receiving high doses (more than 500 mg daily) because toxic reactions may occur with blood level above 30 mcg/ml.
- Monitor results of hematologic tests and renal and liver function studies.
- Be alert for adverse reactions and drug interactions.
- Assess patient's and family's knowledge of drug therapy.

Nursing diagnoses

- Ineffective health maintenance related to presence of tuberculosis
- Risk for injury related to drug-induced CNS adverse reactions
- Deficient knowledge related to drug therapy

Planning and implementation

- Always give with other antituberculotics to prevent development of resistant organisms. Drug is considered second-line treatment for tuberculosis
- Adjust dose according to level, toxicity, or effectiveness.
- Give pyridoxine, anticonvulsants, tranquilizers, or sedatives to relieve adverse reactions.
- Pyridoxine may prevent neurotoxicity.

ALERT: Don't confuse cycloserine with cyclophosphamide or cyclosporine.

Patient teaching

- Warn patient to avoid alcohol, which may cause serious neurologic reactions.
- Instruct patient to take drug exactly as prescribed, and warn against stopping drug without prescriber's approval.
- Stress importance of having laboratory studies done to monitor drug effectiveness and toxicity.

Evaluation

- Patient maintains health after drug therapy.
- Patient has no injury as a result of drug-induced adverse reactions.
- Patient and family state understanding of drug therapy.

cyclosporine (cyclosporin)

(sigh-kloh-SPOOR-een)

Sandimmun ◇, Sandimmune

cyclosporine, modified

Gengraf, Neoral

Pharmacologic class: polypeptide antibiotic
Therapeutic class: immunosuppressant
Pregnancy risk category: C

Indications and dosages

▶ **To prevent organ rejection in kidney, liver, or heart transplantation.** *Adults and children:* 15 mg/kg P.O. 4 to 12 hours before transplantation and continued daily postoperatively for 1 to 2 weeks. Reduce dosage by 5% each week to maintenance level of 5 to 10 mg/kg daily. Or 5 to 6 mg/kg I.V. concentrate 4 to 12 hours before transplantation. Postoperatively, repeat dosage daily until patient can tolerate P.O. forms. When converting from Sandimmune to Neoral or Gengraf, use same daily dose as previously used for Sandimmune. Monitor level q 4 to 7 days after converting, and monitor blood pressure and creatinine level q 2 weeks during the first 2 months.

▶ **Severe, active rheumatoid arthritis that hasn't adequately responded to methotrexate.** *Adults:* 1.25 mg/kg Gengraf or Neoral P.O. b.i.d. Increase dosage by 0.5 to 0.75 mg/kg daily after 8 weeks and again after 12 weeks to a maximum of 4 mg/kg daily. If no response is seen after 16 weeks, stop therapy.

▶ **Recalcitrant plaque psoriasis that isn't adequately responsive to at least one systemic therapy or in patients for whom other systemic therapy is contraindicated or isn't tolerated.** *Adults:* Initially, 2.5 mg/kg Gengraf or Neoral P.O. daily divided b.i.d. Maintain initial dose for 4 weeks. Increase by 0.5 mg/kg daily to a maximum of 4 mg/kg daily at 2-week intervals, if needed.

Adjust-a-dose: In patients with rheumatoid arthritis or plaque psoriasis, decrease dose by 25% to 50% at any time to control adverse events (such as hypertension), elevated serum creatinine level (25% or more above baseline), or clinically significant laboratory abnormalities.

I.V. administration

- Give drug I.V. to patients who can't tolerate oral drugs.
- Dilute each milliliter of concentrate in 20 to 100 ml of D_5W or normal saline solution for injection. Dilute immediately before infusion; infuse over 2 to 6 hours.
- Give I.V. concentrate at one-third oral dose and dilute before use.
- Protect I.V. solution from light.

⊗ **Incompatibilities**

None reported.

Contraindications and cautions

- Contraindicated in patients hypersensitive to drug or to polyoxyethylated castor oil (found in injectable form). Neoral and Gengraf are contraindicated in patients with psoriasis or rheumatoid arthritis who also have renal impairment, uncontrolled hypertension, or malignancies.

Lifespan: In pregnant women, use cautiously. In breast-feeding women, safety and effectiveness haven't been established.

Adverse reactions

CNS: headache, ***seizures***, *tremor.*
CV: flushing, hypertension.
EENT: sinusitis.
GI: diarrhea, *gum hyperplasia,* nausea, oral thrush, vomiting.
GU: NEPHROTOXICITY.
Hematologic: anemia, LEUKOPENIA, THROMBOCYTOPENIA.

Hepatic: *hepatotoxicity.*
Skin: acne, *hirsutism.*
Other: ***anaphylaxis,*** infections.

Interactions

Drug-drug. *Aminoglycosides, amphotericin B, co-trimoxazole, NSAIDs:* May increase risk of nephrotoxicity. Monitor patient for toxicity.
Amphotericin B, cilastatin, cimetidine, diltiazem, erythromycin, imipenem, ketoconazole, metoclopramide, prednisolone: May increase level of cyclosporine. Monitor patient for increased toxicity.
Azathioprine, corticosteroids, cyclophosphamide, verapamil: May increase immunosuppression. Monitor patient closely for infection.
Carbamazepine, isoniazid, phenobarbital, phenytoin, rifampin: May decrease immunosuppressant effect. Increase cyclosporine dosage.
Vaccines: May decrease immune response. Postpone routine immunization.
Drug-herb. *Pill-bearing spurge:* May inhibit CYP3A enzymes affecting drug metabolism. Discourage use together.
St. John's wort: May significantly lower drug level and contribute to organ rejection. Discourage use together.
Drug-food. *Grapefruit:* May increase drug level and cause toxicity. Discourage use together.

Effects on lab test results

- May increase BUN, creatinine, LDL, bilirubin, AST, ALT, and glucose levels. May decrease hemoglobin level and hematocrit.
- May decrease WBC and platelet counts.

Pharmacokinetics

Absorption: Varies widely. Only 30% of Sandimmune oral dose reaches systemic circulation, while 60% of Neoral reaches systemic circulation. Gengraf absorption is 10% to 89%, depending on patient population.
Distribution: Wide. 90% protein-bound.
Metabolism: Extensive, in liver.
Excretion: Mainly in feces. *Half-life:* 10 to 27 hours.

Route	Onset	Peak	Duration
P.O.	Unknown	1½–3 hr	Unknown
I.V.	Unknown	Unknown	Unknown

Action

Chemical effect: Inhibits proliferation of T lymphocytes.
Therapeutic effect: Prevents organ rejection.

Available forms

Capsules: 25 mg, 50 mg, 100 mg
Capsules for microemulsion: 25 mg, 100 mg.
Injection: 50 mg/ml
Oral solution: 100 mg/ml

NURSING PROCESS

Assessment

- Assess patient's organ transplant before therapy.
- Monitor drug effectiveness by evaluating patient for signs and symptoms of organ rejection.
- Check drug level at regular intervals.
- Monitor BUN and creatinine levels because nephrotoxicity may develop 2 to 3 months after transplant surgery and require reducing the dose.
- Monitor liver function tests for hepatotoxicity, which usually occurs during first month after transplant.
- Monitor CBC and platelet counts regularly.
- Be alert for adverse reactions and drug interactions.
- Assess patient's and family's knowledge of drug therapy.

Nursing diagnoses

- Risk for injury related to potential for organ rejection
- Ineffective protection related to drug-induced immunosuppression
- Deficient knowledge related to drug therapy

Planning and implementation

- Don't give psoralen plus ultraviolet A or ultraviolet B therapy, methotrexate, other immunosuppressants, coal tar, or radiation therapy to psoriasis patient taking Neoral or Gengraf.
- Always give drug with adrenal corticosteroids.
- Measure oral dose carefully in oral syringe. To increase palatability of conventional oral solution, mix with whole milk, chocolate milk, or fruit juice (except grapefruit juice). Modified oral solution (Gengraf or Neoral) is less palatable when mixed with milk; to increase its palatability, mix with room-temperature orange

or apple juice. Use glass container to minimize adherence to container walls.
• Give drug with meals to minimize GI distress.
ALERT: Sandimmune isn't bioequivalent with Neoral or Gengraf. When converting from Sandimmune to either of these drugs, increase monitoring to detect inadequate doses. Gengraf is bioequivalent to and interchangeable with Neoral capsules.
• Before giving drug to patient with rheumatoid arthritis, measure blood pressure at least twice and obtain two creatinine levels to estimate baseline. Evaluate patient's blood pressure and creatinine level every 2 weeks during first 3 months, then monthly if patient is stable. Monitor blood pressure and creatinine level after an increase in NSAID dosage or introduction of a new NSAID. If hypertension occurs, decrease dosage of Gengraf or Neoral by 25% to 50%. If hypertension persists, decrease dosage further or control blood pressure with antihypertensives.
• If patient also receives methotrexate, monitor CBC and liver function tests monthly.
• For patient with psoriasis, watch for occult infection and tumors before and during therapy.
• Before starting therapy in psoriasis patient, take blood pressure at least twice and obtain two creatinine levels. Also, obtain CBC and BUN, magnesium, uric acid, potassium, and lipid levels. Evaluate blood pressure, CBC, uric acid, creatinine, BUN, potassium, lipid, and magnesium levels every 2 weeks for the first 3 months, then monthly if patient is stable, or more frequently when adjusting dose. Reduce dose by 25% to 50% in case of significant abnormality.
• Monitor blood pressure and creatinine level after an increase in NSAID dosage or introduction of a new NSAID.
ALERT: Don't confuse cyclosporine with cyclophosphamide or cycloserine.
ALERT: Don't confuse Sandimmune with Sandoglobulin or Sandostatin.

Patient teaching

• Encourage patient to take drug at the same time each day.
• Advise patient to take Neoral or Gengraf on an empty stomach and not to mix with grapefruit juice.
• Advise patient to take drug with meals if it causes nausea.
• Tell patient not to stop taking drug without prescriber's approval.
• Instruct patient to swish and swallow nystatin four times daily to prevent oral thrush.
• Instruct patient on infection control and bleeding precautions, as indicated by CBC and platelet count results.

Evaluation

• Patient doesn't experience organ rejection while taking drug.
• Patient is free from infection and serious bleeding episodes throughout drug therapy.
• Patient and family state understanding of drug therapy.

cytarabine (ara-C, cytosine arabinoside)

(sigh-TAR-uh-been)
Cytosar ♦, Cytosar-U, Tarabine PFS

Pharmacologic class: antimetabolite
Therapeutic class: antineoplastic
Pregnancy risk category: D

Indications and dosages

▶ **Acute nonlymphocytic leukemia.** *Adults and children:* 100 mg/m²/day by continuous I.V. infusion (days 1 to 7) or 100 mg/m² I.V. q 12 hours (days 1 to 7). Give with other anticancer drugs.
▶ **Acute lymphocytic leukemia.** Consult literature for current recommendations.
▶ **Refractory acute leukemia.** *Adults and children:* 3 g/m² I.V. over 2 hours q 12 hours for 4 to 12 doses (repeated at 2- to 3-week intervals).
▶ **Meningeal leukemia.** *Adults and children:* Highly variable from 5 to 75 mg/m² intrathecally. Frequency also varies from once a day for 4 days to once q 4 days. Most common dosage is 30 mg/m², q 4 days until CSF is normal, followed by one more dose.

I.V. administration

• Preparing and giving I.V. form are linked to carcinogenic, mutagenic, and teratogenic risks. Follow facility policy to reduce risks.
• To reduce nausea, give antiemetic before drug. Nausea and vomiting are more frequent when large doses are given rapidly by I.V. push. These

reactions are less frequent when given by infusion. Dizziness may occur with rapid infusion.
• Reconstitute drug using provided diluent, which is bacteriostatic water for injection containing benzyl alcohol. Avoid this diluent when preparing drug for neonates or for intrathecal use. Reconstitute 100-mg vial with 5 ml of diluent or 500-mg vial with 10 ml of diluent. Reconstituted solution is stable for 48 hours. Discard cloudy reconstituted solution.
• For I.V. infusion, further dilute using normal saline solution for injection, D_5W, or sterile water for injection.

⊗ **Incompatibilities**
Allopurinol sodium, fluorouracil, ganciclovir sodium, heparin sodium, insulin (regular), methylprednisolone sodium succinate, nafcillin, oxacillin, penicillin.

Contraindications and cautions

• Contraindicated in patients hypersensitive to drug.
• Use cautiously in patients with hepatic disease.
Lifespan: In pregnant women, drug isn't recommended because fetal harm may occur. In breast-feeding women, drug is contraindicated.

Adverse reactions

CNS: neurotoxicity, including ataxia and cerebellar dysfunction (with high doses).
EENT: keratitis, nystagmus.
GI: *anal ulceration, anorexia, constipation,* diarrhea, *nausea, vomiting,* dysphagia, projectile vomiting from large I.V. dose given rapidly, reddened area at juncture of lips followed by sore mouth and oral ulcers in 5 to 10 days.
GU: urate nephropathy.
Hematologic: anemia; ***leukopenia,*** with initial WBC count nadir 7 to 9 days after drug is stopped and second (more severe) nadir 15 to 24 days after drug is stopped; reticulocytopenia; ***thrombocytopenia,*** with platelet count nadir occurring on day 10; *megaloblastosis.*
Hepatic: ***hepatotoxicity*** (usually mild and reversible).
Metabolic: hyperuricemia.
Skin: rash.
Other: ***anaphylaxis,*** flulike syndrome.

Interactions

Drug-drug. *Digoxin:* May decrease digoxin level. Monitor digoxin level.
Flucytosine: May decrease flucytosine activity. Monitor patient closely.
Gentamicin: May decrease activity against *Klebsiella pneumoniae.* Avoid use together.

Effects on lab test results

• May increase uric acid level. May decrease hemoglobin level and hematocrit.
• May increase megaloblasts. May decrease WBC, RBC, platelet, and reticulocyte counts.

Pharmacokinetics

Absorption: Good.
Distribution: Rapid and wide. 13% protein-bound. Drug penetrates the blood–brain barrier only slightly after rapid I.V. dose; however, when drug is given by continuous I.V. infusion, CSF level reaches 40% to 60% of plasma level.
Metabolism: Mainly in liver but also in kidneys, GI mucosa, and granulocytes.
Excretion: In urine. Less than 10% of dose as unchanged drug in urine. *Half-life:* Initial, 8 minutes; terminal, 1 to 3 hours; in CSF, 2 hours.

Route	Onset	Peak	Duration
I.V., intrathecal	Unknown	Unknown	Unknown
SubQ	Unknown	20–60 min	Unknown

Action

Chemical effect: Inhibits DNA synthesis.
Therapeutic effect: Kills selected cancer cells.

Available forms

Injection: 100-mg, 500-mg, 1-g, 2-g vials

NURSING PROCESS

Assessment

• Assess patient's underlying condition before and regularly throughout therapy.
• Monitor uric acid level, hepatic and renal function studies, and CBC.
• Be alert for adverse reactions and drug interactions.
• If patient receives high doses, watch for neurotoxicity, which may first appear as nystagmus but can progress to ataxia and cerebellar dysfunction.
• Assess patient's and family's knowledge of drug therapy.

Nursing diagnoses

- Ineffective health maintenance related to underlying condition
- Risk for injury related to drug-induced adverse hematologic reactions
- Deficient knowledge related to drug therapy

Planning and implementation

- When giving intrathecally, use preservative-free normal saline solution. Add 5 ml to 100-mg vial or 10 ml to 500-mg vial. Use immediately after reconstitution. Discard unused drug.
- Maintain high fluid intake and give allopurinol to avoid urate nephropathy in leukemia induction therapy.
- If granulocyte count is below 1,000/mm³ or if platelet count is below 50,000/mm³, modify or stop therapy.
- Corticosteroid eyedrops are prescribed to prevent drug-induced keratitis.
- Potential benefit must be judged against known adverse effects.

Patient teaching

- Warn patient to watch for signs of infection (fever, sore throat, fatigue) and bleeding (easy bruising, nosebleeds, bleeding gums, melena). Tell patient to take temperature daily.
- Instruct patient on infection control and bleeding precautions.
- Advise woman of childbearing age to avoid becoming pregnant during therapy. Also recommend consulting with prescriber before becoming pregnant.
- Encourage patient to drink at least 3 L of fluids daily.
- Instruct patient about need for frequent oral hygiene.

Evaluation

- Patient demonstrates positive response to drug therapy.
- Patient doesn't experience injury as result of drug therapy.
- Patient and family state understanding of drug therapy.

cytomegalovirus immune globulin, intravenous (CMV-IGIV)

(sigh-toh-MEH-gah-loh-VIGH-rus ih-MYOON GLOH-byoo-lin)

CytoGam

Pharmacologic class: immune globulin
Therapeutic class: immune serum
Pregnancy risk category: C

Indications and dosages

▶ To attenuate primary CMV disease in seronegative kidney transplant recipients who receive kidney from a CMV seropositive donor. *Adults:* Give I.V. based on time after transplantation:

- Within 72 hours, 150 mg/kg
- 2 weeks after, 100 mg/kg
- 4 weeks after, 100 mg/kg
- 6 weeks after, 100 mg/kg
- 8 weeks after, 100 mg/kg
- 12 weeks after, 50 mg/kg
- 16 weeks after, 50 mg/kg.

Give first dose at 15 mg/kg/hour. If no adverse reactions occur after 30 minutes, increase to 30 mg/kg/hour. If no adverse reactions occur after another 30 minutes, increase to 60 mg/kg/hour. Don't exceed 75 ml/hour. Subsequent doses may be given at 15 mg/kg/hour for 15 minutes, increasing at 15-minute intervals in stepwise fashion to 60 mg/kg/hour. Don't exceed 75 ml/hour. Monitor patient closely during and after rate change.

▶ Prophylaxis of CMV disease related to lung, liver, pancreas, and heart transplants. *Adults:* Use with ganciclovir in organ transplants from CMV seropositive donors into seronegative recipients. Maximum total dose per infusion is 150 mg/kg I.V. Give as follows based on time after transplantation:

- Within 72 hours, 150 mg/kg
- 2 weeks after, 150 mg/kg
- 4 weeks after, 150 mg/kg
- 6 weeks after, 150 mg/kg
- 8 weeks after, 150 mg/kg
- 12 weeks after, 100 mg/kg
- 16 weeks after, 100 mg/kg.

Give first dose at 15 mg/kg/hour. If no adverse reactions occur after 30 minutes, increase to 30 mg/kg/hour. If no adverse reactions occur after another 30 minutes, increase to 60 mg/kg/

hour. (Don't exceed 75 ml/hour.) Later doses may be given at 15 mg/kg/hour for 15 minutes, increasing q 15 minutes in a stepwise fashion to a maximum of 60 mg/kg/hour. (Don't exceed 75 ml/hour.) Monitor patient closely during and after each rate change.

I.V. administration

- Remove tab portion of vial cap and clean rubber stopper with 70% alcohol or equivalent. Don't shake vial; avoid foaming. Don't infuse if the solution has color or particulate matter or is turbid. Don't predilute.
- Give through separate I.V. line using constant infusion pump. Filters aren't needed. If unable to give through separate line, piggyback into existing line of saline solution injection or one of the following dextrose solutions with or without saline solution: dextrose 2.5% in water, D_5W, dextrose 10% in water, or dextrose 20% in water. Don't dilute more than 1:2 with any of these solutions.
- Begin infusion within 6 hours of entering vial; finish within 12 hours.
- Refrigerate drug at 36° to 46° F (2° to 8° C).

⊗ **Incompatibilities**
Other I.V. drugs.

Contraindications and cautions

- Contraindicated in patients with selective immunoglobulin (Ig)A deficiency or history of sensitivity to other human immunoglobulin preparations.

Lifespan: In pregnant women, use cautiously. In breast-feeding women and in children, safety and effectiveness haven't been established.

Adverse reactions

CNS: fever.
CV: flushing, hypotension.
GI: nausea, vomiting.
Musculoskeletal: back pain, muscle cramps.
Respiratory: wheezing.
Other: ***anaphylaxis,*** chills.

Interactions

Drug-drug. *Live-virus vaccines:* May interfere with immune response to live-virus vaccines. Defer vaccination for at least 3 months.

Effects on lab test results

None reported.

Pharmacokinetics

Absorption: Given I.V.
Distribution: Unknown.
Metabolism: Unknown.
Excretion: Unknown. *Half-life:* Immediately after transplantation, 8 days; 60 or more days after transplantation, 13 to 15 days.

Route	Onset	Peak	Duration
I.V.	Unknown	Unknown	Unknown

Action

Chemical effect: Supplies relatively high concentration of IgG antibodies against CMV. Increasing these antibody levels in CMV-exposed patients may reduce risk of serious CMV disease.
Therapeutic effect: Provides passive immunity to CMV.

Available forms

Solution for injection: 50 ± 10 mg protein/ml

NURSING PROCESS

Assessment

- Assess patient's underlying condition before therapy starts.
- Take vital signs before starting therapy, mid-infusion, post-infusion, and before any increase in infusion rate.
- Monitor drug's effectiveness by evaluating kidney function.
- Be alert for adverse reactions and drug interactions.
- Assess patient's and family's knowledge of drug therapy.

Nursing diagnoses

- Risk for injury related to potential for organ rejection
- Decreased cardiac output related to drug-induced hypotension
- Deficient knowledge related to drug therapy

Planning and implementation

- If patient develops anaphylaxis or if blood pressure drops, stop infusion, notify prescriber, and give CPR and drugs, such as diphenhydramine and epinephrine.

Patient teaching

- Teach patient about drug therapy.

• Instruct patient to notify prescriber immediately if adverse reactions develop.

Evaluation

• Patient doesn't reject transplanted kidney during drug therapy.
• Patient maintains normal cardiac output throughout drug therapy.
• Patient and family state understanding of drug therapy.

dacarbazine

(deh-KAR-buh-zeen)
DTIC-Dome ♦

Pharmacologic class: alkylating drug
Therapeutic class: antineoplastic
Pregnancy risk category: C

Indications and dosages

▶ **Metastatic malignant melanoma.** *Adults:* 2 to 4.5 mg/kg I.V. daily for 10 days; then q 4 weeks, as tolerated. Or, 250 mg/m² I.V. daily for 5 days; repeat at 3-week intervals.
▶ **Hodgkin lymphoma.** *Adults:* 150 mg/m² I.V. daily (with other drugs) for 5 days; repeat q 4 weeks. Or, 375 mg/m² on first day of combined regimen; repeat q 15 days.

I.V. administration

• Preparing and giving drug raises risk of carcinogenic, mutagenic, and teratogenic effects. Follow facility policy to reduce risks.
• Reconstitute drug with sterile water for injection. Add 9.9 ml to 100-mg vial or 19.7 ml to 200-mg vial. Solution should be colorless to clear yellow. For infusion, further dilute, using up to 250 ml of normal saline solution or D_5W. Infuse over 30 minutes.
• During infusion, protect bag from direct sunlight to avoid drug breakdown. Dilute solution further or slow infusion to decrease pain at infusion site.
• If infiltration occurs, stop infusion immediately, apply ice to area for 24 to 48 hours, and notify prescriber.
• Reconstituted solutions are stable for 8 hours at room temperature under normal lighting conditions and up to 3 days if refrigerated. Diluted solutions are stable for 8 hours at room temperature under normal light and up to 24 hours if refrigerated. If solutions turn pink, this is a sign of decomposition. Discard drug.

⊗ **Incompatibilities**
Allopurinol sodium, cefepime, hydrocortisone sodium succinate, piperacillin with tazobactam.

Contraindications and cautions

• Contraindicated in patients hypersensitive to drug.
• Use cautiously in impaired bone marrow function.
Lifespan: In pregnant women, use cautiously and only when absolutely needed because fetal harm may occur. In breast-feeding women, drug is contraindicated. In children, safety and effectiveness haven't been established.

Adverse reactions

GI: *anorexia, severe nausea and vomiting.*
Hematologic: ***leukopenia, thrombocytopenia*** (nadir at 3 to 4 weeks).
Hepatic: ***hepatotoxicity.***
Metabolic: hyperuricemia.
Skin: alopecia, phototoxicity.
Other: ***anaphylaxis,*** *flulike syndrome,* severe pain with concentrated solution or extravasation, tissue damage.

Interactions

Drug-drug. *Allopurinol:* May have additive hypouricemic effects. Monitor patient closely.
Anticoagulants, aspirin: May increase risk of bleeding. Avoid use together.
Bone marrow suppressants: May increase toxicity. Monitor hematologic studies closely.
Phenobarbital, phenytoin, and other drugs that induce hepatic metabolism: May increase dacarbazine metabolism. Adjust dosage.
Drug-lifestyle. *Sun exposure:* May cause photosensitivity reactions, especially during the first 2 days of therapy. Advise patient to avoid prolonged sun exposure and to wear protective clothing and sunblock.

Effects on lab test results

• May increase BUN and liver enzyme levels.
• May decrease WBC, RBC, and platelet counts.

Pharmacokinetics

Absorption: Given I.V.
Distribution: May localize in body tissues, especially the liver. Minimally protein-bound.
Metabolism: Rapid to several compounds, some of which may be active.
Excretion: About 30% to 45% in urine. *Half-life:* Initial, 19 minutes; terminal, 5 hours.

Route	Onset	Peak	Duration
I.V.	Unknown	Unknown	Unknown

Action

Chemical effect: May cross-link strands of cellular DNA and interfere with RNA transcription, causing imbalance of growth that leads to cell death.
Therapeutic effect: Kills selected cancer cells.

Available forms

Injection: 100-mg, 200-mg, 500-mg, 600-mg ♦ vials

NURSING PROCESS

Assessment

- Obtain history of patient's underlying disease before therapy, and reassess regularly throughout therapy.
- Monitor CBC and platelet count.

ALERT: Monitor liver function closely because toxicity is possible.

- Look for adverse reactions and drug interactions.
- Assess patient's and family's knowledge of drug therapy.

Nursing diagnoses

- Ineffective health maintenance related to presence of neoplastic disease
- Risk for injury related to risk of drug-induced adverse reactions
- Deficient knowledge related to drug therapy

Planning and implementation

- For Hodgkin lymphoma, drug usually is given with other antineoplastic drugs.
- To help decrease nausea, give antiemetics before use. Nausea and vomiting may subside after several doses.
- To prevent bleeding, avoid all I.M. injections when platelet count is below 50,000/mm^3.
- Use blood transfusions to combat anemia. Patient may receive injections of RBC colony-stimulating factors to promote RBC production and decrease need for blood transfusions.

ALERT: Don't confuse dacarbazine with Dicarbosil, carbamazepine, or procarbazine.

Patient teaching

- Warn patient to watch for signs of infection (fever, sore throat, fatigue) and bleeding (easy bruising, nosebleeds, bleeding gums, melena). Tell patient to take temperature daily.
- Instruct patient to avoid OTC products containing aspirin.
- Advise patient to avoid sunlight and sunlamps for first 2 days after therapy.
- Reassure patient that flulike syndrome may be treated with mild antipyretics, such as acetaminophen.

Evaluation

- Patient has positive response to therapy, as shown on follow-up diagnostic studies and overall physical condition.
- Patient has no injury from drug-induced adverse reactions.
- Patient and family state understanding of drug therapy.

daclizumab

(da-KLIZ-yoo-mab)
Zenapax

Pharmacologic class: humanized immunoglobulin G1 monoclonal antibody
Therapeutic class: immunosuppressant
Pregnancy risk category: C

Indications and dosages

▶ **To prevent acute organ rejection in renal transplant patients receiving an immunosuppressive regimen that includes cyclosporine and corticosteroids.** *Adults:* 1 mg/kg I.V. Standard course of therapy is five doses. Give first dose no more than 24 hours before transplantation; give remaining four doses at 14-day intervals.

I.V. administration

- Don't give drug in a direct I.V. injection. Dilute in 50 ml of sterile normal saline solution before administration. To avoid foaming, don't shake. Inspect for particulates and discoloration before use.

• Infuse over 15 minutes via a central or peripheral line. Don't add or infuse other drugs simultaneously through the same line.

• Drug may be refrigerated at 36° to 46° F (2° to 8° C) for 24 hours and is stable at room temperature for 4 hours. Discard solution if not used within 24 hours.

• Protect undiluted solution from direct light.

⊗ **Incompatibilities**

Other drugs infused through same I.V. line.

Contraindications and cautions

• Contraindicated in patients hypersensitive to drug or any of its components.

Lifespan: In pregnant or breast-feeding women, use cautiously. Tell women of childbearing age to use contraception before, during, and for 4 months after drug therapy.

Adverse reactions

CNS: *anxiety,* depression, dizziness, fatigue, fever, generalized weakness, headache, insomnia, pain, prickly sensation, tremors.
CV: aggravated hypertension, chest pain, edema, fluid overload, hypertension, hypotension, tachycardia.
EENT: blurred vision, pharyngitis, rhinitis.
GI: abdominal distention, *abdominal pain, constipation, diarrhea, dyspepsia,* epigastric pain, flatulence, gastritis, hemorrhoids, *nausea, pyrosis,* vomiting.
GU: dysuria, hydronephrosis, lymphocele, ***oliguria,*** renal damage, renal insufficiency, ***renal tubular necrosis,*** urinary tract bleeding, urinary tract disorder, urine retention.
Hematologic: bleeding.
Metabolic: dehydration, diabetes mellitus.
Musculoskeletal: arthralgia, leg cramps, musculoskeletal or back pain, myalgia.
Respiratory: abnormal breath sounds, atelectasis, congestion, coughing, crackles, dyspnea, ***hypoxia,*** pleural effusion, ***pulmonary edema.***
Skin: acne, cellulitis, hirsutism, impaired wound healing without infection, *increased sweating,* night sweats, *pruritus, rash,* wound infections.
Other: ***anaphylaxis,*** limb edema, ***severe infection,*** shivering.

Interactions

Drug-drug. *Corticosteroids, cyclosporine, mycophenolate mofetil:* May increase mortality. Monitor patient closely for lymphoproliferative disorders and opportunistic infections.

Effects on lab test results

• May increase BUN and creatinine levels.

Pharmacokinetics

Absorption: Given I.V.
Distribution: Unknown.
Metabolism: Unknown.
Excretion: Unknown. *Half-life:* 20 days.

Route	Onset	Peak	Duration
I.V.	Unknown	Unknown	Unknown

Action

Chemical effect: Inhibits interleukin-2 (IL-2) binding to prevent IL-2 from activating lymphocytes. Once in circulation, drug impairs response of immune system.
Therapeutic effect: Prevents organ rejection.

Available forms

Injection: 25 mg/5 ml

NURSING PROCESS

Assessment

• Obtain history of patient's underlying condition before therapy, and reassess regularly.

• Check for opportunistic infections.

ALERT: Monitor patient for severe, acute hypersensitivity reactions when giving each dose (includes anaphylaxis, hypotension, bronchospasm, loss of consciousness, injection site reactions, edema, and arrhythmias). Stop drug if severe reaction occurs.

• Assess patient's and family's knowledge of drug therapy.

Nursing diagnoses

• Risk for injury related to potential for organ rejection

• Ineffective protection related to drug-induced immunosuppression

• Deficient knowledge related to drug therapy

Planning and implementation

• Use only with a prescriber experienced in immunosuppressant therapy and management of organ transplantation.

ALERT: Using daclizumab as part of an immunosuppressive regimen that includes cyclosporine, mycophenolate mofetil, and corticosteroids may increase the patient's risk of death.

Patient teaching

• Tell patient to consult prescriber before taking other drugs during therapy.
• Advise patient to take precautions against infection.
• Inform patient that neither he nor any household member should receive vaccinations unless medically approved.
• Tell patient to immediately report wounds that fail to heal, unusual bruising or bleeding, or fever.
• Advise patient to drink plenty of fluids during therapy and to report painful urination, blood in the urine, or a decrease in urine output.
• Instruct women of childbearing age to use effective contraception before starting therapy, during therapy, and to continue until 4 months after completing therapy.

Evaluation

• Patient doesn't experience organ rejection while taking drug.
• Patient is free from infection and serious bleeding episodes throughout drug therapy.
• Patient and family state understanding of drug therapy.

dalteparin sodium

(dal-TEH-peh-rin SOH-dee-um)
Fragmin

Pharmacologic class: low–molecular-weight heparin
Therapeutic class: anticoagulant
Pregnancy risk category: B

Indications and dosages

▶ **Prevention of deep vein thrombosis (DVT) in patients undergoing abdominal surgery who are at risk for thromboembolic complications.** *Adults:* 2,500 international units subcutaneously daily, starting 1 to 2 hours before surgery and repeated once daily for 5 to 10 days postoperatively. In abdominal surgery patients at high risk for thromboembolic complications (such as those with malignant disease), 5,000 international units subcutaneously daily starting on the evening before surgery and repeated once daily for 5 to 10 days postoperatively. Or, 2,500 international units subcutaneously within 1 to 2 hours before surgery, followed 12 hours later by a second dose of 2,500 international units subcutaneously and then 5,000 international units subcutaneously once daily for 5 to 10 days postoperatively.

▶ **Prevention of DVT in patients undergoing hip replacement surgery.** *Adults:* 2,500 international units subcutaneously within 2 hours before surgery and second dose 2,500 international units subcutaneously in the evening following surgery (at least 6 hours after first dose). If surgery is performed in the evening, omit second dose on day of surgery. Starting on first postoperative day, give 5,000 international units subcutaneously once daily for 5 to 10 days. Or, 5,000 international units subcutaneously on the evening before surgery, followed by 5,000 international units subcutaneously once daily starting in the evening of surgery for 5 to 10 days postoperatively. If the initial dose is scheduled after surgery, give 2,500 international units subcutaneously 4 to 8 hours following surgery, provided hemostasis has been achieved. Then begin 5,000 international units subcutaneously once daily, allowing at least 6 hours between the initial post-operative dose and the second dose.

▶ **To decrease risk of thromboembolism in patients with severely restricted mobility during acute illness.** *Adults:* 5,000 international units subcutaneously daily for 12 to 14 days.

▶ **Unstable angina, non–ST-segment elevation MI.** *Adults:* 120 international units/kg up to 10,000 international units subcutaneously q 12 hours with oral aspirin (75 to 165 mg/day) therapy. Continue until patient is stable. Usual duration of treatment is 5 to 8 days.

Contraindications and cautions

• Contraindicated in patients hypersensitive to drug, heparin, or pork products, and in those with major bleeding or thrombocytopenia with positive in vitro tests for antiplatelet antibody in presence of drug.
• Use cautiously in patients with a history of heparin-induced thrombocytopenia; in patients

with an increased risk of hemorrhage, such as those with severe uncontrolled hypertension, bacterial endocarditis, congenital or acquired bleeding disorders, active ulceration, angiodysplastic GI disease, or hemorrhagic stroke; and in those who recently underwent brain, spinal, or ophthalmologic surgery.

• Also use cautiously in patients with bleeding diathesis, thrombocytopenia, platelet defects, severe liver or kidney insufficiency, hypertensive or diabetic retinopathy, or recent GI bleeding.

Lifespan: In pregnant and breast-feeding women, use cautiously. In children, safety and effectiveness haven't been established.

Adverse reactions

CNS: fever.
Hematologic: bleeding complications, ***hemorrhage, thrombocytopenia.***
Skin: ecchymosis, pruritus, rash.
Other: ***anaphylaxis,*** *hematoma at injection site* (when given with heparin), pain at injection site.

Interactions

Drug-drug. *Antiplatelet drugs, oral anticoagulants:* May increase risk of bleeding. Use together cautiously; monitor patient for bleeding.

Effects on lab test results

• May increase ALT and AST levels.
• May decrease platelet count.

Pharmacokinetics

Absorption: Absolute bioavailability of anti-factor Xa is 87%.
Distribution: Volume is 40 to 60 ml/kg.
Metabolism: Unknown.
Excretion: In urine. *Half-life:* 3 to 5 hours.

Route	Onset	Peak	Duration
SubQ	Unknown	4 hr	Unknown

Action

Chemical effect: Enhances inhibition of factor Xa and thrombin by antithrombin.
Therapeutic effect: Prevents DVT.

Available forms

Multidose vial: 10,000 anti-factor Xa international units/ml
Syringe: 2,500 anti-factor Xa international units/0.2 ml; 5,000 anti-factor Xa international units/0.2 ml

NURSING PROCESS

Assessment

• Obtain history of patient's underlying condition before starting therapy.
• Those at risk for DVT include obese patients older than age 40 who are having surgery under general anesthesia that lasts longer than 30 minutes. Other risk factors include cancer and a history of DVT or pulmonary embolism.
• Monitor effectiveness by assessing patient for evidence of DVT.
• Perform routine CBCs (including platelet count) and fecal occult blood tests.

ALERT: Low–molecular-weight heparins used during neuraxial anesthesia or spinal puncture increase risk of epidural or spinal hematoma. Monitor patient closely for neurologic impairment.

• Look for adverse reactions and drug interactions.
• Assess patient's and family's knowledge of drug therapy.

Nursing diagnoses

• Risk for injury related to risk of DVT as result of underlying condition
• Ineffective protection related to drug-induced adverse hematologic reactions
• Deficient knowledge related to drug therapy

Planning and implementation

• Place patient in sitting or supine position when giving drug. Give by deep subcutaneous injection. Injection sites include U-shaped area below navel, upper outer side of thigh, and upper outer quadrangle of buttock. Rotate sites daily.

ALERT: Drug should never be given I.M. or I.V.

• Don't mix with other injections or infusions unless specific compatibility data are available that support such mixing.

ALERT: Drug isn't interchangeable unit for unit with unfractionated heparin or other low–molecular-weight heparin derivatives.

• Stop drug and notify prescriber if a thromboembolism occurs despite therapy.

Patient teaching
- Instruct patient and family to immediately notify the prescriber if signs of bleeding occur.
- Tell patient to avoid OTC medications containing aspirin or other salicylates.

Evaluation
- Patient doesn't develop DVT.
- Patient maintains stable hematologic function.
- Patient and family state understanding of drug therapy.

dantrolene sodium

(DAN-troh-leen SOH-dee-um)
Dantrium, Dantrium Intravenous

Pharmacologic class: hydantoin derivative
Therapeutic class: skeletal muscle relaxant
Pregnancy risk category: C

Indications and dosages

▶ **Spasticity and sequelae from severe chronic disorders (such as multiple sclerosis, cerebral palsy, spinal cord injury, stroke).** *Adults:* 25 mg P.O. daily. Increase in 25-mg increments up to 100 mg b.i.d. to q.i.d. Maximum, 400 mg daily. Maintain each dosage level for 4 to 7 days to determine response.
Children: Initially, 0.5 mg/kg P.O. b.i.d., increase to t.i.d. and then to q.i.d. Increase dosage as needed by 0.5 mg/kg daily to 3 mg/kg b.i.d. to q.i.d. Maximum, 100 mg q.i.d.

▶ **To manage malignant hyperthermic crisis.** *Adults and children:* 1 mg/kg I.V. initially, then repeat as needed up to a total dosage of 10 mg/kg.

▶ **To prevent or lessen malignant hyperthermia in susceptible patients who need surgery.** *Adults:* 4 to 8 mg/kg P.O. daily in three or four divided doses for 1 or 2 days before procedure. Final dose 3 to 4 hours before procedure. Or 2.5 mg/kg I.V. infused over 1 hour about 1 hour before anesthesia. Additional doses, which must be individualized, may be given intraoperatively.

▶ **To prevent recurrence of malignant hyperthermia.** *Adults:* 4 to 8 mg/kg P.O. daily in four divided doses for up to 3 days after hyperthermic crisis.

▶ **To reduce succinylcholine-induced muscle fasciculations and postoperative muscle pain‡.** *Adults weighing less than 45 kg (99 lb):* 100 mg P.O. 2 hours before succinylcholine. *Adults weighing more than 45 kg:* 150 mg P.O. 2 hours before succinylcholine.

I.V. administration

- Give as soon as malignant hyperthermia reaction is recognized.
- Reconstitute each vial with 60 ml of sterile water for injection, and shake vial until clear. Don't use diluent that contains bacteriostatic agent.
- Protect contents from light and use within 6 hours.
- Monitor patient for extravasation.

⊗ **Incompatibilities**
D_5W, normal saline solution, other I. V. drugs mixed in a syringe.

Contraindications and cautions

- Contraindicated in patients whose spasticity is used to maintain motor function and in patients with upper motor neuron disorders, spasms from rheumatic disorders, or active hepatic disease.
- Use cautiously in women, and in patients with hepatic disease or severely impaired cardiac or pulmonary function.

Lifespan: In pregnant women and patients older than age 35, use cautiously. In breast-feeding women, drug is contraindicated.

Adverse reactions

CNS: confusion, *dizziness, drowsiness,* fever, hallucinations, headache, insomnia, light-headedness, *malaise,* nervousness, ***seizures.***
CV: blood pressure changes, tachycardia.
EENT: auditory or visual disturbances, excessive tearing.
GI: anorexia, ***bleeding,*** constipation, cramping, drooling, dysphagia, metallic taste, severe diarrhea.
GU: crystalluria, difficulty achieving erection, dysuria, hematuria, incontinence, nocturia, urinary frequency.
Hepatic: ***hepatitis***.
Musculoskeletal: *muscle weakness,* myalgia.
Respiratory: pleural effusion.
Skin: abnormal hair growth, diaphoresis, eczematous eruption, photosensitivity, pruritus, urticaria.
Other: chills.

D

Interactions

Drug-drug. *CNS depressants:* May increase CNS depression. Avoid use together.
Estrogens: May increase risk of hepatotoxicity. Use together cautiously.
I.V. verapamil: May cause CV collapse when used together in anesthetized patients. Manufacturer recommends stopping verapamil before giving I.V. dantrolene based on animal studies
Drug-lifestyle. *Alcohol use:* May increase CNS depression. Avoid use together.
Sun exposure: Photosensitivity may occur. Urge patient to avoid prolonged and unprotected sun exposure.

Effects on lab test results

- May increase BUN, ALT, AST, and bilirubin levels.

Pharmacokinetics

Absorption: 35% of P.O. dose.
Distribution: Substantially protein-bound, mainly to albumin.
Metabolism: In liver to its less active 5-hydroxy derivatives and to its amino derivative by reductive pathways.
Excretion: In urine as metabolites. *Half-life:* P.O., 9 hours; I.V., 4 to 8 hours.

Route	Onset	Peak	Duration
P.O.	≤ 1 wk	5 hr	Unknown
I.V.	Unknown	Unknown	Unknown

Action

Chemical effect: Acts directly on skeletal muscle to interfere with intracellular calcium movement.
Therapeutic effect: Relieves muscle spasms.

Available forms

Capsules: 25 mg, 50 mg, 100 mg
Injection: 20 mg/vial

NURSING PROCESS

Assessment

- Obtain history of patient's disorder before therapy.
- Obtain liver function tests at start of therapy.
- Monitor effectiveness by evaluating severity of spasticity.
- Be alert for adverse reactions and drug interactions.
- Assess patient's and family's knowledge of drug therapy.

Nursing diagnoses

- Acute pain related to presence of spasticity
- Risk for injury related to drug-induced adverse reactions
- Deficient knowledge related to drug therapy

Planning and implementation

- For optimum drug effect, divide daily dose into four doses.
- Give drug with meals or milk to prevent GI distress.
- Prepare oral suspension for each dose by dissolving capsule contents in juice or other suitable liquid. For multiple doses, use acid vehicle, such as citric acid in USP syrup. Refrigerate, and use within several days.
- Amount of relief determines whether dose can be reduced.
- If hepatitis, severe diarrhea, severe weakness, or sensitivity reaction occurs, don't give the drug, and immediately notify prescriber.

ALERT: Don't confuse Dantrium with Daraprim.

Patient teaching

- Tell patient to use caution when eating to avoid choking. Some patients may have trouble swallowing during therapy.
- Warn patient to avoid hazardous activities until the drug's full CNS effects are known.
- Advise patient to avoid combining dantrolene with alcohol or other CNS depressants.
- Tell patient to use sunblock and wear protective clothing, to report GI problems immediately, and to follow prescriber's orders regarding rest and physical therapy.

Evaluation

- Patient states that pain from muscle spasticity has lessened.
- Patient has no injury from drug-induced adverse reactions.
- Patient and family state understanding of drug therapy.

daptomycin

(dapp-toh-MY-sin)
Cubicin

Pharmacologic class: cyclic lipopeptide antibacterial
Therapeutic class: antibiotic
Pregnancy risk category: B

Indications and dosages

▶ **Complicated skin and skin-structure infections caused by susceptible strains of *Staphylococcus aureus* (including methicillin-resistant strains), *Streptococcus pyogenes, Streptococcus agalactiae, Streptococcus dysgalactiae,* and *Enterococcus faecalis* (vancomycin-susceptible strains only).** *Adults:* 4 mg/kg by I.V. infusion over 30 minutes q 24 hours for 7 to 14 days.

▶ **Bacteremia caused by *S. aureus* (including right-sided endocarditis caused by methicillin-susceptible and methicillin-resistant strains).** *Adults:* 6 mg/kg I.V. over 30 minutes q 24 hours for at least 2 to 6 weeks.

Adjust-a-dose: In patients with infections of skin or skin structure whose creatinine clearance is less than 30 ml/minute (including those receiving hemodialysis or continuous ambulatory peritoneal dialysis), give 4 mg/kg I.V. q 48 hours. For bacteremic patients with a clearance less than 30 ml/minute, give 6 mg/kg I.V. q 48 hours. When possible, give drug after hemodialysis.

I.V. administration

- Reconstitute 250-mg vial with 5 ml of normal saline solution and 500-mg vial with 10 ml. Further dilute admixture with normal saline solution. Vials are for single use. Discard excess.
- Compatible with normal saline solution and lactated Ringer's injection. Flush line also used for other drugs with compatible fluids.
- For intermittent infusion, give drug over 30 minutes.
- Refrigerate vials at 36° to 46° F (2° to 8° C). Reconstituted and diluted solutions are stable 12 hours at room temperature or 48 hours at 36° to 46° F.

⊗ **Incompatibilities**

Dextrose-containing solutions. Any other I.V. drugs and solutions.

Contraindications and cautions

- Contraindicated in patients hypersensitive to drug or any of its components.
- Use cautiously in those with renal insufficiency.

Lifespan: In pregnant women, use cautiously. In breast-feeding women, use cautiously because it's unknown if drug appears in breast milk. In children, safety and effectiveness haven't been established. In patients older than age 65, use cautiously because drug may be less effective and cause more adverse reactions.

Adverse reactions

CNS: anxiety, confusion, dizziness, fever, headache, insomnia.
CV: chest pain, edema, ***heart failure,*** hypertension, hypotension.
EENT: sore throat.
GI: abdominal pain, constipation, decreased appetite, diarrhea, nausea, ***pseudomembranous colitis,*** vomiting.
GU: ***renal failure,*** UTI.
Hematologic: anemia.
Metabolic: hyperglycemia, ***hypoglycemia,*** hypokalemia.
Musculoskeletal: limb and back pain.
Respiratory: cough, dyspnea.
Skin: cellulitis, pruritus, rash.
Other: fungal infections, injection site reactions.

Interactions

Drug-drug. *HMG-CoA reductase inhibitors:* May increase risk of myopathy. Consider stopping these drugs while giving daptomycin.
Tobramycin: May affect levels of both drugs. Use together cautiously.
Warfarin: May alter anticoagulant activity. Monitor PT and INR for the first several days of daptomycin therapy.

Effects on lab test results

- May increase CK and alkaline phosphatase levels. May decrease potassium and hemoglobin levels and hematocrit. May increase or decrease glucose level.
- May increase liver function test values.

Pharmacokinetics

Absorption: Given I.V.
Distribution: 92% protein-bound, mainly to albumin.

Metabolism: Unknown.
Excretion: Mainly by kidneys. *Half-life:* About 8 hours.

Route	Onset	Peak	Duration
I.V.	Rapid	< 1 hr	Unknown

Action

Chemical effect: Binds to and depolarizes bacterial membranes to inhibit protein, DNA, and RNA synthesis.
Therapeutic effect: Kills bacteria in susceptible organisms.

Available forms

Powder for injection: 250-mg vial, 500-mg vial

NURSING PROCESS

Assessment
- Monitor CBC and renal and liver function tests periodically.
- Monitor patient for superinfection because drug may cause overgrowth of nonsusceptible organisms.
- Watch for evidence of pseudomembranous colitis, and treat accordingly.
- Assess patient's and family's knowledge of drug therapy.

Nursing diagnoses
- Risk for infection related to bacteria
- Impaired urinary elimination related to daptomycin-induced renal impairment
- Deficient knowledge related to drug therapy

Planning and implementation
- Obtain specimen for culture and sensitivity tests before giving the first dose. Begin therapy pending test results.

ALERT: Because drug may increase the risk of myopathy, monitor CK level weekly. If it rises, check it more often. Stop giving drug to a patient with evidence of myopathy and CK level that exceeds 1,000 units/L. Also stop giving the drug to a patient with CK level more than 10 times the upper limit of normal. Consider stopping all other drugs linked with myopathy (such as HMG-CoA reductase inhibitors).

Patient teaching
- Advise patient to immediately report muscle weakness and infusion site irritation.
- Tell patient to report severe diarrhea, rash, and infection.
- Inform patient about adverse reactions.

Evaluation
- Patient's infection is eradicated.
- Patient's renal function test values remain unchanged.
- Patient and family state understanding of drug therapy.

darbepoetin alfa
(dar-beh-POE-eh-tin AL-fah)
Aranesp

Pharmacologic class: hematopoietic
Therapeutic class: antianemic
Pregnancy risk category: C

Indications and dosages

▶ **Anemia from chronic renal failure.** *Adults:* 0.45 mcg/kg I.V. or subcutaneously once weekly. The I.V. route is preferred for patients undergoing dialysis. Adjust dose so hemoglobin level doesn't exceed 12 g/dl. Don't increase dose more often than once a month.
Adults and children older than age 1 who are converting from epoetin alfa: Base starting dose on the previous epoetin alfa dose, as shown in the table.

Previous epoetin alfa dose (units/wk)	Darbepoetin alfa dose (mcg/wk)	
	Adults	Children
< 1,500	6.25	Unknown
1,500–2,499	6.25	6.25
2,500–4,999	12.5	10
5,000–10,999	25	20
11,000–17,999	40	40
18,000–33,999	60	60
34,000–89,999	100	100
≥ 90,000	200	200

Give darbepoetin alfa less often than epoetin alfa. If patient was receiving epoetin alfa two to three times weekly, give darbepoetin alfa once weekly. If patient was receiving epoetin alfa once weekly, give darbepoetin alfa once q 2 weeks.

Adjust-a-dose: If increasing hemoglobin level approaches 12 g/dl, reduce dose by 25%. If level continues to increase, withhold dose until it begins to decrease; then restart drug at a dose 25% below the previous dose. If hemoglobin level increases more than 1 g/dl in 2 weeks, decrease dose by 25%. If it increases less than 1 g/dl over 4 weeks and iron stores are adequate, increase dose by 25% of previous dose. Make further increases at 4-week intervals until target hemoglobin level is reached. Patients who don't need dialysis may need lower maintenance doses.

▶ **Anemia from chemotherapy in patients with nonmyeloid malignancies.** *Adults:* 2.25 mcg/kg subcutaneously once weekly or 500 mcg subcutaneously once q 3 weeks.

Adjust-a-dose: For either dosage schedule, adjust dose to keep hemoglobin level below 12 g/dl. If hemoglobin level exceeds 13 g/dl, hold drug until it drops to 12 g/dl; then resume at 40% of previous dose. If hemoglobin level increases more than 1 g/dl in 2 weeks or it exceeds 11 g/dl, reduce dose by 40%. If patient receives drug once weekly and hemoglobin level increases less than 1 g/dl in 6 weeks, increase dose to 4.5 mcg/kg.

I.V. administration

- Don't shake drug because doing so can denature it.
- Drug is provided in single-dose vials without a preservative. Don't pool or retain unused portions.
- If drug has particulate matter or is discolored, don't use.
- Give undiluted by I.V. injection.
- Store drug in refrigerator; don't freeze. Protect drug from light.

⊗ **Incompatibilities**
Other I.V. drugs and solutions.

Contraindications and cautions

- Contraindicated in patients hypersensitive to drug or any of its components and in patients with uncontrolled hypertension.
- Use cautiously in patients with underlying hematologic disease, such as hemolytic anemia, sickle cell anemia, thalassemia, or porphyria, because safety and effectiveness haven't been established.

Lifespan: In pregnant women, safety and effectiveness haven't been established. In breast-feeding women, use cautiously because it's unknown whether drug appears in breast milk. In children with chronic renal failure, use as initial treatment to correct anemia hasn't been studied. Elderly patients may have greater sensitivity to the drug.

Adverse reactions

CNS: asthenia, dizziness, fatigue, fever, headache, ***seizures, stroke, TIA.***
CV: ***acute MI,*** angina, CARDIAC ARREST, CARDIAC ARRHYTHMIA, chest pain, *edema,* fluid overload, ***heart failure,*** *hypertension, hypotension, thrombosis.*
GI: abdominal pain, constipation, diarrhea, nausea, vomiting.
Metabolic: dehydration.
Musculoskeletal: arthralgia, back pain, limb pain, myalgia.
Respiratory: bronchitis, cough, dyspnea, pneumonia, ***pulmonary embolism,*** upper respiratory tract infection.
Skin: ***hemorrhage at access site,*** pruritus, rash.
Other: flulike symptoms, *infection.*

Interactions

None reported.

Effects on lab test results

- May increase hemoglobin level and hematocrit. May decrease ferritin level.
- May increase RBC count.

Pharmacokinetics

Absorption: Slow and rate limiting. Bioavailability ranges from 30% to 50% (mean: 37%).
Distribution: Mostly to vascular space.
Metabolism: Unknown.
Excretion: Steady-state levels occur within 4 weeks. *Half-life:* 21 hours (I.V.); 49 hours (subcutaneous).

Route	Onset	Peak	Duration
I.V.	Unknown	Unknown	21 hr
SubQ	Unknown	34 hr	49 hr

Action

Chemical effect: Stimulates erythropoiesis the same way as endogenous erythropoietin produced by the kidneys. In a healthy patient, erythropoiesis increases the number of RBCs.

Therapeutic effect: Corrects anemia in patients with chronic renal failure.

Available forms

Injection (albumin solution): 25 mcg/ml, 40 mcg/ml, 60 mcg/ml, 100 mcg/ml, 200 mcg/ml single-dose vials
Injection (polysorbate solution): 25 mcg/ml, 40 mcg/ml, 60 mcg/ml, 100 mcg/ml, 200 mcg/ml single-dose vials

NURSING PROCESS

Assessment

- Drug may increase blood pressure. Blood pressure should be controlled before starting therapy. Obtain baseline blood pressure before therapy, and carefully monitor and control patient's blood pressure during therapy.
- Monitor renal function and electrolytes in predialysis patients.

ALERT: Hemoglobin level may not increase until 2 to 6 weeks after therapy starts. Monitor level weekly until stabilized. Don't exceed the target level of 12 g/dl in patients with chronic renal impairment.

- Drug may increase risk of CV events, so carefully monitor and assess patient.
- Patient may have seizures. Follow patient closely, especially during the first several months of therapy.

Nursing diagnoses

- Risk for injury related to drug-induced adverse cardiac events
- Fatigue related to underlying anemia
- Deficient knowledge related to darbepoetin alfa therapy

Planning and implementation

ALERT: If hemoglobin level increases 1 g/dl in any 2-week period, decrease dose. Any increase greater than 1 g/dl within a 2-week period will increase the risk of adverse CV reactions, such as seizures, stroke, exacerbation of hypertension, heart failure, acute MI, fluid overload, edema, or vascular thrombosis, infarction, or ischemia. If symptoms occur, decrease drug dose by 25%.

ALERT: If patient suddenly loses response to drug and has severe anemia and a low reticulocyte count, withhold drug and test patient for antierythropoietin antibodies. If they're present, stop treatment. Don't switch to another erythropoietic protein because a cross reaction is possible.

- Monitor iron level before and during therapy. If ferritin level is less than 100 mcg/L and transferrin saturation is less than 20%, provide supplemental iron.
- Serious allergic reactions, including rash and urticaria, may occur. If an anaphylactic reaction occurs, stop giving drug and provide appropriate therapy.
- The maximum safe dose isn't known. Although doses greater than 3 mcg/kg/week for up to 28 weeks can be given, an excessive rise or rate of rise of hemoglobin level leads to adverse reactions. If patient has polycythemia, don't give drug.
- If patient doesn't respond to therapy, reevaluate patient for other etiologies that may inhibit erythropoiesis, such as folic acid or vitamin B_{12} deficiencies, infections, inflammatory or malignant processes, osteofibrosis cystica, occult blood loss, hemolysis, severe aluminum toxicity, and bone marrow fibrosis.

Patient teaching

- Teach patient how to give drug properly, including how to use and dispose of needles.
- Advise patient of adverse effects and allergic reactions.
- Inform patient of need to frequently monitor blood pressure, hemoglobin level, and hematocrit. Advise him to comply with antihypertensive therapy and dietary restrictions to keep blood pressure under control. Uncontrolled blood pressure is believed to cause seizures and hypertensive encephalopathy in patients with chronic renal impairment.

Evaluation

- Patient's hemoglobin level increases to no more than 12 g/dl.
- Patient's blood pressure remains adequately controlled, and patient doesn't suffer any adverse reactions related to drug therapy.
- Patient and family state understanding of drug therapy.

darifenacin

(dare-ee-PHEN-uh-sin)
Enablex

Pharmacologic classification: muscarinic receptor antagonist
Therapeutic classification: anticholinergic
Pregnancy risk category: C

Indications and dosages

▶ **Symptoms of urge incontinence, urgency, and frequency from an overactive urinary bladder.** *Adults:* Initially, 7.5 mg P.O. once daily. If needed, may increase to 15 mg P.O. once daily after 2 weeks.

Adjust-a-dose: If patient has moderate hepatic impairment (Child-Pugh class B) or takes a potent CYP3A4 inhibitor (such as clarithromycin, itraconazole, ketoconazole, nefazodone, nelfinavir, or ritonavir), don't exceed 7.5 mg P.O. once daily.

Contraindications and cautions

• Contraindicated in patients hypersensitive to drug or its ingredients. Also contraindicated in patients with or at risk for urine retention, gastric retention, or uncontrolled narrow-angle glaucoma. Avoid use in patients with severe hepatic impairment (Child-Pugh C).
• Use cautiously in patients with bladder outflow obstruction, decreased GI motility, GI obstruction, ulcerative colitis, myasthenia gravis, severe constipation, controlled narrow-angle glaucoma, or moderate hepatic impairment (Child-Pugh B).

Lifespan: In pregnant women, use only if benefit to mother outweighs risk to fetus. In breast-feeding women, use cautiously; it isn't known if drug appears in breast milk. In children, safety and effectiveness haven't been established.

Adverse reactions

CNS: asthenia, dizziness.
CV: hypertension.
EENT: abnormal vision, dry eyes, pharyngitis, rhinitis, sinusitis.
GI: abdominal pain, *constipation,* diarrhea, *dry mouth,* dyspepsia, nausea, vomiting.
GU: urinary tract disorder, UTI, vaginitis.
Metabolic: weight gain.
Musculoskeletal: arthralgia, back pain.
Respiratory: bronchitis.
Skin: dry skin, pruritus, rash.
Other: accidental injury, flu syndrome, pain, peripheral edema.

Interactions

Drug-drug. *Anticholinergics:* May increase anticholinergic effects, such as dry mouth, blurred vision, and constipation. Monitor patient closely.
Digoxin: May increase digoxin level. Monitor digoxin level.
Drugs metabolized by CYP2D6 (such as flecainide, thioridazine, tricyclic antidepressants): May increase levels of these drugs. Use together cautiously.
Drugs that are potent CYP3A4 inhibitors (such as clarithromycin, itraconazole, ketoconazole, nefazodone, nelfinavir, ritonavir): May increase darifenacin levels. Maximum darifenacin dose is 7.5 mg P.O. daily.
Midazolam: May increase midazolam level. Monitor patient carefully.
Drug-lifestyle. *Hot weather:* May cause heat prostration from decreased sweating. Advise caution.

Effects on lab test results

None reported.

Pharmacokinetics

Absorption: Level peaks 7 hours after multiple doses.
Distribution: 98% bound to plasma proteins, mainly to alpha$_1$-acid glycoprotein.
Metabolism: Extensive, in liver (CYP2D6, CYP3A4).
Excretion: 60% in urine, 40% in feces; 3% unchanged. *Half-life:* 13 to 19 hours.

Route	Onset	Peak	Duration
P.O.	Unknown	7 hr	Unknown

Action

Chemical effect: Antagonizes muscarinic (M$_3$) receptors, increasing bladder capacity and decreasing unstable detrusor contractions.
Therapeutic effect: Relieves symptoms of overactive bladder.

Available forms

Tablets (extended-release): 7.5 mg, 15 mg

NURSING PROCESS

Assessment

- Assess bladder function before therapy starts.
- Monitor drug effects.
- If patient has bladder outlet obstruction, watch for urine retention.
- Assess patient for decreased gastric motility and constipation.
- Assess patient's and family's knowledge of drug therapy.

Nursing diagnoses

- Impaired urinary elimination related to underlying medical condition
- Risk for injury related to drug-induced adverse effects
- Deficient knowledge related to drug therapy

Planning and implementation

- If patient has a UTI, give antibiotics.
- Reduce GI distress by giving drug with food.
- If patient develops urine retention, notify physician and prepare for urinary catheterization.

Patient teaching

- Tell patient to swallow tablet whole with plenty of liquid; caution against crushing or chewing the tablets.
- Inform patient that drug may be taken with or without food.
- Explain that drug may cause blurred vision. Tell patient to use caution, especially when performing hazardous tasks, until drug effects are known.
- Tell patient to report blurred vision, constipation, and urine retention.
- Discourage use of other drugs that may cause dry mouth, constipation, urine retention, or blurred vision.
- Tell patient that drug decreases sweating. Advise caution in hot environments and during strenuous activity.

Evaluation

- Patient experiences improved bladder function with drug therapy.
- Patient sustains no injuries from drug-induced effects.
- Patient and family state understanding of drug therapy.

darunavir ethanolate

(duh-ROO-nah-veer eh-THAH-nuh-layt)
Prezista

Pharmacologic class: protease inhibitor
Therapeutic class: antiretroviral
Pregnancy risk category: B

Indications and dosages

▶ **HIV infection in antiretroviral treatment–experienced patients, with ritonavir and other antiretrovirals.** *Adults:* 600 mg P.O. b.i.d., given with ritonavir 100 mg P.O. b.i.d. and food.

Contraindications and cautions

- Contraindicated in patients hypersensitive to drug or its components and in patient taking drugs metabolized by CYP3A, such as astemizole, dihydroergotamine, ergonovine, ergotamine, methylergonovine, midazolam, pimozide, terfenadine, and triazolam.
- Use cautiously in patients with liver or renal impairment, diabetes mellitus, hemophilia, sulfonamide allergy, or a history of opportunistic infections.

Lifespan: In pregnant patients, use only if potential benefits to mother justify risk to fetus. HIV-infected mothers shouldn't breast-feed to avoid transmitting HIV to their infants. In children, safety and efficacy haven't been established. In elderly patients, use cautiously because these patients are more likely to have decreased hepatic function.

Adverse reactions

CNS: altered mood, anxiety, asthenia, confusion, disorientation, fatigue, *headache,* hypoesthesia, irritability, memory impairment, nightmares, paresthesia, peripheral neuropathy, somnolence, transient ischemic attack, vertigo.
CV: hypertension, ***MI***, tachycardia.
EENT: *nasopharyngitis.*
GI: abdominal distension, abdominal pain, anorexia, constipation, *diarrhea,* dry mouth, dyspepsia, flatulence, *nausea,* polydipsia, vomiting.
GU: ***acute renal failure***, renal insufficiency, nephrolithiasis, polyuria.

Hematologic: LEUKOPENIA, ***neutropenia, thrombocytopenia.***
Metabolic: decreased appetite, diabetes mellitus, hypercholesterolemia, hyperlipidemia, hypernatremia, hyperuricemia, hyponatremia, obesity.
Musculoskeletal: arthralgia, limb pain, myalgia, osteopenia, osteoporosis.
Respiratory: cough, dyspnea, hiccups.
Skin: allergic dermatitis, alopecia, dermatitis medicamentosa, eczema, ***erythema multiforme***, folliculitis, increased sweating, inflammation, lipoatrophy, maculopapular rash, night sweats, ***Stevens-Johnson syndrome***, toxic skin eruption.
Other: fat redistribution, gynecomastia, hyperthermia, peripheral edema, pyrexia, rigors.

Interactions

Drug-drug. *Amiodarone, bepridil, cyclosporine, felodipine, fluticasone, lidocaine, nicardipine, nifedipine, quinidine, rifabutin, sildenafil, sirolimus, tacrolimus, tadalafil, trazodone, vardenafil:* May increase levels of these drugs and risk of adverse reactions. Use caution, and monitor patient carefully.
Astemizole, cisapride, ergot derivatives, midazolam, pimozide, terfenadine, triazolam: May cause serious or life-threatening reactions. Use together is contraindicated.
Atorvastatin, pravastatin: May increase levels of these drugs. Start at the lowest dose, and monitor patient carefully.
Clarithromycin: May increase clarithromycin level. Reduce clarithromycin dose in patients with renal impairment.
CYP3A inducers (carbamazepine, dexamethasone, phenobarbital, phenytoin, rifabutin, rifampin), efavirenz, lopinavir, saquinavir: May increase darunavir clearance and decrease darunavir level. Avoid use together.
Ethinyl estradiol, norethindrone: May decrease estrogen level. Recommend alternative or additional contraception.
Itraconazole, ketoconazole: May increase levels of these drugs and darunavir. Don't exceed 200 mg of itraconazole or ketoconazole daily.
Lovastatin, simvastatin: May increase risk of myopathy, including rhabdomyolysis. Use caution.
Methadone: May decrease methadone level. Monitor patient for opioid abstinence syndrome, and consider increasing methadone dosage.
Rifabutin: May decrease darunavir level. If used together, give rifabutin as 150 mg every other day.
SSRIs (paroxetine, sertraline): May decrease levels of these drugs. Adjust dosage carefully based on antidepressant response.
Trazodone: May increase trazodone level and risk of toxicity. Decrease trazodone dosage.
Warfarin: May decrease warfarin level. Monitor patient carefully.
Drug-food. *Food:* Increases darunavir absorption, which is needed for adequate therapeutic effect. Always give with food.
Drug-herb. *St. John's wort:* May decrease darunavir level significantly. Discourage use together.

Effects on lab test results

- May increase AST, ALT, GGT, alkaline phosphatase, bilirubin, pancreatic amylase, pancreatic lipase, cholesterol, triglyceride, and uric acid levels. May decrease albumin, bicarbonate, and calcium levels. May increase or decrease sodium and glucose levels.
- May decrease WBC, neutrophil, lymphocyte, and platelet counts.

Pharmacokinetics

Absorption: Greater when taken with ritonavir and food.
Distribution: About 95% bound to plasma proteins.
Metabolism: Metabolized extensively in the liver by CYP3A.
Excretion: Mainly in feces, with a small amount in urine. *Half-life:* About 15 hours when combined with ritonavir.

Route	Onset	Peak	Duration
P.O.	Unknown	2½–4 hr	Unknown

Action

Chemical effect: Drug binds to the protease-active site and selectively inhibits enzyme activity. This inhibition prevents cleavage of viral polyproteins, resulting in the formation of immature noninfectious viral particles.
Therapeutic effect: Treats HIV infection.

Available forms

Tablets: 300 mg

NURSING PROCESS

Assessment

- Assess patient for appropriateness of drug therapy.
- Because drug may interact with other drugs, obtain patient's complete drug history.
- Monitor patient for diarrhea, nausea, headache, and signs and symptoms of a common cold. If patient develops a rash, report it to prescriber.
- Find out whether patient is pregnant or plans to become pregnant.
- Assess patient's and family's knowledge about drug therapy.

Nursing diagnoses

- Risk for infection secondary to presence of HIV
- Ineffective coping related to HIV infection
- Deficient knowledge related to drug therapy

Planning and implementation

- Always give drug with ritonavir and food.
- Drug may cause spontaneous bleeding in some patients with hemophilia. Monitor patient closely.
- Patients with hepatic impairment, diabetes mellitus, sulfonamide allergy, or hemophilia must be monitored closely while taking this drug.

Patient teaching

- Explain that many drugs interact with darunavir; advise patient to report all drugs he takes, including OTC products.

ALERT: Instruct patient to take darunavir and ritonavir at the same time every day, with food.

- Advise patient to swallow the tablet whole and not to chew it.
- Tell patient that darunavir doesn't cure HIV infection or AIDS and doesn't reduce the risk of passing HIV to others.
- Explain that opportunistic infections and other complications of HIV infection may still develop.
- If patient misses a dose by more than 6 hours, tell him to wait and take the next dose at the regularly scheduled time. If he remembers within 6 hours, tell him to take the missed dose immediately.

Evaluation

- Patient has reduced signs and symptoms of infection.
- Patient demonstrates adequate coping mechanisms.
- Patient and family state understanding of drug therapy.

D

dasatinib

(duh-SAH-tih-nib)

Sprycel

Pharmacologic class: protein-tyrosine kinase inhibitor
Therapeutic class: antineoplastic
Pregnancy risk category: D

Indications and dosages

▶ **Chronic, accelerated, myeloid, or lymphoid blast phase chronic myeloid leukemia with resistance or intolerance to earlier treatment, including imatinib; Philadelphia chromosome–positive acute lymphoblastic leukemia with resistance or tolerance to previous therapy.** *Adults:* 70 mg P.O. b.i.d. in the morning and evening with or without food. If patient tolerates this dose but fails to respond, may increase to 90 or 100 mg b.i.d. Continue until disease progresses or intolerable adverse effects occur.

Adjust-a-dose: If patient has hematologic toxicity, consider reducing dose or interrupting or stopping therapy. If patient has severe, nonhematologic toxicity, hold dose until condition resolves; then resume at previous or reduced dose.

Contraindications and cautions

- No known contraindications.
- Use cautiously in patients receiving antiarrhythmics, antiplatelets, or anticoagulants; patients receiving cumulative high-dose anthracycline therapy; patients with a prolonged QT interval or risk of prolonged QT interval (those with hypokalemia, hypomagnesemia, or current use of drugs that prolong the QT interval); patients with liver impairment; and patients who are lactose intolerant.

Lifespan: In pregnant patients, drug may cause fetal harm. Mothers shouldn't breast-feed during treatment. In children, safety and efficacy haven't been established. Elderly patients may be more sensitive to drug's effects.

Adverse reactions

CNS: anxiety, *asthenia*, ***bleeding***, *chills*, confusion, depression, *dizziness*, *fatigue*, *headache*, insomnia, malaise, *neuropathy*, ***pyrexia***, ***seizures***, somnolence, syncope, tremor, vertigo.
CV: *arrhythmias*, ***cardiac dysfunction***, *chest pain*, *edema*, ***heart failure***, ***hemorrhage***, hypertension, hypotension, pericardial effusion.
EENT: conjunctivitis, dry eyes, dysgeusia, *mucositis*, *stomatitis*, tinnitus.
GI: *abdominal distention and pain*, *anorexia*, anal fissure, ***bleeding***, colitis, *constipation*, *diarrhea*, dyspepsia, dysphagia, *nausea*, *vomiting*.
GU: ***renal failure***, urinary frequency.
Hematologic: *anemia*, ***febrile neutropenia***, ***pancytopenia***, ***thrombocytopenia***.
Hepatic: cholecystitis, cholestasis, ***hepatitis***.
Metabolic: hyperuricemia, *weight loss or gain*.
Musculoskeletal: *arthralgia*, inflammation, *myalgia*, muscle stiffness, *pain*.
Respiratory: asthma, *cough*, *dyspnea*, ***pleural effusion***, ***pneumonia***, pulmonary edema and hypertension, *upper respiratory tract infection*.
Skin: acne, alopecia, dry skin, nail or pigment disorders, *pruritus*, *rash*, sweating.
Other: ascites, gynecomastia, herpes infection, *infection*, ***tumor lysis syndrome***.

Interactions

Drug-drug. *Antacids:* May decrease dasatinib absorption. Give antacid 2 hours before or 2 hours after dasatinib.
CYP3A4 inducers (carbamazepine, dexamethasone, phenobarbital, phenytoin, rifampicin): May decrease dasatinib level. Avoid use together, or increase dasatinib dose in 20-mg increments.
CYP3A4 inhibitors (atazanavir, clarithromycin, erythromycin, indinavir, itraconazole, ketoconazole, nefazodone, nelfinavir, ritonavir, saquinavir, telithromycin): May increase dasatinib level and toxicity. Avoid use together; if it can't be avoided, monitor patient closely. Dasatinib dose may be decreased 20 to 40 mg daily.
CYP3A4 substrates (cyclosporine, ergot alkaloids, fentanyl, pimozide, quinidine, sirolimus, tacrolimus): May alter levels of these drugs. Use cautiously together, and monitor patient.
H_2-blockers, proton pump inhibitors: May decrease dasatinib level because of gastric acid suppression. Avoid use together. Consider antacids as an alternative.
Drug-herb. *St. John's wort:* May decrease dasatinib level. Discourage use together.

Effects on lab test results

- May increase uric acid, bilirubin, creatinine, AST, ALT, CK, and troponin levels. May decrease phosphate and calcium levels.
- May decrease RBC, platelet, and neutrophil counts.

Pharmacokinetics

Absorption: Well absorbed. Absorption is pH dependent.
Distribution: 96% protein-bound.
Metabolism: Mainly by CYP3A4.
Excretion: Mainly in feces as metabolites. *Half-life:* 3 to 5 hours.

Route	Onset	Peak	Duration
P.O.	Unknown	½–6 hr	Unknown

Action

Chemical effect: Reduces leukemic cell growth by inhibiting tyrosine kinase BRC-ABL.
Therapeutic effect: Bone marrow is able to resume production of normal red cells, white cells, and platelets.

Available forms

Tablets: 20 mg, 50 mg, 70 mg

NURSING PROCESS

Assessment

- Ask patient if he is lactose intolerant because drug contains lactose.
- Monitor CBC weekly for the first 2 months of treatment, then monthly thereafter, or as clinically indicated.
- If patient develops dyspnea or a dry cough, notify prescriber. Obtain a chest X-ray and give oxygen, diuretics, and steroids, as indicated.
- Monitor patient for easy bruising or bleeding, and report it to the prescriber.
- Assess patient's and family's knowledge of drug therapy.

Nursing diagnoses

- Ineffective breathing pattern related to pulmonary edema and fluid retention

• Risk for infection related to drug's adverse reaction
• Deficient knowledge related to drug therapy

Planning and implementation

ALERT: Don't crush or cut tablets. If tablet is crushed or broken, wear chemotherapy gloves to dispose of it. Pregnant women shouldn't handle broken tablets.
• Obtain patient's baseline weight, and check regularly for swelling or weight gain.
• Correct electrolyte imbalances, especially of potassium and magnesium, before treatment.

Patient teaching

• Tell patient to take tablets at about the same time each day.
• Caution patient not to crush or cut the tablets.
• Warn women of childbearing potential to use reliable contraception during treatment. Men who take dasatinib should use condoms to avoid impregnating their partners.
• Tell patient to report weight gain, swelling, and shortness of breath.
• Advise patient to notify prescriber immediately about easy or unusual bruising.

Evaluation

• Patient maintains adequate respiratory function.
• Patient is free from infection.
• Patient and family state understanding of drug therapy.

daunorubicin citrate liposomal

(daw-noh-ROO-buh-sin SIH-trayt li-poh-SOE-mul)
DaunoXome

Pharmacologic class: anthracycline
Therapeutic class: antineoplastic
Pregnancy risk category: D

Indications and dosages

▶ **First-line cytotoxic therapy for advanced HIV-related Kaposi sarcoma.** *Adults:* 40 mg/m² I.V. over 60 minutes once q 2 weeks. Continue therapy unless patient shows signs of progressive disease or until drugs has to be stopped from other complications of HIV.

Adjust-a-dose: For patients with renal or hepatic impairment, if bilirubin is 1.2 to 3 mg/dl, give ¼ of normal dose; if bilirubin or creatinine level is greater than 3 mg/dl, give ½ of normal dose.

I.V. administration

• Preparing and giving drug raises carcinogenic, mutagenic, and teratogenic risks. Follow facility policy to reduce risks.
• Dilute drug with D_5W only. Withdraw the calculated volume of drug from the vial, and transfer it into an equivalent amount of D_5W to yield 1 mg/ml.
• After dilution, immediately give I.V. over 60 minutes. If unable to use drug immediately, refrigerate at 36° to 46° F (2° to 8° C) for a maximum of 6 hours.
• Don't use in-line filters for I.V. infusion.
• Because local tissue necrosis may occur, monitor I.V. site closely to avoid extravasation. If extravasation occurs, stop I.V., apply ice, and notify prescriber.
• Monitor patient for adverse reactions. A triad of back pain, flushing, and chest tightness may occur within the first 5 minutes of the infusion. These symptoms subside after stopping the infusion and typically don't recur when the infusion resumes at a slower rate.
• Follow facility policy for handling and disposing of antineoplastics.

⊗ **Incompatibilities**

Bacteriostatic agents, other I.V. drugs, saline and other solutions.

Contraindications and cautions

• Contraindicated in patients hypersensitive to drug or any of its components.
• Use cautiously in patients with myelosuppression, cardiac disease, previous radiotherapy involving the heart, previous anthracycline use (doxorubicin greater than 300 mg/m² or equivalent), or hepatic or renal impairment.

Lifespan: In pregnant women, avoid use because the drug may harm the fetus. In children and the elderly, safety and effectiveness haven't been established.

Adverse reactions

CNS: abnormal gait, abnormal thinking, amnesia, anxiety, ataxia, confusion, depression, dizziness, emotional lability, *fatigue, fever,* hallucinations, *headache,* hyperkinesia, hypertonia, insomnia, malaise, meningitis, *neuropathy, **seizures,*** somnolence, syncope, tremor.

CV: angina pectoris, ***arrhythmias, cardiac arrest, cardiac tamponade, cardiomyopathy,*** chest pain, edema, flushing, hypertension, ***MI,*** palpitations, ***pericardial effusion, pulmonary hypertension,*** tachycardia.
EENT: abnormal vision, conjunctivitis, deafness, dry mouth, earache, eye pain, gingival bleeding, *rhinitis,* sinusitis, taste disturbance, tinnitus, tooth caries.
GI: *abdominal pain, anorexia,* constipation, *diarrhea,* dysphagia, gastritis, ***hemorrhage,*** hemorrhoids, increased appetite, melena, *nausea,* stomatitis, tenesmus, vomiting.
GU: dysuria, nocturia, polyuria.
Hematologic: lymphadenopathy, **NEUTROPENIA,** splenomegaly.
Hepatic: hepatomegaly.
Metabolic: dehydration.
Musculoskeletal: arthralgia, *back pain,* myalgia, *rigors.*
Respiratory: *cough, dyspnea,* hemoptysis, hiccups, increased sputum, pulmonary infiltration.
Skin: alopecia, dry skin, folliculitis, increased sweating, pruritus, seborrhea.
Other: *allergic reactions,* flulike symptoms, injection site inflammation, *opportunistic infections,* thirst.

Interactions

None reported.

Effects on lab test results

- May decrease neutrophil and platelet counts.

Pharmacokinetics

Absorption: Given I.V.
Distribution: Probably mainly in vascular fluid volume.
Metabolism: By the liver into active metabolites.
Excretion: Unknown. *Half-life:* 4½ hours.

Route	Onset	Peak	Duration
I.V.	Unknown	Unknown	Unknown

Action

Chemical effect: Exerts cytotoxic effects by intercalating between DNA base pairs and uncoiling the DNA helix. This inhibits DNA synthesis and DNA-dependent RNA synthesis. Also inhibits polymerase activity. The liposomal preparation maximizes the selectivity of daunorubicin for solid tumors in situ.
Therapeutic effect: Decreases tumor growth for advanced HIV-related Kaposi sarcoma.

Available forms

Injection: 2 mg/ml (equivalent to 50 mg daunorubicin base)

NURSING PROCESS

Assessment

- Obtain history of patient's underlying condition before therapy, and reassess regularly thereafter.
- Obtain hepatic and renal studies before therapy.
- Monitor cardiac function regularly, especially immediately before giving a dose, because of the risk of cardiac toxicity and heart failure. Determine left ventricular ejection fraction at a total cumulative dose of 320 mg/m^2 and every 160 mg/m^2 thereafter.
- Monitor patient closely for signs of opportunistic infections.
- Be alert for adverse reactions and drug interactions.
- Assess patient's and family's knowledge of drug therapy.

Nursing diagnoses

- Risk for injury related to drug-induced adverse reactions
- Risk for infection related to myelosuppression
- Deficient knowledge related to drug therapy

Planning and implementation

- Drug causes less nausea, vomiting, alopecia, neutropenia, thrombocytopenia, and potentially less cardiotoxicity than conventional daunorubicin.
- Give only under the supervision of a prescriber specializing in cancer chemotherapy.
- Monitor hematology closely because severe myelosuppression may occur. Obtain and check blood counts before each dose. If absolute granulocyte count is less than 750 cells/mm^3, withhold drug.

ALERT: Drug has unique kinetic properties that are different from the conventional daunorubicin hydrochloride. Don't substitute or interchange the drugs on a milligram-to-milligram basis.

Patient teaching
- Inform patient that alopecia may occur, but that it's usually reversible.
- Tell patient to notify prescriber about sore throat, fever, or other signs of infection. Tell patient to avoid exposure to people with infections.
- Advise patient to report suspected or known pregnancy during therapy.
- Tell patient to report back pain, flushing, and chest tightness during the infusion.

Evaluation
- Patient has no injury as a result of drug-induced adverse reactions.
- Patient remains free of infection.
- Patient and family state understanding of drug therapy.

daunorubicin hydrochloride
(daw-noh-ROO-buh-sin high-droh-KLOR-ighd)
Cerubidine

Pharmacologic class: anthracycline antineoplastic
Therapeutic class: antineoplastic
Pregnancy risk category: D

Indications and dosages

▶ **To induce remission in acute nonlymphocytic (myelogenous, monocytic, erythroid) leukemia.** *Adults younger than age 60:* When given with other drugs, 45 mg/m² I.V. daily on days 1, 2, and 3 of first course and on days 1 and 2 of subsequent courses with cytarabine infusions.
Adults age 60 or older: When given with other drugs, 30 mg/m² I.V. daily on days 1, 2, and 3 of first course and on days 1 and 2 of subsequent courses with cytarabine infusions.

▶ **To induce remission in acute lymphocytic leukemia.** *Adults:* 45 mg/m² I.V. daily on days 1, 2, and 3.
Children age 2 and older: 25 mg/m² I.V. on day 1 q week for up to 6 weeks, if needed.
Children younger than age 2 or with body surface area smaller than 0.5 m²: Calculate dose based on body weight (1 mg/kg).

Adjust-a-dose: For patients with impaired hepatic or renal function, reduce dosage as follows: If bilirubin level is 1.2 to 3 mg/dl, give 75% of normal dose; if bilirubin or creatinine level exceeds 3 mg/dl, give 50% of the normal dose.

I.V. administration
- Preparing and giving drug raises carcinogenic, mutagenic, and teratogenic risks. Follow institutional policy to reduce risks.
- Reconstitute drug using 4 ml of sterile water for injection to produce a 5-mg/ml solution.
- Withdraw desired dose into syringe containing 10 to 15 ml of normal saline solution for injection. Over 2 to 3 minutes, inject into I.V. line containing free-flowing D_5W or normal saline solution.
- Monitor I.V. site for extravasation. If it occurs, stop I.V. injection immediately, notify prescriber, and apply ice to area for 24 to 48 hours.
- Don't inject with dexamethasone or heparin because a precipitate may form.
- Use within 8 hours of preparation. Reconstituted undiluted solution is stable 24 hours at room temperature, 48 hours if refrigerated.

⊗ **Incompatibilities**
Other I.V. drugs.

Contraindications and cautions
- Use cautiously in patients with myelosuppression and in those with impaired cardiac, renal, or hepatic function.

Lifespan: In pregnant women, avoid use because of potential fetal abnormality or death. Women of childbearing age should avoid becoming pregnant while on drug. Males being treated have increased risk of fertility impairment. Breast-feeding isn't recommended during therapy because of possible increased risk of breast tumors. In children and the elderly, cardiotoxicity may be more frequent and occur at lower cumulative doses.

Adverse reactions
CNS: fever.
CV: ***arrhythmias,*** ECG changes, ***irreversible cardiomyopathy,*** myocarditis, ***pericarditis.***
GI: anorexia, diarrhea, esophagitis, nausea, stomatitis, vomiting.
GU: red urine.
Hematologic: ***bone marrow suppression.***
Hepatic: ***hepatotoxicity.***
Metabolic: hyperuricemia.

Skin: *generalized alopecia*, pigmentation of fingernails and toenails, rash, *tissue sloughing with extravasation.*
Other: ***anaphylaxis,*** chills, severe cellulitis.

Interactions

Drug-drug. *Bone marrow suppressants:* May increase risk of myelosuppression. Monitor patient closely.
Cyclophosphamide: May increase risk of cardiotoxicity. Monitor patient closely.
Doxorubicin: May increase risk of cardiotoxicity. Monitor patient closely.
Hepatotoxic drugs: May increase risk of hepatotoxicity. Monitor hepatic function closely.

Effects on lab test results

• May increase uric acid level.

Pharmacokinetics

Absorption: Given I.V. only.
Distribution: Wide. Drug doesn't cross blood–brain barrier.
Metabolism: Extensive. One of metabolites has cytotoxic activity.
Excretion: Mainly in bile, with small portion in urine. *Half-life:* Initial, 45 minutes; terminal, 18½ hours.

Route	Onset	Peak	Duration
I.V.	Unknown	Unknown	Unknown

Action

Chemical effect: May interfere with DNA-dependent RNA synthesis by intercalation.
Therapeutic effect: Kills selected cancer cells.

Available forms

Injection: 20 mg/vial

NURSING PROCESS

Assessment

• Obtain history of patient's underlying disease before therapy, and reassess regularly throughout therapy.
• Check ECG before therapy.
• Monitor CBC and liver function tests; monitor ECG every month (or more frequently if needed) during therapy.
• Monitor pulse rate closely.
• Look for adverse reactions and drug interactions.
• Monitor patient for nausea and vomiting, which may be severe and may last 24 to 48 hours. Monitor patient's hydration during episodes of nausea and vomiting.
• Assess patient's and family's knowledge of drug therapy.

Nursing diagnoses

• Risk for injury related to presence of neoplastic disease
• Risk for deficient fluid volume related to drug-induced nausea and vomiting
• Deficient knowledge related to drug therapy

Planning and implementation

ALERT: Never give drug by I.M. or subcutaneous route.
• Limit cumulative dose to 500 to 600 mg/m² (450 mg/m² if patient receives or has received cyclophosphamide or radiation therapy to cardiac area).
ALERT: Color is similar to that of doxorubicin. Don't confuse these two drugs.
• If signs of heart failure or cardiomyopathy develop, stop giving the drug and immediately notify the prescriber.
ALERT: The risk of myocardial toxicity increases after a total cumulative dose higher than 400 to 550 mg/m² in adults, 300 mg/m² in children older than age 2, and 10 mg/kg in children younger than age 2.
• Give antiemetics to help control nausea and vomiting.

Patient teaching

• Warn patient to watch for signs of infection and bleeding.
• Advise patient that red urine for 1 to 2 days is normal and doesn't indicate blood in urine.
• Inform patient that alopecia may occur, but that it's usually reversible.
• Advise women of childbearing age to avoid becoming pregnant during therapy.
• Instruct patient about need for protective measures, including conservation of energy, balanced diet, adequate rest, personal hygiene, clean environment, and avoidance of people with infections.

Evaluation

• Patient shows positive response to therapy as shown by reports of follow-up diagnostic tests and improved physical condition.

• Patient maintains adequate hydration throughout therapy.
• Patient and family state understanding of drug therapy.

delavirdine mesylate

(deh-luh-VEER-deen MES-ih-layt)
Rescriptor

Pharmacologic class: nonnucleoside reverse transcriptase inhibitor
Therapeutic class: antiretroviral
Pregnancy risk category: C

Indications and dosages

▶ **HIV-1 infection.** *Adults:* 400 mg P.O. t.i.d. with other appropriate antiretrovirals.

Contraindications and cautions

• Contraindicated in patients hypersensitive to drug or any of its components.
• Use cautiously in patients with impaired hepatic function.
Lifespan: In pregnant women, use only if potential benefits to the woman outweigh risks to the fetus. Breast-feeding women can transmit HIV to their infants. In children younger than age 16, safety and effectiveness haven't been established.

Adverse reactions

CNS: anxiety, *asthenia,* depression, *fatigue,* fever, *headache,* insomnia, pain.
EENT: pharyngitis, sinusitis.
GI: abdominal pain (generalized or localized), diarrhea, nausea, vomiting.
Respiratory: bronchitis, cough, upper respiratory tract infection.
Skin: *rash.*
Other: flulike syndrome.

Interactions

Drug-drug. *Amphetamines, antihistamines (nonsedating), benzodiazepines, calcium channel blockers, clarithromycin, dapsone, ergot alkaloids, indinavir, quinidine, rifabutin, sedative hypnotics, warfarin:* May increase or prolong therapeutic and adverse effects of these drugs. Avoid use together; however, reduced doses of indinavir and clarithromycin may be used.
Antacids: May reduce absorption of delavirdine. Separate doses by at least 1 hour.
Carbamazepine, phenobarbital, phenytoin: May decrease delavirdine level; use together cautiously.
Clarithromycin, fluoxetine, ketoconazole: May cause a 50% increase in delavirdine bioavailability. Monitor patient. Reduce dose of clarithromycin.
Didanosine: May decrease absorption of both drugs by 20%. Separate doses by at least 1 hour.
H_2-receptor antagonists: May increase gastric pH, reducing absorption of delavirdine. Long-term use together isn't recommended.
HMG-CoA reductase inhibitors, such as atorvastatin, lovastatin, and simvastatin: May increase levels of these drugs, raising risk for myopathy, including rhabdomyolysis. Avoid use together.
Rifabutin, rifampin: May decrease delavirdine levels. Rifabutin levels are increased by 100%. Avoid use together.
Saquinavir: May increase bioavailability of saquinavir fivefold. Monitor AST and ALT levels frequently when used together.
Sildenafil: May increase sildenafil level and risk of hypotension, visual changes, and priapism. Tell patient not to exceed 25 mg of sildenafil in a 48-hour period.

Effects on lab test results

• May increase ALT, GGT, amylase, bilirubin, and AST levels. May decrease hemoglobin level and hematocrit. May increase or decrease glucose level.
• May increase PT, PTT, and eosinophil count. May decrease granulocyte, neutrophil, WBC, RBC, and platelet counts.

Pharmacokinetics

Absorption: Rapid.
Distribution: 98% protein-bound.
Metabolism: Extensive, to inactive metabolites. Mainly in liver by cytochrome P-450 enzyme systems.
Excretion: 51% in the urine (less than 5% unchanged), 44% in the feces. *Half-life:* 5.8 hours.

Route	Onset	Peak	Duration
P.O.	Unknown	1 hr	Unknown

Action

Chemical effect: Drug binds directly to reverse transcriptase and blocks RNA- and DNA-dependent DNA polymerase activities.
Therapeutic effect: Inhibits HIV replication.

Available forms

Tablets: 100 mg, 200 mg

NURSING PROCESS

Assessment

- Assess patient's underlying condition before therapy and regularly thereafter.
- Be alert for adverse reactions and drug interactions.
- Monitor patient for drug-induced rash.
- Assess patient's and family's knowledge of drug therapy.

Nursing diagnoses

- Risk for impaired skin integrity related to potential adverse effects of medication
- Risk for infection related to patient's underlying condition
- Deficient knowledge related to drug therapy

Planning and implementation

- If rash develops, give diphenhydramine, hydroxyzine, or topical corticosteroids to relieve symptoms.
- Resistance develops rapidly when drug is used as monotherapy. Always give with appropriate antiretroviral therapy.
- If patient has trouble swallowing pills, add tablets to at least 3 oz (90 ml) of water, let stand for a few minutes, then stir well. Have patient drink promptly, rinse the glass, and swallow the rinse to make sure entire dose is consumed.

Patient teaching

- Tell patient to stop taking the drug and to call prescriber if he develops a severe rash or rash accompanied by symptoms such as fever, blistering, oral lesions, conjunctivitis, swelling, or muscle or joint aches.
- Tell patient that drug doesn't cure HIV-1 infection and that he may continue to acquire illnesses related to HIV-1 infection.
- Urge patient to remain under medical supervision when taking drug because long-term effects aren't known.
- Advise patient to take drug as prescribed and not to alter doses without prescriber's approval. If a dose is missed, tell him to take the next dose as soon as possible but not to double the next dose.
- Inform patient that drug may be taken with or without food.
- Tell patient with achlorhydria to take drug with an acidic beverage, such as orange or cranberry juice.
- Advise patient taking sildenafil of increased risk for sildenafil-associated adverse events, including hypotension, vision changes, and priapism. Tell him to promptly report any symptoms to prescriber. Tell him not to exceed 25 mg of sildenafil in a 48-hour period.
- Advise patient to report use of other prescription drugs, OTC medicines, or herbal remedies.

Evaluation

- Patient's skin integrity is maintained.
- Patient is free from opportunistic infections.
- Patient and family state understanding of drug therapy.

desipramine hydrochloride

(deh-SIP-rah-meen high-droh-KLOR-ighd)
Norpramin

Pharmacologic class: tricyclic antidepressant (TCA)
Therapeutic class: antidepressant
Pregnancy risk category: C

Indications and dosages

▶ **Depression.** *Adults:* Initially, 100 to 200 mg P.O. daily in divided doses; increase to maximum, 300 mg daily. Or, entire dose can be given at bedtime.
Elderly patients and adolescents: 25 to 100 mg P.O. daily in divided doses; increase gradually to maximum, 150 mg daily, if needed.

Contraindications and cautions

- Contraindicated in patients hypersensitive to drug or any of its components, in those in acute recovery phase of MI, and within 14 days of MAO inhibitor therapy.
- Use cautiously in patients taking thyroid medication and in those with CV disease, seizure disorder, glaucoma, thyroid disorder, or history of urine retention.

Lifespan: In pregnant and breast-feeding women, use cautiously. In children younger than age 12, use is contraindicated.

Adverse reactions

CNS: confusion, *dizziness, drowsiness,* EEG changes, excitation, extrapyramidal reactions, headache, nervousness, ***seizures, suicidal thinking and behavior in adolescents,*** tremors, weakness.
CV: ECG changes, hypertension, orthostatic hypotension, tachycardia.
EENT: *blurred vision,* mydriasis, tinnitus.
GI: anorexia, *constipation, dry mouth,* nausea, paralytic ileus, vomiting.
GU: urine retention.
Skin: *diaphoresis,* photosensitivity, rash, urticaria.
Other: hypersensitivity reaction, ***sudden death.***

Interactions

Drug-drug. *Anticholinergics:* May enhance anticholinergic effects. Monitor patient closely.
Barbiturates, CNS depressants: May enhance CNS depression. Avoid use together.
Cimetidine, methylphenidate: May increase desipramine levels. Monitor patient for adverse reactions.
Clonidine: May cause loss of blood pressure control with potentially life-threatening elevations in blood pressure. Don't use together.
Epinephrine, norepinephrine: May increase hypertensive effect. Use together cautiously.
MAO inhibitors: May cause severe excitation, hyperpyrexia, or seizures, usually with high dosage. Contraindicated within 14 days of MAO inhibitor therapy.
SSRIs: May inhibit the metabolism of TCAs, causing toxicity. Symptoms of TCA toxicity may persist for several weeks after stopping SSRI. At least 5 weeks may be needed when switching from fluoxetine to a tricyclic antidepressant because of the long half-life of the active and parent metabolite.
Drug-lifestyle. *Alcohol use:* May enhance CNS depression. Discourage use together.
Smoking: May lower desipramine level. Monitor patient for lack of effect; encourage smoking cessation.
Sun exposure: May increase risk of photosensitivity. Advise against unprotected or prolonged sun exposure.

Effects on lab test results

- May increase or decrease glucose level.
- May increase liver function test values.

Pharmacokinetics

Absorption: Rapid.
Distribution: Wide, including CNS. 90% protein-bound.
Metabolism: By the liver; significant first-pass effect may explain different levels in patients taking same dosage.
Excretion: Mainly in urine. *Half-life:* Unknown.

Route	Onset	Peak	Duration
P.O.	2–4 wk	4–6 hr	Unknown

Action

Chemical effect: May increase amount of norepinephrine, serotonin, or both in the CNS by blocking their reuptake by neurons.
Therapeutic effect: Relieves depression.

Available forms

Tablets: 10 mg, 25 mg, 50 mg, 75 mg, 100 mg, 150 mg

NURSING PROCESS

Assessment

- Obtain history of patient's depression before therapy, and reassess regularly.
- Be alert for adverse reactions and drug interactions.
- Assess patient's and family's knowledge of drug therapy.

Nursing diagnoses

- Ineffective coping related to depression
- Risk for injury related to drug-induced adverse reactions
- Deficient knowledge related to drug therapy

Planning and implementation

ALERT: Short-term studies in children and adolescents with major depressive disorder and other psychiatric disorders have shown an increased risk of suicidal thinking and behavior. Observe for clinical worsening, suicidality, or unusual behavior changes.

• Don't abruptly stop giving the drug. Abruptly stopping long-term therapy may cause nausea, headache, and malaise.
• Because drug produces fewer anticholinergic effects than other TCAs, it's prescribed often for patients with cardiac problems.
• Because hypertensive episodes may occur during surgery, stop drug gradually several days before surgery.
ALERT: This drug may cause sudden death in children, although the cause isn't clearly defined.
• If signs of psychosis occur or increase, reduce dosage.

Patient teaching

• Advise parents and caregivers to closely observe adolescents for suicidality, behavior changes, or worsening of depression.
• Warn patient to avoid hazardous activities until the drug's CNS effects are known. Drowsiness and dizziness usually subside after a few weeks.
• Tell patient to avoid alcohol during therapy because it may antagonize drug effects.
• Warn patient not to abruptly stop taking the drug.
• Advise patient to consult prescriber before taking other prescription drugs, OTC medications, or herbal remedies.
• Instruct patient to use sunblock, wear protective clothing, and avoid prolonged exposure to strong sunlight.

Evaluation

• Patient behavior and communication indicate improvement of depression.
• Patient has no injury as a result of drug-induced adverse reactions.
• Patient and family state understanding of drug therapy.

desloratadine

(des-lor-AT-ah-deen)
Clarinex, Clarinex RediTabs

Pharmacologic class: selective H_1-receptor antagonist
Therapeutic class: antihistamine
Pregnancy risk category: C

Indications and dosages

▶ **Perennial allergic rhinitis; chronic idiopathic urticaria.** *Adults and children age 12 and older:* 5 mg P.O. using tablets, RediTabs, or syrup.
Children ages 6 to 11 years: 2.5 mg (5 ml) syrup P.O. daily or one 2.5-mg RediTab P.O. once daily.
Children ages 1 to 5 years: 1.25 mg (2.5 ml) syrup P.O. daily.
Children ages 6 to 11 months: 1 mg (2 ml) syrup P.O. daily.
▶ **Seasonal allergic rhinitis.** *Adults and children age 12 and older:* 5 mg P.O. daily using tablets, RediTabs, or syrup.
Children ages 6 to 11: Give 2.5 mg (5 ml) syrup P.O. daily or one 2.5-mg RediTab P.O. once daily.
Children ages 2 to 5: Give 1.25 mg (2.5 ml) syrup P.O. daily.
Adjust-a-dose: In patients with hepatic or renal impairment, start with 5 mg P.O. q other day.

Contraindications and cautions

• Contraindicated in patients hypersensitive to drug or any of its components, or loratadine. Drug can't be eliminated by hemodialysis.
Lifespan: Breast-feeding women should stop nursing or stop taking the drug because drug appears in breast milk. In children younger than age 6 months, safety and effectiveness haven't been established. In elderly patients, use cautiously because they may have decreased hepatic, renal, or cardiac function or other diseases and may be taking other drugs.

Adverse reactions

CNS: dizziness, fatigue, *fever, headache,* somnolence.
CV: tachycardia.
EENT: pharyngitis, sore throat.
GI: *diarrhea,* dry mouth, dyspepsia, nausea.
GU: dysmenorrhea.
Musculoskeletal: myalgia.
Respiratory: upper respiratory tract infection.

Interactions

None reported.

Effects on lab test results

• May increase liver enzyme and bilirubin levels.

Pharmacokinetics

Absorption: Readily absorbed in plasma. Doesn't cross the blood–brain barrier. All forms equal in pharmacokinetics.
Distribution: 82% to 87% protein-bound. Active metabolite is 85% to 89% protein-bound.
Metabolism: Extensive, to inactive metabolite.
Excretion: Equal in urine and feces, mainly as metabolites. *Half-life:* 27 hours.

Route	Onset	Peak	Duration
P.O.	1 hr	3 hr	Unknown

Action

Chemical effect: Inhibits histamine release from human mast cells in vitro.
Therapeutic effect: Relieves allergy symptoms.

Available forms

Syrup: 0.5 mg/ml
Tablets: 5 mg
Tablets (orally disintegrating): 2.5 mg, 5 mg

NURSING PROCESS

Assessment

- Assess patient's condition before therapy and regularly thereafter.
- Be alert for adverse reactions.
- Assess patient's and family's knowledge of drug therapy.

Nursing diagnoses

- Ineffective health maintenance related to underlying allergic condition
- Fatigue related to drug-induced reaction
- Deficient knowledge related to drug therapy

Planning and implementation

- Drug may be taken with or without food.
- Overdose may cause somnolence and increased heart rate. If these symptoms occur, consider removing unabsorbed drug through standard measures; treat symptoms and provide supportive therapy.

Patient teaching

- Inform phenylketonuric patients that RediTabs contain phenylalanine.
- Advise patient not to exceed prescribed dosage. Doses of more than 5 mg don't increase effectiveness and may cause somnolence.
- Tell patient to report adverse effects.
- Store all forms at room temperature, not to exceed 86° F (30° C), and avoid exposure to light and moisture.
- Inform patient that orally disintegrating tablet may be taken with or without water.
- Instruct patient to remove a tablet from the blister pack and immediately place it on his tongue. The tablet will dissolve.
- Teach parents to use properly calibrated 5- to 10-ml dropper or syringe for syrup administration, not household measuring devices.

Evaluation

- Patient's allergic symptoms are relieved.
- Patient doesn't suffer any drug-induced adverse effects.
- Patient and family state understanding of drug therapy.

desmopressin acetate

(dez-moh-PREH-sin AS-ih-tayt)
DDAVP, Minirin, Stimate

Pharmacologic class: posterior pituitary hormone
Therapeutic class: antidiuretic, hemostatic
Pregnancy risk category: B

Indications and dosages

▶ **Nonnephrogenic diabetes insipidus, temporary polyuria, and polydipsia from pituitary trauma.** *Adults:* 10 to 40 mcg intranasally daily in one to three divided doses. Adjust morning and evening doses separately for adequate diurnal rhythm of water turnover. Or 0.05 mg P.O. b.i.d. Adjust each dose separately for an adequate diurnal rhythm of water turnover. Increase or decrease total oral daily dosage as needed to achieve desired response. Dosage may range from 0.1 to 1.2 mg, divided into two or three daily doses. Start oral therapy 12 hours after last intranasal dose. Or, give 2 to 4 mcg I.V. or subcutaneously daily, usually in two equally divided doses.
Children ages 3 months to 12 years: 0.05 to 0.3 ml intranasally daily in one or two doses.
Children age 4 and older: Begin with 0.05 mg oral form P.O. b.i.d. Adjust each dose separately for an adequate diurnal rhythm of water turnover. Increase or decrease total oral daily dosage to achieve desired response. Dosages may range

from 0.1 to 1.2 mg, divided into two or three daily doses. Start oral therapy 12 hours after the last intranasal dose.
Children younger than age 4: Adjust dosage of oral form individually to prevent an excessive decrease in blood osmolality.

▶ **Hemophilia A and von Willebrand disease.** *Adults and children:* 0.3 mcg/kg diluted in normal saline solution and infused I.V. over 15 to 30 minutes. May repeat dose, if needed, based on laboratory response and patient's condition. Intranasal dose is 1 spray (of solution containing 1.5 mg/ml) into each nostril to provide total of 300 mcg.
Adults and children weighing less than 50 kg (110 lb): 1 spray into a single nostril (150 mcg).

▶ **Primary nocturnal enuresis.** *Children age 6 and older:* Initially, 20 mcg intranasally at bedtime. Adjust dosage according to response. Maximum, 40 mcg daily. Or 0.2 mg P.O. at bedtime. Adjust dose up to 0.6 mg P.O. to achieve desired response. Oral therapy may start 24 hours after last intranasal dose.

I.V. administration

- For adults and children weighing more than 10 kg (22 lb), dilute with 50 ml sterile physiologic saline solution. For children weighing 10 kg or less, use 10 ml of diluent.
- Inspect for particulate matter and discoloration before infusing drug.
- Monitor blood pressure and pulse during infusion.

⊗ **Incompatibilities**
None reported.

Contraindications and cautions

- Contraindicated in patients hypersensitive to drug (or any of its components), and in those with type IIB von Willebrand disease.
- Use cautiously in patients with coronary artery insufficiency or hypertensive CV disease and in those with conditions linked to fluid and electrolyte imbalance, such as cystic fibrosis, because these patients are prone to hyponatremia.

Lifespan: In pregnant and breast-feeding women, use cautiously. In infants younger than age 3 months, use of drug isn't recommended because of their increased tendency to develop fluid imbalance. In children younger than age 12, safety of parenteral form of drug hasn't been established for management of diabetes insipidus.

Adverse reactions

CNS: headache.
CV: slight rise in blood pressure.
EENT: epistaxis, nasal congestion, rhinitis, sore throat.
GI: abdominal cramps, nausea.
GU: vulvar pain.
Respiratory: cough.
Other: flushing, local erythema, swelling or burning after injection.

Interactions

Drug-drug. *Carbamazepine, chlorpropamide:* May potentiate effects of desmopressin. Monitor patient.
Demeclocycline, epinephrine, heparin, lithium: May decrease response to desmopressin. Monitor patient closely.
Vasopressors: May potentiate pressor effect of these drugs. Use large intranasal or parenteral doses cautiously.
Drug-lifestyle. *Alcohol use:* May increase risk of adverse effects. Discourage use together.

Effects on lab test results

None reported.

Pharmacokinetics

Absorption: After intranasal use, 10% to 20% by nasal mucosa. After subcutaneous use, unknown. After P.O. use, minimal.
Distribution: Unknown.
Metabolism: Unknown.
Excretion: Unknown. *Half-life (injection):* Fast phase, about 8 minutes; slow phase, 75.5 minutes. *Half-life (intranasal):* 3.3 to 3.5 hours. *Half-life (oral):* 1.5 to 2.5 hours.

Route	Onset	Peak	Duration
P.O.	1 hr	4–7 hr	8–12 hr
I.V.	15–30 min	½–2 hr	4–12 hr
SubQ	Unknown	Unknown	Unknown
Intranasal	≤ 1 hr	1–5 hr	8–12 hr

Action

Chemical effect: Increases flow of adenosine monophosphate and water through the kidneys, promoting reabsorption of water and producing concentrated urine (ADH effect). Releases factor VIII from plasma.
Therapeutic effect: Decreases diuresis and promotes clotting.

Available forms

Injection: 4 mcg/ml
Nasal solution: 0.1 mg/ml, 1.5 mg/ml
Nasal spray: 0.1 mg/ml (10 mcg/spray)
Tablets: 0.1 mg, 0.2 mg.

NURSING PROCESS

Assessment

- Obtain history of patient's underlying condition before therapy.
- Monitor effectiveness for diabetes insipidus or relief of symptoms of other disorders by checking patient's fluid intake and output, serum and urine osmolality, and urine specific gravity.
- Be alert for adverse reactions and drug interactions.
- Monitor patient carefully for hypertension during high-dose therapy.
- Assess patient's and family's knowledge of drug therapy.

Nursing diagnoses

- Deficient fluid volume related to underlying condition
- Acute pain related to drug-induced headache
- Deficient knowledge related to drug therapy

Planning and implementation

- When giving drug subcutaneously, rotate injection sites.
- Follow manufacturer's instructions exactly for intranasal administration.
- Ensure nasal passages are intact, clean, and free of obstruction before intranasal use.
- Intranasal use can cause changes in nasal mucosa, resulting in erratic, unreliable absorption. Report worsening condition to prescriber, who may prescribe injectable DDAVP.
- Don't use drug to treat severe cases of von Willebrand disease or hemophilia A with factor VIII levels of 0% to 5%.
- Patients may be switched from intranasal to subcutaneous form, such as during episodes of rhinorrhea. Give 1/10 or 1/4 of their usual nasal dose subcutaneously.
- When drug is used to treat diabetes insipidus, adjust dosage according to patient's fluid output. Adjust morning and evening doses separately for adequate diurnal rhythm of water turnover.

ALERT: Don't confuse desmopressin with vasopressin.

Patient teaching

- Instruct patient to clear nasal passages before using intranasal form of the drug.
- Teach patient and caregiver correct method of administration. Patient may have trouble measuring and inhaling drug into nostrils.
- Advise patient to report conditions such as nasal congestion, allergic rhinitis, or upper respiratory tract infection because dose adjustment may be required.
- Teach patient using subcutaneous desmopressin to rotate injection sites to avoid tissue damage.
- Warn patient to drink only enough water to satisfy thirst.
- Inform patient that when treating hemophilia A and von Willebrand disease, giving desmopressin may avoid hazards of using blood products.
- Advise patient to wear or carry medical identification indicating use of drug.

Evaluation

- Patient achieves normal fluid and electrolyte balance.
- Patient states that headache is relieved with mild analgesic.
- Patient and family state understanding of drug therapy.

dexamethasone

(deks-oh-METH-uh-sohn)
Decadron*, Dexamethasone Intensol*, Dexasone ♦, Dexpak, Mymethasone*, Oradexon ♦

dexamethasone acetate

Cortastat LA, Decaject-L.A., Dexasone L.A., Dexone L.A., Solurex-LA

dexamethasone sodium phosphate

Cortastat, Dalalone, Decadron Phosphate, Decaject, Dexone, Hexadrol Phosphate, Solurex

Pharmacologic class: glucocorticoid
Therapeutic class: anti-inflammatory, immunosuppressant
Pregnancy risk category: NR

Indications and dosages

▶ **Cerebral edema.** *Adults:* Initially, 10 mg dexamethasone sodium phosphate I.V. Then 4 mg I.M. q 6 hours until symptoms subside (usually 2 to 4 days). Then taper down over 5 to 7 days.

▶ **Inflammatory conditions, allergic reactions, neoplasias.** *Adults:* 4 mg dexamethasone sodium phosphate I.M. as a single dose. Continue maintenance therapy with dexamethasone tablets, 1.5 mg P.O. b.i.d. for 2 days; then 0.75 mg P.O. b.i.d. for 1 day; then 0.75 mg P.O. once daily for 2 days; then stop drug. Or 4 to 16 mg dexamethasone acetate I.M. into joint or soft tissue q 1 to 3 weeks. Or 0.8 to 1.6 mg into lesions q 1 to 3 weeks.

▶ **Shock.** *Adults:* 1 to 6 mg/kg dexamethasone sodium phosphate I.V. as single dose or 40 mg I.V. q 2 to 6 hours, as needed. Or 20 mg I.V. as a single dose, followed by continuous infusion of 3 mg/kg q 24 hours. Limit high-dose therapy to 48 to 72 hours.

▶ **Suppression test for Cushing syndrome.** *Adults:* After determining baseline 24-hour urine levels of 17-hydroxycorticosteroids, 0.5 mg P.O. q 6 hours for 48 hours; perform 24-hour urine collection to determine 17-hydroxycorticosteroid excretion again during second 24 hours of dexamethasone administration. Or 1 mg P.O. as a single dose at 11 PM. Draw blood for cortisol level at 8 AM the following day.

▶ **Tuberculous meningitis.** *Adults:* 8 to 12 mg (phosphate) I.M. daily tapered over 6 to 8 weeks.

▶ **Bacterial meningitis‡.** *Adults, infants, and children:* 0.15 mg/kg (phosphate) I.V. q.i.d. for the first 2 to 4 days of anti-infective therapy.

▶ **To prevent hyaline membrane disease in premature infants‡.** *Adults:* 4 mg dexamethasone sodium phosphate I.M. t.i.d. to mother for 2 days before delivery.

▶ **To prevent chemotherapy-induced nausea and vomiting‡.** *Adults:* 10 to 20 mg I.V. before giving chemotherapy. Additional doses (individualized for each patient and usually lower than initial dose) may be given I.V. or P.O. for 24 to 72 hours following cancer chemotherapy.

I.V. administration

- When giving as direct injection, inject undiluted over at least 1 minute.
- When giving as intermittent or continuous infusion, dilute solution in normal saline solution or D_5W. For continuous infusion, change solution every 24 hours.

⊗ **Incompatibilities**
Ciprofloxacin, daunorubicin, diphenhydramine, doxapram, doxorubicin, glycopyrrolate, idarubicin, midazolam, vancomycin.

Contraindications and cautions

- Contraindicated in patients hypersensitive to drug or any of its components and in those with systemic fungal infections.
- Use cautiously in patients with seizures, emotional instability, psychotic tendencies, recent MI, thromboembolic disorders, heart failure, hypertension, GI ulcer, diverticulitis, nonspecific ulcerative colitis, recent intestinal anastomoses, renal disease, ocular herpes simplex, cirrhosis, diabetes mellitus, hypothyroidism, myasthenia gravis, osteoporosis, or tuberculosis. Because some forms contain sulfite preservatives, use cautiously in patients sensitive to sulfites.

Lifespan: In pregnant women, use cautiously. In breast-feeding women, drug isn't recommended. In children, long-term use of drug may delay growth and maturation.

Adverse reactions

CNS: *euphoria, insomnia,* pseudotumor cerebri, psychotic behavior, ***seizures,*** headache, vertigo.
CV: ***arrhythmias,*** edema, ***heart failure,*** hypertension, ***thromboembolism.***
EENT: cataracts, glaucoma.
GI: GI irritation, increased appetite, ***pancreatitis,*** *peptic ulceration.*
GU: menstrual irregularities.
Metabolic: carbohydrate intolerance, hyperglycemia, hypokalemia, negative nitrogen balance caused by protein catabolism.
Musculoskeletal: growth suppression in children, muscle weakness, osteoporosis.
Skin: acne, allergic dermatitis, angioneurotic edema, atrophy at I.M. injection sites, delayed wound healing, hirsutism, skin eruptions, thin fragile skin, urticaria.
Other: ***acute adrenal insufficiency*** (may follow abrupt withdrawal after long-term therapy or such increased stress as infection, surgery, or trauma), cushingoid state (moonface, buffalo hump, central obesity), susceptibility to infections.

Interactions

Drug-drug. *Antidiabetics, including insulin:* May decrease corticosteroid response. May need dosage adjustment.
Aspirin, indomethacin, other NSAIDs: May increase risk of GI distress and bleeding. Give together cautiously.
Barbiturates, phenytoin, rifampin: May decrease corticosteroid effect. Increase corticosteroid dosage.
Digoxin: May increase risk of arrhythmia from hypokalemia. May need dosage adjustment.
Oral anticoagulants: May alter dosage requirements. Monitor PT and INR closely.
Potassium-depleting drugs: May enhance potassium-wasting effects of dexamethasone. Monitor potassium level.
Salicylates: May decrease salicylate level. Monitor patient for lack of therapeutic effects.
Skin-test antigens: May decrease response of skin-test antigens. Defer skin testing until therapy is completed.
Toxoids, vaccines: May decrease antibody response and increase risk of neurologic complications. Avoid use together.
Drug-lifestyle. *Alcohol use:* May increase risk of gastric irritation and GI ulceration. Discourage use together.

Effects on lab test results

- May increase glucose and cholesterol levels. May decrease potassium, calcium, T_3, and T_4 levels.
- May cause false negative dexamethasone suppression test in patients taking indomethacin.

Pharmacokinetics

Absorption: For P.O. use, good. For injections, depends on location.
Distribution: To muscle, liver, skin, intestines, and kidneys. Bound weakly to transcortin and albumin. Only unbound portion is active.
Metabolism: In liver to inactive glucuronide and sulfate metabolites.
Excretion: Inactive metabolites and small amounts of unmetabolized drug by kidneys. Insignificant in feces. *Half-life:* About 1 to 2 days.

Route	Onset	Peak	Duration
P.O.	1–2 hr	1–2 hr	2½ days
I.V., I.M.	≤ 1 hr	1 hr	2 days–3 wk

Action

Chemical effect: May stabilize leukocyte lysosomal membranes; stimulate bone marrow; and influence protein, fat, and carbohydrate metabolism.
Therapeutic effect: Relieves cerebral edema, reduces inflammation and immune response, and reverses shock.

Available forms

dexamethasone
Elixir: 0.5 mg/5 ml
Oral solution: 0.5 mg/5 ml, 1 mg/ml
Tablets: 0.25 mg, 0.5 mg, 0.75 mg, 1 mg, 1.5 mg, 2 mg, 4 mg, 6 mg
dexamethasone acetate
Injection: 8 mg/ml, 16 mg/ml suspension
dexamethasone sodium phosphate
Injection: 4 mg/ml, 10 mg/ml, 20 mg/ml, 24 mg/ml

NURSING PROCESS

Assessment

- Obtain history of patient's underlying condition before therapy.
- Monitor patient's weight, blood pressure, glucose level, and electrolyte levels.
- Look for adverse reactions and drug interactions. Most adverse reactions to corticosteroids are dosage-dependent.
- Watch for depression or psychotic episodes, especially in high-dose therapy.
- Assess patient's and family's knowledge of drug therapy.

Nursing diagnoses

- Ineffective health maintenance related to underlying condition
- Risk for injury related to drug-induced adverse reactions
- Deficient knowledge related to drug therapy

Planning and implementation

- For better results and less toxicity, give once-daily dose in the morning.
- Give with food when possible.
- Give I.M. deep into gluteal muscle. Rotate injection sites to prevent muscle atrophy.
- If possible, avoid giving drug subcutaneously because atrophy and sterile abscesses may occur.
- Always adjust to lowest effective dose.

• Corticosteroids may mask signs of infection and new infections may arise during their use.

ALERT: When stopping drug after long-term use, reduce dose gradually. Stopping drug abruptly may cause rebound inflammation, fatigue, weakness, arthralgia, fever, dizziness, lethargy, depression, fainting, orthostatic hypotension, dyspnea, anorexia, or hypoglycemia, or may be fatal.

ALERT: Give patient low-sodium diet high in potassium and protein. Also, give potassium supplements as directed.

• If patient's stress level (physical or psychological) increases, notify prescriber and increase dose.

• If patient has adverse reaction, notify prescriber, treat symptoms, and provide supportive therapy.

ALERT: Don't confuse dexamethasone with desoximetasone.

Patient teaching

• Tell patient not to abruptly stop taking the drug because this may be fatal.

• Teach patient the early signs of adrenal insufficiency (fatigue, muscle weakness, joint pain, fever, anorexia, nausea, dyspnea, dizziness, and fainting).

• Instruct patient to wear or carry medical identification that indicates need for supplemental systemic glucocorticoids during stress, especially as dose is decreased.

• Warn patient receiving long-term therapy about cushingoid symptoms and the need to notify prescriber about sudden weight gain or swelling.

• Warn patient about easy bruising.

• Advise patient receiving long-term therapy to consider exercise or physical therapy. Give vitamin D or calcium supplements.

• Advise patient receiving long-term therapy to have periodic ophthalmologic examinations.

Evaluation

• Patient's condition improves with drug therapy.

• Patient has no injury as a result of drug therapy.

• Patient and family state understanding of drug therapy.

dexmedetomidine hydrochloride

(dex-meh-dih-TOE-mih-deen high-droh-KLOR-ighd)

Precedex

Pharmacologic class: selective $alpha_2$-adrenoreceptor agonist with sedative properties
Therapeutic class: sedative
Pregnancy risk category: C

Indications and dosages

▶ **Sedation of initially intubated and mechanically ventilated patients in the ICU.** *Adults:* Loading infusion of 1 mcg/kg I.V. over 10 minutes; then a maintenance infusion of 0.2 to 0.7 mcg/kg/hour for up to 24 hours; adjust to achieve the desired level of sedation.

Adjust-a-dose: In elderly patients and those with renal or hepatic failure, reduce dosage.

I.V. administration

• Dilute in normal saline solution. To prepare the infusion, withdraw 2 ml of drug and add to 48 ml of normal saline injection to a total of 50 ml. Shake gently to mix well.

• Don't give through the same I.V. line with blood or plasma because physical compatibility hasn't been established.

• Administer using a controlled infusion device.

• Infusion is compatible with lactated Ringer's solution, D_5W, normal saline solution, 20% mannitol, many anesthetic agents, atropine sulfate, morphine sulfate, and plasma substitute.

• Don't give infusion for longer than 24 hours.

⊗ **Incompatibilities**

Amphotericin B, blood, diazepam, plasma.

Contraindications and cautions

• Contraindicated in patients with hypersensitivity to dexmedetomidine.

• Use cautiously in patients with chronic hypertension, diabetes mellitus, advanced heart block, or renal or hepatic impairment.

Lifespan: In pregnant women, use only if potential benefits to the woman outweigh risks to the fetus because drug may be toxic to fetus. In breast-feeding women, use cautiously. In children, use isn't recommended. In elderly patients, use cautiously.

Adverse reactions

CNS: pain, fever.
CV: ***arrhythmias, bradycardia,*** *hypotension, hypertension.*
GI: *nausea,* thirst.
GU: oliguria.
Hematologic: anemia, leukocytosis.
Respiratory: ***hypoxia,*** pleural effusion, ***pulmonary edema.***
Other: infection.

Interactions

Drug-drug. *Anesthetics, hypnotics, opioids, sedatives:* May enhance effects. May need to reduce dexmedetomidine dose.

Effects on lab test results

- May decrease hemoglobin level and hematocrit.
- May increase WBC count.

Pharmacokinetics

Absorption: Given I.V.
Distribution: Rapid and wide. 94% protein-bound.
Metabolism: Almost complete.
Excretion: 95% in urine and 4% in feces. *Half-life:* About 2 hours.

Route	Onset	Peak	Duration
I.V.	Unknown	Unknown	Unknown

Action

Chemical effect: Selectively stimulates $alpha_2$-adrenoceptors in the CNS.
Therapeutic effect: Produces sedation of initially intubated and mechanically ventilated patients.

Available forms

Injection: 100 mcg/ml in 2-ml vials and 2-ml ampules

NURSING PROCESS

Assessment

- Assess renal and hepatic function before administration, particularly in elderly patients.
- Assess patient's response to drug. Some patients may stir and be alert when stimulated. This doesn't necessarily indicate lack of effectiveness.
- Look for adverse reactions and drug interactions.
- Assess patient's and family's knowledge of drug therapy.

Nursing diagnoses

- Risk for injury related to drug-induced adverse reactions
- Impaired spontaneous ventilation related to underlying disease process
- Deficient knowledge related to drug therapy

Planning and implementation

ALERT: Use a controlled infusion device at the rate calculated for patient's body weight.
- Continuously monitor cardiac condition.
- Drug may be continuously infused in mechanically ventilated patients before, during, and after extubation. Drug doesn't need to be stopped before extubation.

Patient teaching
- Tell patient that he'll be sedated while the drug is given, but that he may wake when stimulated.
- Tell patient that he'll be closely monitored and attended while sedated.

Evaluation

- Patient has no injury as a result of drug-induced adverse reactions.
- Patient regains spontaneous ventilation.
- Patient and family state understanding of drug therapy.

dexmethylphenidate hydrochloride

(dex-meth-il-FEN-uh-date high-droh-KLOR-ighd)
Focalin, Focalin XR

Pharmacologic class: CNS stimulant
Therapeutic class: CNS stimulant
Pregnancy risk category: C
Controlled substance schedule: II

Indications and dosages

▶ **Attention deficit hyperactivity disorder (ADHD).**
Immediate-release tablets
Children age 6 and older: For patients who aren't taking racemic methylphenidate or who

are taking another stimulant, start with 2.5 mg P.O. twice daily, at least 4 hours apart. For patients who are being switched from methylphenidate, start with one-half of the current methylphenidate dosage. Additionally, adjust dose weekly in increments of 2.5 to 5 mg daily to maximum of 20 mg daily in two divided doses.

Extended-release capsules

Adults: If patient takes neither dexmethylphenidate nor methylphenidate or takes a stimulant other than methylphenidate, 10 mg P.O. once daily in the morning. May adjust by 10 mg weekly. If patient takes methylphenidate, start with half the total daily methylphenidate dose. If patient takes immediate-release dexmethylphenidate, may switch to same daily dose of extended-release form. Maximum, 20 mg daily.

Children age 6 and older: If patient takes neither dexmethylphenidate nor methylphenidate, or takes a stimulant other than methylphenidate, 5 mg P.O. once daily in the morning. May adjust by 5 mg weekly. If patient takes methylphenidate, start with half the total daily methylphenidate dose. If patient takes immediate-release dexmethylphenidate, may switch to same daily dose of extended-release form. Maximum, 20 mg daily.

Contraindications and cautions

- Contraindicated in patients hypersensitive to drug or any of its components. Also contraindicated in patients with severe anxiety, tension, agitation, or glaucoma and in those who have motor tics or a family history or diagnosis of Tourette syndrome. Also contraindicated within 14 days of MAO inhibitor therapy because hypertensive crisis may occur. Don't use to treat severe depression or to prevent or treat normal fatigue states. Don't use drug in children or adolescents with structural cardiac abnormalities or other serious heart problems.
- Use cautiously in patients with a history of seizures, drug abuse, alcoholism, psychiatric illness, bipolar disorder, depression, or family history of suicide. Also use cautiously in patients whose underlying condition may be worsened by an increase in blood pressure or heart rate (such as those with hypertension, heart failure, recent MI).

Lifespan: In pregnant women, use only if the potential benefits to the woman outweigh the risks to the fetus. In breast-feeding women, use cautiously because it's unknown if drug appears in breast milk. In children younger than age 6, don't use.

Adverse reactions

CNS: blurred vision, fever, growth suppression, insomnia, nervousness, psychosis, dizziness, drowsiness.
CV: hypertension, tachycardia, angina, ***arrhythmia.***
GI: *abdominal pain,* anorexia, nausea.
Hematologic: anemia, ***leukopenia.***
Hepatic: abnormal liver function.
Metabolic: weight loss.
Musculoskeletal: arthralgia, twitching (motor or vocal tics).
Skin: scalp hair loss.

Interactions

Drug-drug. *Anticoagulants, anticonvulsants, SSRIs, tricyclic antidepressants:* May inhibit metabolism of these drugs. May need to decrease dosage of these drugs; monitor drug levels.
Antihypertensives: May decrease effectiveness of these drugs. Use together cautiously; monitor blood pressure.
Clonidine, other centrally acting alpha$_2$ agonists: May cause serious adverse effects. Use together cautiously.
MAO inhibitors: May increase risk of hypertensive crisis. Avoid use within 14 days of using MAO inhibitors.

Effects on lab test results

- May decrease hemoglobin level and hematocrit.
- May increase liver function test values. May decrease WBC count.

Pharmacokinetics

Absorption: Food delays rate of peak level but doesn't affect the amount absorbed.
Distribution: Rapid.
Metabolism: Extensive via de-esterification. Doesn't inhibit the cytochrome P-450 system. No active metabolites.
Excretion: 90% in urine. *Half-life:* About 2 hours.

Route	Onset	Peak	Duration
P.O.			
immediate-release	Unknown	1–1½ hr	Unknown
extended-release	Unknown	1–4 hr; 4½–7 hr	Unknown

Action

Chemical effect: May block presynaptic reuptake of norepinephrine and dopamine and increase the release of these neurotransmitters.
Therapeutic effect: Increases attention span and decreases hyperactivity and impulsiveness related to ADHD.

Available forms

Capsules (extended-release): 5 mg, 10 mg, 20 mg
Tablets: 2.5 mg, 5 mg, 10 mg

NURSING PROCESS

Assessment

- Diagnosis must be based on complete history and evaluation of the child in consultation with psychological, educational, and social specialists.
- Obtain a detailed patient history, including a family history for mental disorders, family suicide, ventricular arrhythmias, or sudden death.
- Monitor blood pressure and pulse routinely during drug therapy.
- Look for adverse reactions.
- Check CBC with differential and platelet counts during long-term use.

Nursing diagnoses

- Ineffective health maintenance related to underlying condition
- Compromised family coping because of patient's underlying hyperactivity condition
- Deficient knowledge of drug therapy

Planning and implementation

- Drug is meant to be an adjunct to comprehensive therapy program that includes psychological, educational, and social support.
- Drug contains only the active isomer required to effectively manage the symptoms of ADHD, at half the dose of Ritalin.
- Growth may be suppressed with long-term stimulant use. Monitor children for growth and weight gain. If growth is suppressed or if weight gain is lower than expected, stop giving the drug.
- If symptoms are aggravated or adverse reactions occur, reduce dosage or stop drug.
- If seizures occur, stop giving the drug.
- Symptoms of overdose include vomiting, agitation, tremors, hyperreflexia, muscle twitching, convulsions, euphoria, confusion, hallucinations, delirium, sweating, flushing, headache, hyperpyrexia, tachycardia, palpitations, cardiac arrhythmias, hypertension, mydriasis, and dry mucous membranes. Give supportive care and protection against self-injury and additional overstimulation.
- Stop drug if symptoms don't improve after 1 month.

Patient teaching

ALERT: Warn patient that misuse of amphetamines can cause serious adverse cardiovascular events, including sudden death.

- Caution patient that drug may cause blurred vision or trouble focusing. Urge patient to use caution during activities that require a clear visual field.
- Inform parents that children may show increased aggression or hostility. Urge them to report worsening behavior.
- Advise parents to monitor child's height and weight and to tell prescriber if they suspect any growth suppression.
- If patient can't swallow capsules, tell him to empty the contents onto a spoonful of applesauce and eat immediately.

ALERT: Tell patient or parent not to cut, crush, or chew contents of extended-release capsules.

- Advise patient to take drug at the same time every day at the prescribed dose. Tell patient to report any adverse reactions to prescriber immediately.

Evaluation

- Patient responds positively to drug therapy.
- Patient and family are effectively coping with patient's underlying condition.
- Patient and family state understanding of drug therapy.

dextran, high–molecular-weight (dextran 70, dextran 75)

(DEKS-tran, high moh-LEH-kyoo-ler wayt)

Dextran 70, Dextran 75, Gentran 70, Macrodex

Pharmacologic class: glucose polymer
Therapeutic class: plasma volume expander
Pregnancy risk category: C

Indications and dosages

▶ **Plasma expander.** *Adults:* 30 g (500 ml of 6% solution) I.V. In emergencies, may give 1.2 to 2.4 g (20 to 40 ml)/minute. In normovolemic or nearly normovolemic patients, don't infuse faster than 240 mg (4 ml)/minute. Don't give more than 1.2 g/kg during the first 24 hours of therapy. Actual dosage depends on amount of fluid loss and resulting hemoconcentration and must be determined for each patient. *Children:*‡ Don't exceed total dosage of 20 ml/kg.

I.V. administration

- Use D_5W instead of normal saline solution because drug is hazardous for patients with heart failure, especially when given in normal saline solution.
- Give 20 ml of dextran 1 (containing 150 mg/ml) I.V. over 60 seconds 1 to 2 minutes before I.V. infusion of dextran, to protect against drug-induced anaphylaxis.
- Observe patient closely during early phase of infusion, when most anaphylactic reactions occur.
- Store drug at constant 77° F (25° C). Precipitate may form in storage. Heat to dissolve.

⊗ **Incompatibilities**

Any other I.V. drug added to a bottle of dextran, ascorbic acid, phytonadione, promethazine, protein hydrolysate.

Contraindications and cautions

- Contraindicated in patients hypersensitive to drug and in those with marked hemostatic defects, marked cardiac decompensation, renal disease with severe oliguria or anuria, hypervolemic conditions, or severe bleeding disorders.
- Use cautiously in patients with active hemorrhage, thrombocytopenia, impaired renal clearance, chronic liver disease, or abdominal conditions, and in patients undergoing bowel surgery.

Lifespan: In pregnant women, use cautiously. Breast-feeding women should stop nursing or stop the drug. In children, safety and effectiveness haven't been established.

Adverse reactions

CNS: fever.
CV: fluid overload, thrombophlebitis.
EENT: nasal congestion.
GI: nausea, vomiting.
GU: ***anuria,*** increased specific gravity and viscosity of urine, oliguria, ***tubular stasis and blocking.***
Musculoskeletal: arthralgia.
Skin: urticaria.
Other: ***anaphylaxis,*** hypersensitivity reactions.

Interactions

Drug-drug. *Abciximab, aspirin, heparin, thrombolytics, warfarin:* May increase bleeding. Use together cautiously; monitor patient for bleeding.

Effects on lab test results

- May increase ALT and AST levels. May decrease hemoglobin level and hematocrit.
- May increase bleeding time.

Pharmacokinetics

Absorption: Given I.V.
Distribution: Throughout vascular system.
Metabolism: Drug molecules with molecular weights above 50,000 are degraded to glucose at rate of about 70 to 90 mg/kg/day.
Excretion: Drug molecules with molecular weights below 50,000 in urine. *Half-life:* Unknown.

Route	Onset	Peak	Duration
I.V.	Immediate	Immediate	Unknown

Action

Chemical effect: Expands plasma volume by way of colloidal osmotic effect, drawing fluid from interstitial to intravascular space, providing fluid replacement.
Therapeutic effect: Expands plasma volume.

Available forms

Injection: Dextran 70 in normal saline solution or D_5W; 6% dextran 75 in normal saline solution or D_5W

NURSING PROCESS

Assessment

- Obtain history of patient's underlying condition and hydration before therapy, and reassess regularly. Frequently assess vital signs, fluid intake and output, and urine or serum osmolarity levels.
- Be alert for adverse reactions.
- Watch for circulatory overload and rise in central venous pressure. Plasma expansion is slightly greater than volume infused.
- Monitor hemoglobin level and hematocrit.
- Assess patient's and family's knowledge of drug therapy.

Nursing diagnoses

- Decreased cardiac output related to underlying condition
- Risk for injury related to potential for drug-induced hypersensitivity reaction
- Deficient knowledge related to drug therapy

Planning and implementation

- May significantly suppress platelet function with doses of 15 ml/kg.
- If oliguria or anuria occurs or isn't relieved by infusion, stop dextran and give loop diuretic.
- If hematocrit values fall below 30% by volume, notify prescriber.
- Drug may interfere with analyses of blood grouping, crossmatching, and bilirubin, glucose, and protein levels.

ALERT: Low– and high–molecular-weight dextrans aren't interchangeable. Verify preparation before use.

Patient teaching

- Inform patient or family about drug therapy.
- Instruct patient to notify prescriber if adverse reactions, such as itching, occur.

Evaluation

- Patient's vital signs and urine output return to normal.
- Patient doesn't develop hypersensitivity reaction to drug.
- Patient and family state understanding of drug therapy.

dextran, low–molecular-weight (dextran 40)

(DEKS-tran, LOH moh-LEH-kyoo-ler wayt)

Dextran 40, Gentran 40, 10% LMD, Rheomacrodex

Pharmacologic class: glucose polymer
Therapeutic class: plasma volume expander
Pregnancy risk category: C

Indications and dosages

▶ **Plasma volume expansion.** *Adults:* Dosage by I.V. infusion depends on amount of fluid loss. Initially, 10 ml/kg of dextran infused rapidly with central venous pressure monitoring; remainder of dose given slowly. Total dosage not to exceed 20 ml/kg in the first 24 hours. If therapy is continued longer than 24 hours, don't exceed 10 ml/kg daily. Continue for no longer than 5 days.

▶ **To prevent venous thrombosis.** *Adults:* 10 ml/kg (500 to 1,000 ml) I.V. on day of procedure; 500 ml on days 2 and 3.

▶ **Hemodiluent in extracorporeal circulation.** *Adults:* 10 to 20 ml/kg added to perfusion circuit. Total dosage not to exceed 20 ml/kg.

I.V. administration

- Use D_5W solution instead of normal saline solution because drug is hazardous for patients with heart failure, especially when given in normal saline solution.
- Prescriber may order dextran 1, a dextran adjunct, to protect against drug-induced anaphylaxis. Give 20 ml of dextran 1 (containing 150 mg/ml) I.V. over 60 seconds, 1 to 2 minutes before I.V. infusion of dextran.
- Observe patient closely during early phase of infusion, when most anaphylactic reactions occur.
- Store at constant 77° F (25° C). Precipitate may form during storage. Heat to dissolve.
- Discard partially used containers.

⊗ **Incompatibilities**

Any other I.V. drug added to a bottle of dextran, ascorbic acid, phytonadione, promethazine, protein hydrolysate.

Contraindications and cautions

- Contraindicated in patients hypersensitive to drug and in those with marked hemostatic defects, marked cardiac decompensation, and renal disease with severe oliguria or anuria.
- Use cautiously in patients with active hemorrhage, thrombocytopenia, or diabetes mellitus.

Lifespan: In pregnant women, use cautiously. Breast-feeding women should stop breast-feeding or not use the drug. In children, safety and effectiveness haven't been established.

Adverse reactions

CV: thrombophlebitis.
GI: nausea, vomiting.
GU: increased urine viscosity, ***tubular stasis and blocking.***
Hematologic: anemia.
Skin: urticaria.
Other: ***anaphylaxis,*** hypersensitivity reactions.

Interactions

None significant.

Effects on lab test results

- May increase ALT and AST levels. May decrease hemoglobin level and hematocrit.
- May increase bleeding time.

Pharmacokinetics

Absorption: Given I.V.
Distribution: Throughout vascular system.
Metabolism: Drug molecules with molecular weights above 50,000 are degraded to glucose at about 70 to 90 mg/kg/day.
Excretion: By kidneys for drug molecules with molecular weights below 50,000. *Half-life:* Unknown.

Route	Onset	Peak	Duration
I.V.	Immediate	Immediate	≤ 3 hr

Action

Chemical effect: Expands plasma volume by colloidal osmotic effect, drawing fluid from interstitial to intravascular space, providing fluid replacement.
Therapeutic effect: Expands plasma volume.

Available forms

Injection: 10% dextran 40 in D_5W or normal saline solution

NURSING PROCESS

Assessment

- Obtain history of patient's underlying condition and hydration before therapy, and reassess regularly. Frequently assess vital signs, fluid intake and output, and urine or serum osmolarity levels.
- Be alert for adverse reactions.
- Watch for circulatory overload and rise in central venous pressure. Plasma expansion is slightly greater than volume infused.
- Check hemoglobin level and hematocrit.
- Assess patient's and family's knowledge of drug therapy.

Nursing diagnoses

- Decreased cardiac output related to underlying condition
- Risk for injury related to potential for drug-induced hypersensitivity reaction
- Deficient knowledge related to drug therapy

Planning and implementation

- If oliguria or anuria occurs or isn't relieved by infusion, stop dextran and give loop diuretic.
- If hematocrit falls below 30% by volume, notify prescriber.
- Drug may interfere with analyses of blood grouping, crossmatching, and bilirubin, glucose, and protein levels.

ALERT: Low– and high–molecular-weight dextrans aren't interchangeable. Verify preparation before use.

Patient teaching

- Tell patient and family about therapy.
- Instruct patient to notify prescriber if adverse reactions, such as itching, occur.

Evaluation

- Patient's vital signs and urine output return to normal.
- Patient has no hypersensitivity reaction to drug.
- Patient and family state understanding of drug therapy.

dextroamphetamine sulfate

(deks-troh-am-FET-uh-meen SUL-fayt)

Dexedrine*, Dexedrine Spansule, DextroStat

Pharmacologic class: amphetamine
Therapeutic class: CNS stimulant
Pregnancy risk category: C
Controlled substance schedule: II

Indications and dosages

▶ **Narcolepsy.** *Adults:* 5 to 60 mg P.O. daily in divided doses.
Children age 12 and older: 10 mg P.O. daily; increase by 10-mg increments weekly until desired response occurs or adult dose is reached.
Children ages 6 to 11: Give 5 mg P.O. daily; increase by 5-mg increments weekly until desired response occurs. Give first dose on awakening, additional doses (one or two) at intervals of 4 to 6 hours.

▶ **Attention deficit hyperactivity disorder.** *Children age 6 and older:* 5 mg P.O. once daily or b.i.d.; increase by 5-mg increments weekly, as needed.
Children ages 3 to 5: Give 2.5 mg P.O. daily; increase by 2.5-mg increments weekly, as needed. In rare cases, more than 40 mg daily is needed.

▶ **Short-term adjunct in exogenous obesity ‡.** *Adults:* 5 to 30 mg P.O. daily 30 to 60 minutes before meals in divided doses of 5 to 10 mg. Or one 10- or 15-mg sustained-released capsule daily as a single dose in the morning.

Contraindications and cautions

- Contraindicated in patients hypersensitive to sympathomimetic amines and those with idiosyncratic reactions to them; within 14 days of MAO inhibitor use; and in those with hyperthyroidism, glaucoma, advanced arteriosclerosis, or a history of drug abuse.
- Don't use in children or adolescents with structural cardiac abnormalities or other serious heart problems.
- Use cautiously in patients whose underlying condition may be worsened by an increase in blood pressure or heart rate (pre-existing hypertension, heart failure, recent MI); patients with a psychiatric illness, bipolar disorder, depression, or family history of suicide; those with a seizure disorder or in patients with motor and phonic tics, Tourette syndrome, and agitated states.

Lifespan: In pregnant women, use cautiously. In breast-feeding women, safety and effectiveness haven't been established.

Adverse reactions

CNS: dizziness, dysphoria, headache, *insomnia,* overstimulation, *restlessness,* tremors.
CV: ***arrhythmias,*** hypertension, palpitations, tachycardia, ***cardiomyopathy.***
GI: anorexia, constipation, diarrhea, dry mouth, other GI disturbances, unpleasant taste, weight loss.
GU: impotence.
Skin: urticaria.
Other: altered libido, chills.

Interactions

Drug-drug. *Acetazolamide, alkalizing drugs, antacids, sodium bicarbonate:* May increase renal reabsorption. Monitor patient for enhanced amphetamine effects.
Acidifying drugs, ammonium chloride, ascorbic acid: May decrease level and increase renal clearance of dextroamphetamine. Monitor patient for decreased amphetamine effects.
Adrenergic blockers: May be inhibited by amphetamines. Avoid use together.
Antihistamines: May counteract sedative effects of antihistamines. Monitor patient for loss of therapeutic effects.
Chlorpromazine: May inhibit central stimulant effects of amphetamines, and may be used to treat amphetamine poisoning. Monitor patient closely.
Haloperidol, phenothiazines, tricyclic antidepressants: May decrease amphetamine effect. Increase dose as needed.
Insulin, oral antidiabetics: May decrease antidiabetic requirement. Monitor glucose levels.
Lithium carbonate: May inhibit antiobesity and stimulating effects of amphetamines. Monitor patient closely.
MAO inhibitors: May cause severe hypertension; possibly hypertensive crisis. Don't use within 14 days of MAO inhibitor therapy.
Meperidine: Amphetamines may potentiate analgesic effect. Use together cautiously.
Methenamine: May increase urinary excretion and reduces effectiveness of amphetamines. Monitor effects.

Norepinephrine: May enhance adrenergic effect of norepinephrine. Monitor patient closely.
Phenobarbital, phenytoin: May delay absorption of dextroamphetamine. Monitor patient closely.
Propoxyphene: In cases of propoxyphene overdose, amphetamine CNS stimulation may be potentiated and fatal seizures can occur. Don't use together.
Drug-food. *Caffeine:* May increase amphetamine and related amine effects. Monitor patient closely.

Effects on lab test results

- May increase corticosteroid level.

Pharmacokinetics

Absorption: Rapid; for sustained-release capsules, more slowly.
Distribution: Wide.
Metabolism: Unknown.
Excretion: In urine. *Half-life:* 10 to 12 hours.

Route	Onset	Peak	Duration
P.O.	Unknown	Unknown	Unknown

Action

Chemical effect: Unknown; probably promotes nerve impulse transmission by releasing stored norepinephrine from nerve terminals in brain. Main sites of activity appear to be the cerebral cortex and reticular activating system.
Therapeutic effect: Helps prevent sleep and calms hyperactive children.

Available forms

Capsules (sustained-release): 5 mg, 10 mg, 15 mg
Tablets: 5 mg, 10 mg

NURSING PROCESS

Assessment

- Obtain history of patient's underlying condition before therapy, and reassess regularly throughout therapy.
- Obtain a detailed patient history, including a family history for mental disorders, family suicide, ventricular arrhythmias, or sudden death.
- Monitor for growth retardation in children
- Be alert for adverse reactions and drug interactions.
- Monitor sleeping pattern, and observe patient for signs of excessive stimulation.
- Assess patient's and family's knowledge of drug therapy.

Nursing diagnoses

- Ineffective health maintenance related to underlying condition
- Insomnia related to adverse effect of drug
- Deficient knowledge related to drug therapy

Planning and implementation

- Give at least 6 hours before bedtime to avoid sleep interference.
- Prolonged use may cause psychological dependence or habituation, especially in patients with history of drug addiction. After prolonged use, reduce dose gradually to prevent acute rebound depression.

Patient teaching

ALERT: Warn patient that misuse of amphetamines can cause serious adverse cardiovascular events, including sudden death.

- Caution patient that drug may cause blurred vision or trouble focusing. Urge patient to use caution during activities that require a clear visual field.
- Inform parents that children may show increased aggression or hostility. Urge them to report worsening behavior.
- Tell patient to avoid drinks containing caffeine, which increases the effects of amphetamines and related amines.
- Inform patient that fatigue may result as drug effects wear off.
- Instruct patient to report signs of excessive stimulation.
- Inform patient that when tolerance to anorexigenic effect develops, he should stop the drug, not increase the dose. Tell him to report decreased effectiveness of drug. Warn patient against stopping drug abruptly.

Evaluation

- Patient shows improvement in underlying condition.
- Patient can sleep without difficulty.
- Patient and family state understanding of drug therapy.

D

diazepam

(digh-AZ-uh-pam)

Apo-Diazepam ♦, Diastat, Diazemuls ♦ ◇, Diazepam Intensol, Novo-Dipam ♦, PMS-Diazepam ♦, Valium, Vivol ♦

Pharmacologic class: benzodiazepine
Therapeutic class: anxiolytic, skeletal muscle relaxant, anticonvulsant, sedative-hypnotic
Pregnancy risk category: D
Controlled substance schedule: IV

Indications and dosages

▶ **Anxiety.** *Adults:* Depending on severity, 2 to 10 mg P.O. b.i.d. to q.i.d. Or 2 to 10 mg I.M. or I.V. q 3 to 4 hours, if needed.
Elderly patients: 2 to 2.5 mg P.O. once or twice daily; increase gradually, as needed.
Children age 6 months and older: 1 to 2.5 mg P.O. t.i.d. or q.i.d.; increase gradually, as needed and tolerated.

▶ **Acute alcohol withdrawal.** *Adults:* 10 mg P.O. t.i.d. or q.i.d. for the first 24 hours and reduce to 5 mg P.O. t.i.d. or q.i.d., as appropriate. Or, initially, 10 mg I.M. or I.V.; then 5 to 10 mg I.M. or I.V. in 3 to 4 hours, if needed.

▶ **Before endoscopic procedures.** *Adults:* Titrate I.V. dose to desired sedative response (up to 20 mg). Or 5 to 10 mg I.M. 30 minutes before procedure.

▶ **Muscle spasm.** *Adults:* 2 to 10 mg P.O. b.i.d. to q.i.d. daily. Or 5 to 10 mg I.M. or I.V. initially; then 5 to 10 mg I.M. or I.V. in 3 to 4 hours, as needed. For tetanus, larger doses may be required.
Elderly patients: 2 to 2.5 mg I.M. or I.V. once or twice daily; increase as needed.
Children age 5 and older: 5 to 10 mg I.M. or I.V. q 3 to 4 hours, as needed.
Infants older than age 30 days and children younger than age 5: Give 1 to 2 mg I.M. or I.V. slowly repeated q 3 to 4 hours, as needed.

▶ **Preoperative sedation.** *Adults:* 10 mg I.M. (preferred) or I.V. before surgery.

▶ **Cardioversion.** *Adults:* 5 to 15 mg I.V. 5 to 10 minutes before procedure.

▶ **Adjunct in seizure disorders.** *Adults:* 2 to 10 mg P.O. b.i.d. to q.i.d.
Elderly patients: 2 to 2.5 mg P.O. once or twice daily; increase as needed.
Children and infants age 6 months and older: 1 to 2.5 mg P.O. t.i.d. or q.i.d. initially; increase as tolerated and needed.

▶ **Status epilepticus.** *Adults:* 5 to 10 mg I.V. (preferred) or I.M. initially. Repeat q 10 to 15 minutes, as needed, to maximum, 30 mg. Repeat in 2 to 4 hours, if needed.
Children age 5 and older: 1 mg I.V. q 2 to 5 minutes to maximum, 10 mg. Repeat in 2 to 4 hours, if needed.
Infants older than age 30 days and children younger than age 5: Give 0.2 to 0.5 mg I.V. slowly q 2 to 5 minutes to maximum, 5 mg. Repeat in 2 to 4 hours, if needed.

▶ **To control acute repetitive seizure activity in patients already taking anticonvulsants.** *Adults and children age 12 and older:* 0.2 mg/kg P.R. using applicator. A second dose may be given 4 to 12 hours after the first dose, if needed.
Children ages 6 to 11: Give 0.3 mg/kg P.R. using applicator. A second dose may be given 4 to 12 hours after the first dose, if needed.
Children ages 2 to 5: Give 0.5 mg/kg P.R. using applicator. A second dose may be given 4 to 12 hours after the first dose, if needed.

▼ I.V. administration

- Give drug I.V. at no more than 5 mg/minute.
- Inject drug directly into vein. If this is impossible, inject slowly through infusion tubing as near to venous insertion site as possible. Watch closely for phlebitis at injection site.
- To avoid extravasation, don't inject into small veins.
- Monitor respirations every 5 to 15 minutes and before each I.V. dose. Have emergency resuscitation equipment and oxygen at bedside when giving drug I.V.

⊗ **Incompatibilities**
All other I.V. drugs, most I.V. solutions.

Contraindications and cautions

- Contraindicated in patients hypersensitive to drug or any of its components and in those with angle-closure glaucoma, shock, coma, or acute alcohol intoxication (parenteral form).
- Use cautiously in patients with hepatic or renal impairment, depression, or chronic open-angle glaucoma.

Lifespan: In pregnant women (especially during the first trimester) and in breast-feeding women, avoid using the drug. In infants younger than age 6 months, oral form of drug is contraindicated. Safety and efficacy of parenteral form in neonates younger than 30 days haven't been established. In elderly and debilitated patients, use cautiously and give a lower dose because these patients may be more susceptible to adverse CNS effects of drug.

Adverse reactions

CNS: anterograde amnesia, *ataxia,* depression, *drowsiness,* fainting, *hangover,* headache, insomnia, *lethargy, pain,* psychosis, restlessness, slurred speech, tremors.
CV: ***bradycardia, CV collapse,*** transient hypotension.
EENT: blurred vision, diplopia, nystagmus.
GI: abdominal discomfort, constipation, nausea, vomiting.
GU: incontinence, urine retention.
Respiratory: ***respiratory depression.***
Skin: desquamation, rash, urticaria.
Other: ***acute withdrawal syndrome*** after stopping drug suddenly in physically dependent person, *phlebitis at injection site,* physical or psychological dependence.

Interactions

Drug-drug. *Cimetidine:* May increase sedation. Monitor patient carefully.
CNS depressants: May increase CNS depression. Avoid use together.
Digoxin: May increase digoxin level and toxicity. Monitor digoxin level.
Diltiazem: May increase CNS depression and prolong effects of diazepam. Use lower dose of diazepam.
Fluconazole, ketoconazole, itraconazole, miconazole: May increase and prolong diazepam level, CNS depression, and psychomotor impairment. Don't use together.
Phenobarbital: May increase effects of both drugs. Use together cautiously.
Phenytoin: May increase level of phenytoin. Monitor patient for toxicity.
Ranitidine: May decrease absorption. Monitor patient for decreased effect.
Drug-herb. *Kava, sassafras, valerian:* Sedative effects may be enhanced. Discourage use together.
St. John's wort: May decrease drug effects. Discourage use together.
Drug-food: *Grapefruit juice:* May increase sedative effects. Advise patient to take with a beverage other than grapefruit juice.
Drug-lifestyle. *Alcohol use:* May cause additive CNS effects. Strongly discourage use of alcohol with these drugs.
Smoking: May increase benzodiazepine clearance. Monitor patient for lack of drug effect.

Effects on lab test results

• May increase liver function test values. May decrease neutrophil count.

Pharmacokinetics

Absorption: For I.M. use, erratic.
Distribution: Wide. About 85% to 95% bound to plasma protein.
Metabolism: In liver to active metabolite, desmethyldiazepam.
Excretion: Most metabolites in urine, with small amount in feces. *Half-life:* About 1 to 12 days.

Route	Onset	Peak	Duration
P.O.	30 min	½–2 hr	3–8 hr
I.V.	1–5 min	≤ 15 min	15–60 min
I.M.	Unknown	2 hr	Unknown
P.R.	Unknown	1–5 hr	Unknown

Action

Chemical effect: May depress CNS at limbic and subcortical levels of brain; suppresses spread of seizure activity produced by epileptogenic foci in cortex, thalamus, and limbic system.
Therapeutic effect: Relieves anxiety, muscle spasms, and seizures (parenteral form); promotes calmness and sleep.

Available forms

Injection: 5 mg/ml
Oral solution: 5 mg/ml, 5 mg/5 ml
Rectal gel: 2.5 mg*, 5 mg*, 10 mg*, 15 mg*, 20 mg*
Sterile emulsion for injection: 5 mg/ml*
Tablets: 2 mg, 5 mg, 10 mg

NURSING PROCESS

Assessment

• Obtain history of patient's underlying condition before therapy, and reassess regularly thereafter.

• Periodically monitor liver, kidney, and hematopoietic function studies in patient receiving repeated or prolonged therapy.
• Look for adverse reactions and drug interactions.
• Assess patient's and family's knowledge of drug therapy.

Nursing diagnoses

• Ineffective health maintenance related to underlying condition
• Risk for injury related to drug-induced adverse CNS reactions
• Deficient knowledge related to drug therapy

Planning and implementation

• When oral concentrate solution is used, dilute dose just before giving. Use water, juice, or carbonated beverages, or mix with semisolid food such as applesauce or pudding.
• Avoid P.R. use of Diastat for more than 5 episodes per month or one episode every 5 days.
ALERT: Drug should be given only by caregivers who can distinguish the distinct cluster of seizures or events from the patient's ordinary seizure activity, who can give the drug competently, who understand which seizure characteristics can be treated with drug, and who can monitor the patient's response and recognize when immediate professional help is needed.
• Give drug I.M. only when giving I.V. or P.O. isn't possible because absorption is variable and injection is painful.
• Don't mix injectable form with other drugs because diazepam is incompatible with most drugs.
• Don't store parenteral solution in plastic syringes.
• Parenteral emulsion—a stabilized oil-in-water emulsion—should appear milky white and uniform. Avoid mixing with any other drugs or solutions, and avoid infusion sets or containers made from polyvinyl chloride. If diluting, mix drug with I.V. fat emulsion. Use admixture within 6 hours.
• Possibility of abuse and addiction exists. Don't withdraw drug abruptly after long-term use. Withdrawal symptoms may occur.
ALERT: Don't confuse diazepam with diazoxide.

Patient teaching

• Warn patient to avoid hazardous activities until the drug's CNS effects are known.
• Tell patient to avoid using alcohol during therapy.
• Warn patient to take drug only as directed and not to stop it without prescriber's approval.
• Warn patient about risk of physical and psychological dependence.

Evaluation

• Patient shows improvement in underlying condition.
• Patient has no injury as result of drug-induced adverse CNS reactions.
• Patient and family state understanding of drug therapy.

diclofenac potassium

(digh-KLOH-fen-ek poh-TAH-see-um)
Cataflam

diclofenac sodium

Solaraze, Voltaren, Voltaren SR ♦, Voltaren-XR

Pharmacologic class: NSAID
Therapeutic class: antiarthritic, antiinflammatory
Pregnancy risk category: B

Indications and dosages

▶ **Ankylosing spondylitis.** *Adults:* 25-mg delayed-release tablets P.O. q.i.d. (may give another 25 mg at bedtime, if needed). Or, 50 mg (diclofenac potassium) P.O. b.i.d.
▶ **Osteoarthritis.** *Adults:* 50-mg immediate- or delayed-release tablets P.O. b.i.d. or t.i.d. Or 75 mg P.O. b.i.d. Or 100-mg extended-release tablets P.O. daily.
▶ **Rheumatoid arthritis.** *Adults:* 50-mg immediate- or delayed-release tablets P.O. t.i.d. or q.i.d. Or 75 mg P.O. b.i.d. Or 50 to 100 mg P.R. (where available) at bedtime as substitute for last P.O. dose of day. Not to exceed 225 mg daily. Or 100-mg extended-release tablets P.O. daily or b.i.d.
▶ **Analgesia and primary dysmenorrhea.** *Adults:* 50 mg diclofenac potassium P.O. t.i.d. If needed, 100 mg may be given for first dose only. Maximum total daily dose is 150 mg.
▶ **Actinic keratosis.** *Adults:* Apply gel to lesion b.i.d.

Contraindications and cautions

• Contraindicated in patients hypersensitive to drug or any of its components and in those with hepatic porphyria or a history of asthma, urticaria, or other allergic reactions after taking aspirin or other NSAIDs. Also contraindicated for treatment of perioperative pain in patients undergoing CABG surgery.
• Use cautiously in patients with history of peptic ulcer disease, hepatic dysfunction, cardiac disease, hypertension, conditions that cause fluid retention, or impaired kidney function.
Lifespan: For women in late pregnancy or who are breast-feeding, drug isn't recommended. In children, safety and effectiveness haven't been established.

Adverse reactions

CNS: anxiety, depression, dizziness, drowsiness, headache, insomnia, irritability, migraine, myoclonus.
CV: edema, fluid retention, ***heart failure,*** hypertension.
EENT: blurred vision, epistaxis, eye pain, ***laryngeal edema,*** night blindness, reversible hearing loss, swelling of lips and tongue, tinnitus.
GI: abdominal distention, *abdominal pain or cramps,* appetite change, ***bleeding,*** bloody diarrhea, colitis, *constipation, diarrhea,* flatulence, *indigestion,* melena, *nausea,* peptic ulceration, taste disorder.
GU: ***acute renal failure,*** azotemia, *fluid retention,* interstitial nephritis, nephrotic syndrome, ***oliguria,*** papillary necrosis, proteinuria.
Hepatic: ***hepatitis, hepatotoxicity,*** jaundice.
Metabolic: hyperglycemia, ***hypoglycemia.***
Musculoskeletal: back, leg, or joint pain.
Respiratory: ***asthma.***
Skin: allergic purpura, alopecia, bullous eruption, dermatitis, eczema, photosensitivity, pruritus, rash, ***Stevens-Johnson syndrome,*** urticaria.
Other: ***anaphylaxis, angioedema.***

Interactions

Drug-drug. *Anticoagulants, including warfarin:* May increase risk of bleeding. Monitor patient closely for bleeding.
Aspirin: May increase risk of bleeding. Don't use together.
Beta blockers: Antihypertensive effect of beta blocker may be blunted. Monitor blood pressure closely.
Cyclosporine, digoxin, lithium, methotrexate: May reduce renal clearance of these drugs and increase risk of toxicity. Monitor patient closely; monitor drug levels if appropriate.
Diuretics: May decrease diuretic effectiveness. Monitor patient for fluid retention.
Insulin, oral antidiabetics: May alter antidiabetic requirement. Monitor glucose level.
Potassium-sparing diuretics: May enhance potassium retention and increases potassium levels. Monitor patient for hyperkalemia.
Drug-herb. *Dong quai, feverfew, garlic, ginger, horse chestnut, red clover:* May increase risk of bleeding. Discourage use together.
St. John's wort: May increase risk of photosensitivity. Advise against unprotected and prolonged exposure to sunlight.
Drug-lifestyle. *Sun exposure:* May cause photosensitivity reactions. Urge patient to wear protective clothing and sunblock.

Effects on lab test results

• May increase ALT, AST, alkaline phosphatase, bilirubin, BUN, creatinine, and LDH levels. May increase or decrease glucose level.

Pharmacokinetics

Absorption: Rapid and almost complete. Delayed by food.
Distribution: Almost 100% protein-bound.
Metabolism: Undergoes first-pass metabolism, with 60% of unchanged drug reaching systemic circulation.
Excretion: About 40% to 60% in urine; balance in bile. *Half-life:* 1 to 2 hours.

Route	Onset	Peak	Duration
P.O., P.R.	30 min	Unknown	8 hr
P.O. enteric-coated	30 min	2–3 hr	8 hr

Action

Chemical effect: Produces anti-inflammatory, analgesic, and antipyretic effects, possibly by inhibiting prostaglandin synthesis.
Therapeutic effect: Relieves inflammation, pain, and fever.

Available forms

diclofenac potassium
Tablets: 50 mg

diclofenac sodium
Suppositories: 50 mg ♦, 100 mg ♦
Tablets (delayed-release/enteric-coated): 25 mg, 50 mg, 75 mg
Tablets (extended-release): 100 mg ♦

NURSING PROCESS

Assessment

- Obtain history of patient's underlying condition before therapy.
- Monitor effectiveness by assessing patient for pain relief.
- Liver enzyme level may elevate. Monitor transaminase level, especially ALT level, periodically in a patient undergoing long-term therapy. Take first level within the first 8 weeks of therapy.
- Look for adverse reactions and drug interactions.
- Assess patient's and family's knowledge of drug therapy.

Nursing diagnoses

- Acute pain related to underlying condition
- Risk for injury related to drug-induced adverse reactions
- Deficient knowledge related to drug therapy

Planning and implementation

ALERT: NSAIDs may cause an increased risk of serious or fatal cardiovascular thrombotic events, including MI and stroke.

ALERT: NSAIDs increase the risk of serious GI adverse events, including inflammation, bleeding, ulceration, and perforation, which can be fatal.

- If drug causes GI distress. Give with milk or food.
- Notify prescriber immediately if patient develops signs of GI bleeding, hepatotoxicity, or other adverse reactions.
- The sodium and potassium preparations may not be bioequivalent.
- Rectal preparation isn't commercially available in the United States. Elsewhere, it may be substituted for the last oral dose of the day to decrease GI distress if can't take with food.

Patient teaching

- Tell patient to take drug with milk or food to minimize GI distress.
- Instruct patient not to crush, break, or chew enteric-coated tablets.
- Teach patient signs and symptoms of GI bleeding, and tell him to contact prescriber immediately if they occur.
- Teach patient signs and symptoms of hepatotoxicity, including nausea, fatigue, lethargy, pruritus, jaundice, right upper quadrant tenderness, and flulike symptoms. Tell him to contact prescriber immediately if these symptoms appear.

Evaluation

- Patient is free from pain.
- Patient has no injury as result of drug-induced adverse reactions.
- Patient and family state understanding of drug therapy.

dicyclomine hydrochloride

(digh-SIGH-kloh-meen high-droh-KLOR-ighd)
Antispas, Bemote, Bentyl, Bentylol ♦, Byclomine, Dibent, Dilomine, Di-Spaz, Formulex ♦, Lomine ♦, Merbenty ◇, Or-Tyl, Spasmoban ♦

Pharmacologic class: anticholinergic
Therapeutic class: antimuscarinic, GI antispasmodic
Pregnancy risk category: B

Indications and dosages

▶ **Irritable bowel syndrome and other functional GI disorders.** *Adults:* Initially, 20 mg P.O. q.i.d.; increase to 40 mg q.i.d. Or 80 mg I.M. daily in four divided doses.
Children age 2 and older: 10 mg P.O. t.i.d. or q.i.d.
Infants ages 6 months to 2 years: 5 to 10 mg P.O. t.i.d. or q.i.d.

▶ **Colic‡.** *Infants age 6 months and older:* 5 to 10 mg P.O. t.i.d. or q.i.d. Adjust dosage according to patient's needs and response.

Contraindications and cautions

- Contraindicated in patients hypersensitive to anticholinergics and in those with obstructive uropathy, obstructive disease of GI tract, reflux esophagitis, severe ulcerative colitis, myasthenia gravis, unstable CV status in acute hemorrhage, or glaucoma.
- Use cautiously in patients with autonomic neuropathy, hyperthyroidism, coronary artery disease, arrhythmias, heart failure, hypertension,

hiatal hernia, hepatic or renal disease, prostatic hypertrophy, or ulcerative colitis.
Lifespan: In pregnant patients, use cautiously. In breast-feeding women and in infants younger than age 6 months, drug is contraindicated.

Adverse reactions

CNS: *dizziness;* drowsiness; fever; *headache;* insomnia; nervousness, confusion, and excitement in elderly patients.
CV: *palpitations,* tachycardia.
EENT: blurred vision, increased intraocular pressure, mydriasis.
GI: abdominal distention, *constipation, dry mouth,* heartburn, nausea, paralytic ileus, vomiting.
GU: impotence, urinary hesitancy, urine retention.
Skin: decreased sweating or possibly anhidrosis, other dermal changes, urticaria.
Other: allergic reactions.

Interactions

Drug-drug. *Amantadine, antihistamines, antiparkinsonians, disopyramide, glutethimide, MAO inhibitors, meperidine, phenothiazines, procainamide, quinidine, tricyclic antidepressants:* May cause additive adverse effects. Avoid use together.
Antacids: May decrease absorption of oral anticholinergics. Separate doses by 2 to 3 hours.
Ketoconazole: May interfere with ketoconazole absorption. Give at least 2 hours after ketoconazole.

Effects on lab test results

None reported.

Pharmacokinetics

Absorption: 67% of P.O. dose.
Distribution: Extensive in tissue.
Metabolism: Unknown.
Excretion: 80% of P.O. dose in urine and 10% in feces. *Half-life:* Initial, about 2 hours; secondary, 9 to 10 hours.

Route	Onset	Peak	Duration
P.O.	Unknown	1–½ hr	Unknown
I.M.	Unknown	Unknown	Unknown

Action

Chemical effect: Appears to exert nonspecific, indirect spasmolytic action on smooth muscle. Dicyclomine also possesses local anesthetic properties that may be partly responsible for spasmolysis.
Therapeutic effect: Relieves GI spasms.

Available forms

Capsules: 10 mg, 20 mg
Injection: 10 mg/ml
Syrup: 5 mg/5 ml ◇, 10 mg/5 ml
Tablets: 10 mg ◇, 20 mg

NURSING PROCESS

Assessment

- Obtain history of patient's underlying condition before therapy.
- Monitor the drug's effectiveness by regularly assessing patient for pain relief and improvement of underlying condition.
- Look for adverse reactions and drug interactions.
- Assess patient's and family's knowledge of drug therapy.

Nursing diagnoses

- Acute pain related to underlying condition
- Risk for injury related to drug-induced adverse CNS reactions
- Deficient knowledge related to drug therapy

Planning and implementation

- Drug is synthetic tertiary derivative that may cause atropine-like adverse reactions. Overdose may cause curare-like effects, such as respiratory paralysis.
- High environmental temperatures may induce heatstroke during drug use. If symptoms occur, stop giving the drug.
- Give 30 to 60 minutes before meals and at bedtime. Bedtime dose can be larger; give at least 2 hours after last meal of the day.

ALERT: Don't give drug subcutaneously or I.V.

- Adjust dosage according to patient's needs and response. Up to 40 mg P.O. q.i.d. may be used in adults, but safety and effectiveness for more than 2 weeks haven't been established.

ALERT: The dicyclomine label may be misleading. The ampule label reads 10 mg/ml, but doesn't indicate that the ampule contains 2 ml of solution (20 mg of drug).

ALERT: Don't confuse dicyclomine with dyclonine or doxycycline; don't confuse Bentyl with Aventyl or Benadryl.

Patient teaching

- Instruct patient to refrain from driving and performing other hazardous activities if he's drowsy or dizzy or has blurred vision.
- Tell him to drink plenty of fluids to help prevent constipation.
- Urge patient to report rash or skin eruption.
- Tell patient to use sugarless gum or hard candy to relieve dry mouth.

Evaluation

- Patient is free from pain.
- Patient doesn't experience injury as a result of drug-induced adverse CNS reactions.
- Patient and family state understanding of drug therapy.

didanosine (ddI)

(digh-DAN-uh-zeen)

Videx, Videx EC

Pharmacologic class: nucleoside reverse transcriptase inhibitor
Therapeutic class: antiretroviral
Pregnancy risk category: B

Indications and dosages

▶ **HIV infection.** *Adults weighing 60 kg (132 lb) and more:* 400 mg delayed-release form P.O. daily.
Adults weighing less than 60 kg: 250 mg delayed-release form P.O. daily.
Children older than age 8 months: 120 mg/m² P.O. b.i.d.
Children ages 2 weeks to 8 months: 100 mg/m² P.O. b.i.d.

Adjust-a-dose: In adults who weigh 60 kg or more with creatinine clearance of 30 to 59 ml/minute, give 200 mg once daily. For clearance of 10 to 29 ml/minute, give 125-mg delayed-release capsule once daily. For clearance less than 10 ml/minute, give 125-mg delayed-release capsule once daily.

In adults who weigh less than 60 kg and have a clearance of 10 to 59 ml/minute, give 125-mg delayed-release capsule once daily. For clearance less than 10 ml/minute or patients on dialysis, give alternate form. No additional dose is needed after hemodialysis.

▶ **Postexposure prevention following occupational or nonoccupational exposure to HIV, with other antiretrovirals‡.** *Adults weighing 60 kg or more:* 400 mg P.O. once daily or divided b.i.d. for 4 weeks.
Adults weighing less than 60 kg: 250 mg P.O. once daily or divided b.i.d. for 4 weeks.

Contraindications and cautions

- Contraindicated in patients hypersensitive to drug or any of its components.
- Use cautiously in patients with a history of pancreatitis and in patients with peripheral neuropathy, renal or hepatic impairment, or hyperuricemia.

Lifespan: In pregnant women, use cautiously. In breast-feeding women, drug isn't recommended.

Adverse reactions

CNS: abnormal thinking, asthenia, anxiety, confusion, depression, *dizziness, fever, headache,* hypertonia, insomnia, nervousness, pain, *peripheral neuropathy,* ***seizures,*** twitching.
CV: edema, ***heart failure,*** hyperlipidemia, hypertension.
GI: abdominal pain, diarrhea, dry mouth, dyspepsia, flatulence, nausea, ***pancreatitis,*** vomiting.
Hematologic: anemia, granulocytosis, ***leukopenia, thrombocytopenia.***
Hepatic: ***hepatic failure***, liver abnormalities, ***severe hepatomegaly***.
Metabolic: lactic acidosis.
Musculoskeletal: arthritis, myalgia, myopathy, ***rhabdomyolysis.***
Respiratory: cough, dyspnea, pneumonia.
Skin: alopecia, pruritus, rash.
Other: ***anaphylactoid reaction,*** chills, infection, sarcoma.

Interactions

Drug-drug. *Amprenavir, delavirdine, indinavir, nelfinavir, ritonavir, saquinavir:* May alter pharmacokinetics. Separate doses.
Antacids containing magnesium or aluminum hydroxides: Enhances adverse effects of antacid component (including diarrhea or constipation). Avoid use together.

Dapsone, ketoconazole, drugs that require gastric acid for adequate absorption: May decrease absorption from buffering action. Give these drugs 2 hours before didanosine.
Fluoroquinolones, tetracyclines: May decrease absorption because of buffers in didanosine antacids in pediatric solution. Monitor patient for decreased effectiveness.
Itraconazole: May decrease levels of itraconazole. Avoid use together.
Tenofovir: May cause high rate of early virologic failure and emerging resistance. Don't use together. Switch patients currently on this regimen to eliminate tenofovir.
Drug-food. *Any food:* May increase rate of absorption. Give drug on an empty stomach.
Drug-herb. *St. John's wort:* May decrease drug levels, decreasing therapeutic effect. Discourage use together.

Effects on lab test results

- May increase uric acid, AST, ALT, alkaline phosphatase, and bilirubin levels. May decrease hemoglobin level and hematocrit.
- May decrease WBC, granulocyte, and platelet counts.

Pharmacokinetics

Absorption: Rapid. Commercially available forms contain buffers to raise stomach pH. Bioavailability averages 33%. Food decreases absorption by 50%.
Distribution: Wide. Drug penetration into CNS varies, but CSF levels average 46% of concurrent plasma levels in children and 21% in adults.
Metabolism: Probably similar to that of endogenous purines.
Excretion: In urine. *Half-life:* 48 minutes; half-life increases as creatinine clearance decreases.

Route	Onset	Peak	Duration
P.O.	Unknown	30 min–1 hr	Unknown

Action

Chemical effect: Unknown; appears to inhibit replication of HIV by preventing DNA replication.
Therapeutic effect: Inhibits replication of HIV.

Available forms

Delayed-release capsules: 125 mg, 200 mg, 250 mg, 400 mg
Powder for oral solution (pediatric): 10 mg/ml in 2- and 4-g bottles

NURSING PROCESS

Assessment

- Obtain history of patient's underlying condition before therapy, and reassess regularly thereafter.
- Be alert for adverse reactions and drug interactions.
- Assess patient's and family's knowledge of drug therapy.

Nursing diagnoses

- Ineffective protection related to presence of HIV infection
- Diarrhea related to drug-induced adverse effect on bowel
- Deficient knowledge related to drug therapy

Planning and implementation

- Give drug on empty stomach at least 30 minutes before or 2 hours after meals, regardless of dosage form used, because giving drug with meals can decrease absorption by 50%.
- Pharmacist must prepare pediatric powder for oral solution to a final concentration of 10 mg/ml. The solution is stable for 30 days if refrigerated. Shake well before measuring dose.
- If pancreatitis is suspected, stop drug and don't continue until pancreatitis is ruled out.

Patient teaching

- Tell patient to take drug on an empty stomach and to drink at least 1 oz (30 ml) water with each dose.
- Instruct patient not to crush or break capsules.
- Explain the importance of complying with drug regimen for treatment of HIV infection.
- Warn patient about adverse CNS reactions, and tell patient to take safety precautions.
- Tell patient to notify prescriber if adverse GI reaction occurs.

Evaluation

- Patient improves with therapy.
- Patient regains normal bowel pattern.
- Patient and family state understanding of drug therapy.

diflunisal

(digh-FLOO-neh-sol)

Dolobid

Pharmacologic class: NSAID
Therapeutic class: analgesic, anti-inflammatory
Pregnancy risk category: C

Indications and dosages

▶ **Mild to moderate pain.** *Adults:* Initially, 500 mg to 1 g P.O., followed by 250 to 500 mg q 8 to 12 hours.

▶ **Osteoarthritis, rheumatoid arthritis.** *Adults:* 500 mg to 1 g P.O. daily in two divided doses, usually q 12 hours. Maximum, 1,500 mg daily.

Adjust-a-dose: For patients older than age 65, give half the usual adult dose.

Contraindications and cautions

- Contraindicated in patients hypersensitive to drug or any of its components and in those who develop acute asthmatic attacks, urticaria, or rhinitis after taking aspirin or other NSAIDs.
- Use cautiously in patients with GI bleeding, history of peptic ulcer disease, renal impairment, compromised cardiac function, hypertension, or other conditions predisposing patient to fluid retention.

Lifespan: In breast-feeding women, drug isn't recommended. In children and teenagers with chickenpox or flulike illness, salicylates aren't recommended because of epidemiologic connection to Reye syndrome.

Adverse reactions

CNS: *dizziness,* fatigue, *headache,* insomnia, somnolence.
EENT: *tinnitus,* visual disturbances.
GI: constipation, *diarrhea, dyspepsia,* flatulence, *GI pain, nausea,* vomiting.
GU: hematuria, interstitial nephritis, renal impairment.
Skin: ***erythema multiforme,*** pruritus, rash, ***Stevens-Johnson syndrome,*** stomatitis, sweating.
Other: dry mucous membranes.

Interactions

Drug-drug. *Acetaminophen, hydrochlorothiazide, indomethacin, lithium:* May substantially increase levels of these drugs, increasing risk of toxicity. Avoid use together, or monitor patient closely.
Antacids: May decrease diflunisal level. Monitor patient for decreased therapeutic effect.
Aspirin: May increase adverse effects. Monitor patient closely.
Cyclosporine: May increase nephrotoxicity of cyclosporine. Avoid use together.
Methotrexate: May increase toxicity of methotrexate. Avoid use together.
Oral anticoagulants, thrombolytics: May enhance effects of these drugs. Use together cautiously.
Sulindac: May decrease level of sulindac's active metabolite. Monitor patient for decreased effect.
Drug-herb. *Dong quai, feverfew, garlic, ginger, horse chestnut, red clover:* May increase risk of bleeding. Discourage use together.

Effects on lab test results

- May falsely elevate serum salicylate levels.

Pharmacokinetics

Absorption: Rapid and complete.
Distribution: Highly protein-bound.
Metabolism: In liver.
Excretion: In urine. *Half-life:* 8 to 12 hours.

Route	Onset	Peak	Duration
P.O.	1 hr	2–3 hr	8–12 hr

Action

Chemical effect: May inhibit prostaglandin synthesis.
Therapeutic effect: Relieves inflammation and pain; reduces body temperature.

Available forms

Tablets: 250 mg, 500 mg

NURSING PROCESS

Assessment

- Obtain history of patient's underlying condition before therapy, and reassess regularly thereafter.

• Look for adverse reactions and drug interactions.
• Assess patient's and family's knowledge of drug therapy.

Nursing diagnoses
• Acute pain related to underlying condition
• Risk for deficient fluid volume related to drug-induced adverse reactions
• Deficient knowledge related to drug therapy

Planning and implementation
• Give drug with milk or food to minimize adverse GI reactions.
ALERT: Don't confuse Dolobid with Slo-bid.
Patient teaching
• Advise patient to take with water, milk, or meals.
• Warn patient to avoid drug interactions by checking with prescriber or pharmacist before taking OTC drugs or herbal remedies, such as those containing aspirin or salicylates.

Evaluation
• Patient is free from pain.
• Patient maintains adequate hydration throughout therapy.
• Patient and family state understanding of drug therapy.

digoxin
(dih-JOKS-in)
Digitek, Digoxin, Lanoxicaps, Lanoxin*

Pharmacologic class: cardiac glycoside
Therapeutic class: antiarrhythmic, inotropic
Pregnancy risk category: C

Indications and dosages
▶ **Heart failure, paroxysmal supraventricular tachycardia, atrial fibrillation and flutter.**
Tablets, elixir
Adults: For rapid digitalization, give 0.75 to 1.25 mg P.O. over 24 hours in two or more divided doses q 6 to 8 hours. For slow digitalization, give 0.125 to 0.5 mg daily for 5 to 7 days. Maintenance dose is 0.125 to 0.5 mg daily.
Children age 10 and older: 10 to 15 mcg/kg P.O. over 24 hours in two or more divided doses q 6 to 8 hours. Maintenance dose is 25% to 35% of total digitalizing dose.
Children ages 5 to 10: Give 20 to 35 mcg/kg P.O. over 24 hours in two or more divided doses q 6 to 8 hours. Maintenance dose is 25% to 35% of total digitalizing dose.
Children ages 2 to 5: Give 30 to 40 mcg/kg P.O. over 24 hours in two or more divided doses q 6 to 8 hours. Maintenance dose is 25% to 35% of total digitalizing dose.
Infants ages 1 month to 2 years: 35 to 60 mcg/kg P.O. over 24 hours in two or more divided doses q 6 to 8 hours. Maintenance dose is 25% to 35% of total digitalizing dose.
Neonates: 25 to 35 mcg/kg P.O. over 24 hours in two or more divided doses q 6 to 8 hours. Maintenance dose is 25% to 35% of total digitalizing dose.
Premature infants: 20 to 30 mcg/kg P.O. over 24 hours in two or more divided doses q 6 to 8 hours. Maintenance dose is 20% to 30% of total digitalizing dose.
Capsules
Adults: For rapid digitalization, give 0.4 to 0.6 mg P.O. initially, followed by 0.1 to 0.3 mg q 6 to 8 hours, as needed and tolerated, for 24 hours. For slow digitalization, give 0.05 to 0.35 mg daily in two divided doses for 7 to 22 days until therapeutic levels are reached. Maintenance dose is 0.05 to 0.35 mg daily in one or two divided doses.
Adjust-a-dose: In children, digitalizing dose is based on child's age and is given in three or more divided doses over the first 24 hours. First dose is 50% of the total dose; subsequent doses are given q 4 to 8 hours as needed and tolerated.
Children age 10 and older: For rapid digitalization, give 8 to 12 mcg/kg P.O. over 24 hours, divided as above. Maintenance dose is 25% to 35% of total digitalizing dose, given daily as a single dose.
Children ages 5 to 10: For rapid digitalization, give 15 to 30 mcg/kg P.O. over 24 hours, divided as above. Maintenance dose is 25% to 35% of total digitalizing dose, divided and given in two or three equal portions daily.
Children ages 2 to 5: For rapid digitalization, give 25 to 35 mcg/kg P.O. over 24 hours, divided as above. Maintenance dose is 25% to 35% of total digitalizing dose, divided and given in two or three equal portions daily.
Injection
Adults: For rapid digitalization, give 0.4 to 0.6 mg I.V. initially, followed by 0.1 to 0.3 mg

I.V. q 4 to 8 hours, as needed and tolerated, for 24 hours. For slow digitalization, give appropriate daily maintenance dose for 7 to 22 days as needed until therapeutic levels are reached. Maintenance dose is 0.125 to 0.5 mg I.V. daily in one or two divided doses.
Children: Digitalizing dose is based on child's age and is given in three or more divided doses over the first 24 hours. First dose is 50% of total dose; subsequent doses are given q 4 to 8 hours as needed and tolerated.
Children age 10 and older: For rapid digitalization, give 8 to 12 mcg/kg I.V. over 24 hours, divided as above. Maintenance dose is 25% to 35% of total digitalizing dose, given daily as a single dose.
Children ages 5 to 10: For rapid digitalization, give 15 to 30 mcg/kg I.V. over 24 hours, divided as above. Maintenance dose is 25% to 35% of total digitalizing dose, divided and given in two or three equal portions daily.
Children ages 2 to 5: For rapid digitalization, give 25 to 35 mcg/kg I.V. over 24 hours, divided as above. Maintenance dose is 25% to 35% of total digitalizing dose, divided and given in two or three equal portions daily.
Infants ages 1 month to 2 years: For rapid digitalization, give 30 to 50 mcg/kg I.V. over 24 hours, divided as above. Maintenance dose is 25% to 35% of total digitalizing dose, divided and given in two or three equal portions daily.
Neonates: For rapid digitalization, give 20 to 30 mcg/kg I.V. over 24 hours, divided as above. Maintenance dose is 25% to 35% of the total digitalizing dose, divided and given in two or three equal portions daily.
Premature infants: For rapid digitalization, give 15 to 25 mcg/kg I.V. over 24 hours, divided as above. Maintenance dose is 20% to 30% of the total digitalizing dose, divided and given in two or three equal portions daily.
Adjust-a-dose: In all dosage forms, give smaller loading and maintenance doses to patients with impaired renal function.

For patients with renal impairment, decrease dosage. For patients with hyperthyroidism, may need to increase dosage.

I.V. administration

- Dilute fourfold with D_5W, normal saline solution, or sterile water for injection to reduce the chance of precipitation.
- Infuse drug slowly over at least 5 minutes.
- Protect prepared drug from light.

⊗ **Incompatibilities**
Amiodarone, dobutamine, doxapram, drugs or solutions given through the same I.V. line, fluconazole, foscarnet, other I.V. drugs, propofol.

Contraindications and cautions

- Contraindicated in patients hypersensitive to the drug or any of its components and in those with digoxin-induced toxicity, ventricular fibrillation, or ventricular tachycardia unless caused by heart failure.
- Use cautiously in patients with acute MI, incomplete AV block, sinus bradycardia, PVCs, chronic constrictive pericarditis, hypertrophic cardiomyopathy, renal insufficiency, severe pulmonary disease, or hypothyroidism.

Lifespan: In pregnant women, use cautiously. In breast-feeding women, use cautiously; it's unknown if the drug appears in breast milk. In elderly patients, use cautiously.

Adverse reactions

CNS: agitation, dizziness, fatigue, generalized muscle weakness, hallucinations, headache, malaise, paresthesia, stupor, vertigo.
CV: ***arrhythmias, heart failure,*** hypotension.
EENT: blurred vision, diplopia, light flashes, photophobia, yellow-green halos around visual images.
GI: anorexia, diarrhea, nausea, vomiting.

Interactions

Drug-drug. *Amiloride:* May inhibit digoxin effect and increase digoxin excretion. Monitor patient for altered digoxin effect.
Amiodarone, diltiazem, nifedipine, quinidine, rifampin, verapamil: May increase digoxin level. Monitor patient for digoxin toxicity.
Amphotericin B, carbenicillin, corticosteroids, diuretics (including loop diuretics, chlorthalidone, metolazone, and thiazides), ticarcillin: May decrease potassium level, predisposing patient to digoxin toxicity. Monitor potassium levels.
Antacids, kaolin-pectin: May decrease digoxin absorption. Schedule doses as far as possible from P.O. digoxin administration.
Cholestyramine, colestipol, metoclopramide: May decrease absorption of P.O. digoxin. Moni-

tor patient for decreased effect and low blood levels. Increase dosage.
Parenteral calcium, thiazides: May increase calcium level and decrease magnesium level, predisposing patient to digoxin toxicity. Monitor calcium and magnesium levels.
Drug-herb. *Betel palm, fumitory, goldenseal, lily of the valley, motherwort, rue, shepherd's purse:* May increase cardiac effect. Discourage use together.
Horsetail, licorice: May deplete potassium stores, leading to digoxin toxicity. Monitor potassium level closely.
Oleander, Siberian ginseng, squill: May enhance toxicity. Discourage use together.
St. John's wort: May reduce therapeutic effect of digoxin, requiring an increased dosage. Monitor patient for loss of therapeutic effect, and advise patient to avoid this herb.
Drug-lifestyle. *Alcohol use:* May increase CNS effects. Discourage use together.

Effects on lab test results

None reported.

Pharmacokinetics

Absorption: For tablet or elixir, 60% to 85%. For capsule, 90% to 100%.
Distribution: Wide. About 20% to 30% bound to plasma proteins.
Metabolism: Small amount in liver and gut by bacteria. This varies and may be substantial in some patients. Drug undergoes some enterohepatic recirculation (also variable). Metabolites have minimal cardiac activity.
Excretion: Mostly by kidneys as unchanged drug, although a substantial amount of metabolized or reduced drug may be excreted. In patients with renal impairment, biliary excretion is most important. *Half-life:* 30 to 40 hours.

Route	Onset	Peak	Duration
P.O.	30 min–2 hr	2–6 hr	3–4 days
I.V.	5–30 min	1–4 hr	3–4 days

Action

Chemical effect: Inhibits sodium-potassium-activated adenosine triphosphatase, thereby promoting movement of calcium from extracellular to intracellular cytoplasm and strengthening myocardial contraction. Also acts on CNS to enhance vagal tone, slowing conduction through SA and AV nodes and providing antiarrhythmic effect.
Therapeutic effect: Strengthens myocardial contractions and slows conduction through SA and AV nodes.

Available forms

Capsules: 0.05 mg, 0.1 mg, 0.2 mg
Elixir: 0.05 mg/ml
Injection: 0.05 mg/ml, 0.1 mg/ml (pediatric), 0.25 mg/ml
Tablets: 0.125 mg, 0.25 mg

NURSING PROCESS

Assessment

- Obtain history of patient's underlying condition before therapy.
- Monitor effectiveness by taking apical pulse for 1 full minute before giving a dose. Evaluate ECG, and regularly assess patient's cardiopulmonary condition for signs of improvement.
- Monitor drug level. Therapeutic level ranges from 0.5 to 2 nanograms/ml. Take level 8 hours after last P.O. dose.
- Monitor potassium level carefully.
- Look for adverse reactions and drug interactions. In children, arrhythmias are the earliest and most frequent manifestation of excessive dosing.
- Assess patient's and family's knowledge of drug therapy.

Nursing diagnoses

- Decreased cardiac output related to underlying condition
- Ineffective protection related to digoxin toxicity caused by drug
- Deficient knowledge related to drug therapy

Planning and implementation

- Adjust dosages as needed. Hypothyroid patients are extremely sensitive to drug, and hyperthyroid patients may need a larger dosage. Reduce the dosage in patients with renal impairment.
- Before giving loading dose, obtain baseline data (heart rate and rhythm, blood pressure, and electrolyte levels) and question patient about use of drug within the previous 2 to 3 weeks.
- Loading dose is always divided over first 24 hours unless patient's condition indicates otherwise.

• Before giving drug, take apical pulse for 1 full minute. Record and report to prescriber significant changes (sudden increase or decrease in pulse rate, pulse deficit, irregular beats, and regularization of previously irregular rhythm). If these changes occur, check blood pressure and obtain 12-lead ECG.

ALERT: If pulse rate slows to 60 beats/minute or less, withhold drug and notify prescriber.

• Reduce dosage by 20% to 25% when changing from tablets or elixir to liquid-filled capsules or injection because the new forms are better absorbed.

• For digoxin toxicity, give drugs that bind drug in intestine (for example, colestipol or cholestyramine). Treat arrhythmias with phenytoin I.V. or lidocaine I.V., and treat potentially life-threatening toxicity with specific antigen-binding fragments (such as digoxin immune Fab).

• Withhold drug for 1 to 2 days before elective cardioversion. Adjust dose after cardioversion.

ALERT: Be careful when calculating doses. A tenfold miscalculation of a child's dose can easily occur.

ALERT: Don't confuse digoxin with doxepin.

Patient teaching

• Instruct patient and caregiver about drug action, dosage regimen, pulse taking, reportable signs, and follow-up plans.

• Instruct patient not to substitute one brand of digoxin for another.

• Tell patient to eat potassium-rich foods.

Evaluation

• Patient has adequate cardiac output.

• Patient has no digoxin toxicity.

• Patient and family state understanding of drug therapy.

digoxin immune Fab (ovine)

(dih-JOKS-in ih-MYOON Fab)

Digibind, DigiFab

Pharmacologic class: antibody fragment
Therapeutic class: cardiac glycoside antidote
Pregnancy risk category: C

Indications and dosages

▶ **Life-threatening digoxin toxicity.** *Adults and children:* Dosage based on ingested amount or level of digoxin. When calculating amount of antidote, round up to the nearest whole number.

For digoxin tablets, find the number of antidote vials by multiplying the ingested amount by 0.8 and dividing answer by 0.5. For example, if patient takes 25 tablets of 0.25-mg digoxin, the ingested amount is 6.25 mg. Multiply 6.25 mg by 0.8 and divide answer by 0.5 to obtain 10 vials of antidote.

For digoxin capsules, find the number of antidote vials by dividing the ingested dose in mg by 0.5. For example, if patient takes 50 of 0.2-mg capsules, the ingested amount is 10 mg. Divide 10 mg by 0.5 to obtain 20 vials of antidote.

If the digoxin level is known, determine the number of antidote vials as follows: multiply the digoxin level in nanograms/ml by patient's weight in kg, divide by 100. For example, if digoxin is 4 nanograms/ml, and patient weighs 60 kg, multiply together to obtain 240. Divide by 100 to obtain 2.4 vials; then round up to 3 vials.

▶ **Acute toxicity or if estimated ingested amount or digoxin level is unknown.** *Adults and children:* Consider giving 10 vials of digoxin immune Fab and observing patient's response. Follow with another 10 vials. Dose is effective in most life-threatening ingestions in adults and children but may cause volume overload in young children.

I.V. administration

• Reconstitute with 4 ml of sterile water for injection. For infusion, further dilute solution with normal saline. For children or other patients who need small doses, reconstitute Digibind in 38-mg vial with 34 ml of normal saline for 1 mg/ml concentration; reconstitute DigiFab in 40-mg vial with 36 ml of normal saline for 1 mg/ml concentration.

• Infuse over 30 minutes. If cardiac arrest is imminent, give as a bolus injection. Infuse via a 0.22-micron membrane filter to ensure no undissolved particulate matter is infused.

• Use reconstituted solution promptly. If not used immediately, refrigerate for up to 4 hours.

⊗ **Incompatibilities**

None reported.

Contraindications and cautions

• Use cautiously in patients allergic to ovine proteins. In these high-risk patients, perform skin test because drug is derived from digoxin-specific antibody fragments obtained from immunized sheep.

Lifespan: In pregnant women, use cautiously. In breast-feeding women, use cautiously; it's unknown if the drug appears in breast milk.

Adverse reactions

CV: ***heart failure, rapid ventricular rate.***
Metabolic: hypokalemia.
Other: ***anaphylaxis,*** hypersensitivity reactions.

Interactions

None reported.

Effects on lab test results

• May decrease potassium level.

Pharmacokinetics

Absorption: Given I.V.
Distribution: Unknown.
Metabolism: Unknown.
Excretion: In urine. *Half-life:* 15 to 20 hours.

Route	Onset	Peak	Duration
I.V.	Varies	End of dose	2–6 hr

Action

Chemical effect: Binds molecules of digoxin, making them unavailable for binding at site of action on cells.
Therapeutic effect: Reverses digoxin toxicity.

Available forms

Injection: 38-mg vial (Digibind) and 40-mg vial (DigiFab)

NURSING PROCESS

Assessment

• Obtain history of patient's digoxin intoxication before therapy.
• Monitor effectiveness by watching for decreased signs and symptoms of digoxin toxicity. In most patients, signs of digoxin toxicity disappear within a few hours.
• Because drug interferes with digoxin immunoassay measurements, standard digoxin levels are misleading until drug is cleared from body (about 2 days).
• Watch for adverse reactions.
• Assess patient's and family's knowledge of drug therapy.

Nursing diagnoses

• Ineffective health maintenance related to digoxin intoxication
• Decreased cardiac output related to drug-induced heart failure
• Deficient knowledge related to drug therapy

Planning and implementation

• Drug is used only for life-threatening overdose in patients with shock or cardiac arrest; ventricular arrhythmias, such as ventricular tachycardia or fibrillation; progressive bradycardia, such as severe sinus bradycardia; or second- or third-degree AV block not responsive to atropine.
• Give oxygen. Keep resuscitation equipment nearby.

Patient teaching

• Instruct patient to report respiratory difficulty, chest pain, or dizziness immediately.

Evaluation

• Patient exhibits improved health with alleviation of digoxin toxicity.
• Patient demonstrates adequate cardiac output through normal vital signs and urine output and clear mental condition.
• Patient and family state understanding of drug therapy.

diltiazem hydrochloride

(dil-TIGH-uh-zem high-droh-KLOR-ighd)

Cardizem, Cardizem CD, Cardizem LA, Cartia XT, Dilacor XR, Dilt-XR, Diltia XT, Taztia XT, Tiazac

Pharmacologic class: calcium channel blocker
Therapeutic class: antianginal, antihypertensive
Pregnancy risk category: C

Indications and dosages

▶ **Vasospastic angina (Prinzmetal [variant] angina), classic chronic stable angina pectoris.** *Adults:* 30 mg P.O. t.i.d. or q.i.d. before meals and at bedtime. Increase dosage gradually to maximum, 360 mg daily in divided doses. Or

120- to 180-mg extended-release capsules P.O. once daily. Adjust dosage up to 480 mg once daily.

▶ **Chronic stable angina.** *Adults:* Initially, 180 mg (Cardizem LA, Cardizem CD, or extended-release capsules) once daily in the morning or evening. May increase at intervals of 1 to 2 weeks if needed to maximum 360 mg.

▶ **Hypertension.** *Adults:* Initially, 180- to 240-mg extended-release capsules daily. Adjust dosage as needed. As monotherapy, 120 to 240 mg Cardizem LA P.O. once daily at the same time each day, either in the morning or at bedtime. Adjust dosage about q 14 days. Maximum, 540 mg daily.

▶ **Atrial fibrillation or flutter; paroxysmal supraventricular tachycardia.** *Adults:* 0.25 mg/kg as I.V. bolus injection over 2 minutes. If response is inadequate, 0.35 mg/kg I.V. after 15 minutes, followed with continuous infusion of 10 mg/hour. May increase in increments of 5 mg/hour. Maximum, 15 mg/hour.

I.V. administration

- For direct I.V. injection, no dilution of 5 mg/ml injection is needed.
- For continuous I.V. infusion, add 5 mg/ml injection to 100, 200, or 500 ml of normal saline solution, D_5W, or 5% dextrose and half-normal saline solution to produce a final concentration of 1, 0.83, or 0.45 mg/ml, respectively.
- Reconstitute drug in monovials and store up to 24 hours in PVC bag as directed.
- For direct injection or continuous infusion, give slowly while continuously monitoring ECG and blood pressure.
- Don't give reconstituted solutions stored longer than 24 hours or those with discoloration or visible particulate matter.

⊗ **Incompatibilities**

Acetazolamide, acyclovir, aminophylline, ampicillin, cefoperazone, diazepam, furosemide, heparin, hydrocortisone, insulin, methylprednisolone, nafcillin, phenytoin, rifampin, sodium bicarbonate, thiopental.

Contraindications and cautions

- Contraindicated in patients hypersensitive to drug and in those with sick sinus syndrome, second- or third-degree AV block without artificial pacemaker, hypotension (systolic blood pressure below 90 mm Hg), acute MI, or pulmonary congestion (documented by X-ray).
- Use cautiously in patients with heart failure and those with impaired liver or kidney function.

Lifespan: In pregnant women, use cautiously. Women who are breast-feeding should stop breast-feeding or not use this drug. In children, safety and effectiveness haven't been established. In elderly patients, use cautiously.

Adverse reactions

CNS: asthenia, dizziness, *headache,* insomnia, somnolence.
CV: abnormal ECG, ***arrhythmias, AV block, bradycardia,*** conduction abnormalities, *edema,* flushing, ***heart failure,*** hypotension.
GI: abdominal discomfort, constipation, diarrhea, nausea, vomiting.
GU: nocturia, polyuria.
Skin: photosensitivity, pruritus, rash.

Interactions

Drug-drug. *Anesthetics:* May potentiate effects. Monitor patient.
Carbamazepine: May cause increased carbamazepine levels. Monitor serum levels and adjust dosage as needed.
Cimetidine: May inhibit diltiazem metabolism. Monitor patient for toxicity.
Cyclosporine: May increase cyclosporine levels by decreasing its metabolism, leading to increased risk of cyclosporine toxicity. Avoid use together.
Diazepam, midazolam, triazolam: May increase CNS depression and prolong effects of these drugs. Use lower dose of these benzodiazepines.
Digoxin: May increase levels of digoxin. Monitor patient and digoxin levels.
Propranolol, other beta blockers: May precipitate heart failure or prolong cardiac conduction time. Use together cautiously.
Quinidine: May cause increased quinidine effects. Use together cautiously.
Drug-lifestyle. *Sun exposure:* May cause photosensitivity reactions. Advise patient to avoid unprotected or prolonged sun exposure.

Effects on lab test results

- May cause transient increase in liver enzyme levels.

Pharmacokinetics

Absorption: 80%. 40% of drug enters systemic circulation because of significant first-pass effect in liver.
Distribution: 70% to 85% of circulating drug is bound to plasma proteins.
Metabolism: In liver.
Excretion: 35% in urine and 65% in bile as unchanged drug and inactive and active metabolites. *Half-life:* 2 to 11 hours.

Route	Onset	Peak	Duration
P.O.	30 min–4 hr	2–18 hr	6–24 hr
I.V.			
bolus	3 min	Immediate	1–3 hr
infusion	3 min	Immediate	< 10 hr

Action

Chemical effect: Inhibits calcium ion influx across cardiac and smooth muscle cells, decreasing myocardial contractility and oxygen demand; also dilates coronary arteries and arterioles.
Therapeutic effect: Relieves anginal pain, lowers blood pressure, and restores normal sinus rhythm.

Available forms

Capsules (extended-release): 60 mg, 90 mg, 120 mg, 180 mg, 240 mg, 300 mg, 360 mg, 420 mg
Injection: 5 mg/ml (25 mg and 50 mg)
Tablets: 30 mg, 60 mg, 90 mg, 120 mg

NURSING PROCESS

Assessment

- Obtain history of patient's underlying condition before therapy, and reassess regularly thereafter.
- Monitor blood pressure when therapy starts and when dosage changes.
- Monitor patient's ECG and heart rate and rhythm regularly.
- Be alert for adverse reactions and drug interactions.
- Assess patient's and family's knowledge of drug therapy.

Nursing diagnoses

- Ineffective health maintenance related to underlying condition
- Decreased cardiac output related to drug-induced adverse reactions
- Deficient knowledge related to drug therapy

Planning and implementation

- Give tablets before meals and at bedtime.
- Patients controlled on diltiazem alone or with other medications may be switched to Cardizem LA tablets once a day at the nearest equivalent total daily dose.

ALERT: If systolic blood pressure is below 90 mm Hg or heart rate is below 60 beats/minute, don't give the dose and notify prescriber.

- Assist patient with ambulation during start of therapy because dizziness may occur.
- To minimize edema, restrict the patient's fluid and sodium intake.

Patient teaching

- If nitrate therapy is prescribed during adjustment of diltiazem dosage, urge patient compliance. Tell patient that S.L. nitroglycerin may be taken p.r.n. and as directed when angina is acute.
- Instruct patient to call prescriber if he experiences chest pain, shortness of breath, dizziness, palpitations, or swelling of the limbs.
- Tell patient to swallow extended-release capsules whole and not to open, crush, or chew them.
- Instruct patient to take drug exactly as prescribed, even when feeling better.
- Advise patient to minimize exposure to direct sunlight and to take precautions when in sun because of drug-induced photosensitivity.
- Instruct patient to limit fluid and sodium intake to minimize edema.

Evaluation

- Patient exhibits improvement in underlying condition.
- Patient maintains adequate cardiac output throughout therapy.
- Patient and family state understanding of drug therapy.

diphenhydramine hydrochloride

(digh-fen-HIGH-drah-meen high-droh-KLOR-ighd)

Allerdryl ♦ †, AllerMax Caplets†, Banophen†, Banophen Caplets†, Beldin† Benadryl†, Benadryl 25†, Benadryl Kapseals, Benylin Cough†, Bydramine Cough†, Compoz†, Diphenadryl†, Diphen Cough†, Diphenhist†, Diphenhist Captabs†, Genahist†, Hyrexin-50, Nytol Maximum Strength†, Nytol with DPH†, Sleep-Eze 3†, Sominex Formula 2†, Tusstat†, Twilite Caplets†, Uni-Bent Cough†

Pharmacologic class: nonselective ethanolamine derivative antihistamine
Therapeutic class: antihistamine (H_1-receptor antagonist), antitussive, sleep aid
Pregnancy risk category: B

Indications and dosages

▶ **Rhinitis, allergy symptoms, motion sickness, Parkinson disease.** *Adults and children age 12 and older:* 25 to 50 mg P.O. t.i.d. or q.i.d. Or 10 to 50 mg deep I.M. or I.V. Maximum I.M. or I.V. dosage, 400 mg daily.
Children younger than age 12: Give 5 mg/kg daily P.O., deep I.M., or I.V. in divided doses q.i.d. Maximum, 300 mg daily.

▶ **Sedation.** *Adults:* 25 to 50 mg P.O. or deep I.M., p.r.n.

▶ **Nighttime sleep aid.** *Adults:* 50 mg P.O. at bedtime.

▶ **Nonproductive cough.** *Adults:* 25 mg P.O. q 4 to 6 hours (up to 150 mg daily).
Children ages 6 to 11: Give 12.5 mg P.O. q 4 to 6 hours (up to 75 mg daily).
Children ages 2 to 5: Give 6.25 mg P.O. q 4 to 6 hours (up to 25 mg daily).

I.V. administration

- Make sure I.V. site is patent, and monitor it for irritation.
- Don't give I.V. drug faster than 25 mg/minute.

⊗ **Incompatibilities**

Allopurinol, amobarbital, amphotericin B, cefepime, dexamethasone, foscarnet, haloperidol lactate, pentobarbital, phenytoin, phenobarbital, thiopental.

Contraindications and cautions

- Contraindicated in patients hypersensitive to drug and in patients having acute asthma attacks.
- Use cautiously in patients with CV disease, hypertension, angle-closure glaucoma, increased intraocular pressure, stenosing peptic ulcer, pyloroduodenal and bladder-neck obstruction, prostatic hyperplasia, hyperthyroidism, asthma, or COPD.

Lifespan: In pregnant women, use cautiously. In neonates, premature neonates, and breast-feeding women, drug is contraindicated. In children younger than age 12, safety and effectiveness as a night-time sleep aid haven't been established. Children younger than age 6 should use only when directed by prescriber. Age restrictions for topical preparations vary depending on drug's formulation and manufacturer.

Adverse reactions

CNS: confusion, *dizziness, drowsiness,* fatigue, headache, incoordination, insomnia, nervousness, restlessness, *sedation,* ***seizures,*** *sleepiness,* tremor, vertigo.
CV: hypotension, palpitations, tachycardia.
EENT: blurred vision, diplopia, nasal congestion, tinnitus.
GI: anorexia, constipation, diarrhea, *dry mouth, epigastric distress, nausea,* vomiting.
GU: dysuria, urinary frequency, urine retention.
Hematologic: ***agranulocytosis,*** hemolytic anemia, ***thrombocytopenia.***
Respiratory: thickening of bronchial secretions.
Skin: photosensitivity, rash, urticaria.
Other: ***anaphylactic shock.***

Interactions

Drug-drug. *CNS depressants:* May increase sedation. Use together cautiously; monitor patient for increased sedation.
MAO inhibitors: May increase anticholinergic effects. Don't use together.
Other products containing diphenhydramine, including topical forms: May increase risk of adverse reactions. Avoid use together.
Drug-lifestyle. *Alcohol use:* May increase adverse CNS effects. Discourage use together.
Sun exposure: May cause photosensitivity reactions. Urge patient to wear protective clothing and sunblock.

Effects on lab test results

- May decrease hemoglobin level and hematocrit.
- May decrease platelet and granulocyte counts.

Pharmacokinetics

Absorption: Good after P.O. use.
Distribution: Wide, including CNS. About 82% protein-bound.
Metabolism: In liver.
Excretion: Drug and metabolites mainly in urine. *Half-life:* About 3½ hours.

Route	Onset	Peak	Duration
P.O.	≤ 15 min	1–4 hr	6–8 hr
I.V.	Immediate	1–4 hr	6–8 hr
I.M.	Unknown	1–4 hr	6–8 hr

Action

Chemical effect: Competes with histamine for H_1-receptor sites on effector cells. Prevents but doesn't reverse histamine-mediated responses, particularly histamine's effects on smooth muscle of bronchial tubes, GI tract, uterus, and blood vessels. Provides local anesthesia by preventing initiation and transmission of nerve impulses, and suppresses cough reflex by direct effect in medulla of brain.
Therapeutic effect: Relieves allergy symptoms, motion sickness, and cough; improves voluntary movement; and promotes sleep and calmness.

Available forms

Capsules: 25 mg†, 50 mg†
Chewable tablets: 12.5 mg†
Elixir: 12.5 mg/5 ml*†
Injection: 10 mg/ml, 50 mg/ml
Syrup: 12.5 mg/5 ml†, 6.25 mg/5 ml†
Tablets: 25 mg†, 50 mg†

NURSING PROCESS

Assessment

- Obtain history of patient's underlying condition before therapy, and reassess regularly thereafter.
- Be alert for adverse reactions and drug interactions.
- Assess patient's and family's knowledge of drug therapy.

Nursing diagnoses

- Ineffective health maintenance related to underlying condition
- Risk for injury related to drug-induced adverse CNS reactions
- Deficient knowledge related to drug therapy

Planning and implementation

- Reduce GI distress by giving drug with food or milk.
- Alternate injection sites to prevent irritation. Give I.M. injection deep into large muscle.
- If tolerance is observed, notify prescriber because another antihistamine may need to be substituted.

ALERT: Don't confuse diphenhydramine with dicyclomine, or Benadryl with Bentyl or Benylin.

Patient teaching

- Instruct patient to take drug 30 minutes before travel, to prevent motion sickness.
- Warn patient to avoid alcohol and to refrain from driving or performing other hazardous activities that require alertness.
- Tell patient that coffee or tea may reduce drowsiness.
- Inform patient that ice chips, sugarless gum, or hard candy may relieve dry mouth.
- Advise patient to stop taking the drug 4 days before allergy skin tests to preserve test accuracy.
- Tell patient to notify prescriber if tolerance develops because different antihistamine may need to be prescribed.
- Warn patient that he may be photosensitive. Advise use of sunblock or protective clothing.
- Warn patient to avoid using other products containing diphenhydramine, including topical forms, because of risk of adverse reactions.

Evaluation

- Patient shows improvement in underlying condition.
- Patient has no injury as result of therapy.
- Patient and family state understanding of drug therapy.

diphenoxylate hydrochloride and atropine sulfate

(digh-fen-OKS-ul-ayt high-droh-KLOR-ighd and AH-troh-peen SUL-fayt)

Logen, Lomanate, Lomotil*, Lonox

Pharmacologic class: opioid
Therapeutic class: antidiarrheal
Pregnancy risk category: C
Controlled substance schedule: V

Indications and dosages

▶ **Acute, nonspecific diarrhea.** *Adults:* Initially, 5 mg P.O. q.i.d.; then reduce dosage as soon as initial control is achieved. Maximum, 20 mg P.O. daily.
Children ages 2 to 12: Give 0.3 to 0.4 mg/kg liquid form P.O. daily in four divided doses. Maintenance dosage may be as low as 25% of initial dosage. Maximum, 20 mg P.O. daily.

Contraindications and cautions

- Contraindicated in patients hypersensitive to drug or any of its components and in those with acute diarrhea from poison (until toxic material is eliminated), acute diarrhea caused by organisms that penetrate the intestinal mucosa, or diarrhea from antibiotic-induced pseudomembranous enterocolitis. Also contraindicated in jaundiced patients.
- Use cautiously in patients with hepatic disease, opioid dependence, or acute ulcerative colitis. If abdominal distention or other signs of toxic megacolon develop, stop therapy immediately and notify prescriber.

Lifespan: In pregnant women, use cautiously. In breast-feeding women, drug isn't recommended. In children ages 2 to 12, use cautiously and in liquid form only. In children younger than age 2, drug is contraindicated.

Adverse reactions

CNS: confusion, depression, *dizziness,* drowsiness, euphoria, headache, lethargy, malaise, numbness in limbs, restlessness, *sedation.*
CV: tachycardia.
EENT: mydriasis.
GI: abdominal discomfort or distention, anorexia, *dry mouth,* fluid retention in bowel, nausea, ***pancreatitis,*** paralytic ileus, vomiting.
GU: urine retention.
Respiratory: ***respiratory depression.***
Skin: pruritus, rash.
Other: ***angioedema, anaphylaxis,*** possible physical dependence with long-term use.

Interactions

Drug-drug. *Barbiturates, CNS depressants, opioids, tranquilizers:* May increase CNS depression. Monitor patient closely for increased sedation.
MAO inhibitors: May cause a hypertensive crisis. Don't use together.
Drug-lifestyle. *Alcohol use:* May increase CNS depression. Discourage use together.

Effects on lab test results

None reported.

Pharmacokinetics

Absorption: 90%.
Distribution: Unknown.
Metabolism: Extensive.
Excretion: Metabolites mainly in feces with lesser amounts in urine. *Half-life:* Diphenoxylate, 2½ hours; its major metabolite, diphenoxylic acid, 4½ hours; atropine, 2½ hours.

Route	Onset	Peak	Duration
P.O.	45–60 min	2 hr	3–4 hr

Action

Chemical effect: Unknown; probably increases smooth-muscle tone in GI tract, inhibits motility and propulsion, and diminishes secretions.
Therapeutic effect: Relieves diarrhea.

Available forms

Liquid: 2.5 mg/5 ml (with atropine sulfate 0.025 mg/5 ml)*
Tablets: 2.5 mg (with atropine sulfate 0.025 mg)

NURSING PROCESS

Assessment

- Assess patient's diarrhea before and regularly during therapy.
- Be alert for adverse reactions and drug interactions.
- Assess patient's and family's knowledge of drug therapy.

Nursing diagnoses
- Diarrhea related to underlying condition
- Ineffective breathing pattern related to drug-induced respiratory depression
- Deficient knowledge related to drug therapy

Planning and implementation
- Fluid retention in the bowel may mask depletion of extracellular fluid and electrolytes, especially in young children with acute gastroenteritis. Correct fluid and electrolyte disturbances before starting therapy. Dehydration may increase risk of delayed toxicity.
- A 2.5-mg dose is as effective as 5 ml of camphorated opium tincture.
- Drug isn't indicated for treating antibiotic-induced diarrhea.
- Drug is unlikely to be effective if patient doesn't respond within 48 hours.
- Risk of physical dependence increases with high dosage and long-term use. Atropine sulfate helps discourage abuse.
- Use naloxone to treat respiratory depression caused by overdose.

ALERT: Don't confuse Lomotil (diphenoxylate hydrochloride and atropine sulfate) with Lamictal (lamotrigine).

Patient teaching
- Tell patient not to exceed prescribed dosage.
- Warn patient not to use drug to treat acute diarrhea for longer than 2 days. Encourage him to seek medical attention if diarrhea persists.
- Advise patient to avoid hazardous activities, such as driving, until CNS effects of drug are known.

Evaluation
- Patient regains normal bowel pattern.
- Patient maintains normal breathing pattern throughout therapy.
- Patient and family state understanding of drug therapy.

dipyridamole
(digh-peer-IH-duh-mohl)

Apo-Dipyridamole ♦, Novo-Dipiradol ♦, Persantin ◇, Persantin 100 SR ◇, Persantine

Pharmacologic class: pyrimidine analogue
Therapeutic class: coronary vasodilator, platelet aggregation inhibitor
Pregnancy risk category: B

Indications and dosages
▶ **To inhibit platelet adhesion in prosthetic heart valves.** *Adults:* 75 to 100 mg P.O. q.i.d. (with warfarin or aspirin).

▶ **Alternative to exercise in evaluation of coronary artery disease during thallium-201 myocardial perfusion scintigraphy.** *Adults:* 0.57 mg/kg as I.V. infusion at constant rate over 4 minutes (0.142 mg/kg/minute).

▶ **Chronic angina pectoris‡.** *Adults:* 50 mg P.O. t.i.d. at least 1 hour before meals; 2 to 3 months of therapy may be required to achieve therapeutic response.

▶ **To prevent thromboembolic complications in patients with thromboembolic disorders other than prosthetic heart valves‡.** *Adults:* 150 to 400 mg P.O. daily (with warfarin or aspirin).

I.V. administration
- If giving drug as a diagnostic agent, dilute in half-normal or normal saline solution or D_5W in at least a 1:2 ratio for total volume of 20 to 50 ml.
- Inject thallium-201 within 5 minutes of completing 4-minute infusion.
- Avoid freezing and protect from direct light.

⊗ Incompatibilities
Other I.V. drugs.

Contraindications and cautions
- Use cautiously in patients with hypotension.

Lifespan: In pregnant women, use cautiously. In breast-feeding women and in children, safety and effectiveness haven't been established.

Adverse reactions
CNS: *dizziness, headache,* weakness.

CV: blood pressure lability, chest pain, ECG abnormalities, fainting, flushing, hypertension (with I.V. infusion), hypotension.
GI: abdominal distress, diarrhea, nausea, vomiting.
Skin: irritation (with undiluted injection), pruritus, rash.

Interactions

Drug-drug. *Heparin:* May increase bleeding. Monitor patient closely for increased bleeding; monitor PTT.
Theophylline: May prevent coronary vasodilation by I.V. dipyridamole. Avoid use together.
Drug-herb. *Dong quai, feverfew, garlic, ginger, horse chestnut, red clover:* May increase risk of bleeding. Discourage use together.

Effects on lab test results

None reported.

Pharmacokinetics

Absorption: Variable and slow; 27% to 59%.
Distribution: Wide. 91% to 97% protein-bound.
Metabolism: By liver.
Excretion: By way of biliary excretion of glucuronide conjugates. Some dipyridamole and conjugates may undergo enterohepatic circulation and fecal excretion; small amount in urine. *Half-life:* 10 to 12 hours

Route	Onset	Peak	Duration
P.O.	Unknown	45–150 min	Unknown
I.V.	Unknown	2 min after therapy	Unknown
I.M.	Unknown	Unknown	Unknown

Action

Chemical effect: May involve its ability to increase adenosine, which is a coronary vasodilator and platelet aggregation inhibitor.
Therapeutic effect: Dilates coronary arteries and helps prevent clotting.

Available forms

Injection: 10 mg/2 ml
Tablets: 25 mg, 50 mg, 75 mg

NURSING PROCESS

Assessment

- Obtain history of patient's underlying condition before therapy, and reassess regularly thereafter.
- Be alert for adverse reactions and drug interactions.
- Assess patient's and family's knowledge of drug therapy.

Nursing diagnoses

- Ineffective cardiopulmonary tissue perfusion related to underlying condition
- Acute pain related to drug-induced headache
- Deficient knowledge related to drug therapy

Planning and implementation

- Give drug 1 hour before meals. If patient develops adverse GI reactions, give drug with meals.
- The value of dipyridamole as part of an antithrombotic regimen is controversial; its use may not provide significantly better results than aspirin alone.

ALERT: Don't confuse dipyridamole with disopyramide; or Persantine with Periactin.

Patient teaching

- Instruct patient when to take drug.
- Tell patient to have his blood pressure checked frequently.
- Advise patient to take mild analgesic if headache occurs.
- Instruct patient to notify prescriber if chest pain occurs.

Evaluation

- Patient maintains adequate tissue perfusion and cellular oxygenation.
- Patient obtains relief from drug-induced headache with use of mild analgesic.
- Patient and family state understanding of drug therapy.

disopyramide
(digh-so-PEER-uh-mighd)
Rythmodan ♦ ◇

disopyramide phosphate
Norpace, Norpace CR, Rythmodan LA ♦

Pharmacologic class: pyridine derivative
Therapeutic class: antiarrhythmic
Pregnancy risk category: C

Indications and dosages

▶ **Symptomatic PVCs (unifocal, multifocal, or coupled); ventricular tachycardia not severe enough to require cardioversion.**
Adults: For parenteral use, initially give 2 mg/kg I.V. slowly (over at least 15 minutes). Give drug until arrhythmia is gone or patient has received 150 mg. If conversion is successful but arrhythmia returns, repeat dosage. Don't exceed total I.V. dosage of 300 mg in first hour. Follow with I.V. infusion of 0.4 mg/kg/hour (usually 20 to 30 mg/hour) to maximum, 800 mg daily.
Adults weighing more than 50 kg (110 lb): Initial loading dose is 300 mg P.O. for rapid control of ventricular arrhythmia. Follow with 150 mg q 6 hours or 300 mg q 12 hours with controlled-release capsules.
Adults weighing 50 kg or less: Initial loading dose is 200 mg P.O., then 100 mg P.O. q 6 hours as conventional capsules or 200 mg P.O. q 12 hours with controlled-release capsules.
Children ages 12 to 18: Give 6 to 15 mg/kg P.O. daily, divided into equal amounts and given q 6 hours.
Children ages 4 to 12: Give 10 to 15 mg/kg P.O. daily, divided into equal amounts and given q 6 hours.
Children ages 1 to 4: Give 10 to 20 mg/kg P.O. daily, divided into equal amounts and given q 6 hours.
Children younger than age 1: Give 10 to 30 mg/kg P.O. daily, divided into equal amounts and given q 6 hours.
Adjust-a-dose: For patients with renal impairment, if creatinine clearance is 30 to 40 ml/minute, give 100 mg q 8 hours. If creatinine clearance is 15 to 30 ml/minute, give 100 mg q 12 hours. If creatinine clearance is less than 15 ml/minute, give 100 mg q 24 hours.

I.V. administration

- Add 200 mg to 500 ml of compatible solution, such as normal saline solution or D_5W.
- Use an infusion pump. Don't mix with other drugs.
- Give slowly over at least 15 minutes.
- Switch to P.O. therapy as soon as possible.

⊗ **Incompatibilities**
Other I.V. drugs.

Contraindications and cautions

- Contraindicated in patients hypersensitive to the drug or any of its components and in those with cardiogenic shock or second- or third-degree heart block without an artificial pacemaker.
- Use cautiously or avoid using, if possible, in patients with heart failure.
- Use cautiously in patients with underlying conduction abnormalities, urinary tract diseases (especially prostatic hypertrophy), hepatic or renal impairment, myasthenia gravis, or acute angle-closure glaucoma.

Lifespan: In pregnant women, use cautiously. In breast-feeding women, drug isn't recommended.

Adverse reactions

CNS: *acute psychosis,* agitation, depression, dizziness, fatigue, headache, syncope.
CV: ***arrhythmias,*** chest pain, edema, ***heart block, heart failure,*** hypotension.
EENT: blurred vision, dry eyes, dry nose.
GI: abdominal pain, anorexia, bloating, *constipation,* diarrhea, *dry mouth,* nausea, vomiting.
GU: *urinary hesitancy,* urine retention.
Hepatic: cholestatic jaundice.
Metabolic: weight gain.
Musculoskeletal: aches, muscle weakness, pain.
Respiratory: shortness of breath.
Skin: dermatosis, pruritus, rash.

Interactions

Drug-drug. *Antiarrhythmics:* May cause additive or antagonized antiarrhythmic effects. Monitor patient ECG closely.
Erythromycin: May increase disopyramide level, causing arrhythmias and prolonged QTc interval. Monitor ECG closely.

Phenytoin: May increase metabolism of disopyramide. Monitor patient for decreased antiarrhythmic effect.
Rifampin: May decrease disopyramide level. Monitor patient for decreased effectiveness.
Drug-herb. *Jimson weed:* May adversely affect CV function. Discourage use together.

Effects on lab test results

None reported.

Pharmacokinetics

Absorption: Rapid and good.
Distribution: Throughout extracellular fluid but not extensively bound to tissues. 50% to 65% protein-bound.
Metabolism: In liver.
Excretion: In urine. *Half-life:* 7 hours.

Route	Onset	Peak	Duration
P.O.	½–3½ hr	2–2½ hr	1½–8½ hr
I.V.	Unknown	Unknown	Unknown

Action

Chemical effect: May depress phase 0 and prolong action potential. All class I drugs have membrane-stabilizing effects.
Therapeutic effect: Restores normal sinus rhythm.

Available forms

disopyramide
Capsules: 100 mg ♦, 150 mg ♦
disopyramide phosphate
Capsules: 100 mg, 150 mg
Capsules (controlled-release): 100 mg, 150 mg
Injection: 10 mg/ml ♦ ◊
Tablets (sustained-release): 150 mg ♦

NURSING PROCESS

Assessment

- Obtain history of patient's arrhythmia before therapy.
- Monitor drug effectiveness by assessing patient's ECG pattern and apical pulse rate.
- Be alert for adverse reactions and drug interactions.
- Assess patient's and family's knowledge of drug therapy.

Nursing diagnoses

- Decreased cardiac output related to underlying arrhythmia
- Ineffective protection related to drug-induced proarrhythmias
- Deficient knowledge related to drug therapy

Planning and implementation

- Correct electrolyte abnormalities before therapy begins.
- Check apical pulse before therapy. Notify prescriber if pulse rate is slower than 60 beats/minute or faster than 120 beats/minute.
- Don't use sustained- and controlled-release preparations for rapid control of ventricular arrhythmias, when therapeutic levels must be rapidly attained; in patients with cardiomyopathy or suspected cardiac decompensation; or in those with severe renal impairment.
- For young children, pharmacist may prepare disopyramide suspension from 100-mg capsules using cherry syrup. Suspension should be dispensed in amber glass bottles and protected from light.
- If heart block develops, QRS complex widens by more than 25%, or QT interval is prolonged by more than 25% above baseline; stop the drug and notify the prescriber.

Patient teaching

- When switching patient from immediate- to sustained-release capsules, advise taking sustained-release capsule 6 hours after last immediate-release capsule.
- Teach patient importance of taking drug on time and exactly as prescribed. This may require use of alarm clock for night doses.
- Advise patient to use sugarless gum or hard candy to relieve dry mouth.
- Tell patient not to crush or chew extended-release tablets.

Evaluation

- Patient's ECG reveals that arrhythmia has been corrected.
- Patient develops no new arrhythmias as result of therapy.
- Patient and family state understanding of drug therapy.

disulfiram

(digh-SUL-fih-ram)
Antabuse

Pharmacologic class: aldehyde dehydrogenase inhibitor
Therapeutic class: alcohol deterrent
Pregnancy risk category: C

Indications and dosages

▶ **Adjunct to manage alcohol dependence.** *Adults:* 250 to 500 mg P.O. as single dose in morning for 1 to 2 weeks. If drowsiness occurs, give in the evening. Maintenance dosage is 125 to 500 mg P.O. daily (average dosage, 250 mg) until permanent self-control is established. Therapy may continue for months or years.

Contraindications and cautions

- Contraindicated during alcohol intoxication and within 12 hours of alcohol ingestion. Also contraindicated in patients hypersensitive to disulfiram or thiram derivatives used in pesticides and rubber vulcanization; patients with psychoses, myocardial disease, or coronary occlusion; and patients receiving metronidazole, paraldehyde, alcohol, or alcohol-containing preparations.
- Use cautiously in patients receiving phenytoin therapy and in patients with diabetes mellitus, hypothyroidism, seizure disorder, cerebral damage, nephritis, or hepatic cirrhosis or insufficiency.

Lifespan: In pregnant women, don't use. In breast-feeding women, use cautiously. In children, safety and effectiveness haven't been established.

Adverse reactions

CNS: delirium, depression, drowsiness, fatigue, headache, neuritis, peripheral neuritis, polyneuritis, psychotic reactions, restlessness.
EENT: optic neuritis.
GI: metallic or garlic aftertaste.
GU: impotence.
Hepatic: ***hepatitis, hepatic failure.***
Skin: acneiform or allergic dermatitis.
Other: ***disulfiram reaction.***

Interactions

Drug-drug. *Alfentanil:* May prolong duration of effect. Monitor patient closely.
Anticoagulants: May increase anticoagulant effect. Adjust dosage of anticoagulant accordingly; monitor patient for bleeding.
CNS depressants: May increase CNS depression. Use together cautiously.
Isoniazid: May cause ataxia or marked change in behavior. Avoid use together.
Metronidazole: May cause psychotic reaction. Avoid use together; wait for 2 weeks following disulfiram.
Midazolam: May increase plasma levels of midazolam. Use together cautiously.
Paraldehyde: May cause toxic level of acetaldehyde. Don't use together.
Phenytoin: May increase toxic effects of phenytoin. Monitor phenytoin levels closely and adjust dose.
Tricyclic antidepressants, especially amitriptyline: May cause transient delirium. Monitor patient closely.
Drug-herb. *Passion flower, pill-bearing spurge, pokeweed, squaw vine, squill, sundew, sweet flag, tormentil, valerian, yarrow:* May cause disulfiram reaction if herb contains alcohol. Discourage use together.
Drug-food: *Caffeine:* May increase cardiovascular and CNS stimulant effects of caffeine. Advise against caffeine use.
Drug-lifestyle. *Alcohol use:* May cause disulfiram reaction, including flushing, tachycardia, bronchospasm, sweating, nausea, and vomiting. Death may also occur. Warn against any alcohol consumption.
Cocaine use: May increase adverse cardiovascular effects of cocaine. Inform patient of this interaction.

Effects on lab test results

- May increase cholesterol level.

Pharmacokinetics

Absorption: Complete.
Distribution: Highly lipid soluble and initially localized in fat.
Metabolism: Mostly oxidized in liver.
Excretion: Mainly in urine; 5% to 20% in feces. *Half-life:* Unknown.

Route	Onset	Peak	Duration
P.O.	1–2 hr	Unknown	< 14 days

Action

Chemical effect: Blocks oxidation of ethanol at acetaldehyde stage. Excess acetaldehyde produces highly unpleasant reaction in presence of even small amounts of ethanol.
Therapeutic effect: Deters alcohol consumption.

Available forms

Tablets: 250 mg, 500 mg

NURSING PROCESS

Assessment

- Obtain history of patient's alcoholism before therapy.
- Do a complete physical examination and laboratory studies, including CBC, chemistry panel, and transaminase determination before therapy. Repeat physical examination and laboratory studies regularly.
- Monitor the drug's effectiveness by assessing patient's abstinence from alcohol.
- Measure blood alcohol level weekly.
- Be alert for adverse reactions and drug interactions. Disulfiram reaction is precipitated by alcohol use and may include flushing, throbbing headache, dyspnea, nausea, copious vomiting, diaphoresis, thirst, chest pain, palpitations, hyperventilation, hypotension, syncope, anxiety, weakness, blurred vision, and confusion. Severe reaction may cause respiratory depression, CV collapse, arrhythmias, MI, acute heart failure, seizures, unconsciousness, and death.
- Mild reactions may occur in sensitive patients with blood alcohol levels of 5 to 10 mg/dl; symptoms are fully developed at 50 mg/dl. At 125 to 150 mg/dl, patient typically is unconscious. Reaction may last from 30 minutes to several hours or as long as alcohol remains in blood.
- Assess patient's and family's knowledge of drug therapy.

Nursing diagnoses

- Ineffective health maintenance related to alcoholism
- Acute pain related to drug-induced headache
- Deficient knowledge related to drug therapy

Planning and implementation

- Use only under close medical and nursing supervision. Only give drug to patient who hasn't used alcohol for at least 12 hours. Make sure that patient clearly understands consequences of therapy and gives permission for its use. Use drug only if patient is cooperative, well-motivated, and receiving supportive psychiatric therapy.
- Drug is usually given during the day, although it may be given at night if drowsiness occurs. Establish lowered maintenance dose until permanent self-control is practiced. Therapy may continue for months or years.

Patient teaching

- Caution patient's family that drug should never be given to the patient without his knowledge because severe reaction or death could result if the patient ingests alcohol.
- Warn patient to avoid all sources of alcohol (including, for example, sauces and cough syrups). Even external application of liniments, shaving lotion, and back-rub preparations may cause disulfiram reaction. Tell patient that alcohol reaction may occur as long as 2 weeks after single dose of disulfiram, and that the longer he remains on drug, the more sensitive he becomes to alcohol.
- Tell patient to wear or carry medical identification identifying him as a disulfiram user.
- Reassure patient that drug-induced adverse reactions (unrelated to alcohol use), such as drowsiness, fatigue, impotence, headache, peripheral neuritis, and metallic or garlic taste, subside after about 2 weeks of therapy.

Evaluation

- Patient abstains from alcohol consumption.
- Patient's headache is relieved with mild analgesic therapy.
- Patient and family state understanding of drug therapy.

dobutamine hydrochloride

(doh-BYOO-tuh-meen high-droh-KLOR-ighd)
Dobutrex

Pharmacologic class: adrenergic, $beta_1$ agonist
Therapeutic class: inotropic drug
Pregnancy risk category: B

Indications and dosages

▶ To increase cardiac output in short-term treatment of cardiac decompensation caused

by depressed contractility, such as during refractory heart failure, and as adjunct in cardiac surgery. *Adults:* 2 to 20 mcg/kg/minute I.V. infusion. Usual dosage range is 2.5 to 10 mcg/kg/minute. Rarely, rates up to 40 mcg/kg/minute may be needed; however, such doses may worsen ischemia.

I.V. administration

- Dilute concentrate for injection to no more than 5 mg/ml. Compatible solutions include D_5W, half-normal saline solution injection, normal saline solution injection, and lactated Ringer's injection. The contents of one vial (250 mg) diluted with 1,000 ml of solution yield 250 mcg/ml; diluted with 500 ml, 500 mcg/ml; diluted with 250 ml, 1,000 mcg/ml.
- Oxidation of drug may slightly discolor admixtures containing dobutamine. This doesn't indicate significant loss of potency, provided drug is used within 24 hours of reconstitution.
- Don't mix with sodium bicarbonate injection because drug is incompatible with alkaline solutions.
- Don't give in same I.V. line with other drugs. Drug is incompatible with heparin, hydrocortisone sodium succinate, cefazolin, neutral cephalothin, penicillin, and ethacrynate sodium.
- Give drug using central venous catheter or large peripheral vein. Titrate infusion according to patient's condition per prescriber's guidelines. Use infusion pump.
- Watch for irritation and infiltration. Extravasation can cause inflammation, tissue damage, and necrosis. Change I.V. sites regularly to avoid phlebitis.
- Solutions remain stable for 24 hours.

⊗ **Incompatibilities**
Acyclovir, alkaline solutions, alteplase, aminophylline, bretylium, bumetanide, calcium chloride, calcium gluconate, cefepime, diazepam, digoxin, doxapram, furosemide, heparin, indomethacin, insulin, magnesium sulfate, midazolam, piperacillin with tazobactam, phenytoin, phytonadione, potassium chloride, sodium bicarbonate, thiopental, verapamil, warfarin.

Contraindications and cautions

- Contraindicated in patients hypersensitive to drug or any of its components and in those with idiopathic hypertrophic subaortic stenosis.
- Use cautiously in patients with history of hypertension. Drug may cause exaggerated pressor response.

Lifespan: In pregnant and breast-feeding women and in children, safety and effectiveness haven't been established.

Adverse reactions

CNS: headache.
CV: angina, *hypertension, hypotension, increased heart rate,* nonspecific chest pain, phlebitis, *PVCs.*
GI: nausea, vomiting.
Musculoskeletal: mild leg cramps or tingling sensation.
Respiratory: ***asthma attacks,*** shortness of breath.
Other: ***anaphylaxis.***

Interactions

Drug-drug. *Beta blockers:* May antagonize dobutamine effects. Don't use together.
Bretylium: May potentiate action of vasopressors on adrenergic receptors; arrhythmias may result. Monitor ECG closely.
General anesthetics: May increase risk of ventricular arrhythmias. Monitor patient closely.
Guanethidine: May increase pressor response possibly causing severe hypertension. Monitor closely.
Oxytocic drugs: May cause severe persistent hypertension. Use with caution.
Tricyclic antidepressants: May potentiate the pressor response and cause arrhythmias. Use with caution.
Drug-herb. *Rue:* May increase inotropic potential. Monitor vital signs closely.

Effects on lab test results

- May decrease potassium level.

Pharmacokinetics

Absorption: Given I.V.
Distribution: Wide.
Metabolism: By liver.
Excretion: Mainly in urine with minor amounts in feces. *Half-life:* 2 minutes.

Route	Onset	Peak	Duration
I.V.	1–2 min	≤ 10 min	Unknown

Action

Chemical effect: Directly stimulates $beta_1$ receptors to increase myocardial contractility and stroke volume. Decreases peripheral vascular resistance (afterload), reduces ventricular filling pressure (preload), and may facilitate AV node conduction.
Therapeutic effect: Increases cardiac output.

Available forms

Injection: 12.5 mg/ml in 20-ml vials.
Premixed: 0.5 mg/ml (125 mg or 250 mg) in D_5W, 1 mg/ml (250 mg or 500 mg) in D_5W 2 mg/ml (500 mg) in D_5W, 4 mg/ml (1000 mg) in D_5W

NURSING PROCESS

Assessment

- Assess patient's condition before therapy and regularly thereafter.
- Continuously monitor ECG, blood pressure, pulmonary capillary wedge pressure, cardiac condition, and urine output.
- Monitor electrolyte level.
- Be alert for adverse reactions and drug interactions.
- Assess patient's and family's knowledge of drug therapy.

Nursing diagnoses

- Decreased cardiac output related to underlying condition
- Acute pain related to headache
- Deficient knowledge related to drug therapy

Planning and implementation

- Before starting therapy, correct hypovolemia with plasma volume expanders.
- Give digoxin before giving this drug. Because drug increases AV node conduction, patients with atrial fibrillation may develop rapid ventricular rate.

ALERT: Don't confuse dobutamine with dopamine.

Patient teaching

- Tell patient to report chest pain, shortness of breath, and headache.

Evaluation

- Patient regains adequate cardiac output exhibited by stable vital signs, normal urine output, and clear mental condition.
- Patient's headache is relieved with analgesic administration.
- Patient and family state understanding of drug therapy.

docetaxel

(doks-uh-TACKS-ul)
Taxotere

Pharmacologic class: taxoid antineoplastic
Therapeutic class: antineoplastic
Pregnancy risk category: D

Indications and dosages

▶ **Locally advanced or metastatic breast cancer for which prior chemotherapy has failed.** *Adults:* 60 to 100 mg/m^2 I.V. over 1 hour q 3 weeks.

▶ **Locally advanced or metastatic non–small-cell lung cancer after failure of platinum-based chemotherapy.** *Adults:* 75 mg/m^2 I.V. over 1 hour q 3 weeks.

▶ **Unresectable, locally advanced, or metastatic non–small-cell lung cancer in patient who has not previously received chemotherapy for this condition with cisplatin.** *Adults:* 75 mg/m^2 I.V. over 1 hour immediately followed by cisplatin 75 mg/m^2 I.V. over 30 to 60 minutes q 3 weeks.

▶ **Androgen-independent metastatic prostate cancer in combination with prednisone.** *Men:* 75 mg/m^2 I.V. as a 1-hour infusion q 3 weeks given with prednisone, 5 mg P.O. b.i.d. continuously. Premedicate with dexamethasone 8 mg P.O. at 12 hours, 3 hours, and 1 hour before the infusion.

▶ **Adjuvant post-surgery treatment of operable node-positive breast cancer.** *Adults:* 75 mg/m^2 I.V. as a 1-hour infusion given 1 hour after doxorubicin 50 mg/m^2 and cyclophosphamide 500 mg/m^2 q 3 weeks for 6 cycles. Patient's neutrophil count should be 1,500 cells/mm^3 or higher.

▶ **Advanced gastric adenocarcinoma, with cisplatin and fluorouracil (5–FU), in patients who haven't received chemotherapy for advanced disease.** *Adults:* Premedicate with antiemetics and hydration according to cisplatin recommendations. Give 75 mg/m^2 docetaxel I.V. over 1 hour, followed by cisplatin 75 mg/m^2 I.V. over 1 to 3 hours on day 1. Then give fluorouracil 750 mg/m^2 I.V. daily as a 24-hour continuous infusion for 5 days starting when cisplatin infusion ends. Repeat cycle every 3 weeks.

Adjust-a-dose: If patient develops hematologic, GI, or hepatic toxicities, reduce dose or stop treatment. In some cases, colony-stimulating factor may be helpful.

I.V. administration

• Premedicate with oral corticosteroids for 3 days, starting 1 day before treatment to reduce fluid retention and hypersensitivity reactions.
• Wear gloves while preparing and giving drug. If solution contacts skin, wash immediately and thoroughly with soap and water. If drug contacts mucous membranes, flush thoroughly with water. Mark all waste materials with chemotherapy hazard labels.
• Prepare and store infusion solutions in bottles (glass or polypropylene) or plastic bags, and give through polyethylene-lined administration sets.
• Dilute drug with diluent supplied. Allow drug and diluent to stand at room temperature for 5 minutes before mixing. After adding diluent contents to vial, rotate vial gently for 15 seconds. Let solution stand for a few minutes for foam to dissipate.
• To prepare solution for infusion, withdraw required amount of premixed solution from vial and add it to 250 ml normal saline solution or D_5W to yield 0.3 to 0.9 mg/ml. Doses exceeding 240 mg need a larger volume of infusion solution to stay below 0.9 mg/ml of drug. Mix infusion thoroughly by manual rotation.
• Give drug as a 1-hour infusion; store unopened vials in the refrigerator.
• If solution isn't clear or if it contains precipitates, discard it. Use infusion solution within 8 hours.

⊗ Incompatibilities
None reported.

Contraindications and cautions

• Contraindicated in patients hypersensitive to drug or other drugs containing polysorbate 80 and in those with neutrophil counts below 1,500 cells/mm^3.
• Don't give drug to patients with severe hepatic impairment, bilirubin level higher than the upper limits of normal (ULN) or with AST or ALT level higher than 1.5 times ULN and alkaline phosphatase level higher than 2.5 times ULN.

Lifespan: In pregnant and breast-feeding women, drug is contraindicated. In children younger than age 16, safety and effectiveness haven't been established.

Adverse reactions

CNS: *asthenia,* dysesthesia, pain, paresthesia, weakness.
CV: fluid retention, hypotension.
GI: diarrhea, nausea, stomatitis, vomiting.
Hematologic: *anemia,* FEBRILE NEUTROPENIA, LEUKOPENIA, MYELOSUPPRESSION, NEUTROPENIA, THROMBOCYTOPENIA.
Musculoskeletal: arthralgia, back pain, *myalgia.*
Respiratory: dyspnea.
Skin: *alopecia,* desquamation, flushing, nail pain, nail pigment changes, rash, skin eruptions.
Other: chest tightness, chills, drug fever, HYPERSENSITIVITY REACTIONS, infection, ***septic and nonseptic death.***

Interactions

Drug-drug. *Drugs that are induced, inhibited, or metabolized by CYP3A4 (cyclosporin, ketoconazole, erythromycin, troleandomycin):* May modify docetaxel metabolism. Use together cautiously.

Effects on lab test results

• May increase ALT, AST, bilirubin, and alkaline phosphatase levels. May decrease hemoglobin level and hematocrit.
• May decrease WBC and platelet counts.

Pharmacokinetics

Absorption: Given I.V.
Distribution: 94% protein-bound.
Metabolism: Partly by liver.
Excretion: Mainly in feces. *Half-life:* About 12 hours.

Route	Onset	Peak	Duration
I.V.	Immediate	Unknown	Unknown

Action

Chemical effect: Disrupts the microtubular network essential for mitotic and interphase cellular functions.
Therapeutic effect: Inhibits mitosis, producing antineoplastic effect.

Available forms

Injection: 20 mg, 80 mg

D

NURSING PROCESS

Assessment
- Monitor blood count often during therapy.
- Assess patient's and family's knowledge of drug therapy.

Nursing diagnoses
- Ineffective health maintenance related to neoplastic disease
- Deficient knowledge related to drug therapy

Planning and implementation
- Don't give drug to patients with baseline neutrophil count less than 1,500/mm³.

ALERT: Don't confuse Taxotere with Taxol.

Patient teaching
- Warn patient that alopecia occurs in almost 80% of patients.
- Tell patient to promptly report sore throat, fever, unusual bruising or bleeding, or signs of fluid retention.

Evaluation
- Patient shows positive response to drug.
- Patient and family state understanding of drug therapy.

docusate calcium (dioctyl calcium sulfosuccinate)
(DOK-yoo-sayt KAL-see-um)
DC Softgels, Pro-Cal-Sof, Surfak

docusate potassium (dioctyl potassium sulfosuccinate)
Diocto-K†, Kasof†

docusate sodium (dioctyl sodium sulfosuccinate)
Colace†, Coloxyl ◇, Coloxyl Enema Concentrate ◇, Dialose†, Diocto†, Dioeze†, Disonate†, DOK†, DOS Softgels†, Doxinate†, D-S-S†, Modane Soft†, Pro-Sof†, Regulax SS†, Regutol†, Therevac-SB†

Pharmacologic class: surfactant
Therapeutic class: emollient laxative
Pregnancy risk category: C

Indications and dosages
▶ **Stool softener.** *Adults and children age 12 and older:* 50 to 360 mg P.O. daily until bowel movements are normal. Or give enema (where available). Dilute 1:24 with sterile water before administration, and give 100 to 150 ml (retention enema), 300 to 500 ml (evacuation enema), or 0.5 to 1.5 liters (flushing enema).
Children ages 6 to 12: Give 40 to 120 mg docusate sodium P.O. daily.
Children ages 3 to 6: Give 20 to 60 mg docusate sodium P.O. daily.
Children younger than age 3: Give 10 to 40 mg docusate sodium P.O. daily. Higher dosages used for initial therapy. Adjust dosage to individual response.
Adults and children: Usual dosage 240 mg docusate calcium P.O. daily until bowel movements are normal.

Contraindications and cautions
- Contraindicated in patients hypersensitive to drug or any of its components and in those with intestinal obstruction, undiagnosed abdominal pain, signs of appendicitis, fecal impaction, or acute surgical abdomen.

Lifespan: In pregnant women, use cautiously.

Adverse reactions
CNS: fainting.
EENT: throat irritation.
GI: bitter taste, diarrhea, laxative dependence with long-term or excessive use, mild abdominal cramping.

Interactions
Drug-drug. *Mineral oil:* May increase mineral oil absorption and cause toxicity and lipoid pneumonia. Separate doses.

Effects on lab test results
None reported.

Pharmacokinetics
Absorption: Minimal.
Distribution: Mainly local.
Metabolism: None.
Excretion: In feces. *Half-life:* Unknown.

Route	Onset	Peak	Duration
P.O.	Varies	Varies	24–72 hr
P.R.	Unknown	Unknown	Unknown

Action

Chemical effect: Reduces surface tension of interfacing liquid contents of bowel. This detergent activity promotes incorporation of additional liquid into stool, thus forming softer mass.
Therapeutic effect: Softens stool.

Available forms

docusate calcium
Capsules: 50 mg†, 240 mg†
docusate potassium
Capsules: 100 mg†, 240 mg†
docusate sodium
Capsules: 50 mg† 60 mg†, 100 mg†, 240 mg†, 250 mg†
Enema concentrate: 18 g/100 ml (must be diluted) ◊
Oral liquid: 150 mg/15 ml†
Oral solution: 50 mg/ml†
Syrup: 20 mg/5 ml*†, 50 mg/15 ml†, 60 mg/15 ml†, 100 mg/30 ml†
Tablets: 100 mg†

NURSING PROCESS

Assessment

- Obtain history of patient's bowel patterns before therapy, and reassess regularly thereafter.
- Before giving drug for constipation, determine if patient has adequate fluid intake, exercise, and diet.
- Be alert for adverse reactions and drug interactions.
- Assess patient's and family's knowledge of drug therapy.

Nursing diagnoses

- Constipation related to underlying condition
- Diarrhea related to prolonged or excessive use of drug
- Deficient knowledge related to drug therapy

Planning and implementation

- Give liquid in milk, fruit juice, or infant formula to mask bitter taste.
- Drug is the laxative of choice for patients who shouldn't strain during defecation, including patients recovering from MI or rectal surgery, patients with a rectal or anal disease that makes passage of firm stool difficult, or patients with postpartum constipation.
- Store drug at 59° to 86° F (15° to 30° C), and protect liquid from light.
- If abdominal cramping occurs, stop drug and notify prescriber.
- Drug doesn't stimulate intestinal peristaltic movements.

ALERT: Don't confuse Colace and Calan.

Patient teaching

- Teach patient about dietary sources of bulk, which include bran and other cereals, fresh fruit, and vegetables.
- Instruct patient to use only occasionally and not to use for more than 1 week without prescriber's knowledge.
- Tell patient to stop taking the drug and to notify the prescriber if severe cramping occurs.

Evaluation

- Patient's constipation is relieved.
- Patient remains free from diarrhea during therapy.
- Patient and family state understanding of drug therapy.

dofetilide

(doh-FET-eh-lighd)
Tikosyn

Pharmacologic class: antiarrhythmic
Therapeutic class: class III antiarrhythmic
Pregnancy risk category: C

Indications and dosages

▶ **To maintain normal sinus rhythm in patients with symptomatic atrial fibrillation or atrial flutter for longer than 1 week who have been converted to normal sinus rhythm; to convert atrial fibrillation and atrial flutter to normal sinus rhythm.** *Adults:* Dosage is individualized and is based on creatinine clearance and QT interval, which must be obtained before first dose. (If pulse is less than 60 beats/minute, use QT interval.) Usual dosage is 500 mcg P.O. b.i.d. for patients with creatinine clearance above 60 ml/minute.

Adjust-a-dose: For patients with renal impairment, if creatinine clearance is 40 to 60 ml/minute, give 250 mcg P.O. b.i.d. If creatinine clearance is 20 to 39 ml/minute, give 125 mcg P.O. b.i.d. If creatinine clearance is less than 20 ml/minute, drug is contraindicated.

For patients who develop prolonged QT interval, adjust dosage or stop drug.

Contraindications and cautions

- Contraindicated in patients with congenital or acquired prolonged QT-interval syndromes. Also contraindicated in patients with baseline QTc interval greater than 440 msec (500 msec in patients with ventricular conduction abnormalities). Also contraindicated in patients with creatinine clearance below 20 ml/min and in patients hypersensitive to drug and in those receiving verapamil, cimetidine, hydrochlorothiazide (alone or with triamterene), trimethoprim (alone or with sulfamethoxazole), or ketoconazole.
- Use cautiously in patients with severe hepatic impairment.

Lifespan: In pregnant women, use cautiously. In breast-feeding women, drug isn't recommended. In children, safety and effectiveness haven't been established.

Adverse reactions

CNS: anxiety, asthenia, ***cerebral ischemia,*** dizziness, *headache,* insomnia, migraine, paresthesia, ***stroke,*** syncope.
CV: angina, atrial fibrillation, ***bradycardia,*** bundle branch block, ***cardiac arrest,*** chest pain, edema, heart block, hypertension, ***MI,*** palpitations, peripheral edema, ***torsades de pointes, ventricular fibrillation, ventricular tachycardia.***
EENT: facial paralysis.
GI: abdominal pain, diarrhea, nausea.
GU: UTI.
Hepatic: ***liver damage.***
Musculoskeletal: arthralgia, back pain.
Respiratory: dyspnea, increased cough, respiratory tract infection.
Skin: rash, sweating.
Other: ***angioedema,*** flulike syndrome.

Interactions

Drug-drug. *Amiloride, metformin, triamterene:* May increase dofetilide level. Use together cautiously.
Cimetidine, ketoconazole, sulfamethoxazole, trimethoprim, verapamil: May increase dofetilide level. Don't use together.
Inhibitors of CYP3A4 (amiodarone, azole antifungals, cannabinoids, diltiazem, macrolide antibiotics, nefazodone, norfloxacin, protease inhibitors, quinine, serotonin reuptake inhibitors, zafirlukast): May decrease metabolism and increase dofetilide level. Use together cautiously; monitor patient for toxicity.
Inhibitors of renal cationic secretion (megestrol, prochlorperazine): May increase dofetilide level. Avoid use together.
Drug-food. *Grapefruit juice:* May decrease dofetilide's hepatic metabolism and increase its level. Avoid use together.

Effects on lab test results

None reported.

Pharmacokinetics

Absorption: More than 90%; levels peak at 2 to 3 hours. Steady-state levels are achieved in 2 to 3 days. Unaffected by food or antacid.
Distribution: Wide with a volume of distribution of 3 L/kg. 60% to 70% protein-bound.
Metabolism: Small, by the CYP3A4 isoenzyme in the liver.
Excretion: 80% in urine, of which 80% is unchanged drug while the rest is inactive or minimally active metabolites. *Half-life:* 10 hours.

Route	Onset	Peak	Duration
P.O.	Unknown	2–3 hr	Unknown

Action

Chemical effect: Prolongs repolarization without affecting conduction velocity by blocking the cardiac ion channel carrying potassium current.
Therapeutic effect: Converts atrial fibrillation and atrial flutter to normal sinus rhythm, and maintains normal rhythm.

Available forms

Capsules: 125 mcg (0.125 mg), 250 mcg (0.25 mg), 500 mcg (0.5 mg)

NURSING PROCESS

Assessment

- Obtain accurate medication list (prescription, OTC, and herbal) from patient before starting drug; stop antiarrhythmic under careful monitoring for at least 2 days before giving second antiarrhythmic. Don't give drug within 3 months of amiodarone unless level is below 0.3 mcg/ml.
- Assess patient's QTc interval, cardiac rhythm, creatinine clearance, and vital signs before starting medication. Prolongation of the QTc inter-

val requires subsequent dosage adjustments or discontinuation. Continuous ECG monitoring is required for a minimum of 3 days for maintenance therapy, or 12 hours after conversion to normal sinus rhythm.

- Obtain potassium level before starting therapy and regularly thereafter. Hypokalemia and hypomagnesemia may occur when giving potassium-depleting diuretics, increasing the risk of torsades de pointes. Achieve and maintain normal potassium level.
- Monitor patient for prolonged diarrhea, sweating, and vomiting, and report any such symptoms to the prescriber because electrolyte imbalance may increase the risk of arrhythmias.
- Monitor renal function and QTc interval every 3 months.
- Assess patient's and family's knowledge of drug therapy.

Nursing diagnoses

- Decreased cardiac output related to underlying arrhythmia
- Risk for injury related to drug-induced adverse reactions
- Deficient knowledge related to drug therapy

Planning and implementation

- Drug is distributed only to hospitals and other institutions with dosage and treatment initiation programs. Inpatient and outpatient discharge and refills of prescriptions are allowed only with confirmation that prescriber has access to these programs.
- If patient doesn't convert to normal sinus rhythm within 24 hours after starting drug, use electrical cardioversion.
- Drug must be given by specially certified prescriber in an acute care facility because of potentially high risk of torsades de pointes.
- If drug must be stopped to allow administration of other interacting drugs, allow washout period of at least 2 days before starting other drug.

Patient teaching

- Instruct patient to notify prescriber about any change in prescription drugs, OTC medications, or herbal remedies.
- Urge patient to immediately report excessive or prolonged diarrhea, sweating, vomiting, or loss of appetite or thirst to prescriber.
- Inform patient that dofetilide can be taken without regard to meals or antacids.
- Tell patient not to take drug with grapefruit juice.
- Warn patient not to use OTC Tagamet-HB for ulcers or heartburn. Explain that antacids and OTC acid reducers such as Zantac 75 mg, Pepcid, Axid, and Prevacid are acceptable.
- Instruct woman to notify prescriber about planned, suspected, or known pregnancy.
- Advise patient not to breast-feed while taking dofetilide.
- If patient misses a dose, tell him to skip it and wait for the next scheduled dose. Caution against doubling the dose.

Evaluation

- Patient maintains normal sinus rhythm.
- Patient has no injury as a result of drug-induced adverse reactions.
- Patient and family state understanding of drug therapy.

dolasetron mesylate

(doh-LEH-seh-trohn MES-ih-layt)

Anzemet

Pharmacologic class: selective serotonin ($5\text{-}HT_3$) receptor antagonist
Therapeutic class: antiemetic
Pregnancy risk category: B

Indications and dosages

▶ **To prevent nausea and vomiting after cancer chemotherapy.** *Adults:* 100 mg P.O. given as a single dose 1 hour before chemotherapy. Or 1.8 mg/kg (or a fixed dose of 100 mg) as a single I.V. dose given 30 minutes before chemotherapy.

Children ages 2 to 16: Give 1.8 mg/kg P.O. 1 hour before chemotherapy. Or 1.8 mg/kg as single I.V. dose 30 minutes before chemotherapy. Injectable form can be mixed with apple juice and given P.O. Maximum dose, 100 mg.

▶ **To prevent postoperative nausea and vomiting.** *Adults:* 100 mg P.O. within 2 hours before surgery. Or 12.5 mg as single I.V. dose about 15 minutes before cessation of anesthesia.

Children ages 2 to 16: Give 1.2 mg/kg P.O. within 2 hours before surgery, to maximum, 100 mg. Or 0.35 mg/kg (up to 12.5 mg) as single I.V. dose about 15 minutes before cessation of anesthesia. Injectable form can be mixed with apple juice and given P.O.

▶ **Postoperative nausea and vomiting.** *Adults:* 12.5 mg as a single I.V. dose as soon as nausea or vomiting begins.

Children ages 2 to 16: Give 0.35 mg/kg to maximum, 12.5 mg, as a single I.V. dose as soon as nausea or vomiting begins.

I.V. administration

- Drug can be injected as rapidly as 100 mg in 30 seconds, or diluted in 50 ml of compatible solution and infused over 15 minutes.
- If an arrhythmia develops, stop the drug and notify prescriber immediately.
- After dilution, solution is stable for 24 hours at room temperature or 48 hours if refrigerated.

⊗ **Incompatibilities**

Injection shouldn't be mixed with other drugs.

Contraindications and cautions

- Contraindicated in patients hypersensitive to drug or any of its components.
- Give cautiously to patients who have or may develop prolonged cardiac conduction intervals, such as those with electrolyte abnormalities, history of arrhythmias, and cumulative high-dose anthracycline therapy.

Lifespan: In breast-feeding women, use cautiously because it's unknown if drug appears in breast milk. In infants, drug isn't recommended.

Adverse reactions

CNS: dizziness, drowsiness, fatigue, fever, *headache.*

CV: ***arrhythmias, bradycardia,*** ECG changes, hypertension, hypotension, tachycardia.

GI: abdominal pain, anorexia, constipation, *diarrhea,* dyspepsia.

GU: oliguria, urine retention.

Skin: pruritus, rash.

Other: chills, pain at injection site.

Interactions

Drug-drug. *Drugs that induce cytochrome P-450 enzymes (such as rifampin):* May decrease hydrodolasetron level. Monitor patient for decreased effectiveness of drug.

Drugs that inhibit cytochrome P-450 enzymes (such as atenolol, cimetidine): May increase hydrodolasetron level. Monitor patient for adverse effects.

Drugs that prolong ECG intervals (such as antiarrhythmics): May increase risk of arrhythmia. Monitor patient closely.

Effects on lab test results

- May increase ALT and AST levels.

Pharmacokinetics

Absorption: Rapid for hydrodolasetron, an active metabolite that has an absolute bioavailability of 75%.

Distribution: Wide, with 69% to 77% bound to plasma protein.

Metabolism: Rapid and complete.

Excretion: Two-thirds of hydrodolasetron is in urine; rest in feces. *Half-life:* 8 hours.

Route	Onset	Peak	Duration
P.O.	Rapid	1 hr	8 hr
I.V.	Rapid	36 min	7 hr

Action

Chemical effect: Blocks the action of serotonin, thereby preventing serotonin from stimulating the vomiting reflex.

Therapeutic effect: Prevents nausea and vomiting.

Available forms

Injection: 20 mg/ml as 12.5 mg/0.625 ml-ampule or 100 mg/5 ml-vial

Tablets: 50 mg, 100 mg

NURSING PROCESS

Assessment

- Assess patient for history of nausea and vomiting related to chemotherapy or postoperative recovery.
- Be alert for adverse reactions and drug interactions.
- Monitor ECG carefully in patients who have or may develop prolonged cardiac conduction intervals.
- Assess patient's and family's knowledge of drug therapy.

Nursing diagnoses

- Imbalanced nutrition: less than body requirements, related to nausea and vomiting
- Risk for injury related to drug-induced adverse CNS reaction
- Deficient knowledge related to drug therapy

Planning and implementation

- Injection for P.O. use is stable in apple juice for 2 hours at room temperature.

ALERT: Don't confuse Anzemet with Avandamet.

Patient teaching

- Tell patient about potential adverse effects.
- Instruct patient not to mix injection in juice for P.O. use until just before taking the dose.
- Tell patient to report nausea or vomiting.

Evaluation

- Patient has no nausea and vomiting.
- Patient is free from injury.
- Patient and family state understanding of drug therapy.

donepezil hydrochloride

(doh-NEH-peh-zil high-droh-KLOR-ighd)

Aricept, Aricept ODT

Pharmacologic class: reversible inhibitor of acetylcholinesterase
Therapeutic class: psychotherapeutic drug for Alzheimer disease
Pregnancy risk category: C

Indications and dosages

▶ **Mild to moderate and severe dementia of the Alzheimer type.** *Adults:* Initially, 5 mg P.O. daily at bedtime. After 4 to 6 weeks, may increase dosage to 10 mg daily.

Contraindications and cautions

- Contraindicated in patients hypersensitive to drug or to piperidine derivatives.
- Use cautiously in patients with history of ulcer disease, CV disease, asthma or COPD, or urinary outflow impairment. Also use cautiously in patients currently taking NSAIDs.

Lifespan: In pregnant women, use only if benefits to the woman outweigh risks to the fetus. Breast-feeding women shouldn't nurse during therapy. In children, safety and effectiveness haven't been established.

Adverse reactions

CNS: abnormal crying, abnormal dreams, aggression, aphasia, ataxia, depression, dizziness, fatigue, *headache,* insomnia, irritability, nervousness, pain, paresthesia, restlessness, ***seizures,*** somnolence, syncope, tremor, vertigo.
CV: atrial fibrillation, chest pain, hypertension, hypotension, vasodilation.
EENT: blurred vision, cataracts, eye irritation, sore throat.
GI: anorexia, bloating, *diarrhea,* epigastric pain, fecal incontinence, ***GI bleeding,*** *nausea,* vomiting.
GU: frequent urination, nocturia, urinary incontinence.
Metabolic: dehydration, weight decrease.
Musculoskeletal: arthritis, bone fracture, muscle cramps, toothache.
Respiratory: bronchitis, dyspnea.
Skin: diaphoresis, ecchymosis, pruritus, urticaria.
Other: accident, hot flushes, increased libido, influenza.

Interactions

Drug-drug. *Anticholinergics:* May interfere with anticholinergic activity. Monitor patient for effects.
Bethanechol, succinylcholine: May have additive effects. Monitor patient closely.
Carbamazepine, dexamethasone, phenytoin, phenobarbital, rifampin: May increase rate of donepezil elimination. Monitor patient for effects.
Cholinomimetics, cholinesterase inhibitors: May have synergistic effect. Monitor patient closely.
NSAIDs: May increase gastric acid secretion. Monitor patient for occult bleeding.
Drug-herb. *Jaborandi tree, pill-bearing spurge:* May cause additive effect and increased risk of toxicity. Discourage use together.

Effects on lab test results

None reported.

Pharmacokinetics

Absorption: Good.
Distribution: 96% bound to plasma proteins, mainly to albumin.
Metabolism: Extensive.
Excretion: In urine and feces. *Half-life:* 70 hours.

Route	Onset	Peak	Duration
P.O.	Unknown	3–4 hr	Unknown

Action

Chemical effect: Reversibly inhibits acetylcholinesterase in the CNS, thereby increasing the acetylcholine level.
Therapeutic effect: Temporarily improves cognitive function in patients with Alzheimer disease.

Available forms

Tablets: 5 mg, 10 mg
Tablets (orally disintegrating): 5 mg, 10 mg

NURSING PROCESS

Assessment

- Monitor patient for symptoms of active or occult GI bleeding.
- Assess patient's and family's knowledge of drug therapy.

Nursing diagnoses

- Risk for injury related to adverse effects of drug
- Deficient knowledge related to drug therapy

Planning and implementation

- Give drug at bedtime, with or without food.
- If cholinergic crisis (severe nausea, vomiting, salivation, sweating, bradycardia, hypotension, respiratory depression, convulsions, and collapse) occurs, treat with an anticholinergic such as atropine.

Patient teaching

- Explain that drug doesn't alter underlying degenerative disease but can alleviate symptoms.
- Tell caregiver to give drug in the evening, just before bedtime.
- Advise patient and caregiver to immediately report significant adverse effects or changes in overall health condition.
- Tell caregiver to inform health care team that patient is taking drug before patient receives anesthesia.

Evaluation

- Patient remains free from injury.
- Patient and family state understanding of drug therapy.

dopamine hydrochloride

(DOH-puh-meen high-droh-KLOR-ighd)
Intropin, Revimine ♦

Pharmacologic class: adrenergic
Therapeutic class: inotropic, vasopressor
Pregnancy risk category: C

Indications and dosages

▶ **To treat shock and correct hemodynamic imbalances; to improve perfusion to vital organs; to increase cardiac output; to correct hypotension.** *Adults and children:* Initially, 2 to 5 mcg/kg/minute by I.V. infusion. Adjust dosage to desired hemodynamic or renal response, increase by 1 to 4 mcg/kg/minute at 10- to 30-minute intervals.

I.V. administration

- Dilute with D_5W, normal saline solution, or combination of D_5W and normal saline solution. Mix just before use.
- Use continuous infusion pump to regulate flow rate.
- Use central line or large vein, such as in antecubital fossa, to minimize risk of extravasation. If extravasation occurs, stop infusion immediately and call prescriber. Extravasation may require treatment by infiltration of area with 5 to 10 mg of phentolamine and 10 to 15 ml of normal saline solution.
- If solution is discolored, discard within 24 hours.

⊗ Incompatibilities

Acyclovir sodium, additives with a dopamine and dextrose solution, alteplase, amphotericin B, cefepime, furosemide, gentamicin, indomethacin sodium trihydrate, iron salts, insulin, oxidizing agents, penicillin G potassium, sodium bicarbonate or other alkaline solutions, thiopental.

Contraindications and cautions

- Contraindicated in patients with uncorrected tachyarrhythmias, pheochromocytoma, or ventricular fibrillation.
- Use cautiously in patients with occlusive vascular disease, cold injuries, diabetic endarteritis, and arterial embolism, and in those taking MAO inhibitors.

Lifespan: In pregnant women, use cautiously. In breast-feeding women, safety and effectiveness haven't been established.

Adverse reactions

CNS: headache, anxiety.
CV: anginal pain, ***arrhythmias, bradycardia,*** conduction disturbances, ectopic beats, hypertension, ***hypotension,*** palpitations, tachycardia, vasoconstriction, ***widening of QRS complex.***
GI: nausea, vomiting.
GU: azotemia.
Respiratory: *asthma attacks,* dyspnea.
Skin: necrosis, piloerection, tissue sloughing with extravasation.
Other: ***anaphylaxis.***

Interactions

Drug-drug. *Alpha and beta blockers:* May antagonize dopamine effects. Monitor patient for effect.
Ergot alkaloids: May increase blood pressure. Don't use together.
Inhaled anesthetics: May increase risk of arrhythmias or hypertension. Monitor vital signs and ECG closely.
Oxytocic drugs: May potentiate pressor effect, resulting in severe hypertension. Avoid use together, if possible.
Phenelzine, tranylcypromine: May cause severe headache, hypertension, fever, and hypertensive crisis. Avoid use together.
Phenytoin: May lower blood pressure in dopamine-stabilized patients. Monitor blood pressure carefully.
Tricyclic antidepressants: May decrease pressor response. Monitor patient closely.

Effects on lab test results

- May increase glucose and urea levels.

Pharmacokinetics

Absorption: Given I.V.
Distribution: Wide; doesn't cross blood–brain barrier.
Metabolism: To inactive compounds in liver, kidneys, and plasma.
Excretion: In urine, mainly as its metabolites. *Half-life:* 2 minutes in adults; 5 to 11 minutes in neonates.

Route	Onset	Peak	Duration
I.V.	≤ 5 min	Unknown	≤ 10 min

Action

Chemical effect: Stimulates dopaminergic, beta-adrenergic, and alpha-adrenergic receptors of sympathetic nervous system.
Therapeutic effect: Increases cardiac output, blood pressure, and renal perfusion (in low doses).

Available forms

Injection: 40 mg/ml, 80 mg/ml, 160 mg/ml as concentrate for injection for I.V. infusion; 0.8 mg/ml (200 or 400 mg) in D_5W; 1.6 mg/ml (400 or 800 mg) in D_5W; 3.2 mg/ml (800 mg) in D_5W as parenteral injection for I.V. infusion

NURSING PROCESS

Assessment

- Obtain history of patient's underlying condition before therapy.
- During infusion, frequently monitor ECG, blood pressure, cardiac output, central venous pressure, pulmonary capillary wedge pressure, pulse rate, urine output, and color and temperature of limbs.
- Be alert for adverse reactions and drug interactions.
- Be aware that acidosis decreases effectiveness of dopamine.
- After drug is stopped, watch closely for sudden drop in blood pressure.
- Assess patient's and family's knowledge of drug therapy.

Nursing diagnoses

- Ineffective tissue perfusion (cerebral, cardiopulmonary, and renal) related to underlying condition
- Risk for injury related to drug-induced adverse reactions
- Deficient knowledge related to drug therapy

Planning and implementation

- Be aware that dosages of 0.5 to 2 mcg/kg/minute mainly stimulate dopamine receptors and dilate renal vasculature increasing urine output. Dosages of 2 to 10 mcg/kg/minute stimulate beta receptors for increased cardiac output. Higher dosages also stimulate alpha-adrenergic receptors, causing vasoconstriction and increased blood pressure. Most patients are satisfactorily maintained on dosages below 20 mcg/kg/minute.

• Drug isn't used to treat blood or fluid volume deficit. If deficit exists, replace fluid before giving vasopressors.
• Taper dosage slowly to evaluate stability of blood pressure.
• If patient receiving dopamine has disproportionate rise in diastolic pressure (a marked decrease in pulse pressure), decrease infusion rate, and watch carefully for further evidence of predominant vasoconstrictor activity, unless such effect is desired.
• If an adverse reaction develops, notify prescriber, who will reduce the dosage or stop the drug.
• If urine flow decreases without hypotension, notify prescriber and reduce dosage.
ALERT: Don't confuse dopamine with dobutamine.

Patient teaching
• Emphasize importance of reporting discomfort at I.V. site immediately.
• Explain to patient the need for drug therapy.

Evaluation
• Patient regains adequate cerebral, cardiopulmonary, and renal tissue perfusion.
• Patient doesn't experience injury as result of drug-induced adverse reactions.
• Patient and family state understanding of drug therapy.

dorzolamide hydrochloride
(dor-ZOLE-uh-mighd high-droh-KLOR-ighd)
Trusopt

Pharmacologic class: carbonic anhydrase inhibitor, sulfonamide
Therapeutic class: antiglaucoma drug
Pregnancy risk category: C

Indications and dosages
▶ **Increased intraocular pressure (IOP) in patients with ocular hypertension or open-angle glaucoma.** *Adults and children:* Instill 1 drop in the conjunctival sac of affected eye t.i.d.

Contraindications and cautions
• Contraindicated in patients hypersensitive to drug or any of its components Also contraindicated in those with renal impairment.
• Use cautiously in patients with impaired hepatic function.
Lifespan: In pregnant women, use only if potential benefits to the woman outweigh the risks to the fetus. In breast-feeding women, drug isn't recommended because it's unknown if it appears in breast milk. In elderly patients, use cautiously because they may have greater sensitivity to drug.

Adverse reactions
CNS: asthenia, dizziness, fatigue, headache, paresthesia.
EENT: blurred vision; dryness; eyelid crusting; iridocyclitis; lacrimation; ocular allergic reactions, including conjunctivitis, itching, and lid reactions; ocular burning, stinging, and discomfort; ocular pain; photophobia; redness; superficial punctate keratitis; throat irritation; transient myopia.
GI: bitter taste, nausea.
GU: urolithiasis.
Respiratory: ***bronchospasm,*** dyspnea.
Skin: contact dermatitis, pruritus, rash, urticaria.
Other: ***angioedema.***

Interactions
Drug-drug. *Oral carbonic anhydrase inhibitors:* May cause additive effects. Don't use together.
Topical beta blockers: May cause additive effects. Give drugs 10 minutes apart.

Effects on lab tests results
• May decrease potassium and pH levels.

Pharmacokinetics
Absorption: Systemic.
Distribution: 33% bound to plasma proteins. Accumulates in RBCs during regular therapy.
Metabolism: In the liver by cytochrome P-450 isoenzymes.
Excretion: Mainly unchanged in urine. *Half-life:* 4 months.

Route	Onset	Peak	Duration
Ophthalmic	1–2 hr	2–3 hr	8 hr

Action
Chemical effect: Inhibits carbonic anhydrase in the ciliary processes of the eye. This action reduces aqueous humor secretion, presumably by

slowing the formation of bicarbonate ions with subsequent reduction in sodium and fluid transport.
Therapeutic effect: Reduces IOP.

Available forms

Ophthalmic solution: 2%

NURSING PROCESS

Assessment

- Assess patient before starting therapy.
- Because drug is a sulfonamide that is absorbed systemically, the adverse reactions caused by sulfonamides, such as Stevens-Johnson syndrome, agranulocytosis, and aplastic anemia, may occur. Although these symptoms haven't been shown with this drug, monitor for them during therapy.
- Overdose may result in electrolyte imbalance, acidosis, and CNS effects. Monitor electrolyte levels (especially potassium) and pH levels. Provide supportive therapy for any overdose.
- Assess patient's and family's understanding of drug therapy.

Nursing diagnoses

- Risk for infection to the eyes related to inadvertent contamination of the multidose container
- Disturbed visual perception related to underlying ocular condition
- Deficient knowledge related to drug therapy

Planning and implementation

- If patient is wearing contact lenses, remove lenses before giving the drug. Contact lenses may be reinserted 15 minutes after the drug is given.
- Instruct patient not to blink after administration, just close eyes. Apply light finger pressure on lacrimal sac for 1 minute after instillation to minimize systemic absorption of drug.
- If more than one topical ophthalmic drug is being used, give drugs at least 10 minutes apart.

Patient teaching

- Teach patient how to instill drops properly. Advise him to wash hands before and after instilling solution, and warn him not to touch dropper or tip to eye or surrounding tissue, to prevent contamination to the dropper.
- If patient wears contact lenses, instruct him to remove them before instilling the drops and to reinsert them 15 minutes after instillation.
- Advise patient to report ocular reactions, particularly conjunctivitis and lid reactions, immediately to prescriber and to stop drug.

Evaluation

- Patient doesn't suffer from any infection related to drug administration.
- Patient's underlying condition is resolved with drug therapy.
- Patient and family state understanding of drug therapy.

doxapram hydrochloride

(DOKS-uh-prahm high-droh-KLOR-ighd)
Dopram

Pharmacologic class: analeptic
Therapeutic class: CNS and respiratory stimulant
Pregnancy risk category: B

Indications and dosages

▶ **Postanesthesia respiratory stimulation, drug-induced CNS depression, chronic pulmonary disease with acute hypercapnia.** *Adults:* 0.5 to 1 mg/kg of body weight (up to 2 mg/kg in CNS depression) by I.V. injection or infusion. Repeat q 5 minutes, if needed. Maximum, 4 mg/kg, up to 3 g daily

▶ **COPD.** *Adults:* 1 to 2 mg/minute by I.V. infusion. Maximum, 3 mg/minute for maximum duration of 2 hours.

I.V. administration

- For I.V. infusion, add 250 mg of drug to 250 ml of 5% or 10% dextrose or normal saline solution injection; concentration equals 1 mg/ml.
- For acute hypercapnia related to COPD, add 400 mg of drug to 180 ml of dextrose or normal saline solution to equal 2 mg/ml. Infuse at 1 to 3 mg/minute.
- Give drug slowly because rapid infusion may cause hemolysis.
- Watch for irritation and infiltration.

⊗ **Incompatibilities**

Aminophylline, ascorbic acid, cefoperazone, cefotaxime, cefuroxime sodium, dexamethasone sodium phosphate, diazepam, digoxin, dobutamine, folic acid, furosemide, hydrocortisone sodium phosphate, hydrocortisone sodium succinate, ketamine, methylprednisolone sodium succinate, minocycline, thiopental, ticarcillin disodium.

Contraindications and cautions

• Contraindicated in patients with seizure disorders; head injury; CV disorders; frank, uncompensated heart failure; severe hypertension; stroke; respiratory failure or incompetence secondary to neuromuscular disorders, muscle paresis, flail chest, obstructed airway, pulmonary embolism, pneumothorax, restrictive respiratory disease, acute bronchial asthma, or dyspnea; or hypoxia not related to hypercapnia.
• Don't use in patients with severe hypotension. If sudden hypotension occurs, stop drug.
• Use cautiously in patients with bronchial asthma, severe tachycardia or arrhythmias, cerebral edema or increased CSF pressure, hyperthyroidism, pheochromocytoma, or metabolic disorders.
Lifespan: In pregnant women, use cautiously. In breast-feeding women and in children, safety and effectiveness haven't been established.

Adverse reactions

CNS: apprehension, bilateral Babinski signs, disorientation, dizziness, fever, *headache,* paresthesia, pupil dilation, ***seizures.***
CV: ***arrhythmias,*** chest pain and tightness, depressed T waves, flushing, increased blood pressure, variations in heart rate.
EENT: *laryngospasm,* sneezing.
GI: diarrhea, nausea, urge to defecate, vomiting.
GU: bladder stimulation with incontinence, urine retention, albuminuria.
Musculoskeletal: muscle spasms.
Respiratory: ***bronchospasm,*** cough, dyspnea, hiccups, rebound hypoventilation.
Skin: diaphoresis, pruritus.

Interactions

Drug-drug. *MAO inhibitors, sympathomimetics:* May potentiate adverse CV effects. Use together cautiously.

Effects on lab test results

• May increase BUN and hemoglobin levels and hematocrit.
• May decrease erythrocyte, WBC, and RBC counts.

Pharmacokinetics

Absorption: Given I.V.
Distribution: Wide.
Metabolism: 99% by liver.
Excretion: In urine. *Half-life:* 2½ to 4 hours.

Route	Onset	Peak	Duration
I.V.	20–40 sec	1–2 min	5–12 min

Action

Chemical effect: Not clearly defined; acts either directly on central respiratory centers in medulla or indirectly on chemoreceptors.
Therapeutic effect: Stimulates respirations.

Available forms

Injection: 20 mg/ml (benzyl alcohol 0.9%)

NURSING PROCESS

Assessment

• Obtain history of patient's underlying condition before beginning therapy.
• Assess blood pressure, heart rate, deep tendon reflexes, and arterial blood gases before giving drug, and monitor closely throughout therapy.
• Monitor the drug's effectiveness by observing patient for improvement in CNS and respiratory function.
• Be alert for adverse reactions and drug interactions.
• Assess patient's and family's knowledge of drug therapy.

Nursing diagnoses

• Ineffective breathing pattern related to underlying condition
• Risk for trauma related to potential for drug-induced seizure activity
• Deficient knowledge related to drug therapy

Planning and implementation

• Don't use in patients with severe hypotension. If sudden hypotension occurs or dyspnea develops, stop giving the drug.
• Establish adequate airway before giving the drug. Prevent patient from aspirating vomitus by

placing him on his side. Have suction equipment nearby.

• Drug is used only in surgical or emergency situations.

• If patient's arterial carbon dioxide or oxygen tension increases, or if mechanical ventilation is started, stop drug and notify prescriber.

ALERT: Don't confuse doxapram with doxorubicin, doxepin, doxacurium, or doxazosin.

Patient teaching

• If patient is alert, instruct him to report chest pain or tightness immediately.

Evaluation

• Patient regains normal respiratory pattern.
• Patient has no seizures as result of therapy.
• Patient and family state understanding of drug therapy.

doxazosin mesylate

(doks-AY-zoh-sin MES-ih-layt)

Cardura

Pharmacologic class: alpha blocker
Therapeutic class: antihypertensive
Pregnancy risk category: C

Indications and dosages

▶ **Essential hypertension.** *Adults:* Initially, 1 mg P.O. daily. Increase to 2 mg daily, then 4 mg daily, then 8 mg. Maximum, 16 mg daily, but dosage above 4 mg daily increases risk of adverse reactions. To minimize adverse reactions, adjust dosage slowly (typically increase only q 2 weeks).

▶ **BPH.** *Adults:* Initially, 1 mg P.O. once daily, morning or evening; may increase to 2 mg and, thereafter, to 4 mg and to 8 mg once daily or as needed. Adjust dosage in 1- to 2-week intervals.

Contraindications and cautions

• Contraindicated in patients hypersensitive to drug and to quinazoline derivatives (including prazosin and terazosin).

• Use cautiously in patients with impaired liver function.

Lifespan: In pregnant women, use cautiously. In breast-feeding women, drug isn't recommended because it appears in breast milk at levels about 20 times greater than those in maternal plasma. In children, safety and effectiveness haven't been established.

Adverse reactions

CNS: *asthenia, dizziness,* drowsiness, *headache,* pain, somnolence, vertigo.
CV: ***arrhythmias,*** edema, hypotension, palpitations, *orthostatic hypotension,* tachycardia.
EENT: abnormal vision, pharyngitis, rhinitis.
GI: constipation, diarrhea, nausea, vomiting.
Musculoskeletal: arthralgia, myalgia.
Respiratory: dyspnea.
Skin: pruritus, rash.

Interactions

Drug-drug. *Clonidine:* May decrease clonidine effects. Adjust dosage.

Drug-herb. *Butcher's broom:* May reduce drug effects. Discourage use together.

Effects on lab test results

• May decrease WBC and neutrophil counts.

Pharmacokinetics

Absorption: Good.
Distribution: 98% protein-bound.
Metabolism: Extensive.
Excretion: 63% in bile and feces; 9% in urine. *Half-life:* 19 to 22 hours.

Route	Onset	Peak	Duration
P.O.	1–2 hr	2–6 hr	24 hr

Action

Chemical effect: Acts on peripheral vasculature to produce vasodilation.
Therapeutic effect: Lowers blood pressure.

Available forms

Tablets: 1 mg, 2 mg, 4 mg, 8 mg

NURSING PROCESS

Assessment

• Obtain history of patient's blood pressure before beginning therapy, and reassess regularly thereafter.

• Determine effect on standing and supine blood pressure at 2 to 6 hours and 24 hours after giving the drug.

• Be alert for adverse reactions.

• Monitor patient's ECG for arrhythmias.

• Assess patient's and family's knowledge of drug therapy.

Nursing diagnoses

• Risk for injury related to presence of hypertension
• Decreased cardiac output related to drug-induced adverse CV reactions
• Deficient knowledge related to drug therapy

Planning and implementation

• Increase dosage gradually, with adjustments every 2 weeks for hypertension and every 1 to 2 weeks for BPH.
• If syncope occurs, place patient in recumbent position and provide supportive therapy. A transient hypotensive response isn't considered a contraindication to continued therapy.
ALERT: Don't confuse doxazosin with doxapram, doxorubicin, or doxepin. Don't confuse Cardura with Coumadin, K-Dur, Cardene, or Cordarone.

Patient teaching

• Advise patient that he's susceptible to a first-dose effect similar to that produced by other alpha blockers: marked orthostatic hypotension, accompanied by dizziness or syncope. Orthostatic hypotension is most common after first dose, but it can also occur when stopping therapy or adjusting dosage.
• Warn patient that dizziness or fainting may occur. Advise patient to refrain from driving and performing other hazardous activities until drug's adverse CNS effects are known.
• Stress importance of regular follow-up visits.

Evaluation

• Patient's blood pressure becomes normal.
• Patient maintains adequate cardiac output throughout therapy.
• Patient and family state understanding of drug therapy.

doxepin hydrochloride

(DOKS-eh-pin high-droh-KLOR-ighd)
Novo-Doxepin ♦, Sinequan

Pharmacologic class: tricyclic antidepressant
Therapeutic class: antidepressant
Pregnancy risk category: C

Indications and dosages

▶ **Depression, anxiety.** *Adults and children age 12 and older:* Initially, 25 to 75 mg P.O. daily in divided doses to maximum, 300 mg daily. Or, give entire maintenance dosage once daily. Maximum, 150 mg.
Adjust-a-dose: In elderly or debilitated patients, adolescents, and those receiving other drugs (especially anticholinergics), reduce dosage.

Contraindications and cautions

• Contraindicated in patients hypersensitive to the drug or any of its components and in those with glaucoma or a tendency for urine retention.
Lifespan: In pregnant women and in children younger than age 12, safety and effectiveness haven't been established. In breast-feeding women, drug isn't recommended.

Adverse reactions

CNS: ataxia, confusion, *dizziness, drowsiness,* EEG changes, excitation, extrapyramidal reactions, hallucinations, headache, nervousness, paresthesia, ***seizures, suicidal thinking,*** tremors, weakness.
CV: ECG changes, hypertension, orthostatic hypotension, tachycardia.
EENT: *blurred vision,* mydriasis, tinnitus.
GI: anorexia, constipation, dry mouth, glossitis, nausea, vomiting.
GU: urine retention.
Hematologic: ***bone marrow depression, including agranulocytosis, aplastic anemia, leukopenia, and thrombocytopenia;*** eosinophilia.
Skin: *diaphoresis,* photosensitivity, rash, urticaria.
Other: hypersensitivity reaction.

Interactions

Drug-drug. *Barbiturates, CNS depressants:* May increase CNS depression. Avoid use together.
Cimetidine, fluoxetine, methylphenidate, sertraline: May increase doxepin level. Monitor patient for increased adverse reactions.
Clonidine: May cause loss of blood pressure control with potentially life-threatening elevations in blood pressure. Don't use together.
Epinephrine, norepinephrine: May increase hypertensive effect. Use cautiously; monitor blood pressure closely.

MAO inhibitors: May cause severe excitation, hyperpyrexia, or seizures, usually with high dosage. Avoid use together.
Drug-herb. *SAMe, St. John's wort, yohimbe:* May elevate serotonin level. Discourage use together.
Drug-food. *Carbonated beverages, grape juice:* May be incompatible. Avoid use together.
Drug-lifestyle. *Alcohol use:* May increase CNS depression. Discourage use together.
Sun exposure: May increase risk of photosensitivity reactions. Discourage unprotected or prolonged exposure to the sun.

Effects on lab test results

• May increase liver enzyme levels. May decrease hemoglobin level and hematocrit. May increase or decrease glucose level.
• May increase eosinophil count. May decrease RBC, WBC, granulocyte, and platelet counts.

Pharmacokinetics

Absorption: Rapid.
Distribution: Wide, including CNS. 90% protein-bound.
Metabolism: By liver. A significant first-pass effect may explain varying levels in patients with same dosage.
Excretion: Mainly in urine. *Half-life:* 6 to 8 hours.

Route	Onset	Peak	Duration
P.O.	Unknown	≤ 2 hr	Unknown

Action

Chemical effect: Unknown; increases amount of norepinephrine, serotonin, or both in CNS by blocking their reuptake by presynaptic neurons.
Therapeutic effect: Relieves depression and anxiety.

Available forms

Capsules: 10 mg, 25 mg, 50 mg, 75 mg, 100 mg, 150 mg
Oral concentrate: 10 mg/ml

NURSING PROCESS

Assessment

• Assess patient's depression or anxiety before and during therapy.
• Be alert for adverse reactions and drug interactions.
• Assess patient's and family's knowledge of drug therapy.

Nursing diagnoses

• Ineffective coping related to underlying condition
• Risk for injury related to drug-induced adverse CNS reactions
• Deficient knowledge related to drug therapy

Planning and implementation

• Dilute oral concentrate with 120 ml of water, milk, or juice (except grape juice). Don't mix with carbonated beverages because they are incompatible.
• Don't stop long-term therapy abruptly; doing so can cause nausea, headache, and malaise, which don't indicate addiction.
• Stop drug gradually several days before surgery because hypertensive episodes may occur.
• If signs of psychosis occur or increase, notify prescriber and reduce dosage.
ALERT: Antidepressants may increase the risk of suicidal thinking and behavior in children and adolescents with major depressive disorder and other psychiatric disorders. Balance risk with patient's need for drug.
ALERT: Don't confuse doxepin with doxazosin, digoxin, doxapram, or Doxidan; don't confuse Sinequan with saquinavir.

Patient teaching

• Tell patient to dilute oral concentrate with 120 ml of water, milk, or juice (orange, grapefruit, tomato, prune, or pineapple). Drug is incompatible with carbonated beverages and grape juice.
• Advise patient to take full dose at bedtime, but warn him that he may have morning orthostatic hypotension.
• Warn patient to avoid hazardous activities that require alertness and good psychomotor coordination until the drug's CNS effects are known. Drowsiness and dizziness usually subside after a few weeks.
• Tell patient to avoid using alcohol while taking the drug.
• Warn patient not to stop drug therapy suddenly.
• Advise patient to consult prescriber before taking prescription drugs, OTC medications, or herbal remedies.

• Advise patient to use sunblock, wear protective clothing, and avoid prolonged exposure to strong sunlight.

Evaluation

• Patient behavior and communication indicate improvement of depression or anxiety.
• Patient has no injury as result of drug-induced adverse CNS reactions.
• Patient and family state understanding of drug therapy.

doxercalciferol

(dox-er-kal-SIF-eh-rol)
Hectorol

Pharmacologic class: synthetic vitamin D analogue
Therapeutic class: parathyroid hormone antagonist
Pregnancy risk category: B

Indications and dosages

▶ **To reduce intact parathyroid hormone (iPTH) levels to manage secondary hyperparathyroidism in patients undergoing long-term renal dialysis.** *Adults:* Initially, 10 mcg P.O. three times weekly at dialysis. Adjust dosage as needed to lower iPTH level to 150 to 300 picograms per milliliter (pg/ml). Increase dosage by 2.5 mcg at 8-week intervals if iPTH level doesn't decline by 50% and fails to reach target range. Maximum, 20 mcg P.O. three times weekly. If iPTH level falls below 100 pg/ml, stop drug for 1 week and then resume at a dose that's at least 2.5 mcg lower than the last dose. Or, 4 mcg I.V. bolus three times weekly (about every other day) at the end of dialysis. Adjust dose as needed to lower iPTH level to 150 to 300 pg/ml. Dosage may be increased by 1 to 2 mcg at 8-week intervals if iPTH level isn't decreased by 50% and fails to reach target range. Maximum, 18 mcg weekly. If iPTH level goes below 100 pg/ml, suspend drug for 1 week; then resume at a dosage that's at least 1 mcg P.O. lower than the last dose.

▶ **Secondary hyperparathyroidism in predialysis patients with stage 3 or 4 chronic kidney disease.** *Adults:* 1 mcg P.O. daily. Adjust dosage as needed to lower blood iPTH level to target range. Target range for stage 3 is 35 to 70 pg/ml. Target range for stage 4 is 70 to 110 pg/ml. Increase dosage at 2-week intervals by 0.5 mcg if level is above 70 pg/ml (stage 3) or above 110 pg/ml (stage 4). If level falls below 35 pg/ml for stage 3 or 70 pg/ml for stage 4, stop drug for 1 week, then resume at a dosage at least 0.5 mcg lower than the last dose. Maximum dose is 3.5 mcg daily.

I.V. administration

• Administer by bolus injection.
• Store at a controlled room temperature.
• Protect from light.

⊗ **Incompatibilities**

None reported.

Contraindications and cautions

• Contraindicated in patients with a recent history of hypercalcemia, hyperphosphatemia, or vitamin D toxicity.
• Use cautiously in patients with hepatic insufficiency, and frequently monitor calcium, phosphorus, and iPTH levels in these patients.

Lifespan: In breast-feeding women, and in children younger than age 12, drug isn't recommended. In elderly patients, use cautiously because adverse CNS reactions, orthostatic hypotension, and GI and GU distresses are more likely to develop.

Adverse reactions

CNS: dizziness, headache, malaise, sleep disorder.
CV: *bradycardia,* edema.
GI: anorexia, constipation, dyspepsia, *nausea, vomiting.*
Metabolic: weight gain or loss.
Musculoskeletal: arthralgia.
Respiratory: *dyspnea.*
Skin: pruritus.
Other: abscess.

Interactions

Drug-drug. *Calcium-containing or non–aluminum-containing phosphate binders:* May cause hypercalcemia or hyperphosphatemia and decrease effectiveness of doxercalciferol. Use together cautiously, and adjust dosage of phosphate binders as directed.
Cholestyramine, mineral oil: May decrease intestinal absorption of doxercalciferol. Avoid use together.

Glutethimide, phenobarbital, and other enzyme inducers; phenytoin and other enzyme inhibitors: May affect doxercalciferol metabolism. Adjust dosage as directed.
Magnesium-containing antacids: May cause hypermagnesemia. Monitor patient for toxicity.
Orlistat: May interfere with intestinal absorption of vitamin D analogues. Give drug at least 2 hours before or 2 hours after Orlistat administration.
Vitamin D supplements: May cause additive effects and hypercalcemia. Monitor patient for toxicity.

Effects on lab test results

None reported.

Pharmacokinetics

Absorption: Good.
Distribution: Unknown.
Metabolism: To its active forms in the liver.
Excretion: Major metabolite attains peak levels at 11 to 12 hours after repeated doses. *Half-life:* 32 to 37 hours, with a range of up to 96 hours.

Route	Onset	Peak	Duration
P.O.	Unknown	11–12 hr	Unknown

Action

Chemical effect: Regulates calcium levels. Acts directly on the parathyroid glands to suppress PTH synthesis and secretion.
Therapeutic effect: Reduces elevated iPTH levels.

Available forms

Capsules: 0.5 mcg, 2.5 mcg
Injection: 4 mcg/2 ml

NURSING PROCESS

Assessment

- Assess hepatic function before starting therapy.
- Monitor calcium, phosphorus, and iPTH levels. Monitor them more frequently in patients with hepatic insufficiency.
- Be alert for adverse reactions and drug interactions.
- Assess patient's and family's knowledge of drug therapy.

Nursing diagnoses

- Imbalanced nutrition: less than body requirements related to adverse GI effects
- Risk for injury related to adverse CNS effects
- Deficient knowledge related to drug therapy

Planning and implementation

- Give drug with dialysis (about q other day). Individualize doses based on intact PTH levels, with monitoring of calcium and phosphorus levels before therapy and weekly thereafter.
- If patient has hypercalcemia or hyperphosphatemia, or if the calcium level multiplied by the phosphorus level (Ca × P) is greater than 70, immediately stop doxercalciferol until these values decrease.
- Progressive hypercalcemia from vitamin D overdose may require emergency attention. Acute hypercalcemia may worsen arrhythmias and seizures and affect the action of digoxin. Chronic hypercalcemia can lead to vascular and soft-tissue calcification.
- Calcium-based or non–aluminum-containing phosphate binders and a low-phosphate diet are used to control phosphorus levels in patients undergoing dialysis. Adjust dosage of this drug and other therapies to maintain PTH suppression and calcium and phosphorus levels.

Patient teaching

- Inform patient that dosage will be adjusted over several months to achieve satisfactory PTH suppression.
- Tell patient to adhere to a low-phosphorus diet and to follow instructions regarding calcium supplements.
- Tell patient to obtain prescriber's approval before using OTC drugs, including antacids and vitamin preparations containing calcium or vitamin D.
- Inform patient that early signs and symptoms of hypercalcemia include weakness, headache, somnolence, nausea, vomiting, dry mouth, constipation, muscle pain, bone pain, and metallic taste. Late signs and symptoms include polyuria, polydipsia, anorexia, weight loss, nocturia, conjunctivitis, pancreatitis, photophobia, rhinorrhea, pruritus, hyperthermia, decreased libido, hypertension, and arrhythmias.

Evaluation

- Patient has no nausea and vomiting.
- Patient remains free from injury.

• Patient and family state understanding of drug therapy.

doxorubicin hydrochloride

(doks-oh-ROO-bih-sin high-droh-KLOR-ighd)
Adriamycin ◇, Adriamycin PFS, Adriamycin RDF, Rubex

Pharmacologic class: anthracycline antibiotic
Therapeutic class: antineoplastic
Pregnancy risk category: D

Indications and dosages

▶ **Bladder, breast, lung, ovarian, stomach, testicular, and thyroid cancers; Hodgkin lymphoma; acute lymphoblastic and myeloblastic leukemia; Wilms tumor; neuroblastoma; lymphoma; sarcoma.** *Adults:* 60 to 75 mg/m² I.V. as single dose q 3 weeks; or 30 mg/m² I.V. in single daily dose on days 1 through 3 of 4-week cycle. Or, 20 mg/m² I.V. once weekly. Maximum cumulative dose, 550 mg/m².

Adjust-a-dose: In elderly patients and those with myelosuppression or impaired cardiac or hepatic function, dosage may need adjustment.

If bilirubin level increases, decrease dosage: 50% of dosage when bilirubin level is 1.2 to 3 mg/dl; 25% of dosage when bilirubin level is greater than 3 mg/dl.

I.V. administration

• Preparing and giving drug carry carcinogenic, mutagenic, and teratogenic risks. Follow facility policy to reduce risks.
• Reconstitute using preservative-free normal saline solution injection. Add 5 ml to 10-mg vial, 10 ml to 20-mg vial, or 25 ml to 50-mg vial. Shake vial, and allow drug to dissolve; final concentration is 2 mg/ml.
• Give by direct injection into I.V. line of free-flowing compatible I.V. solution containing D_5W or normal saline solution injection in no less than 3 minutes.
• Drug is a severe vesicant, and extravasation may cause tissue necrosis. To avoid extravasation, don't place I.V. line over joints or in limbs with poor venous or lymphatic drainage.
• If extravasation occurs, stop I.V. injection immediately, notify prescriber, and apply ice to area for 24 to 48 hours. Monitor area closely because extravasation reaction may be progressive. Early consultation with plastic surgeon may be advisable.
• If vein streaking occurs, slow administration rate. If welts occur, stop administration and notify prescriber.
• Refrigerated, reconstituted solution is stable for 48 hours; at room temperature, it's stable for 24 hours.

⊗ **Incompatibilities**

Allopurinol, aluminum, aminophylline, bacteriostatic diluents, cefepime, cephalothin, dexamethasone sodium phosphate, diazepam, fluorouracil, furosemide, ganciclovir, heparin sodium, hydrocortisone sodium succinate, piperacillin with tazobactam.

Contraindications and cautions

• Contraindicated in patients with marked myelosuppression induced by previous therapy with other antitumor drugs or radiotherapy and in those who have received lifetime cumulative dose of 550 mg/m².

Lifespan: In pregnant and breast-feeding women, drug isn't recommended. In children, safety and effectiveness haven't been established.

Adverse reactions

CV: ***arrhythmias;*** cardiac depression, seen in ECG changes, such as sinus tachycardia, T-wave flattening, ST-segment depression, voltage reduction; ***irreversible cardiomyopathy.***
EENT: conjunctivitis.
GI: anorexia, diarrhea, esophagitis, *nausea, stomatitis, vomiting.*
GU: transient red urine.
Hematologic: ***leukopenia*** during days 10 through 15, with recovery by day 21; **MYELOSUPPRESSION;** ***thrombocytopenia.***
Skin: *complete alopecia;* facial flushing; *hyperpigmentation of nails, dermal creases,* or skin (especially in previously irradiated areas); urticaria.
Other: ***anaphylaxis,*** hyperuricemia, severe cellulitis or tissue sloughing if drug extravasates.

Interactions

Drug-drug. *Calcium channel blockers:* May potentiate cardiotoxic effects. Monitor patient closely.
Digoxin: May decrease digoxin level. Monitor patient closely.

Paclitaxel: May decrease doxorubicin clearance. Monitor patient for toxicity.
Phenobarbital: May increase doxorubicin clearance. Monitor patient closely.
Phenytoin: May decrease phenytoin level. Check level.
Progesterone: May enhance doxorubicin-induced neutropenia and thrombocytopenia. Monitor closely.
Streptozocin: May increase and prolong blood level of doxorubicin HCl. Dosage may need adjustment.
Drug-herb. *Green tea:* May enhance antitumor effects of drug. Urge patient to discuss with prescriber before using together.

Effects on lab test results

- May increase bilirubin, uric acid, and glucose levels. May decrease calcium and hemoglobin levels and hematocrit.
- May decrease WBC, neutrophil, and platelet counts.

Pharmacokinetics

Absorption: Given I.V.
Distribution: Wide; doesn't cross blood–brain barrier.
Metabolism: Extensive, by hepatic microsomal enzymes to several metabolites, one of which has cytotoxic activity.
Excretion: Mainly in bile, minimally in urine. *Half-life:* Triphasic pattern of 12 minutes, 3.3 hours, and 30 to 40 hours.

Route	Onset	Peak	Duration
I.V.	Unknown	Unknown	Unknown

Action

Chemical effect: May interfere with DNA-dependent RNA synthesis by intercalation.
Therapeutic effect: Hinders or kills certain cancer cells.

Available forms

Injection (preservative-free): 2 mg/ml
Powder for injection: 10-mg, 20-mg, 50-mg, 100-mg, 150-mg vials

NURSING PROCESS

Assessment

- Obtain history of patient's neoplastic disorder before therapy, and reassess regularly thereafter.
- Assess ECG before therapy.
- Monitor CBC and liver function tests; monitor ECG monthly during therapy.
- Be alert for adverse reactions and drug interactions.
- Assess patient's and family's knowledge of drug therapy.

Nursing diagnoses

- Ineffective health maintenance related to presence of neoplastic disease
- Decreased cardiac output related to drug-induced cardiotoxicity
- Deficient knowledge related to drug therapy

Planning and implementation

- To reduce nausea, premedicate with antiemetic.
- If skin or mucosal contact occurs, immediately wash area with soap and water.
- In case of leak or spill, inactivate drug with 5% sodium hypochlorite solution (household bleach).
- Never give drug I.M. or subcutaneously.
- If tachycardia develops, stop giving the drug or slow infusion rate, and notify the prescriber.
- If signs of heart failure develop, stop drug immediately and notify prescriber. Limit cumulative dose to 550 mg/m^2 (400 mg/m^2 when patient also receives or has received cyclophosphamide or radiation therapy to cardiac area) to prevent heart failure.
- Alternate dosage schedule (once weekly) to lower the risk of cardiomyopathy.
- Provide adequate hydration. Alkalinizing urine or giving allopurinol may prevent or minimize uric acid nephropathy.
- Radiation may increase radiation-induced toxicity to the myocardium, mucosa, skin, and liver. Monitor patient.
- Report adverse reactions to prescriber and provide supportive care.

ALERT: Avoid confusing doxorubicin and daunorubicin. Red color is similar.

ALERT: Liposomal doxorubicin and conventional doxorubicin aren't interchangeable. Clearance of liposomal form is significantly less than conventional form. Decrease liposomal doxorubicin dose.

Patient teaching

- Warn patient to watch for signs of infection (fever, sore throat, fatigue) and bleeding (easy

bruising, nosebleed, bleeding gums, melena). Have patient take temperature daily.
- Advise patient that orange to red urine for 1 to 2 days is normal and doesn't indicate presence of blood in urine.
- Tell patient that total alopecia may occur within 3 to 4 weeks. Hair may regrow 2 to 5 months after drug is stopped.
- Instruct patient to report symptoms of heart failure and other cardiac signs and symptoms promptly to prescriber.
- Tell patient to use safety precautions to prevent injury.

Evaluation
- Patient exhibits positive response to therapy, as noted on improved follow-up studies.
- Patient maintains adequate cardiac output throughout therapy.
- Patient and family state understanding of drug therapy.

doxorubicin hydrochloride liposomal
(doks-oh-ROO-bih-sin high-droh-KLOR-ighd ly-puh-SOE-mul)
Doxil

Pharmacologic class: anthracycline antibiotic
Therapeutic class: antineoplastic
Pregnancy risk category: D

Indications and dosages
► **Metastatic ovarian cancer in women with disease refractory to paclitaxel- and platinum-based chemotherapy regimens.** *Women:* 50 mg/m² (doxorubicin hydrochloride equivalent) I.V. at an initial infusion rate of 1 mg/minute once q 4 weeks for at least four courses. Continue as long as patient doesn't progress, shows no evidence of cardiotoxicity, and continues to tolerate treatment. If no infusion-related adverse events occur, increase infusion rate to complete administration over 1 hour.

► **AIDS-related Kaposi sarcoma in patients with disease that has progressed with previous combination chemotherapy or in patients who are intolerant to such therapy.** *Adults:* 20 mg/m² (doxorubicin hydrochloride equivalent) I.V. over 30 minutes, once q 3 weeks, for as long as patient responds satisfactorily and tolerates therapy.

Adjust-a-dose: For patients with impaired hepatic function, if bilirubin level is 1.2 to 3 mg/dl, give one-fourth of the normal dose; if bilirubin level is more than 3 mg/dl, give one-half of the normal dose. Consult package insert for dose modifications for hand-foot syndrome, hematologic toxicity, and stomatitis.

I.V. administration
- Follow facility procedures for proper handling and disposal of antineoplastics.
- Dilute dose (maximum, 90 mg) in 250 ml of D_5W using aseptic technique.
- Carefully check label on the I.V. bag before giving drug. Accidentally substituting Doxil for conventional doxorubicin hydrochloride can cause severe adverse effects.
- Infuse I.V. over 30 to 60 minutes, depending on the dose. Don't use with in-line filters.
- Monitor patient carefully during infusion. Flushing, shortness of breath, facial swelling, headache, chills, back pain, tightness in the chest or throat, or hypotension may occur. These reactions resolve over several hours to a day once the infusion is stopped; they may also resolve by slowing the infusion rate.
- If extravasation occurs, stop infusion immediately and restart in another vein. Applying ice over the extravasation site for about 30 minutes may help to alleviate the local reaction.
- Refrigerate diluted solution at 36° to 46° F (2° to 8° C), and give within 24 hours.

⊗ **Incompatibilities**
Other I.V. drugs.

Contraindications and cautions
- Contraindicated in patients hypersensitive to the conventional form of doxorubicin hydrochloride or any component in the liposomal form. Also contraindicated in patients with marked myelosuppression or those who have received a lifetime cumulative dosage of 550 mg/m² (400 mg/m² if patient received radiotherapy to the mediastinal area or simultaneous therapy with other cardiotoxic drugs, such as cyclophosphamide).
- Use in patients with a history of CV disease only when the potential benefits of the drug outweigh the risks.

• Use cautiously in patients who have received another anthracycline.
Lifespan: In women of child-bearing age, avoid pregnancy during therapy; don't start drug if patient is pregnant. In breast-feeding women, drug is contraindicated. In children, safety and effectiveness haven't been established. In elderly patients, use cautiously because they may have greater sensitivity to the drug.

Adverse reactions

CNS: anxiety, *asthenia,* depression, dizziness, emotional lability, fatigue, fever, headache, insomnia, malaise, paresthesia, somnolence.
CV: ***arrhythmias, cardiomyopathy,*** chest pain, ***heart failure,*** hypotension, ***pericardial effusion,*** peripheral edema, tachycardia.
EENT: conjunctivitis, mouth ulceration, mucous membrane disorder, optic neuritis, pharyngitis, retinitis, rhinitis.
GI: abdominal pain, anorexia, constipation, diarrhea, dyspepsia, dysphagia, enlarged abdomen, esophagitis, glossitis, *nausea,* oral candidiasis, *stomatitis,* taste disturbance, vomiting.
GU: albuminuria.
Hematologic: *anemia,* ***leukopenia,*** **NEUTROPENIA, THROMBOCYTOPENIA.**
Hepatic: hyperbilirubinemia.
Metabolic: dehydration, hyperglycemia, hypocalcemia, weight loss.
Musculoskeletal: back pain, myalgia.
Respiratory: dyspnea, increased cough, pneumonia.
Skin: *alopecia,* dry skin, exfoliative dermatitis, hand-foot syndrome, herpes zoster, pruritus, *rash,* skin discoloration, skin disorder, sweating.
Other: ***allergic reaction,*** chills, *infection,* infusion-related reactions, ***sepsis.***

Interactions

No drug interactions have been reported; however, doxorubicin hydrochloride liposomal may interact with drugs known to interact with the conventional form of doxorubicin hydrochloride.

Effects on lab test results

• May increase bilirubin and glucose levels. May decrease calcium and hemoglobin levels and hematocrit.
• May increase PT. May decrease WBC, neutrophil, and platelet counts.

Pharmacokinetics

Absorption: Given I.V.
Distribution: Mostly to vascular fluid.
Metabolism: Doxorubicinol, the major metabolite, is detected at very low levels.
Excretion: Slow, in two phases. *Half-life:* 5 hours in the first phase, 55 hours in the second phase with doses of 10 to 20 mg/m^2.

Route	Onset	Peak	Duration
I.V.	Unknown	Unknown	Unknown

Action

Chemical effect: Doxil is doxorubicin hydrochloride encapsulated in liposomes that, because of their small size and persistence in circulation, can penetrate the altered vasculature of tumors. The mechanism of action of doxorubicin hydrochloride is probably related to its ability to bind DNA and inhibit nucleic acid synthesis.
Therapeutic effect: Hinders or kills certain cancer cells in patients with ovarian cancer or AIDS-related Kaposi sarcoma.

Available forms

Injection: 2 mg/ml, 20 mg/10 ml, 50 mg/30 ml

NURSING PROCESS

Assessment

• Obtain an accurate medication list from patient, including previous or current chemotherapeutic drugs.
• Evaluate patient's hepatic function before beginning therapy, and adjust dose accordingly.
• Monitor cardiac function closely by endomyocardial biopsy, echocardiography, or gated radionuclide scans. If results indicate that the patient may have cardiac injury, the benefit of continued therapy must be weighed against the risk of myocardial injury.
• Be alert for adverse reactions.
• Assess patient's and family's knowledge of drug therapy.

Nursing diagnoses

• Risk for infection related to myelosuppression
• Risk for injury related to drug-induced adverse reactions
• Deficient knowledge related to drug therapy

Planning and implementation

• Don't give drug I.M. or subcutaneously.

ALERT: Don't substitute on a milligram-per-milligram basis with conventional doxorubicin hydrochloride.

• Drug may increase the toxicity of other antineoplastic therapies.

• Take into account any earlier or simultaneous therapy with related compounds, such as daunorubicin, when giving total dose. Heart failure and cardiomyopathy may occur after therapy stops.

• Monitor CBC, including platelets, before each dose and frequently throughout therapy. Leukopenia is usually transient. Hematologic toxicity may require dosage reduction or suspension or delay of therapy. Persistent severe myelosuppression may result in superinfection or hemorrhage. Patient may need granulocyte colony-stimulating factor (or granulocyte-macrophage colony-stimulating factor) to support blood counts.

Patient teaching

• Tell patient to notify prescriber about symptoms of hand-foot syndrome, such as tingling or burning, redness, flaking, bothersome swelling, small blisters, or small sores on the palms of hands or soles of feet.

• Advise patient to report symptoms of stomatitis, such as painful redness, swelling, or sores in the mouth.

• Advise patient to avoid exposure to people with infections. Tell patient to report fever of 100.5° F (38° C) or higher.

• Urge patient to report nausea, vomiting, tiredness, weakness, rash, or mild hair loss.

• Advise woman of childbearing age to avoid pregnancy during therapy.

Evaluation

• Patient has no infection.

• Patient has no injury as a result of drug-induced adverse reactions.

• Patient and family state understanding of drug therapy.

doxycycline
(docks-ih-SYE-kleen)
Oracea

doxycycline hyclate
Apo-Doxy ♦, Doryx, Doxy-100, Doxy-200, Doxycin ♦, Doxytec ♦, Novo-Doxylin ♦, Nu-Doxycycline ♦, Periostat, Vibramycin, Vibra-Tabs

doxycycline hydrochloride ◇
Doryx ◇, Doxylin ◇, Doxy Tablets ◇, Vibramycin ◇, Vibra-Tabs ◇

doxycycline monohydrate
Adoxa, Monodox, Vibramycin

Pharmacologic class: tetracycline
Therapeutic class: antibiotic
Pregnancy risk category: D

Indications and dosages

▶ **Infections caused by sensitive gram-negative and gram-positive organisms, *Chlamydia, Mycoplasma, Rickettsia,* and organisms that cause trachoma.** *Adults and children weighing more than 45 kg (99 lb):* 100 mg P.O. q 12 hours on first day; then 100 mg P.O. daily. Or, 200 mg I.V. on first day in one or two infusions; then 100 to 200 mg I.V. daily. For severe infections, 100 mg P.O. q 12 hours may be used.
Children older than age 8 and weighing less than 45 kg: 4.4 mg/kg P.O. or I.V. daily in divided doses q 12 hours on first day, then 2.2 to 4.4 mg/kg daily.

▶ **Gonorrhea in patients allergic to penicillin.** *Adults:* 100 mg P.O. b.i.d. for 7 days. Or 300 mg P.O. initially; repeat dose in 1 hour.

▶ **Primary or secondary syphilis in patients allergic to penicillin.** *Adults and children older than age 8:* Give 100 mg P.O. b.i.d. for 2 weeks (early detection) or for 4 weeks (if more than 1 year's duration).

▶ **Uncomplicated urethral, endocervical, or rectal infection caused by *Chlamydia trachomatis* or *Ureaplasma urealyticum.*** *Adults:* 100 mg P.O. b.i.d. for at least 7 days.

▶ **To prevent malaria.** *Adults:* 100 mg P.O. daily.

Children older than age 8: Give 2 mg/kg P.O. once daily. Don't exceed adult dose. Begin 1 to 2 days before travel to malarious area and continue throughout travel and for 4 weeks thereafter.

▶ **Adjunct to scaling and root planing to promote attachment level gain and to reduce pocket depth in patients with adult periodontitis.** *Adults:* 20 mg Periostat P.O. b.i.d. more than 1 hour before or 2 hours after the morning and evening meals and after scaling and root planing. Effective for 9 months.

▶ **Adjunct to other antibiotics for inhalation, GI, and oropharyngeal anthrax.** *Adults:* 100 mg I.V. q 12 hours initially until susceptibility test results are known. Switch to 100 mg P.O. b.i.d. when appropriate. Treat for 60 days total.

Children older than age 8 and weighing more than 45 kg: 100 mg I.V. q 12 hours, then switch to 100 mg P.O. b.i.d. when appropriate. Treat for 60 days total.

Children older than age 8 and weighing 45 kg or less: 2.2 mg/kg I.V. q 12 hours, then switch to 2.2 mg/kg P.O. b.i.d. when appropriate. Treat for 60 days total.

Children age 8 and younger: 2.2 mg/kg I.V. q 12 hours, then switch to 2.2 mg/kg P.O. b.i.d. when appropriate. Treat for 60 days total.

▶ **Cutaneous anthrax.** *Adults:* 100 mg P.O. b.i.d. for 60 days.

Children older than age 8 and weighing more than 45 kg: 100 mg P.O. q 12 hours for 60 days.

Children older than age 8 and weighing 45 kg or less: 2.2 mg/kg P.O. q 12 hours for 60 days.

Children age 8 and younger: 2.2 mg/kg P.O. q 12 hours for 60 days.

▶ **Adjunct to severe acne.** *Adults:* 200 mg Adoxa P.O. on day 1 (give as 100 mg q 12 hours or 50 mg q 6 hours); follow with a maintenance dose of 100 mg P.O. daily, or 50 mg P.O. b.i.d.

▶ **Inflammatory lesions (papules and pustules) of rosacea.** *Adults:* 40 mg P.O. once daily in the morning, 1 hour before or 2 hours after a meal, with a full glass of water.

▶ **To prevent traveler's diarrhea commonly caused by enterotoxigenic *Escherichia coli*‡.** *Adults:* 100 mg P.O. daily for up to 3 days.

▶ **To prevent sexually transmitted diseases in rape victims‡.** *Adults and adolescents:* 100 mg Adoxa P.O. b.i.d. for 7 days after a single 2-g oral dose of metronidazole is given with a single 125-mg I.M. dose of ceftriaxone.

▶ **Lyme disease‡.** *Adults and children older than age 9:* 100 mg Adoxa P.O. b.i.d. or t.i.d. for 10 to 30 days.

▶ **Pleural effusions related to cancer‡.** *Adults:* 500 mg of doxycycline diluted in 250 ml of normal saline solution and instilled into pleural space via chest tube.

I.V. administration

- Reconstitute powder for injection with sterile water for injection. Use 10 ml in 100-mg vial and 20 ml in 200-mg vial. Dilute solution to 100 to 1,000 ml for I.V. infusion.
- Don't expose drug to light or heat. Protect it from sunlight during infusion.
- Don't infuse solutions that are more concentrated than 1 mg/ml.
- Depending on the dose, infusion lasts typically 1 to 4 hours. Complete infusion within 12 hours.
- Monitor I.V. infusion site for signs of thrombophlebitis.
- Monitor for infiltration or irritation.
- Reconstituted injectable solution is stable for 72 hours if refrigerated.

⊗ **Incompatibilities**

Allopurinol; drugs unstable in acidic solutions, such as barbiturates; erythromycin lactobionate; heparin; meropenem; nafcillin; penicillin G potassium; piperacillin with tazobactam; riboflavin; and sulfonamides.

Contraindications and cautions

- Contraindicated in patients hypersensitive to drug or other tetracyclines.
- Use cautiously in patients with impaired kidney or liver function.

Lifespan: In the first half of pregnancy, drug isn't recommended unless other options aren't available because of the risk of bone growth retardation and neural tube defects in the fetus. In breast-feeding women, avoid drug because of possible adverse effects on the infant. In children younger than age 8 and in the fetus during last half of pregnancy, these drugs may cause permanent tooth discoloration, enamel defects, and retarded bone growth. These effects are dose-limited; therefore, drug may be used for a short course (7 to 14 days) and not repeated. For anthrax in pregnant women, children younger than age 8, and immunocompromised patients, give the usual dose and regimen.

Adverse reactions

CNS: ***intracranial hypertension (pseudotumor cerebri).***
CV: pericarditis, thrombophlebitis.
EENT: dysphagia, glossitis.
GI: anogenital inflammation, anorexia, *diarrhea,* enterocolitis, *epigastric distress,* nausea, oral candidiasis, vomiting.
Hematologic: eosinophilia, hemolytic anemia, ***neutropenia, thrombocytopenia.***
Musculoskeletal: bone growth retardation if used in children younger than age 8.
Skin: increased pigmentation, maculopapular and erythematous rash, photosensitivity, urticaria.
Other: ***anaphylaxis,*** enamel defects, hypersensitivity reactions, permanent discoloration of teeth, superinfection.

Interactions

Drug-drug. *Antacids (including sodium bicarbonate) and laxatives containing aluminum, magnesium, or calcium; antidiarrheals:* May decrease antibiotic absorption. Give antibiotic 1 hour before or 2 hours after these drugs.
Carbamazepine, phenobarbital: May decrease antibiotic effect. Avoid use together, if possible.
Digoxin: May increase serum digoxin levels. Monitor levels and signs of toxicity.
Ferrous sulfate and other iron products, zinc: May decrease antibiotic absorption. Give drug 3 hours after or 2 hours before iron.
Hormonal contraceptives: May decrease contraceptive effectiveness and increase risk of breakthrough bleeding. Recommend nonhormonal form of birth control.
Isotretinoin: May cause pseudotumor cerebri. Avoid concomitant use.
Methoxyflurane: May cause nephrotoxicity with tetracyclines. Avoid use together.
Oral anticoagulants: May increase anticoagulant effect. Monitor PT and INR, and adjust dosage.
Penicillins: May interfere with bactericidal action of penicillins. Avoid use together.
Drug-lifestyle. *Alcohol use:* May decrease antibiotic effect. Avoid use together.
Sun exposure: May cause photosensitivity reactions. Urge patient to avoid unprotected and prolonged sun exposure.

Effects on lab test results

- May increase BUN and liver enzyme levels. May decrease hemoglobin level and hematocrit.
- May increase eosinophil count. May decrease platelet, neutrophil, and WBC counts.
- May cause false-negative reading of glucose oxidase reagent (Diastix or Chemstrip uG). May cause false-positive reading of copper sulfate tests (Clinitest) with parenteral form.
- May falsely elevate urinary catecholamine levels.

D

Pharmacokinetics

Absorption: 90% to 100%.
Distribution: Wide, but poor in CSF. 25% to 93% protein-bound.
Metabolism: Insignificant; some hepatic degradation occurs.
Excretion: Mainly unchanged in urine; some in feces. *Half-life:* About 1 day after multiple doses.

Route	Onset	Peak	Duration
P.O.	Unknown	1½–4 hr	Unknown
I.V.	Immediate	Unknown	Unknown

Action

Chemical effect: May exert bacteriostatic effect by binding to 30S ribosomal subunit of microorganisms, thus inhibiting protein synthesis.
Therapeutic effect: Hinders bacterial growth.

Available forms

doxycycline calcium
Capsules: 40 mg
Syrup: 50 mg/5 ml
doxycycline hyclate
Capsules: 20 mg, 50 mg, 100 mg
Capsules (coated pellets): 75 mg, 100 mg
Injection: 100 mg, 200 mg
Tablets: 20 mg, 100 mg
doxycycline hydrochloride ◇
Capsules: 50 mg ◇, 100 mg ◇
Tablets: 50 mg ◇, 100 mg ◇
doxycycline monohydrate
Capsules: 50 mg, 100 mg
Oral suspension: 25 mg/5 ml
Tablets: 50 mg, 75 mg, 100 mg

NURSING PROCESS

Assessment

- Obtain history of patient's infection before therapy, and reassess regularly thereafter.

• Obtain specimen for culture and sensitivity tests before giving the first dose. Begin therapy pending test results.
• Be alert for adverse reactions and drug interactions.
• If patient has adverse GI reactions, monitor his hydration.
• Assess patient's and family's knowledge of drug therapy.

Nursing diagnoses

• Ineffective protection related to presence of susceptible bacteria
• Risk for deficient fluid volume related to drug-induced adverse GI reactions
• Deficient knowledge related to drug therapy

Planning and implementation

• Check expiration date. Outdated or deteriorated tetracyclines may cause reversible nephrotoxicity (Fanconi syndrome).
• If drug causes adverse GI reaction, may give with milk or food.
• Follow current Centers for Disease Control and Prevention recommendations for anthrax.
• Ciprofloxacin and doxycycline are first-line therapy for anthrax; 500 mg amoxicillin P.O. t.i.d. for adults and 80 mg/kg/day divided q 8 hours for children is an option for completing therapy after improvement.
• Cutaneous anthrax with signs of systemic involvement, extensive edema, or lesions on the head or neck requires I.V. therapy and a multidrug approach.
• Additional antimicrobials for anthrax multidrug regimens can include rifampin, vancomycin, penicillin, ampicillin, chloramphenicol, imipenem, clindamycin, and clarithromycin.
• Steroids may be considered as adjunctive therapy for anthrax patients with severe edema and for meningitis, based on experience with bacterial meningitis of other etiologies.
• If meningitis is suspected, doxycycline would be less optimal because of poor CNS penetration.
• Notify prescriber of adverse reactions. Some adverse reactions, such as superinfection, may necessitate substitution of another antibiotic.
ALERT: Don't confuse doxycycline with doxylamine or dicyclomine.

Patient teaching

• Tell patient to take entire amount of medication exactly as prescribed, even after he feels better.
• Instruct patient to take oral drug with milk or food but not with antacids if adverse GI reaction develops. Tell patient to take drug no less than 1 hour before bedtime to prevent irritation from esophageal reflux.
• Advise parent giving drug to a child that tablets may be crushed and mixed with low-fat milk, low-fat chocolate milk, regular (whole) chocolate milk, chocolate pudding, or apple juice mixed with sugar in equal proportions. Store mixtures in refrigerator, except apple juice mixture (which can be stored at room temperature), and discard after 24 hours.
• Tell patient to use sunscreen and avoid strong sunlight during therapy to prevent photosensitivity reactions.
• Stress good oral hygiene.
• Tell patient to check expiration dates and to discard outdated doxycycline because it may become toxic.
• Advise patient taking hormonal contraceptive to use alternative means of contraception within 1 week of therapy.

Evaluation

• Patient is free from infection.
• Patient maintains adequate hydration throughout therapy.
• Patient and family state understanding of drug therapy.

dronabinol (delta-9-tetrahydrocannabinol)

(droh-NAB-eh-nohl)
Marinol

Pharmacologic class: cannabinoid
Therapeutic class: antiemetic, appetite stimulant
Pregnancy risk category: C
Controlled substance schedule: III

Indications and dosages

▶ **Nausea and vomiting from chemotherapy.** *Adults:* 5 mg/m^2 P.O. 1 to 3 hours before administration of chemotherapy. Then same dose q

2 to 4 hours after chemotherapy for total of four to six doses daily. If needed, increase dosage in increments of 2.5 mg/m² to maximum dose, 15 mg/m².

▶ **Anorexia and weight loss in patients with AIDS.** *Adults:* 2.5 mg P.O. b.i.d. before lunch and dinner, increase as needed to maximum, 20 mg daily.

Contraindications and cautions

- Contraindicated in patients hypersensitive to sesame oil or cannabinoids.
- Use cautiously in patients with heart disease, psychiatric illness, or history of drug abuse.

Lifespan: In breast-feeding women, drug isn't recommended. In children, safety and effectiveness haven't been established. In elderly patients, use cautiously.

Adverse reactions

CNS: amnesia, asthenia, ataxia, confusion, depersonalization, disorientation, *dizziness, drowsiness, euphoria,* hallucinations, headache, muddled thinking, *paranoia, somnolence.*
CV: orthostatic hypotension, palpitations, tachycardia, vasodilation.
EENT: visual disturbances.
GI: abdominal pain, diarrhea, dry mouth, nausea, vomiting.

Interactions

Drug-drug. *CNS depressants, psychotomimetic substances, sedatives:* May have additive effects. Avoid use together.
Drug-lifestyle. *Alcohol use:* May have additive effects. Discourage use together.

Effects on lab test results

None reported.

Pharmacokinetics

Absorption: 95%.
Distribution: Rapid. 97% to 99% protein-bound.
Metabolism: Extensive.
Excretion: Mainly in feces. *Half-life:* 1 to 1½ days.

Route	Onset	Peak	Duration
P.O.	Unknown	2–4 hr	4–6 hr; ≥ 24 hours for appetite stimulation

Action

Chemical effect: Unknown.
Therapeutic effect: Relieves nausea and vomiting caused by chemotherapy and stimulates appetite.

Available forms

Capsules: 2.5 mg, 5 mg, 10 mg

NURSING PROCESS

Assessment

- Obtain history of patient's underlying condition before therapy.
- Monitor the drug's effectiveness by assessing for nausea, vomiting, or weight gain. Drug effects may persist for days after therapy ends.
- Be alert for adverse reactions and drug interactions.
- Monitor patient for dependence. Dronabinol is the principal active substance in *Cannabis sativa* (marijuana). It can produce physical and psychological dependence and has high potential for abuse.
- Monitor patient's hydration, weight, and nutrition regularly.
- Assess patient's and family's knowledge of drug therapy.

Nursing diagnoses

- Risk for deficient fluid volume related to nausea and vomiting from chemotherapy
- Disturbed thought processes related to drug-induced adverse CNS reactions
- Deficient knowledge related to drug therapy

Planning and implementation

- Give drug only to patients who haven't responded satisfactorily to other antiemetics.
- Give drug 1 to 3 hours before chemotherapy starts and again 2 to 4 hours after chemotherapy.

Patient teaching

- Inform patient that drug may cause unusual changes in mood or other adverse behavioral effects.
- Caution patient to avoid hazardous activities until the drug's CNS effects are known.
- Warn family members to make sure patient is supervised by a responsible person during and immediately after therapy.

Evaluation

- Patient maintains adequate hydration.

• Patient regains normal thought processes after effects of drug therapy have dissipated.
• Patient and family state understanding of drug therapy.

drotrecogin alfa (activated)

(droh-truh-KO-jin AL-fah)
Xigris

Pharmacologic class: recombinant protease of human activated protein C
Therapeutic class: antithrombotic
Pregnancy risk category: C

Indications and dosages

▶ **Reduction of mortality in patients with severe sepsis (sepsis from acute organ dysfunction).** *Adults:* 24 mcg/kg/hour I.V. infusion for a total of 96 hours.

I.V. administration

• Reconstitute 5-mg vials with 2.5 ml sterile water for injection, USP, and 20-mg vials with 10 ml of sterile water for injection, USP. The resulting concentration is 2 mg/ml. Gently swirl each vial until powder is completely dissolved; avoid inverting or shaking the vial.
• If the reconstituted vial isn't used immediately, it may be held at controlled room temperature of 59° to 86° F (15° to 30° C) for up to 3 hours, or stored in a refrigerator at 36° to 46° F (2° to 8° C).
• Further dilute the reconstituted solution with sterile normal saline injection. Withdraw appropriate amount of reconstituted drug into a prepared infusion bag of sterile normal saline solution. When adding the drug, direct the stream to the side of the bag to minimize agitation of the solution.
• Gently invert the infusion bag to obtain a homogenous solution. Don't transport the infusion bag between locations using mechanical delivery systems.
• Inspect for particulate matter and discoloration before giving.
• Give drug within 12 hours of preparing solution for infusion. Don't freeze. Avoid heat and direct sunlight.
• For an I.V. pump, the solution of reconstituted drug is typically diluted into an infusion bag containing sterile normal saline solution to a final concentration between 100 mcg/ml and 200 mcg/ml.
• For a syringe pump, the reconstituted solution is typically diluted with sterile normal saline solution to a final concentration between 100 mcg/ml and 1,000 mcg/ml. When giving less than 200 mcg/ml at less than 5 ml/hour, the infusion set must be primed for about 15 minutes at a flow rate of about 5 ml/hour.
• Give via a dedicated I.V. line or lumen of a multilumen central venous catheter. The only other solutions that can be given through the same line are normal saline solution, lactated Ringer's injection, dextrose, or dextrose and saline mixtures.

⊗ **Incompatibilities**
Other I.V. drugs.

Contraindications and cautions

• Contraindicated in patients with active internal bleeding, hemorrhagic stroke within 3 months, intracranial or intraspinal surgery within 2 months, severe head trauma, trauma with an increased risk of life-threatening bleeding, an epidural catheter, intracranial neoplasm or mass lesion, or evidence of cerebral herniation. Drug is also contraindicated in patients hypersensitive to drotrecogin alfa (activated) or any of its components.
• Use cautiously in patients with a high risk of bleeding, such as those who are taking heparin (15 units/kg/hour or more); those with a platelet count less than 30,000 × 10^6/L (even if platelet count increases after transfusions); those with an INR greater than 3; those who have experienced GI bleeding within 6 weeks; those who have had thrombolytic therapy within 3 days; those who have been given oral anticoagulants, glycoprotein IIb/IIIa inhibitors, aspirin (more than 650 mg/day) or other platelet inhibitors within 7 days; those who have had an ischemic stroke within 3 months; and those who have had intracranial arteriovenous malformation or aneurysm, bleeding diathesis, chronic severe hepatic disease, or any other condition in which bleeding constitutes a significant hazard or would be particularly difficult to manage because of its location.
• Use only after careful consideration of the risk versus benefit in patients with single-organ dysfunction and recent surgery because they may not be at high risk of death.

Lifespan: In pregnant women, drug should be used only if benefit to patient exceeds risk to the fetus. Breast-feeding women should stop nursing or stop taking the drug because it's unknown whether drug appears in breast milk. In children, safety and effectiveness haven't been established.

Adverse reactions

Hematologic: HEMORRHAGE.

Interactions

Drug-drug. *Drugs that affect hemostasis:* May increase risk of bleeding. Use together cautiously; monitor patient for bleeding.

Effects on lab test results

- May increase PTT and PT.
- May interfere with one-stage coagulation assays based on PTT (such as factors VIII, IX, and XI assays), causing inconclusive results.

Pharmacokinetics

Absorption: Given I.V.
Distribution: Steady-state levels within 2 hours.
Metabolism: Unknown.
Excretion: Unknown. *Half-life:* Unknown.

Route	Onset	Peak	Duration
I.V.	Rapid	Unknown	Unknown

Action

Chemical effect: Inhibits monocytes from producing human tumor necrosis factor, by blocking leukocyte from adhering to selectins, and by limiting the thrombin-induced inflammatory response.
Therapeutic effect: Prevents clots and blocks cell death.

Available forms

Injection: 5 mg; 20 mg

NURSING PROCESS

Assessment

- Assess patient before starting and during drug therapy for risk of bleeding or contraindications.
- Monitor patient closely for bleeding. If significant bleeding occurs, immediately stop the infusion.
- Because drug may prolong PTT, it can't be used to reliably assess the condition of the coagulopathy during infusion. Because drug has minimal effect on PT, PT can be used instead.

Nursing diagnoses

- Risk for injury caused by increased bleeding potential related to drug therapy.
- Deficient knowledge related to drug therapy.

Planning and implementation

- If the infusion is interrupted, restart at the baseline 24-mcg/kg/hour infusion rate. Dose escalation, bolus doses, and dose adjustment based on observation or laboratory parameters aren't recommended.
- Stop drug 2 hours before an invasive surgical procedure with a risk of bleeding. After hemostasis is reached, drug may be restarted 12 hours after major invasive procedures or surgery or immediately after uncomplicated, less-invasive procedures.

Patient teaching

- Inform patient of potential adverse reactions.
- Instruct patient to report signs of bleeding promptly.
- Advise patient that bleeding may occur for up to 28 days after therapy.

Evaluation

- Patient doesn't experience any hemorrhaging during and 28 days after drug therapy.
- Patient and family state understanding of drug therapy.

duloxetine hydrochloride

(dull-OX-uh-teen high-droh-KLOR-idgh)

Cymbalta

Pharmacologic class: selective serotonin and norepinephrine reuptake inhibitor
Therapeutic class: antidepressant, central pain inhibitor
Pregnancy risk category: C

Indications and dosages

▶ **Major depressive disorder.** *Adults:* Initially, 20 mg P.O. bid to 60 mg P.O. once daily or in two divided doses. Maximum, 60 mg daily.

▶ **Neuropathic pain from diabetic peripheral neuropathy.** *Adults:* 60 mg P.O. once daily.

Adjust-a-dose: Patients with renal impairment may need a lower initial dose and gradual dose increases.

Contraindications and cautions

- Contraindicated in patients hypersensitive to drug or its ingredients, those taking MAO inhibitors, and those with uncontrolled narrow angle-closure glaucoma or a creatinine clearance less than 30 ml/minute. Drug isn't recommended for patients with hepatic dysfunction, or end-stage renal disease or those who drink substantial amounts of alcohol.
- Use cautiously in patients with a history of mania or seizures and those with hypertension, controlled narrow angle-closure glaucoma, or conditions that slow gastric emptying.

Lifespan: In pregnant women, use during third trimester may cause complications for the neonate, including respiratory distress, cyanosis, apnea, seizures, vomiting, hypoglycemia, and hyperreflexia, that may require prolonged hospitalization, respiratory support, and tube feeding. Weigh potential benefit for the mother versus risks to the fetus. Breast-feeding women shouldn't use. Safety and effectiveness in children haven't been established.

Adverse reactions

CNS: anxiety, asthenia, *dizziness, fatigue,* fever, *headache,* hypoesthesia, initial insomnia, *insomnia,* irritability, lethargy, nervousness, nightmares, restlessness, sleep disorder, *somnolence,* ***suicidal ideation,*** tremor.
CV: hot flushes, hypertension, increased heart rate.
EENT: blurred vision, nasopharyngitis, pharyngolaryngeal pain.
GI: *constipation, diarrhea, dry mouth,* dyspepsia, gastritis, nausea, vomiting.
GU: abnormal orgasm, abnormally increased frequency of urination, delayed or dysfunctional ejaculation, dysuria, erectile dysfunction, urinary hesitancy.
Metabolic: *decreased appetite,* ***hypoglycemia,*** increased appetite, weight gain or loss.
Musculoskeletal: muscle cramps, myalgia.
Respiratory: cough.
Skin: increased sweating, night sweats, pruritus, rash.
Other: decreased libido, rigors.

Interactions

Drug-drug. *CNS drugs:* May increase adverse effects. Use cautiously together.
CYP1A2 inhibitors (cimetidine, fluvoxamine, certain quinolones): May increase duloxetine level. Avoid use together.
CYP2D6 inhibitors (fluoxetine, paroxetine, quinidine): May increase duloxetine level. Use together cautiously.
Drugs that reduce gastric acidity: May cause premature breakdown of duloxetine's protective coating and early release of the drug. Monitor patient for effects.
MAO inhibitors: May cause hyperthermia, rigidity, myoclonus, autonomic instability, rapid fluctuations of vital signs, agitation, and eventually, delirium and coma. Wait at least 14 days after stopping an MAO inhibitor before starting duloxetine; wait at least 5 days after stopping duloxetine before starting an MAO inhibitor.
Thioridazine: May prolong the QT interval and increase the risk of serious ventricular arrhythmias and sudden death. Avoid use together.
Tricyclic antidepressants (amitriptyline, nortriptyline, imipramine): May increase levels of these drugs. Tricyclic antidepressant dose may need to be reduced and levels monitored closely.
Type 1C antiarrhythmics (flecainide, propafenone), phenothiazines (except thioridazine): May increase levels of these drugs. Use cautiously together.
Drug-lifestyle. *Alcohol use:* May increase the risk of liver damage. Discourage alcohol use.

Effects on lab test results

- May increase alkaline phosphatase, ALT, AST, bilirubin, and CK levels.

Pharmacokinetics

Absorption: Compared with the morning dose, the evening dose has a 3-hour delay in absorption and a one-third increase in clearance.
Distribution: More than 90% protein-bound to albumin and alpha$_1$-acid glycoprotein.
Metabolism: Numerous metabolites by the liver via CYP2D6 and CYP1A2.
Excretion: 70% in urine and 20% in feces as metabolites. *Half-life:* 12 hours.

Route	Onset	Peak	Duration
P.O.	Unknown	6 hr	Unknown

Action

Chemical effect: May inhibit serotonin and norepinephrine reuptake in the CNS.
Therapeutic effect: Relieves depression. Relieves neuropathic pain in patients with diabetic peripheral neuropathy.

Available forms

Capsules (delayed-release): 20 mg, 30 mg, 60 mg

NURSING PROCESS

Assessment

- Monitor patient for worsening depression or suicidal behavior, especially during dosage initiation or changes.
- Monitor blood pressure periodically during therapy.
- Reassess patient periodically to determine whether therapy needs to continue.
- Assess patient's and family's knowledge of drug therapy.

Nursing diagnoses

- Disturbed thought processes related to presence of depression
- Chronic pain related to underlying disease process and neuropathic pain
- Deficient knowledge related to drug therapy

Planning and implementation

- Monitor older patient for increased effect, and adjust dosage. Old and young adults respond similarly, but older patients may be more sensitive to drug effects.
- Decrease dosage gradually, and watch for symptoms such as dizziness, nausea, headache, paresthesia, vomiting, irritability, and nightmares. If symptoms occur, restart at previous dose and decrease even more gradually.

ALERT: Antidepressants may increase the risk of suicidal thinking and behavior in children and adolescents with major depressive disorder and other psychiatric disorders. Balance risk with patient's need for drug.

Patient teaching

ALERT: Warn families or caregivers to report signs of worsening depression (such as agitation, irritability, insomnia, hostility, impulsivity) or suicidal behavior to prescriber immediately.

- Tell patient to consult his prescriber or pharmacist if he plans to take other prescription or OTC drugs or an herbal or other dietary supplement.
- Instruct patient to swallow capsules whole and not to chew, crush, or open them because they have an enteric coating.
- Urge patient to avoid activities that are hazardous or require mental alertness until he knows the drug's effects.
- Warn against drinking substantial amounts of alcohol because of risk of severe liver toxicity.
- If patient takes drug for depression, explain that it may take 1 to 4 weeks to take effect.

Evaluation

- Patient's behavior and communication indicate improved thought processes.
- Patient reports decreased pain.
- Patient and family state understanding of drug therapy.

dutasteride

(doo-TAS-teer-ighd)
Avodart

Pharmacologic class: 5-alpha-reductase enzyme inhibitor
Therapeutic class: BPH drug
Pregnancy risk category: X

Indications and dosages

▶ **BPH.** *Men:* 0.5 mg P.O. once daily.

Contraindications and cautions

- Contraindicated in patients hypersensitive to drug, its components, or other 5-alpha-reductase inhibitors.
- Use cautiously in patients with hepatic disease and in those taking long-term potent CYP3A4 inhibitors.

Lifespan: In pregnant and breast-feeding women and in children, drug is contraindicated. It's unknown if drug appears in breast milk.

Adverse reactions

GU: decreased libido, ejaculation disorder, impotence.
Other: gynecomastia.

Interactions

Drug-drug. *CYP3A4 inhibitors (cimetidine, diltiazem, itraconazole, ketoconazole, macrolide* *antibiotics, protease inhibitors, ritonavir, verapamil):* May increase dutasteride level. Use together cautiously.

Effects on lab test results

• May decrease prostate-specific antigen (PSA) level.

Pharmacokinetics

Absorption: Bioavailability of about 60%.
Distribution: 99% bound to albumin and 96.6% bound to $alpha_1$-acid glycoprotein.
Metabolism: Extensive, by CYP3A4.
Excretion: Mainly in feces, 5% unchanged and 40% as metabolites, trace amounts in urine.
Half-life: 5 weeks.

Route	Onset	Peak	Duration
P.O.	Unknown	2–3 hr	Unknown

Action

Chemical effect: Inhibits conversion of testosterone to dihydrotestosterone, the androgen mainly responsible for initial development and later enlargement of the prostate gland.
Therapeutic effect: Resolves BPH.

Available forms

Capsules: 0.5 mg

NURSING PROCESS

Assessment

• Before therapy, assess patient to rule out other urologic diseases.
• Carefully monitor patients with a large residual urine volume, severely diminished urine flow, or both, for obstructive uropathy.
• Perform digital rectal examinations and other evaluations for prostate cancer on patients with BPH before starting therapy, and reassess periodically thereafter.
• Be alert for adverse effects.
• Assess patient's and family's knowledge of drug therapy.

Nursing diagnoses

• Impaired urinary elimination related to underlying condition
• Sexual dysfunction related to adverse effects of medication
• Deficient knowledge related to drug therapy

Planning and implementation

• Because drug may be absorbed through the skin, don't allow women who are or may become pregnant to handle the drug.
• If capsule leaks onto skin, wash the area immediately with soap and water.
• Patient shouldn't donate blood within 6 months of last dose.
• Establish new baseline PSA level in men treated for 3 to 6 months, and use it to assess potentially cancer-related changes in PSA level.
• To interpret PSA level in men treated for 6 months or more, double the PSA level for comparison with normal levels in untreated men.

Patient teaching

• Tell patient to swallow the capsule whole and to take with or without food.
• Inform patient that ejaculate volume may decrease, but sexual function will remain normal.
• Tell patient that pregnant women shouldn't handle drug. A boy born to a woman who was exposed to the drug during pregnancy may have abnormal sex organs.
• Tell patient not to donate blood within 6 months of his final dose.

Evaluation

• Patient has normal urinary flow without urinary residual volume.
• Patient doesn't experience adverse effects.
• Patient and family state understanding of drug therapy.

edetate calcium disodium (calcium EDTA)

(ED-eh-tayt KAL-see-um digh-SOH-dee-um)
Calcium Disodium Versenate

Pharmacologic class: chelating drug
Therapeutic class: heavy metal antagonist
Pregnancy risk category: B

Indications and dosages

▶ **Acute lead encephalopathy or lead level above 70 mcg/dl.** *Adults and children:* 1.5 g/m²

I.V. or I.M. daily in divided doses at 12-hour intervals for 3 to 5 days, usually with dimercaprol. Give a second course in 5 to 7 days.

▶ **Lead poisoning without encephalopathy, or asymptomatic patient with lead level between 20 mcg/dl and 70 mcg/dl.** *Children:* 1 g/m^2 I.V. or I.M. daily in divided doses for 5 days. Give second course after 2 to 4 days, as needed.

Adjust-a-dose: In patients with lead nephropathy, decrease dose and frequency as follows. If serum creatinine level is 2 to 3 mg/dl, give 500 mg/m^2/day for 5 days. If serum creatinine level is 3 to 4 mg/dl, give 500 mg/m^2/day q 48 hours for three doses. If serum creatinine level exceeds 4 mg/dl, give 500 mg/m^2 once weekly.

I.V. administration

- I.V. use may increase intracranial pressure. To treat lead encephalopathy, give by I.M. route instead.
- Dilute drug with 250 to 500 ml of D_5W or normal saline injection.
- Infuse half of daily dose over 1 hour in asymptomatic patients or over 2 hours in symptomatic patients. Give rest of infusion at least 6 hours later. Or give by slow infusion over 4 to 24 hours.

⊗ **Incompatibilities**

Amphotericin B, dextrose 10% in water, hydralazine hydrochloride, invert sugar 10% in normal saline solution, invert sugar 10% in water, lactated Ringer's solution, Ringer's injection, 1/6 M sodium lactate.

Contraindications and cautions

- Contraindicated in patients with anuria, acute renal disease, or hepatitis.
- Use cautiously and reduce dosage in patients with mild renal disease. Drug may cause life-threatening toxic effects.

Lifespan: In pregnant and breast-feeding women, use cautiously.

Adverse reactions

CNS: fatigue, headache, numbness, paresthesia, sudden fever.
CV: ***arrhythmias,*** hypotension.
EENT: nasal congestion, sneezing.
GI: anorexia, cheilosis, nausea, vomiting.
GU: acute necrosis of proximal tubules, hematuria, ***nephrotoxicity,*** proteinuria.
Hematologic: anemia, transient bone marrow depression.
Metabolic: hypercalcemia, zinc deficiency.
Musculoskeletal: arthralgia, myalgia.
Skin: rash.
Other: allergic histamine-like reaction, chills, excessive thirst.

Interactions

Drug-drug. *Zinc insulin:* May interfere with action of insulin by binding with zinc. Monitor patient closely.
Zinc supplements: May decrease effectiveness of edetate calcium disodium and zinc supplements because of chelation. Withhold zinc supplements until therapy is complete.

Effects on lab test results

- May increase AST, ALT, and calcium levels. May decrease zinc and hemoglobin levels and hematocrit.

Pharmacokinetics

Absorption: Well absorbed after I.M. use.
Distribution: Mainly in extracellular fluid.
Metabolism: None.
Excretion: In urine. *Half-life:* 20 minutes to 1½ hours.

Route	Onset	Peak	Duration
I.V., I.M.	1 hr	1–2 days	Unknown

Action

Chemical effect: Forms stable, soluble complexes with metals, particularly lead.
Therapeutic effect: Abolishes effects of lead poisoning.

Available forms

Injection: 200 mg/ml

NURSING PROCESS

Assessment

- Obtain history of patient's underlying condition before therapy.
- Monitor drug's effectiveness by checking lead level and watching for decreasing evidence of lead poisoning.
- Monitor fluid intake and output; conduct urinalysis, BUN, and ECG daily.
- Be alert for adverse reactions.

• Assess patient's and family's knowledge of drug therapy.

Nursing diagnoses

• Risk for injury related to lead poisoning
• Ineffective renal tissue perfusion related to drug-induced fatal nephrosis
• Deficient knowledge related to drug therapy

Planning and implementation

• When giving I.M., add procaine hydrochloride to I.M. solution to minimize pain. Watch for local reactions.
• Use I.M. route for children and patients with lead encephalopathy.
• Force fluids to facilitate lead excretion, except in patients with lead encephalopathy.
• To avoid toxicity, use with dimercaprol.
• Apply ice or cold compresses to injection site to ease local reaction.

ALERT: Don't confuse edetate calcium disodium with edetate disodium, which is used to treat hypercalcemia.

Patient teaching

• Warn patient that some adverse reactions, such as fever, chills, thirst, and nasal congestion, may occur 4 to 8 hours after use.
• Encourage patient and family to identify and remove source of lead in home.

Evaluation

• Patient sustains no injury as a result of lead poisoning.
• Patient has no signs of altered renal tissue perfusion.
• Patient and family state understanding of drug therapy.

edetate disodium

(ED-eh-tayt digh-SOH-dee-um)

Disodium EDTA, Endrate, Sodium Edetate

Pharmacologic class: chelating drug
Therapeutic class: heavy metal antagonist
Pregnancy risk category: C

Indications and dosages

▶ **Hypercalcemic crisis.** *Adults:* 50 mg/kg/day by slow I.V. infusion for 5 days; no drug for 2 days; then repeat course, as needed. Maximum, 3 g I.V. daily and 15 doses total.
Children: 40 to 70 mg/kg/day by slow I.V. infusion. Maximum, 70 mg/kg I.V. daily.

▶ **Digoxin-induced arrhythmias.** *Adults and children:* 15 mg/kg/hour I.V. daily. Maximum, 60 mg/kg I.V. daily.

I.V. administration

• Drug isn't recommended for direct or intermittent injection.
• Keep I.V. calcium available to treat hypocalcemia.
• Dilute before use. For adults, add dose to 500 ml of D_5W or normal saline solution and give over 3 or more hours. For children, dilute to maximum of 30 mg/ml in D_5W or normal saline solution and give over 3 or more hours.
• Don't exceed recommended dose or rate of administration.
• Avoid rapid I.V. infusion, which may result in profound hypocalcemia and lead to tetany, seizures, arrhythmias, and respiratory arrest.
• Extravasation can cause tissue damage and necrosis; watch for irritation and infiltration.
• Record I.V. site used and avoid repeated use of same site to decrease likelihood of thrombophlebitis.
• Keep patient in bed for 15 minutes after infusion to avoid orthostatic hypotension.

⊗ Incompatibilities

None reported.

Contraindications and cautions

• Contraindicated in patients hypersensitive to the drug or any of its components and in those with anuria, known or suspected hypocalcemia, significant renal disease, active or healed tubercular lesions, or a history of seizures or intracranial lesions.
• Use cautiously in patients with limited cardiac reserve, heart failure, or hypokalemia.

Lifespan: In pregnant and breast-feeding women, use cautiously.

Adverse reactions

CNS: circumoral paresthesia, numbness, headache.
CV: hypertension, orthostatic hypotension, thrombophlebitis.
GI: abdominal cramps, anorexia, diarrhea, nausea, vomiting.
GU: dysuria, ***nephrotoxicity,*** nocturia, polyuria, proteinuria, ***renal failure,*** renal insufficiency, ***tubular necrosis,*** urinary urgency.

Metabolic: hypocalcemia, ***hypomagnesia.***
Skin: dermatitis, erythema.
Other: infusion site pain.

Interactions

Drug-drug. *Digoxin:* May reverse effects of digoxin overdose because of drop in calcium caused by edetate disodium. If hypercalcemia recurs, monitor patient closely for renewed digoxin toxicity.
Zinc insulins: May decrease glucose and chelate zinc in some insulin. Dosage adjustments of insulin may be required.

Effects on lab test results

- May increase uric acid level. May decrease calcium, magnesium, potassium, zinc, and hemoglobin levels and hematocrit.

Pharmacokinetics

Absorption: Administered I.V.
Distribution: Distributed widely throughout body but doesn't enter CSF in significant amounts.
Metabolism: None.
Excretion: In urine. *Half-life:* Unknown.

Route	Onset	Peak	Duration
I.V.	Unknown	Unknown	Unknown

Action

Chemical effect: Chelates with metals, such as calcium, to form stable, soluble complex.
Therapeutic effect: Lowers calcium level and stabilizes heart rhythm in emergency conditions.

Available forms

Injection: 150 mg/ml

NURSING PROCESS

Assessment

- Obtain history of patient's calcium level before therapy.
- Monitor drug's effectiveness by obtaining calcium level after each dose. If drug is used to treat digoxin-induced arrhythmias, evaluate patient's ECG often.
- Monitor kidney function tests often.
- Be alert for adverse reactions.
- Assess patient's and family's knowledge of drug therapy.

Nursing diagnoses

- Risk for injury related to hypercalcemia
- Ineffective protection related to drug-induced hypocalcemia
- Deficient knowledge related to drug therapy

Planning and implementation

- If generalized systemic reactions (fever, chills, back pain, emesis, muscle cramps, urinary urgency) occur 4 to 8 hours after infusion, report them to prescriber. Treatment is usually symptomatic. Effects usually subside within 12 hours.
- Other drugs for hypercalcemia are safer and more effective than edetate disodium.

ALERT: Don't confuse edetate disodium with edetate calcium disodium, which is used to treat lead toxicity.

Patient teaching

- Instruct patient to immediately report respiratory difficulty, dizziness, and muscle cramping.
- Advise patient to move from sitting or lying position slowly to avoid dizziness.
- Reassure patient that generalized systemic reaction usually subsides within 12 hours.
- If treating digoxin toxicity, instruct patient on correct usage of drug and required laboratory follow-up.

Evaluation

- Patient sustains no injury as result of hypercalcemia.
- Patient's calcium level doesn't fall below normal after edetate disodium therapy.
- Patient and family state understanding of drug therapy.

efalizumab

(eh-fah-LEE-zoo-mab)
Raptiva

Pharmacologic class: immunosuppressant
Therapeutic class: antipsoriatic
Pregnancy risk category: C

Indications and dosages

▶ **Chronic moderate-to-severe plaque psoriasis when systemic therapy or phototherapy is appropriate.** *Adults:* Single dose of 0.7 mg/kg subcutaneously; follow with weekly doses of 1 mg/kg subcutaneously. Maximum single dose, 200 mg.

Contraindications and cautions

- Contraindicated in patients hypersensitive to drug or any of its components and in patients with significant infection.
- Use cautiously in patients with chronic infection or a history of recurrent infection. Also use cautiously in patients with a history of or high risk for malignancy.

Lifespan: In pregnant women, use cautiously; it isn't known whether drug harms fetus. Tell breast-feeding women to stop breast-feeding or to stop using the drug because risk to the infant is unknown. In children, safety and effectiveness haven't been established. In elderly patients, use cautiously because of their increased risk of infection.

Adverse reactions

CNS: fever, *headache,* pain, ***stroke.***
GI: *nausea.*
Hematologic: ***thrombocytopenia.***
Musculoskeletal: back pain, myalgia.
Skin: acne.
Other: chills, flulike syndrome, hypersensitivity reaction, *infection,* ***malignancy.***

Interactions

Drug-drug. *Immunosuppressants:* May increase risk of infection and malignancy. Avoid use together.
Vaccines: May decrease or eliminate immune response to vaccine. Avoid use together.

Effects on lab test results

- May increase alkaline phosphatase level.
- May increase lymphocyte and leukocyte counts. May decrease platelet count.

Pharmacokinetics

Absorption: 50% bioavailable.
Distribution: Unknown.
Metabolism: Unknown.
Excretion: Unknown. *Half-life:* Unknown.

Route	Onset	Peak	Duration
SubQ	1–2 days	Unknown	25 days

Action

Chemical effect: Binds to a leukocyte function antigen and decreases its expression, thus inhibiting the action of T lymphocytes at sites of inflammation, including psoriatic skin.

Therapeutic effect: Decreases inflammation of psoriatic skin.

Available forms

Injection: 125-mg single-use vial

NURSING PROCESS

Assessment

- Watch for thrombocytopenia. Check patient's platelet count monthly before start of treatment, monthly until laboratory effects are stable, and then every 3 months.
- Monitor patient for worsening of psoriasis during or after therapy.
- Assess patient's and family's knowledge of drug therapy.

Nursing diagnoses

- Impaired skin integrity related to underlying condition
- Ineffective protection related to drug-induced thrombocytopenia
- Deficient knowledge related to drug therapy

Planning and implementation

- To reconstitute, inject 1.3 ml of sterile water for injection into the vial. Swirl gently to dissolve powder, which takes less than 5 minutes. Don't shake the vial.
- Reconstitute drug immediately before use.
- Don't use any other diluent besides sterile water, and use a vial only once.
- The reconstituted solution should be colorless to pale yellow and free of particulates. Don't use solution that contains particulates or is discolored.
- Use reconstituted solution immediately, or store it at room temperature and use within 8 hours.
- Rotate injection sites.
- Don't add other drugs to solution.
- Keep powder refrigerated, and protect vials from light.
- Stop drug if patient develops severe infection or malignancy.
- Don't give vaccines to patients taking this drug because the immune response may be inadequate.
- If patient becomes pregnant while taking the drug or within 6 weeks after stopping it, enroll her in the Raptiva Pregnancy Registry by calling 1-877-727-8482.

Patient teaching

- Tell patient to take drug exactly as prescribed.
- Explain that platelet counts will be monitored during therapy.
- Urge patient to immediately report evidence of severe thrombocytopenia, such as bleeding gums, bruising, or petechiae.
- Tell patient to report weight changes because dosage may need to be changed.
- Advise patient to report any newly diagnosed infection or malignancy.
- Tell patient to report worsening psoriasis.
- Caution patient to immediately report pregnancy or suspected pregnancy while taking drug or within 6 weeks of stopping drug.

☑ Evaluation

- Patient's underlying condition improves with drug therapy.
- Patient has no serious complications from drug-induced thrombocytopenia.
- Patient and family state understanding of drug therapy.

efavirenz

(eh-FAH-veer-enz)
Sustiva

Pharmacologic class: nonnucleoside reverse transcriptase inhibitor (NNRTI)
Therapeutic class: antiretroviral
Pregnancy risk category: D

Indications and dosages

▶ **HIV-1 infection.** *Adults:* 600 mg P.O. daily with a protease inhibitor or nucleoside analogue reverse transcriptase inhibitors.
Children age 3 and older who weigh 10 to less than 15 kg (22 to less than 33 lb): 200 mg P.O. daily.
Children who weigh 15 to less than 20 kg (33 to 44 lb): 250 mg P.O. daily.
Children who weigh 20 to less than 25 kg (44 to 55 lb): 300 mg P.O. daily.
Children who weigh 25 to less than 32.5 kg (55 to 72 lb): 350 mg P.O. daily.
Children who weigh 32.5 to less than 40 kg (72 to 88 lb): 400 mg P.O. daily.
Children who weigh 40 kg (88 lb) or more: 600 mg P.O. once daily.

Contraindications and cautions

- Contraindicated in patients hypersensitive to drug or any of its components.
- Use cautiously in patients with hepatic impairment or in those receiving hepatotoxic drugs.

Lifespan: In pregnant and breast-feeding women, drug is contraindicated. In children and elderly patients, use cautiously.

Adverse reactions

CNS: abnormal dreams or thinking, agitation, amnesia, confusion, depersonalization, depression, dizziness, euphoria, fatigue, hallucinations, headache, hypoesthesia, impaired concentration, insomnia, somnolence, nervousness, fever.
GI: abdominal pain, anorexia, constipation, diarrhea, dyspepsia, flatulence, malabsorption, nausea, vomiting.
GU: hematuria, renal calculi.
Skin: ***erythema multiforme,*** increased sweating, pruritus, rash, ***Stevens-Johnson syndrome, toxic epidermal necrolysis.***
Other: gynecomastia.

Interactions

Drug-drug. *Amprenavir, indinavir, lopinavir:* May decrease levels of these drugs. Consider alternative therapy or dosage adjustment.
Bepridil: May cause life-threatening adverse events, such as arrhythmias. Avoid use together.
Clarithromycin: May decrease clarithromycin level and increase level of main metabolite. Also increases risk of rash. Consider using azithromycin instead.
Drugs that induce the cytochrome P-450 enzyme system (such as phenobarbital, rifampin): May increase clearance of efavirenz, resulting in lower level. Avoid use together.
Ergot derivatives, midazolam, triazolam: May inhibit metabolism of these drugs through competition for the cytochrome P-450 enzyme system, possibly causing serious or life-threatening adverse events (such as arrhythmias, prolonged sedation, or respiratory depression). Avoid use together.
Ethinyl estradiol: May increase level of ethinyl estradiol. Advise use of a reliable method of barrier contraception in addition to hormonal contraceptive.
Pimozide: May cause serious or life-threatening adverse events, such as arrhythmias. Avoid use together.

Psychoactive drugs: May cause additive CNS effects. Avoid use together.
Rifabutin: May decrease rifabutin level. Increase dosage of rifabutin to 450 to 600 mg once daily or 600 mg two to three times a week.
Ritonavir: May increase levels of efavirenz and ritonavir. Monitor patient closely.
Saquinavir: May significantly decrease saquinavir level. Don't use with saquinavir as sole protease inhibitor.
Voriconazole: May significantly decrease voriconazole level while significantly increasing efavirenz level. Avoid use together.
Warfarin: May increase or decrease level and effects of warfarin. Monitor INR.
Drug-herb. *St. John's wort:* May decrease efavirenz level. Discourage use together.
Drug-food. *High-fat meals:* May increase absorption of drug, increasing risk of adverse effects. Instruct patient to maintain a low-fat diet.
Drug-lifestyle. *Alcohol use:* Enhances CNS effects. Discourage alcohol use.

Effects on lab test results

- May increase ALT, AST, amylase, and cholesterol levels.

Pharmacokinetics

Absorption: Steady-state levels reached in 6 to 10 days. Food increases amount of drug in body.
Distribution: Highly protein-bound, mainly to albumin.
Metabolism: Mainly by cytochrome P-450 system to metabolites that are inactive against HIV-1.
Excretion: Mainly in feces. *Half-life:* 40 to 76 hours.

Route	Onset	Peak	Duration
P.O.	Unknown	3–5 hr	Unknown

Action

Chemical effect: An NNRTI that inhibits the transcription of HIV-1 RNA to DNA, a critical step in the viral replication process.
Therapeutic effect: Lowers viral load of HIV in the blood and increases CD4+ lymphocytes.

Available forms

Capsules: 50 mg, 100 mg, 200 mg
Tablets: 600 mg

NURSING PROCESS

Assessment

- Monitor liver function test results in a patient with a history of hepatitis B or C and in those taking ritonavir.
- Monitor cholesterol level.
- Children may be more susceptible to adverse reactions, especially diarrhea, nausea, vomiting, and rash.
- Observe skin before starting drug and regularly thereafter for signs of rash.
- Assess patient's and family's knowledge of drug therapy.

Nursing diagnoses

- Risk for infection related to patient's underlying condition
- Risk for impaired skin integrity related to potential adverse effects of drug
- Deficient knowledge related to drug therapy

Planning and implementation

- Use drug with other antiretrovirals and not as monotherapy because resistant viruses emerge rapidly when it's used alone. Don't add it as a single drug to a failing regimen.
- Using drug with ritonavir may cause a higher occurrence of adverse effects, such as dizziness, nausea, paresthesia, and elevated liver enzyme levels.
- Rule out pregnancy before starting therapy in women of childbearing age.
- Give drug at bedtime on an empty stomach to decrease adverse effects.

Patient teaching

- Instruct patient to take drug on an empty stomach, preferably at bedtime, and to take it with water, juice, milk, or soda.
- Inform patient about need for scheduled blood tests to monitor liver function and cholesterol levels.
- Tell patient to use reliable method of barrier contraception in addition to hormonal contraceptives, and to notify prescriber immediately if pregnancy is suspected. Drug is a known risk to the fetus.
- Inform patient that drug doesn't cure HIV infection and that it won't affect the complications of HIV. Explain that it doesn't reduce the risk of HIV transmission through sexual contact or blood contamination.

- Instruct patient to take drug at the same time each day and always with other antiretrovirals.
- Tell patient to take drug exactly as prescribed and not to stop without medical approval.
- Inform patient that rash is the most common adverse effect. Tell patient to immediately report any rash or any other adverse effects. Rash may be serious in rare cases.
- Instruct patient to report use of other drugs.
- Advise patient that dizziness, difficulty sleeping or concentrating, drowsiness, or unusual dreams may occur during the first few days of therapy. Reassure patient that these symptoms typically resolve after 2 to 4 weeks and that it may help to take drug at bedtime.
- Tell patient not to use alcohol and not to drive or operate machinery until drug's effects are known.

Evaluation

- Patient is free of opportunistic infections.
- Patient's skin integrity is maintained.
- Patient and family state understanding of drug therapy.

eletriptan hydrobromide

(el-eh-TRIP-tan high-dro-BRO-mighd)
Relpax

Pharmacologic class: serotonin receptor agonist
Therapeutic class: antimigraine
Pregnancy risk category: C

Indications and dosages

▶ **Acute migraine with or without aura.** *Adults:* 20 to 40 mg P.O. at the first migraine symptom. If headache recurs after initial relief, repeat dose at least 2 hours later. Maximum, 80 mg daily.

Contraindications and cautions

- Contraindicated in patients hypersensitive to drug or any of its components and in those with severe hepatic impairment; ischemic heart disease, such as angina pectoris, a history of MI, or silent ischemia; coronary artery vasospasm, including Prinzmetal variant angina; and other CV conditions. Also contraindicated in patients with cerebrovascular disorders, such as stroke or transient ischemic attack; peripheral vascular disease, including ischemic bowel disease; uncontrolled hypertension; or hemiplegic or basilar migraine.
- Avoid use within 24 hours of another serotonin agonist or an ergotamine-containing or ergot-type drug.

Lifespan: In pregnant women, use drug only when benefits outweigh risks to fetus. In breastfeeding women, use cautiously because drug appears in breast milk. In children, safety and effectiveness haven't been established. In elderly patients, use cautiously because they may have 15% lower drug clearance, the half-life of the drug is prolonged to about 6 hours, and these patients may develop higher blood pressure than younger patients.

Adverse reactions

CNS: *asthenia,* dizziness, headache, hypertonia, hypesthesia, pain, paresthesia, somnolence, vertigo.
CV: chest tightness, pain, and pressure; flushing; palpitations.
EENT: abnormal accommodation, abnormal vision, conjunctivitis, dry eyes, eye hemorrhage, *lacrimation disorder,* melanin toxicity, photophobia, transient corneal opacity.
GI: abdominal pain, discomfort, or cramps; dry mouth; dyspepsia; dysphagia; nausea.
Musculoskeletal: back pain.
Respiratory: pharyngitis.
Skin: increased sweating.
Other: chills.

Interactions

Drug-drug. *CYP3A4 inhibitors, such as clarithromycin, itraconazole, ketoconazole, nefazodone, nelfinavir, ritonavir, and troleandomycin:* May decrease eletriptan metabolism. Avoid use within 72 hours of these drugs.
Ergotamine-containing or ergot-type drugs, such as dihydroergotamine or methysergide; serotonin agonists: May prolong vasospastic reactions. Avoid use within 24 hours of these drugs.
Propranolol: May increase bioavailability of eletriptan. No dosage adjustment is needed.

Effects on lab test results

None reported.

Pharmacokinetics

Absorption: Oral bioavailability is 50%. Drug level peaks in 1½ to 2 hours.
Distribution: About 85% protein-bound.
Metabolism: Mainly by CYP3A4. The metabolite of eletriptan is active but without therapeutic effect.
Excretion: Clearance is 10% renal and 90% nonrenal. *Half-life:* About 4 hours.

Route	Onset	Peak	Duration
P.O.	½ hr	1½–2 hr	Unknown

Action

Chemical effect: Binds to serotonin receptors and may constrict intracranial blood vessels and inhibit proinflammatory neuropeptide release.
Therapeutic effect: Relieves migraine symptoms.

Available forms

Tablets: 20 mg, 40 mg

NURSING PROCESS

Assessment

- Obtain history of patient's underlying condition before therapy.
- Assess patient for medical history or risk factors for liver disease, heart disease, cerebrovascular disease, peripheral vascular disease, ischemic bowel, or uncontrolled hypertension.
- Be alert for adverse reactions.
- Assess patient's and family's knowledge of drug therapy.

Nursing diagnoses

- Acute pain related to migraine headaches
- Risk for injury related to adverse reactions
- Deficient knowledge related to drug therapy

Planning and implementation

- Use only in patients with a clear diagnosis of migraine, not for prevention.
- If first use produces no response, reconsider diagnosis; a second dose will probably not be effective if the first dose causes no response.
- The safety of treating more than three migraines in 30 days hasn't been established.

ALERT: Serious cardiac events, including acute MI, arrhythmias, and death, occur rarely—usually within a few hours after use.

- Don't use in patient with risk factors for coronary artery disease, in a postmenopausal woman, or in a man older than age 40, unless patient is reasonably free of underlying CV disease. If drug must be used because of intractable migraine pain unresponsive to other drugs, give the first dose under medical supervision.
- Ocular effects, such as melanin-binding and toxicity, and corneal opacities, may occur with long-term use.

Patient teaching

- Instruct patient to take dose at the first sign of a migraine headache. If headache returns after the first dose, he may take a second dose after 2 hours. Caution patient not to take more than 80 mg in 24 hours.
- Warn patient to avoid driving and operating machinery if he feels dizzy or fatigued after taking drug.
- Tell patient to immediately report pain, tightness, heaviness, or pressure in the chest, throat, neck, or jaw.

Evaluation

- Patient experiences relief from migraine headache.
- Patient has no signs of adverse reaction to the drug.
- Patient and family state understanding of drug therapy and conditions that are contraindications for use of this drug.

emtricitabine

(em-trih-SIGH-tah-been)
Emtriva

Pharmacologic class: nucleoside reverse transcriptase inhibitor (NRTI)
Therapeutic class: antiretroviral
Pregnancy risk category: B

Indications and dosages

▶ **HIV-1 infection with other antiretrovirals.** *Adults:* 200 mg capsule P.O. once daily or 240 mg (24 ml) oral solution P.O. once daily. *Children age 3 months to 17 years:* For children who weigh more than 33 kg (73 lb) and can swallow intact capsule, give one 200-mg capsule P.O. once daily. Otherwise, give 6 mg/kg oral solution, up to a maximum dose of 240 mg once daily.

Children younger than age 3 months: 3 mg/kg oral solution P.O. once daily.
Adjust-a-dose: For adults who have baseline creatinine clearance of 30 to 49 ml/minute, give 200-mg capsule q 48 hours or 120 mg oral solution q 24 hours. If creatinine clearance is 15 to 29 ml/minute, give 200-mg capsule q 72 hours or 80-mg oral solution q 24 hours. If clearance is less than 15 ml/minute (including patients requiring dialysis), give 200-mg capsule q 96 hours or 60-mg oral solution q 24 hours. If dose is scheduled on the day of hemodialysis, give it after dialysis. For children with renal insufficiency, there's no established dosage reduction. Consider reducing the dose and increasing the interval.

Contraindications and cautions

- Contraindicated in patients hypersensitive to drug or any of its components.
- Lactic acidosis and severe hepatomegaly with steatosis, including fatal cases, have been reported with the use of nucleoside analogues alone and in combination with other antiretrovirals.
- In patients with renal impairment, lower the dose and use drug cautiously.
- Drug isn't indicated for chronic hepatitis B virus infection, and safety and effectiveness of the drug haven't been established in patients infected with hepatitis B virus and HIV.

Lifespan: In pregnant women, use cautiously because there are no adequate and well-controlled studies in this group. Women should avoid breast-feeding to prevent transmitting HIV to infants.

Adverse reactions

CNS: *asthenia,* depression, *headache,* insomnia, neuritis, nightmares, paresthesia, peripheral neuropathy.
EENT: rhinitis.
GI: abdominal pain, *diarrhea,* dyspepsia, *nausea,* vomiting.
Hepatic: ***severe hepatomegaly, steatosis.***
Metabolic: ***lactic acidosis.***
Musculoskeletal: arthralgia, myalgia.
Respiratory: *cough.*
Skin: rash.

Interactions

None reported.

Effects on lab test results

- May increase ALT, AST, bilirubin, triglyceride, amylase, lipase, CK, and glucose levels.

Pharmacokinetics

Absorption: Rapid.
Distribution: At peak level, the mean plasma-to-blood ratio is about 1, and the mean semen-to-plasma ratio is about 4.
Metabolism: Not metabolized by cytochrome P-450 enzymes. Less than 15% undergoes oxidation and glucuronidation by the liver.
Excretion: Mainly in urine. *Half-life:* About 10 hours.

Route	Onset	Peak	Duration
P.O.	Unknown	1–2 hr	Unknown

Action

Chemical effect: Inhibits activity of HIV-1 reverse transcriptase by competing with natural substrate and being incorporated into new viral DNA chains, which results in their destruction.
Therapeutic effect: Helps block HIV replication.

Available forms

Capsules: 200 mg
Oral solution: 10 mg/ml

NURSING PROCESS

Assessment

- Monitor liver and renal function tests.
- Assess all HIV-positive patients for chronic HBV infection before starting therapy.
- In a patient infected with both HBV and HIV, hepatitis B may worsen after therapy. Monitor patient closely for at least several months.
- Assess patient's and family's knowledge of drug therapy.

Nursing diagnoses

- Risk for infection related to patient's underlying condition
- Disturbed body image related to redistribution of body fat due to antiretroviral therapy
- Deficient knowledge related to drug therapy

Planning and implementation

- If patient develops symptoms of lactic acidosis or pronounced hepatotoxicity, stop drug.

• Drug may cause redistribution or accumulation of body fat, including central obesity, dorsocervical fat enlargement (buffalo hump), peripheral wasting, facial wasting, breast enlargement, and cushingoid appearance.
• Effects of higher doses aren't known; overdose can be treated with hemodialysis.

Patient teaching

• Tell patient that drug doesn't cure HIV infection and doesn't reduce the risk of transmitting HIV to others.
• Tell patient that drug must be taken for life.
• Stress importance of compliance and of planning compliance strategies in advance.
• Inform patient of potential adverse reactions, including lactic acidosis, hepatotoxicity, and redistribution or accumulation of body fat.
• Tell patient to contact prescriber immediately if she suspects she is pregnant.
• Instruct patient or family to refrigerate the oral solution. If it's stored at room temperature, they should use it within 3 months.

Evaluation

• Patient remains free of opportunistic infection.
• Patient has no adverse drug effects.
• Patient and family state understanding of drug therapy.

enalaprilat

(eh-NAH-leh-prel-at)

enalapril maleate

Amprace ◇, Renitec ◇, Vasotec

Pharmacologic class: ACE inhibitor
Therapeutic class: antihypertensive
Pregnancy risk category: C (D in second and third trimesters)

Indications and dosages

▶ **Hypertension.** *Adults:* Initially 5 mg P.O. once daily; adjust according to response. Usual dosage range is 10 to 40 mg daily as single dose or two divided doses. Or 1.25 mg I.V. over 5 minutes q 6 hours.

Adjust-a-dose: For patient taking a diuretic, initially 2.5 mg P.O. once daily. Or 0.625 mg I.V. over 5 minutes, repeated in 1 hour, if needed, and followed by 1.25 mg I.V. q 6 hours. In patients with creatinine clearance of 30 ml/minute or less, initial dose is 2.5 mg P.O. daily, increased gradually to maximum of 40 mg daily. Or give 0.625 mg I.V. and repeat in 1 hour if needed. Then give 1.25 mg I.V. q 6 hours. In hemodialysis patients, give 2.5 mg P.O. on dialysis days and adjust dose on nondialysis days based on blood pressure. Or give 0.625 mg I.V. q 6 hours.

▶ **Heart failure.** *Adults:* Initially 2.5 mg P.O. daily. Increase dosage after a few days or weeks according to response. Recommended range is 2.5 to 20 mg b.i.d.

Adjust-a-dose: In patients with hyponatremia (serum sodium level less than 130 mEq/L) or severe renal impairment (creatinine clearance 30 ml/minute or less), initial dose is 2.5 mg P.O. daily given under close supervision. Increase at intervals of 4 or more days to 2.5 mg b.i.d., then 5 mg b.i.d., to a maximum of 40 mg daily.

▶ **Asymptomatic left ventricular dysfunction.** *Adults:* 2.5 mg P.O. b.i.d.; adjust as tolerated to target of 20 mg P.O. daily in divided doses.

I.V. administration

• Giving doses greater than 1.25 mg isn't more effective.
• Compatible solutions include D_5W, normal saline solution, dextrose 5% in lactated Ringer's solution, and D_5W in normal saline solution.
• Inject drug slowly over at least 5 minutes, or dilute in 50 ml of compatible solution and infuse over 15 minutes.

⊗ Incompatibilities

Amphotericin B, phenytoin sodium.

Contraindications and cautions

• Contraindicated in patients hypersensitive to drug or any of its components and in those with a history of angioedema from ACE inhibitor.
• Use cautiously in patients with renal impairment, especially those with bilateral renal artery stenosis or unilateral renal artery stenosis in a single functioning kidney.

Lifespan: In pregnant women, use only when benefits outweigh risks to the fetus. In second and third trimesters, ACE inhibitors may be harmful or fatal to fetus. In breast-feeding women and in children, safety hasn't been established.

Adverse reactions

CNS: asthenia, *dizziness, fatigue, headache,* syncope, vertigo.
CV: chest pain, *hypotension.*
GI: abdominal pain, diarrhea, nausea, vomiting.
GU: decreased renal function.
Hematologic: ***agranulocytosis, neutropenia, thrombocytopenia.***
Metabolic: ***hyperkalemia.***
Respiratory: dry, persistent, tickling, nonproductive cough; dyspnea.
Skin: rash.
Other: ***angioedema.***

Interactions

Drug-drug. *Diuretics:* May cause excessive reduction of blood pressure. Monitor patient.
Insulin, oral antidiabetics: May increase risk of hypoglycemia, especially at start of enalapril therapy. Monitor patient and glucose levels closely.
Lithium: May increase risk of lithium toxicity. Monitor lithium level.
NSAIDs: May reduce antihypertensive effect. Monitor blood pressure.
Potassium supplements, potassium-sparing diuretics: May increase risk of hyperkalemia. Avoid these drugs unless hypokalemic blood levels are confirmed.
Drug-herb. *Licorice:* May cause sodium retention and increase blood pressure, interfering with ACE inhibitor effects. Discourage licorice intake during drug therapy.
Drug-lifestyle. *Alcohol use*: May produce additive hypotensive effect. Discourage use together.
Sun exposure: May increase risk of photosensitivity reaction. Urge patient to avoid unprotected or prolonged sun exposure.

Effects on lab test results

- May increase ALT, AST, bilirubin, BUN, creatinine, and potassium levels. May decrease sodium and hemoglobin levels and hematocrit.
- May decrease neutrophil, granulocyte, and platelet counts.

Pharmacokinetics

Absorption: About 60% of P.O. dose absorbed from GI tract.
Distribution: Unknown.
Metabolism: Metabolized extensively to active metabolite.
Excretion: About 94% in urine and feces as enalaprilat and enalapril. *Half-life:* 35 to 38 hours.

Route	Onset	Peak	Duration
P.O.	1 hr	4–6 hr	24 hr
I.V.	15 min	1–4 hr	6 hr

Action

Chemical effect: May inhibit ACE, preventing conversion of angiotensin I to angiotensin II, a potent vasoconstrictor. Reduced formation of angiotensin II decreases peripheral arterial resistance, thus decreasing aldosterone secretion.
Therapeutic effect: Lowers blood pressure.

Available forms

Injection: 1.25 mg/ml
Tablets: 2.5 mg, 5 mg, 10 mg, 20 mg

NURSING PROCESS

Assessment

- Obtain history of patient's blood pressure before starting therapy, and reassess regularly.
- Monitor CBC with differential counts before therapy, every 2 weeks for first 3 months of therapy, and periodically thereafter.
- Monitor potassium intake and serum potassium level.
- Be alert for adverse reactions and drug interactions.
- Assess patient's and family's knowledge of drug therapy.

Nursing diagnoses

- Risk for injury related to presence of hypertension
- Risk for infection related to drug-induced adverse hematologic reactions
- Deficient knowledge related to drug therapy

Planning and implementation

- If patient has hypotension after first dose, adjust dose as long as patient is under medical supervision.
- If CBC becomes abnormal or evidence of infection arises, notify prescriber immediately.
- If angioedema (including laryngeal edema) occurs, notify prescriber and stop drug immediately. Institute appropriate therapy (epinephrine

solution 1:1,000 [0.3 to 0.5 ml] subcutaneously), and take measures to ensure patent airway.

Patient teaching

- Advise patient to report evidence of angioedema, such as breathing difficulty and swelling of face, eyes, lips, or tongue.
- Instruct patient to report signs of infection, such as fever and sore throat.
- Advise patient that light-headedness can occur, especially during first few days of therapy. Tell patient to rise slowly to minimize this effect and to report symptoms to prescriber. If patient experiences syncope, tell him to stop taking drug and to call prescriber immediately.
- Tell patient to use caution in hot weather and during exercise. Inadequate fluid intake, vomiting, diarrhea, and excessive perspiration can lead to light-headedness and syncope.
- Advise patient to avoid sodium substitutes; these products may contain potassium, which can cause hyperkalemia.
- Tell patient to notify prescriber if pregnancy occurs. Drug will probably need to be changed.

Evaluation

- Patient's blood pressure becomes normal.
- Patient's CBC remains normal throughout therapy.
- Patient and family state understanding of drug therapy.

enfuvirtide

(ehn-FOO-ver-tighd)

Fuzeon

Pharmacologic class: fusion inhibitor
Therapeutic class: antiretroviral
Pregnancy risk category: B

Indications and dosages

▶ **HIV-1 infection, with other antiretrovirals, in patients with continued HIV-1 replication despite antiretroviral therapy.** *Adults:* 90 mg subcutaneously b.i.d., injected into the upper arm, anterior thigh, or abdomen.
Children ages 6 to 16: Give 2 mg/kg subcutaneously b.i.d.; maximum dose, 90 mg.

Contraindications and cautions

- Contraindicated in patients hypersensitive to drug or any of its components.

Lifespan: In pregnant women, use only when benefits outweigh risks to the fetus. Breast-feeding women should stop breast-feeding to prevent transmitting HIV to infants. In children younger than age 6, safety and effectiveness haven't been established.

Adverse reactions

CNS: anxiety, asthenia, depression, *insomnia,* peripheral neuropathy.
EENT: conjunctivitis, sinusitis, taste disturbance.
GI: abdominal pain, constipation, *diarrhea, nausea,* ***pancreatitis.***
Hematologic: lymphadenopathy.
Metabolic: anorexia, weight decrease.
Musculoskeletal: myalgia.
Respiratory: *bacterial pneumonia,* cough.
Skin: *ecchymosis,* pruritus, skin papilloma.
Other: flulike illness, herpes simplex, influenza, *injection-site reactions.*

Interactions

None reported.

Effects on lab test results

- May increase triglyceride, amylase, lipase, ALT, AST, CK, and GGT levels. May decrease hemoglobin level and hematocrit.
- May decrease eosinophil count.

Pharmacokinetics

Absorption: Absorbed well after subcutaneous administration into arm, thigh, or abdomen.
Distribution: 92% protein-bound.
Metabolism: May undergo catabolism to its constituent amino acids; hydrolyzed to a metabolite detectable in plasma.
Excretion: Unknown. *Half-life:* 4 hours.

Route	Onset	Peak	Duration
SubQ	Unknown	4–8 hr	Unknown

Action

Chemical effect: Interferes with entry of HIV-1 into cells by inhibiting fusion of HIV-1 to cell membranes.
Therapeutic effect: Controls symptoms of HIV infection.

Available forms

Injection: 108-mg single-use vials (90 mg/ml after reconstitution)

NURSING PROCESS

Assessment

- Use drug only in patients who are HIV-positive.
- Assess patient for evidence of bacterial pneumonia.
- Observe injection site for local reaction.
- Assess patient's and family's knowledge of drug therapy.

Nursing diagnoses

- Risk for infection related to underlying condition
- Deficient knowledge related to drug therapy

Planning and implementation

- Reconstitute vial with 1.1 ml sterile water for injection. Tap vial for 10 seconds, and then gently roll it between hands to prevent foaming. Let drug stand for up to 45 minutes to ensure reconstitution. Or gently roll vial between hands until product is completely dissolved. Then draw up correct dose and inject drug.
- If drug isn't used immediately after reconstitution, refrigerate in original vial and use within 24 hours. Don't inject drug until it's at room temperature.
- Store vials that haven't been reconstituted at room temperature.
- Vial is for single use; discard unused portion.
- Rotate injection sites. Don't inject into same site for two consecutive doses, and don't inject into moles, scar tissue, bruises, or the navel.
- Injection site reactions (pain, discomfort, induration, erythema, pruritus, nodules, cysts, ecchymosis) are common and may require analgesics or rest.

ALERT: Monitor patient closely for bacterial pneumonia. Patients at high risk include those with a low initial CD4+ count or high initial viral load, those who use I.V. drugs or smoke, and those with a history of lung disease.

- Hypersensitivity may occur with the first dose or later doses. If symptoms occur, stop drug.
- Register pregnant women in the Antiretroviral Pregnancy Registry by phoning 1-800-258-4263.

Patient teaching

- Teach patient how to prepare and give drug and how to safely dispose of used needles and syringes.
- Tell patient to rotate injection sites and to watch for cellulitis or local infection.
- Urge patient to immediately report evidence of pneumonia, such as cough with fever, rapid breathing, or shortness of breath.
- Tell patient to stop taking drug and seek medical attention if evidence of hypersensitivity develops, such as rash, fever, nausea, vomiting, chills, rigors, and hypotension.
- Inform patient that drug doesn't cure HIV infection and that it must be taken with other antiretrovirals.
- Tell patient to inform prescriber if she's pregnant, plans to become pregnant, or is breastfeeding while taking this drug.
- Tell patient that drug may impair the ability to drive or operate machinery.

Evaluation

- Patient is free from opportunistic infections.
- Patient and family state understanding of drug therapy.

enoxaparin sodium

(eh-NOKS-uh-pah-rin SOH-dee-um)
Lovenox

Pharmacologic class: low–molecular-weight heparin derivative
Therapeutic class: anticoagulant
Pregnancy risk category: B

Indications and dosages

▶ **To prevent deep vein thrombosis (DVT) following hip or knee replacement surgery.** *Adults:* 30 mg subcutaneously q 12 hours for 7 to 10 days. Initial dose given 12 to 24 hours after surgery, provided hemostasis has been established. Or, for hip replacement surgery, 40 mg subcutaneously once daily given initially 9 to 15 hours before surgery. May continue with 40 mg subcutaneously once daily or 30 mg subcutaneously q 12 hours for 3 weeks.

▶ **To prevent DVT following abdominal surgery.** *Adults:* 40 mg subcutaneously once daily for 7 to 10 days with initial dose given 2 hours before surgery.

▶ **To prevent ischemic complications of unstable angina and non–ST-segment elevation MI (NSTEMI).** *Adults:* 1 mg/kg subcutaneously q 12 hours for 2 to 8 days with oral aspirin therapy (100 to 325 mg daily).

▶ **Inpatient with acute DVT with or without pulmonary embolism.** *Adults:* 1 mg/kg subcutaneously q 12 hours. Or 1.5 mg/kg subcutaneously once daily (at same time every day) for 5 to 7 days until therapeutic oral anticoagulant effect (INR of 2 to 3) is achieved. Warfarin therapy usually starts within 72 hours of enoxaparin injection.

▶ **Outpatient with acute DVT and without pulmonary embolism.** *Adults:* 1 mg/kg subcutaneously q 12 hours for 5 to 7 days until INR of 2 to 3 is achieved. Warfarin therapy is usually started within 72 hours of the enoxaparin injection.

▶ **Immobile patients during an acute illness.** *Adults:* 40 mg subcutaneously given once daily for 6 to 11 days. Up to 14 days may be tolerated.

Adjust-a-dose: In patients with a creatinine clearance less than 30 ml/minute receiving drug as prophylaxis following abdominal surgery or hip or knee replacement surgery, and in medical patients for prophylaxis during acute illness, decrease dosage to 30 mg subcutaneously daily. In patients with creatinine clearance less than 30 ml/minute receiving drug for acute DVT or prophylaxis of ischemic complications of unstable angina and NSTEMI, give 1 mg/kg subcutaneously daily.

Contraindications and cautions

- Contraindicated in patients hypersensitive to drug or any of its components, to heparin, or to pork products; in those with active major bleeding or thrombocytopenia; and in those who have antiplatelet antibodies in presence of drug.
- Not recommended for thromboprophylaxis in patients with prosthetic heart valves.
- Use cautiously in patients with postoperative indwelling epidural catheters and patients who have had epidural or spinal anesthesia. Epidural and spinal hematomas may result in long-term or permanent paralysis. Also use cautiously in patients with a history of heparin-induced thrombocytopenia; in patients with conditions that increase their risk of hemorrhage (such as bacterial endocarditis); and in patients with congenital or acquired bleeding disorders, ulcer disease, angiodysplastic GI disease, hemorrhagic stroke, or recent spinal, eye, or brain surgery.

Lifespan: In pregnant women, use cautiously, and only when benefits outweigh risks to fetus. In breast-feeding women, use cautiously because it's unknown if drug appears in breast milk. In children, safety and effectiveness haven't been established.

Adverse reactions

CNS: confusion, fever, pain.
CV: edema, peripheral edema.
GI: nausea.
Hematologic: *anemia,* ***bleeding complications, hemorrhage, thrombocytopenia.***
Skin: ecchymosis; hematoma, irritation, pain, or erythema at injection site; rash; urticaria.
Other: ***angioedema, anaphylaxis.***

Interactions

Drug-drug. *Anticoagulants, antiplatelet drugs, dipyridamole, NSAIDs, sulfinpyrazone:* May increase risk of bleeding. Don't use together.
Plicamycin, valproic acid: May cause hypoprothrombinemia and inhibit platelet aggregation. Monitor patient closely.

Effects on lab test results

- May increase ALT and AST levels. May decrease hemoglobin level and hematocrit.
- May decrease platelet count.

Pharmacokinetics

Absorption: Unknown.
Distribution: Unknown.
Metabolism: Unknown.
Excretion: Unknown. *Half-life:* 4½ hours.

Route	Onset	Peak	Duration
SubQ	Unknown	3–5 hr	< 24 hr

Action

Chemical effect: Accelerates formation of antithrombin IIIB–thrombin complex and deactivates thrombin, preventing conversion of fibrinogen to fibrin.
Therapeutic effect: Prevents pulmonary embolism and DVT.

Available forms

Ampules: 30 mg/0.3 ml
Syringes (prefilled, graduated): 60 mg/0.6 ml, 80 mg/0.8 ml, 100 mg/ml, 120 mg/0.8 ml, 150 mg/ml

Syringes (prefilled): 30 mg/0.3 ml, 40 mg/0.4 ml
Vial (multidose): 300 mg/3 ml (contains 15 mg/ml of benzyl alcohol)

NURSING PROCESS

Assessment

- Obtain history of patient's coagulation parameters before starting therapy.
- Monitor drug's effectiveness by evaluating patient for evidence of pulmonary embolism or DVT.
- Monitor platelet counts regularly. Patient with normal coagulation doesn't require regular monitoring of PT, INR, or PTT.
- If patient has had spinal or epidural anesthesia, monitor neurologic condition often. If abnormalities are discovered, alert prescriber immediately.
- Be alert for adverse reactions and drug interactions.
- Assess patient's and family's knowledge of drug therapy.

Nursing diagnoses

- Risk for injury related to risk for pulmonary embolism or DVT after knee or hip replacement surgery
- Ineffective protection related to drug-induced bleeding complications
- Deficient knowledge related to drug therapy

Planning and implementation

ALERT: To avoid drug loss, don't expel air bubble from 30- or 40-mg prefilled syringes.
ALERT: Never give drug I.M.

- Don't massage after subcutaneous injection. Rotate sites among the left and right anterolateral and the left and right posterolateral abdominal walls.

ALERT: Drug can't be used interchangeably (unit for unit) with unfractionated heparin or other low–molecular-weight heparins.

- Avoid excessive I.M. injections of other drugs to prevent or minimize hematomas. Don't give I.M. injections when patient is anticoagulated.
- To treat severe overdose, give protamine sulfate (a heparin antagonist) by slow I.V. infusion at concentration of 1% to equal dosage of enoxaparin injected.

Patient teaching

- Instruct patient and family to watch for signs of bleeding and to notify prescriber at once.
- Tell patient to avoid OTC drugs that contain aspirin or other salicylates.
- Tell pregnant women and women of childbearing potential about the potential hazard to fetus and mother if drug is used during pregnancy.

Evaluation

- Patient doesn't develop pulmonary embolism or DVT.
- Patient has no bleeding complications during therapy.
- Patient and family state understanding of drug therapy.

entacapone

(en-TAK-uh-pohn)
Comtan

Pharmacologic class: COMT inhibitor
Therapeutic class: antiparkinsonian
Pregnancy risk category: C

Indications and dosages

▶ **Adjunct to levodopa and carbidopa in idiopathic Parkinson disease in patients who experience end-of-dose wearing-off.** *Adults:* 200 mg P.O. with each dose of levodopa and carbidopa up to eight times daily. Maximum, 1,600 mg daily. Reducing daily levodopa dose or extending interval between doses may optimize patient's response.

Contraindications and cautions

- Contraindicated in patients hypersensitive to the drug or any of its components.
- Use cautiously in patients with hepatic impairment, biliary obstruction, or orthostatic hypotension.

Lifespan: In pregnant women, use drug only when benefits outweigh risks to the fetus. In breast-feeding women, use cautiously because it's unknown if the drug appears in breast milk.

Adverse reactions

CNS: agitation, anxiety, asthenia, dizziness, *dyskinesia,* fatigue, hallucinations, *hyperkinesia,* hypokinesia, somnolence.

GI: abdominal pain, constipation, *diarrhea,* dry mouth, dyspepsia, flatulence, gastritis, *nausea,* taste perversion, vomiting.
GU: urine discoloration.
Hematologic: purpura.
Musculoskeletal: back pain, ***rhabdomyolysis.***
Respiratory: dyspnea.
Skin: sweating.
Other: bacterial infection.

Interactions

Drug-drug. *Ampicillin, chloramphenicol, cholestyramine, erythromycin, probenecid, rifampin:* May block biliary excretion, resulting in higher levels of entacapone. Use cautiously.
CNS depressants: May have additive effects. Use cautiously.
Drugs metabolized by COMT, such as bitolterol, dobutamine, dopamine, epinephrine, isoetharine, isoproterenol, and norepinephrine: May increase levels of these drugs, which may increase heart rate, change blood pressure, or cause arrhythmias. Use cautiously.
Nonselective MAO inhibitors, such as phenelzine and tranylcypromine: May inhibit normal catecholamine metabolism. Don't use together.
Drug-lifestyle. *Alcohol use:* May cause additive CNS effects. Discourage use together.

Effects on lab test results

None reported.

Pharmacokinetics

Absorption: Rapid, with level peaking in about 1 hour. Food doesn't affect absorption.
Distribution: About 98% protein-bound, mainly to albumin. Doesn't distribute widely into tissues.
Metabolism: Almost completely metabolized by glucuronidation before elimination.
Excretion: About 10% in urine; the remainder in bile and feces. *Half-life:* 0.4 to 0.7 hours for first phase and 2.4 hours for second phase.

Route	Onset	Peak	Duration
P.O.	1 hr	1 hr	6 hr

Action

Chemical effect: Drug is a reversible inhibitor of peripheral COMT, which is responsible for elimination of various catecholamines, including dopamine. Blocking this pathway when giving levodopa and carbidopa may result in higher levels of levodopa, which allows greater dopaminergic stimulation in the CNS and leads to a greater effect on parkinsonian symptoms.
Therapeutic effect: Controls idiopathic Parkinson disease signs and symptoms.

Available forms

Tablets: 200 mg

NURSING PROCESS

Assessment

- Assess hepatic and biliary function before starting therapy.
- Monitor blood pressure closely. Watch for orthostatic hypotension.
- Monitor patient for hallucinations.
- Assess patient's and family's knowledge of drug therapy.

Nursing diagnoses

- Impaired physical mobility related to presence of parkinsonism
- Disturbed thought processes related to drug-induced adverse reactions
- Deficient knowledge related to drug therapy

Planning and implementation

- Use with levodopa and carbidopa. Drug isn't effective when given as monotherapy.
- Drug may be given with immediate- or sustained-release levodopa and carbidopa and may be taken with or without food.
- Decrease levodopa and carbidopa dose or increase interval to avoid adverse effects.
- Drug may cause or worsen dyskinesia despite reduction of levodopa dosage.
- Watch for diarrhea, which usually begins 4 to 12 weeks after therapy starts but may begin as early as the first week or as late as many months after therapy starts.
- Stopping drug abruptly or lowering dosage abruptly could lead to sudden worsening of Parkinson disease; it also may lead to hyperpyrexia and confusion, a symptom complex resembling neuroleptic malignant syndrome. Taper dose, and monitor patient closely. Adjust other antiparkinson drugs as needed.
- Assess patient for urine discoloration.
- Rarely, rhabdomyolysis may occur with drug use.

Patient teaching

- Instruct patient not to crush or break tablet and to take it at same time as levodopa and carbidopa.
- Warn patient to avoid hazardous activities until drug's CNS effects are known.
- Advise patient not to consume alcohol.
- Instruct patient to use caution when standing after a prolonged period of sitting or lying down because dizziness may occur. This effect is more common early in therapy.
- Warn patient that hallucinations, dyskinesia, nausea, diarrhea, and urine discoloration may occur.
- Inform patient that abruptly stopping drug therapy can cause sudden severe symptoms.
- Advise female patient to notify prescriber if she's pregnant or breast-feeding or if she plans to become pregnant.

Evaluation

- Patient has improved physical mobility.
- Patient maintains normal thought process.
- Patient and family state understanding of drug therapy.

entecavir
(ehn-TECK-ah-veer)
Baraclude

Pharmacologic class: guanosine nucleoside analogue
Therapeutic class: antiviral
Pregnancy risk category: C

Indications and dosages

▶ **Chronic hepatitis B infection in patients with active viral replication and either persistently increased serum aminotransferase levels or histologically active disease.** *Adults and adolescents age 16 and older who have had no previous nucleoside treatment:* 0.5 mg P.O. once daily on an empty stomach.
Adults and adolescents age 16 and older who have a history of viremia and are taking lamivudine or have resistance mutations: 1 mg P.O. once daily on an empty stomach.

Adjust-a-dose: *Patients with no previous nucleoside treatment:* If creatinine clearance is 30 to 49 ml/minute, give 0.25 mg P.O. once daily. If clearance is 10 to 29 ml/minute, give 0.15 mg P.O. once daily. If clearance is less than 10 ml/minute or patient is undergoing hemodialysis or continuous ambulatory peritoneal dialysis, give 0.05 mg P.O. once daily.

Patients with lamivudine resistance: If creatinine clearance is 30 to 49 ml/minute, give 0.5 mg P.O. once daily. If clearance is 10 to 29 ml/minute, give 0.3 mg P.O. once daily. If clearance is less than 10 ml/minute or patient is undergoing hemodialysis or continuous ambulatory peritoneal dialysis, give 0.1 mg P.O. once daily.

Contraindications and cautions

- Contraindicated in patients hypersensitive to drug or its components.
- Use cautiously in patients with renal impairment and after liver transplantation.
- Lactic acidosis and severe hepatomegaly with steatosis, including fatal cases, have been reported with the use of nucleoside analogues alone and in combination with other antiretrovirals.

Lifespan: In pregnant women, use only when benefits outweigh risks to fetus. In breast-feeding women, avoid use; it's unknown if drug appears in breast milk. In patients younger than age 16, safety and effectiveness haven't been established. In elderly patients, adjust dosage for age-related decreases in renal function.

Adverse reactions

CNS: dizziness, fatigue, headache.
GI: diarrhea, dyspepsia, nausea.
GU: glycosuria, hematuria.
Hepatic: ***hepatomegaly with steatosis.***
Other: ***lactic acidosis.***

Interactions

Drug-drug. *Cyclosporine, tacrolimus:* May further decrease renal function. Monitor renal function carefully.
Drugs that reduce renal function or compete for active tubular secretion: May increase serum levels of either drug. Monitor renal function, and watch for adverse effects.
Drug-food. *Food:* May delay absorption and decrease serum drug level. Give drug on an empty stomach, at least 2 hours before or after a meal.

Effects on lab test results

- May increase ALT, amylase, AST, blood glucose, creatinine, lipase, and total bilirubin levels.
- May decrease platelet count.

Pharmacokinetics

Absorption: Absorbed through the GI tract. Food delays and decreases absorption.
Distribution: Extensive in tissues. 13% bound to plasma proteins.
Metabolism: Drug isn't a substrate, inhibitor, or inducer of the cytochrome P-450 enzyme system.
Excretion: By kidneys, 62% to 73% unchanged. *Half-life:* 128 to 149 hours.

Route	Onset	Peak	Duration
P.O.	Unknown	½–1½ hr	Unknown

Action

Chemical effect: Inhibits hepatitis B virus polymerase and reduces viral DNA levels.
Therapeutic effect: Reduces symptoms of hepatitis B infection.

Available forms

Oral solution: 0.05 mg/ml
Tablets: 0.5 mg, 1 mg

NURSING PROCESS

Assessment

- Assess patient's condition before therapy and regularly thereafter.
- Monitor renal and liver function tests during therapy.

ALERT: Hepatitis B may worsen severely after entecavir therapy stops.

- Monitor hepatic function for several months in patients who stop therapy. If appropriate, restart therapy for hepatitis B.
- Assess patient's and family's knowledge of drug therapy.

Nursing diagnoses

- Risk for injury related to development of lactic acidosis and severe hepatomegaly with steatosis secondary to drug therapy
- Ineffective therapeutic regimen management secondary to long-term drug therapy
- Deficient knowledge related to drug therapy

Planning and implementation

ALERT: The drug may cause life-threatening lactic acidosis and severe hepatomegaly with steatosis.

- Register pregnant women in the Antiretroviral Pregnancy Registry by phoning 1-800-258-4263.
- The optimal duration of treatment hasn't been established.

Patient teaching

- Tell patient that drug should be taken on an empty stomach at least 2 hours before or after a meal.
- Caution against mixing or diluting oral solution with any other substances. Teach proper use of spoon used to measure dose.
- Advise patient to report new adverse effects or new therapy with another drug.
- Explain that drug doesn't reduce the risk of transmitting hepatitis B virus to others.
- Teach patient the signs and symptoms of lactic acidosis, such as muscle pain, weakness, dyspnea, GI distress, cold extremities, dizziness, and fast or irregular heartbeat.
- Teach patient the signs and symptoms of hepatotoxicity, such as jaundice, dark urine, light-colored stool, loss of appetite, nausea, and lower stomach pain.
- Warn patient not to stop drug abruptly.

Evaluation

- Patient remains free from lactic acidosis and severe hepatomegaly with steatosis during therapy.
- Patient maintains therapeutic regimen as shown by improvement of hepatitis B viral infection.
- Patient and family state understanding of drug therapy.

ephedrine sulfate

(eh-FED-rihn SUL-fayt)

Pharmacologic class: adrenergic
Therapeutic class: bronchodilator, vasopressor
Pregnancy risk category: C

Indications and dosages

▶ **Hypotension.** *Adults:* 25 to 50 mg I.M. or subcutaneously, or 10 to 25 mg I.V. infusion, or

5 to 25 mg by slow I.V. bolus injection, p.r.n., up to maximum of 150 mg/24 hours.
Children: 3 mg/kg or 100 mg/m^2 subcutaneously or I.V. daily in four to six divided doses.
▶ **Bronchodilation.** *Adults and children older than age 12:* Give 25 to 50 mg P.O. q 3 to 4 hours p.r.n. For use as a bronchodilator, 12.5 to 25 mg P.O. q 4 hours. Maximum, 150 mg in 24 hours.
Children ages 2 to 12: Give 2 to 3 mg/kg or 100 mg/m^2 P.O. daily in four to six divided doses.

I.V. administration

- Drug is compatible with most common I.V. solutions.
- For vasopressor action, use I.V. route initially. Give slowly until systolic blood pressure is 30 to 40 mm Hg below patient's normal systolic pressure or 80 to 100 mm Hg.

⊗ **Incompatibilities**
Fructose 10% in normal saline solution; hydrocortisone sodium succinate; Ionosol B, D-CM, and D solutions; pentobarbital sodium; phenobarbital sodium; thiopental.

Contraindications and cautions

- Contraindicated in patients hypersensitive to drug, to any of its components, or to other sympathomimetic drugs; in those with porphyria, severe coronary artery disease, arrhythmias, angle-closure glaucoma, psychoneurosis, angina pectoris, substantial organic heart disease, or CV disease; and in those taking MAO inhibitors.
- Use cautiously in patients with hypertension, hyperthyroidism, nervous or excitable states, diabetes, or prostatic hyperplasia.

Lifespan: In pregnant women, children, and older men, use cautiously. In breast-feeding women, drug is contraindicated.

Adverse reactions

CNS: *confusion, delirium, dizziness, euphoria, headache, insomnia, nervousness.*
CV: hypertension, *palpitations,* precordial pain, *tachycardia.*
GI: *anorexia, nausea, vomiting.*
GU: painful urination from visceral sphincter spasm, *urine retention.*
Musculoskeletal: muscle weakness.
Skin: diaphoresis.

Interactions

Drug-drug. *Acetazolamide:* May increase ephedrine level. Monitor patient for toxicity.
Alpha blockers: Doesn't counteract beta blocker effects, resulting in hypotension. Monitor blood pressure.
Antihypertensives: May decrease effects. Monitor blood pressure.
Beta blockers: Doesn't counteract alpha-adrenergic effects, resulting in hypertension. Monitor blood pressure.
Digoxin, general anesthetics (halogenated hydrocarbons): May increase risk of ventricular arrhythmias. Monitor patient closely.
Ergot alkaloids: May enhance vasoconstrictor activity. Monitor patient closely.
Guanadrel, guanethidine: May enhance pressor effects of ephedrine. Monitor patient closely.
MAO inhibitors: When given with sympathomimetics, may cause hypertensive crisis. Don't use together.
Methyldopa, reserpine: May inhibit effects of ephedrine. Use together cautiously.
Phenelzine, tranylcypromine: May cause severe headache, hypertension, fever, and hypertensive crisis. Avoid use together.
Tricyclic antidepressants: May decrease pressor response. Monitor patient's blood pressure closely.

Effects on lab test results

None reported.

Pharmacokinetics

Absorption: Rapid and complete after P.O., I.M., or subcutaneous use; unknown after I.V. use.
Distribution: Widely distributed throughout body.
Metabolism: Slow, in liver.
Excretion: Unchanged in urine. Rate of excretion depends on urine pH. *Half-life:* 3 to 6 hours.

Route	Onset	Peak	Duration
P.O.	15–60 min	Unknown	3–5 hr
I.V.	≤ 5 min	Unknown	1 hr
I.M.	10–20 min	Unknown	1 hr
SubQ	Unknown	Unknown	1 hr

Action

Chemical effect: Stimulates alpha and beta receptors; direct- and indirect-acting sympathomimetic.
Therapeutic effect: Raises blood pressure and causes bronchodilation.

Available forms

Capsules: 25 mg, 50 mg
Injection: 25 mg/ml, 50 mg/ml
Tablets: 30 mg†

NURSING PROCESS

Assessment
- Obtain history of patient's underlying condition before starting therapy, and reassess regularly.
- Be alert for adverse reactions and drug interactions.
- Assess patient's and family's knowledge of drug therapy.

Nursing diagnoses
- Ineffective health maintenance related to underlying condition
- Risk for deficient fluid volume related to drug-induced adverse GI reactions
- Deficient knowledge related to drug therapy

Planning and implementation
- Hypoxia, hypercapnia, and acidosis, which may reduce drug effectiveness or increase adverse reactions, must be identified and corrected before or during ephedrine administration for shock.
- Volume deficit must be corrected before giving vasopressors. This drug isn't a substitute for blood or fluid volume replenishment.
- To prevent insomnia, avoid giving within 2 hours of bedtime.
- When effectiveness decreases, notify prescriber. Effectiveness decreases after 2 to 3 weeks, as tolerance develops. Drug isn't addictive.

Patient teaching
- Warn patient not to take OTC drugs that contain ephedrine without consulting prescriber.
- Advise patient to notify prescriber if effectiveness decreases and to adjust dosage as instructed.
- Instruct patient to notify prescriber if adverse reactions occur.
- Caution patient not to perform hazardous activities if adverse CNS reactions occur.

Evaluation
- Patient shows improvement in underlying condition.
- Patient maintains adequate hydration throughout therapy.
- Patient and family state understanding of drug therapy.

epinephrine hydrochloride
(eh-pih-NEF-rin high-droh-KLOR-ighd)
Adrenalin Chloride†, Ana-Guard, EpiPen Auto-Injector, EpiPen Jr. Auto-Injector

Pharmacologic class: adrenergic
Therapeutic class: bronchodilator, vasopressor, cardiac stimulant, topical antihemorrhagic
Pregnancy risk category: C

Indications and dosages

▶ **Bronchospasm, hypersensitivity reactions, anaphylaxis.** *Adults:* 0.1 to 0.5 ml of 1:1,000 subcutaneously or I.M.; repeat q 10 to 15 minutes, p.r.n. Or 1 to 2.5 ml of 1:10,000 injection I.V. slowly over 5 to 10 minutes.
Children: 0.01 ml (10 mcg) of 1:1,000/kg subcutaneously; repeat q 20 minutes to 4 hours, p.r.n.

▶ **Hemostasis.** *Adults:* 1:50,000 to 1:1,000 applied topically.

▶ **Prolonging local anesthetic effect.** *Adults and children:* Mix 1:500,000 to 1:50,000 with local anesthetic.

▶ **Restoring cardiac rhythm in cardiac arrest.** *Adults:* 1 to 10 ml of 1:10,000 solution by slow I.V., q 3 to 5 minutes, as needed. Or 2 to 25 ml with 10 ml normal saline solution or D_5W for injection via endotracheal tube. If no I.V. route or intratracheal route is available, give drug intracardiac. Intracardiac dose is 0.3 to 0.5 mg (1:10,000 solution). Up to 5 mg may be given, especially in patients who don't respond to usual I.V. dose. After initial I.V. bolus administration, drug may be infused I.V. at 1 to 4 mcg/minute.
Children: 10 mcg/kg I.V., or 5 to 10 mcg (0.05 to 0.1 ml of 1:10,000)/kg intracardiac.

I.V. administration

- Use D_5W, normal saline injection, lactated Ringer's injection, or combinations of dextrose in sodium chloride. Mix just before use.
- Give 1:10,000 dilution prepared by diluting 1 ml of commercially available 1:1,000 injection with 10 ml of water for injection or normal saline injection.
- In emergency situations, epinephrine hydrochloride may be injected slowly as a dilute solution or infused slowly I.V. Injection may be repeated in 5 to 10 minutes, as needed. Dosages in emergencies are controversial; some researchers may use higher than usual dosages for cardiac resuscitation.
- Follow peripheral administration with a 20-ml flush, and elevate the site for 10 to 20 seconds to ensure delivery to the central circulation.
- Discard solution after 24 hours or if solution is discolored or contains precipitate. Keep solution in light-resistant container, and don't remove before use.

⊗ Incompatibilities

Aminophylline; ampicillin sodium; cephapirin; furosemide; Ionosol D-CM, PSL, and T solutions with D_5W; mephentermine. Rapidly destroyed by alkaline solutions or oxidizing drugs, including halogens, nitrates, nitrites, permanganates, sodium bicarbonate, and salts of easily reducible metals, such as iron, copper, and zinc.

Contraindications and cautions

- Contraindicated in patients with angle-closure glaucoma, shock (other than anaphylactic shock), organic brain damage, cardiac dilation, arrhythmias, coronary insufficiency, or cerebral arteriosclerosis. Also contraindicated in patients receiving general anesthesia with halogenated hydrocarbons or cyclopropane and in patients in labor (may delay second stage).
- Some commercial products contain sulfites and are contraindicated in patients with sulfite allergies except when drug is used for serious allergic reactions or in other emergency situations.
- In conjunction with local anesthetics, epinephrine is contraindicated for use in fingers, toes, ears, nose, or genitalia.
- Use cautiously in patients with long-standing bronchial asthma or emphysema who have developed degenerative heart disease and in those with hyperthyroidism, CV disease, hypertension, psychoneurosis, or diabetes.

Lifespan: In pregnant women in labor, drug is contraindicated. In pregnant women not in labor, in children, and in elderly patients, use cautiously. Breast-feeding women should stop breast-feeding or stop taking the drug.

Adverse reactions

CNS: agitation, anxiety, ***cerebral hemorrhage,*** cold limbs, diaphoresis, disorientation, *drowsiness,* euphoria, fear, *headache,* increased rigidity and tremors in patients with Parkinson disease, *nervousness,* ***stroke,*** *tremors,* vertigo, weakness.
CV: anginal pain, ECG changes, *hypertension, palpitations,* ***shock,*** *tachycardia,* ***ventricular fibrillation,*** widened pulse pressure.
GI: nausea, vomiting.
Metabolic: glycosuria, hyperglycemia.
Respiratory: dyspnea.
Skin: pain, urticaria.
Other: hemorrhage at injection site, pallor.

Interactions

Drug-drug. *Alpha blockers:* May cause hypotension from unopposed beta blocker effects. Monitor blood pressure.
Antihistamines, thyroid hormones: May cause severe adverse cardiac effects when given with sympathomimetics. Avoid giving together.
Carteolol, nadolol, penbutolol, pindolol, propranolol, timolol: May cause an initial hypertensive episode followed by bradycardia. Stop the beta blocker 3 days before anticipated epinephrine use. Monitor patient closely.
Digoxin, general anesthetics (halogenated hydrocarbons): May increase risk of ventricular arrhythmias. Monitor patient closely.
Doxapram, methylphenidate: May increase CNS stimulation or pressor effects. Monitor patient closely.
Ergot alkaloids: May increase vasoconstrictor activity. Monitor patient closely.
Guanadrel, guanethidine: May increase pressor effects of epinephrine. Monitor the patient closely.
Levodopa: May increase risk of cardiac arrhythmias. Monitor patient closely.
MAO inhibitors: May increase risk of hypertensive crisis. Don't use together.
Methyldopa: May increase pressor effects. Monitor patient closely.

Oxytoxic drugs: May cause persistent hypertension. Don't use together.
Tricyclic antidepressants: May increase the pressor response and cause arrhythmias. Use cautiously.

Effects on lab test results

- May increase BUN, glucose, and lactic acid levels.

Pharmacokinetics

Absorption: Well absorbed after subcutaneous or I.M. injection.
Distribution: Wide, throughout body.
Metabolism: Metabolized at sympathetic nerve endings, liver, and other tissues to inactive metabolites.
Excretion: In urine. *Half-life:* Unknown.

Route	Onset	Peak	Duration
I.V.	Immediate	≤ 5 min	1–4 hr
I.M.	Varies	Unknown	1–4 hr
SubQ	6–15 min	≤ 30 min	1–4 hr

Action

Chemical effect: Stimulates alpha and beta receptors in sympathetic nervous system.
Therapeutic effect: Relaxes bronchial smooth muscle, causes cardiac stimulation, relieves allergic signs and symptoms, helps stop local bleeding, and decreases pain sensation.

Available forms

Injection: 0.01 mg/ml (1:100,000), 0.1 mg/ml (1:10,000), 0.5 mg/ml (1:2,000), 1 mg/ml (1:1,000)
Nebulizer inhaler: 1% (1:100) ♦ †, 2.25% (racepinephrine) ◊ †
Parenteral: 5 mg/ml (1:200) parenteral suspension

NURSING PROCESS

Assessment

- Obtain history of patient's underlying condition before starting therapy; reassess regularly.
- When giving drug I.V., monitor blood pressure, heart rate, and ECG when therapy starts and frequently thereafter.
- Be alert for adverse reactions and drug interactions.
- Assess patient's and family's knowledge of drug therapy.

Nursing diagnoses

- Ineffective health maintenance related to underlying condition
- Decreased cardiac output related to drug-induced adverse CV effects
- Deficient knowledge related to drug therapy

Planning and implementation

ALERT: 1 mg of epinephrine is equal to 1 ml of 1:1,000 or 10 ml of 1:10,000.
- Epinephrine is drug of choice in emergency treatment of anaphylactic reaction.
- Avoid I.M. injection of parenteral suspension into buttocks. Gas gangrene may occur because epinephrine reduces oxygen tension of tissues, encouraging growth of contaminating organisms.
- Massage site after I.M. injection to counteract vasoconstriction. Repeated local injection can cause necrosis, resulting from vasoconstriction at injection site.
- Giving drug on time is important.
- If adverse reactions develop, notify prescriber, and adjust dosage or stop the drug. If patient's pulse increases by 20% or more when drug is given, notify prescriber.
- If blood pressure rises sharply, rapid-acting vasodilators, such as nitrites or alpha blockers, can be given to counteract marked pressor effect of large doses of epinephrine.

Patient teaching

- Tell patient to take drug exactly as prescribed and to take it around the clock.
- Instruct patient who has acute hypersensitivity reactions, such as to bee stings, to self-inject epinephrine at home.
- Tell patient to reduce intake of foods containing caffeine, such as coffee, colas, and chocolates, when taking bronchodilator.
- Instruct patient to contact prescriber immediately if he experiences fluttering of heart, rapid beating of heart, shortness of breath, or chest pain.
- Tell patient to obtain approval from prescriber before taking OTC medicines or herbal remedies.
- Show patient how to check pulse. Instruct him to check pulse before and after using bronchodilator and to call prescriber if pulse rate increases by more than 20 beats/minute.

Evaluation

- Patient shows improvement in underlying condition.
- Patient maintains adequate cardiac output throughout therapy.
- Patient and family state understanding of drug therapy.

epirubicin hydrochloride

(ep-uh-ROO-bih-sin high-droh-KLOR-ighd)
Ellence

Pharmacologic class: anthracycline
Therapeutic class: antineoplastic
Pregnancy risk category: D

Indications and dosages

▶ **Adjuvant therapy for breast cancer with lymph node metastasis after resection.** *Adults:* 100 to 120 mg/m² I.V. infusion over 3 to 20 minutes via a free-flowing I.V. solution on day 1 of each cycle q 3 to 4 weeks; or divided equally in two doses on days 1 and 8 of each cycle. Maximum cumulative (lifetime) dosage is 900 mg/m².

Adjust-a-dose: Dosage change after the first cycle is based on toxicity. If patient has a platelet count below 50,000/mm³, absolute neutrophil count (ANC) below 250/mm³, neutropenic fever, or grade 3 or 4 nonhematologic toxicity, give 75% of day 1 dose in later cycles. Delay day 1 therapy in later cycles until platelet count is 100,000/mm³ or above, ANC is 1,500/mm³ or above, and nonhematologic toxicities recover to grade 1.

For patients receiving divided doses (days 1 and 8), give 75% of the day 1 dose on day 8 if platelet count is 75,000 to 100,000/mm³ and ANC is 1,000 to 1,499/mm³. If day 8 platelet count is below 75,000/mm³, ANC is below 1,000/mm³, or grade 3 or 4 nonhematologic toxicity occurs, skip the day 8 dose.

In patients with bone marrow impairment, start dose at 75 to 90 mg/m². Reduce dosage in patients with hepatic or severe renal impairment.

I.V. administration

- Drug is a vesicant. Never give I.M. or subcutaneously. Always give through free-flowing I.V. solution of normal saline solution or D_5W over 3 to 20 minutes. Initial doses at recommended dosages should be infused over 15 to 20 minutes.
- Give prophylactic antibiotic therapy with trimethoprim and sulfamethoxazole or a fluoroquinolone to patients receiving 120 mg/m² dose.
- Give antiemetics before giving drug to reduce nausea and vomiting.
- Avoid veins over joints and limbs with compromised venous or lymphatic drainage.
- If burning or stinging occurs, immediately stop infusion and restart in another vein.
- Facial flushing and local erythematous streaking along the vein may indicate too-rapid administration.
- Discard unused solution in vial 24 hours after vial is penetrated.

⊗ **Incompatibilities**
Fluorouracil, heparin, other I.V. drugs.

Contraindications and cautions

- Contraindicated in patients hypersensitive to drug or its components, other anthracyclines, or anthracenediones. Also contraindicated in patients with baseline neutrophil count below 1,500/mm³, those with severe myocardial insufficiency or recent MI, those previously treated with anthracyclines to total cumulative dosages, and those with severe hepatic dysfunction.
- Use cautiously in patients with active or dormant cardiac disease, previous or simultaneous radiotherapy to the mediastinal and pericardial area, or previous therapy with other anthracyclines or anthracenediones. Also use cautiously with other cardiotoxic drugs.

Lifespan: In pregnant and breast-feeding women, drug is contraindicated. In children, safety and effectiveness haven't been established. In elderly patients, especially women older than age 70, use cautiously because of greater chance of toxicity.

Adverse reactions

CNS: fever, *lethargy.*
CV: ***cardiomyopathy, heart failure.***
EENT: *conjunctivitis, keratitis.*
GI: anorexia, *diarrhea, mucositis, nausea, vomiting.*
GU: *amenorrhea.*
Hematologic: *anemia,* **LEUKOPENIA, NEUTROPENIA, THROMBOCYTOPENIA.**
Skin: *alopecia,* itch, rash, skin changes.
Other: *hot flushes, infection, local toxicity.*

Interactions

Drug-drug. *Calcium channel blockers, other cardioactive compounds:* May increase risk of heart failure. Monitor cardiac function closely.
Cimetidine: May increase epirubicin level (by 50%) and decrease clearance. Avoid use together.
Cytotoxic drugs: May result in additive toxicities (especially hematologic and GI). Monitor patient closely.
Radiation therapy: May enhance effects. Monitor patient carefully.

Effects on lab test results

- May decrease hemoglobin level and hematocrit.
- May decrease WBC, neutrophil, and platelet counts.

Pharmacokinetics

Absorption: Given I.V.
Distribution: Rapid and widely distributed into tissues. About 77% protein-bound, mainly to albumin. Appears to concentrate in RBCs.
Metabolism: Extensive and rapid.
Excretion: Mostly biliary. *Half-life:* 31 to 35 hours.

Route	Onset	Peak	Duration
I.V.	Unknown	Unknown	Unknown

Action

Chemical effect: The precise mechanism of drug's cytotoxic effects isn't completely known. It's thought to form a complex with DNA by intercalation between nucleotide base pairs, thereby inhibiting DNA, RNA, and protein synthesis, resulting in cytocidal activity. Drug may also interfere with replication and transcription of DNA.
Therapeutic effect: Kills certain cancer cells.

Available forms

Injection: 2 mg/ml

NURSING PROCESS

Assessment

- Obtain baseline total bilirubin, AST, creatinine, and CBC (including ANC). Evaluate cardiac function by obtaining an ECG and measuring left ventricular ejection fraction (LVEF) before therapy.
- Monitor LVEF regularly during therapy, and stop drug at first sign of cardiac impairment. Monitor patient for early signs of cardiac toxicity, including sinus tachycardia, ECG abnormalities, tachyarrhythmias, bradycardia, AV block, and bundle branch block.
- Obtain total and differential WBC, RBC, and platelet counts before and during each therapy cycle.
- Assess patient's and family's knowledge of drug therapy.

Nursing diagnoses

- Risk for injury related to drug-induced adverse reactions
- Risk for infection related to myelosuppression
- Deficient knowledge related to drug therapy

Planning and implementation

- Give drug under supervision of a prescriber experienced in the use of cancer chemotherapy.
- Wear protective clothing (goggles, gown, disposable gloves) when handling this drug. Pregnant health care providers shouldn't handle this drug because of risks to fetus.
- Cardiac toxicity may occur 2 to 3 months after stopping drug, causing reduced LVEF, evidence of heart failure (tachycardia, dyspnea, pulmonary edema, dependent edema, hepatomegaly, ascites, pleural effusion, and gallop rhythm). Delayed cardiac toxicity depends on the cumulative dosage of epirubicin. Don't exceed a cumulative dose of 900 mg/m^2.
- Monitor uric acid, potassium, calcium phosphate, and creatinine levels immediately after initial chemotherapy in patients susceptible to tumor lysis syndrome. Hydration, urine alkalinization, and prophylaxis with allopurinol may prevent hyperuricemia and minimize complications of tumor lysis syndrome.
- Lowest WBC count usually occurs 10 to 14 days after drug administration and returns to normal by day 21.
- Anthracycline-induced leukemia may occur.
- Giving drug after previous radiation therapy may induce an inflammatory cell reaction at the site of irradiation.

ALERT: Don't confuse epirubicin with other anthracyclines, such as daunorubicin, doxorubicin, or idarubicin.

Patient teaching

- Advise patient to report nausea, vomiting, stomatitis, dehydration, fever, evidence of infec-

tion, symptoms of heart failure (tachycardia, dyspnea, edema), or injection-site pain.
• Inform patient of the risk of cardiac damage and drug-related leukemia.
• Tell women of childbearing age not to become pregnant. Tell men to use effective contraception.
• Advise women that irreversible amenorrhea or premature menopause may occur.
• Advise patient about probable hair loss. Tell patient that hair usually regrows 2 to 3 months after therapy is stopped.
• Advise patient that urine may appear red 1 to 2 days after administration of the drug.

Evaluation

• Patient sustains no injury from drug-induced adverse reactions.
• Patient remains free of infection.
• Patient and family state understanding of drug therapy.

eplerenone

(eh-PLAIR-eh-nown)
Inspra

Pharmacologic class: aldosterone receptor antagonist
Therapeutic class: antihypertensive
Pregnancy risk category: B

Indications and dosages

▶ **Heart failure post-MI.** *Adults:* Initially 25 mg P.O. daily or q other day. Increase to 50 mg P.O. daily if needed within 4 weeks, according to potassium level.
Adjust-a-dose: In patients with potassium level less than 5 mEq/L, increase dosage from 25 mg every other day to 25 mg daily, or increase dosage from 25 mg daily to 50 mg daily. For potassium level of 5 to 5.4 mEq/L, no dosage adjustment needed. For potassium level of 5.5 to 5.9 mEq/L, decrease dosage from 50 mg daily to 25 mg daily, or decrease dosage from 25 mg daily to 25 mg every other day; or if dosage was 25 mg every other day, withhold drug. For potassium level greater than 6 mEq/L, withhold drug. May restart drug at 25 mg every other day when potassium level is less than 5.5 mEq/L.

▶ **Hypertension.** *Adults:* 50 mg P.O. once daily alone or with other antihypertensives. If response is inadequate after 4 weeks, increase dosage to 50 mg P.O. b.i.d. Maximum, 100 mg daily.
Adjust-a-dose: For either indication, patients who also take a weak CYP3A4 inhibitor (such as erythromycin, verapamil, or fluconazole) need a reduced starting dose of 25 mg P.O. daily.

Contraindications and cautions

• Contraindicated in patients with potassium level greater than 5.5 mEq/L at start of treatment, type 2 diabetes with microalbuminuria, serum creatinine level greater than 2 mg/dl in men or greater than 1.8 mg/dl in women, or creatinine clearance less than 30 ml/minute (less than 50 ml/minute if patient is being treated for high blood pressure). Also contraindicated in patients treated simultaneously with potassium supplements, potassium-sparing diuretics (amiloride, spironolactone, or triamterene), or strong CYP3A4 inhibitors, such as ketoconazole, itraconazole, clarithromycin, nefazodone, nelfinavir, and ritonavir.
• Use cautiously in patients with mild to moderate hepatic impairment.
Lifespan: In pregnant women, use only if benefits outweigh risks to fetus. In breast-feeding women, use cautiously because it's unknown whether drug appears in breast milk. In children, safety and effectiveness haven't been established.

Adverse reactions

CNS: dizziness, fatigue.
GI: abdominal pain, diarrhea.
GU: abnormal vaginal bleeding, albuminuria.
Metabolic: ***hyperkalemia.***
Respiratory: cough.
Other: flulike syndrome, gynecomastia.

Interactions

Drug-drug. *ACE inhibitors, angiotensin II receptor antagonists*: May increase risk of hyperkalemia. Use together cautiously.
Lithium: May increase risk of lithium toxicity. Monitor lithium level.
NSAIDs: May reduce the antihypertensive effect and cause severe hyperkalemia in patients with renal impairment. Monitor blood pressure and potassium level.

Potassium supplements, potassium-sparing diuretics (amiloride, spironolactone, triamterene): May increase risk of hyperkalemia and sometimes fatal arrhythmias. Avoid use together.
Strong CYP3A4 inhibitors (clarithromycin, itraconazole, ketoconazole, nefazodone, nelfinavir, ritonavir, troleandomycin): May increase eplerenone level. Avoid use together.
Weak CYP3A4 inhibitors (erythromycin, fluconazole, saquinavir, verapamil): May increase eplerenone level. Reduce eplerenone starting dose to 25 mg P.O. once daily.
Drug-herb. *St. John's wort:* May decrease eplerenone level over time. Discourage use together.

Effects on lab test results

- May increase potassium, creatinine, BUN, triglyceride, cholesterol, ALT, and GGT levels. May decrease sodium level.

Pharmacokinetics

Absorption: Bioavailability of drug is unknown.
Distribution: About 50% protein-bound.
Metabolism: Mainly by CYP3A4.
Excretion: Mainly in urine. *Half-life:* 4 to 6 hours.

Route	Onset	Peak	Duration
P.O.	Unknown	1½ hr	Unknown

Action

Chemical effect: Binds to mineralocorticoid receptors and blocks aldosterone. Aldosterone may increase blood pressure through induction of sodium reabsorption and other mechanisms.
Therapeutic effect: Lowers blood pressure.

Available forms

Tablets: 25 mg, 50 mg

NURSING PROCESS

Assessment

- Obtain history of patient's underlying condition before starting therapy.
- Obtain patient's baseline blood pressure and potassium levels and reassess regularly.
- Assess patient's and family's knowledge of drug therapy.

Nursing diagnoses

- Ineffective health maintenance related to hypertension
- Risk for injury related to the presence of hypertension
- Deficient knowledge related to drug therapy

Planning and implementation

- Drug may be used alone or with other antihypertensives.
- The drug's full therapeutic effect occurs within 4 weeks.
- Monitor patient for signs and symptoms of hyperkalemia.
- Overdose may cause hypotension and hyperkalemia. Treat symptoms and provide support. Drug binds extensively to charcoal but can't be removed by hemodialysis.

ALERT: Don't confuse Inspra (eplerenone) with Spiriva (tiotropium bromide).

Patient teaching

- Tell patient drug can be taken with or without food.
- Advise patient to avoid potassium supplements and salt substitutes.
- Tell patient to report adverse reactions.

Evaluation

- Patient's blood pressure remains within normal limits.
- Patient's potassium remains within normal limits.
- Patient and family state understanding of drug therapy.

epoetin alfa (erythropoietin)

(ee-POH-eh-tin AL-fah)
Epogen, Eprex ◇, Procrit

Pharmacologic class: glycoprotein
Therapeutic class: hematopoietic
Pregnancy risk category: C

Indications and dosages

▶ **Anemia caused by chronic renal disease.** *Adults:* Starting dosage is 50 to 100 units/kg I.V. or subcutaneously three times weekly. Maintenance dosage is highly individualized.
Infants and children ages 1 month to 16 years who are on dialysis: 50 units/kg I.V. or subcutaneously three times weekly. Maintenance dos-

age is highly individualized to keep hemoglobin level in target range.

Adjust-a-dose: When target hemoglobin level approaches 12 g/dl or if it rises more than 1 g/dl in any 2-week period, reduce dosage. If hemoglobin level doesn't increase by 2 g/dl after 8 weeks of therapy and is below the target range, increase dosage.

▶ **Anemia from zidovudine therapy in HIV-infected patients.** *Adults:* 100 units/kg I.V. or subcutaneously three times weekly for 8 weeks or until target hemoglobin level is reached. If response isn't satisfactory after 8 weeks, increase dosage by 50 to 100 units/kg I.V. or subcutaneously three times weekly. After 4 to 8 weeks, further increase dosage in increments of 50 to 100 units/kg three times weekly, up to a maximum of 300 units/kg three times weekly.

Infants and children ages 8 months to 17 years‡: 50 to 400 units/kg subcutaneously or I.V. two to three times weekly.

▶ **Anemia from cancer chemotherapy.** *Adults:* 150 units/kg subcutaneously three times weekly for 8 weeks or until target hemoglobin level is reached. If response isn't satisfactory after 8 weeks, increase dosage up to 300 units/kg subcutaneously three times weekly. Or 40,000 units subcutaneously once weekly. If hemoglobin level hasn't increased by at least 1 g/dl in the absence of RBC transfusion, increase dose to 60,000 units subcutaneously weekly.

Infants and children ages 6 months to 18 years‡: 25 to 300 units/kg subcutaneously or I.V. three to seven times weekly.

Adjust-a-dose: Withhold drug if hemoglobin level exceeds 13 g/dl. Reduce dose by 25% and resume therapy when hemoglobin level is less than 12 g/dl. If hemoglobin level increases by more than 1 g/dl in any 2-week period, reduce dose by 25%.

▶ **To reduce need for allogenic blood transfusion in anemic patients undergoing elective, noncardiac, nonvascular surgery.** *Adults:* 300 units/kg subcutaneously once daily for 10 days before surgery, on the day of surgery, and for 4 days after surgery. Or 600 units/kg subcutaneously in once-weekly doses (21, 14, and 7 days before surgery), plus a fourth dose on day of surgery.

▶ **Anemia related to rheumatoid arthritis and rheumatic disease**‡. *Adults:* 50 to 200 units/kg subcutaneously three times weekly.

▶ **Anemia related to prematurity**‡. *Neonates:* 25 to 100 units/kg subcutaneously three times weekly.

I.V. administration

- Don't shake.
- Give drug by direct injection without dilution.
- If patient is having dialysis, drug may be given into venous return line after dialysis session. To keep drug from adhering to tubing, inject drug with blood still in the line; then flush with normal saline solution.

⊗ **Incompatibilities**

Other I.V. drugs.

Contraindications and cautions

- Contraindicated in patients with uncontrolled hypertension and in patients with hypersensitivity to mammal-cell–derived products or albumin.

Lifespan: In pregnant women, use cautiously. In breast-feeding women, use cautiously because it's unknown if the drug appears in breast milk. In children younger than age 1 month, safety and effectiveness haven't been established.

Adverse reactions

CNS: asthenia, dizziness, fatigue, fever, headache, paresthesia, ***seizures.***
CV: *edema, hypertension,* increased clotting of arteriovenous grafts.
GI: abdominal pain and constipation in children, diarrhea, nausea, vomiting.
Hematologic: iron deficiency, thrombocytosis.
Metabolic: ***hyperkalemia,*** hyperphosphatemia, hyperuricemia.
Musculoskeletal: *arthralgia.*
Respiratory: cough, shortness of breath.
Skin: rash, urticaria.
Other: injection-site reaction.

Interactions

None significant.

Effects on lab test results

- May increase BUN, creatinine, uric acid, potassium, phosphate, and hemoglobin levels and hematocrit.
- May increase platelet count.

Pharmacokinetics

Absorption: After subcutaneous use, systemic absorption is delayed, incomplete, and variable compared with I.V. use.

Distribution: Unknown.
Metabolism: Unknown.
Excretion: Unknown. *Half-life:* 4 to 13 hours.

Route	Onset	Peak	Duration
I.V.	1 wk	Immediate	Unknown
SubQ	1–6 wk	5–24 hr	Unknown

Action

Chemical effect: Mimics effects of erythropoietin, a naturally occurring hormone produced by the kidneys. It functions as both growth and differentiating factors, enhancing the rate of RBC production.
Therapeutic effect: Corrects anemia.

Available forms

Injection: 2,000 units/ml, 3,000 units/ml, 4,000 units/ml, 10,000 units/ml, 20,000 units/ml, 40,000 units/ml

NURSING PROCESS

Assessment

- Assess patient's CBC and blood pressure before starting therapy.
- Assess effectiveness by monitoring CBC results. Suggested target hemoglobin range is 10 to 12 g/dl. Hematocrit may rise and cause excessive clotting. Watch for evidence of blood clot formation, such as shortness of breath and cold, swollen, or pulseless limb.
- Patient's response depends on amount of endogenous erythropoietin. Patients with 500 units/L or more usually have transfusion-dependent anemia and probably won't respond to drug. Those with levels below 500 units/L usually respond well.
- Before and during therapy, monitor patient's serum iron level. Most patients need supplemental iron to support erythropoiesis.
- Monitor blood pressure closely. Up to 80% of patients with chronic renal impairment have hypertension. Blood pressure may rise, especially when hematocrit is increasing in early part of therapy.
- After injection (usually within 2 hours), some patients complain of pain or discomfort in their limbs (long bones) and pelvis and of coldness and sweating. Symptoms may persist for up to 12 hours and then disappear.
- If adverse GI reaction occurs, monitor patient's hydration.
- Assess patient's and family's knowledge of drug therapy.

Nursing diagnoses

- Ineffective protection related to reduced production of endogenous erythropoietin
- Risk for deficient fluid volume related to drug-induced adverse GI reactions
- Deficient knowledge related to drug therapy

Planning and implementation

- When used in an HIV-infected patient, individualize the dose based on response. Dosage recommendations are for patients with endogenous erythropoietin levels of 500 units/L or less and cumulative zidovudine doses of 4.2 g per week or less.
- Patient may need additional heparin to prevent clotting during dialysis.
- Start diet restrictions or drug therapy to control blood pressure.

Patient teaching

- Advise patient that blood specimens will be drawn weekly for blood counts and that dose adjustments may be made based on results.
- Warn patient to avoid hazardous activities, such as driving or operating heavy machinery, early in therapy; excessively rapid rise in hematocrit may increase the risk of seizures.
- Tell patient to notify prescriber if adverse reactions occur.

Evaluation

- Patient's blood count is normal.
- Patient maintains adequate hydration throughout therapy.
- Patient and family state understanding of drug therapy.

eprosartan mesylate

(eh-proh-SAR-ten MEH-sih-layt)
Teveten

Pharmacologic class: angiotensin II receptor antagonist
Therapeutic class: antihypertensive
Pregnancy risk category: C (D in second and third trimesters)

Indications and dosages

▶ **Hypertension.** *Adults:* Initially 600 mg P.O. daily. Daily dosage ranges from 400 to 800 mg given as single daily dose or two divided doses. Drug can be given alone or with other antihypertensives.

Contraindications and cautions

- Contraindicated in patients hypersensitive to drug or any of its components.
- Use cautiously in patients with an activated renin-angiotensin system, such as volume- or salt-depleted patients, and in patients whose renal function may depend on the activity of the renin-angiotensin-aldosterone system, such as patients with severe heart failure.
- Use cautiously in patients with renal artery stenosis.

Lifespan: In pregnant and breast-feeding women, drug is contraindicated. In children, safety and effectiveness haven't been established. In elderly patients, use cautiously because of decreased response to drug.

Adverse reactions

CNS: depression, dizziness, fatigue, headache.
CV: chest pain, dependent edema, hypertriglyceridemia.
EENT: pharyngitis, rhinitis, sinusitis.
GI: abdominal pain, diarrhea, dyspepsia.
GU: UTI.
Hematologic: ***neutropenia.***
Musculoskeletal: arthralgia, myalgia.
Respiratory: bronchitis, cough, upper respiratory tract infection.
Other: injury, viral infection.

Interactions

None significant.

Effects on lab test results

- May increase BUN and triglyceride levels. May decrease hemoglobin level and hematocrit.
- May decrease neutrophil count.

Pharmacokinetics

Absorption: Absolute bioavailability of single oral dose is about 13%.
Distribution: About 98% protein-bound.
Metabolism: No active metabolites.
Excretion: Eliminated by biliary and renal excretion. *Half-life:* 5 to 9 hours.

Route	Onset	Peak	Duration
P.O.	1–2 hr	1–3 hr	24 hr

Action

Chemical effect: Blocks vasoconstrictor and aldosterone-secreting effects of angiotensin II by selectively blocking binding of angiotensin II to its receptor sites in many tissues, such as vascular smooth muscle and the adrenal gland.
Therapeutic effect: Lowers blood pressure.

Available forms

Tablets: 400 mg, 600 mg

NURSING PROCESS

Assessment

- Monitor blood pressure closely at start of therapy. If hypotension occurs, place patient in supine position and give normal saline solution I.V.
- Determine patient's fluid balance and sodium level before starting drug therapy.
- In elderly patients, watch for a slightly decreased response to drug.
- Be alert for adverse reactions.
- Assess patient's and family's knowledge of drug therapy.

Nursing diagnoses

- Risk for injury related to presence of hypertension
- Risk for infection related to neutropenia
- Deficient knowledge related to drug therapy

Planning and implementation

- Correct hypovolemia and hyponatremia before starting therapy to reduce risk of symptomatic hypotension.
- A transient episode of hypotension isn't cause for stopping therapy altogether. Restart once patient's blood pressure is stabilized.
- Drug may be used alone or with other antihypertensives, such as diuretics and calcium channel blockers. Maximum blood pressure response may take 2 to 3 weeks.
- Monitor patient for facial or lip swelling because angioedema has occurred with other angiotensin II antagonists.

Patient teaching

- Advise woman of childbearing age to use reliable contraception and to notify prescriber immediately if pregnancy is suspected. Drug will need to be stopped under medical supervision.
- Advise patient to report facial or lip swelling and signs and symptoms of infection, such as fever or sore throat.
- Tell patient to notify prescriber before taking OTC product to treat a dry cough.
- Inform patient that drug may be taken without regard to meals.
- Tell patient to store drug at a controlled room temperature (68° to 77° F [20° to 25° C]).

Evaluation

- Patient's blood pressure is well controlled, and patient remains free of injury.
- WBC count is normal.
- Patient and family state understanding of drug therapy.

eptifibatide

(ep-tih-FIH-beh-tide)
Integrilin

Pharmacologic class: glycoprotein IIb/IIIa inhibitor
Therapeutic class: antiplatelet
Pregnancy risk category: B

Indications and dosages

▶ **Acute coronary syndrome (unstable angina or non–ST segment elevation MI) in patients with serum creatinine level below 2 mg/dl, being managed medically and in those undergoing percutaneous coronary intervention (PCI).** *Adults:* 180 mcg/kg I.V. bolus as soon as possible after diagnosis, followed by a continuous I.V. infusion of 2 mcg/kg per minute until hospital discharge or start of coronary artery bypass graft surgery, up to 72 hours. If undergoing PCI, continue infusion until hospital discharge, or for up to 18 to 24 hours after the procedure, whichever comes first, up to 96 hours. Give patients weighing more than 121 kg (267 lb) a maximum bolus of 22.6 mg followed by a maximum infusion rate of 15 mg/hour.

Adjust-a-dose: For adults with creatinine clearance less than 50 ml/minute or a creatinine level between 2 and 4 mg/dl, give 180 mcg/kg I.V. bolus as soon as possible after diagnosis, followed by an infusion rate of 1 mcg/kg per minute. For patients weighing more than 121 kg (267 lb), the maximum bolus dose is 22.6 mg and the maximum infusion rate is 7.5 mg/hour.

▶ **Patients with serum creatinine level below 2 mg/dl, undergoing PCI.** *Adults:* 180 mcg/kg I.V. bolus given immediately before the procedure, immediately followed by an infusion of 2 mcg/kg/minute and a second I.V. bolus of 180 mcg/kg given 10 minutes after the first bolus. Continue infusion until hospital discharge or for up to 18 to 24 hours, whichever comes first; a minimum of 12 hours of eptifibatide infusion is recommended. Give patients weighing more than 121 kg a maximum bolus of 22.6 mg followed by a maximum of 15 mg/hour.

Adjust-a-dose: For adults with creatinine clearance less than 50 ml/minute or a creatinine level between 2 and 4 mg/dl, give 180 mcg/kg immediately before the procedure, immediately followed by an infusion of 1 mcg/kg per minute and a second bolus of 180 mcg/kg given 10 minutes after the first bolus. Give patients weighing more than 121 kg a maximum of 22.6 mg/bolus followed by a maximum rate of 7.5 mg/hour.

I.V. administration

- Drug is intended for use with heparin and aspirin.
- Inspect solution for particulate matter before use. If particles are visible, sterility is suspect. Discard the solution.
- Drug may be given in same I.V. line with normal saline solution or normal saline and 5% dextrose; main infusion may also contain up to 60 mEq/L of potassium chloride.
- Drug may be given in same I.V. line as alteplase, atropine, dobutamine, heparin, lidocaine, meperidine, metoprolol, midazolam, morphine, nitroglycerin, or verapamil.
- When obtaining I.V. access, avoid use of noncompressible sites (such as subclavian or jugular veins).
- Withdraw bolus dose from 10-ml vial into a syringe and give by I.V. push over 1 to 2 minutes. Give I.V. infusion undiluted directly from 100-ml vial using an infusion pump.

• If patient needs thrombolytic therapy, stop infusion.

• Refrigerate vials at 36° to 46° F (2° to 8° C). Protect from light until use. Discard any unused solution left in vial.

⊗ **Incompatibility**

Furosemide.

Contraindications and cautions

• Contraindicated in patients hypersensitive to drug or its components and in those with a history of bleeding diathesis, evidence of active abnormal bleeding within previous 30 days, severe hypertension (systolic blood pressure over 200 mm Hg or diastolic blood pressure over 110 mm Hg) not adequately controlled with antihypertensives, major surgery within previous 6 weeks, history of stroke within 30 days, history of hemorrhagic stroke, current or planned use of another parenteral glycoprotein IIb/IIIa inhibitor, or platelet count below 100,000/mm^3. Also contraindicated in patients whose creatinine level is 2 mg/dl or higher (for the 180-mcg/kg bolus and 2-mcg/kg/minute infusion) or 4 mg/dl or higher (for the 135-mcg/kg bolus and 0.5-mcg/kg/minute infusion) and in patients dependent on dialysis.

Lifespan: In pregnant women, use cautiously. In breast-feeding women, use cautiously because it's unknown if the drug appears in breast milk. In children, safety and effectiveness haven't been established.

Adverse reactions

CV: hypotension.
GU: hematuria.
Hematologic: BLEEDING, *thrombocytopenia.*
Other: bleeding at femoral artery access site.

Interactions

Drug-drug. *Clopidogrel, dipyridamole, NSAIDs, warfarin, thrombolytics, ticlopidine:* May increase risk of bleeding. Monitor patient closely.

Glycoprotein IIb/IIIa inhibitors: May increase risk of serious bleeding. Don't give together.

Effects on lab test results

• May decrease platelet count.

Pharmacokinetics

Absorption: Given I.V.
Distribution: 25% protein-bound.
Metabolism: None reported. No major metabolites are detected.
Excretion: 50% of drug is excreted in urine. *Half-life:* 2½ hours.

Route	Onset	Peak	Duration
I.V.	Immediate	Immediate	4–6 hr after therapy

Action

Chemical effect: Reversibly binds to the glycoprotein IIb/IIIa receptor on human platelets and inhibits platelet aggregation.
Therapeutic effect: Prevents clot formation.

Available forms

Injection: 10-ml (2 mg/ml), 100-ml (0.75 mg/ml, 2 mg/ml) vials

NURSING PROCESS

Assessment

• Obtain history of patient's underlying medical conditions, especially conditions that increase risk of bleeding.

• Obtain accurate patient weight. Use drug cautiously in patients weighing more than 143 kg (315 lb).

• Determine creatinine and hemoglobin levels, hematocrit, platelet count, PT, INR, and PTT before start of therapy and regularly thereafter.

• Monitor patient for bleeding.

• Assess patient's and family's knowledge of drug therapy.

Nursing diagnoses

• Ineffective cardiopulmonary tissue perfusion related to presence of acute coronary syndrome

• Risk for injury related to increased bleeding tendencies

• Deficient knowledge related to drug therapy

Planning and implementation

• Stop this drug and heparin, and achieve sheath hemostasis by standard compressive techniques at least 4 hours before hospital discharge.

• In patients undergoing coronary artery bypass graft surgery, stop infusion before surgery.

• Minimize use of arterial and venous punctures, I.M. injections, urinary catheters, and nasotracheal and nasogastric tubes.

• If platelet count is less than 100,000/mm^3, notify prescriber and stop both this drug and heparin.

Patient teaching

• Explain that drug is a blood thinner used to prevent heart attack.
• Explain that the benefits of the drug far outweigh the risk of serious bleeding.
• Instruct patient to report chest discomfort or other adverse events immediately.

Evaluation

• Patient maintains adequate cardiopulmonary tissue perfusion.
• Patient has no life-threatening bleeding episode.
• Patient and family state understanding of drug therapy.

erlotinib

(ur-LOE-tih-nib)
Tarceva

Pharmacologic class: human epidermal growth factor receptor 1 (HER1)/epidermal growth factor receptor (EGFR)–tyrosine kinase inhibitor
Therapeutic class: antineoplastic
Pregnancy risk category: D

Indications and dosages

▶ **Locally advanced or metastatic non–small-cell lung cancer after failure of at least one other chemotherapeutic agent.** *Adults:* 150 mg P.O. once daily taken at least 1 hour before or 2 hours after meals. Continue until disease progresses or intolerable toxicity occurs.

▶ **First line treatment of locally advanced, unresectable or metastatic pancreatic cancer in combination with gemcitabine.** *Adults:* 100 mg P.O. once daily taken at least 1 hour before or 2 hours after meals. Continue until disease progression or intolerable toxicity occurs.

Adjust-a-dose: In patients with severe skin reactions or severe diarrhea refractory to loperamide, reduce dosage in 50-mg decrements or stop therapy.

Contraindications and cautions

• Use cautiously in patients with pulmonary disease or liver impairment and those who have received or are receiving chemotherapy because it may worsen adverse pulmonary effects.

Lifespan: In pregnant women, use only if benefits outweigh risks to fetus. If patient becomes pregnant during therapy, drug may harm fetus and increase risk of miscarriage. Women shouldn't breast-feed while taking this drug. In children, safety and effectiveness haven't been established.

Adverse reactions

CNS: *fatigue.*
EENT: *conjunctivitis, keratoconjuctivitis sicca.*
GI: abdominal pain, *anorexia, diarrhea, nausea,* stomatitis, *vomiting.*
Respiratory: cough, dyspnea, ***pulmonary toxicity.***
Skin: *acne, dry skin,* pruritus, *rash.*
Other: *infection.*

Interactions

Drug-drug. *Anticoagulants, such as warfarin:* May increase risk of bleeding. Monitor PT and INR.
Atazanavir, clarithromycin, indinavir, itraconazole, ketoconazole, nefazodone, nelfinavir, ritonavir, saquinavir, telithromycin, troleandomycin, voriconazole: May decrease erlotinib metabolism. Use together cautiously, and consider reducing erlotinib dosage.
Carbamazepine, phenobarbital, phenytoin, rifabutin, rifampicin: May increase erlotinib metabolism. Erlotinib dosage may need to be increased.
Drug-herb. *St. John's wort:* May increase erlotinib metabolism. Erlotinib dosage may need to be increased. Discourage use together.

Effects on lab test results

• May increase ALT, AST, and bilirubin levels.
• May increase PT and INR.

Pharmacokinetics

Absorption: About 60%.
Distribution: About 93% protein-bound to albumin and alpha$_1$-acid glycoprotein.
Metabolism: Mainly by CYP3A4 and partly by CYP1A2 and CYP1A1.
Excretion: 83% in feces. *Half-life:* 36 hours.

Route	Onset	Peak	Duration
P.O.	Unknown	4 hr	Unknown

Action

Chemical effect: Probably inhibits tyrosine kinase activity in EGFR, which is expressed on the surface of normal and cancer cells, and is particularly selective for HER1.
Therapeutic effect: Increases survival of patients with locally advanced or metastatic non–small-cell lung cancer.

Available forms

Tablets: 25 mg, 100 mg, 150 mg

NURSING PROCESS

Assessment

- Assess patient's underlying condition before therapy.
- Monitor liver function tests periodically during therapy. If values change dramatically, consider reducing dosage or stopping drug.
- Monitor patient for severe diarrhea, and give loperamide if needed.
- Assess patient's and family's knowledge of drug therapy.

Nursing diagnoses

- Ineffective health maintenance related to presence of neoplastic disease
- Risk for deficient fluid volume related to drug-induced adverse GI reactions
- Deficient knowledge related to drug therapy

Planning and implementation

- Rarely, serious interstitial lung disease may occur. If patient develops dyspnea, cough, or fever, withhold therapy. Stop drug if interstitial lung disease develops.
- Overdose may cause diarrhea, rash, and liver transaminase elevations. If overdose occurs, withhold drug and treat symptoms.

Patient teaching

- Tell woman of childbearing age to use contraception while taking drug and for 2 weeks afterward.
- Tell patient to immediately report new or worsened cough, shortness of breath, eye irritation, or severe or persistent diarrhea, nausea, anorexia, or vomiting.
- Instruct patient to take drug 1 hour before or 2 hours after food.
- Explain the likelihood of serious interactions with other drugs and herbal supplements and the need to tell prescriber about any change in drugs and supplements taken.

Evaluation

- Patient responds to drug therapy.
- Patient maintains adequate hydration.
- Patient and family state understanding of drug therapy.

E

ertapenem sodium

(ur-tah-PEN-uhm SOH-dee-um)
Invanz

Pharmacologic class: carbapenem
Therapeutic class: antibiotic
Pregnancy risk category: B

Indications and dosages

▶ **Complicated intra-abdominal infections caused by *Escherichia coli, Clostridium clostridioforme, Eubacterium lentum, Peptostreptococcus,* or *Bacteroides fragilis, distasonis, ovatus, thetaiotaomicron,* or *uniformis*.** *Adults and children age 13 and older:* 1 g I.V. or I.M. once daily for 5 to 14 days.
Infants and children age 3 months to 12 years: 15 mg/kg I.V. q 12 hours for 5 to 14 days. Don't exceed 1 g daily.

▶ **Complicated skin and skin-structure infections, including diabetic foot infection without osteomyelitis, caused by *Staphylococcus aureus* (methicillin-susceptible strains), *Streptococcus agalactiae, Streptococcus pyogenes, E. coli, Klebsiella pneumoniae, Proteus mirabilis, B. fragilis, Peptostreptococcus* species, *Porphyromonas asaccharolytica,* or *Prevotella bivia*.** *Adults and children age 13 and older:* 1 g I.M. or I.V. over 30 minutes once daily for 7 to 14 days. Diabetic foot infection may need up to 28 days of treatment.
Infants and children age 3 months to 12 years: 15 mg/kg I.M. or I.V. over 30 minutes q 12 hours for 7 to 14 days. Don't exceed 1 g daily.

▶ **Community-acquired pneumonia caused by *Streptococcus pneumoniae* (penicillin-susceptible strains), *Haemophilus influenzae* (beta-lactamase–negative strains), or *Moraxella catarrhalis*.** *Adults and children age 13 and older:* 1 g I.V. or I.M. once daily for 10 to 14 days. If improvement occurs after at least

3 days of therapy, appropriate oral therapy may be used to complete the full course of therapy.
Infants and children age 3 months to 12 years: 15 mg/kg I.V. q 12 hours for 10 to 14 days. Don't exceed 1 g daily. If patient improves after at least 3 days of treatment, use appropriate oral therapy to complete the full course of treatment.

▶ **Complicated UTI, including pyelonephritis, caused by *E. coli* or *K. pneumoniae*.** *Adults and children age 13 and older:* 1 g I.V. or I.M. once daily for 10 to 14 days. If improvement occurs after at least 3 days, appropriate oral therapy may be used to complete the full course of therapy.
Infants and children age 3 months to 12 years: 15 mg/kg I.V. q 12 hours for 10 to 14 days. Don't exceed 1 g daily. If patient improves after at least 3 days of treatment, use appropriate oral therapy to complete the full course of treatment.

▶ **Acute pelvic infections, including postpartum endomyometritis, septic abortion, and postsurgical gynecologic infections caused by *S. agalactiae, E. coli, B. fragilis, Peptostreptococcus* species, or *P. bivia*.** *Adults and children age 13 and older:* 1 g I.V. or I.M. once daily for 3 to 10 days.
Infants and children age 3 months to 12 years: 15 mg/kg I.V. q 12 hours for 3 to 10 days. Don't exceed 1 g daily.

Adjust-a-dose: In adults, if creatinine clearance is 30 ml/minute or less, give 500 mg daily. A supplemental dose of 150 mg is recommended after a hemodialysis session only in patients who receive the recommended daily ertapenem dose of 500 mg within 6 hours before hemodialysis. If ertapenem is given 6 hours or more before hemodialysis, no supplemental dose is needed.

I.V. administration

• Reconstitute the contents of a 1-g drug vial with 10 ml of water for injection, normal saline injection, or bacteriostatic water for injection. Don't use diluents containing dextrose. Shake well to dissolve, and immediately transfer contents of the reconstituted vial to 50 ml of normal saline injection.
• Infuse over 30 minutes. Complete the infusion within 6 hours of reconstitution.
• Don't store lyophilized powder above 77° F (25° C).
• Reconstituted solution, immediately diluted in normal saline injection, may be stored at room temperature and used within 6 hours or stored for 24 hours under refrigeration (41° F [5° C]) and used within 4 hours after removal from refrigeration. Don't freeze solutions of ertapenem.

⊗ **Incompatibilities**

Diluents containing dextrose (alpha-D-glucose), other I.V. drugs.

Contraindications and cautions

• Contraindicated in patients hypersensitive to the drug or any of its components or to other drugs in the same class; also contraindicated in patients who have had anaphylactic reactions to beta-lactams. I.M. use is contraindicated in patients hypersensitive to local anesthetics of the amide type. (Lidocaine hydrochloride is used as the diluent.)
• Use cautiously in patients with CNS disorders or compromised renal function because seizures may occur. Ertapenem sodium may be removed by hemodialysis, if needed.

Lifespan: In pregnant women, use only if benefits outweigh risks to the fetus. In breast-feeding women, drug appears in breast milk. In elderly patients with renal impairment, select dose carefully and monitor renal function.

Adverse reactions

CNS: altered mental status, anxiety, asthenia, dizziness, fatigue, fever, headache, insomnia, pain, ***seizures***.
CV: chest pain, edema, hypertension, hypotension, swelling, tachycardia.
EENT: pharyngitis.
GI: abdominal distention, abdominal pain, acid regurgitation, constipation, *diarrhea,* dyspepsia, oral candidiasis, nausea, ***pseudomembranous colitis,*** *vomiting.*
GU: hematuria, renal dysfunction, urine retention, vaginitis.
Hematologic: anemia, coagulation abnormalities, eosinophilia, ***leukopenia, neutropenia, thrombocytopenia,*** thrombocytosis.
Hepatic: jaundice.
Metabolic: hyperglycemia, ***hyperkalemia,*** hypernatremia.
Musculoskeletal: leg pain.
Respiratory: cough, crackles, dyspnea, ***respiratory distress,*** rhonchi.
Skin: erythema, extravasation, infused vein complication, infusion site pain and redness, phlebitis, pruritus, rash, thrombophlebitis.

Other: chills, hypersensitivity reactions, *septicemia.*

Interactions

Drug-drug. *Probenecid:* May reduce renal clearance and increase half-life. Avoid use together.

Effects on lab test results

- May increase ALT, AST, alkaline phosphatase, BUN, creatinine, glucose, potassium, sodium, and bilirubin levels. May decrease albumin, sodium bicarbonate, and hemoglobin levels and hematocrit.
- May increase PT, PTT, eosinophil count, and urinary RBC and WBC counts. May decrease segmented neutrophil and WBC counts. May increase or decrease platelet count.

Pharmacokinetics

Absorption: Almost completely absorbed after I.M. use. Mean bioavailability of 90%.
Distribution: Highly protein-bound, mainly to albumin.
Metabolism: Doesn't inhibit metabolism mediated by any cytochrome P-450 isoforms. Stable against hydrolysis by a variety of betalactamases, including penicillinase, cephalosporinase, and extended-spectrum beta-lactamase. Hydrolyzed by metallo-beta-lactamases.
Excretion: Mainly by the kidneys. *Half-life:* 4 hours.

Route	Onset	Peak	Duration
I.V.	Immediate	30 min	24 hr
I.M.	Unknown	2 hr	24 hr

Action

Chemical effect: Inhibition of cell wall synthesis is mediated through ertapenem binding to penicillin-binding proteins.
Therapeutic effect: Kills susceptible bacteria.

Available forms

Injection: 1 g

NURSING PROCESS

Assessment

- Check for previous penicillin, cephalosporin, or other beta-lactam hypersensitivity.
- If giving I.M., check for hypersensitivity to local, amide-type anesthetics.
- Obtain specimens for culture and sensitivity testing before giving first dose. Therapy may start before results are available.
- Monitor renal, hepatic, and hematopoietic function during prolonged therapy.
- Be alert for adverse reactions, particularly diarrhea, seizures, and superinfection.
- Assess patient's and family's knowledge of drug therapy.

Nursing diagnoses

- Diarrhea related to drug-induced adverse reaction
- Ineffective health maintenance related to underlying infectious disease process
- Deficient knowledge related to anti-infective therapy

Planning and implementation

ALERT: Don't mix or infuse with other drugs.

- When giving I.M., reconstitute contents of a 1-g vial of drug with 3.2 ml of 1% lidocaine hydrochloride injection (without epinephrine). See prescribing information for lidocaine hydrochloride. Shake vial thoroughly to form solution. Immediately withdraw contents of the vial and give by deep I.M. injection into a large muscle, such as gluteal muscles or lateral part of the thigh. Use reconstituted I.M. solution within 1 hour of preparing. Don't give reconstituted solution I.V.
- Avoid inadvertent injection into a blood vessel during I.M. delivery.
- If diarrhea persists during therapy, stop drug and collect stool specimen for culture to rule out pseudomembranous colitis.
- Vomiting is more common in children than in adults.
- If allergic reaction occurs, stop drug immediately and give immediate treatment with airway management, epinephrine, oxygen, and I.V. steroids.
- Continue anticonvulsants in patients with known seizure disorders. If focal tremors, myoclonus, or seizures occur, evaluate patient neurologically and give anticonvulsants if not given before. Decrease or stop drug after reexamining dosage.
- Overdose may cause nausea, diarrhea, and dizziness. If an overdose occurs, stop drug and

treat supportively until drug has been eliminated from the body.

ALERT: Don't confuse Avinza with Invanz.

Patient teaching

- Inform patient of potential adverse reactions and urge him to notify prescriber immediately if they occur.
- Tell patient to alert prescriber if he develops diarrhea.

Evaluation

- Patient tolerates and responds well to drug therapy.
- Patient doesn't develop colitis or any other adverse reactions from drug therapy.
- Patient and family state understanding of drug therapy.

erythromycin base

(eh-rith-roh-MIGH-sin bays)

Apo-Erythro ♦, E-Base, E-Mycin, Erybid ♦, Eryc, Ery-Tab, Erythromycin Delayed-Release, Erythromycin Filmtabs, PCE Dispertab

erythromycin estolate

erythromycin ethylsuccinate

Apo-Erythro-ES ♦, E.E.S., E.E.S. Granules, EryPed, EryPed 200, EryPed 400

erythromycin lactobionate

Erythrocin Lactobionate

erythromycin stearate

Apo-Erythro-S ♦, Erythrocin Stearate

Pharmacologic class: macrolide
Therapeutic class: antibiotic
Pregnancy risk category: B

Indications and dosages

► **Acute pelvic inflammatory disease caused by *Neisseria gonorrhoeae*.** *Adults:* 500 mg erythromycin lactobionate I.V. q 6 hours for 3 days; then 250 mg erythromycin base, estolate, or stearate P.O. q 6 hours or 333 mg q 8 hours for 7 days. Or 400 mg ethylsuccinate P.O. q 6 hours for 7 days.

► **Endocarditis prophylaxis for dental procedures in patients allergic to penicillin.** *Adults:* Initially 800 mg ethylsuccinate or 1 g stearate P.O. 1 hour before procedure; then 400 mg ethylsuccinate or 500 mg stearate P.O. 6 hours later.
Children: Initially 20 mg/kg ethylsuccinate or stearate P.O. 1 hour before procedure; then 10 mg/kg 6 hours later.

► **Intestinal amebiasis.** *Adults:* 250 mg erythromycin base, estolate, or stearate, or 400 mg ethylsuccinate, P.O. q 6 hours, or 333 mg erythromycin base q 8 hours, or 500 mg q 12 hours for 10 to 14 days.
Children: 30 to 50 mg/kg erythromycin base, estolate, ethylsuccinate, or stearate P.O. daily in divided doses q 6 hours for 10 to 14 days.

► **Mild to moderately severe respiratory tract, skin, and soft-tissue infections caused by sensitive *Streptococcus pyogenes, Bordetella pertussis, Corynebacterium diphtheriae, Diplococcus pneumoniae, Listeria monocytogenes,* or *Mycoplasma pneumoniae*.** *Adults:* 250 to 500 mg erythromycin base, estolate, or stearate P.O. q 6 hours; or 400 to 800 mg erythromycin ethylsuccinate P.O. q 6 hours; or 15 to 20 mg/kg I.V. daily as continuous infusion or in divided doses q 6 hours for 10 to 21 days, depending on severity and source of infection, until oral dosage can be taken.
Children: 20 to 50 mg/kg oral erythromycin salts P.O. daily in divided doses q 6 hours; or 15 to 20 mg/kg I.V. daily in divided doses q 4 to 6 hours.

► **Syphilis.** *Adults:* 500 mg erythromycin base, estolate, or stearate P.O. q.i.d. for 15 days.

► **Legionnaires disease.** *Adults:* 1 to 4 g P.O. or I.V. daily in divided doses for 10 to 14 days.

► **Uncomplicated urethral, endocervical, or rectal infections when tetracyclines are contraindicated.** *Adults:* 500 mg erythromycin base, estolate, or stearate or 800 mg ethylsuccinate P.O. q.i.d. or 666 mg erythromycin base P.O. q 8 hours for at least 7 days.

► **Urogenital *Chlamydia trachomatis* infections during pregnancy.** *Adults:* 500 mg erythromycin base, estolate, or stearate P.O. q.i.d. or 666 mg q 8 hours for at least 7 days; or 250 mg erythromycin base, estolate, or stearate, or 333 mg q 8 hours, or 500 mg q 12 hours, or 400 mg ethylsuccinate P.O. q.i.d. for at least 14 days.

► **Conjunctivitis caused by *C. trachomatis* in neonates.** *Neonates:* 50 mg/kg P.O. daily in four divided doses for 14 days or more.

▶ **Pneumonia of infancy caused by *C. trachomatis.*** *Infants:* 50 mg/kg P.O. daily in four divided doses for at least 2 but usually 3 weeks; a second course may be needed.
▶ **Early form of Lyme disease in persons allergic to penicillins and cephalosporins and in whom tetracyclines are contraindicated‡.** *Adults and children age 8 and older:* 250 to 500 mg erythromycin base P.O. t.i.d. or q.i.d. Or 30 to 40 mg/kg P.O. daily in divided doses for 10 to 30 days.
Children younger than age 8: Give 30 to 40 mg/kg erythromycin base P.O. daily in divided doses (not to exceed adult dose) for 10 to 30 days.
▶ **Early Lyme disease manifested as erythema migrans‡.** *Adults:* 500 mg erythromycin base P.O. q.i.d. for 14 to 21 days.
Children: 12.5 mg/kg erythromycin base P.O. q.i.d. (maximum, 500 mg/dose) for 14 to 21 days.
▶ **Diarrhea caused by *Campylobacter jejuni*‡.** *Adults:* 500 mg erythromycin base P.O. q.i.d. for 7 days.
▶ **Genital, inguinal, or anorectal lymphogranuloma venereum‡.** *Adults:* 500 mg erythromycin base P.O. q.i.d. for 21 days.
▶ **Chancroid caused by *Haemophilus ducreyi*‡.** *Adults:* 500 mg P.O. t.i.d. or q.i.d. for 7 days, until ulcers or lymph nodes are healed.
▶ **Tetanus caused by *Clostridium tetani*‡.** *Adults:* 500 mg P.O. q 6 hours for 10 days.
▶ **Granuloma inguinale‡.** *Adults:* 500 mg P.O. q.i.d. for at least 21 days.

I.V. administration

- Prepare the initial solution by adding 10 ml sterile water for injection to the 500-mg vial or 20 ml diluent to the 1-g vial. All other diluents may cause precipitation. Use only preservative-free sterile water for injection. Dilute each 250 mg in at least 100 ml of normal saline solution, lactated Ringer's injection, or Normosol-R.
- Don't give by I.V. bolus.
- Infuse over 1 hour or by continuous infusion.

⊗ **Incompatibilities**
Ascorbic acid injection, colistimethate, dextrose 2.5% in half-strength Ringer's lactate, dextrose 5% in lactated Ringer's solution, dextrose 5% in normal saline solution, D_5W, dextrose 10% in water, floxacillin, furosemide, heparin sodium, linezolid, metoclopramide, dextrose 5% in Normosol-M, Ringer's injection, vitamin B complex with C. Manufacturer recommends not administering with other I.V. drugs.

Contraindications and cautions

- Contraindicated in patients hypersensitive to drug, any of its components, or other macrolides. Also contraindicated in patients taking pimozide. Erythromycin estolate is contraindicated in patients with hepatic disease.
- Use other erythromycin salts cautiously in patients with impaired liver function.

Lifespan: In pregnant women, use cautiously. In breast-feeding women, use cautiously because the drug appears in breast milk. The American Academy of Pediatrics considers erythromycin compatible with breast-feeding. In neonates, avoid I.V.drug because it may contain benzyl alcohol.

E

Adverse reactions

CNS: dizziness, fever, headache.
CV: venous irritation or thrombophlebitis after I.V. injection, ***ventricular arrhythmias.***
EENT: hearing loss.
GI: abdominal pain and cramping, diarrhea, nausea, ***pseudomembranous colitis,*** vomiting.
Hepatic: cholestatic hepatitis.
Skin: eczema, rash, urticaria.
Other: ***anaphylaxis,*** overgrowth of nonsusceptible bacteria or fungi.

Interactions

Drug-drug. *Carbamazepine:* May increase carbamazepine level and risk of toxicity. Avoid use together.
Clindamycin, lincomycin: May be antagonistic. Don't use together.
Cyclosporine: May increase cyclosporine level. Monitor patient closely for toxicity.
Digoxin: May increase digoxin level. Monitor patient for digoxin toxicity.
Disopyramide: May increase disopyramide level; may result, in some cases, in arrhythmias and prolonged QT intervals. Monitor ECG.
Ergot alkaloids: May cause acute ergot toxicity. Monitor carefully.
HMG-CoA reductase inhibitors: May increase risk of myopathy and rhabdomyolysis. Avoid use together.
Midazolam, triazolam: May increase effects of these drugs. Monitor patient closely.

Oral anticoagulants: May increase anticoagulant effects. Monitor PT and INR closely; monitor patient for bleeding.
Strong CYP3A inhibitors (such as diltiazem or verapamil): May increase risk of life-threatening cardiac condition. Don't use together.
Tacrolimus: May increase tacrolimus level and risk of adverse reactions, such as nephrotoxicity. Use together cautiously.
Theophylline: May decrease erythromycin level and increase risk of theophylline toxicity. Use together cautiously.
Vinblastine: May increase risk of vinblastine toxicity. Use together cautiously.
Drug-herb. *Pill-bearing spurge:* May inhibit CYP3A enzymes and alter drug metabolism. Discourage use together.

Effects on lab test results

- May increase CK, ASP, ALT, alkaline phosphatase, and bilirubin levels. May decrease bicarbonate level.
- May increase eosinophil, neutrophil, and platelet counts.
- May falsely elevate urinary catecholamines, 17-hydroxycorticosterone, and 17-ketosteroids. May interfere with colorimetric assays, resulting in falsely elevated AST and ALT levels.

Pharmacokinetics

Absorption: Most erythromycin salts are absorbed in duodenum. Because erythromycin base is acid-sensitive, it must be buffered or have enteric coating to prevent destruction by gastric acid. Acid salts and esters (estolate, ethylsuccinate, and stearate) aren't affected by gastric acidity; they're unaffected or may even be enhanced by food. Give erythromycin base and stearate preparations on empty stomach.
Distribution: Widely distributed in most body tissues and fluids except CSF, where it appears at low levels. About 80% of erythromycin base and 96% of erythromycin estolate are protein-bound.
Metabolism: Partially metabolized in liver.
Excretion: Mainly unchanged in bile. *Half-life:* 1.6 hours.

Route	Onset	Peak	Duration
P.O.	Unknown	1–4 hr	Unknown
I.V.	Immediate	Immediate	Unknown

Action

Chemical effect: Inhibits bacterial protein synthesis by binding to 50S subunit of ribosome.
Therapeutic effect: Inhibits bacterial growth.

Available forms

erythromycin base
Capsules (delayed-release): 250 mg
Tablets (enteric-coated): 250 mg, 333 mg, 500 mg
Tablets (filmtabs): 250 mg, 500 mg
erythromycin estolate
Capsules: 250 mg
Oral suspension: 125 mg/5 ml, 250 mg/5 ml
erythromycin ethylsuccinate
Oral suspension: 100 mg/2.5 ml, 200 mg/5 ml, 400 mg/5 ml
Powder for oral suspension: 200 mg/5 ml, 400 mg/5ml
Tablets: 400 mg
erythromycin lactobionate
Injection: 500-mg, 1-g vials
erythromycin stearate
Tablets (film-coated): 250 mg, 500 mg

NURSING PROCESS

Assessment

- Obtain history of patient's infection before starting therapy, and reassess regularly.
- Obtain appropriate specimen for culture and sensitivity tests before starting therapy. Begin therapy pending test results.
- Be alert for adverse reactions and drug interactions.
- If adverse GI reaction occurs, monitor patient's hydration.
- Monitor liver function. Drug may increase levels of alkaline phosphatase, ALT, AST, and bilirubin. Erythromycin estolate (most frequently used of all forms of erythromycin) may cause serious hepatotoxicity in adults (reversible cholestatic jaundice). A patient who develops hepatotoxicity may react similarly to other erythromycin forms.
- If high doses given I.V., monitor patient for hearing loss.
- Assess patient's and family's knowledge of drug therapy.

Nursing diagnoses

- Risk for infection related to presence of susceptible bacteria

- Risk for deficient fluid volume related to potential for drug-induced adverse GI reactions
- Deficient knowledge related to drug therapy

Planning and implementation

ALERT: The American Heart Association no longer recommends using erythromycin to prevent bacterial endocarditis. However, practitioners who have successfully used the drug as prophylaxis in individual patients may continue to do so.

- When giving suspension, note concentration.
- For best absorption, give oral form with full glass of water 1 hour before or 2 hours after meals. Coated tablets may be taken with meals. Tell patient not to drink fruit juice with drug.
- Coated tablets or encapsulated pellets cause less GI upset; they may be more tolerable in patients who can't tolerate drug.

Patient teaching

- Tell patient how to take oral drug.
- Tell patient to take entire amount of drug exactly as prescribed, even after he feels better.
- Instruct patient to notify prescriber if adverse reaction occurs, especially nausea, abdominal pain, and fever.

Evaluation

- Patient is free from infection.
- Patient maintains adequate hydration with therapy.
- Patient and family state understanding of drug therapy.

escitalopram oxalate

(es-sigh-TAL-uh-pram OCKS-uh-layt)

Lexapro

Pharmacologic class: SSRI
Therapeutic class: anxiolytic, antidepressant
Pregnancy risk category: C

Indications and dosages

▶ **Major depressive disorder; generalized anxiety disorder.** *Adults:* Initially 10 mg P.O. daily, increasing to 20 mg, if needed, after at least 1 week.

▶ **Panic disorder‡.** *Adults:* 10 mg P.O. daily.

Adjust-a-dose: For elderly patients and those with hepatic impairment, 10 mg P.O. daily initially and as maintenance dosage.

Contraindications and cautions

- Contraindicated in patients hypersensitive to drug or its components or to citalopram. Also contraindicated within 14 days of MAO inhibitor therapy.
- Use cautiously in patients with suicidal ideation, a history of mania, seizure disorders, or renal or hepatic impairment. Also use cautiously in patients with diseases that produce altered metabolism or hemodynamic responses.

Lifespan: In pregnant women, use drug only if the benefits to the woman outweigh the risks to the fetus. Breast-feeding women should stop breast-feeding or stop drug. Drug appears in breast milk. In children, safety and effectiveness haven't been established. In elderly patients, use cautiously because they may have greater sensitivity to drug.

Adverse reactions

CNS: abnormal dreams, dizziness, fatigue, fever, *headache,* impaired concentration, *insomnia,* irritability, lethargy, light-headedness, migraine, paresthesia, *somnolence,* tremor, vertigo.
CV: chest pain, flushing, hypertension, palpitations.
EENT: blurred vision, earache, rhinitis, sinusitis, tinnitus.
GI: abdominal pain, constipation, cramps, diarrhea, dry mouth, flatulence, gastroesophageal reflux, heartburn, increased or decreased appetite, indigestion, *nausea,* vomiting.
GU: anorgasmia, *ejaculation disorder,* impotence, menstrual cramps, urinary frequency, UTI.
Metabolic: weight gain or loss.
Musculoskeletal: arthralgia, extremity pain, muscle cramps, myalgia.
Respiratory: bronchitis, cough.
Skin: increased sweating, rash.
Other: decreased libido, flulike symptoms, toothache, yawning.

Interactions

Drug-drug. *Carbamazepine:* May increase escitalopram clearance caused by cytochrome P-450 induction. Monitor patient for expected antidepressant effect, and adjust dose if needed.
Cimetidine: May increase escitalopram level. Monitor patient for adverse reactions to escitalopram.
Citalopram: May cause additive effects. Avoid use together.

CNS drugs: May cause additive effects. Use together cautiously.
Desipramine, other drugs metabolized by CYP2D6: May increase levels of these drugs. Use together cautiously.
Lithium: May enhance serotonergic effect of escitalopram. Use together cautiously, and monitor lithium level.
MAO inhibitors: May cause serious, sometimes fatal, reactions. Avoid using drug within 14 days of MAO inhibitor.
Sumatriptan: May increase serotonergic effects, leading to weakness, enhanced reflex response, and incoordination. Use these drugs together cautiously.
Tricyclic antidepressants: May increase antidepressant level. Use together cautiously. Monitor antidepressant level. Reduce antidepressant dose if needed.
Drug-lifestyle. *Alcohol use:* May increase CNS effects. Discourage using together.

Effects on lab test results

None reported.

Pharmacokinetics

Absorption: Absolute bioavailability is 80%.
Distribution: About 56% protein-bound.
Metabolism: Extensive, mainly by CYP3A4 and CYP2C19 to inactive metabolites.
Excretion: About 8% unchanged in urine. *Half-life:* 27 to 32 hours.

Route	Onset	Peak	Duration
P.O.	Unknown	5 hr	Unknown

Action

Chemical effect: May increase serotonergic activity in the CNS by inhibiting neuronal reuptake of serotonin.
Therapeutic effect: Relieves depression and anxiety.

Available forms

Oral solution: 5 mg/5 ml
Tablets: 5 mg, 10 mg, 20 mg

NURSING PROCESS

Assessment

- Obtain history of patient's medical condition before starting therapy.
- Closely monitor patients at high risk of suicide.
- Assess patient for history of drug abuse, and observe for signs of misuse or abuse.
- Assess patient's and family's knowledge of drug therapy.

Nursing diagnoses

- Ineffective coping related to underlying condition
- Interrupted family processes related to underlying condition
- Deficient knowledge related to drug therapy

Planning and implementation

- In case of overdose, establish and maintain an airway, induce vomiting, and give activated charcoal. Closely observe and monitor vital signs and cardiac health, and maintain supportive care. Dialysis isn't effective, and no known antidote exists.

ALERT: Don't confuse Lexapro with Celexa or Loxitane.

Patient teaching

- Inform patient that symptoms will improve gradually over several weeks rather than immediately.
- Tell patient to continue taking drug as prescribed even though improvement may not occur for 1 to 4 weeks.
- Tell patient to use caution while driving or operating hazardous machinery because of drug's potential to impair judgment, thinking, and motor skills.
- Advise patient to consult prescriber before taking other prescription or OTC drugs.
- Tell patient that drug may be taken in the morning or evening with or without food.
- Encourage patient to avoid alcohol while taking drug.
- Tell patient to notify prescriber if she's pregnant or breast-feeding.

Evaluation

- Patient is able to carry out activities vital to usual role performance.
- Patient doesn't experience interrupted family processes.
- Patient and family state understanding of drug therapy.

esmolol hydrochloride
(EZ-moh-lohl high-droh-KLOR-ighd)
Brevibloc

Pharmacologic class: beta blocker
Therapeutic class: antiarrhythmic
Pregnancy risk category: C

Indications and dosages

▶ **Supraventricular tachycardia; control of ventricular rate in patients with atrial fibrillation or flutter in perioperative, postoperative, or other emergent circumstances; noncompensatory sinus tachycardia when heart rate requires specific interventions.** *Adults:* Loading dose is 500 mcg/kg/minute by I.V. infusion over 1 minute, followed by 4-minute maintenance infusion of 50 mcg/kg/minute. If adequate response doesn't occur within 5 minutes, repeat loading dose and infuse 100 mcg/kg/minute for 4 minutes. Repeat loading dose and increase maintenance infusion stepwise, as needed. Maximum maintenance infusion for tachycardia is 200 mcg/kg/minute.

▶ **Management of perioperative and postoperative tachycardia or hypertension.** *Adults:* For perioperative therapy, 80 mg (about 1 mg/kg) I.V. bolus over 30 seconds, followed by 150 mcg/kg/minute I.V., if needed. Adjust infusion rate, as needed, to maximum of 300 mcg/kg/ minute. Postoperative therapy is the same as for supraventricular tachycardia, although dosages adequate for control may be as high as 300 mcg/kg/minute.

I.V. administration

- Don't give by I.V. push; use infusion-control device. The 10-mg/ml single-dose vial may be used without diluting, but injection concentrate (250 mg/ml) must be diluted to no more than 10 mg/ml before infusion. Remove 20 ml from 500 ml of D_5W, lactated Ringer's solution, or half-normal or normal saline solution, and add two ampules of drug.
- Doses greater than 200 mcg/kg/minute aren't recommended.
- When patient's heart rate becomes stable, replace drug with a longer-acting antiarrhythmic, such as propranolol, digoxin, or verapamil; 30 minutes after giving the first dose of a replacement, reduce infusion rate by 50%. Monitor patient response, and if pulse is controlled for 1 hour after giving second dose of replacement, stop infusion.
- If local reaction develops at infusion site, change to another site. Avoid using butterfly needles.
- Don't abruptly stop giving the drug because withdrawal effects may occur. If immediate withdrawal is needed, use caution.
- Drug is intended for short-term use, no longer than 48 hours.
- Watch for irritation and infiltration because extravasation may cause tissue damage or necrosis.

⊗ **Incompatibilities**
Diazepam, furosemide, procainamide, thiopental sodium, warfarin sodium, 5% sodium bicarbonate injection.

Contraindications and cautions

- Contraindicated in patients with sinus bradycardia, heart block greater than first-degree, cardiogenic shock, or overt heart failure.
- Use cautiously in patients with impaired kidney function, diabetes, or bronchospasm.

Lifespan: In pregnant women, use cautiously. In breast-feeding women, use cautiously because it's unknown if the drug appears in breast milk. In children, safety and effectiveness haven't been established.

Adverse reactions

CNS: agitation, confusion, dizziness, fatigue, headache, somnolence.
CV: HYPOTENSION, peripheral ischemia.
EENT: nasal congestion.
GI: *nausea,* vomiting.
Respiratory: ***bronchospasm,*** dyspnea, wheezing.
Other: induration at infusion site, inflammation.

Interactions

Drug-drug. *Digoxin:* May increase digoxin level by 10% to 20%. Monitor digoxin level.
Morphine: May increase esmolol level. Adjust esmolol carefully.
Prazosin: May increase the risk of orthostatic hypotension in the early phases of use together. Assist patient to stand slowly until effects are known.

Reserpine, other catecholamine-depleting drugs: May cause additive bradycardia and hypotension. Adjust esmolol carefully.
Succinylcholine: Esmolol may prolong neuromuscular blockade. Monitor patient.
Verapamil: May increase the effects of both drugs. Monitor cardiac function closely, and decrease dosages if needed.

Effects on lab test results

• May increase LDH level. May decrease hemoglobin level.

Pharmacokinetics

Absorption: Given I.V.
Distribution: Rapid. 55% protein-bound.
Metabolism: Rapid.
Excretion: By kidneys as metabolites. *Half-life:* About 9 minutes.

Route	Onset	Peak	Duration
I.V.	Immediate	30 min	< 30 min

Action

Chemical effect: Decreases heart rate, myocardial contractility, and blood pressure.
Therapeutic effect: Restores normal sinus rhythm.

Available forms

Injection: 10 mg/ml, 250 mg/ml

NURSING PROCESS

Assessment

• Obtain history of patient's arrhythmias before starting therapy.
• Monitor ECG and blood pressure continuously during infusion. Up to 50% of patients develop hypotension. Monitor patient closely, especially if blood pressure was low before therapy.
• Be alert for adverse reactions and drug interactions.
• Assess patient's and family's knowledge of drug therapy.

Nursing diagnoses

• Decreased cardiac output related to presence of arrhythmias
• Ineffective cerebral tissue perfusion related to drug-induced hypotension
• Deficient knowledge related to drug therapy

Planning and implementation

• If patient develops severe dose-related hypotension, decrease dose or stop infusion and immediately notify prescriber. Hypotension will reverse within 30 minutes.
• If patient develops symptoms of heart failure (shortness of breath, night cough, swelling of the limbs), notify prescriber.

Patient teaching

• Inform patient of need for continuous ECG, blood pressure, and heart rate monitoring to assess effectiveness of drug and detect adverse reactions.

Evaluation

• Patient regains normal cardiac output with correction of arrhythmias.
• Patient's blood pressure remains normal throughout therapy.
• Patient and family state understanding of drug therapy.

esomeprazole magnesium

(ee-soh-MEP-rah-zohl mag-NEEZ-ee-uhm)
Nexium

esomeprazole sodium

Nexium I.V.

Pharmacologic class: proton pump inhibitor
Therapeutic class: antisecretory
Pregnancy risk category: B

Indications and dosages

▶ **Gastroesophageal reflux disease (GERD), healing of erosive esophagitis.** *Adults:* 20 or 40 mg P.O. daily for 4 to 8 weeks. If symptoms persist, use for an additional 4 to 8 weeks. *Children and adolescents age 12 to 17:* Give 20 or 40 mg P.O. once daily for up to 8 weeks.

▶ **Long-term maintenance of healing in erosive esophagitis.** *Adults:* 20 mg P.O. daily for no more than 6 months.

▶ **Long-term treatment of pathological hypersecretory conditions, including Zollinger-Ellison syndrome.** *Adults:* 40 mg P.O. b.i.d. Adjust dosage based on patient response.

▶ **Eradication of *Helicobacter pylori* to reduce duodenal ulcer recurrence.** *Adults:* Combination triple therapy with esomeprazole magnesium 40 mg P.O. daily plus amoxicillin

1,000 mg P.O. b.i.d. and clarithromycin 500 mg P.O. b.i.d., all for 10 days.

▶ **Short-term treatment of GERD in patients with a history of erosive esophagitis who are unable to take drug orally.** *Adults:* 20 or 40 mg I.V. once daily by direct injection over 3 minutes or by I.V. infusion over 10 to 30 minutes for up to 10 days. Switch patient to oral therapy as soon as possible.

▶ **Reduction of risk of gastric ulcers in patients on continuous NSAID therapy.** *Adults:* 20 to 40 mg P.O. once daily for up to 6 months.

Adjust-a-dose: For patients with severe hepatic impairment, maximum dosage is 20 mg P.O. daily.

I.V. administration

• Reconstitute 20- or 40-mg vial with 5 ml of D_5W, normal saline solution, or lactated Ringer's injection, and give by I.V. bolus over 3 minutes. Or further dilute to a total volume of 50 ml and give I.V. over 10 to 30 minutes.

• Flush I.V. line with D_5W, normal saline solution, or lactated Ringer's injection before and after administration.

• Store reconstituted solution and admixture at room temperature. Use reconstituted solution within 12 hours. For admixture diluted with D_5W, give within 6 hours. If diluted with normal saline solution or lactated Ringer's injection, use within 12 hours.

⊗ **Incompatibilities**
Don't infuse with other I.V. drugs.

Contraindications and cautions

• Contraindicated in patients hypersensitive to any component of esomeprazole or omeprazole. Combination triple therapy for the eradication of *H. pylori* is contraindicated in patients hypersensitive to clarithromycin, macrolide antibiotics, amoxicillin, or penicillin.

• Use cautiously in patients with severe hepatic insufficiency.

Lifespan: In pregnant women, use only if benefits outweigh risks to the fetus. In breast-feeding women, use cautiously because it's unknown whether drug appears in breast milk. In children, safety and effectiveness haven't been established.

Adverse reactions

CNS: headache.

GI: abdominal pain, constipation, diarrhea, dry mouth, flatulence, nausea, vomiting.

Interactions

Drug-drug. *Amoxicillin, clarithromycin:* May increase esomeprazole level. Monitor patient for toxicity.

Diazepam: May decrease diazepam clearance and increase level of diazepam. Monitor patient for diazepam toxicity.

Digoxin, iron salts, ketoconazole: May interfere with drug absorption. Monitor patient closely.

Other drugs metabolized by CYP2C19: May alter esomeprazole clearance. Monitor patient closely, especially elderly patient or patient with hepatic insufficiency.

Warfarin: May prolong PT and INR causing abnormal bleeding. Monitor the patient and PT and INR carefully.

Drug-food. *Any food:* May reduce bioavailability. Advise patient to take drug 1 hour before eating.

Effects on lab test results

• May increase creatinine, uric acid, bilirubin, alkaline phosphatase, ALT, AST, potassium, sodium, thyroxine, thyroid-stimulating hormone, and hemoglobin levels and hematocrit.

• May increase WBC and platelet counts.

Pharmacokinetics

Absorption: The level following a 40-mg dose is three times higher than after a 20-mg dose. Repeated daily 40-mg doses yield systemic bioavailability of 90%; a single 40-mg dose yields 64%. Giving drug with food reduces mean level by 33% to 53%.

Distribution: About 97% protein-bound.

Metabolism: Extensive in the liver by CYP2C19 to form hydroxy and desmethyl metabolites. CYP2C19 exhibits polymorphism. About 3% of whites and 15% to 20% of Asians who lack CYP2C19 may have decreased levels. CYP3A4 metabolizes the remaining amount.

Excretion: About 80% excreted as inactive metabolites in urine. Systemic clearance of esomeprazole decreases with multiple doses. *Half-life:* 1 to 1½ hours.

Route	Onset	Peak	Duration
P.O.	Unknown	1½ hr	13–17 hr
I.V.	Unknown	Unknown	Unknown

Action

Chemical effect: Suppresses gastric secretion through proton pump inhibition. Inhibits the H^+-K^+-ATPase pump in gastric parietal cells, thereby reducing gastric acidity by blocking the final step in acid production.
Therapeutic effect: Decreases gastric acid.

Available forms

Capsules (delayed-release containing enteric-coated pellets): 20 mg, 40 mg
Powder for injection: 20 mg, 40 mg in single-use vials

NURSING PROCESS

Assessment

- Assess patient's condition before and during drug therapy. Patients with a history of gastric ulcers or those age 60 and older on continuous NSAID therapy have increased risk of gastric ulcers.
- Monitor liver function test results because drug is extensively metabolized by CYP2C19. In patients with hepatic insufficiency, drug increases liver function test values.
- Long-term therapy with omeprazole has caused atrophic gastritis. Be alert for adverse reactions.
- Assess patient's and family's knowledge of drug therapy.

Nursing diagnoses

- Impaired tissue integrity related to underlying gastroesophageal condition
- Imbalanced nutrition: less than body requirements related to decreased oral intake due to underlying gastroesophageal disorder
- Deficient knowledge related to drug therapy

Planning and implementation

- Give esomeprazole at least 1 hour before meals because food decreases the extent of absorption.
- Overdose may result in confusion, drowsiness, blurred vision, tachycardia, nausea, diaphoresis, dry mouth, and headache. Provide supportive care. Dialysis is not effective.
- Urge patient to avoid alcohol and foods that increase gastric secretions.

Patient teaching

- Tell patient to take drug exactly as prescribed and at least 1 hour before meals.
- If patient has trouble swallowing capsule, suggest that he open it, sprinkle contents into applesauce, and swallow applesauce immediately. Warn against crushing or chewing the drug pellets.
- Tell patient to report continued or worsened symptoms or any adverse reaction.

Evaluation

- Patient responds positively to drug therapy.
- Patient is able to tolerate liquids and foods orally without any nausea or vomiting.
- Patient and family state understanding of drug therapy.

estazolam

(eh-STAZ-uh-lam)

ProSom

Pharmacologic class: benzodiazepine
Therapeutic class: hypnotic
Pregnancy risk category: X
Controlled substance schedule: IV

Indications and dosages

▶ **Insomnia.** *Adults:* 1 mg P.O. at bedtime. Some patients may need 2 mg.

Adjust-a-dose: For elderly patients, give 1 mg P.O. at bedtime; use higher doses cautiously. Frail, elderly, or debilitated patients may take 0.5 mg, but this low dose may be only marginally effective.

Contraindications and cautions

- Contraindicated in patients hypersensitive to drug or any of its components.
- Use cautiously in patients with hepatic, renal, or pulmonary disease; depression; or suicidal tendencies.

Lifespan: In pregnant or breast-feeding women, drug is contraindicated. In children, safety and effectiveness haven't been established.

Adverse reactions

CNS: abnormal thinking, asthenia, daytime drowsiness, dizziness, fatigue, headache, hypokinesia, somnolence.
GI: abdominal pain, dyspepsia.
Musculoskeletal: back pain, stiffness.
Respiratory: cold symptoms, pharyngitis.

Interactions

Drug-drug. *Cimetidine, disulfiram, hormonal contraceptives, isoniazid:* May impair metabolism and clearance of benzodiazepines and prolong their half-life. Monitor patient for CNS depression.
CNS depressants, including antihistamines, benzodiazepines, opioid analgesics: May increase CNS depression. Avoid use together.
Digoxin, phenytoin: May increase levels of these drugs, resulting in toxicity. Monitor levels closely.
Fluconazole, itraconazole, ketoconazole, miconazole: May increase and prolong drug level, CNS depression, and psychomotor impairment. Don't use together.
Rifampin: May increase metabolism and clearance and decrease half-life. Watch for decreased effectiveness.
Theophylline: May act as a drug antagonist. Watch for decreased effectiveness.
Drug-herb. *Catnip, kava, lady's slipper, lemon balm, passionflower, sassafras, skullcap, valerian:* May enhance sedative effects. Discourage use together.
Drug-lifestyle. *Alcohol use:* May increase CNS and respiratory depression. Strongly discourage use together.
Smoking: May increase drug metabolism and clearance and decrease half-life. Monitor patient for decreased effectiveness.

Effects on lab test results

- May increase ALT and AST levels.

Pharmacokinetics

Absorption: Rapid and complete.
Distribution: 93% protein-bound.
Metabolism: Extensive.
Excretion: Metabolites excreted mainly in urine. *Half-life:* 10 to 24 hours.

Route	Onset	Peak	Duration
P.O.	Unknown	1–3 hr	Unknown

Action

Chemical effect: May act on limbic system and thalamus of CNS by binding to specific benzodiazepine receptors.
Therapeutic effect: Promotes sleep.

Available forms

Tablets: 1 mg, 2 mg

NURSING PROCESS

Assessment

- Obtain history of patient's sleep pattern before starting therapy, and reassess regularly.
- Monitor liver and kidney function and CBC periodically during long-term therapy.
- Be alert for adverse reactions and drug interactions.
- Watch for withdrawal symptoms. If drug is stopped suddenly, patients who have received 6 weeks of continuous therapy may experience withdrawal.
- Assess patient's and family's knowledge of drug therapy.

Nursing diagnoses

- Sleep deprivation related to underlying condition
- Risk for trauma related to drug-induced adverse CNS reactions
- Deficient knowledge related to drug therapy

Planning and implementation

- Before leaving bedside, make sure patient has swallowed drug.
- Take precautions to prevent hoarding by depressed, suicidal, or drug-dependent patient, or patient who has history of drug abuse.

Patient teaching

- Tell patient not to increase drug dose on his own, but to inform prescriber if he thinks that drug is no longer effective.
- Warn patient to avoid hazardous activities that require mental alertness or physical coordination. For inpatient (particularly elderly patient), supervise walking and raise side rails.
- Warn patient that additive depressant effects can occur if alcohol is consumed while taking drug or within 24 hours afterward.
- If patient uses a hormonal contraceptive, recommend an alternative birth-control method during therapy because drug may enhance contraceptive hormone metabolism and decrease its effect.

Evaluation

- Patient is able to sleep.
- Patient's safety is maintained.
- Patient and family state understanding of drug therapy.

estradiol (oestradiol)

(eh-stray-DYE-ol)
Alora, Climara, Esclim, Estrace, Estrace Vaginal Cream, Estraderm, Estraderm MX ◇, Estring, FemPatch, Femtran ◇, Gynodiol, Menorest ◇, Menostar, Oesclim ♦, Vivelle, Vivelle-Dot

estradiol acetate

Femring Vaginal Ring

estradiol cypionate

Depo-Estradiol

estradiol gel

EstroGel

estradiol hemihydrate

Estrasorb, Vagifem

estradiol valerate (oestradiol valerate)

Delestrogen

Pharmacologic class: hormone
Therapeutic class: estrogen replacement, antineoplastic
Pregnancy risk category: X

Indications and dosages

▶ **Vasomotor symptoms, vulvar and vaginal atrophy, hypoestrogenism from hypogonadism, castration, or primary ovarian failure.** *Adults:* 1 to 2 mg estradiol P.O. daily in cycles of 21 days on and 7 days off or cycles of 5 days on and 2 days off. Or 0.025-mg daily Esclim transdermal system applied to a clean, dry area of the trunk twice weekly. Adjust dose, if needed, after the first 2 or 3 weeks of therapy, then at 3 to 6 months, as needed. Or 1 Estraderm transdermal system delivering 0.05 mg/24 hours applied twice weekly. Or, the Vivelle transdermal system delivering either 0.05 mg/24 hours or 0.0375 mg/24 hours applied twice weekly. Or, the Climara system delivering 0.05 mg/24 hours or 0.1 mg/24 hours applied transdermally once weekly in cycles of 3 weeks on and 1 week off. Or, 1 to 5 mg estradiol cypionate I.M. q 3 to 4 weeks. Or 10 to 20 mg estradiol valerate I.M. q 4 weeks, p.r.n. Or Estrasorb topical emulsion delivering 0.05 mg estradiol/day: Apply contents of two 1.74-g foil pouches daily, using one pouch for each thigh and calf.

▶ **Atrophic vaginitis, kraurosis vulvae.** *Women:* 2 to 4 g estradiol intravaginal applications of cream daily for 1 to 2 weeks. When vaginal mucosa is restored, maintenance dosage of 1 g one to three times weekly in a cycle. Or 0.05 mg/24 hours Climara applied weekly in a cycle. Or 0.05 mg/24 hours Estraderm applied twice weekly in a cycle. Or 10 to 20 mg estradiol valerate I.M. q 4 weeks, as needed.

▶ **Palliative therapy for advanced, inoperable breast cancer.** *Men and postmenopausal women:* 10 mg estradiol P.O. t.i.d. for 3 months.

▶ **Palliative therapy for advanced inoperable prostate cancer.** *Men:* 1 to 2 mg estradiol P.O. t.i.d. Or 30 mg estradiol valerate I.M. q 1 to 2 weeks.

▶ **To prevent postmenopausal osteoporosis in high-risk patients for whom non-estrogen therapy is inappropriate.** *Women:* 0.025 mg daily Vivelle-Dot, or Alora, or 0.5 mg daily Estraderm applied to a clean, dry area of the trunk twice weekly. Or 0.025 mg daily Climara patch applied once weekly, continuously. Or 0.014 mg daily Menostar patch applied to clean, dry area of the lower abdomen once weekly.

▶ **Vasomotor symptoms.** *Women:* 0.05 mg daily Climara patch applied once weekly, continuously.

▶ **Moderate to severe vasomotor symptoms and vulvar and vaginal atrophy unresponsive to vaginal products.** *Women:* 1.25 EstroGel applied to skin in thin layer, wrist to shoulder, once daily.

Contraindications and cautions

- Contraindicated in patients with thrombophlebitis, thromboembolic disorders, estrogen-dependent neoplasia, breast or reproductive organ cancer (except as palliative therapy), or undiagnosed abnormal genital bleeding. Also contraindicated in patients with history of thrombophlebitis or thromboembolic disorders linked to estrogen use (except as palliative therapy of breast and prostate cancer) and in patients with liver dysfunction or disease.
- Use cautiously in patients with cerebrovascular or coronary artery disease, asthma, bone diseases, migraine, seizures, or cardiac or renal dysfunction and in women with strong family history of breast cancer or who have breast nod-

ules, fibrocystic disease, or abnormal mammogram findings. Use the lowest effective dose.
• This drug hasn't been approved for prevention of cognitive disorders or memory loss.
Lifespan: In pregnant and breast-feeding women, drug is contraindicated. In children, use is contraindicated except in some adolescents with pubertal delay because of risk of early epiphyseal closure, breast enlargement, vaginal cornification or bleeding, and male pubertal abnormalities.

Adverse reactions

CNS: chorea, depression, *dizziness, headache,* ***seizures.***
CV: edema, hypertension, ***thromboembolism,*** thrombophlebitis.
EENT: abdominal cramps, bloating, diarrhea, intolerance of contact lenses, worsening of myopia or astigmatism.
GI: constipation, *nausea,* ***pancreatitis,*** vomiting.
GU: altered cervical secretions, altered menstrual flow, amenorrhea, breakthrough bleeding, cervical erosion, dysmenorrhea, ***endometrial cancer,*** enlargement of uterine fibromas, impotence, testicular atrophy, vaginal candidiasis.
Hepatic: cholestatic jaundice, gallbladder disease, ***hepatic adenoma.***
Metabolic: hypercalcemia, hyperglycemia, hyperthyroidism, hypothyroidism, increased appetite, weight changes.
Respiratory: *upper respiratory infection.*
Skin: dermatitis, erythema nodosum, hair loss, melasma, pruritus, urticaria.
Other: abnormal Pap smear, ***breast cancer,*** *breast changes* (tenderness, enlargement, secretion), flulike syndrome, gynecomastia.

Interactions

Drug-drug. *Bromocriptine:* May cause amenorrhea, interfering with bromocriptine effects. Avoid use together.
Carbamazepine, phenobarbital, rifampin: May decrease estrogen effectiveness. Monitor patient closely.
Corticosteroids: May enhance effects. Monitor patient closely.
Cyclosporine: May increase risk of toxicity. Monitor cyclosporine levels often.
Dantrolene, other hepatotoxic drugs: May increase risk of hepatotoxicity. Monitor patient closely.
Hydantoins: May cause loss of seizure control and increase risk of breakthrough bleeding, spotting, and pregnancy. Monitor patient closely.
Itraconazole, ketoconazole, macrolides, ritonavir: May increase estrogen level. Watch for increased adverse effects.
Oral anticoagulants: May decrease anticoagulant effects; may need to adjust dosage. Monitor PT and INR.
Tamoxifen: May interfere with tamoxifen effectiveness. Avoid use together.
Thyroid hormones: May alter serum thyroxine and thyrotropin levels. Increase thyroid hormone dose as needed.
Topiramate: May increase estrogen metabolism and decrease effectiveness. Monitor patient closely.
Drug-herb. *St. John's wort:* May decrease estrogen level. Monitor patient for decreased effectiveness and changes in bleeding patterns.
Drug-food. *Caffeine:* May increase caffeine level. Monitor effects.
Drug-lifestyle. *Smoking:* May increase risk of CV effects. If smoking continues, may need alternative therapy. Urge patient to stop smoking.

Effects on lab test results

• May increase total T_4, thyroid-binding globulin, triglyceride, and clotting factor VII, VIII, IX, and X levels.
• May increase PT and norepinephrine-induced platelet aggregation.

Pharmacokinetics

Absorption: Well absorbed but substantially inactivated by liver after P.O. use. Absorbed rapidly and lasts days after I.M. use. Readily absorbed into systemic circulation after transdermal use.
Distribution: Highest levels in fat. About 50% to 80% protein-bound.
Metabolism: Mainly in liver.
Excretion: Mainly through kidneys. *Half-life:* Unknown.

Route	Onset	Peak	Duration
P.O., I.M., vaginal	Unknown	Unknown	Unknown
Transdermal			
Esclim	Unknown	27–30 hr	Unknown
Estrasorb	Immediate	Unknown	Unknown
EstroGel	Immediate	1 hr	24–36 hr

Action

Chemical effect: Increases synthesis of DNA, RNA, and protein and reduces release of follicle-stimulating hormone and luteinizing hormone from pituitary gland.
Therapeutic effect: Replaces estrogen in women and treats some male prostate and breast cancers.

Available forms

estradiol
Tablets (micronized): 0.5 mg, 1 mg, 1.5 mg, 2 mg
Transdermal gel: 0.06%
Transdermal patch: 0.014 mg/day, 0.025 mg/24 hours, 0.0375 mg/24 hours, 0.05 mg/24 hours, 0.06 mg/day, 0.075 mg/24 hours, 0.1 mg/24 hours
Vaginal cream (in nonliquefying base): 0.01%
Vaginal ring: 0.0075 mg/24 hours
estradiol acetate
Vaginal ring: 0.05 mg/24 hours, 0.1 mg/24 hours
estradiol cypionate
Injection (in oil): 5 mg/ml
estradiol hemihydrate
Topical emulsion: 4.35 mg hemihydrate/1.74 g; 3.48 g emulsion delivers 0.05 mg estradiol/day
Vaginal tablets: 25 mcg
estradiol valerate
Injection (in oil): 10 mg/ml, 20 mg/ml, 40 mg/ml

NURSING PROCESS

Assessment

- Obtain history of patient's underlying condition before starting therapy, and reassess regularly.
- Make sure patient has thorough physical examination before starting estrogen therapy.
- Ask patient about allergies, especially to foods or plants. Estradiol is available as aqueous solution or as solution in peanut oil; estradiol cypionate, as solution in cottonseed oil or vegetable oil; estradiol valerate, as solution in castor oil, sesame oil, or vegetable oil.
- Patient receiving long-term therapy should have yearly gynecologic and physical examinations. Periodically monitor lipid level, blood pressure, body weight, and liver function.
- Assess patient's and family's knowledge of drug therapy.

Nursing diagnoses

- Ineffective health maintenance related to underlying condition
- Ineffective tissue perfusion (cerebral, peripheral, pulmonary, or myocardial) related to drug-induced thromboembolism
- Deficient knowledge related to drug therapy

Planning and implementation

- Give oral drug at mealtimes or at bedtime (for once-daily dose) to minimize nausea.
- To give as I.M. injection, make sure drug is well-dispersed in solution by rolling vial between palms. Inject deep into large muscle. Rotate injection sites to prevent muscle atrophy. Never give drug I.V.
- Apply transdermal patch to clean, dry, hairless, intact skin on abdomen or buttocks. Don't apply to breasts, waistline, or other areas where clothing can loosen patch. When applying, ensure good contact with skin, especially around edges, and hold in place with palm for about 10 seconds. Rotate application sites.
- Begin transdermal patch 1 week after withdrawal of oral therapy, or sooner if menopausal symptoms appear before end of week.

ALERT: Risk of MI, deep vein thrombosis, invasive breast cancer, pulmonary embolism, and stroke is increased in postmenopausal women ages 50 to 79 who are being treated with estrogen and progestin. Risk of dementia is increased in postmenopausal women age 65 or older.

ALERT: EstroGel dries in 2 to 5 minutes. Avoid fire, flame, or smoking until gel is dry because gel contains alcohol.

- Because of risk of thromboembolism, stop therapy at least 1 month before procedures that increase risk of prolonged immobilization or thromboembolism, such as knee or hip surgery. If you suspect thromboembolism, withhold drug and notify prescriber.

ALERT: Estrogen preparations aren't interchangeable.

Patient teaching

- Inform patient about adverse effects of estrogen.
- Emphasize importance of regular physical examinations. In postmenopausal women, estrogen replacement therapy for longer than 5 years may increase risk of endometrial cancer. Tell patient that risk is reduced by using cyclic rather than continuous therapy and lowest dosages of

estrogen. Drug probably doesn't increase risk of breast cancer.
- Teach patient how to use vaginal cream. Tell her to wash vaginal area with soap and water before applying. Tell her to apply drug at bedtime or to lie flat for 30 minutes after application to minimize drug loss.
- Warn patient to immediately report abdominal pain; pain, numbness, or stiffness in legs or buttocks; pressure or pain in chest; shortness of breath; severe headaches; visual disturbances, such as blind spots, flashing lights, or blurriness; vaginal bleeding or discharge; breast lumps; swelling of hands or feet; yellow skin or sclera; dark urine; and light-colored stools.
- Explain to patient receiving cyclic therapy for postmenopausal symptoms that, although withdrawal bleeding may occur during week off drug, fertility hasn't been restored. Pregnancy can't occur because she hasn't ovulated.
- Teach patient using Estrasorb topical emulsion to rub into thigh and calf until thoroughly absorbed, rub excess on hands into buttocks, and let dry before covering with clothing. Tell patient to wash hands thoroughly.
- Teach patient using transdermal gel (EstroGel) to apply in a thin layer on one arm and let dry before smoking, nearing flames, dressing, or letting someone touch that arm. Recommend bathing before application to maintain full dosage.
- Tell diabetic patient to report elevated glucose test results so antidiabetic dosage can be adjusted.
- Teach woman how to perform routine breast self-examination.

☑ Evaluation
- Patient shows improvement in underlying condition.
- Patient has no thromboembolic event during therapy.
- Patient and family state understanding of drug therapy.

estradiol and norgestimate
(eh-stray-DYE-ol and nor-JESS-tih-mayt)
Prefest

estrogens, conjugated, and medroxyprogesterone
(ESS-troh-jenz, KAHN-jih-gayt-ed, and med-roks-ee-proh-JESS-ter-ohn)
Premphase, Prempro

Pharmacologic class: hormones
Therapeutic class: combined estrogen and progestin
Pregnancy risk category: X

Indications and dosages
▶ **Moderate to severe vasomotor symptoms and vulvar and vaginal atrophy caused by menopause; prevention of osteoporosis in women with an intact uterus.** *Women:* 1 mg estradiol (pink tablet) P.O. daily for 3 days; then 1 mg estradiol/0.09 mg norgestimate (white tablet) P.O. daily for 3 days (Prefest). Repeat cycle until blister card is empty. Or 0.625 mg/2.5 mg (Prempro) P.O. once daily; can increase to 0.625 mg/5 mg tablet if needed. Or 0.625 mg conjugated estrogens (maroon tablet) P.O. once daily on days 1 through 14 and 0.625 mg conjugated estrogen/5 mg medroxyprogesterone (light blue tablet) P.O. once daily (Premphase) on days 15 through 28.

Contraindications and cautions
- Contraindicated in patients hypersensitive to any component of drugs and in patients with cancer of the breast, estrogen-dependent neoplasia, undiagnosed abnormal vaginal bleeding, or active or previous thrombophlebitis or thromboembolic disorders. Hormone replacement therapy is contraindicated for cardiac disease prevention.
- Use cautiously in women who have had a hysterectomy, are overweight, or have abnormal lipid profiles, gallbladder disease, or impaired liver function.

ALERT: Don't use estrogens and progestins to prevent CV disease. The Women's Health Initiative study reported increased risks of MI, stroke, invasive breast cancer, pulmonary embolism, and deep vein thrombosis in postmenopausal women during 5 years of combination therapy.

Because of these risks, give estrogens and progestins at the lowest effective dose and for the shortest duration.

Lifespan: In women who are or may be pregnant, drug is contraindicated.

Adverse reactions

CNS: depression, dizziness, fatigue, *headache,* pain, ***seizures, stroke.***

CV: edema, ***pulmonary embolism, MI, thromboembolism.***

EENT: intolerance of contact lenses, pharyngitis, sinusitis, worsening of myopia or astigmatism.

GI: abdominal pain, flatulence, *nausea,* weight changes.

GU: decreased libido, dysmenorrhea, ***endometrial cancer,*** vaginal bleeding, vaginitis.

Hepatic: gallbladder disease, ***hepatic adenoma.***

Musculoskeletal: arthralgia, back pain, myalgia.

Respiratory: cough, upper respiratory tract infection.

Other: ***breast cancer,*** breast pain, flulike symptoms, tooth disorder, viral infection.

Interactions

Drug-drug. *Bromocriptine:* May cause amenorrhea, interfering with bromocriptine effects. Avoid use together.

Carbamazepine, phenobarbital, rifampin: May decrease effectiveness of estrogen therapy. Monitor patient closely.

Corticosteroids: May enhance effects. Monitor patient closely.

Cyclosporine: May increase risk of toxicity. Monitor cyclosporine level often.

Dantrolene, other hepatotoxic drugs: May increase risk of hepatotoxicity. Monitor patient closely.

Hydantoins: May cause loss of seizure control and increased risk of breakthrough bleeding, spotting, and pregnancy. Monitor patient closely.

Itraconazole, ketoconazole, macrolides, ritonavir: May increase estrogen level. Monitor patient for increased adverse effects.

Oral anticoagulants: May decrease anticoagulant effects. Dosage adjustments may be needed. Monitor PT and INR.

Tamoxifen: May interfere with tamoxifen effectiveness. Avoid use together.

Thyroid hormones: May alter serum thyroxine and thyrotropin levels. Increase thyroid hormone dose as needed.

Topiramate: May increase estrogen metabolism and decrease effectiveness. Monitor patient closely.

Drug-herb. *St. John's wort:* May decrease estrogen level. Watch for decreased effectiveness and changes in bleeding patterns.

Drug-food. *Caffeine:* May increase caffeine level. Monitor effects.

Drug-lifestyle. *Smoking:* May increase risk of CV effects. If smoking continues, patient may need alternative therapy. Urge patient to stop smoking.

Effects on lab test results

- May increase glucose, calcium, thyroxine-binding globulin, LDL, triglyceride, total circulating corticosteroid and sex steroid, total plasma cortisol, fibrinogen, plasminogen antigen, and blood clotting factor VII, VIII, IX, and X levels. May decrease folate, metyrapone, HDL, and antithrombin III levels.
- May increase PT, PTT, platelet aggregation time, and platelet count. May decrease T_3 resin uptake, glucose tolerance, and cortisol secretion rate.

Pharmacokinetics

Absorption: Unknown.

Distribution: Wide. Highly protein-bound.

Metabolism: Mainly metabolized in the liver.

Excretion: Mainly in urine. *Half-life:* About 16 hours for estrogens and 8 to 9 hours for progestins in postmenopausal women.

Route	Onset	Peak	Duration
P.O.			
estrogens	Unknown	Varies	Unknown
progestins	Rapid	1–2 hr	Several days

Action

Chemical effect: Circulating estrogens modulate pituitary secretion of gonadotropins, luteinizing hormone, and follicle-stimulating hormone. Estrogen-replacement therapy reduces elevated levels of these hormones in postmenopausal women. Estrogens also contribute to the reduction of the rate of bone turnover. Progestins counter estrogenic effects by decreasing the number of nuclear estradiol receptors and suppressing epithelial DNA synthesis in endometrial tissue.

Therapeutic effect: Relieves menopausal vasomotor symptoms and vaginal dryness; reduces the severity of osteoporosis.

Available forms

Prefest

Blister card of 15 pink and 15 white tablets. Pink tablets are 1 mg estradiol; white tablets are 1 mg estradiol and 0.09 mg norgestimate.

Premphase

Dial pack of 14 maroon and 14 light blue tablets. Maroon tablets are 0.625 mg estrogen; light blue tablets are 0.625 mg estrogen and 5 mg medroxyprogesterone.

Prempro

Dial pack of 28 tablets, available in these doses: 0.3 mg estrogen and 1.5 mg medroxyprogesterone, 0.45 mg and 1.5 mg, 0.625 mg and 2.5 mg, 0.625 mg and 5 mg.

NURSING PROCESS

Assessment

- Obtain history of patient's underlying condition before therapy, and reassess regularly thereafter.
- Make sure patient has a thorough physical examination before starting drug therapy.
- Assess patient's risk of venous thromboembolism.
- Assess patient's risk of cancer because hormone replacement therapy may increase the risk of breast cancer in postmenopausal women.
- Be alert for adverse reactions.
- Assess patient's and family's knowledge of drug therapy.

Nursing diagnoses

- Ineffective peripheral tissue perfusion related to drug-induced thromboembolism
- Ineffective health maintenance related to underlying condition
- Deficient knowledge related to drug therapy

Planning and implementation

ALERT: Combined product may increase risk of MI, stroke, invasive breast cancer, pulmonary embolism, and deep vein thrombosis in postmenopausal women ages 50 to 79. There's also an increased risk of probable dementia in postmenopausal women age 65 and older.

- Reassess patient at 6-month intervals to make sure treatment is still needed.
- Monitor patient for hypercalcemia if she has breast cancer and bone metastases. If severe hypercalcemia occurs, notify the prescriber and stop the drug; take the appropriate measures to reduce calcium level.

Patient teaching

- Explain the risks of estrogen therapy, including breast cancer, uterine cancer, abnormal blood clotting, gallbladder disease, heart disease, and stroke.
- Tell patient to immediately report any undiagnosed, persistent, or recurring abnormal vaginal bleeding.
- Instruct women to perform monthly breast examinations and have a yearly breast examination by a health care provider. Also recommend annual mammogram if patient is older than age 50.
- Tell patient to immediately report pain in the calves or chest, sudden shortness of breath, coughing blood, severe headache, vomiting, dizziness, faintness, changes in vision or speech, and weakness or numbness in arms or legs. These are warning signals of blood clots.
- Urge patient to report evidence of liver problems, such as yellowing of skin or eyes and upper right quadrant pain.
- Instruct patient to report pain, swelling, or tenderness in abdomen, which may indicate gallbladder problems.
- Tell patient to store drug at room temperature away from excessive heat and moisture. It remains stable for 18 months.

Evaluation

- Patient has no thromboembolic event during therapy.
- Patient's underlying condition improves.
- Patient and family state understanding of drug therapy.

estrogens, conjugated (estrogenic substances, conjugated; oestrogens, conjugated)

(ESS-troh-jenz, KAHN-jih-gayt-ed)

C.E.S. ♦, Cenestin, Enjuvia, Premarin, Premarin Intravenous

Pharmacologic class: hormone
Therapeutic class: estrogen, antineoplastic, antiosteoporotic
Pregnancy risk category: X

Indications and dosages

▶ **Abnormal uterine bleeding caused by hormonal imbalance.** *Women:* 25 mg I.V. or I.M. Repeat dose in 6 to 12 hours, if needed.

▶ **Vulvar or vaginal atrophy.** *Women:* 0.5 to 2 g cream intravaginally once daily in cycles of 3 weeks on, 1 week off. Or 0.3 mg P.O. daily.

▶ **Female castration, primary ovarian failure.** *Adults:* Initially 1.25 mg P.O. daily in cycles of 3 weeks on, 1 week off. Adjust dosage as needed.

▶ **Hypogonadism.** *Women:* 0.3 to 0.625 mg P.O. daily, given cyclically 3 weeks on, 1 week off.

▶ **Moderate to severe vasomotor symptoms with or without moderate to severe symptoms of vulvar and vaginal atrophy related to menopause.** *Women:* 0.3 mg P.O. daily, or cyclically 25 days on, 5 days off for atrophy; 0.45 mg P.O. daily for vasomotor symptoms.

▶ **Palliative therapy for inoperable prostate cancer.** *Men:* 1.25 to 2.5 mg P.O. t.i.d.

▶ **Palliative therapy for breast cancer.** *Adults:* 10 mg P.O. t.i.d. for 3 months or more.

▶ **To prevent osteoporosis in women with an increased risk but for whom non-estrogen therapy is inappropriate.** *Adults:* 0.3 to 0.625 mg P.O. daily, or cyclically, 25 days on, 5 days off.

I.V. administration

- Refrigerate before reconstituting.
- Withdraw 5 ml of air from vial before adding diluent.
- Reconstitute powder for injection with diluent provided (sterile water for injection with benzyl alcohol). Gently agitate to mix drug. Avoid shaking container.
- When giving by direct I.V. injection, give slowly to avoid flushing.

⊗ **Incompatibilities**
Acidic solutions, ascorbic acid.

Contraindications and cautions

- Contraindicated in patients with thrombophlebitis, thromboembolic disorders, estrogen-dependent neoplasia, breast or reproductive organ cancer (except for palliative therapy), or undiagnosed abnormal genital bleeding.
- Use cautiously in patients with cerebrovascular or coronary artery disease, asthma, bone disease, migraine, seizures, or cardiac, hepatic, or renal dysfunction and in women with a close family history of breast or genital tract cancer or who have breast nodules, fibrocystic disease, or abnormal mammogram findings.

Lifespan: In children and in pregnant or breast-feeding women, drug is contraindicated.

Adverse reactions

CNS: chorea, depression, dizziness, headache, lethargy, ***seizures, stroke.***
CV: edema, hypertension, ***MI, pulmonary embolism, thromboembolism,*** thrombophlebitis.
EENT: intolerance of contact lenses, worsening of myopia or astigmatism.
GI: abdominal cramps, anorexia, bloating, constipation, diarrhea, *nausea,* ***pancreatitis,*** vomiting.
GU: altered cervical secretions, altered menstrual flow, amenorrhea, breakthrough bleeding, cervical erosion, dysmenorrhea, ***endometrial cancer,*** enlargement of uterine fibromas, impotence, testicular atrophy, vaginal candidiasis.
Hepatic: cholestatic jaundice, gallbladder disease, ***hepatic adenoma.***
Metabolic: hypercalcemia, hyperglycemia, increased appetite, weight changes.
Skin: dermatitis, erythema nodosum, flushing (with rapid I.V. use), hair loss, hirsutism, melasma, urticaria.
Other: ***breast cancer,*** breast changes (tenderness, enlargement, secretion), gynecomastia.

Interactions

Drug-drug. *Bromocriptine:* May cause amenorrhea, interfering with bromocriptine effects. Avoid use together.

Carbamazepine, phenobarbital, rifampin: May decrease estrogen effectiveness. Monitor patient closely.
Corticosteroids: May enhance effects. Monitor patient closely.
Cyclosporine: May increase risk of toxicity. Monitor cyclosporine level often.
Dantrolene, other hepatotoxic drugs: May increase risk of hepatotoxicity. Monitor patient closely.
Hydantoins: May cause loss of seizure control and increased risk of breakthrough bleeding, spotting, and pregnancy. Monitor patient closely.
Itraconazole, ketoconazole, macrolides, ritonavir: May increase estrogen level. Monitor patient for increased adverse effects.
Oral anticoagulants: May decrease anticoagulant effects. Dosage adjustments may be needed. Monitor PT and INR.
Tamoxifen: May interfere with tamoxifen effectiveness. Avoid use together.
Thyroid hormones: May alter serum thyroxine and thyrotropin levels. Increase thyroid hormone dose as needed.
Topiramate: May increase estrogen metabolism and decrease effectiveness. Monitor patient closely.
Drug-herb. *St. John's wort:* May decrease estrogen level. Watch for decreased effectiveness and changes in bleeding patterns.
Drug-food. *Caffeine:* May increase caffeine level. Monitor effects.
Drug-lifestyle. *Smoking:* May increase risk of CV effects. If smoking continues, consider alternative therapy. Urge patient to stop smoking.

Effects on lab test results

- May increase glucose, calcium, total T_4, thyroid-binding globulin, phospholipid, triglyceride, and clotting factor VII, VIII, IX, and X levels.
- May increase PT and norepinephrine-induced platelet aggregation.

Pharmacokinetics

Absorption: Rapid, continuing for days after I.M. use.
Distribution: Highest levels in fat. About 50% to 80% protein-bound.
Metabolism: Mainly in liver.
Excretion: Mostly through kidneys. *Half-life:* Unknown.

Route	Onset	Peak	Duration
P.O., I.V., I.M., vaginal	Unknown	Unknown	Unknown

Action

Chemical effect: Increases synthesis of DNA, RNA, and protein in responsive tissues; also reduces release of follicle-stimulating hormone and luteinizing hormone from pituitary gland.
Therapeutic effect: Provides estrogen replacement, relieves vasomotor menopausal symptoms and vaginal dryness, helps prevent severity of osteoporosis, and provides palliation for prostate and breast cancer.

Available forms

Injection: 25 mg/5 ml
Tablets: 0.3 mg, 0.45 mg, 0.625 mg, 0.9 mg, 1.25 mg
Vaginal cream: 0.625 mg/g

NURSING PROCESS

Assessment

- Obtain history of patient's underlying condition before starting therapy, and reassess regularly.
- Make sure patient has thorough physical examination before starting estrogen therapy.
- Patient receiving long-term therapy should have yearly examinations. Periodically monitor lipid levels, blood pressure, body weight, and liver function.
- Be alert for adverse reactions and drug interactions.
- Assess patient's and family's knowledge of drug therapy.

Nursing diagnoses

- Ineffective health maintenance related to underlying condition
- Ineffective tissue perfusion (cerebral, peripheral, pulmonary, or myocardial) related to drug-induced thromboembolism
- Deficient knowledge related to drug therapy

Planning and implementation

- Give oral forms at mealtimes or at bedtime (for once-daily dose) to minimize nausea.
- When giving I.M., inject deep into large muscle. Rotate injection sites to prevent muscle atrophy.

• Use I.M. or I.V. to rapidly treat dysfunctional uterine bleeding or to reduce surgical bleeding.
• Because of risk of thromboembolism, stop therapy at least 1 month before procedures that may prolong immobilization, such as knee or hip surgery. If thromboembolism is suspected, withhold drug, notify prescriber, and provide supportive care.
ALERT: Estrogens aren't interchangeable.

Patient teaching

• Inform patient about adverse effects.
• Emphasize importance of regular physical examinations. In postmenopausal women, using the drug for longer than 5 years may increase risk of endometrial carcinoma. This risk is reduced by using cyclic rather than continuous therapy and lowest dosages. Drug probably doesn't increase risk of breast cancer.
• Teach patient how to use vaginal cream. Tell her to wash vaginal area with soap and water before applying. Tell her to apply drug at bedtime or to lie flat for 30 minutes after application to minimize drug loss.
• Explain to patient on cyclic therapy for postmenopausal symptoms that, although withdrawal bleeding may occur during week off drug, fertility hasn't been restored. Pregnancy can't occur because she hasn't ovulated.
• Warn patient to immediately report abdominal pain; pain, numbness, or stiffness in legs or buttocks; pressure or pain in chest; shortness of breath; severe headaches; visual disturbances, such as blind spots, flashing lights, or blurriness; vaginal bleeding or discharge; breast lumps; swelling of hands or feet; yellow skin or sclera; dark urine; and light-colored stools.
• Tell diabetic patient to report elevated glucose test results so antidiabetic dosage can be adjusted.
• Teach woman how to perform routine breast self-examination.

Evaluation

• Patient shows improvement in underlying condition.
• Patient has no thromboembolic event during therapy.
• Patient and family state understanding of drug therapy.

estrogens, esterified

(ESS-troh-jenz, ESS-tehr-eh-fighd)
Estratab, Menest, Neo-Estrone

Pharmacologic class: hormone
Therapeutic class: antineoplastic, estrogen
Pregnancy risk category: X

Indications and dosages

▶ **Inoperable prostate cancer.** *Men:* 1.25 to 2.5 mg P.O. t.i.d.
▶ **Breast cancer with metastasis.** *Men and postmenopausal women:* 10 mg P.O. t.i.d. for 3 or more months.
▶ **Hypogonadism.** *Women*: 2.5 to 7.5 mg P.O. daily in divided doses in cycles of 20 days on, 10 days off.
▶ **Female castration, primary ovarian failure.** *Women:* 2.5 mg P.O. daily to t.i.d. in cycles of 3 weeks on, 1 week off.
▶ **Vasomotor menopausal symptoms.** *Women:* Average dosage is 1.25 mg P.O. daily in cycles of 3 weeks on, 1 week off.
▶ **Atrophic vaginitis or urethritis.** *Women:* 0.3 to 1.25 mg P.O. daily in cycles of 3 weeks on, 1 week off.
▶ **Prevention of osteoporosis in women at significant risk for whom non-estrogen therapy is inappropriate.** *Women:* Initially 0.3 mg P.O. daily; may increase to maximum, 1.25 mg daily.

Contraindications and cautions

• Contraindicated in patients with breast cancer (except when metastatic disease is present), estrogen-dependent neoplasia, active thrombophlebitis or thromboembolic disorders, undiagnosed abnormal genital bleeding, hypersensitivity to drug, or history of thromboembolic disease.
• Use cautiously in patients with history of hypertension, depression, cardiac or renal dysfunction, liver impairment, bone diseases, migraine, seizures, or diabetes mellitus.
Lifespan: In children and in pregnant or breast-feeding women, drug is contraindicated.

Adverse reactions

CNS: headache, dizziness, chorea, depression, lethargy, ***seizures, stroke.***

CV: edema, hypertension, ***MI, pulmonary embolism,*** thrombophlebitis, ***thromboembolism.***
EENT: intolerance of contact lenses, worsening of myopia or astigmatism.
GI: abdominal cramps, anorexia, bloating, constipation, diarrhea, nausea, ***pancreatitis,*** vomiting.
GU: altered cervical secretions, altered menstrual flow, amenorrhea, breakthrough bleeding, ***breast and endometrial cancers,*** cervical erosion, dysmenorrhea, enlargement of uterine fibromas, impotence, testicular atrophy, vaginal candidiasis.
Hepatic: cholestatic jaundice, gallbladder disease, ***hepatic adenoma.***
Metabolic: hypercalcemia, increased appetite, weight changes.
Skin: dermatitis, erythema nodosum, hair loss, hirsutism, melasma, rash.
Other: breast changes (tenderness, enlargement, secretion), gynecomastia.

Interactions

Drug-drug. *Bromocriptine:* May cause amenorrhea, interfering with bromocriptine effects. Avoid use together.
Carbamazepine, phenobarbital, rifampin: May decrease estrogen effectiveness. Monitor patient closely.
Corticosteroids: May enhance effects. Monitor patient closely.
Cyclosporine: May increase risk of toxicity. Monitor cyclosporine level often.
Dantrolene, other hepatotoxic drugs: May increase risk of hepatotoxicity. Monitor patient closely.
Hydantoins: May cause loss of seizure control and increased risk of breakthrough bleeding, spotting, and pregnancy. Monitor patient closely.
Itraconazole, ketoconazole, macrolides, ritonavir: May increase estrogen level. Watch for increased adverse effects.
Oral anticoagulants: May decrease anticoagulant effects. Dosage adjustments may be needed. Monitor PT and INR.
Tamoxifen: May interfere with tamoxifen effectiveness. Avoid use together.
Thyroid hormones: May alter serum thyroxine and thyrotropin levels. Increase thyroid hormone dose as needed.
Topiramate: May increase estrogen metabolism and decrease effectiveness. Monitor patient closely.
Drug-herb. *St. John's wort:* May decrease estrogen level. Watch for decreased effectiveness and changes in bleeding patterns.
Drug-food. *Caffeine:* May increase caffeine level. Monitor effects.
Drug-lifestyle. *Smoking:* May increase risk of CV effects. Urge patient to stop smoking. If smoking continues, patient may need alternative therapy.

Effects on lab test results

- May increase glucose, calcium, total T_4, thyroid-binding globulin, phospholipid, triglyceride, and clotting factor VII, VIII, IX, and X levels.
- May increase PT and norepinephrine-induced platelet aggregation.

Pharmacokinetics

Absorption: Well absorbed but substantially inactivated by liver.
Distribution: Highest levels in fat. About 50% to 80% protein-bound.
Metabolism: Mainly in liver.
Excretion: Mainly by kidneys. *Half-life:* Unknown.

Route	Onset	Peak	Duration
P.O.	Unknown	Unknown	Unknown

Action

Chemical effect: Increases synthesis of DNA, RNA, and protein and reduces release of follicle-stimulating hormone and luteinizing hormone from pituitary gland.
Therapeutic effect: Provides estrogen replacement, hinders prostate and breast cancer cell growth, and relieves menopausal vasomotor symptoms and vaginal dryness.

Available forms

Tablets: 0.3 mg, 0.625 mg, 1.25 mg, 2.5 mg
Tablets (film-coated): 0.3 mg, 0.625 mg, 1.25 mg, 2.5 mg

NURSING PROCESS

Assessment

- Obtain history of patient's underlying condition before starting therapy, and reassess regularly thereafter.
- Make sure patient has thorough physical examination before starting drug therapy.

• Patient receiving long-term therapy should have yearly examinations. Periodically monitor lipid levels, blood pressure, body weight, and liver function.
• Be alert for adverse reactions and drug interactions.
• Assess patient's and family's knowledge of drug therapy.

Nursing diagnoses

• Ineffective health maintenance related to underlying condition
• Ineffective tissue perfusion (cerebral, peripheral, pulmonary, or myocardial) related to drug-induced thromboembolism
• Deficient knowledge related to drug therapy

Planning and implementation

• Give oral forms at mealtimes or bedtime (for once-daily dose) to minimize nausea.
• Because of risk of thromboembolism, stop therapy at least 1 month before procedures that may cause prolonged immobilization or thromboembolism, such as knee or hip surgery. If thromboembolism is suspected, withhold drug, notify prescriber, and provide supportive care.
ALERT: Estrogens aren't interchangeable.

Patient teaching

• Inform patient about adverse effects.
• Emphasize importance of regular physical examinations. Tell postmenopausal women who use the drug for more than 5 years that it may increase their risk for endometrial carcinoma, but that this risk is reduced by using cyclic rather than continuous therapy and the lowest dosages of estrogen. Also inform her that the drug probably doesn't increase risk of breast cancer.
• Explain to patient on cyclic therapy for postmenopausal symptoms that although withdrawal bleeding may occur during the week off, fertility hasn't been restored. Pregnancy can't occur because she hasn't ovulated.
• Warn patient to immediately report abdominal pain; pain, numbness, or stiffness in legs or buttocks; pressure or pain in chest; shortness of breath; severe headaches; visual disturbances, such as blind spots, flashing lights, or blurriness; vaginal bleeding or discharge; breast lumps; swelling of hands or feet; yellow skin or sclera; dark urine; and light-colored stools.
• Tell diabetic patient to report elevated glucose test results so antidiabetic dosage can be adjusted.
• Teach woman how to perform routine breast self-examination.

Evaluation

• Patient shows improvement in underlying condition.
• Patient has no thromboembolic event during therapy.
• Patient and family state understanding of drug therapy.

estropipate (piperazine estrone sulfate)

(ess-troh-PIH-payt)
Ogen, Ortho-Est

Pharmacologic class: hormone
Therapeutic class: estrogen
Pregnancy risk category: X

Indications and dosages

▶ **Management of moderate-to-severe vasomotor symptoms, vulvar and vaginal atrophy.** *Women:* 0.75 to 6 mg P.O. daily 3 weeks on, 1 week off, or 2 to 4 g of vaginal cream daily. Typically dosage given on cyclic, short-term basis.
▶ **Primary ovarian failure, female castration, hypogonadism.** *Women:* Given cyclically with 1.5 to 9 mg P.O. daily for first 3 weeks and then 8 to 10 day rest period. If bleeding doesn't occur by end of rest period, repeat cycle.
▶ **To prevent osteoporosis.** *Women:* 0.75 mg P.O. daily for 25 days of 31-day cycle. Repeat cycle p.r.n.

Contraindications and cautions

• Contraindicated in patients with active thrombophlebitis, thromboembolic disorders, estrogen-dependent neoplasia, undiagnosed genital bleeding, or breast, reproductive organ, or genital cancer.
• Use cautiously in patients with cerebrovascular or coronary artery disease, asthma, depression, bone disease, migraine, seizures, or cardiac, hepatic, or renal dysfunction and in women with family history (mother, grandmoth-

er, sister) of breast or genital tract cancer or who have breast nodules, fibrocystic disease, or abnormal mammogram findings. Use the lowest effective dose for the shortest duration.
• This drug has not been approved for the prevention of cognitive disorders or memory loss.
Lifespan: In children and in pregnant or breast-feeding women, drug is contraindicated.

Adverse reactions

CNS: depression, dizziness, headache, migraine, ***seizure, stroke.***
CV: edema, ***MI, pulmonary embolism, thromboembolism,*** thrombophlebitis.
GI: abdominal cramps, bloating, *nausea,* vomiting.
GU: breakthrough bleeding, candidiasis, cystitis-like syndrome, dysmenorrhea, ***endometrial and breast cancers,*** increased size of uterine fibromas, vaginal amenorrhea.
Hepatic: cholestatic jaundice.
Metabolic: hypercalcemia, weight changes.
Skin: ***erythema multiforme,*** erythema nodosum, hair loss, hemorrhagic eruption, hirsutism, melasma.
Other: aggravation of porphyria, breast engorgement or enlargement, libido changes.

Interactions

Drug-drug. *Bromocriptine:* May cause amenorrhea, interfering with bromocriptine effects. Avoid use together.
Carbamazepine, phenobarbital, rifampin: May decrease estrogen effectiveness. Monitor patient closely.
Corticosteroids: May enhance effects. Monitor patient closely.
Cyclosporine: May increase risk of toxicity. Monitor cyclosporine level often.
Dantrolene, other hepatotoxic drugs: May increase risk of hepatotoxicity. Monitor patient closely.
Hydantoins: May cause loss of seizure control and increased risk of breakthrough bleeding, spotting, and pregnancy. Monitor patient closely.
Itraconazole, ketoconazole, macrolides, ritonavir: May increase estrogen level. Watch for increased adverse effects.
Oral anticoagulants: May decrease anticoagulant effects. Dosage adjustments may be needed. Monitor PT and INR.
Tamoxifen: May interfere with tamoxifen effectiveness. Avoid use together.
Thyroid hormones: May alter serum thyroxine and thyrotropin levels. Increase thyroid hormone dose as needed.
Topiramate: May increase estrogen metabolism and decrease effectiveness. Monitor patient closely.
Drug-herb. *St. John's wort:* May decrease estrogen level. Watch for decreased effectiveness and changes in bleeding patterns.
Drug-food. *Caffeine:* May increase caffeine level. Monitor effects.
Drug-lifestyle. *Smoking:* May increase risk of CV effects. Urge patient to stop smoking. If smoking continues, patient may need alternate therapy.

Effects on lab test results

• May increase calcium, total T_4, thyroid-binding globulin, phospholipid, triglyceride, and clotting factor VII, VIII, IX, and X levels.
• May increase PT and norepinephrine-induced platelet aggregation.

Pharmacokinetics

Absorption: Not well characterized after P.O. or intravaginal use.
Distribution: Highest levels in fat. About 50% to 80% protein-bound.
Metabolism: Mainly in liver.
Excretion: Mainly by kidneys. *Half-life:* Unknown.

Route	Onset	Peak	Duration
P.O., vaginal	Unknown	Unknown	Unknown

Action

Chemical effect: Increases synthesis of DNA, RNA, and protein and reduces release of follicle-stimulating hormone and luteinizing hormone from pituitary gland.
Therapeutic effect: Provides estrogen replacement, relieves menopausal vasomotor symptoms, and helps reduce severity of osteoporosis.

Available forms

Tablets: 0.625 mg, 1.25 mg, 2.5 mg, 5 mg as sodium estrone sulfate (equivalent to 0.75 mg, 1.5 mg, 3 mg, 6 mg as estropipate)
Vaginal cream: 1.5 mg/g (0.15%)

NURSING PROCESS

Assessment

- Obtain history of patient's underlying condition before starting therapy, and reassess regularly.
- Make sure patient has thorough physical examination before starting drug therapy.
- Patient receiving long-term therapy should have yearly examinations. Periodically monitor lipid level, blood pressure, body weight, and liver function.
- Be alert for adverse reactions and drug interactions.
- Assess patient's and family's knowledge of drug therapy.

Nursing diagnoses

- Ineffective health maintenance related to underlying condition
- Ineffective tissue perfusion (cerebral, peripheral, pulmonary, or myocardial) related to drug-induced thromboembolism
- Deficient knowledge related to drug therapy

Planning and implementation

- Give oral forms with meals or at bedtime (for once-daily dose) to minimize nausea.
- Because of risk of thromboembolism, stop therapy at least 1 month before procedures that may cause prolonged immobilization or thromboembolism, such as knee or hip surgery. If thromboembolism is suspected, withhold drug, notify prescriber, and provide supportive care.

ALERT: Estrogens aren't interchangeable.

Patient teaching

- Inform patient about adverse effects.
- Emphasize importance of regular physical examinations. Tell postmenopausal women who use the drug for more than 5 years that it may increase their risk of endometrial carcinoma, but that the risk is reduced by using cyclic rather than continuous therapy and the lowest dosages of estrogen. Also inform her that the drug probably doesn't increase risk of breast cancer.
- Teach patient how to use vaginal cream. Tell her to wash vaginal area with soap and water before applying. Tell her to use drug at bedtime or to lie flat for 30 minutes after application to minimize drug loss.
- Explain to patient on cyclic therapy for postmenopausal symptoms that although withdrawal bleeding may occur during the week off, fertility hasn't been restored. Pregnancy can't occur because she hasn't ovulated.
- Explain to patient being treated for hypogonadism that therapy length depends on her endometrial response to drug. If satisfactory withdrawal bleeding doesn't occur, oral progestin may be added. Explain to patient that despite return of withdrawal bleeding, pregnancy can't occur because she isn't ovulating.
- Warn patient to immediately report abdominal pain; pain, numbness, or stiffness in legs or buttocks; pressure or pain in chest; shortness of breath; severe headaches; visual disturbances, such as blind spots, flashing lights, or blurriness; vaginal bleeding or discharge; breast lumps; swelling of hands or feet; yellow skin or sclera; dark urine; and light-colored stools.
- Tell diabetic patient to report elevated glucose test results so antidiabetic dosage can be adjusted.
- Teach woman how to perform routine breast self-examination.

Evaluation

- Patient shows improvement in underlying condition.
- Patient has no thromboembolic event during therapy.
- Patient and family state understanding of drug therapy.

eszopiclone

(ess-zoe-PICK-lone)

Lunesta

Pharmacologic class: pyrrolopyrazine derivative
Therapeutic class: hypnotic
Pregnancy risk category: C
Controlled substance schedule: IV

Indications and dosages

▶ **Insomnia.** *Adults:* 2 mg P.O. immediately before bedtime. Increase to 3 mg if needed.
Elderly patients having trouble falling asleep: 1 mg P.O. immediately before bedtime. Increase to 2 mg if needed.
Elderly patients having trouble staying asleep: 2 mg P.O. immediately before bedtime.
Adjust-a-dose: In patients with severe hepatic impairment, start with 1 mg P.O. In patients

who also take a potent CYP3A4 inhibitor, start with 1 mg and increase to 2 mg if needed.

Contraindications and cautions

• Use cautiously in patients with diseases or conditions that could affect metabolism or hemodynamic responses. Also use cautiously in patients with compromised respiratory function, severe hepatic impairment, or signs and symptoms of depression.

Lifespan: In pregnant women, use only if benefits outweigh risk to the fetus. In breast-feeding women, use cautiously because it isn't known if drug appears in breast milk. In children, safety and effectiveness haven't been established. Elderly patients may be more sensitive to drug effects.

Adverse reactions

CNS: abnormal dreams, anxiety, confusion, depression, dizziness, hallucinations, *headache,* nervousness, neuralgia, pain, *somnolence.*
EENT: unpleasant taste.
GI: diarrhea, dry mouth, dyspepsia, nausea, vomiting.
GU: UTI.
Respiratory: respiratory infection.
Skin: pruritus, rash.
Other: accidental injury, decreased libido, viral infection, ***anaphylaxis, angioedema.***

Interactions

Drug-drug. *CNS depressants:* May have additive CNS effects. Adjust dosage of either drug as needed.
CYP3A4 inhibitors (clarithromycin, itraconazole, ketoconazole, nefazodone, nelfinavir, ritonavir, troleandomycin): May decrease eszopiclone elimination, increasing the risk of toxicity. Use together cautiously.
Olanzapine: May impair cognitive function or memory. Use together cautiously.
Rifampicin: May decrease eszopiclone activity. Don't use together.
Drug-food. *High-fat meals:* May decrease eszopiclone absorption and decrease drug effects. Discourage high-fat meals with or just before taking drug.
Drug-lifestyle. *Alcohol:* May decrease psychomotor ability. Discourage use together.

Effects on lab test results

None reported.

Pharmacokinetics

Absorption: Rapid.
Distribution: In plasma. About 50% to 60% protein-bound.
Metabolism: By CYP3A4 in the liver, with two mainly inactive metabolites.
Excretion: In urine, mainly as metabolites. *Half-life:* 6 hours.

Route	Onset	Peak	Duration
P.O.	Rapid	1 hr	Unknown

Action

Chemical effect: Drug probably interacts with gamma amino-butyric acid receptors at binding sites close to or connected to benzodiazepine receptors.
Therapeutic effect: Promotes sleep.

Available forms

Tablets: 1 mg, 2 mg, 3 mg

NURSING PROCESS

Assessment

• Evaluate patient for physical and psychiatric disorders before treatment.
• Be alert for drug interactions and adverse reactions. Anaphylaxis and angioedema may occur as early as the first dose.
• If patient is still having trouble sleeping after using drug for short-term therapy, check for other psychological disorders.
• Monitor patient for changes in behavior, including complex sleep disorders and those that suggest depression or suicidal thinking.
• Assess patient's and family's knowledge of drug therapy.

Nursing diagnoses

• Sleep deprivation related to insomnia
• Risk for injury related to drug-induced adverse CNS reactions
• Deficient knowledge related to drug therapy

Planning and implementation

ALERT: Give drug immediately before patient goes to bed or after patient has gone to bed and has trouble falling asleep.
• Use the lowest effective dose.
• Use only for short periods (for example, 7 to 10 days).

• Overdose may cause impaired consciousness, hypotension, and CNS depression.
• Treat overdose symptomatically and supportively; flumazenil may be helpful. It isn't known if eszopiclone is removed by dialysis.

Patient teaching

• Urge patient to take drug immediately before going to bed because drug may cause dizziness or light-headedness.
• Caution patient not to take eszopiclone unless he can get a full night's sleep.
• Advise patient to avoid taking drug after a high-fat meal.
• Tell patient to avoid activities that require mental alertness until the drug's effects are known.
• Advise patient to avoid alcohol while taking drug.
• Urge patient to immediately report changes in behavior and thinking, including complex sleep-related behaviors.
• Warn patient not to stop drug abruptly or change dose without consulting the prescriber.
• Inform patient that tolerance or dependence may develop if drug is taken for a prolonged period.

☑ Evaluation

• Patient no longer experiences insomnia with drug therapy.
• Patient does not experience injury from adverse CNS reactions.
• Patient and family state understanding of drug therapy.

etanercept

(ee-TAN-er-sept)
Enbrel

Pharmacologic class: tumor necrosis factor (TNF) blocker
Therapeutic class: antirheumatic
Pregnancy risk category: B

Indications and dosages

▶ **Psoriatic arthritis, ankylosing spondylitis, moderately to severely active rheumatoid arthritis.** *Adults:* 25 mg subcutaneously twice weekly, on same day or 72 to 96 hours apart, or 50 mg subcutaneously from prefilled syringe once weekly. Continue methotrexate, glucocorticoids, salicylates, NSAIDs, or analgesics during therapy.

▶ **Moderate to severely active polyarticular-course juvenile rheumatoid arthritis in patients who have had an inadequate response to one or more disease-modifying antirheumatic drugs.** *Children ages 4 to 17:* Give 0.4 mg/kg (maximum, 25 mg/dose) subcutaneously twice weekly, on same day or 72 to 96 hours apart.

▶ **Chronic moderate to severe plaque psoriasis in patients who are candidates for systemic therapy or phototherapy.** *Adults:* 50 mg subcutaneously twice weekly, 3 to 4 days apart for 3 months. Then, reduce dosage to 50 mg subcutaneously once weekly.

Contraindications and cautions

• Contraindicated in patients hypersensitive to drug or any of its components and in those with sepsis. Stop giving the drug to a patient who develops a serious infection or sepsis. Use of live vaccines during drug therapy is contraindicated.
• Use cautiously in patients with a history of recurring infections and in those with underlying diseases that predispose them to infection, such as diabetes or heart failure. Also use cautiously in patients with CNS demyelinating disorders and in those with a history of significant hematologic abnormalities.
Lifespan: In pregnant women, use cautiously. Breast-feeding women should stop drug or stop breast-feeding. In children younger than age 4, safety and effectiveness haven't been established.

Adverse reactions

CNS: asthenia, dizziness, *headache.*
EENT: pharyngitis, rhinitis, sinusitis.
GI: abdominal pain, dyspepsia.
Respiratory: cough, respiratory disorder, *upper respiratory tract infections.*
Skin: rash.
Other: infections, injection site reaction, ***malignancies.***

Interactions

Drug-drug. *Live-virus vaccinations:* Transmission of infection remains unknown. Avoid use together.

Effects on lab test results

• May cause positive antinuclear antibody or positive anti–double-stranded DNA antibodies measured by radioimmunoassay and *Crithidia luciliae* assay.

Pharmacokinetics

Absorption: Level peaks in 72 hours.
Distribution: Unknown.
Metabolism: Unknown.
Excretion: Unknown. *Half-life:* 115 hours.

Route	Onset	Peak	Duration
SubQ	Unknown	3 days	Unknown

Action

Chemical effect: Binds specifically to TNF and blocks its action, reducing inflammatory and immune responses found in rheumatoid arthritis.
Therapeutic effect: Reduces signs and symptoms of rheumatoid arthritis.

Available forms

Injection: 25-mg single-use vial, 50-mg/ml prefilled syringe

NURSING PROCESS

Assessment

• Obtain history of patient's underlying condition before starting therapy, and reassess regularly.
• Obtain accurate immunization history from parents or guardians of juvenile rheumatoid arthritis patients. Patient should be brought up-to-date with all immunizations before starting drug.
• Monitor patient for infection.
• Assess patient's and family's knowledge of drug therapy.

Nursing diagnoses

• Acute pain related to underlying condition
• Risk for infection related to drug-induced adverse reactions
• Deficient knowledge related to drug therapy

Planning and implementation

• Drug is for subcutaneous injection only.
• Reconstitute aseptically with 1 ml of supplied sterile bacteriostatic water for injection, USP (0.9% benzyl alcohol). Don't filter reconstituted solution during preparation or administration. Inject diluent slowly into vial. Minimize foaming by gently swirling during dissolution rather than shaking. Dissolution takes less than 5 minutes.
• Inspect solution for particulates and discoloration before use. Reconstituted solution should be clear and colorless. Don't use solution if it's discolored or cloudy, or if particulates exist.
• Don't add other drugs or diluents to reconstituted solution.
• Use reconstituted solution as soon as possible. Solution may be refrigerated in vial for up to 6 hours at 36° to 46° F (2° to 8° C).
• Inject at least 1 inch from another injection site; don't use areas where skin is tender, bruised, red, or hard. Recommended sites include the thigh, abdomen, and upper arm. Rotate sites regularly.
• Don't give live vaccines during therapy.
• Drug may affect defenses against infection. If serious infection occurs, notify prescriber and stop therapy.
• Needle cover of diluent syringe contains dry natural rubber (latex). Don't allow those sensitive to latex to handle cover.
ALERT: Don't confuse Enbrel with Levbid.

Patient teaching

• If patient will be administering drug, teach mixing and injection techniques, including rotation of injection sites.
• Instruct patient to use puncture-resistant container to dispose of needles and syringes.
• Tell patient that injection site reactions typically occur within first month of therapy and decrease thereafter.
• Urge patient to avoid live vaccines during therapy. Stress importance of alerting other health care providers of etanercept use.
• Instruct patient to promptly report evidence of infection to prescriber.

Evaluation

• Patient's pain decreases.
• Patient is free from infection.
• Patient and family state understanding of drug therapy.

ethacrynate sodium

(eth-uh-KRIH-nayt SOH-dee-um)

Sodium Edecrin

ethacrynic acid

Edecril ◇, Edecrin

Pharmacologic class: loop diuretic
Therapeutic class: diuretic
Pregnancy risk category: B

Indications and dosages

▶ **Acute pulmonary edema.** *Adults:* 50 mg or 0.5 to 1 mg/kg I.V. to maximum dose of 100 mg. Usually, only one dose is needed; occasionally, second dose may be required.

▶ **Edema.** *Adults:* 50 to 200 mg P.O. daily. Refractory cases may require up to 200 mg b.i.d. *Children age 1 and older:* Initial dose is 25 mg P.O.; increase cautiously in 25-mg increments daily until desired effect is achieved.

▶ **Hypertension**‡. *Adults:* Initially 25 mg P.O. daily. Adjust dosage as needed. Maximum maintenance dosage is 200 mg P.O. daily in two divided doses.

I.V. administration

- Reconstitute vacuum vial with 50 ml of D_5W or normal saline solution.
- Give slowly through I.V. line of running infusion or by direct injection over several minutes.
- If more than one I.V. dose is needed, use new injection site to avoid thrombophlebitis.
- Discard unused solution after 24 hours. Don't use cloudy or opalescent solutions.

⊗ **Incompatibilities**

Hydralazine, Normosol-M, procainamide, ranitidine, reserpine, solutions or drugs with pH below 5, tolazoline, triflupromazine, whole blood and its derivatives.

Contraindications and cautions

- Contraindicated in patients hypersensitive to the drug or any of its components and in those with anuria.
- Use cautiously in patients with electrolyte abnormalities, advanced cirrhosis of the liver, hepatic encephalopathy, or renal impairment.

Lifespan: In pregnant women, use cautiously. In breast-feeding women, it's unknown if drug appears in breast milk. In infants, drug is contraindicated.

Adverse reactions

CNS: confusion, fatigue, fever, headache, malaise, nervousness, vertigo.
CV: orthostatic hypotension, volume depletion and dehydration.
EENT: blurred vision, hearing loss, tinnitus, transient deafness (with too-rapid I.V. injection).
GI: anorexia, cramping, diarrhea, GI bleeding, nausea, ***pancreatitis,*** vomiting.
GU: frequent urination, hematuria, nocturia, oliguria, polyuria.
Hematologic: ***agranulocytosis, azotemia, neutropenia, thrombocytopenia.***
Metabolic: dilutional hyponatremia, hyperglycemia, hyperuricemia, hypochloremic alkalosis, hypocalcemia, hypokalemia, ***hypomagnesemia,*** impaired glucose tolerance.
Skin: dermatitis, rash.
Other: chills.

Interactions

Drug-drug. *Aminoglycoside antibiotics:* May potentiate ototoxic adverse reactions of both drugs. Use together cautiously.
Antihypertensives: May increase risk of hypotension. Use together cautiously.
Chlorothiazide, chlorthalidone, hydrochlorothiazide, indapamide, metolazone: May cause excessive diuretic response, resulting in serious electrolyte abnormalities or dehydration. Adjust doses carefully while monitoring patient closely for excessive diuretic responses.
Cisplatin: May increase risk of ototoxicity. Avoid use together.
Digoxin: May increase risk of digoxin toxicity from ethacrynate-induced hypokalemia. Monitor potassium and digoxin levels.
Lithium: May decrease lithium clearance, increasing risk of lithium toxicity. Monitor lithium level.
Metolazone: May cause profound diuresis and enhance electrolyte loss. Use together cautiously.
NSAIDs: May decrease diuretic effectiveness. Use together cautiously.
Warfarin: May potentiate anticoagulant effect. Use together cautiously.
Drug-herb. *Licorice root:* May contribute to potassium depletion caused by diuretics. Discourage licorice root intake.

Drug-lifestyle. *Sun exposure:* Photosensitivity may occur. Discourage prolonged or unprotected exposure to sunlight.

Effects on lab test results

- May increase glucose, BUN, and uric acid levels. May decrease potassium, sodium, calcium, and magnesium levels.
- May decrease granulocyte, neutrophil, and platelet counts.

Pharmacokinetics

Absorption: Ethacrynic acid is absorbed rapidly from GI tract. Ethacrynate sodium is given I.V.
Distribution: Unknown.
Metabolism: Unknown.
Excretion: Unknown. *Half-life:* 1 hour.

Route	Onset	Peak	Duration
P.O.	30 min	2 hr	6–8 hr
I.V.	5 min	15–30 min	2 hr

Action

Chemical effect: Inhibits sodium and chloride reabsorption at renal tubules and ascending loop of Henle.
Therapeutic effect: Promotes sodium and water excretion.

Available forms

Injection: 50 mg (with 62.5 mg of mannitol and 0.1 mg of thimerosal)
Tablets: 25 mg, 50 mg

NURSING PROCESS

Assessment

- Obtain history of patient's underlying condition before starting therapy.
- Monitor effectiveness by regularly checking urine output, weight, peripheral edema, and breath sounds.
- Monitor fluid intake, blood pressure, and electrolyte levels.
- Monitor uric acid levels, especially in patients with history of gout.
- Be alert for adverse reactions and drug interactions.
- Assess patient's and family's knowledge of drug therapy.

Nursing diagnoses

- Excess fluid volume related to underlying condition
- Impaired urinary elimination related to diuretic therapy
- Deficient knowledge related to drug therapy

Planning and implementation

- Give drug with food or milk because P.O. use may cause GI upset.
- To prevent nocturia, give P.O. doses in morning.
- Don't mix with whole blood or its derivatives.
- Don't give subcutaneously or I.M. because of local pain and irritation.
- Potassium chloride and sodium supplements may be needed.
- If diarrhea occurs, notify prescriber because severe diarrhea may warrant stopping drug.

Patient teaching

- Advise patient to avoid sudden posture changes and to rise slowly to avoid orthostatic hypotension.
- Advise diabetic patient to closely monitor glucose level.
- Teach patient and family to identify and report signs of hypersensitivity or fluid and electrolyte disturbances.
- Teach patient to monitor fluid volume by daily weight and intake and output.
- Tell patient to take oral drug early in day to avoid interruption of sleep by nocturia.

Evaluation

- Patient is free from edema.
- Patient demonstrates adjustment of lifestyle to deal with altered patterns of urinary elimination.
- Patient and family state understanding of drug therapy.

ethambutol hydrochloride

(ee-THAM-byoo-tall high-droh-KLOR-ighd)
Etibi ♦, Myambutol

Pharmacologic class: semisynthetic antituberculotic
Therapeutic class: antituberculotic
Pregnancy risk category: B

Indications and dosages

▶ **Adjunct therapy for pulmonary tuberculosis.** *Adults and children age 13 and older:* For patients who haven't received previous antitubercular therapy, 15 mg/kg P.O. daily. For patients who have received previous antitubercular therapy, 25 mg/kg P.O. daily for 60 days until cultures are negative; then decrease to 15 mg/kg P.O. daily.

▶ **Adjunct therapy for pulmonary *Mycobacterium avium* complex infections in patients without HIV‡.** *Adults:* 25 mg/kg P.O. daily for 2 months followed by 15 mg/kg P.O. daily until cultures are negative for 1 year.

▶ **Adjunct therapy for disseminated *Mycobacterium avium* complex infections‡.** *Adults:* 15 mg/kg P.O. daily for patient's lifetime.

Contraindications and cautions

- Contraindicated in patients hypersensitive to drug and in patients with optic neuritis.
- Use cautiously in patients with impaired kidney function, cataracts, recurrent eye inflammations, gout, or diabetic retinopathy.

Lifespan: In pregnant women, use cautiously. In breast-feeding women, use cautiously because it's unknown if the drug appears in breast milk. In children younger than age 13, drug is contraindicated.

Adverse reactions

CNS: confusion, dizziness, fever, hallucinations, headache, malaise, peripheral neuritis.
EENT: dose-related optic neuritis; loss of color discrimination, especially red and green; vision loss.
GI: abdominal pain, anorexia, nausea, vomiting.
Hematologic: ***thrombocytopenia.***
Respiratory: bloody sputum.
Skin: dermatitis, pruritus, ***toxic epidermal necrolysis.***
Other: ***anaphylactoid reactions,*** precipitation of gout.

Interactions

Drug-drug. *Aluminum salts:* May delay and reduce absorption of ethambutol. Separate doses by several hours.

Effects on lab test results

- May increase ALT, AST, bilirubin, and uric acid levels. May decrease glucose level.
- May decrease platelet count.

Pharmacokinetics

Absorption: Rapid.
Distribution: Wide. 8% to 22% protein-bound.
Metabolism: Undergoes partial hepatic metabolism.
Excretion: After 24 hours, about 50% of unchanged drug and 8% to 15% of its metabolites in urine; 20% to 25% in feces. *Half-life:* About 3½ hours.

Route	Onset	Peak	Duration
P.O.	Unknown	2–4 hr	Unknown

Action

Chemical effect: May interfere with synthesis of one or more metabolites of susceptible bacteria, altering cellular metabolism during cell division.
Therapeutic effect: Hinders bacterial growth.

Available forms

Tablets: 100 mg, 400 mg

NURSING PROCESS

Assessment

- Obtain history of patient's infection before starting therapy.
- Perform visual acuity and color discrimination tests before and during therapy (monthly when dose is 25 mg/kg or more).
- Monitor the drug's effectiveness by regularly assessing for improvement in patient's condition and evaluating culture and sensitivity test results.
- Obtain AST and ALT levels before starting therapy. Then monitor AST and ALT levels every 2 to 4 weeks.
- Monitor uric acid level; observe patient for symptoms of gout.
- Be alert for adverse reactions and drug interactions.
- Assess patient's and family's knowledge of drug therapy.

Nursing diagnoses

- Risk for infection related to presence of susceptible bacteria
- Disturbed sensory perception (visual) related to drug-induced adverse reactions
- Deficient knowledge related to drug therapy

Planning and implementation

- Anticipate the need for a lower dose in a patient with impaired kidney function.
- Always give ethambutol with other antituberculotics to prevent development of resistant organisms.

ALERT: Don't confuse ethambutol with Ethmozine.

Patient teaching

- Reassure patient that visual disturbances will disappear several weeks to months after the therapy ends.
- Warn patient not to perform hazardous activities if visual disturbances or adverse CNS reactions occur.
- Emphasize need for regular follow-up care.

Evaluation

- Patient is free from infection.
- Patient regains pretreatment vision.
- Patient and family state understanding of drug therapy.

ethinyl estradiol and desogestrel

(ETH-ih-nill es-truh-DIGH-ol and DAY-so-jest-rul)

monophasic: **Apri, Desogen, Ortho-Cept**
biphasic: **Kariva, Mircette**
triphasic: **Cyclessa, Velivet**

ethinyl estradiol and ethynodiol diacetate

monophasic: **Demulen 1/35, Demulen 1/50, Zovia 1/35E, Zovia 1/50E**

ethinyl estradiol and levonorgestrel

emergency: **Preven**
extended cycle: **Seasonique**
monophasic: **Alesse, Aviane, Lessina, Levlen, Levlite, Levora, Nordette, Portia**
triphasic: **Enpresse, Tri-Levlen, Triphasil, Trivora**

ethinyl estradiol and norethindrone

monophasic: **Balziva, Brevicon, Genora 0.5/35, Genora 1/35, ModiCon, Norethin 1/35E, Norinyl 1+35, Ortho-Novum 1/35, Ovcon-35, Ovcon-50**
biphasic: **Necon 10/11, Nortrel, Ortho-Novum 10/11**
triphasic: **Necon 7/7/7, Nortrel 7/7/7, Ortho-Novum 7/7/7, Tri-Norinyl**

ethinyl estradiol and norethindrone acetate

monophasic: **Junel 1/20, Junel 1.5/30, Loestrin 21 1/20, Loestrin 21 1.5/30, Necon 1/35, Nortrel 1/35**
triphasic: **Estrostep**

ethinyl estradiol and norgestimate

monophasic: **MonoNessa, Ortho-Cyclen, Sprintec**
triphasic: **Ortho Tri-Cyclen, Ortho Tri-Cyclen Lo, Tri-Sprintec**

ethinyl estradiol and norgestrel

monophasic: **Cryselle, Lo/Ovral, Lo/Ovral 28, Low-Ogestrel, Ogestrel 0.5/50, Ovral**

ethinyl estradiol, norethindrone acetate, and ferrous fumarate

monophasic: **Junel Fe 1/5/30, Junel Fe 1/20, Loestrin Fe 1/20, Loestrin Fe 1.5/30, Loestrin 24 Fe, Microgestin Fe 1/20, Microgestin Fe 1.5/30**

mestranol and norethindrone

monophasic: **Necon 1/50, Norinyl 1+50, Ortho-Novum 1/50**
triphasic: **Estrostep Fe, Estrostep 21**

Pharmacologic class: hormonal contraceptive
Therapeutic class: estrogen with progestin
Pregnancy risk category: X

Indications and dosages

▶ **Contraception.** *Women:* 1 monophasic tablet P.O. daily, beginning on day 5 of menstrual cycle (first day of menstrual flow is day 1). With 20- and 21-tablet packages, new cycle begins

7 days after last tablet taken. With 28-tablet packages, dosage is 1 tablet daily without interruption; extra tablets are placebos or contain iron. Or first-color biphasic tablet P.O. daily for 10 days; then next color tablet for 11 days. Or 1 triphasic tablet P.O. daily in sequence specified by brand. Or 1 transdermal patch, changed weekly. Or 1 extended-cycle light blue–green tablet P.O. once daily for 84 consecutive days followed by one yellow tablet for consecutive 7 days; then repeat cycle.

▶ **Moderate acne vulgaris in women and girls age 15 and older who have no known contraindications to hormonal contraceptive therapy, desire hormonal contraception, have achieved menarche, and are unresponsive to topical antiacne drugs.** *Women and girls age 15 and older:* 1 tablet Estrostep, Ortho Tri-Cyclen, or Tri-Sprintec P.O. daily. (Twenty-one tablets contain active ingredients, and seven are inert.)

Contraindications and cautions

- Contraindicated in patients with thromboembolic disorders, cerebrovascular or coronary artery disease, diplopia or ocular lesion arising from ophthalmic vascular disease, classic migraine, MI, known or suspected breast cancer, known or suspected estrogen-dependent neoplasia, benign or malignant liver tumors, active liver disease or history of cholestatic jaundice with pregnancy or prior use of hormonal contraceptives, or undiagnosed abnormal vaginal bleeding.
- Use cautiously in patients with cardiac, renal, or hepatic insufficiency; hyperlipidemia; hypertension; migraine; seizure disorders; or asthma.

Lifespan: In adolescents, hormonal contraception isn't advised until after at least 2 years of well-established menstrual cycles and completion of physiologic maturation to avoid later fertility and menstrual problems. In women who are pregnant or suspect they may be pregnant and in breast-feeding women, drug is contraindicated.

Adverse reactions

CNS: depression, *dizziness, headache,* lethargy, migraine, ***stroke.***
CV: edema, hypertension, ***pulmonary embolism,*** thromboembolism.
EENT: diplopia, exophthalmos, intolerance of contact lenses, worsening of myopia or astigmatism.
GI: abdominal cramps, anorexia, bloating, constipation, diarrhea, granulomatous colitis, nausea, ***pancreatitis,*** vomiting.
GU: amenorrhea, *breakthrough bleeding,* cervical erosion or abnormal secretions, dysmenorrhea, enlargement of uterine fibromas, vaginal candidiasis.
Hepatic: cholestatic jaundice, gallbladder disease, ***liver tumors.***
Metabolic: changes in appetite, hypercalcemia, hyperglycemia, weight gain.
Skin: acne, ***erythema multiforme,*** rash.
Other: breast changes (tenderness, enlargement, secretion).

Interactions

Drug-drug. *Alprazolam, chlordiazepoxide, diazepam, temazepam:* May prolong the half-life of these drugs. Watch for adverse effects.
Atorvastatin: May increase estrogen level. Monitor patient closely.
Beta blockers, corticosteroids, theophyllines, tricyclic antidepressants: May enhance effects of these drugs. Monitor patient closely.
Bromocriptine: May cause amenorrhea, interfering with bromocriptine effects. Avoid use together.
Carbamazepine, phenobarbital, phenytoin, rifampin: May decrease effectiveness of estrogen therapy. Monitor patient closely.
Cyclosporine: May inhibit cyclosporine metabolism, increasing the risk of toxicity. Avoid use together, if possible. If given together, monitor cyclosporine level and renal and hepatic function. Adjust cyclosporine dose as needed.
Dantrolene, other hepatotoxic drugs: May increase risk of hepatotoxicity. Monitor patient closely.
Griseofulvin, penicillins, sulfonamides, tetracyclines: May decrease effectiveness of hormonal contraceptives. Discourage use together, or suggest barrier contraception for the duration of therapy.
Lamotrigine, lorazepam, oxazepam, temazepam: May increase clearance of these drugs. Monitor patient for lack of effect.
Oral anticoagulants: May decrease anticoagulant effects. Dosage adjustments may be needed. Monitor PT and INR.
Selegiline: May increase selegiline levels. Monitor patient closely.
Tamoxifen: May interfere with tamoxifen effectiveness. Avoid use together.

Drug-herb. *St. John's wort:* May decrease estrogen level. Watch for decreased effectiveness and changes in bleeding patterns.
Drug-food. *Caffeine:* May increase caffeine level. Monitor effects.
Drug-lifestyle. *Smoking:* May increase risk of CV effects and thrombosis. Discourage patient from smoking. If smoking continues, patient may need a different form of contraception.

Effects on lab test results

- May increase glucose, calcium, fibrinogen, triglyceride, phospholipid, total T_4, thyroid-binding globulin, plasminogen, liver enzyme, and clotting factor II, VII, VIII, IX, X, and XII levels.
- May increase PT and norepinephrine-induced platelet aggregation.

Pharmacokinetics

Absorption: Mostly well absorbed.
Distribution: Wide. Extensively protein-bound.
Metabolism: Mainly in liver.
Excretion: In urine and feces. *Half-life:* 6 to 20 hours.

Route	Onset	Peak	Duration
P.O., transdermal	Unknown	Varies	Unknown

Action

Chemical effect: Inhibits ovulation through negative feedback mechanism directed at hypothalamus. Estrogen suppresses secretion of follicle-stimulating hormone, blocking follicle development and ovulation. Progestin suppresses secretion of luteinizing hormone so ovulation can't occur. Progestin thickens cervical mucus, which interferes with sperm migration and prevents implantation.
Therapeutic effect: Prevents pregnancy and relieves signs and symptoms of endometriosis.

Available forms

monophasic
ethinyl estradiol and desogestrel
Tablets: ethinyl estradiol 30 mcg and desogestrel 0.15 mg (Apri, Desogen, Ortho-Cept); ethinyl estradiol 25 mcg and desogestrel 0.1 mg
ethinyl estradiol and ethynodiol diacetate
Tablets: ethinyl estradiol 35 mcg and ethynodiol diacetate 1 mg (Demulen 1/35, Zovia 1/35E); ethinyl estradiol 50 mcg and ethynodiol diacetate 1 mg (Demulen 1/50, Zovia 1/50E)
ethinyl estradiol and levonorgestrel
Tablets: ethinyl estradiol 30 mcg and levonorgestrel 0.15 mg (Levlen, Levora, Nordette, Portia); ethinyl estradiol 20 mcg, levonorgestrel 0.1 mg (Alesse, Aviane, Lessina, Levlite); levonorgestrel/ethinyl estradiol tablets 0.15 mg/0.03 mg and ethinyl estradiol tablets 0.01 mg (Seasonique)
ethinyl estradiol and norethindrone
Tablets: ethinyl estradiol 35 mcg and norethindrone 0.4 mg (Balziva, Ovcon-35); ethinyl estradiol 35 mcg and norethindrone 0.5 mg (Brevicon, Necon, Nortrel, ModiCon); ethinyl estradiol 35 mcg and norethindrone 1 mg (Necon 1/35, Nortrel 1/35, Norinyl 1+35, Ortho-Novum 1/35); ethinyl estradiol 50 mcg and norethindrone 1 mg (Ovcon-50)
ethinyl estradiol and norethindrone acetate
Tablets: ethinyl estradiol 20 mcg and norethindrone acetate 1 mg (Loestrin 21 1/20); ethinyl estradiol 30 mcg and norethindrone acetate 1.5 mg (Loestrin 21 1.5/30)
ethinyl estradiol and norgestimate
Tablets: ethinyl estradiol 35 mcg and norgestimate 0.25 mg (Ortho-Cyclen)
ethinyl estradiol and norgestrel
Tablets: ethinyl estradiol 30 mcg and norgestrel 0.3 mg (Cryselle, Lo/Ovral, Lo/Ovral 28, Low-Ogestrel); ethinyl estradiol 50 mcg and norgestrel 0.5 mg (Ovral, Ovral 28, Ogestrel 0.5/50)
ethinyl estradiol, norethindrone acetate, and ferrous fumarate
Tablets: ethinyl estradiol 20 mcg, norethindrone acetate 1 mg, and ferrous fumarate 75 mg (Loestrin Fe 1/20, Microgestin Fe 1/20); ethinyl estradiol 30 mcg, norethindrone acetate 1.5 mg, and ferrous fumarate 75 mg (Loestrin Fe 1.5/30, Microgestin Fe 1.5/30)
mestranol and norethindrone
Tablets: mestranol 50 mcg and norethindrone 1 mg (Necon 1/50, Norinyl 1+50, Ortho-Novum 1/50)
biphasic
ethinyl estradiol and desogestrel
Tablets: ethinyl estradiol 20 mcg and desogestrel 0.15 mg (Kariva, Mircette)
ethinyl estradiol and norethindrone
Tablets: ethinyl estradiol 35 mcg and norethindrone 0.5 mg during phase 1 (10 days); ethinyl estradiol 35 mcg and norethindrone 1 mg during

phase 2 (11 days) (Necon 10/11, Ortho-Novum 10/11)

triphasic

ethinyl estradiol and desogestrel

Tablets: desogestrel 0.1 mg and ethinyl estradiol 25 mcg (7 tablets); desogestrel 0.125 mg and ethinyl estradiol 25 mcg (7 tablets); desogestrel 0.15 mg and ethinyl estradiol 25 mcg (7 tablets) (Cyclessa); 0.1 mg desogestrel and 0.025 mg ethinyl estradiol (7 tablets); 0.125 mg desogestrel and 0.025 mg ethinyl estradiol (7 tablets); and 0.15 mg desogestrel and 0.025 mg ethinyl estradiol (7 tablets) (Velivet)

ethinyl estradiol and levonorgestrel

Tablets: ethinyl estradiol 30 mcg and levonorgestrel 0.05 mg during phase 1 (6 days); ethinyl estradiol 40 mcg and levonorgestrel 0.075 mg during phase 2 (5 days); ethinyl estradiol 30 mcg and levonorgestrel 0.125 mg during phase 3 (10 days) (Tri-Levlen, Triphasil, Trivora-28, Enpresse)

Transdermal patch: ethinyl estradiol 0.045 mg and levonorgestrel 0.015 mg

ethinyl estradiol and norethindrone

Tablets: ethinyl estradiol 35 mcg and norethindrone 0.5 mg during phase 1 (7 days); ethinyl estradiol 35 mcg and norethindrone 1 mg during phase 2 (9 days); ethinyl estradiol 35 mcg and norethindrone 0.5 mg during phase 3 (5 days) (Tri-Norinyl); ethinyl estradiol 35 mcg and norethindrone 0.5 mg during phase 1 (7 days); ethinyl estradiol 35 mcg and norethindrone 0.75 mg during phase 2 (7 days); ethinyl estradiol 35 mcg and norethindrone 1 mg during phase 3 (7 days) (Necon 7/7/7, Nortrel 7/7/7, Ortho-Novum 7/7/7)

ethinyl estradiol and norethindrone acetate

Tablets: ethinyl estradiol 0.02 mg and norethindrone acetate 1 mg (5 tablets), ethinyl estradiol 0.03 mg and norethindrone acetate 1 mg (7 tablets), ethinyl estradiol 0.035 mg and norethindrone acetate 1 mg (9 tablets) (Estrostep Fe, Estrostep 21)

ethinyl estradiol and norgestimate

Tablets: ethinyl estradiol 35 mcg and norgestimate 0.18 mg during phase 1 (7 days); ethinyl estradiol 35 mcg and norgestimate 0.215 mg during phase 2 (7 days); ethinyl estradiol 35 mcg and norgestimate 0.25 mg during phase 3 (7 days) (Ortho Tri-Cyclen)

NURSING PROCESS

Assessment

- Obtain history of patient's fertility or underlying endometriosis before starting therapy.
- Monitor the drug's effectiveness by determining if pregnancy test is negative or if patient with endometriosis has diminished signs and symptoms.
- Periodically monitor lipid levels, blood pressure, body weight, and liver function.
- Be alert for adverse reactions and drug interactions.
- Assess patient's and family's knowledge of drug therapy.

Nursing diagnoses

- Health-seeking behavior (prevention of pregnancy) related to family planning
- Acute pain related to drug-induced headache
- Deficient knowledge related to drug therapy

Planning and implementation

- Make sure patient has been properly instructed about prescribed hormonal contraceptive before she takes first dose.

ALERT: Make sure patient has negative pregnancy test before therapy starts.

- If patient develops granulomatous colitis, stop therapy and notify prescriber.
- Stop drug at least 1 week before surgery to decrease risk of thromboembolism. Tell patient to use other, nonhormonal method of birth control.

ALERT: Don't confuse Nortrel 7/7/7 with Nortrel 0.5/35 or Nortrel 1/35.

ALERT: Don't confuse Necon 7/7/7 with Nortrel 7/7/7.

Patient teaching

- Tell patient to take tablets at same time each day; nighttime doses may reduce nausea and headaches.
- Advise patient to use barrier method of birth control for first week of first cycle.
- Tell patient that missed doses in midcycle greatly increase likelihood of pregnancy.
- If 1 pill is missed, take pill as soon as possible; if remembered on the next day, take 2 pills, then continue regular dosage schedule. Use additional method of contraception for remainder of cycle.
- If 2 consecutive pills are missed, take 2 pills a day for next 2 days; then resume regular dosage

schedule. Use additional method of contraception for the next 7 days or preferably for the remainder of cycle.

- If 2 consecutive pills are missed in the third week or if patient misses 3 consecutive pills, tell patient to contact prescriber for dosage instructions.
- Warn patient that headache, nausea, dizziness, breast tenderness, spotting, and breakthrough bleeding are common at first. Effects will diminish after 3 to 6 months.
- Instruct patient to weigh herself at least twice weekly and to report sudden weight gain or edema to prescriber.
- Warn patient to avoid exposure to ultraviolet light or prolonged exposure to sunlight.

ALERT: Warn patient to immediately report abdominal pain; numbness, stiffness, or pain in legs or buttocks; pressure or pain in chest; shortness of breath; severe headache; visual disturbances, such as blind spots, blurriness, or flashing lights; undiagnosed vaginal bleeding or discharge; two consecutive missed menstrual periods; lumps in breast; swelling of hands or feet; or severe pain in abdomen.

- Advise patient that smoking while using hormonal contraceptives increases risks of thromboembolic events.
- Teach patient how to perform breast self-examination.
- If one menstrual period is missed and tablets have been taken on schedule, tell patient to continue taking them. If two consecutive menstrual periods are missed, tell patient to stop drug and have pregnancy test. Progestins may cause birth defects if taken early in pregnancy.
- Advise patient not to take same drug for longer than 12 months without consulting prescriber. Stress importance of Papanicolaou test and annual gynecologic examination.
- Advise patient to check with prescriber about how soon pregnancy may be attempted after hormonal therapy is stopped.
- Warn patient that she may not be able to become pregnant immediately after drug is stopped.
- Advise women on prolonged contraceptive therapy to stop drug and use other nonhormonal birth control methods. Periodically reassess patient while off hormone therapy.

☑ Evaluation

- Patient doesn't become pregnant.
- Patient obtains relief from drug-induced headache with administration of mild analgesic.
- Patient and family state understanding of drug therapy.

ethinyl estradiol and drospirenone

(ETH-ih-nill es-truh-DIGH-ol and droh-SPEER-ih-nohn)

Yasmin, YAZ

Pharmacologic class: hormonal contraceptive
Therapeutic class: estrogen and progestin
Pregnancy risk category: X

Indications and dosages

▶ **Contraception (Yasin).** *Women and postpubertal girls:* 1 yellow tablet P.O. for 21 consecutive days; then 1 white inert tablet on days 22 through 28 per menstrual cycle. Begin either on the first day of menstrual period (day 1 start) or on the first Sunday after menstruation starts (Sunday start).

▶ **Premenstrual dysphoric disorder; contraception (YAZ).** *Women:* 1 light-pink tablet P.O. daily for 24 consecutive days followed by 1 white tablet P.O. for 4 consecutive days per menstrual cycle. Begin either on the first day of menstrual period (day 1 start) or on the first Sunday after menstruation starts (Sunday start).

Contraindications and cautions

- Contraindicated in women with hepatic dysfunction, tumor, or disease; renal or adrenal insufficiency; thrombophlebitis, thromboembolic disorders, or history of deep vein thrombosis or thromboembolic disorders; cerebrovascular or coronary artery disease; known or suspected breast cancer, endometrial cancer, or other estrogen-dependent neoplasia; unexplained vaginal bleeding; or cholestatic jaundice of pregnancy or jaundice with other contraceptive pill use. Also contraindicated in women older than age 35 who smoke 15 or more cigarettes daily.
- Use cautiously in patients with risk factors for CV disease, such as hypertension, hyperlipidemias, obesity, and diabetes.

Lifespan: In women who are pregnant or suspect they may be pregnant, drug is contraindicated. In breast-feeding women, drug is contraindicated. In girls who haven't reached menarche, drug is contraindicated.

Adverse reactions

CNS: asthenia, depression, dizziness, emotional lability, headache, migraine, nervousness, ***stroke.***
CV: edema, hypertension, ***mesenteric thrombosis, MI, thromboembolism,*** thrombophlebitis.
EENT: cataracts, intolerance to contact lenses, pharyngitis, retinal thrombosis, sinusitis, steepening of corneal curvature.
GI: abdominal cramping, abdominal pain, bloating, changes in appetite, colitis, diarrhea, gastroenteritis, nausea, vomiting.
GU: amenorrhea, breakthrough bleeding, change in cervical erosion and secretion, change in menstrual flow, cystitis, cystitis-like syndrome, dysmenorrhea, ***hemolytic uremic syndrome,*** leukorrhea, menstrual disorder, premenstrual syndrome, renal impairment, spotting, temporary infertility, UTI, vaginal candidiasis, vaginitis.
Hepatic: benign liver tumors, ***Budd-Chiari syndrome,*** cholestatic jaundice, gallbladder disease, ***hepatic adenomas.***
Metabolic: porphyria, reduced tolerance to carbohydrates, weight gain.
Musculoskeletal: back pain.
Respiratory: bronchitis, ***pulmonary embolism,*** upper respiratory tract infection.
Skin: acne, ***erythema multiforme,*** erythema nodosum, hemorrhagic eruption, hirsutism, loss of scalp hair, melasma, pruritus, rash.
Other: breast changes, changes in libido, decreased lactation.

Interactions

Drug-drug. *ACE inhibitors, aldosterone antagonists, angiotensin II receptor antagonists, heparin, NSAIDs, potassium-sparing diuretics:* May increase risk of hyperkalemia. Monitor potassium level.
Acetaminophen: May decrease acetaminophen level. Adjust acetaminophen dose as needed.
Ampicillin, griseofulvin, tetracycline: May decrease contraceptive effect. Encourage use of additional method of birth control while taking the antibiotic.
Ascorbic acid, atorvastatin: May increase contraceptive level. Monitor patient for adverse effects.
Carbamazepine, phenobarbital, phenytoin: May increase metabolism of ethinyl estradiol and decrease contraceptive effectiveness. Encourage use of alternative method of birth control.
Clofibrate, morphine, salicylic acid, temazepam: May decrease levels and increase clearance of these drugs. Monitor effectiveness.
Cyclosporine, prednisolone, theophylline: May increase levels of these drugs. Monitor patient for adverse effects and toxicity.
Phenylbutazone, rifampin: May decrease contraceptive effectiveness and increase breakthrough bleeding. Encourage use of alternative method of birth control.
Drug-herb. *St. John's wort:* May decrease contraceptive effect and increase breakthrough bleeding. Encourage use of additional method of birth control, or discourage use together.
Drug-lifestyle. *Smoking:* May increase risk of CV adverse effects and thromboembolism. Warn patient to avoid smoking and tobacco products while taking hormonal contraceptives.

Effects on lab test results

- May increase circulating total thyroid hormone, triglyceride, other binding protein, sex hormone–binding globulin, total circulating endogenous sex steroid, corticoid, potassium, folate, liver enzyme, and clotting factors VII, VIII, IX, and X levels.
- May increase PT. May decrease glucose tolerance.

Pharmacokinetics

Absorption: Steady-state level occurs after 10 days for drospirenone and during second half of treatment cycle for ethinyl estradiol.
Distribution: Wide. Drospirenone is about 97% bound to nonspecific proteins. Ethinyl estradiol is about 98% bound to albumin and other nonspecific proteins.
Metabolism: Drospirenone is metabolized mainly by metabolites in plasma and to a minor extent in the liver by CYP3A4 to inactive metabolites. Ethinyl estradiol is mainly metabolized by hydroxylation and subject to presystemic conjugation in the small bowel and the liver.
Excretion: Small amounts of drospirenone unchanged in urine and feces. Ethinyl estradiol as metabolites in urine and feces. *Half-life:* drospirenone, 30 hours; ethinyl estradiol, 24 hours.

Route	Onset	Peak	Duration
P.O.	Unknown	1–3 hr	Unknown

Action

Chemical effect: Suppresses gonadotropins, follicle-stimulating hormone, and luteinizing hormone, thereby preventing ovulation, changing the cervical mucus to increase the difficulty of penetration by sperm and changing the endometrium to increase the difficulty of implantation.

Therapeutic effect: Reduces the opportunity for conception.

Available forms

Tablets: 21 yellow tablets containing 3 mg drospirenone and 30 mcg ethinyl estradiol, and 7 inert white tablets (Yasmin); 3 mg drospirenone and 20 mcg ethinyl estradiol (YAZ)

NURSING PROCESS

Assessment

- Determine if patient is pregnant before giving drug.
- Find out if the patient smokes, and investigate her medical history, CV health, and potassium level before starting therapy.
- Assess and be alert for adverse reactions. The use of contraceptives increases the risk of MI, thromboembolism, stroke, hepatic neoplasia, gallbladder disease, and hypertension, especially in patients with hypertension, diabetes, hyperlipidemia, and obesity.
- Monitor patient's laboratory results during drug therapy.
- Assess patient's and family's knowledge of contraception and drug therapy.

Nursing diagnoses

- Risk for injury related to drug-induced adverse reactions
- Health seeking behavior for the prevention of pregnancy related to family planning
- Deficient knowledge of contraceptive drug therapy

Planning and implementation

- Because of the postpartum risk of thromboembolism, don't start drug earlier than 4 to 6 weeks after delivery.
- If patient misses two consecutive periods, tell her to obtain a negative pregnancy test result before continuing contraceptive. If pregnancy test is positive, tell her to immediately stop taking the drug.
- In patients scheduled to have elective surgery that may increase the risk of thromboembolism, stop contraceptive use from at least 4 weeks before until 2 weeks after surgery. Also avoid use during and after prolonged immobilization. Advise patient to use alternative methods of birth control.
- Overdose may cause nausea and withdrawal bleeding. Monitor potassium and sodium levels, and watch for signs of metabolic acidosis.
- If loss of vision, proptosis, diplopia, papilledema, or retinal vascular lesions occur, stop use and evaluate patient. Recommend that contact lens wearers be evaluated by an ophthalmologist if they have changes in vision or lens intolerance.
- Evaluate patient who has unusual breakthrough bleeding for malignancy or pregnancy.
- If patient develops sharp or crushing chest pains, hemoptysis, sudden shortness of breath, calf pain, breast lumps, severe stomach pains, difficulty sleeping, weakness, fatigue, or jaundice, stop drug. Notify prescriber immediately and offer supportive treatment p.r.n.

Patient teaching

- Inform patient that pills are used to prevent pregnancy and don't protect against HIV and other sexually transmitted diseases.
- Advise patient of the dangers of smoking while taking hormonal contraceptives. Suggest that she choose a different form of birth control if she continues smoking.
- Tell patient to schedule yearly gynecologic examinations and perform monthly breast self-examinations.
- Inform patient that spotting, light bleeding, or stomach upset may occur during the first one to three packs of pills. Tell her to continue taking the pills and to notify prescriber if these symptoms persist.
- Tell patient to take the pill at the same time each day, preferably during the evening or at bedtime.
- Tell patient to immediately report sharp chest pain, coughing of blood, or sudden shortness of breath, pain in the calf, crushing chest pain or chest heaviness, sudden severe headache or vomiting, dizziness or fainting, visual or speech disturbances, weakness or numbness in an arm or leg, loss of vision, breast lumps, severe stom-

ach pain or tenderness, difficulty sleeping, lack of energy, fatigue, change in mood, jaundice with fever, loss of appetite, dark urine, or light-colored bowel movements.
• Tell patient to notify prescriber if she wears contact lenses and notices a change in vision or has difficulty wearing the lenses.
• Advise patient to use additional method of birth control during the first 7 days of the first cycle of hormonal contraceptive.
• Tell patient that the risk of pregnancy increases with each active yellow tablet she forgets to take.
• If patient misses 1 tablet, tell her to take it as soon as she remembers and to take the next pill at the regular time.
• Tell patient to use an additional method of birth control and notify prescriber if she isn't sure what to do about missed pills.

Evaluation
• Patient doesn't suffer from any drug-induced adverse reactions.
• Patient doesn't become pregnant.
• Patient and family state understanding of drug therapy.

ethinyl estradiol and etonogestrel vaginal ring

(ETH-ih-nill es-truh-DIGH-ol and et-oh-noe-JESS-trel)
NuvaRing

Pharmacologic class: intravaginal hormonal contraceptive
Therapeutic class: progestin and estrogen
Pregnancy risk category: X

Indications and dosages

▶ **Contraception.** *Women:* Insert one ring vaginally, and leave in place for 3 weeks. Insert new ring exactly 1 week after the previous ring was removed, even if still menstruating.

Contraindications and cautions

• Contraindicated in patients hypersensitive to the drug or any of its components and in patients older than age 35 who smoke 15 or more cigarettes daily. Also contraindicated in patients with thrombophlebitis, thromboembolic disorder, history of deep vein thrombophlebitis, cerebral vascular or coronary artery disease (current or previous), valvular heart disease with complications, severe hypertension, diabetes with vascular complications, headache with focal neurologic symptoms, major surgery with prolonged immobilization, known or suspected cancer of the endometrium or breast, estrogen-dependent neoplasia, abnormal undiagnosed vaginal bleeding, jaundice related to pregnancy or previous use of hormonal contraceptive, active liver disease, or benign or malignant hepatic tumors.
• Use cautiously in patients with hypertension, hyperlipidemias, obesity, diabetes, a condition that could be aggravated by fluid retention, a history of depression, or impaired liver function.
Lifespan: In women who are or may be pregnant, drug is contraindicated. In breast-feeding women, drug isn't recommended; tell patient to use alternative forms of contraception until baby is weaned. In women who choose not to breast-feed, don't start drug earlier than 4 weeks after delivery. In girls who haven't reached menarche, drug is contraindicated. In postmenopausal women, don't use.

Adverse reactions

CNS: emotional lability, *headache.*
EENT: sinusitis.
GI: nausea.
GU: device-related events (such as foreign body sensation, coital difficulties, device expulsion), *leukorrhea*, vaginal discomfort, *vaginitis.*
Metabolic: weight gain.
Respiratory: upper respiratory tract infection.

Interactions

Drug-drug. *Acetaminophen, ascorbic acid, atorvastatin, itraconazole:* May increase ethinyl estradiol level. Monitor patient for adverse effects.
Ampicillin, barbiturates, carbamazepine, felbamate, griseofulvin, oxcarbazepine, phenylbutazone, phenytoin, rifampin, tetracyclines, topiramate: May decrease contraceptive effectiveness and increase risk of pregnancy, breakthrough bleeding, or both. Tell patient to use an additional form of contraception while taking these drugs.
Clofibric acid, morphine, salicylic acid, temazepam: May increase clearance of these drugs. Monitor patient for effectiveness.
Cyclosporine, prednisolone, theophylline: May increase levels of these drugs. Monitor cyclo-

sporine and theophylline levels, and adjust dosages if needed.
Protease inhibitors: May increase or decrease the bioavailability of estrogen or progestin. Suggest other methods of birth control.
Drug-herb. *St. John's wort:* May reduce contraceptive effectiveness, increase risk of pregnancy, and increase risk of breakthrough bleeding. Discourage use together.
Drug-lifestyle. *Smoking:* May increase risk of serious CV side effects and thromboembolism, especially in women age 35 and older who smoke 15 or more cigarettes daily. Urge patient to quit smoking.

Effects on lab test results

- May increase prothrombin, thyroid-binding globulin (leading to increased circulating total thyroid hormone levels), other binding protein, sex hormone–binding globulin, triglyceride, lipoprotein, other lipid, and clotting factor VII, VIII, IX, and X levels. May decrease antithrombin III and folate levels.
- May increase norepinephrine-induced platelet aggregation. May decrease T_3 resin uptake and glucose tolerance.

Pharmacokinetics

Absorption: Rapid. Bioavailability of etonogestrel is 100% and ethinyl estradiol is 55.6%.
Distribution: Etonogestrel is 66% protein-bound and 32% bound to sex hormone–binding globulin. Ethinyl estradiol is about 98% nonspecific protein-bound and increases levels of sex hormone–binding globulin.
Metabolism: Both components of drug are metabolized in the liver by CYP3A4.
Excretion: Mainly in urine, bile, and feces.
Half-life: ethinyl estradiol, 45 hours; etonogestrel, 29 hours.

Route	Onset	Peak	Duration
Vaginal	Immediate	Unknown	Unknown

Action

Chemical effect: Suppresses gonadotropins, which inhibits ovulation, increases the viscosity of cervical mucus (decreasing the ability of sperm to enter the uterus), and alters the endometrial lining (reducing potential for implantation).
Therapeutic effect: Decreases risk of pregnancy.

Available forms

Vaginal ring: Delivers 0.120 mg etonogestrel and 0.015 mg ethinyl estradiol daily

NURSING PROCESS

Assessment

- Assess patient for pregnancy before giving the drug.
- Find out if the patient smokes, and investigate her medical history, CV health, and risk factors before starting drug.
- Be alert for adverse reactions.
- Use of contraceptives increases the risk of MI, thromboembolism, stroke, hepatic neoplasia, gallbladder disease, and hypertension, especially in patients with hypertension, diabetes, hyperlipidemia, and obesity. Monitor patient for related signs and symptoms.
- Monitor patient's laboratory results during drug therapy.
- Assess patient's and family's knowledge of contraception and drug therapy.

Nursing diagnoses

- Risk for injury related to drug-induced adverse reactions
- Health seeking behavior for the prevention of pregnancy related to family planning
- Deficient knowledge of contraceptive drug therapy

Planning and implementation

- Stop drug at least 4 weeks before and for 2 weeks after procedures that may increase the risk of thromboembolism and during and after prolonged immobilization.
- If patient develops unexplained partial or complete loss of vision, proptosis, diplopia, papilledema, or retinal vascular lesions, stop drug.
- If patient has hypertension or renal disease, monitor blood pressure closely. If blood pressure rises, stop drug.
- If migraine begins or worsens or if patient has recurrent, persistent, or severe headaches, stop drug.
- If jaundice occurs, stop drug. The hormones may be poorly metabolized in patients with liver disease.
- If patient has persistent or severe abnormal menstrual bleeding, look for cause. If amenorrhea occurs, rule out pregnancy.

• If depression occurs, stop drug to determine whether depression is drug-related.
• If patient hasn't adhered to the prescribed regimen and a menstrual period is missed, if prescribed regimen is adhered to and two periods are missed, or if the patient has retained the ring for longer than 4 weeks, rule out pregnancy.
• Overdose may cause nausea, vomiting, vaginal bleeding, or other menstrual irregularities. Offer supportive treatment.

Patient teaching

• Teach patient or provide patient with instructions for proper placement of vaginal ring. Also encourage proper handwashing before and after ring insertion to prevent vaginal infections.
• If the ring is removed or expelled (for example, while removing a tampon or moving the bowels), tell patient to wash with cool to lukewarm water and reinsert immediately. If the ring stays out for more than 3 hours, contraceptive may not be effective, and a backup method of contraception should be recommended until the reinserted ring is used continuously for 7 days.
• Emphasize the importance of having annual physical examinations to check for adverse effects or developing contraindications.
• Tell patient that drug doesn't protect against HIV and other sexually transmitted diseases.
• Advise patient not to smoke while using contraceptive.
• Tell patient not to use a diaphragm if a backup method of birth control is needed.
• Tell patient who wears contact lenses to contact an ophthalmologist if vision or lens tolerance changes.

☑ Evaluation

• Patient doesn't suffer from any drug-induced adverse reactions or vaginal infections.
• Patient doesn't become pregnant.
• Patient and family state understanding of drug therapy.

ethinyl estradiol and norelgestromin transdermal system

(ETH-ih-nill es-truh-DIGH-ol and nor-el-GESS-troh-min)
Ortho Evra

Pharmacologic class: transdermal hormonal contraceptive
Therapeutic class: estrogen and progestin
Pregnancy risk category: X

Indications and dosages

▶ **Contraception.** *Women:* Apply one patch weekly for 3 weeks. Week 4 is patch-free. On the day after week 4 ends, apply a new patch to start a new 4-week cycle. Apply each new patch on the same day of the week.

Contraindications and cautions

• Contraindicated in patients hypersensitive to the drug or any of its components and in those with a history of deep vein thrombosis or related disorder; history of cerebrovascular or coronary artery disease; past or current known or suspected breast cancer, endometrial cancer, or other known or suspected estrogen-dependent neoplasia; hepatic adenoma or carcinoma; or known or suspected pregnancy. Also contraindicated in patients with thrombophlebitis, thromboembolic disorders, valvular heart disease with complications, severe hypertension, diabetes with vascular involvement, headaches with focal neurologic symptoms, major surgery with prolonged immobilization, undiagnosed abnormal genital bleeding, cholestatic jaundice of pregnancy or jaundice with previous hormonal contraceptive use, or acute or chronic hepatocellular disease with abnormal liver function.
• Use cautiously in patients with CV disease risk factors, with conditions that might be aggravated by fluid retention, or with a history of depression.
Lifespan: In breast-feeding women, safety and effectiveness haven't been established; advise an alternative method of birth control. In girls who haven't reached menarche, safety and effectiveness haven't been evaluated; don't use.

Adverse reactions

CNS: *cerebral hemorrhage,* emotional lability, headache.

CV: edema, hypertension, MI, thromboembolic events.
EENT: contact lens intolerance.
GI: abdominal pain, nausea, vomiting.
GU: changes in menstrual flow, menstrual cramps, vaginal candidiasis.
Hepatic: benign liver tumors, gallbladder disease, ***hepatic adenomas.***
Metabolic: weight changes.
Respiratory: upper respiratory tract infection.
Skin: application site reaction.
Other: breast tenderness, enlargement, or secretion.

Interactions

Drug-drug. *Acetaminophen, clofibric acid, morphine, salicylic acid, temazepam:* May decrease levels or increase clearance of these drugs. Monitor patient closely for lack of drug effect.
Ampicillin, barbiturates, carbamazepine, felbamate, griseofulvin, oxcarbazepine, phenylbutazone, phenytoin, rifampin, topiramate: May decrease contraceptive effectiveness, resulting in unintended pregnancy or breakthrough bleeding. If used together, encourage backup contraceptive.
Ascorbic acid, atorvastatin, itraconazole, ketoconazole: May increase hormone levels. Use together cautiously.
Cyclosporine, prednisolone, theophylline: May increase levels of these drugs. Monitor patient for adverse effects.
Protease inhibitors: May alter contraceptive effectiveness and safety. Use together cautiously.
Drug-herb. *St. John's wort:* May reduce contraceptive effectiveness and cause breakthrough bleeding. Discourage use together.
Drug-lifestyle. *Smoking:* May increase risk of serious CV side effects, especially in those older than age 35 who smoke 15 or more cigarettes daily. Urge patient to stop smoking.

Effects on lab test results

- May increase clotting factor VII, VIII, IX, and X; prothrombin; circulating total thyroid hormone; triglyceride; other binding protein; sex hormone–binding globulin; total circulating endogenous sex steroid; and corticoid levels. May decrease antithrombin III and folate levels.
- May decrease free T_3 resin uptake and glucose tolerance.

Pharmacokinetics

Absorption: Rapid. Maintained at a steady state while the patch is worn.
Distribution: Norelgestromin and norgestrel (a metabolite) are more than 97% protein-bound. Ethinyl estradiol is extensively bound to albumin.
Metabolism: In the liver.
Excretion: Norelgestromin and ethinyl estradiol are eliminated in 28 hours and 17 hours, respectively. The metabolites are eliminated in the urine and feces. *Half-life:* 6 to 45 hours (ethinyl estradiol); 28 hours (norelgestromin).

Route	Onset	Peak	Duration
Transdermal	Rapid	2 days	Unknown

Action

Chemical effect: Suppresses gonadotropins and inhibits ovulation. Changes cervical mucus, complicating entry of sperm into the uterus, and changes endometrium, decreasing the likelihood of implantation.
Therapeutic effect: Reduces risk of pregnancy.

Available forms

Transdermal patch: norelgestromin 6 mg and ethinyl estradiol 0.75 mg (releases 150 mcg of norelgestromin and 20 mcg of ethinyl estradiol every 24 hours)

NURSING PROCESS

Assessment

- Rule out pregnancy before giving drug.
- Find out if the patient smokes, and investigate her medical history and CV health before starting drug.
- Be alert for any drug-induced adverse reactions.
- Monitor patient for adverse signs and symptoms related to contraceptive use: increased risk of MI, thromboembolism, stroke, hepatic neoplasia, gallbladder disease, and hypertension, especially in patients with hypertension, diabetes, hyperlipidemia, and obesity.
- Monitor patient's laboratory results during drug therapy.
- Assess patient's knowledge of contraception and drug therapy.

Nursing diagnoses

- Risk for injury related to drug-induced adverse reactions
- Health seeking behavior for the prevention of pregnancy related to family planning
- Deficient knowledge of contraceptive drug therapy

Planning and implementation

- Encourage women with a history of hypertension or renal disease to use a different method of contraception. If Ortho Evra is used, monitor blood pressure closely; if hypertension occurs, stop use.
- Drug may be less effective in women weighing 90 kg (198 lb) or more.
- Cigarette smoking increases the risk of serious CV adverse effects. This risk increases especially in women age 35 and older who smoke 15 or more cigarettes per day.
- If used postpartum or postabortion, risk of thromboembolic disease increases.
- If breakthrough bleeding occurs for more than a few cycles, remove patch and assess cause.
- If no withdrawal bleeding occurs on patch-free week, resume on the next scheduled patch-change day. If withdrawal bleeding fails to occur for two consecutive cycles, rule out pregnancy.
- If skin becomes irritated, the patch may be removed and a new patch applied at a different site until the next patch-change day.
- Stop use at least 4 weeks before and for 2 weeks after elective surgery that increases risk of thromboembolism and during and after prolonged immobilization.
- If patient has vision loss, proptosis, diplopia, papilledema, retinal vascular lesions, or recurrent, persistent, or severe headaches, stop use.
- If jaundice occurs, stop use.
- If patient becomes severely depressed, stop use and evaluate whether the depression is drug related.

Patient teaching

- Emphasize the importance of having annual physical examinations to check for adverse effects or developing contraindications.
- Tell patient that the contraceptive patch doesn't protect against HIV and other sexually transmitted diseases.
- Advise patient to immediately apply a new patch once the used patch is removed, on the same day of the week, every 7 days for 3 weeks. Week 4 is patch-free. Tell patient to expect bleeding to occur during this time.
- Advise patient to start a new cycle, applying a new patch on the usual patch-change day, regardless of when the menstrual period starts or ends.
- Teach patient how to properly apply the patch.
- Tell patient to apply each patch to a new clean, dry area of the skin on the buttocks, abdomen, upper outer arm, or upper torso to avoid irritation. Tell patient not to apply to the breasts or to skin that's red, irritated, or cut. Instruct patient to avoid creams, oils, powder, or makeup on or near the skin where the patch will be placed because it may cause the patch to become loose.
- Tell patient what to do if a patch is partially or completely detached.
- Tell patient what to do if she forgets to change her patch.
- If patient wants to change her patch-change day, tell her to complete her current cycle and apply a new patch on the desired day during the patch-free week. There shouldn't be more than 7 consecutive patch-free days.
- Tell patient what to do if she misses a menstrual period.
- Tell patient to immediately stop drug if pregnancy is confirmed.
- Tell patient who wears contact lenses to contact an ophthalmologist if visual changes or changes in lens tolerance develop.
- Stress that if patient isn't sure what to do about mistakes with patch use, she should use a backup method of birth control, such as a condom, spermicide, or diaphragm. She should contact her prescriber for further instructions.

Evaluation

- Patient doesn't have any drug-induced adverse reactions.
- Patient doesn't become pregnant.
- Patient and family state understanding of drug therapy.

etodolac (ultradol)

(eh-toh-DOH-lak)

Lodine, Lodine XL

Pharmacologic class: NSAID
Therapeutic class: analgesic, antiarthritic
Pregnancy risk category: C (D in third trimester)

Indications and dosages

▶**Acute pain.** *Adults:* 200 to 400 mg P.O. of film-coated tablets or capsules q 6 to 8 hours. Maximum dose is 1,200 mg daily.

▶**Acute or long-term management of osteoarthritis or rheumatoid arthritis.** *Adults:* 600 to 1,000 mg P.O. daily of film-coated tablets or capsules in two divided doses. For extended-release tablets, usual dosage is 400 to 1,000 mg P.O. once daily. Maximum dose is 1,200 mg daily.

Contraindications and cautions

• Contraindicated in patients hypersensitive to the drug or any of its components and in those with history of aspirin- or NSAID-induced asthma, rhinitis, urticaria, or other allergic reactions.

• Use cautiously in patients with history of GI bleeding, ulceration, and perforation; in patients with renal or hepatic impairment, heart failure, hypertension, or cardiac function impairments; and in those predisposed to fluid retention.

Lifespan: In pregnant women during first and second trimesters, use cautiously. During third trimester, drug is contraindicated. In breast-feeding women, use cautiously because it's unknown if the drug appears in breast milk. In children younger than age 18, safety and effectiveness haven't been established.

Adverse reactions

CNS: *asthenia,* depression, *dizziness,* drowsiness, fever, headache, insomnia, *malaise,* nervousness, syncope.
CV: edema, fluid retention, flushing, ***heart failure,*** hypertension, palpitations.
EENT: blurred vision, dry mouth, photophobia, tinnitus.
GI: abdominal pain, anorexia, constipation, diarrhea, *dyspepsia,* flatulence, gastritis, ***GI bleeding,*** melena, nausea, peptic ulceration, ***perforation,*** thirst, ulcerative stomatitis, vomiting.
GU: dysuria, ***renal impairment,*** urinary frequency.
Hematologic: hemolytic anemia, ***leukopenia, thrombocytopenia, agranulocytosis.***
Hepatic: ***hepatitis.***
Metabolic: weight gain.
Respiratory: ***asthma.***
Skin: pruritus, rash, photosensitivity, ***Stevens-Johnson syndrome.***
Other: chills.

Interactions

Drug-drug. *ACE inhibitors, beta blockers, diuretics:* May blunt the effects of these drugs. Monitor patient closely.
Antacids: May decrease peak drug levels. Monitor patient for decreased etodolac effect.
Aspirin: May reduce protein-binding of etodolac without altering its clearance. Significance isn't known. Avoid use together.
Cyclosporine: May impair elimination and increase risk of nephrotoxicity. Avoid use together.
Digoxin, lithium, methotrexate: May impair elimination of these drugs, increasing levels and risk of toxicity. Monitor blood levels.
Phenytoin: May increase phenytoin level. Monitor patient and level for toxicity.
Warfarin: May decrease protein-binding of warfarin but doesn't alter clearance. Although no dosage adjustment is needed, monitor PT and INR closely, and watch for bleeding.
Drug-herb. *Dong quai, feverfew, garlic, ginger, horse chestnut, red clover:* May increase risk of bleeding. Discourage use together.
St. John's wort: May increase risk of photosensitivity. Discourage use together.
Drug-lifestyle. *Alcohol use:* May increase chance of adverse effects. Discourage use together.
Sun exposure: May cause photosensitivity reactions. Urge patient to avoid unprotected or prolonged exposure to sunlight.

Effects on lab test results

• May increase BUN and creatinine levels. May decrease uric acid and hemoglobin levels and hematocrit.

• May increase liver function test values. May decrease platelet, granulocyte, and WBC counts.

• May cause false-positive test for urinary bilirubin.

Pharmacokinetics

Absorption: Well absorbed from GI tract.
Distribution: To liver, lungs, heart, and kidneys.
Metabolism: Extensive.
Excretion: In urine, mainly as metabolites; 16% is excreted in feces. *Half-life:* 7¼ hours.

Route	Onset	Peak	Duration
P.O.	≤ 30 min	1–2 hr	4–12 hr

Action

Chemical effect: May inhibit prostaglandin synthesis.
Therapeutic effect: Relieves inflammation and pain.

Available forms

Capsules: 200 mg, 300 mg
Tablets (extended-release): 400 mg, 500 mg, 600 mg
Tablets (film-coated): 400 mg, 500 mg

NURSING PROCESS

Assessment

• Obtain history of patient's underlying condition before starting therapy.
• Be alert for adverse reactions and drug interactions.
• Assess patient's and family's knowledge of drug therapy.

Nursing diagnoses

• Acute pain related to underlying condition
• Risk for injury related to drug-induced adverse reactions
• Deficient knowledge related to drug therapy

Planning and implementation

• Give drug with milk or meals to minimize GI discomfort.
ALERT: Don't confuse Lodine with iodine.

Patient teaching

• Advise patient that serious GI toxicity, including peptic ulceration and bleeding, can occur as a result of taking NSAIDs, despite absence of GI symptoms. Teach patient the signs and symptoms of GI bleeding, such as dark tarry stools, generalized weakness, and coffee-ground emesis, and tell him to contact prescriber immediately if they occur.
• Tell patient to take drug with milk or food.
• Instruct patient to notify prescriber if other adverse reactions occur or if drug doesn't relieve pain.
• Advise patient to use sunblock, wear protective clothing, and avoid prolonged exposure to sunlight to prevent photosensitivity reactions.
• Tell patient not to use drug during last trimester of pregnancy.

Evaluation

• Patient is free from pain.
• Patient has no injury as result of drug-induced adverse reactions.
• Patient and family state understanding of drug therapy.

etoposide (VP-16)

(eh-toh-POH-sighd)
Etopophos, Toposar, VePesid

Pharmacologic class: podophyllotoxin
Therapeutic class: antineoplastic
Pregnancy risk category: D

Indications and dosages

▶ **Testicular cancer.** *Adults:* 50 to 100 mg/m² I.V. on 5 consecutive days q 3 to 4 weeks; or 100 mg/m² on days 1, 3, and 5 q 3 to 4 weeks for three to four courses of therapy.
▶ **Small-cell carcinoma of lung.** *Adults:* 35 mg/m²/day I.V. for 4 days; or 50 mg/m²/day I.V. for 5 days. P.O. dose is two times I.V. dose rounded to nearest 50 mg.
▶ **AIDS-related Kaposi sarcoma‡.** *Adults:* 150 mg/m² I.V. for 3 consecutive days q 4 weeks. Repeat cycles as needed.

I.V. administration

• Keep diphenhydramine, hydrocortisone, epinephrine, and needed emergency equipment available to establish airway in case of anaphylaxis.
• Don't give drug through membrane-type in-line filter because diluent may dissolve filter.
• Dilute drug for infusion in either D_5W or normal saline solution to 0.2 or 0.4 mg/ml. Higher concentrations may crystallize.

• Give drug by slow I.V. infusion (over at least 30 minutes) to prevent severe hypotension.
• If systolic blood pressure falls below 90 mm Hg, stop infusion and notify prescriber.
• Solutions diluted to 0.2 mg/ml are stable 96 hours at room temperature in plastic or glass unprotected from light; solutions diluted to 0.4 mg/ml are stable 48 hours under same conditions.

⊗ **Incompatibilities**

Cefepime hydrochloride, filgrastim, gallium nitrate, idarubicin.

Contraindications and cautions

• Contraindicated in patients hypersensitive to the drug or any of its components.
• Use cautiously in patients who have had cytotoxic or radiation therapy.

Lifespan: In pregnant women, use cautiously and only when benefits outweigh risks to fetus. In breast-feeding women, drug is contraindicated. In children, safety and effectiveness haven't been established.

Adverse reactions

CNS: peripheral neuropathy.
CV: hypotension.
GI: abdominal pain, anorexia, diarrhea, nausea, stomatitis, vomiting.
Hematologic: anemia, **LEUKOPENIA,** ***myelosuppression*** (dose-limiting), **THROMBOCYTOPENIA.**
Skin: reversible alopecia.
Other: ***anaphylaxis,*** rash.

Interactions

Drug-drug. *Warfarin:* May further prolong PT. Monitor patient for bleeding, and monitor PT and INR.

Effects on lab test results

• May decrease hemoglobin level and hematocrit.
• May decrease WBC, RBC, platelet, and neutrophil counts.

Pharmacokinetics

Absorption: Moderate across GI tract after P.O. use. Bioavailability ranges from 25% to 75%, with average of 50% of dose being absorbed.
Distribution: Wide in body tissues. Crosses blood–brain barrier to limited and variable extent. About 94% protein-bound.
Metabolism: Only small portion of dose is metabolized in liver.
Excretion: Mainly in urine as unchanged drug; smaller amount in feces. *Half-life:* Initial, 30 minutes to 2 hours; terminal, 5¼ to 11 hours.

Route	Onset	Peak	Duration
P.O., I.V.	Unknown	Unknown	Unknown

Action

Chemical effect: Unknown.
Therapeutic effect: Inhibits selected cancer cell growth.

Available forms

Capsules: 50 mg
Injection: 20 mg/ml
Powder for injection: 100 mg

NURSING PROCESS

Assessment

• Obtain history of patient's underlying condition before starting therapy.
• Obtain baseline blood pressure before therapy, and monitor blood pressure at 30-minute intervals during infusion.
• Monitor effectiveness by noting results of follow-up diagnostic tests and overall physical health and by regularly checking tumor size and rate of growth through appropriate studies. Etoposide has produced complete remission in small-cell lung cancer and testicular cancer.
• Monitor CBC. Observe patient for signs of bone marrow suppression.
• Be alert for adverse reactions and drug interactions.
• Assess patient's and family's knowledge of drug therapy.

Nursing diagnoses

• Ineffective health maintenance related to presence of neoplastic disease
• Ineffective protection related to drug induced adverse hematologic reactions
• Deficient knowledge related to drug therapy

Planning and implementation

• Follow facility policy to reduce risks. Preparation and administration of parenteral form cre-

ates carcinogenic, mutagenic, and teratogenic risks for staff.
• Store capsules in refrigerator.

Patient teaching
• Warn patient to watch for signs of infection and bleeding. Teach patient how to take infection-control and bleeding precautions.
• Tell patient that reversible hair loss may occur.
• Instruct patient to report discomfort, pain, or burning at I.V. insertion site.

Evaluation
• Patient exhibits positive response to therapy.
• Patient's immune function returns to normal when therapy stops.
• Patient and family state understanding of drug therapy.

exemestane
(ecks-eh-MES-tayn)
Aromasin

Pharmacologic class: aromatase inhibitor
Therapeutic class: antineoplastic
Pregnancy risk category: D

Indications and dosages

▶ **Advanced breast cancer in postmenopausal women whose disease has progressed after tamoxifen therapy.** *Women:* 25 mg P.O. once daily after a meal.
▶ **Adjuvant treatment of postmenopausal women with estrogen-receptor–positive early breast cancer after 2 to 3 years of tamoxifen therapy, to complete 5 consecutive years of adjuvant hormonal therapy.** *Women:* 25 mg P.O. once daily after a meal.

Contraindications and cautions

• Contraindicated in patients hypersensitive to drug or any of its components.
Lifespan: In premenopausal women, drug is contraindicated.

Adverse reactions

CNS: *anxiety,* asthenia, confusion, *depression,* dizziness, *fatigue, fever,* generalized weakness, headache, hypoesthesia, *insomnia, pain,* paresthesia.
CV: chest pain, edema, *hot flashes,* hypertension.
EENT: pharyngitis, rhinitis, sinusitis.
GI: abdominal pain, anorexia, constipation, diarrhea, dyspepsia, nausea, vomiting.
GU: UTI.
Metabolic: increased appetite.
Musculoskeletal: *arthralgia,* back pain, pathologic fractures, skeletal pain.
Respiratory: bronchitis, coughing, *dyspnea,* upper respiratory tract infection.
Skin: *alopecia,* dermatitis, *increased sweating,* itching, rash.
Other: flulike syndrome, infection, lymphedema.

Interactions

Drug-drug. *CYP3A4 inducers, such as phenytoin and rifampicin:* May reduce therapeutic effects of exemestane; increase dose to 50 mg once daily.
Drugs that contain estrogen: May interact. Don't give together.
Drug-herb. *St. John's wort:* May decrease effectiveness of drug. Discourage use together.

Effects on lab test results

• May increase bilirubin, alkaline phosphatase, and creatinine levels.

Pharmacokinetics

Absorption: Rapid, with about 42% of dose absorbed from the GI tract after P.O. use. Level increases by 40% after a high-fat meal.
Distribution: Extensive in tissues. 90% protein-bound.
Metabolism: Extensive by the liver. Main liver isoenzyme is CYP3A4.
Excretion: Equal in urine and feces. *Half-life:* 24 hours.

Route	Onset	Peak	Duration
P.O.	Unknown	1–2 hr	Unknown

Action

Chemical effect: Acts as a false substrate for the aromatase enzyme, the principal enzyme that converts androgens to estrogens in premenopausal and postmenopausal women. Results in lower levels of circulating estrogens.
Therapeutic effect: Hinders growth of estrogen-dependent breast cancer cells.

Available forms

Tablets: 25 mg

NURSING PROCESS

Assessment

- Assess patient's breast cancer before starting therapy and regularly thereafter.
- Monitor patient for adverse reactions.
- If adverse GI reactions occur, monitor patient's hydration.
- Assess patient's and family's knowledge of drug therapy.

Nursing diagnoses

- Ineffective health maintenance related to presence of breast cancer
- Impaired physical mobility related to potential adverse musculoskeletal effects
- Deficient knowledge related to drug therapy

Planning and implementation

- Give drug only to postmenopausal women.
- Don't give with drugs that contain estrogen because doing so could interfere with intended action.
- Continue treatment in patients with advanced breast cancer until tumor progression is evident.
- Patients with early breast cancer who have taken tamoxifen for 2 to 3 years should take exemestane to complete the 5-year course, unless cancer reoccurs or is found in the other breast.

ALERT: Don't confuse exemestane with estramustine.

Patient teaching

- Tell patient to take drug after a meal.
- Inform patient that she may need to take drug for a long period.
- Advise patient to report adverse effects to prescriber.

Evaluation

- Patient responds well to drug.
- Patient has no musculoskeletal adverse reactions.
- Patient and family state understanding of drug therapy.

exenatide

(ecks-EHN-uh-tighd)

Byetta

Pharmacologic class: incretin mimetic
Therapeutic class: antidiabetic
Pregnancy risk category: C

Indications and dosages

▶ **Adjunctive therapy to improve glycemic control in patients with type 2 diabetes who take metformin, a sulfonylurea, a thiazolidinedione, or a combination of metformin and a sulfonylnurea or a thiazolidinedione, but haven't achieved adequate glycemic control.** *Adults:* 5 mcg subcutaneously b.i.d. within 60 minutes before morning and evening meals (or before the two main meals of the day, about 6 hours or more apart). Increase to 10 mcg b.i.d. after 1 month, as needed.

Contraindications and cautions

- Contraindicated in patients hypersensitive to drug or its components. Don't give to patients with type 1 diabetes or diabetic ketoacidosis. Avoid in patients with end-stage renal disease, creatinine clearance less than 30 ml/minute, or severe GI disease.

Lifespan: In pregnant women, use only if benefits justify risks to the fetus. In breast-feeding women, use cautiously because it isn't known if drug appears in breast milk. In children, safety and effectiveness haven't been established.

Adverse reactions

CNS: dizziness, headache, jittery feeling.
GI: diarrhea, dyspepsia, nausea, vomiting.
Metabolic: ***hypoglycemia.***
Skin: excessive sweating.
Other: injection site reaction.

Interactions

Drug-drug. *Drugs that are rapidly absorbed:* May slow gastric emptying and reduce absorption of some oral drugs. Use cautiously together.
Oral drugs that need to maintain a threshold level to maintain effectiveness (antibiotics, hormonal contraceptives): May reduce rate and extent of absorption of these drugs. Give these drugs at least 1 hour before giving exenatide.

Sulfonylureas: May increase the risk of hypoglycemia. Reduce sulfonylurea dose as needed, and monitor patient closely.

Effects on lab test results

None reported.

Pharmacokinetics

Absorption: Peaks in plasma in about 2 hours.
Distribution: Volume of about 28.3 L after a single dose.
Metabolism: Not metabolized.
Excretion: Mainly by glomerular filtration.
Half-life: 2.4 hours.

Route	Onset	Peak	Duration
SubQ	Unknown	2 hr	10 hr

Action

Chemical effect: Reduces fasting and postprandial glucose levels in type 2 diabetes by stimulating insulin production in response to elevated glucose levels, inhibiting glucagon release after meals and slowing gastric emptying.
Therapeutic effect: Lowers glucose level.

Available forms

Injection: 5 mcg/dose in 1.2-ml prefilled pen, 10 mcg/dose in 2.4-ml prefilled pen (60 doses).

NURSING PROCESS

Assessment

- Assess GI function before treatment starts.
- Monitor blood glucose level regularly and glycosylated hemoglobin level periodically.
- Monitor patient for adverse reactions and drug interactions.
- Assess patient's and family's knowledge of drug therapy.

Nursing diagnoses

- Risk for injury related to drug-induced hypoglycemia
- Ineffective health maintenance related to hyperglycemia
- Deficient knowledge related to drug therapy

Planning and implementation

- Drug comes in two strengths; check cartridge carefully before use.
- Overdose may cause rapid decline in blood glucose levels, leading to severe nausea and vomiting, tachycardia, restlessness, and dizziness.
- Provide symptomatic care for hypoglycemia. If patient is responsive, give fast-acting oral carbohydrate. If unresponsive, give I.V. glucose.
- Store drug in refrigerator at 36° to 46° F (2° to 8° C).

ALERT: Don't confuse exenatide (Byetta) with ezetimibe (Zetia).

Patient teaching

- Explain the risks of exenatide.
- Review proper use and storage of dosage pen, particularly the one-time setup for each new pen.
- Inform patient that prefilled pen doesn't include a needle; explain which needle length and gauge is appropriate.
- Instruct patient to inject drug in the thigh, abdomen, or upper arm within 60 minutes before morning and evening meals. Caution against injecting drug after a meal.
- Advise patient that drug may decrease appetite, food intake, and body weight and that these changes don't warrant a change in dosage.
- Review steps for managing hypoglycemia, especially if patient takes a sulfonylurea.
- Stress importance of proper storage (refrigerated), infection prevention, and timing of exenatide dose in relation to other oral drugs.

Evaluation

- Patient sustains no injury.
- Patient's glucose level is normal with drug therapy.
- Patient and family state understanding of drug therapy.

ezetimibe

(eh-ZET-eh-mighb)
Zetia

Pharmacologic class: selective cholesterol absorption inhibitor
Therapeutic class: antilipemic
Pregnancy risk category: C

Indications and dosages

▶ **Primary hypercholesterolemia, alone or with HMG-CoA reductase inhibitors; adjunct to atorvastatin or simvastatin in patients with homozygous familial hypercholesterolemia; homozygous sitosterolemia to**

reduce sitosterol and campesterol levels. *Adults:* 10 mg P.O. daily.

▶ **Adjunct to fenofibrate and diet to reduce elevated total-C, LDL-C, Apo B and non-HDL-C in patients with mixed hyperlipidemia.** *Adults:* 10 mg P.O. once daily with or without food, taken at the same time as fenofibrate.

Contraindications and cautions

- Contraindicated in patients allergic to any component of the drug. Use with a HMG-CoA reductase inhibitor is contraindicated in patients with active hepatic disease or unexplained increase in transaminase levels.

Lifespan: In pregnant women, use only if benefits outweigh risks to fetus. If used in pregnant women, don't give with an HMG-CoA reductase inhibitor. In breast-feeding women, use cautiously because it's unknown if drug appears in breast milk. In children, safety and effectiveness haven't been established. In elderly patients, use cautiously because they may have a greater sensitivity to drug.

Adverse reactions

CNS: dizziness, fatigue, headache.
CV: chest pain.
EENT: pharyngitis, sinusitis.
GI: abdominal pain, diarrhea.
Musculoskeletal: arthralgia, back pain, myalgia.
Respiratory: cough, upper respiratory tract infection.
Other: viral infection.

Interactions

Drug-drug. *Aluminum/magnesium antacids, bile acid sequestrant (cholestyramine):* May decrease ezetimibe level. Give ezetimibe at least 2 hours before or 4 hours after cholestyramine.
Cyclosporine, fenofibrate, gemfibrozil: May increase ezetimibe level. Monitor patient closely for adverse effects.
Fibrates: May increase excretion of cholesterol into gallbladder bile. Avoid use together.

Effects on lab test results

- May increase liver function test values.

Pharmacokinetics

Absorption: Absorbed and conjugated to an active metabolite.
Distribution: More than 90% protein-bound.
Metabolism: Mainly and rapidly in the small intestine and liver via glucuronide conjugation.
Excretion: Biliary and renal. *Half-life:* 22 hours.

Route	Onset	Peak	Duration
P.O.	Unknown	4–12 hr	Unknown

Action

Chemical effect: Inhibits absorption of cholesterol by the small intestine. Decreases hepatic cholesterol stores and increases cholesterol clearance.
Therapeutic effect: Lowers cholesterol levels.

Available forms

Tablets: 10 mg

NURSING PROCESS

Assessment

- Obtain history of patient's underlying condition before starting therapy.
- Monitor total cholesterol, LDL, HDL, and triglyceride levels before and during therapy.
- Assess patient's and family's knowledge of drug therapy.

Nursing diagnoses

- Risk for injury related to elevated cholesterol levels
- Deficient knowledge related to drug therapy

Planning and implementation

- Use drug only after diet and other nondrug therapy prove ineffective. Have patient follow a standard low-cholesterol diet before and during therapy.
- Before starting drug, evaluate patient for secondary causes of dyslipidemia.
- When drug is used with an HMG-CoA reductase inhibitor, check liver function test results at start of therapy and thereafter according to the recommendations relevant to the HMG-CoA reductase inhibitor being used.
- Use with an HMG-CoA reductase inhibitor significantly reduces total cholesterol, LDL, apolipoprotein B, and triglyceride levels and (except with pravastatin) increases HDL level more than use of an HMG-CoA reductase inhibitor alone.

ALERT: Don't confuse Zetia with Zebeta, Zestril, or Zyrtec.

Patient teaching

- Emphasize importance of following a cholesterol-lowering diet.
- Tell patient he may take drug without regard to meals.
- Advise patient to notify prescriber of unexplained muscle pain, weakness, or tenderness.
- Urge patient to tell prescriber if he's taking herbal or dietary supplements.
- Advise patient to visit his prescriber for routine follow-up and blood tests.
- Tell patient to notify prescriber if she becomes pregnant.

Evaluation

- Patient's cholesterol level is within normal limits.
- Patient and family state understanding of drug therapy.

F

famciclovir

(fam-SIGH-kloh-veer)
Famvir

Pharmacologic class: synthetic acyclic guanine derivative
Therapeutic class: antiviral
Pregnancy risk category: B

Indications and dosages

▶ **Acute herpes zoster.** *Adults:* 500 mg P.O. q 8 hours for 7 days.
Adjust-a-dose: For patients with renal impairment, if creatinine clearance is 40 to 59 ml/minute, give 500 mg q 12 hours. If clearance is 20 to 39 ml/minute, give 500 mg q 24 hours. If clearance is less than 20 ml/minute, give 250 mg q 24 hours.

▶ **Recurrent genital herpes.** *Adults:* 1,000 mg P.O. b.i.d. for a single day. Start therapy at the first sign or symptom.
Adjust-a-dose: If creatinine clearance is 40 to 59 ml/minute, give 500 mg q 12 hours for 1 day. If clearance is 20 to 39 ml/minute, give 500 mg P.O. as a single dose. If clearance is less than 20 ml/minute, give 250 mg as a single dose. If patient is undergoing hemodialysis, give 250 mg as a single dose after dialysis session.

▶ **Long-term suppressive therapy of recurrent episodes of genital herpes.** *Adults:* 250 mg P.O. b.i.d. for up to 1 year.
Adjust-a-dose: If creatinine clearance is 20 to 39 ml/minute, give 125 mg q 12 hours. If clearance is less than 20 ml/minute, give 125 mg q 24 hours.

▶ **Recurrent herpes labialis (cold sores).** *Adults:* 1,500 mg P.O. for one dose. Give at the first sign or symptom of cold sore.
Adjust-a-dose: If creatinine clearance is 40 to 59 ml/minute, give 750 mg as a single dose. If clearance is 20 to 39 ml/minute, give 500 mg P.O. as a single dose. If clearance is less than 20 ml/minute, give 250 mg as a single dose. If patient is undergoing hemodialysis, give 250 mg as a single dose after dialysis session.

▶ **Recurrent herpes simplex virus infections in HIV-infected patients.** *Adults:* 500 mg P.O. b.i.d. for 7 days.
Adjust-a-dose: If creatinine clearance is 20 to 39 ml/minute, give 500 mg q 24 hours. If clearance is less than 20 ml/minute, give 250 mg q 24 hours.

Contraindications and cautions

- Contraindicated in patients hypersensitive to drug or any of its components.
- Use cautiously in patients with renal or hepatic impairment. Dosage adjustment may be needed.

Lifespan: In pregnant women, use only if benefits outweigh risks to fetus. In breast-feeding women, use cautiously because it's unknown if drug appears in breast milk. In men, use cautiously because of risk of decreased fertility. In children, safety and effectiveness haven't been established.

Adverse reactions

CNS: dizziness, fatigue, *headache,* paresthesia, somnolence.
EENT: pharyngitis, sinusitis.
GI: abdominal pain, anorexia, constipation, diarrhea, *nausea,* vomiting.
Musculoskeletal: arthralgia, back pain.
Skin: pruritus; zoster-related signs, symptoms, and complications.

Interactions

Drug-drug. *Probenecid:* May increase level of famciclovir. Monitor patient for increased adverse effects.

Effects on lab test results

• May increase AST, ALT, total bilirubin, creatinine, amylase, and lipase levels. May decrease hemoglobin level and hematocrit.
• May decrease WBC and neutrophil counts.

Pharmacokinetics

Absorption: Absolute bioavailability is 77%.
Distribution: Less than 20% protein-bound.
Metabolism: Extensive, in liver to active drug, penciclovir, and inactive metabolites.
Excretion: Mainly in urine. *Half-life:* 2 to 3 hours.

Route	Onset	Peak	Duration
P.O.	Unknown	≤ 1 hr	Unknown

Action

Chemical effect: Converted to penciclovir, which enters viral cells and inhibits DNA polymerase and viral DNA synthesis.
Therapeutic effect: Inhibits viral replication. Spectrum of activity includes herpes simplex types 1 and 2 and varicella zoster viruses.

Available forms

Tablets: 125 mg, 250 mg, 500 mg

NURSING PROCESS

Assessment

• Assess patient's viral infection before starting therapy, and reassess regularly throughout therapy.
• Be alert for adverse reactions and drug interactions.
• If adverse GI reactions occur, monitor patient's hydration.
• Assess patient's and family's knowledge of drug therapy.

Nursing diagnoses

• Risk for infection related to presence of virus susceptible to famciclovir
• Risk for deficient fluid volume related to drug's adverse GI reactions
• Deficient knowledge related to drug therapy

Planning and implementation

• Give a lower dose in patients with renal insufficiency.
• Drug may be taken with or without food.

Patient teaching

• Teach patient how to prevent spread of infection to others.
• Urge patient to recognize and report early symptoms of herpes infection, such as tingling, itching, or pain.

Evaluation

• Patient is free from infection.
• Patient maintains adequate hydration.
• Patient and family state understanding of drug therapy.

famotidine

(fam-OH-tih-deen)
Pepcid†✐, Pepcid AC†, Pepcid RPD, Pepcidine ◇

Pharmacologic class: H_2-receptor antagonist
Therapeutic class: antisecretory
Pregnancy risk category: B

Indications and dosages

▶ **Duodenal ulcer (short-term therapy).** *Adults:* For acute therapy, 40 mg P.O. once daily at bedtime or 20 mg P.O. b.i.d. Maintenance, 20 mg P.O. once daily at bedtime.
▶ **Benign gastric ulcer (short-term therapy).** *Adults:* 40 mg P.O. daily at bedtime for 8 weeks.
▶ **Pathologic hypersecretory conditions (such as Zollinger-Ellison syndrome).** *Adults:* 20 mg P.O. q 6 hours up to 160 mg q 6 hours.
▶ **Gastroesophageal reflux disease (GERD).** *Adults:* 20 mg P.O. b.i.d. for up to 6 weeks. For esophagitis caused by GERD, 20 to 40 mg b.i.d. for up to 12 weeks.
Children ages 1 to 16: Give 1 mg/kg/day P.O. in divided doses b.i.d. up to 80 mg daily.
▶ **Peptic ulcer in children.** *Children ages 1 to 16:* Give 0.5 mg/kg/day P.O. at bedtime or divided b.i.d. up to 40 mg daily.
▶ **Heartburn, prevention of heartburn.** *Adults:* 10 mg Pepcid AC P.O. 15 to 60 minutes before meals (prevention) or 10 mg Pepcid AC P.O. with water when symptoms occur. Maximum, 20 mg daily. Drug shouldn't be taken dai-

ly for longer than 2 weeks without prescriber authorization.

▶ **Hospitalized patients with intractable ulcerations or hypersecretory conditions or patients who can't take oral drugs.** *Adults:* 20 mg I.V. q 12 hours.
Children ages 1 to 16: Give 0.25 mg/kg I.V. q 12 hours, up to 40 mg daily.

Adjust-a-dose: If creatinine clearance is less than 50 ml/minute (moderate renal impairment) or less than 10 ml/minute (severe renal impairment) dose may be reduced to half-strength or interval prolonged to 36 to 48 hours, if needed, to avoid excess drug accumulation.

I.V. administration

- For I.V. injection, dilute 2 ml (20 mg) with compatible I.V. solution to total volume of either 5 or 10 ml. Compatible solutions include sterile water for injection, normal saline injection, D_5W or dextrose 10% in water injection, 5% sodium bicarbonate injection, and lactated Ringer's injection. Inject over at least 2 minutes.
- For intermittent I.V. infusion, dilute 20 mg (2 ml) drug in 100 ml of compatible solution. Solution is stable for 48 hours at room temperature after dilution. Infuse over 15 to 30 minutes.
- If infiltration or phlebitis occurs, apply warm compresses and use different site for next dose.
- Store premixed injection at room temperature. Store unmixed injection in refrigerator at 36° to 46° F (2° to 8° C).

⊗ **Incompatibilities**
Amphotericin B cholesterol complex, azithromycin, cefepime, piperacillin with tazobactam.

Contraindications and cautions

- Contraindicated in patients hypersensitive to drug or any of its components. Injection may contain benzyl alcohol as a preservative; some preparations contain phenylalanine.

Lifespan: In pregnant women, use cautiously. In breast-feeding women, use cautiously because it's unknown if the drug appears in breast milk. In children younger than 1 year old, drug is contraindicated.

Adverse reactions

CNS: dizziness, fever, *headache,* malaise, paresthesia, vertigo.
CV: flushing, palpitations.
EENT: orbital edema, tinnitus.
GI: anorexia, constipation, diarrhea, dry mouth, taste disorder.
Musculoskeletal: musculoskeletal pain.
Skin: acne, dry skin.
Other: transient irritation at I.V. site.

Interactions

None significant.

Effects on lab test results

- May increase BUN, creatinine, and liver enzyme levels.

Pharmacokinetics

Absorption: 40% to 45%.
Distribution: Wide.
Metabolism: 30% to 35% by liver.
Excretion: Mostly unchanged in urine. *Half-life:* 2½ to 3½ hours.

Route	Onset	Peak	Duration
P.O.	≤ 1 hr	1–3 hr	10–12 hr
I.V.	≤ 1 hr	20 min	10–12 hr

Action

Chemical effect: Competitively inhibits action of H_2 at receptor sites of parietal cells, decreasing gastric acid secretion.
Therapeutic effect: Decreases gastric acid levels and prevents heartburn.

Available forms

Gelcaps: 10 mg
Injection: 10 mg/ml, 20 mg/50 ml (premixed)
Powder for oral suspension: 40 mg/5 ml after reconstitution
Tablets: 10 mg†, 20 mg, 40 mg
Tablets (chewable): 10 mg†
Tablets (orally-disintegrating): 20 mg, 40 mg

NURSING PROCESS

Assessment

- Assess creatinine clearance before treatment.
- Assess patient's GI disorder before starting therapy and reassess regularly.
- Be alert for adverse reactions.
- Determine if patient has phenylalanine sensitivity.
- Assess patient's and family's knowledge of drug therapy.

Nursing diagnoses
- Impaired tissue integrity related to underlying GI disorder
- Deficient knowledge related to drug therapy

Planning and implementation
- Give daily doses or last dose of the day at bedtime.
- Store reconstituted oral suspension below 86° F (30° C). Discard after 30 days.

Patient teaching
- Tell patient to take drug with food. Remind him that drug is most effective if taken at bedtime. Tell patient taking 20 mg b.i.d. to take one dose at bedtime.
- With prescriber's knowledge, allow patient to take antacids, especially at beginning of therapy when pain is severe.
- Urge patient not to smoke because it may increase gastric acid secretion and worsen disease.
- Advise patient not to take drug for more than 8 weeks unless specifically ordered by prescriber. Tell patient not to self-medicate for heartburn longer than 2 weeks without prescriber's knowledge.

Evaluation
- Patient reports decrease in or relief of GI pain with drug.
- Patient and family state understanding of drug therapy.

felodipine
(feh-LOH-dih-peen)

Agon ◇, Agon SR ◇, Plendil, Plendil ER ◇, Renedil ◆

Pharmacologic class: calcium channel blocker
Therapeutic class: antihypertensive
Pregnancy risk category: C

Indications and dosages
▶ **Hypertension.** *Adults:* Initially, 5 mg P.O. daily. Adjust dosage based on response, usually at no less than 2-week intervals. Usual dosage is 2.5 to 10 mg daily.
Elderly patients: 2.5 mg P.O. daily; adjust as for adults. Maximum, 10 mg daily.

Contraindications and cautions
- Contraindicated in patients hypersensitive to drug or any of its components.
- Use cautiously in patients with heart failure, particularly those receiving beta blockers, and in patients with impaired hepatic function.

Lifespan: In pregnant and breast-feeding women, use cautiously. In children, safety and effectiveness haven't been established.

Adverse reactions
CNS: asthenia, dizziness, *headache,* paresthesia.
CV: chest pain, *flushing,* palpitations, *peripheral edema.*
EENT: gingival hyperplasia, rhinorrhea, pharyngitis.
GI: abdominal pain, constipation, diarrhea, nausea.
Musculoskeletal: back pain, muscle cramps.
Respiratory: cough, upper respiratory infection.
Skin: rash.

Interactions
Drug-drug. *Anticonvulsants:* May decrease felodipine level. Avoid use together.
Cimetidine, erythromycin, itraconazole, ketoconazole: May decrease felodipine clearance. Give lower doses of felodipine.
Metoprolol: May alter pharmacokinetics of metoprolol. No dosage adjustment needed. Monitor patient for adverse effects.
Tacrolimus: May increase tacrolimus level. Monitor tacrolimus level and adjust dose as needed.
Theophylline: May slightly decrease theophylline level. Monitor patient's response carefully.
Drug-herb. *St. John's wort:* May increase felodipine metabolism. Discourage use together.
Drug-food. *Grapefruit, lime:* May increase level and adverse effects of drug. Discourage use together.

Effects on lab test results
None reported.

Pharmacokinetics
Absorption: Almost complete, but extensive first-pass metabolism reduces absolute bioavailability to about 20%.
Distribution: More than 99% protein-bound.
Metabolism: Possibly hepatic.

Excretion: More than 70% in urine and 10% in feces as metabolites. *Half-life:* 11 to 16 hours.

Route	Onset	Peak	Duration
P.O.	2–5 hr	2½–5 hr	24 hr

Action

Chemical effect: Prevents entry of calcium ions into vascular smooth muscle and cardiac cells.
Therapeutic effect: Lowers blood pressure.

Available forms

Tablets: 5 mg ◇
Tablets (extended-release): 2.5 mg, 5 mg, 10 mg

NURSING PROCESS

Assessment

- Assess patient's blood pressure before starting therapy, and reassess regularly.
- Be alert for adverse reactions and drug interactions.
- Assess patient's and family's knowledge of drug therapy.

Nursing diagnoses

- Risk for injury related to presence of hypertension
- Excess fluid volume related to drug-induced peripheral edema
- Deficient knowledge related to drug therapy

Planning and implementation

- Drug may be given with or without food.

ALERT: Don't confuse Plendil with Isordil.

Patient teaching

- Instruct patient to swallow tablets whole and not to crush or chew them.
- Tell patient to take drug even when he feels better, to watch his diet, and to check with prescriber or pharmacist before taking other drugs, including OTC and herbal remedies.
- Advise patient to practice good oral hygiene and to see dentist regularly.

Evaluation

- Patient's blood pressure is normal.
- Patient doesn't develop complications from peripheral edema.
- Patient and family state understanding of drug therapy.

fenofibrate

(feh-noh-FIGH-brayt)
Antara, Lipofen, Lofibra, TriCor, Triglide

Pharmacologic class: fibric acid derivative
Therapeutic class: antilipemic
Pregnancy risk category: C

Indications and dosages

▶ **Hypertriglyceridemia (Fredrickson types IV and V hyperlipidemia) in patients who don't respond adequately to diet alone.** For all forms, adjust dosage based on patient response and lipid determinations performed at 4- to 8-week intervals.

Antara
Adults: Initially, 43 to 130 mg P.O. daily. Maximum, 130 mg daily.
Lipofen
Adults: Initially, 50 to 150 mg daily. Maximum, 150 mg daily.
Lofibra
Adults: Initially, 67 to 200 mg (capsules) or 54 to 160 mg (tablets) daily. Maximum, 200 mg (capsules) or 160 mg (tablets) daily.
TriCor
Adults: Initially, 48 to 145 mg daily. Maximum, 145 mg daily.
Triglide
Adults: Initially, 50 to 160 mg daily. Maximum, 160 mg daily.

▶ **Primary hypercholesterolemia or mixed dyslipidemia (Fredrickson types IIa and IIb) in patients who don't respond adequately to diet alone.** May reduce following dosages if lipid levels fall significantly below target range.

Antara
Adults: Initially, 130 mg P.O. daily.
Lipofen
Adults: Initially, 150 mg daily.
Lofibra
Adults: Initially, 200 mg (capsules) or 160 mg (tablets) daily.
TriCor
Adults: Initially, 145 mg daily.
Triglide
Adults: Initially, 160 mg daily.

Adjust-a-dose: If creatinine clearance is less than 50 ml/minute or patient is elderly, start with 43 mg (Antara), 50 mg (Lipofen), 67 mg (Lofibra capsules), 54 mg (Lofibra tablets),

48 mg (TriCor), or 50 mg (Triglide) daily. Increase only after evaluating renal function and triglyceride level at this dose.

Contraindications and cautions

• Contraindicated in patients hypersensitive to drug or any of its components and in those with gallbladder disease, hepatic dysfunction, primary biliary cirrhosis, severe renal dysfunction, or unexplained persistent liver function abnormalities.
• Use cautiously in patients with history of pancreatitis.

Lifespan: In pregnant women, use only if benefits outweigh risks to fetus. Breast-feeding women should stop the drug or stop breast-feeding. In children, safety and effectiveness haven't been established. In elderly patients, start with lower dosage.

Adverse reactions

CNS: asthenia, *dizziness,* fatigue, *headache,* insomnia, pain, paresthesia.
CV: ***arrhythmias.***
EENT: blurred vision, conjunctivitis, earache, eye floaters, eye irritation, rhinitis, sinusitis.
GI: abdominal pain, constipation, diarrhea, dyspepsia, eructation, flatulence, increased appetite, nausea, ***pancreatitis,*** vomiting.
GU: polyuria, vaginitis.
Hepatic: cholelithiasis.
Musculoskeletal: arthralgia, myalgia, myositis, ***rhabdomyolysis.***
Respiratory: cough.
Skin: pruritus, rash.
Other: decreased libido, flulike syndrome, hypersensitivity reaction, *infection.*

Interactions

Drug-drug. *Bile acid sequestrants:* May bind drug and inhibit absorption. Give drug 1 hour before or 4 to 6 hours after bile acid sequestrants.
Coumarin-type anticoagulants: May increase anticoagulant effect. Monitor PT and INR closely. Reduce anticoagulant dosage if needed.
Cyclosporine, immunosuppressants, nephrotoxic drugs: May cause renal dysfunction, which may compromise the elimination of drug. Use together cautiously.
HMG-CoA reductase inhibitors: May increase risk of myopathy, rhabdomyolysis, and acute renal impairment from use of HMG-CoA reductase inhibitors with gemfibrozil (another fibrate derivative). Don't use together.
Drug-food. *Any food:* May increase absorption. Give drug with meals.
Drug-lifestyle. *Alcohol use:* May elevate triglyceride level. Discourage use together.

Effects on lab test results

• May increase BUN, creatinine, ALT, and AST levels. May decrease uric acid and hemoglobin levels and hematocrit.
• May decrease WBC count.

Pharmacokinetics

Absorption: Good.
Distribution: 99% protein-bound.
Metabolism: Rapidly hydrolyzed by esterases to active metabolite, fenofibric acid.
Excretion: 60% in urine, mainly as metabolites, and 25% in feces. *Half-life:* 20 hours.

Route	Onset	Peak	Duration
P.O.	Unknown	6–8 hr	Unknown

Action

Chemical effect: May inhibit triglyceride synthesis, decreasing amount of very–low-density lipoproteins released into circulation. May stimulate breakdown of triglyceride-rich protein.
Therapeutic effect: Decreases triglyceride levels.

Available forms

Capsules (micronized): 43 mg, 50 mg, 67 mg, 87 mg, 100 mg, 130 mg, 134 mg, 150 mg, 200 mg
Tablets: 48 mg, 50 mg, 54 mg, 145 mg, 160 mg

NURSING PROCESS

Assessment

• Assess baseline lipid levels and liver function test results before starting therapy and periodically thereafter.
• Be alert for adverse reactions and drug interactions.
• Assess patient's and family's knowledge of drug therapy.

Nursing diagnoses

• Impaired tissue integrity: muscular related to adverse drug reaction
• Risk for infection related to adverse drug reactions
• Deficient knowledge related to drug therapy

Planning and implementation

- Stop giving the drug to a patient who doesn't have an adequate response after 2 months of therapy with maximum dose.
- Give tablets with meals to increase bioavailability.
- Evaluate renal function and triglyceride levels in patient with severe renal impairment before increasing dose.
- Counsel patient on importance of adhering to triglyceride-lowering diet.

ALERT: Don't confuse Tricor with Tracleer.

Patient teaching

- Advise patient to promptly report symptoms of unexplained muscle weakness, pain, or tenderness, especially if accompanied by malaise or fever.
- Urge patient to take drug with meals to optimize drug absorption.
- Advise patient to continue weight-control measures, including diet and exercise, and to reduce alcohol intake before starting therapy.
- Instruct patient who also takes bile acid resin to take fenofibrate 1 hour before or 4 to 6 hours after bile acid resin.

Evaluation

- Patient remains free of myositis and rhabdomyolysis.
- Patient remains free from infection.
- Patient and family state understanding of drug therapy.

fentanyl citrate

(FEN-tuh-nihl SIGH-trayt)

Sublimaze

fentanyl iontophoretic transdermal system

Ionsys

fentanyl transdermal system

Duragesic-12, Duragesic-25, Duragesic-50, Duragesic-75, Duragesic-100

fentanyl transmucosal

Actiq, Fentora

Pharmacologic class: opioid
Therapeutic class: analgesic, anesthetic
Pregnancy risk category: C
Controlled substance schedule: II

Indications and dosages

▶ **Adjunct to general anesthetic.** *Adults and children older than age 12:* For low-dose therapy, 2 mcg/kg I.V. For moderate-dose therapy, 2 to 20 mcg/kg I.V.; then 25 to 100 mcg I.V. or I.M., p.r.n. For high-dose therapy, 20 to 50 mcg/kg I.V.; then 25 mcg to one-half initial loading dose I.V., p.r.n.
Children ages 2 to 12: Give 2 to 3 mcg/kg I.V. or I.M. during induction and maintenance phases of general anesthesia.

▶ **Adjunct to regional anesthesia.** *Adults:* 50 to 100 mcg I.M. or slow I.V. over 1 to 2 minutes.

▶ **Postoperative pain.** *Adults:* 50 to 100 mcg I.M. q 1 to 2 hours, p.r.n.

▶ **Short-term management of acute postoperative pain in patients who need opioid analgesia during hospitalization.** *Adults:* First, give a different opioid until patient is comfortable. Then, apply Ionsys system to intact, nonirritated skin on the chest or upper outer arm. To activate a dose, instruct the patient to firmly press the dose-delivery button twice within 3 seconds. Each actuation of the system delivers 40 mcg of fentanyl. A beep indicates the start of delivery of each dose, and a red light remains on throughout the 10-minute delivery period. A maximum of six 40-mcg doses can be delivered each hour. Each system operates for 80 doses or up to 24 hours. A maximum of three systems can be used sequentially, applied to a different skin site, for a total of 72 hours of pain management.

▶ **To manage persistent, moderate to severe chronic pain in opioid-tolerant patients who require continuous, around-the-clock opioid analgesics for an extended period of time.** *Adults and children age 2 or older:* When converting to Duragesic, the initial dose is based on the daily dose, potency and characteristics of the current opioid therapy, the reliability of the relative potency estimates used to calculate the needed dose of fentanyl, the degree of opioid tolerance, and the condition of the patient. Each system may be worn for 72 hours, although some adult patients may need systems to be applied q 48 hours during the initial period. May increase dose 3 days after the first dose and then q 6 days thereafter.

▶ **Breakthrough cancer pain in opioid-tolerant patients.** *Adults:* Initially, 200 mcg Actiq P.O. (transmucosally); adjust dosage based on response. Have patient suck on each unit for 15 minutes. An additional unit may be given 30 minutes after start of the previous dose. Don't use more than 2 units per episode of breakthrough pain. Or, initially, 100 mcg Fentora between the upper cheek and gum. May repeat same dose once per breakthrough episode after at least 30 minutes. Adjust in 100-mcg increments. Doses above 400 mcg can be increased by 200 mcg. Generally, dosage should be increased when patient needs more than one dose per breakthrough episode. Once a successful maintenance dose has been established, reevaluate if patient has more than four breakthrough episodes per day.

▶ **Switching from Actiq to Fentora to manage breakthrough cancer pain in opioid-tolerant patients.** *Adults:* If current Actiq dose is 200 to 400 mcg, start with 100 mcg Fentora. If current Actiq dose is 600 to 800 mcg, use 200 mcg Fentora. If current Actiq dose is 1,200 to 1,600 mcg, use 400 mcg Fentora.

I.V. administration

- Only staff trained in giving I.V. anesthetics and managing their adverse effects should give drug I.V.
- Keep naloxone and resuscitation equipment available when giving drug I.V.
- Drug is commonly used I.V. with droperidol to produce neuroleptanalgesia.

⊗ **Incompatibilities**

Azithromycin, fluorouracil, lidocaine, methohexital, pentobarbital sodium, phenytoin, thiopental.

Contraindications and cautions

- Contraindicated in patients intolerant of drug. Transdermal fentanyl is contraindicated in patients hypersensitive to adhesives; patients who need postoperative pain management; patients who have acute, mild, or intermittent pain that can be managed with nonopioid drugs; and patients who aren't opioid tolerant. Don't use in patients with increased intracranial pressure, impaired consciousness, or coma.
- Use cautiously in debilitated patients and in patients with brain tumors, increased CSF pressure, COPD, decreased respiratory reserve, potentially compromised respirations, hepatic or renal disease, or bradyarrhythmias.

Lifespan: In pregnant women, use cautiously. In breast-feeding women, use cautiously because it's unknown if the drug appears in breast milk. Actiq is contraindicated for use during labor and delivery. In children younger than age 2, safety and effectiveness of I.V. drug haven't been established. In children younger than age 16, safety and effectiveness of Actiq haven't been established. In children younger than age 12 and children younger than age 18 weighing less than 50 kg (110 lb), transdermal system is contraindicated. In elderly patients, use all forms cautiously because dosages may have prolonged CNS and respiratory effects.

Adverse reactions

CNS: anxiety, *asthenia, clouded sensorium, confusion,* depression, dizziness, *euphoria,* hallucinations, headache, nervousness, *sedation, somnolence.*
CV: ***arrhythmias, bradycardia,*** chest pain, hypertension, hypotension.
EENT: dry mouth.
GI: abdominal pain, constipation, ileus, nausea, vomiting.
GU: urine retention.
Respiratory: ***apnea,*** dyspnea, hypoventilation, ***respiratory depression.***
Skin: diaphoresis, pruritus.
Other: physical dependence, reaction at application site (edema, erythema, papules).

Interactions

Drug-drug. *CNS depressants, general anesthetics, hypnotics, MAO inhibitors, opioid analgesics, sedatives, tricyclic antidepressants:* May have additive effects. Use together cautiously. Reduce fentanyl dose by one-fourth or one-third. Reduce dosages of other drugs.
Diazepam: May cause CV depression when given with high doses of fentanyl. Monitor patient closely.
Droperidol: May cause hypotension and decreased pulmonary arterial pressure. Monitor patient closely.
Potent CYP3A4 inhibitors (clarithromycin, erythromycin, itraconazole, ketoconazole, nefazodone, nelfinavir, ritonavir, troleandomycin): May increase analgesia, CNS depression, and hypotensive effects. Monitor patient's respiratory status and vital signs.

Protease inhibitors: May increase CNS and respiratory depression. Monitor patient closely.
Drug-lifestyle. *Alcohol use:* May have additive effects. Discourage use together.

Effects on lab test results

None reported.

Pharmacokinetics

Absorption: Varies with drug route.
Distribution: Accumulates in adipose tissue and skeletal muscle.
Metabolism: In liver.
Excretion: In urine. *Half-life:* 3½ hours (parenteral), 5 to 15 hours (transmucosal), 18 hours (transdermal).

Route	Onset	Peak	Duration
I.V.	1–2 min	3–5 min	30–60 min
I.M.	7–15 min	20–30 min	1–2 hr
Transmucosal	15 min	20–30 min	Unknown
Transdermal	12–24 hr	1–3 days	Varies

Action

Chemical effect: May bind with opiate receptors in CNS, altering both perception of and emotional response to pain.
Therapeutic effect: Relieves pain.

Available forms

Injection: 50 mcg/ml
Iontophoretic transdermal system: 40 mcg/dose
Transdermal system: patches designed to release 12.5, 25, 50, 75, or 100 mcg of fentanyl per hour
Transmucosal (Actiq): 200 mcg, 400 mcg, 600 mcg, 800 mcg, 1,200 mcg, 1,600 mcg
Transmucosal (Fentora): 100 mcg, 200 mcg, 400 mcg, 600 mcg, 800 mcg

NURSING PROCESS

Assessment

- Assess patient's underlying condition before starting therapy.
- Evaluate degree of pain relief provided by each dose.
- Periodically monitor postoperative vital signs and bladder function. Because drug decreases both rate and depth of respirations, monitoring of arterial oxygen saturation (Sa_{O_2}) may help assess respiratory depression.

ALERT: Transdermal patch levels peak between 24 and 72 hours after initial application and dose increases. Monitor patients for life-threatening hypoventilation, especially during these times.

- Be alert for adverse reactions and drug interactions.
- Assess patient's and family's knowledge of drug therapy.

Nursing diagnoses

- Acute pain related to underlying condition
- Ineffective breathing pattern related to respiratory depression
- Deficient knowledge related to drug therapy

Planning and implementation

- For better analgesic effect, give drug before patient has intense pain.
- When drug is used postoperatively, encourage patient to turn, cough, and breathe deeply to prevent atelectasis.

ALERT: Only the patient should activate the iontophoretic transdermal system.
ALERT: Fentora and Actiq aren't bioequivalent and can't be substituted on a mcg-per-mcg basis.

- To give transmucosal lozenge:
  - Open childproof foil package with scissors immediately before use.
  - Place lozenge or tablet in patient's mouth between the cheek and gum.
  - Actiq should be actively sucked while Fentora should be allowed to dissolve.
  - Make sure patient consumes the lozenge or tablet in about 15 minutes. Faster or slower consumption may reduce its effects.
  - If signs of excess opioid effects appear before the entire lozenge or tablet dissolves, remove it from the patient's mouth and decrease future doses.

ALERT: Ask patient and caregivers about the presence of children in the home because lozenges and tablets may be fatal to a child. Explain how to dispose of lozenges properly.

- Transdermal patch isn't recommended for postoperative pain.
- Use dosage equivalency charts to calculate transdermal dose based on daily morphine intake—for example, for every 90 mg of oral morphine or 15 mg of I.M. morphine daily, give 25 mcg/hour of transdermal drug.
- Adjust dosage gradually in patient using transdermal patch. Delay dosage adjustment un-

til after at least two applications. Reaching steady-state levels of new dosage may take up to 6 days.
• High doses can produce muscle rigidity, which can be reversed with neuromuscular blockers; however, patient must be artificially ventilated.
• Immediately report respiratory rate below 12 breaths/minute or decreased respiratory volume or Sao_2.
• Most patients have good control of pain for 3 days while wearing transdermal patch, but a few may need a new application after 48 hours. Because drug level rises for first 24 hours after application, analgesic effect can't be evaluated on the first day. Make sure patient has adequate supplemental analgesic to prevent breakthrough pain.
• When reducing opioid therapy or switching to a different analgesic, withdraw transdermal patch gradually. Because drug level drops gradually after removal, give half of equianalgesic dose of new analgesic 12 to 18 hours after removal.
ALERT: Don't confuse fentanyl with sufentanil.

Patient teaching

• Teach patient proper application of transdermal patch. Instruct patient to clip hair at application site, but to avoid razors, which may irritate skin. Tell him to wash area with clear water if needed, but not with soaps, oils, lotions, alcohol, or other substances that may irritate skin or prevent adhesion. Urge him to dry area completely before application.
• Tell patient to remove transdermal system from package just before applying, to hold in place for 10 to 20 seconds, and to be sure edges of patch adhere to the skin.
• Teach patient to dispose of transdermal patch by folding so that adhesive side adheres to itself, and then flushing it down toilet.
• If patient needs another patch after 72 hours, tell him to apply it to new site.
• Inform patient that heat from fever or environment may increase transdermal delivery and cause toxicity, which requires dosage adjustment. Instruct patient to notify prescriber if fever occurs or if he will be spending time in hot climate.
ALERT: Strongly warn patient to keep drug safely secured, away from children.
• Advise parent or caregiver to place transdermal patch on the upper back for a child or a patient who's cognitively impaired, to reduce the chance the patch will be removed and placed in the mouth.
• Teach patient how to properly take transmucosal Actiq, and to apply transdermal systems.
ALERT: Teach patient proper disposal of transmucosal Actiq units.

☑ Evaluation

• Patient is free from pain.
• Patient maintains adequate ventilation throughout drug therapy.
• Patient and family state understanding of drug therapy.

ferrous fumarate

(FEH-rus FYOO-muh-rayt)

Femiron†, Feostat†, Feostat Drops†, Ferretts†, Fumasorb†, Fumerin†, Hemocyte†, Ircon†, Neo-Fer ♦ †, Nephro-Fer†, Novofumar ♦ †, Palafer ♦ †, Span-FF†

ferrous gluconate

Fergon†, Fertinic ♦, Novoferrogluc ♦

ferrous sulfate

Apo-Ferrous Sulfate, ED-IN-SOL, Feosol*†, Feratab, Fer-Gen-Sol Drops†, Fer-In-Sol*†, Fer-Iron Drops†, Fero-Grad ♦, Fero-Gradumet†, Irospan†, Mol-Iron

ferrous sulfate, dried

Feosol, Fer-In-Sol, Fe50, Slow-Fe†

Pharmacologic class: oral iron supplement
Therapeutic class: hematinic
Pregnancy risk category: A

Indications and dosages

▶ **Iron deficiency.** *Adults:* 150 to 300 mg elemental iron P.O. daily given in three divided doses.
Children: 3 to 6 mg/kg P.O. daily given in one to three divided doses.
Premature infants: 2 to 4 mg/kg P.O. daily given in one to two divided doses. Maximum, 15 mg/day.

Contraindications and cautions

- Contraindicated in patients hypersensitive to drug or its ingredients; patients with primary hemochromatosis, hemosiderosis, hemolytic anemia (unless iron deficiency anemia is also present), peptic ulcer disease, regional enteritis, or ulcerative colitis; and patients receiving repeated blood transfusions.
- Use cautiously on long-term basis.

Lifespan: In breast-feeding women, iron supplements usually are recommended. In children, use cautiously. Extended-release forms aren't recommended for children. In elderly patients, may cause constipation.

Adverse reactions

GI: anorexia, *black stools, constipation,* diarrhea, epigastric pain, *nausea,* vomiting.
Other: temporary staining of teeth (drops, suspension).

Interactions

Drug-drug. *Antacids, cholestyramine resin, levodopa, tetracycline, vitamin E:* May decrease iron absorption. Separate doses by 2 to 4 hours.
Chloramphenicol: May increase iron response. Watch patient carefully.
Fluoroquinolones, penicillamine, tetracyclines: May decrease GI absorption of these drugs, possibly decreasing levels and effectiveness. Separate doses by 2 to 4 hours.
L-thyroxine: May decrease L-thyroxine absorption. Separate doses by at least 2 hours. Monitor thyroid function.
Levodopa, methyldopa: May decrease absorption and effectiveness of levodopa and methyldopa. Monitor patient for decreased effects of these drugs.
Vitamin C: May increase iron absorption. Suggest patient take vitamin C with drug.
Drug-food. *Cereals, cheese, coffee, eggs, milk, tea, whole-grain breads, yogurt:* May impair oral iron absorption. Advise against use together.

Effects on lab test results

None reported.

Pharmacokinetics

Absorption: Mainly at duodenum and proximal jejunum. For enteric-coated and some extended-release formulas, may be decreased. With food, may decrease by 33% to 50%.
Distribution: Binds immediately to carrier protein, transferrin, then to bone marrow for incorporation into hemoglobin.
Metabolism: Liberated by destruction of hemoglobin but is conserved and reused by body.
Excretion: Healthy people lose only small amounts of mineral each day. Men and postmenopausal women lose about 1 mg daily and premenopausal women about 1.5 mg daily. The loss usually occurs in nails, hair, feces, and urine. *Half-life:* Unknown.

Route	Onset	Peak	Duration
P.O.	≤ 4 days	7–10 days	2–4 mo

Action

Chemical effect: Provides elemental iron, an essential component in formation of hemoglobin.
Therapeutic effect: Relieves iron deficiency.

Available forms

ferrous fumarate
(Each 100 mg provides 33 mg of elemental iron.)
Tablets: 90 mg, 324 mg, 325 mg, 350 mg
Tablets (chewable): 100 mg†
Tablets (timed-release): 150 mg†
ferrous gluconate
(Each 100 mg provides 11.6 mg of elemental iron.)
Tablets: 225 mg, 300 mg†, 324 mg† (contains 37 mg elemental iron), 325 mg†
ferrous sulfate
(About 20% elemental iron; dried and powdered, it's about 32% elemental iron.)
Drops: 75 mg/0.6 ml
Elixir: 220 mg/5 ml*†
Tablets: 195 mg†, 300 mg†, 325 mg†, 187 mg (dried), 200 mg (dried)
Tablets (extended-release): 160 mg (dried)†

NURSING PROCESS

Assessment

- Obtain baseline assessment of patient's iron deficiency before starting therapy.
- Evaluate hemoglobin level, hematocrit, and reticulocyte count during therapy.
- Be alert for adverse reactions and drug interactions.

• Assess patient's and family's knowledge of drug therapy.

Nursing diagnoses

• Fatigue related to iron deficiency
• Constipation related to adverse effect of drug therapy on GI tract
• Deficient knowledge related to drug therapy

Planning and implementation

• Give tablets with juice or water, but not with milk or antacids.
• Dilute liquid forms in juice or water, but not in milk or antacids.
• To avoid staining teeth, give suspension or elixir with straw and place drops at back of throat.
• Don't crush or allow patient to chew extended-release forms.
• GI upset may be related to dose. Preferably give drug between meals, but if GI upset continues, may give with food, except eggs, milk products, coffee, and tea, which may impair absorption. Enteric-coated or sustained-release forms reduce GI upset but also reduce amount absorbed.
• Oral iron may turn stools black. Although this unabsorbed iron is harmless, it could mask presence of melena. Have stools tested for presence of blood.

Patient teaching

ALERT: Inform parents that as few as three tablets can poison a child.
• If patient misses a dose, tell him to take it as soon as he remembers but not to double the dose.
• Advise patient to avoid taking drug with certain foods that may impair oral iron absorption, including yogurt, cheese, eggs, milk, whole-grain breads and cereals, tea, and coffee.
• Teach dietary measures for preventing constipation.
• Advise patient to report costipation and changes in stool color or consistency.

Evaluation

• Patient reports fatigue is no longer a problem in daily life.
• Patient states appropriate measures to prevent or relieve constipation.
• Patient and family state understanding of drug therapy.

fexofenadine hydrochloride

(feks-oh-FEN-uh-deen high-droh-KLOR-ighd)
Allegra, Telfast ♦

Pharmacologic class: H_1-receptor antagonist
Therapeutic class: antihistamine
Pregnancy risk category: C

Indications and dosages

▶ **Seasonal allergic rhinitis.** *Adults and children age 12 and older:* 60 mg P.O. b.i.d. or 180 mg P.O. once daily.
Children ages 2 to 11: Give 30 mg P.O. b.i.d.
▶ **Chronic idiopathic urticaria.** *Children age 12 and older:* 60 mg P.O. b.i.d. or 180 mg P.O. once daily.
Children ages 2 to 11: Give 30 mg P.O. b.i.d.
Children ages 6 months to 2 years: 15 mg (2.5 ml) P.O. b.i.d.
Adjust-a-dose: For adults with renal impairment, increase dosage interval to q 24 hours. For children ages 2 to 11, give 30 mg daily. For children ages 6 months to 2 years, give 15 mg daily.

Contraindications and cautions

• Contraindicated in patients hypersensitive to the drug or any of its components.
• Use cautiously in patients with renal impairment.
Lifespan: In pregnant women, use only if benefits outweigh risks to the fetus, and avoid use in the third trimester. In breast-feeding women, use cautiously because it's unknown if drug appears in breast milk.

Adverse reactions

CNS: fatigue, drowsiness, *headache.*
GI: dyspepsia, nausea.
GU: dysmenorrhea.
Musculoskeletal: back pain.
Respiratory: cough, sinusitis.
Other: viral infection.

Interactions

Drug-drug. *Aluminum- or magnesium-containing antacids:* May interfere with absorption of fexofenadine. Separate doses.
Erythromycin, ketoconazole: May increase fexofenadine levels. Prolonged QT interval has occurred with other antihistamines. Monitor patient closely.

Drug-lifestyle. *Alcohol:* May increase sedative effects. Discourage use together.

Drug-food. *Apple, grapefruit, and orange juice:* May decrease GI absorption of drug, reducing effects. Discourage use together.

Effects on lab test results

None reported.

Pharmacokinetics

Absorption: Rapid.
Distribution: 60% to 70% protein-bound.
Metabolism: Unknown.
Excretion: Mainly in feces. *Half-life:* 14½ hours.

Route	Onset	Peak	Duration
P.O.	Unknown	3 hr	14 hr

Action

Chemical effect: Selectively inhibits peripheral H_1-receptors.

Therapeutic effect: Relieves symptoms of seasonal allergies.

Available forms

Capsules: 60 mg
Oral suspension: 30 mg/5 ml
Tablets: 30 mg, 60 mg, 180 mg

NURSING PROCESS

Assessment

- Assess patient's seasonal allergy symptoms before starting therapy and regularly thereafter.
- Monitor patient for adverse reactions.
- Assess patient's and family's knowledge of drug therapy.

Nursing diagnoses

- Risk for injury related to fatigue and drowsiness caused by drug
- Ineffective health maintenance related to underlying condition
- Deficient knowledge related to drug therapy

Planning and implementation

- Reduce daily dosage in patient with renal impairment or currently on dialysis.
- Avoid giving with apple, orange, or grapefruit juice.

ALERT: Don't confuse Allegra with Viagra.

Patient teaching

- Instruct patient not to exceed prescribed dose and to take drug only when affected by seasonal allergy symptoms.
- Warn patient not to drink alcohol and to avoid hazardous activities that require alertness until the drug's CNS effects are known.
- Tell patient that coffee or tea may reduce drowsiness. Suggest sugarless gum, hard candy, or ice chips to relieve dry mouth.
- Tell patient to avoid taking drug with apple, orange, or grapefruit juice.
- Tell parents to keep oral solution tightly closed in a cool, dry place and to shake it well before using.

Evaluation

- Patient experiences limited fatigue and drowsiness caused by the drug.
- Patient responds well to the drug.
- Patient and family state understanding of drug therapy.

filgrastim (granulocyte colony-stimulating factor; G-CSF)

(fil-GRAH-stem)

Neupogen

Pharmacologic class: biologic response modifier
Therapeutic class: colony-stimulating factor, hematopoietic
Pregnancy risk category: C

Indications and dosages

▶ **To decrease risk of infection in patients with nonmyeloid cancers receiving myelosuppressive antineoplastics followed by bone marrow transplant.** *Adults and children:* 10 mcg/kg I.V. or subcutaneously daily at least 24 hours after cytotoxic chemotherapy and bone marrow infusion. Adjust later doses according to neutrophil response.

▶ **Congenital neutropenia.** *Adults:* 6 mcg/kg subcutaneously b.i.d. Adjust dosage based on response.

▶ **Idiopathic or cyclic neutropenia.** *Adults:* 5 mcg/kg subcutaneously daily. Adjust dosage based on response.

▶ **Peripheral blood progenitor cell collection.** *Adults:* 10 mcg/kg subcutaneously daily for at least 4 days before first leukapheresis and continuing until the last leukapheresis is completed.

▶ **To decrease risk of infection in patients with nonmyeloid cancers receiving myelosuppressive antineoplastics, agranulocytosis‡, pancytopenia with colchicine overdose‡, acute leukemia‡, hematologic toxicity with zidovudine therapy‡.** *Adults and children:* 5 mcg/kg I.V. or subcutaneously daily as single dose. May increase in increments of 5 mcg/kg for each chemotherapy cycle, depending on duration and severity of nadir of absolute neutrophil count (ANC).

▶ **Myelodysplasia‡.** *Adults:* 0.3 to 10 mcg/kg subcutaneously daily.

▶ **Neutropenia from HIV infection‡.** *Adults and adolescents:* 5 to 10 mcg/kg subcutaneously or I.V. daily for 2 to 4 weeks.

I.V. administration

- Dilute in 50 to 100 ml of D_5W. If final concentration will be 2 to 15 mcg/ml, add albumin at 2 mg/ml (0.2%) to minimize binding of drug to plastic containers or tubing.
- Give by intermittent infusion over 15 to 60 minutes or continuous infusion over 24 hours.
- Refrigerate drug at 36° to 46° F (2° to 8° C). Don't freeze; avoid shaking. Store at room temperature for maximum of 6 hours; discard after 6 hours.

⊗ **Incompatibilities**

Amphotericin B, cefepime, cefonicid, cefotaxime, cefoxitin, ceftizoxime, ceftriaxone, cefuroxime, clindamycin, dactinomycin, etoposide, fluorouracil, furosemide, heparin sodium, mannitol, methylprednisolone sodium succinate, metronidazole, mitomycin, piperacillin, prochlorperazine edisylate, sodium solutions, thiotepa.

Contraindications and cautions

- Contraindicated in patients hypersensitive to proteins derived from *Escherichia coli* or to the drug or any of its components.

Lifespan: In pregnant women, use cautiously. In breast-feeding women, use cautiously because it's unknown if the drug appears in breast milk.

Adverse reactions

CNS: *fatigue, fever,* headache, weakness.
CV: ***arrhythmias,*** chest pain, ***MI.***
GI: constipation, *diarrhea, mucositis, nausea,* stomatitis, *vomiting.*
GU: hematuria, proteinuria.
Hematologic: leukocytosis, ***thrombocytopenia.***
Musculoskeletal: *skeletal pain.*
Respiratory: cough, dyspnea.
Skin: *alopecia,* cutaneous vasculitis, rash.
Other: hypersensitivity reactions.

Interactions

Drug-drug. *Chemotherapeutics:* May cause sensitivity in rapidly dividing myeloid cells. Don't use filgrastim within 24 hours of chemotherapy.

Effects on lab test results

- May increase creatinine, uric acid, alkaline phosphatase, and LDH levels.
- May increase WBC count. May decrease platelet count.

Pharmacokinetics

Absorption: Rapid.
Distribution: Unknown.
Metabolism: Unknown.
Excretion: Unknown. *Half-life:* About 3½ hours.

Route	Onset	Peak	Duration
I.V.	5–60 min	24 hr	1–7 days
SubQ	5–60 min	2–8 hr	1–7 days

Action

Chemical effect: Stimulates proliferation and differentiation of hematopoietic cells. Drug is specific for neutrophils.
Therapeutic effect: Raises WBC count.

Available forms

Injection: 300 mcg/ml in 1-ml and 1.6-ml single-use vials; 300 mcg/0.5 ml, 480 mcg/0.8 ml in prefilled syringes

NURSING PROCESS

Assessment

- Assess patient's underlying condition before starting therapy.
- Obtain baseline CBC and platelet count before and during therapy.
- Be alert for adverse reactions and drug interactions.
- Ask patient about skeletal pain.

• Assess patient's and family's knowledge of drug therapy.

Nursing diagnoses

• Ineffective protection related to underlying condition or treatment
• Acute pain related to adverse drug effects on skeletal muscle
• Deficient knowledge related to drug therapy

Planning and implementation

• Don't give drug within 24 hours of cytotoxic chemotherapy.
• Once dose is withdrawn from vial, discard the unused portion. Vials are for single-dose use and contain no preservatives.
• Give daily for up to 2 weeks or until ANC has returned to 10,000/mm^3 after the expected chemotherapy-induced neutrophil nadir.

ALERT: Rare cases of splenic rupture have occurred.

ALERT: Don't confuse Neupogen with Neumega or Neulasta.

Patient teaching

• Teach patient how to give drug and how to dispose of used needles, syringes, drug containers, and unused drug.
• Tell patient to report bruising or spontaneous bleeding, such as frequent nosebleeds.
• Teach patient how to manage skeletal pain.
• Tell patient to immediately report upper left abdominal or shoulder pain, because these may be signs of splenic rupture.

Evaluation

• Patient's WBC count is normal.
• Patient reports skeletal pain is bearable or relieved with analgesic administration and comfort measures.
• Patient and family state understanding of drug therapy.

finasteride

(fin-ES-teh-righd)
Propecia, Proscar

Pharmacologic class: steroid derivative
Therapeutic class: androgen synthesis inhibitor
Pregnancy risk category: X

Indications and dosages

▶ **To reduce the progression of BPH symptoms.** *Men:* 5 mg Proscar P.O. daily with or without doxazosin.
▶ **To reduce risk of acute urine retention and need for surgery, including prostatectomy and transurethral resection of prostate; symptomatic BPH; adjunct therapy after radical prostatectomy‡, first-stage prostate cancer‡, acne‡, or hirsutism‡.** *Adults:* 5 mg Proscar P.O. daily.
▶ **Male pattern baldness.** *Men:* 1 mg Propecia P.O. daily.

Contraindications and cautions

• Contraindicated in patients hypersensitive to drug or any of its components or to other 5-alpha-reductase inhibitors, such as dutasteride. Use cautiously in patients with liver dysfunction.

Lifespan: In women and children, drug is contraindicated.

Adverse reactions

GU: decreased volume of ejaculate, impotence.
Other: decreased libido.

Interactions

None significant.

Effects on lab test results

• May decrease prostate-specific antigen (PSA) level.

Pharmacokinetics

Absorption: Not clearly defined, but average bioavailability may be as high as 63%.
Distribution: 90% protein-bound. Crosses blood–brain barrier.
Metabolism: Extensive.
Excretion: 39% in urine as metabolites; 57% in feces. *Half-life:* Unknown.

Route	Onset	Peak	Duration
P.O.	Unknown	1–2 hr	2 wk

Action

Chemical effect: Competitively inhibits steroid 5-reductase, an enzyme that forms potent androgen 5-dihydrotestosterone (DHT) from testosterone. Because DHT influences development of the prostate gland, lower levels will relieve symptoms of BPH. For male pattern baldness, a

balding scalp contains higher amounts of DHT; drug lowers scalp and serum DHT levels.
Therapeutic effect: Relieves symptoms of BPH, reduces hair loss, and promotes hair growth.

Available forms

Tablets: 1 mg, 5 mg

NURSING PROCESS

Assessment

- Before starting therapy, assess patient's BPH and evaluate him for conditions that could mimic BPH, including hypotonic bladder; prostate cancer, infection, or stricture; and neurologic conditions. Carefully monitor patients with large residual urine volume or severely diminished urine flow. These patients may not be candidates for therapy.
- Assess patient for improvement in BPH symptoms.
- Perform periodic digital rectal examinations.
- Be alert for adverse reactions and drug interactions.
- Carefully evaluate sustained increases in PSA levels, which could indicate noncompliance or disease progression.
- Assess patient's and family's knowledge of drug therapy.

Nursing diagnoses

- Impaired urinary elimination related to BPH
- Ineffective sexuality pattern related to drug-induced impotence
- Deficient knowledge related to drug therapy

Planning and implementation

- Because it's impossible to identify which patients will respond to therapy, keep in mind that a minimum of 6 months of therapy may be needed.

Patient teaching

- Warn woman who is or may become pregnant not to handle crushed or broken tablets because of risk of adverse effects on fetus.
- Reassure patient that, although drug may decrease volume of ejaculate, it doesn't appear to impair normal sexual function. Impotence and decreased libido have occurred in less than 4% of patients.
- Tell patient taking drug for male pattern baldness that he may not notice any effects for 3 months or more.
- Warn patient not to donate blood until at least 1 month after final dose.
- Tell patient that drug may be taken without regard to meals.

Evaluation

- Patient's BPH symptoms diminish.
- Patient states appropriate ways to manage sexual dysfunction.
- Patient and family state understanding of drug therapy.

F

flecainide acetate

(FLEH-kay-nighd AS-ih-tayt)
Tambocor

Pharmacologic class: benzamide derivative
Therapeutic class: antiarrhythmic
Pregnancy risk category: C

Indications and dosages

▶ **Paroxysmal supraventricular tachycardia; paroxysmal atrial fibrillation or flutter in patients without structural heart disease.** *Adults:* 50 mg P.O. q 12 hours. Increase in increments of 50 mg b.i.d. q 4 days until effectiveness is achieved. Maximum, 300 mg daily.
▶ **Life-threatening ventricular arrhythmias, such as sustained ventricular tachycardia.** *Adults:* 100 mg P.O. q 12 hours. Increase in increments of 50 mg b.i.d. q 4 days until effectiveness is achieved. Maximum, 400 mg daily for most patients. Or, where available (Australia), give 2 mg/kg I.V. push over at least 10 minutes; or dilute dose and give as infusion.
Adjust-a-dose: For patients with renal impairment, if creatinine clearance is more than 35 ml/minute, initial dose is 100 mg q 12 hours. If clearance is 35 ml/minute or less, initial dose is 100 mg once daily or 50 mg b.i.d. Adjust doses cautiously for all renally impaired patients. When flecainide is used with amiodarone, decrease flecainide dose by 50%.

I.V. administration ◇

- For I.V. infusion, mix only with D_5W.
- When giving by I.V. push, give over at least 10 minutes.

⊗ Incompatibilities
Saline solutions.

Contraindications and cautions

- Contraindicated in patients hypersensitive to the drug or any of its components and in those with cardiogenic shock, second- or third-degree AV block, recent MI, or right bundle branch block related to left hemiblock (in absence of artificial pacemaker).
- Use cautiously in patients with heart failure, cardiomyopathy, severe renal or hepatic disease, prolonged QT interval, sick sinus syndrome, or blood dyscrasia.

Lifespan: In pregnant women, use cautiously. Breast-feeding women should stop breast-feeding or not use the drug. In children, safety and effectiveness haven't been established.

Adverse reactions

CNS: anxiety, asthenia, ataxia, depression, *dizziness,* fatigue, fever, *headache,* insomnia, *light-headedness,* malaise, paresthesia, *syncope,* tremor, vertigo.
CV: ***arrhythmias, cardiac arrest,*** chest pain, edema, flushing, ***heart failure,*** palpitations.
EENT: blurred vision, other visual disturbances.
GI: abdominal pain, anorexia, constipation, diarrhea, dyspepsia, nausea, vomiting.
Respiratory: *dyspnea.*
Skin: rash.

Interactions

Drug-drug. *Amiodarone, cimetidine:* May alter pharmacokinetics. Watch for toxicity. Decrease flecainide dose by 50%.
Digoxin: May increase digoxin level by 15% to 25%. Monitor digoxin level; watch for toxicity.
Disopyramide, verapamil: May have additive negative inotropic properties with flecainide. Avoid use together.
Propranolol, other beta blockers: May increase flecainide and propranolol levels by 20% to 30%. Monitor patient for propranolol and flecainide toxicity.
Urine acidifying and alkalinizing drugs: May substantially alter excretion of flecainide. Monitor patient for flecainide toxicity or decreased effectiveness.
Drug-lifestyle. *Smoking:* May lower drug level. Discourage smoking.

Effects on lab test results

None reported.

Pharmacokinetics

Absorption: Rapid and almost complete; bioavailability is 85% to 90%.
Distribution: Possibly wide. 40% protein-bound.
Metabolism: In liver to inactive metabolites; 30% escapes metabolism.
Excretion: In urine. *Half-life:* 12 to 27 hours.

Route	Onset	Peak	Duration
P.O.	Unknown	2–3 hr	Unknown
I.V.	Immediate	Immediate	Unknown

Action

Chemical effect: Decreases excitability, conduction velocity, and automaticity as result of slowed atrial, AV node, His-Purkinje system, and intraventricular conduction and causes slight but significant prolongation of refractory periods in these tissues.
Therapeutic effect: Restores normal sinus rhythm.

Available forms

Injection: 10 mg/ml ◊
Tablets: 50 mg, 100 mg, 150 mg

NURSING PROCESS

Assessment

- Assess patient's arrhythmia before starting therapy.
- Monitor effectiveness by continuous ECG monitoring initially; long-term oral administration requires regular ECG readings.
- Monitor level, especially in patient with renal impairment or heart failure. Therapeutic level ranges from 0.2 to 1 mcg/ml. Risk of adverse effects increases when trough level exceeds 1 mcg/ml.
- Monitor potassium level regularly.
- Be alert for adverse reactions and drug interactions.
- Assess patient's and family's knowledge of drug therapy.

Nursing diagnoses

- Decreased cardiac output related to underlying arrhythmia
- Ineffective protection related to drug-induced new arrhythmias
- Deficient knowledge related to drug therapy

Planning and implementation

- If used to prevent ventricular arrhythmias, give drug only to patient with documented life-threatening arrhythmias.
- If patient has pacemaker, check that pacing threshold was determined 1 week before and after starting therapy because drug can alter endocardial pacing thresholds.
- Correct hypokalemia or hyperkalemia before giving drug because these electrolyte disturbances may alter effect.
- Twice-daily administration enhances patient compliance.
- Because of drug's long half-life, its full effect may take 3 to 5 days. Give I.V. lidocaine with drug for first several days.
- Keep emergency equipment nearby when giving drug.
- If ECG disturbances occur, withhold drug, obtain rhythm strip, and notify prescriber immediately.

Patient teaching

- Stress importance of taking oral drug exactly as prescribed.
- Warn patient to avoid hazardous activities that require alertness or good vision if adverse CNS or visual reaction occurs.
- Tell patient to limit fluid and sodium intake to minimize heart failure or fluid retention and to weigh himself daily on the same scale at around the same time. Urge him to report promptly sudden weight gain.

Evaluation

- Patient regains normal cardiac output with abolishment of underlying arrhythmia after drug therapy.
- Patient doesn't develop new arrhythmias.
- Patient and family state understanding of drug therapy.

fluconazole

(floo-KON-uh-zohl)

Diflucan

Pharmacologic class: bis-triazole derivative
Therapeutic class: antifungal
Pregnancy risk category: C

Indications and dosages

▶ **Oropharyngeal and esophageal candidiasis.** *Adults:* 200 mg P.O. or I.V. on first day, followed by 100 mg daily. Higher doses (up to 400 mg daily) may be used for esophageal disease. Continue for 2 weeks after symptoms resolve.
Children: 6 mg/kg P.O. or I.V. on first day, followed by 3 mg/kg daily for at least 2 weeks.

▶ **Systemic candidiasis.** *Adults:* 400 mg P.O. or I.V. on first day, followed by 200 mg daily. Continue at least 4 weeks or for 2 weeks after symptoms resolve.
Children: 6 to 12 mg/kg P.O. or I.V. daily.

▶ **Cryptococcal meningitis.** *Adults:* 400 mg P.O. or I.V. on first day, followed by 200 mg once daily. Higher doses (up to 400 mg daily) may be used. Continue for 10 to 12 weeks after CSF culture is negative.
Children: 12 mg/kg P.O. or I.V. on first day; follow with 6 mg/kg P.O. or I.V. daily for 10 to 12 weeks after CSF culture becomes negative.

▶ **To prevent candidiasis in bone marrow transplant.** *Adults:* 400 mg. P.O. or I.V. once daily. Start prophylaxis several days before anticipated granulocytopenia. Continue therapy for 7 days after neutrophil count rises above 1,000/mm³.

▶ **To suppress relapse of cryptococcal meningitis in patients with AIDS.** *Adults:* 200 mg P.O. or I.V. daily.
Children: 3 to 6 mg/kg P.O. daily.

▶ **Vulvovaginal candidiasis.** *Adults:* 150 mg P.O. as a single dose.

▶ **Candidal infection, long-term suppression in patients with HIV infection‡.** *Adults:* 100 to 200 mg P.O. or I.V. daily.

▶ **To prevent mucocutaneous candidiasis, cryptococcosis, coccidioidomycosis, or histoplasmosis in patients with HIV infection‡.**
Adults: 200 to 400 mg P.O. or I.V. daily.
Children and infants: 2 to 8 mg/kg P.O. daily.

Adjust-a-dose: For patients with renal impairment, give an initial loading dose of 50 to 400 mg. If creatinine clearance is 50 ml/minute or less, reduce dose by 50% in patients not receiving dialysis. For patients on hemodialysis, give 100% of usual dose after each dialysis session.

I.V. administration

- Don't remove protective overwrap from I.V. bags until just before use to ensure product sterility. Plastic container may show some opacity from moisture absorbed during sterilization. This is normal; it won't affect the drug and will dissipate over time.

• Give by continuous infusion at no more than 200 mg/hour. Use infusion pump. To prevent air embolism, don't connect in series with other infusions.

⊗ **Incompatibilities**
Amphotericin B, amphotericin B cholesteryl sulfate complex, ampicillin sodium, calcium gluconate, cefotaxime sodium, ceftazidime, ceftriaxone, cefuroxime sodium, chloramphenicol sodium succinate, clindamycin phosphate, diazepam, digoxin, erythromycin lactobionate, furosemide, haloperidol lactate, hydroxyzine hydrochloride, imipenem and cilastatin sodium, pentamidine, piperacillin sodium, ticarcillin disodium, trimethoprim-sulfamethoxazole. Don't add other drugs.

Contraindications and cautions

• Contraindicated in patients hypersensitive to drug or any of its components.

• Although no information exists regarding cross-sensitivity, use cautiously in patients hypersensitive to other antifungal azole compounds.

Lifespan: In pregnant women, use cautiously. In breast-feeding women, drug isn't recommended.

Adverse reactions

CNS: headache.
GI: abdominal pain, diarrhea, *nausea,* vomiting.
Hepatic: ***hepatotoxicity.***
Skin: rash, ***Stevens-Johnson syndrome.***
Other: ***anaphylaxis.***

Interactions

Drug-drug. *Alprazolam, chlordiazepoxide, clonazepam, clorazepate, diazepam, estazolam, flurazepam, midazolam, quazepam, triazolam:* May increase and prolong levels of these drugs, CNS depression, and psychomotor impairment. Don't use together.
Amitriptyline: May increase amitriptyline levels. Avoid combining, if possible.
Atorvastatin, fluvastatin, lovastatin, pravastatin, simvastatin: May increase levels and adverse effects of these HMG-CoA reductase inhibitors. Avoid use together. If they must be given together, reduce dose of HMG-CoA reductase inhibitor.
Carbamazepine: May increase carbamazepine level. Monitor levels closely.
Cyclosporine, phenytoin, tacrolimus: May increase levels of these drugs. Monitor cyclosporine or phenytoin level, and watch for drug toxicity.
Isoniazid, oral sulfonylureas, phenytoin, rifampin, valproic acid: May increase risk of elevated hepatic transaminases. Monitor patient and level closely.
Oral antidiabetics (glipizide, glyburide, tolbutamide): May increase levels of these drugs. Monitor patient for enhanced hypoglycemic effect.
Rifampin: May enhance fluconazole metabolism. Monitor patient for lack of response.
Theophylline: May decrease theophylline clearance. Monitor level.
Warfarin: May increase risk of bleeding. Monitor PT and INR.
Zidovudine: May increase zidovudine activity. Monitor patient closely.
Drug-lifestyle. *Alcohol use:* May increase risk of hepatotoxicity. Discourage use together.

Effects on lab test results

• May increase alkaline phosphatase, ALT, AST, bilirubin, and GGT levels.
• May decrease WBC and platelet counts.

Pharmacokinetics

Absorption: Rapid and complete.
Distribution: Wide. 12% protein-bound.
Metabolism: Partial.
Excretion: Mainly by kidneys; more than 80% unchanged in urine. *Half-life:* 20 to 50 hours.

Route	Onset	Peak	Duration
P.O.	Unknown	1–2 hr	Unknown
I.V.	Immediate	Immediate	Unknown

Action

Chemical effect: Inhibits fungal cytochrome P-450, an enzyme responsible for fungal sterol synthesis, and weakens fungal cell walls.
Therapeutic effect: Hinders fungal growth.

Available forms

Injection: 200 mg/100 ml, 400 mg/200 ml

Powder for oral suspension: 10 mg/ml, 40 mg/ml
Tablets: 50 mg, 100 mg, 150 mg, 200 mg

NURSING PROCESS

Assessment

- Assess patient's fungal infection before starting therapy, and reassess regularly.
- Periodically monitor liver function during prolonged therapy. Although adverse hepatic effects are rare, they can be serious.
- Be alert for adverse reactions and drug interactions.
- If adverse GI reactions occur, monitor patient's hydration.
- Assess patient's and family's knowledge of drug therapy.

Nursing diagnoses

- Risk for infection related to presence of susceptible fungi
- Risk for deficient fluid volume related to adverse GI reactions
- Deficient knowledge related to drug therapy

Planning and implementation

- If patient develops mild rash, monitor him closely. If lesions progress, stop drug and notify prescriber.

Patient teaching

- Urge patient to adhere to regimen and to return for follow-up.
- Tell patient to report adverse reactions to prescriber.

Evaluation

- Patient is free from infection.
- Patient maintains adequate hydration.
- Patient and family state understanding of drug therapy.

flucytosine (5-fluorocytosine, 5FC)

(floo-SIGH-toh-seen)
Ancobon, Ancotil ◇

Pharmacologic class: fluorinated pyrimidine
Therapeutic class: antifungal
Pregnancy risk category: C

Indications and dosages

▶ **Severe fungal infections caused by susceptible strains of *Candida* (including septicemia, endocarditis, urinary tract and pulmonary infections) and *Cryptococcus* (meningitis, pulmonary infection, and possible UTI).** *Adults:* 50 to 150 mg/kg P.O. daily in divided doses given q 6 hours. Use the lower initial dose in patients with renal insufficiency.

▶ **Chromomycosis‡.** *Adults:* 150 mg/kg P.O. daily.

Contraindications and cautions

- Contraindicated in patients hypersensitive to the drug or any of its components.
- Use cautiously in those with hepatic or renal impairment or bone marrow suppression.

Lifespan: In pregnant women, use cautiously. Breast-feeding women should stop breast-feeding or not use the drug. In children, safety and effectiveness haven't been established.

Adverse reactions

CNS: ataxia, confusion, dizziness, fatigue, hallucinations, headache, paresthesia, parkinsonism, peripheral neuropathy, psychosis, sedation, vertigo, weakness.
CV: ***cardiac arrest,*** chest pain.
EENT: hearing loss.
GI: abdominal pain, diarrhea, dry mouth, duodenal ulcer, ***hemorrhage,*** nausea, ulcerative colitis, vomiting.
GU: azotemia, crystalluria, ***renal impairment.***
Hematologic: agranulocytosis, anemia, ***aplastic anemia, bone marrow suppression,*** eosinophilia, ***leukopenia, thrombocytopenia.***
Hepatic: jaundice.
Metabolic: ***hypoglycemia,*** hypokalemia.
Respiratory: dyspnea, ***respiratory arrest.***
Skin: occasional rash, photosensitivity, pruritus, urticaria.

Interactions

Drug-drug. *Amphotericin B:* May have synergistic effects and enhance toxicity when used together. Monitor patient.
Cytosine: May inactivate the antifungal activity of flucytosine. Monitor patient.

Effects on lab test results

- May increase urine urea, alkaline phosphatase, ALT, AST, bilirubin, creatinine, and

BUN levels. May decrease glucose, potassium, and hemoglobin levels and hematocrit.
• May increase eosinophil count. May decrease WBC, platelet, and granulocyte counts.

Pharmacokinetics

Absorption: 75% to 90%; food decreases absorption rate.
Distribution: Wide. CSF levels vary from 60% to 100% of blood levels. 2% to 4% protein-bound.
Metabolism: Only small amounts.
Excretion: 75% to 95% unchanged in urine. *Half-life:* 2½ to 6 hours.

Route	Onset	Peak	Duration
P.O.	Unknown	1–2 hr	Unknown

Action

Chemical effect: May penetrate fungal cells where it's converted to fluorouracil—a known metabolic antagonist—and causes defective protein synthesis.
Therapeutic effect: Hinders fungal growth, including some strains of *Cryptococcus* and *Candida.*

Available forms

Capsules: 250 mg, 500 mg

NURSING PROCESS

Assessment

• Assess patient's fungal infection before starting therapy, and reassess regularly.
• Before starting therapy, obtain hematologic tests and renal and liver function studies. Make sure susceptibility tests showing that organism is flucytosine-sensitive are on chart.
• Monitor blood, liver, and renal function studies frequently; obtain susceptibility tests weekly to monitor drug resistance.
• If possible, regularly perform blood level assays of drug to maintain flucytosine at therapeutic level (25 to 120 mcg/ml). Higher levels may be toxic.
• Be alert for adverse reactions and drug interactions.
• If adverse GI reaction occurs, monitor patient's hydration.
• Assess patient's and family's knowledge of drug therapy.

Nursing diagnoses

• Risk for infection related to presence of susceptible fungi
• Risk for deficient fluid volume related to adverse GI reactions
• Deficient knowledge related to drug therapy

Planning and implementation

• Give capsules over 15 minutes to reduce adverse GI reactions.

Patient teaching

• Inform patient that therapeutic response may take weeks or months.
• Tell patient how to take capsules.
• Warn patient to avoid activities requiring mental alertness if adverse CNS reactions occur.

Evaluation

• Patient is free from infection.
• Patient maintains adequate hydration throughout drug therapy.
• Patient and family state understanding of drug therapy.

fludarabine phosphate

(floo-DAR-uh-been FOS-fayt)
Fludara

Pharmacologic class: antimetabolite, purine antagonist
Therapeutic class: antineoplastic
Pregnancy risk category: D

Indications and dosages

▶ **B-cell chronic lymphocytic leukemia in patients who either haven't responded or have responded inadequately to at least one standard alkylating drug regimen, mycosis fungoides‡, hairy cell leukemia‡, and Hodgkin and malignant lymphoma‡.** *Adults:* 25 mg/m² I.V. over 30 minutes for 5 consecutive days. Repeat cycle q 28 days.
Adjust-a-dose: For patients with renal impairment, if creatinine clearance is 30 to 70 ml/minute, decrease dose by 20%. If clearance is less than 30 ml/minute, don't give drug.
▶ **Chronic lymphocytic leukemia‡.** *Adults:* Usually, 18 to 30 mg/m² I.V. over 30 minutes for 5 consecutive days q 28 days. Therapy is based on patient's response and tolerance.

I.V. administration

• Preparing and giving the drug have mutagenic, teratogenic, and carcinogenic risks. Follow facility policy to reduce risks.
• To prepare solution from lyophilized powder, add 2 ml of sterile water for injection to solid cake of drug. Drug will dissolve within 15 seconds; each ml will contain 25 mg of drug. Dilute this solution or injection further in 100 or 125 ml of D_5W or normal saline injection.
• Check injection for particulate matter or discoloration; reconstituted solution should be clear.
• Use within 8 hours of reconstitution.
• Store drug in refrigerator at 36° to 46° F (2° to 8° C).

⊗ Incompatibilities
Acyclovir sodium, amphotericin B, chlorpromazine, daunorubicin, ganciclovir, hydroxyzine hydrochloride, prochlorperazine edisylate.

Contraindications and cautions

• Contraindicated in patients hypersensitive to the drug or any of its components.
• Use cautiously in patients with renal insufficiency.

Lifespan: In pregnant women, use only if benefits outweigh risks to fetus. In breast-feeding women and in children, safety and effectiveness haven't been established.

Adverse reactions

CNS: agitation, cerebellar syndrome, ***coma,*** *confusion,* depression, *fatigue, fever,* headache, *malaise,* pain, *paresthesia,* peripheral neuropathy, sleep disorder, ***stroke,*** transient ischemic attack, *weakness.*
CV: aneurysm, angina, ***arrhythmias,*** deep venous thrombosis, edema, ***heart failure, hemorrhage, MI,*** phlebitis, ***supraventricular tachycardia.***
EENT: delayed blindness (with high doses), epistaxis, hearing loss, pharyngitis, sinusitis, *visual disturbances.*
GI: *anorexia,* constipation, *diarrhea,* esophagitis, GI BLEEDING, mucositis, *nausea,* stomatitis, *vomiting.*
GU: dysuria, hematuria, proteinuria, ***renal impairment,*** urinary hesitancy, *UTI.*
Hematologic: anemia, myelosuppression, ***neutropenia, thrombocytopenia.***
Hepatic: cholelithiasis, ***liver failure.***
Metabolic: dehydration, hyperglycemia, hyperphosphatemia, hyperuricemia.
Musculoskeletal: myalgia.
Respiratory: allergic pneumonitis, bronchitis, *cough, dyspnea,* hemoptysis, ***hypoxia,*** *pneumonia,* ***pulmonary toxicity,*** *upper respiratory infection.*
Skin: alopecia, diaphoresis, pruritus, *rash,* seborrhea.
Other: ***anaphylaxis,*** chills, INFECTION, tumor lysis syndrome.

Interactions

Drug-drug. *Anticoagulants:* May interfere with anticoagulant response. Monitor PT; adjust dosage as needed.
Estrogens: May decrease fludarabine metabolism. Monitor patient.
Other myelosuppressants: May increase toxicity. Avoid use together.
Pentostatin: May increase risk of pulmonary toxicity. Avoid use together.
Salicylates: May decrease effect of salicylates and increase ulcerogenic effects. Avoid use together.

Effects on lab test results

• May increase glucose, phosphate, potassium, and uric acid levels. May decrease hemoglobin level and hematocrit.
• May decrease platelet and neutrophil counts.

Pharmacokinetics

Absorption: Given I.V.
Distribution: Unknown.
Metabolism: Rapidly dephosphorylated and then phosphorylated intracellularly to its active metabolite.
Excretion: 23% in urine as unchanged active metabolite. *Half-life:* About 10 hours.

Route	Onset	Peak	Duration
I.V.	7–21 hr	Unknown	Unknown

Action

Chemical effect: Unknown; actions may be multifaceted. After conversion to its active metabolite, fludarabine interferes with DNA synthesis by inhibiting DNA polymerase alpha, ribonucleotide reductase, and DNA primase.
Therapeutic effect: Kills susceptible cancer cells.

Available forms

Injection: 50 mg/2 ml
Powder for injection: 50 mg

NURSING PROCESS

Assessment

- Assess patient's underlying condition before starting therapy, and reassess regularly.
- Careful hematologic monitoring is needed, especially of neutrophil and platelet counts, because bone marrow suppression can be severe.
- Be alert for adverse reactions and drug interactions.
- Assess patient's and family's knowledge of drug therapy.

Nursing diagnoses

- Ineffective health maintenance related to presence of leukemia
- Ineffective protection related to drug-induced immunosuppression
- Deficient knowledge related to drug therapy

Planning and implementation

- Optimum duration of therapy isn't known. Recommendations suggest three additional cycles after achieving maximum response.

Patient teaching

- Warn patient to watch for evidence of infection and bleeding.
- Tell patient to notify prescriber if adverse reactions occur.

Evaluation

- Patient shows positive response to fludarabine therapy.
- Patient develops no serious infections or bleeding complications.
- Patient and family state understanding of drug therapy.

fludrocortisone acetate

(floo-droh-KOR-tuh-sohn AS-ih-tayt)
Florinef

Pharmacologic class: mineralocorticoid
Therapeutic class: adrenocortical steroid
Pregnancy risk category: C

Indications and dosages

▶ **Adrenal insufficiency (partial replacement), adrenogenital syndrome.** *Adults:* 0.1 to 0.2 mg P.O. daily.

▶ **Orthostatic hypotension‡.** *Adults:* 0.1 to 0.4 mg P.O. daily.

Contraindications and cautions

- Contraindicated in patients hypersensitive to drug or any of its components and in those with systemic fungal infections.
- Use cautiously in patients with hypothyroidism, cirrhosis, ocular herpes simplex, emotional instability with psychotic tendencies, nonspecific ulcerative colitis, diverticulitis, fresh intestinal anastomoses, active or latent peptic ulcer, renal insufficiency, hypertension, osteoporosis, and myasthenia gravis.

Lifespan: In pregnant women, use only if benefits outweigh risks to fetus. In breast-feeding women, use cautiously because it's unclear if the drug appears in breast milk. In children, long-term use may delay growth and maturation.

Adverse reactions

CNS: dizziness, headache, ***seizures.***
CV: cardiac hypertrophy, *edema,* ***heart failure,*** hypertension, *sodium and water retention.*
EENT: cataracts, glaucoma.
GI: peptic ulcer.
Metabolic: hyperglycemia, hypokalemia.
Musculoskeletal: weakness.
Skin: allergic rash, ***anaphylaxis,*** bruising, diaphoresis, urticaria.

Interactions

Drug-drug. *Amphotericin B, drugs that deplete potassium (such as thiazide diuretics):* May enhance potassium-wasting effects of fludrocortisone. Monitor potassium levels.
Barbiturates, phenytoin, rifampin: May increase clearance of fludrocortisone acetate. Monitor patient for effect.
Drug-food. *Food containing sodium:* May increase blood pressure. Advise patient to limit sodium intake.

Effects on lab test results

- May increase glucose level. May decrease potassium level.

Pharmacokinetics

Absorption: Good.
Distribution: To muscle, liver, skin, intestines, and kidneys. Extensively protein-bound. Only unbound portion is active.
Metabolism: In liver to inactive metabolites.
Excretion: In urine; insignificant amount in feces. *Half-life:* 18 to 36 hours.

Route	Onset	Peak	Duration
P.O.	Varies	Varies	1–2 days

Action

Chemical effect: Increases sodium reabsorption and potassium and hydrogen secretion at distal convoluted tubule of nephron.
Therapeutic effect: Increases sodium level and decreases potassium and hydrogen levels.

Available forms

Tablets: 0.1 mg

NURSING PROCESS

Assessment

- Assess patient's underlying condition before starting therapy, and reassess regularly.
- Monitor patient's blood pressure, weight, and electrolyte levels.
- Be alert for adverse reactions and drug interactions.
- Assess patient's and family's knowledge of drug therapy.

Nursing diagnoses

- Ineffective health maintenance related to underlying adrenal condition
- Excess fluid volume related to drug-induced adverse reactions
- Deficient knowledge related to drug therapy

Planning and implementation

- Drug is used with cortisone or hydrocortisone in patients with adrenal insufficiency.
- If hypertension occurs, notify prescriber, who may lower dose by 50%.
- Potassium supplements may be needed for excessive potassium loss.
- Signs of overdose include excessive weight gain, edema, hypertension, hypokalemia, and enlarged heart. Stop therapy for a few days until symptoms subside, and then resume drug at a lower dose.

Patient teaching

- Tell patient to notify prescriber about worsened symptoms, such as hypotension, weakness, cramping, and palpitations.
- Warn patient that mild peripheral edema is common.

Evaluation

- Patient's health is improved.
- Patient develops no sodium and water retention.
- Patient and family state understanding of drug therapy.

flumazenil

(floo-MAZ-ih-nil)
Romazicon

Pharmacologic class: benzodiazepine antagonist
Therapeutic class: antidote
Pregnancy risk category: C

Indications and dosages

▶ **Complete or partial reversal of sedative effects of benzodiazepines after anesthesia or short diagnostic procedures (conscious sedation).** *Adults:* Initially, 0.2 mg I.V. over 15 seconds. If patient doesn't reach desired level of consciousness (LOC) after 45 seconds, repeat dose. Repeat at 1-minute intervals until cumulative dose of 1 mg has been given (initial dose plus four more doses), if needed. Most patients respond after 0.6 to 1 mg of drug. In case of resedation, repeat dose after 20 minutes, but don't give more than 1 mg at any one time and no more than 3 mg/hour.

▶ **Suspected benzodiazepine overdose.** *Adults:* Initially, 0.2 mg I.V. over 30 seconds. If patient doesn't reach desired LOC after 30 seconds, give 0.3 mg over 30 seconds. If patient still doesn't respond adequately, give 0.5 mg over 30 seconds; repeat 0.5-mg doses p.r.n. at 1-minute intervals up to a cumulative dose of 3 mg. Most patients with benzodiazepine overdose respond to cumulative doses between 1 and 3 mg; rarely, patients who respond partially after 3 mg may need additional doses. Don't give more than 5 mg over 5 minutes initially. Sedation that persists after this dosage is unlikely to be caused by benzodiazepines. In case of resedation, repeat dose after 20 minutes, but don't give more than 1 mg at any one time and no more than 3 mg/hour.

I.V. administration

- Compatible solutions include D_5W, lactated Ringer's injection, and normal saline solution.
- Give drug into I.V. line in large vein with free-flowing I.V. solution to minimize pain at injection site.
- Discard within 24 hours any unused drug that has been drawn into syringe or diluted.

⊗ **Incompatibilities**

None reported.

Contraindications and cautions

- Contraindicated in patients hypersensitive to drug, any of its components, or benzodiazepines; patients who show evidence of serious cyclic antidepressant overdose; and those who received a benzodiazepine to treat a potentially life-threatening condition (such as status epilepticus).
- Use cautiously in patients at high risk for developing seizures; patients who recently have received multiple doses of parenteral benzodiazepine; patients displaying signs of seizure activity; patients who may be at risk for unrecognized benzodiazepine dependence, such as ICU patients; and patients with head injury, psychiatric, or alcohol-dependency problems.

Lifespan: In pregnant women, use cautiously. In breast-feeding women, use cautiously because it's unknown if the drug appears in breast milk. In children, safety and effectiveness haven't been established.

Adverse reactions

CNS: agitation, *dizziness,* emotional lability, *headache,* insomnia, ***seizures,*** tremor.
CV: ***arrhythmias,*** cutaneous vasodilation, palpitations.
EENT: abnormal or blurred vision.
GI: nausea, vomiting.
Respiratory: dyspnea, hyperventilation.
Skin: diaphoresis.
Other: pain at injection site.

Interactions

Drug-drug. *Antidepressants, drugs that can cause seizures or arrhythmias:* May cause seizures or arrhythmias after effect of benzodiazepine overdose is removed. Use with caution, if at all, in cases of mixed overdose.

Effects on lab test results

None reported.

Pharmacokinetics

Absorption: Given I.V.
Distribution: Rapid. 50% protein-bound.
Metabolism: By liver.
Excretion: 90% to 95% appears in urine as metabolites. *Half-life:* 54 minutes.

Route	Onset	Peak	Duration
I.V.	Unknown	Unknown	Unknown

Action

Chemical effect: Competitively inhibits actions of benzodiazepines on GABA-benzodiazepine receptor complex.
Therapeutic effect: Awakens patient from sedative effects of benzodiazepines.

Available forms

Injection: 0.1 mg/ml in 5- and 10-ml multiple-dose vials

NURSING PROCESS

Assessment

- Assess patient's sedation before starting therapy.
- Assess patient's LOC often.
- Be alert for adverse reactions and drug interactions.

ALERT: Monitor patient closely for resedation that may occur after reversal of benzodiazepine effects because drug's duration of action is shorter than that of benzodiazepines. Monitor patient closely after long-acting benzodiazepines, such as diazepam, or high doses of short-acting benzodiazepines, such as 10 mg of midazolam. In most cases, severe resedation is unlikely in patient who shows no signs of resedation 2 hours after 1-mg dose of flumazenil.

- Monitor patient's ECG for evidence of arrhythmias.
- Assess patient's and family's knowledge of drug therapy.

Nursing diagnoses

- Ineffective protection related to sedated state

• Decreased cardiac output related to drug-induced seizures
• Deficient knowledge related to drug therapy

Planning and implementation

• If arrhythmias or other adverse reactions occur, notify prescriber and treat accordingly.

Patient teaching

• Warn patient to avoid hazardous activities within 24 hours.
• Tell patient not to use alcohol, CNS depressants, or OTC drugs for 24 hours.
• Give family members important instructions or provide patient with written instructions.

Evaluation

• Patient is awake and alert.
• Patient maintains adequate cardiac output.
• Patient and family state understanding of drug therapy.

fluorouracil (5-fluorouracil, 5-FU)

(floo-roh-YOOR-uh-sil)
Adrucil, Carac, Efudex, Fluoroplex

Pharmacologic class: antimetabolite
Therapeutic class: antineoplastic
Pregnancy risk category: D (injection); X (topical)

Indications and dosages

▶ **Colon, rectal, breast, stomach, and pancreatic cancers.** *Adults:* 12 mg/kg I.V. daily for 4 days; if no toxicity, give 6 mg/kg on days 6, 8, 10, and 12; then begin single weekly maintenance dose of 10 to 15 mg/kg I.V. after toxicity (if any) from initial course subsides. Dosages based on lean body weight. Maximum single dose, 800 mg.

▶ **Palliative therapy of advanced colorectal cancer.** *Adults:* 425 mg/m^2 I.V. daily for 5 consecutive days. Give with 20 mg/m^2 of leucovorin I.V. Repeat at 4-week intervals for two additional courses; then repeat at intervals of 4 to 5 weeks, as tolerated.

▶ **Multiple actinic (solar) keratoses; superficial basal cell carcinoma.** *Adults:* Apply cream or topical solution b.i.d.

▶ **Multiple actinic (solar) keratosis of the face and anterior scalp.** *Adults:* Apply a thin layer of cream or topical solution to the washed and dried affected area daily for up to 4 weeks.

I.V. administration

• Give antiemetic to reduce nausea before giving drug.
• Preparing and giving drug create carcinogenic, mutagenic, and teratogenic risks for staff. Follow facility policy to reduce risks.
• Drug may be given by direct injection without dilution.
• For I.V. infusion, drug may be diluted with D_5W, sterile water for injection, or normal saline injection.
• Infuse slowly over 2 to 8 hours. Don't use cloudy solution. If crystals form, dissolve by warming.
• Use plastic I.V. containers for giving continuous infusions. Solution is more stable in plastic I.V. bags than in glass bottles.

⊗ Incompatibilities

Aldesleukin, amphotericin B cholesterol complex, carboplatin, cisplatin, cytarabine, diazepam, doxorubicin, droperidol, epirubicin, fentanyl citrate, filgrastim, gallium nitrate, leucovorin calcium, metoclopramide, morphine sulfate, ondansetron, topotecan, vinorelbine tartrate.

Contraindications and cautions

• Contraindicated in patients hypersensitive to the drug or any of its components; in those with poor nutrition, bone marrow suppression (WBC count of 5,000/mm^3 or less or platelet counts of 100,000/mm^3 or less), or potentially serious infections; and in those who have had major surgery within the previous month.
• Use cautiously after high-dose pelvic radiation therapy and in patients who have received alkylating drugs. Also use cautiously in patients who have impaired hepatic or renal function or widespread neoplastic infiltration of bone marrow.

Lifespan: In pregnant and breast-feeding women, drug is contraindicated. In children, safety and effectiveness haven't been established.

Adverse reactions

CNS: acute cerebellar syndrome, ataxia, confusion, disorientation, euphoria, headache, *malaise,* nystagmus, *weakness.*

CV: angina, ***myocardial ischemia,*** thrombophlebitis.
EENT: epistaxis, lacrimal duct stenosis, lacrimation, photophobia, visual changes.
GI: anorexia, diarrhea, ***GI bleeding,*** GI ulcer, nausea, stomatitis, vomiting.
Hematologic: ***agranulocytosis,*** anemia, ***leukopenia, thrombocytopenia.***
Skin: *burning, pain,* soreness, suppuration, and swelling with topical use; contact dermatitis; *dermatitis; erythema;* erythematous, desquamative rash of hands and feet; nail changes; photosensitivity; pigmented palmar creases; *pruritus; reversible alopecia; scaling.*
Other: ***anaphylaxis.***

Interactions

Drug-drug. *Leucovorin calcium, previous therapy with alkylating drugs:* May increase fluorouracil toxicity. Use cautiously.
Drug-lifestyle. *Sun exposure:* Photosensitivity reactions may occur. Urge patient to avoid unprotected or prolonged sun exposure.

Effects on lab test results

- May increase alkaline phosphatase, AST, ALT, bilirubin, LDH, and urine 5-hydroxyindoleacetic acid levels. May decrease hemoglobin level and hematocrit.
- May decrease WBC, RBC, platelet, and granulocyte counts.

Pharmacokinetics

Absorption: Unknown for topical forms.
Distribution: Wide; crosses blood–brain barrier.
Metabolism: Most of drug degraded in liver; small amount converted in tissues to active metabolite.
Excretion: Metabolites mainly through lungs as carbon dioxide. *Half-life:* 20 minutes.

Route	Onset	Peak	Duration
I.V., topical	Unknown	Unknown	Unknown

Action

Chemical effect: Inhibits DNA synthesis.
Therapeutic effect: Inhibits cell growth of selected cancers.

Available forms

Cream: 0.5%, 1%, 5%
Injection: 50 mg/ml
Topical solution: 1%, 2%, 5%

NURSING PROCESS

Assessment

- Assess patient's condition before starting therapy and reassess regularly.
- Monitor fluid intake and output, CBC, platelet count, and renal and hepatic function tests.
- Be alert for adverse reactions and interactions.
- Fluorouracil toxicity may be delayed for 1 to 3 weeks. Lowest WBC count is 9 to 14 days after each dose; lowest platelet count is 7 to 14 days after each dose.
- Monitor patient receiving topical form for serious adverse reaction. Ingestion and systemic absorption may cause leukopenia, thrombocytopenia, stomatitis, diarrhea, or GI ulceration, bleeding, and hemorrhage. Application to large ulcerated areas may cause systemic toxicity.
- Watch for stomatitis or diarrhea (signs of toxicity).
- Assess patient's and family's knowledge of drug therapy.

Nursing diagnoses

- Ineffective health maintenance related to underlying neoplastic condition
- Ineffective protection related to adverse hematologic reactions
- Deficient knowledge related to drug therapy

Planning and implementation

ALERT: Drug sometimes is ordered as 5-fluorouracil or 5-FU. The numeral 5 is part of drug name and shouldn't be confused with dosage units.
- When giving topically, apply cautiously near eyes, nose, and mouth.
- Avoid occlusive dressings because they increase risk of inflammatory reactions in adjacent normal skin.
- Wash hands immediately after handling topical form.
- Wash and dry affected area; wait 10 minutes. Apply thin layer of cream to affected area.
- Use 1% topical form on face. Higher concentrations are used for thicker-skinned areas or resistant lesions.
- Use 5% topical form for superficial basal cell carcinoma confirmed by biopsy.
- May apply sunscreen and moisturizer 2 hours after application.
- Risk of local irritation isn't increased by extending therapy from 2 to 4 weeks; irritation

typically resolves within 2 weeks of stopping drug.

- Don't refrigerate fluorouracil.
- Use sodium hypochlorite 5% (household bleach) to inactivate drug if it spills.
- If diarrhea occurs, stop giving the drug and notify prescriber.
- If WBC count is less than 2,000/mm^3, consider protective isolation.

Patient teaching

- Warn patient that alopecia may occur, but it's reversible.
- Advise patient to avoid prolonged exposure to sunlight or ultraviolet light when topical form is used.
- Tell patient to use sunblock to avoid inflammatory erythematous dermatitis. Long-term use of drug may cause erythematous, desquamative rash of hands and feet, which may be treated with pyridoxine (50 to 150 mg P.O. daily) for 5 to 7 days.
- Warn patient that topically treated area may be unsightly during therapy and for several weeks after. Full healing may take 1 to 2 months. Local irritation typically resolves 2 weeks after drug is stopped.
- Inform patient that sunscreen and a moisturizer may be applied 2 hours after drug application.

☑ Evaluation

- Patient shows positive response to fluorouracil therapy.
- Patient develops no serious adverse hematologic reactions.
- Patient and family state understanding of drug therapy.

fluoxetine hydrochloride

(floo-OKS-eh-teen high-droh-KLOR-ighd)

Prozac✐, Prozac-20 ◇, Prozac Weekly, Sarafem Pulvules

Pharmacologic class: SSRI
Therapeutic class: antidepressant
Pregnancy risk category: C

Indications and dosages

▶ **Depression, obsessive-compulsive disorder (OCD).** *Adults:* Initially, 20 mg P.O. in morning; increase by patient's response. May be given b.i.d. in morning and at noon. Maximum, 80 mg daily.

Children ages 7 to 17: For OCD, 10 mg P.O. daily. After 2 weeks, increase dose to 20 mg daily to maximum of 60 mg daily. In lower-weight children, increase dose to 20 to 30 mg daily after several weeks. Maximum, 60 mg daily.

Children ages 8 to 18: For depression, 10 to 20 mg P.O. daily. After 1 week, increase to 20 mg daily. Start lower-weight children at 10 mg daily and increase dose to 20 mg daily after several weeks.

▶ **Maintenance therapy for depression in stabilized patients.** *Adults:* 90 mg Prozac Weekly P.O. once weekly. Start 7 days after the last daily dose of Prozac 20 mg.

▶ **Moderate to severe bulimia nervosa.** *Adults:* 60 mg daily P.O. in the morning.

▶ **Premenstrual dysphoric disorder (PMDD).** *Adults:* 20 mg Sarafem P.O. daily every day of the menstrual cycle or starting 14 days before the anticipated onset of menstruation through the first full day of menses and repeating with each new cycle. Maximum, 80 mg daily.

▶ **Panic disorder with or without agoraphobia.** *Adults:* 10 mg P.O. daily. May increase in 10-mg increments at intervals of no less than 1 week to maximum dosage of 60 mg.

▶ **Anorexia nervosa‡.** *Adults:* 40 mg P.O. daily in weight-restored patients.

▶ **Depression linked to bipolar disorder‡.** *Adults:* 20 to 60 mg P.O. daily.

▶ **Cataplexy‡.** *Adults:* 20 mg P.O. daily or b.i.d. in conjunction with CNS stimulant therapy.

▶ **Alcohol dependence‡.** *Adults:* 60 mg P.O. daily.

▶ **To prevent migraine headaches‡.** *Adults:* 10 to 40 mg P.O. daily.

▶ **Posttraumatic stress disorder‡, Raynaud phenomenon‡.** *Adults:* 20 to 60 mg P.O. daily.

▶ **Generalized anxiety disorder‡, hot flashes‡.** *Adults:* 20 mg P.O. daily.

Contraindications and cautions

- Contraindicated in patients hypersensitive to the drug or any of its components and in those taking MAO inhibitors within 14 days of starting therapy. Don't give MAO inhibitors or thioridazine within 5 weeks of discontinuing fluoxetine.
- Use cautiously in patients at high risk for suicide and in those with history of mania, sei-

zures, diabetes mellitus, or hepatic, renal, or CV disease.

Lifespan: In pregnant women, use cautiously. In breast-feeding women, it's unknown if drug appears in breast milk. In children younger than age 7, safety and effectiveness in OCD haven't been established. In children younger than age 8, safety and effectiveness in major depressive disorder haven't been established. In children, safety and effectiveness for panic disorder, PMDD, and bulimia nervosa haven't been established. In adults age 65 and older treated for depression, start with lower dosage.

Adverse reactions

CNS: anxiety, asthenia, dizziness, drowsiness, fatigue, fever, headache, insomnia, nervousness, somnolence, tremor.
CV: palpitations.
EENT: nasal congestion, pharyngitis, sinusitis.
GI: abdominal pain, *anorexia,* constipation, *diarrhea, dry mouth,* dyspepsia, flatulence, increased appetite, *nausea,* vomiting.
Metabolic: weight loss.
Musculoskeletal: muscle pain.
Respiratory: cough, ***respiratory distress,*** upper respiratory infection.
Skin: pruritus, rash, urticaria.
Other: flulike syndrome, hot flushes, sexual dysfunction.

Interactions

Drug-drug. *Amphetamines, dextromethorphan, dihydroergotamine, meperidine, SSRIs, sumatriptan, tramadol, trazodone:* May increase risk of serotonin syndrome. Avoid use together.
Benzodiazepines, tricyclic antidepressants: May increase CNS effects. Monitor patient and level closely; adjust doses if needed.
Carbamazepine, clozapine, cyclosporine, flecainide, haloperidol, propafenone, ritonavir, vinblastine: May increase levels of these drugs. Monitor levels and patient for adverse effects.
Cyproheptadine: May reverse or decrease pharmacologic effect. Monitor patient closely.
Insulin, oral antidiabetics: May alter glucose levels and need for antidiabetic. Adjust dosage.
Lithium: May alter lithium level. Monitor lithium level closely.
Phenelzine, selegiline, tranylcypromine: May cause serotonin syndrome (CNS irritability, shivering, and altered consciousness). Don't give drug within 2 weeks of an SSRI.
Phenytoin: May increase phenytoin level and risk of toxicity. Monitor phenytoin level and adjust dosage.
Sumatriptan: May cause weakness, hyperreflexia, and incoordination. Monitor the patient closely.
Thioridazine: May raise level of thioridazine, leading to a higher risk of serious ventricular arrhythmias and sudden death. Don't give within 5 weeks of each other.
Tryptophan: May increase toxic reaction with agitation, GI distress, and restlessness. Don't use together.
Warfarin, other highly protein-bound drugs: May increase level of fluoxetine or other highly protein-bound drugs. Monitor level of these drugs closely.
Drug-herb. *St. John's wort:* May increase the risk of serotonin syndrome. Discourage use together.
Drug-lifestyle. *Alcohol use:* May increase CNS depression. Discourage use together.

Effects on lab test results

None reported.

Pharmacokinetics

Absorption: Good.
Distribution: 95% protein-bound.
Metabolism: Mainly in liver to active metabolites.
Excretion: By kidneys. *Half-life:* 2 to 3 days.

Route	Onset	Peak	Duration
P.O.	1–4 wk	6–8 hr	Unknown

Action

Chemical effect: May inhibit CNS neuronal uptake of serotonin.
Therapeutic effect: Relieves depression and obsessive-compulsive behaviors.

Available forms

Capsules: 90 mg (Prozac Weekly)
Oral solution: 20 mg/5 ml
Pulvules: 10 mg, 20 mg, 40 mg
Tablets: 10 mg

NURSING PROCESS

Assessment

- Assess patient's condition before starting therapy, and reassess regularly.

• Be alert for adverse reactions and drug interactions.
• Observe closely for evidence of suicidal thoughts or behaviors until depression is relieved.
• Assess patient's and family's knowledge of drug therapy.

Nursing diagnoses

• Ineffective coping related to patient's underlying condition
• Sleep deprivation related to drug-induced insomnia
• Deficient knowledge related to drug therapy

Planning and implementation

• An elderly or debilitated patient, or a patient with renal or hepatic dysfunction, may need a lower dose or less frequent administration.
• Give drug in morning to prevent insomnia.
• Give antihistamines or topical corticosteroids to treat rashes or pruritus.
• Low-weight children may need several weeks between dosage increases.

ALERT: Don't confuse Prozac with Prilosec.

ALERT: Don't confuse Sarafem with Serophene.

Patient teaching

• Tell patient not to take drug in afternoon or evening because fluoxetine commonly causes nervousness and insomnia.
• Instruct patient to take drug with or without food.
• Warn patient to avoid hazardous activities that require alertness and psychomotor coordination until the drug's CNS effects are known.
• Advise patient to consult prescriber before taking any other prescription or OTC drugs.

Evaluation

• Patient behavior and communication indicate an improvement of depression with drug therapy.
• Patient has no insomnia with drug use.
• Patient and family state understanding of drug therapy.

fluphenazine decanoate

(floo-FEN-uh-zeen deh-kuh-NOH-ayt)

Modecate ♦ ◇, Modecate Concentrate, Prolixin Decanoate

fluphenazine hydrochloride

Anatensol ◇ *, Apo-Fluphenazine ♦, Modecate Concentrate ♦, Moditen HCl ♦, Prolixin*

Pharmacologic class: phenothiazine (piperazine derivative)
Therapeutic class: antipsychotic
Pregnancy risk category: C

Indications and dosages

▶ **Psychotic disorders.** *Adults:* Initially, 2.5 to 10 mg hydrochloride P.O. daily in divided doses q 6 to 8 hours; may increase cautiously to 20 mg. Maintenance, 1 to 5 mg P.O. daily. Or 1.25 mg hydrochloride I.M. initially; then 2.5 to 10 mg I.M. daily in divided doses q 6 to 8 hours. Or 12.5 to 25 mg decanoate I.M. or subcutaneously q 4 to 6 weeks. Maximum dose, 100 mg.
Elderly patients: Initially 1 to 2.5 mg P.O. daily. Adjust according to response.

Contraindications and cautions

• Contraindicated in patients hypersensitive to drug or any of its components and in those with CNS depression, bone marrow suppression, other blood dyscrasia, subcortical damage, liver damage, or coma.
• Use cautiously in debilitated patients and those with pheochromocytoma, severe CV disease, peptic ulcer, fever, exposure to extreme heat or cold or phosphorous insecticides, respiratory disorder, hypocalcemia, seizure disorder, severe reactions to insulin or electroconvulsive therapy, mitral insufficiency, glaucoma, or prostatic hyperplasia. Use parenteral form cautiously in patients with asthma and patients allergic to sulfites.

Lifespan: In pregnant women, use cautiously. In breast-feeding women, use cautiously because it's unknown if the drug appears in breast milk. In children, safety and effectiveness haven't been established. In elderly patients, use cautiously.

Adverse reactions

CNS: dizziness, drowsiness, EEG changes, extrapyramidal reactions, ***neuroleptic malignant syndrome,*** pseudoparkinsonism, sedation, ***seizures,*** tardive dyskinesia.
CV: ECG changes, orthostatic hypotension, tachycardia.
EENT: *blurred vision, dry mouth,* nasal congestion, ocular changes.
GI: constipation.
GU: dark urine, inhibited ejaculation, menstrual irregularities, *urine retention.*
Hematologic: ***agranulocytosis, aplastic anemia,*** eosinophilia, hemolytic anemia, ***leukopenia.***
Hepatic: cholestatic jaundice.
Metabolic: increased appetite, weight gain.
Skin: mild photosensitivity.
Other: allergic reactions, gynecomastia.

Interactions

Drug-drug. *Antacids:* May inhibit absorption of oral phenothiazines. Separate doses by at least 2 hours.
Anticholinergics: May increase anticholinergic effects. Avoid use together.
Barbiturates, lithium: May decrease phenothiazine effect. Observe patient.
Centrally acting antihypertensives: May decrease antihypertensive effect. Monitor blood pressure.
CNS depressants: May increase CNS depression. Avoid use together.
Drug-lifestyle. *Alcohol use:* May increase CNS depression, particularly psychomotor skills. Strongly discourage use together.
Sun exposure: May increase risk of photosensitivity. Discourage prolonged or unprotected exposure to sun.

Effects on lab test results

- May decrease hemoglobin level and hematocrit.
- May increase eosinophil count. May decrease WBC, granulocyte, and platelet counts. May alter liver function test values.

Pharmacokinetics

Absorption: For tablet, erratic and variable.
Distribution: Wide. CNS levels are usually higher than those in blood. 91% to 99% protein-bound.
Metabolism: Extensive.
Excretion: Mostly in urine. *Half-life:* Hydrochloride, 15 hours; decanoate, 7 to 10 days.

Route	Onset	Peak	Duration
P.O.	≤ 1 hr	30 min	6–8 hr
I.M., SubQ	1–3 days	Unknown	1–6 wk

Action

Chemical effect: Unknown; may block dopamine receptors in brain.
Therapeutic effect: Relieves psychotic signs and symptoms.

Available forms

fluphenazine decanoate
Depot injection: 25 mg/ml, 100 mg/ml ◆
fluphenazine hydrochloride
Elixir: 2.5 mg/5 ml*
I.M. injection: 2.5 mg/ml
Oral concentrate: 5 mg/ml*
Tablets: 1 mg, 2.5 mg, 5 mg, 10 mg

NURSING PROCESS

Assessment

- Assess patient's condition before starting therapy and regularly thereafter.
- Monitor therapy with weekly bilirubin tests during first month, periodic blood tests (CBC and liver function), and periodic renal function and ophthalmic tests (long-term use).
- Be alert for adverse reactions and drug interactions.
- Monitor patient for tardive dyskinesia, which may occur after prolonged use. Reaction may not appear until months or years later and may disappear spontaneously or persist for life despite no longer taking the drug.
- Assess patient's and family's knowledge of drug therapy.

Nursing diagnoses

- Disturbed thought processes related to psychosis
- Impaired physical mobility related to extrapyramidal reactions
- Deficient knowledge related to drug therapy

Planning and implementation

ALERT: Oral concentrates are up to 10 times more concentrated than elixir. Check dosage order carefully.

- Dilute liquid concentrate with water, fruit juice (except apple), milk, or semisolid food just before administration.
- When giving I.M. or subcutaneously, for long-acting oil preparation form (decanoate), use dry needle of at least 21G. Allow 24 to 96 hours for onset of action. Note and report adverse reactions in patient taking these drug forms.
- Oral liquid and parenteral forms can cause contact dermatitis. Wear gloves when preparing solutions, and avoid contact with skin and clothing.
- Protect drug from light. Slight yellowing of liquid or concentrate is common and doesn't affect potency. Discard markedly discolored solutions.
- If patient, especially a pregnant woman or a child, develops symptoms of blood dyscrasia (fever, sore throat, infection, cellulitis, weakness) or extrapyramidal reactions for longer than a few hours, don't give the next dose. Notify prescriber.
- Acute dystonic reactions may be treated with diphenhydramine.
- Don't abruptly stop the drug unless a severe adverse reaction occurs. After abruptly stopping long-term therapy, patient may experience gastritis, nausea, vomiting, dizziness, tremor, feeling of warmth or cold, diaphoresis, tachycardia, headache, and insomnia.

Patient teaching

- Warn patient to avoid activities that require alertness and psychomotor coordination until the drug's CNS effects are known.
- Tell patient not to mix concentrate with beverages containing caffeine, tannics (such as tea), or pectinates (such as apple juice).
- Tell patient not to drink alcohol during therapy.
- Advise patient to relieve dry mouth with sugarless gum or hard candy.
- Have patient report urine retention or constipation.
- Tell patient to use sunblock and to wear protective clothing.
- Inform patient that drug may discolor urine.
- Stress importance of not stopping drug suddenly.

☑ Evaluation

- Patient demonstrates decrease in psychotic behavior.
- Patient maintains pretreatment physical mobility.
- Patient and family state understanding of drug therapy.

flurazepam hydrochloride

(floo-RAH-zuh-pam high-droh-KLOR-ighd)

Apo-Flurazepam ♦, Dalmane, Novo-Flupam ♦, Somnol ♦

F

Pharmacologic class: benzodiazepine
Therapeutic class: sedative-hypnotic
Pregnancy risk category: X
Controlled substance schedule: IV

Indications and dosages

▶ **Insomnia.** *Adults:* 15 to 30 mg P.O. at bedtime. Dose repeated once, if needed.

Contraindications and cautions

- Contraindicated in patients hypersensitive to drug or any of its components and in pregnancy.
- Use cautiously in patients with impaired hepatic or renal function, chronic pulmonary insufficiency, mental depression, suicidal tendencies, or history of drug abuse.

Lifespan: In pregnant women, drug is contraindicated. In breast-feeding women, drug is contraindicated because it isn't known if drug appears in breast milk. In children younger than age 15, safety and effectiveness haven't been established. In elderly patients, use cautiously and at a lower dose because they're more susceptible to CNS effects of drug.

Adverse reactions

CNS: ataxia, ***coma,*** confusion, *daytime sedation,* disorientation, *disturbed coordination, dizziness, drowsiness,* hallucinations, *headache,* lethargy, light-headedness, nervousness, staggering.
GI: abdominal pain, diarrhea, heartburn, nausea, vomiting.
Other: ***anaphylaxis, angioedema,*** physical or psychological dependence.

Interactions

Drug-drug. *Cimetidine:* May increase sedation from decreased hepatic metabolism of benzodiazepines. Monitor patient carefully.

CNS depressants, including opioid analgesics: May cause excessive CNS depression. Use together cautiously.
Digoxin: May increase digoxin level and risk of digoxin toxicity. Monitor patient and digoxin level closely.
Disulfiram, hormonal contraceptives, isoniazid: May decrease metabolism of benzodiazepines, leading to toxicity. Monitor patient closely.
Fluconazole, itraconazole, ketoconazole, miconazole: May increase and prolong level, CNS depression, and psychomotor impairment. Don't use together.
Phenytoin: May increase phenytoin level. Monitor patient for toxicity.
Rifampin: May increase benzodiazepine metabolism. Monitor patient for decreased effectiveness.
Theophylline: May antagonize flurazepam. Monitor patient for decreased effectiveness.
Drug-herb. *Catnip, kava, lady's slipper, lemon balm, passionflower, sassafras, skullcap, valerian:* May increase sedative effects. Discourage use together.
Drug-lifestyle. *Alcohol use:* May cause additive CNS and respiratory depression. Strongly discourage use together.
Smoking: May increase benzodiazepine metabolism. Discourage use together.

Effects on lab test results

• May increase AST, ALT, total and direct bilirubin, and alkaline phosphatase levels.

Pharmacokinetics

Absorption: Rapid.
Distribution: Wide. About 97% protein-bound.
Metabolism: In liver to active metabolite.
Excretion: In urine. *Half-life:* 2 to 4 days.

Route	Onset	Peak	Duration
P.O.	Unknown	30 min–1 hr	Unknown

Action

Chemical effect: Unknown; may act on limbic system, thalamus, and hypothalamus of CNS to produce hypnotic effects.
Therapeutic effect: Promotes sleep and calmness.

Available forms

Capsules: 15 mg, 30 mg
Tablets: 15 mg ♦, 30 mg ♦

NURSING PROCESS

Assessment

• Assess patient's sleep patterns and CNS before starting therapy.
• Be alert for adverse reactions and drug interactions. Anaphylaxis and angioedema may occur as early as first dose.
• Assess patient's and family's knowledge of drug therapy.

Nursing diagnoses

• Sleep deprivation related to underlying problem
• Risk for trauma related to drug-induced adverse CNS reactions
• Deficient knowledge related to drug therapy

Planning and implementation

• Before leaving bedside, make sure patient has swallowed capsule.

Patient teaching

• Encourage patient to continue drug, even if it doesn't relieve insomnia on the first night.
• Warn patient to avoid activities that require alertness or physical coordination. For inpatient, particularly for elderly patient, supervise walking and raise bed rails.
• Advise patient that physical and psychological dependence is possible with long-term use.
• Warn patient about possible complex sleep-related behaviors.

Evaluation

• Patient notes drug-induced sleep.
• Patient's safety is maintained.
• Patient and family state understanding of drug therapy.

flutamide

(FLOO-tuh-mighd)
Euflex ♦, Eulexin

Pharmacologic class: nonsteroidal antiandrogen
Therapeutic class: antineoplastic
Pregnancy risk category: D

Indications and dosages

▶ **Locally advanced (stage B2) or metastatic (stage D2) prostatic carcinoma.** *Adults:*

250 mg P.O. q 8 hours. Used with luteinizing hormone–releasing hormone analogs such as leuprolide acetate.

▶ **Hirsutism in women‡.** *Adults:* 250 mg P.O. daily.

Contraindications and cautions

- Contraindicated in patients hypersensitive to the drug or any of its components and in those with severe hepatic impairment.

Lifespan: In women and girls, drug is contraindicated. In boys, safety and effectiveness haven't been established. In elderly patients, use drug cautiously because its half-life is prolonged.

Adverse reactions

CNS: anxiety, confusion, depression, drowsiness, nervousness, paresthesia.
CV: hypertension, peripheral edema.
GI: anorexia, diarrhea, nausea, vomiting.
GU: impotence, urine discoloration.
Hematologic: anemia, hemolytic anemia, ***leukopenia, thrombocytopenia.***
Hepatic: ***hepatic encephalopathy, hepatitis.***
Skin: photosensitivity, rash.
Other: gynecomastia, hot flashes, loss of libido.

Interactions

Drug-drug. *Warfarin:* May increase PT. Monitor patient's PT and INR.
Drug-lifestyle. *Sun exposure:* May cause sensitivity reactions. Warn patient to avoid unprotected or prolonged sun exposure.

Effects on lab test results

- May increase BUN, creatinine, and liver enzyme levels. May decrease hemoglobin level and hematocrit.
- May decrease WBC and platelet counts.

Pharmacokinetics

Absorption: Rapid and complete.
Distribution: Concentrates in prostate. 95% protein-bound.
Metabolism: More than 97% occurs rapidly, with at least six metabolites.
Excretion: More than 95% in urine. *Half-life:* 6 hours.

Route	Onset	Peak	Duration
P.O.	Unknown	2 hr	Unknown

Action

Chemical effect: Inhibits androgen uptake or prevents androgen binding in cell nuclei in target tissues.
Therapeutic effect: Hinders prostatic cancer cell activity.

Available forms

Capsules: 125 mg
Tablets: 250 mg ♦

NURSING PROCESS

Assessment

- Assess patient's prostatic cancer before starting therapy.
- Monitor liver function test results periodically.
- Be alert for adverse reactions.
- If adverse GI reaction occurs, monitor hydration.
- Assess patient's and family's knowledge of drug therapy.

Nursing diagnoses

- Ineffective health maintenance related to presence of prostatic cancer
- Risk for deficient fluid volume related to adverse GI reactions
- Deficient knowledge related to drug therapy

Planning and implementation

- Drug may be given with or without meals.
- Give with luteinizing hormone–releasing antagonist (such as leuprolide acetate).

Patient teaching

- Make sure patient knows that flutamide must be taken continuously with drug used for medical castration (such as leuprolide acetate) to allow full benefit of therapy. Leuprolide suppresses testosterone production, and flutamide inhibits testosterone action at cellular level. Together they can impair growth of androgen-responsive tumors. Advise patient not to stop either drug.
- Tell patient to notify prescriber if adverse reactions occur.
- Instruct patient to avoid prolonged exposure to sun and other UV light. Use sunscreens and protective clothing until tolerance is determined.

Evaluation

- Patient responds well to drug.

F

• Patient maintains adequate hydration throughout drug therapy.
• Patient and family state understanding of drug therapy.

fluticasone propionate

(FLOO-tih-ka-sohn proh-PIGH-oh-nayt)

Flonase, Flovent Diskus ♦, Flovent HFA, Flovent Inhalation Aerosol

Pharmacologic class: corticosteroid
Therapeutic class: intranasal and inhalation anti-inflammatory
Pregnancy risk category: C

Indications and dosages

▶ **Asthma prevention and chronic asthma in patients who need oral corticosteroids.** *Adults and children age 12 and older previously taking bronchodilators alone:* Initially, 88 mcg Flovent HFA or Inhalation Aerosol b.i.d. to maximum of 440 mcg b.i.d. Or 100 mcg Flovent Diskus b.i.d. to maximum of 500 mcg b.i.d.
Adults and children age 12 and older previously taking inhaled corticosteroids: Initially, 88 to 220 mcg Flovent HFA or Inhalation Aerosol b.i.d. to maximum of 440 mcg b.i.d. In patients with poor asthma control, initial doses of Flovent HFA or Inhalation Aerosol may be above 88 mcg b.i.d. Or 100 to 250 mcg Flovent Diskus b.i.d. to maximum of 500 mcg b.i.d. In patients with poor asthma control, initial doses of Flovent Diskus may be above 100 mcg b.i.d.
Adults and children age 12 and older previously taking oral corticosteroids: 440 mcg to a maximum of 880 mcg Flovent HFA or Inhalation Aerosol b.i.d. Or 500 to 1,000 mcg Flovent Diskus b.i.d. to maximum of 1,000 mcg b.i.d.
Adults and children age 12 and older starting HFA or inhalation aerosol therapy who are receiving oral corticosteroid therapy: Reduce prednisone dose to no more than 2.5 mg daily on a weekly basis, beginning after at least 1 week of therapy with fluticasone.
Children ages 4 to 11: Give 88 mcg Flovent Diskus b.i.d.
▶ **Management of nasal symptoms of seasonal and perennial allergic and nonallergic rhinitis.** *Adults:* 2 sprays (100 mcg) Flonase in each nostril once daily or 1 spray (50 mcg) b.i.d. Reduce dosage to 1 spray in each nostril daily for maintenance therapy. Or, for seasonal allergic rhinitis, 2 sprays (100 mcg) in each nostril once daily p.r.n. for symptom control, although greater symptom control may be achieved with regular use.
Children age 4 and older: Initially 1 spray (50 mcg) Flonase in each nostril once daily. If patient doesn't respond, increase to 2 sprays (100 mcg) in each nostril daily. Once adequate control is achieved, decrease dose to 1 spray in each nostril daily. Maximum dosage is 2 sprays in each nostril daily.

Contraindications and cautions

• Contraindicated in patients hypersensitive to any of the components of these preparations. Also contraindicated as primary therapy for patients with status asthmaticus or other acute episodes of asthma in whom intensive measures are needed.
• Use cautiously in patients with ocular herpes simplex or untreated systemic, bacterial, viral, fungal, or parasitic infection, and in those with active or quiescent pulmonary tuberculosis.
Lifespan: In pregnant women, use only if benefits outweigh risks to fetus. In breastfeeding women, use cautiously because it's unknown if the drug appears in breast milk. In children younger than age 12, safety and effectiveness of the HFA and inhalation aerosols haven't been studied. In children younger than age 4, safety and effectiveness of the nasal formulation hasn't been studied.

Adverse reactions

CNS: dizziness, fever, *headache,* migraine, nervousness.
EENT: acute nasopharyngitis, conjunctivitis, dysphonia, earache, epistaxis, eye irritation, hoarseness, laryngitis, mouth irritation, nasal congestion, nasal discharge, *oral candidiasis,* otitis media, *pharyngitis,* rhinitis, sinusitis, sneezing, tonsillitis.
GI: abdominal discomfort, abdominal pain, colitis, diarrhea, nausea, viral gastroenteritis, vomiting.
GU: candidiasis of vagina, dysmenorrhea, irregular menstrual cycle, pelvic inflammatory disease, vaginitis, vulvovaginitis.
Metabolic: cushingoid features, weight gain.
Musculoskeletal: aches and pains, disorder or symptoms of neck sprain or strain, growth retardation in children, pain in joints, sore muscles.

Respiratory: bronchitis, chest congestion, dyspnea, irritation from inhalant, *upper respiratory tract infection.*
Skin: dermatitis, urticaria.
Other: dental problems, influenza.

Interactions

Drug-drug. *Ketoconazole:* May increase mean fluticasone level. Use care when giving fluticasone with long-term ketoconazole and other CYP3A4 inhibitors.

Effects on lab test results

- May increase glucose level.
- May cause an abnormal response to the 6-hour cosyntropin stimulation test with high doses.

Pharmacokinetics

Absorption: Mostly systemic, with 30% of the delivered dose reaching the lungs. Less than 2% from the nasal mucosa.
Distribution: 91% protein-bound.
Metabolism: Via CYP3A4.
Excretion: In feces, mainly as unchanged drug and metabolites. *Half-life:* 3 hours.

Route	Onset	Peak	Duration
Inhalation	24 hr	1–2 wk	Several days
Nasal	12 hr–3 days	4–7 days	Several days

Action

Chemical effect: Inhibits many cell types and mediator production or secretion involved in asthma.
Therapeutic effect: Improves breathing ability by reducing inflammation.

Available forms

Nasal suspension: 50-mcg metered inhaler
Oral HFA and inhalation aerosol: 44 mcg, 110 mcg, 220 mcg
Oral inhalation powder: 50 mcg/actuation, 100 mcg/actuation, 250 mcg/actuation

NURSING PROCESS

Assessment

- Obtain history of patient's underlying condition before starting therapy, and reassess regularly.
- Because of risk of systemic absorption of inhaled corticosteroids, observe patient carefully for evidence of systemic corticosteroid effects.
- Monitor patient, especially postoperatively or during periods of stress, for evidence of inadequate adrenal response.
- Monitor growth in children closely because growth suppression may occur.
- Assess patient's and family's knowledge of drug therapy.

Nursing diagnoses

- Ineffective breathing pattern related to respiratory condition
- Impaired oral mucous membrane related to potential adverse effect of oral candidiasis
- Deficient knowledge related to drug therapy

Planning and implementation

- During withdrawal from oral corticosteroids, patient may have symptoms of systemically active corticosteroid withdrawal, such as joint or muscle pain, lethargy, and depression, despite maintenance or even improvement of respiratory function.
- Bronchospasm may occur with an immediate increase in wheezing after a dose. If bronchospasm occurs following inhalation, treat immediately with a fast-acting inhaled bronchodilator.
- If patient is using a bronchodilator regularly, administer it at least 5 minutes before corticosteroid.

ALERT: Use lowest effective dose in children to minimize growth suppression.

Patient teaching

- Tell patient that drug isn't intended to relieve acute bronchospasm.
- For proper use of drug and to attain maximum improvement, tell patient to use drug at regular intervals as directed.
- Instruct patient not to increase dosage but to contact prescriber if symptoms don't improve or if condition worsens.
- Instruct patient to contact prescriber immediately if episodes of asthma aren't responsive to bronchodilators. During such episodes, patients may need therapy with oral corticosteroids.
- Warn patient to avoid exposure to chickenpox or measles, and if exposed to immediately consult prescriber.
- Tell patient to carry or wear medical identification indicating that he may need supplemen-

tary corticosteroids during stress or a severe asthma attack.

- During periods of stress or a severe asthma attack, instruct patient who has been withdrawn from systemic corticosteroids to immediately resume oral corticosteroids (in large doses) and to contact prescriber for further instruction. Instruct him to rinse his mouth after inhalation.
- Instruct patient to shake canister well before using inhalation aerosol or HFA and to avoid spraying either into the eyes.
- Inform patient that inhalation aerosol is being replaced with the HFA version for environmental reasons; doses and effectiveness remain the same.

Evaluation

- Patient has normal breathing pattern.
- Patient doesn't develop oral candidiasis.
- Patient and family state understanding of drug therapy.

fluticasone propionate and salmeterol inhalation powder

(FLOO-tih-ka-sohn proh-PIGH-oh-nayt and sal-MEH-teh-rohl)

Advair Diskus 100/50, Advair Diskus 250/50, Advair Diskus 500/50

Pharmacologic class: corticosteroid, long-acting beta$_2$ agonist
Therapeutic class: anti-inflammatory, bronchodilator
Pregnancy risk category: C

Indications and dosages

▶ **Chronic asthma.** *Adults and children age 12 and older:* 1 oral inhalation b.i.d., morning and evening, at least 12 hours apart. Maximum oral inhalation of Advair Diskus 500/50 is b.i.d.
Adults and children older than age 12 not taking an inhaled corticosteroid: 1 oral inhalation of Advair Diskus 100/50 b.i.d.
Adults and children older than age 12 taking beclomethasone dipropionate: If daily dose of beclomethasone dipropionate is 420 mcg or less, start with 1 oral inhalation of Advair Diskus 100/50 b.i.d. If beclomethasone dipropionate daily dose is 462 to 840 mcg, start with one oral inhalation of Advair Diskus 250/50 b.i.d.
Adults and children older than age 12 taking budesonide: If daily dose of budesonide is 400 mcg or less, start with 1 oral inhalation of Advair Diskus 100/50 b.i.d. If budesonide daily dose is 800 to 1,200 mcg, start with 1 oral inhalation of Advair Diskus 250/50 b.i.d. If budesonide daily dose is 1,600 mcg, start with 1 oral inhalation of Advair Diskus 500/50 b.i.d.
Adults and children older than age 12 taking flunisolide: If daily dose of flunisolide is 1,000 mcg or less, start with 1 oral inhalation of Advair Diskus 100/50 b.i.d. If flunisolide daily dose is 1,250 to 2,000 mcg, start with 1 oral inhalation of Advair Diskus 250/50 b.i.d.
Adults and children older than age 12 taking fluticasone propionate inhalation aerosol: If daily dose of fluticasone propionate inhalation aerosol is 176 mcg or less, start with 1 oral inhalation of Advair Diskus 100/50 b.i.d. If fluticasone propionate inhalation aerosol daily dose is 440 mcg, start with 1 oral inhalation of Advair Diskus 250/50 b.i.d. If fluticasone propionate inhalation aerosol daily dose is 660 to 880 mcg, start with 1 oral inhalation of Advair Diskus 500/50 b.i.d.
Adults and children older than age 12 taking fluticasone propionate inhalation powder: If fluticasone propionate inhalation powder daily dose is 200 mcg or less, start with 1 oral inhalation of Advair Diskus 100/50 b.i.d. If fluticasone propionate inhalation powder daily dose is 500 mcg, start with 1 oral inhalation of Advair Diskus 250/50 b.i.d. If fluticasone propionate inhalation powder daily dose is 1,000 mcg, start with 1 oral inhalation of Advair Diskus 500/50 b.i.d.
Adults and children older than age 12 taking triamcinolone acetonide: If triamcinolone acetonide daily dose is 1,000 mcg or less, start with 1 oral inhalation of Advair Diskus 100/50 b.i.d. If triamcinolone acetonide daily dose is 1,100 to 1,600 mcg, start with 1 oral inhalation of Advair Diskus 250/50 b.i.d.
Children ages 4 to 11: Give 1 oral inhalation of Advair Diskus 100/50 b.i.d., morning and evening, at least 12 hours apart.
Adjust-a dose: In all patients, after asthma has been controlled, adjust to lowest effective dosage.

▶ **Maintenance therapy for airflow obstruction in patients with COPD from chronic bronchitis.** *Adults:* 1 inhalation 250/50 b.i.d., about 12 hours apart.

Contraindications and cautions

• Contraindicated in patients hypersensitive to the drug or any of its components. Also contraindicated as primary therapy for status asthmaticus or other potentially life-threatening acute asthmatic episodes.

• Drug isn't indicated for exercise-induced bronchospasms.

• Use cautiously in patients with active or quiescent respiratory tuberculosis infection; untreated systemic fungal, bacterial, viral, or parasitic infection; or ocular herpes simplex. Also use cautiously in patients with CV disorders, especially coronary insufficiency, cardiac arrhythmias, and hypertension; in patients with seizure disorders or thyrotoxicosis; in patients unusually responsive to sympathomimetic amines; and in patients with hepatic impairment (because salmeterol is metabolized mainly in the liver).

Lifespan: In pregnant women, use only if benefits outweigh risks to fetus. In breast-feeding women, use cautiously; it isn't known if drug is found in breast milk. In children younger than age 4, safety and effectiveness haven't been established. Closely monitor growth in children because growth suppression may occur. Maintain child on lowest effective dose to minimize potential for growth suppression.

Adverse reactions

CNS: agitation, compressed nerve syndromes, fever, *headache,* hypnagogic effects, nervousness, pain, sleep disorder, tremor.
CV: ***arrhythmias,*** chest pains, fluid retention, palpitations, rapid heart rate.
EENT: blood in nasal mucosa, congestion, conjunctivitis, dysphonia, eye redness, hoarseness, keratitis, nasal irritation, oral candidiasis, *pharyngitis,* rhinitis, rhinorrhea, sinusitis, sneezing, viral eye infections.
GI: abdominal pain and discomfort, appendicitis, constipation, diarrhea, gastroenteritis, nausea, oral discomfort and pain, oral erythema and rashes, oral ulcerations, unusual taste, vomiting.
Musculoskeletal: arthralgia, articular rheumatism, back pain, bone and cartilage disorders, muscle pain, muscle stiffness, rigidity, tightness.
Respiratory: bronchitis, cough, lower viral respiratory infection, ***paradoxical bronchospasms,*** pneumonia, ***severe asthma or asthma-related deaths,*** upper respiratory tract infection.
Skin: disorders of sweat and sebum, skin flakiness, sweating, urticaria, viral skin infections.
Other: allergic reactions, allergies, bacterial infections, dental discomfort and pain, influenza.

Interactions

Drug-drug. *Beta blockers:* May block pulmonary effect of salmeterol, producing severe bronchospasm in patients with asthma. Avoid use together. If needed, use a cardioselective beta blocker cautiously.
Cytochrome P-450 inhibitors (such as ketoconazole): May increase fluticasone level and adverse effects. Use together cautiously.
Loop diuretics, thiazide diuretics: May cause or worsen ECG changes or hypokalemia. Use together cautiously.
MAO inhibitors, tricyclic antidepressants: May potentiate the action of salmeterol on the vascular system. Avoid use within 2 weeks of these drugs.

Effects on lab test results

• May increase or decrease liver function test values.

Pharmacokinetics

Absorption: *Fluticasone propionate:* systemic. *Salmeterol:* local. With long-term therapy, salmeterol appears in blood within 45 minutes.
Distribution: *Fluticasone:* 91% protein-bound and weakly and reversibly bound to erythrocytes. *Salmeterol:* 96% protein-bound.
Metabolism: Mainly by CYP3A4.
Excretion: *Fluticasone:* less than 5% of a dose in urine as metabolites, with remainder in feces as an unchanged drug and metabolite. *Salmeterol xinafoate:* 25% and 60% in urine and feces, respectively, over 7 days. *Fluticasone half-life:* 8 hours; *salmeterol half-life:* 5½ hours.

Route	Onset	Peak	Duration
Inhalation			
salmeterol	Unknown	5 min	Unknown
fluticasone	Unknown	1–2 hr	Unknown

Action

Chemical effect: Fluticasone's action is unknown. Salmeterol xinafoate stimulates intracellular adenyl cyclase, the enzyme that catalyzes

F

conversion of adenosine triphosphate (ATP) to cAMP. Increased cAMP levels relax bronchial smooth muscle and inhibit release of mediators of immediate hypersensitivity from cells, especially mast cells.
Therapeutic effect: Reduces inflammation in the lungs and opens airways to improve pulmonary function.

Available forms

Inhalation powder: 100 mcg fluticasone and 50 mcg salmeterol, 250 mcg fluticasone and 50 mcg salmeterol, 500 mcg fluticasone and 50 mcg salmeterol

NURSING PROCESS

Assessment

- Obtain patient's medical history, and assess patient before starting therapy.

ALERT: Chronic overdose of fluticasone may cause signs and symptoms of hypercorticism. Salmeterol overdose may cause seizures, angina, hypertension, hypotension, tachycardia, arrhythmias, nervousness, headache, tremor, muscle cramps, dry mouth, palpitations, nausea, prolonged QT interval, ventricular arrhythmia, hypokalemia, hyperglycemia, cardiac arrest, and death. Stop drug and give a cardioselective beta blocker. Monitor cardiac condition.

- Monitor patient for urticaria, angioedema, rash, bronchospasm, or other signs of hypersensitivity, which may occur immediately after a dose of Advair Diskus.
- Monitor patient for increased use of inhaled short-acting $beta_2$ agonist. The dose of Advair Diskus may need to be increased.
- Monitor patient for hypercorticism and adrenal suppression. If these occur, reduce dosage slowly.
- Monitor patient for eosinophilia, vasculitic rash, worsening pulmonary symptoms, cardiac complications, or neuropathy, which may be signs of a serious eosinophilic condition.
- Monitor patient for signs or symptoms of thrush.
- Assess patient's and family's knowledge of drug therapy.

Nursing diagnoses

- Ineffective airway clearance related to underlying asthmatic condition
- Activity intolerance related to underlying asthmatic condition
- Deficient knowledge related to proper inhalation with the device and drug therapy

Planning and implementation

ALERT: Don't switch patient directly from systemic corticosteroids to Advair Diskus. Hypothalamic-pituitary-adrenal axis suppression from corticosteroid therapy requires gradual weaning of steroid before replacement with inhaled steroid to avoid risk of death from adrenal insufficiency.

- After asthma has been controlled, adjust to the lowest effective dosage.

ALERT: Don't start Advair Diskus therapy during rapidly deteriorating or potentially life-threatening episodes of asthma. Serious acute respiratory events, including death, can occur, especially in blacks.

ALERT: When a patient uses Advair Diskus, make sure the patient has an inhaled, short-acting $beta_2$ agonist (such as albuterol) for acute symptoms that occur between doses of Advair Diskus.

ALERT: Advair Diskus can produce paradoxical bronchospasm. If it does, treat immediately with a short-acting, inhaled bronchodilator (such as albuterol) and stop Advair Diskus therapy.

- If patient is exposed to chickenpox, give varicella zoster immune globulin as prophylaxis. If chickenpox develops, give an antiviral.
- If patient is exposed to measles, give pooled I.M. immunoglobulin as prophylaxis.
- Store at controlled room temperature (68° F to 77° F [20° to 25° C]) in a dry place away from direct heat or sunlight. Discard the device 1 month after removal from the moisture-protective overwrap pouch or after every foil-wrapped blister has been used, whichever comes first. Don't attempt to take the device apart.

Patient teaching

- Instruct patient on most effective use of the Advair Diskus.
- Instruct patient to keep the Advair Diskus in a dry place, to avoid washing the mouthpiece or other parts of the device, and to avoid taking the Diskus apart.
- Tell patient to stop taking an oral or inhaled long-acting $beta_2$ agonist simultaneously when beginning Advair Diskus.

ALERT: Explain that Advair Diskus is used only for long-term maintenance and not for acute symptoms of asthma or for prevention of exercise-induced bronchospasm. Urge patient to use a short-acting $beta_2$ agonist (such as albuterol) for relief of acute symptoms.
- Instruct patient to rinse mouth after each inhalation to prevent oral candidiasis.
- Inform patient that improvement may be seen within 30 minutes after an Advair dose; however, the full benefit may not occur for 1 week or more.

ALERT: Instruct patient not to exceed prescribed dose under any circumstances.
- Instruct patient to report decreasing effects or increasing use of the short-acting $beta_2$ agonist inhaler immediately to his prescriber.
- Instruct patient not to use Advair Diskus with a spacer device.
- Tell patient to report palpitations, chest pain, rapid heart rate, tremor, or nervousness immediately to prescriber. Also instruct patient to avoid stimulants, such as caffeine, while on Advair Diskus therapy because they may increase these adverse reactions.
- Instruct patient to contact prescriber immediately if exposed to chickenpox or measles.

Evaluation
- Patient's activity tolerance increases.
- Patient has a normal breathing pattern and optimal air exchange.
- Patient and family state understanding of drug therapy.

fluvastatin sodium
(floo-vuh-STAH-tin SOH-dee-um)
Lescol, Lescol XL

Pharmacologic class: HMG-CoA reductase inhibitor
Therapeutic class: cholesterol inhibitor
Pregnancy risk category: X

Indications and dosages

▶ **To reduce LDL and total cholesterol levels in patients with primary hypercholesterolemia (types IIa and IIb) or to slow progression of coronary atherosclerosis in patients with coronary artery disease; elevated triglyceride and apolipoprotein B levels in patients with primary hypercholesterolemia and mixed dyslipidemia whose response to dietary restriction and other nonpharmacologic measures has been inadequate.** *Adults:* Initially, 20 to 40 mg P.O. at bedtime. Increase if needed to maximum of 80 mg daily (in divided doses). Or 80 mg extended-release tablet P.O. daily.

▶ **To reduce the risk of undergoing coronary revascularization procedures.** *Adults:* For patients who need LDL cholesterol reduction of 25% or more, initially 40 mg (regular-release) P.O. or 80 mg (extended-release) P.O. once daily in the evening. Or 40 mg (regular-release) P.O. b.i.d. For patients requiring LDL cholesterol reduction of less than 25%, initially 20 mg P.O. daily. The recommended range is 20 to 80 mg daily.

Adjust-a-dose: If levels of ALT or AST persist at least three times the upper limit of normal, stop giving the drug. Drug is primarily cleared hepatically, so dosage adjustments for mild to moderate renal impairment aren't needed. Exercise caution with severe renal impairment.

Contraindications and cautions
- Contraindicated in patients hypersensitive to drug or any of its components and in those with active liver disease or conditions that cause unexplained, persistent elevations of transaminase levels. Also contraindicated during pregnancy.
- Use cautiously in patients with severe renal impairment or with history of liver disease or heavy alcohol use.

Lifespan: In pregnant and breast-feeding women and women of childbearing age, drug is contraindicated. In children, safety and effectiveness haven't been established.

Adverse reactions
CNS: dizziness, fatigue, headache, insomnia.
EENT: pharyngitis, rhinitis, sinusitis.
GI: abdominal pain, constipation, diarrhea, dyspepsia, flatulence, nausea, vomiting.
Hematologic: hemolytic anemia, ***leukopenia, thrombocytopenia.***
Musculoskeletal: arthralgia, arthropathy, myalgia.
Respiratory: bronchitis, cough, *upper respiratory infection.*
Skin: rash.

Other: hypersensitivity reactions, tooth disorder.

Interactions

Drug-drug. *Cholestyramine, colestipol:* May bind with fluvastatin in GI tract and decrease absorption. Separate administration times by at least 4 hours.
Cimetidine, omeprazole, ranitidine: May decrease fluvastatin metabolism. Monitor patient for enhanced effects.
Cyclosporine and other immunosuppressants, erythromycin, gemfibrozil, niacin: May increase risk of polymyositis and rhabdomyolysis. Avoid use together.
Digoxin: May increase digoxin level. Monitor digoxin level carefully.
Fluconazole, itraconazole, ketoconazole: May increase fluvastatin level and adverse effects. Avoid use together. If they must be given together, reduce dose of fluvastatin.
Rifampin: May increase rifampin metabolism and decrease level. Monitor patient for lack of effect.
Drug-herb. *Red yeast rice:* May increase the risk of adverse events or toxicity. Discourage use together.
Drug-lifestyle. *Alcohol use:* May increase risk of hepatotoxicity. Discourage use together.

Effects on lab test results

- May increase ALT, AST, bilirubin, and CK levels. May decrease hemoglobin level and hematocrit.
- May decrease platelet and WBC counts.

Pharmacokinetics

Absorption: Rapid and almost complete on empty stomach.
Distribution: More than 98% protein-bound.
Metabolism: Complete.
Excretion: About 5% in urine, 90% in feces as metabolites. *Half-life:* Less than 1 hour.

Route	Onset	Peak	Duration
P.O.	Unknown	30–45 min	Unknown

Action

Chemical effect: Inhibits HMG-CoA reductase, an early (and rate-limiting) step in synthetic pathway of cholesterol.
Therapeutic effect: Lowers blood LDL and cholesterol levels.

Available forms

Capsules: 20 mg, 40 mg
Tablets (extended-release): 80 mg

NURSING PROCESS

Assessment

- Assess patient's LDL and total cholesterol levels before starting therapy, and evaluate regularly.
- Perform liver function tests periodically.
- Be alert for adverse reactions and drug interactions.
- Assess patient's and family's knowledge of drug therapy.

Nursing diagnoses

- Risk for injury related to elevated LDL and cholesterol blood levels
- Diarrhea related to adverse effect of drug on GI tract
- Deficient knowledge related to drug therapy

Planning and implementation

- Start drug only after diet and other nondrug therapies have proven ineffective.
- Give drug at bedtime to enhance effectiveness.
- Maintain standard low-cholesterol diet during therapy.

Patient teaching

- Tell patient that drug may be taken with or without food; effectiveness is enhanced if taken in evening.
- Teach patient about proper dietary management, weight control, and exercise. Explain their importance in controlling lipid levels.
- Warn patient to restrict alcohol consumption.
- Tell patient to inform prescriber of any adverse reactions, particularly muscle aches and pains.
- Tell patient to stop drug and notify prescriber about planned, suspected, or known pregnancy.

Evaluation

- Patient's LDL and total cholesterol levels are within normal limits.
- Patient maintains normal bowel pattern.
- Patient and family state understanding of drug therapy.

fluvoxamine maleate

(floo-VOKS-uh-meen MAL-ee-ayt)
Luvox

Pharmacologic class: SSRI
Therapeutic class: antidepressant
Pregnancy risk category: C

Indications and dosages

▶ **Obsessive-compulsive disorder (OCD), depression‡.** *Adults:* Initially, 50 mg P.O. daily at bedtime. Increase in 50-mg increments q 4 to 7 days until maximum benefit occurs. Maximum, 300 mg daily. If total daily amount exceeds 100 mg, divide and give in two doses. *Children ages 8 to 17:* Give 25 mg P.O. at bedtime. Maximum daily dose for children ages 8 to 11 is 200 mg. Maximum daily dose for children ages 12 to 17 is 300 mg. Increase initial dosage q 4 to 7 days, as needed. Divide doses greater than 50 mg b.i.d.

Adjust-a-dose: For elderly patients and patients with hepatic impairment, initially 25 mg P.O. daily then increase gradually to a maximum daily dose of 200 mg.

Contraindications and cautions

- Contraindicated in patients hypersensitive to SSRIs or any of their ingredients and within 2 weeks of an MAO inhibitor. Use with thioridazine or pimozide is contraindicated because ventricular arrhythmias and death may occur.
- Use cautiously in patients with hepatic dysfunction, suicidal ideation, conditions that may affect hemodynamic responses or metabolism, or history of mania or seizures.

Lifespan: In pregnant women and in breastfeeding women, use cautiously. In children younger than age 8, drug is contraindicated for OCD. In children, drug is contraindicated for major depressive disorder. In elderly patients, use cautiously and start at a lower dose.

Adverse reactions

CNS: agitation, anxiety, asthenia, CNS stimulation, depression, *dizziness,* headache, hypertonia, *insomnia, nervousness, somnolence,* tremor.
CV: palpitations, vasodilation.
EENT: amblyopia.
GI: anorexia, constipation, *diarrhea, dry mouth,* dyspepsia, dysphagia, flatulence, *nausea,* taste perversion, vomiting.
GU: abnormal ejaculation, anorgasmia, impotence, urinary frequency, urine retention.
Respiratory: dyspnea, upper respiratory tract infection, yawning.
Skin: sweating.
Other: chills, flulike syndrome, decreased libido, tooth disorder.

Interactions

Drug-drug. *Benzodiazepines, theophylline, warfarin:* May reduce clearance of these drugs. Use together cautiously (except for diazepam, which shouldn't be given with fluvoxamine). Adjust dosage as needed.
Carbamazepine, clozapine, haloperidol, methadone, metoprolol, propranolol, tricyclic antidepressants: May increase levels of these drugs. Use together cautiously. Monitor patient closely for adverse reactions. Adjust dosage if needed.
Diltiazem: May cause bradycardia. Monitor heart rate.
Lithium, tryptophan: May increase fluvoxamine effects. Use together cautiously.
Phenelzine, selegiline, tranylcypromine: May cause serotonin syndrome, which may include CNS irritability, shivering, and altered consciousness. Use together may also cause severe excitation, hyperpyrexia, myoclonus, delirium, and coma. Don't give an MAO inhibitor within 2 weeks of an SSRI.
Pimozide, thioridazine: May prolong QT interval. Avoid use together.
Sumatriptan: May cause weakness, hyperreflexia, and incoordination. Monitor patient closely.
Drug-herb. *St. John's wort:* May cause serotonin syndrome. Discourage use together.
Drug-food. *Caffeine:* May decrease caffeine elimination and increase caffeine effects. Discourage use together.
Drug-lifestyle. *Alcohol use:* May increase CNS effects. Discourage use together.
Smoking: May decrease effectiveness of drug. Discourage patient from smoking.
Sun exposure: May cause photosensitivity. Discourage prolonged or unprotected exposure to sunlight.

Effects on lab test results

None reported.

Pharmacokinetics

Absorption: Good.
Distribution: 77% protein-bound.
Metabolism: In liver.
Excretion: In urine. *Half-life:* 17 hours.

Route	Onset	Peak	Duration
P.O.	3–10 wk	3–8 hr	Unknown

Action

Chemical effect: May selectively inhibit neuronal uptake of serotonin, which is thought to reduce obsessive-compulsive disorders.
Therapeutic effect: Decreases obsessive-compulsive behavior.

Available forms

Tablets: 25 mg, 50 mg, 100 mg

NURSING PROCESS

Assessment

- Assess patient's condition before starting therapy, and reassess regularly. Patient may need several weeks of therapy before having a positive response.
- Be alert for adverse reactions and drug interactions.
- Assess child with OCD for signs of depression, including suicidal thoughts and behaviors.
- Assess patient's and family's knowledge of drug therapy.

Nursing diagnoses

- Ineffective coping related to underlying condition
- Diarrhea related to adverse effect of drug on GI tract
- Deficient knowledge related to drug therapy

Planning and implementation

- Don't give drug within 14 days of MAO inhibitor therapy.
- Give drug at bedtime, with or without food.

ALERT: Don't confuse Luvox with Lasix.
ALERT: Don't confuse fluvoxamine with fluvoxate or fluoxetine.

Patient teaching

- Instruct patient not to stop drug abruptly but to first consult prescriber.
- Warn patient to avoid hazardous activities until the drug's CNS effects are known.
- Advise patient not to drink alcoholic beverages during therapy.
- Inform patient that smoking may decrease effectiveness of drug.
- Tell patient that drug may be taken with or without food.
- Instruct woman to notify prescriber about planned, suspected, or known pregnancy.
- Tell patient who develops rash, hives, or related allergic reaction to notify prescriber.
- Inform patient that several weeks of therapy may be needed to obtain full antidepressant effect. Once improvement has occurred, advise patient not to stop drug unless directed by prescriber.
- Advise patient to check with prescriber before taking OTC drugs or herbal remedies because interactions can occur.

☑ Evaluation

- Patient's obsessive-compulsive behaviors are diminished.
- Patient maintains normal bowel patterns.
- Patient and family state understanding of drug therapy.

folic acid (vitamin B_9)

(FOH-lek AS-id)
Apo-Folic ♦, Folvite, Novo-Folacid ♦

Pharmacologic class: folic acid derivative
Therapeutic class: vitamin
Pregnancy risk category: A

Indications and dosages

▶ **To maintain health.** *Adults and children age 4 and older:* 0.4 mg P.O. daily.
Pregnant or lactating women: 0.8 mg P.O. daily.
Children younger than age 4: Up to 0.3 mg P.O. daily.
Infants: Up to 0.1 mg P.O. daily.

▶ **Megaloblastic or macrocytic anemia caused by folic acid or other nutritional deficiency, hepatic disease, alcoholism, intestinal obstruction, excessive hemolysis.** *Adults and children age 4 and older:* 0.4 mg to 1 mg P.O., subcutaneously, or I.M. daily. After anemia caused by folic acid deficiency is corrected, proper diet and supplements are needed to prevent recurrence.

Pregnant and breast-feeding women: 0.8 mg P.O., subcutaneously, or I.M. daily.
Children younger than age 4: Up to 0.3 mg P.O., subcutaneously, or I.M. daily.
▶ **Prevention of megaloblastic anemia in pregnancy.** *Adults:* Up to 1 mg P.O., subcutaneously, or I.M. daily throughout pregnancy.
▶ **Nutritional supplement.** *Adults:* 0.1 mg P.O., subcutaneously, or I.M. daily.
Children: 0.05 mg P.O. daily.
▶ **To test folic acid deficiency in patients with megaloblastic anemia without masking pernicious anemia.** *Adults and children:* 0.1 to 0.2 mg P.O. or I.M. for 10 days with diet low in folate and vitamin B_{12}.
▶ **Tropical sprue.** *Adults:* 3 to 15 mg P.O. daily.

Contraindications and cautions

• Contraindicated in patients with vitamin B_{12} deficiency or undiagnosed anemia.
Lifespan: In pregnant women, folic acid therapy is recommended to prevent fetal neural tube defects.

Adverse reactions

CNS: general malaise.
GI: anorexia, bitter taste, flatulence, nausea.
Respiratory: ***bronchospasm.***
Other: allergic reactions (erythema, pruritus, rash).

Interactions

Drug-drug. *Aminosalicylic acid, chloramphenicol, methotrexate, sulfasalazine, trimethoprim:* May antagonize folic acid. Monitor patient for decreased folic acid effect. Use together cautiously.
Anticonvulsants (such as phenobarbital, phenytoin): May increase anticonvulsant metabolism and decrease anticonvulsant blood levels. Monitor patient closely.

Effects on lab test results

• May decrease RBC count.

Pharmacokinetics

Absorption: Rapid after P.O. use.
Distribution: Complete; liver contains about half of total body stores. Concentrated actively in CSF.
Metabolism: In liver.
Excretion: Excess is unchanged in urine; small amounts in feces. *Half-life:* Unknown.

Route	Onset	Peak	Duration
P.O., I.M., SubQ	Unknown	30–60 min	Unknown

Action

Chemical effect: Stimulates normal erythropoiesis and nucleoprotein synthesis.
Therapeutic effect: Nutritional supplement.

Available forms

Injection: 5 mg/ml with 1.5% benzyl alcohol
Tablets: 0.1 mg†, 0.4 mg†, 0.8 mg†, 1 mg

NURSING PROCESS

Assessment

• Assess patient's folic acid deficiency before starting therapy.
• Evaluate CBC and assess patient's physical status throughout therapy.
• Be alert for adverse reactions and drug interactions.
• Assess patient's and family's knowledge of drug therapy.

Nursing diagnoses

• Imbalanced nutrition: less than body requirements related to presence of folic acid deficiency
• Deficient knowledge related to drug therapy

Planning and implementation

• Patient with small-bowel resection and intestinal malabsorption may need parenteral administration.
• Don't mix with other drugs in same syringe for I.M. injections.
• Protect from light and heat; store at room temperature.
• Give vitamin B_{12} with this therapy if needed.
• Make sure patient is getting properly balanced diet.
ALERT: Some preparations contain benzyl alcohol. Don't use in infants and children.
ALERT: Don't confuse folic acid with folinic acid.

Patient teaching

• Teach patient proper nutrition to prevent recurrence of anemia.

• Tell patient to report hypersensitivity reactions or breathing difficulty.
• Urge patient to avoid alcohol because it increases folic acid requirements.

Evaluation
• Patient's CBC is normal.
• Patient and family state understanding of drug therapy.

fondaparinux sodium
(fon-duh-PAIR-in-ux SOH-dee-uhm)
Arixtra

Pharmacologic class: inhibitor of activated factor X (Xa)
Therapeutic class: anticoagulant
Pregnancy risk category: B

Indications and dosages

▶ **To prevent deep vein thrombosis and pulmonary embolism in patients undergoing abdominal surgery or surgery for hip fracture, hip replacement, or knee replacement.** *Adults who weigh 50 kg (110 lb) or more:* 2.5 mg subcutaneously once daily for 5 to 9 days. Give initial dose after hemostasis is established, 6 to 8 hours after surgery. Giving the dose earlier than 6 hours after surgery increases the risk for major bleeding.

▶ **Acute deep vein thrombosis with warfarin; acute pulmonary embolism with warfarin when therapy is initiated in the hospital.** *Adults who weigh more than 100 kg (220 lb):* 10 mg subcutaneously daily for 5 to 9 days. *Adults who weigh 50 to 100 kg:* 7.5 mg subcutaneously daily for 5 to 9 days. *Adults who weigh less than 50 kg:* 5 mg subcutaneously daily for 5 to 9 days.

For all patients, begin oral anticoagulant therapy as soon as possible, usually within 72 hours.

Contraindications and cautions

• Contraindicated in patients with creatinine clearance less than 30 ml/minute; in those who are hypersensitive to the drug or as prophylaxis for abdominal, hip, or knee surgery in patients who weigh less than 50 kg; and in those with active major bleeding, bacterial endocarditis, or thrombocytopenia with a positive test result for antiplatelet antibody during therapy.
• Use cautiously in patients also being treated with platelet inhibitors and in those at increased risk for bleeding, such as patients who have congenital or acquired bleeding disorders, a bleeding diathesis, active ulcerative and angiodysplastic GI disease, or hemorrhagic stroke; and patients who recently had brain, spinal, or ophthalmologic surgery. Also use cautiously in patients who have had epidural or spinal anesthesia or spinal puncture because they have an increased risk of epidural or spinal hematoma (which may cause permanent paralysis). Use cautiously in patients undergoing elective hip surgery with mild or moderate renal impairment. Also use caution in patients with a creatinine clearance of 30 to 50 ml/minute, a history of heparin-induced thrombocytopenia, uncontrolled arterial hypertension, or a history of recent GI ulceration, diabetic retinopathy, or hemorrhage.
Lifespan: In pregnant women, use only if benefits outweigh risks to fetus. In breast-feeding women, use cautiously because it's unknown if drug appears in breast milk. In children, safety and effectiveness haven't been established. In elderly patients, use cautiously because the risk of major bleeding increases with age.

Adverse reactions

CNS: confusion, dizziness, *fever,* headache, insomnia, pain, ***spinal and epidural hematomas.***
CV: edema, hypotension.
GI: constipation, diarrhea, dyspepsia, *nausea,* vomiting.
GU: urine retention, UTI.
Hematologic: anemia, hematoma, ***hemorrhage, postoperative hemorrhage, thrombocytopenia.***
Metabolic: hypokalemia.
Skin: bullous eruption, increased wound drainage, mild local irritation (injection site bleeding, pruritus, rash), purpura, rash.

Interactions

Drug-drug. *Drugs that increase risk of bleeding (anticoagulants, NSAIDs, platelet inhibitors, salicylates):* May increase risk of hemorrhage. If drugs must be used together, monitor patient closely.

Effects on lab test results

• May increase creatinine, AST, ALT, and bilirubin levels. May decrease potassium and hemoglobin levels and hematocrit.
• May decrease platelet count.

Pharmacokinetics

Absorption: Rapid and complete; 100% bioavailability.
Distribution: Mainly in blood. At least 94% bound to antithrombin III (AT-III).
Metabolism: Not studied.
Excretion: Up to 77% in urine unchanged in 72 hours. *Half-life:* 17 to 21 hours.

Route	Onset	Peak	Duration
SubQ	Unknown	2–3 hr	Unknown

Action

Chemical effect: Binds to AT-III and potentiates the natural neutralization of factor Xa by AT-III. Neutralization of factor Xa interrupts the coagulation cascade, thereby inhibiting formation of thrombin and thrombus development.
Therapeutic effect: Prevents the formation of blood clots.

Available forms

Injection (single-dose prefilled syringes): 2.5 mg/0.5 ml, 5 mg/0.4 ml, 7.5 mg/0.6 ml, 10 mg/0.8 ml

NURSING PROCESS

Assessment

• Assess patient's underlying condition before starting therapy.
• Be alert for adverse reactions and drug interactions.
• Patient who has received epidural or spinal anesthesia is at increased risk for epidural or spinal hematoma, which may result in long-term or permanent paralysis. Monitor patient closely for neurological impairment.
• Monitor renal function periodically, and stop drug in patient who develops unstable renal function or severe renal impairment.
• Routinely assess patient for signs and symptoms of bleeding, and regularly monitor CBC, platelet count, creatinine level, and stool occult blood test results. If platelet count is less than 100,000/mm^3, stop drug.
• Effect may last for 2 to 4 days after stopping drug in patient with normal renal function.
• Don't use PT and PTT tests to measure effectiveness.
• Assess patient's and family's knowledge of drug therapy.

Nursing diagnoses

• Risk for injury related to potential for thrombosis or pulmonary emboli development from underlying condition
• Risk for trauma related to increased risk of bleeding and hemorrhaging due to drug therapy
• Deficient knowledge related to anticoagulant therapy

Planning and implementation

• Give by subcutaneous injection only, in fatty tissue only, rotating injection sites.
• Visually inspect the single-dose prefilled syringe for particulate matter and discoloration before administration.
• Don't mix with other injections.
ALERT: Don't use interchangeably with heparin, low–molecular-weight heparins, or heparinoids.
• To avoid loss of drug, don't expel air bubble from the syringe.
• If patient begins to overtly bleed while being given the drug, apply strong pressure to the injection area and immediately notify the prescriber.
• Overdose may lead to hemorrhagic complications. Stop giving the drug and treat bleeding appropriately.
ALERT: Don't confuse Arixtra with the lab test anti-factor Xa, sometimes written anti-Xa.
ALERT: Don't confuse Arixtra with Bextra.

Patient teaching

• Teach patient signs and symptoms of bleeding. If any occur, patient should immediately contact the prescriber.
• Instruct patient to avoid OTC products that contain aspirin, other salicylates, or NSAIDs and other non-prescribed anticoagulants.
• Teach patient the correct way to give drug to himself subcutaneously.
• Show patient the different sites for injection, and explain that he must alternate injection sites to prevent hardening of fatty tissues.
• Teach patient the proper disposal of the syringe.

Evaluation

- Patient has no pulmonary embolus or thrombus during drug therapy.
- Patient is free from any injury or bleeding.
- Patient and family state understanding of drug therapy.

formoterol fumarate inhalation powder

(for-MOE-tur-all FYOO-muh-rayt)
Foradil Aerolizer

Pharmacologic class: selective long-acting $beta_2$ agonist
Therapeutic class: bronchodilator
Pregnancy risk category: C

Indications and dosages

▶ **Preventive and maintenance therapy for bronchospasm in patients with reversible obstructive airway disease or nocturnal asthma who usually need short-acting inhaled $beta_2$ agonists.** *Adults and children age 5 and older:* One 12-mcg capsule by inhalation via Aerolizer inhaler q 12 hours. Don't give more than one capsule b.i.d. (24 mcg daily). If symptoms are present between doses, use a short-acting $beta_2$ agonist for immediate relief.

▶ **To prevent exercise-induced bronchospasm.** *Adults and children age 12 and older:* One 12-mcg capsule by inhalation via Aerolizer inhaler at least 15 minutes before exercise, given occasionally, p.r.n. Avoid giving additional doses within 12 hours of first dose.

▶ **Maintenance therapy for COPD.** *Adults:* One 12-mcg capsule by inhalation via Aerolizer inhaler q 12 hours. Total daily dosage of greater than 24 mcg isn't recommended.

Contraindications and cautions

- Contraindicated in patients hypersensitive to drug or any of its components.
- Use cautiously in patients with CV disease, particularly coronary insufficiency, cardiac arrhythmias, and hypertension; in those who are unusually responsive to sympathomimetic amines; and in those with diabetes mellitus because hyperglycemia and ketoacidosis have occurred rarely with use of beta agonists. Also use cautiously in patients with lactose or milk allergy, seizure disorders, or thyrotoxicosis.
- Do not use to treat acute asthma attack or bronchospasm.

Lifespan: In pregnant women, use cautiously because drug may interfere with uterine contractility. In breast-feeding women, use cautiously because it isn't known if drug appears in breast milk. In children younger than age 5, safety and effectiveness haven't been established for asthma. In children younger than age 12, safety and effectiveness haven't been established for exercise-induced bronchospasm.

Adverse reactions

CNS: dizziness, fatigue, headache, insomnia, malaise, nervousness, tremor.
CV: angina, ***arrhythmias,*** chest pain, hypertension, hypotension, palpitations, tachycardia.
EENT: dry mouth, dysphonia, tonsillitis.
GI: nausea.
Metabolic: hyperglycemia, hypokalemia, ***metabolic acidosis.***
Musculoskeletal: muscle cramps.
Respiratory: bronchitis, chest infection, dyspnea.
Skin: rash.
Other: viral infection.

Interactions

Drug-drug. *Adrenergics:* May potentiate sympathetic effects of formoterol. Use together cautiously.
Beta blockers: May antagonize effects of beta agonists, causing bronchospasm in asthmatic patients. Avoid use except when benefits outweigh risks. Use cardioselective beta blockers cautiously to minimize risk of bronchospasm.
Corticosteroids, diuretics, xanthine derivatives: May potentiate hypokalemic effect of formoterol. Use together cautiously.
Loop or thiazide diuretics: May worsen ECG changes or hypokalemia with beta agonists. Use together cautiously, and monitor patient closely.
MAO inhibitors, tricyclic antidepressants, and other drugs that prolong the QT interval: May increase risk of ventricular arrhythmias. Use together cautiously.

Effects on lab test results

- May decrease potassium level. May increase glucose level.

Pharmacokinetics

Absorption: Rapid. Drug levels peak within 5 minutes after a 120-mcg dose.
Distribution: 61% to 64% protein-bound.
Metabolism: Mainly by CYP2D6, CYP2C19, CYP2C9, and CYP2A6. At therapeutic level, doesn't appear to inhibit cytochrome P-450 enzymes.
Excretion: 59% to 62% in urine and 32% to 34% in feces over 5 days. *Half-life:* Unknown.

Route	Onset	Peak	Duration
Inhalation	1–3 min	½–1½ hr	12 hr

Action

Chemical effect: Relaxes bronchial smooth muscle by acting on $beta_2$-adrenergic receptors; stimulates intracellular adenyl cyclase, the enzyme responsible for catalyzing the conversion of adenosine triphosphate (ATP) to cAMP. Increase in cAMP leads to relaxation of bronchial smooth muscle and inhibition of mediator release from mast cells.
Therapeutic effect: Prevents and controls bronchospasm.

Available forms

Capsules for inhalation: 12 mcg

NURSING PROCESS

Assessment

- Assess patient's underlying condition before starting therapy, and reassess regularly.
- Evaluate patient's use of short-acting $beta_2$ agonists for immediate relief of bronchospasm. Drug may be used with short-acting $beta_2$ agonists, inhaled corticosteroids, and theophylline therapy to manage asthma.
- Assess patient's and family's knowledge of drug therapy.

Nursing diagnoses

- Impaired gas exchange related to underlying pulmonary condition
- Risk for activity intolerance related to underlying pulmonary condition
- Deficient knowledge related to formoterol fumarate therapy

Planning and implementation

- Before use, store drug in refrigerator. After use, drug may be stored at room temperature.
- Don't remove capsule from unopened blister until immediately before use.
- Give capsules only by oral inhalation and only with the Aerolizer inhaler.
- Don't use Foradil Aerolizer with a spacer device.
- For patient using drug twice daily, don't give additional doses to prevent exercise-induced bronchospasm.
- Don't use as a substitute for short-acting $beta_2$ agonists for immediate relief of bronchospasm, or as a substitute for inhaled or oral corticosteroids.
- Don't begin use in patients with rapidly deteriorating or significantly worsening asthma.
- If usual dose doesn't control symptoms of bronchoconstriction and the patient's short-acting $beta_2$ agonist becomes less effective, reevaluate patient and therapy.
- For patient who formerly used regularly scheduled short-acting $beta_2$ agonists, decrease use of these drugs to an as-needed basis when long-acting therapy starts.
- Don't let the patient exhale into the device.
- Pierce capsules only once. To minimize risk of shattering capsule, strictly follow storage and use instructions. The Aerolizer contains a screen that will catch any broken pieces of the capsule before they enter the patient's mouth or lungs.
- Drug may cause life-threatening paradoxical bronchospasm. If this occurs, immediately stop giving the drug and use a different drug.
- Monitor patient for tachycardia, hypertension, and other adverse CV effects. If they occur, stop drug.
- Watch for immediate hypersensitivity reactions, such as anaphylaxis, urticaria, angioedema, rash, and bronchospasm.
- Signs and symptoms of overdose include excessive beta blocker stimulation (tachycardia, tremor, hypotension) and exaggerated adverse effects, leading to cardiac arrest and death. To treat overdose, stop drug, monitor cardiac condition, give appropriate symptomatic relief or supportive therapy, and use cardioselective beta blockers cautiously. It's unknown whether dialysis is beneficial.

ALERT: Capsules shouldn't be swallowed.
ALERT: Don't confuse Foradil with Toradol.

Patient teaching

- Tell patient not to increase the dosage or frequency of use without medical advice.

• Warn patient not to stop or reduce other drugs taken for asthma.
• Advise patient that drug isn't for acute asthmatic episodes; instead, he should use short-acting $beta_2$ agonist.
• Advise patient to report worsening symptoms, decreasing effectiveness, or increasing use of short-acting $beta_2$ agonist.
• Tell patient to report nausea, vomiting, shakiness, headache, fast or irregular heartbeat, chest pain, or sleeplessness.
• Tell patient being treated for exercise-induced bronchospasm to take drug at least 15 minutes before exercise. Additional doses can't be taken for 12 hours.
• Tell patient not to use the Foradil Aerolizer with a spacer device or to exhale or blow into the inhaler.
• Advise patient to avoid washing the Aerolizer and to always keep it dry. Advise patient to use the new device that comes with each refill.
• Tell patient to avoid exposing capsules to moisture and to handle them only with dry hands.

Evaluation

• Patient's pulmonary symptoms improve.
• Patient's activity intolerance improves.
• Patient and family state understanding of drug therapy.

fosamprenavir calcium

(foss-am-PREH-nuh-veer CAL-see-um)
Lexiva

Pharmacologic class: protease inhibitor
Therapeutic class: antiretroviral
Pregnancy risk category: C

Indications and dosages

▶ **HIV infection with other antiretrovirals.** *Adults:* In patients previously untreated, 1,400 mg P.O. b.i.d. (without ritonavir). Or 1,400 mg P.O. once daily and ritonavir 200 mg P.O. once daily. Or 700 mg P.O. b.i.d. and ritonavir 100 mg P.O. b.i.d. In patients previously treated with a protease inhibitor, 700 mg P.O. b.i.d. plus ritonavir 100 mg P.O. b.i.d.

Adjust-a-dose: If patient takes efavirenz, fosamprenavir, and ritonavir once daily, give an additional 100 mg daily of ritonavir (300 mg total). If patient has mild or moderate hepatic impairment and takes fosamprenavir without ritonavir, reduce dosage to 700 mg P.O. b.i.d. Avoid use in patients with severe hepatic impairment because dose can't be reduced below 700 mg.

Contraindications and cautions

• Contraindicated in patients hypersensitive to amprenavir or any of its components. Also contraindicated with dihydroergotamine, ergonovine, ergotamine, flecainide, methylergonovine, midazolam, pimozide, propafenone, and triazolam.
• Use cautiously in patients allergic to sulfonamides and those with mild to moderate hepatic impairment. Avoid use in patients with severe hepatic impairment.

Lifespan: In pregnant women, breast-feeding women, and children, safety and effectiveness haven't been established.

Adverse reactions

CNS: depression, fatigue, headache, oral paresthesia.
GI: abdominal pain, diarrhea, nausea, vomiting.
Skin: pruritus, *rash.*

Interactions

Drug-drug. *Amitriptyline, cyclosporine, imipramine, tacrolimus:* May increase levels of these drugs. Monitor drug levels.
Antiarrhythmics (amiodarone, lidocaine, quinidine): May increase antiarrhythmic level. Use together cautiously, and monitor antiarrhythmic levels.
Atorvastatin: May increase atorvastatin level. Give 20 mg daily or less of atorvastatin and monitor patient carefully. Or consider other HMG-CoA reductase inhibitors, such as fluvastatin, pravastatin, or rosuvastatin.
Benzodiazepines (alprazolam, clorazepate, diazepam, flurazepam): May increase benzodiazepine level. Decrease benzodiazepine dosage if needed.
Calcium channel blockers (amlodipine, diltiazem, felodipine, isradipine, nicardipine, nifedipine, nimodipine, nisoldipine, verapamil): May increase calcium channel blocker level. Use together cautiously.
Carbamazepine, dexamethasone, H_2-receptor antagonists, phenobarbital, phenytoin, proton-pump inhibitors: May decrease amprenavir level. Use together cautiously.

Delavirdine: May cause loss of virologic response and resistance to delavirdine. Avoid use together.
Dihydroergotamine, ergonovine, ergotamine, flecainide, methylergonovine, midazolam, pimozide, propafenone, triazolam: May cause serious adverse reactions. Avoid use together.
Efavirenz, nevirapine, saquinavir: May decrease amprenavir level. Appropriate combination doses haven't been established.
Efavirenz with ritonavir: May decrease amprenavir level. Increase ritonavir by 100 mg daily (300 mg total) when giving efavirenz, fosamprenavir, and ritonavir once daily. No change needed in ritonavir when giving efavirenz, fosamprenavir, and ritonavir twice daily.
Ethinyl estradiol and norethindrone: May increase ethinyl estradiol and norethindrone levels. Recommend nonhormonal contraception.
Indinavir, nelfinavir: May increase amprenavir level. Appropriate combination doses haven't been established.
Itraconazole, ketoconazole: May increase ketoconazole and itraconazole levels. Reduce ketoconazole or itraconazole dosage as needed if patient takes more than 400 mg daily of fosamprenavir. Don't give more than 200 mg daily.
Lopinavir with ritonavir: May decrease amprenavir and lopinavir levels. Appropriate combination doses haven't been established.
Lovastatin, simvastatin: May increase risk of myopathy, including rhabdomyolysis. Avoid use together.
Methadone: May decrease methadone level. Increase methadone dosage if needed.
Rifabutin: May increase rifabutin level. Obtain CBC weekly to watch for neutropenia and decrease rifabutin dosage by at least half. If patient takes ritonavir, decrease dosage by at least 75% from the usual 300 mg daily. Maximum, 150 mg q other day or three times weekly.
Rifampin: May decrease amprenavir level and drug effect. Avoid use together.
Sildenafil, tadalafil, vardenafil: May increase levels of these drugs. Recommend cautious use of sildenafil at 25 mg q 48 hours, tadalafil 10 mg q 72 hours, or vardenafil at no more than 2.5 mg q 24 hours. If patient takes ritonavir, recommend cautious use of vardenafil at no more than 2.5 mg q 72 hours. Tell patient to report adverse events.
Warfarin: May alter warfarin level. Monitor INR.

Drug-herb. *St. John's wort:* May cause loss of virologic response and resistance to fosamprenavir or its class of protease inhibitors. Discourage use together.

Effects on lab test results

- May increase lipase, triglyceride, AST, and ALT levels.
- May decrease neutrophil count.

Pharmacokinetics

Absorption: Food has no effect.
Distribution: 90% protein-bound.
Metabolism: Rapid and almost complete via CYP3A4.
Excretion: Unknown. *Half-life:* About 8 hours.

Route	Onset	Peak	Duration
P.O.	Unknown	1½–4 hr	Unknown

Action

Chemical effect: Converts rapidly to amprenavir, which binds to the active site of HIV-1 protease and causes formation of immature noninfectious viral particles.
Therapeutic effect: Hinders HIV activity.

Available forms

Tablets: 700 mg

NURSING PROCESS

Assessment

- Monitor patient with hemophilia for spontaneous bleeding.
- During initial therapy, monitor patient for such opportunistic infections as *Mycobacterium avium* complex, CMV, *Pneumocystis jiroveci (carinii)* pneumonia, and tuberculosis.
- Assess patient for redistribution or accumulation of body fat, as in central obesity, dorsocervical fat enlargement (buffalo hump), peripheral wasting, facial wasting, breast enlargement, and a cushingoid appearance.
- Assess patient's and family's knowledge of drug therapy.

Nursing diagnoses

- Risk for infection related to presence of HIV
- Risk for deficient fluid volume related to adverse GI reactions
- Deficient knowledge related to drug therapy

Planning and implementation

- Patient with hepatitis B or C, or noticeable increase in transaminase level before therapy, may have an increased risk of transaminase elevation. Monitor patient.

Patient teaching

- Tell patient that drug doesn't reduce the risk of transmitting HIV to others.
- Inform patient that the drug may reduce the risk of progression to AIDS and death.
- Explain that drug must be used with other antiretrovirals.
- Tell patient not to alter the dosage or stop taking drug without consulting the prescriber.
- Urge patient to inform the prescriber about sulfa allergy.
- Because this drug may interact with many drugs, urge patient to tell the prescriber about any prescription or OTC drugs and herbal products that he takes (especially St. John's wort).
- Explain that body fat may redistribute or accumulate.

Evaluation

- Patient responds well to therapy.
- Patient maintains adequate hydration.
- Patient and family state understanding of drug therapy.

foscarnet sodium (phosphonoformic acid)

(fos-KAR-net SOH-dee-um)

Foscavir

Pharmacologic class: pyrophosphate analog
Therapeutic class: antiviral
Pregnancy risk category: C

Indications and dosages

▶ **CMV retinitis in patients with AIDS.** *Adults:* Initially, 60 mg/kg I.V. over 1 hour q 8 hours, or 90 mg/kg I.V. over 1½ to 2 hours q 12 hours for 2 to 3 weeks, depending on response. Follow with maintenance infusion of 90 to 120 mg/kg I.V. daily over 2 hours.

Adjust-a-dose: In patients with renal impairment, adjust dosage if creatinine clearance is less than 1.5 ml/kg/minute. If clearance is less than 0.4 ml/kg/minute, stop drug.

▶ **Mucocutaneous acyclovir-resistant herpes simplex virus infections.** *Adults:* 40 mg/kg I.V. infused over at least 1 hour, q 8 or 12 hours for 2 to 3 weeks or until healed.

Adjust-a-dose: In patients with renal impairment, if creatinine clearance is less than 1.5 ml/kg/minute, adjust dosage. If clearance is less than 0.4 ml/kg/minute, stop drug.

▶ **Varicella zoster infection‡.** *Adults:* 40 mg/kg I.V. q 8 hours for 14 to 21 days.

I.V. administration

- If infusing via central venous access, the standard 24-mg/ml solution may or may not be diluted. When using a peripheral venous catheter, dilute solution to 12 mg/ml with D_5W or normal saline solution.
- To reduce the risk of nephrotoxicity, give 750 to 1,000 ml of normal saline solution or D_5W before first dose and then with each subsequent dose.
- Don't exceed recommended dosage, infusion rate, or frequency of administration. All doses must be individualized based on patient's renal function.
- Use infusion pump to give drug over at least 1 hour.
- Use solution within 24 hours of first entry into sealed bottle.

⊗ **Incompatibilities**

Acyclovir, amphotericin B, co-trimoxazole, dextrose 30%, diazepam, digoxin, diphenhydramine, dobutamine, droperidol, ganciclovir, gentamicin, haloperidol, lactated Ringer's solution, leucovorin, lorazepam, midazolam, morphine, pentamidine, phenytoin, prochlorperazine, promethazine, solutions containing calcium (such as total parenteral nutrition), trimetrexate, vancomycin.

Contraindications and cautions

- Contraindicated in patients hypersensitive to drug or any of its components.
- Use cautiously and at a lower dose in a patient with abnormal renal function because drug will accumulate and toxicity will increase. Because drug is nephrotoxic, it may worsen renal impairment. Some nephrotoxicity occurs in most patients treated with drug.

Lifespan: In pregnant women, use cautiously. In breast-feeding women, use cautiously because it's unknown if the drug appears in breast milk. In children, safety and effectiveness haven't been established. In elderly patients, use cautiously because they are more likely to have decreased renal function.

Adverse reactions

CNS: abnormal coordination, aggressive reaction, agitation, amnesia, anxiety, aphasia, *asthenia,* ataxia, cerebrovascular disorder, confusion, dementia, depression, *dizziness,* EEG abnormalities, *fatigue, fever,* generalized spasms, *headache, hypoesthesia,* insomnia, *malaise,* meningitis, nervousness, *neuropathy,* pain, *paresthesia,* ***seizures,*** sensory disturbances, somnolence, stupor, tremor.
CV: ECG abnormalities, edema, facial edema, first-degree AV block, flushing, hypertension, hypotension, palpitations, sinus tachycardia.
EENT: conjunctivitis, eye pain, pharyngitis, rhinitis, sinusitis, visual disturbances.
GI: *abdominal pain, anorexia,* constipation, *diarrhea,* dry mouth, dysphagia, flatulence, melena, *nausea,* ***pancreatitis, rectal hemorrhage,*** taste perversion, ulcerative stomatitis, *vomiting.*
GU: abnormal renal function, ***acute renal impairment,*** albuminuria, candidiasis, dysuria, ***nephrotoxicity,*** polyuria, urethral disorder, urine retention, UTI.
Hematologic: anemia, ***bone marrow suppression, granulocytopenia, leukopenia,*** lymphadenopathy, ***thrombocytopenia, thrombosis.***
Hepatic: abnormal hepatic function.
Metabolic: hypocalcemia, hypokalemia, ***hypomagnesemia,*** hyponatremia, hypophosphatemia or hyperphosphatemia.
Musculoskeletal: arthralgia, leg cramps, myalgia.
Respiratory: ***bronchospasm,*** *cough, dyspnea,* hemoptysis, pneumonic respiratory insufficiency, ***pneumothorax,*** pulmonary infiltration, ***stridor.***
Skin: erythematous rash, *increased sweating,* pruritus, *rash,* seborrhea, skin discoloration, skin ulceration.
Other: abscess, back or chest pain, bacterial or fungal infections, flulike symptoms, inflammation, lymphoma-like disorder, pain at infusion site, rigors, sarcoma, ***sepsis.***

Interactions

Drug-drug. *Nephrotoxic drugs (such as aminoglycosides, amphotericin B):* May increase risk of nephrotoxicity. Avoid use together.
Pentamidine: May increase risk of nephrotoxicity and severe hypocalcemia. Don't use together.
Zidovudine: May increase risk or severity of anemia. Monitor blood counts.

Effects on lab test results

- May increase BUN, creatinine, phosphate, ALT, AST, alkaline phosphatase, and bilirubin levels. May decrease calcium, magnesium, phosphate, potassium, sodium, and hemoglobin levels and hematocrit.
- May decrease granulocyte and WBC counts. May increase or decrease platelet count.

Pharmacokinetics

Absorption: Given I.V.
Distribution: 14% to 17% protein-bound.
Metabolism: None.
Excretion: 80% to 90% unchanged in urine. *Half-life:* 3 hours.

Route	Onset	Peak	Duration
I.V.	Immediate	Immediate	Unknown

Action

Chemical effect: Blocks pyrophosphate binding sites on DNA polymerases and reverse transcriptases.
Therapeutic effect: Kills virus.

Available forms

Injection: 24 mg/ml in 250- and 500-ml bottles

NURSING PROCESS

Assessment

- Assess patient's infection before therapy and regularly thereafter.
- Obtain electrolyte levels and creatinine clearance before therapy, two or three times weekly during induction and at least once every 1 or 2 weeks during maintenance.
- Drug may cause dose-related transient decrease in ionized calcium, which may not show up in laboratory values. Watch for tetany and seizures with abnormal electrolyte levels.
- Monitor patient's hemoglobin level and hematocrit. Patient may develop anemia severe enough that he needs transfusions.
- Be alert for adverse reactions and drug interactions.
- Assess patient's and family's knowledge of drug therapy.

Nursing diagnoses
• Risk for infection related to presence of herpes virus susceptible to drug
• Disturbed sensory perception (tactile) related to drug's adverse effect
• Deficient knowledge related to drug therapy

Planning and implementation
• Because drug is highly toxic and toxicity is probably dose-related, use lowest effective maintenance dosage.

Patient teaching
• Advise patient to report circumoral tingling, numbness in limbs, and paresthesia.

Evaluation
• Patient is free from infection.
• Patient has no adverse neurologic reactions.
• Patient and family state understanding of drug therapy.

fosinopril sodium
(foh-SIN-oh-pril SOH-dee-um)
Monopril

Pharmacologic class: ACE inhibitor
Therapeutic class: antihypertensive
Pregnancy risk category: C (D in second and third trimesters)

Indications and dosages
▶ **Hypertension.** *Adults:* Initially, 10 mg P.O. daily. Adjust dosage based on blood pressure at peak and trough levels. Usual dosage, 20 to 40 mg daily. Maximum, 80 mg daily. May divide dosage.
Children ages 6 to 16, weighing 50 kg (110 lb) or more: Give 5 to 10 mg P.O. daily.
▶ **Adjunct therapy for heart failure.** *Adults:* Initially, 10 mg P.O. once daily. Increase dosage over several weeks to maximum tolerable, but no more than 40 mg P.O. daily. If possible, stop diuretic therapy.
Adjust-a-dose: For patients who have heart failure with moderate to severe renal impairment or who are being vigorously diuresed, give initial dose of 5 mg P.O. daily.

Contraindications and cautions
• Contraindicated in patients hypersensitive to drug or any of its components or to other ACE inhibitors, including patients with a history of ACE inhibitor–induced angioedema and patients with hereditary or idiopathic angioedema. Avoid use in patients with renal artery stenosis.
• Use cautiously in patients with impaired renal or hepatic function.
Lifespan: In pregnant women, use only if benefits outweigh risks to fetus. In breast-feeding women, drug is contraindicated. In children younger than age 6 or those weighing less than 50 kg, safety and effectiveness haven't been established.

Adverse reactions
CNS: dizziness, fatigue, headache, paresthesia, sleep disturbance, ***stroke,*** syncope.
CV: angina, chest pain, hypotension, ***MI,*** orthostatic hypotension, palpitations, rhythm disturbances.
EENT: sinusitis, tinnitus.
GI: abdominal distention, abdominal pain, constipation, diarrhea, dry mouth, nausea, ***pancreatitis,*** vomiting.
GU: renal insufficiency.
Hepatic: ***hepatitis.***
Metabolic: ***hyperkalemia.***
Musculoskeletal: arthralgia, musculoskeletal pain, myalgia.
Respiratory: ***bronchospasm;*** dry, persistent, tickling, nonproductive cough.
Skin: photosensitivity, pruritus, rash, urticaria.
Other: ***angioedema,*** decreased libido, gout, sexual dysfunction.

Interactions
Drug-drug. *Antacids:* May impair absorption. Separate administration times by at least 2 hours.
Diuretics, other antihypertensives: May increase risk of excessive hypotension. Stop diuretic or lower fosinopril dosage.
Lithium: May increase lithium level and toxicity. Avoid use together.
Potassium-sparing diuretics, potassium supplements, sodium substitutes containing potassium: May increase risk of hyperkalemia. Monitor potassium level.
Drug-herb. *Licorice:* May cause sodium retention and increase blood pressure, interfering with ACE inhibitor effect. Discourage ingestion of licorice during drug therapy.
Drug-food. *Salt substitutes containing potassium:* May increase risk of hyperkalemia. Monitor potassium closely.

Drug-lifestyle. *Alcohol use:* May have additive hypotensive effects. Discourage use together.

Effects on lab test results

- May increase BUN, creatinine, and potassium levels. May decrease hemoglobin level and hematocrit.
- May increase liver function test values.

Pharmacokinetics

Absorption: Slow, mainly in proximal small intestine.
Distribution: More than 95% protein-bound.
Metabolism: Mainly in liver and gut.
Excretion: 50% in urine; remainder in feces. *Half-life:* 11½ hours.

Route	Onset	Peak	Duration
P.O.	≤ 1 hr	2–6 hr	24 hr

Action

Chemical effect: Inhibits ACE, preventing conversion of angiotensin I to angiotensin II, a potent vasoconstrictor, which decreases peripheral arterial resistance, and aldosterone secretion.
Therapeutic effect: Lowers blood pressure.

Available forms

Tablets: 10 mg, 20 mg, 40 mg

NURSING PROCESS

Assessment

- Assess blood pressure before starting therapy and regularly thereafter.
- Assess renal and hepatic function before starting therapy and regularly thereafter.
- Monitor potassium intake and potassium level. Diabetic patients, those with renal impairment, and those receiving drugs that can increase potassium levels may develop hyperkalemia.
- Other ACE inhibitors have been linked to agranulocytosis and neutropenia. Monitor CBC with differential counts before therapy, every 2 weeks for first 3 months of therapy, and periodically thereafter.
- If adverse GI reaction occurs, monitor patient's hydration.
- Assess patient's and family's knowledge of drug therapy.

Nursing diagnoses

- Risk for injury related to presence of hypertension
- Risk for deficient fluid volume related to adverse GI reactions
- Deficient knowledge related to drug therapy

Planning and implementation

- Drug may be taken with food, but it slows absorption.

Patient teaching

- Tell patient to avoid salt substitutes because they may contain potassium, which increases the risk of hyperkalemia.
- Urge patient to report signs of infection (such as fever and sore throat); easy bruising or bleeding; swelling of tongue, lips, face, eyes, mucous membranes, or limbs; difficulty swallowing or breathing; and hoarseness.
- Tell patient to use caution in hot weather and during exercise. Inadequate fluid intake, vomiting, diarrhea, and excessive perspiration can lead to light-headedness and syncope.
- Tell woman to notify prescriber about planned, suspected, or known pregnancy. Drug will probably need to be stopped.

Evaluation

- Patient's blood pressure is normal.
- Patient maintains adequate hydration throughout drug therapy.
- Patient and family state understanding of drug therapy.

fosphenytoin sodium

(fahs-FEN-eh-toyn SOH-dee-um)
Cerebyx

Pharmacologic class: hydantoin
Therapeutic class: anticonvulsant
Pregnancy risk category: D

Indications and dosages

▶ **Status epilepticus.** *Adults:* 15 to 20 mg phenytoin sodium equivalent (PE)/kg I.V. at 100 to 150 mg PE/minute as loading dose; then 4 to 6 mg PE/kg I.V. daily as maintenance dose. (Phenytoin may be used instead of fosphenytoin as maintenance, using the appropriate dose.)

▶ **To prevent and treat seizures during neurosurgery (nonemergent loading or mainte-**

nance doses). *Adults:* Loading dose of 10 to 20 mg PE/kg I.M. or I.V. at infusion rate not exceeding 150 mg PE/minute. Maintenance dosage is 4 to 6 mg PE/kg I.V. or I.M. daily.

▶ **Short-term substitution for oral phenytoin therapy.** *Adults:* Same total daily dosage equivalent as oral phenytoin sodium therapy given as a single daily dose I.M. or I.V. at infusion rate not exceeding 150 mg PE/minute. Some patients may need more frequent doses.

I.V. administration

- Dilute drug in D_5W or normal saline solution for injection to yield 1.5 to 25 mg PE/ml.
- Don't exceed 150 mg PE/minute.
- Monitor patient's ECG, blood pressure, and respirations throughout period of highest phenytoin levels—about 10 to 20 minutes after end of fosphenytoin infusion.
- Refrigerate at 36° to 46° F (2° C to 8° C). Don't keep at room temperature for longer than 48 hours.

⊗ **Incompatibilities**
Other I.V. drugs.

Contraindications and cautions

- Contraindicated in patients hypersensitive to drug or any of its components, phenytoin, or other hydantoins. Also contraindicated in patients with sinus bradycardia, SA block, second- or third-degree AV block, Adams-Stokes syndrome, or acute hepatotoxicity. Drug isn't indicated for absence seizures.
- Use cautiously in patients with renal and hepatic disease or in those with hypoalbuminemia.

Lifespan: In pregnant women, use drug only if nature, frequency, and severity of seizures pose a serious threat to the patient. In breast-feeding women, use cautiously. In children, safety and effectiveness haven't been established. In elderly patients, use a lower dose because of their decreased metabolism and decreased phenytoin clearance.

Adverse reactions

CNS: abnormal thinking, agitation, asthenia, *ataxia*, ***brain edema***, decreased reflexes, *dizziness*, dysarthria, headache, extrapyramidal syndrome, fever, hypoesthesia, increased reflexes, incoordination, ***intracranial hypertension***, nervousness, paresthesia, speech disorder, *somnolence*, stupor, vertigo.
CV: hypotension, hypertension, tachycardia, tremor, facial edema, vasodilation, ***severe CV reactions, ventricular fibrillation.***
EENT: amblyopia, deafness, diplopia, *nystagmus*, tinnitus.
GI: constipation, dry mouth, nausea, taste perversion, tongue disorder, vomiting.
Hepatic: ***hepatotoxicity.***
Metabolic: hypokalemia.
Musculoskeletal: back pain, myasthenia, pelvic pain.
Respiratory: pneumonia.
Skin: ecchymosis, *pruritus*, rash.
Other: accidental injury, chills, infection, injection-site reaction and pain.

Interactions

Drug-drug. *Amiodarone, chloramphenicol, chlordiazepoxide, cimetidine, diazepam, dicumarol, disulfiram, estrogens, ethosuximide, fluoxetine, H_2-receptor antagonists, halothane, isoniazid, methylphenidate, phenothiazines, phenylbutazone, salicylates, succinimides, sulfonamides, tolbutamide, trazodone:* May increase phenytoin level and therapeutic effects. Use together cautiously.
Carbamazepine, reserpine: May decrease phenytoin level. Monitor patient.
Coumarin, digitoxin, doxycycline, estrogens, furosemide, hormonal contraceptives, quinidine, rifampin, theophylline, vitamin D: May decrease effectiveness of these drugs because of increased hepatic metabolism. Monitor patient closely.
Phenobarbital, sodium valproate, valproic acid: May increase or decrease phenytoin level. Monitor patient.
Tricyclic antidepressants: May lower seizure threshold and require adjustments in phenytoin dosage. Use cautiously.
Drug-lifestyle. *Acute alcohol use:* May increase phenytoin level and toxic effects. Discourage alcohol use.
Chronic alcohol use: May decrease phenytoin level. Monitor patient; discourage alcohol use.

Effects on lab test results

- May increase alkaline phosphatase, GGT, and glucose levels. May decrease potassium and T_4 levels.
- May decrease platelet, WBC, granulocyte, leukocyte, and RBC counts.

Pharmacokinetics

Absorption: Complete.
Distribution: Wide. 95% to 99% protein-bound.
Metabolism: In the liver; undergoes rapid hydrolysis to phenytoin.
Excretion: In the urine as phenytoin metabolites. *Half-life:* 15 minutes.

Route	Onset	Peak	Duration
I.V.	Unknown	Immediate	Unknown
I.M.	Unknown	30 min	Unknown

Action

Chemical effect: Because fosphenytoin is a prodrug of phenytoin, their action is the same: stabilizing neuronal membranes.
Therapeutic effect: Prevents and controls seizures.

Available forms

Injection: 2 ml (150 mg fosphenytoin sodium equivalent to 100 mg phenytoin sodium), 10 ml (750 mg fosphenytoin sodium equivalent to 500 mg phenytoin sodium)

NURSING PROCESS

Assessment
- Don't give drug I.M. for status epilepticus because therapeutic phenytoin levels may not occur as rapidly as with I.V. use.
- Don't monitor phenytoin level until about 2 hours after the end of I.V. infusion or 4 hours after I.M. injection.
- Assess patient's and family's knowledge of drug therapy.

Nursing diagnoses
- Risk for trauma related to seizures
- Deficient knowledge related to drug therapy

Planning and implementation
- Drug should always be prescribed and dispensed in PE units. Don't make any adjustments in recommended dose when substituting fosphenytoin for phenytoin, or vice versa.
- I.M. use generates systemic phenytoin levels similar to oral phenytoin sodium, allowing essentially interchangeable use.

ALERT: Abruptly stopping the drug may cause status epilepticus. Substitute another drug, or reduce the dosage of this drug gradually.

ALERT: Don't confuse Cerebyx with Celexa or Celebrex.

Patient teaching
- Warn patient that sensory disturbances may occur with I.V. use.
- Instruct patient to immediately report adverse reactions, especially rash.

Evaluation
- Patient is free from seizures.
- Patient and family state understanding of drug therapy.

frovatriptan succinate
(froh-vah-TRIP-tan SUK-seh-nayt)
Frova

Pharmacologic class: serotonin 5-HT_1 receptor agonist
Therapeutic class: antimigraine drug
Pregnancy risk category: C

Indications and dosages

▶ **Migraine attacks with or without aura.** *Adults:* 2.5 mg P.O. taken at the first sign of migraine. If headache recurs after initial relief, a second tablet may be given after waiting at least 2 hours. Don't give more than 3 tablets daily.

Contraindications and cautions

- Contraindicated in patients hypersensitive to drug or any of the inactive ingredients. Also contraindicated in patients with history of or current ischemic heart disease, coronary artery vasospasm (including Prinzmetal variant angina), or other significant underlying CV conditions. Don't use in patients with cerebrovascular syndromes, such as stroke of any type or transient ischemic attacks, or in patients with peripheral vascular disease, including, but not limited to, ischemic bowel disease. Contraindicated in patients with uncontrolled hypertension and in patients with hemiplegic or basilar migraine.

Lifespan: In pregnant women, use drug only if benefits outweigh risks to fetus. In breast-feeding women, use cautiously because it's unknown if drug appears in breast milk. In children, safety and effectiveness haven't been established. In elderly patients, no special dosage has been suggested, but experience is limited.

Adverse reactions

CNS: anxiety, dizziness, dysesthesia, headache, hypoesthesia, insomnia, fatigue, pain, paresthesia, somnolence, ***stroke.***
CV: ***cardiac arrhythmias,*** chest pain, flushing, hypertension, ***MI,*** palpitations.
EENT: abnormal vision, rhinitis, sinusitis, tinnitus.
GI: abdominal pain, diarrhea, dry mouth, dyspepsia, nausea, vomiting.
Musculoskeletal: skeletal pain.
Skin: increased sweating.
Other: hot or cold sensation.

Interactions

Drug-drug. *Ergotamine or ergot-type drugs (such as dihydroergotamine or methysergide):* May cause prolonged vasospastic reactions. Don't use within 24 hours of each other.
5-$HT_{1B/1D}$ agonists: May have additive effects. Use of other 5-HT_1 agonists within 24 hours of frovatriptan isn't recommended.
Hormonal contraceptives, propranolol: May increase bioavailability of frovatriptan. Monitor patient for adverse effects.
SSRIs (such as citalopram, fluoxetine, fluvoxamine, paroxetine, sertraline): May cause serotonin syndrome. Monitor patient closely.

Effects on lab test results

None reported.

Pharmacokinetics

Absorption: Oral bioavailability 20% in men and 30% in women. Food delays the time to peak, but not bioavailability.
Distribution: 15% protein-bound.
Metabolism: In the liver, by CYP1A2. Drug doesn't appear to induce or inhibit cytochrome P-450.
Excretion: In urine and feces. *Half-life:* 26 hours.

Route	Onset	Peak	Duration
P.O.	Unknown	2–4 hr	Unknown

Action

Chemical effect: May inhibit excessive dilation of extracerebral intracranial arteries in migraine headaches.
Therapeutic effect: Relieves pain caused by migraines.

Available forms

Tablets: 2.5 mg

NURSING PROCESS

Assessment

- Assess underlying condition before starting therapy, and reassess regularly throughout therapy.
- Obtain complete medical history, paying particular attention to history of CV and cerebrovascular disease.
- Assess patient's and family's knowledge of drug therapy.

Nursing diagnoses

- Acute pain related to migraine headache
- Activity intolerance related to migraine headache
- Deficient knowledge related to frovatriptan succinate therapy

Planning and implementation

ALERT: Don't give within 24 hours of another 5-HT_1 agonist or an ergotamine or ergotlike drug.
ALERT: Serious cardiac events, including acute MI and life-threatening cardiac rhythm disturbances may occur within a few hours of giving 5-HT_1 agonists.

- Drug may bind to the melanin of the eye and cause ophthalmic effects. No specific ophthalmic monitoring is recommended.
- The safety of treating an average of more than four migraine attacks in a 30-day period hasn't been established.
- If used in a patient with risk factors for unrecognized coronary artery disease (such as hypertension, hypercholesterolemia, smoking, obesity, strong family history of coronary artery disease, woman with surgical or physiologic menopause, man older than age 40), give the first dose in a medically staffed and equipped facility. Obtain an ECG after the first dose. Periodically assess cardiac condition in intermittent, long-term users of 5-HT_1 agonists or those who have or acquire risk factors during therapy.

Patient teaching

- Instruct patient to take the dose at the first sign of a migraine headache. If the headache comes back after the first dose, a second dose may be taken after 2 hours. Tell patient not to take more than 3 tablets in a 24-hour period.

• Inform patient that, in rare cases, patients have experienced serious heart problems, stroke, or high blood pressure after taking the drug.
• Advise patient to take extra care or avoid driving and operating machinery if dizziness or fatigue develops.
• Emphasize importance of immediately reporting rash, itching, or pain, tightness, heaviness, or pressure in the chest, throat, neck, or jaw after taking the drug.
• Instruct patient not to take drug within 24 hours of taking another serotonin receptor agonist or ergotamine-type drugs.

Evaluation

• Patient is relieved of pain.
• Patient's activity tolerance returns to baseline.
• Patient and family state understanding of drug therapy.

fulvestrant

(full-VESS-trant)
Faslodex

Pharmacologic class: estrogen receptor antagonist
Therapeutic class: antineoplastic
Pregnancy risk category: D

Indications and dosages

▶ **Hormone-receptor–positive metastatic breast cancer in postmenopausal women with disease progression following antiestrogen therapy.** *Adults:* 250 mg by slow I.M. injection into buttock once monthly.

Contraindications and cautions

• Contraindicated in patients hypersensitive to drug or any of its components.
• Use cautiously in patients with moderate or severe hepatic impairment.
Lifespan: In pregnant women, drug is contraindicated. Women of childbearing age should avoid getting pregnant while taking the drug. Breast-feeding women should stop breast-feeding or not take the drug. In children, safety and effectiveness haven't been established.

Adverse reactions

CNS: anxiety, *asthenia,* depression, dizziness, fever, *headache,* insomnia, *pain,* paresthesia.
CV: chest pain, peripheral edema, *vasodilation.*
EENT: *pharyngitis.*
GI: *abdominal pain,* anorexia, *constipation, diarrhea, nausea, vomiting.*
GU: UTI.
Hematologic: anemia.
Musculoskeletal: arthritis, *back pain, bone pain,* pelvic pain.
Respiratory: *cough, dyspnea.*
Skin: rash, sweating.
Other: accidental injury, flulike syndrome, *injection-site pain.*

Interactions

None reported.

Effects on lab test results

• May decrease hemoglobin level and hematocrit.

Pharmacokinetics

Absorption: Unknown.
Distribution: Extensive and rapid. 99% protein-bound.
Metabolism: Extensive, via several pathways.
Excretion: Hepatically cleared, 90% in feces.
Half-life: 29 to 51 days.

Route	Onset	Peak	Duration
I.M.	Unknown	7 days	1 mo

Action

Chemical effect: Competitively binds estrogen receptors and down-regulates estrogen-receptor protein in breast cancer cells.
Therapeutic effect: Fights cancer cells.

Available forms

Injection: 50 mg/ml in 2.5-ml and 5-ml prefilled syringes

NURSING PROCESS

Assessment

• Monitor hemoglobin level and hematocrit before starting therapy and during therapy.
• Confirm that patient isn't pregnant before starting therapy.
• Observe injection site for local reaction.
• Assess patient's and family's knowledge of drug therapy.

Nursing diagnoses

- Risk for imbalanced nutrition: less than body requirements, related to side effects of therapy
- Acute pain related to side effects of therapy
- Deficient knowledge related to drug therapy

Planning and implementation

- Because drug is given I.M., don't use in patients with bleeding diatheses or thrombocytopenia or in those taking anticoagulants.

ALERT: The drug is packaged in one 5-ml prefilled syringe or two 2.5-ml prefilled syringes. If using the 2.5-ml syringes, both syringes must be given to achieve the full 250-mg recommended monthly dose.

- Expel the gas bubble from syringe before administration.

Patient teaching

- Tell patient the most common adverse reactions are GI symptoms, headache, back pain, hot flushes, and sore throat.
- Advise women of childbearing age to avoid pregnancy and to report suspected pregnancy immediately. Drug crosses the placenta after a single I.M. dose and harms the fetus.

Evaluation

- Patient maintains adequate nutrition during therapy.
- Patient doesn't experience pain as an adverse effect.
- Patient and family state understanding of therapy.

furosemide (frusemide)

(fyoo-ROH-seh-mighd)

Apo-Furosemide ♦, Furoside ♦, Lasix, Lasix Special ♦, Novosemide ♦, Uritol ♦

Pharmacologic class: loop diuretic
Therapeutic class: diuretic, antihypertensive
Pregnancy risk category: C

Indications and dosages

▶ **Acute pulmonary edema.** *Adults:* 40 mg I.V. injected slowly over 1 to 2 minutes; then 80 mg I.V. in 1 to 1½ hours, if needed.
Infants and children: 1 mg/kg I.M. or I.V. If desired results don't occur after 2 hours, may increase initial dose by 1 mg/kg. Separate doses by at least 2 hours.

▶ **Edema.** *Adults:* 20 to 80 mg P.O. daily in morning; second dose in 6 to 8 hours. Carefully adjust up to 600 mg daily if needed. Or 20 to 40 mg I.M. or I.V.; increase by 20 mg q 2 hours until desired response occurs. Give I.V. dose slowly over 1 to 2 minutes.
Infants and children: 2 mg/kg P.O. daily; increase by 1 to 2 mg/kg in 6 to 8 hours, if needed. Carefully adjust up to 6 mg/kg daily, if needed. Or 1 mg/kg slow IV; increase by 1 mg/kg q 2 hours until desired response.

▶ **Heart failure and chronic renal impairment.** *Adults:* 2 to 2.5 g daily P.O. or I.V. Maximum I.V. injection, 1 g daily over 30 minutes.

▶ **Hypertension.** *Adults:* 40 mg P.O. b.i.d. Adjust dosage according to response.

▶ **Hypercalcemia‡.** *Adults:* 80 to 100 mg I.V. q 1 to 2 hours. Or 120 mg P.O. daily.

I.V. administration

- Dilute with D_5W, normal saline solution, or lactated Ringer's solution,
- Infuse no more than 4 mg/minute to avoid ototoxicity.
- Give drug by direct injection over 1 to 2 minutes.
- Avoid exposing injection to light; it may discolor and become useable.
- Use prepared infusion solution within 24 hours.

⊗ Incompatibilities

Acidic solutions, aminoglycosides, amiodarone, ascorbic acid, bleomycin, buprenorphine, chlorpromazine, diazepam, dobutamine, doxapram, doxorubicin, droperidol, epinephrine, erythromycin, esmolol, fluconazole, fructose 10% in water, gentamicin, hydralazine, idarubicin, invert sugar 10% in electrolyte #2, isoproterenol, meperidine, metoclopramide, milrinone, morphine, netilmicin, norepinephrine, ondansetron, prochlorperazine, promethazine, quinidine, vinblastine, vincristine.

Contraindications and cautions

- Contraindicated in patients hypersensitive to drug or any of its components and in those with anuria.
- Use cautiously in patients with hepatic cirrhosis.
- Patients with allergy to sulfonamides may also be allergic to furosemide.

Lifespan: In pregnant women, use only if benefits outweigh risks to fetus. In breast-feeding women, don't use drug.

Adverse reactions

CNS: dizziness, fever, headache, paresthesia, restlessness, vertigo, weakness.
CV: orthostatic hypotension, thrombophlebitis (with I.V. use), volume depletion, dehydration.
EENT: blurred or yellow vision, transient deafness.
GI: abdominal discomfort, anorexia, constipation, diarrhea, nausea, ***pancreatitis,*** vomiting.
GU: azotemia, frequent urination, nocturia, oliguria, polyuria.
Hematologic: ***agranulocytosis,*** anemia, ***aplastic anemia, leukopenia, thrombocytopenia.***
Hepatic: hepatic dysfunction.
Metabolic: asymptomatic hyperuricemia; fluid and electrolyte imbalances, including dilutional hyponatremia, hypocalcemia, and hypomagnesemia; glucose intolerance; hyperglycemia; hypochloremic alkalosis; hypokalemia.
Musculoskeletal: muscle spasm.
Skin: dermatitis, photosensitivity, purpura.
Other: gout, transient pain at I.M. injection site.

Interactions

Drug-drug. *Aminoglycoside antibiotics, cisplatin:* May potentiate ototoxicity. Use together cautiously.
Amphotericin B, corticosteroids, corticotropin: May increase risk of hypokalemia. Monitor potassium level closely.
Antidiabetics: May decrease hypoglycemic effects. Monitor glucose level.
Antihypertensives: May increase risk of hypotension. Use together cautiously.
Chlorothiazide, chlorthalidone, hydrochlorothiazide, indapamide, metolazone: May cause excessive diuretic response, resulting in serious electrolyte abnormalities or dehydration. Adjust doses carefully while monitoring patient closely.
Digoxin, neuromuscular blockers: May increase toxicity from furosemide-induced hypokalemia. Monitor potassium level closely.
Ethacrynic acid: May increase risk of ototoxicity. Don't use together.
Lithium: May decrease lithium excretion, resulting in lithium toxicity. Monitor lithium level.
NSAIDs: May inhibit diuretic response. Use together cautiously.
Salicylates: May cause salicylate toxicity. Use together cautiously.
Drug-herb. *Aloe:* May increase drug effects. Monitor patient for dehydration.
Licorice: May cause rapid potassium loss. Monitor patient for hypokalemia; discourage licorice intake.
Drug-lifestyle. *Alcohol use:* May cause additive hypotensive and diuretic effect. Discourage use together.
Sun exposure: May cause photosensitivity reactions. Urge patient to avoid unprotected or prolonged sun exposure.

Effects on lab test results

- May increase glucose, cholesterol, and uric acid levels. May decrease potassium, sodium, calcium, magnesium, and hemoglobin levels and hematocrit.
- May decrease granulocyte, WBC, and platelet counts.

Pharmacokinetics

Absorption: 60% after P.O. use; unknown after I.M. use.
Distribution: 95% protein-bound.
Metabolism: Minimal.
Excretion: 50% to 80% in urine. *Half-life:* 30 minutes.

Route	Onset	Peak	Duration
P.O.	20–60 min	1–2 hr	6–8 hr
I.V.	5 min	30 min	2 hr
I.M.	Unknown	Unknown	Unknown

Action

Chemical effect: Inhibits sodium and chloride reabsorption at proximal and distal tubules and ascending loop of Henle.
Therapeutic effect: Promotes water and sodium excretion.

Available forms

Injection: 10 mg/ml
Oral solution: 40 mg/5 ml, 10 mg/ml
Tablets: 20 mg, 40 mg, 80 mg, 500 mg ♦

NURSING PROCESS

Assessment

- Assess patient's underlying condition before starting therapy.

• Monitor weight, peripheral edema, breath sounds, blood pressure, fluid intake and output, and electrolyte, glucose, BUN, and carbon dioxide levels.
• Monitor uric acid level, especially if patient has a history of gout.
• Be alert for adverse reactions and drug interactions.
• Assess patient's and family's knowledge of drug therapy.

Nursing diagnoses

• Excess fluid volume related to presence of edema
• Impaired urinary elimination related to diuretic therapy
• Deficient knowledge related to drug therapy

Planning and implementation

• Give a P.O. or I.M. dose in the morning to prevent nocturia. Give a second dose in early afternoon.
• Store tablets in light-resistant container to prevent discoloration. Don't use yellowed injectable preparation.
• Refrigerate oral furosemide solution to ensure drug stability.
• If oliguria or azotemia develops or increases, notify prescriber.

Patient teaching

• Advise patient to stand slowly to prevent dizziness, not to drink alcohol, and to minimize strenuous exercise in hot weather.
• Instruct patient to report ringing in ears, severe abdominal pain, or sore throat and fever because they may indicate toxicity.

ALERT: Discourage patient from storing different drugs in same container because this increases risk of errors. The most popular strengths of furosemide and digoxin are white tablets of similar size.

• Tell patient to check with prescriber before taking OTC drugs or herbal remedies.

Evaluation

• Patient is free from edema.
• Patient demonstrates adjustment of lifestyle to cope with altered patterns of urinary elimination.
• Patient and family state understanding of drug therapy.

G

gabapentin

(geh-buh-PEN-tin)
Gabarone, Neurontin

Pharmacologic class: anticonvulsant
Therapeutic class: anticonvulsant
Pregnancy risk category: C

Indications and dosages

▶ **Adjunct therapy of partial seizures with and without secondary generalization in patients with epilepsy.** *Adults and children older than age 12:* Initially, 300 mg P.O. t.i.d. Increase dosage gradually based on response. Dosages of 900 to 1,800 mg daily in three divided doses are effective for most patients. Dosages up to 3,600 mg daily are well tolerated.
Children ages 3 to 12: Starting dosage, 10 to 15 mg/kg P.O. daily in three divided doses; adjust over 3 days to reach effective dosage.
Children ages 5 to 12: Effective dosage, 25 to 35 mg/kg P.O. daily in three divided doses.
Children ages 3 to 4: Effective dosage, 40 mg/kg P.O. daily in three divided doses.

Adjust-a-dose: For adults and children age 12 and older with renal impairment or undergoing hemodialysis, if creatinine clearance is 30 to 59 ml/minute, give 400 to 1,400 mg P.O. daily, divided b.i.d. If clearance is 15 to 29 ml/minute, give 200 to 700 mg P.O. daily. If clearance is less than 15 ml/minute, give 100 to 300 mg P.O. daily; reduce dosage in proportion to creatinine clearance (for example, for patients with a clearance of 7.5 ml/minute, give one-half the dose that a patient with 15 ml/minute would receive).

For dialysis patients, maintenance dosages are based on estimated creatinine clearance. Give supplemental postdialysis dose of 125 to 350 mg after each 4 hours of dialysis.

▶ **Postherpetic neuralgia.** *Adults:* 300 mg P.O. once daily on day 1, then 300 mg b.i.d. on day 2, and 300 mg t.i.d. on day 3. Adjust as needed for pain relief to maximum daily dosage, 1,800 mg, divided t.i.d.

Contraindications and cautions

• Contraindicated in patients hypersensitive to the drug or any of its components.
Lifespan: In pregnant women, use cautiously. In breast-feeding women and in children younger than age 3, safety and effectiveness haven't been established. In children ages 3 to 12, use cautiously; drug may cause mild to moderate emotional lability, hostility, aggressive behavior, and hyperkinesias.

Adverse reactions

CNS: abnormal coordination, abnormal thinking, amnesia, *ataxia,* depression, *dizziness,* dysarthria, *fatigue,* nervousness, *nystagmus, somnolence, tremor,* twitching.
CV: peripheral edema, vasodilation.
EENT: *amblyopia, diplopia,* dry throat, pharyngitis, *rhinitis.*
GI: constipation, dry mouth, dyspepsia, nausea, vomiting.
GU: impotence.
Hematologic: ***leukopenia.***
Metabolic: increased appetite, weight gain.
Musculoskeletal: back pain, fractures, myalgia.
Respiratory: cough.
Skin: abrasion, pruritus.
Other: dental abnormalities.

Interactions

Drug-drug. *Antacids:* May decrease gabapentin absorption. Separate administration times by at least 2 hours.
Morphine: May increase gabapentin level and risk of CNS depression. Decrease dose of either drug.
Drug-lifestyle. *Alcohol use:* May increase CNS depression. Discourage use together.

Effects on lab test results

• May decrease WBC count.
• May cause false-positive tests for urine protein when using Ames-N-Multistix SG dipstick test.

Pharmacokinetics

Absorption: Bioavailability isn't dose-proportional but averages 60%.
Distribution: Circulates largely unbound to protein.
Metabolism: Insignificant.
Excretion: By kidneys as unchanged drug. *Half-life:* 5 to 7 hours.

Route	Onset	Peak	Duration
P.O.	Unknown	2–4 hr	Unknown

Action

Chemical effect: Unknown; although structurally related to GABA, drug doesn't interact with GABA receptors and isn't converted metabolically into GABA or a GABA agonist.
Therapeutic effect: Prevents and treats partial seizures and treats postherpetic neuralgia.

Available forms

Capsules: 100 mg, 300 mg, 400 mg
Solution: 250 mg/5 ml
Tablets (film-coated): 100 mg, 300 mg, 400 mg, 600 mg, 800 mg

NURSING PROCESS

Assessment

• Assess patient's disorder before starting therapy and regularly thereafter.
• Assess patient's renal function before starting therapy.
• Routine monitoring of level isn't needed. Drug doesn't appear to alter levels of other anticonvulsants.
• Be alert for adverse reactions and drug interactions.
• Assess patient's and family's knowledge of drug therapy.

Nursing diagnoses

• Risk for trauma related to seizures
• Risk for injury related to drug-induced adverse CNS reactions
• Deficient knowledge related to drug therapy

Planning and implementation

• Give first dose at bedtime to minimize drowsiness, dizziness, fatigue, and ataxia.
ALERT: If stopping drug or substituting another drug, do so gradually over at least 1 week to minimize risk of seizures. Don't abruptly stop other anticonvulsants when starting therapy.
• Take seizure precautions.
ALERT: Don't confuse Neurontin with Noroxin.

Patient teaching

• Tell patient drug can be taken with or without food.
• Warn patient to avoid hazardous activities until the drug's CNS effects are known.

Evaluation

- Patient is free from seizures.
- Patient has no injury from adverse CNS reactions.
- Patient and family state understanding of drug therapy.

galantamine hydrobromide

(gah-LAN-tah-meen high-droh-BROH-mighd)
Razadyne, Razadyne ER

Pharmacologic class: reversible, competitive acetylcholinesterase inhibitor
Therapeutic class: cholinomimetic
Pregnancy risk category: B

Indications and dosages

▶ **Mild to moderate dementia of Alzheimer type.** *Adults:* Initially, 4 mg P.O. b.i.d., preferably with morning and evening meals. If dose is well tolerated after minimum of 4 weeks of therapy, increase to 8 mg b.i.d. A further increase to 12 mg b.i.d. may be attempted only after at least 4 weeks of the previous dose. Recommended dosage range is 16 to 24 mg daily in two divided doses. Or if using the extended-release form, 8 mg P.O. once daily in the morning with food. Increase to 16 mg P.O. once daily after a minimum of 4 weeks. May further increase to 24 mg once daily after a minimum of 4 weeks, based on patient response and tolerability.

Adjust-a-dose: For patients with hepatic impairment (Child-Pugh score of 7 to 9), don't exceed 16 mg daily. For patients with a Child-Pugh score of 10 to 15, don't give drug. For patients with moderate renal impairment, don't exceed 16 mg daily. For patients with creatinine clearance less than 9 ml/minute, don't give drug. Adjusted dose is the same for regular and extended-release forms.

Contraindications and cautions

- Contraindicated in patients hypersensitive to the drug or any of its components.
- Use cautiously in patients with supraventricular cardiac conduction disorders and in those taking other drugs that significantly slow the heart rate. Use cautiously before or during procedures involving anesthesia with succinylcholine-type or other similar neuromuscular blockers. Use cautiously in patients with a history of peptic ulcer disease and in those taking NSAIDs. Because of the potential for cholinomimetic effects, use cautiously in patients with bladder outflow obstruction, seizures, asthma, or COPD.

Lifespan: In pregnant women, use only if benefits outweigh risks to fetus. In breast-feeding women, use cautiously because it's unknown if drug appears in breast milk. In children, safety and effectiveness haven't been established.

Adverse reactions

CNS: depression, dizziness, fatigue, headache, insomnia, somnolence, syncope, tremor.
CV: ***bradycardia,*** heart block.
EENT: rhinitis.
GI: abdominal pain, anorexia, *diarrhea,* dyspepsia, *nausea, vomiting.*
GU: hematuria, UTI.
Hematologic: anemia.
Metabolic: weight loss.

Interactions

Drug-drug. *Amitriptyline, fluoxetine, fluvoxamine, quinidine:* May decrease galantamine clearance. Monitor patient closely.
Anticholinergics: May antagonize activity of anticholinergics. Monitor patient.
Cholinergics (such as bethanechol, succinylcholine): May have a synergistic effect. Monitor patient closely. May need to avoid use before procedures using general anesthesia with succinylcholine-type neuromuscular blockers.
Cimetidine, erythromycin, ketoconazole, paroxetine: May increase bioavailability of galantamine. Monitor patient closely.

Effects on lab test results

- May decrease hemoglobin level and hematocrit.

Pharmacokinetics

Absorption: Rapid and good, with an oral bioavailability of about 90%. Levels peak in 1 hour. In elderly patients, levels are 30% to 40% higher than in young, healthy people.
Distribution: Mainly to blood. Protein-binding isn't significant.
Metabolism: In liver by CYP2D6 and CYP3A4 and glucuronidated. Using with inhibitors of

these enzyme systems may modestly increase bioavailability.
Excretion: In urine, unchanged, as glucuronide and metabolites. *Half-life:* About 7 hours.

Route	Onset	Peak	Duration
P.O.	Unknown	1 hr	Unknown

Action

Chemical effect: Unknown; may enhance cholinergic function by increasing acetylcholine level in the brain.
Therapeutic effect: Improves cognition in patients with Alzheimer disease.

Available forms

Oral solution: 4 mg/ml
Tablets: 4 mg, 8 mg, 12 mg
Capsules (extended-release): 8 mg, 16 mg, 24 mg

NURSING PROCESS

Assessment

- Assess underlying condition before starting therapy, and reassess regularly.
- Bradycardia and heart block have been reported in patients with and without underlying cardiac conduction abnormalities. Consider all patients at risk for adverse effects on cardiac conduction.
- Patients are at increased risk for gastric ulcers because of the potential for increased gastric acid secretion. Monitor patient closely for symptoms of active or occult GI bleeding.
- Assess patient's and family's knowledge of drug therapy.

Nursing diagnoses

- Risk for injury due to wandering related to Alzheimer disease
- Risk for imbalanced fluid volume related to drug-induced adverse GI reactions
- Deficient knowledge related to drug therapy

Planning and implementation

ALERT: Razadyne tablets should be given twice daily and Razadyne ER capsules once daily. To avoid errors, verify any prescription that suggests a different dosing schedule.

- Give drug with food and ensure adequate fluid intake to decrease the risk of nausea and vomiting.
- If drug is stopped for several days, restart at the lowest dose and increase, at a minimum of 4-week intervals, to the previous dose.
- Use proper technique when dispensing the oral solution with the pipette. Dispense measured amount in a liquid and give right away. Oral solution and tablets are bioequivalent.
- Don't give more than 16 mg daily in patients with moderate hepatic or renal impairment.
- In case of overdose, contact a poison control center. Treat symptoms and provide support. Atropine I.V. may be used as an antidote; give an initial dose of 0.5 to 1 mg and base subsequent doses on response. It's unknown if drug is removed by dialysis.

Patient teaching

- Advise patient or his caregiver that the conventional tablets should be taken with morning and evening meals and the extended-release capsules should be taken with the morning meal.
- Inform patient or caregiver that dosage increases should occur at no more than 4-week intervals.
- Explain that nausea and vomiting occur in less than 25% of patients.
- Advise patient or caregiver that following the recommended dosing and administration schedule can minimize common adverse effects.
- Tell patient or caregiver, if therapy is interrupted for several days or longer, to restart the drug at the lowest dose and increase based on the prescriber's dosing schedule.
- Advise patient or caregiver to report signs and symptoms of bradycardia immediately to the prescriber.
- Advise patient or caregiver that drug may enhance cognitive function, but may not alter the underlying disease process.

Evaluation

- Patient's cognition improves and tendency to wander decreases.
- Patient and family state that drug-induced adverse GI reactions haven't occurred.
- Patient and family state understanding of drug therapy.

ganciclovir (DHPG)

(gan-SIGH-kloh-veer)

Cytovene, Cytovene-IV

Pharmacologic class: synthetic nucleoside
Therapeutic class: antiviral
Pregnancy risk category: C

Indications and dosages

▶ **CMV retinitis in immunocompromised patients, including those with AIDS.** *Adults:* 5 mg/kg I.V. over 1 hour q 12 hours for 14 to 21 days, followed by 5 mg/kg I.V. daily for 7 days weekly, or 6 mg/kg I.V. daily for 5 of 7 days weekly. Or, following I.V. induction therapy, give 1,000 mg P.O. t.i.d. with food or 500 mg P.O. six times a day q 3 hours with food while awake.

▶ **To prevent CMV disease in transplant recipients at risk for CMV disease.** *Adults:* 5 mg/kg I.V. over 1 hour q 12 hours for 7 to 14 days, followed by 5 mg/kg I.V. once daily, or 6 mg/kg I.V. once daily for 5 of 7 days weekly. Alternatively, 1,000 mg P.O. t.i.d. with food. Length of therapy in transplant recipients depends on duration and degree of immunosuppression.

▶ **To prevent CMV disease in patients with advanced HIV infection at risk for development of CMV disease.** *Adults:* 1,000 mg P.O. t.i.d. with food.

▶ **Other CMV infections‡.** *Adults:* 5 mg/kg I.V. over 1 hour q 12 hours for 14 to 21 days. Or 2.5 mg/kg I.V. over 1 hour q 8 hours for 14 to 21 days.

Adjust-a-dose: For patients with renal impairment, adjust dosage according to the table at the top of page 603. For patients receiving hemodialysis, see dosages for creatinine clearance greater than 10 ml/minute.

I.V. administration

- Reconstitute with 10 ml sterile water for injection. Shake vial to dissolve drug.
- Further dilute appropriate dose in normal saline solution, D_5W, Ringer's lactate, or Ringer's solution (typically 100 ml).
- Use caution when preparing alkaline solution.
- Infuse over 1 hour. Faster infusions will cause increased toxicity. Never exceed recommended infusion rate. Use infusion pump. Don't give as I.V. bolus or by rapid infusion.
- Infusion concentrations greater than 10 mg/ml aren't recommended.

⊗ **Incompatibilities**

Aldesleukin, amifostine, aztreonam, cefepime, cytarabine, doxorubicin hydrochloride, fludarabine, foscarnet, ondansetron, paraben (bacteriostatic agent), piperacillin sodium with tazobactam, sargramostim, vinorelbine. Manufacturer recommends not giving with other I.V. drugs.

Contraindications and cautions

- Contraindicated in patients hypersensitive to ganciclovir or acyclovir. Patients with allergies to acyclovir may also react to ganciclovir. Also contraindicated in those with absolute neutrophil count below 500/mm^3 or platelet count below 25,000/mm^3.
- Use cautiously and at a lower dosage in patients with renal impairment.

Lifespan: In pregnant women, use only if benefits outweigh risks to the fetus. In breast-feeding women, use cautiously because it isn't known if drug appears in breast milk. In children, safety and effectiveness haven't been established.

Adverse reactions

CNS: altered dreams, ataxia, behavioral changes, ***coma,*** confusion, dizziness, headache, pain, ***seizures.***
CV: ***arrhythmias,*** hypertension, hypotension.
EENT: retinal detachment in CMV retinitis.
GI: anorexia, diarrhea, nausea, vomiting.
GU: hematuria.
Hematologic: ***agranulocytosis,*** anemia, ***granulocytopenia, leukopenia, thrombocytopenia.***
Other: inflammation, phlebitis at injection site.

Interactions

Drug-drug. *Cytotoxic drugs:* May increase toxic effects, especially hematologic effects and stomatitis. Monitor patient closely.
Imipenem and cilastatin: May heighten seizure activity. Monitor patient closely.
Immunosuppressants (such as azathioprine, corticosteroids, cyclosporine): May enhance immune and bone marrow suppression. Use together cautiously.
Probenecid: May increase ganciclovir level. Monitor patient closely.

Creatinine clearance (ml/min)	Initial I.V. dosage Dose (mg/kg)	Interval	Maintenance I.V. dosage Dose (mg/kg)	Interval	P.O. dosage Dose (mg)	Interval
50–69	2.5	12 hr	2.5	24 hr	1,500 500	24 hr 8 hr
25–49	2.5	24 hr	1.25	24 hr	1,000 500	24 hr 12 hr
10–24	1.25	24 hr	0.625	24 hr	500	24 hr
< 10	1.25	3 times/wk	0.625	3 times/wk	500	3 times/wk

Zidovudine: May increase risk of granulocytopenia. Monitor patient closely.

Effects on lab test results

- May increase creatinine, ALT, AST, GGT, and alkaline phosphatase levels. May decrease hemoglobin level and hematocrit.
- May decrease granulocyte, platelet, neutrophil, and WBC counts.

Pharmacokinetics

Absorption: Poor. Bioavailability is about 5% under fasting conditions.
Distribution: Concentrates in CMV-infected cells.
Metabolism: Less than 10%.
Excretion: Mostly unchanged. *Half-life:* About 3 hours.

Route	Onset	Peak	Duration
P.O.	Unknown	3 hr	Unknown
I.V.	Immediate	Immediate	Unknown

Action

Chemical effect: Unknown, may inhibit viral DNA synthesis of CMV.
Therapeutic effect: Inhibits CMV.

Available forms

Capsules: 250 mg, 500 mg
Injection: 500 mg/vial

NURSING PROCESS

Assessment

- Assess patient's condition before starting therapy and regularly thereafter.
- Obtain CBC, neutrophil, and platelet counts every 2 days during twice-daily ganciclovir use and at least weekly thereafter.
- Monitor hydration if adverse GI reaction occurs with oral drug.
- Be alert for adverse reactions and drug interactions.
- Assess patient's and family's knowledge of drug therapy.

Nursing diagnoses

- Risk for infection related to CMV retinitis
- Ineffective protection related to adverse hematologic reactions
- Deficient knowledge related to drug therapy

Planning and implementation

- Give oral form of drug with food.

ALERT: Don't give drug subcutaneously or I.M. because severe tissue irritation could result.

ALERT: Encourage fluid intake; ensure adequate hydration during drug infusion.

- Alert prescriber to signs of renal impairment because the dosage will need adjustment.
- Capsules are linked to a risk of rapid progression of CMV retinitis. Don't use capsules for induction therapy; use only as maintenance therapy in patients who benefit from not taking drug I.V.

Patient teaching

- Tell patient to take oral form of drug with food.
- Stress importance of drinking adequate fluids throughout therapy.
- Advise patient to report pain or discomfort at I.V. site.
- Instruct patient about infection-control and bleeding precautions.

Evaluation

- Patient is free from infection.
- Patient has no serious adverse hematologic reactions.

• Patient and family state understanding of drug therapy.

gatifloxacin ophthalmic solution

(gah-ti-FLOCKS-ah-sin off-THAL-mick suh-LOO-shun)
Zymar

Pharmacologic class: fluoroquinolone
Therapeutic class: antibiotic
Pregnancy risk category: C

Indications and dosages

▶ **Bacterial conjunctivitis.** *Adults and children age 1 and older:* While patient is awake, instill 1 drop into affected eyes q 2 hours up to eight times daily for 2 days. Then, instill 1 drop up to q.i.d. for 5 more days.

Contraindications and cautions

• Contraindicated in patients hypersensitive to the drug or any of its components or to quinolones or any of their components.

Lifespan: In pregnant women, use cautiously. In breast-feeding women, use cautiously because it's unknown if the drug appears in breast milk. In children younger than age 1 year, drug is contraindicated.

Adverse reactions

CNS: headache.
EENT: chemosis, conjunctival hemorrhage, *conjunctival irritation,* discharge, dry eyes, eye irritation, eyelid edema, *increased lacrimation, keratitis,* pain, *papillary conjunctivitis,* red eyes, reduced visual acuity.
GI: taste disturbance.

Interactions

None reported.

Effects on lab test results

None reported.

Pharmacokinetics

Absorption: Unknown.
Distribution: Unknown.
Metabolism: Unknown.
Excretion: Unknown. *Half-life:* Unknown.

Route	Onset	Peak	Duration
Ophthalmic	Unknown	Unknown	Unknown

Action

Chemical effect: Inhibits DNA gyrase and topoisomerase, preventing cell replication and division.
Therapeutic effect: Kills susceptible bacteria.

Available forms

Solution: 0.3% in 2.5- and 5-ml bottles

NURSING PROCESS

Assessment

• Monitor therapy for effectiveness.
• Monitor patient for adverse reactions.
• Assess patient's and family's knowledge of drug therapy.

Nursing diagnoses

• Disturbed sensory perception (visual) related to eye infection
• Deficient knowledge related to drug therapy

Planning and implementation

• Don't inject solution subconjunctivally or into the anterior chamber of the eye.
• Systemic drug causes serious hypersensitivity reactions. If allergic reaction occurs, stop giving the drug and treat symptoms.
• Monitor patient for superinfection.

Patient teaching

• Tell patient to immediately stop taking the drug and seek medical treatment if evidence of a serious allergic reaction develops, such as itching, rash, swelling of the face or throat, or difficulty breathing.
• Tell patient not to wear contact lenses.
• Warn patient to avoid touching the applicator tip to anything, including eyes and fingers.
• Teach patient that prolonged use may encourage infections with nonsusceptible bacteria.

Evaluation

• Patient recovers from infection.
• Patient and family state understanding of drug therapy.

gemfibrozil

(jem-FIGH-broh-zil)

Apo-Gemfibrozil ♦, Gen-Fibro ♦, Lopid, Novo-Gemfibrozil ♦, Nu-Gemfibrozil ♦

Pharmacologic class: fibric acid derivative
Therapeutic class: antilipemic
Pregnancy risk category: C

Indications and dosages

▶ **Type IV and V hyperlipidemia unresponsive to diet and other drugs; reduction of risk of coronary heart disease in patients with type IIb hyperlipidemia who can't tolerate or who are refractory to therapy with bile acid sequestrants or niacin.** *Adults:* 1,200 mg P.O. daily in two divided doses, 30 minutes before morning and evening meals. If no benefit occurs after 3 months, stop drug.

Contraindications and cautions

• Contraindicated in patients hypersensitive to the drug or any of its components and in those with hepatic or severe renal dysfunction (including primary biliary cirrhosis) or gallbladder disease.

Lifespan: In pregnant women, use cautiously. In breast-feeding women and in children, safety and effectiveness haven't been established.

Adverse reactions

CNS: blurred vision, dizziness, fatigue, headache.
GI: *abdominal and epigastric pain,* diarrhea, *dyspepsia,* flatulence, nausea, taste perversion, vomiting.
Hematologic: ***bone marrow hypoplasia, leukopenia, severe anemia, thrombocytopenia.***
Hepatic: bile duct obstruction, gallstones.
Musculoskeletal: painful limbs, ***rhabdomyolysis.***
Skin: dermatitis, pruritus, rash.

Interactions

Drug-drug. *Cyclosporine:* May decrease cyclosporine effects. Monitor cyclosporine level.
HMG-CoA reductase inhibitors: May lead to myopathy with rhabdomyolysis. Don't use together.
Oral anticoagulants: May increase effects of oral anticoagulants. Monitor patient.
Repaglinide: May increase repaglinide level. Avoid use together.

Effects on lab test results

• May increase ALT, AST, and CK levels. May decrease potassium and hemoglobin levels and hematocrit.
• May decrease eosinophil, WBC, and platelet counts.

Pharmacokinetics

Absorption: Good.
Distribution: 95% protein-bound.
Metabolism: By liver.
Excretion: Mainly in urine. *Half-life:* 1¼ hours.

Route	Onset	Peak	Duration
P.O.	2–5 days	> 4 wk	Unknown

Action

Chemical effect: Inhibits peripheral lipolysis and also reduces triglyceride synthesis in liver.
Therapeutic effect: Lowers triglyceride levels and raises HDL levels.

Available forms

Tablets: 600 mg

NURSING PROCESS

Assessment

• Obtain patient's triglyceride and HDL levels before starting therapy and regularly thereafter.
• Obtain CBC and liver function tests periodically during first 12 months of therapy.
• Be alert for adverse reactions and drug interactions.
• Assess patient's and family's knowledge of drug therapy.

Nursing diagnoses

• Risk for injury related to elevated blood lipids and cholesterol levels
• Diarrhea related to drug's adverse effect on GI tract
• Deficient knowledge related to drug therapy

Planning and implementation

• Give drug 30 minutes before breakfast and dinner.

• Make sure patient is following standard low-cholesterol diet.

Patient teaching

• Instruct patient to take drug 30 minutes before breakfast and dinner.

• Teach patient dietary management of lipids (restricting total fat and cholesterol intake) and measures to control other cardiac disease risk factors. If appropriate, suggest weight control, exercise, and smoking cessation programs.

• Advise patient to avoid driving or other potentially hazardous activities until drug's CNS effects are known.

• Tell patient to observe bowel movements and to report signs of steatorrhea or bile duct obstruction (nausea, vomiting, abdominal or epigastric pain, and diarrhea).

Evaluation

• Patient's triglyceride and cholesterol levels are normal.

• Patient regains normal bowel patterns.

• Patient and family state understanding of drug therapy.

gemifloxacin mesylate

(geh-mih-FLOCKS-a-sin MESS-ih-late)

Factive

Pharmacologic class: fluoroquinolone
Therapeutic class: antibacterial
Pregnancy risk category: C

Indications and dosages

▶ **Acute bacterial exacerbation of chronic bronchitis caused by *Streptococcus pneumoniae, Haemophilus influenzae, Haemophilus parainfluenzae, Moraxella catarrhalis.*** *Adults:* 320 mg P.O. once daily for 5 days.

▶ **Mild to moderate community-acquired pneumonia caused by *S. pneumoniae* (including penicillin-resistant strains), *H. influenzae, M. catarrhalis, Mycoplasma pneumoniae, Chlamydia pneumoniae, Klebsiella pneumoniae.*** *Adults:* 320 mg P.O. once daily for 7 days.

Adjust-a-dose: For patients with renal impairment, if creatinine clearance is 40 ml/minute or less or if patient receives routine hemodialysis or continuous ambulatory peritoneal dialysis, reduce dosage to 160 mg P.O. once daily.

Contraindications and cautions

• Contraindicated in patients hypersensitive to fluoroquinolones or any of their components, those with a history of prolonged QT interval, those with uncorrected electrolyte disorders, and those taking a class IA or III antiarrhythmic.

• Use cautiously in patients with epilepsy, predisposition to seizures, or renal impairment.

Lifespan: In pregnant women, use only if benefits outweigh risks to fetus. In breast-feeding women, use cautiously because it isn't known if drug appears in breast milk. In children, safety and effectiveness of drug haven't been established.

Adverse reactions

CNS: dizziness, fatigue, headache.
GI: abdominal pain, diarrhea, nausea, ***pseudomembranous colitis,*** vomiting.
Musculoskeletal: ruptured tendons.
Skin: rash.
Other: ***hypersensitivity reactions.***

Interactions

Drug-drug. *Antacids (magnesium or aluminum), didanosine, iron, multivitamins containing metal cations (such as zinc), sucralfate:* May decrease gemifloxacin level. Give gemifloxacin at least 3 hours before or 2 hours after these drugs.

Antiarrhythmics (amiodarone, procainamide, quinidine, sotalol): May increase risk of prolonged QT interval. Avoid use together.

Drugs that affect QT interval (such as antidepressants, antipsychotics, erythromycin): May increase risk of prolonged QT interval. Use together cautiously.

Probenecid: May increase gemifloxacin level. Use together cautiously.

Warfarin: May increase anticoagulation effects. Monitor patient's PT and INR.

Drug-lifestyle. *Sun exposure:* May increase risk of photosensitivity. Discourage excessive or unprotected exposure to ultraviolet light or sunlight.

Effects on lab test results

• May increase ALT and AST levels.

Pharmacokinetics

Absorption: Rapid and unaffected by food.
Distribution: Wide, especially to lung tissue and fluids. 60% to 70% protein-bound.
Metabolism: Limited, mainly hepatic; some minor metabolites formed.
Excretion: In feces and urine as unchanged drug and metabolites. *Half-life:* 4 to 12 hours.

Route	Onset	Peak	Duration
P.O.	Unknown	½–2 hr	Unknown

Action

Chemical effect: Prevents cell growth by inhibiting DNA gyrase and topoisomerase IV, which interferes with DNA synthesis.
Therapeutic effect: Kills susceptible bacteria.

Available forms

Tablets: 320 mg

NURSING PROCESS

Assessment

- Serious and occasionally fatal hypersensitivity reaction may occur. Monitor patient carefully.
- Drug may cause CNS effects, such as tremors and anxiety. Monitor patient carefully.
- Carefully monitor patient's liver enzyme levels. Liver enzyme levels may rise during therapy but will resolve afterward.
- Assess patient's and family's knowledge of drug therapy.

Nursing diagnoses

- Risk for infection related to presence of bacteria susceptible to drug
- Risk for injury related to adverse effects of drug therapy
- Deficient knowledge related to drug therapy

Planning and implementation

- Rash is more likely to appear in a patient younger than age 40, especially women and those taking hormone therapy. Stop giving drug if rash appears.
- Drug may cause tendon rupture, arthropathy, or osteochondrosis. Stop drug if patient reports pain, inflammation, or signs of muscle rupture.
- If patient has a photosensitivity reaction, stop giving drug.
- Serious diarrhea may indicate pseudomembranous colitis. Stop drug if needed.
- Keep patient adequately hydrated to avoid concentration of urine.
- In acute overdose, empty patient's stomach by inducing vomiting or performing gastric lavage. Hydrate patient if needed, and continue treating symptoms. Hemodialysis removes 20% to 30% of a dose.

Patient teaching

- Instruct patient to finish full course of therapy, even if symptoms improve.
- Tell patient to stop drug and seek medical care if evidence of hypersensitivity reaction develops.
- Tell patient to report serious diarrhea.
- Instruct patient to drink fluids liberally.
- Warn patient against taking OTC drugs or dietary supplements with this drug without consulting prescriber.
- Tell patient to avoid excessive exposure to sunlight or ultraviolet light.
- Urge patient to report pain, inflammation, or rupture of tendons.
- Warn patient to avoid driving or other hazardous activities until effects of drug are known.

Evaluation

- Patient is free from infection after drug treatment.
- Patient remains free from injury from adverse reactions.
- Patient and family state understanding of drug therapy.

gemtuzumab ozogamicin

(gem-TOO-zuh-mab oh-zoh-GAM-ih-sin)
Mylotarg

Pharmacologic class: monoclonal antibody
Therapeutic class: chemotherapeutic drug
Pregnancy risk category: D

Indications and dosages

▶ **Patients with CD33-positive acute myeloid leukemia in first relapse who are not considered candidates for cytotoxic chemotherapy.** *Adults age 60 and older:* 9 mg/m² I.V. infusion over 2 hours q 14 days for a total of two doses. One hour before the infusion, give 50 mg of diphenhydramine P.O. and 650 to 1,000 mg of acetaminophen P.O. Additional doses of acetaminophen 650 to 1,000 mg P.O. can be given q 4 hours, p.r.n.

I.V. administration

- During preparation and administration, protect from direct and indirect sunlight and unshielded fluorescent light.
- Administer in 100 ml of normal saline injection. Place the 100-ml I.V. bag into an ultraviolet light protectant bag. Use drug solution in I.V. bag immediately.
- Use a separate I.V. line equipped with a low–protein-binding 1.2-micron terminal filter for administration of drug. May be infused by central or peripheral line.
- Don't give I.V. push or bolus.
- Monitor vital signs during infusion and for 4 hours after infusion.

Incompatibilities
None reported.

Contraindications and cautions

- Contraindicated in patients hypersensitive to drug or any of its components.
- Use cautiously in patients with hepatic impairment.

Lifespan: Drug is indicated only for adults age 60 and older. In pregnant women, avoid using drug. Advise women of childbearing age not to become pregnant. Breast-feeding women should stop nursing or stop taking drug. It's unknown whether drug appears in breast milk. In children, safety and effectiveness haven't been established.

Adverse reactions

CNS: *asthenia, depression, dizziness, fever, headache, insomnia, pain.*
CV: hypertension, hypotension, tachycardia.
EENT: *epistaxis, pharyngitis, rhinitis.*
GI: *abdominal pain, anorexia, constipation, diarrhea, dyspepsia, enlarged abdomen, nausea, stomatitis, vomiting.*
GU: *hematuria,* **VAGINAL HEMORRHAGE.**
Hematologic: *anemia,* **BLEEDING, LEUKOPENIA, NEUTROPENIA, NEUTROPENIC FEVER, SEVERE MYELOSUPPRESSION, THROMBOCYTOPENIA.**
Hepatic: ***hepatotoxicity, hyperbilirubinemia, veno-occlusive disease.***
Metabolic: hyperglycemia, hypokalemia, ***hypomagnesemia.***
Musculoskeletal: arthralgia, back pain.
Respiratory: ***acute respiratory distress syndrome,*** dyspnea, ***hypoxia,*** *increased cough,* pneumonia, ***pulmonary edema.***
Skin: *rash.*
Other: chills, herpes simplex, **SEPSIS, *severe hypersensitivity reactions.***

Interactions

None reported.

Effects on lab test results

- May increase liver enzyme, LDH, and glucose levels. May decrease potassium, magnesium, and hemoglobin levels and hematocrit.
- May decrease leukocyte, neutrophil, and platelet counts.

Pharmacokinetics

Absorption: Given I.V.
Distribution: Unknown.
Metabolism: Unknown. Liver microsomal enzymes may be involved.
Excretion: Unknown. *Half-life:* Total and unconjugated calicheamicin, 45 and 100 hours, respectively, after the first dose. After the second dose, total calicheamicin, 60 hours.

Route	Onset	Peak	Duration
I.V.	Unknown	Unknown	Unknown

Action

Chemical effect: May bind to CD33 antigen on the surface of leukemic blasts in patients with acute myeloid leukemia, resulting in formation of a complex that's internalized by the cell. The calicheamicin derivative is then released inside the cell, causing DNA double-strand breaks and cell death.
Therapeutic effect: Kills cancer cells.

Available forms

Powder for injection: 5 mg

NURSING PROCESS

Assessment

- Monitor CBC and platelets before starting and during therapy.
- Monitor liver enzymes before and during therapy.

• Monitor patient for postinfusion reactions and tumor lysis syndrome.
• Monitor I.V. site for local reactions.
• Assess patient's and family's knowledge of drug therapy.

Nursing diagnoses

• Risk for injury related to adverse effects of drug
• Risk for infection related to drug-induced adverse hematologic reactions
• Deficient knowledge related to drug therapy

Planning and implementation

• Use only under the supervision of a prescriber experienced in the use of cancer drugs.
• Drug may produce a postinfusion symptom complex in the 24 hours immediately after the infusion; symptoms include chills, fever, hypotension, hypertension, hyperglycemia, hypoxia, or dyspnea.
• Tumor lysis syndrome may occur. Provide adequate hydration, and treat with allopurinol to prevent hyperuricemia.
• Drug isn't dialyzable.
• Severe myelosuppression will occur in all patients given the recommended dose. Careful hematologic monitoring is required.
• Monitor electrolytes, hepatic function, CBC, and platelets during therapy.

Patient teaching

• Inform patient about postinfusion symptoms, and instruct him to continue to take acetaminophen 650 to 1,000 mg q 4 hours p.r.n.
• Tell patient to watch for signs of infection (fever, sore throat, and fatigue) and bleeding (easy bruising, nosebleeds, bleeding gums, and melena). Tell patient to take temperature daily, before acetaminophen dose.

Evaluation

• Patient remains free from infection.
• Patient's laboratory values remain above critical levels throughout course of therapy.
• Patient and family state understanding of drug therapy.

gentamicin sulfate

(jen-tuh-MIGH-sin SUL-fayt)
Cidomycin ♦, Garamycin, Gentamicin Sulfate ADD-Vantage, Jenamicin

Pharmacologic class: aminoglycoside
Therapeutic class: antibiotic
Pregnancy risk category: D

Indications and dosages

▶ **Serious infections caused by sensitive strains of *Pseudomonas aeruginosa, Escherichia coli, Proteus, Klebsiella, Serratia, Enterobacter, Citrobacter, Staphylococcus.*** *Adults:* 3 mg/kg daily in divided doses I.M. or I.V. q 8 hours. For life-threatening infections, up to 5 mg/kg daily in three to four divided doses. Reduce to 3 mg/kg daily as soon as indicated.
Children: 2 to 2.5 mg/kg I.M. or I.V. q 8 hours.
Neonates older than age 1 week and infants: 2.5 mg/kg I.M. or I.V. q 8 hours.
Preterm infants and neonates age 1 week and younger: 2.5 mg/kg I.V. q 12 hours.
▶ **Meningitis.** *Adults:* 3 mg/kg daily in divided doses I.M. or I.V. q 8 hours. For life-threatening infections, up to 5 mg/kg daily in three to four divided doses. Reduce to 3 mg/kg daily as soon as indicated. Or 4 to 8 mg intrathecally daily.
Children and infants older than age 3 months: 2 to 2.5 mg/kg I.M. or I.V. q 8 hours. Or 1 to 2 mg intrathecally daily.
▶ **Endocarditis prophylaxis for GI or GU procedure or surgery.** *Adults:* 1.5 mg/kg to maximum dose, 80 mg, I.M. or I.V. 30 to 60 minutes before procedure or surgery. Give separately with ampicillin I.M. or I.V. followed in 6 hours by ampicillin or amoxicillin alone.
Children: 2 mg/kg I.M. or I.V. 30 to 60 minutes before procedure or surgery. Give separately with ampicillin I.M. or I.V. followed in 6 hours by ampicillin or amoxicillin alone.
▶ **Posthemodialysis to maintain therapeutic level.** *Adults:* 1 to 1.7 mg/kg I.M. or I.V. after each dialysis session.
Children: 2 to 2.5 mg/kg I.M. or by I.V. infusion after each dialysis session.

I.V. administration

• When giving drug by intermittent I.V. infusion, dilute with 50 to 200 ml of D_5W or normal saline injection.

• Infuse over 30 minutes to 2 hours.
• After infusion, flush line with normal saline solution or D_5W.

⊗ Incompatibilities

Allopurinol, amphotericin B, ampicillin, azithromycin, cefazolin, cefepime, cefotaxime, ceftazidime, ceftriaxone sodium, cefuroxime, certain parenteral nutrition formulations, cytarabine, dopamine, fat emulsions, furosemide, heparin, hetastarch, idarubicin, indomethacin sodium trihydrate, nafcillin, propofol, ticarcillin, warfarin.

Contraindications and cautions

• Contraindicated in patients hypersensitive to drug or other aminoglycosides.
• Use cautiously in patients with renal impairment or neuromuscular disorders.

Lifespan: In pregnant women, don't use because drug is teratogenic. Beast-feeding women should stop the drug or stop breast-feeding. In neonates, infants, and the elderly, use drug cautiously.

Adverse reactions

CNS: headache, lethargy, numbness, paresthesias, peripheral neuropathy, ***neurotoxicity, seizures,*** twitching.
EENT: *ototoxicity.*
GU: NEPHROTOXICITY.
Hematologic: ***agranulocytosis, leukopenia, thrombocytopenia.***
Other: hypersensitivity reactions.

Interactions

Drug-drug. *Acyclovir, amphotericin B, cisplatin, methoxyflurane, other aminoglycosides, vancomycin:* May increase ototoxicity and nephrotoxicity. Use together cautiously.
Atracurium, pancuronium, rocuronium, vecuronium: May increase neuromuscular blockade. Monitor patient closely.
Cephalothin: May increase nephrotoxicity. Use together cautiously; monitor renal function.
Dimenhydrinate: May mask symptoms of ototoxicity. Use with caution.
Diuretics: May increase ototoxicity. Avoid use together.
General anesthetics: May increase effects of nondepolarizing muscle relaxant, including prolonged respiratory depression. Use together only when necessary.
Indomethacin: May decrease renal clearance of gentamicin, leading to increased risk of toxicity.
I.V. loop diuretics (such as furosemide): May increase ototoxicity. Use cautiously.
Neurotoxic drugs: May increase neurotoxicity. Avoid use together.
Parenteral penicillins (such as ampicillin, ticarcillin): May inactivate gentamicin in vitro. Don't mix together.

Effects on lab test results

• May increase BUN, creatinine, nonprotein nitrogen, ALT, AST, bilirubin, and LDH levels. May decrease hemoglobin level and hematocrit.
• May increase eosinophil count. May decrease WBC, platelet, and granulocyte counts.

Pharmacokinetics

Absorption: Rapid and complete after I.M. use.
Distribution: Wide. CSF penetration is low even in adults with inflamed meninges. CSF levels are higher in neonates than adults. Protein-binding is minimal.
Metabolism: None.
Excretion: Mainly in urine. *Half-life:* 2 to 3 hours.

Route	Onset	Peak	Duration
I.V.	Immediate	15–30 min	Unknown
I.M.	Unknown	30–90 min	Unknown
Intrathecal	Unknown	Unknown	Unknown

Action

Chemical effect: Inhibits protein synthesis by binding to ribosomes.
Therapeutic effect: Kills susceptible bacteria (many aerobic gram-negative organisms and some aerobic gram-positive organisms). Drug may act against some aminoglycoside-resistant bacteria.

Available forms

Injection: 40 mg/ml (adult), 10 mg/ml (pediatric), 2 mg/ml (intrathecal)
I.V. infusion (premixed): 40 mg, 60 mg, 70 mg, 80 mg, 90 mg, 100 mg, 120 mg, 160 mg, 180 mg available in normal saline solution

NURSING PROCESS

Assessment

• Assess patient's infection and hearing before starting therapy and regularly thereafter.

• Obtain specimen for culture and sensitivity tests before giving the first dose. Begin therapy pending test results.
• Weigh patient and review baseline renal function studies before therapy and regularly during therapy. Notify prescriber of any changes; adjust dosage.
• Obtain blood for peak drug level 1 hour after I.M. injection and 30 minutes to 1 hour after I.V. infusion; for trough levels, draw blood just before next dose. Don't collect blood in heparinized tube because heparin is incompatible with aminoglycosides.
• Peak level above 12 mcg/ml and trough level above 2 mcg/ml may increase risk of toxicity.
• Be alert for adverse reactions and drug interactions.
• Assess patient's and family's knowledge of drug therapy.

Nursing diagnoses

• Risk for infection related to presence of susceptible bacteria
• Impaired urinary elimination related to nephrotoxicity
• Deficient knowledge related to drug therapy

Planning and implementation

• Give I.M. injection deep into large muscle mass (gluteal or midlateral thigh); rotate injection sites. Don't inject more than 2 g of drug per site.
ALERT: Use preservative-free forms of gentamicin for intrathecal route.
• Hemodialysis (8 hours) removes up to 50% of drug.
• Notify prescriber about signs of decreasing renal function or changes in hearing.
• Therapy usually continues for 7 to 10 days. If no response occurs in 3 to 5 days, therapy may be stopped and new specimens obtained for culture and sensitivity testing.
• Therapeutic peak and trough levels are 4 to 12 mcg/ml and less than 2 mcg/ml, respectively.
• Make sure patient is well hydrated to minimize chemical irritation of renal tubules.

Patient teaching

• Instruct patient to notify prescriber about adverse reactions, such as changes in hearing.
• Emphasize importance of drinking at least 2 L of fluids daily, if not contraindicated.

Evaluation

• Patient is free from infection.
• Patient maintains normal renal function throughout drug therapy.
• Patient and family state understanding of drug therapy.

glimepiride

(gligh-MEH-peh-righd)
Amaryl

Pharmacologic class: sulfonylurea
Therapeutic class: antidiabetic
Pregnancy risk category: C

Indications and dosages

▶ **Type 2 diabetes mellitus when hyperglycemia can't be managed by diet and exercise alone.** *Adults:* Initially, 1 to 2 mg P.O. once daily with first main meal of day. Usual maintenance dosage is 1 to 4 mg P.O. once daily. After reaching 2 mg, increase dosage in increments not exceeding 2 mg q 1 to 2 weeks, based on patient's response. Maximum, 8 mg daily.
▶ **Adjunct to insulin therapy in patients with type 2 diabetes mellitus whose hyperglycemia can't be managed by diet and exercise with oral antidiabetics.** *Adults:* 8 mg P.O. once daily with first main meal of day with low-dose insulin. Adjust insulin upward weekly based on patient's response.
▶ **Adjunct to metformin therapy in patients with type 2 diabetes mellitus whose hyperglycemia can't be managed by diet, exercise, and glimepiride or metformin alone.** *Adults:* 8 mg P.O. once daily with first main meal of the day with metformin. Adjust dosages based on patient's blood glucose response to determine minimum effective dosage of each drug.
Adjust-a-dose: For patients with renal or hepatic impairment, initial dose is 1 mg P.O. daily with breakfast; then adjust based on the patient's fasting glucose levels.

Contraindications and cautions

• Contraindicated in patients hypersensitive to the drug or any of its components, in those with diabetic ketoacidosis, and in those with allergies to sulfonamides or thiazide diuretics.

• Use cautiously in debilitated or malnourished patients and in those with adrenal, pituitary, hepatic, or renal insufficiency.

Lifespan: In pregnant and breast-feeding women, drug is contraindicated. In children, safety and effectiveness haven't been established. In elderly patients, use cautiously because they might be more sensitive to the drug.

Adverse reactions

CNS: asthenia, dizziness, headache.
EENT: changes in accommodation.
GI: nausea.
Hematologic: ***agranulocytosis, aplastic anemia,*** hemolytic anemia, ***leukopenia, pancytopenia, thrombocytopenia.***
Hepatic: cholestatic jaundice.
Metabolic: ***hypoglycemia.***
Skin: allergic skin reactions.

Interactions

Drug-drug. *Beta blockers:* May mask symptoms of hypoglycemia. Monitor glucose level carefully.
Drugs that produce hyperglycemia, thiazides and other diuretics: May lead to loss of glucose control. May require dosage adjustment.
Insulin: May increase risk of hypoglycemia. Monitor glucose level closely.
NSAIDs, other highly protein-bound drugs: May increase hypoglycemic action of sulfonylureas, such as glimepiride. Monitor patient carefully.
Drug-herb. *Aloe, bilberry leaf, bitter melon, burdock, dandelion, fenugreek, garlic, ginseng:* May improve glucose control, which may allow reduction of oral hypoglycemic. Tell patient to discuss herbs with prescriber before use.
Drug-lifestyle. *Alcohol use:* May alter glycemic control, most commonly toward hypoglycemia. May cause disulfiram-like reaction. Discourage use together.
Sun exposure: May cause photosensitivity. Discourage prolonged or unprotected exposure to the sun.

Effects on lab test results

• May increase BUN, creatinine, alkaline phosphatase, ALT, and AST levels. May decrease glucose, sodium, and hemoglobin levels and hematocrit.
• May decrease WBC, RBC, platelet, and granulocyte counts.

Pharmacokinetics

Absorption: Complete.
Distribution: Almost completely protein-bound.
Metabolism: Complete.
Excretion: In urine and feces. *Half-life:* 9 hours.

Route	Onset	Peak	Duration
P.O.	≤ 1 hr	2–3 hr	24 hr

Action

Chemical effect: Stimulates release of insulin from pancreatic beta cells; increases sensitivity of peripheral tissues to insulin.
Therapeutic effect: Lowers glucose levels.

Available forms

Tablets: 1 mg, 2 mg, 4 mg

NURSING PROCESS

Assessment

• Monitor fasting glucose periodically to determine therapeutic response. Also monitor glycosylated hemoglobin level, usually every 3 to 6 months, to more precisely assess long-term glycemic control.
• Assess patient's and family's knowledge of drug therapy.

Nursing diagnoses

• Ineffective health maintenance related to hyperglycemia
• Risk for injury related to drug-induced hypoglycemia
• Deficient knowledge related to drug therapy

Planning and implementation

• Oral hypoglycemic drugs have been linked to an increased risk of CV mortality compared with diet alone or with diet and insulin therapy.
• Give drug with the first meal of the day.

Patient teaching

• Tell patient to take drug with first meal of day.
• Stress importance of adhering to diet, weight-reduction, exercise, and personal hygiene programs.
• Explain to patient and family how to monitor glucose levels, identify signs and symptoms, and treat hyperglycemia and hypoglycemia.

• Advise patient to wear or carry medical identification that describes his condition.
• Instruct patient to avoid alcohol consumption during therapy.

Evaluation

• Patient's glucose level is normal.
• Patient recognizes hypoglycemia early and treats it before injury occurs.
• Patient and family state understanding of drug therapy.

glipizide

(GLIH-pih-zighd)
Glucotrol, Glucotrol XL, Minidiab ◇

Pharmacologic class: sulfonylurea
Therapeutic class: antidiabetic
Pregnancy risk category: C

Indications and dosages

▶ **Adjunct to diet to lower glucose level in patients with type 2 diabetes mellitus.** *Adults:* Initially 5 mg immediate-release P.O. daily 30 minutes before breakfast. Maximum recommended total daily dose, 40 mg. Or 5 mg extended-release tablets P.O. daily. Adjust in 5-mg increments q 3 months depending on level of glycemic control. Maximum daily dose for extended-release tablets, 20 mg.
Adjust-a-dose: In elderly patients with liver disease, 2.5 mg immediate-release or 5 mg extended-release. Maximum once-daily dose is 15 mg.
▶ **To replace insulin therapy.** *Adults:* If insulin dosage is more than 20 units daily, patient is started at usual dosage in addition to 50% of insulin. If insulin dosage is less than 20 units, stop insulin.

Contraindications and cautions

• Contraindicated in patients hypersensitive to the drug or any of its components, in those with diabetic ketoacidosis, and in those with allergies to sulfonamides or thiazide diuretics.
• Use cautiously in patients with renal and hepatic disease and in debilitated or malnourished patients.
Lifespan: In pregnant and breast-feeding women, drug is contraindicated. In children, safety and effectiveness haven't been established because of the rarity of type 2 diabetes mellitus in this population. In elderly patients, use cautiously.

Adverse reactions

CNS: dizziness, drowsiness, headache.
CV: facial flushing.
GI: constipation, nausea, vomiting.
Hematologic: ***agranulocytosis, aplastic anemia, thrombocytopenia.***
Hepatic: cholestatic jaundice.
Metabolic: ***hypoglycemia.***
Skin: rash, pruritus.

Interactions

Drug-drug. *Anabolic steroids, antifungal antibiotics, chloramphenicol, cimetidine, clofibrate, guanethidine, MAO inhibitors, phenylbutazone, probenecid, salicylates, sulfonamides:* May increase hypoglycemic activity. Monitor glucose level.
Beta blockers: May prolong hypoglycemic effect and mask symptoms of hypoglycemia. Use together cautiously.
Corticosteroids, glucagon, rifampin, thiazide diuretics: May decrease hypoglycemic response. Monitor glucose level.
Hydantoins: May increase hydantoin level. Monitor level.
Oral anticoagulants: May increase hypoglycemic activity or enhance anticoagulant effect. Monitor glucose level, PT, and INR.
Drug-herb. *Aloe, bilberry leaf, bitter melon, burdock, dandelion, fenugreek, garlic, ginseng:* May improve glucose control, which may allow reduction of oral hypoglycemic. Tell patient to discuss herbs with prescriber before use.
Drug-lifestyle. *Alcohol use:* May alter glycemic control, most commonly toward hypoglycemia. May also cause disulfiram-like reaction. Discourage use together.
Sun exposure: May cause photosensitivity. Discourage prolonged or unprotected sun exposure.

Effects on lab test results

• May increase BUN, creatinine, alkaline phosphatase, AST, and LDH levels. May decrease glucose and hemoglobin levels and hematocrit.
• May decrease granulocyte and platelet counts.

Pharmacokinetics

Absorption: Rapid and complete.
Distribution: In extracellular fluid. 98% to 99% protein-bound.
Metabolism: By liver to inactive metabolites.
Excretion: Mainly in urine. *Half-life:* 2 to 4 hours.

Route	Onset	Peak	Duration
P.O.	15–30 min	1–3 hr	10–24 hr

Action

Chemical effect: May stimulate insulin release from pancreas, reduce glucose output by liver, and increase peripheral sensitivity to insulin.
Therapeutic effect: Lowers glucose level.

Available forms

Tablets: 5 mg, 10 mg
Tablets (extended-release): 2.5 mg, 5 mg, 10 mg

NURSING PROCESS

Assessment

- Assess glucose level before starting therapy and regularly thereafter.
- Patient transferring from insulin therapy to oral antidiabetic needs glucose monitoring at least three times daily before meals.
- During periods of increased stress, such as from infection, fever, surgery, or trauma, patient may need insulin therapy. Monitor patient closely for hyperglycemia in these situations.
- Be alert for adverse reactions and drug interactions.
- Assess patient's and family's knowledge of drug therapy.

Nursing diagnoses

- Ineffective health maintenance related to hyperglycemia
- Risk for injury related to drug-induced hypoglycemia
- Deficient knowledge related to drug therapy

Planning and implementation

- Give drug about 30 minutes before meals.
- Some patients may attain effective control with once-daily dose; others show better response with divided doses.
- For a hypoglycemic reaction, give oral form of fast-acting carbohydrates or glucagon or I.V. glucose (if patient can't swallow or is comatose). Then give patient a complex carbohydrate snack when he awakens, and determine cause of the reaction.
- Make sure adjunct therapies, such as diet and exercise, are being used appropriately.

ALERT: Don't confuse glipizide with glyburide.

Patient teaching

- Teach patient about diabetes and the importance of following a therapeutic regimen: adhering to specific diet, weight reduction, exercise and personal hygiene programs, and avoiding infection.
- Explain how to monitor glucose level and how to recognize and treat hypoglycemia and hyperglycemia.
- Tell patient not to change dosage without prescriber's consent and to report any adverse reactions.
- Advise patient not to take other drugs, including OTC drugs or herbal remedies, without first checking with prescriber.
- Instruct patient not to drink alcohol during drug therapy.
- Advise patient to carry medical identification at all times.

Evaluation

- Patient's glucose level is normal with drug therapy.
- Patient doesn't experience hypoglycemia or hyperglycemia.
- Patient and family state understanding of drug therapy.

glucagon

(GLOO-kuh-gon)

Pharmacologic class: pancreatic hormone
Therapeutic class: antihypoglycemic
Pregnancy risk category: B

Indications and dosages

▶ **Hypoglycemia.** *Adults and children who weigh more than 20 kg (44 lb):* 1 mg I.V., I.M., or subcutaneously.
Children who weigh 20 kg or less: 0.5 mg I.V., I.M., or subcutaneously.

▶ **Diagnostic aid for radiologic examination.** *Adults:* 0.25 to 2 mg I.V. or 1 to 2 mg I.M. before start of radiologic procedure.

I.V. administration

- Reconstitute drug in 1-unit vial with 1 ml of diluent. Use only diluent supplied by manufacturer.
- Don't exceed concentration of 1 mg/ml (1 unit/ml).
- For I.V. drip infusion, use dextrose solution, which is compatible with glucagon. Drug forms precipitate in chloride solutions.
- Inject directly into vein or into I.V. tubing of free-flowing compatible solution over 2 to 5 minutes. Interrupt primary infusion during glucagon injection (if using same I.V. line). Repeat in 15 minutes if needed.
- If patient fails to respond, give I.V. glucose. When patient responds, give supplemental carbohydrate promptly.

⊗ **Incompatibilities**
Sodium chloride solution, solutions with pH of 3 to 9.5.

Contraindications and cautions

- Contraindicated in patients hypersensitive to the drug or any or its components and in those with pheochromocytoma.
- Use cautiously in patients with history of insulinoma or pheochromocytoma.

Lifespan: In pregnant women, use only if benefits outweigh risks to the fetus. In breastfeeding women, use cautiously because it's unknown if the drug appears in breast milk. In children, safety and effectiveness as a diagnostic aid haven't been established.

Adverse reactions

CV: hypotension.
GI: nausea, vomiting.
Respiratory: ***respiratory distress.***
Skin: urticaria.
Other: ***allergic reactions.***

Interactions

Drug-drug. *Oral anticoagulants:* May increase anticoagulant effect. Monitor PT and INR closely; monitor patient for bleeding.

Effects on lab test results

- May decrease potassium level.

Pharmacokinetics

Absorption: Unknown.
Distribution: Unknown.
Metabolism: Extensive by liver, in kidneys and plasma, and at its tissue receptor sites in plasma membranes.
Excretion: By kidneys. *Half-life:* 8 to 18 minutes.

Route	Onset	Peak	Duration
I.V., I.M., SubQ	Immediate	≤ 30 min	1–2 hr

Action

Chemical effect: Promotes catalytic depolymerization of hepatic glycogen to glucose.
Therapeutic effect: Raises glucose level.

Available forms

Powder for injection: 1 mg (1 unit)/vial

NURSING PROCESS

Assessment

- Assess patient's glucose level before starting therapy and after giving the drug.
- Be alert for adverse reactions and drug interactions.
- If patient vomits, monitor his hydration.
- Assess patient's and family's knowledge of drug therapy.

Nursing diagnoses

- Risk for injury related to hypoglycemia
- Risk for deficient fluid volume related to drug-induced vomiting
- Deficient knowledge related to drug therapy

Planning and implementation

- For I.M use, reconstitute drug in 1-unit vial with 1 ml of diluent; reconstitute drug in 10-unit vial with 10 ml of diluent. Use only diluent supplied by manufacturer when preparing doses of 2 mg or less. For larger doses, dilute with sterile water for injection.
- Arouse lethargic patient as quickly as possible and give additional carbohydrates orally to prevent secondary hypoglycemic reactions. Notify prescriber that patient's hypoglycemic episode required glucagon use. If patient doesn't respond to drug, provide emergency intervention. Unstable hypoglycemic diabetic

patient may not respond to drug. Give glucose I.V. instead.

• If patient can't retain some form of sugar for 1 hour because of nausea or vomiting, notify prescriber.

Patient teaching

• Instruct patient and family in proper drug administration.

• Teach them to recognize signs and symptoms of hypoglycemia, and tell them to notify prescriber immediately in emergencies.

Evaluation

• Patient's glucose level returns to normal.

• Patient remains well hydrated.

• Patient and family state understanding of drug therapy.

glyburide (glibenclamide)

(GLIGH-byoo-righd)

Albert Glyburide ♦, Apo-Glyburide ♦, DiaBeta, Euglucon ♦, Gen-Glybe ♦, Glynase PresTab, Micronase, Novo-Glyburide ♦, Nu-Glyburide ♦

Pharmacologic class: sulfonylurea
Therapeutic class: antidiabetic
Pregnancy risk category: B (for Micronase, Glynase); C (for DiaBeta)

Indications and dosages

▶ **Adjunct to diet to lower glucose level in patients with type 2 diabetes mellitus.** *Adults:* Initially, 1.25- to 5-mg regular tablets P.O. once daily with breakfast. For maintenance, 1.25 to 20 mg daily as single dose or in divided doses. Or, initially, 0.75- to 3-mg micronized formulation P.O. daily. For maintenance, 0.75 to 12 mg P.O. daily in single or divided doses.

▶ **To replace insulin therapy.** *Adults:* Initially, if insulin dosage is more than 40 units daily, 5-mg regular tablets or 3-mg micronized form P.O. once daily in addition to 50% of insulin dosage. If insulin dosage is 20 to 40 units daily, 5-mg regular tablets or 3-mg micronized form P.O. once daily while abruptly stopping insulin. If insulin dosage is less than 20 units daily, 2.5- to 5-mg regular tablets or 1.5- to 3-mg micronized form P.O. once daily while abruptly stopping insulin.

Contraindications and cautions

• Contraindicated in patients hypersensitive to the drug or any of its components, in those with diabetic ketoacidosis, and in those with allergies to sulfonamides or thiazide diuretics.

• Use cautiously in patients with hepatic or renal impairment and in debilitated or malnourished patients.

Lifespan: In pregnant women, breast-feeding women, and children, drug is contraindicated. In elderly patients, use cautiously.

Adverse reactions

CV: facial flushing.
GI: epigastric fullness, heartburn, nausea.
Hematologic: ***agranulocytosis, aplastic anemia, thrombocytopenia.***
Hepatic: cholestatic jaundice.
Metabolic: ***hypoglycemia.***
Skin: pruritus, rash.

Interactions

Drug-drug. *Anabolic steroids, chloramphenicol, clofibrate, guanethidine, MAO inhibitors, phenylbutazone, salicylates, sulfonamides:* May increase hypoglycemic activity. Monitor glucose level.

Beta blockers: May prolong hypoglycemic effect and mask symptoms of hypoglycemia. Use together cautiously.

Corticosteroids, glucagon, rifampin, thiazide diuretics: May decrease hypoglycemic response. Monitor glucose level.

Hydantoins: May increase hydantoin level. Monitor level.

Oral anticoagulants: May increase hypoglycemic activity or enhance anticoagulant effect. Monitor glucose level, PT, and INR.

Drug-herb. *Aloe, bilberry leaf, bitter melon, burdock, dandelion, fenugreek, garlic, ginseng:* May improve glucose control and allow reduction of oral hypoglycemic. Tell patient to discuss herbs with prescriber before use.

Drug-lifestyle. *Alcohol use:* May alter glycemic control, most commonly hypoglycemia. May also cause disulfiram-like reaction. Discourage use together.

Sun exposure: May cause photosensitivity. Discourage prolonged or unprotected exposure to sunlight.

Effects on lab test results

- May increase BUN, alkaline phosphatase, bilirubin, AST, ALT, and LDH levels. May decrease glucose and hemoglobin levels and hematocrit.
- May decrease WBC, platelet, and granulocyte counts.

Pharmacokinetics

Absorption: Almost complete.
Distribution: 99% protein-bound.
Metabolism: Complete.
Excretion: As metabolites in urine and feces in equal proportions. *Half-life:* 10 hours.

Route	Onset	Peak	Duration
P.O.	45–60 min	2–4 hr	24 hr

Action

Chemical effect: May stimulate insulin release from pancreas, reduce glucose output by liver, increase peripheral sensitivity to insulin, and cause mild diuresis.
Therapeutic effect: Lowers glucose levels.

Available forms

Tablets: 1.25 mg, 2.5 mg, 5 mg
Tablets (micronized): 1.5 mg, 3 mg, 4.5 mg, 6 mg

NURSING PROCESS

Assessment

- Assess glucose level before starting therapy and regularly thereafter.
- Patient transferring from insulin therapy to oral antidiabetic needs glucose monitoring at least three times daily before meals.
- During periods of increased stress, such as from infection, fever, surgery, or trauma, patient may need insulin therapy. Monitor patient closely for hyperglycemia in these situations.
- Be alert for adverse reactions and drug interactions.
- Assess patient's and family's knowledge of drug therapy.

Nursing diagnoses

- Ineffective health maintenance related to hyperglycemia
- Risk for injury related to drug-induced hypoglycemia
- Deficient knowledge related to drug therapy

Planning and implementation

- Micronized glyburide (Glynase PresTab) contains drug in smaller particle size and isn't bioequivalent to regular tablets. Adjust dose in a patient who has been taking Micronase or DiaBeta.
- Although most patients take drug once daily, patient taking more than 10 mg daily may achieve better results with twice-daily dosage.
- For hypoglycemic reaction, give oral form of fast-acting carbohydrates or, if patient can't swallow or is comatose, glucagon or I.V. glucose. Then give patient a complex carbohydrate snack when patient is conscious, and determine cause of reaction.
- Make sure that adjunct therapy, such as diet and exercise, is appropriate.
- **ALERT:** Don't confuse glyburide with glipizide.

Patient teaching

- Teach patient about diabetes and the importance of following therapeutic regimen by adhering to specific diet, weight reduction, exercise, and personal hygiene programs and by avoiding infection.
- Explain how to monitor glucose level and recognize and treat hypoglycemia and hyperglycemia.
- Tell patient not to change dosage without prescriber's consent and to report any adverse reactions.
- Advise patient not to take OTC drugs or herbal remedies without first checking with prescriber.
- Instruct patient not to drink alcohol during drug therapy.
- Advise patient to wear or carry medical identification at all times.

Evaluation

- Patient's glucose level is normal with drug therapy.
- Patient doesn't experience hypoglycemia.
- Patient and family state understanding of drug therapy.

goserelin acetate

(GOH-seh-reh-lin AS-ih-tayt)

Zoladex, Zoladex 3-Month

Pharmacologic class: luteinizing hormone–releasing hormone (LH-RH) analog
Therapeutic class: antineoplastic
Pregnancy risk category: X (for endometriosis); D (for advanced breast cancer)

Indications and dosages

▶ **Endometriosis, advanced breast cancer.** *Women:* One 3.6-mg implant subcutaneously q 28 days into upper abdominal wall for 6 months in endometriosis, longer in breast cancer. For endometriosis, maximum duration of therapy is 6 months.

▶ **Palliative therapy of advanced carcinoma of the prostate.** *Men:* One 10.8-mg implant subcutaneously q 12 weeks or 3.6 mg implant subcutaneously q 4 weeks into upper abdominal wall, given with radiotherapy and Flutamide.

▶ **Endometrial thinning before endometrial ablation for dysfunctional uterine bleeding.** *Women:* One or two 3.6-mg implants subcutaneously into upper abdominal wall. Give each implant 4 weeks apart.

Contraindications and cautions

- Contraindicated in patients hypersensitive to LH-RH, LH-RH agonist analogs, goserelin acetate, or any of its components.
- The 10.8-mg implant is contraindicated for use in women.
- Use cautiously in patients with risk factors for osteoporosis, such as family history of osteoporosis, chronic alcohol or tobacco abuse, or use of drugs that affect bone density.

Lifespan: In pregnant women, breast-feeding women, and children, drug is contraindicated.

Adverse reactions

CNS: anxiety, depression, dizziness, emotional lability, fever, headache, insomnia, lethargy, pain, ***stroke.***
CV: ***arrhythmias,*** chest pain, edema, ***heart failure,*** hypertension, ***MI,*** peripheral vascular disorder.
GI: constipation, diarrhea, nausea, ulcer, vomiting.
GU: amenorrhea, *impotence, lower urinary tract symptoms,* renal insufficiency, urinary obstruction, UTI, vaginal dryness.
Hematologic: anemia.
Metabolic: hyperglycemia, weight increase.
Musculoskeletal: loss of bone mineral density.
Respiratory: COPD, upper respiratory tract infection.
Skin: diaphoresis, rash.
Other: breast swelling and tenderness, changes in breast size, chills, gout, *hot flushes, sexual dysfunction.*

Interactions

None reported.

Effects on lab test results

- May increase ALT, AST, LDL, HDL, cholesterol, triglyceride, calcium, and glucose levels. May decrease hemoglobin level and hematocrit.
- May alter diagnostic tests of pituitary-gonadotropic and gonadal function.

Pharmacokinetics

Absorption: Slow.
Distribution: Minimally protein-bound.
Metabolism: Hydrolysis of C-terminal amino acids.
Excretion: Mostly via kidneys, 20% unchanged. *Half-life:* About 4 hours.

Route	Onset	Peak	Duration
SubQ	2–4 wk	12–15 days	Throughout therapy

Action

Chemical effect: Acts on pituitary to decrease release of follicle-stimulating hormone and LH, resulting in dramatically lowered levels of sex hormones.
Therapeutic effect: Decreases effects of sex hormones on tumor growth in prostate gland and tissue growth in uterus.

Available forms

Implants: 3.6 mg, 10.8 mg

NURSING PROCESS

Assessment
- Assess patient's condition before starting therapy and regularly thereafter.
- When used for prostate cancer, drug may initially worsen symptoms because it initially increases testosterone levels. Patient may have increased bone pain. Rarely, disease (spinal cord compression or ureteral obstruction) may worsen.
- Be alert for adverse reactions.
- Assess patient's and family's knowledge of drug therapy.

Nursing diagnoses
- Ineffective health maintenance related to underlying condition
- Acute pain related to drug's adverse effect
- Deficient knowledge related to drug therapy

Planning and implementation
- Give under supervision of prescriber.
- Give drug into upper abdominal wall. After cleaning area with alcohol swab (and injecting local anesthetic), stretch patient's skin with one hand while grasping barrel of syringe with the other. Insert needle into subcutaneous fat; then change direction of needle so that it parallels abdominal wall. Push in needle until hub touches patient's skin, and then withdraw about 1 cm (this creates a gap for drug to be injected) before depressing plunger completely.
- To avoid need for new syringe and injection site, don't aspirate after inserting needle.
- Implant comes in preloaded syringe. If package is damaged, don't use syringe. Make sure drug is visible in translucent chamber.
- After implantation, area requires bandage after needle is withdrawn.
- If implants require removal, schedule patient for ultrasound to locate them.
- Notify prescriber of adverse reactions, and provide supportive care.

Patient teaching
- Advise patient to report every 28 days for new implant. A delay of a couple of days is permissible.
- Tell patient to call prescriber if menstruation persists or breakthrough bleeding occurs. Menstruation should stop during therapy.
- After therapy ends, inform patient that she may experience delayed return of menses. Persistent amenorrhea is rare.
- Warn patient that pain may occur.

Evaluation
- Patient responds well to drug.
- Patient has no pain.
- Patient and family state understanding of drug therapy.

granisetron hydrochloride
(grah-NEEZ-eh-trohn high-droh-KLOR-ighd)
Kytril

Pharmacologic class: selective 5-hydroxytryptamine ($5\text{-}HT_3$) receptor antagonist
Therapeutic class: antiemetic, antinauseant
Pregnancy risk category: B

Indications and dosages
▶ **Prevention of nausea and vomiting caused by emetogenic chemotherapy.** *Adults and children age 2 and older:* 10 mcg/kg undiluted and given by direct injection over 30 seconds, or diluted and infused over 5 minutes. Begin infusion within 30 minutes before chemotherapy starts. Or, for adults, 1 mg P.O. up to 1 hour before chemotherapy and repeated 12 hours later. Or, for adults, 2 mg P.O. daily within 1 hour before chemotherapy.

▶ **Prevention of nausea and vomiting from radiation, including total body irradiation and fractionated abdominal radiation.** *Adults:* 2 mg P.O. once daily within 1 hour of radiation.

▶ **Postoperative nausea and vomiting.** *Adults:* 1 mg I.V. undiluted and given over 30 seconds. For prevention, give before anesthesia induction or immediately before reversal.

I.V. administration
- Dilute drug with normal saline injection or D_5W to make 20 to 50 ml.
- Infuse over 5 minutes, beginning within 30 minutes before chemotherapy starts and only on days chemotherapy is given.
- Diluted solutions are stable for 24 hours at room temperature.

⊗ **Incompatibilities**
Other I.V. drugs.

Contraindications and cautions

- Contraindicated in patients hypersensitive to the drug or any of its components.

Lifespan: In pregnant women, use cautiously. In breast-feeding women, use cautiously because it's unknown if the drug appears in breast milk. In children, safety and effectiveness haven't been established for postoperative nausea and vomiting. In children younger than age 2, safety and effectiveness haven't been established for nausea and vomiting from chemotherapy. Safety and effectiveness of oral drug haven't been established in children of any age.

Adverse reactions

CNS: agitation, anxiety, *asthenia,* CNS stimulation, *dizziness, fever, headache,* insomnia, *pain,* somnolence.
CV: ***bradycardia,*** hypertension, ***hypotension.***
GI: abdominal pain, *constipation,* decreased appetite, diarrhea, dyspepsia, flatulence, *nausea,* taste disorder, *vomiting.*
GU: ***oliguria,*** UTI.
Hematologic: anemia, ***leukopenia, leukocytosis, thrombocytopenia.***
Respiratory: cough, ***dyspnea,*** increased sputum.
Skin: alopecia, dermatitis, rash, ***urticaria.***
Other: ***anaphylaxis, hypersensitivity reactions,*** infection.

Interactions

Drug-herb. *Horehound:* May enhance serotonergic effects. Discourage use together.

Effects on lab test results

- May increase ALT and AST levels. May decrease hemoglobin level and hematocrit.
- May decrease WBC and platelet counts.

Pharmacokinetics

Absorption: Unknown.
Distribution: Distributed freely between plasma and RBCs. About 65% protein-bound.
Metabolism: By liver.
Excretion: In urine and feces. *Half-life:* 5 to 9 hours.

Route	Onset	Peak	Duration
P.O., I.V.	Unknown	Unknown	Unknown

Action

Chemical effect: Located in the CNS at the area postrema (chemoreceptor trigger zone) and in the peripheral nervous system on nerve terminals of the vagus nerve. Drug's blocking action may occur at both sites.
Therapeutic effect: Prevents nausea and vomiting from chemotherapy and anesthesia.

Available forms

Injection: 0.1 mg/ml, 1 mg/ml
Oral solution: 1 mg/5 ml
Tablets: 1 mg

NURSING PROCESS

Assessment

- Assess patient's chemotherapy and GI reactions before starting therapy.
- Monitor patient for nausea and vomiting.
- Be alert for adverse reactions.
- If drug is ineffective or diarrhea occurs, monitor hydration.
- Assess patient's and family's knowledge of drug therapy.

Nursing diagnoses

- Risk for deficient fluid volume related to nausea and vomiting
- Acute pain related to drug-induced headache
- Deficient knowledge related to drug therapy

Planning and implementation

- Give oral form of drug 1 hour before chemotherapy; repeat in 12 hours.

ALERT: Don't mix with other drugs. Compatibility data are limited.

- If patient has nausea or vomits, alert prescriber.

Patient teaching

- Tell patient to notify prescriber if adverse drug reactions occur.

Evaluation

- Patient has no nausea or vomiting with chemotherapy.
- Patient's headache is relieved with mild analgesic.
- Patient and family state understanding of drug therapy.

guaifenesin (glyceryl guaiacolate)

(gwah-FEH-nih-sin)

Diabetic Tussin EX, Guiatuss*†, Hytuss†, Hytuss-2X†, Mucinex†, Mucinex ER, Naldecon Senior EX†, Organidin NR, Robitussin*†

Pharmacologic class: propanediol derivative
Therapeutic class: expectorant
Pregnancy risk category: C

Indications and dosages

▶ **Expectorant.** *Adults and children age 12 and older:* Give 200 to 400 mg P.O. q 4 hours, or 600 to 1,200 mg extended-release capsules q 12 hours. Maximum, 2,400 mg daily.
Children ages 6 to 11: Give 100 to 200 mg P.O. q 4 hours. Maximum, 1,200 mg daily.
Children ages 2 to 5: Give 50 to 100 mg P.O. q 4 hours. Maximum, 600 mg daily.

Contraindications and cautions

- Contraindicated in patients hypersensitive to the drug or any of its components.

Lifespan: In pregnant women, use cautiously. In breast-feeding women, safety and effectiveness haven't been established. In children younger than age 2 years, safety and effectiveness haven't been established. For children younger than age 12, don't give extended-release form.

Adverse reactions

CNS: drowsiness.
GI: diarrhea, stomach pain, nausea (with large doses), vomiting.
Skin: rash.

Interactions

None significant.

Effects on lab test results

- May decrease serum uric acid level.
- May falsify results of 5-hydroxyindoleacetic acid and vanillylmandelic acid tests.

Pharmacokinetics

Absorption: Good.
Distribution: Unknown.
Metabolism: Unknown.
Excretion: Renal, as inactive metabolites. *Half-life:* Unknown.

Route	Onset	Peak	Duration
P.O.	Unknown	Unknown	Unknown

Action

Chemical effect: Increases production of respiratory tract fluids to help liquefy and reduce viscosity of tenacious secretions.
Therapeutic effect: Thins respiratory secretions for easier removal.

Available forms

Capsules: 200 mg†
Liquid: 100 mg/5 ml, 200 mg/5 ml
Syrup: 100 mg/5 ml†
Tablets: 100 mg†, 200 mg†, 200 mg, 400 mg
Tablets (extended-release): 600 mg†, 1,200 mg†

NURSING PROCESS

Assessment

- Assess patient's sputum production before and after giving drug.
- Be alert for adverse reactions.
- If adverse GI reactions occur, monitor patient's hydration.
- Assess patient's and family's knowledge of drug therapy.

Nursing diagnoses

- Ineffective airway clearance related to underlying condition
- Risk for deficient fluid volume related to adverse GI reactions
- Deficient knowledge related to drug therapy

Planning and implementation

- Give drug with a full glass of water.

Patient teaching

- Inform patient that persistent cough may indicate a serious condition. Tell him to contact prescriber if cough lasts longer than 1 week, recurs frequently, or accompanies a high fever, rash, or severe headache.
- Advise patient to take each dose with a full glass of water before and after dose. Increasing fluid intake may prove beneficial.

ALERT: Advise patient not to break, crush, or chew extended-release tablets.

• Encourage patient to perform deep-breathing exercises.

Evaluation
• Patient's lungs are clear and respiratory secretions are normal.
• Patient maintains adequate hydration.
• Patient and family state understanding of drug therapy.

H

haloperidol
(hal-oh-PER-uh-dol)
Apo-Haloperidol ♦, Haldol, Novo-Peridol ♦, Peridol ♦, PMS-Haloperidol ♦, Serenace ◊

haloperidol decanoate
Haldol Decanoate, Haldol LA ♦

haloperidol lactate
Haldol

Pharmacologic class: butyrophenone derivative
Therapeutic class: antipsychotic
Pregnancy risk category: C

Indications and dosages

▶ **Psychotic disorders.** *Adults and children age 12 and older:* Initial range is 0.5 to 5 mg P.O. b.i.d. or t.i.d. Or 2 to 5 mg I.M. q 4 to 8 hours, although hourly administration may be needed until control is obtained. Maximum, 100 mg P.O. daily.
Children ages 3 to 11: Give 0.05 to 0.15 mg/kg P.O. given b.i.d. or t.i.d. Severely disturbed children may need higher doses.

▶ **Chronically psychotic patients who need prolonged therapy.** *Adults:* Initially, 10 to 20 times previous daily dosage of oral haloperidol equivalent up to a maximum of 100 mg decanoate given I.M. q 4 weeks. Usual maintenance dosage, 10 to 15 times previous daily dosage in oral haloperidol equivalents.

▶ **Nonpsychotic behavior disorders.** *Children ages 3 to 12:* Give 0.05 to 0.075 mg/kg P.O. b.i.d. or t.i.d. Maximum, 6 mg P.O. daily.

▶ **Tourette syndrome.** *Adults:* 0.5 to 1.5 mg P.O. t.i.d. Some patients may require up to 10 mg/day in two or three divided doses.
Children ages 3 to 12: Give 0.05 to 0.075 mg/kg P.O. b.i.d. or t.i.d.

▶ **Delirium**‡. *Adults:* 1 to 2 mg I.V. q 2 to 4 hours.

I.V. administration

• I.V. form not recommended; best I.V. dosage hasn't been established.

⊗ **Incompatibilities**
Allopurinol, amphotericin B, benztropine, cefepime, diphenhydramine, fluconazole, foscarnet, heparin, hydromorphone, hydroxyzine, ketorolac, morphine, nitroprusside, piperacillin, and tazobactam.

Contraindications and cautions

• Contraindicated in patients hypersensitive to the drug or any of its components and in those with parkinsonism, coma, or CNS depression.
• Use cautiously in debilitated patients; in patients who take anticonvulsants, anticoagulants, antiparkinsonians, or lithium; and in patients with a history of seizures or EEG abnormalities, severe CV disorders, allergies, glaucoma, or urine retention.

Lifespan: In pregnant women, use only if benefits outweigh risks to fetus. In breast-feeding women, drug is contraindicated. In children younger than age 3 or those who weigh less than 15 kg (33 lb), use is contraindicated. In elderly patients, use cautiously. Elderly patients need a lower initial dose and a more gradual dosage adjustment.

Adverse reactions

CNS: ***neuroleptic malignant syndrome,*** sedation, ***seizures, severe extrapyramidal reactions,*** tardive dyskinesia.
CV: ***bradycardia,*** ECG changes, hypertension, hypotension, tachycardia, ***torsades de pointes.***
EENT: blurred vision.
GU: menstrual irregularities, urine retention.
Hematologic: leukocytosis, ***leukopenia.***
Hepatic: jaundice.
Skin: rash.
Other: gynecomastia.

Interactions

Drug-drug. *Carbamazepine:* May decrease haloperidol level. Monitor patient.

CNS depressants: May increase CNS depression. Avoid use together.
Fluoxetine: May cause severe extrapyramidal reaction. Don't use together.
Lithium: May cause lethargy and confusion with high doses. Monitor patient.
Methyldopa: May cause symptoms of dementia or psychosis. Monitor patient.
Phenytoin, rifampin: May decrease haloperidol level. Monitor patient.
Drug-herb. *Nutmeg:* May cause loss of symptom control or interference with therapy for psychiatric illness. Discourage use together.
Drug-lifestyle. *Alcohol use:* May increase CNS depression. Discourage use together.

Effects on lab test results

• May increase liver function test values. May increase or decrease WBC count.

Pharmacokinetics

Absorption: 60% after P.O. use; 70% of I.M. dose within 30 minutes. I.M. route provides 4 to 10 times more active drug than oral route.
Distribution: Wide, with high levels in adipose tissue. 91% to 99% protein-bound.
Metabolism: Extensive.
Excretion: 40% in urine within 5 days; 15% in feces by way of biliary tract. *Half-life:* P.O., 24 hours; I.M., 21 hours.

Route	Onset	Peak	Duration
P.O.	Unknown	3–6 hr	Unknown
I.M.			
lactate	Unknown	10–20 min	Unknown
decanoate	Unknown	3–9 days	Unknown

Action

Chemical effect: May block postsynaptic dopamine receptors in brain.
Therapeutic effect: Decreases psychotic behaviors.

Available forms

haloperidol
Tablets: 0.5 mg, 1 mg, 2 mg, 5 mg, 10 mg, 20 mg
haloperidol decanoate
Injection: 50 mg/ml, 100 mg/ml
haloperidol lactate
Injection: 5 mg/ml
Oral concentrate: 2 mg/ml

NURSING PROCESS

Assessment

• Assess patient's disorder before starting therapy and regularly thereafter.
• Be alert for adverse reactions and drug interactions.
• Monitor patient for tardive dyskinesia, which may not appear until months or years later and may disappear spontaneously or persist for life despite stopping use of the drug.
• Assess patient's and family's knowledge of drug therapy.

Nursing diagnoses

• Disturbed thought processes related to underlying condition
• Impaired physical mobility related to extrapyramidal effects
• Deficient knowledge related to drug therapy

Planning and implementation

ALERT: Give long-acting form of the drug by deep I.M. injection in gluteal region, using a 21G needle. Don't exceed 3 ml for each injection.
ALERT: I.V. form not recommended; optimum I.V. dosage has not been established.
• When changing from oral to injection form, give patient 10 to 15 times oral dose once monthly (maximum, 100 mg).
• Protect drug from light. Slight yellowing of liquid or concentrate is common and doesn't affect potency. Discard markedly discolored solutions.
• Don't abruptly stop giving the drug unless severe adverse reaction occurs.
• Acute dystonic reactions may be treated with diphenhydramine.

Patient teaching

• Warn patient to avoid activities that require alertness and psychomotor coordination until the drug's CNS effects are known.
• Tell patient not to drink alcohol while taking drug.
• Tell patient to relieve dry mouth with sugarless gum or hard candy.
• Instruct patient to take drug exactly as prescribed and not to double doses to compensate for missed ones.

Evaluation
- Patient has decreased psychotic behavior and agitation.
- Patient maintains physical mobility.
- Patient and family state understanding of drug therapy.

heparin sodium
(HEH-prin SOH-dee-um)

Hepalean ♦, Heparin Leo ♦, Heparin Lock Flush Solution (with Tubex), Hep-Lock, Uniparin ◇

Pharmacologic class: anticoagulant
Therapeutic class: heparin
Pregnancy risk category: C

Indications and dosages
Heparin dosage is highly individualized depending on patient's disease state, age, and renal and hepatic health.

▶ **Deep vein thrombosis, pulmonary embolism.** *Adults:* Initially, 10,000 units as I.V. bolus; then adjust according to PTT and give I.V. q 4 to 6 hours (5,000 to 10,000 units). Or 5,000 units as I.V. bolus; then 20,000 to 40,000 units in 24 hours by I.V. infusion pump. Adjust hourly rate 4 to 6 hours after bolus dose according to PTT.
Children: Initially, 50 units/kg I.V. drip. Maintenance dosage is 100 units/kg I.V. drip over 4 hours. For constant infusion, 20,000 units/m^2 daily. Adjust dosages according to PTT.

▶ **Embolism prevention.** *Adults:* 5,000 units subcutaneously q 8 to 12 hours. In surgical patients, give first dose 2 hours before procedure; follow with 5,000 units subcutaneously q 8 to 12 hours for 5 to 7 days or until patient is fully ambulatory.

▶ **Open-heart surgery.** *Adults:* (total body perfusion) 150 to 400 units/kg continuous I.V. infusion.

▶ **DIC.** *Adults:* 50 to 100 units/kg I.V. q 4 hours as a single injection or constant infusion. If no improvement in 4 to 8 hours, stop drug.
Children: 25 to 50 units/kg I.V. q 4 hours as a single injection or constant infusion. If no improvement in 4 to 8 hours, stop drug.

▶ **Maintaining patency of I.V. indwelling catheters.** *Adults:* 10 to 100 units I.V. flush. Use sufficient volume to fill device. Not intended for therapeutic use.

▶ **Unstable angina‡.** *Adults:* 70 to 80 units/kg I.V. loading dose; follow by infusion maintaining PTT at 1.5 to 2 times control level during first week of anginal pain.

▶ **Post MI, cerebral thrombosis in evolving stroke, left ventricular thrombi, heart failure, history of embolism, and atrial fibrillation‡.** *Adults:* 5,000 units subcutaneously q 12 hours empirically. Or 75 units/kg continuous infusion to maintain PTT at 1.5 to 2 times control value; follow by warfarin sodium.

I.V. administration
- Check order and vial carefully. Heparin comes in various concentrations.
- Give drug I.V. using infusion pump to provide maximum safety because of long-term effects and irregular absorption when given subcutaneously.
- Check constant I.V. infusions regularly, even when pumps are in good working order, to prevent giving too much or too little.
- Never piggyback other drugs into infusion line while heparin infusion is running. Many antibiotics and other drugs deactivate heparin. Never mix any drug with heparin in syringe when bolus therapy is used.
- If I.V. bag is empty, restart it as soon as possible and reschedule bolus dose immediately. Don't skip dose or increase rate to catch up.

⊗ Incompatibilities
Alteplase, amikacin, amiodarone, ampicillin sodium, atracurium, chlorpromazine, ciprofloxacin, codeine phosphate, cytarabine, dacarbazine, daunorubicin, dextrose 4.3% in sodium chloride solution 0.18%, diazepam, diltiazem, dobutamine, doxorubicin, doxycycline hyclate, droperidol, ergotamine, erythromycin gluceptate or lactobionate, filgrastim, gentamicin, haloperidol lactate, hydrocortisone sodium succinate, hydroxyzine hydrochloride, idarubicin, kanamycin, labetalol, levorphanol, meperidine, methadone, methotrimeprazine, methylprednisone sodium succinate, morphine sulfate, netilmicin, nicardipine, penicillin G potassium, penicillin G sodium, pentazocine lactate, phenytoin sodium, polymyxin B sulfate, prochlorperazine edisylate, promethazine hydrochloride, quinidine gluconate, 1/6 M sodium lactate, streptomycin, tobramycin sulfate, trifluoperazine, triflupromazine, vancomycin, vinblastine,

warfarin; solutions containing a phosphate buffer, sodium carbonate, or sodium oxalate.

Contraindications and cautions

- Contraindicated in patients hypersensitive to the drug or any of its components.
- Use very cautiously in patients with active bleeding; blood dyscrasia; bleeding tendencies, such as hemophilia, thrombocytopenia, or hepatic disease with hypoprothrombinemia; suspected intracranial hemorrhage; suppurative thrombophlebitis; inaccessible ulcerative lesions (especially of GI tract) and open ulcerative wounds; extensive denudation of skin; ascorbic acid deficiency and other conditions causing increased capillary permeability; subacute bacterial endocarditis; shock; advanced renal disease; threatened abortion; and severe hypertension. Also use very cautiously during or after brain, eye, or spinal cord surgery; during spinal tap or spinal anesthesia; and during continuous tube drainage of stomach or small intestine. Although heparin is clearly hazardous in these conditions, risk versus benefits must be evaluated. Use cautiously in patients with mild hepatic or renal disease, alcoholism, an occupation with a risk of physical injury, or a history of allergies, asthma, or GI ulcerations.

Lifespan: In pregnant women who need anticoagulation, most clinicians use heparin. Use it cautiously, especially during the last trimester and immediately postpartum, because of the increased risk of maternal hemorrhage. Heparin doesn't appear in breast milk. In neonates, safety and effectiveness haven't been established. In elderly patients, use cautiously and at a lower dosage.

Adverse reactions

CNS: fever.
EENT: conjunctivitis, lacrimation, rhinitis.
Hematologic: ***hemorrhage,*** *overly prolonged clotting time,* ***thrombocytopenia.***
Skin: cutaneous or subcutaneous necrosis, hematoma, irritation, mild pain, pruritus, ulceration, urticaria.
Other: ***anaphylaxis,*** burning feet, chills, ***hypersensitivity reactions, white clot syndrome.***

Interactions

Drug-drug. *Antiplatelet drugs, aspirin, salicylates:* May increase the risk of bleeding. Monitor coagulation tests and patient closely for bleeding.
Oral anticoagulants: May cause additive anticoagulation. Monitor PT, INR, and PTT; monitor patient for bleeding.
Thrombolytics: May increase risk of hemorrhage. Monitor patient closely for bleeding.
Drug-herb. *Dong quai, feverfew, garlic, ginger, horse chestnut, motherwort, red clover:* May increase risk of bleeding. Monitor patient closely for bleeding.

Effects on lab test results

- May increase ALT and AST levels.
- May increase INR, PT, and PTT. May decrease platelet count.

Pharmacokinetics

Absorption: Peak level varies.
Distribution: Extensively bound to lipoprotein, globulins, and fibrinogen.
Metabolism: Thought to be removed by reticuloendothelial system, with some metabolism occurring in liver.
Excretion: Small amount in urine as unchanged drug. *Half-life:* 1 to 2 hours. Half-life is dose-dependent and nonlinear and may be disproportionately prolonged at higher doses.

Route	Onset	Peak	Duration
I.V.	Immediate	Unknown	Unknown
SubQ	20–60 min	2–4 hr	Unknown

Action

Chemical effect: Accelerates formation of antithrombin III–thrombin complex and deactivates thrombin, preventing conversion of fibrinogen to fibrin.
Therapeutic effect: Decreases ability of blood to clot.

Available forms

Products are derived from beef lung or porcine intestinal mucosa.
heparin sodium
Carpuject: 5,000 units/ml
Disposable syringes: 1,000 units/ml; 2,500 units/ml; 5,000 units/ml; 7,500 units/ml; 10,000 units/ml; 15,000 units/ml; 20,000 units/ml; 40,000 units/ml
Premixed I.V. solutions: 1,000 units in 500 ml of normal saline solution; 2,000 units in 1,000 ml of normal saline solution; 12,500 units

in 250 ml of half-normal saline solution; 25,000 units in 250 ml of half-normal saline solution; 25,000 units in 500 ml of half-normal saline solution; 10,000 units in 100 ml of D_5W; 12,500 units in 250 ml of D_5W; 25,000 units in 250 ml of D_5W; 25,000 units in 500 ml of D_5W; 20,000 units in 500 ml of D_5W
Unit-dose ampules: 1,000 units/ml; 5,000 units/ml; 10,000 units/ml
Vials: 1,000 units/ml; 2,500 units/ml; 5,000 units/ml; 7,500 units/ml; 10,000 units/ml; 15,000 units/ml; 20,000 units/ml; 40,000 units/ml
heparin sodium flush
Disposable syringes: 10 units/ml, 100 units/ml
Vials: 10 units/ml, 100 units/ml

NURSING PROCESS

Assessment

- Assess patient's underlying condition before starting therapy.
- Draw blood to establish baseline coagulation values before starting therapy.
- Monitor the drug's effectiveness by measuring PTT carefully and regularly. Anticoagulation is present when PTT values are 1½ to 2 times control values.
- To avoid falsely elevated PTT, always draw blood 30 minutes before next dose. Draw blood for PTT 8 hours after start of continuous I.V. heparin therapy. Don't draw blood for PTT from I.V. tubing of heparin infusion; draw blood from opposite arm.
- Be alert for adverse reactions and drug interactions.
- Monitor platelet counts regularly. Thrombocytopenia caused by heparin may be linked to a type of arterial thrombosis known as white clot syndrome.
- Solutions more concentrated than 100 units/ml can irritate blood vessels.
- Assess patient's and family's knowledge of drug therapy.

Nursing diagnoses

- Risk for injury related to potential for thrombosis or emboli development from underlying condition
- Ineffective protection related to increased bleeding risks
- Deficient knowledge related to drug therapy

Planning and implementation

- Give low-dose injections sequentially between iliac crests in lower abdomen deep into subcutaneous fat. Inject drug slowly. Leave needle in place for 10 seconds after injection, then withdraw. Don't massage after subcutaneous injection. Watch for bleeding at injection site. Alternate sites every 12 hours.
- Drug requirements are higher in early phases of thrombogenic diseases and febrile states, lower when patient's condition stabilizes.
- Place notice above patient's bed to inform I.V. team or laboratory staff to apply pressure dressings after taking blood.
- Take precautions to reduce bleeding.
- To minimize the risk of hematoma, avoid excessive I.M. injection of other drugs. If possible, don't give I.M. injections at all.

ALERT: To treat severe overdose, use protamine sulfate, a heparin antagonist. Base dosage on heparin dose, the route used, and time elapsed since it was given. As a general rule, 1 to 1.5 units of protamine/100 units of heparin are given if only a few minutes have elapsed; 0.5 to 0.75 mg protamine/100 units heparin if 30 to 60 minutes have elapsed; and 0.25 to 0.375 mg protamine/100 units heparin if 2 or more hours have elapsed.

- Abruptly stopping the drug may increase coagulability, and heparin therapy is usually followed by oral anticoagulants for prophylaxis.

ALERT: Don't give heparin I.M.
ALERT: Don't give heparin with low–molecular-weight heparins.
ALERT: Spell out "units" to reduce the risk of misreading "U" as a zero.
ALERT: Don't confuse heparin with Hespan.

Patient teaching

- Instruct patient and family to watch for signs of bleeding and to immediately notify the prescriber.
- Tell patient to avoid OTC drugs containing aspirin, other salicylates, some herbal remedies, and other drugs that may interact with heparin.

Evaluation

- Patient's PTT reflects goal of heparin therapy.
- Patient has no injury from bleeding.
- Patient and family state understanding of drug therapy.

hepatitis B immune globulin, human

(hep-uh-TIGH-tus bee ih-MYOON GLOH-byoo-lin, HYOO-mun)

BayHep B, HBIG, HyperHEP B S/D, Nabi-HB

Pharmacologic class: immunoglobulin
Therapeutic class: hepatitis B prophylaxis
Pregnancy risk category: C

Indications and dosages

▶ **Hepatitis B exposure in high-risk patients.** *Adults and children:* 0.06 ml/kg I.M. within 7 days after exposure (preferably within first 24 hours). If patient refuses hepatitis B vaccine, repeat dosage 28 days after exposure.
Neonates born to patients who test positive for hepatitis B surface antigen (HBsAg): 0.5 ml I.M. within 12 hours of birth.

Contraindications and cautions

- Contraindicated in patients with a history of anaphylactic reactions to immune serum.
- Use cautiously in patients with severe thrombocytopenia or any coagulation disorder that would contraindicate I.M. injections.

Lifespan: In pregnant women, use cautiously. In breast-feeding women, use cautiously because it's unknown if drug appears in breast milk.

Adverse reactions

CNS: *headache.*
Musculoskeletal: *myalgia.*
Skin: urticaria.
Other: ***anaphylaxis, angioedema,*** *injection-site reactions.*

Interactions

Drug-drug. *Live-virus vaccines:* May interfere with response to live-virus vaccines. Defer routine immunization for 3 months.

Effects on lab test results

None reported.

Pharmacokinetics

Absorption: Slow.
Distribution: Unknown.
Metabolism: Unknown.
Excretion: Unknown. *Half-life:* Antibodies to HBsAg, 21 days.

Route	Onset	Peak	Duration
I.M.	1–6 days	3–11 days	≥ 2 mo

Action

Chemical effect: Provides passive immunity to hepatitis B.
Therapeutic effect: Prevents hepatitis B.

Available forms

Injection: 1-ml, 5-ml vials; 0.5 ml and 1.0 ml prefilled syringes

NURSING PROCESS

Assessment

- Assess patient's allergies and reaction to immunizations before starting therapy.
- Monitor effectiveness by checking patient's antibody titers.
- Be alert for anaphylaxis.
- Assess patient's and family's knowledge of drug therapy.

Nursing diagnoses

- Ineffective protection related to lack of immunity to hepatitis B
- Deficient knowledge related to drug therapy

Planning and implementation

- Do not give I.V.
- Inject drug into anterolateral aspect of thigh or deltoid muscle in older children and adults; inject into anterolateral aspect of thigh for neonates and children younger than age 3.
- Make sure epinephrine 1:1,000 is available in case anaphylaxis occurs.
- To prevent neutralization, do not give Hep B immune globulin and Hep B vaccine in same site or same syringe.
- For postexposure prophylaxis (for example, needle stick, direct contact), drug is usually given with hepatitis B vaccine.

Patient teaching

- Instruct patient to immediately report respiratory difficulty.

Evaluation

- Patient exhibits passive immunity to hepatitis B.

H

• Patient and family state understanding of drug therapy.

high–molecular-weight hyaluronan

(HI–mow-LECK-yuh-lerr-wayt high-al-your-RON-ann)
Hyalgan, Orthovisc, Supartz, Synvisc

Pharmacologic class: hyaluronic acid derivative
Therapeutic class: viscosupplement; analgesic
Pregnancy risk category: NR

Indications and dosages

▶ **To reduce pain caused by osteoarthritis of the knee in patients who haven't responded to nondrug therapy or simple analgesics.**
Adults: Intra-articular injection (one syringe) into affected knee once weekly for a total of three to five injections.

Contraindications and cautions

• Contraindicated in patients allergic to hyaluronate preparations, birds, eggs, feathers, and poultry.
• Contraindicated in patients with infection or skin disease in area of injection site or joint.
Lifespan: In pregnant women, use only if benefits outweigh risks to fetus. In breast-feeding women and in children, safety and effectiveness haven't been established.

Adverse reactions

CNS: dizziness, *headache,* pain.
CV: ***hypotensive crisis.***
Musculoskeletal: *arthralgia,* back pain, bursitis.
Other: anaphylactoid reaction, injection-site pain.

Interactions

Drug-drug. *Skin preparation disinfectants that contain quaternary ammonium salts:* May cause hyaluronan to precipitate. Don't use together.

Effects on lab test results

None reported.

Pharmacokinetics

Absorption: None.
Distribution: None.
Metabolism: None.
Excretion: None. *Half-life:* Unknown.

Route	Onset	Peak	Duration
Intra-articular	Unknown	Unknown	Unknown

Action

Chemical effect: Supplements body's natural supply of hyaluronan, which acts as a shock absorber and lubricant in the joints.
Therapeutic effect: Relief of pain in knee joints in osteoarthritis patients.

Available forms

Injection: 16 mg/2 ml (Synvisc), 20 mg/2 ml (Hyalgan), 25 mg/2.5 ml (Supartz), 30 mg/2 ml (Orthovisc)

NURSING PROCESS

Assessment

• Assess patient for joint effusion before giving the drug. Remove joint effusion before injecting drug.
• Evaluate patient's degree of pain relief. Pain may not be relieved until after the third injection.
• Assess patient for injection-site reactions. Inflammation may increase briefly in affected knee in a patient with inflammatory osteoarthritis.
• Assess patient's and family's knowledge of drug therapy.

Nursing diagnoses

• Acute pain related to underlying medical condition
• Impaired physical mobility related to underlying medical condition
• Deficient knowledge related to drug therapy

Planning and implementation

• Drug should be given by staff trained in intra-articular administration.
• Use an 18G to 21G needle. Inject contents of one syringe into one knee. If needed, use a second syringe for the second knee.
• Don't give less than three injections in a treatment cycle.
• Safety and effectiveness of drug use for more than one treatment cycle or in joints other than the knee aren't known.

• Give drug immediately after opening. Store in original package at room temperature (lower than 77° F [25° C]); don't freeze. Discard unused drug.

Patient teaching

• Tell patient that pain and inflammation may increase briefly after the injection.

• Urge patient to avoid strenuous or weight-bearing activity, such as running or tennis, for more than an hour within 48 hours of an injection.

• Tell patient to report injection-site reactions, such as pain, swelling, itching, heat, rash, bruising, or redness.

• Inform patient that a treatment cycle includes at least three injections and that pain may not be relieved until after the third injection.

• Caution patient to report planned or suspected pregnancy.

Evaluation

• Patient is free from pain.

• Patient has full physical mobility.

• Patient and family state understanding of drug therapy.

hydralazine hydrochloride

(high-DRAL-uh-zeen high-droh-KLOR-ighd)

Alphapress ◇, Apresoline, Novo-Hylazin ♦

Pharmacologic class: peripheral vasodilator
Therapeutic class: antihypertensive
Pregnancy risk category: C

Indications and dosages

▶ **Essential hypertension (orally, alone or with other antihypertensives); severe essential hypertension (parenterally, to lower blood pressure quickly).** *Adults:* Initially, 10 mg P.O. q.i.d.; gradually increase to 50 mg q.i.d. if needed. Maximum recommended dosage is 200 mg daily, but some patients may need 300 to 400 mg daily. Or give 10 to 20 mg I.V. slowly and repeat if needed. Switch to P.O. antihypertensives as soon as possible. Or 10 to 50 mg I.M.; repeat if needed. Switch to P.O. form as soon as possible.

▶ **To manage hypertensive emergencies related to pregnancy (preeclampsia, eclampsia).** *Adults:* 5 to 10 mg I.V.; repeat q 20 to 30 minutes if needed to achieve adequate blood pressure control. Or, infuse at 0.5 to 10 mg/hour.

▶ **To manage severe heart failure‡.** *Adults:* Initially 50 to 75 mg P.O.; then adjust according to patient's response. Most patients respond to 200 to 600 mg daily, divided q 6 to 12 hours, but daily dosages as high as 3 g have been given.

I.V. administration

• Drug is compatible with normal saline solution, Ringer's and lactated Ringer's solutions, and several other common I.V. solutions. Manufacturer doesn't recommend mixing drug in infusion solutions.

• Drug changes color in most infusion solutions, but the change doesn't indicate loss of potency.

• Give drug slowly and repeat if needed, usually q 4 to 6 hours.

• Monitor blood pressure closely.

⊗ Incompatibilities

Aminophylline, ampicillin sodium, chlorothiazide, dextrose 10% in lactated Ringer's solution, dextrose 10% in normal saline solution, D_5W, diazoxide, doxapram, edetate calcium disodium, ethacrynate, fructose 10% in normal saline solution, fructose 10% in water, furosemide, hydrocortisone sodium succinate, mephentermine, metaraminol bitartrate, methohexital, nitroglycerin, phenobarbital sodium, verapamil.

Contraindications and cautions

• Contraindicated in patients hypersensitive to the drug or any of its components and in those with coronary artery disease or mitral valvular rheumatic heart disease.

• Use cautiously in patients with suspected cardiac disease, stroke, or severe renal impairment, and in those taking other antihypertensives.

Lifespan: In pregnant women, use cautiously. In breast-feeding women and in children, safety and effectiveness haven't been established.

Adverse reactions

CNS: dizziness, *headache,* peripheral neuritis.
CV: angina, ***arrhythmias,*** orthostatic hypotension, palpitations, tachycardia.
GI: anorexia, diarrhea, nausea, vomiting.
Hematologic: ***agranulocytopenia, leukopenia, neutropenia.***

H

Metabolic: sodium retention, *weight gain.*
Skin: rash.
Other: *lupus-like syndrome.*

Interactions

Drug-drug. *Diazoxide, MAO inhibitors:* May cause severe hypotension. Use together cautiously.
Epinephrine: May decrease pressor effects of epinephrine. Monitor patient's response.
Indomethacin: May decrease hydralazine effects. Monitor patient.
Metoprolol, propranolol: May increase levels and effects of these drugs. Monitor patient closely; adjust dosage of either drug if needed.

Effects on lab test results

- May decrease hemoglobin level and hematocrit.
- May decrease neutrophil, WBC, RBC, granulocyte, and platelet counts.

Pharmacokinetics

Absorption: Rapid after P.O. use; food enhances absorption. Unknown after I.M. use.
Distribution: Wide. 88% to 90% protein-bound.
Metabolism: Extensive, in GI mucosa and liver.
Excretion: Mainly in urine. *Half-life:* 3 to 7 hours.

Route	Onset	Peak	Duration
P.O.	20–30 min	1–2 hr	2–4 hr
I.V.	≤ 5 min	15–30 min	2–6 hr
I.M.	10–30 min	1 hr	2–6 hr

Action

Chemical effect: Unknown. As a direct-acting vasodilator, it relaxes arteriolar smooth muscle.
Therapeutic effect: Lowers blood pressure.

Available forms

Injection: 20 mg/ml
Tablets: 10 mg, 25 mg, 50 mg, 100 mg

NURSING PROCESS

Assessment

- Assess blood pressure before starting therapy and regularly thereafter.
- Monitor CBC, lupus erythematosus cell preparation, and antinuclear antibody titer determination during long-term therapy.
- Be alert for adverse reactions and drug interactions, especially lupus-like reactions at high drug dosages.
- Assess patient's and family's knowledge of drug therapy.

Nursing diagnoses

- Risk for injury related to presence of hypertension
- Excess fluid volume related to sodium retention
- Deficient knowledge related to drug therapy

Planning and implementation

- Give oral form of drug with meals to increase absorption.
- Some clinicians combine hydralazine therapy with diuretics and beta blockers to decrease sodium retention and tachycardia and to prevent angina.
- Compliance may be improved by giving drug twice daily. Check with prescriber.

ALERT: Don't confuse hydralazine with hydroxyzine.

Patient teaching

- Instruct patient to take oral form with meals.
- Inform patient that orthostatic hypotension can be minimized by rising slowly and not changing position suddenly.
- Tell patient not to abruptly stop taking the drug, but to call prescriber if adverse reactions occur.
- Tell patient to limit sodium intake.

Evaluation

- Patient's blood pressure is normal.
- Fluid retention doesn't develop.
- Patient and family state understanding of drug therapy.

hydrochlorothiazide

(high-droh-klor-oh-THIGH-uh-zighd)

Apo-Hydro ♦, Aquazide-H, Dichlotride ◇, Dithiazide ◇, Diuchlor HI, Esidrix, Ezide, HydroDIURIL, Hydro-Par, Microzide, Neo-Codema ♦, Novo-Hydrazide ♦, Nu-Hydro ♦, Oretic, Urozide ♦

Pharmacologic class: thiazide diuretic
Therapeutic class: diuretic, antihypertensive
Pregnancy risk category: D

Indications and dosages

▶ **Edema.** *Adults:* 25 to 100 mg P.O. daily or intermittently.

▶ **Hypertension.** *Adults:* 12.5 to 50 mg P.O. once daily. May increase or decrease daily dosage based on blood pressure.
Children ages 2 to 12: Give 2.2 mg/kg or 60 mg/m^2 P.O. daily in two divided doses. Usual dosage range is 37.5 to 100 mg P.O. daily.
Infants and children ages 6 months to younger than 2 years: 2.2 mg/kg or 60 mg/m^2 P.O. daily in two divided doses. Usual dosage range is 12.5 to 37.5 mg P.O. daily.
Infants younger than age 6 months: Up to 3.3 mg/kg daily in two divided doses.

Contraindications and cautions

- Contraindicated in patients with anuria and in patients hypersensitive to other thiazides or sulfonamide derivatives.
- Use cautiously in patients with severe renal disease, impaired hepatic function, and progressive hepatic disease.

Lifespan: In pregnant women, drug isn't recommended. In breast-feeding women, safety and effectiveness haven't been established. In elderly patients, use lower initial dose.

Adverse reactions

CV: orthostatic hypotension, volume depletion and dehydration.
GI: anorexia, nausea, ***pancreatitis.***
GU: frequent urination, nocturia, polyuria, ***renal impairment.***
Hematologic: ***agranulocytosis, aplastic anemia, leukopenia, thrombocytopenia.***
Hepatic: ***hepatic encephalopathy.***
Metabolic: asymptomatic hyperuricemia, dilutional hyponatremia, fluid and electrolyte imbalances, hypercalcemia, hyperglycemia, hypochloremia, hypokalemia, impaired glucose tolerance, ***metabolic alkalosis.***
Skin: dermatitis, photosensitivity, rash.
Other: ***anaphylactic reactions;*** gout; hypersensitivity reactions, such as pneumonitis and vasculitis.

Interactions

Drug-drug. *Antidiabetics:* May decrease hypoglycemic effectiveness. Monitor glucose level, and adjust dosage if needed.
Antihypertensives: May have additive antihypertensive effect. Use together cautiously; monitor blood pressure closely.
Barbiturates, opioids: May increase orthostatic hypotensive effect. Monitor patient closely.
Bumetanide, ethacrynic acid, furosemide, torsemide: May cause excessive diuretic response, resulting in serious electrolyte abnormalities or dehydration. Adjust doses while monitoring patient for excessive diuretic responses.
Cholestyramine, colestipol: May decrease intestinal absorption of thiazides. Give drugs separately.
Diazoxide: May increase antihypertensive, hyperglycemic, and hyperuricemic effects. Use together cautiously.
Digoxin: May increase risk of digoxin toxicity from hydrochlorothiazide-induced hypokalemia. Monitor potassium and digoxin levels.
Lithium: May decrease lithium excretion, increasing risk of toxicity. Monitor level.
NSAIDs: May increase risk of NSAID-induced renal impairment. Monitor patient closely.
Drug-herb. *Dandelion:* May interfere with diuretic activity. Discourage use together.
Licorice root: May contribute to the potassium depletion caused by thiazides. Discourage use together.
Drug-lifestyle. *Alcohol use:* May increase orthostatic hypotensive effect. Discourage use together.
Sun exposure: May increase photosensitivity. Urge patient to avoid unprotected or prolonged sun exposure.

Effects on lab test results

- May increase glucose, cholesterol, triglyceride, calcium, and uric acid levels. May decrease potassium, sodium, chloride, and hemoglobin levels and hematocrit.
- May decrease granulocyte, WBC, and platelet counts.

Pharmacokinetics

Absorption: Varies with drug forms.
Distribution: 40% to 68% protein-bound.
Metabolism: None.
Excretion: Unchanged in urine. *Half-life:* 5½ to 15 hours.

Route	Onset	Peak	Duration
P.O.	2 hr	4–6 hr	6–12 hr

Action

Chemical effect: Increases sodium and water excretion by inhibiting sodium and chloride reabsorption in the distal segment of the nephron.
Therapeutic effect: Promotes sodium and water excretion, thereby lowering blood pressure.

Available forms

Capsules: 12.5 mg
Oral solution: 50 mg/5 ml
Tablets: 25 mg, 50 mg, 100 mg

NURSING PROCESS

Assessment

- Assess patient's edema or blood pressure before starting therapy.
- Monitor the drug's effectiveness by regularly checking blood pressure, urine output, and weight. In a patient with hypertension, therapeutic response may be delayed several days.
- Monitor electrolyte levels.
- Monitor creatinine and BUN levels regularly. If these levels are more than twice normal, monitor patient for decreased effectiveness.
- Monitor uric acid level, especially in patient with history of gout.
- Be alert for adverse reactions and drug interactions.
- Assess patient's and family's knowledge of drug therapy.

Nursing diagnoses

- Ineffective health maintenance related to presence of edema or hypertension
- Impaired urinary elimination related to diuretic effect of drug
- Deficient knowledge related to drug therapy

Planning and implementation

- Give drug in morning to prevent nocturia.
- If nausea occurs, give drug with food.
- Drug may be used with potassium-sparing diuretic to prevent potassium loss.

Patient teaching

- Advise patient to take drug with food to minimize GI upset.
- Warn patient not to change position suddenly and to rise slowly to avoid orthostatic hypotension.
- Instruct patient not to drink alcohol during drug therapy.
- Advise patient to use sunblock to prevent photosensitivity reactions.
- Tell patient to check with prescriber before taking OTC drugs or herbal remedies.

Evaluation

- Patient's blood pressure is normal, and no edema is present.
- Patient demonstrates adjustment of lifestyle to accommodate altered patterns of urinary elimination.
- Patient and family state understanding of drug therapy.

hydrocortisone
(high-droh-KOR-tuh-sohn)
Cortef, Cortenema, Hydrocortone

hydrocortisone acetate
Cortifoam, Hydrocortone Acetate

hydrocortisone cypionate
Cortef

hydrocortisone sodium phosphate
Hydrocortone Phosphate

hydrocortisone sodium succinate
A-hydroCort, Solu-Cortef

Pharmacologic class: adrenocortical steroid
Therapeutic class: glucocorticoid
Pregnancy risk category: NR

Indications and dosages

▶ **Severe inflammation, adrenal insufficiency.** *Adults:* 20 to 240 mg hydrocortisone or cypionate P.O. daily. Or 5 to 75 mg acetate injected into joints or soft tissue. Give once q 2 to 3 weeks, although some conditions may require weekly injections. Dosage varies with degree of inflammation and size and location of the joint or soft tissues. Or 15 to 240 mg phosphate I.V., I.M., or subcutaneously daily, divided into 12-hour intervals. Or, initially, 100 to 500 mg succinate I.V. or I.M.; may repeat q 2 to 6 hours if needed.

▶ **Adjunct for ulcerative colitis and proctitis.** *Adults:* 1 enema (100 mg) hydrocortisone or acetate P.R. nightly for 21 days.

▶ **Shock.** *Adults:* Initially, 50 mg/kg succinate I.V. repeated in 4 hours or q 24 hours, as needed. Or 0.5 mg to 2 g I.V. q 2 to 6 hours, as needed.

Children: 0.16 to 1 mg/kg or 6 to 30 mg/m^2 phosphate I.M. or succinate I.M. or I.V. daily or b.i.d.

I.V. administration

- Don't use acetate or suspension form I.V.
- Hydrocortisone sodium phosphate may be added directly to D_5W or normal saline solution for I.V. administration.
- Reconstitute hydrocortisone sodium succinate with bacteriostatic water or bacteriostatic sodium chloride solution before adding to I.V. solutions. When giving by direct I.V. injection, inject over at least 30 seconds. For infusion, dilute with D_5W, normal saline solution, or D_5W in normal saline solution to 1 mg/ml or less.
- When giving as direct injection, inject directly into vein or I.V. line containing free-flowing compatible solution over 30 seconds to several minutes.
- When giving as intermittent or continuous infusion, dilute solution per manufacturer's instructions and give over prescribed duration. If used for continuous infusion, change solution every 24 hours.

⊗ **Incompatibilities**

Hydrocortisone sodium phosphate: doxapram, mitoxantrone, sargramostim.

Hydrocortisone sodium succinate: amobarbital, ampicillin sodium, bleomycin, ciprofloxacin, colistimethate, cytarabine, dacarbazine, diazepam, dimenhydrinate, ephedrine, ergotamine, furosemide, heparin sodium, hydralazine, idarubicin, Ionosol B with invert sugar 10%, kanamycin, methylprednisolone sodium succinate, midazolam, nafcillin, pentobarbital sodium, phenobarbital sodium, phenytoin, prochlorperazine edisylate, promethazine hydrochloride, sargramostim, vancomycin, vitamin B complex with C.

Contraindications and cautions

- Contraindicated in patients hypersensitive to drug or any of its components, and in those with systemic fungal infections. Hydrocortisone sodium succinate is contraindicated in premature infants.
- Use cautiously in patients with GI ulcer, renal disease, hypertension, osteoporosis, diabetes mellitus, hypothyroidism, cirrhosis, diverticulitis, nonspecific ulcerative colitis, recent intestinal anastomoses, thromboembolic disorders, seizures, myasthenia gravis, heart failure, tuberculosis, ocular herpes simplex, emotional instability, psychotic tendencies, and recent MI.

Lifespan: In pregnant women, use cautiously. In breast-feeding women, use cautiously. Drug isn't recommended in high doses. In children, use cautiously because long-term use may delay growth and maturation.

Adverse reactions

Most adverse reactions are dose- or duration-dependent.

CNS: *euphoria, insomnia,* pseudotumor cerebri, psychotic behavior, ***seizures.***

CV: ***arrhythmias,*** edema, ***heart failure,*** hypertension, ***thromboembolism.***

EENT: cataracts, glaucoma.

GI: GI irritation, increased appetite, ***pancreatitis,*** peptic ulceration.

Metabolic: carbohydrate intolerance, hyperglycemia, hypokalemia.

Musculoskeletal: growth suppression in children, muscle weakness, osteoporosis.

Skin: acne, delayed wound healing, easy bruising, hirsutism, various skin eruptions.

Other: ***acute adrenal insufficiency with increased stress (infection, surgery, or trauma) or abrupt withdrawal after long-term therapy,*** susceptibility to infections.

Interactions

Drug-drug. *Aspirin, indomethacin, NSAIDs:* May increase risk of GI distress and bleeding. Give together cautiously.

Barbiturates, phenytoin, rifampin: May decrease corticosteroid effect; may require increased dosage.

Live-attenuated virus vaccines, other toxoids and vaccines: May decrease antibody response and increase risk of neurologic complications. Avoid use together.

Oral anticoagulants: May alter dosage requirements. Monitor PT and INR closely.

Potassium-depleting drugs (such as thiazide diuretics): May enhance potassium-wasting effects of hydrocortisone. Monitor potassium level.

Skin-test antigens: May decrease skin response. Defer skin testing until therapy is completed.
Drug-lifestyle. *Alcohol use:* May increase risk of GI effects. Discourage use together.

Effects on lab test results

- May increase glucose and cholesterol levels. May decrease potassium and calcium levels.

Pharmacokinetics

Absorption: Rapid after P.O. use. Variable after I.M. or intra-articular injection. Unknown after rectal use.
Distribution: To muscle, liver, skin, intestines, and kidneys. Extensively protein-bound. Only unbound portion is active.
Metabolism: Metabolized in liver.
Excretion: Inactive metabolites and small amounts of unmetabolized drug excreted in urine; insignificant amount in feces. *Half-life:* 8 to 12 hours.

Route	Onset	Peak	Duration
P.O., I.V., I.M., P.R.	Varies	Varies	Varies

Action

Chemical effect: Not clearly defined; may stabilize leukocyte lysosomal membranes, suppress immune response, stimulate bone marrow, and influence nutrient metabolism.
Therapeutic effect: Reduces inflammation, suppresses immune function, and raises adrenocorticoid hormonal levels.

Available forms

hydrocortisone
Enema: 100 mg/60 ml
Tablets: 5 mg, 10 mg, 20 mg
hydrocortisone acetate
Enema: 10% aerosol foam (provides 90 mg/application)
Injection: 25-mg/ml*, 50-mg/ml* suspension
Suppositories: 25 mg
hydrocortisone cypionate
Oral suspension: 10 mg/5 ml
hydrocortisone sodium phosphate
Injection: 50-mg/ml solution
hydrocortisone sodium succinate
Injection: 100 mg/vial*, 250 mg/vial*, 500 mg/vial*, 1,000 mg/vial*

NURSING PROCESS

Assessment

- Assess patient's condition before starting therapy and regularly thereafter.
- Monitor patient's weight, blood pressure, and electrolyte levels.
- Monitor patient for stress. Fever, trauma, surgery, and emotional problems may increase adrenal insufficiency.
- Periodically measure growth and development during high-dose or prolonged therapy in infants and children.
- Be alert for adverse reactions and drug interactions.
- Assess patient's and family's knowledge of drug therapy.

Nursing diagnoses

- Ineffective health maintenance related to underlying condition
- Ineffective protection related to immunosuppression
- Deficient knowledge related to drug therapy

Planning and implementation

- For better results and less toxicity, give once-daily dose in morning.
- Give oral dose with food.
- Give I.M. injection deep into gluteal muscle. Rotate injection sites to prevent muscle atrophy.
- Rectal suppositories may produce the same systemic effects as other forms of hydrocortisone. If therapy must exceed 21 days, stop gradually by giving every other night for 2 or 3 weeks.

ALERT: Avoid subcutaneous injection because atrophy and sterile abscesses may occur.

- Injectable forms aren't used for alternate-day therapy.
- High-dose therapy usually doesn't continue beyond 48 hours.
- Always adjust to lowest effective dose, and gradually reduce dosage after long-term therapy.
- Give potassium supplements.
- If evidence of adrenal insufficiency appears, notify prescriber and increase dosage.
- Notify prescriber about adverse reactions. Provide supportive care.

ALERT: Avoid abbreviating drug as HCT, which can be misread as HCTZ (hydrochlorothiazide).

ALERT: Don't confuse Solu-Cortef with Solu-Medrol.

Patient teaching

- Teach patient signs of early adrenal insufficiency (fatigue, muscle weakness, joint pain, fever, anorexia, nausea, dyspnea, dizziness, and fainting).
- Instruct patient to carry or wear medical identification that identifies need for supplemental systemic glucocorticoids during stress.

ALERT: Tell patient not to abruptly stop taking the drug without prescriber's consent. Abruptly stopping therapy may lead to rebound inflammation, fatigue, weakness, arthralgia, fever, dizziness, lethargy, depression, fainting, orthostatic hypotension, dyspnea, anorexia, and hypoglycemia. After prolonged use, sudden withdrawal may be fatal.

- Warn patient receiving long-term therapy about cushingoid symptoms, and tell him to report sudden weight gain or swelling to prescriber.
- Advise him to consider exercise or physical therapy, to ask his prescriber about vitamin D or calcium supplements, and to have periodic ophthalmic examinations.
- Warn patient about easy bruising.

Evaluation

- Patient's condition improves.
- Serious complications related to drug-induced immunosuppression don't develop.
- Patient and family state understanding of drug therapy.

hydromorphone hydrochloride (dihydromorphinone hydrochloride)

(high-droh-MOR-fohn high-droh-KLOR-ighd)

Dilaudid, Dilaudid-HP

Pharmacologic class: opioid
Therapeutic class: analgesic, antitussive
Pregnancy risk category: C
Controlled substance schedule: II

Indications and dosages

▶ **Moderate to severe pain.** *Adults:* 2 to 4 mg P.O. q 4 to 6 hours p.r.n. Or 1 to 2 mg I.M., subcutaneously, or I.V. (slowly over at least 2 to 3 minutes) q 4 to 6 hours p.r.n. Or 3-mg rectal suppository q 6 to 8 hours p.r.n.

▶ **Cough.** *Adults:* 1 mg P.O. q 3 to 4 hours p.r.n.
Children ages 6 to 12: Give 0.5 mg P.O. q 3 to 4 hours p.r.n.

I.V. administration

- For infusion, drug may be mixed in D_5W, normal saline solution, D_5W in normal saline solution, D_5W in half-normal saline solution, or Ringer's or lactated Ringer's solutions.
- For direct injection, give over at least 2 minutes.
- Respiratory depression and hypotension may occur. Monitor respiration and circulation often.

⊗ Incompatibilities

Alkalines, amphotericin B cholesterol complex, ampicillin sodium, bromides, cefazolin, dexamethasone, diazepam, gallium nitrate, haloperidol, heparin sodium, iodides, minocycline, phenobarbital sodium, phenytoin sodium, prochlorperazine edisylate, sargramostim, sodium bicarbonate, sodium phosphate, thiopental.

Contraindications and cautions

- Contraindicated in patients hypersensitive to drug or any of its components, patients with intracranial lesions from increased intracranial pressure, patients with status asthmaticus, and whenever ventilatory function is depressed in the absence of resuscitative equipment. Also contraindicated as obstetric analgesia.
- Use with extreme caution in patients with COPD, cor pulmonale, a substantially decreased respiratory reserve, hypoxia, hypercapnia, or respiratory depression. Use cautiously in debilitated patients and in patients with hepatic or renal disease, hypothyroidism, Addison disease, prostatic hypertrophy, urethral stricture, CNS depression or coma, toxic psychosis, gallbladder disease, acute alcoholism, alcohol withdrawal, kyphoscoliosis, or sulfite sensitivity (because drug contains sodium metabisulfite and may cause allergic-type reactions, including anaphylactic symptoms or asthmatic episodes, especially in people with asthma). Also use cautiously after GI surgery.

Lifespan: In pregnant women, use only if potential benefits to mother outweigh risks to fetus. During labor and delivery, don't use drug. Women shouldn't breast-feed while receiving drug. In children, safety and effectiveness haven't been established except as listed for cough. In elderly patients, use cautiously.

Adverse reactions

CNS: *clouded sensorium, dizziness, euphoria, sedation,* ***seizures,*** *somnolence.*
CV: ***bradycardia,*** hypotension.
EENT: blurred vision, diplopia, nystagmus.
GI: constipation, ileus, nausea, vomiting.
GU: urine retention.
Respiratory: ***bronchospasm, respiratory depression.***
Other: induration with repeated subcutaneous injections, physical dependence.

Interactions

Drug-drug. *CNS depressants, general anesthetics, hypnotics, MAO inhibitors, other opioid analgesics, sedatives, tranquilizers, tricyclic antidepressants:* May have additive effects. Use together cautiously. Reduce hydromorphone dose, and monitor patient response.
Drug-lifestyle. *Alcohol use:* May have additive effects. Discourage use together.

Effects on lab test results

- May increase amylase and lipase levels.

Pharmacokinetics

Absorption: Good.
Distribution: Unknown.
Metabolism: Mainly in liver.
Excretion: Mainly in urine. *Half-life:* 2½ to 4 hours.

Route	Onset	Peak	Duration
P.O.	30 min	30 min–2 hr	4–5 hr
I.V.	10–15 min	15–30 min	2–3 hr
I.M.	15 min	30–60 min	4–5 hr
SubQ	15 min	30–90 min	4 hr
P.R.	Unknown	Unknown	4 hr

Action

Chemical effect: Binds with opiate receptors in CNS, altering perception of and emotional response to pain. Suppresses cough reflex by direct action on cough center in medulla.
Therapeutic effect: Relieves pain and cough.

Available forms

Injection: 1 mg/ml, 2 mg/ml, 4 mg/ml, 10 mg/ml
Injection (lyophilized powder): 250 mg/vial
Liquid: 5 mg/5 ml
Suppositories: 3 mg
Tablets: 2 mg, 4 mg, 8 mg

NURSING PROCESS

Assessment

- Assess patient's pain or cough before and after giving drug.
- Drug may worsen or mask gallbladder pain.
- Drug is a commonly abused opioid. Be alert for addictive behavior or drug abuse.
- Be alert for adverse reactions and drug interactions.
- Assess patient's and family's knowledge of drug therapy.

Nursing diagnoses

- Acute pain related to underlying condition
- Ineffective breathing pattern related to respiratory depression
- Deficient knowledge related to drug therapy

Planning and implementation

- For better analgesic effect, give drug before patient's pain becomes intense.
- Dilaudid-HP, a highly concentrated form (10 mg/ml), may be given in smaller volumes to prevent discomfort caused by large-volume I.M. or subcutaneous injections. Check dosage carefully.
- To avoid induration with subcutaneous injection, rotate injection sites.
- Keep resuscitation equipment and opioid antagonist (naloxone) available.
- Postoperatively, encourage patient to turn, cough, and deep-breathe to avoid atelectasis.
- Recommend increased intake of fiber and fluids and a stool softener to prevent constipation during maintenance therapy.
- Signs and symptoms of overdose include respiratory depression, CNS depression progressing to stupor or coma, flaccid muscles, cold and clammy skin, bradycardia, hypotension, and constricted pupils. Severe overdose may include apnea, circulatory collapse, cardiac arrest, and death.
- To treat overdose, ensure a patent airway and provide ventilation as needed. If patient is con-

scious and received the oral form of drug, gastric lavage or induced emesis may be useful in removing unabsorbed drug. If patient is unconscious and has a secure airway, activated charcoal may be given by NG tube; a saline cathartic or sorbitol may be added to the first dose. If patient has significant respiratory or circulatory depression, give naloxone; use caution if patient may be physically dependent on hydromorphone. Provide symptomatic and supportive treatment, including I.V. fluids, vasopressors, and other measures as needed.

Patient teaching

- Advise ambulatory patient to be careful when getting out of bed or walking. Warn patient to avoid activities that require mental alertness until the drug's CNS effects are known.
- Encourage patient to ask for drug before pain becomes severe.
- If patient's respiratory rate decreases, tell patient or caregiver to notify prescriber.
- Instruct patient to avoid alcohol consumption during drug therapy.

Evaluation

- Patient is free from pain.
- Patient maintains adequate breathing patterns.
- Patient and family state understanding of drug therapy.

hydroxychloroquine sulfate

(high-droks-ee-KLOR-oh-kwin SUL-fayt)
Plaquenil

Pharmacologic class: 4-aminoquinoline
Therapeutic class: antimalarial, anti-inflammatory
Pregnancy risk category: C

Indications and dosages

▶ **Suppressive prophylaxis of malaria attacks caused by *Plasmodium vivax, P. malariae, P. ovale,* and susceptible strains of *P. falciparum.*** *Adults:* 310 mg base P.O. weekly on same day of week. Begin 1 to 2 weeks before exposure and continue for 4 weeks after leaving endemic areas.
Children: 5 mg base/kg P.O. weekly, not to exceed 310 mg.
Patients untreated before exposure: Initial loading dose is doubled (620 mg for adults, 10 mg/kg for children) P.O. in two divided doses 6 hours apart.

▶ **Acute malarial attacks.** *Adults:* Initially, 620 mg base P.O.; then 310 mg base after 6 hours; then 310 mg base daily for 2 days.
Children: Initial dose, 10 mg base/kg (up to 620 mg base); second dose, 5 mg base/kg (up to 310 mg base) 6 hours after first dose; third dose, 5 mg base/kg 18 hours after second dose; fourth dose, 5 mg base/kg 24 hours after third dose.

▶ **Lupus erythematosus (chronic discoid and systemic).** *Adults:* 400 mg (sulfate) P.O. daily or b.i.d., continued for several weeks or months, depending on response. Prolonged maintenance dosage: 200 to 400 mg (sulfate) daily.

▶ **Rheumatoid arthritis.** *Adults:* Initially, 400 to 600 mg (sulfate) P.O. daily. When good response occurs (usually in 4 to 12 weeks), reduce dosage by 50% and continue at 200 to 400 mg daily.

Contraindications and cautions

- Contraindicated in patients hypersensitive to the drug or any of its components and in patients with retinal or visual field changes or porphyria.
- Use cautiously in patients with severe GI, neurologic, or blood disorders, and in patients with hepatic disease or alcoholism because drug concentrates in liver. Also use cautiously in those with G6PD deficiency or psoriasis because drug may worsen these conditions.

Lifespan: In pregnant women, use cautiously. In breast-feeding women, safety and effectiveness haven't been established. In children who need long-term therapy, drug is contraindicated.

Adverse reactions

CNS: ataxia, dizziness, fatigue, hypoactive deep tendon reflexes, irritability, lassitude, nightmares, nystagmus, psychic stimulation, ***seizures,*** toxic psychosis, vertigo.
EENT: ototoxicity, retinopathy, serious visual disturbances.
GI: abdominal cramps, anorexia, diarrhea, nausea, vomiting.
Hematologic: ***agranulocytosis, aplastic anemia, hemolysis in patients with G6PD deficiency, leukopenia, thrombocytopenia.***
Metabolic: weight loss.

Musculoskeletal: skeletal muscle weakness.
Skin: alopecia, bleaching of hair, lichen planus eruptions, pleomorphic skin eruptions, pruritus, skin and mucosal pigment changes.

Interactions

Drug-drug. *Aluminum and magnesium salts, kaolin:* May decrease GI absorption. Separate administration times.
Cimetidine: May decrease hepatic metabolism of hydroxychloroquine. Monitor patient for toxicity.
Epinephrine: Vasopressor effects are inhibited by hydroxyzine. Use a different vasopressor, if needed.

Effects on lab test results

- May decrease hemoglobin level and hematocrit.
- May decrease granulocyte, WBC, and platelet counts.

Pharmacokinetics

Absorption: Good and almost complete.
Distribution: Concentrates in liver, spleen, kidneys, heart, and brain and is strongly bound in melanin-containing cells. Drug is protein-bound.
Metabolism: By liver.
Excretion: Mostly unchanged in urine. *Half-life:* 32 to 50 days.

Route	Onset	Peak	Duration
P.O.	Unknown	2–4½ hr	Unknown

Action

Chemical effect: May bind to and alter properties of DNA in susceptible organisms.
Therapeutic effect: Prevents or hinders growth of *P. malariae, P. ovale, P. vivax,* and *P. falciparum.* Relieves inflammation.

Available forms

Tablets: 200 mg (equivalent to 155-mg base)

NURSING PROCESS

Assessment

- Assess patient's condition before starting therapy and regularly thereafter.
- Make sure baseline and periodic ophthalmic examinations are performed because blindness can occur. Check periodically for ocular muscle weakness after long-term use.
- Obtain audiometric tests before, during, and after therapy, especially long-term therapy.
- Monitor CBC and liver function studies periodically during long-term therapy.
- Assess patient for overdose, which can quickly lead to headache, drowsiness, visual disturbances, CV collapse, and seizures, followed by cardiopulmonary arrest. Children are extremely susceptible to toxicity, so don't give them long-term therapy.
- Be alert for adverse reactions and drug interactions.
- Assess patient's and family's knowledge of drug therapy.

Nursing diagnoses

- Risk for infection related to susceptible organisms
- Disturbed sensory perception (visual and auditory) related to adverse reactions to drug
- Deficient knowledge related to drug therapy

Planning and implementation

- Give drug right before or after meals on same day of each week.
- Notify prescriber immediately about severe blood disorder that can't be attributed to disease. Blood reaction may require stopping the drug.

Patient teaching

- Advise patient to take drug immediately before or after meals on same day each week to enhance compliance for prophylaxis.
- If adverse CNS or visual disturbances occur, warn patient to avoid hazardous activities.
- Tell patient to promptly report visual or auditory changes.

Evaluation

- Patient is free from infection.
- Patient maintains normal visual and auditory function.
- Patient and family state understanding of drug therapy.

hydroxyurea

(high-droks-ee-yoo-REE-uh)

Droxia, Hydrea, Mylocel

Pharmacologic class: antimetabolite
Therapeutic class: antineoplastic; antisickling drug
Pregnancy risk category: D

Indications and dosages

Dosage and indications for hydroxyurea may vary. Check current literature for recommended protocol.

▶ **Solid tumors.** *Adults:* 80 mg/kg Hydrea or Mylocel P.O. as a single dose q 3 days; or 20 to 30 mg/kg Hydrea or Mylocel P.O. as a single daily dose.

▶ **Head and neck cancers, excluding the lip.** *Adults:* 80 mg/kg Hydrea or Mylocel P.O. as a single dose q 3 days.

▶ **Resistant chronic myelocytic leukemia.** *Adults:* 20 to 30 mg/kg Hydrea or Mylocel P.O. as a single daily dose.

▶ **To reduce the frequency of painful crises and to reduce the need for blood transfusions in patients with sickle cell anemia with recurrent moderate-to-severe painful crises (typically at least 3 during the preceding 12 months).** *Adults:* Base dosage on the patient's actual or ideal weight, whichever is less. The initial dose is 15 mg/kg Droxia P.O. as a single daily dose. The patient's blood count must be monitored every 2 weeks; see package insert for dosage adjustment.

Contraindications and cautions

- Contraindicated in patients hypersensitive to the drug or any of its components and in those with marked bone marrow depression and severe anemia.
- Use cautiously in patients with renal dysfunction and in the elderly.

Lifespan: In pregnant women, use only if benefits outweigh risks to fetus. In breast-feeding women, drug is contraindicated. In children, safety and effectiveness haven't been established. Elderly patients may be more sensitive to the drug and require a lower dosage.

Adverse reactions

CNS: disorientation, dizziness, drowsiness, fever, hallucinations, headache, malaise, ***seizures.***
GI: anorexia, diarrhea, nausea, stomatitis, vomiting.
GU: ***renal toxicity.***
Hematologic: anemia, ***bone marrow suppression, leukopenia, megaloblastosis, thrombocytopenia.***
Metabolic: hyperuricemia.
Skin: mucositis, pruritus, rash.
Other: chills.

Interactions

Drug-drug. *Cytotoxic drugs, radiation therapy:* May enhance toxicity of hydroxyurea. Use together cautiously.

Effects on lab test results

- May increase liver enzyme, BUN, creatinine, and uric acid levels. May decrease hemoglobin level and hematocrit.
- May decrease WBC, RBC, and platelet counts.

Pharmacokinetics

Absorption: Good. Level is higher with a large, single dose than with divided doses.
Distribution: Crosses blood-brain barrier.
Metabolism: 50% of dose degraded in liver.
Excretion: 50% of drug in urine as unchanged drug; metabolites excreted through lungs as carbon dioxide and in urine as urea. *Half-life:* 3 to 4 hours.

Route	Onset	Peak	Duration
P.O.	Unknown	2 hr	Unknown

Action

Chemical effect: Unknown; thought to inhibit DNA synthesis.
Therapeutic effect: Hinders growth of certain cancer cells.

Available forms

Capsules: 200 mg, 300 mg, 400 mg, 500 mg
Tablets: 1,000 mg

NURSING PROCESS

Assessment

- Assess patient's condition before therapy and regularly thereafter.

• Measure CBC, BUN, uric acid, and creatinine levels.
• Auditory and visual hallucinations and hematologic toxicity increase with decreased renal function.
• Radiation therapy may increase risk or severity of GI distress or stomatitis.
• Be alert for adverse reactions and drug interactions.
• Assess patient's and family's knowledge of drug therapy.

Nursing diagnoses

• Ineffective health maintenance related to presence of neoplastic disease
• Ineffective protection related to adverse hematologic reactions
• Deficient knowledge related to drug therapy

Planning and implementation

ALERT: Patients who have received or are currently receiving interferon may be at a greater risk of cutaneous vasculitic toxicities. Monitor them closely.
• Keep patient hydrated.
• Dosage modification may be needed after chemotherapy or radiation therapy.
• Bone marrow suppression is dose-limited and dose-related, with rapid recovery.

Patient teaching

• If patient can't swallow capsules, tell him to empty contents of capsules into water and drink immediately.
• Warn patient to watch for signs of infection (fever, sore throat, fatigue) and bleeding (easy bruising, nosebleed, bleeding gums, melena). Instruct patient to take infection-control and bleeding precautions. Tell patient to take temperature daily.
• Tell patient or caregiver to wear gloves when handling drug or its container and to wash their hands before and after contact with the bottle or capsule. If powder from capsule is spilled, wipe it up immediately with a damp towel and dispose of the towel in a closed container, such as a plastic bag.
• Advise woman of childbearing age not to become pregnant during therapy and to consult with prescriber before becoming pregnant.

Evaluation

• Patient responds well to drug therapy.
• Serious infections or bleeding complications don't develop.
• Patient and family state understanding of drug therapy.

hydroxyzine embonate ◇

(high-DROKS-ih-zeen EM-boh-nayt)
Atarax

hydroxyzine hydrochloride

Apo-Hydroxyzine ♦, Atarax, Hydroxacen, Hyzine-50, Multipax ♦, Neucalm, Novo-Hydroxyzin ♦, QYS, Vistacon-50, Vistaject-50, Vistaril

hydroxyzine pamoate

Vistaril

Pharmacologic class: piperazine derivative
Therapeutic class: anxiolytic, sedative, antihistamine, antipruritic, antiemetic, antispasmodic
Pregnancy risk category: C

Indications and dosages

▶ **Anxiety.** *Adults:* 50 to 100 mg P.O. q.i.d.
Children age 6 and older: 50 to 100 mg P.O. daily in divided doses.
Children younger than age 6: Give 50 mg P.O. daily in divided doses.
▶ **Preoperative and postoperative adjunct therapy.** *Adults:* 25 to 100 mg I.M. q 4 to 6 hours.
Children: 1.1 mg/kg I.M. q 4 to 6 hours.
▶ **Pruritus from allergies.** *Adults:* 25 mg P.O. t.i.d. or q.i.d.
Children age 6 and older: 50 to 100 mg P.O. daily in divided doses.
Children younger than age 6: Give 50 mg P.O. daily in divided doses.
▶ **Psychiatric and emotional emergencies, including acute alcoholism.** *Adults:* 50 to 100 mg I.M. q 4 to 6 hours p.r.n.
▶ **Nausea and vomiting (excluding nausea and vomiting of pregnancy).** *Adults:* 25 to 100 mg I.M.
Children: 1.1 mg/kg I.M.
▶ **Prepartum and postpartum adjunct therapy.** *Adults:* 25 to 100 mg I.M.

Contraindications and cautions

- Contraindicated in patients hypersensitive to hydroxyzine or cetirizine.

Lifespan: In early pregnancy, drug is contraindicated. In breast-feeding women, safety and effectiveness haven't been established. In elderly patients, use cautiously and at lower doses.

Adverse reactions

CNS: *drowsiness,* involuntary motor activity.
GI: *dry mouth.*
Other: hypersensitivity reactions, marked discomfort at I.M. injection site.

Interactions

Drug-drug. *CNS depressants:* May increase CNS depression. Avoid use together.
Epinephrine: Inhibits and reverses vasopressor effect of epinephrine. If vasopressor is required, don't use epinephrine.
MAO inhibitors: May enhance anticholinergic effects. Use together cautiously.
Drug-lifestyle. *Alcohol use:* May increase CNS depression. Discourage use together.
Sun exposure: Photosensitivity may occur. Urge patient to avoid unprotected or prolonged sun exposure.

Effects on lab test results

- May cause false elevations of urine 17-hydroxycorticosteroids, depending on test method used.

Pharmacokinetics

Absorption: Rapid and complete after P.O. use. Unknown for I.M. use.
Distribution: Unknown.
Metabolism: Almost complete.
Excretion: Mainly in urine. *Half-life:* 3 hours.

Route	Onset	Peak	Duration
P.O.	15–30 min	2 hr	4–6 hr
I.M.	Unknown	Unknown	4–6 hr

Action

Chemical effect: Unknown; may suppress activity in key regions of subcortical area of CNS.
Therapeutic effect: Relieves anxiety and itching, promotes calmness, and alleviates nausea and vomiting.

Available forms

hydroxyzine embonate
Capsules: 25 mg, 50 mg
hydroxyzine hydrochloride
Capsules: 10 mg ◇, 25 mg, 50 mg, 100 mg
Injection: 25 mg/ml*, 50 mg/ml*
Syrup: 10 mg/5 ml*
Tablets: 10 mg, 25 mg, 50 mg, 100 mg
Tablets (film-coated): 10 mg, 25 mg, 50 mg
hydroxyzine pamoate
Capsules: 25 mg, 50 mg, 100 mg
Oral suspension: 25 mg/5 ml

NURSING PROCESS

Assessment

- Assess patient's condition before therapy and regularly thereafter.
- Be alert for adverse reactions and drug interactions.
- Assess patient's and family's knowledge of drug therapy.

Nursing diagnoses

- Ineffective health maintenance related to underlying condition
- Risk for injury related to adverse CNS reactions
- Deficient knowledge related to drug therapy

Planning and implementation

- Give a lower dose to an elderly or debilitated patient.
- Parenteral form (hydroxyzine hydrochloride) for I.M. use only; Z-track injection method is preferred. Aspirate I.M. injection carefully to prevent inadvertent intravascular injection. Inject deep into large muscle mass.

ALERT: Never give drug I.V.
ALERT: Don't confuse hydroxyzine with hydralazine.

Patient teaching

- Warn patient to avoid hazardous activities until CNS effects of drug are known.
- Tell patient to avoid alcohol during drug therapy.
- Suggest sugarless hard candy or gum to relieve dry mouth.

Evaluation

- Patient has improved health.
- Patient doesn't experience injury.

H

• Patient and family state understanding of drug therapy.

ibandronate sodium

(ih-BAN-druh-nayt SOH-dee-um)
Boniva

Pharmacologic class: bisphosphonate
Therapeutic class: bone resorption inhibitor
Pregnancy risk category: C

Indications and dosages

▶ **Postmenopausal osteoporosis.** *Adults:* For treatment or prevention, 2.5 mg P.O. daily or 150 mg P.O. once monthly. Drug should be taken first thing in the morning with a large glass of plain water, 1 hour before food or other drugs, and patient must remain standing or seated upright for 60 minutes. Or, for treatment only, 3 mg I.V. bolus over 15 to 30 seconds once q 3 months.

I.V. administration

• Injection is for I.V. use only. Don't give I.M. or subcutaneously.
• Give the 3-mg/3-ml dose using the ¾-inch safety needle provided with the prefilled 5-ml syringe.
• Syringes are for single use only.
• Inspect prefilled syringe for particles and discoloration before giving. Don't use if particles are visible or product is discolored.

⊗ **Incompatibilities**
Calcium-containing solutions and other I.V. drugs.

Contraindications and cautions

• Contraindicated in patients hypersensitive to ibandronate and patients with uncorrected hypocalcemia. Oral form contraindicated in patients who are unable to stand or sit upright for 60 minutes. Not recommended for patients with severe renal impairment (creatinine clearance less than 30 ml/minute).
• Use cautiously in patients with a history of GI disorders.

Lifespan: In pregnant women, use only if benefits outweigh risks to fetus. In breast-feeding women, use cautiously because it isn't known if drug appears in breast milk. In children, safety and effectiveness haven't been established.

Adverse reactions

CNS: asthenia, dizziness, headache, insomnia, nerve root lesion, vertigo.
CV: hypertension.
EENT: nasopharyngitis, pharyngitis.
GI: abdominal pain, constipation, diarrhea, *dyspepsia,* gastritis, nausea, vomiting.
GU: UTI.
Musculoskeletal: arthralgia, arthritis, *back pain,* joint disorder, limb pain, localized osteoarthritis, muscle cramps, myalgia, osteonecrosis.
Respiratory: bronchitis, pneumonia, upper respiratory tract infection.
Skin: rash.
Other: allergic reaction, infection, influenza, tooth disorder.

Interactions

Drug-drug. *Aspirin, NSAIDs:* May increase GI irritation. Use together cautiously.
Aluminum-, calcium-, magnesium-, or iron-containing products: May decrease ibandronate absorption. Give ibandronate 60 minutes before vitamins, minerals, or antacids.
Drug-food. *Food, milk, and beverages other than water:* May decrease ibandronate absorption. Give drug on an empty stomach with plain water.
Drug-lifestyle. *Alcohol use:* May decrease ibandronate absorption and increase risk of esophageal irritation. Discourage use together.

Effects on lab test results

• May increase cholesterol level. May decrease total alkaline phosphatase level.
• May interfere with bone-imaging agents.

Pharmacokinetics

Absorption: Absorbed in the upper GI tract; bioavailability is low and significantly impaired by food or non-water beverages.
Distribution: Rapidly binds to bone or is eliminated.
Metabolism: Not metabolized.

Excretion: Unchanged in urine and feces; 50% to 60% excreted by kidneys. *Half-life:* 37 to 157 hours in patients taking the 150-mg dose.

Route	Onset	Peak	Duration
P.O.	Unknown	½–2 hr	Unknown
I.V.	Rapid	Unknown	Unknown

Action

Chemical effect: Inhibits the osteoclast activity of bone breakdown and removal to reduce bone loss.

Therapeutic effect: Increases bone mass.

Available forms

Injection: 3-mg/3-ml prefilled syringe
Tablets: 2.5 mg, 150 mg

NURSING PROCESS

Assessment

- Assess patient for adequate intake of calcium and vitamin D.
- Monitor patient for signs or symptoms of esophageal irritation, including dysphagia, painful swallowing, retrosternal pain, and heartburn.
- Monitor patient for bone, joint, and muscle pain, which may be severe or incapacitating.
- Watch for signs and symptoms of uveitis and scleritis.
- Assess patient's and family's knowledge of drug therapy.

Nursing diagnoses

- Risk for injury related to decreased bone mass
- Risk for deficient fluid volume related to drug-induced GI upset
- Deficient knowledge related to drug therapy

Planning and implementation

- Correct hypocalcemia or other disturbances of bone and mineral metabolism before therapy.
- Give drug in the morning 60 minutes before the first meal or fluid and before any other drugs.

ALERT: Bisphosphonates may lead to osteonecrosis, mainly in the jaw. Dental surgery may worsen the condition. If the patient needs dental procedures, assess the risk of stopping ibandronate.

- Signs of possible overdose include hypocalcemia, hypophosphatemia, upset stomach, dyspepsia, esophagitis, gastritis, or ulcer.
- Treatment of overdose includes giving milk or antacids to enhance binding of ibandronate. Avoid emesis to minimize gastric irritation. Keep patient upright during management of overdose. Dialysis isn't helpful.

Patient teaching

- Tell patient receiving I.V. form, if she misses a dose, reschedule the missed dose as soon as possible. Subsequent injections should be rescheduled once every 3 months from that dose. She shouldn't receive more than one dose in a 3-month timeframe.
- Tell patient taking the monthly dose to take it on the same date each month and to wait at least 7 days between doses if she misses a scheduled dose.
- Instruct patient to take drug 60 minutes before eating or drinking in the morning and before any other drugs, including OTC products, such as calcium, antacids, and vitamins.
- Advise patient to swallow drug whole with a full glass of plain water while standing or sitting and to remain upright for at least 60 minutes after taking drug.
- Caution patient to take only with plain water and no other beverage.
- Instruct patient not to chew or suck on the tablet.
- Advise patient to take calcium and vitamin D supplements as directed by prescriber.
- Tell patient to report any bone, joint, or muscle pain.
- Advise patient to stop drug and immediately report signs and symptoms of esophageal irritation, such as dysphagia, painful swallowing, retrosternal pain, or heartburn.

Evaluation

- Patient does not suffer any injury related to decreased bone mass.
- Patient maintains adequate hydration.
- Patient and family state understanding of drug therapy.

ibuprofen

(igh-byoo-PROH-fen)

ACT-3 ◇, Advil†, Advil Children's, Advil Infants' Drops†, Advil Junior Strength†, Advil Liqui-Gels†, Advil Migraine†, Apo-Ibuprofen ♦, Brufen ◇, Genpril Caplets†, Genpril Tablets†, Haltran†, IBU†, Ibu-Tab†, Junior Strength Motrin†, Menadol, Midol Cramp†, Midol IB, Motrin, Motrin Children's†, Motrin Drops†, Motrin IB Caplets†, Motrin IB Gelcaps†, Motrin IB Tablets† Motrin Infants' Drops†, Motrin Migraine Pain Caplets†, Novo-Profen, Nurofen, Rafen ◇, Saleto-200

Pharmacologic class: NSAID
Therapeutic class: analgesic, antipyretic, anti-inflammatory
Pregnancy risk category: B

Indications and dosages

▶ **Rheumatoid arthritis, osteoarthritis.** *Adults:* 300 to 800 mg P.O. t.i.d. or q.i.d., not to exceed 3.2 g P.O. daily.
Children: 20 to 40 mg/kg P.O. daily, divided into three to four doses.

▶ **Mild to moderate pain, dysmenorrhea.** *Adults:* 400 mg P.O. q 4 to 6 hours p.r.n.
Children ages 6 months to 12 years: 10 mg/kg per dose P.O. q 6 to 8 hours. Maximum, 40 mg/kg daily.

▶ **Fever, minor aches and pains.** *Adults and children older than age 12:* Give 200 to 400 mg P.O. q 4 to 6 hours p.r.n. Don't exceed 1.2 g P.O. daily or give for longer than 3 days for fever or 10 days for pain unless directed by prescriber.
Children ages 6 months to 12 years: If temperature is below 102.5° F (39° C), recommended dosage is 5 mg/kg P.O. q 6 to 8 hours p.r.n. Treat higher temperatures with 10 mg/kg P.O. q 6 to 8 hours p.r.n. to maximum dosage of 40 mg/kg daily.

Contraindications and cautions

- Contraindicated in patients hypersensitive to the drug or any of its components and in those with nasal polyps, angioedema, and bronchospastic reaction to aspirin or other NSAIDs.
- Use cautiously in patients with GI disorders, history of peptic ulcer disease, hepatic or renal disease, cardiac decompensation, hypertension, or intrinsic coagulation defects.

Lifespan: In pregnant and breast-feeding women, use cautiously. In infants younger than age 6 months, safety and effectiveness haven't been established. In elderly patients, use with caution and at a lower dose because they are at greater risk for adverse GI effects.

Adverse reactions

CNS: aseptic meningitis, cognitive dysfunction, *dizziness, drowsiness, headache.*
CV: edema, ***heart failure,*** hypertension, *peripheral edema.*
EENT: *tinnitus,* visual disturbances.
GI: epigastric distress, nausea, ***occult blood loss,*** peptic ulceration.
GU: reversible renal failure.
Hematologic: agranulocytosis, anemia, ***aplastic anemia, leukopenia, neutropenia, pancytopenia,*** prolonged bleeding time, ***thrombocytopenia.***
Respiratory: ***bronchospasm.***
Skin: photosensitivity reactions, pruritus, rash, ***Stevens-Johnson syndrome,*** urticaria.

Interactions

Drug-drug. *Antihypertensives, furosemide, thiazide diuretics:* May decrease effectiveness of diuretics or antihypertensives. Monitor patient.
Aspirin: May decrease drug level and increase risk of adverse GI reactions. Monitor patient.
Corticosteroids: May increase risk of adverse GI reactions. Avoid use together.
Cyclosporine: May increase nephrotoxicity of both drugs. Avoid use together.
Digoxin: May increase digoxin level. Monitor level closely for digoxin toxicity.
Lithium, oral anticoagulants: May increase levels or effects of these drugs. Monitor patient for toxicity.
Methotrexate: May increase risk of methotrexate toxicity. Monitor patient closely.
Probenecid: May increase level and toxicity of NSAIDs. Monitor patient for signs of toxicity.
Drug-herb. *Dong quai, feverfew, garlic, ginger, horse chestnut, red clover:* May increase risk of bleeding. Monitor patient closely for bleeding.
St. John's wort: May increase risk of photosensitivity reactions. Advise patient to avoid unprotected or prolonged exposure to sunlight.

Drug-lifestyle. *Alcohol use:* May increase risk of adverse GI reactions. Discourage use together.
Smoking: May increase risk for gastric ulceration. Discourage use together.
Sun exposure: May cause photosensitivity reactions. Advise patient to avoid unprotected or prolonged exposure to sunlight.

Effects on lab test results

- May increase BUN, creatinine, ALT, AST, potassium levels. May decrease glucose and hemoglobin levels and hematocrit.
- May decrease neutrophil, WBC, RBC, platelet, and granulocyte counts.

Pharmacokinetics

Absorption: Rapid and complete from GI tract.
Distribution: Highly protein-bound.
Metabolism: Undergoes biotransformation in liver.
Excretion: Mainly in urine, with some biliary excretion. *Half-life:* 2 to 4 hours.

Route	Onset	Peak	Duration
P.O.	≤ 30 min	2–4 hr	≥ 4 hr

Action

Chemical effect: May inhibit prostaglandin synthesis.
Therapeutic effect: Relieves pain, fever, and inflammation.

Available forms

Caplets: 200 mg†
Capsules (liquid-filled): 200 mg†
Oral drops: 40 mg/ml†
Oral suspension: 100 mg/5 ml†
Tablets: 100 mg†, 200 mg†, 400 mg†, 600 mg, 800 mg
Tablets (chewable): 50 mg†, 100 mg†
Tablets (film-coated): 100 mg†, 200 mg†, 400 mg†, 600 mg, 800 mg

NURSING PROCESS

Assessment

- Assess patient's underlying condition before starting therapy.
- Evaluate patient for relief from pain, fever, or inflammation. Full effects on arthritis may take 2 to 4 weeks.
- Check renal and hepatic function periodically in long-term therapy.
- Be alert for adverse reactions and drug interactions.
- Assess patient's and family's knowledge of drug therapy.

Nursing diagnoses

- Chronic pain related to underlying condition
- Risk for injury related to drug-induced adverse reactions
- Deficient knowledge related to drug therapy

Planning and implementation

- Give with meals or milk to reduce adverse GI reactions.
- If drug is ineffective, notify prescriber.
- If renal or hepatic abnormalities occur, stop drug and notify prescriber.

Patient teaching

- Tell patient to take drug with meals or milk to reduce adverse GI reactions.
- Tell adult patient using OTC drug not to exceed 1.2 g daily, not to give drug to children younger than age 12, and not to take drug for extended periods without consulting prescriber.
- Ibuprofen can negate the antiplatelet effect of low-dose aspirin therapy. Tell patient how to safely use ibuprofen in relation to aspirin therapy.
- Warn patient that using drug with aspirin, alcohol, or corticosteroids may increase the risk of adverse GI reactions.
- Serious GI toxicity, including peptic ulceration and bleeding, can occur in patients taking NSAIDs, despite absence of GI symptoms.
- Teach patient to recognize and report signs and symptoms of GI bleeding.
- Instruct patient not to drink alcohol during therapy.
- Instruct patient to use sunblock, wear protective clothing, and avoid prolonged exposure to sunlight.
- Inform patient that some ankle swelling may occur, but tell him to call prescriber promptly if weight increases by 3 to 5 pounds/week, or he develops shortness of breath, cough, or palpitations.

Evaluation

- Patient is free from pain.
- Patient doesn't experience injury from adverse reactions.

• Patient and family state understanding of drug therapy.

ibutilide fumarate

(igh-BYOO-tih-lighd FYOO-muh-rayt)
Corvert

Pharmacologic class: ibutilide derivative
Therapeutic class: class III antiarrhythmic
Pregnancy risk category: C

Indications and dosages

▶ **Rapid conversion of recent atrial fibrillation or atrial flutter to sinus rhythm.** *Adults who weigh 60 kg (132 lb) or more:* 1 mg I.V. over 10 minutes.
Adults who weigh less than 60 kg (132 lb): 0.01 mg/kg I.V. over 10 minutes.

I.V. administration

• Give undiluted or diluted in 50 ml of diluent. Add to normal saline solution for injection or D_5W injection before infusion. Add contents of one 10-ml vial (0.1 mg/ml) to a 50-ml infusion bag to form admixture of about 0.017 mg/ml ibutilide fumarate. Drug is compatible with polyvinyl chloride plastic bags and polyolefin bags.
• Admixtures with approved diluents are chemically and physically stable for 24 hours at room temperature or 48 hours if refrigerated.
• Inspect parenteral drugs for particles and discoloration before giving.
• Stop infusion if arrhythmia stops or if patient develops sustained or nonsustained ventricular tachycardia or significantly prolonged QT interval. If arrhythmia doesn't stop within 10 minutes after infusion ends, give a second 10-minute infusion of equal strength.

⊗ **Incompatibilities**
None reported.

Contraindications and cautions

• Contraindicated in patients hypersensitive to the drug or any of its components.
• Contraindicated for use in patients with history of polymorphic ventricular tachycardia, such as torsades de pointes.
• Use cautiously in patients with hepatic or renal dysfunction; usually, no dosage adjustments are needed.

Lifespan: In pregnant women, use cautiously. In breast-feeding women and in children, safety and effectiveness haven't been established.

Adverse reactions

CNS: headache, syncope.
CV: ***AV block, bradycardia,*** bundle branch block, ***heart failure,*** hypertension, hypotension, ***nonsustained ventricular tachycardia,*** palpitations, ***QT interval prolongation, sustained polymorphic ventricular tachycardia,*** tachycardia, ventricular extrasystoles.
GI: nausea.
GU: ***renal failure.***

Interactions

Drug-drug. *Class IA antiarrhythmics (such as disopyramide, procainamide, quinidine), other class III drugs (such as amiodarone, sotalol):* May increase risk of prolonged refractory state. Avoid use together.
Digoxin: Supraventricular arrhythmias may mask cardiotoxicity from excessive digoxin levels. Use cautiously.
H_1-receptor antagonist antihistamines, phenothiazines, tetracyclic antidepressants, tricyclic antidepressants, other drugs that prolong QT interval: May increase risk of proarrhythmias. Monitor patient closely.

Effects on lab test results

None reported.

Pharmacokinetics

Absorption: Given I.V.
Distribution: Highly distributed. About 40% protein-bound.
Metabolism: Not clearly defined.
Excretion: In urine and feces. *Half-life:* Averages about 6 hours.

Route	Onset	Peak	Duration
I.V.	Unknown	Unknown	Unknown

Action

Chemical effect: Prolongs action potential in isolated cardiac myocyte and increases atrial and ventricular refractoriness; has mainly class III properties.
Therapeutic effect: Restores normal sinus rhythm.

Available forms

Injection: 0.1 mg/ml in 10-ml vials

NURSING PROCESS

Assessment

- Assess patient's arrhythmia before starting therapy.

ALERT: Monitor ECG continuously during therapy and for at least 4 hours afterward (or until QT interval returns to baseline) because drug can induce or worsen ventricular arrhythmias. If ECG shows arrhythmias, monitor it longer.

- Be alert for adverse reactions and drug interactions.
- Assess patient's and family's knowledge of drug therapy.

Nursing diagnoses

- Decreased cardiac output related to arrhythmias
- Risk for injury related to life-threatening arrhythmias
- Deficient knowledge related to drug therapy

Planning and implementation

- Drug should be given only by skilled personnel. During and after administration, have available proper equipment and facilities for a cardiac emergency, such as cardiac monitor, intracardiac pacer, cardioverter or defibrillator, and drugs for sustained ventricular tachycardia.
- Correct hypokalemia and hypomagnesemia before therapy to reduce risk of proarrhythmia.

Patient teaching

- Tell patient to promptly report adverse reactions, especially headaches, dizziness, weakness, palpitations, or chest pains.
- Instruct patient to report any discomfort at injection site.

Evaluation

- Patient regains normal sinus rhythm.
- Life-threatening arrhythmia doesn't develop.
- Patient and family state understanding of drug therapy.

idarubicin hydrochloride

(igh-duh-ROO-bih-sin high-droh-KLOR-ighd)

Idamycin PFS

Pharmacologic class: anthracycline antibiotic
Therapeutic class: antineoplastic
Pregnancy risk category: D

Indications and dosages

▶ **Acute myeloid leukemia, including French-American-British classifications M1 through M7, with other approved antileukemic drugs.** *Adults:* 12 mg/m² by slow I.V. injection (over 10 to 15 minutes) daily for 3 days with 100 mg/m² of cytarabine by continuous I.V. infusion daily for 7 days or cytarabine as 25-mg/m² bolus followed by 200 mg/m² by continuous infusion daily for 5 days. Give second course, if needed. If patient develops severe mucositis, don't give until recovery is complete, and reduce dosage by 25%.

Adjust-a-dose: For patients with hepatic or renal impairment, reduce dosage. If bilirubin level is above 5 mg/dl, withhold drug.

I.V. administration

- Preparation and administration of drug have carcinogenic, mutagenic, and teratogenic risks. Follow facility policy to reduce risks.
- Reconstitute to final concentration of 1 mg/ml using normal saline solution for injection. Add 5 ml to 5-mg vial or 10 ml to 10-mg vial. Don't use bacteriostatic saline solution. Vial is under negative pressure.
- Give over 10 to 15 minutes into free-flowing I.V. infusion of normal saline solution or D_5W running into large vein. If extravasation occurs, stop infusion immediately, elevate limb, and notify prescriber. Apply intermittent ice packs for 30 minutes immediately and then 30 minutes q.i.d. for 4 days. Consult plastic surgery promptly if pain, erythema, edema, vesication, or ulceration occurs.
- Reconstituted solutions are stable for 72 hours at 59° to 86° F (15° to 30° C), 7 days if refrigerated. Label unused solutions with chemotherapy hazard label.

⊗ **Incompatibilities**

Acyclovir sodium, alkaline solutions, allopurinol, ampicillin sodium with sulbactam, cefazolin, cefepime, ceftazidime, clindamycin phosphate, dexamethasone sodium phosphate, etoposide, furosemide, gentamicin, heparin, hydrocortisone sodium succinate, lorazepam, meperidine, methotrexate sodium, piperacillin sodium with tazobactam, sodium bicarbonate, teniposide, vancomycin, vincristine.

Contraindications and cautions

- Use cautiously in patients with bone marrow suppression induced by previous drug therapy or radiotherapy and in patients with impaired hepatic or renal function, heart disease, or previous therapy with anthracyclines at high cumulative doses or other potentially cardiotoxic drugs.

Lifespan: In pregnant and breast-feeding women, use cautiously. In children, safety and effectiveness haven't been established.

Adverse reactions

CNS: *altered mental status, fever, headache,* peripheral neuropathy, ***seizures.***
CV: ***arrhythmias,*** atrial fibrillation, ***cardiomyopathy,*** chest pain, ***heart failure, MI,*** myocardial insufficiency, ***myocardial toxicity.***
GI: *cramps, diarrhea, mucositis, nausea,* ***severe enterocolitis with perforation,*** *vomiting.*
Hematologic: HEMORRHAGE, MYELOSUPPRESSION.
Skin: *alopecia,* bullous erythrodermatous rash on palms and soles, erythema at previously irradiated sites, rash, tissue necrosis at injection site if extravasation occurs, urticaria, urticaria at injection site.
Other: INFECTION.

Interactions

None reported.

Effects on lab test results

- May increase BUN, creatinine, and uric acid and levels. May decrease hemoglobin level and hematocrit.
- May increase liver function test values. May decrease RBC, WBC, and platelet counts.

Pharmacokinetics

Absorption: Given I.V.
Distribution: 97% lipophilic and tissue-bound, with highest levels in nucleated blood and bone marrow cells.
Metabolism: Extensively outside of liver. Metabolite is cytotoxic.
Excretion: Mainly biliary. *Half-life:* 20 to 22 hours.

Route	Onset	Peak	Duration
I.V.	Unknown	≤ 3 min	Unknown

Action

Chemical effect: May inhibit nucleic acid synthesis by intercalation; interacts with enzyme topoisomerase II.
Therapeutic effect: Hinders growth of susceptible leukemic cells.

Available forms

Powder for injection: 1 mg/ml available in 5-, 10-, and 20-mg vials

NURSING PROCESS

Assessment

- Assess patient's condition before starting therapy and regularly thereafter.
- Assess patient for systemic infection, and control infection before therapy begins.
- Monitor CBC and hepatic and renal function test results frequently.
- Be alert for adverse reactions and drug interactions, especially signs of heart failure, infection, and hemorrhage.
- Assess patient's and family's knowledge of drug therapy.

Nursing diagnoses

- Ineffective health maintenance related to presence of underlying condition
- Ineffective protection related to adverse hematologic reactions
- Deficient knowledge related to drug therapy

Planning and implementation

- Take appropriate preventive measures (including adequate hydration) before starting treatment.

ALERT: Never give drug I.M. or subcutaneously.

- Hyperuricemia may result from rapid destruction of leukemic cells. Give allopurinol.

ALERT: Don't confuse idarubicin with daunorubicin, doxorubicin, or epirubicin.

Patient teaching

- Teach patient to recognize and report signs of extravasation, infection, bleeding, and heart failure, such as shortness of breath and leg swelling.

• Advise patient that red urine for several days is normal and doesn't indicate blood in urine.
• Advise women of childbearing age to use a reliable contraceptive during therapy and to consult with prescriber before becoming pregnant.

Evaluation
• Patient responds well to drug.
• Serious adverse hematologic reactions don't develop.
• Patient and family state understanding of drug therapy.

ifosfamide

(igh-FOHS-fuh-mighd)
IFEX

Pharmacologic class: alkylating drug
Therapeutic class: antineoplastic
Pregnancy risk category: D

Indications and dosages

▶ **Testicular cancer.** *Adults:* 1.2 g/m² I.V. daily for 5 consecutive days. Repeat q 3 weeks or after patient recovers from hematologic toxicity.
▶ **Lung cancer, Hodgkin and malignant lymphoma, breast cancer, acute lymphocytic leukemia, ovarian cancer, gastric cancer, pancreatic cancer, sarcomas, cervical cancer, and uterine cancer‡.** *Adults:* 1.2 to 2.5 g/m² I.V. daily for 3 to 5 days, with cycles of therapy repeated as needed.

I.V. administration

• Follow facility policy to reduce risks. Preparation and administration are linked to carcinogenic, mutagenic, and teratogenic risks.
• Reconstitute each gram of drug with 20 ml of diluent to yield 50 mg/ml. Use sterile water for injection or bacteriostatic water for injection. Solutions may be further diluted with sterile water, dextrose 2.5% or 5% in water, half-normal or normal saline solution for injection, D_5W and normal saline solution for injection, or lactated Ringer's injection.
• Infuse each dose over at least 30 minutes.
• Ifosfamide and mesna are physically compatible and may be mixed in same I.V. solution.
• Reconstituted solution is stable for 1 week at room temperature or 6 weeks if refrigerated. If drug was reconstituted with sterile water, however, use solution within 6 hours.

⊗ **Incompatibilities**
Cefepime, methotrexate sodium.

Contraindications and cautions

• Contraindicated in patients hypersensitive to the drug or any of its components and in those with severely depressed bone marrow function.
• Use cautiously in patients with renal impairment or compromised bone marrow from leukopenia, granulocytopenia, extensive bone marrow metastases, previous radiation therapy, or previous therapy with cytotoxic drugs.
Lifespan: In pregnant and breast-feeding women, drug is contraindicated. In children, safety and effectiveness haven't been established.

Adverse reactions

CNS: ataxia, ***coma,*** *confusion, depressive psychosis,* lethargy, ***seizures,*** *somnolence.*
GI: *nausea, vomiting.*
GU: *hematuria, hemorrhagic cystitis,* ***nephrotoxicity.***
Hematologic: ***leukopenia, myelosuppression, thrombocytopenia.***
Metabolic: ***metabolic acidosis.***
Skin: *alopecia.*
Other: infection.

Interactions

Drug-drug. *Anticoagulants, aspirin:* May increase risk of bleeding. Avoid use together.
Barbiturates, chloral hydrate, phenytoin: May increase ifosfamide toxicity by inducing hepatic enzymes that hasten formation of toxic metabolites. Monitor patient closely.
Mesna: May decrease ifosfamide-induced bladder toxicity. May be given together.
Myelosuppressants: May enhance hematologic toxicity. Dosage adjustment may be needed.

Effects on lab test results

• May increase BUN, creatinine, bilirubin, and liver enzyme levels. May decrease hemoglobin level and hematocrit.
• May decrease WBC, RBC, and platelet counts.

Pharmacokinetics

Absorption: Given I.V.

Distribution: Crosses blood-brain barrier, but its metabolites don't, so alkylation doesn't occur in CSF.
Metabolism: About 50% of dose is metabolized in liver.
Excretion: Mainly in urine. *Half-life:* About 14 hours.

Route	Onset	Peak	Duration
I.V.	Unknown	Unknown	Unknown

Action

Chemical effect: Cross-links strands of cellular DNA and interferes with RNA transcription, which causes growth imbalance that leads to cell death.
Therapeutic effect: Kills cancer cells.

Available forms

Injection: 1 g (supplied with 200-mg ampule of mesna), 3 g (supplied with 400-mg ampule of mesna)

NURSING PROCESS

Assessment

- Assess patient's condition before starting therapy and regularly thereafter.
- Obtain urinalysis before each dose. If microscopic hematuria is present, evaluate patient for hemorrhagic cystitis. Adjust dosage of mesna, a protecting agent given with drug, if needed.
- Monitor CBC and renal and liver function test results.
- Be alert for adverse reactions and drug interactions.
- Assess patient for mental status changes. Dosage may need to be decreased or therapy stopped.
- Assess patient's and family's knowledge of drug therapy.

Nursing diagnoses

- Ineffective health maintenance related to presence of cancer
- Ineffective protection related to adverse CNS and hematologic reactions
- Deficient knowledge related to drug therapy

Planning and implementation

- Give antiemetic before giving drug to decrease nausea.
- Give drug with mesna to prevent hemorrhagic cystitis. Give mesna with or before drug to prevent cystitis. Give at least 2 L of fluids daily, either P.O. or I.V.
- Don't give drug at bedtime; infrequent voiding at night may increase risk of cystitis. If cystitis develops, stop giving drug and notify prescriber.
- Bladder irrigation with normal saline solution may decrease possibility of cystitis.
- Institute infection control and bleeding precautions.

ALERT: Don't confuse ifosfamide with cyclophosphamide.

Patient teaching

- Tell patient to void frequently to minimize contact of drug and its metabolites with bladder mucosa.
- Warn patient to watch for evidence of infection (fever, sore throat, fatigue), CNS effects (somnolence and dizziness), and bleeding (easy bruising, nosebleed, bleeding gums, melena). Teach patient about infection-control and bleeding precautions, and tell him to report adverse effects. Tell him to take his temperature daily.
- Instruct patient to avoid OTC drugs that contain aspirin.
- Stress importance of adequate fluid intake. Explain that it may help prevent hemorrhagic cystitis.
- Warn patient that hyperpigmentation may occur.

Evaluation

- Patient responds well to drug.
- Serious infections and CNS and bleeding complications don't develop.
- Patient and family state understanding of drug therapy.

iloprost

(IGH-loe-prost)
Ventavis

Pharmacologic class: prostacyclin analogue
Therapeutic class: vasodilator
Pregnancy risk category: C

Indications and dosages

▶ **Pulmonary arterial hypertension in patients with New York Heart Association Class**

III or IV symptoms. *Adults:* Initially, 2.5 mcg inhaled using the Prodose AAD System. As tolerated, increase to 5 mcg inhaled six to nine times daily while awake, p.r.n., but no more than q 2 hours. Maximum, 5 mcg nine times daily.

Contraindications and cautions

- No known contraindications. Don't use in patients whose systolic blood pressure is less than 85 mm Hg.
- Use drug cautiously in patients who have hepatic or renal impairment and in patients with COPD, severe asthma, or acute pulmonary infection.

Lifespan: In pregnant women, use only if benefits outweigh risk to fetus. In breast-feeding women, breast-feeding should be stopped because it isn't known if drug appears in breast milk. In children, safety and effectiveness haven't been established. In elderly patients, use cautiously and start with a low dosage.

Adverse reactions

CNS: *headache,* insomnia, *syncope.*
CV: chest pain, ***heart failure,*** *hypotension,* palpitations, peripheral edema, ***supraventricular tachycardia,*** *vasodilation.*
EENT: tongue pain.
GI: *nausea,* vomiting.
GU: ***renal failure.***
Musculoskeletal: back pain, muscle cramps, *trismus.*
Respiratory: *cough,* dyspnea, hemoptysis, pneumonia, ***pulmonary edema.***
Other: *flulike syndrome.*

Interactions

Drug-drug. *Anticoagulants:* May increase the risk of bleeding. Monitor patient closely.
Antihypertensive drugs, vasodilators: May increase effects of these drugs. Monitor patient's blood pressure.

Effects on lab test results

- May increase alkaline phosphatase and GGT levels.

Pharmacokinetics

Absorption: No GI absorption.
Distribution: 60% protein-bound, mainly to albumin.
Metabolism: To inactive metabolites.
Excretion: Mainly in urine; some in feces. *Half-life:* 20 to 30 minutes.

Route	Onset	Peak	Duration
Inhalation	Unknown	Unknown	30–60 min

Action

Chemical effect: Lowers pulmonary arterial pressure by dilating systemic and pulmonary arterial beds. Drug also affects platelet aggregation, although effect in pulmonary hypertension treatment isn't known.
Therapeutic effect: Improved exercise tolerance, fewer symptoms, and lack of deterioration.

Available forms

Inhalation solution: 10 mcg/ml (given only using the I-neb delivery system); 20 mcg/2-ml single-use ampule (should be given using the Prodose AAD delivery system, but can be done with the I-neb)

NURSING PROCESS

Assessment

- Assess patient's underlying condition, and assess regularly thereafter.
- Monitor patient's vital signs carefully at start of treatment.
- Monitor patient for syncope.
- Monitor patient for evidence of pulmonary edema; stop treatment immediately.
- Assess patient's and family's knowledge of drug therapy.

Nursing diagnoses

- Ineffective tissue perfusion (cardiopulmonary) related to underlying condition
- Risk for injury related to drug-induced syncope
- Deficient knowledge related to drug therapy

Planning and implementation

- Keep drug away from skin and eyes.
- Administer drug only through Prodose AAD device.
- Take care not to inhale drug while providing treatment.
- Overdose may cause hypotension, headache, flushing, nausea, vomiting, and diarrhea.

• To treat overdose, stop the inhalation session as needed. Monitor patient closely, and provide symptomatic treatment.

Patient teaching

• Advise patient to take drug exactly as prescribed using Prodose AAD.
• Urge patient to follow manufacturer's instructions for preparing and inhaling drug.
• Advise patient to keep a backup Prodose AAD in case the original malfunctions.
• Tell patient to keep drug away from skin and eyes and to rinse the area immediately if contact occurs.
• Caution patient not to ingest the drug solution.
• Inform patient that drug may cause dizziness and fainting. Urge him to stand up slowly from a sitting or lying position and to report worsening of symptoms.
• Tell patient to take drug before physical exertion but no more than every 2 hours.
• Discourage exposing other people—especially pregnant women and babies—to drug.
• Teach patient how to clean equipment and safely dispose of used ampules after each treatment. Caution patient not to save or use leftover solution.

Evaluation

• Patient's pulmonary artery pressure decreases and patient reaches pulmonary hemodynamic stability.
• Patient maintains a stable blood pressure and doesn't experience syncope.
• Patient and family state understanding of drug therapy.

imatinib mesylate

(ih-MAH-tin-nib MEH-suh-layt)
Gleevec

Pharmacologic class: protein-tyrosine kinase inhibitor
Therapeutic class: antineoplastic
Pregnancy risk category: D

Indications and dosages

▶ **Chronic myeloid leukemia (CML) in blast crisis, in accelerated phase, or in chronic phase after failure of interferon-alpha therapy; newly diagnosed Philadelphia chromosome–positive (Ph+) chronic-phase CML.** *Adults:* For chronic-phase CML, 400 mg P.O. daily as single dose with a meal and large glass of water. For accelerated-phase CML or blast crisis, 600 mg P.O. daily as single dose with a meal and large glass of water. Continue treatment as long as patient continues to benefit. May increase daily dose to 600 mg P.O. in chronic phase or to 800 mg P.O. (400 mg P.O. b.i.d.) in accelerated phase or blast crisis. Increase dosage only if no severe adverse reactions and no severe non–leukemia-related neutropenia or thrombocytopenia occur in the following circumstances: disease progression (at any time), failure to achieve a satisfactory hematologic response after at least 3 months of treatment, or loss of a previously achieved hematologic response.
Children age 2 and older: For newly diagnosed Ph+ chronic-phase CML only, give 340 mg/m²/day P.O. Don't exceed 600 mg.
▶ **Patients with kit (CD117)-positive unresectable or metastatic malignant GI stromal tumors (GIST).** *Adults:* 400 or 600 mg P.O. daily.
▶ **Philadelphia chromosome–positive chronic-phase CML in patients whose disease has recurred after stem cell transplant or who are resistant to interferon-alpha therapy.** *Children age 3 and older:* 260 mg/m² P.O. as single daily dose or divided into two doses, taken with a meal and large glass of water. May increase dosage to 340 mg/m² daily.
Adjust-a-dose: Withhold treatment or reduce dosage based on bilirubin or liver transaminase levels, severity of fluid retention, or hematologic toxicities.

Contraindications and cautions

• Contraindicated in patients hypersensitive to the drug or any of its components.
• Use cautiously in hepatically impaired patients.
Lifespan: In pregnant and breast-feeding women, drug is contraindicated. In children younger than age 3, safety and effectiveness haven't been established. In elderly patients, use cautiously because they may have an increased risk of edema when taking drug.

Adverse reactions

CNS: CEREBRAL HEMORRHAGE, *dizziness, fatigue, fever, headache, insomnia,* weakness.
CV: *edema,* ***heart failure.***

EENT: *epistaxis,* nasopharyngitis.
GI: *abdominal pain, anorexia,* constipation, *diarrhea, dyspepsia,* **GI HEMORRHAGE,** *nausea, vomiting.*
GU: ***renal failure.***
Hematologic: *anemia,* **HEMORRHAGE,** ***neutropenia, thrombocytopenia.***
Hepatic: ***liver toxicity.***
Metabolic: *hypokalemia, weight increase.*
Musculoskeletal: arthralgia, *muscle cramps, musculoskeletal pain, myalgia.*
Respiratory: *cough,* dyspnea, *nasopharyngitis, pleural effusion,* pneumonia, ***pulmonary edema,*** *upper respiratory tract infection.*
Skin: petechiae, pruritus, *rash.*
Other: night sweats.

Interactions

Drug-drug. *Acetaminophen:* May increase risk of liver toxicity. Monitor patient.
Cyclosporine, dihydropyridine calcium channel blockers, certain HMG-CoA reductase inhibitors, pimozide, triazolobenzodiazepines: May increase levels of these drugs. Monitor drug levels and patient for toxicity.
CYP3A4 inducers (carbamazepine, dexamethasone, phenobarbital, phenytoin, rifampin): May increase metabolism and decrease imatinib level. Use cautiously.
CYP3A4 inhibitors (clarithromycin, erythromycin, itraconazole, ketoconazole): May decrease metabolism and increase imatinib level. Monitor patient for toxicity.
Warfarin: May alter warfarin metabolism. Avoid use together; instead, use standard heparin or a low–molecular-weight heparin.
Drug-herb. *St. John's wort:* May decrease drug effects. Warn patient not to use together.

Effects on lab test results

- May increase creatinine, bilirubin, alkaline phosphatase, AST, and ALT levels. May decrease potassium and hemoglobin levels and hematocrit.
- May decrease neutrophil and platelet counts.

Pharmacokinetics

Absorption: Well absorbed.
Distribution: 98% protein-bound.
Metabolism: Mainly by CYP3A4.
Excretion: Mainly in feces as metabolites.
Half-life: 18 to 40 hours.

Route	Onset	Peak	Duration
P.O.	Unknown	2–4 hr	Unknown

Action

Chemical effect: Inhibits Bcr-Abl tyrosine kinase, the abnormal tyrosine kinase created in CML. Inhibits tumor growth of Bcr-Abl–transfected murine myeloid cells and Bcr-Abl–positive leukemia lines derived from CML patients in blast crisis.
Therapeutic effect: Stops tumor growth.

Available forms

Tablets: 100 mg, 400 mg

NURSING PROCESS

Assessment

- Assess neoplastic disease before starting therapy, and reassess regularly.
- Obtain baseline weight before starting therapy, and then weigh patient daily. Evaluate and treat unexpected and rapid weight gain.
- Assess patient's and family's knowledge of drug therapy.
- Monitor patient closely for fluid retention, which can be severe.
- Monitor CBC weekly for first month, biweekly for second month, and periodically thereafter.
- Monitor liver function test results carefully because severe hepatotoxicity may occur. Decrease dosage as needed.
- Because the long-term safety of this drug isn't known, carefully monitor renal toxicity, liver toxicity, and immunosuppression.

Nursing diagnoses

- Ineffective health maintenance related to neoplastic disease
- Risk for falls related to drug-induced adverse reactions
- Deficient knowledge related to drug therapy

Planning and implementation

- For CML, increase dosage only if no severe adverse reactions and no severe non–leukemia-related neutropenia or thrombocytopenia has occurred under the following circumstances: disease progression (at any time), failure to achieve a satisfactory hematologic response after at least 3 months of treatment, or loss of a previously achieved hematologic response.

• Because GI irritation is common, give drug with food.
• For patients unable to swallow tablets, dissolve tablets in water or apple juice (50 ml for 100-mg tablet or 200 ml for 400-mg tablet). Stir and have patient drink immediately.

Patient teaching
• Instruct patient to take drug with food and a large glass of water.
• Urge patient to report to the prescriber any adverse effects, such as fluid retention, signs of bleeding, or infection.
• Advise patient to have periodic liver and kidney function tests and tests to determine blood counts.
• Tell patient to avoid OTC products with acetaminophen.

Evaluation
• Patient shows positive response to drug therapy on follow-up studies.
• Patient doesn't experience falls.
• Patient and family state understanding of drug therapy.

imipenem and cilastatin sodium
(im-ih-PEN-em and sigh-luh-STAT-in SO-dee-um)
Primaxin IM, Primaxin IV

Pharmacologic class: carbapenem (thienamycin class); beta-lactam antibiotic
Therapeutic class: antibiotic
Pregnancy risk category: C

Indications and dosages
▶ **Mild to moderate lower respiratory tract, skin, skin structure, intra-abdominal, and gynecologic infections; serious lower respiratory and urinary tract, intra-abdominal, and gynecologic infections; bacterial septicemia; bone and joint infections; serious soft-tissue infections; endocarditis; polymicrobic infections.** *Adults who weigh at least 70 kg (154 lb):* 500 to 750 mg I.M. q 12 hours. Or 250 mg to 1 g I.V. q 6 to 8 hours. Maximum I.V. dosage is 50 mg/kg or 4 g daily, whichever is less.
Children age 3 months and older: 15 to 25 mg/kg I.V. q 6 hours. Maximum dosage for fully susceptible organisms is 2 g daily and for moderately susceptible organisms, 4 g daily (based on adult studies).
Infants ages 4 weeks to 3 months and weighing at least 1.5 kg (3.3 lb): 25 mg/kg I.V. q 6 hours.
Neonates ages 1 to 4 weeks and weighing at least 1.5 kg: 25 mg/kg I.V. q 8 hours.
Neonates younger than 1 week and weighing at least 1.5 kg: 25 mg/kg I.V. q 12 hours.
Adjust-a-dose: For patients who weigh less than 70 kg (154 lb), use lower dose or longer intervals between doses if needed.

For patients with renal impairment, if creatinine clearance is 6 to 20 ml/minute, give 125 to 250 mg I.V. q 12 hours. If clearance is less then 5 ml/minute, withhold drug unless hemodialysis starts within 48 hours.

I.V. administration
• When reconstituting powder, shake until solution is clear. Solutions may range from colorless to yellow; variations of color within this range don't affect drug's potency. After reconstitution, solution is stable for 10 hours at room temperature and for 48 hours when refrigerated.
• Don't give drug by direct I.V. bolus injection. Give 250- or 500-mg dose by I.V. infusion over 20 to 30 minutes. Infuse each 1-g dose over 40 to 60 minutes. If nausea occurs, slow infusion.

⊗ **Incompatibilities**
Antibiotics, dextrose 5% in lactated Ringer's injection, other I.V. drugs including allopurinol, amiodarone, amphotericin B cholesterol complex, azithromycin, etoposide, fluconazole, gemcitabine, lorazepam, meperidine, midazolam, milrinone, sargramostim, sodium bicarbonate.

Contraindications and cautions
• Contraindicated in patients hypersensitive to drug or any of its components.
• Use cautiously in patients allergic to penicillins or cephalosporins and in those with history of seizure disorders, especially if they also have compromised renal function.
Lifespan: In pregnant women, use cautiously. In breast-feeding women, use cautiously because it's unknown if drug appears in breast milk. In children younger than age 12, I.M. safety and effectiveness haven't been established. In children with CNS infections, I.V. use isn't recommended because of risk of seizures. In children who weigh less than 30 kg (66 lb)

with renal impairment, use is contraindicated. In elderly patients, use cautiously because they may have decreased renal function.

Adverse reactions

CNS: dizziness, fever, ***seizures,*** somnolence.
CV: hypotension, thrombophlebitis.
GI: diarrhea, nausea, ***pseudomembranous colitis,*** vomiting.
Skin: pruritus, rash, urticaria.
Other: hypersensitivity reactions ***(anaphylaxis),*** pain at injection site.

Interactions

Drug-drug. *Beta-lactam antibiotics:* May cause in vitro antagonism. Avoid use together.
Cyclosporine: May increase adverse CNS effects of both drugs, possibly because of additive or synergistic toxicity. Avoid use together.
Ganciclovir: May cause seizures. Avoid use together.
Probenecid: May increase cilastatin levels. Avoid use together.

Effects on lab test results

- May increase BUN, creatinine, ALT, AST, alkaline phosphatase, bilirubin, and LDH levels. May decrease hemoglobin level and hematocrit.
- May increase eosinophil count. May decrease WBC and platelet counts.

Pharmacokinetics

Absorption: Imipenem is about 75% bioavailable; cilastatin is about 95% bioavailable.
Distribution: Rapid and wide. About 20% of imipenem is protein-bound; 40% of cilastatin is protein-bound.
Metabolism: Imipenem is metabolized by kidney dehydropeptidase I, resulting in low urine levels. Cilastatin inhibits this enzyme, reducing imipenem metabolism.
Excretion: About 70% excreted unchanged by kidneys. *Half-life:* 1 hour after I.V. dose; 2 to 3 hours after I.M. dose.

Route	Onset	Peak	Duration
I.V.	Unknown	Immediate	Unknown
I.M.	Unknown	1–2 hr	Unknown

Action

Chemical effect: Imipenem is bactericidal and inhibits bacterial cell wall synthesis. Cilastatin inhibits enzymatic breakdown of imipenem in kidneys, making it effective in urinary tract.
Therapeutic effect: Kills susceptible organisms, including many gram-positive, gram-negative, and anaerobic bacteria.

Available forms

Powder for I.M. injection: 500- and 750-mg vials
Powder for I.V. injection: 250- and 500-mg vials

NURSING PROCESS

Assessment

- Assess patient's infection before starting therapy and regularly thereafter.
- Obtain urine specimen for culture and sensitivity tests before starting therapy. Start therapy pending test results.
- Be alert for adverse reactions and drug interactions.
- If adverse GI reaction occurs, monitor patient's hydration status.
- Assess patient's and family's knowledge of drug therapy.

Nursing diagnoses

- Risk for infection related to presence of susceptible organisms
- Risk for deficient fluid volume related to adverse GI reactions
- Deficient knowledge related to drug therapy

Planning and implementation

- Reconstitute drug for I.M. injection with 1% lidocaine hydrochloride (without epinephrine) as directed.

ALERT: If seizures develop and persist despite anticonvulsants, notify prescriber, stop giving the drug, and institute seizure precautions and protocols.

Patient teaching

- Instruct patient to report adverse reactions because supportive therapy may be needed.
- Warn patient about pain at injection site.

Evaluation

- Patient is free from infection.
- Patient maintains adequate hydration throughout therapy.
- Patient and family state understanding of drug therapy.

imipramine hydrochloride
(ih-MIP-ruh-meen high-droh-KLOR-ighd)
Apo-Imipramine ♦, Impril ♦, Melipramine ◇, Norfranil, Novopramine ♦, Tipramine, Tofranil

imipramine pamoate
Tofranil-PM

Pharmacologic class: dibenzazepine-derivative tricyclic antidepressant
Therapeutic class: antidepressant
Pregnancy risk category: D

Indications and dosages

▶ **Depression.** *Adults:* 75 to 100 mg P.O. daily in divided doses; increase in 25- to 50-mg increments to maximum dosage. Or 25 mg P.O. daily; increase in 25-mg increments every other day. Or entire dosage may be given at bedtime. Maximum dosage is 200 mg P.O. daily for outpatients, 300 mg P.O. daily for inpatients, and 100 mg P.O. daily for elderly patients.

▶ **Enuresis.** *Children age 6 and older:* 25 mg P.O. 1 hour before bedtime. If no response within 1 week, increase dosage 50 mg nightly for children younger than age 12 or 75 mg nightly for children age 12 and older. Maximum, 2.5 mg/kg P.O. daily.

▶ **Attention-deficit/hyperactivity disorder**‡. *Children age 6 and older:* 2 to 5 mg/kg P.O. given in two to three divided daily doses.

Contraindications and cautions

• Contraindicated in patients hypersensitive to the drug or any of its components, patients receiving MAO inhibitors, and patients in acute recovery phase of MI.

• Use cautiously in patients at risk for suicide, those receiving thyroid drugs, and those with a history of urine retention or angle-closure glaucoma, increased intraocular pressure, CV disease, impaired hepatic function, hyperthyroidism, seizure disorder, or renal impairment.

Lifespan: In pregnant and breast-feeding women, don't use. In children, safety and effectiveness haven't been established for treating depression. In elderly patients, use lower dose and more gradual dose increases to avoid toxicity.

Adverse reactions

CNS: confusion, *dizziness, drowsiness,* EEG changes, excitation, extrapyramidal reactions, headache, nervousness, ***seizures, stroke,*** tremor, weakness.
CV: ***arrhythmias,*** ECG changes, ***heart block,*** hypertension, ***MI,*** *orthostatic hypotension,* tachycardia.
EENT: *blurred vision,* mydriasis, tinnitus.
GI: anorexia, *constipation, dry mouth,* nausea, paralytic ileus, vomiting.
GU: impotence, testicular swelling, *urine retention.*
Metabolic: hyperglycemia, ***hypoglycemia.***
Skin: *diaphoresis,* photosensitivity reactions, rash, urticaria.
Other: altered libido, galactorrhea and breast enlargement, gynecomastia, hypersensitivity reactions, SIADH.

Interactions

Drug-drug. *Barbiturates, CNS depressants:* May increase CNS depression. Avoid use together.
Cimetidine, methylphenidate: May increase imipramine level. Monitor patient for adverse reactions.
Clonidine: May cause loss of blood pressure control with potentially life-threatening elevations in blood pressure. Don't use together.
Epinephrine, norepinephrine: May cause life-threatening hypertensive effect. Use cautiously; monitor patient's blood pressure.
MAO inhibitors: May cause hyperpyretic crisis, severe seizures, and death. Don't use together.
SSRIs: May increase effects of tricyclic antidepressants; symptoms may persist several weeks after fluoxetine therapy stops. Monitor symptoms closely.
Drug-herb. *SAMe, St. John's wort:* May increase serotonin level. Discourage use together.
Yohimbe: May increase blood pressure effects. Avoid use together.
Drug-lifestyle. *Alcohol use:* May increase CNS depression. Discourage use together.
Smoking: May decrease imipramine level. Monitor patient for lack of effect; discourage patient from smoking.
Sun exposure: May increase risk of photosensitivity reactions. Advise patient to avoid unprotected or prolonged exposure to sunlight.

Effects on lab test results

- May increase or decrease glucose level.
- May increase liver function test values.

Pharmacokinetics

Absorption: Rapid and complete.
Distribution: Wide. 90% protein-bound.
Metabolism: By liver. A significant first-pass effect may explain variable level in different patients taking same dose.
Excretion: Mostly in urine. *Half-life:* 11 to 25 hours.

Route	Onset	Peak	Duration
P.O.	Unknown	1–2 hr	Unknown

Action

Chemical effect: Increases amount of norepinephrine, serotonin, or both in CNS by blocking their reuptake by presynaptic neurons.
Therapeutic effect: Relieves depression and childhood enuresis (hydrochloride form).

Available forms

imipramine hydrochloride
Tablets: 10 mg, 25 mg, 50 mg
imipramine pamoate
Capsules: 75 mg, 100 mg, 125 mg, 150 mg

NURSING PROCESS

Assessment

- Assess patient's condition before starting therapy and regularly thereafter.
- Observe patient closely for evidence of suicidal thoughts or behaviors until depression is relieved.
- Be alert for adverse reactions and drug interactions.
- Assess patient's and family's knowledge of drug therapy.

Nursing diagnoses

- Ineffective coping related to depression
- Deficient knowledge related to drug therapy

Planning and implementation

- Give a lower dose to an elderly or a debilitated patient, an adolescent, or a patient with aggravated psychotic symptoms.
- Although doses can be given up to four times daily, patients also may receive entire daily dose at one time because of drug's long action.
- Don't abruptly stop giving the drug. After abruptly stopping long-term therapy, the patient may experience nausea, headache, and malaise. These symptoms don't indicate addiction. Provide supportive treatment.
- Drug causes high risk of orthostatic hypotension. Check sitting and standing blood pressures after initial dose.
- Because of hypertensive episodes during surgery in patients receiving tricyclic antidepressants, gradually stop giving the drug over several days before surgery.
- If signs of psychosis occur or increase, notify prescriber, lower the dose, and institute safety precautions.

ALERT: Don't confuse imipramine with desipramine or amitriptyline.

Patient teaching

- Advise patient to take full dose at bedtime, but warn about possible morning orthostatic hypotension.
- Suggest taking drug with food or milk if it causes stomach upset.
- Suggest relieving dry mouth with sugarless chewing gum or hard candy. Encourage good dental prophylaxis because persistent dry mouth may increase the risk of dental caries.
- Tell patient not to drink alcohol or smoke during therapy.
- Warn patient to avoid hazardous activities until the drug's CNS effects are known.
- Warn the patient not to abruptly stop taking the drug.
- Advise patient to consult prescriber before taking other prescription drugs, OTC drugs, or herbal remedies.
- Advise patient to use sunblock, wear protective clothing, and avoid prolonged exposure to sunlight to prevent photosensitivity reactions.

Evaluation

- Patient behavior and communication show diminished depression.
- Patient and family state understanding of drug therapy.

immune globulin intramuscular (gamma globulin, IG, IGIM)

(ih-MYOON GLOB-yoo-lin in-truh-MUS-kyoo-ler)

BayGam

immune globulin intravenous (IGIV)

Carimune, Gammagard S/D, Gammar-P IV, Iveegam EN, Octagam, Panglobulin, Polygam S/D, Venoglobulin-S

Pharmacologic class: immunologic drug
Therapeutic class: immune serum
Pregnancy risk category: C

Indications and dosages

▶ **Primary humoral immunodeficiency (IGIV); primary defective antibody synthesis, such as agammaglobulinemia or hypogammaglobulinemia, in patients who are at increased risk of infection.**

BayGam
Adults and children: Initially, 1.3 ml/kg I.M. Maintenance, 0.66 ml/kg (at least 100 mg/kg) q 3 to 4 weeks. Maximum single dose of IGIM is 30 to 50 ml in adults and 20 to 30 ml in infants and small children.

Carimune, Panglobulin
Adults and children: 200 mg/kg I.V. monthly. Start with 0.5 to 1 ml/minute of 3% solution; gradually increase to 2.5 ml/minute after 15 to 30 minutes.

Gammagard S/D
Adults and children: 200 to 400 mg/kg I.V.; then monthly doses of 100 mg/kg. Start infusion at 0.5 ml/kg/hour and increase to maximum of 4 ml/kg/hour. Dosage is related to patient response.

Gammar-P IV
Adults: 200 to 400 mg/kg I.V. q 3 to 4 weeks, infused at 0.01 ml/kg/minute; if no problems develop, increase to 0.02 ml/kg/minute after 15 to 30 minutes. Maximum infusion rate is 0.06 ml/kg/minute.
Adolescents and children: 200 to 400 mg/kg I.V. q 3 to 4 weeks.

Iveegam EN
Adults and children: 200 mg/kg I.V. monthly, infused at 1 to 2 ml/minute for 5% solution. May increase to maximum of 800 mg/kg or give more often to produce desired effect.

Octagam
Adults and children: 100 to 200 mg/kg I.V. monthly at 0.01 to 0.02 ml/kg/minute for 30 minutes. If no discomfort, rate can slowly be increased to a maximum of 0.08 ml/kg/minute.

Polygam S/D
Adults and children: 200 to 400 mg/kg I.V. at 0.5 ml/kg/hour, increasing to a maximum of 4 ml/kg/hour. Subsequent dose is 100 mg/kg I.V. monthly.

Venoglobulin-S
Adults and children: 200 mg/kg I.V. monthly, infused at 0.01 to 0.02 ml/kg/minute for 30 minutes; if tolerated, increase 5% solution to 0.08 ml/kg/minute and 10% solution to 0.05 ml/kg/minute. If immune globulin G levels aren't adequate, increase to 300 to 400 mg/kg and give more than once monthly.

▶ **Idiopathic thrombocytopenic purpura (IGIV).**

Carimune, Panglobulin
Adults and children: 400 mg/kg I.V. for 2 to 5 consecutive days, depending on platelet count and immune response.

Gammagard S/D, Polygam S/D
Adults and children: 1,000 mg/kg I.V. as a single dose. Give up to three doses on alternate days, if needed.

Octagam
Adults and children: 400 mg/kg of 5% solution I.V. for 5 days, or 1,000 mg/kg of 10% solution I.V. for 1 to 2 days with maintenance dosage of 10% solution at 400 to 1,000 mg/kg I.V. single infusion to maintain 30,000/mm^3 platelet count.

Venoglobulin-S
Adults and children: Maximum of 2,000 mg/kg I.V. over 5 days or less. Maintenance, 1,000 mg/kg, if needed.

▶ **Bone marrow transplant (IGIV).** *Adults older than age 20:* Give 500 mg/kg of 5% or 10% solution I.V. Octagam on days 7 and 2 before transplantation, and then weekly until 90 days after transplantation.

▶ **B-cell chronic lymphocytic leukemia (IGIV).** *Adults:* 400 mg/kg I.V. Gammagard S/D or Polygam S/D q 3 to 4 weeks.

▶ **Pediatric HIV infection (IGIV).** *Children:* 400 mg/kg I.V. once q 2 to 4 weeks.

▶ **Kawasaki syndrome (IGIV).**
Iveegam EN
Adults: 400 mg/kg I.V. daily over 2 hours for 4 consecutive days, or a single dose of 2,000 mg/kg I.V. over 10 to 12 hours. Start within 10 days of disease onset. Give with aspirin (80 to 100 mg/kg P.O. daily through day 14; then 3 to 10 mg/kg P.O. daily for 5 weeks).
Gammagard S/D, Polygam S/D
Adults: Either a single dose of 1 g/kg or 400 mg/kg I.V. daily for 4 days starting within 7 days of fever onset. Give with aspirin (80 to 100 mg/kg in four divided daily doses).
▶ **Hepatitis A exposure (IGIM).** *Adults and children:* 0.02 ml/kg I.M. as soon as possible after exposure. Up to 0.06 ml/kg may be given for prolonged or intense exposure.
▶ **Measles exposure (IGIM).** *Adults and children:* 0.02 ml/kg I.M. within 6 days after exposure.
▶ **Measles postexposure prophylaxis (IGIM).** *Immunocompromised children:* 0.5 ml/kg I.M. (maximum, 15 ml) within 6 days after exposure.
▶ **Chickenpox exposure (IGIM).** *Adults and children:* 0.6 to 1.2 ml/kg I.M. as soon as possible after exposure.
▶ **Rubella exposure in first trimester of pregnancy (IGIM).** *Women:* 0.55 ml/kg I.M. as soon as possible after exposure (within 72 hours).

I.V. administration

- I.V. products aren't interchangeable. Gammagard requires a filter, which is supplied by the manufacturer.
- Most adverse effects are related to rapid infusion rate. Infuse slowly.
- In patients with a risk of a thrombotic event, avoid infusion solutions more concentrated than 5%, start infusion at no more than 0.5 ml/kg/hour, and speed up slowly and only if well tolerated to a maximum rate of 4 ml/kg/hour.

⊗ **Incompatibilities**
Don't mix with other I.V. drugs.

Contraindications and cautions

- Contraindicated in patients hypersensitive to the drug or any of its components, in patients with a history of an allergic response to thimerosal, and in patients with selective immune globulin A deficiencies.
- I.M. administration contraindicated in patients with severe thrombocytopenia or other coagulation-bleeding disorders.
- Use Gammagard S/D cautiously in patients with renal impairment. Renal dysfunction may occur more often with preparations stabilized in glucose (Carimune NF, Gammar P IV).
- Use caution when giving drug to patients with a history of CV disease or thrombotic episodes because I.V. drug may cause thrombotic events. The exact cause of this is unknown.

Lifespan: In pregnant women, use cautiously. In breast-feeding women, use cautiously because it's unknown if the drug appears in breast milk.

Adverse reactions

CNS: faintness, fever, malaise, severe headache requiring hospitalization.
CV: chest pain, ***heart failure*** (Gammagard S/D), ***MI.***
GI: nausea, vomiting.
GU: ***acute renal impairment, acute tubular necrosis, nephrotic syndrome,*** osmotic nephrosis.
Musculoskeletal: muscle stiffness at injection site.
Respiratory: ***pulmonary embolism,*** transfusion-related acute lung injury.
Skin: erythema, urticaria.
Other: ***anaphylaxis.***

Interactions

Drug-drug. *Live-virus vaccines:* Antibodies in the vaccine may interfere with drug therapy. Don't give within 6 months after giving immune globulin.

Effects on lab test results

- May increase BUN and creatinine levels.

Pharmacokinetics

Absorption: Slow.
Distribution: Evenly between intravascular and extravascular spaces.
Metabolism: Unknown.
Excretion: Unknown. *Half-life:* 21 to 24 days in immunocompromised patients.

Route	Onset	Peak	Duration
I.V.	Immediate	Immediate	Unknown
I.M.	Unknown	2–5 days	Unknown

Action

Chemical effect: Provides passive immunity by increasing antibody titer. The primary component is immune globulin G.

Therapeutic effect: Helps prevent infections.

Available forms

IGIM

Injection: 2-ml and 10-ml vials

IGIV

Injection: 5% in 1-g, 2.5-g, 5-g, and 10-g single-use bottles (Octagam); 5% and 10% in 50-ml, 100-ml, and 200-ml vials (Venoglobulin-S); 5% in 1-g, 2.5-g, 5-g, and 10-g single-use bottles

Powder for injection: 50 mg protein/ml in 2.5-g, 5-g, and 10-g vials (Gammagard S/D); 1-g, 2.5-g, and 5-g vials (Gammar-P IV); 500-mg and 1-g, 2.5-g, and 5-g vials (Iveegam); 2.5-g, 5-g, and 10-g vials (Polygam S/D); 3-g, 6-g, and 12-g vials (Panglobulin, Carimune)

NURSING PROCESS

Assessment

- Obtain history of allergies and reactions to immunizations.
- Observe patient for signs of anaphylaxis or other adverse reactions immediately after injection.
- Inspect injection site for local reactions.
- Monitor effectiveness by checking antibody titers after administration.
- Assess patient's and family's knowledge of drug therapy.

Nursing diagnoses

- Ineffective protection related to lack of or decreased immunity
- Ineffective breathing pattern related to anaphylaxis
- Deficient knowledge related to drug therapy

Planning and implementation

- Give I.M. injection in gluteal region. Divide any dose larger than 10 ml, and inject into several muscle sites to reduce local discomfort.
- If 6 weeks or more have passed since exposure or since symptoms have begun, don't give immune globulin to help prevent hepatitis A.
- Make sure epinephrine 1:1,000 is available in case of anaphylaxis.

ALERT: I.V. and I.M. products aren't interchangeable.

Patient teaching

- Instruct patient to immediately report respiratory difficulty.
- Tell patient that local reactions may occur at injection site.
- Instruct patient to promptly notify prescriber if adverse reaction persists or becomes severe.

Evaluation

- Patient exhibits increased passive immunity.
- Patient shows no signs of anaphylaxis.
- Patient and family state understanding of drug therapy.

indapamide

(in-DAP-uh-mighd)

Lozide ♦ Lozol, Natrilix ◇

Pharmacologic class: thiazide-like diuretic

Therapeutic class: diuretic, antihypertensive

Pregnancy risk category: B

Indications and dosages

▶ **Edema.** *Adults:* Initially, 2.5 mg P.O. daily in morning. Increase to 5 mg daily after 1 week, if needed.

▶ **Hypertension.** *Adults:* Initially, 1.25 mg P.O. daily in morning. Increase to 2.5 mg daily after 4 weeks. Increase to 5 mg daily after 4 more weeks.

Contraindications and cautions

- Contraindicated in patients hypersensitive to the drug, any of its components, or other sulfonamide-derived drugs. Also contraindicated in patients with anuria.
- Use cautiously in patients with severe renal disease, impaired hepatic function, and progressive hepatic disease.

Lifespan: In pregnant women, use cautiously. In breast-feeding women and children, safety and effectiveness haven't been established.

Adverse reactions

CNS: *dizziness, headache,* irritability, *lightheadedness,* nervousness, weakness.

CV: orthostatic hypotension, volume depletion and dehydration.

GI: nausea, *pancreatitis.*
GU: frequent urination, nocturia, polyuria.
Metabolic: anorexia, hyperuricemia, hypochloremia, hypokalemia, hyponatremia, metabolic alkalosis.
Musculoskeletal: muscle cramps and spasms.
Skin: dermatitis, photosensitivity reactions, rash.
Other: gout.

Interactions

Drug-drug. *Antihypertensives:* May cause severe hypotension. Use together cautiously.
Bumetanide, ethacrynic acid, furosemide, torsemide: May cause excessive diuretic response, resulting in serious electrolyte abnormalities or dehydration. Adjust dosages carefully while monitoring the patient for excessive diuretic responses.
Diazoxide: May increase antihypertensive, hyperglycemic, and hyperuricemic effects. Use together cautiously.
Digoxin: May increase risk of digoxin toxicity from indapamide-induced hypokalemia. Monitor potassium and digoxin levels.
Lithium: May decrease lithium clearance and increase risk of toxicity. Use together cautiously.
NSAIDs: May reduce the diuretic, natriuretic, and antihypertensive effects. Monitor patient.
Drug-lifestyle. *Sun exposure:* May cause photosensitivity reactions. Avoid prolonged and unprotected exposure to sunlight.

Effects on lab test results

- May increase glucose, cholesterol, triglyceride, and uric acid levels. May decrease potassium, sodium, and chloride levels.

Pharmacokinetics

Absorption: Complete.
Distribution: Wide because of its lipophilicity. 71% to 79% protein-bound.
Metabolism: Undergoes significant hepatic metabolism.
Excretion: Mainly in urine; smaller amounts in feces. *Half-life:* About 14 hours.

Route	Onset	Peak	Duration
P.O.	1–2 hr	≤ 2 hr	≤ 36 hr

Action

Chemical effect: Unknown; probably inhibits sodium reabsorption in distal segment of nephron. Also has direct vasodilating effect, possibly from calcium channel-blocking action.
Therapeutic effect: Promotes water and sodium excretion and lowers blood pressure.

Available forms

Tablets: 1.25 mg, 2.5 mg

NURSING PROCESS

Assessment

- Assess patient's underlying condition before starting therapy.
- Monitor effectiveness by assessing fluid intake and output, weight, and blood pressure. In hypertensive patient, therapeutic response may be delayed several days.
- Monitor electrolytes and glucose levels.
- Monitor creatinine and BUN levels regularly. If these levels are more than twice normal, drug is less effective.
- Monitor uric acid level, especially if patient has history of gout.
- Be alert for adverse reactions and drug interactions.
- Assess patient's and family's knowledge of drug therapy.

Nursing diagnoses

- Risk for injury related to presence of hypertension
- Excessive fluid volume related to presence of edema
- Deficient knowledge related to drug therapy

Planning and implementation

- To prevent nocturia, give drug in the morning.
- Drug may be used with potassium-sparing diuretic to prevent potassium loss.

Patient teaching

- Advise patient not to suddenly change position, and to rise slowly to avoid orthostatic hypotension.
- Advise patient to use sunblock and avoid prolonged exposure to sunlight to prevent photosensitivity reactions.
- Teach patient to monitor fluid volume by recording daily weight and intake and output.
- Tell patient to avoid high-sodium foods and to choose high-potassium foods.

• Advise patient to take drug early in day to avoid nocturia.

Evaluation

• Patient's blood pressure is normal.
• Patient is free from edema.
• Patient and family state understanding of drug therapy.

indinavir sulfate

(in-DIH-nuh-veer SUL-fayt)
Crixivan

Pharmacologic class: protease inhibitor
Therapeutic class: antiretroviral
Pregnancy risk category: C

Indications and dosages

▶ **HIV infection.** *Adults:* 800 mg P.O. q 8 hours, 1 hour before or 2 hours after a meal.
Adjust-a-dose: For patients with mild to moderate hepatic insufficiency resulting in cirrhosis, reduce dosage to 600 mg P.O. q 8 hours.

Contraindications and cautions

• Contraindicated in patients hypersensitive to the drug or any of its components.
• Use cautiously and at a reduced dosage in patients with hepatic insufficiency.
Lifespan: In pregnant women, use only if benefits outweigh risks to fetus. In breast-feeding women, use cautiously because it isn't known if drug appears in breast milk. In children, safety and effectiveness haven't been established.

Adverse reactions

CNS: asthenia, dizziness, fatigue, headache, insomnia, malaise, somnolence.
GI: *abdominal pain,* acid regurgitation, anorexia, diarrhea, dry mouth, *nausea,* taste perversion, vomiting.
GU: ***acute renal failure,*** *nephrolithiasis.*
Hematologic: ***hemolytic anemia, neutropenia.***
Hepatic: ***hepatic failure,*** hyperbilirubinemia.
Metabolic: ***hyperglycemia,*** new onset diabetes mellitus.
Musculoskeletal: back pain, flank pain.
Other: redistribution and accumulation of body fat.

Interactions

Drug-drug. *Amprenavir, saquinavir:* May increase levels of these drugs. Dosage adjustments probably aren't needed.
Carbamazepine: May decrease indinavir level. Avoid use together.
Clarithromycin: May alter clarithromycin level. Monitor patient.
Delavirdine, itraconazole, ketoconazole: May increase indinavir level. Consider reducing indinavir dosage to 600 mg q 8 hours.
Didanosine: May need normal gastric pH for optimal absorption of indinavir. Give these drugs and indinavir at least 1 hour apart on an empty stomach.
Efavirenz, nevirapine: May decrease indinavir level. Increase indinavir to 1,000 mg q 8 hours.
Ergot derivatives, pimozide: May result in life-threatening events. Avoid use together.
HMG-CoA reductase inhibitors: May increase levels of these drugs and increase risk of myopathy and rhabdomyolysis. Avoid use together.
Midazolam, triazolam: May inhibit metabolism of these drugs (because of competition for CYP3A4 by indinavir) and increase risk of serious or life-threatening events, such as arrhythmias or prolonged sedation. Don't give together.
Nelfinavir: May increase levels of indinavir by 50% and nelfinavir by 80%. Monitor patient closely.
Rifabutin: May increase rifabutin level and decrease indinavir level. Give indinavir 1,000 mg q 8 hours and decrease rifabutin to either 150 mg daily or 300 mg two to three times weekly.
Rifampin: May significantly decrease indinavir level because rifampin is a potent inducer of CYP3A4. Avoid use together.
Ritonavir: May increase indinavir level by two to five times. Adjust dosage to indinavir 400 mg b.i.d. and ritonavir 400 mg b.i.d., or indinavir 800 mg b.i.d. and ritonavir 100 to 200 mg b.i.d.
Sildenafil, tadalafil, vardenafil: May increase levels of these drugs and the risk of adverse effects (hypotension, visual changes, priapism). Tell patient not to exceed 25 mg of sildenafil in a 48-hour period, 10 mg of tadalafil in a 72-hour period, or 2.5 mg vardenafil in a 24-hour period.
Drug-herb. *St. John's wort:* May reduce indinavir level by more than 50%. Discourage use together.

Drug-food. *Any food:* May substantially decrease absorption of oral indinavir. Give drug on an empty stomach.
Grapefruit juice: May decrease level and therapeutic effect of indinavir. Advise patient to take drug with liquid other than grapefruit juice.

Effects on lab test results

• May increase ALT, AST, bilirubin, amylase, triglyceride, cholesterol, and glucose levels. May decrease hemoglobin level and hematocrit.
• May decrease neutrophil and platelet counts.

Pharmacokinetics

Absorption: Rapid.
Distribution: 60% protein-bound.
Metabolism: By liver and kidneys.
Excretion: In urine. *Half-life:* 2 hours.

Route	Onset	Peak	Duration
P.O.	Unknown	< 1 hr	1–8 hr

Action

Chemical effect: Binds to and inhibits protease active sites. Prevents cleavage of viral polyproteins, resulting in formation of immature, noninfectious viral particles.
Therapeutic effect: Reduces symptoms of HIV.

Available forms

Capsules: 100 mg, 200 mg, 333 mg, 400 mg

NURSING PROCESS

Assessment

• Monitor adverse reactions and drug interactions.
• Assess patient's and family's knowledge of drug therapy.

Nursing diagnoses

• Risk for infection related to presence of virus
• Risk for deficient fluid volume related to effect on kidneys
• Deficient knowledge related to drug therapy

Planning and implementation

• Give at least 48 oz (1.5 L) of fluids every 24 hours to maintain adequate hydration.
• Give drug on an empty stomach, 1 hour before or 2 hours after a meal.

Patient teaching

• Instruct patient to use barrier contraception.
• If patient misses a dose, advise him to take the next dose at regularly scheduled time and not to double the dose.
• Instruct patient to take drug on an empty stomach with water 1 hour before or 2 hours after a meal.
• Instruct patient to store capsules in the original container and to keep the desiccant in the bottle.
• Instruct patient to drink at least 48 oz (1.5 L) of fluid daily.
• Advise HIV-positive women to prevent transmitting virus to infant by not breast-feeding.
• Instruct patient to promptly report evidence of nephrolithiasis (flank pain, hematuria) or diabetes (increased thirst, polyuria).
• Advise patient taking sildenafil, tadalafil, or vardenafil that he may be at increased risk for adverse reactions, such as hypotension, visual changes, and priapism, and that he should promptly report any symptoms to prescriber. Patient shouldn't take more than 25 mg of sildenafil in a 48-hour period, 10 mg of tadalafil in a 72-hour period, or 2.5 mg of vardenafil in a 24-hour period.

Evaluation

• Patient's health improves, and signs and symptoms of underlying condition diminish with use of drug.
• Patient maintains adequate hydration.
• Patient and family state understanding of drug therapy.

indomethacin

(in-doh-METH-uh-sin)

Apo-Indomethacin ♦, Arthrexin ◇, Indocid ♦ ◇, Indocid SR ♦, Indocin*, Indocin SR, Indomethagan, Novo-Methacin ♦

indomethacin sodium trihydrate

Apo-Indomethacin ♦, Indocid PDA ♦, Indocin I.V., Novo-Methacin ♦

Pharmacologic class: NSAID
Therapeutic class: analgesic, antipyretic, anti-inflammatory
Pregnancy risk category: C (D in third trimester)

Indications and dosages

▶ **Moderate to severe rheumatoid arthritis or osteoarthritis, ankylosing spondylitis.** *Adults:* 25 mg P.O. b.i.d. or t.i.d. with food or antacids. Increase by 25 mg or 50 mg daily q 7 days up to 200 mg daily. Or 50 mg P.R. q.i.d. Or 75-mg sustained-release capsule P.O. to start, in morning or at bedtime, followed, if needed, by another 75 mg b.i.d.

▶ **Acute gouty arthritis.** *Adults:* 50 mg P.O. t.i.d. Reduce dose as soon as possible; then stop. Don't use sustained-release capsules.

▶ **Acute painful shoulders (bursitis or tendinitis).** *Adults:* 75 to 150 mg P.O. daily t.i.d. or q.i.d. with food or antacids for 7 to 14 days.

▶ **To close hemodynamically significant patent ductus arteriosus in premature infants.** *Neonates less than 48 hours old:* 0.2 mg/kg I.V. followed by two doses of 0.1 mg/kg at 12- to 24-hour intervals.
Neonates ages 2 to 7 days: 0.2 mg/kg I.V. followed by two doses of 0.2 mg/kg at 12- to 24-hour intervals.
Neonates more than 7 days old: 0.2 mg/kg I.V. followed by two doses of 0.25 mg/kg at 12- to 24-hour intervals.

▶ **Pericarditis‡.** *Adults:* 75 to 200 mg P.O. daily in three to four divided doses.

▶ **Dysmenorrhea‡.** *Adults:* 25 mg P.O. t.i.d. with food or antacids.

▶ **Bartter syndrome‡.** *Adults:* 150 mg P.O. daily with food or antacids.
Children: 0.5 to 2 mg/kg P.O. in divided doses.

I.V. administration

• Reconstitute powder for injection with sterile water for injection or normal saline solution. For each 1-mg vial, add 1 ml of diluent to yield 1 mg/ml; add 2 ml of diluent to yield 0.5 mg/ml.
• Use only preservative-free diluents to prepare I.V. injection. Never use diluents containing benzyl alcohol because it has been linked to fatal gasping syndrome in neonates. Because injection contains no preservatives, reconstitute immediately before administration and discard unused solution.
• Give by direct injection over 20 to 30 minutes per published literature although the optimum rate has not been established by the manufacturer.
• If patient has anuria or marked oliguria, don't give second or third scheduled I.V. dose; instead, notify prescriber.

⊗ Incompatibilities
Amino acid injection, calcium gluconate, cimetidine, dextrose injection, dobutamine, dopamine, gentamicin, levofloxacin, solutions with pH less than 6, tobramycin sulfate, tolazoline.

Contraindications and cautions

• Contraindicated in patients hypersensitive to the drug or any of its components and in those with a history of aspirin- or NSAID-induced asthma, rhinitis, or urticaria. Suppositories contraindicated in patients with a history of proctitis or recent rectal bleeding.
• Because of its high risk of adverse effects during prolonged use, don't use drug routinely as analgesic or antipyretic.
• Use cautiously in patients with epilepsy, parkinsonism, hepatic or renal disease, CV disease, infection, mental illness or depression, or history of GI disease.
Lifespan: In pregnant and breast-feeding women, drug is contraindicated. In children younger than age 14, safety and effectiveness haven't been established by manufacturer. In infants with untreated infection, active bleeding, coagulation defects, thrombocytopenia, congenital heart disease (in whom patency of ductus arteriosus is needed for satisfactory pulmonary or systemic blood flow), necrotizing enterocolitis, or renal impairment, drug is contraindicated. In elderly patients, use cautiously.

Adverse reactions

P.O. and P.R.
CNS: confusion, drowsiness, depression, *dizziness, headache,* peripheral neuropathy, psychic disturbances, ***seizures,*** syncope, vertigo.
CV: edema, ***heart failure,*** hypertension.
EENT: blurred vision, corneal and retinal damage, hearing loss, tinnitus.
GI: anorexia, diarrhea, ***GI bleeding,*** nausea, peptic ulceration, vomiting.
GU: ***acute renal failure,*** hematuria.
Hematologic: ***aplastic anemia, agranulocytosis,*** hemolytic anemia, iron-deficiency anemia, ***leukopenia, thrombocytopenic purpura.***
Metabolic: ***hyperkalemia.***
Respiratory: respiratory distress.
Skin: pruritus, rash, ***Stevens-Johnson syndrome,*** urticaria.
Other: ***anaphylaxis, angioedema,*** hypersensitivity reactions.

I.V.
GI: ***GI bleeding,*** vomiting.
GU: azotemia, renal dysfunction.
Metabolic: ***hyperkalemia, hypoglycemia,*** hyponatremia.
Respiratory: ***respiratory distress.***
Other: ***anaphylaxis, angioedema,*** hypersensitivity reactions, rash.

Interactions

Drug-drug. *Aminoglycosides, cyclosporine, methotrexate:* May increase toxicity of these drugs. Avoid use together.
Antihypertensives: May decrease antihypertensive effect. Monitor blood pressure closely.
Aspirin: May decrease indomethacin level and increase the risk of GI toxicity. Avoid use together.
Corticosteroids: May increase risk of GI toxicity. Don't use together.
Diflunisal, probenecid: May decrease indomethacin excretion. Monitor patient for increased adverse reactions to indomethacin.
Digoxin: May prolong digoxin half-life. Use together cautiously; monitor digoxin level.
Dipyridamole: May enhance fluid retention. Avoid use together.
Furosemide, thiazide diuretics: May impair response to both drugs. Avoid using together, if possible.
Lithium: May increase lithium level. Monitor patient for lithium toxicity.
Triamterene: May cause nephrotoxicity. Monitor patient closely.
Drug-herb. *Dong quai, feverfew, garlic, ginger, horse chestnut, red clover:* May increase risk of bleeding. Monitor patient closely for bleeding.
Senna: May block laxative effects. Discourage use together.
St. John's wort: May increase risk of photosensitivity. Advise patient to avoid unprotected or prolonged exposure to sunlight.
Drug-lifestyle. *Alcohol use:* May increase risk of GI toxicity. Discourage use together.

Effects on lab test results

- May increase AST, ALT, BUN, creatinine, and potassium levels. May decrease glucose, sodium, and hemoglobin levels and hematocrit.
- May decrease WBC, granulocyte, and platelet counts.

Pharmacokinetics

Absorption: Rapid and complete.
Distribution: Highly protein-bound.
Metabolism: In liver.
Excretion: Mainly in urine, with some biliary excretion. *Half-life:* 4¼ hours.

Route	Onset	Peak	Duration
P.O.	30 min	1–4 hr	4–6 hr
I.V.	Immediate	Immediate	Unknown
P.R.	2–4 hr	Unknown	4–6 hr

Action

Chemical effect: Unknown; produces anti-inflammatory, analgesic, and antipyretic effects, possibly by inhibiting prostaglandin synthesis.
Therapeutic effect: Relieves pain, fever, and inflammation.

Available forms

indomethacin
Capsules: 25 mg, 50 mg
Capsules (sustained-release): 75 mg
Oral suspension: 25 mg/5 ml
Suppositories: 50 mg
indomethacin sodium trihydrate
Injection: 1-mg vials

NURSING PROCESS

Assessment

- Assess patient's condition before starting therapy and regularly thereafter.
- Monitor patient carefully for bleeding and for reduced urine output during I.V. use.
- Be alert for adverse reactions and drug interactions.
- Assess patient's and family's knowledge of drug therapy.

Nursing diagnoses

- Chronic pain related to underlying condition
- Risk for injury related to adverse reactions
- Deficient knowledge related to drug therapy

Planning and implementation

- If GI upset occurs, give oral form of drug with food, milk, or antacid.
- If ductus arteriosus reopens, give second course of one to three doses. If ineffective, surgery may be needed.

• If patient has bleeding or reduced urine output, stop giving the drug and notify prescriber.
• Drug may enhance hypothalamic-pituitary-adrenal axis response to dexamethasone suppression test.
• Notify prescriber if drug is ineffective.

Patient teaching

• Tell patient to take oral form of drug with food, milk, or antacid if GI upset occurs.
• Inform patient that use of oral form with aspirin, alcohol, or corticosteroids may increase risk of adverse GI reactions.
• Teach patient signs and symptoms of GI bleeding, and tell him to report them to prescriber. Serious GI toxicity, including peptic ulceration and bleeding despite absence of GI symptoms, can occur in patients taking oral NSAIDs.
• Instruct patient not to drink alcohol during therapy.
• Tell patient to notify prescriber immediately about visual or hearing changes. Patient receiving long-term oral therapy should have regular eye and hearing examinations, CBC, and renal function tests to detect toxicity.
• Advise patient to avoid hazardous activities if adverse CNS reactions occur.

✓ Evaluation

• Patient is free from pain.
• Patient doesn't experience injury from adverse reactions.
• Patient and family state understanding of drug therapy.

infliximab

(in-FLICKS-ih-mab)

Remicade

Pharmacologic class: monoclonal antibody
Therapeutic class: anti-inflammatory
Pregnancy risk category: B

Indications and dosages

▶ **Moderate to severe active Crohn disease; to reduce the number of draining fistulas and maintain fistula closure in patients with Crohn disease.** *Adults:* 5 mg/kg by I.V. infusion over at least 2 hours, given as an induction regimen at 0, 2, and 6 weeks, followed by a maintenance regimen of 5 mg/kg q 8 weeks thereafter. For adults who respond and then stop responding, consider giving 10 mg/kg. Patients who don't respond by week 14 are unlikely to respond to continued therapy; consider stopping drug.

▶ **Moderate to severe active Crohn disease.** *Children:* 5 mg/kg given as I.V. induction regimen at 0, 2, and 6 weeks, followed by a maintenance regimen of 5 mg/kg q 8 weeks.

▶ **Moderate to severe active rheumatoid arthritis, with methotrexate.** *Adults:* 3 mg/kg by I.V. infusion over at least 2 hours. Give additional doses of 3 mg/kg at 2 and 6 weeks after initial infusion and q 8 weeks thereafter. If response is inadequate, increase to 10 mg/kg or give q 4 weeks.

▶ **Ankylosing spondylitis.** *Adults:* 5 mg/kg by I.V. infusion over at least 2 hours. Give additional doses of 5 mg/kg at 2 and 6 weeks after first infusion and then q 6 weeks thereafter.

▶ **Psoriatic arthritis, with or without methotrexate.** *Adults:* 5 mg/kg by I.V. infusion over at least 2 hours. Give additional doses of 5 mg/kg at 2 and 6 weeks after first infusion and then q 8 weeks thereafter.

▶ **Moderate to severe ulcerative colitis.** *Adults:* Induction dose, 5 mg/kg I.V. over 2 hours given at 0, 2, and 6 weeks, followed by a maintenance dose of 5 mg/kg q 8 weeks thereafter.

▶ **Chronic severe plaque psoriasis.** *Adults:* 5 mg/kg by I.V. infusion over at least 2 hours. Repeat dosage in 2 and 6 weeks; then give 5 mg/kg q 8 weeks thereafter.

I.V. administration

• Drug is incompatible with plasticized polyvinyl chloride equipment or devices; prepare only in glass infusion bottles or polypropylene or polyolefin infusion bags.
• Give through polyethylene-lined administration sets with an in-line, sterile, nonpyrogenic, low–protein-binding filter (pore size of 1.2 mm or less).
• Reconstitute with 10 ml sterile solution for injection using syringe with 21G or smaller needle. Don't shake; gently swirl to dissolve powder. Solution should be colorless to light yellow and opalescent; it may contain a few translucent particles. If you see other particles or discoloration, don't use.

• Vials don't contain antibacterial preservatives; use reconstituted drug immediately.
• Dilute total volume of reconstituted drug to 250 ml with normal saline solution for injection. Infusion concentration range is 0.4 to 4 mg/ml.
• Infuse within 3 hours of preparation and for at least 2 hours after starting.
• If an infusion reaction occurs, stop the infusion, notify prescriber, and give acetaminophen, antihistamines, corticosteroids, and epinephrine.

⊗ **Incompatibilities**
Other I.V. drugs.

Contraindications and cautions

• Contraindicated in patients hypersensitive to murine proteins or any other of the drug's components.
• In patients with mild heart failure (New York Heart Association [NYHA] Class I or II), use cautiously. Doses greater than 5 mg/kg are contraindicated in patients with moderate to severe heart failure (NYHA Class III or IV).
• Use cautiously in patients with a history of hematologic abnormalities or those with CNS demyelinating or seizure disorders.
Lifespan: In pregnant women, give only if benefits outweigh risks to fetus. In breast-feeding women, stop breast-feeding or don't use the drug. In elderly patients, use cautiously.

Adverse reactions

CNS: depression, dizziness, *fatigue, fever, headache,* insomnia, malaise, pain, systemic and cutaneous vasculitis.
CV: chest pain, flushing, *hypertension,* hypotension, ***pericardial effusion,*** peripheral edema, tachycardia.
EENT: conjunctivitis, *pharyngitis,* rhinitis, *sinusitis.*
GI: *abdominal pain,* constipation, *diarrhea, dyspepsia,* flatulence, intestinal obstruction, mouth pain, *nausea,* ulcerative stomatitis, vomiting.
GU: dysuria, increased urinary frequency, *UTI.*
Hematologic: anemia, hematoma, ***leukopenia, neutropenia, pancytopenia.***
Musculoskeletal: *arthralgia,* arthritis, *back pain,* myalgia.
Respiratory: *bronchitis, coughing,* dyspnea, *upper respiratory tract infection.*
Skin: acne, alopecia, candidiasis, dry skin, ecchymosis, eczema, erythema, erythematous rash, increased sweating, maculopapular rash, papular rash, pruritus, *rash,* urticaria.
Other: abscess, chills, flulike syndrome, hot flushes, hypersensitivity reaction, ***severe opportunistic infections,*** toothache, ***tuberculosis.***

Interactions

Drug-drug. *Anakinra:* May increase the risk of serious infection and neutropenia. Avoid use together.
Live-virus vaccines: No data are available on response to vaccines or on the secondary transmission of infection by live-virus vaccines. Don't use together.

Effects on lab test results

• May increase liver enzyme levels. May decrease hemoglobin level and hematocrit.

Pharmacokinetics

Absorption: Given I.V.
Distribution: Mainly in the vascular compartment.
Metabolism: Unknown.
Excretion: Unknown. *Half-life:* 9½ days.

Route	Onset	Peak	Duration
I.V.	Unknown	Unknown	Unknown

Action

Chemical effect: Binds to tumor necrosis factor (TNF)-alpha to neutralize it and inhibit its binding with receptors, reducing the infiltration of inflammatory cells and production of TNF-alpha in inflamed areas of the intestine.
Therapeutic effect: Relieves inflammation.

Available forms

Injection: 100-mg vials

NURSING PROCESS

Assessment

• Obtain history of patient's underlying condition before starting therapy, and reassess regularly.
• Use in Crohn disease and ulcerative colitis only after patient has had an inadequate response to conventional therapy.
• Observe patient for infusion-related reactions, including fever, chills, pruritus, urticaria, dysp-

nea, hypotension, hypertension, and chest pain, within 2 hours of infusion.
• Monitor liver function test results.
• Observe patient for development of lymphomas and infection. Patients with chronic Crohn disease and long-term exposure to immunosuppressants are more likely to develop lymphomas and infections.
• Consider stopping treatment in patient who develops significant hematologic abnormalities or CNS adverse reactions.
• Drug may affect normal immune responses. Monitor patient for development of autoimmune antibodies and lupus-like syndrome; stop giving the drug if symptoms develop. Symptoms should resolve.
• Tuberculosis, invasive fungal infections, and other fatal opportunistic infections may occur.
• In patient with heart failure, monitor patient's cardiac status.
• Assess patient's and family's knowledge of drug therapy.

Nursing diagnoses

• Chronic pain related to inflammation of the GI tract
• Imbalanced nutrition: less than body requirements related to underlying medical condition
• Deficient knowledge related to drug therapy

Planning and implementation

• If patient develops new or worsening symptoms of heart failure, notify the prescriber.
• Patient may develop tuberculosis, invasive fungal infections, or other opportunistic infection. Test patient for latent tuberculosis infection with a tuberculin skin test. Start treatment of latent tuberculosis infection before therapy.
• Patient may develop histoplasmosis, listeriosis, and pneumocystosis. For patients who have lived in regions where histoplasmosis is endemic, carefully consider the benefits and risks before starting therapy.

Patient teaching

• Tell patient about infusion reaction symptoms and the need to report them to prescriber.
• Inform patient of postinfusion adverse effects, and tell him to promptly report them.
• Advise patient to seek immediate medical attention for signs and symptoms of infection or strange or unusual bleeding or bruising.
• Advise parent to have child up-to-date for all vaccines before therapy starts.

Evaluation

• Patient is free from pain.
• Patient maintains adequate nutrition.
• Patient and family state understanding of drug therapy.

influenza virus vaccine live, intranasal

(inn-floo-EHN-zah VY-russ vack-SEEN LYV inn-truh-NAZ-ul)
FluMist

Pharmacologic class: neuraminidase inhibitor
Therapeutic class: antiviral
Pregnancy risk category: C

Indications and dosages

▶ **Active immunization for influenza A and B viruses.** *Adults and children ages 9 to 49:* Give 0.5 ml per season.
Children ages 5 to 8 (not previously vaccinated with FluMist): Two doses of 0.5 ml each, 60 days apart (± 14 days for initial season).
Children ages 5 to 8 (previously vaccinated with FluMist): 0.5 ml per season.

Contraindications and cautions

• Contraindicated in patients hypersensitive to the drug or any of its components, including eggs or egg products. Also contraindicated in patients who may be immunosuppressed or have altered or compromised immune status as a consequence of treatment with systemic corticosteroids, alkylating drugs, antimetabolites, radiation, or other immunosuppressive therapies. Contraindicated in patients with known or suspected immune deficiency diseases, such as combined immunodeficiency, agammaglobulinemia, or thymic abnormalities; conditions such as HIV infection, malignancy, leukemia, or lymphoma; or a history of Guillain-Barré syndrome or asthma or reactive airway disease.
Lifespan: In pregnant women, drug is contraindicated. In breast-feeding women, use cautiously because it's unknown if drug appears in breast milk. In children ages 5 to 17 receiving aspirin or drugs that contain aspirin, drug is contraindicated because of the link with Reye syndrome. In children younger than age 5 and

adults age 50 and older, safety and effectiveness haven't been established.

Adverse reactions

CNS: fever, headache, irritability.
EENT: nasal congestion, runny nose, sore throat.
GI: vomiting.
Musculoskeletal: muscle aches.
Respiratory: cough.
Other: chills, decreased activity.

Interactions

Drug-drug. *Antivirals active against influenza A or B viruses:* May cause synergistic or decreased effect. Wait 48 hours after stopping antiviral therapy before giving vaccine. Don't give antivirals within 2 weeks of vaccine.
Aspirin: May cause Reye syndrome. Avoid use together.

Effects on lab test results

None reported.

Pharmacokinetics

Absorption: Unknown.
Distribution: Unknown.
Metabolism: Unknown.
Excretion: Unknown. *Half-life:* Unknown.

Route	Onset	Peak	Duration
Intranasal	Unknown	Unknown	Unknown

Action

Chemical effect: May play a role in prevention and recovery from infection. Induces influenza strain-specific serum antibodies.
Therapeutic effect: Protects against influenza.

Available forms

Intranasal spray: 0.5 ml

NURSING PROCESS

Assessment

- Assess patient's health and immune status.
- To prevent allergic or other adverse reaction, review patient's history for possible sensitivity to influenza vaccine components, including eggs and egg products.
- Be alert for adverse reactions.
- Assess patient's and family's knowledge of therapy.

Nursing diagnoses

- Risk for infection related to influenza A and B virus
- Deficient knowledge related to vaccine therapy

Planning and implementation

ALERT: Keep epinephrine injection (1:1,000) or compatible treatment readily available in case of an acute anaphylactic reaction.

- Don't give drug until at least 72 hours after a patient's fever has started.
- Advise vaccine recipient and the parents of immunized child to avoid close contact within the same household with immunocompromised people for at least 21 days.
- Report adverse reactions. The U.S. Department of Health and Human Services has established a Vaccine Adverse Event Reporting System to manage reports of suspected adverse reactions for any vaccine (1-800-822-7967). Reporting forms may also be obtained at the FDA Web site (http://vaers.hhs.gov).
- Give drug before exposure to influenza. The peak of influenza varies from year to year, but typically occurs between late December and early March. Because the duration of protection from drug isn't known and yearly variation in the influenza strains is possible, revaccinate annually to increase the likelihood of protection.
- Don't give with other vaccines.
- Drug may not protect 100% of patients.
- Thaw drug before giving. To thaw, hold the sprayer in the palm of the hand and support the plunger rod with the thumb. Give the vaccine immediately. Or thaw drug in a refrigerator, and store at 36° to 46° F (2° to 8° C) for no more than 24 hours before use. When thawed, drug is a colorless to pale yellow liquid that's clear to slightly cloudy. Some particulates may be present, but they don't affect use.
- Give about 0.25 ml into each nostril while the recipient is in an upright position. Insert the tip of the sprayer just inside the nose, and depress the plunger to spray. The dose-divider clip is removed from the sprayer to give the second half of the dose into the other nostril.

Patient teaching

- Inform parents of children ages 5 to 8 that two doses of the drug are required the first time it's used.

• Tell patient to avoid close contact within the same household with immunocompromised people for at least 21 days.
• Instruct patient to report any suspected adverse reaction to the prescriber or clinic where the vaccine was given.
• Inform patient that annual revaccination may increase the likelihood of protection and that not every person who receives the vaccine will be protected.

Evaluation

• Patient remains free of adverse effects of the therapy.
• Patient does not contract influenza A or B virus.
• Patient and family state understanding of vaccine therapy.

insulin aspart (rDNA origin) injection

(IN-suh-lin AS-part)

NovoLog

insulin aspart (rDNA origin) protamine suspension and insulin aspart (rDNA origin) injection

NovoLog 70/30

Pharmacologic class: human insulin analogue
Therapeutic class: antidiabetic
Pregnancy risk category: B

Indications and dosages

▶ **Control of hyperglycemia in diabetes mellitus.** *Adults and children age 6 and older:* 0.5 to 1 unit/kg NovoLog subcutaneously daily within 5 to 10 minutes of start of meal. About 50% to 70% of the daily insulin requirement may be provided by this drug and the remainder by intermediate-acting or long-acting insulin. Initially, dosage for NovoLog external insulin infusion pumps is based on the total daily insulin dosage of the previous regimen. Give 50% of the total dosage as a bolus at mealtime and the remainder as basal infusion. Adjust dosage as needed. Or give NovoLog 70/30 b.i.d. within 15 minutes of meals.

Contraindications and cautions

• Contraindicated during episodes of hypoglycemia and in patients hypersensitive to NovoLog or its excipients.
• Use cautiously in patients prone to hypoglycemia and hypokalemia, such as patients who are fasting, have autonomic neuropathy, or are using potassium-lowering drugs or drugs sensitive to potassium levels.
Lifespan: In breast-feeding women, use cautiously because it's unknown if drug appears in breast milk. In children younger than age 6, safety and effectiveness haven't been established.

Adverse reactions

Metabolic: ***hyperkalemia, hypoglycemia.***
Skin: lipodystrophy, pruritus, rash.
Other: allergic reactions, injection site reactions.

Interactions

Drug-drug. *ACE inhibitors, disopyramide, fibrates, fluoxetine, MAO inhibitors, oral antidiabetics, propoxyphene, salicylates, somatostatin analogue (octreotide), sulfonamide antibiotics:* May enhance the blood glucose–lowering effects of insulin and increase risk of hypoglycemia. Monitor glucose level and signs of hypoglycemia. May require insulin dosage adjustment.
Beta blockers, clonidine, guanethidine, reserpine: May mask symptoms of hypoglycemia. Use cautiously in patients with diabetes.
Corticosteroids, danazol, diuretics, estrogens, isoniazid, niacin, phenothiazine derivatives, progestogens (hormonal contraceptives), somatropin, sympathomimetics (such as epinephrine, salbutamol, terbutaline), thyroid hormones: May reduce the blood glucose–lowering effect of insulin and may cause hyperglycemia. Monitor glucose level. May require insulin dosage adjustment.
Lithium salts, pentamidine: May enhance or weaken blood glucose–lowering effect of insulin, causing hypoglycemia or hyperglycemia. Pentamidine may cause hypoglycemia, which may sometimes be followed by hyperglycemia. Monitor glucose level.
Drug-lifestyle. *Alcohol use:* May increase the blood glucose–lowering effects of insulin. Discourage use together.

Marijuana use: May increase glucose level. Tell patient about this interaction.
Smoking: May increase glucose level and decrease response to insulin. Discourage patient from smoking; have patient monitor glucose level closely.

Effects on lab test results

- May decrease glucose and potassium levels.

Pharmacokinetics

Absorption: Bioavailable as regular human insulin. Faster absorption and onset and shorter duration of action compared to regular human insulin.
Distribution: 0% to 9% protein-bound, similar to regular insulin.
Metabolism: Unknown.
Excretion: Unknown. *Half-life:* 81 minutes.

Route	Onset	Peak	Duration
SubQ			
NovoLog	15–30 min	1–3 hr	3–5 hr
NovoLog 70/30	Rapid	1–4 hr	24 hr

Action

Chemical effect: Binds to insulin receptors on muscle and fat cells, lowers glucose level, facilitates the cellular uptake of glucose, and inhibits the output of glucose from the liver.
Therapeutic effect: Lowers glucose level.

Available forms

10-ml vial for injection: 100 units of insulin aspart per ml (U-100)
3-ml PenFill cartridges: 100 units/ml

NURSING PROCESS

Assessment

- Assess underlying condition before starting therapy, and reassess regularly.
- Monitor glucose level before starting therapy and regularly throughout therapy.
- Monitor patient's glycosylated hemoglobin level regularly.
- Monitor urine ketones when glucose level is elevated.
- Monitor patient for injection-site reactions.
- Monitor patient with an external insulin pump for erythematous, pruritic, or thickened skin at injection site.
- Assess patient's and family's knowledge of drug therapy.

Nursing diagnoses

- Risk for impaired skin integrity related to adverse drug effects
- Risk for injury related to drug-induced hypoglycemia
- Deficient knowledge related to insulin aspart therapy

Planning and implementation

- Give NovoLog 5 to 10 minutes before the start of a meal. Give NovoLog 70/30 up to 15 minutes before the start of a meal. Because of drug's rapid onset and short duration of action, patients may need the addition of longer-acting insulins to prevent before-meal hyperglycemia.
- Give subcutaneously into the abdominal wall, thigh, or upper arm. Rotate sites to minimize lipodystrophies.
- Monitor patient for hypoglycemia, which may occur as a result of an excess of insulin relative to food intake, energy expenditure, or both. The warning signs and symptoms of hypoglycemia include shaking, sweating, dizziness, fatigue, hunger, irritability, confusion, blurred vision, headaches, or nausea and vomiting. Treat mild episodes of hypoglycemia with oral glucose. Adjust drug dosage, meal patterns, or exercise, if needed. Treat more severe episodes involving coma, seizure, or neurologic impairment with I.M. or subcutaneous glucagon or concentrated I.V. glucose. Sustain carbohydrate intake and observe because hypoglycemia may recur.
- Look at insulin vial before use. NovoLog should appear as a clear, colorless solution. It should never contain particulate matter, appear cloudy or viscous, or be discolored. NovoLog 70/30 should appear uniformly white and cloudy and should never contain particulate matter or be discolored.
- Don't use drug after its expiration date. Discard after expiration date.
- Store drug between 36° and 46° F (2° and 8° C). Don't freeze. Don't expose vials to excessive heat or sunlight. Open vials are stable at room temperature for 28 days.

ALERT: Pump or infusion-set malfunctions or insulin degradation can lead to hyperglycemia and ketosis in a short time because of a subcutaneous depot of fast-acting insulin.

• Don't dilute or mix insulin aspart with any other insulin when using an external insulin pump.
• Insulin aspart is recommended for use with Disetronic H-TRON plus V100 with Disetronic 3.15 plastic cartridges and Classic or Tender infusion sets, and MiniMed Models 505, 506, and 507 with MiniMed 3-ml syringes and Polyfin or Sof-set infusion sets. The use of insulin aspart in quick-release infusion sets and cartridge adapters has not been assessed.
• Replace infusion sets and insulin aspart in the reservoir and choose a new infusion site every 48 hours or less to avoid insulin degradation and infusion set malfunction.
• Discard drug exposed to temperatures higher than 98.6° F (37° C). The temperature may exceed room temperature when the pump housing, cover, tubing, or sport case is exposed to sunlight or radiant heat.
ALERT: Spell out "units" to reduce the risk of error of misreading "U" as a zero.
ALERT: Don't confuse NovoLog 70/30 with Novolin 70/30.
ALERT: Don't confuse NovoLog with Novolin or Humalog.

Patient teaching

• Inform patient of the drug's risks and benefits.
• Teach patient to recognize symptoms of hypoglycemia and hyperglycemia and how to treat them.
• Instruct patient on injection techniques, timing of dose to meals, adherence to meal planning, importance of regular glucose monitoring and periodic glycosylated hemoglobin testing, and proper storage of insulin.
• Tell woman to notify prescriber if she plans to become or becomes pregnant. Information on drug in pregnancy or lactation isn't available.
• Instruct patient to report changes at injection site, including redness, itchiness, or thickened skin.
• Tell patient not to dilute or mix insulin aspart with any other insulin when using an external insulin pump.
• Teach patient how to properly use the external insulin pump.

Evaluation

• Patient doesn't experience adverse reactions from drug.
• Patient's glucose level is within the normal range.
• Patient and family state understanding of drug therapy.

insulin detemir

(IN-suh-lin DEH-teh-meer)
Levemir

Pharmacologic class: insulin analogue
Therapeutic class: antidiabetic
Pregnancy risk category: C

Indications and dosages

▶ **Hyperglycemia in patients with diabetes mellitus who need basal (long-acting) insulin.** *Adults and children age 6 and older:* Base dosage on patient response and glucose level. In insulin-naive patients with type 2 diabetes, start with 0.1 to 0.2 units/kg subcutaneously once daily in the evening or 10 units once or b.i.d. based on glucose level. Patients with type 1 or 2 diabetes receiving basal-bolus treatment or basal insulin only may switch to insulin detemir on a unit-to-unit basis adjusted to glycemic target.

Contraindications and cautions

• Contraindicated in patients hypersensitive to insulin detemir or its excipients. Don't give drug with an insulin infusion pump.
• Use cautiously in patients with hepatic or renal impairment; they may need dosage adjustment.
Lifespan: In pregnant women, use only if benefits outweigh risks to the fetus. In breast-feeding women, use cautiously; it isn't known whether drug appears in breast milk. In children, safety and efficacy haven't been established. In elderly patients, starting dosage, increments of change, and maintenance dosage should be conservative; hypoglycemia may be harder to recognize in these patients.

Adverse reactions

CV: edema.
Metabolic: HYPOGLYCEMIA, sodium retention, *weight gain.*
Skin: injection site reactions, lipodystrophy, pruritus, rash.
Other: allergic reactions.

Interactions

Drug-drug. *ACE inhibitors, antidiabetic drugs, disopyramide, fibrates, fluoxetine, MAO inhibitors, octreotide, propoxyphene, salicylates, sulfonamides:* May increase blood glucose–lowering effect of insulin and risk of hypoglycemia. Monitor blood glucose carefully.
Beta blockers, clonidine, guanethidine, reserpine: May decrease or conceal signs of hypoglycemia. Avoid use together if possible.
Beta blockers, clonidine, lithium salts: May increase or decrease blood glucose–lowering effect of insulin. Monitor blood glucose level carefully.
Corticosteroids, danazol, diuretics, estrogens, isoniazid, phenothiazines, progestogens (hormonal contraceptives), somatropin, sympathomimetics, thyroid hormones: May decrease blood glucose–lowering effect of insulin. Monitor blood glucose level carefully.
Insulin other than insulin detemir: May alter the action of one or both insulins if mixed together. Don't mix or dilute insulin detemir with other insulins.
Pentamidine: May cause initial hypoglycemia followed by hyperglycemia. Use together cautiously.
Drug-lifestyle. *Alcohol use:* May increase or decrease blood glucose–lowering effect of insulin. Discourage use together.
Marijuana use: May increase glucose level. Tell patient about this interaction.
Smoking: May increase glucose level and decrease response to insulin. Discourage patient from smoking; have patient monitor glucose level closely.

Effects on lab test results

- May decrease glucose level.

Pharmacokinetics

Absorption: Slow and prolonged.
Distribution: 98% bound to albumin.
Metabolism: Unknown.
Excretion: Unknown. *Half life:* 5 to 7 hours.

Route	Onset	Peak	Duration
SubQ	Unknown	6–8 hr	6–23 hr

Action

Chemical effect: Regulates glucose metabolism by binding to insulin receptors, facilitating cellular uptake of glucose into muscle and fat, and inhibiting release of glucose from liver.
Therapeutic effect: Lowers glucose level.

Available forms

Injection: 100 units/ml in 10-ml vials, 3-ml cartridges (PenFill), 3-ml prefilled syringes (InnoLet, FlexPen)

NURSING PROCESS

Assessment

- Monitor blood glucose level routinely in all patients receiving insulin.
- Measure patient's glycosylated hemoglobin level periodically.
- Watch for hyperglycemia, especially if patient's diet or exercise patterns change.
- Assess patient for signs and symptoms of hypoglycemia. Insulin dosages may need adjustment.
- Assess patient's and family's knowledge of drug therapy.

Nursing diagnoses

- Risk for injury related to drug-induced hypoglycemia
- Ineffective health maintenance related to hyperglycemia
- Deficient knowledge related to drug therapy

Planning and implementation

ALERT: Don't give this drug by I.V. or I.M. route.
ALERT: Don't mix or dilute insulin detemir with other insulins.
ALERT: Spell out "units" to reduce the risk of misreading "U" as a zero.
- Early warning symptoms of hypoglycemia may be less pronounced in patients who take beta blockers and patients with long-standing diabetes, diabetic nerve disease, or intensified diabetes control. Monitor glucose level closely in these patients because severe hypoglycemia could develop before symptoms do.
- Insulin dosages may need adjustment if patient experiences illness, emotional disturbance, or other stresses or if patient changes his usual meal plan or exercise level.

Patient teaching

- Teach diabetes management, including glucose monitoring, injection techniques, and continuous rotation of injection sites.

ALERT: Teach patient not to mix insulin detemir with any other insulin or solution.
- Instruct patient to use only solution that's clear and colorless, with no visible particles.
- Tell patient to recognize and report signs and symptoms of hyperglycemia, such as nausea, vomiting, drowsiness, flushed dry skin, dry mouth, increased urination, thirst, and loss of appetite.
- Urge patient to check blood glucose level often to achieve control and to avoid hyperglycemia and hypoglycemia.
- Teach patient to recognize and report signs and symptoms of hypoglycemia, such as sweating, dizziness, light-headedness, headache, drowsiness, and irritability.
- Advise patient to carry a quick source of simple sugar, such as hard candy or glucose tablets, in case of hypoglycemia.
- Caution patient not to stop insulin abruptly or change the amount or type of insulin used without consulting prescriber.
- Advise patient to avoid alcohol because it lowers the glucose level.
- Caution woman to consult prescriber before trying to become pregnant.
- Tell patient to store unused vials, cartridges, and prefilled syringes in the refrigerator at 36° to 46° F (2° to 8° C).
- After initial use, vials may be refrigerated or stored at room temperature, below 86° F (30° C), away from direct heat and light, for up to 42 days. Cartridges or prefilled syringes may be stored at room temperature, below 86° F (30° C). Tell patient not to store or refrigerate insulin with a needle in place.
- Caution against freezing insulin detemir and against using insulin detemir that has been frozen.

Evaluation

- Patient does not experience drug-induced hypoglycemia.
- Patient's glucose level remains within normal limits with drug therapy.
- Deficient knowledge related to drug therapy.

insulin glargine (rDNA)

(IN-suh-lin GLAR-gene)

Lantus

Pharmacologic class: insulin analogue
Therapeutic class: antidiabetic
Pregnancy risk category: C

Indications and dosages

▶ **Management of type 1 or type 2 diabetes mellitus in patients who need basal (long-acting) insulin for the control of hyperglycemia.** *Adults and children age 6 and older:* Individualize dosage. Start drug subcutaneously at the same dose as the current insulin dose at the same time each day.

▶ **Management of type 2 diabetes mellitus in patients previously treated with oral antidiabetics.** *Adults:* 10 units subcutaneously once daily at bedtime. Adjust as needed to total daily dosage of 2 units to 100 units subcutaneously at the same time each day.

Contraindications and cautions

- Contraindicated in patients hypersensitive to insulin glargine or its excipients. Don't use drug during episodes of hypoglycemia.
- Use cautiously in patients with renal or hepatic impairment, and adjust dosage as directed.

Lifespan: In breast-feeding women, use cautiously because it's unknown if the drug appears in breast milk. In children younger than age 6, safety and effectiveness haven't been established. In elderly patients, use cautiously to avoid hypoglycemia.

Adverse reactions

EENT: retinopathy.
Metabolic: *hypoglycemia.*
Skin: lipodystrophy, pruritus, rash.
Other: allergic reactions, pain at injection site.

Interactions

Drug-drug. *ACE inhibitors, disopyramide, fibrates, fluoxetine, MAO inhibitors, octreotide, oral antidiabetics, propoxyphene, salicylates, sulfonamide antibiotics:* May cause hypoglycemia and increased insulin effect. Monitor glucose level. Insulin glargine dosage may need adjustment.

Beta blockers, clonidine, guanethidine, reserpine: May decrease or conceal signs of hypoglycemia. Use cautiously.
Beta blockers, clonidine, lithium salts: May increase or decrease blood glucose–lowering effect of insulin. Monitor blood glucose level carefully.
Corticosteroids, danazol, diuretics, estrogens, isoniazid, phenothiazines (prochlorperazine, promethazine), progestins (hormonal contraceptives), sympathomimetics (albuterol, epinephrine, terbutaline), thyroid hormones: May reduce the blood glucose–lowering effect of insulin. Monitor glucose level. Insulin glargine dosage may need adjustment.
Guanethidine, reserpine: May mask signs of hypoglycemia. Avoid using together, if possible. Monitor glucose level carefully.
Lithium: May increase or decrease blood glucose–lowering effect of insulin. Monitor glucose level. Insulin glargine dosage may need adjustment.
Pentamidine: May cause hypoglycemia, which may be followed by hyperglycemia. Avoid using together, if possible.
Drug-herb. *Aloe, bilberry leaf, bitter melon, burdock, dandelion, fenugreek, garlic, ginseng:* May improve glucose control and allow a reduced antidiabetic dosage. Tell patient to discuss the use of herbal remedies with prescriber before use.
Licorice root: May increase dosage requirements of insulin. Discourage use together.
Drug-lifestyle. *Alcohol use:* May increase glucose-lowering effects of insulin. Discourage use together.
Emotional stress, exercise: May increase or decrease glucose-lowering effect of insulin. Monitor glucose level. Insulin glargine dosage may need adjustment.
Marijuana use: May increase glucose level. Tell patient about this interaction.
Smoking: May increase glucose level and decrease response to insulin. Discourage patient from smoking; have patient monitor glucose level closely.

Effects on lab test results

- May decrease glucose level.

Pharmacokinetics

Absorption: Slower, more prolonged absorption than NPH and a relatively constant level over 24 hours with no pronounced peak when compared with NPH insulin. After injection into subcutaneous tissue, the acidic solution is neutralized, leading to formation of microprecipitates. From these microprecipitates, small amounts of insulin glargine are slowly released.
Distribution: Unknown.
Metabolism: Partly metabolized to form two active metabolites similar to insulin.
Excretion: Unknown. *Half-life:* Unknown.

Route	Onset	Peak	Duration
SubQ	Slow	None	10¾–24 hr

Action

Chemical effect: Increases glucose transport across muscle and fat cell membranes to reduce glucose level. Promotes conversion of glucose to its storage form, glycogen.
Therapeutic effect: Lowers glucose level.

Available forms

Injection: 10-ml vial or 3 ml cartridges (for OptiPen) of 100 units/ml

NURSING PROCESS

Assessment

- Obtain history of patient's underlying condition before starting therapy, and reassess regularly. As with any insulin, the desired glucose level and the doses and timing of antidiabetic drug must be determined individually.
- Monitor glucose level closely.
- Monitor patient for hypoglycemia. Early symptoms may be different or less pronounced in patients with long-standing diabetes, diabetic nerve disease, or intensified diabetes control.
- Assess patient's and family's knowledge of drug therapy.

Nursing diagnoses

- Ineffective health maintenance related to hyperglycemia
- Risk for injury related to drug-induced hypoglycemia
- Deficient knowledge related to drug therapy

Planning and implementation

- Drug isn't intended for I.V. use. Its prolonged action depends on injection into the subcutaneous space.

• Because of its prolonged duration, insulin glargine isn't the insulin of choice for diabetic ketoacidosis.
• The rate of absorption and onset and the duration of action may be affected by exercise and other circumstances, such as illness and emotional stress.
• Don't dilute drug or mix it with any other insulin or solution.
• As with any insulin therapy, lipodystrophy may occur at injection site and delay insulin absorption. Rotate injection sites to reduce lipodystrophy.
ALERT: Spell out "units" to reduce the risk of misreading "U" as a zero.
• Store unopened vials at 36° F to 46° F (2° to 8° C). Don't freeze. Discard opened vials, whether refrigerated or not, after 28 days. May store opened vials at room temperature away from direct heat and light.
ALERT: Don't confuse Lantus with Lente.

Patient teaching

• Teach patient proper glucose-monitoring techniques and proper diabetes management.
• Teach diabetic patient signs and symptoms of hypoglycemia, such as fatigue, weakness, confusion, headache, and pale skin.
• Advise patient to treat mild episodes of hypoglycemia with oral glucose tablets. Encourage patient to always carry glucose tablets in case of a hypoglycemic episode.
• Teach patient the importance of maintaining a diabetic diet. Explain that adjustments in drug dosage, meal patterns, and exercise may be needed to regulate blood glucose.
• Tell patient that any change of insulin should be made cautiously and only under medical supervision. Changes in insulin strength, manufacturer, type (regular, NPH, insulin analogues), species (animal, human), or method of manufacture (ribosomal DNA versus animal source) may warrant a dosage change. Oral antidiabetic treatment may need to be adjusted.
• Tell patient to consult prescriber before using OTC drugs.
• Advise patient not to dilute or mix any other insulin or solution with insulin glargine. Tell patient to discard the vial if the solution is cloudy.
• Instruct patient to store insulin glargine vials in the refrigerator, if possible.

Evaluation

• Patient's blood glucose level is normal.
• Patient doesn't experience hypoglycemic reactions.
• Patient and family state understanding of drug therapy.

insulin glulisine (rDNA origin)

(IN-suh-lin GLUE-lih-seen)
Apidra

Pharmacologic class: human insulin analogue
Therapeutic class: antidiabetic
Pregnancy risk category: C

Indications and dosages

▶ **Diabetes mellitus.** *Adults:* Individualize dosage. Give subcutaneous injection within 15 minutes before a meal or within 20 minutes after meal starts if regimen also includes a longer-acting insulin or basal insulin analogue. Or give subcutaneous infusion using an external infusion pump.

Contraindications and cautions

• Contraindicated during periods of hypoglycemia and in patients hypersensitive to insulin glulisine or one of its excipients.
• Use cautiously in patients with moderate to severe renal or hepatic dysfunction.
Lifespan: In pregnant women, safety and effectiveness haven't been established. In breastfeeding women, use cautiously because it's unknown if the drug appears in breast milk. In children, safety and effectiveness haven't been established.

Adverse reactions

Metabolic: ***hypoglycemia.***
Skin: *injection-site reactions,* lipodystrophy, pruritus, rash.
Other: allergic reactions, ***anaphylaxis,*** insulin antibody production.

Interactions

Drug-drug. *ACE inhibitors, disopyramide, fibrates, fluoxetine, MAO inhibitors, oral antidiabetics, pentoxifylline, propoxyphene, salicylates, sulfonamide antibiotics:* May increase blood glucose–lowering effects. Monitor glu-

cose level, and watch for evidence of hypoglycemia.
Beta blockers, clonidine, guanethidine, reserpine: May decrease or conceal signs of hypoglycemia. Avoid use together if possible.
Beta blockers, clonidine, lithium, pentamidine: May cause unpredictable response to insulin. Use together cautiously; monitor patient closely.
Clozapine, corticosteroids, danazol, diazoxide, diuretics, estrogens, glucagons, isoniazid, olanzapine, phenothiazines, progestogens, protease inhibitors, somatropin, sympathomimetics (such as albuterol, epinephrine, and terbutaline), thyroid hormones: May decrease blood glucose–lowering effects. Monitor glucose level carefully.
Drug-lifestyle. *Alcohol:* May increase or decrease drug effects, resulting in either hypoglycemia or hyperglycemia. Discourage alcohol use.
Marijuana use: May increase glucose level. Tell patient about this interaction.
Smoking: May increase glucose level and decrease response to insulin. Discourage patient from smoking; have patient monitor glucose level closely.

Effects on lab test results

- May decrease glucose level.

Pharmacokinetics

Absorption: Absorbed rapidly, faster than regular insulin.
Distribution: Wide.
Metabolism: Bound and inactivated in peripheral tissues plus primary metabolism in the liver.
Excretion: Renal filtration. *Half-life:* 42 minutes.

Route	Onset	Peak	Duration
SubQ	15 min	34–91 min	105–210 min

Action

Chemical effect: Increases peripheral glucose uptake by skeletal muscle and fat and decreases hepatic glucose production.
Therapeutic effect: Lowers glucose level.

Available forms

Injection: 10-ml vial of 100 units/ml

NURSING PROCESS

Assessment

- Monitor patient for signs and symptoms of hyperglycemia, including drowsiness, fruity breath, frequent urination, and thirst.
- Monitor patient for signs and symptoms of hypoglycemia, including cool, diaphoretic skin; shaking; trembling; confusion; headache; irritability; hunger; tachycardia; and nausea.
- Look for early warning signs of hypoglycemia. They may be different or less pronounced in patients who take beta blockers, who have had an oral antidiabetic added to the regimen, or who have long-term diabetes or diabetic nerve disease.
- Assess injection site for redness, swelling, or itching.
- Monitor patient for lipodystrophy at injection site. Lipodystrophy may delay insulin absorption.
- Assess patient's and family's knowledge of drug therapy.

Nursing diagnoses

- Ineffective health maintenance related to presence of underlying disease
- Risk for injury related to drug-induced hypoglycemia
- Deficient knowledge related to drug therapy

Planning and implementation

- Use with a longer-acting or basal insulin analogue.

ALERT: Drug has a more rapid onset and shorter duration of action than regular human insulin. Give within 15 minutes before or immediately after a meal.

ALERT: Spell out "units" to reduce the risk of misreading "U" as a zero.

- Don't mix drug in a syringe with other insulins except NPH.
- When drug is used in an external subcutaneous infusion pump, don't mix with other insulins or with a diluent.
- Adjust dosage for changes in insulin strength, manufacturer, or type.
- Adjust dosage for changes in physical activity or usual meal plan.
- Adjust dosage during illness, emotional disturbances, or stress.

Patient teaching

- Tell patient to take drug within 20 minutes of eating.
- Teach patient how to give subcutaneous insulin injections.
- Tell patient not to mix drug in a syringe with any insulin other than NPH.
- If patient is mixing drug with NPH, tell patient to use U-100 syringes, to draw insulin glulisine into the syringe before NPH insulin, and to inject the mixture immediately.
- Instruct patient to rotate injection sites to avoid injection-site reactions.
- If patient is using an external infusion pump, teach proper use of the device. Tell patient not to mix drug with other insulin or diluents. Instruct patient to change the infusion set, reservoir with insulin, and infusion site every 48 hours.
- Teach patient the signs and symptoms of hypoglycemia (sweating, rapid pulse, trembling, confusion, headache, irritability, and nausea). Advise the patient to treat these symptoms by eating or drinking something containing sugar.
- Tell the patient to contact his prescriber for dosage adjustments if hypoglycemia occurs frequently.
- Show patient how to monitor and log his glucose levels to assess diabetes control.
- Explain the possible long-term complications of diabetes and the importance of regular preventive therapy. Urge patient to follow prescribed diet and exercise regimen. To further reduce the increased risk of heart disease, encourage patient to stop smoking and lose weight.
- Instruct patient to wear or carry identification showing that he has diabetes.
- Tell patient to store unopened vials in the refrigerator. Opened vials must be stored below 77° F (25° C) and should be used within 28 days. Drug should be protected from direct heat and light.

☑ Evaluation

- Patient's glucose level is normal.
- Patient doesn't experience hypoglycemia.
- Patient and family state understanding of drug therapy.

insulin (regular)

(IN-suh-lin)

Humulin R, Humulin R Regular U-500 (concentrated), Novolin R, Novolin R PenFill, Novolin R Prefilled

insulin (rDNA) inhalation powder

Exubera

insulin (lispro)

Humalog

insulin lispro protamine and insulin lispro

Humalog Mix 75/25

isophane insulin suspension (NPH)

Humulin N, Novolin N, Novolin N PenFill, Novolin N Prefilled

isophane insulin suspension and insulin injection combinations

Humulin 50/50, Humulin 70/30, Novolin 70/30, Novolin 70/30 PenFill, Novolin 70/30 Prefilled

Pharmacologic class: pancreatic hormone
Therapeutic class: antidiabetic
Pregnancy risk category: B (C; oral inhalation)

Indications and dosages

▶ **Moderate to severe diabetic ketoacidosis or hyperosmolar hyperglycemia (regular insulin).** *Adults older than age 20:* Give loading dose of 0.15 units/kg I.V. by direct injection, followed by 0.1 unit/kg/hour as a continuous infusion. When glucose level reaches 250 to 300 mg/dl, decrease insulin infusion to 0.05 to 0.1 unit/kg/hour. When glucose level is 150 to 200 mg/dl in patients with diabetic ketoacidosis or 250 to 300 mg/dl in those with hyperosmolar hyperglycemia, start infusion of D_5W in half-normal saline solution separately from the insulin infusion. Give insulin dose (intermediate-acting insulin is recommended) subcutaneously 1 to 2 hours before stopping insulin infusion.
Adults and children age 20 or younger: Loading dose isn't recommended. Start with 0.1 unit/kg/

hour by I.V. infusion. Once condition improves, decrease insulin infusion to 0.05 unit/kg/hour. When glucose level is 250 mg/dl, start infusion of D_5W in half-normal saline solution separately from the insulin infusion.

▶ **Mild diabetic ketoacidosis (regular insulin).** *Adults older than age 20:* Give loading dose of 0.4 to 0.6 unit/kg divided in two equal parts, with half the dose given by direct I.V. injection and half given I.M. or subcutaneously. Subsequent doses can be based on 0.1 unit/kg/hour I.M. or subcutaneously.

▶ **Newly diagnosed diabetes mellitus (regular insulin).** *Adults older than age 20:* Individualize therapy. Initially, 0.5 to 1 unit/kg/day subcutaneously as part of a regimen with short-acting and long-acting insulin therapy.
Adults and children age 20 or younger: Individualize therapy. Initially, 0.1 to 0.25 unit/kg subcutaneously q 6 to 8 hours for 24 hours; then adjust accordingly.

▶ **Control of hyperglycemia with Humalog and longer-acting insulin in patients with type 1 diabetes mellitus.** *Adults:* Dosage varies among patients and must be determined by prescriber familiar with patient's metabolic needs, eating habits, and other lifestyle variables. Inject subcutaneously within 15 minutes before or after a meal.

▶ **Control of hyperglycemia with Humalog and sulfonylureas in patients with type 2 diabetes mellitus.** *Adults and children older than age 3:* Dosage varies among patients and must be determined by prescriber familiar with patient's metabolic needs, eating habits, and other lifestyle variables. Inject subcutaneously within 15 minutes before or after a meal.

▶ **Control of hyperglycemia of type 1 or type 2 diabetes with inhalation powder (Exubera).** *Adults:* Initially, 0.05 mg/kg Exubera oral inhalation per meal, rounded down to the nearest whole milligram. Give within 10 minutes of a meal. Adjust dosage based on patient's need and glucose response.

▶ **Hyperkalemia‡.** *Adults:* 50 ml of dextrose 50% given over 5 minutes, followed by 5 to 10 units of regular insulin by I.V. push.

I.V. administration

- Give only regular insulin I.V. Inject directly into vein or into a port close to I.V. access site. Intermittent infusion isn't recommended. If given by continuous infusion, infuse drug diluted in normal saline solution at prescribed rate.
- Regular insulin is used in patients with circulatory collapse, diabetic ketoacidosis, or hyperkalemia.
- Don't use Humulin R (concentrated) U-500 I.V.
- Don't use intermediate- or long-acting insulins for coma or other emergency requiring rapid drug action.
- Ketosis-prone type 1, severely ill, and newly diagnosed diabetic patients with very high glucose levels may need hospitalization and I.V. treatment with regular fast-acting insulin.

⊗ Incompatibilities

Aminophylline, amobarbital, chlorothiazide, cytarabine, digoxin, diltiazem, dobutamine, dopamine, levofloxacin, methylprednisolone sodium succinate, nafcillin, norepinephrine, pentobarbital sodium, phenobarbital sodium, phenytoin sodium, ranitidine, sodium bicarbonate, thiopental.

Contraindications and cautions

- Contraindicated in hypoglycemia and in patients hypersensitive to insulin or any of its ingredients. Inhaled form is contraindicated in patients who smoke, quit smoking within the past 6 months, or have poorly controlled lung disease.

Lifespan: In pregnant and breast-feeding women, insulin is drug of choice to treat diabetes.

Adverse reactions

Metabolic: hyperglycemia (rebound or Somogyi effect), ***hypoglycemia.***
Respiratory: dyspnea, *increased cough,* reduced pulmonary function, *respiratory tract infection.*
Skin: itching, rash, redness, stinging, swelling, urticaria, warmth at injection site.
Other: ***anaphylaxis,*** hypersensitivity reactions, lipoatrophy, lipohypertrophy, rash.

Interactions

Drug-drug. *AIDS antiretrovirals, corticosteroids, dextrothyroxine, epinephrine, thiazide diuretics:* May decrease insulin response. Monitor patient for hyperglycemia.
Anabolic steroids, clofibrate, guanethidine, MAO inhibitors, salicylates, tetracyclines: May

prolong hypoglycemic effect. Monitor glucose level carefully.
Beta blockers, clonidine: May decrease or conceal signs of hypoglycemia. Use together cautiously.
Hormonal contraceptives: May decrease glucose tolerance in diabetic patients. Monitor glucose level, and adjust insulin dosage carefully.
Inhaled drugs, such as bronchodilators: May alter absorption of inhaled insulin. Time doses of other inhaled drugs consistently with inhaled insulin, and monitor glucose level closely.
Drug-herb. *Basil, bay, bee pollen, burdock, ginseng, glucomannan, horehound, marshmallow, myrrh, sage:* May affect glycemic control. Monitor glucose level carefully.
Drug-lifestyle. *Alcohol use:* May increase the blood glucose–lowering effects of insulin. Discourage use together.
Marijuana use: May increase glucose level. Tell patient about this interaction.
Smoking: May increase glucose level and decrease response to insulin. Discourage smoking; have patient monitor glucose level closely.

Effects on lab test results

• May decrease glucose, magnesium, and potassium levels.

Pharmacokinetics

Absorption: Highly variable after subcutaneous use depending on insulin type and injection site.
Distribution: Wide.
Metabolism: Some is bound and inactivated by peripheral tissues, but most appears to be degraded in liver and kidneys.
Excretion: Filtered by renal glomeruli; undergoes some tubular reabsorption. *Half-life:* About 9 minutes after I.V. use.

Route	Onset	Peak	Duration
I.V.	≤ 30 min	15–30 min	30 min–1 hr
SubQ	15 min–8 hr	2–30 hr	5–36 hr
Inhalation (oral)	10–20 min	2 hr	6 hr

Action

Chemical effect: Increases glucose transport across muscle and fat cell membranes to reduce glucose level. Promotes conversion of glucose to its storage form, glycogen.
Therapeutic effect: Lowers blood glucose level.

Available forms

Available without a prescription
insulin (regular)
Injection (human): 100 units/ml (Humulin R, Novolin R, Novolin R PenFill, Novolin R Prefilled)
isophane insulin suspension (NPH)
Injection (human): 100 units/ml (Humulin N, Novolin N, Novolin N PenFill, Novolin N Prefilled)
insulin zinc suspension (lente)
Injection (human): 100 units/ml (Novolin L)
isophane insulin suspension and insulin injection combinations
Injection (human): 100 units/ml (Humulin 50/50, Humulin 70/30, Novolin 70/30, Novolin 70/30 PenFill, Novolin 70/30 Prefilled,)
Available by prescription only
insulin (regular)
Injection (human): 500 units/ml (Humulin R Regular U-500 [concentrated])
insulin (rDNA) inhalation powder
Dose blisters: 1 mg, 3 mg
insulin (lispro)
Injection (human): 100 units/ml (Humalog)
insulin lispro protamine and insulin lispro
Injection (human): 100 units/ml (Humalog Mix 75/25)

NURSING PROCESS

Assessment

• Assess patient's glucose level before starting therapy and regularly thereafter. If patient is under stress, unstable, pregnant, recently diagnosed, or taking drugs that can interact with insulin, monitor level more frequently.
• Monitor patient's glycosylated hemoglobin level regularly.
• Monitor urine ketone level when glucose level is elevated.
• Be alert for adverse reactions and drug interactions.
• Monitor injection sites for local reactions.
• Assess patient's and family's knowledge of drug therapy.

Nursing diagnoses

• Ineffective health maintenance related to hyperglycemia
• Risk for injury related to drug-induced hypoglycemia
• Deficient knowledge related to drug therapy

Planning and implementation

ALERT: Dose is always expressed in USP units. Use only syringes calibrated for particular concentration of insulin given (such as U-100 for 100 units/ml insulin).

ALERT: Spell out "units" to reduce the risk of misreading the "U" as a zero.

- Insulin resistance may develop; large insulin doses are needed to control symptoms of diabetes in these patients. U-500 insulin is available as Regular (Concentrated) for such patients. Although not normally stocked in every pharmacy, it's readily available. Give hospital pharmacy sufficient notice before the need to refill in-house prescription. Never store U-500 insulin in same area with other insulin preparations because of danger of severe overdose if given accidentally to other patients.
- To mix insulin suspension, swirl vial gently or rotate between palms or between palm and thigh. Don't shake vigorously because doing so causes bubbling and air in syringe.
- Humalog insulin has a rapid onset of action. Give 15 minutes before meals.
- Regular insulin may be mixed with NPH insulins in any proportion.
- Switching from separate injections to prepared mixture may alter patient response. Whenever NPH is mixed with regular insulin in same syringe, give immediately to avoid loss of potency.
- Don't use insulin that has changed color or become clumped or granular.
- Check expiration date on vial before using.
- Usual route is subcutaneous. Pinch fold of skin with fingers starting at least 3 inches apart, and insert needle at 45- to 90-degree angle.
- Press but don't rub site after injection. Rotate and chart injection sites to avoid overuse of one area. Rotate injection sites within same anatomic region to help diabetic patients achieve better control.
- Ketosis-prone type 1, severely ill, and newly diagnosed diabetic patients with very high glucose levels may require hospitalization and I.V. treatment with regular fast-acting insulin.
- For a patient using inhaled insulin, obtain baseline and periodic pulmonary function tests. Carefully monitor glucose levels when switching from subcutaneous to inhaled insulin.
- Patient's with type 1 diabetes should use inhaled form with a longer-acting insulin. Patient's with type 2 diabetes may use inhaled form as monotherapy or with oral antidiabetics or a longer-acting insulin.
- Store drug in cool area. Refrigeration is desirable but not essential except for concentrated regular insulin.
- Notify prescriber of sudden changes in glucose levels, dangerously high or low levels, or ketosis.
- If patient develops diabetic ketoacidosis or hyperglycemic hyperosmolar nonketotic coma, provide supportive treatment.
- Treat hypoglycemic reaction with oral form of rapid-acting glucose if patient can swallow, or with glucagon or I.V. glucose if patient can't be roused. Follow with complex carbohydrate snack when patient is awake, and determine cause of reaction.
- Make sure patient is following appropriate diet and exercise programs. Adjust insulin dosage when other aspects of regimen are changed.
- Discuss with prescriber how to deal with noncompliance.
- Treat lipoatrophy or lipohypertrophy according to prescribed protocol.

Patient teaching

- Tell patient that insulin relieves symptoms but doesn't cure disease.
- Inform patient about nature of disease; importance of following therapeutic regimen; adherence to specific diet, weight reduction, exercise, and personal hygiene programs; and ways of avoiding infection. Review timing of injections and eating, and explain that meals must not be skipped.
- Stress that accuracy of measurement is very important, especially with concentrated regular insulin. Aids, such as a magnifying sleeve or dose magnifier, may improve accuracy. Instruct patient and family how to measure and give insulin.
- Advise patient not to alter order of mixing insulins or change model or brand of syringe or needle.
- Tell patient that glucose monitoring and urine ketone tests are essential guides to dosage and success of therapy. Stress the importance of recognizing hypoglycemic symptoms because insulin-induced hypoglycemia is hazardous and may cause brain damage if prolonged. Most adverse effects are self-limiting and temporary.
- Teach patient about proper use of equipment for monitoring glucose level.

• For patient using the inhaled form, make sure that he reads and understands the copy of the medication guide, detailing use, monitoring, care of the inhaler, and storage.
• Instruct patient not to drink alcohol during therapy.
• Advise patient not to smoke within 30 minutes after insulin injection. Smoking decreases absorption.
• Tell patient that marijuana use may increase insulin requirements.
• Advise patient to wear or carry medical identification at all times, to carry ample insulin supply and syringes on trips, to have carbohydrates (lump of sugar or candy) on hand for emergencies, and to note time-zone changes for dose scheduling when traveling.

☑ Evaluation

• Patient's glucose level is normal.
• Patient sustains no injury from drug-induced hypoglycemia.
• Patient and family state understanding of drug therapy.

interferon alfa-2a, recombinant (rIFN-A)

(in-ter-FEER-on AL-fuh too-ay ree-COM-bih-nent)
Roferon-A

interferon alfa-2b, recombinant (IFN-alpha 2)

Intron-A

Pharmacologic class: biological response modifier
Therapeutic class: antineoplastic, immunomodulator
Pregnancy risk category: C

Indications and dosages

▶ **Hairy cell leukemia.** *Adults:* For induction, 3 million international units alfa-2a subcutaneously or I.M. daily for 16 to 24 weeks. For maintenance, 3 million international units alfa-2a subcutaneously or I.M. three times weekly. Or 2 million international units/m^2 alfa-2b I.M. or subcutaneously three times weekly for induction and maintenance.

▶ **Condylomata acuminata.** *Adults:* 1 million international units alfa-2b per lesion, intralesionally, three times weekly for 3 weeks. May repeat after 12 to 16 weeks if results are not satisfactory

▶ **Kaposi sarcoma.** *Adults:* For induction, 36 million international units alfa-2a subcutaneously or I.M. daily for 10 to 12 weeks; for maintenance, 36 million international units alfa-2a three times weekly. Doses may begin at 3 million international units and escalate every 3 days until patient is given 36 million international units daily, in order to decrease toxicity. Or 30 million international units/m^2 alfa-2b subcutaneously or I.M. three times weekly. Maintain dose unless disease progresses rapidly or intolerance occurs.

▶ **Chronic hepatitis C.** *Adults:* 3 million international units alfa-2a three times weekly subcutaneously or I.M. for 12 months (48 to 52 weeks). Alternatively, induction dose of 6 million international units alfa-2a three times weekly for the first 3 months (12 weeks) followed by 3 million international units alfa-2a three times weekly for 9 months (36 weeks). If no response after 3 months, stop therapy. Retreatment with either 3 or 6 million international units alfa-2a three times weekly for 6 to 12 months may be considered. Or 3 million international units alfa-2b subcutaneously or I.M. three times weekly. In patients tolerating therapy with normalization of ALT at 16 weeks of treatment, extend therapy to 18 to 24 months. If no normalization of ALT at 16 weeks of treatment, consider stopping therapy.

▶ **Chronic hepatitis B.** *Adults:* 30 to 35 million international units alfa-2b subcutaneously or I.M. weekly either as 5 million international units daily or 10 million international units three times weekly for 16 weeks.
Children ages 1 to 17: Give 3 million international units/m^2 alfa-2b subcutaneously three times weekly for 1 week; then escalate dosage to 6 million international units/m^2 subcutaneously three times weekly (up to 10 million international units/m^2 subcutaneously three times weekly) for 16 to 24 weeks.

▶ **Chronic myelogenous leukemia.** *Adults:* 9 million international units alfa-2a daily I.M. or subcutaneously. An escalating dosage regimen, in which daily doses of 3 million and 6 million international units are given over 3 days followed by 9 million international units

daily for remainder of therapy, may produce increased short-term tolerance.
Children: 2.5 to 5 million international units/m^2 alfa-2a I.M. daily.

▶ **Malignant melanoma.** *Adults:* 20 million international units/m^2 alfa-2b daily given as I.V. infusion 5 days in a row for 4 weeks. For maintenance therapy, 10 million international units/m^2 subcutaneously three times weekly for 48 weeks. If adverse effects occur, stop therapy until they subside, and then resume therapy at 50% of the previous dose. If intolerance persists, stop therapy.

▶ **Initial treatment of aggressive follicular malignant lymphoma with combination chemotherapy containing anthracycline.** *Adults:* 5 million international units alfa-2b subcutaneously three times weekly for up to 18 months.

▶ **Metastatic renal cell carcinoma‡.** *Adults:* 5 to 20 million international units alfa-2b subcutaneously daily or three times weekly.

Contraindications and cautions

- Contraindicated in patients hypersensitive to the drug, its components, or mouse protein.
- Use cautiously in patients with severe hepatic or renal function impairment, seizure disorders, compromised CNS function, cardiac disease, or myelosuppression.
- Alpha interferons cause or aggravate fatal or life-threatening neuropsychiatric, autoimmune, ischemic, and infectious disorders. Monitor patient closely. Stop drug in patients with persistently severe or worsening signs or symptoms of these conditions.

Lifespan: In pregnant women, use cautiously. In breast-feeding women, stop drug or stop breast-feeding. In children, safety and effectiveness haven't been established.

Adverse reactions

CNS: anxiety, apathy, confusion, *depression,* difficulty in thinking or concentrating, *dizziness,* fatigue, gait disturbances, *headache, insomnia, irritability,* lethargy, nervousness, numbness, paresthesia, poor coordination, sedation, syncope, vertigo.
CV: ***arrhythmias,*** chest pain, ***cyanosis,*** edema, flushing, ***heart failure,*** *hypertension,* hypotension, ***MI,*** palpitations.
EENT: conjunctivitis, dry or inflamed oropharynx, earache, excessive salivation, eye irritation, pharyngitis, rhinitis, rhinorrhea, sinusitis, visual disturbances.
GI: abdominal fullness, *abdominal pain, anorexia,* constipation, *diarrhea,* dysgeusia, esophagitis, flatulence, gastric distress, gingivitis, hypermotility, *nausea,* stomatitis, vomiting.
GU: transient impotence.
Hematologic: anemia, ***leukopenia, mild thrombocytopenia, neutropenia.***
Hepatic: ***hepatitis.***
Respiratory: *coughing, dyspnea,* tachypnea.
Skin: *diaphoresis,* dryness, partial alopecia, *pruritus, rash,* urticaria.
Other: *flulike syndrome,* hot flushes, *injection site reaction.*

Interactions

Drug-drug. *Aminophylline, theophylline:* May reduce theophylline clearance. Monitor level.
Cardiotoxic, hematotoxic, or neurotoxic drugs: May increase effects of these drugs. Monitor patient closely.
CNS depressants: May increase CNS effects. Avoid use together.
Interleukin-2: May increase risk of renal impairment from interleukin-2. Monitor patient closely.
Live-virus vaccines: May increase risk of adverse reactions and decreased antibody response. Don't use together.
Zidovudine: May have synergistic adverse effects between alfa-2b and zidovudine. Carefully monitor WBC count.
Drug-lifestyle. *Alcohol use:* May increase risk of GI bleeding. Discourage use together.
Sun exposure: May cause photosensitivity reactions. Discourage prolonged or unprotected sun exposure.

Effects on lab test results

- May increase calcium, potassium, AST, ALT, alkaline phosphatase, LDH, triglyceride, and fasting glucose levels. May decrease hemoglobin level and hematocrit.
- May increase PT, INR, and PTT. May decrease WBC, neutrophil, and platelet counts.

Pharmacokinetics

Absorption: More than 80% absorbed after I.M. or subcutaneous injection.
Distribution: Wide and rapid.
Metabolism: Drug appears to be metabolized in liver and kidneys.

Excretion: Reabsorbed from glomerular filtrate with minor biliary elimination. *Half-life:* 3½ to 8½ hours.

Route	Onset	Peak	Duration
I.M.	Unknown	3¾ hr	Unknown
SubQ	Unknown	7¼ hr	Unknown
Intralesional	Unknown	Unknown	Unknown

Action

Chemical effect: May involve direct antiproliferative action against tumor cells or viral cells to inhibit replication and change immune response by enhancing phagocytic macrophages and by augmenting specific cytotoxicity of lymphocytes for target cells.
Therapeutic effect: Inhibits growth of certain tumor cells and viral cells.

Available forms

alfa-2a (Roferon-A)
Prefilled syringes for subcutaneous use only: 3 million international units/0.5 ml; 6 million international units/0.5 ml; 9 million international units/0.5 ml
Solution for injection: 18 million international units/multidose vial; 36 million international units/single-dose vial
alfa-2b (Intron A)
Powder for injection with diluent: 5 million international units/vial; 10 million international units/vial; 18 million international units/multidose vial; 25 million international units/vial; 50 million international units/vial
Solution for injection: 3 million international units/vial or syringe; 5 million international units/vial or syringe; 10 million international units/vial; 18 million international units/multidose vial; 25 million international units/vial
Multidose pens: 18 million international units (3 million international units per dose); 30 million international units (5 million international units per dose); 60 million international units (10 million international units per dose)

NURSING PROCESS

Assessment

- Assess patient's condition before starting therapy and regularly thereafter.
- Obtain allergy history. Drug contains phenol as preservative and albumin as stabilizer.
- Assess patient for flulike symptoms before starting therapy; these tend to diminish with continued therapy.
- Alpha interferons may cause or aggravate fatal or life-threatening neuropsychiatric, autoimmune, ischemic, and infectious disorders. Monitor patients closely. Stop drug in patients with persistently severe or worsening signs or symptoms of these conditions. In many, but not all, cases, these disorders resolve after stopping therapy.
- Monitor blood studies. Tests include CBC with differential, platelet count, blood chemistry and electrolyte studies, liver function, and, if patient has cardiac disorder or advanced stages of cancer, ECGs. Any effects are dose-related and reversible. Recovery occurs within several days or weeks after withdrawal.
- Be alert for adverse reactions and drug interactions.
- Assess patient's and family's knowledge of drug therapy.

Nursing diagnoses

- Ineffective health maintenance related to underlying condition
- Risk for injury related to drug-induced adverse CNS reactions
- Deficient knowledge related to drug therapy

Planning and implementation

- Premedicate patient with acetaminophen to minimize flulike symptoms.
- Give drug at bedtime to minimize daytime drowsiness.
- Make sure patient is well hydrated, especially during initial stages of treatment.

ALERT: Different brands of interferon may not be equivalent and may require different dosages.

- Give subcutaneously if patient's platelet count is below 50,000/mm³.
- When giving interferon alfa-2b for condylomata acuminata, use only 10 million–international units vial because dilution of other strengths for intralesional use results in hypertonic solution. Don't reconstitute 10 million–international units vial with more than 1 ml of diluent. Use tuberculin or similar syringe and 25G to 30G needle. Don't inject too deeply beneath lesion or too superficially. As many as five lesions can be treated at one time. To ease discomfort, give drug in evening with acetaminophen.

• Refrigerate drug.
• Notify prescriber of severe adverse reactions, which may require a lower dose or stopping the drug.
• Using drug with blood dyscrasia–causing drugs, bone marrow suppressants, or radiation therapy may increase bone marrow suppression. A lower dose may be needed.

Patient teaching

• Advise patient that laboratory tests will be performed before starting therapy and periodically thereafter.
• Instruct patient in proper oral hygiene because bone marrow–suppressant effects may lead to microbial infection, delayed healing, and gingival bleeding. Drug may decrease salivary flow.
• Emphasize need to follow prescriber's instructions about taking and recording temperature. Explain how and when to take acetaminophen.
• Advise patient to check with prescriber for instructions after missing dose.
• Tell patient that drug may cause temporary hair loss; explain that it will grow back when therapy ends.
• Teach patient how to prepare and give drug and how to dispose of used needles, syringes, containers, and unused drug. Give him a copy of information for patients included with product, and make sure he understands it. Also provide information on drug stability.
• Warn patient not to receive any immunization without prescriber's approval and to avoid contact with people who have taken polio vaccine. Use with live-virus vaccine may increase adverse reactions and decrease patient's antibody response. Patient is at increased risk for infection.
• Instruct patient to avoid alcohol during drug therapy.
• Advise patient to report signs of depression.

☑ Evaluation

• Patient shows improved health.
• Patient sustains no injury from adverse CNS reactions.
• Patient and family state understanding of drug therapy.

interferon beta-1b, recombinant

(in-ter-FEER-on BAY-tuh wun bee ree-CAHM-bih-nehnt)
Betaseron

Pharmacologic class: biological response modifier
Therapeutic class: antiviral, immunoregulator
Pregnancy risk category: C

Indications and dosages

▶ **To reduce frequency of exacerbations in patients with relapsing multiple sclerosis.**
Adults: 0.0625 mg subcutaneously q other day for weeks 1 and 2; then 0.125 mg subcutaneously q other day for weeks 3 and 4; then 0.1875 mg subcutaneously q other day for weeks 5 and 6; then 0.25 mg subcutaneously q other day thereafter.

Contraindications and cautions

• Contraindicated in patients hypersensitive to interferon beta or human albumin.
Lifespan: In pregnant and breast-feeding women, use only if benefits outweigh risks to the fetus or infant. In children, safety and effectiveness haven't been established.

Adverse reactions

CNS: anxiety, confusion, depersonalization, depression, dizziness, emotional lability, headache, ***malaise, seizures,*** somnolence, ***suicidal tendencies.***
CV: ***hemorrhage,*** peripheral edema.
EENT: laryngitis.
GI: abdominal pain, constipation, diarrhea, nausea, vomiting.
GU: impotence, menstrual disorders, urinary urgency.
Hematologic: ***leukopenia, neutropenia.***
Hepatic: ***liver failure.***
Respiratory: bronchitis, dyspnea, sinusitis, upper respiratory tract infection.
Skin: alopecia, skin disorders, sweating.
Other: breast pain, flulike symptoms, hypersensitivity reaction, inflammation, lymphadenopathy, necrosis at injection site, pain, pelvic pain, thyroid disorders.

Interactions

Drug-lifestyle. *Sun exposure:* May cause photosensitivity reactions. Discourage prolonged or unprotected sun exposure.

Effects on lab test results

- May increase ALT and bilirubin levels.
- May decrease WBC and neutrophil counts.

Pharmacokinetics

Absorption: Bioavailability is 50% after subcutaneous injection.
Distribution: Unknown.
Metabolism: Unknown.
Excretion: Unknown. *Half-life:* 8 minutes to 4¼ hours.

Route	Onset	Peak	Duration
SubQ	Unknown	1–8 hr	Unknown

Action

Chemical effect: Attaches to membrane receptors and causes cellular changes, including increased protein synthesis.
Therapeutic effect: Decreases neurologic disturbances seen during exacerbations of multiple sclerosis.

Available forms

Powder for injection: 0.3 mg with separate 1.2-ml prefilled syringe of sodium chloride, 0.54% diluent.

NURSING PROCESS

Assessment

- Assess patient's underlying condition before starting therapy.
- Monitor frequency of exacerbations after drug therapy begins.
- Monitor WBC counts, platelet counts, and blood chemistries, including liver function test results.

ALERT: Serious liver damage can occur with therapy, including hepatic failure and need for liver transplant. Monitor liver function 1, 3, and 6 months after treatment starts, then periodically thereafter.

- Be alert for adverse reactions.
- Monitor patient for depression and suicidal ideation.
- Assess patient's and family's knowledge of drug therapy.

Nursing diagnoses

- Ineffective health maintenance related to exacerbations of multiple sclerosis
- Risk for injury related to drug-induced adverse CNS reactions
- Deficient knowledge related to drug therapy

Planning and implementation

- Premedicate patient with acetaminophen to minimize flulike symptoms.
- To reconstitute, inject 1.2 ml of supplied diluent (0.54% saline solution for injection) into vial and gently swirl to dissolve drug. Don't shake. Reconstituted solution will contain 8 million units (0.25 mg)/ml. Discard vials that contain particles or discolored solution.
- Inject preparation immediately.
- Store at room temperature. Once reconstituted, may refrigerate for up to 3 hours before use.
- Rotate injection sites to minimize local reactions.

Patient teaching

- Warn woman of childbearing age about dangers to fetus. Tell her to notify prescriber promptly if she becomes pregnant.
- Teach patient how to give subcutaneous injections, including solution preparation, use of aseptic technique, rotation of injection sites, and equipment disposal. Periodically reevaluate patient's technique.
- Advise patient to take drug at bedtime to minimize mild flulike symptoms.
- Advise patient of need for blood testing to check liver status and need to report anorexia, fatigue, malaise, dark urine, light feces, or jaundice to prescriber promptly.
- Advise patient to report thoughts of depression or suicidal ideation.

Evaluation

- Patient exhibits decreased frequency of exacerbations.
- Patient sustains no injury from adverse CNS reactions.
- Patient and family state understanding of drug therapy.

interferon gamma-1b

(in-ter-FEER-on GAH-muh wun bee)

Actimmune

Pharmacologic class: biological response modifier

Therapeutic class: immunomodulator; antineoplastic

Pregnancy risk category: C

Indications and dosages

▶ **To delay disease progression in patients with severe, malignant osteopetrosis; chronic granulomatous disease.** *Patients with body surface area greater than 0.5 m²:* 50 mcg/m² (1 million international units/m²) subcutaneously three times weekly in the deltoid or anterior thigh.

Patients with body surface area 0.5 m² or less: 1.5 mcg/kg/dose subcutaneously three times weekly in the deltoid or anterior thigh.

Contraindications and cautions

- Contraindicated in patients hypersensitive to the drug or any of its components or to genetically engineered products derived from *Escherichia coli.*
- Use cautiously in patients with cardiac disease, compromised CNS function, or seizure disorders.
- Drug metabolized by cytochrome P-450. Use cautiously with other drugs using same system of metabolism.

Lifespan: In pregnant women, use cautiously. In breast-feeding women, use cautiously because it's unknown if drug appears in breast milk. In children younger than age 1, safety and effectiveness haven't been established.

Adverse reactions

CNS: decreased mental status, depression, fatigue, gait disturbance.
GI: diarrhea, nausea, vomiting.
Hematologic: ***neutropenia, thrombocytopenia.***
Skin: rash.
Other: flulike syndrome, erythema and tenderness at injection site.

Interactions

Drug-drug. *Myelosuppressive drugs:* May have additive myelosuppression. Monitor patient closely.
Zidovudine: May have additive bone marrow suppression. Consider reducing dosage.

Effects on lab test results

- May increase liver enzyme levels.
- May decrease neutrophil and platelet counts.

Pharmacokinetics

Absorption: About 90% absorbed after subcutaneous or I.M. use.
Distribution: Unknown.
Metabolism: Unknown.
Excretion: Unknown. *Half-life:* 6 hours.

Route	Onset	Peak	Duration
SubQ	Unknown	≤ 7 hr	Unknown

Action

Chemical effect: Acts as interleukin-type lymphokine. Drug has potent phagocyte-activating properties and enhances oxidative metabolism of tissue macrophages.
Therapeutic effect: Promotes phagocytes.

Available forms

Injection: 100 mcg (2 million international units)/0.5-ml vial

NURSING PROCESS

Assessment

- Assess patient's condition before starting therapy and regularly thereafter.
- Be alert for adverse reactions and drug interactions. Flulike symptoms include headache, fever, chills, myalgia, and arthralgia.
- If adverse GI reactions occur, monitor patient's hydration status.
- Assess patient's and family's knowledge of drug therapy.

Nursing diagnoses

- Ineffective health maintenance related to underlying condition
- Risk for deficient fluid volume related to adverse GI reactions
- Deficient knowledge related to drug therapy

Planning and implementation

• Premedicate with acetaminophen to minimize symptoms at beginning of therapy. Flulike symptoms tend to diminish with continued therapy.
• Discard unused portion. Each vial is for single-dose use and doesn't contain preservative.
• Give drug at bedtime to reduce discomfort from flulike symptoms.
• Refrigerate drug immediately. Vials must be stored at 36° to 46° F (2° to 8° C). Don't freeze. Don't shake vial; avoid excessive agitation. Discard vials that have been left at room temperature for longer than 12 hours.

Patient teaching

• Teach patient and family how to give drug and how to dispose of used needles, syringes, containers, and unused drug. Give him a copy of patient information included with product, and make sure he understands it.
• Instruct patient to notify prescriber if adverse reaction occurs.

Evaluation

• Patient responds well to drug.
• Patient maintains adequate hydration.
• Patient and family state understanding of drug therapy.

ipratropium bromide

(ip-ruh-TROH-pee-um BROH-mighd)
Atrovent

Pharmacologic class: anticholinergic
Therapeutic class: bronchodilator
Pregnancy risk category: B

Indications and dosages

▶ **Bronchospasm caused by COPD.** *Adults and children age 12 and older:* 2 inhalations q.i.d. Additional inhalations may be needed. However, don't exceed 12 total inhalations in 24 hours. Or use inhalation solution, giving up to 500 mcg q 6 to 8 hours via oral nebulizer.

▶ **Rhinorrhea linked to allergic and nonallergic perennial rhinitis.** *Adults and children age 6 and older:* 2 sprays of 0.03% nasal spray in each nostril b.i.d. or t.i.d.

▶ **Rhinorrhea caused by the common cold.** *Adults and children age 12 and older:* 2 sprays of 0.06% nasal spray per nostril t.i.d. or q.i.d. *Children ages 5 to 11:* Give 2 sprays of 0.06% nasal spray per nostril t.i.d.

▶ **Rhinorrhea linked to seasonal allergic rhinitis.** *Adults and children age 5 and older:* 2 sprays of 0.06% nasal spray per nostril q.i.d.

Contraindications and cautions

• Contraindicated in patients hypersensitive to the drug, its components, or atropine or its derivatives and in those hypersensitive to soya lecithin or related food products, such as soybeans and peanuts.
• Use cautiously in patients with angle-closure glaucoma, prostatic hyperplasia, or bladder-neck obstruction.
• Safety and effectiveness of use beyond 4 days for rhinorrhea from the common cold or 3 weeks for seasonal allergic rhinitis haven't been established.

Lifespan: In pregnant women, use cautiously. In breast-feeding women, use cautiously because it's unknown if the drug appears in breast milk. In children younger than age 12, safety of oral inhaler or nebulizer hasn't been established.

Adverse reactions

CNS: dizziness, headache, nervousness.
CV: chest pain, palpitations.
EENT: blurred vision, burning eyes, epistaxis.
GI: constipation, dry mouth, GI distress, nausea.
Respiratory: bronchitis, ***bronchospasm,*** cough, upper respiratory tract infection.
Skin: rash.

Interactions

Drug-drug. *Anticholinergics:* May increase anticholinergic effects. Avoid use together.
Cromolyn sodium: Will precipitate if mixed in same nebulizer. Don't use together.
Drug-herb. *Jaborandi tree, pill-bearing spurge:* May decrease drug effects. Use cautiously.

Effects on lab test results

None reported.

Pharmacokinetics

Absorption: Not readily absorbed into systemic circulation.
Distribution: Not distributed.
Metabolism: Small amount that's absorbed is metabolized in liver.

Excretion: Absorbed drug excreted in urine and bile; remainder excreted unchanged in feces. *Half-life:* About 2 hours.

Route	Onset	Peak	Duration
Inhalation	5–15 min	1–2 hr	3–6 hr

Action

Chemical effect: Inhibits vagally mediated reflexes by antagonizing acetylcholine.
Therapeutic effect: Relieves bronchospasms and symptoms of seasonal allergic rhinitis.

Available forms

Inhaler: 18 mcg/metered dose
Nasal spray: 0.03% (21 mcg/spray), 0.06% (42 mcg/spray)
Solution for inhalation: 0.02% (500-mcg vial)
Solution for nebulizer: 0.02% (200 mcg/ml), 0.025% (250 mcg/ml) ◇

NURSING PROCESS

Assessment

- Assess patient's condition before and after drug therapy; monitor peak expiratory flow.
- Be alert for adverse reactions and drug interactions.
- Assess patient's and family's knowledge of drug therapy.

Nursing diagnoses

- Ineffective breathing pattern related to patient's underlying condition
- Acute pain related to drug-induced headache
- Deficient knowledge related to drug therapy

Planning and implementation

ALERT: Drug isn't effective for treating acute episodes of bronchospasm when rapid response is needed.

- Don't exceed 12 total inhalations in 24 hours; total nasal sprays shouldn't exceed 8 in each nostril in 24 hours.
- If giving more than one inhalation, let 2 minutes elapse between inhalations. If giving more than one type of inhalant, always give bronchodilator first and wait 5 minutes before giving the other.
- Give drug on time to ensure maximal effect.
- If drug fails to relieve bronchospasms, notify prescriber.

ALERT: Don't confuse Atrovent with Alupent.

Patient teaching

- Warn patient that drug isn't effective for treating acute episodes of bronchospasm where rapid response is needed.
- Give patient these instructions for using metered-dose inhaler: clear nasal passages and throat. Breathe out, expelling as much air from lungs as possible. Place mouthpiece well into mouth, and inhale deeply as you release dose from inhaler. Hold breath for several seconds, remove mouthpiece, and exhale slowly.
- Tell patient to avoid accidentally spraying into eyes. Temporary blurring of vision may result.
- Tell patient to wait at least 2 minutes before repeating when using more than one inhalation.
- If patient also uses a corticosteroid inhaler, tell him to use ipratropium first and then wait about 5 minutes before using the corticosteroid. This process allows bronchodilator to open air passages for maximum effectiveness of the corticosteroid.
- Tell patient to take a missed dose as soon as remembered, unless it's almost time for next dose. In that case, tell him to skip the missed dose and not to double the dose.
- Tell patient to rinse mouth after using oral inhaler.

Evaluation

- Patient's bronchospasms are relieved.
- Patient doesn't suffer from any drug-induced headaches.
- Patient and family state understanding of drug therapy.

irbesartan

(ir-buh-SAR-tun)
Avapro

Pharmacologic class: angiotensin II receptor antagonist
Therapeutic class: antihypertensive
Pregnancy risk category: C (D in second and third trimesters)

Indications and dosages

▶ **Hypertension.** *Adults and children age 13 and older:* Initially 150 mg P.O. daily; increase to a maximum of 300 mg daily, if needed.

Children ages 6 to 12 years: Initially, 75 mg P.O. daily; increase to a maximum of 150 mg daily, if needed.

▶ **Nephropathy in type 2 diabetic patients.**
Adults: 300 mg P.O. daily.

Adjust-a-dose: In patients who are volume- or salt-depleted, give lower initial dose of 75 mg P.O. daily.

Contraindications and cautions

- Contraindicated in patients hypersensitive to the drug or any of its components.
- Use cautiously in volume- or salt-depleted patients and in patients with renal impairment or renal artery stenosis.

Lifespan: In pregnant women, drug should be stopped as soon as possible; use in the second and third trimesters can cause fetal death. Breast-feeding women should stop the drug or stop breast-feeding. In children younger than age 6, safety and effectiveness haven't been established.

Adverse reactions

CNS: anxiety, dizziness, fatigue, headache.
CV: chest pain, edema, tachycardia.
EENT: pharyngitis, rhinitis, sinus abnormality.
GI: abdominal pain, diarrhea, dyspepsia, nausea, vomiting.
GU: UTI.
Metabolic: ***hyperkalemia.***
Musculoskeletal: musculoskeletal trauma or pain.
Respiratory: *upper respiratory tract infection.*
Skin: rash.

Interactions

Drug-drug. *Potassium-sparing drugs, potassium supplements:* Use cautiously because of risk of hyperkalemia.

Effects on lab test results

- May increase potassium level.

Pharmacokinetics

Absorption: Rapid and complete, with an average absolute bioavailability of 60% to 80%.
Distribution: Wide. 90% protein-bound.
Metabolism: Mainly by conjugation and oxidation.
Excretion: Biliary and renal. About 20% is recovered in urine and the rest in feces. *Half-life:* 11 to 15 hours.

Route	Onset	Peak	Duration
P.O.	Unknown	1½–2 hr	24 hr

Action

Chemical effect: Inhibits the vasoconstricting and aldosterone-secreting effects of angiotensin II by selectively blocking binding of angiotensin II to receptor sites in many tissues.
Therapeutic effect: Lowers blood pressure.

Available forms

Tablets: 75 mg, 150 mg, 300 mg

NURSING PROCESS

Assessment

- Monitor patient's blood pressure regularly. Dizziness and orthostatic hypotension may occur more frequently in patients with type 2 diabetes mellitus and renal disease.
- Monitor patient's electrolytes, particularly potassium, and assess patient for volume or salt depletion before starting drug therapy.
- Make sure a woman of childbearing age uses effective birth control before starting this drug because of danger to fetus in second and third trimesters.
- Assess patient's and family's knowledge of drug therapy.

Nursing diagnoses

- Risk for deficient fluid volume in volume- or sodium-depleted patients
- Risk of injury related to the presence of hypertension
- Deficient knowledge related to drug therapy

Planning and implementation

- If drug is needed to control blood pressure, give with a diuretic or other antihypertensive.
- If patient becomes hypotensive, place in a supine position and give an I.V. infusion of normal saline solution.

Patient teaching

- Warn woman of childbearing age about consequences of exposing fetus to drug. Tell her to call prescriber immediately if she suspects she is pregnant.
- Tell patient that drug may be taken once daily with or without food.
- Instruct patient to avoid driving and hazardous activities until CNS effects of drug are known.

Evaluation

- Patient doesn't experience hypotension as a result of volume or salt depletion.
- Patient's blood pressure remains within normal limits, and drug therapy doesn't cause injury.
- Patient and family state understanding of drug therapy.

iron dextran

(IGH-ern DEKS-tran)

DexFerrum, DexIron ♦, InFeD

Pharmacologic class: parenteral iron supplement
Therapeutic class: hematinic
Pregnancy risk category: C

Indications and dosages

▶ **Iron deficiency anemia.** Total dose (in ml) is based on patient's weight and hemoglobin (Hgb) level using the following formula:

Dose (ml) = 0.0442 (desired Hgb − observed Hgb) × weight** + (0.26 × weight)

**Ideal body weight (IBW) or actual body weight if less than IBW, in kilograms

For children 5 to 15 kg, use actual weight in kg.

One ml iron dextran provides 50 mg elemental iron.

Adults and children: For I.M. use, 0.5-ml test dose injected by Z-track method. If no reactions occur, maximum daily doses are 0.5 ml (25 mg) for infants weighing less than 5 kg (11 lb), 1 ml (50 mg) for children weighing less than 10 kg (22 lb), and 2 ml (100 mg) for heavier children and adults. For I.V. use, 0.5-ml test dose injected over 30 seconds for InFeD, but for DexFerrum, inject over at least 5 minutes. If no reactions occur in 1 hour, remainder of therapeutic dose is given I.V. Therapeutic dose repeated I.V. daily. Maximum single dose is 100 mg of undiluted iron. Give slowly (1 ml/minute).

I.V. administration

- Check facility policy before giving drug I.V.
- Use I.V. when patient has insufficient muscle mass for deep I.M. injection, impaired absorption from muscle as a result of stasis or edema, possibility of uncontrolled I.M. bleeding from trauma (as may occur in hemophilia), or massive and prolonged parenteral therapy (as may be needed in chronic substantial blood loss).
- When I.V. dose is complete, flush vein with 10 ml of normal saline solution. Have patient rest for 15 to 30 minutes after I.V. administration.

⊗ **Incompatibilities**

Other I.V. drugs, parenteral nutrition solutions for I.V. infusion.

Contraindications and cautions

- Contraindicated in patients hypersensitive to drug or any of its components and in those with acute infectious renal disease or anemia disorders (except iron deficiency anemia).
- Use cautiously in patients who have serious hepatic impairment, rheumatoid arthritis, or other inflammatory diseases, and in patients with history of significant allergies or asthma.

Lifespan: In pregnant women, use only when benefits outweigh risks to the fetus. In breast-feeding women, use cautiously because it's unknown if the drug appears in breast milk. In children younger than age 4 months, safety and effectiveness haven't been studied.

Adverse reactions

CNS: arthralgia, dizziness, headache, malaise, myalgia, syncope, transitory paresthesia, weakness.
CV: ***arrhythmias,*** bradycardia, chest pain, chest tightness, hypertension, hypotensive reaction, peripheral vascular flushing with overly rapid I.V. administration, ***shock,*** tachycardia.
GI: abdominal pain, diarrhea, metallic taste, nausea, transient loss of taste, vomiting.
Respiratory: ***bronchospasm.***
Skin: *brown discoloration* at I.M. injection site, rash, urticaria.
Other: ***anaphylaxis;*** atrophy; delayed sensitivity reactions; fibrosis; necrosis; *soreness, inflammation, and local phlebitis* at I.V. injection site; sterile abscess.

Interactions

Drug-drug. *Chloramphenicol:* May increase iron level because of decreased iron clearance and erythropoiesis. Consult prescriber about using together.

Effects on lab test results

- May increase bilirubin and hemoglobin levels and hematocrit. May decrease calcium level.
- May falsely increase bilirubin level. May falsely decrease calcium level.
- May interfere with bone scans involving 99m Tc-diphosphonate.

Pharmacokinetics

Absorption: In two stages: 60% after 3 days and up to 90% by 3 weeks. Remainder is absorbed over several months or longer.
Distribution: During first 3 days, local inflammation facilitates passage of drug into lymphatic system; drug is then ingested by macrophages, which enter lymph and blood.
Metabolism: Cleared from plasma by reticuloendothelial cells of liver, spleen, and bone marrow.
Excretion: Trace amounts in urine, bile, and feces. *Half-life:* 6 hours.

Route	Onset	Peak	Duration
I.V., I.M.	72 hr	Unknown	3–4 wk

Action

Chemical effect: Provides elemental iron, a component of hemoglobin.
Therapeutic effect: Increases level of iron, an essential component of hemoglobin.

Available forms

Injection: 50 mg elemental iron/ml

NURSING PROCESS

Assessment

- Assess patient's iron deficiency before starting therapy.
- Monitor the drug's effectiveness by evaluating hemoglobin level, hematocrit, and reticulocyte count, and monitor patient's health status.
- Be alert for adverse reactions and drug interactions.
- Observe patient for delayed reactions (1 to 2 days), which may include arthralgia, backache, chills, dizziness, headache, malaise, fever, myalgia, nausea, and vomiting.
- Assess patient's and family's knowledge of drug therapy.

Nursing diagnoses

- Ineffective health maintenance related to iron deficiency
- Risk for injury related to potential drug-induced anaphylaxis
- Deficient knowledge related to drug therapy

Planning and implementation

- Don't give iron dextran with oral iron preparations.
- I.M. or I.V. injections of iron are recommended only for patients for whom oral administration is impossible or ineffective.

ALERT: I.M. or I.V. test dose is required.

- When giving I.M., use a 19G or 20G needle that is 2 to 3 inches long. Inject drug deep into upper outer quadrant of buttock—never into arm or other exposed area. Use Z-track method to avoid leakage into subcutaneous tissue and staining of skin.
- Minimize skin staining by using separate needle to withdraw drug from its container.
- Keep epinephrine and resuscitation equipment readily available to treat anaphylaxis.

Patient teaching

- Warn patient to avoid OTC vitamins that contain iron.
- Teach patient to recognize and report symptoms of reaction or toxicity.

Evaluation

- Patient's hemoglobin level, hematocrit, and reticulocyte count are normal.
- Patient doesn't experience anaphylaxis.
- Patient and family state understanding of drug therapy.

iron sucrose

(IGH-ern SOO-krohs)
Venofer

Pharmacologic class: polynuclear iron (III)-hydroxide in sucrose
Therapeutic class: hematinic
Pregnancy risk category: B

Indications and dosages

▶ **Iron deficiency anemia in patients undergoing long-term hemodialysis who are receiving supplemental erythropoietin therapy.**
Adults: 100 mg (5 ml) of elemental iron I.V. di-

rectly in the dialysis line either by slow injection over 2 to 5 minutes or by infusion over 15 minutes during the dialysis session, one to three times weekly for a total of 1,000 mg in 10 doses. Repeat, if needed.

▶ **Iron deficiency anemia in chronic kidney disease patients not on dialysis.** *Adults:* 200 mg by slow I.V. injection undiluted over 2 to 5 minutes on five separate occasions during a 14-day period to a total cumulative dose of 1,000 mg.

I.V. administration

- Inspect drug for particulates and discoloration before giving it.
- For slow injection, give 1 ml (20 mg elemental iron) undiluted solution per minute, not exceeding one vial (100 mg elemental iron) per injection.
- For infusion, dilute to a maximum of 100 ml in normal saline solution immediately before infusion, and infuse 100 mg elemental iron over at least 15 minutes.
- Giving by infusion may reduce the risk of hypotension.
- Transferrin saturation values increase rapidly after I.V. delivery of iron sucrose. Measure iron level 48 hours after an I.V. dose.

⊗ **Incompatibilities**
Other I.V. drugs, parenteral nutrition infusions.

Contraindications and cautions

- Contraindicated in patients with evidence of iron overload, patients hypersensitive to drug or its components, and patients with anemia not caused by iron deficiency.

Lifespan: In pregnant women, use cautiously. In breast-feeding women, use cautiously because it's not known whether drug appears in breast milk. In children, safety and effectiveness of drug haven't been established. In elderly patients, make dose selection conservatively; these patients may have decreased hepatic, renal, and cardiac function and other diseases and drug therapies.

Adverse reactions

CNS: asthenia, dizziness, fever, headache, malaise, pain.
CV: chest pain, fluid retention, ***heart failure,*** hypertension, *hypotension.*
GI: abdominal pain, diarrhea, nausea, taste perversion, vomiting.
Musculoskeletal: bone and muscle pain, *leg cramps.*
Respiratory: cough, dyspnea, pneumonia.
Skin: pruritus.
Other: accidental injury, ***anaphylaxis,*** hypersensitivity reaction, injection-site reaction, ***sepsis.***

Interactions

Drug-drug. *Oral iron preparations:* May reduce absorption of these compounds. Avoid use together.

Effects on lab test results

- May increase liver enzyme levels.

Pharmacokinetics

Absorption: Given I.V.
Distribution: Mainly in blood and somewhat in extravascular fluid. A significant amount of iron is also distributed in the liver, spleen, and bone marrow.
Metabolism: Dissociated by reticuloendothelial system into iron and sucrose.
Excretion: About 75% of sucrose and 5% of the iron component are eliminated by urinary excretion in 24 hours. *Half-life:* 6 hours.

Route	Onset	Peak	Duration
I.V.	Unknown	Unknown	Variable

Action

Chemical effect: Iron component of dissociated drug eventually replenishes depleted body iron stores, significantly increasing iron and ferritin levels and decreasing total iron-binding capacity.
Therapeutic effect: Increases iron level.

Available forms

Injection: 20 mg/ml of elemental iron in 5-ml vial

NURSING PROCESS

Assessment

- Assess underlying condition before starting therapy, and reassess regularly.
- Monitor ferritin and hemoglobin levels, hematocrit, and transferrin saturation.
- Monitor patient for adverse reactions or hypersensitivity reactions to the drug.

• Assess patient's and family's knowledge of drug therapy.

Nursing diagnoses

• Acute pain related to adverse drug effects
• Ineffective health maintenance related to iron deficiency
• Deficient knowledge related to iron sucrose therapy

Planning and implementation

• Monitor patient for symptoms of overdose or too-rapid infusion, which include hypotension, headache, nausea, dizziness, joint aches, paresthesia, abdominal and muscle pain, edema, and CV collapse.
• Observe patient for rare but fatal hypersensitivity reactions characterized by anaphylaxis, loss of consciousness, collapse, hypotension, dyspnea, or seizures.
• Withhold dose in patient with evidence of iron overload.

Patient teaching

• Instruct patient to notify prescriber if symptoms of overdose occur, such as headache, nausea, dizziness, joint aches, paresthesia, or abdominal and muscle pain.
• Warn patient not to take OTC vitamins containing iron.

Evaluation

• Patient doesn't experience pain.
• Patient's hemoglobin level and hematocrit are normal.
• Patient and family state understanding of iron sucrose therapy.

isoniazid (isonicotinic acid hydride INH)

(igh-soh-NIGH-uh-sid)

Isotamine ♦, Laniazid, Nydrazid, PMS Isoniazid ♦

Pharmacologic class: isonicotinic acid hydrazine
Therapeutic class: antituberculotic
Pregnancy risk category: C

Indications and dosages

▶ **Actively growing tubercle bacilli with other antituberculotics.** *Adults and children age 15 and older:* 5 mg/kg P.O. or I.M. daily in single dose, maximum 300 mg P.O. or I.M. daily, continued for 6 months to 2 years. Or 15 mg/kg (maximum dose 900 mg/daily) two to three times weekly.
Infants and children: 10 to 15 mg/kg P.O. or I.M. daily in single dose, maximum 300 mg P.O. or I.M. daily, continued for 18 months to 2 years. Or 20 to 40 mg/kg (maximum dose 900 mg/daily) two to three times weekly.

▶ **Prevention of tubercle bacilli in those closely exposed to tuberculosis or those with positive skin tests whose chest X-rays and bacteriologic studies are consistent with nonprogressive tuberculosis.** *Adults:* 300 mg P.O. daily in single dose, for 6 months to 1 year.
Infants and children: 10 mg/kg P.O. daily in single dose. Maximum, 300 mg P.O. daily for 1 year.

Contraindications and cautions

• Contraindicated in patients with acute hepatic disease or isoniazid-related liver damage.
• Use cautiously in patients with chronic non–isoniazid-related liver disease, seizure disorders (especially in those taking phenytoin), severe renal impairment, chronic alcoholism, or I.V. drug abuse.

Lifespan: In pregnant women, use cautiously. In breast-feeding women, small amounts of drug appear in breast milk but aren't sufficient to cause harm or therapeutic benefit to the infant. In elderly patients, use cautiously.

Adverse reactions

CNS: paresthesias, *peripheral neuropathy,* psychosis, ***seizures.***
GI: constipation, dry mouth, epigastric distress, nausea, vomiting.
Hematologic: ***agranulocytosis, aplastic anemia,*** eosinophilia, hemolytic anemia, ***leukopenia, methemoglobinemia, neutropenia,*** pyridoxine-responsive hypochromic anemia, ***thrombocytopenia.***
Hepatic: ***hepatitis.***
Metabolic: hyperglycemia, ***metabolic acidosis.***
Other: hypersensitivity reactions, irritation at I.M. injection site, rheumatic syndrome and lupuslike syndrome.

Interactions

Drug-drug. *Acetaminophen:* May increase hepatotoxic effects of acetaminophen. Don't give together.

Antacids and laxatives containing aluminum: May decrease rate and amount of isoniazid absorbed. Give isoniazid at least 1 hour before antacid or laxative.

Carbamazepine: May increase risk of isoniazid hepatotoxicity. Use together cautiously.

Carbamazepine, phenytoin: May increase levels of these anticonvulsants. Monitor patient closely.

Corticosteroids: May decrease therapeutic effect of isoniazid. Monitor patient's need for larger isoniazid dose.

Cyclosporine: May increase adverse CNS effects of cyclosporine. Monitor patient closely.

Disulfiram: May cause neurologic symptoms, including changes in behavior and coordination. Avoid use together.

Ketoconazole: May decrease ketoconazole level. Monitor patient closely.

Oral anticoagulants: May increase anticoagulation. Monitor patient for signs of bleeding.

Rifampin: May increase risk of hepatotoxicity. Monitor patient closely.

SSRIs: May cause serotonin syndrome. Use with caution.

Theophylline: May increase theophylline level. Monitor level closely, and adjust theophylline dosage.

Drug-food. *Foods containing tyramine:* May cause hypertensive crisis. Tell patients to avoid such foods altogether.

Drug-lifestyle. *Alcohol use:* May increase risk of isoniazid-related hepatitis. Discourage use together.

Effects on lab test results

- May increase transaminase, glucose, and bilirubin levels. May decrease calcium, phosphate, and hemoglobin levels and hematocrit.
- May increase eosinophil count. May decrease WBC, granulocyte, neutrophil, and platelet counts.

Pharmacokinetics

Absorption: Complete and rapid after P.O. use. Also absorbed readily after I.M. injection.

Distribution: Wide.

Metabolism: Mainly in liver. Rate of metabolism varies individually; fast acetylators metabolize drug five times faster than others. About 50% of blacks and whites are slow acetylators; more than 80% of Chinese, Japanese, and Eskimos are fast acetylators.

Excretion: Mainly in urine; some in saliva, sputum, feces, and breast milk. *Half-life:* 1 to 4 hours.

Route	Onset	Peak	Duration
P.O., I.M.	Unknown	1–2 hr	Unknown

Action

Chemical effect: May inhibit cell wall biosynthesis by interfering with lipid and DNA synthesis.

Therapeutic effect: Kills susceptible bacteria, such as *Mycobacterium tuberculosis, M. bovis,* and some strains of *M. kansasii.*

Available forms

Injection: 100 mg/ml
Oral solution: 50 mg/5 ml
Tablets: 100 mg, 300 mg

NURSING PROCESS

Assessment

- Assess patient's infection before starting therapy by physical examination and culture and sensitivity testing.
- Monitor patient for improvement, and evaluate culture and sensitivity tests.
- Be alert for adverse reactions and drug interactions.
- Monitor hepatic function closely for changes.
- Monitor patient for paresthesia of hands and feet, which usually precedes peripheral neuropathy, especially in patients who are malnourished, alcoholic, diabetic, or slow acetylators.
- Assess patient's and family's knowledge of drug therapy.

Nursing diagnoses

- Risk for infection related to presence of susceptible bacteria
- Disturbed sensory perception (tactile) related to drug-induced peripheral neuropathy
- Deficient knowledge related to drug therapy

Planning and implementation

- Give oral form of drug 1 hour before or 2 hours after meals to avoid decreased absorption.

• Switch from I.M. to P.O. form as soon as possible.

ALERT: Always give isoniazid with other antituberculotics to prevent development of resistant organisms.

• Give pyridoxine to prevent peripheral neuropathy, especially in malnourished patients.

Patient teaching

• Tell patient to take drug as prescribed; warn against stopping drug without prescriber's consent.

• Advise patient to take with food if GI irritation occurs.

• Instruct patient not to drink alcohol during therapy.

• Instruct patient to avoid certain foods (fish, such as skip jack and tuna, and foods containing tyramine, such as aged cheese, beer, and chocolate) because drug acts like an MAO inhibitor.

• Tell patient to notify prescriber immediately if symptoms of liver impairment occur (loss of appetite, fatigue, malaise, jaundice, dark urine).

• Urge patient to comply with treatment, which may last for months or years.

Evaluation

• Patient is free from infection.

• Patient maintains normal peripheral nervous system function.

• Patient and family state understanding of drug therapy.

isoproterenol (isoprenaline)

(igh-soh-proh-TEER-uh-nol)

Isuprel

isoproterenol hydrochloride

isoproterenol sulfate

Medihaler-Iso

Pharmacologic class: adrenergic
Therapeutic class: bronchodilator, cardiac stimulant
Pregnancy risk category: C

Indications and dosages

▶ **Bronchospasm.** *Adults and children:* For acute dyspneic episodes, one inhalation of sulfate form initially. Repeat, if needed, after 2 to 5 minutes. Maintenance dosage is one to two inhalations four to six times daily. Repeat once more 10 minutes after second dose. Give no more than three doses for each attack.

▶ **Bronchospasm in COPD.** Give by intermittent positive pressure breathing or for nebulization by compressed air or oxygen.
Adults: 2 ml of 0.125% or 2.5 ml of 0.1% solution (prepared by diluting 0.5 ml of 0.5% solution to 2 or 2.5 ml or by diluting 0.25 ml of 1% solution to 2 or 2.5 ml with water or half-normal or normal saline solution) up to five times daily.
Children: 2 ml of 0.125% solution or 2.5 ml of 0.1% solution up to five times daily.

▶ **Heart block and ventricular arrhythmias.**
Adults: Initially, 0.02 to 0.06 mg hydrochloride I.V. Subsequent doses 0.01 to 0.2 mg I.V. or 5 mcg/minute I.V. Or 0.2 mg I.M. initially; then 0.02 to 1 mg, as needed.
Children: Give half of initial adult dosage of hydrochloride.

▶ **Shock.** *Adults and children:* 0.5 to 5 mcg/minute hydrochloride by continuous I.V. infusion. Usual concentration is 1 mg (5 ml) in 500 ml D_5W. Infusion rate adjusted according to heart rate, central venous pressure, blood pressure, and urine flow.

▶ **Postoperative cardiac patients with bradycardia‡.** *Children:* I.V. infusion of 0.029 mcg/kg/minute.

▶ **As an aid in diagnosing the cause of mitral regurgitation‡.** *Adults:* 4 mcg/minute I.V. infusion.

▶ **As an aid in diagnosing coronary artery disease or lesions‡.** *Adults:* 1 to 3 mcg/minute I.V. infusion.

I.V. administration

• If injection solution is discolored or contains precipitate, don't use.

• Give drug by direct injection or I.V. infusion. For infusion, drug may be diluted with most common I.V. solutions.

• If heart rate exceeds 110 beats/minute with I.V. infusion, notify prescriber. Doses sufficient to increase heart rate to more than 130 beats/minute may induce ventricular arrhythmias.

• When giving I.V. isoproterenol to treat shock, closely monitor blood pressure, central venous pressure, ECG, arterial blood gas measurements, and urine output. Carefully adjust infusion rate according to these measurements. Use continuous infusion pump to regulate flow rate.

⊗ Incompatibilities

Alkalies, aminophylline, furosemide, metals, sodium bicarbonate.

Contraindications and cautions

- Contraindicated in patients with tachycardia caused by digitalis intoxication, in those with arrhythmias (other than those that may respond to treatment with isoproterenol), and in those with angina pectoris.
- Use cautiously in patients with renal or CV disease, coronary insufficiency, diabetes, hyperthyroidism, or history of sensitivity to sympathomimetic amines.

Lifespan: In pregnant and breast-feeding women, use cautiously. In children and elderly patients, use cautiously.

Adverse reactions

CNS: ***Adams-Stokes syndrome,*** dizziness, *headache,* insomnia, mild tremor, nervousness, weakness.
CV: angina, ***arrhythmias, cardiac arrest,*** flushing of face, labile blood pressure, palpitations, tachycardia.
GI: nausea, vomiting.
Metabolic: hyperglycemia.
Respiratory: ***bronchospasm.***
Skin: diaphoresis.

Interactions

Drug-drug. *Beta blockers, such as propranolol:* May block bronchodilating effect of isoproterenol. If used together, monitor patient carefully.
Sympathomimetics, such as epinephrine: May increase risk of arrhythmias. Avoid use together.

Effects on lab test results

- May increase glucose level.

Pharmacokinetics

Absorption: Rapid after P.O. inhalation.
Distribution: Wide.
Metabolism: By conjugation in GI tract and by enzymatic reduction in liver, lungs, and other tissues.
Excretion: Mainly in urine. *Half-life:* Unknown.

Route	Onset	Peak	Duration
I.V.	Immediate	Unknown	< 1 hr
Inhalation	2–5 min	Unknown	½–2 hr

Action

Chemical effect: Relaxes bronchial smooth muscle by acting on beta$_2$-adrenergic receptors. As cardiac stimulant, acts on beta$_1$-adrenergic receptors in heart.
Therapeutic effect: Relieves bronchospasms and heart block and restores normal sinus rhythm after ventricular arrhythmia.

Available forms

isoproterenol
Nebulizer inhaler: 0.25%, 0.5%, 1%
isoproterenol hydrochloride
Aerosol inhaler: 131 mcg/metered spray
Injection: 20 mcg/ml, 200 mcg/ml
Solution for inhalation: 0.5%, 1%
isoproterenol sulfate
Aerosol inhaler: 80 mcg/metered spray

NURSING PROCESS

Assessment

- Assess patient's underlying condition before starting therapy.
- Monitor cardiopulmonary status frequently.
- Be alert for adverse reactions and drug interactions.
- This drug may aggravate ventilation and perfusion abnormalities. Even when ease of breathing is improved, arterial oxygen tension may fall paradoxically.
- Assess patient's and family's knowledge of drug therapy.

Nursing diagnoses

- Ineffective health maintenance related to underlying condition
- Risk for injury related to drug-induced adverse reactions
- Deficient knowledge related to drug therapy

Planning and implementation

- Drug doesn't treat blood or fluid volume deficit. Correct volume deficit before giving vasopressors.
- If drug is given by inhalation with oxygen, make sure oxygen concentration won't suppress respiratory drive.
- Follow same instructions for metered powder nebulizer, although deep inhalation isn't needed.
- If adverse reactions occur, notify prescriber; adjust dosage or stop drug if needed.

• If precordial distress or angina occurs, stop drug immediately.

ALERT: Don't confuse Isuprel with Ismelin or Isordil.

Patient teaching

• Give patient the following instructions for using metered-dose inhaler: Clear nasal passages and throat. Breathe out, expelling as much air from lungs as possible. Place mouthpiece well into mouth, and inhale deeply as you release dose from inhaler. Hold breath for several seconds, remove mouthpiece, and exhale slowly.

• Tell patient to wait at least 2 minutes before repeating when using more than one inhalation.

• If patient also uses a corticosteroid inhaler, tell him to use bronchodilator first, and then wait about 5 minutes before using corticosteroid. This process allows bronchodilator to open air passages for maximum effectiveness of the corticosteroid.

• Warn patient using oral inhalant that this drug may turn sputum and saliva pink.

• Tell patient to stop drug and notify prescriber about chest tightness or dyspnea.

• Warn patient against overuse of drug. Tell him that tolerance can develop.

• Tell patient to reduce caffeine intake during therapy.

Evaluation

• Patient has improved health.

• Patient sustains no injury from adverse reactions.

• Patient and family state understanding of drug therapy.

isosorbide dinitrate

(igh-soh-SOR-bighd digh-NIGH-trayt)

Apo-ISDN ♦, Cedocard SR ♦, Coronex ♦, Dilatrate-SR, Isordil, Isordil Titradose, Isotrate

isosorbide mononitrate

IMDUR, ISMO, Isotrate ER, Monoket

Pharmacologic class: nitrate
Therapeutic class: antianginal, vasodilator
Pregnancy risk category: C

Indications and dosages

▶ **Acute angina (S.L. form only), prophylaxis in situations likely to cause angina.** *Adults:* 2.5 to 5 mg S.L. tablets for prompt relief of angina, repeated q 5 to 10 minutes (maximum of three doses for each 30-minute period). For prevention, 2.5 to 10 mg q 2 to 3 hours. Or, 5 to 40 mg isosorbide dinitrate P.O. b.i.d. or t.i.d. for prevention only (use smallest effective dose). Or, 30 to 60 mg isosorbide mononitrate using Imdur P.O. once daily on arising; increased to 120 mg once daily after several days, if needed. Or, 20 mg isosorbide mononitrate using ISMO or Monoket b.i.d. with the two doses given 7 hours apart.

▶ **Adjunctive treatment of heart failure‡.** *Adults:* 80 mg isosorbide dinitrate P.O. daily with hydralazine. Maximum dose is 160 mg isosorbide dinitrate and 300 mg hydralazine.

▶ **Diffuse esophageal spasm without gastroesophageal reflux‡.** *Adults:* 10 to 30 mg isosorbide dinitrate P.O. q.i.d.

Contraindications and cautions

• Contraindicated in patients hypersensitive to nitrates, in those with idiosyncratic reactions to nitrates, and in those with severe hypotension, shock, or acute MI with low left ventricular filling pressure.

• Use cautiously in patients with blood volume depletion (such as that resulting from diuretic therapy) or mild hypotension.

Lifespan: In pregnant women, use cautiously. In breast-feeding women, use cautiously because it's unknown if drug appears in breast milk. In children, safety and effectiveness haven't been established.

Adverse reactions

CNS: dizziness, *headache,* weakness.
CV: ankle edema, fainting, *flushing,* orthostatic hypotension, palpitations, tachycardia.
GI: nausea, vomiting.
Skin: cutaneous vasodilation.
Other: hypersensitivity reactions, sublingual burning.

Interactions

Drug-drug. *Antihypertensives:* May increase hypotensive effects. Monitor patient closely during initial therapy.
Sildenafil, tadalafil, vardenafil: May increase hypotensive effects. Avoid use together.

Drug-lifestyle. *Alcohol use:* May increase hypotension. Discourage use together.

Effects on lab test results

None reported.

Pharmacokinetics

Absorption: Dinitrate is well absorbed from GI tract but undergoes first-pass metabolism, resulting in bioavailability of about 50% (depending on dosage form used). Mononitrate is also absorbed well, with almost 100% bioavailability.
Distribution: Widely throughout body.
Metabolism: In liver to active metabolites.
Excretion: In urine. *Half-life:* Dinitrate P.O., 5 to 6 hours; S.L., 2 hours; mononitrate, about 5 hours.

Route	Onset	Peak	Duration
P.O.	2–60 min	2–60 min	1–12 hr
S.L.	2–5 min	2–5 min	1–2 hr

Action

Chemical effect: May reduce cardiac oxygen demand by decreasing left ventricular end diastolic pressure (preload) and, to a lesser extent, systemic vascular resistance (afterload). May increase blood flow through collateral coronary vessels.
Therapeutic effect: Relieves angina.

Available forms

isosorbide dinitrate
Capsules (extended-release): 40 mg
Tablets: 5 mg, 10 mg, 20 mg, 30 mg, 40 mg
Tablets (S.L.): 2.5 mg, 5 mg, 10 mg
Tablets (sustained-release): 40 mg
isosorbide mononitrate
Tablets: 10 mg, 20 mg
Tablets (extended-release): 30 mg, 60 mg, 120 mg

NURSING PROCESS

Assessment

- Assess patient's angina before and regularly during therapy.
- Monitor blood pressure, heart rate and rhythm, and intensity and duration of drug response.
- Be alert for adverse reactions and drug interactions.
- Assess patient's and family's knowledge of drug therapy.

Nursing diagnoses

- Acute pain related to angina
- Risk for injury related to drug-induced adverse reactions
- Deficient knowledge related to drug therapy

Planning and implementation

- To prevent tolerance, don't give drug during an 8- to 12-hour period daily. The dosage regimen for isosorbide mononitrate (one tablet on awakening with second dose in 7 hours, or one extended-release tablet daily) is intended to offer a nitrate-free period during the day to minimize nitrate tolerance.
- Give drug on empty stomach, either 30 minutes before or 1 to 2 hours after meals, and have patient swallow tablets whole.
- Give S.L. form of drug at first sign of angina. Have patient wet tablet with saliva, place it under his tongue until completely absorbed, and sit down and rest. Dose may be repeated every 10 to 15 minutes for maximum of three doses.

ALERT: Don't stop therapy abruptly because coronary vasospasm may occur.

- If patient's pain doesn't subside, notify prescriber immediately.

ALERT: Don't confuse Isordil with Isuprel or Inderal.

ALERT: Don't confuse Coronex (isosorbide dinitrate) with Coronex (the herbal supplement for male virility and vitality).

Patient teaching

- Advise patient to take drug regularly, as prescribed, and to keep it accessible at all times.

ALERT: Advise patient that stopping drug abruptly causes coronary vasospasm.

- Tell patient to take S.L. tablet at first sign of attack. Explain that tablet should be wet with saliva and placed under tongue until completely absorbed, and that patient should sit down and rest until pain subsides. Tell patient that dose may be repeated every 10 to 15 minutes for up to three doses. If pain doesn't subside, tell patient to get medical help promptly.
- If patient complains of tingling sensation with S.L. use, suggest holding tablet in buccal pouch.

ALERT: Warn patient not to confuse S.L. form with P.O. form.

- Instruct patient taking P.O. form to take tablet on empty stomach, either 30 minutes before or

1 to 2 hours after meals, and to swallow tablet whole.

- Tell patient to minimize orthostatic hypotension by changing to upright position slowly. Tell him to go up and down stairs carefully and to lie down at first sign of dizziness.
- Instruct patient to avoid alcohol during therapy.
- Tell patient to store drug in cool place, in tightly closed container, away from light.

☑ Evaluation

- Patient is free from pain.
- Patient sustains no injury from adverse reactions.
- Patient and family state understanding of drug therapy.

isotretinoin

(igh-soh-TREH-tih-noyn)

Accutane, Accutane Roche ♦, Claravis, Roaccutane ◇, Sotret

Pharmacologic class: retinoic acid derivative
Therapeutic class: antiacne drug
Pregnancy risk category: X

Indications and dosages

▶ **Severe recalcitrant nodular acne unresponsive to conventional therapy.** *Adults and children ages 12 to 17:* Give 0.5 to 1 mg/kg P.O. daily in two divided doses for 15 to 20 weeks. Maximum daily dosage, 2 mg/kg.

▶ **Keratinization disorders resistant to conventional therapy, prevention of skin cancer‡.** *Adults:* Dosage varies with specific disease and severity of the disorder. Dosages up to 2 to 4 mg/kg P.O. daily have been used. Consult literature for specific recommendations.

▶ **Squamous cell cancer of the head and neck‡.** *Adults:* 50 to 100 mg/m² P.O.

Contraindications and cautions

- Contraindicated in patients hypersensitive to parabens, which are used as preservatives.
- Use cautiously in patients with genetic predisposition or history of osteoporosis, osteomalacia, or other disorders of bone metabolism. Also use cautiously in patients with a history of mental illness or family history of psychiatric disorders, asthma, liver disease, diabetes, heart disease, osteoporosis, weak bones, or anorexia nervosa.

Lifespan: In women of childbearing age, drug is contraindicated unless patient has had negative serum pregnancy test within 2 weeks of beginning therapy, will begin drug therapy on second or third day of next menstrual period, and will comply with stringent contraceptive measures for 1 month before therapy, during therapy, and at least 1 month after therapy. In pregnant women, drug is contraindicated. In breast-feeding women, use cautiously. In children younger than age 12, safety and effectiveness haven't been established. In children ages 12 to 17, use cautiously.

Adverse reactions

CNS: ***aggressive and violent behavior,*** depression, emotional instability, *fatigue, headache,* pseudotumor cerebri (benign intracranial hypertension), psychosis, ***seizure, stroke, suicide.***
CV: hypertriglyceridemia.
EENT: *conjunctivitis,* corneal deposits, decreased night vision, dry eyes, hearing impairment, intolerance to contact lenses, visual disturbances.
GI: ***acute pancreatitis,*** gum bleeding and inflammation, inflammatory bowel disease, nausea, nonspecific GI symptoms, vomiting.
Hepatic: ***hepatitis,*** increased liver enzymes.
Hematologic: anemia.
Metabolic: hyperglycemia.
Musculoskeletal: *arthralgia,* arthritis, back pain, bone abnormalities, calcification of tendons and ligaments, decreases in bone mineral density, musculoskeletal symptoms, premature epiphyseal closure, ***rhabdomyolysis,*** skeletal hyperostosis, tendonitis.
Skin: *cheilosis, dry skin,* peeling of palms and toes, photosensitivity, *rash,* skin infection, thinning of hair.

Interactions

Drug-drug. *Corticosteroids:* May increase risk of osteoporosis. Use together cautiously.
Medicated soaps and cleansers, medicated cover-ups, topical resorcinol peeling agents (benzoyl peroxide), and preparations containing alcohol: May have cumulative drying effect. Use cautiously.
Microdosed progesterone birth control pills that don't contain estrogen: May decrease contra-

ceptive effectiveness. Advise using alternative contraceptive methods.
Phenytoin: May increase risk of osteomalacia. Use together cautiously.
Tetracyclines: May increase risk of pseudotumor cerebri. Avoid use together.
Vitamin A products: May have additive toxic effect. Avoid use together.
Drug-food. *Any food:* May increase absorption of drug. Have patient take drug with food.
Drug-lifestyle. *Alcohol use:* May increase risk of hypertriglyceridemia. Discourage use together.
Sun exposure: May increase photosensitivity reactions. Advise patient to use sunscreen and wear protective clothing.

Effects on lab test results

- May increase CK, ALT, AST, alkaline phosphatase, uric acid, glucose, and triglyceride levels. May decrease hemoglobin level and hematocrit.
- May increase platelet count.

Pharmacokinetics

Absorption: Rapid.
Distribution: Wide. 99.9% protein-bound, mainly to albumin.
Metabolism: In liver and possibly in gut wall.
Excretion: Unknown. *Half-life:* 30 minutes to 39 hours.

Route	Onset	Peak	Duration
P.O.	Unknown	3 hr	Unknown

Action

Chemical effect: May normalize keratinization, reversibly decrease size of sebaceous glands, and alter composition of sebum to less viscous form that is less likely to plug follicles.
Therapeutic effect: Improves skin integrity.

Available forms

Capsules: 10 mg, 20 mg, 30 mg, 40 mg

NURSING PROCESS

Assessment

- Assess patient's skin before starting therapy and regularly thereafter.
- Obtain baseline lipid studies, liver function test results, and pregnancy test before therapy. Monitor these values at regular intervals until response to drug is established (usually about 4 weeks).
- Monitor glucose and CK levels in patients who engage in vigorous physical activity.
- Be alert for adverse reactions and drug interactions.
- Osteoporosis, osteopenia, bone fractures, and delayed healing of bone fractures have been seen in patients taking isotretinoin. While a causal relationship hasn't been established, an effect can't be ruled out. Long-term effects haven't been studied. It's important not to exceed the recommended dose or duration.
- Most adverse reactions appear to be dose-related, occurring at dosages greater than 1 mg/kg daily. They're usually reversible when therapy is stopped or dosage reduced.
- To minimize the risk of fetal exposure, drug is only available through restricted distribution program approved by the FDA called iPLEDGE.
- Actively monitor mood and behavioral changes because of risk of significant psychological changes including suicidal thoughts and behavior.
- Assess patient's and family's knowledge of drug therapy.

Nursing diagnoses

- Impaired skin integrity related to underlying skin condition
- Impaired tissue integrity related to adverse reactions
- Deficient knowledge related to drug therapy

Planning and implementation

- Start second course of therapy at least 8 weeks after completion of first course because improvement may continue after stopping drug.
- Any suspected fetal exposure to drug must be immediately reported to the FDA's MedWatch program at 1-800-FDA-1088 and the iPLEDGE pregnancy registry at 1-866-495-0654 or www.ipledgeprogram.com.
- Give drug with meals or shortly thereafter to enhance absorption.

ALERT: Screen patient with headache, nausea and vomiting, or visual disturbances for papilledema. Signs and symptoms of pseudotumor cerebri require an immediate stop to therapy and prompt neurologic intervention.

Patient teaching

- Advise patient to take drug with milk, meals, or shortly after meals to ensure adequate absorption.
- Tell patient to immediately report visual disturbances and bone, muscle, or joint pain.
- Warn patient that contact lenses may feel uncomfortable during therapy.
- Warn patient against using abrasives, medicated soaps and cleansers, acne preparations containing peeling agents, and topical alcohol preparations (including cosmetics, aftershave, cologne) because these agents cause cumulative irritation or excessive drying of skin.
- Instruct patient not to drink alcohol during therapy.
- Urge patient to report mood changes, such as increased hostility or depression, and suicidal thinking immediately; these may be drug related.
- Tell patient to avoid prolonged exposure to sunlight, to use sunblock, and to wear protective clothing.

ALERT: Advise patient not to donate blood during or for 30 days after therapy; severe fetal abnormalities may occur if a pregnant woman receives blood containing isotretinoin.

- Advise women of childbearing age to use two reliable forms of contraception simultaneously within 1 month of treatment, during treatment and for 1 month after treatment as prescribed under the iPLEDGE program, and to report suspected pregnancy immediately.

Evaluation

- Patient has improved skin condition.
- Patient is free from conjunctivitis, corneal deposits, and dry eyes.
- Patient and family state understanding of drug therapy.

itraconazole

(ih-truh-KAHN-uh-zohl)

Sporanox

Pharmacologic class: synthetic triazole
Therapeutic class: antifungal
Pregnancy risk category: C

Indications and dosages

▶ **Pulmonary and extrapulmonary blastomycosis, histoplasmosis.** *Adults:* 200 mg P.O. (capsules) daily. Dosage may be increased as needed and tolerated in 100-mg increments to maximum of 400 mg daily. Divide doses larger than 200 mg daily into two doses. Continue treatment for at least 3 months. In life-threatening illness, loading dose of 200 mg t.i.d. is given for 3 days. Or give 200 mg by I.V. infusion over 1 hour b.i.d. for four doses; then 200 mg I.V. once daily.

▶ **Aspergillosis.** *Adults:* 200 to 400 mg P.O. (capsules) daily. Or give 200 mg by I.V. infusion over 1 hour b.i.d. for four doses; then decrease to 200 mg I.V. once daily for up to 14 days.

▶ **Onychomycosis for toenails with or without fingernail involvement.** *Adults:* 200 mg P.O. (capsules) once daily for 12 weeks.

▶ **Onychomycosis for fingernails.** *Adults:* Two treatment phases, each consisting of 200 mg P.O. (capsules) b.i.d. for 1 week. Phases are separated by a 3-week period without drug.

▶ **Esophageal candidiasis.** *Adults:* 100 to 200 mg P.O. (oral solution) swished in mouth vigorously and swallowed daily for a minimum of 3 weeks.

▶ **Oropharyngeal candidiasis.** *Adults:* 200 mg P.O. (oral solution) swished in mouth vigorously and swallowed daily for 1 to 2 weeks. For patients unresponsive to fluconazole tablets, give 100 mg swished in mouth vigorously and swallowed b.i.d. for 2 to 4 weeks.

I.V. administration

- Injection form shouldn't be used in patients with creatinine clearance below 30 ml/minute.
- Distributed in a kit that includes a 50-ml bag of normal saline solution for injection and filtered infusion set.
- Don't give drug by I.V. bolus injection.
- Infuse over 60 minutes, using an infusion set with a filter.
- Flush I.V. line with 15 to 20 ml of normal saline solution after each infusion.

⊗ **Incompatibilities**

- Dextrose solution, lactated Ringer's solution.

Contraindications and cautions

- Contraindicated in patients hypersensitive to the drug or any of its components. Also contraindicated in patients with ventricular dysfunction, heart failure, or a history of heart failure. Also contraindicated in patients receiving cisapride, oral midazolam, triazolam, pimozide, dofetilide, or quinidine; HMG-CoA reductase inhibitors metabolized by CYP3A4 (lovastatin, simvastatin); ergot alkaloids (dihydroergotamine, ergonovine, methylergonovine).

• Use cautiously in patients with hypochlorhydria (they may not absorb drug as readily as patients with normal gastric acidity), in HIV-infected patients (hypochlorhydria can accompany HIV infection), and in those with liver disease.

Lifespan: In pregnant women, use cautiously. In breast-feeding women, drug is contraindicated because it appears in breast milk. In children, safety and effectiveness haven't been established.

Adverse reactions

CNS: abnormal dreaming, anxiety, asthenia, depression, dizziness, fatigue, fever, *headache,* malaise, pain, somnolence, tremor.
CV: edema, ***heart failure,*** hypertension, hypertriglyceridemia, orthostatic hypotension.
EENT: pharyngitis, rhinitis, sinusitis.
GI: abdominal pain, anorexia, constipation, diarrhea, dyspepsia, flatulence, increased appetite, gastritis, gastroenteritis, gingivitis, *nausea,* ulcerative stomatitis, vomiting.
GU: albuminuria, cystitis, impotence, UTI.
Hematologic: ***neutropenia.***
Hepatic: ***hepatotoxicity, impaired hepatic function, liver failure.***
Metabolic: hypokalemia.
Musculoskeletal: myalgia.
Respiratory: ***pulmonary edema,*** upper respiratory tract infection.
Skin: pruritus, rash.
Other: ***angioedema,*** decreased libido, herpes zoster, hypersensitivity reactions, injury, ***Stevens-Johnson syndrome,*** urticaria.

Interactions

Drug-drug. *Alprazolam, chlordiazepoxide, clonazepam, clorazepate, diazepam, estazolam, flurazepam, midazolam, quazepam, triazolam:* May increase and prolong levels of these drugs, CNS depression, and psychomotor impairment. Don't use together.
Antacids, H_2-receptor antagonists, phenytoin, rifampin: May decrease itraconazole level. Avoid use together.
Antineoplastics (busulfan, docetaxel, vinca alkaloids): May inhibit metabolism of these drugs, resulting in toxicity. Avoid use together.
Aripiprazole: May increase levels of this drug. Decrease aripiprazole dosage by 50%.
Atorvastatin, fluvastatin, lovastatin, pravastatin, simvastatin: May increase levels and adverse effects of these HMG-CoA reductase inhibitors. Don't use together.
Buspirone, carbamazepine, corticosteroids, cyclosporine, digoxin: May increase levels of these drugs. Monitor level closely.
Calcium channel blockers: May increase negative inotropic effect, causing edema. Use together with caution, and adjust dosages as necessary.
Cisapride, dofetilide, pimozide, quinidine: May increase levels of these drugs by CYP3A4 metabolism, causing serious CV events, including torsades de pointes, prolonged QT interval, ventricular tachycardia, cardiac arrest, or sudden death. Use together is contraindicated.
Didanosine: May decrease therapeutic effect of itraconazole. Give itraconazole at least 2 hours before didanosine.
Isoniazid: May decrease itraconazole level. Monitor patient closely.
Macrolide antibiotics (clarithromycin, erythromycin): May increase concentrations of itraconazole. Adjust dosage accordingly.
Oral anticoagulants: May enhance anticoagulant effects. Monitor PT and INR closely.
Oral antidiabetics: May cause hypoglycemia. Monitor glucose level.
Protease inhibitors: May increase concentrations of protease inhibitors, resulting in toxicity. Use together with caution.
Rifabutin, rifampin, rifamycin: May reduce the effectiveness of itraconazole. Avoid use together.
Drug-food. *Cola:* May increase drug level and adverse effects. Advise patient to take drug with water.
Grapefruit: May delay absorption of drug. Advise patient to avoid grapefruit products.
Orange juice: May decrease level and therapeutic effects of drug. Advise patient to avoid taking drug with orange juice.

Effects on lab test results

• May increase alkaline phosphatase, ALT, AST, bilirubin, and GGT levels. May decrease potassium level.

Pharmacokinetics

Absorption: For oral solution, bioavailability is maximal when taken without food; for capsules, it's with a full meal.

Distribution: 99.8% protein-bound. Extensively distributed in tissues susceptible to infection.
Metabolism: Extensively by liver.
Excretion: In feces and urine. *Half-life:* 1 to 8¼ hours.

Route	Onset	Peak	Duration
P.O.			
Fasting	Unknown	2 hr	Unknown
Non-fasting	Unknown	5 hr	Unknown
I.V.	Unknown	Unknown	Unknown

Action

Chemical effect: Interferes with fungal cell wall synthesis by inhibiting formation of ergosterol and increasing cell wall permeability.
Therapeutic effect: Hinders fungi, including *Aspergillus* sp. and *Blastomyces dermatitidis.*

Available forms

Capsules: 100 mg
Injection: 10 mg/ml in a kit with 25-ml ampule, 50-ml bag of normal saline solution for injection, and a filtered infusion set
Oral solution: 10 mg/ml

NURSING PROCESS

Assessment

- Assess patient's infection before starting therapy and regularly thereafter.
- Before starting treatment, obtain nail specimens for potassium hydroxide preparation, fungal culture, or nail biopsy to confirm diagnosis of onychomycosis.
- Monitor liver and renal function test results.
- Be alert for adverse reactions and drug interactions.
- Assess patient's and family's knowledge of drug therapy.

Nursing diagnoses

- Risk for infection related to presence of susceptible fungi
- Risk for deficient fluid volume related to adverse reactions
- Deficient knowledge related to drug therapy

Planning and implementation

- Don't use in patient with baseline liver impairment, unless in a life-threatening situation where benefit exceeds risk. If signs of liver dysfunction occur, monitor liver function closely and stop therapy; don't restart unless the benefit exceeds the risk.
- Give capsules with food. Don't give oral solution with food.

ALERT: Oral solution and capsules aren't interchangeable.

- If signs and symptoms of heart failure occur, stop drug.
- Report signs and symptoms of liver disease and abnormal liver test results.

Patient teaching

- Teach patient to recognize and report signs and symptoms of liver disease (anorexia, dark urine, pale feces, unusual fatigue, or jaundice) and heart failure (weight gain more than 3 to 5 lb in 1 week, ankle or leg swelling, new shortness of breath).
- Tell patient to take capsules with food to ensure maximum absorption.
- Instruct patient to swish oral solution vigorously in the mouth (10 ml at a time) for several seconds and then swallow. Oral solution should be taken without food, if possible.

Evaluation

- Patient is free from infection.
- Patient maintains adequate fluid balance.
- Patient and family state understanding of drug therapy.

kaolin and pectin mixtures

(KAY-oh-lin and PEK-tin MIX-cherz)
K-Pek, Kaodene Non-Narcotic†, Kaolin w/Pectin†, Kao-Spen, Kapectolin†

Pharmacologic class: absorbent
Therapeutic class: antidiarrheal
Pregnancy risk category: NR

Indications and dosages

▶ **Mild, nonspecific diarrhea.** *Adults:* With regular-strength suspension, 60 to 120 ml P.O. after each bowel movement. With liquid, 45 ml P.O. one to three times daily or after each loose bowel movement.

Children ages 6 to 12: With regular-strength suspension, 30 to 60 ml P.O. after each bowel movement. With liquid, 22.5 ml P.O. one to three times daily or after each loose bowel movement.
Children ages 3 to 6: With regular-strength suspension, 15 to 30 ml P.O. after each bowel movement. With liquid, 15 ml P.O. one to three times daily or after each loose bowel movement.

Contraindications and cautions

- Don't use in patients with diarrhea linked to pseudomembranous colitis or caused by toxigenic bacteria.
- Use cautiously in patients with bleeding disorders or salicylate sensitivity.

Lifespan: In pregnant women and in children, use cautiously.

Adverse reactions

GI: constipation; fecal impaction or ulceration (in infants and elderly or debilitated patients after long-term use).

Interactions

Drug-drug. *Oral drugs:* May decrease drug absorption. Separate administration times by at least 2 or 3 hours.

Effects on lab test results

None reported.

Pharmacokinetics

Absorption: None.
Distribution: None.
Metabolism: None.
Excretion: In stool. *Half-life:* Unknown.

Route	Onset	Peak	Duration
P.O.	Unknown	Unknown	Unknown

Action

Chemical effect: Decreases fluid content of feces, although total water loss seems to remain the same.
Therapeutic effect: Alleviates diarrhea.

Available forms

Liquid: 3.9 g kaolin and 194.4 mg pectin per 30 ml with bismuth subsalicylate (Kaodene)
Oral suspension: 5.2 g kaolin and 260 mg pectin per 30 ml† (Kao-Spen), 90 g kaolin and 2 g pectin per 30 ml† (Kapectolin†, Kaolin w/Pectin†)

NURSING PROCESS

Assessment

- Assess patient's bowel patterns before and after therapy.
- Be alert for adverse GI reactions and drug interactions.
- Assess patient's and family's knowledge of drug therapy.

Nursing diagnoses

- Diarrhea related to underlying condition
- Constipation related to long-term use of drug
- Deficient knowledge related to drug therapy

Planning and implementation

- Read label carefully. Check dosage and strength.
- Give dose after each loose bowel movement.
- Don't use in place of specific therapy for underlying cause of diarrhea.

Patient teaching

- Warn patient not to use drug to replace therapy for underlying cause of the disease.
- Advise patient not to use drug for longer than 2 days.

Evaluation

- Patient reports decrease in or absence of loose stools.
- Patient doesn't have constipation.
- Patient and family state understanding of drug therapy.

ketoconazole

(kee-toh-KAHN-uh-zohl)
Nizoral, Nizoral A-D

Pharmacologic class: imidazole derivative
Therapeutic class: antifungal
Pregnancy risk category: C

Indications and dosages

▶ **Systemic candidiasis, chronic mucocandidiasis, oral thrush, candiduria, coccidioidomycosis, histoplasmosis, chromomycosis, paracoccidioidomycosis, severe cutaneous dermatophyte infection resistant to therapy**

with topical or oral griseofulvin. *Adults and children who weigh more than 40 kg (88 lb):* Initially, 200 mg P.O. daily in single dose. Increase to 400 mg once daily in patients who don't respond to lower dosage.
Children age 2 and older: 3.3 to 6.6 mg/kg P.O. daily as single dose.
Note: Minimum treatment for candidiasis is 7 to 14 days; for other systemic fungal infections, 6 months; for resistant dermatophyte infections, at least 4 weeks.
▶ **Cutaneous candidiasis, tinea corporis, tinea pedis, tinea cruris, and tinea versicolor.** *Adults:* Apply cream once daily to cover the affected area and area immediately surrounding it. Treat candidal infection, tinea cruris, tinea corporis, and tinea versicolor for 2 weeks. Patients with tinea pedis require 6 weeks of treatment.
▶ **Seborrheic dermatitis.** *Adults:* Apply cream to affected area b.i.d. for 4 weeks or until resolved.
▶ **Dandruff.** *Adults:* Moisten hair and scalp with water. Gently massage shampoo over the entire scalp area for about 1 minute. Rinse thoroughly with warm water. Repeat, leaving shampoo on scalp for an additional 3 minutes. After second thorough rinse, dry hair with towel or warm air flow. Use shampoo twice weekly for 4 weeks with at least 3 days between each shampooing. Then use as needed.

Contraindications and cautions

- Contraindicated in patients hypersensitive to the drug or any of its components, and in those taking oral midazolam or triazolam.
- Use cautiously in patients with hepatic disease and in those taking other hepatotoxic drugs.

Lifespan: In pregnant women, use cautiously. Breast-feeding women should stop breast-feeding or use another drug. In children younger than age 2, safety hasn't been established.

Adverse reactions

CNS: dizziness, headache, nervousness, ***suicidal tendencies.***
GI: abdominal pain, constipation, diarrhea, *nausea, vomiting.*
Hematologic: ***thrombocytopenia.***
Hepatic: ***hepatotoxicity.***
Skin: itching, stinging (cream).
Other: gynecomastia with tenderness.

Interactions

Drug-drug. *Alprazolam, chlordiazepoxide, clonazepam, clorazepate, diazepam, estazolam, flurazepam, midazolam, quazepam, triazolam:* May increase and prolong levels, CNS depression, and psychomotor impairment. Don't use together.
Antacids, anticholinergics, H_2-receptor antagonists, proton pump inhibitors, sucralfate: May decrease ketoconazole absorption. Wait at least 2 hours after ketoconazole dose before giving these drugs.
Atorvastatin, fluvastatin, lovastatin, pravastatin, simvastatin: May increase level and adverse effects of these HMG-CoA reductase inhibitors. Avoid this combination. If they must be given together, reduce dosage of HMG-CoA reductase inhibitor.
Corticosteroids: May increase corticosteroid bioavailability and may decrease clearance, possibly resulting in toxicity. Monitor patient closely.
Cyclosporine, methylprednisolone, tacrolimus: May increase levels of these drugs. Adjust their dosages, and monitor their levels closely.
Didanosine: Therapeutic effects of ketoconazole may be decreased by the buffers in the chewable tablets.
Isoniazid, rifampin: May increase ketoconazole metabolism. Monitor patient for decreased antifungal effect.
Oral anticoagulants: May enhance anticoagulant response may be enhanced. Monitor PT and INR.
Oral midazolam, triazolam: May elevate levels of these drugs, which may increase or prolong sedative or hypnotic effects. Avoid using together.

Effects on lab test results

- May increase lipid, alkaline phosphatase, ALT, and AST levels. May decrease hemoglobin level and hematocrit.
- May decrease platelet and WBC counts.

Pharmacokinetics

Absorption: Decreased by raised gastric pH and may be increased in extent and consistency by food.
Distribution: Into bile, saliva, cerumen, synovial fluid, and sebum. Penetration into CSF is erratic and probably minimal. About 84% to 99% protein-bound.

Metabolism: In liver.
Excretion: Mainly in feces, with smaller amount in urine. *Half-life:* 8 hours.

Route	Onset	Peak	Duration
P.O.	Unknown	1–2 hr	Unknown

Action

Chemical effect: Inhibits purine transport and DNA, RNA, and protein synthesis; increases cell wall permeability, making fungus more susceptible to osmotic pressure.
Therapeutic effect: Kills or hinders growth of susceptible fungi, including most pathogenic fungi.

Available forms

Cream: 2%
Shampoo: 1%†, 2%
Tablets: 200 mg

NURSING PROCESS

Assessment

- Assess patient's infection before starting therapy and regularly thereafter.
- Evaluate laboratory studies for eradication of fungi.
- Be alert for adverse reactions and drug interactions.
- If adverse GI reactions occur, monitor patient's hydration.
- Assess patient's and family's knowledge of drug therapy.

Nursing diagnoses

- Risk for infection related to presence of susceptible fungi
- Risk for deficient fluid volume related to adverse GI reactions
- Deficient knowledge related to drug therapy

Planning and implementation

- Because of risk of serious hepatotoxicity, don't use for less serious conditions, such as fungus infections of skin or nails.
- To minimize nausea, divide daily amount into two doses. Also, giving drug with meals helps to decrease nausea.
- Have patient dissolve each tablet in 4 ml aqueous solution of 0.2N hydrochloric acid and sip mixture through straw to avoid contact with teeth. Have patient drink full glass (8 oz) of water afterward.

ALERT: Cream contains sulfites, which can cause allergic reactions in susceptible individuals.

Patient teaching

- Instruct patient with achlorhydria to dissolve each tablet in 4 ml aqueous solution of 0.2N hydrochloric acid, sip mixture through a straw (to avoid contact with teeth), and drink a glass of water after the dose because drug requires gastric acidity to dissolve and absorb completely.
- Make sure patient understands that therapy will continue until all tests indicate that active fungal infection has subsided. If drug is stopped too soon, infection will recur.
- Reassure patient that nausea will subside.
- Tell patient that shampoo and cream are for external use only and to avoid contact with eyes.
- Instruct patient to separate doses of H_2-receptor antagonists, antacids, anticholinergics, proton pump inhibitors, and sucralfate at least 2 hours from drug, as drug requires stomach acidity to work properly.

Evaluation

- Patient is free from infection.
- Patient maintains adequate hydration.
- Patient and family state understanding of drug therapy.

ketoprofen

(kee-toh-PROH-fen)
Actron†, Apo-Keto ♦, Apo-Keto-E ♦, Novo-Keto-EC ♦, Orudis, Orudis-E ♦, Orudis KT†, Orudis SR ♦ ◊, Oruvail, Rhodis ♦, Rhodis-EC ♦

Pharmacologic class: NSAID
Therapeutic class: analgesic, antipyretic, anti-inflammatory
Pregnancy risk category: B (D in third trimester)

Indications and dosages

▶ **Rheumatoid arthritis and osteoarthritis.** *Adults:* 75 mg t.i.d., 50 mg q.i.d., or 200 mg as sustained-release tablet once daily. Maximum, 300 mg daily. Or, where suppository is avail-

K

able, 100 mg P.R. b.i.d. or one suppository at bedtime (with ketoprofen P.O. during day).

▶ **Mild to moderate pain; dysmenorrhea.** *Adults:* 25 to 50 mg P.O. q 6 to 8 hours, p.r.n. Maximum, 300 mg daily.

▶ **Minor aches and pain or fever†.** *Adults:* 12.5 mg with full glass of water q 4 to 6 hours. Don't exceed 25 mg in 4 hours or 75 mg in 24 hours.

Adjust-a-dose: In patients with mildly impaired renal function, the maximum total daily dosage is 150 mg. In more severe renal impairment (GFR less than 25 ml/minute or end-stage renal impairment), the maximum total daily dose is 100 mg. In patients with impaired liver function and serum albumin level less than 3.5 g/dl, the maximum initial total daily dosage is 100 mg. Reduce initial dosage in patients age 75 and older.

Contraindications and cautions

- Contraindicated in patients hypersensitive to the drug or any of its components, and in those with a history of aspirin- or NSAID-induced asthma, urticaria, or other allergic reactions.
- Use cautiously in patients with a history of peptic ulcer disease, renal or liver dysfunction, hypertension, heart failure, or fluid retention.

Lifespan: In pregnant women, don't use drug during the third trimester. In breast-feeding women, don't use because drug appears in breast milk. In children, safety and effectiveness haven't been established. In children younger than age 16, safety and effectiveness of OTC use haven't been established.

Adverse reactions

CNS: *depression,* dizziness, *excitation, headache, malaise, nervousness.*
EENT: ***laryngeal edema,*** tinnitus, visual disturbances.
GI: *abdominal pain,* anorexia, *constipation, diarrhea, flatulence, nausea,* peptic ulceration, stomatitis, vomiting.
GU: ***nephrotoxicity.***
Hematologic: ***agranulocytosis,*** prolonged bleeding time, ***thrombocytopenia.***
Metabolic: *edema.*
Respiratory: ***bronchospasm,*** dyspnea.
Skin: exfoliative dermatitis, photosensitivity, rash.

Interactions

Drug-drug. *Anticoagulants:* May increase anticoagulant effect. Monitor patient for signs and symptoms of bleeding.
Aspirin: May increase risk of adverse GI reactions and increase ketoprofen levels. Avoid use together.
Corticosteroids: May increase risk of adverse GI reactions. Avoid use together.
Hydrochlorothiazide, other diuretics: May decrease diuretic effectiveness. Monitor patient for lack of effect.
Lithium, methotrexate: May increase levels of these drugs, leading to toxicity. Monitor levels closely.
Other NSAIDs: May increase risk of bleeding. Monitor patient.
Probenecid: May increase ketoprofen level. Avoid use together.
Drug-herb. *Dong quai, feverfew, garlic, ginger, horse chestnut, red clover:* May increase risk of bleeding. Monitor patient closely.
St. John's wort: May increase risk of photosensitivity reactions. Advise patient to avoid unprotected or prolonged exposure to sunlight.
Drug-lifestyle. *Alcohol use:* May increase risk of GI toxicity. Discourage use together.
Sun exposure: May cause photosensitivity reactions. Advise patient to avoid unprotected or prolonged exposure to sunlight.

Effects on lab test results

- May increase BUN level.
- May increase bleeding time and liver function test values. May decrease WBC and platelet counts.
- May interfere with glucose and iron levels, depending on test used.

Pharmacokinetics

Absorption: Rapid and complete.
Distribution: Highly protein-bound.
Metabolism: Extensive, in liver.
Excretion: In urine. *Half-life:* 2 to 5½ hours for extended-release forms.

Route	Onset	Peak	Duration
P.O., P.R.	1–2 hr	½–2 hr	3–4 hr
P.O.			
Extended-release	2–3 hr	6–9 hr	24–48 hr

Action

Chemical effect: May inhibit prostaglandin synthesis.

Therapeutic effect: Relieves pain, fever, and inflammation.

Available forms

Capsules: 25 mg, 50 mg, 75 mg
Capsules (extended-release): 100 mg, 150 mg, 200 mg
Suppositories: 100 mg ♦
Tablets: 12.5 mg†
Tablets (enteric-coated): 50 mg ♦, 100 mg ♦
Tablets (sustained-release): 200 mg ♦

NURSING PROCESS

Assessment

- Assess patient's pain before and after giving the drug. Full effect may not occur for 2 to 4 weeks.
- Check renal and hepatic function every 6 months during long-term therapy.
- Be alert for adverse reactions and drug interactions.
- If adverse GI reactions occur, monitor patient's hydration.
- Assess patient's and family's knowledge of drug therapy.

Nursing diagnoses

- Chronic pain related to underlying condition
- Risk for deficient fluid volume related to adverse GI reactions
- Deficient knowledge related to drug therapy

Planning and implementation

- Sustained-release form isn't recommended for patients in acute pain.
- May give drug with antacids, food, or milk to minimize adverse GI effects.
- Inform lab technician that patient is taking drug; it may interfere with tests for glucose and iron levels, depending on testing method used.

Patient teaching

- Patient may take drug with milk or meals if he experiences adverse GI effects.
- Tell patient that full therapeutic effect may be delayed for 2 to 4 weeks.
- Instruct patient to report adverse visual or auditory reactions immediately.
- Teach patient to recognize and immediately report evidence of GI bleeding. Explain that serious GI toxicity, including peptic ulceration and bleeding, can occur in patients taking NSAIDs even without GI symptoms.
- Inform patient that use with aspirin, alcohol, or corticosteroids may increase risk of adverse GI reactions.
- Advise patient to use sunblock, wear protective clothing, and avoid prolonged exposure to sunlight. Explain that drug may cause photosensitivity reactions.

Evaluation

- Patient is free from pain.
- Patient maintains normal hydration.
- Patient and family state understanding of drug therapy.

ketorolac tromethamine

(KEE-toh-roh-lak troh-METH-uh-meen)
Acular, Acular LS, Toradol

Pharmacologic class: NSAID
Therapeutic class: analgesic, anti-inflammatory
Pregnancy risk category: C (D in third trimester)

Indications and dosages

▶ **Short-term management of pain.** *Adults younger than age 65:* Base dosage on patient response. Initially, 60 mg I.M. or 30 mg I.V. as single dose or doses of 30 mg I.M. or I.V. q 6 hours. Maximum, 120 mg daily. To switch to P.O. route, initially give 20 mg P.O., and then 10 mg P.O. q 4 to 6 hours, p.r.n., up to 40 mg daily. Maximum combined use of drug not to exceed 5 days.

Adults age 65 and older, patients with renal impairment, and those weighing less than 50 kg (110 lb): Initially, 30 mg I.M. or 15 mg I.V. as single dose or doses of 15 mg I.M. or I.V. q 6 hours. Maximum, 60 mg daily. To switch to P.O. route, 10 mg P.O. q 4 to 6 hours, if needed, up to 40 mg daily. Maximum combined use of drug not to exceed 5 days.

▶ **Ocular itching caused by seasonal allergic rhinitis.** *Adults:* 1 drop (0.25 mg) q.i.d.

▶ **Postoperative inflammation following cataract surgery.** *Adults:* 1 drop to affected eye q.i.d. starting 24 hours after surgery and continuing for the first 2 postoperative weeks.

▶ **Pain and burning or stinging following corneal refractive surgery.** *Adults:* 1 drop in the operated eye q.i.d., p.r.n., for up to 4 days.

I.V. administration

- Injection solution contains alcohol.
- Give I.V. bolus over at least 15 seconds.

⊗ **Incompatibilities**

Haloperidol lactate; nalbuphine; solutions that result in a relatively low pH, such as hydroxyzine, meperidine, morphine sulfate, and prochlorperazine; thiethylperazine.

Contraindications and cautions

- Contraindicated in patients hypersensitive to the drug or any of its components; in those with a history of nasal polyps, angioedema, bronchospastic reactivity, or allergic reactions to aspirin or other NSAIDs; in patients receiving aspirin or other NSAIDs; in those with advanced renal impairment; and in those at risk for renal impairment as a result of volume depletion. Also contraindicated in patients with a high risk of bleeding and in those with suspected or confirmed cerebrovascular bleeding, hemorrhagic diathesis, and incomplete hemostasis.
- Not recommended for intrathecal or epidural administration because of its alcohol content.
- Use cautiously in patients in the perioperative period, and in patients with hepatic or renal impairment, history of serious GI events or peptic ulcer disease, cardiac decompensation, hypertension, or coagulation disorders.

Lifespan: In pregnant women, safety during first two trimesters hasn't been established; drug is contraindicated in third trimester. In breast-feeding women, use cautiously because trace amounts have been detected in breast milk. In children, safety of oral form hasn't been established; I.M. and I.V. use are safe in children age 2 and older; ophthalmic solutions are safe for children age 3 and older.

Adverse reactions

CNS: dizziness, drowsiness, *headache,* insomnia, syncope.
CV: edema, hypertension, palpitations.
EENT: corneal edema, keratitis (ocular form), ocular irritation, *transient stinging and burning.*
GI: diarrhea, *dyspepsia, GI pain, nausea.*
GU: hematuria, polyuria, ***renal failure.***
Hematologic: anemia, eosinophilia, purpura.
Skin: sweating.
Other: pain at injection site.

Interactions

Drug-drug. *Antihypertensives, diuretics:* May decrease effectiveness of these drugs. Monitor reactions closely.
Cyclosporine: May increase risk of nephrotoxicity. Use together cautiously.
Lithium: May increase lithium level. Monitor level closely.
Low–molecular-weight heparin, salicylates, warfarin: May increase levels of free (unbound) salicylates or warfarin in blood. Significance is unknown.
Methotrexate: May decrease methotrexate clearance and increase toxicity. Don't use together.
Drug-herb. *Dong quai, feverfew, garlic, ginger, horse chestnut, red clover:* May increase risk of bleeding. Monitor patient closely.
St. John's wort: May increase risk of photosensitivity reactions. Advise patient to avoid unprotected or prolonged exposure to sunlight.

Effects on lab test results

- May decrease hemoglobin level and hematocrit.
- May increase eosinophil count and liver function test values.

Pharmacokinetics

Absorption: Complete after I.M. use. After P.O. use, food delays absorption but doesn't decrease amount absorbed.
Distribution: More than 99.9% protein-bound.
Metabolism: Mainly in liver.
Excretion: More than 90% in urine, with the remainder in feces. *Half-life:* 4 to 6 hours.

Route	Onset	Peak	Duration
P.O.	30–60 min	30–60 min	6–8 hr
I.V.	Immediate	Immediate	8 hr
I.M.	≤ 30 min	1–2 hr	6–8 hr

Action

Chemical effect: May inhibit prostaglandin synthesis.
Therapeutic effect: Relieves pain and inflammation.

Available forms

Injection: 15 mg/ml, 30 mg/ml
Ophthalmic solution: 0.4%, 0.5%
Tablets: 10 mg

NURSING PROCESS

Assessment

- Assess patient's pain before and after drug therapy.
- Be alert for adverse reactions and drug interactions.
- Assess patient's and family's knowledge of drug therapy.

Nursing diagnoses

- Acute pain related to underlying condition
- Risk for injury related to drug-induced adverse CNS reactions
- Deficient knowledge related to drug therapy

Planning and implementation

- When switching from I.M. to P.O., don't exceed 120 mg (including maximum of 40 mg P.O.) on day of transition.
- I.M. use may cause pain at injection site. Apply pressure to site for 15 to 30 seconds after injection to minimize local effects.
- If pain persists or worsens, notify prescriber.

ALERT: Don't confuse Toradol with Foradil.

Patient teaching

- Teach patient to recognize and immediately report signs and symptoms of GI bleeding. Explain that serious GI toxicity, even without any symptoms, can occur.
- Advise patient to report persistent or worsening pain.
- Explain that drug is intended only for short-term use.

Evaluation

- Patient is free from pain.
- Patient sustains no injury from adverse reactions.
- Patient and family state understanding of drug therapy.

ketotifen fumarate

(kee-toe-TYE-fen FOO-muh-rayt)
Zaditor

Pharmacologic class: histamine antagonist and mast cell stabilizer
Therapeutic class: ophthalmic antihistamine
Pregnancy risk category: C

Indications and dosages

▶ **To temporarily prevent itching of eye caused by allergic conjunctivitis.** *Adults and children age 3 and older:* Instill 1 drop in affected eye q 8 to 12 hours.

Contraindications and cautions

- Contraindicated in patients hypersensitive to the drug or any of its components.

Lifespan: In pregnant women, use cautiously. In breast-feeding women, use cautiously; it's unknown if topical ocular drug appears in breast milk. In children younger than age 3, safety and effectiveness haven't been established.

Adverse reactions

CNS: *headaches.*
EENT: burning or stinging of eyes, *conjunctival infection,* conjunctivitis, dry eyes, eye discharge, eye pain, eyelid disorder, itching of eyes, keratitis, lacrimation disorder, mydriasis, ocular allergic reactions, ocular rash, pharyngitis, photophobia, *rhinitis.*
Other: flulike syndrome.

Interactions

None reported.

Effects on lab test results

None reported.

Pharmacokinetics

Absorption: Unknown.
Distribution: Unknown.
Metabolism: Unknown.
Excretion: Unknown. *Half-life:* Unknown.

Route	Onset	Peak	Duration
Ophthalmic	Within min	Unknown	Unknown

K

Action

Chemical effect: Inhibits release of mediators from cells involved in hypersensitivity reactions.

Therapeutic effect: Temporary prevention of eye itching.

Available forms

Ophthalmic solution: 0.025% solution in 5-ml and 7.5-ml bottles

NURSING PROCESS

Assessment

- Assess underlying condition before starting therapy, and reassess regularly during therapy.
- Monitor patient for sensitivity reactions.
- Monitor patient for signs of infection.
- Assess patient's and family's knowledge of drug therapy.

Nursing diagnoses

- Impaired tissue integrity related to drug-induced adverse EENT reactions
- Deficient knowledge related to ketotifen fumarate therapy

Planning and implementation

- Drug is for ophthalmic use only and not for injection or oral use.
- Drug isn't indicated for use with irritation related to contact lenses.
- Preservative in drug may be absorbed by soft contact lenses. Have patient remove contact lenses before giving drops, and tell him not to reinsert them for at least 10 minutes.

Patient teaching

- Teach patient proper instillation technique. Tell him to avoid contaminating dropper tip and solution and not to touch eyelids or surrounding areas with dropper tip of bottle.
- Tell patient not to wear contact lenses if eyes are red. Warn patient not to use drug to treat irritation related to contact lenses.
- Instruct patient who wears soft contact lenses and whose eyes aren't red to wait at least 10 minutes after instilling drug before inserting contact lenses.
- Advise patient to report adverse reactions to prescriber.
- Instruct patient to keep bottle tightly closed when not in use.

Evaluation

- Patient demonstrates appropriate management of any adverse EENT reactions.
- Patient and family state understanding of therapy.

labetalol hydrochloride

(lah-BAY-tuh-lol high-droh-KLOR-ighd)

Normodyne, Presolol ◇, Trandate

Pharmacologic class: alpha and beta blocker
Therapeutic class: antihypertensive
Pregnancy risk category: C

Indications and dosages

▶ **Hypertension.** *Adults:* 100 mg P.O. b.i.d. with or without diuretic. Adjust dosage in increments of 100 mg b.i.d. q 2 or 3 days. Maintenance dosage, 200 to 400 mg b.i.d. Some patients may need 1.2 to 2.4 g/day.

▶ **Severe hypertension, hypertensive emergency.** *Adults:* 200 mg I.V. diluted for infusion at 2 mg/minute until obtaining satisfactory response; then stop infusion. Or give by repeated I.V. injection; initially, 20 mg I.V. slowly over 2 minutes. Then repeat injections of 40 to 80 mg q 10 minutes, p.r.n. to maximum dose, 300 mg.

I.V. administration

- Dilute 200 mg in 160 ml for 1 mg/ml solution for infusion. May use 200 mg/250 ml solution.
- Dilute with D_5W, normal saline solutions, Ringer's solution, or lactated Ringer's solution.
- Give diluted infusion with infusion-control device.
- Give direct I.V. injection over 2 minutes at 10-minute intervals.
- Monitor blood pressure every 5 minutes for 30 minutes, then q 30 minutes for 2 hours, then every hour for 6 hours.
- When given I.V. for hypertensive emergency, drug produces rapid, predictable fall in blood pressure within 5 to 10 minutes.
- Have patient lie down for 3 hours after infusion.

• Store drug at 36° to 86° F (2° to 30° C) and protect from light.

⊗ **Incompatibilities**

Alkali solutions, cefoperazone, ceftriaxone, furosemide, heparin, nafcillin, sodium bicarbonate, thiopental, warfarin.

Contraindications and cautions

• Contraindicated in patients hypersensitive to the drug or any of its components and in those with bronchial asthma, overt cardiac failure, greater than first-degree heart block, cardiogenic shock, severe bradycardia, and other conditions linked to severe and prolonged hypotension.

• Use cautiously in patients with heart failure, hepatic impairment, chronic bronchitis, emphysema, peripheral vascular disease, or pheochromocytoma.

Lifespan: In pregnant and breast-feeding women, use cautiously. In children, safety and effectiveness haven't been established. Elderly patients typically need a lower maintenance dosage.

Adverse reactions

CNS: *dizziness,* fatigue, headache, transient scalp tingling, vivid dreams.
CV: ***bradycardia,*** *orthostatic hypotension,* peripheral vascular disease, ***ventricular arrhythmias.***
EENT: nasal stuffiness.
GI: diarrhea, nausea, vomiting.
GU: sexual dysfunction, urine retention.
Respiratory: increased airway resistance.
Skin: rash.

Interactions

Drug-drug. *Beta agonists:* May blunt the bronchodilator effect of these drugs in patients with bronchospasm. Increase dosage of these bronchodilators.

Cimetidine: May enhance labetalol's effect. Give together cautiously; monitor patient for adverse reactions.

Diuretics and other antihypertensives: May increase hypotension. Monitor patient and adjust dosage.

Glutethimide: May decrease effects of labetalol. Adjust labetalol dosage carefully to reach optimal blood pressure control.

Halothane: May increase hypotension. Monitor blood pressure.

Insulin, oral antidiabetics: May change required dosage in previously stabilized diabetic patients. Observe patient carefully.

Tricyclic antidepressants: May increase risk of tremor. Monitor patient.

Effects on lab test results

• May increase glucose, transaminase, and blood urea levels.

• May cause false-positive result for amphetamines in urine drug screen.

Pharmacokinetics

Absorption: 90% to 100%, but drug undergoes extensive first-pass metabolism in liver and only about 25% reaches circulation unchanged.
Distribution: Wide. About 50% protein-bound.
Metabolism: Extensive, in liver and possibly GI mucosa.
Excretion: About 5% unchanged in urine; remainder as metabolites in urine and feces.
Half-life: About 5½ hours after I.V. use; 6 to 8 hours after P.O. use.

Route	Onset	Peak	Duration
P.O.	≤ 20 min	2–4 hr	8–12 hr
I.V.	2–5 min	5 min	2–4 hr

Action

Chemical effect: May be related to reduced peripheral vascular resistance as result of alpha-adrenergic blockade.
Therapeutic effect: Lowers blood pressure.

Available forms

Injection: 5 mg/ml
Tablets: 100 mg, 200 mg, 300 mg

NURSING PROCESS

Assessment

• Obtain history of patient's hypertension before starting therapy.

• Check blood pressure often. Drug masks common signs of shock.

• Be alert for adverse reactions and drug interactions.

• With oral form, full antihypertensive effect is usually seen within the first 1 to 3 hours of initial dose or dose change.

• Assess patient's and family's knowledge of drug therapy.

Nursing diagnoses
- Ineffective health maintenance related to presence of hypertension
- Risk for trauma related to drug-induced hypotension
- Deficient knowledge related to drug therapy

Planning and implementation
- If dizziness occurs, give at bedtime or give smaller doses t.i.d. to help minimize it.

ALERT: Don't confuse Trandate with Tridrate or Trental.

Patient teaching
- Tell patient that abruptly stopping therapy can worsen angina and cause MI.
- Inform patient that rising slowly and avoiding sudden position changes can minimize dizziness.

Evaluation
- Patient's blood pressure is normal.
- Patient doesn't experience trauma caused by drug-induced hypotension.
- Patient and family state understanding of drug therapy.

lactulose
(LAK-tyoo-lohs)

Cephulac, Cholac, Chronulac, Constilac, Constulose, Duphalac, Enulose, Generlac, Kristalose, Lac-Dol ◇

Pharmacologic class: disaccharide
Therapeutic class: laxative
Pregnancy risk category: B

Indications and dosages
▶ **Constipation.** *Adults:* 10 to 20 g (15 to 30 ml) P.O. daily, increase to 60 ml/day, if needed.

▶ **To prevent and treat hepatic encephalopathy, including hepatic precoma and coma in patients with severe hepatic disease.** *Adults:* Initially, 20 to 30 g (30 to 45 ml) P.O. t.i.d. or q.i.d. until two to three soft stools are produced daily. Usual dosage, 60 to 100 g total daily. Or 200 g (300 ml) diluted with 700 ml of water or normal saline solution and given as retention enema q 4 to 6 hours, p.r.n.
Adolescents and older children: 27 to 60 g (40 to 90 ml) daily in divided doses.
Infants: 1.67 to 6.67 g (2.5 to 10 ml) daily in divided doses.

For all patients, the desired effect is two to three stools daily. If diarrhea occurs with first dose, reduce dose immediately. If diarrhea persists, stop drug.

▶ **To induce bowel evacuation in geriatric patients with colonic retention of barium and severe constipation after a barium meal examination‡.** *Adults:* 3.3 to 6.7 g P.O. b.i.d. for 1 to 4 weeks.

▶ **To restore bowel movements after hemorrhoidectomy‡.** *Adults:* 10 g P.O. twice during day before surgery and 5 days afterward.

Contraindications and cautions
- Contraindicated in patients on low-galactose diet.
- Use cautiously in patients with diabetes mellitus because drug contains lactose, galactose, and other sugars.

Lifespan: In pregnant women, use only when clearly needed. In breast-feeding women, use cautiously; it's unknown if the drug appears in breast milk. In children, use for chronic constipation is contraindicated. In elderly patients, use cautiously because they may be more susceptible to hyponatremia.

Adverse reactions
GI: *abdominal cramps and distention, belching, diarrhea, flatulence,* nausea, vomiting.

Interactions
Drug-drug. *Antacids, antibiotics, oral neomycin:* May decrease effectiveness of lactulose. Avoid use together.

Effects on lab test results
- May increase glucose level. May decrease ammonia, chloride, potassium, and sodium levels.

Pharmacokinetics
Absorption: Minimal.
Distribution: Local, mainly in colon.
Metabolism: By colonic bacteria.
Excretion: Mostly in feces; absorbed portion in urine.

Route	Onset	Peak	Duration
P.O.	24–48 hr	Varies	Varies
P.R.	Unknown	Unknown	Unknown

Action

Chemical effect: Produces osmotic effect in colon. Resulting distention promotes peristalsis. Decreases blood ammonia build-up that causes hepatic encephalopathy, probably as result of bacterial degradation, which lowers pH of colon contents.

Therapeutic effect: Relieves constipation, decreases blood ammonia concentration.

Available forms

Crystals for reconstitution: 10 g/packet, 20 g/packet

Solution: 10 g/15 ml, 3.33 g/5 ml

NURSING PROCESS

Assessment

- Assess patient's condition before starting therapy and regularly thereafter to monitor drug effectiveness. If patient has hepatic encephalopathy, assess mental condition.
- Monitor patient's electrolyte levels during long-term use.
- Monitor ammonia level in patient with hepatic disease.
- Be alert for adverse reactions and drug interactions.
- Assess patient's and family's knowledge of drug therapy.

Nursing diagnoses

- Constipation related to underlying condition
- Deficient knowledge related to drug therapy

Planning and implementation

ALERT: Don't confuse lactulose with lactose.

- Replace fluid loss.
- Diarrhea may indicate overdose.
- To minimize sweet taste, dilute with water or fruit juice or give with food.
- If enema isn't retained for at least 30 minutes, repeat dose.

ALERT: For a patient undergoing electrocautery procedures during proctoscopy or colonoscopy, the accumulation of hydrogen gas, combined with an electrical spark may cause an explosion. For a patient undergoing electrocautery procedures, give an enema with a nonfermentable solution.

- Store drug at room temperature, preferably below 86° F (30° C); don't freeze.

Patient teaching

- Advise patient to dilute drug with juice or water, or to take with food to improve taste.
- Inform patient of adverse reactions and tell him to notify prescriber if reactions become bothersome or if having more than two or three soft stools daily.

Evaluation

- Patient's constipation is relieved.
- Patient and family state understanding of drug therapy.

lamivudine (3TC)

(la-MIH-vyoo-deen)

Epivir, Epivir-HBV

Pharmacologic class: nucleoside reverse transcriptase inhibitor

Therapeutic class: antiretroviral

Pregnancy risk category: C

L

Indications and dosages

▶ **HIV infection (with other antiretrovirals).** *Adults and children age 16 and older:* 300 mg Epivir P.O. once daily or 150 mg P.O. b.i.d.

Children ages 3 months to 16 years: 4 mg/kg Epivir P.O. b.i.d. Maximum, 150 mg b.i.d.

Neonates age 30 days and younger‡: 2 mg/kg Epivir P.O. b.i.d.

Adjust-a-dose: For adults and adolescents with renal impairment, if creatinine clearance is 30 to 49 ml/minute, give 150 mg Epivir P.O. daily; if clearance is 15 to 29 ml/minute, give 150 mg P.O. on day 1, then 100 mg daily; if clearance is 5 to 14 ml/minute, give 150 mg on day 1, then 50 mg daily; if clearance is less than 5 ml/minute, give 50 mg on day 1, then 25 mg daily.

▶ **Chronic hepatitis B with evidence of hepatitis B virus (HBV) replication and active liver inflammation.** *Adults:* 100 mg Epivir-HBV P.O. once daily.

Children ages 2 to 17: Give 3 mg/kg Epivir-HBV once daily. Maximum daily, 100 mg.

Adjust-a-dose: For adult patients with renal impairment, if creatinine clearance is 30 to 49 ml/minute, give 100 mg Epivir-HBV as first dose, then 50 mg P.O. daily; if clearance is 15 to 29 ml/minute, give 100 mg first dose, then 25 mg P.O. daily; if clearance is 5 to 14 ml/

minute, give 35 mg first dose, then 15 mg P.O. daily; if clearance is less than 5 ml/minute, give 35 mg first dose, then 10 mg P.O. daily.

Contraindications and cautions

- Contraindicated in patients hypersensitive to the drug or any of its components, as well as in combination antiretroviral therapy with abacavir, lamivudine, and tenofovir, and with didanosine, lamivudine, and tenofovir because of early drug resistance in HIV-infected patients.
- Epivir-HBV is contraindicated for patients co-infected with HBV and HIV.
- Safety and effectiveness of Epivir-HBV in all patients for longer than 1 year haven't been established; ideal duration of therapy isn't known.
- Use cautiously in patients with decompensated liver disease or organ transplant. Use cautiously and at a reduced dosage in patients with renal impairment.

Lifespan: In pregnant women, use only if benefits outweigh risks to the fetus. Breast-feeding women should stop breast-feeding or take another drug. In children younger than age 2, safety and effectiveness in chronic hepatitis B haven't been established. In children with history of pancreatitis or other significant risk factors for pancreatitis, use cautiously, if at all.

Adverse reactions

For HIV-infected patients

CNS: depressive disorders, *dizziness, fatigue, fever, headache, insomnia, malaise, neuropathy, sleep disorders.*

EENT: *nasal symptoms.*

GI: abdominal cramps, abdominal pain, *anorexia, diarrhea,* dyspepsia, *hepatomegaly* (in children), *nausea, **pancreatitis,** vomiting.*

Hematologic: anemia, lymphadenopathy (in children), ***neutropenia, thrombocytopenia.***

Musculoskeletal: arthralgia, *musculoskeletal pain,* myalgia.

Respiratory: *cough.*

Skin: rash (*rashes* in children).

Other: *chills, **lactic acidosis.***

For hepatitis B patients

CNS: *fatigue, fever, headache, malaise.*

EENT: ear, nose, and throat infections; sore throat.

GI: abdominal pain and discomfort, *diarrhea, nausea, vomiting.*

Musculoskeletal: arthralgia, *myalgia.*

Skin: rash.

Other: ***lactic acidosis.***

Interactions

Drug-drug. *Co-trimoxazole:* May increase lamivudine bioavailability. Dosage adjustment isn't needed. Avoid giving lamivudine with high doses of co-trimoxazole for *Pneumocystis jiroveci (carinii)* pneumonia and toxoplasmosis.

Zalcitabine: May inhibit activation of one another. Avoid use together.

Effects on lab test results

- May increase ALT and bilirubin levels. May decrease hemoglobin level and hematocrit.
- May decrease neutrophil and platelet counts.

Pharmacokinetics

Absorption: Rapid for HIV-infected patients.

Distribution: Possibly into extravascular spaces. Volume is independent of dose and doesn't correlate with body weight. Less than 36% protein-bound.

Metabolism: To trans-sulfoxide.

Excretion: Mainly unchanged in urine. *Half-life:* 5 to 7 hours.

Route	Onset	Peak	Duration
P.O.	Unknown	1–3 hr	Unknown

Action

Chemical effect: Inhibits HIV reverse transcription by viral DNA chain termination and RNA- and DNA-dependent DNA polymerase activities.

Therapeutic effect: Reduces the symptoms of HIV infection, reduces liver inflammation of chronic hepatitis B and may seroconvert some patients.

Available forms

Epivir

Oral solution: 10 mg/ml

Tablets: 150 mg, 300 mg

Epivir-HBV

Oral solution: 5 mg/ml

Tablets: 100 mg

NURSING PROCESS

Assessment

- Obtain history of patient's underlying condition before starting therapy, and reassess regularly thereafter to monitor drug effectiveness.

• Test patient with HBV for HIV before and throughout therapy, because drug isn't appropriate for those dually infected.

ALERT: Some patients with chronic HBV infection may have recurrent hepatitis after stopping the drug. Patients with liver disease may have more severe effects; monitor liver function tests, markers of HBV replication, and clinical signs regularly after stopping therapy.

• Monitor renal function before and during therapy.

• Monitor patient's CBC, platelet count, and liver function. Report any abnormalities to prescriber.

• Assess patient's and family's knowledge of drug therapy.

Nursing diagnoses

• Risk for infection related to the presence of HIV

• Risk for injury related to drug-induced CNS adverse reactions

• Deficient knowledge related to drug therapy

Planning and implementation

• Safety and effectiveness of drug haven't been established for chronic hepatitis B in a patient infected with both HIV and HBV. Drug-resistant HBV variations may occur in such a patient; HIV drug resistance often occurs also.

ALERT: Lactic acidosis and severe hepatomegaly, including fatal cases, have been reported.

• If signs, symptoms, or laboratory abnormalities suggest pancreatitis, stop therapy immediately and notify prescriber.

• An Antiretroviral Pregnancy Registry has been established to monitor maternal-fetal outcomes of pregnant women exposed to drug. To register a pregnant woman, call 1-800-258-4263, or register online at www.apregistry.com.

ALERT: Don't confuse lamivudine with lamotrigine.

Patient teaching

• Inform patient that long-term effects of drug are unknown.

• Stress importance of taking drug exactly as prescribed.

• Teach patient the signs and symptoms of pancreatitis. Advise him to report signs and symptoms immediately.

Evaluation

• Patient responds well to drug therapy.

• Patient sustains no injury as a result of drug-induced CNS adverse reactions.

• Patient and family state understanding of drug therapy.

lamivudine and zidovudine

(la-MIH-vyoo-deen and zye-DOE-vyoo-deen)

Combivir

Pharmacologic class: nucleoside reverse transcriptase inhibitor

Therapeutic class: antiretroviral

Pregnancy risk category: C

Indications and dosages

▶ **HIV infection.** *Adults and children age 12 and older who weigh more than 50 kg (110 lb):* One tablet P.O. b.i.d.

Contraindications and cautions

• Contraindicated in patients hypersensitive to the drug or any of its components, those who need dosage adjustments (such as those who weigh less than 50 kg), those with creatinine clearance less than 50 ml/minute, and those with impaired hepatic function. Also contraindicated in patients with dose-limiting adverse effects.

• Safety and effectiveness of lamivudine haven't been established for patients infected with HIV and hepatitis B virus (HBV). Drug-resistant HBV variations may occur in these patients after receiving combination drug.

Lifespan: In pregnant women, use only if benefits outweigh risks to the fetus. Breast-feeding women should stop breast-feeding or use another drug. In children younger than age 12, drug is contraindicated.

Adverse reactions

CNS: depression, *dizziness, fatigue, fever, headache, insomnia, malaise, neuropathy.*

EENT: *nasal signs and symptoms.*

GI: abdominal cramps, abdominal pain, *anorexia, diarrhea,* dyspepsia, *nausea, vomiting.*

Hematologic: ***neutropenia,*** severe anemia.

Hepatic: ***severe hepatomegaly with steatosis.***

Musculoskeletal: arthralgia, *musculoskeletal pain,* myalgia.

Respiratory: *cough.*
Skin: rash.
Other: *chills, **lactic acidosis.***

Interactions

Drug-drug. *Atovaquone, fluconazole, methadone, probenecid, valproic acid given with zidovudine:* May increase bioavailability of zidovudine. Dosage adjustment isn't needed.
Co-trimoxazole, nelfinavir: May increase bioavailability of lamivudine. Dosage adjustment isn't needed. Avoid giving lamivudine with high doses of co-trimoxazole for *Pneumocystis jiroveci (carinii)* pneumonia and toxoplasmosis.
Ganciclovir, interferon-alfa, and other bone marrow suppressive or cytotoxic drugs: May increase hematologic toxicity of zidovudine. Use cautiously as with other reverse transcriptase inhibitors.
Nelfinavir, ritonavir: May decrease bioavailability of zidovudine. Dosage modification isn't needed.
Zalcitabine: May inhibit intracellular phosphorylation of one another. Avoid using these drugs together.

Effects on lab test results

- May increase ALT, AST, and amylase levels. May decrease hemoglobin level and hematocrit.
- May decrease neutrophil count.

Pharmacokinetics

Absorption: Rapid for both drugs, with bioavailability of 86% and 64%, respectively.
Distribution: Extensive for both drugs with low protein-binding.
Metabolism: About 5% for lamivudine; 74% for zidovudine.
Excretion: Mainly in urine. *Half-lives of lamivudine and zidovudine:* 5 to 7 hours and ½ to 3 hours, respectively.

Route	Onset	Peak	Duration
P.O.	Unknown	Unknown	Unknown

Action

Chemical effect: Inhibits reverse transcriptase by DNA chain termination. Both drugs are also weak inhibitors of DNA polymerase. Together, they act synergistically by suppressing or delaying the emergence of resistant strains that can occur with retroviral monotherapy, because dual resistance requires multiple mutations.
Therapeutic effect: Reduces the symptoms of HIV infection.

Available forms

Tablets: 150 mg lamivudine and 300 mg zidovudine

NURSING PROCESS

Assessment

- Obtain history of patient's underlying condition before starting therapy, and reassess regularly thereafter to monitor the drug's effectiveness.
- Watch for hematologic toxicity by taking frequent blood counts, especially in patients with advanced HIV infection.
- Assess patient's fine motor skills and peripheral sensation for evidence of peripheral neuropathies.

ALERT: In a patient with chronic HBV infection, hepatitis may recur when drug is stopped. Patients with pre-existing liver disease may have more severe consequences. Periodically monitor liver function test results and markers of HBV replication in patient with liver disease and HBV.

- Assess patient's and family's knowledge of drug therapy.

Nursing diagnoses

- Risk for infection related to the presence of HIV
- Disturbed sensory perception (tactile) related to drug-induced peripheral neuropathy
- Deficient knowledge related to drug therapy

Planning and implementation

ALERT: Fatal lactic acidosis and severe hepatomegaly with steatosis may occur. If patient develops signs or symptoms of lactic acidosis or severe hepatotoxicity, stop drug.

- Use drug cautiously in patients with bone marrow suppression (granulocyte count below 1,000/mm³ or hemoglobin level below 9.5 g/dl).
- An Antiretroviral Pregnancy Registry has been established to monitor maternal-fetal outcomes of pregnant women exposed to drug. To register a pregnant patient call 1-800-258-4263 or register online at www.apregistry.com.

Patient teaching

- Explain to patient that therapy won't cure HIV infection and that he may continue to have illness.
- Warn patient that HIV transmission can still occur with drug therapy. Educate patient about using barrier contraception when engaging in sexual activities to prevent disease transmission.
- Teach patient signs and symptoms of neutropenia and anemia (fever, chills, infection, fatigue), and instruct him to immediately report them to the prescriber.
- Tell patient to have blood counts followed closely while taking drug, especially if he has advanced disease.
- Advise patient to consult prescriber or pharmacist before taking other drugs.
- Warn patient to report abdominal pain immediately.
- Instruct patient to report evidence of myopathy or myositis, such as muscle inflammation, pain, weakness, and a decrease in muscle size.
- Stress importance of taking combination drug therapy exactly as prescribed to reduce the development of drug resistance.
- Tell patient he may take combination with or without food.
- Inform woman that breast-feeding is contraindicated with an HIV infection, whether or not she is taking drug.

☑ Evaluation

- Patient responds well to drug.
- Patient doesn't develop peripheral neuropathy.
- Patient and family state understanding of drug therapy.

lamotrigine

(lah-MOH-trih-jeen)

Lamictal

Pharmacologic class: phenyltriazine
Therapeutic class: anticonvulsant, mood stabilizer
Pregnancy risk category: C

Indications and dosages

▶ **Adjunct therapy for partial seizures caused by epilepsy or generalized seizures of Lennox-Gastaut syndrome.** *Adults and children older than age 12:* For patients taking valproic acid with other enzyme-inducing anticonvulsants, 25 mg P.O. q other day for 2 weeks; then 25 mg P.O. daily for 2 weeks. Continue to increase, as appropriate, by 25 to 50 mg/day q 1 to 2 weeks until effective maintenance dosage of 100 to 400 mg daily, given in one or two divided doses, is reached. When added to valproic acid alone, maintenance dosage is 100 to 200 mg P.O. daily. For patients receiving enzyme-inducing anticonvulsants and not valproic acid, 50 mg P.O. daily for 2 weeks; then 100 mg P.O. daily in two divided doses for 2 weeks. Increase, as needed, by 100 mg daily q 1 to 2 weeks. Maintenance dosage, 300 to 500 mg P.O. daily in two divided doses.
Children ages 2 to 12 who weigh 6.7 to 40 kg (15 to 88 lb): For patients taking valproic acid with other enzyme-inducing anticonvulsants, 0.15 mg/kg P.O. daily in one or two divided doses (round down to nearest whole tablet) for 2 weeks, followed by 0.3 mg/kg daily in one or two divided doses for another 2 weeks. Then maintenance dosage, 1 to 5 mg/kg daily (maximum, 200 mg daily in one to two divided doses). For patients receiving enzyme-inducing anticonvulsants and not valproic acid, 0.6 mg/kg P.O. daily in two divided doses (round down to nearest whole tablet) for 2 weeks, followed by 1.2 mg/kg daily in two divided doses for another 2 weeks. Maintenance dosage, 5 to 15 mg/kg daily (maximum, 400 mg daily in two divided doses).

▶ **Adjunctive therapy for primary generalized tonic-clonic seizures.** *Adults and children age 12 and older:* Dosage is based on other antiepileptics taken. For patients also taking valproate: for weeks 1 and 2, give 25 mg P.O. q other day; for weeks 3 and 4, give 25 mg daily; then increase by 25 to 50 mg/day q 1 to 2 weeks to maintenance dosage of 100 to 400 mg daily in one or two divided doses or, 100 to 200 mg daily with valproate alone. For patients taking antiepileptics other than carbamazepine, phenobarbital, phenytoin, primidone, or valproate: for weeks 1 and 2, give 25 mg P.O. daily; for weeks 3 and 4, give 50 mg P.O. daily; then increase by 50 mg/day every 1 to 2 weeks to maintenance dosage of 225 to 375 mg daily in two divided doses. For patients taking carbamazepine, phenobarbital, phenytoin, or primidone, and not valproate: for weeks 1 and 2, give 50 mg P.O. daily; for weeks 3 and 4, give 100 mg daily in two divided doses; then in-

crease by 100 mg daily q 1 to 2 weeks to maintenance dosage of 300 to 500 mg daily in 2 divided dosages.
Children ages 2 to 12: Dosage is based on other antiepileptics taken. For patients also taking valproate: for weeks 1 and 2, give 0.15 mg/kg P.O. daily in one or two divided doses; for weeks 3 and 4, give 0.3 mg/kg daily in one or two divided doses; then increase to maintenance dosage of 1 to 5 mg/kg daily; maximum dosage, 200 mg daily, or 1 to 3 mg/kg daily with valproate alone. For patients taking antiepileptics other than carbamazepine, phenobarbital, phenytoin, primidone, or valproate: for weeks 1 and 2, give 0.3 mg/kg P.O. daily in one or two divided doses; for weeks 3 and 4, give 0.6 mg/kg daily in two divided doses; then increase to maintenance dosage of 4.5 to 7.5 mg/kg daily; maximum dosage, 300 mg daily. For patients taking carbamazepine, phenobarbital, phenytoin, or primidone, and not valproate: for weeks 1 and 2, give 0.6 mg/kg P.O. daily in two divided doses; for weeks 3 and 4, give 1.2 mg/kg daily in two divided doses; increase to maintenance dosage of 5 to 15 mg/kg daily in two divided doses; maximum dosage, 400 mg daily.

▶ **To convert patients from monotherapy with a hepatic enzyme-inducing anticonvulsant to lamotrigine.** *Adults and children age 16 and older:* Add 50 mg P.O. once daily to current therapy for 2 weeks, followed by 100 mg P.O. daily in two divided doses for 2 weeks. Then increase daily dosage by 100 mg q 1 to 2 weeks until maintenance dosage of 500 mg daily in two divided doses is reached. Gradually withdraw hepatic enzyme-inducing anticonvulsant in 20% decrements weekly for 4 weeks.

Adjust-a-dose: For patients with severe renal impairment or moderate to severe hepatic impairment, use lower maintenance dosage.

▶ **Bipolar disorder.** *Adults not taking carbamazepine (or other enzyme-inducing drugs) or valproic acid:* Target dose, 200 mg daily. Initially, 25 mg daily for weeks 1 and 2; then 50 mg daily for weeks 3 and 4; then 100 mg daily for week 5; then 200 mg daily for weeks 6 and 7.
Adults taking carbamazepine (or other enzyme-inducing drugs) and not taking valproic acid: Target dose, 400 mg/day. Initially, 50 mg daily for weeks 1 and 2; then 100 mg daily in divided doses for weeks 3 and 4; then 200 mg daily in divided doses for week 5; then 300 mg daily in divided doses for week 6; and up to 400 mg daily in divided doses for week 7.
Adults taking valproic acid: Target dosage is 100 mg/day. Initially, 25 mg q other day for weeks 1 and 2; then 25 mg daily for weeks 3 and 4; then 50 mg daily for week 5; then 100 mg daily for weeks 6 and 7.

Adjust-a-dose: If other psychotropic drugs are withdrawn following stabilization, adjust dosage.

Contraindications and cautions

- Contraindicated in patients hypersensitive to the drug or any of its components.
- Use cautiously in patients with renal, hepatic, or cardiac impairment.

Lifespan: In pregnant women, use only when benefits outweigh risks to the fetus. In breast-feeding women, use cautiously, it isn't known if drug appears in breast milk. In children, drug is only indicated as adjunctive therapy for the generalized seizures of Lennox-Gastaut syndrome. For other uses, safety and effectiveness haven't been established in children younger than age 16.

Adverse reactions

CNS: aggravated reaction, anxiety, *ataxia,* concentration disturbance, decreased memory, depression, *dizziness,* emotional lability, fever, *headache,* incoordination, insomnia, irritability, malaise, mind racing, ***seizures,*** sleep disorder, *somnolence,* speech disorder, ***suicide attempts,*** tremor, vertigo.
CV: palpitations.
EENT: *blurred vision, diplopia,* nystagmus, pharyngitis, rhinitis, vision abnormality.
GI: abdominal pain, anorexia, constipation, diarrhea, dry mouth, dyspepsia, *nausea, vomiting.*
GU: amenorrhea, dysmenorrhea, vaginitis.
Musculoskeletal: dysarthria, muscle spasm, neck pain.
Respiratory: cough, dyspnea.
Skin: acne, alopecia, pruritus, rash, ***Stevens-Johnson syndrome, toxic epidermal necrolysis.***
Other: chills, flulike syndrome, hot flushes, infection, tooth disorder.

Interactions

Drug-drug. *Acetaminophen:* May reduce lamotrigine level, decreasing therapeutic effects. Monitor patient.

Carbamazepine, oxcarbazepine, phenobarbital, phenytoin, primidone, rifamycins: May decrease lamotrigine steady-state level. Monitor patient closely for decreased effect.
Folate inhibitors (such as co-trimoxazole, methotrexate): May have additive effect because lamotrigine inhibits dihydrofolate reductase, an enzyme involved in folic acid synthesis. Monitor patient closely for adverse effects and toxicities.
Hormonal contraceptives, progestins: May reduce lamotrigine level. Adjust lamotrigine dosage if needed.
Valproic acid: May decrease lamotrigine clearance, which increases steady-state levels. Monitor patient closely for toxicity.
Drug-herb. *Evening primrose oil:* May lower the seizure threshold. Discourage use together.
Drug-lifestyle. *Sun exposure:* May cause photosensitivity reactions. Urge patient to avoid unprotected or prolonged exposure to sunlight.

Effects on lab test results

None reported.

Pharmacokinetics

Absorption: Rapid and complete with negligible first-pass metabolism.
Distribution: 55% protein-bound.
Metabolism: Mainly by glucuronic acid conjugation.
Excretion: Mainly in urine. *Half-life:* 14½ to 70¼ hours, depending on dosage schedule and use of other anticonvulsants.

Route	Onset	Peak	Duration
P.O.	Unknown	1½–4½ hr	Unknown

Action

Chemical effect: May inhibit release of glutamate and aspartate, excitatory neurotransmitters in the brain, through action at sodium channels.
Therapeutic effect: Prevents partial seizures, stabilizes mood.

Available forms

Tablets: 25 mg, 100 mg, 150 mg, 200 mg
Tablets (chewable dispersible): 2 mg, 5 mg, 25 mg

NURSING PROCESS

Assessment

- Obtain history of patient's disorder before starting therapy.
- Evaluate patient for reduction in frequency and duration of seizures after therapy begins. Check adjunct anticonvulsant level periodically.
- Monitor signs and symptoms of bipolar disorder and suicidal thoughts.
- Assess patient's and family's knowledge of drug therapy.

Nursing diagnoses

- Risk for trauma related to seizures
- Risk for impaired skin integrity related to dermatologic reactions
- Deficient knowledge related to drug therapy

Planning and implementation

- If drug is added to therapy that includes valproic acid, lower dosage.

ALERT: Don't abruptly stop giving the drug because doing so increases the risk of seizures and unstable mood. Taper drug over at least 2 weeks.
ALERT: Rash may be life-threatening. If one develops, stop giving the drug and immediately notify prescriber. Don't restart.
ALERT: Don't confuse Lamictal with Lamisil or Lomotil.

Patient teaching

- Inform patient that drug may cause rash. Combination therapy with valproic acid and lamotrigine is more likely to cause a serious rash. Tell patient to immediately report rash or signs or symptoms of hypersensitivity because they could be life-threatening.
- Instruct patient to avoid prolonged exposure to sunlight, use sunblock, and wear protective clothing to avoid photosensitivity.
- Warn patient not to engage in hazardous activity until the drug's CNS effects are known.

Evaluation

- Patient is seizure-free.
- Patient doesn't develop drug-induced skin reactions.
- Patient and family state understanding of drug therapy.

lansoprazole

(lan-soh-PRAY-zohl)

Prevacid, Prevacid I.V., Prevacid SoluTab

Pharmacologic class: proton-pump inhibitor
Therapeutic class: gastric antisecretory
Pregnancy risk category: B

Indications and dosages

▶ **Short-term therapy for active duodenal ulcer.** *Adults:* 15 mg P.O. daily for 4 weeks.

▶ **Maintenance of healed duodenal ulcers; maintenance of healing erosive esophagitis.** *Adults:* 15 mg P.O. daily.

▶ **Short-term therapy for erosive esophagitis.** *Adults:* 30 mg P.O. daily for up to 8 weeks. If healing doesn't occur, give additional 8 weeks of therapy. Maintenance dosage for healing is 15 mg P.O. daily.
Children ages 12 to 17: Give 30 mg P.O. once daily for up to 8 weeks.
Children ages 1 to 11 who weigh 30 kg (66 lb) or less: 15 mg P.O. daily for up to 12 weeks.
Children ages 1 to 11 who weigh more than 30 kg: 30 mg P.O. daily for up to 12 weeks.

▶ **Short-term therapy for erosive esophagitis when the patient isn't able to take oral drug.** *Adults:* 30 mg I.V. daily, over 30 minutes, for up to 7 days. As soon as the patient can take oral drug, switch to P.O. and continue for 6 to 8 weeks.

▶ **Short-term therapy for active benign gastric ulcer.** *Adults:* 30 mg P.O. daily for up to 8 weeks.

▶ ***Helicobacter pylori* eradication to reduce risk of duodenal ulcer recurrence.** *Adults:* For triple therapy, 30 mg P.O. lansoprazole with 500 mg P.O. clarithromycin and 1 g P.O. amoxicillin, each given q 12 hours for 14 days. For dual therapy, 30 mg P.O. lansoprazole with 1 g P.O. amoxicillin, each given q 8 hours for 14 days.

▶ **Long-term therapy for pathologic hypersecretory conditions, including Zollinger-Ellison syndrome.** *Adults:* Initially, 60 mg P.O. daily. Increase dosage as needed. If more than 120 mg daily, give in divided doses.

▶ **Short-term therapy for symptomatic gastroesophageal reflux disease.** *Adults:* 15 mg P.O. daily for up to 8 weeks.
Children ages 12 to 17: Give 15 mg P.O. daily for up to 8 weeks.
Children ages 1 to 11 who weigh 30 kg (66 lb) or less: 15 mg P.O. daily for up to 12 weeks.
Children ages 1 to 11 who weigh more than 30 kg: 30 mg P.O. daily for up to 12 weeks.

▶ **NSAID-related ulcer in patients who are continuing NSAIDs.** *Adults:* 30 mg P.O. daily for 8 weeks.

▶ **To reduce risk of NSAID-related ulcer in a patient who has a history of gastric ulcer and needs NSAIDs.** *Adults:* 15 mg P.O. daily for up to 12 weeks.

I.V. administration

- Reconstitute with 5 ml sterile water for injection only.
- Mix gently until the powder is dissolved.
- Infuse over 30 minutes using the provided 1.2 micron in-line filter, which will remove any precipitate that forms when reconstituted solution comes in contact with I.V. solutions.

⊗ **Incompatibilities**
Other I.V. drugs.

Contraindications and cautions

- Contraindicated in patients hypersensitive to the drug or any of its components.
- Drug isn't recommended as maintenance therapy for patients with active duodenal ulcers or erosive esophagitis.

Lifespan: In pregnant women, use only when benefits outweigh risks to the fetus. In breast-feeding women, don't use; it isn't known if drug appears in breast milk. In children younger than age 1, safety and effectiveness haven't been established.

Adverse reactions

GI: abdominal pain, diarrhea, nausea.

Interactions

Drug-drug. *Ampicillin esters, digoxin, iron salts, ketoconazole:* May interfere with absorption of these drugs. Monitor patient closely.
Sucralfate: May delay lansoprazole absorption. Give lansoprazole at least 30 minutes before sucralfate.
Theophylline: May slightly increase theophylline clearance. Use together cautiously. Adjust dosage, if needed, when lansoprazole is started or stopped.

Drug-herb. *Male fern:* May inactivate drug in alkaline environments. Discourage use together. *St. John's wort:* May increase risk of photosensitivity reactions. Advise patient to avoid unprotected or prolonged exposure to sunlight.
Drug-food. *Food:* May decrease absorption of drug when taken with meals. Take drug on an empty stomach, before meals.

Effects on lab test results

None reported.

Pharmacokinetics

Absorption: Rapid.
Distribution: 97% protein-bound.
Metabolism: Extensive, in liver.
Excretion: Mainly in feces, minimally in urine. *Half-life:* Less than 2 hours.

Route	Onset	Peak	Duration
P.O.	Unknown	2 hr	> 24 hr

Action

Chemical effect: Inhibits proton pump and binds to hydrogen or potassium adenosine triphosphatase, located at secretory surface of gastric parietal cells.
Therapeutic effect: Decreases gastric acid formation.

Available forms

Capsules (delayed-release): 15 mg, 30 mg
Injection: 30-mg single-use vial
Oral suspension (delayed-release): 15 mg/packet, 30 mg/packet
Tablets (delayed-release, orally disintegrating): 15 mg (contains 2.5 mg phenylalanine), 30 mg (contains 5.1 mg phenylalanine)

NURSING PROCESS

Assessment

- Assess patient's condition before starting therapy and regularly thereafter to monitor drug's effectiveness.
- Be alert for adverse reactions and drug interactions.
- Assess patient's and family's knowledge of drug therapy.

Nursing diagnoses

- Impaired tissue integrity related to underlying condition
- Ineffective health maintenance related to drug-induced adverse reactions
- Deficient knowledge related to drug therapy

Planning and implementation

ALERT: Orally disintegrating tablets contain phenylalanine. Assess patient for sensitivity before starting therapy.

- Give drug on an empty stomach.
- If giving by NG tube, mix contents of capsule with 40 ml of apple juice in a syringe and give within 3 to 5 minutes. Flush with additional apple juice to ensure entire dose is given and to maintain patency of the tube.
- If giving capsule to a patient who has difficulty swallowing, empty contents of capsule into about 2 oz (60 ml) of apple, cranberry, grape, orange, pineapple, prune, tomato, or vegetable juice, mix briefly, and use within 30 minutes. To ensure complete dose, rinse glass with two or more servings of juice and have patient drink immediately. Or mix contents of capsule with 1 tbs of applesauce, pudding, cottage cheese, yogurt, or strained pears and have patient swallow immediately. Tell him not to chew or crush granules.
- For the oral suspension, empty packet contents into 30 ml of water. Stir well and have patient drink immediately. Tell patient not to chew or crush the contents of the capsules or the suspension. Don't use with other liquids or food. If any material remains after drinking, add more water, stir, and have patient drink immediately.
- Place orally disintegrating tablets on the patient's tongue and allow to dissolve completely. Water isn't needed. If using NG tube or oral syringe, dissolve 15-mg tablet in 4 ml water or 30-mg tablet in 10 ml water.

ALERT: Don't crush drug or allow patient to chew it.

- If adverse reaction occurs, notify prescriber and provide supportive care.
- Adjust dosage in patients with severe liver disease.

Patient teaching

- Tell patient not to crush or chew drug and to take it before a meal.
- Explain how to mix drug with other liquids if patient has difficulty swallowing.
- Tell patient to allow orally disintegrating tablets to dissolve on tongue until the particles can be swallowed.

- Instruct patient to notify prescriber if any adverse reactions occur.

Evaluation

- Patient regains normal GI tissue integrity.
- Patient doesn't experience serious adverse reactions.
- Patient and family state understanding of drug therapy.

leflunomide

(leh-FLOO-noh-mighd)

Arava

Pharmacologic class: pyrimidine synthesis inhibitor
Therapeutic class: immunomodulator
Pregnancy risk category: X

Indications and dosages

▶ **Active rheumatoid arthritis, to reduce signs and symptoms, to retard structural damage based on X-ray evidence of erosions and joint space narrowing, to improve physical function.** *Adults:* 100 mg P.O. q 24 hours for 3 days followed by 20 mg (daily maximum) P.O. q 24 hours. If this dosage isn't tolerated, decrease to 10 mg daily.

Contraindications and cautions

- Contraindicated in patients hypersensitive to the drug or any of its components.
- Use cautiously in patients with hepatic insufficiency, hepatitis B or C, severe immunodeficiency, bone marrow dysplasia, or severe uncontrolled infections.
- Use cautiously in patients with renal insufficiency.

Lifespan: In pregnant and breast-feeding women, drug is contraindicated. In children, safety and effectiveness haven't been established. In men attempting to father children, drug isn't recommended.

Adverse reactions

CNS: anxiety, asthenia, depression, dizziness, fever, headache, insomnia, malaise, migraine, neuralgia, neuritis, paresthesia, sleep disorder, vertigo.
CV: angina pectoris, chest pain, *hypertension,* palpitations, peripheral edema, tachycardia, varicose veins, vasculitis, vasodilation.
EENT: blurred vision, cataracts, conjunctivitis, enlarged salivary gland, epistaxis, eye disorders, pharyngitis, rhinitis, sinusitis.
GI: abdominal pain, anorexia, cholelithiasis, colitis, constipation, *diarrhea,* dry mouth, dyspepsia, esophagitis, flatulence, gastritis, gastroenteritis, gingivitis, melena, mouth ulcer, nausea, oral candidiasis, stomatitis, taste perversion, vomiting.
GU: albuminuria, cystitis, dysuria, hematuria, menstrual disorder, pelvic pain, prostate disorder, urinary frequency, UTI, vaginal candidiasis.
Hematologic: anemia, hyperlipidemia.
Metabolic: ***diabetes mellitus,*** hyperglycemia, hyperthyroidism, hypokalemia, weight loss.
Musculoskeletal: arthralgia, arthrosis, back pain, bone necrosis, bone pain, bursitis, joint disorder, leg cramps, muscle cramps, myalgia, neck pain, synovitis, tendon rupture, tenosynovitis.
Respiratory: ***asthma,*** bronchitis, dyspnea, increased cough, lung disorders, pneumonia, *respiratory infection.*
Skin: acne, *alopecia,* contact dermatitis, dry skin, ecchymosis, eczema, fungal dermatitis, hair discoloration, hematoma, increased sweating, maculopapular rash, nail disorder, pruritus, *rash,* skin nodule, skin discoloration, skin disorder, subcutaneous nodule, skin ulcer.
Other: abscess, allergic reaction, cyst, flulike syndrome, hernia, herpes simplex, herpes zoster, injury or accident, pain, tooth disorder.

Interactions

Drug-drug. *Charcoal, cholestyramine:* May decrease leflunomide level. Sometimes used for this effect in overdose.
Live vaccines: May alter immune response. Avoid live vaccines during therapy, and remember leflunomide's long half-life when considering a live vaccine after therapy stops.
Methotrexate, other hepatotoxic drugs: May increase risk of hepatotoxicity. Monitor liver enzyme levels.
NSAIDs (diclofenac, ibuprofen): May increase NSAID level. Significance is unknown; monitor patient.
Rifampin: May increase active leflunomide metabolite level. Use together cautiously.

Tolbutamide: May increase tolbutamide levels. Significance is unknown; monitor patient.

Effects on lab test results

- May increase AST, ALT, glucose, lipid, T_4, and CK levels. May decrease potassium, TSH, and hemoglobin levels and hematocrit.

Pharmacokinetics

Absorption: 80%.
Distribution: Low. Extensively bound to albumin.
Metabolism: Main route unknown.
Excretion: Renal and biliary; 43% in urine, 48% in feces. *Half-life:* 15 to 18 days.

Route	Onset	Peak	Duration
P.O.	Unknown	6–12 hr	Unknown

Action

Chemical effect: Inhibits dihydroorotate dehydrogenase, an enzyme involved in pyrimidine synthesis, and is antiproliferative and anti-inflammatory.
Therapeutic effect: Reduces pain and inflammation related to rheumatoid arthritis.

Available forms

Tablets: 10 mg, 20 mg, 100 mg

NURSING PROCESS

Assessment

- Assess patient's condition before starting therapy, and regularly thereafter to monitor drug effectiveness.
- Be alert for adverse reactions and drug interactions.
- Monitor platelet and WBC counts, ALT and hemoglobin levels, and hematocrit, at baseline and at monthly intervals during the first 6 months; if stable, continue monitoring q 6 to 8 weeks. If used with methotrexate or other immunosuppressant, monitor patient's AST, ALT, and albumin levels monthly.

ALERT: Severe liver damage, sometimes fatal, may rarely occur. Most cases of severe liver damage occur within 6 months of therapy in a patient with multiple risk factors for hepatotoxicity (liver disease, other hepatotoxins).

- Monitor for overlapping hematologic toxicity when switching to another antirheumatic.
- Because of drug's long half-life, carefully observe patient after reducing dosage because level may take several weeks to decline.
- Assess patient's and family's knowledge of drug therapy.

Nursing diagnoses

- Ineffective health maintenance related to underlying disease
- Deficient knowledge related to drug therapy

Planning and implementation

- If ALT level increases to between two and three times the upper limit of normal (ULN), lower the dose to 10 mg daily. This may allow you to continue use under close monitoring. If ALT stays between two and three times ULN despite the lower dose, or if ALT level increases to more than three times ULN, stop giving the drug, give cholestyramine or charcoal, and monitor the patient closely. Give additional doses of cholestyramine or charcoal if needed.

ALERT: Drug can cause fetal harm when given during pregnancy. Stop giving the drug to a woman planning to become pregnant, and notify prescriber.

- Stop drug in a man who plans to father a child. Tell him to take 8 g cholestyramine P.O. t.i.d. for 11 days to remove drug. Check levels.
- If bone marrow suppression occurs, stop the drug and start cholestyramine or charcoal therapy.
- Some immunosuppressants, possibly including leflunomide, increase the risk of cancer, particularly lymphoproliferative disorders. Use drug only when benefits exceed risks.

Patient teaching

- Explain the need for frequent blood test monitoring.
- Instruct patient to use contraceptive measures during drug therapy and until drug is no longer active.
- If a patient suspects she is pregnant, advise her to immediately notify the prescriber.
- Advise breast-feeding woman not to breast-feed during therapy.
- Tell patient that he may continue taking aspirin, other NSAIDs, and low-dose corticosteroids, but that combined use of drug with antimalarials, I.M. or P.O. gold, penicillamine, azathioprine, or methotrexate hasn't been adequately studied. Instruct patient to review all drugs with prescriber before use.

Evaluation

- Patient's symptoms of rheumatoid arthritis improve.
- Patient and family state understanding of drug therapy.

leucovorin calcium (citrovorum factor, folinic acid)

(loo-koh-VOR-in KAL-see-um)

Pharmacologic class: formyl derivative (active reduced form of folic acid)
Therapeutic class: vitamin, antidote
Pregnancy risk category: C

Indications and dosages

▶ **Overdose of folic acid antagonist.** *Adults and children:* P.O., I.M., or I.V. dose equivalent to weight of antagonist given.

▶ **Rescue after high methotrexate dose given as cancer therapy.** *Adults and children:* 10 mg/m² P.O., I.M., or I.V. q 6 hours until methotrexate level falls below 5×10^{-8} M.

▶ **Megaloblastic anemia caused by congenital enzyme deficiency.** *Adults and children:* 3 to 6 mg I.M. daily; then 1 mg P.O. or I.M. daily for life.

▶ **Folate-deficient megaloblastic anemia.** *Adults and children:* Up to 1 mg P.O. or I.M. daily. Duration of therapy depends on hematologic response.

▶ **Hematologic toxicity caused by pyrimethamine or trimethoprim therapy.** *Adults and children:* 5 to 15 mg P.O. or I.M. daily.

▶ **Palliative treatment of advanced colorectal carcinoma.** *Adults:* 20 mg/m² I.V., followed by fluorouracil, for 5 consecutive days. Repeat q 4 weeks for two more courses; then q 4 to 5 weeks, if tolerated.

I.V. administration

- Give leucovorin I.V. to patients with GI toxicity (diarrhea, stomatitis, vomiting) when doses exceed 25 mg.
- When using powder for injection, reconstitute drug in 50-mg vial with 5 ml, 100 mg vial with 10 ml, or 350-mg vial with 17 ml of sterile water or bacteriostatic water for injection. When doses are greater than 10 mg/m² don't use diluents containing benzyl alcohol, especially in neonates.
- Don't give faster than 160 mg/minute because of the calcium concentration.
- Protect drug from light and heat, especially reconstituted parenteral forms.

⊗ **Incompatibilities**
Droperidol, fluorouracil, foscarnet, sodium bicarbonate.

Contraindications and cautions

- Contraindicated in patients with pernicious anemia and other megaloblastic anemias caused by lack of vitamin B_{12}.

Lifespan: In breast-feeding women, use cautiously; it's unknown if drug appears in breast milk. In neonates, injection form is contraindicated because it contains benzyl alcohol. In children, use cautiously because drug may increase risk of seizures.

Adverse reactions

Respiratory: ***bronchospasm.***
Skin: hypersensitivity reactions (erythema, pruritus, rash).

Interactions

Drug-drug. *Anticonvulsants:* May decrease anticonvulsant effectiveness. Monitor patient closely.
Fluorouracil: May enhance fluorouracil toxicity. Adjust fluorouracil dosage if needed.
Methotrexate: May decrease intrathecal methotrexate effectiveness. Avoid use together.

Effects on lab test results

None reported.

Pharmacokinetics

Absorption: Rapid after P.O. use.
Distribution: Throughout body; liver contains about one-half of total body folate stores.
Metabolism: In liver.
Excretion: By kidneys. *Half-life:* 6¼ hours.

Route	Onset	Peak	Duration
P.O.	20–30 min	2–3 hr	3–6 hr
I.V.	5 min	10 min	3–6 hr
I.M.	10–20 min	< 1 hr	3–6 hr

Action

Chemical effect: Readily converts to other folic acid derivatives.

Therapeutic effect: Raises folic acid level.

Available forms

Injection: 3 mg/ml in 1-ml ampule; 10 mg/ml in 5-ml vial

Powder for injection: 50-mg, 100-mg, and 350-mg vials for reconstitution

Tablets: 5 mg, 15 mg, 25 mg

NURSING PROCESS

Assessment

- Assess patient's condition before starting therapy and regularly thereafter to monitor drug effectiveness.
- Monitor creatinine level daily to detect renal dysfunction.
- Be alert for adverse reactions and drug interactions.
- Monitor patient for rash, wheezing, pruritus, and urticaria, which can signal drug allergy.
- Assess patient's and family's knowledge of drug therapy.

Nursing diagnoses

- Ineffective health maintenance related to underlying condition
- Deficient knowledge related to drug therapy

Planning and implementation

- Drug may mask diagnosis of pernicious anemia.
- Follow leucovorin rescue schedule and protocol closely to maximize therapeutic response.
- Don't give simultaneously with systemic methotrexate.

ALERT: Don't confuse leucovorin (folinic acid) with folic acid. To avoid confusion, don't refer to leucovorin as folinic acid.

Patient teaching

- Explain to patient reasons for drug therapy.

Evaluation

- Patient's condition improves.
- Patient and family state understanding of drug therapy.

leuprolide acetate

(loo-PROH-lighd AS-ih-tayt)

Eligard, Lucrin ◇, Lupron, Lupron Depot, Lupron Depot-Ped, Lupron Depot-3 Month, Lupron Depot-4 Month, Lupron for Pediatric Use, Viadur

Pharmacologic class: synthetic analogue of gonadotropin-releasing hormone

Therapeutic class: antineoplastic, luteinizing hormone-releasing hormone agonist

Pregnancy risk category: X

Indications and dosages

▶ **Advanced prostate cancer.** *Men:* 1 mg subcutaneously daily. Or 7.5 mg I.M. depot injection monthly. Or 7.5 mg Eligard subcutaneously once monthly. Or 22.5 mg I.M. q 3 months (84 days). Or 22.5 mg Eligard subcutaneously q 3 months. Or 30 mg I.M. depot injection q 4 months (16 weeks). Or 30 mg Eligard subcutaneously q 4 months. Or 45 mg Eligard subcutaneously q 6 months. Or 72 mg Viadur implant subcutaneously q 12 months.

▶ **Endometriosis.** *Women:* 3.75 mg I.M. as single injection once monthly. Or 11.25 mg I.M. q 3 months (depot injection only). Recommended duration of treatment is 6 months.

▶ **Central precocious puberty.** *Children:* Initially, 0.3 mg/kg (minimum, 7.5 mg) I.M. depot injection as a single injection q 4 weeks. Increase dosage in increments of 3.75 mg q 4 weeks, if needed. This will be considered the maintenance dosage. Or 50 mcg/kg subcutaneously (injection form) daily. If total down-regulation isn't achieved, increase dosage by 10 mcg/kg daily. This becomes the maintenance dosage. Stop drug before girls reach age 11 and before boys reach age 12.

▶ **Uterine leiomyomata (depot only).** *Women:* 3.75 mg I.M. monthly or one dose of 11.25 mg I.M. with iron therapy. Recommended duration of therapy is 3 months or less.

Contraindications and cautions

- Contraindicated in patients hypersensitive to drug, its components, or other gonadotropin-releasing hormone analogues and in women with undiagnosed vaginal bleeding. Viadur implant is contraindicated in women and children.

• Use cautiously in patients hypersensitive to benzyl alcohol.

Lifespan: In women, the 30-mg depot form is contraindicated. In pregnant and breast-feeding women, drug is contraindicated. In neonates, drug is contraindicated because it contains benzyl alcohol.

Adverse reactions

CNS: *depression,* dizziness, *headache, pain.*
CV: angina, ***arrhythmias, MI,*** *peripheral edema.*
GI: *nausea, vomiting.*
GU: impotence.
Musculoskeletal: *decreased bone density,* transient bone pain (during first week of therapy).
Respiratory: ***pulmonary embolism.***
Skin: skin reactions at injection site.
Other: decreased libido, gynecomastia, *hot flushes.*

Interactions

None significant.

Effects on lab test results

• May increase BUN, creatinine, bilirubin, alkaline phosphatase, LDH, glucose, uric acid, albumin, calcium, phosphorus, total cholesterol, LDL, and triglyceride levels. May decrease potassium, HDL, and hemoglobin levels and hematocrit.
• May increase WBC count. May decrease PT, PTT, RBC, and platelet counts.
• May give inaccurate reading of pituitary gonadotropic and gonadal functions during therapy and for up to 12 weeks afterwards.

Pharmacokinetics

Absorption: Rapid and complete after subcutaneous use; unknown for I.M. use.
Distribution: Unknown. About 7% to 15% protein-bound at therapeutic level.
Metabolism: Unknown.
Excretion: Unknown. *Half-life:* 3 hours.

Route	Onset	Peak	Duration
I.M., SubQ	Unknown	4 hr	1–3 mo
Implant	Unknown	4 hr	12 mo

Action

Chemical effect: Initially stimulates but then inhibits release of gonadotropin-releasing hormone, resulting in testosterone and estrogen suppression.
Therapeutic effect: Hinders prostatic cancer cell growth, eases signs and symptoms of endometriosis, and inhibits progression of puberty in children. Also decreases uterine and fibroid volume.

Available forms

Implant: 72 mg
Injection: 5 mg/ml in 2.8-ml multiple-dose vial
Microspheres for injection, lyophilized: 3.75 mg, 7.5 mg, 11.25 mg, 15 mg, 22.5 mg, 30 mg
Suspension for depot injection: 7.5 mg, 22.5 mg, 30 mg, 45 mg (single-use kit)

NURSING PROCESS

Assessment

• Assess patient's condition before starting therapy and regularly thereafter to monitor drug effectiveness.
• Be alert for adverse reactions.
• Assess patient's and family's knowledge of drug therapy.

Nursing diagnoses

• Ineffective health maintenance related to underlying condition
• Disturbed thought processes related to drug-induced depression
• Deficient knowledge related to drug therapy

Planning and implementation

ALERT: Never give drug by I.V. injection.
ALERT: Different products have specific mixing and administration instructions. Read the manufacturer's directions closely. When using the two-syringe mixing system, after connecting the syringes, inject the liquid contents from syringe A into the powder in syringe B. Mix product by pushing contents back and forth between syringes for about 45 seconds. (Shaking syringes won't provide adequate mixing.) The suspension will be colorless to pale yellow. The 7.5-mg suspension should be light tan to tan. Use immediately after mixing. Attach the needle provided in the kit and inject subcutaneously.
• Give once-monthly depot injection under medical supervision. Use supplied diluent to reconstitute. (Discard extra diluent.) Draw 1 ml into syringe with 22G needle. (When preparing

Lupron Depot-3 Month 22.5 mg, use a 23G or larger needle.) Withdraw 1.5 ml from ampule for the 3-month formulation. Inject into vial and shake well. Suspension will appear milky. Although suspension is stable for 24 hours after reconstitution, it doesn't contain a bacteriostatic agent. Use immediately.

- When using prefilled dual-chamber syringes, screw white plunger into end stopper until stopper begins to turn. Remove and discard tab around base of needle. Hold syringe upright and release diluent by slowly pushing plunger until first stopper is at blue line in middle of barrel. Gently shake syringe to form a uniform milky suspension. If particles adhere to stopper, tap syringe. Remove needle guard and advance plunger to expel air from syringe. Inject entire contents I.M. as for a normal injection.
- Drug is a nonsurgical alternative to orchiectomy or estrogen therapy for advanced prostate cancer.
- The 12-month subcutaneous implant is surgically placed in the upper inner arm.

ALERT: A fractional dose of drug formulated to be given q 3 months isn't equivalent to same dose of once-monthly formulation.

Patient teaching

- Before starting therapy in a child with central precocious puberty, make sure parents understand importance of continuous therapy.
- Carefully instruct patient who will give subcutaneous injection about proper administration technique, and advise him to use only syringes provided by manufacturer.
- Advise patient that if another syringe must be substituted, a low-dose insulin syringe (U-100, 0.5 ml) is acceptable.
- Advise patient to store drug at room temperature, protected from light and heat.
- Reassure patient with a history of undesirable effects from other endocrine therapies that this drug is much easier to tolerate. Tell patient that adverse effects are transient and will disappear after about 1 week.
- Warn patient that worsening of prostate cancer symptoms may occur when therapy starts.
- Instruct woman to have a bone-density evaluation before and after therapy. Recommend supplemental calcium to minimize bone loss.

Evaluation

- Patient exhibits improvement in underlying condition.
- Patient demonstrates pretherapy thought processes.
- Patient and family state understanding of drug therapy.

levalbuterol hydrochloride

(leev-al-BYOO-teh-rohl high-droh-KLOR-ighd)

Xopenex, Xopenex HFA

Pharmacologic class: $beta_2$ agonist
Therapeutic class: bronchodilator
Pregnancy risk category: C

Indications and dosages

▶ **To prevent or treat bronchospasm in patients with reversible obstructive airway disease.** *Adults and children age 12 and older:* 0.63 mg (3 ml) solution for inhalation by nebulizer t.i.d. q 6 to 8 hours. Patients with more severe asthma who don't respond adequately to 0.63-mg doses may benefit from 1.25 mg t.i.d. *Children ages 6 to 11:* Give 0.31 mg given t.i.d. by nebulizer. Maximum dosage 0.63 mg t.i.d.

▶ **Treatment of acute episode of bronchospasm or prevention of asthmatic symptoms.** *Adults and children age 4 and older:* 2 inhalations (90 mcg) q 4 to 6 hours. In some patients, 1 inhalation q 4 hours is sufficient.

Contraindications and cautions

- Contraindicated in patients hypersensitive to the drug or any of its components, or racemic albuterol.
- Use cautiously in patients with CV disorders, especially coronary insufficiency, hypertension, and arrhythmias. Also use cautiously in patients with seizure disorders, hyperthyroidism, or diabetes mellitus and in patients who are unusually responsive to sympathomimetic amines.

Lifespan: In pregnant women, use only when benefits outweigh risks to fetus. In breastfeeding women, use cautiously. In children younger than age 6 and patients age 65 and older, safety and effectiveness are unknown.

Adverse reactions

CNS: anxiety, dizziness, *headache,* migraine, nervousness, pain, tremor.
CV: tachycardia.
EENT: *rhinitis,* sinusitis, turbinate edema.
GI: dyspepsia.

L

Musculoskeletal: leg cramps.
Respiratory: ***asthma exacerbation, bronchospasm,*** increased cough.
Other: accidental injury, flulike syndrome, *viral infection.*

Interactions

Drug-drug. *Beta blockers:* May block pulmonary effect of drug and may cause severe bronchospasm. Don't use together. If drug is needed, a cardioselective beta blocker may be considered, but give it with caution.
Digoxin: May decrease digoxin level up to 22%. Monitor digoxin level, and monitor patient for loss of therapeutic effect.
Epinephrine, short-acting sympathomimetic aerosol bronchodilators: May increase adverse adrenergic effects. To avoid serious CV effects, use additional adrenergics with caution.
Loop and thiazide diuretics: May increase risk of ECG changes and hypokalemia. Use together cautiously; monitor cardiac condition and potassium level.
MAO inhibitors, tricyclic antidepressants: May increase levalbuterol action on the vascular system. Use caution when giving these drugs within 2 weeks of each other.

Effects on lab test results

None reported.

Pharmacokinetics

Absorption: Some.
Distribution: Unknown.
Metabolism: Unknown.
Excretion: Unknown. *Half-life:* 3¼ to 4 hours.

Route	Onset	Peak	Duration
Inhalation			
Solution	10–17 min	90 min	5–8 hr
Aerosol	Unknown	< 1 hr	Unknown

Action

Chemical effect: Activates $beta_2$ receptors on airway smooth muscle, which causes smooth muscle from trachea to terminal bronchioles to relax, relieving bronchospasm and reducing airway resistance. Inhibits the release of mediators from mast cells in the airway.
Therapeutic effect: Improves ventilation.

Available forms

Inhalation aerosol: 15 g containing 200 actuations
Solution for inhalation: 0.31 mg, 0.63 mg, or 1.25 mg in 3-ml vials

NURSING PROCESS

Assessment

- Obtain history of patient's underlying condition before starting therapy, and reassess regularly to monitor drug effectiveness.
- Make sure that patient has a thorough physical examination before starting drug therapy.
- Be alert for adverse reactions and drug interactions.
- Assess patient's and family's knowledge of drug therapy.

Nursing diagnoses

- Impaired gas exchange related to underlying respiratory condition
- Risk for injury related to drug-induced adverse reactions
- Deficient knowledge related to drug therapy

Planning and implementation

ALERT: Drug may produce life-threatening paradoxical bronchospasm. If this reaction occurs, immediately stop giving the drug and start alternative therapy.

- Rarely, drug may produce significant CV effects. If they occur, stop the drug.
- Compatibility, effectiveness, and safety of levalbuterol when mixed with other drugs in a nebulizer haven't been established.

Patient teaching

- Warn patient to stop taking the drug and notify prescriber if drug worsens breathing.
- Tell patient to call prescriber immediately if drug becomes less effective, if signs and symptoms worsen, or if drug is needed more often than usual.
- Urge patient not to increase the dose or frequency without consulting prescriber.
- Tell patient to prime the inhaler before first use or if it has not been used for more than 3 days. To prime inhaler, release 4 test sprays into the air away from the face.
- Tell patient to breathe as calmly, deeply, and evenly as possible until no more mist is formed in the nebulizer reservoir (5 to 15 minutes).

• Teach patient to correctly use and clean nebulizer unit.
• Tell patient that the drug's effects may last up to 8 hours.
• Urge patient to use other inhalations and antiasthma drugs only as directed while taking this drug.
• Tell woman to notify prescriber if she becomes pregnant or intends to breast-feed.
• Tell patient to keep unopened vials in foil pouch. Once the foil pouch is opened, use vials within 2 weeks. Inform patient that vials removed from the pouch should be protected from light and heat and used within 1 week.

Evaluation

• Patient's respiration improves.
• Patient doesn't experience injury from adverse reactions caused by drug.
• Patient and family state understanding of drug therapy.

levetiracetam

(lee-veh-tih-RACE-ah-tam)
Keppra

Pharmacologic class: pyrrolidine derivative
Therapeutic class: anticonvulsant
Pregnancy risk category: C

Indications and dosages

▶ **Adjunctive treatment of partial-onset seizures in epilepsy.** *Adults and adolescents 16 years and older:* Initially, 500 mg P.O. or I.V. b.i.d. Increase dosage 500 mg b.i.d., if needed, for seizure control at 2-week intervals to maximum, 1,500 mg b.i.d.
Children ages 4 to 16: Give 10 mg/kg P.O. b.i.d. Increase dosage by 10 mg/kg b.i.d. at 2-week intervals to recommended dose of 30 mg/kg b.i.d. If patient can't tolerate this dose, it may be reduced. Patients who weigh 20 kg or less should use the oral solution.
▶ **Adjunctive treatment of myoclonic seizures in juvenile myoclonic epilepsy.** *Adults and adolescents age 12 and older:* Initially, 500 mg P.O. b.i.d. Increase by 1,000 mg/day q 2 weeks to 3,000 mg daily.
Adjust-a-dose: For adults with renal impairment, if creatinine clearance is greater than 80 ml/minute, give 500 to 1,500 mg q 12 hours; if clearance is 50 to 80 ml/minute, give 500 to 1,000 mg q 12 hours; if clearance is 30 to 50 ml/minute, give 250 to 750 mg q 12 hours; if clearance is less than 30 ml/minute, give 250 to 500 mg q 12 hours. For dialysis patients, give 500 to 1,000 mg q 24 hours. Give one dose of 250 to 500 mg after dialysis.

I.V. administration

• Dilute drug before giving it.
• Dilute 500-mg, 1,000-mg, or 1,500-mg dose in 100 ml normal saline, D_5W, or lactated Ringer's injection, and infuse over 15 minutes.
• Drug is compatible with diazepam, lorazepam, and valproate sodium for 24 hours at a controlled room temperature.
⊗ **Incompatibilities**
None reported.

Contraindications and cautions

• Contraindicated in patients hypersensitive to the drug or any of its components.
• Use cautiously in immunocompromised patients and in those with poor renal function.
Lifespan: In breast-feeding women, use cautiously; it isn't known if the drug appears in breast milk. In children younger than age 4, drug isn't indicated. I.V. form should not be used for children. In elderly patients, use cautiously because of their greater risk of falls.

Adverse reactions

CNS: amnesia, anxiety, *asthenia,* ataxia, depression, dizziness, emotional lability, *headache,* hostility, nervousness, paresthesia, *somnolence,* vertigo.
EENT: diplopia, pharyngitis, rhinitis, sinusitis.
GI: anorexia.
Hematologic: ***leukopenia, neutropenia.***
Musculoskeletal: pain.
Respiratory: cough.
Other: infection.

Interactions

Drug-drug. *Antihistamines, benzodiazepines, opioids, tricyclic antidepressants, other drugs that cause drowsiness:* May lead to severe sedation. Avoid use together.
Carbamazepine, clozapine, and other drugs known to cause leukopenia or neutropenia: May increase the risk of infection. Monitor patient closely; monitor hematologic studies.

Drug-lifestyle. *Alcohol use:* Increases risk of severe sedation. Discourage use together.

Effects on lab test results

- May decrease WBC and neutrophil counts.

Pharmacokinetics

Absorption: Rapid. Level peaks in about 1 hour. When given with food, peak level is delayed by about 1½ hours and level will be slightly lower. Level reaches steady-state in about 2 days.
Distribution: Minimally protein-bound.
Metabolism: No active metabolites.
Excretion: About 66% of drug is unchanged by glomerular filtration and tubular reabsorption. *Half-life:* About 7 hours in patients with normal renal function.

Route	Onset	Peak	Duration
P.O., I.V.	1 hr	1 hr	12 hr

Action

Chemical effect: May inhibit kindling in hippocampus, preventing simultaneous neuronal firing that leads to seizures.
Therapeutic effect: Prevents seizures.

Available forms

Injection: 100 mg/ml in 5-ml single-use vials
Oral solution: 100 mg/ml
Tablets: 250 mg, 500 mg, 750 mg

NURSING PROCESS

Assessment

- Obtain history of patient's underlying condition before starting therapy, and reassess regularly to monitor drug effectiveness.
- Assess renal function before starting therapy.
- Monitor patient closely for dizziness, which may lead to falls.
- Assess patient's and family's knowledge of drug therapy.

Nursing diagnoses

- Risk for trauma related to seizures
- Risk for infection related to drug-induced leukopenia and neutropenia
- Deficient knowledge related to drug therapy

Planning and implementation

- Drug can be taken with or without food.
- Use drug only with other anticonvulsants. It isn't recommended for monotherapy.
- Taper drug to reduce the risk of seizures.

ALERT: Don't confuse Keppra with Kaletra.

Patient teaching

- Tell patient to use a calibrated device for measuring a dose of oral solution; a household spoon is inadequate.
- Warn patient that drug may cause dizziness and somnolence and to use extra care when rising to a sitting or standing position to avoid becoming dizzy or falling; also to avoid driving, bike riding or other activities that may be hazardous until drugs effects are known.
- Advise patient to call prescriber, but not to abruptly stop taking drug, if an adverse reaction occurs.
- Tell patient to take drug with other prescribed seizure drugs.
- Inform patient that drug can be taken with or without food.

Evaluation

- Patient is free from seizures.
- Patient doesn't develop infection.
- Patient and family state understanding of drug therapy.

levodopa

(lee-voh-DOH-puh)
Larodopa

Pharmacologic class: precursor of dopamine
Therapeutic class: antiparkinsonian
Pregnancy risk category: C

Indications and dosages

▶ **Idiopathic parkinsonism, postencephalitic parkinsonism, and symptomatic parkinsonism after carbon monoxide or manganese intoxication or with cerebral arteriosclerosis.** *Adults and children older than age 12:* Initially, 0.5 to 1 g P.O. daily divided into two or more doses with food; increase by no more than 0.75 g daily q 3 to 7 days until daily dosage of 3 to 6 g is reached. Maximum, 8 g daily. Adjust dosage carefully to patient requirements, tolerance, and response. Closely supervise higher dosages.

Contraindications and cautions

- Contraindicated in patients hypersensitive to the drug or any of its components, in those who have taken an MAO inhibitor within 14 days, and in those with acute angle-closure glaucoma, melanoma, or undiagnosed skin lesions.
- Use cautiously in patients with severe CV, renal, hepatic, or pulmonary disorders; peptic ulcer; psychiatric illness; MI with residual arrhythmias; bronchial asthma; emphysema; or endocrine disease.

Lifespan: In pregnant women, use cautiously; safety hasn't been established. In breastfeeding women, drug is contraindicated. In children age 12 and younger, safety and effectiveness haven't been established.

Adverse reactions

CNS: *abnormal movements (choreiform, dyskinetic, dystonic), aggressive behavior, anxiety, ataxia, bradykinetic episodes, delirium, dementia, disturbing dreams, euphoria, fatigue, hallucinations, involuntary grimacing and head movements, malaise, memory loss, mood changes, muscle twitching, myoclonic body jerks, nervousness, psychiatric disturbance,* ***seizures,*** *severe depression,* ***suicidal tendencies,*** *tremor.*
CV: cardiac irregularities, flushing, hypertension, *orthostatic hypotension,* phlebitis.
EENT: activation of latent Horner syndrome, *blepharospasm,* blurred vision, diplopia, mydriasis or miosis, nasal discharge, oculogyric crises, widening of palpebral fissures.
GI: *anorexia,* bitter taste, constipation, diarrhea, dry mouth, epigastric pain, excessive salivation, flatulence, *nausea, vomiting.*
GU: darkened urine, incontinence, priapism, urinary frequency, urine retention.
Hematologic: ***agranulocytosis,*** hemolytic anemia, ***leukopenia.***
Hepatic: ***hepatotoxicity.***
Metabolic: weight loss.
Respiratory: hiccups, hyperventilation.
Other: dark perspiration, excessive and inappropriate sexual behavior.

Interactions

Drug-drug. *Antacids:* May increase levodopa absorption. Give antacids 1 hour after levodopa.
Anticholinergics: May increase gastric deactivation and decrease intestinal absorption of levodopa. Avoid use together.
Benzodiazepines: May decrease levodopa's therapeutic value. Monitor patient closely.
Furazolidone, procarbazine: May increase risk of severe hypertension. Avoid use together.
Inhaled halogen anesthetics, sympathomimetics: May increase risk of arrhythmias. Monitor ECG and vital signs closely.
MAO inhibitors (phenelzine, tranylcypromine): May cause a hypertensive reaction. Don't use together.
Metoclopramide: May accelerate gastric emptying of levodopa. Give metoclopramide 1 hour after levodopa.
Papaverine, phenothiazines and other antipsychotics, phenytoin, rauwolfia alkaloids: May decrease levodopa effect. Use together cautiously.
Pyridoxine (vitamin B_6): May decrease the effectiveness of levodopa. Avoid use together. (Pyridoxine has little to no effect on the combination drug levodopa and carbidopa.)
Tricyclic antidepressants: May delay absorption and decrease bioavailability of levodopa. Hypertensive episodes have occurred. Monitor patient closely.
Drug-herb. *Kava:* May interfere with drug and with natural dopamine, worsening symptoms of Parkinson disease. Discourage use together.
Rauwolfia: May decrease effectiveness of levodopa. Discourage use together.
Drug-food. *Foods high in protein:* May decrease levodopa absorption. Don't give with high-protein foods.
Drug-lifestyle. *Cocaine:* May increase risk of arrhythmias. Inform patient of this interaction.

Effects on lab test results

- May increase BUN, ALT, AST, alkaline phosphatase, LDH, bilirubin, and uric acid levels. May decrease hemoglobin level and hematocrit.
- May decrease WBC and granulocyte counts.
- May falsely increase urine catecholamine level. May falsely decrease urine vanillylmandelic acid level. May cause false-positive Coombs test or tests for urine glucose with reagents that use copper sulfate. May cause false-negative results with tests that use glucose enzymatic methods. May cause false-positive or false-negative tests for urine ketones and urine phenylketonuria.

L

Pharmacokinetics

Absorption: Rapid, by active amino acid transport system, with 30% to 50% reaching general circulation.
Distribution: Wide to most body tissues but not CNS, which receives less than 1% of dose because of extensive metabolism in periphery.
Metabolism: 95% of levodopa is converted to dopamine.
Excretion: Mainly in urine. *Half-life:* 1 to 3 hours.

Route	Onset	Peak	Duration
P.O.	Unknown	1–3 hr	About 5 hr but varies greatly

Action

Chemical effect: May be decarboxylated to dopamine, countering dopamine depletion in extrapyramidal centers.
Therapeutic effect: Improves voluntary movement.

Available forms

Capsules: 100 mg, 250 mg, 500 mg
Tablets: 100 mg, 250 mg, 500 mg

NURSING PROCESS

Assessment

- Assess patient's condition before starting therapy and regularly thereafter to monitor drug effectiveness.
- Observe and monitor vital signs, especially during dosage adjustments.
- Test patient receiving long-term therapy regularly for diabetes and acromegaly; periodically monitor kidney, liver, and hematopoietic function.
- Assess mental status before initiation of treatment and periodically thereafter.
- Be alert for adverse reactions and drug interactions.
- Assess patient's and family's knowledge of drug therapy.

Nursing diagnoses

- Impaired physical mobility related to presence of parkinsonism
- Disturbed thought processes related to drug-induced adverse reactions
- Deficient knowledge related to drug therapy

Planning and implementation

- To minimize GI upset, give drug with food but not a high-protein meal, which can impair absorption and reduce effectiveness.
- In a patient undergoing surgery, continue drug as long as oral intake is permitted, usually until 6 to 24 hours before surgery. Resume drug as soon as patient can take oral drug.
- Protect drug from heat, light, and moisture. If preparation darkens, discard because it has lost potency.

ALERT: Muscle twitching and eyelid twitching may be early signs of drug overdose. Report signs immediately.

- Reestablish effectiveness of lower dose by not giving the drug for a period of time (called a drug holiday). Because the drug holiday may cause symptoms that resemble neuroleptic malignant syndrome, observe patient when drug is abruptly stopped or the dose is abruptly lowered.

Patient teaching

- Advise patient to take drug with food, but not with high-protein meals. If patient has trouble swallowing pills, tell him or family member to crush tablets and mix with applesauce or baby food.
- Teach patient and family that behavioral or thought changes may occur and to report symptoms promptly for evaluation.
- Warn patient and family not to increase dosage without prescriber's orders.
- Warn patient about dizziness and lightheadedness, especially at start of therapy. Tell patient to change positions slowly and dangle legs before getting out of bed. Elastic stockings may help control this reaction.
- Advise patient and family that multivitamin preparations, fortified cereals, and certain OTC drugs may contain pyridoxine (vitamin B_6), which can block effects of levodopa.
- Warn patient about risk of arrhythmias if he uses cocaine while taking drug.

Evaluation

- Patient has improved physical mobility.
- Patient maintains normal thought process.
- Patient and family state understanding of drug therapy.

levodopa and carbidopa

(lee-vuh-DOH-puh and kar-bih-DOH-puh)

Parcopa, Sinemet, Sinemet CR

Pharmacologic class: dopamine precursor and decarboxylase inhibitor combination
Therapeutic class: antiparkinsonian
Pregnancy risk category: C

Indications and dosages

▶ **Idiopathic Parkinson disease, postencephalitic parkinsonism, and symptomatic parkinsonism resulting from carbon monoxide or manganese intoxication.** *Adults:* 1 tablet of 100 mg levodopa and 25 mg carbidopa or 1 tablet of 100 mg levodopa and 10 mg carbidopa P.O. t.i.d. followed by increase of 1 tablet daily or q other day if needed.; maximum daily, 8 tablets. Substitute 250 mg levodopa and 25 mg carbidopa or 100 mg levodopa and 10 mg carbidopa tablets as required. Determine optimum daily dosage by carefully adjusting dosage for each patient. Patients taking conventional tablets may receive extended-release tablets; dosage is calculated on current levodopa intake. Initially, give extended-release tablets equal to 10% more levodopa per day, increase as needed and tolerated to 30% more levodopa per day. Give in divided doses at intervals of 4 to 8 hours.

Contraindications and cautions

- Contraindicated in patients hypersensitive to drugs or any of its components; in patients with acute angle-closure glaucoma, melanoma, or undiagnosed skin lesions; and within 14 days of MAO inhibitor therapy.
- Use cautiously in patients with severe CV, renal, hepatic, endocrine, or pulmonary disorders; history of peptic ulcer; psychiatric illness; MI with residual arrhythmias; bronchial asthma; emphysema; or well-controlled, chronic, open-angle glaucoma.

Lifespan: In pregnant women, use cautiously. In breast-feeding women, drug combination is contraindicated. In children, safety and effectiveness haven't been established.

Adverse reactions

CNS: *abnormal movements (choreiform, dyskinetic, dystonic),* anxiety, *ataxia,* bradykinetic episodes, delirium, dementia, disturbing dreams, euphoria, fatigue, hallucinations, *head movements, involuntary grimacing,* malaise, memory loss, muscle twitching, *myoclonic body jerks,* nervousness, psychiatric disturbances, ***severe depression, suicidal tendencies,*** tremors.
CV: ***cardiac irregularities,*** flushing, hypertension, orthostatic hypotension.
EENT: activation of latent Horner syndrome, *blepharospasm,* blurred vision, diplopia, excessive salivation, mydriasis or miosis, nasal discharge, oculogyric crises, widening of palpebral fissures.
GI: anorexia, bitter taste, dry mouth, nausea, vomiting, and weight loss at start of therapy; constipation; diarrhea; epigastric pain; flatulence.
GU: darkened urine, priapism, urinary frequency, urinary incontinence, urine retention.
Hematologic: hemolytic anemia.
Hepatic: ***hepatotoxicity.***
Respiratory: hiccups, hyperventilation.
Skin: dark perspiration, phlebitis.
Other: excessive and inappropriate sexual behavior.

L

Interactions

Drug-drug. *Antacids:* May increase absorption of levodopa components. Monitor patient closely.
Antihypertensives: May have additive hypotensive effects. Use together cautiously; monitor blood pressure.
Iron salts: May decrease bioavailability of levodopa and carbidopa. Give iron 1 hour before or 2 hours after giving levodopa and carbidopa.
MAO inhibitors: May increase risk of severe hypertension. Don't use together.
Papaverine, phenytoin: May antagonize antiparkinsonian. Avoid use together.
Phenothiazines, other antipsychotics: May antagonize antiparkinsonian. Use together cautiously; monitor for decreased effect.
Drug-herb. *Kava:* May interfere with action of levodopa and natural dopamine, worsening Parkinson symptoms. Discourage use together.
Octacosanol: May worsen dyskinesia. Discourage use together.
Drug-food. *Foods high in protein:* May decrease absorption of levodopa. Warn against taking drug with high-protein foods.

Effects on lab test results

- May decrease hemoglobin level and hematocrit.
- May decrease platelet, granulocyte, and WBC counts.
- May falsely increase levels of uric acid, urine ketones, urine catecholamines, and urine vanillylmandelic acid, depending on reagent and test method used.

Pharmacokinetics

Absorption: 40% to 70%.
Distribution: Wide to most body tissues, except CNS.
Metabolism: For carbidopa, not extensive. It inhibits levodopa, increasing its own absorption.
Excretion: 30% unchanged in urine within 24 hours. When given with carbidopa, amount of levodopa unchanged in urine is increased by about 6%. *Half-life:* 1 to 2 hours.

Route	Onset	Peak	Duration
P.O.			
Regular-release	Unknown	40 min	Unknown
Extended-release	Unknown	2½ hr	Unknown

Action

Chemical effect: Unknown for levodopa. May be decarboxylated to dopamine, countering depletion of striatal dopamine in extrapyramidal centers. Carbidopa inhibits peripheral decarboxylation of levodopa without affecting levodopa's metabolism within CNS, making more levodopa available to be decarboxylated to dopamine in brain.
Therapeutic effect: Improves voluntary movement.

Available forms

Tablets: carbidopa 10 mg with levodopa 100 mg (Sinemet 10-100), carbidopa 25 mg with levodopa 100 mg (Sinemet 25-100), carbidopa 25 mg with levodopa 250 mg (Sinemet 25-250)
Tablets (extended-release): carbidopa 25 mg with levodopa 100 mg, carbidopa 50 mg with levodopa 200 mg (Sinemet CR)
Tablets (orally disintegrating): carbidopa 10 mg with levodopa 100 mg, carbidopa 25 mg with levodopa 100 mg, carbidopa 25 mg with levodopa 250 mg

NURSING PROCESS

Assessment

- Assess patient's underlying condition before therapy and regularly thereafter. Therapeutic response usually follows each dose, disappears within 5 hours, and may vary considerably.
- Be alert for adverse reactions and drug interactions.

ALERT: Immediately report muscle twitching and blepharospasm, which may be early signs of drug overdose.

- Test patients receiving long-term therapy regularly for diabetes and acromegaly, and perform periodic tests of liver, renal, and hematopoietic function.
- Assess patient's and family's knowledge of drug therapy.

Nursing diagnoses

- Impaired physical mobility related to underlying parkinsonian syndrome
- Disturbed thought processes related to drug-induced CNS adverse reactions
- Deficient knowledge related to drug therapy

Planning and implementation

- If patient is being treated with levodopa only, stop that drug at least 8 hours before starting levodopa and carbidopa combination.
- Give drug with food to minimize adverse GI reactions.
- Adjust dosage according to patient's response and tolerance.
- If vital signs or mental condition change significantly, don't give drug. Notify the prescriber, and then lower the dose or stop giving the drug.
- Treat patient with open-angle glaucoma with caution. Monitor patient closely. Watch for change in intraocular pressure and arrange for periodic eye exams.

Patient teaching

- Caution patient and family not to increase dosage without consulting the prescriber.
- Warn patient of dizziness and orthostatic hypotension, especially at start of therapy. Tell patient to change positions slowly and to dangle legs before getting out of bed. Elastic stockings may control this adverse reaction.

• Teach patient and family that behavioral or thought changes may occur and to report symptoms promptly for evaluation.
• Instruct patient to report adverse reactions and therapeutic effects.
• Inform patient that pyridoxine (vitamin B_6) doesn't reverse beneficial effects of levodopa and carbidopa. Multivitamins can be taken without decreased drug effectiveness.

☑ Evaluation

• Patient exhibits improved mobility with reduction of muscular rigidity and tremor.
• Patient remains mentally alert.
• Patient and family state understanding of drug therapy.

levodopa, carbidopa, and entacapone

(lee-vuh-DOH-puh, kar-bih-DOH-puh, and en-TAH-kah-pohn)
Stalevo 50, Stalevo 100, Stalevo 150

Pharmacologic class: dopamine precursor, decarboxylase inhibitor, and catechol-O-methyltransferase (COMT) inhibitor
Therapeutic class: antiparkinsonian
Pregnancy risk category: C

Indications and dosages

▶ **Idiopathic parkinsonism.** *Adults:* Individualize and carefully adjust the optimum daily dosage according to response. For maintenance therapy, reduce the total daily dosage by either decreasing the strength of this drug or by decreasing the frequency by extending the time between doses. When more levodopa is needed, give the next higher strength of this drug or increase the frequency to maximum, eight doses daily without exceeding the maximum daily dosage.

Contraindications and cautions

• Contraindicated in patients hypersensitive to drug or any of its components and in patients with angle-closure glaucoma, suspicious undiagnosed skin lesions, or a history of melanoma. Also contraindicated within 14 days of MAO inhibitor therapy. If the intraocular pressure is well controlled, patients with chronic open-angle glaucoma may use drug.
• Use cautiously in patients with liver, renal, or endocrine disease or biliary obstruction. Also use cautiously in patients with past or current psychosis, severe CV or pulmonary disease, bronchial asthma, or history of MI with residual arrhythmias.
Lifespan: In pregnant women, use only if benefits outweigh risks to the fetus. In breast-feeding women, use cautiously. In children, safety and effectiveness haven't been established.

Adverse reactions

CNS: agitation, anxiety, asthenia, dizziness, *dyskinesia,* fatigue, hallucinations, *hyperkinesia,* hypokinesia, ***neuroleptic malignant syndrome,*** somnolence, syncope.
CV: chest pain, hypotension.
GI: abdominal pain, constipation, *diarrhea,* dry mouth, dyspepsia, flatulence, gastritis, gastrointestinal disorder, *nausea,* taste disorder, vomiting.
GU: ***nephrotoxicity,*** urine discoloration.
Hematologic: ***agranulocytosis,*** anemia, ***leukopenia, thrombocytopenia.***
Musculoskeletal: back pain.
Respiratory: dyspnea.
Skin: sweating.
Other: bacterial infection.

Interactions

Drug-drug. *Antihypertensives:* May cause postural hypotension. Adjust antihypertensive dosage, if needed.
Dopamine D2-receptor antagonists (such as butyrophenones, isoniazid, metoclopramide, phenothiazines, and risperidone): May reduce levodopa effects. Avoid use together.
Drugs metabolized by COMT, such as alpha-methyldopa, apomorphine, bitolterol, dobutamine, dopamine, epinephrine, isoetharine, isoproterenol, and norepinephrine: May increase heart rate, arrhythmias, and excessive changes in blood pressure. Use together cautiously.
Drugs that interfere with biliary excretion, glucuronidation, and intestinal beta-glucuronidase, including cholestyramine, probenecid, and some antibiotics (ampicillin, chloramphenicol, erythromycin, rifampicin): May interfere with entacapone excretion. Use together cautiously.

L

Hydantoin, papaverine: May reduce levodopa effects. Avoid use together.
Iron salts: May reduce the bioavailability of drug. Adjust dosage if needed.
Metoclopramide: May increase bioavailability of carbidopa and levodopa by increasing gastric emptying. Adjust dosage if needed.
Nonselective MAO inhibitors: May cause a hypertensive reaction. Don't use within 14 days of each other.
Selegiline: May cause severe hypotension. Avoid use together.
Tricyclic antidepressants: May cause hypertension and dyskinesia. Use together cautiously.
Drug-food. *Foods high in protein, such as legumes, liquid protein shakes, and red meat:* May delay and reduce the absorption of levodopa. Give drug on an empty stomach.

Effects on lab test results

- May increase growth hormone level. May decrease prolactin level. May increase or decrease BUN and bilirubin levels.
- May increase liver function test values.
- May cause a false-positive Coombs test. May cause a false-positive reaction for urinary ketone bodies when using a test tape.

Pharmacokinetics

Absorption: Varies. Carbidopa level peaks within 2½ to 3½ hours. Levodopa level peaks in 1 to 1½ hours. Entacapone level peaks within 1½ hours.
Distribution: Levodopa and carbidopa are minimally protein-bound. Entacapone is 98% bound to albumin.
Metabolism: Carbidopa is metabolized to two main metabolites. Levodopa is extensively metabolized to various metabolites. Entacapone is almost completely metabolized.
Excretion: Carbidopa, primarily in urine unchanged; entacapone, 10% in urine, 90% in feces; levodopa, unknown. *Half-life:* 1½ to 2 hours carbidopa, 1 to 5 hours levodopa, and 1 to 4 hours entacapone.

Route	Onset	Peak	Duration
P.O.	< 1 hr	1–1½ hr	Unknown

Action

Chemical effect: Levodopa, a dopamine precursor, converts to dopamine in the brain. Carbidopa inhibits the decarboxylation of peripheral levodopa. When given with levodopa, carbidopa permits more intact levodopa to be transported into the brain. Entacapone is a selective and reversible inhibitor of COMT.
Therapeutic effect: Decreases symptoms of Parkinson disease.

Available forms

Tablets: 12.5 mg carbidopa, 50 mg levodopa, and 200 mg entacapone (Stalevo 50); 25 mg carbidopa, 100 mg levodopa, and 200 mg entacapone (Stalevo 100); 37.5 mg carbidopa, 150 mg levodopa, and 200 mg entacapone (Stalevo 150)

NURSING PROCESS

Assessment

- Periodically evaluate hepatic, hematopoietic, CV, and renal function.
- Monitor patient for mental disturbances such as hallucinations or depression with suicidal tendencies.
- Be alert for adverse reactions and interactions.
- Assess patient's and family's knowledge of drug therapy.

Nursing diagnoses

- Impaired physical mobility related to underlying parkinsonism
- Risk for injury related to drug-induced adverse reactions
- Deficient knowledge related to drug therapy

Planning and implementation

- Patients taking 200-mg entacapone tablet with each dose of standard-release levodopa and carbidopa can be switched to the corresponding strength of this drug containing the same amount of levodopa and carbidopa.
- Patients who experience signs and symptoms of end-of-dose "wearing off" on standard-release levodopa and carbidopa and have a history of moderate or severe dyskinesia, or take more than 600 mg of levodopa per day are likely to require a reduction in daily levodopa dose when entacapone is added. Adjust dosage with levodopa and carbidopa (1:4 ratio) and entacapone, then transfer to a corresponding dose of this drug once the patient is stabilized.
- Don't cut or break tablets.
- If dyskinesia occurs, reduce dosage.

ALERT: If abruptly reducing or stopping drug, especially in a patient also taking an antipsychotic, observe him carefully for a syndrome resembling neuroleptic malignant syndrome: elevated temperature, muscle rigidity, involuntary movements, altered consciousness, confusion, tachycardia, tachypnea, sweating, hypertension or hypotension, leukocytosis, myoglobinuria, and increased myoglobin level.

ALERT: Check for overdose by monitoring respiratory, renal, and CV functions. Use supportive measures along with repeated doses of charcoal over time. Also give I.V. fluids and ensure adequate airway.

Patient teaching

- Advise patient to take drug on an empty stomach preferably, or at least not with high-protein meals or drinks.
- Tell patient to take drug exactly as prescribed.
- Tell patient not to cut or break tablets.
- Warn patient of adverse reactions, such as hallucinations, diarrhea, nausea, and discolored urine, and instruct him to notify prescriber if they occur.
- Instruct patient to notify prescriber of any and all drugs taken to prevent any drug interactions.

Evaluation

- Patient has improved physical mobility.
- Patient doesn't suffer any injury from adverse reactions.
- Patient and family state understanding of drug therapy.

levofloxacin

(lee-voh-FLOCKS-uh-sihn)

Levaquin

Pharmacologic class: fluorinated carboxyquinolone
Therapeutic class: broad-spectrum antibiotic
Pregnancy risk category: C

Indications and dosages

▶ **Acute bacterial sinusitis caused by susceptible strains of *Streptococcus pneumoniae, Moraxella catarrhalis,* or *Haemophilus influenzae.*** *Adults:* 500 mg P.O. or I.V. daily for 10 to 14 days; or, 750 mg P.O. or I.V. daily for 5 days.

▶ **Acute bacterial exacerbation of chronic bronchitis caused by *Staphylococcus aureus, S. pneumoniae, M. catarrhalis,* or *H. influenzae* or *parainfluenzae.*** *Adults:* 500 mg P.O. or I.V. daily for 7 days.

▶ **Community-acquired pneumonia caused by *S. pneumoniae* resistant to two or more of the following antibiotics: penicillin, second-generation cephalosporins, macrolides, tetracyclines, trimethoprim, and sulfamethoxazole; or by *S. aureus, M. catarrhalis, H. influenzae, H. parainfluenzae, Klebsiella pneumoniae, Chlamydia pneumoniae, Legionella pneumophila, Mycoplasma pneumoniae,* or *S. pneumoniae.*** *Adults:* 500 mg P.O. or I.V. daily for 7 to 14 days. Or, 750 mg P.O. or I.V. once daily for 5 days (not for multidrug-resistant *S. pneumoniae*).

▶ **Mild to moderate skin and skin-structure infections caused by *S. aureus* or *Streptococcus pyogenes.*** *Adults:* 500 mg P.O. or I.V. daily for 7 to 10 days.

▶ **Chronic bacterial prostatitis caused by *E. coli, E. faecalis,* or *Staphylococcus epidermidis.*** *Adults:* 500 mg P.O. or I.V. daily for 28 days.

▶ **Prevention of inhalation anthrax following confirmed or suspected exposure to *Bacillus anthracis.*** *Adults:* 500 mg I.V. or P.O. q 24 hours for 60 days.

Adjust-a-dose: For patients with renal impairment, if creatinine clearance is 20 to 49 ml/minute, give initial dose of 500 mg and then 250 mg once daily; or (if not treating multidrug-resistant *S. pneumoniae*), give 750 mg initially and then 750 mg q 48 hours. If clearance is 10 to 19 ml/minute, initial dose is 500 mg and then 250 mg q 48 hours; or give 750 mg initially and then 500 mg q 48 hours. For patients on hemodialysis or chronic ambulatory peritoneal dialysis, give initial dose of 500 mg and then 250 mg q 48 hours; or give 750 mg initially and then 500 mg q 48 hours.

▶ **Complicated skin and skin structure infections caused by methicillin-sensitive *S. aureus, E. faecalis, S. pyogenes, P. mirabilis;* nosocomial pneumonia caused by methicillin-susceptible *S. aureus, P. aeruginosa, Serratia marcescens, E. coli, K. pneumoniae, H. influenzae,* or *S. pneumoniae.*** *Adults:* 750 mg P.O or I.V. daily for 7 to 14 days.

Adjust-a-dose: For patients with renal impairment, if creatinine clearance is 20 to 49 ml/

L

minute, give 750 mg initially and then 750 mg q 48 hours. If clearance is 10 to 19 ml/minute or patient is on hemodialysis or chronic ambulatory peritoneal dialysis, give 750 mg initially and then 500 mg q 48 hours.

▶ **Mild to moderate UTI caused by *Enterococcus faecalis, Enterobacter cloacae, E. coli, K. pneumoniae, Proteus mirabilis,* or *Pseudomonas aeruginosa.*** *Adults:* 250 mg P.O. or I.V. daily for 10 days.

▶ **Mild to moderate acute pyelonephritis caused by *E. coli.*** *Adults:* 250 mg P.O. or I.V. daily for 10 days.

Adjust-a-dose: For patients with renal impairment, if creatinine clearance is 10 to 19 ml/minute, give 250 mg initially and then 250 mg q 48 hours.

▶ **Mild to moderate uncomplicated UTI caused by *Escherichia coli, K. pneumoniae,* or *Staphylococcus saprophyticus.*** *Adults:* 250 mg P.O. daily for 3 days.

▶ **Traveler's diarrhea‡.** *Adults:* 500 mg P.O. as a single dose with loperamide hydrochloride.

▶ **To prevent traveler's diarrhea‡.** *Adults:* 500 mg P.O. daily during period of risk, for up to 3 weeks.

▶ **Uncomplicated cervical, urethral, or rectal gonorrhea‡.** *Adults and adolescents:* 250 mg P.O. as a single dose.

▶ **Disseminated gonococcal infection‡.** *Adults and adolescents:* 250 mg I.V. daily and continue for 24 to 48 hours after improvement begins. Switch to 500 mg P.O. daily to complete at least 1 week of therapy.

▶ **Nongonococcal urethritis; urogenital chlamydial infections‡.** *Adults and adolescents:* 500 mg P.O. daily for 7 days.

▶ **Acute pelvic inflammatory disease‡.** *Adults and adolescents:* 500 mg I.V. daily with or without metronidazole 500 mg q 8 hours. Stop parenteral drug 24 hours after improvement; then begin 100 mg P.O. b.i.d. of doxycycline to complete 14 days of therapy. Or give 500 mg P.O. levofloxacin daily for 14 days with or without metronidazole 500 mg b.i.d. for 14 days.

I.V. administration

- Dilute in single-use vials with D_5W or normal saline solution for injection to yield 5 mg/ml.
- Make sure reconstituted solution is clear, slightly yellow, and free of particulates.
- Give only by I.V. infusion over 60 minutes for 500 mg or 90 minutes for 750 mg.
- Diluted solution is stable for 72 hours at room temperature, 14 days when refrigerated in plastic containers, and 6 months when frozen. Thaw at room temperature or in refrigerator.

⊗ **Incompatibilities**

Mannitol 20%, multivalent cations (such as magnesium), sodium bicarbonate 5%. Don't mix drug with other drugs.

Contraindications and cautions

- Contraindicated in patients hypersensitive to the drug, any of its components, or other fluoroquinolones.

Lifespan: In pregnant women, use only when benefits outweigh risks to fetus. Breast-feeding women should either stop breast-feeding or use another drug. In children, safety and effectiveness haven't been established. In elderly patients with renal impairment, adjust dosage.

Adverse reactions

CNS: dizziness, ***encephalopathy,*** headache, insomnia, pain, paresthesia, ***seizures.***
CV: abnormal ECG, chest pain, palpitations, vasodilation.
GI: abdominal pain, constipation, diarrhea, dyspepsia, flatulence, nausea, ***pseudomembranous colitis,*** vomiting.
GU: vaginitis.
Hematologic: eosinophilia, hemolytic anemia, ***lymphocytopenia.***
Metabolic: ***hypoglycemia.***
Musculoskeletal: back pain, tendon rupture.
Respiratory: allergic pneumonitis.
Skin: ***erythema multiforme,*** photosensitivity reactions, pruritus, rash, ***Stevens-Johnson syndrome.***
Other: ***anaphylaxis,*** hypersensitivity reactions, ***multisystem organ failure.***

Interactions

Drug-drug. *Aluminum hydroxide, aluminum-magnesium hydroxide, calcium carbonate, magnesium hydroxide:* May decrease levofloxacin effects. Give antacid at least 6 hours before or 2 hours after levofloxacin.
Antidiabetics: May alter glucose level. Monitor it closely.
Iron salts: May decrease levofloxacin absorption, reducing anti-infective response. Give at least 2 hours apart.

NSAIDs: May increase CNS stimulation. Monitor patient for seizures.
Sucralfate, zinc-containing products: May interfere with GI absorption of levofloxacin. Give at least 2 hours apart.
Theophylline: May decrease theophylline clearance with some fluoroquinolones. Monitor theophylline levels.
Warfarin: May increase anticoagulant effects. Monitor PT and INR closely.
Drug-lifestyle. *Sun exposure:* May cause photosensitivity reactions. Urge patient to avoid unprotected or prolonged exposure to sunlight.

Effects on lab test results

- May decrease glucose and hemoglobin levels and hematocrit.
- May increase eosinophil count. May decrease WBC and lymphocyte counts.
- May cause false-positive opiate assay results.

Pharmacokinetics

Absorption: Rapid and complete.
Distribution: Wide.
Metabolism: Limited.
Excretion: Mainly unchanged in urine. *Half-life:* About 6 to 8 hours.

Route	Onset	Peak	Duration
P.O.	Unknown	1–2 hr	30–36 hr
I.V.	Immediate	1–1½ hr	30–36 hr

Action

Chemical effect: Inhibits bacterial DNA gyrase and prevents DNA replication, transcription, repair, and recombination in susceptible bacteria.
Therapeutic effect: Kills susceptible bacteria.

Available forms

Infusion (premixed): 250 mg in 50 ml D_5W, 500 mg in 100 ml D_5W, 750 mg in 150 ml D_5W (5 mg/ml)
Oral solution: 25 mg/ml
Single-use vials: 500 mg, 750 mg (25 mg/ml)
Tablets: 250 mg, 500 mg, 750 mg

NURSING PROCESS

Assessment

- Obtain specimen for culture and sensitivity tests before starting therapy and as needed to detect bacterial resistance. Therapy may begin pending results.
- Obtain history of seizure disorders or other CNS diseases, such as cerebral arteriosclerosis, before starting therapy.
- Monitor glucose level and renal, hepatic, and hematopoietic blood studies.
- Assess patient's and family's knowledge of drug therapy.

Nursing diagnoses

- Risk for infection related to presence of bacteria susceptible to drug
- Risk for deficient fluid volume related to drug-induced adverse GI reactions
- Deficient knowledge related to drug therapy

Planning and implementation

- Give oral drugs with plenty of fluids.
- Oral solution should be taken 1 hour before or 2 hours after eating.
- P.O. and I.V. dosages are interchangeable.
- Oral solution is as effective as tablet form and is flexible, which is helpful for patients with renal impairment.

ALERT: If *P. aeruginosa* is or is suspected to be the cause, give combination therapy with an antipseudomonal beta-lactam.

- Treat acute hypersensitivity reactions with epinephrine, oxygen, I.V. fluids, antihistamines, corticosteroids, pressor amines, and airway management.
- If patient has symptoms of excessive CNS stimulation (restlessness, tremor, confusion, hallucinations), stop drug and notify prescriber. Take seizure precautions.
- Most antibacterials can cause pseudomembranous colitis. If diarrhea occurs, notify prescriber. If symptoms are severe or unrelieved by appropriate treatment, stop giving the drug.

Patient teaching

- Tell patient to take drug as prescribed, even if symptoms resolve.
- Advise patient to take drug with plenty of fluids and to avoid antacids, sucralfate, and products containing iron or zinc for at least 2 hours before and after each dose.
- Warn patient to avoid hazardous tasks until the drug's CNS effects are known.
- Advise patient to avoid excessive sunlight, use sunblock, and wear protective clothing when outdoors.

• Instruct patient to stop taking the drug and notify prescriber if rash or other signs or symptoms of hypersensitivity develop.
• Tell patient to notify prescriber if he experiences pain or inflammation; tendon rupture can occur with drug.
• Instruct diabetic patient to monitor glucose level and notify prescriber if a hypoglycemic reaction occurs; may need to stop drug.
• Instruct patient to notify prescriber about loose stools or diarrhea.

Evaluation

• Patient is free from infection after drug therapy.
• Patient maintains adequate hydration throughout drug therapy.
• Patient and family state understanding of drug therapy.

levothyroxine sodium (T_4, L-thyroxine sodium)

(lee-voh-thigh-ROKS-een SOH-dee-um)

Eltroxin ♦, Levo-T, Levothroid, Levoxine, Levoxyl, Oroxine ◇, Synthroid, Thyro-Tabs, Unithroid

Pharmacologic class: thyroid hormone
Therapeutic class: thyroid hormone replacement
Pregnancy risk category: A

Indications and dosages

▶ **Myxedema coma.** *Adults:* 300 to 500 mcg I.V., followed by parenteral maintenance dosage of 75 to 100 mcg I.V. daily. Switch patient to oral maintenance as soon as possible.

▶ **Thyroid hormone replacement.** *Adults:* Initially, 25 to 50 mcg P.O. daily; increase by 25 mcg P.O. q 4 to 8 weeks until desired response occurs. Maintenance dosage is 75 to 200 mcg P.O. daily.
Children older than age 12: More than 150 mcg or 2 to 3 mcg/kg P.O. daily.
Children ages 6 to 12: Give 100 to 150 mcg or 4 to 5 mcg/kg P.O. daily.
Children ages 1 to 5: Give 75 to 100 mcg or 5 to 6 mcg/kg P.O. daily.
Children ages 6 months to 1 year: Give 50 to 75 mcg or 6 to 8 mcg/kg P.O. daily.
Children younger than age 6 months: Give 25 to 50 mcg or 8 to 10 mcg/kg P.O. daily.
Patients older than age 65: Give 2.5 to 50 mcg P.O. daily; increase by 12.5 to 25 mcg q 6 to 8 weeks, depending on response.

I.V. administration

• Don't confuse mg with mcg dosage (1 mg = 1,000 mcg).
• Initial I.V. dose is about half the previously established oral dose of tablets when used for maintenance of euthyroid state.
• Prepare dose immediately before injection. Dilute powder for injection with 5 ml of normal saline solution for injection or bacteriostatic saline solution injection with benzyl alcohol to 200- or 500-mcg vial; don't use other diluents. Resulting solutions contain 40 or 100 mcg/ml, respectively.
• Inject into vein over 1 to 2 minutes.
• Monitor blood pressure and heart rate closely. High initial dosage is usually tolerated by patients in myxedema coma. Normal levels of T_4 occur within 24 hours, followed by a threefold increase in T_3 in 3 days.

⊗ **Incompatibilities**
Other I.V. solutions.

Contraindications and cautions

• Contraindicated in patients hypersensitive to the drug or any of its components, and in patients with acute MI uncomplicated by hypothyroidism, untreated thyrotoxicosis, or uncorrected adrenal insufficiency.
• Use cautiously in patients with angina pectoris, hypertension, other CV disorders, renal insufficiency, or ischemia. Also use cautiously in patients with diabetes mellitus, diabetes insipidus, myxedema, or dysphagia.
• Use cautiously in patients with arteriosclerosis. Rapid replacement in these patients may precipitate angina, coronary occlusion, or stroke.
Lifespan: In breast-feeding women, use cautiously; it's unknown if the drug appears in breast milk. Children typically need a higher dose than adults. Adults older than age 60 typically need a lower dose than younger adults.

Adverse reactions

CNS: fever, headache, *insomnia, nervousness, tremor.*

CV: angina pectoris, ***arrhythmias, cardiac arrest,*** hypertension, palpitations, tachycardia.
GI: appetite change; choking, gagging, or dysphagia, particularly when not taken with fluids; diarrhea; nausea.
GU: menstrual irregularities.
Metabolic: weight loss.
Musculoskeletal: leg cramps.
Skin: diaphoresis.
Other: heat intolerance.

Interactions

Drug-drug. *Cholestyramine, colestipol:* May impair levothyroxine absorption. Separate doses by 4 to 5 hours.
Insulin, oral antidiabetics: May increase glucose level. Monitor glucose level when starting or changing dosage, and adjust dosage if needed.
I.V. phenytoin: May release free thyroid. Monitor patient for tachycardia.
Oral anticoagulants: May increase PT. Decrease anticoagulants by about one-third when initiating thyroid replacement therapy, monitor PT and INR, and adjust dosage to desired range, if needed.
Sympathomimetics (such as epinephrine): May increase risk of coronary insufficiency. Monitor patient closely.

Effects on lab test results

- May alter results of radioactive iodine uptake studies.

Pharmacokinetics

Absorption: Good.
Distribution: Wide. 99% protein-bound.
Metabolism: Mainly in liver, kidneys, and intestines.
Excretion: 20% to 40% in feces. *Half-life:* 3 to 4 days in hyperthyroidism, 9 to 10 days in hypothyroidism.

Route	Onset	Peak	Duration
P.O. I.V., I.M.	24 hr	Unknown	Unknown

Action

Chemical effect: Not fully defined; stimulates metabolism by accelerating cellular oxidation.
Therapeutic effect: Raises thyroid hormone levels in body.

Available forms

Powder for injection: 200 mcg/vial, 500 mcg/vial
Tablets: 0.025 mg, 0.05 mg, 0.075 mg, 0.088 mg, 0.1 mg, 0.112 mg, 0.125 mg, 0.137 mg, 0.15 mg, 0.175 mg, 0.2 mg, 0.3 mg

NURSING PROCESS

Assessment

- Assess patient's condition before starting therapy and regularly thereafter to monitor drug effectiveness. Monitor TSH monthly until stable, then yearly if asymptomatic.
- Be alert for adverse reactions and drug interactions.
- In patient with coronary artery disease who must receive thyroid hormone, monitor carefully for coronary insufficiency.
- Assess patient for swallowing difficulties before giving the drug. Advise all patients to take tablet with water.
- Assess patient's and family's knowledge of drug therapy.

Nursing diagnoses

- Ineffective health maintenance related to presence of hypothyroidism
- Risk for injury related to drug-induced adverse reactions
- Deficient knowledge related to drug therapy

Planning and implementation

ALERT: Doses of alternative brands of thyroid replacement drugs may not be equivalent, particularly between levothyroxine sodium (synthetic T_4), liothyronine (synthetic T_3), and thyroid hormone from animals (Armour thyroid, desiccated thyroid).
- Thyroid hormone replacement requirements are about 25% lower in patients older than age 60 than in younger adults.
- I.M. use typically isn't recommended because of variable absorption and difficulty regulating dose.
- Patients with adult hypothyroidism are unusually sensitive to thyroid hormone. Start patient at lowest dose and adjust to higher dose until reaching a euthyroid state based on symptoms and laboratory data.
- When changing from levothyroxine to liothyronine, stop levothyroxine then begin liothyronine at a low dose. Increase liothyronine dosage

in small increments after residual effects of levothyroxine disappear. When changing from liothyronine to levothyroxine, to avoid relapse start levothyroxine several days before stopping liothyronine.

- Thyroid hormones alter thyroid non-serum test results. Stop drug 4 weeks before test.
- In patient taking a prescribed anticoagulant with thyroid hormones, lower the dosage of anticoagulant if needed.

ALERT: Don't confuse levothyroxine sodium with liothyronine sodium or liotrix.

Patient teaching

- Stress importance of compliance. Tell patient to take thyroid hormones at same time each day, preferably 30 to 60 minutes before breakfast, to maintain constant hormone levels, prevent insomnia, and increase absorption.
- Instruct patient (especially an elderly patient) to immediately notify prescriber about chest pain, palpitations, sweating, nervousness, shortness of breath, or other signs of overdose or aggravated CV disease.
- Advise patient who has achieved stable response not to change brands without physician advice.
- Advise female patient to alert prescriber if she becomes pregnant.
- Tell patient to report unusual bleeding and bruising.

Evaluation

- Patient's thyroid hormone levels are normal.
- Patient doesn't experience any adverse reactions.
- Patient and family state understanding of drug therapy.

lidocaine hydrochloride (lignocaine hydrochloride)

(LIGH-doh-kayn high-droh-KLOR-ighd)

LidoPen Auto-Injector, Xylocaine, Xylocard ♦ ◇

Pharmacologic class: amide derivative
Therapeutic class: ventricular antiarrhythmic
Pregnancy risk category: B

Indications and dosages

▶ **Ventricular arrhythmias resulting from MI, cardiac manipulation, or digoxin toxicity.** *Adults:* 50 to 100 mg (1 to 1.5 mg/kg) by I.V. bolus at 25 to 50 mg/minute. Repeat bolus dose q 3 to 5 minutes until arrhythmias subside or adverse reactions develop. Don't exceed 300-mg total bolus during 1-hour period. Simultaneously, start a constant infusion of 20 to 50 mcg/kg/minute (or 1 to 4 mg/minute). If single bolus has been given, smaller bolus dose may be repeated 5 to 10 minutes after start of infusion to maintain therapeutic level. After 24 hours of continuous infusion, decrease rate by half. Or 200 to 300 mg I.M., followed by second I.M. dose 60 to 90 minutes later, if needed. Change to I.V. form as soon as possible.
Children: 1 mg/kg by I.V. bolus, followed by infusion of 20 to 50 mcg/kg/minute.

Adjust-a-dose: For elderly patients, patients who weigh less than 50 kg (110 lb) and patients with heart failure or hepatic disease, give half the normal adult dose.

▶ **Status epilepticus‡.** *Adults:* 1 mg/kg I.V. bolus; then, if seizures continue, give 0.5 mg/kg 2 minutes after first dose. May use an infusion of 30 mcg/kg/minute.

I.V. administration

- Use drug without preservatives. Read label carefully.
- Injections (additive syringes and single-use vials) containing 40, 100, or 200 mg/ml are for preparing I.V. infusion solutions and must be diluted before use.
- Add 1 g of drug (using 25 ml of 4% or 5 ml of 20% injection) to 1 L of D_5W injection to provide a solution containing 1 mg/ml.
- If patient is fluid restricted, use a more concentrated solution of up to 8 mg/ml.
- Patients receiving infusion must be on a cardiac monitor and must be attended at all times. Use infusion-control device to give infusion precisely. Don't exceed 4 mg/minute because doing so greatly increases the risk of toxicity.

⊗ **Incompatibilities**

Fentanyl citrate (higher pH formulations), methohexital sodium, phenytoin sodium.

Contraindications and cautions

- Contraindicated in patients hypersensitive to amide-type local anesthetics and in those with

Adams-Stokes syndrome, Wolff-Parkinson-White syndrome, or severe degrees of SA, AV, or intraventricular block in absence of artificial pacemaker.

• Use cautiously and reduce dosage in patients with complete or second-degree heart block or sinus bradycardia, in those with heart failure or renal or hepatic disease, and in those who weigh less than 50 kg.

Lifespan: In pregnant women, use only when benefits outweigh risks to the fetus. In breast-feeding women and in children, safety and effectiveness haven't been established. In elderly patients, use cautiously.

Adverse reactions

CNS: *confusion,* depression, euphoria, lethargy, *light-headedness,* muscle twitching, paresthesia, *restlessness,* ***seizures,*** slurred speech, somnolence, *stupor, tremor.*
CV: ***bradycardia, cardiac arrest,*** hypotension, ***new or worsened arrhythmias.***
EENT: *blurred or double vision, tinnitus.*
Respiratory: ***respiratory arrest, status asthmaticus.***
Skin: diaphoresis.
Other: ***anaphylaxis,*** cold sensation, soreness at injection site.

Interactions

Drug-drug. *Atenolol, metoprolol, nadolol, pindolol, propranolol:* May reduce hepatic metabolism of lidocaine, increasing risk of lidocaine toxicity. Give bolus doses of lidocaine at a slower rate, and monitor lidocaine level closely.
Cimetidine: May decrease lidocaine clearance, increasing the risk of lidocaine toxicity. Use a different H_2-antagonist. Monitor lidocaine level closely.
Phenytoin, procainamide, propranolol, quinidine: May have additive cardiac depressant effects. Monitor patient.
Succinylcholine: May prolong neuromuscular blockage. Monitor patient for increased effects.
Tocainide: May increase risk of adverse reactions. Avoid use together.
Drug-herb. *Pareira:* May increase neuromuscular blockade. Avoid use together.
Drug-lifestyle. *Smoking:* May increase lidocaine metabolism. Monitor patient closely; discourage patient from smoking.

Effects on lab test results

• May increase CK level.

Pharmacokinetics

Absorption: Nearly complete.
Distribution: Wide, especially to adipose tissue.
Metabolism: Most of drug in liver to two active metabolites.
Excretion: 90% as metabolites; less than 10% in urine unchanged. *Half-life:* 1½ to 2 hours (may be prolonged in patients with heart failure or hepatic disease).

Route	Onset	Peak	Duration
I.V.	Immediate	30–60 min	10–20 min
I.M.	5–15 min	10 min	2 hr

Action

Chemical effect: Decreases depolarization, automaticity, and excitability in ventricles during diastolic phase by direct action on tissues.
Therapeutic effect: Abolishes ventricular arrhythmias.

Available forms

Infusion (premixed): 0.2% (2 mg/ml), 0.4% (4 mg/ml), 0.8% (8 mg/ml)
Injection for direct I.V. use: 1% (10 mg/ml), 2% (20 mg/ml)
Injection for I.M. use: 300 mg/3 ml automatic injection device
Injection for I.V. admixtures: 4% (40 mg/ml), 10% (100 mg/ml), 20% (200 mg/ml)

NURSING PROCESS

Assessment

• Assess patient's condition before starting therapy and regularly thereafter to monitor drug effectiveness.
ALERT: Patient receiving infusion must be on cardiac monitor and attended to at all times.
• Monitor patient's response, especially ECG, blood pressure, and electrolytes, BUN, and creatinine levels.
• Check for therapeutic level (2 to 5 mcg/ml).
• Be alert for adverse reactions and drug interactions.
ALERT: Monitor patient for toxicity. Seizures may be the first sign. Severe reactions usually

are preceded by somnolence, confusion, and paresthesia.
• Assess patient's and family's knowledge of drug therapy.

Nursing diagnoses

• Decreased cardiac output related to presence of ventricular arrhythmia
• Disturbed thought processes related to adverse CNS reactions
• Deficient knowledge related to drug therapy

Planning and implementation

ALERT: If using I.M. drug in patient with suspected MI, test isoenzymes before starting therapy because patients receiving I.M. drug show sevenfold increase in CK level. Such an increase originates in skeletal muscle, not cardiac muscle.
ALERT: Give I.M. injections only in deltoid muscle.
• Use only the 10% solution for I.M. injection. Read label carefully.
• If signs of toxicity (such as dizziness) occur, immediately stop giving the drug and notify prescriber. Continued infusion could lead to seizures and coma. Give oxygen by way of nasal cannula. Keep oxygen and cardiopulmonary resuscitation equipment available.
• If arrhythmias worsen or if ECG changes, such as with a widening QRS complex or substantially prolonged PR interval, stop drug and notify prescriber.

Patient teaching

• Explain purpose of drug to patient.
• Tell patient or caregiver to report any adverse reactions.
• Instruct patient to avoid smoking during drug therapy.

Evaluation

• Patient's cardiac output returns to normal with abolishment of ventricular arrhythmia.
• Patient maintains normal thought processes throughout therapy.
• Patient and family state understanding of drug therapy.

linezolid

(lih-NEH-zoe-lid)
Zyvox

Pharmacologic class: oxazolidinone
Therapeutic class: antibiotic
Pregnancy risk category: C

Indications and dosages

▶ **Vancomycin-resistant *Enterococcus faecium* infections, including those with bacteremia.** *Adults and children age 12 and older:* 600 mg I.V. or P.O. q 12 hours for 14 to 28 days.
Neonates 7 days or older, infants, and children age 11 and younger: 10 mg/kg I.V. or P.O. q 8 hours for 14 to 28 days.
Neonates younger than 7 days old: 10 mg/kg I.V. or P.O. q 12 hours for 14 to 28 days. If neonate doesn't respond or when he is 7 days old, increase to 10 mg/kg q 8 hours.
▶ **Nosocomial pneumonia caused by *Staphylococcus aureus* (methicillin-susceptible [MSSA] and methicillin-resistant [MRSA] strains) or *Streptococcus pneumonia* (multidrug-resistant strains [MDRSP] only); complicated skin and skin-structure infections, including diabetic foot infections without osteomyelitis, caused by *S. aureus* (MSSA and MRSA), *Streptococcus pyogenes*, or *Streptococcus agalactiae*; community-acquired pneumonia caused by *S. pneumoniae* (including MDRSP), including those with bacteremia, or *S. aureus* (MSSA only).** *Adults and children age 12 and older:* 600 mg I.V. or P.O. q 12 hours for 10 to 14 days.
Neonates 7 days or older, infants, and children age 11 and younger: 10 mg/kg I.V. or P.O. q 8 hours for 10 to 14 days.
Preterm neonates younger than 7 days old: 10 mg/kg I.V. or P.O. q 12 hours for 10 to 14 days. Increase to 10 mg/kg q 8 hours if neonate doesn't respond or when he is 7 days old.
▶ **Uncomplicated skin and skin-structure infections caused by *S. aureus* (MSSA only) or *S. pyogenes*.** *Adults:* 400 mg P.O. q 12 hours for 10 to 14 days.
Children ages 12 to 18: Give 600 mg P.O. q 12 hours for 10 to 14 days.

Children ages 5 to 11: Give 10 mg/kg P.O. q 12 hours for 10 to 14 days.
Neonates 7 days or older, infants, and children younger than age 5: Give 10 mg/kg P.O. q 8 hours for 10 to 14 days.
Neonates younger than 7 days old: 10 mg/kg I.V. or P.O. q 12 hours for 10 to 14 days. Increase to 10 mg/kg q 8 hours if neonate doesn't respond or when he is 7 days old.

I.V. administration

- Drug is compatible with D_5W, normal saline solution for injection, and lactated Ringer's injection.
- Infuse over 30 to 120 minutes. Don't infuse in a series connection.
- Store drug at room temperature in its protective overwrap. The solution may turn yellow over time, but potency isn't affected. Use within 21 days.

⊗ **Incompatibilities**
Amphotericin B, ceftriaxone sodium, chlorpromazine hydrochloride, diazepam, erythromycin lactobionate, pentamidine isethionate, phenytoin sodium, trimethoprim-sulfamethoxazole. Don't mix with other I.V. drugs.

Contraindications and cautions

- Contraindicated in patients hypersensitive to the drug or any of its components.
- Safety and effectiveness of therapy for longer than 28 days haven't been studied.

Lifespan: In pregnant women, use only if benefits outweigh risks to the fetus. In breast-feeding women, use cautiously.

Adverse reactions

CNS: dizziness, fever, *headache,* insomnia.
GI: altered taste, constipation, *diarrhea, nausea,* oral candidiasis, ***pseudomembranous colitis,*** tongue discoloration, vomiting.
GU: vaginal candidiasis.
Hematologic: anemia, ***leukopenia, neutropenia, thrombocytopenia.***
Skin: rash.
Other: fungal infection.

Interactions

Drug-drug. *Adrenergics (such as dopamine, epinephrine, pseudoephedrine):* Increases risk of hypertension. Monitor blood pressure and heart rate. Start continuous infusions of dopamine and epinephrine at lower doses, and adjust to response.
Serotoninergics: Increases risk of serotonin syndrome (confusion, delirium, restlessness, tremor, blushing, diaphoresis, hyperpyrexia). If these symptoms occur, stop serotoninergic.
Drug-food. *Foods and beverages high in tyramine (such as aged cheese, air-dried meat, draft beer, red wine, sauerkraut, soy sauce):* May increase blood pressure. Advise patient to avoid these foods; explain that tyramine content of meals shouldn't exceed 100 mg.

Effects on lab test results

- May increase ALT, AST, bilirubin, alkaline phosphatase, creatinine, BUN, amylase, and lipase levels. May decrease hemoglobin level and hematocrit.
- May decrease WBC, neutrophil, and platelet counts.

Pharmacokinetics

Absorption: Rapid and complete. Bioavailability is about 100%.
Distribution: Good. About 31% protein-bound.
Metabolism: Undergoes oxidative metabolism to two inactive metabolites.
Excretion: At steady-state, about 30% unchanged in urine and about 50% as metabolites. *Half-life:* 6¼ hours.

Route	Onset	Peak	Duration
P.O.			
Tablet	Unknown	1 hr	4¾–5½ hr
Suspension	Unknown	1 hr	4½ hr
I.V.	Unknown	½ hr	4¾ hr

Action

Chemical effect: Bacteriostatic against enterococci and staphylococci. Bactericidal against most strains of streptococci. Interferes with bacterial protein synthesis.
Therapeutic effect: Hinders or kills susceptible bacteria.

Available forms

Injection: 2 mg/ml
Powder for oral suspension: 100 mg/5 ml when reconstituted
Tablets: 400 mg, 600 mg

NURSING PROCESS

Assessment
- Obtain history of patient's underlying condition before starting therapy, and reassess regularly to monitor drug effectiveness.
- Obtain specimen for culture and sensitivity tests before starting therapy. Use sensitivity results to guide subsequent therapy.
- Monitor platelet count in patient with increased risk of bleeding, patient with thrombocytopenia, patient taking drugs that may cause thrombocytopenia, or patient taking linezolid for longer than 14 days.
- Monitor patient for persistent diarrhea; if it occurs, consider the possibility of pseudomembranous colitis.
- Assess patient's and family's knowledge of drug therapy.

Nursing diagnoses
- Risk for infection related to presence of susceptible bacteria
- Risk for injury related to drug-induced adverse reactions
- Deficient knowledge related to drug therapy

Planning and implementation
- Because inappropriate use of antibiotics may lead to resistant organisms, carefully consider other drugs before starting therapy, especially in an outpatient setting.
- No dosage adjustment is needed when switching from I.V. to P.O. dosage forms.

ALERT: Don't confuse Zyvox with Zovirax. They both come in a 400-mg tablet.

Patient teaching
- Inform patient that tablets and oral suspension may be taken with or without meals.
- Stress to patient the importance of completing the entire course of therapy, even if he feels better.
- Tell patient to alert prescriber if he has hypertension, is taking cough or cold preparations, or is taking a selective serotonin reuptake inhibitor or another antidepressant.
- Inform patient with phenylketonuria that each 5 ml of oral suspension contains 20 mg of phenylalanine. Tablets and injection don't contain phenylalanine.

Evaluation
- Patient is free from infection.
- Patient sustains no injury as a result of drug-induced adverse reactions.
- Patient and family state understanding of drug therapy.

lisinopril
(ligh-SIN-uh-pril)
Prinivil, Zestril

Pharmacologic class: ACE inhibitor
Therapeutic class: antihypertensive
Pregnancy risk category: C (D in second and third trimesters)

Indications and dosages

▶ **Hypertension.** *Adults:* Initially, 10 mg P.O. daily. If patient also takes a diuretic, reduce initial dosage to 5 mg P.O. daily. Usual effective dosage is 20 to 40 mg daily. Maximum dosage, 80 mg daily.
Children ages 6 to 16: Initially, 0.07 mg/kg P.O. once daily (up to 5 mg total). Adjust dosage by blood pressure response. Doses above 0.61 mg/kg (or in excess of 40 mg) haven't been tested in children.

▶ **Adjunct therapy in heart failure (with diuretics and digoxin).** *Adults:* Initially, 5 mg P.O. daily. Usual effective dosage range is 5 to 20 mg daily. In patients with hyponatremia (sodium level below 130 mEq/L) or creatinine above 3 mg/dl, start with 2.5 mg P.O. once daily.

▶ **Hemodynamically stable patients within 24 hours of acute MI to improve survival.** *Adults:* Initially, 5 mg P.O. Then 5 mg P.O. after 24 hours, 10 mg P.O. after 48 hours, and 10 mg P.O. once daily for 6 weeks. In patients with systolic blood pressure of 120 mm Hg or less at start of therapy or during first 3 days after an MI, reduce dosage to 2.5 mg.

Contraindications and cautions
- Contraindicated in patients hypersensitive to ACE inhibitors and in those with a history of angioedema from previous therapy with an ACE inhibitor.
- Use cautiously in patients with impaired kidney function; adjust dosage as directed. Also use cautiously in patients at risk for hyperkalemia (those with renal insufficiency or diabetes or who use drugs that raise potassium level).

Lifespan: In pregnant women, use in first trimester when benefits to woman exceed risks to fetus. In last two trimesters, drug is contraindicated. In breast-feeding women, use cautiously. In children younger than age 6 and in children with GFR of less than 30 ml/minute, safety and effectiveness haven't been established.

Adverse reactions

CNS: depression, *dizziness, fatigue, headache,* paresthesia, somnolence.
CV: chest pain, hypotension, *orthostatic hypotension.*
EENT: *nasal congestion.*
GI: *diarrhea,* dysgeusia, dyspepsia, nausea.
GU: impotence.
Metabolic: ***hyperkalemia.***
Musculoskeletal: *muscle cramps.*
Respiratory: *dry, persistent, tickling, nonproductive cough.*
Skin: rash.
Other: ***angioedema, anaphylaxis,*** decreased libido.

Interactions

Drug-drug. *Capsaicin:* May cause or worsen coughing caused by ACE inhibitors. Monitor patient closely.
Digoxin: May increase digoxin level. Monitor level.
Diuretics: May cause excessive hypotension. Stop diuretics for 2 to 3 days or increase salt intake before lisinopril therapy or reduce lisinopril dosage to 5 mg P.O. once daily. Monitor blood pressure closely until stabilized.
Indomethacin: May lessen hypotensive effect. Monitor blood pressure.
Insulin, oral antidiabetics: May increase risk of hypoglycemia, especially when starting lisinopril. Monitor glucose closely.
Lithium: May increase lithium level. Monitor patient for toxicity.
Phenothiazines: May increase effects of drug. Monitor blood pressure.
Potassium-sparing diuretics, potassium supplements: May increase risk of hyperkalemia. Monitor potassium level.
Thiazide diuretics: May lessen potassium loss caused by thiazide diuretics. Monitor potassium level.
Tizanidine: May cause severe hypotension. Monitor patient closely.
Drug-herb. *Licorice:* May cause sodium retention and increase blood pressure, interfering with ACE inhibitor effects. Discourage use together.
Drug-food. *Salt substitutes with potassium:* May increase risk of hyperkalemia. Monitor patient closely; discourage patient from using unless directed by prescriber.

Effects on lab test results

- May increase BUN, creatinine, potassium, and bilirubin levels.
- May increase liver function test values.

Pharmacokinetics

Absorption: Variable.
Distribution: Wide, although minimally to brain. Insignificantly protein-bound.
Metabolism: None.
Excretion: Unchanged in urine. *Half-life:* 12 hours.

Route	Onset	Peak	Duration
P.O.	1 hr	7 hr	24 hr

Action

Chemical effect: Unknown; may result primarily from suppression of renin-angiotensin-aldosterone system.
Therapeutic effect: Lowers blood pressure.

Available forms

Tablets: 2.5 mg, 5 mg, 10 mg, 20 mg, 40 mg

NURSING PROCESS

Assessment

- Assess patient's condition before starting therapy and regularly thereafter to monitor drug effectiveness. Beneficial effects may take several weeks to appear.
- Monitor WBC with differential counts before therapy, q 2 weeks for first 3 months, and periodically thereafter.
- Be alert for adverse reactions and drug interactions.
- Assess patient's and family's knowledge of drug therapy.

Nursing diagnoses

- Risk for injury related to presence of hypertension

• Decreased cardiac output related to drug-induced hypotension
• Deficient knowledge related to drug therapy

Planning and implementation

• If drug doesn't control blood pressure, add diuretics.
ALERT: Don't confuse lisinopril with fosinopril or Lioresal.
ALERT: Don't confuse Prinivil with Proventil or Prilosec.
ALERT: Don't confuse Zestril with Zostrix, Zetia, Zebeta, or Zyrtec.

Patient teaching

• Advise patient to report signs or symptoms of angioedema (including laryngeal edema), such as breathing difficulty or swelling of face, eyes, lips, or tongue.
• Tell patient that light-headedness may occur, especially during first few days of therapy. Tell him to rise slowly to avoid this effect and to report symptoms to prescriber. If syncope occurs, tell patient to stop taking drug and call prescriber immediately.
• Tell patient not to abruptly stop taking the drug but to call the prescriber if an adverse reaction occurs.
• Advise patient to report signs of infection, such as fever and sore throat.
• Tell patient to notify prescriber and stop taking the drug if she becomes pregnant.

Evaluation

• Patient's blood pressure is within normal limits.
• Patient maintains adequate cardiac output throughout therapy.
• Patient and family state understanding of drug therapy.

lithium carbonate

(LITH-ee-um KAR-buh-nayt)

Carbolith ♦, Duralith ♦, Eskalith, Eskalith CR, Lithane, Lithicarb ◇, Lithizine ♦, Lithobid, Lithonate, Lithotabs

lithium citrate

Lithium Citrate Syrup*

Pharmacologic class: alkali metal
Therapeutic class: antipsychotic
Pregnancy risk category: D

Indications and dosages

▶ **To prevent or control acute manic or mixed episodes in patients with bipolar disorder.** *Adults:* 300 to 600 mg P.O. up to q.i.d., increasing on basis of drug level to achieve therapeutic dosage, usually 1,800 mg P.O. daily. Therapeutic drug level is 1 to 1.5 mEq/L for acute mania; 0.6 to 1.2 mEq/L for maintenance therapy; and 2 mEq/L as maximum level.

▶ **Major depression, schizoaffective disorder, schizophrenic disorder, alcohol dependence‡.** *Adults:* 300 mg lithium carbonate P.O. t.i.d. or q.i.d.

▶ **Apparent mixed bipolar disorder in children‡.** *Children:* Initially, 15 to 60 mg/kg or 0.5 to 1.5 g/m^2 lithium carbonate P.O. daily in three divided doses. Don't exceed usual adult dosage. Adjust dosage based on patient's response and lithium level. Usual range, 150 to 300 mg daily in divided doses to maintain lithium level of 0.5 to 1.2 mEq/L.

▶ **Chemotherapy-induced neutropenia in children and patients with AIDS receiving zidovudine‡.** *Adults and children:* 300 to 1,000 mg P.O. daily.

Contraindications and cautions

• Contraindicated if therapy can't be closely monitored.
• Use cautiously in patients receiving neuroleptics, neuromuscular blockers, or diuretics; in debilitated patients; and in patients with thyroid disease, seizure disorder, renal or CV disease, severe debilitation or dehydration, or sodium depletion.
Lifespan: In pregnant and breast-feeding women, drug is contraindicated. In children younger than age 12, safety and effectiveness haven't been established. In elderly patients, use cautiously because of possible decreased rate of excretion.

Adverse reactions

CNS: ataxia, ***coma,*** confusion, dizziness, drowsiness, EEG changes, ***epileptiform seizures,*** headache, impaired speech, incoordination, lethargy, psychomotor retardation, restlessness, stupor, syncope, tremor, worsened organic mental syndrome, weakness.
CV: ankle and wrist edema, ***arrhythmias,*** hypotension, *reversible ECG changes.*
EENT: blurred vision, tinnitus.

GI: abdominal pain, anorexia, diarrhea, dry mouth, flatulence, indigestion, metallic taste, nausea, thirst, vomiting.
GU: albuminuria, glycosuria, polyuria, ***renal toxicity.***
Hematologic: *reversible leukocytosis.*
Metabolic: goiter, hyponatremia, hypothyroidism, transient hyperglycemia.
Skin: acne, alopecia, diminished or absent sensation, drying and thinning of hair, pruritus, psoriasis, rash.

Interactions

Drug-drug. *Acetazolamide, aminophylline, sodium bicarbonate, urine alkalinizers:* May increase lithium excretion. Avoid salt loads; monitor lithium levels for increase.
Carbamazepine, indomethacin, methyldopa, NSAIDS, piroxicam, probenecid: May increase lithium effects. Monitor patient for lithium toxicity.
Diuretics: May increase reabsorption of lithium by kidneys with a toxic effect. Use cautiously, and monitor lithium and electrolyte levels (especially sodium).
Fluoxetine: May increase lithium level. Monitor patient for toxicity.
Neuroleptics: May cause encephalopathy. Watch for signs and symptoms (lethargy, tremor, extrapyramidal symptoms), and stop drug if they occur.
Neuromuscular blockers: May cause prolonged paralysis or weakness. Monitor patient closely.
Thyroid hormones: May induce hypothyroidism. Monitor thyroid function, and treat with thyroid hormones as needed.

Effects on lab test results

- May increase glucose level. May decrease sodium, T_3, T_4, and protein-bound iodine levels.
- May increase ^{131}I uptake and WBC and neutrophil counts.

Pharmacokinetics

Absorption: Complete within 8 hours.
Distribution: Wide. Levels in thyroid gland, bone, and brain exceed serum levels.
Metabolism: Not metabolized.
Excretion: 95% unchanged in urine. *Half-life:* 18 hours (adolescents) to 36 hours (elderly).

Route	Onset	Peak	Duration
P.O.	Unknown	½–3 hr	Unknown

Action

Chemical effect: Unknown; probably alters chemical transmitters in CNS, possibly by interfering with ionic pump mechanisms in brain cells, and may compete with sodium ions.
Therapeutic effect: Stabilizes mood.

Available forms

lithium carbonate
Capsules: 150 mg, 300 mg, 600 mg
Tablets: 300 mg (300 mg = 8.12 mEq lithium)
Tablets (controlled-release): 300 mg, 450 mg
lithium citrate
Syrup (sugarless)*: 8 mEq of lithium per 5 ml (8 mEq lithium = 300 mg of lithium carbonate)

NURSING PROCESS

Assessment

- Assess patient's condition before starting therapy and regularly thereafter to monitor drug effectiveness. Expect delay of 1 to 3 weeks before drug's beneficial effects occur.
- Monitor baseline ECG, thyroid and kidney studies, and electrolyte levels.
- Monitor lithium blood level 8 to 12 hours after first dose, usually before morning dose, two or three times weekly in first month, and then weekly to monthly during maintenance therapy. With blood levels below 1.5 mEq/L, adverse reactions usually remain mild, although toxicity may occur even at therapeutic levels.
- Check urine-specific gravity, and report level below 1.005, which may indicate diabetes insipidus.
- Monitor glucose level closely. Lithium may alter glucose tolerance in diabetic patient.
- Be alert for adverse reactions and drug interactions.
- Assess patient's and family's knowledge of drug therapy.

Nursing diagnoses

- Disturbed thought processes related to presence of bipolar disorder
- Ineffective health maintenance related to drug-induced endocrine dysfunction
- Deficient knowledge related to drug therapy

Planning and implementation

ALERT: Don't confuse Lithobid with Levbid, Lithonate with Lithostat, or Lithotabs with Lithobid or Lithostat.

- Monitoring lithium level is crucial to safe use of drug. Don't use in patient who can't have level checked regularly.
- Give with plenty of water and after meals to minimize GI reactions.
- Before leaving bedside, make sure patient has swallowed drug.
- Notify prescriber if patient's behavior hasn't improved in 3 weeks or if it worsens.
- Perform outpatient follow-up of thyroid and kidney function q 6 to 12 months. Palpate thyroid to check for enlargement.

Patient teaching

- Tell patient to take drug with plenty of water and after meals to minimize GI upset.
- Explain that lithium has narrow therapeutic margin of safety. A blood level that's even slightly high can be dangerous.
- Warn patient and family to watch for signs of toxicity (diarrhea, vomiting, tremor, drowsiness, muscle weakness, ataxia) and to expect transient nausea, polyuria, thirst, and discomfort during the first few days. Tell patient not to stop taking the drug abruptly unless he has symptoms of toxicity. If he does, he should call his prescriber and not take the next dose.
- Warn patient to avoid activities that require alertness and good psychomotor coordination until the drug's CNS effects are known.
- Tell patient not to switch brands or take other prescription or OTC drugs without prescriber's approval.
- Advise patient to wear or carry medical identification.

Evaluation

- Patient exhibits improved behavior and thought processes.
- Patient maintains normal endocrine function throughout therapy.
- Patient and family state understanding of drug therapy.

lomustine (CCNU)

(loh-MUH-steen)

CeeNU

Pharmacologic class: alkylating drug, nitrosourea
Therapeutic class: antineoplastic
Pregnancy risk category: D

Indications and dosages

▶ **Brain tumor, Hodgkin and other lymphomas.** *Adults and children:* 100 to 130 mg/m^2 P.O. as single dose q 6 weeks. Reduce dosage according to degree of bone marrow suppression. Don't repeat doses until WBC count is more than 4,000/mm^3 and platelet count is more than 100,000/mm^3.

Contraindications and cautions

- Contraindicated in patients hypersensitive to the drug or any of its components.
- Use cautiously in patients with lowered platelet, WBC, or RBC count and in those receiving other myelosuppressant drugs.

Lifespan: In pregnant and breast-feeding women, drug is contraindicated.

Adverse reactions

GI: *nausea,* stomatitis, *vomiting.*
GU: ***nephrotoxicity,*** progressive azotemia, ***renal impairment.***
Hematologic: anemia, ***bone marrow suppression, leukopenia, thrombocytopenia.***
Hepatic: ***hepatotoxicity.***
Respiratory: ***pulmonary fibrosis.***
Other: ***secondary malignant disease.***

Interactions

Drug-drug. *Anticoagulants, aspirin:* Increases bleeding risk. Avoid use together.

Effects on lab test results

- May increase urine urea, liver enzyme, BUN, and creatinine levels. May decrease hemoglobin level and hematocrit.
- May decrease WBC, RBC, and platelet counts.

Pharmacokinetics

Absorption: Rapid and good.

Distribution: Wide. Crosses blood–brain barrier to significant extent.
Metabolism: Rapid and extensive in liver.
Excretion: Metabolites mainly in urine. *Half-life:* 1 to 2 days.

Route	Onset	Peak	Duration
P.O.	Unknown	Unknown	Unknown

Action

Chemical effect: Cross-links strands of cellular DNA and interferes with RNA transcription.
Therapeutic effect: Kills selected cancer cells.

Available forms

Capsules: 10 mg, 40 mg, 100 mg, dose pack (two 10-mg, two 40-mg, two 100-mg capsules)

NURSING PROCESS

Assessment

- Assess patient's condition before starting therapy and regularly thereafter to monitor drug effectiveness.
- Monitor CBC weekly because bone marrow toxicity is delayed by 4 to 6 weeks after treatment.
- Periodically monitor liver function test results.
- Be alert for adverse reactions and drug interactions.
- Assess patient's and family's knowledge of drug therapy.

Nursing diagnoses

- Ineffective health maintenance related to presence of neoplastic disease
- Ineffective protection related to adverse hematologic reactions
- Deficient knowledge related to drug therapy

Planning and implementation

- Give antiemetic before giving drug to help patient avoid nausea.
- Give 2 to 4 hours after meals because drug is better absorbed on an empty stomach.
- Repeat dose only when CBC results reveal safe blood counts.
- Institute infection control and bleeding precautions.

Patient teaching

- Warn patient to watch for signs of infection (fever, sore throat, fatigue) and bleeding (easy bruising, nosebleeds, bleeding gums, melena) and to take temperature daily.
- Instruct patient to avoid OTC products containing aspirin.
- Advise woman of childbearing age to avoid pregnancy during therapy and to consult with prescriber before becoming pregnant.

Evaluation

- Patient responds well to therapy.
- Patient regains normal hematologic function.
- Patient and family state understanding of drug therapy.

loperamide

(loh-PEH-ruh-mighd)
Imodium, Imodium A-D†, Kaopectate II Caplets†, Maalox Anti-Diarrheal Caplets†, Neo-Diaral†, Pepto Diarrhea Control†

Pharmacologic class: piperidine derivative
Therapeutic class: antidiarrheal
Pregnancy risk category: B

L

Indications and dosages

▶ **Acute diarrhea.** *Adults and children age 12 and older:* Initially, 4 mg P.O.; then 2 mg after each unformed stool. Maximum dosage, 16 mg daily.
Children ages 8 to 12 who weigh more than 30 kg (66 lb): 2 mg P.O. t.i.d. on first day. On subsequent days, doses of 1 mg/10 kg of body weight may be given after each unformed stool. Maximum dosage, 6 mg daily.
Children ages 6 to 8 who weigh 20 to 30 kg (44 to 66 lb): 2 mg P.O. b.i.d. on first day. On subsequent days, doses of 1 mg/10 kg of body weight may be given after each unformed stool. Maximum dosage, 4 mg daily.
Children ages 2 to 5 who weigh 13 to 20 kg (29 to 44 lb): 1 mg P.O. t.i.d. on first day. On subsequent days, give doses of 1 mg/10 kg of body weight after each unformed stool. Maximum dosage, 3 mg daily.
▶ **Chronic diarrhea.** *Adults:* Initially, 4 mg P.O.; then 2 mg after each unformed stool until diarrhea subsides. Adjust dosage to individual response. Maximum dosage, 16 mg daily. If patient doesn't improve in 10 days, consider different therapy.

Children‡: 0.08 to 0.24 mg/kg P.O. daily in two to three divided doses. Report persistent diarrhea to prescriber.

▶ **Self-medication of acute diarrhea including traveler's diarrhea.** *Adults:* 4 mg† after first loose bowel movement followed by 2 mg† after each subsequent loose bowel movement; maximum, 8 mg P.O. daily for 2 days.

Contraindications and cautions

- Contraindicated in patients hypersensitive to the drug or any of its components; in patients for whom constipation must be avoided; in patients with pseudomembranous colitis from antibiotic use; and patients with *Shigella, Salmonella,* or enteroinvasive *Escherichia coli* infection. OTC form is contraindicated in patients with bloody diarrhea and those with temperature over 101° F (38° C).
- Use cautiously in patients with hepatic disease because of risk of encephalopathy.

Lifespan: In pregnant women, use cautiously. In breast-feeding women, use cautiously; it's unknown if the drug appears in breast milk. In children younger than age 2, drug is contraindicated.

Adverse reactions

CNS: dizziness, drowsiness, fatigue.
GI: abdominal pain, distention, or discomfort; *constipation;* dry mouth; nausea; vomiting.
Skin: rash.
Other: hypersensitivity reactions.

Interactions

Drug-drug. *Saquinavir:* May increase loperamide level and decrease saquinavir level. Avoid use together.

Effects on lab test results

None reported.

Pharmacokinetics

Absorption: Poor.
Distribution: Unknown.
Metabolism: In liver.
Excretion: Mainly in feces; less than 2% in urine. *Half-life:* 9 to 14½ hours.

Route	Onset	Peak	Duration
P.O.	Unknown	2½–5 hr	24 hr

Action

Chemical effect: Inhibits peristalsis, prolonging passage of intestinal contents.
Therapeutic effect: Relieves diarrhea.

Available forms

Capsules: 2 mg
Oral liquid*: 1 mg/5 ml†, 1 mg/ml†
Tablets: 2 mg†

NURSING PROCESS

Assessment

- Assess patient's diarrhea before starting therapy and regularly thereafter to monitor drug effectiveness.
- Be alert for adverse reactions.

ALERT: Monitor children closely for CNS effects because they may be more sensitive than adults.

- Monitor patient's hydration.
- Assess patient's and family's knowledge of drug therapy.

Nursing diagnoses

- Diarrhea related to underlying condition
- Risk for deficient fluid volume related to drug-induced adverse GI reactions
- Deficient knowledge related to drug therapy

Planning and implementation

- If patient doesn't improve in 48 hours, stop therapy.
- If patient has severe abdominal pain, bloating, or firmness or if drug is ineffective, notify prescriber.
- If drug is given by NG tube, flush tube to clear it and ensure drug's passage to stomach.

ALERT: Oral liquids are available in different concentrations. Check dose carefully. For children, consider an oral liquid product that doesn't contain alcohol.

ALERT: Don't confuse Imodium with Ionamin.

Patient teaching

- Advise patient not to exceed recommended dosage.
- Tell patient with acute diarrhea to contact prescriber if patient doesn't improve within 48 hours. For chronic diarrhea, tell patient to notify prescriber and stop taking the drug if no improvement occurs after taking 16 mg daily for at least 10 days.

• Advise patient to stop taking drug and to notify prescriber immediately if abdominal pain, bloating, or firmness develop because of risk of toxic megacolon.

Evaluation

• Patient's diarrhea is relieved.
• Patient is adequately hydrated throughout therapy.
• Patient and family state understanding of drug therapy.

lopinavir and ritonavir

(loe-PIN-a-veer and rih-TOH-nuh-veer)
Kaletra

Pharmacologic class: protease inhibitor
Therapeutic class: antiretroviral
Pregnancy risk category: C

Indications and dosages

▶ **HIV infection, with other antiretrovirals in treatment-naive adults.** *Adults:* 800 mg lopinavir and 200 mg ritonavir (4 tablets or 10 ml) P.O. with food once daily or 400 mg lopinavir and 100 mg ritonavir with food b.i.d.
▶ **HIV infection, with other antiretrovirals in treatment-experienced patients.** *Adults and children older than age 12:* Give 400 mg lopinavir and 100 mg ritonavir (2 tablets or 5 ml) P.O. b.i.d.
Children ages 6 months to 12 years who weigh 15 to 40 kg (33 to 88 lb): 10 mg/kg (lopinavir content) P.O. b.i.d. with food up to a maximum of 400 mg lopinavir and 100 mg ritonavir in children weighing more than 40 kg.
Children ages 6 months to 12 years who weigh 7 to 15 kg (15 to 33 lb): 12 mg/kg (lopinavir content) P.O. b.i.d. with food.
Adjust-a-dose: In treatment-experienced patients older than age 12 also taking efavirenz, nevirapine, fosamprenavir without ritonavir, or nelfinavir, consider dosage of 600 mg lopinavir and 150 mg ritonavir (3 tablets) P.O. b.i.d. For patients using oral solution and also taking efavirenz, nevirapine, amprenavir, or nelfinavir, 533 mg lopinavir and 133 mg ritonavir (6.5 ml) b.i.d. with food is recommended.

In treatment-experienced patients ages 6 months to 12 years also taking amprenavir, efavirenz, or nevirapine and weighing 7 to 15 kg, give 13 mg/kg (lopinavir content) P.O. b.i.d. with food. For patients weighing 15 to 45 kg, give 11 mg/kg (lopinavir content) P.O. b.i.d. with food up to a maximum dose of 533 mg lopinavir and 133 mg ritonavir b.i.d. In children weighing more than 45 kg, use adult dosage.

Contraindications and cautions

• Contraindicated in patients hypersensitive to the drug or any of its components.
• Use cautiously in patients with a history of pancreatitis or with hepatic impairment, hepatitis B or C, marked elevations in liver enzyme levels, or hemophilia.
Lifespan: In breast-feeding women, either stop breast-feeding or use another drug. In infants younger than age 6 months, safety and effectiveness haven't been established. In elderly patients, use cautiously because of possible decreased rate of excretion.

Adverse reactions

CNS: abnormal dreams, abnormal thinking, agitation, amnesia, anxiety, asthenia, ataxia, confusion, depression, dizziness, dyskinesia, emotional lability, ***encephalopathy,*** fever, headache, hypertonia, insomnia, malaise, nervousness, neuropathy, pain, paresthesia, peripheral neuritis, somnolence, tremor.
CV: chest pain, ***deep vein thrombosis,*** edema, facial edema, hypertension, palpitations, peripheral edema, thrombophlebitis, vasculitis.
EENT: abnormal vision, eye disorder, otitis media, sialadenitis, sinusitis, stomatitis, taste perversion, tinnitus, ulcerative stomatitis.
GI: abdominal pain, abnormal stools, anorexia, cholecystitis, constipation, *diarrhea,* dry mouth, dyspepsia, dysphagia, enterocolitis, eructation, esophagitis, fecal incontinence, flatulence, gastritis, gastroenteritis, GI disorder, ***hemorrhagic colitis,*** increased appetite, *nausea,* ***pancreatitis,*** vomiting.
GU: abnormal ejaculation, decreased libido, gynecomastia, hypogonadism, renal calculus, urine abnormality.
Hematologic: anemia, ***leukopenia,*** lymphadenopathy, ***neutropenia, thrombocytopenia*** in children.
Hepatic: hyperbilirubinemia in children.
Metabolic: Cushing syndrome, dehydration, decreased glucose tolerance, *hypercholesterolemia,* hyperglycemia, hyperuricemia, hypona-

L

tremia in children, hypothyroidism, ***lactic acidosis,*** weight loss.
Musculoskeletal: arthralgia, arthrosis, back pain, myalgia.
Respiratory: bronchitis, dyspnea, ***lung edema.***
Skin: acne, alopecia, benign skin neoplasm, dry skin, exfoliative dermatitis, furunculosis, nail disorder, pruritus, rash, skin discoloration, sweating.
Other: chills, flulike syndrome, viral infection.

Interactions

Drug-drug. *Amiodarone, bepridil, lidocaine, quinidine:* May increase antiarrhythmic levels. Use cautiously. Monitor levels of these drugs; adjust dosage, if needed.
Amprenavir, efavirenz, nelfinavir, nevirapine: May decrease lopinavir level. Consider increasing lopinavir and ritonavir dose. Don't use a once-daily Kaletra regimen with these drugs.
Antiarrhythmics (flecainide, propafenone), pimozide: May increase risk of cardiac arrhythmias. Don't use together.
Atovaquone, methadone: May decrease levels of these drugs. Consider increasing doses of these drugs.
Carbamazepine, corticosteroids, phenobarbital, phenytoin: May decrease lopinavir level. Use cautiously.
Clarithromycin: May increase clarithromycin levels in patients with renal impairment. Adjust clarithromycin dosage.
Cyclosporine, rapamycin, tacrolimus: May increase levels of these drugs. Monitor therapeutic levels.
Delavirdine: May increase lopinavir level. May be prescribed together for this effect.
Didanosine: May decrease absorption of didanosine because lopinavir and ritonavir dose is taken with food. Give didanosine 1 hour before or 2 hours after lopinavir and ritonavir.
Dihydroergotamine, ergonovine, ergotamine, methylergonovine: May increase risk of ergot toxicity characterized by peripheral vasospasm and ischemia. Don't use together.
Disulfiram, metronidazole: May increase risk of disulfiram-like reaction. Avoid use together.
Felodipine, nicardipine, nifedipine: May increase levels of these drugs. Use cautiously. Monitor patient.
Fluticasone: May significantly increase fluticasone exposure and significantly decreased cortisol level, which may lead to systemic corticosteroid effects (including Cushing syndrome). Don't use together, if possible.
HMG-CoA reductase inhibitors: May increase risk of adverse reactions, such as myopathy and rhabdomyolysis. Atorvastatin, fluvastatin, and pravastatin may be used with careful monitoring; Avoid using lovastatin or simvastatin.
Hormonal contraceptives (ethinyl estradiol): May decrease effectiveness of contraceptives. Recommend nonhormonal contraception.
Indinavir, saquinavir: May increase level of these drugs. May be prescribed together for this effect.
Itraconazole, ketoconazole: May increase levels of these drugs. Don't give more than 200 mg/day of these drugs.
Methadone: May decrease methadone absorption. May need to increase dosage. Monitor patient closely.
Midazolam, triazolam: May prolong or increase sedation or respiratory depression. Don't use together.
Phosphodiesterase type 5 inhibitors (sildenafil, tadalafil, vardenafil): May increase levels and risk of adverse effects of these drugs, such as hypotension and prolonged erection. Don't exceed 25 mg of sildenafil in a 48 hours, 10 mg of tadalafil in 72 hours, or 2.5 mg of vardenafil in 72 hours. Use cautiously, and monitor patient for adverse reactions.
Rifabutin: May increase rifabutin level. Decrease rifabutin dosage by 75%; monitor patient for adverse effects.
Rifampin: May decrease effectiveness of lopinavir and ritonavir. Avoid use together.
Trazodone: May increase trazodone level, causing nausea, dizziness, hypotension, and syncope. Avoid use together. If unavoidable, use cautiously with a lower dose of trazodone.
Warfarin: May affect warfarin level. Monitor PT and INR.
Drug-herb. *St. John's wort:* May cause loss of virologic response and resistance to drug. Discourage use together.
Drug-food. *Any food:* May increase absorption of oral solution. Give drug with food.

Effects on lab test results

- May increase amylase, liver enzyme, glucose, uric acid, cholesterol, and triglyceride levels. May decrease hemoglobin level and hematocrit. In children, may increase bilirubin level and decrease sodium level.

• May decrease WBC, neutrophil, and platelet counts.

Pharmacokinetics

Absorption: Levels peak in 4 hours. Drug is better absorbed when taken with food.
Distribution: Lopinavir is 98% or 99% protein-bound.
Metabolism: Lopinavir is extensively metabolized by the CYP3A isoenzyme. Ritonavir is a potent inhibitor of CYP3A, which inhibits lopinavir metabolism and increases lopinavir level.
Excretion: In urine and feces. Less than 3% of drug is excreted unchanged. *Half-life:* About 6 hours.

Route	Onset	Peak	Duration
P.O.	Unknown	4 hr	6 hr

Action

Chemical effects: Inhibits HIV protease. Ritonavir inhibits lopinavir metabolism, increasing lopinavir level.
Therapeutic effect: Prevents cleavage of the Gag-Pol polyprotein, resulting in the production of immature, noninfectious viral particles.

Available forms

Capsule: 133.3 mg lopinavir and 33.3 mg ritonavir
Solution: lopinavir 400 mg and ritonavir 100 mg per 5 ml (80 mg and 20 mg per ml)
Tablets: 200 mg lopinavir and 50 mg ritonavir

NURSING PROCESS

Assessment

• Assess underlying condition before starting therapy, and reassess regularly to monitor drugs' effectiveness.
• Monitor total cholesterol and triglycerides before starting therapy and periodically thereafter.
• To monitor maternal-fetal outcomes of pregnant women exposed to lopinavir and ritonavir, an Antiretroviral Pregnancy Registry has been established. Enroll patients by calling 1-800-258-4263, or register online at www.apregistry.com.
ALERT: This drug interacts with many other drugs. Review all drugs that patient is currently taking.
• Assess patient's and family's knowledge of drug therapy.

Nursing diagnoses

• Risk for falls related to drug-induced adverse CNS effects
• Risk for powerlessness related to chronic disease and need for aggressive medical management
• Deficient knowledge related to drug therapy

Planning and implementation

• Tablets may be taken without regard to meals. Oral solution must be taken with food.
ALERT: Tablets must be swallowed whole. Don't crush, divide, or let patient chew.
• Refrigerated drug remains stable until expiration date on package. If stored at room temperature, use drug within 2 months.
• Monitor patient for signs of fat redistribution, including central obesity, buffalo hump, peripheral wasting, breast enlargement, and cushingoid appearance.
• Watch for evidence of pancreatitis: nausea, vomiting, abdominal pain, and increased lipase and amylase values.
• Monitor patient for signs of bleeding.
• For an overdose, induce emesis or perform gastric lavage. Activated charcoal may be used to aid in removing unabsorbed drug. Dialysis is unlikely to help remove drug.
ALERT: Don't confuse Kaletra with Keppra.

Patient teaching

• Tell patient to take oral solution with food.
• Tell patient also taking didanosine to take it 1 hour before or 2 hours after lopinavir and ritonavir.
• Advise patient to report side effects to prescriber.
• Tell patient to immediately report severe nausea, vomiting, or abdominal pain.
• Warn patient to tell prescriber about any other prescription or nonprescription drug he is taking, including herbal supplements.
• Tell patient that drug doesn't cure HIV.
• If patient takes a drug for erectile dysfunction, caution about an increased risk of adverse events, including hypotension, visual changes, and priapism, and the need to promptly report any symptoms. Tell him not to take more than directed.

• Advise HIV-infected mothers not to breast-feed because breast-feeding may transmit HIV to their infants.

Evaluation
• Patient doesn't experience falls.
• Patient has adequate support, personal and professional, to deal with emotional aspects of having HIV disease.
• Patient and family state understanding of drug therapy.

loracarbef
(loh-ruh-KAR-bef)
Lorabid

Pharmacologic class: synthetic beta-lactam antibiotic of carbacephem class
Therapeutic class: cephalosporin
Pregnancy risk category: B

Indications and dosages

▶ **Secondary bacterial infections of acute bronchitis.** *Adults:* 200 to 400 g P.O. q 12 hours for 7 days.
▶ **Acute bacterial exacerbations of chronic bronchitis.** *Adults:* 400 mg P.O. q 12 hours for 7 days.
▶ **Pneumonia.** *Adults:* 400 mg P.O. q 12 hours for 14 days.
▶ **Pharyngitis and tonsillitis.** *Adults:* 200 mg P.O. q 12 hours for 10 days.
Children: 15 mg/kg P.O. daily in divided doses q 12 hours for 10 days.
▶ **Sinusitis:** *Adults:* 400 mg P.O. q 12 hours for 10 days.
Children: 15 mg/kg P.O. daily in divided doses q 12 hours for 10 days.
▶ **Acute otitis media.** *Children:* 30 mg/kg (oral suspension) P.O. daily in divided doses q 12 hours for 10 days.
▶ **Uncomplicated skin and skin-structure infections.** *Adults:* 200 mg P.O. q 12 hours for 7 days.
▶ **Impetigo.** *Children:* 15 mg/kg P.O. daily in divided doses q 12 hours for 7 days.
▶ **Uncomplicated cystitis.** *Adults:* 200 mg P.O. daily for 7 days.
▶ **Uncomplicated pyelonephritis.** *Adults:* 400 mg P.O. q 12 hours for 14 days.

Adjust-a-dose: For patients with renal impairment, if creatinine clearance is 10 to 49 ml/minute, give half of usual dose at same intervals. If clearance is below 10 ml/minute, give usual dose q 3 to 5 days. Give hemodialysis patients another dose after dialysis.

Contraindications and cautions

• Contraindicated in patients hypersensitive to drug, other cephalosporins, or related antibiotics, and in patients with diarrhea caused by pseudomembranous colitis.
Lifespan: In pregnant women, use cautiously. In breast-feeding women, use cautiously; it's unknown if the drug appears in breast milk. In infants younger than age 6 months, safety and effectiveness haven't been established.

Adverse reactions

CNS: dizziness, headache, insomnia, nervousness, ***seizures,*** somnolence.
CV: vasodilation.
GI: abdominal pain, anorexia, diarrhea, nausea, ***pseudomembranous colitis,*** vomiting.
GU: vaginal candidiasis.
Hematologic: eosinophilia, ***leukopenia, transient thrombocytopenia.***
Skin: ***erythema multiforme,*** pruritus, rash, urticaria.
Other: ***anaphylaxis,*** hypersensitivity reactions.

Interactions

Drug-drug. *Aminoglycosides, loop diuretics:* May increase risk of nephrotoxicity. Use together cautiously.
Probenecid: May decrease loracarbef excretion, increasing level. Monitor patient for toxicity.
Drug-food. *Any food:* May decrease absorption. Give drug 1 hour before or 2 hours after meals.

Effects on lab test results

• May increase BUN, creatinine, ALT, AST, and alkaline phosphatase levels.
• May increase PT, INR, and eosinophil count. May decrease platelet, WBC, RBC, and neutrophil counts.
• May cause false-positive direct Coombs test.

Pharmacokinetics

Absorption: About 90%.
Distribution: About 25% of circulating drug is protein-bound.
Metabolism: None.

Excretion: Mainly in urine. *Half-life:* About 1 hour.

Route	Onset	Peak	Duration
P.O.	Unknown	30–60 min	Unknown

Action

Chemical effect: Inhibits cell-wall synthesis, promoting osmotic instability; usually bactericidal.

Therapeutic effect: Kills susceptible bacteria.

Available forms

Powder for oral suspension: 100 mg/5 ml, 200 mg/5 ml

Pulvules: 200 mg, 400 mg

NURSING PROCESS

Assessment

- Assess patient's infection before starting therapy and regularly thereafter to monitor drug effectiveness.
- Obtain specimen for culture and sensitivity tests before starting therapy. Begin therapy pending test results.
- Be alert for adverse reactions and drug interactions.

ALERT: Watch for seizures. Beta-lactam antibiotics may trigger seizures in a susceptible patient, especially when given without dosage adjustment to a patient with renal impairment.

- If patient has an adverse GI reaction, monitor his hydration.
- Assess patient's and family's knowledge of drug therapy.

Nursing diagnoses

- Risk for infection related to presence of susceptible bacteria
- Risk for deficient fluid volume related to drug-induced adverse GI reactions
- Deficient knowledge related to drug therapy

Planning and implementation

- To reconstitute powder for oral suspension, add 30 ml of water in two portions to 50-ml bottle, or add 60 ml of water in two portions to 100-ml bottle. Shake after each addition.
- After reconstitution, store oral suspension for 14 days at constant room temperature (59° to 86° F [15° to 30° C]).
- If seizure occurs, stop giving the drug and tell prescriber. Give anticonvulsants.

ALERT: Don't confuse Lorabid with Lortab.

Patient teaching

- Tell patient to take drug on an empty stomach, at least 1 hour before or 2 hours after meals.
- Tell patient to shake suspension well before measuring dose and to take drug exactly as prescribed.
- Instruct patient to discard unused portion after 14 days.

Evaluation

- Patient is free from infection.
- Patient maintains adequate hydration throughout therapy.
- Patient and family state understanding of drug therapy.

loratadine

(loo-RAH-tuh-deen)

Alavert†, Claratyne ◇, Claritin†, Claritin Reditabs† Claritin Syrup†, Claritin-D 12 Hour†, Claritin-D 24 Hour†, Tavist ND Allergy†

Pharmacologic class: peripherally selective piperidine

Therapeutic class: antihistamine

Pregnancy risk category: B

Indications and dosages

▶ **Allergic rhinitis, chronic idiopathic urticaria.** *Adults and children age 6 and older:* 10 mg P.O. daily.

Children ages 2 to 5: Give 5 mg P.O. daily.

Adjust-a-dose: For patients with renal or hepatic impairment, adjust dosage as follows: in adults and children age 6 and older with liver impairment or creatinine clearance less than 30 ml/minute, give 10 mg q other day. In children ages 2 to 5 with liver impairment or renal insufficiency, give 5 mg q other day.

Contraindications and cautions

- Contraindicated in patients hypersensitive to the drug or any of its components.
- Use cautiously in patients with hepatic impairment.

Lifespan: In pregnant women, use only when benefits outweigh risks to the fetus. In breast-feeding women, use cautiously because it isn't known if drug appears in breast milk. In children younger than age 2, safety and effectiveness haven't been established.

Adverse reactions

CNS: drowsiness, fatigue, *headache,* insomnia, nervousness.
EENT: *dry mouth.*

Interactions

Drug-drug. *Erythromycin, ketoconazole:* May increase loratadine level. Monitor patient closely.
Drug-lifestyle. *Alcohol use:* May increase CNS depression. Discourage use together.

Effects on lab test results

None reported.

Pharmacokinetics

Absorption: Good. Food may delay peak levels by 1 hour.
Distribution: Doesn't readily cross blood-brain barrier. About 97% protein-bound.
Metabolism: Extensive, although specific enzyme system hasn't been identified.
Excretion: About 80%, distributed equally between urine and feces. *Half-life:* 8½ hours.

Route	Onset	Peak	Duration
P.O.	1 hr	4–6 hr	24 hr

Action

Chemical effect: Blocks effects of histamine at H_1-receptor sites. Drug's chemical structure prevents entry into CNS, preventing sedation.
Therapeutic effect: Relieves allergy symptoms.

Available forms

Syrup: 1 mg/ml†
Tablets: 10 mg†
Tablets (chewable): 5 mg
Tablets (rapidly disintegrating): 10 mg†

NURSING PROCESS

Assessment

- Assess patient's condition before starting therapy and regularly thereafter to monitor drug effectiveness.
- Be alert for adverse reactions and drug interactions.
- Assess patient's and family's knowledge of drug therapy.

Nursing diagnoses

- Ineffective health maintenance related to underlying allergy condition
- Fatigue related to drug's adverse effect
- Deficient knowledge related to drug therapy

Planning and implementation

- Give drug on an empty stomach.
- If drug is ineffective, notify prescriber.

Patient teaching

- Tell patient to take drug at least 2 hours after a meal, to avoid eating for at least 1 hour after taking drug, and to take drug only once daily.
- Advise patient taking rapidly disintegrating tablets to place tablet on the tongue, where it disintegrates within a few seconds. It can be swallowed with or without water.
- Tell patient to contact prescriber if symptoms persist or worsen.
- Advise patient to stop taking drug 4 days before allergy skin tests to preserve accuracy of tests.
- Tell patient not to drink alcohol and not to drive or engage in other activities that require alertness until the drug's CNS effects are known.

Evaluation

- Patient states that allergy symptoms are relieved.
- Patient describes coping strategies for fatigue.
- Patient and family state understanding of drug therapy.

lorazepam

(loo-RAZ-eh-pam)

Apo-Lorazepam♦, Ativan, Lorazepam Intensol, Novo-Lorazem♦, Nu-Loraz♦

Pharmacologic class: benzodiazepine
Therapeutic class: anxiolytic, sedative-hypnotic
Pregnancy risk category: D
Controlled substance schedule: IV

Indications and dosages

▶ **Anxiety.** *Adults:* 2 to 6 mg P.O. daily in divided doses. Maximum, 10 mg daily.

▶ **Insomnia caused by anxiety.** *Adults:* 2 to 4 mg P.O. at bedtime.

Adjust-a-dose: For elderly patients, initially, 1 to 2 mg P.O. daily in divided doses. Adjust as needed and as tolerated.

▶ **Status epilepticus.** *Adults:* 4 mg I.V. If seizures continue or recur after 10 to 15 minutes, another 4 mg may be given. Drug may be given I.M. if I.V. access is not available. *Children‡:* 0.05 to 0.1 mg/kg I.V.

▶ **Premedication before operative procedure.** *Adults:* 0.05 mg/kg I.M. 2 hours before procedure. Maximum dosage, 4 mg. Or 2 mg total or 0.044 mg/kg I.V., whichever is smaller.

▶ **Nausea and vomiting caused by emetogenic cancer chemotherapy‡.** *Adults:* 2.5 mg P.O. the evening before chemotherapy; repeat just after the initiation of chemotherapy. Or 1.5 mg/m^2 (maximum, 3 mg) I.V. over 5 minutes, 45 minutes before chemotherapy.

I.V. administration

- Have emergency resuscitation equipment and oxygen available.
- Dilute with equal volume of sterile water for injection, normal saline solution for injection, or D_5W injection.
- Don't exceed 2-mg dose preoperatively in patients older than age 50.
- Check respirations before each dose and every 5 to 15 minutes thereafter until respiratory condition is stable.
- Give drug slowly, at no more than 2 mg/minute.

⊗ **Incompatibilities**
Aldesleukin, aztreonam, buprenorphine, foscarnet, idarubicin, imipenem-cilastatin sodium, ondansetron hydrochloride, sargramostim, sufentanil citrate, thiopental.

Contraindications and cautions

- Contraindicated in patients hypersensitive to the drug, any of its components, or other benzodiazepines. Contraindicated in patients with acute angle-closure glaucoma or acute alcohol intoxication. I.M. and I.V. forms contraindicated in patients with renal or hepatic impairment.
- Use cautiously in patients with pulmonary impairment. Use oral forms cautiously in patients with renal or hepatic impairment. Also use cautiously and at a reduced dosage in acutely ill or debilitated patients.

Lifespan: In pregnant and breast-feeding women, drug is contraindicated. In elderly patients, use cautiously and at a lower dosage.

Adverse reactions

CNS: anterograde amnesia, *drowsiness,* fainting, *hangover, lethargy,* psychosis, restlessness.
CV: transient hypotension.
EENT: visual disturbances.
GI: abdominal discomfort, dry mouth.
GU: incontinence, urine retention.
Other: ***acute withdrawal syndrome.***

Interactions

Drug-drug. *CNS depressants:* May increase CNS depression. Avoid use together.
Digoxin: May increase digoxin level, increasing toxicity. Monitor level.
Levodopa: May decrease antiparkinson effect. Monitor patient.
Scopolamine: May increase the risk of sedation, hallucinations, and irrational behavior. Monitor patient.
Drug-herb. *Catnip, kava, lady's slipper, lemon balm, passion flower, sassafras, skullcap, valerian:* May enhance sedative effects. Discourage use together.
Drug-lifestyle. *Alcohol use:* May cause additive CNS effects. Strongly discourage use together.
Smoking: May decrease drug effectiveness. Monitor patient closely; discourage patient from smoking.

Effects on lab test results

- May increase liver function test values.

Pharmacokinetics

Absorption: Good with P.O. use; unknown with I.M. use.
Distribution: Wide. 85% protein-bound.
Metabolism: In liver.
Excretion: In urine. *Half-life:* 10 to 20 hours.

Route	Onset	Peak	Duration
P.O.	1 hr	2 hr	12–24 hr
I.V.	1–5 min	1–1½ hr	6–8 hr
I.M.	15–30 min	1–1½ hr	6–8 hr

Action

Chemical effect: May stimulate gamma-aminobutyric receptors in ascending reticular activating system.
Therapeutic effect: Relieves anxiety and promotes calmness and sleep.

Available forms

Injection: 2 mg/ml, 4 mg/ml

Oral solution (concentrated): 2 mg/ml
S.L. tablets: 0.5 mg ♦, 1 mg ♦, 2 mg ♦
Tablets: 0.5 mg, 1 mg, 2 mg

NURSING PROCESS

Assessment
- Assess patient's condition before starting therapy and regularly thereafter to monitor drug effectiveness.
- Monitor liver, kidney, and hematopoietic function studies periodically in patient receiving repeated or prolonged therapy.
- Be alert for adverse reactions and drug interactions.
- Assess patient's and family's knowledge of drug therapy.

Nursing diagnoses
- Anxiety related to underlying condition
- Risk for injury related to drug-induced adverse CNS effects
- Deficient knowledge related to drug therapy

Planning and implementation
- For I.M. injection, inject drug deep into muscle mass. Don't dilute.
- Refrigerate parenteral form to prolong shelf life.

ALERT: Possibility of abuse and addiction exists. Don't abruptly stop giving the drug after long-term use. Withdrawal symptoms may occur.

ALERT: Don't confuse lorazepam with alprazolam.

Patient teaching
- Warn patient to avoid hazardous activities until the drug's CNS effects are known.
- Tell patient not to drink alcohol or smoke during therapy.
- Explain the risks of dependence and addiction with prolonged use of drug.
- Teach patient not to stop drug abruptly after prolonged use because of risk of seizures or other withdrawal symptoms.

Evaluation
- Patient is less anxious.
- Patient doesn't experience injury as result of adverse CNS reactions.
- Patient and family state understanding of drug therapy.

losartan potassium
(loh-SAR-tan poh-TAH-see-um)
Cozaar

Pharmacologic class: angiotensin II receptor antagonist
Therapeutic class: antihypertensive
Pregnancy risk category: C (D in second and third trimesters)

Indications and dosages
▶ **Nephropathy in type 2 diabetes mellitus.** *Adults:* 50 mg P.O. daily. Increase dose to 100 mg daily based on blood pressure response.

▶ **Hypertension.** *Adults:* Initially, 25 to 50 mg P.O. daily. Maximum, 100 mg daily in one or two divided doses.

▶ **To reduce risk of stroke in patients with hypertension and left ventricular hypertrophy.** *Adults:* Initially, 50 mg P.O. once daily. Adjust dosage based on blood pressure response, adding hydrochlorothiazide 12.5 mg once daily, increasing losartan to 100 mg daily, or both. If further adjustments are needed, may increase the daily dose of hydrochlorothiazide to 25 mg.

Adjust-a-dose: In patient with impaired liver function or volume depletion (such as patient taking diuretic), use initial dose of 25 mg.

Contraindications and cautions
- Contraindicated in patients hypersensitive to the drug or any of its components.
- Use cautiously in patients with impaired kidney or liver function and in volume-depleted, hypotensive patients.

Lifespan: In pregnant women, drug is contraindicated in second and third trimesters; use very cautiously in first trimester. If pregnancy occurs, stop drug as soon as possible. Breastfeeding women should stop breast-feeding or use another drug. In children, safety and effectiveness haven't been established.

Adverse reactions
For hypertension and left ventricular hypertrophy
CNS: asthenia, dizziness, fatigue, headache, insomnia.
CV: chest pain, edema.
EENT: nasal congestion, pharyngitis, sinus disorder, sinusitis.

GI: abdominal pain, diarrhea, dyspepsia, nausea.
Musculoskeletal: back or leg pain, muscle cramps, myalgia.
Respiratory: cough, upper respiratory tract infection.
Other: ***anaphylaxis, angioedema.***
For nephropathy
CNS: *asthenia,* diabetic neuropathy, *fatigue,* fever, hypoesthesia.
CV: *chest pain, diabetic vascular disease,* hypotension, orthostatic hypotension.
EENT: cataract, sinusitis.
GI: *diarrhea,* dyspepsia, gastritis.
GU: UTI.
Hematologic: *anemia.*
Metabolic: ***hyperkalemia,*** **HYPOGLYCEMIA,** weight gain.
Musculoskeletal: *back pain,* leg or knee pain, muscle weakness.
Respiratory: *bronchitis, cough.*
Skin: cellulitis.
Other: ***anaphylaxis, angioedema,*** infection, *flulike syndrome,* trauma.

Interactions

Drug-drug. *Fluconazole:* May increase antihypertensive effects and adverse reactions. Monitor patient.
Indomethacin: May decrease hypotensive effect. Monitor blood pressure.
Phenobarbital: May decrease losartan absorption. Monitor patient.
Potassium-sparing diuretics, potassium supplements: May cause hyperkalemia. Monitor potassium level.
Rifamycins: May decrease antihypertensive effects. Monitor blood pressure.
Drug-herb. *Red yeast rice:* May increase the risk of adverse events or toxicity because herb contains components similar to those of statin drugs. Discourage use together.
Drug-food. *Salt substitutes containing potassium:* May increase risk of hyperkalemia. Monitor patient closely; advise patient to use only under prescriber's guidance.

Effects on lab test results

None reported.

Pharmacokinetics

Absorption: Good with extensive first-pass metabolism; systemic bioavailability of drug is 33%.
Distribution: Highly protein-bound.
Metabolism: Involves CYP2C9 and CYP3A4.
Excretion: Mainly in feces with smaller amount in urine. *Half-life:* 2 hours.

Route	Onset	Peak	Duration
P.O.	Unknown	1–4 hr	Unknown

Action

Chemical effect: Inhibits vasoconstricting and aldosterone-secreting effects of angiotensin II by selectively blocking binding of angiotensin II to receptor sites in many tissues, including vascular smooth muscle and adrenal glands.
Therapeutic effect: Lowers blood pressure.

Available forms

Tablets: 25 mg, 50 mg, 100 mg

NURSING PROCESS

Assessment

- Assess patient's blood pressure before starting therapy and regularly thereafter to monitor drug's effectiveness. When drug is used alone, its effect on blood pressure is notably less in black patients than in patients of other races.
- Regularly assess creatinine and BUN levels to check kidney function. Patients with severe heart failure whose kidney function depends on angiotensin-aldosterone system may develop acute renal impairment during therapy. Monitor patient closely, especially during first few weeks of therapy.
- Be alert for adverse reactions.
- If patient is taking a diuretic, watch for symptomatic hypotension.
- Assess patient's and family's knowledge of drug therapy.

Nursing diagnoses

- Risk for injury related to presence of hypertension
- Sleep deprivation related to drug-induced insomnia
- Deficient knowledge related to drug therapy

Planning and implementation

- Black patients with hypertension and left ventricular hypertrophy have a lower risk of stroke with atenolol than with this drug, but the cause is unknown.
- Drug can be used alone or with other antihypertensives.
- Determine trough level to measure effect. If giving once daily isn't effective, divide same total daily into two daily doses or increase dose.
- Give once-daily dose in the morning to prevent insomnia.
- If pregnancy is suspected, stop giving the drug and immediately notify prescriber.

ALERT: Don't confuse Cozaar with Zocor.

Patient teaching

- Tell patient to avoid sodium substitutes because they may contain potassium, which can cause hyperkalemia in patients taking drug.
- Tell woman of childbearing age to notify prescriber immediately if she suspects she is pregnant.

Evaluation

- Patient's blood pressure is normal.
- Patient states that insomnia hasn't occurred.
- Patient and family state understanding of drug therapy.

lovastatin (mevinolin)

(loh-vuh-STAH-tin)

Altoprev, Mevacor

Pharmacologic class: HMG-CoA reductase inhibitor
Therapeutic class: cholesterol-lowering drug
Pregnancy risk category: X

Indications and dosages

▶ **Primary prevention of coronary artery disease; coronary artery disease; hyperlipidemia.** *Adults:* Initially, 20 mg immediate-release tablets P.O. once daily with evening meal. Recommended range is 10 to 80 mg in single or two divided doses; maximum dosage, 80 mg daily. Or 20 to 60 mg extended-release P.O. at bedtime. Starting dose of 10 mg can be used for patients requiring smaller reductions. Usual dosage range is 10 to 60 mg daily for the extended-release tablets.

▶ **Heterozygous familial hypercholesterolemia.** *Children ages 10 to 17:* Give 10 to 40 mg P.O. (immediate-release) daily with evening meal. In patients requiring reductions in LDL level of 20% or more, start with 20 mg daily.

Adjust-a-dose: For patients also taking cyclosporine, give 10 mg P.O. daily, not to exceed 20 mg daily. Avoid use of drug with fibrates or niacin; if used with either, don't give more than 20 mg of lovastatin daily. If using with amiodarone or verapamil (immediate-release), don't exceed 40 mg/day.

For patients with renal impairment, if creatinine clearance is less than 30 ml/minute, take care when considering dosage increase above 20 mg daily.

Contraindications and cautions

- Contraindicated in patients hypersensitive to the drug or any of its components, and in those with active liver disease or conditions linked to unexplained persistent elevations of transaminase levels.
- Use cautiously in patients who consume substantial quantities of alcohol or have history of liver disease.

Lifespan: In pregnant and breast-feeding women, drug is contraindicated. In women of childbearing age, drug is contraindicated unless they have no risk of pregnancy. In children younger than age 10, safety and effectiveness haven't been established.

Adverse reactions

CNS: dizziness, headache, peripheral neuropathy.
EENT: blurred vision.
GI: abdominal pain or cramps, constipation, diarrhea, dysgeusia, dyspepsia, flatulence, heartburn, nausea.
Musculoskeletal: muscle cramps, myalgia, myositis, ***rhabdomyolysis.***
Skin: pruritus, rash.

Interactions

Drug-drug. *Bile acid sequestrants:* May decrease lovastatin bioavailability. Give separately.
Cyclosporine or other immunosuppressants, erythromycin, gemfibrozil, niacin: May increase risk of polymyositis and rhabdomyolysis. Monitor patient closely.
Digoxin: May slightly elevate digoxin level. Monitor patient.

Fluconazole, itraconazole, ketoconazole: May increase lovastatin level and adverse effects. Avoid this combination. If drugs must be given together, reduce lovastatin dosage.
Isradipine: May increase lovastatin clearance and its metabolites by increasing hepatic blood flow. Monitor patient for loss of therapeutic effect.
Nicotinic acid: May increase risk of severe myopathy or rhabdomyolysis. Monitor patient closely.
Oral anticoagulants: May enhance oral anticoagulant effects. Monitor PT and INR.
Drug-herb. *Red yeast rice:* May increase risk of adverse events or toxicity because herb contains components similar to those of drug. Discourage use together.
Drug-lifestyle. *Alcohol use:* May increase risk of hepatotoxicity. Discourage use together.
Sun exposure: May cause photosensitivity reactions. Tell patient to avoid unprotected or prolonged exposure to sunlight.

Effects on lab test results

- May increase ALT, AST, and CK levels. May decrease lipid level.

Pharmacokinetics

Absorption: About 30%. Giving with food improves levels of total inhibitors by about 30%. Extended-release tablets have greater bioavailability than immediate-release tablets.
Distribution: Less than 5% because of extensive first-pass hepatic extraction. More than 95% protein-bound.
Metabolism: In liver.
Excretion: About 80% in feces, about 10% in urine. *Half-life:* 3 hours.

Route	Onset	Peak	Duration
P.O.	Unknown	2–6 hr	4–6 wk
P.O. Extended-release	Unknown	14 hr	Unknown

Action

Chemical effect: Inhibits HMG-CoA reductase. This enzyme is an early and rate-limiting step in synthetic pathway of cholesterol.
Therapeutic effect: Lowers LDL and total cholesterol levels.

Available forms

Tablets: 10 mg, 20 mg, 40 mg
Tablets (extended-release): 10 mg, 20 mg, 40 mg, 60 mg

NURSING PROCESS

Assessment

- Obtain history of patient's lipoprotein and cholesterol levels before starting therapy, and reassess regularly to monitor drug effectiveness.
- Use for heterozygous familial hypercholesterolemia in girls who are at least 1 year postmenarche and boys (ages 10 to 17) who have the following findings after an adequate trial of diet therapy: LDL level higher than 189 mg/dl or LDL level higher than 160 mg/dl with a family history of premature CV disease or two or more other CV disease risk factors.
- Perform liver function tests before starting therapy and periodically thereafter.
- Be alert for adverse reactions and drug interactions.
- Assess patient's and family's knowledge of drug therapy.

Nursing diagnoses

- Risk for injury related to underlying condition
- Acute pain related to drug-induced adverse musculoskeletal reactions
- Deficient knowledge related to drug therapy

Planning and implementation

- Begin drug therapy only after diet and other nondrug therapies have proven ineffective. Make sure patient follows a low-cholesterol diet.
- Give drug with evening meal; absorption is enhanced and cholesterol biosynthesis is greater in evening.

ALERT: Don't confuse lovastatin with Lotensin, Leustatin, or Livostin. Don't confuse Mevacor with Mivacron.

Patient teaching

- Instruct patient to take drug with evening meal.
- Advise patient not to crush or chew extended-release tablets.
- Teach patient to manage lipid level by restricting total fat and cholesterol intake. If appropriate, recommend weight control, exercise, and smoking cessation programs to control other cardiac disease risk factors.

L

• Advise patient to have periodic eye examinations.
• Tell patient to store drug at room temperature in light-resistant container.
• Instruct patient to avoid alcohol consumption during drug therapy.
ALERT: Inform patient that drug is contraindicated during pregnancy. Tell her to notify prescriber immediately if she becomes pregnant.

Evaluation
• Patient's LDL and cholesterol levels are within normal limits.
• Patient doesn't experience musculoskeletal pain.
• Patient and family state understanding of drug therapy.

lubiprostone
(loo-bee-PROSS-tohn)
Amitiza

Pharmacologic class: chloride channel activator
Therapeutic class: laxative
Pregnancy risk category: C

Indications and dosages
▶ **Chronic idiopathic constipation.** *Adults:* 24 mcg P.O. b.i.d. with food.

Contraindications and cautions
• Contraindicated in patients hypersensitive to drug or its components and in those with a history of mechanical GI obstruction.
• Use cautiously in women who are or may become pregnant.
Lifespan: In pregnant patients, use only if benefits outweigh risks to fetus. In breast-feeding patients, mother should stop breast-feeding or stop drug therapy. In children, safety and effectiveness haven't been established. In elderly patients, use cautiously due to increased likelihood of hepatic or renal insufficiency.

Adverse reactions
CNS: anxiety, depression, dizziness, fatigue, *headache,* insomnia, pyrexia.
CV: chest pain, peripheral edema.
EENT: nasopharyngitis, pharyngolaryngeal pain, sinusitis.
GI: abdominal distention, abdominal pain or discomfort, constipation, *diarrhea,* dry mouth, dyspepsia, flatulence, gastroesophageal reflux disease, loose stools, *nausea,* stomach discomfort, viral gastroenteritis, vomiting.
GU: UTI.
Metabolic: weight gain.
Musculoskeletal: arthralgia, back pain, limb pain, muscle cramps.
Respiratory: bronchitis, cough, dyspnea, upper respiratory tract infection.
Other: influenza.

Interactions
None reported.

Effects on lab test results
None reported.

Pharmacokinetics
Absorption: Low systemic availability.
Distribution: 94% bound to plasma proteins.
Metabolism: Rapid and extensive in stomach and jejunum.
Excretion: Trace amount in feces. *Half-life:* Unknown.

Route	Onset	Peak	Duration
P.O.	Unknown	1 hr	Unknown

Action
Chemical effect: Increases intestinal fluid secretion by activating chloride channels, and increases intestinal motility.
Therapeutic effect: Relieves constipation.

Available forms
Capsules: 24 mcg

NURSING PROCESS

Assessment
• Obtain history of bowel disorder, GI status, fluid intake, nutritional status, exercise habits, and normal patterns of elimination.
• Monitor effectiveness by checking frequency and characteristics of stools. Relief is defined as three or more spontaneous bowel movements weekly.
• Be alert for adverse reactions. Nausea, diarrhea, and headache are the most common.
• Assess patient's and family's understanding of drug therapy.

Nursing diagnoses
- Constipation related to interruption of normal pattern of elimination
- Risk for deficient fluid volume due to drug-induced diarrhea
- Deficient knowledge related to drug therapy

Planning and implementation
- Auscultate bowel sounds at least once per shift. Check for pain and cramping.
- Don't give drug to a patient with severe diarrhea.

Patient teaching
- Tell patient to take drug with food.
- Explain that patient may have diarrhea during treatment; advise against taking the drug if he develops severe diarrhea.
- Advise patient about a proper diet and the need to drink plenty of fluids.

Evaluation
- Patient reports return of normal bowel pattern of elimination.
- Patient is free from deficient fluid volume.
- Patient and family state understanding of drug therapy.

lymphocyte immune globulin (LIG) (antithymocyte globulin [equine], ATG),

(LIM-foh-sight ih-MYOON GLOH-byoo-lin)
Atgam

Pharmacologic class: immunoglobulin
Therapeutic class: immunosuppressant
Pregnancy risk category: C

Indications and dosages

▶ **To prevent acute renal allograft rejection.** *Adults and children:* 15 mg/kg I.V. daily for 14 days, followed by alternate-day doses for 14 days. Give first dose within 24 hours of transplantation.

▶ **Acute renal allograft rejection.** *Adults and children:* 10 to 15 mg/kg I.V. daily for 14 days, followed by alternate-day doses for 14 days. Start therapy when rejection is diagnosed.

▶ **Aplastic anemia.** *Adults:* 10 to 20 mg/kg I.V. daily for 8 to 14 days. Additional alternate-day therapy up to total of 21 doses can be given.

▶ **Skin allotransplantation‡.** *Adults:* 10 mg/kg I.V. 24 hours before allograft; then 10 to 15 mg/kg q other day. Maintenance dosage ranges from 5 to 40 mg/kg daily based on response. Therapy usually continues until allograft covers less than 20% of total body surface area, usually 40 to 60 days.

I.V. administration
- Dilute dose in 250 to 1,000 ml of half-normal or normal saline solution for injection. Don't exceed final concentration of 4 mg/ml. When adding drug to solution, make sure container is inverted so drug doesn't contact air inside container. The proteins in drug can be denatured by air. Gently rotate or swirl container to mix contents; don't shake because this may cause excessive foaming and may alter drug.
- Allow diluted drug to reach room temperature before infusion.
- Infuse with in-line filter with pore size of 0.2 to 1 micron over no less than 4 hours (most facilities specify 4 to 8 hours) into a vascular shunt, arterial venous fistula, or high-flow central vein.
- Don't use solutions that are more than 12 hours old, including actual infusion time.
- Refrigerate drug at 35° to 47° F (2° to 8° C). Don't freeze. Drug is heat sensitive.

⊗ **Incompatibilities**
Acidic solutions, dextrose solutions, solutions with low salt concentration.

Contraindications and cautions
- Contraindicated in patients hypersensitive to the drug or any of its components.
- Use cautiously in patients receiving additional immunosuppressive therapy (such as corticosteroids and azathioprine) because of increased risk of infection.

Lifespan: In pregnant women, use cautiously. In breast-feeding women, drug isn't recommended because it is unknown if drug is excreted in breast milk.

Adverse reactions
CNS: headache, malaise, ***seizures.***
CV: *chest pain,* edema, *hypotension,* ***iliac vein obstruction,*** renal artery stenosis, tachycardia, thrombophlebitis.
EENT: ***laryngospasm.***
GI: abdominal distention, diarrhea, epigastric pain, *nausea,* stomatitis, *vomiting.*

Hematologic: ***aplastic anemia,*** hemolysis, ***leukopenia,*** lymphadenopathy, ***thrombocytopenia.***
Metabolic: hyperglycemia.
Musculoskeletal: arthralgia.
Respiratory: *dyspnea,* hiccups, ***pulmonary edema.***
Skin: rash.
Other: ***anaphylaxis,*** febrile reactions, infection, night sweats, serum sickness.

Interactions

Drug-drug. *Immunosuppressants, muromonab-CD3:* May increase risk of infection. Monitor patient closely.

Effects on lab test results

- May increase liver enzyme and glucose levels. May decrease hemoglobin level and hematocrit.
- May decrease WBC and platelet counts.

Pharmacokinetics

Absorption: Given I.V.
Distribution: Unknown.
Metabolism: Unknown.
Excretion: About 1% in urine, mainly as unchanged drug. *Half-life:* About 6 days.

Route	Onset	Peak	Duration
I.V.	Unknown	5 days	Unknown

Action

Chemical effect: Inhibits cell-mediated immune responses by either altering T-cell function or eliminating antigen-reactive T cells.
Therapeutic effect: Prevents or relieves evidence of renal allograft rejection; also relieves signs and symptoms of aplastic anemia.

Available forms

Injection: 50 mg of equine immunoglobulin/ml

NURSING PROCESS

Assessment

- Assess patient's condition before starting therapy and regularly thereafter to monitor drug effectiveness.
- Be alert for adverse reactions and drug interactions.
- Assess patient's and family's knowledge of drug therapy.

Nursing diagnoses

- Ineffective health maintenance related to underlying condition
- Ineffective immune protection related to adverse hematologic reactions
- Deficient knowledge related to drug therapy

Planning and implementation

- Perform an intradermal skin test at least 1 hour before giving the first dose. Marked local swelling or erythema larger than 10 mm indicates increased risk of severe systemic reaction, such as anaphylaxis. Severe reactions to skin test, such as hypotension, tachycardia, dyspnea, generalized rash, or anaphylaxis, rule out further use.

ALERT: Keep airway adjuncts and anaphylaxis drugs at bedside while giving the drug.

Patient teaching

- Warn patient that he'll likely develop a fever. Instruct him to report adverse drug effects.
- Instruct patient to take infection-control and bleeding precautions.

Evaluation

- Patient responds well to therapy.
- Patient doesn't experience serious adverse hematologic reactions.
- Patient and family state understanding of drug therapy.

magnesium chloride

(mag-NEE-see-um KLOR-ighd)
Slow-Mag

magnesium sulfate

Pharmacologic class: magnesium salts
Therapeutic class: anticonvulsant, mineral, antiarrhythmic
Pregnancy risk category: A

Indications and dosages

▶ **Mild hypomagnesemia.** *Adults:* 1 g I.M. q 6 hours for four doses, depending on magnesium level.

▶ **Severe hypomagnesemia (magnesium level 0.8 mEq/L or less with symptoms).** *Adults:* Up to 2 mEq (0.5 ml of 50% solution)/kg I.M. within a 4- hour period may be given, or 5 g (about 40 mEq) I.V. in 1 L of solution over 3 hours. Subsequent doses depend on magnesium level.
▶ **Magnesium supplementation.** *Adults:* 54 to 483 mg P.O. daily in divided doses (chloride form only).
▶ **Magnesium supplementation in total parenteral nutrition (TPN).** *Adults:* 8 to 24 mEq I.V. daily added to TPN solution.
Infants: 2 to 10 mEq I.V. daily added to TPN solution. Each 2 ml of 50% solution contains 1 g, or 8.12 mEq, magnesium sulfate.
▶ **Hypomagnesemic seizures.** *Adults:* 1 to 2 g of 10% solution I.V. over 15 minutes; then 1 g I.M. q 4 to 6 hours, based on patient's response and magnesium level.
▶ **Seizures caused by hypomagnesemia in acute nephritis.** *Children:* 20 to 40 mg/kg I.M. p.r.n. to control seizures. Dilute the 50% concentration to a 20% solution and give 0.1 to 0.2 ml/kg of the 20% solution. Or, 100 to 200 mg/kg as a 1% to 3% solution I.V. slowly over one hour with 50% of dose given in first 15 to 20 minutes. Adjust dosage according to magnesium level and seizure response.
▶ **Paroxysmal atrial tachycardia in patients unresponsive to other therapies‡.** *Adults:* 3 to 4 g I.V. of 10% solution over 30 seconds with close monitoring of ECG.
▶ **To reduce CV morbidity and mortality from acute MI‡.** *Adults:* 2 g I.V. over 5 to 15 minutes, followed by infusion of 18 g over 24 hours (12.5 mg/minute). Start as soon as possible, and no longer than 6 hours after MI.
▶ **To manage preterm labor‡.** *Adults:* 4 to 6 g I.V. over 20 minutes as a loading dose, followed by maintenance infusions of 2 to 4 g/hour for 12 to 24 hours, as tolerated, after contractions subside.
▶ **Severe acute asthma unresponsive to conventional therapy‡.** *Children:* 25 to 50 mg/kg (up to 2 g) I.V. over 10 to 20 minutes.

I.V. administration

- Solutions must be diluted to 20% (200 mg/ml) or less before administration.
- Inject I.V. bolus dose slowly. Use infusion pump for continuous infusion to avoid respiratory or cardiac arrest. Don't exceed 150 mg/minute (1.5 ml of a 10% solution). Rapid drip causes heat sensation.
- When giving I.V. for severe hypomagnesemia, watch for respiratory depression and evidence of heart block. Give dose only when respirations are more than 16 breaths/minute.
- Monitor vital signs q 15 minutes when giving drug I.V.
- For preterm labor, monitor I.V. fluids and rates carefully to avoid circulatory overload. Monitor patient for pulmonary edema.

⊗ **Incompatibilities**
Alcohol in high concentrations, alkali carbonates and bicarbonates, amiodarone, amphotericin B, arsenates, barium, calcium gluconate, cefepime, ciprofloxacin, clindamycin, cyclosporine, dobutamine, ethanol, heavy metals, hydrocortisone sodium succinate, I.V. fat emulsion 10%, polymyxin B, procaine, salicylates, sodium bicarbonate, soluble phosphates, tartrates.

Contraindications and cautions

- Contraindicated in patients with myocardial damage, marked myocardial disease, or heart block. I.V. form is contraindicated in patients with preeclampsia during the 2 hours preceding delivery. Magnesium chloride is contraindicated in patients with renal impairment.
- Use magnesium sulfate cautiously in patients with impaired kidney function.

Lifespan: Use during all trimesters of pregnancy if clearly needed except during active labor when drug is contraindicated. Continuous I.V. infusion longer than 24 hours in toxemic mothers may cause neonatal magnesium toxicity. In breast-feeding women small amount of drug is excreted in breast milk but use if clearly needed. Elderly patients may need a lower dose because of renal insufficiency. If patient is severely renally impaired, don't exceed 20 g in 48 hours.

Adverse reactions

CNS: *depressed deep tendon reflexes,* drowsiness, flaccid paralysis, hypothermia, perioral paresthesia, ***seizures,*** tetany, twitching carpopedal spasm.
CV: ***arrhythmias; circulatory collapse; depressed cardiac function; heart block;*** *hypotension;* ***slow, weak pulse.***
Metabolic: hypocalcemia.
Respiratory: ***respiratory paralysis.***
Other: diaphoresis, flushing.

Interactions

Drug-drug. *Anesthetics, CNS depressants:* May cause additive CNS depression. Use together cautiously.
Digoxin: May cause serious cardiac conduction changes. Give cautiously.
Neuromuscular blockers: May increase neuromuscular blockage. Use cautiously; monitor patient for increased effects.
Nitrofurantoin, penicillamine, tetracyclines: May decrease bioavailability with oral magnesium supplements. Separate doses by 2 to 3 hours.

Effects on lab test results

- May increase magnesium level. May decrease calcium and potassium levels.

Pharmacokinetics

Absorption: 35% to 40% of P.O. dose. High-fat diets may interfere.
Distribution: About 30% is bound intracellularly to proteins and energy-rich phosphates.
Metabolism: None.
Excretion: Parenteral dose mainly in urine, P.O. dose in urine and feces. *Half-life:* Unknown.

Route	Onset	Peak	Duration
P.O.	Unknown	4 hr	4–6 hr
I.V.	Immediate	Unknown	30 min
I.M.	1 hr	Unknown	3–4 hr

Action

Chemical effect: Replaces and maintains magnesium levels; as anticonvulsant, reduces muscle contractions by interfering with release of acetylcholine at myoneural junction.
Therapeutic effect: Raises magnesium levels, alleviates seizures, and restores normal sinus rhythm.

Available forms

magnesium chloride
Injectable solutions: 20% (1.97 mEq/ml)
Tablets (delayed-release): 64 mg elemental magnesium
magnesium sulfate
Injectable solutions: 4% (0.325 mEq/ml), 8% (0.65 mEq/ml), 10% (0.8 mEq/ml), 12.5% (1 mEq/ml), 50% (4 mEq/ml)

NURSING PROCESS

Assessment

- Assess patient's condition before therapy and regularly thereafter to monitor drug effectiveness.
- Check magnesium level after repeated doses.

ALERT: Watch for respiratory depression and signs of heart block. Make sure respirations are 16 breaths/minute before each dose.

- Monitor patient's fluid intake and output. Make sure output is 100 ml or more during the 4 hours before giving.
- Be alert for adverse reactions and drug interactions.
- Assess patient's and family's knowledge of drug therapy.

Nursing diagnoses

- Ineffective health maintenance related to underlying condition
- Risk for injury related to drug-induced adverse reactions
- Deficient knowledge related to drug therapy

Planning and implementation

- Keep I.V. calcium gluconate available at bedside to reverse magnesium intoxication.
- For cases of severe hypermagnesemia, peritoneal dialysis or hemodialysis may be needed.
- Undiluted 50% solutions may be given to adults by deep I.M. injection. When giving to children, dilute solutions to 20% or less.

ALERT: Test knee-jerk (patellar) reflexes before each additional dose. If no reflex, notify prescriber and withhold magnesium until reflexes return. Check magnesium level because it may be toxic. Signs of hypermagnesemia begin to appear at a level of 4 mEq/L.

- If used to treat seizures, take appropriate seizure precautions.

Patient teaching

- Instruct patient taking parenteral drug to immediately report any adverse reactions.
- Review oral administration schedule with patient. Tell him not to take more than prescribed.

Evaluation

- Patient has positive response to drug administration.
- Patient sustains no injury from adverse reactions.

• Patient and family state understanding of drug therapy.

magnesium citrate (citrate of magnesia)

(mag-NEE-see-um SIH-trayt)

Citro-Mag ♦, Evac-Q-Mag

magnesium hydroxide

Milk of Magnesia†, Milk of Magnesia Concentrated†, Phillips' Milk of Magnesia†, Phillips' Milk of Magnesia Concentrated†

magnesium sulfate

Epsom salts†

Pharmacologic class: magnesium salts
Therapeutic class: saline laxatives
Pregnancy risk category: NR

Indications and dosages

▶ **Constipation, to evacuate bowel before surgery.** *Adults and children age 12 and older:* 11 to 25 g magnesium citrate P.O. daily as single dose or divided. Or 2 to 4 tbs magnesium hydroxide at bedtime or on rising, followed by 240 ml (8 oz) of liquid. Or 10 to 30 g magnesium sulfate P.O. daily as single dose or divided.

Children ages 6 to 11: Give 5.5 to 12.5 g magnesium citrate P.O. daily as single dose or divided. Or 1 to 2 tbs magnesium hydroxide followed by 240 ml (8 oz) of liquid. Don't use dosage cup. Or 5 to 10 g magnesium sulfate P.O. daily as single dose or divided.

Children ages 2 to 5: Give 2.7 to 6.25 g magnesium citrate P.O. daily as single dose or divided. Or 1 to 3 tsp magnesium hydroxide followed by 240 ml (8 oz) of liquid. Don't use dosage cup. Or 2.5 to 5 g magnesium sulfate P.O. daily as single dose or divided.

▶ **Acid indigestion, gastroesophageal reflux disease, peptic ulcer disease, heartburn.** *Adults and children age 12 and older:* Don't use dosage cup. 1 to 3 tsp magnesium hydroxide with a little water, up to q.i.d., or as directed by prescriber. Or, for adults, 5 to 15 ml magnesium citrate P.O. t.i.d. or q.i.d.

Contraindications and cautions

• Contraindicated in patients with abdominal pain, nausea, vomiting, other symptoms of appendicitis or acute surgical abdomen, myocardial damage, heart block, fecal impaction, rectal fissures, intestinal obstruction or perforation, or renal disease.

• Use cautiously in patients with rectal bleeding.

Lifespan: In pregnant women, use cautiously. During labor and delivery, drug is contraindicated. In breast-feeding women, use cautiously; small amounts of the drug appears in breast milk. In children, use cautiously.

Adverse reactions

GI: *abdominal cramping, diarrhea,* laxative dependence with long-term or excessive use, *nausea.*

Metabolic: fluid and electrolyte disturbances.

Interactions

Drug-drug. *Benzodiazepines, chloroquine, corticosteroids, digoxin, H_2 antagonists, hydantoins, iron, nitrofurantoin, penicillamine, phenothiazines, tetracyclines:* May decrease pharmacologic effects of these drugs. Monitor patient.

Ciprofloxacin, levofloxacin, lomefloxacin, moxifloxacin, norfloxacin, ofloxacin: May decrease effects of quinolones. Give drug at least 6 hours before or 2 hours after quinolones.

Dicumarol, quinidine, sulfonylureas: May increase effects of these drugs. Monitor patient.

Oral drugs: May impair absorption. Separate doses.

Effects on lab test results

• May increase or decrease fluid and electrolyte levels with prolonged use.

Pharmacokinetics

Absorption: About 15% to 30% may be systemic (posing risk to patients with renal impairment).

Distribution: Unknown.

Metabolism: Unknown.

Excretion: Unabsorbed drug in feces; absorbed drug rapidly in urine. *Half-life:* Unknown.

Route	Onset	Peak	Duration
P.O.	30 min–3 hr	Varies	Varies

M

Action

Chemical effect: Reduces total acid load in GI tract, elevates gastric pH to inhibit pepsin, strengthens gastric mucosal barrier, and increases esophageal sphincter tone.
Therapeutic effect: Soothes stomach upset, relieves constipation, and raises magnesium level.

Available forms

magnesium citrate
Oral solution: about 3.85 to 4.71 mEq magnesium/5 ml†
magnesium hydroxide
Liquid: 400 mg/5 ml, 800 mg/5 ml
Tablets (chewable): 311 mg
magnesium sulfate
Granules: about 40 mEq magnesium/5 g†

NURSING PROCESS

Assessment

- Assess patient's condition before therapy and regularly thereafter to monitor drug effectiveness.
- Before giving drug for constipation, determine whether patient has adequate fluid intake, exercise, and diet.

ALERT: Monitor electrolyte levels during prolonged use. Magnesium may accumulate in patients with renal insufficiency.

- Be alert for adverse reactions and drug interactions.
- Assess patient's and family's knowledge of drug therapy.

Nursing diagnoses

- Constipation related to underlying condition
- Diarrhea related to therapy
- Deficient knowledge related to drug therapy

Planning and implementation

- Give the drug at a time that doesn't interfere with scheduled activities or sleep.
- Chill magnesium citrate before use to improve its palatability.
- Shake suspension well. Give with large amount of water when used as laxative. When giving through NG tube, make sure tube is placed properly and is patent. After instilling drug, flush tube with water to ensure passage to stomach and to maintain tube patency.

ALERT: Drug is for short-term therapy only.

- Magnesium sulfate is more potent than other saline laxatives.

Patient teaching

- Teach patient about dietary sources of bulk, such as bran, other high-fiber cereals, and fresh fruit and vegetables.
- Warn patient that frequent or prolonged use may cause dependence.

Evaluation

- Patient's constipation is relieved.
- Diarrhea doesn't develop.
- Patient and family state understanding of drug therapy.

magnesium oxide

(mag-NEE-see-um OKS-ighd)
Mag-Caps, Mag-Ox 400†, Maox 420†, Uro-Mag†

Pharmacologic class: magnesium salt
Therapeutic class: antacid, mineral
Pregnancy risk category: NR

Indications and dosages

▶ **Antacid.** *Adults:* 140 mg (capsules) P.O. 3 to 4 times daily, or 400 to 800 mg (tablets) daily.
▶ **Mild hypomagnesemia.** *Adults:* 400 to 840 mg P.O. daily based on magnesium level.

Contraindications and cautions

- In patients with renal disease, use cautiously and under the supervision of a physician.

Lifespan: In pregnant women, use cautiously. In breast-feeding women, use cautiously; it's unknown if the drug appears in breast milk.

Adverse reactions

GI: abdominal pain, *diarrhea,* nausea.
Metabolic: hypermagnesemia.

Interactions

Drug-drug. *Allopurinol, antibiotics (including fluoroquinolones and tetracyclines), diflunisal, digoxin, iron, isoniazid, penicillamine, phenothiazines, quinidine:* May decrease pharmacologic effect, possibly because of impaired absorption. Separate doses.

Enteric-coated drugs: May release prematurely in stomach. Separate doses by at least 1 hour.

Effects on lab test results

- May increase magnesium level.

Pharmacokinetics

Absorption: Small.
Distribution: Unknown.
Metabolism: None.
Excretion: Unabsorbed drug in feces; absorbed drug in urine. *Half-life:* Unknown.

Route	Onset	Peak	Duration
P.O.			
Fasting	20 min	Unknown	20–60 min
Non-fasting	20 min	Unknown	20–60 min

Action

Chemical effect: Reduces total acid load in GI tract, elevates gastric pH to inhibit pepsin, strengthens gastric mucosal barrier, and increases esophageal sphincter tone.
Therapeutic effect: Soothes stomach upset, relieves constipation, and raises magnesium level.

Available forms

Capsules: 140 mg (84.5 mg elemental magnesium)†
Tablets: 400 mg (241.3 mg elemental magnesium)†, 420 mg†, 500 mg†

NURSING PROCESS

Assessment

- Assess patient's condition before therapy and regularly thereafter to monitor drug effectiveness.

ALERT: Monitor magnesium level. In a patient with renal impairment on long-term therapy, watch for signs and symptoms of hypermagnesemia (hypotension, nausea, vomiting, depressed reflexes, respiratory depression, and coma).

- Be alert for adverse reactions and drug interactions.
- Assess patient's and family's knowledge of drug therapy.

Nursing diagnoses

- Ineffective health maintenance related to underlying condition
- Risk for injury related to potential for hypermagnesemia
- Deficient knowledge related to drug therapy

Planning and implementation

- Don't give other oral drugs 1 to 2 hours before or after therapy.
- If patient has diarrhea, use a different drug.

Patient teaching

- Advise patient not to take drug indiscriminately or to switch antacids without prescriber's advice.

Evaluation

- Patient responds well to therapy.
- Patient maintains normal magnesium level throughout therapy.
- Patient and family state understanding of drug therapy.

mannitol

(MAN-ih-tol)
Osmitrol

Pharmacologic class: osmotic diuretic
Therapeutic class: diuretic
Pregnancy risk category: C

Indications and dosages

▶ **Test dose for marked oliguria or suspected inadequate kidney function.** *Adults and children older than age 12:* Give 200 mg/kg or 12.5 g as 15% or 20% I.V. solution over 3 to 5 minutes. Response is adequate if 30 to 50 ml of urine/hour is excreted over 2 to 3 hours. If response is inadequate, give second test dose. If still no response after second dose, stop drug. *Children age 12 and younger‡:* 200 mg/kg or 6 g/m² I.V. as a 15 or 20% solution over 3 to 5 minutes. Measure response adequacy as above.

▶ **Oliguria.** *Adults and children older than age 12:* Give 50 to 100 g I.V. of a 15% to 25% solution.
Children age 12 and younger‡: 2 g/kg or 60 g/m² I.V. as a 15% or 20% solution.

▶ **To prevent oliguria or acute renal impairment.** *Adults and children older than age 12:* Give 50 to 100 g I.V. of concentrated solution, followed by 5% to 10% solution. Exact concentration determined by fluid requirements.

▶ **Edema; ascites caused by renal, hepatic, or cardiac failure.** *Adults and children older than age 12:* Give 100 g I.V. as 10% to 20% solution over 2 to 6 hours.

Children age 12 and younger‡: 2 g/kg or 60 g/m^2 I.V. as a 15% or 20% solution over 2 to 6 hours.

▶ **To reduce intraocular or intracranial pressure.** *Adults and children older than age 12:* Give 1.5 to 2 g/kg as 15% to 25% I.V. solution over 30 to 60 minutes.

Children age 12 and younger‡: 2 g/kg or 60 g/m^2 I.V. as a 15% or 20% solution over 30 to 60 minutes.

▶ **Diuresis in drug intoxication.** *Adults and children older than age 12:* Concentration depends on fluid requirement and urine output. If benefit not seen after 200 mg, discontinue infusion.

Children age 12 and younger‡: 2 g/kg or 60 g/m^2 I.V. as a 5% or 10% solution, p.r.n.

▶ **Irrigating solution during transurethral resection of prostate.** *Adults:* 2.5% solution, p.r.n.

I.V. administration

• Crystals may form in solution at low temperatures or in concentrations greater than 15%. To dissolve, warm bottle in hot water bath and shake vigorously. Cool to body temperature before giving. Don't use solution with undissolved crystals.

• Give as intermittent or continuous infusion, using in-line filter and infusion pump. Direct injection isn't recommended. Check I.V. line patency at infusion site before and during administration.

• Watch for signs of infiltration, including inflammation, edema, and necrosis.

⊗ **Incompatibilities**

Blood products, cefepime, doxorubicin liposomal, filgrastim, imipenem-cilastatin, meropenem, potassium chloride, sodium chloride, strongly acidic or alkaline solutions.

Contraindications and cautions

• Contraindicated in patients hypersensitive to the drug or any of its components, and in those with anuria, severe pulmonary congestion, frank pulmonary edema, severe heart failure, severe dehydration, metabolic edema, progressive renal disease or dysfunction, or active intracranial bleeding except during craniotomy.

Lifespan: In pregnant women, use cautiously. In breast-feeding women, use cautiously; it's unknown if drug appears in breast milk.

Adverse reactions

CNS: headache, confusion, ***seizures.***
CV: ***circulatory overload, heart failure,*** tachycardia; chest pain.
EENT: blurred vision, rhinitis.
GI: thirst, nausea, vomiting, *diarrhea.*
GU: urine retention.
Metabolic: ***water intoxication,*** cellular dehydration, electrolyte imbalances.

Interactions

Drug-drug. *Lithium:* Increases urinary excretion of lithium. Monitor patient closely; monitor lithium level.

Effects on lab test results

• May cause electrolyte imbalance.

Pharmacokinetics

Absorption: Given I.V.
Distribution: Remains in extracellular compartment; doesn't cross blood-brain barrier.
Metabolism: Minimal.
Excretion: In urine. *Half-life:* About 1½ hours.

Route	Onset	Peak	Duration
I.V.	30–60 min	≤ 1 hr	6–8 hr

Action

Chemical effect: Increases osmotic pressure of glomerular filtrate, inhibiting tubular reabsorption of water and electrolytes. This elevates blood osmolality, enhancing water and sodium flow into extracellular fluid.
Therapeutic effect: Increases water excretion, decreases intracranial or intraocular pressure, prevents or treats kidney dysfunction, and promotes excretion of drug overdosage.

Available forms

Injection: 5%, 10%, 15%, 20%, 25%

NURSING PROCESS

Assessment

• Assess patient's condition before therapy and regularly thereafter to monitor the drug's effectiveness.

• Monitor vital signs, central venous pressure, and fluid intake and output hourly. Insert urethral catheter in comatose or incontinent patient because therapy is based on strict evaluation of fluid intake and output. In patient with urethral catheter, use hourly urometer collection bag for accurate evaluation.

• Monitor weight and kidney function, as well as serum and urine sodium and potassium levels, daily.

• Be alert for adverse reactions and drug interactions.

• Assess patient's and family's knowledge of drug therapy.

Nursing diagnoses

• Ineffective health maintenance related to underlying condition

• Risk for deficient fluid volume related to drug-induced adverse GI reactions

• Deficient knowledge related to drug therapy

Planning and implementation

• For maximum intraocular pressure reduction before surgery, give 1 to 1½ hours before surgery.

• When used as irrigating solution for prostate surgery, a concentration of 3.5% or greater is needed to avoid hemolysis.

• If patient's oliguria increases or he has adverse reactions, notify prescriber immediately.

Patient teaching

• Tell patient he may feel thirsty or have a dry mouth, and emphasize the importance of drinking only the amount of fluid provided.

• Instruct patient to immediately report pain in chest, back, or legs, or shortness of breath.

Evaluation

• Patient responds well to mannitol.

• Patient maintains adequate hydration throughout therapy.

• Patient and family state understanding of drug therapy.

mebendazole

(meh-BEN-duh-zohl)

Vermox

Pharmacologic class: benzimidazole

Therapeutic class: anthelmintic

Pregnancy risk category: C

Indications and dosages

▶ **Pinworm.** *Adults and children older than age 2:* Give 100 mg P.O. as single dose. If infection persists for 3 weeks, repeat therapy.

▶ **Roundworm, whipworm, hookworm.** *Adults and children older than age 2:* Give 100 mg P.O. b.i.d. for 3 days. If infection persists for 3 weeks, repeat therapy.

▶ **Trichinosis‡.** *Adults and children older than age 2:* Give 200 to 400 mg P.O. t.i.d. for 3 days, then 400 to 500 mg t.i.d. for 10 days.

▶ **Capillariasis‡.** *Adults and children older than age 2:* Give 200 mg P.O. b.i.d. for 20 days.

▶ **Toxocariasis‡.** *Adults and children:* 100 to 200 mg P.O. b.i.d. for 5 days.

▶ **Dracunculiasis‡.** *Adults and children older than age 2:* Give 400 to 800 mg P.O. daily for 6 days.

Contraindications and cautions

• Contraindicated in patients hypersensitive to the drug or any of its components.

Lifespan: In pregnant women, use cautiously. In breast-feeding women, safety and effectiveness haven't been established. In children younger than 2 years, safety and effectiveness haven't been established.

Adverse reactions

GI: diarrhea, transient abdominal pain.

Interactions

Drug-drug. *Carbamazepine, hydantoins:* May reduce level of mebendazole, possibly decreasing its therapeutic effect. Monitor patient for effect.

Cimetidine: Increases mebendazole level. Monitor patient for toxicity.

Effects on lab test results

None reported.

M

Pharmacokinetics

Absorption: About 5% to 10%; varies widely among patients.
Distribution: Highly protein-bound.
Metabolism: To inactive metabolites.
Excretion: Mostly in feces; 2% to 10% in urine. *Half-life:* 3 to 9 hours.

Route	Onset	Peak	Duration
P.O.	Unknown	2–5 hr	Varies

Action

Chemical effect: Selectively and irreversibly inhibits uptake of glucose and other nutrients in susceptible helminths.
Therapeutic effect: Kills helminth infestation.

Available forms

Tablets (chewable): 100 mg

NURSING PROCESS

Assessment

- Assess patient's condition before therapy and regularly thereafter to monitor the drug's effectiveness.
- Be alert for adverse reactions and drug interactions.
- Assess patient's and family's knowledge of drug therapy.

Nursing diagnoses

- Risk for infection related to presence of helminths
- Diarrhea related to drug-induced adverse GI reactions
- Deficient knowledge related to drug therapy

Planning and implementation

- Tablets may be chewed, swallowed whole, or crushed and mixed with food.
- Give drug to all family members to decrease risk of spreading infection.
- No dietary restrictions, laxatives, or enemas are needed.

Patient teaching

- Teach patient about personal hygiene, especially good hand-washing technique. To avoid reinfection, teach patient to wash perianal area daily, to change undergarments and bedclothes daily, and to wash hands and clean fingernails before meals and after bowel movements.
- Advise patient not to prepare food for others.

Evaluation

- Patient is free from infestation.
- Patient's bowel pattern returns to normal after therapy is stopped.
- Patient and family state understanding of drug therapy.

mecasermin rinfabate

(meh-KAH-sur-men RIHN-fah-bayt)
Iplex

Pharmacologic class: human insulin growth factor
Therapeutic class: growth factor
Pregnancy risk category: C

Indications and dosages

▶ **Growth failure in children with severe primary insulin growth factor-1 (IGF-1) deficiency or children with growth hormone gene deletion who have developed neutralizing antibodies to growth hormone.** *Children age 3 and older:* Initially, 0.5 mg/kg subcutaneously. Adjust to therapeutic range (1 to 2 mg/kg once daily) based on glucose and IGF-1 levels. Give at about the same time each day, before the morning or evening meal, as long as the child maintains a balanced diet.

Contraindications and cautions

- Contraindicated in patients with closed epiphyses, active or suspected cancer, or allergy to mecasermin rinfabate or any component of the drug. I.V. use is also contraindicated. Don't use in place of growth hormone or for other causes of growth failure.

Lifespan: In pregnant or breast-feeding women, use cautiously. In children younger than age 3, safety and effectiveness haven't been established.

Adverse reactions

CNS: dizziness, *headache,* intracranial hypertension.
EENT: otitis media, papilledema, *tonsillar hypertrophy.*
GI: vomiting.
GU: hematuria, ovarian cysts.
Hematologic: *iron deficiency anemia.*
Metabolic: hyperglycemia, ***hypoglycemia.***

Musculoskeletal: arthralgia, bone pain, *muscle atrophy,* scoliosis.
Other: *enlarged thyroid, pain,* injection site reaction, lymphadenopathy, snoring.

Interactions

None known.

Effects on lab test results

• May increase AST, LDH, and transaminase levels. May increase or decrease glucose level.

Pharmacokinetics

Absorption: Rapid.
Distribution: Less than 2% of total IGF-1 exists as free form.
Metabolism: None.
Excretion: *IGF-1 half-life:* More than 12 hours.

Route	Onset	Peak	Duration
SubQ			
IGF-1	1 hr	5–17½ hr	Unknown
IGFBP-3	1 hr	10½–28½ hr	Unknown

Action

Chemical effect: Promotes growth because synthetic drug is identical to endogenous insulin-like growth factor-binding protein-3 (IGFBP-3) and IGF-1.
Therapeutic effect: Promotes growth.

Available forms

Injection: 36 mg/0.6-ml vial

NURSING PROCESS

Assessment

• Make sure child has had a fundoscopic eye exam before therapy starts.
• Monitor blood glucose level carefully, especially in small children, whose oral intake can be inconsistent.
• Check patient regularly for adenotonsillar enlargement. Ask parent or caregiver if the child has developed snoring, sleep apnea, or reduced hearing.
• Monitor patient for changes typical of acromegaly.

Nursing diagnoses

• Delayed growth and development related to primary IGF-1 deficiency
• Ineffective health maintenance related to adverse metabolic reactions
• Deficient knowledge related to drug therapy

Planning and implementation

• Give drug at the same time each day. Because of its insulin-like effects, withhold dose if patient can't or won't eat.
• If drug produces rapid growth, patient may be at risk for slipped capital femoral epiphysis or progression of scoliosis. Monitor patient closely.
• Acute overdose may produce hypoglycemia (dizziness, tiredness, hunger, irritability, sweating, nausea, fast or irregular heartbeat). If mild, treat with oral glucose. If severe, give parenteral glucagon or I.V. glucose.
• Long-term overdose may cause acromegaly (enlarged hands and feet; increased sweating; oily skin; acne; thickening of facial features, especially the nose; increased prominence of jaw or forehead). Notify prescriber, and monitor patient.

Patient teaching

• Explain that drug must be kept frozen until ready to use. Tell parent or caregiver to discard unused drug after 2 months, even if it has been frozen.
• Instruct parent to thaw drug at room temperature for about 45 minutes before giving it and to give it within 1 hour of thawing. Explain that drug must be discarded if not used within 2 hours of thawing because it may not work.
• Warn parent not to use drug if it's cloudy.
• Tell parent to give drug before the same meal daily and to withhold dose if the child is unable or unwilling to eat.
• Teach parent how to inject drug and dispose of syringes properly.
• Tell parent to inject drug into child's upper arm, upper thigh, stomach area, or buttocks. Caution against injecting it into a muscle or vein.
• To decrease injection site reactions, advise parent to rotate injection sites.
• Tell parent to regularly monitor the child's blood glucose level. Review signs and symptoms of hypoglycemia, including dizziness, tiredness, hunger, irritability, sweating, nausea, and a fast or irregular heartbeat.
• Advise parent and child to keep a quick source of sugar (such as orange juice, glucose

gel, or candy) readily available in case of hypoglycemia.

- Explain that child should avoid hazardous activities while the dosage is being adjusted. Hypoglycemia can cause unconsciousness, seizures, or death.
- Advise parent to have the child's tonsils checked regularly and to monitor child for enlarged tonsils and snoring or sleep apnea.
- Tell parent to notify prescriber if child develops nausea and vomiting with headache, hypoglycemic episodes, a limp, hip or knee pain, snoring, trouble swallowing, earaches, or breathing problems.

☑ Evaluation

- Patient exhibits growth.
- Patient's thyroid function studies and glucose level are normal.
- Patient and family state understanding of drug therapy.

mechlorethamine hydrochloride (nitrogen mustard)

(meh-klor-ETH-uh-meen high-droh-KLOR-ighd)

Mustargen

Pharmacologic class: alkylating drug
Therapeutic class: antineoplastic
Pregnancy risk category: D

Indications and dosages

▶ **Hodgkin lymphoma.** *Adults and children:* 6 mg/m^2 I.V. daily on days 1 and 8 of 28-day cycle given with other antineoplastics, such as mechlorethamine-vincristine-procarbazine-prednisone (MOPP). Repeat dosage for six cycles.

Adjust-a-dose: Reduce subsequent doses by 50% during MOPP therapy when WBC count is between 3,000 and 3,999/mm^3, and by 75% when WBC count is between 1,000 and 2,999/mm^3; or when platelet count is between 50,000 and 100,000/mm^3.

▶ **Polycythemia vera, chronic lymphocytic leukemia, chronic myelocytic leukemia, bronchogenic cancer, lymphosarcoma, mycosis fungoides.** *Adults and children:* 0.4 mg/kg I.V. daily as a single dose or divided into 2 doses of 0.2 mg/kg or 4 doses of 0.1 mg/kg. Base dosage on ideal dry body weight without edema or ascites. Subsequent courses can't be given until patient has recovered hematologically, usually within 3 weeks.

I.V. administration

- Preparation and administration of parenteral form are linked to carcinogenic, mutagenic, and teratogenic risks. Follow facility protection policy to reduce risks.
- Prepare solution immediately before infusion because it's unstable. Use within 15 minutes, and discard unused solution.
- Reconstitute drug using 10 ml of sterile water for injection. Resulting solution contains 1 mg/ml of drug. Give by direct injection into I.V. line containing free-flowing compatible solution.
- Don't use solutions that are discolored or contain particulates. Don't use vials that appear to contain droplets of water.
- Make sure I.V. solution doesn't extravasate because drug is a potent vesicant. If it does, infiltrate area with sterile (1/6 molar) isotonic sodium thiosulfate and apply cold compresses for 6 to 12 hours.
- Dispose of used equipment properly and according to facility policy. Neutralize unused solution with equal volume of 5% sodium bicarbonate and 5% sodium thiosulfate for 45 minutes.

⊗ Incompatibilities

Allopurinol, cefepime, methohexital.

Contraindications and cautions

- Contraindicated in patients with infectious disease or previous anaphylactic reactions to the drug.
- Use cautiously in patients with chronic lymphatic lymphoma caused by increased drug toxicity.
- Use cautiously in patients with widely disseminated neoplasms. In patients with inoperable neoplasms or in the terminal stage of the disease, weigh risks and discomfort from use against limited potential gain.

Lifespan: Women of childbearing age shouldn't become pregnant while taking drug. In pregnant women, use cautiously because of risks to the fetus. Breast-feeding women should stop breast-feeding or not take the drug. In children, safety and effectiveness of drug haven't been established.

Adverse reactions

CNS: drowsiness, headache, vertigo, weakness.
CV: thrombophlebitis.
EENT: hearing loss, tinnitus.
GI: anorexia, metallic taste, nausea, vomiting.
Hematologic: ***agranulocytosis,*** anemia, lymphocytopenia, ***myelosuppression, thrombocytopenia.***
Skin: *alopecia,* rash, severe irritation if drug extravasates or touches skin, sloughing.
Other: ***anaphylaxis,*** herpes zoster, ***secondary malignant disease.***

Interactions

Drug-drug. *Anticoagulants, aspirin:* May increase risk of bleeding. Monitor PT and INR and monitor patient for bleeding; adjust dosage, if needed.

Effects on lab test results

- May increase urine urea level. May decrease hemoglobin level and hematocrit.
- May increase PT and INR. May decrease platelet, granulocyte, lymphocyte, WBC, and RBC counts.

Pharmacokinetics

Absorption: Incomplete, probably from deactivation by body fluids in cavity.
Distribution: Doesn't cross blood–brain barrier.
Metabolism: Converted rapidly to its active form, which reacts quickly with various cellular components before being deactivated.
Excretion: Metabolites in urine.

Route	Onset	Peak	Duration
I.V., intracavitary	Rapid	Unknown	Unknown

Action

Chemical effect: Cross-links strands of cellular DNA and interferes with RNA transcription, causing imbalance of growth that leads to cell death.
Therapeutic effect: Kills certain cancer cells.

Available forms

Injection: 10-mg vials

NURSING PROCESS

Assessment

- Assess patient's condition before therapy and regularly thereafter to monitor drug effectiveness.
- Monitor CBC and platelet counts regularly. Mild anemia begins in 2 to 3 weeks.
- Monitor uric acid level.
- Be alert for adverse reactions and drug interactions.
- Monitor patient for signs and symptoms of infection caused by immunosuppression. Myelosuppression peaks in 4 to 10 days and lasts 10 to 21 days per cycle.
- Neurotoxicity and ototoxicity increases with dose and patient age.
- Assess patient's and family's knowledge of drug therapy.

Nursing diagnoses

- Ineffective health maintenance related to presence of neoplastic disease
- Risk for infection related to adverse hematologic reactions
- Deficient knowledge related to drug therapy

Planning and implementation

ALERT: Drug is highly toxic. Avoid inhaling dust or vapors. Also avoid contact with skin or mucous membranes. Use personal protection equipment, clean drug equipment, and neutralize unused drug according to manufacturer's instructions.

- Give under the supervision of a physician experienced in the use of chemotherapy drugs.
- To prevent hyperuricemia with resulting uric acid nephropathy, make sure patient is adequately hydrated.
- If patient develops the acute phase of herpes zoster, stop giving the drug to avoid progression to generalized herpes zoster.

Patient teaching

- Warn patient to watch for signs of infection (fever, sore throat, fatigue) and bleeding (easy bruising, nosebleeds, bleeding gums, melena). Have patient take temperature daily.
- Instruct patient to avoid OTC products that contain aspirin.
- Advise woman of childbearing age to avoid becoming pregnant during therapy and to consult with prescriber before attempting to become pregnant.

M

Evaluation
- Patient responds positively to drug.
- Patient regains normal hematologic parameters.
- Patient and family state understanding of drug therapy.

meclizine hydrochloride (meclozine hydrochloride)

(MEK-lih-zeen high-droh-KLOR-ighd)

Ancolan ◇, Antivert†, Antivert/25, Antivert/50, Antrizine, Bonamine ♦, Bonine†, Dramamine Less Drowsy Formula†, Meni-D, Vergon†

Pharmacologic class: piperazine-derivative antihistamine; anticholinergic
Therapeutic class: antiemetic, antivertigo drug
Pregnancy risk category: B

Indications and dosages

▶ **Vertigo, dizziness.** *Adults:* 25 to 100 mg P.O. daily in divided doses. Dosage varies with patient response.

▶ **Motion sickness.** *Adults:* 25 to 50 mg P.O. 1 hour before travel, repeat daily for duration of journey.

Contraindications and cautions
- Contraindicated in patients hypersensitive to the drug or any of its components.
- Use cautiously in patients with asthma, glaucoma, or prostatic hyperplasia.

Lifespan: In pregnant women, safety and effectiveness haven't been established. In breast-feeding women, use cautiously; it's unknown if drug appears in breast milk. In children, safety and effectiveness haven't been established.

Adverse reactions
CNS: *drowsiness,* excitation, fatigue, nervousness.
CV: hypotension, palpitations, tachycardia.
EENT: blurred vision.
GI: anorexia, diarrhea, dry mouth, nausea, vomiting.
GU: urinary frequency.
Skin: rash, urticaria.

Interactions
Drug-drug. *CNS depressants:* May increase drowsiness. Use together cautiously; monitor patient for safety.

Effects on lab test results
None reported.

Pharmacokinetics
Absorption: Unknown.
Distribution: Good.
Metabolism: May be in liver.
Excretion: Unchanged in feces; metabolites in urine. *Half-life:* About 6 hours.

Route	Onset	Peak	Duration
P.O.	30–60 min	Unknown	4–24 hr

Action
Chemical effect: May affect neural pathways originating in labyrinth to inhibit nausea and vomiting.
Therapeutic effect: Relieves vertigo and nausea.

Available forms
Capsules: 25 mg, 30 mg†
Tablets: 12.5 mg, 25 mg†, 50 mg
Tablets (chewable): 25 mg†

NURSING PROCESS

Assessment
- Assess patient's condition before therapy and regularly thereafter to monitor drug effectiveness.
- Be alert for adverse reactions and drug interactions.
- Assess patient's and family's knowledge of drug therapy.

Nursing diagnoses
- Risk for injury related to vertigo
- Risk for deficient fluid volume related to motion sickness
- Deficient knowledge related to drug therapy

Planning and implementation
- Don't abruptly stop giving the drug after long-term therapy. Paradoxical reactions or sudden reversal of improved state may occur.

ALERT: Don't confuse Antivert with Axert.

Patient teaching

- Advise patient to refrain from driving and performing other hazardous activities that require alertness until the drug's CNS effects are known.
- If drug is to be used long-term, stress the importance of not abruptly stopping it.
- Advise patient not to use alcohol while taking this drug and to consult prescriber before taking this drug if he's already taking sedatives or tranquilizers.

Evaluation

- Patient states that vertigo is relieved.
- Patient states that motion sickness doesn't occur.
- Patient and family state understanding of drug therapy.

medroxyprogesterone acetate

(med-roks-ee-proh-JES-ter-ohn AS-ih-tayt)

Amen, Cycrin, Depo-Provera, Provera

Pharmacologic class: synthetic hormone
Therapeutic class: progestin, antineoplastic
Pregnancy risk category: X

Indications and dosages

▶ **Abnormal uterine bleeding caused by hormonal imbalance.** *Women:* 5 or 10 mg P.O. daily for 5 to 10 days beginning on day 16 or 21 of menstrual cycle. If patient also has received estrogen, 10 mg P.O. daily for 10 days beginning on day 16 of cycle.

▶ **Secondary amenorrhea.** *Women:* 5 or 10 mg P.O. daily for 5 to 10 days.

▶ **Endometrial or renal carcinoma.** *Adults:* 400 to 1,000 mg I.M. weekly. If disease improves within a few weeks to months and seems stable, it may be possible to maintain response with 400 mg monthly.

▶ **Endometrial hyperplasia.** *Postmenopausal women who haven't had a hysterectomy and are taking 0.625 mg conjugated estrogens:* 5 or 10 mg P.O. daily for 12 to 14 consecutive days per month, starting on day 1 or day 16 of the cycle.

▶ **Contraception.** *Women:* 150 mg I.M. once q 3 months.

▶ **Paraphilia‡.** *Men:* Initially, 200 mg I.M. b.i.d. or t.i.d. or 500 mg I.M. weekly. Base dosage on response.

Contraindications and cautions

- Contraindicated in patients hypersensitive to the drug or any of its components and in those with active thromboembolic disorders, breast cancer, undiagnosed abnormal vaginal bleeding, missed abortion, hepatic dysfunction, or a history of thromboembolic disorders, cerebrovascular disease, or stroke. Tablets are contraindicated in patients with liver dysfunction or known or suspected genital cancer.
- Use cautiously in patients with diabetes mellitus, seizure disorder, migraine, cardiac or renal disease, asthma, or depression.

Lifespan: In pregnant women, drug is contraindicated. In breast-feeding women, drug has no adverse effects on infants; it may increase milk production and duration of lactation.

Adverse reactions

CNS: asthenia, depression, dizziness, lethargy, migraine, nervousness, ***stroke.***
CV: edema, hypertension, ***thromboembolism,*** thrombophlebitis.
EENT: intolerance of contact lenses.
GI: abdominal cramps, nausea, vomiting.
GU: abnormal secretions, amenorrhea, breakthrough bleeding, cervical erosion, dysmenorrhea, uterine fibromas, vaginal candidiasis.
Hepatic: *cholestatic jaundice,* gallbladder disease, ***tumors.***
Metabolic: hyperglycemia, *weight gain.*
Respiratory: ***pulmonary embolism.***
Skin: acne, alopecia, induration, melasma, pain, rash, sterile abscesses.
Other: breast tenderness, enlargement, or secretion; decreased libido; hypersensitivity reactions.

Interactions

Drug-drug. *Aminoglutethimide, rifampin:* May decrease progestin effects. Monitor patient for diminished therapeutic response. Tell patient to use nonhormonal contraceptive during therapy with these drugs.
Bromocriptine: May cause amenorrhea, interfering with bromocriptine's effects. Avoid use together.
Drug-food. *Caffeine:* May increase caffeine levels. Monitor patient for effect.

Drug-lifestyle. *Smoking:* May increase risk of adverse CV effects. If smoking continues, may need alternative therapy. Discourage patient from smoking.

Effects on lab test results

- May increase thyroxin-binding globulin and T_4 levels.
- May increase liver function test values.

Pharmacokinetics

Absorption: Rapid.
Distribution: Extensively protein-bound, mainly to albumin and corticosteroid-binding globulin.
Metabolism: Rapid, mainly in the liver.
Excretion: Mainly in urine. *Half-life:* 2¼ to 9 hours P.O., 10 weeks I.M.

Route	Onset	Peak	Duration
P.O.	Rapid	1–2 hr	3–5 days
I.M.	Rapid	24 hr	3–4 mo

Action

Chemical effect: Acts as progestin: suppresses ovulation, possibly by inhibiting pituitary gonadotropin secretion.
Therapeutic effect: Regulates menses or acts as a contraceptive depending on dose; promotes anti-androgenic effects in men; and slows growth of some cancer cells.

Available forms

Injection (suspension): 150 mg/ml, 400 mg/ml
Tablets: 2.5 mg, 5 mg, 10 mg

NURSING PROCESS

Assessment

- Assess patient's condition before therapy and regularly thereafter to monitor drug effectiveness.
- Be alert for adverse reactions and drug interactions.
- Monitor injection sites for evidence of sterile abscess.
- Assess patient's and family's knowledge of drug therapy.

Nursing diagnoses

- Ineffective health maintenance related to underlying condition
- Excessive fluid volume related to drug-induced edema
- Deficient knowledge related to drug therapy

Planning and implementation

- Rotate injection sites to prevent muscle atrophy.

Patient teaching

- Explain to patient adverse effects of progestins before giving the first dose.
- Instruct patient not to smoke or use caffeine during therapy.

ALERT: Tell patient to immediately report unusual symptoms and to stop taking drug and notify prescriber about disturbed vision or migraine.

- Teach woman how to perform routine monthly breast self-examination.
- Warn patient that I.M. injection may be painful.

Evaluation

- Patient responds well to drug therapy.
- Patient doesn't develop fluid excess throughout drug therapy.
- Patient and family state understanding of drug therapy.

mefloquine hydrochloride

(MEF-loh-kwin high-droh-KLOR-ighd)
Lariam

Pharmacologic class: quinine derivative
Therapeutic class: antimalarial
Pregnancy risk category: C

Indications and dosages

▶ **Acute malaria infections caused by mefloquine-sensitive strains of *Plasmodium falciparum* and *P. vivax*.** *Adults age 17 and older:* 1,250 mg P.O. as single dose, with 240 ml (8 oz) water. Give patients with *P. vivax* infections primaquine or other 8-aminoquinoline to avoid relapse of initial infection after therapy. *Children age 6 months to 16 years:* 20 to 25 mg/kg in 2 divided doses given 6 to 8 hours apart, with ample water.

▶ **To prevent malaria.** *Adults:* 250 mg P.O. once weekly. Give 1 week before patient enters endemic area and continue for 4 weeks after return. Can begin prophylaxis 2 to 3 weeks before departure when taken with other drugs.

Contraindications and cautions

- Contraindicated in patients hypersensitive to the drug or related compounds. Don't give as prevention to patients with active depression, a recent history of depression, generalized anxiety disorder, psychosis, schizophrenia, other major psychiatric disorder, or a history of seizures.
- Use cautiously in patients with a history of depression and in patients with cardiac disease or seizure disorders.

Lifespan: In pregnant women, use cautiously. In breast-feeding women, use cautiously; it's unknown if the drug appears in breast milk. In infants less than 6 months, safety and effectiveness haven't been established.

Adverse reactions

CNS: ataxia, dizziness, fatigue, fever, headache, mood changes, panic attacks, ***seizures, suicide,*** syncope, tremor.
CV: chest pain, edema, extrasystoles.
EENT: tinnitus.
GI: diarrhea, dyspepsia, GI discomfort, loose stools, loss of appetite, *nausea,* vomiting.
Skin: rash.
Other: chills.

Interactions

Drug-drug. *Beta blockers, quinidine, quinine:* May cause ECG abnormalities and cardiac arrest. Avoid use together.
Chloroquine, quinine: May increase risk of seizures. Do not use together.
Halofantrine: May increase risk of fatal prolongation of QTc interval. Don't use together.
Oral live typhoid vaccine: May reduce effectiveness of immunization. Complete immunization at least 3 days before giving drug.
Valproic acid, other anticonvulsants: May cause loss of seizure control by lowering drug levels. Check anticonvulsant level.

Effects on lab test results

- May increase transaminase levels. May decrease hemoglobin level and hematocrit.
- May decrease WBC and platelet counts.

Pharmacokinetics

Absorption: Good, enhanced with food.
Distribution: Concentrated in RBCs. About 98% protein-bound.
Metabolism: By liver.
Excretion: Primarily by liver; small amounts in urine. *Half-life:* About 21 days.

Route	Onset	Peak	Duration
P.O.	Unknown	7–24 hr	Unknown

Action

Chemical effect: May be related to its ability to form complexes with hemin.
Therapeutic effect: Inhibits or kills malaria-causing organisms.

Available forms

Tablets: 250 mg

NURSING PROCESS

Assessment

- Assess patient's condition before therapy and regularly thereafter to monitor drug effectiveness.
- Periodically monitor liver function.
- Be alert for adverse reactions and drug interactions.
- If patient has an adverse GI reaction, monitor his hydration.
- Assess patient's and family's knowledge of drug therapy.

Nursing diagnoses

- Risk for infection related to presence of malaria organisms
- Risk for deficient fluid volume related to drug-induced adverse reactions
- Deficient knowledge related to drug therapy

Planning and implementation

ALERT: During preventive use, psychiatric symptoms may precede a more serious reaction. Stop giving the drug, and use an alternative.
- If *P. falciparum* infection is life-threatening or overwhelming, start with an I.V. antimalarial drug, and complete therapy with mefloquine.
- Because health risks from simultaneous administration of quinine and mefloquine are great, don't begin therapy within 12 hours of last dose of quinine or quinidine.

M

• Patients with infections caused by *P. vivax* are at high risk for relapse because drug doesn't eliminate hepatic phase (exoerythrocytic parasites). Follow-up therapy with primaquine or an 8-aminoquinoline is advisable.
• Give drug with food and full glass of water to minimize adverse GI reactions.

Patient teaching

• Advise patient to take drug on the same day each week when using it for prevention and to take with food and a full 8-ounce glass of water.
• Advise patient to use caution when performing hazardous activities that require alertness and coordination because dizziness, disturbed sense of balance, and neuropsychiatric reactions may occur.
• Instruct patient taking drug as prevention to stop taking the drug and notify prescriber if he notices signs or symptoms of impending toxicity, such as unexplained anxiety, depression, confusion, or restlessness.
• For patient undergoing long-term therapy, recommend that he have periodic ophthalmologic examinations.

✔ Evaluation

• Patient is free from infection.
• Patient maintains adequate hydration throughout therapy.
• Patient and family state understanding of drug therapy.

megestrol acetate
(meh-JES-trol AS-ih-tayt)
Megace, Megace ES, Megostat ◇

Pharmacologic class: synthetic progestin
Therapeutic class: antineoplastic
Pregnancy risk category: D (tablets); X (oral suspension)

Indications and dosages

▶ **Breast cancer.** *Adults:* 40 mg P.O. q.i.d.
▶ **Endometrial cancer.** *Women:* 40 to 320 mg P.O. daily in divided doses.
▶ **Anorexia, cachexia, or unexplained significant weight loss in patients with AIDS.** *Adults:* 800 mg P.O. (20 ml regular oral suspension) or 625 mg P.O. (5 ml concentrated ES oral suspension) once daily.
▶ **Anorexia or cachexia in patients with neoplastic disease‡.** *Adults:* 480 to 600 mg P.O. daily.

Contraindications and cautions

• Contraindicated in patients hypersensitive to the drug or any of its components.
• Use cautiously in patients with history of thrombophlebitis.
Lifespan: In pregnant women, drug is contraindicated in the first 4 months of pregnancy. In breast-feeding women, use cautiously; it's unknown if drug appears in breast milk. In children, safety and effectiveness haven't been established.

Adverse reactions

CV: ***heart failure,*** hypertension, ***thromboembolism,*** thrombophlebitis.
GI: abdominal pain, nausea, vomiting.
GU: breakthrough menstrual bleeding.
Metabolic: increased appetite, weight gain.
Musculoskeletal: back pain, carpal tunnel syndrome.
Respiratory: ***pulmonary embolism.***
Skin: alopecia, hirsutism.
Other: breast tenderness.

Interactions

Drug-drug. *Dofetilide:* May increase risk of cardiotoxicity. Monitor QT interval.

Effects on lab test results

• May increase glucose level.

Pharmacokinetics

Absorption: Good.
Distribution: May be stored in fatty tissue. Highly protein-bound.
Metabolism: Complete.
Excretion: In urine. *Half-life:* 2¼ to 9 hours.

Route	Onset	Peak	Duration
P.O.	Rapid	1–2 hr	3–5 days

Action

Chemical effect: Changes tumor's hormonal environment and alters neoplastic process. Mechanism of appetite stimulation is unknown.
Therapeutic effect: Hinders cancer cell growth and increases appetite.

Available forms

Oral suspension: 40 mg/ml
Oral suspension (concentrated): 125 mg/ml
Tablets: 20 mg, 40 mg

NURSING PROCESS

Assessment

- Assess patient's condition before therapy and regularly thereafter to monitor drug effectiveness.
- Be alert for adverse reactions.
- If patient has an adverse GI reaction, monitor his hydration.
- Assess patient's and family's knowledge of drug therapy.

Nursing diagnoses

- Ineffective health maintenance related to underlying condition
- Risk for deficient fluid volume related to drug-induced adverse GI reactions
- Deficient knowledge related to drug therapy

Planning and implementation

- Two months is adequate trial when treating cancer.
- If patient develops pronounced back pain, abdominal pain, headache, or nausea and vomiting, notify prescriber.

Patient teaching

- Inform patient that therapeutic response isn't immediate.

ALERT: Tell patient the ES oral suspension is more concentrated than the regular oral suspension so a smaller amount is needed for the proper dose.

- Advise breast-feeding woman to stop breast-feeding during therapy because of infant toxicity.
- Encourage women to use nonhormonal contraceptives during therapy.

Evaluation

- Patient responds well to therapy.
- Patient maintains adequate hydration throughout therapy.
- Patient and family state understanding of drug therapy.

meloxicam
(mell-OX-ih-kam)
Mobic

Pharmacologic class: NSAID
Therapeutic class: anti-inflammatory, analgesic
Pregnancy risk category: C

Indications and dosages

▶ **Osteoarthritis or rheumatoid arthritis.** *Adults:* 7.5 mg P.O. once daily. May increase to maximum of 15 mg P.O. once daily.

▶ **Pauciarticular or polyarticular course juvenile rheumatoid arthritis.** *Children ages 2 to 17:* Give 0.125 mg/kg P.O. once daily, up to a maximum of 7.5 mg daily.

Contraindications and cautions

- Contraindicated in patients hypersensitive to the drug or any of its components and in those who have had asthma, urticaria, or allergic-type reactions after taking aspirin or other NSAIDs. Contraindicated in patients with severe renal impairment and for treating perioperative pain after coronary artery bypass surgery.
- Use cautiously in patients with a history of ulcers or GI bleeding and in patients with dehydration, anemia, hepatic disease, renal disease, hypertension, fluid retention, heart failure, or asthma.

Lifespan: In pregnant women, avoid use especially during the third trimester. In breast-feeding women, don't use drug. In children younger that age 2, safety and effectiveness haven't been established. In elderly and debilitated patients, use cautiously because of greater risk of fatal GI bleeding.

Adverse reactions

CNS: anxiety, confusion, depression, dizziness, fatigue, fever, headache, insomnia, malaise, nervousness, paresthesia, ***seizures,*** somnolence, syncope, tremor, vertigo.
CV: angina, ***arrhythmias,*** edema, ***heart failure,*** hypertension, hypotension, ***MI,*** palpitations, tachycardia.
EENT: abnormal vision, conjunctivitis, pharyngitis, tinnitus.
GI: abdominal pain, colitis, constipation, diarrhea, dry mouth, duodenal ulcer, dyspepsia,

M

esophagitis, flatulence, gastric ulcer, gastritis, GI reflux, ***hemorrhage,*** increased appetite, nausea, ***pancreatitis,*** taste perversion, vomiting.
GU: albuminuria, hematuria, ***renal impairment,*** urinary frequency, UTI.
Hematologic: ***agranulocytosis,*** anemia, ***leukopenia,*** purpura, ***thrombocytopenia.***
Hepatic: bilirubinemia, ***hepatitis,*** jaundice, ***liver failure.***
Metabolic: dehydration, weight changes.
Musculoskeletal: arthralgia, back pain.
Respiratory: ***asthma, bronchospasm,*** cough, dyspnea, upper respiratory tract infection.
Skin: alopecia, bullous eruption, ***erythema multiforme, exfoliative dermatitis,*** photosensitivity reactions, pruritus, rash, ***Stevens-Johnson syndrome,*** sweating, ***toxic epidermal necrolysis,*** urticaria.
Other: accidental injury, allergic reaction, ***anaphylactoid reactions, angioedema,*** flulike symptoms, ***shock.***

Interactions

Drug-drug. *ACE inhibitors:* May decrease antihypertensive effects. Monitor patient's blood pressure.
Aspirin: May increase risk of adverse effects. Avoid use together.
Bile acid sequestrants: May increase clearance of meloxicam. Monitor patient's pain level.
Cyclosporine: May increase risk of nephrotoxicity. Monitor patient.
Lithium: May increase lithium level. Monitor lithium level closely for toxicity.
Methotrexate: May increase the toxicity of methotrexate. Use cautiously together.
Thiazide and loop diuretics: May reduce sodium excretion linked to diuretics, leading to sodium retention. Monitor patient for edema and increased blood pressure.
Warfarin: May increase PT or INR. Monitor PT and INR, and check for signs and symptoms of bleeding.
Drug-herb. *Dong quai, feverfew, garlic, ginger, horse chestnut, ma huang, meadowsweet, red clover:* May increase risk of bleeding. Discourage use together.
St. John's wort: May increase risk of photosensitivity reactions. Advise patient to avoid unprotected or prolonged exposure to sunlight.
Drug-lifestyle. *Alcohol use:* May increase risk of GI irritation and bleeding. Monitor patient for bleeding; discourage use together.
Smoking: May increase risk of GI irritation and bleeding. Monitor patient for bleeding; discourage patient from smoking.

Effects on lab test results

- May increase BUN, creatinine, ALT, AST, and bilirubin levels. May decrease hemoglobin level and hematocrit.
- May decrease WBC and platelet counts.

Pharmacokinetics

Absorption: Bioavailability is 89% and doesn't appear to be affected by food or antacids. Steady-state conditions are reached after 5 days of daily administration.
Distribution: 99.4% protein-bound.
Metabolism: Almost complete, to pharmacologically inactive metabolites.
Excretion: In both urine and feces, mainly as metabolites. *Half-life:* 15 to 20 hours.

Route	Onset	Peak	Duration
P.O.	Unknown	Unknown	Unknown

Action

Chemical effect: May be related to prostaglandin (cyclooxygenase) synthetase inhibition.
Therapeutic effect: Relief of signs and symptoms of osteoarthritis.

Available forms

Oral suspension: 7.5 mg/5 ml
Tablets: 7.5 mg, 15 mg

NURSING PROCESS

Assessment

- Obtain accurate history of drug allergies. Drug can produce allergic-like reactions in patients hypersensitive to aspirin and other NSAIDs.
- Assess patient for increased risk of GI bleeding. Risk factors include history of ulcers or GI bleeding, therapy with corticosteroids or anticoagulants, long duration of NSAID therapy, smoking, alcoholism, old age, and poor overall health.
- Monitor patient for signs and symptoms of overt and occult bleeding.

ALERT: NSAIDs may increase the risk of serious thrombotic events, MI, or stroke. The risk may increase with duration of use and be higher in patients with CV disease or risk factors for CV disease.

• Monitor children for abdominal pain, vomiting, diarrhea, headache, and pyrexia, which may occur more commonly than in adults.

• Monitor patient for fluid retention; closely monitor patient who has hypertension, edema, or heart failure.

• Monitor liver function.

• Assess patient's and family's knowledge of drug therapy.

Nursing diagnoses

• Chronic pain related to underlying condition

• Risk for injury related to drug-induced adverse reactions

• Deficient knowledge related to drug therapy

Planning and implementation

• Drug may be taken with food to prevent GI upset.

• Rehydrate dehydrated patient before therapy.

• If patient develops evidence of liver disease (eosinophilia, rash), stop giving the drug.

• Use oral suspension to improve accuracy of doses in lighter-weight children.

Patient teaching

• Tell patient to notify prescriber about history of allergic reactions to aspirin or other NSAIDs before therapy.

• Oral solution may be substituted on a milligram-per-milligram basis for tablets. Shake suspension gently before use.

• Tell patient to report signs and symptoms of GI ulcerations and bleeding, such as vomiting blood, blood in stool, and black, tarry stools.

• Instruct patient to report skin rash, weight gain, or edema.

• Advise patient to report warning signs of hepatotoxicity (nausea, fatigue, lethargy, pruritus, jaundice, right upper quadrant tenderness, and flulike symptoms).

• Warn patient with a history of asthma that it may recur during therapy and that he should stop taking the drug and notify prescriber if it does.

• Tell woman to notify prescriber if she becomes pregnant or is planning to become pregnant during therapy.

• Inform patient that it may take several days before consistent pain relief is achieved.

Evaluation

• Patient is free from pain.

• Patient sustains no injury as a result of drug-induced adverse reactions.

• Patient and family state understanding of drug therapy.

melphalan (L-phenylalanine mustard)

(MEL-feh-len)

Alkeran

Pharmacologic class: nitrogen mustard; alkylating drug
Therapeutic class: antineoplastic
Pregnancy risk category: D

Indications and dosages

▶ **Multiple myeloma.** *Adults:* 6 mg P.O. daily for 2 to 3 weeks; then stop drug for up to 4 weeks or until WBC and platelet counts begin to rise again; then give maintenance dosage of 2 mg daily.

▶ **Alternative therapy for multiple myeloma.** *Adults:* 0.15 mg/kg P.O. daily for 7 days at 2- to 6-week intervals, then begin maintenance therapy at or less than 0.05 mg/kg/day when WBC and platelet counts increase. Or 0.25 mg/kg P.O. daily for 4 days, repeat q 4 to 6 weeks. Or 10 mg/day for 7 to 10 days, maintenance therapy at 2 mg/day, adjust dosage within 1- to 3-mg range daily based on hematological response. Or for patients who can't tolerate oral therapy, give 16 mg/m^2 by I.V. infusion over 15 to 20 minutes q 2 weeks for four doses. After patient has recovered from toxicity, give drug q 4 weeks.

Adjust-a-dose: For patients with renal impairment, reduce I.V. dosage by 50% to reduce risk of severe leukopenia and drug-related death.

▶ **Nonresectable advanced ovarian cancer.** *Women:* 0.2 mg/kg P.O. daily for 5 days. Repeat q 4 to 6 weeks, depending on bone marrow recovery.

I.V. administration

• Follow facility policy to reduce risks. Preparation and administration of parenteral form are linked to carcinogenic, mutagenic, and teratogenic risks for personnel.

M

• Because drug isn't stable in solution, reconstitute immediately before giving, using 10 ml of sterile diluent supplied by manufacturer. Shake vigorously until solution is clear. Resulting solution contains 5 mg/ml. Immediately dilute required dose in normal saline solution for injection. Don't exceed a final concentration of 0.45 mg/ml.
• Give promptly after diluting because reconstituted product begins to degrade within 30 minutes. After final dilution, nearly 1% of drug degrades q 10 minutes. Administration must be completed within 60 minutes of reconstitution.
• Give by I.V. infusion over 15 to 20 minutes.
• Don't refrigerate reconstituted product because precipitate will form.

⊗ **Incompatibilities**

Amphotericin B, chlorpromazine, D_5W, lactated Ringer's injection. Compatibility with normal saline injection depends on concentration.

Contraindications and cautions

• Contraindicated in patients hypersensitive to the drug or any of its components and in those whose disease is resistant to drug. Patients hypersensitive to chlorambucil may have cross-sensitivity to drug.
• Drug isn't recommended for patients with severe leukopenia, thrombocytopenia, anemia, or chronic lymphocytic leukemia.

Lifespan: In pregnant and breast-feeding women, drug isn't recommended. In children, safety and effectiveness haven't been established.

Adverse reactions

Hematologic: ***bone marrow suppression, leukopenia, thrombocytopenia.***
Hepatic: ***hepatotoxicity.***
Respiratory: pneumonitis, ***pulmonary fibrosis.***
Skin: alopecia, dermatitis, pruritus, rash.
Other: ***anaphylaxis,*** hypersensitivity reactions.

Interactions

Drug-drug. *Anticoagulants, aspirin:* May increase risk of bleeding. Use cautiously together.
Antigout drugs: May decrease effectiveness. Dosage adjustments may be needed.
Bone marrow suppressants: May have additive toxicity. Monitor patient closely.
Carmustine: May reduce carmustine lung toxicity threshold. Monitor patient closely for signs of toxicity.
Cisplatin: May affect melphalan's pharmacokinetics by inducing renal dysfunction and altering melphalan clearance. Monitor patient for toxicity.
Cyclosporine: May increase toxicity of cyclosporine, particularly nephrotoxicity. Monitor cyclosporine level and renal function tests.
Interferon alfa: May decrease melphalan level. Monitor level closely.
Nalidixic acid: May increase risk of severe hemorrhagic necrotic enterocolitis in children. Monitor patient closely.
Vaccines: May decrease effectiveness of killed-virus vaccines and increase risk of toxicity from live-virus vaccines. Postpone routine immunization for at least 3 months after last dose of melphalan.
Drug-food. *Any food:* May decrease absorption of oral drug. Separate administration times; give drug on an empty stomach.

Effects on lab test results

• May increase urine urea level. May decrease hemoglobin level and hematocrit.
• May decrease RBC, WBC, and platelet counts.

Pharmacokinetics

Absorption: Incomplete and variable.
Distribution: Rapid and wide in total body water. Initially 50% to 60% protein-bound, increasing to 80% to 90%.
Metabolism: Extensively deactivated by hydrolysis.
Excretion: Mainly in urine. *Half-life:* 2 hours.

Route	Onset	Peak	Duration
P.O., I.V.	Unknown	Unknown	Unknown

Action

Chemical effect: Cross-links strands of cellular DNA and interferes with RNA transcription.
Therapeutic effect: Kills certain cancer cells.

Available forms

Injection: 50 mg
Tablets (scored): 2 mg

NURSING PROCESS

Assessment
- Assess patient's condition before therapy and regularly thereafter to monitor drug effectiveness.
- Monitor uric acid level and CBC.
- Be alert for adverse reactions and drug interactions.
- Assess patient's and family's knowledge of drug therapy.

Nursing diagnoses
- Ineffective health maintenance related to presence of neoplastic disease
- Risk for infection related to adverse hematologic reactions
- Deficient knowledge related to drug therapy

Planning and implementation
- Give under the supervision of a physician experienced in using chemotherapy drugs.

ALERT: Drug may cause leukemia. Use proper precautions.
- Dosage may need to be reduced in patient with renal impairment.
- Melphalan is drug of choice with prednisone in patients with multiple myeloma.
- Give drug on empty stomach.
- Anaphylaxis may occur. Keep antihistamines and steroids readily available.

ALERT: Don't confuse melphalan with Mephyton.

Patient teaching
- Tell patient to take oral drug on empty stomach.
- Warn patient to watch for signs of infection (fever, sore throat, fatigue) and bleeding (easy bruising, nosebleed, bleeding gums, melena). Have patient take temperature daily.
- Instruct patient to avoid OTC products that contain aspirin.
- Advise woman of childbearing age not to become pregnant during therapy and to consult with prescriber before becoming pregnant.

Evaluation
- Patient responds well to therapy.
- Patient regains normal hematologic function when therapy is completed.
- Patient and family state understanding of drug therapy.

memantine hydrochloride
(MEHM-en-teen high-droh-KLOR-ighd)
Namenda

Pharmacologic class: N-methyl-D-aspartate (NMDA) receptor antagonist
Therapeutic class: Alzheimer disease drug
Pregnancy risk category: B

Indications and dosages

▶ **Moderate to severe Alzheimer-type dementia.** *Adults:* Initially, 5 mg P.O. once daily. Increase by 5 mg/day each week up to the target dosage. Maximum, 10 mg P.O. b.i.d. Divide doses larger than 5 mg b.i.d.

Adjust-a-dose: If the patient has moderate renal impairment, reduce dosage.

Contraindications and cautions

- Contraindicated in patients allergic to the drug or any of its components. In patients with severe renal impairment, drug isn't recommended.
- Use cautiously in patients with seizures, hepatic impairment, or moderate renal impairment. Also use cautiously in patients who may have an increased urine pH (from drugs, diet, renal tubular acidosis, or severe UTI).

Lifespan: In pregnant women, use only if benefits outweigh risks to the fetus. In breast-feeding women, use cautiously; it's unknown if the drug appears in breast milk. In children, safety and effectiveness haven't been established. In elderly patients, use cautiously.

Adverse reactions

CNS: abnormal gait, aggressiveness, agitation, anxiety, ataxia, confusion, depression, dizziness, fatigue, hallucinations, headache, hypokinesia, insomnia, pain, somnolence, ***stroke,*** syncope, transient ischemic attack, vertigo.
CV: edema, ***heart failure,*** hypertension.
EENT: cataracts, conjunctivitis.
GI: anorexia, constipation, diarrhea, nausea, vomiting.
GU: incontinence, urinary frequency, UTI.
Hematologic: anemia.
Metabolic: weight loss.
Musculoskeletal: arthralgia, back pain.

Respiratory: bronchitis, coughing, dyspnea, pneumonia, upper respiratory tract infection.
Skin: rash.
Other: falls, flulike symptoms, inflicted injury.

Interactions

Drug-drug. *Cimetidine, hydrochlorothiazide, quinidine, ranitidine, triamterene:* May alter drug levels. Monitor patient.
NMDA antagonists (amantadine, dextromethorphan, ketamine): May interact. Use together cautiously.
Urine alkalinizers (carbonic anhydrase inhibitors, sodium bicarbonate): May decrease memantine clearance. Monitor patient for adverse effects.
Drug-herb. *Herbs that alkalinize urine:* May increase drug level and adverse effects. Discourage use together.
Drug-food. *Foods that alkalinize urine:* May increase drug level and adverse effects. Discourage use together.
Drug-lifestyle. *Alcohol use:* May decrease drug's effectiveness or increase adverse effects. Discourage use together.
Smoking: May alter levels of drug and nicotine. Discourage use together.

Effects on lab test results

- May increase alkaline phosphatase level. May decrease hemoglobin level and hematocrit.

Pharmacokinetics

Absorption: Good.
Distribution: About 45% protein-bound.
Metabolism: Little.
Excretion: Unchanged, mainly in urine. *Half-life:* 60 to 80 hours.

Route	Onset	Peak	Duration
P.O.	Unknown	3–7 hr	Unknown

Action

Chemical effect: Antagonizes NMDA receptors, the persistent activation of which seems to increase Alzheimer symptoms.
Therapeutic effect: Decreases dementia.

Available forms

Oral solution: 2 mg/ml
Tablets: 5 mg, 10 mg

NURSING PROCESS

Assessment

- Assess patient's condition before therapy and regularly thereafter to monitor drug effectiveness.
- Assess patient's and family's knowledge of drug therapy.

Nursing diagnoses

- Acute or chronic confusion related to underlying disease
- Risk for imbalanced fluid volume related to drug-induced GI effects
- Deficient knowledge related to drug therapy

Planning and implementation

- Drug isn't indicated for mild Alzheimer disease or other types of dementia.
- Give drug with or without food.

Patient teaching

- Explain that drug doesn't cure Alzheimer disease but may improve the symptoms.
- Tell patient to report adverse effects.
- Urge patient not to drink alcohol during therapy.
- Advise patient not to take herbal or OTC cold and cough or GI products without consulting the prescriber.

Evaluation

- Patient's cognition improves, and he experiences less confusion.
- Patient and family state that adverse GI effects haven't occurred or have been managed effectively.
- Patient and family state understanding of drug therapy.

menotropins

(meh-noh-TROH-pins)
Menopur, Repronex

Pharmacologic class: gonadotropin
Therapeutic class: ovulation stimulant
Pregnancy risk category: X

Indications and dosages

▶ **Stimulation of ovulation in patients who have received gonadotropin-releasing hormone agonist pituitary suppression.** *Adults:*

Initially, 225 units subcutaneously. Repronex may also be given I.M. Adjust subsequent dosages based on serum estradiol level, vaginal ultrasound, and patient response. Don't adjust more than once q 2 days, and don't exceed 75 to 150 units per adjustment for Repronex, or 150 units per adjustment for Menopur. Maximum daily dose is 450 units. Use beyond 12 days for Repronex, or 20 days for Menopur, isn't recommended.

Once follicular development is adequate, give 5,000 to 10,000 units of human chorionic gonadotropin (hCG) to induce final follicular maturation in preparation for oocyte retrieval. If the ovaries are abnormally enlarged on the last day of therapy, withhold hCG to reduce the chance of developing ovarian hyperstimulation syndrome.

Contraindications and cautions

• Contraindicated in patients hypersensitive to the drug or any of its components and in women with primary ovarian failure, uncontrolled thyroid or adrenal dysfunction, pituitary tumor, abnormal uterine bleeding, uterine fibromas, or ovarian cysts or enlargement.

Lifespan: In pregnant women, breast-feeding women, and children, drug is contraindicated.

Adverse reactions

CNS: *headache, stroke.*
CV: ***arterial occlusion,*** fever, tachycardia.
GI: diarrhea, nausea, vomiting.
GU: multiple births, *ovarian enlargement,* ovarian hyperstimulation syndrome.
Hematologic: hemoconcentration with fluid loss into abdomen.
Respiratory: ***acute respiratory distress syndrome,*** atelectasis, ***pulmonary embolism, pulmonary infarction.***
Other: ***anaphylaxis,*** *gynecomastia,* hypersensitivity reactions.

Interactions

None significant.

Effects on lab test results

None reported.

Pharmacokinetics

Absorption: Unknown.
Distribution: Unknown.
Metabolism: Unknown.
Excretion: In urine. *Half-life:* I.M., 60 hours.

Route	Onset	Peak	Duration
SubQ, I.M.	9–12 days	Unknown	Unknown

Action

Chemical effect: When given to women who haven't had primary ovarian failure, mimics follicle-stimulating hormone (FSH) in inducing follicular growth and luteinizing hormone (LH) in aiding follicular maturation.
Therapeutic effect: Stimulates ovulation.

Available forms

Injection: 75 units of LH and 75 units of FSH activity per ampule; 150 units of LH and 150 units of FSH activity per ampule

NURSING PROCESS

Assessment

• Assess patient's condition before therapy and regularly thereafter to monitor drug effectiveness.
• Be alert for adverse reactions.

ALERT: Monitor women for rare ovarian hyperstimulation syndrome (ovarian enlargement with possible pain and abdominal distention, ascites, and possible pleural effusion with hemoconcentration). Stop drug immediately and hospitalize patient for symptomatic treatment.

• Assess patient's and family's knowledge of drug therapy.

Nursing diagnoses

• Sexual dysfunction related to underlying disorder
• Risk for deficient fluid volume related to drug-induced adverse reactions
• Deficient knowledge related to drug therapy

Planning and implementation

• Monitor patient closely to ensure adequate hormonal stimulation.
• Reconstitute with 1 ml (Menopur) or 1 to 2 ml (Repronex) of sterile normal saline solution. Use immediately.
• Rotate injection sites.

Patient teaching

• Teach patient correct administration technique.
• Discuss risk of multiple births.

M

• Encourage patient to have intercourse daily from the day before hCG is given until ovulation occurs.
• Tell patient that pregnancy usually occurs 4 to 6 weeks after therapy.
• Instruct patient to immediately report severe abdominal pain, bloating, swelling of hands or feet, nausea, vomiting, diarrhea, substantial weight gain, or shortness of breath.

Evaluation
• Patient or partner becomes pregnant.
• Patient maintains adequate hydration throughout therapy.
• Patient and family state understanding of drug therapy.

meperidine hydrochloride (pethidine hydrochloride)
(meh-PER-uh-deen high-droh-KLOR-ighd)
Demerol

Pharmacologic class: opioid
Therapeutic class: analgesic, adjunct to anesthesia
Pregnancy risk category: B; D (injection, for prolonged periods or high doses at term)
Controlled substance schedule: II

Indications and dosages
▶ **Moderate to severe pain.** *Adults:* 50 to 150 mg P.O., I.M., or subcutaneously q 3 to 4 hours, p.r.n. Or 15 to 35 mg/hour by continuous I.V. infusion.
Children: 1.1 to 1.75 mg/kg P.O., I.M., or subcutaneously, up to the adult dose, q 3 to 4 hours, p.r.n.
▶ **Preoperatively.** *Adults:* 50 to 100 mg I.M., I.V., or subcutaneously 30 to 90 minutes before surgery.
Children: 1 to 2.2 mg/kg I.M., I.V., or subcutaneously up to adult dose 30 to 90 minutes before surgery.
▶ **Adjunct to anesthesia.** *Adults:* Repeat slow I.V. injections of fractional doses (such as 10 mg/ml). Or continuous I.V. infusion of more dilute solution (1 mg/ml); adjust to needs of patient.
▶ **Obstetric analgesia.** *Adults:* 50 to 100 mg I.M. or subcutaneously when pain becomes regular; repeat at 1- to 3-hour intervals.

I.V. administration
• Drug is compatible with most I.V. solutions, including D_5W, normal saline solution, and Ringer's or lactated Ringer's solutions.
• Keep resuscitation equipment and naloxone available.
• Give slowly by direct I.V. injection or slow continuous I.V. infusion.

⊗ **Incompatibilities**
Acyclovir, allopurinol, aminophylline, amobarbital, amphotericin B, cefepime, cefoperazone, doxorubicin liposomal, ephedrine, furosemide, heparin, hydrocortisone sodium succinate, idarubicin, imipenem-cilastatin sodium, methylprednisolone sodium succinate, morphine, pentobarbital, phenobarbital sodium, phenytoin, sodium bicarbonate, sodium iodide, sulfonamides, thiopental.

Contraindications and cautions
• Contraindicated in patients hypersensitive to the drug or any of its components and in those who have received MAO inhibitors within 14 days.
• Use cautiously in debilitated patients and in patients with increased intracranial pressure, head injury, asthma, other respiratory conditions, supraventricular tachycardias, seizures, acute abdominal conditions, hepatic or renal disease, hypothyroidism, Addison disease, urethral stricture, or prostatic hyperplasia.
Lifespan: In pregnant women, use cautiously. In breast-feeding women, use cautiously because it's unknown if drug appears in breast milk. In the elderly, use cautiously because of increased risk of renal insufficiency.

Adverse reactions
CNS: *clouded sensorium,* dizziness, *euphoria,* paradoxical excitement, *sedation,* ***seizures,*** *somnolence,* tremors.
CV: ***bradycardia, cardiac arrest,*** hypotension, ***shock,*** tachycardia.
GI: constipation, ileus, nausea, vomiting.
GU: urine retention.
Musculoskeletal: muscle twitching.
Respiratory: ***respiratory arrest, respiratory depression.***

Skin: local tissue irritation and induration, phlebitis.
Other: pain at injection site, physical dependence.

Interactions

Drug-drug. *Chlorpromazine:* May cause excessive sedation and hypotension. Don't use together.
CNS depressants, general anesthetics, hypnotics, other opioid analgesics, phenothiazines, sedatives, tricyclic antidepressants: May cause respiratory depression, hypotension, profound sedation, or coma. Use together cautiously. Reduce meperidine dosage as directed.
MAO inhibitors: May increase CNS excitation or depression that can be severe or fatal. Don't use together.
Phenytoin: May decrease meperidine level. Monitor patient for decreased analgesia.
Drug-lifestyle. *Alcohol use:* May have additive CNS effects. Discourage use together.

Effects on lab test results

- May increase amylase and lipase levels.

Pharmacokinetics

Absorption: Unknown.
Distribution: Wide.
Metabolism: Mainly by hydrolysis in liver.
Excretion: Mainly in urine, enhanced by acidifying urine. *Half-life:* 2½ to 4 hours.

Route	Onset	Peak	Duration
P.O.	15 min	60–90 min	2–4 hr
I.V.	1 min	5–7 min	2–4 hr
I.M., SubQ	10–15 min	30–50 min	2–4 hr

Action

Chemical effect: Binds with opioid receptors in CNS, altering both perception of and emotional response to pain through unknown mechanism.
Therapeutic effect: Relieves pain.

Available forms

Injection: 25 mg/ml, 50 mg/ml, 75 mg/ml, 100 mg/ml
Injection (for infusion only): 10 mg/ml
Syrup: 50 mg/5 ml
Tablets: 50 mg, 100 mg

NURSING PROCESS

Assessment

- Assess patient's pain before therapy and regularly thereafter to monitor drug effectiveness.
- Be alert for adverse reactions and drug interactions.
- Meperidine and its active metabolite normeperidine accumulate in the body. Monitor patient for increased toxic effect, especially in patient with renal impairment.
- Monitor respirations of neonate exposed to drug during labor.
- Don't stop drug abruptly after long-term use; doing so may cause withdrawal symptoms.
- Assess patient's and family's knowledge of drug therapy.

Nursing diagnoses

- Acute pain related to underlying condition
- Risk for injury related to drug-induced adverse reactions
- Deficient knowledge related to drug therapy

Planning and implementation

- Drug may be used in patients with pain who are allergic to morphine.
- Because drug toxicity often appears after several days of therapy, it isn't recommended for chronic pain.

ALERT: If respiratory rate is less than 12 breaths/minute, if respiratory depth decreases, or if pupil size decreases, don't give drug.
ALERT: Oral dose is less than half as effective as parenteral dose. Give I.M., if possible. When changing from parenteral to oral route, increase dose.

- Syrup has local anesthetic effect. Give with full glass of water.
- Subcutaneous injection is painful; avoid if possible.

ALERT: Don't confuse Demerol with Demulen, Dymelor, or Temaril.

Patient teaching

- Warn outpatient to avoid hazardous activities until the drug's CNS effects are known.
- Instruct patient not to use alcohol during therapy.
- Teach patient to manage adverse reactions, such as constipation.
- Tell family members not to give the drug and to notify the prescriber if patient's respiratory rate decreases.

Evaluation

- Patient is free from pain.
- Patient doesn't experience injury.
- Patient and family state understanding of drug therapy.

mercaptopurine (6-mercaptopurine, 6-MP)

(mer-cap-toh-PYOO-reen)
Purinethol

Pharmacologic class: antimetabolite
Therapeutic class: antineoplastic
Pregnancy risk category: D

Indications and dosages

▶ **Acute lymphatic leukemia (lymphocytic, lymphoblastic), acute myelogenous and acute myelomonocytic leukemia.** *Adults:* 2.5 mg/kg P.O. daily as single dose, up to 5 mg/kg P.O. daily. Maintenance dosage is 1.5 to 2.5 mg/kg P.O. daily.
Children age 5 and older: 2.5 mg/kg P.O. daily. Maintenance dosage is 1.5 to 2.5 mg/kg P.O. daily.

▶ **Intractable Crohn disease‡.** *Adults:* 1 to 1.5 mg/kg P.O. daily (maximum 125 mg/day) with other therapies.
Children: 1 to 1.5 mg/kg P.O. daily (maximum 75 mg/day) with other therapies.

Contraindications and cautions

- Contraindicated in patients whose disease has resisted drug.

Lifespan: In pregnant and breast-feeding women, drug is contraindicated.

Adverse reactions

GI: anorexia, nausea, ***pancreatitis,*** stomatitis, vomiting.
Hematologic: anemia, ***leukopenia, thrombocytopenia.***
Hepatic: biliary stasis, ***hepatotoxicity,*** jaundice.
Metabolic: hyperuricemia.
Skin: hyperpigmentation, rash.

Interactions

Drug-drug. *Allopurinol:* May slow inactivation of mercaptopurine. Decrease mercaptopurine to one-fourth or one-third normal dose.
Hepatotoxic drugs: May enhance hepatotoxicity of mercaptopurine. Monitor patient closely; monitor liver function test results.
Warfarin: May antagonize anticoagulant effect. Monitor PT and INR.

Effects on lab test results

- May increase alkaline phosphatase, bilirubin, and liver enzyme levels. May decrease hemoglobin level and hematocrit.
- May decrease WBC, RBC, and platelet counts.
- May falsely increase glucose and uric acid levels.

Pharmacokinetics

Absorption: Incomplete and variable; about 50%.
Distribution: Wide in total body water.
Metabolism: Extensive.
Excretion: In urine. *Half-life:* Unknown.

Route	Onset	Peak	Duration
P.O.	Unknown	Unknown	Unknown

Action

Chemical effect: Inhibits RNA and DNA synthesis. Strongly inhibits primary immune response by suppressing humoral immunity.
Therapeutic effect: Inhibits growth of certain cancer cells.

Available forms

Tablets (scored): 50 mg

NURSING PROCESS

Assessment

- Assess patient's condition before therapy and regularly thereafter to monitor drug effectiveness.
- Monitor blood count and transaminase, alkaline phosphatase, and bilirubin levels weekly during initiation of treatment until remission is achieved and monthly during maintenance.
- Observe patient for signs of bleeding and infection.
- Monitor fluid intake and output and uric acid level.
- Be alert for adverse reactions and drug interactions. Adverse GI reactions are less common in children.

ALERT: Watch for jaundice, clay-colored stools, and frothy, dark urine. Hepatic dysfunction is reversible when drug is stopped. If hepatic tenderness occurs, stop giving the drug and notify prescriber.
- Assess patient's and family's knowledge of drug therapy.

Nursing diagnoses
- Ineffective health maintenance related to presence of leukemia
- Risk for infection related to drug-induced adverse hematologic reactions
- Deficient knowledge related to drug therapy

Planning and implementation
- Calculate dosage to the closest multiple of 25 mg.
- Adjust dosage after chemotherapy or radiation therapy and in a patient with depressed neutrophil or platelet count, or impaired liver or kidney function.
- Be aware that drug is usually used with other antineoplastics because response to monotherapy is poor.

ALERT: Sometimes drug is ordered as 6-mercaptopurine or 6-MP. The numeral 6 is part of drug name and doesn't signify number of dosage units. To prevent confusion, avoid these designations.
- Therapy must continue despite nausea and vomiting. If patient has an adverse GI reaction, notify prescriber and give an antiemetic.
- Encourage adequate fluid intake (3 L daily).
- Give allopurinol cautiously.
- If hepatic tenderness occurs, stop giving the drug and notify prescriber.

ALERT: Don't confuse Purinethol with propylthiouracil.

Patient teaching
- Tell patient to notify prescriber if vomiting occurs shortly after taking dose because antiemetic will be needed so drug therapy can continue.
- Instruct patient to watch for signs of infection (fever, sore throat, fatigue) and bleeding (easy bruising, nosebleed, bleeding gums, melena). Have patient take his temperature daily.
- Advise woman of childbearing age not to become pregnant during therapy and to consult with prescriber before becoming pregnant after therapy.

Evaluation
- Patient responds well to therapy.
- Patient doesn't develop serious ill effects when hematologic studies are abnormal.
- Patient and family state understanding of drug therapy.

meropenem
(mer-oh-PEN-em)
Merrem I.V.

Pharmacologic class: synthetic broad-spectrum carbapenem
Therapeutic class: antibiotic
Pregnancy risk category: B

Indications and dosages
▶ **Complicated skin and skin structure infections caused by *Staphylococcus aureus* (beta-lactamase and non–beta-lactamase producing, methicillin-susceptible isolates only), *Streptococcus pyogenes, Streptococcus agalactiae, viridans group streptococci, Enterococcus faecalis* (excluding vancomycin-resistant isolates), *Pseudomonas aeruginosa, Escherichia coli, Proteus mirabilis, Bacteroides fragilis,* and *Peptostreptococcus* species.** *Adults and children weighing more than 50 kg (110 lb):* 500 mg I.V. q 8 hours over 15 to 30 minutes as I.V. infusion.
Children ages 3 months and older weighing 50 kg or less: 10 mg/kg I.V. q 8 hours over 15 to 30 minutes as I.V. infusion or over 3 to 5 minutes as I.V. bolus injection (5 to 20 ml); maximum dose is 500 mg I.V. q 8 hours.
▶ **Complicated appendicitis and peritonitis caused by viridans group streptococci, *E. coli, Klebsiella pneumoniae, P. aeruginosa, Bacteroides fragilis, Bacteroides thetaiotaomicron,* and *Peptostreptococcus* species.** *Adults and children weighing more than 50 kg:* 1 g I.V. q 8 hours over 15 to 30 minutes as I.V. infusion or over 3 to 5 minutes as I.V. bolus injection (5 to 20 ml).
Children ages 3 months and older, weighing 50 kg or less: 20 mg/kg I.V. q 8 hours over 15 to 30 minutes as I.V. infusion or over 3 to 5 minutes as I.V. bolus injection (5 to 20 ml); maximum dosage is 1 g I.V. q 8 hours.
Adjust-a-dose: For adults with creatinine clearance of 26 to 50 ml/minute, give usual dose

M

q 12 hours. If clearance is 10 to 25 ml/minute, give half usual dose q 12 hours; if clearance is less than 10 ml/minute, give half usual dose q 24 hours.

▶ **Bacterial meningitis caused by *Streptococcus pneumoniae, Haemophilus influenzae,* and *Neisseria meningitides.*** *Children weighing more than 50 kg:* 2 g I.V. q 8 hours.
Children ages 3 months and older weighing 50 kg or less: 40 mg/kg I.V. q 8 hours; maximum dose, 2 g I.V. q 8 hours.

I.V. administration

- For I.V. bolus, add 10 ml of sterile water for injection to 500-mg/20-ml vial or add 20 ml to 1-g/30-ml vial. Shake to dissolve, and let stand until clear.
- For I.V. infusion, infusion vials (500 mg/100 ml and 1 g/100 ml) may be directly reconstituted with compatible infusion fluid. Or an injection vial may be reconstituted, then the resulting solution added to an I.V. container, and further diluted with appropriate infusion fluid. Don't use ADD-Vantage vials for this purpose.
- Follow manufacturer's guidelines closely when using ADD-Vantage vials.
- Use freshly prepared solutions of drug immediately.
- Stability of drug varies with form of drug used (injection vial, infusion vial, or ADD-Vantage container).

⊗ **Incompatibilities**
Other I.V. drugs.

Contraindications and cautions

- Contraindicated in patients hypersensitive to the drug, its components, or other drugs in the class. Also contraindicated in those who have had anaphylactic reactions to beta-lactams.
- Use cautiously and at a reduced dosage in patients with renal impairment.

Lifespan: In pregnant women, use only when benefits outweigh risks to the fetus. In breast-feeding women, use cautiously because it's unknown if the drug appears in breast milk. In infants younger than age 3 months, safety and effectiveness haven't been established.

Adverse reactions

CNS: agitation, confusion, headache, insomnia, nervousness, somnolence.
CV: ***bradycardia, cardiac arrest, heart failure,*** hypertension, hypotension, ***MI, pulmonary embolism,*** tachycardia, thrombophlebitis at injection site.
GI: anorexia, cholestatic jaundice, constipation, diarrhea, glossitis, nausea, oral candidiasis, ***pseudomembranous colitis,*** vomiting.
GU: dysuria, ***renal failure.***
Hematologic: anemia, eosinophilia.
Respiratory: ***apnea.***
Skin: pruritus, rash, urticaria.
Other: ***anaphylaxis, hypersensitivity reactions,*** inflammation at injection site, pain.

Interactions

Drug-drug. *Probenecid:* May inhibit renal meropenem excretion. Don't give together.

Effects on lab test results

- May increase ALT, AST, bilirubin, alkaline phosphatase, LDH, creatinine, and BUN levels. May decrease hemoglobin level and hematocrit.
- May increase eosinophil count. May decrease WBC count. May increase or decrease platelet count and PT.

Pharmacokinetics

Absorption: Given I.V.
Distribution: 2% protein-bound. Penetrates into most body fluids and tissues, including CSF.
Metabolism: In kidneys.
Excretion: In urine. *Half-life:* 1 hour.

Route	Onset	Peak	Duration
I.V.	Unknown	< 1 hr	Unknown

Action

Chemical effect: Readily penetrates the cell wall of most gram-positive and gram-negative bacteria to reach penicillin-binding protein targets, where it inhibits cell wall synthesis.
Therapeutic effect: Bactericidal.

Available forms

Powder for injection: 500 mg/15 ml, 500 mg/20 ml, 500 mg/100 ml, 1 g/15 ml, 1 g/30 ml, 1 g/100 ml

NURSING PROCESS

Assessment

- Obtain specimen for culture and sensitivity tests before giving first dose. Therapy may begin pending test results.

ALERT: Serious and occasionally fatal hypersensitivity reactions may occur. Before therapy, determine whether patient has ever had a hypersensitivity reaction to penicillins, cephalosporins, other beta-lactams, or other allergens.

- Monitor patient for signs and symptoms of superinfection.
- Periodically assess organ-system functions during prolonged therapy.
- Assess patient's and family's knowledge of drug therapy.

Nursing diagnoses

- Risk for infection related to bacteria
- Risk for deficient fluid volume related to effect on kidneys
- Deficient knowledge related to drug therapy

Planning and implementation

- Drug isn't used to treat methicillin-resistant staphylococci.
- If patient develops diarrhea, suspect pseudomembranous colitis. If confirmed, stop giving the drug, begin fluid and electrolyte management, and give an antibacterial effective against *Clostridium difficile.*
- If overdose occurs (usually in patients with renal impairment), stop giving the drug and provide general supportive therapy until renal elimination occurs. Drug is removable by hemodialysis, if needed.

Patient teaching

- Instruct patient to report adverse reactions.

Evaluation

- Patient is free from infection.
- Patient maintains adequate hydration.
- Patient and family state understanding of drug therapy.

mesalamine

(mez-AL-uh-meen)

Asacol, Canasa, Lialda, Mesasal ♦, Novo-5 ASA ♦, Pentasa, Rowasa, Salofalk ♦

Pharmacologic class: salicylate
Therapeutic class: anti-inflammatory
Pregnancy risk category: B

Indications and dosages

▶ **Active mild to moderate distal ulcerative colitis, proctitis, proctosigmoiditis.** *Adults:* 800 mg P.O. (tablets) t.i.d. for total dose of 2.4 g daily for 6 weeks, or 1 g P.O. (capsules) q.i.d. for total dose of 4 g daily up to 8 weeks. Or, 1,000 mg suppository retained in the rectum for 1 to 3 hours or longer, if possible, once daily at bedtime. Or 4 g as retention enema once daily (preferably at bedtime) retained for about 8 hours. Usual course of therapy for P.R. form is 3 to 6 weeks.

▶ **Induction of remission of active, mild to moderate ulcerative colitis.** *Adults:* Two to four 1.2-g tablets P.O. once daily with a meal for a total daily dose of 2.4 to 4.8 g, for maximum of 8 weeks.

▶ **Maintenance of remission of ulcerative colitis.** *Adults:* 1.6 g P.O. daily in divided doses for 6 months. Or, 60 ml (4 g) rectal suspension q 2 to 3 nights or 1 to 3 g rectal suspension daily; retain for about 8 hours.

Contraindications and cautions

- Contraindicated in patients hypersensitive to the drug, any of its components, or salicylates.
- Use cautiously in patients with renal impairment; absorbed drug may cause nephrotoxicity.

Lifespan: In pregnant women, use cautiously. In breast-feeding women, rectal form of drug is contraindicated. Oral form may be used with caution. It's unknown if the drug appears in breast milk. In children, drug is contraindicated. In the elderly, use cautiously.

Adverse reactions

CNS: dizziness, fatigue, fever, headache, malaise.
GI: abdominal cramps, discomfort, or pain; *belching;* bloating; diarrhea; flatulence; *nausea; pancolitis; pancreatitis;* rectal pain; vomiting.
Respiratory: upper respiratory tract infection, wheezing.
Skin: acne, hair loss, pruritus, rash, urticaria.
Other: ***anaphylaxis,*** pain.

Interactions

None significant.

Effects on lab test results

- May increase BUN, creatinine, AST, ALT, alkaline phosphatase, LDH, amylase, and lipase levels.

Pharmacokinetics

Absorption: Poor with P.R. use.
Distribution: Not clearly defined.
Metabolism: Undergoes acetylation, but whether this takes place at colonic or systemic sites is unknown.
Excretion: P.O. form mainly in urine; most of P.R. form in feces. *Half-life:* about 5 to 10 hours.

Route	Onset	Peak	Duration
P.O., P.R.	Unknown	3–12 hr	Unknown

Action

Chemical effect: May act topically by inhibiting prostaglandin production in colon.
Therapeutic effect: Relieves inflammation in lower GI tract.

Available forms

Capsules (controlled-release): 250 mg, 500 mg
Rectal suspension: 4 g/60 ml
Suppositories: 1,000 mg
Tablets (delayed-release): 400 mg, 1.2 g

NURSING PROCESS

Assessment

- Assess patient's condition before therapy and regularly thereafter to monitor drug effectiveness.
- Periodically monitor kidney function in patient on long-term therapy.
- Because it contains potassium metabisulfite, drug may cause hypersensitivity reactions in patient sensitive to sulfites.
- Be alert for adverse reactions.
- Assess patient's and family's knowledge of drug therapy.

Nursing diagnoses

- Impaired tissue integrity related to underlying condition
- Acute pain related to drug-induced adverse GI reactions
- Deficient knowledge related to drug therapy

Planning and implementation

- Have patient swallow tablets and capsules whole; don't crush or let him chew them.
- For maximum effectiveness, have patient retain suppository as long as possible. When giving rectal suspension, shake bottle before application.

ALERT: Don't confuse Asacol with Os-Cal or mesalamine with mecamylamine.

Patient teaching

- Teach patient how to take oral and rectal form, and instruct him to carefully follow instructions supplied with drug.
- Instruct patient to stop taking drug if he experiences fever or rash. Patient intolerant of sulfasalazine or aminosalicylic acid may also be hypersensitive to this drug.

Evaluation

- Patient reports relief from GI symptoms.
- Patient states that no new pain is experienced during therapy.
- Patient and family state understanding of drug therapy.

mesna

(MEZ-nah)
Mesnex, Uromitexan ♦

Pharmacologic class: thiol derivative
Therapeutic class: uroprotectant
Pregnancy risk category: B

Indications and dosages

▶ **To prevent hemorrhagic cystitis in patients taking ifosfamide.** *Adults:* Dosage varies with amount of ifosfamide given. If using 1.2-g/m^2 ifosfamide, give 240 mg/m^2 as I.V. bolus with ifosfamide dose. Repeat dose at 4 hours and 8 hours to a total of 60% of the ifosfamide dose. Or, give 20% as a single bolus injection followed by two oral doses (40% each). If using 1.2-g/m^2 ifosfamide, give 240 mg/m^2 I.V. mesna with ifosfamide, then 480 mg/m^2 P.O. at 2 and 6 hours.

▶ **To prevent hemorrhagic cystitis in bone marrow recipients taking cyclophosphamide‡.** *Adults:* Give 60% to 160% of the cyclophosphamide daily dose I.V. in three to five divided doses or by continuous infusion. Or, in patients receiving 50 to 60 mg/kg cyclophosphamide I.V. daily for 2 to 4 days, give 10 mg/kg I.V. loading dose followed by 60 mg/kg by continuous infusion over 24 hours. Give with each cyclophosphamide dose and continue for 24 hours after last dose of cyclophosphamide.

I.V. administration

- Dilute drug in D_5W, dextrose 5% combined with normal saline solution for injection, normal saline solution for injection, or lactated Ringer's solution to obtain final solution of 20 mg/ml.
- After mixing, inspect drug for particulate matter and discoloration before administering.
- Drug and ifosfamide are compatible in same I.V. infusion.
- Although diluted solution is stable for 24 hours at room temperature, refrigerate after preparation and use within 6 hours. After opening ampule, discard any unused drug because it decomposes quickly into inactive compound.

⊗ **Incompatibilities**
Amphotericin B, carboplatin, cisplatin.

Contraindications and cautions

- Contraindicated in patients hypersensitive to the drug or other compounds containing thiol.

Lifespan: In pregnant women, use cautiously. In breast-feeding women and in children, safety and effectiveness haven't been established.

Adverse reactions

CNS: anxiety, *asthenia,* confusion, dizziness, *fatigue, fever,* headache, insomnia, pain, somnolence.
CV: chest pain, edema, flushing, hypotension, tachycardia.
GI: abdominal pain, anorexia, constipation, diarrhea, dyspepsia, nausea, vomiting.
GU: hematuria.
Hematologic: ***anemia, granulocytopenia, leukopenia, thrombocytopenia.***
Metabolic: dehydration, hypokalemia.
Musculoskeletal: back pain.
Respiratory: dyspnea, coughing, pneumonia.
Skin: alopecia, increased sweating, pallor.
Other: *allergy,* injection site reaction.

Interactions

None significant.

Effects on lab test results

- May interfere with diagnostic tests for urine ketones.

Pharmacokinetics

Absorption: Unaffected by food.
Distribution: Remains in vascular compartment.
Metabolism: Rapid, to one metabolite.
Excretion: In urine. *Half-life:* 4 to 8 hours.

Route	Onset	Peak	Duration
P.O., I.V.	Unknown	Unknown	Unknown

Action

Chemical effect: Detoxifies urotoxic ifosfamide metabolites.
Therapeutic effect: Prevents ifosfamide from adversely affecting bladder tissue.

Available forms

Injection: 100 mg/ml in 2- and 10-ml vials (contains benzyl alcohol)
Tablets: 400 mg

NURSING PROCESS

Assessment

- Assess patient's condition before therapy and regularly thereafter to monitor drug effectiveness.
- Up to 6% of patients may not respond to drug's protective effects.
- Monitor urine samples for hematuria daily in patient taking mesna.
- Be alert for adverse reactions.
- If patient has an adverse GI reaction, monitor his hydration.
- Assess patient's and family's knowledge of drug therapy.

Nursing diagnoses

- Risk for deficient fluid volume related to drug-induced adverse GI reactions
- Deficient knowledge related to drug therapy

Planning and implementation

- If patient vomits within 2 hours of taking drug P.O., repeat the dose or give I.V.
- Because drug is used with ifosfamide and other chemotherapeutics, it's difficult to determine adverse reactions attributable solely to this drug.
- Drug isn't effective in preventing hematuria from other causes (such as thrombocytopenia).
- Although formulated to prevent hemorrhagic cystitis from ifosfamide, drug won't protect against other toxicities linked to ifosfamide.

Patient teaching

- Instruct patient to report hematuria immediately and to notify prescriber about adverse GI reactions.

M

Evaluation

- Patient maintains adequate hydration throughout therapy.
- Patient and family state understanding of drug therapy.

metaproterenol sulfate

(met-uh-proh-TER-eh-nul SUL-fayt)

Alupent

Pharmacologic class: beta agonist
Therapeutic class: bronchodilator
Pregnancy risk category: C

Indications and dosages

▶ **Asthma; bronchospasm.**
Oral
Adults and children age 9 and older or weighing more than 27.3 kg (60 lb): 20 mg P.O. t.i.d. to q.i.d.
Adults and children younger than age 9 or weighing less 27.3 kg (60 lb): 10 mg P.O. t.i.d. to q.i.d.
Children younger than age 6: Give 1.3 to 2.6 mg/kg/day P.O. in divided doses.
Aerosol inhalation
Adults and children older than age 12: Give 2 to 3 inhalations with at least 2 minutes between inhalations. Don't repeat inhalations more often than q 3 to 4 hours. Maximum, 12 inhalations daily.
Intermittent positive-pressure breathing (IPPB) or nebulizer
Adults and children age 12 and older: 0.2 to 0.3 ml of 5% solution diluted in 2.5 ml of normal saline solution or 2.5 ml of commercially available 0.4% or 0.6% solution q 4 hours, p.r.n.
Hand-bulb nebulizer
Adults and children age 12 and older: 10 inhalations of an undiluted 5% solution.

▶ **Acute asthma attacks.** *Children age 6 and older:* Use 5% solution for inhalation only. Give 0.1 to 0.2 ml in saline to a total volume of 3 ml given by nebulizer at time of attack.

Contraindications and cautions

- Contraindicated in patients hypersensitive to the drug or any of its components, in those receiving cyclopropane or halogenated hydrocarbon general anesthetics, and in those with tachycardia or arrhythmias caused by tachycardia, peripheral or mesenteric vascular thrombosis, or profound hypoxia or hypercapnia.
- Use cautiously in patients with hypertension, hyperthyroidism, heart disease, diabetes, or cirrhosis and in patients who are receiving digoxin.

Lifespan: In pregnant women, use cautiously. In breast-feeding women, use cautiously. It's unknown if the drug appears in breast milk.

Adverse reactions

CNS: drowsiness, *nervousness,* tremors, *weakness.*
CV: ***cardiac arrest,*** ECG changes, hypertension, palpitations, tachycardia.
GI: heartburn, nausea, taste perversion, vomiting.
Respiratory: ***paradoxical bronchoconstriction.***

Interactions

Drug-drug. *Aminophylline, theophylline:* May increase risk of cardiotoxicity. Monitor ECG and vital signs closely.
Other sympathomimetics: May have additive effects and toxicity. Separate administration times.
Propranolol, other beta blockers: May block bronchodilating effect of metaproterenol. Monitor patient.

Effects on lab test results

None reported.

Pharmacokinetics

Absorption: Good in GI tract. Minimally through the lungs.
Distribution: Wide.
Metabolism: Extensive on first pass through liver.
Excretion: In urine. *Half-life:* Unknown.

Route	Onset	Peak	Duration
P.O.	15 min	1 hr	1–4 hr
Inhalation	1 min	1 hr	2–6 hr
Nebulization	5–30 min	1 hr	2–6 hr

Action

Chemical effect: Relaxes bronchial smooth muscle by acting on $beta_2$-adrenergic receptors.
Therapeutic effect: Improves breathing.

Available forms

Aerosol inhaler: 0.65 mg/metered spray

Solution for nebulizer inhalation: 0.4%, 0.6%
Syrup: 10 mg/5 ml
Tablets: 10 mg, 20 mg

NURSING PROCESS

Assessment

- Assess patient's condition before therapy and regularly thereafter to monitor drug effectiveness.
- Be alert for adverse reactions and drug interactions.
- If patient has an adverse GI reaction, monitor his hydration.
- Assess patient's and family's knowledge of drug therapy.

Nursing diagnoses

- Impaired gas exchange related to underlying respiratory condition
- Risk for deficient fluid volume related to drug-induced adverse GI reactions
- Deficient knowledge related to drug therapy

Planning and implementation

- Aerosol nebulization solution can be given by IPPB with drug diluted in normal saline solution or by hand-bulb nebulizer at full strength.

ALERT: Don't use solution if discolored or precipitated.
ALERT: Don't confuse metaproterenol with metoprolol or metipranolol.
ALERT: Don't confuse Alupent with Atrovent.

Patient teaching

- Give patient the following instructions for using metered-dose inhaler: clear nasal passages and throat. Breathe out, expelling as much air from lungs as possible. Place mouthpiece well into mouth and inhale deeply as you release a dose from inhaler. Hold breath for several seconds, remove mouthpiece, and exhale slowly. Allow 2 minutes between inhalations.
- Instruct patient to store drug in light-resistant container.
- Tell patient using corticosteroid inhaler to use bronchodilator first and then to wait 5 to 15 minutes before using corticosteroid. This allows bronchodilator to open air passages for maximum effectiveness of corticosteroid.
- Warn patient to immediately stop taking the drug and notify the prescriber if he has paradoxical bronchospasm.
- Tell patient that if dose doesn't work, he should notify his prescriber for an increase.

Evaluation

- Patient's respiratory status improves.
- Patient maintains adequate hydration.
- Patient and family state understanding of drug therapy.

metformin hydrochloride

(met-FOR-min high-droh-KLOR-ighd)
Apo-Metformin ♦, Fortamet, Gen-Metformin ♦, Glucophage, Glucophage XR, Glumetza, Nu-Metformin ♦, PMS-Metformin ♦, Rhoxal-metformin ♦, Riomet

Pharmacologic class: biguanide
Therapeutic class: antidiabetic
Pregnancy risk category: B

Indications and dosages

▶ **Adjunct to diet and exercise to lower glucose level in patients with type 2 diabetes mellitus.** *Adults (immediate-release form):* 500 mg P.O. b.i.d. or 850 mg P.O. daily, given with meals. Increase doses in increments of 500 mg weekly or 850 mg q 2 weeks to 2,000 mg daily, in divided doses. May also increase from 500 mg b.i.d. to 850 mg b.i.d. after 2 weeks. Maximum daily dose is 2,550 mg daily. Doses above 2,000 mg may be better tolerated given t.i.d. with meals.
Adults (extended-release form): 500 mg P.O. daily with the evening meal. Increase in increments of 500 mg weekly to a maximum of 2,000 mg once daily (2,500 mg for Fortamet) with the evening meal. If glycemic control isn't achieved with 2,000 mg once daily, consider a trial of 1,000 mg b.i.d. If higher doses are required, use immediate-release form.
Children ages 10 to 16: Give 500 mg P.O. b.i.d. (regular-release form). Increase dosage in increments of 500 mg weekly to a maximum of 2,000 mg daily in divided doses. Don't use extended-release form in children.
▶ **Adjunct to diet and exercise in type 2 diabetes, as monotherapy or with a sulfonylurea or insulin.** *Adults and adolescents age 17 and older:* Initially, 500 to 1,000 mg of Fortamet P.O. with evening meal. Increase dosage based

M

on glucose level in increments of 500 mg/week to a maximum of 2,500 mg daily. When used with a sulfonylurea or insulin, base dosage on blood glucose level, and adjust slowly until desired therapeutic effect occurs. Decrease insulin dosage by 10% to 25% when fasting blood glucose level is less than 120 mg/dl.

▶ **Adjunct to diet and exercise in type 2 diabetes as monotherapy or with a sulfonylurea or insulin (Glumetza).** *Adults:* Initially, 1,000 mg P.O. once daily in the evening with food. Increase, as needed, by 500 mg in weekly increments up to a maximum of 2,000 mg daily. If glycemic control not attained at this dose, give 1,000 mg b.i.d.

When used with a sulfonylurea or insulin, base dosage on glucose level and adjust slowly until desired therapeutic effect occurs. Decrease insulin dose by 10% to 25% when fasting blood glucose level is less than 120 mg/dl.

Adjust-a-dose: For malnourished or debilitated patients, don't adjust to maximum dosage.

Contraindications and cautions

- Contraindicated in patients hypersensitive to the drug or any of its components; those with hepatic disease, renal disease or dysfunction, or acute or chronic metabolic acidosis; and in heart failure patients who need other drugs. Temporarily withhold drug in patients undergoing radiologic studies involving parenteral administration of iodinated contrast materials; using such products may result in acute renal dysfunction. If patient enters hypoxic state, stop drug.
- Use cautiously in debilitated or malnourished patients and in those with adrenal or pituitary insufficiency because of increased risk of hypoglycemia.

Lifespan: In pregnant women, safety and effectiveness haven't been established. In breastfeeding women, use cautiously; it's unknown if drug appears in breast milk. In children younger than age 10, safety and effectiveness of regular form haven't been established. In children younger than age 17, safety and effectiveness of extended-release form haven't been established. In elderly patients, use cautiously.

Adverse reactions

CNS: asthenia, dizziness, headache.
GI: abdominal discomfort, *diarrhea, flatulence,* indigestion, *nausea,* unpleasant or metallic taste, *vomiting.*
Hematologic: megaloblastic anemia.
Metabolic: *lactic acidosis.*

Interactions

Drug-drug. *Calcium channel blockers, corticosteroids, estrogens, hormonal contraceptives, isoniazid, nicotinic acid, phenothiazines, phenytoin, sympathomimetics, thiazide and other diuretics, thyroid drugs:* May cause hyperglycemia. Monitor patient's glycemic control. Increase metformin dosage.
Cationic drugs (such as amiloride, cimetidine, digoxin, morphine, procainamide, quinidine, quinine, ranitidine, triamterene, trimethoprim, vancomycin): May reduce metformin clearance and increase metformin level. Monitor patient's glucose level. Adjust dosages, if needed.
Furosemide, nifedipine: May increase metformin level. Monitor patient and decrease dosage.
Iodinated contrast material: May cause lactic acidosis, leading to acute renal impairment. Withhold metformin on or before the day of the study, and resume after 48 hours, if renal function is normal.
Drug-herb. *Aloe, bilberry leaf, bitter melon, burdock, dandelion, fenugreek, garlic, ginseng:* May improve glucose control and allow reduction of antidiabetic. Tell patient to discuss use of herbal remedies with prescriber before therapy.
Drug-lifestyle. *Alcohol use:* May increase drug effects. Discourage use together.

Effects on lab test results

- May decrease pH, bicarbonate, triglyceride, total cholesterol, LDL, glucose, hemoglobin, and glycosylated hemoglobin levels and hematocrit.
- May decrease RBC count.

Pharmacokinetics

Absorption: Food decreases rate and extent for tablets, but increases extent for oral solution.
Distribution: Negligible.
Metabolism: None.
Excretion: Unchanged in urine. *Half-life:* About 6 hours.

Route	Onset	Peak	Duration
P.O.			
Regular	Unknown	2–4 hr	Unknown
Solution	Unknown	2½ hr	Unknown
Extended-release	Unknown	4–8 hr	24–48 hr

Action

Chemical effect: Decreases hepatic glucose production and intestinal absorption of glucose and improves insulin sensitivity (increases peripheral glucose uptake and utilization).
Therapeutic effect: Lowers blood glucose level.

Available forms

Oral solution: 500 mg/5 ml
Tablets: 500 mg, 850 mg, 1,000 mg
Tablets (extended-release): 500 mg, 750 mg, 1,000 mg

NURSING PROCESS

Assessment

- Assess patient's glucose level before therapy and regularly thereafter to monitor drug effectiveness.
- Assess patient's kidney function before therapy and reassess at least annually. If renal impairment is detected, expect prescriber to switch to different antidiabetic.
- Monitor patient's hematologic lab test results for megaloblastic anemia. Patients with low vitamin B_{12} or calcium intake or absorption may be more likely to develop a below-normal vitamin B_{12} level. Check their vitamin B_{12} level every 2 to 3 years.
- Be alert for adverse reactions and drug interactions.
- Monitor patient closely during times of stress, such as infection, fever, surgery, or trauma. Insulin therapy may be needed.
- The risk of drug-induced lactic acidosis is very low but may occur in diabetics with significant renal or hepatic insufficiency, other medical or surgical problems, and multiple drug therapies. The risk of lactic acidosis increases with the degree of renal impairment and patient's age. Don't give drug to patient age 80 or older unless measurement of creatinine clearance shows renal function is normal.
- Assess patient's and family's knowledge of drug therapy.

Nursing diagnoses

- Ineffective health maintenance related to presence of hyperglycemia
- Risk for deficient fluid volume related to drug-induced adverse GI reactions
- Deficient knowledge related to drug therapy

Planning and implementation

- When switching from standard oral antidiabetic (except chlorpropamide) to metformin, usually no transition period is needed. When switching from chlorpropamide to metformin, use care during first 2 weeks of metformin therapy because prolonged retention of chlorpropamide increases risk of hypoglycemia during this time.

ALERT: Don't use extended-release formulation in children.

ALERT: Don't cut, crush or chew extended-release tablets; swallow whole.

- If glucose level rises despite therapy, notify prescriber.
- If patient hasn't responded to 4 weeks of therapy using maximum dosage, add oral sulfonylurea while continuing metformin at maximum dosage. If patient still doesn't respond after several months, stop both drugs and start insulin therapy.

ALERT: If patient develops conditions linked to hypoxemia or dehydration, stop giving the drug immediately and notify prescriber because of risk of lactic acidosis.

- Stop therapy temporarily for a surgical procedure (except minor procedures not related to restricted intake of food and fluids), and don't restart until patient's oral intake and kidney function are normal.

Patient teaching

- Tell patient to take once-daily dose with breakfast (except Fortamet or Glumetza, which is to be taken with dinner) and twice-daily dose with breakfast and dinner.
- Tell patient not to crush or chew extended-release tablets.
- Instruct patient to stop drug and tell prescriber about unexplained hyperventilation, myalgia, malaise, unusual somnolence, or other symptoms of early lactic acidosis.
- Warn patient to avoid alcohol consumption while taking drug.

ALERT: Teach patient about diabetes and the importance of complying with therapy; adhering to diet, weight reduction, exercise, and hygiene programs; and avoiding infection. Explain how and when to monitor glucose level and how to differentiate between hypoglycemia and hyperglycemia.

- Tell patient not to change dose without prescriber's consent. Encourage patient to report abnormal glucose test results.

M

• Advise patient not to take other drugs, including OTC drugs, without checking with prescriber.
• Instruct patient to wear or carry medical identification.

Evaluation

• Patient's glucose level is normal.
• Patient maintains adequate hydration throughout therapy.
• Patient and family state understanding of drug therapy.

methadone hydrochloride

(METH-eh-dohn high-droh-KLOR-ighd)

Dolophine, Methadose, Physeptone ◇

Pharmacologic class: opioid
Therapeutic class: analgesic, opioid detoxification adjunct
Pregnancy risk category: C
Controlled substance schedule: II

Indications and dosages

▶ **Severe pain.** *Adults:* 2.5 to 10 mg P.O., I.M., or subcutaneously q 3 to 4 hours, p.r.n. If patient is opioid-naive, give q 8 to 12 hours.
Children‡: 0.7 mg/kg P.O. q 4 to 6 hours.

▶ **Opioid withdrawal syndrome.** *Adults:* 15 to 40 mg P.O. daily initially based on previous opioid exposure (highly individualized). Maintenance dosage is 20 to 120 mg P.O. daily. Adjust dosage as needed. Daily doses greater than 120 mg require state and federal approval.

Contraindications and cautions

• Contraindicated in patients hypersensitive to the drug or any of its components.
• Use cautiously in debilitated patients and in patients with acute abdominal conditions, severe hepatic or renal impairment, hypothyroidism, Addison disease, prostatic hyperplasia, urethral stricture, head injury, increased intracranial pressure, asthma, or other respiratory conditions.

Lifespan: In pregnant women, use cautiously. In breast-feeding women, don't use. It's unknown if the drug appears in breast milk. In children, safety and effectiveness haven't been established. In elderly patients, use cautiously.

Adverse reactions

CNS: agitation, chorea, *clouded sensorium,* dizziness, *euphoria,* headache, insomnia, lightheadedness, *sedation,* ***seizures,*** *somnolence,* syncope.
CV: ***arrhythmias, bradycardia, cardiac arrest,*** hypotension, ***shock.***
EENT: visual disturbances.
GI: constipation, ileus, nausea, vomiting.
GU: urine retention.
Respiratory: ***respiratory arrest, respiratory depression.***
Skin: diaphoresis.
Other: decreased libido, induration after subcutaneous injection, pain at injection site, *physical dependence,* tissue irritation.

Interactions

Drug-drug. *Ammonium chloride and other urine acidifiers, phenytoin:* May reduce methadone effect. Monitor patient for decreased pain control.
Cimetidine: May increase methadone level. Monitor patient for increased CNS and respiratory depression.
CNS depressants, general anesthetics, hypnotics, MAO inhibitors, sedatives, tranquilizers, tricyclic antidepressants: May cause respiratory depression, hypotension, profound sedation, or coma. Use together cautiously and monitor patient.
Rifampin: May cause withdrawal symptoms; reduces blood levels of methadone. Use together cautiously.
Drug-lifestyle. *Alcohol use:* May have additive effects. Discourage patient from use together.

Effects on lab test results

• May increase amylase or lipase levels.

Pharmacokinetics

Absorption: Good in P.O. use; unknown in I.M. use.
Distribution: Highly bound to tissue protein.
Metabolism: Mainly in liver.
Excretion: Mainly in urine; metabolites in feces. *Half-life:* 15 to 25 hours.

Route	Onset	Peak	Duration
P.O.	30–60 min	1–2 hr	4–7 hr
I.M.	10–30 min	½–1 hr	4–7 hr
SubQ	Unknown	1–1½ hr	4–7 hr

Action

Chemical effect: Binds to opioid receptors at many sites in CNS, altering both perception of and emotional response to pain through unknown mechanism.
Therapeutic effect: Relieves pain and symptoms of opioid withdrawal.

Available forms

Dispersible tablets (for maintenance therapy): 40 mg
Injection: 10 mg/ml
Oral solution (contains 8% alcohol): 5 mg/5 ml, 10 mg/5 ml, 10 mg/ml (concentrate)
Tablets: 5 mg, 10 mg

NURSING PROCESS

Assessment

- Assess patient's pain or opioid dependence before and during therapy.
- Monitor patient closely because drug has cumulative effect. Marked sedation can occur after repeated doses.
- Be alert for adverse reactions and drug interactions.
- Assess patient's and family's knowledge of drug therapy.

Nursing diagnoses

- Chronic pain related to underlying condition
- Ineffective coping related to opioid dependence
- Deficient knowledge related to drug therapy

Planning and implementation

- Liquid form is legally required in maintenance programs. Dissolve tablets in 120 ml of orange juice or powdered citrus drink.
- P.O. dose is one-half as potent as injected dose.
- For parenteral use, I.M. injection is preferred. Rotate injection sites.
- Around-the-clock therapy is needed to manage severe, chronic pain.
- Duration of action is prolonged to 22 to 48 hours with repeated doses of drug. Depressant effects from overdosage can also last 36 to 48 hours.

ALERT: Very high doses of methadone may cause QT interval prolongation and torsades de pointes.

ALERT: Don't confuse methadone with Metadate.

Patient teaching

- Warn patient about getting out of bed or walking. Warn outpatient to avoid hazardous activities until drug's CNS effects are known.
- Instruct patient to avoid alcohol consumption during drug therapy.

Evaluation

- Patient is free from pain.
- Patient doesn't exhibit opioid withdrawal symptoms.
- Patient and family state understanding of drug therapy.

methamphetamine hydrochloride

(meth-am-FET-uh-meen high-droh-KLOR-ighd)
Desoxyn

Pharmacologic class: amphetamine
Therapeutic class: CNS stimulant, short-term adjunct anorexigenic, sympathomimetic amine
Pregnancy risk category: C
Controlled substance schedule: II

Indications and dosages

▶ **Attention deficit hyperactivity disorder.** *Children age 6 and older:* Initially, 5 mg P.O. once daily or b.i.d., increase by 5-mg increments weekly as needed. Usual effective dosage is 20 to 25 mg daily.

▶ **Short-term adjunct in exogenous obesity.** *Adults and children older than age 12:* Give 5 mg P.O. 30 minutes before each meal. Treatment should not exceed a few weeks.

Contraindications and cautions

- Contraindicated in patients hypersensitive to sympathomimetic amines; patients with idiosyncratic reactions to sympathomimetic amines; patients with moderate to severe hypertension, hyperthyroidism, symptomatic CV disease, advanced arteriosclerosis, glaucoma, or history of drug abuse; patients who have taken an MAO inhibitor within 14 days; and agitated patients.
- Use cautiously in patients who are debilitated, asthenic, psychopathic, or patients who have a history of suicidal or homicidal tendencies.

Lifespan: In pregnant and breast-feeding women, drug is contraindicated. In children

M

younger than age 6, safety and effectiveness haven't been established. In elderly patients, use cautiously.

Adverse reactions

CNS: dizziness, euphoria, headache, hyperexcitability, *insomnia,* irritability, *nervousness,* psychotic episodes, *talkativeness,* tics, tremors, worsening of Tourette syndrome.
CV: ***arrhythmias, cardiomyopathy,*** hypertension, *palpitations,* ***reflex bradycardia,*** tachycardia.
EENT: blurred vision, mydriasis.
GI: abdominal cramps, *anorexia,* constipation, diarrhea, dry mouth, metallic taste, nausea, vomiting.
GU: impotence.
Skin: urticaria.
Other: altered libido, growth suppression in children.

Interactions

Drug-drug. *Acetazolamide, antacids, sodium bicarbonate:* May increase renal reabsorption. Monitor patient for enhanced effects.
Ammonium chloride, ascorbic acid: May decrease level and increase renal excretion of methamphetamine. Monitor patient for decreased methamphetamine effects.
Furazolidone: May increase sensitivity to amphetamines. Monitor patient for toxicity and adjust dosage as needed.
Guanethidine: May decrease the antihypertensive effectiveness of guanethidine. Monitor blood pressure.
Haloperidol, phenothiazines, tricyclic antidepressants: May increase CNS effects. Avoid use together.
Insulin, oral antidiabetics: May decrease antidiabetic requirement. Monitor glucose level.
MAO inhibitors: May cause severe hypertension; possible hypertensive crisis. Don't use within 14 days of MAO inhibitor therapy.
SSRIs: May increase sensitivity to sympathomimetics and increase risk of serotonin syndrome. Monitor and adjust dosage as needed.
Drug-herb. *Melatonin:* May enhance monoaminergic effects of drug; may worsen insomnia. Discourage use together.
Drug-food. *Caffeinated beverages:* May increase drug effects. Discourage use together.

Effects on lab test results

• May increase corticosteroid level.

Pharmacokinetics

Absorption: Rapid.
Distribution: Wide.
Metabolism: In liver to at least seven metabolites.
Excretion: In urine. *Half-life:* 4 to 5 hours.

Route	Onset	Peak	Duration
P.O.	Unknown	Unknown	≤ 24 hr

Action

Chemical effect: Probably promotes nerve impulse transmission by releasing stored norepinephrine from nerve terminals in brain. Main sites appear to be cerebral cortex and reticular activating system. In hyperkinetic children, drug has paradoxical calming effect.
Therapeutic effect: Promotes calmness in children with attention deficit disorder and causes weight loss.

Available forms

Tablets: 5 mg

NURSING PROCESS

Assessment

• Assess patient's condition before therapy, and regularly thereafter to monitor drug effectiveness.
• Be alert for adverse reactions and drug interactions particularly growth suppression in children and cardiomyopathy with prolonged use.
• Assess patient's and family's knowledge of drug therapy.

Nursing diagnoses

• Ineffective health maintenance related to underlying condition
• Sleep deprivation related to drug-induced insomnia
• Deficient knowledge related to drug therapy

Planning and implementation

ALERT: Don't confuse Desoxyn with digitoxin or digoxin.
• Drug isn't the first-line therapy for obesity. Use as anorexigenic is prohibited in some states.
• When used for obesity, make sure patient is on weight-reduction program.

• If tolerance to anorexigenic effect develops, notify prescriber and stop giving the drug.

Patient teaching

• Warn patient of high risk of abuse. Advise him that drug shouldn't be used to prevent fatigue.
• Advise patient to take last dose of drug at least 6 hours before bedtime.
• Warn patient to avoid activities that require alertness or good coordination until the drug's CNS effects are known.
• Tell patient not to use caffeine during therapy.
• Instruct patient to report signs of excessive stimulation.
• Instruct patient not to crush long-acting tablets.

Evaluation

• Patient has positive response to drug therapy.
• Patient doesn't experience insomnia.
• Patient and family state understanding of drug therapy.

methimazole

(meth-IH-muh-zohl)
Tapazole

Pharmacologic class: thyroid hormone antagonist
Therapeutic class: antithyroid drug
Pregnancy risk category: D

Indications and dosages

▶ **Hyperthyroidism.** *Adults:* If mild, 15 mg P.O. daily. If moderately severe, 30 to 40 mg daily. If severe, 60 mg daily. Daily dosage divided into three doses at 8-hour intervals. Maintenance dosage is 5 to 15 mg daily.
Children: 0.4 mg/kg P.O. daily in divided doses q 8 hours. Maintenance dosage is 0.2 mg/kg P.O. daily in divided doses q 8 hours. Or 0.5 to 0.7 mg/kg P.O. daily in three divided doses. Maintenance dosage is one-third to two-thirds of initial dose. Maximum dosage 30 mg/24 hours.

Contraindications and cautions

• Contraindicated in patients hypersensitive to the drug or any of its components.
Lifespan: In pregnant women, use cautiously. In breast-feeding women, use cautiously; it's unknown if drug appears in breast milk.

Adverse reactions

CNS: CNS stimulation, depression, drowsiness, headache, neuritis, neuropathies, paresthesias, vertigo.
GI: diarrhea, epigastric distress, loss of taste, nausea, salivary gland enlargement, vomiting.
Hematologic: ***agranulocytosis, aplastic anemia, leukopenia,*** lymphadenopathy, ***thrombocytopenia.***
Hepatic: jaundice.
Metabolic: hypothyroidism.
Musculoskeletal: arthralgia, myalgia.
Skin: alopecia, rash, skin discoloration, urticaria.
Other: drug-induced fever.

Interactions

Drug-drug. *Anticoagulants:* May enhance anti–vitamin K effects. Monitor PT and INR.
Beta blockers, digoxin, theophylline: May increase levels of these drugs when a hyperthyroid patient becomes euthyroid. Reduce dosage of these drugs, if needed.

Effects on lab test results

• May decrease hemoglobin level and hematocrit.
• May decrease granulocyte, WBC, RBC, and platelet counts.

Pharmacokinetics

Absorption: Rapid.
Distribution: Concentrated in thyroid and isn't protein-bound.
Metabolism: Hepatic.
Excretion: Mainly in urine. *Half-life:* 5 to 13 hours.

Route	Onset	Peak	Duration
P.O.	Unknown	30 min–1 hr	Unknown

Action

Chemical effect: Inhibits oxidation of iodine in thyroid gland, blocking iodine's ability to combine with tyrosine to form T_4. Also may prevent coupling of monoiodotyrosine and diiodotyrosine to form T_4 and T_3.
Therapeutic effect: Reduces thyroid hormone level.

Available forms

Tablets: 5 mg, 10 mg

NURSING PROCESS

Assessment

- Assess patient's thyroid condition before therapy and regularly thereafter to monitor the drug's effectiveness.
- Monitor thyroid function studies.
- Monitor CBC and liver function periodically.

ALERT: Dosages higher than 30 mg daily increase risk of agranulocytosis, especially in patients older than age 40.

- Be alert for adverse reactions.
- Assess patient's and family's knowledge of drug therapy.

Nursing diagnoses

- Ineffective health maintenance related to presence of hyperthyroidism
- Risk for infection related to drug-induced adverse hematologic reactions
- Deficient knowledge related to drug therapy

Planning and implementation

- Pregnant women may need a lower dosage as pregnancy progresses. Thyroid hormone may be added. Drug may be stopped during last weeks of pregnancy.
- Notify prescriber about signs and symptoms of hypothyroidism and adjust dosage.

ALERT: If severe rash occurs or cervical lymph nodes become enlarged, stop giving the drug and notify prescriber.

ALERT: Don't confuse methimazole with mebendazole, methazolamide, or rabeprazole.

Patient teaching

- Tell patient to take drug with meals.
- Warn patient to immediately report fever, sore throat, or mouth sores (signs of agranulocytosis); skin eruptions (sign of hypersensitivity); or anorexia, pruritus, right upper quadrant pain, and yellow skin or sclera (signs of hepatic dysfunction).
- Tell patient to ask prescriber about using iodized salt and eating shellfish.
- Warn patient against taking OTC cough products, because many contain iodine.
- Instruct patient to store drug in light-resistant container.

Evaluation

- Patient has normal thyroid hormone level.
- Patient maintains normal hematologic parameters and remains free from infection throughout therapy.
- Patient and family state understanding of drug therapy.

methotrexate (amethopterin, MTX)

(meth-oh-TRECKS-ayt)
Trexall

methotrexate sodium

Methotrexate LPF, Rheumatrex Dose Pack

Pharmacologic class: antimetabolite
Therapeutic class: antineoplastic, immunosuppressant, antirheumatic
Pregnancy risk category: X

Indications and dosages

▶ **Trophoblastic tumors (choriocarcinoma, hydatidiform mole).** *Adults:* 15 to 30 mg P.O. or I.M. daily for 5 days. May repeat course after 1 or more weeks, based on response or toxicity. Three to five courses usually are used.

▶ **Acute lymphoblastic and lymphatic leukemia.** *Adults and children:* 3.3 mg/m² P.O. or I.M. daily for 4 to 6 weeks or until remission occurs; then 20 to 30 mg/m² P.O. or I.M. twice weekly. Or, 2.5 mg/kg I.V. q 14 days.

▶ **Meningeal leukemia.** *Adults and children:* 12 mg/m² intrathecally (maximum of 15 mg) q 2 to 5 days and repeat until cell count of CSF returns to normal, then give one additional dose. Or, 12 mg/m² once weekly for 2 weeks, then once monthly thereafter. Or intrathecal dose based on age in years: younger than 1 year, 6 mg; 1 year, 8 mg; 2 years, 10 mg; 3 years or older, 12 mg.

▶ **Burkitt lymphoma (stage I or stage II).** *Adults:* 10 to 25 mg P.O. daily for 4 to 8 days with 7- to 10-day rest intervals.

▶ **Lymphosarcoma (stage III).** *Adults:* 0.625 to 2.5 mg/kg P.O., I.M., or I.V. daily.

▶ **Osteosarcoma.** *Adults:* 12 g/m² I.V. as a 4-hour infusion. May increase to 15 g/m² in subsequent treatments if peak serum concentration at the end of infusion does not reach 1,000 micromolar (10^{-3} mol/L).

▶ **Mycosis fungoides.** *Adults:* 5 to 50 mg P.O. or I.M. once weekly. Or, 15 to 37.5 mg P.O. or I.M. twice weekly.
▶ **Psoriasis.** *Adults:* 10 to 25 mg P.O., I.M., or I.V. as single weekly dose. Do not exceed 30 mg/week. Or, 2.5 mg q. 12 hours for 3 doses each week. Do not exceed 30 mg/week. A 5- to 10-mg test dose should be tried the week before therapy starts.
▶ **Rheumatoid arthritis.** *Adults:* Initially, 7.5 mg P.O. once weekly, or divided as 2.5 mg P.O. q 12 hours for three doses once a week. Gradually increase dosage to maximum, 20 mg weekly.
Adults‡: 7.5 to 15 mg I.M. once weekly.
▶ **Head and neck carcinoma‡.** *Adults:* 40 to 60 mg/m^2 I.V. once weekly. Response to therapy is limited to 4 months.

I.V. administration

• Follow facility policy to reduce risks. Preparation and administration of parenteral forms are linked to carcinogenic, mutagenic, and teratogenic risks.
• Liquid methotrexate sodium injection with preservatives may be given undiluted except intrathecally or in high I.V. doses.
• Preservative-free liquid methotrexate sodium injection may be given undiluted or may be further diluted with normal saline solution.
• For reconstitution of lyophilized powders, reconstitute immediately before use, and discard unused drug. Dilute with D_5W or normal saline solution. Dilute the 20-mg vial to a concentration no greater than 25 mg/ml. Reconstitute 1-g vial with 19.4 ml of diluent for a maximum concentration of 50 mg/ml.
• For intrathecal use, only use 20-mg vials of powder with no preservatives. Reconstitute immediately before using, with preservative-free normal saline solution injection. Dilute to maximum of 1 mg/ml. Use only new vials of drug and diluent.
• Drug may be given daily or weekly, depending on the disease.
• Storage for 24 hours at 70° to 77° F (21° to 25° C) results in a product that is within 90% of label potency. Protect from light.

⊗ **Incompatibilities**
Bleomycin, chlorpromazine, dexamethasone sodium phosphate, droperidol, fluorouracil, gemcitabine, idarubicin, ifosfamide, metoclopramide, midazolam, nalbuphine, prednisolone, promethazine, propofol, sodium phosphate, vancomycin.

Contraindications and cautions

• Contraindicated in patients hypersensitive to the drug or any of its components and in those with psoriasis or rheumatoid arthritis who also have alcoholism, alcoholic liver, chronic liver disease, immunodeficiency syndromes, or blood dyscrasias.
• Use cautiously and at modified dosage in patients with impaired liver or kidney function, bone marrow suppression, aplasia, leukopenia, thrombocytopenia, or anemia. Also use cautiously in patients with infection, peptic ulceration, or ulcerative colitis and in debilitated patients.
Lifespan: In pregnant and breast-feeding women, drug is contraindicated. In children younger than age 2, safety and effectiveness haven't been established for uses other than cancer. In elderly patients, use cautiously.

Adverse reactions

CNS: ***arachnoiditis,*** dizziness, headache, ***leukoencephalopathy,*** malaise, neurotoxicity, ***seizures,*** subacute demyelination.
EENT: blurred vision, gingivitis, pharyngitis.
GI: diarrhea, enteritis, ***intestinal perforation,*** nausea, stomatitis, vomiting.
GU: nephropathy, ***renal impairment, renal failure,*** TUBULAR NECROSIS.
Hematologic: *anemia,* ***leukopenia, thrombocytopenia.***
Hepatic: ***acute toxicity, chronic toxicity, cirrhosis, hepatic fibrosis.***
Metabolic: hyperuricemia.
Musculoskeletal: osteoporosis in children with long-term use.
Respiratory: pneumonitis, ***pulmonary fibrosis, pulmonary interstitial infiltrates.***
Skin: alopecia, hyperpigmentation, photosensitivity reactions, pruritus, psoriatic lesions, rash, *urticaria.*
Other: ***severe infections, sudden death.***

Interactions

Drug-drug. *Digoxin:* May decrease digoxin level. Monitor digoxin level.
Folic acid derivatives: May antagonize methotrexate effect. Monitor patient.
NSAIDs, phenylbutazone, salicylates, sulfonamides: May increase methotrexate toxicity.

Use together cautiously; monitor methotrexate levels.
Phenytoin: May decrease phenytoin level. Monitor phenytoin level.
Probenecid: May impair excretion of methotrexate, causing increased levels, effects, and toxicity. Monitor level closely, and decrease dosage accordingly.
Procarbazine: May increase nephrotoxicity of methotrexate. Monitor renal function closely.
Vaccines: May inactivate vaccine; may increase risk of disseminated infection with live-virus vaccines. Consult with prescriber about safe time to give vaccine.
Drug-food. *Food:* May delay drug absorption and reduce peak levels of methotrexate. Take on empty stomach.
Drug-lifestyle. *Alcohol use:* May increase hepatotoxicity. Discourage use together.
Sun exposure: May cause photosensitivity reactions. Urge patient to avoid unprotected or prolonged exposure to sunlight.

Effects on lab test results

- May increase uric acid, BUN, creatinine, and liver enzyme levels. May decrease hemoglobin level and hematocrit.
- May decrease WBC, RBC, and platelet counts.

Pharmacokinetics

Absorption: For small P.O. doses, almost complete, but for large doses, incomplete and variable. For I.M. use, complete.
Distribution: Wide, with highest levels in kidneys, gallbladder, spleen, liver, and skin. About 50% protein-bound.
Metabolism: Only slight.
Excretion: Primarily in urine. *Half-life for doses below 30 mg/m²:* About 3 to 10 hours. *Half-life for doses of 30 mg/m² and above:* 8 to 15 hours.

Route	Onset	Peak	Duration
P.O.	Unknown	1–2 hr	Unknown
I.V., intrathecal	Unknown	Immediate	24 hr
I.M.	Unknown	30 min–1 hr	Unknown

Action

Chemical effect: Prevents reduction of folic acid to tetrahydrofolate by binding to dihydrofolate reductase.
Therapeutic effect: Kills certain cancer cells and reduces inflammation.

Available forms

methotrexate
Tablets: 2.5 mg, 5 mg, 7.5 mg, 10 mg, 15 mg
methotrexate sodium
Injection (lyophilized powder, preservative free): 20 mg (as base); 1-g (as base) vials
Injection (preservative free): 25 mg/ml in 2-, 4-, 8-,10-, 20-, and 40-ml vials
Injection (with preservatives): 25 mg/ml in 2- and 10-ml vials
Tablets: 2.5 mg

NURSING PROCESS

Assessment

- Assess patient's condition before therapy and regularly thereafter to monitor drug effectiveness.
- Perform baseline pulmonary function tests before therapy, and repeat periodically.
- Monitor fluid intake and output daily.
- Monitor uric acid level.
- Watch for increases in AST, ALT, and alkaline phosphatase levels, which are signs of hepatic dysfunction.
- Regularly monitor CBC.
- Be alert for adverse reactions and drug interactions.
- Assess patient's and family's knowledge of drug therapy.

Nursing diagnoses

- Ineffective health maintenance related to underlying condition
- Risk for infection related to drug-induced adverse hematologic reactions
- Deficient knowledge related to drug therapy

Planning and implementation

- CSF volume depends on age, not body surface area (BSA). Basing dose on BSA for meningeal leukemia may cause low CSF methotrexate level in children and high level and neurotoxicity in adults. Instead, base dose on patient's age. Elderly patients may need a reduced dosage because CSF volume and turnover may decrease with age.
- Arachnoiditis can develop within hours of intrathecal use but subacute neurotoxicity may begin a few weeks later.

• Have patient drink 2 to 3 L of fluids daily.

ALERT: Alkalinize urine by giving sodium bicarbonate tablets to prevent precipitation of drug, especially with high doses. Maintain urine pH at more than 6.5. If BUN level reaches 20 to 30 mg/dl or creatinine level reaches 1.2 to 2 mg/dl, reduce dosage. Report BUN level over 30 mg/dl or creatinine level over 2 mg/dl, and stop drug.

• Rash, redness, ulcerations in the mouth, or adverse pulmonary reactions may signal serious complications. If patient develops ulcerative stomatitis, other severe adverse GI reaction, or pulmonary toxicity, stop giving the drug.

• Leucovorin rescue is used with high-dose (greater than 100 mg) protocols. This technique works against systemic toxicity but doesn't interfere with tumor cells' absorption of methotrexate.

Patient teaching

• Teach and encourage diligent mouth care to reduce risk of superinfection in mouth.

• Tell patient to take oral form on empty stomach.

• Advise patient to avoid prolonged exposure to sunlight, wear protective clothing, and use highly protective sunblock.

• Tell patient to continue leucovorin rescue despite severe nausea and vomiting and to tell prescriber. Parenteral leucovorin therapy may be needed.

• Warn patient not to become pregnant during or immediately after therapy, because of risk of spontaneous abortion or congenital anomalies.

• Instruct patient not to use alcohol during therapy.

Evaluation

• Patient exhibits positive response to drug therapy.

• Patient has no serious complications when hematologic parameters are depressed during therapy.

• Patient and family state understanding of drug therapy.

methyldopa

(meth-il-DOH-puh)

Aldomet, Apo-Methyldopa ♦, Dopamet ♦, Hydopa ◇, Novomedopa ♦, Nu-Medopa ♦

methyldopate hydrochloride

Aldomet

Pharmacologic class: centrally acting antiadrenergic

Therapeutic class: antihypertensive

Pregnancy risk category: B (P.O.), C (I.V.)

Indications and dosages

▶ **Hypertension, hypertensive crisis.** *Adults:* Initially, 250 mg P.O. b.i.d. to t.i.d. in first 48 hours. Then increase as needed q 2 days. Entire daily dosage may be given in evening or at bedtime. If other antihypertensives are added to or removed from therapy, adjust dosages as needed. Maintenance dosage, 500 mg to 2 g daily divided b.i.d. or q.i.d. Maximum daily dosage, 3 g. Or, 250 to 500 mg I.V. q 6 hours. Maximum dosage, 1 g q 6 hours. Switch to P.O. antihypertensives as soon as possible.

Children: Initially, 10 mg/kg P.O. daily in two to four divided doses. Or, 20 to 40 mg/kg I.V. daily in four divided doses. Increase dosage at least q 2 days until desired response occurs. Maximum, 65 mg/kg, 2 g/m^2, or 3 g daily, whichever is least.

I.V. administration

• Dilute appropriate dose in 100 ml D_5W. Or, the required dose may be given in 5% dextrose injection at 10 mg/ml.

• Infuse slowly over 30 to 60 minutes.

• When control has been obtained, substitute oral therapy starting with the same parenteral dosage schedule.

⊗ **Incompatibilities**

Amphotericin B; drugs with poor solubility in acidic media, such as barbiturates and sulfonamides; methohexital; some total parenteral nutrition solutions.

Contraindications and cautions

• Contraindicated in patients hypersensitive to drug or any of its components (including sulfites), those with active hepatic disease (such as acute hepatitis) or active cirrhosis, and those

M

taking MAO inhibitors. Also contraindicated if previous methyldopa therapy has been linked to liver disorders.

• Use cautiously in patients with renal impairment or a history of impaired liver function.

Lifespan: Drug has been used effectively in pregnant women without apparent harm to the fetus. In breast-feeding women, use cautiously; it's unknown if the drug appears in breast milk. In elderly patients, use cautiously because they may experience syncope from increased sensitivity.

Adverse reactions

CNS: asthenia, *decreased mental acuity,* depression, dizziness, headache, involuntary choreoathetoid movements, nightmares, psychic disturbances, *sedation,* weakness.
CV: aggravated angina, ***bradycardia,*** edema, ***heart failure, myocarditis,*** orthostatic hypotension.
EENT: nasal congestion.
GI: constipation, diarrhea, *dry mouth,* nausea, ***pancreatitis,*** vomiting.
GU: decreased libido, impotence.
Hematologic: hemolytic anemia, ***thrombocytopenia.***
Hepatic: ***hepatic necrosis.***
Metabolic: weight gain.
Skin: rash.
Other: *drug-induced fever,* galactorrhea, gynecomastia.

Interactions

Drug-drug. *Amphetamines, norepinephrine, phenothiazines, tricyclic antidepressants:* May decrease hypotensive effects. Monitor blood pressure carefully.
Antihypertensives, diuretics: May increase hypotensive effects. Decrease the methyldopa dosage.
Barbiturates: May increase likelihood of orthostatic hypotension. Monitor patient and blood pressure.
Haloperidol: May produce dementia and sedation. Use together cautiously.
Levodopa: May have additive hypotensive effects and may increase adverse CNS reactions. Monitor patient closely.
Lithium: May increase lithium level. Monitor lithium level and toxicity.
MAO inhibitors: May increase sympathetic stimulation, which may result in hypertensive crisis. Don't use together.
Oral iron therapy: May increase hypotensive effects. Use together cautiously; monitor blood pressure.
Drug-herb. *Capsicum:* May reduce antihypertensive effectiveness. Discourage use together.
Yohimbe: May interfere with blood pressure. Discourage use together.

Effects on lab test results

• May increase creatinine level. May decrease hemoglobin level and hematocrit.
• May decrease liver function test values and granulocyte, platelet, RBC, and WBC counts.
• May cause positive direct Coombs test.

Pharmacokinetics

Absorption: Partial.
Distribution: Wide. Weakly protein-bound.
Metabolism: Extensive in liver and intestinal cells.
Excretion: Absorbed drug in urine; unabsorbed drug in feces. *Half-life:* About 2 hours.

Route	Onset	Peak	Duration
P.O.	Unknown	4–6 hr	12–48 hr
I.V.	Unknown	4–6 hr	10–16 hr

Action

Chemical effect: May involve inhibition of central vasomotor centers, decreasing sympathetic outflow to heart, kidneys, and peripheral vasculature.
Therapeutic effect: Lowers blood pressure.

Available forms

methyldopa
Tablets: 250 mg, 500 mg
methyldopate hydrochloride
Injection: 50 mg/ml in 5- and 10-mg vials

NURSING PROCESS

Assessment

• Assess patient's blood pressure before therapy and regularly thereafter to monitor drug effectiveness.
• Monitor CBC with differential counts before therapy, every 2 weeks for first 3 months, and periodically thereafter.

• Monitor patient's Coombs test results. In patient who has received this drug for several months, positive reaction to direct Coombs test indicates hemolytic anemia.
• Be alert for adverse reactions and drug interactions.
• Assess patient's and family's knowledge of drug therapy.

Nursing diagnoses

• Ineffective health maintenance related to presence of hypertension
• Risk for injury related to drug-induced adverse CNS reactions
• Deficient knowledge related to drug therapy

Planning and implementation

• Report involuntary choreoathetoid movements. Drug may be stopped.
• Tolerance may occur, usually between the second and third months of therapy, and addition of a diuretic or a dosage adjustment may be needed. If patient's response changes significantly, notify prescriber.
• If hypertension occurs after dialysis, notify prescriber. Patient may need extra dose of drug.
• In a patient who needs blood transfusions, perform direct and indirect Coombs tests to prevent crossmatching problems.
ALERT: Don't confuse Aldomet with Aldoril or Anzemet.

Patient teaching

• Advise patient to report signs of infection, such as fever and sore throat.
• Tell patient to report adverse reactions but not to stop taking drug.
• Tell patient to check his weight daily and to report weight gain of more than 5 lb (2.27 kg). Diuretics can relieve sodium and water retention.
• Warn patient that drug may impair mental alertness, particularly at start of therapy. Once-daily dose at bedtime minimizes daytime drowsiness.
• Tell patient to rise slowly and avoid sudden position changes.
• Tell patient that dry mouth can be relieved with ice chips, sugarless gum, or hard candy.
• Advise patient that urine may turn dark in bleached toilet bowls.

Evaluation

• Patient's blood pressure is normal.
• Patient doesn't experience injury as result of drug-induced adverse CNS reactions.
• Patient and family state understanding of drug therapy.

methylphenidate hydrochloride

(meth-il-FEN-ih-dayt high-droh-KLOR-ighd)

Concerta, Metadate CD, Metadate ER, Methylin, Methylin ER, Ritalin, Ritalin LA, Ritalin SR

methylphenidate transdermal system

Daytrana

Pharmacologic class: piperidine derivative
Therapeutic class: CNS stimulant
Pregnancy risk category: NR (Metadate ER, Methylin, Methylin ER, Ritalin, Ritalin SR); C (Concerta, Daytrana, Metadate CD, Ritalin LA)
Controlled substance schedule: II

Indications and dosages

▶ **Attention deficit hyperactivity disorder (ADHD).** *Children age 6 and older:* Initially 5 mg, Methylin or Ritalin P.O. b.i.d. before breakfast and lunch. Increase in 5- to 10-mg increments weekly, as needed until an optimum daily dosage of 2 mg/kg is reached, not to exceed 60 mg/day. Ritalin SR, Metadate ER, Methylin ER, Metadate CD, or Ritalin LA may be used in place of above tablets by calculating the dose of methylphenidate in 8 hours, and giving the total dosage P.O. once daily before breakfast. Or, initially, 20 mg Metadate CD or Ritalin LA P.O. daily before breakfast; increase in 10-mg increments weekly to maximum, 60 mg daily. Or, for children age 6 to 12, initially, apply one 10-mg patch (Daytrana) to clean, dry, nonirritated skin on the hip, alternating sites daily. Avoid the waistline or where tight clothing may rub off the patch. Apply 2 hours before desired effect, and remove 9 hours later. Increase dosage weekly, as needed, to a maximum of 30 mg daily. Base final dose and wear time on patient response.
Adolescents ages 13 to 17 not on methylphenidate, or for patients on other stimulants: 18 mg P.O. extended-release Concerta once daily in the morning. Adjust dosage by 18 mg at weekly in-

tervals to a maximum of 72 mg P.O. (not to exceed 2 mg/kg) once daily in the morning.
Children ages 6 to 12 not on methylphenidate, or for patients on other stimulants: 18 mg P.O. extended-release Concerta once daily in the morning. Adjust dosage by 18 mg at weekly intervals to a maximum of 54 mg P.O. once daily in the morning.
Children age 6 and older on methylphenidate: If the previous methylphenidate daily dosage is 5 mg b.i.d. or t.i.d. or 20 mg of sustained-release, the recommended dose of Concerta is 18 mg P.O. q morning. If the previous methylphenidate daily dose is 10 mg b.i.d. or t.i.d. or 40 mg sustained-release, the recommended dosage of Concerta is 36 mg P.O. q morning. If the previous methylphenidate daily dosage is 15 mg b.i.d. or t.i.d. or 60 mg of sustained-release, the recommended dose of Concerta is 54 mg P.O. q morning. Maximum conversion daily dose is 54 mg. After conversion is complete, adjust adolescents ages 13 to 17 to maximum, 72 mg once daily (not to exceed 2 mg/kg).

▶ **Narcolepsy.** *Adults:* 10 mg Methylin or Ritalin P.O. b.i.d. or t.i.d. 30 to 45 minutes before meals. Dosage varies with patient needs; average dose is 40 to 60 mg P.O. daily. Ritalin SR, Metadate ER, and Methylin ER tablets may be used in place of methylphenidate tablets by calculating the dosage of methylphenidate in 8 hours and administering the total dosage P.O. once daily before breakfast.

Contraindications and cautions

- Contraindicated in patients hypersensitive to the drug or any of its components and in those with glaucoma, motor tics, family history or diagnosis of Tourette syndrome, or history of marked anxiety, tension, or agitation. Also contraindicated within 14 days of taking an MAO inhibitor. Avoid use in patients with structural cardiac abnormalities.
- Use cautiously in patients with hypertension, history of drug abuse, GI stricture or narrowing, seizures, or EEG abnormalities.

Lifespan: In pregnant women, use cautiously. In breast-feeding women, use cautiously. It's unknown if the drug appears in breast milk. In children younger than age 6, safety and effectiveness haven't been established.

Adverse reactions

CNS: akathisia, dizziness, dyskinesia, headache, *insomnia,* mood swings, *nervousness, seizures,* Tourette syndrome.
CV: angina, changes in blood pressure and pulse rate, *palpitations, tachycardia.*
EENT: dry throat, pharyngitis, sinusitis.
GI: *abdominal pain, anorexia, decreased appetite, nausea, vomiting.*
Hematologic: ***leukopenia, thrombocytopenia, thrombocytopenic purpura.***
Metabolic: delayed growth, weight loss.
Respiratory: cough, upper respiratory tract infection.
Skin: application site reaction (redness, swelling, papules), ***erythema multiforme,*** exfoliative dermatitis, rash, urticaria.
Other: viral infection.

Interactions

Drug-drug. *Anticonvulsants (such as phenobarbital, phenytoin, primidone), SSRIs, tricyclic antidepressants (clomipramine, desipramine, imipramine), warfarin:* May increase levels of these drugs. Monitor patient for adverse reactions, and decrease dosage of these drugs as needed. Monitor drug levels (or coagulation times if patient is also taking warfarin).
Centrally acting antihypertensives: Decreases antihypertensive effect. Monitor blood pressure.
Clonidine: May cause serious adverse events. Avoid use together.
Coumadin: May increase levels. Monitor PT and INR and monitor patient for bleeding.
Drugs that increase gastric pH (antacids, H_2-receptor antagonists, proton pump inhibitors): May alter the release of Ritalin LA extended-release capsules. Separate administration times.
MAO inhibitors: May cause severe hypertension or hypertensive crisis. Don't use together or within 14 days of each other.
Drug-food. *Caffeine:* May increase amphetamine and related amine effects. Discourage use together.

Effects on lab test results

- May decrease hemoglobin level and hematocrit.
- May decrease WBC and platelet counts.

Pharmacokinetics

Absorption: Rapid and complete. Ritalin LA and Metadate CD have two distinct peaks.

Distribution: Unknown. Ritalin LA is 10% to 33% protein-bound.
Metabolism: By the liver.
Excretion: In urine. *Half-life:* 12 hours.

Route	Onset	Peak	Duration
P.O.			
Methylin, Ritalin	Unknown	2 hr	3–6 hr
Concerta	Unknown	6–8 hr	8–12 hr
Methylin ER, Ritalin SR	Unknown	4¾ hr	3–8 hr
Metadate CD	Unknown	1st peak, 1½ hr 2nd peak, 4½ hr	8–12 hr
Ritalin LA	Unknown	1st peak, 1–3 hr 2nd peak, 4–7 hr	8–12 hr
Transdermal	2 hr	Variable	12 hr

Action

Chemical effect: Probably promotes nerve impulse transmission by releasing stored norepinephrine from nerve terminals in brain. Main site appears to be cerebral cortex and reticular activating system.
Therapeutic effect: Promotes calmness in hyperkinesis, and prevents sleep.

Available forms

Capsules (extended-release) (Metadate CD, Ritalin LA): 10 mg, 20 mg, 30 mg, 40 mg
Oral solution: 5 mg/5 ml, 10 mg/5 ml
Tablets (chewable) (Methylin): 2.5 mg, 5 mg, 10 mg
Tablets (extended-release) (Metadate ER, Methylin ER, Ritalin SR): 10 mg, 20 mg
Tablets (extended-release core) (Concerta): 18 mg, 27 mg, 36 mg, 54 mg
Tablets (immediate-release) (Methylin, methylphenidate, Ritalin): 5 mg, 10 mg, 20 mg
Transdermal patch: 10 mg, 15 mg, 20 mg, 30 mg

NURSING PROCESS

Assessment

- Assess patient's condition before therapy and regularly thereafter to monitor drug effectiveness.
- Drug may precipitate Tourette syndrome in children. Monitor effects, especially at start of therapy.
- Observe patient for signs of excessive stimulation. Monitor blood pressure.
- Check CBC, differential, and platelet counts with long-term use, particularly if patient shows signs or symptoms of hematologic toxicity (fever, sore throat, easy bruising).
- Monitor height and weight in child receiving long-term therapy. Drug may delay growth, but child will attain normal height when drug is stopped.

ALERT: Chronic abuse can lead to marked tolerance and psychological dependence. Careful supervision is needed. Monitor patient for tolerance or psychological dependence.

- Be alert for adverse reactions and drug interactions.
- Assess patient's and family's knowledge of drug therapy.

Nursing diagnoses

- Ineffective health maintenance related to underlying condition
- Sleep deprivation related to drug induced insomnia
- Deficient knowledge related to drug therapy

Planning and implementation

ALERT: This is drug of choice for ADHD and is usually stopped after puberty.

- Don't use to prevent fatigue.
- Metadate CD and Ritalin-LA may be swallowed whole, or the contents of the capsule may be sprinkled onto a small amount of cool applesauce and given immediately with a full glass of water.
- Give at least 6 hours before bedtime to prevent insomnia. Give after meals to reduce appetite suppression.
- Methylin ER and Ritalin SR tablets have a duration of about 8 hours and may be used in place of regular tablets when 8-hour dosage of sustained release tablets corresponds to the adjusted dosage of the regular tablets.

ALERT: Don't confuse Ritalin with Rifadin or Metadate with methadone.

Patient teaching

- Tell patient to swallow Ritalin SR and Concerta tablets whole and not to chew or crush them. Metadate CD or Ritalin LA may be swallowed whole, or the contents of the capsule may be sprinkled onto a small amount of cool applesauce and given immediately.

• Warn patient to avoid activities that require alertness until the drug's CNS effects are known.
• Tell patient to avoid caffeine.
• Advise patient with seizure disorder to notify prescriber.
• Inform patient that he will need more rest as drug effects wear off.
• Warn patient that the shell of the Concerta tablet may appear in the stool.
• Tell parent to apply patch immediately after opening; don't use if pouch seal is broken. Press firmly in place for about 30 seconds using the palm of your hand, being sure there is good contact with the skin—especially around the edges. Once applied correctly, the child may shower, bathe, or swim as usual.
• Inform parent if patch comes off, a new one may be applied on a different site, but the total wear time for that day should be 9 hours. Upon removal, fold patch in half so the sticky sides adhere to itself, and then flush down toilet or dispose of in a lidded container.
• Tell parent if the applied patch is missing, to ask the child when or how the patch came off.
• Encourage parent to use the application chart provided with the patch carton to keep track of application and removal.
• Tell parent to remove patch sooner than 9 hours if the child has decreased evening appetite or has difficulty sleeping.
• Tell parent the effects of the patch lasts for several hours after its removal.
• Warn parent and patient to avoid exposing patch to direct external heat sources such as heating pads, electric blankets, and heated water beds.
• Tell parent to notify prescriber if the child develops bumps, swelling, or blistering at the application site or is experiencing blurred vision or other serious side effects.

☑ Evaluation

• Patient responds positively to drug therapy.
• Patient doesn't experience insomnia during therapy.
• Patient and family state understanding of drug therapy.

methylprednisolone

(meth-il-pred-NIS-uh-lohn)
Medrol, Meprolone

methylprednisolone acetate

depMedalone 40, depMedalone 80, Depo-Medrol, Depopred-40, Depopred-80

methylprednisolone sodium succinate

A-MethaPred, Solu-Medrol

Pharmacologic class: glucocorticoid
Therapeutic class: anti-inflammatory, immunosuppressant
Pregnancy risk category: C (oral); NR (parenteral)

Indications and dosages

▶ **Severe inflammation or immunosuppression.** *Adults:* 2 to 60 mg methylprednisolone P.O. daily in four divided doses. Or 10 to 80 mg methylprednisolone acetate I.M. daily, or 4 to 80 mg into joint or soft tissue, as needed. May repeat q 1 to 5 weeks as needed. Or 10 to 250 mg methylprednisolone succinate I.M. or I.V. q 4 hours.
Children: 0.03 to 0.2 mg/kg or 1 to 6.25 mg/m^2 methylprednisolone succinate I.M. once or twice daily. Although dosage may be reduced in infants and children, give dose based more on severity of condition and response than by age or size. Don't give less than 0.5 mg/kg daily.
▶ **Shock.** *Adults:* 100 to 250 mg methylprednisolone succinate I.V. at 2- to 6-hour intervals. Or 30 mg/kg I.V. initially, repeat q 4 to 6 hours, as needed. Continue therapy for 2 to 3 days or until patient is stable.
▶ **Acute exacerbations of multiple sclerosis.** *Adults:* Give 200 mg I.M. prednisolone daily for 1 week, followed by 80 mg I.M. q other day for 1 month. (Note that 5 mg of prednisolone is equivalent to 4 mg of methylprednisolone.)
▶ **Severe lupus nephritis‡.** *Adults:* 1 g methylprednisolone succinate I.V. over 1 hour for 3 days. Continue orally at 0.5 mg/kg daily using prednisone or prednisolone.
Children: 30 mg/kg methylprednisolone succinate I.V. q other day for 6 doses.
▶ **To minimize motor and sensory defects caused by acute spinal cord injury‡.** *Adults:*

Initially, 30 mg/kg I.V. over 15 minutes, followed in 45 minutes by 5.4 mg/kg/hour I.V. infusion for 23 hours.

▶ **Adjunct treatment for moderate to severe *Pneumocystis jiroveci (carinii)* pneumonia‡.** *Adults and children older than age 13:* Give 30 mg I.V. b.i.d. for 5 days; then 30 mg I.V. daily for 5 days; then 15 mg I.V. daily for 11 days (or until completion of anti-infective therapy).

I.V. administration

• Compatible solutions include D_5W, normal saline solution, and D_5W in normal saline solution.
• Use within 48 hours after mixing.
• Give only methylprednisolone sodium succinate I.V., never the acetate form. Reconstitute according to manufacturer's directions using supplied diluent or bacteriostatic water for injection with benzyl alcohol.
• For direct injection, inject diluted drug into vein or I.V. line containing free-flowing compatible solution over at least 1 minute. For shock, give massive doses over at least 10 minutes to prevent arrhythmias and circulatory collapse.
• For intermittent or continuous infusion, dilute solution according to manufacturer's instructions and give over prescribed duration. In continuous infusion, change solution q 24 hours.
• Rapid administration of large I.V. doses (0.5 to 1 g in less than 10 to 120 minutes) may result in circulatory collapse, cardiac arrhythmias, or fatal cardiac arrest.

⊗ **Incompatibilities**

Allopurinol, aminophylline, calcium gluconate, cephalothin, ciprofloxacin, cytarabine, diltiazem, docetaxel, doxapram, etoposide, gemcitabine, filgrastim, glycopyrrolate, metaraminol, nafcillin, ondansetron, paclitaxel, penicillin G sodium, potassium chloride, propofol, sargramostim, vinorelbine, vitamin B complex with C.

Contraindications and cautions

• Contraindicated in patients hypersensitive to drug or any of its components, and in those with systemic fungal infections.
• Use cautiously in patients with GI ulceration or renal disease, hypertension, osteoporosis, diabetes mellitus, hypothyroidism, cirrhosis, diverticulitis, nonspecific ulcerative colitis, recent intestinal anastomoses, thromboembolic disorders, seizures, myasthenia gravis, heart failure, tuberculosis, ocular herpes simplex, emotional instability, or psychotic tendencies.

Lifespan: In pregnant women, use cautiously. In breast-feeding women, don't use because it's unknown if drug appears in breast milk. In premature infants, methylprednisolone acetate and methylprednisolone succinate are contraindicated because they contain benzyl alcohol.

Adverse reactions

CNS: *euphoria, insomnia,* ***pseudotumor cerebri,*** psychotic behavior.
CV: ***arrhythmias, circulatory collapse,*** edema, ***fatal arrest, heart failure,*** hypertension, ***thromboembolism.***
EENT: cataracts, glaucoma.
GI: GI irritation, increased appetite, ***pancreatitis,*** peptic ulceration.
Metabolic: carbohydrate intolerance, growth suppression in children, hyperglycemia, hypokalemia.
Musculoskeletal: muscle weakness, osteoporosis.
Skin: acne, delayed wound healing, hirsutism, various skin eruptions.
Other: ***acute adrenal insufficiency,*** susceptibility to infections.

Interactions

Drug-drug. *Anticholinesterases:* May cause profound weakness. Use together cautiously.
Aspirin, indomethacin, other NSAIDs: May increase risk of GI distress and bleeding. Give together cautiously.
Cyclosporins: May increase risk of adverse events and convulsions. May need to increase methylprednisolone dose.
CYP3A4 inducers (barbiturates, ephedrine, phenytoin, rifampin): May decrease corticosteroid effect. Increase corticosteroid dosage.
CYP3A4 inhibitors (ketoconazole, macrolides): May decrease glucocorticoid clearance. Adjust dosage, if needed.
Hormonal contraceptives: May decrease corticosteroid metabolism. Dosage of steroid may need to be reduced.
Oral anticoagulants: May alter dosage requirements. Monitor PT and INR closely.
Potassium-depleting drugs (such as thiazide and loop diuretics): May increase potassium-wasting effects. Monitor potassium level.
Skin-test antigens: May decrease response. Defer skin testing until therapy is completed.

M

Toxoids, live-virus vaccines: May decrease antibody response and increase risk of neurologic complications. Avoid use together.

Effects on lab test results

- May increase glucose and cholesterol levels. May decrease potassium and calcium levels.

Pharmacokinetics

Absorption: Good after P.O. use; sodium succinate is rapid while acetate is much slower.
Distribution: Rapid to muscle, liver, skin, intestines, and kidneys.
Metabolism: In liver.
Excretion: Primarily in urine. *Half-life:* 18 to 36 hours.

Route	Onset	Peak	Duration
P.O.	Rapid	1–2 hr	30–36 hr
I.V.	Immediate	Immediate	Unknown
I.M.	6–48 hr	Unknown	4–8 days

Action

Chemical effect: Not clear; decreases inflammation, mainly by stabilizing leukocyte lysosomal membranes. Drug also suppresses immune response, stimulates bone marrow, and influences protein, fat, and carbohydrate metabolism.
Therapeutic effect: Relieves inflammation and suppresses immune system function.

Available forms

methylprednisolone
Tablets: 2 mg, 4 mg, 8 mg, 16 mg, 24 mg, 32 mg
methylprednisolone acetate
Injection (suspension): 20 mg/ml, 40 mg/ml, 80 mg/ml
methylprednisolone sodium succinate (contains benzyl alcohol)
Injection: 40-, 125-, 500-, 1,000-, and 2,000-mg vials

NURSING PROCESS

Assessment

- Assess patient's condition before therapy and regularly thereafter to monitor drug effectiveness.
- Watch for enhanced response in patient with hypothyroidism or cirrhosis.
- Monitor patient's weight, blood pressure, electrolyte levels (especially glucose), and sleep patterns. Euphoria may initially interfere with sleep, but patient typically adjusts to drug after 1 to 3 weeks.
- Be alert for adverse reactions and drug interactions.
- Assess patient's and family's knowledge of drug therapy.

Nursing diagnoses

- Ineffective health maintenance related to underlying condition
- Risk for injury related to drug-induced adverse reactions
- Deficient knowledge related to drug therapy

Planning and implementation

ALERT: Salt formulations are not interchangeable.
- Drug may be used for alternate-day therapy.
- For better results and less risk of toxicity, give once-daily dose in morning.
- Don't inject subcutaneously. Atrophy and sterile abscesses may occur.
- Give with food whenever possible. Critically ill patients may also need antacid or H_2-receptor antagonist therapy.
- Give I.M. injection deep into gluteal muscle.
- Dermal atrophy may occur with large dose of acetate salt. Use multiple small injections rather than single large dose, and rotate injection sites.

ALERT: Don't give intrathecally because severe adverse reactions may occur.
- Don't use acetate salt when immediate onset of action is needed.

ALERT: Acute adrenal insufficiency may occur in patients on long term therapy who are under stress (infection, surgery, or trauma).
- Always adjust to lowest effective dosage.
- Give potassium supplements as appropriate.
- Gradually stop giving the drug after long-term therapy. Abruptly stopping drug may be fatal or cause inflammation, fatigue, weakness, arthralgia, fever, dizziness, lethargy, depression, fainting, orthostatic hypotension, dyspnea, anorexia, or hypoglycemia.

ALERT: Don't confuse Solu-Medrol with Solu-Cortef.

ALERT: Don't confuse methylprednisolone with medroxyprogesterone.

Patient teaching
- Tell patient most adverse reactions are dose or duration dependent.

• Tell patient not to abruptly stop taking the drug without prescriber's consent.
• Teach patient signs of early adrenal insufficiency: fatigue, muscle weakness, joint pain, fever, anorexia, nausea, dyspnea, dizziness, and fainting.
• Instruct patient to wear or carry medical identification.
• Warn patient receiving long-term therapy about cushingoid symptoms, and tell him to report sudden weight gain or swelling. Suggest exercise or physical therapy, and advise him to ask prescriber about vitamin D or calcium supplements.

Evaluation

• Patient responds positively to drug therapy.
• Patient sustains no injury from adverse reactions.
• Patient and family state understanding of drug therapy.

metoclopramide hydrochloride

(met-oh-KLOH-preh-mighd high-droh-KLOR-ighd)

Apo-Metoclop ♦, Clopra, Maxeran ♦, Maxolon, Octamide, Octamide PFS, Pramin ◇, Reclomide, Reglan

Pharmacologic class: para-aminobenzoic acid derivative; dopamine-receptor agonist
Therapeutic class: antiemetic, GI stimulant
Pregnancy risk category: B

Indications and dosages

▶ **To prevent or reduce nausea and vomiting induced by cisplatin alone or with other chemotherapeutics.** *Adults:* 1 to 2 mg/kg I.V. 30 minutes before chemotherapy; then repeat q 2 hours for two doses; then q 3 hours for three doses.

▶ **To prevent or reduce postoperative nausea and vomiting.** *Adults:* 10 to 20 mg I.M. near end of surgical procedure, repeat q 4 to 6 hours, p.r.n.

▶ **To facilitate small-bowel or upper G.I. intubation and aid in radiologic examinations.** *Adults and children older than age 14:* Give 10 mg (2 ml) I.V. as single dose over 1 to 2 minutes.
Children ages 6 to 14: Give 2.5 to 5 mg I.V. (0.5 to 1 ml).
Children younger than age 6: Give 0.1 mg/kg I.V.

▶ **Delayed gastric emptying caused by diabetic gastroparesis.** *Adults:* 10 mg P.O. for mild symptoms; slow I.V. infusion for severe symptoms 30 minutes before meals and at bedtime for 2 to 8 weeks, depending on response.

▶ **Gastroesophageal reflux disease.** *Adults:* 10 to 15 mg P.O. q.i.d., p.r.n., 30 minutes before meals and at bedtime.

Adjust-a-dose: For patients with renal impairment, if creatinine clearance is less than 40 ml/minute, reduce initial dose by 50% and adjust dosage, as tolerated.

I.V. administration

• Drug is compatible with D_5W, normal saline solution for injection, dextrose 5% in half-normal saline solution, Ringer's solution, and lactated Ringer's solution. Normal saline is the preferred diluent because drug is most stable in this solution.
• Dilute doses larger than 10 mg in 50 ml of compatible diluent, and infuse over at least 15 minutes.
• Give doses of 10 mg or less by direct injection over 1 to 2 minutes.
• Closely monitor blood pressure.
• If giving infusion mixture within 24 hours, protection from light is unnecessary. If protected from light and refrigerated, it's stable for 48 hours.

⊗ **Incompatibilities**

Allopurinol, amphotericin B, ampicillin, calcium gluconate, cefepime, chloramphenicol sodium succinate, cisplatin, doxorubicin liposomal, erythromycin lactobionate, fluorouracil, furosemide, methotrexate sodium, penicillin G potassium, propofol, sodium bicarbonate.

Contraindications and cautions

• Contraindicated in patients hypersensitive to the drug or any of its components; patients allergic to procainamide may also be allergic to metoclopramide. Also contraindicated in patients taking drugs that are likely to cause extrapyramidal reactions (butyrophenones, phenothiazines), in those for whom stimulation of GI motility might be dangerous (such as those with hemorrhage), and in those with pheochromocytoma or seizure disorder.

• Use cautiously in patients with a history of depression, Parkinson disease, hypertension, or renal impairment.
• Safety and effectiveness haven't been established for therapy that lasts longer than 12 weeks.
Lifespan: In pregnant women, use cautiously. In breast-feeding women, use cautiously; it's unknown if the drug appears in breast milk. In elderly patients, use cautiously and at a reduced dosage.

Adverse reactions

CNS: *anxiety,* dizziness, *drowsiness,* dystonic reactions, extrapyramidal symptoms, fatigue, fever, headache, insomnia, *lassitude, restlessness,* sedation, ***seizures, suicidal ideation,*** tardive dyskinesia.
CV: ***arrhythmias, AV block, bradycardia, heart failure,*** hypotension, transient hypertension.
GI: bowel disturbances, diarrhea, nausea.
Hematologic: ***agranulocytosis, leukopenia, neonatal methemoglobinemia, neutropenia.***
Skin: rash.
Other: loss of libido, prolactin secretion.

Interactions

Drug-drug. *Acetaminophen, aspirin, cyclosporine, diazepam, levodopa, lithium, tetracycline:* May increase absorption of these drugs. Monitor patient for adverse effects.
Anticholinergics, opioid analgesics: May antagonize GI motility effects of metoclopramide. Use together cautiously.
CNS depressants: May cause additive CNS depression. Avoid use together.
Digoxin: May decrease absorption of digoxin. Monitor digoxin levels.
Insulin: May influence the rate of food absorption. Adjust insulin dosage, if needed.
Drug-lifestyle. *Alcohol use:* May cause additive CNS depression. Discourage use together.

Effects on lab test results

• May increase aldosterone and prolactin levels.
• May decrease neutrophil and granulocyte counts.

Pharmacokinetics

Absorption: After P.O. use, rapid and complete. After I.M. use, about 74% to 96% bioavailable.
Distribution: To most body tissues and fluids, including brain.
Metabolism: Not extensive.
Excretion: In urine and feces. *Half-life:* 4 to 6 hours.

Route	Onset	Peak	Duration
P.O.	30–60 min	1–2 hr	1–2 hr
I.V.	1–3 min	Unknown	1–2 hr
I.M.	10–15 min	Unknown	1–2 hr

Action

Chemical effect: Stimulates motility of upper GI tract by increasing lower esophageal sphincter tone. Blocks dopamine receptors at chemoreceptor trigger zone.
Therapeutic effect: Prevents or minimizes nausea and vomiting. Also reduces gag reflex, improves gastric emptying, and reduces gastric reflux.

Available forms

Injection: 5 mg/ml
Syrup: 5 mg/5 ml (sugar-free), 10 mg/ml
Tablets: 5 mg, 10 mg

NURSING PROCESS

Assessment

• Assess patient's condition before therapy and regularly thereafter to monitor drug effectiveness.
• Monitor blood pressure often in patient taking I.V. form of drug.
• Be alert for adverse reactions and drug interactions.
• Assess patient's and family's knowledge of drug therapy.

Nursing diagnoses

• Risk for deficient fluid volume related to nausea and vomiting
• Risk for injury related to drug-induced adverse CNS reactions
• Deficient knowledge related to drug therapy

Planning and implementation

• Dilute oral concentrate with water, juice, or carbonated beverage just before administration. Semisolid food, such as applesauce or pudding, also may be used.
• Commercially available I.M. preparations may be used without further dilution.

Photoguide to tablets and capsules

This photoguide provides full-color photographs of some of the most commonly prescribed tablets and capsules. These drugs, organized by generic name, are shown in actual size and color with page references to corresponding drug information. Each drug is labeled with its trade name and its strength.

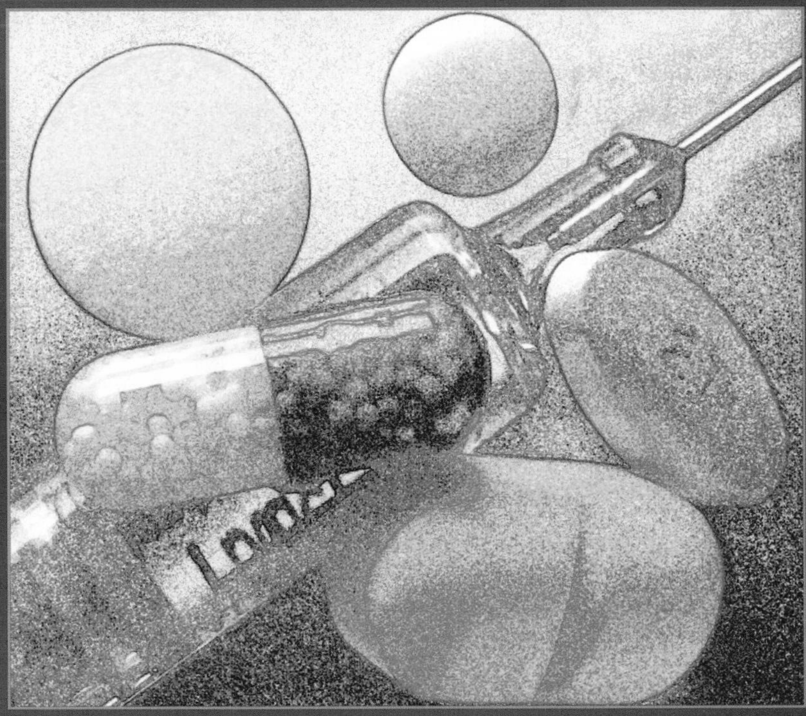

Adapted from Facts & Comparisons, St. Louis, Mo.

For the list of companies permitting the use of these photographs, see pages 1407–1408.

ACAMPROSATE CALCIUM

Campral

(page 95)

333 mg

ALENDRONATE SODIUM

Fosamax

(page 120)

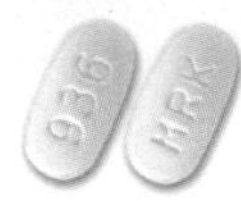

10 mg

40 mg

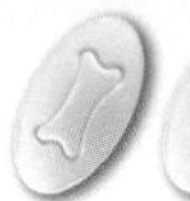

70 mg

ALPRAZOLAM

Xanax

(page 128)

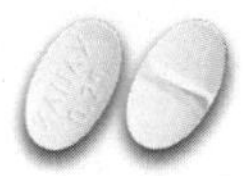

0.25 mg

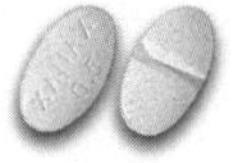

0.5 mg

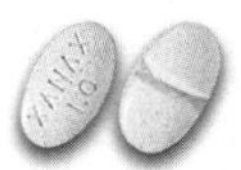

1 mg

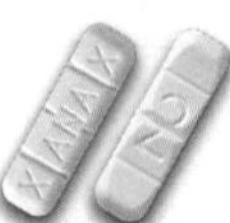

2 mg

AMLODIPINE BESYLATE

Norvasc

(page 141)

2.5 mg

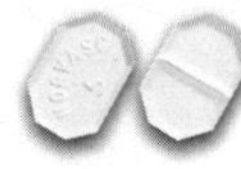

5 mg

ANASTROZOLE

Arimidex

(page 160)

1 mg

ARIPIPRAZOLE

Abilify

(page 169)

10 mg

15 mg

30 mg

ATENOLOL

Tenormin

(page 177)

25 mg

50 mg

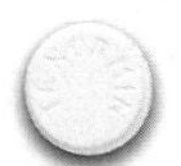

100 mg

ATOMOXETINE HYDROCHLORIDE

Strattera

(page 178)

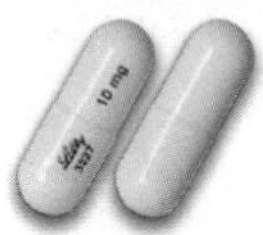

10 mg

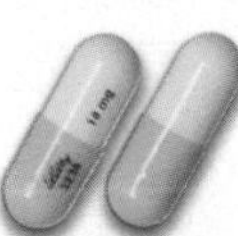

18 mg

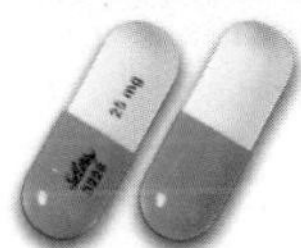

25 mg

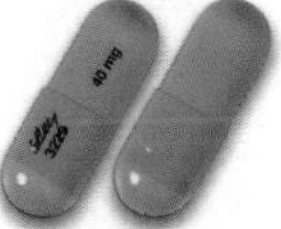

40 mg

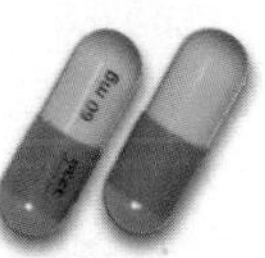

60 mg

ATORVASTATIN CALCIUM

Lipitor

(page 180)

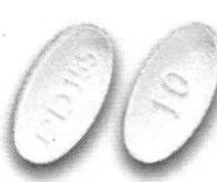

10 mg

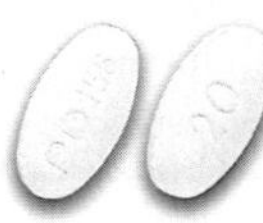

20 mg

40 mg

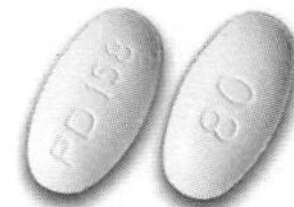

80 mg

AZITHROMYCIN

Zithromax

(page 191)

250 mg

500 mg

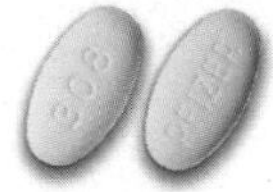

600 mg

BUPROPION HYDROCHLORIDE

Wellbutrin SR

(page 231)

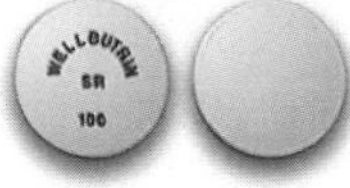

100 mg

150 mg

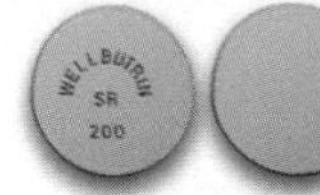

200 mg

CAPTOPRIL

Capoten

(page 249)

12.5 mg

25 mg

CEFADROXIL MONOHYDRATE

Duricef

(page 262)

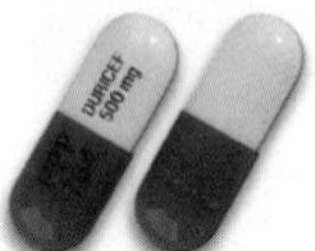

500 mg

1,000 mg

CELECOXIB

Celebrex

(page 286)

100 mg

200 mg

CIPROFLOXACIN HYDROCHLORIDE

Cipro

(page 311)

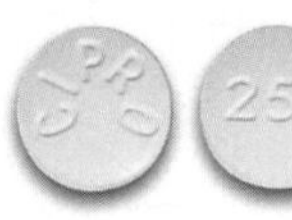

250 mg

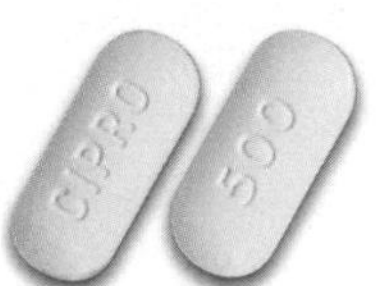

500 mg

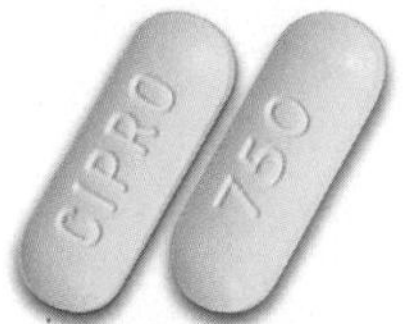

750 mg

CITALOPRAM HYDROBROMIDE

Celexa

(page 316)

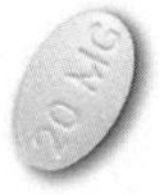

20 mg

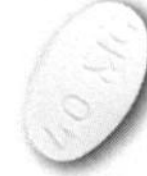
40 mg

DARIFENACIN HYDROBROMIDE

Enablex

(page 370)

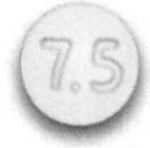

7.5 mg

15 mg

DESLORATADINE

Clarinex
(page 382)

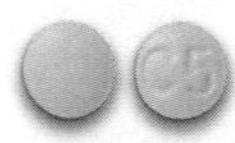

5 mg

DIAZEPAM

Valium
(page 397)

2 mg

5 mg

10 mg

DIGOXIN

Lanoxin
(page 406)

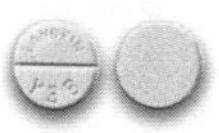

0.125 mg

0.25 mg

DILTIAZEM HYDROCHLORIDE

Cardizem
(page 410)

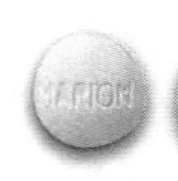

30 mg

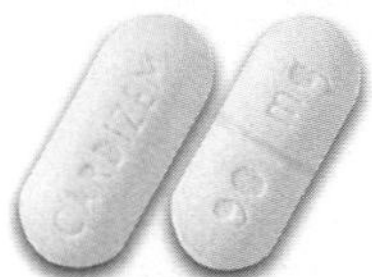

90 mg

Cardizem CD
(page 410)

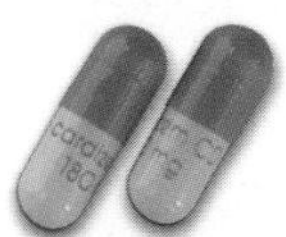

180 mg

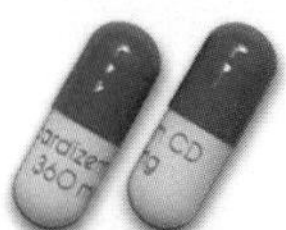

360 mg

Cardizem LA
(page 410)

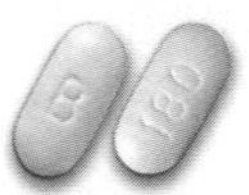

180 mg

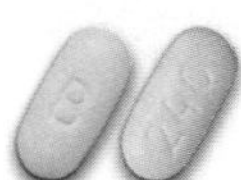

240 mg

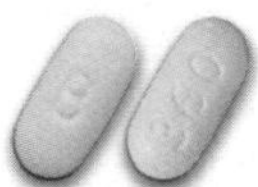

360 mg

DIVALPROEX SODIUM

Depakote
(page 1284)

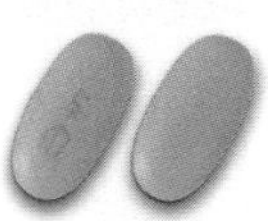

125 mg

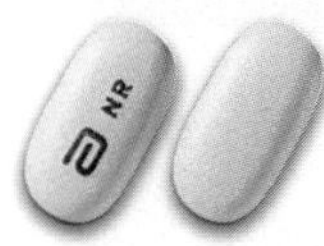

250 mg

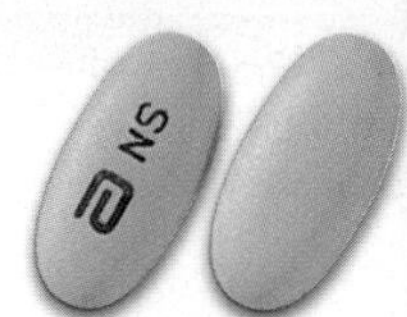

500 mg

DULOXETINE HYDROCHLORIDE

Cymbalta

(page 451)

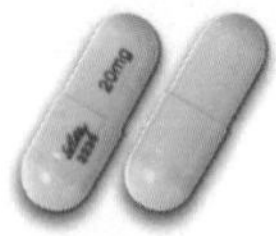

20 mg

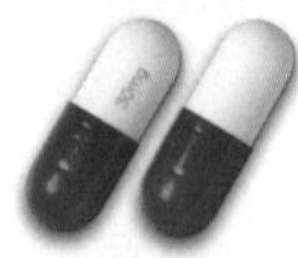

30 mg

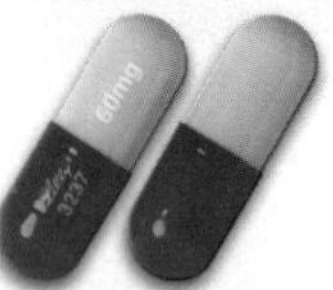

60 mg

ENALAPRIL MALEATE

Vasotec

(page 464)

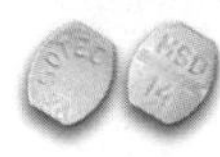

2.5 mg

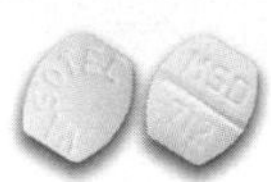

5 mg

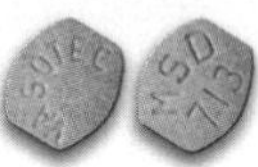

10 mg

20 mg

ERYTHROMYCIN BASE

Eryc

(page 490)

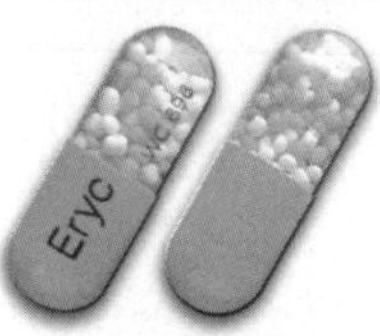

250 mg

ESCITALOPRAM OXALATE

Lexapro

(page 493)

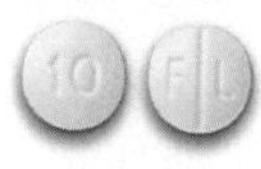

10 mg

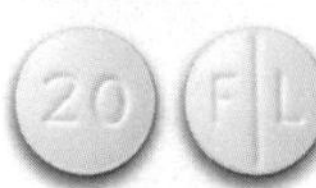

20 mg

ESTRADIOL

Estrace

(page 500)

0.5 mg

1 mg

2 mg

ESZOPICLONE

Lunesta

(page 512)

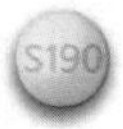

1 mg

2 mg

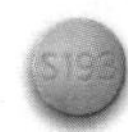

3 mg

EZETIMIBE

Zetia
(page 536)

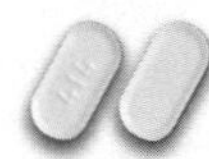
10 mg

FAMOTIDINE

Pepcid
(page 539)

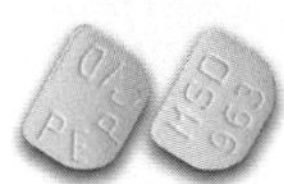

20 mg

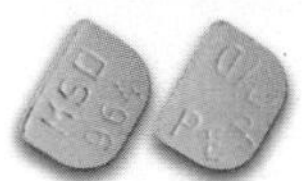
40 mg

FLUCONAZOLE

Diflucan
(page 555)

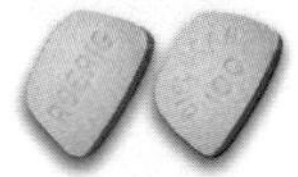

100 mg

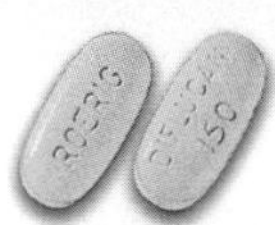

150 mg

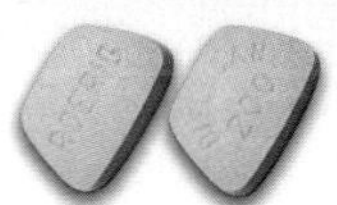

200 mg

FLUOXETINE HYDROCHLORIDE

Prozac
(page 565)

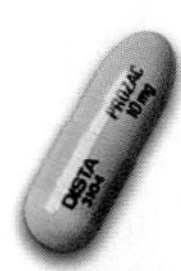

10 mg

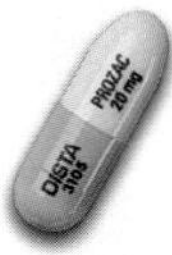

20 mg

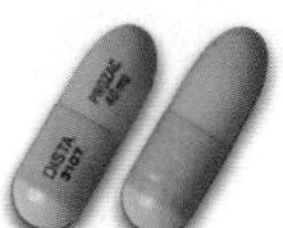

40 mg

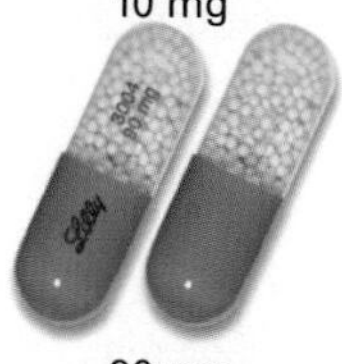

90 mg

FOSINOPRIL SODIUM

Monopril
(page 590)

10 mg

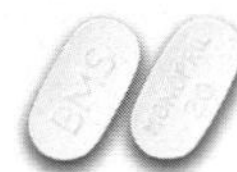

20 mg

40 mg

FROVATRIPTAN SUCCINATE

Frova
(page 593)

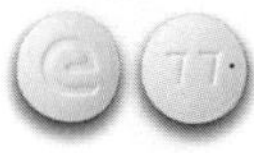
2.5 mg

FUROSEMIDE

Lasix

(page 596)

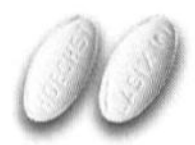

20 mg

40 mg

80 mg

GABAPENTIN

Neurontin

(page 598)

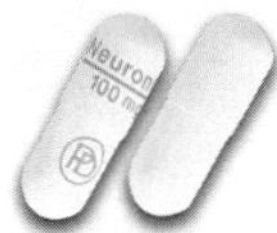

100 mg

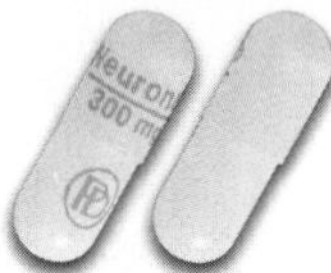

300 mg

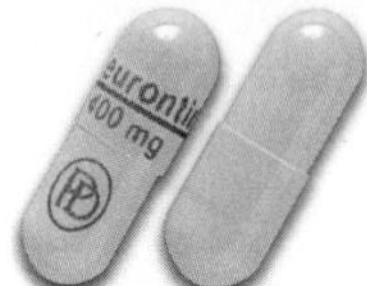

400 mg

GLIPIZIDE

Glucotrol

(page 613)

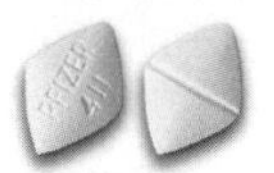

5 mg

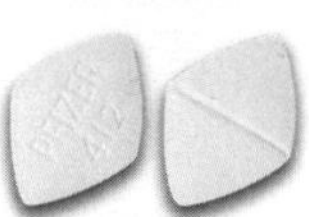

10 mg

Glucotrol XL

(page 613)

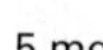

5 mg

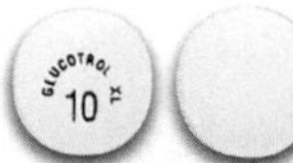

10 mg

GLYBURIDE

DiaBeta

(page 616)

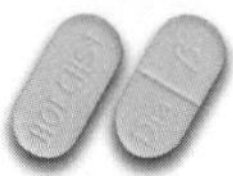

1.25 mg

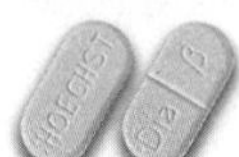

2.5 mg

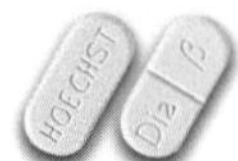

5 mg

Micronase

(page 616)

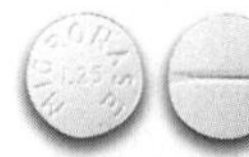

1.25 mg

2.5 mg

5 mg

LANSOPRAZOLE

Prevacid

(page 722)

15 mg

30 mg

LEVOFLOXACIN

Levaquin

(page 739)

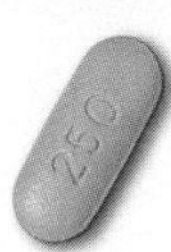

250 mg

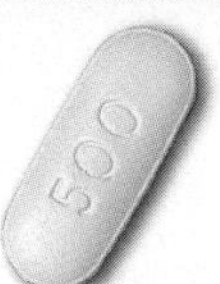

500 mg

LEVOTHYROXINE SODIUM

Levoxyl

(page 742)

25 mcg

50 mcg

75 mcg

88 mcg

100 mcg

112 mcg

125 mcg

137 mcg

150 mcg

175 mcg

200 mcg

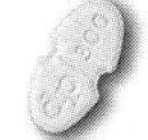

300 mcg

LISINOPRIL

Prinivil

(page 748)

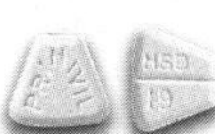

5 mg

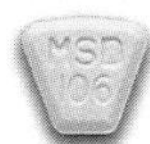

10 mg

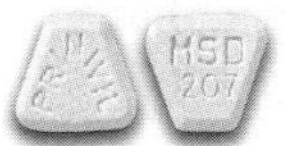

20 mg

LOPINAVIR AND RITONAVIR

Kaletra

(page 755)

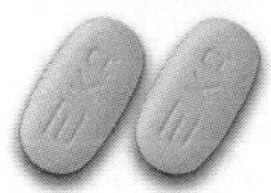

200mg/50 mg

LOSARTAN POTASSIUM

Cozaar

(page 762)

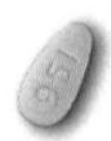

25 mg

50 mg

LOVASTATIN

Mevacor

(page 764)

10 mg

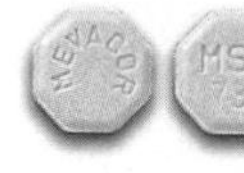

20 mg

40 mg

LUBIPROSTONE

Amitiza

(page 766)

24 mcg

MEDROXYPROGESTERONE ACETATE

Provera

(page 781)

2.5 mg

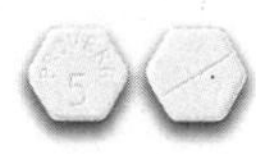

5 mg

10 mg

METFORMIN HYDROCHLORIDE

Glucophage

(page 801)

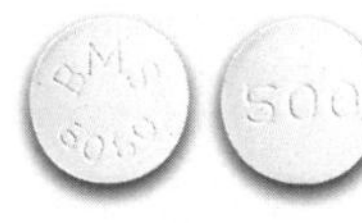

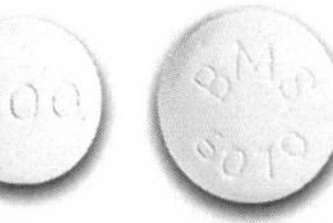

500 mg

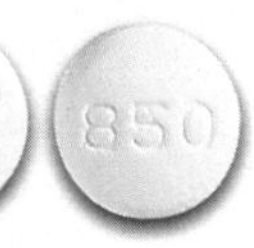

850 mg

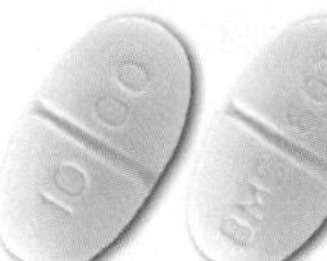

1,000 mg

Glucophage XR

(page 801)

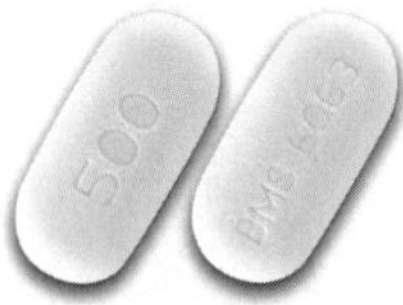

500 mg

METHYLPHENIDATE HYDROCHLORIDE

Ritalin
(page 813)

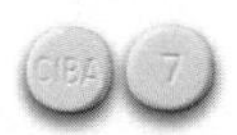

5 mg

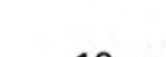

10 mg

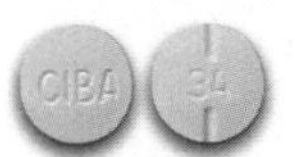

20 mg

METOPROLOL SUCCINATE

Toprol-XL
(page 822)

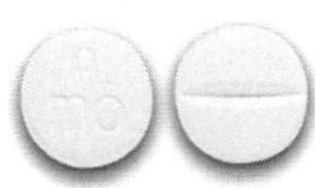

50 mg

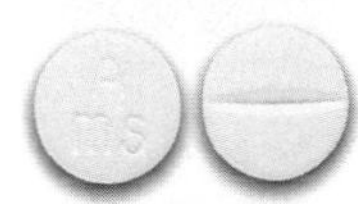

100 mg

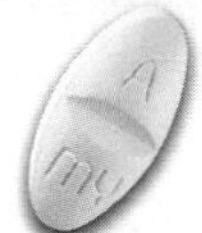

200 mg

MONTELUKAST SODIUM

Singulair
(page 849)

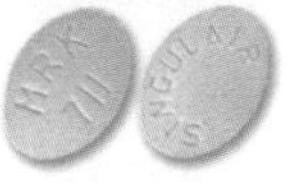

4 mg

5 mg

10 mg

NIFEDIPINE

Procardia XL
(page 891)

30 mg

60 mg

90 mg

NORTRIPTYLINE HYDROCHLORIDE

Pamelor
(page 907)

10 mg

25 mg

50 mg

OMEPRAZOLE

Prilosec
(page 921)

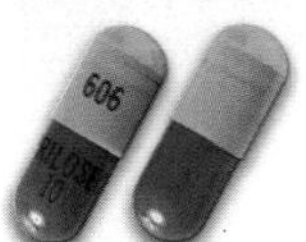

10 mg

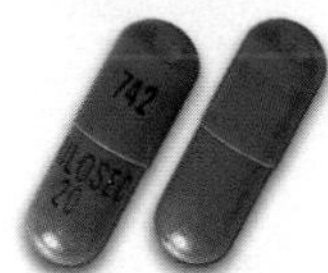

20 mg

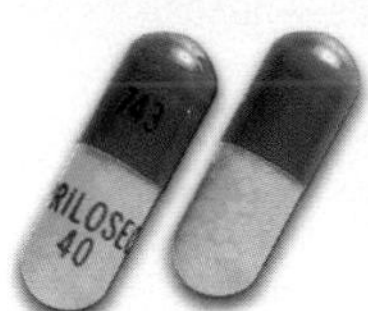

40 mg

OXYCODONE HYDROCHLORIDE

OxyContin

(page 937)

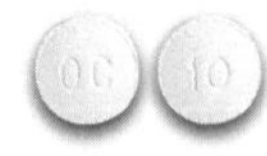

10 mg

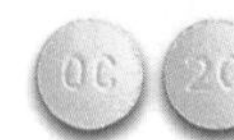

20 mg

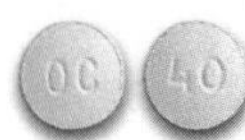

40 mg

80 mg

PHENYTOIN SODIUM

Dilantin Kapseals

(page 1000)

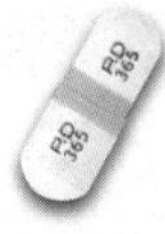

30 mg

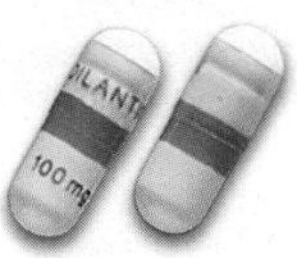

100 mg

POTASSIUM CHLORIDE

K-Dur 20

(page 1017)

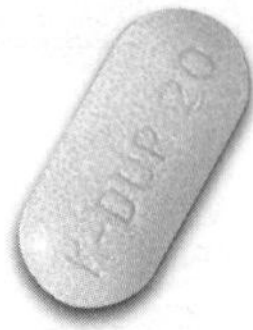

20 mEq

PRAVASTATIN SODIUM

Pravachol

(page 1027)

10 mg

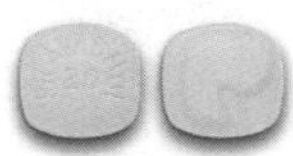

20 mg

40 mg

QUINAPRIL HYDROCHLORIDE

Accupril

(page 1066)

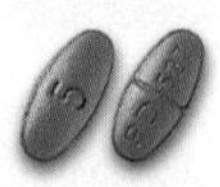

5 mg

10 mg

20 mg

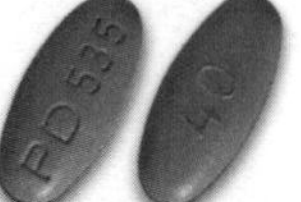

40 mg

RANOLAZINE

Ranexa
(page 1081)

500 mg

RASAGILINE

Azilect
(page 1082)

0.5 mg

1 mg

RISEDRONATE SODIUM

Actonel
(page 1098)

5 mg

35 mg

RISPERIDONE

Risperdal
(page 1100)

0.25 mg

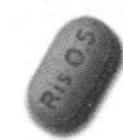

0.5 mg

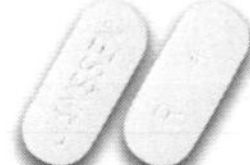
1 mg

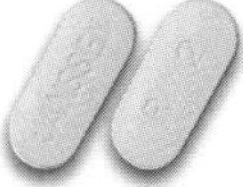
2 mg

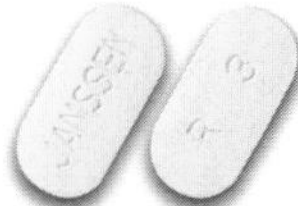

3 mg

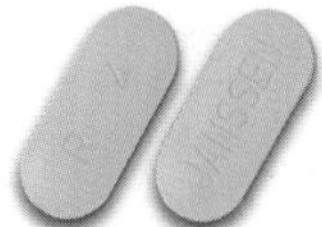

4 mg

Risperdal M-Tab
(page 1100)

0.5 mg

ROSIGLITAZONE MALEATE

Avandia
(page 1111)

2 mg

4 mg

8 mg

ROSUVASTATIN CALCIUM

Crestor
(page 1116)

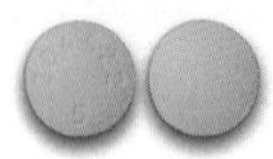

5 mg

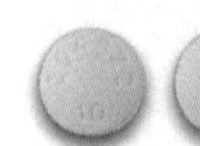

10 mg

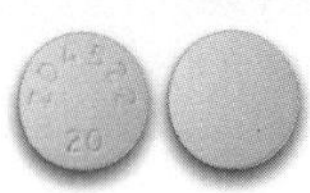

20 mg

40 mg

SERTRALINE HYDROCHLORIDE

Zoloft
(page 1130)

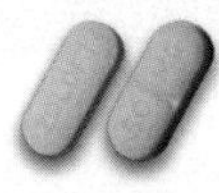

50 mg

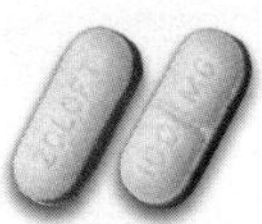

100 mg

SILDENAFIL CITRATE

Viagra
(page 1137)

25 mg

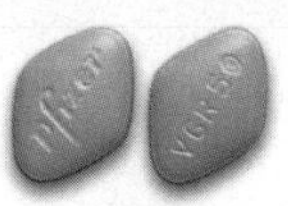

50 mg

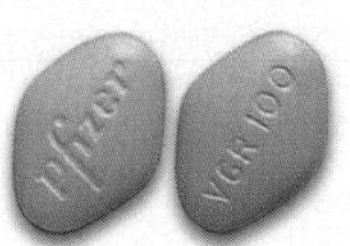

100 mg

SIMVASTATIN

Zocor
(page 1139)

5 mg

10 mg

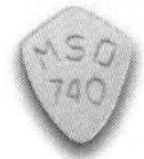

20 mg

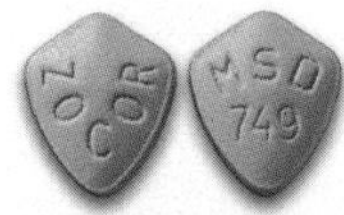

40 mg

SITAGLIPTIN PHOSPHATE

Januvia
(page 1143)

100 mg

SORAFENIB

Nexavar

(page 1157)

200 mg

SUNITINIB MALATE

Sutent

(page 1182)

12.5 mg

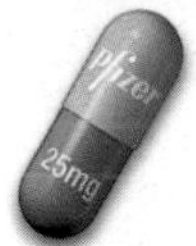

25 mg

50 mg

TERAZOSIN HYDROCHLORIDE

Hytrin

(page 1205)

1 mg

5 mg

10 mg

VARDENAFIL HYDROCHLORIDE

Levitra

(page 1290)

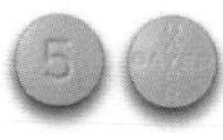

5 mg

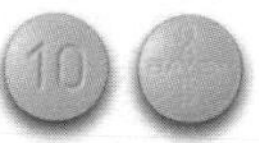

10 mg

20 mg

VARENICLINE TARTRATE

Chantix

(page 1291)

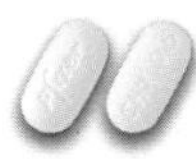

0.5 mg

1 mg

VENLAFAXINE HYDROCHLORIDE

Effexor XR

(page 1296)

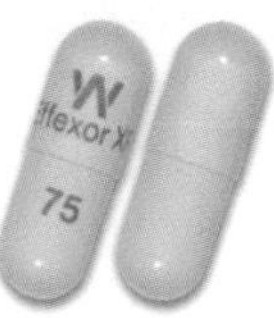

75 mg

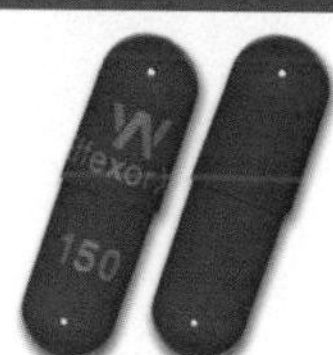

150 mg

VERAPAMIL HYDROCHLORIDE

Calan

(page 1298)

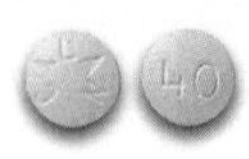
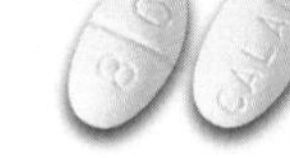
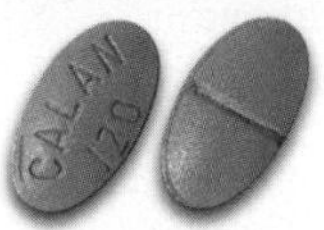

40 mg | 80 mg | 120 mg

WARFARIN SODIUM

Coumadin

(page 1315)

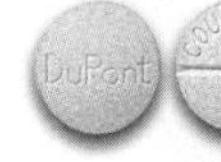
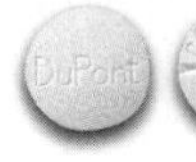

1 mg | 2 mg | 2.5 mg

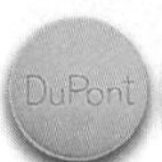
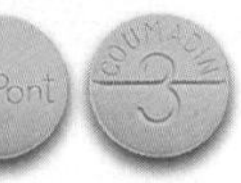
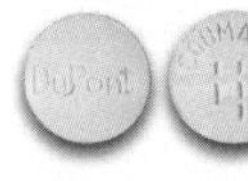

3 mg | 4 mg | 5 mg

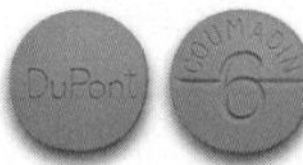
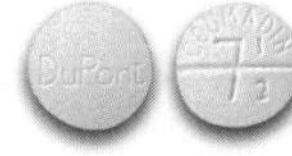
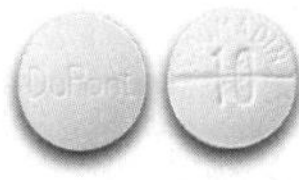

6 mg | 7.5 mg | 10 mg

ZOLPIDEM TARTRATE

Ambien

(page 1329)

5 mg | 10 mg

ⓢ **ALERT:** Extrapyramidal effects caused by high drug doses are counteracted by 25 mg diphenhydramine I.V.

ⓢ **ALERT:** Don't confuse Reglan with Relafen.

Patient teaching

- Instruct patient not to drink alcohol during therapy.
- Advise patient to avoid activities requiring alertness for 2 hours after taking each dose.

Evaluation

- Patient responds positively to drug and doesn't develop fluid volume deficit.
- Patient doesn't experience injury from adverse reactions.
- Patient and family state understanding of drug therapy.

metolazone

(meh-TOH-luh-zohn)

Zaroxolyn

Pharmacologic class: quinazoline derivative
Therapeutic class: diuretic, antihypertensive
Pregnancy risk category: B

Indications and dosages

▶ **Edema in heart failure or renal disease.** *Adults:* 5 to 10 mg P.O. daily; may increase to 20 mg daily.

▶ **Mild to moderate essential hypertension.** *Adults:* Initially, 1.25 to 2.5 mg P.O. daily; increase gradually until desired therapeutic response has been achieved. Usual maintenance dose is 2.5 to 5 mg daily. Maintenance dosage determined by patient's blood pressure. If response is inadequate, add another antihypertensive.

Contraindications and cautions

- Contraindicated in patients hypersensitive to thiazides or other sulfonamide-derived drugs and in patients with anuria, hepatic coma, or precoma.
- Use cautiously in patients with impaired kidney or liver function.

Lifespan: In pregnant women, use only when benefits outweigh risks to the fetus. In breast-feeding women and in children, safety and effectiveness haven't been established.

Adverse reactions

CNS: *dizziness,* fatigue, headache.
CV: chest pain, orthostatic hypotension, palpitations, volume depletion.
GI: anorexia, nausea, ***pancreatitis.***
GU: frequent urination, nocturia, polyuria.
Hematologic: ***agranulocytosis, aplastic anemia,*** hyperlipidemia, ***leukopenia, thrombocytopenia.***
Hepatic: ***hepatic encephalopathy.***
Metabolic: dehydration, dilutional hyponatremia, glucose tolerance impairment, hypercalcemia, hypochloremia, hyperglycemia, hyperuricemia, hypokalemia, ***metabolic alkalosis.***
Musculoskeletal: acute gouty attacks, muscle cramps, swelling.
Skin: dermatitis, photosensitivity reactions, rash.
Other: hypersensitivity reactions.

Interactions

Drug-drug. *Amphotericin B, corticosteroids:* May cause hypokalemia. Monitor potassium level.
Barbiturates, opioids: May increase orthostatic hypotensive effect. Monitor blood pressure closely.
Bumetanide, ethacrynic acid, furosemide, torsemide: May cause excessive diuretic response resulting in serious electrolyte abnormalities or dehydration. Adjust dosages carefully while monitoring patient closely.
Cholestyramine, colestipol: May decrease intestinal absorption of thiazides. Separate doses by 1 hour.
Diazoxide: May increase antihypertensive, hyperglycemic, and hyperuricemic effects. Use together cautiously.
Digoxin: May increase risk of digoxin toxicity from metolazone-induced hypokalemia. Monitor potassium and digitalis levels.
Insulin, sulfonylureas: May increase requirements in diabetic patients. Adjust dosages.
Lithium: May decrease lithium clearance, increasing risk of lithium toxicity. Avoid giving together.
NSAIDs: May increase risk of NSAID-induced renal impairment. Monitor patient for signs of renal impairment.
Drug-lifestyle. *Alcohol use:* May increase orthostatic hypotensive effect. Discourage use together.

Sun exposure: May cause photosensitivity reactions. Urge patient to avoid unprotected or prolonged exposure to sunlight.

Effects on lab test results

• May increase glucose, calcium, cholesterol, pH, bicarbonate, uric acid, and triglyceride levels. May decrease potassium, sodium, magnesium, chloride, and hemoglobin levels and hematocrit.
• May decrease granulocyte, platelet, and WBC counts.

Pharmacokinetics

Absorption: About 65% in healthy adults; in cardiac patients, falls to 40%.
Distribution: 50% to 70% erythrocyte-bound. 33% protein-bound.
Metabolism: Insignificant.
Excretion: 70% to 95% unchanged in urine.
Half-life: About 14 hours.

Route	Onset	Peak	Duration
P.O.	≤ 1 hr	2–8 hr	12–24 hr

Action

Chemical effect: Increases sodium and water excretion by inhibiting sodium reabsorption in cortical diluting site of ascending loop of Henle.
Therapeutic effect: Promotes water and sodium elimination and lowers blood pressure.

Available forms

Tablets: 2.5 mg, 5 mg, 10 mg

NURSING PROCESS

Assessment

• Assess patient's condition before therapy and regularly thereafter to monitor the drug's effectiveness. In hypertensive patients, therapeutic response may be delayed several days.
• Unlike thiazide diuretics, drug is effective in patients with decreased kidney function.
• Monitor fluid intake and output, weight, blood pressure, and electrolyte level.
• Monitor uric acid level, especially in patient with a history of gout.
• Be alert for adverse reactions and drug interactions.
• Assess patient's and family's knowledge of drug therapy.

Nursing diagnoses

• Excess fluid volume related to presence of edema
• Risk for injury related to presence of hypertension
• Deficient knowledge related to drug therapy

Planning and implementation

• Drug may be used with potassium-sparing diuretic to prevent potassium loss.
• Give drug in morning to prevent nocturia.
• Drug is used as adjunct in furosemide-resistant edema.
ALERT: Don't confuse Zaroxolyn with Zarontin or metolazone with metoprolol.

Patient teaching

• Advise patient to not change position suddenly and to rise slowly, to avoid orthostatic hypotension.
• Advise patient to wear protective clothing, avoid prolonged exposure to sunlight, and use sunblock to prevent photosensitivity reactions.
• Instruct patient to avoid alcohol consumption during drug therapy.

Evaluation

• Patient doesn't have edema.
• Patient's blood pressure is normal.
• Patient and family state understanding of drug therapy.

metoprolol succinate

(meh-TOH-pruh-lol SUHK-seh-nayt)
Toprol-XL

metoprolol tartrate

(meh-TOH-pruh-lol TAR-trayt)
Apo-Metoprolol ♦, Apo-Metoprolol (Type L) ♦, Betalo ♦ ◇, Betaloc Durules ♦, Lopresor ♦, Lopressor, Minax ◇, Novometoprol ♦, Nu-Metop ♦

Pharmacologic class: selective $beta_1$ blocker
Therapeutic class: antihypertensive, adjunct therapy of acute MI
Pregnancy risk category: C

Indications and dosages

▶ **Hypertension.** *Adults:* Initially, 50 to 100 mg succinate P.O. once daily. Adjust dosage as needed and tolerated at intervals of no less than 1 week to maximum, 400 mg daily. For metoprolol tartrate, initially, 100 mg P.O. daily in single or divided doses; usual maintenance dosage is 100 to 450 mg daily.

▶ **Early intervention in acute MI.** *Adults:* 5 mg tartrate I.V. push q 2 to 5 minutes up to a total of 15 mg based on hemodynamic status. Then, 15 minutes after last dose, 25 to 50 mg P.O. q 6 hours for 48 hours. Maintenance dosage is 100 mg P.O. b.i.d. In patients who do not tolerate full 15 mg dose in 10 to 15 minutes, may decrease oral dose to 25 mg initially. If severe intolerance, discontinue drug.

▶ **Angina pectoris.** *Adults:* Initially, 100 mg succinate P.O. daily as single dose. Increase at weekly intervals until adequate response or pronounced decrease in heart rate is seen. Safety and effectiveness of daily dose higher than 400 mg aren't known. Or, 100 mg metoprolol tartrate P.O. in two divided doses. Increase at weekly intervals until adequate response or pronounced decrease in heart rate is seen. Maintenance dosage, 100 to 400 mg P.O. daily.

▶ **Stable, symptomatic heart failure (New York Heart Association class II) resulting from ischemia, hypertension, or cardiomyopathy.** *Adults:* 25 mg succinate P.O. once daily for 2 weeks. In patients with more severe heart failure, start with 12.5 mg P.O. once daily for 2 weeks. Double the dose q 2 weeks as tolerated to a maximum of 200 mg daily.

▶ **Atrial tachyarrhythmias after acute MI‡.** *Adults:* 2.5 to 5 mg I.V. q 2 to 5 minutes to control rate up to 15 mg over a 10- to 15-minute period. Once heart rate is controlled or normal sinus rhythm is restored, therapy may continue with 50 mg P.O. b.i.d. for 24 hours starting 15 minutes after the last I.V. dose. Increase dosage to 100 mg P.O. b.i.d. as tolerated. When therapeutic response is achieved or if systolic blood pressure is less than 100 mm Hg or heart rate is less than 50 beats/minute, stop drug.

▶ **Unstable angina or non–ST-segment elevation MI at high risk for ischemic events‡.** *Adults:* 5 mg I.V. bolus q 5 minutes for 3 doses. May continue therapy with P.O. drug.

I.V. administration

- Give drug undiluted and by direct injection.
- Drug is only compatible with meperidine hydrochloride or morphine sulfate, or with alteplase infusions at Y-site connection.
- Store drug at room temperature and protect from light. If solution is discolored or contains particulates, discard.

⊗ **Incompatibilities**

Amphotericin B, other I.V. drugs.

Contraindications and cautions

- Contraindicated in patients hypersensitive to the drug or other beta blockers, and in those with sinus bradycardia, heart block greater than first-degree, cardiogenic shock, or overt cardiac failure when used to treat hypertension or angina. When used to treat MI, drug is also contraindicated in patients with heart rate below 45 beats/minute, second- or third-degree heart block, PR interval of 0.24 second or more with first-degree heart block, systolic blood pressure lower than 100 mm Hg, or moderate-to-severe cardiac failure.
- Use cautiously in patients with heart failure, diabetes, or respiratory or hepatic disease.

Lifespan: In pregnant women, use cautiously. In breast-feeding women, don't use; it's unknown if drug appears in breast milk. In children, safety and effectiveness haven't been established.

Adverse reactions

CNS: dizziness, fatigue, fever, lethargy.
CV: ***AV block, bradycardia, heart failure,*** hypotension, peripheral vascular disease.
GI: diarrhea, nausea, vomiting.
GU: decreased libido.
Musculoskeletal: arthralgia.
Respiratory: ***bronchospasm,*** dyspnea.
Skin: rash.

Interactions

Drug-drug. *Amobarbital, aprobarbital, butabarbital, butalbital, mephobarbital, pentobarbital, phenobarbital, primidone, secobarbital:* May reduce the effects of metoprolol. Increase beta blocker dose.

Antihypertensives: May produce additive effects. Monitor blood pressure.

Chlorpromazine: May decrease hepatic clearance. Monitor patient for increased beta blockade.

Cimetidine: May increase the pharmacologic effects of beta blocker. Consider another H_2 agonist or decrease the dose of beta blocker.

CYP2D6 inhibitors, such as amiodarone, fluoxetine, paroxetine, propafenone, quinidine: May

M

increase metoprolol level. Monitor patient for increased adverse effects.
Digoxin, diltiazem: May cause excessive bradycardia and increase depressant effect on myocardium. Use together cautiously.
Hydralazine: May increase levels and effects of both drugs. Monitor patient closely. Adjust dosage of either drug, if needed.
Indomethacin: May decrease antihypertensive effect. Monitor blood pressure and adjust dosage.
Insulin, oral antidiabetics: May alter dosage requirements in previously stabilized diabetic patient. Observe patient carefully.
I.V. lidocaine: May reduce metabolism of lidocaine, increasing the risk of toxicity. Give bolus doses of lidocaine at a slower rate, and monitor lidocaine levels closely.
MAO inhibitors: May cause bradycardia during use with MAO inhibitors. Monitor ECG and patient closely.
Prazosin: May increase the risk of orthostatic hypotension in the early phases of use together. Assist patient to stand slowly until effects are known.
Rifampin: May increase metabolism of metoprolol. Monitor patient for decreased effect.
Thioamine: May alter pharmacokinetics of metoprolol, increasing the effects of metoprolol. Monitor patient.
Thyroid hormones: May impair actions of metoprolol when patient is converted to euthyroid state. Monitor patient.
Verapamil: May increase the effects of both drugs. Monitor cardiac function closely, and decrease dosages if needed.
Drug-food. *Any food:* May increase absorption. Give together.

Effects on lab test results

- May increase transaminase, alkaline phosphatase, LDH, and uric acid levels.

Pharmacokinetics

Absorption: Rapid and almost complete; food enhances absorption of metoprolol tartrate.
Distribution: Wide. About 12% protein-bound.
Metabolism: In liver.
Excretion: About 95% in urine. *Half-life:* 3 to 7 hours.

Route	Onset	Peak	Duration
P.O.	≤ 15 min	1–12 hr	6–24 hr
I.V.	≤ 5 min	20 min	5–8 hr

Action

Chemical effect: Unknown. Known to depress renin secretion.
Therapeutic effect: Reduces blood pressure; decreases myocardial contractility, heart rate, and cardiac output; reduces myocardial oxygen consumption; and helps to prevent myocardial tissue damage.

Available forms

metoprolol succinate
Tablets (extended-release): 25 mg, 50 mg, 100 mg, 200 mg
metoprolol tartrate
Injection: 1 mg/ml in 5-ml ampules
Tablets: 50 mg, 100 mg
Tablets (extended-release): 100 mg ♦, 200 mg ♦

NURSING PROCESS

Assessment

- Assess patient's condition before therapy and regularly thereafter to monitor drug effectiveness.
- Monitor blood pressure often. Drug masks common signs of shock.
- Be alert for adverse reactions and drug interactions.
- Assess patient's and family's knowledge of drug therapy.

Nursing diagnoses

- Ineffective health maintenance related to underlying disorder
- Risk for injury related to drug-induced adverse CNS reactions
- Deficient knowledge related to drug therapy

Planning and implementation

ALERT: Always check patient's apical pulse rate before giving drug. If it's slower than 60 beats/minute, don't give the drug and immediately call the prescriber.
- Give drug with meals because food may increase absorption.

ALERT: Don't confuse metoprolol with metaproterenol or metolazone or Toprol XL with Topamax, Tegretol, or Tegretol-XR.

Patient teaching

- Tell patient that abruptly stopping therapy can worsen angina and precipitate MI. He should stop taking the drug gradually over 1 to 2 weeks.
- Instruct patient to take oral form with meals to enhance absorption.
- Advise patient to report adverse reactions to prescriber.
- Warn patient to avoid performing hazardous activities until the drug's CNS effects are known.

☑ Evaluation

- Patient responds well to therapy.
- Patient doesn't experience injury from adverse CNS reactions.
- Patient and family state understanding of drug therapy.

metronidazole

(met-roh-NIGH-duh-zohl)

Apo-Metronidazole ♦, Flagyl, Flagyl ER, Flagyl 375, Metric 21, MetroCream, MetroGel, MetroGel-vaginal, Metrogyl ◇, MetroLotion, Metrozine ◇, NidaGel ♦, Noritate, Novonidazol ♦, Protostat, Trikacide ♦

metronidazole hydrochloride

Flagyl I.V. RTU, Metro I.V., Novonidazol ♦

Pharmacologic class: nitroimidazole
Therapeutic class: antibacterial, antiprotozoal, amebicide
Pregnancy risk category: B

Indications and dosages

▶ **Amebic hepatic abscess.** *Adults:* 500 to 750 mg P.O. t.i.d. for 5 to 10 days.
Children: 35 to 50 mg/kg daily (in three doses) for 10 days.

▶ **Intestinal amebiasis.** *Adults:* 750 mg P.O. t.i.d. for 5 to 10 days.
Children: 35 to 50 mg/kg daily (in three doses) for 10 days; maximum of 750 mg/dose. Therapy is followed by P.O. iodoquinol.

▶ **Trichomoniasis.** *Adults:* 250 mg P.O. t.i.d. for 7 days, or 500 mg b.i.d. for 7 days or 2 g P.O. in single dose (may give 2-g dose as two 1-g doses on same day); allow 4 to 6 weeks between courses of therapy. Both partners should be treated.
Children: 5 mg/kg dose P.O. t.i.d. for 7 days. Maximum dosage, 2 g daily.

▶ **Refractory trichomoniasis.** *Adults:* 500 mg P.O. b.i.d. for 7 days. For repeated failures, 2 g P.O. daily for 3 to 5 days.

▶ **Bacterial infections caused by anaerobic microorganisms.** *Adults:* Loading dose, 15 mg/kg I.V. infused over 1 hour (about 1 g for 70-kg [154-lb] adult). Maintenance dosage, 7.5 mg/kg I.V. or P.O. q 6 hours (about 500 mg for 70-kg adult). Give first maintenance dose 6 hours after loading dose. Maximum, 4 g daily.

▶ **To prevent postoperative infection in contaminated or potentially contaminated colorectal surgery.** *Adults:* 15 mg/kg I.V. infused over 30 to 60 minutes and completed about 1 hour before surgery. Then, 7.5 mg/kg I.V. infused over 30 to 60 minutes at 6 and 12 hours after initial dose.

▶ **Inflammatory papules and pustules of acne rosacea.** *Adults:* If using a 0.75% preparation, apply thin film to affected area b.i.d., morning and evening. If using a 1% preparation, apply thin film to affected area once daily. Frequency and duration of therapy are adjusted after response is seen. Results are usually noticed within 3 weeks.

▶ **Pelvic inflammatory disease‡.** *Adults:* 500 mg I.V. q 8 hours with other drugs. Or, 500 mg P.O. b.i.d. for 14 days given with ofloxacin, 400 mg P.O. b.i.d.

▶ **Bacterial vaginosis‡.** *Adults:* 500 mg P.O. b.i.d. for 7 days. Or, 2 g P.O. as a single dose. Or, 250 mg P.O. t.i.d. for 7 days.

▶ **Active Crohn disease‡.** *Adults:* 400 mg P.O. b.i.d. For refractory perineal disease, 20 mg/kg (1 to 1.5 g) P.O. daily in three to five divided doses.

▶ **To prevent sexually transmitted diseases in sexual assault victims‡.** *Adults:* 2 g P.O. given with other drugs.

▶ ***Helicobacter pylori* with peptic ulcer disease‡.** *Adults:* 250 to 500 mg P.O. t.i.d. to q.i.d. given with other drugs. Continue for 7 to 14 days depending on the regimen used.

Children: 15 to 20 mg/kg P.O. daily, divided in two doses for 4 weeks given with other drugs.

▶ **Giardiasis‡.** *Adults:* 250 mg P.O. t.i.d. for 7 days.

▼I.V. administration

- No preparation is needed for Flagyl I.V. RTU form.
- Add 4.4 ml of sterile water for injection, bacteriostatic water for injection, sterile normal saline solution injection, or bacteriostatic normal saline solution injection. Reconstituted drug contains 100 mg/ml.
- Add contents of vial to 100 ml of D_5W, lactated Ringer's injection, or normal saline solution for final concentration of 5 mg/ml. Do not exceed a concentration of 8 mg/ml.
- The resulting highly acidic solution must be neutralized before giving. Carefully add 5 mEq of sodium bicarbonate for each 500 mg of metronidazole. Carbon dioxide will form and may need to be vented.
- Don't use equipment (needles, hubs) containing aluminum to reconstitute the drug or to transfer reconstituted drug. Equipment that contains aluminum will turn the solution orange; the potency isn't affected.
- Infuse drug over at least 1 hour. Don't give I.V. push.
- Don't refrigerate neutralized diluted solution. Precipitation may occur. If Flagyl I.V. RTU is refrigerated, crystals may form. These will disappear after solution is gently warmed to room temperature.

⊗ **Incompatibilities**
Aluminum, amino acid 10%, amphotericin B, aztreonam, ceftriaxone, dopamine, filgrastim, meropenem, warfarin; other I.V. drugs.

Contraindications and cautions

- Contraindicated in patients hypersensitive to the drug or other nitroimidazole derivatives.
- Use cautiously in patients receiving hepatotoxic drugs and in patients with history of blood dyscrasia or CNS disorder, retinal or visual field changes, hepatic disease, or alcoholism.

Lifespan: In pregnant women, don't use during first trimester unless benefits outweigh risks to the fetus. In breast-feeding women, use cautiously. It isn't known if drug appears in breast milk.

Adverse reactions

CNS: ataxia, confusion, depression, drowsiness, fatigue, fever, headache, incoordination, insomnia, irritability, neuropathy, paresthesia of limbs, psychic stimulation, restlessness, ***seizures,*** sensory neuropathy, vertigo, weakness.
CV: edema, flattened T wave, flushing, thrombophlebitis.
EENT: eye tearing.
GI: abdominal cramping, *anorexia,* constipation, diarrhea, dry mouth, metallic taste, *nausea,* proctitis, stomatitis, *vomiting.*
GU: cystitis, darkened urine, dry vagina and vulva, dyspareunia, dysuria, incontinence, polyuria, pyuria, sense of pelvic pressure.
Hematologic: ***neutropenia, thrombocytopenia, transient leukopenia.***
Skin: burning and stinging, contact dermatitis, dry skin, local allergic reaction or irritation, pruritus, rash, worsening of rosacea.
Other: decreased libido, glossitis, gynecomastia, overgrowth of nonsusceptible organisms.

Interactions

Drug-drug. *Azathioprine, fluorouracil:* May increase risk of transient neutropenia. Use cautiously.
Barbiturates, phenobarbital, phenytoin: May decrease metronidazole effectiveness because of increased hepatic clearance. Monitor patient closely for effect.
Cimetidine: May increase risk of metronidazole toxicity because of inhibited hepatic metabolism. Monitor patient.
Disulfiram: May cause acute psychoses and confusional states. Don't use together.
Lithium: May increase lithium level, resulting in toxicity. Monitor lithium level closely.
Oral anticoagulants: May increase anticoagulant effects. Monitor patient for bleeding; monitor PT and INR.
Drug-lifestyle. *Alcohol use:* May cause disulfiram-like reaction (nausea, vomiting, headache, cramps, flushing). Discourage use together.

Effects on lab test results

- May decrease WBC and neutrophil counts.

Pharmacokinetics

Absorption: About 80%; food delays peak levels to about 2 hours.

Distribution: To most body tissues and fluids. Less than 20% protein-bound.
Metabolism: To active metabolite and to other metabolites.
Excretion: Primarily in urine; 6% to 15% in feces. *Half-life:* 6 to 8 hours.

Route	Onset	Peak	Duration
P.O.	Unknown	1–2 hr	Unknown
I.V.	Immediate	Immediate	Unknown
Topical	Unknown	6–10 hr	Unknown

Action

Chemical effect: Direct-acting trichomonacide and amebicide that works at both intestinal and extraintestinal sites.
Therapeutic effect: Hinders growth of selected organisms, including most anaerobic bacteria and protozoa.

Available forms

Capsules: 375 mg
Injection: 5 mg/ml
Oral suspension (benzoyl metronidazole): 200 mg/5 ml ◊
Tablets: 200 mg ◊ 250 mg, 400 mg ◊, 500 mg
Tablets (extended-release): 750 mg
Topical gel: 0.75%; 1%

NURSING PROCESS

Assessment

- Assess patient's infection before therapy and regularly thereafter to monitor drug effectiveness.
- Watch carefully for edema, especially in patients also receiving corticosteroids, because Flagyl I.V. RTU may cause sodium retention.
- Record number and character of stools when used in amebiasis.
- Be alert for adverse reactions and drug interactions.
- I.V. infusion may cause thrombophlebitis at site; observe closely.
- Assess skin for severity, areas of rosacea before and after therapy, and any local adverse reactions.
- Assess patient's and family's knowledge of drug therapy.

Nursing diagnoses

- Risk for infection related to presence of susceptible organisms
- Risk for deficient fluid volume related to drug-induced adverse GI reactions
- Deficient knowledge related to drug therapy

Planning and implementation

- Give drug (except Flagyl ER) with meals to minimize GI distress. Give Flagyl ER at least 1 hour before or 2 hours after meals.
- Use only after *T. vaginalis* has been confirmed by wet smear or culture or *E. histolytica* has been identified; simultaneously treat asymptomatic sexual partners to avoid reinfection.
- To treat trichomoniasis during pregnancy, give drug for 7 days instead of 2-g single dose.

Patient teaching

- Tell patient not to use alcohol or drugs that contain alcohol during therapy and for at least 48 hours after therapy is completed.
- Tell patient that metallic taste and dark or red-brown urine may occur.
- Instruct patient to take oral form with meals to minimize reactions.
- Urge patient to complete full course of therapy even if he feels better.
- Instruct patient in proper hygiene.
- Teach patient to cleanse affected skin areas twice daily before applying MetroLotion.
- Instruct users of topical drug to report worsening of rosacea promptly to prescriber.

Evaluation

- Patient is free from infection.
- Patient maintains adequate hydration throughout therapy.
- Patient and family state understanding of drug therapy.

mexiletine hydrochloride

(MEKS-il-eh-teen high-droh-KLOR-ighd)
Mexitil

Pharmacologic class: lidocaine analogue, sodium channel antagonist
Therapeutic class: class IB ventricular antiarrhythmic
Pregnancy risk category: C

Indications and dosages

▶ **Refractory life-threatening ventricular arrhythmias, including ventricular tachycardia and PVCs.** *Adults:* 200 mg (if rapid control of arrhythmia is not necessary) to 400 mg (for rapid arrhythmia control) P.O., followed by 200 mg q 8 hours. If satisfactory control isn't obtained, increase dosage in 2 to 3 days to 400 mg q 8 hours. Patients who respond well to a 12-hour schedule may be given up to 450 mg q 12 hours. Maximum daily dose is 1,200 mg.

▶ **Diabetic neuropathy**‡. *Adults:* 150 mg P.O. daily for 3 days; then give 300 mg P.O. daily for 3 days followed by 10 mg/kg P.O. daily.

Contraindications and cautions

- Contraindicated in patients with cardiogenic shock or second- or third-degree AV block in absence of artificial pacemaker.
- Use cautiously in patients with first-degree heart block, ventricular pacemaker, sinus node dysfunction, intraventricular conduction disturbances, hypotension, severe heart failure, or seizure disorder.

Lifespan: In pregnant women, use cautiously. In breast-feeding women, use cautiously; it isn't known if drug appears in breast milk. In children, safety and effectiveness haven't been established.

Adverse reactions

CNS: ataxia, blurred vision, confusion, diplopia, *dizziness,* headache, nervousness, nystagmus, *tremor.*
CV: ***arrhythmias, bradycardia,*** chest pain, ***hypotension,*** palpitations, ***widened QRS complex.***
GI: constipation, diarrhea, *heartburn,* nausea, vomiting.
Skin: rash.

Interactions

Drug-drug. *Antacids, atropine, opioids:* May slow mexiletine absorption. Monitor patient; separate doses.
Cimetidine: May increase or decrease mexiletine level. Monitor patient for effect or toxicities.
Methylxanthines (such as theophylline): May reduce clearance of methylxanthines, possibly resulting in toxicity. Monitor levels.
Metoclopramide: May accelerate absorption. Monitor patient for toxicity.
Phenobarbital, phenytoin, rifampin, urine acidifiers: May decrease mexiletine level. Monitor patient.
Urine alkalinizers: May increase mexiletine level. Monitor patient.
Drug-food. *Caffeine:* May reduce clearance of methylxanthines, resulting in toxicity. Monitor patient.

Effects on lab test results

- May increase AST level.

Pharmacokinetics

Absorption: About 90%.
Distribution: Wide. Volume declines in patients with liver disease, resulting in toxic levels with usual doses. About 50% to 60% of circulating drug is protein-bound.
Metabolism: Almost complete, in liver.
Excretion: In urine. *Half-life:* 10 to 12 hours.

Route	Onset	Peak	Duration
P.O.	½–2 hr	2–3 hr	Unknown

Action

Chemical effect: Blocks fast sodium channel in cardiac tissues without involvement of autonomic nervous system. Reduces acceleration and amplitude of action potential and decreases automaticity in Purkinje fibers. It also shortens action potential and, to a lesser extent, decreases the effective refractory period in Purkinje fibers.
Therapeutic effect: Abolishes ventricular arrhythmias.

Available forms

Capsules: 100 mg ♦, 150 mg, 200 mg, 250 mg

NURSING PROCESS

Assessment

- Assess patient's condition until arrhythmia is abolished.
- Monitor drug levels. Therapeutic levels are 0.75 to 2 mcg/ml.
- Be alert for adverse reactions and drug interactions.
- Monitor patient for toxicity. Early signs include tremors—usually fine tremor of hands. As drug's blood level increases, additional signs of toxicity such as dizziness, ataxia, and nystagmus may develop. Ask patient about these symptoms.
- If patient has an adverse GI reaction, monitor his hydration.
- Assess patient's and family's knowledge of drug therapy.

Nursing diagnoses

- Decreased cardiac output related to presence of ventricular arrhythmia
- Risk for deficient fluid volume related to drug-induced adverse GI reactions
- Deficient knowledge related to drug therapy

Planning and implementation

- Give with meals or antacids to lessen GI distress.
- If patient appears to be good candidate for twice-a-day therapy, notify prescriber. This dose enhances compliance.
- Notify prescriber of any significant changes in blood pressure, heart rate, and heart rhythm.

Patient teaching

- Instruct patient taking oral form of drug to take it with food.
- Instruct patient to report adverse reactions.

Evaluation

- Patient regains normal cardiac output.
- Patient maintains adequate hydration throughout therapy.
- Patient and family state understanding of drug therapy.

micafungin sodium

(my-kah-FUN-jin SOE-dee-um)

Mycamine

Pharmacologic class: echinocandin antifungal
Therapeutic class: antifungal
Pregnancy risk category: C

Indications and dosages

▶ **Esophageal candidiasis.** *Adults:* 150 mg I.V. daily for 10 to 30 days.

▶ **Prevention of candidal infection in hematopoietic stem cell transplant recipients.** *Adults:* 50 mg I.V. daily for 6 to 51 days.

I.V. administration

- Use aseptic technique when preparing micafungin.
- Reconstitute each 50-mg vial with 5 ml of normal saline solution for injection or D_5W.
- To minimize foaming, dissolve powder by swirling the vial; don't shake it.
- Dilute dose in 100 ml of normal saline solution for injection.
- Flush I.V. line with normal saline solution for injection before infusing drug.
- Infuse drug over 1 hour.
- Reconstituted product and diluted infusion may be stored for up to 24 hours at room temperature.
- Protect diluted solution from light.

⊗ **Incompatibilities**

Other I.V. drugs.

Contraindications and cautions

- Contraindicated in patients hypersensitive to drug.
- Use cautiously in patients with severe hepatic disease.

Lifespan: In pregnant women, only use if clearly needed. Use cautiously in breast-feeding women; it isn't known whether micafungin appears in breast milk. In children, safety hasn't been established.

Adverse reactions

CNS: delirium, headache.
GI: abdominal pain, diarrhea, nausea, vomiting.
Hematologic: anemia, ***leukopenia, neutropenia, thrombocytopenia.***
Hepatic: hepatocellular damage, hyperbilirubinemia.
Metabolic: hemolytic anemia, hypocalcemia, hypokalemia, ***hypomagnesemia,*** hypophosphatemia.
Skin: infusion site inflammation, phlebitis, pruritus, rash.
Other: pyrexia, rigors, ***shock.***

Interactions

Drug-drug. *Nifedipine:* May increase nifedipine level. Monitor blood pressure, and decrease nifedipine dosage if needed.
Sirolimus: May increase sirolimus level. Monitor patient for evidence of toxicity, and decrease the sirolimus dosage if needed.

Effects on lab test results

- May increase alkaline phosphatase, ALT, AST, bilirubin, BUN, creatinine, and LDH levels. May decrease calcium, magnesium, phosphorus, potassium, and hemoglobin levels and hematocrit.
- May decrease neutrophil and platelet counts.

Pharmacokinetics

Absorption: Given I.V.

M

Distribution: More than 99% protein-bound, mainly to albumin.
Metabolism: By several pathways in the liver.
Excretion: Mainly fecal.

Route	Onset	Peak	Duration
I.V.	Unknown	Unknown	Unknown

Action

Chemical effect: Inhibits synthesis of 1,3-β-D-glucan, which is an essential component of fungal cell walls that isn't found in mammal cells.
Therapeutic effect: Hinders fungal growth, including *Candida albicans, C. glabrata, C. krusei, C. parapsilosis,* and *C. tropicalis.*

Available forms

Lyophilized powder for injection: 50-mg single-use vial

NURSING PROCESS

Assessment

- Assess patient's fungal infection before treatment and regularly thereafter.
- Be alert for adverse reactions and drug interactions.
- Monitor hepatic and renal function during therapy.
- Monitor patient for hemolysis and hemolytic anemia.
- Assess patient's and family's knowledge of drug therapy.

Nursing diagnoses

- Infection related to presence of susceptible fungi
- Risk for injury related to potential for drug-induced hypersensitivity reaction
- Deficient knowledge related to drug therapy

Planning and implementation

- Injection site reactions occur more often in patients receiving drug by peripheral I.V. route.
- Histamine-mediated reactions may occur more often if drug is infused over less than 1 hour.
- Stop infusion if patient develops signs of serious hypersensitivity reaction, including shock.
- Micafungin isn't removed by dialysis.

Patient teaching

- Advise patient to report pain or redness at infusion site.
- Tell patient to expect to undergo laboratory tests during treatment to monitor hematologic, renal, and hepatic function.

Evaluation

- Patient responds to drug therapy and is free from infection.
- Patient has no hypersensitivity reaction.
- Patient and family state understanding of drug therapy.

midazolam hydrochloride

(mid-AYZ-oh-lam high-droh-KLOR-ighd)
Hypnovel ◇

Pharmacologic class: benzodiazepine
Therapeutic class: sedative
Pregnancy risk category: D
Controlled substance schedule: IV

Indications and dosages

▶ **Preoperative sedation (to induce sleepiness or drowsiness and relieve apprehension).** *Adults younger than age 60:* Give 0.07 mg to 0.08 mg/kg I.M. about 1 hour before surgery.

▶ **Moderate sedation before short diagnostic or endoscopic procedures.** *Adults younger than age 60:* Initially, up to 2.5 mg slow I.V.; repeat in 2 minutes if needed, in small increments of initial dose over at least 2 minutes. Total dose that exceeds 5 mg usually isn't needed.

Adults age 60 and older: 1.5 mg or less over at least 2 minutes. If additional adjustment is needed, give at no more than 1 mg over 2 minutes. Total doses exceeding 3.5 mg aren't usually needed.

▶ **Induction of general anesthesia.** *Adults younger than age 55:* If patient hasn't received preanesthesia drug, 0.3 to 0.35 mg/kg I.V. over 20 to 30 seconds. If patient has received preanesthesia drug, 0.15 to 0.35 mg/kg I.V. over 20 to 30 seconds. To complete induction, give additional increments of 25% of initial dose p.r.n. Total dose that exceeds 0.6 mg/kg usually isn't needed.

Adults age 55 and older: If patient hasn't been premedicated, 0.3 mg/kg I.V. over 20 to 30 seconds. If patient has received sedation or opioid, 0.2 mg/kg I.V. over 20 to 30 seconds. To complete induction, give additional increments of 25% of initial dose p.r.n.

▶ **To induce sleepiness and amnesia and to relieve apprehension before anesthesia or before or during procedures in children.**
Children: 0.1 to 0.15 mg/kg I.M. Doses up to 0.5 mg/kg can be used for more anxious patients. Total dose usually doesn't exceed 10 mg. I.M. depending on age of child.
Children ages 12 to 16: Initially, give dose of 2.5 mg or less I.V. slowly; repeat in 2 minutes, if needed, in small increments of initial dose over at least 2 minutes to achieve desired effect. Slowly titrate additional doses to maintain desired level of sedation in increments of 25% of dose used to first reach the sedative endpoint. Total dose that exceeds 5 mg usually isn't needed.
Children ages 6 to 12: Give 0.025 to 0.05 mg/kg I.V. over 2 to 3 minutes. Additional doses may be given in small increments after 2 to 3 minutes. Total dose that exceeds 0.4 mg/kg usually isn't needed.
Children ages 6 months to 5 years: Initially, 0.05 to 0.1 mg/kg I.V. over 2 to 3 minutes. Additional doses may be given in small increments after 2 to 3 minutes. Total dose that exceeds 0.6 mg/kg usually isn't needed.

▶ **Continuous infusion for sedation of intubated patients in the critical care setting.**
Adults: Initially, 0.01 to 0.05 mg/kg I.V. over several minutes, repeat at 10- to 15-minute intervals, until adequate sedation is achieved. To maintain sedation, infuse initially at 0.02 to 0.1 mg/kg/hour. Some patients may need higher loading doses or infusion rates. Use the lowest effective rate.
Children: Initially, 0.05 to 0.2 mg/kg I.V. over at least 2 to 3 minutes; then continuous infusion at 0.06 to 0.12 mg/kg/hour. Increase or decrease infusion to maintain desired effect.
Neonates born at 32 weeks' gestation or later: Initially 0.06 mg/kg/hour. Adjust rate, as needed, using lowest possible rate.
Neonates born earlier than 32 weeks' gestation: Initially 0.03 mg/kg/hour. Adjust rate, as needed, using lowest possible rate.

I.V. administration

- When mixing infusion, use 5-mg/ml vial, dilute to 0.5 mg/ml with D_5W or normal saline solution.
- Give slowly over at least 2 minutes, and wait at least 2 minutes when adjusting doses to desired effect.
- Watch for irritation and infiltration. Extravasation can cause tissue damage and necrosis.

⊗ **Incompatibilities**
Albumin, amphotericin B, ampicillin sodium, bumetanide, butorphanol, ceftazidime, cefuroxime, clonidine, dexamethasone sodium phosphate, dimenhydrinate, dobutamine, foscarnet, fosphenytoin, furosemide, hydrocortisone, imipenem-cilastatin sodium, methotrexate sodium, nafcillin, pentobarbital sodium, perphenazine, prochlorperazine edisylate, ranitidine hydrochloride, sodium bicarbonate, thiopental, some total parenteral nutrition formulations, trimethoprim-sulfamethoxazole.

Contraindications and cautions

- Contraindicated in patients hypersensitive to the drug or any of its components and in those with acute angle-closure glaucoma, shock, coma, or acute alcohol intoxication.
- Use cautiously in patients with uncompensated acute illness and in debilitated patients.

Lifespan: In pregnant women, drug is contraindicated. In breast-feeding women, use cautiously; it's unknown if the drug appears in breast milk. In elderly patients, use drug cautiously.

Adverse reactions

CNS: amnesia, combativeness, headache, involuntary movements, oversedation.
CV: ***cardiac arrest, hypotension,*** variations in blood pressure and pulse rate.
GI: hiccups, nausea, vomiting.
Respiratory: **APNEA,** decreased respiratory rate.
Other: pain, tenderness at injection site.

Interactions

Drug-drug. *Cimetidine, verapamil:* May increase effects of benzodiazepine. Monitor patient closely.
CNS depressants: May increase risk of apnea. Monitor vital signs and respiratory condition closely.

M

CYP3A4 inducers (carbamazepine, phenobarbital, phenytoin, rifampin): May decrease midazolam level. Monitor patient for effect; adjust dosage if needed.
Diltiazem: May increase CNS depression and prolong midazolam effects. Use lower dose of midazolam.
Fluconazole, itraconazole, ketoconazole, miconazole: May increase and prolong levels, and may increase CNS depression and psychomotor impairment. Don't use together.
Hormonal contraceptives: May prolong benzodiazepine half-life. Monitor patient closely.
Indinavir, ritonavir: May cause prolonged or severe sedation and respiratory depression. Monitor patient closely.
Opioid analgesics: May increase midazolam's hypnotic effect and increase risk of hypotension. Monitor patient closely; adjust dosage as needed.
Rifamycin: May decrease midazolam levels. Monitor patient for effect.
Drug-food. *Grapefruit juice:* May increase bioavailability of oral midazolam. Discourage use together.
Drug-lifestyle. *Alcohol use:* May cause additive CNS effects. Strongly discourage use together.

Effects on lab test results

None reported.

Pharmacokinetics

Absorption: 80% to 100%.
Distribution: Large volume. About 97% protein-bound.
Metabolism: In liver by CYP3A4 isoenzyme.
Excretion: In urine. *Half-life:* 2 to 6 hours.

Route	Onset	Peak	Duration
P.O.	10–20 min	45–60 min	2–6 hr
I.V.	1½–5 min	Rapid	2–6 hr
I.M.	≤ 15 min	15–60 min	2–6 hr

Action

Chemical effect: May depress CNS at limbic and subcortical levels of brain by potentiating effects of GABA.
Therapeutic effect: Promotes calmness and sleep.

Available forms

Injection: 1 mg/ml, 5 mg/ml
Syrup: 2 mg/ml

NURSING PROCESS

Assessment

- Assess patient's condition before therapy and regularly thereafter to monitor drug effectiveness.
- Monitor blood pressure, heart rate and rhythm, respirations, airway integrity, and arterial oxygen saturation during procedure, especially in patients premedicated with opioids.
- Assess patient's and family's knowledge of drug therapy.

Nursing diagnoses

- Anxiety related to surgery
- Ineffective breathing pattern related to drug's effect on respiratory system
- Deficient knowledge related to drug therapy

Planning and implementation

ALERT: Have oxygen and resuscitation equipment available in case of severe respiratory depression. Excessive dose or too rapid infusion may cause respiratory arrest, particularly in an elderly or debilitated patient.

- Abrupt withdrawal of drug can cause seizures.
- For I.M. dose, give deep into large muscle mass.

ALERT: Don't give by rapid injection to neonates.

- Drug contains benzyl alcohol preservative. Don't give by intrathecal or epidural route.

Patient teaching

- Use extra caution when teaching patient because drug will diminish predrug memory. Provide written information, family member instruction, and follow-up contact to ensure that patient has adequate information.
- Instruct patient not to use alcohol during therapy.

Evaluation

- Patient exhibits calmness.
- Patient maintains adequate breathing pattern throughout therapy.
- Patient and family state understanding of drug therapy.

miglitol

(MIG-lih-tall)
Glyset

Pharmacologic class: alpha-glucosidase inhibitor
Therapeutic class: antidiabetic
Pregnancy risk category: B

Indications and dosages

▶ **Type 2 diabetes mellitus where hyperglycemia can't be managed with diet alone; with a sulfonylurea when diet plus either miglitol or sulfonylurea alone yield inadequate glycemic control.** *Adults:* 25 mg P.O. t.i.d. with the first bite of each main meal; some patients may start at 25 mg P.O. daily to minimize GI side effects. Increase dosage after 4 to 8 weeks to maintenance dosage of 50 mg P.O. t.i.d. Further increase dosage after 3 months, based on glycosylated hemoglobin level, to maximum of 100 mg P.O. t.i.d.

Contraindications and cautions

- Contraindicated in patients hypersensitive to the drug or any of its components. Also contraindicated in patients with diabetic ketoacidosis, inflammatory bowel disease, colonic ulceration, or partial intestinal obstruction; patients predisposed to intestinal obstruction or those with chronic intestinal diseases related to disorders of digestion or absorption; and patients with conditions that may deteriorate as a result of increased gas formation in the intestine.
- Use cautiously in patients with serum creatinine more than 2 mg/dl.
- Use cautiously in patients also receiving insulin or oral sulfonylureas.

Lifespan: In pregnant women, use cautiously when benefits outweigh risks to the fetus. In breast-feeding women, don't use. In children, safety and effectiveness haven't been established.

Adverse reactions

GI: abdominal pain, diarrhea, flatulence.
Skin: rash.

Interactions

Drug-drug. *Digestive enzyme preparations (such as amylase, pancreatin), intestinal absorbents (such as charcoal):* May reduce the effectiveness of miglitol. Avoid use together.
Digoxin, propranolol, ranitidine: May decrease the bioavailability of these drugs. Monitor patient for loss of effectiveness and adjust dosages.
Insulin, oral sulfonylureas: May increase the effect of these drugs. Adjust dosage of these drugs if needed. Monitor these patients for hypoglycemia.
Drug-herb. *Aloe, bilberry leaf, bitter melon, burdock, dandelion, fenugreek, garlic, ginseng, stinging nettle:* May improve glucose level control, allowing for a reduced antidiabetic dosage. Advise patient to discuss the use of herbal remedies with prescriber before therapy.

Effects on lab test results

- May decrease iron and glucose levels.

Pharmacokinetics

Absorption: A 25-mg dose is completely absorbed, whereas a 100-mg dose is only 50% to 70% absorbed.
Distribution: Mainly into the extracellular fluid. Less than 4% protein-bound.
Metabolism: None.
Excretion: Mainly renal. More than 95% of a dose in urine as unchanged drug. *Half-life:* About 2 hours.

Route	Onset	Peak	Duration
P.O.	Unknown	2–3 hr	Unknown

Action

Chemical effect: Lowers glucose level through reversible inhibition of alpha glucosidases in the small intestine; they convert oligosaccharides and disaccharides to glucose. Inhibiting these enzymes delays glucose absorption. Drug has no effect on insulin secretion.
Therapeutic effect: Lowers glucose level.

Available forms

Tablets: 25 mg, 50 mg, 100 mg

M

NURSING PROCESS

Assessment

- Obtain history of patient's condition before therapy, and reassess regularly to monitor drug effectiveness.
- Regularly monitor glucose level, especially during increased stress, such as infection, fever, surgery, and trauma.
- Check glycosylated hemoglobin level every 3 months to monitor long-term glycemic control.
- Assess patient's and family's knowledge of drug therapy.

Nursing diagnoses

- Ineffective health maintenance related to hyperglycemia
- Risk for injury related to drug-induced hypoglycemia
- Deficient knowledge related to drug therapy

Planning and implementation

- Give with the first bite of each main meal.
- Manage type 2 diabetes with diet control, exercise program, and regular testing of urine and glucose levels.
- Treat mild to moderate hypoglycemia with dextrose, such as glucose tablets or gel, or orange juice with sugar packets. Severe hypoglycemia may require I.V. glucose or glucagon.
- GI adverse effects decrease with continued treatment.

Patient teaching

- Tell patient about the importance of adhering to prescriber's diet, weight reduction, and exercise instructions and to have glucose and glycosylated hemoglobin level tested regularly.
- Inform patient that drug therapy relieves symptoms but doesn't cure diabetes.
- Teach patient the signs and symptoms of hyperglycemia and hypoglycemia.
- Instruct patient to treat hypoglycemia with glucose tablets and to have a source of glucose readily available when miglitol is taken with a sulfonylurea or insulin.
- Advise patient to promptly seek medical advice during periods of stress such as fever, trauma, infection, or surgery, because drug requirements may change.
- Instruct patient to take drug three times a day with the first bite of each main meal.
- Show patient how and when to monitor glucose level.
- Advise patient that adverse GI effects are most common during the first few weeks of therapy and should improve over time.
- Urge patient to always carry medical identification.

Evaluation

- Patient's glucose level is normal.
- Patient sustains no injury from drug-induced hypoglycemia.
- Patient and family state understanding of drug therapy.

milrinone lactate

(MIL-rih-nohn LAK-tayt)
Primacor

Pharmacologic class: bipyridine phosphodiesterase inhibitor
Therapeutic class: inotropic vasodilator
Pregnancy risk category: C

Indications and dosages

▶ **Short-term therapy for acute decompensated heart failure.** *Adults:* Loading dose is 50 mcg/kg I.V., given slowly over 10 minutes, followed by continuous I.V. infusion of 0.375 to 0.75 mcg/kg/minute. Adjust infusion dose based on response. Maximum dosage is 1.13 mg/kg daily.

Adjust-a-dose: For patients with renal impairment, if creatinine clearance is 50 ml/minute or less, decrease dosage to achieve maximum effect, not to exceed 1.13 mg/kg I.V. daily.

I.V. administration

- Dilute with half-normal or normal saline solution or D_5W. Prepare 100-mcg/ml solution by adding 180 ml of diluent per 20-mg (20-ml) vial, 150-mcg/ml solution by adding 113 ml of diluent per 20-mg (20-ml) vial, and 200-mcg/ml solution by adding 80 ml of diluent per 20-mg (20-ml) vial.
- Decreased blood pressure requires stopping or slowing infusion.
- Drug hasn't been shown to be safe or effective for more than 48 hours. Avoid using longer.

⊗ Incompatibilities

Bumetanide, furosemide, procainamide.

Contraindications and cautions

• Contraindicated in patients hypersensitive to the drug, or any of its components.
• Use cautiously in patients with severe aortic or pulmonic valvular disease in place of surgical correction of obstruction, or for patients in acute phase of MI.
• Use cautiously in patients with atrial flutter or fibrillation because drug slightly shortens AV node conduction time and may increase ventricular response rate.
Lifespan: In pregnant women, use cautiously. In breast-feeding women, use cautiously; it's unknown if the drug appears in breast milk. In children, safety and effectiveness haven't been established.

Adverse reactions

CNS: headache.
CV: chest pain, hypotension, VENTRICULAR ARRHYTHMIAS, ***ventricular ectopic activity, ventricular fibrillation, ventricular tachycardia.***

Interactions

Drug-drug. *Nesiritide:* May increase hypotensive effect. Avoid use together.

Effects on lab test results

None reported.

Pharmacokinetics

Absorption: Given I.V.
Distribution: About 70% protein-bound.
Metabolism: About 12% to glucuronide metabolite.
Excretion: About 83% unchanged in urine. *Half-life:* 2½ to 2¾ hours.

Route	Onset	Peak	Duration
I.V.	5–15 min	1–2 hr	3–6 hr

Action

Chemical effect: Produces inotropic action by increasing cellular levels of cAMP; produces vasodilation by relaxing vascular smooth muscle.
Therapeutic effect: Relieves acute signs and symptoms of heart failure.

Available forms

Injection: 1 mg/ml
Premixed injection: 200 mcg/ml in 100 ml D_5W injection; 200 mcg/ml in 200 ml D_5W injection

NURSING PROCESS

Assessment

• Assess patient's heart failure before therapy and regularly thereafter to monitor drug effectiveness.
• Monitor fluid and electrolyte levels, blood pressure, heart rate, and kidney function during therapy.
• Continuously monitor patient's ECG.
• Be alert for adverse reactions.
• Assess patient's and family's knowledge of drug therapy.

Nursing diagnoses

• Impaired gas exchange related to presence of heart failure
• Decreased cardiac output related to drug-induced cardiac arrhythmias
• Deficient knowledge related to drug therapy

Planning and implementation

• Drug is typically given with digoxin and diuretics.
• Inotropics may aggravate outflow tract obstruction in hypertrophic subaortic stenosis.
ALERT: Improvement of cardiac output may result in enhanced urine output. Reduce diuretic dose as heart failure improves. Potassium loss may predispose patient to digitalis toxicity.
ALERT: Don't confuse milrinone with inamrinone.

Patient teaching

• Tell patient to report headache. Mild analgesic can be given for relief.

Evaluation

• Patient exhibits adequate gas exchange as heart failure is resolved.
• Drug-induced arrhythmias don't develop during therapy.
• Patient and family state understanding of drug therapy.

minocycline hydrochloride

(migh-noh-SIGH-kleen high-droh-KLOR-ighd)
Akamin ◇, Alti-Minocycline ♦, Apo-Minocycline ♦, Dynacin, Minocin, Minomycin ◇, Novo-Minocycline ♦, PMS-Minocycline ♦, Vectrin

Pharmacologic class: tetracycline
Therapeutic class: antibiotic
Pregnancy risk category: D

Indications and dosages

▶ **Infections caused by sensitive gram-negative and gram-positive organisms, trachoma, amebiasis.** *Adults:* 200 mg I.V.; then 100 mg I.V. q 12 hours. Maximum 400 mg I.V. daily. Or 200 mg P.O. initially; then 100 mg P.O. q 12 hours. Some clinicians use 100 or 200 mg P.O. initially, followed by 50 mg q.i.d. *Children older than age 8:* Initially, 4 mg/kg P.O. or I.V., then 2 mg/kg P.O. q 12 hours. Give I.V. in 500- to 1,000-ml solution without calcium over 6 hours.

▶ **Gonorrhea in patients sensitive to penicillin.** *Adults:* Initially, 200 mg P.O.; then 100 mg q 12 hours for at least 4 days.

▶ **Syphilis in patients sensitive to penicillin.** *Adults:* Initially, 200 mg P.O.; then 100 mg q 12 hours for 10 to 15 days.

▶ **Meningococcal carrier state.** *Adults:* 100 mg P.O. q 12 hours for 5 days.

▶ **Uncomplicated urethral, endocervical, or rectal infection caused by *Chlamydia trachomatis* or *Ureaplasma urealyticum*.** *Adults:* 100 mg P.O. b.i.d. for at least 7 days.

▶ **Uncomplicated gonococcal urethritis in men.** *Adults:* 100 mg P.O. b.i.d. for 5 days.

▶ **Cholera.** *Adults:* Initially, 200 mg P.O., then 100 mg P.O. q 12 hours for 2 to 3 days.

▶ **Multibacillary leprosy‡.** *Adults:* 100 mg P.O. daily with clofazimine and ofloxacin for 6 months, followed by 100 mg P.O. daily for an additional 18 months in conjunction with clofazimine.

▶ **Nongonococcal urethritis caused by *C. trachomatis* or *mycoplasma*‡.** *Adults:* 100 mg P.O. daily in one or two divided doses for 1 to 3 weeks.

Adjust-a-dose: Decrease dosage or extend dosing intervals in patients with renal impairment to a maximum of 200 mg Minocin in 24 hours.

I.V. administration

- Reconstitute 100 mg of powder with 5 ml of sterile water for injection, with further dilution of 500 to 1,000 ml for I.V. infusion.
- Infusions are usually given over 6 hours.
- Thrombophlebitis may develop. Watch for irritation and infiltration; extravasation can cause tissue damage and necrosis.
- Switch to P.O. form as soon as possible.
- Solution is stable for 24 hours at room temperature.

⊗ **Incompatibilities**
Adrenocorticotropic hormone, allopurinol, amifostine, aminophylline, amobarbital sodium, amphotericin B, bicarbonate infusion mixtures, calcium gluconate or calcium chloride, carbenicillin, cefazolin sodium, cephalothin sodium, chloramphenicol succinate, colistin sulfate, doxapram, heparin sodium, hydrocortisone sodium succinate, hydromorphone, iodine sodium, meperidine, morphine, penicillin, pentobarbital, phenytoin sodium, piperacillin sodium-tazobactam sodium, polymyxin, prochlorperazine, propofol, rifampin, sodium ascorbate, sulfadiazine, sulfisoxazole, thiopental sodium, thiotepa, vitamin K (sodium bisulfate or sodium salt), whole blood.

Contraindications and cautions

- Contraindicated in patients hypersensitive to the drug or other tetracyclines.
- Use cautiously in patients with impaired kidney or liver function.

Lifespan: In breast-feeding women, don't use because it's unknown if drug appears in breast milk. In children younger than age 8, don't use. Drug may cause permanent discoloration of teeth, enamel defects, and bone growth retardation. In pregnant women, don't use in the last trimester because of these same effects on the fetus.

Adverse reactions

CNS: ***intracranial hypertension (pseudotumor cerebri)***, light-headedness or dizziness from vestibular toxicity.
CV: pericarditis, *thrombophlebitis.*
EENT: dysphagia, glossitis.

GI: *anorexia, diarrhea,* enterocolitis, epigastric distress, inflammatory anogenital lesions, oral candidiasis, *nausea,* vomiting.
Hematologic: eosinophilia, ***neutropenia, thrombocytopenia.***
Musculoskeletal: bone growth retardation.
Skin: increased pigmentation, maculopapular and erythematous rashes, photosensitivity reactions, urticaria.
Other: ***anaphylaxis,*** enamel defects, ***hypersensitivity reactions,*** permanent discoloration of teeth, superinfection.

Interactions

Drug-drug. *Antacids (including sodium bicarbonate) and laxatives containing aluminum, magnesium, or calcium; antidiarrheals:* May decrease antibiotic absorption. Give antibiotic 1 hour before or 2 hours after these drugs.
Cimetidine: May decrease absorption of minocycline. Monitor patient.
Digoxin: May increase digoxin level. Decrease digoxin dose, if needed.
Ferrous sulfate, other iron products, zinc: May decrease antibiotic absorption. Administer drug 3 hours after or 2 hours before iron.
Hormonal contraceptives: May decrease contraceptive effectiveness and increase risk of breakthrough bleeding. Recommend a nonhormonal contraceptive.
Methoxyflurane: May cause nephrotoxicity with tetracyclines. Avoid use together; monitor patient carefully.
Oral anticoagulants: May increase anticoagulant effect. Monitor PT and INR. Adjust dosage if needed.
Penicillins: May interfere with bactericidal action of penicillins. Avoid use together.
Drug-herb. *St. John's wort:* May increase photosensitivity reactions. Urge patient to avoid unprotected or prolonged exposure to sunlight.
Drug-lifestyle. *Sun exposure:* May cause photosensitivity reaction. Urge patient to avoid unprotected or prolonged exposure to sunlight.

Effects on lab test results

- May increase BUN and liver enzyme levels. May decrease hemoglobin level and hematocrit.
- May increase eosinophil count. May decrease platelet and neutrophil counts.
- May cause false-positive reading of copper sulfate tests, such as Clinitest (parenteral form). May cause false-negative reading of glucose enzymatic tests, such as Diastix (all forms).

Pharmacokinetics

Absorption: 90% to 100%.
Distribution: Wide, including into synovial, pleural, prostatic, and seminal fluids; bronchial secretions; saliva; and aqueous humor. CSF penetration is poor. 70% to 80% protein-bound.
Metabolism: Partial.
Excretion: In bile salts, urine, and feces. *Half-life:* 11 to 26 hours.

Route	Onset	Peak	Duration
P.O.	Unknown	1–4 hr	Unknown
I.V.	Immediate	Immediate	Unknown

Action

Chemical effect: May exert bacteriostatic effect by binding to ribosomal subunit of microorganisms, inhibiting protein synthesis.
Therapeutic effect: Hinders bacterial cell growth.

Available forms

Akamin ◇, ***Minomycin*** ◇
Capsules: 100 mg
Tablets: 50 mg
Alti-Minocycline ♦, ***Apo-Minocycline*** ♦, ***Novo-Minocycline*** ♦, ***PMS-Minocycline*** ♦
Capsules: 50 mg, 100 mg
Dynacin
Capsules: 50 mg, 75 mg, 100 mg
Tablets: 50 mg, 75 mg, 100 mg
Minocin
Capsules (pellet-filled): 50 mg, 100 mg
Injection: 100 mg/vial

NURSING PROCESS

Assessment

- Assess patient's infection before therapy and regularly thereafter to monitor drug effectiveness.
- Obtain specimen for culture and sensitivity tests before giving first dose. Begin therapy pending results.
- Be alert for adverse reactions and drug interactions.
- If patient has an adverse GI reaction, monitor patient's hydration.

M

• Assess patient's and family's knowledge of drug therapy.

Nursing diagnoses

• Risk for infection related to presence of susceptible bacteria
• Risk for deficient fluid volume related to drug-induced adverse reactions
• Deficient knowledge related to drug therapy

Planning and implementation

ALERT: Check expiration date. Outdated or degraded tetracyclines have been linked to reversible nephrotoxicity (Fanconi syndrome).
• Don't expose these drugs to light or heat. Keep cap tightly closed.
• Drug may cause tooth discoloration in children and young adults. If it occurs, inform prescriber.
ALERT: Don't confuse Minocin with niacin and Mithracin.
ALERT: Don't confuse Dynacin with DynaCirc.

Patient teaching

• Inform patient that drug may be taken with food, and instruct him to take drug exactly as prescribed.
• Instruct patient to take oral form with full glass of water and to avoid taking it within 1 hour of bedtime to avoid esophagitis.
• Warn patient to avoid hazardous tasks until the drug's CNS effects are known.
• Instruct patient to avoid direct sunlight and ultraviolet light, to use sunblock, and to wear protective clothing in order to avoid photosensitivity reaction.
• Advise patient who uses hormonal contraceptives that barrier method of contraception should also be used. Also inform her that she may experience breakthrough bleeding.

Evaluation

• Patient is free from infection.
• Patient maintains adequate hydration throughout therapy.
• Patient and family state understanding of drug therapy.

mirtazapine

(mir-TAH-zuh-peen)
Remeron, Remeron SolTab

Pharmacologic class: piperazinoazepine
Therapeutic class: antidepressant
Pregnancy risk category: C

Indications and dosages

▶ **Depression.** *Adults:* Initially, 15 mg P.O. at bedtime. Maintenance dosage is 15 to 45 mg daily. Adjust dosage at intervals of at least 1 to 2 weeks.

Contraindications and cautions

• Contraindicated in patients hypersensitive to the drug or any of its components and in those taking MAO inhibitors.
• Use cautiously in patients with CV or cerebrovascular disease, seizure disorders, suicidal ideation, impaired hepatic or renal function, or history of mania or hypomania.
Lifespan: In pregnant women, use only if benefits outweigh risks to the fetus. In breastfeeding women, use cautiously; it's unknown if the drug appears in breast milk. In children, safety and effectiveness haven't been established, and drug shouldn't be used to treat major depressive disorder. Increased risk of suicidal behavior has been noted in this population, although not proven to be attributable to drug.

Adverse reactions

CNS: abnormal dreams, abnormal thinking, asthenia, confusion, dizziness, neuropathy, neurosis, *somnolence,* tremor.
CV: edema, peripheral edema.
GI: constipation, dry mouth, increased appetite, nausea.
GU: urinary frequency.
Hematologic: ***agranulocytosis, neutropenia.***
Metabolic: *weight gain.*
Musculoskeletal: back pain, myalgia.
Respiratory: dyspnea.
Other: flulike syndrome.

Interactions

Drug-drug. *Diazepam, other CNS depressants:* May have additive CNS effects. Avoid use together.

MAO inhibitors: May cause serious and sometimes fatal reactions. Don't use drug within 14 days of an MAO inhibitor.

Drug-lifestyle. *Alcohol use:* May have additive CNS effects. Discourage use together.

Effects on lab test results

- May increase ALT level.
- May decrease neutrophil and granulocyte counts.

Pharmacokinetics

Absorption: Rapid.
Distribution: 85% protein-bound.
Metabolism: Extensive.
Excretion: Mainly in urine; some in feces. *Half-life:* About 20 to 40 hours.

Route	Onset	Peak	Duration
P.O.	Unknown	< 2 hr	Unknown

Action

Chemical effect: Enhances central noradrenergic and serotonergic action; potent antagonist of histamine receptors.
Therapeutic effect: Relieves depression.

Available forms

Orally disintegrating tablets: 15 mg, 30 mg, 45 mg
Tablets: 15 mg, 30 mg, 45 mg

NURSING PROCESS

Assessment

- Assess mental status before and regularly during treatment.
- Monitor for signs of infection and other adverse reactions.
- Assess patient's and family's knowledge of drug therapy.

Nursing diagnoses

- Disturbed thought processes related to adverse effects
- Risk for injury related to sedation and orthostatic hypotension
- Deficient knowledge related to drug therapy

Planning and implementation

- If patient develops a sore throat, fever, stomatitis, or other signs of infection with a low WBC count, stop giving the drug and monitor him closely.

ALERT: Don't stop drug therapy abruptly because doing so increases the patient's risk of suicide. Monitor patient and take suicide precautions.

Patient teaching

- Instruct patient to remove orally disintegrating tablet from blister pack and immediately place on the tongue. Tell him he won't need water to swallow the tablet because drug dissolves rapidly.
- Tell patient not to break or split tablet.
- Warn patient to avoid hazardous activities if somnolence occurs.
- Tell patient to report signs and symptoms of infection or flulike symptoms.
- Advise patient not to use alcohol or take other CNS depressants.
- Stress importance of compliance with therapy.
- Instruct patient not to take other drugs without prescriber's approval.
- Tell woman to notify prescriber if she suspects pregnancy or if she is breast-feeding.

Evaluation

- Patient regains normal thought processes.
- Patient sustains no injury from adverse reactions.
- Patient and family state understanding of drug therapy.

misoprostol

(migh-soe-PROST-ole)
Cytotec

Pharmacologic class: prostaglandin E_1 analogue
Therapeutic class: gastric mucosal protectant
Pregnancy risk category: X

Indications and dosages

▶ **Prevention of NSAID-induced gastric ulcer in elderly or debilitated patients at high risk for complications from gastric ulcer and in patients with history of NSAID-induced ulcer.** *Adults:* 200 mcg P.O. q.i.d. with food. If dosage isn't tolerated, decrease to 100 mcg P.O. q.i.d.

▶ **Duodenal or gastric ulcer‡.** *Adults:* 100 to 200 mcg P.O. q.i.d. with meals and at bedtime for 4 to 8 weeks.

Contraindications and cautions

- Contraindicated in patients with a known allergy to prostaglandins.

Lifespan: In pregnant women, don't use because of risk of uterine rupture and fetal death. In breast-feeding women, don't use because significant diarrhea in infants has been reported. In children, safety and effectiveness haven't been established.

Adverse reactions

CNS: headache, lethargy, vertigo.
GI: *abdominal pain,* constipation, *diarrhea,* dyspepsia, flatulence, nausea, ***pancreatitis,*** vomiting.
GU: cramps, dysmenorrhea, hematuria, hypermenorrhea, menstrual disorders, spotting, UTI.
Other: ***anaphylaxis.***

Interactions

Drug-drug. *Antacids:* May reduce misoprostol level insignificantly. Monitor patient.

Effects on lab test results

- May increase alkaline phosphatase, aminotransferase, and cardiac enzyme levels. May decrease hemoglobin level and hematocrit.
- May increase erythrocyte sedimentation rate. May decrease platelet count.

Pharmacokinetics

Absorption: Rapid.
Distribution: Highly protein-bound.
Metabolism: Rapidly de-esterified to misoprostol acid, the biologically active metabolite.
Excretion: About 15% in feces; rest in urine. *Half-life:* 20 to 40 minutes.

Route	Onset	Peak	Duration
P.O.	30 min	60–90 min	3 hr

Action

Chemical effect: Replaces gastric prostaglandins depleted by NSAID therapy. Decreases basal and stimulated gastric acid secretion and may increase gastric mucus and bicarbonate production.
Therapeutic effect: Protects gastric mucosa from ulcerating.

Available forms

Tablets: 100 mcg, 200 mcg

NURSING PROCESS

Assessment

- Obtain history of patient's GI condition before therapy.
- In woman of childbearing age, make sure that negative pregnancy test is obtained within 2 weeks before therapy begins.
- Be alert for adverse reactions and drug interactions.
- Assess patient's and family's knowledge of drug therapy.

Nursing diagnoses

- Risk for injury related to potential for gastric ulceration
- Acute pain related to headache
- Deficient knowledge related to drug therapy

Planning and implementation

ALERT: Take special precautions not to use drug in a pregnant woman. Make sure she is fully aware of dangers to fetus and that she receives both verbal and written warnings of these dangers. Also, make sure she can comply with effective contraceptive use.

- Uterine rupture is linked to certain risk factors, including later trimester pregnancies, higher doses of the drug, previous cesarean delivery or uterine surgery, and five or more previous pregnancies.

ALERT: Don't confuse misoprostol with mifepristone.

Patient teaching

- Instruct patient to report to prescriber headache, diarrhea that doesn't resolve within three weeks or is severe, and severe abdominal pain.
- Instruct patient not to share drug because it may cause miscarriage, usually with life-threatening bleeding, in women of childbearing age.
- Advise patient not to start therapy until the second or third day of the next normal menstrual period.

Evaluation

- Patient remains free from signs and symptoms of gastric ulceration.

• Patient states that drug-induced headache doesn't occur.
• Patient and family state understanding of drug therapy.

mitomycin (mitomycin-C)

(might-oh-MIGH-sin)
Mutamycin

Pharmacologic class: antibiotic
Therapeutic class: antineoplastic
Pregnancy risk category: NR

Indications and dosages

▶ **Disseminated adenocarcinomas of the pancreas and stomach.** *Adults:* 20 mg/m² I.V. as single dose. Repeat cycle after 6 to 8 weeks when WBC and platelet counts have returned to normal.

Adjust-a-dose: If WBC count at nadir after last dose is 2,000 to 2,999 mm³ and platelet count is 25,000 to 74,999 mm³, give 70% of regular dose. If WBC count is less than 2,000 mm³ and platelet count is less than 25,000 mm³, give 50% of regular dose.

▶ **Bladder cancer ‡.** *Adults:* 20 to 60 mg intravesically once per week for 8 weeks.

I.V. administration

• Preparation and administration are related to mutagenic, teratogenic, and carcinogenic risks to personnel. Follow facility policy to reduce risks.
• To reconstitute 5-mg vial use 10 ml sterile water for injection; to reconstitute 20-mg vial, use 40 ml of sterile water for injection; to reconstitute a 40-mg vial, use 80 ml sterile water for injection, to give a concentration of 0.5 mg/ml. Let stand at room temperature until complete dissolution occurs.
• Give drug into the Y-connector of a free-flowing I.V. line.
• Watch for irritation and infiltration. Extravasation can cause tissue damage, severe ulceration, and necrosis. If it occurs, stop infusion immediately and notify prescriber.
• When reconstituted with sterile water for injection to 0.5 mg/ml, drug is stable for 14 days refrigerated or 7 days at room temperature. When diluted to 20 to 40 mcg/ml, it's stable in D_5W for 3 hours, in normal saline solution for 12 hours, and in sodium lactate for 24 hours.
• The combination of 5 to 15 mg mitomycin and 1,000 to 10,000 units heparin in 30 ml of normal saline solution for injection is stable at room temperature for 48 hours.

⊗ **Incompatibilities**
Aztreonam, bleomycin, cefepime, etoposide, filgrastim, gemcitabine, piperacillin sodium-tazobactam sodium, sargramostim, vinorelbine.

Contraindications and cautions

• Contraindicated in patients hypersensitive to the drug or any of its components and in those with thrombocytopenia, coagulation disorder, or increased bleeding tendency from other causes.

Lifespan: In pregnant and breast-feeding women, use only when benefits outweigh risks to the fetus and infant. In children, safety and effectiveness haven't been established.

Adverse reactions

CNS: confusion, drowsiness, fatigue, *fever,* headache, neurologic abnormalities.
GI: anorexia, *nausea,* stomatitis, *vomiting.*
GU: ***hemolytic uremic syndrome, renal toxicity.***
Hematologic: LEUKOPENIA, ***microangiopathic hemolytic anemia,*** THROMBOCYTOPENIA.
Respiratory: ***acute respiratory distress syndrome,*** dyspnea, ***interstitial pneumonitis,*** nonproductive cough, ***pulmonary edema.***
Skin: cellulitis, ulceration, and sloughing with extravasation; desquamation, induration, pruritus, and *pain* at injection site; purple coloration of nail beds; *reversible alopecia.*
Other: ***septicemia.***

Interactions

Drug-drug. *Vinca alkaloids:* May cause acute respiratory distress. Avoid use together.

Effects on lab test results

• May decrease hemoglobin level and hematocrit.
• May decrease platelet and WBC counts.

Pharmacokinetics

Absorption: Given I.V.
Distribution: Wide. Doesn't cross blood-brain barrier.

M

Metabolism: By hepatic microsomal enzymes and deactivated in kidneys, spleen, brain, and heart.
Excretion: Mainly in urine; small portion in bile and feces. *Half-life:* About 50 minutes.

Route	Onset	Peak	Duration
I.V.	Unknown	Unknown	Unknown

Action

Chemical effect: Acts like alkylating drug, cross-linking strands of DNA. This causes imbalance of cell growth, leading to cell death.
Therapeutic effect: Kills certain cancer cells.

Available forms

Injection: 5-, 20-, and 40-mg vials

NURSING PROCESS

Assessment

- Assess patient's condition before therapy and regularly thereafter to monitor drug effectiveness.
- Obtain CBC and blood studies.
- Monitor kidney function tests.
- Be alert for adverse reactions and drug interactions.
- Assess patient's and family's knowledge of drug therapy.

Nursing diagnoses

- Ineffective health maintenance related to presence of neoplastic disease
- Ineffective protection related to adverse hematologic reactions
- Deficient knowledge related to drug therapy

Planning and implementation

- Never give drug I.M. or subcutaneously.
- Base dosage adjustments on nadir of leukocyte and platelet counts after previous dose.
- Hemolytic uremic syndrome is characterized by microangiopathic hemolytic anemia, thrombocytopenia, and renal impairment.
- Watch for leukopenia up to 8 weeks post infusion; also can be cumulative with successive doses.

ALERT: Don't confuse mitomycin with mithramycin.

Patient teaching

- Instruct patient to watch for signs of infection and bleeding and to take temperature daily.
- Warn patient that alopecia may occur, but assure him that it's reversible.
- Tell patient to promptly report to prescriber any adverse reaction.

Evaluation

- Patient responds well to therapy.
- Patient doesn't develop serious complications.
- Patient and family state understanding of drug therapy.

mitoxantrone hydrochloride

(migh-toh-ZAN-trohn high-droh-KLOR-ighd)
Novantrone

Pharmacologic class: antibiotic
Therapeutic class: antineoplastic
Pregnancy risk category: D

Indications and dosages

▶ **Combination initial therapy for acute nonlymphocytic leukemia.** *Adults:* Induction begins with 12 mg/m² I.V. daily on days 1 through 3, given with 100 mg/m² daily of cytarabine on days 1 through 7. If response isn't adequate, give second induction. Maintenance therapy includes 12 mg/m² on days 1 and 2, given with cytarabine on days 1 through 5.

▶ **To reduce neurologic disability and frequency of relapse in chronic progressive, progressive relapsing, or worsening relapsing-remitting multiple sclerosis.** *Adults:* 12 mg/m² I.V. infusion over 5 to 15 minutes q 3 months.

▶ **Pain from advanced hormone-refractory prostate cancer.** *Adults:* 12 to 14 mg/m² I.V. infusion over 15 to 30 minutes q 21 days with corticosteroids.

I.V. administration

- Preparation and administration of parenteral form carries mutagenic, teratogenic, and carcinogenic risks. Check facility policy.
- Dilute dose (available as aqueous solution of 2 mg/ml in volumes of 10, 12.5, and 15 ml) in at least 50 ml of normal saline solution injection or D_5W injection. Give drug by direct injection into free-flowing I.V. line of normal saline solution or D_5W injection over at least 3 minutes, usually 15 to 30 minutes.

• Although drug isn't a vesicant, if dose extravasates, stop infusion immediately and notify prescriber.
• Never give by subcutaneous, I.M., intra-arterial, or intrathecal route.
• Store undiluted solution at room temperature. Once vial is penetrated, undiluted solution may be stored at room temperature for 7 days, or 14 days in refrigerator. Don't freeze.

⊗ **Incompatibilities**
Amphotericin B, aztreonam, cefepime, doxorubicin liposomal, heparin sodium, hydrocortisone, other I.V. drugs, paclitaxel, piperacillin sodium and tazobactam sodium, propofol, sargramostim.

Contraindications and cautions

• Contraindicated in patients hypersensitive to the drug or any of its components.
• Use cautiously in patients previously exposed to anthracyclines or other cardiotoxic drugs.
Lifespan: In pregnant and breast-feeding women, drug is contraindicated. In children, safety and effectiveness haven't been established.

Adverse reactions

CNS: headache, ***seizures.***
CV: ***arrhythmias, fatal myocardial toxicity, heart failure,*** tachycardia.
EENT: conjunctivitis.
GI: abdominal pain, **BLEEDING,** diarrhea, mucositis, nausea, stomatitis, vomiting.
GU: ***renal impairment,*** uric acid nephropathy.
Hematologic: ***myelosuppression, secondary acute myelogenous leukemia.***
Hepatic: *jaundice.*
Metabolic: hyperuricemia.
Respiratory: cough, dyspnea.
Skin: alopecia, ecchymoses, petechiae.

Interactions

None significant.

Effects on lab test results

• May increase ALT, AST, bilirubin, BUN, creatinine, and uric acid levels. May decrease hemoglobin level and hematocrit.
• May decrease WBC, RBC, and platelet counts.

Pharmacokinetics

Absorption: Given I.V.
Distribution: 78% protein-bound.
Metabolism: In liver.
Excretion: By renal and hepatobiliary systems. *Half-life:* 5¾ days.

Route	Onset	Peak	Duration
I.V.	Unknown	Unknown	Unknown

Action

Chemical effect: Not fully understood; may be cell cycle–nonspecific. Drug reacts with DNA, producing cytotoxic effect.
Therapeutic effect: Hinders susceptible cancer cell growth.

Available forms

Injection: 2 mg/ml in 10-, 12.5-, and 15-ml vials

NURSING PROCESS

Assessment

• Assess patient's condition before therapy and regularly thereafter to monitor drug effectiveness.
• Monitor CBC and other lab test results regularly.
• Monitor left ventricular ejection fraction and signs of heart failure or cardiac toxicity with each dose.
• Be alert for adverse reactions and drug interactions.
• Assess patient's and family's knowledge of drug therapy.

Nursing diagnoses

• Ineffective health maintenance related to presence of leukemia
• Risk for infection related to drug-induced myelosuppression
• Deficient knowledge related to drug therapy

Planning and implementation

• Give under the supervision of a physician experienced in the use of cytotoxic chemotherapeutics.
• Don't give drug to a patient with neutrophil count below 1,500 cells/mm^3 or left ventricular ejection fraction less than 50% unless benefits outweigh risks.
• Cardiotoxicity is linked to a cumulative dose greater than 140 mg/m^2.

• Myocardial toxicity may occur during treatment or months to years after therapy ends.
• Give allopurinol, if needed. Uric acid nephropathy can be avoided by adequately hydrating patient before and during therapy.
• If severe nonhematologic toxicity occurs during first course of therapy, delay second course until patient recovers.

Patient teaching

• Inform patient that urine may appear blue-green within 24 hours after administration, and that some bluish discoloration of sclera may occur. These effects aren't harmful.
• Teach patient infection control and bleeding precautions. Tell him to watch for and report signs of bleeding and infection.
• Tell patient to report sudden weight gain, peripheral edema, shortness of breath, or chest discomfort to prescriber immediately.
• Advise woman of childbearing age not to become pregnant during therapy and to consult prescriber before becoming pregnant.

Evaluation

• Patient responds well to therapy.
• Patient develops no serious complications from drug-induced myelosuppression.
• Patient and family state understanding of drug therapy.

modafinil

(moh-DAFF-ih-nil)
Provigil

Pharmacologic class: CNS stimulant
Therapeutic class: analeptic
Pregnancy risk category: C
Controlled substance schedule: IV

Indications and dosages

▶ **Narcolepsy, obstructive sleep apnea/hypopnea syndrome.** *Adults:* 200 mg P.O. daily, given as a single dose in the morning.
▶ **Shift-work sleep disorder.** *Adults:* 200 mg P.O. once daily 1 hour before start of shift work.
Adjust-a-dose: For patients with severe hepatic impairment, reduce dosage by 50%.

Contraindications and cautions

• Contraindicated in patients hypersensitive to the drug or any of its components. Don't use in patients with a history of left ventricular hypertrophy or ischemic ECG changes, chest pain, arrhythmias, or other signs or symptoms of mitral valve prolapse caused by CNS stimulant use.
• Use cautiously in patients with recent MI or unstable angina, in those with history of psychosis, and in those receiving therapy with MAO inhibitors.
• Use cautiously and at reduced dosage in patients with severe hepatic impairment, with or without cirrhosis.
• Safety and effectiveness of drug in patients with severe renal impairment hasn't been established.
Lifespan: In pregnant women, use only when benefits outweigh risks to the fetus. In breast-feeding women, use cautiously because it's unknown if the drug appears in breast milk. In children younger than age 16, safety and effectiveness haven't been established. In elderly patients with renal or hepatic impairment, use cautiously and at a low dose.

Adverse reactions

CNS: amnesia, anxiety, ataxia, cataplexy, confusion, depression, dizziness, dyskinesia, emotional lability, fever, *headache,* hypertonia, insomnia, nervousness, paresthesia, syncope, tremor.
CV: ***arrhythmias,*** chest pain, hypertension, hypotension, vasodilation.
EENT: abnormal vision, amblyopia, epistaxis, *rhinitis,* pharyngitis.
GI: anorexia, diarrhea, dry mouth, gingivitis, mouth ulcer, *nausea,* thirst, vomiting.
GU: abnormal ejaculation, abnormal urine, urine retention.
Hematologic: eosinophilia.
Metabolic: hyperglycemia.
Musculoskeletal: joint disorder, neck pain, rigid neck.
Respiratory: ***asthma,*** dyspnea, lung disorders.
Skin: dry skin, herpes simplex.
Other: chills, infection.

Interactions

Drug-drug. *Cyclosporine, theophylline:* May reduce levels of these drugs. Use together cautiously.

Drugs that induce CYP3A4 (carbamazepine, phenobarbital, rifampin), drugs that inhibit CYP3A4 (itraconazole, ketoconazole): May alter modafinil level. Monitor patient closely.
Drugs metabolized by CYP2C9 (diazepam, phenytoin, propranolol): May increase levels of these drugs. Use together cautiously, and adjust dosage as needed.
Hormonal contraceptives: May reduce levels of these drugs, resulting in reduced contraceptive effectiveness. Recommend additional or alternative contraceptive method during modafinil therapy and for 1 month afterward.
Methylphenidate: May delay modafinil absorption. Separate doses.
Phenytoin, warfarin: May inhibit CYP2C9 and increase levels of phenytoin and warfarin. Monitor patient closely for signs of toxicity.
Tricyclic antidepressants (clomipramine, desipramine): May increase tricyclic antidepressant levels. Reduce dosage of these drugs.

Effects on lab test results

- May increase glucose, GGT, and AST levels.
- May increase eosinophil count.

Pharmacokinetics

Absorption: Rapid, with levels peaking in 2 to 4 hours.
Distribution: Good. About 60% protein-bound, mainly to albumin.
Metabolism: About 90% in the liver.
Excretion: Less than 10% from the kidneys as unchanged drug. *Half-life:* 15 hours.

Route	Onset	Peak	Duration
P.O.	Unknown	2–4 hr	Unknown

Action

Chemical effect: Unknown. It provides wake-promoting actions similar to those of sympathomimetics, including amphetamines, but it's structurally distinct from amphetamines and doesn't appear to alter the release of either dopamine or norepinephrine to produce CNS stimulation.
Therapeutic effect: Improves daytime wakefulness.

Available forms

Tablets: 100 mg, 200 mg

NURSING PROCESS

Assessment

- Obtain history of patient's condition before therapy, and reassess regularly thereafter to monitor drug effectiveness.
- Assess patient's renal function before therapy.
- Closely monitor hypertensive patient.
- Assess patient's and family's knowledge of drug therapy.

Nursing diagnoses

- Sleep deprivation related to drug-induced insomnia
- Risk for injury related to drug-induced CNS adverse effects
- Deficient knowledge related to drug therapy

Planning and implementation

- Food has no effect on overall bioavailability, but it may delay modafinil absorption by 1 hour.
- Although single, daily, 400-mg dose is usually well tolerated, no consistent evidence exists that this dosage provides additional benefit beyond daily 200-mg doses.

Patient teaching

- Drug may impair judgment. Advise patient to be careful while driving or performing other activities that require alertness until the drug's CNS effects are known.
- Instruct patient not to take other prescription or OTC drugs without consulting prescriber because of possible drug interactions.
- Advise patient not to drink alcohol during therapy.
- Tell patient to notify prescriber if he develops a rash, hives, or a related allergic reaction.
- Caution woman that use of hormonal contraceptives (including depot or implantable contraceptives) with modafinil tablets may increase the risk of pregnancy. Recommend barrier method as alternative or additional contraception during therapy and for 1 month after therapy ends.
- Advise woman to notify prescriber if she becomes pregnant or intends to become pregnant during therapy.
- Tell woman to notify prescriber if she's breast-feeding.

Evaluation

- Patient develops and maintains normal sleep-wake patterns.

M

• Patient has no adverse CNS effects.
• Patient and family state understanding of drug therapy.

moexipril hydrochloride
(moh-EKS-eh-pril high-droh-KLOR-ighd)
Univasc

Pharmacologic class: ACE inhibitor
Therapeutic class: antihypertensive
Pregnancy risk category: C (D in second and third trimesters)

Indications and dosages

▶ **Hypertension.** *Adults:* Initially, 7.5 mg P.O. daily in patients not receiving a diuretic, given 1 hour before meals. If inadequate response, increase or divide dose. Maintenance dosage, 7.5 to 30 mg daily in one or two divided doses 1 hour before meals.

Adjust-a-dose: For patients with renal impairment, if creatinine clearance is 40 ml/minute or less, start dosage at 3.75 mg P.O. daily. Maximum, 15 mg P.O. daily. For patients taking diuretics, if diuretic can't be discontinued, start dosage at 3.75 mg P.O. daily.

Contraindications and cautions

• Contraindicated in patients hypersensitive to the drug or any of its components, and in those with history of angioedema with previous ACE inhibitor therapy.
• Use cautiously in patients with impaired kidney function, heart failure, or renal artery stenosis.

Lifespan: In pregnant women, use cautiously during first trimester; contraindicated in second and third trimesters. In breast-feeding women, use cautiously; it's unknown if the drug appears in breast milk. In children, safety and effectiveness haven't been established.

Adverse reactions

CNS: *dizziness,* fatigue, headache, pain.
CV: chest pain, flushing, hypotension, orthostatic hypotension, peripheral edema.
EENT: pharyngitis, rhinitis, sinusitis.
GI: diarrhea, dyspepsia, nausea.
GU: urinary frequency.
Hematologic: ***neutropenia.***
Metabolic: ***hyperkalemia.***
Musculoskeletal: myalgia.
Respiratory: *persistent, nonproductive cough;* upper respiratory tract infection.
Skin: rash.
Other: ***anaphylaxis, angioedema,*** flulike syndrome.

Interactions

Drug-drug. *Antacids:* May decrease bioavailability of ACE inhibitors. Give drug on an empty stomach.
Digoxin: May increase or decrease digoxin level. Monitor digoxin level and patient closely.
Diuretics: May increase risk of excessive hypotension. Monitor blood pressure closely.
Indomethacin: May reduce hypotensive effects of ACE inhibitors. Avoid use together; monitor blood pressure.
Lithium: May increase lithium level and toxicity. Use together cautiously. Monitor lithium level often.
Potassium-sparing diuretics, potassium supplements: May increase risk of hyperkalemia. Monitor potassium level closely.
Drug-herb. *Capsaicin:* May cause or worsen coughing from ACE inhibitor therapy. Discourage use together.
Drug-food. *Salt substitutes that contain potassium:* May increase risk of hyperkalemia. Monitor potassium level closely; urge patient to avoid salt substitutes containing potassium.

Effects on lab test results

• May increase potassium level.
• May decrease neutrophil and granulocyte counts.

Pharmacokinetics

Absorption: Incomplete, with bioavailability of about 13%. Food significantly decreases bioavailability.
Distribution: About 50% protein-bound.
Metabolism: Extensive, to the active metabolite moexiprilat.
Excretion: Mainly in feces, with small amount in urine. *Half-life:* 2 to 9 hours.

Route	Onset	Peak	Duration
P.O.	1 hr	3–6 hr	24 hr

Action

Chemical effect: May suppress renin-angiotensin-aldosterone system. Inhibits ACE, inhibiting production of angiotensin II (a potent vasoconstrictor and stimulator of aldosterone secretion).

Therapeutic effect: Lowers blood pressure.

Available forms

Tablets: 7.5 mg, 15 mg

NURSING PROCESS

Assessment

- Assess patient's blood pressure before therapy begins.
- Measure blood pressure at lowest point just before dose to verify adequate control. Drug is less effective in reducing trough blood pressure in blacks than in others.
- Monitor patient for hypotension.
- Assess kidney function before therapy and periodically thereafter. Monitor potassium level.
- Monitor CBC with differential counts before therapy, especially in patient who has collagen-vascular disease with impaired kidney function.
- Be alert for adverse reactions and interactions.
- Assess patient's and family's knowledge of drug therapy.

Nursing diagnoses

- Risk for injury related to presence of hypertension
- Sleep deprivation related to cough
- Deficient knowledge related to drug therapy

Planning and implementation

ALERT: Excessive hypotension can occur when drug is given with diuretics. If possible, stop giving diuretics 2 to 3 days before giving this drug to decrease risk of reaction. If drug doesn't adequately control blood pressure, restart diuretic with care.

ALERT: Angioedema involving tongue, glottis, or larynx may be fatal because of airway obstruction. Give epinephrine and ensure a patent airway.

- If cough interferes with patient's ability to sleep, notify prescriber.

Patient teaching

- Instruct patient to take drug on an empty stomach; high-fat meals can impair absorption.
- Tell patient to avoid salt substitutes. These products may contain potassium, which can cause hyperkalemia.
- Advise patient to rise slowly to minimize light-headedness. If syncope occurs, tell him to stop taking the drug and immediately call the prescriber.
- Urge patient to use caution in hot weather and during exercise. Inadequate fluid intake, vomiting, diarrhea, and excessive perspiration can lead to light-headedness and syncope.
- Advise patient to report signs of infection, such as fever and sore throat; easy bruising or bleeding; swelling of tongue, lips, face, eyes, mucous membranes, or limbs; difficulty swallowing or breathing; and hoarseness.
- Tell woman to notify prescriber if she becomes pregnant.

Evaluation

- Patient's blood pressure is normal.
- Patient states that sleep disturbance doesn't occur.
- Patient and family state understanding of drug therapy.

mometasone furoate

(moe-MEH-tah-zone FUHR-oh-ayt)

Asmanex Twisthaler

Pharmacologic class: corticosteroid

Therapeutic class: anti-inflammatory, anti-asthmatic

Pregnancy risk category: C

Indications and dosages

▶ **Maintenance therapy for asthma; asthma in patients who need oral corticosteroids.** *Adults and children age 12 and older who use a bronchodilator or inhaled corticosteroids:* Initially, 220 mcg by oral inhalation q day in the evening. Maximum, 440 mcg/day.

Adults and children age 12 and older who take oral corticosteroids: 440 mcg b.i.d. by oral inhalation. Maximum, 880 mcg/day. Reduce oral corticosteroid dosage by no more than 2.5 mg/day at weekly intervals starting at least 1 week after starting mometasone. After stopping oral corticosteroids, reduce mometasone dosage to the lowest effective amount.

Contraindications and cautions

- Contraindicated in patients hypersensitive to drug or its ingredients and as primary treatment

M

of status asthmaticus or other acute episodes of asthma or bronchospasm.

• Use cautiously in patients at high risk for decreased bone mineral content (those with a family history of osteoporosis, prolonged immobilization, long-term use of drugs that reduce bone mass), patients switching from systemic to inhaled corticosteroids, and patients with active or quiescent tuberculosis, untreated systemic infections, ocular herpes simplex, or immunosuppression.

Lifespan: In pregnant women, use only if benefits outweigh risks to the fetus. In breast-feeding women; use cautiously; it isn't known if drug appears in breast milk. In children younger than age 12, safety hasn't been established.

Adverse reactions

CNS: depression, fatigue, *headache,* insomnia.
EENT: *allergic rhinitis,* dry throat, dysphonia, earache, epistaxis, nasal irritation, *pharyngitis,* sinus congestion, sinusitis.
GI: abdominal pain, anorexia, dyspepsia, flatulence, gastroenteritis, nausea, oral candidiasis, vomiting.
GU: dysmenorrhea, menstrual disorder, UTI.
Musculoskeletal: arthralgia, back pain, myalgia, pain.
Respiratory: respiratory disorder, *upper respiratory tract infection.*
Other: accidental injury, flulike symptoms, infection.

Interactions

Drug-drug. *Ketoconazole:* May increase mometasone level. Use together cautiously.

Effects on lab test results

None reported.

Pharmacokinetics

Absorption: Low in plasma.
Distribution: None in RBCs.
Metabolism: Extensive in the liver by CYP3A4 to multiple metabolites.
Excretion: Mainly in feces; some in urine.

Route	Onset	Peak	Duration
Inhalation	Unknown	Unknown	Unknown

Action

Chemical effect: Unknown, although corticosteroids inhibit many cells and mediators involved in inflammation and the asthmatic response.
Therapeutic effect: Reduces inflammation in the lungs and airways to improve pulmonary function.

Available forms

Inhalation powder: 220 mcg per inhalation

NURSING PROCESS

Assessment

• Obtain patient's medical history, including current treatments for asthma, before starting drug therapy.

ALERT: If patient is switching from an oral corticosteroid to an inhaled form, watch closely for evidence of adrenal insufficiency, such as fatigue, lethargy, weakness, nausea, vomiting, and hypotension.

• Because inhaled corticosteroids can be systemically absorbed, watch for cushingoid effects.
• If a woman takes corticosteroids during pregnancy, monitor newborn for hypoadrenalism.
• Assess patient for bone loss during long-term use.
• Watch for evidence of localized mouth infections, glaucoma, and immunosuppression.
• Monitor elderly patients for increased sensitivity to drug effects.
• Assess patient's and family's knowledge of drug therapy.

Nursing diagnoses

• Impaired gas exchange related to underlying condition and poor pulmonary function
• Activity intolerance related to underlying asthmatic condition
• Deficient knowledge related to drug therapy

Planning and implementation

ALERT: Don't use this drug to treat acute bronchospasm.

• Wean patient slowly from systemic corticosteroids once he switches to mometasone. Monitor lung function tests, beta-agonist use, and asthma symptoms.
• After oral corticosteroids are withdrawn, it may take months for hypothalamic-pituitary-adrenal (HPA) function to recover. Patients are particularly vulnerable to adrenal insufficiency or adrenal crisis during this period of HPA re-

covery if they experience trauma, stress, infection, or surgery.

• Maximum benefits may not occur for 1 to 2 weeks or longer after mometasone therapy is initiated.

Patient teaching

• Tell patient to use the mometasone inhaler regularly and at the same time each day. If he uses it only once daily, tell him to do so in the evening.

• Caution patient not to use drug for immediate relief of an asthmatic attack or bronchospasm.

• Inform patient that maximum benefits may not occur for 1 to 2 weeks or longer after mometasone therapy starts; instruct him to notify the prescriber if his condition fails to improve or if it worsens.

• Explain that, if bronchospasm develops after taking mometasone, he should immediately use a fast-acting bronchodilator. Urge him to contact the prescriber immediately if bronchospasm doesn't respond to the fast-acting bronchodilator.

ALERT: If patient has been weaned from oral corticosteroids, urge him to resume them during severe asthmatic attack or periods of stress and to contact the prescriber for instructions.

• Warn patient to avoid exposure to chickenpox or measles and to notify the prescriber if such exposure occurs.

• Tell patient to report vision changes; long-term use of an inhaled corticosteroid may increase the risk of cataracts or glaucoma.

• Advise patient to write the date on a new inhaler on the day he opens it and to discard the unit after 45 days or when the dose counter reads "00".

• Instruct patient on the proper use and routine care of the inhaler.

☑ Evaluation

• Patient has normal respiratory rate and optimal air exchange.

• Patient experiences improved exercise and activity tolerance.

• Patient and family state understanding of drug therapy.

montelukast sodium

(mon-tih-LOO-kist SOH-dee-um)

Singulair

Pharmacologic class: leukotriene receptor antagonist

Therapeutic class: antiasthmatic

Pregnancy risk category: B

Indications and dosages

▶ **Asthma, seasonal allergic rhinitis.** *Adults and children age 15 and older:* One 10-mg tablet P.O. daily in the evening.
Children ages 6 to 14: Give 5-mg chewable tablet P.O. daily in the evening.
Children ages 2 to 5: Give 4-mg chewable tablet P.O. or one packet (4-mg) oral granules daily in the evening.

▶ **Asthma.** *Children ages 12 to 23 months:* One packet (4-mg) granules P.O. daily in the evening.

▶ **Perennial allergic rhinitis in children.** *Children 6 to 23 months:* One packet (4-mg) granules P.O. daily in the evening.

▶ **Prevention of exercise-induced bronchospasm‡.** *Adults and children age 15 and older:* 10 mg P.O. daily.
Children ages 6 to 14: Give 5 mg P.O. daily.

Contraindications and cautions

• Contraindicated in patients hypersensitive to the drug or any of its components and in patients with acute asthmatic attacks or status asthmaticus.

• Use cautiously and with appropriate monitoring when systemic corticosteroid dosages are reduced.

Lifespan: In children younger than age 6 months, safety and effectiveness haven't been established.

Adverse reactions

CNS: asthenia, dizziness, fatigue, fever, *headache.*
EENT: nasal congestion.
GI: abdominal pain, dyspepsia, infectious gastroenteritis.
GU: pyuria.
Respiratory: cough.
Skin: rash.
Other: dental pain, influenza, trauma.

M

Interactions

Drug-drug. *Phenobarbital, rifampin:* May decrease bioavailability of montelukast by inducing hepatic metabolism. Monitor patient closely for decreased effects.

Effects on lab test results

- May increase ALT and AST levels.

Pharmacokinetics

Absorption: Rapid with an oral bioavailability of 64% in adults without regard to meals.
Distribution: More than 99% bound to plasma proteins.
Metabolism: Extensive, by cytochrome P-450 isoenzymes in GI tract.
Excretion: About 86% in the feces. *Half-life:* 2¾ to 5½ hours.

Route	Onset	Peak	Duration
P.O.			
Chewable	Unknown	2–2½ hr	24 hr
Coated	Unknown	3–4 hr	24 hr
Granules	Unknown	2 hr	24 hr

Action

Chemical effect: Inhibits action of cysteinyl leukotriene$_1$ ($CysLT_1$) receptor by binding with $CysLT_1$. This reduces early- and late-phase bronchoconstriction caused by antigen challenge.
Therapeutic effect: Improves breathing.

Available forms

Granules: 4-mg packet
Tablets (chewable): 4 mg, 5 mg
Tablets (film-coated): 10 mg

NURSING PROCESS

Assessment

- Assess patient's underlying condition before therapy and regularly thereafter to monitor drug effectiveness.
- Monitor patient for adverse reactions and drug interactions.
- Assess patient's and family's knowledge of drug therapy.

Nursing diagnoses

- Impaired gas exchange related to asthma
- Activity intolerance related to asthma
- Deficient knowledge related to drug therapy

Planning and implementation

- Don't abruptly substitute drug for inhaled or oral corticosteroids.
- Drug isn't indicated for patients with acute asthmatic attacks or status asthmaticus. It's also not indicated as monotherapy for managing exercise-induced bronchospasm. Continue rescue drug for acute exacerbations.
- Give oral granules directly in mouth or mixed with a teaspoonful of cold or room-temperature applesauce, carrots, rice, or ice cream. After opening packet, give within 15 minutes. If mixed with food, don't store excess for future use; discard any unused portion.
- Granules aren't intended to be dissolved in liquid other than formula or breast milk. Other liquids may be given afterwards.
- Don't give oral granules with high-fat meals.
- Give drug daily in the evening for asthma or asthma with allergic rhinitis; in the morning, give only for allergic rhinitis.

Patient teaching

- Advise patient not to use drug on an as-needed basis but to take drug daily, even if asymptomatic, and to contact prescriber if asthma isn't well controlled.
- Warn patient not to reduce or stop taking any other prescribed antiasthma drugs without the prescriber's approval.
- Tell parent the oral granules may be given directly into the child's mouth, dissolved in 1 tsp of cold or room temperature baby formula or breast milk, or mixed in a spoonful of applesauce, carrots, rice, or ice cream.
- Warn patient that drug isn't beneficial in acute asthma attacks or in exercise-induced bronchospasm, and advise him to keep appropriate rescue drugs available.
- Advise patient with known aspirin sensitivity to continue not to use aspirin or other NSAIDs.
- Advise patient with phenylketonuria that chewable tablet contains phenylalanine.

Evaluation

- Patient's respiratory signs and symptoms improve.
- Patient can perform normal activities of daily living.
- Patient and family state understanding of drug therapy.

moricizine hydrochloride

(mor-IH-sih-zeen high-droh-KLOR-ighd)
Ethmozine

Pharmacologic class: sodium channel blocker
Therapeutic class: antiarrhythmic
Pregnancy risk category: B

Indications and dosages

▶ **Life-threatening ventricular arrhythmias.** *Adults:* Individualized dosage is based on response and patient tolerance. Begin therapy in hospital. Most patients respond to 600 to 900 mg P.O. daily in divided doses q 8 hours. Increase daily dosage within this range q 3 days by 150 mg until desired effect is achieved.

Adjust-a-dose: For patients with hepatic or renal impairment, give 600 mg or less P.O. daily. Monitor ECG before increasing dosage.

Contraindications and cautions

- Contraindicated in patients hypersensitive to the drug or any of its components, in patients with second- or third-degree AV block or right bundle-branch heart block when linked to left hemiblock (bifascicular block) unless artificial pacemaker is present, and in patients with cardiogenic shock.
- Use cautiously in patients with sick sinus syndrome because drug may cause sinus bradycardia or sinus arrest. Also use cautiously in patients with coronary artery disease and left ventricular dysfunction because these patients may be at risk for sudden death when treated with drug.
- Give cautiously to patients with hepatic or renal impairment.

Lifespan: In pregnant and breast-feeding women use only if benefits outweigh risks to fetus and infant; drug does appear in breast milk. In children, safety and effectiveness haven't been established.

Adverse reactions

CNS: anxiety, asthenia, *dizziness, fatigue, headache,* hypoesthesia, nervousness, paresthesia, sleep disorders.
CV: ***AV block, cardiac death,*** chest pain, ECG abnormalities, ***heart failure,*** palpitations, ***PVCs,*** *supraventricular arrhythmias, ventricular tachycardia.*
EENT: blurred vision.
GI: abdominal pain, diarrhea, dry mouth, dyspepsia, nausea, vomiting.
GU: dysuria, urinary frequency, urine retention.
Musculoskeletal: muscle pain.
Respiratory: dyspnea.
Skin: diaphoresis, rash.
Other: drug-induced fever.

Interactions

Drug-drug. *Cimetidine:* May decrease clearance and increase level of moricizine. Start moricizine therapy at low dosage (not more than 600 mg daily), and monitor therapeutic effect and signs of toxicity closely.
Digoxin, propranolol: May cause additive prolongation of PR interval, but doesn't increase the occurrence of second or third degree heart block. Monitor patient closely; monitor ECG.
Theophylline: May increase clearance and decrease level of theophylline. Monitor level and therapeutic response; adjust theophylline dosage.

Effects on lab test results

None reported.

Pharmacokinetics

Absorption: Using within 30 minutes of a meal delays absorption and lowers peak levels but has no effect on extent.
Distribution: 95% protein-bound.
Metabolism: Significant in first-pass.
Excretion: 50% in feces; 39% in urine. *Half-life:* 1½ to 3½ hours.

Route	Onset	Peak	Duration
P.O.	≤ 2 hr	30 min–2 hr	10–24 hr

Action

Chemical effect: Reduces fast inward current carried by sodium ions across myocardial cell membranes. Stabilizes membranes.
Therapeutic effect: Reduces risk of recurrence of ventricular arrhythmias.

Available forms

Tablets: 200 mg, 250 mg, 300 mg

NURSING PROCESS

Assessment

- Assess patient's condition before therapy and regularly thereafter to monitor drug effectiveness.
- Be alert for adverse reactions and drug interactions.
- Assess patient's and family's knowledge of drug therapy.
- The use of this drug should be reserved for those patients in whom the benefits of treatment outweigh the risks.

Nursing diagnoses

- Decreased cardiac output related to presence of ventricular arrhythmia
- Risk for injury related to drug-induced adverse reactions
- Deficient knowledge related to drug therapy

Planning and implementation

- When substituting this drug for another antiarrhythmic, stop giving previous drug for one or two of drug's half-lives before giving this drug. When stopping or adjusting drug, hospitalize patient with tendency to develop life-threatening arrhythmias after stopping the drug. Start this drug as follows: 6 to 12 hours after last dose of disopyramide; 8 to 12 hours after last dose of mexiletine; 3 to 6 hours after last dose of procainamide; 8 to 12 hours after last dose of propafenone; 6 to 12 hours after last dose of quinidine; 8 to 12 hours after last dose of tocainide.
- Obtain electrolyte levels and correct imbalances before therapy. Hypokalemia, hyperkalemia, and hypomagnesemia may alter effects of drug.

ALERT: Don't confuse Ethmozine with Erythrocin.

Patient teaching

- Tell patient to promptly report adverse reactions.

Evaluation

- Patient regains normal cardiac output with alleviation of ventricular arrhythmia.
- Patient sustains no injury from adverse reactions.
- Patient and family state understanding of drug therapy.

morphine hydrochloride

(MOR-feen high-droh-KLOR-ighd)

M.O.S. ♦, M.O.S.-SR ♦

morphine sulfate

Astramorph PF, Avinza, DepoDur, DMS Concentrate, Duramorph PF, Infumorph 200, Infumorph 500, Kadian, Morphine H.P. ♦, MS Contin, MSIR, MS/L, MS/L Concentrate, OMS Concentrate, Oramorph SR, RMS Uniserts, Roxanol, Roxanol 100, Roxanol T, Statex ♦

morphine tartrate ◇

Pharmacologic class: opioid agonist
Therapeutic class: analgesic
Pregnancy risk category: C
Controlled substance schedule: II

Indications and dosages

▶ **Severe pain.** *Adults:* 5 to 20 mg/70 kg subcutaneously or I.M. q 4 hours, p.r.n. Or 2 to 10 mg/70 kg I.V. q 4 hours, p.r.n. Or 10 to 30 mg P.O. q 4 hours, p.r.n. Or, 10 to 20 mg P.R. q 4 hours, p.r.n. Or 15 to 30 mg of controlled-release tablets P.O. q 8 to 12 hours. Or 5 mg of epidural injection by epidural catheter. Maximum total epidural dose, 10 mg. If adequate pain relief not obtained within 1 hour, give additional doses of 1 to 2 mg at intervals sufficient to assess effectiveness.
Children: 0.1 to 0.2 mg/kg I.M. or subcutaneously q 4 hours, p.r.n. Maximum single dose is 15 mg. Or, 0.05 to 0.1 mg/kg by slow I.V. injection.

▶ **Moderate to severe pain requiring continuous, around-the-clock opioid therapy.** *Adults:* Give loading dose of 15 mg or more by continuous I.V. infusion; then continuous infusion (concentration of 1 mg/ml) of 0.8 to 80 mg/hour. Or individualize dosage of Avinza according to patient's previous drug schedule.
Children: Give 0.025 to 2.6 mg/kg/hour by I.V. infusion.

▶ **Pain following major surgery.** *Adults:* Inject 10 to 15 mg DepoDur (maximum 20 mg) by lumbar epidural administration into lumbar epidural space before surgery or after clamping of umbilical cord during cesarean delivery. Inject undiluted or dilute up to 5 ml total volume with preservative-free normal saline solution. Don't mix with other drugs. Don't give other drugs into epidural space for at least 48 hours.

I.V. administration

- Drug is compatible with most common I.V. solutions.
- For direct injection, dilute 2.5 to 15 mg in 4 or 5 ml of sterile water for injection and give over 4 to 5 minutes.
- For continuous infusion, mix with D_5W to yield 0.1 to 1 mg/ml.

⊗ **Incompatibilities**

Aminophylline, amobarbital, cefepime, chlorothiazide, fluorouracil, haloperidol, heparin sodium, meperidine, pentobarbital, phenobarbital sodium, phenytoin sodium, prochlorperazine, promethazine hydrochloride, sodium bicarbonate, thiopental.

Contraindications and cautions

- Contraindicated in patients hypersensitive to the drug or any of its components and in those with conditions that preclude I.V. administration of opioids (acute bronchial asthma or upper airway obstruction).
- Use cautiously in debilitated patients and in patients with head injury, increased intracranial pressure, seizures, chronic pulmonary disease, prostatic hyperplasia, severe hepatic or renal disease, acute abdominal conditions, hypothyroidism, Addison disease, or urethral stricture.

Lifespan: In pregnant women, use cautiously. In breast-feeding women, wait 2 to 3 hours after last dose before breast-feeding to avoid sedation in infant. In elderly patients, use cautiously.

Adverse reactions

CNS: *clouded sensorium,* dizziness, *euphoria,* nightmares, *sedation,* ***seizures,*** *somnolence.*
CV: ***bradycardia, cardiac arrest,*** flushing, *hypotension,* ***shock.***
GI: constipation, ileus, nausea, vomiting.
GU: urine retention.
Hematologic: ***thrombocytopenia.***
Respiratory: ***respiratory arrest, respiratory depression.***
Skin: pruritus.
Other: *physical dependence.*

Interactions

Drug-drug. *Antihistamines, chloral hydrate, CNS depressants, general anesthetics, glutethimide, hypnotics, MAO inhibitors, methocarbamol, opioid analgesics, sedatives, tranquilizers, tricyclic antidepressants:* May cause respiratory depression, hypotension, profound sedation, or coma. Use cautiously. Reduce morphine dosage, and monitor patient.
Drug-lifestyle. *Alcohol use:* May have additive CNS effects. Also, use with Avinza and Kadian may compromise the extended-release capsule characteristics and cause a life-threatening dose of morphine to be released. Urge patient to avoid using alcohol during drug therapy.

Effects on lab test results

- May increase amylase level.
- May decrease platelet count.

Pharmacokinetics

Absorption: Variable when given P.O.; unknown for other routes.
Distribution: Wide.
Metabolism: Mainly in liver.
Excretion: In urine and bile. *Half-life:* 2 to 3 hours.

Route	Onset	Peak	Duration
P.O.	1 hr	1–2 hr	4–12 hr
I.V.	< 5 min	20 min	4–5 hr
I.M.	10–30 min	30–60 min	4–5 hr
SubQ	10–30 min	50–90 min	4–5 hr
P.R.	20–60 min	20–60 min	4–5 hr
Epidural	15–60 min	15–60 min	24 hr
Intrathecal	15–60 min	Unknown	24 hr

Action

Chemical effect: Binds with opioid receptors in CNS, altering both perception of and emotional response to pain through unknown mechanism.
Therapeutic effect: Relieves pain.

Available forms

morphine hydrochloride ♦
Oral solution ♦: 1 mg/ml, 5 mg/ml, 10 mg/ml, 20 mg/ml, 50 mg/ml
Suppositories ♦: 10 mg, 20 mg, 30 mg
Syrup ♦: 1 mg/ml, 5 mg/ml, 10 mg/ml, 20 mg/ml, 50 mg/ml
Tablets ♦: 10 mg, 20 mg, 40 mg, 60 mg
Tablets (extended-release) ♦: 30 mg, 60 mg

M

morphine sulfate
Capsules: 15 mg, 30 mg
Capsules (extended-release beads) (Avinza): 30 mg, 60 mg, 90 mg, 120 mg
Capsules (extended-release pellets) (Kadian): 20 mg, 30 mg, 50 mg, 60 mg, 80 mg, 100 mg
Injection (with preservative): 1 mg/ml, 2 mg/ml, 4 mg/ml, 5 mg/ml, 8 mg/ml, 10 mg/ml, 15 mg/ml, 25 mg/ml, 50 mg/ml
Injection (without preservative): 0.5 mg/ml, 1 mg/ml, 10 mg/ml, 15 mg/ml, 25 mg/ml, 50 mg/ml
Liposomal injection (preservative-free): 10 mg/ml, 15 mg/1.5 ml, 20 mg/2 ml
Oral solution: 10 mg/5 ml, 20 mg/5 ml
Oral solution (concentrated): 20 mg/ml, 100 mg/5 ml
Soluble tablets: 10 mg, 15 mg, 30 mg
Suppositories: 5 mg, 10 mg, 20 mg, 30 mg
Tablets: 15 mg, 30 mg
Tablets (extended-release): 15 mg, 30 mg, 60 mg, 100 mg, 200 mg
Tablets (sustained-release): 15 mg, 30 mg, 60 mg, 100 mg, 200 mg
morphine tartrate ◇
Injection: 80 mg/ml ◇

NURSING PROCESS

Assessment
- Assess patient's pain before therapy and regularly thereafter to monitor drug effectiveness.
- Drug may worsen or mask gallbladder pain.
- Monitor patient for respiratory depression after administration. When given epidurally, monitor patient for up to 24 hours after injection. Check respiratory rate and depth q 30 to 60 minutes for 24 hours.
- Assess patient for constipation often; adjust GI drugs as needed when increasing morphine dose.
- Be alert for adverse reactions and drug interactions.
- Assess patient's and family's knowledge of drug therapy.

Nursing diagnoses
- Acute pain related to underlying condition
- Ineffective breathing pattern related to drug's depressive effect on respiratory system
- Deficient knowledge related to drug therapy

Planning and implementation
- Preservative-free preparations are available for giving by epidural or intrathecal route.

ALERT: Highly concentrated injections containing 10 or 25 mg/ml are meant for continuous, controlled microinfusion devices. Don't use for I.M., subcutaneous, I.V epidural, or intrathecal individual doses because of the risk of substantial overdose.

- Solutions of various strengths are available as well as concentrated P.O. solutions (20 mg/ml, 100 mg/5 ml). Double-check the orders written against the strength you are giving carefully. Serious events and fatalities may occur from dispensing and using wrong concentrations.
- Don't crush or break extended- or sustained-release tablets.
- For use with gastrostomy tube, immediately give opened Kadian capsule pellets in 10 ml water, swirling them into prewetted gastrostomy tube. Flush with additional water to clear all pellets; don't use in NG tube and don't crush pellets.
- May open controlled-release capsules and sprinkle beads or pellets onto small amount of applesauce for immediate use P.O. Follow with 4 to 8 oz water.
- Store DepoDur in refrigerator. Unopened vials can be stored at room temperature for up to 7 days. After withdrawn from vial, drug can be stored at room temperature for up to 4 hours before use.
- No need to refrigerate rectal suppositories.
- If using S.L., measure solution with tuberculin syringe. Give dose a few drops at a time to maximize S.L. absorption and minimize swallowing.
- In some patients, P.R. and P.O. absorption may not be equivalent.
- Morphine is drug of choice in relieving pain of MI. It may cause transient decrease in blood pressure.
- Keep opioid antagonist and resuscitation equipment available.
- Around-the-clock therapy best manages severe, chronic pain.

ALERT: If respiratory rate is below 12 breaths/minute except in terminal conditions, don't give the dose. Notify prescriber.

- Because constipation is often severe with maintenance dosage, give stool softener or other laxative.

ALERT: Don't confuse morphine with hydromorphone. Don't confuse Avinza with Invanz.

ALERT: Dose of Kadian is not bioequivalent to other controlled-release formulations. Therefore, observe patient carefully for oversedation or inadequate analgesia, and adjust dosage or time interval accordingly.

Patient teaching

- Teach patient use of standardized pain-rating scale to facilitate communication about analgesic effectiveness.

ALERT: Consuming alcoholic beverages or drugs containing alcohol while taking Avinza may cause extended-release coating to fail, releasing a potentially fatal dose of morphine. Warn patient against the use of alcohol in any form, and stress need to read labels on OTC products carefully.

- Warn patient about getting out of bed or walking without assistance. Warn outpatient not to drive or perform other hazardous activities until the drug's CNS effects are known.
- Tell patient to report continued pain and not to increase dose independently.
- Instruct patient to keep opioids locked safely out of reach of children or cognitively impaired individuals.
- Instruct patient not to consume alcohol during therapy.

Evaluation

- Patient states that pain is relieved.
- Patient maintains adequate breathing patterns throughout therapy.
- Patient and family state understanding of drug therapy.

moxifloxacin hydrochloride

(mox-ih-FLOX-uh-sin high-droh-CLOR-ighd)
Avelox, Avelox I.V.

Pharmacologic class: fluoroquinolone
Therapeutic class: antibiotic
Pregnancy risk category: C

Indications and dosages

▶ **Acute bacterial sinusitis caused by *Streptococcus pneumoniae, Haemophilus influenzae,* or *Moraxella catarrhalis.*** *Adults:* 400 mg P.O. or I.V. once daily for 10 days.

▶ **Acute bacterial exacerbation of chronic bronchitis caused by *S. pneumoniae, H. influenzae, H. parainfluenzae, Klebsiella pneumoniae, Staphylococcus aureus,* or *M. catarrhalis.*** *Adults:* 400 mg P.O. or I.V. once daily for 5 days.

▶ **Community-acquired pneumonia caused by multidrug-resistant *S. pneumoniae* (resistance to two or more of the following antibiotics: penicillin, second-generation cephalosporins, macrolides, tetracyclines, trimethoprim and sulfamethoxazole), *Chlamydia pneumoniae, H. influenzae, K. pneumoniae, Mycoplasma pneumoniae, M. catarrhalis,* or *S. aureus.*** *Adults:* 400 mg P.O. or I.V. once daily for 7 to 14 days.

▶ **Uncomplicated skin and skin-structure infections caused by *S. aureus* and *Streptococcus pyogenes.*** *Adults:* 400 mg P.O daily for 7 days.

▶ **Complicated skin and skin structure infections caused by methicillin-susceptible *S. aureus, Escherichia coli, K. pneumoniae,* or *Enterobacter cloacae.*** *Adults:* 400 mg P.O. or I.V. q 24 hours for 7 to 21 days.

▶ **Complicated intra-abdominal infections caused by *E. coli, Bacteroides fragilis, Streptococcus anginosis, Streptococcus constellatus, Enterococcus faecalis, Proteus mirabilis, Clostridium perfringens, Bacteroides thetaiotaomicron, or Peptostreptococcus* species.** *Adults:* 400 mg P.O. or I.V. q 24 hours for 5 to 14 days. Therapy usually begins with the I.V. formulation.

I.V. administration

- If particulate matter is visible, don't use.
- Flush I.V. line with a compatible solution such as D_5W, normal saline solution, or Ringer's lactate solution before and after use.
- Infuse over 60 minutes by direct infusion or through a Y-type IV infusion set. Avoid rapid infusion or bolus injection.
- Switch from I.V. to P.O. form when warranted.

Incompatibilities
Other I.V. drugs or additives.

Contraindications and cautions

- Contraindicated in patients hypersensitive to drug, any of its components, or other fluoroquinolones.
- Use cautiously in patients with known or suspected CNS disorders and in patients with risk factors that may predispose them to seizures or lower the seizure threshold. Use cautiously in

M

patients with prolonged QT interval or uncorrected hypokalemia.

Lifespan: In pregnant women, breast-feeding women, and children, safety and effectiveness haven't been established. In elderly patients, monitor cardiac function carefully, especially with I.V. form.

Adverse reactions

CNS: anxiety, asthenia, confusion, dizziness, headache, insomnia, malaise, nervousness, pain, paresthesia, somnolence, tremor, vertigo.
CV: chest pain, hypertension, palpitations, peripheral edema, ***prolonged QT interval,*** tachycardia.
GI: abdominal pain, anorexia, constipation, diarrhea, dry mouth, dyspepsia, flatulence, GI disorder, glossitis, nausea, oral candidiasis, ***pseudomembranous colitis,*** stomatitis, taste perversion, vomiting.
GU: vaginal candidiasis, vaginitis.
Hematologic: eosinophilia, ***leukopenia, thrombocytopenia, thrombocytosis.***
Hepatic: cholestatic jaundice, liver dysfunction.
Musculoskeletal: arthralgia, back pain, leg pain, myalgia, tendon rupture.
Respiratory: dyspnea.
Skin: phototoxicity, pruritus, rash (maculopapular, purpuric, pustular), sweating.
Other: ***allergic reaction,*** candidiasis, injection site reaction.

Interactions

Drug-drug. *Aluminum hydroxide, aluminum-magnesium hydroxide, calcium carbonate, magnesium hydroxide:* May decrease moxifloxacin effects. Give antacid at least 4 hours before or 8 hours after.
Class IA (procainamide, quinidine) or Class III (amiodarone, sotalol) antiarrhythmics: May enhance adverse CV effects. Avoid use together.
Didanosine, metal cations (such as aluminum, iron, magnesium, zinc), multivitamins: May decrease absorption and lower levels. Give moxifloxacin at least 4 hours before or 8 hours after these drugs.
Drugs known to prolong the QT interval, such as antipsychotics, erythromycin, tricyclic antidepressants: May have an additive effect when combined with these drugs. Avoid use together.
NSAIDs: May increase risk of CNS stimulation and seizures. Don't use together.
Sucralfate: May decrease absorption of moxifloxacin, reducing anti-infective effect. If use together can't be avoided, give at least 6 hours apart.
Warfarin: May enhance anticoagulant effects. Monitor PT and INR closely.
Drug-lifestyle. *Sun exposure:* May cause photosensitivity reactions. Discourage prolonged or unprotected exposure to sunlight or tanning bed use.

Effects on lab test results

- May increase GGT, glucose, amylase, lipid, and LDH levels.
- May increase eosinophil count. May decrease WBC count. May increase or decrease platelet count, PT, and INR.

Pharmacokinetics

Absorption: Good.
Distribution: Wide. About 50% protein-bound.
Metabolism: About 50% to inactive conjugates.
Excretion: About 45% of dose unchanged in urine and feces. *Half-life:* About 12 hours.

Route	Onset	Peak	Duration
P.O., I.V.	Unknown	1–3 hr	24 hr

Action

Chemical effect: Inhibits the enzymes needed for bacterial DNA replication, transcription, repair, and recombination.
Therapeutic effect: Kills susceptible bacteria.

Available forms

Injection (premixed solution): 400 mg
Tablets (film-coated): 400 mg

NURSING PROCESS

Assessment

- Obtain history of patient's condition before therapy, and reassess regularly to monitor drug effectiveness.
- Obtain specimen for culture and sensitivity tests before first dose. Begin therapy pending culture results.
- Monitor patient for hypersensitivity reactions and symptoms of CNS toxicity, including seizures, prolonged QT interval, pseudomembranous colitis, phototoxicity, and tendon rupture.
- Assess patient's and family's knowledge of drug therapy.

Nursing diagnoses

- Risk for infection related to presence of bacteria susceptible to drug
- Risk for injury related to drug-induced adverse reactions
- Deficient knowledge related to drug therapy

Planning and implementation

- Correct hypokalemia before therapy.
- Give with or without food. Give at same time each day to provide consistent absorption.
- Provide plenty of fluids.
- The most common adverse reactions are nausea, vomiting, stomach pain, diarrhea, dizziness, and headache.
- Store drug at controlled room temperature.

Patient teaching

- Instruct patient to take drug once daily, at the same time each day.
- Tell patient to finish the entire course of therapy, even if symptoms resolve.
- Advise the patient to drink plenty of fluids and to take moxifloxacin 6 hours before or 2 hours after antacids, sucralfate, or products containing iron and zinc.
- Tell patient to avoid hazardous activities, such as driving or operating machinery, until the drug's CNS effects are known.
- Instruct patient to contact prescriber if he experiences adverse effects.

Evaluation

- Patient is free from infection after drug therapy.
- Patient sustains no injury as a result of drug-induced adverse reactions.
- Patient and family state understanding of drug therapy.

moxifloxacin hydrochloride ophthalmic solution

(mocks-ih-FLOCKS-ah-sin high-droe-KLOR-ighd off-THAL-mick suh-LOO-shun)

Vigamox

Pharmacologic class: fluoroquinolone
Therapeutic class: antibiotic
Pregnancy risk category: C

Indications and dosages

▶ **Bacterial conjunctivitis.** *Adults and children age 1 and older:* 1 drop into affected eye t.i.d. for 7 days.

Contraindications and cautions

- Contraindicated in patients hypersensitive to the drug, any of its components, or other fluoroquinolones. Contraindicated in patients with epithelial herpes simplex keratitis, vaccinia, varicella, mycobacterial infections of the eye, fungal diseases of the ocular structure, or use of steroid combinations after uncomplicated removal of a corneal foreign body.

Lifespan: In pregnant women, use only when benefits of therapy outweigh risks to the fetus. In breast-feeding women, use cautiously because it's unknown if the drug appears in breast milk. In children younger than age 1, don't use drug.

Adverse reactions

EENT: conjunctivitis; dry eyes; increased lacrimation; keratitis; ocular hyperemia; ocular discomfort, pain, and pruritus; otitis media; pharyngitis; reduced visual acuity; rhinitis; subconjunctival hemorrhage.
Respiratory: increased cough.
Skin: rash.
Other: fever, infection.

Interactions

None reported.

Effects on lab test results

None reported.

Pharmacokinetics

Absorption: Local.
Distribution: Local tissues and plasma 1,000 to 1,600 times less than oral doses.
Metabolism: Unknown.
Excretion: In urine and bile. *Half-life:* 13 hours.

Route	Onset	Peak	Duration
Ocular	Immediate	Unknown	Unknown

Action

Chemical effect: Inhibits DNA gyrase and topoisomerase IV, preventing cell replication, transcription, repair of bacterial DNA, and cell division.

M

Therapeutic effect: Kills susceptible bacteria causing infection.

Available forms

Solution: 0.5%

NURSING PROCESS

Assessment

- Assess patient's allergy history before therapy.
- Monitor patient for superinfection, particularly with repeated use.
- Monitor patient for adverse reactions.
- Assess patient's and family's knowledge of drug therapy.

Nursing diagnoses

- Risk for infection related to presence of bacteria susceptible to drug
- Disturbed visual sensory perception related to adverse effects of the drug
- Deficient knowledge related to drug therapy

Planning and implementation

- Don't inject solution subconjunctivally, or into the eye's anterior chamber.
- Drug has caused serious hypersensitivity reactions; if patient has an allergic reaction, stop giving the drug and treat symptoms.

Patient teaching

- Tell patient to stop taking the drug and immediately seek medical treatment if he develops an allergic reaction (itching, rash, swelling of the face or throat, or difficulty breathing).
- Tell patient not to wear contact lenses during therapy.
- Instruct patient not to touch dropper tip to anything, including eyes and fingers.

Evaluation

- Patient is free from infection after drug therapy.
- Patient doesn't experience adverse drug effects.
- Patient and family state understanding of drug therapy.

muromonab-CD3

(myoo-roh-MOH-nab see dee three)

Orthoclone OKT*3

Pharmacologic class: monoclonal antibody
Therapeutic class: immunosuppressive
Pregnancy risk category: C

Indications and dosages

▶ **Acute allograft rejection in heart, liver, or kidney transplant.** *Adults:* 5 mg I.V. daily for 10 to 14 days.
Children: Initially, 2.5 mg/day (if 30 kg or less) or 5 mg/day (if more than 30 kg) I.V. as a single bolus over less than 1 minute for 10 to 14 days. Increase daily dosage in 2.5 mg increments to decrease CD3-positive cells.

I.V. administration

- Don't give by infusion.
- Draw solution into syringe through low–protein-binding 0.2- or 0.22-micron filter. Discard filter and attach needle for bolus injection.
- Give bolus over less than 1 minute.
- Store drug in the refrigerator at 2° to 8° C (36° to 46° F). Do not freeze.

⊗ **Incompatibilities**
Other I.V. drugs.

Contraindications and cautions

- Contraindicated in patients hypersensitive to the drug or to other products of murine origin. Also contraindicated in patients who have antimouse antibody titers of 1:1,000 or more; who have fluid overload, as evidenced by chest X-ray or weight gain greater than 3% in the week before therapy; and who have history of or predisposition to seizures.

Lifespan: In pregnant and breast-feeding women, drug is contraindicated. In children, safety and effectiveness haven't been established.

Adverse reactions

CNS: *asthenia,* confusion, depression, dizziness, fatigue, *fever, headache,* lethargy, malaise, ***meningitis,*** nervousness, ***seizures,*** somnolence, *tremor.*
CV: ***arrhythmia, bradycardia,*** chest pain, edema, hypertension, hypotension, tachycardia, ***vascular occlusion,*** vasodilation.

EENT: photophobia, tinnitus.
GI: abdominal pain, anorexia, *diarrhea,* GI pain, *nausea, vomiting.*
GU: ***renal dysfunction.***
Hematologic: anemia, ***leukocytosis, leukopenia, thrombocytopenia.***
Musculoskeletal: arthralgia, myalgia.
Respiratory: ***acute respiratory distress syndrome,*** *dyspnea,* hyperventilation, ***hypoxia,*** pneumonia, ***pulmonary edema,*** respiratory congestion, wheezing.
Skin: diaphoresis, pruritus, *rash.*
Other: chills, ***cytokine release syndrome, hypersensitivity reactions,*** pain in trunk area.

Interactions

Drug-drug. *Immunosuppressants:* May increase risk of infection. Monitor patient closely.
Indomethacin: May increase muromonab-CD3 levels with CNS effects, including encephalopathy. Monitor patient closely.
Live-virus vaccines: May increase replication and effects of vaccine. Postpone vaccination when possible, and consult prescriber.

Effects on lab test results

- May increase BUN and creatinine levels. May decrease hemoglobin level and hematocrit.
- May decrease platelet count. May increase or decrease WBC count.

Pharmacokinetics

Absorption: Given I.V.
Distribution: Unknown.
Metabolism: Unknown.
Excretion: Unknown. *Half-life:* Unknown.

Route	Onset	Peak	Duration
I.V.	Immediately	Unknown	1 wk after therapy

Action

Chemical effect: Reacts in T-lymphocyte membrane with CD3 needed for antigen recognition and depletes blood of CD3-positive T cells.
Therapeutic effect: Halts acute allograft rejection in kidney transplantation.

Available forms

Injection: 1 mg/ml in 5-ml ampules

NURSING PROCESS

Assessment

- Assess patient's condition before therapy and regularly thereafter to monitor drug effectiveness.
- Obtain chest X-ray within 24 hours before drug therapy.
- Assess patient for signs of fluid overload before therapy.
- Be alert for adverse reactions and drug interactions.
- If patient has an adverse GI reaction, monitor his hydration.
- Assess patient's and family's knowledge of drug therapy.

Nursing diagnoses

- Risk for injury related to presence of acute allograft rejection
- Risk for deficient fluid volume related to drug-induced adverse GI reactions
- Deficient knowledge related to drug therapy

Planning and implementation

- Begin therapy in facility equipped and staffed for cardiopulmonary resuscitation where patient can be closely monitored.
- Most adverse reactions develop within 30 minutes to 6 hours after first dose.

ALERT: Give antipyretic before giving drug to lower risk of expected pyrexia and chills. It is recommended that methylprednisolone sodium succinate 8 mg/kg be administered I.V. 1 to 4 hours before initial dose of muromonab-CD3 to reduce the risk for and severity of cytokine release syndrome.

- If second course of therapy is attempted, patient may develop antibodies to drug that can lead to loss of effectiveness and more severe adverse reactions; use for one course of therapy only.

Patient teaching

- Inform patient of expected adverse reactions, and reassure him that they will lessen as therapy progresses.

Evaluation

- Patient shows no signs of organ rejection.
- Patient maintains adequate hydration.
- Patient and family state understanding of drug therapy.

M

mycophenolate mofetil

(migh-koh-FEN-oh-layt MOH-feh-til)
CellCept

mycophenolate mofetil hydrochloride

CellCept Intravenous

Pharmacologic class: mycophenolic acid derivative
Therapeutic class: immunosuppressant
Pregnancy risk category: C

Indications and dosages

▶ **Prevention of organ rejection in patients receiving allogenic renal transplant.** *Adults:* 1 g I.V. infused over 2 hours b.i.d. with cyclosporine and corticosteroids. Begin I.V. infusion within 24 hours after transplantation. For oral use, give 1 g P.O. b.i.d. as soon as possible after surgery.
Children age 1 and older: 600 mg/m^2 oral suspension P.O. b.i.d. up to a maximum daily dosage of 2 g/10 ml. Or give child with 1.25 m^2 to 1.5 m^2 body surface area 750 mg capsules P.O. b.i.d. Give child with a greater than 1.5 m^2 body surface area 1 g P.O. tablets or capsules b.i.d. For oral use, give as soon as possible after surgery.
Adjust-a-dose: For patients with renal impairment, if GFR is less than 25 ml/minute outside the immediate post-transplant period, avoid doses above 1 g b.i.d. If neutropenia develops, interrupt or reduce dose.

▶ **Prevention of organ rejection in patients receiving allogenic cardiac transplant.** *Adults:* 1.5 g P.O. or I.V. b.i.d. over no less than 2 hours, with cyclosporine and corticosteroids.

▶ **Prevention of organ rejection in patients receiving allogenic hepatic transplants.** *Adults:* 1 g I.V. b.i.d. over no less than 2 hours or 1.5 g P.O. b.i.d., with cyclosporine and corticosteroids.
Adjust-a-dose: If neutropenia develops, interrupt or reduce dose.

I.V. administration

- Avoid direct contact with solution.
- Reconstitute under aseptic conditions.
- Reconstitute the contents of each CellCept Intravenous vial with 14 ml of D_5W. Use two vials to prepare a 1-g dose and 3 vials for a 1.5-g dose. Gently shake the vial to dissolve drug.
- For a 1-g dose, dilute 2 vials further into 140 ml of D_5W; for a 1.5-g dose, dilute three vials further into 210 ml of 5% dextrose injection. The final concentration of both solutions is 6 mg/ml.
- Never give drug by rapid or bolus I.V. injection. Give infusion over at least 2 hours.
- Use within 4 hours of reconstitution and dilution.

⊗ Incompatibilities
- Other I.V. solutions.

Contraindications and cautions

- Contraindicated in patients hypersensitive to the drug or any of its components.
- Use cautiously in patients with GI disorders.

Lifespan: In pregnant and breast-feeding women, use only when benefits outweigh risks to fetus and infant. In children, safety and effectiveness for cardiac and hepatic transplantation haven't been established.

Adverse reactions

CNS: asthenia, dizziness, fever, headache, insomnia, pain, tremor.
CV: *chest pain, edema, hypertension,* peripheral edema, tachycardia.
EENT: pharyngitis.
GI: abdominal pain, constipation, diarrhea, dyspepsia, **HEMORRHAGE,** nausea, oral candidiasis, vomiting.
GU: hematuria, ***kidney tubular necrosis,*** UTI.
Hematologic: anemia, hypochromic anemia, leukocytosis, ***leukopenia,*** **THROMBOCYTOPENIA.**
Metabolic: *hypercholesteremia, hyperglycemia,* ***hyperkalemia,*** *hypokalemia, hypophosphatemia.*
Musculoskeletal: *back pain.*
Respiratory: bronchitis, *cough, dyspnea,* infection, pneumonia.
Skin: *acne,* rash.
Other: infection, ***sepsis.***

Interactions

Drug-drug. *Acyclovir, ganciclovir, other drugs known to undergo tubular secretion:* May increase risk of toxicity for both drugs. Monitor patient closely.

Antacids with magnesium and aluminum hydroxides: May decrease mycophenolate mofetil absorption. Separate doses.
Azathioprine: Hasn't been studied. Avoid use together.
Cholestyramine: May interfere with enterohepatic recirculation, reducing mycophenolate bioavailability. Don't give together.
Hormonal contraceptives: May reduce effectiveness of hormonal contraceptives. Advise patient to use barrier birth control methods.

Effects on lab test results

- May increase cholesterol and glucose levels. May decrease phosphorus and hemoglobin levels and hematocrit. May increase or decrease potassium level.
- May decrease platelet count. May increase or decrease WBC count.

Pharmacokinetics

Absorption: Good.
Distribution: 97% protein-bound.
Metabolism: Complete, to mycophenolic acid.
Excretion: Mainly in urine, with small amount in feces. *Half-life:* About 18 hours.

Route	Onset	Peak	Duration
P.O.	Unknown	Unknown	Unknown
I.V.	Unknown	Unknown	10–17 hr

Action

Chemical effect: Inhibits proliferative responses of T- and B-lymphocytes, suppresses antibody formation by B-lymphocytes, and may inhibit recruitment of leukocytes into sites of inflammation and graft rejection.
Therapeutic effect: Prevents organ rejection.

Available forms

mycophenolate mofetil
Capsules: 250 mg
Powder for oral suspension (contains aspartame): 200 mg/ml
Tablets: 500 mg
mycophenolate mofetil hydrochloride
Injection: 500 mg/vial

NURSING PROCESS

Assessment

- Obtain history of patient's kidney transplant.
- Monitor CBC regularly.
- Be alert for adverse reactions and drug interactions.
- Assess patient's and family's knowledge of drug therapy.

Nursing diagnoses

- Ineffective health maintenance related to need for kidney transplant
- Risk for infection related to drug-induced immunosuppression
- Deficient knowledge related to drug therapy

Planning and implementation

- Administer drug under the supervision of a physician experienced in immunosuppressive therapy and management of renal, hepatic, or cardiac transplant patients.
- Give drug on an empty stomach.

ALERT: Because of risk of teratogenic effects, don't open or crush capsules. Avoid inhaling powder in capsules or letting it contact skin or mucous membranes. If it does, wash skin thoroughly with soap and water and rinse eyes with plain water.

- If patient develops neutropenia, notify prescriber.

Patient teaching

- Warn patient not to open or crush capsule but to swallow it whole on an empty stomach.
- Stress importance of not interrupting therapy without consulting prescriber.
- Tell woman to do a pregnancy test 1 week before therapy. Tell her to use two forms of contraception simultaneously unless abstinent and to use effective contraception until at least 6 weeks after therapy ends, even if she has a history of infertility (unless she has had a hysterectomy). If patient becomes pregnant, tell her to immediately contact her prescriber.

Evaluation

- Patient shows no signs and symptoms of organ rejection.
- Neutropenia doesn't develop.
- Patient and family state understanding of drug therapy.

M

nabilone
(NAH-bi-lohn)
Cesamet

Pharmacologic class: cannabinoid
Therapeutic class: antiemetic
Pregnancy risk category: C
Controlled substance schedule: II

Indications and dosages

▶ **Chemotherapy-induced nausea and vomiting unresponsive to other antiemetic therapy.** *Adults:* Usually 1 or 2 mg P.O. b.i.d. Give first dose 1 to 3 hours before chemotherapy starts and then b.i.d. to t.i.d. throughout the cycle. If needed, start with 1- or 2-mg dose the night before chemotherapy starts and continue 48 hours after the cycle ends. Maximum dosage is 6 mg daily, divided and given t.i.d.

Contraindications and cautions

• Contraindicated in patients hypersensitive to cannabinoids.
• Use cautiously in patients taking highly protein-bound drugs; patients taking sedatives, hypnotics, or other psychoactive drugs; and patients with hypertension, heart disease, hepatic or renal impairment, or current or previous mental illness or substance abuse.
Lifespan: In pregnant patients, use only if potential benefit justifies risk to fetus. Breastfeeding isn't recommended during treatment with nabilone. In children, safety and efficacy aren't known; use cautiously because of drug's psychoactive effects. In elderly patients, use cautiously because of drug's effects on heart rate and blood pressure.

Adverse reactions

CNS: anorexia, asthenia, *ataxia,* depersonalization, *depression, difficulty concentrating,* disorientation, *drowsiness,* dysphoria, *euphoria,* headache, *sleep disturbance, vertigo.*
CV: hypotension, orthostatic hypotension, tachycardia.
EENT: *visual disturbance.*
GI: *dry mouth,* nausea, thirst.
Metabolic: increased appetite.

Interactions

Drug-drug. *Anticholinergics, sympathomimetics, tricyclic antidepressants:* May increase hypertension, tachycardia, and drowsiness. Avoid use together if possible.
CNS depressants: May increase CNS depression. Use with extreme caution, and monitor patient carefully.
Highly protein-bound drugs: May be displaced by nabilone. Monitor patient and drug levels, as needed. Dosages may need adjustment.
Drug-lifestyle. *Alcohol use:* May increase CNS depression. Tell patient to avoid alcohol.
Marijuana: May cause additive effects. Discourage use.

Effects on lab test results

None reported.

Pharmacokinetics

Absorption: Complete in the GI tract.
Distribution: Rapid. Highly protein-bound.
Metabolism: Extensive in the liver through multiple cytochrome P-450 pathways. Several metabolites are formed.
Excretion: Mainly in feces via the biliary tract, less by the kidneys. *Half-life:* 2 hours for drug; 35 hours for metabolites.

Route	Onset	Peak	Duration
P.O.	Rapid	2 hr	Unknown

Action

Chemical effect: Drug probably exerts antiemetic effects by interacting with cannabinoid receptors in the CNS.
Therapeutic effect: Relieves chemotherapy-induced nausea and vomiting.

Available forms

Capsules: 1 mg

NURSING PROCESS

Assessment

• Obtain a detailed health history before treatment starts to rule out mental illness and substance abuse.

• Monitor drug's effectiveness by assessing patient for nausea and vomiting. Drug effects may persist for days after therapy ends.
• Be alert for adverse reactions and drug interactions.
• Monitor patient for physical or psychological dependence. Drug has high potential for abuse.
• Check supine and standing pulse and blood pressure before and periodically during treatment.
• Monitor patient's hydration, weight, and nutrition regularly.
• Assess patient's and family's knowledge of drug therapy.

Nursing diagnoses

• Risk for deficient fluid volume related to nausea and vomiting from chemotherapy
• Disturbed thought processes related to drug-induced adverse CNS reactions
• Deficient knowledge related to drug therapy

Planning and implementation

• Give drug only to patients who haven't responded satisfactorily to other antiemetics.
• Give drug 1 to 3 hours before chemotherapy starts and then 2 to 3 times daily throughout the cycle. Continue for up to 48 hours post-treatment.
• Make sure patient will remain under the supervision of a responsible adult during treatment.
• When stopping drug, monitor patient for evidence of withdrawal, including mental distress, insomnia, and autonomic hyperactivity (sweating, rhinorrhea, loose stools, hiccups). Psychiatric reactions may persist up to 72 hours after treatment stops.
• In case of overdose, if patient is psychotic, keep the environment quiet and offer reassurance as needed. Monitor vital signs closely; watch especially for hypotension, orthostatic hypotension, hypertension, and tachycardia. Activated charcoal may decrease systemic absorption. Protect patient's airway, and maintain ventilation, perfusion, and circulation. Treatment is symptomatic and supportive.

Patient teaching

• Tell patient that drug commonly causes dizziness, euphoria, disorientation, and drowsiness. Explain that depression, hallucinations, and psychosis are also possible.
• Stress that patient should remain under the supervision of a responsible adult, especially when treatment starts or dosage changes, because of drug's psychoactive effects.
• Advise patient to rise slowly from a reclining position and to sit with his feet on the floor before standing until drug's effects are known.
• Urge patient to avoid alcohol, sedatives, and hypnotics because of the increased risk of adverse effects.
• Caution patient to avoid driving and other hazardous activities during treatment.
• Explain that drug has a high abuse potential and should be used only as prescribed.

Evaluation

• Patient maintains adequate hydration.
• Patient regains normal thought processes after effects of drug therapy have dissipated.
• Patient and family state understanding of drug therapy.

nabumetone

(nuh-BYOO-meh-tohn)

Apo-Nabumetone ♦, Relafen

Pharmacologic class: NSAID
Therapeutic class: anti-inflammatory, analgesic, antipyretic
Pregnancy risk category: C; D (third trimester)

Indications and dosages

▶ **Rheumatoid arthritis, osteoarthritis.** *Adults:* Initially, 1,000 mg P.O. daily as single dose or in divided doses b.i.d. Maximum, 2,000 mg daily.

Contraindications and cautions

• Contraindicated in patients hypersensitive to the drug or any of its components and in patients with history of aspirin- or NSAID-induced asthma, urticaria, or other allergic reactions.
• Use cautiously in patients with renal or hepatic impairment, peptic ulcer disease, heart failure, hypertension, or other conditions that may predispose patient to fluid retention.
Lifespan: In pregnant and breast-feeding women, only use when benefits outweigh risks to fetus and infant. In children, safety and effec-

tiveness haven't been established. In the elderly, use cautiously because of possible impaired excretion.

Adverse reactions

CNS: *dizziness,* fatigue, *headache,* insomnia, nervousness, somnolence.
CV: *edema,* vasculitis.
EENT: tinnitus.
GI: abdominal pain, ***bleeding,*** constipation, diarrhea, dry mouth, dyspepsia, flatulence, gastritis, nausea, stomatitis, ulceration, vomiting.
Respiratory: dyspnea, pneumonitis.
Skin: increased sweating, *pruritus, rash.*

Interactions

Drug-drug. *Diuretics:* May decrease diuretic effectiveness. Monitor patient for effect.
Drugs highly bound to proteins (such as warfarin): May increase risk of adverse effects from displacement of drug by nabumetone. Use together cautiously; monitor patient for adverse effects.
Drug-herb. *Dong quai, feverfew, garlic, ginger, horse chestnut, red clover:* May increase risk of bleeding. Discourage use together.
St. John's wort: May increase risk of photosensitivity. Advise patient to avoid unprotected or prolonged exposure to sunlight.
Drug-food. *Any food:* May increase absorption rate. Give together.
Drug-lifestyle. *Alcohol use:* May increase risk of additive GI toxicity. Discourage use together.

Effects on lab test results

None reported.

Pharmacokinetics

Absorption: Good. Taking with food increases absorption rate and peak levels of principal metabolite but doesn't change total amount absorbed.
Distribution: More than 99% of metabolite is protein-bound.
Metabolism: To inactive metabolites in liver.
Excretion: Metabolites mainly in urine; about 9% in feces. *Half-life:* About 24 hours.

Route	Onset	Peak	Duration
P.O.	Unknown	2–4 hr	Unknown

Action

Chemical effect: Unknown; may inhibit prostaglandin synthesis.
Therapeutic effect: Relieves pain.

Available forms

Tablets: 500 mg, 750 mg

NURSING PROCESS

Assessment

- Assess patient's arthritis before starting therapy and regularly thereafter to monitor drug effectiveness.
- During long-term therapy, periodically monitor renal and liver function, CBC, and hematocrit; assess patient for evidence of GI bleeding.
- Watch for fluid retention, especially in a patient with heart failure and hypertension.
- Be alert for adverse reactions and drug interactions.
- Assess patient's and family's knowledge of drug therapy.

Nursing diagnoses

- Chronic pain related to arthritic condition
- Impaired tissue integrity related to adverse drug effect on GI mucosa
- Deficient knowledge related to drug therapy

Planning and implementation

- Give drug with food to increase absorption rate.
- Notify prescriber about adverse reactions.

ALERT: Don't confuse Relafen with Rifadin.

Patient teaching

- Instruct patient to take drug with food, milk, or antacids for best absorption.
- Advise patient to limit alcohol intake because of additive GI toxicity.
- Teach patient to recognize and report signs and symptoms of GI bleeding.

Evaluation

- Patient is free from pain.
- Patient's GI tissue integrity is maintained throughout drug therapy.
- Patient and family state understanding of drug therapy.

nadolol

(nay-DOH-lol)

Apo-Nadol ♦, Corgard

Pharmacologic class: nonselective beta blocker
Therapeutic class: antihypertensive, antianginal
Pregnancy risk category: C

Indications and dosages

▶ **Angina pectoris.** *Adults:* Initially, 40 mg P.O. once daily. Increase in 40- to 80-mg increments q 3 to 7 days until optimum response occurs. Usual maintenance dosage is 40 or 80 mg daily; a maximum dose of 160 or 240 mg may be needed.

▶ **Hypertension.** *Adults:* Initially, 20 to 40 mg P.O. once daily. Increase by 40- to 80-mg increments q 2 to 14 days until optimum response occurs. Usual maintenance dosage is 40 or 80 mg daily; doses up to 240 or 320 mg may be needed.

Adjust-a-dose: In patients with renal impairment, if creatinine clearance is 31 to 50 ml/minute, give q 24 to 36 hours; if 10 to 30 ml/minute, give q 24 to 48 hours; if less than 10 ml/minute, give q 40 to 60 hours.

▶ **Arrhythmias‡.** *Adults:* 60 to 160 mg P.O. daily or in divided doses.

▶ **To prevent vascular headaches‡.** *Adults:* 20 to 40 mg P.O. daily; gradually increase to 120 mg daily, if needed.

Contraindications and cautions

- Contraindicated in patients with bronchial asthma, sinus bradycardia, greater than first-degree heart block, and cardiogenic shock.
- Use cautiously in patients undergoing major surgery involving general anesthesia and in those with heart failure, chronic bronchitis, emphysema, renal or hepatic impairment, or diabetes.

Lifespan: In pregnant women, use only if benefits outweigh risks to the fetus. In breast-feeding women, don't use because it's unknown if drug appears in breast milk. In children, safety and effectiveness haven't been established.

Adverse reactions

CNS: dizziness, fatigue, fever, lethargy.
CV: ***bradycardia, heart failure,*** *hypotension,* peripheral vascular disease.
GI: constipation, diarrhea, nausea, vomiting.
Respiratory: *increased airway resistance.*

Interactions

Drug-drug. *Antihypertensives:* May enhance antihypertensive effect. Monitor patient's blood pressure closely.
Digoxin, diltiazem: May cause excessive bradycardia and affect AV conduction. Use together cautiously; monitor ECG.
Epinephrine: May cause an initial hypertensive episode followed by bradycardia. Stop beta blocker 3 days before anticipated epinephrine use. Monitor patient closely.
Insulin: May mask symptoms of hypoglycemia as a result of beta blockade (such as tachycardia). Use cautiously in patients with diabetes.
I.V. lidocaine: May reduce hepatic metabolism of lidocaine, increasing the risk of toxicity. Give bolus doses of lidocaine at a slower rate, and monitor lidocaine level closely.
NSAIDs: May decrease antihypertensive effect. Monitor blood pressure and adjust dosage.
Oral antidiabetics: May alter dosage requirements in diabetic patients. Monitor glucose level.
Prazosin: May increase the risk of orthostatic hypotension early in use together. Teach patient to stand slowly until effects are known.
Verapamil: May increase the effects of both drugs. Monitor cardiac function closely for excessive bradycardia and decrease dosage.

Effects on lab test results

None reported.

Pharmacokinetics

Absorption: 30% to 40% without regard to meals.
Distribution: Distributed throughout body. About 30% protein-bound.
Metabolism: None.
Excretion: Most excreted unchanged in urine; remainder in feces. *Half-life:* About 10 to 24 hours.

Route	Onset	Peak	Duration
P.O.	Unknown	2–4 hr	24 hr

N

Action

Chemical effect: Reduces cardiac oxygen demand by blocking catecholamine-induced increases in heart rate, blood pressure, and myocardial contraction. Depresses renin secretion.
Therapeutic effect: Lowers blood pressure, relieves and prevents recurrence of angina.

Available forms

Tablets: 20 mg, 40 mg, 80 mg, 120 mg, 160 mg

NURSING PROCESS

Assessment

- Assess patient's condition before starting therapy and regularly thereafter to monitor drug effectiveness.
- Drug masks common signs of shock, hyperthyroidism, and hypoglycemia.
- Be alert for adverse reactions and drug interactions.
- Assess patient's and family's knowledge of drug therapy.

Nursing diagnoses

- Risk for injury related to presence of hypertension
- Acute pain related to angina
- Deficient knowledge related to drug therapy

Planning and implementation

ALERT: Always check apical pulse before giving drug. If slower than 60 beats/minute, don't give the dose. Notify prescriber.
- If patient develops severe hypotension, give vasopressor.

ALERT: Reduce dosage gradually over 1 to 2 weeks. Abruptly stopping the drug can worsen angina and MI.
ALERT: Don't confuse Corgard with Coreg.

Patient teaching
- Explain importance of taking drug as prescribed, even when feeling well.
- Warn patient not to abruptly stop taking the drug.

Evaluation

- Patient's blood pressure is normal.
- Patient reports reduced angina.
- Patient and family state understanding of drug therapy.

nafcillin sodium

(naf-SIL-in SOH-dee-um)

Pharmacologic class: penicillinase-resistant penicillin
Therapeutic class: antibiotic
Pregnancy risk category: B

Indications and dosages

▶ **Systemic infections caused by susceptible organisms (including methicillin-sensitive *Staphylococcus aureus*).** *Adults and children who weigh 40 kg (88 lb) or more:* 500 mg to 1 g I.V. q 4 hours depending on severity of the infection.
Infants and children older than age 1 month: 50 to 200 mg/kg I.V. or I.M. daily in equally divided doses q 4 to 6 hours depending severity of the infection.
Neonates younger than age 7 days who weigh less than 2 kg (4.4 lb): 25 mg/kg I.V. or I.M. q 12 hours.
Neonates younger than age 7 days who weigh more than 2 kg: 25 mg/kg I.V. or I.M. q 8 hours.
Neonates ages 1 to 4 weeks who weigh less than 2 kg: 25 mg/kg I.V. or I.M. q 8 hours. Or 25 mg/kg q 12 hours for those who weigh less than 1.2 kg (2.6 lb).
Neonates ages 1 to 4 weeks who weigh more than 2 kg: 25 to 35 mg/kg I.V. or I.M. q 6 hours.

▶ **Meningitis.** *Adults and children who weigh 40 kg or more:* 100 to 200 mg/kg I.V. daily in divided doses q 4 to 6 hours.
Neonates younger than age 7 days who weigh more than 2 kg: 25 mg/kg I.V. or I.M. q 8 hours.
Neonates ages 1 to 4 weeks who weigh more than 2 kg: 35 mg/kg I.V. or I.M. q 6 hours.

▶ **Acute or chronic osteomyelitis caused by susceptible organism.** *Adults:* 1 to 2 g I.V. q 4 hours.

▶ **Native valve endocarditis caused by susceptible organisms.** *Adults and children who weigh 40 kg or more:* 2 g I.V. q 4 hours for 4 to 6 weeks, with gentamicin for the first 3 to 5 days.
Children: 200 mg/kg I.V. daily in equally divided doses q 4 to 6 hours for 6 weeks, with gentamicin for the first 3 to 5 days.

I.V. administration

- After thawing at room temperature or under refrigeration, check and discard container with leaks, cloudiness, or precipitate.
- Give by intermittent I.V. infusion over at least 30 to 60 minutes.
- Give by intermittent I.V. injection, slowly giving the properly diluted nafcillin sodium over 5 to 10 minutes.
- Change I.V. site q 48 hours to reduce the risk of vein irritation.

⊗ Incompatibilities

Aminoglycosides, aminophylline, ascorbic acid, aztreonam, bleomycin, cytarabine, diltiazem, droperidol, gentamicin, hydrocortisone sodium succinate, insulin, labetalol, meperidine, methylprednisolone sodium succinate, midazolam, nalbuphine, pentazocine lactate, promazine, vancomycin, verapamil hydrochloride, vitamin B complex with C.

Contraindications and cautions

- Contraindicated in patients hypersensitive to the drug or other penicillins.
- Use cautiously in patients with GI distress and those with other drug allergies, especially to cephalosporins.

Lifespan: In pregnant women, use cautiously. In breast-feeding women, use cautiously because penicillins appear in breast milk.

Adverse reactions

CV: thrombophlebitis.
GI: *nausea,* vomiting, diarrhea.
Hematologic: ***transient leukopenia, neutropenia, granulocytopenia, thrombocytopenia.***
Other: ***anaphylaxis,*** hypersensitivity reactions, vein irritation.

Interactions

Drug-drug. *Aminoglycosides:* May have synergistic effect; may use together for this effect. Monitor patient closely.
Cyclosporine: May cause subtherapeutic cyclosporine level. Monitor level.
Probenecid: May increase level of nafcillin. Probenecid may be used for this purpose.
Rifampin: May cause dose-dependent antagonism. Monitor patient closely.
Warfarin: May increase risk of bleeding when used with I.V. nafcillin. Monitor patient for bleeding.

Effects on lab test results

- May decrease neutrophil, granulocyte, WBC, and platelet counts.
- May falsely elevate urine or serum proteins or cause false-positive results in certain tests for them.

Pharmacokinetics

Absorption: Administered I.V. or I.M.
Distribution: Wide. CSF penetration is poor but enhanced by meningeal inflammation. 70% to 90% protein-bound.
Metabolism: Metabolized primarily in liver; undergoes enterohepatic circulation.
Excretion: Excreted primarily in bile; 25% to 30% is excreted in urine unchanged. *Half-life:* 30 to 90 minutes.

Route	Onset	Peak	Duration
I.V.	Immediate	Immediate	Unknown
I.M.	Unknown	30–60 min	Unknown

Action

Chemical effect: Inhibits cell wall synthesis during microorganism multiplication; resists bacteria-produced penicillinases.
Therapeutic effect: Kills susceptible bacteria, such as penicillinase-producing staphylococci, and some gram-positive aerobic and anaerobic bacilli.

Available forms

Injection: 1 g, 2 g

NURSING PROCESS

Assessment

- Assess patient's infection before starting therapy and regularly thereafter to monitor the drug's effectiveness.
- Before giving drug, ask patient about allergic reactions to penicillins and cephalosporins. Remember that allergic reactions may occur even in patients with no history of penicillin allergy.
- Obtain specimen for culture and sensitivity tests before giving first dose. Begin therapy pending results.

ALERT: Monitor WBC counts twice weekly in patients receiving nafcillin for longer than 2 weeks. Neutropenia commonly occurs in the third week.

- Be alert for adverse reactions and drug interactions.

N

• If patient has an adverse GI reaction, monitor his hydration.
• Assess patient's and family's knowledge of drug therapy.

Nursing diagnoses

• Risk for infection related to susceptible bacteria
• Risk for deficient fluid volume related to drug-induced adverse GI reactions
• Deficient knowledge related to drug therapy

Planning and implementation

• Give drug at least 1 hour before bacteriostatic antibiotics.
• If urinalysis is abnormal, notify prescriber because this may indicate drug-induced interstitial nephritis.

Patient teaching

• Tell patient to notify prescriber if rash, fever, or chills develop.
• Instruct patient to report pain, burning, edema, or redness at I.V. site.

Evaluation

• Patient is free from infection.
• Patient maintains adequate hydration throughout drug therapy.
• Patient and family state understanding of drug therapy.

nalbuphine hydrochloride

(NAL-byoo-feen high-droh-KLOR-ighd)
Nubain

Pharmacologic class: synthetic opioid partial agonist/antagonist
Therapeutic class: analgesic, adjunct to anesthesia
Pregnancy risk category: B

Indications and dosages

▶ **Moderate to severe pain.** *Adults:* For patient who weighs about 70 kg (154 lb), give 10 to 20 mg I.V., I.M., or subcutaneously q 3 to 6 hours, as appropriate. Maximum daily dosage is 160 mg.
▶ **Adjunct in balanced anesthesia.** *Adults:* 0.3 mg/kg to 3 mg/kg I.V. over 10 to 15 minutes, followed by maintenance doses of 0.25 to 0.5 mg/kg in single I.V. doses, p.r.n.

I.V. administration

• Keep resuscitation equipment available.
• Inject slowly over at least 2 minutes into vein or into line containing compatible, free-flowing solution, such as D_5W, normal saline solution, or lactated Ringer's solution.
• Respiratory depression can be reversed with naloxone.

⊗ Incompatibilities
Allopurinol, amphotericin B, cefepime, diazepam, docetaxel, ketorolac, methotrexate sodium, nafcillin, pentobarbital sodium, piperacillin and tazobactam sodium, promethazine, sargramostim, sodium bicarbonate, thiethylperazine.

Contraindications and cautions

• Contraindicated in patients hypersensitive to the drug or sulfites present in some preparations of drug.
• Use cautiously in substance abusers and in those with emotional instability, head injury, increased intracranial pressure, impaired ventilation, MI accompanied by nausea and vomiting, upcoming biliary surgery, and hepatic or renal disease.
Lifespan: In pregnant women, use cautiously. In breast-feeding women, use cautiously because it's unknown if drug appears in breast milk. In children, safety and effectiveness haven't been established.

Adverse reactions

CNS: confusion, crying, delusions, depression, dizziness, euphoria, hallucinations, headache, hostility, nervousness, restlessness, *sedation,* speech difficulty, unusual dreams, vertigo.
CV: ***bradycardia,*** hypertension, hypotension, tachycardia.
EENT: blurred vision.
GI: bitter taste, constipation, cramps, dry mouth, dyspepsia, nausea, vomiting.
GU: urinary urgency.
Respiratory: ***pulmonary edema, respiratory depression.***
Skin: burning; itching; sweaty, clammy feeling; urticaria.

Interactions

Drug-drug. *CNS depressants, hypnotics, MAO inhibitors, sedatives, tranquilizers, tricyclic antidepressants:* May cause respiratory depression, hypertension, profound sedation, or coma.

Dose of one or both drugs may need to be decreased.
General anesthetics: May increase respiratory depression, sedation, and coma; may cause hypertension or hypotension.
Opioid analgesics: May decrease analgesic effect and increase withdrawal symptoms. Avoid use together.
Drug-lifestyle. *Alcohol use:* May cause respiratory depression, hypertension, profound sedation, or coma. Discourage use together.

Effects on lab test results

None reported.

Pharmacokinetics

Absorption: Unknown.
Distribution: Not measurably protein-bound.
Metabolism: In liver.
Excretion: In urine and bile. *Half-life:* 5 hours.

Route	Onset	Peak	Duration
I.V.	2–3 min	≤ 30 min	3–4 hr
I.M.	≤ 15 min	≤ 60 min	3–6 hr
SubQ	≤ 15 min	30–60 min	3–6 hr

Action

Chemical effect: Binds with opioid receptors in CNS, altering pain perception and response to pain by unknown mechanism.
Therapeutic effect: Relieves pain and enhances anesthesia.

Available forms

Injection: 10 mg/ml, 20 mg/ml

NURSING PROCESS

Assessment

- Assess patient's pain or anesthetic requirement before starting therapy and regularly thereafter to monitor drug effectiveness.
- Observe for signs of withdrawal in patient receiving long-term opioid therapy.
- Monitor patient closely for respiratory depression.
- Monitor patient for signs and symptoms of constipation.
- Be alert for adverse reactions and drug interactions.
- Assess patient's and family's knowledge of drug therapy.

Nursing diagnoses

- Acute pain related to underlying condition
- Disturbed thought processes related to drug's effect on CNS
- Deficient knowledge related to drug therapy

Planning and implementation

- Psychological and physical dependence may occur with prolonged use.
- Drug acts as an opioid antagonist and may precipitate withdrawal syndrome. For patients receiving long-term opioid therapy, start with 25% of usual dose.
- Give stool softener or other laxative to prevent constipation. Encourage patient to drink fluids and eat fiber.

ALERT: If patient's respirations are shallow or rate is below 12 breaths/minute, withhold dose and notify prescriber.
ALERT: Don't confuse Nubain with Navane.

Patient teaching

- Warn ambulatory patient about getting out of bed or walking.
- Instruct outpatient to avoid hazardous activities until the drug's CNS effects are known.

Evaluation

- Patient is free from pain.
- Patient maintains normal thought processes throughout therapy.
- Patient and family state understanding of drug therapy.

naloxone hydrochloride

(nal-OKS-ohn high-droh-KLOR-ighd)
Narcan

Pharmacologic class: opioid antagonist
Therapeutic class: antidote
Pregnancy risk category: B

Indications and dosages

▶ **Known or suspected opioid-induced respiratory depression, including that caused by pentazocine and propoxyphene.** *Adults:* 0.4 to 2 mg I.V. May be given I.M. or subcutaneously if I.V. route unavailable. Repeat q 2 to 3 minutes, if needed. If no response is observed after 10 mg has been given, reevaluate diagnosis.

▶ **Postoperative reversal of opioid effects.** *Adults:* 0.1 to 0.2 mg I.V. q 2 to 3 minutes, if needed.
Children: 0.005 to 0.01 mg/kg dose I.V. Repeat q 2 to 3 minutes, if needed.
Neonates (asphyxia neonatorum): 0.01 mg/kg I.V. into umbilical vein. May repeat q 2 to 3 minutes until response is obtained.
▶ **Naloxone challenge for diagnosing opiate dependence**‡. *Adults:* 0.16 mg I.M. naloxone; if no signs of withdrawal after 20 to 30 minutes, give second dose of 0.24 mg. Test is negative if no withdrawal symptoms within 30 minutes.

I.V. administration

- If 0.02 mg/ml isn't available for neonatal concentration, adult concentration (0.4 mg) may be diluted by mixing 0.5 ml with 9.5 ml of sterile water or saline solution for injection.
- Give continuous I.V. infusion to control adverse effects of epidural morphine.

⊗ **Incompatibilities**
All other I.V. drugs, especially preparations containing bisulfite, sulfite, long-chain or high–molecular-weight anions, or alkaline solutions.

Contraindications and cautions

- Contraindicated in patients hypersensitive to drug or any of its components.
- Use cautiously in patients with cardiac irritability and opioid addiction. Abrupt reversal of opioid-induced CNS depression may cause nausea, vomiting, diaphoresis, tachycardia, CNS excitement, and increased blood pressure.

Lifespan: In pregnant women, use cautiously. In breast-feeding women, safety and effectiveness haven't been established.

Adverse reactions

CNS: ***seizures,*** tremors.
CV: tachycardia and hypertension with high doses, ***ventricular fibrillation.***
GI: nausea and vomiting with high doses.
Respiratory: ***pulmonary edema.***
Other: ***withdrawal symptoms.***

Interactions

None significant.

Effects on lab test results

None reported.

Pharmacokinetics

Absorption: Unknown.
Distribution: Rapid.
Metabolism: Rapid.
Excretion: In urine. *Half-life:* 60 to 90 minutes in adults, 3 hours in neonates.

Route	Onset	Peak	Duration
I.V.	1–2 min	Unknown	Varies
I.M., SubQ	2–5 min	Unknown	Varies

Action

Chemical effect: Unknown; may displace opioid analgesics from their receptors (competitive antagonism). Has no pharmacologic activity.
Therapeutic effect: Reverses opioid effects.

Available forms

Injection: 0.02 mg/ml, 0.4 mg/ml, 1 mg/ml

NURSING PROCESS

Assessment

- Assess patient's opioid use before starting therapy, and reassess regularly to monitor drug effectiveness.
- Duration of opioid action may exceed that of naloxone, causing relapse into respiratory depression. Monitor patient's respiratory depth and rate.
- Patients who receive naloxone to reverse opioid-induced respiratory depression may develop tachypnea.
- If patient has an adverse GI reaction, monitor his hydration.
- Assess patient's and family's knowledge of drug therapy.

Nursing diagnoses

- Ineffective health maintenance related to opioid use
- Risk for deficient fluid volume related to drug-induced adverse GI reactions
- Deficient knowledge related to drug therapy

Planning and implementation

- High doses of drug may cause withdrawal symptoms in opioid-dependent patients.

ALERT: Drug is effective only in reversing respiratory depression caused by opioids. Use flumazenil to treat respiratory depression caused by diazepam or other benzodiazepines.

ALERT: Provide oxygen, ventilation, and other resuscitation measures to patient with severe respiratory depression from acute opioid overdose.
ALERT: Don't confuse naloxone with naltrexone.

Patient teaching

- Instruct patient and family to report adverse reactions.

Evaluation

- Patient responds well to drug.
- Patient maintains adequate hydration.
- Patient and family state understanding of drug therapy.

naltrexone hydrochloride
(nal-TREKS-ohn high-droh-KLOR-ighd)
Depade, ReVia, Vivitrol

Pharmacologic class: opioid antagonist
Therapeutic class: adjunct in opioid detoxification/cessation
Pregnancy risk category: C

Indications and dosages

▶ **Adjunct in maintaining opioid-free state in detoxified patients.** *Adults:* Initially, 25 mg P.O. If no withdrawal signs occur within 1 hour, additional 25 mg is given. Once patient takes 50 mg q 24 hours, flexible maintenance schedule may be used.
▶ **Alcohol dependence in combination with a treatment program.** *Adults:* 50 mg P.O. once daily for up to 12 weeks. Or, 380 mg I.M. q 4 weeks or once each month.

Contraindications and cautions

- Contraindicated in patients hypersensitive to the drug or any of its components; those who are receiving opioid analgesics, have a positive urine screen for opioids, or are opioid dependent; those who have acute opioid withdrawal; and those with acute hepatitis or liver failure.
- Use cautiously in patients with mild hepatic disease or history of recent hepatic disease.

Lifespan: In pregnant women, use cautiously. In breast-feeding women and in children, safety and effectiveness haven't been established.

Adverse reactions

CNS: *anxiety,* depression, *headache, insomnia, nervousness,* ***suicidal ideation.***
GI: *abdominal pain,* anorexia, *nausea, vomiting.*
Hematologic: lymphocytosis.
Hepatic: ***hepatotoxicity.***
Musculoskeletal: *muscle and joint pain.*
Other: *injection site reaction* (I.M. form).

Interactions

Drug-drug. *Products containing opioids (such as cough and cold and antidiarrheal products):* May decrease response to these products. Recommend a nonopioid product.
Thioridazine: May increase somnolence and lethargy. Monitor patient closely.

Effects on lab test results

- May increase AST, ALT, and LDH levels.
- May increase lymphocyte count. May decrease platelet count (I.M. form).

Pharmacokinetics

Absorption: Good.
Distribution: Wide but variable. About 21% to 28% protein-bound.
Metabolism: Extensive. Its major metabolite may be pure antagonist and contribute to its effectiveness. Drug and metabolites may undergo enterohepatic recirculation.
Excretion: Mainly by kidneys. *Half-life:* About 4 hours; 5 to 10 days with I.M. form.

Route	Onset	Peak	Duration
P.O.	15–30 min	1–2 hr	24 hr
I.M.	unknown	2 hr; then again in 2–3 days	> 1 month

Action

Chemical effect: May reversibly block subjective effects of I.V. opioids by occupying opiate receptors in brain.
Therapeutic effect: Helps prevent opioid dependence and treats alcohol dependence.

Available forms

Injectable suspension: 380 mg vial in single-use kit
Tablets: 25 mg, 50 mg, 100 mg

N

NURSING PROCESS

Assessment
- Assess patient's opioid or alcohol dependence before starting therapy and regularly thereafter to monitor drug effectiveness.
- Assess patient's and family's knowledge of drug therapy.

Nursing diagnoses
- Health-seeking behavior related to desire to remain free from opioid dependence
- Sleep deprivation related to drug-induced insomnia
- Deficient knowledge related to drug therapy

Planning and implementation
ALERT: Begin therapy for opioid dependence after giving naloxone challenge, a provocative test of opioid dependence. If signs of opioid withdrawal persist after challenge, don't give the drug.

ALERT: Patient must be completely free from opioids before taking the drug, or severe withdrawal symptoms may occur. Wait at least 7 days in patient addicted to short-acting opioids, such as heroin and meperidine. Wait at least 10 days in patient addicted to longer-acting opioids, such as methadone.

- Use a nonopioid analgesic for analgesia. If an opioid analgesic is needed in an emergency, give an opioid analgesic in a higher dose than usual to surmount naltrexone's effect. Respiratory depression caused by opioid analgesic may be longer and deeper.
- For patient with opioid dependence who isn't expected to comply, use flexible maintenance regimen: 100 mg on Monday and Wednesday, 150 mg on Friday.
- I.M. injection should be given in gluteal muscle, alternating buttocks, using the kit components provided.
- Store Vivitrol in the refrigerator. Unrefrigerated, it can be stored at temperatures not exceeding 25°C (77° F) for no longer than 7 days before use. Vivitrol shouldn't be frozen.
- Use naltrexone only as part of comprehensive rehabilitation program.

ALERT: Don't confuse naltrexone with naloxone.

Patient teaching
- Advise patient to wear or carry medical identification. Warn him to tell medical personnel that he takes naltrexone.
- Give patient names of nonopioid drugs he can take for pain, diarrhea, or cough.

Evaluation
- Patient maintains opioid-free state.
- Patient reports no insomnia.
- Patient and family state understanding of drug therapy.

naproxen
(nuh-PROK-sin)

Apo-Naproxen ♦, EC-Naprosyn, Naprosyn, Naprosyn SR ♦ ◇, Naxen ♦ ◇, Novo-Naprox ♦, Nu-Naprox ♦

naproxen sodium

Aleve†, Anaprox, Anaprox DS, Apo-Napro-Na ♦, Apo-Napro-Na DS ♦, Naprelan, Novo-Naprox Sodium ♦, Synflex ♦, Synflex DS ♦

Pharmacologic class: NSAID
Therapeutic class: analgesic, antipyretic, anti-inflammatory
Pregnancy risk category: B; D (third trimester)

Indications and dosages
▶ **Rheumatoid arthritis, osteoarthritis, ankylosing spondylitis.** *Adults:* 250 to 500 mg naproxen P.O. b.i.d. Or, 375 mg to 500 mg EC-Naprosyn P.O. b.i.d. Or, 275 to 550 mg naproxen sodium P.O. b.i.d. Or, 750 mg or 1,000 mg Naprelan P.O. daily; may use 1,500 mg daily for limited periods. Or, where suppository is available, 500 mg P.R. at bedtime with naproxen P.O. during day.

▶ **Juvenile arthritis.** *Children age 2 and older:* 10 mg/kg naproxen P.O. in two divided doses.

▶ **Acute gout.** *Adults:* 750 mg naproxen P.O., followed by 250 mg q 8 hours until attack subsides. Or 825 mg naproxen sodium initially; then 275 mg q 8 hours until attack subsides. Or 1,000 mg to 1,500 mg Naprelan P.O. on the first day; then 1,000 mg daily until attack subsides.

▶ **Mild to moderate pain, primary dysmenorrhea, acute tendinitis and bursitis.** *Adults:*

500 mg naproxen P.O., followed by 250 mg q 6 to 8 hours p.r.n. Or 550 mg naproxen sodium P.O. initially; then 275 mg P.O. q 6 to 8 hours p.r.n. Or 1,000 mg Naprelan P.O. daily; use 1,500 mg P.O. daily for limited period.

Contraindications and cautions

- Contraindicated in patients hypersensitive to the drug or any of its components and in patients with asthma, rhinitis, or nasal polyps.
- Use cautiously in those with renal disease, CV disease, GI disorders, hepatic disease, or peptic ulcer disease.

Lifespan: In women in the last trimester of pregnancy and in breast-feeding women, drug is contraindicated. In children younger than age 2, safety and effectiveness haven't been established. In elderly patients, use cautiously because of possible delayed excretion.

Adverse reactions

CNS: aseptic meningitis, cognitive dysfunction, *dizziness, drowsiness, headache.*
CV: digital vasculitis, palpitations, *peripheral edema.*
EENT: *tinnitus,* visual disturbances.
GI: *epigastric distress,* nausea, *occult blood loss,* peptic ulceration.
GU: ***nephrotoxicity.***
Hematologic: ***agranulocytosis, neutropenia, thrombocytopenia.***
Metabolic: ***hyperkalemia.***
Respiratory: dyspnea.
Skin: *pruritus, rash,* urticaria.

Interactions

Drug-drug. *ACE inhibitors:* May increase risk of renal disease. Don't use together.
Aspirin, corticosteroids: May increase risk of adverse GI reactions. Use cautiously, and monitor patient for abdominal pain and bleeding.
Cyclosporine: May increase nephrotoxicity of both drugs. Monitor renal function tests.
Diuretics: May decrease effect of these drugs. Monitor patient.
Drugs that are highly protein-bound, oral anticoagulants, sulfonylureas: May increase risk of toxicity. Monitor patient closely.
Methotrexate: May increase risk of toxicity. Monitor levels.
Probenecid: May decrease naproxen elimination. Monitor patient for toxicity.
Drug-herb. *Dong quai, feverfew, garlic, ginger, horse chestnut, red clover:* May increase risk of bleeding. Discourage use together.
St. John's wort: May increase risk of photosensitivity. Advise patient to avoid unprotected or prolonged exposure to sunlight.
Drug-lifestyle. *Alcohol use:* May increase risk of adverse GI reactions. Discourage use together.

Effects on lab test results

- May increase BUN, creatinine, ALT, AST, and potassium levels.
- May increase bleeding time. May decrease granulocyte, platelet, and neutrophil counts.
- May interfere with urinary assays of 5-hydroxyindoleacetic acid and may falsely elevate urine 17-ketosteroid concentrations.

Pharmacokinetics

Absorption: Rapid and complete.
Distribution: Highly protein-bound.
Metabolism: In liver.
Excretion: In urine. *Half-life:* 10 to 20 hours.

Route	Onset	Peak	Duration
P.O.	≤ 1 hr	1–6 hr	7–12 hr
P.R.	Unknown	Unknown	Unknown

Action

Chemical effect: Unknown; produces anti-inflammatory, analgesic, and antipyretic effects, possibly by inhibiting prostaglandin synthesis.
Therapeutic effect: Relieves pain, fever, and inflammation.

Available forms

naproxen
Oral suspension: 125 mg/5 ml
Suppositories: 500 mg ◊
Tablets: 250 mg, 375 mg, 500 mg
Tablets (delayed-release, enteric-coated): 375 mg, 500 mg
Tablets (extended-release) ♦: 750 mg, 1,000 mg
naproxen sodium
275 mg naproxen sodium equals 250 mg naproxen.
Tablets: 220 mg†, 275 mg, 550 mg
Tablets (controlled-release): 375 mg, 500 mg

N

NURSING PROCESS

Assessment

- Assess patient's condition before starting therapy and regularly thereafter to monitor drug effectiveness.
- Monitor CBC, electrolytes, and renal and hepatic function q 4 to 6 months during long-term therapy.
- NSAIDs may mask signs and symptoms of infection.
- If patient has an adverse GI reaction, monitor his hydration.
- Assess patient's and family's knowledge of drug therapy.

Nursing diagnoses

- Acute pain related to underlying condition
- Risk for deficient fluid volume related to drug-induced adverse GI reactions
- Deficient knowledge related to drug therapy

Planning and implementation

ALERT: Don't exceed 1.25 g of naproxen or 1.375 g of naproxen sodium daily.

- Give drug with food or milk to minimize GI upset.
- Suppository form isn't available in the United States.
- Don't use in patients with inflammatory lesion of the rectum or anus.

Patient teaching

- Tell patient taking prescription doses of naproxen for arthritis that full therapeutic effect may take 2 to 4 weeks.
- Tell patient to take a full glass of water or other liquid with each dose.
- Tell patient not to break, crush, or chew delayed-release tablets.

ALERT: Warn patient against taking naproxen and naproxen sodium at the same time.

- Teach patient to recognize and report evidence of GI bleeding. Serious GI toxicity, including peptic ulceration and bleeding, can occur in patients taking NSAIDs, despite absence of GI symptoms.
- Warn patient that use with aspirin, alcohol, or corticosteroids may increase risk of adverse GI reactions.
- Advise patient to have periodic eye examinations.

Evaluation

- Patient is free from pain.
- Patient maintains adequate hydration.
- Patient and family state understanding of drug therapy.

naratriptan hydrochloride

(nah-rah-TRIP-tin high-droh-KLOR-ighd)

Amerge, Naramig ◇

Pharmacologic class: selective agonist of serotonin
Therapeutic class: antimigraine drug
Pregnancy risk category: C

Indications and dosages

▶ **Acute migraine headaches with or without aura.** *Adults:* 1 or 2.5 mg P.O. as a single dose. If headache returns or responds only partially, dose may be repeated after 4 hours, for maximum dosage of 5 mg in 24 hours.

Adjust-a-dose: For patients with mild or moderate renal or hepatic impairment, don't use more than 2.5 mg P.O. in 24 hours. If creatinine clearance is less than 15 ml/minute or if patient has severe hepatic impairment, don't use drug.

Contraindications and cautions

- Contraindicated in patients hypersensitive to the drug or any of its components and in those who have received ergot-containing, ergot-type, or other 5-HT_1 agonists in the previous 24 hours. Also contraindicated in patients with a history or evidence of cardiac ischemia, cerebrovascular disease, peripheral vascular disease, significant underlying CV disease, uncontrolled hypertension, creatinine clearance below 15 ml/minute, or severe hepatic impairment (Child-Pugh grade C).
- Unless a CV evaluation deems patient free from cardiac disease, use cautiously in patient with risk factors for coronary artery disease, such as hypertension, hypercholesterolemia, obesity, diabetes, a strong family history of coronary artery disease, surgical or physiologic menopause (women), age older than 40 (men), and smoking. For patients with cardiac risk factors but a satisfactory CV evaluation, give first dose in a medical facility and consider ECG monitoring.

• Safety and effectiveness haven't been established for cluster headaches or for treating more than four migraine headaches in a 30-day period.

Lifespan: In pregnant women, drug is contraindicated. In breast-feeding women, small amounts of drug may appear in breast milk. In children, safety and effectiveness haven't been established. In elderly patients, drug is contraindicated.

Adverse reactions

CNS: dizziness, drowsiness, fatigue, malaise, paresthesias, syncope, vertigo.
CV: ***atrial fibrillation, atrial flutter, coronary artery vasospasm,*** increased blood pressure, ***MI,*** palpitations, ***PR- and QT-interval prolongation, PVCs, ST/T wave abnormalities, tachyarrhythmias,*** transient myocardial ischemia, ***ventricular fibrillation, ventricular tachycardia.***
EENT: ear, nose, and throat infections; photophobia.
GI: hyposalivation, nausea, vomiting.
Other: pressure, tightness, and heaviness sensations; warm or cold temperature sensations.

Interactions

Drug-drug. *Ergot-containing or ergot-type drugs (dihydroergotamine, methysergide), other 5-HT_1 agonists:* May prolong vasospastic reactions. Don't give within 24 hours of naratriptan.
Hormonal contraceptives: May slightly increase naratriptan levels. Monitor patient.
Sibutramine: May cause signs of serotonin syndrome, including CNS irritability, motor weakness, shivering, myoclonus may occur. Use together cautiously.
SSRIs, such as fluoxetine, fluvoxamine, paroxetine, sertraline: May cause weakness, hyperreflexia, and incoordination. Monitor patient.
Drug-lifestyle. *Smoking:* May increase naratriptan clearance. Discourage use together; urge patient to stop smoking.

Effects on lab test results

None reported.

Pharmacokinetics

Absorption: Good. Bioavailability of 70%.
Distribution: About 28% to 31% protein-bound.
Metabolism: To a number of inactive metabolites by wide range of cytochrome P-450 isoenzymes.
Excretion: Mainly in urine with 50% of dose recovered unchanged and 30% as metabolites. *Half-life:* 6 hours.

Route	Onset	Peak	Duration
P.O.	Unknown	2–3 hr	Unknown

Action

Chemical effect: May activate receptors in intracranial blood vessels, leading to vasoconstriction and relief of migraine headache; activation of receptors on sensory nerve endings in trigeminal system may inhibit proinflammatory neuropeptide release.
Therapeutic effect: Relieves migraine pain.

Available forms

Tablets: 1 mg, 2.5 mg

NURSING PROCESS

Assessment

• Assess baseline cardiac function before starting therapy. Perform periodic cardiac evaluation in patients who develop risk factors for coronary artery disease.

• Assess renal and liver function test results before starting drug therapy, and report abnormalities.

• Assess patient's and family's knowledge of drug therapy.

Nursing diagnoses

• Acute pain related to presence of migraine headache
• Risk for injury related to drug-induced adverse CV reactions
• Deficient knowledge related to drug therapy

Planning and implementation

• Give drug only for a definite diagnosis of migraine. Drug isn't intended to prevent migraine headaches or treat hemiplegic headaches, basilar migraines, or cluster headaches.
• If patient has pain or tightness in chest or throat, arrhythmias, or increased blood pressure, withhold the drug and notify prescriber.
• Don't give drug to a patient with history of coronary artery disease, hypertension, arrhyth-

N

mias, or risk factors for coronary artery disease because drug may cause coronary vasospasm and hypertension.

- For patients with cardiac risk factors who have had a satisfactory cardiac evaluation, give first dose while monitoring ECG. Keep emergency equipment readily available.

Patient teaching

- Instruct patient to take drug only as prescribed.
- Tell patient that drug is intended to relieve migraine headaches, not to prevent them.
- Instruct patient to take dose soon after headache starts. If no response occurs to first tablet, tell patient to seek prescriber approval before taking second tablet. If prescriber approves a second dose, patient may take a second tablet, but no sooner than 4 hours after first tablet. Advise patient not to exceed two tablets in 24 hours.
- Teach patient to alert prescriber about risk factors for coronary artery disease or bothersome adverse effects.

Evaluation

- Patient has relief from migraine headache.
- Patient has no pain or tightness in chest or throat, arrhythmias, or increase in blood pressure.
- Patient and family state understanding of drug therapy.

natalizumab

(nah-tah-LIZ-yoo-mab)
Tysabri

Pharmacologic class: monoclonal antibody
Therapeutic class: immune response modifier
Pregnancy risk category: C

Indications and dosages

▶ **To slow the accumulation of physical disabilities and reduce the frequency of flare-ups in relapsing forms of multiple sclerosis for patients who failed to respond or were unable to tolerate other therapies.** *Adults:* 300 mg in 100 ml normal saline solution infused I.V. over 1 hour q 4 weeks.

I.V. administration

- Dilute 300 mg in 100 ml normal saline solution.
- Invert I.V. bag gently to mix solution; don't shake.
- Infuse over 1 hour; don't give by I.V. push or bolus.
- Flush I.V. line with normal saline solution after infusion is complete.
- Refrigerate solution and use within 8 hours if not used immediately.

⊗ Incompatibilities

Any diluent other than normal saline solution. Don't mix or infuse with other drugs.

Contraindications and cautions

- Contraindicated in patients hypersensitive to drug or its components and in those with current or previous progressive multifocal leukoencephalopathy. Use with other immunosuppressants isn't recommended.

Lifespan: In pregnant patients, use only if clearly needed. In breast-feeding women, don't use drug. In children, safety and effectiveness haven't been established. In elderly patients, use caution; it isn't known whether they respond differently than younger adults.

Adverse reactions

CNS: *depression, fatigue, headache,* ***progressive multifocal leukoencephalopathy,*** *somnolence, vertigo.*
CV: chest discomfort.
EENT: tonsillitis.
GI: *abdominal discomfort, diarrhea, gastroenteritis.*
GU: amenorrhea, dysmenorrhea, irregular menstruation, urinary frequency, urinary urgency, *UTI, vaginitis.*
Metabolism: weight increase or decrease.
Musculoskeletal: *arthralgia, extremity pain,* muscle cramps, swollen joints.
Respiratory: *lower respiratory tract infection.*
Skin: dermatitis, pruritus, *rash.*
Other: herpes, ***hypersensitivity reaction,*** infection, ***infusion-related reaction,*** rigors, seasonal allergy, *tooth infections.*

Interactions

Drug-drug. *Corticosteroids, other immunosuppressants:* May increase risk of infection. Don't use together.

Effects on lab test results

- May increase liver function test values and lymphocyte, monocyte, eosinophil, basophil, and nucleated RBC counts.

Pharmacokinetics

Absorption: Unknown.
Distribution: Unknown.
Metabolism: Unknown.
Excretion: Unknown. *Half-life:* 7 to 15 days.

Route	Onset	Peak	Duration
I.V.	Unknown	Unknown	Unknown

Action

Chemical effect: Not fully defined. May block interaction between adhesion molecules on inflammatory cells and receptors on endothelial cells of vessel walls.
Therapeutic effect: Slows progression of multiple sclerosis.

Available forms

Injection: 300 mg/15 ml single-use vials

NURSING PROCESS

Assessment

- Make sure patient has had a brain MRI before therapy starts.
- Assess patient's condition before therapy and regularly thereafter to monitor drug effectiveness.
- Be alert for adverse reactions and drug interactions.
- Assess patient's and family's knowledge of drug therapy.

Nursing diagnoses

- Ineffective health maintenance related to underlying condition
- Risk for injury related to drug-induced adverse reactions
- Deficient knowledge related to drug therapy

Planning and implementation

- Watch for evidence of hypersensitivity reaction during and for 1 hour after infusion. Evidence may include dizziness, urticaria, fever, rash, rigors, pruritus, nausea, flushing, hypotension, dyspnea, and chest pain.
- Patients who develop antibodies to natalizumab have an increased risk of infusion-related reaction.

ALERT: Drug may cause progressive multifocal leukoencephalopathy. Withhold drug and notify prescriber at the first evidence that suggests progressive multifocal leukoencephalopathy.

Patient teaching

- Tell patient to read the Medication Guide for Tysabri before each infusion.
- Urge patient to immediately report progressively worsening symptoms persisting over several days, including changes in thinking, eyesight, balance, or strength.
- Advise patient to inform all the healthcare providers caring for him that he is receiving this drug.
- Tell patient to schedule follow-up appointments with prescriber at 3 and 6 months after the first infusion, then at least every 6 months thereafter.
- Urge patient to immediately report rash, hives, dizziness, fever, shaking chills, or itching while drug is infusing or up to 1 hour afterward.

Evaluation

- Patient responds positively to drug therapy.
- Patient sustains no injury from adverse reactions.
- Patient and family state understanding of drug therapy.

nateglinide

(na-TEG-lih-nighd)
Starlix

Pharmacologic class: amino acid derivative
Therapeutic class: antidiabetic
Pregnancy risk category: C

Indications and dosages

▶ **Alone or with metformin or a thiazolidinedione to lower glucose levels in patients with type 2 diabetes whose hyperglycemia isn't adequately controlled by diet and exercise and who haven't received long-term therapy with other antidiabetics.** *Adults:* 120 mg P.O. t.i.d., taken 1 to 30 minutes before meals. If patient's glycosylated hemoglobin level is near normal when therapy starts, he may receive 60 mg P.O. t.i.d.

Contraindications and cautions

- Contraindicated in patients hypersensitive to the drug or any of its components and in patients with type 1 diabetes or diabetic ketoacidosis.
- Use cautiously in malnourished patients and patients with moderate to severe liver dysfunction or adrenal or pituitary insufficiency.

Lifespan: In pregnant women, don't use. In breast-feeding women, use cautiously; it's unknown if the drug appears in breast milk. In children, safety and effectiveness haven't been established. In elderly patients, use cautiously because some of these patients have greater sensitivity to the glucose-lowering effects than others.

Adverse reactions

CNS: dizziness.
GI: diarrhea.
Metabolic: ***hypoglycemia.***
Musculoskeletal: arthropathy, back pain.
Respiratory: bronchitis, coughing, upper respiratory tract infection.
Other: accidental trauma, flulike symptoms.

Interactions

Drug-drug. *Corticosteroids, sympathomimetics, thiazides, thyroid drugs:* May reduce hypoglycemic action of nateglinide. Monitor patient for hyperglycemia, and monitor glucose levels closely.
MAO inhibitors, nonselective beta blockers, NSAIDs, salicylates: May increase hypoglycemic action of nateglinide. Monitor patient for hypoglycemia and monitor glucose levels closely.

Effects on lab test results

- May decrease glucose level.

Pharmacokinetics

Absorption: Rapid when taken immediately before a meal.
Distribution: 98% protein-bound, mainly to albumin.
Metabolism: In the liver.
Excretion: Rapid and complete. *Half-life:* About 1½ hours.

Route	Onset	Peak	Duration
P.O.	20 min	1 hr	4 hr

Action

Chemical effect: Stimulates insulin secretion from the pancreas.
Therapeutic effect: Lowers glucose level.

Available forms

Tablets: 60 mg, 120 mg

NURSING PROCESS

Assessment

- Assess underlying condition before starting therapy, and reassess regularly to monitor drug effectiveness.
- Monitor glucose level regularly to evaluate drug effectiveness.
- When other drugs are started or stopped, monitor glucose level closely to detect interactions.
- Periodically monitor glycosylated hemoglobin level.
- Assess patient's and family's knowledge of drug therapy.

Nursing diagnoses

- Ineffective health maintenance related to hyperglycemia
- Risk for injury related to adverse drug effect of hypoglycemia
- Deficient knowledge related to nateglinide therapy

Planning and implementation

- Don't use with or instead of glyburide or other oral antidiabetics. Drug may be used with metformin.
- Give drug 1 to 30 minutes before a meal. If patient misses a meal, skip the scheduled dose.

ALERT: Risk of hypoglycemia rises with strenuous exercise, alcohol ingestion, insufficient caloric intake, and use with other oral antidiabetics.

- Symptoms of hypoglycemia may be masked in patients with autonomic neuropathy and in those who use beta blockers.
- Insulin may be needed for glycemic control in patients with fever, infection, trauma, or impending surgery.
- Effectiveness may decline over time.

ALERT: Observe patient for evidence of hypoglycemia, including sweating, rapid pulse, trembling, confusion, headache, irritability, and nausea. To minimize the risk of hypoglycemia, follow dose immediately with a meal. If hypoglycemia occurs and the patient remains conscious, give an oral form of glucose. If unconscious, give I.V. glucose.

Patient teaching

- Tell patient to take nateglinide 1 to 30 minutes before a meal.
- To reduce the risk of hypoglycemia, advise patient to skip the scheduled dose if he misses a meal.
- Educate patient about the risk of hypoglycemia and its signs and symptoms (sweating, rapid pulse, trembling, confusion, headache, irritability, and nausea). Advise patient to treat these symptoms by eating or drinking something containing sugar.
- Teach patient how to monitor and log glucose levels to evaluate diabetes control.
- Instruct patient to adhere to the prescribed diet and exercise regimen.
- Explain the long-term complications of diabetes and the importance of regular preventive therapy.
- Encourage patient to wear or carry medical identification that shows he has diabetes.

☑ Evaluation

- Patient's glucose level is normal.
- Patient doesn't become hypoglycemic and sustains no injury.
- Patient and family state understanding of drug therapy.

nefazodone hydrochloride

(nef-AZ-oh-dohn high-droh-KLOR-ighd)

Pharmacologic class: serotonin modulator
Therapeutic class: antidepressant
Pregnancy risk category: C

Indications and dosages

▶ **Depression.** *Adults:* Initially, 200 mg P.O. daily in two divided doses. Increase dosage in increments of 100 to 200 mg daily at intervals of no less than 1 week. Usual daily dosage range, 300 to 600 mg. Maximum dosage is 600 mg.

Contraindications and cautions

- Contraindicated in patients hypersensitive to the drug or any of its components, other phenylpiperazine antidepressants, or in patients who are withdrawn from drug because of liver injury. Also contraindicated within 14 days of MAO inhibitor therapy.
- Use cautiously in patients with CV or cerebrovascular disease that could be worsened by hypotension (such as history of MI, angina, or stroke) and conditions that predispose to hypotension (such as dehydration, hypovolemia, and therapy with antihypertensives).
- Also use cautiously in patients with history of mania.

Lifespan: In pregnant women, use cautiously. In breast-feeding women, use cautiously; it's unknown if drug appears in breast milk. In children, drug isn't approved for use because children may have an increased risk of suicidal behavior.

Adverse reactions

CNS: abnormal dreams, *asthenia,* ataxia, *confusion,* decreased concentration, *dizziness,* fever, headache, hypertonia, incoordination, insomnia, *light-headedness,* memory impairment, paresthesia, psychomotor retardation, *somnolence,* ***suicidal ideation,*** tremor.
CV: hypotension, orthostatic hypotension, peripheral edema, vasodilation.
EENT: *abnormal vision, blurred vision,* pharyngitis, tinnitus, visual field defect.
GI: *constipation,* diarrhea, *dry mouth,* dyspepsia, increased appetite, *nausea,* taste perversion, vomiting.
GU: urinary frequency, urine retention, UTI, vaginitis.
Hepatic: ***liver failure.***
Metabolic: hyponatremia.
Musculoskeletal: arthralgia, neck rigidity.
Respiratory: cough.
Skin: pruritus, rash.
Other: breast pain, chills, flulike syndrome, infection, thirst.

Interactions

Drug-drug. *Alprazolam, triazolam:* May increase effects of these drugs. Avoid using together or substantially reduce dosage of alprazolam and triazolam.
Calcium channel blockers, HMG-CoA reductase inhibitors: May increase levels of these drugs. Adjust dosage if needed.
CNS-active drugs: May alter CNS activity. Use together cautiously.

Digoxin: May increase digoxin level. Use together cautiously and monitor digoxin levels.
MAO inhibitors (phenelzine, selegiline, tranylcypromine): May cause serotonin syndrome (CNS irritability, shivering, and altered consciousness). Don't give together. Wait at least 2 weeks after stopping an MAO inhibitor before giving any selective serotonin reuptake inhibitors.
Other drugs highly bound to proteins: May increase adverse reactions. Monitor patient closely.
Sibutramine, sumatriptan: May cause severe excitation, hyperpyrexia, seizures, delirium, coma, or a fatal reaction. Avoid using together.
Drug-herb. *St. John's wort:* May cause additive effects and serotonin syndrome (CNS irritability, shivering, and altered consciousness). Discourage using together.
Drug-lifestyle. *Alcohol use:* Enhances CNS depression. Discourage using together.

Effects on lab test results

- May decrease sodium level.

Pharmacokinetics

Absorption: Rapid and complete.
Distribution: Wide. Extensively protein-bound.
Metabolism: Extensive.
Excretion: In urine. *Half-life:* 2 to 4 hours.

Route	Onset	Peak	Duration
P.O.	Unknown	1 hr	Unknown

Action

Chemical effect: Not precisely defined. Drug inhibits neuronal uptake of serotonin ($5\text{-}HT_2$) and norepinephrine; it also occupies serotonin and $alpha_1$-adrenergic receptors in CNS.
Therapeutic effect: Relieves depression.

Available forms

Tablets: 50 mg, 100 mg, 150 mg, 200 mg, 250 mg

NURSING PROCESS

Assessment

- Assess patient's depression before starting therapy and regularly thereafter to monitor the drug's effectiveness.

ALERT: Calculate a risk-benefit ratio before using drug for depression because of the risk for hepatic failure and emergence of suicidal ideation and attempts.

- Record mood changes. Monitor patient for suicidal tendencies.
- Be alert for adverse reactions and drug interactions.
- Assess patient's and family's knowledge of drug therapy.

Nursing diagnoses

- Disturbed thought processes related to depression
- Risk for injury related to drug-induced adverse CNS reactions
- Deficient knowledge related to drug therapy

Planning and implementation

ALERT: Allow at least 7 days after stopping drug before starting patient on an MAO inhibitor. Allow at least 14 days after stopping an MAO inhibitor before starting patient on the drug.
ALERT: Don't initiate therapy in patients with active liver disease or with elevated baseline transaminase levels. Preexisting liver disease doesn't appear to increase the likelihood of developing liver failure, but baseline abnormalities can complicate patient monitoring.
ALERT: If patient has signs and symptoms of liver dysfunction, such as AST or ALT levels greater than or equal to 3 times upper limit of normal, stop giving the drug and don't restart.

Patient teaching

- Warn patient not to engage in hazardous activity until the drug's CNS effects of drug are known.

ALERT: Instruct man with prolonged or inappropriate erections to stop drug at once and call prescriber.

- Instruct woman to call prescriber if she becomes pregnant or intends to become pregnant during therapy.
- Teach patient the signs and symptoms of liver dysfunction (jaundice, anorexia, GI complaints, and malaise), and tell him to immediately report them to prescriber.
- Instruct patient not to drink alcohol during therapy.
- Tell patient who develops rash, hives, or related allergic reaction to notify prescriber.

• Inform patient that several weeks of therapy may be needed to obtain full antidepressant effect. Once improvement occurs, tell patient not to stop drug until directed by prescriber.

ALERT: Inform family members to be particularly vigilant for suicidal tendencies during therapy with nefazodone.

• Urge patient to notify prescriber before taking any OTC drugs.

Evaluation

• Patient exhibits improved thought processes.
• Patient sustains no injuries from drug-induced adverse CNS reactions.
• Patient and family state understanding of drug therapy.

nelfinavir mesylate

(nel-FIN-uh-veer MES-ih-layt)
Viracept

Pharmacologic class: protease inhibitor
Therapeutic class: antiretroviral
Pregnancy risk category: B

Indications and dosages

▶ **HIV infection when antiretroviral therapy is warranted.** *Adults and children older than age 13:* Give 750 mg P.O. t.i.d., or 1,250 mg P.O. b.i.d. with meal.
Children ages 2 to 13: Give 45 to 55 mg/kg b.i.d. or 25 to 35 mg/kg t.i.d. with meal. Maximum dosage, 2,500 mg daily.

▶ **Prophylaxis after occupational exposure to HIV‡.** *Adults:* 750 mg P.O. t.i.d. with two other antiretrovirals for 4 weeks.

Contraindications and cautions

• Contraindicated in patients hypersensitive to the drug or any of its components and in patients receiving amiodarone, ergot derivatives, lovastatin, midazolam, pimozide, quinidine, simvastatin, or triazolam.
• Use cautiously in patients with hepatic dysfunction or hemophilia type A and B.

Lifespan: In pregnant women, use only when clearly needed. Women shouldn't breastfeed to avoid transmitting HIV to infant.

Adverse reactions

CNS: anxiety, asthenia, depression, dizziness, emotional lability, headache, malaise, paresthesia, ***seizures,*** sleep disorders, ***suicidal ideation.***
EENT: conjunctivitis, iritis, pharyngitis, rhinitis, sinusitis.
GI: *diarrhea,* flatulence, mouth ulceration, nausea, ***pancreatitis.***
GU: renal calculus, sexual dysfunction.
Hematologic: anemia, ***leukopenia, thrombocytopenia.***
Hepatic: ***hepatitis.***
Metabolic: dehydration, hyperlipidemia, hyperuricemia, ***hypoglycemia.***
Musculoskeletal: arthralgia, myalgia, myasthenia, myopathy.
Respiratory: diaphoresis, dyspnea.
Skin: dermatitis, pruritus, rash, urticaria.
Other: allergic reactions, fever, redistribution or accumulation of body fat.

Interactions

Drug-drug. *Amiodarone, ergot derivatives, lovastatin, midazolam, pimozide, quinidine, simvastatin, triazolam:* May increase levels of these drugs, causing increased risk of serious or life-threatening adverse reactions. Avoid use together.
Atorvastatin, lovastatin, simvastatin: May increase level of these drugs. Use lowest dose, or consider using pravastatin or fluvastatin instead.
Azithromycin: May increase azithromycin level. Monitor patient for liver impairment.
Carbamazepine, phenobarbital: May reduce the nelfinavir effectiveness. Use together cautiously; monitor drug level and virologic response.
Cyclosporine, sirolimus, tacrolimus: May increase levels of these immunosuppressants. Use together cautiously.
Delavirdine, HIV protease inhibitors (indinavir or saquinavir), nevirapine: May increase protease inhibitor level. Use together cautiously.
Didanosine: May decrease didanosine absorption. Give nelfinavir with food at least 2 hours before or 1 hour after didanosine.
Ethinyl estradiol: May decrease level of contraceptive. Advise patient to use alternative contraceptive measures during therapy.
Methadone, phenytoin: May decrease levels of these drugs. Adjust dosage of these drugs accordingly.

Phosphodiesterase type 5 inhibitors (sildenafil, tadalafil, vardenafil): May increase adverse effects of these drugs. Use together cautiously. Don't exceed 25 mg of sildenafil in a 48-hour period, 10 mg of tadalafil in a 72-hour period, or 2.5 mg of vardenafil in a 72-hour period.
Rifabutin: May increase rifabutin level and decrease nelfinavir level. Reduce rifabutin dosage to half the usual amount, and increase nelfinavir to 1,250 mg b.i.d.
Drug-herb. *St. John's wort:* May decrease nelfinavir level. Discourage use together.

Effects on lab test results

- May increase ALT, AST, alkaline phosphatase, bilirubin, GGT, amylase, CK, and uric acid levels. May decrease hemoglobin level and hematocrit. May increase or decrease glucose level.
- May decrease WBC and platelet counts.

Pharmacokinetics

Absorption: Level peaks higher when drug is taken with food.
Distribution: More than 98% protein-bound.
Metabolism: Mainly by CYP3A and CYP2C19.
Excretion: Mainly in feces. *Half-life:* 3½ to 5 hours.

Route	Onset	Peak	Duration
P.O.	Unknown	2–4 hr	Unknown

Action

Chemical effect: Inhibits protease enzyme and prevents splitting of the viral polyprotein.
Therapeutic effect: Produces immature, noninfectious virus; prevention of AIDS progression.

Available forms

Powder (for suspension): 50 mg/g powder
Tablets (film-coated): 250 mg, 625 mg

NURSING PROCESS

Assessment

- Obtain baseline assessment of patient's condition before starting therapy, and reassess regularly to monitor drug's effectiveness.
- Monitor liver function test results.
- Assess patient for increased bleeding tendencies, especially if he has hemophilia type A or B.
- Monitor patient for excessive diarrhea, and treat as directed.
- Assess patient's and family's knowledge of drug therapy.

Nursing diagnoses

- Risk for injury related to adverse GI effects of drug
- Risk for impaired skin integrity secondary to drug-induced adverse effects
- Deficient knowledge related to drug therapy

Planning and implementation

- Give oral powder to children unable to take tablets. Mix powder with small amount of water, milk, formula, soy formula, soy milk, or dietary supplements. Tell patient to consume entire contents.
- Don't reconstitute drug with water in its original container.
- Use reconstituted powder within 6 hours.
- Mixing with acidic foods or juice isn't recommended because of the bitter taste.
- Enroll pregnant women with the Antiretroviral Pregnancy Registry by calling 1-800-258-4263 or visiting www.apregistry.com.

ALERT: Don't confuse nelfinavir with nevirapine.

Patient teaching

- Advise patient to take drug with food.
- Explain that drug doesn't cure HIV infection or reduce the risk of transmitting HIV to others.
- Tell patient that the drug's long-term effects are unknown.
- Instruct patient to take drug daily as prescribed and not to alter dose or stop drug without medical approval.
- Tell patient that diarrhea is the most common adverse effect and that it can be controlled with loperamide.
- If patient misses a dose, tell him to take it immediately and then return to his normal schedule, but do not double the dose.
- Instruct patient taking hormonal contraceptives to use an additional (or different) contraceptive measure while taking drug.

ALERT: Warn patient with phenylketonuria that powder contains 11.2 mg phenylalanine per gram.

- Instruct patient to report use of other prescribed or OTC drugs because of interactions.

• Advise patient taking sildenafil, tadalafil, or vardenafil of an increased risk of adverse events, including hypotension, visual changes, and priapism; tell him to promptly report any symptoms to prescriber. Tell him not to exceed 25 mg of sildenafil in a 48-hour period, 10 mg of tadalafil in a 72-hour period, or 2.5 mg of vardenafil in a 72-hour period.

Evaluation

• Patient has no adverse GI reactions.
• Patient and family state understanding of drug therapy.
• Skin integrity remains intact.

neomycin sulfate

(nee-oh-MIGH-sin SUL-fayt)
Mycifradin, Neo-Fradin, Neo-Tabs

Pharmacologic class: aminoglycoside
Therapeutic class: antibiotic
Pregnancy risk category: D

Indications and dosages

▶ **Infectious diarrhea caused by enteropathogenic *Escherichia coli*.** *Adults:* 50 mg/kg daily P.O. in four divided doses for 2 to 3 days.
Children: 50 to 100 mg/kg daily P.O. divided q 4 to 6 hours for 2 to 3 days.
▶ **Preoperative suppression of intestinal bacteria.** *Adults:* 1 g P.O. q hour for four doses; then 1 g q 4 hours for balance of 24 hours. For the 2- to 3-day regimen, 88 mg/kg/day in 6 equally divided doses at 4-hour intervals. Give a saline cathartic before first dose.
Children: 40 to 100 mg/kg daily P.O. divided q 4 to 6 hours. Give a saline cathartic before first dose.
▶ **Adjunct in hepatic coma.** *Adults:* 1 to 3 g P.O. q.i.d. for 5 to 6 days. Or 200 ml of 1% solution or 100 ml of 2% solution as enema retained for 20 to 60 minutes q 6 hours.
▶ **Hypercholesterolemia‡.** *Adults:* 500 mg to 2 g P.O. daily in 2 to 3 divided doses with or immediately after meals.

Contraindications and cautions

• Contraindicated in patients hypersensitive to other aminoglycosides and in those with intestinal obstruction.
• Use cautiously in patients with renal impairment, neuromuscular disorders, or ulcerative bowel lesions.
Lifespan: In pregnant women, only use drug when clearly needed because of the potential for harm. In breast-feeding women, safety and effectiveness haven't been established. In elderly patients, use cautiously.

Adverse reactions

CNS: headache, lethargy.
EENT: *ototoxicity.*
GI: nausea, vomiting.
GU: ***nephrotoxicity.***
Skin: rash, urticaria.
Other: ***hypersensitivity reactions.***

Interactions

Drug-drug. *Acyclovir, amphotericin B, cisplatin, methoxyflurane, other aminoglycosides, vancomycin:* May increase risk of nephrotoxicity. Use together cautiously.
Atracurium, pancuronium, rocuronium, vecuronium: May increase effects of nondepolarizing muscle relaxant, such as prolonged respiratory depression. Use together only when needed, and reduce dosage.
Cephalothin: May increase risk of nephrotoxicity. Use together cautiously; monitor renal function.
Digoxin: May decrease digoxin absorption. Monitor patient for loss of therapeutic effect.
Dimenhydrinate: May mask symptoms of ototoxicity. Use cautiously.
I.V. loop diuretics (such as furosemide): May increase risk of ototoxicity. Use cautiously; monitor hearing function.
Methotrexate: May decrease methotrexate effects. Monitor patient for decreased effect.
Oral anticoagulants: May inhibit vitamin K–producing bacteria; may increase anticoagulant effect. Monitor patient for bleeding; monitor PT and INR.

Effects on lab test results

• May increase BUN, creatinine, and nonprotein nitrogen levels.

Pharmacokinetics

Absorption: About 3%. Enhanced in patients with impaired GI motility or mucosal intestinal ulcerations.

N

Distribution: Local.
Metabolism: None.
Excretion: Mainly unchanged in feces. *Half-life:* 2 to 3 hours.

Route	Onset	Peak	Duration
P.O.	Unknown	1–4 hr	8 hr

Action

Chemical effect: Inhibits protein synthesis by binding directly to 30S ribosomal subunit.
Therapeutic effect: Kills susceptible bacteria, such as many aerobic gram-negative organisms and some aerobic gram-positive organisms. Inhibits ammonia-forming bacteria in GI tract, reducing ammonia and improving neurologic status of patients with hepatic encephalopathy.

Available forms

Oral solution: 125 mg/5 ml
Tablets: 500 mg

NURSING PROCESS

Assessment

- Assess patient's condition before starting therapy and regularly thereafter to monitor drug effectiveness.
- Evaluate patient's hearing before starting therapy and regularly thereafter.
- Monitor renal function (output, specific gravity, urinalysis, BUN and creatinine levels, and creatinine clearance).
- Be alert for adverse reactions and drug interactions.
- If patient has adverse GI reactions, monitor his hydration.
- Assess patient's and family's knowledge of drug therapy.

Nursing diagnoses

- Risk for infection related to organisms
- Risk for deficient fluid volume related to drug-induced adverse GI reactions
- Deficient knowledge related to drug therapy

Planning and implementation

ALERT: Never give drug parenterally.
- Drug is nonabsorbable at recommended dosage. More than 4 g daily may be systemically absorbed and lead to nephrotoxicity.
- Make sure patient is well hydrated while taking drug to minimize chemical irritation of renal tubules.
- For preoperative disinfection, provide low-residue diet and cathartic immediately before giving the drug orally.
- In adjunct therapy of hepatic coma, decrease patient's dietary protein and assess neurologic status frequently during therapy.
- The ototoxic and nephrotoxic properties of neomycin limit its usefulness.
- Drug is available with polymyxin B as urinary bladder irrigant.
- Notify prescriber about signs of decreasing renal function or complaints of tinnitus, vertigo, or hearing loss. Deafness may begin several weeks after drug is stopped.

Patient teaching
- Instruct patient to report adverse reactions, especially hearing loss or change in urinary elimination.
- Emphasize the need to drink 2 L of fluid each day.
- Tell patient to alert prescriber if infection worsens or doesn't improve.

Evaluation

- Patient is free from infection.
- Patient maintains adequate hydration throughout drug therapy.
- Patient and family state understanding of drug therapy.

neostigmine bromide
(nee-oh-STIG-meen BROH-mighd)
Prostigmin

neostigmine methylsulfate
Prostigmin

Pharmacologic class: cholinesterase inhibitor
Therapeutic class: muscle stimulant
Pregnancy risk category: C

Indications and dosages

▶ **Myasthenia gravis.** *Adults:* 15 to 30 mg P.O. t.i.d. (range, 15 to 375 mg daily). Or, 0.5 mg (1:2,000 solution) subcutaneously, I.M., or I.V., as needed.
Children: 7.5 to 15 mg P.O. t.i.d. or q.i.d. or 2 mg/kg/day P.O. divided q 3 to 4 hours. Or,

0.01 to 0.04 mg/kg/dose I.M., I.V., or subcutaneously q 2 to 3 hours, as needed. Later doses must be highly individualized, depending on response and tolerance of adverse effects. Therapy may be required day and night.

▶ **To diagnose myasthenia gravis.** *Adults:* 0.022 mg/kg I.M. 30 minutes after 0.011 mg/kg I.M. of atropine sulfate.
Children: 0.025 to 0.04 mg/kg. I.M. after 0.011 mg/kg atropine sulfate subcutaneously.

▶ **Postoperative abdominal distention and bladder atony.** *Adults:* 0.25 to 0.5 mg (1:4,000 solution) I.M. or subcutaneously q 4 to 6 hours for 2 to 3 days.

▶ **Antidote for nondepolarizing neuromuscular blockers.** *Adults:* 0.5 to 2.5 mg I.V. slowly. Repeat, as needed, to total of 5 mg. Before antidote dose, give 0.6 to 1.2 mg I.V. atropine sulfate.
Children age 12 months and older: 0.025 to 0.08 mg/kg/dose I.V. given with atropine or glycopyrrolate.
Infants up to age 12 months: 0.025 to 0.1 mg/kg/dose I.V. given with atropine or glycopyrrolate.

▶ **Supraventricular tachycardia from tricyclic antidepressant overdose‡.** *Children:* 0.5 to 1 mg I.V. slowly, followed by 0.25 to 0.5 mg I.V. q 1 to 3 hours, if needed.

▶ **Decrease small bowel transit time during radiography‡.** *Adults:* 0.5 to 0.75 mg subcutaneously.

I.V. administration

- A 1:1,000 solution of injectable solution contains 1 mg/ml; a 1:2,000 solution contains 0.5 mg/ml.
- Give drug at slow, controlled rate of no more than 1 mg/minute in adults and 0.5 mg/minute in children.

⊗ **Incompatibilities**
None reported.

Contraindications and cautions

- Contraindicated in patients hypersensitive to cholinergics or bromide and in those with peritonitis or mechanical obstruction of intestine or urinary tract.
- Use cautiously in patients with bronchial asthma, bradycardia, seizure disorders, recent coronary occlusion, vagotonia, hyperthyroidism, arrhythmias, or peptic ulcer.

Lifespan: In pregnant women, safety and effectiveness haven't been established.

Adverse reactions

CNS: dizziness, headache, jitters, mental confusion.
CV: ***bradycardia, cardiac arrest,*** hypotension.
EENT: blurred vision, lacrimation, miosis.
GI: *abdominal cramps, diarrhea,* excessive salivation, *nausea, vomiting.*
GU: urinary frequency.
Musculoskeletal: *muscle cramps,* muscle fasciculations, muscle weakness.
Respiratory: ***bronchoconstriction, bronchospasm, depressed respiratory drive, respiratory arrest.***
Skin: diaphoresis, rash (with bromide).
Other: ***anaphylaxis, hypersensitivity reactions.***

Interactions

Drug-drug. *Aminoglycosides, anticholinergics, atropine, corticosteroids, magnesium sulfate, procainamide, quinidine:* May reverse cholinergic effects. Observe patient for lack of drug effect.

Effects on lab test results

None reported.

Pharmacokinetics

Absorption: 1% to 2% after P.O. use. Unknown after subcutaneous or I.M. use.
Distribution: About 15% to 25% of dose binds to serum albumin.
Metabolism: Hydrolyzed by cholinesterases and metabolized by microsomal liver enzymes.
Excretion: About 80% of drug in urine. *Half-life:* 52 to 53 minutes.

Route	Onset	Peak	Duration
P.O.	45–75 min	1–2 hr	2–4 hr
I.V.	4–8 min	1–2 hr	2–4 hr
I.M.	20–30 min	1–2 hr	2–4 hr
SubQ	Unknown	1–2 hr	2–4 hr

Action

Chemical effect: Inhibits destruction of acetylcholine released from parasympathetic and somatic efferent nerves. Acetylcholine accumulates, increasing stimulation of receptor.
Therapeutic effect: Stimulates muscle contraction.

N

Available forms

neostigmine bromide
Tablets: 15 mg
neostigmine methylsulfate
Injection: 0.25 mg/ml, 0.5 mg/ml, 1 mg/ml

NURSING PROCESS

Assessment

- Assess patient's condition before beginning therapy.
- Monitor patient's response after each dose. Watch closely for improvement in strength, vision, and ptosis 45 to 60 minutes after each dose. Show patient how to record variations in muscle strength.
- Monitor vital signs often.
- Assess patient's and family's knowledge of drug therapy.

Nursing diagnoses

- Impaired physical mobility related to condition
- Diarrhea related to drug's adverse effect on GI tract
- Deficient knowledge related to drug therapy

Planning and implementation

ALERT: For diagnosis of myasthenia gravis, stop any anticholinesterases for at least 8 hours before giving drug.

- For myasthenia gravis, schedule doses before fatigue. For example, if patient has dysphagia, schedule dose 30 minutes before each meal.
- Give atropine injection and provide respiratory support as needed.
- When drug is used to prevent abdominal distention and GI distress, use a rectal tube to help passage of gas.

ALERT: Although drug is commonly used to reverse effects of nondepolarizing neuromuscular blockers in patients who have undergone surgery, it may worsen blockade produced by succinylcholine.

- Patient may develop resistance to drug.
- Give oral drug with food or milk.

ALERT: Use I.M. drug instead of edrophonium to diagnose myasthenia gravis when lengthy procedures involving testing of limb strength are used.

ALERT: Don't confuse neostigmine with etomidate (Amidate) vials. They may look alike.

Patient teaching

- Tell patient to take drug with food or milk to reduce GI distress.
- When using for myasthenia gravis, explain that drug will relieve ptosis, double vision, difficulty chewing and swallowing, and trunk and limb weakness. Stress need to take drug exactly as ordered. Explain that it may have to be taken for life.
- Advise patient to wear or carry medical identification indicating that he has myasthenia gravis.

Evaluation

- Patient performs activities of daily living without assistance.
- Patient has normal bowel patterns.
- Patient and family state understanding of drug therapy.

nesiritide

(neh-SIR-ih-tighd)
Natrecor

Pharmacologic class: human B-type natriuretic peptide
Therapeutic class: inotropic vasodilator
Pregnancy risk category: C

Indications and dosages

▶ **Acutely decompensated heart failure in patients with dyspnea at rest or with minimal activity.** *Adults:* 2 mcg/kg by I.V. bolus over 60 seconds followed by continuous infusion of 0.01 mcg/kg/minute.

I.V. administration

- Use these formulas to calculate bolus volume (2 mcg/kg) and infusion flow rate (0.01 mcg/kg/minute):

$$\underset{\text{(ml)}}{\text{Bolus volume}} = 0.33 \times \underset{\text{(kg)}}{\text{patient weight}}$$

$$\underset{\text{(ml/hr)}}{\text{Infusion flow rate}} = 0.1 \times \underset{\text{(kg)}}{\text{patient weight}}$$

- Reconstitute one 1.5-mg vial with 5 ml of diluent (such as D_5W, normal saline solution, 5% dextrose and 0.2% saline solution injection, or 5% dextrose and half-normal saline solution) from a prefilled 250-ml I.V. bag.

- Don't shake vial. Gently rock until solution is clear and colorless.
- Withdraw contents of vial and add back to the 250-ml bag to yield 6 mcg/ml. Invert the bag several times to ensure complete mixing, and use the solution within 24 hours.
- Drug binds heparin and could bind the heparin lining of a heparin-coated catheter, decreasing the amount of nesiritide delivered. Don't give nesiritide through a central heparin-coated catheter.
- Before starting bolus dose, prime the tubing. Give the bolus over 60 seconds through a port in the tubing.
- Immediately after giving bolus, infuse drug at 0.1 ml/kg/hour to deliver 0.01 mcg/kg/minute.
- Store drug at a controlled room temperature.

⊗ **Incompatibilities**

Bumetanide, enalaprilat, ethacrynate sodium, furosemide, heparin, hydralazine, insulin, sodium metabisulfite preservative.

Contraindications and cautions

- Contraindicated in patients hypersensitive to the drug or any of its components.
- Avoid using drug as primary therapy in patients with cardiogenic shock, systolic blood pressure below 90 mm Hg, low cardiac filling pressures, conditions in which cardiac output depends on venous return, or conditions that make vasodilators inappropriate, such as valvular stenosis, restrictive or obstructive cardiomyopathy, constrictive pericarditis, or pericardial tamponade.

Lifespan: In pregnant women, use cautiously. In breast-feeding women, use cautiously; it's unknown if the drug appears in breast milk. In children, safety and effectiveness haven't been established. Some older patients are more sensitive to drug effects than younger patients, but no overall difference in effectiveness has been noted.

Adverse reactions

CNS: anxiety, confusion, dizziness, fever, headache, insomnia, paresthesia, somnolence, tremor.
CV: angina, atrial fibrillation, AV node conduction abnormalities, ***bradycardia, hypotension,*** ventricular extrasystoles, ***ventricular tachycardia.***
GI: abdominal pain, nausea, vomiting.
Hematologic: anemia.
Musculoskeletal: back pain, leg cramps.
Respiratory: *apnea,* cough.
Skin: pruritus, rash, sweating.
Other: injection-site reactions, pain at the site.

Interactions

Drug-drug. *ACE inhibitors:* May increase hypotension symptoms. Monitor blood pressure closely.

Effects on lab test results

- May increase creatinine level more than 0.5 mg/dl above baseline. May decrease hemoglobin level and hematocrit.

Pharmacokinetics

Absorption: Given I.V.
Distribution: Unknown.
Metabolism: Unknown.
Excretion: Three independent paths: lysosomal proteolysis after drug binds to cell surface receptors, proteolytic cleavage by endopeptidases in the vascular lumen, and renal filtration. *Half-life:* 18 minutes.

Route	Onset	Peak	Duration
I.V.	15 min	1 hr	3 hr

Action

Chemical effect: Binds to receptors on vascular smooth muscle and endothelial cells, which leads to relaxation of smooth muscles and dilation of veins and arteries.
Therapeutic effect: Produces a dose-dependent reduction in pulmonary capillary wedge pressure and systemic arterial pressure in patients with heart failure.

Available forms

Injection: Single-dose vials of 1.5-mg sterile, lyophilized powder

NURSING PROCESS

Assessment

- Assess underlying condition before starting therapy, and reassess regularly to monitor drug effectiveness.

ALERT: Drug may cause hypotension. Monitor patient's blood pressure closely, particularly if patient also takes an ACE inhibitor.

• Evaluate patient's renal function because drug affects renal function in some people. In patients with severe heart failure whose renal function depends on the renin-angiotensin-aldosterone system, therapy may lead to azotemia.
• Monitor patient's cardiac status before, during, and after giving drug.
• Assess patient's and family's knowledge of drug therapy.

Nursing diagnoses

• Ineffective tissue perfusion (cardiopulmonary) related to drug-induced hypotension
• Excess fluid volume related to heart failure
• Deficient knowledge related to nesiritide therapy

Planning and implementation

• Because of hypotension, don't start drug at dose higher than recommended. If hypotension develops during administration, reduce dose or stop giving drug; then restart at a lower dose.
• Limited data exist about giving this drug for longer than 48 hours.

Patient teaching

• Tell patient to report discomfort at I.V. site.
• Urge patient to report symptoms of hypotension, such as dizziness, light-headedness, blurred vision, or sweating.
• Tell patient to report other adverse effects promptly.

Evaluation

• Patient's blood pressure remains normal during therapy.
• Patient's volume status improves.
• Patient and family state understanding of drug therapy.

nevirapine

(neh-VEER-uh-peen)
Viramune

Pharmacologic class: nonnucleoside reverse transcriptase inhibitor
Therapeutic class: antiretroviral
Pregnancy risk category: C

Indications and dosages

▶ **Adjunct for deteriorating patients with HIV-1 infection.** *Adults:* 200 mg P.O. daily for first 14 days, followed by 200 mg P.O. b.i.d. with nucleoside analogue antiretroviral drugs.
▶ **Adjunct therapy in children infected with HIV-1.** *Children age 8 and older:* 4 mg/kg P.O. once daily for first 14 days, followed by 4 mg/kg P.O. b.i.d. thereafter. Maximum, 400 mg daily.
Children ages 2 months to 7 years: 4 mg/kg P.O. once daily for first 14 days, followed by 7 mg/kg P.O. b.i.d. thereafter. Maximum dosage is 400 mg daily.
▶ **Prevention of maternal-fetal transmission of HIV‡.** *Mother:* Give 200 mg P.O. as a single dose at the onset of labor.
Neonate: Give 2 mg/kg P.O. as a single dose 48 to 72 hours after birth. Usually given with a three-part zidovudine regimen.

Contraindications and cautions

• Contraindicated in patients hypersensitive to the drug or any of its components and in those with severe hepatic impairment.
• Use cautiously in patients with impaired renal and hepatic function or coinfection with hepatitis B or C. Use extreme caution in women and patients with CD4 counts greater than 250 cells/mm^3.
Lifespan: In pregnant women, use only if benefits outweigh risks to the fetus. Women shouldn't breast-feed to reduce risk of giving HIV to infant. In the elderly, choose dose cautiously.

Adverse reactions

CNS: *fever, headache,* paresthesia.
GI: abdominal pain, diarrhea, *nausea,* ulcerative stomatitis.
Hepatic: ***hepatitis, hepatotoxicity.***
Musculoskeletal: myalgia.
Skin: blistering, rash, ***Stevens-Johnson syndrome, toxic epidermal necrolysis.***
Other: fat redistribution, ***severe hypersensitivity reactions.***

Interactions

Drug-drug. *CYP3A4 inhibitors (cimetidine, macrolides):* May increase nevirapine level. Monitor patient for adverse effects.

Drugs extensively metabolized by CYP3A4 (rifabutin, rifampin): May decrease plasma concentrations of these drugs. Adjust dosages of these drugs if needed.
Hormonal contraceptives, protease inhibitors: May decrease levels of these drugs. Monitor patient for effect; advise patient to use nonhormonal contraception.
Ketoconazole: May decrease ketoconazole level and increase nevirapine level. Avoid use together.
Drug-herb. *St. John's wort:* May decrease nevirapine level. Discourage use together.

Effects on lab test results

- May increase ALT, AST, GGT, and bilirubin levels. May decrease hemoglobin level and hematocrit.
- May decrease neutrophil count.

Pharmacokinetics

Absorption: Greater than 90%.
Distribution: Wide.
Metabolism: By liver.
Excretion: In urine and feces. *Terminal-phase half-life:* 45 hours (single dose); 25 to 30 hours (multiple doses).

Route	Onset	Peak	Duration
P.O.	Unknown	4 hr	Unknown

Action

Chemical effect: Binds to reverse transcriptase and blocks RNA-dependent and DNA-dependent DNA polymerase activities.
Therapeutic effect: May inhibit replication of HIV-1.

Available forms

Oral suspension: 50 mg/5 ml
Tablets: 200 mg

NURSING PROCESS

Assessment

- Obtain lab tests, including liver and renal function tests, before and during therapy.
- Monitor patient for blistering, oral lesions, conjunctivitis, muscle or joint aches, or general malaise. Be especially alert for severe rash, rash with fever, or rash with elevated AST and ALT levels, which require stopping therapy. Report such signs and symptoms immediately to prescriber.

Nursing diagnoses

- Risk for infection related to presence of virus
- Deficient knowledge related to drug therapy

Planning and implementation

- If clinical hepatitis occurs, stop therapy permanently.
- Use drug with at least one other antiretroviral.
- Notify the Antiretroviral Pregnancy Registry if woman is or becomes pregnant while taking drug by calling 1-800-258-4263 or visiting www.apregistry.com.

ALERT: Don't confuse nelfinavir with nevirapine.

Patient teaching

- Inform patient that drug doesn't cure HIV infection and that he can still develop illnesses in advanced HIV infection and can still transmit HIV to others.
- Instruct patient to report rash at once and to stop taking the drug if rash develops.
- Instruct women to use at least two barrier methods of contraception because hormonal contraceptive effectiveness is reduced.
- Tell patient not to take other drugs unless approved by prescriber.
- If therapy is interrupted for longer than 7 days, instruct patient to resume it as if for the first time.
- Tell patient with evidence of hepatitis (fatigue, malaise, anorexia, nausea, jaundice, liver tenderness or hepatomegaly, with or without initially abnormal transaminase levels) to stop taking the drug and immediately seek medical evaluation.

Evaluation

- Patient shows no signs of worsening condition.
- Patient and family state understanding of drug therapy.

N

niacin (nicotinic acid, vitamin B_3)

(NIGH-uh-sin)
Niacin TR Tablets, Niacor, Niaspan, Nicolar, Nicotinex*, Slo Niacin

niacinamide (nicotinamide)†

Pharmacologic class: B-complex vitamin
Therapeutic class: vitamin B_3, antilipemic, peripheral vasodilator
Pregnancy risk category: A (C in dosages that exceed the RDA)

Indications and dosages

▶ **RDA.** *Neonates and infants younger than 6 months:* Give 2 mg.
Infants ages 7 months to 1 year: Give 4 mg.
Children ages 1 to 3: Give 6 mg.
Children ages 4 to 8: Give 8 mg.
Children ages 9 to 13: Give 12 mg.
Males age 14 and older: Give 16 mg.
Females age 14 and older: Give 14 mg.
Pregnant women: Give 18 mg.
Breast-feeding women: Give 17 mg.

▶ **Pellagra.** *Adults:* 300 to 500 mg P.O. daily in divided doses, depending on severity of niacin deficiency.
Children: Up to 300 mg P.O. daily, depending on severity of niacin deficiency. After symptoms subside, advise adequate nutrition and RDA supplements to prevent recurrence.

▶ **Hartnup disease.** *Adults:* 50 to 200 mg P.O. daily.

▶ **Niacin deficiency.** *Adults:* Up to 100 mg P.O. daily.

▶ **Hyperlipidemias, especially with hypercholesterolemia.** *Adults:* Initially, 250 mg P.O. as a single dose following evening meal. Then increase q 4 to 7 days to 1 to 2 g P.O. b.i.d. or t.i.d. with meals until desired LDL level is achieved. Maximum, 6 g daily. Alternatively, for extended-release tablets, start at 500 mg P.O. daily at bedtime for 1 to 4 weeks; then increase to 1,000 mg at bedtime during weeks 5 to 8. After week 8, increase by 500 mg q 4 weeks. Maximum, 2 g daily.

Contraindications and cautions

- Contraindicated in patients hypersensitive to the drug or any of its components and in those with hepatic dysfunction, active peptic ulcers, severe hypotension, or arterial hemorrhage.
- Use cautiously in patients with gallbladder disease, diabetes mellitus, or coronary artery disease and in patients with history of liver disease, peptic ulcer, allergy, or gout.

Lifespan: In pregnant women, use above the RDA hasn't been studied. In breast-feeding women, use above the RDA isn't recommended. In children, safety of doses that exceed the RDA hasn't been established.

Adverse reactions

CNS: dizziness, transient headache.
CV: ***arrhythmias,*** *excessive peripheral vasodilation, flushing.*
GI: activation of peptic ulceration, *diarrhea,* epigastric or substernal pain, *nausea, vomiting.*
Hepatic: ***hepatic dysfunction.***
Metabolic: hyperglycemia, hyperuricemia.
Skin: dryness, pruritus, tingling.

Interactions

Drug-drug. *Antihypertensives:* May increase risk of orthostatic hypotension. Use together cautiously; also warn patient about orthostatic hypotension.
HMG-CoA reductase inhibitors, such as lovastatin: May result in myopathy and rhabdomyolysis. Avoid use together.

Effects on lab test results

- May increase glucose, AST, ALT, and uric acid levels.

Pharmacokinetics

Absorption: Rapid after P.O. use. Unknown after subcutaneous or I.M. use.
Distribution: Wide.
Metabolism: By liver to active metabolites.
Excretion: In urine. *Half-life:* About 45 minutes.

Route	Onset	Peak	Duration
P.O.	Unknown	45 min	Unknown

Action

Chemical effect: Niacin and niacinamide stimulate lipid metabolism, tissue respiration, and glycogenolysis; niacin decreases synthesis of low-density lipoproteins and inhibits lipolysis in adipose tissue.

Therapeutic effect: Restores normal level of vitamin B_3, lowers triglyceride and cholesterol levels, and dilates peripheral blood vessels.

Available forms

niacin
Capsules (timed-release): 125 mg†, 250 mg†, 400 mg†, 500 mg
Elixir: 50 mg/5 ml*†
Tablets: 50 mg†, 100 mg†, 250 mg†, 500 mg
Tablets (extended-release): 500 mg, 750 mg, 1,000 mg
Tablets (timed-release): 250 mg†, 500 mg†, 750 mg†
niacinamide
Tablets: 50 mg†, 100 mg†, 500 mg†

NURSING PROCESS

Assessment

- Assess patient's condition before starting therapy and regularly thereafter to monitor drug effectiveness.
- Monitor hepatic function and glucose levels.
- Be alert for adverse reactions and drug interactions.
- If patient has an adverse GI reaction, monitor his hydration.
- Assess patient's and family's knowledge of drug therapy.

Nursing diagnoses

- Imbalanced nutrition: less than body requirements related to decreased intake of vitamin B_3
- Risk for deficient fluid volume related to drug-induced adverse GI reactions
- Deficient knowledge related to drug therapy

Planning and implementation

ALERT: Give aspirin (325 mg P.O. 30 minutes before niacin dose) to help reduce persistent or distressing flushing.

- Timed-release niacin or niacinamide may prevent excessive flushing that occurs with large doses, but this drug form also has been linked to hepatic dysfunction, even at doses as low as 1 g daily.
- Give drug with meals to minimize GI adverse effects.

ALERT: Don't confuse Nicobid and Nicotinex with Nicoderm, Nicotrol, or Nicorette.

Patient teaching

- Explain that skin flushing or warm sensation is usually harmless and will usually subside with continued use.
- Advise patient to decrease flushing by taking drug with a low-fat snack and not taking it after alcohol, hot beverages, hot or spicy foods, a hot shower, or exercise.
- Stress that drug is a potent drug that may cause serious adverse effects. Explain importance of adhering to therapy.
- Advise patient against self-medicating for hyperlipidemia.

Evaluation

- Patient's vitamin B_3 levels are normal.
- Patient maintains adequate hydration throughout drug therapy.
- Patient and family state understanding of drug therapy.

nifedipine

(nigh-FEH-duh-peen)

Adalat CC, Apo-Nifed ♦, Nifedical XL, Novo-Nifedin ♦, Nu-Nifed ♦, Procardia XL✐

Pharmacologic class: calcium channel blocker
Therapeutic class: antianginal
Pregnancy risk category: C

Indications and dosages

▶ **Vasospastic angina (Prinzmetal or variant angina), classic chronic stable angina pectoris.** *Adults:* Initially, 10 mg (short-acting capsules) P.O. t.i.d. Usual effective dosage range is 10 to 20 mg t.i.d. Some patients may require up to 30 mg q.i.d. Maximum daily dose is 180 mg. Adjust dosage over 7 to 14 days to evaluate response. Or, 30 to 60 mg (extended-release tablets, except Adalat CC) P.O. once daily. Maximum daily dose is 120 mg. Adjust dosage over 7 to 14 days to evaluate response.

▶ **Hypertension.** *Adults:* 30 or 60 mg P.O. (extended-release) once daily. Adjusted over 7 to 14 days. Doses larger than 90 mg (Adalat CC) and 120 mg (Procardia XL) aren't recommended.

Contraindications and cautions

- Contraindicated in patients hypersensitive to the drug or any of its components.

• Use cautiously in those with heart failure or hypotension. Use extended-release tablets cautiously in patients with severe GI narrowing because obstructive symptoms may occur.

Lifespan: In pregnant and breast-feeding women, drug is contraindicated. In children, safety and effectiveness haven't been established. In geriatric patients, use cautiously.

Adverse reactions

CNS: *dizziness, headache, light-headedness,* nervousness, somnolence, syncope, weakness.
CV: *flushing,* ***heart failure,*** hypotension, ***MI,*** palpitations, *peripheral edema.*
EENT: nasal congestion.
GI: abdominal discomfort, constipation, diarrhea, *nausea.*
Metabolic: ***hypokalemia.***
Musculoskeletal: muscle cramps.
Respiratory: cough, dyspnea, ***pulmonary edema.***
Skin: pruritus, rash.

Interactions

Drug-drug. *Antiretrovirals, cimetidine, verapamil:* May decrease nifedipine metabolism. Monitor blood pressure closely, and adjust nifedipine dosage as needed.
Azole antifungals, dalfopristin erythromycin, quinupristin: May increase nifedipine effects. Monitor blood pressure closely, and decrease nifedipine dosage as needed.
Digoxin: May increase digoxin level. Monitor digoxin level.
Diltiazem: May increase nifedipine effects. Monitor patient closely.
Fentanyl: May cause severe hypotension. Monitor blood pressure.
Phenytoin: May reduce phenytoin metabolism. Monitor phenytoin level.
Propranolol, other beta blockers: May cause hypotension and heart failure. Use together cautiously.
Quinidine: May decrease quinidine levels and effects and increase nifedipine effects. Monitor heart rate, and adjust nifedipine dosage as needed.
Rifamycins: May decrease nifedipine level. Monitor patient.
Tacrolimus: May increase tacrolimus level and risk for toxicity. Decrease tacrolimus dosage as needed.
Drug-herb. *Ginkgo:* May increase nifedipine effects. Discourage use together.
Ginseng: May increase nifedipine level and possibly cause toxicity. Discourage use together.
Melatonin, St. John's wort: May interfere with antihypertensive effect. Discourage use together.
Drug-food. *Grapefruit juice:* May increase nifedipine bioavailability. Discourage use together.

Effects on lab test results

• May increase ALT, AST, alkaline phosphatase, and LDH levels.

Pharmacokinetics

Absorption: Rapid and about 90%, but only about 45% to 75% reaches circulation because of significant first-pass effect in liver.
Distribution: About 92% to 98% protein-bound.
Metabolism: In liver.
Excretion: In urine and feces as inactive metabolites. *Half-life:* 2 to 5 hours.

Route	Onset	Peak	Duration
P.O.	20 min	30–60 min	4–8 hr
P.O. Extended release	20 min	6 hr	24 hr

Action

Chemical effect: Unknown; may inhibit calcium ion influx across cardiac and smooth-muscle cells, decreasing myocardial contractility and oxygen demand. Also may dilate coronary arteries and arterioles.
Therapeutic effect: Reduces blood pressure and prevents angina.

Available forms

Capsules: 10 mg, 20 mg
Tablets (extended-release): 30 mg, 60 mg, 90 mg

NURSING PROCESS

Assessment

• Assess patient's condition before starting therapy and regularly thereafter to monitor drug effectiveness.

• Monitor blood pressure regularly, especially in patients who take beta blockers or antihypertensives.

• Monitor potassium level regularly.
• Be alert for adverse reactions and drug interactions.
• Assess patient's and family's knowledge of drug therapy.

Nursing diagnoses
• Risk for injury related to presence of hypertension
• Chronic pain related to angina
• Deficient knowledge related to drug therapy

Planning and implementation
• Don't give immediate-release form within 1 week of acute MI or in acute coronary syndrome.
ALERT: Don't use nifedipine capsules sublingually to rapidly reduce severely high blood pressure. Excessive hypotension, MI, and death may result.
• Watch for symptoms of heart failure.
ALERT: Don't confuse nifedipine with nimodipine or nicardipine.

Patient teaching
• If patient is kept on nitrate therapy while nifedipine dosage is adjusted, urge continued compliance. Patient may take S.L. nitroglycerin, as needed, for acute chest pain.
• Tell patient that chest pain may worsen briefly when therapy starts or dosage increases.
• Instruct patient to swallow extended-release tablets without breaking, crushing, or chewing them.
• Advise patient to avoid taking drug with grapefruit juice.
• Reassure patient taking the extended-release form that a wax-matrix "ghost" from the tablet may be passed in the stool. Drug is completely absorbed before this occurs.
• Tell patient to protect capsules from direct light and moisture and to store at room temperature.

Evaluation
• Patient's blood pressure is normal.
• Patient's angina is less frequent and severe.
• Patient and family state understanding of drug therapy.

nisoldipine
(nigh-SOHL-dih-peen)
Sular

Pharmacologic class: calcium channel blocker
Therapeutic class: antihypertensive
Pregnancy risk category: C

Indications and dosages
▶ **Hypertension.** *Adults:* Initially, 20 mg P.O. once daily; then increase by 10 mg weekly or at longer intervals, as indicated. Usual maintenance dosage is 20 to 40 mg once daily. Dosages above 60 mg daily aren't recommended.
Adjust-a-dose: For patients older than age 65 and those who have liver dysfunction, initial dosage is 10 mg P.O. daily.

Contraindications and cautions
• Contraindicated in patients hypersensitive to dihydropyridine calcium channel blockers.
• Use cautiously in patients with severe hepatic impairment, heart failure, or compromised ventricular function, and particularly in those taking beta blockers.
Lifespan: In pregnant women, use cautiously. In breast-feeding women, don't use drug. In children, safety and effectiveness haven't been established.

Adverse reactions
CNS: dizziness, *headache.*
CV: chest pain, palpitations, *peripheral edema,* vasodilation.
EENT: pharyngitis, sinusitis.
GI: nausea.
Skin: rash.

Interactions
Drug-drug. *Cimetidine:* May increase nisoldipine bioavailability and peak level. Monitor patient for increased adverse effects.
Quinidine: May decrease nisoldipine bioavailability but not peak level. Monitor patient.
Drug-food. *Grapefruit juice:* May increase peak drug level, increasing therapeutic and adverse effects. Give drug 1 hour before or after patient eats or drinks grapefruit.
High-fat meal: May increase peak drug level. Don't give drug with a high-fat meal.

N

Effects on lab test results

None reported.

Pharmacokinetics

Absorption: Good; high-fat foods significantly affect rate of release of drug.
Distribution: About 99% protein-bound.
Metabolism: Extensive.
Excretion: In urine. *Half-life:* 7 to 12 hours.

Route	Onset	Peak	Duration
P.O.	Unknown	6–12 hr	24 hr

Action

Chemical effect: Prevents entry of calcium ions into vascular smooth-muscle cells, causing dilation of arterioles, which decreases peripheral vascular resistance.
Therapeutic effect: Lowers blood pressure.

Available forms

Extended-release tablets: 10 mg, 20 mg, 30 mg, 40 mg

NURSING PROCESS

Assessment

- Assess patient's blood pressure before starting therapy, and monitor regularly, especially during dose adjustment.
- Monitor patient carefully. Some patients, especially those with severe obstructive coronary artery disease, may develop increased frequency, duration, or severity of angina or acute MI when starting calcium channel blocker therapy or increasing dose.
- Be alert for adverse reactions and interactions.
- Assess patient's and family's knowledge of drug therapy.

Nursing diagnoses

- Risk for injury related to hypertension
- Excess fluid volume related to edema
- Deficient knowledge related to drug therapy

Planning and implementation

- Don't give drug with a high-fat meal or grapefruit products.

ALERT: Don't confuse nisoldipine with nifedipine or nicardipine.

Patient teaching

- Tell patient to take drug as prescribed.
- Instruct patient to swallow tablet whole and not to chew, divide, or crush it.

Evaluation

- Patient's blood pressure is normal.
- Patient doesn't exhibit signs of edema.
- Patient and family state understanding of drug therapy.

nitrofurantoin macrocrystals

(nigh-troh-fyoo-RAN-toyn MAH-kroh-kris-tuls)
Macrobid, Macrodantin

nitrofurantoin microcrystals

Apo-Nitrofurantoin ♦, Furadantin, Furalan, Macrodantin

Pharmacologic class: nitrofuran
Therapeutic class: urinary tract anti-infective
Pregnancy risk category: B

Indications and dosages

▶ **UTI caused by susceptible *Escherichia coli, Staphylococcus aureus,* enterococci, and certain strains of *Klebsiella* and *Enterobacter.*** *Adults and children older than age 12:* Give 50 to 100 mg P.O. q.i.d. with milk or meals. Or 100 mg Macrobid PO q 12 hours for 7 days.
Children ages 1 month to 12 years: 5 to 7 mg/kg P.O. daily, divided q.i.d.

▶ **Long-term suppression therapy.** *Adults:* 50 to 100 mg P.O. at bedtime.
Children age 1 month and older: 1 to 2 mg/kg P.O. at bedtime.

Contraindications and cautions

- Contraindicated in patients who are hypersensitive to the drug or any of its components. Contraindicated in patients with moderate to severe renal impairment (creatinine clearance less than 60 ml/minute), anuria, or oliguria.
- Use cautiously in patients with renal impairment, anemia, diabetes mellitus, electrolyte abnormalities, vitamin B deficiency, debilitating disease, or G6PD deficiency.

Lifespan: In pregnant women, use cautiously. In breast-feeding women, use cautiously; it's unknown if the drug appears in breast milk. In infants age 1 month and younger, drug is contraindicated.

Adverse reactions

CNS: ***ascending polyneuropathy,*** dizziness, drowsiness, headache, *peripheral neuropathy.*
GI: abdominal pain, anorexia, diarrhea, nausea, vomiting.
Hematologic: ***agranulocytosis, hemolysis in patients with G6PD deficiency, leukopenia, thrombocytopenia.***
Hepatic: ***hepatic necrosis, hepatitis.***
Respiratory: ***asthma,*** pulmonary sensitivity.
Skin: eczematous, erythematous, or maculopapular eruption; exfoliative dermatitis; pruritus; ***Stevens-Johnson syndrome,*** urticaria.
Other: ***anaphylaxis,*** drug fever, hypersensitivity reactions, overgrowth of nonsusceptible organisms in urinary tract, transient alopecia.

Interactions

Drug-drug. *Magnesium-containing antacids:* May decrease nitrofurantoin absorption. Separate ingestion by 1 hour.
Probenecid, sulfinpyrazone: May increase blood level and decrease urine level. May result in increased toxicity and lack of therapeutic effect. Don't use together.
Quinolones (such as nalidixic acid, norfloxacin): May decrease effectiveness of quinolone derivatives. Avoid use together.
Drug-food. *Any food:* May increase drug absorption. Give drug with food.

Effects on lab test results

- May increase phosphorus, bilirubin, and alkaline phosphatase levels. May decrease glucose and hemoglobin levels and hematocrit.
- May decrease granulocyte and platelet counts.
- May cause false-positive results with urine glucose test using copper sulfate reduction method (Clinitest), Benedict solution, or Fehling solution, but not with glucose enzymatic test.

Pharmacokinetics

Absorption: Good. Food aids drug's dissolution and speeds absorption. Macrocrystal form has slower dissolution and absorption.
Distribution: Into bile. 60% protein-bound.
Metabolism: Partially in liver.
Excretion: About 30% to 50% in urine. *Half-life:* 15 minutes to 1 hour.

Route	Onset	Peak	Duration
P.O.	Unknown	Unknown	Unknown

Action

Chemical effect: Unknown; may interfere with bacterial enzyme systems and cell wall formation.
Therapeutic effect: Hinders growth of many common gram-positive and gram-negative urinary pathogens.

Available forms

nitrofurantoin macrocrystals
Capsules: 25 mg, 50 mg, 100 mg
Capsules (dual-release): 100 mg
nitrofurantoin microcrystals
Capsules: 50 mg, 100 mg
Oral suspension: 25 mg/5 ml
Tablets: 50 mg, 100 mg

NURSING PROCESS

Assessment

- Assess patient's infection before starting therapy and regularly thereafter to monitor drug effectiveness.
- Obtain urine specimen for culture and sensitivity tests before starting therapy, and repeat as needed. Start therapy pending results.
- Monitor fluid intake and output. May turn urine darker or even brown.
- Monitor CBC and pulmonary status regularly.
- Assess patient for renal impairment before and during therapy, especially with high doses, and increased risk of ascending polyneuropathy.
- Be alert for adverse reactions and drug interactions.
- If patient has adverse GI reactions, monitor his hydration.
- Assess patient's and family's knowledge of drug therapy.

Nursing diagnoses

- Risk for infection related to susceptible bacteria
- Risk for deficient fluid volume related to drug-induced adverse GI reactions
- Deficient knowledge related to drug therapy

Planning and implementation

- Drug has no effect on blood or tissue outside urinary tract.

N

• Notify prescriber if patient develops cough, chest pains, fever, chills, and dyspnea (signs of pulmonary sensitivity).
• Be aware that patients with G6PD deficiency who develop hemolysis during therapy will recover when drug is stopped.
ALERT: Hypersensitivity may develop during long-term therapy.
• Dual-release capsules (25-mg nitrofurantoin macrocrystals combined with 75-mg nitrofurantoin monohydrate) enable twice-daily dosing.
• Continue therapy for 3 days after urine specimens become sterile.
• Patient may experience fewer adverse GI effects with nitrofurantoin macrocrystals.
• Store drug in amber container. Avoid metals other than stainless steel or aluminum to avoid precipitate formation.

Patient teaching
• Tell patient to take drug with food or milk to minimize GI distress.
• Teach patient how to measure intake and output. Warn him that drug will turn urine darker or even brown.
• Instruct patient how to store drug.

Evaluation
• Patient is free from infection.
• Patient maintains adequate hydration throughout drug therapy.
• Patient and family state understanding of drug therapy.

nitroglycerin (glyceryl trinitrate)
(nigh-troh-GLIH-suh-rin)
Anginine ◇, Deponit, Minitran, Nitradisc ◇, Nitro-Bid, Nitro-Bid IV, Nitrodisc, Nitro-Dur, Nitrogard, Nitroglyn, Nitrolingual, NitroQuick, Nitrostat, Nitro-Time, Transderm-Nitro, Transiderm-Nitro ◇, Tridil

Pharmacologic class: nitrate
Therapeutic class: antianginal, vasodilator
Pregnancy risk category: C

Indications and dosages
▶ **Prevention of chronic anginal attacks.** *Adults:* 2.5 mg or 2.6 mg sustained-release capsule q 8 to 12 hours. Or 2% ointment: Start with ½ inch of ointment and increase by ½-inch increments until headache occurs; then decrease to previous dose. Range of dosage with ointment is ½ to 5 inches. Usual dose is 1 to 2 inches. Or Nitrodisc, Nitro-Dur, or Transderm-Nitro transdermal disk or pad, 0.2 to 0.4 mg/hour once daily.
▶ **Acute angina pectoris; to prevent or minimize anginal attacks when taken immediately before stressful events.** *Adults:* 1 S.L. tablet (grain [gr] 1/200, 1/150, 1/100) dissolved under tongue or in buccal pouch as soon as angina begins. Repeat q 5 minutes for up to 15 minutes if symptoms persist. Or, using Nitrolingual spray, 1 or 2 sprays into mouth, preferably onto or under tongue. Repeat q 3 to 5 minutes if symptoms persist, to maximum of three doses in 15-minute period. Or, 1 to 3 mg transmucosally q 3 to 5 hours during waking hours.
▶ **Hypertension related to surgery; heart failure linked to MI; angina pectoris in acute situations; to produce controlled hypotension during surgery.** *Adults:* Initial infusion rate is 5 mcg/minute. Increase as needed by 5 mcg/minute q 3 to 5 minutes until response occurs. If 20-mcg/minute rate doesn't produce response, increase dosage by as much as 20 mcg/minute q 3 to 5 minutes. Up to 100 mcg/minute I.V. may be needed.
▶ **Hypertensive crisis‡.** *Adults:* Infuse at 5 to 100 mcg/minute I.V.

I.V. administration
• Mix in glass bottles, and avoid I.V. filters because drug binds to plastic. Regular polyvinyl chloride tubing can bind up to 80% of drug, requiring higher doses. Special nonabsorbent, nonpolyvinyl chloride tubing is available from manufacturer.
• Dilute drug with D_5W or normal saline solution for injection to no more than 400 mcg/ml.
• Always use same type of infusion set when changing I.V. lines.
• When changing concentration of nitroglycerin infusion, flush I.V. administration set with 15 to 20 ml of new concentration before use. This will clear line of old drug solution.
• Give with infusion control device and titrate to desired response.

⊗ Incompatibilities
Alteplase, bretylium, hydralazine, levofloxacin, phenytoin sodium, other I.V. drugs.

Contraindications and cautions

• Contraindicated in patients hypersensitive to nitrates and in those with early MI (S.L. form), severe anemia, increased intracranial pressure, angle-closure glaucoma, orthostatic hypotension, and allergy to adhesives (transdermal form). I.V. nitroglycerin is contraindicated in patients with hypovolemia, hypotension, cardiac tamponade, restrictive cardiomyopathy, constrictive pericarditis, or hypersensitivity to I.V. form.

• Use cautiously in patients with hypotension or volume depletion.

Lifespan: In pregnant women, use cautiously. In breast-feeding women, use cautiously; it's unknown if the drug appears in breast milk. In children, safety and effectiveness haven't been established.

Adverse reactions

CNS: *dizziness, headache, throbbing,* weakness.
CV: fainting, *flushing, orthostatic hypotension,* palpitations, *tachycardia.*
EENT: sublingual burning.
GI: nausea, vomiting.
Skin: contact dermatitis (patch), cutaneous vasodilation, rash.
Other: hypersensitivity reactions.

Interactions

Drug-drug. *Alteplase:* May decrease t-PA antigen level. Avoid use together. If use together is unavoidable, use the lowest effective dose of nitroglycerin.
Antihypertensives: May increase hypotensive effect. Monitor patient closely.
Dihydroergotamine: May decrease antianginal effect or increase mean standing systolic blood pressure. Avoid use together.
Phosphodiesterase type 5 inhibitors (sildenafil, tadalafil, vardenafil): May cause severe hypotension. Use of nitrates in any form with erectile dysfunction drugs is contraindicated.
Drug-lifestyle. *Alcohol use:* May increase hypotension. Urge patient to avoid alcohol during therapy.

Effects on lab test results

• May interfere with Zlatkis-Zak color reaction, causing false report of decreased cholesterol level.

Pharmacokinetics

Absorption: For P.O. use, good but incomplete. For S.L. use, relatively complete. For topical or transdermal use, good.
Distribution: Wide. About 60% protein-bound.
Metabolism: In liver.
Excretion: Metabolites in urine. *Half-life:* About 1 to 4 minutes.

Route	Onset	Peak	Duration
P.O.	20–45 min	Unknown	3–8 hr
I.V.	Immediate	Immediate	3–5 min
Topical	30 min	Unknown	2–12 hr
Transdermal	30 min	Unknown	≤ 24 hr
S.L.	1–3 min	Unknown	30–60 min
Buccal	3 min	Unknown	5 hr
Translingual	2–4 min	Unknown	30–60 min

Action

Chemical effect: Reduces cardiac oxygen demand by decreasing left ventricular end-diastolic pressure (preload) and, to a lesser extent, systemic vascular resistance (afterload). Also increases blood flow through collateral coronary vessels.
Therapeutic effect: Prevents or relieves acute angina, lowers blood pressure, and helps minimize heart failure caused by MI.

Available forms

Aerosol (translingual): 0.4 mg metered spray
Capsules (sustained-release): 2.5 mg, 6.5 mg, 9 mg
I.V.: 0.5 mg/ml, 0.8 mg/ml, 5 mg/ml
I.V. premixed solutions in dextrose: 100 mcg/ml, 200 mcg/ml, 400 mcg/ml
Tablets (buccal): 2 mg, 3 mg
Tablets (S.L.): 0.3 mg (gr 1/200) 0.4 mg (gr 1/150), 0.6 mg (gr 1/100)
Topical: 2% ointment
Transdermal: 2.5 mg/24 hours, 5 mg/24 hours, 7.5 mg/24 hours, 10 mg/24 hours, 15 mg/24 hours, 20 mg/24 hours

NURSING PROCESS

Assessment

• Assess patient's condition before starting therapy and regularly thereafter to monitor drug effectiveness.

- Monitor vital signs and drug response. Be particularly aware of blood pressure. Excessive hypotension may worsen MI.
- Be alert for adverse reactions and drug interactions.
- Assess patient's and family's knowledge of drug therapy.

Nursing diagnoses

- Acute or chronic pain related to angina
- Risk for injury related to drug-induced adverse reactions
- Deficient knowledge related to drug therapy

Planning and implementation

- Give P.O. tablets on empty stomach, either 30 minutes before or 1 to 2 hours after meals.
- Don't allow patient to swallow or chew S.L. tablets.
- Give S.L. tablet at first sign of attack. Wet tablet with patient's saliva, then place under patient's tongue until completely absorbed. Have patient sit and rest until pain subsides.
- Repeat dose q 5 minutes for up to three doses. If drug doesn't provide relief, immediately notify prescriber.
- If patient complains of tingling sensation with S.L. form, place tablet in buccal pouch.
- When giving translingual aerosol form, make sure patient doesn't inhale spray. Release it onto or under tongue, and have patient wait about 10 seconds or so before swallowing.
- To apply ointment, measure prescribed amount on application paper, and then place paper on any nonhairy area. Don't rub in. Cover with plastic film to aid absorption and protect clothing.
- If using Tape-Surrounded Appli-Ruler (TSAR) system, keep TSAR on skin to protect patient's clothing and to make sure that ointment remains in place.
- Remove excess ointment from previous site before applying next dose. Avoid getting ointment on fingers.
- Apply transdermal forms to any nonhairy area, except lower parts of arms or legs, to promote maximum absorption.

ALERT: Remove transdermal patch before defibrillation. Electric current may cause patch to arc, causing burn to patient or damage to paddles.

- When stopping transdermal therapy for angina, gradually reduce dose and frequency of application over 4 to 6 weeks.
- If drug is ineffective, immediately notify prescriber and keep patient at rest.
- Drug may cause headache, especially at start of therapy. Lower the dose temporarily. Tolerance to drug without headache response may develop. Treat headache with aspirin or acetaminophen.
- Minimize drug tolerance with 10- to 12-hour daily nitrate-free interval. For example, remove transdermal system in early evening and apply a new system the next morning. Or omit the last daily dose of buccal, sustained-release, or ointment form. If tolerance is suspected, alter dosage.

ALERT: Don't confuse Nitro-Bid with Nicobid.

ALERT: Don't confuse nitroglycerin with nitroprusside.

Patient teaching

- Teach patient how to use prescribed form of drug.
- Tell patient to place transmucosal tablet between lip and gum above incisors, or between cheek and gum.
- Tell patient to swallow oral tablets whole and not to chew them.
- Instruct patient to take drug regularly, as prescribed, and to have it accessible at all times.
- Tell patient that abruptly stopping the drug causes coronary vasospasm.
- Inform patient that an additional dose may be taken before anticipated stress or at bedtime if angina is nocturnal.
- Instruct patient to use caution when wearing transdermal patch near microwave oven. Leaking radiation may heat metallic backing of patch and cause burns.
- Advise patient not to drink alcohol during therapy.
- Tell patient to change to upright position slowly. Advise him to go up and down stairs carefully and to lie down at first sign of dizziness.
- Urge patient to store drug in cool, dark place in tightly closed container. To ensure potency, tell him to replace S.L. tablets 6 months after opening (mark bottle with date opened), and to remove cotton because it absorbs drug.

• Tell patient to store S.L. tablets in original container or other container specifically approved for this use and to carry container in jacket pocket or purse, not in a pocket close to body.

Evaluation

• Patient reports pain relief.
• Patient sustains no injury from adverse reactions.
• Patient and family state understanding of drug therapy.

nitroprusside sodium

(nigh-troh-PRUHS-ighd SOH-dee-um)
Nipride ♦, Nitropress

Pharmacologic class: vasodilator
Therapeutic class: antihypertensive
Pregnancy risk category: C

Indications and dosages

▶ **To lower blood pressure quickly in hypertensive emergencies; to produce controlled hypotension during anesthesia; to reduce preload and afterload in cardiac pump failure or cardiogenic shock (may be used with or without dopamine).** *Adults:* Begin infusion at 0.25 to 0.3 mcg/kg/minute I.V. and gradually titrate q few minutes to a maximum infusion rate of 10 mcg/kg/minute. Average dose is 3 mcg/kg/minute. Patients taking other antihypertensives are extremely sensitive to nitroprusside. Adjust dosage.

I.V. administration

• Dissolve 50 mg in 2 to 3 ml of D_5W injection. Further dilute in 250, 500, or 1,000 ml of D_5W to provide solutions of 200, 100, or 50 mcg/ml, respectively. Reconstitute ADD-Vantage vials labeled as containing 50 mg of drug according to manufacturer's directions.
• Because drug is sensitive to light, wrap infusion bag in foil; wrapping the tubing isn't needed.
• Infuse with infusion pump. Drug is best given by piggyback through peripheral line with no other drug. Don't adjust rate of main line while drug is being infused. Even small bolus of nitroprusside can cause severe hypotension.
• Check blood pressure every 5 minutes at start of infusion and every 15 minutes thereafter.
• If severe hypotension occurs, stop infusion. Effects of drug reverse quickly. Notify prescriber.
• Start arterial pressure line. Adjust flow to specified level.
• If cyanide toxicity occurs, stop drug immediately and notify prescriber.
• Fresh solution will have faint brownish tint. Discard drug after 24 hours.

⊗ **Incompatibilities**
Bacteriostatic water for injection, other I.V. drug, or preservative.

Contraindications and cautions

• Contraindicated in patients hypersensitive to the drug or any of its components, and in those with compensatory hypertension (as in arteriovenous shunt or coarctation of aorta), inadequate cerebral circulation, congenital optic atrophy, or tobacco-induced amblyopia.
• Use cautiously in patients with increased intracranial pressure and in those with hypothyroidism, hepatic or renal disease, hyponatremia, or low vitamin B_{12} level.

Lifespan: In pregnant women, use cautiously. In breast-feeding women and in children, safety and effectiveness haven't been established.

Adverse reactions

CNS: absent reflexes, ataxia, ***coma,*** dilated pupils, *dizziness, headache,* ***increased intracranial pressure,*** loss of consciousness, *muscle twitching, restlessness.*
CV: ***bradycardia,*** distant heart sounds, ***hypotension,*** palpitations, tachycardia, weak pulse.
GI: abdominal pain, nausea, vomiting.
Hematologic: ***methemoglobinemia.***
Metabolic: ***acidosis.***
Respiratory: dyspnea, shallow breathing.
Skin: *diaphoresis,* pink color.
Other: ***cyanide toxicity, thiocyanate toxicity.***

Interactions

Drug-drug. *Antihypertensives:* May cause sensitivity to nitroprusside. Adjust dosage.
Ganglionic blockers, general anesthetics, negative inotropics, other antihypertensives: May have additive effects. Monitor blood pressure closely.

Sildenafil, tadalafil, vardenafil: May increase hypotensive effects. Don't use together.
Tricyclic antidepressants: May increase the pressor response and cause arrhythmias. Use with caution.

Effects on lab test results

- May increase creatinine, thiocyanide, and methemoglobin levels.

Pharmacokinetics

Absorption: Given I.V.
Distribution: Unknown.
Metabolism: Rapid in erythrocytes and tissues to cyanide radical and then converted to thiocyanate in liver.
Excretion: Mainly as metabolites in urine.
Half-life: 2 minutes.

Route	Onset	Peak	Duration
I.V.	Immediate	1–2 min	10 min

Action

Chemical effect: Relaxes arteriolar and venous smooth muscle.
Therapeutic effect: Lowers blood pressure and reduces preload and afterload.

Available forms

Injection: 50 mg/vial in 2-ml, 5-ml vials

NURSING PROCESS

Assessment

- Assess patient's condition before starting therapy.
- Obtain baseline vital signs before giving drug, and find out what parameters prescriber wants to achieve.

ALERT: Excessive doses or rapid infusion (greater than 15 mcg/kg/minute) can cause cyanide toxicity; check thiocyanate levels q 72 hours. Levels above 100 mcg/ml may cause toxicity. Watch for profound hypotension, metabolic acidosis, dyspnea, headache, loss of consciousness, ataxia, and vomiting.

- Be alert for adverse reactions and drug interactions.
- Assess patient's (if appropriate) and family's knowledge of drug therapy.

Nursing diagnoses

- Risk for injury related to hypertension
- Decreased cardiac output related to heart failure
- Deficient knowledge related to drug therapy

Planning and implementation

- Keep patient in supine position when starting therapy or adjusting dose.

ALERT: Don't confuse nitroprusside with nitroglycerin.

Patient teaching

- Advise patient, if alert, to report adverse reactions or discomfort at the I.V. site immediately.

Evaluation

- Patient's blood pressure is normal.
- Patient has normal cardiac output.
- Patient and family state understanding of drug therapy.

nizatidine

(nigh-ZAT-ih-deen)
Axid, Axid AR†, Tazac ♦

Pharmacologic class: histamine$_2$ (H_2)-receptor antagonist
Therapeutic class: gastric antisecretory
Pregnancy risk category: B

Indications and dosages

▶ **Active duodenal ulcer.** *Adults:* 300 mg P.O. daily at bedtime. Or, 150 mg P.O. b.i.d.
▶ **Maintenance therapy for duodenal ulcer.** *Adults:* 150 mg P.O. daily at bedtime.
▶ **Benign gastric ulcer.** *Adults:* 150 mg P.O. b.i.d. or 300 mg P.O. at bedtime for 8 weeks.
▶ **Gastroesophageal reflux disease.** *Adults:* 150 mg P.O. b.i.d.
▶ **Relief or prevention of heartburn†.** *Adults:* 75-mg tablet 1 to 2 times daily.
Adjust-a-dose: For patients with renal impairment, if creatinine clearance is 20 to 50 ml/minute, give 150 mg P.O. daily for active duodenal ulcer or 150 mg q other day for maintenance therapy. If creatinine clearance is less than 20 ml/minute, give 150 mg P.O. q other day for active ulcer or 150 mg q third day for maintenance.

Contraindications and cautions

- Contraindicated in patients hypersensitive to H_2-receptor antagonists.
- Use cautiously in patients with renal impairment.

Lifespan: In pregnant women, use cautiously. In breast-feeding women, use cautiously; it's unknown if the drug appears in breast milk. In children, safety and effectiveness haven't been established.

Adverse reactions

CNS: fever, *somnolence.*
CV: ***arrhythmias.***
Hematologic: ***thrombocytopenia.***
Hepatic: *liver damage.*
Metabolic: hyperuricemia.
Skin: *diaphoresis,* exfoliative dermatitis, rash, urticaria.

Interactions

Drug-drug. *Aspirin:* May increase salicylate level (with high doses). Monitor patient for salicylate toxicity.
Drug-lifestyle. *Alcohol use:* May increase alcohol level. Discourage use together.

Effects on lab test results

- May increase liver enzyme and uric acid levels.
- May decrease platelet count.
- May cause false-positive test results for urobilinogen.

Pharmacokinetics

Absorption: Greater than 90%. May be slightly enhanced by food and slightly impaired by antacids.
Distribution: About 35% protein-bound.
Metabolism: Unknown, but may undergo hepatic metabolism.
Excretion: More than 90% excreted in urine; less than 6% in feces. *Half-life:* 1 to 2 hours.

Route	Onset	Peak	Duration
P.O.	≤ 30 min	30 min–3 hr	≤ 12 hr

Action

Chemical effect: Competitively inhibits action of H_2 at receptor sites of parietal cells.
Therapeutic effect: Decreases gastric acid secretion.

Available forms

Capsules: 75 mg†, 150 mg, 300 mg

NURSING PROCESS

Assessment

- Assess patient's condition before starting therapy and regularly thereafter to monitor drug effectiveness.
- Be alert for adverse reactions and drug interactions.
- Assess patient for abdominal pain. Note presence of blood in emesis, stool, or gastric aspirate.
- Assess patient's and family's knowledge of drug therapy.

Nursing diagnoses

- Impaired tissue integrity related to ulceration of GI mucosa
- Decreased cardiac output related to drug-induced arrhythmias
- Deficient knowledge related to drug therapy

Planning and implementation

- If needed, open capsules and mix contents with apple juice.

Patient teaching

- Urge patient not to smoke cigarettes because they may increase gastric acid secretion and worsen disease.
- Have patient report blood in stool or emesis.
- Warn patient to take drug as directed, even after pain subsides, to allow for adequate healing.
- Instruct users of OTC dose to report worsening symptoms to provider and not to exceed recommended dose without provider instruction.

Evaluation

- Patient reports pain relief.
- Patient maintains normal cardiac output throughout drug therapy.
- Patient and family state understanding of drug therapy.

N

norepinephrine bitartrate (levarterenol bitartrate, noradrenaline acid tartrate)

(nor-ep-ih-NEF-rin bigh-TAR-trayt)
Levophed

Pharmacologic class: adrenergic
Therapeutic class: vasopressor
Pregnancy risk category: C

Indications and dosages

▶ **To restore blood pressure in severe hypotension, shock, and during cardiac arrest.** *Adults:* Initially, 8 to 12 mcg/minute by I.V. infusion, adjust to maintain low normal blood pressure (systolic blood pressure 80 to 100 mm Hg). Or 0.5 to 1 mcg/minute I.V. infusion, titrate to effect. Average maintenance dosage is 2 to 4 mcg/minute.
Children: 2 mcg/m^2/minute by I.V. infusion; adjust dosage based on patient response. Or, initial I.V. infusion rate of 0.1 mcg/kg/minute, titrate to effect.

▶ **GI bleeding**‡. *Adults:* Give 8 mg in 250 ml normal saline solution intraperitoneally. Or give 8 mg in 100 ml of normal saline solution by NG tube q 1 hour for 6 to 8 hours and then q 2 hours for 4 to 6 hours.

I.V. administration

- Prepare by adding 4 mg of norepinephrine to 1 L of 5% dextrose injection to equal a concentration of 4 mcg/ml.
- Never leave patient unattended during infusion.
- Use central venous catheter or large vein, such as in antecubital fossa, to minimize risk of extravasation. Dilute in dextrose 5% in normal saline solution for injection. Use continuous infusion pump to regulate flow rate and piggyback setup so I.V. line remains open if drug is stopped.
- Titrate infusion rate according to assessment findings and prescriber's guidelines. In previously hypertensive patients, don't raise blood pressure higher than 30 to 40 mm Hg below previous systolic pressure.
- Check site often for blanching and other signs of extravasation. If they occur, change infusion site immediately and call prescriber. Counteract effect by infiltrating area with 5 to 10 mg phentolamine and 10 to 15 ml of normal saline solution. Untreated extravasation can lead to tissue necrosis.
- If prolonged I.V. therapy is needed, change injection site often.
- Protect drug from light. Discard discolored solutions or solutions that contain precipitate. Drug solutions deteriorate after 24 hours.

⊗ **Incompatibilities**
Alkaline solutions, aminophylline, amobarbital, chlorothiazide, chlorpheniramine, iron salts, lidocaine, normal saline solution, oxidizing drugs, pentobarbital sodium, phenobarbital sodium, phenytoin sodium, ranitidine hydrochloride, sodium bicarbonate, streptomycin, thiopental, whole blood.

Contraindications and cautions

- Contraindicated in patients receiving cyclopropane or halothane anesthesia and in patients with mesenteric or peripheral vascular thrombosis, profound hypoxia, hypercapnia, or hypotension caused by blood volume deficits.
- Use cautiously in patients receiving MAO inhibitors, tricyclic antidepressants, or certain antihistamines and in patients with sulfite sensitivity.

Lifespan: In pregnant and breast-feeding women, drug is contraindicated. Use cautiously in elderly patients because of increased risk of vasoconstrictive adverse reactions.

Adverse reactions

CNS: anxiety, dizziness, fever, *headache,* insomnia, restlessness, tremor, weakness.
CV: ***arrhythmias, bradycardia, decreased cardiac output,*** marked increase in peripheral resistance, ***severe hypertension.***
GU: decreased urine output.
Metabolic: hyperglycemia, increased glycogenolysis, ***metabolic acidosis.***
Respiratory: ***asthmatic episodes, respiratory difficulties.***
Other: ***anaphylaxis,*** swelling and enlargement of thyroid, tissue sloughing with extravasation.

Interactions

Drug-drug. *Alpha blockers:* May antagonize drug effects. Monitor patient.
Antihistamines, ergot alkaloids, guanethidine, methyldopa: May cause severe hypertension. Don't give together.
Bretylium: May cause arrhythmias. Monitor ECG closely.

Inhaled anesthetics: May increase risk of arrhythmias. Monitor ECG closely.
MAO inhibitors: May increase risk of hypertensive crisis. Monitor patient closely.
Tricyclic antidepressants: May increase the pressor response and cause arrhythmias. Use with caution.

Effects on lab test results

- May increase glucose level.

Pharmacokinetics

Absorption: Given I.V.
Distribution: Drug localizes in sympathetic nerve tissues.
Metabolism: Metabolized in liver and other tissues to inactive compounds.
Excretion: Excreted in urine. *Half-life:* About 1 minute.

Route	Onset	Peak	Duration
I.V.	Immediate	Immediate	1–2 min

Action

Chemical effect: Stimulates alpha- and $beta_1$-adrenergic receptors in sympathetic nervous system.
Therapeutic effect: Raises blood pressure.

Available forms

Injection: 1 mg/ml in 4-ml ampules

NURSING PROCESS

Assessment

- Assess patient's condition before starting therapy.
- During infusion, frequently monitor ECG, cardiac output, central venous pressure, pulmonary capillary wedge pressure, pulse rate, urine output, and color and temperature of limbs. Also, check blood pressure q 2 minutes until stabilized; then check q 5 minutes.
- Be alert for adverse reactions and drug interactions.
- Monitor vital signs closely when therapy ends. Watch for sudden drop in blood pressure.
- Assess patient's and family's knowledge of drug therapy.

Nursing diagnoses

- Decreased cardiac output related to hypotension
- Risk for injury related to drug-induced adverse reactions
- Deficient knowledge related to drug therapy

Planning and implementation

- Drug isn't a substitute for blood or fluid volume deficit. If deficit exists, replace fluid before giving vasopressors.
- Keep emergency drugs on hand to reverse effects of norepinephrine: atropine for reflex bradycardia, phentolamine for vasopressor effects, and propranolol for arrhythmias.
- Immediately report to prescriber any decrease in urine output.
- When stopping drug, gradually slow infusion rate and report sudden drop in blood pressure.

Patient teaching

- Tell patient to immediately report discomfort at infusion site or difficulty breathing.

Evaluation

- Patient has normal cardiac output.
- Patient sustains no injuries from drug-induced adverse reactions.
- Patient and family state understanding of drug therapy.

norethindrone

(nor-ETH-in-drohn)

Camila, Errin, Jolivette, Micronor, Nora-BE, Nor-QD

norethindrone acetate

Aygestin, Norlutate ♦

Pharmacologic class: progestin
Therapeutic class: contraceptive
Pregnancy risk category: X

Indications and dosages

▶ **Amenorrhea, abnormal uterine bleeding.** *Women:* 2.5 to 10 mg norethindrone acetate P.O. daily for 5 to 10 days during second half of the theoretical menstrual cycle.

▶ **Endometriosis.** *Women:* 5 mg norethindrone acetate P.O. daily for 14 days; then increase by 2.5 mg daily q 2 weeks up to 15 mg daily.

▶ **To prevent pregnancy.** *Women:* Initially, 0.35 mg norethindrone P.O. on first day of menstruation; then 0.35 mg daily.

Contraindications and cautions

• Contraindicated in patients hypersensitive to the drug or any of its components; patients with thromboembolic disorders, cerebrovascular insufficiency, or a history of these conditions; and patients with breast cancer, undiagnosed abnormal vaginal bleeding, severe hepatic disease, or missed abortion.

• Use cautiously in patients with diabetes mellitus, seizure disorder, migraine, cardiac or renal disease, asthma, or depression.

Lifespan: In pregnant women, drug is contraindicated. Breast-feeding woman may start taking progestin-only pills 6 weeks after delivery. A woman who is partially breast-feeding (supplementing with formula) can start taking drug by 3 weeks after delivery. In children, safety and effectiveness haven't been established.

Adverse reactions

CNS: depression, dizziness, lethargy, migraine, ***stroke.***
CV: *edema,* hypertension, ***pulmonary embolism, thromboembolism,*** thrombophlebitis.
GI: abdominal cramps, nausea, vomiting.
GU: abnormal secretions, amenorrhea, breakthrough bleeding, cervical erosion, dysmenorrhea, uterine fibromas, vaginal candidiasis.
Hepatic: cholestatic jaundice.
Metabolic: hyperglycemia, weight changes.
Skin: hirsutism, melasma, rash.
Other: breast tenderness, enlargement, or secretion; decreased libido.

Interactions

Drug-drug. *Barbiturates, carbamazepine, rifampin:* May decrease progestin effects. Monitor patient for lack of effect.
Bromocriptine: May cause amenorrhea, thus interfering with bromocriptine effects. Avoid use together.
Drug-food. *Caffeine:* May increase caffeine level. Monitor patient for caffeine effects.
Drug-lifestyle. *Smoking:* May increase risk of CV effects. If patient continues smoking, may need alternative therapy.

Effects on lab test results

• May increase glucose level.
• May increase liver function test values. May decrease T_3 uptake and glucose tolerance.

Pharmacokinetics

Absorption: Well absorbed from GI tract.
Distribution: Distributed widely. About 80% protein-bound.
Metabolism: Metabolized mainly in liver; undergoes extensive first-pass metabolism.
Excretion: Excreted primarily in feces. *Half-life:* 5 to 14 hours.

Route	Onset	Peak	Duration
P.O.	Unknown	1–2 hr	Unknown

Action

Chemical effect: Suppresses ovulation, possibly by inhibiting pituitary gonadotropin secretion, and forms thick cervical mucus.
Therapeutic effect: Prevents pregnancy and relieves symptoms of endometriosis, amenorrhea, and abnormal uterine bleeding.

Available forms

norethindrone
Tablets: 0.35 mg, 0.5 mg
norethindrone acetate
Tablets: 5 mg

NURSING PROCESS

Assessment

• Assess patient's condition before starting therapy and regularly thereafter to monitor drug effectiveness.
• Be alert for adverse reactions and drug interactions.
• Assess patient's and family's knowledge of drug therapy.
• Monitor blood pressure and edema.

Nursing diagnoses

• Ineffective health maintenance related to underlying condition
• Excess fluid volume related to drug-induced edema
• Deficient knowledge related to drug therapy

Planning and implementation

ALERT: Norethindrone acetate is twice as potent as norethindrone. Don't use as contraception.
• Preliminary estrogen therapy is usually needed by patients with menstrual disorders.
ALERT: If visual disturbance, migraine, or headache occurs or if pulmonary emboli are

suspected, withhold drug, notify prescriber, and provide supportive care.

ALERT: Don't confuse Micronor with Micro-K or Micronase.

Patient teaching

- If switching from combined hormonal contraceptives to progestin-only pill (POP), tell patient to take the first POP the day after the last active combined pill.
- If switching from POPs to combined pills, tell patient to take the first active combined pill on the first day of menstruation, even if the POPs pack isn't finished.
- Explain adverse effects of progestin and have patient read package insert before taking first dose.
- Tell patient to take drug at same time each day when used as a contraceptive. If she is more than 3 hours late or has missed a pill, tell her to take pill as soon as she remembers, to continue with her normal schedule, and to use backup contraception for the next 48 hours.
- Instruct patient to immediately report unusual symptoms. Tell her to stop taking the drug and call prescriber if visual disturbance or migraine occurs.
- Teach patient how to perform routine monthly breast self-examination.
- Warn patient that edema and weight gain are likely. Advise her to restrict sodium intake.

Evaluation

- Patient responds well to therapy.
- Patient's drug-induced edema is minimized with sodium restriction.
- Patient and family state understanding of drug therapy.

norfloxacin

(nor-FLOKS-uh-sin)

Noroxin

Pharmacologic class: fluoroquinolone
Therapeutic class: broad-spectrum antibiotic
Pregnancy risk category: C

Indications and dosages

▶ **UTI caused by susceptible strains of *Escherichia coli, Klebsiella, Enterobacter, Proteus, Pseudomonas aeruginosa, Citrobacter, Staphylococcus aureus, Staphylococcus epidermidis,* and group D streptococci.** *Adults:* For uncomplicated infections, 400 mg P.O. b.i.d. for 7 to 10 days. For complicated infections, 400 mg b.i.d. for 10 to 21 days.

▶ **UTI caused by *E. coli, K. pneumoniae,* or *Proteus mirabilis.*** *Adults:* 400 mg P.O. b.i.d. for 3 days.

▶ **Acute, uncomplicated gonorrhea.** *Adults:* 800 mg P.O. as single dose, followed by doxycycline therapy to treat coexisting chlamydial infection.

▶ **Prostatitis from *E. coli.*** *Men:* 400 mg P.O. q 12 hours for 28 days.

▶ **Gastroenteritis‡.** *Adults:* 400 mg P.O. b.i.d. for 5 days.

▶ **Traveler's diarrhea‡.** *Adults:* 400 mg P.O. b.i.d. for 3 days.

Adjust-a-dose: For patients with renal impairment, if creatinine clearance is less than 30 ml/minute, give 400 mg once daily.

Contraindications and cautions

- Contraindicated in patients hypersensitive to fluoroquinolones. Contraindicated in patients with a history of tendonitis or tendon rupture associated with fluoroquinolones.
- Use cautiously in patients with conditions that may predispose them to seizure disorders, such as cerebral arteriosclerosis and epilepsy.

Lifespan: In pregnant women, breast-feeding women, adolescents, and children, safety and effectiveness haven't been established.

Adverse reactions

CNS: dizziness, fatigue, fever, headache, ***seizures,*** somnolence.
GI: constipation, dry mouth, flatulence, heartburn, nausea.
GU: crystalluria.
Hematologic: eosinophilia.
Musculoskeletal: arthralgia, arthritis, joint swelling, myalgia.
Skin: photosensitivity reaction, rash.
Other: ***anaphylactoid reactions,*** hypersensitivity reaction, rash.

Interactions

Drug-drug. *Aluminum hydroxide, aluminum-magnesium hydroxide, calcium carbonate, magnesium hydroxide:* May decrease effects of norfloxacin. Give antacid at least 6 hours before or 2 hours after norfloxacin.

N

Cimetidine: May interfere with norfloxacin elimination. Use cautiously.
Cyclosporine: May increase cyclosporine level. Monitor level.
Didanosine: May decrease norfloxacin absorption. Avoid use together.
Iron salts: May decrease norfloxacin absorption, reducing anti-infective response. Give at least 2 hours apart.
Nitrofurantoin: May decrease norfloxacin effectiveness. Don't use together.
NSAIDs: May increase risk of CNS stimulation and seizures. Monitor patient closely.
Oral anticoagulants: May increase anticoagulant effect. Monitor patient closely for bleeding; monitor PT and INR.
Probenecid: May increase norfloxacin level by decreasing its excretion. Monitor patient for toxicity.
Sucralfate: May decrease norfloxacin absorption, reducing anti-infective response. If use together can't be avoided, give at least 6 hours apart.
Theophylline: May impair theophylline metabolism, resulting in increased theophylline level and risk of toxicity. Monitor theophylline level closely.
Warfarin: May increase anticoagulant effect. Monitor patient and INR closely.
Drug-food. *Any food:* May decrease drug absorption. Give drug 1 hour before or 2 hours after meals.
Caffeine: May increase caffeine effects. Discourage caffeine use.
Drug-lifestyle. *Sunlight:* May cause photosensitivity reaction. Urge patient to avoid unprotected or prolonged sun exposure.

Effects on lab test results

- May increase BUN, creatinine, ALT, AST, and alkaline phosphatase levels. May decrease hemoglobin level and hematocrit.
- May increase eosinophil count. May decrease neutrophil count.

Pharmacokinetics

Absorption: About 30% to 40%. As dose increases, percentage absorbed decreases. Food may reduce absorption.
Distribution: Into renal tissue, liver, gallbladder, prostatic fluid, testicles, seminal fluid, bile, and sputum. About 10% to 15% protein-bound.
Metabolism: Unknown.
Excretion: Mostly excreted by kidneys with about 30% appearing in bile. *Half-life:* 3 to 4 hours.

Route	Onset	Peak	Duration
P.O.	Unknown	1–2 hr	Unknown

Action

Chemical effect: Inhibits bacterial DNA synthesis, mainly by blocking DNA gyrase.
Therapeutic effect: Kills certain bacteria.

Available forms

Tablets: 400 mg

NURSING PROCESS

Assessment

- Assess patient's infection before starting therapy and regularly thereafter to monitor drug effectiveness.
- Obtain a sample for culture and sensitivity tests before starting therapy, and repeat as needed throughout therapy. May begin therapy pending test results.
- Be alert for adverse reactions and drug interactions.
- Assess patient's and family's knowledge of drug therapy.

Nursing diagnoses

- Risk for infection related to bacteria
- Risk for injury related to drug-induced adverse CNS reactions
- Deficient knowledge related to drug therapy

Planning and implementation

- Give drug on empty stomach.
- Make sure patient is well hydrated before and during therapy to avoid crystalluria.

ALERT: Don't confuse Noroxin with Neurontin or Floxin.

Patient teaching

- Urge patient to take drug 1 hour before or 2 hours after meals to promote absorption.
- Warn patient not to exceed recommended dosage.
- Encourage patient to drink several glasses of water throughout the day to maintain hydration and adequate urine output.
- Warn patient to avoid hazardous activities until the drug's CNS effects are known.

☑ Evaluation

- Patient is free from infection.
- Patient has no injuries from drug-induced adverse CNS reactions.
- Patient and family state understanding of drug therapy.

nortriptyline hydrochloride

(nor-TRIP-teh-leen high-droh-KLOR-ighd)
Allegron ◇, Aventyl*, Pamelor*🖉

Pharmacologic class: tricyclic antidepressant
Therapeutic class: antidepressant
Pregnancy risk category: D

Indications and dosages

▶ **Depression.** *Adults:* 25 mg P.O. t.i.d. or q.i.d.; gradually increase up to maximum of 150 mg daily. Or entire dosage may be given at bedtime.

▶ **Premenstrual symptoms‡.** *Adults:* 50 to 125 mg daily.

▶ **Dermatologic disorders (chronic urticaria, angioedema, nocturnal pruritus in atopic eczema)‡.** *Adults:* 20 to 75 mg/day.

Adjust-a-dose: For elderly and debilitated patients, give 30 mg to 50 mg P.O. once daily or in divided doses.

Contraindications and cautions

- Contraindicated in patients hypersensitive to the drug or any of its components, patients in acute recovery phase after MI, and patients who have taken an MAO inhibitor within 14 days.
- Use cautiously in patients taking thyroid drugs and patients with glaucoma, suicidal tendency, history of urine retention or seizures, CV disease, or hyperthyroidism.

Lifespan: In pregnant women, breast-feeding women, and children, don't use unless benefits outweigh risks. In elderly patients, use cautiously and at a lower dose.

Adverse reactions

CNS: confusion, *dizziness, drowsiness,* EEG changes, excitation, extrapyramidal reactions, headache, nervousness, ***seizures, stroke, suicidal ideation,*** tremor, weakness.
CV: ECG changes, ***heart block,*** hypertension, ***MI,*** *tachycardia.*
EENT: *blurred vision,* mydriasis, tinnitus.
GI: anorexia, *constipation,* dry mouth, nausea, paralytic ileus, vomiting.
GU: urine retention.
Hematologic: ***agranulocytosis, bone marrow depression,*** eosinophilia, ***thrombocytopenia.***
Skin: diaphoresis, photosensitivity, rash, urticaria.
Other: hypersensitivity reaction.

Interactions

Drug-drug. *Anticholinergics:* May increase anticholinergic effect. Paralytic ileus may occur. Monitor patient.
Barbiturates, CNS depressants: May increase CNS depression. Avoid use together.
Bupropion, cimetidine, methylphenidate, SSRIs, valproic acid: May increase nortriptyline level. Monitor patient for adverse reactions.
Carbamazepine: May increase nortriptyline and carbamazepine levels, leading to toxicity. Use with caution.
Clonidine: May cause loss of blood pressure control with potentially life-threatening increases in blood pressure. Don't use together.
Epinephrine, norepinephrine: May increase hypertensive effect. Use together cautiously; monitor blood pressure.
MAO inhibitors: May cause severe excitation, hyperpyrexia, or seizures. Don't use together.
Quinolones: May increase the risk of life-threatening arrhythmias, including torsades de pointes. Don't use together.
Rifamycin: May decrease nortriptyline level. Monitor it for decreased effect.
Drug-herb. *SAMe, St. John's wort, yohimbe:* Use with some tricyclic antidepressants may increase serotonin levels. Discourage use together.
Drug-lifestyle. *Alcohol use:* May increase CNS depression. Discourage use together.
Smoking: May decrease nortriptyline level. Monitor patient for lack of drug effect.
Sun exposure: May increase risk of photosensitivity reaction. Urge patient to avoid unprotected or prolonged exposure to sunlight.

Effects on lab test results

- May increase or decrease glucose level.
- May increase liver function test values and eosinophil count. May decrease RBC, WBC, granulocyte, and platelet counts.

N

Pharmacokinetics

Absorption: Rapid.
Distribution: Distributed widely into body, including CNS. 95% protein-bound.
Metabolism: Metabolized by liver; significant first-pass effect may account for variability of levels in different patients taking same dosage.
Excretion: Most excreted in urine; some in feces. *Half-life:* 18 to 24 hours.

Route	Onset	Peak	Duration
P.O.	Unknown	7–8½ hr	16–90 hr

Action

Chemical effect: Unknown; increases amount of norepinephrine, serotonin, or both in CNS by blocking their reuptake by presynaptic neurons.
Therapeutic effect: Relieves depression.

Available forms

Capsules: 10 mg, 25 mg, 50 mg, 75 mg
Oral solution: 10 mg/5 ml*
Tablets: 10 mg ◇, 25 mg ◇

NURSING PROCESS

Assessment

- Assess patient's depression before starting therapy and regularly thereafter to monitor drug effectiveness.
- Be alert for adverse reactions and drug interactions.
- If dosage is greater than 100 mg/day, monitor drug level and maintain a range of 50 to 150 nanograms/ml.
- Assess patient's and family's knowledge of drug therapy.

Nursing diagnoses

- Disturbed thought processes related to depression
- Risk for injury related to drug-induced adverse CNS reactions
- Deficient knowledge related to drug therapy

Planning and implementation

- Lower the dosage in elderly or debilitated patient.

ALERT: Stopping long-term therapy abruptly may cause nausea, headache, and malaise.
ALERT: Because hypertensive episodes may occur during surgery in patients receiving tricyclic antidepressants, gradually stop therapy starting several days before surgery.

- If signs of psychosis occur or increase, reduce dosage.

ALERT: Don't confuse nortriptyline with amitriptyline.

Patient teaching

- Advise patient to take full dose at bedtime to reduce risk of orthostatic hypotension.
- Warn patient to avoid hazardous activities until CNS effects of drug are known. Drowsiness and dizziness usually subside after a few weeks.
- Tell patient to avoid alcohol during drug therapy.
- Warn patient not to stop drug suddenly.
- Advise patient to consult prescriber before taking other prescription or OTC drugs.
- Advise patient to use sunblock, wear protective clothing, and avoid prolonged exposure to sunlight to avoid photosensitivity.

Evaluation

- Patient's depression improves.
- Patient sustains no injuries from drug-induced adverse CNS reactions.
- Patient and family state understanding of drug therapy.

nystatin

(nigh-STAT-in)
Mycostatin*, Nilstat, Nystex*, Nystop

Pharmacologic class: polyene macrolide
Therapeutic class: antifungal
Pregnancy risk category: C

Indications and dosages

▶ **GI tract infections.** *Adults:* 500,000 to 1 million units as oral tablets P.O. t.i.d.
▶ **Oral infections caused by *Candida albicans* and other *Candida* species.** *Adults and children:* 400,000 to 600,000 units suspension P.O. q.i.d. Or 200,000 or 400,000 units (1 or 2 lozenges) 4 or 5 times daily.
Infants: 200,000 units suspension P.O. q.i.d.
▶ **Vaginal infections.** *Adults:* 100,000 units, as vaginal tablets, inserted high into vagina, daily for 14 days.

▶ **Cutaneous or mucocutaneous yeast infections.** *Adults:* Apply topical products to affected areas b.i.d. to t.i.d.

▶ **Candidal diaper dermatitis‡.** *Infants:* 100,000 units suspension P.O. q.i.d. as an adjunct to topical nystatin therapy.

Contraindications and cautions

• Contraindicated in patients hypersensitive to the drug or any of its components.

Lifespan: In pregnant women, use only when benefits outweigh risks to the fetus. In breast-feeding women, safety and effectiveness haven't been established.

Adverse reactions

GI: diarrhea, transient nausea, vomiting.
Skin: rash.

Interactions

None significant.

Effects on lab test results

None reported.

Pharmacokinetics

Absorption: Not absorbed from GI tract, intact skin, or mucous membranes.
Distribution: None.
Metabolism: None.
Excretion: Oral form excreted almost entirely unchanged in feces. *Half-life:* Unknown.

Route	Onset	Peak	Duration
P.O., topical, vaginal	Unknown	Unknown	Unknown

Action

Chemical effect: Unknown; probably acts by binding to sterols in fungal cell membrane, altering cell permeability and allowing leakage of intracellular components.
Therapeutic effect: Kills susceptible yeasts and fungi.

Available forms

Cream/ointment/powder: 100,000 units/g
Lozenges: 200,000 units
Oral suspension: 100,000 units/ml*
Tablets: 500,000 units
Vaginal tablets: 100,000 units

NURSING PROCESS

Assessment

• Assess patient's infection before starting therapy and regularly thereafter to monitor drug effectiveness.
• Be alert for adverse reactions.
• If patient has adverse GI reactions, monitor his hydration.
• Assess patient's and family's knowledge of drug therapy.

Nursing diagnoses

• Risk for infection related to organisms
• Risk for deficient fluid volume related to drug-induced adverse GI reactions
• Deficient knowledge related to drug therapy

Planning and implementation

• Drug isn't effective against systemic infections.
• When treating oral candidiasis (thrush), clean food debris from patient's mouth and have patient hold suspension in mouth for several minutes before swallowing.
• When treating an infant, swab drug on oral mucosa.
• Immunosuppressed patients with oral candidiasis are sometimes instructed by prescriber to suck on vaginal tablets (100,000 units) because doing so provides prolonged contact with oral mucosa.
• Pregnant patients can use vaginal tablets up to 6 weeks before term to treat infection that may cause thrush in neonates.

Patient teaching

• Advise patient to take drug for at least 2 days after symptoms disappear to prevent reinfection. Consult prescriber for duration of therapy.
• Tell patient not to chew or swallow lozenge (troche) but to allow it to dissolve slowly in the mouth.
• Tell patient to premoisten oral mucosa and maintain adequate hydration when using lozenge (troche) formulation.
• Instruct patient to continue therapy during menstruation.
• Instruct patient in oral hygiene techniques. Poorly fitting dentures and overuse of mouthwash may alter oral flora and promote infection.
• Explain that predisposing factors for vaginal infection include use of antibiotics, hormonal contraceptives, and corticosteroids; diabetes; re-

infection by sexual partner; and tight-fitting undergarments. Encourage patient to wear cotton (not synthetic) underpants.

• Teach patient about hygiene for affected areas, including wiping perineal area from front to back.

• Advise patient to report redness, swelling, or irritation.

☑ Evaluation

• Patient is free from infection.

• Patient maintains adequate hydration throughout drug therapy.

• Patient and family state understanding of drug therapy.

octreotide acetate

(ok-TREE-oh-tighd AS-ih-tayt)

Sandostatin, Sandostatin LAR Depot

Pharmacologic class: synthetic polypeptide
Therapeutic class: somatotropic hormone
Pregnancy risk category: B

Indications and dosages

▶ **Flushing and diarrhea caused by carcinoid tumors.** *Adults:* 100 to 600 mcg daily subcutaneously in two to four divided doses for first 2 weeks (usual daily dosage 300 mcg). Subsequent dosage based on patient's response. Patients currently on Sandostatin can switch to Sandostatin LAR Depot 20 mg I.M. to gluteal area q 4 weeks for 2 months. Octreotide immediate-release injection should be continued at the previous dosage during at least the first 2 weeks of therapy with the long-acting formulation.

▶ **Watery diarrhea caused by vasoactive intestinal polypeptide secreting tumors (VIPomas).** *Adults:* 200 to 300 mcg daily subcutaneously in two to four divided doses for first 2 weeks of therapy. Subsequent dosage based on individual response; typically doesn't exceed 450 mcg daily. Patients currently on Sandostatin can switch to Sandostatin LAR Depot 20 mg I.M. to gluteal area q 4 weeks for 2 months.

▶ **Acromegaly.** *Adults:* Initially, 50 mcg subcutaneously t.i.d.; then adjust by somatomedin C (IGF-1) or growth hormone (GH) level q 2 weeks. Usual effective dosage, 100 mcg subcutaneously t.i.d. Some patients may need up to 500 mcg subcutaneously t.i.d., but dosages higher than 300 mg t.i.d. often add no benefits. Switch patients on Sandostatin to 20 mg Sandostatin LAR Depot I.M. to gluteal area q 4 weeks for 3 months.

▶ **GI fistula‡.** *Adults:* 0.05 to 0.2 mg subcutaneously q 8 hours.

▶ **Variceal bleeding‡.** *Adults:* 0.025 to 0.05 mg/hour continuous I.V. infusion. Duration is from 18 hours to 5 days.

▶ **AIDS-related diarrhea‡.** *Adults:* 0.1 to 0.5 mg subcutaneously t.i.d.

▶ **Short bowel (ileostomy) syndrome‡.** *Adults:* 0.025 mg/hour continuous I.V. infusion or 0.05 mg subcutaneously b.i.d.

▶ **Chemotherapy- and radiation-induced diarrhea‡.** *Adults:* 0.05 to 0.1 mg subcutaneously t.i.d. for 1 to 3 days.

▶ **Pancreatic fistula‡.** *Adults:* 0.05 to 0.2 mg subcutaneously q 8 hours.

▶ **Irritable bowel syndrome‡.** *Adults:* 0.1 mg single dose to 0.125 mg subcutaneously b.i.d.

▶ **Dumping syndrome‡.** *Adults:* 0.05 to 0.15 mg subcutaneously daily.

Contraindications and cautions

• Contraindicated in patients hypersensitive to the drug or any of its components.

Lifespan: In pregnant women, use cautiously. In breast-feeding women and in children, safety and effectiveness haven't been established.

Adverse reactions

CNS: dizziness, fatigue, headache, lightheadedness, pain.
CV: ***arrhythmias, bradycardia,*** flushing.
GI: *abdominal pain or discomfort, diarrhea,* fat malabsorption, gallbladder abnormalities, loose stools, *nausea,* vomiting.
Metabolic: *hyperglycemia,* ***hypoglycemia,*** hypothyroidism.
Skin: edema, erythema, pain, and wheal at injection site.
Other: burning at subcutaneous injection site.

Interactions

Drug-drug. *Cyclosporine:* May decrease cyclosporine level. Monitor patient.

Drug-food. *Dietary fats:* Drug may alter the absorption of dietary fats.
Vitamin B_{12}: May decrease vitamin B_{12} level; monitor level.

Effects on lab test results

• May decrease T_4 and thyroid-stimulating hormone levels. May increase or decrease glucose level.

Pharmacokinetics

Absorption: Rapid and complete after subcutaneous use.
Distribution: To plasma, where it binds to lipoprotein and albumin.
Metabolism: Not clearly defined.
Excretion: About 35% unchanged in urine. *Half-life:* About 1½ hours.

Route	Onset	Peak	Duration
I.M., SubQ	≤ 30 min	30–60 min	12 hr–6 wk

Action

Chemical effect: Mimics action of naturally occurring somatostatin.
Therapeutic effect: Relieves flushing and diarrhea caused by certain tumors and treats acromegaly.

Available forms

Depot: 10 mg/5 ml, 20 mg/5 ml, 30 mg/5 ml
Injection: 0.05-mg, 0.1-mg, 0.5-mg ampules; 0.2-mg/ml, 1-mg/ml multidose vials

NURSING PROCESS

Assessment

• Assess patient's condition before starting therapy, and regularly thereafter to monitor the drug's effectiveness.
• Monitor IGF-1 or GH level every 2 weeks. Base dosage on this level.
• Monitor laboratory tests, such as thyroid function tests, urine 5-hydroxyindoleacetic acid, serotonin, substance P (for carcinoid tumors), and vasoactive intestinal peptide levels (for VIPomas), at baseline and then periodically.
• Monitor fluid and electrolyte levels.
• Be alert for adverse reactions and drug interactions.
• Assess patient's and family's knowledge of drug therapy.

Nursing diagnoses

• Diarrhea related to condition
• Fatigue related to drug-induced adverse CNS reaction
• Deficient knowledge related to drug therapy

Planning and implementation

• Give drug in divided doses for first 2 weeks of therapy; subsequent daily dosage depends on patient's response.
• Read drug labels carefully, and check dosage and strength.
ALERT: For LAR Depot injection, give drug I.M. only. Avoid deltoid muscle because of discomfort at site.
• Drug therapy may alter fluid and electrolyte balance and may require adjustment of other drugs.
• Adjust LAR Depot dosage q 3 months based on GH level; range for depot dosage, 10 to 40 mg at intervals no sooner than 4 weeks.

Patient teaching

• Tell patient to report signs of gallbladder disease such as abdominal discomfort. Drug may be linked to cholelithiasis.
• Inform patient that laboratory tests are needed during therapy.
• Advise diabetic patient to monitor glucose level closely. Antidiabetics may need dosage adjustment.

Evaluation

• Patient's bowel pattern is normal.
• Patient uses energy-saving measures to combat fatigue.
• Patient and family state understanding of drug therapy.

ofloxacin

(oh-FLOKS-eh-sin)
Apo-Oflox ♦, Floxin, Floxin Otic, Ocuflox

Pharmacologic class: fluoroquinolone
Therapeutic class: antibiotic
Pregnancy risk category: C

Indications and dosages

▶ **Lower respiratory tract infections caused by susceptible strains of *Haemophilus influenzae* or *Streptococcus pneumoniae*.** *Adults:* 400 mg P.O. q 12 hours for 10 days.

▶ **Cervicitis or urethritis caused by *Chlamydia trachomatis* or *Neisseria gonorrhoeae*.** *Adults:* 300 mg P.O. q 12 hours for 7 days.
▶ **Acute pelvic inflammatory disease.** *Adults:* 400 mg P.O. q 12 hours for 10 to 14 days.
▶ **Acute uncomplicated gonorrhea.** *Adults:* 400 mg P.O. as single dose.
▶ **Mild to moderate skin and skin-structure infections caused by susceptible strains of *Staphylococcus aureus, Staphylococcus epidermidis, Streptococcus pyogenes,* or *Proteus mirabilis.*** *Adults:* 400 mg P.O. q 12 hours for 10 days.
▶ **Cystitis caused by *Escherichia coli* or *Klebsiella pneumoniae.*** *Adults:* 200 mg P.O. q 12 hours for 3 days.
▶ **UTIs caused by susceptible strains of *Citrobacter diversus, Enterobacter aerogenes, E. coli, P. mirabilis,* or *Pseudomonas aeruginosa.*** *Adults:* 200 mg P.O. q 12 hours for 7 days. Complicated infections may need 10 days of therapy.
▶ **Prostatitis caused by *E. coli.*** *Adults:* 300 mg P.O. q 12 hours for 6 weeks.
▶ **Bacterial conjunctivitis.** *Adults and children age 1 year and older:* 1 or 2 drops every 2 to 4 hours in the affected eye on days 1 and 2, then 1 or 2 drops q.i.d. on days 3 through 7.
▶ **Otitis externa (swimmer's ear).** *Adults and children age 13 and older:* 10 drops (or 2 single-dispensing containers) into affected ear b.i.d. for 10 days.
Children 1 to 12 years old: 5 drops (or 1 single-dispensing container) into affected ear b.i.d. for 10 days.
▶ **Otitis media with tympanostomy tubes.** *Children ages 1 to 12:* Give 1 single-dispensing container into affected ear b.i.d. for 10 days.
▶ **Chronic suppurative otitis media with perforated tympanic membranes.** *Adults and children age 12 and older:* 2 dispensing-containers in affected ear b.i.d. for 14 days.
▶ **Adjunct for *Brucella* infections‡.** *Adults:* 400 mg P.O. daily for 6 weeks.
▶ **Typhoid fever‡.** *Adults:* 200 to 400 mg P.O. q 12 hours for 7 to 14 days.
▶ **Tuberculosis adjunct ‡.** *Adults:* 300 mg P.O. daily.
▶ **Postoperative sternotomy or soft tissue wounds caused by *Mycobacterium fortuitum*‡.** *Adults:* 300 or 600 mg P.O. daily for 3 to 6 months.
▶ **Acute Q fever pneumonia‡.** *Adults:* 600 mg P.O. daily for up to 16 days.
▶ **Mediterranean spotted fever‡.** *Adults:* 200 mg P.O. q 12 hours for 7 days.
▶ **Traveler's diarrhea‡.** *Adults:* 300 mg P.O. b.i.d. for 3 days.
▶ **Inhalational anthrax post-exposure prophylaxis/treatment‡.** *Adults:* 400 mg P.O. b.i.d. for 60 days.
▶ **Legionnaire disease‡.** *Adults:* 400 mg P.O. q 12 hours for 2 to 3 weeks.

Adjust-a-dose: For patients with renal impairment, if creatinine clearance is 20 to 50 ml/minute, give usual recommended dose q 24 hours; if creatinine clearance is less than 20 ml/minute, give one-half of recommended dose q 24 hours.

For patients with hepatic impairment, maximum daily dosage is 400 mg.

Contraindications and cautions

- Contraindicated in patients hypersensitive to drug or other fluoroquinolones.
- Use cautiously in patients with renal impairment, history of seizures, or other CNS diseases such as cerebral arteriosclerosis.

Lifespan: In pregnant women, use cautiously. In breast-feeding women and in infants younger than age 1, safety and effectiveness haven't been established.

Adverse reactions

CNS: dizziness, drowsiness, fatigue, fever, *headache,* insomnia, lethargy, lightheadedness, malaise, nervousness, ***seizures,*** sleep disorders.
CV: chest pain.
EENT: visual disturbances.
GI: abdominal pain or discomfort, anorexia, diarrhea, dry mouth, dysgeusia, flatulence, *nausea,* vomiting.
GU: genital pruritus, vaginal discharge, vaginitis.
Hematologic: anemia, eosinophilia, leukocytosis, ***leukopenia, lymphocytopenia, neutropenia.***
Metabolic: hyperglycemia, ***hypoglycemia.***
Musculoskeletal: myalgia, transient arthralgia, trunk pain.
Skin: photosensitivity reaction, pruritus, rash.
Other: ***anaphylaxis,*** hypersensitivity reactions.

Interactions

Drug-drug. *Aluminum hydroxide, aluminum-magnesium hydroxide, calcium carbonate, mag-*

nesium hydroxide: May decrease ofloxacin effects. Give antacid at least 6 hours before or 2 hours after oral ofloxacin.
Cimetidine: May interfere with ofloxacin elimination. Monitor patient for toxicity.
Divalent or trivalent cations (such as zinc), or didanosine (chewable or buffered tablets or pediatric powder for oral solution): May interfere with GI absorption of ofloxacin. Give these drugs at least 2 hours before or 2 hours after taking oral ofloxacin.
Iron salts: May decrease ofloxacin absorption, reducing anti-infective response. Give at least 2 hours apart.
NSAIDs: May increase risk of CNS stimulation and convulsive seizures. Avoid using together. Monitor patient for tremors and seizures if used together.
Oral anticoagulants: May increase anticoagulant effect. Monitor patient for bleeding and altered PT and INR.
Procainamide: May increase procainamide level. Monitor procainamide level; adjust dosage accordingly.
Sucralfate: May decrease absorption of oral ofloxacin, reducing anti-infective response. If use together can't be avoided, give at least 2 hours apart.
Theophylline: Some fluoroquinolones may decrease theophylline clearance. Monitor theophylline level.
Drug-food. *Any food:* May decrease oral drug absorption. Give drug on an empty stomach.
Drug-lifestyle. *Sun exposure:* May cause photosensitivity reactions. Urge patient to avoid unprotected or prolonged sun exposure.

Effects on lab test results

- May increase ALT, AST, and alkaline phosphatase levels. May decrease hemoglobin level and hematocrit. May increase or decrease glucose level.
- May increase eosinophil count. May decrease neutrophil and lymphocyte counts. May increase or decrease WBC count.
- May produce false-positive opiate assay results.

Pharmacokinetics

Absorption: Good.
Distribution: Wide.
Metabolism: Pyridobenzoxazine ring decreases extent.
Excretion: 68% to 90% unchanged in urine; less than 5% in feces. *Half-life:* 4 to 7½ hours.

Route	Onset	Peak	Duration
P.O.	Unknown	1–2 hr	Unknown
Topical	Unknown	Unknown	Unknown

Action

Chemical effect: May inhibit bacterial DNA gyrase and prevent DNA replication in susceptible bacteria.
Therapeutic effect: Kills susceptible aerobic gram-positive and gram-negative organisms.

Available forms

Tablets: 200 mg, 300 mg, 400 mg
Ophthalmic solution: 0.3% in 1ml, 5 ml, 10 ml
Otic solution: 0.3% in 0.25-ml single-dispensing containers, 5 ml, 10 ml

NURSING PROCESS

Assessment

- Assess patient's infection before starting therapy and regularly thereafter to monitor the drug's effectiveness.
- Monitor regular blood studies and hepatic and renal function tests during long-term therapy.
- Give serologic test for syphilis to patient treated for gonorrhea. Drug isn't effective against syphilis, and treating gonorrhea may mask or delay symptoms of syphilis.
- Be alert for adverse reactions and drug interactions.
- If patient has an adverse GI reaction, monitor his hydration.
- Assess patient's and family's knowledge of drug therapy.

Nursing diagnoses

- Risk for infection related to presence of bacteria
- Risk for deficient fluid volume related to drug-induced adverse GI reactions
- Deficient knowledge related to drug therapy

Planning and implementation

- Give oral drug on empty stomach.

ALERT: If patient develops restlessness, tremor, confusion, or hallucinations, stop giving the drug and notify prescriber. Take seizure precautions.

O

ALERT: Ophthalmic and otic forms both come in 3% strengths. Don't confuse them; they're not interchangeable.

Patient teaching

- Advise patient to take oral drug with plenty of fluids but not with meals. Also, tell patient to avoid antacids, sucralfate, and products containing iron or zinc for at least 2 hours before and after each dose.
- Advise patient to complete full course of antibiotics, as directed.
- Warn patient to avoid hazardous tasks until the drug's CNS effects are known.
- Advise patient to use sunblock and protective clothing to avoid photosensitivity reactions.
- Tell patient to stop taking the drug and notify prescriber if rash or other signs of hypersensitivity reactions develop.
- Tell patient to warm ear drops before instilling by holding the bottle in his hands for 1 or 2 minutes; this will avoid dizziness that may occur following instillation of cold solution.
- Give the patient these instructions for using eardrops: lie down with the affected ear upward and drop in the prescribed amount of drops. Remain lying down for 5 minutes to allow the drug to reach the ear canal. If treating middle ear infections, press the cartilage by the opening of the ear four times to help drug get to the middle ear.
- Advise patient using ear drops or eye drops to avoid contaminating the tip of the multidose container with his fingers, infectious material or other sources.

Evaluation

- Patient is free from infection.
- Patient maintains adequate hydration throughout drug therapy.
- Patient and family state understanding of drug therapy.

olanzapine

(oh-LAN-za-peen)

Zyprexa, Zyprexa Intramuscular, Zyprexa Zydis

Pharmacologic class: thienobenzodiazepine derivative
Therapeutic class: atypical antipsychotic
Pregnancy risk category: C

Indications and dosages

▶ **Short-term therapy for acute manic episodes related to bipolar I disorder.** *Adults:* Initially, 10 or 15 mg P.O. daily. Adjust dosage as needed by increments of 5 mg daily at intervals of 24 hours or more. Maximum, 20 mg P.O. daily. Therapy lasts 3 or 4 weeks.

▶ **Short-term therapy for acute manic episodes of bipolar I disorder, given with lithium or valproate.** *Adults:* 10 mg P.O. once daily. Dosage range, 5 to 20 mg daily. Therapy lasts for 6 weeks.

▶ **Long-term therapy for bipolar I disorder.** *Adults:* 5 to 20 mg P.O. daily.

▶ **Agitation from schizophrenia and bipolar I mania.** *Adults:* 2.5 to 10 mg I.M. Maximum daily dosage, 30 mg I.M., in no more than 3 divided doses.

▶ **Long-term therapy for schizophrenia.** *Adults:* Initially, 5 to 10 mg P.O. daily. Goal, 10 mg P.O. daily within several days of starting therapy. Increase dosage weekly in increments of 5 mg daily to a maximum of 20 mg daily.

Adjust-a-dose: For patients who are debilitated, are predisposed to hypotensive reactions, have risk factors for slower drug metabolism (nonsmoking women older than age 65), or may be more pharmacodynamically sensitive to drug, the recommended starting dosage is 5 mg P.O. or 2.5 to 5 mg I.M. daily. In these patients, increase dosage with caution.

Contraindications and cautions

- Contraindicated in patients hypersensitive to the drug or any of its components.
- Use cautiously in patients with heart disease, cerebrovascular disease, diabetes, conditions that predispose patient to hypotension, history of seizures or conditions that might lower the seizure threshold, or hepatic impairment. Also use cautiously in patients with a history of paralytic ileus and in those at risk for aspiration pneumonia, prostatic hyperplasia, or angle-closure glaucoma.

Lifespan: In pregnant women, use drug only if benefits outweigh risks to the fetus. Breast-feeding women should stop breast-feeding or use another drug. Safety and effectiveness haven't been established in children younger than age 18. In elderly people with dementia, don't use; such patients may have an increased risk of stroke while using this drug.

Adverse reactions

CNS: abnormal gait, akathisia, *asthenia, dizziness,* extrapyramidal events, fever, *insomnia,* ***neuroleptic malignant syndrome,*** *parkinsonism,* personality disorder, *somnolence,* speech impairment, ***suicide attempt*** (P.O.), tardive dyskinesia.
CV: chest pain, hypertension, orthostatic hypotension, peripheral edema, tachycardia.
EENT: amblyopia, conjunctivitis, pharyngitis, rhinitis.
GI: *constipation, dry mouth, dyspepsia,* increased appetite, increased salivation and thirst, vomiting.
GU: amenorrhea, hematuria, metrorrhagia, urinary incontinence, UTI, vaginitis.
Hematologic: ***leukopenia.***
Metabolic: ***hyperglycemia,*** weight gain.
Musculoskeletal: back pain, extremity pain, hypertonia, joint pain, joint stiffness and twitching.
Respiratory: dyspnea, increased cough.
Skin: ecchymosis, injection site pain, sweating.
Other: dental pain, flulike syndrome, injury.

Interactions

Drug-drug. *Antihypertensives:* May increase hypotensive effects. Monitor blood pressure closely.
Carbamazepine, omeprazole, rifampin: May increase olanzapine clearance. Monitor patient.
Diazepam: May increase CNS effects. Monitor patient closely.
Dopamine agonists, levodopa: May antagonize these drugs. Monitor patient.
Fluvoxamine: May decrease olanzapine clearance. Consider lower olanzapine dosage.
Drug-herb. *Nutmeg:* May reduce effectiveness of or interfere with drug therapy. Discourage using together.
Drug-lifestyle. *Alcohol use:* May increase CNS effects. Discourage using together.

Effects on lab test results

- May increase AST, ALT, GGT, CK, and prolactin levels.

Pharmacokinetics

Absorption: Food doesn't affect rate or extent. About 40% of dose is limited by first-pass metabolism.
Distribution: Extensive, with a volume of distribution of about 1,000 L. About 93% protein-bound, mainly to albumin and alpha$_1$-acid glycoprotein.
Metabolism: By direct glucuronidation and cytochrome P-450–mediated oxidation.
Excretion: About 57% in urine and 30% in feces as metabolites. Only 7% of dose is recovered in urine unchanged. *Half-life:* 21 to 54 hours.

Route	Onset	Peak	Duration
P.O.	Unknown	6 hr	Unknown
I.M.	Rapid	15–45 min	Unknown

Action

Chemical effect: Binds to dopamine and serotonin receptors; may antagonize adrenergic, cholinergic, and histaminergic receptors.
Therapeutic effect: Relieves signs and symptoms of psychosis.

Available forms

Powder for injection: 10 mg
Tablets: 2.5 mg, 5 mg, 7.5 mg, 10 mg, 15 mg, 20 mg
Tablets (orally disintegrating): 5 mg, 10 mg, 15 mg, 20 mg

NURSING PROCESS

Assessment

- Obtain history of patient's underlying condition before starting therapy, and reassess regularly thereafter to monitor drug's effectiveness.
- Obtain baseline and periodic liver function tests.
- Monitor patient for signs of neuroleptic malignant syndrome (hyperpyrexia, muscle rigidity, altered mental condition, autonomic instability), which is rare but fatal. If patient has symptoms, stop drug immediately, notify prescriber, and treat symptoms.
- Monitor patient for tardive dyskinesia, which may occur after prolonged use. It may not appear until months or years later, and it may disappear spontaneously or persist for life despite stopping therapy.
- Monitor patient for abnormal body temperature regulation, especially if patient is exercising strenuously, exposed to extreme heat, receiving anticholinergics, or at risk for dehydration.

ALERT: Hyperglycemia may occur. If patient has diabetes, check blood glucose level regularly. If patient has risk factors for diabetes, check

O

fasting blood glucose level at baseline and periodically thereafter. In some cases, hyperglycemia is reversible when antipsychotic therapy is stopped.
- Monitor patient for symptoms of hyperglycemia, including polydipsia, polyuria, polyphagia, and weakness; if symptoms develop, test fasting glucose level.
- Regularly re-evaluate the drug's long-term effectiveness, especially in patients taking more than 20 mg daily.
- Assess patient's and family's knowledge of drug therapy.

Nursing diagnoses
- Disturbed thought processes related to underlying condition
- Risk for injury related to drug-induced adverse CNS reactions
- Deficient knowledge related to drug therapy

Planning and implementation
- Start with a 5-mg dose in a patient who is debilitated, predisposed to hypotension, sensitive to drug, or affected by altered metabolism caused by smoking, gender, or age.
- Orally disintegrating tablets contain phenylalanine.
- Inspect I.M. solution for particulate matter and discoloration before administration.
- Store vials at 68 to 77° F (20 to 25° C). Protect from light and don't freeze. To reconstitute I.M. injection, dissolve contents of 1 vial with 2.1 ml of sterile water for injection to yield a 5 mg/ml solution that is clear and yellow in appearance. Store at room temperature and administer within 1 hour of reconstitution. Discard any unused solution.
- Postural hypotension and bradycardia may be lessened after I.M. injection by keeping patient recumbent.

ALERT: Don't confuse olanzapine with olsalazine or ondansetron.

ALERT: Don't confuse Zyprexa with Zyrtec or Celexa.

Patient teaching
- Drug can be taken with or without food.
- Tell patient to avoid hazardous tasks until the drug's CNS effects are known.
- Warn patient against exposure to extreme heat; drug may impair body's ability to reduce core temperature.
- Tell patient not to drink alcohol during therapy.
- Tell patient to rise slowly to avoid effects of orthostatic hypotension.
- Instruct patient to relieve dry mouth with ice chips or sugarless candy or gum.
- Advise woman to notify prescriber if she becomes pregnant or intends to become pregnant during drug therapy. Advise her not to breastfeed during therapy.

Evaluation
- Patient's behavior and communication show improved thought processes.
- Patient sustains no injury from adverse CNS reactions.
- Patient and family state understanding of drug therapy.

olmesartan medoxomil
(ol-meh-SAHR-tan me-DOKS-oh-mil)
Benicar

Pharmacologic class: angiotensin II receptor antagonist
Therapeutic class: antihypertensive
Pregnancy risk category: C (first trimester) and D (second and third trimesters)

Indications and dosages
▶ **Hypertension.** *Adults:* 20 mg P.O. daily in patients who aren't volume-contracted. If blood pressure isn't reduced after 2 weeks of therapy, increase dosage to 40 mg P.O. once daily.

Adjust-a-dose: In patients whose intravascular volume may be depleted, consider lower starting dose.

Contraindications and cautions
- Contraindicated in patients hypersensitive to drug or any of its components.
- Use cautiously in patients who are volume- or salt-depleted, in those whose renal function depends on the renin-angiotensin-aldosterone system (such as patients with severe heart failure), and in those with renal artery stenosis.

Lifespan: In pregnant women, drug isn't recommended. If woman becomes pregnant, stop drug immediately. Breast-feeding women should either stop breast-feeding or use another drug. In children, safety and effectiveness haven't been established. In elderly patients, use cautiously because they may have greater sensitivity to drug.

Adverse reactions

CNS: headache.
EENT: pharyngitis, rhinitis, sinusitis.
GI: diarrhea.
GU: hematuria.
Metabolic: hypercholesterolemia, hyperglycemia, hypertriglyceridemia.
Musculoskeletal: back pain.
Respiratory: bronchitis, cough, upper respiratory tract infection.
Other: accidental injury, flulike symptoms.

Interactions

None reported.

Effects on lab test results

- May increase glucose, triglyceride, uric acid, liver enzyme, bilirubin, cholesterol, potassium, and CK levels. May decrease hemoglobin level and hematocrit.

Pharmacokinetics

Absorption: Rapid and complete. Steady-state level occurs within 3 to 5 days.
Distribution: 99% protein-bound.
Metabolism: None.
Excretion: In the urine and feces. *Half-life:* 13 hours.

Route	Onset	Peak	Duration
P.O.	Rapid	1–2 hr	24 hr

Action

Chemical effect: Blocks the vasoconstrictor and aldosterone-secreting effects of angiotensin II by selectively blocking the binding of angiotensin II to the angiotensin receptor in the vascular smooth muscle.
Therapeutic effect: Lowers blood pressure.

Available forms

Tablets: 5 mg, 20 mg, 40 mg

NURSING PROCESS

Assessment

- Monitor patients with heart failure closely for oliguria, azotemia, and acute renal impairment.
- Monitor BUN and creatinine levels in patients with renal artery stenosis.
- Be alert for adverse reactions.
- Assess patient's and family's knowledge of drug therapy.

Nursing diagnoses

- Risk for injury related to presence of hypertension
- Sleep deprivation related to drug-induced cough
- Deficient knowledge related to drug therapy

Planning and implementation

- Symptomatic hypotension may occur in patients who are volume- or salt-depleted, especially those being treated with high doses of a diuretic. If hypotension occurs, place patient supine and treat supportively. When blood pressure is stabilized, therapy can continue.
- If blood pressure isn't adequately controlled, a diuretic or other antihypertensive may be added.

Patient teaching

- Tell patient to take drug exactly as prescribed and not to stop even if he feels better.
- Tell patient that drug may be taken with or without food.
- Tell patient to immediately report adverse reactions, especially lightheadedness and syncope, to prescriber.
- Advise a woman of childbearing age to immediately report pregnancy to prescriber.
- Inform diabetic patient that glucose readings may become higher, and the dosage of their antidiabetics may need adjustment.
- Warn patient that reduced fluid volume from inadequate fluid intake, excessive perspiration, diarrhea, or vomiting may cause a drop in blood pressure, leading to lightheadedness and fainting.
- Inform patient that other antihypertensives can have additive or synergistic effects. Patient should inform prescriber of all drugs (including OTC) that he's taking.

Evaluation

- Patient's blood pressure is normal.
- Patient's sleep patterns are undisturbed throughout therapy.
- Patient and family state understanding of drug therapy.

O

olsalazine sodium

(olh-SAL-uh-zeen SOH-dee-um)
Dipentum

Pharmacologic class: salicylate
Therapeutic class: anti-inflammatory
Pregnancy risk category: C

Indications and dosages

▶ **Maintenance of remission of ulcerative colitis in patients intolerant of sulfasalazine.**
Adults: 500 mg P.O. b.i.d. with meals.

Contraindications and cautions

- Contraindicated in patients hypersensitive to salicylates.
- Use cautiously in patients with renal disease. Renal tubular damage may result from absorbed drug or its metabolites.

Lifespan: In pregnant women, use cautiously. In breast-feeding women, use cautiously; it's unknown if the drug appears in breast milk. In children, safety and effectiveness haven't been established.

Adverse reactions

CNS: depression, dizziness, headache, vertigo.
GI: abdominal pain, *diarrhea,* heartburn, nausea.
Musculoskeletal: arthralgia.
Skin: itching, rash.

Interactions

Drug-drug. *Anticoagulants, coumarin derivatives:* May increase anticoagulant effects. Monitor patient closely for bleeding.

Effects on lab test results

- May increase AST and ALT levels.

Pharmacokinetics

Absorption: About 2%.
Distribution: Liberated mesalamine is absorbed slowly from colon, resulting in very high local level.
Metabolism: 0.1% in liver; remainder reaches colon, where it's rapidly converted to mesalamine by colonic bacteria.
Excretion: About 80% in feces; less than 1% in urine. *Half-life:* About 1 hour.

Route	Onset	Peak	Duration
P.O.	Unknown	1 hr	Unknown

Action

Chemical effect: May convert to 5-aminosalicylic acid (5-ASA or mesalamine) in colon, where it has local anti-inflammatory effect.
Therapeutic effect: Prevents flare-up of ulcerative colitis.

Available forms

Capsules: 250 mg

NURSING PROCESS

Assessment

- Assess patient's condition before starting therapy and regularly thereafter to monitor drug's effectiveness.
- Monitor BUN and creatinine levels and urinalysis in patient with renal disease.
- Be alert for adverse reactions.
- Assess patient's and family's knowledge of drug therapy.

Nursing diagnoses

- Impaired tissue integrity related to ulcerative colitis
- Diarrhea related to drug's adverse effect on GI tract
- Deficient knowledge related to drug therapy

Planning and implementation

- To decrease GI irritation, give drug in evenly divided doses with food.
- Report diarrhea to prescriber. Although diarrhea appears dose-related, it's difficult to distinguish from worsening of disease symptoms. Worsening of disease has been noted with similar drugs.

ALERT: Don't confuse olsalazine with olanzapine.

Patient teaching

- Tell patient to take drug in evenly divided doses, with food, to minimize GI irritation.
- Urge patient to notify prescriber about adverse reactions, especially diarrhea or increased pain.

Evaluation

- Patient has no evidence of ulcerative colitis.
- Patient is free from diarrhea.
- Patient and family state understanding of drug therapy.

omalizumab

(oh-mah-LIZZ-uh-mahb)
Xolair

Pharmacologic class: monoclonal antibody
Therapeutic class: antasthmatic
Pregnancy risk category: B

Indications and dosages

▶ **Moderate to severe persistent asthma in patients with positive skin test or in vitro reactivity to a seasonal allergen and whose symptoms are inadequately controlled with inhaled corticosteroids.** *Adults and children age 12 and older:* Dosage is determined by total immunoglobulin E (IgE) level (international unit/ml) measured before the start of therapy and by body weight (kg). See tables on this page. Divide doses greater than 150 mg and use more than one injection site. Inject subcutaneously q 2 or 4 weeks.

Contraindications and cautions

• Contraindicated in patients hypersensitive to the drug or any of its components.
Lifespan: In pregnant women, use only when potential benefits outweigh risks to the fetus. In breast-feeding women, use cautiously; it's unclear if drug appears in breast milk. In children younger than age 12, safety and effectiveness of drug haven't been established.

Adverse reactions

CNS: dizziness, fatigue, *headache,* pain.
EENT: earache, pharyngitis, *sinusitis.*
Musculoskeletal: arm pain, arthralgia, fracture, leg pain.
Respiratory: *upper respiratory tract infection.*
Skin: dermatitis, pruritus.
Other: ***anaphylaxis*** (immediate or delayed), hypersensitivity reaction, *injection site reaction, **malignancy**, viral infections.*

Interactions

None reported.

Effects on lab test results

• May increase IgE level for up to 1 year after therapy.

Pharmacokinetics

Absorption: Slow, with a bioavailability of about 62%.
Distribution: None specified.
Metabolism: Unknown.
Excretion: In liver and bile. *Half-life:* About 26 days.

Route	Onset	Peak	Duration
SubQ	Unknown	7–8 days	Unknown

DOSE EVERY 4 WEEKS

Pretreatment IgE (international unit/ml)	Body weight (kg) 30–60	> 60–70	> 70–90	> 90–150
≥ 30–100	150 mg	150 mg	150 mg	300 mg
> 100–200	300 mg	300 mg	300 mg	See table below.
> 200–300	300 mg	See table below.	See table below.	See table below.

DOSE EVERY 2 WEEKS

Pretreatment IgE (international unit/ml)	Body weight (kg) 30–60	> 60–70	> 70–90	> 90–150
> 100–200	See table above.	See table above.	See table above.	225 mg
> 200–300	See table above.	225 mg	225 mg	300 mg
> 300–400	225 mg	225 mg	300 mg	Don't give.
> 400–500	300 mg	300 mg	375 mg	Don't give.
> 500–600	300 mg	375 mg	Don't give.	Don't give.
> 600–700	375 mg	Don't give.	Don't give.	Don't give.

Action

Chemical effect: Inhibits binding of IgE to a high-affinity receptor on the surface of mast cells and basophils. Reducing IgE limits the release of mediators of the allergic response and reduces the number of receptors on basophils.
Therapeutic effect: Treats asthma symptoms.

Available forms

Powder for injection: 150 mg in 5-ml vial

NURSING PROCESS

Assessment

- Assess patient's respiratory condition before starting therapy and regularly thereafter to monitor drug's effectiveness.
- Be alert for adverse reactions.

ALERT: Observe patient after injection, and have drugs available to treat severe hypersensitivity reactions. If a severe hypersensitivity reaction occurs, stop therapy.

- Assess patient's and family's knowledge of drug therapy.

Nursing diagnoses

- Impaired gas exchange related to bronchospasm
- Acute pain related to drug-induced headache
- Deficient knowledge related to drug therapy

Planning and implementation

ALERT: Don't use for acute bronchospasm or status asthmaticus.

ALERT: Life-threatening anaphylactic reactions have occurred, usually within 2 hours of subcutaneous injection; reaction can be delayed.

- Don't abruptly stop giving systemic or inhaled corticosteroids when starting this drug. Gradually decrease corticosteroids with prescriber nearby.
- Because the solution is slightly viscous, it may take 5 to 10 seconds to inject.
- Patient may have injection site reactions, including bruising, redness, warmth, burning, stinging, itching, hives, pain, induration, and inflammation. Most reactions occur within 1 hour of injection, last less than 8 days, and decrease in frequency with subsequent injections.
- Total IgE level may elevate during therapy and remain elevated for up to 1 year after therapy stops; testing IgE level during therapy can't be used as a guide to determine dosage. If therapy has been stopped for less than 1 year, use IgE level from the original dosage determination. If therapy has been stopped for 1 year or more, retest total IgE level.

Patient teaching

- Tell patient not to decrease the dosage or stop taking his other antasthmatics unless directed by prescriber.
- Tell patient not to expect immediate improvement in his asthma after starting therapy.

Evaluation

- Patient exhibits normal breathing pattern.
- Patient states that drug-induced headache is relieved by analgesic.
- Patient and family state understanding of drug therapy.

omega-3 acid ethyl esters

(oh-MAY-gah THREE ASS-id ETH-ill ESS-turs)
Omacor

Pharmacologic class: ethyl ester
Therapeutic class: lipid regulator
Pregnancy risk category: C

Indications and dosages

▶ **Adjunct to diet to reduce triglyceride level of 500 mg/dl or more.** *Adults:* 4 g P.O. once daily or divided equally b.i.d.

Contraindications and cautions

- Contraindicated in patients hypersensitive to drug or any of its components.
- Use cautiously in patients sensitive to fish.

Lifespan: In pregnant women, use only if benefits outweigh risks to the fetus. In breast-feeding women, use cautiously. Safety and effectiveness in children haven't been established.

Adverse reactions

CNS: pain.
CV: angina pectoris.
GI: altered taste, belching, dyspepsia.
Musculoskeletal: back pain.
Skin: rash.
Other: flulike syndrome, infection.

Interactions

Drug-drug. *Anticoagulants:* May prolong bleeding time. Monitor patient.

Effects on lab test results

- May increase ALT and LDL levels.

Pharmacokinetics

Absorption: Good.
Distribution: Unknown.
Metabolism: Unknown.
Excretion: Unknown.

Route	Onset	Peak	Duration
P.O.	Unknown	Unknown	Unknown

Action

Chemical effect: May be a poor substrate for the enzymes needed for triglyceride synthesis. Blocks formation of other fatty acids.
Therapeutic effect: Decreases triglyceride level.

Available forms

Capsules: 1 g

NURSING PROCESS

Assessment

- Before therapy, assess patient for conditions that increase triglyceride level, such as diabetes and hypothyroidism.
- Assess patient's current history for drugs known to sharply increase triglyceride level, including estrogen therapy, thiazide diuretics, and beta blockers. Drug made not be needed after stopping these drugs.
- Monitor patient for adverse drug effects.
- Assess patient's and family's knowledge of drug therapy.

Nursing diagnoses

- Ineffective health maintenance related to elevated triglyceride level
- Risk for injury related to very high triglyceride level
- Deficient knowledge related to drug therapy

Planning and implementation

- Start therapy only after diet and lifestyle modifications have proven unsuccessful.
- Obtain baseline triglyceride level to confirm that they're consistently abnormal before therapy; then recheck periodically during therapy. If patient has an inadequate response after 2 months, stop drug.
- Monitor LDL level to make sure it doesn't increase excessively during therapy.

ALERT: Don't confuse Omacor with Amicar.

Patient teaching

- Explain that drug doesn't reduce the importance of following the recommended diet and exercise plan.
- Remind patient of the need for follow-up blood work to evaluate progress.
- Advise patient to notify prescriber about bothersome side effects.
- Tell patient to report planned or suspected pregnancy.

Evaluation

- Patient reduces triglyceride level with diet, exercise, lifestyle modifications, and drug therapy.
- Patient has reduced triglyceride level.
- Patient and family state understanding of drug therapy.

omeprazole

(oh-MEH-pruh-zohl)

Losec ♦ ◊, Prilosec, Prilosec OTC†, Zegerid

Pharmacologic class: substituted benzimidazole
Therapeutic class: proton pump inhibitor
Pregnancy risk category: C

Indications and dosages

▶ **Erosive esophagitis; symptomatic, poorly responsive gastroesophageal reflux disease (GERD).** *Adults with GERD who are unresponsive to H_2-receptor antagonist:* 20 mg P.O. daily for 4 to 8 weeks. May increase dosage to 40 mg daily if needed and extend therapy up to 12 weeks.
Children 2 to 16 years weighing less than 20 kg: 10 mg P.O. daily.
Children 2 to 16 years weighing 20 kg or more: 20 mg P.O. daily.

▶ **GERD without erosive esophagitis.** *Adults:* 20 mg P.O. daily for 4 weeks.

▶ **Pathologic hypersecretory conditions (such as Zollinger-Ellison syndrome).** *Adults:* Initially, 60 mg P.O. daily; adjust to patient's response. If daily amount exceeds 80 mg, give in divided doses. Dosages up to 120 mg t.i.d. may be given.

O

▶ **Duodenal ulcer (short-term therapy).** *Adults:* 20 mg P.O. daily for 2 to 8 weeks.

▶ **Gastric ulcer.** *Adults:* 40 mg P.O. daily for 4 to 8 weeks.

▶ ***Helicobacter pylori* eradication to reduce risk of duodenal ulcer recurrence as part of triple therapy with clarithromycin and amoxicillin.** *Adults:* 20 mg P.O. with 500 mg clarithromycin P.O. and 1,000 mg amoxicillin P.O., each given b.i.d. for 10 days. For patients with ulcers when therapy starts, another 18 days of 20 mg omeprazole P.O. once daily is recommended.

▶ ***Helicobacter pylori* eradication to reduce risk of duodenal ulcer recurrence as part of dual therapy with clarithromycin.** *Adults:* 40 mg P.O. once daily with clarithromycin 500 mg, P.O., t.i.d. for 14 days. For patients with ulcers present at the start of therapy, give 20 mg omeprazole P.O. once daily for 14 more days.

▶ **Heartburn on 2 or more days per week.** *Adults:* 20 mg P.O. (Prilosec OTC) daily before breakfast for 14 days. May repeat the 14-day course q 4 months.

▶ **Posterior laryngitis‡.** *Adults:* 40 mg at bedtime for 6 to 24 weeks.

Contraindications and cautions

• Contraindicated in patients hypersensitive to the drug or any of its components.

Lifespan: In pregnant women, use cautiously. In breast-feeding women, use cautiously; it's unknown if the drug appears in breast milk. In children ages 2 to 16 years, drug may be used to treat GERD, erosive esophagitis, and for maintenance of healing in erosive esophagitis (tablets and capsules only).

Adverse reactions

CNS: dizziness, headache.
GI: abdominal pain, constipation, diarrhea, flatulence, nausea, vomiting.
Musculoskeletal: back pain.
Respiratory: cough.
Skin: rash.

Interactions

Drug-drug. *Ampicillin esters, iron derivatives, ketoconazole:* May decrease absorption. Give separately.
Clarithromycin: May increase level of either drug. Monitor patient for drug toxicity.
Diazepam, phenytoin, warfarin: May decrease hepatic clearance of these drugs, possibly leading to increased levels. Monitor patient closely.
Sucralfate: May delay absorption and reduce omeprazole bioavailability. Separate administration times by 30 minutes or more.
Drug-herb. *Male fern:* May inactivate herb. Discourage using together.
Pennyroyal: May change the rate at which toxic metabolites of herb form. Discourage using together.

Effects on lab test results

None reported.

Pharmacokinetics

Absorption: Rapid, but bioavailability is about 40% because of instability in gastric acid as well as substantial first-pass effect. Bioavailability increases slightly with repeated doses.
Distribution: 95% protein-bound.
Metabolism: Mainly in liver.
Excretion: Mainly in urine. *Half-life:* 30 to 60 minutes.

Route	Onset	Peak	Duration
P.O.	≤ 1 hr	30 min–2 hr	< 3 days

Action

Chemical effect: Inhibits acid (proton) pump and binds to hydrogen-potassium adenosine triphosphatase on secretory surface of gastric parietal cells to block formation of gastric acid.
Therapeutic effect: Relieves symptoms caused by excessive gastric acid.

Available forms

Capsules (delayed-release): 10 mg, 20 mg, 40 mg
Tablets (delayed-release): 20 mg
Powder for oral suspension: 20 mg

NURSING PROCESS

Assessment

• Assess patient's condition before starting therapy and regularly thereafter to monitor drug's effectiveness.
• Be alert for adverse reactions and drug interactions.
• If adverse GI reaction occurs, monitor patient's hydration.

• Assess patient's and family's knowledge of drug therapy.

Nursing diagnoses

• Impaired tissue integrity related to upper gastric disorder

• Risk for deficient fluid volume related to drug-induced adverse GI reactions

• Deficient knowledge related to drug therapy

Planning and implementation

• Give tablets or capsules 30 minutes before meals; powder for oral suspension 1 hour before meals.

• Zegerid powder for oral suspension may be used for short-term treatment of duodenal ulcers, GERD, and maintenance of healing of erosive esophagitis; don't use in children younger than age 18.

• Use 2 tbs of water to mix 1 packet of powder for oral suspension; don't use any other liquids or food.

• Powder for oral suspension contains 460 mg of sodium per dose and 20 mEq of sodium bicarbonate.

• Lower doses aren't needed for patients with renal or hepatic impairment.

ALERT: Don't confuse Prilosec with Prozac, prilocaine, or Prinivil.

ALERT: Don't confuse Losec with Lasix.

Patient teaching

• Explain importance of taking drug exactly as prescribed.

• Warn patient not to crush or chew tablets or capsules.

• Explain to patient how to reconstitute powder for oral suspension: Empty packet contents into a small cup containing 2 tbs of water; stir well and drink immediately. Refill cup with water and drink.

• Advise patient that OTC drug isn't intended for immediate relief of heartburn or to treat occasional heartburn (one episode of heartburn a week or less).

• Inform patient that OTC drug may require 1 to 4 days for full effect, although some patients may get complete relief of symptoms within 24 hours.

Evaluation

• Patient responds well to therapy.

• Patient maintains adequate hydration throughout drug therapy.

• Patient and family state understanding of drug therapy.

ondansetron hydrochloride

(on-DAN-seh-tron high-droh-KLOR-ighd)

Zofran, Zofran ODT

Pharmacologic class: serotonin receptor antagonist

Therapeutic class: antiemetic

Pregnancy risk category: B

Indications and dosages

▶ **To prevent nausea and vomiting caused by moderately emetogenic chemotherapy.** *Adults and children age 12 and older:* 8 mg P.O. 30 minutes before start of chemotherapy. Follow with 8 mg P.O. 8 hours after first dose. Then follow with 8 mg q 12 hours for 1 to 2 days. Or, three doses of 0.15 mg/kg I.V. Give first dose 30 minutes before chemotherapy; give subsequent doses 4 and 8 hours after first dose. Infuse drug over 15 minutes. Or, adults may receive a single dose of 32 mg I.V. infused over 15 minutes, 30 minutes before chemotherapy. Don't repeat this dose.

Children ages 4 to 11: Give 4 mg P.O. 30 minutes before start of chemotherapy. Follow with 4 mg P.O. 4 and 8 hours after first dose. Then follow with 4 mg q 8 hours for 1 to 2 days.

Children ages 6 months to 11 years: Three doses of 0.15 mg/kg I.V. Give first dose 30 minutes before chemotherapy; give subsequent doses 4 and 8 hours after first dose. Infuse drug over 15 minutes.

▶ **To prevent nausea and vomiting caused by highly emetogenic chemotherapy.** *Adults:* 24 mg P.O. 30 minutes before start of chemotherapy.

▶ **To prevent postoperative nausea and vomiting.** *Adults:* 4 mg I.V. (undiluted) over 2 to 5 minutes immediately before induction of anesthesia or postoperatively. Or, 4 mg I.M. as a single injection immediately before induction of anesthesia or postoperatively. Or, 16 mg P.O. 1 hour before induction of anesthesia.

Children ages 1 month to 12 years who weigh 40 kg (88 lb) or less: 0.1 mg/kg I.V. Give dose over 2 to 5 minutes as a single dose.

O

Children ages 1 month to 12 years who weigh more than 40 kg: Give 4 mg I.V. over 2 to 5 minutes as a single dose.

▶ **To prevent nausea and vomiting from radiation therapy—total body irradiation, a single high-dose fraction, or daily fractions to the abdomen.** *Adults:* 8 mg P.O. t.i.d.

Adjust-a-dose: For patients with severe liver impairment, don't exceed total daily dosage of 8 mg P.O. or a single maximum dose of 8 mg I.V. over 15 minutes.

I.V. administration

- Dilute drug in 50 ml of D_5W injection or normal saline solution for injection before giving.
- Infuse drug over 15 minutes.
- Drug is stable for up to 48 hours after dilution in 5% dextrose and normal saline injection, 5% dextrose in half-normal saline injection, and 3% saline injection.

⊗ **Incompatibilities**

Acyclovir sodium, allopurinol, aminophylline, amphotericin B, ampicillin sodium, ampicillin sodium and sulbactam sodium, cefepime, cefoperazone, dexamethasone sodium phosphate, droperidol, fluorouracil, furosemide, ganciclovir, lorazepam, meropenem, methylprednisolone sodium succinate, piperacillin sodium, sargramostim, sodium bicarbonate.

Contraindications and cautions

- Contraindicated in patients hypersensitive to the drug or any of its components.
- Use cautiously and at a lower dose in patients with liver failure.

Lifespan: In pregnant women, use cautiously. In breast-feeding women, use cautiously; it's unknown if the drug appears in breast milk. In children, safety and effectiveness of the 24-mg tablet or the use of oral forms of drug for postoperative nausea and vomiting or radiation-induced nausea and vomiting haven't been established. In infants younger than age 1 month who are undergoing surgery, information on safety and effectiveness of drug is limited.

Adverse reactions

CNS: extrapyramidal syndrome, *headache.*
CV: ***arrhythmias, bradycardia,*** chest pain, hypotension.
GI: constipation, diarrhea.
Skin: pruritus, rash.

Interactions

Drug-drug. *Drugs that alter hepatic drug-metabolizing enzymes (such as cimetidine, phenobarbital):* May alter pharmacokinetics of ondansetron. No dosage adjustment is needed.
Rifampin: May reduce ondansetron level, decreasing antiemetic effect. Monitor patient for adequate antiemetic effect; adjust dosage.

Effects on lab test results

- May increase ALT and AST levels.

Pharmacokinetics

Absorption: Variable; bioavailability is 50% to 60%.
Distribution: 70% to 76% protein-bound.
Metabolism: Extensive.
Excretion: Mainly in urine. *Half-life:* 4 hours.

Route	Onset	Peak	Duration
P.O., I.V.	Unknown	Unknown	Unknown

Action

Chemical effect: Blocking action may take place in CNS at chemoreceptor trigger zone and in peripheral nervous system on terminals of vagus nerve.
Therapeutic effect: Prevents nausea and vomiting from emetogenic chemotherapy or surgery.

Available forms

Injection: 2 mg/ml
Oral solution: 4 mg/5 ml
Tablets: 4 mg, 8 mg, 24 mg
Tablets (orally disintegrating): 4 mg, 8 mg

NURSING PROCESS

Assessment

- Assess patient's condition before starting therapy and regularly thereafter to monitor drug's effectiveness.
- Be alert for adverse reactions and drug interactions.
- Assess patient's and family's knowledge of drug therapy.

Nursing diagnoses

- Risk for deficient fluid volume related to nausea and vomiting
- Acute pain related to drug-induced headache
- Deficient knowledge related to drug therapy

Planning and implementation

ALERT: Don't confuse Zofran with Zantac or Zosyn.

ALERT: Don't confuse Zofran with Precedex. These vials appear very similar.

ALERT: Don't confuse ondansetron with olanzapine.

Patient teaching

- Instruct patient when to take drug.
- Tell patient to report adverse reactions.
- Advise patient to report discomfort at I.V. site.

Evaluation

- Patient maintains adequate hydration.
- Patient has no drug-induced headaches.
- Patient and family state understanding of drug therapy.

orlistat

(OR-lih-stat)

Xenical

Pharmacologic class: lipase inhibitor
Therapeutic class: antiobesity drug
Pregnancy risk category: B

Indications and dosages

▶ **Management of obesity, including weight loss and weight maintenance, given with a reduced-calorie diet; reduction of risk of weight regain after weight loss.** *Adults:* 120 mg P.O. t.i.d. with each main meal containing fat (during or up to 1 hour after the meal).

Contraindications and cautions

- Contraindicated in patients hypersensitive to the drug or any of its components and in patients with chronic malabsorption syndrome or cholestasis.
- Use cautiously in patients with a history of hyperoxaluria or calcium oxalate nephrolithiasis, patients who are at risk for anorexia nervosa or bulimia, and patients who are receiving cyclosporine therapy because of changes in cyclosporine absorption related to variations in diet.

Lifespan: In pregnant and breast-feeding women, drug isn't recommended. In children, safety and effectiveness haven't been established.

Adverse reactions

CNS: anxiety, depression, dizziness, fatigue, *headache,* sleep disorder.
CV: pedal edema.
EENT: otitis.
GI: *abdominal pain, fatty or oily stool,* fecal incontinence, *fecal urgency, flatus with discharge, increased defecation,* infectious diarrhea, nausea, *oily evacuation, oily spotting,* ***pancreatitis,*** rectal pain, vomiting.
GU: menstrual irregularity, UTI, vaginitis.
Musculoskeletal: arthritis, *back pain,* joint disorder, leg pain, myalgia, tendinitis.
Respiratory: *influenza,* lower respiratory tract infection, *upper respiratory tract infection.*
Skin: dry skin, rash.
Other: gingival and tooth disorders.

Interactions

Drug-drug. *Cyclosporine:* May alter cyclosporine absorption. Monitor cyclosporine level.
Fat-soluble vitamins such as vitamin E, beta-carotene: May decrease vitamin absorption. Separate doses by 2 hours.
Pravastatin: May slightly increase pravastatin level and lipid-lowering effects. Monitor patient.
Warfarin: May change coagulation parameters. Monitor INR.

Effects on lab test results

- May decrease vitamin D, beta-carotene, LDL, and total cholesterol levels.

Pharmacokinetics

Absorption: Only a small amount.
Distribution: More than 99% protein-bound. Lipoproteins and albumin are major binding proteins.
Metabolism: Mainly in GI wall.
Excretion: Mostly unchanged in feces. *Half-life:* 1 to 2 hours.

Route	Onset	Peak	Duration
P.O.	Unknown	Unknown	Unknown

Action

Chemical effect: Binds with the active site of gastric and pancreatic lipases. These inactivated enzymes are thus unavailable to hydrolyze dietary fat, in the form of triglycerides, into absorbable free fatty acids and monoglycerides. Because the undigested triglycerides aren't ab-

sorbed, the resulting caloric deficit may help with weight control. The recommended dosage of 120 mg t.i.d. inhibits dietary fat absorption by about 30%.
Therapeutic effect: Weight loss and weight maintenance.

Available forms

Capsules: 120 mg

NURSING PROCESS

Assessment

- Obtain history of patient's underlying condition before starting therapy; reassess regularly thereafter to monitor the drug's effectiveness.
- Screen patient for anorexia nervosa or bulimia; as with any weight-loss drug, drug can be misused.
- Organic causes of obesity, such as hypothyroidism, must be ruled out before patient starts orlistat therapy.
- In diabetic patient, monitor glucose level frequently during weight loss. Dose of oral antidiabetic or insulin may need to be reduced.
- Assess patient's and family's knowledge of drug therapy.

Nursing diagnoses

- Imbalanced nutrition: More than body requirements related to obesity
- Disturbed body image related to obesity
- Deficient knowledge related to drug therapy

Planning and implementation

ALERT: Pancreatitis has occurred with use of drug. Monitor patient closely.

- Use drug for a patient with an initial body mass index of 30 kg/m^2 or more (27 kg/m^2 or more if patient has other risk factors, such as hypertension, diabetes, or dyslipidemia).
- It's unknown whether drug is safe and effective to use longer than 2 years.
- Tell patient to follow dietary guidelines. GI effects may increase when patient takes drug with high-fat foods—specifically, when more than 30% of total daily calories come from fat.
- Drug reduces absorption of some fat-soluble vitamins and beta-carotene.

ALERT: Don't confuse Xenical with Xeloda.

Patient teaching

- Advise patient to follow a nutritionally balanced, reduced-calorie diet that derives only 30% of its calories from fat. Daily intake of fat, carbohydrate, and protein should be distributed over three main meals. If a meal is occasionally missed or contains no fat, tell patient that dose can be skipped.
- To ensure adequate nutrition, advise patient to take a daily multivitamin supplement that contains fat-soluble vitamins no sooner than within 2 hours of taking drug, such as at bedtime.
- Tell patient with diabetes that weight loss may improve glycemic control, so his oral antidiabetic or insulin dosage may need to be reduced.
- Tell woman to inform prescriber if she is pregnant, plans to become pregnant, or is breast-feeding.

Evaluation

- Patient's nutritional intake is adequate according to proper dietary guidelines.
- Patient reaches and maintains a stable weight.
- Patient and family state understanding of drug therapy.

oseltamivir phosphate

(ah-sul-TAM-ih-veer FOS-fayt)
Tamiflu

Pharmacologic class: neuraminidase inhibitor
Therapeutic class: antiviral
Pregnancy risk category: C

Indications and dosages

▶ **Uncomplicated, acute illness from influenza in patients who have been symptomatic for 2 days or less.** *Adults, children age 13 and older, and children age 1 and older who weigh more than 40 kg (88 lb):* 75 mg P.O. b.i.d. for 5 days.
Children age 1 and older who weigh 23 to 40 kg (51 to 88 lb): 60 mg oral suspension P.O. b.i.d. for 5 days.
Children age 1 and older who weigh 15 to 23 kg (33 to 51 lb): 45 mg oral suspension P.O. b.i.d. for 5 days.
Children age 1 and older who weigh 15 kg (33 lb) or less: 30 mg oral suspension P.O. b.i.d. for 5 days.
Adjust-a-dose: For adults and adolescents with renal impairment, if creatinine clearance is 10 to 30 ml/minute, give 75 mg P.O. once daily for 5 days.

▶ **Prevention of influenza after close contact with infected person (beginning within 2 days of exposure).** *Adults and children age 13 and older, and children age 1 and older who weigh more than 40 kg (88 lb):* 75 mg P.O. once daily for at least 10 days.
Children age 1 and older who weigh 23 to 40 kg (51 to 88 lb): 60 mg oral suspension P.O. once daily for 10 days.
Children age 1 and older who weigh 15 to 23 kg (33 to 51 lb): 45 mg oral suspension P.O. once daily for 10 days.
Children age 1 and older who weigh 15 kg (33 lb) or less: 30 mg oral suspension P.O. once daily for 10 days.
Adjust-a-dose: For adults and adolescents with renal impairment, if creatinine clearance is 10 to 30 ml/minute, give 75-mg capsule once q other day or 30 mg of oral suspension daily.
▶ **Prevention of influenza during a community outbreak.** *Adults and children age 13 and older:* 75 mg P.O. daily for up to 6 weeks.
Adjust-a-dose: For patients with renal impairment, if creatinine clearance is 10 to 30 ml/minute, give 75 mg once q other day or 30 mg of oral suspension daily.

Contraindications and cautions

• Contraindicated in patients hypersensitive to the drug or any of its components.
Lifespan: In breast-feeding women, use only if benefits outweigh risks to the infant. In children younger than age 1, use for treatment or prevention of influenza hasn't been established.

Adverse reactions

CNS: dizziness, fatigue, headache, insomnia, vertigo.
GI: abdominal pain, diarrhea, nausea, vomiting.
Respiratory: bronchitis, cough.

Interactions

None significant.

Effects on lab test results

None reported.

Pharmacokinetics

Absorption: Good. More than 75% reaches systemic circulation as oseltamivir carboxylate.
Distribution: 3% to 42% protein-bound.
Metabolism: Extensive.
Excretion: Mostly in urine by glomerular filtration and tubular secretion. Less than 20% is eliminated in feces. *Half-life:* 1 to 10 hours.

Route	Onset	Peak	Duration
P.O.	Unknown	Unknown	Unknown

Action

Chemical effect: Inhibits the enzyme neuraminidase in influenza virus particles. This action may inhibit viral replication, possibly by interfering with viral particle aggregation and release from the host cell.
Therapeutic effect: Lessens the symptoms of influenza.

Available forms

Capsules: 75 mg
Oral suspension: 12 mg/ml after reconstitution

NURSING PROCESS

Assessment

• Obtain complete medical history before starting therapy.
• Assess renal function before giving drug, as directed.
• Assess patient's and family's knowledge of drug therapy.

Nursing diagnoses

• Risk for infection related to influenza virus
• Imbalanced nutrition: Less than body requirements related to drug's adverse GI effects
• Deficient knowledge related to drug therapy

Planning and implementation

• Drug is used mainly to treat symptoms and isn't a replacement for an annual influenza vaccination.
• No evidence supports use in treating other viral infections.
• Drug may be given with meals to decrease adverse GI effects.
• Safety and effectiveness of repeated courses of therapy haven't been established.

Patient teaching

• Tell patient to start drug within 2 days of start of symptoms.
• Inform patient that receiving this drug isn't a substitute for receiving the flu vaccination. Urge

O

patient to continue receiving an annual vaccination.

Evaluation

- Patient recovers from influenza.
- Patient has no adverse GI effects and maintains adequate hydration.
- Patient and family state understanding of drug therapy.

oxaliplatin

(ox-ah-leh-PLA-tin)
Eloxatin

Pharmacologic class: alkylating drug
Therapeutic class: antineoplastic
Pregnancy risk category: D

Indications and dosages

▶ **Advanced colorectal cancer when given with 5-fluorouracil (5-FU) and leucovorin.** *Adults:* On day one, 85 mg/m^2 oxaliplatin I.V. in 250 to 500 ml D_5W and 200 mg/m^2 leucovorin I.V. in D_5W, given simultaneously over 120 minutes in separate bags using a Y-line. Then, 400 mg/m^2 5-FU I.V. bolus given over 2 to 4 minutes, followed by 600 mg/m^2 5-FU I.V. infusion in 500 ml D_5W over 22 hours. On day two, 200 mg/m^2 leucovorin I.V. infusion over 120 minutes. Then, 400 mg/m^2 5-FU I.V. bolus given over 2 to 4 minutes, followed by 600 mg/m^2 5-FU I.V. infusion in 500 ml D_5W over 22 hours. Repeat cycle q 2 weeks.

Adjust-a-dose: In patients with unresolved, persistent, grade 2 neurosensory events (events that interfere with function, but not daily activities), reduce dose to 65 mg/m^2. In patients with persistent grade 3 neurosensory events (pain and functional impairment that affect daily activity), consider stopping drug. In patients recovering from grade 3/4 GI (despite prophylaxis) or hematologic (neutrophil count less than 1.5 $\times$ 10^9/L and platelet count less than 100 $\times$ 10^9/L) events, reduce dose to 65 mg/m^2. Also reduce dose of 5-FU by 20%.

▶ **With 5-FU and leucovorin for the adjuvant treatment of stage III colon cancer in patients who have undergone complete resection of the primary tumor.** *Adults:* On day one, give oxaliplatin, 85 mg/m^2 I.V. in 250 to 500 ml D_5W and leucovorin 200 mg/^{2} I.V. infusion in D_5W, both at the same time over 120 minutes, in separate bags, using a Y-line. Follow with 5-FU 400 mg/m^2 I.V. bolus over 2 to 4 minutes, then 600 mg/m^2 5-FU in 500 ml D_5W as a 22-hour continuous infusion. On day two, give leucovorin, 200 mg/m^2 I.V. infused over 120 minutes followed by 5-FU 400 mg/m^2 as an I.V. bolus over 2 to 4 minutes; then, give 600 mg/m^2 5-FU infusion in 500 ml D_5 over 22 hours. Repeat cycle q 2 weeks for a total of 6 months. Premedicate with antiemetics, with or without dexamethasone.

Adjust-a-dose: For patients with persistent grade 2 neurotoxicity, consider reducing oxaliplatin dose to 75 mg/m^2. For patients with persistent grade 3 neurosensory events, consider discontinuing oxaliplatin therapy. For patients who recovered from a grade 3/4 GI event (despite prophylaxis) or grade 3/4 hematologic toxicity, reduce oxaliplatin to 75 mg/m^2 and 5-FU to a 300 mg/m^2 bolus and 500 mg/m^2 22-hour infusion. Delay dose until neutrophils are $\geq 1.5 \times 10^9$/L and platelets are $\geq 75 \times 10^9$/L.

I.V. administration

- Preparing and giving drug may have carcinogenic, mutagenic, and teratogenic risks. Follow facility policy to reduce risks.
- Reconstitute powder using sterile water for injection or D_5W. Add 10 ml to a 50-mg vial or 20 ml to a 100-mg vial for a final concentration of 5 mg/ml. Never reconstitute with sodium chloride solution or other solution containing chloride.
- Further dilute reconstituted solutions in an infusion solution of 250 to 500 ml of D_5W.
- Inspect bag for particulate matter and discoloration before giving; discard the solution if present.
- Don't use needles or I.V. administration sets that contain aluminum because they will react with platinum in drug, causing loss of potency and formation of a black precipitate.
- Drug doesn't require prehydration.
- Premedicate with antiemetics with or without dexamethasone.
- Flush infusion line with D_5W before giving any other drugs simultaneously.
- Give drug and leucovorin over 2 hours at the same time in separate bags, using a Y-line. May extend the infusion time of the oxaliplatin to 6 hours to decrease acute toxicities.

• Avoid ice and cold exposure during infusion of drug because cold temperatures can exacerbate acute neurologic symptoms. Cover patient with a blanket during infusion.
• Store unopened vials at room temperature. Reconstituted solutions are stable if refrigerated (36° to 46° F [2° to 8° C]) for up to 24 hours. After final dilution, solutions are stable for 6 hours at room temperature and up to 24 hours under refrigeration.

⊗ **Incompatibilities**
Alkaline solutions, solutions containing chloride, or drugs such as 5-FU.

Contraindications and cautions

• Contraindicated in patients allergic to the drug or other compounds containing platinum.
• Use cautiously in patients with preexisting renal impairment or peripheral sensory neuropathy.
Lifespan: In pregnant women, drug is contraindicated. In breast-feeding women and in children, safety and effectiveness haven't been established. In the elderly, use cautiously because diarrhea, dehydration, hypokalemia, and fatigue may occur more frequently in these patients.

Adverse reactions

CNS: *dizziness, fatigue, fever, headache, insomnia, pain, peripheral neuropathy.*
CV: chest pain, edema, flushing, peripheral edema, ***thromboembolism.***
EENT: abnormal lacrimation, epistaxis, pharyngitis, *rhinitis.*
GI: *abdominal pain, anorexia, constipation, diarrhea, dyspepsia,* flatulence, gastroesophageal reflux, mucositis, *nausea, stomatitis, vomiting, taste perversion.*
GU: dysuria, hematuria.
Hematologic: *anemia,* **FEBRILE NEUTROPENIA, LEUKOPENIA, THROMBOCYTOPENIA.**
Metabolic: dehydration, hypokalemia.
Musculoskeletal: *arthralgia, back pain.*
Respiratory: *cough, dyspnea,* hiccups, ***pulmonary toxicity,*** *upper respiratory tract infection.*
Skin: alopecia, rash.
Other: allergic reaction, ***anaphylaxis,*** *hand-foot syndrome, injection site reaction,* rigors.

Interactions

Drug-drug. *Nephrotoxic drugs (such as gentamicin):* May decrease oxaliplatin elimination and increase level. Monitor patient for signs and symptoms of toxicity.

Effects on lab test results

• May increase creatinine, bilirubin, AST, and ALT levels. May decrease potassium and hemoglobin levels and hematocrit.
• May decrease neutrophil, WBC, and platelet counts.

Pharmacokinetics

Absorption: Given I.V.
Distribution: Wide. More than 90% protein-bound.
Metabolism: Undergoes non-enzymatic biotransformation.
Excretion: Mainly renal. *Half-life:* Unknown.

Route	Onset	Peak	Duration
I.V.	Unknown	Unknown	Unknown

Action

Chemical effect: May inhibit cell replication and transcription by forming platinum complexes that cross-link with DNA molecules.
Therapeutic effect: Inhibits cancer cell formation.

Available forms

Powder for injection: 50- or 100-mg vials
Injection: 5 mg/ml

NURSING PROCESS

Assessment

• Monitor CBC, platelet count, and liver and kidney function before each chemotherapy cycle.
• Monitor patient for hypersensitivity reactions, which may occur within minutes of giving drug.
• Monitor patient for injection site reaction. Extravasation may occur.
• Monitor patient for neuropathy and pulmonary toxicity. Peripheral neuropathy may be acute or persistent. Acute neuropathy is reversible; it occurs within 2 days of therapy and resolves within 14 days. Persistent peripheral neuropathy occurs more than 14 days after therapy and causes paresthesias, dysesthesias, hypoesthesias, and decrease in sensation that can interfere with daily activities, such as walking or swallowing.

O

• Assess patient's and family's knowledge of drug therapy.

Nursing diagnoses
• Ineffective health maintenance related to cancer
• Ineffective protection related to drug-induced adverse hematologic reactions
• Deficient knowledge related to drug therapy

Planning and implementation
• Drug clearance is reduced in patients with renal impairment. Dosage adjustment for patients with renal impairment hasn't been established.

Patient teaching
• Inform patient about potential adverse reactions.
• Tell patient to avoid exposure to cold or cold objects (such as cold drinks or ice cubes), which can bring on or worsen acute symptoms of peripheral neuropathy. Advise patient to have warm drinks, wear warm clothing, and cover any exposed skin. Have patient warm the air going into his lungs by wearing a scarf or ski mask. Have him wear gloves when touching cold objects (such as foods in the freezer, outside door handles, and mailbox).
• Tell patient to immediately notify prescriber if he has trouble breathing or has signs and symptoms of an allergic reaction (rash, hives, swelling of lips or tongue, sudden cough).
• Tell patient to contact prescriber if fever, signs and symptoms of an infection, persistent vomiting, diarrhea, or signs and symptoms of dehydration (thirst, dry mouth, lightheadedness, and decreased urination) occur.

Evaluation
• Patient responds well to therapy.
• Patient develops no serious complications from drug-induced adverse hematologic reactions.
• Patient and family state understanding of drug therapy.

oxaprozin potassium
(oks-uh-PROH-zin puh-TAH-see-um)

Apo-Oxaprozin ♦, Daypro, Daypro ALTA, Rhoxal-Oxaprozin ♦

Pharmacologic class: NSAID
Therapeutic class: anti-inflammatory, analgesic
Pregnancy risk category: C

Indications and dosages
▶ **Osteoarthritis, rheumatoid arthritis.** *Adults:* 1,200 mg P.O. once daily. Divide doses in patients unable to tolerate single doses. For osteoarthritis patients with low body weight and milder disease, give an initial dose of 600 mg once daily. Maximum daily dosage, 1,800 mg.
Adjust-a-dose: For patients with renal impairment and those undergoing hemodialysis, initial dose is 600 mg P.O. daily.

Contraindications and cautions
• Contraindicated in patients hypersensitive to the drug or any of its components and in those with syndrome of nasal polyps, angioedema, and bronchospastic reactions to aspirin or other NSAIDs.
• Use cautiously in patients with history of peptic ulcer disease, hepatic or renal dysfunction, hypertension, CV disease, or conditions that predispose to fluid retention.
Lifespan: In pregnant women, use cautiously. In breast-feeding women, use cautiously; it's unknown if the drug appears in breast milk. In children, safety and effectiveness haven't been established.

Adverse reactions
CNS: confusion, depression, sedation, sleep disturbances, somnolence.
EENT: tinnitus, visual disturbances.
GI: abdominal pain or distress, anorexia, *constipation, diarrhea, dyspepsia,* flatulence, ***GI hemorrhage,*** *nausea,* vomiting.
GU: dysuria, renal insufficiency, urinary frequency.
Skin: photosensitivity, *rash.*

Interactions
Drug-drug. *Antihypertensives, diuretics:* May decrease effect. Monitor patient closely, and adjust dosage.

Aspirin: May displace salicylates from protein-binding sites, increasing risk of salicylate toxicity. Avoid using together.
Aspirin, corticosteroids: May increase risk of adverse GI reactions. Avoid using together.
Cyclosporine: May increase risk of nephrotoxicity by both drugs. Monitor renal function tests.
Methotrexate: Increases risk of methotrexate toxicity. Avoid using together.
Oral anticoagulants: May increase risk of bleeding. Use together cautiously; monitor patient for bleeding.
Drug-herb. *Dong quai, feverfew, garlic, ginger, horse chestnut, red clover:* May increase risk of bleeding. Discourage using together.
St. John's wort: May increase risk of photosensitivity. Advise patient to avoid unprotected or prolonged exposure to sunlight.
Drug-lifestyle. *Alcohol use:* May increase risk of adverse GI reactions. Discourage using together.
Sun exposure: May cause photosensitivity reactions. Urge patient to avoid unprotected or prolonged exposure to sunlight.

Effects on lab test results

- May increase ALT, AST, BUN, and creatinine levels. May decrease hemoglobin level and hematocrit.
- May increase bleeding time.

Pharmacokinetics

Absorption: Bioavailability is 95%; food may reduce rate but not extent.
Distribution: About 99.9% protein-bound.
Metabolism: In liver.
Excretion: In urine (65%) and feces (35%). *Half-life:* 42 to 50 hours.

Route	Onset	Peak	Duration
P.O.	Unknown	2 hr	Unknown

Action

Chemical effect: May inhibit prostaglandin synthesis.
Therapeutic effect: Relieves pain, fever, and inflammation.

Available forms

Caplets: 600 mg
Tablets: 600 mg

NURSING PROCESS

Assessment

- Assess patient's condition before starting therapy and regularly thereafter to monitor drug's effectiveness.
- Monitor liver function test results periodically during long-term therapy, and closely monitor patient with abnormal test results. Liver function values may be elevated. These abnormal findings may persist, worsen, or resolve with continued therapy. Rarely, patient may progress to severe hepatic dysfunction.
- Be alert for adverse reactions and drug interactions.
- Assess patient's and family's knowledge of drug therapy.

Nursing diagnoses

- Chronic pain related to condition
- Impaired tissue integrity related to adverse GI effects of drug
- Deficient knowledge related to drug therapy

Planning and implementation

- Give drug on empty stomach unless adverse GI reactions occur.
- Notify prescriber immediately about adverse reactions, especially GI symptoms.

ALERT: Don't confuse oxaprozin with oxazepam.

Patient teaching

- Tell patient experiencing adverse GI effects, to take drug with milk or meals.
- Explain that full therapeutic effects may be delayed for 2 to 4 weeks.
- Tell patient to report adverse visual or auditory reactions immediately.
- Teach patient to recognize and promptly report signs and symptoms of GI bleeding.
- Advise patient to use sunscreen, wear protective clothing, and avoid prolonged exposure to sunlight.
- Warn patient to avoid hazardous activities until CNS effects of drug are known.

Evaluation

- Patient is free from pain.
- Patient maintains GI tissue integrity.
- Patient and family state understanding of drug therapy.

O

oxazepam

(oks-AZ-ih-pam)

Alepam ◇, Apo-Oxazepam ♦, Murelax ◇, Novoxapam ♦, Serax, Serepax ◇

Pharmacologic class: benzodiazepine
Therapeutic class: anxiolytic
Pregnancy risk category: D
Controlled substance schedule: IV

Indications and dosages

▶ **Alcohol withdrawal.** *Adults:* 15 to 30 mg P.O. t.i.d. or q.i.d.

▶ **Severe anxiety.** *Adults:* 15 to 30 mg P.O. t.i.d. or q.i.d.

▶ **Mild to moderate anxiety.** *Adults:* 10 to 15 mg P.O. t.i.d. or q.i.d.

▶ **Older patients with anxiety, tension, irritability, and agitation.** *Adults:* 10 mg P.O. t.i.d. May increase cautiously to 15 mg P.O. t.i.d. to q.i.d.

Contraindications and cautions

- Contraindicated in patients hypersensitive to the drug or any of its components.
- Use cautiously in patients with history of drug abuse and in those for whom a drop in blood pressure could lead to cardiac problems.

Lifespan: In pregnant and breast-feeding women, don't use. In children, safety and effectiveness haven't been established. In the elderly, use cautiously.

Adverse reactions

CNS: drowsiness, fainting, hangover, lethargy, *mental changes.*
CV: transient hypotension.
GI: abdominal discomfort, nausea, vomiting.
Hepatic: ***hepatic dysfunction.***
Other: increased risk of falls.

Interactions

Drug-drug. *CNS depressants:* May increase CNS depression. Avoid using together.
Digoxin: May increase digoxin level, increasing toxicity. Monitor level closely.
Hormonal contraceptives: May increase oxazepam clearance. Monitor patient for decreased effect.
Lamotrigine: May decrease lamotrigine level. Adjust lamotrigine dosage as needed.
Phenytoin: May increase oxazepam clearance and phenytoin level. Monitor patient closely for phenytoin toxicity.
Drug-herb. *Catnip, kava, lady's slipper, lemon balm, passionflower, sassafras, skullcap, valerian:* May increase sedative effects. Discourage using together.
Drug-lifestyle. *Alcohol use:* May increase CNS depression. Discourage using together.
Smoking: May increase benzodiazepine clearance. Monitor patient for lack of drug effect.

Effects on lab test results

- May increase liver function test values.

Pharmacokinetics

Absorption: Good.
Distribution: Wide. 85% to 95% protein-bound.
Metabolism: In liver.
Excretion: In urine. *Half-life:* 5 to 13 hours.

Route	Onset	Peak	Duration
P.O.	Unknown	3 hr	Unknown

Action

Chemical effect: May stimulate GABA receptors in ascending reticular activating system.
Therapeutic effect: Relieves anxiety and promotes calmness.

Available forms

Capsules: 10 mg, 15 mg, 30 mg
Tablets: 10 mg, 15 mg, 30 mg

NURSING PROCESS

Assessment

- Assess patient's condition before starting therapy and regularly thereafter to monitor drug's effectiveness.
- Monitor liver, renal, and hematopoietic function studies periodically in patient receiving repeated or prolonged therapy.
- Be alert for adverse reactions and drug interactions.
- Assess patient's and family's knowledge of drug therapy.

Nursing diagnoses

- Disturbed thought processes related to condition

• Risk for injury related to drug-induced adverse CNS reactions
• Deficient knowledge related to drug therapy

Planning and implementation

• Lower the dosage in an elderly or debilitated patient.
• Possibility of abuse and addiction exists. Don't abruptly stop giving the drug; withdrawal symptoms may occur.

ALERT: Don't confuse oxazepam with oxaprozin.

Patient teaching

• Warn patient to avoid hazardous activities until CNS effects of drug are known.
• Tell patient to avoid alcohol during therapy.
• Warn patient not to stop drug abruptly; withdrawal signs may occur.

Evaluation

• Patient has less anxiety.
• Patient sustains no injury as result of drug therapy.
• Patient and family state understanding of drug therapy.

oxcarbazepine

(ox-car-BAY-zah-peen)
Trileptal

Pharmacologic class: carboxamide derivative
Therapeutic class: antiepileptic
Pregnancy risk category: C

Indications and dosages

▶ **Adjunctive therapy for partial seizures in patients with epilepsy.** *Adults:* Initially, 300 mg P.O. b.i.d. Increase by maximum of 600 mg daily (300 mg P.O. b.i.d.) at weekly intervals. Recommended daily dosage is 600 mg P.O. b.i.d.
Children ages 4 to 16: Initially, 4 to 5 mg/kg P.O. b.i.d., not to exceed 600 mg P.O. daily. Target maintenance dosage depends on patient weight. If patient weighs 20 to 29 kg (44 to 64 lb), target maintenance dosage is 900 mg daily. If 29.1 to 39 kg (64 to 86 lb), target maintenance dosage is 1,200 mg daily. If more than 39 kg (86 lb), target maintenance dosage is 1,800 mg daily. Achieve target dosage over 2 weeks.

▶ **Conversion to monotherapy for partial seizures in patients with epilepsy.** *Adults:* Initially, 300 mg P.O. b.i.d. with simultaneous reduction in dosage of other antiepileptics. Increase by a maximum of 600 mg daily at weekly intervals over 2 to 4 weeks. Recommended daily dosage is 2,400 mg P.O., divided b.i.d. Withdraw other antiepileptics completely over 3 to 6 weeks.
Children ages 4 to 16: Initially, 8 to 10 mg/kg P.O. daily divided b.i.d., with simultaneous reduction in dosage of other antiepileptics. Increase by a maximum of 10 mg/kg daily at weekly intervals. Withdraw other antiepileptics completely over 3 to 6 weeks.

▶ **Initial monotherapy for partial seizures in patients with epilepsy.** *Adults:* Initially, 300 mg P.O. b.i.d. Increase by 300 mg daily q third day to a total daily dosage of 1,200 mg.
Children ages 4 to 16: Initially, 8 to 10 mg/kg P.O. daily divided b.i.d., increasing the dosage by 5 mg/kg daily q third day to the recommended daily dosage:
20 to 24 kg (44 to 54 lb): 600 to 900 mg
25 to 34 kg (55 to 76 lb): 900 to 1,200 mg
35 to 44 kg (77 to 98 lb): 900 to 1,500 mg
45 to 49 kg (99 to 109 lb): 1,200 to 1,500 mg
50 to 59 kg (110 to 131 lb): 1,200 to 1,800 mg
60 to 69 kg (132 to 153 lb): 1,200 to 2,100 mg
70 kg (154 lb): 1,500 to 2,100 mg.

Adjust-a-dose: For patients with renal impairment, if creatinine clearance is less than 30 ml/minute, therapy starts at 150 mg P.O. b.i.d. (one-half the usual starting dose) and increases slowly to achieve desired clinical response.

Contraindications and cautions

• Contraindicated in patients hypersensitive to the drug or any of its components.
• Use cautiously in patients who have had hypersensitivity reactions to carbamazepine.

Lifespan: Effects during pregnancy are unknown. Breast-feeding women should either stop breast-feeding or use another drug.

Adverse reactions

CNS: abnormal coordination, *abnormal gait, aggravated seizures,* agitation, amnesia, anxiety, asthenia, *ataxia,* confusion, *dizziness,* emotional lability, *fatigue,* feeling abnormal, fever, *headache,* hypoesthesia, impaired concentra-

O

tion, insomnia, nervousness, *somnolence,* speech disorder, *tremor, vertigo.*
CV: chest pain, edema, hypotension.
EENT: abnormal accommodation, *abnormal vision, diplopia,* epistaxis, *nystagmus,* pharyngitis, rhinitis, sinusitis.
GI: *abdominal pain,* anorexia, constipation, diarrhea, dry mouth, dyspepsia, gastritis, *nausea,* rectal hemorrhage, taste perversion, thirst, *vomiting.*
GU: urinary frequency, UTI, vaginitis.
Metabolic: hyponatremia, weight gain.
Musculoskeletal: back pain, muscle weakness.
Respiratory: bronchitis, chest infection, coughing, *upper respiratory tract infection.*
Skin: acne, bruising, increased sweating, purpura, rash, ***Stevens–Johnson syndrome, toxic epidermal necrosis.***
Other: allergic reaction, hot flushes, toothache.

Interactions

Drug-drug. *Carbamazepine, valproic acid, verapamil:* May decrease level of the active metabolite of oxcarbazepine. Monitor patient and level closely.
Felodipine: May decrease felodipine level. Monitor patient closely.
Hormonal contraceptives: May decrease levels of ethinyl estradiol and levonorgestrel, which reduces contraceptive effect. Women of childbearing age should use other forms of contraception.
Lamotrigine: May decrease lamotrigine level. Adjust lamotrigine dosage as needed.
Phenobarbital: May decrease level of the active metabolite of oxcarbazepine and increase phenobarbital level. Monitor patient closely.
Phenytoin: May decrease level of the active metabolite of oxcarbazepine. Watch for reduced effect. May increase phenytoin level in adults receiving high doses of oxcarbazepine. Monitor phenytoin level closely when starting therapy in these patients.
Drug-lifestyle. *Alcohol use:* Increases CNS depression. Discourage using together.

Effects on lab test results

- May decrease sodium and T_4 levels.

Pharmacokinetics

Absorption: Complete.
Distribution: About 40% of active metabolite is protein-bound, mostly to albumin.
Metabolism: Rapid; 4% of dose is oxidized to inactive metabolite.
Excretion: Mainly by the kidneys. *Half-life:* About 2 hours for drug, about 9 hours for active metabolite. Children younger than age 8 have about 30% to 40% increased clearance of drug.

Route	Onset	Peak	Duration
P.O.	Unknown	Variable	Unknown

Action

Chemical effect: May result from blockade of voltage-sensitive sodium channels, which causes stabilized hyperexcited neural membranes, inhibited repetitive neuronal firing, and reduced synaptic impulses. May stem from increased potassium conductance and modulation of high-voltage activated calcium channels.
Therapeutic effect: Controls partial seizures.

Available forms

Oral suspension: 60 mg/ml, 300 mg/5 ml*
Tablets (film-coated): 150 mg, 300 mg, 600 mg

NURSING PROCESS

Assessment

ALERT: Ask patient about history of hypersensitivity reaction to carbamazepine because 25% to 30% of affected patients may develop hypersensitivity to this drug. If signs or symptoms of hypersensitivity occur, stop drug immediately.
- Obtain history of patient's underlying condition before starting therapy, and reassess regularly thereafter to monitor the drug's effectiveness.

ALERT: Drug is linked to several adverse neurologic events, including psychomotor slowing, difficulty with concentration, speech or language problems, somnolence, fatigue, and abnormal coordination (including ataxia and gait disturbances). Monitor patient closely.
- Monitor patient for evidence of hyponatremia, including nausea, malaise, headache, lethargy, confusion, and decreased sensation.
- Assess patient's and family's knowledge of drug therapy.

Nursing diagnoses

- Risk for trauma related to seizures
- Risk for injury related to drug-induced adverse reactions
- Deficient knowledge related to drug therapy

Planning and implementation

ALERT: Gradually stop giving the drug to minimize risk of increased seizure frequency.
- Correct hyponatremia as needed.
- Shake oral suspension well before giving. Suspension can be mixed with water or may be swallowed directly from the syringe. Oral suspension and tablets may be interchanged at equal doses. Suspension can be taken without regard to food.
- Serious skin reactions including Stevens-Johnson syndrome and toxic epidermal necrosis can occur.

Patient teaching
- Advise patient to tell prescriber if he has ever had a hypersensitivity reaction to carbamazepine.
- Tell patient that drug may be taken with or without food.
- Warn patient to avoid hazardous activities until the drug's CNS effects are known.
- Tell patient not to drink alcohol while taking drug.
- Advise patient not to interrupt therapy without consulting prescriber.
- Advise patient to immediately report skin rashes to his prescriber.
- Advise patient to report fever and swollen lymph nodes to his prescriber; multi-organ hypersensitivity reactions may occur, with diverse signs and symptoms.
- Advise patient to report signs and symptoms of hyponatremia, such as nausea, malaise, headache, lethargy, or confusion.
- Advise women using hormonal contraceptives to use a barrier method of birth control while taking drug.

Evaluation
- Patient experiences no or fewer seizures during drug therapy.
- Patient sustains no injury from drug-induced adverse reactions.
- Patient and family state understanding of drug therapy.

oxybutynin chloride
(oks-ee-BYOO-tih-nin KLOR-ighd)

Apo-Oxybutynin ♦, Ditropan, Ditropan XL, Oxytrol

Pharmacologic class: synthetic tertiary amine
Therapeutic class: urinary antispasmodic
Pregnancy risk category: B

Indications and dosages

▶ **Uninhibited or reflex neurogenic bladder.** *Adults:* 5 mg P.O. b.i.d. to t.i.d., up to 5 mg q.i.d.
Children older than age 5: Give 5 mg P.O. b.i.d., up to 5 mg t.i.d.

▶ **Overactive bladder.** *Adults:* Initially, 5 mg Ditropan XL P.O. once daily. Adjust dosage weekly in 5-mg increments, as needed, to a maximum of 30 mg P.O. daily. Or, 1 transdermal patch (Oxytrol) twice weekly applied to dry, intact skin on abdomen, hip, or buttocks.

Contraindications and cautions

- Contraindicated in patients hypersensitive to the drug or any of its components, in debilitated patients with intestinal atony, in hemorrhaging patients with unstable CV condition, and in patients with myasthenia gravis, GI obstruction, glaucoma, adynamic ileus, megacolon, severe colitis, ulcerative colitis with megacolon, or obstructive uropathy.
- Use cautiously in patients with autonomic neuropathy, reflux esophagitis, or hepatic or renal disease. Use transdermal patch cautiously in patients with bladder outflow obstruction, gastroesophageal reflux, intestinal atony, and in those taking bisphosphonates.

Lifespan: In pregnant women, use cautiously. In breast-feeding women, use cautiously; it's unknown if the drug appears in breast milk. In the elderly, use cautiously. In the elderly who have intestinal atony, drug is contraindicated.

Adverse reactions

Oral form
CNS: dizziness, *drowsiness,* fever, impaired alertness, insomnia, restlessness.
CV: flushing, palpitations, tachycardia.
EENT: cycloplegia, mydriasis, *transient blurred vision.*

GI: bloated feeling, *constipation, dry mouth,* nausea, vomiting.
GU: impotence, urinary hesitancy, urine retention.
Skin: decreased diaphoresis, rash, urticaria.
Other: allergic reactions, suppressed lactation.
Transdermal form
CNS: fatigue, headache, somnolence.
CV: flushing.
EENT: abnormal vision.
GI: abdominal pain, diarrhea, *dry mouth,* flatulence, nausea.
GU: dysuria.
Musculoskeletal: back pain.
Skin: burns, erythema, macules, *pruritus,* rash, vesicles.

Interactions

Drug-drug. *Amantadine, anticholinergics:* May increase anticholinergic effects. Use together cautiously.
Atenolol, digoxin: May increase levels of these drugs. Monitor patient closely. Use of digoxin elixir or capsules may avoid the interaction.
CNS depressants: May increase CNS effects. Use cautiously.
Drug-lifestyle. *Alcohol use:* May increase CNS effects. Discourage using together.
Exercise, hot weather: May precipitate heatstroke. Urge patient to stay hydrated and to avoid exercise or increased activity during hot and humid weather.

Effects on lab test results

None reported.

Pharmacokinetics

Absorption: Rapid.
Distribution: Unknown. Transdermal system is widely distributed.
Metabolism: By liver. Transdermal system is metabolized by liver and gut wall by CYP3A4; bypasses first-pass metabolism.
Excretion: Mainly in urine. *Transdermal half-life:* 2 hours.

Route	Onset	Peak	Duration
P.O.	30–60 min	3–4 hr	6–10 hr
Transdermal	24–48 hr	Varies	96 hr

Action

Chemical effect: Produces direct spasmolytic effect and antimuscarinic (atropine-like) effect on smooth muscles of urinary tract, increasing bladder capacity and providing some local anesthesia and mild analgesia.
Therapeutic effect: Relieves bladder spasms.

Available forms

Syrup: 5 mg/5 ml
Tablets: 5 mg
Tablets (extended-release): 5 mg, 10 mg, 15 mg
Transdermal patch: 36-mg patch (delivers 3.9 mg/day)

NURSING PROCESS

Assessment

- Assess patient's bladder condition before starting therapy.
- Before giving drug, confirm neurogenic bladder by cystometry and rule out partial intestinal obstruction in patients with diarrhea, especially those with colostomy or ileostomy.
- Prepare patient for periodic cystometry to evaluate response to therapy.
- Watch geriatric patients for confusion and mental changes.
- Be alert for adverse reactions.
- Drug may aggravate symptoms of hyperthyroidism, coronary artery disease, heart failure, arrhythmias, tachycardia, hypertension, or prostatic hyperplasia.
- Assess patient's and family's knowledge of drug therapy.

Nursing diagnoses

- Acute pain related to bladder spasms
- Risk for injury related to drug-induced adverse CNS reactions
- Deficient knowledge related to drug therapy

Planning and implementation

- If patient has a UTI, give prescribed antibiotics.
- To minimize tendency toward tolerance, periodically stop therapy to determine whether patient can be weaned off drug.

ALERT: Don't confuse Ditropan with diazepam or Dithranol.

Patient teaching

- Warn patient to avoid hazardous activities until the drug's CNS effects are known.
- Tell patient not to drink alcohol during therapy.

• Advise patient that taking drug in hot weather raises the risk of fever or heatstroke, and urge patient to take precautions to avoid excessive heat and maintain adequate hydration.
• Instruct patient to change transdermal patch two times weekly and to avoid using the same site within 7 days. Also warn patient to wear only one patch at a time and to properly dispose of old patches to prevent accidental application or ingestion.
• Advise patient to store drug in tightly closed container at room temperature.

Evaluation
• Patient is free from bladder pain.
• Patient sustains no injuries from drug-induced adverse CNS reactions.
• Patient and family state understanding of drug therapy.

oxycodone hydrochloride
(oks-ee-KOH-dohn high-droh-KLOR-ighd)
Endocodone, Endone ◇, M-Oxy, OxyContin, Oxydose, OxyFAST, OxyIR, OxyNorm ◇, Percolone, Roxicodone*, Roxicodone Intensol, Supeudol

oxycodone pectinate
Proladone ◇

Pharmacologic class: opioid
Therapeutic class: analgesic
Pregnancy risk category: B
Controlled substance schedule: II

Indications and dosages

▶ **Moderate to severe pain.** *Adults:* 5 mg P.O. q 6 hours, p.r.n. Or, 1 to 3 suppositories P.R. daily, p.r.n.
Adults not taking opioids who need a continuous around-the-clock analgesic for an extended period: 10 mg extended-release tablets P.O. q 12 hours. May increase dosage q 1 to 2 days, as needed. The 80-mg form is for opioid-tolerant patients only.
Adjust-a-dose: For patients with impaired hepatic function, start extended-release tablets at one-third to one-half of usual dosage and adjust carefully. In patients with impaired renal function, if creatinine clearance is less than 60 ml/minute, reduce initial extended-release dose and adjust carefully.

Contraindications and cautions

• Contraindicated in patients hypersensitive to the drug or any of its components.
• Oxycodone extended-release tablets are contraindicated in patients with known or suspected paralytic ileus.
• Use cautiously in debilitated patients and in those with head injury, increased intracranial pressure, seizures, asthma, COPD, prostatic hyperplasia, severe hepatic or renal disease, acute abdominal conditions, urethral stricture, hypothyroidism, Addison disease, or arrhythmias.
Lifespan: In pregnant women, use cautiously. In breast-feeding women, use cautiously; it's unknown if the drug appears in breast milk. In children, drug isn't recommended. In the elderly, use cautiously due to increased risk of delayed renal excretion and of CNS effects.

Adverse reactions

CNS: *clouded sensorium,* dizziness, *euphoria, sedation, somnolence.*
CV: ***bradycardia,*** *hypotension.*
GI: constipation, ileus, nausea, vomiting.
GU: urine retention.
Respiratory: ***respiratory depression.***
Other: physical dependence.

Interactions

Drug-drug. *Anticoagulants:* May increase anticoagulant effect if combination product with aspirin is used. Monitor PT and INR. Use together cautiously; monitor patient for bleeding.
CNS depressants, general anesthetics, hypnotics, MAO inhibitors, other opioid analgesics, protease inhibitors, sedatives, tranquilizers, tricyclic antidepressants: May have additive effects. Use together cautiously. Reduce oxycodone dosage as directed, and monitor patient response.
Drug-lifestyle. *Alcohol use:* May increase CNS depression. Discourage using together.

Effects on lab test results

• May increase amylase and lipase levels.

Pharmacokinetics

Absorption: Unknown.
Distribution: Unknown.
Metabolism: In liver.

Excretion: Mainly in urine. *Half-life:* 2 to 3 hours.

Route	Onset	Peak	Duration
P.O.	10–15 min	≤ 1 hr	3–6 hr
P.R.	Unknown	Unknown	Unknown

Action

Chemical effect: Binds with opiate receptors in CNS, altering response to pain by an unknown mechanism.
Therapeutic effect: Relieves pain.

Available forms

oxycodone hydrochloride
Capsules: 5 mg
Oral solution: 5 mg/5 ml, 20 mg/ml
Tablets: 5 mg, 15 mg, 30 mg
Tablets (extended-release): 10 mg, 20 mg, 40 mg, 80 mg
oxycodone pectinate
Suppositories: 10 mg ♦, 30 mg ◇

NURSING PROCESS

Assessment

- Assess patient's pain before and after giving drug.
- Monitor circulation and respirations.
- Be alert for adverse reactions and drug interactions.
- Monitor patient for development of constipation.
- Assess patient's and family's knowledge of drug therapy.

Nursing diagnoses

- Acute pain related to condition
- Ineffective breathing pattern related to drug-induced respiratory depression
- Deficient knowledge related to drug therapy

Planning and implementation

- Give drug with food or milk to avoid GI upset.

ALERT: Drug isn't intended for p.r.n. use or for immediate postoperative pain. Drug is only indicated for postoperative use if patient was receiving it before surgery or if pain is expected to persist for an extended length of time.

- For best results, give drug before patient has intense pain.
- Single-agent oxycodone solution or tablet is especially useful for patient who can't take aspirin or acetaminophen.

ALERT: If respirations are shallow or rate falls below 12 breaths/minute, withhold dose and notify prescriber.

ALERT: Don't confuse oxycodone immediate-release tablets with OxyContin extended-release tablets.

ALERT: Drug is addictive and abused as much as morphine. Chewing, crushing, snorting, or injecting it can lead to overdose and death.

ALERT: Don't confuse Roxicodone Intensol with other Intensol products manufactured by Roxane.

Patient teaching

- Instruct patient to take drug with food or milk to minimize GI upset.
- Tell patient to ask for drug before pain becomes intense.
- Tell patient not to chew or crush OxyIR or extended-release forms.
- Warn ambulatory patient about getting out of bed or walking. Warn outpatient to avoid hazardous activities until CNS effects of drug are known.

Evaluation

- Patient is free from pain.
- Patient's respiratory rate and pattern remain within normal limits.
- Patient and family state understanding of drug therapy.

oxymorphone hydrochloride

(oks-ee-MOR-fohn high-droh-KLOR-ighd)
Numorphan, Opana, Opana ER

Pharmacologic class: opioid
Therapeutic class: analgesic
Pregnancy risk category: C; D if used for prolonged periods or high doses at term
Controlled substance schedule: II

Indications and dosages

▶ **Moderate to severe pain.** *Adults:* 1 to 1.5 mg I.M. or subcutaneously q 4 to 6 hours, p.r.n. Or, 0.5 mg I.V. q 4 to 6 hours, p.r.n. Or, in opioid-naive patients, give 10 to 20 mg P.O. q 4 to 6 hours. If needed, start with 5 mg P.O. and adjust based on patient response.

▶ **Moderate to severe pain in patients who need continuous, around-the-clock opioid treatment for an extended time.** *Opioid-naive adults:* 5 mg extended-release form P.O. q 12 hours. Increase by 5 to 10 mg q 12 hours every 3 to 7 days as needed and tolerated. Patients taking Opana immediate-release tablets can be switched to extended-release Opana ER tablets by giving one-half the patient's total daily dosage of Opana as Opana ER q 12 hours.

Adjust-a-dose: For patients with mild hepatic impairment or creatinine clearance less than 50 ml/minute, start with the lowest possible dose and increase slowly as tolerated.

I.V. administration

- Give drug by direct I.V. injection. If needed, dilute in normal saline solution.
- To minimize hypotension, keep patient supine while giving drug.

⊗ **Incompatibilities**
None reported.

Contraindications and cautions

- Contraindicated in patients hypersensitive to drug and in those with acute asthma attacks, severe respiratory depression, upper airway obstruction, paralytic ileus, moderate to severe hepatic impairment, or pulmonary edema caused by a respiratory irritant.
- Use cautiously in debilitated patients and those with head injury, increased intracranial pressure, seizures, asthma, COPD, acute abdominal conditions, biliary tract disease (including pancreatitis), acute alcoholism, delirium tremens, prostatic hyperplasia, renal or mild hepatic impairment, urethral stricture, respiratory depression, hypothyroidism, Addison disease, or arrhythmias.

Lifespan: In pregnant women, use cautiously. In breast-feeding women, use cautiously; it's unknown if the drug appears in breast milk. In the elderly, use cautiously due to increased risk of delayed renal excretion and of CNS effects. In children, drug is contraindicated.

Adverse reactions

CNS: *clouded sensorium, dizziness,* dysphoria, *euphoria,* hallucinations, *headache,* physical dependence, lightheadedness, restlessness, *sedation,* ***seizures*** with large doses, *somnolence.*
CV: ***bradycardia,*** *hypotension.*
EENT: blurred vision, diplopia, miosis.
GI: *constipation,* ileus, *nausea, vomiting.*
GU: urine retention.
Respiratory: ***respiratory depression.***
Skin: *increased sweating,* pruritus.

Interactions

Drug-drug. *Agonist/antagonist analgesics:* May reduce analgesic effect or cause withdrawal symptoms. Don't use together.
Anticholinergics: May increase risk of urine retention, severe constipation, and paralytic ileus. Monitor patient for abdominal pain or distention.
CNS depressants, general anesthetics, MAO inhibitors, tricyclic antidepressants: May have additive effects. Use together cautiously, and reduce opioid dosage.
Drug-lifestyle. *Alcohol use:* May have additive effects. Discourage using together.

Effects on lab test results

- May increase amylase and lipase levels.

Pharmacokinetics

Absorption: Good.
Distribution: Wide.
Metabolism: Mainly in liver.
Excretion: Mainly in urine. *Half-life:* For parenteral use, unknown. For ER tablets, 7 to 12 hours. For immediate-release tablets, 3 to 12 hours.

Route	Onset	Peak	Duration
I.V.	5–10 min	15–30 min	3–4 hr
I.M.	10–15 min	30–90 min	3–6 hr
P.O.	Variable	Variable	Variable
SubQ	10–15 min	60–90 min	3–6 hr

Action

Chemical effect: Binds with opiate receptors in CNS, altering response to pain by an unknown mechanism.
Therapeutic effect: Relieves pain.

Available forms

Injection: 1 mg/ml
Tablets: 5 mg, 10 mg
Tablets (extended-release): 5 mg, 10 mg, 20 mg, 40 mg

O

NURSING PROCESS

Assessment
- Assess patient's pain before and after giving drug.
- Be alert for adverse reactions and drug interactions.
- Assess patient's and family's knowledge of drug therapy.

Nursing diagnoses
- Acute pain related to condition
- Ineffective breathing pattern related to drug-induced respiratory depression
- Deficient knowledge related to drug therapy

Planning and implementation
- Keep opioid antagonist (naloxone) and resuscitation equipment available.
- Use of this drug may worsen gallbladder pain.
- Drug isn't for mild pain. For better effect, give drug before patient has intense pain.
- Extended-release tablets aren't for p.r.n. use.
- Monitor CV and respiratory status. If respirations decrease or rate is below 12 breaths/minute, withhold dose and notify prescriber.
- Monitor bladder and bowel function. Patient may need a laxative.

ALERT: Don't confuse oxymorphone with oxymetholone or oxycodone, and don't confuse Numorphan with nalbuphine.

Patient teaching
- Instruct patient to ask for drug before pain is intense. Make sure patient knows that extended-release tablets must be taken around-the-clock.
- When drug is used I.M. or I.V. after surgery, encourage patient to turn, cough, and deep-breathe and to use incentive spirometer to avoid lung problems.
- Caution ambulatory patient about getting out of bed or walking. Warn outpatient to avoid driving and other hazardous activities that require mental alertness until drug's CNS effects are known.

ALERT: Caution patient not to consume alcohol or take any prescription or OTC product containing alcohol with oral form of drug because doing so can lead to oxymorphone overdose.

ALERT: Warn patient not to crush, break, chew, or dissolve extended-release tablets; may lead to a fatal dose of oxymorphone.

- Instruct patient to keep oral form in a child-resistant container in a safe place. Accidental ingestion by a child can result in death.
- Advise patient or family to report a decreased respiratory rate.
- Teach patient about increasing fluid and fiber intake to prevent constipation.

Evaluation
- Patient is free from pain.
- Patient's respiration is normal.
- Patient and family state understanding of drug therapy.

oxytocin, synthetic injection
(oks-ih-TOH-sin, sin-THET-ik in-JEK-shun)

Pitocin, Syntocinon

Pharmacologic class: exogenous hormone
Therapeutic class: lactation stimulant, oxytocic
Pregnancy risk category: NR

Indications and dosages

▶ **To induce or stimulate labor.** *Adults:* Initially, 1-ml ampule (10 units) I.V. in 1,000 ml of D_5W, lactated Ringer's, or normal saline solution infused at 0.5 to 2 milliunits/minute. Increase rate in increments of no more than 1 to 2 milliunits/minute at 30- to 60-minute intervals until normal contraction pattern is established. Decrease rate when labor is firmly established. Rates exceeding 9 to 10 milliunits/minute rarely are required; maximum dose 20 milliunits/minute.

▶ **To reduce postpartum bleeding after expulsion of placenta.** *Adults:* 10 to 40 units I.V. in 1,000 ml of D_5W or normal saline solution infused at rate that controls bleeding, usually 20 to 40 milliunits/minute. Give 10 units I.M. after delivery of placenta.

▶ **Incomplete or inevitable abortion.** *Adults:* 10 units I.V. in 500 ml of normal saline solution or dextrose 5% in normal saline solution or D_5W. Infuse at 10 to 20 milliunits/minute (20 to 40 gtt/minute).

▶ **Oxytocin challenge test to assess fetal distress in high-risk pregnancies greater than 31 weeks' gestation‡.** *Adults:* 5 to 10 units I.V. in 1 L of D_5W injection, yielding a solution of 5 to 10 milliunits per ml. Infuse 0.5 milliunits/minute, gradually increasing at 15-minute intervals to a maximum infusion of 20 milliunits/ minute. Stop infusion when three moderate uterine contractions occur within a 10-minute period. Response of fetal heart rate may be used to evaluate prognosis.

I.V. administration

- Give only by infusion.
- Give by piggyback infusion so drug can be stopped without interrupting I.V. line.
- Use an infusion pump.

⊗ **Incompatibilities**
Plasmin, norepinephrine bitartrate, Normosol-M with dextrose 5%, prochlorperazine, warfarin sodium.

Contraindications and cautions

- Contraindicated in patients hypersensitive to the drug or any of its components. Also contraindicated in cephalopelvic disproportion or delivery that requires conversion, as in transverse lie; in fetal distress when delivery isn't imminent; in prematurity; in other obstetric emergencies; and in severe toxemia, hypertonic uterine patterns, total placenta previa, or vasa previa.
- During first and second stages of labor, use cautiously because cervical laceration, uterine rupture, and maternal and fetal death may occur. In patients with grand multiparity, uterine sepsis, traumatic delivery, or overdistended uterus, use cautiously.
- Use cautiously in patients with invasive cervical carcinoma and in patients with history of cervical or uterine surgery.

Lifespan: Drug is only indicated for pregnant and postpartum women.

Adverse reactions

Maternal
CNS: ***coma from water intoxication, seizures, subarachnoid hemorrhage from hypertension.***
CV: ***arrhythmias; hypertension;*** increased heart rate, systemic venous return, and cardiac output.
GI: nausea, vomiting.
GU: ***abruptio placentae, increased uterine motility, impaired uterine blood flow, pelvic hematoma, tetanic uterine contractions, uterine rupture.***
Hematologic: afibrinogenemia (may be related to postpartum bleeding).
Other: ***anaphylaxis,*** hypersensitivity reactions.

Fetal
CV: ***bradycardia,*** PVCs, tachycardia.
Hematologic: hyperbilirubinemia.
Respiratory: ***anoxia, asphyxia.***

Interactions

Drug-drug. *Cyclopropane anesthetics:* May cause less pronounced tachycardia but more severe hypotension. May cause maternal sinus bradycardia with abnormal atrioventricular arrhythmias. Use together cautiously.
Thiopental anesthetics: May delay induction. Use together cautiously.
Vasoconstrictors: May cause severe hypertension in patients receiving caudal block anesthetic. Avoid using together.

Effects on lab test results

None reported.

Pharmacokinetics

Absorption: Unknown.
Distribution: Through extracellular fluid.
Metabolism: Rapid, in kidneys and liver. In early pregnancy, a circulating enzyme, oxytocinase, can inactivate drug.
Excretion: Small amounts in urine. *Half-life:* 3 to 5 minutes.

Route	Onset	Peak	Duration
I.V.	Immediate	Unknown	1 hr
I.M.	3–5 min	Unknown	2–3 hr

Action

Chemical effect: Causes potent and selective stimulation of uterine and mammary gland smooth muscle.
Therapeutic effect: Induces labor and milk ejection and reduces postpartum bleeding.

Available forms

Injection: 10 units/ml in ampule, vial, or syringe

NURSING PROCESS

Assessment

- Assess patient's condition before starting therapy and regularly thereafter.
- Monitor and record uterine contractions, heart rate, blood pressure, intrauterine pressure, fetal heart rate, and blood loss q 15 minutes.

O

• Be alert for adverse reactions and drug interactions.
• Monitor fluid intake and output. Antidiuretic effect may lead to fluid overload, seizures, and coma.
• Assess patient's and family's knowledge of drug therapy.

Nursing diagnoses

• Risk for deficient fluid volume related to postpartum bleeding
• Excessive fluid volume related to drug-induced antidiuretic effect
• Deficient knowledge related to drug therapy

Planning and implementation

• Drug is used to induce or reinforce labor only when pelvis is known to be adequate, vaginal delivery is indicated, fetal maturity is ensured, and fetal position is favorable. Use only in hospital where critical care facilities and experienced clinician are immediately available.
• Drug isn't recommended for routine I.M. use, but 10 units may be given I.M. after delivery of placenta to control postpartum uterine bleeding.
• Never give oxytocin simultaneously by more than one route.
• Have 20% solution of magnesium sulfate available for relaxation of myometrium.
ALERT: If contractions are less than 2 minutes apart, if they're above 50 mm Hg, or if they last 90 seconds or longer, stop infusion, turn patient on her side, and notify prescriber.
ALERT: Don't confuse Pitocin with Pitressin.
ALERT: Don't confuse oxytocin with OxyContin.

Patient teaching

• Instruct patient to report unusual feelings or adverse effects at once.
• Instruct patient to remain lying down during administration.

Evaluation

• Patient maintains adequate fluid balance with drug therapy.
• Patient doesn't develop edema.
• Patient and family state understanding of drug therapy.

paclitaxel

(pak-lih-TAK-sil)
Onxol, Taxol

Pharmacologic class: antimitotic
Therapeutic class: antineoplastic
Pregnancy risk category: D

Indications and dosages

▶ **First-line and subsequent therapy for advanced ovarian cancer.** *Previously untreated adults:* 175 mg/m^2 over 3 hours q 3 weeks followed by cisplatin 75 mg/m^2 or 135 mg/m^2 over 24 hours followed by cisplatin 75 mg/m^2 q 3 weeks.
Previously treated adults: 135 or 175 mg/m^2 I.V. over 3 hours q 3 weeks.
▶ **Breast cancer that doesn't respond to combination chemotherapy for metastatic disease or relapse within 6 months of chemotherapy that included an anthracycline; node-positive breast cancer (after combination chemotherapy that includes doxorubicin).** *Adults:* 175 mg/m^2 I.V. over 3 hours q 3 weeks.
▶ **Initial therapy for advanced non–small-cell lung cancer in patients who aren't candidates for curative surgery or radiation.** *Adults:* 135 mg/m^2 I.V. infusion over 24 hours; follow with cisplatin 75 mg/m^2. Repeat cycle q 3 weeks.
Adjust-a-dose: For all indications, give subsequent courses when neutrophil count is at least 1,500/mm^3 and platelet count is at least 100,000/mm^3. For patients who experience severe neutropenia (neutrophil count less than 500/mm^3 for at least 7 days) or severe peripheral neuropathy, reduce dose by 20% for subsequent courses.
▶ **AIDS-related Kaposi sarcoma.** *Adults:* 135 mg/m^2 I.V. over 3 hours q 3 weeks, or 100 mg/m^2 I.V. over 3 hours q 2 weeks. Don't give if baseline or subsequent neutrophil counts are less than 1,000/mm^3.
Adjust-a-dose: In patients who experience severe neutropenia (neutrophil count less than

500/mm^3 for a week or longer) or severe peripheral neuropathy, reduce dose by 20% for subsequent courses. In patients with elevated liver enzymes, toxicity increases. Adjust dosage.

I.V. administration

• Preparing and giving drug are linked to carcinogenic, mutagenic, and teratogenic risks. Follow facility policy for safe handling.
• Dilute concentrate to 0.3 to 1.2 mg/ml before infusion. Compatible solutions include normal saline solution for injection, D_5W, dextrose 5% in normal saline for injection, and dextrose 5% in lactated Ringer's injection.
• Don't allow undiluted concentrate to come in contact with polyvinyl chloride I.V. bags or tubing. Prepare and store infusion solutions in glass containers. Store diluted solution in glass or polypropylene bottles, or use polypropylene or polyolefin bags. Administer through polyethylene-lined administration sets, and use in-line 0.22-micron filter.
• If extravasation occurs, stop infusion and notify prescriber.
• Diluted solutions are stable for 27 hours at room temperature. Prepared solution may appear hazy.

⊗ **Incompatibilities**
Amphotericin B, chlorpromazine, cisplatin, doxorubicin liposomal, hydroxyzine hydrochloride, methylprednisolone sodium succinate, mitoxantrone.

Contraindications and cautions

• Contraindicated in patients hypersensitive to the drug or to polyoxyethylated castor oil, a vehicle used in drug solution, and in patients with solid tumors with baseline neutrophil counts below 1,500/mm^3. When used to treat AIDS-related Kaposi sarcoma, contraindicated in patients with baseline neutrophil counts below 1,000/mm^3.
• Use cautiously in patients who have received radiation therapy; they may have more frequent or severe myelosuppression.

Lifespan: In pregnant and breast-feeding women, drug isn't recommended. In children, safety and effectiveness haven't been established.

Adverse reactions

CNS: fever, peripheral neuropathy.
CV: abnormal ECG, ***bradycardia,*** hypotension.
GI: diarrhea, mucositis, nausea, vomiting.
Hematologic: anemia, ***bleeding, leukopenia, neutropenia, thrombocytopenia.***
Musculoskeletal: arthralgia, myalgia.
Skin: *alopecia,* cellulitis at injection site, phlebitis.
Other: ***anaphylaxis,*** hypersensitivity reactions.

Interactions

Drug-drug. *Carbamazepine, phenobarbital:* May increase the metabolism of paclitaxel. Monitor patient for effectiveness.
Cisplatin: May have additive myelosuppressive effects. Use together cautiously.
Cyclosporine, dexamethasone, diazepam, estradiol, etoposide, ketoconazole, quinidine, retinoic acid, teniposide, testosterone, verapamil, vincristine: May inhibit paclitaxel metabolism. Use together cautiously.
Doxorubicin: May increase levels of doxorubicin and its metabolites. Dose adjustments may be needed.

Effects on lab test results

• May increase alkaline phosphatase, AST, and triglyceride levels. May decrease hemoglobin level and hematocrit.
• May decrease neutrophil, WBC, and platelet counts.

Pharmacokinetics

Absorption: Given I.V.
Distribution: About 89% to 98% protein-bound.
Metabolism: May be metabolized in liver by CYP2C8 and CYP3A4.
Excretion: Unknown. *Half-life:* 2¼ to 5¾ hours.

Route	Onset	Peak	Duration
I.V.	Unknown	Unknown	Unknown

Action

Chemical effect: Inhibits normal reorganization of microtubule network needed for mitosis and other vital cellular functions.
Therapeutic effect: Stops ovarian and breast cancer cell activity.

Available forms

Injection: 6 mg/ml

NURSING PROCESS

Assessment
- Assess patient's condition before starting therapy and regularly thereafter to monitor drug's effectiveness.
- Continuously monitor patient for first 30 minutes of infusion. Monitor patient closely throughout infusion.
- Monitor blood counts and liver function test results frequently during therapy.
- Be alert for adverse reactions and drug interactions.
- Assess patient's and family's knowledge of drug therapy.

Nursing diagnoses
- Ineffective health maintenance related to cancer
- Ineffective protection related to drug-induced adverse hematologic reactions
- Deficient knowledge related to drug therapy

Planning and implementation
ALERT: Severe hypersensitivity reactions occur in about 4% of patients, usually within 2 or 3 minutes and almost always within 10 minutes.
- To reduce the risk of severe hypersensitivity, pretreat patient with corticosteroids, such as dexamethasone, and antihistamines. H_1-receptor antagonists, such as diphenhydramine, and H_2-receptor antagonists, such as cimetidine or ranitidine, may be used.

ALERT: Don't confuse paclitaxel with paroxetine. Don't confuse Taxol with Paxil or Taxotere.

Patient teaching
- Warn patient to watch for signs of bleeding and infection.
- Teach patient symptoms of peripheral neuropathy, such as tingling, burning, or numbness in limbs, and urge him to report them immediately to prescriber. Dose reduction may be needed.
- Warn patient that alopecia occurs in up to 82% of patients.
- Advise woman of childbearing age not to become pregnant during therapy. Recommend consulting prescriber before becoming pregnant.

Evaluation
- Patient responds well to therapy.
- Patient develops no serious complications from drug-induced adverse hematologic reactions.
- Patient and family state understanding of drug therapy.

paclitaxel protein-bound particles
(pack-lih-TAK-sil)
Abraxane

Pharmacologic class: antimicrotubule drug
Therapeutic class: antineoplastic
Pregnancy risk category: D

Indications and dosages
▶ **Metastatic breast cancer after failure of combination chemotherapy or relapse within 6 months of adjuvant chemotherapy.** Previous therapy should have included an anthracycline unless clinically contraindicated. *Adults:* 260 mg/m^2 I.V. over 30 minutes q 3 weeks.

Adjust-a-dose: For patients with severe sensory neuropathy or a neutrophil count less than 500 cells/mm^3 for a week or longer, reduce dose to 220 mg/m^2. For recurrence of severe sensory neuropathy or severe neutropenia, reduce dose to 180 mg/m^2. For grade 3 sensory neuropathy, hold drug until condition improves to a grade 1 or 2; then resume drug at a reduced dose for the duration of treatment.

I.V. administration
- Because of the drug's cytotoxicity, handle it cautiously and wear gloves. If the drug contacts your skin, wash thoroughly with soap and water. If it contacts mucous membranes, flush them thoroughly with water.
- Reconstitute the vial with 20 ml of normal saline solution. Direct the stream slowly, over at least 1 minute, onto the inside wall of the vial to avoid foaming.
- Let the vial sit for 5 minutes to ensure proper wetting of the powder.
- Gently swirl or invert the vial for at least 2 minutes until completely dissolved. If foaming occurs, let the solution stand for 15 minutes for the foam to subside.
- If particles are visible, gently invert the vial again to ensure complete resuspension. The so-

lution should be milky and uniform in appearance.
• Each reconstituted vial contains 5 mg/ml paclitaxel. Inject the dose into an empty polyvinyl chloride I.V. bag.
• Give the drug I.V. over 30 minutes.
• Store unopened vials at room temperature in the original package. Use the contents of reconstituted vials immediately, or, if needed, refrigerate at 36° to 46° F (2° to 8° C) for a maximum of 8 hours. If not used immediately, the vial should be protected from light.
• The suspension for infusion prepared as recommended in an infusion bag is stable at room temperature and ambient lighting for up to 8 hours.

⊗ Incompatibilities
None known.

Contraindications and cautions
• Contraindicated in patients with baseline neutrophil counts of less than 1,500/mm³.
• Use hasn't been studied in patients with serum creatinine level more than 2 mg/dl or bilirubin level more than 1.5 mg/dl.
Lifespan: Women of childbearing age should avoid becoming pregnant during treatment. Women shouldn't breast-feed during treatment. In children, safety and effectiveness haven't been established.

Adverse reactions
CNS: *asthenia, sensory neuropathy.*
CV: *abnormal ECG,* ***cardiac arrest, chest pain,*** *edema,* hypertension, hypotension, ***PE, supraventricular tachycardia, thromboembolism, thrombosis.***
EENT: visual disturbances.
GI: *diarrhea,* ***intestinal obstruction, ischemic colitis,*** mucositis, *nausea, oral candidiasis,* ***pancreatitis, perforation,*** *vomiting.*
Hematologic: *anemia,* bleeding, **NEUTROPENIA,** ***thrombocytopenia.***
Hepatic: ***hepatic encephalopathy, hepatic necrosis.***
Musculoskeletal: *arthralgia, myalgia.*
Respiratory: cough, *dyspnea, pneumonia, respiratory tract infection.*
Skin: *alopecia,* injection site reactions.
Other: ***anaphylaxis, angioedema,*** *hypersensitivity reactions, infections.*

Interactions
Cytochrome P-450 inhibitors: May decrease Abraxane metabolism. Use together cautiously.

Effects on lab test results
• May increase alkaline phosphatase, AST, bilirubin, creatinine, and GGT levels. May decrease hemoglobin level.
• May decrease neutrophil and platelet counts.

Pharmacokinetics
Absorption: Given I.V.
Distribution: 89% to 98% bound by serum proteins.
Metabolism: Heavily metabolized by several isoenzymes in the cytochrome P-450 pathway.
Excretion: 4% of drug recovered in urine unchanged. Less than 1% recovered in urine as metabolites. Fecal excretion 20% of the dose. *Half life:* 27 hours.

Route	Onset	Peak	Duration
I.V.	Unknown	Unknown	Unknown

Action
Chemical effect: Prevents depolymerization of cellular microtubules, inhibiting reorganization of the microtubule network and disrupting mitosis and other vital cell functions.
Therapeutic effect: Inhibits breast cancer cell growth.

Available forms
Lyophilized powder for injection: 100 mg in single-use vial

NURSING PROCESS

Assessment
• Assess patient's condition before starting therapy and regularly thereafter to monitor drug's effectiveness.
• Assess the patient for symptoms of sensory neuropathy and severe neutropenia.
• Monitor liver and kidney function tests.
• Monitor infusion site closely.
• Assess patient's and family's knowledge of drug therapy.

Nursing diagnoses
• Risk for injury related to drug-induced hematologic reactions

P

• Ineffective health maintenance related to presence of neoplastic disease
• Deficient knowledge related to drug therapy

Planning and implementation

• Give only under the supervision of a practitioner experienced in using chemotherapy in a facility that can manage its complications.
ALERT: Don't substitute this drug for other forms of paclitaxel.
• Because Abraxane contains human albumin, there's a remote risk of transmitting viral disease and Creutzfeldt-Jakob disease.
• Complications of overdose may include bone marrow suppression, sensory neurotoxicity, and mucositis; there's no known antidote for overdose.

Patient teaching

• Advise male patients to avoid fathering children while taking this drug.
• Warn the patient that alopecia is common, but is reversible when treatment ends.
• Teach the patient to recognize signs of neuropathy, such as tingling, burning, and numbness in limbs.
• Tell the patient to report fever or other signs of infection, severe abdominal pain, or severe diarrhea.
• Advise the patient to contact her health care provider if nausea and vomiting persist or interfere with her ability to maintain nutrition. Reassure her that a drug can be prescribed that may help.
• Explain that many patients experience weakness and fatigue, so it's important to rest. Tiredness, paleness, and shortness of breath may result from low blood counts, and the patient may need a transfusion.
• To reduce or prevent mouth sores, remind the patient to perform proper oral hygiene.

Evaluation

• Patient does not develop serious adverse hematologic reactions.
• Patient responds to pharmacologic therapy.
• Patient and family state understanding of drug therapy.

palifermin
(pahl-ee-FUR-mihn)
Kepivance

Pharmacologic class: human keratinocyte growth factor
Therapeutic class: growth factor
Pregnancy risk category: C

Indications and dosages

▶ **To decrease the occurrence and duration of severe oral mucositis in patients with hematologic malignancies who are receiving myelotoxic therapy that requires hematopoietic stem cell support.** *Adults:* 60 mcg/kg/day by I.V. bolus for 3 consecutive days before myelotoxic therapy, with the third dose 24 to 48 hours before myelotoxic therapy starts. Repeat dose for 3 consecutive days after myelotoxic therapy, for a total of six doses. The first dose after myelotoxic therapy should be given after, but on the same day of, hematopoietic stem cell infusion and at least 4 days after the most recent palifermin dose.

I.V. administration

• To reconstitute powder, slowly add 1.2 ml sterile water for injection to the vial.
• Swirl the vial gently; don't shake or agitate.
• The final concentration will be 5 mg/ml, and the solution should be clear and colorless.
• Use drug immediately after preparing it or refrigerate it for up to 24 hours.
• Discard any drug that sits at room temperature for more than 1 hour.
• Don't filter drug while preparing or giving it.
• Give palifermin by I.V. bolus; if the I.V. line has been flushed with heparin, flush it with normal saline solution before and after giving palifermin.
• Protect drug from light.

Incompatibilities
Heparin.

Contraindications and cautions

• Contraindicated in patients hypersensitive to *Escherichia coli*–derived proteins, palifermin, or any other component of the product.
• Use cautiously in patients with nonhematologic malignancies.
Lifespan: In pregnant women, use drug only if benefits outweigh risk to the fetus. Use cau-

tiously in breast-feeding women; it's unknown if drug appears in breast milk. In children, safety and effectiveness haven't been established.

Adverse reactions

CNS: *dysesthesia, fever, hyperesthesia, hypoesthesia, pain, paresthesia.*
CV: *edema,* hypertension.
GI: *mouth or tongue thickness or discoloration, taste alteration.*
Musculoskeletal: *arthralgia.*
Skin: *erythema, pruritus, rash.*

Interactions

Drug-drug. *Heparin:* May bind to palifermin and alter dose. Flush I.V. line with normal saline solution before and after giving palifermin.
Myelotoxic chemotherapy: May increase severity and duration of oral mucositis. Don't give palifermin within 24 hours before, during, or within 24 hours after chemotherapy.

Effects on lab test results

- May increase amylase and lipase levels.

Pharmacokinetics

Absorption: Unknown.
Distribution: Extravascular.
Metabolism: Unknown.
Excretion: Unknown. *Half-life:* 3¼ to 5¾ hours.

Route	Onset	Peak	Duration
I.V.	Immediate	1–4 hr	Unknown

Action

Chemical effect: Increases proliferation of epithelial cells, increasing the thickness of tongue tissue, buccal mucosa, and GI tract.
Therapeutic effect: Prevents the development of mouth sores (oral mucositis) caused by chemotherapy or radiation therapy; expedites the healing of the sores if they develop.

Available forms

Lyophilized powder for injection: 6.25-mg vials

NURSING PROCESS

Assessment

- Assess patient's condition before starting therapy and regularly thereafter to monitor drug's effectiveness.
- Monitor patient for fever, arthralgia, and adverse mucocutaneous effects.
- Assess patient's and family's knowledge of drug therapy.

Nursing diagnoses

- Impaired oral mucous membrane related to myelotoxic therapy
- Risk for injury related to drug-induced growth of tumor cells
- Deficient knowledge related to drug therapy

Planning and implementation

ALERT: To avoid increasing the severity and duration of oral mucositis, don't give palifermin within 24 hours of myelotoxic chemotherapy.

- Skin-related toxicities are most likely to occur 6 days after the first three consecutive doses.
- Drug may enhance growth of tumor cells.

Patient teaching

- Tell patient to report rash, reddening of the skin, swelling, itching, an unpleasant sensation around the mouth, tongue discoloration or thickening, altered taste, fever, and joint pain.
- Explain that palifermin may stimulate the growth of other types of cancer cells.
- Urge patient to keep all scheduled appointments for treatment.

Evaluation

- Patient responds to palifermin therapy.
- Patient does not experience increased growth of tumor cells.
- Patient and family state understanding of drug therapy.

palivizumab

(pal-ih-VYE-zoo-mab)
Synagis

Pharmacologic class: monoclonal antibody
Therapeutic class: antiviral
Pregnancy risk category: C

Indications and dosages

► **To prevent serious lower respiratory tract disease caused by RSV in children at high risk.** *Infants and children:* 15 mg/kg I.M. monthly throughout RSV season, with first dose before RSV season.

P

Contraindications and cautions

• Contraindicated in children hypersensitive to the drug or any of its components.
• Use cautiously in children with thrombocytopenia or other coagulation disorders.
Lifespan: Drug is only indicated in children.

Adverse reactions

CNS: nervousness, pain.
EENT: conjunctivitis, *otitis media,* pharyngitis, *rhinitis,* sinusitis.
GI: diarrhea, gastroenteritis, oral candidiasis, vomiting.
Hematologic: anemia.
Respiratory: ***apnea, asthma,*** bronchiolitis, bronchitis, cough, croup, dyspnea, pneumonia, *upper respiratory tract infection,* wheeze.
Skin: *rash,* fungal dermatitis, eczema, seborrhea.
Other: ***anaphylaxis, failure to thrive,*** flulike syndrome, hernia, hypersensitivity, injection site reaction, viral infection.

Interactions

None significant.

Effects on lab test results

• May increase ALT and AST levels. May decrease hemoglobin level and hematocrit.

Pharmacokinetics

Absorption: Absorbed well.
Distribution: Unknown.
Metabolism: Unknown.
Excretion: Unknown. *Half-life:* About 18 days.

Route	Onset	Peak	Duration
I.M.	Unknown	Unknown	Unknown

Action

Chemical effect: Inhibits RSV replication.
Therapeutic effect: Prevents RSV infection in high-risk children.

Available forms

Injection (single-use vial): 50 mg, 100 mg

NURSING PROCESS

Assessment

• Obtain accurate medical history before giving drug; ask if child has any coagulation disorders or liver dysfunction.
• Be alert for adverse reactions.
• Assess patient's and family's knowledge of drug therapy.

Nursing diagnoses

• Risk for infection related to RSV infection
• Risk for injury related to drug-induced adverse reactions
• Deficient knowledge related to drug therapy

Planning and implementation

• Very rarely, nonfatal cases of anaphylaxis may occur following re-exposure to drug. Rare severe acute hypersensitivity reactions may occur on initial exposure or re-exposure to drug. If a severe hypersensitivity reaction occurs, permanently stop drug. If milder hypersensitivity reactions occur, restart drug cautiously. If anaphylaxis or severe allergic reactions occur, give drug such as epinephrine and provide supportive care as needed.
• To reconstitute, slowly add 0.6 ml of sterile water for injection to the 50-mg vial or 1 ml of sterile water for injection into a 100-mg vial. Gently swirl vial for 30 seconds to avoid foaming; don't shake. Let reconstituted solution stand at room temperature for 20 minutes. Give within 6 hours of reconstitution.
• Give drug in front thigh muscle, off to one side. Don't use gluteal muscle routinely as an injection site because of risk of damage to sciatic nerve. Divide injections larger than 1 ml.
• Give monthly doses throughout RSV season, even if RSV infection develops. In the northern hemisphere, RSV season typically lasts from November to April.
• For patients undergoing cardiopulmonary bypass, give dose immediately after the bypass, even if it's been less than a month since the last dose.

Patient teaching

• Explain to parent or caregiver that drug is used to prevent RSV and not to treat it.
• Advise parent that monthly injections are recommended throughout RSV season.
• Tell parent to immediately report adverse reactions or unusual bruising, bleeding, or weakness.

Evaluation

• Patient doesn't develop RSV infection.
• Patient sustains no injury from drug-induced adverse reactions.

• Patient and family state understanding of drug therapy.

palonosetron hydrochloride

(pa-LOW-no-suh-tron high-droh-KLOHR-ighd)
Aloxi

Pharmacologic class: selective serotonin receptor antagonist
Therapeutic class: antiemetic
Pregnancy risk category: B

Indications and dosages

▶ **To prevent acute nausea and vomiting caused by moderately or highly emetogenic chemotherapy or delayed nausea and vomiting caused by moderately emetogenic chemotherapy.** *Adults:* 0.25 mg I.V. over 30 seconds; give 30 minutes before the start of chemotherapy. Give once per cycle, not more than q 7 days.

I.V. administration

• Don't mix with other drugs.
• Give by either peripheral or central I.V. access.
• Give by rapid I.V. injection over 30 seconds. Flush I.V. line before and after with normal saline solution.

⊗ **Incompatibilities**
Don't mix (Y-site or otherwise) with other I.V. drugs.

Contraindications and cautions

• Contraindicated in patients hypersensitive to the drug or any of its components.
• Use cautiously in patients hypersensitive to other selective serotonin receptor antagonists; cross-sensitivity may occur. Also use cautiously in patients with cardiac conduction abnormalities, hypokalemia, or hypomagnesemia and in patients taking drugs that affect cardiac conduction.

Lifespan: In pregnant women, use only if benefits outweigh risks to fetus. Breast-feeding women should stop breast-feeding or use a different antiemetic; it's unknown if drug appears in breast milk. In children, safety and effectiveness haven't been established.

Adverse reactions

CNS: anxiety, dizziness, headache, weakness.
CV: ***bradycardia,*** hypotension, ***nonsustained ventricular tachycardia.***
GI: constipation, diarrhea.
Metabolic: ***hyperkalemia.***

Interactions

Drug-drug. *Antiarrhythmics or other drugs that may prolong the QT interval, diuretics with potential for inducing electrolyte abnormalities, high doses of anthracycline:* May increase risk of prolonged QT interval. Use together cautiously.

Effects on lab test results

• May increase potassium level.

Pharmacokinetics

Absorption: Given I.V.
Distribution: Distributes well into tissues. 60% protein-bound.
Metabolism: 50% metabolized to inactive metabolites by CYP2D6 and, to a lesser extent, CYP3A4 and CYP1A2.
Excretion: 80% of drug and inactive metabolites is eliminated in the urine. *Half-life:* 40 hours.

Route	Onset	Peak	Duration
I.V.	30 min	Unknown	5 days

Action

Chemical effect: Binds to the 5-HT_3 receptor, which inhibits emesis caused by cytotoxic chemotherapy.
Therapeutic effect: Prevents vomiting from chemotherapy.

Available forms

Injection: 0.25 mg/5 ml (single-use vial).

NURSING PROCESS

Assessment

• Assess patient's condition before starting therapy and regularly thereafter to monitor drug's effectiveness.
• Obtain baseline potassium level.
• In patients with known cardiac conduction abnormalities, obtain baseline ECG.

• Be alert for adverse reactions and drug interactions.
• Assess patient's and family's knowledge of drug therapy.

Nursing diagnoses

• Risk for deficient fluid volume related to nausea and vomiting
• Acute pain related to drug-induced headache
• Deficient knowledge related to drug therapy

Planning and implementation

• Give 30 minutes before chemotherapy on day 1 of each cycle.
• Consider giving with corticosteroids as part of the antiemetic therapy, particularly for patients receiving highly emetogenic chemotherapy.
• Give additional antiemetics for breakthrough nausea and vomiting.

Patient teaching

• Advise patients to take a different antiemetic for breakthrough nausea and vomiting, and tell patient to take it at the first sign of nausea and not to wait until symptoms are severe.
• Tell patients with a history of cardiac conduction abnormalities to report any changes in their drug regimen, such as the adding or stopping of antiarrhythmics.

Evaluation

• Patient maintains adequate hydration.
• Patient doesn't experience drug-induced headaches.
• Patient and family state understanding of drug therapy.

pamidronate disodium

(pam-ih-DROH-nayt digh-SOH-dee-um)
Aredia

Pharmacologic class: bisphosphonate, pyrophosphate analogue
Therapeutic class: bone resorption inhibitor
Pregnancy risk category: D

Indications and dosages

▶ **Moderate to severe hypercalcemia related to malignancy (with or without metastases).** *Adults:* Dosage depends on severity of hypercalcemia. Calcium level is corrected for serum albumin as follows:

$$\text{Corrected serum calcium (cCa) (in mg/dl)} = \text{serum calcium (in mg/dl)} + 0.8\,(4 - \text{serum albumin) (in g/dl)}$$

Patients with moderate hypercalcemia (cCa level of 12 to 13.5 mg/dl) may receive 60 to 90 mg I.V. infusion as a single dose over 2 to 24 hours. Patients with severe hypercalcemia (cCa level higher than 13.5 mg/dl) may receive 90 mg over 2 to 24 hours. Wait at least 7 days to give repeat dose to allow for full response to initial dose.

▶ **Osteolytic bone lesions of multiple myeloma.** *Adults:* 90 mg I.V. over 4 hours once monthly.

▶ **Osteolytic bone lesions of breast cancer.** *Adults:* 90 mg I.V. over 2 hours q 3 to 4 weeks.

▶ **Moderate to severe Paget disease.** *Adults:* 30 mg I.V. as 4-hour infusion on 3 consecutive days for total dose of 90 mg. Cycle repeated, as needed.

I.V. administration

• Reconstitute vial with 10 ml sterile water for injection. Once drug is completely dissolved, add to 250-ml (2-hour infusion), 500-ml (4-hour infusion), or 1,000-ml (up to 24-hour infusion) bag of half-normal or normal saline solution injection or D_5W. Inspect for precipitate before administering.
• Give drug only by I.V. infusion. Nephropathy may occur with rapid bolus injections.
• Infusions of more than 2 hours may reduce the risk of renal toxicity, particularly in patients with renal insufficiency.
• Solution is stable for 24 hours at room temperature.

⊗ **Incompatibilities**
Calcium-containing infusion solutions, such as Ringer's injection or lactated Ringer's solution.

Contraindications and cautions

• Contraindicated in patients hypersensitive to the drug or to other bisphosphonates, such as etidronate.
• Use cautiously in patients with renal impairment.

Lifespan: In pregnant women, drug is contraindicated. In breast-feeding women, use cautiously; it's unknown if the drug appears in breast milk. In children, safety and effectiveness haven't been established.

Adverse reactions

CNS: *anxiety, fatigue, fever, headache, insomnia, pain,* ***seizures.***
CV: atrial fibrillation, hypertension.
GI: *abdominal pain, anorexia, constipation, diarrhea, dyspepsia,* ***GI hemorrhage,*** *nausea, vomiting,*
GU: ***renal failure,*** *UTI.*
Hematologic: *anemia,* **GRANULOCYTOPENIA,** ***leukopenia,*** **THROMBOCYTOPENIA.**
Metabolism: hypocalcemia, *hypokalemia, hypomagnesemia,* hypophosphatemia.
Musculoskeletal: *arthralgia, bone pain, myalgia.*
Other: **METASTASES.**

Interactions

None significant.

Effects on lab test results

- May increase creatinine level. May decrease phosphate, potassium, magnesium, calcium, and hemoglobin levels and hematocrit.
- May decrease WBC and platelet counts.

Pharmacokinetics

Absorption: Given I.V.
Distribution: About 50% to 60% of dose is rapidly taken up by bone; drug is also taken up by kidneys, liver, spleen, teeth, and tracheal cartilage.
Metabolism: None.
Excretion: By kidneys. *Half-life:* Alpha, 1½ hours; beta, 27¼ hours.

Route	Onset	Peak	Duration
I.V.	Unknown	Unknown	Unknown

Action

Chemical effect: Inhibits bone resorption. Adsorbs to hydroxyapatite crystals in bone and may directly block calcium phosphate dissolution.
Therapeutic effect: Lowers calcium level.

Available forms

Powder for injection: 30 mg/vial, 90 mg/vial
Solution for injection: 3 mg/ml, 6 mg/ml, 9 mg/ml in 10-ml vials

NURSING PROCESS

Assessment

- Assess patient's condition before starting therapy and regularly thereafter to monitor drug's effectiveness.
- Assess hydration before therapy.
- Closely monitor electrolyte level, CBC and differential. Check creatinine level before each dose.
- Carefully monitor patient with anemia, leukopenia, or thrombocytopenia during first 2 weeks of therapy.
- Monitor patient's temperature. Fever is most likely 24 to 48 hours after therapy.
- Be alert for adverse reactions and drug interactions. Patients with renal impairment are at a greater risk for adverse reactions.
- Assess patient's and family's knowledge of drug therapy.

Nursing diagnoses

- Ineffective health maintenance related to hypercalcemia
- Risk for injury related to drug-induced hypocalcemia
- Deficient knowledge related to drug therapy

Planning and implementation

- Use drug only after patient has been vigorously hydrated with saline solution. In patients with mild to moderate hypercalcemia, hydration alone may be sufficient.
- If patient has severe hypocalcemia, short-term administration of calcium may be needed.
- For a patient with multiple myeloma, limited information is available on those with creatinine level greater than 3 mg/dl. Before infusion, adequately hydrate patient with marked Bence Jones proteinuria and dehydration. Optimal duration of therapy is unknown, but may be 21 months.

ALERT: Because of the risk of renal dysfunction leading to renal failure, don't give single doses of more than 90 mg.

- In patient treated for bone metastases who has renal dysfunction, don't give the dose until renal function returns to baseline. Use in patient with severe renal impairment isn't recommended.
- In patient with breast cancer, optimal duration of therapy isn't known; may be 24 months for overall benefit.

ALERT: Don't confuse Aredia with Meridia.

P

Patient teaching

- Instruct patient to report unusual signs or symptoms at once.
- Inform patient of need for frequent tests to monitor effectiveness of drug and detect adverse reactions.

Evaluation

- Patient's calcium level returns to normal.
- Patient doesn't develop hypocalcemia during drug therapy.
- Patient and family state understanding of drug therapy.

pancuronium bromide

(pan-kyoo-ROH-nee-um BROH-mighd)

Pharmacologic class: nondepolarizing neuromuscular blocker
Therapeutic class: skeletal muscle relaxant
Pregnancy risk category: C

Indications and dosages

▶ **Adjunct to anesthesia to induce skeletal muscle relaxation; to facilitate intubation; to lessen muscle contractions in pharmacologically or electrically induced seizures; to assist with mechanical ventilation.** Dosage depends on anesthetic used, individual needs, and response. Dosages shown are representative; individualize dosage.
Adults and children age 1 month and older: Initially, 0.04 to 0.1 mg/kg I.V.; then 0.01 mg/kg q 25 to 60 minutes.
Neonates younger than age 1 month: Individualize dosages. Give a test dose of 0.02 mg/kg to assess response.

I.V. administration

- Mix drug only with fresh solutions.
- Store drug in refrigerator. Don't store in plastic containers or syringes, although plastic syringes may be used for administration.

⊗ **Incompatibilities**
Barbiturates, diazepam, other alkaline solutions.

Contraindications and cautions

- Contraindicated in patients hypersensitive to bromides, in those with tachycardia, and in those for whom even a minor increase in heart rate is undesirable.
- Use cautiously in debilitated patients and in those with respiratory depression, myasthenia gravis, myasthenic syndrome of lung cancer, bronchogenic carcinoma, dehydration, thyroid disorders, collagen diseases, porphyria, electrolyte disturbances, hyperthermia, toxemic states, or renal, hepatic, or pulmonary impairment.

Lifespan: In pregnant women undergoing cesarean section and in breast-feeding women, use large doses cautiously. In the elderly, use cautiously.

Adverse reactions

CV: increased blood pressure, tachycardia.
EENT: excessive salivation.
Musculoskeletal: residual muscle weakness.
Respiratory: ***prolonged, dose-related respiratory insufficiency or apnea;*** wheezing.
Skin: excessive diaphoresis, transient rashes.
Other: ***allergic or idiosyncratic hypersensitivity reactions,*** burning sensation.

Interactions

Drug-drug. *Amikacin, gentamicin, neomycin, streptomycin, tobramycin:* May increase the effects of nondepolarizing muscle relaxant, including prolonged respiratory depression. Use together only when needed. Dose of nondepolarizing muscle relaxant may need to be reduced.
Carbamazepine, phenytoin: May decrease the effects of pancuronium causing it to be less effective. May need to increase the dose of pancuronium.
Clindamycin; general anesthetics; kanamycin; ketamine; polymyxin antibiotics, such as polymyxin B sulfate and colistin; quinidine: May increase neuromuscular blockade, leading to an increase in skeletal muscle relaxation and prolonged effect. Use cautiously during surgical and postoperative periods.
Lithium, opioid analgesics, verapamil: May increase neuromuscular blockade, leading to an increase in skeletal muscle relaxation and respiratory paralysis. Use cautiously, and reduce pancuronium dose, as directed.
Succinylcholine: May increase intensity and duration of blockade. Allow succinylcholine effects to subside before giving pancuronium.
Theophylline: May reverse the neuromuscular blocking effects of pancuronium.

Effects on lab test results

None reported.

Pharmacokinetics

Absorption: Given I.V.
Distribution: About 87% bound to plasma proteins.
Metabolism: Unknown.
Excretion: Mainly in urine; some biliary. *Half-life:* About 2 hours.

Route	Onset	Peak	Duration
I.V.	30–45 sec	3–4½ min	35–45 min

Action

Chemical effect: Prevents acetylcholine from binding to receptors on muscle end plate, thus blocking depolarization.
Therapeutic effect: Relaxes skeletal muscles.

Available forms

Injection: 1 mg/ml, 2 mg/ml

NURSING PROCESS

Assessment

- Assess patient's condition before starting therapy and regularly thereafter to monitor drug's effectiveness.
- Monitor baseline electrolyte determinations (electrolyte imbalance can increase neuromuscular effects) and vital signs.
- Measure fluid intake and output; renal dysfunction may prolong duration of action because 25% of drug is unchanged before excretion.
- Monitor nerve stimulator and train-of-four to avoid overdosage and to confirm antagonism of neuromuscular blockade and recovery of muscle strength. Don't attempt reversal with neostigmine until you see signs of spontaneous recovery.
- Monitor respirations closely until patient fully recovers from neuromuscular blockade, as evidenced by tests of muscle strength (hand grip, head lift, and ability to cough).
- Be alert for adverse reactions and drug interactions.
- Assess patient's and family's knowledge of drug therapy.

Nursing diagnoses

- Ineffective health maintenance related to condition
- Ineffective breathing pattern related to drug's effect on respiratory muscles
- Deficient knowledge related to drug therapy

Planning and implementation

- Administer sedatives or general anesthetics before neuromuscular blockers. Neuromuscular blockers don't reduce consciousness or alter pain threshold. Give analgesics for pain.
- Give drug only if skilled in airway management.
- Have emergency respiratory support equipment (endotracheal equipment, ventilator, oxygen, atropine, edrophonium, epinephrine, and neostigmine) immediately available.
- If giving with succinylcholine, allow succinylcholine effects to subside before giving this drug.
- Once spontaneous recovery starts, drug-induced neuromuscular blockade may be reversed with an anticholinesterase (such as neostigmine or edrophonium). Usually given with an anticholinergic such as atropine.

ALERT: Don't confuse pancuronium with pipecuronium.

Patient teaching

- Explain all events to patient because he can still hear.
- Reassure patient that he'll be monitored at all times and that pain drug will be provided, if appropriate.
- Tell patient that he may feel burning sensation at injection site.

Evaluation

- Patient's condition improves.
- Patient maintains adequate ventilation with mechanical assistance.
- Patient and family state understanding of drug therapy.

panitumumab

(pan-eh-TOO-moo-mab)
Vectibix

Pharmacologic class: monoclonal antibody
Therapeutic class: antineoplastic
Pregnancy risk category: C

Indications and dosages

▶ **Human epidermal growth factor receptor-expressing metastatic colorectal cancer with**

P

disease progression during or following fluoropyrimidine-, oxaliplatin-, and irinotecan-containing regimens. *Adults:* 6 mg/kg I.V. infusion over 60 minutes q 14 days. For doses greater than 1,000 mg, infuse over 90 minutes.

Adjust-a-dose: For patients with mild or moderate (grade 1 or 2) infusion reactions, reduce infusion rate by 50%. For patients with severe (grade 3 or 4) infusion reactions, stop drug permanently.

For skin toxicities grade 3 or greater, or if considered intolerable, stop drug. If toxicity doesn't improve to grade 2 or less within 1 month, permanently stop therapy. If toxicity improves to grade 2 or less, and patient is symptomatically improved after withholding 2 or fewer doses, restart treatment at 50% of original dose. If toxicity recurs, permanently stop drug. If toxicity doesn't recur, increase subsequent doses in increments of 25% of original dose until a 6 mg/kg dose is reached.

I.V. administration

- Flush I.V. line with normal saline solution before and after giving drug.
- Dilute drug using aseptic technique. The solution should be colorless but may contain white or translucent particles which will be filtered out during infusion. Don't shake vials.
- Withdraw drug and dilute to a total volume of 100 ml with normal saline solution. For doses higher than 1,000 mg, dilute to 150 ml. Final concentration shouldn't exceed 10 mg/ml. Use within 6 hours if stored at room temperature or within 24 hours if refrigerated. Dispose of any unused drug.
- Give by I.V. infusion using a pump with a low–protein binding 0.2 or 0.22 micrometer in-line filter. Don't give by I.V. push or bolus.
- Refrigerate vials, don't freeze. Protect from sunlight.

⊗ **Incompatibilities**

Other drugs and solutions.

Contraindications and cautions

- Contraindicated in patients hypersensitive to drug or its components.
- Use cautiously in patients with skin conditions, or preexisting lung or ocular disease.

Lifespan: Advise pregnant women or women wanting to become pregnant about the potential hazard to the fetus. Advise breast-feeding patients to stop breast-feeding during and for 2 months after treatment ends. In children, safety and effectiveness haven't been studied. In elderly patients, there's no difference in safety and effectiveness compared to younger patients.

Adverse reactions

CNS: *chills, fatigue, fever.*
CV: ***hypotension,*** *peripheral edema.*
EENT: *eyelash growth, ocular toxicities, oral mucositis.*
GI: *abdominal pain, constipation, diarrhea,* mucosal inflammation, *nausea,* stomatitis, *vomiting.*
Metabolic: *hypomagnesemia.*
Respiratory: *cough,* pulmonary toxicity.
Skin: *acne, acneiform dermatitis, dry skin, fissures, nail infection, pruritus, rash, redness,* ***skin exfoliation, skin toxicity.***
Other: ***anaphylaxis,*** *general deterioration,* ***severe infusion reaction.***

Interactions

None known.

Effects on lab test results

- May decrease calcium and magnesium levels.

Pharmacokinetics

Absorption: Given I.V.
Distribution: Unknown.
Metabolism: Unknown.
Excretion: Unknown. *Half-life:* 7½ days.

Route	Onset	Peak	Duration
I.V.	Unknown	Unknown	Unknown

Action

Chemical effect: Inhibits actions between proteins and cell surface receptors that would normally allow proliferation of cells and new blood vessel growth.
Therapeutic effect: Inhibits metastatic colon tumor growth.

Available forms

Solution for infusion: 20 mg/ml in 5-ml, 10-ml, and 20-ml vials

NURSING PROCESS

Assessment

- Assess patient's condition before therapy and regularly thereafter.

ALERT: Drug may cause severe infusion reactions including anaphylaxis, bronchospasm, fever, chills, and hypotension. Monitor patient closely. Keep emergency treatment available to treat severe infusion reactions.

- Monitor for severe skin, eye, and pulmonary toxicities. Stop the drug or lower the dose if necessary.
- Assess patient's and family's knowledge of drug therapy.

Nursing diagnoses

- Ineffective health maintenance related to presence of neoplastic disease
- Risk for impaired skin integrity related to drug-induced skin toxicities
- Deficient knowledge related to drug therapy

Planning and implementation

- Drug-induced diarrhea can be very severe when the drug is combined with other chemotherapy drugs. Monitor patient for dehydration. Use with the irinotecan, bolus 5-fluorouracil, or leucovorin regimen isn't recommended.
- Monitor patient's electrolytes, especially calcium and magnesium, periodically during and for 8 weeks after treatment. Supplementation may be needed.

Patient teaching

- Warn patient that drug can cause photosensitivity reactions and have him wear a hat, sunscreen, and protective clothing, and limit sun exposure.
- Warn patient about the risk of severe skin, eye, infusion-related, and pulmonary reactions. Advise him to report any skin changes, eye problems, or difficulty breathing to his prescriber.
- Diarrhea may be severe, especially if more than one chemotherapy drug is used. Remind patient to stay well hydrated.
- Tell women of childbearing age that contraception must be used during and for 6 months following treatment.
- Advise mothers who are breast-feeding to stop breast-feeding during and for 2 months after treatment ends.

Evaluation

- Patient responds to drug therapy.
- Patient doesn't experience serious skin toxicities.
- Patient and family state understanding of drug therapy.

pantoprazole sodium

(pan-TOE-pra-zole SOH-dee-um)

Protonix, Protonix IV

Pharmacologic class: proton pump inhibitor
Therapeutic class: gastric acid suppressant
Pregnancy risk category: B

Indications and dosages

▶ **Short-term therapy for erosive esophagitis related to gastroesophageal reflux disease (GERD).** *Adults:* 40 mg P.O. once daily for up to 8 weeks. For those patients who haven't healed after 8 weeks of therapy, an additional 8-week course may be considered.

▶ **Patients with GERD who are unable to continue pantoprazole sodium delayed-release tablets.** *Adults:* 40 mg I.V. daily for 7 to 10 days. Switch to oral form as soon as patient is able to take oral drugs.

▶ **Long-term maintenance of healing erosive esophagitis and reduction in relapse rates of daytime and nighttime heartburn symptoms in patients with GERD.** *Adults:* 40 mg P.O. once daily.

▶ **Pathological hypersecretion conditions related to Zollinger-Ellison syndrome or other neoplastic conditions.** *Adults:* Individualize dosage. Usual starting dose is 40 mg P.O. b.i.d. Adjust dosage to a maximum of 240 mg daily. Or, 80 mg I.V. q 12 hours for no more than 6 days. For those needing a higher dosage, 80 mg q 8 hours is expected to maintain acid output below 10 mEq/h. Maximum daily dose, 240 mg.

I.V. administration

- Reconstitute each vial with 10 ml of normal saline solution.
- Compatible diluents for infusion include 5% dextrose, normal saline solution, or lactated Ringer's injection.
- For GERD, further dilute with 100 ml of diluent to a final concentration of 0.4 mg/ml.

• For hypersecretion conditions, combine two reconstituted vials and further dilute with 80 ml of diluent to a total volume of 100 ml, with a final concentration of 0.8 mg/ml.
• Infuse diluted solutions I.V. over 15 minutes at no more than 3 mg/min (7 ml/min) for GERD and 6 mg/min (7 ml/min) for pathological hypersecretory conditions.
• Don't give another infusion simultaneously through the same line.
• The reconstituted solution may be stored for up to 2 hours at room temperature, and the diluted solutions may be stored for up to 12 hours at room temperature.
• Stop I.V. drug as soon as P.O. use is possible.

⊗ **Incompatibilities**
Midazolam (Y-site), zinc-containing products or solutions.

Contraindications and cautions

• Contraindicated in patients hypersensitive to the drug or any of its components.
Lifespan: Use in pregnancy only when clearly needed. In breast-feeding women, use cautiously. In children, safety and effectiveness haven't been established.

Adverse reactions

CNS: anxiety, asthenia, dizziness, headache, insomnia, migraine, pain.
CV: chest pain.
EENT: pharyngitis, rhinitis, sinusitis.
GI: abdominal pain, constipation, diarrhea, dyspepsia, eructation, flatulence, gastroenteritis, gastrointestinal disorder, nausea, vomiting.
GU: rectal disorder, urinary frequency, UTI.
Metabolic: hyperglycemia, hyperlipidemia.
Musculoskeletal: arthralgia, back pain, hypertonia, neck pain.
Respiratory: bronchitis, dyspnea, increased cough, upper respiratory tract infection.
Skin: rash.
Other: flulike syndrome, infection.

Interactions

Drug-drug. *Ampicillin esters, iron salts, ketoconazole:* May decrease absorption of these drugs. Monitor patient closely, and try to separate doses.
Drug-herb. *St. John's wort:* May increase risk of sunburn. Discourage use together.
Drug-food. *Food:* May delay absorption of pantoprazole for up to 2 hours, but the extent of absorption isn't affected. Give with or without meals.

Effects on lab test results

• May increase glucose, uric acid, and lipid levels.
• May increase or decrease liver function test values.
• May cause false-positive urine screen for tetrahydrocannabinol.

Pharmacokinetics

Absorption: Good, with an absolute bioavailability of 77%. Peak level occurs at 2½ hours. Food may delay absorption up to 2 hours, but the extent of absorption isn't affected.
Distribution: Mainly in the extracellular fluid; 98% protein-bound, mainly to albumin.
Metabolism: Extensive.
Excretion: About 71% in urine and 18% in feces through bile. *Half-life:* 1 hour.

Route	Onset	Peak	Duration
P.O.	Unknown	2½	24 hr
I.V.	15–30 min	Unknown	24 hr

Action

Chemical effect: Inhibits the activity of the proton pump by binding to hydrogen-potassium adenosine triphosphatase, located at secretory surface of the gastric parietal cells.
Therapeutic effect: Suppresses gastric acid secretion.

Available forms

Injection: 40-mg vial
Tablets (delayed-release): 20 mg, 40 mg

NURSING PROCESS

Assessment

• Assess underlying condition before starting therapy and regularly thereafter to monitor drug's effectiveness.
• Assess patient for complaints of epigastric or abdominal pain and for bleeding (such as blood in stool or emesis).
• Be alert for adverse reactions and interactions.
• Assess patient's and family's knowledge of drug therapy.

Nursing diagnoses

- Risk for imbalanced fluid volume related to drug-induced adverse reactions
- Risk for aspiration related to underlying gastrointestinal disorder
- Deficient knowledge related to pantoprazole therapy

Planning and implementation

- Symptomatic response to therapy doesn't rule out gastric malignancy.

ALERT: Don't confuse Protonix with Lotronex, Prilosec, Prozac, or Prevacid.

Patient teaching

- Instruct patient to take exactly as prescribed and at approximately the same time every day.
- Tell patient that drug can be taken with or without food.
- Inform patient that tablet is to be swallowed whole and not crushed, split, or chewed.
- Tell patient that antacids don't affect the absorption of pantoprazole.
- Instruct patient to report abdominal pain or signs of bleeding, such as tarry stool.
- Advise patient not to drink alcohol, eat food, or take other drugs (such as aspirin, NSAIDs) that could cause gastric irritation.

Evaluation

- Patient maintains adequate hydration throughout therapy.
- Patient responds well to therapy and doesn't aspirate.
- Patient and family state understanding of pantoprazole therapy.

paroxetine hydrochloride

(par-OKS-eh-teen high-droh-KLOR-ighd)

Paxil, Paxil CR

Pharmacologic class: SSRI
Therapeutic class: antidepressant
Pregnancy risk category: D

Indications and dosages

▶ **Major depressive disorder.** *Adults:* Initially, 20 mg P.O. daily, preferably in morning, as directed. Increase by 10 mg daily at weekly intervals, to maximum of 50 mg daily, if needed. Or, initially, 25 mg Paxil CR P.O. as a single daily dose, usually in the morning, with or without food. May increase dose at intervals of at least 1 week by 12.5 mg daily increments, up to a maximum of 62.5 mg daily.

▶ **Obsessive-compulsive disorder.** *Adults:* Initially, 20 mg P.O. daily, preferably in morning, as directed. Increase by 10 mg daily at weekly intervals to target dose of 40 mg daily. Maximum daily dose, 60 mg.

▶ **Panic disorder.** *Adults:* Initially, 10 mg P.O. daily. Increase by 10-mg increments at no less than weekly intervals to target dose of 40 mg daily. Maximum daily dose is 60 mg. Or, initially, 12.5 mg Paxil CR P.O. as a single daily dose, usually in the morning, with or without food. May increase dose at intervals of at least 1 week by 12.5 mg daily increments, up to a maximum of 75 mg daily.

▶ **Generalized anxiety disorder.** *Adults:* Initially, 20 mg P.O. daily. Increase dosage by 10 mg daily at increments of at least 1 week. Maximum daily dose, 50 mg.

▶ **Posttraumatic stress disorder.** *Adults:* Initially, 20 mg P.O. daily. Increase dosage by 10 mg daily at intervals of at least 1 week. Maximum daily dose, 50 mg.

▶ **Premenstrual dysphoric disorder (PMDD).** *Adults:* Initially, 12.5 mg P.O. (Paxil CR) once daily as a single daily dose, usually in the morning, with or without food. May increase to 25 mg daily after at least 1 week. May be given either daily or limited to the luteal phase of the menstrual cycle.

▶ **Social anxiety disorder.** *Adults:* 20 mg P.O. (Paxil) once daily in the morning. Or, initially, 12.5 mg P.O (Paxil CR) once daily in the morning. Increase dose at weekly intervals in increments of 12.5 mg/day, up to a maximum of 37.5 mg. daily.

Adjust-a-dose: For geriatric or debilitated patients and patients with severe hepatic or renal disease, initially, give 10 mg P.O. (immediate-release) daily, preferably in morning. If patient doesn't respond, increase by 10-mg increments at weekly intervals to maximum daily dose of 40 mg. The recommended initial dose of Paxil CR is 12.5 mg daily. Don't exceed 50 mg daily.

▶ **Diabetic neuropathy‡.** *Adults:* 40 mg P.O. daily.

▶ **Headache‡.** *Adults:* 10 to 50 mg P.O daily for 3 to 9 months.

P

▶ **Premature ejaculation‡.** *Adults:* 20 mg P.O. 3 to 4 hours before planned intercourse or 10 to 40 mg daily to increase ejaculatory latency time.

Contraindications and cautions

- Contraindicated in patients taking MAO inhibitors or thioridazine. Don't give drug within 14 days of an MAO inhibitor. Also, contraindicated in patients hypersensitive to the drug or any ingredient in the formulation.
- Use cautiously in patients with a history of seizures or mania; patients with severe, concomitant systemic illness; and patients at risk for volume depletion.
- Adults and children with major depressive disorders may experience suicidal ideation and behavior even while taking an antidepressant. Monitor patients for worsening depression or suicidal ideation, especially when therapy starts or dosage changes.

Lifespan: In pregnant women, use cautiously in first trimester because of risk of congenital malformations in the fetus. Neonates of women taking drug in the latter part of the third trimester may require prolonged hospitalization due to respiratory problems and feeding difficulties. In breast-feeding women, use cautiously; drug is distributed in breast milk. Not approved for use in children.

Adverse reactions

CNS: anxiety, *asthenia,* blurred vision, confusion, *dizziness, headache, insomnia,* nervousness, paresthesia, *somnolence, tremor.*
CV: orthostatic hypotension, palpitations, vasodilation.
EENT: dysgeusia, lump or tightness in throat.
GI: ***bleeding,*** *constipation, diarrhea, dry mouth,* dyspepsia, flatulence, increased or decreased appetite, *nausea,* taste perversion, vomiting.
GU: abnormal ejaculation, *female genital disorder (including anorgasmy, difficulty with orgasm), male genital disorders (including anorgasmy, erectile difficulties, delayed ejaculation or orgasm, impotence, and sexual dysfunction),* other urinary disorder, urinary frequency.
Metabolic: hyponatremia.
Musculoskeletal: myalgia, myopathy, myasthenia.
Skin: excessive sweating, rash.
Other: decreased libido, yawning.

Interactions

Drug-drug. *Buspirone, dextromethorphan, dihydroergotamine, isoniazid, lithium, meperidine, sumatriptan, tramadol, trazodone, tricyclic antidepressants:* May cause serotonin syndrome. Avoid use together.
Cimetidine: May decrease hepatic metabolism of paroxetine, leading to risk of toxicity. Dosage adjustments may be needed.
Digoxin: May decrease digoxin level. Monitor level closely.
NSAIDs, warfarin: May increase risk of bleeding. Use with caution; monitor patient closely for bleeding.
Phenelzine, selegiline, tranylcypromine: May cause serotonin syndrome, including CNS irritability, shivering, and altered consciousness. Don't give together. Wait at least 2 weeks after stopping an MAO inhibitor before giving any SSRI.
Phenobarbital, phenytoin: May alter pharmacokinetics of both drugs. Dosage adjustments may be needed.
Procyclidine: May increase procyclidine level. Monitor patient for excessive anticholinergic effects.
Sumatriptan: May cause weakness, hyperreflexia, and incoordination. Monitor patient.
Theophylline: Theophylline clearance may decrease threefold. Dosage reduction may be needed.
Thioridazine: May prolong QT interval and increase risk of serious ventricular arrhythmias, such as torsades de pointes and sudden death. Avoid use together.
Tricyclic antidepressants: May inhibit tricyclic antidepressant metabolism. Dose of tricyclic antidepressant may need to be reduced. Monitor patient closely.
Tryptophan: May increase risk of adverse reactions, such as nausea and dizziness. Avoid using together.
Drug-herb. *St. John's wort:* May result in sedative-hypnotic intoxication. Discourage using together.
Drug-lifestyle. *Alcohol use:* May alter psychomotor function. Discourage using together.

Effects on lab test results

- May decrease sodium level.
- May alter platelet count.

Pharmacokinetics

Absorption: Complete.
Distribution: Throughout body, including CNS; only 1% remains in plasma. About 93% to 95% protein-bound.
Metabolism: About 36%.
Excretion: About 64% in urine. *Half-life:* About 24 hours.

Route	Onset	Peak	Duration
P.O.			
immediate-release	1–4 wk	2–8 hr	Unknown
controlled-release	Unknown	6–10 hr	Unknown

Action

Chemical effect: May inhibit CNS neuronal uptake of serotonin.
Therapeutic effect: Relieves depression.

Available forms

Suspension: 10 mg/5ml
Tablets: 10 mg, 20 mg, 30 mg, 40 mg
Tablets (controlled-release): 12.5 mg, 25 mg, 37.5 mg

NURSING PROCESS

Assessment

- Assess patient's depression before starting therapy and regularly thereafter to monitor drug's effectiveness.
- Be alert for adverse reactions and drug interactions.
- Assess patient's and family's knowledge of drug therapy.
- For PMDD, the effectiveness of Paxil CR for longer than 3 menstrual cycles hasn't been established.
- Periodically reassess the need for continuing therapy.

Nursing diagnoses

- Disturbed thought processes related to depression
- Risk for injury related to drug-induced adverse CNS reactions
- Deficient knowledge related to drug therapy

Planning and implementation

- Don't give drug within 14 days of MAO inhibitor therapy.
- Don't crush CR tablet. If patient can't swallow a CR tablet whole, give a regular-release form.
- If signs of psychosis occur or increase, reduce dosage.
- Gradually reduce dosage to prevent withdrawal symptoms.

ALERT: Don't confuse paroxetine with paclitaxel.

ALERT: Don't confuse Paxil with Doxil, Taxol, or Plavix.

Patient teaching

- Warn patient to avoid hazardous activities until the drug's CNS effects are known.
- Warn patient not to chew or crush Paxil CR tablet but to swallow it whole.
- Tell patient that he may notice improvement in 1 to 4 weeks but that he must continue with prescribed regimen to continue feeling benefits.
- Tell patient to abstain from alcohol during drug therapy.

ALERT: If patient wishes to switch from an SSRI to St. John's wort, tell him to wait a few weeks for the SSRI to fully leave his system before starting the herb. The exact time required will depend on which SSRI he takes.

Evaluation

- Patient's depression improves.
- Patient sustains no injuries because of drug-induced adverse CNS reactions.
- Patient and family state understanding of drug therapy.

pegaspargase (PEG-L-asparaginase)

(peg-AHS-per-jays)
Oncaspar

Pharmacologic class: modified version of enzyme L-asparaginase
Therapeutic class: antineoplastic
Pregnancy risk category: C

Indications and dosages

▶ **Acute lymphoblastic leukemia (ALL) in patients who need L-asparaginase but have developed hypersensitivity to native forms of L-asparaginase; as a component of a multi-drug chemotherapeutic regimen for first-line**

treatment of patients with ALL. *Adults and children:* 2,500 international units/m^2 I.M. or I.V. no more often than q 14 days.

I.V. administration

- Handle and give solution with care; wear gloves. Avoid inhaling vapors and contact with skin or mucous membranes, especially in eyes. If contact occurs, wash with plenty of water for at least 15 minutes.
- Avoid excessive agitation; don't shake. Keep refrigerated at 36° to 46° F (2° to 8° C). If cloudy, precipitated, or stored at room temperature for more than 48 hours, don't use.
- Give drug over 1 to 2 hours in 100 ml of normal saline solution or D_5W through infusion that is already running.
- Keep patient under observation for 1 hour after use and keep resuscitation equipment (such as epinephrine, oxygen, and I.V. steroids) within reach to treat anaphylaxis. If moderate to life-threatening hypersensitivity reactions occur, stop drug.
- Increased risk of hepatotoxicity, coagulopathy, and GI and renal disorders when compared to the I.M. route. Use only when clearly needed.
- Discard unused portions. Use only one dose per vial; don't reenter vial. Don't save unused drug for later use.

⊗ Incompatibilities
Other I.V. drugs.

Contraindications and cautions

- Contraindicated in patients with pancreatitis or history of pancreatitis; in those who have had significant hemorrhagic events with previous L-asparaginase therapy; and in those with previous serious allergic reactions, such as generalized urticaria, bronchospasm, laryngeal edema, hypotension, or other unacceptable adverse reactions to pegaspargase.
- Use cautiously in patients with liver dysfunction.

Lifespan: In pregnant and breast-feeding women, use only when benefits outweigh risks.

Adverse reactions

CNS: ***coma,*** confusion, disorientation, dizziness, emotional lability, fatigue, headache, malaise mental status changes, mood changes, paresthesia, parkinsonism, ***seizures***, somnolence, ***status epilepticus.***
CV: chest pain, edema, endocarditis, hypotension, subacute bacterial hypertension, tachycardia.
EENT: epistaxis.
GI: abdominal pain, anorexia, colitis, constipation, diarrhea, flatulence, GI pain, indigestion, mouth tenderness, mucositis, nausea, ***pancreatitis,*** vomiting.
GU: hematuria, increased urinary frequency, renal dysfunction, ***renal failure,*** severe hemorrhagic cystitis.
Hematologic: ***agranulocytosis, disseminated intravascular coagulation,*** easy bruising, hemolytic anemia, ***hemorrhage, leukopenia, pancytopenia, thrombocytopenia, thrombosis.***
Hepatic: ascites, bilirubinemia, fatty changes in liver, hypoalbuminemia, jaundice, ***liver failure.***
Metabolic: hyperglycemia, hyperuricemia, ***hypoglycemia,*** hyponatremia, hypoproteinemia, ***metabolic acidosis,*** proteinuria, uric acid nephropathy, weight loss.
Musculoskeletal: arthralgia, cramps, joint stiffness, musculoskeletal pain, myalgia.
Respiratory: cough, ***severe bronchospasm,*** upper respiratory tract infection.
Skin: alopecia, ecchymosis, erythema simplex, fever blister, fungal changes, itching, nail whiteness and ridging, nighttime sweating, petechial rash, purpura, urticaria, white hands.
Other: ***hypersensitivity reactions*** (***including anaphylaxis,*** pain, fever, chills, peripheral edema; infection); injection pain or reaction; localized edema, ***sepsis; septic shock.***

Interactions

Drug-drug. *Aspirin, dipyridamole, heparin, NSAIDs, warfarin:* Imbalances in coagulation factors may occur, predisposing patient to bleeding or thrombosis. Use together cautiously.
Methotrexate: May interfere with action of methotrexate, which requires cell replication for its lethal effect. Monitor patient for decreased effectiveness.
Protein-bound drugs: Protein depletion may increase toxicity of other drugs that bind to proteins. Monitor patient for toxicity. May interfere with enzymatic detoxification of other drugs, particularly in liver. Give together cautiously.

Effects on lab test results

- May increase antithrombin III, fibrinogen, BUN, creatinine, amylase, lipase, bilirubin, ALT, AST, uric acid, and ammonia levels. May

decrease sodium, protein, and hemoglobin levels and hematocrit. May increase or decrease glucose level.
• May increase PT, INR, and PTT. May decrease WBC, RBC, platelet, and granulocyte counts.

Pharmacokinetics

Absorption: Unknown.
Distribution: Unknown.
Metabolism: Unknown.
Excretion: Unknown. *Half-life:* 2 to 6 days.

Route	Onset	Peak	Duration
I.M., I.V.	Unknown	Unknown	Unknown

Action

Chemical effect: Destroys cancer cells by inactivating the amino acid asparagine. Asparagine is required by tumor cells to synthesize proteins. Because tumor cells can't synthesize their own asparagine, protein synthesis and, eventually, synthesis of DNA and RNA are inhibited.
Therapeutic effect: Kills selected leukemic cells.

Available forms

Injection: 750 international units/ml

NURSING PROCESS

Assessment

• Assess patient's condition before starting therapy and regularly thereafter to monitor drug's effectiveness.
• Closely monitor patient for hypersensitivity reactions, including life-threatening anaphylaxis, which may occur during therapy, especially in patient hypersensitive to other forms of L-asparaginase.
• Monitor patient's peripheral blood count and bone marrow. A drop in circulating lymphoblasts may occur with a marked rise in uric acid level.
• Monitor amylase level to detect early evidence of pancreatitis. Monitor patient's glucose level during therapy because hyperglycemia may occur.
• Monitor patient for liver dysfunction when used with hepatotoxic chemotherapeutics.
• Drug may affect a number of plasma proteins; monitor fibrinogen, PT, and PTT.
• Be alert for adverse reactions and drug interactions.
• Assess patient's and family's knowledge of drug therapy.

Nursing diagnoses

• Ineffective health maintenance related to leukemia
• Ineffective protection related to drug-induced adverse hematologic reactions
• Deficient knowledge related to drug therapy

Planning and implementation

• Use as monotherapy only in unusual situation when combined regimen that uses other chemotherapeutic drugs is inappropriate because of toxicity, because patient is refractory to other therapy, or because of other specific patient-related factors.
• Don't use thawed drug. Although drug may look unchanged, freezing destroys its activity. Obtain new dose from pharmacist.
• Hydrate patient before therapy. Hyperuricemia may result from rapid lysis of leukemic cells. Allopurinol may be ordered.
• Limit volume administered at single injection site to 2 ml. If volume is larger than 2 ml, use multiple injection sites.

Patient teaching

• Inform patient about hypersensitivity reactions and importance of alerting staff at once.
• Instruct patient to ask prescriber before taking other drugs, including OTC preparations. Using together may increase risk of bleeding, or may increase toxicity of other drugs.
• Instruct patient to report signs and symptoms of infection (fever, chills, and malaise) to prescriber because drug may suppress immune system.

Evaluation

• Patient responds well to therapy.
• Patient develops no serious complications caused by drug-induced adverse hematologic reactions.
• Patient and family state understanding of drug therapy.

P

pegfilgrastim
(peg-FILL-grass-tihm)
Neulasta

Pharmacologic class: colony-stimulating factor
Therapeutic class: neutrophil-growth stimulator
Pregnancy risk category: C

Indications and dosages

▶ **To reduce frequency of infection in patients with nonmyeloid malignancies taking myelosuppressive anticancer drugs that may cause febrile neutropenia.** *Adults:* 6 mg subcutaneously once per chemotherapy cycle. Don't give in the period between 14 days before and 24 hours after administration of cytotoxic chemotherapy.

Contraindications and cautions

- Contraindicated in patients hypersensitive to *Escherichia coli*–derived proteins, filgrastim, or any component of the drug.
- Don't use for peripheral blood progenitor cell mobilization.
- Use cautiously in patients with sickle cell disease, those receiving chemotherapy causing delayed myelosuppression, and those receiving radiation therapy.

Lifespan: In pregnant women, use drug only if benefits outweigh risks to the fetus. In breast-feeding women, use cautiously; it's unknown if the drug appears in breast milk. In infants, children, and adolescents who weigh less than 45 kg (99 lb), don't use the 6-mg single-use syringe dose. In children, safety and effectiveness haven't been established.

Adverse reactions

CNS: *dizziness, fatigue, fever, headache, insomnia.*
CV: *peripheral edema.*
GI: *abdominal pain, anorexia, constipation, diarrhea, dyspepsia, mucositis, nausea, stomatitis, taste perversion, vomiting.*
Hematologic: GRANULOCYTOPENIA, NEUTROPENIC FEVER, ***splenic rupture.***
Musculoskeletal: arthralgia, bone pain, generalized weakness, myalgia, skeletal pain.
Respiratory: ***acute respiratory distress syndrome (ARDS).***
Skin: alopecia.

Interactions

Drug-drug. *Lithium:* May increase the release of neutrophils. Monitor neutrophil counts closely.

Effects on lab test results

- May increase LDH, alkaline phosphatase, and uric acid levels.
- May increase WBC, granulocyte, and neutrophil counts.

Pharmacokinetics

Absorption: Unknown.
Distribution: Unknown.
Metabolism: Unknown.
Excretion: Unknown. *Half-life:* 15 to 80 hours.

Route	Onset	Peak	Duration
SubQ	Unknown	Unknown	Unknown

Action

Chemical effect: Binds cell receptors to stimulate proliferation, differentiation, commitment, and end-cell function of neutrophils. Pegfilgrastim and filgrastim have the same mechanism of action. Pegfilgrastim has a reduced renal clearance and therefore a longer half-life than filgrastim.
Therapeutic effect: Increases WBC count.

Available forms

Injection: 6 mg/0.6 ml single-use, preservative-free, prefilled syringes

NURSING PROCESS

Assessment

- Assess patient's underlying condition before starting therapy and regularly thereafter to monitor drug's effectiveness.
- Obtain CBC and platelet count before starting therapy.
- Monitor patient's hemoglobin level, hematocrit, and CBC and platelet count; as well as LDH, alkaline phosphatase, and uric acid levels during therapy.
- Assess patient's and family's knowledge of drug therapy.

Nursing diagnoses

- Acute pain related to adverse musculoskeletal effects of drug
- Risk for infection related to underlying condition and treatment
- Deficient knowledge related to pegfilgrastim therapy

Planning and implementation

- The maximum amount of filgrastim that can be given is unknown. Treat patient having symptomatic leukocytosis with leukapheresis.

ALERT: Splenic rupture may occur rarely with filgrastim use. Evaluate patient who experiences signs or symptoms of left upper abdominal or shoulder pain for an enlarged spleen or splenic rupture.

- Monitor patient for allergic reactions, including anaphylaxis, skin rash, and urticaria.
- Evaluate patient who develops fever, lung infiltrates, or respiratory distress for ARDS. If ARDS occurs, stop drug.
- Keep patient with sickle cell disease well hydrated, and monitor patient for symptoms of sickle cell crisis.
- Pegfilgrastim may act as a growth factor for tumors.

Patient teaching

- Inform patient of the drug's potential side effects.
- Advise patient to immediately report upper left abdominal or shoulder tip pain.
- Tell patient to report signs and symptoms of allergic reactions, fever, or breathing problems.
- Tell patient with sickle cell disease to maintain hydration and report signs or symptoms of sickle cell crisis.
- Instruct patient or caregiver how to give drug if it is to be given at home.
- Instruct patient or caregiver not to freeze drug. If accidentally frozen, thaw in refrigerator before administration. Tell them to discard if frozen twice.

Evaluation

- Patient states that pain management is adequate.
- Patient's WBC count is normal.
- Patient and family state understanding of drug therapy.

peginterferon alfa-2a

(peg-inter-FEAR-on AL-fah TOO AY)

Pegasys

Pharmacologic class: biological response modifier

Therapeutic class: antiviral

Pregnancy risk category: C (X if used with ribavirin)

Indications and dosages

▶ **Chronic hepatitis C in patients with compensated liver disease and not previously treated with interferon alfa.** *Adults:* 180 mcg subcutaneously in abdomen or thigh, once weekly for 48 weeks, on the same day each week.

▶ **Chronic hepatitis C (regardless of genotype) in HIV-infected patients not previously treated with interferon.** *Adults:* 180 mcg subcutaneously weekly along with ribavirin (Copegus) 800 mg P.O. daily given in 2 divided doses for 48 weeks.

Adjust-a-dose: If patient has moderate to severe adverse reactions, decrease dose to 135 mcg subcutaneously once a week; in some cases, decrease to 90 mcg subcutaneously once a week.

If patient has hematologic reactions and absolute neutrophil count (ANC) is less than 750/mm^3, reduce dose to 135 mcg subcutaneously once a week; if ANC is less than 500/mm^3, stop drug until ANC exceeds 1,000/mm^3 and restart at 90 mcg subcutaneously once a week. If platelet count is less than 50,000/mm^3, reduce dose to 90 mcg subcutaneously once a week; stop drug if platelet count drops below 25,000/mm^3.

In patients on hemodialysis, decrease dose to 135 mcg subcutaneously once a week.

In patients with ALT level increases above baseline, decrease dose to 135 mcg subcutaneously once a week; if hepatic impairment worsens or bilirubin level increases, stop therapy.

If patient develops mild depression, continue drug, but evaluate weekly. For moderate depression, reduce dose to 135 mcg for 4 to 8 weeks and evaluate patient q week; in some cases, reduce to 90 mcg. If symptoms improve and remain stable for 4 weeks, continue at present dose or resume previous dose. If severe depression occurs, discontinue drug permanently.

Contraindications and cautions

• Contraindicated in patients hypersensitive to interferon alfa-2a or its components and in patients with autoimmune hepatitis or decompensated liver disease before or during therapy.
• Use cautiously in patients with a history of depression, drug addiction, suicidal ideation, or suicide attempts. Also use cautiously in patients with baseline ANC less than 1,500/mm^3, baseline platelet counts less than 90,000/mm^3, or baseline hemoglobin level less than 10 g/dl. Use cautiously in patients with cardiac disease or hypertension, thyroid disease, autoimmune disorders, pulmonary disorders, colitis, pancreatitis, or ophthalmologic disorders. Also use cautiously in patients with creatinine clearance less than 50 ml/minute.
• Safety and effectiveness of drug haven't been established for hepatitis C in organ-transplant recipients, for patients with hepatitis C infected with hepatitis B, or in patients who haven't responded to other alpha interferon therapy.
Lifespan: In pregnant women, use only if benefits outweigh risks to the fetus; women of childbearing age must use effective contraception. In breast-feeding women, use cautiously; it's unknown whether drug appears in breast milk. In neonates and premature infants, don't use the drug because it contains benzyl alcohol. In children, safety and effectiveness of drug haven't been established. In the elderly, use cautiously because risk for adverse reactions increases.

Adverse reactions

CNS: aggressive behavior, anxiety, bipolar disorder, ***cerebral hemorrhage, coma,*** concentration and memory impairment, *depression, dizziness,* ***drug overdose*** and relapse of drug addiction, *insomnia, irritability, pain,* ***suicide.***
CV: arrhythmias, hypotension, ***myocardial infarction, pulmonary embolism.***
GI: *abdominal pain,* anorexia, *diarrhea,* dry mouth, ***hemorrhagic or ischemic colitis,*** *nausea,* ***pancreatitis, ulcerative colitis,*** vomiting.
Hematologic: *anemia, lymphopenia,* NEUTROPENIA, ***thrombocytopenia.***
Metabolic: diabetes mellitus, hyper- or hypothyroidism, ***hypoglycemia.***
Musculoskeletal: *arthralgia,* back pain, *myalgia.*
Respiratory: ***interstitial pneumonitis, pneumonia.***
Skin: *alopecia,* dermatitis, increased sweating, *pruritus,* rash.
Other: *flulike symptoms, infection, injection site reaction.*

Interactions

Drug-drug. *Ribavirin:* May increase risk of hematologic toxicity (neutropenia, anemia). The two drugs are commonly given together for additive therapeutic benefit, but laboratory values and symptoms must be monitored closely.
Theophylline: May increase theophylline level. Monitor theophylline level and adjust dose as needed.

Effects on lab test results

• May increase ALT and triglyceride levels. May decrease hemoglobin level and hematocrit. May increase or decrease glucose level.
• May decrease ANC, WBC, and platelet counts. May increase or decrease thyroid function test values.

Pharmacokinetics

Absorption: Unknown.
Distribution: Unknown.
Metabolism: Possibly in liver and kidney.
Excretion: Unknown, about 30% is excreted by the kidneys. *Half-life:* 80 hours.

Route	Onset	Peak	Duration
SubQ	Unknown	3–4 days	≤ 1 wk

Action

Chemical effect: Binds to specific receptors on the cell surface, which causes rapid gene transcription that starts complex intracellular events and immunomodulation.
Therapeutic effect: Inhibits viral replication in infected cells and decreases cell proliferation.

Available forms

Injection: 180-mcg/ml single-dose vials, 180-mcg/0.5 ml prefilled syringes

NURSING PROCESS

Assessment

- Monitor patient weekly for psychiatric reactions, such as depression and thoughts of suicide, during the first 8 weeks of therapy. These symptoms may occur in a patient without earlier psychiatric illness. If moderate depression occurs and doesn't go away after decreasing dose, refer patient for psychiatric consultation. If severe depression occurs, immediately stop the drug and start psychiatric therapy.
- Obtain CBC and differential before starting therapy, and monitor it routinely thereafter. Stop giving the drug in the case of a large decrease in neutrophil or platelet counts.
- Obtain baseline eye examination and repeat periodically thereafter during therapy. If patient has a new or worsening eye disorder, stop the drug.
- Monitor lab values for kidney or liver impairment and for thyroid or glucose level changes that require therapy.

Nursing diagnoses

- Ineffective health maintenance related to underlying condition
- Risk for suicide related to adverse CNS effects of drug
- Deficient knowledge related to peginterferon alfa-2a therapy

Planning and implementation

- If uncontrollable thyroid disease, hyperglycemia, hypoglycemia, or diabetes mellitus occurs, stop giving the drug. Thyroid dysfunction may persist after drug is stopped.
- If persistent or unexplained pulmonary infiltrates or pulmonary dysfunction occur, stop giving the drug.
- If signs and symptoms of colitis (abdominal pain, bloody diarrhea, and fever) occur, stop giving the drug. Symptoms will resolve within 3 weeks.
- If signs and symptoms of pancreatitis or autoimmune hepatitis occur, stop giving the drug.

Patient teaching

- Teach patient proper technique for giving himself the drug and for properly disposing of needles and syringes.
- Tell patient to immediately report depression, mood or sleep changes, or thoughts of suicide.
- Tell patient to report signs and symptoms of pancreatitis, GI upset, eye disorders, flulike symptoms, or respiratory disorders.
- Instruct women of childbearing age who are taking drug or who are sexual partners of men taking drug to use two forms of effective contraception during therapy and for 6 months following the end of therapy.
- Inform patient, or partner of patient, who becomes pregnant during or for 6 months post-treatment, to notify prescriber immediately or call the Pregnancy Registry at 1-800-526-6367.
- Advise patient to avoid driving or operating machinery if dizziness, fatigue, confusion, or somnolence occur.

Evaluation

- Patient has improved health.
- Patient denies suicidal ideation.
- Patient and family state understanding of drug therapy.

peginterferon alfa-2b

(pehg-in-ter-FEAR-ahn AL-fah TOO BEE)

PEG-Intron

Pharmacologic class: biological response modifier

Therapeutic class: antiviral

Pregnancy risk category: C (X if used with ribavirin)

Indications and dosages

▶ **Chronic hepatitis C in patients with compensated liver disease not previously treated with interferon alfa therapy.** *Adults:* Recommended regimen is about 1 mcg/kg subcutaneously once weekly for 48 weeks on the same day each week. Recommended doses are as follows:

37 to 45 kg (81 to 99 lb): 40 mcg (0.4 ml) of 100-mcg/ml strength

46 to 56 kg (100 to 123 lb): 50 mcg (0.5 ml) of 100-mcg/ml strength

57 to 72 kg (124 to 158 lb): 64 mcg (0.4 ml) of 160-mcg/ml strength

73 to 88 kg (159 to 194 lb): 80 mcg (0.5 ml) of 160-mcg/ml strength

89 to 106 kg (195 to 233 lb): 96 mcg (0.4 ml) of 240-mcg/ml strength

P

107 to 136 kg (234 to 299 lb): 120 mcg (0.5 ml) of 240-mcg/ml strength
137 to 160 kg (300 to 352 lb): 150 mcg (0.5 ml) of 300-mcg/ml strength

▶ **Chronic hepatitis C in patients not previously treated with interferon alpha, given with ribavirin.** *Adults:* Recommended regimen is about 1.5 mcg/kg subcutaneously once weekly for 48 weeks on same day each week. Specific doses are as follows:
Less than 40 kg (88 lb): 50 mcg (0.5 ml) of 100-mcg/ml strength
40 to 50 kg (88 to 110 lb): 64 mcg (0.4 ml) of 160-mcg/ml strength
51 to 60 kg (111 to 132 lb): 80 mcg (0.5 ml) of 160-mcg/ml strength
61 to 75 kg (133 to 165 lb): 96 mcg (0.4 ml) of 240 mcg-mcg/ml strength
76 to 85 kg (166 to 187 lb): 120 mcg (0.5 ml) of 240 mcg-mcg/ml strength
More than 85 kg (187 lb): 150 mcg (0.5 ml) of 300-mcg/ml strength

Adjust-a-dose: In patients with WBC counts less than 1,500/mm^3, neutrophil counts less than 750/mm^3, or platelet counts less than 80,000/mm^3, decrease dose by one-half. Oral ribavirin dose can be continued. If hemoglobin level is less than 10 g/dl, reduce oral ribavirin dose by 200 mg daily. If hemoglobin level is less than 8.5 g/dl, WBC counts less than 1,000/mm^3, neutrophil counts less than 500/mm^3, or platelet counts less than 50,000/mm^3, stop both drugs.

If patient develops mild depression, continue drug, but evaluate weekly. For moderate depression, reduce dose by one-half for 4 to 8 weeks and evaluate patient q week. If symptoms improve and remain stable for 4 weeks, continue at present dose or resume previous dose. If severe depression occurs, stop drug.

For patients with stable CV disease whose hemoglobin level decreases more than 2 g/dl in any 4-week period, decrease peginterferon alfa-2b dose by one-half and ribavirin dose by 200 mg daily. If hemoglobin level is less than 12 g/dl after 4 weeks of reduced doses, stop both drugs.

Contraindications and cautions

• Contraindicated in patients hypersensitive to the drug or any of its components, and in patients with renal impairment (creatinine clearance below 50 ml/minute), pulmonary infiltrates, autoimmune hepatitis, or decompensated liver disease (Child-Pugh class B and C).
• Don't use drug in organ transplant recipients, patients who haven't responded to other alpha interferon therapy, or those with HIV or hepatitis B virus.
• Use cautiously in patients with psychiatric disorders; diabetes mellitus; cardiovascular disease; pulmonary function impairment; or autoimmune, ischemic, and infectious disorders.

Lifespan: In pregnant women and men whose sexual partners are pregnant, drug is contraindicated. Breast-feeding women should either stop breast-feeding or drug. In neonates and infants, drug is contraindicated because it contains benzyl alcohol. In children, safety and effectiveness haven't been established.

Adverse reactions

CNS: anxiety, depression, dizziness, emotional lability, fatigue, fever, headache, hypertonia, insomnia, irritability, malaise, ***suicidal behavior.***
CV: flushing.
EENT: pharyngitis, sinusitis.
GI: abdominal pain, anorexia, colitis, diarrhea, dyspepsia, nausea, right upper quadrant pain, vomiting.
Hematologic: ***neutropenia, thrombocytopenia.***
Hepatic: hepatomegaly.
Metabolic: hyperthyroidism, hypothyroidism, weight decrease.
Musculoskeletal: musculoskeletal pain.
Respiratory: cough.
Skin: alopecia, dry skin, increased sweating, pruritus, rash.
Other: flulike symptoms, injection site pain, injection site reaction (inflammation), rigors, viral infection.

Interactions

None reported.

Effects on lab test results

• May increase ALT, bilirubin, and uric acid levels. May increase or decrease TSH level.
• May decrease neutrophil and platelet counts.

Pharmacokinetics

Absorption: Slowed to mean of 4½ hours by pegylation of interferon alfa-2b.
Distribution: Unknown.
Metabolism: Unknown.

Excretion: Unknown, about 30% is excreted by the kidneys. *Half-life:* 40 hours.

Route	Onset	Peak	Duration
SubQ	Unknown	15–44 hr	48–72 hr

Action

Chemical effect: Binds to specific receptors on the cell surface, which causes rapid gene transcription that initiates complex intracellular events and various immunomodulating activities.

Therapeutic effect: Inhibits viral replication in infected cells, and decreases cell proliferation.

Available forms

Injection: 100 mcg/ml, 160 mcg/ml, 240 mcg/ml, 300 mcg/ml

NURSING PROCESS

Assessment

- Assess underlying condition before starting therapy and regularly thereafter to monitor drug's effectiveness.
- Assess patient for preexisting uncontrolled diabetes or thyroid disorder. Drug may cause or aggravate hypothyroidism, hyperthyroidism, or diabetes.
- If patient has cardiac history, obtain ECG before starting therapy.
- Evaluate patient's volume and make sure patient is hydrated before starting therapy.
- Obtain eye examination in patients with diabetes or hypertension before starting therapy. Retinal hemorrhages, cotton wool spots, and retinal artery or vein obstruction may occur.
- Monitor CBC, platelet count, and AST, ALT, bilirubin, and TSH levels before starting therapy and periodically during therapy.
- Assess patient's and family's knowledge of drug therapy.

Nursing diagnoses

- Ineffective health maintenance related to underlying condition
- Risk for suicide related to adverse CNS effects of drug
- Deficient knowledge related to peginterferon alfa-2b therapy

Planning and implementation

- Drug may be used alone or with ribavirin for chronic hepatitis B.
- If patient has history of MI or arrhythmias, watch closely for hypotension, arrhythmias, tachycardia, cardiomyopathy, and MI.

ALERT: Alpha interferons may cause or aggravate life-threatening neuropsychiatric, autoimmune, ischemic, and infectious disorders. Monitor patient closely and periodically assess for them. Stop therapy in patient with persistently severe or worsening signs or symptoms of these disorders. In many cases, they resolve after stopping therapy.

- Monitor patient for depression and other psychiatric illness. If symptoms are severe, stop giving the drug and refer patient for psychiatric care.
- Monitor patient for signs and symptoms of colitis, such as abdominal pain, bloody diarrhea, and fever. If colitis occurs, stop giving the drug. Symptoms will resolve 1 to 3 weeks after stopping drug.
- Monitor patient for signs and symptoms of pancreatitis or hypersensitivity reactions. If these occur, stop giving the drug.
- Monitor patient with pulmonary disease for dyspnea, pulmonary infiltrates, pneumonitis, and pneumonia.
- If patient has renal disease, watch for signs and symptoms of toxicity.
- If patient has severe neutropenia or thrombocytopenia, stop giving the drug.

Patient teaching

- Explain appropriate use of the drug and its benefits and risks. Tell patient that adverse reactions may continue for several months after therapy is stopped.
- Advise patient that laboratory tests are required before therapy starts and periodically thereafter.
- Tell patient to take drug at bedtime and to use antipyretics to decrease the effect of flulike symptoms.
- Emphasize the importance of properly disposing of needles and syringes, and warn against reusing old needles and syringes.
- Tell patient that drug isn't known to prevent transmission of hepatitis C. It also isn't known whether drug cures hepatitis C or prevents cirrhosis, liver failure, or liver cancer that may result from hepatitis C.

P

• Advise patient to immediately report symptoms of depression or thoughts of suicide.

Evaluation

• Patient has improved health.
• Patient reports no suicidal ideation.
• Patient and family state understanding of drug therapy.

pemetrexed
(peh-meh-TREK-sed)
Alimta

Pharmacologic class: folate antagonist
Therapeutic class: antineoplastic
Pregnancy risk category: D

Indications and dosages

▶ **With cisplatin, malignant pleural mesothelioma in patients whose disease is unresectable or who aren't candidates for surgery.** *Adults:* 500 mg/m^2 I.V. over 10 minutes on day 1 of each 21-day cycle. 30 minutes after infusion ends, give 75 mg/m^2 cisplatin I.V. over 2 hours.

▶ **Locally advanced or metastatic non–small-cell lung cancer after chemotherapy.** *Adults:* 500 mg/m^2 I.V. over 10 minutes on day 1 of each 21-day cycle.

Adjust-a-dose: For patients who develop toxic reactions, see table on next page.

I.V. administration

• Reconstitute 500-mg vial with 20 ml of preservative-free normal saline solution to yield 25 mg/ml.
• Swirl the vial gently until powder is completely dissolved. The solution will be clear and colorless to yellow or yellow-green.
• Calculate the appropriate dose, and further dilute with 100 ml normal saline solution.
• Give I.V. over 10 minutes.
• Reconstituted solution and dilution are stable for 24 hours refrigerated or at room temperature under ambient lighting.

⊗ **Incompatibilities**
Calcium-containing diluents including Ringer's or lactated Ringer's for injection; other drugs or diluents.

Contraindications and cautions

• Contraindicated in patients with a history of severe hypersensitivity reaction to drug or its components. Don't use in patients with creatinine clearance less than 45 ml/minute.

Lifespan: In pregnant women, use only when benefits outweigh risks to the fetus. Breast-feeding women should stop breast-feeding or stop drug. In children, drug hasn't been adequately studied.

Adverse reactions

CNS: *depression, fatigue, fever, neuropathy.*
CV: cardiac ischemia, *chest pain, edema, emboli,* thrombosis.
EENT: *pharyngitis*
GI: *anorexia, constipation, diarrhea, esophagitis, nausea,* painful difficult swallowing, *stomatitis, vomiting.*
GU: ***renal failure.***
Hematologic: ANEMIA, LEUKOPENIA, NEUTROPENIA, THROMBOCYTOPENIA.
Metabolic: dehydration.
Musculoskeletal: arthralgia, *myalgia.*
Respiratory: *dyspnea.*
Skin: *alopecia, rash.*
Other: allergic reaction, *infection.*

Interactions

Drug-drug. *Ibuprofen:* May decrease pemetrexed clearance in patients with mild to moderate renal insufficiency (creatinine clearance 45-79 ml/minute). Use together cautiously.
Nephrotoxic drugs, probenecid: May delay pemetrexed clearance. Monitor patient.
NSAIDs: May decrease pemetrexed clearance in patients with mild to moderate renal insufficiency. For NSAIDs with short half-lives, avoid use for 2 days before, during, and 2 days after pemetrexed therapy. For NSAIDs with long half-lives, avoid use for 5 days before, during, and 2 days after pemetrexed therapy.

Effects on lab test results

• May increase ALT, AST, and creatinine levels. May decrease hemoglobin level and hematocrit.
• May decrease absolute neutrophil, platelet, and WBC counts.

Pharmacokinetics

Absorption: Given I.V.
Distribution: 81% bound by plasma proteins.
Metabolism: None significant.

Toxic reaction	Dosage adjustment
Grade 3 (severe or undesirable) or 4 (life-threatening or disabling) diarrhea Diarrhea that calls for hospitalization Grade 3 toxicity (except mucositis and increased transaminase levels) Grade 4 toxicity (except mucositis) Platelet count ≥ 50,000/mm³ and absolute neutrophil count < 500/mm³	Give 75% of previous pemetrexed and cisplatin doses.
Platelet count < 50,000/mm³	Give 50% of previous pemetrexed and cisplatin doses.
Grade 3 or 4 mucositis	Give 50% of previous pemetrexed dose and 100% of previous cisplatin dose.
Grade 2 neurotoxicity	Give 100% of previous pemetrexed dose and 50% of previous cisplatin dose.
Grade 3 or 4 neurotoxicity Any grade 3 or 4 toxicity (except increased transaminase levels) after two dose reductions	Stop therapy.

Excretion: 70% to 90% is unchanged in urine. *Half life:* 3½ hours.

Route	Onset	Peak	Duration
I.V.	Unknown	Unknown	Unknown

Action

Chemical effect: Disturbs cell replication by inhibiting several folate-dependent enzymes involved in nucleotide synthesis. When given with other antineoplastics, drug inhibits growth of certain mesothelioma cell lines.

Therapeutic effect: Inhibits replication of certain cancer cells.

Available forms

Injection: 500 mg in single-use vials

NURSING PROCESS

Assessment

- Assess patient's condition before therapy and regularly thereafter to monitor drug's effectiveness.
- Monitor renal function, CBC, platelet count, hemoglobin level, hematocrit, and liver function test values.
- Assess patient for neurotoxicity, mucositis, and diarrhea. Severe symptoms may warrant dose reduction.
- If the patient has an adverse GI reaction, monitor his hydration.
- Assess patient's and family's knowledge of drug therapy.

Nursing diagnoses

- Ineffective protection related to drug-induced adverse hematologic reactions
- Risk for deficient fluid volume related to drug-induced adverse GI reactions
- Deficient knowledge related to drug therapy

Planning and implementation

- For a patient with pleural effusion and ascites, drain effusion before therapy.
- Don't start a new cycle of therapy unless absolute neutrophil count is 1,500/mm³ or more, platelet count is 100,000/mm³ or more, and creatinine clearance is 45 ml/minute or more.

ALERT: To reduce the occurrence and severity of cutaneous reactions, give a corticosteroid, such as dexamethasone 4 mg P.O. b.i.d., the day before, the day of, and the day after giving drug.

ALERT: To reduce toxicity, give 350 to 1,000 mcg of folic acid starting 5 days before the first drug dose and ending 21 days after therapy.

ALERT: Give 1,000 mcg vitamin B_{12} I.M. once during the week before the first dose and q three cycles thereafter. After the first cycle, vitamin injections may be given on the first day of the cycle.

Patient teaching

- Inform patient that he may receive corticosteroids and vitamins before pemetrexed to help minimize its adverse effects.
- Tell patient to avoid NSAIDs for several days before, during, and after therapy.

• Urge patient to report adverse reactions, especially fever, sore throat, infection, diarrhea, fatigue, limb pain, unusual bleeding or bruising, black tarry stools, blood in urine or stools, and pinpoint red spots on skin.

Evaluation

• Patient doesn't develop serious complications from adverse hematologic reactions.
• Patient maintains adequate hydration.
• Patient and family state understanding of drug therapy.

penicillamine

(pen-ih-SIL-uh-meen)
Cuprimine, Depen

Pharmacologic class: chelate
Therapeutic class: antirheumatic, heavy metal antagonist
Pregnancy risk category: D

Indications and dosages

▶ **Wilson disease.** *Adults and children:* 0.75 to 1.5 g P.O. in divided doses 60 minutes before meals. Initially, adjust dosage to achieve urinary copper excretion of greater than 2 mg daily. After 3 months, base dose on maintaining a serum free copper level of less than 10 mcg/dL.
▶ **Cystinuria.** *Adults:* 250 mg to 1 g P.O. q.i.d. 60 minutes before meals. Adjust dosage to achieve urinary cystine excretion of less than 100 mg daily when renal calculi are present or 100 to 200 mg daily when no calculi are present. Maximum, 4 g daily.
Children: 30 mg/kg P.O. daily divided q.i.d. 60 minutes before meals. Adjust dosage to achieve urinary cystine excretion of less than 100 mg daily when renal calculi are present or 100 to 200 mg daily when no calculi are present.
▶ **Severe, active rheumatoid arthritis unresponsive to conventional therapy.** *Adults:* Initially, 125 to 250 mg P.O. daily, with increases of 125 to 250 mg q 1 to 3 months, if needed. Maximum, 1.5 g daily.
▶ **Adjunct in heavy metal poisoning‡.** *Adults:* 500 to 1,500 mg P.O. daily for 1 to 2 months.
▶ **Primary biliary cirrhosis‡.** *Adults:* Initially, 250 mg P.O. daily with increases of 250 mg P.O. q 2 weeks. Maximum, 1 g daily in divided doses.
Adjust-a-dose: Reduce dose to 250 mg daily if elective surgery is necessary during penicillamine therapy.

Contraindications and cautions

• Contraindicated in patients with previous penicillamine-related aplastic anemia or agranulocytosis; patients with rheumatoid arthritis and history or other evidence of renal insufficiency.
• Use cautiously, in patients hypersensitive to penicillin.
Lifespan: In pregnant women, except those with Wilson disease or certain patients with cystinuria, drug is contraindicated. Breast-feeding women should stop breast-feeding or use another drug. In children with rheumatoid arthritis, safety and effectiveness haven't been established. In elderly patients, use cautiously due to possible increase in adverse reactions.

Adverse reactions

CNS: agitation, anxiety, mental disorders, optic neuritis, peripheral sensory and motor neuropathies, tinnitus, visual and psychic disturbances.
GI: *anorexia, epigastric pain, diarrhea, loss of taste or altered taste perception, nausea,* oral ulcerations, ***pancreatitis,*** reactivated peptic ulcer, stomatitis, *vomiting.*
GU: ***glomerulonephritis,*** hematuria, ***nephrotic syndrome,*** proteinuria, ***renal failure, renal vasculitis.***
Hematologic: ***agranulocytopenia, aplastic anemia,*** *eosinophilia,* ***leukopenia,*** *lymphadenopathy, monocytosis,* sideroblastic anemia, ***thrombocytopenia,***
Hepatic: ***hepatic failure, hepatotoxicity.***
Metabolic: ***hypoglycemia,*** thyroiditis.
Musculoskeletal: migratory polyarthralgia, synovitis.
Respiratory: ***bronchial asthma,*** *interstitial pneumonitis, obliterative bronchiolitis, pulmonary fibrosis* in patients with severe rheumatoid arthritis.
Skin: alopecia, early and late rashes, ecchymoses, erythema, exfoliative dermatitis, friability (especially at pressure spots), pemphigus, urticaria, wrinkling.
Other: lupus-like syndrome, myasthenia gravis syndrome with long-term use, drug fever, *aller-*

gic reactions, ***Goodpasture syndrome,*** vasculitis.

Interactions

Drug-drug. *Antacids, oral iron:* May decrease effectiveness of penicillamine. Give at least 2 hours apart.
Antimalaria drugs, cytotoxic drugs, gold therapy, oxyphenbutazone, phenylbutazone: May increase risk of toxicity. Avoid giving together.
Digoxin: May decrease digoxin effect. Adjust dose if needed.
Drug-food. *Any food:* May delay absorption of drug. Give drug 1 hour before or 2 hours after meals.

Effects on lab test results

- May increase liver enzyme and urinary protein levels. May decrease glucose and hemoglobin levels and hematocrit.
- May increase eosinophil count, antinuclear antibody titer, and sedimentation rate. May decrease platelet, WBC, and granulocyte counts.

Pharmacokinetics

Absorption: Readily absorbed from the GI tract.
Distribution: Highly protein-bound.
Metabolism: In liver to inactive disulfides.
Excretion: Slow, mainly renal. *Half-life:* 1½ to 3 hours.

Route	Onset	Peak	Duration
P.O.	Unknown	1–3 hr	4–6 days

Action

Chemical effect: Chelates heavy metals, binds cystine into more soluble form, dissociates macroglobulins like rheumatoid factor without causing overall immunoglobulin suppression, depresses T-cell activity, and interferes with cross-links between tropocollagen molecules.
Therapeutic effect: Binds copper for renal excretion in Wilson disease, enhances excretion of cystine, and relieves symptoms of rheumatoid arthritis.

Available forms

Capsules: 125 mg, 250 mg
Tablets (scored): 250 mg

NURSING PROCESS

Assessment

- Obtain history of patient's underlying condition before starting therapy.
- Obtain baseline 24-hour urinary copper excretion before giving the drug for Wilson disease. Goal is more than 2 mg copper excreted daily.
- Monitor CBC with differential and urinalysis two times a week for one month, then q 2 weeks for 5 months, then monthly throughout therapy; observing for hematologic and GU adverse effects. Assess patient's skin, lymph nodes, and body temperature on same schedule.
- Monitor liver function tests q 3 months for first year of therapy for Wilson disease, and q 6 months thereafter. For patient taking drug for other diagnoses, monitor liver function tests q 6 months.
- If patient has rheumatoid arthritis, check 24-hour urinary protein q 1 to 2 weeks.
- In patient with rheumatoid arthritis, check joint mobility and range of motion, pain, and swelling to evaluate the drug's effectiveness.
- Monitor yearly X-ray for renal calculi in patients with cystinuria.
- Be alert for adverse reactions and drug interactions.
- Assess patient's and family's knowledge of drug therapy.

Nursing diagnoses

- Impaired physical mobility related to Wilson disease
- Impaired urinary elimination related to drug-induced renal dysfunction
- Deficient knowledge related to drug therapy

Planning and implementation

- Give dose on an empty stomach to facilitate absorption, preferably 1 hour before or 2 hours after meals. Don't give drug within 1 hour of any other drug, milk, antacid, or preparation that contains zinc or iron due to risk of metal binding in GI tract.
- Penicillamine therapy should be continued on daily basis. Sensitivity reactions may occur when therapy is reinstituted following interruptions.
- Give 25 mg supplemental pyridoxine daily to patients with Wilson disease or cystinuria.

P

• If annoying GI symptoms or rash don't resolve within 6 weeks of starting therapy, reduce dosage to minimum of 250 mg daily and then increase more slowly.
• If patient has mild skin reaction, give antihistamines. Handle patient carefully to avoid skin damage.
ALERT: Immediately report rash and fever (important signs of toxicity to prescriber). If pemphigus, unexplained gross hematuria or persistent microscopic hematuria is noted, stop the drug.
• If WBC count falls below 3,500/mm^3 or platelet count falls below 100,000/mm^3, don't give the drug and notify prescriber. A progressive decline in platelet or WBC count in three successive blood tests may require a temporary stop, even if the counts are within normal limits.
• If 24-hour urinary protein is greater than 1 g or is progressively increasing, reduce or stop drug.
ALERT: Don't confuse penicillamine with penicillin.

Patient teaching

• Tell patient with rheumatoid arthritis or Wilson disease that drug may not take effect for up to 3 months.
• Tell patient with cystinuria to drink 1 L (1 qt) of water throughout the night.
• Teach patient with Wilson disease to follow low-copper diet: no chocolate, nuts, shellfish, mushrooms, liver, molasses, broccoli, and cereals or products containing added copper such as multivitamins.
• Advise patient to report early signs of granulocytopenia or thrombocytopenia: fever, sore throat, chills, bruising, and bleeding.
• Reassure patient that taste impairment usually resolves in 6 weeks without change in dosage.

Evaluation

• Patient reports increase in physical mobility.
• Patient maintains normal urinary elimination pattern.
• Patient and family state understanding of drug therapy.

penicillin G benzathine (benzylpenicillin benzathine)

(pen-ih-SIL-in gee BENZ-uh-theen)
Bicillin L-A, Permapen

Pharmacologic class: natural penicillin
Therapeutic class: long-acting antibiotic
Pregnancy risk category: B

Indications and dosages

▶ **Congenital syphilis.** *Children younger than age 2:* Give 50,000 units/kg I.M. as single dose.
▶ **Group A streptococcal upper respiratory tract infections.** *Adults:* 1.2 million units I.M. as single injection.
Children who weigh 27 kg (60 lb) or more: 900,000 units I.M. as single injection.
Children who weigh less than 27 kg (60 lb): 300,000 to 600,000 units I.M. as single injection.
▶ **To prevent poststreptococcal rheumatic fever and glomerulonephritis.** *Adults and children:* 1.2 million units I.M. once monthly or 600,000 units twice monthly.
▶ **Syphilis of less than 1 year's duration.** *Adults:* 2.4 million units I.M. as single dose.
Children: 50,000 units/kg I.M. up to adult dosage as a single dose.
▶ **Syphilis of more than 1 year's duration.** *Adults:* 2.4 million units I.M. weekly for 3 successive weeks.
Children: 50,000 units/kg I.M. up to adult dosage weekly for 3 successive weeks.
▶ **Yaws, bejel, and pinta.** *Adults:* 1.2 million units I.M. as a single dose.
▶ **To prevent diphtheria‡.** *Adults and children older than age 6 or weighing 30 kg (66 lb) or more:* 1.2 million units I.M. as a single injection.
Children younger than age 6 or weighing less than 30 kg (66 lb): 600,000 units I.M. as a single dose.
Adjust-a-dose: Decrease dose in patients with severe renal or hepatic disease.

Contraindications and cautions

• Contraindicated in patients hypersensitive to drug or other penicillins.
• Use cautiously in patients with other drug allergies, especially to cephalosporins.

Lifespan: In pregnant women, use cautiously. In breast-feeding women, don't use; drug appears in breast milk and may sensitize infant to drug, causing an adverse reaction.

Adverse reactions

CNS: neuropathy, pain, ***seizures.***
Hematologic: eosinophilia, hemolytic anemia, ***leukopenia, thrombocytopenia.***
Other: hypersensitivity reactions (***anaphylaxis,*** chills, edema, fever, maculopapular and exfoliative dermatitis), sterile abscess at injection site.

Interactions

Drug-drug. *Aspirin, ethacrynic acid, furosemide, indomethacin, phenylbutazone, sulfonamides, thiazide diuretics:* May compete with penicillin G for renal tubular secretion and prolong penicillin half-life.
Heparin, oral anticoagulants: May increase risk of bleeding. Monitor PT, PTT, and INR. Monitor patient for bleeding.
Hormonal contraceptives: May decrease effectiveness of hormonal contraceptives and increase breakthrough bleeding. Advise patient to use another method during therapy.
Probenecid: May increase level of penicillin. Probenecid may be used for this purpose.

Effects on lab test results

- May decrease hemoglobin level and hematocrit.
- May increase eosinophil count. May decrease platelet, WBC, and granulocyte counts.
- May cause false-positive urine glucose test results.

Pharmacokinetics

Absorption: Slow.
Distribution: Wide. CSF penetration is poor but enhanced in patients with inflamed meninges. 45% to 68% protein-bound.
Metabolism: At injection site. 16% to 30% to inactive compounds.
Excretion: Mainly in urine. *Half-life:* 30 to 60 minutes.

Route	Onset	Peak	Duration
I.M.	Unknown	13–24 hr	1–4 wk

Action

Chemical effect: Inhibits cell wall synthesis during microorganism multiplication.
Therapeutic effect: Kills susceptible bacteria.

Available forms

Injection: 300,000 units/ml, 600,000 units/ml

NURSING PROCESS

Assessment

- Assess patient's infection before starting therapy and regularly thereafter to monitor drug's effectiveness.
- Before giving drug, ask the patient about allergic reactions to penicillin, cephalosporins, and cephamycins. Absence of past reactions is no guarantee against future allergic reactions.
- Obtain specimen for culture and sensitivity tests before giving first dose. If a sexually transmitted disease (STD) is suspected, obtain baseline venereal disease research laboratory, or VDRL, and rapid plasma reagin, or RPR, tests. Start therapy pending test results.
- Be alert for adverse reactions and drug interactions.
- Observe patient closely. Large doses and prolonged therapy raise the risk of bacterial or fungal superinfection, especially in an elderly, debilitated, or immunosuppressed patient.
- Assess patient's and family's knowledge of drug therapy.

Nursing diagnoses

- Risk for infection related to presence of bacteria
- Ineffective protection related to risk of hypersensitivity reactions to drug
- Deficient knowledge related to drug therapy

Planning and implementation

- Shake drug well before injection.
- Inject at a slow, steady rate to prevent needle from becoming blocked by suspended material in product.

ALERT: Never give drug I.V.; doing so has caused cardiac arrest and death.

- Inject deep into upper outer quadrant of buttocks in adult; in midlateral thigh in infant and young child. Avoid injection into or near major nerves or blood vessels to prevent severe neurovascular damage.
- If a high dose of penicillin is required for several days, change to an I.V. formulation (penicillin G potassium or penicillin G sodium) to avoid muscle fibrosis and atrophy from repeated

I.M. injections (particularly in neonates and infants).
- Drug's extremely slow absorption makes allergic reactions difficult to treat. If patient develops signs of anaphylactic shock, such as rapidly developing dyspnea and hypotension, immediately stop giving the drug. Notify prescriber and immediately administer epinephrine, corticosteroids, antihistamines, or other resuscitative measures.

ALERT: Be aware of the various preparations of penicillin. They aren't interchangeable.
- Periodically monitor renal and hematopoietic function in patient receiving long-term therapy.

ALERT: Don't confuse penicillin with penicillamine. Don't confuse penicillin G potassium with penicillin G sodium, penicillin G procaine, or penicillin G benzathine.

ALERT: Bicillin L-A is the only penicillin G benzathine product indicated for the treatment of sexually transmitted infections, including syphilis. Don't substitute Bicillin C-R in its place as this may cause ineffective treatment.

Patient teaching
- Tell patient to call prescriber if rash, fever, or chills develop.
- Tell patient taking drug for active STD to take safe sex precautions, to reduce risks to fetus and neonate of syphilis during pregnancy, and to complete full drug course and follow-up testing.
- Instruct patient treated for active STD to bring partners in for therapy as well.
- Warn patient that injection may be painful but that ice applied to site may ease discomfort.

Evaluation
- Patient is free from infection.
- Patient shows no signs of allergy.
- Patient and family state understanding of drug therapy.

penicillin G potassium (benzylpenicillin potassium)

(pen-ih-SIL-in gee poh-TAH-see-um)

Pfizerpen

Pharmacologic class: natural penicillin
Therapeutic class: rapid-acting antibiotic
Pregnancy risk category: B

Indications and dosages

▶ **Moderate to severe systemic infection.** *Adults and children age 12 and older:* Individualize dosage. 1 to 24 million units I.M. or I.V. daily in divided doses q 4 to 6 hours.
Children younger than age 12: Highly individualized; 25,000 to 400,000 units/kg I.M. or I.V. daily in divided doses q 4 to 6 hours.

▶ **Anthrax.** *Adults:* 5 to 20 million units I.V. daily in divided doses q 4 to 6 hours for at least 14 days after symptoms subside. Or, 80,000 units/kg in the first hour followed by a maintenance dose of 320,000 units/kg/day. Average adult dosage, 4 million units q 4 hours or 2 million units q 2 hours.
Children: 100,000 to 150,000 units/kg/day I.V. in divided doses q 4 to 6 hours for at least 14 days after symptoms subside.

▶ **Necrotizing ulcerative gingivitis.** *Adults:* 5 to 10 million units I.M. or I.V. daily.

▶ **To eliminate the diphtheria carrier-state:** *Adults:* 2 to 3 million units per day I.M. in divided doses q 4 to 6 hours for 10 to 12 days.

Adjust-a-dose: For patients with renal impairment, if creatinine clearance is less than 10 ml/min, give full loading dose and then one-half of usual dose q 8 to 10 hours or usual dose q 12 to 18 hours; if creatinine clearance is more than 10 ml/minute, give full loading dose and then give one-half dose q 4 to 6 hours for additional doses.

I.V. administration
- Use continuous I.V. infusion when large doses are required (10 million units or more). Otherwise, give by intermittent I.V. infusion over 1 to 2 hours.

Incompatibilities

Alcohol 5%, amikacin, aminoglycosides, aminophylline, amphotericin B sodium, chlorpromazine, dextran, dopamine, heparin sodium, hydroxyzine hydrochloride, lincomycin, metoclopramide, pentobarbital sodium, phenytoin sodium, prochlorperazine mesylate, promethazine hydrochloride, sodium bicarbonate, thiopental, vancomycin, vitamin B complex with C.

Contraindications and cautions
- Contraindicated in patients hypersensitive to the drug or other penicillins.

• Use cautiously in patients with other drug allergies, especially to cephalosporins and cephamycins.

Lifespan: In pregnant women, use cautiously. In breast-feeding women, don't use; drug appears in breast milk and may sensitize infant to penicillin and cause an adverse reaction.

Adverse reactions

CNS: ***coma***, neuropathy, ***seizures.***
CV: thrombophlebitis.
Hematologic: hemolytic anemia, ***leukopenia, thrombocytopenia.***
Metabolic: ***severe potassium poisoning.***
Other: hypersensitivity reactions (***anaphylaxis,*** chills, edema, exfoliative dermatitis, fever, maculopapular eruptions, rash, urticaria), overgrowth of nonsusceptible organisms, pain at injection site.

Interactions

Drug-drug. *Aminoglycoside antibiotics:* May be synergistic with some penicillins but can deactivate some beta-lactam penicillins if mixed in same syringe or I.V. solution and administration set. May reduce oral aminoglycoside level when given with parenteral penicillins to renally impaired patients.
Aspirin, ethacrynic acid, furosemide, indomethacin, phenylbutazone, sulfonamides, thiazide diuretics: May compete with penicillin G for renal tubular secretion and prolong penicillin half-life.
Heparin, oral anticoagulants: May increase risk of bleeding. Monitor PT, PTT, and INR. Monitor patient for bleeding.
Hormonal contraceptives: May decrease effectiveness of hormonal contraceptives and increase breakthrough bleeding. Advise patient to use another contraceptive during therapy.
Potassium-sparing diuretics: May increase risk of hyperkalemia. Don't use together.
Probenecid: May increase level of penicillin. Probenecid may be used for this purpose.

Effects on lab test results

• May increase potassium level. May decrease hemoglobin level and hematocrit.
• May increase eosinophil count. May decrease platelet, WBC, and granulocyte counts.

Pharmacokinetics

Absorption: Rapid from I.M. injection site.
Distribution: Wide. CSF penetration is poor but is enhanced in patients with inflamed meninges. 45% to 68% protein-bound.
Metabolism: At injection site.
Excretion: Mainly in urine. *Half-life:* 30 to 60 minutes.

Route	Onset	Peak	Duration
I.V.	Immediate	Immediate	4 hr
I.M.	Unknown	15–30 min	4 hr

Action

Chemical effect: Inhibits cell wall synthesis during microorganism multiplication.
Therapeutic effect: Kills susceptible bacteria.

Available forms

Injection (powder): 5 million units, 20 million units
Injection (premixed in dextrose): 1 million units, 2 million units, 3 million units

NURSING PROCESS

Assessment

• Assess patient's infection before starting therapy and regularly thereafter to monitor drug's effectiveness.
• Before giving, ask the patient about any allergic reactions to penicillin, cephalosporins, and cephamycins. Negative history of penicillin allergy is no guarantee against future allergic reactions.
• Obtain specimen for culture and sensitivity tests before first dose. Start therapy pending test results.
• Assess renal, cardiac, and vascular conditions with physical exams and laboratory testing before start of therapy. Drug contains 1.7 mEq potassium and 0.3 mEq sodium per 1 million units. If risk of fluid overload or electrolyte imbalance, decrease dosage and monitor electrolytes and renal tests frequently during therapy.
• Be alert for adverse reactions and drug interactions.
• Observe patient closely. Large doses and prolonged therapy raise the risk of neutropenia and bacterial or fungal superinfection especially in an elderly, debilitated, or immunosuppressed patient.
• Assess patient's and family's knowledge of drug therapy.

P

Nursing diagnoses
- Risk for infection related to presence of bacteria
- Ineffective protection related to risk of hypersensitivity reactions to drug
- Deficient knowledge related to drug therapy

Planning and implementation
- Reconstitute vials with sterile water for injection, D_5W, or normal saline solution for injection. Volume of diluent varies by manufacturer.
- Inject deep into upper outer quadrant of buttocks in adult and in midlateral thigh in infant and young child. Avoid injection into or near major nerves or blood vessels to prevent severe neurovascular damage.

ALERT: The various preparations of penicillin aren't interchangeable.
- Monitor level in patients taking large doses. A high level may lead to seizures. Take precautions and periodically monitor renal and hematopoietic function in patient receiving long-term therapy.
- Give drug I.M. deep into large muscle; warn patient that injection may be painful.

ALERT: Don't confuse penicillamine with penicillin. Don't confuse penicillin G potassium with penicillin G sodium, penicillin G procaine, or penicillin G benzathine.

Patient teaching
- Tell patient to call prescriber if rash, fever, or chills develop.
- Warn patient that I.M. injection may be painful but that ice applied to site may ease discomfort.

Evaluation
- Patient is free from infection.
- Patient shows no signs of allergy.
- Patient and family state understanding of drug therapy.

penicillin G procaine (benzylpenicillin procaine)
(pen-ih-SIL-in gee PROH-kayn)
Wycillin

Pharmacologic class: natural penicillin
Therapeutic class: long-acting antibiotic
Pregnancy risk category: B

Indications and dosages
▶ **Moderately severe infections of upper respiratory tract including pneumococcal pneumonia; tonsils; pharynx; and skin and soft tissues.** *Adults and children who weigh 27 kg (60 lb) or more:* 600,000 to 1.2 million units I.M. daily in 1 or 2 doses for at least 10 days. *Children who weigh less than 27 kg (60 lb):* 300,000 units I.M. daily in single dose for at least 10 days.

▶ **Anthrax caused by *Bacillus anthracis,* including prophylaxis after exposure to inhalation anthrax.** *Adults:* 1.2 million units I.M. q 12 hours for up to 60 days.
Children: 25,000 units/kg I.M. (maximum, 1.2 million units) q 12 hours for up to 60 days.

▶ **Cutaneous anthrax.** *Adults:* 600,000 to 1 million units I.M. daily for 5 to 60 days depending on source of exposure.

▶ **Necrotizing ulcerative gingivitis.** *Adults:* 600,000 to 1 million units I.M. daily.

▶ **Syphilis with negative CSF test.** *Adults and children older than age 12:* Give 600,000 units I.M. daily for 8 days.

▶ **Syphilis with no CSF test or positive CSF test.** *Adults and children older than age 12:* Give 600,000 units I.M. daily for 10 to 15 days.

▶ **Neurosyphilis.** *Adults and children older than age 12:* Give 2.4 million units I.M. daily with probenecid 500 mg P.O. q.i.d. for 10 to 14 days.

▶ **Congenital syphilis.** *Children less than 32 kg (70 lb):* Give 50,000 units/kg/day I.M. for 10 to 14 days.

Contraindications and cautions
- Contraindicated in patients hypersensitive to drug, other penicillins, or procaine.
- Use cautiously in patients with other drug allergies, especially to cephalosporins, and cephamycins.

Lifespan: In pregnant women, use cautiously. In breast-feeding women, don't use; drug appears in breast milk and drug use may sensitize infant to penicillin and cause adverse effects. Avoid use in newborns due to concern of sterile abscesses and procaine toxicity.

Adverse reactions
CNS: ***seizures.***
Hematologic: hemolytic anemia, ***leukopenia, thrombocytopenia.***
Musculoskeletal: arthralgia.

Other: hypersensitivity reactions (***anaphylaxis,*** chills, edema, fever, prostration, rash, urticaria), overgrowth of nonsusceptible organisms.

Interactions

Drug-drug. *Aspirin, ethacrynic acid, furosemide, indomethacin, phenylbutazone, sulfonamides, thiazide diuretics:* May compete with penicillin G for renal tubular secretion and prolong penicillin half-life.
Heparin, oral anticoagulants: May increase risk of bleeding. Monitor PT, PTT, and INR. Monitor patient for bleeding.
Hormonal contraceptives: May decrease effectiveness of hormonal contraceptives and increase breakthrough bleeding. Advise patient to use alternative method during therapy.
Probenecid: May increase level of penicillin. Probenecid may be used for this purpose.

Effects on lab test results

- May decrease hemoglobin level and hematocrit.
- May increase eosinophil count. May decrease platelet, WBC, and granulocyte counts.

Pharmacokinetics

Absorption: Slow.
Distribution: Distributed widely. CSF penetration poor. 45% to 68% protein-bound.
Metabolism: Occurs at injection site. From 16% to 30% metabolized to inactive compounds.
Excretion: Mainly in urine. *Half-life:* 30 to 60 minutes.

Route	Onset	Peak	Duration
I.M.	Unknown	1–4 hr	1–2 days

Action

Chemical effect: Inhibits cell wall synthesis during microorganism multiplication.
Therapeutic effect: Kills susceptible bacteria.

Available forms

Injection: 600,000 units/ml

NURSING PROCESS

Assessment

- Assess patient's infection before starting therapy and regularly thereafter to monitor drug's effectiveness.
- Before giving, ask patient about allergic reactions to penicillin, cephalosporins, and cephamycins. Negative history of penicillin allergy is no guarantee against future allergic reaction.
- Assess for allergy to drug. Give test dose of 0.1 ml of 1% or 2% intradermally and observe for erythema, wheal, flare, or eruption. If positive for sensitivity, drug is contraindicated.
- Obtain specimen for culture and sensitivity tests before giving first dose. Start therapy pending test results.
- Be alert for adverse reactions and drug interactions. Observe patient closely. Large doses and prolonged therapy raise the risk of neutropenia and bacterial or fungal superinfection, especially in a geriatric, debilitated, or immunosuppressed patient.
- Assess patient's and family's knowledge of drug therapy.

Nursing diagnoses

- Risk for infection related to presence of bacteria
- Ineffective protection related to risk of hypersensitivity reactions to drug
- Deficient knowledge related to drug therapy

Planning and implementation

- Shake drug well before injection.
- Inject at a slow, steady rate to prevent needle from becoming blocked by suspended material in product.
- Inject deep into upper outer quadrant of buttocks in adults; in midlateral thigh in infants and small children. Avoid injection into or near major nerves or blood vessels to prevent severe neurovascular damage.

ALERT: Never give I.V.; doing so has caused cardiac arrest and death.

- If high dose is required for several days, consider change to I.V. penicillin G potassium or penicillin G sodium to avoid muscle fibrosis and atrophy from repeated I.M. injections.
- In patients with renal insufficiency or those taking high doses of I.M. drug, give penicillin G procaine at least 1 hour before bacteriostatic oral antibiotics such as aminoglycosides because it may inactivate such oral drugs.

ALERT: Don't confuse penicillin G procaine, with penicillin G sodium, penicillin G potassium, or penicillin G benzathine.

- The drug's extremely slow absorption makes allergic reactions difficult to treat. If patient de-

P

velops signs of anaphylactic shock, such as rapidly developing dyspnea and hypotension, immediately stop giving the drug. Notify prescriber and immediately administer epinephrine, corticosteroids, antihistamines, or other resuscitative measures.

- For a patient receiving long-term therapy, periodically monitor renal and hematopoietic function.

ALERT: Be aware of the various preparations of penicillin. They aren't interchangeable.

Patient teaching

- Tell patient to call prescriber if rash, fever, or chills develop.
- Warn patient that injection may be painful but that ice applied to site may ease discomfort.
- Teach patient taking drug for active sexually transmitted disease (STD) about safe sex practices, and address the risks of syphilis to fetus and neonate during pregnancy and the need to complete full drug course and follow-up testing.
- Instruct patient treated for active STD to bring partners in for treatment as well.

Evaluation

- Patient is free from infection.
- Patient shows no signs of allergy.
- Patient and family state understanding of drug therapy.

penicillin G sodium (benzylpenicillin sodium)

(pen-ih-SIL-in gee SOH-dee-um)

Crystapen ♦

Pharmacologic class: natural penicillin
Therapeutic class: rapid-acting antibiotic
Pregnancy risk category: B

Indications and dosages

▶ **Moderate to severe systemic infections.** *Adults and children age 12 and older:* Highly individualized; 1 to 24 million units daily I.M. or I.V. in divided doses q 4 to 6 hours.
Children younger than age 12: Highly individualized; 25,000 to 400,000 units/kg daily I.M. or I.V. in divided doses q 4 to 6 hours.

▶ **Bacterial endocarditis.** *Adults and children age 12 and older:* 5 to 30 million units daily I.V. in divided doses q 4 to 6 hours for 2 to 6 weeks depending on bacterial strain and severity of infection.
Children younger than age 12: Give 50,000 to 250,000 units/kg daily I.M. or I.V. in divided doses q 4 weeks.

▶ **Anthrax.** *Adults:* 5 to 20 million units I.V. daily in divided doses q 4 to 6 hours, for at least 14 days after symptoms abate. Or, 80,000 units/kg in the first hour, followed by a maintenance dose of 320,000 units/kg/day. The average adult dosage is 4 million units q 4 hours or 2 million units q 2 hours.
Children: 100,000 to 150,000 units/kg/day I.V. in divided doses q 4 to 6 hours for at least 14 days after symptoms lessen.

▶ **Neurosyphilis.** *Adults:* 18 to 24 million units I.V. daily in divided doses q 4 hours for 10 to 14 days.

▶ **Necrotizing ulcerative gingivitis.** *Adults:* 5 to 10 million units I.M. or I.V. daily.

Adjust-a-dose: For patients with renal impairment, if creatinine clearance is less than 10 ml/min, give full loading dose and then half of usual dose q 8 to 10 hours or usual dose q 12 to 18 hours; if creatinine clearance is more than 10 ml/minute, give full loading dose and then give half dose q 4 to 6 hours.

I.V. administration

- Reconstitute vials with sterile water for injection, normal saline solution for injection, or D_5W. Volume of diluent varies with manufacturer and concentration needed.
- For patient receiving 10 million units of drug or more daily, dilute in 1 to 2 liters of compatible solution and administer over 24 hours. Otherwise, give by intermittent I.V. infusion: Dilute drug in 50 to 100 ml and give over 1 to 2 hours every 4 to 6 hours.
- In a neonate or child, give divided doses, usually over 15 to 30 minutes.

⊗ Incompatibilities

Aminoglycosides, amphotericin B, bleomycin, chlorpromazine, cytarabine, fat emulsions 10%, heparin sodium, hydroxyzine hydrochloride, invert sugar 10%, lincomycin, methylprednisolone sodium succinate, potassium chloride, prochlorperazine mesylate, promethazine hydrochloride.

Contraindications and cautions

- Contraindicated in patients hypersensitive to the drug or other penicillins.

• Use cautiously in patients with other drug allergies, especially to cephalosporins, and cephamycins.
Lifespan: In pregnant women, use cautiously. In breast-feeding women, don't use; drug appears in breast milk and may sensitize infant to penicillin and cause adverse effects.

Adverse reactions

CNS: neuropathy, ***seizures.***
CV: thrombophlebitis.
Hematologic: hemolytic anemia, ***leukopenia, thrombocytopenia.***
Musculoskeletal: arthralgia.
Other: hypersensitivity reactions (***anaphylaxis,*** exfoliative dermatitis, urticaria), overgrowth of nonsusceptible organisms, pain at injection site, vein irritation,

Interactions

Drug-drug. *Aminoglycoside antibiotics:* May deactivate some beta-lactam penicillins if mixed in same syringe or I.V. solution and administration set. Oral aminoglycoside level may be reduced when given with parenteral penicillins to a renally compromised patient.
Aspirin, ethacrynic acid, furosemide, indomethacin, phenylbutazone, sulfonamides, thiazide diuretics: May compete with penicillin G for renal tubular secretion and prolong penicillin half-life. Monitor patient.
Heparin, oral anticoagulants: May increase risk of bleeding. Monitor PT, PTT, and INR. Monitor patient for bleeding.
Hormonal contraceptives: May decrease effectiveness of hormonal contraceptives and increase breakthrough bleeding. Advise patient to use alternative contraception during therapy.
Probenecid: May increase level of penicillin. Probenecid may be used for this purpose.

Effects on lab test results

• May decrease hemoglobin level and hematocrit.
• May increase eosinophil count. May decrease platelet, WBC, and granulocyte counts.

Pharmacokinetics

Absorption: Rapid.
Distribution: Wide. CSF penetration is poor but is enhanced in patients with inflamed meninges. 45% to 68% protein-bound.
Metabolism: At injection site. 16% to 30% to inactive compounds.
Excretion: Mainly in urine. *Half-life:* 30 to 60 minutes.

Route	Onset	Peak	Duration
I.V.	Immediate	Immediate	4 hr
I.M.	Unknown	15–30 min	4 hr

Action

Chemical effect: Inhibits cell wall synthesis during microorganism multiplication.
Therapeutic effect: Kills susceptible bacteria.

Available forms

Injection: 5-million-unit vial

NURSING PROCESS

Assessment

• Assess patient's infection before starting therapy and regularly thereafter to monitor drug's effectiveness.
• Before giving, ask patient about allergic reactions to penicillin, cephalosporins, and cephamycins. Negative history of penicillin allergy is no guarantee against future allergic reaction.
• Obtain specimen for culture and sensitivity tests before first dose. Start therapy pending test results.
• Assess renal, cardiac, and vascular conditions with physical exams and laboratory testing before the start of therapy. Drug contains 2 mEq sodium per 1 million units. Assess risk of fluid overload or electrolyte imbalance; decrease dose and monitor electrolytes and renal tests frequently during therapy.
• Be alert for adverse reactions and drug interactions.
• Observe patient closely. Large doses and prolonged therapy raise the risk of neutropenia and bacterial or fungal superinfection, especially in geriatric, debilitated, or immunosuppressed patients.
• Assess patient's and family's knowledge of drug therapy.

Nursing diagnoses

• Risk for infection related to presence of bacteria
• Ineffective protection related to risk of hypersensitivity reactions to drug
• Deficient knowledge related to drug therapy

P

Planning and implementation

- Give drug I.M. deep in upper outer quadrant of buttocks in adult; in midlateral thigh in young child. Don't massage injection site. Avoid injection near major nerves or blood vessels to prevent severe neurovascular damage.
- Give penicillin G sodium at least 1 hour before bacteriostatic antibiotics, and if given I.M., at different sites.
- Periodically monitor renal and hematopoietic function in patient receiving long-term therapy.

ALERT: Be aware of the various preparations of penicillin. They aren't interchangeable.

- Monitor level in patient taking large doses. A high level may lead to seizures. Take precautions.

ALERT: Don't confuse penicillamine with penicillin. Don't confuse penicillin G sodium with penicillin G potassium, penicillin G procaine, or penicillin G benzathine.

Patient teaching

- Tell patient to report discomfort at I.V. site
- Warn patient that I.M. injection may be painful but that ice applied to site may ease discomfort.

Evaluation

- Patient is free from infection.
- Patient shows no signs of allergy.
- Patient and family state understanding of drug therapy.

penicillin V (phenoxymethyl penicillin)

(pen-ih-SIL-in VEE)

penicillin V potassium (phenoxymethyl penicillin potassium)

Abbocillin VK ◇, Apo-Pen-VK ♦, Cilicaine VK ◇, Nadopen-V ♦, Nadopen-V-2006 ♦, Nadopen-V-400 ♦, Novo-Pen-VK ♦, Nu-Pen-VK, Penicillin VK, PVF K ♦, PVK ◇, Veetids

Pharmacologic class: natural penicillin
Therapeutic class: antibiotic
Pregnancy risk category: B

Indications and dosages

▶ **Mild to moderately severe infections of upper respiratory tract (including pneumococcal pneumonia), oropharynx, sinuses, and skin and soft tissues; necrotizing ulcerative gingivitis.** *Adults and children older than age 12:* Give 125 to 500 mg (200,000 to 800,000 units) P.O. q 6 to 8 hours.
Children age 1 month to 12 years: Give 15 to 62.5 mg/kg (25,000 to 100,000 units/kg) P.O. daily, in divided doses q 4 to 8 hours.

▶ **Prophylaxis for rheumatic fever.** *Adults and children older than age 12:* Give 125 to 250 mg P.O. b.i.d.

▶ **Prophylaxis for pneumococcal infections in children with sickle cell anemia or splenectomy‡.** *Children age 5 and older:* 250 mg P.O. b.i.d.
Children 3 months to younger than age 5: Give 125 mg P.O. b.i.d.

▶ **Lyme disease‡.** *Adults:* 500 mg P.O. q.i.d. for 10 to 20 days.

▶ **Actinomycosis‡.** *Adults:* Penicillin G 10 to 20 mg/day I.V. for 4 to 6 weeks; then penicillin V 2 to 4 g/day for 6 to 12 months.

▶ **Confirmed or suspected exposure to *Bacillus anthracis*‡.** *Adults:* 7.5 mg/kg P.O. q.i.d. Continue prophylaxis until exposure to *B. anthracis* has been ruled out. If exposure is confirmed and vaccine is available, continue prophylaxis for 4 weeks and until three doses of vaccine have been given or for 30 to 60 days if vaccine isn't available.
Children younger than age 9: Give 50 mg/kg P.O. daily in four divided doses. Continue prophylaxis until exposure to *B. anthracis* has been ruled out. If exposure is confirmed and vaccine is available, continue prophylaxis for 4 weeks and until three doses of vaccine have been given or for 30 to 60 days if vaccine isn't available.

Contraindications and cautions

- Contraindicated in patients hypersensitive to the drug or other penicillins.
- Use cautiously in patients with other drug allergies, especially to cephalosporins and cephamycins and in patients with hyperacidity of the GI tract since decreased pH can inactivate drug.

Lifespan: In pregnant women, use cautiously. In breast-feeding women, don't use; drug appears in breast milk and use of drug may sensitize infant to penicillin and cause adverse effects.

Adverse reactions

CNS: neuropathy, ***seizures.***
GI: diarrhea, *epigastric distress, nausea,* vomiting.
Hematologic: eosinophilia, hemolytic anemia, ***leukopenia, thrombocytopenia.***
Other: hypersensitivity reactions (***anaphylaxis,*** chills, edema, fever, rash, urticaria), overgrowth of nonsusceptible organisms.

Interactions

Drug-drug. *Beta blockers:* May increase risk of anaphylactic reactions to oral penicillins.
Hormonal contraceptives containing estrogen: May decrease effectiveness of hormonal contraceptive. Monitor patient for breakthrough bleeding. Advise patient to use alternative forms of birth control.
Methotrexate: May increase methotrexate level, increasing risk of toxicity. Monitor patient.
Oral neomycin: May reduce oral penicillin level. Monitor patient.
Probenecid: May increase level of penicillin. Probenecid may be used for this purpose.

Effects on lab test results

- May decrease hemoglobin level and hematocrit.
- May increase eosinophil count. May decrease platelet, WBC, and granulocyte counts.

Pharmacokinetics

Absorption: About 60% to 75%.
Distribution: Wide. CSF penetration is poor. 75% to 89% protein-bound.
Metabolism: Mainly in small intestine.
Excretion: Mainly in urine. *Half-life:* 30 minutes.

Route	Onset	Peak	Duration
P.O.	Unknown	30–60 min	6–8 hr

Action

Chemical effect: Inhibits cell wall synthesis during microorganism multiplication.
Therapeutic effect: Kills susceptible bacteria.

Available forms

penicillin V
Oral suspension: 125 mg/5 ml, 250 mg/5 ml (after reconstitution)
Tablets: 250 mg, 500 mg

penicillin V potassium
Capsules: 250 mg ◇
Oral suspension: 125 mg/5 ml, 250 mg/5 ml (after reconstitution)
Tablets: 125 mg, 250 mg, 500 mg
Tablets (film-coated): 250 mg, 500 mg

NURSING PROCESS

Assessment

- Assess patient's infection before starting therapy and regularly thereafter to monitor drug's effectiveness.
- Before giving drug, ask patient about any allergic reactions to penicillin, cephalosporins, and cephamycins. Negative history of penicillin allergy is no guarantee against future allergic reaction.
- Obtain specimen for culture and sensitivity tests before giving first dose. Start therapy pending test results.
- Periodically assess renal and hematopoietic function in patient receiving long-term therapy.
- Be alert for adverse reactions and drug interactions.
- If patient develops diarrhea during therapy, consider possibility of pseudomembranous colitis.
- Observe patient closely. Large doses and prolonged therapy raise the risk of bacterial or fungal superinfection, especially in geriatric, debilitated, or immunosuppressed patients.
- Assess patient's and family's knowledge of drug therapy.

Nursing diagnoses

- Risk of infection related to presence of bacteria
- Ineffective protection related to risk of hypersensitivity reactions to drug
- Deficient knowledge related to drug therapy

Planning and implementation

- Give drug at least 1 hour before bacteriostatic antibiotics.

ALERT: Don't confuse penicillamine with penicillin.

Patient teaching

- Tell patient to take drug exactly as prescribed, even after he feels better.
- Tell patient that drug may be taken without regard to meals. If GI disturbances occur, drug may be taken with meals.

P

• Warn patient never to use leftover penicillin V for new illness or to share penicillin with family and friends.
• Inform patients using oral solution that any remaining solution must be discarded after 14 days.
• Drug of choice for endocarditis prophylaxis is amoxicillin
• Tell patient to call prescriber if rash, fever, or chills develop.

Evaluation
• Patient is free from infection.
• Patient shows no signs of allergy.
• Patient and family state understanding of drug therapy.

pentamidine isethionate
(pen-TAM-eh-deen ighs-eh-THIGH-oh-nayt)
NebuPent, Pentacarinat ♦, Pentam 300

Pharmacologic class: diamidine derivative
Therapeutic class: antiprotozoal
Pregnancy risk category: C

Indications and dosages

▶ ***Pneumocystis jiroveci (carinii)* pneumonia.** *Adults and children:* 4 mg/kg I.V. or I.M. once daily for 14 to 21 days.
▶ **Prevention of *P. jiroveci (carinii)* pneumonia in high-risk patients.** *Adults:* 300 mg by inhalation (using Respirgard II jet nebulizer) once q 4 weeks.

I.V. administration

• Reconstitute drug with 3 ml of sterile water for injection; then dilute in 50 to 250 ml of D_5W. Inject over 1 to 2 hours.
• To minimize hypotension, infuse drug slowly with patient lying down.
⊗ **Incompatibilities**
Aldesleukin, cephalosporins, fluconazole, foscarnet.

Contraindications and cautions

• Contraindicated in patients with history of anaphylactic reaction to drug.
• Use cautiously in patients with hypertension, hypotension, hypoglycemia, hypocalcemia, leukopenia, thrombocytopenia, anemia, pancreatitis, hepatic or renal dysfunction or history of ventricular tachycardia or Stevens-Johnson syndrome.

Lifespan: In pregnant women, use cautiously. In breast-feeding women, drug isn't recommended.

Adverse reactions

Parenteral form
CNS: confusion, dizziness, fever, hallucinations, neuralgia.
CV: cardiac arrhythmias, facial flushing, ***hypotension, ventricular tachycardia.***
GI: abdominal discomfort, anorexia, diarrhea, *metallic taste,* nausea, ***pancreatitis,*** vomiting.
GU: ***acute renal failure, renal toxicity.***
Hematologic: ***anemia, leukopenia, thrombocytopenia.***
Metabolic: hyperglycemia, ***hyperkalemia, hypocalcemia, hypoglycemia.***
Respiratory: ***bronchospasm,*** cough.
Skin: pruritus, rash, ***Stevens-Johnson syndrome.***
Other: ***anaphylactoid reactions,*** *pain and induration at injection site* with I.M. route, phlebitis, tissue necrosis or sloughing from extravasation with I.V. route, *sterile abscess.*
Aerosol form
CNS: confusion, decreased taste or smell, *dizziness, fatigue,* fever, headache, tremors.
CV: *chest pain,* hypertension, hypotension.
GI: abdominal discomfort, anorexia, diarrhea, *metallic taste, nausea,* ***pancreatitis,*** *pharyngitis, vomiting.*
Hematologic: ***anemia, leukopenia, thrombocytopenia.***
Metabolic: hyperglycemia, ***hypocalcemia, hypoglycemia.***
Respiratory: **BRONCHOSPASM,** *chest congestion, cough, shortness of breath.*
Skin: *rash.*
Other: *chills, night sweats.*

Interactions

Drug-drug. *Aminoglycosides, amphotericin B, capreomycin, cisplatin, colistin, methoxyflurane, polymyxin B, vancomycin:* Increases risk of nephrotoxicity. Monitor patient closely.

Effects on lab test results

• May increase BUN, creatinine, potassium, and liver enzyme levels. May decrease calcium and hemoglobin levels and hematocrit. May increase or severely decrease glucose level.
• May decrease WBC and platelet counts.

Pharmacokinetics

Absorption: Limited after aerosol use. Well absorbed after I.M. use.
Distribution: Drug appears to be extensively tissue-bound. CNS penetration is poor. Extent of protein-binding is unknown.
Metabolism: Unknown.
Excretion: Excreted unchanged in urine. *Half-life:* Varies according to route of administration: 9 to 13¼ hours for I.M., about 6½ hours for I.V., and unknown for aerosol.

Route	Onset	Peak	Duration
I.V.	Unknown	Immediate	Unknown
I.M.	Unknown	30 min–1 hr	Unknown
Aerosol	Unknown	Unknown	Unknown

Action

Chemical effect: Interferes with infectious organism's biosynthesis of DNA, RNA, phospholipids, and proteins.
Therapeutic effect: Hinders growth of susceptible organisms.

Available forms

Aerosol: 300-mg vial
Injection: 300-mg vial

NURSING PROCESS

Assessment

- Assess patient's infection before starting therapy and regularly thereafter to monitor drug's effectiveness.

ALERT: Monitor glucose level before therapy, daily during parenteral administration, and regularly afterwards. Glucose level may decrease initially, and hypoglycemia may be severe. Hyperglycemia and insulin-dependent diabetes mellitus may follow months after therapy ends and may be permanent.

- Monitor CBC, platelet count, calcium, liver function tests, potassium, and renal function tests before, during, and after therapy. Monitor BUN, creatinine, calcium, and potassium levels daily during parenteral therapy due to risks of acute renal failure, hypocalcemia, and hyperkalemia.
- Closely monitor blood pressure during I.V. administration.

ALERT: Screen and treat patient for tuberculosis (TB) before using inhaled form. The risk of spreading TB to health care personnel and family members increases with high-pressure nebulizer use due to cough and droplet spread. If you're pregnant or plan to become pregnant, have another staff member care for this patient. Standard personal protection equipment is ineffective. Use care in choosing a room for patient using inhaled form.

- Be alert for adverse reactions and drug interactions.
- Assess patient's and family's knowledge of drug therapy.

Nursing diagnoses

- Risk for infection related to presence of organisms
- Risk for injury related to drug-induced adverse CNS reactions
- Deficient knowledge related to drug therapy

Planning and implementation

- For I.M. use, reconstitute drug with 3 ml of sterile water to make solution containing 100 mg/ml; administer deeply using Z-track technique. Expect pain and induration at site.
- In patient with AIDS, this drug may produce less severe adverse reactions than co-trimoxazole and may be drug of choice.
- Give aerosol form only by Respirgard II jet nebulizer manufactured by Marquest (flow rate of 5 to 7 liters/minute from 40 to 50 pounds per square inch [psi] compressor). Dosage is based on particle size and delivery rate of this device; don't change to low-pressure (below 20 psi) compressors.
- To use aerosol, mix contents of one vial in 6 ml of sterile water for injection. Don't use normal saline solution; it will cause precipitation.
- Don't mix with other drugs.
- Inhaling drug may induce bronchospasm or cough, especially in patients with a history of smoking or asthma.

Patient teaching

- Instruct patient to use aerosol device until chamber is empty, which may take up to 45 minutes.
- Advise patient with significant cough and bronchospasm to report effects to prescriber. Aerosol bronchodilator may be prescribed for use just before therapy.
- Warn patient that I.M. injection is painful. Application of warm soaks is helpful.
- Tell patient to report lightheadedness or signs and symptoms of hypoglycemia immediately.

P

Evaluation
- Patient is free from infection.
- Patient sustains no injuries because of drug-induced adverse CNS reactions.
- Patient and family state understanding of drug therapy.

pentazocine hydrochloride
(pen-TAZ-oh-seen high-droh-KLOR-ighd)

pentazocine hydrochloride and acetaminophen
Talacen

pentazocine and naloxone hydrochlorides
Talwin NX

pentazocine lactate
Talwin

Pharmacologic class: opioid partial agonist, opioid agonist-antagonist
Therapeutic class: analgesic, adjunct to anesthesia
Pregnancy risk category: C
Controlled substance schedule: IV

Indications and dosages

▶ **Moderate to severe pain.** *Adults:* 50 to 100 mg Talwin NX P.O. q 3 to 4 hours, p.r.n. Maximum oral dose, 600 mg daily. Or, 1 tablet Talacen P.O. q 4 hours, up to 6 tablets daily. Or, 30 mg I.M., I.V., or subcutaneously q 3 to 4 hours, p.r.n. Maximum total parenteral dose is 360 mg in 24 hours. Single doses above 30 mg I.V. or 60 mg I.M. or subcutaneously aren't recommended.

▶ **Labor.** *Women:* 30 mg I.M. as a single dose or 20 mg I.V. q 2 to 3 hours when contractions become regular.

I.V. administration
- Give drug by direct I.V. injection.
- Administer slowly.

⊗ **Incompatibilities**
Aminophylline, amobarbital, glycopyrrolate, heparin sodium, nafcillin sodium, pentobarbital sodium, phenobarbital sodium, sodium bicarbonate.

Contraindications and cautions
- Contraindicated in patients hypersensitive to the drug or any of its components.
- Use cautiously in patients with hepatic or renal disease, acute MI, head injury, increased intracranial pressure, or respiratory depression.

Lifespan: In pregnant women, use cautiously. In breast-feeding women, use cautiously; it's unknown if the drug appears in breast milk. In children younger than age 12, drug isn't recommended. In the elderly, use cautiously because they may be more sensitive to the drug's CNS effects.

Adverse reactions
CNS: confusion, *dizziness*, drowsiness, *euphoria*, hallucinations, headache, *lightheadedness*, psychotomimetic effects, *sedation*, visual disturbances.
CV: flushing, hypertension, hypotension, ***shock***, tachycardia.
EENT: dry mouth, dysgeusia.
GI: constipation, nausea, vomiting.
GU: urine retention.
Respiratory: ***respiratory depression.***
Skin: diaphoresis, induration, nodules, pruritus, rash, sloughing, and sclerosis of injection site.
Other: hypersensitivity reactions ***(anaphylaxis)***, physical and psychological dependence.

Interactions
Drug-drug. *CNS depressants:* May have additive effects. Use together cautiously.
Fluoxetine: May cause diaphoresis, ataxia, flushing, and tremor suggestive of serotonin syndrome. Use together cautiously.
Opioid analgesics: May decrease analgesic effect. Avoid using together.
Drug-lifestyle. *Alcohol use:* May have additive effects. Discourage using together.
Smoking: May increase requirements for pentazocine. Monitor drug's effectiveness; urge patient to stop smoking.

Effects on lab test results
- May interfere with laboratory tests for urinary 17-hydroxycorticosteroids.

Pharmacokinetics
Absorption: Well absorbed after P.O. or parenteral use, although P.O. form undergoes first-pass metabolism in liver and less than 20% of dose reaches systemic circulation unchanged.

Bioavailability is increased in patients with hepatic dysfunction; patients with cirrhosis absorb 60% to 70% of drug.
Distribution: Appears to be wide.
Metabolism: In liver; may be prolonged in patients with impaired hepatic function.
Excretion: Mainly in urine, with very small amounts in feces. *Half-life:* 2 to 3 hours.

Route	Onset	Peak	Duration
P.O.	15–30 min	60–90 min	2–3 hr
I.V.	2–3 min	15–30 min	2–3 hr
I.M., SubQ	15–20 min	15–60 min	4–6 hr

Action

Chemical effect: Binds with opiate receptors at many sites in CNS, altering pain response by unknown mechanism.
Therapeutic effect: Relieves pain.

Available forms

pentazocine hydrochloride
Tablets: 50 mg ◇
pentazocine hydrochloride and acetaminophen
Tablets: 25 mg pentazocine hydrochloride and 650 mg acetaminophen
pentazocine and naloxone hydrochlorides
Tablets: 50 mg pentazocine hydrochloride and 0.5 mg naloxone hydrochloride
pentazocine lactate
Injection: 30 mg/ml

NURSING PROCESS

Assessment

- Assess patient's pain before and after giving the drug.
- Monitor vital signs closely, especially respirations.
- Be alert for adverse reactions and drug interactions.
- Assess patient's and family's knowledge of drug therapy.

Nursing diagnoses

- Acute pain related to condition
- Ineffective breathing pattern related to drug-induced respiratory depression
- Deficient knowledge related to drug therapy

Planning and implementation

- Talwin NX, the oral pentazocine available in the U.S., contains the opioid antagonist naloxone, which prevents illicit use.

ALERT: Talwin NX is for P.O. use only. Severe, potentially fatal reaction may occur if given by injection.

- When giving I.M. or subcutaneously, rotate injection sites to minimize tissue irritation. If possible, avoid giving subcutaneously.
- Drug has opioid antagonist properties. May precipitate withdrawal syndrome in an opioid-dependent patient.
- Dependence may occur with prolonged use.

ALERT: If respiratory rate drops significantly, hold drug and notify prescriber. Have naloxone readily available to reverse respiratory depression.

Patient teaching

- Warn ambulatory patient about getting out of bed or walking. Warn outpatient to avoid hazardous activities until the drug's CNS effects are known.
- Inform patient about the risk of dependence.

Evaluation

- Patient is free from pain.
- Patient maintains respiratory rate and pattern within normal limits.
- Patient and family state understanding of drug therapy.

P

pentetate calcium trisodium (Ca-DTPA)

(PEN-tuh-tayt KAL-see-um try-SOE-dee-um)

pentetate zinc trisodium (Zn-DTPA)

Pharmacologic class: chelate
Therapeutic class: radiation emergency drug
Pregnancy risk category: C (Ca-DTPA); B (Zn-DTPA)

Indications and dosages

▶ **To increase the rate of plutonium, americium, or curium elimination in patients with internal contamination.** *Adults and children age 12 and older:* Initially, 1 g Ca-DTPA by slow I.V. push over 3 to 4 minutes (or dilute in

100 to 250 ml D_5W, Ringer's lactate, or normal saline solution and infuse over 30 minutes) within the first 24 hours of exposure. Then, 1 g once daily of Zn-DTPA by slow I.V. push over 3 to 4 minutes (or dilute in 100 to 250 ml D_5W, Ringer's lactate, or normal saline solution and infuse over 30 minutes) until radioactive substances are removed. If patient was exposed by inhalation, give solution by nebulizer at a ratio of 1:1 with sterile water or saline.
Children younger than age 12: Initially, 14 mg/kg Ca-DTPA (maximum dose, 1 g) by slow I.V. push over 3 to 4 minutes within the first 24 hours of exposure. Then, 14 mg/kg once daily of Zn-DTPA by slow I.V. push over 3 to 4 minutes (maximum dose, 1 g) until radioactive substances are removed.

I.V. administration

- Use a sterile filter if particles appear after ampule is opened.
- Administer by slow I.V. push over 3 to 4 minutes or dilute in 100 to 250 ml of D_5W, lactated Ringer's solution, or normal saline solution and infuse over 30 minutes.
- Store at room temperature.

⊗ **Incompatibilities**
None reported.

Contraindications and cautions

- Use cautiously in patients with severe hemochromatosis. Use inhalation route cautiously in patients with asthma.

Lifespan: In pregnant women, start and continue with Zn-DTPA unless patient has a high level of internal radioactive contamination. If the level of contamination is high, start with a single dose of Ca-DTPA and vitamin or mineral supplements containing zinc. Breast-feeding women should stop breast-feeding or use a different drug; it's unknown if drug appears in breast milk, but radiocontaminants do. Patient shouldn't breast-feed during therapy and should take precautions when discarding breast milk. In children, safety and effectiveness of inhaled form haven't been established.

Adverse reactions

CNS: headache, lightheadedness.
CV: chest pain.
GI: diarrhea, metallic taste, nausea.
Skin: dermatitis, injection site reactions.
Other: allergic reaction.

Interactions

None known.

Effects on lab test results

- May decrease manganese, magnesium, and zinc levels with prolonged therapy.

Pharmacokinetics

Absorption: Unknown, not in GI system, organs, erythrocytes; 20% in lungs with inhalational route.
Distribution: Rapid, throughout extracellular space after I.V. use.
Metabolism: Minimal.
Excretion: Almost exclusively in urine by glomerular filtration. *Half-life:* About 7 hours.

Route	Onset	Peak	Duration
I.V., inhalation	1½ min	Unknown	< 24 hr

Action

Chemical effect: Forms stable complexes with metal ions by exchanging calcium or zinc ions for radioactive plutonium, americium, or curium ions. The complexes are excreted into urine faster than the unbound radioactive contaminants, thus speeding removal from the body.
Therapeutic effect: Reduces the effects of exposure to radioactive plutonium, americium, or curium.

Available forms

Injection: 200 mg/ml in 5-ml single-use vials

NURSING PROCESS

Assessment

- Obtain history of patient's radiation exposure before therapy.
- Obtain baseline CBC, zinc, BUN, and electrolyte levels, urinalysis, and blood and urine radioassays before starting therapy.
- During therapy, measure the radioactivity of blood, urine, and feces weekly.
- Regularly monitor urinalysis, CBC, BUN, and electrolyte levels during therapy.
- Assess patient's and family's knowledge of drug therapy.

Nursing diagnoses

- Risk for injury related to internal radioactive contamination

• Ineffective protection related to drug-induced depletion of endogenous trace metals
• Deficient knowledge related to drug therapy

Planning and implementation

• The binding capacity of Ca-DTPA is greatest in the first 24 hours after exposure.

ALERT: If patient needs further therapy after Ca-DTPA, switch to Zn-DTPA to avoid mineral depletion. If Zn-DTPA isn't available, continue Ca-DTPA as long as the patient receives supplemental zinc, magnesium, and manganese.

• When the route of contamination is unknown or if contamination occurs by multiple routes, use I.V. drug.
• If contamination occurs only by inhalation and within 24 hours, use nebulizer. Dilute drug 1:1 with sterile water or saline solution.
• The elimination rate is based on the quantity of radioactivity taken in.

Patient teaching

• Instruct patient to drink plenty of fluids so he urinates often.
• Remind patient that drug eliminates radioactivity through urine, which may make urine highly radioactive and dangerous to others.
• Instruct patient to flush the toilet several times after each use and to wash hands thoroughly after urinating.
• If the patient is coughing, tell him to dispose of phlegm carefully and not to swallow it, if possible.
• Tell parents of a young child to dispose of dirty diapers properly and to avoid handling urine, feces, or phlegm.

Evaluation

• The effects of radiation contamination are reduced.
• Patient experiences minimal loss of trace metals or receives mineral supplements as appropriate.
• Patient and family state understanding of drug therapy.

pentobarbital (pentobarbitone)

(pen-toh-BAR-beh-tol)

Nembutal

pentobarbital sodium

Nembutal Sodium, Novo-Pentobarb ◊

Pharmacologic class: barbiturate
Therapeutic class: anticonvulsant, sedative-hypnotic
Pregnancy risk category: D
Controlled substance schedule: II (oral and parenteral); III (rectal)

Indications and dosages

▶ **Sedation.** *Adults:* 20 to 40 mg P.O. b.i.d., t.i.d., or q.i.d.
Children: 2 to 6 mg/kg daily P.O. or P.R. t.i.d. Maximum dose, 100 mg daily.

▶ **Short-term therapy for insomnia.** *Adults:* 100 to 200 mg P.O. at bedtime or 150 to 200 mg I.M. Or, 120 to 200 mg P.R. Or, initially, 100 mg I.V. with additional small doses, to a total of 500 mg.
Children: 2 to 6 mg/kg I.M. Maximum dose is 100 mg. Or, for children ages 2 months to 1 year, give 30 mg P.R.; for children ages 1 to 4 years, give 30 or 60 mg P.R.; for children ages 5 to 12 years, give 60 mg P.R.; for children ages 12 to 14 years, give 60 or 120 mg P.R.

▶ **Preoperative sedation.** *Adults:* 150 to 200 mg I.M.
Children: 5 mg/kg P.O. or I.M. In children younger than age 10, the dose is usually given rectally.

I.V. administration

• I.V. use of barbiturates may cause severe respiratory depression, laryngospasm, or hypotension. Have emergency resuscitation equipment available.
• To minimize deterioration, use I.V injection solution within 30 minutes after opening container. Don't use cloudy solution.
• Reserve I.V. injection for emergencies and give under close supervision. Give slowly (50 mg/minute or less).
• Parenteral solution is alkaline. Local tissue reactions and injection site pain may result. Monitor site for irritation and infiltration; extravasation can lead to tissue damage and necrosis.

P

Assess patency of I.V. site before and during administration.

⊗ **Incompatibilities**

Other I.V. drugs or solutions.

Contraindications and cautions

• Contraindicated in patients with porphyria or hypersensitivity to barbiturates.

• Use cautiously in debilitated patients and in those with acute or chronic pain, depression, suicidal tendencies, history of drug abuse, or renal or hepatic impairment.

Lifespan: In pregnant and breast-feeding women, drug isn't recommended. In the elderly, use cautiously because of possible delayed renal excretion.

Adverse reactions

CNS: *drowsiness, hangover, lethargy,* paradoxical excitement in elderly patients.
GI: nausea, vomiting.
Hematologic: worsening of porphyria.
Respiratory: ***respiratory depression.***
Skin: rash, ***Stevens-Johnson syndrome,*** urticaria.
Other: ***angioedema.***

Interactions

Drug-drug. *CNS depressants, including opioid analgesics:* May cause excessive CNS and respiratory depression. Use together cautiously.
Corticosteroids, doxycycline, estrogens and hormonal contraceptives, oral anticoagulants quinidine, theophylline, verapamil: May enhance metabolism of these drugs. Monitor patient for decreased effect.
MAO inhibitors: May inhibit barbiturate metabolism and prolong CNS depression. Reduce barbiturate dose.
Metoprolol, propranolol: May reduce the effects of these drugs. Increase beta blocker dose.
Rifampin: May decrease barbiturate level. Monitor patient for decreased effect.
Drug-lifestyle. *Alcohol use:* May impair coordination, increase CNS effects, and cause death. Strongly discourage use together.

Effects on lab test results

None reported.

Pharmacokinetics

Absorption: Rapid after P.O. use. Unknown after I.M. use.
Distribution: Wide. About 35% to 45% protein-bound.
Metabolism: In liver.
Excretion: 99% in urine. *Half-life:* 35 to 50 hours.

Route	Onset	Peak	Duration
P.O.	≤ 15 min	30–60 min	1–4 hr
I.V.	Immediate	Immediate	15 min
I.M.	10–25 min	Unknown	Unknown

Action

Chemical effect: May interfere with transmission of impulses from thalamus to cortex of brain.
Therapeutic effect: Promotes sleep and calmness.

Available forms

Capsules: 50 mg, 100 mg
Elixir: 20 mg/5ml
Injection: 50 mg/ml
Suppositories: 30 mg, 60 mg, 120 mg, 200 mg

NURSING PROCESS

Assessment

• Assess patient's condition before starting therapy and regularly thereafter to monitor drug's effectiveness.

• An elderly patient may be more sensitive to the drug's CNS effects.

• Inspect patient's skin. Skin eruptions may precede life-threatening reactions to barbiturate therapy.

• Be alert for adverse reactions and drug interactions.

• Assess patient's and family's knowledge of drug therapy.

Nursing diagnoses

• Sleep deprivation related to condition
• Risk for injury related to drug-induced adverse CNS reactions
• Deficient knowledge related to drug therapy

Planning and implementation

• Give I.M. injection deep into muscle. Superficial injection may cause pain, sterile abscess, and sloughing.

ALERT: If skin reactions occur, stop drug and notify prescriber. In some patients, high fever, stomatitis, headache, or rhinitis may precede skin reactions.

- Drug has no analgesic effect and may cause restlessness or delirium in a patient with pain.

ALERT: Long-term use isn't recommended; drug loses its effectiveness in promoting sleep after 14 days of continued use. Long-term high doses may cause dependence and may lead to withdrawal symptoms if drug is suddenly stopped. Gradually stop giving barbiturates.

ALERT: Don't confuse pentobarbital with phenobarbital.

Patient teaching

- Warn patient about performing activities that require alertness or physical coordination. For an acute care inpatient, particularly an elderly patient, supervise walking and raise bed rails.
- Inform patient that morning hangover is common after hypnotic dose, which suppresses REM sleep. Patient's dreams may increase after therapy stops.
- Tell woman who uses hormonal contraceptives to use barrier-method birth control because drug may decrease contraceptive effect.

Evaluation

- Patient reports satisfactory sleep.
- Patient sustains no injuries from drug-induced adverse CNS reactions.
- Patient and family state understanding of drug therapy.

pentoxifylline

(pen-tok-SIH-fi-lin)

Trental

Pharmacologic class: xanthine derivative
Therapeutic class: hemorheologic
Pregnancy risk category: C

Indications and dosages

▶ **Intermittent claudication caused by chronic occlusive vascular disease.** *Adults:* 400 mg P.O. t.i.d. with meals for at least 8 weeks.

Contraindications and cautions

- Contraindicated in patients who are intolerant of methylxanthines, such as caffeine and theophylline, and in those with recent cerebral or retinal hemorrhage.

Lifespan: In pregnant women, use cautiously. In breast-feeding women, drug isn't recommended. In children, safety and effectiveness haven't been established.

Adverse reactions

CNS: dizziness, headache.
GI: dyspepsia, nausea, vomiting.

Interactions

Drug-drug. *Anticoagulants:* May increase anticoagulant effect. Monitor PT and INR, and adjust anticoagulant dose as needed.
Antihypertensives: May increase hypotensive effect. Adjust dose; monitor patient's blood pressure closely.
Theophylline: May increase theophylline level. Monitor level; adjust theophylline dose.
Drug-lifestyle. *Smoking:* May cause vasoconstriction. Advise patient to avoid smoking because it may worsen his condition.

Effects on lab test results

None reported.

Pharmacokinetics

Absorption: Rapid and almost completely absorbed by the GI tract.
Distribution: Bound by erythrocyte membrane.
Metabolism: Extensively by erythrocytes and liver.
Excretion: Mainly in urine. *Half-life:* About 30 to 45 minutes.

Route	Onset	Peak	Duration
P.O.	Unknown	1 hr	Unknown

Action

Chemical effect: May increase RBC flexibility and lower blood viscosity.
Therapeutic effect: Improves capillary blood flow.

Available forms

Tablets (controlled-release): 400 mg
Tablets (extended-release): 400 mg

P

NURSING PROCESS

Assessment
- Assess patient's condition before starting therapy and regularly thereafter to monitor drug's effectiveness.
- Be alert for adverse reactions and drug interactions.
- In patients with other risk factors complicated by hemorrhage (recent surgery, peptic ulceration), assess for bleeding, and obtain hemoglobin level and hematocrit.
- In an elderly patient, watch for increased CNS effects.
- If adverse GI reaction occurs, monitor patient's hydration.
- Assess patient's and family's knowledge of drug therapy.

Nursing diagnoses
- Ineffective peripheral tissue perfusion related to condition
- Risk for deficient fluid volume related to drug-induced adverse GI reactions
- Deficient knowledge related to drug therapy

Planning and implementation
- Drug is useful in patient who isn't a good surgical candidate.
- Report adverse reactions to prescriber; dose may need to be lowered.
- Monitor blood pressure for hypotension, particularly in patients also on antihypertensive therapy.

ALERT: Don't confuse Trental with Trendar or Trandate.

Patient teaching
- Advise patient to take drug with meals to minimize GI upset.
- Instruct patient to swallow drug whole, without breaking, crushing, or chewing.
- Tell patient to report adverse GI or CNS reactions.
- Advise patient not to smoke because nicotine causes vasoconstriction that can worsen his condition.
- Advise patient that effects of drug may not be seen for 2 to 4 weeks.
- Tell patient not to stop taking the drug during first 8 weeks of therapy unless directed by prescriber.

Evaluation
- Patient has adequate peripheral tissue perfusion.
- Patient maintains adequate hydration throughout therapy.
- Patient and family state understanding of drug therapy.

pergolide mesylate
(PER-goh-lighd MES-ih-layt)
Permax

Pharmacologic class: dopaminergic agonist
Therapeutic class: antiparkinsonian
Pregnancy risk category: B

Indications and dosages
▶**Adjunct therapy with levodopa and carbidopa in management of symptoms caused by Parkinson disease.** *Adults:* Initially, 0.05 mg P.O. daily for first 2 days; increase dose by 0.1 to 0.15 mg q third day over 12 days. Increase later doses by 0.25 mg q third day until optimum response is seen. Drug usually is given in divided doses t.i.d. Gradual reductions in levodopa and carbidopa doses may be made during dosage adjustment. Usual total daily dose, 3 mg.

Contraindications and cautions
- Contraindicated in patients hypersensitive to the drug or ergot alkaloids.
- Use cautiously in patients prone to arrhythmias and in patients with a history of pleuritis, pleural effusion, pleural fibrosis, pericarditis, pericardial effusion, cardiac valvulopathy or retroperitoneal fibrosis.
- Because of the risk of increased sedative effects, use caution when patient is also taking other CNS depressants.
- Hypotension may occur, especially during initial therapy.
- Symptoms similar to neuroleptic malignant syndrome may occur with rapid dose reduction.

Lifespan: In pregnant women, use cautiously. In breast-feeding women and in children, safety and effectiveness haven't been established.

Adverse reactions
CNS: abnormal dreams, abnormal gait, akathisia, akinesia, anxiety, asthenia, confusion,

depression, *dizziness, dyskinesia,* dystonia, extrapyramidal syndrome, *hallucinations,* headache, hypertonia, incoordination, insomnia, neuralgia, paresthesia, personality disorder, psychosis, *somnolence,* speech disorder, syncope, tremor, twitching.
CV: ***arrhythmias;*** chest pain; facial, peripheral, or generalized edema; ***fibrosis;*** hypertension; hypotension; ***MI;*** *orthostatic hypotension;* palpitations; ***valvulopathy;*** vasodilation.
EENT: abnormal vision, diplopia, epistaxis, eye disorder, *rhinitis.*
GI: abdominal pain, anorexia, *constipation,* diarrhea, dry mouth, dysgeusia, dyspepsia, *nausea,* vomiting.
GU: hematuria, urinary frequency, UTI.
Hematologic: anemia.
Metabolic: weight gain.
Musculoskeletal: arthralgia, bursitis, myalgia, neck and back pain.
Skin: diaphoresis, rash.
Other: chills, flulike syndrome, infection.

Interactions

Drug-drug. *Butyrophenones, metoclopramide, other dopamine antagonists, phenothiazines, thioxanthenes:* May antagonize effects of pergolide. Avoid using together.
CNS depressants: May cause additive CNS effects. Monitor patient closely.
Levodopa: May cause additive neurologic effects, such as hallucinations. Monitor patient closely.

Effects on lab test results

- May decrease hemoglobin level and hematocrit.

Pharmacokinetics

Absorption: Well absorbed.
Distribution: About 90% protein-bound.
Metabolism: To at least 10 different compounds, some of which retain pharmacologic activity.
Excretion: Mainly by kidneys. *Half-life:* Unknown.

Route	Onset	Peak	Duration
P.O.	Unknown	Unknown	Unknown

Action

Chemical effect: Directly stimulates dopamine receptors in nigrostriatal system.
Therapeutic effect: Helps to relieve signs and symptoms of Parkinson disease.

Available forms

Tablets: 0.05 mg, 0.25 mg, 1 mg

NURSING PROCESS

Assessment

- Assess patient's condition before starting therapy. Monitor drug effectiveness by regularly checking patient's body movements for improvement.
- Monitor blood pressure and heart rate and rhythm. Symptomatic orthostatic or sustained hypotension may occur, especially at start of therapy. Drug also may induce arrhythmias.
- Evaluate patient for underlying valvular disease, including echocardiogram, before beginning therapy with pergolide.
- Be alert for adverse reactions and drug interactions.
- Assess patient's and family's knowledge of drug therapy.
- Periodically evaluate patient for somnolence. If a patient develops significant daytime sleepiness or episodes of falling asleep during activities that require participation (such as conversations or eating), stop the drug. If patient continues therapy, advise patient not to drive and to avoid other potentially dangerous activities. Dose reduction may reduce the degree of somnolence, but not enough information is available to establish that dose reduction will stop it.

Nursing diagnoses

- Impaired physical mobility related to Parkinson disease
- Decreased cardiac output related to drug-induced adverse CV reactions
- Deficient knowledge related to drug therapy

Planning and implementation

- Gradually increase dose by patient's response and tolerance.
- Perform regular cardiovascular follow-up during the course of the drug therapy.
- Stop therapy if patient develops a fibrotic condition or cardiac valvular disease during treatment.
- If patient has significant changes in vital signs or mental status, notify prescriber.

• When stopping drug, taper slowly to avoid malignant neuroleptic syndrome, confusion, and hallucinations.

Patient teaching

• Inform patient of potential adverse reactions, especially hallucinations and confusion.
• Warn patient to avoid activities that could result in injury from orthostatic hypotension and syncope.
• Advise patient of the possibility of suddenly falling asleep while performing daily activities, including driving a car. Many patients who fall asleep have no warning of somnolence. Advise patient with increased somnolence or new episodes of falling asleep during daily living not to drive or participate in potentially dangerous activities until he has contacted his prescriber.

☑ Evaluation

• Patient has improved mobility.
• Patient maintains cardiac output.
• Patient and family state understanding of drug therapy.

perphenazine

(per-FEN-uh-zeen)

Apo-erphenazine ♦

Pharmacologic class: phenothiazine (piperazine derivative)
Therapeutic class: antiemetic, antipsychotic
Pregnancy risk category: C

Indications and dosages

▶ **Psychosis in nonhospitalized patients.** *Adults:* Initially, 4 to 8 mg P.O. t.i.d. Reduce to minimum effective dose as soon as possible.
Children older than age 12: Lowest adult dose.
▶ **Psychosis in hospitalized patients.** *Adults:* Initially, 8 to 16 mg P.O. b.i.d., t.i.d., or q.i.d., increase to 64 mg daily, as needed. Or, 5 to 10 mg I.M. q 6 hours, p.r.n. Maximum daily I.M. dose, 30 mg.
Children older than age 12: Lowest limit of adult dosage.
▶ **Severe nausea and vomiting.** *Adults:* 5 to 10 mg I.M., p.r.n.

Contraindications and cautions

• Contraindicated in patients hypersensitive to the drug or any of its components; in comatose patients; in patients with CNS depression, blood dyscrasia, bone marrow depression, liver damage, or subcortical damage; and in those taking large doses of CNS depressants and itraconazole.
• Use cautiously with other CNS depressants or anticholinergics. Also use cautiously in debilitated patients and patients with alcohol withdrawal, depression, suicidal tendency, severe adverse reactions to other phenothiazines, impaired renal function, or respiratory disorders.
Lifespan: In pregnant women, use cautiously; a neonate whose mother uses drug during pregnancy may have prolonged jaundice, extrapyramidal signs, hyperreflexia or hyporeflexia. In breast-feeding women, drug appears in breast milk; avoid using unless the benefit outweighs the risk to the infant. In children age 12 and younger, safety and effectiveness haven't been established. In the elderly, use cautiously because of risk of increased effects.

Adverse reactions

CNS: dizziness, EEG changes, *extrapyramidal reaction,* ***neuroleptic malignant syndrome,*** pseudoparkinsonism, sedation, ***seizures,*** *tardive dyskinesia.*
CV: ***cardiac arrest,*** ECG changes, *orthostatic hypotension,* tachycardia.
EENT: blurred vision, ocular changes.
GI: constipation, dry mouth.
GU: dark urine, inhibited ejaculation, menstrual irregularities, *urine retention,*
Hematologic: ***agranulocytosis, hemolytic anemia,*** hyperprolactinemia, ***thrombocytopenia, transient leukopenia.***
Hepatic: cholestatic jaundice.
Metabolic: increased appetite, weight gain.
Skin: *mild photosensitivity reaction,* sterile abscess.
Other: allergic reactions, gynecomastia, pain at I.M. injection site.

Interactions

Drug-drug. *Antacids:* May inhibit oral phenothiazine absorption. Administer drugs separately.
Anticonvulsants: May lower the seizure threshold. Monitor patient.
Barbiturates: May decrease phenothiazine effect. Observe patient closely.
Bromocriptine: May decrease bromocriptine effectiveness. Monitor patient for effect.

CNS depressants: May increase CNS depression. Avoid using together.
Lithium: May cause severe neurological toxicity with encephalitis-like syndrome; decreased therapeutic response to perphenazine. Don't use together.
Drug-herb. *Dong quai, St. John's wort:* May increase photosensitivity. Discourage using together.
Evening primrose oil: May increase risk of seizures. Discourage using together.
Kava: May increase risk of dystonic reactions. Discourage using together.
Milk thistle: May decrease liver toxicity caused by phenothiazines. Monitor liver enzyme level.
Yohimbe: May increase risk of yohimbe toxicity. Discourage using together.
Drug-lifestyle. *Alcohol use:* May increase CNS depression, particularly psychomotor skills. Strongly discourage use together.
Sun exposure: May increase photosensitivity reaction. Urge patient to avoid unprotected or prolonged exposure to sunlight.

Effects on lab test results

- May increase prolactin level. May decrease hemoglobin level and hematocrit.
- May increase liver function test values and eosinophil count. May decrease WBC, granulocyte, and platelet counts.
- May produce false-positive phenylketonuria or pregnancy test results.

Pharmacokinetics

Absorption: Rate and extent vary. Erratic and variable for P.O. tablet; much more predictable for P.O. concentrate. Rapid from I.M. injection.
Distribution: Wide. 91% to 99% protein-bound.
Metabolism: Extensive in liver.
Excretion: Mainly in urine; some in feces.
Half-life: 9 to 12 hours.

Route	Onset	Peak	Duration
P.O., I.M.	Varies	1–3 hr	Unknown

Action

Chemical effect: Probably blocks postsynaptic dopamine receptors in brain and inhibits medullary chemoreceptor trigger zone.
Therapeutic effect: Relieves signs and symptoms of psychosis; also relieves nausea and vomiting.

Available forms

Injection: 5 mg/ml
Oral concentrate: 16 mg/5 ml*
Syrup: 2 mg/5 ml ♦
Tablets: 2 mg, 4 mg, 8 mg, 16 mg

NURSING PROCESS

Assessment

- Assess patient's condition before starting therapy and regularly thereafter to monitor drug's effectiveness.
- Obtain baseline blood pressure before starting therapy, and monitor it regularly. Watch for orthostatic hypotension, especially with I.M. administration.
- Test bilirubin level weekly during first month, and obtain periodic blood tests (CBC and liver function) and ophthalmic tests (long-term use).
- Be alert for adverse reactions and drug interactions.
- Monitor patient for tardive dyskinesia, which may occur after prolonged use. It may not appear until months or years later and may disappear spontaneously or persist for life despite no longer using the drug.
- If drug is used for nausea and vomiting, monitor patient's hydration.
- Assess patient's and family's knowledge of drug therapy.

Nursing diagnoses

- Disturbed thought processes related to psychosis
- Risk for deficient fluid volume related to nausea or vomiting
- Deficient knowledge related to drug therapy

Planning and implementation

- When giving liquid form, dilute with fruit juice, milk, carbonated beverage, or semisolid food just before giving.
- Concentrate causes turbidity or precipitation in colas, black coffee, grape or apple juice, or tea. Don't mix with them.
- When given I.M., inject drug deep in upper outer quadrant of buttocks. Injection may sting.
- Massage slowly after injection to prevent sterile abscess.
- Keep patient supine for 1 hour after injection because of risk of hypotension.

P

• Prevent contact dermatitis by keeping drug away from skin and clothes. Wear gloves when preparing liquid forms.
• Protect drug from light. Slight yellowing of injection or concentrate doesn't affect potency. Discard markedly discolored solutions.
• Don't abruptly stop giving the drug unless severe adverse reaction occurs. After abruptly stopping long-term therapy, patient may experience gastritis, nausea, vomiting, dizziness, tremors, feeling of warmth or cold, diaphoresis, tachycardia, headache, or insomnia.
• If patient develops jaundice, symptoms of blood dyscrasia (fever, sore throat, infection, cellulitis, weakness), or extrapyramidal reactions that last longer than a few hours, withhold dose and notify prescriber.
• Acute dystonic reactions may be treated with diphenhydramine.
ALERT: Don't confuse perphenazine with prochlorperazine.

Patient teaching

• Advise patient to change positions slowly to minimize orthostatic hypotension.
• Teach patient which fluids are appropriate for diluting concentrate.
• Warn patient to avoid hazardous activities until the drug's CNS effects are known. Drowsiness and dizziness usually subside after a few weeks.
• Tell patient to avoid alcohol during drug therapy.
• Advise patient to report urine retention or constipation.
• Tell patient to use sunblock and to wear protective clothing to avoid photosensitivity reactions.
• Tell patient to relieve dry mouth with sugarless gum or hard candy.

Evaluation

• Patient's thought processes are normal.
• Patient maintains adequate hydration throughout drug therapy.
• Patient and family state understanding of drug therapy.

phenazopyridine hydrochloride (phenylazo diamino pyridine hydrochloride)

(fen-eh-soh-PEER-eh-deen high-droh-KLOR-ighd)
Azo-Dine, Azo-Gesic, Azo-Standard†, Baridium†, Geridium, Phenazo†, Prodium†, Pyridiate, Pyridium, Pyridium Plus, RE-Azo, Urodine†, Urogesic, UTI Relief

Pharmacologic class: azo dye
Therapeutic class: urinary analgesic
Pregnancy risk category: B

Indications and dosages

▶ **Relief of symptoms of urinary tract irritation or infection.** *Adults:* 200 mg P.O. t.i.d. *Children ages 6 to 12 years:* 12 mg/kg P.O. daily divided into three equal doses.

Contraindications and cautions

• Contraindicated in patients with glomerulonephritis, severe hepatitis, uremia, or renal insufficiency.
Lifespan: In pyelonephritis during pregnancy, drug is contraindicated. In breast-feeding women, safety and effectiveness haven't been established. In children younger than age 12, don't use.

Adverse reactions

CNS: headache, vertigo.
EENT: staining of contact lenses.
GI: mild GI disturbance, nausea.
Skin: pruritus, rash.

Interactions

None significant.

Effects on lab test results

• May alter urine glucose results when Diastix is used. May interfere with urinalysis based on spectrometry or color reactions.

Pharmacokinetics

Absorption: Unknown.
Distribution: Unknown.
Metabolism: In liver.
Excretion: 65% in urine unchanged. *Half-life:* Unknown.

Route	Onset	Peak	Duration
P.O.	Unknown	Unknown	Unknown

Action

Chemical effect: Unknown; has local anesthetic effect on urinary mucosa.
Therapeutic effect: Relieves urinary tract pain.

Available forms

Tablets: 95 mg†, 97.2 mg, 100 mg†, 200 mg

NURSING PROCESS

Assessment

- Assess patient's pain before and after giving drug.
- Be alert for adverse reactions.
- If nausea occurs, monitor patient's hydration.
- Assess patient's and family's knowledge of drug therapy.

Nursing diagnoses

- Acute pain related to underlying urinary tract condition
- Risk for deficient fluid volume related to drug-induced nausea
- Deficient knowledge related to drug therapy

Planning and implementation

- Administer drug with food to minimize nausea.

ALERT: Don't confuse Pyridium with pyridoxine, pyrimethamine, or pyridine.

Patient teaching

- Advise patient that taking drug with meals may minimize nausea.
- Tell patient to stop taking drug and notify prescriber if skin or sclera becomes yellow-tinged.
- Warn patient that drug colors urine red or orange. Drug may stain fabrics and contact lenses.
- Tell patient to notify prescriber if urinary tract pain persists after 2 days and the patient isn't also taking an antibiotic. If using drug with an antibiotic, stop drug after 2 days because it has no additional effectiveness. Drug isn't for long-term use.

Evaluation

- Patient is free from pain.
- Patient maintains adequate hydration.
- Patient and family state understanding of drug therapy.

phenobarbital (phenobarbitone)

(feen-oh-BAR-bih-tol)
Solfoton

phenobarbital sodium (phenobarbitone sodium)

Luminal Sodium

Pharmacologic class: barbiturate
Therapeutic class: anticonvulsant, sedative-hypnotic
Pregnancy risk category: D
Controlled substance schedule: IV

Indications and dosages

▶ **All forms of epilepsy except absence seizures; febrile seizures in children.** *Adults:* 60 to 250 mg P.O. daily, in divided doses t.i.d. or as single dose at bedtime
Children: 1 to 6 mg/kg P.O. daily, divided q 12 hours for total of 100 mg; can be given once daily, usually at bedtime
▶ **Status epilepticus.** *Adults:* 200 to 600 mg by slow I.V. injection; may repeat in 6 hours, if needed.
Children: 15 to 20 mg/kg by slow I.V. injection.
▶ **Sedation.** *Adults:* 30 to 120 mg P.O. daily in two or three divided doses.
Children: 8 to 32 mg P.O. daily in divided doses t.i.d.
▶ **Insomnia.** *Adults:* 100 to 200 mg P.O. or I.M. at bedtime
▶ **Preoperative sedation.** *Adults:* 100 to 200 mg I.M. 60 to 90 minutes before surgery.
Children: 1 to 3 mg/kg I.V. or I.M. 60 to 90 minutes before surgery.
▶ **Prevention and treatment of hyperbilirubinemia‡.** *Neonates:* 7 mg/kg P.O. daily from the 1st to 5th days after birth. Or, 5 mg/kg I.M. on day 1 and then 5 mg/kg P.O. on the 2nd through 7th days after birth.
▶ **To lower serum bilirubin or serum lipid level in the treatment of chronic cholestasis‡.** *Adults:* 90 to 180 mg P.O. daily in two or three divided doses.
Children younger than age 12: Give 3 to 12 mg/kg P.O. daily in two to three divided doses.

I.V. administration

- Injection is reserved for emergencies because patients respond differently.
- Have resuscitation equipment available.
- If injectable solution contains precipitate, don't use.
- Observe patient with status epilepticus for decrease of seizures; stop drug when convulsions cease.
- Don't give more than 60 mg/minute because respiratory depression may occur. Monitor respirations closely.

⊗ **Incompatibilities**

Acidic solutions, amphotericin B, chlorpromazine, dimenhydrinate, diphenhydramine, ephedrine, hydralazine, hydrocortisone sodium succinate, hydromorphone, insulin, kanamycin, levorphanol, meperidine, morphine, norepinephrine, pentazocine lactate, phenytoin, prochlorperazine mesylate, promethazine hydrochloride, ranitidine hydrochloride, streptomycin, vancomycin.

Contraindications and cautions

- Contraindicated in patients hypersensitive to barbiturates and in those with hepatic dysfunction, respiratory disease with dyspnea or obstruction, nephritis, or a history of manifest or latent porphyria.
- Use cautiously in debilitated patients and in patients with acute or chronic pain, depression, suicidal tendencies, history of drug abuse, altered blood pressure, CV disease, shock, or uremia.

Lifespan: In pregnant and breast-feeding women, drug isn't recommended. In the elderly, use cautiously; drug causes paradoxical excitement in these patients.

Adverse reactions

CNS: drowsiness, hangover, lethargy.
CV: ***bradycardia,*** hypotension.
GI: nausea, vomiting.
Hematologic: exacerbation of porphyria.
Respiratory: ***apnea, respiratory depression.***
Skin: ***erythema multiforme,*** rash, ***Stevens-Johnson syndrome,*** urticaria.
Other: ***angioedema;*** necrosis, nerve injury at injection site, pain, swelling, thrombophlebitis.

Interactions

Drug-drug. *Carbamazepine, corticosteroids, digitoxin, doxorubicin, doxycycline, estrogens and hormonal contraceptives, oral anticoagulants, quinidine, theophylline, tricyclic antidepressants, verapamil:* May enhance metabolism of these drugs. Monitor for decreased effect.
Chloramphenicol, MAO inhibitors, valproic acid: May increase barbiturate effect. Monitor patient for increased CNS and respiratory depression.
CNS depressants, including opioid analgesics: May increase CNS depression. Use together cautiously.
Diazepam: May increase effects of both drugs. Use together cautiously.
Griseofulvin: May decrease griseofulvin absorption. Administer drug separately.
Mephobarbital, primidone: May increase phenobarbital level. Monitor patient closely.
Metoprolol, propranolol: May reduce the effects of these drugs. Increase beta blocker dose.
Rifampin: May decrease barbiturate level. Monitor patient for decreased effect.
Drug-lifestyle. *Alcohol use:* May impair coordination, increase CNS effects, and cause death. Strongly discourage use together.

Effects on lab test results

- May decrease bilirubin level.

Pharmacokinetics

Absorption: Good after P.O. use. 100% from I.M. injection.
Distribution: Wide. About 25% to 30% protein-bound.
Metabolism: In liver.
Excretion: In urine. *Half-life:* 5 to 7 days.

Route	Onset	Peak	Duration
P.O.	20–60 min	Unknown	10–12 hr
I.V.	5 min	≥ 15 min	10–12 hr
I.M.	> 60 min	Unknown	10–12 hr

Action

Chemical effect: Unknown; may depress CNS synaptic transmission and increase seizure activity threshold in motor cortex. As sedative, may interfere with transmission of impulses from thalamus to brain cortex.
Therapeutic effect: Prevents and stops seizure activity; promotes calmness and sleep.

Available forms

Capsules: 16 mg
Elixir*: 15 mg/5ml, 20 mg/5 ml
Injection: 30 mg/ml, 60 mg/ml, 65 mg/ml, 130 mg/ml
Tablets: 15 mg, 16 mg, 30 mg, 60 mg, 100 mg

NURSING PROCESS

Assessment

- Assess patient's condition before starting therapy and regularly thereafter to monitor drug's effectiveness.
- Monitor drug level closely. Therapeutic level is 15 to 40 mcg/ml.
- Be alert for adverse reactions and drug interactions.
- Assess patient's and family's knowledge of drug therapy.

Nursing diagnoses

- Risk for trauma related to seizures
- Risk for injury related to drug-induced adverse CNS reactions
- Deficient knowledge related to drug therapy

Planning and implementation

- Don't abruptly stop giving the drug; seizures may worsen. If adverse reaction occurs, immediately notify prescriber.
- Give drug by deep I.M. injection. Superficial injection may cause pain, sterile abscess, and tissue sloughing.

ALERT: Don't confuse phenobarbital with pentobarbital.

Patient teaching

- Tell patient that phenobarbital is available in different strengths and sizes. Advise him to check prescription and refills closely.
- Inform patient that full effects don't occur for 2 to 3 weeks except when loading dose is used.
- Advise patient to avoid hazardous activities until the drug's CNS effects are known.
- Warn patient and parents not to abruptly stop taking the drug.
- Tell patient using hormonal contraceptives to use barrier-method birth control.

Evaluation

- Patient is free from seizure activity.
- Patient has no injury from drug-induced adverse CNS reactions.
- Patient and family state understanding of drug therapy.

phentermine hydrochloride

(FEN-ter-meen high-droh-KLOR-ighd)
Adipex-P, Duromine ◇, Ionamin, Ona Mast, Pro-Fast HS, Pro-Fast SA, Pro-Fast SR

Pharmacologic class: indirect-acting sympathomimetic amine
Therapeutic class: anorexigenic
Pregnancy risk category: C
Controlled substance schedule: IV

Indications and dosages

▶ **Short-term monotherapy in exogenous obesity as an adjunct to exercise, behavioral modification, and caloric restriction.** *Adults:* 8 mg P.O. t.i.d. 30 minutes before meals. Or, 15 to 37.5 mg daily before breakfast or 10 to 14 hours before bedtime. Give Pro-Fast HS or Pro-Fast SR capsules 2 hours after breakfast. Give Adipex-P before breakfast or 1 to 2 hours after breakfast.

Contraindications and cautions

- Contraindicated in agitated patients, patients hypersensitive to sympathomimetic amines, patients who have idiosyncratic reactions to them, patients who have taken an MAO inhibitor within 14 days, and patients with hyperthyroidism, moderate to severe hypertension, advanced arteriosclerosis, symptomatic CV disease, or glaucoma.
- Use cautiously in patients with mild hypertension.

Lifespan: In pregnant and breast-feeding women, drug isn't recommended. Use in children younger than 16 years of age isn't recommended.

Adverse reactions

CNS: dizziness, dysphoria, euphoria, headache, *insomnia,* overstimulation.
CV: increased blood pressure, palpitations, ***pulmonary hypertension,*** tachycardia.
EENT: blurred vision, eye irritation, mydriasis.
GI: constipation, diarrhea, dry mouth, dysgeusia, other GI disturbances.
GU: impotence.

P

Skin: urticaria.
Other: altered libido.

Interactions

Drug-drug. *Acetazolamide, antacids, sodium bicarbonate:* May increase renal reabsorption. Monitor patient.
Ammonium chloride, ascorbic acid: May decrease level and increase renal excretion of phentermine. Monitor patient for decreased effects.
Furazolidone, MAO inhibitors: May cause severe hypertension and hypertensive crisis. Don't use within 14 days of an MAO inhibitor.
Guanethidine: May decrease hypotensive effect. Monitor blood pressure closely.
Haloperidol, phenothiazines, tricyclic antidepressants: May increase CNS effects. Avoid using together.
Insulin, oral antidiabetics: May alter antidiabetic requirements. Monitor glucose level.
SSRIs: May increase sensitivity to phentermine with risk of serotonin syndrome.
Drug-food. *Caffeine:* May increase CNS stimulation. Discourage using together.

Effects on lab test results

None reported.

Pharmacokinetics

Absorption: Absorbed readily from GI tract.
Distribution: Throughout body.
Metabolism: Unknown.
Excretion: In urine. *Half-life:* 19 to 24 hours.

Route	Onset	Peak	Duration
P.O.	Unknown	Unknown	12–14 hr

Action

Chemical effect: Unknown; probably works by releasing stored norepinephrine from nerve terminals in the brain (primarily in the cerebral cortex and reticular activating system), thus promoting nerve impulse transmission.
Therapeutic effect: Depresses appetite.

Available forms

Capsules: 15 mg, 18.75 mg, 30 mg, 37.5 mg
Capsules (extended-release): 15 mg, 30 mg
Tablets: 8 mg, 15 mg, 18.75 mg, 30 mg, 37.5 mg

NURSING PROCESS

Assessment

- Weigh patient before starting therapy and regularly thereafter to monitor drug's effectiveness.
- Be alert for adverse reactions and drug interactions.
- Monitor patient for habituation and tolerance.
- Assess patient's and family's knowledge of drug therapy.

Nursing diagnoses

- Imbalanced nutrition: more than body requirements related to food intake
- Sleep deprivation related to drug-induced insomnia
- Deficient knowledge related to drug therapy

Planning and implementation

- Give drug at least 6 hours before bedtime to avoid insomnia.
- Make sure patient is following a weight-reduction program.

ALERT: Don't confuse phentermine with phentolamine.

Patient teaching

- Instruct patient to take drug at least 6 hours before bedtime to avoid sleep interference.
- Warn patient to avoid hazardous activities until the drug's CNS effects are known.
- Instruct patient that drug is to meant to suppress appetite while patient maintains a reducing diet and that he shouldn't use the drug for more than 3 to 4 weeks.
- Tell patient to avoid caffeine because it increases the effects of amphetamines and related amines.
- Tell patient to report signs of excessive stimulation.
- Inform patient that fatigue may result as drug effects wear off.

Evaluation

- Patient loses weight.
- Patient doesn't have insomnia.
- Patient and family state understanding of drug therapy.

phenylephrine hydrochloride
(fen-il-EF-rin high-droh-KLOR-ighd)
Neo-Synephrine

Pharmacologic class: adrenergic
Therapeutic class: vasoconstrictor
Pregnancy risk category: C

Indications and dosages

▶ **Hypotensive emergencies during spinal anesthesia.** *Adults:* Initially, 0.1 to 0.2 mg I.V., followed by 0.1 to 0.2 mg, p.r.n.

▶ **Maintenance of blood pressure during spinal or inhalation anesthesia.** *Adults:* 2 to 3 mg subcutaneously or I.M. 3 or 4 minutes before anesthesia.
Children: 0.044 to 0.088 mg/kg subcutaneously or I.M.

▶ **Prolongation of spinal anesthesia.** *Adults:* 2 to 5 mg added to anesthetic solution.

▶ **Vasoconstrictor for regional anesthesia.** *Adults:* 1 mg phenylephrine added to 20 ml local anesthetic.

▶ **Mild to moderate hypotension.** *Adults:* 2 to 5 mg subcutaneously or I.M.; repeated in 1 to 2 hours as needed and tolerated. Maximum first dose, 5 mg. Or, 0.1 to 0.5 mg slow I.V., no more than q 10 to 15 minutes.
Children: 0.1 mg/kg I.M. or subcutaneously; repeated in 1 to 2 hours as needed and tolerated.

▶ **Severe hypotension and shock (including drug-induced).** *Adults:* 0.1 to 0.18 mg/minute I.V. infusion. After blood pressure stabilizes, maintain at 0.04 to 0.06 mg/minute and adjust to patient response.

▶ **Paroxysmal supraventricular tachycardia.** *Adults:* Initially, 0.5 mg rapid I.V. Increase later doses by 0.1 to 0.2 mg. Maximum dose, 1 mg.

I.V. administration

- For direct injection, dilute 10 mg (1 ml) with 9 ml sterile water for injection to provide solution containing 1 mg/ml.
- Prepare I.V. infusions by adding 10 mg of drug to 500 ml of D_5W or normal saline solution for injection.
- Initial infusion rate is usually 100 to 180 mcg/minute; maintenance rate is usually 40 to 60 mcg/minute.
- Use central venous catheter or large vein, as in antecubital fossa, to minimize risk of extravasation.
- Use continuous infusion pump to regulate flow rate.
- During infusion, frequently monitor ECG, blood pressure, cardiac output, central venous pressure, pulmonary capillary wedge pressure, pulse rate, urine output, and color and temperature of limbs. Titrate infusion rate according to findings and prescriber's guidelines.
- To treat extravasation, infiltrate site promptly with 10 to 15 ml of normal saline solution for injection that contains 5 to 10 mg phentolamine. Use a fine needle.
- After prolonged I.V. infusion, avoid abrupt withdrawal.
- Store at room temperature and protect from light.

⊗ **Incompatibilities**
Alkaline solutions, butacaine sulfate, iron salts, other metals, phenytoin sodium, thiopental sodium.

Contraindications and cautions

- Contraindicated in patients hypersensitive to the drug or any of its components, and in patients with severe hypertension or ventricular tachycardia.
- Use cautiously in patients with heart disease, hyperthyroidism, severe atherosclerosis, bradycardia, partial heart block, myocardial disease, or sulfite sensitivity.
- Correct blood volume depletion before using phenylephrine.

Lifespan: In pregnant women, use cautiously. In breast-feeding women, use cautiously; it's unknown if the drug appears in breast milk. In the elderly, use cautiously.

Adverse reactions

CNS: *headache, lightheadedness, restlessness, weakness.*
CV: angina, ***arrhythmias, bradycardia,*** decreased cardiac output, hypertension, palpitations.
EENT: blurred vision.
GI: vomiting.
Respiratory: ***asthma attacks.***
Skin: feeling of coolness, pilomotor response.
Other: ***anaphylaxis,*** *decreased organ perfusion with prolonged use,* tachyphylaxis, tissue sloughing with extravasation.

P

Interactions

Drug-drug. *Alpha blockers, phenothiazines:* May decrease vasopressor response. Monitor patient closely.
Bretylium: May increase risk of arrhythmias. Monitor ECG.
Guanethidine, oxytocics: May increase pressor response and cause severe, persistent hypertension. Monitor patient and blood pressure closely.
Halogenated hydrocarbon anesthetics: May lead to serious arrhythmias. Use with caution.
MAO inhibitors: May potentiate cardiac and pressor effects. Avoid use together.
Phenelzine, tranylcypromine: May cause severe headache, hypertension, fever, and hypertensive crisis. Avoid using together.
Tricyclic antidepressants: May increase the pressor response and cause arrhythmias. Use cautiously.

Effects on lab test results

None reported.

Pharmacokinetics

Absorption: Unknown.
Distribution: Unknown.
Metabolism: In liver and intestine.
Excretion: Unknown. *Half-life:* Unknown.

Route	Onset	Peak	Duration
I.V.	Immediate	Unknown	15–20 min
I.M.	10–15 min	Unknown	½–2 hr
SubQ	10–15 min	Unknown	50–60 min

Action

Chemical effect: Mainly stimulates alpha-adrenergic receptors in sympathetic nervous system.
Therapeutic effect: Raises blood pressure and stops paroxysmal supraventricular tachycardia.

Available forms

Injection: 10 mg/ml (1%)

NURSING PROCESS

Assessment

- Assess patient's condition before starting therapy and regularly thereafter to monitor drug's effectiveness.
- Monitor blood pressure often; avoid severe increase.
- Monitor ECG throughout therapy.
- Be alert for adverse reactions and drug interactions.
- Assess patient's and family's knowledge of drug therapy.

Nursing diagnoses

- Ineffective tissue perfusion (cerebral, cardiopulmonary, peripheral, GI, renal) related to underlying condition
- Decreased cardiac output related to drug-induced adverse reaction
- Deficient knowledge related to drug therapy

Planning and implementation

- Maintain blood pressure slightly below patient's normal level. In previously normotensive patient, maintain systolic pressure at 80 to 100 mm Hg; in previously hypertensive patient, maintain systolic pressure at 30 to 40 mm Hg below usual level.

Patient teaching

- Tell patient to immediately report discomfort at infusion site.

Evaluation

- Patient maintains tissue perfusion and cellular oxygenation.
- Patient maintains adequate cardiac output.
- Patient and family state understanding of drug therapy.

phenytoin (diphenylhydantoin)

(FEN-uh-toyn)
Dilantin-125, Dilantin Infatabs

phenytoin sodium (extended)

Dilantin Kapseals✐, Phenytek

phenytoin sodium (prompt)

Dilantin

Pharmacologic class: hydantoin derivative
Therapeutic class: anticonvulsant
Pregnancy risk category: D

Indications and dosages

▶ **Control of tonic-clonic (grand mal) and complex partial (temporal lobe) seizures.** *Adults:* Highly individualized. Initially, 100 mg P.O. t.i.d. Increase in increments of 100 mg P.O.

q 2 to 4 weeks until desired response is obtained. Usual range is 300 to 600 mg daily. If patient is stabilized with extended-release capsules, may give once-daily dose with 300-mg extended-release capsules.
Children: 5 mg/kg or 250 mg/m^2 P.O. extended-release capsules divided b.i.d. or t.i.d. Maximum daily dose is 300 mg.

▶ **For patient requiring a loading dose.** *Adults:* Initially, 1 g P.O. daily divided into three doses and administered at 2-hour intervals. Or, 10 to 15 mg/kg I.V. at a rate not exceeding 50 mg/minute. Normal maintenance dose is started 24 hours later with frequent level determinations.
Children: Initially, 5 mg/kg P.O. daily in two or three equally divided doses with subsequent dose individualized to maximum of 300 mg daily. Usual dose is 4 to 8 mg/kg P.O. daily. Children older than age 6 may require the minimum adult dose (300 mg daily).

▶ **To prevent and treat seizures during neurosurgery.** *Adults:* 100 to 200 mg I.M or I.V. q 4 hours during surgery and continued in the immediate postoperative period.

▶ **Status epilepticus.** *Adults:* Loading dose of 10 to 15 mg/kg I.V. (1 to 1.5 g may be needed) at a rate not exceeding 50 mg/minute; then maintenance dose of 100 mg P.O. or I.V. q 6 to 8 hours.
Children: Loading dose of 15 to 20 mg/kg I.V., at a rate not exceeding 1 to 3 mg/kg/minute; then highly individualized maintenance dosages.

▶ **Alternative to magnesium sulfate for severe preeclampsia‡.** *Women:* 15 mg/kg I.V. given as 10 mg/kg initially and 5 mg/kg 2 hours later.

▶ **Cardiac glycoside–induced arrhythmias‡.** *Adults:* 100 mg I.V. q 5 minutes to a total of 1 g. Or, oral dose of 200 to 400 mg/day P.O.

Adjust-a-dose: Elderly patients may need lower doses.

I.V. administration

- Check patency of I.V. catheter before giving drug. Extravasation may cause severe local tissue damage.
- Never use cloudy solution.
- Avoid giving phenytoin by I.V. push into veins on back of hand to avoid discoloration known as purple glove syndrome. Inject into larger veins or central venous catheter.
- Give drug slowly (50 mg/minute) as an I.V. bolus.
- If giving as infusion, don't mix drug with D_5W because it will precipitate. Clear I.V. tubing first with normal saline solution. May mix with normal saline solution if needed and infuse over 30 to 60 minutes when possible.
- Infusion must begin within 1 hour after preparation and run through in-line filter.
- Discard 4 hours after preparation.

⊗ Incompatibilities
Amikacin, aminophylline, amphotericin B, bretylium, cephapirin, ciprofloxacin, D_5W, diltiazem, dobutamine, enalaprilat, fat emulsions, hydromorphone, insulin (regular), levorphanol, lidocaine, lincomycin, meperidine, morphine sulfate, nitroglycerin, norepinephrine, other I.V. drugs or infusion solutions, pentobarbital sodium, potassium chloride, procaine, propofol, streptomycin, sufentanil citrate, theophylline, vitamin B complex with C.

Contraindications and cautions

- Contraindicated in patients hypersensitive to hydantoin. I.V. use is contraindicated in patients with sinus bradycardia, SA block, second- or third-degree AV block, or Adams-Stokes syndrome.
- Use cautiously in debilitated patients, patients taking other hydantoin derivatives, and patients with hepatic dysfunction, hypotension, myocardial insufficiency, diabetes, or respiratory depression.
- Don't stop drug in pregnant women using the drug to prevent major seizures. An increase in seizure activity may occur in pregnant woman due to changes in drug absorption or metabolism, so monitor level carefully.

Lifespan: In pregnant women, drug isn't recommended; infants born to mothers taking phenytoin may have bleeding defects. Give vitamin K to the mother 1 month before and during delivery and to the neonate immediately after birth. In breast-feeding women, drug isn't recommended. In the elderly, use cautiously; they tend to metabolize drug slowly and may need lower doses.

Adverse reactions

CNS: *ataxia, confusion,* dizziness, headache, insomnia, nervousness, *slurred speech,* twitching.
CV: hypotension.

P

EENT: blurred vision, diplopia, gingival hyperplasia, nystagmus.
GI: nausea, vomiting.
Hematologic: ***agranulocytosis,*** anemia, ***leukopenia,*** macrocythemia, megaloblastic lymphadenopathy, ***pancytopenia, thrombocytopenia.***
Hepatic: ***toxic hepatitis.***
Metabolic: hyperglycemia.
Musculoskeletal: osteomalacia.
Skin: bullous, exfoliative, or purpuric dermatitis; *hirsutism;* hypertrichosis; photosensitivity reaction; scarlatiniform or morbilliform rash; ***Stevens-Johnson syndrome; toxic epidermal necrolysis.***
Other: lupus erythematosus; pain, necrosis, or inflammation at injection site; periarteritis nodosa.

Interactions

Drug-drug. *Amiodarone, allopurinol, antihistamines, chloramphenicol, cimetidine, clonazepam, cycloserine, diazepam, disulfiram, fluconazole, ibuprofen, influenza vaccine, isoniazid, metronidazole, omeprazole, phenylbutazone, phenothiazines, salicylates, sulfamethizole, tricyclic antidepressants, valproate:* May increase therapeutic effects of phenytoin. Monitor patient for toxicity.
Antacids, carbamazepine, dexamethasone, diazoxide, folic acid, phenobarbital, rifampin, theophylline: May decrease phenytoin activity. Monitor patient closely.
Atracurium, cisatracurium, doxacurium, mivacurium, pancuronium, rocuronium, vecuronium: May decrease the effects of nondepolarizing muscle relaxant causing it to be less effective. May need to increase the dose of the nondepolarizing muscle relaxant.
Lithium: May increase toxicity. Monitor lithium level.
Meperidine: May increase toxic effects of meperidine while decreasing analgesic effect. Monitor patient for decreased effect and toxicity.
Warfarin: May displace warfarin. Monitor patient for bleeding complications.
Drug-herb. *Milk thistle:* May decrease risk of liver toxicity. Monitor patient.
Drug-food. *Enteral nutrition therapy:* May reduce orally administered phenytoin concentrations. Consider giving phenytoin 2 hours before starting enteral feeding, or wait 2 hours after stopping enteral feeding to administer phenytoin.
Drug-lifestyle. *Alcohol use:* May decrease phenytoin activity. Discourage using together.

Effects on lab test results

- May increase alkaline phosphatase, GGT, and glucose levels. May decrease protein-bound iodine, free thyroxine, urinary 17-hydroxysteroid, 17-ketosteroid, and hemoglobin levels and hematocrit.
- May increase urine 6-hydroxycortisol excretion. May decrease platelet, WBC, RBC, and granulocyte counts.
- May decrease dexamethasone suppression and metyrapone test values.

Pharmacokinetics

Absorption: Slow after P.O. use. Formulation-dependent; bioavailability may differ among products. Erratic from I.M. site.
Distribution: Wide throughout body. About 90% protein-bound.
Metabolism: In liver.
Excretion: In urine, with dose-dependent (zero-order) elimination kinetics. Above certain dosage level, small increases in dose disproportionately increase level. *Half-life:* Varies with dose and concentration changes.

Route	Onset	Peak	Duration
P.O.	Unknown	½–2 hr	Unknown
P.O. extended-release	Unknown	4–12 hr	Unknown
I.V.	Immediate	1–2 hr	Unknown
I.M.	Unknown	Unknown	Unknown

Action

Chemical effect: Unknown; probably limits seizure activity by either increasing efflux or decreasing influx of sodium ions across cell membranes in motor cortex during generation of nerve impulses.
Therapeutic effect: Prevents and stops seizure activity.

Available forms

phenytoin
Oral suspension: 125 mg/5 ml
Tablets (chewable): 50 mg

phenytoin sodium (extended)
Capsules: 30 mg (27.6-mg base), 100 mg (92-mg base), 200 mg (184-mg base), 300 mg (276-mg base)
phenytoin sodium (prompt)
Capsules: 100 mg (92-mg base)
Injection: 50 mg/ml (46-mg base)

NURSING PROCESS

Assessment

- Assess patient's condition before starting therapy and regularly thereafter to monitor drug's effectiveness.
- Monitor phenytoin level; therapeutic level is 10 to 20 mcg/ml.
- Monitor CBC and calcium level q 6 months, and periodically monitor hepatic function.
- Check vital signs, blood pressure, and ECG during I.V. administration.
- Be alert for adverse reactions and drug interactions.
- Mononucleosis may decrease phenytoin level. Monitor patient for increased seizure activity.
- Assess patient's and family's knowledge of drug therapy.

Nursing diagnoses

- Risk for trauma related to seizures
- Impaired oral mucous membrane related to gingival hyperplasia
- Deficient knowledge related to drug therapy

Planning and implementation

- Use only clear or slightly yellow solution for injection. Don't refrigerate.
- Divided doses given with or after meals may decrease adverse GI reactions.
- Dilantin capsule is only P.O. form that can be given once daily. If any other brand or form is given once daily, toxic level may result.
- Don't give drug I.M. unless dosage adjustments are made. Drug may precipitate at site, cause pain, and be erratically absorbed.
- If rash appears, stop giving the drug. If rash is scarlatiniform or morbilliform, drug may be resumed after rash clears. If rash reappears, stop giving the drug. If rash is exfoliative, purpuric, or bullous, don't resume.
- Don't abruptly stop giving the drug; seizures may worsen. If adverse reaction occurs, immediately notify prescriber.
- If patient has megaloblastic anemia, prescriber may order folic acid and vitamin B_{12}.

ALERT: Don't confuse phenytoin with Mephyton or fosphenytoin.

ALERT: Don't confuse Dilantin with Dilaudid.

Patient teaching

- Advise patient to avoid hazardous activities until the drug's CNS effects are known.
- Advise patient not to change brand, dose, or form.
- Warn patient and parents not to abruptly stop taking the drug.
- Promote oral hygiene and regular dental examinations. Gingivectomy may be needed periodically if dental hygiene is poor.
- Inform patient that drug may color urine pink, red, or red-brown.
- Tell patient that heavy alcohol use may diminish drug's benefits.

Evaluation

- Patient is free from seizure activity.
- Patient expresses importance of good oral hygiene and regular dental examinations.
- Patient and family state understanding of drug therapy.

physostigmine salicylate (eserine salicylate)

(fiz-oh-STIG-meen sa-LIS-il-ayt)
Antilirium

Pharmacologic class: cholinesterase inhibitor
Therapeutic class: antimuscarinic antidote
Pregnancy risk category: C

Indications and dosages

▶ **To reverse CNS toxicity caused by anticholinergics.** *Adults:* 0.5 to 2 mg I.M. or slow I.V. injection (1 mg/minute or slower). If coma, seizures, or arrhythmias recur, dose may be repeated.
Children: 0.02 mg/kg I.M. or slow I.V. injection (0.5 mg/min or slower). Repeat q 5 to 10 minutes until patient responds. Maximum dose, 2 mg. Drug is only for life-threatening situations.

P

I.V. administration

- Use only clear solution. Darkening of solution may indicate loss of potency.
- Give drug I.V. at controlled rate; use direct injection at no more than 1 mg/minute. Rapid administration may cause bradycardia and hypersalivation, leading to respiratory difficulties and seizures.

⊗ Incompatibilities

None reported.

Contraindications and cautions

- Contraindicated in patients taking choline esters or depolarizing neuromuscular blockers and in patients with mechanical obstruction of intestine or urogenital tract, asthma, gangrene, diabetes, CV disease, or vagotonia.
- Use cautiously in patients with sensitivity or allergy to sulfites.

Lifespan: In pregnant women, use cautiously. In breast-feeding women, safety and effectiveness haven't been established. In children, use only in life-threatening situations.

Adverse reactions

CNS: ataxia, *excitability,* hallucinations, muscle twitching, muscle weakness, *restlessness,* ***seizures,*** *sweating.*
CV: ***bradycardia,*** hypotension, irregular pulse, palpitations.
EENT: miosis.
GI: *diarrhea,* epigastric pain, *excessive salivation,* nausea, vomiting.
GU: urinary urgency.
Respiratory: bronchial constriction, ***bronchospasm,*** dyspnea.

Interactions

Drug-drug. *Anticholinergics, atropine, procainamide, quinidine:* May reverse cholinergic effects. Observe patient for lack of drug effect.
Drug-herb. *Jaborandi tree, pill-bearing spurge:* May have additive effects and increase risk of toxicity. Discourage using together.

Effects on lab test results

None reported.

Pharmacokinetics

Absorption: Absorbed well from injection site.
Distribution: Wide, including across blood-brain barrier.
Metabolism: Cholinesterase hydrolyzes physostigmine relatively quickly.
Excretion: Primary mode unknown; small amount excreted in urine. *Half-life:* 1 to 2 hours.

Route	Onset	Peak	Duration
I.V.	3–5 min	≤ 5 min	30–60 min
I.M.	3–5 min	20–30 min	30–60 min

Action

Chemical effect: Inhibits destruction of acetylcholine released from parasympathetic and somatic efferent nerves. Acetylcholine accumulates, promoting increased stimulation of receptor.
Therapeutic effect: Reverses anticholinergic signs and symptoms.

Available forms

Injection: 1 mg/ml

NURSING PROCESS

Assessment

- Assess patient's condition before starting therapy and regularly thereafter. Effect is often immediate and dramatic, but may be transient and require repeated doses.
- Monitor vital signs often, especially respirations.
- Be alert for adverse reactions and drug interactions.
- Assess patient's and family's knowledge of drug therapy.

Nursing diagnoses

- Ineffective health maintenance related to underlying condition
- Risk for injury related to drug-induced adverse CNS reactions
- Deficient knowledge related to drug therapy

Planning and implementation

- Position patient to ease breathing. If hypersensitivity or cholinergic crisis occurs, have atropine injection readily available and give 0.5 mg subcutaneously or slow I.V. push. Provide respiratory support p.r.n. Best administered in presence of prescriber.
- If patient becomes restless or hallucinates, raise side rails of bed. Adverse reaction may indicate drug toxicity. Notify prescriber.

• If patient has excessive salivation or emesis, frequent urination, or diarrhea, stop the drug.
• If patient has excessive sweating or nausea, lower dose.

Patient teaching

• Tell patient to report adverse reactions, especially pain at the I.V. site.

Evaluation

• Patient responds well to therapy.
• Patient doesn't experience injury from adverse CNS reactions.
• Patient and family state understanding of drug therapy.

phytonadione (vitamin K_1)

(figh-toh-neh-DIGH-ohn)

AquaMEPHYTON, Mephyton

Pharmacologic class: synthetic analogue of vitamin K
Therapeutic class: blood coagulation modifier
Pregnancy risk category: C

Indications and dosages

▶ **RDA.** *Infants age 6 months and younger:* 5 mcg.
Infants ages 6 months to 1 year: 10 mcg.
Children ages 1 to 3: Give 15 mcg.
Children ages 4 to 6: Give 20 mcg.
Children ages 7 to 10: Give 30 mcg.
Children ages 11 to 14: Give 45 mcg.
Adolescent males ages 15 to 18: Give 65 mcg.
Men ages 19 to 24: Give 70 mcg.
Men age 25 and older: Give 80 mcg.
Adolescent females ages 15 to 18: Give 55 mcg.
Women ages 19 to 24: Give 60 mcg.
Women age 25 and older, and pregnant or breast-feeding women: Give 65 mcg.

▶ **Hypoprothrombinemia secondary to vitamin K malabsorption, drug therapy, or excessive vitamin A.** *Adults:* Depending on severity, 2.5 to 25 mg P.O., subcutaneously, or I.M.; repeat and increase up to 50 mg, if needed.

▶ **Hypoprothrombinemia secondary to effect of oral anticoagulants.** *Adults:* 2.5 to 10 mg P.O., subcutaneously, or I.M. based on PT; repeat if needed within 12 to 48 hours after P.O. dose or within 6 to 8 hours after parenteral dose.

▶ **To prevent hemorrhagic disease of newborns.** *Neonates:* 0.5 to 1 mg I.M. or subcutaneously within 1 hour after birth.

▶ **Hemorrhagic disease of newborns.** *Neonates:* 1 mg subcutaneously or I.M. based on laboratory tests. Higher doses may be needed if mother has been taking oral anticoagulants.

I.V. administration

ALERT: Severe reactions, including fatalities, may occur with I.V. injection. Use I.V. route only if other routes aren't available and when benefits outweigh serious risks.
• Dilute drug with normal saline solution for injection, D_5W, or 5% dextrose in normal saline solution for injection.
• Protect parenteral products from light. Wrap infusion container with aluminum foil.

⊗ **Incompatibilities**

Dobutamine, phenytoin sodium, ranitidine.

Contraindications and cautions

• Contraindicated in patients hypersensitive to the drug or any of its components.

Lifespan: In pregnant women, use cautiously. In breast-feeding women, use cautiously; it's unknown if the drug appears in breast milk. In neonates, use cautiously and don't exceed recommended dose.

Adverse reactions

CNS: dizziness, seizure-like movements.
CV: cardiac irregularities, flushing, rapid and weak pulse, transient hypotension after I.V. administration.
Skin: diaphoresis, erythema.
Other: ***anaphylaxis and anaphylactoid reactions*** (usually after rapid I.V. administration); cramplike pain; pain, swelling, and hematoma at injection site.

Interactions

Drug-drug. *Anticoagulants:* May cause temporary resistance to prothrombin-depressing anticoagulants, especially when larger doses of phytonadione are used. Monitor patient closely.
Cholestyramine resin, mineral oil: May inhibit GI absorption of oral vitamin K. Administer separately.

Effects on lab test results

• May decrease PT and INR.

Pharmacokinetics

Absorption: Requires bile salts for GI absorption after P.O. use. Unknown after I.M. or subcutaneous use.
Distribution: Concentrates briefly in liver.
Metabolism: Rapid, in liver.
Excretion: Unclear. *Half-life:* Unknown.

Route	Onset	Peak	Duration
P.O.	6–12 hr	Unknown	12–14 hr
I.V., I.M., SubQ	1–2 hr	Unknown	12–14 hr

Action

Chemical effect: An antihemorrhagic factor that promotes hepatic formation of active prothrombin.
Therapeutic effect: Controls abnormal bleeding.

Available forms

Injection (aqueous colloidal solution): 2 mg/ml, 10 mg/ml
Tablets: 5 mg

NURSING PROCESS

Assessment

- Assess patient's condition before starting therapy and regularly thereafter to monitor drug's effectiveness.
- Monitor PT to determine dosage effectiveness.
- Failure to respond to vitamin K may indicate coagulation defects.
- Be alert for adverse reactions and drug interactions.
- If adverse GI reactions occur, monitor patient's hydration.
- Assess patient's and family's knowledge of drug therapy.

Nursing diagnoses

- Ineffective protection related to underlying vitamin K deficiency
- Risk for deficient fluid volume related to adverse GI reactions
- Deficient knowledge related to drug therapy

Planning and implementation

- Check brand name labels for administration route restrictions.
- Subcutaneous is the preferred route of administration.
- Give drug I.M. in upper outer quadrant of buttocks in an adult; inject in infant's outer thigh.
- If severe bleeding occurs, don't delay other therapy, such as fresh frozen plasma or whole blood.
- Does not counteract the anticoagulant effects of heparin or low–molecular-weight heparin.

Patient teaching

- Explain drug's purpose.
- Instruct patient to report adverse reactions.

Evaluation

- Patient achieves normal PT level with drug therapy.
- Patient maintains adequate hydration throughout drug therapy.
- Patient and family state understanding of drug therapy.

pimecrolimus

(py-meck-roh-LY-muhs)
Elidel

Pharmacologic class: topical immunomodulator
Therapeutic class: topical skin product
Pregnancy risk category: C

Indications and dosages

▶ **Short-term and intermittent long-term therapy for mild to moderate atopic dermatitis in nonimmunocompromised patients in whom the use of alternative, conventional therapies is deemed inadvisable or for patients who aren't adequately responding to or are intolerant of conventional therapies.** *Adults and children age 2 and older:* Apply a thin layer to the affected skin twice daily and rub in gently and completely.

Contraindications and cautions

- Contraindicated in patients hypersensitive to the drug or any of the cream's components.
- Don't use on areas of active cutaneous viral infections or infected atopic dermatitis.
- Not recommended for use in patients with Netherton syndrome or in immunocompromised patients.
- Use cautiously in patients with varicella zoster virus infection, herpes simplex virus infection, or eczema herpeticum.

Lifespan: In pregnant women, safety and effectiveness haven't been established. Breast-feeding women should stop breast-feeding or use another drug. In children younger than age 2, drug isn't recommended. In patients age 65 and older, safety and effectiveness haven't been established.

Adverse reactions

CNS: *headache.*
EENT: conjunctivitis, earache, epistaxis, eye infection, nasal congestion, *nasopharyngitis,* otitis media, pharyngitis, rhinitis, rhinorrhea, sinus congestion, sinusitis.
GI: abdominal pain, constipation, diarrhea, gastroenteritis, loose stools, nausea, sore throat, tonsillitis, toothache, vomiting.
GU: dysmenorrhea.
Musculoskeletal: arthralgias, back pain.
Respiratory: asthma, *bronchitis,* cough, dyspnea, *pneumonia, upper respiratory tract infections,* wheezing.
Skin: acne, folliculitis, impetigo, molluscum contagiosum, skin infections, skin papilloma, urticaria, varicella.
Other: *application site reaction* (burning, irritation, erythema, pruritus), bacterial infection, flu-like illness, herpes simplex, hypersensitivity reaction, *influenza, pyrexia,* staphylococcal infection, viral infection.

Interactions

Drug-drug. *CYP3A family of inhibitors (erythromycin, itraconazole, ketoconazole, fluconazole, calcium channel blockers):* May have an effect on metabolism of pimecrolimus. Use together cautiously.
Drug-lifestyle. *Natural or artificial sunlight:* Drug may shorten the time to skin tumor formation. Avoid or minimize exposure to sunlight.

Effects on lab test results

None reported.

Pharmacokinetics

Absorption: Low systemic absorption.
Distribution: 74% to 87% protein-bound.
Metabolism: No evidence of skin-mediated drug metabolism exists.
Excretion: After a single oral radiolabeled dose, about 81% of radioactivity can be recovered, mainly in feces (78.4%), as metabolites. Less than 1% of radioactivity in feces is from unchanged drug. *Half-life:* Unknown.

Route	Onset	Peak	Duration
Topical	Unknown	Unknown	Unknown

Action

Chemical effect: Unknown. May inhibit T cell activation by blocking the transcription of early cytokines. May also prevent the release of inflammatory cytokines and mediators from mast cells in vitro after stimulation by antigen/immunoglobulin E.
Therapeutic effect: Improves skin integrity.

Available forms

Cream: 1% in tubes of 15 g, 30 g, and 100 g (Base contains the following alcohols: benzyl alcohol, cetyl alcohol, oleyl alcohol, and stearyl alcohol.)

NURSING PROCESS

Assessment

- Assess underlying skin condition before starting therapy and regularly thereafter to monitor drug's effectiveness. Clear up infections at disease sites before use.
- Assess patient's and family's knowledge of drug therapy.

Nursing diagnoses

- Risk for situational low self-esteem related to skin disorder
- Impaired skin integrity related to underlying skin condition
- Deficient knowledge related to pimecrolimus therapy

Planning and implementation

- May be used on all skin surfaces, including the head, neck, and intertriginous areas.
- Use only after other treatments have failed because of risk of cancer with its use.
- If disease resolves, stop giving the drug.
- If symptoms persist beyond 6 weeks, reevaluate patient.

ALERT: Don't use with occlusive dressing; this may promote systemic exposure.

- May cause local symptoms such as skin burning. Most local reactions start within 1 to 5 days, are mild to moderately severe, and last no more than 5 days.

P

• Monitor patient for lymphadenopathy. If the cause isn't clear or the patient has acute infectious mononucleosis, consider stopping drug.
• Papillomas or warts may occur. If skin papillomas worsen or don't respond to conventional therapy, consider stopping drug.

Patient teaching

• Instruct patient to use as directed; this drug is for external use on the skin only. Tell patient to report any signs or symptoms of adverse reactions.
• Tell patient not to use drug with an occlusive dressing.
• Instruct patient to wash hands after application if hands aren't being treated.
• Tell patient to stop using the drug after signs and symptoms of atopic dermatitis have resolved. Tell patient to contact prescriber if symptoms persist beyond 6 weeks.
• Advise patient to resume therapy at the first signs or symptoms of recurrence.
• Instruct patient to minimize or avoid exposure to natural or artificial sunlight (including tanning beds and ultraviolet A and B therapy) while using this drug.
• Tell patient that application site reactions are expected, but to notify prescriber if reaction is severe or persists for more than 1 week.

Evaluation

• Patient has improved self-esteem as skin condition clears.
• Patient has improved skin condition.
• Patient and family state understanding of drug therapy.

pioglitazone hydrochloride
(pigh-oh-GLIH-tah-zohn high-droh-KLOR-ighd)
Actos

Pharmacologic class: thiazolidinedione
Therapeutic class: antidiabetic
Pregnancy risk category: C

Indications and dosages

▶ **Monotherapy adjunct to diet and exercise to improve glycemic control in patients with type 2 diabetes mellitus, or combination therapy with a sulfonylurea, metformin, or insulin when diet, exercise, and the single drug don't yield adequate glycemic control.** *Adults:* Initially, 15 or 30 mg P.O. once daily. For patients who respond inadequately to initial dose, increase in increments; maximum daily dose is 45 mg. If used in combination therapy, don't exceed 30 mg daily.

Contraindications and cautions

• Contraindicated in patients hypersensitive to the drug or any of its components. Not recommended for New York Heart Association Class III and IV cardiac patients.
• Also contraindicated in patients with type 1 diabetes mellitus or diabetic ketoacidosis, patients with evidence of active liver disease, patients with ALT level more than 2½ times the upper limit of normal, and patients who experienced jaundice while taking troglitazone.
Lifespan: In pregnant women, use only if benefits outweigh risks to the fetus; insulin is the preferred antidiabetic for use during pregnancy. Potentially excreted in breast milk. Avoid use if breast-feeding. Safety has not been established in children younger than 18.

Adverse reactions

CNS: headache.
CV: edema, ***heart failure.***
EENT: pharyngitis, sinusitis.
Hematologic: anemia.
Metabolic: aggravated diabetes mellitus, ***hypoglycemia with combination therapy,*** weight gain.
Musculoskeletal: myalgia.
Respiratory: upper respiratory tract infection.
Other: tooth disorder.

Interactions

Drug-drug. *Atorvastatin, midazolam, nifedipine:* May reduce levels of these drugs. Monitor patient.
Hormonal contraceptives: May reduce level of hormonal contraceptives, resulting in less effective contraception. Advise patients taking pioglitazone and hormonal contraceptives to consider additional birth control measures.
Ketoconazole and other CYP3A4 inhibitors: May inhibit pioglitazone metabolism. Monitor patient's glucose level more frequently.
Drug-herb. *Aloe, bilberry leaf, bitter melon, burdock, dandelion, fenugreek, garlic, ginseng:* May improve blood glucose control and allow reduction of antidiabetic dose. Advise patient to

discuss herbal remedies with prescriber before using them.

Effects on lab test results

- May increase liver enzyme and HDL levels. May decrease glucose, triglyceride, and hemoglobin levels and hematocrit.

Pharmacokinetics

Absorption: On an empty stomach, rapidly absorbed and measurable in serum within 30 minutes; level peaks within 2 hours. Food slightly delays time to peak level (to 3 to 4 hours), but doesn't affect overall extent of absorption.
Distribution: Drug and its metabolites are more than 98% protein-bound, mainly to albumin.
Metabolism: Extensive, by the liver. Three metabolites, M-II, M-III, and M-IV, are pharmacologically active.
Excretion: About 15% to 30% of dose is recovered in urine, mainly as metabolites and their conjugates. Most of P.O. dose is excreted in bile and eliminated in feces. *Half-life:* 3 to 7 hours.

Route	Onset	Peak	Duration
P.O.	Unknown	< 2 hr	Unknown

Action

Chemical effect: Decreases insulin resistance in the periphery and in the liver, resulting in decreased glucose output by the liver.
Therapeutic effect: Lowers glucose level.

Available forms

Tablets: 15 mg, 30 mg, 45 mg

NURSING PROCESS

Assessment

- Obtain history of patient's underlying condition before starting therapy and regularly thereafter to monitor drug's effectiveness.
- Assess patient for excessive fluid volume. Monitor patient with heart failure for increased edema.
- Measure liver enzymes at start of therapy, q 2 months for the first year of therapy, and periodically thereafter. Obtain liver function test results in patients who develop evidence of liver dysfunction, such as nausea, vomiting, abdominal pain, fatigue, anorexia, or dark urine.
- Monitor hemoglobin level and hematocrit, especially during the first 4 to 12 weeks of therapy.
- Monitor glucose level regularly, especially during situations of increased stress, such as infection, fever, surgery, and trauma.
- Check glycosylated hemoglobin level periodically to evaluate therapeutic response to drug.
- Assess patient's and family's knowledge of drug therapy.

Nursing diagnoses

- Ineffective health maintenance related to hyperglycemia
- Risk for injury related to drug-induced hyperglycemia
- Deficient knowledge related to drug therapy

Planning and implementation

- If patient develops jaundice or if results of liver function tests show ALT elevations greater than three times the upper limit of normal, notify prescriber and stop giving the drug.
- Drug alone or with insulin can cause fluid retention that may lead to or exacerbate heart failure. Observe patients for signs or symptoms of heart failure. If cardiac condition deteriorates, stop drug.
- Watch for hypoglycemia in patients taking pioglitazone with insulin or a sulfonylurea. Dose adjustments of these drugs may be needed.
- Premenopausal, anovulatory women with insulin resistance may need contraception because ovulation may resume.

Patient teaching

- Tell patient to control his diet in order to manage type 2 diabetes because calorie restrictions, weight loss, and exercise improve insulin sensitivity and make drug therapy more effective.
- Instruct patient to adhere to dietary instructions and to have glucose and glycosylated hemoglobin level tested regularly.
- Inform patient taking drug with insulin or an oral antidiabetic about the signs and symptoms of hypoglycemia.
- Tell patient to notify prescriber about periods of stress, such as fever, trauma, infection, or surgery, because drug requirements may change.
- Inform patient that blood tests for liver function will be performed before the start of therapy, every 2 months for the first year, and periodically thereafter.

P

• Tell patient to report unexplained nausea, vomiting, abdominal pain, fatigue, anorexia, or dark urine immediately because these signs and symptoms may indicate liver problems.
• Advise patient to contact prescriber if he has signs or symptoms of heart failure (unusually rapid increase in weight or edema, shortness of breath).
• Inform patient that pioglitazone can be taken with or without meals.
• If patient misses a dose, warn against doubling the dose the following day.
• Advise premenopausal, anovulatory woman with insulin resistance that drug may restore ovulation; recommend that she consider contraception as needed.

Evaluation

• Patient's glucose level is normal with drug therapy.
• Patient doesn't experience hypoglycemia.
• Patient and family state understanding of drug therapy.

piperacillin sodium and tazobactam sodium

(pigh-PER-uh-sil-in SOH-dee-um and taz-oh-BAK-tem SOH-dee-um)
Zosyn

Pharmacologic class: beta-lactamase inhibitor, extended-spectrum penicillin
Therapeutic class: antibiotic
Pregnancy risk category: B

Indications and dosages

▶ **Moderate to severe infections caused by piperacillin-resistant, piperacillin and tazobactam–susceptible, beta-lactamase–producing strains of microorganisms in the following conditions: appendicitis (complicated by rupture or abscess) and peritonitis caused by *Escherichia coli, Bacteroides fragilis, Bacteroides ovatus, Bacteroides thetaiotaomicron, Bacteroides vulgatus;* skin and skin-structure infections caused by *Staphylococcus aureus;* postpartum endometritis or pelvic inflammatory disease caused by *E. coli;* moderately severe community-acquired pneumonia caused by *Haemophilus influenzae.*** *Adults:* 3.375 g (3 g piperacillin and 0.375 g tazobactam) q 6 hours as a 30-minute I.V. infusion for 7 to 10 days.

Adjust-a-dose: For patients with renal impairment, if creatinine clearance is 20 to 40 ml/minute, give 2.25 g (2 g piperacillin and 0.25 g tazobactam) q 6 hours; if clearance is less than 20 ml/minute, give same dose q 8 hours.

In patients undergoing continuous ambulatory peritoneal dialysis (CAPD), give same dose q 12 hours. In hemodialysis patients, give same dose q 12 hours with a supplemental dose of 0.75 g (0.67 g piperacillin and 0.08 g tazobactam) after each dialysis period.

▶ **Moderate to severe nosocomial pneumonia caused by piperacillin-resistant, beta-lactamase–producing strains of *S. aureus* and by piperacillin and tazobactam–susceptible *Acinetobacter baumannii, H. influenzae, Klebsiella pneumoniae,* and *Pseudomonas aeruginosa.*** *Adults:* 4.5 g (4 g piperacillin and 0.5 g tazobactam) q 6 hours given with an aminoglycoside for 7 to 14 days. For patients with *P. aeruginosa,* continue aminoglycoside therapy; if *P. aeruginosa* isn't isolated, may stop aminoglycoside therapy.

Adjust-a-dose: For patients with renal impairment, if creatinine clearance is 20 to 40 ml/minute, give 3.375 g (3 g piperacillin and 0.375 g tazobactam) q 6 hours; if clearance is less than 20 ml/minute, give 2.25 g (2 g piperacillin and 0.25 g tazobactam) q 6 hours. In CAPD patients, give 2.25 g (2 g piperacillin and 0.25 g tazobactam) q 8 hours.

I.V. administration

• Reconstitute each gram of drug with 5 ml of diluent, such as sterile or bacteriostatic water for injection, normal saline solution for injection, bacteriostatic normal saline solution for injection, D_5W, 5% dextrose in normal saline solution for injection, or dextran 6% in normal saline solution for injection. Shake until dissolved. Further dilute to final volume of 50 ml before infusion.
• Infuse drug over at least 30 minutes. Stop other primary infusions during administration if possible. Aminoglycoside antibiotics (such as gentamicin and tobramycin) are chemically incompatible with drug. Don't mix in same I.V. container.
• Use drug immediately after reconstitution. Discard unused drug in single-dose vials after

24 hours if held at room temperature; after 48 hours if refrigerated. Diluted drug is stable in I.V. bags for 24 hours at room temperature or 1 week if refrigerated.
• Change I.V. site every 48 hours.

⊗ **Incompatibilities**
Acyclovir sodium, aminoglycosides, amphotericin B, chlorpromazine, cisatracurium, cisplatin, dacarbazine, daunorubicin, dobutamine, doxorubicin, doxycycline hyclate, droperidol, famotidine, ganciclovir, gemcitabine, haloperidol lactate, hydroxyzine hydrochloride, idarubicin, lactated Ringer's solution, minocycline, mitomycin, mitoxantrone, nalbuphine, prochlorperazine edisylate, promethazine hydrochloride, streptozocin, vancomycin.

Contraindications and cautions

• Contraindicated in patients hypersensitive to the drug or other penicillins.
• Use cautiously in patients with other drug allergies, especially to cephalosporins (risk of cross-sensitivity), and in those with bleeding tendencies, uremia, or hypokalemia.
Lifespan: In pregnant women, use cautiously. In breast-feeding women, use cautiously; it's unknown if the drug appears in breast milk. In children younger than age 12, safety and effectiveness haven't been established.

Adverse reactions

CNS: agitation, anxiety, dizziness, fever, *headache, insomnia,* pain.
CV: chest pain, edema, hypertension, tachycardia.
EENT: rhinitis.
GI: abdominal pain, *constipation, diarrhea,* dyspepsia, *nausea,* stool changes, vomiting.
Hematologic: ***thrombocytopenia.***
Respiratory: dyspnea.
Skin: pruritus, rash (including bullous, eczematoid, maculopapular, and urticarial) .
Other: ***anaphylaxis,*** candidiasis, inflammation and phlebitis at I.V. site.

Interactions

Drug-drug. *Anticoagulants:* May increase risk of bleeding. Monitor PT, PTT, and INR, and monitor patient for bleeding.
Hormonal contraceptives: May decrease effectiveness of hormonal contraceptives. Advise alternative barrier method during therapy.
Probenecid: May increase level of piperacillin. Probenecid may be used for this purpose.
Vecuronium: May prolong neuromuscular blockage. Monitor patient closely.

Effects on lab test results

• May increase AST, ALT, alkaline phosphatase, bilirubin, BUN, and creatinine levels. May decrease hemoglobin level and hematocrit. May increase or decrease sodium, potassium and calcium levels.
• May increase PT, PTT, and eosinophil count. May decrease WBC and platelet counts.

Pharmacokinetics

Absorption: Given I.V.
Distribution: Both drugs are about 30% protein-bound.
Metabolism: Piperacillin is metabolized to a minor, microbiologically active desethyl metabolite. Tazobactam is metabolized to a single metabolite that lacks pharmacologic and antibacterial activities.
Excretion: In urine and bile. *Half-life:* piperacillin, 40 minutes; tazobactam, 70 minutes.

Route	Onset	Peak	Duration
I.V.	Immediate	Immediate	Unknown

Action

Chemical effect: Piperacillin inhibits cell wall synthesis during microorganism multiplication; tazobactam increases piperacillin effectiveness by inactivating beta-lactamases, which destroy penicillins.
Therapeutic effect: Kills susceptible bacteria.

Available forms

Powder for injection: 2 g piperacillin and 0.25 g tazobactam per vial, 3 g piperacillin and 0.375 g tazobactam per vial, 4 g piperacillin and 0.5 g tazobactam per vial

NURSING PROCESS

Assessment

• Before giving drug, ask patient about previous allergic reactions to this drug or other penicillins. Negative history of penicillin allergy doesn't guarantee future safety.
• Assess patient's infection before starting therapy and regularly thereafter to monitor drug's effectiveness.

P

• Obtain specimen for culture and sensitivity tests before first dose. Start therapy pending test results.
• Be alert for adverse reactions and drug interactions. If adverse GI reaction occurs, monitor patient's hydration.
• Assess patient's and family's knowledge of drug therapy.

Nursing diagnoses

• Risk for infection related to presence of bacteria
• Risk of deficient fluid volume related to adverse GI reactions
• Deficient knowledge related to drug therapy

Planning and implementation

• Because hemodialysis removes 6% of piperacillin dose and 21% of tazobactam dose, supplemental doses may be needed after hemodialysis.

Patient teaching

• Tell patient to report pain or discomfort at I.V. site.
• Advise patient to limit salt intake while taking drug because piperacillin contains 1.98 mEq of sodium per gram.
• Tell patient to report adverse reactions.

Evaluation

• Patient is free from infection.
• Patient maintains adequate hydration.
• Patient and family state understanding of drug therapy.

polyethylene glycol and electrolyte solution

(pol-ee-ETH-ih-leen GLIGH-kohl and ee-LEK-troh-light soh-LOO-shun)

CoLyte, GoLYTELY, NuLYTELY, OCL, TriLyte

Pharmacologic class: polyethylene glycol (PEG) 3350 nonabsorbable solution
Therapeutic class: laxative and bowel evacuant
Pregnancy risk category: C

Indications and dosages

▶ **Bowel preparation before GI examination.** *Adults:* 240 ml P.O. q 10 minutes until 4 L are consumed. Typically, give 4 hours before examination, allowing 3 hours for drinking and 1 hour for bowel evacuation.
▶ **Management of acute iron overdose‡.** *Children older than age 3:* Give 2,953 ml/kg over 5 days.

Contraindications and cautions

• Contraindicated in patients with GI obstruction or perforation, gastric retention, toxic colitis, or megacolon.
Lifespan: In pregnant women, use cautiously. In breast-feeding women, use cautiously; it's unknown if the drug appears in breast milk.

Adverse reactions

GI: bloating, cramps, nausea, vomiting.

Interactions

Drug-drug. *Oral drugs:* May decrease absorption if given within 1 hour of starting therapy. Don't give with other oral drugs.

Effects on lab test results

None reported.

Pharmacokinetics

Absorption: None.
Distribution: Not applicable; drug isn't absorbed.
Metabolism: Not applicable; drug isn't absorbed.
Excretion: In GI tract. *Half-life:* None.

Route	Onset	Peak	Duration
P.O.	≤ 1 hr	Varies	Varies

Action

Chemical effect: Acts as an osmotic agent. Sodium sulfate greatly reduces sodium absorption. The electrolyte concentration causes virtually no net absorption or secretion of ions.
Therapeutic effect: Cleanses bowel.

Available forms

Oral solution: PEG 3350 (6 g), sodium sulfate decahydrate (1.29 g), sodium chloride (146 mg), potassium chloride (75 mg), sodium bicarbonate (168 mg), polysorbate 80 (30 mg) per 100 ml (OCL)
Powder for oral solution: PEG 3350 (240 g), sodium sulfate (22.72 g), sodium chloride (5.84 g), potassium chloride (2.98 g), sodium bicarbonate (6.72 g) per 4 L (CoLyte); PEG

3350 (236 g), sodium sulfate (22.74 g), sodium bicarbonate (6.74 g), sodium chloride (5.86 g), potassium chloride (2.97 g) per 4 L (GoLYTELY); PEG 3350 (420 g), sodium bicarbonate (5.72 g), sodium chloride (11.2 g), potassium chloride (1.48 g) per 4 L (NuLYTELY)

NURSING PROCESS

Assessment
- Assess patient's condition before starting therapy and regularly thereafter to monitor drug's effectiveness.
- Be alert for adverse reactions and drug interactions.
- Assess patient's and family's knowledge of drug therapy.

Nursing diagnoses
- Health-seeking behavior (testing) related to need to determine cause of underlying GI problem
- Risk for deficient fluid volume related to adverse GI reactions
- Deficient knowledge related to drug therapy

Planning and implementation
- Use tap water to reconstitute powder. Shake vigorously to make sure all powder is dissolved. Refrigerate solution but use within 48 hours.

ALERT: Don't add flavoring or additional ingredients to solution or administer chilled solution. Hypothermia has developed after ingestion of large amounts of chilled solution.

- If patient is scheduled for midmorning examination, give solution early in morning. Oral solution induces diarrhea in 30 to 60 minutes that rapidly cleans bowel, usually within 4 hours.
- When used as preparation for barium enema, give solution the evening before examination, to avoid interfering with barium coating of colonic mucosa.
- If giving to adult via NG tube infuse at 20 to 30 ml/minute.
- If given to semiconscious patient or to patient with impaired gag reflex, take care to prevent aspiration.
- No major shifts in fluid or electrolyte balance have been reported.

Patient teaching
- Tell patient to fast for 4 hours before taking solution and to ingest only clear fluids until examination is complete.
- Warn patient about adverse GI reactions to drug.
- Advise patient that rapid drinking of each portion is preferred to drinking small amounts continuously.

Evaluation
- Patient is able to have examination.
- Patient maintains adequate fluid volume.
- Patient and family state understanding of drug therapy.

posaconazole
poss-uh-KAHN-uh-zohl
Noxafil

Pharmacologic class: triazole antifungal
Therapeutic class: anti-infective
Pregnancy risk category: C

Indications and dosages

▶ **Prevention of invasive *Aspergillus* and *Candida* infections in high-risk immunocompromised patients.** *Adults and children age 13 and older:* 200 mg (5 ml) P.O. t.i.d. with a full meal or liquid nutritional supplement.

Contraindications and cautions

Contraindicated in patients hypersensitive to drug or its components and in patients taking astemizole, cisapride, ergot derivatives, pimozide, quinidine, or terfenadine.

Use cautiously in patients hypersensitive to other azole antifungals, patients with potentially proarrhythmic conditions, and patients with hepatic or renal insufficiency.

Lifespan: Use drug in pregnant or breast-feeding women only if the benefits outweigh the risks. Use not indicated in children younger than age 13.

Adverse reactions

CNS: *anxiety, dizziness, fatigue, fever, headache, insomnia, weakness.*
CV: *edema, hypertension, hypotension, tachycardia.*
EENT: altered taste, blurred vision, *epistaxis, pharyngitis.*
GI: *abdominal pain, constipation, diarrhea, dyspepsia, mucositis, nausea, vomiting.*
GU: *vaginal hemorrhage.*

Hematologic: *anemia,* FEBRILE NEUTROPENIA, NEUTROPENIA, *petechiae,* THROMBOCYTOPENIA.
Hepatic: *bilirubinemia.*
Metabolic: *hyperglycemia,* hypocalcemia, *hypokalemia, hypomagnesemia.*
Musculoskeletal: *arthralgia, back pain, pain.*
Respiratory: *cough, dyspnea,* upper respiratory tract infection.
Other: *anorexia, bacteremia, cytomegalovirus infection, herpes simplex, rigors.*

Interactions

Drug-drug. *Calcium channel blockers, cyclosporine, HMG-CoA reductase inhibitors, midazolam, phenytoin, sirolimus, tacrolimus, vinca alkaloids:* May increase levels of these drugs. Reduce doses, increase monitoring of levels, and observe patient for adverse effects.
Cimetidine, phenytoin: May decrease level and effectiveness of posaconazole. Avoid use together.
Rifabutin: May decrease level and efficacy of posaconazole while increasing rifabutin level and risk of toxicity. Avoid use together. If unavoidable, monitor patient for uveitis, leukopenia, and other adverse effects.
Drug-food. *Food, liquid nutritional supplements:* May greatly enhance absorption of drug. Always give drug with liquid supplement or food.

Effects on lab test results

- May increase AST, ALT, bilirubin, creatinine, alkaline phosphatase, and glucose levels. May decrease potassium, magnesium, and calcium levels.
- May decrease WBC, RBC, and platelet counts.

Pharmacokinetics

Absorption: Greatly improved when drug is taken with food or a nutritional supplement.
Distribution: Extensive into extravascular space and body tissues. More than 98% protein-bound, mainly to albumin.
Metabolism: Via the liver by glucuronidation.
Excretion: Mainly in feces, and much less in urine. *Half-life:* 35 hours.

Route	Onset	Peak	Duration
P.O.	Unknown	3–5 hr	Unknown

Action

Chemical effect: Drug blocks the synthesis of ergosterol, a vital component of the fungal cell membrane.
Therapeutic effect: Protects high-risk patients from *Aspergillus* and *Candida* infections.

Available forms

Oral solution: 40 mg/ml

NURSING PROCESS

Assessment

- Assess patient for fungal infection before starting therapy, and reassess regularly.
- Correct electrolyte imbalances, especially potassium, magnesium, and calcium imbalances, before therapy starts.
- Be alert for adverse reactions and drug interactions.
- If adverse GI reactions occur, monitor patient's hydration.
- Assess patient's and family's knowledge of drug therapy.

Nursing diagnoses

- Risk for infection related to immunosuppression
- Risk for deficient fluid volume related to adverse GI reactions
- Deficient knowledge related to drug therapy

Planning and implementation

- Obtain baseline liver function tests, including bilirubin level, before therapy starts and periodically during treatment. Notify prescriber if patient develops signs or symptoms of hepatic dysfunction.
- Monitor patient for signs and symptoms of electrolyte imbalance including a slow, weak or irregular pulse; ECG change; nausea; neuromuscular irritability; and tetany.
- Give drug with a full meal or a liquid nutritional supplement.
- Monitor patient who has severe vomiting or diarrhea for breakthrough fungal infection.

Patient teaching

- If patient can't eat or take a liquid supplement, instruct him to notify prescriber. A different anti-infective may be needed, or monitoring may need to be increased.

• Tell patient to notify prescriber about an irregular heartbeat, fainting, or severe diarrhea or vomiting.
• Explain the signs and symptoms of liver dysfunction, including abdominal pain, yellowing skin or eyes, pale stools, and dark urine.
• Urge patient to contact the prescriber or pharmacist before taking other prescription or OTC drugs, and herbal or dietary supplements.
• Tell patient to shake the suspension well before taking it.
• Instruct patient to measure doses using the spoon provided with the drug. Household spoons vary in size and may yield an incorrect dose.
• Point out that the calibrated spoon has two markings, one for 2.5 ml and one for 5 ml. Make sure patient understands which mark to use for his prescribed dose.
• To ensure a full dose, tell patient to fill the spoon with water and drink it after taking a dose. Urge him to clean the spoon with water before putting it away.
• Tell patient to store oral solution at room temperature.

Evaluation

• Patient remains free from infection.
• Patient maintains adequate hydration.
• Patient and family state understanding of drug therapy.

potassium acetate

(poh-TAS-ee-um AS-ih-tayt)

Pharmacologic class: potassium supplement
Therapeutic class: electrolyte
Pregnancy risk category: C

Indications and dosages

▶ **Hypokalemia.** *Adults:* For potassium level above 2.5 mEq/L, no more than 10 mEq I.V. hourly at a concentration of 40 mEq/L or less. Maximum daily dose is 200 mEq. For potassium level less than 2 mEq/L, no more than 40 mEq I.V. hourly at a concentration of 80 mEq/L or less. Maximum daily dose is 400 mEq. Monitor ECG and perform frequent potassium tests with potassium replacement. Use I.V. route only for life-threatening hypokalemia or when oral replacement isn't feasible.

▶ **To prevent hypokalemia.** *Adults:* Dose is individualized to patient's needs, not to exceed 150 mEq daily. Give as an additive to I.V. infusions. Usual dose is 20 mEq/L infused at no more than 20 mEq/hour.
Children: Individualized dose not to exceed 3 mEq/kg daily. Give as an additive to I.V. infusions.

I.V. administration

• Give drug only by I.V. infusion, never by I.V. push or I.M. route.
• Dilute drug before administration and give slowly; life-threatening hyperkalemia may result from a rapid infusion.
• Watch for pain and redness at infusion site. Large-bore needle reduces local irritation.
⊗ **Incompatibilities**
Calcium, phosphate, and sulfate solutions.

Contraindications and cautions

• Contraindicated in patients with severe renal impairment with oliguria, anuria, or azotemia; those with untreated Addison disease or adrenocortical insufficiency; and those with acute dehydration, heat cramps, hyperkalemia, hyperkalemic form of familial periodic paralysis, and conditions related to extensive tissue breakdown.
• Use cautiously in patients with cardiac disease or renal impairment.
Lifespan: In pregnant women, use cautiously. In breast-feeding women, use cautiously; it's unknown if the drug appears in breast milk.

Adverse reactions

CNS: flaccid paralysis, listlessness, mental confusion, paresthesia of limbs, weakness or heaviness of legs.
CV: ***arrhythmias, cardiac arrest,*** ECG changes, ***heart block.***
GI: abdominal pain, diarrhea, nausea, vomiting.
GU: oliguria.
Respiratory: ***respiratory paralysis.***
Skin: cold skin, gray pallor.
Other: pain, redness at infusion site.

Interactions

Drug-drug. *ACE inhibitors, potassium-sparing diuretics:* May increase risk of hyperkalemia. Use cautiously.
Drug-herb. *Cascara, licorice:* May antagonize effects of potassium supplements. Discourage using together.

P

Drug-food. *Salt substitutes:* May increase risk of hyperkalemia. Don't use together.

Effects on lab test results

- May increase potassium level.

Pharmacokinetics

Absorption: Given I.V.
Distribution: Throughout body.
Metabolism: None significant.
Excretion: Mainly by kidneys. *Half-life:* Unknown.

Route	Onset	Peak	Duration
I.V.	Immediate	Immediate	Unknown

Action

Chemical effect: Aids in transmitting nerve impulses, contracting cardiac and skeletal muscle, and maintaining intracellular tonicity, cellular metabolism, acid-base balance, and normal renal function.
Therapeutic effect: Replaces and maintains potassium level.

Available forms

Injection: 2 mEq/ml in 20-ml, 50-ml, 100-ml vials; 4 mEq/ml in 50-ml vial

NURSING PROCESS

Assessment

- Assess patient's condition before starting therapy and regularly thereafter to monitor drug's effectiveness.
- During therapy, monitor ECG, renal function, fluid intake and output, and potassium, creatinine, and BUN levels.
- Be alert for adverse reactions and drug interactions.
- Assess patient's and family's knowledge of drug therapy.

Nursing diagnoses

- Ineffective health maintenance related to presence of hypokalemia
- Risk for injury related to drug-induced hyperkalemia
- Deficient knowledge related to drug therapy

Planning and implementation

- Don't give potassium postoperatively until urine flow is established.

ALERT: Potassium preparations aren't interchangeable. Verify preparation before giving.

Patient teaching

- Inform patient of need for potassium supplementation.
- Tell patient that drug will be given through an I.V. line.
- Instruct patient to report adverse reactions.

Evaluation

- Patient's potassium level returns to normal with drug therapy.
- Patient doesn't develop hyperkalemia as result of drug therapy.
- Patient and family state understanding of drug therapy.

potassium bicarbonate

(poh-TAS-ee-um bigh-KAR-buh-nayt)
K+ Care ET, K-Lyte, Klor Con/EF

Pharmacologic class: potassium supplement
Therapeutic class: mineral
Pregnancy risk category: C

Indications and dosages

▶ **Hypokalemia.** *Adults:* 25 to 50 mEq dissolved in 4 to 8 oz (120 to 240 ml) of water and given P.O. once daily to b.i.d. Maximum 150 mEq daily.

Contraindications and cautions

- Contraindicated in patients with untreated Addison disease, acute dehydration, heat cramps, hyperkalemia, hyperkalemic form of familial periodic paralysis, other conditions linked to extensive tissue breakdown, or severe renal impairment with oliguria, anuria, or azotemia.
- Use cautiously in patients with cardiac disease or renal impairment.

Lifespan: In pregnant women, use cautiously. In breast-feeding women, use cautiously; it's unknown if the drug appears in breast milk. In children, safety and effectiveness haven't been established.

Adverse reactions

CNS: flaccid paralysis, listlessness, mental confusion, paresthesia of limbs, weakness or heaviness of legs.

CV: ***arrhythmias, cardiac arrest,*** ECG changes (prolonged PR interval, widened QRS complex, ST-segment depression, and tall, tented T waves), ***heart block.***
GI: *abdominal pain,* diarrhea, ***hemorrhage,*** *nausea,* ***obstruction, perforation,*** ulcerations, *vomiting.*

Interactions

Drug-drug. *ACE inhibitors, potassium-sparing diuretics:* May increase risk of hyperkalemia. Use cautiously.
Drug-food. *Salt substitutes:* May increase risk of hyperkalemia. Don't use together.

Effects on lab test results

- May increase potassium level.

Pharmacokinetics

Absorption: Well absorbed from GI tract.
Distribution: Throughout body.
Metabolism: None significant.
Excretion: Mainly by kidneys. *Half-life:* Unknown.

Route	Onset	Peak	Duration
P.O.	Unknown	≤ 4 hr	Unknown

Action

Chemical effect: Aids in transmitting nerve impulses, contracting cardiac and skeletal muscle, and maintaining intracellular tonicity, cellular metabolism, acid-base balance, and normal renal function.
Therapeutic effect: Replaces and maintains potassium level.

Available forms

Effervescent tablets: 6.5 mEq, 25 mEq

NURSING PROCESS

Assessment

- Assess patient's condition before starting therapy, and regularly thereafter to monitor the drug's effectiveness.
- During therapy, monitor ECG, renal function, fluid intake and output, and potassium, creatinine, and BUN levels.
- Be alert for adverse reactions and drug interactions.
- Assess patient's and family's knowledge of drug therapy.

Nursing diagnoses

- Ineffective health maintenance related to presence of hypokalemia
- Risk for injury related to potassium-induced hyperkalemia
- Deficient knowledge related to drug therapy

Planning and implementation

- Dissolve potassium bicarbonate tablets completely in 6 to 8 oz of cold water to minimize GI irritation.
- Ask patient's flavor preference. Available in lime, fruit punch, and orange flavors.
- Have patient take with meals and sip slowly over 5 to 10 minutes.
- Don't give potassium supplements postoperatively until urine flow has been established.

ALERT: Potassium preparations aren't interchangeable. Verify preparation before giving.

Patient teaching

- Inform patient about need for potassium supplementation.
- Teach patient how to prepare and take drug.
- Instruct patient to report adverse reactions.

Evaluation

- Patient's potassium level returns to normal.
- Patient doesn't develop hyperkalemia as result of drug therapy.
- Patient and family state understanding of drug therapy.

potassium chloride

(poh-TAS-ee-um KLOR-ighd)

Apo-K*, Cena-K, Gen-K, K-8, K-10*, K+ 10, Kaochlor, Kaochlor S-F*, Kaon-Cl, Kaon-Cl-10, Kaon-Cl 20%*, Kay Ciel*, K+ Care, K-Dur 10, K-Dur 20✐, K-Lease, K-Lor, Klor-Con, Klor-Con 8, Klor-Con 10, Klor-Con/25, Klorvess, Klotrix, K-Lyte/Cl, K-Norm, K-Tab, K-Vescent, Micro-K Extencaps, Micro-K 10 Extencaps, Micro-K LS, Potasalan, Slow-K, Ten-K

Pharmacologic class: potassium supplement
Therapeutic class: mineral
Pregnancy risk category: C

Indications and dosages

▶ **Prevention of hypokalemia.** *Adults and children:* Initially, 20 mEq P.O. daily in divided doses. Adjust dosage, as needed, based on potassium level.

▶ **Hypokalemia.** *Adults and children:* 40 to 100 mEq P.O. daily divided into two to four doses. Use I.V. potassium chloride when oral replacement isn't feasible. Maximum dosage of diluted I.V. potassium chloride is 20 mEq/hour of 40 mEq/L solution. Further doses based on potassium level. Don't exceed 150 mEq P.O. daily in adults and 3 mEq/kg P.O. daily in children. Further doses are based on potassium level and blood pH. Monitor ECG and obtain potassium level frequently when giving I.V. potassium replacement.

▶ **Severe hypokalemia.** *Adults and children:* Dilute potassium chloride in a suitable I.V. solution to 80 mEq/L or less and give at no more than 40 mEq/hour. Base next dose on potassium level. Don't exceed 150 mEq I.V. daily in adults and 3 mEq/kg I.V. daily or 40 mEq/m^2 daily for children.

▶ **Acute MI‡.** *Adults:* High dose—80 mEq/L at 1.5 ml/kg/hour for 24 hours with an I.V. infusion of 25% dextrose and 50 units/L regular insulin. Low dose—40 mEq/L at 1 ml/kg/hour for 24 hours, with an I.V. infusion of 10% dextrose and 20 units/L regular insulin.

I.V. administration

- Give parenteral drug only by infusion, never by I.V. push or I.M. route.
- Give slowly as dilute solution; life-threatening hyperkalemia may result from a rapid infusion.

⊗ **Incompatibilities**

Amikacin, amphotericin B, diazepam, dobutamine, ergotamine, fat emulsion 10%, methylprednisolone sodium succinate, penicillin G sodium, phenytoin sodium, promethazine hydrochloride.

Contraindications and cautions

- Contraindicated in patients with untreated Addison disease, adrenocortical insufficiency, acute dehydration, heat cramps, hyperkalemia, hyperkalemic form of familial periodic paralysis, other conditions linked to extensive tissue breakdown, or severe renal impairment with oliguria, anuria, or azotemia.
- Use cautiously in patients with cardiac disease or renal impairment.

Lifespan: In pregnant women, use cautiously. In breast-feeding women, use cautiously; it's unknown if the drug appears in breast milk.

Adverse reactions

CNS: flaccid paralysis, listlessness, mental confusion, paresthesia of limbs, weakness or heaviness of limbs.
CV: ***arrhythmias, cardiac arrest,*** ECG changes (prolonged PR interval, widened QRS complex, ST-segment depression, and tall, tented T waves), ***heart block.***
GI: abdominal pain, diarrhea, ***GI ulcerations (stenosis, hemorrhage, obstruction, perforation),*** nausea, vomiting.
GU: oliguria.
Respiratory: ***respiratory paralysis.***
Skin: cold skin, gray pallor, phlebitis.

Interactions

Drug-drug. *ACE inhibitors, potassium-sparing diuretics:* May increase risk of hyperkalemia. Use cautiously.
Drug-herb. *Cascara, licorice:* May antagonize effects of potassium supplements. Discourage using together.
Drug-food. *Salt substitutes:* May increase risk of hyperkalemia. Don't use together.

Effects on lab test results

- May increase potassium level.

Pharmacokinetics

Absorption: Well absorbed.
Distribution: Throughout body.
Metabolism: None significant.
Excretion: Mainly by kidneys; small amounts may be excreted by skin and intestinal tract, but intestinal potassium is usually reabsorbed. *Half-life:* Unknown.

Route	Onset	Peak	Duration
P.O.	Unknown	≤ 4 hr	Unknown
I.V.	Immediate	Immediate	Unknown

Action

Chemical effect: Aids in transmitting nerve impulses, contracting cardiac and skeletal muscle, and maintaining intracellular tonicity, cellular metabolism, acid-base balance, and normal renal function.
Therapeutic effect: Replaces and maintains potassium level.

Available forms

Capsules (controlled-release): 8 mEq, 10 mEq
Injection concentrate: 1.5 mEq/ml, 2 mEq/ml

Injection for I.V. infusion: 0.1mEq/ml, 0.2 mEq/ml, 0.3 mEq/ml, 0.4 mEq/ml
Oral liquid: 20 mEq/15 ml*, 30 mEq/15 ml, 40 mEq/15 ml*
Powder for oral administration: 15 mEq/packet, 20 mEq/packet, 25 mEq/packet
Tablets (controlled-release): 6.7 mEq, 8 mEq, 10 mEq, 20 mEq
Tablets (extended-release): 8 mEq, 10 mEq

NURSING PROCESS

Assessment

- Assess patient's condition before starting therapy and regularly thereafter to monitor drug's effectiveness.
- During therapy, monitor ECG, renal function, fluid intake and output, and potassium, creatinine, and BUN levels.
- Be alert for adverse reactions and drug interactions.
- Assess patient's and family's knowledge of drug therapy.

Nursing diagnoses

- Ineffective health maintenance related to presence of hypokalemia
- Risk for injury related to drug-induced hyperkalemia
- Deficient knowledge related to drug therapy

Planning and implementation

- When giving I.V. potassium replacement, monitor ECG and take potassium level frequently.
- Give cautiously because different potassium supplements deliver varying amounts of potassium. Never switch products without prescriber's order.
- Make sure powders are completely dissolved before giving.
- Don't crush sustained-release potassium products.
- Give potassium with or after meals with full glass of water or fruit juice to lessen GI distress.
- If tablet or capsule passage is likely to be delayed, as in GI obstruction, use sugar-free liquid (Kaochlor S-F 10%). Have patient sip slowly to minimize GI irritation.
- Enteric-coated tablets increase risk of GI bleeding and small-bowel ulcerations; use cautiously.
- Tablets in wax matrix sometimes lodge in esophagus and cause ulceration in cardiac patients who have esophageal compression from enlarged left atrium. Use liquid form in such patients and in those with esophageal stasis or obstruction.
- Drug is commonly given with potassium-wasting diuretics to maintain potassium level.

ALERT: Potassium preparations aren't interchangeable. Verify preparation before giving.
ALERT: Don't give potassium postoperatively until urine flow is established.

Patient teaching

- Tell patient that controlled-release tablets may appear in stool but that the drug has already been absorbed.
- Instruct patient to report adverse reactions and pain at the I.V. site.

Evaluation

- Patient's potassium level returns to normal.
- Patient doesn't develop hyperkalemia.
- Patient and family state understanding of drug therapy.

potassium gluconate
(poh-TAS-ee-um GLOO-kuh-nayt)
Kaon, Kaylixir*, K-G Elixir*

Pharmacologic class: potassium supplement
Therapeutic class: mineral
Pregnancy risk category: C

Indications and dosages

▶ **Hypokalemia.** *Adults:* 40 to 100 mEq P.O. daily in three or four divided doses; 20 mEq P.O. daily for prevention. Further doses based on potassium level determinations.

Contraindications and cautions

- Contraindicated in patients with untreated Addison disease, acute dehydration, heat cramps, hyperkalemia, hyperkalemic form of familial periodic paralysis, other conditions related to extensive tissue breakdown, or severe renal impairment with oliguria, anuria, or azotemia.
- Use cautiously in patients with cardiac disease or renal impairment.

Lifespan: In pregnant women, use cautiously. In breast-feeding women, use cautiously; it's unknown if the drug appears in breast milk. In children, safety and effectiveness haven't been established.

Adverse reactions

CNS: flaccid paralysis, listlessness, mental confusion, paresthesia of limbs, weakness or heaviness of legs.
CV: ***arrhythmias,*** ECG changes (prolonged PR interval, widened QRS complex, ST-segment depression, and tall, tented T waves).
GI: *abdominal pain;* diarrhea; ***GI ulcerations*** that may be accompanied by stenosis, ***hemorrhage, obstruction or perforation*** (with oral products, especially enteric-coated tablets); *nausea and vomiting.*

Interactions

Drug-drug. *ACE inhibitors, potassium-sparing diuretics:* May increase risk of hyperkalemia. Use cautiously.
Drug-food. *Salt substitutes:* May increase risk of hyperkalemia. Don't use together.

Effects on lab test results

- May increase potassium level.

Pharmacokinetics

Absorption: Well absorbed from GI tract.
Distribution: Throughout body.
Metabolism: None significant.
Excretion: Mainly by kidneys; small amounts may be excreted by skin and intestinal tract, but intestinal potassium is usually reabsorbed. *Half-life:* Unknown.

Route	Onset	Peak	Duration
P.O.	Unknown	≤ 4 hr	Unknown

Action

Chemical effect: Aids in transmitting nerve impulses, contracting cardiac and skeletal muscle, and maintaining intracellular tonicity, cellular metabolism, acid-base balance, and normal renal function.
Therapeutic effect: Replaces and maintains potassium level.

Available forms

Liquid: 20 mEq/15 ml*
Tablets: 500 mg†, 595 mg† (83.45 mg and 99 mg potassium, respectively)

NURSING PROCESS

Assessment

- Assess patient's condition before starting therapy and regularly thereafter to monitor drug's effectiveness.
- During therapy, monitor ECG, renal function, fluid intake and output, and potassium, creatinine, and BUN levels.
- Be alert for adverse reactions and drug interactions.
- Assess patient's and family's knowledge of drug therapy.

Nursing diagnoses

- Ineffective health maintenance related to presence of hypokalemia
- Risk for injury related to potassium-induced hyperkalemia
- Deficient knowledge related to drug therapy

Planning and implementation

- Give cautiously because different potassium supplements deliver varying amounts of potassium. Never switch products without prescriber's order.
- Give drug with or after meals with glass of water or fruit juice.
- Have patient sip liquid potassium slowly to minimize GI irritation.
- Enteric-coated tablets aren't recommended because of increased risk of GI bleeding and small-bowel ulcerations.

ALERT: Potassium preparations aren't interchangeable. Verify preparation before giving.
ALERT: Don't give potassium supplements postoperatively until urine flow is established.

Patient teaching

- Inform patient of need for potassium supplementation.
- Teach patient how to take drug.
- Instruct patient to report adverse reactions.

Evaluation

- Patient's potassium level returns to normal.
- Patient doesn't develop hyperkalemia as result of drug therapy.
- Patient and family state understanding of drug therapy.

potassium iodide

(poh-TAS-ee-um IGH-uh-dighd)

Losat, Pima, Thyro-Block

potassium iodide, saturated solution (SSKI)

strong iodine solution (Lugol's solution)

Pharmacologic class: antithyroid
Therapeutic class: radiation protectant
Pregnancy risk category: D

Indications and dosages

▶ **Preparation for thyroidectomy.** *Adults and children:* 0.1 to 0.3 ml (2 to 6 drops) strong iodine solution P.O. t.i.d. for 10 days before surgery.

▶ **Thyrotoxic crisis.** *Adults and children:* 500 mg P.O. q 4 hours (about 10 drops of 1 g/ml solution).

▶ **Radiation protectant for thyroid gland.** *Adults:* 130 mg P.O. daily for 10 days after radiation exposure. Start no later than 3 to 4 hours after acute exposure.
Children ages 3 to 18: Give 65 mg P.O. daily for 10 days after exposure. Start no later than 3 to 4 hours after acute exposure.
Children ages 1 month to 3 years: 32.5 mg P.O. daily for 10 days after exposure. Start no later than 3 to 4 hours after acute exposure.
Infants from birth to age 1 month: 16.25 mg P.O. daily for 10 days after exposure. Start no later than 3 to 4 hours after acute exposure.

▶ **Hyperthyroidism.** *Adults and children:* 50 to 250 mg (1 to 5 drops of 1 g/ml solution) potassium iodide t.i.d. for 10 to 14 days before surgery. Or, 0.1 to 0.3 strong iodine solution (3 to 5 drops) t.i.d.

▶ **As an expectorant in chronic pulmonary diseases.** *Adults:* 325 to 650 mg P.O. t.i.d.
Children: 162.5 to 325 mg P.O. t.i.d.

Contraindications and cautions

- Contraindicated in patients with tuberculosis, acute bronchitis, iodide hypersensitivity, impaired renal function, or hyperkalemia. Some forms contain sulfites, which may cause allergic reactions in hypersensitive people.
- Use cautiously in patients with hypocomplementemic vasculitis, goiter, or autoimmune thyroid disease.

Lifespan: In pregnant and breast-feeding women, drug isn't recommended.

Adverse reactions

CNS: fever, frontal headache.
EENT: acute rhinitis, conjunctivitis, hyperemia, inflammation of salivary glands, periorbital edema.
GI: burning, diarrhea (sometimes bloody), irritation, *metallic taste, nausea,* vomiting.
Metabolic: *potassium toxicity* (confusion, irregular heart beat, numbness, tingling, pain or weakness in hands and feet, tiredness).
Skin: acneiform rash, mucous membrane ulceration.
Other: hypersensitivity reactions, tooth discoloration.

Interactions

Drug-drug. *ACE inhibitors, potassium-sparing diuretics:* May increase risk of hyperkalemia. Avoid using together.
Antithyroid drugs: May increase hypothyroid or goitrogenic effects. Monitor effects closely.
Lithium carbonate: May cause hypothyroidism. Use together cautiously.
Drug-food. *Salt substitutes:* May increase risk of hyperkalemia. Don't use together.

Effects on lab test results

- May increase potassium level.
- May increase or decrease thyroid function test results.

Pharmacokinetics

Absorption: Unknown.
Distribution: Unknown.
Metabolism: Unknown.
Excretion: Unknown. *Half-life:* Unknown.

Route	Onset	Peak	Duration
P.O.	≤ 24 hr	10–15 days	Unknown

Action

Chemical effect: Inhibits thyroid hormone formation by blocking iodotyrosine and iodothyronine synthesis, limits iodide transport into thyroid gland, and blocks thyroid hormone release.
Therapeutic effect: Lowers thyroid hormone level.

P

Available forms

potassium iodide
Oral solution: 500 mg/15 ml
Scored tablets: 130 mg
Syrup: 325 mg/5 ml
potassium iodide, saturated solution
Oral solution: 1 g/ml
strong iodine solution
Oral solution: iodine 50 mg/ml and potassium iodide 100 mg/ml

NURSING PROCESS

Assessment

- Assess patient's condition before starting therapy and regularly thereafter to monitor drug's effectiveness.
- Be alert for adverse reactions and drug interactions.
- Earliest signs of delayed hypersensitivity reactions caused by iodides are irritation and swelling of eyelids.
- Assess patient's and family's knowledge of drug therapy.

Nursing diagnoses

- Ineffective health maintenance related to underlying thyroid condition
- Ineffective protection related to hypersensitivity reactions
- Deficient knowledge related to drug therapy

Planning and implementation

- Potassium iodide is usually given with other antithyroid drugs.
- Dilute oral doses in water, milk, or fruit juice to hydrate patient and mask salty taste; give drug after meals to prevent gastric irritation.
- Give iodide through straw to prevent tooth discoloration.
- Store drug in light-resistant container.

Patient teaching

- Warn patient that suddenly stopping the drug may cause thyroid crisis.
- Tell patient to ask prescriber whether he can use iodized salt or eat shellfish.
- Tell patient to report adverse reactions.

Evaluation

- Patient's thyroid hormone level is lower with potassium iodide therapy.
- Patient doesn't experience hypersensitivity reactions.
- Patient and family state understanding of drug therapy.

pralidoxime chloride (pyridine-2-aldoxime methochloride; 2-PAM chloride)

(pral-ih-DOKS-eem KLOR-ighd)
Protopam Chloride

Pharmacologic class: quaternary ammonium oxime
Therapeutic class: antidote
Pregnancy risk category: C

Indications and dosages

▶ **Antidote for organophosphate poisoning.** *Adults:* 1 to 2 g in 100 ml of saline solution by I.V. infusion over 15 to 30 minutes. If patient has pulmonary edema, give by slow I.V. push over at least 5 minutes. Repeat in 1 hour if muscle weakness persists; may give further doses cautiously. Use I.M. or subcutaneous injection if I.V. route isn't feasible.

▶ **Anticholinesterase overdose.** *Adults:* 1 to 2 g I.V., followed by 250 mg I.V. q 5 minutes.

I.V. administration

- Give I.V. preparation slowly as diluted solution. Dilute with unpreserved sterile water.
- To lessen muscarinic effects and block accumulation of acetylcholine from organophosphate poisoning, give atropine 2 to 6 mg I.V. along with pralidoxime unless patient has cyanosis. (If he is cyanotic, give atropine I.M.) Give atropine q 5 to 60 minutes in adults until muscarinic signs and symptoms disappear; if they reappear, repeat the dose. Maintain atropinization for at least 48 hours.
- Infuse slowly since tachycardia, laryngospasm, muscle rigidity, and worsening of cholinergic symptoms may occur with rapid administration. Maximum injection rate is 200 mg/minute.

⊗ **Incompatibilities**
None reported.

Contraindications and cautions

- Use cautiously in patients with myasthenia gravis; overdose may cause myasthenic crisis.

Also use cautiously and with reduced dosage in patients with renal impairment.

Lifespan: In pregnant women, use cautiously. In breast-feeding women and in children, safety and effectiveness haven't been established.

Adverse reactions

CNS: dizziness, drowsiness, excitement, headache, manic behavior after recovery of consciousness.
CV: increased blood pressure, tachycardia.
EENT: blurred vision, diplopia, impaired accommodation.
GI: nausea.
Musculoskeletal: muscle rigidity, muscle weakness.
Respiratory: hyperventilation.
Skin: rash
Other: pain at injection site.

Interactions

Drug-drug. *Atropine:* May cause flushing, tachycardia, dry mouth. Monitor patient.
Barbiturates: May increase the effects of barbiturates. Use together cautiously.

Effects on lab test results

- May increase AST, ALT, and CK levels.

Pharmacokinetics

Absorption: Unknown after I.M. or subcutaneous use.
Distribution: Throughout extracellular fluid. Drug isn't appreciably protein-bound, and it doesn't readily pass into CNS.
Metabolism: Unknown, but hepatic metabolism is likely.
Excretion: Rapid, in urine. *Half-life:* 1½ hours.

Route	Onset	Peak	Duration
I.V.	Unknown	5–15 min	Unknown
I.M.	Unknown	10–20 min	Unknown
SubQ	Unknown	Unknown	Unknown

Action

Chemical effect: Reactivates cholinesterase that has been inactivated by organophosphorus pesticides and related compounds, permitting degradation of accumulated acetylcholine and facilitating normal functioning of neuromuscular junctions.

Therapeutic effect: Alleviates signs and symptoms of organophosphate poisoning and cholinergic crisis in myasthenia gravis.

Available forms

Injection: 1 g/20 ml in 20-ml vial without diluent or syringe; 1 g/20 ml in 20-ml vial with diluent, syringe, needle, and alcohol swab (emergency kit); 600 mg/2 ml autoinjector (may contain benzyl alcohol), parenteral

NURSING PROCESS

Assessment

- Assess patient's condition before starting therapy and regularly thereafter. Drug relieves paralysis of respiratory muscles but is less effective in relieving depression of respiratory center.
- Drug isn't effective against poisoning caused by phosphorus, inorganic phosphates, or organophosphates that have no anticholinesterase activity.
- If poison was ingested, observe patient for 48 to 72 hours. Absorption from lower bowel may be delayed. It's difficult to distinguish between toxic effects produced by atropine or organophosphate compounds and those resulting from this drug.
- Watch for signs of rapid weakening in patient with myasthenia gravis who was treated for overdose of cholinergics. Patient can pass quickly from cholinergic crisis to myasthenic crisis and may need more cholinergic drugs to treat myasthenia. Keep edrophonium (Tensilon) available in such situations for establishing differential diagnosis.
- Be alert for adverse reactions.
- Assess patient's and family's knowledge of drug therapy.

Nursing diagnoses

- Ineffective health maintenance related to underlying condition
- Risk for injury related to adverse CNS reactions
- Deficient knowledge related to drug therapy

Planning and implementation

- Use drug only in hospitalized patients; have respiratory and other supportive measures available. If possible, obtain accurate medical history and chronology of poisoning. Give drug as soon

P

as possible; it's most effective when started within 24 hours.

- Remove secretions, maintain patent airway, and start artificial ventilation if needed. After dermal exposure to organophosphate, remove patient's clothing and wash his skin and hair with sodium bicarbonate, soap, water, and alcohol immediately. A second washing may be needed. When washing patient, wear protective gloves and clothes to avoid exposure.
- Draw blood for cholinesterase level before giving drug.

ALERT: Don't confuse pralidoxime with pramoxine or pyridoxine.

Patient teaching

- Tell patient to report adverse reactions immediately.
- Advise patient treated for organophosphate poisoning to avoid contact with insecticides for several weeks.

Evaluation

- Patient responds well to therapy.
- Patient sustains no injury from adverse CNS reactions.
- Patient and family state understanding of drug therapy.

pramipexole dihydrochloride

(pram-ih-PEKS-ohl digh-high-droh-KLOR-ighd)

Mirapex

Pharmacologic class: dopamine agonist
Therapeutic class: antiparkinsonian
Pregnancy risk category: C

Indications and dosages

▶ **Signs and symptoms of idiopathic Parkinson disease.** *Adults:* Initially, 0.375 mg P.O. daily in three divided doses; don't increase more often than q 5 to 7 days. Maintenance daily dose range is 1.5 to 4.5 mg in three divided doses.

Adjust-a-dose: For patients with renal impairment, if creatinine clearance is greater than 60 ml/minute, initial dose is 0.125 mg P.O. t.i.d., up to 1.5 mg t.i.d. If creatinine clearance is 35 to 59 ml/minute, initial dose is 0.125 mg P.O. b.i.d. up to 1.5 mg b.i.d. If creatinine clearance is 15 to 34 ml/minute, initial dose is 0.125 mg P.O. daily, up to 1.5 mg daily.

Contraindications and cautions

- Contraindicated in patients hypersensitive to the drug or any of its components.
- Use cautiously in patients with renal impairment; adjust dose if needed.

Lifespan: Use during pregnancy only if benefits outweigh risks to the fetus. In breast-feeding women, use cautiously. In children, safety and effectiveness haven't been established. In the elderly, use cautiously.

Adverse reactions

CNS: akathisia, amnesia, *asthenia, confusion,* delusions, *dizziness, dream abnormalities, dyskinesia,* dystonia, *extrapyramidal syndrome,* fever, gait abnormalities, *hallucinations,* hypertonia, hypoesthesia, *insomnia,* malaise, myoclonus, paranoid reaction, sleep disorders, *somnolence,* thought abnormalities.
CV: chest pain, general edema, *orthostatic hypotension,* peripheral edema.
EENT: accommodation abnormalities, diplopia, rhinitis, vision abnormalities.
GI: anorexia, *constipation,* dry mouth, dysphagia, *nausea.*
GU: impotence, urinary frequency, urinary incontinence, UTI.
Metabolic: weight loss.
Musculoskeletal: arthritis, bursitis, myasthenia, twitching.
Respiratory: dyspnea, pneumonia.
Skin: skin disorders.
Other: *accidental injury,* decreased libido.

Interactions

Drug-drug. *Butyrophenones, metoclopramide, phenothiazines, thiothixenes:* May diminish pramipexole effectiveness. Monitor patient closely.
Cimetidine, diltiazem, quinidine, quinine, ranitidine, triamterene, verapamil: May decrease pramipexole clearance. Adjust dose.
Levodopa: May increase adverse effects of levodopa. Decrease levodopa dose, as directed.
Drug-herb. *Black horehound:* May have additive dopaminergic effects. Discourage using together.
Kava: May decrease dopaminergic effects. Discourage use together.

Effects on lab test results

None reported.

Pharmacokinetics

Absorption: Rapid. Absolute bioavailability exceeds 90%.
Distribution: Extensive throughout body.
Metabolism: 90% unchanged in urine.
Excretion: Mainly urinary. *Half-life:* 8 to 12 hours.

Route	Onset	Peak	Duration
P.O.	Rapid	2 hr	8–12 hr

Action

Chemical effect: Precise mechanism is unknown, but drug probably stimulates dopamine receptors in striatum.
Therapeutic effect: Relieves symptoms of idiopathic Parkinson disease.

Available forms

Tablets: 0.125 mg, 0.25 mg, 0.5 mg, 1 mg, 1.5 mg

NURSING PROCESS

Assessment

- Monitor vital signs carefully because drug may cause orthostatic hypotension, especially during dosage escalation.
- Assess patient's risk for physical injury from adverse CNS effects of drug (dyskinesia, dizziness, hallucinations, and somnolence).
- Assess patient's response to drug therapy, and adjust dosage.
- Assess patient's and family's knowledge of drug therapy.

Nursing diagnoses

- Impaired physical mobility related to underlying Parkinson disease
- Disturbed thought processes related to drug-induced CNS adverse reactions
- Deficient knowledge related to drug therapy

Planning and implementation

- Institute safety precautions.

ALERT: Don't abruptly stop giving the drug. Adjust dosage gradually according to patient's response and tolerance.

- Provide ice chips, drinks, or hard, sugarless candy to relieve dry mouth. Increase fluid and fiber intake to prevent constipation.

Patient teaching

- Instruct patient not to rise rapidly after sitting or lying down because of risk of orthostatic hypotension.
- Warn patient to avoid hazardous activities until the drug's CNS effects are known.
- Tell patient to contact prescriber before taking this drug with other drugs.
- Tell patient—especially geriatric patient—that hallucinations may occur.
- If nausea develops, advise patient to take drug with food.
- If woman is breast-feeding or intends to do so, tell her to notify prescriber.

Evaluation

- Patient has improved mobility and reduced muscle rigidity and tremor.
- Patient remains mentally alert.
- Patient and family state understanding of drug therapy.

pramlintide acetate

(PRAM-lihn-tighd AS-ih-tayt)
Symlin

Pharmacologic class: human amylin analogue
Therapeutic class: antidiabetic
Pregnancy risk category: C

Indications and dosages

▶ **Adjunct to insulin in patients with type 1 diabetes who haven't achieved the desired glucose control.** *Adults:* Initially, 15 mcg subcutaneously immediately before major meals (more than 250 calories or 30 g of carbohydrates). Reduce preprandial rapid-acting or short-acting insulin dose, including fixed-mix insulin such as 70/30, by 50%. Increase pramlintide dose by 15-mcg increments every 3 days as long as no nausea has occurred, to a maintenance dose of 30 to 60 mcg. Adjust insulin dose as needed.

▶ **Adjunct to insulin in patients with type 2 diabetes who haven't achieved the desired glucose control, with or without a sulfonylurea or metformin.** *Adults:* Initially, 60 mcg subcutaneously immediately before major meals. Reduce preprandial rapid-acting or short-acting insulin dose, including fixed-mix insulin, by 50%. Increase pramlintide dose to 120 mcg

P

when no significant nausea has occurred for 3 to 7 days. Adjust insulin dosage as needed.

Contraindications and cautions

• Contraindicated in patients hypersensitive to drug or its components, including metacresol, and in patients with gastroparesis or hypoglycemia unawareness. Don't use drug in patients noncompliant with current insulin and glucose monitoring regimen, patients with a glycosylated hemoglobin (HbA_{1c}) level greater than 9%, patients with severe hypoglycemia during the previous 6 months, and patients who take drugs that stimulate GI motility.

Lifespan: Use during pregnancy only if benefits outweigh risks to the fetus. Use cautiously in breast-feeding women; it isn't known whether drug appears in breast milk. Safety and effectiveness haven't been established in children. Use cautiously in elderly patients; drug seems to have similar effects on elderly and younger adults, but some older adults may have greater sensitivity to it.

Adverse reactions

CNS: dizziness, fatigue, *headache.*
EENT: pharyngitis.
GI: abdominal pain, *anorexia, nausea, vomiting.*
Metabolic: ***hypoglycemia.***
Musculoskeletal: arthralgia.
Respiratory: cough.
Skin: injection site reaction.
Other: allergic reaction, *inflicted injury.*

Interactions

Drug-drug. *ACE inhibitors, disopyramide, fibrates, fluoxetine, MAO inhibitors, oral antidiabetics, pentoxifylline, propoxyphene, salicylates, sulfonamide antibiotics:* May increase the risk of hypoglycemia. Monitor blood glucose level closely.
Alpha glucosidase inhibitors (such as acarbose) and anticholinergics (such as atropine, tricyclic antidepressants, benztropine): May alter GI motility. Avoid using together.
Beta blockers, clonidine, guanethidine, reserpine: May mask signs of hypoglycemia. Monitor blood glucose level closely.
Oral drugs dependent on rapid onset of action (such as analgesics): May delay absorption because of slowed gastric emptying. If rapid effect is needed, give oral drug 1 hour before or 2 hours after pramlintide.

Effects on lab test results

None reported.

Pharmacokinetics

Absorption: 30% to 40% bioavailable.
Distribution: Not extensively bound to blood cells or albumin.
Metabolism: Mainly renal.
Excretion: *Half-life of parent drug and active metabolite:* About 48 minutes each.

Route	Onset	Peak	Duration
SubQ	Unknown	19–21 min	Unknown

Action

Chemical effect: Slows the rate at which food leaves the stomach, reducing the initial postprandial increase in plasma glucose level. Drug also reduces postprandial glucagon concentrations, which decreases hyperglycemia, and reduces total caloric intake by modulating appetite.
Therapeutic effect: Lowers glucose level.

Available forms

Injection: 0.6 mg/ml in 50-ml vials

NURSING PROCESS

Assessment

• Before starting drug, review patient's HbA_{1c} level, recent blood glucose monitoring data, history of insulin-induced hypoglycemia, current insulin regimen, and body weight.
• Monitor patient's blood glucose level.
• Assess patient for signs of hypoglycemia including dizziness, restlessness, diaphoresis, tremor, nausea, irritability, and poor concentration.
• Monitor patient for severe nausea and vomiting. Dose reduction may be needed.
• Assess patient's and family's knowledge of drug therapy.

Nursing diagnoses

• Risk for injury related to drug-induced hypoglycemia
• Ineffective health maintenance related to hyperglycemia
• Deficient knowledge related to drug therapy

Planning and implementation

- To give drug, use a U-100 insulin syringe, preferably a 0.3-ml size.
- Don't mix drug with any type of insulin, and give it as a separate injection.
- Give each dose subcutaneously into the abdomen or thigh. Rotate injection sites, and use a site separate from the insulin site used at the same time.

ALERT: Pramlintide may increase the risk of insulin-induced severe hypoglycemia, particularly in patients with type 1 diabetes.

- The risk of severe, drug-related hypoglycemia is highest within the first 3 hours after an injection.
- Symptoms of hypoglycemia may be masked in patients with a long history of diabetes, diabetic nerve disease, or intensified diabetes control.
- Stop drug if patient has persistent nausea or recurrent, unexplained hypoglycemia that requires medical assistance. Also stop drug if patient doesn't comply with blood glucose monitoring or drug dose adjustments.

Patient teaching

- Teach patient how to take drug exactly as prescribed, immediately before mealtimes. Explain that it doesn't replace daily insulin but may lower the amount of insulin needed, especially before meals.
- Explain that a major meal contains more than 250 calories or 30 g of carbohydrates.
- Caution patient not to mix drug with insulin; instruct him to give the injections at separate sites.
- Instruct patient not to change doses of pramlintide or insulin without consulting the prescriber.
- Tell patient to refrain from driving, operating heavy machinery, or performing other risky activities where he could hurt himself or others, until drug affects his blood glucose are known.
- Caution patient about the possibility of severe hypoglycemia, particularly within 3 hours of injection.
- Teach patient and family members the signs and symptoms of hypoglycemia, including hunger, headache, sweating, tremor, irritability, and trouble concentrating.
- Instruct patient and family members what to do if hypoglycemia occurs.
- Tell patient to report severe nausea and vomiting.
- Advise woman of child-bearing potential to tell the prescriber if she is, could be, or is planning to become pregnant.
- Teach patient how to handle unusual situations, such as illness or stress, an inadequate or omitted insulin dose, inadvertent use of too much insulin or pramlintide, inadequate food intake, or missed meals.
- Tell patient to refrigerate vials. Contents of open vials should be used within 28 days and unopened vials before expiration date.

Evaluation

- Patient does not experience hypoglycemia and sustains no injury.
- Patient's glucose level is normal with drug therapy.
- Patient and family state understanding of drug therapy.

pravastatin sodium (eptastatin)

(PRAH-vuh-stat-in SOH-dee-um)

Pravachol

Pharmacologic class: HMG-CoA reductase inhibitor
Therapeutic class: antilipemic
Pregnancy risk category: X

Indications and dosages

▶ **Primary hypercholesterolemia and mixed dyslipidemia; primary and secondary prevention of coronary events; hyperlipidemia; homozygous familial hypercholesterolemia.** *Adults:* Initially, 40 mg P.O. once daily at the same time each day, with or without food. Adjust dosage q 4 weeks based on patient tolerance and response; maximum daily dose, 80 mg.

▶ **Heterozygous familial hypercholesterolemia.** *Children ages 14 to 18:* Give 40 mg P.O. once daily.

Children ages 8 to 13: Give 20 mg P.O. once daily.

Adjust-a-dose: For patients with renal or hepatic impairment, start with 10 mg P.O. daily.

For patients also taking immunosuppressants, start with 10 mg P.O. at bedtime and adjust to higher doses cautiously. Most patients given combination will receive maximum daily dose of 20 mg.

Contraindications and cautions

• Contraindicated in patients hypersensitive to the drug or any of its components, and in patients with active liver disease or unexplained persistent elevations of transaminase level.
• Use cautiously in patients who consume large quantities of alcohol or have a history of liver disease.
Lifespan: In pregnant women, breast-feeding women, and women of childbearing age (unless they have no risk of pregnancy), drug is contraindicated. In children younger than age 8, safety and effectiveness haven't been established.

Adverse reactions

CNS: dizziness, fatigue, headache.
CV: chest pain.
EENT: rhinitis.
GI: diarrhea, heartburn, nausea, vomiting.
GU: ***renal failure*** secondary to myoglobinuria.
Musculoskeletal: localized muscle pain, myalgia, myopathy, myositis, ***rhabdomyolysis.***
Respiratory: cough.
Skin: rash.
Other: flulike symptoms.

Interactions

Drug-drug. *Cholestyramine, colestipol:* May decrease pravastatin level. Give pravastatin 1 hour before or 4 hours after these drugs.
Drugs that decrease level or activity of endogenous steroids (such as cimetidine, spironolactone): May increase risk of endocrine dysfunction. No intervention needed. Take complete drug history in patients who develop endocrine dysfunction.
Erythromycin, fibric acid derivatives (such as clofibrate, gemfibrozil), high doses of niacin, immunosuppressants: May increase risk of rhabdomyolysis. Don't use together.
Fluconazole, itraconazole, ketoconazole: May increase level and adverse effects of pravastatin. Consider reduced dose of pravastatin.
Gemfibrozil: May decrease protein-binding and urinary clearance of pravastatin. Avoid using together.
Hepatotoxic drugs: May increase risk of hepatotoxicity. Avoid using together.
Drug-herb. *Kava:* May increase risk of hepatotoxicity. Discourage using together.
Red yeast rice: May increase the risk of adverse events or toxicity because herb contains components similar to those of statin drugs. Discourage using together.
Drug-lifestyle. *Alcohol use:* May increase risk of hepatotoxicity. Discourage using together.

Effects on lab test results

• May increase ALT, AST, CK, alkaline phosphatase, and bilirubin levels.
• May alter thyroid function test values.

Pharmacokinetics

Absorption: Rapid. Although food reduces bioavailability, drug effects are the same if drug is taken with or 1 hour before meals.
Distribution: About 50% protein-bound. Drug undergoes extensive first-pass extraction, possibly because of active transport system into hepatocytes.
Metabolism: In liver, into at least six metabolites. Some are active.
Excretion: By liver and kidneys. *Half-life:* 1¼ to 2¼ hours.

Route	Onset	Peak	Duration
P.O.	Unknown	1 hr	Unknown

Action

Chemical effect: Inhibits HMG-CoA reductase, which is an early and rate-limiting step in the synthesis of cholesterol.
Therapeutic effect: Lowers LDL and total cholesterol levels in some patients.

Available forms

Tablets: 10 mg, 20 mg, 40 mg, 80 mg

NURSING PROCESS

Assessment

• Assess patient's condition before starting therapy and regularly thereafter to monitor drug's effectiveness.
• Obtain liver function tests at start of therapy and periodically thereafter. If elevations persist, arrange for patient to have a liver biopsy.
• Be alert for adverse reactions and drug interactions.
• Monitor patient for signs of rhabdomyolysis, such as muscle aches and weakness.
• If adverse GI reaction occurs, monitor patient's hydration.

• Assess patient's and family's knowledge of drug therapy.

Nursing diagnoses

• Risk for injury related to elevated cholesterol level
• Risk for deficient fluid volume related to adverse GI reactions
• Deficient knowledge related to drug therapy

Planning and implementation

• Begin only after diet and other nondrug therapies have proved ineffective.

Patient teaching

• Instruct patient to take recommended dosage in evening, preferably at bedtime
• Teach patient about proper cholesterol-lowering diet (restricting total fat and cholesterol), and how to control other cardiac disease risk factors. Recommend weight control, exercise, and smoking cessation programs.
• Inform woman that drug is contraindicated during pregnancy. Advise her to notify prescriber immediately if she becomes pregnant.

Evaluation

• Patient's LDL and total cholesterol levels are within normal range.
• Patient maintains adequate hydration.
• Patient and family state understanding of drug therapy.

prazosin hydrochloride

(PRAH-zoh-sin high-droh-KLOR-ighd)

Minipress

Pharmacologic class: alpha blocker
Therapeutic class: antihypertensive
Pregnancy risk category: C

Indications and dosages

▶**Mild to moderate hypertension, alone or with diuretic or other antihypertensive.** *Adults:* Initial dosage is 1 mg P.O. b.i.d. to t.i.d. Increase slowly; maximum daily dose is 20 mg. Maintenance dosage is 6 to 15 mg daily in three divided doses. Some patients need larger doses (up to 40 mg daily). If other antihypertensives or diuretics are added, decrease to 1 to 2 mg t.i.d. and readjust.

▶**BPH**‡. *Adults:* Initially, 2 mg P.O. b.i.d. Daily dose may range from 1 to 9 mg.

Contraindications and cautions

• Use cautiously in patients taking other antihypertensives.

Lifespan: In pregnant women, use cautiously. In breast-feeding women, drug isn't recommended. In children, safety and effectiveness haven't been established.

Adverse reactions

CNS: depression, *dizziness,* drowsiness, *first-dose syncope,* headache, weakness.
CV: edema, orthostatic hypotension, *palpitations.*
EENT: blurred vision, epistaxis, nasal congestion, reddened sclera.
GI: abdominal cramps, constipation, diarrhea, dry mouth, *nausea,* vomiting.
GU: impotence, priapism, urinary frequency.
Skin: rash.

Interactions

Drug-drug. *Acebutolol, atenolol, betaxolol, carteolol, esmolol, metoprolol, nadolol, pindolol, propranolol, sotalol, timolol:* May increase risk of orthostatic hypotension in the early phases of use together. Assist patient to stand slowly until effects of drug are known.
Clonidine: May decrease antihypertensive effect of clonidine. Monitor blood pressure.
Diuretics: May increase risk of syncope with loss of consciousness.
Indomethacin: May decrease antihypertensive action of prazosin. Monitor blood pressure.
Verapamil: May increase prazosin level and increase risk of postural hypotension. Advise patient to sit or lie down if dizziness occurs.
Drug-herb. *Saw palmetto.* May have additive effect when used together for BPH.
Yohimbe: May antagonize antihypertensive effects. Discourage using together.

Effects on lab test results

• May increase BUN and uric acid levels.
• May increase liver function test values.

Pharmacokinetics

Absorption: Variable.
Distribution: Throughout body. About 97% protein-bound.
Metabolism: Extensive in liver.

Excretion: More than 90% in feces by bile; remainder in urine. *Half-life:* 2 to 4 hours.

Route	Onset	Peak	Duration
P.O.	30–90 min	2–4 hr	7–10 hr

Action

Chemical effect: Unknown; effects probably stem from alpha blocking activity.

Therapeutic effect: Lowers blood pressure.

Available forms

Capsules: 1 mg, 2 mg, 5 mg

NURSING PROCESS

Assessment

- Assess patient's condition before starting therapy and regularly thereafter to monitor drug's effectiveness.
- Frequently monitor patient's blood pressure and pulse rate.
- An elderly patient may be more sensitive to hypotensive effects of drug.
- Be alert for adverse reactions and drug interactions.
- Assess patient's and family's knowledge of drug therapy.

Nursing diagnoses

- Risk for injury related to presence of hypertension
- Sexual dysfunction related to drug-induced impotence
- Deficient knowledge related to drug therapy

Planning and implementation

- If first dose is larger than 1 mg, severe syncope with loss of consciousness may occur (first-dose syncope).

ALERT: Don't stop therapy abruptly.

- If you suspect compliance problems, discuss twice-daily dose with prescriber.

Patient teaching

- Tell patient not to abruptly stop taking drug, but to call prescriber if unpleasant adverse reactions occur.
- Advise patient to minimize effects of orthostatic hypotension by rising slowly and avoiding sudden position changes.
- Dry mouth can be relieved with sugarless chewing gum, sour hard candy, or ice chips.
- Inform male patient of the possibility of impotence, and advise him to seek counseling to learn how to cope with this adverse effect.

Evaluation

- Patient's blood pressure is normal.
- Patient seeks counseling for alternative methods of sexual gratification because of drug-induced impotence.
- Patient and family state understanding of drug therapy.

prednisolone (systemic)

(pred-NIS-uh-lohn)

Delta-Cortef, Prelone

prednisolone acetate

Cotolone, Key-Pred-25, Predalone 50, Predcor-50

prednisolone sodium phosphate

Hydeltrasol, Key-Pred SP, Orapred, Orapred ODT, Pediapred

Pharmacologic class: glucocorticoid, mineralocorticoid

Therapeutic class: anti-inflammatory, immunosuppressant

Pregnancy risk category: C

Indications and dosages

▶ **Severe inflammation, modification of body's immune response to disease.** *Adults:* 2.5 to 15 mg prednisolone P.O. b.i.d., t.i.d., or q.i.d. Or, 2 to 30 mg prednisolone acetate I.M. q 12 hours. Or, 5 to 60 mg prednisolone sodium phosphate I.M., I.V., or P.O. daily.

Children: Initially, 0.14 to 2 mg/kg prednisolone P.O. or 4 to 60 mg/m^2 prednisolone P.O. daily in four divided doses. Or, 0.04 to 0.25 mg/kg prednisolone acetate or 1.5 to 7.5 mg/m^2 prednisolone acetate I.M. once or twice daily. Or, initially, 0.14 to 2 mg/kg prednisolone sodium phosphate or 4 to 60 mg/m^2 prednisolone sodium phosphate I.M., I.V., or P.O. daily in three or four divided doses.

▶ **Acute exacerbations of multiple sclerosis.** *Adults:* 200 mg prednisolone sodium phosphate P.O. daily for 1 week, followed by 80 mg q other day.

▶ **Nephrotic syndrome.** *Children:* 60 mg/m^2 prednisolone sodium phosphate P.O. daily in three divided doses for 4 weeks, followed by 4 weeks of single-dose, alternate-day therapy at 40 mg/m^2.

▶ **Uncontrolled asthma in patients taking inhaled corticosteroids and long-acting bronchodilators.** *Children:* 1 to 2 mg/kg prednisolone sodium phosphate P.O. daily in single or divided doses. Short course or "burst" therapy should continue until a child achieves a peak expiratory flow rate of 80% of his personal best or symptoms resolve. This usually requires 3 to 10 days of therapy, although it can take longer. No evidence shows that tapering the dosage after improvement will prevent a relapse.

I.V. administration

• Give only prednisolone sodium phosphate by I.V. route. Never give acetate form by I.V. route.
• When giving drug as direct injection, inject undiluted over at least 1 minute.
• When giving drug as intermittent or continuous infusion, dilute solution according to the manufacturer's instructions and give over prescribed duration.
• D_5W and normal saline solution are recommended as diluents for I.V. infusions.

⊗ **Incompatibilities**
Calcium gluconate, dimenhydrinate, methotrexate sodium, polymyxin B, prochlorperazine edisylate, promazine, promethazine hydrochloride.

Contraindications and cautions

• Contraindicated in patients hypersensitive to the drug or any of its components, and in those with fungal infections.
• Use cautiously in patients with recent MI, GI ulcer, renal disease, hypertension, osteoporosis, diabetes mellitus, hypothyroidism, cirrhosis, diverticulitis, nonspecific ulcerative colitis, recent intestinal anastomoses, thromboembolic disorders, seizures, myasthenia gravis, heart failure, tuberculosis, ocular herpes simplex, emotional instability, or psychotic tendencies.

Lifespan: In pregnant women, use cautiously. In breast-feeding women, high doses aren't recommended.

Adverse reactions

Most reactions to corticosteroids are dose- or duration-dependent.

CNS: *euphoria, insomnia,* pseudotumor cerebri, psychotic behavior, ***seizures.***
CV: edema, ***heart failure,*** hypertension, ***thromboembolism.***
EENT: cataracts, glaucoma.
GI: GI irritation, increased appetite, ***pancreatitis,*** *peptic ulceration.*
Metabolic: carbohydrate intolerance, growth suppression in children, hyperglycemia, hypokalemia.
Musculoskeletal: muscle weakness, osteoporosis.
Skin: acne, delayed wound healing, hirsutism, various skin eruptions.
Other: ***acute adrenal insufficiency with increased stress (infection, surgery, or trauma) or abrupt withdrawal after long-term therapy;*** susceptibility to infections.

Interactions

Drug-drug. *Antihypertensives:* May counteract effect of antihypertensives. Adjust dose of antihypertensive as needed.
Aspirin, indomethacin, other NSAIDs: Increases risk of GI distress and bleeding. Avoid using together.
Azole antifungals (ketoconazole): May increase corticosteroid effects. Decrease corticosteroid dose.
Barbiturates, phenytoin, rifampin: May decrease corticosteroid effect. Increase corticosteroid dose.
Nondepolarizing muscle relaxants: May potentiate or counteract neuromuscular blocking action. Monitor patient closely.
Oral anticoagulants: May alter dosage requirements. Monitor PT and INR closely.
Potassium-depleting drugs (such as thiazide diuretics): May enhance potassium-wasting effects of prednisolone. Monitor potassium level.
Skin-test antigens: May decrease skin-test response. Defer skin testing until therapy is completed.
Toxoids, vaccines: May decrease antibody response and increase risk of neurologic complications. Check with prescriber about when to reschedule vaccine, if possible.

Effects on lab test results

• May increase glucose and cholesterol levels. May decrease potassium and calcium levels.

P

Pharmacokinetics

Absorption: Absorbed readily after P.O. use; variable with other routes.
Distribution: To muscle, liver, skin, intestine, and kidneys. Extensively protein-bound. Only unbound portion is active.
Metabolism: In liver.
Excretion: Inactive metabolites and small amounts of unmetabolized drug in urine; insignificant amount in feces. *Half-life:* 2 to 4 hours.

Route	Onset	Peak	Duration
P.O.	Rapid	1–2 hr	30–36 hr
I.V.	Rapid	< 1 hr	Unknown
I.M.	Rapid	< 1 hr	< 4 wk
P.R.	Unknown	Unknown	Unknown
Intra-articular, intralesional	1–2 days	Unknown	3 days–4 wk

Action

Chemical effect: Not clearly defined; decreases inflammation, mainly by stabilizing leukocyte lysosomal membranes; suppresses immune response; stimulates bone marrow; and influences protein, fat, and carbohydrate metabolism.
Therapeutic effect: Relieves inflammation and induces immunosuppression.

Available forms

prednisolone
Syrup: 5 mg/ml, 15 mg/5 ml
Tablets: 5 mg
prednisolone acetate
Injection: 25 mg/ml, 50 mg/ml suspension
prednisolone sodium phosphate
Injection: 20 mg/ml solution
Oral liquid: 5 mg/5 ml, 15 mg/5 ml
Tablets (orally disintegrating): 10 mg, 15 mg, 30 mg

NURSING PROCESS

Assessment

- Assess patient's condition before starting therapy and regularly thereafter to monitor drug's effectiveness.
- Monitor patient's weight, blood pressure, and electrolyte level.
- Watch for depression or psychotic episodes, especially with high dose.
- Monitor glucose level in a diabetic patient; he may need increase in insulin.
- Monitor patient's stress level; a dose adjustment may be needed.
- Assess for adequate calcium supplementation.
- Be alert for adverse reactions and drug interactions.
- Assess patient's and family's knowledge of drug therapy.

Nursing diagnoses

- Ineffective health maintenance related to underlying condition
- Ineffective protection related to drug-induced adverse reactions
- Deficient knowledge related to drug therapy

Planning and implementation

- Always adjust to lowest effective dose, which may need to be increased during times of physiologic stress (such as surgery, trauma, or infection).
- Prednisolone salts (acetate and sodium phosphate) are used parenterally less often than other corticosteroids that have more potent anti-inflammatory action.
- Drug may be used for alternate-day therapy.
- Give dose with food when possible to reduce GI irritation.
- Refrigerate Orapred at 36° to 46° F (2° to 8° C).
- Inject drug I.M. deep into gluteal muscle.
- Alternate injection sites to prevent muscle atrophy.
- Avoid subcutaneous injection because atrophy and sterile abscesses may occur.
- Unless contraindicated, give low-sodium diet high in potassium and protein. Give potassium supplements, as needed.
- Notify prescriber immediately if serious adverse reactions occur, and give supportive care.
- After long-term therapy, reduce dose gradually. Abrupt withdrawal may cause rebound inflammation, fatigue, weakness, arthralgia, fever, dizziness, lethargy, depression, fainting, orthostatic hypotension, dyspnea, anorexia, or hypoglycemia. Sudden withdrawal after prolonged use may be fatal.

ALERT: Don't confuse prednisolone with prednisone.

Patient teaching

- Tell patient not to stop drug without the prescriber's knowledge.
- Tell patient that if he misses a dose, he should take it as soon as possible unless it is near the

time for his next dose. Tell him not to attempt to make up missed doses that are long overdue.

- Advise patient to take oral form with meals to minimize GI reactions.

ALERT: Tell patient not to cut, crush, or chew the orally disintegrating tablets.

- Instruct patient to wait to remove the orally disintegrating tablet from the blister pack until he's ready to take it. The tablet can be swallowed whole or allowed to dissolve on the tongue with or without water.
- Warn patient receiving long-term therapy about cushingoid symptoms.
- Teach signs of early adrenal insufficiency: fatigue, muscle weakness, joint pain, fever, anorexia, nausea, dyspnea, dizziness, and fainting.
- Instruct patient to wear or carry medical identification that indicates his need for systemic glucocorticoids during stress.
- Tell patient to report slow healing, sudden weight gain, or swelling.
- Advise patient receiving long-term therapy to exercise or have physical therapy and to ask prescriber about vitamin D or calcium supplements.

☑ Evaluation

- Patient responds well to therapy.
- Patient has no serious adverse reactions.
- Patient and family state understanding of drug therapy.

prednisone

(PRED-nih-sohn)

Apo-Prednisone ♦, Novo-Prednisone ♦, Panafcort ♦, Panasol-S, Prednisone Intensol*, Sone ♦, Sterapred, Winpred ♦

Pharmacologic class: adrenocorticoid
Therapeutic class: anti-inflammatory, immunosuppressant
Pregnancy risk category: C

Indications and dosages

▶ **Severe inflammation or immunosuppression.** *Adults:* 5 to 60 mg P.O. daily in single or divided doses. Maximum, 250 mg daily. Maintenance dose given once daily or q other day. Dosage must be individualized.
Children: 0.14 to 2 mg/kg P.O. daily in four divided doses.

▶ **Acute exacerbations of multiple sclerosis.** *Adults:* 200 mg P.O. daily for 1 week; then 80 mg P.O. q other day for 1 month.

Contraindications and cautions

- Contraindicated in patients hypersensitive to the drug or any of its components, and in those with systemic fungal infections.
- Use cautiously in patients with GI ulcer, renal disease, hypertension, osteoporosis, diabetes mellitus, hypothyroidism, cirrhosis, diverticulitis, nonspecific ulcerative colitis, recent intestinal anastomoses, thromboembolic disorders, seizures, myasthenia gravis, heart failure, tuberculosis, ocular herpes simplex, emotional instability, or psychotic tendencies.

Lifespan: In pregnant women, use cautiously. In breast-feeding women, high doses aren't recommended.

Adverse reactions

Most reactions are dose- or duration-dependent.
CNS: *euphoria, insomnia,* pseudotumor cerebri, psychotic behavior, ***seizures.***
CV: edema, ***heart failure,*** hypertension, ***thromboembolism.***
EENT: cataracts, glaucoma.
GI: GI irritation, increased appetite, *peptic ulceration,* ***pancreatitis.***
Metabolic: carbohydrate intolerance, growth suppression in children, hyperglycemia, hypokalemia.
Musculoskeletal: muscle weakness, osteoporosis.
Skin: acne, delayed wound healing, hirsutism, various skin eruptions.
Other: susceptibility to infections.

Interactions

Drug-drug. *Antihypertensives:* May counteract effect of antihypertensives. Adjust dosage of antihypertensive as needed.
Aspirin, indomethacin, other NSAIDs: May increase risk of GI distress and bleeding. Give together cautiously.
Barbiturates, phenytoin, rifampin: May decrease corticosteroid effect. Increase corticosteroid dose.
Ketoconazole: May increase steroid effects. Decrease glucocorticoid dose.
Oral anticoagulants: May alter dosage requirements. Monitor PT and INR closely.

P

Potassium-depleting drugs (such as thiazide diuretics): May enhance potassium-wasting effects of prednisone. Monitor potassium level.
Skin-test antigens: May decrease skin test response. Defer skin testing until therapy is completed.
Toxoids, vaccines: May decrease antibody response and increases risk of neurologic complications. Don't give together.

Effects on lab test results

- May increase ALT, AST, alkaline phosphatase, glucose, and cholesterol levels. May decrease potassium and calcium levels.

Pharmacokinetics

Absorption: Absorbed readily after P.O. use.
Distribution: To muscle, liver, skin, intestine, and kidneys. Extensively protein-bound. Only unbound portion is active.
Metabolism: In liver.
Excretion: Inactive metabolites and small amounts of unmetabolized drug in urine; insignificant amounts in feces. *Half-life:* 1 hour.

Route	Onset	Peak	Duration
P.O.	Varies	Varies	Varies

Action

Chemical effect: Not clearly defined; decreases inflammation; suppresses immune response; stimulates bone marrow; and influences protein, fat, and carbohydrate metabolism.
Therapeutic effect: Relieves inflammation and induces immunosuppression.

Available forms

Oral solution: 5 mg/5 ml*, 5 mg/ml (concentrate)*
Syrup: 5 mg/5 ml*
Tablets: 1 mg, 2.5 mg, 5 mg, 10 mg, 20 mg, 25 mg, 50 mg

NURSING PROCESS

Assessment

- Assess patient's condition before starting therapy and regularly thereafter to monitor drug's effectiveness.
- Monitor patient's weight, blood pressure, and electrolyte level.
- Watch for depression or psychotic episodes, especially when given in high doses.
- Monitor glucose level in a diabetic patient; he may need an increase in insulin.
- Monitor patient's stress level; dosage adjustment may be needed.
- Be alert for adverse reactions and drug interactions.
- Assess patient's and family's knowledge of drug therapy.

Nursing diagnoses

- Ineffective health maintenance related to underlying condition
- Ineffective protection related to drug-induced adverse reactions
- Deficient knowledge related to drug therapy

Planning and implementation

- Always adjust to lowest effective dose, which may need to be increased during times of physiologic stress (such as surgery, trauma, or infection).
- Drug may be used for alternate-day therapy.
- For better results and less toxicity, give once-daily dose in morning.
- Give oral dose with food to reduce GI irritation.
- After long-term therapy, reduce dosage gradually. Abruptly stopping the drug may cause rebound inflammation, fatigue, weakness, arthralgia, fever, dizziness, lethargy, depression, fainting, orthostatic hypotension, dyspnea, anorexia, or hypoglycemia. After long-term therapy, increased stress or abrupt withdrawal may cause acute adrenal insufficiency. Sudden withdrawal after prolonged use may be fatal.
- Unless contraindicated, give low-sodium diet high in potassium and protein. Give potassium supplements, as needed.
- If serious adverse reactions occur, notify prescriber immediately and give supportive care.

ALERT: Don't confuse prednisone with prednisolone.

Patient teaching

- Tell patient not to stop taking the drug without prescriber's knowledge.
- Advise patient to take oral form with meals to minimize GI reactions.
- Tell patient to report sudden weight gain, swelling, or slow healing.
- Advise patient receiving long-term therapy to exercise or have physical therapy, to ask prescriber about vitamin D or calcium supplements, and to have periodic eye examinations.

• Instruct patient to wear or carry medical identification that indicates his need for systemic glucocorticoids during stress.
• Warn patient receiving long-term therapy about cushingoid symptoms.
• Teach signs of early adrenal insufficiency: fatigue, muscular weakness, joint pain, fever, anorexia, nausea, dyspnea, dizziness, and fainting.

Evaluation
• Patient responds well to therapy.
• Patient doesn't experience serious adverse reactions.
• Patient and family state understanding of drug therapy.

pregabalin
(preh-GAH-bah-linn)
Lyrica

Pharmacologic class: CNS drug
Therapeutic class: analgesic, anticonvulsant
Pregnancy risk category: C
Controlled substance schedule: V

Indications and dosages
▶ **Diabetic peripheral neuropathy.** *Adults:* Initially, 50 mg P.O. t.i.d. May increase to 100 mg P.O. t.i.d. within 1 week.
▶ **Postherpetic neuralgia.** *Adults:* Initially, 75 mg P.O. b.i.d. or 50 mg P.O. t.i.d. May increase to 300 mg/day in two or three equally divided doses within 1 week. If pain relief is insufficient after 2 to 4 weeks, may increase to 300 mg b.i.d. or 200 mg t.i.d.
▶ **Adjunctive treatment of partial onset seizures.** *Adults:* Initially, 75 mg P.O. b.i.d. or 50 mg P.O. t.i.d. Range, 150 to 600 mg/day.
Adjust-a-dose: In patients with renal impairment, if creatinine clearance is 30 to 60 ml/minute, give 75 to 300 mg/day in two to three divided doses. If clearance is 15 to 30 ml/minute, give 25 to 150 mg/day in one dose or divided into two doses. If clearance is less than 15 ml/minute, give 25 to 75 mg/day in one dose.

If patient undergoes hemodialysis, give one supplemental dose according to these guidelines. If patient takes 25 mg daily, give 25 or 50 mg. If patient takes 25 to 50 mg daily, give 50 or 75 mg. If patient takes 75 mg daily, give 100 or 150 mg.

Contraindications and cautions
• Contraindicated in patients hypersensitive to pregabalin or any of its components.
• Use cautiously in patients with New York Heart Association Class III or Class IV heart failure.
Lifespan: Use drug in pregnancy only if benefits outweigh risks to the fetus. It isn't known whether drug appears in breast milk. Patient should either stop breast-feeding or stop drug. Safety and effectiveness haven't been established in pediatric patients. Older adults may be more sensitive to side effects.

Adverse reactions
CNS: abnormal gait, abnormal thinking, amnesia, anxiety, asthenia, *ataxia,* confusion, depersonalization, *dizziness,* euphoria, headache, hypesthesia, hypertonia, incoordination, myoclonus, nervousness, nystagmus, paresthesia, *somnolence,* stupor, tremor, twitching, vertigo.
CV: *edema,* ***PR interval prolongation.***
EENT: blurred or abnormal vision, conjunctivitis, diplopia, eye disorder, otitis media, tinnitus.
GI: abdominal pain, constipation, *dry mouth,* flatulence, gastroenteritis, vomiting.
GU: anorgasmia, impotence, urinary frequency, urinary incontinence.
Metabolic: **HYPOGLYCEMIA,** increased or decreased appetite, *weight gain.*
Musculoskeletal: arthralgia, back and chest pain, leg cramps, myalgia, myasthenia, neuropathy.
Respiratory: bronchitis, dyspnea.
Skin: ecchymosis, pruritus.
Other: accidental injury, ***allergic reaction,*** decreased libido, flu syndrome, *infection,* pain.

Interactions
Drug-drug. *CNS depressants:* May have additive effects on cognitive and gross motor function. Monitor patient for increased dizziness and somnolence.
Pioglitazone, rosiglitazone: May cause additive fluid retention and weight gain. Monitor patient closely.
Drug-lifestyle. *Alcohol use:* May have additive depressant effects on cognitive and gross motor function. Discourage alcohol use.

Effects on lab test results
• May increase CK level.
• May decrease platelet count.

Pharmacokinetics

Absorption: Well absorbed. Bioavailability exceeds 90%. Rate but not extent of absorption is decreased when drug is taken with food.
Distribution: Steady state is achieved in 24 to 48 hours. Not plasma protein–bound.
Metabolism: Negligible.
Excretion: Nearly proportional to creatinine clearance. About 90% eliminated via the kidneys as unchanged drug. *Half-life:* 6½ hours.

Route	Onset	Peak	Duration
P.O.	Unknown	1½–3 hr	Unknown

Action

Chemical effect: Drug may contribute to analgesic and anticonvulsant effects by binding to sites in CNS.
Therapeutic effect: Prevents seizure activity; relieves nerve pain caused by diabetic peripheral neuropathy or postherpetic neuralgia.

Available forms

Capsules: 25 mg, 50 mg, 75 mg, 100 mg, 150 mg, 200 mg, 225 mg, 300 mg

NURSING PROCESS

Assessment

- Assess patient's seizure disorder or diabetic peripheral neuropathy or postherpetic neuralgia prior to therapy and regularly thereafter.
- Monitor patient's weight and fluid status, especially if he has heart failure.
- Check for changes in vision.
- Watch for signs of rhabdomyolysis, such as dark, red, or cola-colored urine; muscle tenderness; generalized weakness; or muscle stiffness or aching.
- Evaluate patient's and family's knowledge of drug therapy.

Nursing diagnoses

- Risk for injury related to seizure disorder
- Acute pain related to diabetic peripheral neuropathy or postherpetic neuralgia
- Deficient knowledge related to drug therapy

Planning and implementation

- Taper drug gradually over at least 1 week. Stopping abruptly may result in increased seizure frequency, insomnia, headache, nausea, and diarrhea.
- In the case of overdose, treatment is supportive. Four hours of hemodialysis removes about 50% of drug. Contact poison control center.

Patient teaching

- Explain that drug may be taken with or without food.
- Warn patient not to stop drug abruptly.
- Caution patient to avoid hazardous activities until drug's effects are known.
- Instruct patient to watch for weight changes and water retention.
- Advise patient to report vision changes and malaise or fever accompanied by muscle pain, tenderness, or weakness.
- Inform a woman of childbearing age to immediately report planned or suspected pregnancy to prescriber.
- Tell a man who plans to father a child to consult prescriber about risks to fetus.
- If patient has diabetes, urge him to inspect his skin closely for ulcer formation.

Evaluation

- Patient does not experience seizures while taking drug.
- Patient reports pain relief.
- Patient and family state understanding of drug therapy.

primidone

(PRIH-mih-dohn)

Apo-Primidone ♦, Mysoline, PMS Primidone, Sertan ♦

Pharmacologic class: barbiturate analogue
Therapeutic class: anticonvulsant
Pregnancy risk category: D

Indications and dosages

▶ **Generalized tonic-clonic, focal, and complex-partial (psychomotor) seizures.** *Adults and children age 8 and older:* Initially, 100 to 125 mg P.O. at bedtime on days 1 to 3; then 100 to 125 mg P.O. b.i.d. on days 4 to 6; then 100 to 125 mg P.O. t.i.d. on days 7 to 9; followed by maintenance dose of 250 mg P.O. t.i.d. to q.i.d.; maximum dose, 2 g daily.
Children younger than age 8: Initially, 50 mg P.O. at bedtime for 3 days; then 50 mg P.O. b.i.d. for 4 to 6 days; then 100 mg P.O. b.i.d. for 7 to 9 days; followed by maintenance dose of

125 to 250 mg P.O. t.i.d., or 10 to 25 mg/kg daily in divided doses.

▶ **Benign familial tremor (essential tremor).** *Adults:* 750 mg P.O. daily.

Contraindications and cautions

- Contraindicated in patients with phenobarbital hypersensitivity or porphyria.

Lifespan: In pregnant and breast-feeding women, drug is contraindicated.

Adverse reactions

CNS: *ataxia, drowsiness,* emotional disturbances, fatigue, hyperirritability, vertigo.
CV: edema.
EENT: *diplopia,* edema of eyelids, nystagmus.
GI: anorexia, nausea, thirst, vomiting.
GU: impotence, polyuria.
Hematologic: eosinophilia, ***leukopenia, thrombocytopenia.***
Skin: alopecia, morbilliform rash.

Interactions

Drug-drug. *Acetazolamide:* May decrease primidone level. Monitor patient for effect.
Anticoagulants: May decrease anticoagulant effects. Adjust anticoagulant dose as needed.
Carbamazepine: May decrease primidone level and increase carbamazepine level. Observe patient for lack of effect or carbamazepine toxicity.
Corticosteroids: May decrease corticosteroid effects. Avoid use together, if possible.
Doxycycline: May decrease doxycycline effects. Consider alternative tetracycline.
Estrogen, oral contraceptives: May decrease contraceptive effectiveness. Recommend alternative contraceptive method.
Felodipine, methadone, metronidazole, nifedipine, quinidine, theophylline: May decrease effectiveness of these drugs. Consider increased dosage.
Isoniazid, nicotinamide: May increase primidone level. Monitor patient for toxicity.
Metoprolol, propranolol: May reduce the effects of these drugs. Consider an increased beta blocker dose.
Phenytoin: May increase conversion of primidone to phenobarbital. Observe patient for increased phenobarbital effect.
Valproic acid: May increase primidone level. Consider decreased primidone dose
Drug-herb. *Glutamate:* May antagonize anticonvulsant effects of drug. Discourage using together.
Drug-lifestyle. *Alcohol use:* May impair coordination, increase CNS effects, and cause death. Strongly discourage use together.

Effects on lab test results

- May decrease hemoglobin level and hematocrit.
- May increase eosinophil count. May decrease WBC and platelet counts.

Pharmacokinetics

Absorption: Absorbed readily.
Distribution: Wide.
Metabolism: Slow, by liver, to phenylethylmalonamide (PEMA) and phenobarbital; PEMA is the major metabolite.
Excretion: In urine. *Half-life:* 5 to 15 hours.

Route	Onset	Peak	Duration
P.O.	Unknown	3–4 hr	Unknown

Action

Chemical effect: Unknown; some activity may be caused by PEMA and phenobarbital.
Therapeutic effect: Prevents seizures.

Available forms

Oral suspension: 250 mg/5 ml
Tablets: 50 mg, 250 mg

NURSING PROCESS

Assessment

- Assess patient's condition before starting therapy and regularly thereafter to monitor drug's effectiveness.
- Monitor blood drug level. Therapeutic primidone level is 5 to 12 mcg/ml. Therapeutic phenobarbital level is 15 to 40 mcg/ml.
- Monitor CBC and routine blood chemistry q 6 months.
- Monitor patient's hydration throughout drug therapy.
- Assess patient's and family's knowledge of drug therapy.

Nursing diagnoses

- Risk for trauma related to seizures
- Risk for deficient fluid volume related to adverse reactions

• Deficient knowledge related to drug therapy

Planning and implementation

• Shake liquid suspension well.
• Don't abruptly stop giving the drug, because seizures may worsen.
• Call prescriber immediately if adverse reactions develop.
ALERT: Don't confuse primidone with prednisone.

Patient teaching

• Advise patient to avoid hazardous activities until the drug's CNS effects are known.
• Warn patient and parents not to stop drug suddenly.
• Tell patient that full therapeutic response may take 2 weeks or more.

Evaluation

• Patient is free from seizure activity.
• Patient maintains adequate hydration throughout drug therapy.
• Patient and family state understanding of drug therapy.

probenecid

(proh-BEN-uh-sid)
Benuryl ◊, Probalan

Pharmacologic class: sulfonamide derivative
Therapeutic class: uricosuric
Pregnancy risk category: B

Indications and dosages

▶ **Adjunct to penicillin therapy.** *Adults and children older than age 14 or who weigh more than 50 kg (110 lb):* 500 mg P.O. q.i.d.
Children ages 2 to 14 or who weigh 50 kg or less: Initially, 25 mg/kg P.O.; then 40 mg/kg in divided doses q.i.d.
▶ **Gonorrhea.** *Adults:* 3.5 g ampicillin P.O. with 1 g probenecid P.O. given together. Or, 1 g probenecid P.O. 30 minutes before 4.8 million units of aqueous penicillin G procaine I.M., injected at two different sites.
▶ **Hyperuricemia of gout, gouty arthritis.** *Adults:* 250 mg P.O. b.i.d. for first week; then 500 mg b.i.d., to maximum of 3 g daily. Reevaluate maintenance dosage q 6 months and reduce in increments of 500 mg.
▶ **To diagnose parkinsonian syndrome or mental depression‡.** *Adults:* 500 mg P.O. q 12 hours for 5 doses.
Adjust-a-dose: For patients with renal impairment with a GFR of 30 ml/minute or greater, dosage may need to be increased. Increases can be made in 0.5 g increments q 4 weeks. Usual daily dose is 2 g or less.

Contraindications and cautions

• Contraindicated in patients hypersensitive to the drug or any of its components, and in patients with uric acid kidney stones, blood dyscrasias, or acute gout attack.
• Use cautiously in patients with history of allergy to sulfa drugs; peptic ulcer or renal impairment.
Lifespan: In pregnant women, use cautiously. In breast-feeding women, use cautiously; it's unknown if the drug appears in breast milk. In children younger than age 2, drug is contraindicated.

Adverse reactions

CNS: dizziness, fever, *headache.*
CV: flushing, hypotension.
GI: anorexia, *gastric distress,* nausea, sore gums, vomiting.
GU: renal colic, urinary frequency.
Hematologic: ***aplastic anemia,*** hemolytic anemia.
Hepatic: ***hepatic necrosis.***
Skin: alopecia, dermatitis, pruritus.
Other: ***anaphylaxis,*** hypersensitivity reaction.

Interactions

Drug-drug. *Methotrexate:* May impair excretion of methotrexate, causing increased level, effects, and toxicity. Monitor level closely and adjust dosage accordingly.
NSAIDs: May increase NSAID level and increase risk of toxicity. Adjust dosage, as needed
Oral antidiabetics: May enhance hypoglycemic effect. Monitor glucose level closely. Dosage adjustment may be needed.
Rifampin: May decrease rifampin level. Monitor patient for lack of effect.
Salicylates: May inhibit uricosuric effect of probenecid, causing urate retention. Don't use together.
Sulfonamides: May decrease sulfonamide excretion. Monitor patient for signs of toxicity.

Sulfonylureas: May increase half-life of these drugs. Monitor blood glucose.
Zidovudine: May increase absorption of zidovudine. Monitor patient for cutaneous drug eruption, malaise, myalgia, and fever.
Drug-lifestyle. *Alcohol use:* May increase urate level. Discourage using together.

Effects on lab test results

- May decrease hemoglobin level and hematocrit.
- May falsely elevate theophylline level. May cause false-positive glucose test results with Benedict solution or Clinitest.

Pharmacokinetics

Absorption: Complete.
Distribution: Throughout body. About 75% protein-bound.
Metabolism: In liver to active metabolites, with some uricosuric effect.
Excretion: Drug and metabolites in urine; probenecid is actively reabsorbed but metabolites aren't. *Half-life:* 3 to 8 hours after 500-mg dose, 6 to 12 hours after larger doses.

Route	Onset	Peak	Duration
P.O.	Unknown	2–4 hr	8 hr

Action

Chemical effect: Blocks renal tubular reabsorption of uric acid, increasing excretion, and inhibits active renal tubular secretion of many weak organic acids, such as penicillins and cephalosporins.
Therapeutic effect: Lowers uric acid and prolongs penicillin action.

Available forms

Tablets: 500 mg

NURSING PROCESS

Assessment

- Assess patient's condition before starting therapy and regularly thereafter to monitor drug's effectiveness.
- Periodically monitor BUN and renal function tests in patient on long-term therapy.
- Be alert for adverse reactions and drug interactions.
- If adverse GI reactions occur, monitor patient's hydration.
- Assess patient's and family's knowledge of drug therapy.

Nursing diagnoses

- Ineffective health maintenance related to underlying condition
- Risk for deficient fluid volume related to adverse GI reactions
- Deficient knowledge related to drug therapy

Planning and implementation

- Drug is ineffective in patients with chronic renal insufficiency and a GFR less than 30 ml/minute.
- Give drug with milk, food, or antacids to minimize GI distress. Continued disturbances may indicate need to lower dosage.
- Encourage patient to drink to maintain minimum daily output of 2 L of water a day. Alkalinize urine with sodium bicarbonate or potassium citrate. These measures will prevent hematuria, renal colic, urate stone development, and costovertebral pain.
- Therapy doesn't start until acute attack subsides. Drug contains no analgesic or anti-inflammatory drug and isn't useful during acute gout attacks.
- Drug may increase frequency, severity, and duration of acute gout attacks during first 6 to 12 months of therapy. Prophylactic colchicine or another anti-inflammatory is given during first 3 to 6 months.

ALERT: Don't confuse probenecid with Procanbid.

Patient teaching

- Instruct patient to take drug with food or milk to minimize GI distress.
- Advise patient with gout to avoid all drugs that contain aspirin, which may precipitate gout. Acetaminophen may be used for pain.
- Tell patient with gout to avoid alcohol during drug therapy; it increases urate level.
- Tell patient with gout to limit intake of foods high in purine, such as anchovies, liver, sardines, kidneys, sweetbreads, peas, and lentils.
- Instruct patient and family that drug must be taken regularly or gout attacks may result. Tell patient to visit prescriber regularly so uric acid can be monitored and dosage adjusted, if needed. Lifelong therapy may be required in patients with hyperuricemia.

P

Evaluation
- Patient responds positively to therapy.
- Patient maintains adequate hydration.
- Patient and family state understanding of drug therapy.

procainamide hydrochloride

(proh-KAYN-uh-mighd high-droh-KLOR-ighd)

Procainamide Durules ♦, Procan SR, Procanbid, Promine, Pronestyl, Pronestyl-SR

Pharmacologic class: procaine derivative
Therapeutic class: antiarrhythmic
Pregnancy risk category: C

Indications and dosages

▶ **Symptomatic PVCs; life-threatening ventricular tachycardia.** *Adults:* 100 mg q 5 minutes by slow I.V. push, no faster than 25 to 50 mg/minute, until arrhythmias disappear, adverse effects develop, or 500 mg have been given. Or, give a loading dose of 500 to 600 mg I.V. infusion over 25 to 30 minutes. Maximum total dose is 1 g. When arrhythmias disappear, give continuous infusion of 2 to 6 mg/minute. If arrhythmias recur, repeat bolus and increase infusion rate. For I.M. administration, give 50 mg/kg/day divided q 3 to 6 hours; for arrhythmias during surgery, 100 to 500 mg I.M. For oral therapy, start with 50 mg/kg P.O. of conventional tablets or capsules in divided doses q 3 hours until therapeutic level is reached. For the maintenance dosage, substitute sustained-release form q 6 hours or extended-release form (Procanbid) at dose of 50 mg/kg P.O. in two divided doses q 12 hours.
Children‡: Dosage not established. Recommendations include 2 to 5 mg/kg, not exceeding 100 mg, repeated, as needed, at 5- to 10-minute intervals not exceeding 15 mg/kg in 24 hours or 500 mg in a 30-minute period; or 15 mg/kg infused over 30 to 60 minutes, followed by maintenance infusion of 0.02 to 0.08 mg/kg/minute.
Adjust-a-dose: For patients with renal or hepatic dysfunction, decrease dose or give at longer intervals.

▶ **To maintain normal sinus rhythm after conversion of atrial flutter‡.** *Adults:* 0.5 to 1 g P.O. of conventional tablets or capsules q 4 to 6 hours.

▶ **Loading dose to prevent atrial fibrillation or paroxysmal atrial tachycardia‡.** *Adults:* 1.25 g P.O. of conventional tablets or capsules. If arrhythmias persist after 1 hour, give additional 750 mg. If no change occurs, give 500 mg to 1 g P.O. q 2 hours until arrhythmias disappear or adverse effects occur. Maintenance dose is 1 g extended release q 6 hours.

▶ **Malignant hyperthermia‡.** *Adults:* 200 to 900 mg I.V., followed by an infusion.

I.V. administration

- Vials for I.V. injection contain 1 g of drug: 100 mg/ml (10 ml) or 500 mg/ml (2 ml).
- Use infusion control device to give infusion precisely.
- Keep patient in supine position during I.V. use. If drug is given too rapidly, hypotension can occur. Watch closely for adverse reactions during infusion, and notify prescriber if they occur.
- Patient receiving infusions must be monitored at all times.
- If solution becomes discolored, check with pharmacy and expect to discard.

⊗ **Incompatibilities**
Bretylium, esmolol, ethacrynate, milrinone, phenytoin sodium.

Contraindications and cautions

- Contraindicated in patients hypersensitive to procaine and related drugs; in those with complete, second-, or third-degree heart block in absence of artificial pacemaker; and in those with myasthenia gravis or systemic lupus erythematosus. Also contraindicated in patients with atypical ventricular tachycardia (torsades de pointes) because procainamide may aggravate this condition.
- Use cautiously to treat ventricular tachycardia during coronary occlusion. Also use cautiously in patients with hepatic or renal insufficiency, blood dyscrasias, bone marrow suppression, heart failure, or other conduction disturbances, such as bundle-branch heart block, sinus bradycardia, or digoxin intoxication.

Lifespan: In pregnant women, use cautiously. In breast-feeding women, drug isn't recommended. In children, safety and effectiveness haven't been established.

Adverse reactions

CNS: confusion, depression, dizziness, fever, hallucinations.
CV: AV block, bradycardia, ***heart failure,*** hypotension, ***ventricular asystole, ventricular fibrillation*** after parenteral use.
GI: anorexia, bitter taste with large doses, diarrhea, nausea, vomiting.
Hematologic: ***agranulocytosis,*** hemolytic anemia, ***neutropenia*** (especially with sustained-release forms), ***thrombocytopenia.***
Musculoskeletal: *myalgia.*
Skin: maculopapular rash.
Other: *lupuslike syndrome* (especially after prolonged use).

Interactions

Drug-drug. *Amiodarone:* May increase procainamide level and toxicity with additive effects on QT interval and QRS complex. Avoid using together.
Anticholinergics: May have additive anticholinergic effects. Monitor patient closely.
Anticholinesterases: May decrease anticholinesterase effect. Anticholinesterase dose may need to be increased.
Cimetidine: May increase procainamide level. Avoid this combination if possible. Monitor procainamide level closely and adjust the dosage as needed.
Lidocaine: May have additive cardiodepressant effects. Monitor ECG.
Neuromuscular skeletal muscle relaxants: May increase skeletal muscle relaxant effects. Monitor patient.
Propranolol, ranitidine: May increase procainamide level. Monitor patient for toxicity.
Quinidine, trimethoprim: May elevate procainamide and *N*-acetylprocainamide (NAPA) levels. Monitor patient for toxicity.
Quinolones: May increase procainamide level and risk of life threatening arrhythmias. Adjust dosage as needed.
Drug-herb. *Jimson weed:* May adversely affect CV function. Discourage using together.
Licorice: May prolong QT interval and be additive. Discourage using together.

Effects on lab test results

- May increase ALT, AST, alkaline phosphatase, LDH, and bilirubin levels. May decrease hemoglobin level and hematocrit.
- May increase antinuclear antibody titer. May decrease neutrophil, granulocyte, and platelet counts.

Pharmacokinetics

Absorption: Usually 75% to 95% of P.O. dose. Unknown after I.M. use.
Distribution: Wide in most body tissues, including CSF, liver, spleen, kidneys, lungs, muscles, brain, and heart. About 15% protein-bound.
Metabolism: In liver.
Excretion: In urine. *Half-life:* About 2½ to 4¾ hours.

Route	Onset	Peak	Duration
P.O.	Unknown	1–2 hr	Unknown
I.V.	Immediate	Immediate	Unknown
I.M.	10–30 min	15–60 min	Unknown

Action

Chemical effect: Class IA antiarrhythmic that decreases excitability, conduction velocity, automaticity, and membrane responsiveness with prolonged refractory period. Larger doses may induce AV block.
Therapeutic effect: Restores normal sinus rhythm.

Available forms

Capsules: 250 mg, 375 mg, 500 mg
Injection: 100 mg/ml, 500 mg/ml
Tablets: 250 mg, 375 mg, 500 mg
Tablets (extended-release): 500 mg, 1000 mg
Tablets (sustained-release): 250 mg, 500 mg, 750 mg

P

NURSING PROCESS

Assessment

- Assess patient's condition before starting therapy and regularly thereafter to monitor drug's effectiveness.
- Monitor level of procainamide and its active metabolite, NAPA. To suppress ventricular arrhythmias, therapeutic level of procainamide is 4 to 8 mcg/ml; therapeutic level of NAPA is 10 to 30 mcg/ml.
- Monitor QT interval closely in patient with renal impairment.

• Hypokalemia predisposes patient to arrhythmias; monitor electrolytes, especially potassium level.
• Monitor blood pressure and ECG continuously during I.V. use. Watch for prolonged QT intervals and QRS complexes, heart block, or increased arrhythmias.
• Monitor CBC frequently during first 3 months, particularly in patient taking sustained-release form.
• Be alert for adverse reactions and drug interactions.
• Assess patient's and family's knowledge of drug therapy.

Nursing diagnoses

• Decreased cardiac output related to presence of arrhythmia
• Ineffective protection related to adverse hematologic reactions
• Deficient knowledge related to drug therapy

Planning and implementation

ALERT: Some drug products contain tartrazine and sulfites. Ask if patient is allergic to these agents.
ALERT: If blood pressure changes significantly or ECG changes occur, withhold drug, obtain rhythm strip, and notify prescriber immediately.
ALERT: Don't confuse procainamide with probenecid.
• Positive antinuclear antibody titer occurs in about 60% of patients without lupuslike symptoms. This response seems to be related to prolonged use, not to dosage. May progress to systemic lupus erythematosus if drug isn't stopped.

Patient teaching

• Instruct patient to report fever, rash, muscle pain, diarrhea, bleeding, bruises, or pleuritic chest pain.
• Stress importance of taking drug exactly as prescribed. This may require use of alarm clock for nighttime doses.
• Inform patient taking extended-release form that wax-matrix "ghost" from tablet may be passed in stool. Assure patient that drug is completely absorbed before this occurs.
• Tell patient not to crush or break sustained-release or extended-release tablets.

Evaluation

• Patient regains normal cardiac output after drug stops abnormal heart rhythm.
• Patient maintains normal CBC.
• Patient and family state understanding of drug therapy.

procarbazine hydrochloride

(proh-KAR-buh-zeen high-droh-KLOR-ighd)
Matulane, Natulan ♦

Pharmacologic class: alkylating agent
Therapeutic class: antineoplastic
Pregnancy risk category: D

Indications and dosages

▶ **Hodgkin lymphoma, non-Hodgkin lymphoma‡, brain tumors‡, small-cell lung cancer‡, melanoma‡, mycosis fungoides‡, and multiple myeloma‡.** *Adults:* 2 to 4 mg/kg P.O. daily in single dose or divided doses for first week. Then, 4 to 6 mg/kg daily until WBC count decreases to less than 4,000/mm^3 or platelet count decreases to less than 100,000/mm^3. If hematologic toxicity occurs, resume at 1 to 2 mg/kg daily.
Children: 50 mg/m^2 P.O. daily for first week; then 100 mg/m^2 until response or toxicity occurs. Maintenance dose is 50 mg/m^2 P.O. daily after bone marrow recovery.

Contraindications and cautions

• Contraindicated in patients hypersensitive to the drug or any of its components and in those with inadequate bone marrow reserve as shown by bone marrow aspiration.
• Use cautiously in patients with impaired hepatic or renal function.
Lifespan: In pregnant and breast-feeding women, drug isn't recommended.

Adverse reactions

CNS: *coma,* confusion, depression, *hallucinations,* insomnia, nervousness, neuropathy, nightmares, paresthesia, ***seizures.***
EENT: nystagmus, photophobia, retinal hemorrhage.
GI: anorexia, constipation, diarrhea, dry mouth, dysphagia, *nausea,* stomatitis, *vomiting.*
Hematologic: anemia, ***bleeding tendency, leukopenia, thrombocytopenia.***
Hepatic: ***hepatotoxicity.***
Respiratory: *pleural effusion,* pneumonitis.
Skin: dermatitis, reversible alopecia.

Interactions

Drug-drug. *CNS depressants:* May have additive depressant effects. Avoid using together.
Digoxin: May decrease digoxin level. Monitor level closely.
Levodopa: May cause flushing and a significant rise in blood pressure within 1 hour of levodopa use. Separate administration times; monitor patient's blood pressure closely.
Local anesthetics, sympathomimetics, tricyclic antidepressants: May cause tremors, palpitations, and increased blood pressure. Monitor patient closely.
Opioids: May cause severe hypotension and death. Don't give together.
Drug-food. *Caffeine:* May result in arrhythmias, severe hypertension. Discourage caffeine intake.
Foods high in tyramine (cheese, red wine): May cause tremors, palpitations, and increased blood pressure. Monitor patient closely.
Drug-lifestyle. *Alcohol use:* May cause mild disulfiram-like reaction. Warn patient to avoid alcohol.

Effects on lab test results

- May increase liver enzyme level. May decrease hemoglobin level and hematocrit.
- May increase eosinophil count. May decrease platelet, WBC, and RBC counts.

Pharmacokinetics

Absorption: Rapid and complete.
Distribution: Wide; throughout body tissues, with highest levels in liver, kidneys, intestinal wall, and skin. Drug crosses blood-brain barrier.
Metabolism: Extensive in liver; some metabolites have cytotoxic activity.
Excretion: Drug and metabolites excreted mainly in urine. *Half-life:* Unknown.

Route	Onset	Peak	Duration
P.O.	Unknown	1 hr	Unknown

Action

Chemical effect: Unknown; thought to inhibit DNA, RNA, and protein synthesis.
Therapeutic effect: Kills selected cancer cells.

Available forms

Capsules: 50 mg

NURSING PROCESS

Assessment

- Assess patient's condition before starting therapy and regularly thereafter to monitor drug's effectiveness.
- Monitor CBC and platelet counts.
- Be alert for adverse reactions and drug interactions.
- Assess patient's and family's knowledge of drug therapy.

Nursing diagnoses

- Ineffective health maintenance related to presence of neoplastic disease
- Ineffective protection related to adverse hematologic reactions
- Deficient knowledge related to drug therapy

Planning and implementation

- Give drug at bedtime to lessen nausea.

ALERT: If patient becomes confused or if paresthesia or other neuropathies develop, stop giving the drug and notify prescriber.

Patient teaching

- Advise patient to take drug at bedtime and in divided doses.
- Warn patient to watch for signs of infection (fever, sore throat, fatigue) and bleeding (easy bruising, nosebleeds, bleeding gums, melena). Tell him to take his temperature daily.
- Warn patient not to drink alcohol during therapy.
- Tell patient to stop taking the drug and immediately notify the prescriber if disulfiram-like reaction occurs (chest pains, rapid or irregular heartbeat, severe headache, stiff neck).
- Tell patient to avoid foods high in tyramine, such as cheese, yogurt, and bananas.
- Warn patient to avoid hazardous activities until the drug's CNS effects are known.
- Advise woman of childbearing age not to become pregnant during therapy, and to consult with prescriber before becoming pregnant.

Evaluation

- Patient responds well to therapy.
- Patient develops no serious adverse hematologic reactions.
- Patient and family state understanding of drug therapy.

P

prochlorperazine
(proh-klor-PER-ah-zeen)
Compazine, Compro

prochlorperazine edisylate
Compazine, Compazine Syrup

prochlorperazine maleate
Compazine, Compazine Spansule

Pharmacologic class: phenothiazine (piperazine derivative)
Therapeutic class: antiemetic, antipsychotic, anxiolytic
Pregnancy risk category: C

Indications and dosages

▶ **Preoperative nausea control.** *Adults:* 5 to 10 mg I.M. 1 to 2 hours before induction of anesthesia; repeat once in 30 minutes, if needed. Or, 5 to 10 mg I.V. 15 to 30 minutes before induction of anesthesia; repeat once if needed. Or, 20 mg/L D_5W or normal saline solution by I.V. infusion. Begin infusion 15 to 30 minutes before induction of anesthesia.

▶ **Severe nausea and vomiting.** *Adults:* 5 to 10 mg P.O., t.i.d. or q.i.d. Or, 15 mg P.O. (sustained-release) on arising. Or, 10-mg sustained-release form P.O. q 12 hours. Or, 25 mg P.R., b.i.d. Or, 5 to 10 mg I.M. repeated q 3 to 4 hours, p.r.n. Or, 2.5 to 10 mg may be given I.V. Maximum parenteral dose is 40 mg daily.
Children who weigh 18 to 39 kg (40 to 85 lb): 2.5 mg P.O. or P.R., t.i.d. Or, 5 mg P.O. or P.R., b.i.d. Maximum dose is 15 mg daily. Or, give 0.132 mg/kg by deep I.M. injection. Control usually is obtained with one dose.
Children who weigh 14 to 18 kg (30 to 39 lb): 2.5 mg P.O. or P.R., b.i.d. or t.i.d. Maximum dose, 10 mg daily. Or give 0.132 mg/kg by deep I.M. injection. Control usually is obtained with one dose.
Children who weigh 9 to 13 kg (20 to 29 lb): 2.5 mg P.O. or P.R. once daily or b.i.d. Maximum dose, 7.5 mg daily. Or give 0.132 mg/kg by deep I.M. injection. Control usually is obtained with one dose.

▶ **To manage symptoms of psychotic disorders.** *Adults and children age 12 and older:* 5 to 10 mg P.O., t.i.d. or q.i.d.
Children ages 2 to 12: Give 2.5 mg P.O. or P.R., b.i.d. or t.i.d. Don't exceed 10 mg on day 1. Increase dosage gradually to recommended maximum, if needed. In children ages 2 to 5, maximum daily dose is 20 mg. In children ages 6 to 12, maximum daily dose is 25 mg.

▶ **To manage symptoms of severe psychoses.** *Adults and children age 12 and older:* 10 to 20 mg I.M. repeated in 1 to 4 hours, if needed. Rarely, patients may require 10 to 20 mg q 4 to 6 hours. Institute P.O. therapy after symptoms are controlled.
Children ages 2 to 12: Give 0.13 mg/kg I.M. then switch to oral dose.

▶ **Nonpsychotic anxiety.** *Adults:* 5 to 10 mg by deep I.M. injection q 3 to 4 hours, not to exceed 40 mg daily; or 5 to 10 mg P.O., t.i.d., or q.i.d. Or, give 15-mg extended-release capsule once daily or 10-mg extended-release capsule q 12 hours.

I.V. administration

- Drug may be given undiluted or diluted in an isotonic solution.
- Don't give faster than 5 mg/minute. Don't give by bolus injection.

⊗ **Incompatibilities**
Aldesleukin, allopurinol, amifostine, aminophylline, amphotericin B, ampicillin sodium, aztreonam, calcium gluconate, chloramphenicol sodium succinate, chlorothiazide, dexamethasone sodium phosphate, dimenhydrinate, etoposide, filgrastim, fludarabine, foscarnet, furosemide, gemcitabine, heparin sodium, hydrocortisone sodium succinate, hydromorphone, ketorolac, solutions containing methylparabens, midazolam hydrochloride, morphine, penicillin G potassium, penicillin G sodium, pentobarbital, phenobarbital sodium, phenytoin sodium, piperacillin sodium and tazobactam sodium, solutions containing propylparabens, thiopental, vitamin B complex with C.

Contraindications and cautions

- Contraindicated in patients hypersensitive to phenothiazines, patients with CNS depression (including coma), patients undergoing pediatric surgery, patients taking adrenergic blockers, and patients under the influence of alcohol.
- Use cautiously in patients who have been exposed to extreme heat and patients with impaired CV function, glaucoma, or seizure disorders.

Lifespan: In pregnant women, drug is contraindicated except in cases of continuous nausea and vomiting when benefits outweigh risk to the fetus. In breast-feeding women, use cautiously; it's unknown if the drug appears in breast milk. In acutely ill children, use cautiously. In children younger than age 2 who weigh less than 9 kg (20 lb), drug is contraindicated. In the elderly, use cautiously, and gradually increase the dosage.

Adverse reactions

CNS: dizziness, EEG changes, *extrapyramidal reactions, **neuroleptic malignant syndrome,*** pseudoparkinsonism, sedation, tardive dyskinesia.
CV: ECG changes, *orthostatic hypotension,* tachycardia.
EENT: blurred vision, ocular changes.
GI: constipation, dry mouth.
GU: dark urine, inhibited ejaculation, menstrual irregularities, *urine retention.*
Hematologic: ***agranulocytosis,*** hyperprolactinemia, ***transient leukopenia.***
Hepatic: cholestatic jaundice.
Metabolic: increased appetite, weight gain.
Skin: exfoliative dermatitis, *mild photosensitivity.*
Other: allergic reactions, gynecomastia.

Interactions

Drug-drug. *Antacids:* May inhibit absorption of oral phenothiazines. Separate antacid doses by at least 2 hours.
Anticholinergics, including antidepressants and antiparkinsonian drugs: May increase anticholinergic activity and aggravated parkinsonian symptoms. Use together cautiously.
Anticonvulsants: Phenothiazines may lower the seizure threshold. Adjust anticonvulsant dosage as needed.
Barbiturates: May decrease phenothiazine effect. Monitor patient for decreased effect.
CNS depressants: May cause additive CNS effects. Use together cautiously.
Lithium: May cause disorientation, unconsciousness, and extrapyramidal symptoms. Monitor patient closely.
Drug-herb. *Dong quai, St. John's wort:* May increase photosensitivity reactions. Discourage using together.
Ginkgo: May decrease effects of phenothiazines. Monitor patient.
Kava: May increase risk of dystonic reactions. Discourage using together.
Milk thistle: May decrease liver toxicity caused by phenothiazines. Monitor liver enzyme level if used together.
Yohimbe: May increase risk for yohimbe toxicity when used together. Discourage using together.
Drug-lifestyle. *Alcohol use:* May increase CNS depression, particularly decreasing psychomotor skills. Strongly discourage alcohol use.
Sun exposure: May cause photosensitivity reaction. Urge patient to avoid unprotected or prolonged sun exposure.

Effects on lab test results

- May decrease WBC and granulocyte counts. May alter liver function test values.
- May cause false-positive results for PKU, urobilinogen, amylase, uroporphyrins, porphobilinogens, and 5-hydroxyindolacetic acid levels. May cause false-positive pregnancy test.

Pharmacokinetics

Absorption: Erratic and variable with P.O. tablets; more predictable with P.O. concentrate. Unknown for P.R. use. Rapid for I.M. use.
Distribution: Widely into body. 91% to 99% protein-bound.
Metabolism: Extensively by liver, but no active metabolites are formed.
Excretion: Mainly in urine; some in feces. *Half-life:* Unknown.

Route	Onset	Peak	Duration
P.O.	30–40 min	Unknown	3–12 hr
I.V.	Immediate	Immediate	Unknown
I.M.	10–20 min	Unknown	3–4 hr
P.R.	60 min	Unknown	3–4 hr

Action

Chemical effect: Acts on chemoreceptor trigger zone to inhibit nausea and vomiting; in larger doses, partially depresses vomiting center.
Therapeutic effect: Relieves nausea and vomiting, signs and symptoms of psychosis, and anxiety.

Available forms

prochlorperazine
Injection: 5 mg/ml
Suppositories: 2.5 mg, 5 mg, 25 mg
Tablets: 5 mg, 10 mg

P

prochlorperazine edisylate
Injection: 5 mg/ml
Syrup: 5 mg/5 ml
prochlorperazine maleate
Capsules (sustained-release): 10 mg, 15 mg
Tablets: 5 mg, 10 mg

NURSING PROCESS

Assessment

- Assess patient's condition before starting therapy and regularly thereafter to monitor drug's effectiveness.
- Watch for orthostatic hypotension, especially when giving drug by I.V. route.
- Monitor CBC and liver function test results during long-term therapy.
- Be alert for adverse reactions and drug interactions.
- Assess patient's and family's knowledge of drug therapy.

Nursing diagnoses

- Risk for deficient fluid volume related to nausea and vomiting
- Disturbed thought processes related to presence of psychosis
- Deficient knowledge related to drug therapy

Planning and implementation

- Dilute solution with tomato or fruit juice, milk, coffee, carbonated beverage, tea, water, or soup; or mix with pudding.
- Inject I.M. deep into upper outer quadrant of gluteal region.
- Don't give subcutaneously or mix in syringe with another drug.
- Avoid getting concentrate or injection solution on hands or clothing.
- Drug is used only if vomiting can't be otherwise controlled or if only a few doses are needed. If more than four doses are needed in 24 hours, notify prescriber.
- Store drug in light-resistant container. Slight yellowing doesn't affect potency; discard extremely discolored solutions.

Patient teaching

- Tell patient to mix oral solution with flavored liquid to mask taste.
- Advise patient to wear protective clothing when exposed to sunlight.
- Tell patient to notify prescriber about adverse reactions.

Evaluation

- Patient's nausea and vomiting are relieved.
- Patient's behavior and communication show better thought processes.
- Patient and family state understanding of drug therapy.

promethazine hydrochloride

(proh-METH-uh-zeen high-droh-KLOR-ighd)
Anergan 50, Phenergan*

promethazine theoclate

Avomine ◇

Pharmacologic class: phenothiazine derivative
Therapeutic class: antiemetic, antihistamine, sedative
Pregnancy risk category: C

Indications and dosages

▶ **Motion sickness.** *Adults:* Give 25 mg P.O. or P.R. b.i.d. Take initial dose 30 to 60 minutes before anticipated travel, and repeat in 8 to 12 hours, if needed.
Children older than age 2: Give 12.5 to 25 mg P.O. or P.R. b.i.d.

▶ **Nausea and vomiting.** *Adults:* Give 12.5 to 25 mg P.O., I.M., or P.R. q 4 to 6 hours, p.r.n.
Children older than age 2: Give 12.5 to 25 mg P.O. or P.R. q 4 to 6 hours, p.r.n. Or, 6.25 to 12.5 mg I.M. q 4 to 6 hours, p.r.n.

▶ **Rhinitis, allergy symptoms.** *Adults:* Give 12.5 mg P.O. or P.R. q.i.d. (before meals and at bedtime). Or, 25 mg P.O. or P.R. at bedtime
Children older than age 2: Give 6.25 to 12.5 mg P.O. or P.R. t.i.d. Or, 25 mg P.O. or P.R. at bedtime

▶ **Sedation.** *Adults:* Give 25 to 50 mg P.O., P.R., or I.M. at bedtime or p.r.n.
Children older than age 2: Give 12.5 to 25 mg P.O., I.M., or P.R. at bedtime

▶ **Routine preoperative or postoperative sedation or adjunct to analgesics.** *Adults:* Give 25 to 50 mg I.M., I.V., P.R., or P.O.
Children older than age 2: Give 0.5 to 1.1 mg/kg I.M., P.R., or P.O.

I.V. administration

- Don't give in concentration greater than 25 mg/ml or at rate exceeding 25 mg/minute.
- Shield I.V. solution from direct light.

⊗ Incompatibilities

Aldesleukin, allopurinol, aminophylline, amphotericin B, cephalosporins, chloramphenicol sodium succinate, chloroquine phosphate, chlorothiazide, diatrizoate meglumine (34.3%) and diatrizoate sodium (35%), diatrizoate meglumine (52%) and diatrizoate sodium (8%), diatrizoate sodium (75%), dimenhydrinate, doxorubicin liposomal, foscarnet, furosemide, heparin sodium, hydrocortisone sodium succinate, iodipamide meglumine (52%), iothalamate meglumine (60%), iothalamate sodium (80%), ketorolac, methohexital, morphine, nalbuphine, penicillin G potassium and sodium, pentobarbital sodium, phenobarbital sodium, phenytoin sodium, thiopental, vitamin B complex.

Contraindications and cautions

• Contraindicated in patients hypersensitive to the drug or any of its components, and in those with intestinal obstruction, prostatic hyperplasia, bladder-neck obstruction, seizure disorders, coma, CNS depression, or stenosing peptic ulcerations.

• Use cautiously in patients with pulmonary, hepatic, or CV disease or asthma.

• Avoid combining drug with other respiratory depressants.

Lifespan: In pregnant women, safety and effectiveness haven't been established. In breastfeeding women, neonates, premature neonates, and acutely ill or dehydrated children, drug is contraindicated. Don't use in children for nausea and vomiting when the cause of the vomiting is unknown. In children younger than age 2, drug is contraindicated. Use with caution in children ages 2 and older, using the lowest effective dose and watch for respiratory depressant effects. In the elderly, use cautiously.

Adverse reactions

CNS: confusion, *drowsiness* (especially geriatric patients), extrapyramidal reactions, restlessness, *sedation,* tremors.
CV: ECG changes, hypotension.
EENT: nasal congestion, transient myopia,
GI: anorexia, constipation, *dry mouth,* nausea, vomiting.
GU: urine retention.
Hematologic: ***agranulocytosis, leukopenia, thrombocytopenia.***
Respiratory: ***respiratory depression*** (in children).
Skin: photosensitivity, venous thrombosis at injection site.

Interactions

Drug-drug. *CNS depressants:* May increase sedation. Use together cautiously.
Epinephrine: May block or reverse effects of epinephrine. Use another vasopressor.
Levodopa: May decrease antiparkinsonian action of levodopa. Avoid using together.
Lithium: May reduce GI absorption or enhance renal elimination of lithium. Avoid using together.
MAO inhibitors: May increase extrapyramidal effects. Don't use together.
Drug-herb. *Dong quai, St. John's wort:* May increase photosensitivity reactions. Discourage using together.
Kava: May increase risk of dystonic reactions. Discourage using together.
Yohimbe: May increase risk of yohimbe toxicity when used together. Discourage using together.
Drug-lifestyle. *Alcohol use:* May increase sedation. Discourage using together.
Sun exposure: May cause photosensitivity reaction. Urge patient to avoid unprotected or prolonged sun exposure.

Effects on lab test results

• May increase glucose and hemoglobin levels and hematocrit.

• May decrease WBC, platelet, and granulocyte counts.

• May cause false-positive immunologic urine pregnancy test using Gravindex and false-negative results using Prepurex or Dap tests. May interfere with blood typing of ABO group.

Pharmacokinetics

Absorption: Well absorbed after P.O. use; fairly rapid after P.R. or I.M. use.
Distribution: Widely throughout body.
Metabolism: In liver.
Excretion: In urine and feces. *Half-life:* Unknown.

Route	Onset	Peak	Duration
P.O.	15–60 min	Unknown	≤ 12 hr
I.V.	3–5 min	Unknown	≤ 12 hr
I.M., P.R.	20 min	Unknown	≤ 12 hr

P

Action

Chemical effect: Competes with histamine for H_1-receptor sites on effector cells. Prevents, but doesn't reverse, histamine-mediated responses.
Therapeutic effect: Prevents motion sickness and relieves nausea, nasal congestion, and allergy symptoms. Also promotes calmness.

Available forms

promethazine hydrochloride
Injection: 25 mg/ml, 50 mg/ml (I.M. use only)
Suppositories: 12.5 mg, 25 mg, 50 mg
Syrup: 6.25 mg/5 ml*
Tablets: 12.5 mg, 25 mg, 50 mg
promethazine theoclate
Tablets: 25 mg†

NURSING PROCESS

Assessment

- Assess patient's condition before starting therapy and regularly thereafter to monitor drug's effectiveness.
- Be alert for adverse reactions and drug interactions.
- Assess patient's and family's knowledge of drug therapy.

Nursing diagnoses

- Ineffective health maintenance related to underlying condition
- Risk for injury related to drug's sedating effects
- Deficient knowledge related to drug therapy

Planning and implementation

- Pronounced sedative effect limits use in many ambulatory patients.
- Drug is used as adjunct to analgesics (usually to increase sedation); it has no analgesic activity.
- Give drug with food or milk to reduce GI distress.

ALERT: Phenergan brand ampules contain sulfite. Check patient for sulfite allergy before administering Phenergan I.M.

- Inject I.M. deep into large muscle mass. Rotate injection sites.
- Don't give subcutaneously.
- Drug may be safely mixed with meperidine (Demerol) in same syringe.
- In patient scheduled for myelogram, stop drug 48 hours before procedure and don't resume giving the drug until 24 hours after the procedure, because of risk of seizures.

ALERT: Caution should be used in children age 2 and older. This includes using the lowest effective dose, monitoring for respiratory depressant effects and avoiding combining promethazine hydrochloride with other drugs that are known to depress the respiratory system.

Patient teaching

- When treating for motion sickness, tell patient to take first dose 30 to 60 minutes before travel. Tell him to take dose after rising and with evening meal on next days of travel.
- Warn patient not to drink alcohol or engage in hazardous activities until the drug's CNS effects are known.
- Tell patient that coffee or tea may reduce drowsiness. Sugarless gum, sugarless sour hard candy, or ice chips may relieve dry mouth.
- Warn patient about photosensitivity and precautions to avoid it.
- Advise patient to stop drug 4 days before allergy skin tests.

Evaluation

- Patient responds well to therapy.
- Patient doesn't experience injury from adverse reactions.
- Patient and family state understanding of drug therapy.

propafenone hydrochloride

(proh-puh-FEE-nohn high-droh-KLOR-ighd)
Rythmol, Rythmol SR

Pharmacologic class: sodium channel antagonist
Therapeutic class: antiarrhythmic (class IC)
Pregnancy risk category: C

Indications and dosages

▶ **Suppression of life-threatening ventricular arrhythmias, such as sustained ventricular tachycardia; prevention of supraventricular tachycardia associated with disabling symptoms and for disabling paroxysmal atrial fibrillation/flutter.** *Adults:* Initially, 150 mg P.O. q 8 hours. May increase dose at 3- to 4-day intervals to 225 mg q 8 hours. If needed, increase dosage to 300 mg q 8 hours. Maximum daily dose is 900 mg.

Adjust-a-dose: For patients with hepatic failure, manufacturer recommends dose reduction of 20% to 30%.

Contraindications and cautions

• Contraindicated in patients hypersensitive to the drug or any of its components, and in those with severe or uncontrolled heart failure, cardiogenic shock, bradycardia, marked hypotension, bronchospastic disorders, electrolyte imbalance, or SA, AV, or intraventricular disorders of impulse conduction in absence of pacemaker.
• Use cautiously in patients with heart failure because propafenone can have negative inotropic effect. Also use cautiously in patients taking other cardiac depressant drugs and in those with hepatic or renal impairment.
Lifespan: In pregnant women, safety and effectiveness haven't been established. In breastfeeding women, drug isn't recommended. In children, safety and effectiveness haven't been established.

Adverse reactions

CNS: anxiety, ataxia, dizziness, drowsiness, fatigue, headache, insomnia, syncope, tremor, weakness.
CV: atrial fibrillation, ***bradycardia,*** bundle branch block, ***heart failure,*** chest pain, edema, first-degree AV block, hypotension, increased QRS duration, intraventricular conduction delay, palpitations, ***proarrhythmic events (ventricular tachycardia, PVCs).***
EENT: blurred vision.
GI: abdominal pain or cramps, anorexia, constipation, diarrhea, dry mouth, dyspepsia, flatulence, nausea, unusual taste, vomiting.
Musculoskeletal: joint pain.
Respiratory: dyspnea.
Skin: diaphoresis, rash.

Interactions

Drug-drug. *Antiarrhythmics:* May increase risk of heart failure. Monitor patient closely.
Cimetidine: May decrease metabolism of propafenone. Monitor patient for toxicity.
Cyclosporine, theophylline: May increase concentrations of these drugs. Monitor for toxicity.
Digoxin, oral anticoagulants: May increase levels of these drugs by about 35% to 85%, resulting in toxicity. Monitor patient's PT, INR, and digoxin level closely.
Local anesthetics: May increase risk of CNS toxicity. Monitor patient closely.
Metoprolol, propranolol: May slow metabolism of these drugs. Monitor patient for toxicity.
Quinidine: May slow propafenone metabolism. Avoid using together.
Rifampin: May increase propafenone clearance. Monitor patient for lack of effect.
Ritonavir, SSRIs: May increase propafenone level. Avoid using together.

Effects on lab test results

• May cause positive ANA titers.

Pharmacokinetics

Absorption: Good. Because of significant first-pass effect, bioavailability is limited, but it increases with dosage.
Distribution: 97% protein-bound.
Metabolism: In liver.
Excretion: Mainly in feces; some in urine. *Half-life:* 2 to 32 hours.

Route	Onset	Peak	Duration
P.O.	Unknown	≤ 3½ hr	Unknown

Action

Chemical effect: Reduces inward sodium current in Purkinje and myocardial cells. Decreases excitability, conduction velocity, and automaticity in AV nodal, His-Purkinje, and intraventricular tissue; causes slight but significant prolongation of refractory period in AV nodal tissue.
Therapeutic effect: Restores normal sinus rhythm.

Available forms

Capsules (extended-release): 225 mg, 325 mg, 425 mg
Tablets: 150 mg, 225 mg, 300 mg

NURSING PROCESS

Assessment

• Assess patient's condition before starting therapy and regularly thereafter to monitor drug's effectiveness.
• Continuous cardiac monitoring is recommended at start of therapy and during dose adjustments.
• Be alert for adverse reactions and drug interactions.

P

- Assess patient's and family's knowledge of drug therapy.

Nursing diagnoses
- Decreased cardiac output related to presence of arrhythmia
- Ineffective protection related to drug-induced proarrhythmias
- Deficient knowledge related to drug therapy

Planning and implementation
- Give drug with food to minimize adverse GI reactions.

ALERT: If PR interval or QRS complex increases by more than 25%, notify prescriber because reduction in dose may be needed.
- During use with digoxin, monitor ECG and digoxin level frequently.

Patient teaching
- Tell patient to take drug with food.
- Stress importance of taking drug exactly as ordered.
- Warn patient to avoid hazardous activities if adverse CNS disturbances occur.

Evaluation
- Patient regains adequate cardiac output when arrhythmia is corrected.
- Patient doesn't develop any proarrhythmic events.
- Patient and family state understanding of drug therapy.

propoxyphene hydrochloride (dextropropoxyphene hydrochloride)
(proh-POK-sih-feen high-droh-KLOR-ighd)
Darvon, 642 ♦

propoxyphene napsylate (dextropropoxyphene napsylate)
Darvon-N

Pharmacologic class: opioid
Therapeutic class: analgesic
Pregnancy risk category: C
Controlled substance schedule: IV

Indications and dosages
▶ **Mild to moderate pain.** *Adults:* 65 mg propoxyphene hydrochloride P.O. q 4 hours, p.r.n. Maximum, 390 mg P.O. daily. Or, 100 mg propoxyphene napsylate P.O. q 4 hours, p.r.n. Maximum, 600 mg P.O. daily.

Contraindications and cautions
- Contraindicated in patients hypersensitive to the drug or any of its components, and in patients who are suicidal or addiction-prone.
- Use cautiously in patients with hepatic or renal disease, emotional instability, or history of drug or alcohol abuse.

Lifespan: In pregnant women, use cautiously. In breast-feeding women, use cautiously; it's unknown if the drug appears in breast milk. In children, safety and effectiveness haven't been established.

Adverse reactions
CNS: *dizziness,* euphoria, headache, insomnia, paradoxical excitement, *sedation.*
GI: *constipation,* nausea, vomiting.
Respiratory: ***respiratory depression.***
Other: physical and psychological dependence.

Interactions
Drug-drug. *Barbiturate anesthetics:* May increase respiratory and CNS depression. Use together cautiously.
Carbamazepine: May increase carbamazepine level. Monitor level closely.
CNS depressants: May have additive effects. Use together cautiously.
Protease inhibitors: May increase CNS and respiratory depression. Monitor patient.
Warfarin: May increase anticoagulant effect. Monitor PT and INR and patient for bleeding.
Drug-lifestyle. *Alcohol use:* May have additive effects. Discourage using together.

Effects on lab test results
- May increase or decrease liver function test values.
- May cause false decreases in urinary steroid excretion tests.

Pharmacokinetics
Absorption: Mainly in upper small intestine.
Distribution: Drug enters CSF.

Metabolism: In liver; about one-quarter of dose is metabolized to norpropoxyphene, an active metabolite.

Excretion: In urine. *Half-life:* 6 to 12 hours.

Route	Onset	Peak	Duration
P.O.	¼–1 hr	2–2½ hr	4–6 hr

Action

Chemical effect: Binds with opioid receptors in CNS, altering both perception of and emotional response to pain through unknown mechanism.

Therapeutic effect: Relieves pain.

Available forms

propoxyphene hydrochloride

Capsules: 65 mg

propoxyphene napsylate

Tablets: 50 mg, 100 mg

NURSING PROCESS

Assessment

- Assess patient's pain before and after giving drug.
- Be alert for adverse reactions and drug interactions.
- If adverse GI reaction occurs, monitor patient's hydration.
- Assess patient's and family's knowledge of drug therapy.

Nursing diagnoses

- Acute pain related to underlying condition
- Risk for deficient fluid volume related to GI upset
- Deficient knowledge related to drug therapy

Planning and implementation

- Give with food to minimize adverse GI reactions.
- Consider giving laxative to prevent constipation.
- Drug can be considered a mild opioid analgesic, but pain relief is equivalent to that provided by aspirin. Tolerance and physical dependence have been observed. Typically used with aspirin or acetaminophen to maximize analgesia.

ALERT: A dose of 65 mg of propoxyphene hydrochloride equals 100 mg of propoxyphene napsylate.

Patient teaching

- Advise patient to take drug with food or milk to minimize GI upset.

ALERT: Warn patient not to exceed recommended dose. Respiratory depression, hypotension, profound sedation, and coma may result if used in excess or with other CNS depressants. Products that contain propoxyphene alone or with other drugs are major cause of drug-related overdose and death.

- Advise patient not to drink alcohol during therapy.
- Warn ambulatory patient about getting out of bed or walking. Warn outpatient to avoid driving and other hazardous activities until drug's CNS effects are known.

Evaluation

- Patient is free from pain.
- Patient maintains adequate hydration.
- Patient and family state understanding of drug therapy.

propranolol hydrochloride

(proh-PRAH-nuh-lohl high-droh-KLOR-ighd)

Apo-Propranolol ♦, Detensol ♦, Inderal, Inderal LA, InnoPran XL, Novopranol ♦, PMS Propranolol ♦

Pharmacologic class: beta blocker

Therapeutic class: antianginal, antiarrhythmic, antihypertensive

Pregnancy risk category: C

Indications and dosages

▶ **Angina pectoris.** *Adults:* Total daily doses of 80 to 320 mg P.O. when given b.i.d., t.i.d., or q.i.d. Or, one 80-mg extended-release capsule daily. Increase dosage at 7- to 10-day intervals.

▶ **Mortality reduction after MI.** *Adults:* 180 to 240 mg P.O. daily in divided doses beginning 5 to 21 days after MI. Usually given t.i.d. or q.i.d.

▶ **Supraventricular, ventricular, and atrial arrhythmias; tachyarrhythmias caused by excessive catecholamine action during anesthesia.** *Adults:* 0.5 to 3 mg by slow I.V. push, not to exceed 1 mg/minute. After 3 mg have been given, another dose may be given in 2 minutes; subsequent doses, no sooner than q 4 hours. May be diluted and infused slowly.

Usual maintenance dosage is 10 to 30 mg P.O. t.i.d. to q.i.d.
Children‡: 0.01 to 0.1 mg/kg I.V. to a maximum of 1 mg/dose by slow infusion over 5 minutes.
▶ **Hypertension.** *Adults:* Initially, 80 mg P.O. daily in two to four divided doses or extended-release form once daily. Increase at 3- to 7-day intervals to maximum daily dose of 640 mg. Usual maintenance dose is 120 to 240 mg daily in two or three divided doses or 120 to 160 mg sustained-release once daily. Or, 80 mg InnoPran XL P.O. once daily at bedtime Take consistently with or without food. Adjust to maximum of 120 mg daily if needed.
Children‡: 1 mg/kg P.O. daily, up to a maximum daily dose of 16 mg/kg.
▶ **Prevention of frequent, severe, uncontrollable, or disabling migraine or vascular headache.** *Adults:* Initially, 80 mg P.O. daily in divided doses or one extended-release capsule daily. Usual maintenance dose is 160 to 240 mg daily.
▶ **Essential tremor.** *Adults:* 40 mg (tablets, solution) P.O. b.i.d. Usual maintenance dose is 120 to 320 mg daily in three divided doses.
▶ **Hypertrophic subaortic stenosis.** *Adults:* 10 to 20 mg P.O. t.i.d. or q.i.d. before meals and at bedtime or 80 to 160 mg extended-release capsule daily.
▶ **Adjunct therapy in pheochromocytoma.** *Adults:* 60 mg P.O. daily in divided doses with alpha blocker 3 days before surgery.
▶ **Adjunctive therapy in anxiety‡.** *Adults:* 10 to 80 mg P.O. 1 hour before anxiety-provoking activity.

I.V. administration

- Drug is compatible with D_5W, half-normal and normal saline solutions, and lactated Ringer's solution.
- Give drug by direct injection into large vessel or I.V. line containing free-flowing, compatible solution; continuous I.V. infusion generally isn't recommended.
- Or dilute drug with normal saline solution and give by intermittent infusion over 10 to 15 minutes in 0.1- to 0.2-mg increments.

⊗ **Incompatibilities**
Amphotericin B, diazoxide.

Contraindications and cautions

- Contraindicated in patients with bronchial asthma, sinus bradycardia, heart block greater than first-degree, cardiogenic shock, or overt cardiac failure (unless failure is secondary to tachyarrhythmia that can be treated with propranolol).
- Use cautiously in patients taking other antihypertensives and in those with renal impairment, nonallergic bronchospastic diseases, Wolff-Parkinson-White syndrome, hepatic disease, diabetes mellitus (drug blocks some symptoms of hypoglycemia), or thyrotoxicosis (drug may mask some signs of that disorder).

Lifespan: In pregnant women, use cautiously. In breast-feeding women, drug isn't recommended.

Adverse reactions

CNS: dizziness (InnoPran XL), *fatigue,* fever, hallucinations, *lethargy,* mental depression, vivid dreams.
CV: ***bradycardia, heart failure,*** hypotension, intermittent claudication.
GI: constipation (InnoPran XL), diarrhea, nausea, vomiting.
Hematologic: ***agranulocytosis.***
Musculoskeletal: arthralgia.
Respiratory: increased airway resistance.
Skin: rash.

Interactions

Drug-drug. *Aminophylline, theophylline:* May act antagonistically reducing the effects of one or both drugs. May reduce theophylline elimination. Monitor theophylline level and patient closely.
Amiodarone, fluconazole, fluoxetine, isoniazid, paroxetine, ritonavir, rizatriptan, zolmitriptan: May increase propranolol level. Use together cautiously.
Amobarbital, aprobarbital, butabarbital, butalbital, mephobarbital, pentobarbital, phenobarbital, primidone, secobarbital: May reduce propranolol effects. Increase beta blocker dose.
Cimetidine: May increase pharmacologic effects of beta blocker. Consider a different H_2-agonist or decrease the beta blocker dose.
Digoxin, diltiazem, verapamil: May cause hypotension, bradycardia, and increased depressant effect on myocardium. Use together cautiously.
Epinephrine: May cause an initial hypertensive episode followed by bradycardia. Stop the beta blocker 3 days before anticipated epinephrine use. Monitor patient closely.

Glucagon, isoproterenol: May antagonize propranolol effect. May be used therapeutically and in emergencies.
Hydralazine: May increase levels and pharmacologic effects of both drugs. Monitor patient closely. Dosage adjustment of either drug may be needed.
Insulin: May mask symptoms of hypoglycemia (such as tachycardia) as a result of beta blockade. Use cautiously in patients with diabetes.
Lidocaine I.V.: May reduce hepatic metabolism of lidocaine, increasing the risk of toxicity. Give bolus doses of lidocaine at a slower rate and monitor lidocaine level closely.
Oral antidiabetics: May alter requirements for these drugs in previously stabilized diabetic patients. Monitor patient for hypoglycemia.
Prazosin: May increase the risk of orthostatic hypotension in the early phases of use together. Assist patient to stand slowly until effects are known.
Verapamil: May increase the effects of both drugs. Monitor cardiac function closely and decrease dosages as needed.
Drug-herb. *Ginkgo:* May alter drug level. Discourage use of herb.
Melatonin: May reverse the negative effects of drug on nocturnal sleep. Advise patient to discuss use with prescriber.
Drug-lifestyle. *Cocaine use:* May increase angina-inducing potential of cocaine. Inform patient of this potentially dangerous combination.

Effects on lab test results

• May increase BUN, transaminase, alkaline phosphatase, and LDH levels.
• May decrease granulocyte count.
• May interfere with glaucoma screening test.

Pharmacokinetics

Absorption: Almost complete, and enhanced when given with food. Food increases the lag time and the time to maximum concentration of InnoPran XL.
Distribution: Widely throughout body. More than 90% protein-bound.
Metabolism: Almost totally in liver. P.O. form undergoes extensive first-pass metabolism.
Excretion: About 96% to 99% in urine as metabolites; remainder in feces as unchanged drug and metabolites. *Half-life:* About 4 hours; 8 hours for InnoPran XL.

Route	Onset	Peak	Duration
P.O.	30 min	60–90 min	12 hr
P.O. InnoPran XL	Unknown	12–14 hr	24 hr
I.V.	≤ 1 min	≤ 1 min	< 5 min

Action

Chemical effect: Reduces cardiac oxygen demand by blocking catecholamine-induced increases in heart rate, blood pressure, and force of myocardial contraction. Depresses renin secretion and prevents vasodilation of cerebral arteries.
Therapeutic effect: Relieves anginal and migraine pain, lowers blood pressure, restores normal sinus rhythm, and helps limit MI damage.

Available forms

Capsules (extended-release): 60 mg, 80 mg, 120 mg, 160 mg
Injection: 1 mg/ml
Oral solution: 4 mg/ml, 8 mg/ml, 80 mg/ml (concentrate)
Tablets: 10 mg, 20 mg, 40 mg, 60 mg, 80 mg, 90 mg

NURSING PROCESS

Assessment

• Assess patient's condition before starting therapy and regularly thereafter to monitor drug's effectiveness.
• Frequently monitor blood pressure, ECG, and heart rate and rhythm, especially when giving by I.V. route.
• Be alert for adverse reactions and drug interactions.
• Assess patient's and family's knowledge of drug therapy.

Nursing diagnoses

• Ineffective health maintenance related to underlying condition
• Impaired gas exchange related to airway resistance
• Deficient knowledge related to drug therapy

Planning and implementation

• Check patient's apical pulse before therapy. If extremes in pulse rate occur, don't give the drug and immediately call the prescriber.

ALERT: Don't confuse Inderal with Inderide or Isordil.

- Double-check dose and route. I.V. doses are much smaller than oral doses.
- Give oral drug with meals. Food may increase absorption.
- Don't stop giving the drug before surgery for pheochromocytoma. Before any surgical procedure, notify anesthesiologist that patient is taking propranolol.
- If patient develops severe hypotension, notify prescriber; vasopressor may be prescribed.
- In an elderly patient, adverse reactions may increase and he may need an adjusted dose.
- Don't abruptly stop giving the drug.
- For overdose, give I.V. isoproterenol, I.V. atropine, or glucagon; refractory cases may require pacemaker.

Patient teaching

- Teach patient how to check pulse rate, and tell him to do so before each dose. Tell him to notify prescriber if rate changes significantly.
- Tell patient that taking drug twice a day or as extended-release capsule may improve compliance. Advise him to check with prescriber.
- Advise patient to continue taking drug as prescribed, even when he's feeling well. Tell him not to stop drug suddenly because doing so can worsen angina and MI.

Evaluation

- Patient responds well to therapy.
- Patient maintains adequate gas exchange.
- Patient and family state understanding of drug therapy.

propylthiouracil (PTU)

(proh-pil-thigh-oh-YOOR-uh-sil)

Propyl-Thyracil ♦

Pharmacologic class: thyroid hormone antagonist

Therapeutic class: antihyperthyroid drug

Pregnancy risk category: D

Indications and dosages

▶ **Hyperthyroidism.** *Adults:* 300 to 450 mg P.O. daily in divided doses. Patients with severe hyperthyroidism or very large goiters may need initial doses of 600 to 1,200 mg daily. Continue until patient is euthyroid; then start maintenance dose of 100 mg to 150 mg P.O. daily.

Children age 10 and older: Initially, 150 to 300 mg P.O. daily in divided doses. Continue until patient is euthyroid. Individualize maintenance dose.

Children ages 6 to 10: Initially, 50 to 150 mg P.O. daily in divided doses q 8 hours. Continue until patient is euthyroid. Individualize maintenance dose.

Neonates and children: 5 to 7 mg/kg P.O. daily in divided doses q 8 hours, or give according to age as above.

▶ **Thyrotoxic crisis.** *Adults and children:* 200 to 400 mg P.O. q 4 to 6 hours on first day; after symptoms are under control, gradually reduce dose to usual maintenance level.

▶ **To reduce mortality caused by alcoholic liver disease‡.** *Adults:* 300 mg/day.

Contraindications and cautions

- Contraindicated in patients hypersensitive to the drug or any of its components.

Lifespan: In pregnant women, use cautiously. Pregnant women may need a lower dose as pregnancy progresses; monitor thyroid function studies closely. In breast-feeding women, drug is contraindicated.

Adverse reactions

CNS: drowsiness, headache, vertigo.
CV: vasculitis.
EENT: visual disturbances.
GI: diarrhea, loss of taste, *nausea,* salivary gland enlargement, *vomiting* (may be dose-related).
Hematologic: ***agranulocytosis, aplastic anemia, leukopenia,*** lymphadenopathy, ***thrombocytopenia.***
Hepatic: jaundice, ***hepatotoxicity.***
Metabolic: dose-related hypothyroidism (mental depression; cold intolerance; hard, nonpitting edema).
Musculoskeletal: arthralgia, myalgia.
Skin: pruritus, rash, skin discoloration, urticaria.
Other: drug-induced fever.

Interactions

Drug-drug. *Aminophylline, oxtriphylline, theophylline:* May decrease drug clearance. Dose may need adjustment.

Anticoagulants: May increase anticoagulant effects. Monitor PT, PTT, and INR and monitor patient for bleeding.
Beta blockers: May decrease T3 level and alter the action of beta blockers. Monitor patient closely.
Digoxin: May increase glycoside level. May need to decrease dose.
Potassium iodide: May decrease response to drug. May need to increase dose of antithyroid drug.

Effects on lab test results

- May increase liver enzyme level. May decrease hemoglobin level and hematocrit.
- May decrease granulocyte, WBC, and platelet counts.

Pharmacokinetics

Absorption: About 80% of drug is absorbed rapidly and readily from GI tract.
Distribution: Appears to be concentrated in thyroid gland. About 75% to 80% protein-bound.
Metabolism: Rapidly in liver.
Excretion: About 35% in urine. *Half-life:* 1 to 2 hours.

Route	Onset	Peak	Duration
P.O.	Unknown	1–1½ hr	Unknown

Action

Chemical effect: Inhibits oxidation of iodine in thyroid gland, blocking iodine's ability to combine with tyrosine to form T_4, and may prevent coupling of monoiodotyrosine and diiodotyrosine to form T_4 and T_3.
Therapeutic effect: Lowers thyroid hormone level.

Available forms

Tablets: 50 mg, 100 mg ♦

NURSING PROCESS

Assessment

- Assess patient's condition before starting therapy and regularly thereafter to monitor drug's effectiveness.
- Watch for signs of hypothyroidism (depression; cold intolerance; hard, nonpitting edema); adjust dosage as directed.
- Monitor CBC to detect impending leukopenia, thrombocytopenia, and agranulocytosis.
- Be alert for adverse reactions.
- If adverse GI reaction occurs, monitor patient's hydration.
- Assess patient's and family's knowledge of drug therapy.

Nursing diagnoses

- Ineffective health maintenance related to thyroid condition
- Risk for deficient fluid volume related to adverse GI reaction
- Deficient knowledge related to drug therapy

Planning and implementation

- Give drug with meals to reduce adverse GI reaction.
- If patient develops severe rash or enlarged cervical lymph nodes, stop giving the drug and notify prescriber.
- Maintenance daily dose is about ⅓ to ⅔ of initial daily dose.
- Store drug in light-resistant container.

ALERT: Don't confuse propylthiouracil with Purinethol.

Patient teaching

- Tell patient to report skin eruptions (sign of hypersensitivity), fever, sore throat, or mouth sores (early signs of agranulocytosis).
- Instruct patient to ask prescriber whether he can use iodized salt and eat shellfish.
- Warn patient against OTC cough medicines because many contain iodine.

Evaluation

- Patient's thyroid hormone level is normal.
- Patient maintains adequate hydration.
- Patient and family state understanding of drug therapy.

protamine sulfate

(PROH-tuh-meen SUL-fayt)

Pharmacologic class: antidote
Therapeutic class: heparin antagonist
Pregnancy risk category: C

Indications and dosages

▶ **Heparin overdose.** *Adults:* Dosage based on venous blood coagulation studies, usually 1 mg

P

for each 90 to 115 units of heparin. Give by slow I.V. injection over 10 minutes, not to exceed 50 mg.

I.V. administration

- May be given without further dilution or diluted in D_5W or normal saline solution.
- Give by slow injection over 10 minutes.
- Refrigerate at 36° to 46° F (2° to 8° C).
- Don't store diluted solutions; they contain no preservatives.

⊗ Incompatibilities
Cephalosporins, diatrizoate meglumine 52% and diatrizoate sodium 8%, diatrizoate sodium 60%, ioxaglate meglumine 39.3% and ioxaglate sodium 19.6%, penicillins.

Contraindications and cautions

- Contraindicated in patients hypersensitive to the drug or any of its components.
- Use cautiously after cardiac surgery.

Lifespan: In pregnant women, use cautiously. In breast-feeding women, use cautiously; it's unknown if the drug appears in breast milk. In children, safety and effectiveness haven't been established.

Adverse reactions

CV: ***bradycardia, circulatory collapse,*** drop in blood pressure, transitory flushing.
Respiratory: ***acute pulmonary hypertension,*** dyspnea, ***pulmonary edema.***
Other: ***anaphylactoid reactions, anaphylaxis,*** feeling of warmth.

Interactions

None significant.

Effects on lab test results

None reported.

Pharmacokinetics

Absorption: Given I.V.
Distribution: Unknown.
Metabolism: Unknown, although it appears to be partially degraded, with release of some heparin.
Excretion: Unknown. *Half-life:* Shorter than heparin.

Route	Onset	Peak	Duration
I.V.	30–60 sec	Unknown	2 hr

Action

Chemical effect: Forms inert complex with heparin sodium.
Therapeutic effect: Blocks heparin's effects.

Available forms

Injection: 10 mg/ml

NURSING PROCESS

Assessment

- Assess patient's heparin overdose before therapy.
- Continually monitor patient; frequently check vital signs.
- Assess patient for fish allergy; hypersensitivity reactions to protamine may develop.
- Watch for spontaneous bleeding (heparin rebound), especially in patients undergoing dialysis and in those who have undergone cardiac surgery. Protamine sulfate may act as anticoagulant in very high doses.
- Assess patient's and family's knowledge of drug therapy.

Nursing diagnoses

- Ineffective protection related to heparin overdose
- Risk for injury related to anaphylaxis
- Deficient knowledge related to drug therapy

Planning and implementation

- Calculate dosage carefully. One milligram of drug neutralizes 90 to 115 units of heparin depending on salt (heparin calcium or heparin sodium) and source of heparin (beef or pork).
- Give drug slowly by direct injection. Treat shock.

ALERT: Don't confuse protamine with Protopam.

Patient teaching

- Instruct patient to report adverse reactions immediately.

Evaluation

- Patient doesn't experience injury.
- Patient and family state understanding of drug therapy.

pseudoephedrine hydrochloride

(soo-doh-eh-FED-rin high-droh-KLOR-ighd)

Cenafed, Children's Sudafed Liquid†, Decofed†, DeFed-60†, Dimetapp†, Dorcol Children's Decongestant†, Drixoral Non-Drowsy Formula ♦ †, Eltor 120 ♦ †, Genaphed†, Halofed†, Halofed Adult Strength†, Maxenal ♦ † Myfedrine†, Novafed†, PediaCare Infants' Oral Decongestant Drops†, Pseudo 60†, Pseudofrin ♦, Pseudogest†, Robidrine ♦ †, Sudafed†, Sudafed 12 Hour†, Sudafed 60†, Sufedrin†, Triaminic†

pseudoephedrine sulfate

Afrin†, Drixoral†, Drixoral 12 Hour Non-Drowsy Formula ♦ †

Pharmacologic class: sympathomimetic
Therapeutic class: decongestant
Pregnancy risk category: C

Indications and dosages

▶ **Nasal and eustachian tube decongestion.** *Adults and children age 12 and older:* 60 mg P.O. q 4 to 6 hours; or 120 mg P.O. extended-release tablet q 12 hours; or 240 mg P.O. controlled-release tablet daily. Maximum dose is 240 mg daily.
Children ages 6 to 11: Give 30 mg P.O. q 4 to 6 hours. Maximum dose, 120 mg daily.
Children ages 2 to 5: Give 15 mg P.O. q 4 to 6 hours. Maximum dose, 60 mg daily, or 4 mg/kg or 125 mg/m^2 P.O. divided q.i.d.
Children younger than age 2: Consult a prescriber for specific dosage.
▶ **Prevention of otitic barotraumas during air travel or underwater diving‡.** *Adults:* 120-mg extended-release tablet P.O. 30 minutes before air travel or 60 mg P.O. 30 minutes before underwater diving.

Contraindications and cautions

- Contraindicated in patients taking MAO inhibitors and in patients with severe hypertension or severe coronary artery disease.
- Use cautiously in patients with hypertension, cardiac disease, diabetes, glaucoma, hyperthyroidism, or prostatic hyperplasia.

Lifespan: Use cautiously during pregnancy and breast-feeding. In children younger than age 12, extended-release forms are contraindicated.

Adverse reactions

CNS: *anxiety,* dizziness, headache, *insomnia, nervousness,* transient stimulation, tremor.
CV: ***arrhythmias,*** hypertension, *palpitations,* tachycardia.
GI: anorexia, dry mouth, nausea, vomiting.
GU: difficulty urinating.
Respiratory: burning, drying, stinging of nasal mucosa; excessive nasal discharge with topical drug forms; ***respiratory difficulty;*** sneezing.
Skin: pallor.

Interactions

Drug-drug. *Antihypertensives:* May attenuate hypotensive effect. Monitor blood pressure.
Phenelzine, tranylcypromine: May cause severe headache, hypertension, fever, and hypertensive crisis. Avoid using together.
Sympathomimetic agents: May cause additive effects and increased toxicity. Use with extreme caution or avoid using together.
Drug-herb. *Bitter orange:* May increase risk of hypertension and adverse CV effects. Discourage using together.

Effects on lab test results

None reported.

Pharmacokinetics

Absorption: Unknown.
Distribution: Wide, throughout body.
Metabolism: Incomplete in liver to inactive compounds.
Excretion: In urine; rate is accelerated with acidic urine. *Half-life:* 3 to 16 hours, depending on urine pH.

Route	Onset	Peak	Duration
P.O.	15–30 min	30–60 min	3–12 hr

Action

Chemical effect: Stimulates alpha-adrenergic receptors in upper respiratory tract, resulting in vasoconstriction.
Therapeutic effect: Relieves congestion of nasal passages and eustachian tube.

P

Available forms

pseudoephedrine hydrochloride
Capsules†: 60 mg
Capsules (liquid gel)†: 30 mg
Liquid†: 7.5 mg/0.8 ml, 15 mg/5 ml, 30 mg/5 ml
Tablets†: 30 mg, 60 mg
Tablets (chewable)†: 15 mg
Tablets (controlled-release)†: 240 mg (60-mg immediate, 180-mg delayed release)
Tablets (extended-release)†: 120 mg
pseudoephedrine sulfate
Tablets (extended-release)†: 120 mg (60-mg immediate, 60-mg delayed release)

NURSING PROCESS

Assessment

- Assess patient's condition before starting therapy and regularly thereafter to monitor drug's effectiveness.
- Be alert for adverse reactions and drug interactions.
- Elderly patients are more sensitive to drug's effects.
- Some OTC topical preparations contain sulfites. Determine patient allergy to sulfites before therapy.
- Assess patient's and family's knowledge of drug therapy.

Nursing diagnoses

- Ineffective health maintenance related to congestion
- Sleep deprivation related to drug-induced insomnia
- Deficient knowledge related to drug therapy

Planning and implementation

- Don't crush or break extended-release forms.
- Give last dose at least 2 hours before bedtime to minimize insomnia.

Patient teaching

- Teach patient to read OTC drug labels so he can avoid using products containing other sympathomimetics or sulfites (if allergic).
- Tell patient not to take immediate-release drug within 2 hours of bedtime because it can cause insomnia.
- Tell patient to relieve dry mouth with sugarless gum or hard candy.
- Instruct patient to stop drug if he becomes unusually restless and to notify prescriber promptly.
- Inform patient about risk of overuse of nasal sprays and consequent rebound congestion. Warn against exceeding recommended dose and use longer than 3 days unless instructed to do so by a physician.
- Instruct patient to stop drug and call prescriber if no improvement with oral dose within 7 days.
- Inform patient of risks of overdosing if he exceeds recommended daily dosage.
- Teach patient proper administration of sprays, drops and inhalers, as needed.

Evaluation

- Patient's congestion is relieved.
- Patient has no insomnia.
- Patient and family state understanding of drug therapy.

pyridostigmine bromide

(peer-ih-doh-STIG-meen BROH-mighd)
Mestinon*, Mestinon SR♦, Mestinon Timespans, Regonol

Pharmacologic class: cholinesterase inhibitor
Therapeutic class: muscle stimulant
Pregnancy risk category: NR

Indications and dosages

▶ **Antidote for nondepolarizing neuromuscular blockers.** *Adults:* 10 to 20 mg I.V. preceded by atropine sulfate 0.6 to 1.2 mg I.V.

▶ **Myasthenia gravis.** *Adults:* 60 to 120 mg P.O. t.i.d. Usual dose is 600 mg daily, but a higher dose may be needed (up to 1,500 mg daily). For I.M. or I.V. use, give 1/30 of oral dose. Adjust dosage for each patient, depending on response and tolerance. Or, 180 to 540 mg sustained-release tablets (1 to 3 tablets) P.O. daily to b.i.d., with at least 6 hours between doses.
Children‡: 7 mg/kg or 200 mg/m^2 P.O. daily in five or six divided doses. Or, 0.05 to 0.15 mg/kg/dose I.V. or I.M.

▶ **Prophylaxis against the lethal effects of the nerve agent Soman.** *Adults in the military:* 30 mg P.O. q 8 hours starting about 8 hours before Soman exposure. Discontinue at first sign of nerve gas poisoning and treat with atropine and pralidoxime immediately.

I.V. administration

• Give I.V. injection no faster than 1 mg/minute. If administration is too rapid, bradycardia and seizures may result.

⊗ **Incompatibilities**
Alkaline solutions.

Contraindications and cautions

• Contraindicated in patients hypersensitive to anticholinesterases, in those with mechanical obstruction of the intestine or urinary tract, and in those with history of a reaction to bromides.
• Use cautiously in patients with bronchial asthma, bradycardia, or arrhythmias.
Lifespan: In pregnant and breast-feeding women, safety and effectiveness haven't been established. In neonates, Regonol is contraindicated because it contains benzyl alcohol.

Adverse reactions

CNS: headache with large doses, ***seizures,*** sweating, weakness.
CV: ***bradycardia,*** hypotension, thrombophlebitis.
EENT: miosis.
GI: abdominal cramps, diarrhea, excessive salivation, nausea, vomiting.
Musculoskeletal: muscle cramps, muscle fasciculations.
Respiratory: ***bronchoconstriction, bronchospasm,*** increased bronchial secretions.
Skin: rash.

Interactions

Drug-drug. *Aminoglycosides:* May increase response to drug. Use together cautiously.
Anesthetics, anticholinergics, atropine, corticosteroids, magnesium, procainamide, quinidine: May antagonize cholinergic effects. Observe patient for lack of drug effect.
Ganglionic blockers: May increase risk of hypotension. Monitor patient closely.

Effects on lab test results

None reported.

Pharmacokinetics

Absorption: Poor.
Distribution: Unknown.
Metabolism: Unknown.
Excretion: In urine. *Half-life:* 1 to 3 hours, depending on route.

Route	Onset	Peak	Duration
P.O.	20–60 min	1–2 hr	3–12 hr
I.V.	2–5 min	Unknown	2–3 hr
I.M.	15 min	Unknown	2–3 hr

Action

Chemical effect: Inhibits destruction of acetylcholine released from parasympathetic and somatic efferent nerves. This allows acetylcholine to accumulate.
Therapeutic effect: Reverses effect of nondepolarizing neuromuscular blockers and myasthenia gravis.

Available forms

Injection: 5 mg/ml in 2-ml ampules or 5-ml vials
Syrup: 60 mg/5 ml
Tablets: 60 mg
Tablets (military use only): 30 mg
Tablets (sustained-release): 180 mg

NURSING PROCESS

Assessment

• Assess patient's condition before starting therapy and regularly thereafter to monitor drug's effectiveness.
• Monitor and document patient's response after each dose; optimum dose is difficult to judge.
• Monitor patient's vital signs, especially respirations.
• Be alert for adverse reactions and drug interactions.
• Assess patient's and family's knowledge of drug therapy.

Nursing diagnoses

• Impaired physical mobility related to underlying condition
• Ineffective breathing pattern related to adverse respiratory reactions
• Deficient knowledge related to drug therapy

Planning and implementation

• Stop all other cholinergics before giving drug.
• Don't crush extended-release tablets.

P

• When using sweet syrup for patient who has difficulty swallowing, pour over ice chips if he can't tolerate flavor.
• Position patient to ease breathing. Have atropine injection readily available, and provide respiratory support as needed.
• If patient's muscle weakness is severe, prescriber will determine if it's caused by drug-induced toxicity or worsening of myasthenia gravis. Test dose of edrophonium I.V. will aggravate drug-induced weakness but will temporarily relieve weakness caused by disease.
• The U.S. formulation of Regonol contains benzyl alcohol preservative, which may cause toxicity in neonates if given in large doses. The Canadian formulation of this drug doesn't contain benzyl ethanol.
• If appropriate, obtain prescriber's order for hospitalized patient to have bedside supply of tablets. Patients with long-standing disease often insist on self-administration.
ALERT: If drug is taken immediately before or during Soman exposure, drug may be ineffective against Soman, and may worsen the effects of Soman.
ALERT: Don't confuse Mestinon with Mesantoin or Metatensin.

Patient teaching

• When giving drug for myasthenia gravis, stress the importance of taking it exactly as ordered, on time, in evenly spaced doses. If prescriber has ordered extended-release tablets, tell patient to take tablets at same time each day, at least 6 hours apart. Tell him that he may have to take drug for life.
• Advise patient to wear or carry medical identification at all times.

Evaluation

• Patient has improved physical mobility.
• Patient maintains adequate respiratory pattern.
• Patient and family state understanding of drug therapy.

pyridoxine hydrochloride (vitamin B_6)

(peer-ih-DOKS-een high-droh-KLOR-ighd)
Aminoxin, Beesix, Nestrex†, Rodex

Pharmacologic class: water-soluble vitamin
Therapeutic class: nutritional supplement
Pregnancy risk category: A

Indications and dosages

▶ **RDA.** *Males age 15 and older:* Give 2 mg. *Adolescent males ages 11 to 14:* Give 1.7 mg. *Women age 19 and older:* Give 1.6 mg. *Females ages 15 to 18:* Give 1.5 mg. *Adolescent females ages 11 to 14:* Give 1.4 mg. *Pregnant women:* Give 2.2 mg. *Breast-feeding women:* Give 2.1 mg. *Children ages 7 to 10:* Give 1.4 mg. *Children ages 4 to 6:* Give 1.1 mg. *Children ages 1 to 3:* Give 1 mg. *Infants ages 6 months to 1 year:* Give 0.6 mg. *Neonates and infants up to age 6 months:* Give 0.3 mg.
▶ **Dietary vitamin B_6 deficiency.** *Adults:* 2.5 to 10 mg P.O. daily for 3 weeks; then 2 to 5 mg daily as supplement to proper diet.
▶ **Seizures related to vitamin B_6 deficiency or dependency.** *Adults and children:* 10 to 100 mg I.M. or I.V. in single dose.
▶ **Vitamin B_6–responsive anemias or dependency syndrome (inborn errors of metabolism).** *Adults:* up to 600 mg I.M., P.O., or I.V. daily until symptoms subside; then 30 mg daily for life.
▶ **Prevention of vitamin B_6 deficiency during drug therapy.** *Adults:* 6 to 100 mg P.O. daily for isoniazid therapy.
▶ **Drug-induced vitamin B_6 deficiency.** *Adults:* 100 to 200 mg P.O. daily for 3 weeks, followed by 25 to 100 mg P.O. daily to prevent relapse.
▶ **Antidote for isoniazid poisoning.** *Adults:* 1 to 4 g I.V., followed by 1 g I.M. q 30 minutes until amount of pyridoxine given equals amount of isoniazid ingested.
▶ **Premenstrual syndrome‡.** *Adults:* 40 to 500 mg P.O., I.M., or I.V. daily.
▶ **Carpal tunnel syndrome‡.** *Adults:* 100 to 200 mg P.O. daily for 12 weeks or longer.
▶ **Hyperoxaluria type I‡.** *Adults:* 25 to 300 mg P.O. daily.

▶ **Adjunctive treatment in toxicity of *Gyromitra* mushroom poisoning.** *Adults:* 25 mg/kg I.V. over 15 to 30 minutes, repeated as needed up to 15 to 20 g daily.

I.V. administration

- Protect drug from light. Don't use solution if it contains precipitate, although slight darkening is acceptable.
- Inject undiluted drug into I.V. line containing free-flowing compatible solution. Or, infuse diluted drug over prescribed duration for intermittent infusions. Don't use for continuous infusion.

⊗ **Incompatibilities**
Alkaline solutions, erythromycin estolate, iron salts, kanamycin, oxidizers, riboflavin phosphate sodium, streptomycin.

Contraindications and cautions

- Contraindicated in patients hypersensitive to the drug or any of its components, and in patients with heart disease.

Lifespan: No considerations reported.

Adverse reactions

CNS: drowsiness, paresthesia, unstable gait.

Interactions

Drug-drug. *Levodopa:* May decrease levodopa effectiveness. Avoid using pyridoxine with levodopa. Pyridoxine has little or no effect on the combination drug levodopa and carbidopa.
Phenobarbital, phenytoin: May decrease anticonvulsant level, increasing risk of seizures. Monitor level closely; institute seizure precautions.
Drug-lifestyle. *Alcohol use:* May increase risk of delirium and lactic acidosis. Discourage using together.

Effects on lab test results

- May increase AST level. May decrease folic acid level.

Pharmacokinetics

Absorption: Drug and its substituents are absorbed readily from GI tract. May be diminished in patients with malabsorption syndromes or following gastric resection.
Distribution: Drug is stored mainly in liver.
Metabolism: In liver.
Excretion: In erythrocytes, pyridoxine is converted to pyridoxal phosphate and pyridoxamine is converted to pyridoxamine phosphate. The phosphorylated form of pyridoxine is transaminated to pyridoxal and pyridoxamine, which is phosphorylated rapidly. Conversion of pyridoxine phosphate to pyridoxal phosphate requires riboflavin. *Half-life:* 15 to 20 days.

Route	Onset	Peak	Duration
P.O., I.V., I.M.	Unknown	Unknown	Unknown

Action

Chemical effect: Vitamin B_6 stimulates various metabolic functions, including amino acid metabolism.
Therapeutic effect: Raises pyridoxine level, prevents and relieves seizure activity related to pyridoxine deficiency or dependency, and blocks effects of isoniazid poisoning.

Available forms

Injection: 100 mg/ml
Tablets: 10 mg†, 25 mg†, 50 mg†, 100 mg†, 200 mg†, 250 mg†, 500 mg†
Tablets (enteric-coated): 20 mg†
Tablets (extended-release): 200 mg

NURSING PROCESS

Assessment

- Assess patient before starting therapy and regularly thereafter to monitor drug's effectiveness.
- Be alert for adverse CNS reactions and drug interactions. Patient taking high dose (2 to 6 g daily) may have difficulty walking because of reduced proprioceptive and sensory function.
- Monitor patient's diet. Excessive protein intake increases daily drug requirements.
- Assess patient's and family's knowledge of drug therapy.

Nursing diagnoses

- Ineffective health maintenance related to underlying condition
- Risk for injury related to drug-induced adverse CNS reactions
- Deficient knowledge related to drug therapy

P

Planning and implementation

- When using drug to treat isoniazid toxicity, give anticonvulsants.
- If sodium bicarbonate is required to control acidosis in isoniazid toxicity, don't mix in same syringe with pyridoxine.

ALERT: Don't confuse pyridoxine with pralidoxime, pyrimethamine, or Pyridium.

Patient teaching

- Advise patient taking levodopa alone to avoid multivitamins containing pyridoxine because of decreased levodopa effect.
- If prescribed for maintenance therapy to prevent recurrence of deficiency, stress importance of compliance and good nutrition. Explain that pyridoxine with isoniazid has specific therapeutic purpose and isn't just a vitamin.

Evaluation

- Patient responds well to therapy.
- Patient doesn't experience injury from adverse CNS reactions.
- Patient and family state understanding of drug therapy.

pyrimethamine

(peer-ih-METH-uh-meen)
Daraprim

pyrimethamine with sulfadoxine

Fansidar

Pharmacologic class: folic acid antagonist
Therapeutic class: antimalarial
Pregnancy risk category: C

Indications and dosages

▶ **Malaria prophylaxis and transmission control.** *Adults and children older than age 10:* Give 25 mg pyrimethamine P.O. weekly.
Children ages 4 to 10: Give 12.5 mg pyrimethamine P.O. weekly.
Children younger than age 4: Give 6.25 mg pyrimethamine P.O. weekly.
Continued in all age groups at least 10 weeks after leaving endemic area.

▶ **Acute attacks of malaria.** *Adults and children older than age 10:* Give 25 mg pyrimethamine P.O. daily for 2 days when used with faster-acting antimalarials; when used alone, 50 mg P.O. daily for 2 days.
Children ages 4 to 10: Give 25 mg pyrimethamine P.O. daily for 2 days.

▶ **Acute attacks of malaria.** *Adults:* Give 2 to 3 tablets pyrimethamine with sulfadoxine as single dose, either alone or in sequence with quinine.
Children ages 9 to 14: Give 2 tablets pyrimethamine with sulfadoxine.
Children ages 4 to 8: Give 1 tablet pyrimethamine with sulfadoxine.
Children younger than age 4: Give ½ tablet pyrimethamine with sulfadoxine.

▶ **Malaria prophylaxis.** *Adults:* Give 1 tablet pyrimethamine with sulfadoxine weekly, or 2 tablets q 2 weeks.
Children ages 9 to 14: Give ¾ tablet pyrimethamine with sulfadoxine weekly, or 1½ tablets q 2 weeks.
Children ages 4 to 8: Give ½ tablet pyrimethamine with sulfadoxine weekly, or 1 tablet q 2 weeks.
Children younger than age 4: Give ¼ tablet pyrimethamine with sulfadoxine weekly, or ½ tablet q 2 weeks.

▶ **Toxoplasmosis.** *Adults:* Initially, 50 to 75 mg pyrimethamine P.O. daily for 1 to 3 weeks; then 25 mg P.O. daily for 4 to 5 weeks along with 1 g sulfadiazine P.O. q 6 hours.
Children: Initially, 1 mg/kg pyrimethamine P.O. daily (not to exceed 100 mg) in two equally divided doses for 2 to 4 days; then 0.5 mg/kg daily for 4 weeks along with 100 mg sulfadiazine/kg P.O. daily, divided q 6 hours.

▶ **Isosporiasis‡.** *Adults:* 50 to 75 mg pyrimethamine P.O. daily.

Contraindications and cautions

- Contraindicated in patients hypersensitive to the drug or any of its components, and in those with megaloblastic anemia caused by folic acid deficiency. Pyrimethamine with sulfadoxine is contraindicated in patients with porphyria because it contains sulfadoxine, a sulfonamide.
- Repeated use of pyrimethamine with sulfadoxine is contraindicated in patients hypersensitive to pyrimethamine or sulfonamides, and in patients with severe renal insufficiency, marked liver parenchymal damage or blood dyscrasias, or megaloblastic anemia caused by folate deficiency.
- Use cautiously in patients with impaired hepatic or renal function, severe allergy or bronchial asthma, or G6PD deficiency; in those with

seizure disorders (smaller doses may be needed); and in those treated with chloroquine.
Lifespan: In pregnant women at term, infants younger than age 2 months, and breast-feeding women, repeated use of pyrimethamine with sulfadoxine is contraindicated.

Adverse reactions

CNS: ***seizures,*** stimulation.
GI: anorexia, atrophic glossitis, diarrhea, vomiting.
Hematologic: ***agranulocytosis, aplastic anemia, bone marrow suppression, leukopenia,*** megaloblastic anemia, ***pancytopenia, thrombocytopenia.***
Skin: ***erythema multiforme,*** rash, ***Stevens-Johnson syndrome, toxic epidermal necrolysis.***

Interactions

Drug-drug. *Co-trimoxazole, methotrexate, sulfonamides, zidovudine:* May increase risk of bone marrow suppression. Don't use together.
Folic acid, PABA: May decrease antitoxoplasmic effects. May require dose adjustment.
Lorazepam: May cause mild hepatotoxicity. Monitor liver enzymes.

Effects on lab test results

- May decrease hemoglobin level and hematocrit.
- May decrease granulocyte, WBC, platelet, and RBC counts.

Pharmacokinetics

Absorption: Well absorbed from intestinal tract.
Distribution: To kidneys, liver, spleen, and lungs. About 80% protein-bound.
Metabolism: To several unidentified compounds.
Excretion: In urine. *Half-life:* 4 days.

Route	Onset	Peak	Duration
P.O.	Unknown	1½–8 hr	Unknown

Action

Chemical effect: Inhibits enzyme dihydrofolate reductase, impeding reduction of this enzyme to tetrahydrofolic acid. Sulfadoxine competitively inhibits use of PABA.
Therapeutic effect: Prevents malaria and treats malaria and toxoplasmosis infections. Spectrum of activity includes asexual erythrocytic forms of susceptible plasmodia and *Toxoplasma gondii.*

Available forms

pyrimethamine
Tablets: 25 mg
pyrimethamine with sulfadoxine
Tablets: pyrimethamine 25 mg, sulfadoxine 500 mg

NURSING PROCESS

Assessment

- Assess patient's condition before starting therapy and regularly thereafter to monitor drug's effectiveness.
- Obtain twice-weekly blood counts, including platelets, for patients with toxoplasmosis because doses used approach toxic levels.
- Be alert for adverse reactions and drug interactions.
- Assess patient's and family's knowledge of drug therapy.

Nursing diagnoses

- Risk for infection related to presence of susceptible organism
- Ineffective protection related to adverse hematologic reactions
- Deficient knowledge related to drug therapy

Planning and implementation

- Give drug with meals to minimize GI distress.
- If signs of folic acid or folinic acid deficiency develop, reduce dose or stop drug while patient receives parenteral folinic acid (leucovorin) until blood counts become normal.
- For toxoplasmosis, patients with AIDS may need lifelong drug therapy and suppressive therapy.
- Leucovorin should be administered concomitantly when drug is used for the treatment of toxoplasmosis.

ALERT: Because of possibly severe skin reactions, use pyrimethamine with sulfadoxine only in regions where chloroquine-resistant malaria is prevalent and only when traveler plans to stay in region longer than 3 weeks.

Patient teaching

- Advise patient to take drug with food.
- Teach patient to watch for and immediately report signs of folic or folinic acid deficiency and acute toxicity.

P

• Warn patient taking pyrimethamine with sulfadoxine to stop drug and notify prescriber at first sign of rash.
• Instruct patient to take first prophylactic dose of pyrimethamine with sulfadoxine 1 to 2 days before traveling to endemic area.

Evaluation

• Patient is free from infection.
• Patient maintains normal hematologic parameters.
• Patient and family state understanding of drug therapy.

quetiapine fumarate

(KWET-ee-uh-peen FYOO-muh-rayt)
Seroquel

Pharmacologic class: dibenzothiazepine derivative
Therapeutic class: antipsychotic
Pregnancy risk category: C

Indications and dosages

▶ **Schizophrenia.** *Adults:* Initially, 25 mg P.O. b.i.d.; increase in increments of 25 to 50 mg b.i.d. or t.i.d. on days 2 and 3, as tolerated. Target dosage range is 300 to 400 mg daily, divided into two or three daily doses by day 4. Make further dosage adjustments at intervals of not less than 2 days. Dosages can be increased or decreased by 25 to 50 mg b.i.d. based on response. Safety of doses above 800 mg daily hasn't been evaluated.

▶ **Monotherapy and adjunct therapy with lithium or divalproex for the short-term treatment of acute manic episodes associated with bipolar I disorder.** *Adults:* Initially, 50 mg P.O. b.i.d. Increase dosage in increments of 100 mg/day in 2 divided doses, to 200 mg P.O. b.i.d. on day 4. May increase dosage in increments not greater than 200 mg/day, up to 800 mg/day by day 6. Usual dose, 400 to 800 mg daily.

▶ **Depression in bipolar disorder.** *Adults:* On day 1, give 50 mg. On day 2, give 100 mg. On day 3, give 200 mg. On day 4 and thereafter, give 300 mg daily. Give drug at bedtime.

Adjust-a-dose: For patients with hepatic impairment, initially give 25 mg P.O. daily. Increase in increments of 25 to 50 mg daily to an effective dose, depending on the patient's response and tolerance.

Contraindications and cautions

• Contraindicated in patients hypersensitive to the drug or any of its ingredients.
• Use cautiously in patients with CV or cerebrovascular disease or conditions that predispose them to hypotension; in those with history of seizures or conditions that lower seizure threshold; in those at risk for aspiration pneumonia; and in those who could experience conditions in which core body temperature may be elevated. Also use cautiously in patients who are debilitated.

Lifespan: In pregnant women, use only if benefits outweigh risks to the fetus. In breast-feeding women, stop breast-feeding or use a different drug. In children, safety and effectiveness haven't been established. In elderly patients, use cautiously and at a lower dose.

Adverse reactions

CNS: asthenia, *dizziness,* dysarthria, dyskinesia, fever, *headache,* hypertonia, ***neuroleptic malignant syndrome, seizures,*** *somnolence,* tardive extrapyramidal symptoms.
CV: orthostatic hypotension, palpitations, peripheral edema, tachycardia.
EENT: cataracts, ear pain, nasal congestion, pharyngitis, rhinitis, sinusitis.
GI: abdominal pain, anorexia, constipation, dry mouth, dyspepsia.
GU: urine retention.
Hematologic: ***leukopenia.***
Metabolic: ***hyperglycemia,*** hypothyroidism, *weight gain.*
Musculoskeletal: back pain.
Respiratory: dyspnea, increased cough.
Skin: rash, sweating.
Other: flulike syndrome.

Interactions

Drug-drug. *Antihypertensives:* May increase drug effects. Monitor blood pressure.
Carbamazepine, glucocorticoids, phenobarbital, phenytoin, rifampin, thioridazine: May in-

crease quetiapine clearance. Increase quetiapine dose, if needed.
Cimetidine, erythromycin, fluconazole, itraconazole, ketoconazole: May decrease quetiapine clearance. Use together cautiously.
CNS depressants: May increase CNS effects. Use together cautiously.
Dopamine agonists, levodopa: May antagonize effects of these drugs. Monitor patient for effects.
Lorazepam: May reduce lorazepam clearance. Monitor patient.
Drug-lifestyle. *Alcohol use:* May increase CNS effects. Discourage use together.

Effects on lab test results

- May increase glucose, liver enzyme, cholesterol, and triglyceride levels. May decrease T_4 and thyroid-stimulating hormone levels.
- May decrease WBC count.

Pharmacokinetics

Absorption: Rapid. 100% bioavailability.
Distribution: Wide. 83% protein-bound.
Metabolism: Extensive.
Excretion: About 73% in urine, 20% in feces. *Half-life:* 6 hours.

Route	Onset	Peak	Duration
P.O.	Unknown	1½ hr	Unknown

Action

Chemical effect: May block dopamine D_2 receptors and serotonin 5-HT_2 receptors in the brain. It also may act at histamine H_1 receptors and alpha$_1$-adrenergic receptors.
Therapeutic effect: Reduces symptoms of psychotic disorders.

Available forms

Tablets: 25 mg, 50 mg, 100 mg, 200 mg, 300 mg, 400 mg

NURSING PROCESS

Assessment

- Monitor patient for tardive dyskinesia. Condition may not appear until months or years after starting drug and may disappear spontaneously or persist for life, despite stopping the drug.
- Monitor patient's vital signs carefully, especially during the 3- to 5-day period of initial use and when restarting or increasing the dose.
- Assess patient's risk of physical injury from adverse CNS effects.
- Be alert for adverse reactions and drug interactions.
- Assess patient's and family's knowledge of drug therapy.

Nursing diagnoses

- Risk for imbalanced body temperature related to drug-induced hyperpyrexia
- Impaired physical mobility related to drug-induced adverse CNS effects
- Deficient knowledge related to drug therapy

Planning and implementation

- An elderly or debilitated patient or a patient with hepatic impairment or tendency for hypotensive reactions usually needs a lower initial dose and more gradual dose adjustment.

ALERT: Elderly patients with dementia-related psychosis are at increased risk of death when treated with atypical antipsychotics.

- Effectiveness for more than 3 weeks hasn't been thoroughly studied. Periodically reevaluate the long-term usefulness of drug.

ALERT: If symptoms of neuroleptic malignant syndrome (hyperpyrexia, muscle rigidity, altered mental status, or autonomic instability) occur, stop the drug and notify prescriber.

- Provide ice chips, drinks, or sugarless hard candy to help relieve dry mouth.

ALERT: Drug may cause hyperglycemia. Monitor patient with diabetes regularly. For patients with risk factors for diabetes, test fasting glucose level at baseline and periodically during therapy. Monitor all patients for symptoms of hyperglycemia, including excessive hunger or thirst, frequent urinating, and weakness; if symptoms develop, test fasting glucose level. Hyperglycemia may reverse once drug is stopped.

Patient teaching

- Warn patient about risk of orthostatic hypotension, especially during initial use or after a dose increase.
- Tell patient to avoid becoming overheated or dehydrated during therapy.
- Advise patient to avoid activities that require mental alertness until the drug's CNS effects are known.

Q

• Remind patient to have eye examination before starting drug therapy and every 6 months during therapy to check for cataract formation.
• Tell patient to notify prescriber of other prescription or OTC drugs he is taking or plans to take.
• Tell woman to notify prescriber if she becomes pregnant or intends to become pregnant during therapy. Advise her not to breast-feed during therapy.
• Advise patient not to drink alcohol during therapy.
• Tell patient that drug may be taken with or without food.

Evaluation

• Patient maintains normal body temperature.
• Patient maintains physical mobility and doesn't experience extrapyramidal effects of drug.
• Patient and family state understanding of drug therapy.

quinapril hydrochloride

(KWIN-eh-pril high-droh-KLOR-ighd)
Accupril, Asig ◇

Pharmacologic class: ACE inhibitor
Therapeutic class: antihypertensive
Pregnancy risk category: C (D in second and third trimesters)

Indications and dosages

▶ **Hypertension.** *Adults younger than age 65:* Initially, 10 to 20 mg P.O. daily. Adjust dosage based on patient response at intervals of about 2 weeks. Most patients are controlled at 20, 40, or 80 mg daily as a single dose or in two divided doses.
Adults age 65 and older: Initially 10 mg P.O. once daily. Adjust dose based on patient's response and tolerance.
Adjust-a-dose: For patients with renal impairment, if creatinine clearance exceeds 60 ml/minute, maximum initial dose is 10 mg P.O.; if clearance is 30 to 60 ml/minute, 5 mg; and if clearance is 10 to 30 ml/minute, 2.5 mg. No dose recommendations are available for creatinine clearance less than 10 ml/minute.
▶ **Heart failure.** *Adults:* Initially, 5 mg P.O. b.i.d. if patient is taking a diuretic and 10 mg P.O. b.i.d. if patient isn't taking a diuretic. Increase dosage at weekly intervals. Usual effective dosage is 20 to 40 mg daily in equally divided doses.
Adjust-a-dose: For patients with renal impairment, if creatinine clearance exceeds 30 ml/minute, the recommended initial dose is 5 mg P.O.; if clearance is 10 to 30 ml/minute, 2.5 mg. No dose recommendations are available for creatinine clearance less than 10 ml/minute.

Contraindications and cautions

• Contraindicated in patients hypersensitive to ACE inhibitors, in those with a history of angioedema during previous ACE inhibitor therapy, and in those with renal artery stenosis.
• Use cautiously in patients with impaired kidney function and increased potassium level.
Lifespan: In pregnant women in the second or third trimester, drug isn't recommended. In breast-feeding women, use cautiously; it's unknown if the drug appears in breast milk. In children, safety and effectiveness haven't been established.

Adverse reactions

CNS: depression, lightheadedness, malaise, nervousness, somnolence, syncope, vertigo.
CV: angina, ***arrhythmias, hypertensive crisis,*** orthostatic hypotension, palpitations, tachycardia, vasodilation.
EENT: dry throat.
GI: abdominal pain, constipation, dry mouth, ***GI hemorrhage.***
Metabolic: hyperkalemia.
Musculoskeletal: back pain.
Respiratory: dry, persistent, tickling, nonproductive cough.
Skin: exfoliative dermatitis, diaphoresis, *photosensitivity reaction,* pruritus.
Other: ***angioedema.***

Interactions

Drug-drug. *Digoxin:* May increase digoxin level. Monitor level.
Diuretics, other antihypertensives: May increase the risk of excessive hypotension. Expect to stop diuretic or lower dosage.
Lithium: May increase lithium level and lithium toxicity. Avoid using together.
Potassium-sparing diuretics: May increase risk of hyperkalemia. Monitor patient, ECG, and potassium level closely.

Quinolones, tetracyclines, and other drugs that interact with magnesium: May decrease absorption of these drugs. Monitor patient.
Drug-herb. *Licorice:* May cause sodium retention and increase blood pressure, interfering with the therapeutic effects of ACE inhibitors. Discourage using together.
Drug-food. *High-fat foods:* May impair absorption. Discourage using together.
Sodium substitutes containing potassium: May increase risk of hyperkalemia. Discourage using together; monitor patient closely.

Effects on lab test results

- May increase potassium level.
- May decrease liver function test values.

Pharmacokinetics

Absorption: At least 60%; rate and extent drop by 25% to 30% when given with high-fat meal.
Distribution: About 97% of drug and active metabolite are protein-bound.
Metabolism: 38% of dose de-esterified in liver to active metabolite.
Excretion: Mainly in urine. *Elimination half-life:* 2 hours; *terminal half-life:* 25 hours.

Route	Onset	Peak	Duration
P.O.	≤ 1 hr	2–4 hr	24 hr

Action

Chemical effect: Inhibits conversion of angiotensin I to angiotensin II, which lowers peripheral arterial resistance and decreases aldosterone secretion.
Therapeutic effect: Lowers blood pressure.

Available forms

Tablets: 5 mg, 10 mg, 20 mg, 40 mg

NURSING PROCESS

Assessment

- Assess patient's blood pressure before therapy and regularly thereafter. Take blood pressure just before giving a dose and then again 2 to 6 hours after dose to make sure blood pressure is controlled.
- Assess kidney and liver function before starting therapy and regularly thereafter.
- Monitor potassium level.
- Other ACE inhibitors have been linked to agranulocytosis and neutropenia. Monitor CBC with differential before therapy, q 2 weeks for first 3 months of therapy, and periodically thereafter.
- Be alert for adverse reactions and drug interactions.
- Assess patient's and family's knowledge of drug therapy.

Nursing diagnoses

- Risk for injury related to presence of hypertension
- Sleep deprivation related to drug-induced cough
- Deficient knowledge related to drug therapy

Planning and implementation

- If patient has renal impairment, give a lower dose.
- Give drug on empty stomach. High-fat meals can impair absorption.

Patient teaching

- Advise patient to report evidence of infection, such as fever and sore throat.
- Tell patient to immediately report evidence of angioedema (breathing difficulty and swelling of face, eyes, lips, or tongue), especially after first dose.
- Warn patient that lightheadedness can occur, especially at start of therapy. Tell him to rise slowly, stop taking the drug, and notify prescriber if he experiences blackouts.
- Inadequate fluid intake, vomiting, diarrhea, and excessive perspiration can lead to lightheadedness and syncope. Tell patient to maintain adequate hydration/fluid intake and to use caution in hot weather and during exercise.
- Warn patient not to take potassium supplements or use sodium substitutes that contain potassium during therapy.
- Tell women to notify prescriber about suspected or confirmed pregnancy. Drug will need to be stopped.

Evaluation

- Patient's blood pressure is normal.
- Patient's sleep patterns are undisturbed throughout therapy.
- Patient and family state understanding of drug therapy.

Q

quinidine bisulfate
(KWIN-eh-deen bigh-SUL-fayt)
(66.4% quinidine base)
Biquin Durules ♦, Kinidin Durules ◇

quinidine gluconate
(62% quinidine base)
Apo-Quin-G ♦, Quinate ♦

quinidine sulfate
(83% quinidine base)
Apo-Quinidine ♦

Pharmacologic class: cinchona alkaloid
Therapeutic class: antiarrhythmic, antimalarial
Pregnancy risk category: C

Indications and dosages

▶ **Atrial flutter or fibrillation.** *Adults:* 200 mg quinidine sulfate or equivalent base P.O. q 2 to 3 hours for five to eight doses, with subsequent daily increases until sinus rhythm is restored or toxic effects develop. Drug is given only after digitalization to avoid increasing AV conduction. Maximum dosage, 3 to 4 g daily. Or 300 mg Quinidex Extentabs P.O. (extended-release) q 8 to 12 hours.

▶ **Paroxysmal supraventricular tachycardia.** *Adults:* 400 to 600 mg quinidine sulfate P.O. q 2 to 3 hours until toxic adverse reactions develop or arrhythmia subsides.

▶ **Premature atrial and ventricular contractions; paroxysmal AV junctional rhythm; paroxysmal atrial tachycardia; paroxysmal ventricular tachycardia; maintenance after cardioversion of atrial fibrillation or flutter.** *Adults:* Test dose: 200 mg quinidine sulfate or equivalent base P.O., then 200 to 300 mg P.O. q 4 to 6 hours. Or give a test dose of 200 mg quinidine gluconate I.M., then initial dose of 600 mg I.M., followed by 400 mg I.M. q 2 hours, p.r.n. Adjust each dose by the effect of the previous. Or 300 to 600 mg quinidine sulfate or gluconate sustained-release tablets P.O. q 8 or 12 hours. Or, 800 mg quinidine gluconate I.V. diluted in 40 ml of D_5W and infused at 1 ml/minute.
Children: Test dose: 2 mg/kg; then 30 mg/kg P.O. daily or 900 mg/m^2 P.O. daily in five divided doses.

▶ **Severe *Plasmodium falciparum* malaria.** *Adults:* 10 mg/kg quinidine gluconate I.V. Dilute in 250 ml of normal saline solution and infuse over 1 to 2 hours; then give continuous maintenance infusion of 0.02 mg/kg/minute for 72 hours or until parasitemia is less than 1%. Or dilute 15 mg/kg quinidine gluconate I.V. in 250 ml of normal saline solution and infuse over 4 hours. Begin maintenance therapy 24 hours after the start of the loading dose, at 7.5 mg/kg infused over 4 hours, q 8 hours for 7 days, or until oral therapy can be instituted.

I.V. administration

- Use drug I.V. only for malaria or acute arrhythmias.
- Mix 10 ml (800 mg) of quinidine gluconate with 40 ml of D_5W and infuse at a slow rate of 1 ml/minute for maximum safety.
- Never use discolored (brownish) quinidine solution.

⊗ **Incompatibilities**
Alkalies, amiodarone, atracurium besylate, furosemide, heparin sodium, iodides.

Contraindications and cautions

- Contraindicated in patients hypersensitive to quinidine or related cinchona derivatives; in patients with idiosyncratic reactions to them; and in patients with intraventricular conduction defects, complete heart block, left bundle branch block, history of drug-induced torsades de pointes or prolonged QT interval, digitalis toxicity with grossly impaired AV conduction, or abnormal rhythms caused by escape mechanisms.
- Use cautiously in patients with asthma, muscle weakness, or infection with fever (hypersensitivity reactions to drug may be masked). Also use cautiously in patients with hepatic, renal, or cardiac impairment.

Lifespan: In pregnant women, use cautiously. In breast-feeding women, drug isn't recommended. In children, safety and effectiveness haven't been established.

Adverse reactions

CNS: cold sweats, confusion, dementia, fainting, fever, *headache, lightheadedness,* pallor, restlessness, *vertigo.*
CV: ***aggravated heart failure, cardiotoxicity, ECG changes (widening of QRS complex, notched P waves, widened QT interval, ST-***

segment depression), hypotension, ***PVCs, SA and AV block, severe hypotension, torsades de pointes,*** tachycardia, ***ventricular fibrillation, ventricular tachycardia.***
EENT: blurred vision, *tinnitus.*
GI: abdominal pain, anorexia, *diarrhea,* excessive salivation, *nausea,* petechial hemorrhage of buccal mucosa, *vomiting.*
Hematologic: ***agranulocytosis,*** hemolytic anemia, ***thrombocytopenia.***
Hepatic: ***hepatotoxicity.***
Respiratory: ***acute asthma attack, respiratory arrest.***
Skin: pruritus, rash.
Other: ***angioedema,*** cinchonism, hypersensitivity reaction, lupus erythematosus.

Interactions

Drug-drug. *Acetazolamide, antacids, sodium bicarbonate, thiazide diuretics:* May increase quinidine level because of alkaline urine. Monitor patient for increased effect.
Amiodarone: May increase quinidine level, producing potentially fatal cardiac arrhythmias. If use together can't be avoided, monitor quinidine level closely. Adjust quinidine as needed.
Antiarrhythmics (such as lidocaine, procainamide, propranolol): May increase risk of toxicity. Use together cautiously.
Anticoagulants: May increase anticoagulant effect. Monitor patient closely for bleeding.
Barbiturates, nifedipine, phenytoin, rifampin: May decrease level of quinidine. Monitor patient for decreased quinidine effect.
Cimetidine: May increase quinidine level. Monitor patient for increased effect.
Digoxin: May increase digoxin level after quinidine therapy starts. Monitor patient closely for digitalis toxicity.
Nondepolarizing neuromuscular blockers, succinylcholine: May increase neuromuscular blockade. Avoid using together.
Propafenone: May increase propafenone level and its effects. Use together cautiously.
Sucralfate: May decrease quinidine level. Adjust dose, p.r.n.
Verapamil: May cause hypotension, bradycardia, or AV block. Monitor blood pressure and heart rate.
Drug-herb. *Jimson weed:* May adversely affect CV function. Discourage using together.
Licorice: May prolong the QT interval. Discourage using together.
Drug-food. *Grapefruit:* May delay absorption and onset of action of drug. Advise patient to avoid eating grapefruit or drinking its juice.

Effects on lab test results

- May increase liver enzyme level. May decrease hemoglobin level and hematocrit.
- May decrease platelet and granulocyte counts.

Pharmacokinetics

Absorption: Although all salts are well absorbed, levels vary greatly among individuals.
Distribution: Well distributed in all tissues except brain. About 80% protein-bound.
Metabolism: About 60% to 80% metabolized in liver to two metabolites.
Excretion: 10% to 30% in urine. Urine acidification increases excretion; alkalinization decreases it. *Half-life:* 5 to 12 hours.

Route	Onset	Peak	Duration
P.O.	1–3 hr	1–2 hr	6–8 hr
I.V.	Immediate	Immediate	Unknown
I.M.	Unknown	Unknown	Unknown

Action

Chemical effect: Has direct and indirect (anticholinergic) effects on cardiac tissue. Automaticity, conduction velocity, and membrane responsiveness are decreased. The effective refractory period is prolonged. Anticholinergic action reduces vagal tone.
Therapeutic effect: Restores normal sinus rhythm and relieves signs and symptoms of malaria infection.

Available forms

quinidine bisulfate
Tablets (sustained-release): 250 mg ♦ ◇
quinidine gluconate
Injection: 80 mg/ml
Tablets (sustained-release): 324 mg, 325 mg, 330 mg
quinidine sulfate
Tablets: 200 mg, 300 mg
Tablets (sustained-release): 300 mg

NURSING PROCESS

Assessment

- Assess patient's arrhythmia before starting therapy and regularly thereafter to monitor drug's effectiveness.

Q

• Monitor drug level. Therapeutic level for arrhythmias is 2 to 5 mcg/ml.
• Check apical pulse rate and blood pressure before starting therapy. Hypotension may occur, usually with parenteral use.
• Monitor liver function test results during first 4 to 8 weeks of therapy.
• Be alert for adverse reactions and drug interactions.
• Assess patient's and family's knowledge of drug therapy.

Nursing diagnoses

• Decreased cardiac output related to presence of arrhythmia
• Risk for deficient fluid volume related to drug-induced adverse GI reactions
• Deficient knowledge related to drug therapy

Planning and implementation

• Give anticoagulant before starting therapy in a patient with long-standing atrial fibrillation because restoration of normal sinus rhythm may dislodge thrombi from atrial wall, causing thromboembolism.
• If patient develops unexplained fever or elevated hepatic enzyme level, monitor him for hepatotoxicity.
• If patient develops symptoms of cardiotoxicity, such as increased PR and QT intervals, 50% widening of the QRS complex, ventricular tachyarrhythmias, frequent ventricular ectopic beats, or tachycardia, stop drug immediately.
• Don't crush sustained-release tablets.
ALERT: Sustained-release preparations aren't interchangeable.
ALERT: Don't confuse quinidine with clonidine.

Patient teaching

• Tell patient to take drug with meals.
• Tell patient to report evidence of toxicity, including ringing in ears, visual disturbances, dizziness, headache, nausea, rash, or shortness of breath.
• Stress importance of follow-up care.

Evaluation

• Patient regains normal cardiac output with resolution of arrhythmia.
• Patient maintains adequate hydration throughout therapy.
• Patient and family state understanding of drug therapy.

quinupristin and dalfopristin
(QUIN-uh-pris-tin and DALF-oh-pris-tin)
Synercid

Pharmacologic class: streptogramin
Therapeutic class: antibiotic
Pregnancy risk category: B

Indications and dosages

▶ **Serious or life-threatening infections linked to vancomycin-resistant *Enterococcus faecium* bacteremia.** *Adults and children age 16 and older:* 7.5 mg/kg I.V. infusion over 1 hour q 8 hours. Length of therapy determined by site and severity of infection.

▶ **Complicated skin and skin-structure infections caused by *Staphylococcus aureus* (methicillin susceptible) or *Streptococcus pyogenes*.** *Adults and children age 16 and older:* 7.5 mg/kg by I.V. infusion over 1 hour q 12 hours for at least 7 days.

I.V. administration

• Flush line with D_5W before and after each dose.
• Reconstitute powder for injection by adding 5 ml of sterile water for injection or D_5W. Gently swirl vial to dissolve powder completely; to limit foaming, don't shake the vial. Reconstituted solutions must be further diluted within 30 minutes.
• Add dose of reconstituted solution to 250 ml of D_5W; maximum concentration, 2 mg/ml. Diluted solution is stable for 5 hours at room temperature or 54 hours when refrigerated.
• Fluid-restricted patient with a central venous catheter may receive dose in 100 ml of D_5W. This concentration isn't recommended for peripheral venous administration.
• Give all doses by I.V. infusion over 1 hour. Use an infusion pump or device to control rate of infusion.
• If moderate to severe peripheral venous irritation occurs, consider increasing infusion volume to 500 or 750 ml, changing injection site, or infusing by central venous catheter.

⊗ **Incompatibilities**
Saline and heparin solutions.

Contraindications and cautions

• Contraindicated in patients hypersensitive to the drug or other streptogramin antibiotics.
Lifespan: In pregnant women, use only if benefits outweigh risks to the fetus. In breast-feeding women, use cautiously; it's unknown if the drug appears in breast milk. In children younger than age 16, safety and effectiveness haven't been established.

Adverse reactions

CNS: headache, pain.
CV: thrombophlebitis.
GI: diarrhea, nausea, vomiting.
Musculoskeletal: arthralgia, myalgia.
Skin: *edema, inflammation, and pain at infusion site;* pruritus; rash.

Interactions

Drug-drug. *Cyclosporine:* May decrease metabolism of cyclosporine and increase level. Monitor cyclosporine level.
Drugs metabolized by CYP3A4 (carbamazepine, delavirdine, diazepam, diltiazem, disopyramide, docetaxel, indinavir, lidocaine, lovastatin, methylprednisolone, midazolam, nevirapine, nifedipine, paclitaxel, ritonavir, tacrolimus, verapamil, vinblastine, and others): May increase levels, therapeutic effects, and adverse reactions of these drugs. Use together cautiously.
Drugs metabolized by CYP3A4 that may prolong the QT interval (such as quinidine): May decrease metabolism of these drugs and prolong QT interval. Avoid using together.

Effects on lab test results

• May increase AST, ALT, and bilirubin levels.

Pharmacokinetics

Absorption: Given I.V.
Distribution: Protein-binding is moderate.
Metabolism: Quinupristin and dalfopristin are converted to several active major metabolites by nonenzymatic reactions.
Excretion: About 75% of both drugs and their metabolites excreted in feces. About 15% of quinupristin and 19% of dalfopristin excreted in urine. *Half-life:* About 1 hour for quinupristin; about ¼ hours for dalfopristin.

Route	Onset	Peak	Duration
I.V.	Unknown	Unknown	Unknown

Action

Chemical effect: Inhibit or destroy susceptible bacteria through combined inhibition of protein synthesis in bacterial cells. Dalfopristin inhibits the early phase of protein synthesis in the bacterial ribosome, and quinupristin inhibits the late phase of protein synthesis.
Therapeutic effect: Inactivation or death of bacterial cells.

Available forms

Injection: 500 mg/10 ml (150 mg quinupristin and 350 mg dalfopristin)

NURSING PROCESS

Assessment

• Obtain history of patient's underlying condition before starting therapy, and reassess regularly thereafter to monitor drug's effectiveness.
• Overgrowth of nonsusceptible organisms may occur. Monitor patient closely for signs and symptoms of superinfection.
• Monitor liver function during therapy.
• Assess patient's and family's knowledge of drug therapy.

Nursing diagnoses

• Risk for infection related to presence of bacteria
• Diarrhea related to drug-induced adverse effect
• Deficient knowledge related to drug therapy

Planning and implementation

ALERT: Drug isn't active against *Enterococcus faecalis*. Make sure cultures are drawn to avoid misidentifying *E. faecalis* as *E. faecium*.
• To reduce adverse reactions, such as arthralgia and myalgia, decrease dose interval to q 12 hours.
• If patient develops diarrhea during or after therapy, notify prescriber because mild to life-threatening pseudomembranous colitis may occur.

Patient teaching

• Advise patient to immediately report irritation at I.V. site, pain in joints or muscles, and diarrhea.
• Tell patient to report persistent or worsening signs and symptoms of infection, such as pain and erythema.

Q

 **Evaluation**

- Patient is free from infection.
- Patient has no diarrhea.
- Patient and family state understanding of drug therapy.

R

rabeprazole sodium

(rah-BEH-pruh-zohl SOH-dee-um)
AcipHex

Pharmacologic class: proton pump inhibitor
Therapeutic class: antiulcerative
Pregnancy risk category: B

Indications and dosages

▶ **Erosive or ulcerative gastroesophageal reflux disease (GERD).** *Adults:* 20 mg P.O. daily for 4 to 8 weeks. Additional 8-week course may be considered, if needed.

▶ **To maintain healing of erosive or ulcerative GERD.** *Adults:* 20 mg P.O. daily.

▶ **Duodenal ulcers.** *Adults:* 20 mg P.O. daily after morning meal for up to 4 weeks.

▶ **Pathological hypersecretory conditions, including Zollinger-Ellison syndrome.** *Adults:* 60 mg P.O. daily; increase as needed to 100 mg P.O. daily or 60 mg P.O. twice daily.

▶ **Symptomatic GERD, including daytime and nighttime heartburn.** *Adults:* 20 mg P.O. daily for 4 weeks. Additional 4-week course may be considered, if needed.

▶ ***Helicobacter pylori* eradication to reduce the risk of duodenal ulcer recurrence.** *Adults:* Three drug regimen: rabeprazole 20 mg P.O. b.i.d. given with amoxicillin 1,000 mg P.O. b.i.d. and clarithromycin 500 mg P.O. b.i.d. for a total of 7 days.

Contraindications and cautions

- Contraindicated in patients hypersensitive to drug, other benzimidazoles (such as lansoprazole or omeprazole), or components in these formulations. For *H. pylori* eradication, clarithromycin is contraindicated in patients hypersensitive to any macrolide antibiotic and in those taking pimozide. Amoxicillin is contraindicated in patients hypersensitive to any penicillin.
- Use cautiously in patients with severe hepatic impairment.

Lifespan: In pregnant women, clarithromycin is contraindicated for *H. pylori* eradication. In children, safety and effectiveness haven't been established.

Adverse reactions

CNS: headache.

Interactions

Drug-drug. *Clarithromycin:* May increase level of rabeprazole. Monitor patient closely.
Cyclosporine: May inhibit cyclosporine metabolism. Use together cautiously.
Digoxin, ketoconazole, other gastric pH–dependent drugs: May decrease or increase drug absorption at increased pH values. Monitor patient closely.
Drug-herb. *St. John's wort:* May increase risk of sunburn. Discourage using together; urge patient to avoid unprotected or prolonged sun exposure.

Effects on lab test results

None reported.

Pharmacokinetics

Absorption: Acid labile; enteric coating allows drug to pass through the stomach relatively intact. Level peaks over a period of 2 to 5 hours.
Distribution: 96.3% protein-bound.
Metabolism: Extensive, in the liver, to inactive compounds.
Excretion: 90% in urine as metabolites. Remaining 10% of metabolites in feces. *Half-life:* 1 to 2 hours.

Route	Onset	Peak	Duration
P.O.	< 1 hr	2–5 hr	> 24 hr

Action

Chemical effect: Blocks activity of the acid (proton) pump by inhibiting gastric hydrogen-potassium adenosine triphosphatase at the secretory surface of gastric parietal cells, thereby blocking gastric acid secretion.
Therapeutic effect: Promotes healing of gastric erosion or ulceration by stopping gastric acid secretion.

Available forms

Tablets (delayed-release): 20 mg

NURSING PROCESS

Assessment

- Obtain history of patient's underlying condition before starting therapy, and reassess regularly thereafter to monitor drug's effectiveness.
- Determine if patient is hypersensitive to penicillin because anaphylaxis may occur.
- Be alert for adverse reactions and drug interactions.
- Assess patient's and family's knowledge of drug therapy.

Nursing diagnoses

- Acute pain related to underlying condition
- Risk for injury related to drug-induced adverse reactions
- Deficient knowledge related to drug therapy

Planning and implementation

- Don't crush, split, or allow patient to chew tablets.
- If duodenal ulcer or GERD isn't healed after first course of therapy, additional courses of therapy may be needed.

ALERT: Symptomatic response to therapy doesn't rule out presence of gastric malignancy.

- In patient who doesn't respond to therapy for *H. pylori,* test for susceptibility. If resistance to clarithromycin occurs or susceptibility testing isn't possible, give a different antimicrobial.

ALERT: For *H. pylori* eradication, pseudomembranous colitis may occur with nearly all antibacterials, including clarithromycin and amoxicillin. Monitor patient closely.

Patient teaching

- Explain importance of taking drug exactly as prescribed.
- Tell patient to swallow delayed-release tablets whole and not crush, chew, or split them.
- Tell patient that drug may be taken without regard to meals, unless patient is being treated for *H. pylori*; then all three drugs should be taken twice daily with the morning and evening meals.

Evaluation

- Patient reports decreased pain with drug therapy.
- Patient sustains no injury as a result of drug-induced adverse reactions.
- Patient and family state understanding of drug therapy.

rabies immune globulin, human

(RAY-bees ih-MYOON GLOH-byoo-lin, HYOO-mun)

BayRab, HyperRAB S/D, Imogam Rabies-HT

Pharmacologic class: immune serum
Therapeutic class: rabies prevention drug
Pregnancy risk category: C

Indications and dosages

▶ **Rabies exposure.** *Adults and children:* 20 international units/kg at time of first dose of rabies vaccine. If feasible, infiltrate the full dose in the area around and in the wounds. Give remainder, if any, I.M. separate from rabies vaccine injection site.

Contraindications and cautions

- Give only one dose to prevent interference with effectiveness of vaccine.
- Use cautiously in patients hypersensitive to thimerosal, in patients with a history of systemic allergic reactions after using human immunoglobulin, and in patients with immunoglobulin A deficiency.

Lifespan: In pregnant women, use cautiously. In breast-feeding women, safety and effectiveness haven't been established.

Adverse reactions

CV: malaise, slight fever, slight headache.
GU: nephrotic syndrome.
Skin: induration at injection site, pain, *rash,* redness.
Other: ***anaphylaxis, angioedema.***

Interactions

Drug-drug. *Corticosteroids, immunosuppressive drugs:* May interfere with the active antibody response, predisposing patient to rabies. Avoid these drugs during postexposure immunization period.
Live-virus vaccines: May interfere with response to vaccine. Delay immunization.
Rabies vaccine: May partially suppress the antibody response to rabies immune globulin. Give

R

full dose of immune globulin into wound, if feasible.

Effects on lab test results

None reported.

Pharmacokinetics

Absorption: Slow.
Distribution: Unknown.
Metabolism: Unknown.
Excretion: Unknown. *Half-life:* About 24 days.

Route	Onset	Peak	Duration
I.M.	Unknown	2–13 days	Unknown

Action

Chemical effect: Provides passive immunity to rabies.
Therapeutic effect: Prevents rabies.

Available forms

Injection: 150 international units/ml in 2-ml, 10-ml vials

NURSING PROCESS

Assessment

- Obtain history of animal bites, allergies, and immunization reactions.
- Ask patient when he last received a tetanus immunization. Prescriber may order booster.
- Be alert for adverse reactions and drug interactions.
- Assess patient's and family's knowledge of drug therapy.

Nursing diagnoses

- Risk for injury related to rabies exposure
- Ineffective protection related to drug-induced hypersensitivity reaction
- Deficient knowledge related to drug therapy

Planning and implementation

- Use only with rabies vaccine and immediate local treatment of wound. Don't give in same syringe or at same site as rabies vaccine. Give drug regardless of interval between exposure and start of therapy.
- Don't give live-virus vaccines within 3 months of this drug.

ALERT: Drug provides passive immunity. Don't confuse with rabies vaccine, which is suspension of attenuated or killed microorganisms used to give active immunity. The two drugs usually are given together for prophylaxis after exposure to known or suspected rabid animals.

ALERT: Have epinephrine 1:1,000 immediately available to treat any acute anaphylactic reactions.

ALERT: Don't give more than 5 ml at one I.M. injection site; instead, divide I.M. doses larger than 5 ml and give at different sites. Use a large muscle, such as the gluteus.

Patient teaching

- Tell patient he may develop a slight fever and pain and redness at injection site.
- Explain that tetanus booster may be needed.
- Instruct patient to report signs of hypersensitivity immediately.

Evaluation

- Patient has passive immunity to rabies.
- Patient shows no signs of hypersensitivity after receiving drug.
- Patient and family state understanding of drug therapy.

raloxifene hydrochloride

(rah-LOKS-ih-feen high-droh-KLOR-ighd)
Evista

Pharmacologic class: selective estrogen receptor modulator (SERM)
Therapeutic class: antiosteoporotic
Pregnancy risk category: X

Indications and dosages

▶ **To prevent and treat osteoporosis.** *Postmenopausal women:* 60 mg P.O. daily.

Contraindications and cautions

- Contraindicated in women hypersensitive to the drug or any of its components, and in those with current or past venous thromboembolic events, including deep vein thrombosis (DVT), pulmonary embolism, or retinal vein thrombosis.
- Use with hormone replacement therapy or systemic estrogen isn't recommended.
- Use cautiously in women with severe hepatic impairment.

Lifespan: In women who are pregnant or planning to become pregnant, in breast-feeding women, and in children, drug is contraindicated.

In men, safety and effectiveness haven't been evaluated.

Adverse reactions

CNS: depression, fever, insomnia, migraine.
CV: chest pain, peripheral edema.
EENT: laryngitis, pharyngitis, *sinusitis.*
GI: abdominal pain, dyspepsia, flatulence, gastroenteritis, GI disorder, nausea, vomiting.
GU: cystitis, endometrial disorder, leukorrhea, UTI, vaginal bleeding, vaginitis.
Metabolic: weight gain.
Musculoskeletal: *arthralgia,* arthritis, leg cramps, myalgia,
Respiratory: increased cough, pneumonia.
Skin: rash, sweating.
Other: breast pain, flulike syndrome, hot flushes, infection.

Interactions

Drug-drug. *Cholestyramine:* May significantly reduce raloxifene absorption. Don't give these drugs together.
Highly protein-bound drugs (such as clofibrate, diazepam, diazoxide, ibuprofen, indomethacin, naproxen): May interfere with binding sites. Use together cautiously.
Warfarin: May decrease PT. Monitor PT and INR closely.

Effects on lab test results

- May increase calcium, inorganic phosphate, total protein, albumin, hormone-binding globulin, and apolipoprotein A levels. May decrease total cholesterol, low-density lipoprotein cholesterol, and apolipoprotein B levels.

Pharmacokinetics

Absorption: Rapid, with about 60% of dose absorbed after P.O. use.
Distribution: Wide. Extensively protein-bound.
Metabolism: Extensive first-pass metabolism to glucuronide conjugates.
Excretion: Mainly in feces, with less than 0.2% unchanged in urine. *Half-life:* 27½ hours.

Route	Onset	Peak	Duration
P.O.	Unknown	Unknown	24 hr

Action

Chemical effect: Reduces resorption of bone and decreases overall bone turnover by selectively activating and blocking estrogen receptors, resulting in increased bone mineral density.
Therapeutic effect: Prevents bone breakdown in postmenopausal women.

Available forms

Tablets: 60 mg

NURSING PROCESS

Assessment

- Obtain history of patient's condition before starting therapy, and reassess regularly thereafter to monitor drug's effectiveness.
- Monitor patient for signs of blood clots. The greatest risk of thromboembolic events is during the first 4 months of therapy.
- Monitor patient for breast abnormalities.
- Monitor lipid level, blood pressure, body weight, and liver function.
- Assess patient's and family's knowledge of drug therapy.

Nursing diagnoses

- Ineffective peripheral tissue perfusion related to potential DVT formation
- Imbalanced nutrition: less than body requirements related to drug-induced adverse GI reactions
- Deficient knowledge related to drug therapy

Planning and implementation

ALERT: Stop drug at least 72 hours before prolonged immobilization, and resume only after patient is fully mobile.
- If you suspect thromboembolic event, stop giving the drug and notify prescriber.
- Report unexplained uterine bleeding immediately to prescriber.
- Effect on bone mineral density with more than 2 years of drug therapy isn't known.

Patient teaching

- Advise patient to avoid long periods of restricted movement (such as during traveling) because it increases the risk of venous thromboembolic events.
- Inform patient that hot flashes or flushing may occur and that drug doesn't aid in reducing them.
- Instruct patient to take other bone-loss prevention measures, including taking supplemental calcium and vitamin D if dietary intake is inade-

R

quate, performing weight-bearing exercises, and stopping alcohol consumption and smoking.
• Tell patient that drug may be taken with or without food.
• Advise patient to report any unexplained uterine bleeding or breast abnormalities.
• Explain drug's adverse effects; instruct patient to read package insert before starting therapy and each time prescription is renewed.

Evaluation
• Patient has no pain, redness, or swelling in legs.
• Patient maintains normal dietary intake.
• Patient and family state understanding of drug therapy.

ramelteon
(rah-MEHL-tee-on)
Rozerem

Pharmacologic class: melatonin receptor agonist
Therapeutic class: hypnotic
Pregnancy risk category: C

Indications and dosages
▶ **Insomnia characterized by trouble falling asleep.** *Adults:* 8 mg P.O. within 30 minutes at bedtime. Don't give with or immediately after a high-fat meal.

Contraindications and cautions
• Contraindicated with hypersensitivity to the drug or its components. Don't use in patients taking fluvoxamine or in those with severe hepatic impairment, sleep apnea, or COPD.
• Use cautiously in patients with depression or moderate hepatic impairment.
Lifespan: Use drug in pregnancy only if benefits outweigh risks to the fetus. In breast-feeding women, avoid use. In children, safety and effectiveness haven't been established.

Adverse reactions
CNS: complex sleep disorders, depression, dizziness, fatigue, headache, somnolence, worsened insomnia.
GI: diarrhea, impaired taste, nausea.
Musculoskeletal: arthralgia, myalgia.
Respiratory: upper respiratory tract infection.
Other: ***anaphylaxis, angioedema,*** flulike syndrome.

Interactions
Drug-drug. *CNS depressants:* May cause excessive CNS depression. Use together cautiously.
Fluconazole (strong CYP2C9 inhibitor), ketoconazole (strong CYP3A4 inhibitor), weak CYP1A2 inhibitors: May increase ramelteon level. Use together cautiously.
Fluvoxamine (strong CYP1A2 inhibitor): May increase ramelteon level. Avoid use together.
Rifampin (strong cytochrome P-450 enzyme inducer): May decrease ramelteon level. Monitor patient for lack of effect.
Drug-food. *Food (especially high-fat meals):* May delay time to peak drug effect. Tell patient to take drug on an empty stomach.
Drug-lifestyle. *Alcohol use:* May cause excessive CNS depression. Discourage alcohol use.

Effects on lab test results
• May increase prolactin level. May alter blood cortisol and testosterone levels.

Pharmacokinetics
Absorption: Rapid. Oral bioavailability is 1.8%. Food consumption decreases and delays peak level by 45 minutes.
Distribution: 82% protein-bound; 70% to serum albumin. Tissue distribution is substantial.
Metabolism: Rapid, first pass metabolism mainly by CYP1A2 (also by CYP2C and CYP3A4), with four active metabolites formed.
Excretion: 84% in urine, 4% in feces. Less than 0.1% as the parent compound. Elimination complete 96 hours after dose. *Half-life:* Parent compound, 1 to 2½ hours; metabolite M-II, 2 to 5 hours.

Route	Onset	Peak	Duration
P.O.	Rapid	½–1½ hr	Unknown

Action
Chemical effect: Acts on receptors believed to maintain the circadian rhythm underlying the normal sleep-wake cycle.
Therapeutic effect: Promotes sleep.

Available forms
Tablets: 8 mg

NURSING PROCESS

Assessment

- Thoroughly evaluate the cause of insomnia before starting drug.
- Assess patient for behavioral or cognitive disorders.
- Evaluate patient's and family's knowledge of drug therapy.

Nursing diagnoses

- Sleep deprivation related to presence of insomnia
- Risk for injury related to drug-induced adverse CNS effects
- Deficient knowledge related to drug therapy

Planning and implementation

- Give drug on an empty stomach to prevent delays in peak effect.
- Drug doesn't cause physical dependence.
- In cases of overdose, consider the possibility of multiple drug ingestion, and contact a poison control center. Treat symptomatically.

Patient teaching

- Instruct patient to take dose within 30 minutes of bedtime.
- Tell patient not to take drug with or after a heavy meal.
- Warn patient about possible complex sleep-related behaviors.
- Caution against performing activities that require mental alertness or physical coordination after taking drug.
- Caution patient to avoid alcohol while taking ramelteon.
- Tell patient to consult prescriber if insomnia worsens or behavior changes.
- Urge woman to consult prescriber if menses stops, libido decreases, or breast discharge or fertility problems develop.

Evaluation

- Patient reports that drug effectively promotes sleep.
- Patient sustains no injury from adverse CNS effects.
- Patient and family state understanding of drug therapy.

ramipril

(reh-MIH-pril)

Altace, Ramace ◊, Tritace ◊

Pharmacologic class: ACE inhibitor
Therapeutic class: antihypertensive
Pregnancy risk category: C (D in second and third trimesters)

Indications and dosages

▶ **Hypertension (either alone or with thiazide diuretics).** *Adults:* Initially, 2.5 mg P.O. daily in patients not receiving diuretic therapy. Adjust dose based on blood pressure response. Usual maintenance dosage is 2.5 to 20 mg daily as a single dose or in two equal doses.

Adjust-a-dose: For patients with renal impairment, if creatinine clearance is less than 40 ml/minute (creatinine higher than 2.5 mg/dl), recommended initial dose is 1.25 mg daily, adjusted upward to maximum dose of 5 mg based on blood pressure response.

In patients receiving diuretic therapy, symptomatic hypotension may occur. To minimize this, stop diuretic, if possible, 2 to 3 days before starting ramipril. When this isn't possible, give initial dose of 1.25 mg.

▶ **Heart failure post-MI.** *Adults:* Initially, 2.5 mg P.O. b.i.d. Adjust to target dose of 5 mg P.O. b.i.d.

Adjust-a-dose: For patients with renal impairment, start therapy with 1.25 mg P.O. once daily, and increase to 1.25 mg b.i.d. Maximum dosage is 2.5 mg b.i.d.

▶ **Reduction in risk of MI, stroke, and death from CV causes.** *Adults age 55 and older:* 2.5 mg P.O. once daily for 1 week, then 5 mg P.O. once daily for 3 weeks. Increase as tolerated to a maintenance dosage of 10 mg P.O. once daily.

Adjust-a-dose: For patients with renal impairment, if creatinine clearance is less than 40 ml/minute, give one-quarter of recommended dose.

Contraindications and cautions

- Contraindicated in patients hypersensitive to ACE inhibitors, in those with history of angioedema during previous therapy with ACE inhibitor, and in those with renal artery stenosis.
- Use cautiously in patients with renal impairment.

R

Lifespan: In pregnant and breast-feeding women, drug isn't recommended. In children, safety and effectiveness haven't been established.

Adverse reactions

CNS: amnesia, anxiety, asthenia, depression, dizziness, fatigue, headache, insomnia, syncope, lightheadedness, malaise, nervousness, neuralgia, neuropathy, paresthesia, ***seizures,*** somnolence, tremors, vertigo.
CV: angina, ***arrhythmias,*** chest pain, edema, ***MI,*** orthostatic hypotension, palpitations.
EENT: epistaxis, tinnitus.
GI: abdominal pain, anorexia, constipation, diarrhea, dry mouth, dyspepsia, gastroenteritis, nausea, vomiting.
GU: impotence.
Metabolic: ***hyperkalemia,*** weight gain.
Musculoskeletal: arthralgia, arthritis, myalgia.
Respiratory: dry, persistent, tickling, nonproductive cough; dyspnea.
Skin: dermatitis, increased diaphoresis, photosensitivity reaction, pruritus, rash.
Other: ***angioedema,*** hypersensitivity reactions.

Interactions

Drug-drug. *Diuretics:* May cause excessive hypotension, especially at start of therapy. Stop diuretic at least 3 days before starting ramipril, increase sodium intake, or reduce starting dose of ramipril.
Insulin, oral antidiabetics: May increase risk of hypoglycemia, especially at start of ramipril therapy. Monitor patient closely.
Lithium: May increase lithium level. Use together cautiously, and monitor lithium level for toxicity.
Potassium-sparing diuretics, potassium supplements: May increase risk of hyperkalemia because ramipril attenuates potassium loss. Monitor potassium level closely.
Drug-herb. *Capsaicin:* May increase risk of cough. Discourage using together.
Licorice: May cause sodium retention and increase blood pressure, interfering with therapeutic effects of ACE inhibitors. Discourage using together.
Drug-food. *Salt substitutes containing potassium:* May increase risk of hyperkalemia because ramipril attenuates potassium loss. Monitor potassium level closely.

Effects on lab test results

- May increase BUN, creatinine, bilirubin, liver enzyme, glucose, and potassium levels. May decrease hemoglobin level and hematocrit.

Pharmacokinetics

Absorption: 50% to 60%.
Distribution: 73% protein-bound; ramiprilat (metabolite), 58%.
Metabolism: Almost completely converted to ramiprilat, which is six times more potent than parent drug.
Excretion: 60% in urine; 40% in feces. *Half-life:* 9 to 18 hours.

Route	Onset	Peak	Duration
P.O.	1–2 hr	3–6 hr	24 hr

Action

Chemical effect: May inhibit conversion from angiotensin I to angiotensin II, a potent vasoconstrictor. This decreases peripheral arterial resistance, thus decreasing aldosterone secretion.
Therapeutic effect: Lowers blood pressure.

Available forms

Capsules: 1.25 mg, 2.5 mg, 5 mg, 10 mg

NURSING PROCESS

Assessment

- Assess patient's blood pressure before starting therapy and regularly thereafter to monitor drug's effectiveness.
- Assess kidney function closely during first few weeks of therapy. Regularly assess creatinine and BUN levels. Patient with severe heart failure whose kidney function depends on angiotensin-aldosterone system may experience acute renal impairment during therapy. Hypertensive patient with renal artery stenosis also may show signs of worsening kidney function at start of therapy.
- Monitor CBC before therapy, q 2 weeks for first 3 months of therapy, and periodically thereafter.
- Monitor potassium level. Risk factors for hyperkalemia include renal insufficiency, diabetes, and use of drugs that raise potassium level.
- Be alert for adverse reactions and drug interactions.
- Assess patient's and family's knowledge of drug therapy.

Nursing diagnoses
- Risk for injury related to presence of hypertension
- Sleep deprivation related to drug-induced cough
- Deficient knowledge related to drug therapy

Planning and implementation
- Stop diuretic 2 to 3 days before starting therapy, if possible.
- If patient has trouble swallowing pills whole, capsule may be opened and the contents sprinkled onto 4 ounces of applesauce or mixed in 4 ounces (118 ml) of water or apple juice. These mixtures may be stored at room temperature for up to 24 hours, or refrigerated for up to 48 hours.

Patient teaching
- Instruct patient not to use salt substitutes or potassium supplements during therapy.
- If patient has trouble swallowing, tell him to open capsules and sprinkle contents on food.
- Tell patient to rise slowly to avoid initial lightheadedness. If syncope occurs, tell him to stop taking the drug and notify the prescriber.
- Tell patient not to abruptly stop therapy.
- Advise patient to report signs of angioedema and laryngeal edema, which may occur after first dose.
- Tell patient to report signs of infection.
- Tell woman to report pregnancy. Drug will need to be stopped.

Evaluation
- Patient's blood pressure is normal.
- Patient's sleep patterns are undisturbed throughout therapy.
- Patient and family state understanding of drug therapy.

ranitidine hydrochloride
(ruh-NIH-tuh-deen high-droh-KLOR-ighd)
Zantac*, Zantac-C ♦, Zantac EFFERdose, Zantac GELdose, Zantac 75†

Pharmacologic class: H_2-receptor antagonist
Therapeutic class: antiulcerative
Pregnancy risk category: B

Indications and dosages
▶ **Intractable duodenal ulcer; pathologic hypersecretory conditions, such as Zollinger-Ellison syndrome; short-term therapy for patients unable to tolerate oral forms (I.V. only).** *Adults:* 150 mg P.O. b.i.d. or 300 mg q at bedtime. Or, 50 mg I.V. or I.M. q 6 to 8 hours. Patients with Zollinger-Ellison syndrome may need up to 6 g P.O. daily. Or, for Zollinger-Ellison syndrome, 1 mg/kg/hour for 4 hours; then increase in increments of 0.5 mg/kg/hr if needed, to a maximum of 2.5 mg/kg/hour.

▶ **Duodenal and gastric ulcer.** *Children ages 1 month to 16 years:* 2 to 4 mg/kg P.O. twice daily to a maximum of 300 mg/day. Maintenance dosage is 2 to 4 mg/kg P.O. once daily to a maximum of 150 mg daily.

▶ **Maintenance therapy for duodenal ulcer.** *Adults:* 150 mg P.O. at bedtime.

▶ **Gastroesophageal reflux disease.** *Adults:* 150 mg P.O. b.i.d.
Children age 1 month and older: 5 to 10 mg/kg P.O. daily in two divided doses.

▶ **Erosive esophagitis.** *Adults:* 150 mg P.O. q.i.d.; maintenance dosage, 150 mg P.O. b.i.d.
Children age 1 month and older: 5 to 10 mg/kg P.O. daily in 2 divided doses.

▶ **Self-medication for occasional heartburn, acid indigestion, and sour stomach.** *Adults and children age 12 and older:* 75 mg† once or twice daily; maximum daily dosage, 150 mg.

Adjust-a-dose: For patients with renal impairment, if creatinine clearance is less than 50 ml/min, give 150 mg P.O. q 24 hours or 50 mg I.M. or I.V. q 18 to 24 hours.

I.V. administration
- To prepare I.V. injection, dilute 2 ml (50 mg) with compatible I.V. solution to a total volume of 20 ml, and inject over at least 5 minutes. Compatible solutions include sterile water for injection, normal saline solution for injection, D_5W, and lactated Ringer's injection.
- To give drug by intermittent I.V. infusion, dilute 50 mg (2 ml) in 100 ml compatible solution and infuse at a rate of 5 to 7 ml/minute. The premixed solution is 50 ml and doesn't need further dilution. Infuse over 15 to 20 minutes. After dilution, solution is stable for 48 hours at room temperature.
- For premixed I.V. infusion, give by slow I.V. drip (over 15 to 20 minutes). Don't add other

R

drugs to solution. If used with primary I.V. fluid system, stop primary solution during infusion.
• Store I.V. vial at 39° to 86° F (4° to 30° C). Store premixed containers at 36° F to 77° F (2° C to 25° C).

⊗ **Incompatibilities**
Amphotericin B, atracurium, cefazolin, cefoxitin, ceftazidime, cefuroxime, chlorpromazine, clindamycin phosphate, diazepam, ethacrynate sodium, hetastarch, hydroxyzine, insulin, methotrimeprazine, midazolam, norepinephrine, pentobarbital sodium, phenobarbital, phytonadione.

Contraindications and cautions

• Contraindicated in patients hypersensitive to the drug or any of its components.
• Use cautiously in patients with hepatic dysfunction. Adjust dosage in patients with impaired kidney function.
Lifespan: In pregnant women, use cautiously. In breast-feeding women, use cautiously; it's unknown if the drug appears in breast milk. In children, safety and effectiveness haven't been established for pathological hypersecretory conditions or the maintenance of healing duodenal ulcer. In neonates younger than 1 month, safety and effectiveness haven't been established. In elderly patients, use cautiously.

Adverse reactions

CNS: malaise, vertigo.
EENT: blurred vision.
Hematologic: ***pancytopenia, reversible leukopenia, thrombocytopenia.***
Hepatic: jaundice.
Other: ***anaphylaxis, angioedema,*** burning and itching at injection site.

Interactions

Drug-drug. *Antacids:* May interfere with ranitidine absorption. Stagger doses.
Diazepam: May decrease diazepam absorption. Monitor patient for decreased effectiveness; adjust dose.
Glipizide: May increase hypoglycemic effect. Adjust glipizide dosage.
Procainamide: May decrease renal clearance of procainamide. Monitor patient for procainamide toxicity.
Warfarin: May interfere with warfarin clearance. Monitor patient closely for bleeding.
Drug-lifestyle. *Smoking:* May increase gastric acid secretion and worsen disease. Discourage using together.

Effects on lab test results

• May increase creatinine and ALT levels.
• May decrease RBC, WBC, and platelet counts.
• May cause false-positive test for urine protein using Multistix.

Pharmacokinetics

Absorption: About 50% to 60% of P.O. dose; rapid from parenteral sites after I.M. dose.
Distribution: To many body tissues and CSF; about 10% to 19% protein-bound.
Metabolism: In liver.
Excretion: In urine and feces. *Half-life:* 2 to 3 hours.

Route	Onset	Peak	Duration
P.O.	≤ 1 hr	1–3 hr	≤ 13 hr
I.V., I.M.	Unknown	Unknown	≤ 13 hr

Action

Chemical effect: Competitively inhibits action of H_2 at receptor sites of parietal cells, decreasing gastric acid secretion.
Therapeutic effect: Relieves GI discomfort.

Available forms

Capsules: 150 mg, 300 mg
Granules (effervescent): 150 mg
Infusion: 0.5 mg/ml in 100-ml containers
Injection: 25 mg/ml
Syrup: 15 mg/ml*
Tablets: 75 mg†, 150 mg, 300 mg
Tablets (dispersible): 150 mg†
Tablets (effervescent): 25 mg, 150 mg

NURSING PROCESS

Assessment

• Assess patient's GI condition before starting therapy and regularly thereafter to monitor drug's effectiveness.
• Zantac EFFERdose contains phenylalanine.
• Be alert for adverse reactions and drug interactions.
• Assess patient's and family's knowledge of drug therapy.

Nursing diagnoses
- Impaired tissue integrity related to underlying GI condition
- Risk for injury related to drug-induced adverse CNS reactions
- Deficient knowledge related to drug therapy

Planning and implementation
- Don't use aluminum-based needles or equipment when mixing or giving drug parenterally because drug is incompatible with aluminum.
- No dilution is needed when giving drug I.M.
- The effervescent tablet may be dissolved in 5 ml of water and given with an oral syringe or in a medicine cup.

ALERT: Don't confuse ranitidine with rimantadine.

ALERT: Don't confuse Zantac with Xanax or Zyrtec.

Patient teaching
- Remind patient taking drug once daily to take it at bedtime.
- Instruct patient to take drug with or without food.
- Urge patient not to smoke cigarettes; smoking may increase gastric acid secretion and worsen disease.

Evaluation
- Patient states that GI discomfort is relieved.
- Patient sustains no injury as result of drug-induced adverse CNS reactions.
- Patient and family state understanding of drug therapy.

ranolazine
(rah-NOH-lah-zeen)

Ranexa

Pharmacologic class: cardiovascular drug
Therapeutic class: antianginal
Pregnancy risk category: C

Indications and dosages
▶ **Chronic angina, given with amlodipine, beta blockers, or nitrates, in patients who haven't achieved an adequate response with other antianginals.** *Adults:* Initially, 500 mg P.O. b.i.d. Increase as needed to maximum of 1,000 mg b.i.d.

Contraindications and cautions
- Contraindicated in patients taking QT interval–prolonging drugs or CYP3A inhibitors (including diltiazem) and in patients with ventricular tachycardia, hepatic impairment, or a prolonged QT interval.
- Use cautiously in patients with renal impairment.

Lifespan: In pregnant patients, use only if benefit to mother outweighs risk to fetus. It isn't known whether drug appears in breast milk. In children, safety and efficacy haven't been established. In elderly patients, start at the low end of the dosage range and adjust slowly.

Adverse reactions
CNS: dizziness, headache.
CV: palpitations, peripheral edema, syncope.
EENT: tinnitus, vertigo.
GI: abdominal pain, constipation, dry mouth, nausea, vomiting.
Respiratory: dyspnea.

Interactions
Drug-drug. *Antipsychotics or tricyclic antidepressants metabolized by CYP2D6:* May increase levels of these drugs. Dosage reduction may be needed.
Cyclosporine, paroxetine, ritonavir: May increase ranolazine level. Use cautiously together, and monitor patient for increased adverse effects.
Digoxin: May increase digoxin level. Monitor digoxin level periodically; digoxin dosage may need to be reduced.
Diltiazem, macrolide antibiotics (azithromycin, erythromycin), protease inhibitors, verapamil: May increase ranolazine level and prolong QT interval. Avoid use together.
Drugs that prolong the QT interval (antiarrhythmics such as quinidine, dofetilide, and sotalol; antipsychotics such as chlorpromazine and ziprasidone): May increase the risk of prolonged QT interval. Avoid use together.
Potent CYP3A inhibitors, such as ketoconazole: May increase ranolazine level. Use together is contraindicated.
Simvastatin: May increase simvastatin level. Monitor patient for adverse effects, and decrease simvastatin dosage as needed.
Drug-food. *Grapefruit:* May increase ranolazine level and prolong QT interval. Avoid use together.

Effects on lab test results

• May increase serum creatinine and BUN levels. May decrease hematocrit level.
• May decrease eosinophil count.

Pharmacokinetics

Absorption: Highly variable. Steady state occurs within 3 days.
Distribution: 62% bound by plasma proteins.
Metabolism: Rapid and extensive in liver and intestine, mainly by CYP3A and CYP2D6, to four metabolites.
Excretion: 75% in urine; 25% in feces. *Half-life:* 7 hours.

Route	Onset	Peak	Duration
P.O.	Rapid	2–5 hr	Unknown

Action

Chemical effect: Unknown. May result from increased efficiency of myocardial oxygen use when myocardial metabolism is shifted away from fatty acid oxidation toward glucose oxidation. Antianginal and anti-ischemic properties don't decrease heart rate or blood pressure and don't increase myocardial work.
Therapeutic effect: Relieves chronic angina.

Available forms

Tablets (extended-release): 500 mg

NURSING PROCESS

Assessment

• Obtain history of patient's underlying condition before therapy, and reassess regularly thereafter.
• Monitor ECG for prolonged QT interval and measure the QTc interval regularly.
• If patient has renal insufficiency, monitor blood pressure closely.

Nursing diagnoses

• Ineffective health maintenance related to underlying condition
• Decreased cardiac output related to drug-induced adverse reactions
• Deficient knowledge related to drug therapy

Planning and implementation

ALERT: Ranolazine prolongs the QT interval in a dose-related manner. If ranolazine is given with other drugs that prolong the QTc interval, torsades de pointes or sudden death may occur. Don't exceed maximum dosage.
• Drug may be taken without regard to meals.
• Don't crush or cut tablets.

Patient teaching

• Educate patient about drug's potential to cause an irregular heartbeat. Advise patient to immediately report palpitations or fainting and to tell prescriber about all other prescription or OTC drugs or herbal supplements he takes.
• Tell patient that he should keep taking other drugs prescribed for angina.
• Explain that drug won't stop a sudden anginal attack; advise him to keep other treatments, such as sublingual nitroglycerin, readily available.
• Tell patient that drug may be taken with or without food.
• Advise patient to avoid grapefruit juice while taking this drug.
• Warn patient that drug must be swallowed whole and not crushed, broken, or chewed.
• Tell patient to avoid activities that require mental alertness until effects of the drug are known.

Evaluation

• Patient shows improvement in underlying condition.
• Patient maintains adequate cardiac output throughout therapy.
• Patient and family state understanding of drug therapy.

rasagiline mesylate

(reh-SAH-jih-leen MEH-sih-layt)
Azilect

Pharmacologic class: irreversible, selective MAO inhibitor type B
Therapeutic class: antiparkinsonian
Pregnancy risk category: C

Indications and dosages

▶ **Idiopathic Parkinson disease, as monotherapy or with levodopa.** *Adults:* As monotherapy, 1 mg P.O. once daily. With levodopa, 0.5 mg P.O. once daily, increased to 1 mg once daily if needed. If patient taking both drugs has hallucinations or dyskinesia, levodopa dosage may be reduced.

Adjust-a-dose: If patient has mild hepatic impairment or takes a CYP1A2 inhibitor, such as ciprofloxacin, give 0.5 mg once daily.

Contraindications and cautions

- Contraindicated in patients with pheochromocytoma, patients with moderate to severe hepatic impairment, and patients taking amphetamines, cold products, dextromethorphan, ephedrine, MAO inhibitors, meperidine, methadone, phenylephrine, propoxyphene, pseudoephedrine, sympathomimetic amines, or tramadol.
- Use cautiously in patients with mild hepatic impairment.

Lifespan: Use cautiously in pregnant or breast-feeding women. In geriatric patients, safety of drug is similar to that in younger adults.

Adverse reactions

Monotherapy
CNS: depression, *dizziness, falls,* fever, hallucinations, *headache,* malaise, paresthesia, syncope, vertigo.
CV: angina pectoris, *chest pain*, postural hypotension.
EENT: gingivitis.
GI: anorexia, diarrhea, dyspepsia, gastroenteritis, vomiting.
GU: albuminuria, impotence.
Hematologic: ***leukopenia.***
Musculoskeletal: arthralgia, arthritis, neck pain.
Respiratory: asthma, flu syndrome, rhinitis.
Skin: alopecia, ***carcinoma,*** ecchymosis, vesiculobullous rash.
Other: allergic reaction, decreased libido.
Combined with levodopa
CNS: abnormal dreams, amnesia, ataxia, confusion, *dyskinesia,* dystonia, *falls,* hallucinations, *headache,* paresthesia, somnolence, sweating.
CV: *bundle branch block,* postural hypotension, ***stroke.***
EENT: epistaxis, gingivitis.
GI: abdominal pain, anorexia, constipation, diarrhea, dry mouth, dyspepsia, dysphagia, *nausea,* vomiting, weight loss.
GU: albuminuria.
Hematologic: anemia, ***hemorrhage.***
Musculoskeletal: arthralgia, arthritis, bursitis, hernia, leg cramps, myasthenia, neck pain, tenosynovitis.
Respiratory: dyspnea.
Skin: ***carcinoma,*** ecchymosis, pruritus, rash, ulcer.
Other: infection.

Interactions

Drug-drug. *Ciprofloxacin and other CYP1A2 inhibitors:* May double rasagiline level. Decrease rasagiline dosage to 0.5 mg daily.
Levodopa: May increase rasagiline level. Watch for dyskinesia, dystonia, hallucinations, and hypotension, and reduce levodopa dosage if needed.
SSRIs, serotonin-norepinephrine reuptake inhibitors, tricyclic antidepressants: May cause severe or fatal CNS toxicity. Stop rasagiline for at least 14 days before starting an antidepressant. Stop fluoxetine for 5 weeks before starting rasagiline.
Drug-food. *Tyramine-rich foods and supplements:* May cause hypertensive crisis. Urge patient to avoid tyramine-rich foods, such as aged meat, salami, pickled herring, aged cheese, unpasteurized beer, red wine, fava beans, sauerkraut, soybean products, and concentrated yeast extract.
Drug-herb. *St. John's wort:* May cause severe reaction. Strongly discourage use together.

Effects on lab test results

- May increase liver enzyme levels.
- May decrease WBC count.

Pharmacokinetics

Absorption: Rapid absorbed after P.O. use.
Distribution: Wide. 88% to 94% plasma protein–bound.
Metabolism: Almost completely metabolized in the liver by CYP1A2.
Excretion: Mainly in urine as glucuronide conjugates, with small amounts in feces. *Half-life:* 3 hours.

Route	Onset	Peak	Duration
P.O.	Variable	1 hr	1 wk

Action

Chemical effect: Unknown. Inhibition of MAO type B may increase extracellular dopamine level in the CNS, improving neurotransmission.
Therapeutic effect: Relieves the signs and symptoms of Parkinson disease.

R

Available forms

Tablets: 0.5 mg, 1 mg

NURSING PROCESS

Assessment

- Assess patient's condition before starting therapy and regularly thereafter to monitor drug's effectiveness.
- Be alert for drug interactions.
- If patient takes levodopa with rasagiline, watch for adverse effects; a reduced dose of levodopa may be needed.
- Assess patient's and family's knowledge of drug therapy.

Nursing diagnoses

- Impaired physical mobility related to underlying condition
- Risk for injury related to drug-induced adverse CNS reactions
- Deficient knowledge related to drug therapy

Planning and implementation

- Protect patient from falls; postural hypotension may occur during first 2 months of therapy.
- Examine the patient's skin periodically for possible melanoma.
- Drug should be stopped at least 14 days before elective surgery.
- Evidence of overdose may not appear for 12 hours and may include cool and clammy skin, diaphoresis, drowsiness, hallucinations, hyperpyrexia, hypertension or hypotension, severe headache, and respiratory depression or failure.
- In case of overdose, hospitalize immediately and give supportive care. Provide respiratory support, monitor body temperature, manage hyperoxia, and maintain fluid and electrolyte balance for at least 2 days.

Patient teaching

- Explain the risk of hypertensive crisis if patient ingests tyramine while taking rasagiline. Give patient a list of tyramine-containing foods and products.
- Tell patient to contact prescriber if hallucinations occur.
- Urge patient to watch for skin changes that could suggest melanoma and to have periodic skin examinations by a health professional.
- Instruct patient to maintain his usual dosage schedule if he misses a dose and not to double the next dose to make up for a missed one.

Evaluation

- Patient has improved physical mobility.
- Patient sustains no injury from adverse CNS reactions.
- Patient and family state understanding of drug therapy.

repaglinide

(reh-PAG-lih-nighd)

Prandin

Pharmacologic class: meglitinide
Therapeutic class: antidiabetic
Pregnancy risk category: C

Indications and dosages

▶ **Adjunct to diet and exercise to lower glucose level in patients with type 2 diabetes mellitus (non–insulin-dependent diabetes mellitus) whose hyperglycemia can't be controlled satisfactorily by diet and exercise alone; adjunct to diet, exercise, and metformin, rosiglitazone, or pioglitazone.** *Adults:* For patients not previously treated or whose glycosylated hemoglobin (HbA_{1c}) is below 8%, start dose at 0.5 mg P.O. given 15 minutes before meal; however, time may vary from immediately before to as long as 30 minutes before meal. For patients previously treated with glucose-lowering drugs and whose HbA_{1c} is 8% or more, initial dose is 1 to 2 mg P.O. with each meal. Recommended dosage range is 0.5 to 4 mg with meals b.i.d., t.i.d., or q.i.d. Maximum, 16 mg daily. Base dosage on glucose-level response. May double dosage up to 4 mg with each meal until satisfactory glucose-level response is achieved. Allow at least 1 week between dosage adjustments to assess response to each dose.

Adjust-a-dose: For patients with severe renal impairment, starting dose is 0.5 mg P.O. with meals.

Contraindications and cautions

- Contraindicated in patients hypersensitive to the drug or any of its components and in those with insulin-dependent diabetes mellitus or diabetic ketoacidosis with or without coma.
- Use cautiously in patients with hepatic insufficiency. Reduced metabolism may increase drug level and cause hypoglycemia. Also use cau-

tiously in debilitated and malnourished patients and in those with adrenal or pituitary insufficiency because they're more susceptible to the hypoglycemic effect of glucose-lowering drugs.
Lifespan: In pregnant women and breast-feeding women, don't use. In children, safety and effectiveness haven't been established. In the elderly, use cautiously.

Adverse reactions

CNS: *headache,* paresthesia.
CV: angina, chest pain.
EENT: rhinitis, sinusitis.
GI: constipation, diarrhea, dyspepsia, nausea, vomiting.
GU: UTI.
Metabolic: hyperglycemia, HYPOGLYCEMIA.
Musculoskeletal: arthralgia, back pain.
Respiratory: bronchitis, upper respiratory infection.
Other: tooth disorder.

Interactions

Drug-drug. *Barbiturates, carbamazepine, rifampin:* May increase repaglinide metabolism. Monitor glucose level.
Beta blockers, chloramphenicol, coumarins, MAO inhibitors, NSAIDs, other drugs that are highly protein-bound, probenecid, salicylates, sulfonamides: May increase hypoglycemic action of repaglinide. Monitor glucose level.
Calcium channel blockers, corticosteroids, estrogens, hormonal contraceptives, isoniazid, nicotinic acid, phenothiazines, phenytoin, sympathomimetics, thiazides and other diuretics, thyroid products: May produce hyperglycemia and loss of glycemic control. Monitor glucose level.
Erythromycin, gemfibrozil, inhibitors of CYP3A4, ketoconazole, miconazole: May inhibit repaglinide metabolism. Monitor glucose level and avoid using gemfibrozil and repaglinide together.
Levonorgestrel and ethinyl estradiol, simvastatin: May increase repaglinide level. Monitor glucose level.
Drug-herb. *Aloe, bilberry leaf, bitter melon, burdock, dandelion, fenugreek, garlic, ginseng:* May improve glucose control so that antidiabetic dosage needs to be reduced. Advise patient to discuss the use of herbal remedies before taking drug.

Effects on lab test results

• May increase or decrease glucose level.

Pharmacokinetics

Absorption: Rapid and complete. Absolute bioavailability is 56%.
Distribution: More than 98% protein-bound.
Metabolism: Completely metabolized by oxidative biotransformation and direct conjugation with glucuronic acid.
Excretion: About 90% is recovered in feces and 8% in urine. *Half-life:* 1 hour.

Route	Onset	Peak	Duration
P.O.	Rapid	1 hr	Unknown

Action

Chemical effect: Stimulates the release of insulin from beta cells in the pancreas.
Therapeutic effect: Lowers glucose level.

Available forms

Tablets: 0.5 mg, 1 mg, 2 mg

NURSING PROCESS

Assessment

• Monitor glucose level before starting therapy, and regularly thereafter to monitor drug's effectiveness.
• Be alert for adverse reactions and drug interactions.
• Monitor elderly patients and patients taking beta blockers carefully because hypoglycemia may be difficult to recognize in these patients.
• Assess patient's and family's knowledge of drug therapy.

Nursing diagnoses

• Imbalanced nutrition: more than body requirements related to patient's underlying condition
• Risk for injury related to drug-induced hypoglycemic episode
• Deficient knowledge related to drug therapy

Planning and implementation

• Increase dose carefully in a patient with renal impairment who needs dialysis.
• If repaglinide alone is inadequate, metformin may be added.
• Loss of glycemic control can occur during stress, such as fever, trauma, infection, or surgery. Stop giving the drug and give insulin.

R

• Oral antidiabetics have been linked to increased CV mortality compared to changing diet alone.
• Give drug immediately or up to 30 minutes before meals.

Patient teaching

• Teach patient about importance of diet and exercise along with drug therapy.
• Discuss symptoms of hypoglycemia with patient and family.
• Advise patient to monitor glucose level periodically to determine minimum effective dose.
• Encourage patient to keep regular medical appointments and have glucose level checked to monitor long-term glucose control.
• Tell patient to take drug before meals, usually 15 minutes before start of meal; however, time can vary from immediately to up to 30 minutes before meal.
• Tell patient to skip dose if he skips a meal and to add dose if he adds a meal.
• Teach patient how to monitor glucose level carefully and what to do when he is ill, undergoing surgery, or under added stress.

Evaluation

• Patient's glucose level is controlled and an adequate nutritional balance is maintained.
• Patient has no severe decreases in glucose level.
• Patient and family state understanding of drug therapy.

reteplase, recombinant

(REE-teh-plays, ree-KUHM-buh-nent)

Retavase

Pharmacologic class: recombinant plasminogen activator
Therapeutic class: thrombolytic enzyme
Pregnancy risk category: C

Indications and dosages

▶ **Acute MI.** *Adults:* Double-bolus injection of 10 + 10 units. Give each bolus I.V. over 2 minutes. If complications don't occur after first bolus, give second bolus 30 minutes after start of first.

I.V. administration

• Reconstitute drug according to manufacturer's instructions.

⊗ **Incompatibilities**

Other I.V. drugs.

Contraindications and cautions

• Contraindicated in patients with active internal bleeding, bleeding diathesis, history of stroke, recent intracranial or intraspinal surgery or trauma, severe uncontrolled hypertension, intracranial neoplasm, arteriovenous malformation, or aneurysm.
• Use cautiously in patients who've had major surgery, obstetric delivery, organ biopsy, or trauma within 10 days and in those with previous puncture of noncompressible vessel, cerebrovascular disease, recent GI or GU bleeding, or heart disease.

Lifespan: Use in pregnancy only if benefits outweigh risks to the fetus. In breast-feeding women, use cautiously; it's unknown if the drug appears in breast milk. In children, safety and effectiveness haven't been established.

Adverse reactions

CNS: ***intracranial hemorrhage.***
CV: ***arrhythmias, cholesterol embolization, hemorrhage.***
GI: ***hemorrhage.***
GU: hematuria.
Hematologic: anemia, ***bleeding tendency.***
Other: bleeding at puncture sites.

Interactions

Drug-drug. *Heparin, oral anticoagulants, platelet inhibitors (abciximab, aspirin, dipyridamole):* May increase risk of bleeding. Use together cautiously.

Effects on lab test results

• May decrease plasminogen, fibrinogen, and hemoglobin level and hematocrit.
• May cause unreliable results of coagulation tests or measurements of fibrinolytic activity.

Pharmacokinetics

Absorption: Given I.V.
Distribution: Rapid distribution.
Metabolism: Unknown.
Excretion: In urine and feces. *Half-life:* 13 to 16 minutes.

Route	Onset	Peak	Duration
I.V.	Unknown	Unknown	Unknown

Action

Chemical effect: Enhances cleavage of plasminogen to generate plasmin.
Therapeutic effect: Dissolves and breaks up clots.

Available forms

Injection: 10.8 international units (18.8 mg)/vial. Supplied in kit with components for reconstitution for 2 single-use vials. Also available in half kits with 1 single use vial.

NURSING PROCESS

Assessment

- Monitor ECG.
- Monitor patient for bleeding. Avoid I.M. injections, invasive procedures, and unneeded handling of patient.
- Assess patient's and family's knowledge of drug therapy.

Nursing diagnoses

- Ineffective cardiopulmonary tissue perfusion related to underlying condition
- Risk for injury related to adverse effects of drug
- Deficient knowledge related to drug therapy

Planning and implementation

- Reteplase is given I.V. as double-bolus injection. If bleeding or allergic reaction occurs after first bolus, notify prescriber.
- Avoid noncompressible pressure sites during therapy. If an arterial puncture is needed, use a vessel in the arm that can be compressed manually. Apply pressure for at least 30 minutes; then apply a pressure dressing. Check site often for bleeding.

Patient teaching

- Teach patient and family about drug.
- Tell patient to report adverse reactions immediately.

Evaluation

- Patient's cardiopulmonary assessment findings show improved perfusion.
- Patient has no serious adverse reactions to therapy.
- Patient and family state understanding of drug therapy.

Rho(D) immune globulin, human

(ARR AITCH OH DEE ih-MYOON GLOH-byoo-lin, HYOO-mun)

Rho(D) immune globulin, human (Rho[D] IGIM)

BayRho-D Full Dose, RhoGAM

Rho(D) immune globulin, human (Rho[D] IGIV)

Rhophylac, WinRho SDF

Rho(D) immune globulin, human, microdose (Rho[D] IG microdose)

HyperRHO S/D Mini-Dose, MICRhoGAM

Pharmacologic class: immune serum
Therapeutic class: anti-Rh_o(D)-positive prevention drug
Pregnancy risk category: C

Indications and dosages

▶ **Rh exposure (postabortion, postmiscarriage, ectopic pregnancy, postpartum, or threatened abortion 13 weeks or later).** *Women:* Transfusion unit or blood bank determines fetal packed RBC volume entering patient's blood. Give one vial I.M. if fetal packed RBC volume is below 15 ml. More than one vial I.M. may be required if large fetomaternal hemorrhage occurs. Must be given within 72 hours after delivery or miscarriage.

▶ **Transfusion accident.** *Adults and children:* Usually, 600 mcg I.V. q 8 hours or 1,200 mcg I.M. q 12 hours until total dose given. Total dose depends on volume of packed RBCs or whole blood infused. Consult blood bank or transfusion unit at once. Must be given within 72 hours.

▶ **Postabortion or postmiscarriage to prevent Rh antibody formation up to and including 12 weeks' gestation.** *Women:* Consult transfusion unit or blood bank. One microdose vial suppresses immune reaction to 2.5 ml Rh_o(D)-positive RBCs. Should be given within

R

3 hours but may be given up to 72 hours after abortion or miscarriage.

▶ **Amniocentesis or abdominal trauma during pregnancy.** *Women:* Base dose on extent of fetomaternal hemorrhage.

▶ **Idiopathic thrombocytopenia purpura.** *Adults and children:* 250 units/kg (50 mcg/kg) I.V. as single dose or in two divided doses given on separate days. If patient responded to initial dose, maintenance dose is 125 to 300 units/kg (25 to 60 mcg/kg) based on platelet count and hemoglobin level. If patient had inadequate response to initial dose and hemoglobin level is more than 10 g/dl, maintenance dose is 250 to 300 units/kg (50 to 60 mcg/kg); for those with hemoglobin level of 8 to 10 g/dl maintenance dose is 125 to 200 units/kg (25 to 40 mcg/kg).

I.V. administration

- Reconstitute only with normal saline solution. For WinRho SDF, use 0.8% saline supplied by manufacturer: 2.5 ml for the 120-mcg and 300-mcg vials and 8.5 ml for the 1,000-mcg vial. Slowly inject diluent into vial and gently swirl vial until dissolved. Don't shake vial.
- Give injection over 3 to 5 minutes.
- Refrigerate drug at 36° to 46° F (2° to 8° C).

⊗ **Incompatibilities**

Other I.V. drugs.

Contraindications and cautions

- Contraindicated in Rh_0(D)-positive or D^u-positive patients, those previously immunized to Rh_0(D) blood factor, those with anaphylactic or severe systemic reaction to human globulin, and those with immunoglobulin A deficiency.
- Use cautiously in patients with thrombocytopenia or bleeding disorders.

Lifespan: In pregnant women, use cautiously. Drug doesn't appear in breast milk. Microdose must not be used for any indication with continuation of pregnancy.

Adverse reactions

CNS: slight fever.
Hematologic: ***intravascular hemolysis.***
Other: ***anaphylaxis,*** discomfort at injection site.

Interactions

Drug-drug. *Live-virus vaccines:* May interfere with response to Rh_o(D) immune globulin. Delay immunization for 3 months.

Effects on lab test results

None reported.

Pharmacokinetics

Absorption: Unknown.
Distribution: Unknown.
Metabolism: Unknown.
Excretion: Unknown. *Half-life:* 24 to 30 days.

Route	Onset	Peak	Duration
I.V., I.M.	Unknown	Unknown	Unknown

Action

Chemical effect: Suppresses active antibody response and formation of anti-Rh_o(D) in Rh_o(D)-negative, D^u-negative people exposed to Rh-positive blood.
Therapeutic effect: Blocks adverse effects of Rh-positive exposure.

Available forms

I.M. injection: 300 mcg of Rh_o(D) immune globulin/vial (standard dose); 50 mcg of Rh_o(D) immune globulin/vial (microdose)
I.V. infusion: 120 mcg, 300 mcg, 1,000 mcg

NURSING PROCESS

Assessment

- Obtain history of Rh-negative patient's Rh-positive exposure, allergies, and reactions to immunizations.
- Assess patient's and family's knowledge of drug therapy.

Nursing diagnoses

- Risk for injury related to Rh-positive exposure
- Ineffective protection related to drug-induced anaphylaxis
- Deficient knowledge related to drug therapy

Planning and implementation

- Inject I.M. into the anterolateral aspect of the upper thigh or deltoid muscle.
- If administering 1,000 mcg, don't give entire dose in one muscle; divide dose between several different sites.
- Make sure epinephrine 1:1,000 is available in case of anaphylaxis.
- After delivery, have neonate's cord blood typed and crossmatched; confirm if mother is Rh_0(D)-negative and D^u-negative. Give to

mother only if infant is Rh_0(D)-positive or D^u-positive.
• Drug gives passive immunity to woman exposed to Rh_0(D)-positive fetal blood during pregnancy and prevents formation of maternal antibodies, which would endanger future Rh_0(D)-positive pregnancies.
• Defer vaccination with live-virus vaccines for 3 months after giving drug.
• MICRhoGAM is recommended for every woman having an abortion or miscarriage up to 12 weeks' gestation unless she is Rh_0(D)-positive or D^u-positive, she has Rh antibodies, or father or fetus is Rh-negative.

Patient teaching

• Explain how drug protects future Rh_0(D)-positive fetuses.

☑ Evaluation

• Patient shows evidence of passive immunity to exposure to Rh_0(D)-positive blood.
• Patient doesn't develop anaphylaxis after drug administration.
• Patient and family state understanding of drug therapy.

ribavirin

(righ-beh-VIGH-rin)
Copegus, Rebetol, Ribaspheres, Ribatab, Virazole

Pharmacologic class: synthetic nucleoside
Therapeutic class: antiviral
Pregnancy risk category: X

Indications and dosages

▶ **Hospitalized patients infected by RSV.** *Infants and young children:* 20-mg/ml solution delivered by small particle aerosol generator (SPAG-2) and mechanical ventilator or oxygen hood, face mask, or oxygen tent at about 12.5 L of mist per minute. Therapy lasts 12 to 18 hours daily for 3 to 7 days.
▶ **Chronic hepatitis C.** *Adults weighing 75 kg (165 lb) or less:* 1,000 mg Rebetol P.O. daily in divided doses (400 mg in morning, 600 mg in evening) with interferon alfa-2b 3 million units subcutaneously three times weekly. Or, 1,000 mg Copegus with 180 mcg of Pegasys (peginterferon alfa-2a).
Adults weighing more than 75 kg: 1,200 mg Rebetol P.O. divided b.i.d. (600 mg in morning, 600 mg in evening) with interferon alfa-2b, 3 million units subcutaneously three times weekly. Or, 1,200 mg Copegus with 180 mcg of Pegasys.
▶ **Chronic hepatitis C (regardless of genotype) in HIV-infected patients who have not previously been treated with interferon.** *Adults:* 800 mg (Copegus) P.O. daily given in two divided doses with peginterferon alfa-2a (Pegasys) 180 mcg subcutaneously weekly for 48 weeks.

Contraindications and cautions

• Contraindicated in patients hypersensitive to the drug or any of its components, and in those with creatinine clearance less than 50 ml/minute, history of significant or unstable cardiac disease, Child-Pugh class B or C, or hemoglobinopathies, such as sickle cell anemia and thalassemia.
• Avoid use in patients with evidence of pancreatitis.
• Use cautiously in patients with renal impairment.
Lifespan: In women who are or may become pregnant and in men whose sexual partners are pregnant, drug is contraindicated. Breast-feeding women should stop breast-feeding or use another drug, taking into consideration the importance of the drug. In children, capsules and tablets are contraindicated. In elderly patients, use cautiously.

Adverse reactions

CNS: anxiety, asthenia, ***depression,*** dizziness, fatigue, headache, insomnia, ***seizures, suicide.***
CV: ***cardiac arrest,*** chest pains, hypotension.
EENT: conjunctivitis, lacrimation, pharyngitis, rash or erythema of eyelids, rhinitis.
GI: nausea.
Hematologic: hemolytic anemia, ***neutropenia,*** reticulocytosis, ***severe anemia, thrombocytopenia.***
Musculoskeletal: arthralgia, myalgia.
Respiratory: ***apnea,*** bacterial pneumonia, ***bronchospasms, pneumothorax, worsening of respiratory state.***
Skin: rash.
Other: *flulike syndrome,* weight decrease.

Interactions

Drug-drug. *Antacids containing magnesium, aluminum, or simethicone:* May affect drug level. Monitor patient.
Didanosine: May increase toxicity. Avoid using together.
Stavudine, zidovudine: May decrease antiretroviral activity. Use together cautiously.

Effects on lab test results

- May increase bilirubin, AST, and ALT levels. May decrease hemoglobin level and hematocrit.
- May increase reticulocyte count. May decrease platelet and WBC counts.

Pharmacokinetics

Absorption: Some ribavirin is absorbed systemically after inhalation. Rapid and extensive absorption with P.O. use.
Distribution: Concentrates in bronchial secretions.
Metabolism: Metabolized to 1,2,4-triazole-3-carboxamide (deribosylated ribavirin).
Excretion: Most of drug in urine. *Half-life:* First phase, 9¼ hours; second phase, 40 hours; after a single P.O. dose, 120 to 170 hours.

Route	Onset	Peak	Duration
P.O.	Unknown	2 hr	Unknown
Inhalation	Immediate	Immediate	Unknown

Action

Chemical effect: Inhibits viral activity by unknown mechanism, possibly by inhibiting RNA and DNA synthesis by depleting intracellular nucleotide pools.
Therapeutic effect: Inhibits RSV activity.

Available forms

Capsules: 200 mg
Oral solution: 40 mg/ml
Powder to be reconstituted for inhalation: 6 g in 100-ml glass vial
Tablets: 200 mg, 400 mg, 600 mg

NURSING PROCESS

Assessment

- Assess patient's respiratory infection before starting therapy, and regularly thereafter to monitor drug's effectiveness.
- Monitor ventilator function. Drug may precipitate in ventilator apparatus, causing equipment malfunction with serious consequences.
- Watch for anemia in patient taking drug longer than 1 to 2 weeks.
- Be alert for adverse reactions.
- Assess patient's and family's knowledge of drug therapy.

Nursing diagnoses

- Risk for infection related to presence of RSV
- Risk for injury related to drug-induced adverse CV reactions
- Deficient knowledge related to drug therapy

Planning and implementation

- Aerosol form is indicated only for severe lower respiratory tract infection caused by RSV. Start therapy pending test results, but existence of RSV infection must be documented.
- Most infants and children with RSV infection don't need treatment. Infants with underlying conditions, such as prematurity or cardiopulmonary disease, benefit most from using aerosol form of drug.
- Give drug by SPAG-2 only. Don't use any other aerosol generator.
- For reconstitution, use sterile USP water for injection, not bacteriostatic water. Water used to reconstitute this drug must not contain an antimicrobial.
- Discard solutions placed in SPAG-2 unit at least every 24 hours before adding newly reconstituted solution.
- Avoid unneeded occupational exposure to drug. Adverse effects reported in health care personnel exposed to aerosolized drug include eye irritation and headache.
- Capsules and tablets aren't effective as monotherapy for chronic hepatitis C.
- Store reconstituted solutions at room temperature for 24 hours.
- Stop drug at first sign of pancreatitis.

ALERT: Don't confuse ribavirin with riboflavin.

Patient teaching

- Inform parents of children with RSV infection of need for drug therapy, and answer their questions.
- Advise patient to use correct device.
- Explain to women of childbearing age and men with sexual partners of childbearing age the effects of drug on a fetus and the need to in-

form the prescriber immediately if pregnancy occurs.
- Reinforce the importance of avoiding pregnancy during and for 6 months after ribavirin therapy stops. Recommend two reliable forms of contraception.

Evaluation
- Patient is free from infection.
- Patient develops no adverse CV reactions after drug administration.
- Parents state understanding of drug therapy.

rifabutin
(rif-uh-BYOO-tin)
Mycobutin

Pharmacologic class: semisynthetic ansamycin
Therapeutic class: antituberculotic
Pregnancy risk category: B

Indications and dosages
▶ **To prevent disseminated *Mycobacterium avium* complex (MAC) in patients with advanced HIV infection.** *Adults:* 300 mg P.O. daily as single dose or divided b.i.d.

Contraindications and cautions
- Contraindicated in patients hypersensitive to drug or other rifamycin derivatives (such as rifampin).
- Use cautiously in patients with neutropenia and thrombocytopenia.

Lifespan: Use during pregnancy only when clearly needed. In breast-feeding women, drug isn't recommended. In children, safety and effectiveness haven't been established.

Adverse reactions
CNS: fever, headache.
CV: ECG changes.
EENT: uveitis.
GI: abdominal pain, diarrhea, dyspepsia, eructation, flatulence, nausea, vomiting.
GU: discolored urine.
Hematologic: anemia, eosinophilia, LEUKOPENIA, NEUTROPENIA, ***thrombocytopenia.***
Musculoskeletal: myalgia.
Skin: *rash.*

Interactions
Drug-drug. *Corticosteroids:* May decrease corticosteroid effects. Double dose of corticosteroids, if needed.
Cyclosporine: May reduce immunosuppressive effects. Don't use together.
Drugs metabolized by the liver, benzodiazepines, beta blockers, buspirone, doxycycline, hydantoins, indinavir, losartan, macrolides, methadone, morphine, nelfinavir, quinidine, theophylline, tricyclic antidepressants, zidovudine: May decrease level of these drugs. Because rifabutin, like rifampin, induces liver enzymes, it may lower levels of many other drugs as well. Monitor patient for effect.
Hormonal contraceptives: May decrease effectiveness. Instruct patient to use an additional form of birth control.
Warfarin: May decrease anticoagulant effect. Monitor INR, and increase anticoagulant dosage as needed.
Drug-food. *High-fat foods:* May slow absorption of drug. Discourage taking drug with high-fat meals.

Effects on lab test results
- May increase alkaline phosphatase, AST, and ALT levels. May decrease hemoglobin level and hematocrit.
- May increase eosinophil count. May decrease neutrophil, WBC, and platelet counts.

Pharmacokinetics
Absorption: Readily absorbed from GI tract.
Distribution: Because of its high lipophilicity, rifabutin has high propensity for distribution and intracellular tissue uptake. About 85% protein-bound.
Metabolism: In liver.
Excretion: Mainly in urine; about 30% in feces. *Half-life:* 45 hours.

Route	Onset	Peak	Duration
P.O.	Unknown	1½–4 hr	Unknown

Action
Chemical effect: Blocks bacterial protein synthesis by inhibiting DNA-dependent RNA polymerase in susceptible bacteria.
Therapeutic effect: Prevents disseminated MAC in patients with advanced HIV infection.

R

Available forms

Capsules: 150 mg

NURSING PROCESS

Assessment

- Assess patient's condition before starting therapy, and regularly thereafter to monitor drug's effectiveness.
- Perform baseline hematologic studies and repeat periodically.
- Be alert for adverse reactions and drug interactions.
- Assess patient's and family's knowledge of drug therapy.

Nursing diagnoses

- Risk for infection related to immune system dysfunction
- Ineffective protection related to drug-induced adverse hematologic reactions
- Deficient knowledge related to drug therapy

Planning and implementation

- High-fat meals slow rate but not extent of absorption.
- Give drug with food. Mix with soft foods for patient who has difficulty swallowing.
- No evidence exists that drug will provide effective prophylaxis against *Mycobacterium tuberculosis.* Patients requiring prophylaxis against both *M. tuberculosis* and MAC may require rifampin and rifabutin.
- Don't use as monotherapy in patients with active tuberculosis. Doing so may foster tuberculosis that's resistant to both rifabutin and rifampin.

ALERT: Don't confuse rifabutin, rifampin, and rifapentine.

Patient teaching

- Tell patient that drug may turn urine, feces, sputum, saliva, tears, and skin brownish-orange. Tell him not to wear soft contacts because they may be permanently stained.
- Instruct patient to report photophobia, excessive lacrimation, or eye pain. Drug may rarely cause uveitis.

Evaluation

- Patient doesn't develop disseminated MAC.
- Patient maintains normal hematologic values throughout therapy.
- Patient and family state understanding of drug therapy.

rifampin (rifampicin)

(rih-FAM-pin)

Rifadin, Rifadin IV, Rimactane, Rimycin◇, Rofact♦

Pharmacologic class: rifamycin derivative antibiotic
Therapeutic class: antituberculotic
Pregnancy risk category: C

Indications and dosages

▶ **Pulmonary tuberculosis.** *Adults:* 10 mg/kg P.O. or I.V. daily in single dose. Maximum, 600 mg daily.
Children older than age 5: Give 10 to 20 mg/kg P.O. or I.V. daily in single dose. Maximum, 600 mg daily. Use with other antituberculotics is recommended.

▶ **Meningococcal carriers.** *Adults:* 600 mg P.O. or I.V. b.i.d. for 2 days or once daily for 4 days.
Children ages 1 month to 12 years: 10 mg/kg P.O. or I.V. b.i.d. for 2 days or once daily for 4 days. Maximum, 600 mg daily.
Neonates: 5 mg/kg P.O. or I.V. b.i.d. for 2 days.

▶ **Prophylaxis of *Haemophilus influenzae* type B.** *Adults and children:* 20 mg/kg P.O. daily for 4 days. Maximum, 600 mg daily.

▶ **Leprosy‡.** *Adults:* 600 mg P.O. once monthly, usually with other drugs.

I.V. administration

- Reconstitute vial with 10 ml of sterile water for injection to make solution containing 60 mg/ml.
- Add to 100 ml of D_5W and infuse over 30 minutes, or add to 500 ml of D_5W and infuse over 3 hours.
- When dextrose is contraindicated, drug may be diluted with normal saline solution for injection.

⊗ **Incompatibilities**
Diltiazem, minocycline, I.V. solutions other than dextrose or normal saline.

Contraindications and cautions

- Contraindicated in patients hypersensitive to the drug or any of its components.
- Use cautiously and under strict medical supervision in patients with liver disease.

Lifespan: In pregnant women, use only when benefits outweigh risks to the fetus. During the last 2 weeks of pregnancy, use of the drug may lead to postnatal hemorrhage in the mother or infant. Monitor clotting factors closely. In breast-feeding women, decide whether to discontinue drug or breast-feeding based on importance of drug to mother; drug appears in breast milk.

Adverse reactions

CNS: ataxia, behavioral changes, confusion, dizziness, drowsiness, fatigue, generalized numbness, headache.
CV: ***shock.***
EENT: exudative conjunctivitis, visual disturbances.
GI: abdominal pain, anorexia, diarrhea, epigastric distress, flatulence, nausea, ***pancreatitis, pseudomembranous colitis,*** sore mouth and tongue, vomiting.
GU: ***acute renal failure,*** hematuria, hemoglobinuria, menstrual disturbances.
Hematologic: eosinophilia, hemolytic anemia ***thrombocytopenia,, transient leukopenia.***
Hepatic: ***hepatotoxicity,*** worsening of porphyria.
Metabolic: hyperuricemia.
Musculoskeletal: osteomalacia.
Respiratory: shortness of breath, wheezing.
Skin: pruritus, rash, urticaria.
Other: discoloration of body fluids, flulike syndrome.

Interactions

Drug-drug. *Analgesics, anticoagulants, anticonvulsants, barbiturates, beta blockers, chloramphenicol, clofibrate, corticosteroids, cyclosporine, dapsone, diazepam, digoxin, disopyramide, doxycycline, hormonal contraceptives, macrolides, methadone, opioids, progestins, protease inhibitors, quinidine, sulfonylureas, theophylline, verapamil:* May reduce effectiveness of these drugs. Avoid using together.
Halothane: May increase risk of hepatotoxicity in both drugs. Monitor liver function closely.
Ketoconazole, para-aminosalicylate sodium: May interfere with absorption of rifampin. Give these drugs 8 to 12 hours apart.
Drug-herb. *Kava:* May increase the risk of hepatotoxicity. Discourage use.
Drug-lifestyle. *Alcohol use:* May increase risk of hepatotoxicity. Discourage using together.

Effects on lab test results

• May increase ALT, AST, alkaline phosphatase, bilirubin, BUN, creatinine, and uric acid levels. May decrease hemoglobin level and hematocrit.
• May increase eosinophil count. May decrease platelet and WBC counts.

Pharmacokinetics

Absorption: Complete. Food delays absorption.
Distribution: Wide. 84% to 91% protein-bound.
Metabolism: Extensive.
Excretion: Mainly in bile; drug, but not metabolite, is reabsorbed. Some in urine. *Half-life:* 1¼ to 5 hours.

Route	Onset	Peak	Duration
P.O.	Unknown	2–4 hr	Unknown
I.V.	Unknown	Unknown	Unknown

Action

Chemical effect: Kills bacteria by inhibiting DNA-dependent RNA polymerase, thus impairing RNA synthesis.
Therapeutic effect: Kills susceptible bacteria.

Available forms

Capsules: 150 mg, 300 mg
Injection: 600 mg

NURSING PROCESS

Assessment

• Assess patient's infection before starting therapy, and regularly thereafter to monitor drug's effectiveness.
• Monitor liver function, hematopoiesis, and uric acid level.
• Be alert for adverse reactions and drug interactions.
• Watch closely for signs of hepatic impairment.
• If adverse GI reaction occurs, monitor hydration.
• Assess patient's and family's knowledge of drug therapy.

Nursing diagnoses

• Risk for infection related to presence of susceptible bacteria

R

• Risk for deficient fluid volume related to drug-induced adverse reactions
• Deficient knowledge related to drug therapy

Planning and implementation

• Give drug 1 hour before or 2 hours after meals for optimal absorption; if GI irritation occurs, patient may take with meals.
• Drug may inhibit standard assays for folate and vitamin B_{12}. Consider alternative assay method.
• Giving at least one additional antituberculotic is recommended.

ALERT: Don't confuse rifampin, rifabutin, and rifapentine. Don't confuse Rifadin with Ritalin.

Patient teaching

• Warn patient about drowsiness and red-orange discoloration of urine, feces, saliva, sweat, sputum, and tears. Soft contact lenses may be permanently stained.
• Advise patient not to drink alcohol while taking the drug.
• Recommend taking drug with a full glass of water to maintain adequate hydration.

Evaluation

• Patient is free from infection.
• Patient maintains adequate hydration throughout therapy.
• Patient and family state understanding of drug therapy.

rifapentine

(rif-ah-PEN-teen)
Priftin

Pharmacologic class: rifamycin derivative antibiotic
Therapeutic class: antituberculotic
Pregnancy risk category: C

Indications and dosages

▶ **Pulmonary tuberculosis, with at least one other antituberculotic to which the isolate is susceptible.** *Adults:* During intensive phase of short-course therapy, 600 mg P.O. twice weekly for 2 months, with an interval between doses of not less than 3 days (72 hours). During the continuation phase of short-course therapy, 600 mg P.O. once weekly for 4 months with isoniazid or another drug to which the isolate is susceptible.

Contraindications and cautions

• Contraindicated in patients hypersensitive to rifamycin (rifapentine, rifampin, or rifabutin).
• Use drug cautiously and with frequent monitoring in patients with liver disease.

Lifespan: During last 2 weeks of pregnancy, drug may lead to postnatal hemorrhage in mother or infant; monitor clotting parameters closely. Use with caution in breast-feeding women. It isn't known if drug appears in breast milk.

Adverse reactions

CNS: dizziness, headache, pain.
CV: hypertension.
GI: anorexia, diarrhea, dyspepsia, nausea, ***pseudomembranous colitis,*** vomiting.
GU: hematuria, proteinuria, pyuria, urinary casts.
Hematologic: anemia, ***leukopenia, lymphopenia, neutropenia,*** thrombocytosis.
Metabolic: *hyperuricemia.*
Musculoskeletal: arthralgia.
Respiratory: hemoptysis.
Skin: rash, acne, maculopapular rash, pruritus.

Interactions

Drug-drug. *Antiarrhythmics, antibiotics, anticonvulsants, antifungals, barbiturates, benzodiazepines, beta blockers, calcium channel blockers, clofibrate, corticosteroids, digoxin, haloperidol, HIV protease inhibitors, hormonal contraceptives, immunosuppressants, levothyroxine, opioid analgesics (methadone), oral anticoagulants, oral hypoglycemics, progestins, quinine, reverse transcriptase inhibitors, sildenafil, theophylline, tricyclic antidepressants:* May increase metabolism and decrease the activity of these drugs. Dosage adjustments may be needed.

Effects on lab test results

• May increase uric acid, ALT, and AST levels. May decrease hemoglobin level and hematocrit.
• May increase platelet count. May decrease neutrophil and WBC counts.

Pharmacokinetics

Absorption: Relative bioavailability is 70%.
Distribution: About 98% protein-bound.
Metabolism: Hydrolyzed by an esterase enzyme to the microbiologically active 25-desacetyl rifapentine. Rifapentine contributes

62% to drug's activity and 25-desacetyl contributes 38%.
Excretion: About 17% in urine and 70% in feces. *Half-life:* 13 hours.

Route	Onset	Peak	Duration
P.O.	Unknown	5–6 hr	Unknown

Action

Chemical effect: Kills susceptible strains of *Mycobacterium tuberculosis,* both inside and outside cells, by inhibiting DNA-dependent RNA polymerase. Rifapentine and rifampin share similar antimicrobial action.
Therapeutic effect: Kills susceptible bacteria.

Available forms

Tablets (film-coated): 150 mg

NURSING PROCESS

Assessment

• Assess patient's condition before starting therapy and regularly thereafter to monitor drug's effectiveness.
• Assess patient's understanding of disease and stress importance of strict compliance with drug and daily companion medications, as well as needed follow-up visits and laboratory tests.
• Monitor liver function, CBC, and uric acid level.
• Monitor patient for persistent or severe diarrhea and notify prescriber if it occurs.
• Assess patient's and family's knowledge of drug therapy.

Nursing diagnoses

• Risk for infection related to patient's underlying condition
• Noncompliance related to long-term therapeutic regimen
• Deficient knowledge related to drug therapy

Planning and implementation

• Give pyridoxine (vitamin B_6) during rifapentine therapy to a malnourished patient, a patient predisposed to neuropathy (alcoholic, diabetic), or an adolescent.
• Drug must be given with appropriate daily companion drugs. Compliance with all drugs, especially with daily companion drugs on the days when rifapentine isn't given, is crucial for early sputum conversion and protection from tuberculosis relapse.
ALERT: Don't confuse rifampin, rifabutin, and rifapentine.

Patient teaching

• Stress importance of strict compliance with regimen of drug and daily companion drugs, as well as needed follow-up visits and laboratory tests.
• Advise patient to use barrier-method of birth control.
• Tell patient to take drug with food if nausea, vomiting, or GI upset occurs.
• Instruct patient to notify prescriber if any of the following occur: fever, loss of appetite, malaise, nausea, vomiting, darkened urine, yellowish discoloration of skin and eyes, pain or swelling of joints, and excessive loose stools or diarrhea.
• Instruct patient to protect pills from excessive heat.
• Tell patient that drug can turn body fluids red-orange. Contact lenses can become permanently stained.

Evaluation

• Patient experiences sputum conversion and recovers from tuberculosis.
• Patient complies with therapeutic regimen.
• Patient and family state understanding of drug therapy.

rifaximin

rih-FAX-ih-mehn
Xifaxan

Pharmacologic class: rifamycin antibacterial
Therapeutic class: nonabsorbed antibiotic
Pregnancy risk category: C

Indications and dosages

▶ **Traveler's diarrhea caused by noninvasive strains of *Escherichia coli.*** *Adults and children age 12 and older:* 200 mg P.O. t.i.d. for 3 days.

Contraindications and cautions

• Contraindicated in patients hypersensitive to rifaximin or any rifamycin antibacterial.
Lifespan: In pregnant women, use only if benefits outweigh risks to the fetus. In breast-feeding women, use cautiously. It isn't known if

drug appears in breast milk. In children younger than age 12, safety and effectiveness haven't been established.

Adverse reactions

CNS: fever, headache.
GI: abdominal pain, constipation, defecation urgency, flatulence, nausea, rectal tenesmus, vomiting.

Interactions

None significant.

Effects on lab test results

None reported.

Pharmacokinetics

Absorption: Poor.
Distribution: In the gut.
Metabolism: Not specified.
Excretion: In feces as unchanged drug.

Route	Onset	Peak	Duration
P.O.	Unknown	Unknown	Unknown

Action

Chemical effect: Drug binds to the beta-subunit of bacterial DNA–dependent RNA polymerase, which inhibits bacterial RNA synthesis and kills the *E. coli.*
Therapeutic effect: Kills susceptible bacteria and resolves traveler's diarrhea.

Available forms

Tablets: 200 mg

NURSING PROCESS

Assessment

- Assess patient's condition before starting therapy and regularly thereafter to monitor drug's effectiveness.
- Monitor patient's hydration status.
- Be alert for adverse drug reactions.
- Monitor patient for overgrowth of nonsusceptible organisms.
- Assess patient's and family's knowledge of drug therapy.

Nursing diagnoses

- Diarrhea related to infection with *E. coli*
- Risk for imbalanced fluid volume related to underlying medical condition and drug-induced adverse GI effects
- Deficient knowledge related to drug therapy

Planning and implementation

- Don't use drug in patients whose illness may be caused by *Campylobacter jejuni, Shigella,* or *Salmonella.*

ALERT: Don't use drug in patients with blood in the stool, diarrhea with fever, or diarrhea from pathogens other than *E. coli.*

- Stop drug if diarrhea worsens or lasts longer than 24 to 48 hours. The patient may need a different antibiotic.
- Patient who has diarrhea after antibiotic therapy may have pseudomembranous colitis, which may range from mild to life-threatening.

Patient teaching

- Explain that drug may be taken with or without food.
- Tell patient to take all of the prescribed drug, even if he feels better before the drug is finished.
- Advise patient to notify his prescriber if diarrhea worsens or lasts longer than 1 or 2 days after starting treatment. A different treatment may be needed.
- Tell patient to call the prescriber if he develops a fever or has blood in his stool.
- Explain that this drug is only for treating diarrhea caused by contaminated foods or beverages while traveling and not for any other type of infection.
- Caution patient not to share this drug with others.

Evaluation

- Patient's diarrhea resolves with drug therapy.
- Patient maintains adequate hydration.
- Patient and family state understanding of drug therapy.

riluzole

(RIGH-loo-zohl)
Rilutek

Pharmacologic class: benzothiazole, glutamate antagonist
Therapeutic class: neuroprotector
Pregnancy risk category: C

Indications and dosages

▶ **Amyotrophic lateral sclerosis (ALS).**
Adults: 50 mg P.O. q 12 hours on empty stomach.

Contraindications and cautions

- Contraindicated in patients hypersensitive to the drug or any of its components.
- Use cautiously in patients with hepatic or renal dysfunction. Also use cautiously in women and Japanese patients (who may have a lower metabolic capacity to eliminate riluzole compared with men and white patients, respectively).

Lifespan: In pregnant patients, use only if benefits outweigh risks; risks specific to fetus aren't known. In breast-feeding women, drug isn't recommended. In children, safety and effectiveness haven't been established. In elderly patients, use cautiously.

Adverse reactions

CNS: aggravation reaction, *asthenia,* circumoral paresthesia, depression, dizziness, headache, hypertonia, insomnia, malaise, somnolence, vertigo.
CV: hypertension, orthostatic hypotension, palpitations, peripheral edema, tachycardia.
EENT: rhinitis, sinusitis.
GI: abdominal pain, anorexia, dry mouth, dyspepsia, diarrhea, flatulence, *nausea,* oral candidiasis, stomatitis, vomiting.
GU: dysuria, UTI.
Hematologic: ***neutropenia.***
Metabolic: weight loss.
Musculoskeletal: arthralgia, back pain.
Respiratory: *decreased lung function,* increased cough.
Skin: alopecia, eczema, exfoliative dermatitis, pruritus.
Other: phlebitis, tooth disorder.

Interactions

Drug-drug. *Inducers of CYP1A2 (omeprazole, rifampicin):* May increase riluzole elimination. Monitor patient for loss of therapeutic effect.
Potential inhibitors of CYP1A2 (amitriptyline, phenacetin, quinolones, theophylline): May decrease riluzole elimination. Monitor patient closely for toxicity.
Drug-food. *Any food:* May decrease drug bioavailability. Give 1 hour before or 2 hours after meals.
Caffeine: May decrease riluzole elimination. Monitor patient for adverse reactions.
Charbroiled foods: May increase riluzole elimination. Discourage patient from eating these foods while on drug therapy.
Drug-lifestyle. *Alcohol use:* May increase risk of hepatotoxicity. Discourage using together.
Smoking: May increase riluzole elimination. Urge patient to stop smoking.

Effects on lab test results

- May increase AST, ALT, bilirubin, and GGT levels.
- May decrease neutrophil count.

Pharmacokinetics

Absorption: Well absorbed from GI tract, with average absolute oral bioavailability of about 60%. High-fat meal decreases absorption.
Distribution: 96% protein-bound.
Metabolism: Extensive in liver.
Excretion: Mainly in urine, with small amount in feces. *Half-life:* 12 hours with repeated doses.

Route	Onset	Peak	Duration
P.O.	Unknown	Unknown	Unknown

Action

Chemical effect: Unknown.
Therapeutic effect: Improves signs and symptoms of ALS.

Available forms

Tablets: 50 mg

NURSING PROCESS

R

Assessment

- Obtain history of patient's ALS.
- Obtain liver and renal function studies and CBC before and during therapy.
- Monitor patient carefully because rare but severe cases of neutropenia have occurred.
- Assess patient's and family's knowledge of drug therapy.

Nursing diagnoses

- Impaired physical mobility related to ALS
- Risk for deficient fluid volume related to adverse GI reactions
- Deficient knowledge related to drug therapy

Planning and implementation

- If baseline liver function test results (especially bilirubin level) rise, don't use drug. Drug may increase aminotransferase level. If level exceeds 10 times upper limit of normal, or if jaundice develops, notify prescriber.
- Give drug at least 1 hour before or 2 hours after a meal.

Patient teaching

- Tell patient to take drug at same time each day. If he misses a dose, instruct him not to double the dose but to take the next dose as scheduled.
- Instruct patient to report febrile illness; check his WBC count.
- Warn patient to avoid hazardous activities until drug's CNS effects are known.
- Advise patient to limit alcohol intake during therapy.
- Tell patient to store drug at room temperature, protected from bright light and out of children's reach.

Evaluation

- Patient responds well to therapy.
- Patient maintains adequate hydration.
- Patient and family state understanding of drug therapy.

risedronate sodium

(ri-SEH-droe-nate SOE-dee-um)

Actonel

Pharmacologic class: bisphosphonate
Therapeutic class: antiresorptive
Pregnancy risk category: C

Indications and dosages

▶ **To prevent and treat postmenopausal osteoporosis.** *Adults:* 5-mg tablet P.O. once daily, or 35-mg tablet once weekly. Give at least 30 minutes before first food or drink (except water) of the day.

▶ **Glucocorticoid-induced osteoporosis in patients who are either starting or continuing glucocorticoid therapy at 7.5 mg or more of prednisone or equivalent daily.** *Adults:* 5 mg P.O. daily.

▶ **Paget disease.** *Adults:* 30 mg P.O. daily for 2 months. If relapse occurs or alkaline phosphatase level doesn't normalize, give same dose for 2 months or longer after first course.

▶ **To increase bone mass in men with osteoporosis.** *Adults:* 35-mg tablet P.O. once weekly. Give at least 30 minutes before first food or drink (except water) of the day.

Contraindications and cautions

- Contraindicated in patients hypersensitive to the drug or any of its components, and in patients who are hypocalcemic or unable to stand or sit upright for 30 minutes after administration.
- Drug isn't recommended for patients with severe renal impairment (creatinine clearance below 30 ml/minute).
- Use cautiously in patients with upper GI disorders such as dysphagia, esophagitis, and esophageal or gastric ulcers.

Lifespan: In pregnant women, use only when benefits outweigh risks to the fetus. In breast-feeding women, use cautiously. It isn't known if drug appears in breast milk. In children, safety and effectiveness of drug haven't been established.

Adverse reactions

CNS: anxiety, asthenia, depression, dizziness, *headache,* hypertonia, insomnia, neuralgia, *pain,* paresthesia, vertigo.
CV: chest pain, CV disorder, *hypertension,* peripheral edema.
EENT: amblyopia, cataract, conjunctivitis, pharyngitis, otitis media, rhinitis, sinusitis, tinnitus.
GI: abdominal pain, constipation, diarrhea, esophageal irritation and ulceration, flatulence, gastritis, nausea, rectal disorder.
GU: cystitis, *UTI.*
Hematologic: anemia.
Musculoskeletal: *arthralgia, back pain,* bone pain, bursitis, leg cramps, myalgia, neck pain, tendon disorder.
Respiratory: bronchitis, dyspnea, pneumonia.
Skin: ***carcinoma,*** ecchymosis, pruritus, *rash.*
Other: *infection,* tooth disorder.

Interactions

Drug-drug. *Calcium supplements, antacids that contain calcium, magnesium, or aluminum:* May interfere with risedronate absorption. Advise patient to separate administration times.

Drug-food. *Any food:* May interfere with risedronate absorption. Advise patient to take drug at least 30 minutes before first food or drink of the day (other than water).

Effects on lab test results

• May decrease calcium, phosphorus, and hemoglobin levels and hematocrit.

Pharmacokinetics

Absorption: Absorbed via the GI tract. Steady state occurs in 57 days. Mean absolute oral bioavailability of 30-mg tablet is 0.63%. Because food alters absorption, give drug at least 30 minutes before breakfast.
Distribution: About 60% distributed to bone. About 24% protein-bound.
Metabolism: No evidence of systemic metabolism.
Excretion: About 50% in urine within 24 hours. Unabsorbed drug is eliminated unchanged in feces. *Half-life:* 20 days.

Route	Onset	Peak	Duration
P.O.	Unknown	1 hr	Unknown

Action

Chemical effect: Reverses the loss of bone mineral density by reducing bone turnover and bone resorption by inhibiting osteoclasts. In patients with Paget disease, drug causes bone turnover to return to normal.
Therapeutic effect: Reverses the loss of bone mineral density.

Available forms

Tablets: 5 mg, 30 mg, 35 mg

NURSING PROCESS

Assessment

• Assess underlying condition before starting therapy and regularly thereafter to monitor drug's effectiveness.
• Evaluate renal function before beginning therapy. Drug isn't recommended for patients with creatinine clearance below 30 ml/minute.
• Assess patient for the following risk factors for the development of osteoporosis: family history, previous fracture, smoking, a decrease in bone mineral density below the premenopausal mean, a thin body frame, white or Asian race, and early menopause.
• Assess patient's and family's knowledge of drug therapy.

Nursing diagnoses

• Risk for injury related to decreased bone mass
• Ineffective health maintenance related to underlying disease
• Deficient knowledge related to risedronate sodium therapy

Planning and implementation

ALERT: Follow dosage instructions carefully because benefits of the drug may be compromised by failure to take it according to instructions. Give drug at least 30 minutes before patient's first food or drink (other than water) of the day.
• Give drug with 6 to 8 oz plain water to facilitate delivery to the stomach. Don't allow patient to lie down for 30 minutes after taking drug.
ALERT: Bisphosphonates have been linked to such GI disorders as dysphagia, esophagitis, and esophageal or gastric ulcers. Monitor patient for symptoms of esophageal disease (such as dysphagia, retrosternal pain, or severe persistent or worsening heartburn).
• If patient's dietary intake of calcium and vitamin D is inadequate, give supplements. However, because calcium supplements and drugs containing calcium, aluminum, or magnesium may interfere with absorption, separate doses.
• Store drug at 68° to 77° F (20° to 25° C).
• Bisphosphonates can interfere with bone-imaging agents.

Patient teaching

• Explain that risedronate is used to replace bone lost as a result of certain disease processes.
• Instruct patient to adhere to dosage instructions.
• Tell patient to take drug at least 30 minutes before the first food or drink (other than water) of the day. Tell patient to take drug with 6 to 8 oz of water while sitting or standing. Warn against lying down for 30 minutes after taking drug.
• Advise patient not to chew or suck the tablet because doing so could cause mouth irritation.
• Advise patient to notify the prescriber immediately if symptoms of esophageal disease (difficulty or pain when swallowing, retrosternal pain, or severe heartburn) develop.

• Advise patient to take calcium and vitamin D if dietary intake is inadequate, but to take them at a different time than risedronate.
• Advise patient to stop smoking and drinking alcohol, as appropriate. Also, instruct patient to perform weight-bearing exercise.
• Tell patient to store drug in a cool (room temperature), dry place and away from children.
• Urge patient to read the patient information guide before starting therapy.
• Tell patient if he misses a dose of the 35-mg tablet, he should take 1 tablet on the morning after he remembers and return to taking 1 tablet once a week, as originally scheduled on his chosen day. Patients shouldn't take 2 tablets on the same day.

Evaluation

• Patient sustains no injury related to decreased bone mass.
• Patient shows improvement in underlying condition.
• Patient and family state understanding of drug therapy.

risperidone

(ris-PER-ih-dohn)

Risperdal, Risperdal Consta, Risperdal M-Tab

Pharmacologic class: benzisoxazole derivative
Therapeutic class: antipsychotic
Pregnancy risk category: C

Indications and dosages

▶ **Short-term therapy for schizophrenia.** *Adults:* Initially, 1 mg P.O. b.i.d. Increase in increments of 1 mg b.i.d. on days 2 and 3 to a target dosage of 3 mg b.i.d. Or, 1 mg P.O. on day 1, increase to 2 mg once daily on day 2, and 4 mg once daily on day 3. Wait at least 1 week before adjusting dosage further. Adjust doses by 1 to 2 mg. Maximum, 8 mg daily. Once tolerance to P.O. formulation has been established, patient may be switched to I.M. formulation, if appropriate. Give 25 mg by deep I.M. gluteal injection q 2 weeks; alternating injections between the two buttocks. Adjust dose no sooner than q 4 weeks. Maximum, 50 mg I.M. q 2 weeks. Continue oral antipsychotic for 3 weeks after first I.M. injection. Then stop oral therapy.

▶ **Delaying relapse in long-term therapy for schizophrenia.** *Adults:* Initially, 1 mg P.O. on day 1, increase to 2 mg once daily on day 2, and 4 mg once daily on day 3. Dosage range, 2 to 8 mg daily.

▶ **Monotherapy or combination therapy with lithium or valproate for short-term (3-week) treatment of acute manic or mixed episodes in bipolar I disorder.** *Adults:* 2 to 3 mg P.O. once daily. Adjust dose by 1 mg daily. Dosage range, 1 to 6 mg daily.

Adjust-a-dose: For elderly or debilitated patients, hypotensive patients, or patients with severe renal or hepatic impairment, initially give 0.5 mg P.O. b.i.d. Increase dosage in increments of 0.5 mg b.i.d. Increase dosages beyond 1.5 mg b.i.d. at intervals of at least 1 week. Subsequent switches to once-daily doses may be made after patient has received a twice-daily regimen for 2 or 3 days at the target dose.

▶ **Irritability in autistic disorder, including aggression, self-injury, mood swings, and temper tantrums.** *Adolescents and children age 5 and older who weigh 20 kg (44 lb) or more:* Initially, 0.5 mg P.O. once daily or divided b.i.d. After 4 days, increase to 1 mg. If needed, may increase in 0.5-mg increments at intervals of at least 2 weeks.
Children age 5 and older who weigh less than 20 kg: Initially, 0.25 mg P.O. once daily or divided b.i.d. After 4 days, increase to 0.5 mg. If needed, may increase in 0.25-mg increments at intervals of at least 2 weeks. Increase cautiously in children who weigh less than 15 kg (33 lb).

Contraindications and cautions

• Contraindicated in patients hypersensitive to the drug or any of its components.
• Use cautiously in patients with prolonged QT interval, CV disease, cerebrovascular disease, dehydration, hypovolemia, history of seizures, exposure to extreme heat, or conditions that could affect metabolism or hemodynamic responses. Also use cautiously in patients at risk for aspiration pneumonia.
• Use I.M. injection cautiously in those with hepatic or renal impairment. Stabilize patient on oral drug before switching to I.M. injection.

Lifespan: In pregnant women, use cautiously. In breast-feeding women, drug is contraindicated. In elderly patients with dementia, drug is contraindicated.

Adverse reactions

CNS: abnormal thinking and dreaming, aggressiveness, agitation, akathisia, anxiety, depression, dizziness, extrapyramidal reactions, fatigue, fever, hallucination, headache, hypoesthesia, insomnia, nervousness (I.M.), ***neuroleptic malignant syndrome,*** pain, parkinsonism, somnolence, ***suicide attempt,*** tardive dyskinesia, ***transient ischemic attack or stroke in elderly patients with dementia,*** tremor.
CV: chest pain, hypertension (I.M.), orthostatic hypotension, peripheral edema, ***prolonged QT interval,*** syncope, tachycardia.
EENT: abnormal vision; ear disorder (I.M.), pharyngitis, *rhinitis,* sinusitis.
GI: *abdominal pain, anorexia, constipation,* diarrhea (I.M.), dry mouth, *dyspepsia,* increased saliva, *nausea,* tooth ache, tooth disorder, *vomiting.*
Hematologic: anemia.
Metabolic: ***hyperglycemia;*** weight decrease (I.M.), *weight gain.*
Musculoskeletal: arthralgia, back pain; leg pain, myalgia (I.M.).
Respiratory: coughing, upper respiratory infection.
Skin: acne, dry skin, injection site pain (I.M.), photosensitivity, rash.

Interactions

Drug-drug. *Antihypertensives:* May enhance hypotensive effects. Monitor blood pressure.
Carbamazepine: May increase risperidone clearance, leading to decreased effectiveness. Monitor patient closely.
Clozapine: May decrease risperidone clearance, increasing toxicity. Monitor patient closely.
CNS depressants: May cause additive CNS depression. Monitor patient closely.
Dopamine agonists, levodopa: May antagonize the effects of these drugs. Monitor patient closely.
Fluoxetine, paroxetine: May increase risperidone level, increasing the risk of adverse reactions, including serotonin syndrome. Monitor patient closely and adjust risperidone dose as needed.
Drug-lifestyle. *Alcohol use:* May cause additive CNS depression. Discourage using together.
Sun exposure: May increase photosensitivity reactions. Discourage prolonged or unprotected sun exposure.

Effects on lab test results

• May increase glucose and prolactin levels. May decrease hemoglobin level and hematocrit.

Pharmacokinetics

Absorption: Well absorbed; absolute oral bioavailability is 70%. Slowly absorbed via I.M. injection.
Distribution: Risperidone about 90% protein-bound; major active metabolite about 77% protein-bound.
Metabolism: Extensive in liver.
Excretion: Metabolite in urine. *Half-life:* 3 to 20 hours.

Route	Onset	Peak	Duration
P.O.	Unknown	1 hr	Unknown
I.M.	3 wk	4–6 wk	7 wk

Action

Chemical effect: Blocks dopamine and serotonin receptors as well as $alpha_1$, $alpha_2$, and H_1 receptors in the CNS.
Therapeutic effect: Relieves signs and symptoms of psychosis.

Available forms

Oral solution: 1 mg/ml
Powder for I.M. injection: 25 mg, 37.5 mg, 50 mg
Tablets: 0.25 mg, 0.5 mg, 1 mg, 2 mg, 3 mg, 4 mg
Tablets (orally disintegrating): 0.5 mg, 1 mg, 2 mg, 3 mg, 4 mg

NURSING PROCESS

Assessment

• Assess patient's psychosis before starting therapy and regularly thereafter to monitor drug's effectiveness.
• Assess blood pressure before starting therapy, and monitor regularly. Watch for orthostatic hypotension, especially during dose adjustment.
• Monitor CBC, liver functions tests, ECG, serum prolactin, and routine chemistry during prolonged administration.
• Be alert for adverse reactions and drug interactions.

ALERT: Watch for tardive dyskinesia. It may occur after prolonged use; it may not appear until months or years later and may disappear spontaneously or persist for life despite stopping the drug.
- Assess patient's and family's knowledge of drug therapy.

Nursing diagnoses
- Disturbed thought processes related to presence of psychosis
- Risk for injury related to drug-induced adverse CNS reactions
- Deficient knowledge related to drug therapy

Planning and implementation
ALERT: Fatal hyperglycemia may occur in a patient taking atypical antipsychotics. Monitor patient with diabetes regularly. For patients with risk factors for diabetes, perform fasting glucose testing at baseline and periodically. Monitor all patients for symptoms of hyperglycemia, including excessive thirst, hunger, frequent urinating, and weakness; if symptoms develop, perform fasting glucose testing. Hyperglycemia may resolve once therapy is stopped.
- When restarting therapy for patient who has been off drug, follow 3-day dose initiation schedule.
- When switching patient to drug from another antipsychotic, stop other drug immediately when risperidone therapy starts.
- When switching from a depot antipsychotic to oral risperidone, start risperidone at the time of the next scheduled injection.
- Orally disintegrating tablets contain phenylalanine; 3-mg tablet contains 0.63 mg phenylalanine and 4-mg tablet contains 0.84 mg phenylalanine.
- Give oral antipsychotic for the first 3 weeks of I.M. injection therapy because of injection's prolonged onset of action. Then stop oral therapy.
- To reconstitute I.M. injection, remove dose pack from the refrigerator and allow it to reach room temperature. Inject premeasured diluent into vial and shake vigorously for at least 10 seconds. Suspension will appear uniform, thick, and milky; particles will be visible, but no dry particles remain. Manufacturer recommends that drug be used immediately; suspension must be used within 6 hours of reconstitution. If more than 2 minutes pass before injection, shake vigorously again. See manufacturer's package insert for more detailed instructions.
- Before reconstitution, store I.M. injection kit in refrigerator and protect from light. Drug can be stored at temperatures less than 77° F (25° C) for no more than 7 days before administration.
- Risperidone oral solution may be mixed with water, coffee, orange juice, or low-fat milk. It isn't compatible with cola or tea.

ALERT: Fatal cerebrovascular adverse events, such as stroke or transient ischemic attacks, may occur in elderly patients with dementia.

Patient teaching
- Warn patient to rise slowly, avoid hot showers, and use extra caution during first few days of therapy to avoid fainting.
- Warn patient to avoid activities that require alertness until the drug's CNS effects are known. Drowsiness and dizziness usually subside after a few days.
- Tell patient not to drink alcohol and to avoid prolonged exposure to sunlight during therapy.
- Tell patient to use sunblock and to wear protective clothing in sunlight.
- Advise patient to use caution in hot weather to prevent heatstroke; drug may affect the body's ability to regulate temperature.
- Tell woman to notify prescriber if she is or plans to become pregnant during therapy and for at least 12 weeks after last I.M. injection.
- Warn patient not to breast-feed during treatment and for at least 12 weeks after last I.M. injection.
- Inform patient that drug may be taken with or without food.
- Tell patient not to remove orally disintegrating tablets from blister pack until just before use. Explain that he should peel the foil apart to expose the tablet rather than pushing the tablet through the foil. Then, tell him to dissolve the tablet on his tongue.
- Tell patient not to split or chew orally disintegrating tablets.

Evaluation
- Patient behavior and communication indicate improved thought processes.
- Patient sustains no injury from drug-induced adverse CNS reactions.
- Patient and family state understanding of drug therapy.

ritonavir

(rih-TOH-nuh-veer)

Norvir

Pharmacologic class: protease inhibitor
Therapeutic class: antiretroviral
Pregnancy risk category: B

Indications and dosages

▶ **HIV infection.** *Adults:* 600 mg P.O. b.i.d. with meals. If adverse events occur, may give 300 mg b.i.d.; then increase at 2- to 3-day intervals by 100 mg b.i.d. If given with saquinavir, reduce saquinavir to 400 mg P.O. b.i.d. and ritonavir to 400 or 600 mg P.O. b.i.d.
Children age 1 month and older: Initially, 250 mg/m^2 P.O. b.i.d. Increase by 50 mg/m^2 b.i.d. at 2- to 3-day intervals to target dose of 400 mg/m^2 b.i.d.

Contraindications and cautions

• Contraindicated in patients hypersensitive to the drug or any of its components, and in those who are taking dihydroergotamine or ergotamine drugs. Also contraindicated with alfuzosin, amiodarone, cisapride, flecainide, propafenone, quinidine, ergot derivatives, lovastatin, simvastatin, midazolam, triazolam, and voriconazole.
Lifespan: Use in pregnancy only if benefits outweigh risks to fetus. If used during pregnancy, contact the antiretroviral pregnancy registry at 800-258-4263 or www.APRegistry.com. In breast-feeding women, use cautiously. It isn't known whether drug appears in breast milk.

Adverse reactions

CNS: anxiety, *asthenia,* circumoral paresthesia, confusion, depression, dizziness, ***generalized tonic-clonic seizure,*** fever, headache, insomnia, malaise, pain, paresthesia, peripheral paresthesia, somnolence, thinking abnormality.
CV: syncope, vasodilation.
EENT: pharyngitis.
GI: abdominal pain, anorexia, constipation, diarrhea, dyspepsia, flatulence, *nausea,* ***pancreatitis, pseudomembranous colitis,*** taste perversion, vomiting.
Hematologic: ***leukopenia, thrombocytopenia.***
Hepatic: ***hepatitis.***
Metabolic: ***diabetes mellitus,*** weight loss.
Musculoskeletal: arthralgia, myalgia.
Skin: rash, sweating.
Other: fat redistribution/accumulation, ***hypersensitivity reactions.***

Interactions

Drug-drug. *Alfuzosin, amiodarone, cisapride, ergot derivatives, flecainide, midazolam, propafenone, quinidine, triazolam, voriconazole:* May cause serious and life-threatening adverse reactions. Use together is contraindicated.
Atovaquone, divalproex, lamotrigine, phenytoin, warfarin: May decrease levels of these drugs. Use together cautiously and monitor drug levels closely, if appropriate.
Beta blockers, disopyramide, fluoxetine, mexiletine, nefazodone: May increase levels of these drugs, causing cardiac and neurologic events. Use together with caution.
Bupropion, buspirone, carbamazepine, calcium channel blockers, clonazepam, clorazepate, cyclosporine, dexamethasone, diazepam, dronabinol, estazolam, ethosuximide, flurazepam, lidocaine, methamphetamine, metoprolol, perphenazine, prednisone, propoxyphene, quinine, risperidone, SSRIs, tacrolimus, tricyclic antidepressants, thioridazine, timolol, tramadol, zolpidem: May increase levels of these drugs. Use cautiously together and consider decreasing the dosage of these drugs by almost 50%.
Clarithromycin: May increase clarithromycin level. Patients with impaired renal function require 50% reduction in clarithromycin if creatinine clearance is 30 to 60 ml/minute, and a 75% reduction if it's below 30 ml/minute.
Delavirdine: Increases ritonavir level. Use together cautiously. Dosage recommendations not established for combined use.
Didanosine: May decrease didanosine absorption. Separate doses by 2½ hours.
Disulfiram, metronidazole: May increase risk of disulfiram-like reactions since ritonavir formulations contain alcohol. Monitor patient.
Ethinyl estradiol: May decrease ethinyl estradiol level. Use a different or another method of birth control.
Fluticasone: May increase fluticasone exposure leading to significantly decreased serum cortisol concentrations, which may lead to systemic corticosteroid effects (including Cushing syndrome). Don't use together, if possible.
HMG-CoA reductase inhibitors: May cause a large increase in statin level, causing myopathy. Avoid use with lovastatin and simvastatin. Use

R

cautiously with atorvastatin. Consider using fluvastatin or pravastatin.
Indinavir: May increase indinavir level. Use together cautiously.
Itraconazole, ketoconazole: May increase levels of these drugs. Don't exceed 200 mg per day of these drugs.
Meperidine: May decrease level of meperidine and its metabolite. Dosage increase and long-term use of meperidine with ritonavir not recommended because of CNS effects. Use cautiously together.
Methadone: May decrease methadone level. Consider increasing methadone dosage.
Phosphodiesterase type 5 (PDE 5) inhibitors (sildenafil, tadalafil, vardenafil): May increase level of PDE 5 inhibitor causing potentially fatal hypotension, syncope, visual changes, or prolonged erection. Use together cautiously and with increased monitoring for adverse reactions. Tell patient not to exceed 25 mg of sildenafil in a 48-hour period, 10 mg of tadalafil in a 72-hour period, or 2.5 mg of vardenafil in a 72-hour period.
Rifabutin: May increase rifabutin level. Monitor patient and reduce rifabutin daily dosage by at least 75% of usual dose.
Rifampin: May decrease ritonavir level. Consider using rifabutin in place of rifampin.
Saquinavir: May increase saquinavir level. Adjust dose by giving 400 mg saquinavir b.i.d. and 400 mg ritonavir b.i.d.
Theophylline: May decrease theophylline level. Increase dose based on level.
Trazodone: May increase trazodone level causing nausea, dizziness, hypotension and syncope. Avoid use together. If unavoidable, use cautiously with a lower dose of trazodone.
Drug-herb. *St. John's wort:* May substantially reduce drug level. Discourage use together.
Drug-food. *Any food:* May increase drug absorption. Give drug with food.
Drug-lifestyle. *Smoking:* May decrease level of ritonavir. Discourage smoking.

Effects on lab test results

- May increase ALT, AST, GGT, glucose, triglyceride, lipid, CPK, and uric acid levels. May decrease hemoglobin level and hematocrit.
- May decrease WBC, RBC, platelet, and neutrophil counts.

Pharmacokinetics

Absorption: Enhanced by food.
Distribution: Absolute bioavailability unknown. 98% to 100% albumin-bound.
Metabolism: In liver and kidneys.
Excretion: In urine and feces. *Half-life:* Unknown.

Route	Onset	Peak	Duration
P.O.	Unknown	2–4 hr	Unknown

Action

Chemical effect: HIV protease inhibitor with activity against HIV-1 and HIV-2 proteases; binds to protease-active site and inhibits enzyme activity.
Therapeutic effect: Prevents cleavage of viral polyproteins, resulting in formation of immature noninfectious viral particles.

Available forms

Capsules: 100 mg
Oral solution: 80 mg/ml

NURSING PROCESS

Assessment

- Use cautiously in patients with hepatic insufficiency.
- Assess patient's and family's knowledge of drug therapy.

Nursing diagnoses

- Risk for infection related to presence of virus
- Deficient knowledge related to drug therapy

Planning and implementation

ALERT: Don't confuse Norvir with Norvasc. Don't confuse ritonavir with Retrovir.

Patient teaching

- Inform patient that drug doesn't reduce the risk of HIV transmission or cure HIV infection or the illnesses it may cause.
- Tell patient that the taste of oral solution may be improved by mixing with flavored milk within 1 hour of dose.
- Tell patient to take drug with meal.
- If patient misses a dose, instruct him to take next dose at once. He shouldn't take double doses.
- Advise patient to report use of other drugs, including OTC drugs.

• Advise patient taking PDE 5 inhibitors about an increased risk of adverse events, including hypotension, visual changes, and prolonged erection. He should promptly report any symptoms to his prescriber. Tell patient not to exceed 25 mg of sildenafil in a 48-hour period, 10 mg of tadalafil in a 72-hour period, or 2.5 mg of vardenafil in a 72-hour period.
• To prevent transmission of disease, HIV-positive women shouldn't breast-feed.

☑ Evaluation

• Patient's infection is controlled.
• Patient and family state understanding of drug therapy.

rivastigmine tartrate

(riv-uh-STIG-meen TAR-trayt)
Exelon

Pharmacologic class: cholinesterase inhibitor
Therapeutic class: Alzheimer disease drug
Pregnancy risk category: B

Indications and dosages

▶ **Mild to moderate dementia of the Alzheimer type.** *Adults:* Initially, 1.5 mg P.O. b.i.d. with food. If tolerated, may be increased to 3 mg b.i.d. after 2 weeks. Further increases to 4.5 mg b.i.d. and 6 mg b.i.d. may be given as tolerated after 2 weeks on the previous dose. Effective dosage range is 6 to 12 mg daily, with maximum recommended dosage of 12 mg daily.
▶ **Mild to moderate dementia in Parkinson disease.** *Adults:* Initially, 1.5 mg P.O. b.i.d. May increase, as tolerated, to 3 mg b.i.d., then to 4.5 mg b.i.d, and finally to 6 mg b.i.d. after at least 4 weeks at each dose.

Contraindications and cautions

• Contraindicated in patients hypersensitive to the drug, any of its components, or other carbamate derivatives.
• Use cautiously in patients who take NSAIDs and who have a history of ulcers or GI bleeding and in patients with sick sinus syndrome or other supraventricular cardiac conditions, asthma or obstructive pulmonary disease, or seizures.
Lifespan: Use in pregnancy if benefits outweigh risks to the fetus. In breast-feeding women, use cautiously because it isn't known if drug appears in breast milk.

Adverse reactions

CNS: aggressive reaction, agitation, anxiety, asthenia, confusion, delusion, depression, *dizziness,* fatigue, hallucination, *headache,* insomnia, malaise, nervousness, pain, paranoid reaction, somnolence, syncope, tremor, vertigo.
CV: chest pain, hypertension, peripheral edema.
EENT: pharyngitis, rhinitis.
GI: *abdominal pain, anorexia,* constipation, *diarrhea,* dyspepsia, eructation, flatulence, GI bleeding, *nausea, vomiting.*
GU: urinary incontinence, urinary obstruction, UTI.
Metabolic: weight loss.
Musculoskeletal: arthralgia, back pain, bone fracture.
Respiratory: bronchitis, cough, upper respiratory tract infection.
Skin: increased sweating, rash.
Other: *accidental trauma,* flulike symptoms.

Interactions

Drug-drug. *Anticholinergics:* May interfere with anticholinergic activity. Monitor patient closely.
Bethanechol, succinylcholine, and other neuromuscular blockers or cholinergic antagonists: May have synergistic effect. Monitor patient closely.
Drug-lifestyle. *Smoking:* May increase rivastigmine clearance. Monitor patient closely.

Effects on lab test results

None reported.

Pharmacokinetics

Absorption: Rapid, with level peaking in about 1 hour. Although drug is given with food, it delays peak level by about 1½ hours. Absolute bioavailability is 36%.
Distribution: Wide, throughout body; drug crosses the blood-brain barrier. About 40% protein-bound.
Metabolism: Rapid and extensive.
Excretion: Mainly through the kidneys. *Half-life:* About 1½ hours in patients with normal renal function.

Route	Onset	Peak	Duration
P.O.	Unknown	1 hr	12 hr

R

Action

Chemical effect: Thought to increase acetylcholine level by reversibly inhibiting its hydrolysis by cholinesterase. Acetylcholine is probably the primary neurotransmitter that is depleted in Alzheimer disease.
Therapeutic effect: Improves cognitive function.

Available forms

Capsules: 1.5 mg, 3 mg, 4.5 mg, 6 mg
Solution: 2 mg/ml

NURSING PROCESS

Assessment

- Assess underlying condition before starting therapy and regularly thereafter to monitor drug's effectiveness.
- Perform complete health history, and carefully monitor for adverse effects any patient with a history of GI bleeding, NSAID use, arrhythmias, seizures, or pulmonary conditions.
- Assess patient's and family's knowledge of drug therapy.

Nursing diagnoses

- Acute or chronic confusion related to underlying disease
- Risk for imbalanced fluid volume related to drug-induced GI effects
- Deficient knowledge related to rivastigmine tartrate therapy

Planning and implementation

- Expect significant GI adverse effects, such as nausea, vomiting, anorexia, and weight loss. They're less common during maintenance doses.

ALERT: Severe vomiting may occur in patient who resumes therapy after an interruption. If therapy is interrupted for more than several days, resume therapy at 1.5 mg b.i.d. to maintenance level.

- Dramatic memory improvement is unlikely. As disease progresses, the benefits of rivastigmine may decline.
- Monitor patient for symptoms of active or occult GI bleeding.
- Monitor patient for severe nausea, vomiting, and diarrhea, which may lead to dehydration and weight loss.

Patient teaching

- Advise patient to report any episodes of nausea, vomiting, or diarrhea.
- Inform patient and caregiver that memory improvement may be subtle and that a more likely result of therapy is a slower decline in memory loss.
- Tell patient to take rivastigmine with food in the morning and evening.
- Instruct patient to consult prescriber before taking OTC drugs.

Evaluation

- Patient's cognition improves and he experiences less confusion.
- Patient and family state that adverse GI effects haven't occurred or have been managed effectively.
- Patient and family state understanding of drug therapy.

rizatriptan benzoate

(rih-zah-TRIP-tin BEN-zoh-ayt)
Maxalt, Maxalt-MLT

Pharmacologic class: selective 5-hydroxytryptamine ($5\text{-}HT_1$) receptor agonist
Therapeutic class: antimigraine drug
Pregnancy risk category: C

Indications and dosages

▶ **Acute migraine headaches with or without aura.** *Adults:* Initially, 5 to 10 mg P.O. If first dose is ineffective, another dose can be given at least 2 hours after first dose. Maximum, 30 mg daily. For patients taking propranolol, 5 mg P.O., up to maximum of three doses (15 mg total) in 24 hours.

Contraindications and cautions

- Contraindicated in patients hypersensitive to the drug or any of its components and in the management of hemiplegic or basilar migraines. Also contraindicated in patients with ischemic heart disease (angina pectoris, history of MI, or documented silent ischemia) or those with evidence of ischemic heart disease, coronary artery vasospasm (Prinzmetal variant angina), or other significant underlying CV disease. Also contraindicated in patients with uncontrolled hypertension and within 24 hours of another $5\text{-}HT_1$

agonist or ergotamine-containing or ergot-type drug, such as dihydroergotamine or methysergide.
• Don't use within 14 days of an MAO inhibitor.
• Use cautiously in patients with hepatic or renal impairment. Also use cautiously in patients with risk factors for coronary artery disease (hypertension, hypercholesterolemia, smoking, obesity, diabetes, strong family history of coronary artery disease, women with surgical or physiologic menopause, or men older than age 40), unless a cardiac evaluation provides evidence that patient is free from cardiac disease.
Lifespan: Use in pregnancy only if benefits clearly outweigh risks to the fetus. In breast-feeding women, don't use drug because the effects on infants are unknown. In children, safety and effectiveness haven't been established.

Adverse reactions

CNS: asthenia, decreased mental acuity, dizziness, euphoria, fatigue, headache, hypesthesia, pain, paresthesia, somnolence, tremor.
CV: chest pain, ***coronary artery vasospasm,*** flushing, pressure or heaviness, palpitations, ***MI, transient myocardial ischemia, ventricular fibrillation, ventricular tachycardia.***
EENT: neck, throat, and jaw heaviness, pain, or pressure.
GI: diarrhea, dry mouth, nausea, vomiting.
Respiratory: dyspnea.
Other: hot flushes, warm or cold sensations.

Interactions

Drug-drug. *Ergot-containing or ergot-type drugs (dihydroergotamine, methysergide), other 5-HT$_1$ agonists:* May prolong vasospastic reactions. Don't use within 24 hours of rizatriptan.
MAO inhibitors: May increase rizatriptan level. Don't use together. Allow at least 14 days between stopping an MAO inhibitor and giving rizatriptan.
Propranolol: May increase rizatriptan level. Reduce rizatriptan dose to 5 mg.
SSRIs: May cause weakness, hyperreflexia, and incoordination. Monitor patient.

Effects on lab test results

None reported.

Pharmacokinetics

Absorption: Complete, with an absolute bioavailability of 45%.
Distribution: Wide. 14% protein-bound.
Metabolism: Mainly by oxidative deamination by MAO-A.
Excretion: 82% in urine. *Half-life:* 2 to 3 hours.

Route	Onset	Peak	Duration
P.O.	Unknown	1–1½ hr	Unknown

Action

Chemical effect: Believed to exert its effect by acting as an agonist at serotonin receptors on extracerebral intracranial blood vessels, which results in vasoconstriction of the affected vessels, inhibition of neuropeptide release, and reduction of pain transmission in the trigeminal pathways.
Therapeutic effect: Relieves migraine pain.

Available forms

Tablets: 5 mg, 10 mg
Tablets (disintegrating): 5 mg, 10 mg

NURSING PROCESS

Assessment

• Use drug only after a definite diagnosis of migraine is established.
• Assess patient for history of coronary artery disease, hypertension, arrhythmias, or presence of risk factors for coronary artery disease.
• Perform baseline and periodic CV evaluation in patients who develop risk factors for coronary artery disease.
• Monitor renal and liver function tests before starting therapy, and report abnormalities.
• Assess patient's and family's knowledge of drug therapy.

Nursing diagnoses

• Acute pain related to presence of migraine headache
• Risk for activity intolerance related to adverse drug reactions
• Deficient knowledge related to drug therapy

Planning and implementation

• Don't give to patient with hemiplegic migraine, basilar migraine, or cluster headaches.

ALERT: Don't give drug within 24 hours of a drug containing ergot or 5-HT_1 agonist or within 14 days of an MAO inhibitor.
- For patient with cardiac risk factors who has had a satisfactory cardiac evaluation, give first dose while monitoring ECG and have emergency equipment readily available.
- If patient develops palpitations or neck, throat, or jaw pain, pressure, or heaviness, stop giving the drug and notify prescriber.
- Safety of treating more than four headaches in a 30-day period, on average, hasn't been established.
- Drug contains phenylalanine.

Patient teaching
- Inform patient that drug doesn't prevent headache.
- For Maxalt-MLT, tell patient to remove blister pack from sachet and to remove drug from blister pack immediately before use. Tell him not to pop tablet out of blister pack but to carefully peel pack away with dry hands, place tablet on tongue, and let it dissolve. Tablet is then swallowed with saliva. No water is needed or recommended. Tell patient that dissolving tablet doesn't provide more rapid headache relief.
- Advise patient that if headache returns after first dose, a second dose may be taken with medical approval at least 2 hours after the first dose. Don't take more than 30 mg in a 24-hour period.
- Tell patient that food may delay onset of drug action.
- Advise patient to notify prescriber if pregnancy occurs or is suspected.

Evaluation
- Patient has relief from migraine headache.
- Patient maintains baseline activity level.
- Patient and family state understanding of drug therapy.

rocuronium bromide
(roh-kyoo-ROH-nee-um BROH-mighd)
Zemuron

Pharmacologic class: nondepolarizing neuromuscular blocker
Therapeutic class: skeletal muscle relaxant
Pregnancy risk category: C

Indications and dosages
▶ **Adjunct to general anesthesia, to facilitate endotracheal intubation, and to provide skeletal muscle relaxation during surgery or mechanical ventilation.** Dosage depends on anesthetic used, individual needs, and response. Dosages are representative and must be adjusted. *Adults and children age 3 months or older:* Initially, 0.6 mg/kg (adults, up to 1.2 mg/kg) I.V. bolus. In most patients, perform tracheal intubation within 2 minutes; muscle paralysis will last about 31 minutes. A maintenance dosage of 0.1 mg/kg will provide additional 12 minutes of muscle relaxation, 0.15 mg/kg will add 17 minutes, and 0.2 mg/kg will add 24 minutes to duration of effect.

I.V. administration
- Compatible solutions include D_5W, normal saline solution for injection, dextrose 5% in normal saline solution for injection, sterile water for injection, and lactated Ringer's injection.
- Give drug by rapid I.V. injection or continuous I.V. infusion. Infusion rates are highly individualized but range from 0.004 to 0.016 mg/kg/minute.
- Store reconstituted solution in refrigerator. Discard after 24 hours.

⊗ Incompatibilities
Alkaline solutions such as barbiturates; other I.V. drugs.

Contraindications and cautions
- Contraindicated in patients hypersensitive to the drug or any of its components.
- Use cautiously in patients with hepatic disease, severe obesity, bronchogenic carcinoma, electrolyte disturbances, neuromuscular disease, or altered circulation time caused by CV disease or edema.

Lifespan: In pregnant women, use cautiously. In breast-feeding women, safety and effectiveness haven't been established. In elderly patients, use cautiously because of slower circulation.

Adverse reactions
CV: abnormal ECG, ***arrhythmias,*** hypertension, tachycardia, transient hypotension.
GI: nausea, vomiting.
Respiratory: ***asthma,*** hiccups.
Skin: pruritus, rash.
Other: injection site edema.

Interactions

Drug-drug. *Amikacin, gentamicin, kanamycin neomycin, streptomycin, tobramycin:* May increase the effects, including prolonged respiratory depression, of nondepolarizing muscle relaxants. Use together only when needed. Dose of nondepolarizing muscle relaxant may need to be reduced.
Anticonvulsants, clindamycin, general anesthetics (such as enflurane, halothane, isoflurane), opioid analgesics, polymyxin antibiotics (colistin, polymyxin B sulfate), quinidine, succinylcholine, tetracyclines: May increase neuromuscular blockade, leading to increased skeletal muscle relaxation and increased effect. Use cautiously during surgical and postoperative periods.
Carbamazepine, phenytoin: May decrease the effects of rocuronium. May need to increase the dose of rocuronium.

Effects on lab test results

None reported.

Pharmacokinetics

Absorption: Given I.V.
Distribution: About 30% protein-bound.
Metabolism: Unknown, although hepatic clearance may be significant.
Excretion: About 33% in urine. *Half-life:* 1 to 2 hours in adults; ¾ to 1¼ hours in children.

Route	Onset	Peak	Duration
I.V.	≤ 1 min	≤ 2 min	Varies

Action

Chemical effect: Prevents acetylcholine from binding to receptors on motor end plate, thus blocking depolarization.
Therapeutic effect: Relaxes skeletal muscles.

Available forms

Injection: 10 mg/ml

NURSING PROCESS

Assessment

- Assess patient's condition before starting therapy and regularly thereafter to monitor drug's effectiveness.
- Be alert for adverse reactions and drug interactions.
- Monitor patients with liver disease. They may need higher doses to achieve adequate muscle relaxation and may exhibit prolonged effects from drug.
- Monitor respirations closely until patient is fully recovered from neuromuscular blockade, as evidenced by tests of muscle strength (hand grip, head lift, and ability to cough).
- Assess patient's and family's knowledge of drug therapy.

Nursing diagnoses

- Ineffective health maintenance related to underlying condition
- Ineffective breathing pattern related to drug's effect on respiratory muscles
- Deficient knowledge related to drug therapy

Planning and implementation

- Give drug only if skilled in airway management.
- Give sedatives or general anesthetics before neuromuscular blockers because neuromuscular blockers don't affect consciousness or pain perception.
- Give analgesics for pain.
- Keep airway clear. Have emergency respiratory support equipment (endotracheal equipment, ventilator, oxygen, atropine, edrophonium, epinephrine, and neostigmine) on hand.
- Nerve stimulator and train-of-four monitoring are recommended to confirm antagonism of neuromuscular blockade and recovery of muscle strength. Before attempting reversal with neostigmine, note signs of spontaneous recovery.
- Previous administration of succinylcholine may enhance neuromuscular blocking effect and duration of action.

Patient teaching

- Explain all events and happenings to patient because he can still hear.
- Reassure patient that he is being monitored and that muscle use will return when drug has worn off.

Evaluation

- Patient has positive response to drug therapy.
- Patient maintains adequate breathing pattern with mechanical assistance throughout therapy.
- Patient and family state understanding of drug therapy.

R

ropinirole hydrochloride
(roh-PIN-er-ohl high-droh-KLOR-ighd)
Requip

Pharmacologic class: nonergoline dopamine agonist
Therapeutic class: antiparkinsonian
Pregnancy risk category: C

Indications and dosages

▶ **Idiopathic Parkinson disease.** *Adults:* Initially, 0.25 mg P.O. t.i.d. Dosages can be adjusted weekly. After week 4, dosage may be increased by 1.5 mg daily on a weekly basis up to dosage of 9 mg daily, and then increased weekly by up to 3 mg daily to maximum daily dose of 24 mg.

▶ **Moderate to severe restless leg syndrome.** *Adults:* Initially, 0.25 mg P.O. 1 to 3 hours before bedtime. May increase dose as needed and tolerated after 2 days to 0.5 mg, then to 1 mg by the end of the first week. May further increase dose as needed and tolerated as follows: week 2, give 1 mg once daily. Week 3, give 1.5 mg once daily. Week 4, give 2 mg once daily. Week 5, give 2.5 mg once daily. Week 6, give 3 mg once daily. And week 7, give 4 mg once daily. All doses should be taken 1 to 2 hours before bedtime.

Contraindications and cautions

- Contraindicated in patients hypersensitive to the drug or any of its components.
- Use cautiously in patients with severe hepatic or renal impairment.

Lifespan: Use during pregnancy only if benefits outweigh risks to fetus. In nursing mothers, decision should be made whether to stop nursing or to stop drug. In patients older than age 65, clearance is reduced; dose is individually adjusted to response.

Adverse reactions

Early Parkinson disease (without levodopa)
CNS: aggravated Parkinson disease, amnesia, asthenia, confusion, *dizziness,* fatigue, hallucinations, headache, hyperkinesia, hypesthesia, impaired concentration, malaise, pain, somnolence, syncope, vertigo.
CV: atrial fibrillation, chest pain, edema, extrasystoles, flushing hypertension, hypotension, orthostatic symptoms, palpitations, peripheral ischemia, tachycardia.
EENT: abnormal vision, eye abnormality, pharyngitis, rhinitis, sinusitis, xerophthalmia.
GI: abdominal pain, anorexia, constipation, dry mouth, *dyspepsia,* flatulence, *nausea, vomiting.*
GU: UTI, impotence (male).
Respiratory: bronchitis, dyspnea.
Skin: increased sweating.
Other: viral infection, yawning.
Advanced Parkinson disease (with levodopa)
CNS: abnormal dreaming, aggravated parkinsonism, amnesia, anxiety, confusion, *dizziness, hallucinations, headache,* insomnia, nervousness, pain, paresthesia, *somnolence,* syncope, tremor.
CV: hypotension.
EENT: diplopia, increased saliva.
GI: abdominal pain, constipation, diarrhea, dry mouth, dysphagia, flatulence, *nausea,* vomiting.
GU: UTI, pyuria, urinary incontinence.
Hematologic: anemia.
Metabolic: weight loss.
Musculoskeletal: arthralgia, arthritis, *dyskinesia,* hypokinesia, paresis.
Respiratory: dyspnea, upper respiratory infection.
Skin: increased sweating.
Other: *falls,* injury, viral infection.
Restless leg syndrome
CNS: *dizziness, fatigue,* paresthesia, *somnolence,* vertigo.
CV: peripheral edema.
EENT: nasal congestion, *nasopharyngitis.*
GI: diarrhea, dry mouth, dyspepsia, *nausea, vomiting.*
Musculoskeletal: arthralgia, extremity pain, muscle cramps,
Respiratory: cough.
Skin: increased sweating.
Other: influenza.

Interactions

Drug-drug. *CNS depressants:* May increase CNS effects. Use together cautiously.
Dopamine antagonists (butyrophenones, metoclopramide, phenothiazines, thioxanthenes): May decrease ropinirole effectiveness. Monitor patient closely.
Estrogens: May decrease ropinirole clearance. If estrogens are started or stopped during therapy, adjust ropinirole dosage.

Inhibitors or substrates of CYP1A2 (cimetidine, ciprofloxacin, erythromycin, fluvoxamine, diltiazem, tacrine): May decrease ropinirole clearance. If these drugs are started or stopped during therapy, adjust ropinirole dosage.
Drug-lifestyle. *Alcohol use:* May increase sedative effects. Discourage using together.
Smoking: May increase drug clearance. Urge patient to stop smoking, especially during drug therapy.

Effects on lab test results

• May increase BUN and alkaline phosphatase levels. May decrease hemoglobin level and hematocrit.

Pharmacokinetics

Absorption: Rapid, with an absolute bioavailability of 55%.
Distribution: Wide. About 40% protein-bound.
Metabolism: Extensive by the liver to inactive metabolites.
Excretion: Less than 10%, unchanged in urine.
Half-life: 6 hours.

Route	Onset	Peak	Duration
P.O.	Unknown	1–2 hr	Unknown

Action

Chemical effect: Unknown. A dopamine agonist thought to stimulate postsynaptic dopamine D_2 receptors in the brain.
Therapeutic effect: Improves physical mobility in patients with parkinsonism.

Available forms

Tablets: 0.25 mg, 0.5 mg, 1 mg, 2 mg, 3 mg, 4 mg, 5 mg

NURSING PROCESS

Assessment

• Assess patient before starting therapy and frequently thereafter to monitor the drug's effectiveness.
• Monitor patient carefully for orthostatic hypotension, especially during dose escalation.
• Assess patient for adequate nutritional intake.
• Assess patient's and family's knowledge of drug therapy.

Nursing diagnoses

• Impaired physical mobility related to underlying Parkinson disease
• Disturbed thought processes related to drug-induced CNS adverse reactions
• Deficient knowledge related to drug therapy

Planning and implementation

• Give drug with food to decrease nausea.
• Drug may increase the risk of dopaminergic adverse effects of levodopa and may cause or worsen dyskinesia. Decrease levodopa dosage if needed.
• Don't abruptly stop drug. Withdraw gradually over 7 days to avoid hyperpyrexia and confusion.
• When used for restless leg syndrome, no dose taper is needed when stopping therapy.

Patient teaching

• Tell patient to take drug with food if nausea occurs.
• Explain that hallucinations may occur, particularly in an elderly patient.
• To minimize effects of orthostatic hypotension, instruct patient not to rise rapidly after sitting or lying down, especially when therapy starts or dosage changes.
• Advise patient to avoid hazardous activities until the drug's CNS effects are known.
• Tell patient not to drink alcohol during therapy.
• Tell woman to notify prescriber if pregnancy is suspected or planned, or if she is breast-feeding.

Evaluation

• Patient has improved mobility and reduced muscle rigidity and tremor.
• Patient remains mentally alert.
• Patient and family state understanding of drug therapy.

rosiglitazone maleate

(roh-sih-GLIH-tah-zohn MAL-ee-ayt)
Avandia✐

Pharmacologic class: thiazolidinedione
Therapeutic class: antidiabetic
Pregnancy risk category: C

Indications and dosages

▶ **Adjunct to diet and exercise (as monotherapy) to improve glycemic control in patients with type 2 diabetes mellitus, or (as combina-**

R

tion therapy) with sulfonylurea, metformin, or insulin when diet, exercise, and a single drug don't result in adequate glycemic control. *Adults:* Initially, 4 mg P.O. daily in the morning or in divided doses b.i.d. in the morning and evening. If fasting glucose level doesn't improve after 12 weeks, increase to 8 mg P.O. daily or in divided doses b.i.d. Maximum dose is 8 mg daily, except in patients taking insulin. For patients stabilized on insulin, continue insulin dose when therapy starts. Doses greater than 4 mg daily with insulin aren't indicated.
Adjust-a-dose: If patient reports hypoglycemia or if fasting glucose level decreases to less than 100 mg/dl, decrease insulin dose by 10% to 25%. Base further adjustments on response.

Contraindications and cautions

• Contraindicated in patients hypersensitive to the drug or any of its components, and in patients with New York Heart Association Class III or IV cardiac status unless expected benefits outweigh risks. Also contraindicated in patients who developed jaundice while taking troglitazone and in patients with active liver disease, increased baseline liver enzyme level (ALT level is greater than three times the upper limit of normal), type 1 diabetes, or diabetic ketoacidosis.
• Combination therapy with metformin and rosiglitazone is contraindicated in patients with renal impairment. Rosiglitazone can be used as monotherapy in patients with renal impairment.
• Use cautiously in patients with edema or heart failure.
Lifespan: Drug isn't recommended for pregnant or breast-feeding women.

Adverse reactions

CNS: headache, fatigue.
CV: edema, ***heart failure,*** peripheral edema.
EENT: sinusitis.
GI: *diarrhea,* weight gain.
Hematologic: anemia.
Metabolic: hyperglycemia, ***hypoglycemia.***
Musculoskeletal: back pain.
Respiratory: *upper respiratory tract infection.*
Other: injury.

Interactions

Drug-drug. *Gemfibrozil:* May increase rosiglitazone level. May need to decrease rosiglitazone dosage if gemfibrozil is added.
Rifamycins (rifabutin, rifampin, rifapentine): May increase rosiglitazone clearance and decrease glucose control. Monitor blood glucose level carefully when starting or stopping rosiglitazone therapy.
Drug-herb. *Bitter melon, fenugreek, ginseng:* May improve glucose control. Patient may need reduced antidiabetic dosage. Discourage using together.

Effects on lab test results

• May increase ALT, HDL, LDL, total cholesterol, and glucose levels. May decrease free fatty acid, glucose, and hemoglobin levels and hematocrit.

Pharmacokinetics

Absorption: Level peaks about 1 hour after a dose. Absolute bioavailability is 99%.
Distribution: About 99.8% protein-bound, mainly to albumin.
Metabolism: Extensive, with no unchanged drug in urine. Mainly through N-demethylation and hydroxylation.
Excretion: About 64% in urine and 23% in feces. *Half-life:* 3 to 4 hours.

Route	Onset	Peak	Duration
P.O.	Unknown	1 hr	Unknown

Action

Chemical effect: Lowers glucose level by improving insulin sensitivity. Highly selective and potent agonist for receptors in key target areas for insulin action, such as adipose tissue, skeletal muscle, and liver.
Therapeutic effect: Lowers glucose level.

Available forms

Tablets: 2 mg, 4 mg, 8 mg

NURSING PROCESS

Assessment

• Obtain history of patient's underlying condition before starting therapy, and reassess regularly thereafter to monitor drug's effectiveness.
• Check liver enzyme level before therapy starts. Don't use drug in patients with increased baseline liver enzyme level. In patients with normal baseline liver enzyme level, monitor level q 2 months for the first 12 months and periodically afterward. If ALT level is elevated,

recheck level as soon as possible. If level remains elevated, notify prescriber and stop drug.
- Monitor glucose level regularly and glycosylated hemoglobin level periodically to determine therapeutic response to drug.
- If patient has heart failure, watch for increased edema during rosiglitazone therapy.
- Assess patient's and family's knowledge of drug therapy.

Nursing diagnoses

- Ineffective health maintenance related to hyperglycemia
- Risk for injury related to drug-induced hypoglycemia
- Deficient knowledge related to drug therapy

Planning and implementation

- Before starting drug, treat patient for other causes of poor glycemic control, such as infection.
- Because calorie restriction, weight loss, and exercise help improve insulin sensitivity and make drug therapy effective, these measures are essential.
- For patients inadequately controlled with a maximum dose of a sulfonylurea or metformin, add this drug to current regimen; don't switch therapies.
- This drug alone or with insulin can cause fluid retention that may lead to or exacerbate heart failure. Observe patient for signs or symptoms of heart failure. If cardiac health deteriorates, stop drug.
- Macular edema may occur or worsen during therapy. If patient reports vision problems, obtain ophthalmic examination.
- Because ovulation may resume in premenopausal, anovulatory woman with insulin resistance, contraceptive measures may need to be considered.

Patient teaching

- Advise patient that rosiglitazone can be taken with or without food.
- Inform patient that blood will be tested to check liver function before therapy starts, every 2 months for the first 12 months, and periodically thereafter.
- Tell patient to immediately report unexplained signs or symptoms—such as nausea, vomiting, abdominal pain, fatigue, anorexia, or dark urine—because they may indicate liver problems.
- Instruct patient to contact prescriber if he has signs or symptoms of heart failure, such as unusually rapid increase in weight, edema, or shortness of breath.
- Urge patient to report vision changes or problems.
- Inform premenopausal, anovulatory woman with insulin resistance that ovulation may resume and that she may want to consider contraceptive measures.
- Advise patient that diabetes management must include diet control because calorie restriction, weight loss, and exercise improve insulin sensitivity and make drug therapy effective.

Evaluation

- Patient's glucose level is normal with drug therapy.
- Patient doesn't have hypoglycemia.
- Patient and family state understanding of drug therapy.

rosiglitazone maleate and metformin hydrochloride

(roh-si-GLI-ta-zone and met-FOR-min)
Avandamet

Pharmacologic class: thiazolidinedione and biguanide
Therapeutic class: antidiabetic
Pregnancy risk category: C

Indications and dosages

▶ **Adjunct to diet and exercise to improve glycemic control in patients with type 2 diabetes mellitus as initial treatment.** *Adults:* For drug-naive patient, give 2 mg rosiglitazone with 500 mg metformin daily or b.i.d. Dosage may be increased in increments of 2 mg/500 mg/day to a maximum of 8 mg/2,000 mg/day given in divided doses if patient isn't adequately controlled after 4 weeks.

▶ **Adjunct to diet and exercise to improve glycemic control in patients with type 2 diabetes mellitus who are already treated with rosiglitazone and metformin or who are inadequately controlled on metformin or rosiglitazone alone.** *Adults:* Dosage is based on patient's current doses of rosiglitazone, metformin, or both. Base dose on effectiveness and tolerance and give in two divided doses with meals. For patients inadequately controlled on metformin alone, 2 mg rosiglitazone P.O. b.i.d., plus the dose of metformin already being taken (500 mg or 1,000 mg P.O. b.i.d.). Dosage may be increased after 8 to 12 weeks. For patients inadequately controlled on rosiglitazone alone, 500 mg metformin P.O. b.i.d., plus the dose of rosiglitazone already being taken (2 mg or 4 mg b.i.d.). Dosage may be increased after 1 to 2 weeks. The total daily dose of this drug may be increased in increments of 4 mg rosiglitazone or 500 mg metformin, or both, up to the maximum daily dose of 8 mg rosiglitazone and 2,000 mg metformin in two divided doses.

Adjust-a-dose: In elderly patients, give conservative initial and maintenance doses because these patients' kidney function may be reduced. Don't give maximum dose to elderly, malnourished, or debilitated patients.

Contraindications and cautions

- Contraindicated in patients hypersensitive to rosiglitazone or metformin and in patients with creatinine level 1.5 mg/dl or higher in men or 1.4 mg/dl or higher in women; heart failure requiring drug therapy; acute or chronic metabolic acidosis, including diabetic ketoacidosis with or without coma; or evidence of active liver disease or ALT more than 2.5 times the upper limit of normal.
- Don't use with insulin or in patients with type 1 diabetes.
- Use cautiously in patients with edema or those at high risk of heart failure.

Lifespan: In pregnant or breast-feeding women, drug isn't recommended. In children, safety and effectiveness haven't been established. In the elderly, use cautiously because aging often reduces renal function. Don't give an elderly patient the maximum daily dose. Don't give drug to a patient older than age 80 unless renal function is normal.

Adverse reactions

CNS: fatigue, headache.
CV: edema, ***heart failure.***
EENT: sinusitis.
GI: *diarrhea,* weight gain, weight loss.
Hematologic: anemia.
Metabolic: hyperglycemia, ***hypoglycemia, lactic acidosis.***
Musculoskeletal: arthralgia, back pain.
Respiratory: upper respiratory tract infection.
Other: injury, viral infection.

Interactions

Drug-drug. *Calcium channel blockers, corticosteroids, diuretics, estrogens, hormonal contraceptives, isoniazid, nicotinic acid, phenothiazines, phenytoin, sympathomimetics, thyroid products:* May cause hyperglycemia. Monitor glucose level; adjust dosage, if needed.
Cationic drugs (amiloride, digoxin, morphine, procainamide, quinidine, quinine, ranitidine, triamterene, trimethoprim, vancomycin): May decrease metformin excretion. Monitor glucose level; adjust cationic drugs or metformin, if needed.
Contrast media containing iodine: May increase risk of lactic acidosis and renal failure with metformin. Make sure noniodine contrast media is used.
Furosemide: May increase metformin level and decrease furosemide level. Monitor patient closely.
Gemfibrozil: May increase rosiglitazone level. May need to decrease rosiglitazone dosage if gemfibrozil is added.
Nifedipine: May increase absorption of metformin. Monitor patient closely.
Drug-lifestyle. *Alcohol use:* May increase effect of metformin on lactate metabolism and increase risk of lactic acidosis. Discourage using together.

Effects on lab test results

- May increase ALT, HDL, LDL, and total cholesterol level. May decrease vitamin B_{12} and hemoglobin levels and hematocrit. May increase or decrease glucose level.

Pharmacokinetics

Absorption: Absolute bioavailability of rosiglitazone and metformin is 99% and 50% to 60%, respectively.
Distribution: Rosiglitazone is 99.8% protein-bound, primarily to albumin; metformin is negligibly protein-bound.
Metabolism: Rosiglitazone is extensively metabolized, mainly by N-demethylation and hydroxylation. It may be mainly metabolized by CYP2C8, with CYP2C9 contributing as a minor pathway. Metformin doesn't undergo hepatic metabolism.

Excretion: 64% of rosiglitazone in urine and 23% in feces. *Rosiglitazone half-life:* 3 to 4 hours. Metformin is excreted unchanged in the urine. *Metformin half-life:* 6¼ hours to 17½ hours.

Route	Onset	Peak	Duration
P.O.			
rosiglitazone	Unknown	1 hr	Unknown
metformin	Unknown	2½–3 hr	Unknown

Action

Chemical effect: Rosiglitazone improves insulin sensitivity. It's a highly selective and potent agonist for receptors in key target areas for insulin action, such as adipose tissue, skeletal muscle, and the liver. Metformin decreases hepatic glucose production and intestinal absorption of glucose and increases insulin sensitivity.
Therapeutic effect: Lowers glucose level.

Available forms

Tablets: 1 mg rosiglitazone maleate and 500 mg metformin hydrochloride, 2 mg rosiglitazone maleate and 500 mg metformin hydrochloride, 2 mg rosiglitazone maleate and 1,000 mg metformin hydrochloride, 4 mg rosiglitazone maleate and 500 mg metformin hydrochloride, 4 mg rosiglitazone maleate and 1,000 mg metformin hydrochloride

NURSING PROCESS

Assessment

- Obtain history of patient's underlying condition before starting therapy, and reassess regularly thereafter to monitor drug's effectiveness.
- Monitor transaminase level at baseline, q 2 months for the first 12 months, and periodically thereafter. If ALT level increases to more than three times the upper limit of normal, recheck liver enzymes as soon as possible. If ALT remains more than three times the upper limit of normal, stop drug.
- Monitor CBC and vitamin B_{12} level.
- Watch for signs and symptoms of heart failure and hepatic dysfunction. If jaundice occurs, stop therapy.
- Monitor renal function at baseline and at least annually during therapy.
- Monitor glycosylated hemoglobin level q 3 months.
- Assess patient's and family's knowledge of drug therapy.

Nursing diagnoses

- Ineffective health maintenance related to hyperglycemia
- Risk for injury related to drug-induced hypoglycemia
- Deficient knowledge related to drug therapy

Planning and implementation

ALERT: Evaluate patient for ketoacidosis or lactic acidosis. Nonspecific symptoms of lactic acidosis include malaise, myalgias, respiratory distress, abdominal distress, hypotension, and bradyarrhythmias.

- In patient undergoing radiologic studies involving iodinated contrast materials, stop drug before or during the procedure, and withhold for 48 hours after the procedure. Resume drug only after renal function has been re-evaluated and documented to be normal.
- Stop therapy temporarily in a patient having surgery. Don't restart until oral intake resumes and renal function is normal.
- If shock, acute heart failure, acute MI, or other conditions linked to hypoxemia occur, stop drug.

ALERT: Don't confuse Avandamet with Anzemet.

Patient teaching

- Stress the importance of dietary instructions, weight loss, and a regular exercise program.
- Tell patient to immediately report unexplained hyperventilation, myalgia, malaise, or unusual somnolence.
- Instruct patient to report a rapid increase in weight, swelling, shortness of breath, or other symptoms of heart failure.
- Tell patient to report unexplained nausea, vomiting, abdominal pain, fatigue, anorexia, or dark urine.
- Urge patient to report vision changes promptly.
- Explain that it may take 1 to 2 weeks for drug to take effect and up to 2 to 3 months for the full effect to occur.
- Stress the importance of avoiding excessive alcohol intake.
- Discuss the need for contraception with premenopausal women because ovulation may resume.

R

• Advise patient to take the drug in divided doses with meals to reduce GI side effects.

Evaluation

• Patient's glucose level is normal with drug therapy.
• Patient doesn't have hypoglycemia.
• Patient and family state understanding of drug therapy.

rosuvastatin calcium

(ro-SOO-va-stat-in KAL-see-uhm)

Crestor

Pharmacologic class: HMG-CoA reductase inhibitor
Therapeutic class: antihyperlipidemic
Pregnancy risk category: X

Indications and dosages

▶ **Adjunct to diet to reduce total cholesterol, LDL, apolipoprotein B (ApoB), non-HDL, and triglyceride levels, as well as to increase HDL level in primary hypercholesterolemia (heterozygous familial and nonfamilial), mixed dyslipidemia (Fredrickson Type IIA and IIB); adjunct to diet to treat elevated triglyceride level (Fredrickson Type IV).** *Adults:* Initially, 10 mg P.O. daily. Increase dosage, if needed, to a maximum of 40 mg daily. Increase q 2 to 4 weeks based on lipid level. If aggressive lipid lowering is needed, drug may be started at 20 mg once daily.

▶ **Adjunct to other lipid-lowering therapies to reduce LDL, ApoB, and total cholesterol levels in homozygous familial hypercholesterolemia.** *Adults:* Initially, 20 mg once daily. Maximum, 40 mg daily.

Adjust-a-dose: For patients with renal impairment, if creatinine clearance is less than 30 ml/minute, start with 5 mg once daily; don't exceed 10 mg once daily. In patients taking 40 mg who develop unexplained persistent proteinuria, reduce dosage. For patients taking gemfibrozil with rosuvastatin, don't exceed 10 mg once daily. For patients requiring less aggressive treatment, those at risk for myopathy, Asian patients, or patients also taking cyclosporine, initial dose is 5 mg.

Contraindications and cautions

• Contraindicated in patients hypersensitive to the drug or any of its components, and in patients with active liver disease or unexplained persistent elevations in transaminases.
• Use cautiously in patients who drink substantial amounts of alcohol and in patients with a history of liver disease. Also use cautiously in patients at increased risk for developing myopathies, such as patients 65 or older or those with renal impairment or hypothyroidism.
• Use with gemfibrozil only when the benefit clearly outweighs the risk. Don't exceed recommended dosage.

Lifespan: In pregnant women, drug is contraindicated. In breast-feeding women, use cautiously; it's unknown if the drug appears in breast milk. In children, safety and effectiveness haven't been established.

Adverse reactions

CNS: anxiety, asthenia, depression, dizziness, headache, hypertonia, insomnia, neuralgia, pain, paresthesia, vertigo.
CV: chest pain, hypertension, palpitation, vasodilation.
EENT: pharyngitis, rhinitis, sinusitis.
GI: abdominal pain, constipation, diarrhea, dyspepsia, nausea, flatulence, gastritis, gastroenteritis, periodontal abscess, vomiting.
GU: proteinuria, UTI.
Hematologic: anemia.
Metabolic: ***diabetes mellitus.***
Musculoskeletal: arthritis, back pain, myalgia, ***myopathy,*** neck pain, pathological fracture, pelvic pain, ***rhabdomyolysis.***
Respiratory: ***asthma,*** bronchitis, dyspnea, increased cough, pneumonia.
Skin: ecchymosis, pruritus, rash.
Other: accidental injury, flulike syndrome.

Interactions

Drug-drug. *Antacids:* May decrease level of rosuvastatin. Give antacids 2 hours after rosuvastatin.
Cyclosporine: May increase rosuvastatin level and increase risk of myopathy or rhabdomyolysis. Don't exceed 10 mg daily. Monitor patient for signs and symptoms of toxicity.
Gemfibrozil: May increase rosuvastatin level and increase risk of myopathy or rhabdomyolysis. Don't exceed 5 mg daily. Monitor patient for signs and symptoms of toxicity.

Warfarin: May increase warfarin level and increase risk of bleeding. Monitor INR and look for signs of increased bleeding.
Drug-lifestyle. *Alcohol use:* May increase risk of hepatotoxicity. Avoid using together.

Effects on lab test results

- May increase CK, transaminase, glucose, glutamyl transpeptidase, alkaline phosphatase, and bilirubin levels.
- May increase thyroid function test values.
- May cause dipstick-positive proteinuria and microscopic hematuria tests.

Pharmacokinetics

Absorption: About 20%; peak level occurs within 3 to 5 hours. Rate of absorption is decreased by food, but the extent of absorption is unaffected. The drug may be given at any time of day without any change in level.
Distribution: About 88% protein-bound, mainly to albumin.
Metabolism: About 10%.
Excretion: 90% in feces. *Half-life:* About 19 hours.

Route	Onset	Peak	Duration
P.O.	Unknown	3–5 hr	Unknown

Action

Chemical effect: Inhibits HMG-CoA reductase, which is an early and rate-limiting step in the synthetic pathway of cholesterol.
Therapeutic effect: Lowers total cholesterol, LDL, ApoB, non-HDL, and triglyceride levels.

Available forms

Tablets: 5 mg, 10 mg, 20 mg, 40 mg

NURSING PROCESS

Assessment

- Assess patient's condition before starting therapy and regularly thereafter to monitor drug's effectiveness.
- Perform liver function tests before therapy and again at 12 weeks. Repeat liver function tests 12 weeks following a dosage increase and then twice a year thereafter. If CK level increases to greater than 10 times the upper limit of normal, stop drug.
- Be alert for adverse reactions and drug interactions.
- If adverse GI reactions occur, monitor hydration.
- Assess patient's and family's knowledge of drug therapy.

Nursing diagnoses

- Risk for injury related to elevated cholesterol level
- Risk for deficient fluid volume related to adverse GI reactions
- Deficient knowledge related to drug therapy

Planning and implementation

- Begin drug only after diet and other nondrug therapies have proven ineffective. Give standard low-cholesterol diet during therapy.
- Withhold drug temporarily in any condition, such as sepsis, hypotension, major surgery, trauma, uncontrolled seizures, and severe metabolic, endocrine, and electrolyte disorders, that may predispose patient to the development of myopathy or rhabdomyolysis.

ALERT: Asian patients are at a greater risk of elevated drug level.

Patient teaching

- Instruct patient to take drug exactly as prescribed.
- Teach patient about restricting total fat and cholesterol intake, and recommend weight control, exercise, and smoking cessation programs.
- Tell patient to immediately report any signs of unexplained muscle pain, tenderness, or weakness, especially if accompanied by malaise or fever.
- Instruct patient that antacids containing aluminum or magnesium should be taken at least 2 hours after this drug.
- Inform woman that drug is contraindicated during pregnancy. Advise her to notify prescriber immediately if she becomes pregnant.

Evaluation

- Patient's LDL and total cholesterol levels are within normal range.
- Patient maintains adequate hydration.
- Patient and family state understanding of drug therapy.

R

S

salmeterol xinafoate
(sal-MEE-ter-ohl zee-neh-FOH-ayt)
Serevent Diskus

Pharmacologic class: selective $beta_2$ agonist
Therapeutic class: bronchodilator
Pregnancy risk category: C

Indications and dosages

▶ **Long-term maintenance therapy for asthma; to prevention bronchospasm in patients with nocturnal asthma or reversible obstructive airway disease who need regular short-acting beta agonists.** *Adults and children older than age 4:* Give 1 inhalation (50 mcg) q 12 hours, morning and evening.

▶ **To prevent exercise-induced bronchospasm.** *Adults and children age 4 and older:* 1 inhalation (50 mcg) at least 30 minutes before exercise.

▶ **Maintenance therapy for bronchospasm with COPD (including emphysema and chronic bronchitis).** *Adults:* 1 inhalation (50 mcg) q 12 hours, morning and evening.

Contraindications and cautions

• Contraindicated in patients hypersensitive to drug or any of its components.

• Use cautiously in patients who are unusually responsive to sympathomimetics and patients with coronary insufficiency, arrhythmias, hypertension or other CV disorders, thyrotoxicosis, or seizure disorders.

Lifespan: In pregnant women, use cautiously. Don't use in breast-feeding women. In children younger than age 4, safety and effectiveness haven't been established.

Adverse reactions

CNS: dizziness, *headache,* nervousness, sinus headache, tremor.
CV: palpitations, tachycardia, ***ventricular arrhythmias.***
EENT: nasal cavity or sinus disorder, *nasopharyngitis,* sore throat.
GI: diarrhea, heartburn, nausea, vomiting.
Musculoskeletal: joint and back pain, myalgia.
Respiratory: ***bronchospasm,*** cough, lower respiratory tract infection, upper respiratory tract infection, ***worsening of asthma.***
Other: ***anaphylaxis,*** hypersensitivity reactions.

Interactions

Drug-drug. *Beta agonists, methylxanthines, theophylline:* May cause adverse cardiac effects with excessive use. Monitor patient closely.
Beta blockers: May negate the beta agonist effects of salmeterol, resulting in severe bronchospasm. Use alternative to beta blocker, if possible. If beta blocker use can't be avoided, use a cardioselective beta blocker and monitor patient closely.
MAO inhibitors, tricyclic antidepressants: May cause severe adverse CV effects. Don't use within 14 days of MAO or tricyclic therapy.

Effects on lab test results

None reported.

Pharmacokinetics

Absorption: Low or undetectable because of low therapeutic dose.
Distribution: Local to lungs. 94% to 99% protein-bound.
Metabolism: Extensive.
Excretion: Primarily in feces.

Route	Onset	Peak	Duration
Inhalation	10–20 min	3 hr	12 hr

Action

Chemical effect: Unclear; selectively activates $beta_2$-adrenergic receptors, which results in bronchodilation, and blocks release of allergic mediators from mast cells in respiratory tract.
Therapeutic effect: Improves breathing ability.

Available forms

Inhalation powder: 50 mcg/blister

NURSING PROCESS

Assessment

• Assess patient's respiratory condition before starting therapy and regularly thereafter to monitor drug's effectiveness.

• Assess peak flow readings before starting therapy and periodically thereafter.

• Be alert for adverse reactions and drug interactions.
• Assess patient's and family's knowledge of drug therapy.

Nursing diagnoses

• Ineffective breathing pattern related to respiratory condition
• Acute pain related to drug-induced headache
• Deficient knowledge related to drug therapy

Planning and implementation

• Don't give drug for acute bronchospasm.
• Report insufficient relief or worsening condition.
• If headache occurs, give mild analgesic.

ALERT: A serious asthma episode or asthma-related death may occur, with black patients at greatest risk.

ALERT: Salmeterol may increase the risk of asthma-related death. Use only in patients not adequately controlled on inhaled corticosteroids.

ALERT: Don't confuse Serevent with Serentil.

Patient teaching

• Tell patient to take drug at about 12-hour intervals, even if he is feeling better.
• Tell patient to prevent exercise-induced bronchospasm by taking drug 30 to 60 minutes before exercise.

ALERT: Instruct patient not to use for acute bronchospasm; have them use a short-acting beta agonist (such as albuterol) instead.

• Tell patient to contact prescriber if short-acting beta agonist no longer provides sufficient relief or if taking more than 4 inhalations daily. Tell patient not to increase the dose.
• If patient is using an inhaled corticosteroid, he should continue. Warn him not to take other drugs without prescriber's consent.
• Instruct patient not to exhale into Diskus, and to only use Diskus in a level, horizontal position.

Evaluation

• Patient exhibits normal breathing pattern.
• Patient states that drug-induced headache is relieved after analgesic administration.
• Patient and family state understanding of drug therapy.

saquinavir mesylate

(suh-KWIN-uh-veer MEH-sih-layt)
Invirase

Pharmacologic class: protease inhibitor
Therapeutic class: antiretroviral
Pregnancy risk category: B

Indications and dosages

▶ **Adjunct therapy for advanced HIV infection in selected patients.** *Adults and children older than age 16:* Give 1,000 mg P.O. b.i.d. with 100 mg ritonavir. Or, 400 mg and 400 mg ritonavir P.O. b.i.d.

Contraindications and cautions

• Contraindicated in patients hypersensitive to the drug and its components, and in patients taking triazolam, midazolam, ergot derivatives, or cisapride.
• Use cautiously in patients with liver impairment.

Lifespan: In pregnant women, breast-feeding women, and children younger than age 16, safety and effectiveness haven't been established.

Adverse reactions

CNS: asthenia, dizziness, headache, paresthesia.
CV: chest pain.
GI: abdominal pain, diarrhea, mouth ulcers, nausea, ***pancreatitis.***
Hematologic: ***pancytopenia, thrombocytopenia.***
Hepatic: cirrhosis, elevated liver enzymes, ***portal hypertension.***
Metabolic: hyperglycemia, new onset diabetes mellitus.
Musculoskeletal: musculoskeletal pain.
Respiratory: bronchitis, cough.
Skin: rash.
Other: adipogenic effects.

Interactions

Drug-drug. *Amitriptyline, imipramine:* May increase levels of these drugs. Monitor drug levels and adjust dose as needed.
Amlodipine, diltiazem, felodipine, isradipine, nicardipine, nifedipine, nimodipine, nisoldipine,

S

verapamil: May increase levels of these drugs. Use together cautiously.
Antiarrhythmics (amiodarone, bepridil, flecainide, propafenone, quinidine): May cause serious or life-threatening reactions. Avoid using together.
Carbamazepine, phenobarbital, phenytoin: May decrease saquinavir level. Use together cautiously.
Cyclosporine, rapamycin, tacrolimus: May increase levels of these drugs. Monitor drug levels.
Delavirdine: May increase saquinavir level. Use cautiously, and monitor hepatic enzymes. Decrease dose when used together.
Dexamethasone: May decrease saquinavir level. Use together cautiously.
Efavirenz: May decrease level of both drugs. Don't use together.
Ergot derivatives (dihydroergotamine, ergonovine, ergotamine, methylergonovine): May cause serious or life threatening reactions such as ergot toxicity characterized by peripheral vasospasm and ischemia of the extremities and other tissues. Avoid using together.
Ethinyl estradiol: May decrease level of contraceptive. Recommend additional contraceptive during therapy.
HMG-CoA reductase inhibitors: May increase levels of these drugs, which increases risk of myopathy, including rhabdomyolysis. Avoid using together.
Indinavir, lopinavir and ritonavir, nelfinavir, ritonavir: May increase level of saquinavir. Use together cautiously.
Lidocaine: May increase antiarrhythmic level. Use together cautiously and monitor level.
Loperamide: May increase loperamide level while decreasing saquinavir level. Avoid use together.
Macrolide antibiotics such as clarithromycin: May increase level of both drugs. Use together cautiously. Reduce antibiotic dose in patients with renal impairment.
Methadone: May decrease methadone level. Increase methadone dose as needed.
Midazolam, triazolam: May cause serious or life threatening reactions such as prolonged or increased sedation or respiratory depression. Avoid using together.
Nevirapine: May decrease saquinavir level. Monitor patient.
Phosphodiesterase type 5 inhibitors (sildenafil, tadalafil, vardenafil): May increase peak level and exposure of these drugs. Use together cautiously. Reduce dose of sildenafil to 25 mg, dose of vardenafil to 2.5 mg and dose of tadalafil to 10 mg when given with saquinavir.
Rifabutin, rifampin: May reduce the steady-state level of saquinavir. Use rifabutin and saquinavir together cautiously. Don't use with rifampin.
Warfarin: May affect warfarin level. Monitor INR.
Drug-herb. *Garlic supplements:* May decrease drug level by half. Discourage using together.
St. John's wort: May substantially reduce level of drug, causing loss of therapeutic effect. Discourage using together.
Drug-food. *Any food:* May increase drug absorption. Advise patient to take drug within 2 hours after eating a meal.
Grapefruit juice: May increase drug level. Give with another liquid.

Effects on lab test results

- May increase liver enzyme level.
- May decrease WBC, RBC, and platelet counts.

Pharmacokinetics

Absorption: Poor.
Distribution: More than 98% protein-bound.
Metabolism: Rapid.
Excretion: Mainly in feces. *Half-life:* 1 to 2 hours.

Route	Onset	Peak	Duration
P.O.	Unknown	Unknown	7 hr

Action

Chemical effect: Inhibits HIV protease and prevents cleavage of HIV polyproteins, which are essential for HIV maturation.
Therapeutic effect: Hinders HIV activity.

Available forms

Capsules (hard gelatin): 200 mg
Tablets (film coated): 500 mg

NURSING PROCESS

Assessment

- Obtain history of patient's HIV infection.

• Monitor CBC and platelet counts and electrolyte, uric acid, liver enzyme, and bilirubin levels before and during therapy.
• Be alert for adverse reactions and drug interactions, including those caused by adjunct therapy (zidovudine or zalcitabine).
• If patient has an adverse GI reaction, monitor his hydration.
• Watch for adipogenic side effects with prolonged therapy (redistribution or accumulation of body fat, dorsocervical fat enlargement, peripheral wasting, breast enlargement, and cushingoid appearance).
• Assess patient's and family's knowledge of drug therapy.

Nursing diagnoses

• Risk for infection related to presence of HIV
• Risk for deficient fluid volume related to adverse GI reactions
• Deficient knowledge related to drug therapy

Planning and implementation

ALERT: If severe toxicity occurs, stop drug until cause is identified or toxicity resolves. Therapy may resume with no dosage change.
• Notify prescriber of adverse reactions, and obtain an order for a mild analgesic, antiemetic, or antidiarrheal, if needed.
ALERT: Don't confuse saquinavir with sinequan.

Patient teaching

• Tell patient to take drug with meals or within 2 hours after a full meal.
• Urge patient to report adverse reactions.
• Reinforce need for adequate protection of sexual partners. Drug doesn't prevent transmission of HIV.
• Inform patient that drug is usually given with other AIDS-related antiviral drugs.
ALERT: Advise patient taking sildenafil, tadalafil, or vardenafil about an increased risk of adverse events, including hypotension, visual changes, and priapism, and the need to report them promptly. Tell patient not to exceed 25 mg of sildenafil in 48 hours; 10 mg of tadalafil in 72 hours; or 2.5 mg of vardenafil in 72 hours.

Evaluation

• Patient responds well to therapy.
• Patient maintains adequate hydration.
• Patient and family state understanding of drug therapy.

sargramostim (granulocyte macrophage colony-stimulating factor, GM-CSF)

(sar-GRAH-moh-stim)
Leukine

Pharmacologic class: biological response modifier
Therapeutic class: hematopoietic growth factor
Pregnancy risk category: C

Indications and dosages

▶ **To accelerate hematopoiesis after autologous bone marrow transplantation (BMT) in patients with malignant lymphoma, acute lymphoblastic leukemia, or chemotherapeutically treated Hodgkin lymphoma.** *Adults:* 250 mcg/m² daily as 2-hour I.V. infusion beginning 2 to 4 hours after BMT and no less than 24 hours after last dose of chemotherapy or radiation. Patient's post-BMT absolute neutrophil count (ANC) must be less than 500/mm³. Continue until ANC exceeds 1,500/mm³ for 3 consecutive days.
▶ **BMT failure or engraftment delay.** *Adults:* 250 mcg/m² as 2-hour I.V. infusion daily for 14 days. May repeat after 7 days off therapy. If engraftment still hasn't occurred, a third course of 500 mcg/m² I.V. daily for 14 days may be tried after another 7 days off therapy.
▶ **Neutrophil recovery following chemotherapy in acute myelogenous leukemia.** *Adults:* 250 mcg/m² I.V. infusion over 4 hours daily. Start therapy about day 11 or 4 days after end of induction therapy.
▶ **To mobilize hematopoietic progenitor cells into peripheral blood for collection by leukapheresis; to accelerate myeloid engraftment after autologous peripheral blood progenitor cell (PBPC) transplantation.** *Adults:* 250 mcg/m² by continuous I.V. infusion over 24 hours or subcutaneously once daily. After PBPC, continue until the ANC exceeds 1,500/mm³ for 3 consecutive days.

I.V. administration

• Reconstitute drug with 1 ml of sterile water for injection. Direct stream of sterile water against side of vial and gently swirl contents to minimize foaming. Avoid excessive or vigorous agitation or shaking.

S

• Dilute in normal saline solution. If final level is less than 10 mcg/ml, add human albumin at final level of 0.1% to saline solution before adding drug to prevent adsorption to components of delivery system. For final level of 0.1% human albumin, add 1 mg human albumin per 1 ml saline solution.
• Give as soon as possible and no later than 6 hours after reconstituting.
• Do not use an in-line membrane filter since adsorption of the drug could occur.
• Vials are for single-dose use and contain no preservatives. Discard unused portion.
• Refrigerate sterile powder, reconstituted solution, and diluted solution for injection. Don't freeze or shake.

⊗ **Incompatibilities**

Other I.V. drugs, unless specific compatibility data are available.

Contraindications and cautions

• Contraindicated in patients hypersensitive to the drug or any of its components or to yeast-derived products. Also contraindicated in patients with excessive leukemic myeloid blasts in bone marrow or peripheral blood and within 24 hours preceding or following chemotherapy or radiotherapy.
• Use cautiously in patients with cardiac disease, hypoxia, fluid retention, pulmonary infiltrates, heart failure, or impaired kidney or liver function.

Lifespan: In pregnant women, use cautiously. In breast-feeding women, use cautiously; it's unknown if the drug appears in breast milk. In children, safety and effectiveness haven't been established.

Adverse reactions

CNS: asthenia, CNS disorders, fever, malaise.
CV: edema, pericardial effusion, ***supraventricular arrhythmia.***
EENT: mucous membrane disorder.
GI: anorexia, diarrhea, GI disorder, ***hemorrhage,*** nausea, stomatitis, vomiting.
GU: abnormal kidney function, *urinary tract disorder.*
Hematologic: ***blood dyscrasias, hemorrhage.***
Hepatic: ***liver damage.***
Respiratory: *dyspnea, lung disorders,* pleural effusion.
Skin: alopecia, rash.
Other: **SEPSIS.**

Interactions

Drug-drug. *Corticosteroids, lithium:* May increase myeloproliferative effects of sargramostim. Use together cautiously.

Effects on lab test results

• May increase BUN, creatinine, AST, ALT, and bilirubin levels.

Pharmacokinetics

Absorption: Given I.V.
Distribution: Bound to specific receptors on target cells.
Metabolism: Unknown.
Excretion: Unknown. *Half-life:* About 2 hours.

Route	Onset	Peak	Duration
I.V.	≤ 30 min	2 hr	6 hr
SubQ	Rapid	1–4 hr	Unknown

Action

Chemical effect: Differs from natural human GM-CSF. Induces cellular responses by binding to specific receptors on surfaces of target cells.
Therapeutic effect: Stimulates formation of granulocytes (neutrophils, eosinophils) and macrophages.

Available forms

Liquid: 500 mcg*
Powder for injection: 250 mcg

NURSING PROCESS

Assessment

• Assess patient's condition before starting therapy and regularly thereafter to monitor drug's effectiveness.
• Monitor CBC with differential biweekly, including examination for presence of blast cells.
• Be alert for adverse reactions and drug interactions.
• Monitor patient's hydration throughout drug therapy.
• Assess patient's and family's knowledge of drug therapy.

Nursing diagnoses

• Ineffective health maintenance related to underlying condition

• Risk for deficient fluid volume related to drug-induced adverse effects
• Deficient knowledge related to drug therapy

Planning and implementation

• Drug's effect may be lessened in patient who has received extensive radiotherapy to hematopoietic sites in abdomen or chest or who has been exposed to multiple drugs (alkylating, anthracycline antibiotics, antimetabolites) before autologous BMT.
• Drug is effective in accelerating myeloid recovery in patients receiving bone marrow purged from monoclonal antibodies.
• Drug can act as growth factor for tumors, particularly myeloid cancers.
• Blood counts return to normal or baseline level within 3 to 7 days after stopping therapy.
• If severe adverse reaction occurs, notify prescriber. Dose may need to be reduced by half or stopped temporarily. Resume therapy when reaction decreases. Transient rashes and local reactions at injection site may occur; serious allergic or anaphylactic reaction isn't common.
• Stimulation of marrow precursors may result in rapid rise of WBC count. If blast cells appear or increase to 10% or more of WBC count or if underlying disease progresses, stop drug. If ANC is more than 20,000/mm^3 or if platelet count is more than 50,000/mm^3, temporarily stop drug or reduce dose by half.
ALERT: Don't confuse Leukine with Leukeran.

Patient teaching

• Inform patient and family about need for therapy and frequent blood tests.
• Advise patient to report adverse reactions immediately.

Evaluation

• Patient exhibits positive response to drug therapy.
• Patient maintains adequate hydration throughout therapy.
• Patient and family state understanding of drug therapy.

scopolamine (hyoscine)

(skoh-POL-uh-meen)
Scōp ◊, Transderm-Scōp

scopolamine butylbromide (hyoscine butylbromide)

Buscopan ♦

scopolamine hydrobromide (hyoscine hydrobromide)

Scopace

Pharmacologic class: anticholinergic
Therapeutic class: antiemetic, antivertigo drug, adjunct to anesthesia
Pregnancy risk category: C

Indications and dosages

▶ **Spastic states.** *Adults:* 0.4 to 0.8 mg Scopace P.O. daily. Or, 0.32 to 0.65 mg scopolamine hydrobromide subcutaneously, I.M. or I.V. t.i.d. or q.i.d.

▶ **To reduce secretions preoperatively.** *Adults:* 0.2 to 0.6 mg scopolamine hydrobromide I.M. 30 to 60 minutes before induction of anesthesia.
Children ages 8 to 12: Give 0.3 mg scopolamine hydrobromide I.M. 45 minutes before induction of anesthesia.
Children ages 3 to 8: Give 0.2 mg scopolamine hydrobromide I.M. 45 minutes before induction of anesthesia.
Children ages 7 months to 3 years: 0.15 mg scopolamine hydrobromide I.M. 45 minutes before induction of anesthesia.
Infants ages 4 to 7 months: 0.1 mcg scopolamine hydrobromide I.M. 45 minutes before induction of anesthesia.

▶ **To prevent nausea and vomiting from motion sickness.** *Adults:* 1 Transderm-Scōp patch (a circular flat unit), which delivers 1 mg over 3 days (72 hours). Apply to skin behind ear at least 4 hours before antiemetic is needed. Or 0.3 to 0.6 mg scopolamine hydrobromide subcutaneously, I.M., or I.V. Or 0.25 to 0.8 mg P.O 1 hour before exposure to motion; subsequent doses of 0.25 to 0.8 mg may be given t.i.d. if needed.

S

Children: 0.006 mg/kg or 0.2 mg/m² scopolamine hydrobromide subcutaneously, I.M., or I.V.

I.V. administration

- Intermittent and continuous infusions aren't recommended.
- For direct injection, dilute with sterile water and inject through patent I.V. line.
- Protect I.V. solutions from freezing and light; store at room temperature.

⊗ **Incompatibilities**
Alkalies, anticholinergics, methohexital.

Contraindications and cautions

- Contraindicated in patients with angle-closure glaucoma, obstructive uropathy, obstructive disease of GI tract, asthma, chronic pulmonary disease, myasthenia gravis, paralytic ileus, intestinal atony, unstable CV status in acute hemorrhage, or toxic megacolon.
- Transderm-Scōp is contraindicated in patients allergic to scopolamine and other belladonna alkaloids.
- Use cautiously in patients with autonomic neuropathy, hyperthyroidism, coronary artery disease, arrhythmias, heart failure, hypertension, hiatal hernia with reflux esophagitis, hepatic or renal disease, or ulcerative colitis. Also use cautiously in patients in hot or humid environments because of drug-induced heatstroke.
- Use Transderm-Scōp cautiously in patients with liver or renal impairment, pyloric obstruction, or urinary bladder and neck obstruction.

Lifespan: In pregnant women and children younger than age 6, use cautiously. In breast-feeding women, don't use. In children, Transderm-Scōp is contraindicated. In the elderly, use Transderm-Scōp cautiously.

Adverse reactions

CNS: confusion, delirium, disorientation, drowsiness, dizziness, fever, hallucinations, headache, irritability, restlessness.
CV: flushing, palpitations, ***paradoxical bradycardia,*** tachycardia.
EENT: blurred vision, difficulty swallowing, dilated pupils, increased intraocular pressure, photophobia.
GI: constipation, dry mouth, epigastric distress, nausea, vomiting.
GU: urinary hesitancy, urine retention.
Respiratory: bronchial plugging, ***depressed respirations.***
Skin: contact dermatitis, dryness, rash with transdermal patch.

Interactions

Drug-drug. *Centrally acting anticholinergics (antihistamines, phenothiazines, tricyclic antidepressants):* May increase risk of adverse CNS reactions. Monitor patient closely.
CNS depressants: May increase risk of CNS depression. Monitor patient closely.
Drug-herb. *Jaborandi tree:* May decrease effects of drug. Discourage using together.
Pill-bearing spurge: May decrease effects of drug. Discourage using together.
Squaw vine: May decrease metabolic breakdown of drug. Discourage using together.
Drug-lifestyle. *Alcohol use:* May increase risk of CNS depression. Discourage using together.

Effects on lab test results

None reported.

Pharmacokinetics

Absorption: Good with P.O., P.R., and transdermal use. Rapidly with I.M. or subcutaneous use.
Distribution: Wide. Probably crosses blood-brain barrier.
Metabolism: Extensively metabolized by the liver.
Excretion: May be in urine as metabolites. *Half-life:* 8 hours.

Route	Onset	Peak	Duration
P.O.	30–60 min	1 hr	4–6 hr
I.V., I.M., SubQ	30 min	Unknown	4 hr
P.R.	Unknown	Unknown	Unknown
Transdermal	3–6 hr	24 hr	≤ 72 hr

Action

Chemical effect: Inhibits muscarinic actions of acetylcholine. It also may affect neural pathways originating in the labyrinth (inner ear) to inhibit nausea and vomiting.
Therapeutic effect: Relieves spasticity, nausea, and vomiting; reduces secretions; and blocks cardiac vagal reflexes.

Available forms

scopolamine
Transdermal patch: 1.5 mg
scopolamine butylbromide
Capsules: 0.25 mg
Suppositories: 10 mg
Tablets: 10 mg
scopolamine hydrobromide
Injection: 0.3, 0.4, 0.5, 0.86, and 1 mg/ml in 1-ml vials and ampules; 0.4 mg/ml and 0.86 mg/ml in 0.5-ml ampules
Tablets (soluble): 0.4 mg

NURSING PROCESS

Assessment

- Assess patient's condition before starting therapy and regularly thereafter to monitor drug's effectiveness.
- Be alert for adverse reactions and drug interactions.
- Assess patient's and family's knowledge of drug therapy.

Nursing diagnoses

- Risk for deficient fluid volume related to nausea and vomiting
- Risk for injury related to drug-induced adverse CNS reactions
- Deficient knowledge related to drug therapy

Planning and implementation

- In therapeutic doses, drug may produce amnesia, drowsiness, and euphoria; patient may need to be reoriented.
- Raise side rails of bed as a precaution because some patients become temporarily excited or disoriented. Symptoms disappear when sedative effect is complete.
- Tolerance may develop when given for a long time.
- Apply patch the night before patient's expected travel.

ALERT: Overdose may cause curarelike effects such as respiratory paralysis.

Patient teaching

- Advise patient to apply patch the night before planned trip. Transdermal form releases controlled amount of drug. Transderm-Scōp is effective if applied 2 or 3 hours before travel but is more effective if applied 12 hours before.
- Advise patient to wash and dry hands thoroughly before applying transdermal patch. After removing patch, he should discard it and wash hands and application site thoroughly, especially before touching eyes because pupils may dilate.
- Inform patient that discarded patch should be folded in half with sticky sides together and disposed out of reach of children and pets.
- Tell patient that if patch becomes displaced, he should remove it and replace it with another patch on fresh site.
- Advise patient not to cut the patch, because this will lead to increased absorption and possible toxicity.
- Alert patient to risk of withdrawal symptoms (nausea, vomiting, headache, dizziness) if transdermal patch is used longer than 72 hours.
- Tell patient to ask pharmacist for the brochure that comes with transdermal patch.
- Tell patient about P.O. or P.R. forms.
- Advise patient to refrain from activities that require alertness until drug's CNS effects are known.
- Instruct patient to report signs of urinary hesitancy or urine retention.
- Recommend use of sugarless gum or hard candy to help minimize dry mouth.

Evaluation

- Patient responds well to therapy.
- Patient doesn't experience injury from adverse CNS reactions.
- Patient and family state understanding of drug therapy.

secobarbital sodium

(sek-oh-BAR-bih-tohl SOH-dee-um)
Seconal Sodium

Pharmacologic class: barbiturate
Therapeutic class: anticonvulsant, sedative-hypnotic
Pregnancy risk category: D
Controlled substance schedule: II

Indications and dosages

▶ **Preoperative sedation.** *Adults:* 200 to 300 mg P.O. 1 to 2 hours before surgery. *Children:* 2 to 6 mg/kg P.O. 1 to 2 hours before surgery. Maximum single dose, 100 mg.

▶ **Insomnia.** *Adults:* 100 mg P.O. at bedtime.

S

Contraindications and cautions

- Contraindicated in patients hypersensitive to barbiturates and in patients with marked liver impairment, porphyria, or respiratory disease in which dyspnea or obstruction is evident.
- Use cautiously in patients with acute or chronic pain, depression, suicidal tendencies, history of drug abuse, or hepatic impairment.

Lifespan: In pregnant or breast-feeding women, drug isn't recommended.

Adverse reactions

CNS: complex sleep disorders, *drowsiness, hangover, lethargy,* paradoxical excitement in geriatric patients, somnolence.
GI: nausea, vomiting.
Hematologic: exacerbation of porphyria.
Respiratory: ***respiratory depression.***
Skin: rash, ***Stevens-Johnson syndrome,*** urticaria.
Other: ***anaphylaxis, angioedema,*** physical or psychological dependence.

Interactions

Drug-drug. *Chloramphenicol, MAO inhibitors, valproic acid:* May inhibit barbiturate metabolism; may cause prolonged CNS depression. Reduce barbiturate dosage.
CNS depressants, including opioid analgesics: May cause excessive CNS and respiratory depression. Use together cautiously.
Corticosteroids, doxycycline, estrogens, hormonal contraceptives, oral anticoagulants, theophylline, tricyclic antidepressants, verapamil: May enhance metabolism of these drugs. Monitor patient for decreased effect.
Griseofulvin: May decrease absorption of griseofulvin. Monitor patient for decreased griseofulvin effectiveness.
Metoprolol, propranolol: May reduce the effects of these drugs. Consider an increased beta blocker dose
Rifampin: May decrease barbiturate level. Monitor patient for decreased effect.
Warfarin: May decrease the anticoagulant effects of warfarin. Monitor INR and adjust warfarin dosage as needed.
Drug-lifestyle. *Alcohol use:* May impair coordination, increase CNS effects, and cause death. Strongly discourage alcohol use with this drug.

Effects on lab test results

- May increase AST and ALT levels.

Pharmacokinetics

Absorption: Rapid. Almost complete.
Distribution: Rapid. About 30% to 45% protein-bound.
Metabolism: Oxidized in liver to inactive metabolites.
Excretion: In urine. *Half-life:* About 30 hours.

Route	Onset	Peak	Duration
P.O.	15 min	5–30 min	1–4 hr

Action

Chemical effect: Probably interferes with transmission of impulses from thalamus to cortex of brain.
Therapeutic effect: Promotes pain relief and calmness and relieves acute seizures.

Available forms

Capsules: 100 mg

NURSING PROCESS

Assessment

- Assess patient's condition before starting therapy and regularly thereafter to monitor drug's effectiveness.
- Assess mental status before therapy. An elderly patient is more sensitive to the drug's CNS effects.
- Be alert for adverse reactions and drug interactions.
- Assess patient's and family's knowledge of drug therapy.

Nursing diagnoses

- Sleep deprivation related to underlying condition
- Risk for injury related to drug-induced adverse CNS reactions
- Deficient knowledge related to drug therapy

Planning and implementation

- Make sure a patient who is depressed, suicidal, or drug-dependent or who has a history of drug abuse isn't hoarding drug or planning an intentional overdose.
- Skin eruptions may precede a fatal reaction. If skin reactions occur, stop giving the drug and notify the prescriber. In some patients, high fever, stomatitis, headache, or rhinitis may precede skin reactions.

• Long-term use isn't recommended because drug loses effectiveness after 14 days of use.
ALERT: Don't confuse Seconal with Sectral.

Patient teaching

• Warn patient about possible complex sleep-related behaviors.
• Warn patient to avoid activities that require mental alertness or physical coordination. For inpatient, supervise walking and raise bed rails, particularly for an elderly patient.
• Inform patient that morning hangover is common after hypnotic dose, which suppresses REM sleep. Patient may experience increased dreaming after drug is stopped.
• Advise woman who uses a hormonal contraceptive to use a barrier method because drug may enhance the metabolism of a hormonal contraceptive and decrease its effect.

Evaluation

• Patient states that drug effectively induces sleep.
• Patient doesn't experience injury from adverse CNS reactions.
• Patient and family state understanding of drug therapy.

selegiline
Emsam

selegiline hydrochloride (L-deprenyl hydrochloride)
(seh-LEJ-eh-leen high-droh-KLOR-ighd)
Carbex, Eldepryl, Novo-Selegiline, Zelapar

Pharmacologic class: MAO inhibitor
Therapeutic class: antidepressant, antiparkinsonian
Pregnancy risk category: C

Indications and dosages

▶ **Adjunctive treatment with levodopa and carbidopa in managing signs and symptoms of Parkinson disease.** *Adults:* 10 mg P.O. daily divided as 5 mg at breakfast and 5 mg at lunch. After 2 or 3 days, levodopa and carbidopa dosage may need gradual decrease. If using Zelapar, begin with 1.25 mg P.O. once daily before breakfast, without liquid. After 6 weeks, increase to 2.5 mg once daily if needed and tolerated. Don't allow patient to eat or drink for 5 minutes after taking the drug.
▶ **Major depressive disorder.** *Adults:* Apply one patch daily to dry, intact skin on the upper torso, upper thigh, or upper arm. Initially, give 6 mg/24 hr. Increase as needed in increments of 3 mg/24 hr at intervals of 2 or more weeks. Maximum dose, 12 mg/24 hr.
Elderly patients: 6 mg/24 hour.

Contraindications and cautions

• Contraindicated in patients hypersensitive to drug, in patients with pheochromocytoma, and in those taking bupropion, carbamazepine, cyclobenzaprine, dextromethorphan, duloxetine, methadone, meperidine, mirtazapine, MAO inhibitors, oxcarbazepine, propoxyphene, SSRIs, sympathomimetics, tramadol, tricyclic antidepressants, venlafaxine. Don't use oral drug with the transdermal system.
Lifespan: In pregnant women, use cautiously. In breast-feeding women and in children, safety and effectiveness haven't been established.

Adverse reactions

Transdermal form
CNS: headache, insomnia.
CV: chest pain, low blood pressure, orthostatic blood pressure.
GI: diarrhea, dry mouth, dyspepsia.
Metabolic: weight gain, weight loss.
Skin: application site reaction, rash.
Oral form
CNS: behavioral changes, chorea, confusion, *dizziness,* dyskinesia, facial grimacing, fatigue, hallucinations, headache, increased apraxia, increased bradykinesia, increased tremors, involuntary movements, loss of balance, malaise, restlessness, stiff neck, syncope, twitching, vivid dreams.
CV: angina, ***arrhythmias,*** hypertension, hypotension, orthostatic hypotension, palpitations, peripheral edema, tachycardia.
EENT: blepharospasm.
GI: abdominal pain, anorexia or poor appetite, constipation, diarrhea, dry mouth, dysphagia, heartburn, *nausea,* vomiting.
GU: prostatic hyperplasia, sexual dysfunction, slow urination, transient nocturia, urinary frequency, urinary hesitancy, urine retention.
Metabolic: weight loss.

S

Skin: *application site reactions,* diaphoresis, hair loss, rash.

Interactions

Drug-drug. *Adrenergics:* May increase pressor response, particularly in patients who have taken overdose of selegiline. Use together cautiously.
Bupropion, cyclobenzaprine, dextromethorphan, meperidine, methadone, mirtazapine, MAO inhibitors, propoxyphene, sympathomimetic amines, including amphetamines, cold products and weight loss preparations containing vasoconstrictors, tramadol, tricyclic antidepressants: May cause hypertensive crisis. Separate use by at least 2 weeks.
Carbamazepine, oxcarbazepine: May increase selegiline level. Use together is contraindicated.
Citalopram, duloxetine, fluoxetine, fluvoxamine, nefazodone, paroxetine, sertraline, venlafaxine: May cause serotonin syndrome involving CNS irritability, shivering, and altered consciousness. Don't give together. Wait at least 2 weeks after stopping an MAO inhibitor before giving any SSRI.
Meperidine: May cause stupor, muscle rigidity, severe agitation, and elevated temperature. Avoid using together.
Drug-herb. *Cacao tree:* May have vasopressor effects. Discourage using together.
Ginseng: May increase risk of adverse reactions, including headache, tremor, and mania. Discourage using together.
St. John's wort: May cause increased serotonergic effects. Warn patient against use together.
Drug-food. *Foods high in tyramine:* May cause hypertensive crisis. Monitor patient's blood pressure; instruct patient to avoid these foods.

Effects on lab test results

- May cause positive result for amphetamine on urine drug screen.

Pharmacokinetics

Absorption: Rapid.
Distribution: Unknown.
Metabolism: Three metabolites include N-desmethyldeprenyl, L-amphetamine, and L-methamphetamine.
Excretion: 45% in urine as metabolite. *Half-life:* selegiline, 2 to 10 hours; N-desmethyldeprenyl, 2 hours; L-amphetamine, 17¾ hours; L-methamphetamine, 20½ hours.

Route	Onset	Peak	Duration
P.O.	Unknown	30 min–2 hr	Unknown
Transdermal	Unknown	Unknown	24 hours

Action

Chemical effect: May act by selectively inhibiting MAO type B (found mostly in brain). Also may directly increase dopaminergic activity by decreasing reuptake of dopamine into nerve cells. Amphetamine and methamphetamine (active metabolites) may contribute to this effect.
Therapeutic effect: Improves physical mobility and elevates mood.

Available forms

Capsules: 5 mg
Tablets: 5 mg
Tablets, orally-disintegrating: 1.25 mg
Transdermal system: 6 mg/24 hours, 9 mg/24 hours, 12 mg/24 hours

NURSING PROCESS

Assessment

- Assess patient's condition before starting therapy and regularly thereafter to monitor drug's effectiveness.
- Monitor patients with major depressive disorder for worsening of symptoms and for suicidal behavior, especially during the first few weeks of treatment and whenever dosage changes.
- Be alert for adverse reactions and drug interactions.
- Assess patient's and family's knowledge of drug therapy.

Nursing diagnoses

- Impaired physical mobility related to underlying condition
- Risk for injury related to depression or drug-induced adverse CNS reactions
- Deficient knowledge related to drug therapy

Planning and implementation

- Some patients experience increased adverse reactions related to levodopa and need a 10% to 30% reduction of levodopa and carbidopa dosage.

ALERT: Drug may increase the risk of suicidal thinking in children and adolescents. Drug isn't approved for use in children.

ALERT: Don't confuse selegiline with Stelazine or Eldepryl with enalapril or Elavil.

Patient teaching

- Advise patient not to take more than 10 mg daily because greater amount of drug won't improve effectiveness and may increase adverse reactions.
- Tell patient to take drug with food.
- Warn patient to move cautiously or change positions slowly at start of therapy because he may become dizzy or lightheaded.
- Caution patient to avoid driving and other hazardous activities that require mental alertness until the drug's effects are known.
- Advise patient not to overindulge in tyramine-rich foods or beverages. If using a 9-mg/24-hour or higher transdermal system, avoid these products all together.

ALERT: Warn patient about the many drugs, including OTC drugs, that may interact with this drug and about the need to consult a pharmacist or his prescriber before using them.

- Teach patient and family the signs and symptoms of hypertensive crisis including severe headache, sore or stiff neck, nausea, vomiting, sweating, rapid heart beat, dilated pupils, and photophobia.

ALERT: Advise family members to watch patient for anxiety, agitation, insomnia, irritability, hostility, and aggressiveness and to report these immediately to prescriber.

- Tell patient not to cut the transdermal system into smaller pieces.
- When disposing of used patch, tell patient to fold sticky sides together and dispose out of reach of children and pets.
- Advise patient to wash hands thoroughly after touching patch.
- Tell patient to avoid exposing transdermal system to direct external heat sources such as heating pads, electric blankets, hot tubs, heated waterbeds, and prolonged sunlight.
- Tell patient to stop using the transdermal system 10 days before having surgery requiring general anesthesia.
- Tell patient the tablet will disintegrate on top of the tongue within seconds and to avoid eating or drinking for 5 minutes after taking the tablet.
- Advise woman planning pregnancy or breast-feeding to first contact her prescriber.

☑ Evaluation

- Patient exhibits improved physical mobility.
- Patient doesn't experience depression or injury from adverse CNS reactions.
- Patient and family state understanding of drug therapy.

sertaconazole nitrate

(sir-tah-CON-ah-zole NIGH-trate)

Ertaczo

Pharmacologic class: imidazole derivative
Therapeutic class: topical antifungal
Pregnancy risk category: C

Indications and dosages

▶ **Tinea pedis caused by *Trichophyton mentagrophytes, T. rubrum,* or *Epidermophyton floccosum* in immunocompetent patients.**
Adults and children age 12 and older: Apply cream twice daily to affected areas between toes and healthy surrounding areas for 4 weeks.

Contraindications and cautions

- Contraindicated in patients hypersensitive to the drug, any of its components, or other imidazoles.

Lifespan: In pregnant women, use cautiously. In breast-feeding women, use cautiously; it's unknown if the drug appears in breast milk. In children younger than age 12, safety and effectiveness haven't been established.

Adverse reactions

Skin: application site reactions, burning skin, contact dermatitis, dry skin, skin tenderness.

Interactions

None known.

Effects on lab test results

None reported.

Pharmacokinetics

Absorption: Unknown.
Distribution: Unknown.
Metabolism: Unknown.
Excretion: Unknown. *Half-life:* Unknown.

Route	Onset	Peak	Duration
Topical	Unknown	Unknown	Unknown

S

Action

Chemical effect: May inhibit the cytochrome P-450–dependent synthesis of ergosterol. The lack of ergosterol in the cell membrane alters cell wall permeability and osmotic instability leading to fungal cell injury and death.
Therapeutic effect: Kills susceptible fungus.

Available forms

Topical cream: 2%, in 15- and 30-g tubes

NURSING PROCESS

Assessment

- Assess area of infection before therapy and regularly thereafter to monitor the drug's effectiveness.
- Monitor patient for adverse effects. Stop giving the drug if skin irritation or sensitivity develops.
- Assess patient's and family's knowledge of drug therapy.

Nursing diagnoses

- Impaired tissue integrity related to infection with susceptible organisms
- Impaired skin integrity related to adverse effects of drug
- Deficient knowledge related to drug therapy

Planning and implementation

- Before treatment starts, make sure diagnosis has been confirmed by direct microscopic examination of infected tissue in potassium hydroxide solution or by culture on an appropriate medium.
- Drug is for use on skin only, not for ophthalmic, oral, or intravaginal use.
- If condition hasn't improved after 2 weeks, review the diagnosis.

Patient teaching

- Warn patient to stop using drug if he develops increased irritation, redness, itching, burning, blistering, swelling, or oozing at the site of application.
- Caution patient that drug is for external use on skin only. Discourage contact with eyes, nose, mouth, and other mucous membranes.
- If cream will be applied after bathing, tell patient to dry the affected area thoroughly before use.
- Tell patient to wash hands after applying cream.
- Urge patient to use the drug for the full duration of treatment, even if symptoms have improved.
- Instruct patient to notify prescriber if condition worsens or fails to improve.
- Caution patient to avoid occlusive coverings unless directed by prescriber.
- Teach patient proper foot hygiene.

Evaluation

- Tissue integrity is restored after treatment.
- Patient doesn't experience adverse drug effects.
- Patient and family state understanding of drug therapy.

sertraline hydrochloride

(SER-truh-leen high-droh-KLOR-ighd)
Zoloft

Pharmacologic class: SSRI
Therapeutic class: antidepressant
Pregnancy risk category: C

Indications and dosages

▶ **Depression.** *Adults:* 50 mg P.O. daily. Adjust dosage as tolerated and needed, at intervals of no less than 1 week. Maximum dosage, 200 mg daily.

▶ **Post-traumatic stress disorder, social anxiety disorder, obsessive compulsive disorder, panic disorder.** *Adults:* Initially, 25 mg P.O. once daily. Increase dosage to 50 mg P.O. once daily after 1 week of therapy. Dosage may be increased at weekly intervals to a maximum of 200 mg daily. Maintain patient on lowest effective dosage.

▶ **Premenstrual dysphoric disorder.** *Women:* Initially, 50 mg daily P.O. continuously, or limited to the luteal phase of the menstrual cycle. Patients not responding may benefit from dose increases at 50-mg increments per menstrual cycle up to 150 mg daily when taken daily throughout the menstrual cycle, or 100 mg daily when taken during the luteal phase of the menstrual cycle. If a 100-mg daily dose has been established with luteal-phase regimen, a 50-mg daily adjustment step for 3 days should be used at the beginning of each luteal phase.

▶ **Premature ejaculation‡.** *Adults:* 25 to 50 mg P.O. daily or p.r.n.

Adjust-a-dose: Give lower or less frequent doses with hepatic impairment.

Contraindications and cautions

- Contraindicated in patients hypersensitive to the drug or any of its components, and in patients receiving pimozide.
- Use cautiously in patients at risk for suicide and in those with seizure disorder, major affective disorder, or diseases or conditions that affect metabolism or hemodynamic responses.
- Drug should not be discontinued abruptly.

Lifespan: In pregnant women, use cautiously. In breast-feeding women, use cautiously; it's unknown if the drug appears in breast milk. In children younger than age 18, drug isn't approved for use in treatment of major depressive disorder due to possible increased risk of suicidal behavior.

Adverse reactions

CNS: anxiety, confusion, *dizziness, fatigue, headache,* hyperesthesia, hypertonia, hypesthesia, *insomnia,* nervousness, paresthesia, *somnolence, tremor,* twitching.
CV: chest pain, flushing, hot flushes, palpitations.
GI: abdominal pain, anorexia, constipation, *diarrhea, dry mouth, dyspepsia,* flatulence, increased appetite, *loose stools, nausea,* thirst, vomiting.
GU: decreased libido, male sexual dysfunction.
Musculoskeletal: myalgia.
Skin: *diaphoresis,* pruritus, rash.

Interactions

Drug-drug. *Benzodiazepines (except lorazepam and oxazepam), phenytoin, tolbutamide:* May decrease clearance of these drugs. Monitor patient for increased drug effects.
Cimetidine: May decrease sertraline clearance. Monitor patient for toxicity.
Clozapine: may increase clozapine level. Monitor and adjust clozapine dose as needed.
Disulfiram: May cause a disulfiram reaction because oral concentrate contains alcohol. Avoid using together.
Phenelzine, selegiline, tranylcypromine: May cause serotonin syndrome, including CNS irritability, shivering, and altered consciousness. Don't give together. Wait at least 2 weeks after stopping an MAO inhibitor before giving any SSRI.
Pimozide: May increase pimozide level and cause bradycardia. Avoid using together.
Sumatriptan: May cause weakness, hyperreflexia, and incoordination. Monitor patient closely.
Tricyclic antidepressants (TCAs): May inhibit TCA metabolism. Reduce TCA dose. Monitor patient closely.
Warfarin, other highly protein-bound drugs: May increase level of warfarin or other highly bound drug. Monitor patient, PT, and INR closely.
Drug-herb. *St. John's wort:* May cause additive effects and serotonin syndrome, including CNS irritability, shivering, and altered consciousness. Discourage use together.
Drug-lifestyle. *Alcohol use:* May enhance CNS effects. Advise patient to avoid alcohol use.

Effects on lab test results

- May increase ALT, AST, cholesterol, and triglyceride levels. May decrease uric acid level.

Pharmacokinetics

Absorption: Well absorbed from GI tract. Rate and extent enhanced when taken with food.
Distribution: More than 98% protein-bound.
Metabolism: Probably hepatic.
Excretion: Mainly as metabolites in urine and feces. *Half-life:* 26 hours.

Route	Onset	Peak	Duration
P.O.	2–4 wk	4½–8½ hr	Unknown

Action

Chemical effect: Unknown; may be linked to inhibited neuronal uptake of serotonin in CNS.
Therapeutic effect: Relieves depression.

Available forms

Oral concentrate: 20 mg/ml
Tablets: 25 mg, 50 mg, 100 mg

NURSING PROCESS

Assessment

- Assess patient's condition before starting therapy and regularly thereafter to monitor drug's effectiveness.
- Assess patient for risk factors for suicide.
- Be alert for adverse reactions and drug interactions.
- Assess patient's and family's knowledge of drug therapy.

S

Nursing diagnoses

- Disturbed thought processes related to presence of depression
- Risk for injury related to drug-induced adverse CNS reactions
- Deficient knowledge related to drug therapy

Planning and implementation

- Give drug once daily, either morning or evening. Drug may be given with or without food.
- Don't give within 14 days of MAO inhibitor therapy.
- In a patient with a latex allergy, don't use the rubber oral concentrate dropper.
- Don't discontinue drug abruptly. Taper gradually over several weeks, and monitor the patient carefully for SSRI discontinuation syndrome.

ALERT: Don't confuse sertraline with selegiline or Serentil. Don't confuse Zoloft with Zocor.

Patient teaching

- Advise patient to use caution when performing hazardous tasks that require alertness and not to drink alcohol or take other drugs that affect CNS while taking this drug.
- Instruct patient to check with prescriber or pharmacist before taking OTC drugs.
- Advise patient to mix the oral concentrate with 4 oz of water, ginger ale, or lemon-lime soda only, and to take the dose right away.
- Instruct patient that sudden discontinuation will cause unpleasant side effects.

Evaluation

- Patient behavior and communication indicate improved thought processes.
- Patient doesn't experience injury from adverse CNS reactions.
- Patient and family state understanding of drug therapy.

sevelamer hydrochloride

(seh-VEL-ah-mer high-droh-KLOR-ighd)

Renagel

Pharmacologic class: polymeric phosphate binder
Therapeutic class: antihyperphosphatemic
Pregnancy risk category: C

Indications and dosages

▶ **To reduce phosphorus level in patients with end-stage renal disease who are undergoing hemodialysis.** *Adults:* Depends on severity of hyperphosphatemia. Gradually adjust dosage based on phosphorus level, with goal of lowering phosphorus to 6 mg/dl or less. If phosphorus level is 9 mg/dl or more, start with 1.6 g P.O. t.i.d. with meals; if phosphorus level is between 7.5 and 9 mg/dl, 1.2 g P.O. t.i.d. or 1.6 g P.O. t.i.d. with meals; if phosphorus level is between 6 and 7.5 mg/dl, 800 mg P.O. t.i.d. with meals.

Dosage may be increased or decreased by one tablet per meal at 2-week intervals according to the patient's serum phosphorus level. If serum phosphorous level is greater than 6 mg/dl, increase by 1 tablet per meal. If serum phosphorous level is less than 3.5 mg/dl, decrease by 1 tablet per meal.

Contraindications and cautions

- Contraindicated in patients hypersensitive to the drug or any of its components, and in those with hypophosphatemia or bowel obstruction.
- Use cautiously in patients with dysphagia, swallowing disorders, severe GI motility disorders, or major GI tract surgery.

Lifespan: Use in pregnancy only if benefits clearly outweigh potential risks to the fetus. In breast-feeding women, use cautiously; it's unknown if the drug appears in breast milk. In children, safety and effectiveness haven't been established.

Adverse reactions

CNS: headache, pain.
CV: hypertension, hypotension, ***thrombosis.***
GI: constipation, *diarrhea, dyspepsia,* flatulence, *nausea, vomiting.*
Respiratory: cough.
Skin: *pruritus.*
Other: infection.

Interactions

Drug-drug. *Antiarrhythmics, anticonvulsants:* May interact. Give drug at least 1 hour before or 3 hours after giving these drugs and monitor levels of these drugs.
Ciprofloxacin: May reduce the bioavailability of ciprofloxacin. Give 1 hour before or 3 hours after sevelamer.

Effects on lab test results

- May increase alkaline phosphatase level.

Pharmacokinetics

Absorption: Unknown.
Distribution: Binds bile acids in the intestines forming a nonabsorbable complex with phosphorus.
Metabolism: None known systemically.
Excretion: In feces. *Half-life:* Unknown.

Route	Onset	Peak	Duration
P.O.	Unknown	Unknown	Unknown

Action

Chemical effect: Inhibits intestinal phosphate absorption.
Therapeutic effect: Decreases phosphorus level.

Available forms

Tablets: 400 mg, 800 mg

NURSING PROCESS

Assessment

- Obtain history of patient's underlying condition before starting therapy, and reassess regularly thereafter to monitor the drug's effectiveness.
- Monitor calcium, bicarbonate, and chloride levels.
- Watch for symptoms of thrombosis (numbness or tingling of limbs, chest pain, shortness of breath), and notify prescriber if they occur.
- Assess patient's and family's knowledge of drug therapy.

Nursing diagnoses

- Ineffective tissue perfusion (cardiopulmonary or peripheral) related to potential drug-induced thrombosis
- Imbalanced nutrition: less than body requirements related to drug-induced adverse GI effects
- Deficient knowledge related to drug therapy

Planning and implementation

- Don't crush or break capsules or tablets, and give only with meals.
- Drug may bind to other drugs given at the same time and decrease their bioavailability. Give other drugs 1 hour before or 3 hours after sevelamer.

ALERT: Drug may reduce vitamins D, E, and K and folic acid. Give a multivitamin supplement.

Patient teaching

- Instruct patient to take with meals and adhere to prescribed diet.
- Inform patient that drug must be taken whole because contents expand in water; tell him not to open or chew capsules.
- Tell patient to take other drugs as directed, but they must be taken either 1 hour before or 3 hours after sevelamer.
- Inform patient about common adverse reactions and instruct him to report them immediately. Teach patient signs and symptoms of thrombosis (numbness, tingling limbs, chest pain, changes in level of consciousness).

Evaluation

- Patient doesn't develop a thrombus.
- Patient maintains adequate nutrition.
- Patient and family state understanding of drug therapy.

sibutramine hydrochloride monohydrate

(sigh-BYOO-truh-meen high-droh-KLOR-ighd mah-noh-HIGH-drayt)
Meridia

Pharmacologic class: dopamine, norepinephrine, and serotonin reuptake inhibitor
Therapeutic class: anorexic
Pregnancy risk category: C
Controlled substance schedule: IV

Indications and dosages

▶ **To manage obesity.** *Adults:* 10 mg P.O. once daily with or without food. If weight loss isn't adequate after 4 weeks, increase dosage to 15 mg P.O. daily. Patients who don't tolerate the 10-mg dose may receive 5 mg P.O. daily. Doses above 15 mg daily aren't recommended.

Contraindications and cautions

- Contraindicated in patients hypersensitive to the drug or any of its components, those taking MAO inhibitors or other centrally acting ap-

S

petite suppressants, and those with anorexia nervosa. Don't use drug in patients with severe renal or hepatic dysfunction, history of hypertension, seizures, coronary artery disease, heart failure, arrhythmias, or stroke.
- Use cautiously in patients with angle-closure glaucoma, and in patients predisposed to bleeding events or taking drugs that affect hemostasis or platelet function.
- Use not recommended for more than 2 years.

Lifespan: In pregnant and breast-feeding women, use isn't recommended. Women of childbearing age should use adequate contraception and notify prescriber promptly if they become pregnant. In children younger than age 16, safety and effectiveness haven't been established.

Adverse reactions

CNS: anxiety, asthenia, CNS stimulation, depression, dizziness, emotional lability, *headache, insomnia,* migraine, nervousness, paresthesia, somnolence.
CV: chest pain, generalized edema, hypertension, palpitations, tachycardia, vasodilation.
EENT: ear disorder, ear pain, laryngitis, *pharyngitis,* sinusitis, thirst, *rhinitis.*
GI: abdominal pain, *anorexia, constipation, dry mouth,* dyspepsia, gastritis, increased appetite, nausea, rectal disorder, taste perversion, vomiting.
GU: dysmenorrhea, metrorrhagia, UTI, vaginal candidiasis.
Musculoskeletal: arthralgia, joint disorder, myalgia, neck or back pain, tenosynovitis.
Respiratory: cough.
Skin: acne, rash, sweating.
Other: accident, allergic reaction, flulike syndrome, herpes simplex, injury.

Interactions

Drug-drug. *CNS depressants:* May enhance CNS depression. Use cautiously.
Dextromethorphan, dihydroergotamine, fentanyl, fluoxetine, fluvoxamine, lithium, MAO inhibitors, meperidine, paroxetine, pentazocine, sertraline, sumatriptan, tryptophan, venlafaxine: May cause hyperthermia, tachycardia, and loss of consciousness. Don't use together.
Ephedrine, pseudoephedrine: May increase blood pressure or heart rate. Use cautiously.
Erythromycin, cimetidine, ketoconazole: May result in small increases in sibutramine metabolites. Use cautiously together.
Drug-lifestyle. *Alcohol use:* May enhance CNS depression. Discourage using together.

Effects on lab test results

- May increase ALT, AST, GGT, LDH, alkaline phosphatase, and bilirubin levels.

Pharmacokinetics

Absorption: Rapid. About 77% of dose is absorbed.
Distribution: Rapid and extensive. Active metabolites are extensively protein-bound.
Metabolism: Extensive in the first pass by the liver to two active metabolites, M_1 and M_2.
Excretion: About 77% in urine. *Half-life:* M_1 is 14 hours and M_2 is 16 hours.

Route	Onset	Peak	Duration
P.O.	Unknown	3–4 hr	Unknown

Action

Chemical effect: Inhibits reuptake of norepinephrine, serotonin, and dopamine.
Therapeutic effect: Facilitates weight loss.

Available forms

Capsules: 5 mg, 10 mg, 15 mg

NURSING PROCESS

Assessment

- Monitor patient for adverse reactions and drug interactions.
- Assess patient for organic causes of obesity before starting therapy.
- Assess patient's dietary intake.
- Measure blood pressure and pulse before starting therapy, with dosage changes, and at regular intervals during therapy.
- Assess patient's and family's knowledge of drug therapy.

Nursing diagnoses

- Imbalanced nutrition: more than body requirements related to increased caloric intake
- Sleep deprivation related to drug-induced insomnia
- Deficient knowledge related to drug therapy

Planning and implementation

- Don't give drug within 14 days of MAO inhibitor therapy.
- Give patient ice chips or sugarless hard candy to relieve dry mouth.
- Make sure patient follows appropriate diet regimen.

Patient teaching

- Advise patient to immediately report rash, hives, or other allergic reactions.
- Instruct patient to inform prescriber if he is taking or plans to take other prescription or OTC drugs.
- Advise patient to have blood pressure and pulse monitored at regular intervals. Stress importance of regular follow-up visits with prescriber.
- Advise patient to use drug with reduced calorie diet.
- Tell patient that weight loss can cause gallstones. Teach patient about signs and symptoms and the need to report them to prescriber promptly.

Evaluation

- Patient achieves nutritional balance with the use of drugs and a reduced-calorie diet.
- Patient experiences normal sleep patterns.
- Patient and family state understanding of drug therapy.

sildenafil citrate

(sil-DEN-ah-fil SIGH-trayt)

Revatio

Pharmacologic class: cyclic guanosine monophosphate (cGMP)–specific phosphodiesterase type 5 (PDE5) inhibitor
Therapeutic class: vasodilator
Pregnancy risk category: B

Indications and dosages

▶ **To improve exercise ability in patients with World Health Organization group I pulmonary arterial hypertension.** *Adults:* 20 mg P.O. t.i.d., 4 to 6 hours apart.

Contraindications and cautions

- Contraindicated in patients hypersensitive to drug or its components and in those taking organic nitrates.
- Don't use in patients with pulmonary veno-occlusive disease.
- Use cautiously in patients with resting hypotension, severe left ventricular outflow obstruction, autonomic dysfunction, and volume depletion.
- Use cautiously in patients with hepatic or severe renal impairment, retinitis pigmentosa, bleeding disorders, or active peptic ulcer disease; those who have had an MI, a stroke, or a life-threatening arrhythmia in last 6 months; those with history of coronary artery disease causing unstable angina or uncontrolled high or low blood pressure; those with deformation of the penis and conditions that may cause priapism (such as sickle cell anemia, multiple myeloma, or leukemia); and those taking bosentan.

Lifespan: In pregnant women, use cautiously. Use cautiously in breast-feeding women; it isn't known whether drug appears in breast milk. Safety and effectiveness haven't been established in children. Use cautiously in elderly patients because they have an increased risk of impaired renal, hepatic, and cardiac function and of concurrent disease.

Adverse reactions

CNS: dizziness, fever, *headache.*
CV: flushing, hypotension, ***MI, sudden cardiac death, stroke, transient ischemic attack, ventricular arrhythmias.***
EENT: blurred vision, burning, epistaxis, impaired color discrimination, photophobia, rhinitis, sinusitis.
GI: diarrhea, dyspepsia, gastritis.
Musculoskeletal: myalgia.
Skin: erythema.

Interactions

Drug-drug. *Alpha blockers:* May cause symptomatic hypotension. Use together cautiously.
Amlodipine: May further reduce blood pressure. Monitor blood pressure closely.
Bosentan: May decrease sildenafil level. Monitor patient.
Cytochrome P-450 inducers, rifampin: May reduce sildenafil level. Monitor effect.
Hepatic isoenzyme inhibitors (such as cimetidine, erythromycin, itraconazole, ketoconazole): May increase sildenafil level. Avoid using together.

Isosorbide, nitroglycerin: May cause severe hypotension. Use of nitrates in any form is contraindicated during therapy.
Protease inhibitors: May significantly increase sildenafil level. Don't use together.
Vitamin K antagonists: May increase risk of bleeding (primarily epistaxis). Monitor patient.
Drug-food. *Grapefruit:* May increase drug level and delay absorption. Advise patient to avoid using together.

Effects on lab test results

None reported.

Pharmacokinetics

Absorption: Rapid. Absolute bioavailability is 40%.
Distribution: Extensively into body tissues. About 96% protein-bound.
Metabolism: Mainly in the liver to an active metabolite with properties similar to those of parent drug.
Excretion: About 80% in feces and 13% in urine. *Half-life:* 4 hours.

Route	Onset	Peak	Duration
P.O.	15–30 min	30 min–2 hr	4 hr

Action

Chemical effect: Increases cyclic guanosine monophosphate level by preventing its breakdown by phosphodiesterase, prolonging smooth muscle relaxation of the pulmonary vasculature, which leads to vasodilation.
Therapeutic effect: Improved exercise tolerance in patients with World Health Organization group I pulmonary arterial hypertension.

Available Forms

Tablets: 20 mg

NURSING PROCESS

Assessment

- Assess patient for underlying conditions that could be adversely affected by vasodilatory effects of the drug including resting hypotension (blood pressure below 90/50 mm Hg), fluid depletion, severe ventricular outflow obstruction, or autonomic dysfunction.
- Monitor patient's vital signs carefully at start of treatment.
- Monitor patient for evidence of pulmonary edema; if it occurs, consider pulmonary veno-occlusive disease.
- Monitor patient for development of visual disturbances such as photophobia, impaired color discrimination, blurred vision, and burning.
- Assess patient's and family's knowledge of drug therapy.

Nursing diagnoses

- Ineffective tissue perfusion (cardiopulmonary) related to underlying condition
- Activity intolerance related to underlying medical condition
- Deficient knowledge related to drug therapy

Planning and implementation

ALERT: Don't substitute Viagra for Revatio because there isn't an equivalent dose.

- Patients with pulmonary arterial hypertension caused by connective tissue disease are more prone to epistaxis during therapy than those with primary pulmonary hypertension.
- The serious CV events linked to this drug's use in erectile dysfunction mainly involve patients with underlying CV disease who are at increased risk for cardiac effects related to sexual activity.

Patient teaching

- Warn patient that drug should never be used with nitrates.
- Advise patient to rise slowly from lying down.
- Inform patient that drug can be taken with or without food.
- Warn patient that discrimination between colors such as blue and green may become impaired during therapy; warn him to avoid hazardous activities that rely on recognizing colors.
- Instruct patient to notify prescriber of visual changes, dizziness, or fainting.
- Caution patient to take drug only as prescribed.

Evaluation

- Patient's pulmonary artery pressure decreases, and patient reaches pulmonary hemodynamic stability.
- Patient experiences improved exercise tolerance with drug therapy.
- Patient and family state understanding of drug therapy.

sildenafil citrate
(sil-DEN-ah-fil SIGH-trayt)
Viagra

Pharmacologic class: phosphodiesterase type 5 (PDE 5) inhibitor
Therapeutic class: erectile dysfunction drug
Pregnancy risk category: B

Indications and dosages

▶ **Erectile dysfunction.** *Men younger than age 65:* Initially, 50 mg P.O., p.r.n., about 1 hour before sexual activity. Dosage range is 25 to 100 mg, based on effectiveness and tolerance. Maximum, 1 dose daily.
Adjust-a-dose: Men age 65 and older or those with hepatic or severe renal impairment or those taking potent CYP3A4 inhibitors (erythromycin, ketoconazole, itraconazole, saquinavir) should take 25 mg P.O. about 1 hour before sexual activity. Base dose on patient response. Maximum, 1 dose daily.

Contraindications and cautions

- Contraindicated in patients hypersensitive to the drug or any of its components, those with underlying CV disease, and those using organic nitrates at any frequency and in any form.
- Use cautiously in patients with hepatic or severe renal impairment; those with anatomic deformation of the penis; those with conditions that may predispose them to priapism (such as sickle cell anemia, multiple myeloma, leukemia), retinitis pigmentosa, bleeding disorders, or active peptic ulcer disease; those who have had an MI, stroke, or life-threatening arrhythmia during previous 6 months; and those with history of cardiac failure, coronary artery disease, or uncontrolled high or low blood pressure.

Lifespan: In men age 65 and older, use cautiously. Not indicated for use in women or children.

Adverse reactions

CNS: anxiety, dizziness, *headache, **seizures,*** somnolence, vertigo.
CV: ***cerebrovascular hemorrhage,*** flushing, hypotension, ***MI, sudden cardiac death, transient ischemic attack, ventricular arrhythmia.***
EENT: abnormal vision (photophobia, color-tinged vision, blurred vision), decreased vision, diplopia, increased intraocular pressure, ocular burning, ocular redness or bloodshot appearance, ocular swelling or pressure, perimacular edema, retinal bleeding, retinal vascular disease, temporary vision loss, vitreous detachment or traction.
GI: diarrhea, dyspepsia.
GU: hematuria, priapism, UTI.
Musculoskeletal: arthralgia, back pain.
Respiratory: respiratory tract infection.
Skin: rash.
Other: flulike syndrome.

Interactions

Drug-drug. *Alpha blockers:* May cause hypotension or syncope. Caution patient not to take 50- to 100-mg doses of sildenafil within 4 hours of an alpha blocker. A dose of 25 mg may be taken at any time.
Azole antifungals (itraconazole, ketoconazole): May increase sildenafil level. Reduce starting dose of sildenafil to 25 mg.
CYP3A4 inducers, rifampin: May decrease sildenafil level. Monitor drug effect.
Delavirdine, protease inhibitors: May increase sildenafil level and sildenafil-related adverse events, including hypotension, visual changes, and priapism. Tell patient not to exceed 25 mg of sildenafil in a 48-hour period.
Hepatic isoenzyme inhibitors (such as cimetidine, erythromycin, itraconazole, ketoconazole): May reduce sildenafil clearance. Avoid using together, or reduce dosage to 25 mg.
Isosorbide, nitroglycerin, other nitrates: May cause severe hypotension. Use of nitrates in any form with sildenafil is contraindicated.
Drug-food. *Grapefruit:* May increase level and delay absorption. Advise patient to avoid consuming grapefruit products.
High-fat meals: Reduces rate of absorption and decreases peak level. Tell patient to separate dose from meals.

Effects on lab test results

None reported.

Pharmacokinetics

Absorption: Rapid. Absolute bioavailability is 40%.
Distribution: Extensively into body tissues. About 96% protein-bound.

S

Metabolism: Mainly in the liver to an active metabolite with properties similar to those of parent drug.
Excretion: About 80% in feces and 13% in urine. *Half-life:* 4 hours.

Route	Onset	Peak	Duration
P.O.	30 min	30 min–2 hr	4 hr

Action

Chemical effect: Enhances the effect of nitric oxide (NO) by inhibiting PDE 5. When sexual stimulation causes local release of NO, inhibition of PDE 5 causes increased level of cyclic guanosine monophosphate in the corpus cavernosum, resulting in smooth muscle relaxation and inflow of blood.
Therapeutic effect: Patient achieves an erection.

Available forms

Tablets: 25 mg, 50 mg, 100 mg

NURSING PROCESS

Assessment

- Discuss patient's history of erectile dysfunction to establish need for drug versus other therapies.
- Assess patient for CV risk factors because serious events have been reported with drug, and report risk factors to prescriber.
- Assess patient's and family's knowledge of drug therapy.

Nursing diagnoses

- Sexual dysfunction related to patient's underlying condition
- Ineffective tissue perfusion (cardiopulmonary) related to drug-induced effects on blood pressure and cardiac output
- Deficient knowledge related to drug therapy

Planning and implementation

ALERT: Serious CV events, including MI, sudden cardiac death, ventricular arrhythmia, cerebrovascular hemorrhage, transient ischemic attack, and hypertension, may occur in patients during or shortly after sexual activity.
ALERT: Drug's systemic vasodilation causes transient decreases in supine blood pressure and cardiac output about 2 hours after use. Together with the cardiac risk of sexual activity, the risk for patients with underlying CV disease is increased.
ALERT: Don't confuse Viagra with Allegra.

Patient teaching

- Explain that drug is contraindicated with regular or intermittent use of nitrates.
- Warn patient about cardiac risk with sexual activity, especially if he has CV risk factors. If patient has symptoms such as angina pectoris, dizziness, or nausea at the start of sexual activity, instruct him to notify prescriber and refrain from further sexual activity.
- Warn patient that erections lasting more than 4 hours and priapism (painful erections more than 6 hours) may occur and should be reported immediately. If priapism isn't treated immediately, penile tissue damage and permanent loss of potency may result.
- Inform patient that drug doesn't protect against sexually transmitted diseases and that protective measures, such as condoms, should be used.
- Instruct patient to take drug 30 minutes to 4 hours before sexual activity; maximum benefit can be expected less than 2 hours after ingesting drug.
- Advise patient that drug is most rapidly absorbed if taken on an empty stomach.
- Inform patient to avoid potentially hazardous activities that rely on color discrimination because blue and green discrimination may be impaired.
- Instruct patient to notify prescriber if visual changes occur.
- Advise patient that drug is effective only with sexual stimulation.
- Tell patient to take drug only as prescribed.
- Advise patient taking HIV drugs or alpha blockers about an increased risk of sildenafil-related adverse events, including hypotension, visual changes, and priapism, and he should promptly report any symptoms to his prescriber. Tell him not to exceed 25 mg of sildenafil in a 48-hour period.

Evaluation

- Sexual activity improves with drug therapy.
- Patient doesn't experience adverse CV events.
- Patient and family state understanding of drug therapy.

simvastatin
(sim-vuh-STAT-in)
Lipex ◇, Zocor✐

Pharmacologic class: HMG-CoA reductase inhibitor
Therapeutic class: antihyperlipidemic
Pregnancy risk category: X

Indications and dosages

▶ **To reduce risk of CAD mortality and CV events in patients at high risk.** *Adults:* Initially, 20 to 40 mg P.O. daily in evening. Dosage adjusted q 4 weeks based on patient tolerance and response. Maximum, 80 mg daily.
▶ **To reduce total cholesterol and LDL levels in patients with homozygous familial hypercholesterolemia.** *Adults:* 40 mg daily in evening; or 80 mg daily in three divided doses of 20 mg in morning, 20 mg in afternoon, and 40 mg in evening.
▶ **Heterozygous familial hypercholesterolemia.** *Children ages 10 to 17:* Give 10 mg P.O. once daily in the evening. Maximum, 40 mg daily.
Adjust-a-dose: For patients taking cyclosporine, initially give 5 mg P.O. daily; don't exceed 10 mg daily. For patients taking fibrates or niacin, maximum is 10 mg P.O. daily. For patients taking amiodarone or verapamil, maximum is 20 mg P.O. daily. For patients with severe renal insufficiency, initially give 5 mg P.O. daily.

Contraindications and cautions

• Contraindicated in patients hypersensitive to the drug or any of its components, and in those with active liver disease or conditions that have unexplained persistent elevations of transaminase level.
• Use cautiously in patients who consume substantial quantities of alcohol or have a history of liver disease.
Lifespan: In pregnant women, breastfeeding women, and women of childbearing age, drug is contraindicated.

Adverse reactions

CNS: asthenia, headache.
GI: abdominal pain, constipation, diarrhea, dyspepsia, flatulence, nausea.
Hepatic: ***cirrhosis, hepatitis, hepatic necrosis.***
Musculoskeletal: myalgia.
Respiratory: upper respiratory tract infection.

Interactions

Drug-drug. *Amiodarone, verapamil:* May increase risk of myopathy and rhabdomyolysis. Don't exceed 20 mg simvastatin daily.
Clarithromycin, erythromycin, HIV protease inhibitors, nefazodone: May increase risk of myopathy and rhabdomyolysis. Avoid using together, or suspend therapy during treatment with clarithromycin or erythromycin.
Cyclosporine, fibrates, niacin: May increase risk of myopathy and rhabdomyolysis. Monitor patient closely if use together can't be avoided. Don't exceed 10 mg simvastatin daily.
Digoxin: May elevate digoxin level slightly. Closely monitor at the start of therapy.
Fluconazole, itraconazole, ketoconazole: May increase level and adverse effects of simvastatin. Avoid this combination. If they must be given together, reduce dose of simvastatin.
Hepatotoxic drugs: May increase risk of hepatotoxicity. Avoid using together.
Non-nucleoside reverse transcriptase inhibitors (delavirdine, efavirenz, nevirapine): May increase or decrease simvastatin level. Monitor patient for unexplained muscle pain.
Warfarin: May enhance anticoagulant effect. Monitor PT and INR at the start of therapy and during dose adjustment.
Drug-herb. *Red yeast rice:* May increase the risk of adverse events or toxicity. Discourage using together.
St. John's wort: May increase clearance of simvastatin, resulting in reduced effectiveness. Avoid using together.
Drug-food. *Grapefruit juice:* May increase drug level and risk of adverse effects, including myopathy and rhabdomyolysis. Advise patient against drinking grapefruit juice.
Drug-lifestyle. *Alcohol use:* May increase the risk of hepatotoxicity. Discourage using together.

Effects on lab test results

• May increase liver enzyme and CK levels.

Pharmacokinetics

Absorption: Good, but extensive hepatic extraction limits availability of active inhibitors to 5% of dose or less.

S

Distribution: More than 95% protein-bound.
Metabolism: Hydrolysis occurs in liver; at least three major metabolites have been identified.
Excretion: Mainly in bile. *Half-life:* 3 hours.

Route	Onset	Peak	Duration
P.O.	Unknown	1½–2½ hr	Unknown

Action

Chemical effect: Inhibits HMG-CoA reductase. This enzyme is early (and rate-limiting) step in synthetic pathway of cholesterol.
Therapeutic effect: Lowers LDL and total cholesterol level.

Available forms

Tablets: 5 mg, 10 mg, 20 mg, 40 mg, 80 mg

NURSING PROCESS

Assessment

- Obtain history of patient's LDL and total cholesterol level before starting therapy, and reassess regularly thereafter to monitor the drug's effectiveness.
- Obtain liver function test results before starting therapy and periodically thereafter. If enzyme level elevations persist, a liver biopsy may be performed.
- Monitor patient for myalgia—muscular weakness—and for elevated CK level, during treatment. Rhabdomyolysis with and without acute renal insufficiency has been reported.
- Be alert for adverse reactions and drug interactions.
- Assess patient's dietary fat intake.
- Assess patient's and family's knowledge of drug therapy.

Nursing diagnoses

- Risk for injury related to presence of elevated cholesterol level
- Constipation related to drug-induced adverse GI reactions
- Deficient knowledge related to drug therapy

Planning and implementation

- Drug therapy starts only after diet and other nondrug therapies have proven ineffective.
- Make sure patient follows a standard low-cholesterol diet during therapy.
- Give drug with evening meal for enhanced effectiveness.
- If cholesterol level falls below target range, dosage may be reduced.

ALERT: Don't confuse Zocor with Cozaar.

Patient teaching

- Tell patient to take drug with evening meal to enhance absorption and cholesterol biosynthesis.
- Teach patient dietary management of lipids (restricting total fat and cholesterol intake) and measures to control other cardiac disease risk factors. If appropriate, suggest weight control, exercise, and smoking cessation programs.
- Tell patient to inform prescriber about adverse reactions, particularly muscle aches and pains.

ALERT: Inform woman that drug is contraindicated during pregnancy. Advise her to notify prescriber immediately if pregnancy occurs.

Evaluation

- Patient's LDL and total cholesterol level are within normal limits.
- Patient regains and maintains normal bowel pattern throughout therapy.
- Patient and family state understanding of drug therapy.

sirolimus

(sir-AH-lih-mus)
Rapamune

Pharmacologic class: macrocyclic lactone
Therapeutic class: immunosuppressant
Pregnancy risk category: C

Indications and dosages

▶ **Prophylaxis of organ rejection in patients receiving renal transplants.** *Adults and children age 13 and older who weigh 40 kg (88 lb) or more:* Initially, 6 mg P.O. as a one-time loading dose as soon as possible after transplantation; then maintenance dose of 2 mg P.O. once daily. Give 4 hours after cyclosporine and corticosteroids. Maximum daily dose is 40 mg. If a daily dose exceeds 40 mg because of loading dose, give the loading dose over 2 days. Monitor trough level at least 3 to 4 days after loading dose.

Children age 13 and older who weigh less than 40 kg: Initially, 3 mg/m² P.O. as a one-time loading dose after transplantation; then maintenance dose of 1 mg/m² P.O. once daily.

Adjust-a-dose: For patients with hepatic impairment, reduce maintenance dose by 33%. Adjusting loading dose isn't needed.

Contraindications and cautions

- Contraindicated in patients hypersensitive to the drug or any of its derivatives or components.
- Use cautiously in patients with hyperlipidemia or impaired liver or renal function.
- Risk for angioedema, particularly when combined with ACE inhibitors.
- Safety and effectiveness of sirolimus haven't been established in liver and lung transplant patients; therefore, such use isn't recommended.

Lifespan: In pregnant women, use only if benefits outweigh risks to the fetus. In breast-feeding women, drug is contraindicated. Women of childbearing age should use contraception before therapy, during, and for 12 weeks after therapy. In children younger than age 13, safety and effectiveness haven't been established.

Adverse reactions

CNS: *anxiety, asthenia,* confusion, *depression,* dizziness, emotional lability, *fever, headache,* hypertonia, hypesthesia, hypotonia, *insomnia,* malaise, neuropathy, paresthesia, *pain,* somnolence, syncope, *tremor.*
CV: atrial fibrillation, *chest pain, edema,* facial edema, ***heart failure, hemorrhage,*** *hypertension,* hypotension, palpitations, *peripheral edema,* peripheral vascular disorder, tachycardia, thrombophlebitis, ***thrombosis,*** vasodilation.
EENT: abnormal vision, cataracts, conjunctivitis, deafness, ear pain, epistaxis, otitis media, *pharyngitis,* rhinitis, sinusitis, tinnitus.
GI: *abdominal pain,* anorexia, ascites, *constipation, diarrhea, dyspepsia,* dysphagia, enlarged abdomen, eructation, esophagitis, flatulence, gastritis, gastroenteritis, gingivitis, gum hyperplasia, hernia, ileus, mouth ulcerations, *nausea,* oral candidiasis, ***peritonitis,*** stomatitis, *vomiting.*
GU: albuminuria, bladder pain, dysuria, glycosuria, hematuria, hydronephrosis, impotence, kidney pain, nocturia, oliguria, pelvic pain, pyuria, scrotal edema, testis disorder, ***toxic nephropathy, tubular necrosis,*** urinary frequency, urinary incontinence, urine retention, *UTI.*
Hematologic: *anemia,* leukocytosis, ***leukopenia,*** lymphadenopathy, polycythemia, **THROMBOCYTOPENIA,** ***thrombotic thrombocytopenic purpura.***
Hepatic: ***hepatic artery thrombosis.***
Metabolic: ***acidosis,*** Cushing syndrome, dehydration, ***diabetes mellitus,*** hypercalcemia, *hypercholesteremia,* hyperglycemia, **HYPERKALEMIA,** *hyperlipidemia,* hyperphosphatemia, hypervolemia, hypocalcemia, ***hypoglycemia,*** *hypokalemia,* hypomagnesemia, hyponatremia, *hypophosphatemia, weight gain,* weight loss.
Musculoskeletal: *arthralgia,* arthrosis, *back pain,* bone necrosis, leg cramps, myalgia, osteoporosis, tetany.
Respiratory: ***asthma,*** atelectasis, bronchitis, cough, dyspnea, ***hypoxia, lung edema,*** pleural effusion, pneumonia, upper respiratory tract infection.
Skin: *acne,* ecchymoses, fungal dermatitis, hirsutism, pruritus, *rash,* skin hypertrophy, skin ulcer, sweating.
Other: abscess, abnormal healing, ***angioedema,*** cellulitis, chills, flulike syndrome, infection, ***sepsis.***

Interactions

Drug-drug. *Aminoglycosides, amphotericin, other nephrotoxic drugs:* May increase risk of nephrotoxicity. Use cautiously.
Bromocriptine, cimetidine, clarithromycin, clotrimazole, danazol, erythromycin, fluconazole, indinavir, itraconazole, metoclopramide, nicardipine, ritonavir, verapamil, other drugs that inhibit CYP3A4: May decrease sirolimus metabolism and increase sirolimus level. Monitor patient for toxicity and elevated liver enzymes.
Carbamazepine, phenobarbital, phenytoin, rifabutin, rifapentine, other drugs that induce CYP3A4: May increase sirolimus metabolism and decrease sirolimus level. Monitor patient closely.
Cyclosporine: May inhibit sirolimus metabolism, increasing levels and toxicity risk. Give sirolimus 4 hours after cyclosporine to prevent variations in sirolimus concentration.
Diltiazem: May increase sirolimus level. Monitor and reduce dosage of sirolimus as needed.
Ketoconazole: May increase rate and extent of sirolimus absorption. Avoid using together.
Rifampin: May decrease sirolimus level. Consider alternatives to rifampin.
Tacrolimus: May increase risk of hepatic artery thrombosis. Don't use together.
Vaccines: May reduce effectiveness of vaccination. Avoid live vaccines.

S

Drug-food. *Grapefruit juice:* May decrease drug metabolism if patient drinks a quart or more of grapefruit juice per day. Discourage overuse or dilution of drug with juice.
Drug-herb. *St. John's wort:* May reduce sirolimus concentrations. Avoid using together.
Drug-lifestyle. *Sun exposure:* May increase risk of skin cancer. Tell patient to take precautions.

Effects on lab test results

- May increase BUN, creatinine, liver enzyme, cholesterol, and lipid levels. May decrease sodium, magnesium, and hemoglobin levels and hematocrit. May increase or decrease phosphate, potassium, glucose, and calcium levels.
- May increase RBC count. May decrease platelet count. May increase or decrease WBC count.

Pharmacokinetics

Absorption: Rapid, with mean peak level occurring in about 1 to 3 hours. Oral bioavailability is about 14% for the oral solution. Food decreases peak level and increases time to peak level.
Distribution: Extensively partitioned into formed blood elements. About 92% protein-bound.
Metabolism: Extensively metabolized by the mixed function oxidase system, mainly CYP3A4. Seven major metabolites have been identified in whole blood.
Excretion: 91% in feces and 2.2% in urine. *Half-life:* About 62 hours.

Route	Onset	Peak	Duration
P.O.	Unknown	1–3 hr	Unknown

Action

Chemical effect: An immunosuppressant that inhibits T-lymphocyte activation and proliferation that occur in response to antigenic and cytokine stimulation. Also inhibits antibody formation.
Therapeutic effect: Immunosuppression in patients receiving renal transplants.

Available forms

Oral solution: 1 mg/ml
Tablets: 1 mg, 2 mg

NURSING PROCESS

Assessment

- Obtain history of patient's organ transplantation before starting therapy.
- Monitor patient's liver and renal function, and triglyceride level, before starting therapy.
- Monitor drug level in children who weigh less than 40 kg (88 lb), patients with hepatic impairment, patients taking drugs that induce or inhibit CYP3A4, and patients whose cyclosporine dose has been drastically reduced or stopped.
- Monitor patient for infection and development of lymphoma, which may result from immunosuppression.
- Watch for development of rhabdomyolysis if patient is taking sirolimus and cyclosporine is started as an HMG-CoA reductase inhibitor.
- Assess patient's and family's knowledge of drug therapy.

Nursing diagnoses

- Risk for injury related to potential for organ rejection
- Ineffective protection related to drug-induced immunosuppression
- Deficient knowledge related to drug therapy

Planning and implementation

- Give drug consistently with or without food.

ALERT: In patient with mild to moderate hepatic impairment, reduce maintenance dose by about one-third. Loading dose doesn't need to be reduced.

- Dilute oral solution before giving. After dilution, use it immediately.
- When diluting drug, empty correct amount into glass or plastic container filled with at least 2 oz (60 ml) of water or orange juice. Don't use grapefruit juice or any other liquid. Stir vigorously and have patient drink immediately. Refill container with at least 4 oz (120 ml) of water or orange juice, stir again, and have patient drink all contents.
- After opening bottle, use contents within 1 month. If needed, bottles and pouches may be stored at room temperature (up to 77° F [25° C]) for several days. Drug can be kept in oral syringe for 24 hours at room temperature or refrigerated at 36° to 46° F (2° to 8° C).
- A slight haze may develop during refrigeration, but this won't affect quality of drug. If

haze develops, bring drug to room temperature and shake gently until haze disappears.

• Use drug in a regimen with cyclosporine and corticosteroids. This drug should be taken 4 hours after cyclosporine dose.

• Two to four months following transplantation, patient with low to moderate risk of graft rejection should be tapered off cyclosporine over 4 to 8 weeks. During the taper, adjust sirolimus dose q 1 to 2 weeks to obtain level between 12 to 24 nanograms/ml. Dosage adjustments should also be based on condition, tissue biopsies, and laboratory findings.

• After transplantation, give antimicrobials for 1 year as directed to prevent *Pneumocystis jiroveci (carinii)* pneumonia and for 3 months as directed to prevent CMV infection.

• If patient has hyperlipidemia, start additional interventions, such as diet, exercise, and lipid-lowering drugs. Use with lipid-lowering drugs is common.

• Don't withdraw cyclosporine in patients with high risk of graft rejection, including patients with Banff grade III acute rejection or vascular rejection before cyclosporine withdrawal, a creatinine level greater than 4.5 mg/dl, or a high panel of reactive antibodies; those who have had retransplants or multi-organ transplants; and those who are dialysis-dependent or who are black.

Patient teaching

• Show patient how to store, dilute, and take drug properly.

• Tell patient to take drug consistently with or without food to minimize absorption variability.

• Advise patient to take drug 4 hours after taking cyclosporine.

• Tell patient to wash area with soap and water if solution touches skin or mucous membranes; tell him to rinse eyes with plain water if solution gets in eyes.

• Inform woman of child-bearing age of risks during pregnancy. Tell her to use effective contraception before and during therapy and for 12 weeks after stopping the drug.

• Advise patient to take precautions against sun exposure.

☑ Evaluation

• Patient doesn't experience organ rejection.

• Patient is free from infection and serious bleeding episodes throughout drug therapy.

• Patient and family state understanding of drug therapy.

sitagliptin phosphate

(SIGH-tuh-glip-ten FOSS-fayt)

Januvia🖉

Pharmacologic class: dipeptidyl peptidase-4 (DPP-4) enzyme inhibitor

Therapeutic class: antidiabetic

Pregnancy risk category: B

Indications and dosages

▶ **To improve glycemic control in type 2 diabetes, alone or with metformin or a thiazolidinedione.** *Adults:* 100 mg P.O. once daily, with or without food.

Adjust-a-dose: For patients with renal impairment, if creatinine clearance is 30 to 50 ml/minute, give 50 mg once daily. If clearance is less than 30 ml/minute or patient has end-stage renal disease with hemodialysis or peritoneal dialysis, give 25 mg once daily. Drug may be taken without regard to timing of dialysis session.

Contraindications and cautions

• Contraindicated in patients with type 1 diabetes or diabetic ketoacidosis.

• Use cautiously in patients with moderate to severe renal insufficiency and in those taking other antidiabetics.

Lifespan: In breast-feeding women, use cautiously. It's unknown if drug appears in breast-milk. In children, safety and effectiveness aren't known. In elderly patients, assess renal function before therapy and periodically throughout. Adjust dosage carefully because these patients are more likely to have decreased renal function.

Adverse reactions

CNS: headache.
EENT: nasopharyngitis.
GI: abdominal pain, diarrhea, nausea.
Metabolic: ***hypoglycemia.***
Respiratory: upper respiratory tract infection.

Interactions

None significant.

S

Effects on Lab test results

- May increase creatinine level.
- May increase WBC count.

Pharmacokinetics

Absorption: Rapidly absorbed with 87% bioavailability.
Distribution: Mean volume is about 198 L. 38% bound by plasma proteins.
Metabolism: Minimal.
Excretion: Mainly renal, with a small amount via feces. *Half-life:* 12½ hours.

Route	Onset	Peak	Duration
P.O.	Rapid	1–4 hr	Unknown

Action

Chemical effect: Inhibits DPP-4, an enzyme that rapidly inactivates incretin hormones, which play a part in the body's regulation of glucose. By increasing and prolonging active incretin level, drug helps to increase insulin release and decrease circulating glucose.
Therapeutic effect: Stabilizes blood glucose level.

Available forms

Tablets: 25 mg, 50 mg, 100 mg

NURSING PROCESS

Assessment

- Obtain history of patient's underlying condition before starting therapy, and reassess regularly.
- In patients at risk for renal insufficiency, periodically assess renal function.
- Monitor glycosylated hemoglobin level periodically to assess long-term glycemic control.
- Assess patient's and family's knowledge of drug therapy.

Nursing diagnoses

- Ineffective health maintenance related to hyperglycemia
- Risk for injury related to drug-induced hypoglycemia
- Deficient knowledge related to drug therapy

Planning and implementation

- Management of type 2 diabetes should include diet control. Because caloric restrictions, weight loss, and exercise help improve insulin sensitivity and help make drug therapy effective, these measures are essential for proper diabetes management.
- Watch for hypoglycemia, especially in patients receiving combination therapy.

Patient teaching

- Tell patient that drug isn't a substitute for diet and exercise and that it's important to follow a prescribed diet and physical activity routine. Urge patient to monitor his glucose level.
- Inform patient and family members of the signs and symptoms of hyperglycemia and hypoglycemia and the steps to take if these symptoms occur.
- Provide patient with information on complications associated with diabetes and ways to assess for them.
- Tell patient to notify prescriber during periods of stress, such as fever, infection, or surgery; dosage may need adjustment.
- Tell patient drug may be taken without regard to food or meals.

Evaluation

- Patient's blood glucose level is within normal limits.
- Patient doesn't experience hypoglycemic reactions.
- Patient and family state understanding of drug therapy.

sodium bicarbonate

(SOH-dee-um bigh-KAR-buh-nayt)
Arm and Hammer Pure Baking Soda†, Bell/ans†

Pharmacologic class: alkalinizer
Therapeutic class: ion buffer, oral antacid
Pregnancy risk category: C

Indications and dosages

▶ **Adjunct to advanced cardiovascular life support during cardiopulmonary resuscitation (no longer routinely recommended).** *Adults:* Inject either 300 to 500 ml of a 5% solution or 200 to 300 mEq of a 7.5% or 8.4% solution as rapidly as possible. Base further doses on subsequent blood gas values. Or, 1-mEq/kg dose, then repeat 0.5 mEq/kg q 10 minutes.
Children age 2 and younger: 1 mEq/kg I.V. or intraosseous injection of a 4.2 % to 8.4% solu-

tion. Give slowly. Don't exceed daily dose of 8 mEq/kg.

▶ **Severe metabolic acidosis.** *Adults:* Dose depends on blood carbon dioxide content, pH, and patient's condition. Generally, give 90 to 180 mEq/L I.V. during first hour, then adjust as needed.

▶ **Less urgent metabolic acidosis.** *Adults and children age 12 and older:* 2 to 5 mEq/kg as a 4- to 8-hour I.V. infusion.

▶ **Urine alkalization.** *Adults:* 48 mEq (4 g) P.O. initially; then 12 to 24 mEq (1 to 2 g) q 4 hours. May need doses of 30 to 48 mEq (2.5 to 4 g) q 4 hours, up to 192 mEq (16 g) daily.
Children: 1 to 10 mEq (84 to 840 mg)/kg P.O. daily.

▶ **Antacid.** *Adults:* 300 mg to 2 g P.O. one to four times daily.

I.V. administration

- Sodium bicarbonate inactivates such catecholamines as norepinephrine and dopamine and forms precipitate with calcium. Don't mix sodium bicarbonate with I.V. solutions of these drugs, and flush I.V. line adequately.
- Usually given by I.V. infusion. For immediate treatment, drug may be given by direct, rapid I.V. injection, however, in neonates and children younger than age 2, slow I.V. administration is preferred to avoid hypernatremia, decreased CSF pressure, and intracranial hemorrhage.

⊗ **Incompatibilities**
Alcohol 5% in dextrose 5%; allopurinol; amiodarone; amphotericin B; amino acids; ascorbic acid injection; bupivacaine; calcium salts; carboplatin; carmustine; cefotaxime; ciprofloxacin; cisatracurium; cisplatin; corticotropin; dextrose 5% in lactated Ringer's injection; diltiazem; dobutamine; dopamine; doxorubicin liposomal; epinephrine hydrochloride; fat emulsion 10%; glycopyrrolate; hydromorphone; idarubicin; imipenem-cilastatin sodium; Ionosol B, D, or G with invert sugar 10%; isoproterenol; labetalol; lactated Ringer's injection; levorphanol; leucovorin calcium; lidocaine; magnesium sulfate; meperidine; meropenem; methylprednisolone sodium succinate; metoclopramide; midazolam; morphine sulfate; nalbuphine; norepinephrine bitartrate; ondansetron; oxacillin; penicillin G potassium; pentazocine lactate; pentobarbital sodium; procaine; Ringer's injection; sargramostim; 1/6 M sodium lactate; streptomycin; succinylcholine; thiopental; ticarcillin disodium and clavulanate potassium; vancomycin; verapamil; vinca alkaloids; vitamin B complex with vitamin C.

Contraindications and cautions

- Contraindicated in patients with metabolic or respiratory alkalosis; patients who are losing chlorides from vomiting or continuous GI suction; patients taking diuretics known to produce hypochloremic alkalosis; and patients with hypocalcemia in which alkalosis may produce tetany, hypertension, seizures, or heart failure. Oral sodium bicarbonate is contraindicated in patients with acute ingestion of strong mineral acids.
- Use cautiously in patients with hypertension, heart failure or other edematous or sodium-retaining conditions or renal insufficiency.

Lifespan: In pregnant women, use cautiously. In breast-feeding women, use cautiously; it's unknown if the drug appears in breast milk.

Adverse reactions

GI: belching, flatulence, gastric distention.
Metabolic: hypernatremia, hyperosmolarity (with overdose), hypokalemia, ***metabolic alkalosis.***
Other: irritation and pain at injection site.

Interactions

Drug-drug. *Anorexigenics, flecainide, mecamylamine, quinidine, sympathomimetics:* May increase urine alkalization, decrease renal clearance, and increase pharmacologic or toxic effects. Monitor patient for toxicity.
Chlorpropamide, lithium, methotrexate, salicylates, tetracycline: May increase renal clearance of these drugs, possibly resulting in decreased pharmacologic effects. Monitor patient for lack of effect.

Effects on lab test results

- May increase sodium and lactate levels. May decrease potassium level.

Pharmacokinetics

Absorption: Good.
Distribution: Bicarbonate is confined to systemic circulation.
Metabolism: None.

S

Excretion: Bicarbonate is filtered and reabsorbed by kidneys; less than 1% of filtered bicarbonate is excreted. *Half-life:* Unknown.

Route	Onset	Peak	Duration
P.O.	Unknown	Unknown	Unknown
I.V.	Immediate	Immediate	Unknown

Action

Chemical effect: Restores body's buffering capacity and neutralizes excess acid.
Therapeutic effect: Restores normal acid-base balance and relieves acid indigestion.

Available forms

Injection: 4% (2.4 mEq/5 ml), 4.2% (5 mEq/10 ml), 5% (297.5 mEq/500 ml), 7.5% (8.92 mEq/10 ml, 44.6 mEq/50 ml and 179 mEq/200 ml), 8.4% (10 mEq/10 ml and 50 mEq/50 ml)
Tablets†: 325 mg, 650 mg

NURSING PROCESS

Assessment

- Assess patient's condition before starting therapy and regularly thereafter to monitor drug's effectiveness.
- To avoid risk of alkalosis, obtain blood pH, Pao_2, $Paco_2$, and electrolyte level.
- If sodium bicarbonate is being used to produce alkaline urine, monitor urine pH (should be greater than 7) q 4 to 6 hours.
- Be alert for adverse reactions and drug interactions.
- Assess patient's and family's knowledge of drug therapy.

Nursing diagnoses

- Ineffective health maintenance related to underlying condition
- Risk for injury related to drug-induced adverse reactions
- Deficient knowledge related to drug therapy

Planning and implementation

- Drug isn't routinely recommended for use in cardiac arrest because it may produce paradoxical acidosis from CO_2 production. It shouldn't be routinely given during early stages of resuscitation unless acidosis is clearly present.
- Drug may be used after such interventions as defibrillation, cardiac compression, and administration of first-line drugs.
- Give drug with water, not milk; drug may cause hypercalcemia, alkalosis, or possibly renal calculi.
- Inform prescriber of laboratory results.

Patient teaching

- Tell patient not to take with milk.
- Discourage use as antacid. Offer nonabsorbable alternate antacid if it is to be used repeatedly.

Evaluation

- Patient regains normal acid-base balance.
- Patient doesn't experience injury from drug-induced adverse reactions.
- Patient and family state understanding of drug therapy.

sodium chloride

(SOH-dee-um KLOR-ighd)

Pharmacologic class: electrolyte
Therapeutic class: chloride and sodium replacement
Pregnancy risk category: C

Indications and dosages

▶ **Fluid and electrolyte replacement in hyponatremia caused by severe electrolyte loss, severe salt depletion or dehydration.** *Adults:* Dosage is highly individualized. The 3% and 5% solutions are used only with frequent electrolyte determination and given only by slow I.V. With half-normal saline solution: 3% to 8% of body weight, according to deficiencies, over 18 to 24 hours. With normal saline solution: 2% to 6% of body weight, according to deficiencies, over 18 to 24 hours.

I.V. administration

- Infuse 3% and 5% solutions very slowly and cautiously to avoid pulmonary edema. Use only for critical situations, and observe patient continually.
- When infusing peripherally, avoid infiltration and use a large vein.

⊗ Incompatibilities
Amphotericin B, chlordiazepoxide, diazepam, fat emulsion, mannitol, methylprednisolone sodium succinate, phenytoin sodium.

Contraindications and cautions

- Contraindicated in patients with conditions in which giving sodium and chloride is detrimental. The 3% and 5% saline solution injections are contraindicated in patients with increased, normal, or only slightly decreased electrolyte level.
- Use cautiously in postoperative patients and patients with heart failure, circulatory insufficiency, renal dysfunction, or hypoproteinemia.

Lifespan: In pregnant women, use cautiously. In breast-feeding women, use cautiously; it's unknown if the drug appears in breast milk. In the elderly, use cautiously.

Adverse reactions

CV: ***aggravation of heart failure,*** edema if given too rapidly or in excess, thrombophlebitis.
Metabolic: ***aggravation of existing metabolic acidosis*** with excessive infusion, electrolyte disturbances, hypernatremia, hypokalemia.
Respiratory: ***pulmonary edema*** if given too rapidly or in excess.
Skin: abscess, local tenderness, tissue necrosis at injection site.

Interactions

None significant.

Effects on lab test results

- May increase sodium and chloride levels. May decrease potassium and bicarbonate levels.

Pharmacokinetics

Absorption: Absorbed readily.
Distribution: Wide.
Metabolism: None significant.
Excretion: Mainly in urine; some in sweat, tears, and saliva. *Half-life:* Unknown.

Route	Onset	Peak	Duration
P.O.	Unknown	Unknown	Unknown
I.V.	Immediate	Immediate	Unknown

Action

Chemical effect: Replaces and maintains sodium and chloride levels.
Therapeutic effect: Restores normal sodium and chloride levels.

Available forms

Injection: *Half-normal saline solution:* 25 ml, 50 ml, 150 ml, 250 ml, 500 ml, 1,000 ml
Normal saline solution: 2 ml, 3 ml, 5 ml, 10 ml, 20 ml, 25 ml, 30 ml, 50 ml, 100 ml, 150 ml, 250 , 500 ml, 1,000 ml
3% saline solution: 500 ml
5% saline solution: 500 ml
14.6% saline solution: 20 ml, 40 ml, 200 ml
23.4% saline solution: 30 ml, 50 ml, 100 ml, 200 ml
Tablets (enteric-coated): 650 mg, 1 g, 2.25 g
Tablets (slow-release): 600 mg

NURSING PROCESS

Assessment

- Obtain history of patient's sodium and chloride levels before starting therapy, and reassess regularly thereafter to monitor drug's effectiveness.
- Monitor other electrolyte levels.
- Assess patient's fluid status.
- Be alert for adverse reactions.
- Assess patient's and family's knowledge of drug therapy.

Nursing diagnoses

- Imbalanced nutrition: less than body requirements related to subnormal levels of sodium and chloride
- Excess fluid volume related to the saline solution's water-drawing power
- Deficient knowledge related to drug therapy

Planning and implementation

- Give tablet with glass of water.

ALERT: Don't confuse concentrates (14.6% and 23.4%) available to add to parenteral nutrient solutions with normal saline solution injection, and never give without diluting. Read label carefully.

Patient teaching

- Tell patient to report adverse reactions promptly.

Evaluation

- Patient's sodium and chloride levels are normal.

• Patient doesn't exhibit signs and symptoms of fluid retention.
• Patient and family state understanding of drug therapy.

sodium ferric gluconate complex
(SOH-dee-um FEH-rik GLOO-kuh-nayt KOM-pleks)
Ferrlecit

Pharmacologic class: macromolecular iron complex
Therapeutic class: hematinic
Pregnancy risk category: B

Indications and dosages

▶ **Iron-deficient anemia in patients undergoing long-term hemodialysis and receiving supplemental erythropoietin therapy.** *Adults and children older than age 15:* Give 10 ml (125 mg elemental iron) diluted in 100 ml normal saline solution I.V. over 1 hour. May also be given undiluted as a slow I.V. infusion at 12.5 mg/min. Most patients need a minimum cumulative dose of 1 g elemental iron given at more than eight sequential dialysis treatments to achieve a favorable hemoglobin level or hematocrit response. May be given during dialysis session.
Children ages 6 to 15: Give 0.12 ml/kg (1.5 mg/kg elemental iron) diluted in 25 ml 0.9% sodium chloride I.V. infusion over 1 hour at eight sequential dialysis sessions. Maximum dosage not to exceed 125 mg/dose.

I.V. administration

• Don't add sodium ferric gluconate complex to parenteral nutrition solutions for I.V. infusion.
• Use immediately after dilution in normal saline solution.
• Dilute in 100 ml normal saline solution and give over 1 hour. Don't exceed 2.1 mg/minute.
• Patient may develop profound hypotension with flushing, lightheadedness, malaise, fatigue, weakness, or severe chest, back, flank, or groin pain after rapid I.V. administration of iron. These reactions don't indicate hypersensitivity and may result from rapid administration of drug. Monitor patient closely during infusion.
⊗ **Incompatibilities**
Other I.V. drugs.

Contraindications and cautions

• Contraindicated in patients hypersensitive to the drug or any of its components (such as benzyl alcohol), and in patients with anemias not linked to iron deficiency. Don't give to patients with iron overload.
Lifespan: In breast-feeding women, use cautiously; it's unknown if the drug appears in breast milk. In children younger than age 6, safety and effectiveness haven't been established. In the elderly, begin treatment at lowest dose and observe closely.

Adverse reactions

CNS: asthenia, headache, fatigue, malaise, dizziness, paresthesia, agitation, insomnia, somnolence, syncope, pain, fever.
CV: hypotension, hypertension, tachycardia, ***bradycardia,*** angina, chest pain, ***MI,*** edema, flushing.
EENT: conjunctivitis, abnormal vision, rhinitis.
GI: nausea, vomiting, diarrhea, rectal disorder, dyspepsia, eructation, flatulence, melena, abdominal pain.
GU: UTI.
Hematologic: abnormal erythrocytes, anemia, lymphadenopathy.
Metabolic: ***hyperkalemia,*** hypervolemia, ***hypoglycemia,*** hypokalemia.
Musculoskeletal: arm pain, arthralgia, back pain, cramps, myalgia.
Respiratory: coughing, dyspnea, pneumonia, ***pulmonary edema,*** upper respiratory tract infections.
Skin: increased sweating, pruritus, rash.
Other: ***carcinoma,*** chills, flulike syndrome, ***hypersensitivity reactions,*** infection, injection site reaction, rigors, ***sepsis.***

Interactions

ACE inhibitors (enalapril): May potentiate adverse effects of I.V. iron therapy. Use together cautiously.
Oral iron supplements: May decrease absorption of oral iron preparations. Monitor patient.

Effects on lab test results

• May decrease glucose and hemoglobin levels and hematocrit. May increase or decrease potassium level.

Pharmacokinetics

Absorption: Given I.V.

Distribution: Unknown.
Metabolism: Unknown.
Excretion: Unknown. *Half-life:* 1 hour in healthy iron-deficient adults.

Route	Onset	Peak	Duration
I.V.	Unknown	Unknown	Unknown

Action

Chemical effect: Drug restores total body iron content, which is critical for normal hemoglobin synthesis and oxygen transport.
Therapeutic effect: Restores total body iron content.

Available forms

Injection: 62.5 mg elemental iron (12.5 mg/ml) in 5-ml ampules

NURSING PROCESS

Assessment

- Obtain history of patient's underlying condition before starting therapy, and reassess regularly to monitor drug's effectiveness.
- Find out about other sources of iron patient may be taking, such as nonprescription iron preparations and iron-containing multivitamin and mineral supplements.
- Monitor hematocrit and hemoglobin, MCV, ferritin, and iron saturation levels during therapy.
- Assess patient's and family's knowledge of drug therapy.

Nursing diagnoses

- Risk for injury related to drug-induced adverse reactions
- Activity intolerance related to underlying condition
- Deficient knowledge related to drug therapy

Planning and implementation

- Dose is expressed in milligrams of elemental iron.
- Don't give drug to patients with iron overload, which commonly occurs in hemoglobinopathies and other refractory anemias.

ALERT: Life-threatening hypersensitivity reactions (characterized by CV collapse, cardiac arrest, bronchospasm, oral or pharyngeal edema, dyspnea, angioedema, urticaria, or pruritus sometimes linked with pain and muscle spasm of chest or back) may occur during infusion. Have adequate supportive measures readily available. Monitor patient closely.

- Some adverse reactions in hemodialysis patients may be related to dialysis itself or to chronic renal impairment.

ALERT: Drug contains benzyl alcohol and may cause "gasping syndrome" in neonates.

ALERT: Don't confuse Ferrlecit with Ferralet.

Patient teaching

- Advise to immediately report signs or symptoms of iron poisoning, which include abdominal pain, diarrhea, vomiting, drowsiness, or hyperventilation.

Evaluation

- Patient doesn't experience injury as a result of drug-induced adverse reactions.
- Patient experiences improved activity tolerance.
- Patient and family state understanding of drug therapy.

sodium phosphate

(SOH-dee-um FOS-fayt)

Fleet Enema, Fleet Pediatric Enema, Fleet Phospho-soda†

Pharmacologic class: acid salt
Therapeutic class: mineral, saline laxative
Pregnancy risk category: C (I.V.), NR (P.R.)

Indications and dosages

▶ **Constipation.** *Adults and children age 12 and older:* 20 to 45 ml of solution mixed with 120 ml of cold water P.O. Or, 120 ml P.R. (as enema).
Children ages 10 to 11: Give 10 to 20 ml of solution mixed with 120 ml of cold water P.O.
Children ages 5 to 9: Give 5 to 10 ml of solution mixed with 120 ml of cold water P.O.
Children older than age 2: Give 60 ml P.R.

▶ **Total parenteral nutrition (TPN).** *Adults and children:* Doses are highly individualized. Usually 10 to 15 millimoles (mM) per liter of TPN solution I.V.; titrate per phosphate level. Normal range 3 to 4.5 mg/dl for adults, 4 to 7 mg/dl for children.
Infants receiving TPN: Usually 1.5 to 2 mM/kg I.V. daily; titrate per phosphate level.

S

I.V. administration

- To avoid errors, drug should be prescribed in terms of millimoles (mM) of phosphorous.
- Dilute and mix with larger volume of fluid.
- To avoid toxicity, infuse slowly.
- Infusions with high concentrations of phosphate may cause hypocalcemia. Monitor calcium level.

⊗ Incompatibilities
None reported.

Contraindications and cautions

- Contraindicated in patients on sodium-restricted diets and in patients with intestinal obstruction or perforation, edema, heart failure, megacolon, impaired renal function, or symptoms of appendicitis or acute surgical abdomen, such as abdominal pain, nausea, and vomiting.
- I.V. sodium phosphate contraindicated in patients with hypernatremia, high phosphate level, or low calcium level.
- Use cautiously in patients with large hemorrhoids or anal abrasions.
- Use I.V. sodium phosphate cautiously in patients with cardiac disease, renal impairment, adrenal insufficiency, and cirrhosis.

Lifespan: In pregnant women, use cautiously. In breast-feeding women, use cautiously because it's unknown if the drug appears in breast milk. In children younger than age 4, use only as directed by prescriber.

Adverse reactions

GI: abdominal cramps.
Metabolic: fluid and electrolyte disturbances (such as hypernatremia, hyperphosphatemia, hypocalcemia) with daily use.
Other: hypocalcemic tetany, laxative dependence with long-term or excessive use.

Interactions

None significant.

Effects on lab test results

- May increase sodium and phosphate levels. May decrease electrolyte level with prolonged use.

Pharmacokinetics

Absorption: About 1% to 20% of P.O. dose absorbed; unknown after P.R. administration. About 80% of I.V. dose reabsorbed through the renal tubules for homeostasis.
Distribution: Unknown.
Metabolism: Unknown.
Excretion: Renal for I.V. route. *Half-life:* Unknown.

Route	Onset	Peak	Duration
P.O.	30 min–3 hr	Varies	Varies
P.R.	5–10 min	Varies	Ends with evacuation
I.V.	Unknown	Unknown	Unknown

Action

Chemical effect: Oral and rectal use produces osmotic effect in small intestine by drawing water into intestinal lumen. I.V. use maintains body's normal phosphate level.
Therapeutic effect: Relieves constipation. Prevents hypophosphatemia.

Available forms

Enema: 160 mg/ml sodium phosphate and 60 mg/ml sodium biphosphate
I.V. infusion: 3 mM phosphate and 4 mEq sodium/L in 10-, 15-, 30-, 50-ml vials
Liquid: 2.4 g/5 ml sodium phosphate and 900 mg/5 ml sodium biphosphate

NURSING PROCESS

Assessment

- Assess patient's condition before starting therapy and regularly thereafter to monitor drug's effectiveness.
- Before giving drug for constipation, determine whether patient has adequate fluid intake, exercise, and diet.
- Be alert for adverse reactions.
- Assess for signs of overdose during I.V. therapy, including paresthesias of extremities, confusion, paralysis, cardiac arrhythmias.

ALERT: Up to 10% of sodium content of drug may be absorbed.

- Assess patient's and family's knowledge of drug therapy.

Nursing diagnoses

- Constipation related to underlying condition
- Acute pain related to drug-induced abdominal cramping
- Deficient knowledge related to drug therapy

Planning and implementation

• Dilute drug with water before giving. Follow administration with full glass of water.

• Make sure that patient has easy access to bathroom facilities, commode, or bedpan.

ALERT: Severe electrolyte imbalances may occur if recommended dose is exceeded.

Patient teaching

• Teach patient about dietary sources of bulk, which include bran and other cereals, fresh fruit, and vegetables.

• Tell patient to maintain adequate fluid intake of at least 6 to 8 glasses of water or juices daily unless contraindicated.

Evaluation

• Patient's constipation is relieved.

• Patient's abdominal cramping ceases.

• Patient and family state understanding of drug therapy.

sodium phosphate monohydrate

(SOE-dee-um FOS-fate maw-no-HIGH-drate)

sodium phosphate dibasic anhydrous

(SOE-dee-um FOS-fate die-BAY-sick an-HIGH-drus)

Visicol

Pharmacologic class: osmotic laxative
Therapeutic class: bowel evacuant
Pregnancy risk category: C

Indications and dosages

▶ To cleanse the bowel before colonoscopy. *Adults:* 40 tablets taken in the following manner: The evening before the procedure, 3 tablets P.O. with at least 8 oz of clear liquid q 15 minutes for a total of 20 tablets. The last dose will be only 2 tablets. The day of the procedure, 3 tablets P.O. with at least 8 oz of clear liquid q 15 minutes for a total of 20 tablets, starting 3 to 5 hours before the procedure. The last dose will be only 2 tablets.

Contraindications and cautions

• Contraindicated in patients hypersensitive to the drug or any of its components. Avoid giving drug to patients with heart failure, ascites, unstable angina, gastric retention, ileus, acute intestinal obstruction, pseudo-obstruction, severe chronic constipation, bowel perforation, acute colitis, toxic megacolon, or hypomotility syndrome (hypothyroidism, scleroderma).

• Use cautiously in patients with a history of electrolyte abnormalities, current electrolyte abnormalities, or impaired renal function. Also, use cautiously in patients who take drugs that can induce electrolyte abnormalities or prolong the QT interval.

Lifespan: In children, safety and effectiveness haven't been established. In the elderly, use cautiously because of greater sensitivity to drug.

Adverse reactions

CNS: dizziness, headache.
GI: abdominal bloating, abdominal pain, nausea, vomiting.

Interactions

Drug-drug. *Oral drugs:* May reduce absorption of these drugs because of rapid peristalsis and diarrhea induced by sodium phosphate monohydrate and sodium phosphate dibasic anhydrous. Separate administration times.

Effects on lab test results

• May increase phosphorus level. May decrease potassium and calcium levels.

Pharmacokinetics

Absorption: Rapid. Duration of action is 1 to 3 hours after administration.
Distribution: Unknown.
Metabolism: Not expected to be metabolized by the liver.
Excretion: Almost entirely via the kidneys. *Half-life:* Unknown.

Route	Onset	Peak	Duration
P.O.	Unknown	3 hr	1–3 hr

Action

Chemical effect: The primary mechanism probably is thought the osmotic action of sodium, which causes large amounts of water to be drawn into the colon.
Therapeutic effect: Cleanses the colon.

Available forms

Tablets: 1.5 g sodium phosphate (1.102 g sodium phosphate monohydrate and 0.398 g sodium phosphate dibasic anhydrous)

NURSING PROCESS

Assessment
- Assess underlying condition before starting therapy, and reassess regularly thereafter to monitor drug's effectiveness.
- Obtain laboratory studies before starting therapy and correct electrolyte imbalances before giving drug.
- Assess patient's and family's knowledge of drug therapy.

Nursing diagnoses
- Acute pain related to abdominal discomfort
- Risk for deficient fluid volume related to adverse GI effects
- Deficient knowledge related to drug therapy

Planning and implementation
- Undigested or partially digested tablets and other drugs may be seen in the stool or during colonoscopy.
- As with other sodium phosphate cathartic preparations, this drug may induce colonic mucosal ulceration.
- Monitor patient for signs of dehydration.
- Don't repeat administration within 7 days.
- No enema or laxative is needed with drug.

ALERT: Giving other sodium phosphate products may result in death from significant fluid shifts, electrolyte abnormalities, and cardiac arrhythmias. Patient with electrolyte disturbances has an increased risk of prolonged QT interval. Use drug cautiously in patient who is taking other drugs known to prolong the QT interval.

Patient teaching
- Instruct patient to drink at least 8 oz of clear liquid with each dose. Inadequate fluid intake may lead to excessive fluid loss and hypovolemia.
- Tell patient to drink only clear liquids for at least 12 hours before starting the purgative regimen.
- Warn patient against taking an additional enema or laxative, particularly one that contains sodium phosphate.
- Tell patient that undigested or partially digested tablets and other drugs may appear in the stool.

Evaluation
- Patient states that pain management methods are effective.
- Patient maintains adequate hydration.
- Patient and family state understanding of therapy.

sodium polystyrene sulfonate
(SOH-dee-um pol-ee-STIGH-reen SUL-fuh-nayt)
Kayexalate, Kionex, SPS

Pharmacologic class: cation-exchange resin
Therapeutic class: potassium-removing resin
Pregnancy risk category: C

Indications and dosages
▶ **Hyperkalemia.** *Adults:* 15 g P.O. daily to q.i.d. in water or sorbitol (3 to 4 ml/g of resin). Or mix powder with appropriate medium—aqueous suspension or diet appropriate for renal impairment—and instill into NG tube. Or, 30 to 50 g q 6 hours as warm emulsion deep into sigmoid colon (20 cm), retained for 30 minutes. In persistent vomiting or paralytic ileus, high-retention enema of sodium polystyrene sulfonate (30 g) suspended in 200 ml of 10% methylcellulose, 10% dextrose, or 25% sorbitol solution may be given.
Children: 1 g of resin P.O. or P.R. for each mEq of potassium to be removed. Or, 1 g/kg every 6 hours. P.O. route preferred because drug should stay in intestine for at least 6 hours.

Contraindications and cautions
- Contraindicated in patients hypersensitive to the drug or any of its components, and in those with hypokalemia.
- Use cautiously in patients with severe heart failure, severe hypertension, or marked edema.

Lifespan: In pregnant women, use cautiously. In breast-feeding women, use cautiously; it's unknown if the drug appears in breast milk.

Adverse reactions
GI: anorexia, *constipation, diarrhea* with sorbitol emulsions, fecal impaction in elderly patients, gastric irritation, nausea, vomiting.
Metabolic: hypocalcemia, hypokalemia, hypomagnesemia, sodium retention.

Interactions
Drug-drug. *Antacids and laxatives (nonabsorbable cation-donating types, including magnesium hydroxide):* May cause systemic alkalo-

sis and reduced potassium exchange capability. Don't use together.

Effects on lab test results

• May increase sodium level. May decrease potassium, calcium, and magnesium levels.

Pharmacokinetics

Absorption: None.
Distribution: None.
Metabolism: None.
Excretion: Unchanged in feces. *Half-life:* Unknown.

Route	Onset	Peak	Duration
P.O., P.R.	2–12 hr	Unknown	Unknown

Action

Chemical effect: Exchanges sodium ions for potassium ions in intestine. Much of exchange capacity is used for cations other than potassium (calcium and magnesium) and, possibly, fats and proteins.
Therapeutic effect: Lowers potassium level.

Available forms

Powder: 1-lb jar (3.5 g/5 ml)
Suspension (1.25 g/5ml): 60 ml*, 120 ml*, 480 ml*

NURSING PROCESS

Assessment

• Obtain history of patient's potassium level before starting therapy.
• Monitor potassium level regularly. Treatment may result in potassium deficiency. Treatment usually stops when potassium level declines to 4 or 5 mEq/L.
ALERT: Watch for other signs of hypokalemia, such as irritability, confusion, arrhythmias, ECG changes, severe muscle weakness and paralysis, and cardiotoxicity in patient taking digitalis.
• Monitor patient for symptoms of other electrolyte deficiencies (magnesium, calcium) because drug is nonselective. Monitor calcium level in patient receiving sodium polystyrene therapy for more than 3 days. Supplementary calcium may be needed.
• Watch for sodium overload. Drug contains about 100 mg of sodium/g. About one-third of sodium in resin is retained.
• Be alert for adverse reactions and drug interactions.
• Watch for constipation with P.O. or NG use.
• Assess patient's and family's knowledge of drug therapy.

Nursing diagnoses

• Ineffective health maintenance related to presence of hyperkalemia
• Constipation related to drug-induced adverse GI reactions
• Deficient knowledge related to drug therapy

Planning and implementation

• Don't heat resin because it will impair drug's effectiveness.
• Mix resin only with water or sorbitol for P.O. use. Never mix with orange juice (high potassium content) to disguise taste.
• Chill oral suspension for greater palatability.
• If sorbitol is given, mix with resin suspension.
• Consider solid form. Resin cookie and candy recipes are available. Ask pharmacist or dietitian to supply.
• To prevent constipation, use sorbitol (10 to 20 ml of 70% syrup q 2 hours, p.r.n.) to produce one or two watery stools daily.
• Premixed forms are available (SPS and others) for P.R. use.
• If preparing manually, mix polystyrene resin only with water and sorbitol for P.R. use. Don't use mineral oil for P.R. administration to prevent impaction. Ion exchange requires aqueous medium. Sorbitol content prevents impaction.
• Prepare P.R. dose at room temperature. Stir emulsion gently during administration.
• Use #28 French rubber tube. Insert tube 20 cm into sigmoid colon and tape in place. Or, consider indwelling urinary catheter with 30-ml balloon inflated distal to anal sphincter to aid in retention. This is especially helpful for patients with poor sphincter control (for example, after stroke). Use gravity flow. Drain returns constantly through Y-tube connection. Place patient in knee-chest position or with hips on pillow for a while if back leakage occurs.
• After P.R. administration, flush tubing with 50 to 100 ml of nonsodium fluid to ensure delivery of all drug. Flush rectum to remove resin.
• Prevent fecal impaction in geriatric patient by giving resin P.R. Give cleansing enema before P.R. administration. The patient will need to re-

S

tain enema, ideally for 6 to 10 hours, but 30 to 60 minutes is acceptable.
• If hyperkalemia is severe, prescriber won't depend solely on polystyrene resin to lower potassium level. Dextrose 50% with regular insulin may be given by I.V. push.

Patient teaching
• Explain importance of following prescribed low-potassium diet.
• Explain need to retain enema, ideally for 6 to 10 hours, but 30 to 60 minutes is acceptable.
• Tell patient to report adverse reactions.

Evaluation
• Patient's potassium level is normal.
• Patient doesn't develop constipation.
• Patient and family state understanding of drug therapy.

solifenacin succinate

(sohl-ih-FEN-ah-sin SUC-sin-eight)
VESIcare

Pharmacologic class: muscarinic receptor antagonist
Therapeutic class: urinary tract antispasmodic
Pregnancy risk category: C

Indications and dosages

▶ **Overactive bladder with urinary urgency, frequency, and urge incontinence.** *Adults:* 5 mg P.O. once daily. May increase to 10 mg once daily if 5-mg dose is well tolerated.
Adjust-a-dose: If creatinine clearance is less than 30 ml/minute or the patient has moderate liver impairment (Child-Pugh score B), maintain the dose at 5 mg.

Contraindications and cautions

• Contraindicated in patients hypersensitive to drug or any of its components and in patients with urine or gastric retention or uncontrolled narrow-angle glaucoma. Don't use in patients with severe hepatic impairment.
• Use cautiously in patients with a history of prolonged QT interval, those being treated for angle-closure glaucoma, and those with bladder outflow obstruction, decreased GI motility, renal insufficiency, or moderate liver impairment.
Lifespan: In pregnant women, use only if benefits outweigh potential risks to the fetus. Women shouldn't breast-feed while taking drug. Safety and effectiveness in children hasn't been established. In elderly patients, level and half-life may increase though safety and effectiveness are similar to those for younger adults.

Adverse reactions

CNS: depression, dizziness, fatigue.
CV: hypertension, leg swelling.
EENT: blurred vision, dry eyes, pharyngitis.
GI: *constipation, dry mouth,* dyspepsia, nausea, upper abdominal pain, vomiting.
GU: urine retention, UTI.
Respiratory: cough.
Other: influenza.

Interactions

Drug-drug. *Drugs that prolong the QT interval:* May increase the risk of serious cardiac arrhythmias. Monitor patient and ECG closely.
Potent CYP3A4 inhibitors (such as ketoconazole): May increase solifenacin level. Don't exceed solifenacin dose of 5 mg daily when used together.

Effects on lab test results

None reported.

Pharmacokinetics

Absorption: Absolute bioavailability is about 90%.
Distribution: Wide, except in CNS. About 90% bound by plasma proteins.
Metabolism: Extensive, mainly by CYP3A4.
Excretion: Mainly in urine and, to a lesser extent, feces. *Half-life:* 2 or 3 days.

Route	Onset	Peak	Duration
P.O.	Unknown	3–8 hr	Unknown

Action

Chemical effect: Relaxes smooth muscle of the bladder by competitively antagonizing the muscarinic receptors.
Therapeutic effect: Relieves symptoms of overactive bladder.

Available forms

Tablets (film-coated): 5 mg, 10 mg

NURSING PROCESS

Assessment
• Assess bladder function, and monitor drug effects.
• Monitor patient for decreased gastric motility and constipation.
• Evaluate patient's and family's knowledge of drug therapy.

Nursing diagnoses
• Impaired urinary elimination related to underlying medical condition
• Constipation related to drug-induced adverse effects
• Deficient knowledge related to drug therapy

Planning and implementation
• If patient has bladder outlet obstruction, watch for urine retention.
• If the patient has urinary retention, notify prescriber and prepare for urinary catheterization.
• Dry mouth and constipation are the most frequently reported adverse effects of drug therapy.
• Chronic overdose may result in fixed, dilated pupils, blurred vision, dry skin, tremors, and inability to perform the heel-to-toe exam. These effects should subside when drug is stopped.

Patient teaching
• Explain that drug may blur vision. Tell patient to use caution when performing hazardous activities or tasks that require clear vision until effects of the drug are known.
• Discourage use of other drugs that may cause dry mouth, constipation, urine retention, or blurred vision.
• Urge patient to notify prescriber about abdominal pain or constipation that lasts 3 days or longer.
• Tell patient that drug decreases the ability to sweat normally, and advise cautious use in hot environments or during strenuous activity.
• Tell patient to swallow tablet whole with liquid.
• Inform patient that drug may be taken with or without food.

Evaluation
• Patient experiences improved bladder function with drug therapy.
• Patient maintains normal bowel regimen.
• Patient and family state understanding of drug therapy.

somatropin
(soh-muh-TROH-pin)

Genotropin, Genotropin MiniQuick, Humatrope, Norditropin, Nutropin, Nutropin AQ, Saizen, Serostim, Tev-Tropin, Zorbtive

Pharmacologic class: anterior pituitary hormone
Therapeutic class: human growth hormone (GH)
Pregnancy risk category: C

Indications and dosages

▶ **Long-term therapy for growth failure in patients with inadequate secretion of endogenous GH.** *Children:* 0.18 to 0.3 mg/kg Humatrope subcutaneously or I.M. weekly, divided equally and given either 3 alternate days, six times weekly, or daily. Or, up to 0.3 mg/kg Nutropin or Nutropin AQ subcutaneously weekly in daily divided doses. Or, 0.06 mg/kg Saizen I.M. or subcutaneously three times weekly. Or, 0.024 to 0.034 mg/kg Norditropin subcutaneously, six to seven times weekly. Or 0.16 to 0.24 mg/kg Genotropin subcutaneously weekly, divided into five to seven doses. Or 1.5 mg/kg somatropin depot subcutaneously once monthly or 0.75 mg/kg subcutaneously twice monthly on the same days of each month.

▶ **Growth failure from chronic renal insufficiency up to time of kidney transplant.** *Children:* Weekly dosage of up to 0.35 mg/kg Nutropin or Nutropin AQ subcutaneously divided into daily doses.

▶ **Long-term therapy for short stature related to Turner syndrome.** *Children:* Up to 0.375 mg/kg Humatrope, Nutropin, or Nutropin AQ subcutaneously weekly, divided into equal doses given three to seven times weekly.

▶ **Long-term therapy for growth failure in children with Prader-Willi syndrome diagnosed by genetic testing.** *Children:* 0.24 mg/kg Genotropin subcutaneously weekly, divided into six to seven doses.

▶ **To replace endogenous GH in patients with GH deficiency.** *Adults:* Initially, not more than 0.006 mg/kg Humatrope, Nutropin, or Nutropin AQ subcutaneously daily. Humatrope may be increased to maximum of 0.0125 mg/kg daily. Nutropin and Nutropin AQ may be increased to maximum of 0.025 mg/kg daily in

S

patients younger than age 35 or 0.0125 mg/kg daily in patients older than age 35. With Genotropin, starting dose isn't more than 0.04 mg/kg subcutaneously weekly, divided into six to seven doses. Dose may be increased at 4- to 8-week intervals to a maximum dose of 0.08 mg/kg subcutaneously weekly, divided into six to seven doses. With Saizen, starting dose isn't more than 0.005 mg/kg/day. May increase after 4 weeks to maximum of 0.01 mg/kg/day based on patient tolerance and clinical response.

▶ **AIDS wasting or cachexia.** *Adults and children weighing more than 55 kg (121 lb):* 6 mg Serostim subcutaneously at bedtime.

Adults and children weighing 45 to 55 kg (99 to 121 lb): 5 mg Serostim subcutaneously at bedtime.

Adults and children weighing 35 to 45 kg (77 to 99 lb): 4 mg Serostim subcutaneously at bedtime.

Adults and children weighing less than 35 kg: 0.1 mg/kg Serostim subcutaneously daily at bedtime.

▶ **Long-term treatment of growth failure in children born small for gestational age who don't achieve catch-up growth by age 2.** *Children:* 0.48 mg/kg Genotropin subcutaneously weekly, divided into five to seven doses.

▶ **Idiopathic short stature.** *Children:* Up to 0.37 mg/kg (Humatrope) subcutaneously weekly, divided into equal doses given 6 to 7 times per week.

Contraindications and cautions

• Contraindicated in patients with closed epiphyses or active underlying intracranial lesion.

• Don't reconstitute Humatrope with supplied diluent for patients with known sensitivity to either m-cresol or glycerin.

• Genotropin is contraindicated in patients with PWS who are severely obese or have severe respiratory impairment.

Lifespan: In pregnant and breast-feeding women, drug isn't indicated. In children with hypothyroidism and in those whose GH deficiency is caused by an intracranial lesion, use cautiously; these children should be examined frequently for progression or recurrence of underlying disease.

Adverse reactions

CNS: headache, weakness.
CV: mild, transient edema.
Hematologic: *leukemia.*
Metabolic: hypothyroidism, mild hyperglycemia.
Musculoskeletal: localized muscle pain.
Other: *antibodies to GH,* injection site pain.

Interactions

Drug-drug. *Corticosteroids, corticotropin:* May inhibit growth response to GH with long-term use. Monitor patient.

Effects on lab test results

• May increase glucose, inorganic phosphorus, alkaline phosphatase, and parathyroid hormone levels.

Pharmacokinetics

Absorption: About 80% bioavailable after subcutaneous injection.
Distribution: Unknown.
Metabolism: About 90% in liver.
Excretion: About 0.1% unchanged in urine. *Half-life:* 3 hours.

Route	Onset	Peak	Duration
I.M, SubQ	Unknown	7½ hr	12–48 hr

Action

Chemical effect: Purified GH of recombinant DNA origin that stimulates linear, skeletal muscle, and organ growth.
Therapeutic effect: Stimulates growth.

Available forms

Genotropin injection: 5.8 mg (about 17.4 international units/vial), 13.8 mg (about 41.4 international units/vial)
Genotropin MiniQuick injection: 0.2 mg/vial, 0.4 mg/vial, 0.6 mg/vial, 0.8 mg/vial, 1 mg/vial, 1.2 mg/vial, 1.4 mg/vial, 1.6 mg/vial, 1.8 mg/vial, 2 mg/vial
Humatrope injection: 5 mg (about 15 international units/vial), 6 mg (18 international units/cartridge), 12 mg (36 international units/cartridge), 24 mg (72 international units/cartridge)
Norditropin injection: 4 mg (about 12 international units/ml), 8 mg (about 24 international units/ml), 5 mg/1.5 ml cartridges, 10 mg/1.5 ml cartridges, 15 mg/1.5 ml cartridges
Nutropin AQ injection: 10 mg (about 30 international units/vial)

Nutropin injection: 5 mg (about 15 international units/vial), 10 mg (about 30 international units/vial)
Saizen injection: 5 mg (about 15 international units/vial)
Serostim injection: 4 mg (about 12 international units/vial), 5 mg (about 15 international units/vial), 6 mg (about 18 international units/vial)
Somatropin depot injection: 13.5 mg/vial, 18 mg/vial, 22.5 mg/vial
Tev-Tropin injection: 5 mg (about 15 international units/vial)
Zorbtive injection: 4 mg (about 12 international units/vial), 5 mg (about 15 international units/vial), 6 mg (about 18 international units/vial), 8.8 mg (about 26.4 international units/vial)

NURSING PROCESS

Assessment

- Assess child's growth before therapy and regularly thereafter to monitor drug's effectiveness.
- Ensure adults taking Saizen for GH replacement have GH deficiency alone or with multiple hormone deficiencies (result of pituitary or hypothalamic disease, surgery, radiation, or trauma) or had GH deficiency during childhood and confirmed deficiency as an adult.
- Be alert for adverse reactions.
- Toxicity in neonates may occur from exposure to benzyl alcohol used in drug as preservative.
- Conduct regular checkup with monitoring of height, blood, and radiologic studies.
- Observe patient for signs of glucose intolerance and hyperglycemia.
- Monitor patient's periodic thyroid function tests for hypothyroidism, which may require treatment with thyroid hormone.
- Assess patient's and family's knowledge of drug therapy.

Nursing diagnoses

- Delayed growth and development related to lack of adequate endogenous GH
- Ineffective health maintenance related to adverse metabolic reactions
- Deficient knowledge related to drug therapy

Planning and implementation

- To prepare solution, inject supplied diluent into vial containing drug by aiming stream of liquid against glass wall of vial. Then swirl vial with gentle rotary motion until contents are completely dissolved; don't shake vial.
- After reconstitution, solution should be clear. Don't inject solution if it's cloudy or contains particles.
- The subcutaneous route is preferred. Rotate injection sites to reduce the risk of lipoatrophy.
- Store reconstituted drug in refrigerator; use within 14 days.
- If sensitivity to diluent develops, drugs may be reconstituted with sterile water for injection. When drug is reconstituted in this manner, use only one reconstituted dose per vial, refrigerate solution if it isn't used immediately after reconstitution, use reconstituted dose within 24 hours, and discard unused portion.
- If final height is achieved, or epiphyseal fusion occurs, do not continue therapy.
- Excessive glucocorticoid therapy inhibits growth-promoting effect of somatropin. In patient with corticotropin deficiency, adjust glucocorticoid-replacement dosage carefully to avoid growth inhibition.

ALERT: Don't confuse somatropin with somatrem or sumatriptan.

Patient teaching

- Inform parents that child with endocrine disorders (including GH deficiency) may develop slipped capital epiphyses. Tell them to notify prescriber if child begins limping.

Evaluation

- Patient exhibits growth.
- Patient's thyroid function studies and glucose level are normal.
- Patient and family state understanding of drug therapy.

S

sorafenib
(soar-uh-PHEN-ihb)
Nexavar

Pharmacologic class: multi-kinase inhibitor
Therapeutic class: antineoplastic
Pregnancy risk category: D

Indications and dosages

▶ **Advanced renal cell carcinoma.** *Adults:* 400 mg P.O. b.i.d. at least 1 hour before or 2 hours after eating. Continue until disease progresses or unacceptable toxicity occurs.

Adjust-a-dose: If patient develops grade 2 skin toxicity (pain and swelling with normal activities), continue treatment and use topical therapy to relieve symptoms. If symptoms don't improve in 1 week or if they occur a second or third time, stop treatment until toxicity resolves to grade 0 or 1 (able to perform daily activities). Resume treatment at 400 mg daily or every other day. At fourth occurrence of grade 2 toxicity, stop treatment.

If patient develops grade 3 skin toxicity (ulceration, blistering, severe pain of hands and feet, leaving patient unable to perform daily activities) or a second occurrence, stop treatment until toxicity resolves to grade 0 or 1. Resume treatment at 400 mg daily or every other day. At third occurrence of grade 3 toxicity, stop treatment.

Contraindications and cautions

- Contraindicated in patients severely hypersensitive to drug or its components.
- Use cautiously in patients with bleeding disorders, healing wounds, current or previous hand-foot skin reactions, or liver, renal, or cardiac disease, such as hypertension, cardiac ischemia, or a history of MI.

Lifespan: Drug may cause serious birth defects or fetal death. Warn women of childbearing potential to avoid pregnancy during and for 2 weeks following treatment. Mothers shouldn't breast-feed during treatment. In children, safety and effectiveness haven't been established. Geriatric patients may be more sensitive to adverse effects.

Adverse reactions

CNS: *asthenia,* depression, *fatigue, headache, neuropathy.*
CV: *hypertension.*
EENT: *hoarseness.*
GI: *abdominal pain, anorexia, constipation, diarrhea,* dyspepsia, dysphagia, mucositis, *nausea,* stomatitis, *vomiting.*
GU: erectile dysfunction.
Hematologic: anemia, *bleeding,* ***hemorrhage, leukopenia, lymphopenia, neutropenia, thrombocytopenia.***
Metabolic: hypothyroidism, *weight loss.*
Musculoskeletal: arthralgia, *joint pain,* myalgia.
Respiratory: *cough, dyspnea.*
Skin: acne, *alopecia, dry skin, erythema,* exfoliative dermatitis, flushing, *hand-foot reaction, pruritus, rash.*
Other: flulike illness, pyrexia.

Interactions

Drug-drug. *CYP2B6 or CYP2C8 substrates:* May increase levels of these drugs. Use cautiously together.
CYP3A4 inducers (such as carbamazepine, dexamethasone, phenobarbital, phenytoin, rifampin): May increase sorafenib metabolism and decrease its effects. Monitor patient.
Doxorubicin, drugs metabolized by the UGT1A1 pathway (such as irinotecan): May increase levels of these drugs. Use cautiously together.
Warfarin: May increase the risk of bleeding. Monitor PT, INR, and patient for bleeding.
Drug-herb. *St. John's wort:* May decrease drug effects. Discourage use together.

Effects on lab test results

- May increase TSH, lipase, amylase, transaminase, and bilirubin levels. May decrease phosphate level.
- May decrease RBC, WBC, and platelet counts.

Pharmacokinetics

Absorption: Well absorbed; food reduces bioavailability.
Distribution: 99.5% bound by plasma proteins.
Metabolism: In the liver by CYP3A4 and by glucuronidation mediated by UGT1A9.
Excretion: 77% in feces, 19% in urine. *Half-life:* 25 to 48 hours.

Route	Onset	Peak	Duration
P.O.	Unknown	3 hr	Unknown

Action

Chemical effect: Decreases tumor cell proliferation by interacting with multiple intracellular and cell-surface kinases that may influence growth of new blood vessels into a tumor.
Therapeutic effect: Slows carcinoma growth.

Available forms

Tablets: 200 mg

NURSING PROCESS

Assessment

- Assess neoplastic disease before starting therapy, and reassess regularly.
- To avoid serious drug interactions, take a careful drug history.
- Monitor patient closely for hand-foot skin reaction, especially during the first 6 weeks of treatment.
- Monitor patient for cardiac ischemia.
- Assess patient for unusual bruising or bleeding.
- Assess patient's and family's knowledge of drug therapy.

Nursing diagnoses

- Ineffective health maintenance related to neoplastic disease
- Risk for falls related to drug-induced adverse reactions
- Deficient knowledge related to drug therapy

Planning and implementation

- Measure blood pressure weekly during the first 6 weeks of treatment to check for hypertension.
- Stop therapy in patients undergoing major surgery. Before restarting therapy, monitor incision for adequate healing.
- Provide patient with contact information for cancer support groups and instructions for managing adverse effects.

Patient teaching

- Tell patient to swallow tablet whole, 1 hour before or 2 hours after a meal, with water.
- Remind patient to have his blood pressure checked weekly for the first 6 weeks of treatment and as needed throughout therapy.
- Explain that hair loss, nausea, vomiting, diarrhea, and fatigue are common.
- Inform patient that mild to moderate skin reactions are common. Tell him to notify prescriber if they occur. If they're severe, treatment may have to be stopped or dosage reduced. Urge patient to report pain, redness, blisters, or skin ulceration to prescriber immediately.
- Tell patient to report bleeding episodes right away.
- Tell patient to notify prescriber if he develops chest pain or other serious heart problem.

ALERT: Advise women to avoid pregnancy during treatment and for at least 2 weeks afterward. Men and women should both use effective contraception during this time.

- Tell patient to keep an up-to-date list of all medications he takes and to tell all health care providers, including dentists, that he takes sorafenib.

Evaluation

- Patient shows positive response to drug therapy on follow-up studies.
- Patient doesn't experience falls.
- Patient and family state understanding of drug therapy.

sotalol hydrochloride

(SOH-tuh-lol high-droh-KLOR-ighd)

Betapace, Betapace AF, Sorine, Sotacor ♦ ◇

Pharmacologic class: beta blocker
Therapeutic class: antianginal, antiarrhythmic, antihypertensive
Pregnancy risk category: B

Indications and dosages

▶ **Documented, life-threatening ventricular arrhythmias.** *Adults:* Initially, 80 mg Betapace P.O. b.i.d. Dosage is increased q 2 to 3 days as needed and tolerated; most patients respond to 160 to 320 mg daily. A few patients with refractory arrhythmias have received as much as 640 mg daily.

Adjust-a-dose: For patients with renal impairment, if creatinine clearance is 30 to 60 ml/minute, interval is increased to q 24 hours; if clearance is 10 to 30 ml/minute, give q 36 to 48 hours; if clearance is less than 10 ml/minute, individualize dosage.

▶ **To maintain normal sinus rhythm (delayed recurrence of atrial fibrillation or flutter) in patients with symptomatic atrial fibrillation or flutter who are currently in sinus rhythm.** *Adults:* Initially, 80 mg Betapace AF P.O. b.i.d. If initial dose doesn't reduce the frequency of relapses of atrial fibrillation or flutter and patient has a QTc interval of less than 520 msec, may increase to 120 mg P.O. b.i.d. after 3 days. Maximum, 160 mg P.O. b.i.d.

Adjust-a-dose: For patients with renal impairment, if creatinine clearance is 40 to 60 ml/minute, give once daily.

S

Contraindications and cautions

• Contraindicated in patients hypersensitive to the drug or any of its components, and patients with severe sinus node dysfunction, sinus bradycardia, second- or third-degree AV block in absence of an artificial pacemaker, congenital or acquired long-QT interval syndrome, cardiogenic shock, uncontrolled heart failure, or bronchial asthma. Don't give to patients with a creatinine clearance less than 40 ml/minute.
• Use cautiously in patients with renal impairment, sick sinus syndrome, or diabetes mellitus.
Lifespan: In pregnant women, use cautiously. In breast-feeding women and in children, safety and effectiveness haven't been established.

Adverse reactions

CNS: asthenia, dizziness, fatigue, headache, lightheadedness, sleep problems, weakness.
CV: ***arrhythmias, AV block, bradycardia,*** chest pain, ECG abnormalities, edema, ***heart failure,*** hypotension, palpitations, ***proarrhythmic events (ventricular tachycardia, PVCs, ventricular fibrillation).***
GI: diarrhea, dyspepsia, *nausea,* vomiting.
Respiratory: ***bronchospasm,*** dyspnea.

Interactions

Drug-drug. *Antiarrhythmics:* May have additive effects. Avoid using together.
Antihypertensives, catecholamine-depleting drugs (such as guanethidine, haloperidol, and reserpine): May enhance hypotensive effects. Monitor patient closely.
Calcium channel blockers: May enhance myocardial depression. Monitor patient carefully.
Clonidine: May enhance rebound effect seen after withdrawal of clonidine. May cause life-threatening or fatal increases in blood pressure. Stop sotalol several days before withdrawing clonidine.
General anesthetics: May cause additional myocardial depression. Monitor patient closely.
Insulin, oral antidiabetics: May cause hyperglycemia and mask its symptoms. Adjust dosage.
Macrolide antibiotics, quinolones: May increase risk of arrhythmias. Use together cautiously.
Prazosin: May increase the risk of orthostatic hypotension in the early phases of use together. Assist patient to stand slowly until effects are known.

Effects on lab test results

• May increase glucose level.

Pharmacokinetics

Absorption: Well absorbed, with bioavailability of 90% to 100%. Food may interfere.
Distribution: Unknown. Doesn't bind to proteins and crosses blood-brain barrier poorly.
Metabolism: Not metabolized.
Excretion: Mainly in urine in unchanged form. *Half-life:* 12 hours.

Route	Onset	Peak	Duration
P.O.	Unknown	2½–4 hr	Unknown

Action

Chemical effect: Depresses sinus heart rate, slows AV conduction, decreases cardiac output, and lowers systolic and diastolic blood pressure.
Therapeutic effect: Restores normal sinus rhythm, lowers blood pressure, and relieves angina.

Available forms

Tablets: 80 mg, 120 mg, 160 mg, 240 mg

NURSING PROCESS

Assessment

• Assess patient's condition before starting therapy and regularly thereafter to monitor drug's effectiveness.
• Monitor patient's electrolyte level and ECG regularly, especially if patient is taking diuretics. Electrolyte imbalances, such as hypokalemia and hypomagnesemia, may enhance QT interval prolongation and increase risk of serious arrhythmias such as torsades de pointes.
• Be alert for adverse reactions and drug interactions.
• Assess patient's and family's knowledge of drug therapy.

Nursing diagnoses

• Ineffective health maintenance related to underlying condition
• Fatigue related to adverse reactions
• Deficient knowledge related to drug therapy

Planning and implementation

• Because proarrhythmic events may occur at start of therapy and during dose adjustments, patient should be hospitalized for a minimum of 3 days on the maintenance dose. Facilities and personnel should be available to monitor cardiac rhythm and interpret ECG.

• Although patient receiving I.V. lidocaine can start therapy with sotalol without ill effect, other antiarrhythmics should be stopped before starting therapy with sotalol. Therapy typically is delayed until two or three half-lives of withdrawn drug have elapsed. After withdrawal of amiodarone, sotalol shouldn't be given until QT interval normalizes.

• Adjust dose slowly, allowing 2 to 3 days between dose increases for adequate monitoring of QT intervals and for drug level to reach steady-state level.

ALERT: The baseline QTc interval must be 450 msec or less in order to start a patient on Betapace AF. During initiation and adjustment, monitor QT interval 2 to 4 hours after each dose. If the QTc interval is 500 msec or longer, reduce dose or stop drug.

ALERT: Don't confuse sotalol with Stadol. Don't substitute Betapace AF for Betapace.

Patient teaching

• Explain importance of taking drug as prescribed, even when feeling well. Instruct patient not to stop drug suddenly.

• Tell patient that drug may be taken without regard to meals, but should be taken the same way consistently.

• Teach patient how to check his pulse rate.

Evaluation

• Patient responds well to therapy.

• Patient states energy-conserving measures to combat fatigue.

• Patient and family state understanding of drug therapy.

spironolactone

(spih-ron-uh-LAK-tohn)

Aldactone, Novospiroton ♦, Spiractin ◇

Pharmacologic class: mineralocorticoid receptor antagonist
Therapeutic class: potassium-sparing diuretic
Pregnancy risk category: C

Indications and dosages

▶ **Edema.** *Adults:* 25 to 200 mg P.O. daily or in divided doses.
Children: 3.3 mg/kg P.O. daily or in divided doses.

▶ **Essential hypertension.** *Adults:* 50 to 100 mg P.O. daily or in divided doses.
Children: 1 to 2 mg/kg P.O. b.i.d.

▶ **Diuretic-induced hypokalemia.** *Adults:* 25 to 100 mg P.O. daily when P.O. potassium supplements are contraindicated.

▶ **Diagnosis of primary hyperaldosteronism.** *Adults:* 400 mg P.O. daily for 4 days (short test) or 3 to 4 weeks (long test). If hypokalemia and hypertension are corrected, presumptive diagnosis of primary hyperaldosteronism is made.

▶ **To manage primary hyperaldosteronism.** *Adults:* 100 to 400 mg P.O. daily. In patients unwilling or unable to undergo surgery, start with 400 mg daily and then maintain at lowest possible dose.

▶ **Hirsutism‡.** *Adults:* 50 to 200 mg P.O. daily.

▶ **Premenstrual syndrome‡.** *Adults:* 25 mg P.O. q.i.d. beginning on day 14 of menstrual cycle.

▶ **Heart failure in patients taking an ACE inhibitor and a loop diuretic with or without digoxin‡.** *Adults:* Initially, 12.5 to 25 mg P.O. daily.

▶ **To decrease risk of metrorrhagia‡.** *Adults:* 50 mg P.O. b.i.d. on days 4 through 21 of menstrual cycle.

▶ **Acne vulgaris‡.** *Adults:* 100 mg P.O. daily.

Contraindications and cautions

• Contraindicated in patients with anuria, acute or progressive renal insufficiency, rapidly deteriorating renal function, or hyperkalemia.

• Contraindicated in patients taking amiloride or triamterene concomitantly.

• Use cautiously in patients with fluid or electrolyte imbalances, impaired kidney function, or hepatic disease.

Lifespan: In pregnant women, use cautiously. In breast-feeding women, safety and effectiveness haven't been established.

Adverse reactions

CNS: ataxia, confusion, drowsiness, headache, lethargy.
GI: cramping, diarrhea, gastric bleeding, gastritis, ulceration, vomiting.

GU: impotence, menstrual disturbances.
Hematologic: ***agranulocytosis.***
Metabolic: dehydration, ***hyperkalemia,*** hyponatremia, mild acidosis.
Skin: erythematous rash, hirsutism, maculopapular eruptions, urticaria.
Other: ***anaphylaxis, angioedema,*** breast soreness, drug fever, gynecomastia.

Interactions

Drug-drug. *ACE inhibitors, indomethacin, other potassium-sparing diuretics, potassium supplements:* May increase risk of hyperkalemia. Don't use together, especially in patients with renal impairment.
Aspirin, other salicylates: May block diuretic effect of spironolactone. Antihypertensive effect of drug not affected. Monitor edema, ascites, fluid overload.
Digoxin: May alter digoxin clearance, increasing risk of digoxin toxicity. Monitor digoxin level.
Lithium: May increase risk of lithium toxicity. Don't use together.
Warfarin, other anticoagulants: May decrease effectiveness of anticoagulants. Monitor PT and INR, increase dosage as needed.
Drug-food. *Potassium-containing salt substitutes, potassium-rich foods (such as citrus fruits, tomatoes):* May increase risk of hyperkalemia. Tell patient to use low-potassium salt substitutes and to eat high-potassium foods cautiously.

Effects on lab test results

- May increase BUN, creatinine, and potassium levels. May decrease sodium level.
- May decrease granulocyte count.
- May falsely increase serum digoxin level.

Pharmacokinetics

Absorption: About 90%.
Distribution: More than 90% protein-bound.
Metabolism: Rapid and extensive.
Excretion: Canrenone and other metabolites mainly in urine, minimally in feces. *Half-life:* 1¼ to 2 hours.

Route	Onset	Peak	Duration
P.O.	Unknown	1–2 hr	Unknown

Action

Chemical effect: Antagonizes aldosterone in distal tubule.
Therapeutic effect: Promotes water and sodium excretion and hinders potassium excretion, lowers blood pressure, and helps to diagnose primary hyperaldosteronism.

Available forms

Tablets: 25 mg, 50 mg, 100 mg

NURSING PROCESS

Assessment

- Assess patient's condition before starting therapy and regularly thereafter to monitor drug's effectiveness. Maximum antihypertensive response may be delayed up to 2 weeks.
- Monitor electrolyte level, fluid intake and output, weight, and blood pressure.
- Be alert for adverse reactions and drug interactions.
- Assess patient's and family's knowledge of drug therapy.

Nursing diagnoses

- Excess fluid volume related to presence of edema
- Impaired urinary elimination related to diuretic therapy
- Deficient knowledge related to drug therapy

Planning and implementation

- Give drug with meals to enhance absorption.
- Protect drug from light.
- Inform laboratory that patient is taking spironolactone because it may interfere with some laboratory tests that measure digoxin level.

ALERT: Don't confuse Aldactone with Aldactazide.

Patient teaching

ALERT: To prevent serious hyperkalemia, warn patient not to eat large amounts of potassium-rich foods and not to use potassium-containing salt substitutes or potassium supplements.

- Tell patient to take drug with meals and, if possible, early in day to avoid interruption of sleep by nocturia.

Evaluation

- Patient shows no signs of edema.

• Patient demonstrates adjustment of lifestyle to deal with altered patterns of urinary elimination.
• Patient and family state understanding of drug therapy.

stavudine (2,3-didehydro-3-deoxythymidine, d4T)
(stay-VYOO-deen)
Zerit, Zerit XR

Pharmacologic class: nucleoside reverse transcriptase inhibitor
Therapeutic class: antiretroviral
Pregnancy risk category: C

Indications and dosages

▶ **Patients with advanced HIV infection who are intolerant of or unresponsive to other antivirals.** *Adults and children who weigh 60 kg (132 lb) or more:* 40 mg P.O. q 12 hours, or 100 mg P.O. extended-release daily.
Adults and children who weigh more than 30 kg (66 lb) but less than 60 kg: 30 mg P.O. q 12 hours, or 75 mg P.O. extended-release daily.
Children who weigh less than 30 kg: 1 mg/kg q 12 hours if at least 14 days old. If 13 days old or less, give 0.5 mg/kg q 12 hours.
Adjust-a-dose: For patients with renal impairment adjust dosage as follows. If creatinine clearance is 26 to 50 ml/min, give 20 mg q 12 hours if patient weighs 60 kg or more or 15 mg q 12 hours if patient weighs less than 60 kg. If creatinine clearance is 10 to 25 ml/min, give 20 mg q 24 hours if patient weighs 60 kg or more or 15 mg q 24 hours if patient weighs less than 60 kg. For adults undergoing hemodialysis, give 20 mg q 24 hours if patient weighs 60 kg or more or 15 mg q 24 hours if patient weighs less than 60 kg. Give dose after hemodialysis.

Contraindications and cautions

• Contraindicated in patients hypersensitive to the drug or any of its components.
• Don't use Zerit XR in patients with creatinine clearance of 50 ml/minute or less.
• Use cautiously in patients with renal impairment or a history of peripheral neuropathy.

Lifespan: In pregnant women, use cautiously. In breast-feeding women, safety and effectiveness haven't been established.

Adverse reactions

CNS: anxiety, asthenia, depression, dizziness, fever, headache, insomnia, malaise, nervousness, peripheral neuropathy.
CV: chest pain.
EENT: conjunctivitis.
GI: abdominal pain, anorexia, constipation, diarrhea, dyspepsia, nausea, ***pancreatitis,*** vomiting, weight loss.
Hematologic: anemia, ***leukopenia, neutropenia, thrombocytopenia.***
Hepatic: ***hepatotoxicity,*** severe hepatomegaly with steatosis.
Metabolic: ***lactic acidosis.***
Musculoskeletal: *arthralgia, back pain,* myalgia.
Respiratory: *dyspnea.*
Skin: diaphoresis, maculopapular rash, pruritus, rash.
Other: breast enlargement, *chills,* redistribution or accumulation of body fat.

Interactions

Drug-drug. *Didanosine, hydroxyurea:* May increase risk of lactic acidosis, hepatotoxicity, pancreatitis, peripheral neuropathy. Monitor patient closely.
Doxorubicin, ribavirin: May increase risk of toxicities. Use together cautiously.
Ketoconazole, ritonavir: May increase stavudine level. Monitor patient closely.
Methadone: May decrease stavudine absorption. Avoid using together.
Myelosuppressants: May cause additive myelosuppression. Avoid using together.
Zidovudine: May inhibit stavudine phosphorylation. Don't use together.

Effects on lab test results

• May increase liver enzyme level. May decrease hemoglobin level and hematocrit.
• May decrease neutrophil and platelet counts.

Pharmacokinetics

Absorption: Rapid with mean absolute bioavailability of 86.4% for immediate release; slower and less bioavailability with extended-release form.

S

Distribution: Equally between RBCs and plasma. Binds poorly to proteins.
Metabolism: Not extensive.
Excretion: About 40% renal. *Half-life:* 1 to 2 hours.

Route	Onset	Peak	Duration
P.O.	Unknown	≤ 1 hr	8 hr
P.O. extended-release	Unknown	3 hr	24 hr

Action

Chemical effect: Prevents replication of HIV by interfering with enzyme reverse transcriptase.
Therapeutic effect: Inhibits HIV replication.

Available forms

Capsules: 15 mg, 20 mg, 30 mg, 40 mg
Capsules (extended-release): 37.5 mg, 50 mg, 75 mg, 100 mg.
Powder for oral solution: 1 mg/ml

NURSING PROCESS

Assessment

- Assess patient's condition before starting therapy and regularly thereafter to monitor drug's effectiveness.
- Periodically monitor CBC and levels of creatinine, AST, ALT, and alkaline phosphatase.
- Be alert for adverse reactions and drug interactions.
- Assess patient's and family's knowledge of drug therapy.

Nursing diagnoses

- Risk for infection related to presence of HIV
- Disturbed sensory perception (peripheral) related to drug-induced peripheral neuropathy
- Deficient knowledge related to drug therapy

Planning and implementation

ALERT: Peripheral neuropathy appears to be major dose-limiting adverse effect. If it occurs, temporarily stop giving the drug; then resume at 50% of recommended dose.

- Dose is calculated based on patient's weight.

ALERT: Don't confuse drug with other antivirals that may use initials for identification.

- Motor weakness that mimics Guillain-Barré syndrome (including respiratory failure) may occur in HIV-positive patient taking this drug with other antiretrovirals, usually in those with lactic acidosis. Monitor patient for evidence of lactic acidosis, including generalized fatigue, GI problems, tachypnea, or dyspnea. Symptoms may continue or worsen when stopping drug. In patients with these symptoms, promptly stop antiretroviral therapy and perform a full medical workup immediately. Permanently stopping drug should be considered.
- Monitor patient for pancreatitis, especially when this drug is used with didanosine or hydroxyurea. Use caution when restarting drug after confirmed diagnosis of pancreatitis.
- If patient has trouble swallowing capsule, mix contents of the capsule in applesauce or yogurt. Instruct patient not to chew or crush the beads while swallowing.

Patient teaching

- Tell patient that drug may be taken with or without food.
- Tell patient to shake oral solution vigorously before taking it, to store it in the refrigerator, and to discard unused solution after 30 days.
- Advise patient that he can't take drug if he developed peripheral neuropathy while taking other nucleoside analogues or if his treatment plan includes cytotoxic antineoplastics.
- Warn patient not to take any other drugs for HIV or AIDS (especially street drugs) unless prescriber has approved them.
- Explain that drug doesn't prevent transmission of virus; tell patient to use a barrier method of contraception.
- Teach patient signs and symptoms of peripheral neuropathy—pain, burning, aching, weakness, or pins and needles in limbs—and tell him to report these immediately.
- Tell patient to report symptoms of lactic acidosis, including fatigue, GI problems, dyspnea, and tachypnea.
- Tell patient to report symptoms of pancreatitis, including abdominal pain, nausea, vomiting, weight loss or fatty stools.

Evaluation

- Patient's infection is controlled.
- Patient maintains normal peripheral neurologic function.
- Patient and family state understanding of drug therapy.

streptokinase

(strep-toh-KIGH-nayz)
Streptase

Pharmacologic class: plasminogen activator
Therapeutic class: thrombolytic enzyme
Pregnancy risk category: C

Indications and dosages

▶ **Arteriovenous cannula occlusion.** *Adults:* 250,000 international units in 2 ml I.V. solution by I.V. pump infusion into each occluded limb of cannula over 25 to 35 minutes. Clamp cannula for 2 hours. Then aspirate contents of cannula, flush with saline solution, and reconnect.
▶ **Venous thrombosis, pulmonary embolism, arterial thrombosis and embolism.** *Adults:* Loading dose is 250,000 international units by I.V. infusion over 30 minutes. Sustaining dose is 100,000 international units/hour by I.V. infusion for 72 hours for deep vein thrombosis and 100,000 international units/hour over 24 hours by I.V. infusion pump for pulmonary embolism.
▶ **Lysis of coronary artery thrombi after acute MI.** *Adults:* I.V. infusion preferred using 1,500,000 international units infused over 60 minutes. Or, if using intracoronary infusion, the total dose for intracoronary infusion is 140,000 international units. Loading dose is 15,000 to 20,000 international units by coronary catheter over 15 seconds to 2 minutes, followed by infusion of maintenance dose of 2,000 international units/minute for 60 minutes.

I.V. administration

- Reconstitute each drug vial with 5 ml of normal saline solution for injection. Further dilute to 45 ml.
- Don't shake; roll gently to mix. Some precipitate may be present; discard if large amounts appear. Filter solution with 0.8-micron or larger filter. Use within 8 hours.
- Administer with a controlled infusion device.
- Store powder at room temperature and refrigerate after reconstitution.

⊗ **Incompatibilities**
Dextrans, other I.V. drugs.

Contraindications and cautions

- Contraindicated in patients with ulcerative wounds, active internal bleeding, uncontrolled hypercoagulation, chronic pulmonary disease with cavitation, subacute bacterial endocarditis or rheumatic valvular disease, visceral or intracranial malignant neoplasms, ulcerative colitis, diverticulitis, severe hypertension, acute or chronic hepatic or renal insufficiency, recent stroke, recent trauma with possible internal injuries, or recent cerebral embolism, thrombosis, or hemorrhage.
- Also contraindicated within 10 days after intra-arterial diagnostic procedure or any surgery, including liver or kidney biopsy, lumbar puncture, thoracentesis, paracentesis, or extensive or multiple cutdowns.
- I.M. injections and other invasive procedures are contraindicated during streptokinase therapy.
- Use cautiously when treating arterial embolism that originates from left side of heart because of danger of cerebral infarction.

Lifespan: In pregnant women, use cautiously. In breast-feeding women and in children, safety and effectiveness haven't been established.

Adverse reactions

CNS: fever, headache, polyradiculoneuropathy.
CV: flushing, hypotension, ***reperfusion arrhythmias,*** vasculitis.
EENT: periorbital edema.
GI: nausea.
Hematologic: ***bleeding.***
Musculoskeletal: musculoskeletal pain.
Respiratory: ***bronchospasm,*** minor breathing difficulty, ***pulmonary edema.***
Skin: pruritus, urticaria.
Other: ***angioedema, delayed hypersensitivity reactions*** (interstitial nephritis, vasculitis, serum-sickness–like reactions), ***hypersensitivity reactions (anaphylaxis),*** phlebitis or bleeding at injection site.

Interactions

Drug-drug. *Anticoagulants:* May increase risk of bleeding. Monitor patient closely.
Antifibrinolytics, such as aminocaproic acid: May inhibit and reverse streptokinase activity. Use only when indicated during streptokinase therapy.
Aspirin, dipyridamole, drugs that affect platelet activity, indomethacin, phenylbutazone: May increase risk of bleeding. Monitor patient closely. Combined therapy with low-dose aspirin

S

(162.5 mg) or dipyridamole has improved acute and long-term results.

Effects on lab test results

- May decrease hemoglobin level and hematocrit.
- May increase PT, PTT, and INR.

Pharmacokinetics

Absorption: Given I.V.
Distribution: Unknown.
Metabolism: Insignificant.
Excretion: Removed from circulation by antibodies and reticuloendothelial system. *Half-life:* First phase, 18 minutes; second phase, 83 minutes.

Route	Onset	Peak	Duration
I.V.	Immediate	20 min–2 hr	4 hr

Action

Chemical effect: Activates plasminogen in two steps. Plasminogen and streptokinase form a complex that exposes plasminogen-activating site. Plasminogen is then converted to plasmin by cleavage of peptide bond.
Therapeutic effect: Dissolves blood clots.

Available forms

Injection: 250,000 international units, 750,000 international units, and 1.5 million international units in vials for reconstitution

NURSING PROCESS

Assessment

- Assess patient's condition before starting therapy and regularly thereafter to monitor drug's effectiveness.
- Assess patient for increased risk of bleeding (such as from recent surgery, stroke, trauma, or hypertension) before starting therapy.
- Before starting therapy, draw blood to determine PTT and PT. Rate of I.V. infusion depends on thrombin time and streptokinase resistance. Then repeat studies often and keep laboratory flow sheet on patient's chart to monitor PTT, PT, hemoglobin level, and hematocrit.
- Monitor patient for excessive bleeding q 15 minutes for first hour, q 30 minutes for second through eighth hours, then once q shift.
- Assess pulses, color, and sensation of limbs q hour.
- Be alert for adverse reactions and drug interactions.
- Assess patient's and family's knowledge of drug therapy.

Nursing diagnoses

- Ineffective cardiopulmonary tissue perfusion related to condition
- Risk for deficient fluid volume related to potential for bleeding
- Deficient knowledge related to drug therapy

Planning and implementation

- Drug should be used only by prescriber with experience in thrombotic disease management and in a setting where close monitoring can be performed.
- Before using streptokinase to clear an occluded arteriovenous cannula, try flushing with heparinized saline solution.

ALERT: Streptokinase may cause life-threatening side effects when used to clear occluded I.V. catheters. Use only if clearly needed.

ALERT: To check for hypersensitivity reactions, give 100 international units I.D.; wheal and flare response within 20 minutes means patient is probably allergic. Monitor vital signs frequently.

- If patient has had either recent streptococcal infection or recent treatment with streptokinase, higher loading dose may be needed.
- If bleeding occurs, stop therapy and notify prescriber. Pretreatment with heparin or drugs affecting platelets causes high risk of bleeding but may improve long-term results.
- Have aminocaproic acid available to treat bleeding and corticosteroids to treat allergic reactions.
- Have typed and crossmatched packed RBCs ready to treat hemorrhage.
- Keep involved limb in straight alignment to prevent bleeding from infusion site.
- Avoid unnecessary handling of patient, and pad side rails. Bruising is more likely during therapy.
- Keep venipuncture sites to minimum; use pressure dressing on puncture sites for at least 15 minutes.

ALERT: Immediately notify prescriber if hypersensitivity occurs. Antihistamines or corticosteroids may be used to treat mild reactions. If

severe reaction occurs, stop infusion and notify prescriber.
- Heparin by continuous infusion is usually started within 1 hour after stopping streptokinase. Use infusion pump to give heparin.
- In patient with acute MI, thrombolytic therapy may decrease infarct size, improve ventricular function, and decrease risk of heart failure. Drug must be given within 6 hours of onset of symptoms for optimal effect, but benefits have been reported up to 24 hours.

Patient teaching
- Tell patient to report oozing, bleeding, or signs of hypersensitivity immediately.

Evaluation
- Patient responds well to therapy.
- Patient maintains adequate fluid balance.
- Patient and family state understanding of drug therapy.

streptomycin sulfate
(strep-toh-MIGH-sin SUL-fayt)

Pharmacologic class: aminoglycoside
Therapeutic class: antibiotic
Pregnancy risk category: D

Indications and dosages

▶ **Streptococcal endocarditis.** *Adults:* 1 g I.M. q 12 hours for 1 week, and then 500 mg q 12 hours for 1 week, given with penicillin.
Adults older than age 60: Give 500 mg I.M. q 12 hours for 14 days.

▶ **Primary and adjunct treatment in tuberculosis.** *Adults:* 1 g or 15 mg/kg I.M. (up to 1 g) daily or 25 to 30 mg/kg (up to 1.5 g) two or three times weekly.
Children: 20 to 40 mg/kg (up to 1 g) I.M. daily in divided doses injected deep into large muscle mass or 25 to 30 mg/kg (up to 1 g) two or three times weekly. Given with other antituberculars but not with capreomycin. Continue until sputum specimen becomes negative.

▶ **Enterococcal endocarditis.** *Adults:* 1 g I.M. q 12 hours for 2 weeks, and then 500 mg q 12 hours for 4 weeks, given with penicillin.

▶ **Tularemia.** *Adults:* 1 to 2 g I.M. daily in divided doses injected deep into upper outer quadrant of buttocks. Continue for 7 to 14 days until patient is afebrile for 5 to 7 days.

Adjust-a-dose: For patients with renal impairment, initial dose is the same as for normal renal function. Later doses and frequency determined by renal function study results and blood level. If creatinine clearance is 50 to 80 ml/minute, give 7.5 mg/kg q 24 hours. If it's 10 to 50 ml/minute, give 7.5 mg/kg q 24 to 72 hours. If it's less than 10 ml/minute, give 7.5 mg/kg q 72 to 96 hours.

Contraindications and cautions

- Contraindicated in patients hypersensitive to the drug or other aminoglycosides and patients with labyrinthine disease.
- Use cautiously in patients with impaired kidney function or neuromuscular disorders.

Lifespan: In pregnant women, drug is contraindicated. In breast-feeding women and in the elderly, use cautiously.

Adverse reactions

CNS: ***neuromuscular blockade.***
EENT: ototoxicity.
GI: nausea, vomiting.
GU: ***nephrotoxicity.***
Hematologic: eosinophilia, ***leukopenia, thrombocytopenia.***
Respiratory: ***apnea.***
Skin: exfoliative dermatitis.
Other: ***anaphylaxis, angioedema,*** hypersensitivity reactions.

Interactions

Drug-drug. *Aminoglycosides, acyclovir, amphotericin B, cisplatin, methoxyflurane, vancomycin:* May increase risk of nephrotoxicity. Monitor patient.
Atracurium, doxacurium, mivacurium, pancuronium, rocuronium, tubocurarine, vecuronium: May increase the effects of nondepolarizing muscle relaxant, including prolonged respiratory depression. Use together only when necessary. Dose of nondepolarizing muscle relaxant may need to be reduced.
Cephalosporins: May increase risk of nephrotoxicity. Use together cautiously.
Dimenhydrinate: May mask symptoms of streptomycin-induced ototoxicity. Use together cautiously.
I.V. loop diuretics (such as furosemide): May increase ototoxicity. Use together cautiously.

S

Effects on lab test results

- May increase BUN, creatinine, and nonprotein nitrogen levels. May decrease hemoglobin level and hematocrit.
- May increase eosinophil count. May decrease WBC and platelet counts.

Pharmacokinetics

Absorption: Unknown after I.M. use.
Distribution: Wide, although CSF penetration is low. 36% protein-bound.
Metabolism: None.
Excretion: Mainly in urine; less in bile. *Half-life:* 2 to 3 hours; up to 100 hours with renal impairment.

Route	Onset	Peak	Duration
I.M.	Unknown	1–2 hr	Unknown

Action

Chemical effect: Inhibits bacterial protein synthesis by binding directly to 30S ribosomal subunit.
Therapeutic effect: Kills bacteria.

Available forms

Injection: 400 mg/ml in 2.5 ml ampules
Powder for injection: 200 mg/ml in 1 g vials

NURSING PROCESS

Assessment

- Assess patient's infection before starting therapy and regularly thereafter to monitor drug's effectiveness.
- Obtain specimen for culture and sensitivity tests before first dose except when treating tuberculosis. Start therapy pending test results.

ALERT: Obtain blood for peak streptomycin level 1 to 2 hours after I.M. injection; for trough level, draw blood just before next dose. Don't use heparinized tube because heparin is incompatible with aminoglycosides.

- Evaluate patient's hearing before therapy, during therapy, and 6 months after therapy ends.
- Be alert for adverse reactions and drug interactions.
- Assess patient's and family's knowledge of drug therapy.

Nursing diagnoses

- Risk for infection related to presence of susceptible bacteria
- Disturbed sensory perception (auditory) related to drug-induced adverse reactions
- Deficient knowledge related to drug therapy

Planning and implementation

- Protect hands when preparing drug because drug is irritating.
- Inject drug deep into upper outer quadrant of buttocks. Rotate injection sites.

ALERT: Never give streptomycin I.V.

- Encourage adequate fluid intake. Patient should be well hydrated while taking drug to minimize chemical irritation of renal tubules.
- In primary treatment of tuberculosis, stop drug when sputum becomes negative.

Patient teaching

- Warn patient that injection may be painful.
- Emphasize the need to drink at least 2,000 ml daily (if not contraindicated) during therapy.
- Instruct patient to report hearing loss, roaring noises, or fullness in ears or dizziness immediately.

Evaluation

- Patient is free from infection.
- Patient's auditory function remains normal.
- Patient and family state understanding of drug therapy.

succimer

(SUK-sih-mer)
Chemet

Pharmacologic class: heavy metal antagonist
Therapeutic class: chelate
Pregnancy risk category: C

Indications and dosages

▶ **Lead poisoning in children with blood lead levels above 45 mcg/dl.** *Children:* 10 mg/kg or 350 mg/m² q 8 hours for 5 days. Round dose to nearest 100 mg (see table). For next 2 weeks, decrease interval to q 12 hours.

Weight (kg)	Dose (mg)
8–15	100
16–23	200
24–34	300
35–44	400
≥ 45	500

Contraindications and cautions

- Contraindicated in patients hypersensitive to the drug or any of its components.
- Use cautiously in patients with compromised kidney function.
- Monitor patient for neutropenia. If absolute neutrophil count falls below 1,200/mm^3, stop drug.

Lifespan: None reported.

Adverse reactions

CNS: dizziness, drowsiness, headache, paresthesia, sensory motor neuropathy, sleepiness.
CV: ***arrhythmias.***
EENT: cloudy film in eyes, nasal congestion, otitis media, plugged ears, rhinorrhea, sore throat, watery eyes.
GI: abdominal cramps, diarrhea, hemorrhoidal symptoms, loose stools, loss of appetite, metallic taste, nausea, stomach pain, vomiting.
GU: decreased urination, difficult urination, *flank pain,* proteinuria.
Hematologic: intermittent eosinophilia, ***neutropenia.***
Musculoskeletal: back, leg, kneecap, or rib pain.
Respiratory: cough, head cold.
Skin: herpetic rash, mucocutaneous eruptions, papular rash, pruritus.
Other: candidiasis, *flulike syndrome.*

Interactions

None reported.

Effects on lab test results

- May increase AST, ALT, alkaline phosphatase, and cholesterol levels.
- May increase eosinophil and platelet counts.
- May cause false-positive results for ketones in urine using nitroprusside reagents (Ketostix) and falsely decreased uric acid and CK levels.

Pharmacokinetics

Absorption: Rapid but variable.
Distribution: Unknown.
Metabolism: Rapid and extensive.
Excretion: 39% in feces unchanged; remainder mainly in urine. *Half-life:* 48 hours.

Route	Onset	Peak	Duration
P.O.	Unknown	1–2 hr	Unknown

Action

Chemical effect: Forms water-soluble complexes with lead and increases its excretion in urine.
Therapeutic effect: Relieves signs and symptoms of lead poisoning.

Available forms

Capsules: 100 mg

NURSING PROCESS

Assessment

- Assess child's condition before starting therapy and regularly thereafter to monitor drug's effectiveness.
- Measure severity by initial blood lead level and by rate and degree of rebound of blood lead level. Use severity as guide for more frequent blood lead monitoring.
- Monitor transaminase level and neutrophil count before starting therapy, and at least weekly during therapy. Transient, mild elevations of transaminase level may occur. Monitor patient with history of hepatic disease more closely.
- Monitor patient at least once weekly for rebound blood lead level. Elevated blood lead level and associated symptoms may return rapidly after drug is stopped because of redistribution of lead from bone to soft tissues and blood.
- Be alert for adverse reactions.
- If adverse GI reactions occur, monitor patient's hydration.
- Evaluate parents' knowledge of drug therapy.

Nursing diagnoses

- Ineffective health maintenance related to presence of lead poisoning
- Risk for deficient fluid volume related to drug-induced adverse GI reactions
- Deficient knowledge related to drug therapy

Planning and implementation

- Course of treatment lasts 19 days. Repeated courses may be needed if indicated by weekly monitoring of blood lead level.
- A minimum of 2 weeks between courses is recommended unless high blood lead level indicates need for immediate therapy.

ALERT: Administration of succimer with other chelates isn't recommended. Patient who has received edetate calcium disodium with or with-

S

out dimercaprol may use succimer as subsequent therapy after 4-week interval.
• Maintain adequate fluid intake.

Patient teaching

• Tell parents of child who can't swallow capsule to open it and sprinkle contents on small amount of soft food. Or, medicated beads from capsule may be poured on spoon and followed with flavored beverage such as a fruit drink.
• Help parents identify and remove sources of lead in child's environment. Chelation therapy isn't a substitute for preventing further exposure.
• Tell parents to consult prescriber if rash occurs. Consider possibility of allergic or other mucocutaneous reactions each time drug is used.

☑ Evaluation

• Patient responds well to therapy.
• Patient maintains adequate hydration.
• Parents state understanding of drug therapy.

succinylcholine chloride (suxamethonium chloride)

(SUK-seh-nil-KOH-leen KLOR-ighd)

Anectine, Anectine Flo-Pack, Quelicin, Scoline ◇

Pharmacologic class: depolarizing neuromuscular blocker
Therapeutic class: skeletal muscle relaxant
Pregnancy risk category: C

Indications and dosages

▶ **Adjunct to anesthesia to induce skeletal muscle relaxation; to facilitate intubation and assist with mechanical ventilation or orthopedic manipulations (drug of choice); to lessen muscle contractions in pharmacologically or electrically induced seizures.** *Adults:* Dosage depends on anesthetic used, individual needs, and response. Give 0.6 mg/kg I.V. over 10 to 30 seconds; then give 2.5 mg/minute, p.r.n. Or, 2.5 to 4 mg/kg I.M. up to maximum of 150 mg I.M. in deltoid muscle. For short procedures, the optimum dose range is 0.3 to 1.1 mg/kg. The average dose is 0.6 mg/kg. Maximum paralysis occurs in 2 minutes. Recovery time is in 4 to 6 minutes. For long procedures, the average rate for adults is 2.5 to 4.3 mg/minute. For prolonged muscular relaxation, give intermittent I.V. injections of 0.3 to 1.1 mg/kg, then 0.04 to 0.07 mg/kg.
Children: 1 to 2 mg/kg I.V. or 2.5 to 4 mg/kg I.M. Maximum I.M. dose is 150 mg.

▼ I.V. administration

• Use immediately after reconstitution.
• Store injectable form in refrigerator. Store powder form at room temperature in tightly closed container.
• Solutions of 0.1% to 0.2% are common for I.V. infusions (1 to 2 mg/ml).

⊗ Incompatibilities
Barbiturates, nafcillin, sodium bicarbonate, solutions with pH above 4.5, thiopental sodium.

Contraindications and cautions

• Contraindicated in patients hypersensitive to the drug or any of its components and in patients with abnormally low pseudocholinesterase level, angle-closure glaucoma, personal or family history of malignant hyperthermia, or penetrating eye injury.
• Use cautiously in debilitated patients, those taking quinidine or digoxin therapy, and those with severe burns or trauma, electrolyte imbalances, hyperkalemia, paraplegia, spinal neuraxis injury, stroke, degenerative or dystrophic neuromuscular disease, myasthenia gravis, myasthenic syndrome of lung cancer, bronchogenic carcinoma, dehydration, thyroid disorders, collagen diseases, porphyria, fractures, muscle spasms, eye surgery, pheochromocytoma, respiratory depression, or hepatic, renal, or pulmonary impairment.
Lifespan: In women undergoing cesarean section and in breast-feeding women, use large doses cautiously. In the elderly, use cautiously.

Adverse reactions

CV: ***arrhythmias, bradycardia, cardiac arrest,*** flushing, hypertension, hypotension, tachycardia.
EENT: increased intraocular pressure.
Musculoskeletal: muscle fasciculation, myoglobinemia, *postoperative muscle pain.*
Respiratory: ***apnea, bronchoconstriction, prolonged respiratory depression.***
Other: allergic or idiosyncratic hypersensitivity reactions ***(anaphylaxis),*** excessive salivation, ***malignant hyperthermia.***

Interactions

Drug-drug. *Aminoglycoside antibiotics, including amikacin, gentamicin, kanamycin, neomycin, and streptomycin; anticholinesterases, such as echothiophate, edrophonium, neostigmine, physostigmine, and pyridostigmine; general anesthetics, such as enflurane, halothane, and isoflurane; polymyxin antibiotics, such as colistin and polymyxin B sulfate:* May potentiate neuromuscular blockade, leading to increased skeletal muscle relaxation and potentiation of effect. Use cautiously during surgical and postoperative periods.

Cyclophosphamide, lithium, MAO inhibitors: May cause prolonged apnea. Avoid using together; monitor patient closely.

Digoxin: May cause arrhythmias. Use together cautiously.

Methotrimeprazine, opioid analgesics: May potentiate neuromuscular blockade, leading to increased skeletal muscle relaxation and, possibly, respiratory paralysis. Use cautiously.

Parenteral magnesium sulfate: May potentiate neuromuscular blockade, leading to increased skeletal muscle relaxation and, possibly, respiratory paralysis. Use cautiously, preferably with reduced doses.

Drug-herb. *Melatonin:* May potentiate blocking properties of succinylcholine. Discourage using together.

Effects on lab test results

- May increase myoglobin and potassium levels.

Pharmacokinetics

Absorption: Unknown.
Distribution: In extracellular fluid and rapidly to site of action.
Metabolism: Rapid, by plasma pseudocholinesterase.
Excretion: About 10% unchanged in urine.
Half-life: Unknown.

Route	Onset	Peak	Duration
I.V.	≤ 1 min	1–2 min	4–10 min
I.M.	2–3 min	Unknown	10–30 min

Action

Chemical effect: Prolongs depolarization of muscle end plate.
Therapeutic effect: Relaxes skeletal muscles.

Available forms

Injection: 20 mg/ml, 50 mg/ml
Powder for infusion: 500-mg, and 1-g vials

NURSING PROCESS

Assessment

- Assess patient's condition before starting therapy and regularly thereafter to monitor the drug's effectiveness.
- Monitor baseline and ongoing electrolyte level and vital signs (check respiratory rate q 5 to 10 minutes during infusion).
- Monitor respiratory rate and pulse oximetry closely until patient is fully recovered from neuromuscular blockade, as evidenced by tests of muscle strength (hand grip, head lift, and ability to cough).
- Be alert for adverse reactions and drug interactions.
- Assess patient's and family's knowledge of drug therapy.

Nursing diagnoses

- Ineffective health maintenance related to underlying condition
- Ineffective breathing pattern related to drug's effect on respiratory muscles
- Deficient knowledge related to drug therapy

Planning and implementation

ALERT: Give drug only if you are skilled in airway management.
- The drug of choice for procedures less than 3 minutes and for orthopedic manipulations—use caution in fractures or dislocations.
- Give sedatives or general anesthetics before neuromuscular blockers. Neuromuscular blockers don't induce unconsciousness or alter pain threshold.
- Keep airway clear. Have emergency respiratory support equipment immediately available.

ALERT: Careful drug calculation is essential. Always verify with another professional.
- To evaluate patient's ability to metabolize drug, give 10-mg I.M. or I.V. test dose after patient is anesthetized. No respiratory depression or transient depression for up to 5 minutes indicates drug may be given. Don't give subsequent doses if patient develops respiratory paralysis sufficient to permit endotracheal intubation. (Recovery within 30 to 60 minutes.)

S

• Give deep I.M., preferably high into deltoid muscle.
• Give analgesics.
ALERT: Don't use reversing drugs. Unlike with nondepolarizing drugs, giving neostigmine or edrophonium with this depolarizing drug may worsen neuromuscular blockade.
• Repeated or continuous infusions of succinylcholine aren't advised, because they may reduce response or prolong muscle relaxation and apnea.
ALERT: Rarely, cardiac arrest may occur within minutes of succinylcholine administration in children. Carefully monitor ECG for peaked T-waves, which may be an early sign of arrhythmias.

Patient teaching

• Explain all events and happenings to patient because he can still hear.
• Reassure patient that he is being monitored at all times.
• Inform patient that postoperative stiffness is normal and will soon subside.

Evaluation

• Patient responds well to therapy.
• Patient maintains adequate respiratory patterns with mechanical assistance.
• Patient and family state understanding of drug therapy.

sucralfate

(SOO-krahl-fayt)
Carafate, Sulcrate ♦

Pharmacologic class: pepsin inhibitor
Therapeutic class: antiulcerative
Pregnancy risk category: B

Indications and dosages

▶ **Maintenance therapy for duodenal ulcer.** *Adults:* 1 g P.O. b.i.d., before meals.
▶ **Therapy for up to 8 weeks for duodenal ulcer; gastric ulcer‡.** *Adults:* 1 g P.O. q.i.d. 1 hour before meals and at bedtime.

Contraindications and cautions

• Use cautiously in patients with chronic renal impairment.

Lifespan: In pregnant women, use cautiously. In breast-feeding women, use cautiously; it's unknown if the drug appears in breast milk. In children, safety and effectiveness haven't been established.

Adverse reactions

CNS: dizziness, headache, sleepiness, vertigo.
GI: bezoar formation, constipation, diarrhea, dry mouth, flatulence, gastric discomfort, indigestion, nausea, vomiting.
Musculoskeletal: back pain.
Skin: pruritus, rash.

Interactions

Drug-drug. *Antacids:* May decrease binding of drug to gastroduodenal mucosa, impairing effectiveness. Don't give within 30 minutes of each other.
Cimetidine, digoxin, phenytoin, ranitidine, tetracycline, theophylline: May decrease absorption. Separate doses by at least 2 hours.
Ciprofloxacin, lomefloxacin, moxifloxacin, norfloxacin, ofloxacin: May decrease absorption of the quinolone, reducing anti-infective response. If use together can't be avoided, give at least 6 hours apart.

Effects on lab test results

None reported.

Pharmacokinetics

Absorption: About 3% to 5%. Acts locally.
Distribution: To GI tract and small amount to tissues.
Metabolism: None.
Excretion: About 90% in feces; absorbed drug excreted unchanged in urine. *Half-life:* 6 to 20 hours.

Route	Onset	Peak	Duration
P.O.	Unknown	≤ 6 hr	6 hr

Action

Chemical effect: May adhere to and protect ulcer's surface by forming barrier.
Therapeutic effect: Aids in duodenal ulcer healing.

Available forms

Suspension: 1 g/10 ml
Tablets: 1 g

NURSING PROCESS

Assessment

- Assess patient's GI symptoms before starting therapy and regularly thereafter to monitor drug's effectiveness.
- Be alert for adverse reactions and drug interactions.
- Monitor patient for severe, persistent constipation.
- Assess patient's and family's knowledge of drug therapy.

Nursing diagnoses

- Impaired tissue integrity related to presence of duodenal ulcer
- Constipation related to drug-induced adverse GI reactions
- Deficient knowledge related to drug therapy

Planning and implementation

- Give drug on an empty stomach for best results.
- Don't give I.V.
- Antacids may be used to relieve symptoms but should be separated from sucralfate doses by at least 30 minutes.

ALERT: Don't confuse sucralfate with salsalate or Carafate with Cafergot.

Patient teaching

- Instruct patient to take drug 1 hour before each meal and bedtime.
- Tell patient to continue on prescribed regimen to ensure complete healing. Pain and ulcerative symptoms may subside within first few weeks of therapy.
- Urge patient to avoid cigarette smoking because it may increase gastric acid secretion and worsen disease. Also tell patient to avoid alcohol, chocolate, and spicy foods.
- Tell patient to sleep with head of bed elevated.
- Tell patient to avoid large meals within 2 hours of bedtime.

Evaluation

- Patient's ulcer pain is gone.
- Patient maintains normal bowel elimination patterns.
- Patient and family state understanding of drug therapy.

sufentanil citrate

(soo-FEN-tih-nil SIGH-trayt)

Sufenta, Sufentanil Citrate Injection

Pharmacologic class: opioid agonist
Therapeutic class: analgesic, anesthetic
Pregnancy risk category: C
Controlled substance schedule: II

Indications and dosages

▶ **Adjunct to general anesthetic.** *Adults:* 1 to 2 mcg/kg I.V. with nitrous oxide and oxygen for 1- to 2-hour duration anesthesia in procedures lasting less than 8 hours. Maintain analgesia with 10 to 25 mcg I.V. in increments for surgical stress or lightening of anesthesia. Or, 2 to 8 mcg/kg I.V. for more complicated procedures lasting longer than 8 hours; duration of anesthesia 2 to 8 hours. Maintain analgesia with 10 to 50 mcg I.V. in increments for surgical stress or lightening of anesthesia. Adjust maintenance infusion rates based on the induction dose so that the total dose does not exceed 1 mcg/kg/hr of expected surgical time.

▶ **As primary anesthetic.** *Adults and children age 12 and older:* 8 to 30 mcg/kg I.V. with 100% oxygen and muscle relaxant. Maintain anesthesia with 0.5 to 10 mcg/kg for surgical stress; base the maintenance infusion rate on the induction dose so that the total dose for the procedure does not exceed 30 mcg/kg.
Children younger than age 12: For induction and maintenance of anesthesia during cardiovascular surgery, 10 to 25 mcg/kg I.V. with 100% oxygen. Maintenance doses of up to 25 to 50 mcg are recommended.

Adjust-a-dose: Reduce dosage in geriatric patients, debilitated patients, and neonates. Base dose on ideal body weight in obese patients whose body weight exceeds 20% of ideal body weight

▶ **Epidural analgesia during labor and vaginal delivery.** *Adults and children age 12 and older:* 10 to 15 mcg with 10 ml bupivacaine 0.125%, with or without epinephrine. Mix drug and bupivacaine before administration. Doses can be repeated twice (for a total of three doses) at 1-hour or longer intervals until delivery.

S

I.V. administration

- Drug is analgesic at doses less than 8 mcg/kg and is anesthetic at doses equal to or greater than 8 mcg/kg.
- For obese patient weighing more than 20% above ideal body weight, base dosage calculations on lean body weight.
- Give drug by direct I.V. injection. May be given by intermittent I.V. infusion, but compatibility and stability in I.V. solutions aren't fully known.
- Don't exceed 1 mcg/kg/hour of expected surgical time.

⊗ **Incompatibilities**

Acidic solutions, diazepam, lorazepam, phenobarbital, phenytoin, thiopental.

Contraindications and cautions

- Contraindicated in patients hypersensitive to the drug or any of its components.
- Drug isn't recommended for prolonged use.
- Use cautiously in debilitated patients and in patients with head injury, decreased respiratory reserve, or pulmonary, hepatic, or renal disease.

Lifespan: In pregnant women, use only if benefits outweigh potential risks to the fetus. In breast-feeding women, safety and effectiveness haven't been established. In the elderly, use cautiously and at a lower dose.

Adverse reactions

CNS: chills, somnolence.
CV: ***arrhythmias, bradycardia,*** hypertension, *hypotension,* increased cardiac index, tachycardia.
GI: nausea, vomiting.
Musculoskeletal: intraoperative muscle movement.
Respiratory: ***apnea, bronchospasm,*** chest wall rigidity, respiratory depression.
Skin: erythema, *pruritus.*

Interactions

Drug-drug. *Anesthetics:* May affect cardiovascular status. Monitor patient closely.
Beta blockers: May need lower sufentanil doses. Assess patient.
CNS depressants: May have additive effects. Use together cautiously.
Drug-lifestyle. *Alcohol use:* May have additive effects. Discourage using together.

Effects on lab test results

None reported.

Pharmacokinetics

Absorption: Given I.V.
Distribution: Rapidly redistributed. Extensively protein-bound.
Metabolism: Probably in liver and small intestine.
Excretion: Mainly in urine. *Half-life:* About 2 ½ hours.

Route	Onset	Peak	Duration
I.V.	Immediate	Unknown	Unknown

Action

Chemical effect: Binds with opiate receptors in CNS, altering perception of and emotional response to pain through unknown mechanism.
Therapeutic effect: Relieves pain and promotes loss of consciousness.

Available forms

Injection: 50 mcg/ml in 1-ml, 2-ml, and 5-ml ampules and vials

NURSING PROCESS

Assessment

- Assess patient's condition before starting therapy and regularly thereafter to monitor drug's effectiveness.
- Because drug decreases rate and depth of respirations, monitor patient's arterial oxygen saturation to help assess respiratory depression.
- Monitor respiratory rate of neonates exposed to drug during labor.
- Monitor postoperative vital signs.
- Be alert for adverse reactions and drug interactions.
- Assess patient's and family's knowledge of drug therapy.

Nursing diagnoses

- Ineffective health maintenance related to underlying condition
- Ineffective breathing pattern related to respiratory depression
- Deficient knowledge related to drug therapy

Planning and implementation

- Only personnel specifically trained in use of I.V. anesthetics should give drug.

• When used at doses larger than 8 mcg/kg, postoperative mechanical ventilation and observation are essential because of prolonged respiratory depression.
• Keep opioid antagonist (naloxone) and resuscitation equipment available.
• If respiratory rate falls below 12 breaths/minute, notify prescriber.
• For epidural use, give by slow injection. Closely monitor respiration following each administration of drug mixture.
ALERT: High doses can produce muscle rigidity reversible by neuromuscular blockers; however, patient must be artificially ventilated.
ALERT: Don't confuse sufentanil with alfentanil or fentanyl, or Sufenta with Survanta.

Patient teaching

• Inform patient and family that drug will be used as part of patient's anesthesia.

Evaluation

• Patient responds well to therapy.
• Patient maintains adequate ventilation with mechanical support, if needed.
• Patient and family state understanding of drug therapy.

sulfasalazine (salazosulfapyridine, sulphasalazine)

(sul-fuh-SAL-uh-zeen)

Azulfidine, Azulfidine EN-Tabs, PMS-Sulfasalazine E.C. ♦, Ratio-Sulfasalazine ♦, Ratio-Sulfasalazine EN ♦, Salazopyrin ♦, Salazopyrin EN-Tabs ♦ ◊

Pharmacologic class: sulfonamide
Therapeutic class: anti-inflammatory
Pregnancy risk category: B

Indications and dosages

▶ **Mild to moderate ulcerative colitis, adjunct therapy in severe ulcerative colitis.** *Adults:* Initially, 3 to 4 g P.O. daily in evenly divided doses. May begin with a lower dose of 1 to 2 g/day to avoid GI intolerance; usual maintenance dosage is 1 to 2 g P.O. daily in divided doses q 6 hours. Dosage may be started with 1 to 2 g, with gradual increase to minimize adverse effects.
Children older than age 2: Initially, 40 to 60 mg/kg P.O. daily, divided into three to six doses; then 30 mg/kg daily in four doses. If GI intolerance occurs, reduce dosage.
▶ **Rheumatoid arthritis in patients who have responded inadequately to salicylates or NSAIDs.** *Adults:* 2 g P.O. daily b.i.d. in evenly divided doses. Dosage may be started at 0.5 to 1 g daily and be gradually increased over 3 weeks to reduce GI intolerance.
▶ **Patients with polyarticular-course juvenile rheumatoid arthritis who have responded inadequately to salicylates or other NSAIDs.** *Children age 6 and older:* 30 to 50 mg/kg P.O. daily in two divided doses (as delayed-release tablet). Maximum dose is 2 g daily. To reduce GI intolerance, start with one-fourth to one-third of planned maintenance dose and increase weekly until maintenance dose is reached at 1 month.
▶ **Crohn disease‡.** *Adults:* 3 to 6 g P.O. in divided doses.

Contraindications and cautions

• Contraindicated in patients hypersensitive to the drug or its metabolites, and patients with porphyria or intestinal or urinary obstruction.
• Use cautiously and in reduced dosages in patients with impaired liver or kidney function, severe allergy, bronchial asthma, or G6PD deficiency.
Lifespan: In pregnant women, use cautiously. In breast-feeding women, use cautiously; it's unknown if the drug appears in breast milk. In infants younger than age 2, drug is contraindicated.

Adverse reactions

CNS: depression, hallucinations, headache, *seizures.*
GI: abdominal pain, anorexia, *diarrhea, nausea,* stomatitis, *vomiting.*
GU: crystalluria, hematuria, infertility, oligospermia, ***toxic nephrosis with oliguria and anuria.***
Hematologic: ***agranulocytosis, aplastic anemia,*** hemolytic anemia, ***leukopenia,*** megaloblastic anemia, ***thrombocytopenia.***
Hepatic: ***hepatotoxicity,*** jaundice.
Skin: ***epidermal necrolysis, erythema multiforme,*** exfoliative dermatitis, generalized skin

S

eruption, photosensitivity reactions, pruritus, ***Stevens-Johnson syndrome,*** urticaria.
Other: ***hypersensitivity reactions*** (***anaphylaxis,*** drug fever, serum sickness).

Interactions

Drug-drug. *Antibiotics:* May alter action of sulfasalazine by altering internal flora. Monitor patient closely.
Digoxin: May reduce digoxin absorption. Monitor patient closely.
Folic acid: May decrease absorption. No intervention needed.
Hormonal contraceptives: May decrease contraceptive effectiveness and increases risk of breakthrough bleeding. Suggest nonhormonal contraceptive.
Iron: May lower sulfasalazine level by iron chelation. Monitor patient closely.
Methotrexate: May increase risk of methotrexate-induced bone marrow suppression. Monitor for hematologic toxicity.
Oral anticoagulants: May increase anticoagulant effect. Monitor patient for bleeding.
Oral antidiabetics: May increase hypoglycemic effect. Monitor glucose level.
Drug-herb. *Dong quai, St. John's wort:* May increase risk of photosensitivity. Discourage using together.

Effects on lab test results

- May increase AST and ALT levels. May decrease hemoglobin level and hematocrit.
- May decrease granulocyte, platelet, RBC, and WBC counts.

Pharmacokinetics

Absorption: Poor. 70% to 90% transported to colon, where intestinal flora metabolize drug to its active ingredients, which exert their effects locally. One metabolite, sulfapyridine, is absorbed from colon, but only small portion of metabolite 5-aminosalicylic acid is absorbed.
Distribution: Distributed locally in colon. Distribution of absorbed metabolites is unknown.
Metabolism: Divided by intestinal flora in colon.
Excretion: Systemically absorbed sulfasalazine is excreted mainly in urine. *Half-life:* 6 to 8 hours.

Route	Onset	Peak	Duration
P.O.			
parent drug	Unknown	1½–6 hr	Unknown
metabolites	Unknown	12–24 hr	Unknown

Action

Chemical effect: Unknown.
Therapeutic effect: Relieves inflammation in GI tract.

Available forms

Oral suspension: 250 mg/5 ml
Tablets (with or without enteric coating): 500 mg

NURSING PROCESS

Assessment

- Assess patient's condition before starting therapy and regularly thereafter to monitor drug's effectiveness.
- Monitor CBC and liver function tests at baseline, every other week for first 3 months, monthly for next 3 months, then as needed.
- Be alert for adverse reactions and drug interactions.
- Monitor patient's hydration throughout drug therapy.
- Assess patient's and family's knowledge of drug therapy.

Nursing diagnoses

- Acute pain related to inflammation of GI tract
- Risk for deficient fluid volume related to drug-induced adverse GI reactions
- Deficient knowledge related to drug therapy

Planning and implementation

- Minimize adverse GI reaction by spacing doses evenly and giving after food intake.
- Drug colors alkaline urine orange-yellow.

ALERT: If patient shows evidence of hypersensitivity, stop immediately and notify prescriber.
ALERT: Don't confuse sulfasalazine with sulfisoxazole, salsalate, or sulfadiazine.

Patient teaching

- Instruct patient to take drug after meals and to space doses evenly.
- Warn patient that drug may cause skin and urine to turn orange-yellow and may permanently stain soft contact lenses yellow.

• Warn patient to avoid direct sunlight and ultraviolet light, to prevent photosensitivity reaction.
• Instruct patient to notify physician immediately with complaints of pallor, sore throat, purpura or jaundice.

Evaluation
• Patient is free from pain.
• Patient maintains adequate hydration.
• Patient and family state understanding of drug therapy.

sulfinpyrazone
(sul-fin-PEER-uh-zohn)
Anturan ♦, Anturane, Apo-Sulfinpyrazone ♦, Nu-Sulfinpyrazone ♦

Pharmacologic class: uricosuric
Therapeutic class: platelet aggregation inhibitor, uricolytic
Pregnancy risk category: NR

Indications and dosages
▶ **Intermittent or chronic gouty arthritis.** *Adults:* Initially, 100 mg to 200 mg P.O. b.i.d. during the first week; then 200 mg to 400 mg P.O. b.i.d. Maximum dosage is 800 mg daily. After urate level is controlled, dosage can sometimes be reduced to 200 mg daily in divided doses.
▶ **Prophylaxis of thromboembolic disorders, including angina, MI, transient (cerebral) ischemic attacks, and presence of prosthetic heart valves‡.** *Adults:* 600 to 800 mg P.O. daily in divided doses to decrease platelet aggregation.

Contraindications and cautions
• Contraindicated in patients hypersensitive to pyrazole derivatives (including oxyphenbutazone and phenylbutazone) and patients with active peptic ulcer, symptoms of GI inflammation or ulceration, or blood dyscrasias.
• Use cautiously in patients with healed peptic ulcer.
Lifespan: In pregnant women, use cautiously. In breast-feeding women and in children, safety and effectiveness haven't been established.

Adverse reactions
GI: *dyspepsia,* epigastric pain, *nausea,* reactivation of peptic ulcerations.
Hematologic: ***agranulocytosis, aplastic anemia,*** anemia, ***blood dyscrasias, leukopenia, thrombocytopenia.***
Respiratory: ***bronchoconstriction*** in patients with aspirin-induced asthma.
Skin: rash.

Interactions
Drug-drug. *Aspirin, niacin, salicylates:* May inhibit uricosuric effect of sulfinpyrazone. Don't use together.
Cholestyramine: May bind and delay absorption of sulfinpyrazone. Give sulfinpyrazone at least 1 hour before or 4 to 6 hours after cholestyramine.
Oral anticoagulants: May increase anticoagulant effect and risk of bleeding. Use together cautiously.
Oral antidiabetics: May increase effects. Monitor glucose level closely.
Probenecid: May inhibit renal excretion of sulfinpyrazone. Use together cautiously.
Protein-bound drugs: May cause interaction. Monitor patient for toxicity.
Theophylline: May increase theophylline clearance. Monitor level.
Verapamil: May decrease verapamil effect. Monitor patient.
Drug-lifestyle. *Alcohol use:* May decrease drug effectiveness. Discourage using together.

Effects on lab test results
• May increase BUN and creatinine levels. May decrease hemoglobin level and hematocrit.
• May decrease RBC, WBC, granulocyte, and platelet counts.

Pharmacokinetics
Absorption: Complete.
Distribution: 98% to 99% protein-bound.
Metabolism: Rapid.
Excretion: In urine, about 50% unchanged.
Half-life: 3 hours.

Route	Onset	Peak	Duration
P.O.	Unknown	1–2 hr	4–6 hr

S

Action

Chemical effect: Blocks renal tubular reabsorption of uric acid, increasing excretion, and inhibits platelet aggregation.
Therapeutic effect: Relieves signs and symptoms of gouty arthritis.

Available forms

Capsules: 200 mg
Tablets: 100 mg

NURSING PROCESS

Assessment

- Assess patient's condition before starting therapy and regularly thereafter to monitor drug's effectiveness.
- Monitor BUN level, CBC, and kidney function studies periodically during long-term use.
- Monitor fluid intake and output. Therapy may lead to renal colic and formation of uric acid stones until acid level are normal (about 6 mg/dl).
- Be alert for adverse reactions and drug interactions.
- Assess patient's and family's knowledge of drug therapy.

Nursing diagnoses

- Ineffective health maintenance related to presence of gouty arthritis
- Risk for injury related to drug-induced adverse CNS reactions
- Deficient knowledge related to drug therapy

Planning and implementation

- Give drug with milk, food, or antacids to minimize GI disturbances.
- Encourage patient to drink fluids to maintain minimum daily output of 2 to 3 L. Alkalinize urine with sodium bicarbonate or other agent. Keep in mind that alkalinizers are used therapeutically to increase drug activity, preventing urolithiasis.
- Drug is recommended for patient unresponsive to probenecid. Suitable for long-term use; neither cumulative effects nor tolerance develops.
- Drug contains no analgesic or anti-inflammatory and is of no value during acute gout attacks.
- Drug may increase frequency, severity, and length of acute gout attacks during first 6 to 12 months of therapy. Give prophylactic colchicine or another anti-inflammatory during first 3 to 6 months.
- Lifelong therapy may be needed in patient with hyperuricemia.
- Drug decreases urinary excretion of aminohippuric acid, interfering with laboratory test results.

ALERT: Don't confuse Anturane with Artane or Antabuse.

Patient teaching

- Warn patient with gout not to take aspirin-containing drugs because they may precipitate gout. Acetaminophen may be used for pain.
- Tell patient to take drug with food, milk, or antacid. Also instruct him to drink plenty of water.
- Instruct patient with gout to avoid foods high in purine, such as anchovies, liver, sardines, kidneys, sweetbreads, peas, and lentils.
- Inform patient and family that drug must be taken regularly or gout attacks may result. Tell patient to see prescriber regularly so blood level can be monitored and dosage adjusted if needed.

Evaluation

- Patient regains and maintains normal uric acid level.
- Patient doesn't experience injury from adverse CNS reactions.
- Patient and family state understanding of drug therapy.

sulindac

(SUL-in-dak)
Aclin ◇, Apo-Sulin ♦, Clinoril, Novo-Sundac ♦

Pharmacologic class: NSAID
Therapeutic class: analgesic, anti-inflammatory
Pregnancy risk category: B (D in third trimester)

Indications and dosages

▶ **Osteoarthritis, rheumatoid arthritis, ankylosing spondylitis.** *Adults:* Initially,

150 mg P.O. b.i.d.; increase to 200 mg b.i.d., as needed.

▶ **Acute subacromial bursitis or supraspinatus tendinitis, acute gouty arthritis.** *Adults:* 200 mg P.O. b.i.d. for 7 to 14 days. Reduce dose as symptoms subside.

Contraindications and cautions

• Contraindicated in patients hypersensitive to the drug or any of its components, and in patients for whom aspirin or NSAIDs precipitate asthma, rhinitis, urticaria, nasal polyps, angioedema, bronchospasm, or other allergic or anaphylactoid symptoms. Contraindicated for treatment of perioperative pain associated with coronary artery bypass graft surgery.

• Use cautiously in patients with history of ulcers and GI bleeding, renal dysfunction, hepatic dysfunction, compromised cardiac function or hypertension, or conditions predisposing to fluid retention.

Lifespan: In pregnant women, drug isn't recommended. In breast-feeding women and in children, safety and effectiveness haven't been established.

Adverse reactions

CNS: dizziness, headache, nervousness, psychosis.
CV: edema, ***heart failure,*** hypertension, palpitations.
EENT: tinnitus, transient visual disturbances.
GI: anorexia, constipation, dyspepsia, *epigastric distress,* flatulence, ***GI bleeding,*** nausea, occult blood loss, ***pancreatitis,*** peptic ulceration.
GU: interstitial nephritis, nephrotic syndrome, ***renal failure.***
Hematologic: ***agranulocytosis, aplastic anemia,*** hemolytic anemia, ***neutropenia, thrombocytopenia.***
Skin: pruritus, *rash.*
Other: ***anaphylaxis, angioedema,*** drug fever, hypersensitivity syndrome.

Interactions

Drug-drug. *ACE inhibitors:* May decrease antihypertensive effects of these drugs. Monitor blood pressure.
Anticoagulants: May increase risk of bleeding. Monitor PT closely.
Aspirin, NSAIDs: May decrease sulindac level and increase risk of adverse GI reactions. Avoid using together.
Cyclosporine: May increase nephrotoxicity of cyclosporine. Monitor renal function.
Diflunisal, dimethyl sulfoxide (DMSO): May decrease metabolism of sulindac to its active metabolite, reducing its effectiveness. Topical DMSO used with sulindac has caused severe peripheral neuropathy. Don't use together.
Diuretics: May increase effects of regular diuretics on blood pressure, but decrease effects of potassium-sparing diuretics. Monitor blood pressure and electrolytes.
Lithium: May decrease lithium level. Monitor patient and blood level carefully.
Methotrexate: May increase methotrexate toxicity. Avoid using together.
Probenecid: May increase level of sulindac and its active metabolite. Monitor patient for toxicity.
Sulfonamides, sulfonylureas, other highly protein-bound drugs: May displace these drugs from protein-binding sites, leading to increased toxicity. Monitor patient closely for toxicity.

Effects on lab test results

• May increase BUN, creatinine, liver enzyme, and potassium levels. May decrease hemoglobin level and hematocrit.
• May increase bleeding time. May decrease platelet, neutrophil, and granulocyte counts.

Pharmacokinetics

Absorption: 90% absorbed.
Distribution: Extensively protein-bound.
Metabolism: Drug is inactive and metabolized in liver to an active sulfide metabolite.
Excretion: In urine. *Half-life:* Parent drug, 8 hours; active metabolite, about 16 hours.

Route	Onset	Peak	Duration
P.O.	Unknown	2–4 hr	Unknown

Action

Chemical effect: Unknown; produces anti-inflammatory, analgesic, and antipyretic effects, possibly by inhibiting prostaglandin synthesis.
Therapeutic effect: Relieves pain and inflammation.

S

Available forms

Tablets: 100 mg ◊, 150 mg, 200 mg

NURSING PROCESS

Assessment

- Assess patient's condition before starting therapy and regularly thereafter to monitor the drug's effectiveness.
- Periodically monitor liver and kidney function and CBC in patient taking long-term therapy.
- Be alert for adverse reactions and drug interactions.
- Assess patient's and family's knowledge of drug therapy.

Nursing diagnoses

- Acute pain related to presence of arthritis
- Impaired tissue integrity related to drug's adverse effect on GI mucosa
- Deficient knowledge related to drug therapy

Planning and implementation

- Notify prescriber of adverse reactions.

ALERT: Don't confuse Clinoril with Clozaril.

Patient teaching

- Tell patient to take drug with food, milk, or antacids to reduce adverse GI reactions.
- Advise patient to refrain from driving or performing other hazardous activities that require mental alertness until the drug's CNS effects are known.
- Teach patient signs and symptoms of GI bleeding, and tell him to contact prescriber immediately if they occur. Serious GI toxicity, including peptic ulceration and bleeding, can occur in patient taking NSAIDs despite absence of GI symptoms.

ALERT: Tell patient to notify prescriber immediately if easy bruising or prolonged bleeding occurs.

- Instruct patient to report any edema and to have his blood pressure checked monthly. Drug causes sodium retention but may not affect kidneys as much as other NSAIDs.
- Instruct patient not to take aspirin, aspirin-containing products, or other NSAIDs with sulindac.
- Tell patient to notify prescriber and undergo complete eye examination if visual disturbances occur.

Evaluation

- Patient is free from pain.
- Patient doesn't experience adverse GI reactions.
- Patient and family state understanding of drug therapy.

sumatriptan succinate

(soo-muh-TRIP-ten SEK-seh-nayt)

Imitrex

Pharmacologic class: selective 5-hydroxytryptamine (5-HT_1) receptor agonist
Therapeutic class: antimigraine drug
Pregnancy risk category: C

Indications and dosages

▶ **Acute migraine attacks (with or without aura).** *Adults:* 6 mg subcutaneously. Maximum recommended dose is two 6-mg injections in 24 hours, separated by at least 1 hour. Or, 25 to 100 mg P.O. initially. If response isn't achieved in 2 hours, may give second dose of 25 to 100 mg. Additional doses may be used in at least 2-hour intervals. Maximum daily oral dose, 200 mg. Or, 5 mg, 10 mg, or 20 mg administered once in one nostril. May repeat once after 2 hours for maximum daily inhalation dose of 40 mg. For 10-mg dose, give a single 5-mg dose in each nostril.

▶ **Acute treatment of cluster headache episodes.** *Adults:* 6 mg subcutaneously. Maximum recommended dose is two 6-mg injections in 24 hours, separated by at least 1 hour.

Adjust-a-dose: For patients with hepatic impairment, don't exceed maximum single oral dose of 50 mg.

Contraindications and cautions

- Contraindicated in patients hypersensitive to the drug or any of its components, and in patients with history, symptoms, or signs of ischemic cardiac, cerebrovascular (stroke, transient ischemic attack), or peripheral vascular (ischemic bowel disease) syndromes, or MI.
- Contraindicated in patients with uncontrolled hypertension, severe hepatic impairment (oral form), and hemiplegic or basilar migraines.
- Contraindicated within 24 hours of another 5-HT agonist or ergotamine-containing drug and within 14 days of MAO inhibitor therapy

(oral form only; decrease dosage of sumatriptan if given by injection while patient is on an MAO inhibitor).

- Don't give drug I.V.; it can cause coronary vasospasms.
- Use cautiously in patients who may have unrecognized coronary artery disease (CAD), such as postmenopausal women, men older than age 40, and patients with risk factors for CAD.

Lifespan: In pregnant women and women who intend to become pregnant, use cautiously. In breast-feeding women and in children, safety and effectiveness haven't been established.

Adverse reactions

CNS: anxiety, *dizziness,* drowsiness, fatigue, headache, malaise, *vertigo.*
CV: ***atrial fibrillation, coronary artery vasospasm,*** hypertension, ***MI,*** pressure or tightness in chest, ***transient myocardial ischemia, ventricular fibrillation, ventricular tachycardia.***
EENT: altered vision; discomfort of jaw, mouth, nasal cavity, sinus, throat, or tongue.
GI: abdominal discomfort, diarrhea, dysphagia, nausea, unusual or bad taste (nasal spray), vomiting.
Musculoskeletal: muscle cramps, myalgia, neck pain.
Respiratory: dyspnea and upper respiratory inflammation (P.O.).
Skin: diaphoresis.
Other: cold sensation; flushing, *tingling,* or *injection site reaction* (subcutaneous); heaviness, pressure, or tightness; numbness; tight feeling in head; *warm, hot, or burning sensation.*

Interactions

Drug-drug. *Ergot and ergot derivatives; other serotonin$_{1B/1D}$ agonists:* May prolong vasospastic effects. Don't use within 24 hours of sumatriptan therapy.
MAO inhibitors: May reduce sumatriptan clearance. Avoid using sumatriptan tablets or nasal spray within 2 weeks of stopping MAO inhibitor. Use injection cautiously in patients and decrease sumatriptan dose.
SSRIs: May cause weakness, hyperreflexia, and incoordination. Monitor patient closely if use together is warranted.
Drug-herb. *Horehound:* May enhance serotonergic effects. Discourage using together.

Effects on lab test results

- May increase liver enzyme level.

Pharmacokinetics

Absorption: Rapid after P.O. and intranasal use but with low absolute bioavailability (about 15% and 17% respectively); absorbed well from injection site after subcutaneous use.
Distribution: Wide, into body tissues. About 14% to 21% protein-bound.
Metabolism: About 80%, in liver.
Excretion: Mainly in urine. *Half-life:* About 2 hours.

Route	Onset	Peak	Duration
P.O.	30 min	2–4 hr	Unknown
SubQ	10–20 min	1–2 hr	Unknown
Intranasal	Rapid	1–2 hr	Unknown

Action

Chemical effect: Unknown; thought to selectively activate vascular serotonin (5-HT) receptors. Stimulation of specific receptor subtype 5-HT$_1$, present on cranial arteries and the dura mater, causes vasoconstriction of cerebral vessels but has minimal effects on systemic vessels, tissue perfusion, and blood pressure.
Therapeutic effect: Relieves acute migraine pain.

Available forms

Injection: 6 mg/0.5 ml (12 mg/ml) in 0.5-ml prefilled syringes and vials
Nasal spray: 5 mg/spray; 20 mg/spray
Tablets: 25 mg, 50 mg, 100 mg (base) ♦

NURSING PROCESS

Assessment

- Assess patient's condition before starting therapy and regularly thereafter to monitor the drug's effectiveness.
- Be alert for adverse reactions and drug interactions.
- Assess patient's and family's knowledge of drug therapy.

Nursing diagnoses

- Acute pain related to presence of acute migraine attack
- Risk for injury related to drug-induced adverse reactions
- Deficient knowledge related to drug therapy

S

Planning and implementation

- If patient has risk of unrecognized CAD, give first dose with prescriber present.
- Give single tablet whole with fluids as soon as patient complains of migraine symptoms. Give second tablet if symptoms come back, but no sooner than 2 hours after first tablet.
- Maximum recommended subcutaneous dosage in 24-hour period is two 6-mg injections separated by at least 1 hour. If patient doesn't experience relief, notify prescriber.
- Patient will most likely experience relief within 1 to 2 hours.
- Redness or pain at injection site should subside within 1 hour after injection.

ALERT: Serious adverse cardiac effects can follow administration of this drug, but such events are rare.

- If patient doesn't experience relief, notify prescriber.

ALERT: Don't confuse sumatriptan with somatropin.

Patient teaching

- Make sure patient understands that drug is intended only to treat migraine attack, not to prevent or reduce number of attacks.
- Tell patient that drug may be given at any time during migraine attack but should be given as soon as symptoms appear.
- Drug is available in spring-loaded injector system that makes it easy for the patient to give injection to himself. Review detailed information with patient. Make sure patient understands how to load injector, give injection, and dispose of used syringes.
- Instruct patient taking P.O. form when and how often to take drug. Warn patient not to take more than 200 mg within 24 hours.
- Instruct patient to use intranasal spray in one nostril. (If giving 10 mg, 1 spray into each nostril.) A second spray may be used if headache returns, but not before 2 hours has elapsed from the first use.
- Tell patient who experiences persistent or severe chest pain to call prescriber immediately. Patient who experiences pain or tightness in throat, wheezing, heart throbbing, rash, lumps, hives, or swollen eyelids, face, or lips should stop using drug and call prescriber.
- Tell woman who is pregnant or intends to become pregnant not to take this drug.

Evaluation

- Patient is free from pain.
- Patient doesn't experience injury from adverse CV reactions.
- Patient and family state understanding of drug therapy.

sunitinib malate
(soo-NIH-tih-nib MAH-layt)
Sutent

Pharmacologic class: multi-kinase inhibitor
Therapeutic class: antineoplastic
Pregnancy risk category: D

Indications and dosages

▶ **GI stromal tumor that's progressing despite imatinib therapy or because patient is intolerant of imatinib; advanced renal cell carcinoma.** *Adults:* 50 mg P.O. once daily for 4 weeks, followed by a 2-week rest period off the drug. Repeat cycle.

Adjust-a-dose: Increase or decrease dosage in 12.5-mg increments based on individual safety and tolerability.

Contraindications and cautions

- Contraindicated in patients who are hypersensitive to the drug or any of its components. Don't use in patients with non–small-cell lung cancer.
- Use cautiously in patients with a history of hypertension, MI, angina, coronary artery bypass graft, symptomatic heart failure, stroke, TIA, or pulmonary embolism.

Lifespan: Drug inhibits angiogenesis, a critical component of embryonic and fetal development. Explain that drug may harm a fetus and that women should avoid becoming pregnant during treatment. Mothers should either stop breast-feeding or stop the drug. In children, safety and efficacy haven't been established.

Adverse reactions

CNS: *asthenia, dizziness, fatigue, fever, headache, peripheral neuropathy.*
CV: ***decreased left ventricular ejection fraction,*** hypertension, peripheral edema, ***thromboembolic events.***

EENT: increased lacrimation, periorbital edema.
GI: abdominal pain, altered taste, anorexia, appetite disturbance, burning sensation in mouth, constipation, diarrhea, dyspepsia, flatulence, ***GI perforation,*** mucositis, nausea, oral pain, ***pancreatitis,*** stomatitis, vomiting.
Hematologic: *anemia,* ***bleeding, leukopenia,*** *lymphopenia,* **NEUTROPENIA, THROMBOCYTOPENIA.**
Metabolic: *dehydration,* hyperkalemia, *hypernatremia, hyperuricemia, hypokalemia,* hyponatremia, hypophosphatemia, hypothyroidism.
Musculoskeletal: *arthralgia, back pain, limb pain, myalgia.*
Respiratory: *cough, dyspnea.*
Skin: *alopecia, dry skin, hair color changes, hand-foot syndrome, rash,* skin blistering, *skin discoloration.*
Other: adrenal insufficiency, hypothyroidism.

Interactions

Drug-drug. *CYP3A4 inducers (such as carbamazepine, dexamethasone, phenobarbital, phenytoin, rifabutin, rifampin, rifapentine):* May decrease sunitinib level and effects. If use together can't be avoided, increase sunitinib dosage to 87.5 mg daily.
Strong CYP3A4 inhibitors (such as atazanavir, clarithromycin, indinavir, itraconazole, ketoconazole, nefazodone, nelfinavir, ritonavir, saquinavir, telithromycin, voriconazole): May increase sunitinib level and toxicity. If use together can't be avoided, decrease sunitinib dosage to 37.5 mg daily.
Drug-food. *Grapefruit:* May increase drug level. Tell patient to avoid grapefruit.
Drug-herb. *St. John's wort:* May cause an unpredictable decrease in drug level. Discourage use together.

Effects on lab test results

- May increase AST, ALT, alkaline phosphatase, total and indirect bilirubin, amylase, lipase, creatinine, uric acid, and TSH levels. May decrease phosphorus and hemoglobin levels and hematocrit. May increase or decrease potassium and sodium levels.
- May decrease RBC, neutrophil, lymphocyte, leukocyte, and platelet counts.

Pharmacokinetics

Absorption: Unaffected by food. Reaches steady-state level in 10 to 14 days.
Distribution: 95% plasma protein–bound. Metabolite is 90% plasma protein–bound.
Metabolism: Mainly in the liver through the CYP3A4 pathway.
Excretion: Via feces (61%) and urine (16%). *Half-life:* 40 to 60 hours; *primary metabolite:* 80 to 110 hours.

Route	Onset	Peak	Duration
P.O.	Rapid	6–12 hr	Unknown

Action

Chemical effect: A multi-kinase inhibitor targeting several receptor tyrosine kinases, which are involved in tumor growth, pathologic angiogenesis, and metastatic progression of cancer.
Therapeutic effect: Slows carcinoma growth.

Available forms

Capsules: 12.5 mg, 25 mg, 50 mg

NURSING PROCESS

Assessment

- Assess neoplastic disease before starting therapy, and reassess regularly.
- Monitor patient's blood pressure, and treat hypertension as needed. If severe hypertension occurs, stop treatment until blood pressure is adequately controlled.
- Monitor patient for signs and symptoms of heart failure, especially if he has a history of heart disease.
- Notify prescriber if patient develops signs or symptoms of heart failure.
- If patient has seizures, consider reversible posterior leukoencephalopathy syndrome. Signs and symptoms include hypertension, headache, decreased alertness, altered mental functioning, and vision loss. Notify prescriber immediately.
- If patient will be undergoing surgery or suffers trauma or severe infection, assess him for adrenal insufficiency (muscle weakness, weight loss, depression, salt craving, low blood pressure).
- Assess patient's and family's knowledge of drug therapy.

S

Nursing diagnoses
- Ineffective health maintenance related to neoplastic disease
- Risk for falls related to drug-induced adverse reactions
- Deficient knowledge related to drug therapy

Planning and implementation
- Obtain baseline weight before starting therapy, and then weigh patient daily. Evaluate and treat unexpected and rapid weight gain.
- Obtain CBC with platelet count and serum chemistries, including phosphate level, before each treatment cycle.
- Obtain baseline evaluation of ejection fraction in all patients before treatment. If patient had a cardiac event in the year preceding treatment, check ejection fraction periodically.
- Patients with an ejection fraction less than 50% and more than 20% below baseline will need a decreased dosage or to interrupt treatment.
- Provide antiemetics or antidiarrheals as needed for adverse GI effects.

Patient teaching
- Advise patient to keep appointments for blood tests before each treatment cycle and, if needed, periodic heart function evaluations.
- Tell patient about common adverse effects, such as diarrhea, nausea, vomiting, fatigue, mouth pain, and taste disturbance.
- Inform patient about changes that may occur in skin and hair, including color changes and dry, red, blistering skin of the hands and feet.
- Urge patient to tell health care providers about all prescribed and OTC drugs or herbal supplements he takes.
- Warn patient not to consume grapefruit products during therapy.
- Tell patient to notify his prescriber about unusual bleeding, trouble breathing, wheezing, severe or prolonged diarrhea or vomiting, or swelling of the hands or lower legs.

Evaluation
- Patient shows positive response to drug therapy on follow-up studies.
- Patient doesn't experience falls.
- Patient and family state understanding of drug therapy.

tacrine hydrochloride
(TAK-reen high-droh-KLOR-ighd)
Cognex

Pharmacologic class: centrally acting reversible anticholinesterase
Therapeutic class: psychotherapeutic for Alzheimer disease
Pregnancy risk category: C

Indications and dosages
▶ **Mild to moderate dementia of Alzheimer type.** *Adults:* Initially, 10 mg P.O. q.i.d. After 4 weeks, if patient tolerates drug and transaminase level isn't elevated, increase dosage to 20 mg q.i.d. After another 4 weeks, increase dosage to 30 mg q.i.d. If still tolerated, increase to 40 mg q.i.d. after another 4 weeks.

Adjust-a-dose: For patients with ALT level three to five times the upper limit of normal (ULN) range, reduce dosage by 40 mg daily and monitor ALT level weekly until normal. If ALT is more than five times ULN, stop therapy and monitor patient for signs and symptoms of hepatitis. May rechallenge when ALT returns to normal. With rechallenge doses, monitor ALT weekly for 16 weeks, then monthly for 2 months, then every 3 months thereafter.

Contraindications and cautions
- Contraindicated in patients hypersensitive to the drug or acridine derivatives, and in those who have previously developed drug-related jaundice and been confirmed with elevated total bilirubin level of more than 3 mg/dl.
- Use cautiously in patients with sick sinus syndrome or bradycardia; those at risk for peptic ulceration (including patients taking NSAIDs or those with history of peptic ulcer); those with history of hepatic disease; and those with renal disease, asthma, prostatic hyperplasia, or other urinary outflow impairment.

Lifespan: In pregnant and breast-feeding women, drug isn't recommended. In children, drug isn't indicated.

Adverse reactions

CNS: abnormal thinking, agitation, anxiety, ataxia, confusion, depression, *dizziness,* fatigue, *headache,* insomnia, somnolence.
CV: chest pain, facial flushing.
EENT: rhinitis.
GI: anorexia, changes in stool color, constipation, *diarrhea,* dyspepsia, loose stools, *nausea, vomiting.*
Hepatic: jaundice.
Metabolic: weight loss.
Musculoskeletal: myalgia.
Respiratory: cough, upper respiratory tract infection.
Skin: rash.

Interactions

Drug-drug. *Anticholinergics:* May decrease effectiveness of anticholinergics. Monitor patient closely.
Anticholinesterases, cholinergics (such as bethanechol): May have additive effects. Monitor patient for toxicity.
Cimetidine: May increase tacrine level. Monitor patient for toxicity.
Fluvoxamine: May increase tacrine level. Monitor patient.
Succinylcholine: May enhance neuromuscular blockade and prolong duration of action. Monitor patient.
Theophylline: May increase theophylline level and prolong theophylline half-life. Carefully monitor theophylline level, and adjust dosage.
Drug-food. *Any food:* May decrease drug absorption. Tell patient to take drug on empty stomach.
Drug-lifestyle. *Smoking:* May decrease level of drug. Monitor response.

Effects on lab test results

- May increase ALT and AST levels.

Pharmacokinetics

Absorption: Rapid, with absolute bioavailability of about 17%. Food reduces bioavailability by 30% to 40%.
Distribution: About 55% bound to plasma proteins.
Metabolism: Undergoes first-pass metabolism, which is dose-dependent. Extensively metabolized.
Excretion: In urine. *Half-life:* 2 to 4 hours.

Route	Onset	Peak	Duration
P.O.	Unknown	30 min–3 hr	Unknown

Action

Chemical effect: Reversibly inhibits enzyme cholinesterase in CNS, allowing buildup of acetylcholine.
Therapeutic effect: Improves thinking in patients with Alzheimer disease.

Available forms

Capsules: 10 mg, 20 mg, 30 mg, 40 mg

NURSING PROCESS

Assessment

- Assess patient's cognitive ability before starting therapy and regularly thereafter to monitor drug's effectiveness.
- Check ALT level every other week from at least week 4 to week 16 of therapy. If ALT is twice the ULN range, check weekly. If no problems occur, decrease frequency of testing to every 3 months. Whenever dosage is increased, resume monitoring every other week.
- Assess patient's and family's knowledge of drug therapy.

Nursing diagnoses

- Disturbed thought processes related to Alzheimer disease
- Diarrhea related to drug-induced adverse GI reactions
- Deficient knowledge related to drug therapy

Planning and implementation

- Stop drug if patient has evidence of jaundice, increase in total serum bilirubin, or hypersensitivity. Don't resume therapy.
- If patient doesn't improve in 3 to 6 months, consider stopping the drug.
- Give drug between meals. If GI upset becomes a problem, give drug with meals, although level may drop by 30% to 40%.
- If drug is stopped for 4 weeks or more, restart at the basic dose and adjust according to the schedule, as if the patient were being started on drug for the first time.
- Obtain order for antidiarrheal, if indicated.

Patient teaching

- Inform patient and family that drug doesn't alter underlying degenerative disease. Instead, it may alleviate symptoms of Alzheimer disease.

T

• Explain to patient and family that the effect of therapy depends on taking the drug at regular intervals.

ALERT: Instruct caregivers when to give drug. Explain that dosage adjustment is integral to safe use. Abruptly stopping or reducing daily dose by 80 mg or more may trigger behavioral disturbances and cognitive decline.

• Advise patient and caregivers to report immediately any significant adverse effects or changes in status.

Evaluation

• Patient exhibits improved cognitive ability.
• Patient or caregiver states that drug-induced diarrhea hasn't occurred.
• Patient and family state understanding of drug therapy.

tacrolimus

(tek-roh-LYE-mus)

Prograf

Pharmacologic class: macrolide
Therapeutic class: immunosuppressant
Pregnancy risk category: C

Indications and dosages

▶ **To prevent organ rejection in allogenic liver, kidney, or heart transplant.** *Adults:* For patients unable to take drug orally, give 0.03 to 0.05 mg/kg/day (liver or kidney) or 0.01 mg/kg/day (heart) I.V. as continuous infusion no sooner than 6 hours after transplant. Switch to oral therapy as soon as possible, with first dose given 8 to 12 hours after stopping I.V. infusion. For renal transplant, give oral dose within 24 hours of transplantation after renal function has recovered. Recommended initial P.O. dosages are as follows: For liver transplant, give 0.1 to 0.15 mg/kg daily in two divided doses q 12 hours. For kidney transplant, give 0.2 mg/kg daily in two divided doses q 12 hours. For heart transplant, give 0.075 mg/kg daily in two divided doses q 12 hours. Adjust dosages based on patient's response.
Children (liver transplant only): Initially, 0.03 to 0.05 mg/kg daily I.V.; then 0.15 to 0.2 mg/kg daily P.O. on schedule similar to that of adults, adjusted as needed.

Adjust-a-dose: Give lowest recommended P.O. and I.V. dosages to patients with renal or hepatic impairment.

▶ **Crohn disease**‡. *Adults and children age 12 and older:* 200 mcg/kg P.O. daily in 2 divided doses for 10 weeks.

I.V. administration

• Dilute drug with normal saline solution injection or D_5W injection to 0.004 to 0.02 mg/ml before use.
• Each required daily dose of diluted drug is infused continuously over 24 hours.
• Monitor patient continuously during first 30 minutes of infusion; then check often for anaphylaxis.
• Keep epinephrine 1:1,000 available to treat anaphylaxis.
• Store diluted solution for no more than 24 hours in glass or polyethylene containers. Don't store drug in polyvinyl chloride container.

⊗ **Incompatibilities**
Solutions or I.V. drugs with a pH above 9, such as acyclovir and ganciclovir.

Contraindications and cautions

• Contraindicated in patients hypersensitive to the drug or any of its components. I.V. form contraindicated in patients hypersensitive to castor oil derivatives.
• Use cautiously in patients with renal or hepatic impairment.

Lifespan: In pregnant or breast-feeding women, drug isn't recommended.

Adverse reactions

CNS: asthenia, ***coma,*** delirium, fever, headache, insomnia, ***neurotoxicity,*** pain, paresthesia, tremor.
CV: hypertension, peripheral edema.
GI: abdominal pain, anorexia, ascites, constipation, diarrhea, nausea, vomiting.
GU: abnormal kidney function, ***nephrotoxicity,*** oliguria, UTI.
Hematologic: *anemia,* leukocytosis, THROMBOCYTOPENIA.
Metabolic: hyperglycemia, ***hyperkalemia,*** hypokalemia, ***hypomagnesemia.***
Musculoskeletal: *back pain.*
Respiratory: atelectasis, dyspnea, pleural effusion.
Skin: photosensitivity reactions.
Other: ***anaphylaxis.***

Interactions

Drug-drug. *Bromocriptine, cimetidine, clarithromycin, clotrimazole, cyclosporine, danazol, diltiazem, erythromycin, ethinyl estradiol, fluconazole, itraconazole, ketoconazole, methylprednisolone, metoclopramide, nefazodone, nicardipine, nifedipine, omeprazole, protease inhibitors, verapamil:* May increase tacrolimus level. Monitor patient for adverse effects.
Carbamazepine, phenobarbital, phenytoin, rifabutin, rifampin: May decrease tacrolimus level. Monitor tacrolimus effectiveness.
Cyclosporine: May increase risk of excess nephrotoxicity. Don't give together.
Immunosuppressants (except adrenocorticosteroids): May oversuppress immune system. Monitor patient closely, especially during times of stress.
Inducers of cytochrome P-450 enzyme system: May increase tacrolimus metabolism and decrease drug level. Dosage adjustment may be needed.
Inhibitors of cytochrome P-450 enzyme system: May decrease tacrolimus metabolism and increase drug level. Dosage adjustment may be needed.
Nephrotoxic drugs (such as aminoglycosides, amphotericin B, cisplatin, cyclosporine): May cause additive or synergistic effects. Monitor patient closely.
Viral vaccines: May interfere with immune response to live-virus vaccines.
Drug-herb. *St. John's wort:* May decrease tacrolimus level. Monitor effectiveness of tacrolimus.
Drug-food. *Any food:* May inhibit drug absorption. Tell patient to take drug on an empty stomach.
Grapefruit juice: May increase drug level in liver transplant patients. Discourage use together.

Effects on lab test results

- May increase glucose, creatinine, and BUN levels. May decrease magnesium and hemoglobin levels and hematocrit. May increase or decrease potassium level.
- May increase liver function test values and WBC and platelet counts.

Pharmacokinetics

Absorption: Variable. Food reduces absorption and bioavailability of drug.
Distribution: Distribution between whole blood and plasma depends on several factors, such as hematocrit, temperature of separation of plasma, drug level, and protein level. Drug is 75% to 99% protein-bound.
Metabolism: Extensive.
Excretion: Mainly in bile. *Half-life:* 33 to 56 hours.

Route	Onset	Peak	Duration
P.O., I.V.	Unknown	1½–3½ hr	Unknown

Action

Chemical effect: Unknown; may inhibit T-lymphocyte activation, which results in immunosuppression.
Therapeutic effect: Prevents organ rejection.

Available forms

Capsules: 0.5 mg, 1 mg, 5 mg
Injection: 5 mg/ml

NURSING PROCESS

Assessment

- Obtain history of patient's organ transplant before starting therapy, and reassess regularly to monitor the drug's effectiveness.
- Monitor patient for signs of neurotoxicity and nephrotoxicity, especially in those receiving high dosage or those with renal dysfunction.
- Obtain potassium and glucose levels regularly. Monitor patient for hyperglycemia.
- Drug increases risk of infections, lymphomas, and other cancers.
- Be alert for adverse reactions and drug interactions.
- Assess patient's and family's knowledge of drug therapy.

Nursing diagnoses

- Risk for injury related to organ transplant rejection
- Ineffective protection related to drug-induced immunosuppression
- Deficient knowledge related to drug therapy

Planning and implementation

- Child with normal kidney and liver function may need a higher dose than an adult.
- Patient with hepatic or renal dysfunction needs lowest possible dosage.
- Black renal transplant patients may require higher doses.
- Use with adrenal corticosteroids for all indications. For heart transplant patients, also use with azathioprine or mycophenolate mofetil.
- Give oral drug on empty stomach.

ALERT: The use of sirolimus with tacrolimus may increase the risk of wound healing complications, renal impairment, and posttransplant type 1 diabetes mellitus in heart transplant patients. Don't use together.

- Because of risk of anaphylaxis, use injection only in patient who can't take oral form.
- Don't use other immunosuppressants (except adrenocorticosteroids) during therapy.
- Avoid potassium-sparing diuretics during therapy.
- Hepatic transplant trough levels are best maintained at 5 to 20 nanograms/ml 1 to 2 months posttransplant. Renal transplant trough levels are best maintained at 7 to 20 nanograms/ml between posttransplant months 1 to 3, and then 1 to 5 nanograms/ml for posttransplant months 4 to 12.

Patient teaching

- Instruct patient to take drug on empty stomach and not to take it with grapefruit juice.
- Explain need for repeated tests during therapy to monitor adverse reactions and drug effectiveness.
- Advise woman of childbearing age to notify prescriber if she becomes pregnant or plans to do so.
- Instruct patient to check with prescriber before taking other drugs.

Evaluation

- Patient has no signs and symptoms of organ rejection.
- Patient develops no serious complications from drug-induced adverse reactions.
- Patient and family state understanding of drug therapy.

tacrolimus (topical)

(tack-row-LYE-mus)

Protopic

Pharmacologic class: macrolide
Therapeutic class: immunosuppressant
Pregnancy risk category: C

Indication and dosages

▶ **Moderate to severe atopic dermatitis in patients unresponsive to other therapies or unable to use other therapies because of risks.** *Adults:* Apply thin layer of 0.03% or 0.1% strength to affected areas twice daily and rub in completely. Continue for 1 week after affected area clears.
Children ages 2 to 15: Apply thin layer of 0.03% strength to affected areas twice daily and rub in completely. Continue for 1 week after affected area clears.

Contraindications and cautions

- Contraindicated in patients hypersensitive to the drug or any of its components.
- Don't use in patients with Netherton syndrome or generalized erythroderma, or in immunocompromised patients.

Lifespan: In pregnant women, use only if benefits to the patient outweigh risks to the fetus. In breast-feeding women, the drug appears in breast milk; weigh benefits to the mother against risks to the infant. In children ages 2 to 15, use only 0.03% ointment.

Adverse reactions

CNS: asthenia, *fever, headache,* hyperesthesia, insomnia, pain.
CV: face edema, peripheral edema.
EENT: conjunctivitis, *otitis media, pharyngitis,* rhinitis, sinusitis.
GI: abdominal pain, diarrhea, dyspepsia, gastroenteritis, nausea, vomiting.
GU: dysmenorrhea.
Hematologic: lymphadenopathy, ***lymphoma.***
Musculoskeletal: back pain, myalgia.
Respiratory: *asthma,* bronchitis, *increased cough,* pneumonia.
Skin: acne, benign skin neoplasm, contact dermatitis, dry skin, eczema, eczema herpeticum, exfoliative dermatitis, *folliculitis,* fungal dermatitis, herpes zoster, maculopapular rash, pus-

tular rash, *pruritus,* rash, *skin burning, **skin cancer,*** skin disorder, *skin erythema, skin infection,* sunburn, tingling, urticaria, vesiculobullous rash.
Other: accidental injury, alcohol intolerance, allergic reaction, cyst, flulike symptoms, herpes simplex, infection, lack of drug effect, periodontal abscess.

Interactions

Drug-drug. *CYP3A4 inhibitors (erythromycin, itraconazole, ketoconazole, fluconazole):* May interfere with effects of tacrolimus. Use together cautiously.
Drug-lifestyle. *Sun exposure:* May cause risk of phototoxicity. Tell patient to avoid or minimize exposure to artificial or natural sunlight.

Effects on lab test results

None reported.

Pharmacokinetics

Absorption: Immediate, with no systemic accumulation.
Distribution: Unknown.
Metabolism: Unknown.
Excretion: Unknown. *Half-life:* Unknown.

Route	Onset	Peak	Duration
Topical	Unknown	Unknown	Unknown

Action

Chemical effect: May inhibit T-lymphocyte activation in the skin, which causes immunosuppression. Also inhibits the release of mediators from mast cells and basophils in skin.
Therapeutic effect: Improves skin condition.

Available forms

Ointment: 0.03%, 0.1%

NURSING PROCESS

Assessment

- Assess patient's underlying condition before starting therapy, and reassess regularly to monitor the drug's effectiveness.
- Assess patient with infected atopic dermatitis; clear infections at treatment site before using drug.
- Assess patient's and family's knowledge of drug therapy.

Nursing diagnoses

- Impaired skin integrity related to underlying skin condition
- Acute pain related to drug-induced adverse effects
- Deficient knowledge related to tacrolimus therapy

Planning and implementation

- Drug is used only for short-term or intermittent therapy. Avoid long-term use.
- Limit application to areas of involvement with atopic dermatitis.
- Only 0.03% ointment is indicated for use in children ages 2 to 15.
- Use only after other treatments have failed because of a possible risk of cancer with Protopic.

ALERT: Don't use occlusive dressings over drug. This may promote systemic absorption.

- Drug may increase the risk of varicella zoster, herpes simplex virus, and eczema herpeticum.
- Assess all cases of lymphadenopathy to determine etiology. If a clear etiology is unknown or acute mononucleosis is diagnosed, consider stopping drug.
- Monitor all cases of lymphadenopathy until resolution.
- Local adverse effects are most common during the first few days of therapy.

Patient teaching

- Tell patient to wash hands before and after applying drug and to avoid applying drug to wet skin. Skin should be completely dry before applying drug.
- Instruct patient not to use bandages or other occlusive dressings.
- Tell patient not to bathe, shower, or swim immediately after application because doing so could wash the ointment off.
- Advise patient to avoid or minimize exposure to natural or artificial sunlight.
- Tell patient that, if he needs to be outdoors after applying drug, he should wear loose-fitting clothing that covers the treated area. Check with prescriber regarding sunscreen use.
- Tell patient not to use drug for any disorder other than that for which it was prescribed.
- Instruct patient to report adverse reactions.
- Tell patient to store the ointment at room temperature.

T

Evaluation

- Patient has improved skin condition.
- Patient states that pain management techniques are effective.
- Patient and family state understanding of drug therapy.

tadalafil

(tah-DAH-lah-phil)
Cialis

Pharmacologic class: phosphodiesterase type 5 inhibitor
Therapeutic class: erectile dysfunction drug, vasodilator
Pregnancy risk category: B

Indications and dosages

▶ **Erectile dysfunction.** *Men:* 10 mg P.O. as a single dose, p.r.n., before sexual activity. Range is 5 to 20 mg based on effectiveness and tolerance. Maximum, one dose daily.
Adjust-a-dose: For patients with renal impairment, if creatinine clearance is 31 to 50 ml/minute, starting dosage is 5 mg once daily and maximum dosage is 10 mg taken once q 48 hours; if 30 ml/minute or less, maximum dosage is 5 mg once daily. For patients with mild to moderate hepatic impairment (Child-Pugh class A or B), dosage shouldn't exceed 10 mg daily. For patients taking potent CYP3A4 inhibitors (such as erythromycin, itraconazole, ketoconazole, ritonavir), don't exceed one 10-mg dose q 72 hours.

Contraindications and cautions

- Contraindicated in patients hypersensitive to the drug or any of its components, and in those taking nitrates or alpha blockers (other than tamsulosin 0.4 mg once daily). Drug isn't recommended for patients with severe hepatic impairment (Child-Pugh class C), MI within 90 days, New York Heart Association Class II or greater heart failure within 6 months, stroke within 6 months, uncontrolled arrhythmias, blood pressure lower than 90/50 mm Hg or higher than 170/100 mm Hg, unstable angina, or angina that occurs during sexual intercourse. Drug also isn't recommended for patients whose cardiac status makes sexual activity inadvisable and for those with hereditary degenerative retinal disorders.
- Use cautiously in patients taking potent CYP3A4 inhibitors and in patients with bleeding disorders, significant peptic ulceration, or renal or hepatic impairment. Use cautiously in patients with conditions that predispose them to priapism (such as sickle cell anemia, multiple myeloma, or leukemia), anatomical penis abnormalities, or left ventricular outflow obstruction.

Lifespan: Drug is for men only. In elderly men, consider a lower dose because they may be more sensitive to drug effects.

Adverse reactions

CNS: headache.
CV: flushing.
EENT: nasal congestion, vision loss.
GI: dyspepsia.
Musculoskeletal: back pain, limb pain, myalgia.

Interactions

Drug-drug. *Alpha blockers (except tamsulosin 0.4 mg daily), nitrates:* May enhance hypotensive effects. Avoid using together.
Potent CYP3A4 inhibitors (such as erythromycin, itraconazole, ketoconazole, ritonavir): May increase tadalafil level. Patient shouldn't exceed 10 mg q 72 hours.
Rifampin and other CYP3A4 inducers: May decrease tadalafil level. Monitor patient closely.
Drug-food. *Grapefruit:* May increase drug level. Discourage use together. Monitor patient closely.
Drug-lifestyle. *Alcohol use:* May increase risk of headache, dizziness, orthostatic hypotension, and increased heart rate. Discourage use together.

Effects on lab test results

None reported.

Pharmacokinetics

Absorption: Median effect occurs in 2 hours.
Distribution: Distributed into tissues. 97% protein-bound.
Metabolism: Mainly through CYP3A4 isoenzymes.
Excretion: In feces and urine. *Half-life:* 17½ hours.

Route	Onset	Peak	Duration
P.O.	30 min	30 min–6 hr	up to 1 day

Action

Chemical effect: Prevents breakdown of cyclic guanosine monophosphate (cGMP) by phosphodiesterase, thus increasing cGMP level.
Therapeutic effect: Prolongs smooth muscle relaxation and promotes blood flow into the corpus cavernosum.

Available forms

Tablets (film-coated): 5 mg, 10 mg, 20 mg

NURSING PROCESS

Assessment

ALERT: Sexual activity may increase cardiac risk. Assess patient's cardiac risk before he starts drug.
- Before patient starts drug, assess for underlying causes of erectile dysfunction.
- Assess patient's and family's knowledge of drug therapy.

Nursing diagnoses

- Sexual dysfunction related to patient's underlying condition
- Risk for injury related to potential for prolonged erections or priapism
- Deficient knowledge related to drug therapy

Planning and implementation

- Drug may cause transient decreases in supine blood pressure.
- Drug increases risk of prolonged erections and priapism.

Patient teaching
- Warn patient that taking drug with nitrates or alpha blockers could cause a serious drop in blood pressure, raising the risk of heart attack or stroke.
- Tell patient to seek immediate medical attention if he develops chest pain or vision problems after taking the drug.
- Urge patient to seek emergency medical care if his erection lasts more than 4 hours.
- Tell patient to take drug about 60 minutes before anticipated sexual activity. Explain that drug has no effect without sexual stimulation.
- Warn patient not to change dose unless directed by prescriber.
- Caution patient against drinking large amounts of alcohol while taking drug.

Evaluation

- Sexual activity improves with drug therapy.
- Patient sustains no injury from prolonged erection or priapism.
- Patient and family state understanding of drug therapy.

tamoxifen citrate

(teh-MOKS-uh-fen SIGH-trayt)
Apo-Tamox ♦, Nolvadex-D ♦ ◇, Novo-Tamoxifen ♦, Soltamox, Tamofen ♦, Tamone ♦

Pharmacologic class: nonsteroidal antiestrogen
Therapeutic class: antineoplastic
Pregnancy risk category: D

Indications and dosages

▶ **Advanced postmenopausal breast cancer.** *Women:* 20 to 40 mg P.O. daily. Give doses greater than 20 mg/day in divided doses (morning and evening).
▶ **Adjunct treatment for breast cancer.** *Adults:* 20 to 40 mg P.O. daily for no more than 5 years. Give doses greater than 20 mg/day in divided doses (morning and evening).
▶ **Reduction of breast cancer risk.** *Women at high risk:* 20 mg P.O. daily for 5 years.
▶ **Ductal carcinoma in situ (DCIS).** *Adults:* 20 mg P.O. daily for 5 years.
▶ **Stimulation of ovulation**‡. *Women:* 5 to 40 mg P.O. b.i.d. for 4 days.

Contraindications and cautions

- Contraindicated in patients hypersensitive to the drug or any of its components, in women receiving coumarin-type anticoagulants, and in those with history of deep vein thrombosis or pulmonary emboli.
- Use cautiously in patients with leukopenia or thrombocytopenia.

Lifespan: In pregnant or breast-feeding women, drug isn't recommended. Patient should avoid pregnancy for at least 2 months after stopping drug. In children, safety and effectiveness haven't been established.

T

Adverse reactions

CNS: confusion, headache, sleepiness, ***stroke,*** weakness.
CV: hot flushes.
EENT: cataracts, corneal changes, retinopathy.
GI: diarrhea, nausea, vomiting.
GU: amenorrhea, ***endometrial cancer,*** irregular menses, vaginal discharge and bleeding, ***uterine sarcoma.***
Hematologic: ***leukopenia, thrombocytopenia.***
Hepatic: cholestasis, fatty liver, ***hepatic necrosis.***
Metabolic: fluid retention, hypercalcemia, weight changes.
Musculoskeletal: brief exacerbation of pain from osseous metastases.
Respiratory: ***pulmonary embolism.***
Skin: rash, skin changes.
Other: temporary bone or tumor pain.

Interactions

Drug-drug. *Antacids:* May affect absorption of enteric-coated tablet. Don't use within 2 hours of tamoxifen dose.
Bromocriptine: May elevate tamoxifen level. Monitor patient for toxicity.
Coumadin-type anticoagulants: May cause significant increase in anticoagulant effect. Monitor patient, PT, and INR closely.
Cytotoxic drugs (methotrexate, fluorouracil): May increase risk of thromboembolic events. Monitor patient, PT, and INR closely.

Effects on lab test results

- May increase BUN, creatinine, calcium, and liver enzyme levels.
- May decrease WBC and platelet counts.

Pharmacokinetics

Absorption: Appears to be well absorbed.
Distribution: Widely in total body water.
Metabolism: Extensive by the liver.
Excretion: Drug and metabolites mainly in feces, mostly as metabolites. *Half-life:* More than 7 days.

Route	Onset	Peak	Duration
P.O.	Unknown	5 hr	Unknown

Action

Chemical effect: Exact antineoplastic action is unknown; acts as estrogen antagonist.
Therapeutic effect: Hinders function of breast cancer cells.

Available forms

Oral solution: 10 mg/5 ml
Tablets: 10 mg, 20 mg
Tablets (enteric-coated): 10 mg, 20 mg

NURSING PROCESS

Assessment

- Assess patient's breast cancer before starting therapy and regularly thereafter to monitor drug's effectiveness.
- Monitor CBC closely in patient with leukopenia or thrombocytopenia.
- Monitor lipid level during long-term therapy in patient with hyperlipidemia.
- Monitor calcium level in early stages of therapy; drug may compound hypercalcemia related to bone metastases.
- Be alert for adverse reactions.
- Monitor patient's hydration status if adverse GI reaction occurs.
- Assess patient's and family's knowledge of drug therapy.

Nursing diagnoses

- Ineffective health maintenance related to presence of breast cancer
- Risk for deficient fluid volume related to drug-induced adverse GI reactions
- Deficient knowledge related to drug therapy

Planning and implementation

- Make sure patient swallows enteric-coated tablets whole.

ALERT: Serious events (including uterine cancer, stroke, DVT, and pulmonary embolism) are linked to use in women at high risk for cancer and women with DCIS. Prescribers should discuss potential benefits and risks with women considering drug to reduce risk of developing breast cancer. The benefits outweigh risks in women already diagnosed with breast cancer.

Patient teaching

- Tell patient to use oral solution within 3 months of opening and not to freeze or refrigerate.
- Instruct patient to report symptoms of pulmonary embolism (chest pain, difficulty breathing, rapid breathing, sweating or fainting).

- Tell patient to report symptoms of stroke (headache, vision changes, confusion, difficulty speaking or walking, and weakness of face, arm or leg, especially on one side of the body).
- Reassure patient that acute bone pain during drug therapy usually means that drug will produce good response. Tell her to take an analgesic for pain.
- Encourage patient who is taking or has taken drug to have regular gynecologic examinations because of increased risk of uterine cancer.
- If patient is taking drug to reduce risk of breast cancer, teach proper technique for breast self-examination.
- Tell patient that annual mammograms are important.
- Advise patient to use barrier form of contraception because short-term therapy induces ovulation in premenopausal women.
- Advise woman of childbearing age to avoid becoming pregnant during therapy and for at least 2 months following discontinuation of therapy. Tell her to consult with prescriber before becoming pregnant.

Evaluation
- Patient responds well to drug.
- Patient maintains adequate hydration.
- Patient and family state understanding of drug therapy.

tamsulosin hydrochloride
(tam-SOO-loh-sin high-droh-KLOR-ighd)
Flomax

Pharmacologic class: alpha$_{1A}$ antagonist
Therapeutic class: BPH drug
Pregnancy risk category: B

Indications and dosages
▶ **BPH.** *Men:* 0.4 mg P.O. once daily, given 30 minutes after same meal each day. If no response after 2 to 4 weeks, increase dosage to 0.8 mg P.O. once daily.

Contraindications and cautions
- Contraindicated in patients hypersensitive to the drug or any of its components.
- Use cautiously in patients who have experienced hepatic or renal insufficiency, priapism, sulfa allergy, or orthostasis.

Lifespan: Drug is indicated for men only.

Adverse reactions
CNS: asthenia, *dizziness, headache,* insomnia, somnolence, syncope, vertigo.
CV: chest pain, orthostatic hypotension.
EENT: amblyopia, pharyngitis, *rhinitis,* sinusitis.
GI: diarrhea, nausea.
GU: abnormal ejaculation.
Musculoskeletal: back pain.
Respiratory: cough.
Other: decreased libido, *infection,* tooth disorder.

Interactions
Drug-drug. *Alpha blockers:* May interact with tamsulosin. Avoid using together.
Cimetidine: May decrease tamsulosin clearance. Use cautiously.
Warfarin: Study results are inconclusive. Use together cautiously.

Effects on lab test results
None reported.

Pharmacokinetics
Absorption: More than 90%. Food increases bioavailability by 30%.
Distribution: Into extracellular fluids. 94% to 99% protein-bound.
Metabolism: Mainly by cytochrome P-450 enzymes in the liver.
Excretion: 76% in urine; 21% in feces. *Half-life:* 9 to 13 hours.

Route	Onset	Peak	Duration
P.O.	Unknown	4–5 hr	9–15 hr

Action
Chemical effect: Selectively blocks alpha receptors in the prostate, leading to relaxation of smooth muscles in the bladder neck and prostate, which improves urine flow and reduces symptoms of BPH.
Therapeutic effect: Improves urine flow.

Available forms
Capsules: 0.4 mg

T

NURSING PROCESS

Assessment
- Assess patient for signs of prostatic hyperplasia, including frequency of urination, nocturnal urination, and urinary hesitancy.
- Monitor patient for decreases in blood pressure and notify prescriber.
- Assess patient's and family's knowledge of drug therapy.

Nursing diagnoses
- Risk for injury related to decreased blood pressure and resulting syncope
- Impaired urinary elimination related to underlying prostatic hyperplasia
- Deficient knowledge related to drug therapy

Planning and implementation
- Symptoms of BPH and cancer of the prostate are similar; cancer should be ruled out before therapy starts.
- If therapy is interrupted for several days or more, restart therapy at one capsule daily.
- Drug may cause a sudden drop in blood pressure, especially after the first dose or when changing doses.
- Patients having cataract surgery may develop intraoperative floppy iris syndrome; alert surgeon so he can modify his surgical technique as appropriate.

ALERT: Don't confuse Flomax with Fosamax.

Patient teaching
- Instruct patient not to crush, chew, or open capsules.
- Tell patient to get up slowly from chair or bed when therapy starts and to avoid situations where injury could occur because of syncope. Advise him that drug may cause a sudden drop in blood pressure, especially after the first dose or when changing doses.
- Instruct patient not to drive or perform hazardous tasks for 12 hours after the initial dose or a change in dose, until response can be monitored.
- Tell patient to take drug about 30 minutes after same meal each day.
- If patient needs cataract surgery, urge him to tell surgeon that he takes tamsulosin.

Evaluation
- Patient has no sudden decreases in blood pressure.
- Patient has normal urinary elimination patterns.
- Patient and family state understanding of drug therapy.

tegaserod maleate
(teh-GAS-uh-rahd MALL-ee-ayt)

Zelnorm

Pharmacologic class: 5-HT_4 receptor partial agonist
Therapeutic class: irritable bowel drug
Pregnancy risk category: B

Indications and dosages

▶ **Short-term treatment for irritable bowel syndrome, when the primary bowel symptom is constipation.** *Women:* 6 mg P.O. b.i.d. before meals for 4 to 6 weeks. May add another 4- to 6-week course for patients who respond to therapy at 4 to 6 weeks.

▶ **Chronic idiopathic constipation.** *Adults younger than age 65:* Give 6 mg P.O. b.i.d. before meals.

Contraindications and cautions

- Contraindicated in patients hypersensitive to the drug or any of its components, and in those with severe renal impairment, moderate or severe hepatic impairment, a history of bowel obstruction, symptomatic gallbladder disease, suspected sphincter of Oddi dysfunction or abdominal adhesions, or frequent or current diarrhea.

Lifespan: In pregnant women, use drug only if clearly needed. In breast-feeding women, either stop breast-feeding or use a different drug, taking into account the importance of the drug to the mother. In children, safety and effectiveness haven't been established.

Adverse reactions

CNS: dizziness, *headache,* migraine.
GI: *abdominal pain,* diarrhea, flatulence, ischemic colitis, nausea.
Musculoskeletal: arthropathy, back pain, leg pain.
Other: accidental injury.

Interactions

Drug-drug. *Digoxin:* May reduce peak level and exposure of digoxin by 15%. Use cautiously.
Drug-food. *Food:* May reduce bioavailability of drug. Advise patient to take drug on an empty stomach.

Effects on lab test results

None reported.

Pharmacokinetics

Absorption: Food reduces bioavailability by 40% to 65%.
Distribution: About 98% protein-bound.
Metabolism: By two pathways. The first is hydrolysis, followed by oxidation and conjugation. The second is direct glucuronidation.
Excretion: Two-thirds of dose unchanged in feces, with remaining one-third in urine, mainly as metabolite. *Half-life:* 6 to 16 hours.

Route	Onset	Peak	Duration
P.O.	Unknown	1 hr	Unknown

Action

Chemical effect: Binds with high affinity to 5-HT_4 receptors and acts as an agonist. Activating 5-HT_4 receptors in the GI tract stimulates the peristaltic reflex and intestinal secretion and inhibits visceral sensitivity.
Therapeutic effect: Relieves constipation.

Available forms

Tablets: 2 mg, 6 mg

NURSING PROCESS

Assessment

- Assess patient's condition before starting therapy, and reassess regularly to monitor the drug's effectiveness.
- Monitor patient for diarrhea and abdominal pain.
- Assess patient's and family's knowledge of drug therapy.

Nursing diagnoses

- Constipation related to irritable bowel syndrome
- Diarrhea related to adverse effect of tegaserod maleate therapy
- Deficient knowledge related to drug therapy

Planning and implementation

- Give drug on an empty stomach before a meal.
- If patient has rectal bleeding or new or sudden worsening of abdominal pain, stop drug.
- Patient may develop diarrhea during therapy; in most cases, it occurs during the first week of therapy and resolves with continued therapy.
- If serious diarrhea develops, with symptoms of hypovolemia, hypotension, and syncope, stop giving the drug. Don't use drug in a patient who has frequent diarrhea.
- Stop therapy in patients who develop ischemic colitis or other forms of intestinal ischemia with by rectal bleeding, bloody diarrhea, or abdominal pain. Don't resume treatment with tegaserod if patient develops ischemic colitis.

Patient teaching

- Tell patient to take drug on an empty stomach, before a meal.
- Inform patient she may have diarrhea during therapy. Tell her to report severe diarrhea or diarrhea accompanied by severe cramping, abdominal pain, or dizziness.
- Tell patient not to take drug if she now has or often has diarrhea.
- Tell patient to report new or worsening abdominal pain.
- Tell patient not to use drug during pregnancy or breast-feeding.

Evaluation

- Patient expresses relief from constipation.
- Patient reports no diarrhea.
- Patient and family state understanding of drug therapy.

telithromycin

(teh-lith-roh-MY-sin)
Ketek

Pharmacologic class: ketolide
Therapeutic class: antibiotic
Pregnancy risk category: C

Indications and dosages

▶ **Mild to moderate community-acquired pneumonia caused by *S. pneumoniae* (including multi–drug-resistant isolates), *H. influenzae, M. catarrhalis, Chlamydophila pneumoni-***

T

ae,* or *Mycoplasma pneumoniae. *Adults:* 800 mg P.O. once daily for 7 to 10 days.
Adjust-a-dose: For patient with renal impairment and a creatinine clearances less than 30 ml/minute, including patients on dialysis, give 600 mg P.O. once daily. On dialysis days, give after session complete. For patient who also has hepatic impairment, give 400 mg once daily.

Contraindications and cautions

• Contraindicated in patients hypersensitive to telithromycin or any macrolide antibiotic, and in patients with myasthenia gravis or a history of hepatitis or jaundice caused by drug. Don't give to patients with congenitally prolonged QTc interval, patients with ongoing proarrhythmic conditions (such as uncorrected hypokalemia or hypomagnesemia or significant bradycardia), or patients who are taking Class IA antiarrhythmics (such as quinidine, procainamide), Class III antiarrhythmics (such as dofetilide), cisapride, or pimozide.
Lifespan: In pregnant or breast-feeding women, use cautiously. In children, safety and effectiveness haven't been established.

Adverse reactions

CNS: dizziness, headache, transient loss of consciousness.
CV: prolonged QTc interval, ***torsades de pointes, ventricular arrhythmias***, vagal syndrome.
EENT: blurred vision, difficulty focusing, diplopia.
GI: *diarrhea,* loose stools, nausea, ***pseudomembranous colitis,*** taste disturbance, vomiting.
Hepatic: hepatic dysfunction, ***hepatitis, hepatotoxicity.***

Interactions

Drug-drug. *Atorvastatin, lovastatin, simvastatin:* May increase levels of these drugs, increasing the risk of myopathy. Avoid use together.
Benzodiazepines (midazolam): May increase benzodiazepine level. Monitor patient closely, and consider adjusting benzodiazepine dosage.
Cisapride: May increase QTc level. Avoid use together.
CYP3A4 inducers (carbamazepine, phenobarbital, phenytoin): May decrease telithromycin level. Avoid use together.
CYP3A4 inhibitors (itraconazole, ketoconazole): May increase telithromycin level. Monitor patient closely.
Digoxin: May increase digoxin level. Monitor digoxin level.
Drugs metabolized by the cytochrome P-450 system (such as carbamazepine, cyclosporine, hexobarbital, phenytoin, sirolimus, tacrolimus): May increase serum levels of these drugs, increasing or prolonging their effects. Use together cautiously, and monitor patient closely.
Ergot alkaloid derivatives (such as ergotamine): May increase the risk of ergot toxicity, characterized by severe peripheral vasospasm and dysesthesia. Avoid use together.
Metoprolol: May increase metoprolol level. Use together cautiously.
Oral anticoagulants: May increase the effects of the anticoagulant. Monitor PT and INR during co-administration.
Pimozide: May increase pimozide level. Use together is contraindicated.
Rifampin: May decrease telithromycin level significantly. Avoid use together.
Sotalol: May decrease sotalol level. Monitor patient for lack of effect.
Theophylline: May increase theophylline level and cause nausea and vomiting. Separate telithromycin and theophylline doses by 1 hour.

Effects on lab test results

• May increase AST and ALT levels.
• May increase platelet count.

Pharmacokinetics

Absorption: Bioavailability is about 57%.
Distribution: 60% to 70% protein-bound.
Metabolism: About 50% by CYP3A4.
Excretion: 13% unchanged in urine, and 7% unchanged in feces. *Half-life:* 10 hours.

Route	Onset	Peak	Duration
P.O.	Unknown	1 hr	Unknown

Action

Chemical effect: Inhibits bacterial protein synthesis.
Therapeutic effect: Hinders or kills susceptible bacteria.

Available forms

Tablets: 300 mg, 400 mg

NURSING PROCESS

Assessment
- Assess patient's history of allergies, especially to macrolides, before starting therapy.
- Obtain patient's medical history before starting therapy, including a list of drugs he's taking.
- Obtain sample for culture and sensitivity tests before giving the first dose. Start therapy pending test results.
- Be alert for adverse reactions and drug interactions.
- Assess patient for diarrhea during therapy; patients with diarrhea may have pseudomembranous colitis.
- Assess patient's and family's knowledge of drug therapy.

Nursing diagnoses
- Risk for injury related to adverse effects of drug
- Risk for deficient fluid volume related to potential for drug-induced adverse GI reactions
- Deficient knowledge related to drug therapy

Planning and implementation
- Monitor electrolyte level before starting therapy and periodically thereafter. Electrolyte imbalances must be corrected before or during therapy to avoid proarrhythmic conditions.
- Obtain hematologic, renal, and hepatic studies before starting therapy and during therapy.

ALERT: Monitor patient for evidence of acute liver failure, including fatigue, nausea, jaundice, pale stools, darkened urine, abdominal pain, and enlarged liver. Fatal liver failure has occurred in patients taking drug. Notify prescriber immediately if signs and symptoms occur.
- Drug may cause visual disturbances including blurred vision, difficulty focusing, and diplopia, particularly in women and patients younger than age 40. Adverse visual effects occur most often after the first or second dose, last several hours, and sometimes return with later doses. For some patients, the symptoms will resolve during treatment; for others, they'll continue until treatment is complete.

ALERT: Drug may prolong the QTc interval. Rarely, an irregular heartbeat may cause the patient to faint.

ALERT: Drug may cause transient loss of consciousness, including instances of associated vagal syndrome.

Patient teaching
- Urge patient to take drug exactly as prescribed until all of the tablets are gone, even if he feels better before the prescription is finished.
- Tell patient that drug can be taken with or without food.
- Warn patient that this drug may cause vision disturbances, liver problems, or fainting. Caution patient to avoid hazardous activities during therapy.
- Tell patient to report diarrhea or any episodes of fainting that occur while taking this drug.
- Tell patient to store tablets at room temperature.
- Tell patient to report new onset of weakness, abdominal pain, or other symptoms of liver problems.

Evaluation
- Patient is free from injury.
- Patient maintains adequate hydration with therapy.
- Patient and family state understanding of drug therapy.

telmisartan
(tel-mih-SAR-tan)
Micardis

Pharmacologic class: angiotensin II receptor antagonist
Therapeutic class: antihypertensive
Pregnancy risk category: C (D in second and third trimesters)

Indications and dosages
▶ **Hypertension (used alone or with other antihypertensives).** *Adults:* 40 mg P.O. daily. Blood pressure response is dose-related between 20 and 80 mg daily.

Contraindications and cautions
- Contraindicated in patients hypersensitive to the drug or any of its components.
- Use cautiously in patients with renal and hepatic insufficiency and in those with an activated renin-angiotensin system, such as volume- or salt-depleted patients (those being treated with high doses of diuretics, for example).

Lifespan: In pregnant women, don't use. If pregnancy is suspected, notify prescriber be-

T

cause drug should be stopped. Breast-feeding women should stop breast-feeding or use another drug, taking into account importance of drug therapy. In children, safety and effectiveness haven't been established.

Adverse reactions

CNS: dizziness, fatigue, headache, pain.
CV: chest pain, hypertension, peripheral edema.
EENT: pharyngitis, sinusitis.
GI: abdominal pain, diarrhea, dyspepsia, nausea.
GU: UTI.
Musculoskeletal: back pain, myalgia.
Respiratory: cough, upper respiratory tract infection.
Other: flulike syndrome.

Interactions

Drug-drug. *Digoxin:* May increase digoxin level. Monitor digoxin level closely.
Warfarin: May slightly decrease warfarin level. Monitor INR.

Effects on lab test results

• May increase liver enzyme and creatinine levels. May decrease hemoglobin level and hematocrit.

Pharmacokinetics

Absorption: Readily absorbed.
Distribution: Extensively protein-bound; volume of distribution is about 500 L.
Metabolism: Metabolized by conjugation to an inactive metabolite.
Excretion: Mainly unchanged in feces. *Half-life:* 24 hours.

Route	Onset	Peak	Duration
P.O.	Unknown	30 min–1 hr	24 hr

Action

Chemical effect: Blocks the vasoconstrictive and aldosterone-secreting effects of angiotensin II by selectively blocking the binding of angiotensin II to the AT_1 receptor in many tissues, such as vascular smooth muscle and adrenal glands.
Therapeutic effect: Lowers blood pressure.

Available forms

Tablets: 40 mg, 80 mg

NURSING PROCESS

Assessment

• In patient whose renal function may depend on activity of the renin-angiotensin-aldosterone system, such as those with severe heart failure, use of ACE inhibitors and angiotensin-receptor antagonists may be related to oliguria or progressive azotemia and (rarely) to acute renal failure or death.
• In patient with biliary obstruction, drug level may elevate because of inability to excrete drug.
• Drug isn't removed by hemodialysis; orthostatic hypotension may develop in patient undergoing dialysis. Closely monitor blood pressure.
• Assess patient's and family's knowledge of drug therapy.

Nursing diagnoses

• Risk for injury related to presence of hypertension
• Ineffective cerebral and cardiopulmonary tissue perfusion related to drug-induced hypotension
• Deficient knowledge related to drug therapy

Planning and implementation

• Most of the antihypertensive effect is present within 2 weeks. Maximal blood pressure reduction is generally attained after 4 weeks. If blood pressure isn't controlled by drug alone, a diuretic may be added.
• If hypotension occurs, place patient in supine position and give normal saline solution I.V. if needed.

Patient teaching

• Inform woman of childbearing age of consequences of second- and third-trimester exposure to drug. Instruct patient to immediately report suspected pregnancy to prescriber.
• Tell patient that transient hypotension may occur. Instruct him to lie down if feeling dizzy and to climb stairs slowly and rise slowly to standing position.
• Instruct patient with heart failure to notify prescriber about decreased urine output.
• Teach patient other means to reduce blood pressure, such as diet control, exercise, smoking cessation, and stress reduction.
• Inform patient that drug shouldn't be removed from blister-sealed packet until immediately before use.

Evaluation

- Patient sustains no injury from underlying disease.
- Patient has no hypotension and maintains adequate tissue perfusion.
- Patient and family state understanding of drug therapy.

temazepam

(teh-MAZ-ih-pam)

Euhypnos ◊, Normison ◊, Restoril, Temaze ◊

Pharmacologic class: benzodiazepine
Therapeutic class: sedative-hypnotic
Pregnancy risk category: X
Controlled substance schedule: IV

Indications and dosages

▶ **Short-term therapy for insomnia.** *Adults:* 15 to 30 mg P.O. 30 minutes before bedtime. In some patients, 7.5mg to 15 mg may be sufficient.
Elderly or debilitated patients: Start with 7.5 mg P.O. at bedtime until response is determined.

Contraindications and cautions

- Contraindicated in patients hypersensitive to benzodiazepines.
- Use cautiously in patients with chronic pulmonary insufficiency, impaired liver or kidney function, severe or latent depression, suicidal tendencies, or history of drug abuse.

Lifespan: In pregnant women, drug is contraindicated. In breast-feeding women, drug isn't recommended. In children, safety and effectiveness haven't been established.

Adverse reactions

CNS: anxiety, confusion, depression, *dizziness, drowsiness,* disturbed coordination, daytime sedation, euphoria, fatigue, headache, *lethargy,* nervousness, nightmares, complex sleep disorders, vertigo, weakness.
CV: hypotension, palpitations.
EENT: blurred vision.
GI: diarrhea, dry mouth, nausea.
Respiratory: dyspnea.
Other: ***anaphylaxis, angioedema,*** physical or psychological dependence.

Interactions

Drug-drug. *CNS depressants, including opioid analgesics:* May increase CNS depression. Use together cautiously.
Drug-herb. *Calendula, catnip, hops, lady's slipper, lemon balm, passion flower, sassafras, skullcap, valerian, yerba maté:* May increase sedative effects. Monitor patient closely; discourage use together.
Kava: May cause excessive sedation. Discourage use together.
Drug-lifestyle. *Alcohol use:* May cause additive CNS effects. Strongly discourage use together.

Effects on lab test results

- May increase liver enzyme level.

Pharmacokinetics

Absorption: Well absorbed.
Distribution: Wide, throughout body. 98% protein-bound.
Metabolism: In liver, mainly to inactive metabolites.
Excretion: As metabolites in urine. *Half-life:* 10 to 17 hours.

Route	Onset	Peak	Duration
P.O.	Unknown	1–2 hr	Unknown

Action

Chemical effect: May act on limbic system, thalamus, and hypothalamus of CNS to produce hypnotic effects.
Therapeutic effect: Promotes sleep.

Available forms

Capsules: 7.5 mg, 15 mg, 20 mg ◊, 30 mg

NURSING PROCESS

Assessment

- Assess patient's sleeping disorder before starting therapy and regularly thereafter to monitor drug's effectiveness.
- Assess mental status before starting therapy. An elderly patient is more sensitive to drug's adverse CNS effects.
- Be alert for adverse reactions and drug interactions.
- Assess patient's and family's knowledge of drug therapy.

T

Nursing diagnoses

- Insomnia related to underlying disorder
- Risk for injury related to drug-induced adverse CNS reactions
- Deficient knowledge related to drug therapy

Planning and implementation

- Before leaving the bedside, make sure patient who is depressed, suicidal, or drug-dependent, or who has history of drug abuse has swallowed the capsule to prevent hoarding.
- Use drug on an "as needed" basis.
- Supervise walking and raise bed rails, particularly for elderly patients.

ALERT: Don't confuse Restoril with Vistaril.

Patient teaching

- Warn patient to avoid activities that require mental alertness or physical coordination.
- Warn patient about possible complex sleep disorders.

Evaluation

- Patient states that drug induces sleep.
- Patient doesn't experience injury from adverse CNS reactions.
- Patient and family state understanding of drug therapy.

tenecteplase
(te-NEK-te-plase)
TNKase

Pharmacologic class: recombinant tissue plasminogen activator
Therapeutic class: thrombolytic
Pregnancy risk category: C

Indications and dosages

▶ **Reduction of mortality from acute MI.** *Adults weighing less than 60 kg (132 lb):* Give 30 mg (6 ml) by I.V. bolus over 5 seconds. *Adults weighing 60 to 69 kg (132 to 152 lb):* Give 35 mg (7 ml) by I.V. bolus over 5 seconds. *Adults weighing 70 to 79 kg (153 to 174 lb):* Give 40 mg (8 ml) by I.V. bolus over 5 seconds. *Adults weighing 80 to 89 kg (175 to 196 lb):* Give 45 mg (9 ml) by I.V. bolus over 5 seconds. *Adults weighing 90 kg (197 lb) or more:* Give 50 mg (10 ml) by I.V. bolus over 5 seconds. Maximum dose is 50 mg.

I.V. administration

- Use syringe prefilled with sterile water for injection, and inject entire contents into drug vial. Don't use bacteriostatic water for injection.
- Gently swirl solution once mixed. Don't shake. Make sure contents are completely dissolved.
- Draw up the appropriate dose needed from the reconstituted vial with the syringe and discard any unused portion.
- Give drug immediately once reconstituted, or refrigerate and use within 8 hours.
- Give drug in a designated line.
- Give heparin with tenecteplase, but not in the same I.V. line.

Incompatibilities
Solutions containing dextrose.

Contraindications and cautions

- Contraindicated in patients with active internal bleeding; history of stroke; intracranial or intraspinal surgery or trauma during previous 2 months; intracranial neoplasm, aneurysm, or arteriovenous malformation; severe uncontrolled hypertension; or known bleeding diathesis.
- Use cautiously in patients who have had recent major surgery (such as coronary artery bypass grafting), organ biopsy, or obstetrical delivery, or previous puncture of noncompressible vessels. Also use cautiously in patients with recent trauma, recent GI or GU bleeding, high risk of left ventricular thrombus, acute pericarditis, hypertension (systolic 180 mm Hg or above, diastolic 110 mm Hg or above), severe hepatic dysfunction, hemostatic defects, subacute bacterial endocarditis, septic thrombophlebitis, diabetic hemorrhagic retinopathy, or cerebrovascular disease.

Lifespan: In pregnant women, use cautiously. In breast-feeding women, use cautiously; it's unknown if the drug appears in breast milk. In children, safety and effectiveness haven't been established. In patients age 75 and older, give cautiously; weigh drug benefits against the risk of increased adverse effects.

Adverse reactions

CNS: fever, ***intracranial hemorrhage, stroke.***
CV: ***cholesterol embolism, coronary reperfusion arrhythmias, major hematoma,*** *minor hematoma.*
EENT: epistaxis, pharyngeal bleeding.

GI: ***GI bleeding,*** nausea, vomiting.
GU: ***hematuria.***
Hematologic: ***bleeding at puncture sites.***

Interactions

Drug-drug. *Anticoagulants (heparin, vitamin K antagonists), drugs that alter platelet function (acetylsalicylic acid, dipyridamole, glycoprotein IIb/IIIa inhibitors):* May increase risk of bleeding when used before, during, or after therapy with tenecteplase. Use cautiously.

Effects on lab test results

- May increase PT, PTT, and INR.

Pharmacokinetics

Absorption: Given I.V.
Distribution: Related to weight and is an approximation of plasma volume.
Metabolism: Mainly hepatic.
Excretion: Unknown. *Half-life:* 20 minutes to 2 hours.

Route	Onset	Peak	Duration
I.V.	Immediate	Immediate	20–24 min

Action

Chemical effect: Binds to fibrin and converts plasminogen to plasmin. Specificity to fibrin decreases systemic activation of plasminogen and the resulting breakdown of circulating fibrinogen.
Therapeutic effect: Dissolves blood clots.

Available forms

Injection: 50 mg

NURSING PROCESS

Assessment

- Assess underlying condition before starting therapy, and reassess regularly to monitor drug's effectiveness.
- Monitor ECG for reperfusion arrhythmias.
- Assess pain before therapy, and reassess regularly.
- Assess patient's and family's knowledge of drug therapy.

Nursing diagnoses

- Ineffective tissue perfusion, coronary, related to presence of blood clots
- Acute pain related to MI
- Deficient knowledge related to tenecteplase therapy

Planning and implementation

- Minimize arterial and venous punctures during therapy.
- Avoid noncompressible arterial punctures and internal jugular and subclavian venous punctures.
- Monitor patient for bleeding. If serious bleeding occurs, immediately stop giving heparin and antiplatelet drugs.
- Cholesterol embolism is rarely related to thrombolytic use, but may be lethal. Signs and symptoms may include livedo reticularis, "purple toe" syndrome, acute renal failure, gangrenous digits, hypertension, pancreatitis, MI, cerebral infarction, spinal cord infarction, retinal artery occlusion, bowel infarction, and rhabdomyolysis.

Patient teaching

- Inform patient about proper dental care to avoid excessive gum bleeding.
- Advise patient to immediately report any adverse effects or excessive bleeding.
- Explain use of drug to patient and family.

Evaluation

- Patient regains tissue perfusion with dissolution of blood clots.
- Patient is relieved of pain.
- Patient and family state understanding of drug therapy.

teniposide (VM-26)

(teh-NIP-uh-sighd)
Vumon

Pharmacologic class: podophyllotoxin
Therapeutic class: antineoplastic
Pregnancy risk category: D

Indications and dosages

▶ **Refractory childhood acute lymphoblastic leukemia.** *Children:* Optimum dosage hasn't been established. One protocol is 165 mg/m^2 I.V. twice weekly for eight or nine doses, usually with other drugs.
Adjust-a-dose: Consider dosage adjustments in patients with renal and hepatic insufficiency. Patients with Down syndrome may have in-

T

creased sensitivity to the drug; begin therapy with a reduced dose, and monitor patient.

I.V. administration

- Preparation and administration have carcinogenic, mutagenic, and teratogenic risks. Follow institutional policy to reduce risks.
- Dilute drug in D_5W or normal saline solution injection to concentration of 0.1, 0.2, 0.4, or 1 mg/ml. Don't agitate vigorously; precipitation may form. Discard cloudy solutions.
- Don't give drug through membrane-type inline filter because diluent may dissolve filter.
- Infuse over 45 to 90 minutes to prevent hypotension. If hypotension occurs, stop infusion.
- Ensure careful placement of catheter. Extravasation can cause local tissue necrosis or sloughing.
- Prepare and store in glass containers. Solutions containing 0.5 to 1 mg/ml teniposide are stable for 4 hours; those containing 0.1 to 0.2 mg/ml are stable for 6 hours at room temperature.

⊗ **Incompatibilities**
Heparin, idarubicin. Don't mix with other drugs or solutions.

Contraindications and cautions

- Contraindicated in patients hypersensitive to the drug or to polyoxyethylated castor oil (an injection vehicle).
- Use cautiously in patients with myelosuppression.

Lifespan: In pregnant and breast-feeding women, drug isn't recommended.

Adverse reactions

CV: hypotension from rapid infusion.
GI: diarrhea, nausea, mucositis, vomiting.
Hematologic: *anemia, **leukopenia**,* myelosuppression, ***neutropenia, thrombocytopenia.***
Skin: alopecia, tissue necrosis, sloughing, or phlebitis at injection site.
Other: ***hypersensitivity reactions*** (***bronchospasm,*** chills, dyspnea, fever, hypotension, flushing, tachycardia, urticaria).

Interactions

Drug-drug. *Methotrexate:* May increase clearance and intracellular level of methotrexate. Monitor patient closely.
Sodium salicylate, sulfamethizole, tolbutamide: May displace teniposide from protein-binding sites and increase toxicity. Monitor patient closely.

Effects on lab test results

- May increase uric acid level. May decrease hemoglobin level and hematocrit.
- May decrease RBC, WBC, platelet, and neutrophil counts.

Pharmacokinetics

Absorption: Given I.V.
Distribution: Mainly in liver, kidneys, small intestine, and adrenals. Drug crosses blood-brain barrier to limited extent. Extensively bound to plasma proteins.
Metabolism: Extensive, in liver.
Excretion: About 40% through kidneys as unchanged drug or metabolites. *Half-life:* 5 hours.

Route	Onset	Peak	Duration
I.V.	Unknown	Unknown	Unknown

Action

Chemical effect: Acts in late S or early G2 phase of cell cycle, thus preventing cells from entering mitosis.
Therapeutic effect: Prevents reproduction of leukemic cells.

Available forms

Injection: 50 mg/5 ml

NURSING PROCESS

Assessment

- Assess patient's condition before starting therapy and regularly thereafter to monitor drug's effectiveness.
- Obtain baseline blood counts and kidney and liver function tests; then monitor periodically.
- Monitor blood pressure before therapy and at 30-minute intervals during infusion.
- Be alert for adverse reactions and drug interactions.
- Assess patient's and family's knowledge of drug therapy.

Nursing diagnoses

- Ineffective health maintenance related to presence of leukemia

• Ineffective protection related to drug-induced immunosuppression
• Deficient knowledge related to drug therapy

Planning and implementation

• Some prescribers may decide to use drug despite patient's history of hypersensitivity because therapeutic benefits may outweigh risks. Give antihistamines and corticosteroids to these patients before infusion begins, and monitor them closely during drug administration.

ALERT: Have diphenhydramine, hydrocortisone, epinephrine, and appropriate emergency equipment available to establish airway in case of anaphylaxis.

ALERT: Report systolic blood pressure below 90 mm Hg, and stop infusion.

Patient teaching

• Tell patient to immediately report discomfort at the I.V. site.
• Encourage adequate fluid intake to increase urine output and facilitate excretion of uric acid.
• Review infection-control and bleeding precautions to take during therapy.
• Reassure patient that hair should grow back after therapy stops.
• Instruct patient and parents to notify prescriber if adverse reactions occur.

Evaluation

• Patient responds well to drug.
• Patient doesn't develop serious complications from immunosuppression.
• Patient and family state understanding of drug therapy.

tenofovir disoproxil fumarate

(teh-NAH-fuh-veer digh-soh-PRAHK-sul FOO-mah-rate)

Viread

Pharmacologic class: nucleotide reverse transcriptase inhibitor
Therapeutic class: antiretroviral
Pregnancy risk category: B

Indications and dosages

▶ **HIV-1 infection, with other antiretrovirals.** *Adults:* 300 mg P.O. once daily without regard to food. When given with didanosine, give 2 hours before or 1 hour after didanosine.

Adjust-a-dose: For patients with renal impairment, if creatinine clearance is 30 to 49 ml/minute, give 300 mg every 48 hours. If creatinine clearance is 10 to 29 ml/minute, give 300 mg twice weekly.
For hemodialysis patients, give 300 mg every 7 days or after a total of 12 hours of hemodialysis.

Contraindications and cautions

• Contraindicated in patients hypersensitive to the drug or any of its components.
• Use cautiously in patients with hepatic impairment or risk factors for liver disease, and in patients with renal impairment.

Lifespan: In pregnant women, use only if benefits to the woman outweigh risks to the fetus. Breast-feeding women should stop breast-feeding or use another drug. In children, safety and effectiveness haven't been established. In the elderly, use cautiously because they are more likely to have renal impairment and to be receiving other drug therapy.

Adverse reactions

CNS: asthenia, depression, fever, headache, insomnia, peripheral neuropathy.
CV: chest pain.
GI: abdominal pain, anorexia, diarrhea, dyspepsia, flatulence, *nausea,* vomiting.
GU: glycosuria, ***renal toxicity.***
Hematologic: ***neutropenia.***
Hepatic: ***hepatomegaly with steatosis, hepatotoxicity.***
Metabolic: hyperglycemia, ***lactic acidosis,*** weight loss.
Musculoskeletal: back pain, decreased bone density, myalgias.
Skin: fat accumulation and redistribution, rash, sweating.

Interactions

Drug-drug. *Acyclovir, cidofovir, ganciclovir, valacyclovir, valganciclovir (drugs that reduce renal function or compete for renal tubular secretion):* May increase level of tenofovir or other renally eliminated drugs. Monitor patient for adverse effects.
Atazanavir: May decrease atazanavir level, causing resistance. Give both drugs with ritonavir.
Didanosine (buffered formulation): May increase didanosine bioavailability. Monitor pa-

tient for didanosine-related adverse effects, such as bone marrow suppression, GI distress, and peripheral neuropathy. Give tenofovir 2 hours before or 1 hour after didanosine.

Effects on lab test results

• May increase amylase, AST, ALT, creatinine kinase, serum and urine glucose, and triglyceride levels. May decrease HIV-1 RNA level.
• May decrease neutrophil and CD4 cell counts.

Pharmacokinetics

Absorption: In fasting patients, tenofovir is poorly absorbed (bioavailability 25%) with peak level in about 1 hour. A high-fat meal delays peak by 1 hour but increases bioavailability to 40%.
Distribution: Minimally bound to plasma proteins.
Metabolism: Neither tenofovir nor tenofovir disoproxil fumarate is metabolized by liver enzymes, including cytochrome P-450 enzymes.
Excretion: Renal, through glomerular filtration and active tubular secretion. *Half-life:* Unknown.

Route	Onset	Peak	Duration
P.O.	Unknown	1–2 hr	Unknown

Action

Chemical effect: Tenofovir disoproxil fumarate is hydrolyzed to produce tenofovir. Tenofovir undergoes sequential phosphorylations to yield tenofovir diphosphate. Tenofovir diphosphate is a competitive antagonist of HIV reverse transcriptase.
Therapeutic effect: Inhibits HIV replication.

Available forms

Tablets: 300 mg as the fumarate salt (equivalent to 245 mg of tenofovir disoproxil)

NURSING PROCESS

Assessment

• Assess patient's viral infection before starting therapy and regularly thereafter to monitor drug's effectiveness.
• Assess patient for risk of severe adverse reactions. Antiretrovirals, alone or combined, have been linked to lactic acidosis and severe (including fatal) hepatomegaly with steatosis. These effects may occur without elevated transaminase level. Risk is increased for women, obese patients, and those exposed to antiretrovirals long-term. Monitor all patients for hepatotoxicity, including lactic acidosis and hepatomegaly with steatosis.
• Assess patient's and family's knowledge of drug therapy.

Nursing diagnoses

• Noncompliance related to long-term therapy
• Risk for infection related to presence of HIV
• Deficient knowledge related to drug therapy

Planning and implementation

• Antiretrovirals have been linked to the accumulation and redistribution of body fat, resulting in central obesity, peripheral wasting, and development of a buffalo hump. The long-term effects of these changes are unknown. Monitor patients for changes in body fat.
• Tenofovir may be linked to bone abnormalities (osteomalacia and decreased bone mineral density) and renal toxicity (increased creatinine and phosphaturia levels). Monitor patient carefully during long-term therapy.
• Drug may lead to decreased HIV-1 RNA level and CD4 cell counts.
• The effects of tenofovir on the progression of HIV infection are unknown.
• Because of a high rate of early virologic resistance, triple antiretroviral therapy with abacavir, lamivudine, and tenofovir shouldn't be used as a new therapy regimen for untreated or pre-treated patients. Monitor patients currently controlled with this drug combination and those who use this combination in addition to other antiretroviral drugs, and consider modifying therapy.
• Because of a high rate of early virologic failure and emergence of resistance, therapy with tenofovir with didanosine and lamivudine isn't recommended as a new treatment regimen for therapy-naïve or therapy-experienced patients with HIV infection. Patients currently on this regimen should be considered for treatment modification.

Patient teaching

• Instruct patient to take tenofovir with a meal to enhance bioavailability.
• Tell patient to report adverse effects, including nausea, vomiting, diarrhea, flatulence, and headache.

Evaluation

- Patient complies with therapy regimen.
- Patient has reduced signs and symptoms of infection.
- Patient and family state understanding of drug therapy.

terazosin hydrochloride

(ter-uh-ZOH-sin high-droh-KLOR-ighd)

Hytrin

Pharmacologic class: selective $alpha_1$ blocker
Therapeutic class: antihypertensive
Pregnancy risk category: C

Indications and dosages

▶ **Hypertension.** *Adults:* Initially, 1 mg P.O. at bedtime, increased gradually based on response. Usual dosage range is 1 to 5 mg daily. Maximum, 20 mg daily.

▶ **Symptomatic BPH.** *Adults:* Initially, 1 mg P.O. at bedtime. Dosage increased in stepwise manner to 2 mg, 5 mg, and 10 mg once daily to achieve optimal response. Most patients require 10 mg daily for optimal response.

Contraindications and cautions

- Contraindicated in patients hypersensitive to the drug or any of its components.

Lifespan: In pregnant women, use cautiously. In breast-feeding women, use cautiously; it's unknown if the drug appears in breast milk. In children, safety and effectiveness haven't been established.

Adverse reactions

CNS: *asthenia, dizziness, headache,* nervousness, paresthesia, somnolence.
CV: atrial fibrillation, palpitations, orthostatic hypotension, *peripheral edema,* tachycardia.
EENT: blurred vision, nasal congestion, sinusitis.
GI: nausea.
GU: impotence, priapism.
Hematologic: ***thrombocytopenia.***
Musculoskeletal: back pain, muscle pain.
Respiratory: dyspnea.
Other: decreased libido.

Interactions

Drug-drug. *Antihypertensives:* May cause excessive hypotension. Use together cautiously.
Clonidine: May decrease antihypertensive effect of clonidine. Monitor patient.
Drug-herb. *Butcher's broom:* May cause diminished effect. Discourage using together.

Effects on lab test results

- May decrease total protein, albumin, and hemoglobin levels and hematocrit.
- May decrease platelet and WBC counts.

Pharmacokinetics

Absorption: Rapid, with about 90% of dose bioavailable.
Distribution: About 90% to 94% bound to plasma proteins.
Metabolism: In liver.
Excretion: About 40% in urine, 60% in feces, mostly as metabolites. Up to 30% may be unchanged. *Half-life:* About 12 hours.

Route	Onset	Peak	Duration
P.O.	≤ 15 min	2–3 hr	24 hr

Action

Chemical effect: Decreases blood pressure by vasodilation produced in response to blockade of $alpha_1$-adrenergic receptors. Improves urine flow by blocking $alpha_1$ receptors in smooth muscle of bladder neck and prostate, thus relieving urethral pressure and reestablishing urine flow.
Therapeutic effect: Lowers blood pressure and relieves symptoms of BPH.

Available forms

Capsules: 1 mg, 2 mg, 5 mg, 10 mg

NURSING PROCESS

Assessment

- Assess patient's condition before starting therapy and regularly thereafter to monitor drug's effectiveness.
- Assess and monitor patient for prostate cancer because it may resemble BPH.
- Monitor blood pressure often.
- Be alert for adverse reactions and drug interactions.
- Assess patient's and family's knowledge of drug therapy.

T

Nursing diagnoses

- Risk for injury related to presence of hypertension
- Sexual dysfunction related to drug-induced impotence
- Deficient knowledge related to drug therapy

Planning and implementation

- Use cautiously with initial dose, and monitor patient—especially elderly patient—for postural hypotension.

ALERT: If drug is stopped for several days, begin again at the initial dose and adjust regimen.

Patient teaching

- Tell patient not to stop drug but to call prescriber if adverse reaction occurs.
- Tell patient to take the first dose at bedtime. If he must get up, he should do so slowly to prevent dizziness or blackouts.
- Warn patient to avoid activities that require mental alertness for 12 hours after first dose.
- Teach patient other means to reduce blood pressure, such as diet control, exercise, smoking cessation, and stress reduction.

Evaluation

- Patient's blood pressure is normal.
- Patient develops and maintains positive attitude toward his sexuality despite impotence.
- Patient and family state understanding of drug therapy.

terbutaline sulfate

(ter-BYOO-tuh-leen SUL-fayt)

Brethine, Bricanyl

Pharmacologic class: $beta_2$ agonist
Therapeutic class: bronchodilator
Pregnancy risk category: B

Indications and dosages

▶ **Bronchospasm in patients with reversible obstructive airway disease.** *Adults and children older than age 15:* Initially, 2.5 mg P.O. t.i.d. or q.i.d. Increase to 5 mg P.O. t.i.d. at 6-hour intervals while awake. Maximum, 15 mg daily. Or, 0.25 mg subcutaneously. May repeat in 15 to 30 minutes. Maximum, 0.5 mg q 4 hours.
Children ages 12 to 15: Give 2.5 mg P.O. t.i.d. Maximum, 7.5 mg daily.

▶ **Premature labor‡.** *Women:* Initially, 2.5 to 10 mcg/minute I.V.; increase dose gradually as tolerated in 10- to 20-minute intervals until desired effects are achieved. Maximum dosages range from 17.5 to 30 mcg/minute, although dosages of up to 80 mcg/minute have been used cautiously. Continue infusion for at least 12 hours after uterine contractions stop. Maintenance therapy, 2.5 to 10 mg P.O. q 4 to 6 hours.

I.V. administration

- Protect injection from light. If discolored, don't use.
- Monitor uterine response, maternal blood pressure, and maternal and fetal heart rates. Also monitor patient for circulatory overload and pulmonary edema.

Incompatibility
Bleomycin.

Contraindications and cautions

- Contraindicated in patients hypersensitive to the drug or any of its components, or to sympathomimetic amines.
- Use cautiously in patient with CV disorders, hyperthyroidism, diabetes, or seizure disorders.

Lifespan: In pregnant women, use cautiously. In breast-feeding women, use cautiously; it's unknown if the drug appears in breast milk. In children age 11 and younger, safety and effectiveness haven't been established.

Adverse reactions

CNS: dizziness, drowsiness, headache, nervousness, tremor, weakness.
CV: ***arrhythmias,*** chest discomfort, flushing, hypertension, *palpitations,* tachycardia.
EENT: tinnitus.
GI: heartburn, nausea, *vomiting.*
Metabolic: hypokalemia.
Respiratory: dyspnea, ***paradoxical bronchospasm.***
Skin: diaphoresis.

Interactions

Drug-drug. *CNS stimulants:* May increase CNS stimulation. Avoid use together.
Cyclopropane, digoxin, halogenated inhaled anesthetics, levodopa: May increase risk of arrhythmias. Monitor patient closely.
MAO inhibitors: May cause severe hypertension (hypertensive crisis). Don't use together.

Propranolol, other beta blockers: May block bronchodilating effects of terbutaline. Avoid use together.
Sympathomimetics: May cause additive cardiovascular effects. Avoid use together.
Theophylline derivatives: May increase risk of cardiotoxic effects. Avoid use together.

Effects on lab test results

• May increase liver enzyme level. May decrease potassium level.

Pharmacokinetics

Absorption: 33% to 50% of P.O. dose; unknown for subcutaneous
Distribution: Widely distributed throughout body.
Metabolism: Partially metabolized in liver to inactive compounds.
Excretion: Excreted primarily in urine. *Half-life:* Unknown.

Route	Onset	Peak	Duration
P.O.	30 min	2–3 hr	4–8 hr
SubQ	≤ 15 min	30–60 min	1½–4 hr

Action

Chemical effect: Relaxes bronchial smooth muscle by acting on beta$_2$-adrenergic receptors.
Therapeutic effect: Improves breathing ability.

Available forms

Injection: 1 mg/ml
Tablets: 2.5 mg, 5 mg

NURSING PROCESS

Assessment

• Assess patient's condition before starting therapy and regularly thereafter to monitor drug's effectiveness.
• Monitor patient closely for toxicity.
• Assess patient's and family's knowledge of drug therapy.

Nursing diagnoses

• Ineffective breathing pattern related to underlying respiratory condition
• Acute pain related to drug-induced headache
• Deficient knowledge related to drug therapy

Planning and implementation

• For subcutaneous administration, inject in lateral deltoid area.
• If bronchospasm develops during therapy, notify prescriber immediately.
• Mild analgesic may be used to treat drug-induced headache.
ALERT: Don't confuse terbutaline with tolbutamide or terbinafine.

Patient teaching

• Explain to patient and family why drug is needed.
• Instruct patient to report paradoxical bronchospasm, and tell him to stop drug if it happens.
• Warn patient that tolerance may develop with prolonged use.

Evaluation

• Patient's breathing is improved.
• Patient's headache is relieved with mild analgesic.
• Patient and family state understanding of drug therapy.

teriparatide (rDNA origin)

(tehr-ih-PAHR-uh-tyd)
Forteo

Pharmacologic class: recombinant human parathyroid hormone (PTH)
Therapeutic class: antiosteoporotic
Pregnancy risk category: C

Indications and dosages

▶ **Osteoporosis in postmenopausal women at high risk for fracture; to increase bone mass in men with primary or hypogonadal osteoporosis who are at high risk for fracture.** *Adults:* 20 mcg subcutaneously in thigh or abdominal wall once daily.

Contraindications and cautions

• Contraindicated in patients hypersensitive to the drug or any of its components. Don't give to patients who have had radiation to the skeleton, those with Paget disease or unexplained alkaline phosphatase elevations, or those at increased risk for osteosarcoma, such as children. Don't give drug to patients with bone metastases, a history of skeletal malignancies, or metabolic bone diseases other than osteoporosis. Avoid

T

use in patients with hypercalcemia or primary hyperparathyroidism. Don't continue therapy beyond 2 years.

- Use cautiously in patients with active or recent urolithiasis and in patients with hepatic, renal, or cardiac disease.

Lifespan: In pregnant and breast-feeding women, drug isn't recommended. In children, safety and effectiveness haven't been established.

Adverse reactions

CNS: asthenia, depression, dizziness, headache, insomnia, *pain,* syncope, vertigo.
CV: angina pectoris, hypertension, orthostatic hypotension.
EENT: pharyngitis, rhinitis.
GI: constipation, diarrhea, dyspepsia, nausea, tooth disorder, vomiting.
Metabolic: hypercalcemia.
Musculoskeletal: *arthralgia,* leg cramps, neck pain.
Respiratory: cough, dyspnea, pneumonia.
Skin: rash, sweating.

Interactions

Drug-drug. *Calcium supplements:* May increase urinary calcium excretion. Dosage may need adjustment.
Digoxin: Hypercalcemia may predispose patient to digitalis toxicity. Use together cautiously.

Effects on lab test results

- May increase calcium and uric acid levels. May decrease phosphorus level.
- May increase urinary calcium and phosphorus excretion.

Pharmacokinetics

Absorption: Rapid and extensive, with level peaking after about 30 minutes. Availability is about 95%.
Distribution: Unknown.
Metabolism: Unknown for drug, but PTH is metabolized in the liver.
Excretion: Unknown for drug, but PTH is excreted by the kidneys. Elimination is rapid. *Half-life:* 1 hour.

Route	Onset	Peak	Duration
SubQ	Rapid	30 min	3 hr

Action

Chemical effect: Regulates calcium and phosphorus metabolism in bones and kidneys, increases calcium, and decreases phosphorus level.
Therapeutic effect: Decreases risk of fractures in patients with osteoporosis.

Available forms

Injection: 750 mcg/3 ml in a prefilled pen

NURSING PROCESS

Assessment

ALERT: Because of the risk of osteosarcoma, give drug only to patient for whom benefits outweigh risks.

- If patient could have urolithiasis or hypercalciuria, measure urinary calcium excretion before therapy.
- Assess patient's and family's knowledge of drug therapy.

Nursing diagnoses

- Risk for falls related to presence of osteoporosis
- Chronic pain related to adverse drug effects
- Deficient knowledge related to drug therapy

Planning and implementation

- Monitor patient for orthostatic hypotension, which may occur within 4 hours after a dose.
- Track calcium level. If patient develops persistent hypercalcemia, stop drug and evaluate its possible cause.
- Safety and effectiveness haven't been established for use beyond 2 years.

Patient teaching

- Instruct patient on the proper use and disposal of the prefilled pen.
- Tell patient not to share pen with others.
- Advise patient to sit or lie down if drug causes a fast heartbeat, lightheadedness, or dizziness. Tell patient to report persistent or worsening symptoms.
- Instruct patient to report persistent symptoms of hypercalcemia (nausea, vomiting, constipation, lethargy, and muscle weakness).

Evaluation

- Patient doesn't fall.
- Patient reports no pain or states that pain is controlled by therapy.

• Patient and family state understanding of drug therapy.

testolactone
(tes-tuh-LAK-tohn)
Teslac

Pharmacologic class: aromatase inhibitor
Therapeutic class: antineoplastic
Pregnancy risk category: C
Controlled substance schedule: III

Indications and dosages

▶ **Advanced postmenopausal breast cancer.** *Women:* 250 mg P.O. q.i.d. Some patients may benefit from 2 g per day. Therapy should continue for at least 3 months unless disease actively progresses.

Contraindications and cautions

• Contraindicated in patients hypersensitive to the drug or any of its components, and in men with breast cancer.

Lifespan: In pregnant women, use cautiously. In breast-feeding women, drug isn't recommended. In children, drug isn't indicated.

Adverse reactions

CNS: paresthesia, peripheral neuropathy.
CV: edema, increased blood pressure.
GI: anorexia, diarrhea, glossitis, nausea, vomiting,
Skin: alopecia, erythema, nail changes.
Other: hot flashes.

Interactions

Drug-drug. *Oral anticoagulants:* May increase pharmacologic effects. Monitor patient carefully.

Effects on lab test results

• May decrease estradiol level. May increase plasma calcium level.
• May increase 24-hour urinary excretion of creatine.

Pharmacokinetics

Absorption: Good.
Distribution: Widely distributed in total body water.
Metabolism: Extensively metabolized in liver.
Excretion: Testolactone and its metabolites excreted mainly in urine. *Half-life:* Unknown.

Route	Onset	Peak	Duration
P.O.	6–12 wk	Unknown	Unknown

Action

Chemical effect: Unknown; may change tumor's hormonal environment and alter neoplastic process.
Therapeutic effect: Hinders breast cancer cell activity.

Available forms

Tablets: 50 mg

NURSING PROCESS

Assessment

• Assess patient's breast cancer before starting therapy and regularly thereafter to monitor drug's effectiveness.
• Monitor fluid and electrolyte levels, especially calcium level.
• Assess patient's and family's knowledge of drug therapy.

Nursing diagnoses

• Ineffective health maintenance related to presence of breast cancer
• Disturbed sensory perception (tactile) related to drug-induced paresthesia and peripheral neuropathy
• Deficient knowledge related to drug therapy

Planning and implementation

• Encourage patient to drink fluids to aid calcium excretion, and encourage exercise to prevent hypercalcemia. Immobilized patient is prone to hypercalcemia.
• Higher-than-recommended doses don't promote remission.
• Continue therapy for at least 3 months unless disease actively progresses.

Patient teaching

• Inform patient that therapeutic response isn't immediate; it may take up to 3 months for benefit to be noted.
• Encourage patient to exercise and drink plenty of fluids to help prevent hypercalcemia.
• Tell patient to report adverse effects.

T

Evaluation
- Patient responds well to drug.
- Patient lists ways to protect against risk of injury caused by diminished tactile sensation.
- Patient and family state understanding of drug therapy.

testosterone
(tess-TOSS-teh-rohn)
Andronaq-50, Histerone-50, Histerone 100, Testamone 100, Testaqua, Testoject-50

testosterone cypionate
Andronate 100, Andronate 200, depAndro 100, depAndro 200, Depotest, Depo-Testosterone, Duratest-100, Duratest-200, T-Cypionate, Tested Cypionate 200, Virilon IM

testosterone enanthate
Andro L.A. 200, Andropository 200, Andryl 200, Delatest, Delatestryl, Durathate-200, Everone 200, Testrin-P.A.

testosterone propionate
Malogen in Oil ♦, Testex

Pharmacologic class: androgen
Therapeutic class: antineoplastic, hormone replacement
Pregnancy risk category: X
Controlled substance schedule: III

Indications and dosages
▶ **Hypogonadism.** *Men:* 10 to 25 mg testosterone I.M. two to three times weekly. Or, 50 to 400 mg testosterone cypionate or testosterone enanthate I.M. q 2 to 4 weeks. Or, 10 to 25 mg testosterone propionate I.M. two to three times weekly. Another alternative is 75 to 150 mg of testosterone cypionate or enanthate I.M. every 7 to 10 days.
▶ **Delayed puberty.** *Boys:* 25 to 50 mg testosterone or testosterone propionate I.M. two or three times weekly for up to 6 months.
▶ **Metastatic breast cancer 1 to 5 years after menopause.** *Women:* 100 mg testosterone I.M. three times weekly. Or, 50 to 100 mg testosterone propionate I.M. three times weekly. Or, 200 to 400 mg testosterone cypionate or testosterone enanthate I.M. q 2 to 4 weeks.
▶ **Postpartum breast pain and engorgement.** *Women:* 25 to 50 mg testosterone or testosterone propionate I.M. daily for 3 to 4 days.

Contraindications and cautions
- Contraindicated in men with breast or prostate cancer; patients with hypercalcemia; and those with cardiac, hepatic, or renal decompensation.

Lifespan: In pregnant and breast-feeding women, drug is contraindicated. In children, use cautiously because of risk of accelerated bone maturation leading to short stature. In the elderly, use cautiously.

Adverse reactions
CNS: anxiety, depression, headache, paresthesia, sleep apnea syndrome.
CV: edema.
GI: nausea.
GU: bladder irritability; excessive hormonal effects in boys and men (prepubertal: *acne, growth of body and facial hair,* phallic enlargement, premature epiphyseal closure, priapism; postpubertal: decreased ejaculatory volume, epididymitis, gynecomastia, impotence, oligospermia, testicular atrophy); hypoestrogenic effects in women (*acne;* clitoral enlargement; decreased or increased libido; diaphoresis; *edema;* flushing; *hirsutism; hoarseness;* menstrual irregularities; *oily skin; weight gain;* vaginitis, including burning, drying, and itching; vaginal bleeding).
Hematologic: polycythemia, suppression of clotting factors.
Hepatic: *cholestatic hepatitis,* reversible jaundice.
Metabolic: hypercalcemia.
Skin: hypersensitivity skin signs and symptoms, local edema.
Other: pain and induration at injection site.

Interactions
Drug-drug. *Hepatotoxic drugs:* May increase risk of hepatotoxicity. Monitor patient closely.
Insulin, oral antidiabetics: May alter dosage requirements. Monitor glucose level in diabetic patients.
Oral anticoagulants: May alter dosage requirements. Monitor PT and INR.

Effects on lab test results

- May increase sodium, potassium, phosphate, cholesterol, liver enzyme, calcium, and creatinine levels. May decrease thyroxine-binding globulin and total T_4 levels.
- May increase RBC count and resin uptake of T_3 and T_4.

Pharmacokinetics

Absorption: Unknown.
Distribution: 98% to 99% protein-bound, mainly to testosterone–estradiol-binding globulin.
Metabolism: In liver.
Excretion: In urine. *Half-life:* 10 to 100 minutes.

Route	Onset	Peak	Duration
I.M.	Unknown	Unknown	Unknown

Action

Chemical effect: Stimulates target tissues to develop normally in androgen-deficient men. Drug may have some antiestrogen properties, making it useful to treat certain estrogen-dependent breast cancers. Its action in postpartum breast engorgement isn't known because drug doesn't suppress lactation.
Therapeutic effect: Increases testosterone level, inhibits some estrogen activity, and relieves postpartum breast pain and engorgement.

Available forms

testosterone
Injection (aqueous suspension): 25 mg/ml, 50 mg/ml, 100 mg/ml
testosterone cypionate
Injection (in oil): 100 mg/ml, 200 mg/ml
testosterone enanthate
Injection (in oil): 200 mg/ml
testosterone propionate
Injection (in oil): 100 mg/ml

NURSING PROCESS

Assessment

- Assess patient's condition before starting therapy and regularly thereafter to monitor drug's effectiveness.
- Periodically monitor calcium level and liver function test results.
- Monitor hemoglobin and hematocrit for polycythemia.
- Monitor prepubertal boys by X-ray for rate of bone maturation.
- Be alert for adverse reactions and drug interactions.
- Assess patient's and family's knowledge of drug therapy.

Nursing diagnoses

- Ineffective health maintenance related to underlying condition
- Disturbed body image related to drug-induced adverse androgenic reactions
- Deficient knowledge related to drug therapy

Planning and implementation

- Give daily dose requirement in divided doses for best results.
- Store preparations at room temperature. If crystals appear, warm and shake bottle to disperse them.
- Inject deep into upper outer quadrant of gluteal muscle. Rotate sites to prevent muscle atrophy. Report soreness at site because of possibility of postinfection furunculosis.
- Unless contraindicated, use with diet high in calories and protein taken in small, frequent meals.
- Report signs of virilization in woman.
- Edema generally can be controlled with sodium restriction or diuretics.

ALERT: Therapeutic response in breast cancer usually appears within 3 months. If signs of disease progression appear, stop giving the drug. In metastatic breast cancer, hypercalcemia usually signals progression of bone metastases. Report signs of hypercalcemia.

- Androgens may alter results of laboratory studies during therapy and for 2 to 3 weeks after therapy ends.

ALERT: Testosterone and methyltestosterone aren't interchangeable. Don't confuse testosterone with testolactone.

Patient teaching

- Tell patient to use effective barrier-method contraception during therapy.
- Instruct man to report priapism, reduced ejaculatory volume, and gynecomastia. Drug may need to be stopped.
- Inform woman that virilization may occur. Tell her to report androgenic effects immediately. Stopping drug will prevent further andro-

T

genic changes but probably won't reverse those already present.
- Teach patient to recognize and report signs of hypoglycemia.
- Instruct patient to follow dietary measures to combat drug-induced adverse reactions.

Evaluation
- Patient responds well to drug.
- Patient states acceptance of altered body image.
- Patient and family state understanding of drug therapy.

testosterone transdermal system
(tess-TOSS-teh-rohn tranz-DER-mal SIHS-tum)
Androderm, AndroGel, Testim

Pharmacologic class: androgen
Therapeutic class: hormone replacement
Pregnancy risk category: X
Controlled substance schedule: III

Indications and dosages
▶ **Primary or hypogonadotropic hypogonadism.** *Men:* 5 mg Androderm daily either as two 2.5-mg systems or one 5-mg system applied at bedtime to clean, dry skin on back, abdomen, upper arms, or thighs. Or, 5 g, 7.5 g, or 10 g AndroGel applied to upper arms, shoulders, and abdomen daily. Or, 5 or 10 g Testim, applied to upper arms and shoulders daily.

Contraindications and cautions
- Contraindicated in patients hypersensitive to the drug or any of its components, and in patients with known or suspected breast or prostate cancer.
- Use cautiously in patients with renal, hepatic, or cardiac disease.

Lifespan: In women, drug is contraindicated. In children, drug isn't indicated. In elderly men, use cautiously because they may be at greater risk for prostatic hyperplasia or prostate cancer.

Adverse reactions
CV: depression, headache, ***stroke.***
GI: ***GI bleeding.***
GU: prostate abnormalities, prostatitis, UTI.
Skin: acne, allergic contact dermatitis, burning, *blister under system,* induration (at application site), irritation, *pruritus.*
Other: breast tenderness, gynecomastia.

Interactions
Drug-drug. *Antidiabetics:* May alter antidiabetic dosage requirements. Monitor glucose level.
Oral anticoagulants: May alter anticoagulant dosage requirements. Monitor PT and INR.
Oxyphenbutazone: May elevate oxyphenbutazone level. Monitor patient for adverse reactions.

Effects on lab test results
- May increase sodium, potassium, phosphate, cholesterol, liver enzyme, calcium, and creatinine levels.
- May increase RBC count.

Pharmacokinetics
Absorption: Continuously absorbed dermally over 24 hours.
Distribution: Chiefly bound to sex–hormone-binding globulin.
Metabolism: In liver.
Excretion: In urine. *Half-life:* 10 to 100 minutes.

Route	Onset	Peak	Duration
Transdermal	Unknown	2–4 hr	2 hr after removal

Action
Chemical effect: Stimulates target tissues to develop normally in androgen-deficient men.
Therapeutic effect: Increases testosterone in androgen-deficient men.

Available forms
1% gel: 2.5 g and 5 g packets, 75 g nonaerosol metered pump, 5 g tube
Transdermal system: 2.5 mg/day, 5 mg/day

NURSING PROCESS

Assessment
- Assess patient's condition before starting therapy and regularly thereafter to monitor drug's effectiveness.
- Because long-term use of systemic androgens is linked to polycythemia, monitor hematocrit

and hemoglobin values periodically in patient on long-term therapy.
- Periodically assess liver function tests, lipid profiles, and prostatic acid phosphatase and prostate-specific antigen levels.
- Be alert for adverse reactions and drug interactions.
- Assess patient's and family's knowledge of drug therapy.

Nursing diagnoses
- Sexual dysfunction related to androgen deficiency
- Risk for impaired skin integrity related to drug-induced irritation at application site
- Deficient knowledge related to drug therapy

Planning and implementation
- Apply Androderm to clean, dry skin on back, abdomen, upper arms, or thighs.
- Apply gel by rubbing entire dose into skin, then don't allow patient to bathe for 2 to 6 hours.

Patient teaching
- Teach patient how to apply transdermal system.
- Tell patient to fully prime the AndroGel pump by depressing the pumping mechanism three times before first use and discarding that portion. For 5 g dose, he should pump 5 times, for 7.5 g, 6 times, and for 10 g, 8 times. The gel can be pumped into the palm of the hand then applied to application sites.
- Tell patient that topical testosterone preparations can cause virilization in women sexual partners. Advise these women to report acne or changes in body hair. Tell patient to wear a shirt during close physical contact or to wash site if applied within 2 to 6 hours of contact.
- Advise patient to report to prescriber persistent erections, nausea, vomiting, changes in skin color, or ankle edema.

Evaluation
- Patient states that he can resume normal sexual activity.
- Patient maintains normal skin integrity.
- Patient and family state understanding of drug therapy.

tetanus immune globulin, human
(TET-nuss ih-MYOON GLOH-byoo-lin)
BayTet

Pharmacologic class: immune serum
Therapeutic class: tetanus prevention drug
Pregnancy risk category: C

Indications and dosages
▶ **Tetanus exposure.** *Adults and children age 7 and older:* 250 units I.M.
Children younger than age 7: Give 4 units/kg I.M.

▶ **Tetanus.** *Adults and children:* Single doses of 3,000 to 6,000 units I.M. Optimal dosage hasn't been established.

Contraindications and cautions
- In patients with thrombocytopenia or coagulation disorders, I.M. injection is contraindicated unless potential benefits outweigh risks.

Lifespan: In pregnant women, use cautiously. In breast-feeding women, use cautiously; it's unknown if the drug appears in breast milk.

Adverse reactions
GU: slight fever, nephrotic syndrome.
Other: ***anaphylaxis; angioedema;*** erythema, pain, stiffness at injection site; hypersensitivity reactions.

Interactions
Drug-drug. *Live-virus vaccines:* May interfere with response. Defer live-virus vaccines for 3 months after tetanus immune globulin.
Measles, mumps, rubella, and varicella vaccines: Tetanus antibodies may interfere with immune response. Separate vaccines by 3 months.

Effects on lab test results
None reported.

Pharmacokinetics
Absorption: Slow.
Distribution: Unknown.
Metabolism: Unknown.
Excretion: Unknown. *Half-life:* About 28 days.

Route	Onset	Peak	Duration
I.M.	Unknown	2–3 days	4 wk

T

Action

Chemical effect: Provides passive immunity to tetanus.
Therapeutic effect: Prevents tetanus.

Available forms

Injection: 250 units per vial or syringe

NURSING PROCESS

Assessment

• Obtain history of injury, tetanus immunizations, last tetanus toxoid injection, allergies, and reaction to immunizations.
• Antibodies remain at effective level for about 4 weeks (several times the duration of antitoxin-induced antibodies), which protects patient for incubation period of most tetanus cases.
• Be alert for adverse reactions and drug interactions.
• Assess patient's and family's knowledge of drug therapy.

Nursing diagnoses

• Risk for injury related to potential for tetanus to occur
• Deficient knowledge related to drug therapy

Planning and implementation

ALERT: Have epinephrine 1:1,000 available to treat hypersensitivity reactions.
• Use drug if wound is more than 24 hours old or if patient has had fewer than two tetanus toxoid injections.
• Keep drug refrigerated.
• Thoroughly clean wound and remove all foreign matter.
• Inject drug into deltoid muscle for adult or child age 3 and older and into anterolateral aspect of thigh in neonate or child younger than age 3.
ALERT: Don't confuse drug with tetanus toxoid. Tetanus immune globulin isn't a substitute for tetanus toxoid, which should be given at same time to produce active immunization. Don't give at same site as toxoid.

Patient teaching
• Warn patient that pain and tenderness at injection site may occur. Suggest mild analgesic for pain relief.
• Tell patient to document date of tetanus immunization, and encourage him to keep immunization current.

Evaluation

• Patient doesn't develop tetanus.
• Patient and family state understanding of drug therapy.

tetracycline hydrochloride

(tet-ruh-SIGH-kleen high-droh-KLOR-ighd)

Achromycin†, Apo-Tetra ♦, Novo-Tetra ♦, Nu-Tetra ♦, Sumycin, Tetrex ◊, Topicycline

Pharmacologic class: tetracycline
Therapeutic class: antibiotic
Pregnancy risk category: D

Indications and dosages

▶ **Infections caused by sensitive gram-negative and gram-positive organisms, including *Chlamydia, Mycoplasma, Rickettsia,* and organisms that cause trachoma.** *Adults:* 1 to 2 g P.O. divided into two to four doses for 10-14 days.
Children older than age 8: Give 25 to 50 mg/kg P.O. daily divided into four doses.

▶ **Uncomplicated urethral, endocervical, or rectal infection caused by *Chlamydia trachomatis.*** *Adults:* 500 mg P.O. q.i.d. for at least 7 days.

▶ **Brucellosis.** *Adults:* 500 mg P.O. q 6 hours for 3 weeks combined with 1 g of streptomycin I.M. q 12 hours first week and daily the second week.

▶ **Gonorrhea in patients sensitive to penicillin.** *Adults:* Initially, 1.5 g P.O.; then 500 mg q 6 hours for 4 days.

▶ **Syphilis in nonpregnant patients sensitive to penicillin.** *Adults:* 500 mg P.O. q.i.d. for 15 days.

▶ **Acne.** *Adults and adolescents:* Initially, 125 to 250 mg P.O. q 6 hours; then 125 to 500 mg daily or q other day. Or, apply 3% ointment or 2.2% solution to affected areas daily or b.i.d.

▶ **Lyme disease‡.** *Adults:* 250 to 500 mg P.O. q.i.d. for 10 to 30 days.

▶ **Adjunct therapy for acute transmitted epididymitis (children older than age 8); pelvic inflammatory disease; and infection with *Helicobacter pylori*‡.** *Adults:* 500 mg P.O. q.i.d. for 10 to 14 days.

▶ **Malaria.**‡ *Adults:* 250 mg P.O. q.i.d. for 7 days with quinine sulfate.

Children older than age 8: Give 25 mg/kg daily in 4 divided doses for 7 days with quinine sulfate.

Contraindications and cautions

- Contraindicated in patients hypersensitive to tetracyclines.
- Use cautiously in patients with impaired kidney or liver function.

Lifespan: In women in the last half of pregnancy and in children younger than age 8, use cautiously, if at all, because drug may cause permanent discoloration of teeth, enamel defects, and bone-growth retardation. In breast-feeding women, drug isn't recommended.

Adverse reactions

CNS: dizziness, headache, ***intracranial hypertension (pseudotumor cerebri).***
CV: ***pericarditis.***
EENT: dysphagia, glossitis, sore throat.
GI: anorexia, *diarrhea,* enterocolitis, *epigastric distress,* esophagitis, inflammatory lesions in anogenital region, oral candidiasis, *nausea,* stomatitis, vomiting.
Hematologic: eosinophilia, ***neutropenia, thrombocytopenia.***
Musculoskeletal: retardation of bone growth if used in children younger than age 9.
Skin: ***candidal superinfection,*** increased pigmentation, maculopapular and erythematous rashes, photosensitivity reactions, urticaria.
Other: enamel defects, ***hypersensitivity reactions,*** permanent discoloration of teeth.

Interactions

Drug-drug. *Antacids (including sodium bicarbonate); antidiarrheals containing bismuth subsalicylate, kaolin, or pectin; laxatives containing aluminum, calcium, or magnesium:* May decrease antibiotic absorption. Give tetracyclines 1 hour before or 2 hours after these drugs.
Ferrous sulfate, other iron products, zinc: May decrease antibiotic absorption. Give tetracyclines 2 hours before or 3 hours after iron.
Hormonal contraceptives: May decrease contraceptive effectiveness and increase risk of breakthrough bleeding. Recommend nonhormonal form of birth control.
Lithium carbonate: May alter lithium level. Monitor patient.
Methoxyflurane: May cause severe nephrotoxicity with tetracyclines. Monitor patient carefully.
Oral anticoagulants: May potentiate anticoagulant effects. Monitor PT and adjust anticoagulant dosage.
Penicillins: May interfere with bactericidal action of penicillins. Avoid using together.
Drug-food. *Milk, dairy products, other foods:* May decrease drug absorption. Give drug 1 hour before or 2 hours after these products.
Drug-lifestyle. *Sun exposure:* May cause photosensitivity reactions. Urge patient to avoid prolonged or unprotected exposure to sunlight.

Effects on lab test results

- May increase BUN and liver enzyme levels.
- May increase eosinophil count. May decrease platelet and neutrophil counts.
- May cause false-negative reading with glucose enzymatic tests (Diastix).

Pharmacokinetics

Absorption: 75% to 80%. Food or milk products significantly reduces.
Distribution: Wide in body tissues and fluids. CSF penetration is poor. 20% to 67% protein-bound.
Metabolism: None.
Excretion: Mainly unchanged in urine. *Half-life:* 6 to 11 hours.

Route	Onset	Peak	Duration
P.O.	Unknown	2–4 hr	Unknown

Action

Chemical effect: Unknown; may act by binding to 30S ribosomal subunit of microorganisms, thus inhibiting protein synthesis.
Therapeutic effect: Hinders bacterial activity.

Available forms

Capsules: 250 mg, 500 mg
Ointment†: 3%
Oral suspension: 125 mg/5 ml
Topical solution: 2.2 mg/ml

NURSING PROCESS

Assessment

- Assess patient's infection before starting therapy and regularly thereafter to monitor drug's effectiveness.
- Obtain specimen for culture and sensitivity tests before giving the first dose. Start therapy pending test results.

• If adverse GI reaction occurs, monitor hydration.
• Be alert for adverse reactions and drug interactions.
• Assess patient's and family's knowledge of drug therapy.

Nursing diagnoses
• Risk for infection related to presence of susceptible bacteria
• Risk for deficient fluid volume related to drug-induced adverse GI reactions
• Deficient knowledge related to drug therapy

Planning and implementation
ALERT: Check expiration date. Outdated or deteriorated tetracyclines have been linked to reversible nephrotoxicity (Fanconi syndrome).
• Give drug on empty stomach.
• Don't expose drug to light or heat.

Patient teaching
• Tell patient to take drug with full glass of water on empty stomach, at least 1 hour before or 2 hours after meals. Also, tell him to take drug at least 1 hour before bedtime to prevent esophagitis. Explain that effectiveness of drug is reduced when taken with milk or other dairy products, food, antacids, or iron products.
• Tell patient to take drug exactly as prescribed, even after he feels better, and to take entire amount prescribed.
• Warn patient to avoid direct sunlight and ultraviolet light. Recommend sunscreen to help prevent photosensitivity reactions. Tell him that photosensitivity persists after drug is stopped.
• Advise patient that topical forms of the drug may stain skin and clothing.
• Tell patient using topical preparation to wash, rinse, and thoroughly dry the affected area before applying the drug. Also, advise him to avoid getting it in his eyes, nose, mouth, or other mucous membranes.

Evaluation
• Patient is free from infection.
• Patient maintains adequate hydration.
• Patient and family state understanding of drug therapy.

theophylline
(thee-OFF-ih-lin)

Immediate-release liquids
Accurbron*, Aquaphyllin, Asmalix*, Bronkodyl*, Elixomin*, Elixophyllin*, Lanophyllin*, Slo-Phyllin, Theolair

Immediate-release tablets and capsules
Bronkodyl, Elixophyllin, Nuelin ◊, Slo-Phyllin

Timed-release capsules
Elixophyllin SR, Nuelin-SR ◊, Slo-bid Gyrocaps, Slo-Phyllin, Theo-24, Theobid Duracaps, Theochron, Theospan-SR, Theovent Long-Acting

Timed-release tablets
Quibron-T/SR Dividose, Respbid, Sustaire, T-Phyl, Theochron, Theolair-SR, Theo-Sav, Theo-Time, Theo-X, Uniphyl

theophylline sodium glycinate

Pharmacologic class: xanthine derivative
Therapeutic class: bronchodilator
Pregnancy risk category: C

Indications and dosages
▶ **Oral theophylline for acute bronchospasm in patients not already receiving theophylline.** *Adults (nonsmokers):* Loading dose of 6 mg/kg P.O.; then 3 mg/kg q 6 hours for two doses. Maintenance dosage is 3 mg/kg q 8 hours.
Children ages 9 to 16 and young adult smokers: Loading dose of 6 mg/kg P.O.; then 3 mg/kg q 4 hours for three doses; then 3 mg/kg q 6 hours.
Children ages 6 months to 9 years: Loading dose of 6 mg/kg P.O.; then 4 mg/kg q 4 hours for three doses; then 4 mg/kg q 6 hours.
Older adults or those with cor pulmonale: Loading dose of 6 mg/kg P.O.; then 2 mg/kg q 6 hours for two doses; then 2 mg/kg q 8 hours.
Adjust-a-dose: For adults with heart failure or liver disease, give loading dose of 6 mg/kg P.O.; then 2 mg/kg q 8 hours for two doses; then 1 to 2 mg/kg q 12 hours.
▶ **Parenteral theophylline for patients not receiving theophylline.** *Adults (nonsmokers):* Loading dose of 4.7 mg/kg given slow I.V.; then

maintenance infusion of 0.55 mg/kg/hour I.V. for 12 hours; then 0.39 mg/kg/hour.
Adults (otherwise healthy smokers): Loading dose of 4.7 mg/kg given slow I.V.; then maintenance infusion of 0.79 mg/kg/hour I.V. for 12 hours; then 0.63 mg/kg/hour.
Older adults or those with cor pulmonale: Loading dose of 4.7 mg/kg given slow I.V.; then maintenance infusion of 0.47 mg/kg/hour I.V. for 12 hours; then 0.24 mg/kg/hour.
Adults with heart failure or liver disease: Loading dose of 4.7 mg/kg given slow I.V.; then maintenance infusion of 0.39 mg/kg/hour I.V. for 12 hours; then 0.08 to 0.16 mg/kg/hour.
Children ages 9 to 16: Loading dose of 4.7 mg/kg given slow I.V.; then maintenance infusion of 0.79 mg/kg/hour I.V. for 12 hours; then 0.63 mg/kg/hour.
Children ages 6 months to 9 years: Loading dose of 4.7 mg/kg given slow I.V.; then maintenance infusion of 0.95 mg/kg/hour I.V. for 12 hours; then 0.79 mg/kg/hour.

▶ **Oral and parenteral theophylline for acute bronchospasm in patients receiving theophylline.** *Adults and children:* Each 0.5 mg/kg I.V. or P.O. (loading dose) increases plasma level by 1 mcg/ml. Ideally, dose is based on current theophylline level. In emergencies, some clinicians recommend 2.5 mg/kg P.O. dose of rapidly absorbed form if no obvious signs of theophylline toxicity are present.

▶ **Chronic bronchospasm.** *Adults and children:* 16 mg/kg or 400 mg P.O. daily (whichever is less) given in three or four divided doses at 6- to 8-hour intervals. Or, 12 mg/kg or 400 mg P.O. daily (whichever is less) using extended-release preparation given in two or three divided doses at 8- or 12-hour intervals. Dosage increased as tolerated at 2- to 3-day intervals to maximum dosage as follows:
Adults and children age 16 and older: Give 13 mg/kg or 900 mg P.O. daily (whichever is less) in divided doses.
Children ages 12 to 16: Give 18 mg/kg P.O. daily in divided doses.
Children ages 9 to 12: Give 20 mg/kg P.O. daily in divided doses.
Children ages 1 to 9: Give 24 mg/kg P.O. daily in divided doses.
Children younger than age 1‡: Loading dose is 1 mg/kg P.O. or I.V. for each 2-mcg/ml increase in theophylline level desired. Maintenance dosage for premature neonates up to 40 weeks postconception age is 1 mg/kg q 12 hours. Maintenance dosage for term neonates up to age 4 weeks is 1 to 2 mg/kg q 12 hours; 1 to 2 mg/kg q 8 hours in those age 4 to 8 weeks; and 1 to 3 mg/kg q 6 hours in those older than age 8 weeks.

▶ **Cystic fibrosis‡.** *Infants:* 10 to 20 mg/kg I.V. daily.

▶ **Promotion of diuresis; Cheyne-Stokes respirations; paroxysmal nocturnal dyspnea‡.** *Adults:* 200 to 400 mg I.V. bolus as a single dose.

I.V. administration

- Use commercially available infusion solution, or mix drug in D_5W.
- Use infusion pump for continuous infusion.

⊗ Incompatibilities
Ascorbic acid, ceftriaxone, cimetidine, hetastarch, phenytoin.

Contraindications and cautions

- Contraindicated in patients with active peptic ulcer or seizure disorders and in those who are hypersensitive to xanthine compounds (caffeine, theobromine).
- Don't use extended-release forms for acute bronchospasm.
- Use cautiously in patients with COPD, cardiac failure, cor pulmonale, cardiac arrhythmias, renal or hepatic disease, peptic ulceration, hyperthyroidism, diabetes mellitus, glaucoma, severe hypoxemia, hypertension, compromised cardiac or circulatory function, angina, acute MI, or sulfite sensitivity.

Lifespan: In pregnant women, use cautiously. In breast-feeding women, use is discouraged; infants of breast-feeding women may exhibit irritability, insomnia, or fretting. In young children, infants, neonates, and the elderly, use cautiously.

Adverse reactions

CNS: *dizziness,* headache, *insomnia,* irritability, muscle twitching, *restlessness,* ***seizures.***
CV: ***arrhythmias,*** extrasystoles, flushing, ***marked hypotension,*** palpitations, sinus tachycardia.
GI: diarrhea, epigastric pain, *nausea, vomiting.*
Respiratory: increased respiratory rate, ***respiratory arrest.***

T

Interactions

Drug-drug. *Adenosine:* May decrease antiarrhythmic effectiveness. Higher doses of adenosine may be needed.
Allopurinol, cimetidine, fluoroquinolones (such as ciprofloxacin), influenza virus vaccine, macrolide antibiotics (such as erythromycin), hormonal contraceptives: May decrease hepatic clearance of theophylline and elevate theophylline level. Monitor patient for toxicity.
Barbiturates, carbamazepine, phenytoin, rifampin: May enhance metabolism and decrease theophylline blood level. Monitor patient for decreased effect.
Carteolol, pindolol, propranolol, timolol: May act antagonistically, reducing the effects of one or both drugs. The elimination of theophylline may also be reduced. Monitor theophylline level and patient closely.
Nadolol: May antagonize drug; may cause bronchospasm in sensitive patients. Use together cautiously.
Drug-herb. *Cacao tree:* May inhibit drug metabolism. Discourage use together.
Cayenne: May increase drug absorption. Discourage use together.
St. John's wort: May decrease drug effectiveness. Discourage use together.
Drug-food. *Any food:* May accelerate absorption. Give drug on an empty stomach.
Caffeine: May decrease hepatic clearance of theophylline and elevate theophylline level. Monitor patient for toxicity.
Drug-lifestyle. *Smoking:* May increase drug elimination, increasing dosage requirements. Monitor drug response and level.

Effects on lab test results

- May increase free fatty acid level.

Pharmacokinetics

Absorption: Well absorbed. Food may further alter rate of absorption, especially of some extended-release preparations.
Distribution: Distributed throughout extracellular fluids. About 50% protein-bound, equilibrium between fluid and tissues occurs within 1 hour of I.V. loading dose.
Metabolism: In liver to inactive compounds.
Excretion: About 10% excreted unchanged in urine. *Half-life:* Adults, 7 to 9 hours; smokers, 4 to 5 hours; children, 3 to 5 hours; premature infants, 20 to 30 hours.

Route	Onset	Peak	Duration
P.O.			
regular	15–60 min	1–2 hr	Unknown
enteric-coated	15–60 min	1–2 hr	5 hr
extended-release	15–60 min	1–2 hr	4–7 hr
I.V.	15 min	15–30 min	Unknown

Action

Chemical effect: Inhibits phosphodiesterase, the enzyme that degrades cAMP, and relaxes smooth muscle of bronchial airways and pulmonary blood vessels.
Therapeutic effect: Improves breathing ability.

Available forms

theophylline
Capsules: 100 mg, 200 mg
Capsules (extended-release): 50 mg, 60 mg, 65 mg, 75 mg, 100 mg, 125 mg, 130 mg, 200 mg, 250 mg, 260 mg, 300 mg
D_5W injection: 200 mg in 50 ml or 100 ml; 400 mg in 100 ml, 250 ml, 500 ml, or 1,000 ml; 800 mg in 500 ml or 1,000 ml
Elixir: 27 mg/5 ml, 50 mg/5 ml*
Oral solution: 27 mg/5 ml, 50 mg/5 ml
Syrup: 27 mg/5 ml, 50 mg/5 ml
Tablets: 100 mg, 125 mg, 200 mg, 250 mg, 300 mg
Tablets (chewable): 100 mg
Tablets (extended-release): 100 mg, 200 mg, 250 mg, 300 mg, 400 mg, 500 mg, 600 mg
theophylline sodium glycinate
Elixir: 110 mg/5 ml (equivalent to 55 mg of anhydrous theophylline/5 ml)

NURSING PROCESS

Assessment

- Assess patient's condition before starting therapy and regularly thereafter to monitor drug's effectiveness.
- Monitor vital signs; measure fluid intake and output. Expect effects such as improvement in quality of pulse and respirations.
- Metabolism rate varies among individuals; dosage is determined by monitoring response, tolerance, pulmonary function, and drug level. Therapeutic level is 10 to 20 mcg/ml in adults and 5 to 15 mcg/ml in children.
- Be alert for adverse reactions and drug interactions.

ALERT: Monitor patient for signs and symptoms of toxicity, including tachycardia, anorexia, nausea, vomiting, diarrhea, restlessness, irritability, and headache. The presence of any of these signs or symptoms in a patient taking theophylline warrants checking theophylline level and adjusting dose as indicated.
- If adverse GI reaction occurs, monitor hydration.
- Assess patient's and family's knowledge of drug therapy.

Nursing diagnoses
- Impaired gas exchange related to presence of bronchospasm
- Risk for deficient fluid volume related to drug-induced adverse GI reactions
- Deficient knowledge related to drug therapy

Planning and implementation
- Give oral drug around the clock, using sustained-release product at bedtime.

ALERT: Don't confuse sustained-release form with standard-release form.
- Dose may need to be increased in a cigarette smoker or a habitual marijuana smoker; smoking causes drug to be metabolized faster.
- Daily dose may need to be decreased in a patient with heart failure or hepatic disease, or in an elderly patient, because metabolism and excretion may be decreased.

ALERT: Don't confuse Theolair with Thyrolar.

Patient teaching
- Instruct patient not to dissolve, crush, or chew sustained-release products. For child unable to swallow capsules, sprinkle contents of capsules over soft food and tell patient to swallow without chewing.
- Supply instructions for home care and dosage schedule.
- Tell patient to relieve GI symptoms by taking oral drug with full glass of water after meals, although food in stomach delays absorption.
- Instruct patient to take drug regularly, as directed.
- Inform elderly patient that dizziness may occur at start of therapy.
- Have patient change position slowly and avoid hazardous activities.
- Tell patient to check with prescriber before taking other drugs, including OTC drugs. OTC drugs may contain ephedrine with theophylline salts; excessive CNS stimulation may result.
- If patient's dose is stabilized while he is smoking and he then quits smoking, tell him to notify his prescriber; the dose may need to be reduced.

Evaluation
- Patient demonstrates improved gas exchange, exhibited in arterial blood gas values and respiratory status.
- Patient maintains adequate hydration.
- Patient and family state understanding of drug therapy.

thiamine hydrochloride (vitamin B_1)

(THIGH-eh-min high-droh-KLOR-ighd)

Betamin ◊, Beta-Sol ◊, Biamine, Thiamilate†

Pharmacologic class: water-soluble vitamin
Therapeutic class: nutritional supplement
Pregnancy risk category: A

Indications and dosages

▶ **RDA.** *Men age 19 and older:* Give 1.2 mg P.O. daily.
Boys ages 14 to 18: Give 1.2 mg P.O. daily.
Women age 19 and older: Give 1.1 mg P.O. daily.
Girls ages 14 to 18: Give 1 mg P.O. daily.
Pregnant women: Give 1.4 mg P.O. daily.
Breast-feeding women: Give 1.5 mg P.O. daily.
Children ages 9 to 13: Give 0.9 mg P.O. daily.
Children ages 4 to 8: Give 0.6 mg P.O. daily.
Children ages 1 to 3: Give 0.5 mg P.O. daily.
Infants age 6 months to 1 year: Give 0.3 mg P.O. daily.
Neonates and infants younger than age 6 months: Give 0.2 mg P.O. daily.

▶ **Beriberi.** *Adults:* Depending on severity, 10 to 20 mg I.M. t.i.d. for 2 weeks, followed by dietary correction and multivitamin supplement containing 5 to 10 mg of thiamine daily for 1 month.
Children: Depending on severity, 10 to 50 mg I.M. daily for several weeks with adequate diet.

▶ **Wet beriberi with myocardial failure.** *Adults and children:* 10 to 30 mg I.V. for emergency therapy.

T

▶ **Wernicke encephalopathy.** *Adults:* Initially, 100 mg I.V.; then 50 to 100 mg I.V. or I.M. daily until patient is consuming regular balanced diet.

I.V. administration

- Keep epinephrine available to treat anaphylaxis; give large I.V. doses cautiously.
- If patient has history of hypersensitivity reactions, apply skin test before starting therapy.
- Dilute drug before administration.

⊗ Incompatibilities

Alkali carbonates, barbiturates, citrates, erythromycin estolate, kanamycin, streptomycin, sulfites. Don't use with materials that yield alkaline solutions. Unstable in alkaline solutions.

Contraindications and cautions

- Contraindicated in patients hypersensitive to thiamine products.

Lifespan: In pregnant women, use cautiously if dose exceeds RDA.

Adverse reactions

CNS: restlessness, weakness.
CV: *CV collapse,* cyanosis.
EENT: tightness of throat.
GI: nausea, ***hemorrhage.***
Respiratory: ***pulmonary edema.***
Skin: diaphoresis, feeling of warmth, pruritus, urticaria.
Other: ***anaphylactic shock, hypersensitivity reactions,*** tenderness and induration after I.M. use.

Interactions

None significant.

Effects on lab test results

None reported.

Pharmacokinetics

Absorption: Absorbed readily after small P.O. doses; after large P.O. dose, total amount absorbed is limited. In alcoholics and patients with cirrhosis or malabsorption, GI absorption is decreased. When given with meals, rate of absorption decreases, but total absorption remains same. After I.M. dose, rapid and complete.
Distribution: Wide. When intake exceeds minimal requirements, tissue stores become saturated.
Metabolism: In liver.
Excretion: In urine. *Half-life:* Unknown.

Route	Onset	Peak	Duration
P.O., I.V., I.M.	Unknown	Unknown	Unknown

Action

Chemical effect: Combines with adenosine triphosphate to form coenzyme needed for carbohydrate metabolism.
Therapeutic effect: Restores normal thiamine level.

Available forms

Elixir: 250 mcg/5 ml
Injection: 100 mg/ml, 200 mg/ml
Tablets: 5 mg†, 10 mg†, 25 mg†, 50 mg†, 100 mg†, 250 mg†, 500 mg†
Tablets (enteric-coated): 20 mg

NURSING PROCESS

Assessment

- Assess patient's condition before starting therapy and regularly thereafter to monitor drug's effectiveness.
- Be alert for adverse reactions.
- Assess patient's and family's knowledge of drug therapy.

Nursing diagnoses

- Imbalanced nutrition: less than body requirements related to presence of thiamine deficiency
- Diarrhea related to drug-induced adverse GI reactions
- Deficient knowledge related to drug therapy

Planning and implementation

- Use parenteral route only when P.O. route isn't feasible.
- For treating alcoholic patient, give thiamine before dextrose infusions to prevent encephalopathy.
- Drug malabsorption is most likely in a patient with alcoholism, cirrhosis, or GI disease.
- Significant deficiency can occur in about 3 weeks of thiamine-free diet. Thiamine deficiency usually requires simultaneous therapy for multiple deficiencies.
- If breast-fed infant develops beriberi, give drug to both mother and child.

ALERT: Don't confuse thiamine with Thorazine.

Patient teaching

- Stress proper nutritional habits to prevent recurrence of deficiency.

Evaluation

- Patient regains normal thiamine level.
- Patient maintains normal bowel pattern.
- Patient and family state understanding of drug therapy.

thioridazine hydrochloride

(thigh-oh-RIGH-duh-zeen high-droh-KLOR-ighd)

Pharmacologic class: phenothiazine (piperidine derivative)
Therapeutic class: antipsychotic
Pregnancy risk category: C

Indications and dosages

▶ **Schizophrenia in patients who don't respond to treatment with other antipsychotic drugs.** *Adults:* Initially, 50 to 100 mg P.O. t.i.d., with gradual, incremental increases up to 800 mg daily in divided doses, if needed. Dosage varies.
Children: Initially, 0.5 mg/kg P.O. daily in divided doses. Increase dose gradually to optimum therapeutic effect. Maximum dose is 3 mg/kg/day.

Contraindications and cautions

- Contraindicated in patients hypersensitive to the drug or any of its components, and in those with CNS depression, severe hypertensive or hypotensive cardiac disease, coma, reduced level of CYP2D6 isoenzyme, congenital long-QT syndrome, or a history of cardiac arrhythmias.
- Don't give to patients taking fluvoxamine, propranolol, pindolol, fluoxetine, or drugs that inhibit the CYP2D6 enzyme or that prolong the QT interval.
- Use cautiously in debilitated patients and in patients with hepatic disease, CV disease, respiratory disorder, hypocalcemia, seizure disorder, severe reactions to insulin or electroconvulsive therapy, and exposure to extreme heat or cold (including antipyretic therapy) or organophosphate insecticides.

Lifespan: In pregnant women, use cautiously. In breast-feeding women, use cautiously; it's unknown if the drug appears in breast milk. In elderly patients, use cautiously.

Adverse reactions

CNS: dizziness, EEG changes, extrapyramidal reactions, ***neuroleptic malignant syndrome,*** sedation, tardive dyskinesia.
CV: ECG changes, *orthostatic hypotension,* tachycardia.
EENT: blurred vision, ocular changes, retinitis pigmentosa.
GI: constipation, dry mouth.
GU: dark urine, inhibited ejaculation, menstrual irregularities, *urine retention.*
Hematologic: ***agranulocytosis,*** hyperprolactinemia, ***transient leukopenia.***
Hepatic: cholestatic jaundice.
Metabolic: increased appetite, weight gain.
Skin: mild photosensitivity reactions.
Other: allergic reaction, gynecomastia.

Interactions

Drug-drug. *Antacids:* May inhibit absorption of oral phenothiazines. Separate doses by at least 2 hours.
Barbiturates, lithium: May decrease phenothiazine effect. Monitor patient.
Centrally acting antihypertensives: May decrease antihypertensive effect. Monitor blood pressure.
CNS depressants: May increase CNS depression. Use together cautiously.
Fluoxetine, fluvoxamine, pindolol, propranolol, drugs that inhibit the CYP2D6 enzyme system, and drugs that prolong the QT interval: May increase risk of serious or fatal cardiac arrhythmias. Don't use together.
Drug-herb. *Dong quai, St. John's wort:* May increase photosensitivity reactions. Discourage use together.
Kava: May increase risk of dystonic reactions. Discourage use together.
Milk thistle: May decrease liver toxicity caused by phenothiazines. If drug and herb are used together, monitor liver enzyme level.
Yohimbe: May increase risk for yohimbe toxicity. Discourage use together.
Drug-lifestyle. *Alcohol use:* May increase CNS depression, particularly psychomotor skills. Strongly discourage use.

T

Sun exposure: May increase photosensitivity reactions. Advise patient to avoid prolonged or unprotected exposure to sunlight.

Effects on lab test results

- May increase liver enzyme and prolactin levels.
- May decrease granulocyte and WBC counts.

Pharmacokinetics

Absorption: Erratic and variable, although P.O. concentrates and syrups are more predictable than tablets.
Distribution: Wide throughout body. 91% to 99% protein-bound.
Metabolism: Extensive, by liver by the CYP2D6 enzyme system.
Excretion: Mainly as metabolites in urine, some in feces. *Half-life:* 20 to 40 hours.

Route	Onset	Peak	Duration
P.O.	Varies	Unknown	Unknown

Action

Chemical effect: Unknown; probably blocks postsynaptic dopamine receptors in brain.
Therapeutic effect: Manages symptoms of schizophrenia.

Available forms

Oral concentrate: 30 mg/ml, 100 mg/ml* (3% to 4.2% alcohol)
Oral suspension: 25 mg/5 ml, 100 mg/5 ml
Tablets: 10 mg, 15 mg, 25 mg, 50 mg, 100 mg, 150 mg, 200 mg

NURSING PROCESS

Assessment

- Assess patient's condition before starting therapy and regularly thereafter to monitor drug's effectiveness.
- Monitor patient for tardive dyskinesia. It may occur after prolonged use or months or years later. It may disappear spontaneously or persist for life, despite stopping the drug.
- Monitor therapy with weekly bilirubin tests during first month, periodic blood tests (CBC and liver function), and ophthalmologic tests (long-term therapy).

ALERT: Monitor patient for symptoms of neuroleptic malignant syndrome (extrapyramidal effects, hyperthermia, autonomic disturbance), which is rare but can be fatal. It may not relate to length of drug use or type of neuroleptic; however, more than 60% of patients are men.

- Before starting therapy, perform baseline ECG and measure potassium level. Don't give drug to a patient with a QTc interval longer than 450 msec. Stop drug in patients with a QTc longer than 500 msec.
- Assess patient's and family's knowledge of drug therapy.

Nursing diagnoses

- Disturbed thought processes related to underlying condition
- Risk for injury related to drug-induced adverse CNS reactions
- Deficient knowledge related to drug therapy

Planning and implementation

ALERT: Different liquid formulations have different concentrations. Check dosage.

ALERT: Thioridazine prolongs the QTc interval in a dose-related manner.

- Prevent contact dermatitis by keeping drug away from skin and clothes. Wear gloves when preparing liquid forms.
- Dilute liquid concentrate with water or fruit juice just before giving.
- Shake suspension well before using.
- Don't abruptly stop giving the drug unless the patient experiences a severe adverse reaction. Abruptly stopping long-term therapy may cause gastritis, nausea, vomiting, dizziness, tremors, feeling of warmth or cold, diaphoresis, tachycardia, headache, or insomnia.
- Report jaundice, symptoms of blood dyscrasia (fever, sore throat, infection, cellulitis, weakness), or persistent extrapyramidal reactions (longer than a few hours), especially in pregnant women and in children, and withhold drug.
- Acute dystonic reactions may be treated with diphenhydramine.

ALERT: Don't confuse thioridazine with Thorazine.

Patient teaching

- Warn patient to avoid activities that require alertness until the drug's CNS effects are known. Drowsiness and dizziness usually subside after a few weeks.
- Tell patient to watch for orthostatic hypotension, especially with parenteral administration. Advise patient to change position slowly.

• Tell patient not to drink alcohol while taking drug.
• Instruct patient to report urine retention or constipation.
• Inform patient that drug may discolor urine.
• Tell patient to watch for and notify prescriber of blurred vision.
• Advise patient to relieve dry mouth with sugarless gum or hard candy.
• Tell patient to use sun block and to wear protective clothing to avoid photosensitivity reactions.

☑ Evaluation
• Patient's behavior and communication exhibit improved thought processes.
• Patient doesn't experience injury from adverse CNS reactions.
• Patient and family state understanding of drug therapy.

thiotepa
(thigh-oh-TEE-puh)
Thioplex

Pharmacologic class: alkylating drug
Therapeutic class: antineoplastic
Pregnancy risk category: D

Indications and dosages
▶ **Breast and ovarian cancers, lymphoma, Hodgkin lymphoma.** *Adults and children older than age 12:* Give 0.3 to 0.4 mg/kg I.V. q 1 to 4 weeks or 0.2 mg/kg for 4 to 5 days at intervals of 2 to 4 weeks.
▶ **Bladder tumor.** *Adults and children older than age 12:* Give 60 mg in 30 to 60 ml of normal saline solution instilled in bladder for 2 hours once weekly for 4 weeks.
▶ **Neoplastic effusions.** *Adults and children older than age 12:* Give 0.6 to 0.8 mg/kg intracavitarily or intratumor q 1 to 4 weeks.
▶ **Malignant meningeal neoplasm‡.** *Adults:* 1 to 10 mg/m^2 intrathecally, once to twice weekly.

I.V. administration
• Follow facility policy to minimize risks. Preparation and administration of parenteral form are linked to mutagenic, teratogenic, and carcinogenic risks to personnel.
• Reconstitute drug with 1.5 ml of sterile water for injection. Don't reconstitute with other solutions.
• Further dilute solution with normal saline solution injection, D_5W, dextrose 5% in normal saline solution for injection, Ringer's injection, or lactated Ringer's injection.
• Drug may be given rapid I.V. in doses of 0.3 to 0.4 mg/kg at intervals of 1 to 4 weeks.
• If pain occurs at insertion site, dilute further or use local anesthetic. Make sure drug doesn't infiltrate.
• Refrigerate and protect dry powder from direct sunlight.
• Solutions are stable for up to 5 days if refrigerated. Solution should be clear to slightly opaque. Discard if solution appears very opaque or contains precipitate.

⊗ **Incompatibilities**
Cisplatin, filgrastim, minocycline, vinorelbine.

Contraindications and cautions
• Contraindicated in patients hypersensitive to the drug or any of its components and in those with severe bone marrow, hepatic, or renal dysfunction.
• Use cautiously in patients with mild bone marrow suppression or renal or hepatic dysfunction.
Lifespan: In pregnant and breast-feeding women, drug isn't recommended. In children age 12 and younger, safety and effectiveness haven't been established.

Adverse reactions
CNS: dizziness, fatigue, fever, headache, weakness.
EENT: blurred vision, conjunctivitis, ***laryngeal edema.***
GI: abdominal pain, anorexia, stomatitis, *nausea, vomiting.*
GU: amenorrhea, decreased spermatogenesis, dysuria, hemorrhagic cystitis, urine retention.
Hematologic: anemia, ***leukopenia, neutropenia, thrombocytopenia.***
Respiratory: ***asthma.***
Skin: alopecia, dermatitis, rash, urticaria.
Other: ***anaphylaxis,*** hypersensitivity reactions, pain at injection site.

T

Interactions

Drug-drug. *Alkylating drugs, radiation therapy:* May intensify toxicity rather than enhance therapeutic response. Avoid using together.
Anticoagulants, aspirin: May increase bleeding risk. Avoid using together.
Neuromuscular blockers: May prolong muscular paralysis. Monitor patient closely.
Succinylcholine: May increase apnea. Monitor patient closely.

Effects on lab test results

- May increase uric acid level. May decrease pseudocholinesterase and hemoglobin levels and hematocrit.
- May decrease lymphocyte, platelet, WBC, RBC, and neutrophil counts.

Pharmacokinetics

Absorption: Absorption from bladder after instillation ranges from 10% to 100% of instilled dose; also variable after intracavitary use. Increased by certain pathologic conditions.
Distribution: Crosses blood-brain barrier.
Metabolism: Extensive, in liver.
Excretion: Drug and metabolites in urine.
Half-life: 2¼ hours.

Route	Onset	Peak	Duration
I.V., bladder instillation, intracavitary	Unknown	Unknown	Unknown

Action

Chemical effect: Cross-links strands of cellular DNA and interferes with RNA transcription, causing growth imbalance that leads to cell death.
Therapeutic effect: Kills certain cancer cells.

Available forms

Injection: 15-mg vials

NURSING PROCESS

Assessment

- Assess patient's condition before starting therapy and regularly thereafter to monitor drug's effectiveness.
- Adverse GU reactions are reversible in 6 to 8 months.
- Monitor CBC weekly for at least 3 weeks after giving the last dose.
- Monitor uric acid level.
- Be alert for adverse reactions and drug interactions.
- Assess patient's and family's knowledge of drug therapy.

Nursing diagnoses

- Ineffective health maintenance related to presence of neoplastic disease
- Ineffective protection related to drug-induced immunosuppression
- Deficient knowledge related to drug therapy

Planning and implementation

- Drug can be given by all parenteral routes, including direct injection into tumor.
- Dehydrate patient 8 to 10 hours before bladder instillation. Instill drug into bladder by catheter; ask patient to retain solution for 2 hours. If discomfort is too great with 60 ml, reduce volume to 30 ml. Reposition patient q 15 minutes for maximum area contact.
- When intracavitary use is needed, for neoplastic effusions, mix drug with 2% procaine hydrochloride or epinephrine hydrochloride 1:1,000.
- Report WBC count below 3,000/mm³ or platelet count below 150,000/mm³ and stop drug.
- To prevent hyperuricemia with resulting uric acid nephropathy, allopurinol may be used with adequate hydration.

Patient teaching

- Tell patient to watch for signs of infection (fever, sore throat, fatigue) and bleeding (easy bruising, nosebleeds, bleeding gums, melena). Tell patient to take temperature daily and to report even mild infections.
- Instruct patient to avoid OTC products containing aspirin.
- Advise woman of childbearing age to avoid becoming pregnant during therapy and to consult with prescriber if pregnancy is suspected.

Evaluation

- Patient responds well to drug.
- Patient doesn't develop serious complications from drug-induced immunosuppression.
- Patient and family state understanding of drug therapy.

thiothixene
(thigh-oh-THIKS-een)
Navane

thiothixene hydrochloride
Navane*

Pharmacologic class: thioxanthene
Therapeutic class: antipsychotic
Pregnancy risk category: C

Indications and dosages

▶ **Mild to moderate psychosis.** *Adults and children age 12 and older:* Initially, 2 mg P.O. t.i.d. Increase gradually to 15 mg daily.

▶ **Severe psychosis.** *Adults and children age 12 and older:* Initially, 5 mg P.O. b.i.d. Increase gradually to 20 to 30 mg daily. Maximum recommended dosage is 60 mg daily.

Contraindications and cautions

- Contraindicated in patients hypersensitive to the drug or any of its components and in those with circulatory collapse, coma, CNS depression, or blood dyscrasia.
- Use cautiously in patients with history of seizure disorder or during alcohol withdrawal. Also use cautiously in debilitated patients and in patients with CV disease (may cause sudden drop in blood pressure), glaucoma, prostatic hyperplasia, or exposure to extreme heat.

Lifespan: In pregnant women, use cautiously. In breast-feeding women, use cautiously; it's unknown if the drug appears in breast milk. In children younger than age 12, drug isn't recommended. In the elderly, use cautiously.

Adverse reactions

CNS: agitation, dizziness, EEG changes, extrapyramidal reactions (pseudoparkinsonism, dystonias, akathisia), insomnia, ***neuroleptic malignant syndrome,*** restlessness, sedation, tardive dyskinesia.
CV: ECG changes, *orthostatic hypotension,* tachycardia.
EENT: *blurred vision,* ocular changes, nasal congestion.
GI: constipation, dry mouth.
GU: inhibited ejaculation, menstrual irregularities, *urine retention.*
Hematologic: ***agranulocytosis,*** leukocytosis, transient leukopenia.
Hepatic: jaundice.
Metabolic: weight gain.
Skin: mild photosensitivity reactions.
Other: allergic reaction, gynecomastia.

Interactions

Drug-drug. *Anticholinergics:* May potentiate anticholinergic effects. Use together cautiously
Antihypertensives: May potentiate antihypertensive effects. Use together cautiously.
Other CNS depressants: May increase CNS depression. Avoid using together.
Drug-herb. *Nutmeg:* May cause a loss of symptom control or interfere with therapy for psychiatric illnesses. Discourage using together.
Drug-lifestyle. *Alcohol use:* May increase CNS depression. Discourage using together.
Sun exposure: May increase photosensitivity reactions. Advise patient to avoid prolonged or unprotected exposure to sunlight.

Effects on lab test results

- May increase liver enzyme level.
- May decrease granulocyte count. May increase or decrease WBC count.

Pharmacokinetics

Absorption: Rapid.
Distribution: Wide, throughout body. 91% to 99% protein-bound.
Metabolism: Minimal.
Excretion: Mainly as parent drug in feces.
Half-life: 20 to 40 hours.

Route	Onset	Peak	Duration
P.O.	Several wk	Unknown	Unknown

Action

Chemical effect: Unknown; probably blocks postsynaptic dopamine receptors in brain.
Therapeutic effect: Relieves signs and symptoms of psychosis.

Available forms

thiothixene
Capsules: 1 mg, 2 mg, 5 mg, 10 mg, 20 mg
thiothixene hydrochloride
Oral concentrate: 5 mg/ml*

NURSING PROCESS

Assessment
- Assess patient's psychosis before starting therapy and regularly thereafter to monitor drug's effectiveness.
- Watch for orthostatic hypotension; monitor blood pressure.
- Monitor patients, especially children, for tardive dyskinesia. It may occur after prolonged use or may not appear until months or years later. It may disappear spontaneously or persist for life, despite stopping the drug.
- Monitor therapy with weekly bilirubin tests during first month, periodic blood tests (CBC and liver function), and ophthalmologic tests for those in long-term therapy.

ALERT: Monitor patient for symptoms of neuroleptic malignant syndrome (extrapyramidal effects, hyperthermia, autonomic disturbance), which is rare but can be fatal. It isn't necessarily related to length of drug use or type of neuroleptic; however, more than 60% of patients are men.

- Be alert for adverse reactions and drug interactions.
- Assess patient's and family's knowledge of drug therapy.

Nursing diagnoses
- Disturbed thought processes related to presence of psychosis
- Risk for injury related to drug-induced adverse CNS reactions
- Deficient knowledge related to drug therapy

Planning and implementation
- Prevent contact dermatitis by keeping drug away from skin and clothes. Wear gloves when preparing liquid form.
- Dilute liquid concentrate with water or fruit juice just before giving.
- Slight yellowing of concentrate is common and doesn't affect potency. Discard markedly discolored solutions.
- Don't abruptly stop giving the drug unless warranted by a severe adverse reaction. Abruptly stopping long-term therapy may cause gastritis, nausea, vomiting, dizziness, tremors, feeling of warmth or cold, diaphoresis, tachycardia, headache, or insomnia.
- Report jaundice, symptoms of blood dyscrasia (fever, sore throat, infection, cellulitis, weakness), or persistent extrapyramidal reactions (longer than a few hours), especially in pregnant woman or in child, and withhold dose.
- Acute dystonic reactions may be treated with diphenhydramine.

ALERT: Don't confuse Navane with Nubain or Norvasc.

Patient teaching
- Warn patient to avoid activities that require alertness until the drug's CNS effects are known. Drowsiness and dizziness usually subside after a few weeks.
- Tell patient not to drink alcohol while taking drug.
- If urine retention or constipation occurs, instruct patient to notify prescriber.
- Tell patient to relieve dry mouth with sugarless gum or hard candy.
- To avoid photosensitivity reactions, tell patient to use sun block and wear protective clothing.
- Tell patient to watch for orthostatic hypotension; advise patient to change position slowly.

Evaluation
- Patient's behavior and communication exhibit improved thought processes.
- Patient doesn't experience injury from adverse CNS reactions.
- Patient and family state understanding of drug therapy.

tiagabine hydrochloride
(tigh-AG-ah-been high-droh-KLOR-ighd)
Gabitril

Pharmacologic class: GABA uptake inhibitor
Therapeutic class: anticonvulsant
Pregnancy risk category: C

Indications and dosages

▶ **Adjunctive therapy in partial seizures.** *Adults:* Initially, 4 mg P.O. once daily. Total daily dosage may be increased by 4 to 8 mg at weekly intervals until response is noted or up to 56 mg daily. Divide dose b.i.d. to q.i.d.
Children ages 12 to 18: Initially, 4 mg P.O. once daily. Total daily dosage may be increased by 4 mg at the beginning of week 2 and by 4 to 8 mg/week until response is noted or up to 32 mg daily. Divide dose b.i.d. to q.i.d.

Adjust-a-dose: Dosage may be decreased in patients with hepatic insufficiency.

Contraindications and cautions

• Contraindicated in patients hypersensitive to the drug or any of its components.
Lifespan: In pregnant women, use only if clearly needed. In breast-feeding women, use cautiously; it's unknown if drug appears in breast milk. In children younger than age 12, safety and effectiveness haven't been established.

Adverse reactions

CNS: abnormal gait, agitation, *asthenia,* ataxia, confusion, depression, difficulty with memory, *dizziness,* difficulty with concentration and attention, emotional lability, generalized weakness, hostility, insomnia, language problems, *nervousness,* pain, paresthesia, *somnolence,* speech disorder, tremor.
CV: vasodilation.
EENT: nystagmus, pharyngitis.
GI: abdominal pain, diarrhea, increased appetite, mouth ulcerations, *nausea,* vomiting.
Musculoskeletal: myasthenia.
Respiratory: increased cough.
Skin: pruritus, rash.

Interactions

Drug-drug. *Carbamazepine, phenobarbital, phenytoin:* May increase tiagabine clearance. Monitor patient for loss of therapeutic effect. May need to increase tiagabine dose.
CNS depressants: May increase CNS effects. Use cautiously.
Drug-lifestyle. *Alcohol use:* May increase CNS effects. Discourage using together.

Effects on lab test results

None reported.

Pharmacokinetics

Absorption: Rapid and more than 95%. Absolute bioavailability is 90%.
Distribution: About 96% bound to plasma proteins.
Metabolism: Likely to be metabolized by CYP3A isoenzymes.
Excretion: About 25% is in urine; 63% in feces. *Half-life:* 7 to 9 hours.

Route	Onset	Peak	Duration
P.O.	Rapid	45 min	7–9 hr

Action

Chemical effect: Unknown; may enhance the activity of GABA, the major inhibitory neurotransmitter in the CNS. It binds to recognition sites related to the GABA uptake carrier and may thus permit more GABA to be available for binding to receptors on postsynaptic cells.
Therapeutic effect: Prevents partial seizures.

Available forms

Tablets: 2 mg, 4 mg, 12 mg, 16 mg

NURSING PROCESS

Assessment

• Assess patient's seizure disorder before starting therapy and regularly thereafter to monitor drug's effectiveness.
• Assess patient's compliance with therapy at each follow-up visit.
ALERT: Monitor patient carefully for status epilepticus, because sudden death may occur in patient taking an anticonvulsant.
• Assess patient for adverse reactions and drug interactions.
• Assess patient's and family's knowledge of drug therapy.

Nursing diagnoses

• Risk for injury related to seizure disorder
• Impaired physical mobility related to drug-induced generalized weakness
• Deficient knowledge related to drug therapy

Planning and implementation

• In patient with impaired liver function, lower initial and maintenance doses or longer dosage intervals may be needed.
ALERT: Never abruptly stop giving the drug, because seizure frequency may increase. Gradually stop giving the drug unless safety concerns require a more rapid withdrawal.
ALERT: Drug may cause seizures and status epilepticus in patients without a history of epilepsy. Nonepileptic patients who develop seizures should stop drug and be evaluated for underlying seizure disorder. Prescribers are discouraged from using the drug for off-label indications.

T

• Patient who isn't receiving at least one enzyme-inducing antiepileptic when starting therapy may require lower dose or slower dose adjustments.
• Report breakthrough seizure activity to prescriber.
ALERT: Don't confuse tiagabine with tizanidine; both have 4-mg starting doses.

Patient teaching

• Advise patient to take drug only as prescribed.
• Advise patient to take drug with food.
• Warn patient that drug may cause dizziness, somnolence, and other symptoms and signs of CNS depression. Advise patient to avoid driving and other potentially hazardous activities that require mental alertness until the drug's CNS effects are known.
• Tell woman to notify prescriber if she becomes pregnant or plans to become pregnant during therapy.
• Tell woman to notify prescriber if planning to breast-feed because drug may appear in breast milk.

Evaluation

• Patient is free from seizure activity.
• Patient receives therapeutic dose and doesn't experience muscle weakness.
• Patient and family state understanding of drug therapy.

ticarcillin disodium

(tigh-kar-SIL-in digh-SOH-dee-um)
Ticar, Ticillin ◇

Pharmacologic class: alpha-carboxypenicillin, extended-spectrum penicillin
Therapeutic class: antibiotic
Pregnancy risk category: B

Indications and dosages

▶ **Severe systemic infections caused by susceptible strains of gram-positive and especially gram-negative organisms (including *Pseudomonas* and *Proteus*).** *Adults and children older than age 1 month:* 200 to 300 mg/kg I.V. daily in divided doses q 4 to 6 hours.
▶ **Uncomplicated UTI.** *Adults and children weighing 40 kg (88 lb) or more:* 1 g I.V. or I.M. q 6 hours. *Infants and children older than age 1 month and weighing less than 40 kg:* 50 to 100 mg/kg I.V. or I.M. daily in divided doses q 6 to 8 hours.
▶ **Complicated UTI.** *Adults:* 150 to 200 mg/kg I.V. daily in divided doses every 4 or 6 hours.
Adjust-a-dose: For patients with renal impairment, give the initial loading dose of 3 g I.V.; then base I.V. doses on creatinine clearance. If creatinine clearance is 30 to 60 ml/minute, dosage is 2 g I.V. q 4 hours; if clearance is 10 to 29 ml/minute, 2 g I.V. q 8 hours; if below 10 ml/minute, 2 g q 12 hours or 1 g I.M. q 6 hours; and if below 10 ml/minute with hepatic dysfunction, 2 g q 24 hours or 1 g I.M. q 12 hours.

I.V. administration

• Reconstitute drug in vials using D_5W, normal saline solution injection, sterile water for injection, or other compatible solution.
• Reconstitute 3-g piggyback vials with a minimum of 30 ml compatible solution; if diluting with 50 ml diluent, dilute to 60 mg/ml. If diluting with 100 ml diluent, dilute to 30 mg/ml.
• Add 4 ml of diluent for each gram of drug to obtain 200 mg/ml. May dilute further, if desired.
• For direct injection, give slowly to avoid vein irritation. For intermittent infusion, give over 30 minutes to 2 hours. Infusing with a concentration of 50 mg/ml may reduce vein irritation.
• Continuous infusion may cause vein irritation. Change site q 48 hours.

⊗ **Incompatibilities**
Aminoglycosides, amphotericin B, ciprofloxacin, doxapram, fluconazole, gentamicin, methylprednisolone sodium succinate, vancomycin.

Contraindications and cautions

• Contraindicated in patients hypersensitive to penicillins.
• Use cautiously in patients with other drug allergies, especially to cephalosporins (possible cross-sensitivity), and those with impaired kidney function, hemorrhagic conditions, hypokalemia, or sodium restrictions (contains 5.2 to 6.5 mEq sodium/g).
Lifespan: In pregnant women and breast-feeding women, use cautiously.

Adverse reactions

CNS: asterixis, lethargy, neuromuscular excitability, ***seizures,*** stupor.

CV: phlebitis, vein irritation.
GI: diarrhea, nausea, vomiting.
Hematologic: eosinophilia, granulocytopenia, hemolytic anemia, ***leukopenia, neutropenia, thrombocytopenia.***
Metabolic: hypokalemia.
Other: ***hypersensitivity reactions, anaphylaxis,*** overgrowth of nonsusceptible organisms, pain at injection site.

Interactions

Drug-drug. *Hormonal contraceptives:* May decrease effectiveness of hormonal contraceptives. Recommend an additional form of contraception during penicillin therapy.
Lithium: May alter renal elimination of lithium. Monitor lithium level closely.
Methotrexate: May decrease renal clearance of methotrexate. Monitor patient carefully.
Probenecid: May increase level of ticarcillin and other penicillins. Probenecid may be used for this purpose.

Effects on lab test results

- May increase ALT, AST, alkaline phosphatase, LDH, and sodium levels. May decrease potassium and hemoglobin levels and hematocrit.
- May increase eosinophil count. May decrease platelet, WBC, neutrophil, and granulocyte counts.

Pharmacokinetics

Absorption: Unknown after I.M. use.
Distribution: Distributed widely. Penetrates minimally into CSF with non-inflamed meninges. 45% to 65% protein-bound.
Metabolism: About 13% metabolized by hydrolysis to inactive compounds.
Excretion: Mainly in urine; also in bile. *Half-life:* About 1 hour.

Route	Onset	Peak	Duration
I.V.	Immediate	Immediate	Unknown
I.M.	Unknown	30–75 min	Unknown

Action

Chemical effect: Inhibits cell-wall synthesis during microorganism multiplication; bacteria resist penicillins by producing penicillinase enzymes that convert penicillins to inactive penicilloic acid. Drug resists these enzymes.
Therapeutic effect: Kills bacteria.

Available forms

Injection: 3 g

NURSING PROCESS

Assessment

- Assess patient's infection before starting therapy and regularly thereafter to monitor drug's effectiveness.
- Before giving drug, find out if patient is allergic to penicillin. Negative history of penicillin allergy is no guarantee against future allergic reaction.
- Obtain specimen for culture and sensitivity tests before giving the first dose. Start therapy pending test results.
- Monitor potassium level.
- Monitor CBC and platelet count.
- Monitor INR in patient taking warfarin therapy because drug may prolong PT.
- Be alert for adverse reactions and drug interactions.
- If adverse GI reaction occurs, monitor patient's hydration.
- Assess patient's and family's knowledge of drug therapy.

Nursing diagnoses

- Risk for infection related to presence of susceptible bacteria
- Risk for deficient fluid volume related to drug-induced adverse GI reactions
- Deficient knowledge related to drug therapy

Planning and implementation

- Lower the dose in a patient with renal impairment.
- Reconstitute drug for I.M. use in vials with sterile water for injection, normal saline solution injection, or lidocaine 1% (without epinephrine). Use 2 ml of diluent per gram of drug.
- Inject I.M. dose deep into large muscle. Don't exceed 2 g per injection.
- Give drug at least 1 hour before bacteriostatic antibiotics.
- Drug is typically used with another antibiotic, such as gentamicin.

ALERT: Institute seizure precautions. Patient with high drug level may develop seizures.

Patient teaching

- Instruct patient to report adverse reactions.

T

Evaluation

- Patient is free from infection.
- Patient maintains adequate hydration.
- Patient and family state understanding of drug therapy.

ticarcillin disodium and clavulanate potassium

(tigh-kar-SIL-in digh-SOH-dee-um and KLAV-yoo-lan-nayt poh-TAH-see-um)

Timentin

Pharmacologic class: beta-lactamase inhibitor, extended-spectrum penicillin
Therapeutic class: antibiotic
Pregnancy risk category: B

Indications and dosages

▶ **Systemic and urinary tract infections.** *Adults weighing 60 kg (132 lb) or more:* 3.1 g (3 g ticarcillin and 100 mg clavulanic acid) I.V. q 4 to 6 hours.

▶ **Moderate gynecologic infections.** *Adults weighing 60 kg or more:* 200 mg of ticarcillin/kg daily I.V. in divided doses q 6 hours.

▶ **Severe gynecologic infections.** *Adults weighing 60 kg or more:* 300 mg of ticarcillin/kg daily I.V. in divided doses q 4 hours.

▶ **Systemic, urinary tract, and gynecologic infections.** *Adults weighing less than 60 kg:* 200 to 300 mg/kg I.V. daily (based on ticarcillin content) in divided doses q 4 to 6 hours.
Children age 3 months and older and weighing less than 60 kg: For mild to moderate infections, 200 mg of ticarcillin/kg I.V. daily in divided doses q 6 hours. For severe infections, 300 mg/kg daily in divided doses q 4 hours.
Children age 3 months and older weighing 60 kg or more: For mild to moderate infections, 3.1 g (3 g ticarcillin and 100 mg clavulanic acid) I.V. q 6 hours; for severe infections, q 4 hours.

Adjust-a-dose: For patients with renal impairment, if creatinine clearance is greater than 60 ml/minute, give 3.1 g q 4 hours; if 30 to 60 ml/minute, give 2 g q 4 hours; if 10 to 30 ml/minute, give 2 g q 8 hours; if less than 10 ml/minute, give 2 g q 12 hours; and if less than 10 ml/minute and the patient has hepatic dysfunction, give 2 g q 24 hours. If the patient is on peritoneal dialysis, give 3.1 g q 12 hours and if the patient is on hemodialysis, give 2 g q 12 hours and 3.1 g after hemodialysis.

I.V. administration

- Reconstitute drug with 13 ml of sterile water for injection or normal saline solution injection.
- Further dilute to maximum of 10 to 100 mg/ml (based on ticarcillin component). In fluid-restricted patient, dilute to maximum of 48 mg/ml if using D_5W, 43 mg/ml if using normal saline solution injection, or 86 mg/ml if using sterile water for injection.
- Infuse over 30 minutes.

⊗ **Incompatibilities**

Aminoglycosides, amphotericin B, cisatracurium, other anti-infectives, sodium bicarbonate, vancomycin.

Contraindications and cautions

- Contraindicated in patients hypersensitive to penicillins.
- Use cautiously in patients with other drug allergies, especially to cephalosporins (possible cross-sensitivity), and those with impaired kidney function, hemorrhagic condition, hypokalemia, or sodium restrictions (contains 4.5 mEq sodium/g).

Lifespan: In pregnant women, use cautiously. In breast-feeding women, use cautiously; it's unknown if the drug appears in breast milk.

Adverse reactions

CNS: asterixis, giddiness, headache, lethargy, neuromuscular excitability, ***seizures,*** stupor.
CV: phlebitis, vein irritation.
GI: diarrhea, epigastric pain, flatulence, nausea, ***pseudomembranous colitis,*** stomatitis, taste and smell disturbances, vomiting.
Hematologic: anemia, eosinophilia, granulocytopenia, hemolytic anemia, ***leukopenia, neutropenia, thrombocytopenia.***
Metabolic: hypokalemia.
Other: ***anaphylaxis,*** *hypersensitivity reactions,* overgrowth of nonsusceptible organisms, pain at injection site.

Interactions

Drug-drug. *Hormonal contraceptives:* May decrease effectiveness of hormonal contraceptives. Recommend an additional form of contraception during ticarcillin therapy.

Lithium: May alter renal elimination of lithium. Monitor level closely.
Methotrexate: May decrease renal clearance of methotrexate. Monitor level.
Probenecid: May increase blood level of ticarcillin. Probenecid may be used for this purpose.

Effects on lab test results

- May increase ALT, AST, alkaline phosphatase, LDH, and sodium levels. May decrease potassium and hemoglobin levels and hematocrit.
- May increase eosinophil count. May decrease platelet, WBC, neutrophil, and granulocyte counts.

Pharmacokinetics

Absorption: Given I.V.
Distribution: Ticarcillin disodium distributed widely. Penetrates minimally into CSF with noninflamed meninges. Clavulanic acid penetrates pleural fluid, lungs, and peritoneal fluid.
Metabolism: About 13% of ticarcillin dose metabolized by hydrolysis to inactive compounds; clavulanic acid is thought to undergo extensive metabolism but its fate is unknown.
Excretion: Ticarcillin mainly in urine; also in bile. Clavulanate metabolites in urine. *Half-life:* About 1 hour.

Route	Onset	Peak	Duration
I.V.	Immediate	Immediate	Unknown

Action

Chemical effect: Inhibits cell wall synthesis during microorganism replication; clavulanic acid increases ticarcillin's effectiveness by inactivating beta lactamases, which destroy ticarcillin.
Therapeutic effect: Kills susceptible bacteria.

Available forms

Injection: 3 g ticarcillin and 100 mg clavulanic acid

NURSING PROCESS

Assessment

- Assess patient's infection before starting therapy and regularly thereafter to monitor drug's effectiveness.
- Before giving drug, find out if patient is allergic to penicillin. Negative history of penicillin allergy is no guarantee against future allergic reaction.
- Obtain specimen for culture and sensitivity tests before giving the first dose. Start therapy pending test results.
- Monitor CBC and platelet count.
- Be alert for adverse reactions and drug interactions.
- If adverse GI reactions occur, monitor patient's hydration.
- Assess patient's and family's knowledge of drug therapy.

Nursing diagnoses

- Risk for infection related to presence of susceptible bacteria
- Risk for deficient fluid volume related to drug-induced adverse GI reactions
- Deficient knowledge related to drug therapy

Planning and implementation

- Lower the dose in patient with renal impairment.
- Give drug at least 1 hour before bacteriostatic antibiotics.

Patient teaching

- Instruct patient to report adverse reactions immediately.

Evaluation

- Patient is free from infection.
- Patient maintains adequate hydration.
- Patient and family state understanding of drug therapy.

ticlopidine hydrochloride

(tigh-KLOH-peh-deen high-droh-KLOR-ighd)
Ticlid

Pharmacologic class: platelet aggregation inhibitor
Therapeutic class: antithrombotic
Pregnancy risk category: B

Indications and dosages

▶ **To reduce risk of thrombotic stroke in patients with history of stroke or stroke precursors.** *Adults:* 250 mg P.O. b.i.d. with meals.
▶ **Prevention of coronary artery stent thrombosis.** *Adults:* 250 mg P.O. b.i.d. taken with

food together with antiplatelet doses of aspirin for up to 30 days.

Contraindications and cautions

• Contraindicated in patients hypersensitive to the drug or any of its components and in those with hematopoietic disorders (such as neutropenia, thrombocytopenia, or disorders of hemostasis), active pathologic bleeding (such as peptic ulceration or active intracranial bleeding), or severe hepatic impairment.
• Drug is reserved for patients intolerant to aspirin.
Lifespan: In pregnant women, use cautiously. In breast-feeding women, drug isn't recommended. In children, safety and effectiveness haven't been established.

Adverse reactions

CNS: dizziness, ***intracerebral bleeding.***
CV: vasculitis.
EENT: conjunctival hemorrhage, epistaxis.
GI: *abdominal pain,* anorexia, ***bleeding,*** *diarrhea,* dyspepsia, flatulence, nausea, vomiting.
GU: dark-colored urine, hematuria, nephrotic syndrome.
Hematologic: ***agranulocytosis, immune thrombocytopenia, neutropenia, pancytopenia.***
Hepatic: cholestatic jaundice, ***hepatitis.***
Metabolic: hyponatremia.
Musculoskeletal: arthropathy, myositis.
Respiratory: ***allergic pneumonitis.***
Skin: ecchymoses, pruritus, purpura, ***thrombocytopenic purpura,*** *rash,* urticaria.
Other: *hypersensitivity reactions,* ***postoperative bleeding,*** serum sickness, systemic lupus erythematosus.

Interactions

Drug-drug. *Antacids:* May decrease ticlopidine level. Separate administration times by at least 2 hours.
Aspirin: May potentiate aspirin effects on platelets. Use together cautiously and for no longer than 30 days.
Cimetidine: May decrease clearance of ticlopidine and increase risk of toxicity. Avoid using together.
Digoxin: May slightly decrease digoxin level. Monitor level.
Heparin, oral anticoagulants: Safety of combined use hasn't been established. Stop these drugs before starting ticlopidine.
Theophylline: May decrease theophylline clearance and risk of toxicity. Monitor patient closely, and adjust theophylline dosage.
Drug-herb. *Red clover:* May increase risk of bleeding. Caution against using together.

Effects on lab test results

• May increase ALT, AST, and alkaline phosphatase levels. May decrease sodium level.
• May decrease neutrophil, WBC, RBC, platelet, and granulocyte counts.

Pharmacokinetics

Absorption: Rapid and extensive; enhanced by food.
Distribution: 98% protein- and lipoprotein-bound.
Metabolism: Extensive, in liver. More than 20 metabolites have been identified; unknown if parent drug or active metabolites are responsible for pharmacologic activity.
Excretion: 60% in urine; 23% in feces. *Half-life:* 1½ hours after single dose; 4 to 5 days after multiple doses.

Route	Onset	Peak	Duration
P.O.	Unknown	2 hr	Unknown

Action

Chemical effect: Unknown; may block adenosine diphosphate-induced platelet-fibrinogen and platelet-platelet binding.
Therapeutic effect: Prevents blood clots from forming.

Available forms

Tablets: 250 mg

NURSING PROCESS

Assessment

• Assess patient's condition before starting therapy and regularly thereafter to monitor drug's effectiveness.
• Obtain baseline liver function tests before starting therapy. Monitor test results closely, especially during first 4 months of therapy, and repeat when liver dysfunction is suspected.
• Determine baseline CBC and WBC differentials, repeat at second week of therapy and q 2 weeks until end of third month. If patient shows signs of declining neutrophil count, or if count falls 30% below baseline, test more fre-

quently. After first 3 months, obtain CBC and WBC differential counts only in patient showing signs of infection.
- Be alert for adverse reactions and drug interactions.
- Assess patient's and family's knowledge of drug therapy.

Nursing diagnoses
- Impaired cerebral tissue perfusion related to stroke potential or history
- Ineffective protection related to drug-induced adverse hematologic reactions
- Deficient knowledge related to drug therapy

Planning and implementation
- Thrombocytopenia may occur rarely. Report platelet count of 80,000/mm^3 or less, and stop giving the drug. Give 20 mg of methylprednisolone I.V. to normalize bleeding time within 2 hours. Platelet transfusions also may be used.
- When used preoperatively, drug may decrease risk of graft occlusion in patient receiving coronary artery bypass grafts and reduce severity of drop in platelet count in patient receiving extracorporeal hemoperfusion during open heart surgery.

Patient teaching
- Tell patient to take drug with meals; this substantially increases bioavailability and improves GI tolerance.
- Tell patient being treated for stroke to avoid aspirin-containing products and to check with prescriber before taking OTC drugs.
- Explain that drug prolongs bleeding time, but that patient should report unusual or prolonged bleeding. Advise him to tell dentist and other health care providers that he is taking this drug.
- Stress importance of regular blood tests.
- Because neutropenia can increase risk of infection, tell patient to promptly report such signs as fever, chills, and sore throat.
- If drug is substituted for a fibrinolytic or anticoagulant, tell patient to stop those drugs before starting ticlopidine.
- Advise patient to stop drug 10 to 14 days before elective surgery.
- Tell patient to report yellow skin or sclera, severe or persistent diarrhea, rashes, subcutaneous bleeding, light-colored stools, and dark urine.

Evaluation
- Patient maintains adequate cerebral perfusion.
- Patient doesn't develop serious complications.
- Patient and family state understanding of drug therapy.

tigecycline
(tigh-geh-SIGH-kleen)
Tygacil

Pharmacologic class: glycylcycline antibacterial
Therapeutic class: antibiotic
Pregnancy risk category: D

Indications and dosages

▶ **Complicated skin and skin structure infections; complicated intra-abdominal infections.** *Adults:* Initially 100 mg I.V.; then 50 mg q 12 hours for 5 to 14 days. Infuse drug over 30 to 60 minutes.

Adjust-a-dose: For patients with severe hepatic impairment, give initial dose of 100 mg I.V. and then 25 mg I.V. q 12 hours.

I.V. administration
- Reconstitute powder with 5.3 ml of normal saline solution or D_5W to yield 10 mg/ml.
- Gently swirl the vial until the powder dissolves.
- Immediately withdraw the dose from the vial and add it to 100 ml of normal saline solution or D_5W. The maximum concentration is 1 mg/ml.
- Inspect the I.V. solution for particulates and discoloration (green or black) before giving it. Reconstituted solution should be yellow to orange.
- Immediately dilute reconstituted drug for I.V. infusion.
- Use a dedicated I.V. line or a Y-site, and flush the line with normal saline or D_5W before and after infusion.
- Infuse the drug over 30 to 60 minutes.
- Store unopened vials at room temperature in the original package. Store diluted solution at room temperature for up to 6 hours, or refrigerate for up to 24 hours.

⊗ Incompatibilities
Amphotericin B, chlorpromazine, methylprednisolone, voriconazole.

T

Contraindications and cautions

• Contraindicated in patients hypersensitive to tigecycline.

• Use cautiously in patients with severe hepatic impairment and in those hypersensitive to tetracycline antibiotics. Also use cautiously as monotherapy in patients with complicated intra-abdominal infections caused by intestinal perforation.

Lifespan: In pregnant women, use drug only if benefits to patient outweigh risks to fetus. In breast-feeding women, use cautiously; it isn't known if drug appears in breast milk. In children, safety and effectiveness haven't been established. Older adults may be more sensitive to drug's adverse effects.

Adverse reactions

CNS: asthenia, dizziness, fever, headache, insomnia, pain, ***pseudotumor cerebri.***
CV: hypertension, hypotension, peripheral edema.
GI: abdominal pain, constipation, *diarrhea,* dyspepsia, *nausea, vomiting.*
Hematologic: anemia, leukocytosis, ***thrombocytopenia.***
Metabolic: hyperglycemia, hypokalemia, hypoproteinemia.
Musculoskeletal: back pain.
Respiratory: cough, dyspnea.
Skin: local reaction, phlebitis, pruritus, rash, sweating.
Other: abscess, abnormal healing, allergic reaction, infection, ***sepsis.***

Interactions

Drug-drug. *Hormonal contraceptives:* May decrease contraceptive effectiveness. Advise patient to use nonhormonal form of contraception during treatment.
Warfarin: May increase risk of bleeding. Monitor INR.

Effects on lab test results

• May increase alkaline phosphatase, amylase, bilirubin, BUN, creatinine, LDH, AST, and ALT levels. May decrease potassium, protein, calcium, sodium, and hemoglobin levels and hematocrit. May increase or decrease blood glucose level.

• May increase INR, PT, PTT, and WBC count. May decrease platelet count.

Pharmacokinetics

Absorption: Given I.V.
Distribution: Extensive in tissues. About 70% to 90% bound to serum proteins.
Metabolism: Not extensively metabolized in the liver.
Excretion: Mainly through bile and feces as unchanged drug and metabolites; lesser amount via kidneys. *Half life:* 27 to 42 hours.

Route	Onset	Peak	Duration
I.V.	Unknown	Unknown	Unknown

Action

Chemical effect: Inhibits protein translation in bacteria by binding to the 30S ribosomal unit.
Therapeutic effect: Kills susceptible bacteria.

Available forms

Lyophilized powder: 50-mg vials

NURSING PROCESS

Assessment

• Assess patient for tetracycline allergy before giving drug.

• Obtain specimen for culture and sensitivity tests before giving first dose. Therapy may begin pending test results.

• If patient develops diarrhea, monitor him closely for pseudomembranous colitis.

• If patient has abdominal infection caused by intestinal perforation, monitor him for sepsis.

• Evaluate patient's and family's knowledge of drug therapy.

Nursing diagnoses

• Ineffective protection related to presence of susceptible bacteria

• Risk for deficient fluid volume related to drug-induced adverse GI reactions

• Deficient knowledge related to drug therapy

Planning and implementation

• Be alert for potentially dangerous toxicities of tetracyclines, such as photosensitivity, pseudotumor cerebri, pancreatitis and anti-anabolic action (increased BUN level, azotemia, acidosis, and hypophosphatemia).

• Excessive doses may increase the risk of nausea and vomiting. Drug isn't removed by hemodialysis.

Patient teaching

- Tell patient that drug is used to treat only bacterial infections, not viral infections.
- Explain that it's common to feel better after a few days of therapy. Stress that patient will need to finish the full course of treatment even if he feels better before it's finished.
- Tell patient to report burning or pain at the I.V. site.
- Tell women of childbearing age to avoid becoming pregnant during treatment. Urge those who use hormonal contraception to also use barrier contraception during treatment.
- Advise patient to notify a health care provider if pregnancy is suspected or confirmed.

Evaluation

- Patient is free from infection.
- Patient maintains adequate hydration.
- Patient and family state understanding of drug therapy.

tinidazole

(ty-NIH-duh-zohl)
Tindamax

Pharmacologic class: antiprotozoal
Therapeutic class: anti-infective
Pregnancy risk category: C (X in first trimester)

Indications and dosages

▶ **Trichomoniasis caused by *Trichomonas vaginalis*.** *Adults:* 2 g P.O. as a single dose taken with food. Sexual partners should be treated at the same time with the same dose.

▶ **Giardiasis caused by *Giardia lamblia (G. duodenalis)*.** *Adults:* 2 g P.O. as a single dose taken with food.
Children older than age 3: Give 50 mg/kg (up to 2 g) as a single dose taken with food.

▶ **Intestinal amebiasis caused by *Entamoeba histolytica*.** *Adults:* 2 g P.O. daily for 3 days, taken with food.
Children older than age 3: Give 50 mg/kg (up to 2 g) P.O. daily for 3 days, taken with food.

▶ **Amebic liver abscess (amebiasis).** *Adults:* 2 g P.O. daily for 3 to 5 days, taken with food.
Children older than age 3: Give 50 mg/kg (up to 2 g) P.O. daily for 3 to 5 days, taken with food.

Adjust-a-dose: For patients on hemodialysis, give an additional dose equal to one-half the recommended dose after the hemodialysis session.

Contraindications and cautions

- Contraindicated in patients hypersensitive to the drug, its components, or other nitroimidazole derivatives.
- Use cautiously in patients with CNS disorders and in those with blood dyscrasias or hepatic dysfunction.

Lifespan: In pregnant women, drug is contraindicated during the first trimester; during the second and third trimesters, use if benefits to the patient outweigh risks to the fetus. Breast-feeding women should stop breast-feeding or use another drug; they should wait 3 days after the last dose before resuming breast-feeding. In children age 3 and younger, safety and effectiveness haven't been established. In elderly patient, dose selection should reflect the possibility of decreased liver or kidney function and other medical conditions or drug therapies.

Adverse reactions

CNS: dizziness, fatigue, headache, malaise, peripheral neuropathy, ***seizures,*** weakness.
GI: anorexia, constipation, cramps, dyspepsia, metallic taste, nausea, vomiting.
Other: hypersensitivity reactions.

Interactions

Drug-drug. *Cholestyramine:* May decrease oral bioavailability of tinidazole. Separate doses to minimize this effect.
Cyclosporine, tacrolimus: May increase cyclosporine and tacrolimus levels. Monitor patient closely for toxicity, including headache, nausea, vomiting, nephrotoxicity, and electrolyte abnormalities.
Cytochrome P-450 inducers, such as fosphenytoin, phenobarbital, phenytoin, and rifampin: May increase tinidazole elimination. Monitor patient.
Cytochrome P-450 inhibitors, such as cimetidine and ketoconazole: May prolong tinidazole half-life and decrease clearance. Monitor patient.
Disulfiram: May increase abdominal cramping, nausea, vomiting, headaches, and flushing. If

T

patient took disulfiram during previous 2 weeks, don't give tinidazole.
Fluorouracil: May decrease fluorouracil clearance, increasing adverse effects without added benefit. Monitor patient for rash, nausea, vomiting, stomatitis, and leukopenia.
Fosphenytoin, phenytoin: May prolong phenytoin half-life and decrease clearance of I.V. drug. Monitor patient for toxicity.
Lithium: May increase lithium level. Monitor patient and serum lithium and creatinine levels.
Oxytetracycline: May antagonize tinidazole. Assess patient for lack of effect.
Warfarin and other oral anticoagulants: May increase anticoagulant effect. Anticoagulant dosage may need adjustment and for up to 8 days after tinidazole therapy.
Drug-herb. *St. John's wort:* May increase or decrease tinidazole level. Discourage use together.
Drug-lifestyle. *Alcohol and alcohol-containing products:* May increase abdominal cramping, nausea, vomiting, headaches, and flushing. Discourage use together and for 3 days after stopping tinidazole.

Effects on lab test results

- May increase AST, ALT, glucose, LDH, and triglyceride levels.
- May decrease WBC count.

Pharmacokinetics

Absorption: Rapid, complete, and unaffected by food.
Distribution: Into body tissues, fluids, and breast milk. Crosses the blood-brain and placental barriers. About 12% bound to plasma proteins.
Metabolism: Mainly by CYP3A4 enzymes and partially by oxidation, hydroxylation, and conjugation in the liver.
Excretion: By liver and kidneys, with 20% to 25% in urine and 12% in feces. *Half-life:* About 12 to 14 hours.

Route	Onset	Peak	Duration
P.O.	Unknown	1½ hr	Unknown

Action

Chemical effect: Against *Trichomonas,* action may result from reduction of the compound's nitro group into a free nitro radical. Mechanism of action against *Giardia* and *Entamoeba* is unknown.
Therapeutic effect: Hinders growth of susceptible organisms.

Available forms

Tablets: 250 mg, 500 mg

NURSING PROCESS

Assessment

- Assess patient's infection before starting therapy and regularly thereafter to monitor drug's effectiveness.
- Children should be monitored closely if therapy exceeds 3 days.
- Be alert for adverse reactions and drug interactions.

ALERT: Stop giving the drug immediately if abnormal neurologic signs or symptoms occur, such as seizures or numbness of the limbs.

- Assess patient's and family's knowledge of drug therapy.

Nursing diagnoses

- Risk for injury related to drug-induced adverse neurologic reactions
- Risk for deficient fluid volume related to drug-induced adverse GI reactions
- Deficient knowledge related to drug therapy

Planning and implementation

- For patients unable to swallow tablets, a suspension may be made by grinding 2 g of tinidazole into a powder and mixing with 10 ml of cherry syrup. Transfer to a graduated amber container with several rinses of cherry syrup to a final volume of 30 ml.
- Drug is stable for 7 days at room temperature. Shake well.
- Give drug with food to minimize adverse GI effects.
- If candidiasis develops during therapy, give an antifungal.

Patient teaching

- Tell patient to take drug with food.
- Warn patient not to drink alcohol or use alcohol-containing products while taking tinidazole and for 3 days afterward.
- Advise patient to immediately report pregnancy.

• If patient is being treated for a sexually transmitted disease, explain that sexual partners should be treated at the same time.

Evaluation

• Patient has no adverse neurological effects.
• Patient maintains adequate hydration during drug therapy.
• Patient and family state understanding of drug therapy.

tinzaparin sodium

(TIN-zuh-pear-in SOE-dee-um)
Innohep

Pharmacologic class: low–molecular-weight heparin (LMWH)
Therapeutic class: anticoagulant
Pregnancy risk category: B

Indications and dosages

▶ **Adjunct treatment (with warfarin sodium) of symptomatic deep vein thrombosis with or without pulmonary embolism.** *Adults:* 175 antifactor Xa international units per kg of body weight subcutaneously once daily for at least 6 days and until the patient is adequately anticoagulated with warfarin (INR at least 2) for 2 consecutive days. Begin warfarin when appropriate, usually within 1 to 3 days after tinzaparin starts. The volume to be given may be calculated as follows:

Patient weight in kg × 0.00875 ml/kg = volume to be given (in ml)

▶ **Deep vein thrombosis prophylaxis‡.** *Adults:* 3,500 antifactor Xa international units or 50 antifactor Xa international units/kg daily for patients at moderate to high risk, respectively. Start 1 to 2 hours before surgery, and continue for 5 to 10 days. For prophylaxis in orthopedic procedures: 75 antifactor Xa international units/kg daily starting 12 to 24 hours postoperatively. Alternative: 4,500 antifactor Xa international units 12 hours before orthopedic surgery followed by 4,500 antifactor Xa international units daily.

Contraindications and cautions

• Contraindicated in patients hypersensitive to the drug or to heparin, sulfites, benzyl alcohol, or pork products. Also contraindicated in patients with active major bleeding and patients with current or previous heparin-induced thrombocytopenia.
• Use cautiously in patients with increased risk of hemorrhage, such as those with bacterial endocarditis, uncontrolled hypertension, diabetic retinopathy, or congenital or acquired bleeding disorders (such as hepatic failure, amyloidosis, GI ulceration, or hemorrhagic stroke). Also use cautiously in patients being treated with platelet inhibitors, in patients who have recently undergone brain, spinal, or ophthalmologic surgery, and in patients with renal insufficiency.
• Use cautiously in patients with neuraxial (spinal or epidural) anesthesia or spinal puncture because these patients have an increased risk of neurologic injury and epidural or spinal hematoma.
• Use cautiously in patients with severe renal impairment and creatinine clearance less than 30 ml/minute.
Lifespan: In pregnant women, use cautiously and only when clearly needed. Vaginal bleeding has been reported in pregnant women receiving tinzaparin; use only if benefits outweigh risks. In breast-feeding women, use cautiously; it's unknown if the drug appears in breast milk. In children, safety and effectiveness haven't been established. In the elderly, use cautiously because they may have reduced elimination of drug.

Adverse reactions

CNS: ***cerebral or intracranial bleeding,*** confusion, dizziness, fever, headache, insomnia, pain.
CV: angina pectoris, ***arrhythmias,*** chest pain, dependent edema, hypertension, hypotension, ***MI, thromboembolism,*** tachycardia.
EENT: epistaxis, ocular hemorrhage.
GI: anorectal bleeding, constipation, dyspepsia, flatulence, hematemesis, hemarthrosis, ***GI hemorrhage,*** melena, nausea, ***retroperitoneal or intra-abdominal bleeding,*** vomiting.
GU: dysuria, hematuria, urine retention, UTI, ***vaginal hemorrhage.***
Hematologic: ***agranulocytosis,*** anemia, granulocytopenia, ***hemorrhage,*** pancytopenia, ***thrombocytopenia.***
Musculoskeletal: back pain.
Respiratory: dyspnea, pneumonia, ***pulmonary embolism,*** respiratory disorder.

T

Skin: bullous eruption, cellulitis, *injection site hematoma,* pruritus, purpura, rash, skin necrosis, wound hematoma.
Other: allergic reaction, congenital anomaly, ***fetal death, fetal distress, hypersensitivity reactions,*** impaired healing, infection, spinal or ***epidural hematoma.***

Interactions

Drug-drug. *Oral anticoagulants, platelet inhibitors (such as dextran, dipyridamole, NSAIDs, salicylates, sulfinpyrazone), thrombolytics:* May increase the risk of bleeding. Use together cautiously, and monitor patient.

Effects on lab test results

- May increase AST and ALT levels. May decrease hemoglobin level and hematocrit.
- May increase granular leukocyte count. May decrease granulocyte, platelet, RBC, and WBC counts.

Pharmacokinetics

Absorption: Plasma level peaks in 4 to 5 hours.
Distribution: The volume of distribution is similar in magnitude to that of blood volume, which suggests that distribution is limited to the central compartment.
Metabolism: Partially metabolized by desulfation and depolymerization, similar to that of other LMWHs.
Excretion: Mainly renal. *Half-life:* 3 to 4 hours.

Route	Onset	Peak	Duration
SubQ	2–3 hr	4–5 hr	Unknown

Action

Chemical effect: Inhibits reactions that lead to blood clotting, including the formation of fibrin clots. The drug also acts as a potent co-inhibitor of several activated coagulation factors, especially factors Xa and IIa (thrombin). It also induces release of tissue factor pathway inhibitor, which may contribute to the antithrombotic effect.
Therapeutic effect: Reduces the ability of blood to clot.

Available forms

Injection: 20,000 anti-Xa international units per ml in 2-ml vials

NURSING PROCESS

Assessment

- Assess patient's condition before starting therapy and regularly thereafter to monitor drug's effectiveness.
- Monitor platelet count during therapy. If platelet count falls below 100,000/mm^3, stop drug.
- Periodically monitor CBC and stool tests for occult blood during therapy.
- Drug may affect PT and INR levels. Patients who also receive warfarin should have blood drawn for PT and INR tests just before the next scheduled dose of this drug.
- Drug contains sodium metabisulfite, which may cause allergic reactions in susceptible people.
- Weigh patient before starting therapy to calculate accurate dose.
- Assess patient's and family's knowledge of drug therapy.

Nursing diagnoses

- Ineffective protection related to increased risk of bleeding
- Ineffective tissue perfusion, peripheral, related to deep vein thrombosis
- Deficient knowledge related to tinzaparin sodium therapy

Planning and implementation

- Dose is based on actual body weight.
- If patient develops serious bleeding or receives a large overdose, replace volume and hemostatic blood elements (such as RBCs, fresh frozen plasma, and platelets), as needed. If this treatment is ineffective, consider giving protamine sulfate.

ALERT: Don't give I.M. or I.V., and don't mix with other injections or infusions.
ALERT: Drug can't be interchanged (unit for unit) with heparin or other LMWHs.

- While giving the drug, have the patient lie or sit down. Give drug by deep subcutaneous injection into the abdominal wall. Insert the whole length of the needle into a skin fold held between your thumb and forefinger. Hold the skin fold throughout the injection. To minimize bruising, don't rub the injection site after administration.

• Rotate injection sites between the right and left anterolateral and posterolateral abdominal wall.
• Use an appropriate calibrated syringe to ensure withdrawal of the correct volume of drug from vial.
ALERT: When neuraxial anesthesia (epidural or spinal anesthesia) or spinal puncture is used, the patient is at risk for spinal hematoma, which can result in long-term or permanent paralysis. Watch for evidence of neurologic impairment. Consider the risks and benefits of neuraxial intervention in patients being anticoagulated with LMWHs or heparinoids.
• Store drug at room temperature.

Patient teaching

• Inform patient that co-administration of warfarin will begin within 1 to 3 days of tinzaparin administration. Explain the importance of warfarin therapy.
• Stress the importance of laboratory monitoring to ensure effectiveness and safety of therapy.
• Instruct patient to take safety measures to prevent cuts and bruises (such as using a soft toothbrush and an electric razor).
• Review the warning signs of bleeding, and instruct the patient to report evidence of bleeding immediately.
• Gasping syndrome may occur in premature infants who receive large amounts of benzyl alcohol. Warn patient about the risks of becoming pregnant during therapy.

Evaluation

• Patient states appropriate bleeding precautions to take.
• Patient's peripheral neurovascular status returns to baseline.
• Patient and family state understanding of tinzaparin sodium therapy.

tiotropium bromide
(tee-oh-TROPE-ee-um BROH-mighd)
Spiriva

Pharmacologic class: long-acting anticholinergic (antimuscarinic)
Therapeutic class: bronchodilator
Pregnancy risk category: C

Indications and dosages

▶ **Maintenance therapy for bronchospasm in COPD, including chronic bronchitis and emphysema.** *Adults:* One capsule (18 mcg) inhaled orally once daily using the HandiHaler inhalation device.

Contraindications and cautions

• Contraindicated in patients hypersensitive to atropine, its derivatives, ipratropium, or any component of the product.
• Use cautiously in patients with creatinine clearance of 50 ml/minute or less and patients with angle-closure glaucoma, prostatic hyperplasia, or bladder neck obstruction.
Lifespan: In pregnant women, use cautiously. In breast-feeding women, use cautiously; it's unknown if the drug appears in breast milk. In children, safety and effectiveness haven't been established.

Adverse reactions

CNS: depression, paresthesia.
CV: ***angina pectoris,*** chest pain, edema.
EENT: cataract, dysphonia, epistaxis, glaucoma, laryngitis, pharyngitis, rhinitis, *sinusitis.*
GI: abdominal pain, constipation, *dry mouth,* dyspepsia, gastroesophageal reflux, stomatitis, vomiting.
GU: UTI.
Metabolic: hypercholesterolemia, hyperglycemia.
Musculoskeletal: arthritis, leg pain, myalgia, skeletal pain.
Respiratory: cough, ***paradoxical bronchospasm,*** upper respiratory tract infection.
Skin: rash.
Other: ***accidental injury, angioedema,*** allergic reaction, candidiasis, flulike syndrome, herpes zoster, infections.

Interactions

Drug-drug. *Anticholinergics:* May increase the risk of adverse reactions. Avoid using together.

Effects on lab test results

• May increase cholesterol and glucose levels.

Pharmacokinetics

Absorption: Poorly absorbed from GI tract; absolute bioavailability is 19.5% after inhaling dry

powder. Plasma level peaks 3 hours after inhalation.
Distribution: Extensively bound to tissues and 72% bound to plasma proteins.
Metabolism: Small amounts by CYP2D6 and CYP3A4 pathways.
Excretion: About 14% in urine, the rest in feces. *Half-life:* 5 to 6 days.

Route	Onset	Peak	Duration
Inhalation	30 min	3 hr	> 24 hr

Action

Chemical effect: Competitive, reversible inhibition of muscarinic receptors leads to bronchodilation.
Therapeutic effect: Improves breathing.

Available forms

Capsules for inhalation: 18 mcg

NURSING PROCESS

Assessment

- Obtain baseline assessment of patient's respiratory status before starting therapy, and assess frequently thereafter to monitor the drug's effectiveness.
- Be alert for adverse reactions; eye pain, blurred vision, visual halos, colored images, or red eyes may be signs of acute narrow-angle glaucoma.

ALERT: Watch for evidence of hypersensitivity (especially angioedema) and paradoxical bronchospasm.

- Assess patient's and family's knowledge of drug therapy.

Nursing diagnoses

- Impaired gas exchange related to underlying respiratory condition
- Risk for activity intolerance related to underlying pulmonary condition
- Deficient knowledge related to drug therapy

Planning and implementation

- Drug is for maintenance treatment of COPD, not for acute bronchospasm.
- Capsules aren't for oral ingestion. Give them only by oral inhalation and only with the HandiHaler device.
- Capsules may be stored at room temperature prior to use. Remove capsule for oral inhalation from blister card just before use. Capsules should not be stored in the HandiHaler device.
- To give the drug, place the capsule in the center chamber of the HandiHaler device. Close the mouthpiece until it clicks, but leave the dust cap open. Press the piercing button one time. Instruct the patient to breathe out completely, raise HandiHaler device to his mouth, and close his lips tightly around the mouthpiece. The patient should keep his head upright and inhale slowly and deeply at a rate sufficient to hear the capsule vibrate. After the patient has inhaled until his lungs are full, have him hold his breath for as long as is comfortable while simultaneously taking the HandiHaler device out of his mouth; he then should resume normal breathing. The patient shouldn't ever breathe into the mouthpiece. The patient should inhale again to ensure a full dose of the drug.
- After taking the daily dose, dispose of the capsule and close the HandiHaler mouthpiece and dust cap for storage.
- Signs of overdose include dry mouth, bilateral conjunctivitis, altered mental state, tremors, abdominal pain, and severe constipation. Alert prescriber if overdose is suspected, and provide supportive care.

Patient teaching

- Inform patient that drug is for maintenance treatment of COPD and not for immediate relief of breathing problems.
- Explain that capsules are for inhalation and shouldn't be swallowed.
- Provide full instructions for the HandiHaler device.
- Tell patient not to get the powder in his eyes.
- Review the signs and symptoms of hypersensitivity (especially angioedema) and paradoxical bronchospasm. Tell patient to stop the drug and contact the prescriber if they arise.
- Advise patient to report eye pain, blurred vision, visual halos, colored images, or red eyes immediately.
- Tell patient to keep capsules in sealed blisters and to remove each capsule just before use. Caution against storing capsules in the HandiHaler device.
- Instruct patient to store capsules at 77° F (25° C) and not to expose them to extreme temperatures or moisture.

Evaluation

- Patient's respiratory signs and symptoms improve.
- Patient's activity intolerance improves.
- Patient and family state understanding of drug therapy.

tipranavir

(tih-PRAN-uh-veer)

Aptivus

Pharmacologic class: non-peptidic protease inhibitor
Therapeutic class: antiretroviral
Pregnancy risk category: C

Indications and dosages

▶ **HIV-1 in patients with viral replication who are highly treatment-experienced or have HIV-1 strains resistant to multiple protease inhibitors.** *Adults:* 500 mg P.O. twice daily with 200 mg of ritonavir. Give with food.

Contraindications and cautions

- Contraindicated in patients hypersensitive to any ingredients of the product, patients with moderate (Child-Pugh class B) and severe (Child-Pugh class C) hepatic insufficiency, and patients taking drugs that depend on CYP3A for clearance, such as amiodarone, astemizole, bepridil, cisapride, dihydroergotamine, ergonovine, ergotamine, flecainide, methylergonovine, midazolam, pimozide, propafenone, quinidine, terfenadine, and triazolam.
- Use cautiously in patients with sulfonamide allergy, diabetes, liver disease, hepatitis B or C, or hemophilia A or B.

Lifespan: In pregnant women, use only if benefits to the patient outweigh risks to the fetus. If patient is pregnant or becomes pregnant and is exposed to drug, register her with the Antiretroviral Pregnancy Registry at 800-258-4263. Breast-feeding isn't recommended during treatment. In children, safety and effectiveness haven't been established. In elderly patients, use cautiously because these patients are more likely to have decreased organ function, multidrug therapy, and multiple illnesses.

Adverse reactions

CNS: asthenia, depression, dizziness, fatigue, headache, insomnia, pyrexia, malaise, peripheral neuropathy, sleep disorder, somnolence.
GI: abdominal distention, abdominal pain, *diarrhea,* dyspepsia, flatulence, GERD, nausea, ***pancreatitis,*** vomiting.
GU: renal insufficiency.
Hematologic: anemia, ***neutropenia, thrombocytopenia.***
Hepatic: ***hepatic failure, hepatitis.***
Metabolic: anorexia, decreased appetite, dehydration, diabetes mellitus, facial wasting, hyperglycemia, weight loss.
Musculoskeletal: muscle cramps, myalgia.
Respiratory: bronchitis, cough, dyspnea.
Skin: acquired lipodystrophy, exanthem, lipoatrophy, lipohypertrophy, pruritus, ***rash.***
Other: flulike illness, hypersensitivity, reactivation of herpes simplex and varicella zoster.

Interactions

Drug-drug. *Amiodarone, bepridil, flecainide, propafenone, quinidine:* May increase levels of these drugs and risk of serious or life-threatening arrhythmias. Avoid use together.
Astemizole, cisapride, pimozide, terfenadine: May cause serious or life-threatening arrhythmias. Avoid use together.
Atorvastatin: May increase levels of both drugs. Start with lowest dose of atorvastatin, and monitor patient closely or consider other drugs.
Clarithromycin: May increase levels of both drugs. If patient's creatinine clearance is 30 to 60 ml/minute, decrease clarithromycin dose by 50%. If creatinine clearance is less than 30 ml/minute, decrease clarithromycin dose by 75%.
Cyclosporine, sirolimus, tacrolimus: May cause unpredictable interaction. Monitor drug level closely until they've stabilized.
Desipramine: May increase desipramine level. Decrease dose, and monitor desipramine level.
Dihydroergotamine, ergonovine, ergotamine, methylergonovine: May cause acute ergot toxicity, including peripheral vasospasm and ischemia of extremities. Avoid use together.
Diltiazem, felodipine, nicardipine, nisoldipine, verapamil: May cause unpredictable interaction. Use together cautiously, and monitor patient closely.
Disulfiram, metronidazole: May cause disulfiram reaction. Use together cautiously.

T

Estrogen-based hormone therapy: May decrease estrogen level, and rash may occur. Monitor patient carefully. Advise using nonhormonal contraception.
Fluoxetine, paroxetine, sertraline: May increase levels of these drugs. Adjust dosages as needed.
Glimepiride, glipizide, glyburide, pioglitazone, repaglinide, tolbutamide: May affect glucose level. Monitor glucose level carefully.
Lovastatin, simvastatin: May increase risk of myopathy and rhabdomyolysis. Avoid use together.
Meperidine: May increase normeperidine metabolite. Avoid use together.
Methadone: May decrease methadone level by 50%. Consider increased methadone dose.
Midazolam, triazolam: May cause prolonged or increased sedation or respiratory depression. Avoid use together.
Rifabutin: May increase rifabutin level. Decrease rifabutin dose by 75%.
Rifampin: May lead to loss of virologic response and resistance to tipranavir and other protease inhibitors. Avoid use together.
Sildenafil, tadalafil, vardenafil: May increase levels of these drugs. Tell patient to use together cautiously. Tell him not to exceed 25 mg of sildenafil in 48 hours, 10 mg of tadalafil in 72 hours, or 2.5 mg of vardenafil in 72 hours.
Warfarin: May cause unpredictable reaction. Check INR often.
Drug-herb. *St. John's wort:* May lead to loss of virologic response and resistance to drug and class. Warn patient to avoid use together.

Effects on lab test results

- May increase total cholesterol, triglyceride, blood glucose, amylase, lipase, ALT, and AST levels.
- May decrease WBC count.

Pharmacokinetics

Absorption: Limited; bioavailability is increased when taken with a high-fat meal.
Distribution: 99.9% bound to plasma proteins.
Metabolism: Mediated by cytochrome P-450; few plasma metabolites found.
Excretion: Mostly unchanged in feces; some in urine. *Half life:* 4¾ to 6 hours.

Route	Onset	Peak	Duration
P.O.	Unknown	3 hr	Unknown

Action

Chemical effect: Inhibits virus-specific processing of polyproteins in HIV-1 infected cells, thus preventing formation of mature virions.
Therapeutic effect: Produces immature, noninfectious virus.

Available forms

Capsules: 250 mg

NURSING PROCESS

Assessment

- Carefully obtain patient's drug history. Many drugs may interact with tipranavir.
- Obtain liver function tests at start of treatment and often during treatment.
- Obtain cholesterol and triglyceride levels at start of and periodically during therapy.
- If patient has diabetes, monitor blood glucose level closely. Hyperglycemia may occur.
- Monitor patient for evidence of hepatitis, such as fatigue, malaise, anorexia, nausea, jaundice, bilirubinemia, acholic stools, liver tenderness, and hepatomegaly.
- Monitor patient for cushingoid symptoms, such as central obesity, buffalo hump, peripheral wasting, facial wasting, and breast enlargement.
- Evaluate patient's and family's knowledge of drug therapy.

Nursing diagnoses

- Risk for injury related to potential for many drugs to interact with tipranavir
- Ineffective protection related to drug-induced adverse hematologic reactions
- Deficient knowledge related to drug therapy

Planning and implementation

ALERT: Don't give this drug to treatment-naive patients.
- To be effective, drug must be given with 200 mg of ritonavir and other antiretrovirals.

ALERT: Patients who have chronic hepatitis B or C have an increased risk of hepatotoxicity.
- If patient has indicators of hepatitis, stop drug.

Patient teaching
- Explain that drug doesn't cure HIV infection and doesn't reduce the risk of transmitting the virus to others.

ALERT: Warn patient that many drugs may interfere with tipranavir. Urge patient to tell pre-

scriber about all prescription drugs, OTC drugs, and herbal products he takes.
• Tell patient that drug is effective only when taken with ritonavir and other antiretroviral drugs.
• Instruct patient to take drug with food.
• Urge patient to stop drug and contact prescriber if he has evidence of hepatitis, such as fatigue, malaise, anorexia, nausea, jaundice, bilirubinemia, acholic stools, or liver tenderness.
• If patient uses hormonal contraceptives, advise additional or alternative contraception during treatment.
• Tell patient that redistribution or accumulation of body fat may occur.

Evaluation
• Patient has no drug interactions.
• Patient has no serious adverse hematologic effects.

tobramycin sulfate
(toh-bruh-MIGH-sin SUL-fayt)
Nebcin, Tobi

Pharmacologic class: aminoglycoside
Therapeutic class: antibiotic
Pregnancy risk category: D

Indications and dosages
▶ **Serious infections caused by sensitive strains of *Citrobacter, Enterobacter, Escherichia coli, Klebsiella, Proteus, Providencia, Pseudomonas, Serratia,* and *Staphylococcus aureus.*** *Adults and children with normal renal function:* 3 mg/kg I.M. or I.V. daily divided q 8 hours. Up to 5 mg/kg daily divided q 6 to 8 hours for life-threatening infections.
Neonates younger than age 1 week or premature infants: Up to 4 mg/kg I.V. or I.M. daily in two equal doses q 12 hours.
▶ **Bronchopulmonary *Pseudomonas aeruginosa* in cystic fibrosis patients.** *Adults and children 6 years and older:* 300 mg by oral inhalation every 12 hours. Intervals should never be less than 6 hours apart, and cycle should be for 28 days, followed by at least 28 days off.

I.V. administration
• Dilute in 50 to 100 ml of normal saline solution or D_5W for adults and in less volume for children.
• Infuse over 20 to 60 minutes. After I.V. infusion, flush line with normal saline solution or D_5W.
⊗ **Incompatibilities**
Allopurinol; amphotericin B; beta lactam antibiotics; dextrose 5% in Isolyte E, M, or P; heparin sodium; hetastarch; indomethacin; I.V. solutions containing alcohol; other I.V. drugs; propofol; sargramostim.

Contraindications and cautions
• Contraindicated in patients hypersensitive to aminoglycosides.
• Use cautiously in patients with impaired kidney function or neuromuscular disorders.
Lifespan: In pregnant and breast-feeding women, drug isn't recommended. In the elderly, use cautiously.

Adverse reactions
CNS: confusion, disorientation, headache, lethargy.
EENT: ototoxicity.
GI: diarrhea, nausea, vomiting.
GU: ***nephrotoxicity.***
Hematologic: ***agranulocytosis,*** anemia, eosinophilia, ***leukopenia, thrombocytopenia.***
Other: ***anaphylaxis,*** hypersensitivity reactions.

Interactions
Drug-drug. *Acyclovir, amphotericin B, cephalothin, cisplatin, methoxyflurane, other aminoglycosides, vancomycin:* May increase nephrotoxicity. Use together cautiously.
Atracurium, pancuronium, rocuronium, vecuronium: May increase the effects of nondepolarizing muscle relaxant, including prolonged respiratory depression. Use together only when necessary. Dose of nondepolarizing muscle relaxant may need to be reduced.
Dimenhydrinate: May mask symptoms of ototoxicity. Use cautiously.
General anesthetics: May potentiate neuromuscular blockade. Monitor patient closely.
I.V. loop diuretics (such as furosemide): May increase ototoxicity. Use together cautiously.
Parenteral penicillins (such as ticarcillin): May inactivate tobramycin. Don't mix.

T

Effects on lab test results

- May increase BUN, creatinine, and nonprotein nitrogen and nitrogenous compound levels.
- May decrease calcium, magnesium, potassium, and hemoglobin levels and hematocrit.
- May increase eosinophil count. May decrease WBC, platelet, and granulocyte counts.

Pharmacokinetics

Absorption: Unknown.
Distribution: Wide, although CSF penetration is low, even in patients with inflamed meninges. Minimally protein-bound.
Metabolism: None.
Excretion: Mainly in urine; small amount may be excreted in bile. Oral inhalation form is excreted in sputum. *Half-life:* 2 to 3 hours.

Route	Onset	Peak	Duration
I.V.	Immediate	Immediate	8 hr
I.M.	Unknown	30–90 min	8 hr
Inhalation	Unknown	10 min	Unknown

Action

Chemical effect: Inhibits protein synthesis by binding directly to 30S ribosomal subunit.
Therapeutic effect: Kills susceptible bacteria.

Available forms

Injection: 40 mg/ml, 10 mg/ml (pediatric)
Powder for injection: 30 mg/ml after reconstitution
Premixed parenteral injection for I.V. infusion: 60 mg or 80 mg in normal saline solution
Solution for nebulization: 300 mg/5 ml.

NURSING PROCESS

Assessment

- Assess patient's infection before starting therapy and regularly thereafter to monitor drug's effectiveness.
- Obtain specimen for culture and sensitivity tests before giving the first dose. Start therapy pending test results.
- Weigh patient and review baseline kidney function studies before starting therapy.
- Assess patient's hearing before starting therapy and during therapy. Report tinnitus, vertigo, or hearing loss.
- Monitor kidney function (output, specific gravity, urinalysis, BUN and creatinine levels, and creatinine clearance).
- Be alert for adverse reactions and drug interactions.
- Assess patient's and family's knowledge of drug therapy.

Nursing diagnoses

- Risk for infection related to susceptible bacteria
- Risk for injury related to potential for drug-induced nephrotoxicity
- Deficient knowledge related to drug therapy

Planning and implementation

- Don't use commercially packaged products in normal saline solution for I.M. injection. For I.M. injection, use tobramycin from multidose vial or prefilled syringes.
- Draw blood for peak tobramycin level 1 hour after I.M. injection and 30 minutes to 1 hour after infusion ends; draw blood for trough level just before next dose. Don't collect blood in heparinized tube because heparin is incompatible with drug.

ALERT: Peak level higher than 12 mcg/ml and trough level higher than 2 mcg/ml may be linked to increased risk of toxicity.

- Nebulizer treatment for inhaled tobramycin should last 15 minutes. Drug shouldn't be diluted or admixed with other drugs.
- Notify prescriber of signs of decreasing kidney function.
- Keep patient well hydrated during therapy to minimize chemical irritation of renal tubules.
- If no response occurs in 3 to 5 days, therapy may be stopped and new specimens obtained for culture and sensitivity testing.

ALERT: Don't confuse tobramycin with Trobicin.

Patient teaching

- Emphasize need to drink 2 L of fluid each day.
- Instruct patient to report adverse reactions.

Evaluation

- Patient is free from infection.
- Patient maintains normal kidney function.
- Patient and family state understanding of drug therapy.

tolcapone

(TOHL-cah-pohn)
Tasmar

Pharmacologic class: COMT inhibitor
Therapeutic class: antiparkinsonian
Pregnancy risk category: C

Indications and dosages

▶ **Adjunct to levodopa and carbidopa for signs and symptoms of idiopathic Parkinson disease.** *Adults:* Initially, 100 mg P.O. t.i.d. (with levodopa and carbidopa). Recommended daily dosage is 100 mg P.O. t.i.d., although 200 mg P.O. t.i.d. may be given if the anticipated benefit is justified. If starting therapy with 200 mg t.i.d. and dyskinesia occurs, reduce dosage of levodopa. Maximum, 600 mg daily.

Contraindications and cautions

- Contraindicated in patients hypersensitive to the drug or any of its components and in patients with liver disease, elevated ALT or AST values, or history of nontraumatic rhabdomyolysis, hyperpyrexia, or confusion possibly related to drug. Also contraindicated in patients withdrawn from drug because of evidence of drug-induced hepatocellular injury.
- Use cautiously in patients with severe renal impairment.

Lifespan: In pregnant women, use only if benefits to patient outweigh risks to fetus. In breast-feeding women, use cautiously.

Adverse reactions

CNS: agitation, balance loss, *confusion,* depression, *dizziness, dyskinesia, dystonia, excessive dreaming,* falling, fatigue, fever, *hallucinations, headache,* hyperactivity, hyperkinesia, hypertonia, hypokinesia, irritability, paresthesia, mental deficiency, *sleep disorder, somnolence,* speech disorder, syncope, tremor.
CV: chest discomfort, chest pain, hypotension, *orthostatic complaints,* palpitations.
EENT: pharyngitis, sinus congestion, tinnitus.
GI: abdominal pain, *anorexia,* constipation, *diarrhea,* dry mouth, dyspepsia, flatulence, *nausea, vomiting.*
GU: hematuria, impotence, micturition disorder, urinary incontinence, urine discoloration, UTI.
Hematologic: ***bleeding.***
Hepatic: ***hepatic failure.***
Musculoskeletal: arthritis, *muscle cramps,* neck pain, stiffness.
Respiratory: bronchitis, dyspnea, upper respiratory tract infection.
Skin: increased sweating, rash.
Other: burning, influenza.

Interactions

Drug-drug. *CNS depressants:* May enhance sedative effects. Use cautiously.
Nonselective MAO inhibitors (phenelzine, tranylcypromine): May increase risk of hypertensive crisis. Don't use together.

Effects on lab test results

- May increase liver function test values.

Pharmacokinetics

Absorption: Rapid. Absolute bioavailability is 65%.
Distribution: Not widely distributed into tissues. 99.9% bound to plasma proteins.
Metabolism: Almost complete, mainly by glucuronidation.
Excretion: 60% in urine; 40% in feces. *Half-life:* 2 to 3 hours.

Route	Onset	Peak	Duration
P.O.	Unknown	2 hr	Unknown

Action

Chemical effect: Unknown; may reversibly inhibit human erythrocyte COMT when given with levodopa and carbidopa, resulting in a decrease in levodopa clearance and a twofold increase in levodopa bioavailability. Decreased clearance of levodopa prolongs half-life of levodopa from 2 to 3½ hours.
Therapeutic effect: Improves physical mobility in patients with parkinsonism.

Available forms

Tablets: 100 mg, 200 mg

NURSING PROCESS

Assessment

- Assess patient's history of Parkinson disease before starting therapy, and reassess during therapy to monitor drug's effectiveness.
- Monitor liver function test results before starting therapy, every 2 to 4 weeks for the first

T

6 months, then as clinically indicated. If the dose is increased to 200 mg t.i.d., resume monitoring as described. Stop drug if AST or ALT exceed 2 times the upper limit of normal or if patient shows signs or symptoms of hepatic dysfunction.
• Assess patient's risk for physical injury because of drug's adverse CNS effects.
• Monitor patient for orthostatic hypotension and syncope.
• Assess patient's and family's knowledge of drug therapy.

Nursing diagnoses
• Impaired physical mobility related to underlying Parkinson disease
• Disturbed thought processes related to drug-induced CNS adverse reactions
• Deficient knowledge related to drug therapy

Planning and implementation
ALERT: Be sure patient has provided written informed consent before drug is used. Give drug only to patient taking levodopa and carbidopa who doesn't respond to, or who isn't an appropriate candidate for, other adjunctive therapies because of risk of liver toxicity.
• Give first dose of the day with first daily dose of levodopa and carbidopa.
• Patient with severe renal dysfunction may need a lower dose.
• Don't give the drug, and notify prescriber, if hepatic transaminases are elevated or if patient appears jaundiced or complains of nausea, upper right quadrant pain, fatigue, lethargy, anorexia, pruritus, or dark urine.
• Because of risk of liver toxicity, stop giving the drug if patient shows no benefit within 3 weeks.
• Because of highly protein-bound nature of drug, dialysis doesn't significantly remove drug.
• If severe diarrhea linked to therapy occurs, notify prescriber.

Patient teaching
• Advise patient to take drug exactly as prescribed.
• Teach patient signs of liver dysfunction (jaundice, fatigue, loss of appetite, persistent nausea, pruritus, dark urine, or right upper quadrant tenderness) and instruct him to report them immediately.
• Warn patient about risk of orthostatic hypotension; tell him to use caution when rising from a seated or lying position.
• Instruct patient to avoid hazardous activities until the drug's CNS effects are known.
• Tell patient nausea may occur at the start of therapy.
• Inform patient about risk of increased dyskinesia or dystonia.
• Tell patient to report planned, suspected, or known pregnancy during therapy.
• Instruct patient to report adverse effects to prescriber, including diarrhea and hallucinations.
• Inform patient that drug may be taken without regard to meals.

Evaluation
• Patient exhibits improved mobility with reduction of muscular rigidity and tremor.
• Patient remains mentally alert.
• Patient and family state understanding of drug therapy.

tolterodine tartrate
(tohl-TER-oh-deen TAR-trate)
Detrol, Detrol LA

Pharmacologic class: muscarinic receptor antagonist
Therapeutic class: anticholinergic
Pregnancy risk category: C

Indications and dosages
▶ **Overactive bladder in patients with symptoms of urinary frequency, urgency, or urge incontinence.** *Adults:* 2 mg P.O. b.i.d. Dosage may be lowered to 1 mg P.O. b.i.d. based on patient response and tolerance. Or, 4 mg of extended-release capsule P.O. daily; may be decreased to 2 mg P.O. daily.
Adjust-a-dose: For patients with significantly reduced hepatic or renal function and patients taking drug that inhibits CYP3A4 isoenzyme system, give 1 mg P.O. b.i.d. or 2 mg P.O. daily of extended-release capsules.

Contraindications and cautions
• Contraindicated in patients hypersensitive to the drug or any of its components and in those

with uncontrolled angle-closure glaucoma or urine or gastric retention.

• Use cautiously in patients with significant bladder outflow obstruction, GI obstructive disorders (such as pyloric stenosis), controlled angle-closure glaucoma, or hepatic or renal impairment.

Lifespan: In pregnant women, use only if benefits outweigh risks. Breast-feeding women should either stop breast-feeding or use another drug. In children, safety and effectiveness haven't been established.

Adverse reactions

CNS: dizziness, fatigue, *headache,* nervousness, paresthesia, somnolence, vertigo.
CV: chest pain, hypertension.
EENT: abnormal vision, pharyngitis, rhinitis, sinusitis, xerophthalmia.
GI: abdominal pain, constipation, diarrhea, *dry mouth,* dyspepsia, flatulence, nausea, vomiting.
GU: dysuria, micturition frequency, urine retention, UTI.
Metabolic: weight gain.
Musculoskeletal: arthralgia, back pain.
Respiratory: bronchitis, cough, upper respiratory tract infection.
Skin: dry skin, erythema, pruritus, rash.
Other: falls, flulike syndrome, fungal infection, infection.

Interactions

Drug-drug. *Antifungals (itraconazole, ketoconazole, miconazole), cyclosporine, CYP3A4 inhibitors (such as macrolide antibiotics clarithromycin and erythromycin), vincristine:* May increase tolterodine concentration. Don't give tolterodine doses above 1 mg b.i.d. (2 mg daily of extended-release capsules) with these drugs.

Effects on lab test results

None reported.

Pharmacokinetics

Absorption: Well absorbed with about 77% bioavailability. Peak level occurs within 1 to 2 hours after administration. Food increases bioavailability by 53%.
Distribution: Volume of distribution is about 113 L. 96% protein-bound.
Metabolism: Mainly by oxidation by the CYP2D6 pathway and forms an active 5-hydroxymethyl metabolite.
Excretion: Mainly in urine, the rest in feces. Less than 1% of dose is recovered as unchanged drug, and 5% to 14% is recovered as the active metabolite. *Half-life:* 1¾ to 3½ hours.

Route	Onset	Peak	Duration
P.O.	Unknown	1–2 hr	Unknown

Action

Chemical effect: A competitive muscarinic receptor antagonist. Both urinary bladder contraction and salivation are mediated via cholinergic muscarinic receptors.
Therapeutic effect: Relieves symptoms of overactive bladder.

Available forms

Capsules (extended-release): 2 mg, 4 mg
Tablets: 1 mg, 2 mg

NURSING PROCESS

Assessment

• Assess baseline bladder function before starting therapy, and reassess frequently to monitor drug's effectiveness.
• Be alert for adverse reactions and drug interactions.
• Assess patient's and family's knowledge of drug therapy.

Nursing diagnoses

• Impaired urinary elimination related to underlying medical condition
• Urinary retention related to drug-induced adverse effects
• Deficient knowledge related to drug therapy

Planning and implementation

• Food increases the absorption of tolterodine, but no dosage adjustment is needed.
• If patient has urine retention, notify prescriber and prepare for urinary catheterization.
• Dry mouth is the most common adverse reaction.

Patient teaching

• Tell patient that sugarless gum, hard candy, or saliva substitute may help relieve dry mouth.

T

• Advise patient to avoid driving or other potentially hazardous activities until visual effects of drug are known.
• Instruct patient to immediately report signs of infection, urine retention, or GI problems.

Evaluation

• Patient experiences improved bladder function with drug therapy.
• Patient doesn't experience urine retention.
• Patient and family state understanding of drug therapy.

topiramate

(toh-PEER-uh-mayt)
Topamax

Pharmacologic class: sulfamate-substituted monosaccharide
Therapeutic class: antiepileptic
Pregnancy risk category: C

Indications and dosages

▶ **Adjunctive therapy for partial seizures, primary generalized tonic-clonic seizures, or Lennox-Gastaut syndrome.** *Adults:* For partial onset seizures, 200 to 400 mg P.O. daily in two divided doses. For primary generalized tonic-clonic seizures, 400 mg P.O. daily in two divided doses. Start at 25 to 50 mg daily, and adjust to an effective dose in increments of 25 to 50 mg weekly.
Children ages 2 to 16: Give 5 to 9 mg/kg P.O. daily in two divided doses. Begin dosage adjustment at 1 to 3 mg/kg nightly for 1 week. Then increase at 1- to 2-week intervals by 1 to 3 mg/kg daily to achieve optimal response.
▶ **Prevention of migraine headaches.** *Adults:* Week one, 25 mg P.O. q p.m. for 7 days. Week two, 25 mg P.O. b.i.d. for 7 days. Week three, 25 mg P.O. q a.m. and 50 mg P.O. q p.m. for 7 days. Maintenance dose 50 mg P.O. bid. If needed, may use longer intervals between dose adjustments.
▶ **Initial monotherapy in patients with partial onset or primary generalized tonic-clonic seizures.** *Adults and children age 10 or older:* The recommended daily dose is 400 mg P.O. divided b.i.d. (morning and evening). To achieve this dose, adjust as follows. The first week, give 25 mg P.O. b.i.d. The second week, give 50 mg P.O. b.i.d. The third week, give 75 mg P.O. b.i.d. The fourth week, give 100 mg P.O. b.i.d. The fifth week, give 150 mg P.O. b.i.d. The sixth week, give 200 mg P.O. b.i.d.
Adjust-a-dose: For patients with creatinine clearance less than 70 ml/minute, reduce dosage by 50%. For patients on hemodialysis, may need to give supplemental doses to avoid rapid drops in drug level during prolonged dialysis treatment.

Contraindications and cautions

• Contraindicated in patients hypersensitive to the drug or any of its components.
• Use cautiously in patients with hepatic and renal impairment. Also use cautiously with other drugs that predispose patients to heat-related disorders, including other carbonic anhydrase inhibitors and anticholinergics.
Lifespan: In pregnant and breast-feeding women, use cautiously.

Adverse reactions

CNS: abnormal coordination; agitation; aggression; apathy; asthenia; *ataxia; confusion;* depression; depersonalization; difficulty with attention, concentration, language, or *memory; dizziness;* emotional lability; euphoria; *fatigue;* fever; ***generalized tonic-clonic seizures;*** hallucinations; hyperkinesias; hypertonia; hypesthesia; hypokinesia; insomnia; malaise; mood problems; *nervousness; nystagmus; paresthesia;* personality disorder; *psychomotor slowing;* psychosis; *somnolence; speech disorders;* stupor; ***suicide attempts;*** *tremor;* vertigo.
CV: chest pain, edema, hot flushes, palpitations.
EENT: *abnormal vision,* conjunctivitis, *diplopia,* eye pain, hearing problems, pharyngitis, sinusitis, tinnitus.
GI: abdominal pain, *anorexia,* constipation, diarrhea, dry mouth, dyspepsia, flatulence, gastroenteritis, gingivitis, *nausea,* taste perversion, vomiting.
GU: amenorrhea, dysuria, dysmenorrhea, hematuria, impotence, intermenstrual bleeding, leukorrhea, menorrhagia, menstrual disorder, micturition frequency, renal calculi, urinary incontinence, UTI, vaginitis.
Hematologic: anemia, epistaxis, ***leukopenia.***
Metabolic: weight changes.
Musculoskeletal: arthralgia, back or leg pain, muscular weakness, myalgia, rigors.

Respiratory: bronchitis, cough, dyspnea, *upper respiratory tract infection.*
Skin: acne, alopecia, increased sweating, pruritus, rash.
Other: body odor, breast pain, decreased libido, flulike syndrome.

Interactions

Drug-drug. *Carbamazepine:* May decrease topiramate level. Monitor patient.
Carbonic anhydrase inhibitors (acetazolamide, dichlorphenamide): May increase risk of renal calculus formation. Avoid use together.
CNS depressants: May increase risk of topiramate-induced CNS depression and other adverse cognitive and neuropsychiatric events. Use cautiously.
Hormonal contraceptives: May decrease effectiveness. Report changes in bleeding patterns; urge patient to use nonhormonal contraceptive.
Phenytoin: May decrease topiramate level and increase phenytoin level. Monitor levels.
Valproic acid: May decrease valproic acid and topiramate levels. Monitor patient.
Drug-lifestyle. *Alcohol use:* May increase risk of topiramate-induced CNS depression and other adverse cognitive and neuropsychiatric events. Discourage use together.

Effects on lab test results

- May increase liver enzyme level. May decrease bicarbonate and hemoglobin levels and hematocrit.
- May decrease WBC count.

Pharmacokinetics

Absorption: Rapid.
Distribution: Up to 17% bound to plasma proteins.
Metabolism: Not extensive.
Excretion: Mainly unchanged in urine. *Half-life:* 21 hours.

Route	Onset	Peak	Duration
P.O.	Unknown	2 hr	Unknown

Action

Chemical effect: May block action potential, suggestive of a sodium channel blocking action. May also potentiate activity of GABA and antagonize ability of kainate to activate the amino acid (glutamate) receptor.
Therapeutic effect: Prevents partial-onset seizures.

Available forms

Capsules, sprinkle: 15 mg, 25 mg
Tablets: 25 mg, 50 mg, 100 mg, 200 mg

NURSING PROCESS

Assessment

- Assess patient's seizure disorder before starting therapy and regularly thereafter to monitor drug's effectiveness.
- Carefully monitor patient taking topiramate with other antiepileptic drugs; dose adjustment may be needed to achieve optimal response.
- Oligohidrosis and hyperthermia have been infrequently reported, mainly in children. Monitor patient closely, especially in hot weather.
- Because Topamax inhibits carbonic anhydrase, it may cause hyperchloremic, non-anion gap metabolic acidosis from renal bicarbonate. Usually, this occurs early in treatment, although it may happen at any time. Assess patient for factors that may predispose him to acidosis, such as renal disease, severe respiratory disorders, status epilepticus, diarrhea, surgery, ketogenic diet, or drugs.
- Monitor patient for serious symptoms of acute and chronic metabolic acidosis, which include abnormal heart rhythms and stupor. Less severe complications include fatigue, anorexia, and hyperventilation. Left untreated, the acidosis can cause kidney damage, osteoporosis, or osteomalacia—also called rickets, in children.
- Assess patient's compliance with therapy at each follow-up visit.
- Assess patient's and family's knowledge of drug therapy.

Nursing diagnoses

- Risk for injury related to seizure disorder
- Acute pain related to increased risk of renal calculi formation
- Deficient knowledge related to drug therapy

Planning and implementation

- Renal insufficiency requires a lower dose. For hemodialysis patients, supplemental doses may be needed to avoid rapid drops in drug level during prolonged dialysis.
- Measure baseline and periodic serum bicarbonate level during topiramate treatment. If

metabolic acidosis develops and persists, consider reducing the dose or stopping the drug (using dose tapering). If patient continues on drug despite persistent acidosis, alkali treatment should be considered.

ALERT: If an ocular adverse event occurs, characterized by acute myopia and secondary angle-closure glaucoma, stop drug.

ALERT: Don't confuse Topamax with Toprol-XL, Tegretol, or Tegretol-XR.

Patient teaching

- Tell patient to maintain adequate fluid intake during therapy to minimize risk of forming renal calculi.
- Advise patient not to drive or operate hazardous machinery until the drug's CNS effects are known.
- Tell patient that drug may decrease effectiveness of hormonal contraceptives, and suggest barrier-method birth control.
- Tell patient to avoid crushing or breaking tablets because of bitter taste.
- Tell patient that drug can be taken without regard to food.
- Tell patient to notify prescriber immediately if he experiences changes in vision.

Evaluation

- Patient is free from seizure activity.
- Patient maintains adequate hydration to prevent renal calculus formation.
- Patient and family state understanding of drug therapy.

topotecan hydrochloride

(toh-poh-TEE-ken high-droh-KLOR-ighd)

Hycamtin

Pharmacologic class: antitumor drug
Therapeutic class: antineoplastic
Pregnancy risk category: D

Indications and dosages

▶ **Metastatic carcinoma of ovary after failure of initial or subsequent chemotherapy; small-cell lung cancer after failure of first-line chemotherapy.** *Adults:* 1.5 mg/m^2 by I.V. infusion over 30 minutes, daily for 5 consecutive days, starting on day 1 of a 21-day cycle, for minimum of four cycles in absence of tumor progression.

▶ **With cisplatin, to treat stage IV-B, recurrent or persistent cervical cancer unresponsive to surgery or radiation.** *Adults:* 0.75 mg/m^2 by I.V. infusion over 30 minutes on days 1, 2, and 3, followed by 50 mg/m^2 cisplatin by I.V. infusion on day 1. Repeat cycle q 21 days. Base subsequent doses of each drug on hematologic toxicities.

Adjust-a-dose: For patients with renal impairment, if creatinine clearance is 20 to 39 ml/minute, decrease dosage to 0.75 mg/m^2. If severe neutropenia occurs, reduce dose by 0.25 mg/m^2 for subsequent courses. Or, in severe neutropenia, give granulocyte-colony stimulating factor (GSF) after subsequent course (before resorting to dose reduction) starting from day 6 of the course (24 hours after topotecan administration).

I.V. administration

- Prepare drug under a vertical laminar flow hood while wearing gloves and protective clothing. If drug contacts skin, wash immediately and thoroughly with soap and water. If mucous membranes are affected, flush with water.
- Reconstitute drug in each 4-mg vial with 4 ml sterile water for injection.
- Dilute appropriate volume of reconstituted solution in normal saline solution or D_5W before use.
- Infuse over 30 minutes.
- Protect unopened vials of drug from light. Reconstituted vials stored at 68° to 77° F (20° to 25° C) and exposed to ambient lighting are stable for 24 hours.

⊗ **Incompatibilities**

Dexamethasone, mitomycin.

Contraindications and cautions

- Contraindicated in patients hypersensitive to the drug or any of its components and in patients with severe bone marrow depression.

Lifespan: In pregnant and breast-feeding women, drug is contraindicated.

Adverse reactions

CNS: *asthenia, fatigue, fever, headache, paresthesia.*
GI: *abdominal pain, anorexia, constipation, diarrhea, stomatitis, nausea, vomiting.*
Hematologic: *anemia,* **LEUKOPENIA, NEUTROPENIA, THROMBOCYTOPENIA.**
Respiratory: *dyspnea.*

Skin: *alopecia.*
Other: *sepsis.*

Interactions

Drug-drug. *Cisplatin:* May increase severity of myelosuppression. Use both drugs very cautiously.
Filgrastim (6-GCSF): May prolong duration of neutropenia. Don't give GCSF until day 6 of regimen, 24 hours after completion of topotecan therapy.

Effects on lab test results

• May increase ALT, AST, and bilirubin levels. May decrease hemoglobin level and hematocrit.
• May decrease WBC, platelet, and neutrophil counts.

Pharmacokinetics

Absorption: Given I.V.
Distribution: About 35% bound to plasma proteins.
Metabolism: In liver.
Excretion: 30% in urine. *Half-life:* 2 to 3 hours.

Route	Onset	Peak	Duration
I.V.	Unknown	Unknown	Unknown

Action

Chemical effect: Results from damage to DNA produced during DNA synthesis when replication enzymes interact with the complex formed.
Therapeutic effect: Kills certain cancer cells.

Available forms

Injection: 4-mg single-dose vial

NURSING PROCESS

Assessment

• Assess patient's and family's knowledge of drug therapy.
• Assess patient's underlying condition before and often during therapy.
• Monitor patient's CBC often during therapy.
• Be alert for adverse reactions and drug interactions.

Nursing diagnoses

• Ineffective health maintenance related to neoplastic disease
• Deficient knowledge related to drug therapy

Planning and implementation

ALERT: Patient must have a baseline neutrophil count greater than 1,500/mm^3 and platelet count greater than 100,000/mm^3 before therapy can start.
• Frequent monitoring of peripheral blood cell count is critical. Don't give repeated doses until neutrophil count is greater than 1,000/mm^3, platelet count is greater than 100,000/mm^3, and hemoglobin is greater than 9 mg/dl.

Patient teaching

• Instruct patient to promptly report sore throat, fever, chills, or unusual bleeding or bruising.
• Advise woman of childbearing age not to become pregnant, and not to breast-feed, during therapy.
• Tell patient and family about need for close monitoring of blood cell counts.

Evaluation

• Patient shows positive response to drug.
• Patient and family state understanding of drug therapy.

torsemide

(TOR-seh-mighd)
Demadex

Pharmacologic class: loop diuretic
Therapeutic class: antihypertensive, diuretic
Pregnancy risk category: B

Indications and dosages

▶ **Diuresis in patients with heart failure.** *Adults:* Initially, 10 to 20 mg P.O. or I.V. once daily. If response is inadequate, double dose until response is obtained. Maximum, 200 mg daily.

▶ **Diuresis in patients with chronic renal impairment.** *Adults:* Initially, 20 mg P.O. or I.V. once daily. If response is inadequate, double dose until response is obtained. Maximum, 200 mg daily.

▶ **Diuresis in patients with hepatic cirrhosis.** *Adults:* Initially, 5 to 10 mg P.O. or I.V. once daily with aldosterone antagonist or potassium-sparing diuretic. If response is inadequate, double dose until response is obtained. Maximum, 40 mg daily.

▶ **Hypertension.** *Adults:* Initially, 5 mg P.O. daily. Increase to 10 mg in 4 to 6 weeks if need-

T

ed and tolerated. If response is still inadequate, add another antihypertensive.

I.V. administration

- Drug may be given by direct injection over at least 2 minutes. Rapid injection may cause ototoxicity. Don't give more than 200 mg at a time.
- Switch to oral form as soon as possible.

⊗ Incompatibilities
None reported.

Contraindications and cautions

- Contraindicated in patients hypersensitive to the drug or other sulfonylurea derivatives and in those with anuria.
- Use cautiously in patients with hepatic disease, cirrhosis, or ascites; sudden changes in fluid and electrolyte balance may precipitate hepatic coma.

Lifespan: In pregnant women, use cautiously. In breast-feeding women, use cautiously; it's unknown if the drug appears in breast milk. In children, safety and effectiveness haven't been established. In elderly patients, use cautiously.

Adverse reactions

CNS: asthenia, dizziness, headache, nervousness, insomnia, syncope.
CV: chest pain, ECG abnormalities, edema, orthostatic hypotension, ***ventricular tachycardia.***
EENT: rhinitis, sore throat.
GI: constipation, diarrhea, dyspepsia, ***hemorrhage,*** nausea.
GU: excessive urination, impotence.
Metabolic: ***alkalosis, dehydration,*** electrolyte imbalances, including hyperglycemia hypocalcemia, *hypokalemia,* ***hypomagnesemia,*** hyperuricemia; ***hypochloremia.***
Musculoskeletal: arthralgia, myalgia.
Respiratory: cough.
Other: excessive thirst, gout.

Interactions

Drug-drug. *Chlorothiazide, chlorthalidone, hydrochlorothiazide, indapamide, metolazone:* May cause excessive diuretic response resulting in serious electrolyte abnormalities or dehydration. Adjust doses carefully and monitor patient for this effect.
Cholestyramine: May decrease absorption of torsemide. Separate administration times by at least 3 hours.
Indomethacin: May decrease diuretic effectiveness in sodium-restricted patients. Avoid use together.
Lithium, ototoxic drugs (such as aminoglycosides, ethacrynic acid): May increase toxicity of these drugs. Avoid use together.
NSAIDs: May potentiate nephrotoxicity of NSAIDs. Use together cautiously.
Probenecid: May decrease diuretic effectiveness. Avoid use together.
Salicylates: May decrease excretion, possibly leading to salicylate toxicity. Avoid use together.
Spironolactone: May decrease renal clearance of spironolactone. Dosage adjustments aren't needed.
Drug-herb. *Licorice:* May cause rapid potassium loss. Discourage use together.

Effects on lab test results

- May increase glucose, BUN, creatinine, cholesterol, and uric acid levels. May decrease calcium, potassium, and magnesium levels.

Pharmacokinetics

Absorption: Little first-pass metabolism.
Distribution: Extensively bound to plasma proteins.
Metabolism: 80% in liver.
Excretion: 22% to 34% unchanged in urine. *Half-life:* 3½ hours.

Route	Onset	Peak	Duration
P.O.	1 hr	1–2 hr	6–8 hr
I.V.	≤ 10 min	≤ 1 hr	6–8 hr

Action

Chemical effect: Enhances excretion of sodium, chloride, and water by acting on ascending portion of loop of Henle.
Therapeutic effect: Promotes water and sodium excretion and lowers blood pressure.

Available forms

Injection: 10 mg/ml
Tablets: 5 mg, 10 mg, 20 mg, 100 mg

NURSING PROCESS

Assessment

- Assess patient's condition before starting therapy and regularly thereafter to monitor drug's effectiveness.

• Monitor an elderly patient, who is especially susceptible to excessive diuresis, with potential for circulatory collapse and thromboembolic complications.
• During rapid diuresis and routinely with long-term use, monitor fluid intake and output, electrolyte level, blood pressure, weight, and pulse rate. Drug may cause profound diuresis and water and electrolyte depletion.
• Watch for signs of hypokalemia, such as muscle weakness and cramps.
• Be alert for adverse reactions and drug interactions.
• Assess patient's and family's knowledge of drug therapy.

Nursing diagnoses

• Excess fluid volume related to presence of edema
• Risk for injury related to presence of hypertension
• Deficient knowledge related to drug therapy

Planning and implementation

• Give oral drug in morning to prevent nocturia.
• Make sure patient is on a high-potassium diet; refer patient to a dietitian for guidance. Foods rich in potassium include citrus fruits, tomatoes, bananas, dates, and apricots.
ALERT: Don't confuse torsemide with furosemide.

Patient teaching

• Tell patient to take drug in the morning to prevent sleep interruption.
• Advise patient to change position slowly to prevent dizziness.
• Advise patient to immediately report ringing in ears because it may indicate toxicity.
• Tell patient to check with prescriber or pharmacist before taking OTC drugs.

Evaluation

• Patient shows no signs of edema.
• Patient's blood pressure is normal.
• Patient and family state understanding of drug therapy.

tramadol hydrochloride

(TRAM-uh-dohl high-droh-KLOR-ighd)
Ultram

Pharmacologic class: opioid agonist
Therapeutic class: analgesic
Pregnancy risk category: C

Indications and dosages

▶ **Moderate to moderately severe pain.**
Adults: 50 to 100 mg P.O. q 4 to 6 hours, p.r.n. Maximum dosage is 400 mg daily.
Adjust-a-dose: Maximum dosage in patients older than age 75 is 300 mg daily. For patients with cirrhosis, give 50 mg P.O. q 12 hours. For patients with renal impairment, if creatinine clearance is less than 30 ml/minute, give dose q 12 hours. Maximum, 200 mg daily. Hemodialysis patients can receive their regular dose on same day of dialysis.

Contraindications and cautions

• Contraindicated in patients hypersensitive to the drug or any of its components, and in those with acute intoxication from alcohol, hypnotics, centrally acting analgesics, opioids, or psychotropic drugs.
• Use cautiously in patients at risk for seizures or respiratory depression; patients with increased intracranial pressure or head injury, acute abdominal conditions, or renal or hepatic impairment; and patients physically dependent on opioids.
Lifespan: In pregnant women and in children, safety and effectiveness haven't been established. In breast-feeding women, drug isn't recommended.

Adverse reactions

CNS: anxiety, *asthenia, CNS stimulation,* confusion, coordination disturbance, *dizziness,* euphoria, *headache,* malaise, nervousness, *seizures,* sleep disorder, *somnolence, vertigo.*
CV: vasodilation.
EENT: visual disturbances.
GI: abdominal pain, anorexia, *constipation,* diarrhea, dry mouth, dyspepsia, flatulence, *nausea, vomiting.*
GU: menopausal symptoms, urinary frequency, urine retention.

T

Musculoskeletal: hypertonia.
Respiratory: ***respiratory depression.***
Skin: *pruritus,* rash, sweating.

Interactions

Drug-drug. *Carbamazepine:* May increase tramadol metabolism. Patients receiving long-term carbamazepine therapy at dosage of up to 800 mg daily may require up to twice the recommended dose of tramadol.
CNS depressants: May have additive effects. Use together cautiously. Dosage of tramadol may need to be reduced.
MAO inhibitors, SSRIs: May increase risk of seizures. Monitor patient closely.
Drug-herb. *5-hydroxytryptophan (5-HTP), SAMe, St. John's wort:* May increase serotonin level. Discourage use together.

Effects on lab test results

- May increase liver enzyme level. May decrease hemoglobin level and hematocrit.

Pharmacokinetics

Absorption: Rapid and almost complete.
Distribution: About 20% bound to plasma proteins.
Metabolism: Extensively metabolized.
Excretion: 30% in urine as unchanged drug and 60% as metabolites. *Half-life:* 6 to 7 hours.

Route	Onset	Peak	Duration
P.O.	Unknown	2 hr	Unknown

Action

Chemical effect: Unknown; centrally acting synthetic analgesic compound not chemically related to opioids that is thought to bind to opioid receptors and inhibit reuptake of norepinephrine and serotonin.
Therapeutic effect: Relieves pain.

Available forms

Tablets: 50 mg

NURSING PROCESS

Assessment

- Assess patient's pain before starting therapy and regularly thereafter to monitor drug's effectiveness.
- Monitor CV and respiratory status.

ALERT: Closely monitor patient at risk for seizures; drug may reduce seizure threshold.

- Monitor patient for drug dependence. Tramadol can produce dependence similar to that of codeine or dextropropoxyphene and thus has potential to be abused.
- Be alert for adverse reactions and drug interactions.
- Assess patient's and family's knowledge of drug therapy.

Nursing diagnoses

- Acute pain related to underlying condition
- Risk for constipation related to drug-induced adverse GI reactions
- Deficient knowledge related to drug therapy

Planning and implementation

- For better analgesic effect, give drug before onset of intense pain.
- If respiratory rate decreases or falls below 12 breaths/minute, withhold dose and notify prescriber.
- Because constipation is a common adverse effect, anticipate need for laxative therapy.

ALERT: Don't confuse tramadol with trazodone or trandolapril.

Patient teaching

- Instruct patient to take drug only as prescribed and not to increase dosage or dosage interval unless instructed by prescriber.
- Tell ambulatory patient to be careful when getting out of bed and walking. Warn outpatient to refrain from driving and performing other potentially hazardous activities that require mental alertness until drug's CNS effects are known.
- Instruct patient to check with prescriber before taking OTC drugs; drug interactions can occur.

Evaluation

- Patient is free from pain.
- Patient regains normal bowel pattern.
- Patient and family state understanding of drug therapy.

trandolapril

(tran-DOH-luh-pril)
Mavik

Pharmacologic class: ACE inhibitor
Therapeutic class: antihypertensive
Pregnancy risk category: C (D in second and third trimesters)

Indications and dosages

▶ **Hypertension.** *Adults:* For patient not receiving a diuretic, initially 1 mg for a nonblack patient and 2 mg for a black patient P.O. once daily. If response isn't adequate, dose may be increased at intervals of at least 1 week. Maintenance dosage is 2 to 4 mg daily for most patients. Some patients receiving 4-mg once-daily doses may need b.i.d. doses. For patient also receiving diuretic, initial dose is 0.5 mg P.O. once daily. Subsequent doses adjusted based on blood pressure response.

▶ **Heart failure or left ventricular dysfunction after acute MI.** *Adults:* Start therapy 3 to 5 days after MI with 1 mg P.O. daily. Adjust as tolerated to target dosage of 4 mg daily.

Contraindications and cautions

• Contraindicated in patients hypersensitive to the drug or any of its components and in patients with a history of angioedema with previous therapy with ACE inhibitor.

• Use cautiously in patients with impaired renal function, heart failure, or renal artery stenosis.

Lifespan: In pregnant women, drug is contraindicated. Breast-feeding women should stop breast-feeding or stop the drug. In children, safety and effectiveness haven't been established.

Adverse reactions

CNS: anxiety, dizziness, drowsiness, fatigue, headache, insomnia, paresthesia, vertigo.
CV: ***bradycardia,*** chest pain, edema, first-degree AV block, flushing, hypotension, palpitations,
EENT: epistaxis, throat irritation.
GI: abdominal distention, abdominal pain or cramps, constipation, diarrhea, dyspepsia, ***pancreatitis,*** vomiting.
GU: impotence, urinary frequency.
Hematologic: ***leukopenia, neutropenia.***
Metabolic: ***hyperkalemia,*** hyponatremia.
Respiratory: dry, persistent, tickling, nonproductive cough; dyspnea; upper respiratory tract infection.
Skin: pemphigus, pruritus, rash.
Other: ***anaphylaxis, angioedema,*** decreased libido.

Interactions

Drug-drug. *Diuretics:* May increase risk of excessive hypotension. Monitor blood pressure closely.
Lithium: May increase lithium level and lithium toxicity. Avoid use together; monitor lithium level.
NSAIDs: May reduce hypotensive effect of trandolapril. Monitor blood pressure.
Potassium-sparing diuretics, potassium supplements: May increase risk of hyperkalemia. Monitor potassium level closely.
Drug-herb. *Licorice:* May increase sodium retention and blood pressure. Discourage use together.
Drug-food. *Salt substitutes containing potassium:* May increase risk of hyperkalemia. Monitor potassium level closely.

Effects on lab test results

• May increase BUN, creatinine, potassium, uric acid, and liver enzyme levels. May decrease sodium level.

• May decrease neutrophil and WBC counts.

Pharmacokinetics

Absorption: Food slows absorption.
Distribution: 80% protein-bound.
Metabolism: In liver.
Excretion: In urine and feces. *Half-life:* 5 to 10 hours. Longer in patients with renal impairment.

Route	Onset	Peak	Duration
P.O.			
drug	Unknown	1 hr	Unknown
metabolite	4–10 hr	1 hr	Unknown

Action

Chemical effect: Inhibits circulating and tissue ACE activity, which reduces angiotensin II formation, decreases vasoconstriction and aldosterone secretion, and increases plasma renin.
Therapeutic effect: Lowers blood pressure.

Available forms

Tablets: 1 mg, 2 mg, 4 mg

NURSING PROCESS

Assessment

- Monitor patient's blood pressure and potassium level before and during therapy.
- Monitor patient for hypotension. If possible, stop diuretic therapy 2 to 3 days before starting drug.
- Monitor patient for jaundice, and immediately alert prescriber if it occurs.
- Monitor patient's compliance with therapy.
- Assess patient's and family's knowledge of drug therapy.

Nursing diagnoses

- Risk for injury related to hypertension
- Deficient knowledge related to drug therapy

Planning and implementation

- Take steps to prevent or minimize orthostatic hypotension.
- Maintain patient's nondrug therapies, such as sodium restriction, stress management, smoking cessation, and exercise program.

ALERT: Angioedema that involves the tongue, glottis, or larynx may be fatal because of airway obstruction. Have resuscitation equipment readily available for maintaining a patent airway; give appropriate therapy, including epinephrine 1:1,000 (0.3 to 0.5 ml) subcutaneously.

Patient teaching

- Advise patient to report infection and other adverse reactions.
- Tell patient to avoid salt substitutes.
- Tell patient to use caution in hot weather and during exercise.
- Tell woman to immediately report suspected pregnancy.
- Advise patient about to undergo surgery or anesthesia to inform prescriber of use of drug.

Evaluation

- Patient's blood pressure is normal.
- Patient and family state understanding of drug therapy.

trastuzumab

(trahs-TOO-zuh-mab)
Herceptin

Pharmacologic class: monoclonal antibody
Therapeutic class: antineoplastic
Pregnancy risk category: B

Indications and dosages

▶ **Monotherapy for patients with metastatic breast cancer whose tumors overexpress the human epidermal growth factor receptor 2 (HER2) protein and who have received one or more chemotherapy regimens for their metastatic disease; or with paclitaxel for metastatic breast cancer in patients whose tumors overexpress the HER2 protein and who haven't received chemotherapy for their metastatic disease.** *Adults:* Initial loading dose of 4 mg/kg I.V. over 90 minutes. If the initial loading dose is well tolerated, maintenance dosage is 2 mg/kg I.V. weekly as a 30-minute I.V. infusion.

I.V. administration

- Reconstitute drug in each vial with 20 ml of bacteriostatic water for injection, USP, 1.1% benzyl alcohol preserved, as supplied, to yield a multidose solution containing 21 mg/ml. Immediately after reconstitution, label vial for drug expiration 28 days from date of reconstitution.
- If patient is hypersensitive to benzyl alcohol, drug must be reconstituted with sterile water for injection. Drug reconstituted with sterile water for injection must be used immediately; unused portion must be discarded. Avoid other reconstitution diluents.
- Determine dose (milligrams) of drug needed, based on loading dose of 4 mg/kg or maintenance dose of 2 mg/kg. Calculate volume of 21-mg/ml solution and withdraw amount from vial; add it to an infusion bag containing 250 ml of normal saline solution.
- Don't give as an I.V. push or bolus.
- Vials of drug are stable at 36° to 46° F (2° to 8° C) before reconstitution. Discard reconstituted solution after 28 days. Store drug solution diluted in normal saline solution for injection at 36° to 46° F before use; it's stable for up to 24 hours.

⊗ **Incompatibilities**
Other I.V. drugs or dextrose solutions.

Contraindications and cautions

• Use cautiously in patients with cardiac dysfunction. Watch closely for ventricular dysfunction and heart failure, and stop drug if signs of decreased left ventricular dysfunction develop.
• Use cautiously in patients hypersensitive to drug or its components. Severe hypersensitivity reactions, infusion reactions, and pulmonary events can develop. Hypersensitivity reaction typically occurs during or within 24 hours of administration.
Lifespan: In pregnant women, use only if clearly needed. Breast-feeding women should stop breast-feeding during therapy and for 6 months after the last dose, or they should use another drug. In children, safety and effectiveness haven't been established. In elderly patients, use cautiously.

Adverse reactions

CNS: *asthenia,* depression, *dizziness, fever, headache, insomnia,* neuropathy, *pain,* paresthesia, peripheral neuritis.
CV: edema, ***heart failure, left ventricular dysfunction,*** peripheral edema, tachycardia.
EENT: pharyngitis, rhinitis, sinusitis.
GI: abdominal pain, anorexia, diarrhea, nausea, vomiting.
GU: UTI.
Hematologic: anemia, ***leukopenia.***
Musculoskeletal: arthralgia, *back pain,* bone pain.
Respiratory: cough, dyspnea.
Skin: acne, *rash.*
Other: allergic reaction, ***anaphylaxis,*** chills, infection, flulike syndrome, herpes simplex, ***hypersensitivity reactions.***

Interactions

Drug-drug. *Anthracyclines, cyclophosphamide:* May increase risk of cardiotoxic effects. Monitor patient closely.
Paclitaxel: May decrease clearance of trastuzumab. Monitor patient closely.

Effects on lab test results

• May decrease hemoglobin level and hematocrit.
• May decrease WBC count.

Pharmacokinetics

Absorption: Given I.V.
Distribution: Volume is 44 ml/kg.
Metabolism: Unknown.
Excretion: Unknown. *Half-life:* 1 to 32 days.

Route	Onset	Peak	Duration
I.V.	Unknown	Unknown	Unknown

Action

Chemical effect: Recombinant DNA-derived monoclonal antibody that selectively binds to HER2. Inhibits proliferation of human tumor cells that overexpress HER2.
Therapeutic effect: Hinders function of specific breast cancer tumor cells that overexpress HER2.

Available forms

Injection: lyophilized sterile powder containing 440 mg per vial

NURSING PROCESS

Assessment

• Before therapy starts, make sure patient has had a thorough baseline cardiac assessment, including history, physical examination, and evaluation, to see if she's at risk for developing cardiotoxicity.
• Use drug only in patients with metastatic breast cancer whose tumors have HER2 protein overexpression.
• Assess patient for chills and fever, especially during the first infusion.
• Monitor patient closely for signs and symptoms of cardiac dysfunction, especially if also receiving anthracyclines and cyclophosphamide.
• Monitor patient for dyspnea, increased cough, paroxysmal nocturnal dyspnea, peripheral edema, and S3 gallop. Monitor patients also receiving chemotherapy closely for cardiac dysfunction or failure, anemia, leukopenia, diarrhea, and infection.
• Assess patient's and family's knowledge of drug therapy.

Nursing diagnoses

• Imbalanced nutrition: less than body requirements related to drug-induced GI adverse effects
• Decreased cardiac output related to drug-induced decreased left ventricular function
• Deficient knowledge related to drug therapy

T

Planning and implementation

- Treat first-dose, infusion-related symptoms with acetaminophen, diphenhydramine, and meperidine (with or without reducing the rate of infusion).
- If patient has a significant decrease in cardiac function, notify prescriber.

Patient teaching

- Tell patient about possibility of first-dose, infusion-related adverse effects.
- Instruct patient to notify prescriber immediately if signs and symptoms of cardiac dysfunction develop, such as shortness of breath, increased cough, or peripheral edema.
- Instruct patient to report adverse effects to prescriber.

Evaluation

- Patient has no adverse GI effects (nausea, vomiting, diarrhea).
- Patient has no dyspnea, increased cough, paroxysmal nocturnal dyspnea, peripheral edema, or S_3 gallop as result of drug-induced cardiac dysfunction.
- Patient and family state understanding of drug therapy.

travoprost
(TRA-voe-prost)
Travatan

Pharmacologic class: prostaglandin analogue
Therapeutic class: antiglaucoma drug, ocular antihypertensive
Pregnancy risk category: C

Indications and dosages

▶ **Reduction of elevated intraocular pressure (IOP) in patients with open-angle glaucoma or ocular hypertension who are intolerant of other IOP-lowering drugs, or in patients who have had insufficient responses to other IOP-lowering drugs.** *Adults:* 1 drop in conjunctival sac of affected eye once daily in evening.

Contraindications and cautions

- Contraindicated in patients hypersensitive to the drug, benzalkonium chloride, or other components.
- Use cautiously in patients with renal or hepatic impairment, active intraocular inflammation (iritis, uveitis), or risk factors for macular edema. Also use cautiously in aphakic patients and pseudophakic patients with a torn posterior lens capsule.
- Don't use in patients with angle-closure glaucoma or inflammatory or neovascular glaucoma.

Lifespan: In pregnant women and in women attempting to become pregnant, drug isn't recommended. In breast-feeding women, use cautiously; it's unknown if the drug appears in breast milk. In children, safety and effectiveness haven't been established.

Adverse reactions

CNS: anxiety, depression, headache, pain.
CV: angina pectoris, ***bradycardia,*** chest pain, hypertension, hypotension.
EENT: abnormal vision, blepharitis, blurred vision, cataracts, conjunctival hyperemia, conjunctivitis, *decreased visual acuity,* dry eyes, *eye discomfort,* eye disorders, *eye pain, eye pruritus, foreign body sensation,* iris discoloration, keratitis, lid margin crusting, *ocular hyperemia,* photophobia, sinusitis, subconjunctival hemorrhage, tearing.
GI: dyspepsia, GI disorder.
GU: prostate disorder, urinary incontinence, UTI.
Metabolic: hypercholesterolemia.
Musculoskeletal: arthritis, back pain.
Respiratory: bronchitis, sinusitis.
Other: accidental injury, cold syndrome, infection.

Interactions

Drug-herb. *Areca, jaborandi:* May cause additive effects. Discourage use together.

Effects on lab test results

- May increase cholesterol level.

Pharmacokinetics

Absorption: Absorbed through the cornea.
Distribution: Level peaks within 30 minutes.
Metabolism: Hydrolyzed by esterases in the cornea to its active free acid. The liver primarily metabolizes the active acid of drug reaching the systemic circulation.
Excretion: Within 1 hour. *Half-life:* 45 minutes.

Route	Onset	Peak	Duration
Ophthalmic	Unknown	30 min	Unknown

Action

Chemical effect: May increase uveoscleral outflow.
Therapeutic effect: Reduces IOP.

Available forms

Ophthalmic solution: 0.004%

NURSING PROCESS

Assessment

- Assess patient's condition before starting therapy and regularly thereafter to monitor drug's effectiveness.
- If a pregnant woman or a woman attempting to become pregnant accidentally comes in contact with drug, immediately cleanse the exposed area thoroughly with soap and water.
- Assess patient's and family's knowledge of drug therapy.

Nursing diagnoses

- Acute pain related to adverse EENT effects of drug
- Risk for activity intolerance related to decreased visual acuity
- Deficient knowledge related to travoprost therapy

Planning and implementation

- Have patient remove contact lenses before you give the drug. Lenses may be reinserted 15 minutes afterward.
- If multiple ophthalmic drugs are being used, separate doses by at least 5 minutes.
- Temporary or permanent increased pigmentation of the iris and eyelid may occur as well as increased pigmentation and growth of the eyelashes.

Patient teaching

- Teach patient to instill drops, and advise him to wash hands before and after doing so. Warn him not to touch dropper or tip to eye or surrounding tissue.
- Advise patient to apply light pressure on lacrimal sac for 1 minute after instillation to minimize systemic absorption of drug.
- Tell patient to remove contact lenses before instilling solution and to leave them out for 15 minutes afterward.
- Advise patient that, if more than one ophthalmic drug is being used, the drugs should be given at least 5 minutes apart.
- Tell patient receiving treatment to only one eye about the potential for increased brown pigmentation of the iris, eyelid skin darkening, and increased length, thickness, pigmentation, or number of lashes in the treated eye.
- Tell patient that, if eye trauma or infection occurs or if eye surgery is needed, he should seek medical advice before continuing to use the multidose container.
- Advise patient to immediately report conjunctivitis or lid reactions.
- Stress importance of compliance with recommended therapy.
- Tell patient to discard container within 6 weeks of removing it from the sealed pouch.
- Tell pregnant woman or woman attempting to become pregnant that, if she accidentally comes in contact with drug, she should immediately cleanse the exposed area with soap and water.

Evaluation

- Patient denies pain.
- Patient's activity level improves.
- Patient and family state understanding of travoprost therapy.

trazodone hydrochloride

(TRAYZ-oh-dohn high-droh-KLOR-ighd)

Pharmacologic class: triazolopyridine derivative
Therapeutic class: antidepressant
Pregnancy risk category: C

Indications and dosages

▶ **Depression.** *Adults:* Initially, 150 mg P.O. daily in divided doses. Increase by 50 mg daily q 3 to 4 days, as needed. Average daily dose ranges from 150 to 400 mg. Maximum, 600 mg daily for inpatients; 400 mg daily for outpatients.

▶ **Aggressive behavior**‡. *Adults:* 50 mg P.O. b.i.d.

▶ **Panic disorder**‡. *Adults:* 300 mg P.O. daily.

▶ **Insomnia**‡. *Adults:* 25 to 75 mg P.O. with an SSRI.

Contraindications and cautions

- Contraindicated in patients in initial recovery phase of MI and in patients hypersensitive to drug.

T

• Use cautiously in patients with cardiac disease and in those at risk for suicide.

Lifespan: In pregnant women, breast-feeding women, and children, safety and effectiveness haven't been established.

Adverse reactions

CNS: anger, confusion, *dizziness, drowsiness,* fatigue, headache, hostility, insomnia, nervousness, nightmares, ***suicidal thinking,*** syncope, tremor, vivid dreams, weakness.
CV: hypertension, orthostatic hypotension, shortness of breath, tachycardia,
EENT: blurred vision, nasal congestion, tinnitus.
GI: anorexia, constipation, dry mouth, dysgeusia, nausea, vomiting.
GU: hematuria, priapism, urine retention.
Hematologic: anemia.
Skin: diaphoresis, rash, urticaria.
Other: decreased libido.

Interactions

Drug-drug. *Antihypertensives:* May increase hypotensive effect of trazodone. Monitor blood pressure; antihypertensive dosage may have to be decreased.
Clonidine, CNS depressants: May increase CNS depression. Avoid use together.
CYP3A4 inducers (carbamazepine): May reduce trazodone level. Monitor patient closely; trazodone dose may need to be increased.
CYP3A4 inhibitors (ketoconazole, ritonavir, and indinavir): May slow the clearance of trazodone and increase trazodone level. May cause nausea, hypotension, and fainting. Consider decreasing trazodone dose.
Digoxin, phenytoin: May increase levels of these drugs. Monitor patient for toxicity.
MAO inhibitors: May cause an unknown interaction. Use together cautiously.
Phenothiazines: May increase trazodone level. Monitor toxic effects.
Venlafaxine, SSRIs: May cause serotonin syndrome. Use together cautiously.
Drug-herb. *St. John's wort:* May cause serotonin syndrome. Discourage use together.
Drug-lifestyle. *Alcohol use:* May increase CNS depression. Discourage use together.

Effects on lab test results

• May increase ALT and AST levels. May decrease hemoglobin level and hematocrit.

Pharmacokinetics

Absorption: Well absorbed from GI tract. Food delays absorption but increases amount of drug absorbed by 20%.
Distribution: Wide in body; isn't concentrated in any particular tissue.
Metabolism: In liver.
Excretion: About 75% in urine; remainder in feces. *Half-life:* First phase, 3 to 6 hours; second phase, 5 to 9 hours.

Route	Onset	Peak	Duration
P.O.	Unknown	1–2 hr	Unknown

Action

Chemical effect: Unknown, although it inhibits serotonin uptake in brain; not a tricyclic derivative.
Therapeutic effect: Relieves depression.

Available forms

Tablets: 50 mg, 100 mg, 150 mg

NURSING PROCESS

Assessment

• Assess patient's condition before starting therapy and regularly thereafter to monitor drug's effectiveness.
• Be alert for adverse reactions and drug interactions.
• Assess patient's and family's knowledge of drug therapy.

Nursing diagnoses

• Disturbed thought processes related to presence of depression
• Risk for injury related to drug-induced adverse CNS reactions
• Deficient knowledge related to drug therapy

Planning and implementation

• Give after meal or light snack for optimal absorption and to decrease risk of dizziness.
• Don't abruptly stop giving the drug, but stop it at least 48 hours before surgery.
• If an adverse reaction occurs, notify prescriber.

ALERT: Don't confuse trazodone with tramadol.

Patient teaching

• Instruct patient to take drug after a meal or light snack.

ALERT: Advise patient to notify prescriber immediately if priapism (prolonged, painful erection unrelated to sexual stimulation) occurs; emergency interventions are needed within 6 hours to prevent permanent erectile dysfunction.

- Warn patient to avoid activities that require alertness and good psychomotor coordination until the drug's CNS effects are known; drowsiness and dizziness usually subside after first few weeks.
- Teach patient's family how to recognize signs of suicidal tendency or suicidal ideation.

Evaluation

- Patient's behavior and communication exhibit improved thought processes.
- Patient doesn't experience adverse CNS reactions.
- Patient and family state understanding of drug therapy.

treprostinil sodium

(treh-PROSS-ti-nil soh-DEE-uhm)
Remodulin

Pharmacologic class: vasodilator
Therapeutic class: antihypertensive
Pregnancy risk category: B

Indications and dosages

▶ **New York Heart Association Class II to IV pulmonary arterial hypertension (PAH) to reduce symptoms caused by exercise.** *Adults:* Initially, 1.25 nanograms/kg/minute by continuous subcutaneous or I.V. infusion. If initial dose isn't tolerated, reduce infusion rate to 0.625 nanograms/kg/minute. Increase by increments of no more than 1.25 nanograms/kg/minute q week for the first 4 weeks, and then by no more than 2.5 nanograms/kg/minute q week for duration of infusion. Maximum infusion rate is 40 nanograms/kg/minute. To determine subcutaneous infusion rate in ml/hour, use this formula:

Infusion rate (ml/hr) =
[dosage (nanograms/kg/min)
× body weight (kg) × 0.00006]
÷ drug strength (mg/ml)

When using an appropriate infusion pump and reservoir, select a predetermined intravenous infusion rate to allow for a desired infusion period length of up to 48 hours between system changeovers. Typical intravenous infusion system reservoirs have volumes of 50 or 100 ml. With this selected intravenous infusion rate (ml/hr), the diluted intravenous Remodulin concentration (mg/ml) can be calculated using this formula:

Diluted I.V. concentration (mg/ml) =
[dosage (nanograms/kg/min)
× weight (kg) × 0.00006]
÷ I.V. infusion rate (ml/minute)

The amount of Remodulin injection needed to make the required diluted intravenous Remodulin concentration for the given reservoir size can then be calculated using this formula:

Amount of Remodulin injection (ml) =
[diluted I.V. concentration (mg/ml)
÷ vial strength (mg/ml)]
× total volume of diluted Remodulin solution in reservoir (ml)

Add the calculated amount of Remodulin injection to the reservoir along with the sufficient volume of diluent to achieve the desired total volume in the reservoir.

Adjust-a-dose: In patients with mild or moderate hepatic insufficiency, initial dose is 0.625 nanograms/kg of ideal body weight per minute; increase cautiously.

▶ **To diminish the rate of clinical deterioration in patients with pulmonary arterial hypertension (PAH) who are transitioning therapy from Flolan (epoprostenol).** *Adults:* Begin treprostinil infusion at a rate that's 10% of starting epoprostenol dose. Decrease epoprostenol in 20% increments while increasing treprostinil in 20% increments, always maintaining a total dose of 110% of epoprostenol starting dose. Once epoprostenol is at 20% of starting dose, and treprostinil is at 90%, decrease epoprostenol to 5% and increase treprostinil to 110%. Finally, stop epoprostenol and maintain treprostinil dose at 110% of epoprostenol starting dose plus an additional 5 to10 % as needed. Change rate based on individual patient response. Treat worsening of PAH symptoms with increases in treprostinil doses. Treat adverse effects associated with prostacyclin and prostacyclin analogs with decreases in epoprostenol doses.

T

I.V. administration

- Remodulin must be diluted with either sterile water for injection or normal saline solution injection.
- Drug must be administered through a surgically placed, indwelling central venous catheter.
- Diluted Remodulin is stable at ambient temperature for up to 48 hours at concentrations as low as 0.004 mg/ml (4,000 nanograms/ml).
- Patient must have access to a backup infusion pump and infusion sets.

⊗ Incompatibilities

Other I.V. drugs.

Contraindications and cautions

- Contraindicated in patients hypersensitive to the drug or to structurally related compounds.
- Use cautiously in patients with hepatic or renal impairment.

Lifespan: In pregnant women, use only if clearly needed. In breast-feeding women, use cautiously; it's unknown if the drug appears in breast milk. In children, safety and effectiveness haven't been established; select dose cautiously. In the elderly, use cautiously.

Adverse reactions

CNS: dizziness, fatigue, *headache.*
CV: chest pain, edema, hypotension, ***right ventricular heart failure,*** vasodilation.
GI: diarrhea, nausea.
Respiratory: dyspnea.
Skin: pallor, pruritus, *rash.*
Other: *infusion site pain,* infusion site reaction, *jaw pain.*

Interactions

Drug-drug. *Anticoagulants:* May increase risk of bleeding. Monitor patient closely for bleeding.
Antihypertensives, diuretics, vasodilators: May worsen reduction in blood pressure. Monitor blood pressure.

Effects on lab test results

None reported.

Pharmacokinetics

Absorption: Rapid and complete. 100% bioavailable.
Distribution: 91% bound to plasma proteins.
Metabolism: By the liver. Five metabolites are known, but their activity isn't.
Excretion: In the urine, 4% as unchanged drug and 64% as metabolites. *Half-life:* 2 to 4 hours.

Route	Onset	Peak	Duration
I.V., SubQ	Unknown	Unknown	Unknown

Action

Chemical effect: Acts by direct vasodilation of pulmonary and systemic arterial vascular beds and inhibition of platelet aggregation.
Therapeutic effect: Reduces pulmonary artery pressure.

Available forms

Injection: 1 mg/ml, 2.5 mg/ml, 5 mg/ml, 10 mg/ml

NURSING PROCESS

Assessment

- Assess patient's condition before starting therapy and regularly thereafter to monitor drug's effectiveness.
- Make sure adequate monitoring and emergency care are available when starting therapy.
- Assess patient's ability to accept, place, and care for subcutaneous catheter and to use infusion pump.
- Assess patient's ability to accept and care for I.V. catheter and to use the infusion pump.
- Be alert for adverse reactions and drug interactions.
- Assess patient's and family's knowledge of drug therapy.

Nursing diagnoses

- Activity intolerance related to presence of pulmonary hypertension
- Acute pain related to adverse drug effect of headache
- Deficient knowledge related to drug therapy

Planning and implementation

- Drug should be used only by prescribers experienced in the diagnosis and treatment of PAH.
- Give by continuous subcutaneous infusion via a self-inserted subcutaneous catheter, using an infusion pump designed for subcutaneous drug delivery. Or give by continuous I.V. infusion through an indwelling central venous catheter.

• The infusion pump should be small and light-weight; be adjustable to approximately 0.002 ml/hour; have occlusion or no-delivery, low-battery, programming-error, and motor-malfunction alarms; have delivery accuracy of ± 6% or better; and be positive-pressure driven.
• The reservoir should be made of polyvinyl chloride, polypropylene, or glass.
• A single syringe can be given up to 72 hours at 99° F (37° C).
• Use a single vial no longer than 14 days after the initial introduction into the vial.
• Inspect for particulate matter and discoloration before giving.
• Unopened vials are stable until the date indicated when stored at 59° to 77° F (15° to 25° C).
• If patient doesn't improve or if symptoms worsen, increase dose. If patient has excessive effects or unacceptable infusion site symptoms, decrease dose.
• Don't abruptly stop giving the drug or reduce the dose by a large amount; symptoms of PAH may worsen.

Patient teaching

• Tell patient drug is infused continuously through subcutaneous or I.V. catheter, via an infusion pump.
• Inform patient that therapy will be needed for prolonged period, possibly years.
• Inform patient that many side effects may be related to the underlying disease (dyspnea, fatigue, chest pain, right ventricular failure, pallor).
• Tell patient that the most common local reactions are pain, erythema, induration, and rash at the infusion site.

☑ Evaluation

• Patient states activity intolerance is improving.
• Patient doesn't have headache.
• Patient and family state understanding of drug therapy.

triamcinolone
(trigh-am-SIN-oh-lohn)
Aristocort, Atolone, Kenacort

triamcinolone acetonide
Kenaject-40, Kenalog-10, Kenalog-40, Tac-3, Tac-40, Triam-A, Triamonide 40, Tri-Kort, Trilog

triamcinolone diacetate
Amcort, Aristocort Forte, Aristocort Intralesional, Clinacort, Triam Forte, Trilone, Tristoject

triamcinolone hexacetonide
Aristospan Intra-Articular, Aristospan Intralesional

Pharmacologic class: glucocorticoid
Therapeutic class: anti-inflammatory, immunosuppressant
Pregnancy risk category: C

Indications and dosages

▶ **Severe inflammation or immunosuppression.** *Adults:* 4 to 48 mg triamcinolone P.O. daily, in one to four divided doses. Or, initially, 2.5 to 60 mg triamcinolone acetonide I.M. Additional doses of 20 to 100 mg may be given, if needed, at 6-week intervals. Or, 2.5 to 15 mg intra-articularly, or up to 1 mg intralesionally, as needed. Or, 40 mg triamcinolone diacetate I.M. weekly; or 5 to 48 mg by intralesional or sublesional injections (at 1- to 2-week intervals); or 2 to 40 mg by intra-articular, intrasynovial, or soft tissue injection (may repeat at 1- to 8-week intervals). Or, with triamcinolone hexacetonide, use up to 0.5 mg per square inch of affected skin intralesionally, or 2 to 20 mg intra-articularly q 3 to 4 weeks, as needed.
Children: Base dosage on the disease severity and the response instead of age and body weight or surface area. Taper to a stop as soon as possible

Contraindications and cautions

• Contraindicated in patients hypersensitive to the drug or any of its components, and in those with systemic fungal infections.
• Use cautiously in patients with GI ulcer, renal disease, hypertension, osteoporosis, diabetes

mellitus, hypothyroidism, cirrhosis, diverticulitis, nonspecific ulcerative colitis, recent intestinal anastomoses, thromboembolic disorders, seizures, myasthenia gravis, heart failure, tuberculosis, ocular herpes simplex, emotional instability, or psychotic tendencies.

Lifespan: In pregnant women, use cautiously. In breast-feeding women, use cautiously; it's unknown if the drug appears in breast milk.

Adverse reactions

CNS: *euphoria,* headache, *insomnia,* paresthesia, ***pseudotumor cerebri,*** psychotic behavior, ***seizures,*** vertigo.
CV: ***arrhythmias,*** edema, ***heart failure,*** hypertension, ***thromboembolism,*** thrombophlebitis.
EENT: cataracts, glaucoma.
GI: GI irritation, increased appetite, nausea, ***pancreatitis,*** *peptic ulceration,* vomiting.
GU: menstrual irregularities.
Metabolic: carbohydrate intolerance, hyperglycemia, hypokalemia.
Musculoskeletal: growth suppression in children, muscular weakness, osteoporosis.
Skin: acne, bruising, delayed wound healing, various skin eruptions, petechiae.
Other: ***acute adrenal insufficiency*** during times of increased stress; cushingoid state (moonface, buffalo hump, central obesity), hirsutism; susceptibility to infections.

Interactions

Drug-drug. *Aspirin, indomethacin, other NSAIDs:* May increase risk of GI distress and bleeding. Give together cautiously.
Barbiturates, phenytoin, rifampin: May decrease corticosteroid effect. Increase corticosteroid dosage.
Drugs that deplete potassium (such as thiazide diuretics): May increase potassium-wasting effects of triamcinolone. Monitor potassium level.
Oral anticoagulants: May alter dosage requirements. Monitor PT closely.
Skin-test antigens: May decrease response. Defer skin testing.
Toxoids, vaccines: May decrease antibody response and increase risk of neurologic complications. Avoid use together.

Effects on lab test results

• May increase glucose and cholesterol levels. May decrease potassium and calcium levels.

Pharmacokinetics

Absorption: Readily after P.O. use. Variable after other routes.
Distribution: To muscle, liver, skin, intestines, and kidneys. Extensively bound to plasma proteins; only unbound portion is active.
Metabolism: In liver.
Excretion: In urine; insignificant amount in feces. *Half-life:* 18 to 36 hours.

Route	Onset	Peak	Duration
P.O., I.M., intralesional, intra-articular, intrasynovial	Varies	Varies	Varies

Actions

Chemical effect: Not clearly defined; decreases inflammation, mainly by stabilizing leukocyte lysosomal membranes; suppresses immune response; stimulates bone marrow; and influences protein, fat, and carbohydrate metabolism.
Therapeutic effect: Relieves inflammation and suppresses immune system function.

Available forms

triamcinolone
Syrup: 4 mg/5 ml
Tablets: 4 mg, 8 mg
triamcinolone acetonide
Injection (suspension): 3 mg/ml, 10 mg/ml, 40 mg/ml
triamcinolone diacetate
Injection (suspension): 25 mg/ml, 40 mg/ml
triamcinolone hexacetonide
Injection (suspension): 5 mg/ml, 20 mg/ml

NURSING PROCESS

Assessment

• Assess patient before and after starting therapy; monitor weight, blood pressure, and electrolyte level.
• Watch for adverse reactions, drug interactions, depression, or psychotic episodes, especially with high doses.
• Assess patient's and family's knowledge of drug therapy.

Nursing diagnoses

• Ineffective health maintenance related to underlying condition

• Risk for injury related to drug-induced adverse reactions
• Deficient knowledge related to drug therapy

Planning and implementation

• Drug isn't used for alternate-day therapy.
• Always adjust to lowest effective dose.
• For better results and less toxicity, give once-daily dose in morning.
• Give oral dose with food when possible to reduce GI irritation.
• For adults, give I.M. injection deep into gluteal muscle; rotate injection sites to prevent muscle atrophy.
• Don't use 10-mg/ml strength for I.M. administration.
• Assist prescriber with intralesional, intra-articular, or intrasynovial administration.
• Don't use 40-mg/ml strength for I.D. or intralesional administration.

ALERT: Parenteral form isn't for I.V. use; different salt formulations aren't interchangeable.

• Don't use diluents that contain preservatives; flocculation may occur.
• Unless contraindicated, give low-sodium diet high in potassium and protein. Give potassium supplements, as needed.
• Gradually reduce drug dose after long-term therapy. After abruptly stopping the drug, the patient may experience rebound inflammation, fatigue, weakness, arthralgia, fever, dizziness, lethargy, depression, fainting, orthostatic hypotension, dyspnea, anorexia, or hypoglycemia. After prolonged use, sudden withdrawal may be fatal.

ALERT: Don't confuse triamcinolone with Triaminicin, Triaminic, or Triaminicol.

Patient teaching

• Tell patient not to abruptly stop taking the drug without prescriber's consent.
• Instruct patient to take oral drug with food.
• Teach patient signs of early adrenal insufficiency (fatigue, muscle weakness, joint pain, fever, anorexia, nausea, dyspnea, dizziness, and fainting).
• Instruct patient to wear or carry medical identification at all times.
• Warn patient receiving long-term therapy about cushingoid symptoms, and tell him to report sudden weight gain and swelling to prescriber.
• Tell patient to report slow healing.
• Advise patient receiving long-term therapy to consider exercise or physical therapy. Also tell patient to ask prescriber about vitamin D or calcium supplements.

Evaluation

• Patient responds well to drug.
• Patient doesn't experience injury from adverse reactions.
• Patient and family state understanding of drug therapy.

triamcinolone acetonide

(trigh-am-SIN-oh-lohn as-EE-tuh-nighd)

Azmacort, Nasacort HFA

Pharmacologic class: glucocorticoid
Therapeutic class: anti-inflammatory, immunosuppressant
Pregnancy risk category: C

Indications and dosages

▶ **Corticosteroid-dependent asthma.** *Adults:* 2 inhalations t.i.d. to q.i.d. Maximum, 16 inhalations daily. In some patients, maintenance can be accomplished when total daily dose is given b.i.d.
Children ages 6 to 12: Give 1 or 2 inhalations t.i.d. to q.i.d. or 2 to 4 inhalations b.i.d. Maximum, 12 inhalations daily.

▶ **Treatment of nasal symptoms of seasonal and perennial allergic rhinitis.** *Adults and children age 12 years and older:* (Nasacort HFA) 2 sprays into each nostril once daily. May increase to 4 sprays into each nostril once daily. Adjust to minimum effective dosage.
Children age 12 years and older: (Nasacort HFA) 2 sprays into each nostril once daily. Adjust to minimum effective dosage.

Contraindications and cautions

• Contraindicated in patients hypersensitive to the drug or any of its components, and in those with status asthmaticus.
• Use cautiously, if at all, in patients with tuberculosis of respiratory tract; untreated fungal, bacterial, or systemic viral infections; or ocular herpes simplex. Also use cautiously in patients receiving systemic corticosteroids.

Lifespan: In pregnant women, use cautiously. In breast-feeding women, drug isn't recommended.

Adverse reactions

CNS: *headache* (Nasacort HFA).
CV: facial edema.
EENT: dry or irritated nose or throat, hoarseness; nasal irritation, rhinitis (Nasacort HFA), *sneezing.*
GI: dry or irritated tongue or mouth, *oral candidiasis.*
Respiratory: cough, wheezing.
Other: adrenal insufficiency, ***hypothalamic-pituitary-adrenal function suppression.***

Interactions

None significant.

Effects on lab test results

None reported.

Pharmacokinetics

Absorption: Slow.
Distribution: Without spacer, about 10% to 25% of dose goes to airways; remainder goes to mouth and throat and is swallowed. Spacer may help a greater percentage reach lungs.
Metabolism: In liver. Some drug that reaches lungs may be metabolized locally.
Excretion: In urine and feces. *Half-life:* 18 to 36 hours; 5½ hours (HFA)

Route	Onset	Peak	Duration
Inhalation	1–4 wk	Unknown	Unknown
Intranasal	Unknown	4 hr	Unknown

Action

Chemical effect: May decrease inflammation by stabilizing leukocyte lysosomal membranes.
Therapeutic effect: Improves breathing ability.

Available forms

Inhalation aerosol: 100 mcg/metered spray
Nasal aerosol: 55 mcg/actuation.

NURSING PROCESS

Assessment

- Assess patient's asthma or allergic rhinitis before starting therapy and regularly thereafter to monitor drug's effectiveness.
- Be alert for adverse reactions.
- Assess patient's and family's knowledge of drug therapy.

Nursing diagnoses

- Ineffective breathing pattern related to presence of asthma
- Impaired tissue integrity related to drug's adverse effect on oral mucosa
- Deficient knowledge related to drug therapy

Planning and implementation

- Patient who has recently been transferred to oral inhaled steroids from systemic administration of steroids may need to be placed back on systemic steroids during periods of stress or severe asthma attacks.
- Taper oral therapy slowly.
- If patient is also to receive bronchodilator by inhalation, give bronchodilator first, wait several minutes, and then give triamcinolone.
- If more than one inhalation is ordered for each dose, wait 1 minute between inhalations.
- Store drug between 36° and 86° F (2° and 30° C).

ALERT: Don't confuse triamcinolone with Triaminicin, Triaminic, or Triaminicol.

Patient teaching

- Inform patient that inhaled steroids don't provide relief for emergency asthma attacks.
- Instruct patient to use drug as prescribed, even when feeling well.
- Advise patient to ensure delivery of proper dose by gently warming canister to room temperature before using and by using the spacer. Patient can carry canister in his pocket to keep it warm.
- Instruct patient requiring bronchodilator to use it several minutes before triamcinolone. Tell him to wait 1 minute before repeat inhalations and to hold his breath for a few seconds to enhance drug action.
- Teach patient to check mucous membranes frequently for signs of fungal infection.
- Tell patient to prevent oral fungal infections by gargling or rinsing mouth with water after each use of inhaler but not to swallow water.
- Tell patient to keep inhaler clean and unobstructed by washing it with warm water and drying it thoroughly after use.
- Instruct patient to contact prescriber if response to therapy decreases; prescriber may need to adjust dosage. Tell patient not to exceed recommended dosage on his own.

• Instruct patient to wear or carry medical identification at all times.

Evaluation

• Patient exhibits improved breathing ability.
• Patient maintains normal oral mucosa integrity.
• Patient and family state understanding of drug therapy.

triamterene

(trigh-AM-tuh-reen)

Dyrenium

Pharmacologic class: potassium-sparing diuretic
Therapeutic class: diuretic
Pregnancy risk category: B

Indications and dosages

▶ **Edema.** *Adults:* Initially, 100 mg P.O. b.i.d. after meals. Total daily dose shouldn't exceed 300 mg.

Contraindications and cautions

• Contraindicated in patients hypersensitive to the drug or any of its components, and in those with anuria, severe or progressive renal disease or dysfunction, severe hepatic disease, or hyperkalemia.
• Use cautiously in patients with impaired liver function or diabetes mellitus, and in debilitated patients.
Lifespan: In pregnant women, use cautiously. In breast-feeding women, safety and effectiveness haven't been established. In children, safety and effectiveness haven't been established. In elderly patients, use cautiously.

Adverse reactions

CNS: dizziness, fatigue, headache, weakness.
CV: hypotension.
GI: diarrhea, dry mouth, stomatitis, nausea, vomiting.
GU: azotemia, interstitial nephritis, nephrolithiasis.
Hematologic: ***agranulocytosis,*** megaloblastic anemia related to low folic acid level, ***thrombocytopenia.***
Hepatic: jaundice.
Metabolic: ***acidosis,*** hyperglycemia, **HYPERKALEMIA,** hypokalemia, hyponatremia.
Musculoskeletal: muscle cramps.
Skin: photosensitivity reactions, rash.
Other: ***anaphylaxis.***

Interactions

Drug-drug. *ACE inhibitors, potassium supplements:* May increase risk of hyperkalemia. Don't use together.
Amantadine: May increase risk of amantadine toxicity. Don't use together.
Lithium: May decrease lithium clearance, increasing risk of lithium toxicity. Monitor lithium level.
NSAIDs (indomethacin): May increase risk of nephrotoxicity. Avoid use together.
Quinidine: May interfere with some laboratory tests that measure quinidine level. Inform laboratory that patient is taking triamterene.
Drug-food. *Potassium-containing salt substitutes, potassium-rich foods:* May increase risk of hyperkalemia. Discourage use together.
Drug-lifestyle. *Sun exposure:* May increase risk of photosensitivity reactions. Urge patient to avoid prolonged or unprotected exposure to sunlight.

Effects on lab test results

• May increase BUN, creatinine, glucose, and uric acid levels. May decrease sodium and hemoglobin levels and hematocrit. May increase or decrease potassium level.
• May increase liver function test values. May decrease RBC, granulocyte, and platelet counts.

Pharmacokinetics

Absorption: Rapid; extent varies.
Distribution: About 67% protein-bound.
Metabolism: By hydroxylation and sulfation.
Excretion: In urine. *Half-life:* 100 to 150 minutes.

Route	Onset	Peak	Duration
P.O.	2–4 hr	6–8 hr	7–9 hr

Action

Chemical effect: Inhibits sodium reabsorption and potassium and hydrogen excretion by direct action on distal tubule.
Therapeutic effect: Promotes water and sodium excretion.

Available forms

Capsules: 50 mg, 100 mg

NURSING PROCESS

Assessment

- Assess patient's edema before starting therapy and regularly thereafter. Full effect of triamterene is delayed 2 to 3 days when used alone.
- Monitor blood pressure, and BUN and electrolyte levels.
- Watch for blood dyscrasia.
- Be alert for adverse reactions and drug interactions.
- Assess patient's and family's knowledge of drug therapy.

Nursing diagnoses

- Excess fluid volume related to underlying condition
- Ineffective health maintenance related to drug-induced hyperkalemia
- Deficient knowledge related to drug therapy

Planning and implementation

- Give drug after meals, to minimize nausea.

ALERT: Withdraw drug gradually to minimize excessive rebound potassium excretion.

- Drug is less potent than thiazides and loop diuretics and is useful as adjunct to other diuretic therapy. Triamterene is usually used with potassium-wasting diuretics.
- When used with other diuretics, lower initial dose of each drug and adjust to individual requirements.

ALERT: Don't confuse triamterene with trimipramine.

Patient teaching

- Tell patient to take drug after meals.

ALERT: Warn patient to avoid excessive ingestion of potassium-rich foods, potassium-containing salt substitutes, and potassium supplements to prevent serious hyperkalemia.

- Instruct patient to avoid direct sunlight, wear protective clothing, and use sunblock to prevent photosensitivity reactions.

Evaluation

- Patient has no signs of edema.
- Patient's potassium level is normal.
- Patient and family state understanding of drug therapy.

triazolam

(trigh-AH-zoh-lam)

Alti-Triazolam ♦, Apo-Triazo ♦, Halcion, Novo-Triolam ♦

Pharmacologic class: benzodiazepine
Therapeutic class: sedative-hypnotic
Pregnancy risk category: X
Controlled substance schedule: IV

Indications and dosages

▶ **Insomnia.** *Adults:* 0.125 to 0.5 mg P.O. at bedtime.

Adults older than age 65: Give 0.125 mg P.O. at bedtime; increased, if needed, to 0.25 mg P.O. at bedtime.

Contraindications and cautions

- Contraindicated in patients hypersensitive to benzodiazepines.
- Use cautiously in patients with impaired liver or kidney function, chronic pulmonary insufficiency, sleep apnea, depression, suicidal tendencies, or history of drug abuse.

Lifespan: In pregnant women, drug is contraindicated. In breast-feeding women, drug isn't recommended. In children, safety and effectiveness haven't been established.

Adverse reactions

CNS: amnesia, ataxia, complex sleep disorders, confusion, depression, *dizziness, drowsiness, headache,* lack of coordination, lightheadedness, nervousness, rebound insomnia.
GI: nausea, stomatitis, vomiting.
Other: ***anaphylaxis, angioedema,*** physical or psychological abuse.

Interactions

Drug-drug. *Cimetidine, erythromycin, hormonal contraceptives, isoniazid, ranitidine:* May cause prolonged triazolam blood level. Monitor patient for increased sedation.

CNS depressants, including opioid analgesics, other psychotropic drugs, anticonvulsants, antihistamines: May cause excessive CNS depression. Use together cautiously.

Diltiazem: May increase CNS depression and prolong effects of triazolam. Use lower dose of triazolam.

Fluconazole, itraconazole, ketoconazole, miconazole: May increase and prolong drug level, CNS depression, and psychomotor impairment. Don't use together.
Potent CYP3A inhibitors, such as nefazodone: May decrease clearance of triazolam. Don't use together.
Drug-herb. *Calendula, catnip, hops, lady's slipper, lemon balm, passion flower, sassafras, skullcap, valerian, yerba maté:* May increase risk of sedative effects. Monitor patient closely if used together.
Kava: May cause excessive sedation. Discourage use together.
Drug-food. *Grapefruit juice:* May delay drug onset and increase effects. Advise patient to avoid use together.
Drug-lifestyle. *Alcohol use:* May cause additive CNS effects. Strongly discourage use together.

Effects on lab test results

- May increase liver function test values.

Pharmacokinetics

Absorption: Good.
Distribution: Wide. 90% protein-bound.
Metabolism: In liver.
Excretion: In urine. *Half-life:* 1½ to 5½ hours.

Route	Onset	Peak	Duration
P.O.	Unknown	1–2 hr	Unknown

Action

Chemical effect: May act on limbic system, thalamus, and hypothalamus of CNS to produce hypnotic effects.
Therapeutic effect: Promotes sleep.

Available forms

Tablets: 0.125 mg, 0.25 mg

NURSING PROCESS

Assessment

- Assess patient before therapy and regularly thereafter to monitor drug's effectiveness.
- Assess mental status and neurologic function before starting therapy. An elderly patient is more sensitive to the drug's CNS effects.
- Be alert for adverse reactions and drug interactions.
- Assess patient's and family's knowledge of drug therapy.

Nursing diagnoses

- Insomnia related to underlying disorder
- Risk for injury related to drug-induced adverse CNS reactions
- Deficient knowledge related to drug therapy

Planning and implementation

- Make plans to prevent hoarding or intentional overdose by patient who's depressed, suicidal, drug-dependent, or has history of drug abuse.
- Store drug in cool, dry place away from light.
- Institute safety precautions once drug has been given.

ALERT: Don't confuse Halcion with Haldol or halcinonide.

Patient teaching

- Warn patient not to take more than prescribed amount because overdose can occur at total daily dosage of 2 mg (four times the highest recommended amount).
- Warn patient about performing activities that require mental alertness or physical coordination. For inpatient, supervise walking and raise bed rails, particularly for elderly patient.
- Warn patient about possible complex sleep disorders.
- Inform patient that drug is short-acting and has less tendency to cause morning drowsiness.
- Tell patient that rebound insomnia may develop for 1 or 2 nights after stopping therapy.

Evaluation

- Patient states that drug produces sleep.
- Patient sustains no injury from adverse CNS reactions.
- Patient and family state understanding of drug therapy.

trifluoperazine hydrochloride

(trigh-floo-oh-PER-eh-zeen high-droh-KLOR-ighd)
Apo-Trifluoperazine ♦, Novo-Flurazine ♦

Pharmacologic class: phenothiazine (piperazine derivative)
Therapeutic class: antiemetic, antipsychotic
Pregnancy risk category: C

Indications and dosages

▶ **Anxiety.** *Adults:* 1 to 2 mg P.O. b.i.d. Maximum, 6 mg daily. Don't use for longer than 12 weeks.

▶ **Schizophrenia and other psychotic disorders.** *Adult outpatients:* 1 to 2 mg P.O. b.i.d., increased if needed. *Adult inpatients:* 2 to 5 mg P.O. b.i.d.; may increase gradually to 40 mg daily.
Children ages 6 to 12 (hospitalized or under close supervision): 1 mg P.O. daily or b.i.d.; may increase gradually to 15 mg daily, if needed.

Contraindications and cautions

- Contraindicated in patients hypersensitive to phenothiazines and in patients experiencing coma, CNS depression, bone marrow suppression, or liver damage.
- Use cautiously in debilitated patients and in patients with CV disease (may cause drop in blood pressure), seizure disorder, glaucoma, or prostatic hyperplasia. Also use cautiously in patients exposed to extreme heat.

Lifespan: In pregnant or breast-feeding women and in children younger than age 6, safety and effectiveness haven't been established. In elderly patients, use cautiously.

Adverse reactions

CNS: dizziness, drowsiness, *extrapyramidal reactions,* fatigue, headache, insomnia, ***neuroleptic malignant syndrome,*** pseudoparkinsonism, *tardive dyskinesia.*
CV: ECG changes, *orthostatic hypotension,* tachycardia.
EENT: *blurred vision,* ocular changes.
GI: constipation, dry mouth, nausea.
GU: menstrual irregularities, *urine retention.*
Hematologic: *agranulocytosis, transient leukopenia.*
Hepatic: cholestatic jaundice.
Metabolic: weight gain.
Skin: *photosensitivity reactions,* rash.
Other: allergic reaction, gynecomastia, inhibited lactation.

Interactions

Drug-drug. *Antacids:* May inhibit absorption of oral phenothiazines. Separate doses by at least 2 hours.
Barbiturates, lithium: May decrease phenothiazine effect. Monitor patient.
Centrally acting antihypertensives: May decrease antihypertensive effect. Monitor blood pressure.
CNS depressants: May increase CNS depression. Use together cautiously.
Propranolol: May increase levels of both propranolol and trifluoperazine. Monitor patient closely.
Warfarin: May decrease effect of oral anticoagulants. Monitor PT and INR.
Drug-herb. *Dong quai, St. John's wort:* May increase photosensitivity reactions. Discourage use together.
Ginkgo: May decrease adverse effects of thioridazine. Monitor patient.
Kava: May increase risk of dystonic reactions. Discourage use together.
Milk thistle: May decrease liver toxicity caused by phenothiazines. Discourage use together; monitor liver enzyme levels if used together.
Yohimbe: May increase risk of yohimbe toxicity. Discourage use together.
Drug-lifestyle. *Alcohol use:* May increase CNS depression, particularly psychomotor skills. Strongly discourage use together.
Sun exposure: May cause photosensitivity reactions. Urge patient to avoid prolonged or unprotected exposure to sunlight.

Effects on lab test results

- May increase liver enzyme levels.
- May decrease WBC and granulocyte counts.

Pharmacokinetics

Absorption: Variable with P.O. use.
Distribution: Wide. 91% to 99% protein-bound.
Metabolism: Extensively by liver.
Excretion: Mainly in urine; some in feces.
Half-life: 20 to 40 hours.

Route	Onset	Peak	Duration
P.O.	Up to several wk	Unknown	Unknown

Action

Chemical effect: Unknown; probably blocks postsynaptic dopamine receptors in brain.
Therapeutic effect: Relieves anxiety and signs and symptoms of psychotic disorders.

Available forms

Oral concentrate: 10 mg/ml
Tablets (regular and film-coated): 1 mg, 2 mg, 5 mg, 10 mg

NURSING PROCESS

Assessment
- Assess patient's condition before starting therapy and regularly thereafter to monitor drug's effectiveness.
- Watch for orthostatic hypotension, especially with parenteral use.
- Monitor patient for tardive dyskinesia, which may occur after prolonged use. It may not appear until months or years later and may disappear spontaneously or persist for life, despite stopping the drug.
- Monitor therapy with weekly bilirubin tests during first month, periodic blood tests (CBC and liver function), and ophthalmologic tests (long-term use).

ALERT: Monitor patient for symptoms of neuroleptic malignant syndrome (extrapyramidal effects, hyperthermia, autonomic disturbance), which is rare but can be fatal. It isn't necessarily related to length of drug use or type of neuroleptic; however, more than 60% of patients are men.
- Assess patient's and family's knowledge of drug therapy.

Nursing diagnoses
- Anxiety related to underlying condition
- Disturbed thought processes related to underlying psychotic disorder
- Deficient knowledge related to drug therapy

Planning and implementation
- Although there's little likelihood of contact dermatitis, those sensitive to phenothiazine drugs should avoid direct contact. Wear gloves when preparing liquid forms.
- Dilute liquid concentrate with 60 ml of tomato or fruit juice, carbonated beverage, coffee, tea, milk, water, or semisolid food.
- Protect concentrate from light. Slight yellowing of drug is common; it doesn't affect potency. Discard markedly discolored solutions.
- Keep patient supine for 1 hour after drug administration, and advise him to change position slowly.
- Don't abruptly stop giving the drug unless a severe adverse reaction occurs. Abruptly stopping long-term therapy may cause gastritis, nausea, vomiting, dizziness, tremor, feeling of warmth or cold, diaphoresis, tachycardia, headache, insomnia, anorexia, muscle rigidity, altered mental status, or evidence of autonomic instability.
- Don't give the dose, and notify prescriber, if patient develops jaundice, symptoms of blood dyscrasia (fever, sore throat, infection, cellulitis, weakness), or extrapyramidal reactions longer than a few hours, especially in pregnant women and in children.
- Acute dystonic reactions may be treated with diphenhydramine.

ALERT: Don't confuse trifluoperazine with triflupromazine.

Patient teaching
- Teach patient or caregiver how to prepare oral form of drug.
- Warn patient to avoid activities that require alertness or good psychomotor coordination until drug's CNS effects are known; drowsiness and dizziness usually subside after a few weeks.
- Tell patient not to drink alcohol during therapy.
- Instruct patient to report urine retention or constipation.
- Tell patient to use sun block and wear protective clothing to avoid photosensitivity reactions.
- Tell patient to relieve dry mouth with sugarless gum or hard candy.

Evaluation
- Patient's anxiety is reduced.
- Patient's behavior and communication exhibit improved thought processes.
- Patient and family state understanding of drug therapy.

trihexyphenidyl hydrochloride
(trigh-heks-eh-FEEN-ih-dil high-droh-KLOR-ighd)
Apo-Trihex ♦, Artane ♦, Trihexy-2, Trihexy-5

Pharmacologic class: anticholinergic
Therapeutic class: antiparkinsonian
Pregnancy risk category: C

Indications and dosages
▶ **All forms of parkinsonism; adjunct with levodopa in managing parkinsonism.** *Adults:*

1 mg P.O. first day, increased by 2 mg q 3 to 5 days until total of 6 to 10 mg is given daily. Usually given t.i.d. with meals. Sometimes given q.i.d. (last dose at bedtime). Postencephalitic parkinsonism may require total daily dosage of 12 to 15 mg.

▶ **Drug-induced extrapyramidal reactions.** *Adults:* 5 to 15 mg P.O. daily. Initial dose of 1 mg may control some reactions.

Contraindications and cautions

• Contraindicated in patients hypersensitive to the drug or any of its components.

• Use cautiously in patients with glaucoma; cardiac, hepatic, or renal disorders; obstructive disease of the GI or GU tract; or prostatic hyperplasia.

Lifespan: In pregnant women, safety and effectiveness haven't been established. In breast-feeding women, drug isn't recommended. In children, safety and effectiveness haven't been established. In elderly patients, watch for mental confusion or disorientation.

Adverse reactions

CNS: dizziness, drowsiness, hallucinations, headache, nervousness, weakness.
CV: tachycardia.
EENT: blurred vision, increased intraocular pressure, mydriasis.
GI: constipation, *dry mouth, nausea,* vomiting.
GU: urinary hesitancy, urine retention.

Interactions

Drug-drug. *Amantadine:* May have additive anticholinergic reactions, such as confusion and hallucinations. Reduce dosage of trihexyphenidyl before giving it.
Levodopa: May increase drug effect. May require lower doses of both drugs.
Drug-lifestyle. *Alcohol use:* May increase sedative effects. Discourage use together.

Effects on lab test results

None reported.

Pharmacokinetics

Absorption: Readily absorbed.
Distribution: Unknown. Crosses blood-brain barrier.
Metabolism: Unknown.
Excretion: In urine. *Half-life:* 5½ to 10¾ hours.

Route	Onset	Peak	Duration
P.O.	1 hr	2–3 hr	6–12 hr

Action

Chemical effect: Unknown; blocks central cholinergic receptors, helping to balance cholinergic activity in basal ganglia.
Therapeutic effect: Improves physical mobility in patients with parkinsonism.

Available forms

Elixir: 2 mg/5 ml
Tablets: 2 mg, 5 mg

NURSING PROCESS

Assessment

• Assess patient's condition before starting therapy and regularly thereafter to monitor drug's effectiveness.

ALERT: Gonioscopic ocular evaluation and monitoring of intraocular pressure are needed, especially if patient is older than age 40.

• Be alert for adverse reactions and drug interactions. Adverse reactions are dose-related and usually transient.

• Assess patient's and family's knowledge of drug therapy.

Nursing diagnoses

• Impaired physical mobility related to presence of parkinsonism
• Risk for injury related to drug-induced adverse CNS reactions
• Deficient knowledge related to drug therapy

Planning and implementation

• Dose may need to be increased gradually in a patient who develops drug tolerance.
• Give drug with meals.

Patient teaching

• Warn patient that drug may cause nausea if taken before meals.
• Tell patient to avoid activities that require alertness until the drug's CNS effects are known.
• Advise patient to report urinary hesitancy or urine retention.
• Tell patient to relieve dry mouth with cool drinks, ice chips, sugarless gum, or hard candy.

Evaluation

- Patient has improved physical mobility.
- Patient sustains no injury from adverse reactions.
- Patient and family state understanding of drug therapy.

trimethobenzamide hydrochloride

(trigh-meth-oh-BEN-zuh-mighd high-droh-KLOR-ighd)

Tebamide, T-Gen, Ticon, Tigan, Triban, Trimazide

Pharmacologic class: ethanolamine-related antihistamine
Therapeutic class: antiemetic
Pregnancy risk category: C

Indications and dosages

▶ **Nausea, vomiting.** *Adults:* 250 mg P.O. t.i.d. or q.i.d.; or 200 mg I.M. or P.R. t.i.d. or q.i.d.

▶ **Prevention of postoperative nausea and vomiting.** *Adults:* 200 mg I.M. or P.R. as single dose before or during surgery; if needed, repeat 3 hours after termination of anesthesia. Limit use to prolonged vomiting from known cause.
Children weighing 13 to 40 kg (28 to 88 lb): 100 to 200 mg P.O. or P.R. t.i.d. or q.i.d.
Children weighing less than 13 kg: 100 mg P.R. t.i.d. or q.i.d. Don't use in premature or newborn infants.

Contraindications and cautions

- Contraindicated in patients hypersensitive to the drug or any of its components. Suppositories are contraindicated in patients hypersensitive to benzocaine hydrochloride or similar local anesthetics.
- **Lifespan:** In pregnant women, use cautiously. In breast-feeding women, safety and effectiveness haven't been established. In children, use cautiously. In children with viral illness, drug isn't recommended because it may contribute to development of Reye syndrome.

Adverse reactions

CNS: ***coma,*** depression, disorientation, dizziness, *drowsiness,* headache, parkinsonian-like symptoms, ***seizures.***
CV: hypotension.
EENT: blurred vision.
GI: diarrhea.
Hepatic: jaundice.
Musculoskeletal: muscle cramps.
Skin: hypersensitivity reaction (burning, pain, redness, stinging, swelling at I.M. injection site).

Interactions

Drug-drug. *CNS depressants:* May cause additive CNS depression. Avoid use together.
Drug-lifestyle. *Alcohol use:* May cause additive CNS depression. Discourage use together.

Effects on lab test results

None reported.

Pharmacokinetics

Absorption: About 60% after P.O. use; unknown after P.R. or I.M. use.
Distribution: Unknown.
Metabolism: About 50% to 70%, probably in liver.
Excretion: In urine and feces. *Half-life:* 7 to 9 hours.

Route	Onset	Peak	Duration
P.O.	10–20 min	Unknown	3–4 hr
I.M.	15–30 min	Unknown	2–3 hr
P.R.	Unknown	Unknown	Unknown

Action

Chemical effect: Unknown; may act on chemoreceptor trigger zone to inhibit nausea and vomiting.
Therapeutic effect: Prevents or relieves nausea and vomiting.

Available forms

Capsules: 100 mg, 250 mg
Injection: 100 mg/ml
Suppositories: 100 mg, 200 mg

NURSING PROCESS

Assessment

- Assess patient's condition before starting therapy and regularly thereafter to monitor drug's effectiveness.
- Be alert for adverse reactions and drug interactions.
- Assess patient's and family's knowledge of drug therapy.

Nursing diagnoses
- Risk for deficient fluid volume related to potential for or presence of nausea and vomiting
- Diarrhea related to drug-induced adverse GI reactions
- Deficient knowledge related to drug therapy

Planning and implementation
- Inject I.M. dose deep into upper outer quadrant of gluteal region to reduce pain and local irritation.
- Refrigerate suppositories.
- If skin hypersensitivity reaction occurs, don't give the drug.

ALERT: Don't confuse Tigan with Ticar.

Patient teaching
- Advise patient of possibility of drowsiness and dizziness, and caution against driving or performing other activities requiring alertness until the drug's CNS effects are known.
- Warn patient that giving the drug I.M. may be painful.
- If patient will be using suppositories, instruct him to remove foil and, if needed, moisten suppository with water for 10 to 30 seconds before inserting. Tell him to store suppositories in refrigerator.

Evaluation
- Patient maintains adequate hydration, and nausea and vomiting cease.
- Patient maintains normal bowel pattern.
- Patient and family state understanding of drug therapy.

trimethoprim
(trigh-METH-uh-prim)

Alprim ◇, Primsol, Proloprim, Trimpex, Triprim ◇

Pharmacologic class: synthetic folate antagonist
Therapeutic class: antibiotic
Pregnancy risk category: C

Indications and dosages
▶ **Acute otitis media caused by susceptible strains of *Streptococcus pneumoniae* and *Haemophilus influenzae*.** *Children age 6 months and older:* 10 mg/kg Primsol daily in divided doses q 12 hours for 10 days.

▶ **Uncomplicated UTI caused by *Escherichia coli, Proteus mirabilis, Klebsiella pneumoniae, Enterobacter* species, coagulase-negative *Staphylococcus* species (including *Staphylococcus saprophyticus*).** *Adults:* 100 mg (10 ml) q 12 hours, or 200 mg (20 ml) daily for 10 days.

▶ **Prophylaxis of chronic and recurrent UTI‡.** *Adults:* 100 mg P.O. at bedtime for 6 weeks to 6 months.

▶ **Traveler's diarrhea‡.** *Adults:* 200 mg P.O. b.i.d. for 3 to 5 days.

▶ ***Pneumocystis jiroveci (carinii)* pneumonia‡.** *Adults:* 5 mg/kg P.O. t.i.d. with dapsone 100 mg daily for 21 days.

Adjust-a-dose: For patients with renal impairment, if creatinine clearance is 15 to 30 ml/minute, give half the recommended dose q 12 hours; if less than 15 ml/minute, don't use drug.

Contraindications and cautions
- Contraindicated in patients hypersensitive to the drug or any of its components, and in those with documented megaloblastic anemia caused by folate deficiency.
- Use cautiously in patients with hepatic impairment.

Lifespan: In pregnant women, use cautiously. In breast-feeding women, drug isn't recommended. In children younger than age 12, safety and effectiveness (other than of Primsol) haven't been established.

Adverse reactions
CNS: fever.
GI: diarrhea, epigastric distress, glossitis, nausea, vomiting.
Hematologic: ***leukopenia,*** megaloblastic anemia, ***methemoglobinemia, thrombocytopenia.***
Skin: exfoliative dermatitis, *pruritus, rash.*

Interactions
Drug-drug. *Phenytoin:* May decrease phenytoin metabolism and increase blood level. Monitor patient for toxicity.

Effects on lab test results
- May increase BUN, creatinine, bilirubin, and aminotransferase levels. May decrease hemoglobin level and hematocrit.
- May decrease platelet and WBC counts.

Pharmacokinetics

Absorption: Quick and complete.
Distribution: Wide. About 42% to 46% protein-bound.
Metabolism: Less than 20% in liver.
Excretion: Mainly in urine. *Half-life:* 8 to 11 hours.

Route	Onset	Peak	Duration
P.O.	Unknown	1–4 hr	Unknown

Action

Chemical effect: Interferes with action of dihydrofolate reductase, inhibiting bacterial synthesis of folic acid.
Therapeutic effect: Inhibits certain bacteria.

Available forms

Oral solution: 50 mg/5 ml
Tablets: 100 mg, 200 mg

NURSING PROCESS

Assessment

- Assess patient's infection before starting therapy and regularly thereafter to monitor drug's effectiveness.
- Obtain urine specimen for culture and sensitivity tests before giving the first dose. Start therapy pending test results.

ALERT: Monitor CBC routinely. Signs and symptoms such as sore throat, fever, pallor, and purpura may be early indications of serious blood disorders. Prolonged use of trimethoprim at high doses may cause bone marrow suppression.

- Be alert for adverse reactions and drug interactions.
- If adverse GI reactions occur, monitor hydration.
- Assess patient's and family's knowledge of drug therapy.

Nursing diagnoses

- Ineffective protection related to presence of susceptible bacteria
- Risk for deficient fluid volume related to drug-induced adverse GI reactions
- Deficient knowledge related to drug therapy

Planning and implementation

- Because resistance to trimethoprim develops rapidly when drug is given alone, it's usually given with other drugs.

ALERT: Trimethoprim is also used with sulfamethoxazole; don't confuse the two.

Patient teaching

- Instruct patient to take drug as prescribed, even if he feels better.

Evaluation

- Patient is free from infection.
- Patient maintains adequate hydration.
- Patient and family state understanding of drug therapy.

triptorelin pamoate

(trip-TOE-reh-lin PAM-o-eight)
Trelstar Depot, Trelstar LA

Pharmacologic class: synthetic luteinizing hormone-releasing hormone (LHRH) analogue
Therapeutic class: antineoplastic
Pregnancy risk category: X

Indications and dosages

▶ **Palliative treatment of advanced prostate cancer.** *Men:* 3.75 mg Trelstar Depot I.M. given monthly as a single injection, or 11.25 mg Trelstar LA I.M. into either buttock q 12 weeks.

Contraindications and cautions

- Contraindicated in patients hypersensitive to the drug or any of its components, other LHRH agonists, or LHRH.
- Use cautiously in patients with metastatic vertebral lesions or upper or lower urinary tract obstruction during the first few weeks of therapy.
- Use cautiously in patients with hepatic and renal impairment; they have a level of exposure to drug two to four times higher than normal.

Lifespan: Drug is used for men only. In boys, safety and effectiveness haven't been studied.

Adverse reactions

CNS: dizziness, emotional lability, fatigue, headache, insomnia, pain, ***spinal cord compression.***

T

CV: hypertension.
GI: diarrhea, vomiting.
GU: impotence, urine retention, UTI.
Hematologic: anemia.
Musculoskeletal: leg pain, *skeletal pain.*
Skin: pruritus.
Other: *hot flushes,* pain at injection site.

Interactions

Drug-drug. *Hyperprolactinemic drugs:* May decrease pituitary gonadotropin-releasing hormone (GnRH) receptors. Don't use together.

Effects on lab test results

- May increase glucose, BUN, AST, ALT, and alkaline phosphatase levels. May transiently increase testosterone level. May decrease hemoglobin level and hematocrit.

Pharmacokinetics

Absorption: Maintains level over a period of a month.
Distribution: No evidence of protein-binding.
Metabolism: Unknown, but is unlikely to involve hepatic microsomal enzymes; no metabolites have been identified.
Excretion: By liver and kidneys. *Half-life:* 2 to 3 hours.

Route	Onset	Peak	Duration
I.M.	Unknown	Unknown	1 mo

Action

Chemical effect: Is a potent inhibitor of gonadotropin secretion. In men, testosterone declines to a level typically seen in surgically castrated men. As a result, tissues and functions that depend on these hormones become inactive.
Therapeutic effect: Decreases effects of sex hormones on tumor growth in the prostate gland.

Available forms

Injection: 3.75 mg, 11.25 mg

NURSING PROCESS

Assessment

- Assess patient's condition before starting therapy and regularly thereafter to monitor drug's effectiveness.
- Monitor testosterone and prostate-specific antigen levels.
- Assess patient's and family's knowledge of drug therapy.

Nursing diagnoses

- Ineffective health maintenance related to underlying condition
- Acute pain related to adverse drug effects
- Deficient knowledge related to drug therapy

Planning and implementation

- Give drug only under the supervision of an experienced prescriber.

ALERT: Only sterile water may be used as a diluent.

- Reconstitute powder with 2 ml of sterile water for injection. Shake well until suspension appears milky. Use 20 G needle.
- Change the injection site periodically.
- Monitor patients with metastatic vertebral lesions or upper or lower urinary tract obstruction during the first few weeks of therapy.
- Initially, drug causes a transient increase in testosterone level. As a result, signs and symptoms of prostate cancer may worsen during the first few weeks of therapy.
- Patients may have worsening of symptoms or onset of new symptoms, including bone pain, neuropathy, hematuria, or urethral or bladder outlet obstruction.

ALERT: Spinal cord compression, which can lead to paralysis and possibly death, may occur. If spinal cord compression or renal impairment develops, give standard treatment. In extreme cases, immediate orchiectomy is considered.

- If patient has an allergic reaction, immediately stop giving the drug, treat symptoms, and give supportive care.
- Diagnostic tests of pituitary-gonadal function conducted during and after therapy may be misleading.

Patient teaching

- Inform the patient about adverse reactions.
- Tell patient that symptoms (including bone pain, neuropathy, hematuria, or urethral or bladder outlet obstruction) may worsen during the first few weeks of therapy.

• Inform patient that a blood test will be used to monitor response to therapy.

Evaluation

• Patient responds well to drug.
• Patient denies pain.
• Patient and family state understanding of drug therapy.

trospium chloride

(TROSE-pee-uhm KLOHR-ighd)
Sanctura

Pharmacologic class: anticholinergic
Therapeutic class: antimuscarinic, antispasmodic
Pregnancy risk category: C

Indications and dosages

▶ **Overactive bladder with symptoms of urinary urge incontinence, urgency, and frequency.** *Adults younger than age 75:* Give 20 mg P.O. b.i.d. taken on an empty stomach or at least 1 hour before a meal.
Adults age 75 and older: Based on patient tolerance, reduce dose to 20 mg once daily.
Adjust-a-dose: If patient's creatinine clearance is less than 30 ml/minute, give 20 mg P.O. once daily at bedtime.

Contraindications and cautions

• Contraindicated in patients hypersensitive to the drug or any of its components and in patients with or at risk for urine retention, gastric retention, or uncontrolled narrow-angle glaucoma.
• Use cautiously in patients with significant bladder outflow obstruction, obstructive GI disorders, ulcerative colitis, intestinal atony, myasthenia gravis, renal insufficiency, moderate or severe hepatic impairment, or controlled narrow-angle glaucoma.
Lifespan: In pregnant women, use only if benefits to the patient outweigh risks to the fetus. In breast-feeding women, use cautiously; it's unknown if the drug appears in breast milk. In children, safety and effectiveness haven't been established. In elderly patients, use a lower dose because they may have an increased risk of anticholinergic effects.

Adverse reactions

CNS: fatigue, headache.
EENT: dry eyes.
GI: abdominal pain, *constipation, dry mouth,* dyspepsia, flatulence.
GU: urine retention.

Interactions

Drug-drug. *Anticholinergics:* May increase dry mouth, constipation, or other adverse effects. Monitor patient.
Digoxin, metformin, morphine, pancuronium, procainamide, tenofovir, vancomycin: May alter elimination of these drugs or trospium, increasing level. Monitor patient closely.
Drug-food. *High-fat food:* May decrease absorption by up to 80%. Give trospium at least 1 hour before meals or on an empty stomach.
Drug-lifestyle. *Alcohol use:* May increase drowsiness. Discourage use together.

Effects on lab test results

None reported.

Pharmacokinetics

Absorption: Less than 10%. Taking drug after a high-fat meal significantly decreases absorption. It should be taken at least 1 hour before meals or on an empty stomach.
Distribution: Mostly in plasma. 50% to 85% protein-bound.
Metabolism: Not defined. Major pathway is most likely is the liver.
Excretion: About 85% appears in feces and about 6% in urine. *Half-life:* About 20 hours.

Route	Onset	Peak	Duration
P.O.	Unknown	5–6 hr	Unknown

Action

Chemical effect: Opposes the effect of acetylcholine on muscarinic receptors, reducing smooth muscle tone in the bladder and increasing maximum bladder capacity and volume at first contraction.
Therapeutic effect: Relieves symptoms of overactive bladder.

Available forms

Tablets: 20 mg

T

NURSING PROCESS

Assessment
• Assess patient before starting therapy to determine baseline bladder function, and reassess during therapy to monitor drug's effectiveness.
• Monitor patient for decreased gastric motility and constipation.
• Assess patient's and family's knowledge of drug therapy.

Nursing diagnoses
• Impaired urinary elimination related to underlying medical condition
• Impaired oral mucous membrane related to drug-induced adverse effects
• Deficient knowledge related to drug therapy

Planning and implementation
• If the patient has bladder-outflow obstruction, watch for evidence of urine retention.
• If the patient has urine retention, notify prescriber and prepare for urinary catheterization.
• Dry mouth and constipation are the most frequently reported adverse effects.

Patient teaching
• Tell patient to take drug on an empty stomach, at least 1 hour before meals.
• Discourage use of other drugs that may cause dry mouth, constipation, blurred vision, or urine retention.
• Tell patient that alcohol may increase drowsiness and fatigue. Urge him not to drink alcohol to excess while taking drug.
• Explain that drug may decrease sweating and increase the risk of heatstroke when used in hot environments or during strenuous activities.
• Urge patient to avoid activities that are hazardous or require mental alertness until the drug's CNS effects are known.

Evaluation
• Patient's bladder function improves with drug therapy.
• Patient has no dry mouth or controls adverse effects with sugarless gum, hard candy, or saliva substitute.
• Patient and family state understanding of drug therapy.

urokinase
(yoo-roh-KIGH-nays)
Abbokinase

Pharmacologic class: enzyme
Therapeutic class: thrombolytic
Pregnancy risk category: B

Indications and dosages
▶ **Lysis of acute massive pulmonary emboli and pulmonary emboli accompanied by unstable hemodynamics.** *Adults:* For I.V. infusion only by constant infusion pump. Priming dose: 4,400 international units/kg over 10 minutes, followed with 4,400 international units/kg/hour for 12 hours. Flush any drug remaining in the I.V. tubing with a volume of compatible I.V. solution about equal to that of the tubing at 15 ml/hour.
▶ **Venous catheter occlusion‡.** *Adults:* Instill 5,000 international units into occluded catheter.

I.V. administration
• Add 5 ml of sterile water for injection to vial. Don't use bacteriostatic water for injection to reconstitute; it contains preservatives. Use immediately after reconstitution.
• Dilute further with normal saline solution or D_5W solution before infusion.
• Solution may be filtered through a 0.45 micron or smaller filter before administration.
• Give by infusion pump. Total volume of fluid given shouldn't exceed 200 ml.
• Store powder at 36° to 46° F (2° to 8° C).

⊗ **Incompatibilities**
Other I.V. drugs.

Contraindications and cautions
• Contraindicated in patients with active internal bleeding; aneurysm; arteriovenous malformation; bleeding diathesis; visceral or intracranial cancer; ulcerative colitis; diverticulitis; severe hypertension; hemostatic defects, including those secondary to severe hepatic or renal insufficiency; uncontrolled hypocoagulation; subacute bacterial endocarditis or rheumatic

valvular disease; history of stroke; recent trauma with possible internal injuries; or recent cerebral embolism, thrombosis, or hemorrhage.
• Also contraindicated within 10 days after intra-arterial diagnostic procedure or surgery (liver or kidney biopsy, lumbar puncture, thoracentesis, paracentesis, or extensive or multiple cutdowns); and within 2 months after intracranial or intraspinal surgery.
• I.M. injections and other invasive procedures are contraindicated during urokinase therapy.
Lifespan: In pregnant women, drug should be used only when clearly needed. Drug is contraindicated during the first 10 days postpartum. In children, safety and effectiveness haven't been established.

Adverse reactions

CNS: fever, hemiplegia, ***stroke.***
CV: ***reperfusion arrhythmias,*** tachycardia, transient hypotension or hypertension.
GI: nausea, vomiting.
Hematologic: ***bleeding.***
Respiratory: ***bronchospasm,*** minor breathing difficulties.
Skin: phlebitis, rash.
Other: ***anaphylaxis,*** chills.

Interactions

Drug-drug. *Anticoagulants:* May increase risk of bleeding. Monitor patient closely.
Aspirin, dipyridamole, indomethacin, phenylbutazone, other drugs affecting platelet activity: May increase risk of bleeding. Monitor patient closely.

Effects on lab test results

• May decrease hemoglobin level and hematocrit.
• May increase PT, PTT, and INR.

Pharmacokinetics

Absorption: Given I.V.
Distribution: Rapidly cleared from circulation. Most of drug accumulates in kidneys and liver.
Metabolism: Rapid, in liver.
Excretion: Small amount in urine and bile.
Half-life: 10 to 20 minutes.

Route	Onset	Peak	Duration
I.V.	Immediate	20 min–2 hr	4 hr

Action

Chemical effect: Activates plasminogen by directly cleaving peptide bonds at two sites.
Therapeutic effect: Dissolves blood clots in lungs, coronary arteries, and venous catheters.

Available forms

Injection: 250,000 international units/vial

NURSING PROCESS

Assessment

• Assess patient's condition before starting therapy and regularly thereafter to monitor drug's effectiveness.
• Assess patient for contraindications to therapy.
• Monitor patient for excessive bleeding q 15 minutes for first hour, q 30 minutes for second through eighth hours, then once every shift. Pretreatment with drugs affecting platelets places patient at high risk for bleeding.
• Monitor pulse rates and color and sensation of limbs every hour.
• Keep laboratory flow sheet on patient's chart to monitor PTT, PT, INR, hemoglobin level, and hematocrit.
• Be alert for adverse reactions and drug interactions.
• Assess patient's and family's knowledge of drug therapy.

Nursing diagnoses

• Ineffective tissue perfusion (cardiopulmonary, peripheral) related to presence of blood clot(s)
• Ineffective protection related to drug-induced bleeding
• Deficient knowledge related to drug therapy

Planning and implementation

• Have typed and crossmatched RBCs and aminocaproic acid available to treat bleeding, and keep corticosteroids available to treat allergic reactions.
• Keep venipuncture sites to a minimum; use pressure dressing on puncture sites for at least 15 minutes.
• Keep limb being treated in alignment to prevent bleeding from infusion site.
• Don't handle the patient unnecessarily; pad side rails. Bruising is more likely during therapy.

U

• To prevent recurrent thrombosis, start heparin by continuous infusion when patient's thrombin time has decreased to less than twice the normal control value after urokinase has been stopped.

ALERT: Rare reports of orolingual edema, urticaria, cholesterol embolization, and infusion reactions causing hypoxia, cyanosis, acidosis, and back pain have occurred in patients receiving this drug.

Patient teaching

• Instruct patient to report symptoms of bleeding and other adverse reactions.

Evaluation

• Patient regains normal tissue perfusion with dissolution of blood clots.
• Patient doesn't experience serious complications from drug-induced bleeding.
• Patient and family state understanding of drug therapy.

ursodiol

(ur-sih-DIGH-al)

Actigall, URSO 250, URSO Forte

Pharmacologic class: bile acid
Therapeutic class: gallstone-dissolving drug
Pregnancy risk category: B

Indications and dosages

▶ **Dissolution of gallstones smaller than 20 mm in diameter in patients who are poor candidates for surgery or who refuse surgery.** *Adults:* 8 to 10 mg/kg P.O. daily in two or three divided doses.

▶ **Prevention of gallstone formation in obese patients experiencing rapid weight loss.** *Adults:* 300 mg P.O. b.i.d.

Contraindications and cautions

• Contraindicated in patients hypersensitive to the drug or other bile acids and in patients with chronic hepatic disease, unremitting acute cholecystitis, cholangitis, biliary obstruction, gallstone-induced pancreatitis, or biliary fistula. Capsules are contraindicated in patients with calcified cholesterol stones, radiopaque stones, or radiolucent bile pigment stones.

Lifespan: In pregnant women, use cautiously. In breast-feeding women, use cautiously; it's unknown if the drug appears in breast milk. In children, safety and effectiveness haven't been established.

Adverse reactions

CNS: anxiety, depression, *dizziness,* fatigue, *headache,* sleep disorders.
EENT: rhinitis.
GI: *abdominal pain,* biliary pain, cholecystitis, *constipation, diarrhea, dyspepsia,* flatulence, metallic taste, *nausea,* stomatitis, *vomiting.*
GU: UTI.
Musculoskeletal: arthralgia, back pain, myalgia.
Respiratory: cough.
Skin: diaphoresis, dry skin, hair thinning, pruritus, rash, urticaria.

Interactions

Drug-drug. *Antacids that contain aluminum, cholestyramine, colestipol:* May bind ursodiol and prevent its absorption. Avoid use together.
Clofibrate, estrogens, hormonal contraceptives: May increase hepatic cholesterol secretion; may counteract effects of ursodiol. Avoid use together.

Effects on lab test results

• May decrease liver enzyme level in patients with liver disease.

Pharmacokinetics

Absorption: About 90%.
Distribution: Conjugated and then secreted into hepatic bile ducts. Drug in bile is concentrated in gallbladder and expelled into duodenum in gallbladder bile. A small amount appears in systemic circulation.
Metabolism: In liver. A small amount undergoes bacterial degradation with each cycle of enterohepatic circulation.
Excretion: Mainly in feces; very small amount in urine. *Half-life:* Unknown.

Route	Onset	Peak	Duration
P.O.	Unknown	1–3 hr	Unknown

Action

Chemical effect: Unknown; probably suppresses hepatic synthesis and secretion of cholesterol as well as intestinal cholesterol absorption. After long-term administration, ursodiol can solubilize cholesterol from gallstones.

Therapeutic effect: Dissolves cholesterol gallstones.

Available forms

Capsules: 300 mg
Tablets: 250 mg, 300 mg

NURSING PROCESS

Assessment

- Assess patient's condition before starting therapy and regularly thereafter to monitor drug's effectiveness.
- Usually, therapy is long-term and requires ultrasound images of gallbladder q 6 months. If partial stone dissolution doesn't occur within 12 months, it's unlikely that complete dissolution will. Safety of use for longer than 24 months hasn't been established.

ALERT: Monitor liver function test results, including AST and ALT levels, at beginning of therapy, after 1 month, after 3 months, and then q 6 months during therapy. Abnormal test results may indicate worsening of disease. A hepatotoxic metabolite of drug may form in some patients.

- Be alert for adverse reactions and drug interactions.
- If adverse GI reaction occurs, monitor patient's hydration.
- Assess patient's and family's knowledge of drug therapy.

Nursing diagnoses

- Risk for injury related to presence of gallstones
- Risk for deficient fluid volume related to drug-induced adverse GI reactions
- Deficient knowledge related to drug therapy

Planning and implementation

- Gallstone dissolution requires months of therapy.
- Recurrence of stones within 5 years has been observed in up to 50% of patients.
- Complete dissolution doesn't occur in all patients.

Patient teaching

- Tell patient about alternative therapies, including watchful waiting (with no intervention) and cholecystectomy because relapse rate after bile acid therapy may be as high as 50% after 5 years.

Evaluation

- Patient is free from gallstones.
- Patient maintains adequate hydration.
- Patient and family state understanding of drug therapy.

valacyclovir hydrochloride

(val-ay-SIGH-kloh-veer high-droh-KLOR-ighd)
Valtrex

Pharmacologic class: synthetic purine nucleoside
Therapeutic class: antiviral
Pregnancy risk category: B

Indications and dosages

▶ **Herpes zoster (shingles) in immunocompetent patients.** *Adults:* 1 g P.O. q 8 hours for 7 days.

Adjust-a-dose: For patient with renal impairment, if creatinine clearance is 30 to 49 ml/minute, give 1 g q 12 hours; if 10 to 29 ml/minute, give 1 g q 24 hours; if less than 10 ml/minute, give 500 mg q 24 hours.

▶ **Initial episodes of genital herpes in immunocompetent adults.** *Adults:* 1 g P.O. q 12 hours for 10 days.

Adjust-a-dose: For patients with renal impairment, if creatinine clearance is 10 to 29 ml/minute, give 1 g q 24 hours; if less than 10 ml/minute, give 500 mg q 24 hours.

▶ **Recurrent genital herpes in immunocompetent patients.** *Adults:* 500 mg P.O. q 12 hours for 3 days.

Adjust-a-dose: For patients with renal impairment, if creatinine clearance is 29 ml/minute or less, give 500 mg q 24 hours.

▶ **Chronic suppression of recurrent genital herpes.** *Adults:* 1 g P.O. once daily.

Adjust-a-dose: For patients with renal impairment, if creatinine clearance is 29 ml/minute or less, give 500 mg q 24 hours.

▶ **Chronic suppression of genital herpes in patients with a history of 9 or fewer recurrences per year.** *Adults:* 500 mg P.O. daily.

V

Adjust-a-dose: For patients with renal impairment, if creatinine clearance is 29 ml/minute or less, give 500 mg q 48 hours.

▶ **Chronic suppression of recurrent genital herpes in HIV-infected patients with CD4 count of 100/mm³ or more.** *Adults:* 500 mg P.O. twice daily. Safety and effectiveness of therapy beyond 6 months hasn't been established.

Adjust-a-dose: For patients with renal impairment, if creatinine clearance is 29 ml/minute or less, give 500 mg q 24 hours.

▶ **Cold sores (herpes labialis).** *Adults:* 2 g P.O. for two doses, taken about 12 hours apart.

Adjust-a-dose: For patient with renal impairment, if creatinine clearance is 30 to 49 ml/minute, give 1 g q 12 hours for two doses; if 10 to 29 ml/minute, give 500 mg q 12 hours for two doses; if less than 10 ml/minute, give 500 mg as a single dose.

Contraindications and cautions

- Contraindicated in patients hypersensitive to or intolerant of valacyclovir, acyclovir, or components of their formulations.
- Drug isn't recommended for immunocompromised patients. Thrombotic thrombocytopenic purpura and hemolytic uremic syndrome have been fatal in some patients with advanced HIV disease and in bone marrow transplant and renal transplant recipients.
- Use cautiously in patients with renal impairment and in those receiving other nephrotoxic drugs.

Lifespan: In pregnant women, use only if benefits to the patient outweigh risks to the fetus. In breast-feeding women, use cautiously; it's unknown if the drug appears in breast milk. In children, safety and effectiveness haven't been established. In elderly patients, a lower dose may be needed, depending on underlying renal status.

Adverse reactions

CNS: depression, dizziness, *headache*.
GI: abdominal pain, diarrhea, *nausea,* vomiting.
GU: dysmenorrhea.
Musculoskeletal: arthralgia.

Interactions

Drug-drug. *Cimetidine, probenecid:* May reduce rate (but not extent) of conversion from valacyclovir to acyclovir and reduce renal clearance of acyclovir, thereby increasing acyclovir level. Monitor patient for possible toxicity.

Effects on lab test results

- May increase AST, ALT, alkaline phosphatase, and creatinine levels. May decrease hemoglobin level and hematocrit.
- May decrease WBC and platelet counts.

Pharmacokinetics

Absorption: Rapid. Absolute bioavailability of about 54.5%.
Distribution: 13.5% to 17.9% protein-bound.
Metabolism: Rapid; nearly completely converted to acyclovir and L-valine by first-pass intestinal or hepatic metabolism.
Excretion: In urine and feces. *Half-life:* Averages 2½ to 3¼ hours.

Route	Onset	Peak	Duration
P.O.	30 min	Unknown	Unknown

Action

Chemical effect: Rapidly converted to acyclovir, which becomes incorporated into viral DNA and inhibits viral DNA polymerase, thereby inhibiting viral replication.
Therapeutic effect: Inhibits susceptible viral growth of herpes zoster.

Available forms

Caplets: 500 mg, 1,000 mg

NURSING PROCESS

Assessment

- Assess patient's infection before starting therapy.
- Assess patient's and family's knowledge of drug therapy.

Nursing diagnoses

- Risk for infection related to herpes zoster
- Deficient fluid volume related to adverse GI reactions
- Deficient knowledge related to drug therapy

Planning and implementation

- Although overdose hasn't been reported, precipitation of acyclovir in renal tubules may occur when solubility (2.5 mg/ml) is exceeded in the intratubular fluid. In the event of acute renal failure and anuria, the patient may benefit from hemodialysis until kidney function is restored.

ALERT: Don't confuse valacyclovir (Valtrex) with valganciclovir (Valcyte).

Patient teaching

- Inform patient that drug may be taken with or without food.
- Review signs and symptoms of herpes infection (rash, tingling, itching, and pain), and advise patient to notify prescriber immediately if they occur. Treatment should begin as soon as possible after symptoms appear, preferably within 48 hours.

Evaluation

- Patient is free from infection.
- Patient maintains adequate hydration.
- Patient and family state understanding of drug therapy.

valganciclovir

(val-gan-SYE-kloh-veer)

Valcyte

Pharmacologic class: synthetic nucleoside
Therapeutic class: antiviral
Pregnancy risk category: C

Indications and dosages

▶ **Active CMV retinitis in patients with AIDS.** *Adults:* Induction dose is 900 mg (two 450-mg tablets) P.O. b.i.d. with food for 21 days; maintenance dose is 900 mg P.O. once daily with food.

▶ **Inactive CMV retinitis.** *Adults:* 900 mg P.O. once daily with food.

▶ **Prevention of CMV in kidney, heart, and pancreas-kidney transplants.** *Adults:* 900 mg P.O. daily with food 10 days before through 100 days after transplant.

Adjust-a-dose: Patients with renal impairment need adjusted dose. For creatinine clearance of 40 to 59 ml/minute, 450 mg b.i.d. for induction followed by 450 mg daily for maintenance. For creatinine clearance of 25 to 39 ml/minute, 450 mg daily for induction followed by 450 mg every two days for maintenance. For creatinine clearance of 10 to 24 ml/minute, 450 mg every other day for induction followed by 450 mg twice weekly for maintenance.

Contraindications and cautions

- Contraindicated in patients hypersensitive to valganciclovir or ganciclovir or in liver transplant patients. Safety and effectiveness in the prevention of CMV disease in other solid-organ transplant patients, such as lung transplant patients, haven't been established.
- Don't use in patients receiving hemodialysis.
- Use cautiously in patients with cytopenias and in those who have received immunosuppressants or radiation.

Lifespan: In pregnant women, use only if benefits to the woman outweigh risks to the fetus. In breast-feeding women, use cautiously; it's unknown if drug appears in breast milk. In children, safety and effectiveness haven't been established.

Adverse reactions

CNS: agitation, confusion, hallucinations, *headache, insomnia,* paresthesia, peripheral neuropathy, psychosis, *pyrexia,* ***seizures.***
EENT: retinal detachment.
GI: *abdominal pain, diarrhea, nausea, vomiting.*
Hematologic: anemia, ***aplastic anemia, bone marrow depression,*** **NEUTROPENIA,** ***pancytopenia, thrombocytopenia.***
Other: catheter-related infection, ***hypersensitivity reactions,*** local or systemic infections, ***sepsis.***

Interactions

Drug-drug. *Didanosine:* May increase absorption of didanosine. Monitor patient closely for didanosine toxicity.
Immunosuppressants, zidovudine: May increase risk of neutropenia, anemia, thrombocytopenia, and bone marrow depression. Monitor CBC.
Mycophenolate mofetil: May increase level of both drugs in renally impaired patients. Use together carefully.
Probenecid: May decrease renal clearance of ganciclovir. Monitor patient for ganciclovir toxicity.
Drug-food. *Any food:* May increase absorption of drug. Give drug with food.

Effects on lab test results

- May increase creatinine level. May decrease hemoglobin level and hematocrit.
- May decrease RBC, WBC, neutrophil, and platelet counts.

Pharmacokinetics

Absorption: Well absorbed from GI tract. Higher when taken with food.
Distribution: Minimally protein-bound.
Metabolism: In intestinal wall and liver to ganciclovir.
Excretion: Renal. *Half-life:* 4 hours.

Route	Onset	Peak	Duration
P.O.	Unknown	1–3 hr	Unknown

Action

Chemical effect: Converted to ganciclovir, which inhibits replication of viral DNA synthesis of CMV.
Therapeutic effect: Inhibits CMV.

Available forms

Tablets: 450 mg

NURSING PROCESS

Assessment

- Assess patient's condition before starting therapy and regularly thereafter to monitor drug's effectiveness.
- Obtain baseline laboratory studies before starting therapy and reassess regularly.
- Assess patient's and family's knowledge of drug therapy.

Nursing diagnoses

- Risk for imbalanced fluid volume related to adverse GI effects
- Ineffective protection related to adverse hematologic reactions
- Deficient knowledge related to valganciclovir therapy

Planning and implementation

- Adhere to dosage guidelines for valganciclovir because ganciclovir and valganciclovir aren't interchangeable, and overdose may occur.
- Cytopenia may occur at any time during treatment and may increase with continued use. Cell counts usually recover 3 to 7 days after stopping the drug. Monitor patient's CBC closely and frequently throughout therapy.
- No drug interaction studies have been conducted; however, because drug is converted to ganciclovir, drug interactions probably are similar.
- Drug may cause temporary or permanent inhibition of spermatogenesis.

ALERT: Severe leukopenia, neutropenia, anemia, pancytopenia, bone marrow depression, aplastic anemia and thrombocytopenia may occur. If patient's absolute neutrophil count is less than 500/mm³, platelet count is less than 25,000/mm³, or hemoglobin level is less than 8 g/dl, don't use the drug.

- Overdose may cause severe or even fatal bone marrow depression and renal toxicity; if overdose occurs, maintain adequate hydration and consider hematopoietic growth factors. Dialysis may be used to reduce level.

ALERT: Don't confuse valganciclovir with valacyclovir or Valcyte with Valtrex.

Patient teaching

- Instruct women of childbearing age to use contraception during treatment. Instruct men to use barrier contraception during and for 90 days after treatment.
- Inform patient about infection control and bleeding precautions.
- Tell patient to take drug with food.

Evaluation

- Patient remains well hydrated throughout therapy.
- Patient has no serious adverse hematologic reactions.
- Patient and family state understanding of drug therapy.

valproate sodium

(val-PROH-ayt SOH-dee-um)
Depacon, Depakene, Epilim ◇, Valpro ◇

valproic acid

Depakene

divalproex sodium

Depakote, Depakote ER, Depakote Sprinkle, Epival ♦

Pharmacologic class: carboxylic acid derivative
Therapeutic class: anticonvulsant
Pregnancy risk category: D

Indications and dosages

▶ **Simple and complex absence seizures, mixed seizure types (including absence seizures).** *Adults and children:* Initially, 15 mg/kg P.O. or I.V. daily; then increase by 5 to 10 mg/kg daily at weekly intervals up to maximum of 60 mg/kg daily. Don't use Depakote ER in children younger than age 10.

▶ **Mania.** *Adults:* Initially, 750 mg divalproex sodium (delayed-release) P.O. daily in divided doses. Adjust dosage based on patient's response; maximum dosage is 60 mg/kg daily.

▶ **Prevention of migraine headache.** *Adults:* Initially, 250 mg divalproex sodium (delayed-release) P.O. b.i.d. Some patients may need up to 1,000 mg daily. Or, 500 mg Depakote ER P.O. daily for 1 week; then 1,000 mg P.O. daily.

▶ **Complex partial seizures.** *Adults and children age 10 and older:* 10 to 15 mg/kg P.O. or I.V. daily; then increase by 5 to 10 mg/kg daily at weekly intervals, up to 60 mg/kg daily.

Adjust-a-dose: For elderly patients, use lower initial dose and adjust more slowly.

I.V. administration

- Dilute with at least 50 ml of a compatible diluent (D_5W, saline solution, lactated Ringer's injection).
- Give I.V. over 1 hour. Don't exceed 20 mg/minute.
- Use of I.V. therapy for more than 14 days hasn't been studied.

⊗ **Incompatibilities**

None reported.

Contraindications and cautions

- Contraindicated in patients hypersensitive to the drug or any of its components and in patients with hepatic dysfunction or urea cycle disorder.

Lifespan: In pregnant and breast-feeding women, drug isn't recommended. In children younger than age 10, safety and effectiveness of Depakote ER haven't been established. In elderly patients, start at lower dose and adjust dose more slowly.

Adverse reactions

CNS: aggressiveness, ataxia, behavioral deterioration, dizziness, emotional upset, depression, headache, hyperactivity, incoordination, muscle weakness, psychosis, *sedation,* tremor.
EENT: diplopia, nystagmus.
GI: abdominal cramps, anorexia, constipation, diarrhea, increased appetite and weight gain, *indigestion, nausea,* ***pancreatitis,*** *vomiting.*
Hematologic: ***bone marrow suppression,*** bruising, eosinophilia, ***hemorrhage, leukopenia,*** petechiae, ***thrombocytopenia.***
Hepatic: ***hepatotoxicity.***
Skin: alopecia, ***erythema multiforme,*** photosensitivity reactions, pruritus, rash, ***Stevens-Johnson syndrome.***
Other: *flulike syndrome,* infection.

Interactions

Drug-drug. *Aspirin, chlorpromazine, cimetidine, felbamate:* May cause valproic acid toxicity. Use together cautiously and monitor levels.
Benzodiazepines, other CNS depressants: May cause excessive CNS depression. Avoid use together.
Carbamazepine: May result in carbamazepine CNS toxicity (acute psychotic reaction). Monitor level carefully.
Cholestyramine: May decrease valproate level. Monitor patient for decreased effect.
Erythromycin: May increase valproate level. Monitor patient for toxicity.
Lamotrigine: May inhibit lamotrigine metabolism. Decrease lamotrigine dosage when valproic acid therapy starts.
Phenobarbital: May increase phenobarbital level. Monitor patient closely.
Phenytoin: May increase or decrease phenytoin level and increase metabolism of valproic acid. Monitor patient closely.
Rifampin: May decrease valproate level. Monitor level.
Warfarin: May displace warfarin from binding sites. Monitor PT and INR.
Drug-herb. *Glutamine:* May increase risk of seizures. Discourage use together.
White willow: May increase risk of adverse effects because herb contains substances similar to aspirin. Discourage use together.
Drug-lifestyle. *Alcohol use:* May cause excessive CNS depression. Discourage use together.

Effects on lab test results

- May increase ALT, AST, and bilirubin levels.
- May increase eosinophil count and bleeding time. May decrease platelet and WBC counts.

V

• May produce false-positive test results for ketones in urine.

Pharmacokinetics

Absorption: Valproate sodium and divalproex sodium quickly convert to valproic acid, which is then quickly and almost completely absorbed.
Distribution: Throughout body. 80% to 95% protein-bound.
Metabolism: In liver.
Excretion: Mainly in urine; some excreted in feces and exhaled in air. *Half-life:* 6 to 16 hours.

Route	Onset	Peak	Duration
P.O.	Unknown	1–4 hr	Unknown
I.V.	Unknown	Unknown	Unknown

Action

Chemical effect: Unknown; may increase brain level of GABA, which transmits inhibitory nerve impulses in CNS.
Therapeutic effect: Prevents and treats certain types of seizure activity.

Available forms

valproate sodium
Injection: 100 mg/ml
Syrup: 250 mg/5 ml
valproic acid
Capsules: 250 mg
Syrup: 200 mg/5 ml ♦
Tablets (crushable): 100 mg ♦
Tablets (enteric-coated): 200 mg ♦, 500 mg ♦
divalproex sodium
Capsules (containing coated particles): 125 mg
Tablets (delayed-release): 125 mg, 250 mg, 500 mg
Tablets (extended-release): 500 mg

NURSING PROCESS

Assessment

• Assess patient's condition before starting therapy and regularly thereafter to monitor drug's effectiveness.

• Monitor drug level; therapeutic level is 50 to 100 mcg/ml.

• Before starting drug and periodically thereafter, monitor liver function studies, platelet counts, and PT.

• Be alert for adverse reactions and drug interactions.

• Assess patient's and family's knowledge of drug therapy.

Nursing diagnoses

• Risk for trauma related to seizure activity

• Disturbed thought processes related to drug-induced adverse CNS reactions

• Deficient knowledge related to drug therapy

Planning and implementation

• To switch adults and children ages 10 and older taking Depakote for seizures to Depakote ER, give dose of new drug that's 8% to 20% larger than previous drug dose.

• Don't give syrup to patient who needs sodium restriction. Check with prescriber.

• Give drug with food or milk to minimize adverse GI reaction.

• Suddenly stopping the drug may worsen seizures. If adverse reaction develops, call prescriber immediately.

ALERT: Serious or fatal hepatotoxicity may follow nonspecific symptoms, such as malaise, fever, and lethargy. If patient has suspected or apparently substantial hepatic dysfunction, notify prescriber immediately and stop giving the drug.

• Patients at high risk for developing hepatotoxicity include those with congenital metabolic disorders, mental retardation, or organic brain disease; those taking other anticonvulsants; and children younger than age 2.

• Divalproex sodium carries a lower risk of adverse GI effects than other drug forms.

• If tremors occur, notify prescriber. Dosage may need to be reduced.

ALERT: Fatal hyperammonemic encephalopathy may occur in patients with a urea cycle disorder, particularly ornithine transcarbamylase deficiency. Evaluate patients with risk factors for urea cycle disorders before starting therapy. If symptoms of unexplained hyperammonemic encephalopathy occur during therapy, stop drug; give prompt, appropriate treatment; and evaluate for underlying urea cycle disorder.

Patient teaching

• Tell patient that drug may be taken with food or milk to reduce adverse GI effects.

• Instruct patient not to chew capsules and not to crush or chew extended-release tablets.

• Tell patient and parents that syrup shouldn't be mixed with carbonated beverages.
• Tell patient and parents to keep drug out of children's reach.
• Warn patient and parents not to stop drug therapy abruptly.
• Advise patient to refrain from driving or performing other potentially hazardous activities that require mental alertness until drug's CNS effects are known.

Evaluation

• Patient is free from seizure activity.
• Patient maintains normal thought processes.
• Patient and family state understanding of drug therapy.

valsartan

(val-SAR-tin)
Diovan

Pharmacologic class: angiotensin II receptor blocker
Therapeutic class: antihypertensive
Pregnancy risk category: C (D in second and third trimesters)

Indications and dosages

▶ **Hypertension, used alone or with other antihypertensives.** *Adults:* Initially, 80 mg P.O. once daily. Expect a reduction in blood pressure in 2 to 4 weeks. If additional antihypertensive effect is needed, increase dosage to 160 or 320 mg daily, or add a diuretic. (Addition of a diuretic has a greater effect than dose increases above 80 mg.) Usual dosage range is 80 to 320 mg daily.

▶ **Heart failure (New York Heart Association classes II to IV).** *Adults:* Initially, 40 mg P.O. b.i.d. Increase as tolerated to 80 mg b.i.d. Maximum dosage is 160 mg b.i.d. Avoid using with ACE inhibitors or beta blockers.

▶ **To reduce CV death in stable post-MI patients with left ventricular failure or dysfunction.** *Adults:* 20 mg P.O. b.i.d. Initial dose may be given as soon as 12 hours following MI. Increase dose to 40 mg b.i.d. within 7 days. Increase subsequent doses as tolerated to target dose of 160 mg b.i.d.

Contraindications and cautions

• Contraindicated in patients hypersensitive to the drug or any of its components.
• Use cautiously in patients with severe renal or hepatic disease.

Lifespan: During second or third trimester of pregnancy or in breast-feeding women, don't give drug. In children, safety and effectiveness haven't been established.

Adverse reactions

CNS: *dizziness,* fatigue, headache, insomnia, vertigo.
CV: edema, hypotension, postural hypotension, syncope.
EENT: blurred vision, pharyngitis, rhinitis, sinusitis.
GI: abdominal pain, diarrhea, dyspepsia, nausea.
GU: renal impairment.
Hematologic: ***neutropenia.***
Metabolic: ***hyperkalemia.***
Musculoskeletal: arthralgia, back pain.
Respiratory: cough, upper respiratory tract infection.
Other: ***angioedema,*** viral infection.

Interactions

Drug-drug. *Other angiotensin II blockers, potassium sparing diuretics, potassium supplements:* May increase potassium level. Avoid use together.
Drug-food. *Salt substitutes containing potassium:* May increase potassium level. In heart failure patients, may also increase creatinine level. Discourage use together.

Effects on lab test results

• May increase potassium level.
• May decrease neutrophil count.

Pharmacokinetics

Absorption: Bioavailability about 25%; food decreases absorption.
Distribution: Not extensive. 95% protein-bound.
Metabolism: In liver and kidneys.
Excretion: In urine and feces. *Half-life:* 6 hours.

Route	Onset	Peak	Duration
P.O.	< 2 hr	2–4 hr	24 hr

V

Action

Chemical effect: Blocks binding of angiotensin II to receptor sites in vascular smooth muscle and adrenal gland.

Therapeutic effect: Inhibits pressor effects of renin-angiotensin system.

Available forms

Tablets: 40 mg, 80 mg, 160 mg, 320 mg

NURSING PROCESS

Assessment

- Monitor patient for hypotension. Correct volume and sodium depletions before starting drug.
- Assess patient's and family's knowledge of drug therapy.

Nursing diagnoses

- Risk for injury related to presence of hypertension
- Deficient knowledge related to drug therapy

Planning and implementation

- Drug can be given with or without food.

Patient teaching

- Tell woman to notify prescriber if she becomes pregnant.
- Teach patient other means of reducing blood pressure, including proper diet, exercise, smoking cessation, and stress reduction.

Evaluation

- Patient's blood pressure becomes normal.
- Patient and family state understanding of drug therapy.

vancomycin hydrochloride

(van-koh-MIGH-sin high-droh-KLOR-ighd)

Vancocin, Vancoled

Pharmacologic class: glycopeptide
Therapeutic class: antibiotic
Pregnancy risk category: C (B for pulvules)

Indications and dosages

▶ **Severe staphylococcal infections when other antibiotics are ineffective or contraindicated.** *Adults:* 500 mg I.V. q 6 hours, or 1 g q 12 hours.
Children: 40 mg/kg I.V. daily in divided doses q 6 hours.
Neonates: Initially, 15 mg/kg; then 10 mg/kg I.V. daily, divided q 12 hours for first week after birth; then q 8 hours up to age 1 month.

▶ **Endocarditis prophylaxis for dental procedures.** *Adults:* 1 g I.V. slowly over 1 hour, starting 1 hour before procedure.
Children: 20 mg/kg I.V. over 1 hour, starting 1 hour before procedure.

Adjust-a-dose: For patients with renal impairment, adjust I.V. dosage.

▶ **Antibiotic-related pseudomembranous and staphylococcal enterocolitis.** *Adults:* 125 to 500 mg P.O. q 6 hours for 7 to 10 days.
Children: 40 mg/kg P.O. daily in divided doses q 6 to 8 hours for 7 to 10 days. Maximum, 2 g daily.

I.V. administration

- Dilute in 200 ml of saline solution injection or D_5W.
- Infuse over 60 minutes.
- Check site daily for phlebitis and irritation. Watch for irritation and infiltration; extravasation can cause tissue damage and necrosis.
- If red-man syndrome occurs because drug is infused too rapidly, stop infusion and report to prescriber.
- Refrigerate I.V. solution after reconstitution, and use within 96 hours.

⊗ **Incompatibilities**

Albumin, alkaline solutions, aminophylline, amobarbital, amphotericin B, aztreonam, cephalosporins, chloramphenicol, chlorothiazide, corticosteroids, dexamethasone sodium phosphate, foscarnet, heavy metals, heparin, hydrocortisone, idarubicin, methotrexate, nafcillin, penicillin G potassium, pentobarbital, phenobarbital, phenytoin, piperacillin, piperacillin sodium-tazobactam sodium, sargramostim, sodium bicarbonate, ticarcillin disodium, ticarcillin disodium and clavulanate potassium, vitamin B complex with C, warfarin.

Contraindications and cautions

- Contraindicated in patients hypersensitive to the drug or any of its components.
- Use cautiously in patients receiving other neurotoxic, nephrotoxic, or ototoxic drugs; patients

older than age 60; and those with impaired liver or kidney function, hearing loss, or allergies to other antibiotics.
Lifespan: In pregnant women, use cautiously. In breast-feeding women, safety and effectiveness haven't been established.

Adverse reactions

CNS: fever, pain.
CV: hypotension.
EENT: ototoxicity, tinnitus.
GI: nausea, ***pseudomembranous colitis.***
GU: ***nephrotoxicity.***
Hematologic: eosinophilia, ***leukopenia.***
Respiratory: dyspnea, wheezing.
Skin: red-man syndrome (maculopapular rash on face, neck, trunk, and limbs with rapid I.V. infusion; pruritus and hypotension with histamine release).
Other: ***anaphylaxis,*** chills, superinfection, thrombophlebitis at injection site.

Interactions

Drug-drug. *Aminoglycosides, amphotericin B, cisplatin, pentamidine:* May increase risk of nephrotoxicity and ototoxicity. Monitor patient closely.

Effects on lab test results

- May increase BUN and creatinine levels.
- May increase eosinophil count. May decrease neutrophil and WBC counts.

Pharmacokinetics

Absorption: Minimal systemic absorption with P.O. use. (Drug may accumulate in patients with colitis or renal failure.)
Distribution: In body fluids. Achieves therapeutic level in CSF if meninges inflamed.
Metabolism: Unknown.
Excretion: In urine with parenteral use; in feces with P.O. use. *Half-life:* 6 hours.

Route	Onset	Peak	Duration
P.O.	Unknown	Unknown	Unknown
I.V.	Immediate	Immediate	Unknown

Action

Chemical effect: Hinders bacterial cell wall synthesis, damaging bacterial plasma membrane and making cell more vulnerable to osmotic pressure.
Therapeutic effect: Kills susceptible bacteria.

Available forms

Powder for injection: 500-mg, 1-g vials
Powder for oral solution: 1-g, 10-g bottles
Pulvules: 125 mg, 250 mg

NURSING PROCESS

Assessment

- Assess patient's infection before starting therapy and regularly thereafter to monitor drug's effectiveness.
- Obtain urine specimen for culture and sensitivity tests before giving first dose. Start therapy pending test results.
- Obtain hearing evaluation and kidney function studies before starting therapy, and repeat during therapy.
- Check level regularly, especially in elderly patients, premature infants, and those with decreased renal function.
- Be alert for adverse reactions and drug interactions.
- Assess patient's and family's knowledge of drug therapy.

Nursing diagnoses

- Risk for infection related to presence of susceptible bacteria
- Risk for injury related to drug-induced adverse reactions
- Deficient knowledge related to drug therapy

Planning and implementation

- In patient with renal dysfunction, use a lower dose.

ALERT: Oral administration is ineffective for systemic infections, and I.V. administration is ineffective for pseudomembranous (*Clostridium difficile*) diarrhea.

- Oral form is stable for 2 weeks when refrigerated.
- Don't give drug I.M.
- When using drug to treat staphylococcal endocarditis, give for at least 4 weeks.

Patient teaching

- Tell patient to take entire amount of drug exactly as directed, even after he feels better.
- Tell patient to stop taking the drug and immediately report any adverse reactions, especially ringing in ears or fullness.

V

Evaluation

- Patient is free from infection.
- Patient doesn't experience injury from adverse reactions.
- Patient and family state understanding of drug therapy.

vardenafil hydrochloride

(var-DEN-ah-phill high-droh-KLOR-ighd)
Levitra

Pharmacologic class: selective inhibitor of cyclic guanosine monophosphate (cGMP)–specific phosphodiesterase type 5 (PDE5)
Therapeutic class: erectile dysfunction drug
Pregnancy risk category: B

Indications and dosages

▶ **Erectile dysfunction.** *Men:* 10 mg P.O. p.r.n., 1 hour before sexual activity. Dose range is 5 to 20 mg based on effectiveness and tolerance. Maximum, 1 dose daily.
Men age 65 and older: Initial dose is 5 mg P.O. p.r.n., 1 hour before sexual activity. Maximum, 1 dose daily.
Adjust-a-dose: For patients with moderate hepatic impairment (Child-Pugh class B), initial dose is 5 mg daily, p.r.n., not to exceed 10 mg daily. Patients taking ritonavir shouldn't exceed 2.5 mg in a 72-hour period. Patients taking itraconazole 400 mg daily or ketoconazole 400 mg daily shouldn't exceed 2.5 mg daily. Patients taking erythromycin, itraconazole 200 mg daily, or ketoconazole 200 mg daily shouldn't exceed 5 mg daily.

Contraindications and cautions

- Contraindicated in patients hypersensitive to the drug or any of its components and in those taking nitrates or alpha blockers.
- Use cautiously in patients with unstable angina; hypotension (systolic pressure lower than 90 mm Hg); uncontrolled hypertension (blood pressure higher than 170/110 mm Hg); stroke, life-threatening arrhythmia, or MI within past 6 months; severe cardiac failure; severe hepatic impairment (Child-Pugh class C); end-stage renal disease requiring dialysis; hereditary degenerative retinal disorders; hepatic or renal dysfunction; anatomical deformation of the penis; or prolonged QT interval. Also use cautiously in patients taking Class IA or Class III antiarrhythmics and in those with conditions that predispose them to priapism (sickle cell anemia, multiple myeloma, or leukemia).

Lifespan: Only indicated for men. Men age 65 and older have reduced drug clearance.

Adverse reactions

CNS: dizziness, *headache.*
CV: *flushing.*
EENT: rhinitis, sinusitis, visual changes.
GI: dyspepsia, nausea.
Musculoskeletal: back pain.
Other: flulike syndrome.

Interactions

Drug-drug. *Alpha blockers:* May increase hypotensive effects. Don't use together.
Erythromycin, itraconazole 200 mg daily, ketoconazole 200 mg daily: May increase vardenafil level. Don't exceed 5 mg daily.
Itraconazole 400 mg daily, ketoconazole 400 mg daily: May increase vardenafil level. Don't exceed 2.5 mg daily.
Nitrates: May increase hypotensive effects. Don't use together.
Ritonavir: May increase vardenafil level. Don't exceed 2.5 mg in a 72-hour period.
Drug-food. *High-fat meals:* May decrease peak level of drug. Advise patient to take on an empty stomach.

Effects on lab test results

- May increase CK level.

Pharmacokinetics

Absorption: Rapid. Absolute bioavailability is 15%.
Distribution: Both drug and its major active metabolite are 95% protein-bound. Protein-binding is reversible and independent of drug level.
Metabolism: Mainly through CYP3A4, along with CYP3A5 and CYP2C isoenzymes. N-demethylation converts drug into the major metabolite, which accounts for 7% of drug.
Excretion: Mainly in feces. *Half-life:* 4 to 5 hours.

Route	Onset	Peak	Duration
P.O.	Immediate	30 min–2 hr	Unknown

Action

Chemical effect: Selectively inhibits cGMP-specific PDE5 and prevents the breakdown of cGMP by phosphodiesterase, leading to increased cGMP level and prolonged smooth muscle relaxation promoting the flow of blood into the corpus cavernosum.
Therapeutic effect: Stimulates penile erection.

Available forms

Tablets: 2.5 mg, 5 mg, 10 mg, 20 mg

NURSING PROCESS

Assessment

- Assess patient's erectile dysfunction before starting therapy and regularly thereafter to monitor drug's effectiveness.
- Be alert for adverse reactions and drug interactions.
- Assess patient's and family's knowledge of drug therapy.

Nursing diagnoses

- Sexual dysfunction related to process of erectile dysfunction
- Chronic low self-esteem related to erectile dysfunction
- Deficient knowledge related to drug therapy

Planning and implementation

ALERT: Because of cardiac risk during sexual activity, drug increases risk for patients with underlying CV disease.

Patient teaching

- Tell patient that drug doesn't protect against sexually transmitted diseases and that he should use protective measures to prevent infection.
- Advise patient that drug is most rapidly absorbed if taken on an empty stomach.
- Tell patient to notify prescriber of visual changes.
- Instruct patient to seek medical attention if erection persists for more than 4 hours because of risk of permanent erectile dysfunction.
- Tell patient to take drug 60 minutes before anticipated sexual activity. The drug will have no effect in the absence of sexual stimulation.
- Tell patient not to take drug more than once per day.

Evaluation

- Patient reports improvement in sexual functioning.
- Patient demonstrates increased self-esteem.
- Patient and family state understanding of drug therapy.

varenicline tartrate

(vah-RENN-ih-kleen TAR-trayt)
Chantix

Pharmacologic class: nicotinic acetylcholine receptor partial agonist
Therapeutic class: smoking cessation aid
Pregnancy risk category: C

Indications and dosages

▶ **Smoking cessation.** *Adults:* Starting 1 week before patient plans to stop smoking, give 0.5 mg P.O. once daily on days 1 through 3. Days 4 through 7, give 0.5 mg P.O. b.i.d. Day 8 through the end of week 12, give 1 mg P.O. b.i.d. If patient successfully stops smoking, give an additional 12-week course of treatment to increase the likelihood of long-term success.
Adjust-a-dose: If patient has severe renal impairment, 0.5 mg P.O. once daily. Adjust as needed to maximum of 0.5 mg b.i.d. If patient has end-stage renal disease and is undergoing dialysis, 0.5 mg once daily.

Contraindications and cautions

- Use cautiously in patients with severe renal impairment.

Lifespan: In pregnant or breast-feeding women, use cautiously. In children, safety and effectiveness haven't been established. In elderly patients, use cautiously.

Adverse reactions

CNS: *abnormal dreams,* altered attention or emotions, anxiety, asthenia, depression, dizziness, fatigue, *headache, insomnia,* irritability, lethargy, malaise, nightmares, restlessness, sensory disturbance, sleep disorder, somnolence.
CV: chest pain, edema, hot flush, hypertension.
EENT: altered taste, epistaxis.
GI: abdominal pain, constipation, diarrhea, dry mouth, dyspepsia, flatulence, gingivitis, *nausea,* vomiting.

GU: menstrual disorder, polyuria.
Metabolic: decreased appetite, increased appetite, thirst.
Musculoskeletal: arthralgia, back pain, muscle cramps, myalgia.
Respiratory: dyspnea, upper respiratory tract disorder.
Skin: rash.
Other: flulike syndrome.

Interactions

Drug-drug. *Nicotine replacement therapy:* May increase nausea, vomiting, dizziness, dyspepsia, and fatigue. Monitor patient closely.

Effects on lab test results

- May increase liver function test values.

Pharmacokinetics

Absorption: Virtually complete after oral use with high systemic availability.
Distribution: Less than 20% bound to plasma proteins.
Metabolism: Minimal.
Excretion: Via the kidneys, mainly through glomerular filtration and active tubular secretion. *Half-life:* 24 hours.

Route	Onset	Peak	Duration
P.O.	4 days	3–4 hr	24 hr

Action

Chemical effect: Blocks the effects of nicotine by binding with high affinity and selectivity at $alpha_4beta_2$ neuronal nicotinic acetylcholine receptors. Drug also provides some of nicotine's effects to ease withdrawal symptoms.
Therapeutic effect: Helps patient quit smoking.

Available forms

Tablets: 0.5 mg, 1 mg

NURSING PROCESS

Assessment

- Assess patient's readiness and motivation to stop smoking.
- Be alert for adverse reactions.
- Assess patient's and family's knowledge of drug therapy.

Nursing diagnoses

- Risk for injury related smoking habit
- Noncompliance related to drug-induced nausea
- Deficient knowledge related to drug therapy

Planning and implementation

- Patients who develop intolerable nausea may need dosage reduction.
- Because smoking affects the action of certain drugs—such as theophylline, warfarin, and insulin—these drug levels may need temporary monitoring after patient stops smoking. Dosage adjustment may be needed.

Patient teaching

- Provide patient with educational materials and needed counseling.
- Instruct patient to choose a date to stop smoking and to begin treatment 1 week before this date.
- Advise patient to take each dose with a full glass of water after eating.
- Teach patient to gradually increase the dose over the first week to a target of 1 mg in the morning and 1 mg in the evening.
- Explain that nausea and insomnia are common and usually temporary. Urge him to contact the prescriber if adverse effects are persistently troubling; a dosage reduction may help.
- Urge patient to continue trying to abstain from smoking if he has early lapses after successfully quitting.
- Tell patient that dosages of other drugs he takes may need adjustment when he stops smoking.
- If patient plans to become pregnant or to breast-feed, explain the risks of smoking and the risks and benefits of taking varenicline to aid smoking cessation.

Evaluation

- Patient remains free of injury.
- Patient remains compliant with drug therapy.
- Patient and family state understanding of drug therapy.

vasopressin (ADH)
(VAY-soh-preh-sin)
Pitressin

Pharmacologic class: posterior pituitary hormone
Therapeutic class: ADH, peristaltic stimulant
Pregnancy risk category: C

Indications and dosages

▶ **Neurogenic diabetes insipidus.** *Adults:* 5 to 10 units I.M. or subcutaneously b.i.d. to q.i.d., p.r.n. Range 5 to 60 units daily. Or, intranasally (aqueous solution used as spray or applied to cotton balls) in individualized doses, based on response.
Children: 2.5 to 10 units I.M. or subcutaneously b.i.d. to q.i.d., p.r.n. Or, intranasally (aqueous solution used as spray or applied to cotton balls) in individualized doses.
▶ **Postoperative abdominal distention.** *Adults:* Initially, 5 units (aqueous) I.M.; then q 3 to 4 hours, increasing dose to 10 units, if needed. Reduce dose proportionately for children.
▶ **To expel gas before abdominal X-ray.** *Adults:* 10 units subcutaneously 2 hours before X-ray; then again 30 minutes later.
▶ **Provocative testing for growth hormone and corticotropin release‡.** *Adults:* 10 units I.M.
Children: 0.3 units/kg I.M.
▶ **GI hemorrhage‡.** *Adults:* 0.2 to 0.4 units/minute I.V. Increase up to 0.9 units/minute if needed. Or, 0.1 to 0.5 units/minute intra-arterially.
▶ **Pulseless arrest (ventricular fibrillation, rapid ventricular tachycardia, asystole, pulseless electrical activity)‡.** *Adults:* 40 units I.V. as a single one-time dose.

I.V. administration

• Drug is used I.V. for GI hemorrhage and pulseless arrest only.
• For GI hemorrhage, dilute with normal saline solution or D_5W to 0.1 to 1 unit/ml.
• For pulseless arrest, give as bolus during advanced cardiac life support (ACLS).
⊗ **Incompatibilities**
None reported.

Contraindications and cautions

• Contraindicated in patients with chronic nephritis accompanied by nitrogen retention.
• Use cautiously in preoperative and postoperative polyuric patients and those with seizure disorders, migraine headache, asthma, CV disease, heart failure, renal disease, goiter with cardiac complications, arteriosclerosis, or fluid overload.
Lifespan: In pregnant women, use cautiously. In breast-feeding women, use cautiously; it's unknown if the drug appears in breast milk. In children and elderly patients, use cautiously.

Adverse reactions

CNS: headache, tremor, vertigo.
CV: angina in patients with vascular disease, ***arrhythmias,*** circumoral pallor, vasoconstriction, decreased cardiac output, ***myocardial ischemia, pulseless arrest.***
GI: abdominal cramps, flatulence, nausea, vomiting.
Skin: cutaneous gangrene, diaphoresis.
Other: hypersensitivity reactions (***anaphylaxis, angioedema, bronchoconstriction,*** urticaria), water intoxication (***coma,*** confusion, drowsiness, headache, listlessness, ***seizures,*** weight gain).

Interactions

Drug-drug. *Carbamazepine, chlorpropamide, clofibrate, fludrocortisone, tricyclic antidepressants:* May increase antidiuretic response. Use together cautiously.
Demeclocycline, heparin, lithium, norepinephrine: May decrease antidiuretic activity. Use together cautiously.
Drug-lifestyle. *Alcohol use:* May decrease antidiuretic activity. Discourage use together.

Effects on lab test results

None reported.

Pharmacokinetics

Absorption: Unknown.
Distribution: Throughout extracellular fluid without evidence of protein-binding.
Metabolism: Most of drug is destroyed rapidly in liver and kidneys.
Excretion: In urine. *Half-life:* 10 to 20 minutes.

Route	Onset	Peak	Duration
I.V	Unknown	Unknown	Unknown
I.M., SubQ, intranasal	Unknown	Unknown	2–8 hr

V

Action

Chemical effect: Increases permeability of renal tubular epithelium to adenosine monophosphate and water; epithelium promotes reabsorption of water and produces concentrated urine (ADH effect).
Therapeutic effect: Promotes water reabsorption and stimulates GI motility.

Available forms

Injection: 0.5-, 1-, and 10-ml ampules (20 units/ml)

NURSING PROCESS

Assessment

- Assess patient's condition before starting therapy and regularly thereafter to monitor drug's effectiveness.
- Monitor specific gravity of urine, and fluid intake and output, to aid evaluation of drug effectiveness.
- To prevent possible seizures, coma, and death, observe patient closely for early signs of water intoxication.
- Monitor patient's blood pressure often; watch for hypertension or lack of response to drug, which may be indicated by hypotension. Also monitor daily weight.
- Be alert for adverse reactions and drug interactions.
- Assess patient's and family's knowledge of drug therapy.

Nursing diagnoses

- Risk for deficient fluid volume related to polyuria from diabetes insipidus
- Diarrhea related to drug-induced increased GI motility
- Deficient knowledge related to drug therapy

Planning and implementation

- Drug may be used for transient polyuria resulting from ADH deficiency related to neurosurgery or head injury.
- To reduce adverse reactions, use minimum effective dose.
- Give drug with one to two glasses of water to reduce adverse reactions and improve therapeutic response.
- A rectal tube facilitates gas expulsion after vasopressin injection.

ALERT: Never inject during first stage of labor; doing so may cause uterus to rupture.
- Aqueous solution can be used as a nasal spray or it can be applied to cotton balls. Follow the manufacturer's guidelines for intranasal use.

ALERT: Don't confuse vasopressin with desmopressin.

Patient teaching
- Instruct patient how to give drug. Tell patient taking drug subcutaneously to rotate injection sites to prevent tissue damage.
- Stress importance of monitoring fluid intake and output.
- Tell patient to immediately notify prescriber if an adverse reaction occurs.

Evaluation

- Patient maintains adequate hydration.
- Patient has no diarrhea.
- Patient and family state understanding of drug therapy.

vecuronium bromide

(veh-kyoo-ROH-nee-um BROH-mighd)

Pharmacologic class: nondepolarizing neuromuscular blocker
Therapeutic class: skeletal muscle relaxant
Pregnancy risk category: C

Indications and dosages

▶ **Adjunct to general anesthesia; to facilitate endotracheal intubation; to provide skeletal muscle relaxation during surgery or mechanical ventilation. Dosage depends on anesthetic used, individual needs, and response. Dosages are representative and must be adjusted.** *Adults and children age 10 and older:* Initially, 0.08 to 0.1 mg/kg I.V. bolus. During prolonged surgery, may give maintenance doses of 0.01 to 0.015 mg/kg within 25 to 40 minutes of initial dose. Maintenance doses may be given q 12 to 15 minutes in patients receiving balanced anesthesia. Or, drug may be given by continuous I.V. infusion of 1 mcg/kg/minute initially, then 0.8 to 1.2 mcg/kg/minute.
Children younger than age 10: May require slightly higher initial dose as well as supplementation slightly more often than adults.

I.V. administration

• Give drug by rapid I.V. injection. Or, 10 to 20 mg may be added to 100 ml of compatible solution and given by I.V. infusion.
• Compatible solutions include D_5W, normal saline solution for injection, dextrose 5% in normal saline solution for injection, and lactated Ringer's injection.
• Store reconstituted solution in refrigerator. Discard after 24 hours.

⊗ **Incompatibilities**
Alkaline solutions, amphotericin B, diazepam, furosemide, thiopental.

Contraindications and cautions

• Contraindicated in patients hypersensitive to bromides.
• Use cautiously in patients with altered circulation caused by CV disease and edematous states and in patients with hepatic disease, severe obesity, bronchogenic carcinoma, electrolyte disturbances, or neuromuscular disease.
Lifespan: In pregnant woman, use cautiously. In breast-feeding women, use cautiously; it's unknown if the drug appears in breast milk. In the elderly, use cautiously.

Adverse reactions

Musculoskeletal: skeletal muscle weakness.
Respiratory: ***apnea,*** respiratory insufficiency.

Interactions

Drug-drug. *Amikacin, gentamicin, neomycin, streptomycin, tobramycin:* May increase the effects of nondepolarizing muscle relaxant, including prolonged respiratory depression. Use together only when necessary. May need to reduce dose of nondepolarizing muscle relaxant.
Bacitracin; clindamycin; general anesthetics, such as enflurane, halothane, isoflurane; kanamycin; other skeletal muscle relaxants; polymyxin antibiotics, such as colistin, polymyxin B sulfate; quinidine; tetracyclines: May potentiate neuromuscular blockade, leading to increased skeletal muscle relaxation and potentiation of effect. Use cautiously during surgical and postoperative periods.
Carbamazepine, phenytoin: May decrease the effects of vecuronium. May need to increase dose of the vecuronium.

Effects on lab test results

None reported.

Pharmacokinetics

Absorption: Given I.V.
Distribution: In extracellular fluid; rapidly reaches its site of action (skeletal muscles). 60% to 90% protein-bound.
Metabolism: Hepatic; rapid and extensive.
Excretion: In feces and urine. *Half-life:* 20 minutes.

Route	Onset	Peak	Duration
I.V.	≤ 1 min	3–5 min	25–30 min

Action

Chemical effect: Prevents acetylcholine from binding to receptors on motor end plate, thus blocking depolarization.
Therapeutic effect: Relaxes skeletal muscle.

Available forms

Injection: 10-mg vial, 20-mg vial

NURSING PROCESS

Assessment

• Assess patient's condition before starting therapy and regularly thereafter to monitor drug's effectiveness.
• Monitor respiratory rate closely until patient is fully recovered from neuromuscular blockade as evidenced by tests of muscle strength (hand grip, head lift, and ability to cough).
• Be alert for adverse reactions and drug interactions.
• Assess patient's and family's knowledge of drug therapy.

Nursing diagnoses

• Ineffective health maintenance related to underlying condition
• Ineffective breathing pattern related to drug's effect on respiratory muscles
• Deficient knowledge related to drug therapy

Planning and implementation

• Keep airway clear. Have emergency respiratory support equipment available immediately.
• Drug should be used only by personnel skilled in airway management.
• Previous administration of succinylcholine may enhance neuromuscular blocking effect and duration of action.
• Give sedatives or general anesthetics before neuromuscular blockers. Neuromuscular block-

V

ers don't obtund consciousness or alter pain threshold.

- Give analgesics for pain.
- Nerve stimulator and train-of-four monitoring are recommended to confirm antagonism of neuromuscular blockade and recovery of muscle strength. Before attempting pharmacologic reversal with neostigmine, some evidence of spontaneous recovery should be seen.

ALERT: Careful dose calculation is essential. Always verify with another health care professional.

- Don't give by I.M. injection.

Patient teaching

- Explain all events and happenings to patient because he can still hear.
- Reassure patient that he is being monitored at all times.

Evaluation

- Patient responds well to drug.
- Patient maintains effective breathing pattern with mechanical assistance.
- Patient and family state understanding of drug therapy.

venlafaxine hydrochloride

(ven-leh-FAKS-een high-droh-KLOR-ighd)
Effexor, Effexor XR

Pharmacologic class: dopamine, neuronal serotonin, and norepinephrine reuptake inhibitor
Therapeutic class: antidepressant
Pregnancy risk category: C

Indications and dosages

▶ **Depression.** *Adults:* Initially, 75 mg P.O. daily in two or three divided doses, or 75 mg (extended-release) P.O. once daily with food. With both forms, increase dosage as tolerated and needed in increments of 75 mg daily at intervals of no less than 4 days. For moderately depressed outpatients, usual maximum dosage is 225 mg daily; in certain severely depressed patients, dosage may be as high as 350 mg daily.

▶ **Generalized or social anxiety disorder.** *Adults:* 75 mg extended-release capsules P.O. once daily. May increase as needed in increments of 75 mg daily at intervals of no less than 4 days to maximum of 225 mg daily.

▶ **Prevention of major depressive disorder relapse‡.** *Adults:* 100 to 200 mg P.O. daily, or 75 to 225 mg (extended-release) P.O. daily.

▶ **Panic disorder.** *Adults:* Initially, 37.5 mg (extended-release) P.O. daily for 1 week. Then, increase dose to 75 mg daily. If no response, increase by up to 75 mg daily in no less than weekly intervals, as needed, to a maximum dosage of 225 mg daily.

Adjust-a-dose: For patients with hepatic impairment, reduce total daily dose by one-half.

For patients with mild to moderate renal impairment (GFR of 10 to 70 ml/minute), reduce total daily dose by one-quarter to one-half. In patients undergoing hemodialysis, don't give the dose until dialysis session is completed; reduce daily dose by one-half.

Contraindications and cautions

- Contraindicated in patients hypersensitive to the drug or any of its components and in those who took an MAO inhibitor within 14 days.
- Use cautiously in patients with renal impairment or diseases, in those with conditions that could affect hemodynamic responses or metabolism, and in those with a history of mania or seizures.

Lifespan: In pregnant women, use cautiously. In breast-feeding women, use cautiously; it's unknown if the drug appears in breast milk. In children, safety and effectiveness haven't been established.

Adverse reactions

CNS: abnormal dreams, agitation, anxiety, *asthenia, dizziness, headache,* insomnia, *nervousness,* paresthesia, *somnolence,* tremor.
CV: hypertension.
EENT: blurred vision.
GI: *anorexia, constipation,* diarrhea, *dry mouth,* dyspepsia, flatulence, *nausea,* vomiting.
GU: *abnormal ejaculation,* impaired urination, impotence, urinary frequency.
Metabolic: weight loss.
Skin: rash, *diaphoresis.*
Other: chills, infection, yawning.

Interactions

Drug-drug. *Haloperidol:* May increase haloperidol level. Use together cautiously.
Phenelzine, selegiline, tranylcypromine: May cause serotonin syndrome, which includes CNS irritability, shivering, and altered consciousness.

Don't give together. Wait at least 2 weeks after stopping an MAO inhibitor before giving any SSRI.
Trazodone: May cause serotonin syndrome. Avoid use together.
Drug-herb. *St. John's wort:* May increase sedative-hypnotic effects. Discourage use together.
Yohimbe: May cause additive stimulation. Discourage use together.

Effects on lab test results

None reported.

Pharmacokinetics

Absorption: About 92%.
Distribution: About 25% to 29% bound to plasma proteins.
Metabolism: Extensive in liver.
Excretion: In urine. *Half-life:* 5 hours.

Route	Onset	Peak	Duration
P.O.	Unknown	Unknown	Unknown

Action

Chemical effect: Blocks reuptake of norepinephrine and serotonin into neurons in CNS.
Therapeutic effect: Relieves depression.

Available forms

Capsules (extended-release): 37.5 mg, 75 mg, 150 mg
Tablets: 25 mg, 37.5 mg, 50 mg, 75 mg, 100 mg

NURSING PROCESS

Assessment

- Assess patient's depression before starting therapy and regularly thereafter to monitor drug's effectiveness.
- Carefully monitor blood pressure. Venlafaxine therapy is linked to sustained, dose-dependent increases in blood pressure. Greatest increases (averaging about 7 mm Hg above baseline) occur in patients taking 375 mg daily.
- Be alert for adverse reactions and drug interactions.
- Assess patient's and family's knowledge of drug therapy.

Nursing diagnoses

- Disturbed thought processes related to presence of depression
- Risk for injury related to drug-induced adverse CNS reactions
- Deficient knowledge related to drug therapy

Planning and implementation

- Give drug with food.

ALERT: If given for 6 weeks or more, don't abruptly stop giving the drug; taper dosage over a 2-week period.

- Closely monitor patients being treated for depression for signs and symptoms of worsening condition and suicidal ideation, especially when therapy starts or dosage is adjusted. Symptoms may include agitation, insomnia, anxiety, aggressiveness, and panic attacks.

Patient teaching

- Instruct patient to take drug with food.
- Warn patient to avoid hazardous activities until the drug's CNS effects are known.
- Caution patient not to become pregnant during treatment. Neonates exposed to drug late in the third trimester have developed complications requiring prolonged hospitalization, respiratory support, and tube feeding, possibly related to serotonin syndrome.
- Tell patient it may take several weeks before the full antidepressant effect is seen.
- Tell patient not to drink alcohol while taking drug and to notify prescriber before taking other medications, including OTC preparations, because of possible interactions.
- Instruct patient to notify prescriber if adverse reaction occurs.
- Urge family members to closely monitor the patient for signs of worsening condition and suicidal ideation.

Evaluation

- Patient's behavior and communication show improved thought processes.
- Patient sustains no injury from adverse CNS reactions.
- Patient and family state understanding of drug therapy.

V

verapamil hydrochloride

(veh-RAP-uh-mil high-droh-KLOR-ighd)

Anpec ◇, Anpec SR ◇, Apo-Verap ♦, Calan, Calan SR, Cordilox ◇, Cordilox SR ◇, Covera-HS, Isoptin ◇, Isoptin SR, Novo-Veramil ♦, Nu-Verap ♦, Veracaps SR ◇, Verelan, Verelan PM

Pharmacologic class: calcium channel blocker
Therapeutic class: antianginal, antiarrhythmic, antihypertensive
Pregnancy risk category: C

Indications and dosages

▶ **Vasospastic angina; classic chronic, stable angina pectoris; unstable angina; chronic atrial fibrillation.** *Adults:* Starting dose is 80 mg P.O. q 6 to 8 hours. Increase at weekly intervals, as needed. Some patients may need up to 480 mg daily. Or, 180 mg Covera-HS P.O. at bedtime; maximum, 480 mg P.O. daily at bedtime.

▶ **Supraventricular arrhythmias.** *Adults:* 0.075 to 0.15 mg/kg (5 to 10 mg) by I.V. push over 2 minutes with ECG and blood pressure monitoring. If no response occurs, give a second dose of 10 mg (0.15 mg/kg) 30 minutes after the initial dose.
Children ages 1 to 15: Give 0.1 to 0.3 mg/kg as I.V. bolus over 2 minutes. If no response, repeat in 30 minutes.
Children younger than age 1: Give 0.1 to 0.2 mg/kg as I.V. bolus over at least 2 minutes with continuous ECG monitoring. If no response, repeat in 30 minutes.

▶ **To prevent recurrent paroxysmal supraventricular tachycardia.** *Adults:* 240 to 480 mg P.O. daily in three or four divided doses.

▶ **To control ventricular rate in digitalized patients with chronic atrial flutter or atrial fibrillation.** *Adults:* 240 to 320 mg P.O. in three or four divided doses.

▶ **Hypertension.** *Adults:* Usual starting dose is 80 mg P.O. t.i.d. Daily dose may be increased to 360 to 480 mg. Initial dose of extended-release tablets or capsules is 120 to 240 mg daily in the morning. Initial dose of Covera-HS is 180 mg at bedtime and of Verelan PM is 200 mg at bedtime. Start therapy with sustained-release capsules at 180 mg (240 mg for Verelan) daily in the morning. Adjust dosage based on effectiveness 24 hours after giving dose. Increase by 120 mg daily until a maximum dose of 480 mg daily is given. Sustained-release capsules should be given only once daily. Antihypertensive effects are usually seen within the first week of therapy. Most patients respond to 240 mg daily.

I.V. administration

- Give drug by direct injection into vein or into tubing of free-flowing, compatible I.V. solution.
- Compatible solutions include D_5W, half-normal and normal saline solutions, and Ringer's and lactated Ringer's solutions.
- Give I.V. doses slowly over at least 2 minutes (3 minutes for elderly patients) to minimize risk of adverse reactions.
- Perform continuous ECG and blood pressure monitoring during administration.

⊗ **Incompatibilities**
Albumin, aminophylline, amphotericin B, ampicillin sodium, co-trimoxazole, dobutamine, hydralazine, nafcillin, oxacillin, propofol, sodium bicarbonate, solutions with a pH greater than 6.

Contraindications and cautions

- Contraindicated in patients hypersensitive to the drug or any of its components and in those with severe left ventricular dysfunction; cardiogenic shock; second- or third-degree AV block or sick sinus syndrome, except in presence of functioning pacemaker; atrial flutter or fibrillation and accessory bypass tract syndrome; severe heart failure (unless secondary to verapamil therapy); or severe hypotension.
- I.V. verapamil is contraindicated in patients with ventricular tachycardia and in those receiving I.V. beta blockers.
- Use cautiously in patients with increased intracranial pressure or hepatic or renal disease.

Lifespan: In pregnant women, use cautiously. In breast-feeding women, avoid drug; it appears in breast milk. In elderly patients, use cautiously.

Adverse reactions

CNS: asthenia, dizziness, headache.
CV: ***AV block, bradycardia, heart failure,*** peripheral edema, transient hypotension, ***ventricular fibrillation, ventricular asystole.***
GI: constipation, nausea.
Respiratory: ***pulmonary edema.***
Skin: rash.

Interactions

Drug-drug. *Acebutolol, atenolol, betaxolol, carteolol, esmolol, metoprolol, nadolol, penbutolol, pindolol, propranolol, timolol:* May increase the effects of both drugs. Monitor cardiac function closely, and decrease dosages as needed.
Antihypertensives, quinidine: May cause hypotension. Monitor blood pressure.
Carbamazepine, digoxin: May increase levels of these drugs. Monitor patient for toxicity.
Cyclosporine: May increase cyclosporine level. Monitor cyclosporine level.
Disopyramide, flecainide, propranolol, other beta blockers: May cause heart failure. Use together cautiously.
Lithium: May decrease lithium level. Monitor patient closely.
Rifampin: May decrease oral bioavailability of verapamil. Monitor patient for lack of effect.
Drug-herb. *Black catechu:* May cause additive effects. Tell patient to use together cautiously.
Yerba maté: May decrease clearance of yerba maté methylxanthines and cause toxicity. Discourage concomitant use.
Drug-food. *Any food:* May increase drug absorption. Tell patient to take drug with food.
Drug-lifestyle. *Alcohol use:* May enhance effects of alcohol. Discourage use together.

Effects on lab test results

- May increase ALT, AST, alkaline phosphatase, and bilirubin levels.

Pharmacokinetics

Absorption: Rapid and complete from GI tract after P.O. use; only about 20% to 35% reaches systemic circulation.
Distribution: About 90% of circulating drug is protein-bound.
Metabolism: In liver.
Excretion: In urine as unchanged drug and active metabolites. *Half-life:* 6 to 12 hours.

Route	Onset	Peak	Duration
P.O.	1–2 hr	1–9 hr	8–24 hr
I.V.	Rapid	Immediate	1–6 hr

Action

Chemical effect: Not clearly defined; inhibits calcium ion influx across cardiac and smooth-muscle cells, thus decreasing myocardial contractility and oxygen demand. Drug also dilates coronary arteries and arterioles.
Therapeutic effect: Relieves angina, lowers blood pressure, and restores normal sinus rhythm.

Available forms

Capsules (extended-release): 120 mg, 180 mg, 240 mg
Capsules (sustained-release): 120 mg, 160 mg ◊, 80 mg, 200 mg, 240 mg, 360 mg
Injection: 2.5 mg/ml
Tablets: 40 mg, 80 mg, 120 mg, 160 mg ◊
Tablets (extended-release): 100 mg, 120 mg, 180 mg, 200 mg, 240 mg, 300 mg
Tablets (sustained-release): 120 mg, 180 mg, 240 mg

NURSING PROCESS

Assessment

- Assess patient's condition before starting therapy and regularly thereafter to monitor drug's effectiveness.
- Monitor blood pressure at start of therapy and during dosage adjustments.
- Monitor liver function studies during long-term treatment.
- Be alert for adverse reactions and drug interactions.
- Assess patient's and family's knowledge of drug therapy.

Nursing diagnoses

- Acute pain related to presence of angina
- Decreased cardiac output related to presence of arrhythmia
- Deficient knowledge related to drug therapy

Planning and implementation

- Give lower doses to patient with severely compromised cardiac function or to a patient taking beta blockers.
- Give drug with food, but keep in mind that giving extended-release tablets with food may decrease rate and extent of absorption. It also produces smaller fluctuations of peak and trough levels.
- If drug is being used to terminate supraventricular tachycardia, prescriber may have patient perform vagal maneuvers after receiving drug.
- Assist patient with walking because dizziness may occur.

V

• If patient has signs of heart failure, such as swelling of hands and feet or shortness of breath, notify prescriber.

ALERT: Don't confuse Isoptin with Intropin; don't confuse Verelan with Vivarin, Voltaren, Ferralyn, or Virilon.

Patient teaching

• Instruct patient to take drug with food.
• If patient continues nitrate therapy during adjustment of oral verapamil dosage, urge continued compliance. S.L. nitroglycerin, especially, may be taken as needed when angina is acute.
• Encourage patient to increase fluid and fiber intake to combat constipation. Give stool softener.
• Instruct patient to report adverse reactions, especially swelling of hands and feet and shortness of breath.

Evaluation

• Patient has reduced severity or frequency of angina.
• Patient regains normal cardiac output with restoration of normal sinus rhythm.
• Patient and family state understanding of drug therapy.

vinblastine sulfate (VLB)

(vin-BLAH-steen SUL-fayt)

Velban, Velbe ♦ ◇

Pharmacologic class: vinca alkaloid
Therapeutic class: antineoplastic
Pregnancy risk category: D

Indications and dosages

▶ **Breast or testicular cancer, Hodgkin and non-Hodgkin lymphoma, choriocarcinoma, lymphosarcoma, mycosis fungoides, Kaposi sarcoma, histiocytosis.** *Adults:* 0.1 mg/kg or 3.7 mg/m^2 I.V. weekly or q 2 weeks. May be increased to maximum of 0.5 mg/kg or 18.5 mg/m^2 weekly according to response. If WBC count is less than 4,000/mm^3, don't repeat dose.

▶ **Letterer-Siwe disease (histiocytosis X).** *Children:* 6.5 mg/m^2. Adjust dosage by hematologic response.

▶ **Hodgkin lymphoma.** *Children:* 6 mg/m^2 with other drugs. Adjust dosage by hematologic response.

▶ **Testicular germ cell carcinoma.** *Children:* 3 mg/m^2 with other drugs. Adjust dosage by hematologic response.

Adjust-a-dose: If bilirubin level is greater than 3 mg/dl, decrease dosage by half.

I.V. administration

• Preparation and administration of parenteral form are linked to carcinogenic, mutagenic, and teratogenic risks. Follow facility policy to reduce risks.
• Reconstitute drug in 10-mg vial with 10 ml of saline solution injection or sterile water. This yields 1 mg/ml.
• Inject drug directly into vein or running I.V. line over 1 minute. Drug also may be given in 50 ml of D_5W or normal saline solution infused over 15 minutes.
• If extravasation occurs, stop infusion immediately and notify prescriber. Manufacturer recommends that moderate heat be applied to area of leakage. Local injection of hyaluronidase may help disperse drug. Some clinicians prefer to apply ice packs on and off q 2 hours for 24 hours, with local injection of hydrocortisone or normal saline solution.
• Refrigerate reconstituted solution. Discard after 30 days.

⊗ **Incompatibilities**

Cefepime, furosemide, heparin.

Contraindications and cautions

• Contraindicated in patients with severe leukopenia or bacterial infection.
• Use cautiously in patients with hepatic dysfunction.

Lifespan: In pregnant women, give only if clearly needed. In breast-feeding women, drug isn't recommended; it isn't known if drug appears in breast milk.

Adverse reactions

CNS: depression, headache, loss of deep tendon reflexes, numbness, paresthesia, peripheral neuropathy and neuritis, ***seizures, stroke.***
CV: hypertension, ***MI, phlebitis.***
EENT: pharyngitis.
GI: abdominal pain, anorexia, ***bleeding,*** constipation, diarrhea, ileus, nausea, stomatitis, ulcer, vomiting.
GU: aspermia, oligospermia, urine retention.

Hematologic: anemia, *leukopenia* (lowest results on days 4 to 10; lasts another 7 to 14 days), ***thrombocytopenia.***
Metabolic: hyperuricemia, *weight loss.*
Musculoskeletal: *muscle pain and weakness,* uric acid nephropathy.
Respiratory: ***acute bronchospasm,*** shortness of breath.
Skin: cellulitis, necrosis with extravasation, reversible alopecia, vesiculation.

Interactions

Drug-drug. *Erythromycin, other drugs that inhibit cytochrome P-450 pathway:* May increase toxicity of vinblastine. Monitor patient closely.
Mitomycin: May increase risk of bronchospasm and shortness of breath. Monitor patient closely.
Phenytoin: May decrease phenytoin level. Monitor patient closely.

Effects on lab test results

- May increase uric acid level. May decrease hemoglobin level and hematocrit.
- May decrease WBC and platelet counts.

Pharmacokinetics

Absorption: Given I.V.
Distribution: Widely in body tissues. Crosses blood-brain barrier but doesn't achieve therapeutic level in CSF.
Metabolism: Partially in liver to active metabolite.
Excretion: Mainly in bile as unchanged drug; smaller portion excreted in urine. *Half-life:* Alpha phase, 3 minutes; beta phase, 1½ hours; terminal phase, 25 hours.

Route	Onset	Peak	Duration
I.V.	Unknown	Unknown	Unknown

Action

Chemical effect: Arrests mitosis in metaphase, blocking cell division.
Therapeutic effect: Inhibits replication of certain cancer cells.

Available forms

Injection: 10-mg vials (lyophilized powder), 1 mg/ml in 10-ml vials

NURSING PROCESS

Assessment

- Assess patient's condition before starting therapy and regularly thereafter to monitor drug's effectiveness.
- Before therapy and each dose, monitor CBC. Leukopenic effects reach lowest point in 4 to 10 days, with recovery in 7 to 14 days.

ALERT: After giving drug, monitor patient for development of life-threatening acute bronchospasm. Reaction is most likely if patient also receives mitomycin.

- Be alert for adverse reactions and drug interactions.
- Assess patient for numbness and tingling in hands and feet. Assess gait for early evidence of footdrop. Drug is less neurotoxic than vincristine.
- Assess patient's and family's knowledge of drug therapy.

Nursing diagnoses

- Ineffective health maintenance related to presence of neoplastic disease
- Ineffective protection related to drug-induced adverse hematologic reactions
- Deficient knowledge related to drug therapy

Planning and implementation

- Give antiemetic before giving drug.
- Don't give drug into limb with compromised circulation.

ALERT: Drug is fatal if given intrathecally; it's for I.V. use only.

- If acute bronchospasm occurs after administration, notify prescriber immediately.
- Make sure patient maintains adequate fluid intake to facilitate excretion of uric acid.
- If stomatitis occurs, stop giving the drug and notify prescriber.
- Don't repeat dose more frequently than q 7 days to prevent severe leukopenia.

ALERT: Don't confuse vinblastine with vincristine or vindesine.

Patient teaching

- Teach patient about infection control and bleeding precautions.
- Warn patient that alopecia may occur, but that it's usually reversible.
- Tell patient to report adverse reactions promptly.

V

• Encourage adequate fluid intake to increase urine output and facilitate excretion of uric acid.

Evaluation
• Patient responds well to drug.
• Patient develops no serious complications from adverse hematologic reactions.
• Patient and family state understanding of drug therapy.

vincristine sulfate
(vin-KRIH-steen SUL-fayt)
Oncovin, Vincasar PFS

Pharmacologic class: vinca alkaloid
Therapeutic class: antineoplastic
Pregnancy risk category: D

Indications and dosages

▶ **Breast cancer‡, acute lymphoblastic and other leukemias, Hodgkin lymphoma, non-Hodgkin lymphoma, neuroblastoma, rhabdomyosarcoma, Wilms tumor.** *Adults:* 1.4 mg/m^2 I.V. weekly. Maximum, 2 mg weekly.
Children weighing more than 10 kg (22 lb): 2 mg/m^2 I.V. weekly. Maximum single dose is 2 mg.
Children weighing 10 kg or less: 0.05 mg/kg I.V. once weekly.
Adjust-a-dose: If serum bilirubin level is greater than 3 mg/dl, decrease dose by half.

I.V. administration

• Preparation and administration of parenteral form are linked to carcinogenic, mutagenic, and teratogenic risks. Follow facility policy to reduce risks.
• Inject drug directly into vein or running I.V. line slowly over 1 minute. Drug also may be given in 50 ml of D_5W or normal saline solution infused over 15 minutes.
• If drug extravasates, stop infusion immediately and notify prescriber. Apply heat on and off q 2 hours for 24 hours. Give 150 units of hyaluronidase to area of infiltrate.
• All vials (1-, 2-, and 5-ml) contain 1 mg/ml solution and should be refrigerated.
⊗ **Incompatibilities**
Cefepime, furosemide, idarubicin, sodium bicarbonate.

Contraindications and cautions

• Contraindicated in patients hypersensitive to the drug or any of its components and in those with demyelinating form of Charcot-Marie-Tooth syndrome. Don't give drug to patients who are receiving radiation therapy through sites that include the liver.
• Use cautiously in patients with hepatic dysfunction, neuromuscular disease, or infection.
Lifespan: In pregnant or breast-feeding women, drug isn't recommended.

Adverse reactions

CNS: acute uric acid neuropathy, ataxia, ***coma,*** cranial nerve palsies, fever, headache, hoarseness, jaw pain, loss of deep tendon reflexes, paresthesia, peripheral neuropathy, ***permanent neurotoxicity, seizures,*** sensory loss, wristdrop and footdrop, vocal cord paralysis.
CV: hypertension, hypotension, *phlebitis.*
EENT: diplopia, optic and extraocular neuropathy, ptosis, visual disturbances.
GI: anorexia, *constipation, cramps,* diarrhea, dysphagia, ileus that mimics surgical abdomen, ***intestinal necrosis,*** *nausea, stomatitis, vomiting.*
GU: dysuria, polyuria, urine retention,
Hematologic: anemia, ***leukopenia, thrombocytopenia.***
Metabolic: hyperuricemia, hyponatremia, weight loss.
Musculoskeletal: muscle weakness and cramps.
Respiratory: ***acute bronchospasm.***
Skin: cellulitis at injection site, rash, *reversible alopecia,* severe local reaction with extravasation.
Other: SIADH.

Interactions

Drug-drug. *Asparaginase:* May decrease hepatic clearance of vincristine. Monitor patient closely for toxicity.
Azole antifungals: May increase vincristine toxicity. If possible, avoid use together.
Calcium channel blockers: May increase vincristine accumulation. Monitor patient for toxicity.
Digoxin: May decrease digoxin effects. Monitor digoxin level.

Mitomycin: May increase frequency of bronchospasm and acute pulmonary reactions. Monitor patient closely.
Phenytoin: May decrease phenytoin level. Monitor patient closely.
Quinolone antibiotics: May decrease antimicrobial effect of quinolones. Monitor response.

Effects on lab test results

- May increase uric acid level. May decrease sodium and hemoglobin levels and hematocrit.
- May decrease WBC and platelet counts.

Pharmacokinetics

Absorption: Given I.V.
Distribution: Wide. Bound to erythrocytes and platelets. Crosses blood-brain barrier but doesn't achieve therapeutic level in CSF.
Metabolism: Extensive, in liver.
Excretion: Mainly in bile; smaller portion in urine. *Half-life:* First phase, 4 minutes; second phase, 2¼ hours; terminal phase, 85 hours.

Route	Onset	Peak	Duration
I.V.	Unknown	Unknown	Unknown

Action

Chemical effect: Arrests mitosis in metaphase, blocking cell division.
Therapeutic effect: Inhibits replication of certain cancer cells.

Available forms

Injection: 1 mg/ml in 1-, 2-, and 5-ml multiple-dose vials; 1 mg/ml in 1- and 2-ml preservative-free vials

NURSING PROCESS

Assessment

- Assess patient's condition before starting therapy and regularly thereafter to monitor drug's effectiveness.

ALERT: After giving drug, monitor patient for development of life-threatening acute bronchospasm. Reaction is most likely to occur if patient also receives mitomycin.

- Monitor patient for hyperuricemia, especially if he has leukemia or lymphoma.
- Be alert for adverse reactions and drug interactions.
- Check for depression of Achilles tendon reflex, numbness, tingling, footdrop or wristdrop, difficulty in walking, ataxia, and slapping gait. Also check ability to walk on heels.
- Monitor bowel function. Constipation may be early sign of neurotoxicity.
- Assess patient's and family's knowledge of drug therapy.

Nursing diagnoses

- Ineffective health maintenance related to presence of neoplastic disease
- Ineffective protection related to drug-induced adverse hematologic reactions
- Deficient knowledge related to drug therapy

Planning and implementation

- Give antiemetic before drug.
- Don't give drug to one patient as single dose. The 5-mg vials are for multiple-dose use.

ALERT: Drug is fatal if given intrathecally; it's for I.V. use only.

- Because of risk of neurotoxicity, don't give drug more than once a week. Children are more resistant to neurotoxicity than adults. Neurotoxicity is dose-related and usually reversible.
- If acute bronchospasm occurs after giving the drug, immediately notify the prescriber.
- Maintain good hydration and give allopurinol to prevent uric acid nephropathy.
- If SIADH develops, fluid restriction may be needed.
- Give stool softener, laxative, or water before each dose to help prevent constipation.

ALERT: Don't confuse vincristine with vinblastine or vindesine.

Patient teaching

- Instruct patient on infection control and bleeding precautions.
- Warn patient that alopecia may occur, but that it's usually reversible.
- Tell patient to report adverse reactions promptly.
- Encourage fluid intake to facilitate excretion of uric acid.
- Advise woman of childbearing age not to become pregnant during therapy. Also recommend that she consult with prescriber when planning a pregnancy.

Evaluation

- Patient responds well to drug.
- Patient doesn't develop serious complications from adverse hematologic reactions.

V

• Patient and family state understanding of drug therapy.

vinorelbine tartrate

(vin-oh-REL-been TAR-trayt)
Navelbine

Pharmacologic class: semisynthetic vinca alkaloid
Therapeutic class: antineoplastic
Pregnancy risk category: D

Indications and dosages

▶ **Alone or as adjunct therapy with cisplatin for first-line treatment of ambulatory patients with nonresectable advanced non–small-cell lung cancer; alone or with cisplatin in stage IV of non–small-cell lung cancer; with cisplatin in stage III of non–small-cell lung cancer.** *Adults:* 30 mg/m² I.V. weekly. In combination treatment, same dosage used along with 120 mg/m² of cisplatin, given on days 1 and 29, and then q 6 weeks, or vinorelbine 25 mg/m² weekly with cisplatin 100 mg/m² given q 4 weeks.

▶ **Breast cancer‡.** *Adults:* 20 to 30 mg/m² I.V. infusion over 20 to 60 minutes weekly. Or, 30 mg/m² direct I.V. injection over 3 to 5 minutes weekly. If used in combination therapy, give 25 or 30 mg/m² I.V. in periodic doses. If used with mitoxantrone and ifosfamide, give 12 mg/m² I.V. in periodic doses.

Adjust-a-dose: Dosage adjustments are made according to hematologic toxicity or hepatic insufficiency, whichever results in lower dosage. If patient's granulocyte count falls between 1,000/mm³ and 1,500/mm³, reduce dosage by half. If three consecutive doses are skipped because of granulocytopenia, stop drug. If total bilirubin is 2.1 to 3 mg/dl, reduce dosage to 15 mg/m²; if total bilirubin is greater than 3 mg/dl, reduce dosage to 7.5 mg/m².

I.V. administration

• Drug must be diluted.
• Give drug I.V. over 6 to 10 minutes into side port of free-flowing I.V. line that is closest to I.V. bag.
• After the infusion, flush the line with 75 to 125 ml of D_5W or normal saline solution.

⊗ Incompatibilities
Acyclovir, allopurinol, aminophylline, amphotericin B, ampicillin sodium, cefazolin, cefoperazone, ceftriaxone, cefuroxime, fluorouracil, furosemide, ganciclovir, methylprednisolone, mitomycin, piperacillin, sodium bicarbonate, thiotepa, trimethoprim-sulfamethoxazole.

Contraindications and cautions

• Contraindicated in patients with pretreatment granulocyte counts below 1,000/mm³.
• Use cautiously in patients whose bone marrow may have been compromised by previous exposure to radiation therapy or chemotherapy or whose bone marrow is still recovering from previous chemotherapy. Also use cautiously in patients with hepatic impairment.

Lifespan: In pregnant and breast-feeding women, drug isn't recommended. In children, safety and effectiveness haven't been established.

Adverse reactions

CNS: asthenia, fatigue, peripheral neuropathy.
GI: anorexia, constipation, diarrhea, nausea, paralytic ileus, stomatitis, vomiting.
Hematologic: ***anemia, bone marrow suppression, granulocytopenia,*** **LEUKOPENIA.**
Hepatic: *bilirubinemia.*
Musculoskeletal: arthralgia, chest pain, jaw pain, loss of deep tendon reflexes, myalgia.
Respiratory: ***ARDS,*** dyspnea, pneumonia.
Skin: *alopecia,* rash.
Other: injection site pain or reaction, SIADH.

Interactions

Drug-drug. *Cisplatin:* May increase risk of bone marrow suppression when given with cisplatin. Monitor hematologic status closely.
Drugs that inhibit CYP3A isoenzymes: May inhibit metabolism of vinorelbine and cause an earlier onset or increased severity of adverse reactions. Exercise caution.
Mitomycin: May cause pulmonary reactions. Monitor patient's respiratory status closely.
Paclitaxel: May increase risk of neuropathy when given with vinorelbine. Monitor patient.

Effects on lab test results

• May increase bilirubin level. May decrease hemoglobin level and hematocrit.
• May decrease liver function test values and granulocyte, WBC, and platelet counts.

Pharmacokinetics

Absorption: Given I.V.
Distribution: Widely in body tissues. Bound to lymphocytes and platelets.
Metabolism: Extensive, in liver.
Excretion: Mainly in bile; smaller portion in urine. *Half-life:* 27¾ to 43½ hours.

Route	Onset	Peak	Duration
I.V.	Unknown	Unknown	Unknown

Action

Chemical effect: Arrests mitosis in metaphase, blocking cell division.
Therapeutic effect: Inhibits replication of selected cancer cells.

Available forms

Injection: 10 mg/ml, 50 mg/5 ml

NURSING PROCESS

Assessment

- Assess patient's condition before starting therapy and regularly thereafter to monitor drug's effectiveness.
- Monitor patient closely for hypersensitivity reactions.
- To determine dose before each treatment, monitor patient's peripheral blood count and bone marrow.
- Be alert for adverse reactions and drug interactions.
- Assess patient for numbness and tingling in hands and feet. Assess gait for early evidence of footdrop.

ALERT: Monitor patient's deep tendon reflexes; loss may indicate cumulative toxicity.

- Assess patient's and family's knowledge of drug therapy.

Nursing diagnoses

- Ineffective health maintenance related to presence of neoplastic disease
- Ineffective protection related to drug-induced adverse hematologic reactions
- Deficient knowledge related to drug therapy

Planning and implementation

- Give antiemetic before giving drug.
- Check patient's granulocyte count before administration; it should be 1,000/mm^3 or more. If it's less, don't give the dose, and notify the prescriber.
- Take care to avoid extravasation because drug can cause considerable irritation, localized tissue necrosis, and thrombophlebitis. If extravasation occurs, stop drug immediately and inject remaining portion of dose into a different vein.

ALERT: Drug is fatal if given intrathecally; it's for I.V. use only.

- Drug may be a contact irritant, and solution must be handled and given with care. Gloves are recommended. Avoid inhaling vapors and don't allow drug to contact skin or mucous membranes, especially those of eyes. In case of contact, wash with copious amounts of water for at least 15 minutes.

Patient teaching

- Instruct patient on infection control and bleeding precautions.
- Warn patient that alopecia may occur, but that it's usually reversible.
- Instruct patient not to take other drugs, including OTC preparations, unless approved by prescriber.
- Instruct patient to tell prescriber about signs and symptoms of infection (fever, chills, malaise) because drug has immunosuppressant activity.

Evaluation

- Patient responds well to drug.
- Patient doesn't develop serious complications from adverse hematologic reactions.
- Patient and family state understanding of drug therapy.

vitamin A (retinol)

(VIGH-tuh-min ay)

Aquasol A, Palmitate-A 5000

Pharmacologic class: fat-soluble vitamin
Therapeutic class: vitamin
Pregnancy risk category: A (C at higher-than-recommended doses)

Indications and dosages

▶ **RDA.** RDAs are in retinol equivalents (RE). 1 RE has activity of 1 mcg of all-trans retinol, 6 mcg of beta carotene, or 12 mcg of carotenoid provitamins.

V

Men older than age 11: Give 1,000 mcg RE or 5,000 international units.
Pregnant women and women older than age 11: Give 800 mcg RE or 4,000 international units.
Breast-feeding women (first 6 months): Give 1,300 mcg RE or 6,500 international units.
Breast-feeding women (second 6 months): Give 1,200 mcg RE or 6,000 international units.
Children ages 7 to 10: Give 700 mcg RE or 3,500 international units.
Children ages 4 to 6: Give 500 mcg RE or 2,500 international units.
Children ages 1 to 3: Give 400 mcg RE or 2,000 international units.
Neonates and infants younger than age 1: Give 375 mcg RE or 1,875 international units.

▶ **Severe vitamin A deficiency.** *Adults and children older than age 8:* Give 100,000 international units I.M. or P.O. daily for 3 days, followed by 50,000 international units I.M. or P.O. daily for 2 weeks; then 10,000 to 20,000 international units P.O. daily for 2 months. Follow with adequate dietary nutrition and RE vitamin A supplements.
Children ages 1 to 8: Give 17,500 to 35,000 international units I.M. daily for 10 days.
Infants younger than age 1: Give 7,500 to 15,000 international units I.M. daily for 10 days.

▶ **Maintenance dosage to prevent recurrence of vitamin A deficiency.** *Children ages 1 to 8:* Give 5,000 to 10,000 international units P.O. daily for 2 months; then adequate dietary nutrition and RE vitamin A supplements.

Contraindications and cautions

• Contraindicated for oral administration in patients with malabsorption syndrome; if malabsorption is from inadequate bile secretion, oral route may be used with administration of bile salts (dehydrocholic acid). Also contraindicated in patients hypersensitive to other ingredients in product and in those with hypervitaminosis A.
• I.V. administration contraindicated except for special water-miscible forms intended for infusion with large parenteral volumes. I.V. push of vitamin A of any type is also contraindicated (anaphylaxis or anaphylactoid reactions and death have resulted).
Lifespan: In pregnant women, use cautiously. In breast-feeding women, use cautiously, avoiding doses exceeding RE.

Adverse reactions

CNS: fatigue, headache, ***increased intracranial pressure,*** irritability, lethargy, malaise.
EENT: exophthalmos, papilledema.
GI: anorexia, epigastric pain, polydipsia, vomiting.
GU: hypomenorrhea, polyuria.
Hepatic: ***cirrhosis,*** hepatomegaly, jaundice.
Metabolic: cortical thickening over radius and tibia, decalcification of bone, hypercalcemia, migratory arthralgia, periostitis, premature closure of epiphyses, slow growth.
Skin: alopecia; dry, cracked, scaly skin; erythema; increased pigmentation; inflamed tongue, lips, and gums; lip fissures; massive desquamation; night sweats, pruritus.
Other: ***anaphylactic shock,*** splenomegaly.

Interactions

Drug-drug. *Cholestyramine resin, mineral oil:* May decrease GI absorption of fat-soluble vitamins. If needed, give mineral oil at bedtime.
Hormonal contraceptives: May increase vitamin A level. Monitor patient.
Isotretinoin, multivitamins containing vitamin A: May increase risk of toxicity. Avoid use together.
Neomycin (oral): May decrease vitamin A absorption. Avoid use together.

Effects on lab test results

• May increase liver enzyme and calcium levels.

Pharmacokinetics

Absorption: Absorbed readily and completely if fat absorption is normal. Larger doses or regular dose in patients with fat malabsorption, low protein intake, or hepatic or pancreatic disease may be absorbed incompletely. Because vitamin A is fat soluble, absorption requires bile salts, pancreatic lipase, and dietary fat.
Distribution: Stored (mainly as palmitate) in liver. Normal adult liver stores are sufficient to provide vitamin A requirements for 2 years. Lesser amounts of retinyl palmitate are stored in kidneys, lungs, adrenal glands, retinas, and intraperitoneal fat. Vitamin A circulates bound to specific alpha-1, retinol-binding protein.
Metabolism: In liver.
Excretion: Retinol (fat-soluble) combines with glucuronic acid and is metabolized to retinal and retinoic acid. Retinoic acid undergoes bil-

iary excretion in feces. Retinal, retinoic acid, and other water-soluble metabolites are excreted in urine and feces. *Half-life:* Unknown.

Route	Onset	Peak	Duration
P.O., I.M.	Unknown	3–5 hr	Unknown

Action

Chemical effect: Stimulates retinal function, bone growth, reproduction, and integrity of epithelial and mucosal tissues.
Therapeutic effect: Raises vitamin A level in body.

Available forms

Capsules: 10,000 international units, 15,000 international units, 25,000 international units, 50,000 international units
Injection: 2-ml vials (50,000 international units/ml with 0.5% chlorobutanol, polysorbate 80, butylated hydroxyanisole, and butylated hydroxytoluene)
Tablets: 5,000 international units

NURSING PROCESS

Assessment

- Assess patient's vitamin A intake from fortified foods, dietary supplements, self-administered drugs, and prescription drug sources before starting therapy, and reassess regularly thereafter to monitor drug's effectiveness.
- If dose is high, watch for adverse reactions. Acute toxicity may result from a single dose of 25,000 international units/kg; 350,000 international units in infants and over 2 million international units in adults may also be acutely toxic. Doses that don't exceed RE are usually nontoxic.
- Chronic toxicity in infants (age 3 to 6 months) may result from doses of 18,500 international units daily for 1 to 3 months. In adults, chronic toxicity has resulted from doses of 50,000 international units daily for more than 18 months; 500,000 international units daily for 2 months, and 1 million international units daily for 3 days.
- Be alert for drug interactions.
- Assess patient's and family's knowledge of drug therapy.

Nursing diagnoses

- Imbalanced nutrition: less than body requirements related to inadequate intake
- Ineffective health maintenance related to vitamin A toxicity caused by excessive intake
- Deficient knowledge related to drug therapy

Planning and implementation

- Adequate vitamin A absorption requires suitable protein, vitamin E, zinc intake, and bile secretion; give supplemental salts, if needed. Zinc supplements may be needed in patient receiving long-term total parenteral nutrition.
- Liquid preparations may be mixed with cereal or fruit juice to be given by NG tube.
- I.M. absorption is most rapid and complete with aqueous preparations, intermediate with emulsions, and slowest with oil suspensions.

ALERT: Give parenteral form by I.M. route or continuous I.V infusion in total parenteral nutrition. Never give as I.V. bolus.

- Protect drug from light.

Patient teaching

- Warn patient against taking megadoses of vitamins without specific indications. Also stress that he not share prescribed vitamins with others.
- Explain importance of avoiding prolonged use of mineral oil while taking this drug because it reduces vitamin A absorption.
- Review the signs and symptoms of vitamin A toxicity, and tell patient to report them immediately.
- Advise patient to consume adequate protein, vitamin E, and zinc, which, along with bile, are needed for vitamin A absorption.
- Instruct patient to store vitamin A in tight, light-resistant container.

Evaluation

- Patient regains normal vitamin A level.
- Patient shows no signs or symptoms of vitamin A toxicity.
- Patient and family state understanding of drug therapy.

vitamin C (ascorbic acid)

(VIGH-tuh-min see)

Ascor L500, Cecon†, Cenolate†, Cevi-Bid, Dull-C†, N'ice Vitamin C Drops†, Penta-vite ◇, Redoxon ♦, Vita-C†

Pharmacologic class: water-soluble vitamin
Therapeutic class: vitamin
Pregnancy risk category: A (C at higher-than-recommended doses)

Indications and dosages

▶ **RDA.** *Men:* 90 mg.
Women: 75 mg.
Pregnant women ages 14 to 18: Give 80 mg.
Pregnant women ages 19 to 50: Give 85 mg.
Breast-feeding women ages 14 to 18: Give 115 mg.
Breast-feeding women ages 19 to 50: Give 120 mg.
Boys ages 9 to 13: Give 45 mg.
Boys ages 14 to 18: Give 75 mg.
Girls ages 9 to 13: Give 45 mg.
Girls ages 14 to 18: Give 65 mg.
Children ages 4 to 8: Give 25 mg.
Children ages 1 to 3: Give 15 mg.
Infants ages 6 months to 1 year: Give 50 mg.
Neonates and infants younger than age 6 months: Give 40 mg.

▶ **Frank and subclinical scurvy.** *Adults:* Depending on severity, 300 mg to 1 g P.O., subcutaneously, I.M., or I.V. daily; then at least 50 mg daily for maintenance.
Children: Depending on severity, 100 to 300 mg P.O., subcutaneously, I.M., or I.V. daily; then at least 30 mg daily for maintenance.
Premature infants: 75 to 100 mg P.O., I.M., I.V., or subcutaneously daily.

▶ **Extensive burns, delayed fracture or wound healing, postoperative wound healing, severe febrile or chronic disease states.** *Adults:* 300 to 500 mg P.O., subcutaneously, I.M., or I.V. daily for 7 to 10 days. For extensive burns, 1 to 2 g daily.
Children: 100 to 200 mg P.O., subcutaneously, I.M., or I.V. daily.

▶ **Prevention of vitamin C deficiency in patients with poor nutritional habits or increased requirements.** *Adults:* 70 to 150 mg P.O., subcutaneously, I.M., or I.V. daily.
Pregnant or breast-feeding women: 70 to 150 mg P.O., subcutaneously, I.M., or I.V. daily.
Children: at least 40 mg P.O., subcutaneously, I.M., or I.V. daily.
Infants: at least 35 mg P.O., subcutaneously, I.M., or I.V. daily.

▶ **Potentiation of methenamine in urine acidification.** *Adults:* 4 to 12 g P.O. daily in divided doses.

I.V. administration

- Avoid rapid I.V. administration. It may cause faintness or dizziness.
- Give I.V. infusion cautiously in patients with renal insufficiency.
- Protect solution from light and refrigerate ampules.

⊗ **Incompatibilities**
Many drugs.

Contraindications and cautions

Lifespan: In pregnant women, give only if clearly needed. In breast-feeding women, use cautiously.

Adverse reactions

CNS: dizziness with rapid I.V. delivery, faintness.
GI: diarrhea.
GU: acid urine, oxaluria, renal calculi.
Other: discomfort at injection site.

Interactions

Drug-drug. *Aspirin (high doses):* May increase risk of ascorbic acid deficiency. Monitor patient closely.
Estrogen, hormonal contraceptives: May increase level of estrogen. Monitor patient.
Oral iron supplements: May increase iron absorption. A beneficial drug interaction. Encourage use together.
Warfarin: May decrease anticoagulant effect. Monitor patient closely.
Drug-herb. *Bearberry:* May inactivate bearberry in urine. Discourage use together.

Effects on lab test results

- May cause false-negative urine glucose determinations with large doses (larger than 500 mg). May cause false-negative results if ingested 48 to 72 hours before amine-dependent stool occult blood tests.

Pharmacokinetics

Absorption: After P.O. use, absorbed readily; may be reduced with very large doses or in patients with diarrhea or GI diseases. Unknown for I.M and subcutaneous use.
Distribution: Wide, with high levels in liver, leukocytes, platelets, glandular tissues, and lens of eyes. Protein-binding is low.
Metabolism: In liver.
Excretion: In urine. Renal excretion is directly proportional to blood level. *Half-life:* Unknown.

Route	Onset	Peak	Duration
P.O., I.V., I.M., SubQ	Unknown	Unknown	Unknown

Action

Chemical effect: Stimulates collagen formation and tissue repair; involved in oxidation-reduction reactions throughout body.
Therapeutic effect: Raises vitamin C level in body.

Available forms

Capsules (timed-release): 500 mg†, 1000 mg†
Crystals: 1000 mg/¼ tsp†
Injection: 500 mg/ml
Lozenges: 25 mg†
Oral liquid: 500 mg/ml†
Oral solution: 100 mg/ml†
Powder: 60 mg/¼ tsp†, 814 mg/¼ tsp†, 1060 mg/¼ tsp†
Tablets: 250 mg†, 500 mg†, 1,000 mg†, 1500 mg†
Tablets (chewable): 50 mg†, 60 mg†, 100 mg†, 200 mg†, 250 mg†, 500 mg†, 1,000 mg†
Tablets (timed-release): 500 mg†, 1,000 mg†

NURSING PROCESS

Assessment

- Assess patient's condition before starting therapy and regularly thereafter to monitor drug's effectiveness.
- When giving for urine acidification, check urine pH to ensure effectiveness.
- Be alert for adverse reactions and drug interactions.
- If adverse GI reactions occur, monitor patient's hydration.
- Assess patient's and family's knowledge of drug therapy.

Nursing diagnoses

- Imbalanced nutrition: less than body requirements related to inadequate intake
- Risk for deficient fluid volume related to drug-induced adverse GI reactions
- Deficient knowledge related to drug therapy

Planning and implementation

- Give P.O. solution directly into mouth, or mix with food.
- Utilization of vitamin may be better with I.M. route, the preferred parenteral route.

Patient teaching

- Stress proper nutritional habits to prevent recurrence of deficiency.
- Advise patient with vitamin C deficiency to decrease or stop smoking.

Evaluation

- Patient regains normal vitamin C level.
- Patient maintains adequate hydration.
- Patient and family state understanding of drug therapy.

vitamin D

(VIGH-tuh-min dee)

cholecalciferol (vitamin D_3)

(koh-lih-kal-SIF-eh-rol)

Delta-D, Vitamin D_3

ergocalciferol (vitamin D_2)

(er-goh-kal-SIF-er-ohl)

Calciferol, Drisdol, Radiostol Forte ♦

Pharmacologic class: fat-soluble vitamin
Therapeutic class: vitamin
Pregnancy risk category: A, C with doses over the RDA

Indications and dosages

▶ **RDA for cholecalciferol.** *Adolescents and adults:* 200 to 400 international units.
Children 4 to 10 years: 400 international units.
Infants and children (birth to 3 years): 300 to 400 international units.

V

Pregnant or breast-feeding women: 400 international units.

▶ **Rickets and other vitamin D deficiency diseases.** *Adults:* Initially, 12,000 international units P.O. daily; increase by response up to 500,000 international units daily. After correcting deficiency, patient should have adequate diet and take supplements.

▶ **Hypoparathyroidism.** *Adults and children:* 50,000 to 200,000 international units P.O. daily with calcium supplement.

▶ **Familial hypophosphatemia.** *Adults:* 10,000 to 80,000 international units P.O. daily with phosphorus supplement.

Contraindications and cautions

- Contraindicated in patients with hypercalcemia, hypervitaminosis D, or renal osteodystrophy with hyperphosphatemia.
- Use cautiously in cardiac patients, especially those receiving digoxin, and in patients with increased sensitivity to these drugs.
- Give ergocalciferol cautiously to patients with impaired kidney function, heart disease, renal calculi, or arteriosclerosis.

Lifespan: In pregnant women and breast-feeding women, use cautiously.

Adverse reactions

Adverse reactions listed are usually seen only in vitamin D toxicity.

CNS: headache, irritability, overt psychosis, somnolence, weakness.
CV: ***arrhythmias,*** calcifications of soft tissues including heart, hypertension.
EENT: conjunctivitis (calcific), photophobia, rhinorrhea,
GI: anorexia, constipation, dry mouth, metallic taste, nausea, polydipsia, vomiting.
GU: albuminuria, hypercalciuria, impaired kidney function, nocturia, polyuria, reversible azotemia.
Metabolic: hypercalcemia, hyperthermia, weight loss.
Musculoskeletal: bone demineralization, bone and muscle pain.
Skin: pruritus.
Other: decreased libido.

Interactions

Drug-drug. *Cholestyramine resin, mineral oil:* May inhibit GI absorption of oral vitamin D. Space doses. Use together cautiously.
Corticosteroids: May antagonize effect of vitamin D. Monitor vitamin D level closely.
Digoxin: May increase risk of arrhythmias. Monitor calcium level.
Phenobarbital, phenytoin: May increase vitamin D metabolism, which decreases half-life as well as drug's effectiveness. Monitor patient closely.
Thiazide diuretics: May cause hypercalcemia in patients with hypoparathyroidism. Monitor patient closely.
Verapamil: May increase risk of atrial fibrillation because of increased calcium. Monitor patient closely.

Effects on lab test results

- May increase BUN, creatinine, AST, ALT, urine urea, albumin, calcium, and cholesterol levels.

Pharmacokinetics

Absorption: From small intestine.
Distribution: Throughout body. Bound to proteins stored in liver.
Metabolism: In liver and kidneys.
Excretion: Mainly in bile; small amount in urine. *Half-life:* 24 hours.

Route	Onset	Peak	Duration
P.O.	2–24 hr	3–12 hr	Varies

Action

Chemical effect: Promotes absorption and utilization of calcium and phosphate, helping to regulate calcium homeostasis.
Therapeutic effect: Helps to maintain normal calcium and phosphate levels in body.

Available forms

Capsules: 1.25 mg (50,000 international units)
Oral liquid: 8,000 international units/ml in 60-ml dropper bottle
Tablets: 400 international units, 1,000 international units

NURSING PROCESS

Assessment

- Assess patient's condition before starting therapy and regularly thereafter to monitor drug's effectiveness.

ALERT: Monitor patient's eating and bowel habits; dry mouth, nausea, vomiting, metallic taste, and constipation may be early evidence of toxicity.

• Monitor serum and urine calcium, potassium, and urea levels when high doses are used.
• Be alert for adverse reactions and drug interactions.
• Assess patient's and family's knowledge of drug therapy.

Nursing diagnoses

• Imbalanced nutrition: less than body requirements related to inadequate intake
• Ineffective health maintenance related to vitamin D toxicity
• Deficient knowledge related to drug therapy

Planning and implementation

• Doses of 60,000 international units a day can cause hypercalcemia.
• Malabsorption from inadequate bile or hepatic dysfunction may require addition of exogenous bile salts with oral form.
• Patient with hyperphosphatemia requires dietary phosphate restrictions and binding agents to avoid metastatic calcifications and renal calculus formation.

Patient teaching

• Warn patient of dangers of increasing dose without consulting prescriber. Vitamin D is fat soluble.
• Tell patient taking vitamin D to restrict his intake of magnesium-containing antacids.

Evaluation

• Patient regains normal vitamin D level.
• Patient doesn't develop vitamin D toxicity.
• Patient and family state understanding of drug therapy.

vitamin E (tocopherol)

(VIGH-tuh-min EE)

Aquasol E Drops†, Aquavit-E, E-200 I.U. Softgels†, E-400 I.U. Softgels†, Mixed E 400 Softgels, Mixed E 1000 Softgels, Nutr-E-Sol, Vitamin E with Mixed Tocopherols, Vita-Plus E Softgels†

Pharmacologic class: fat-soluble vitamin
Therapeutic class: vitamin
Pregnancy risk category: A

Indications and dosages

▶ **RDA.** RDAs are in α-tocopherol equivalents (α-TE). One α-TE equals 1 mg of D-α tocopherol or 1.49 international units.
Adults, pregnant women: Give 15 α-TE.
Breast-feeding women: Give 19 α-TE.
Children ages 14 to 18: Give 15 α-TE.
Children ages 9 to 13: Give 11 α-TE.
Children ages 4 to 8: Give 7 α-TE.
Children ages 1 to 3: Give 6 α-TE.
Infants ages 7 to 12 months: Give 5 α-TE.
Infants age 6 months and younger: Give 4 α-TE.

▶ **Vitamin E deficiency in adults and in children with malabsorption syndrome.** *Adults:* Depending on severity, 60 to 75 international units P.O. daily.
Children: 1 international unit/kg P.O. daily.

Contraindications and cautions

None reported.
Lifespan: In pregnant women, use cautiously. In breast-feeding women, use cautiously.

Adverse reactions

None reported.

Interactions

Drug-drug. *Cholestyramine resin, mineral oil:* May inhibit GI absorption of oral vitamin E. Space doses. Use together cautiously.
Iron: May catalyze oxidation and increase daily requirements. Give separately.
Oral anticoagulants: May increase hypoprothrombinemic effects, possibly causing bleeding. Monitor patient closely.
Vitamin K: May antagonize effects of vitamin K with large doses of vitamin E. Avoid use together.

Effects on lab test results

None reported.

Pharmacokinetics

Absorption: GI absorption depends on presence of bile. Only 20% to 60% of vitamin obtained from dietary sources is absorbed. As dosage increases, fraction of vitamin E absorbed decreases.
Distribution: To all tissues and stored in adipose tissues.
Metabolism: In liver.

V

Excretion: Mainly in bile; small amount in urine. *Half-life:* Unknown.

Route	Onset	Peak	Duration
P.O.	Unknown	Unknown	Unknown

Action

Chemical effect: May act as an antioxidant and protect RBC membranes against hemolysis.
Therapeutic effect: Raises vitamin E level in body.

Available forms

Capsules: 100 international units, 200 international units†, 400 international units†, 1,000 international units†
Drops: 15 international units/0.3 ml
Liquid: 15 international units/30 ml, 798 international units/30 ml
Oral solution: 50 international units/ml
Tablets (chewable): 100 international units, 200 international units†, 400 international units†, 500 international units, 800 international units, 1,000 international units

NURSING PROCESS

Assessment

- Assess patient's condition before starting therapy and regularly thereafter to monitor drug's effectiveness.
- Monitor patient with liver or gallbladder disease for response to therapy. Adequate bile is essential for vitamin E absorption.
- Be alert for drug interactions.
- Assess patient's and family's knowledge of drug therapy.

Nursing diagnoses

- Imbalanced nutrition: less than body requirements related to inadequate intake
- Deficient knowledge related to drug therapy

Planning and implementation

- Requirements increase with rise in dietary polyunsaturated acids.
- Make sure patient swallows tablets or capsules whole.
- Store drug in tightly closed, light-resistant container.
- If patient has malabsorption caused by lack of bile, give vitamin E with bile salts.
- Hypervitaminosis E symptoms include fatigue, weakness, nausea, headache, blurred vision, flatulence, diarrhea.

Patient teaching

- Tell patient not to crush tablets or open capsules. An oral solution and chewable tablets are commercially available.
- Discourage patient from taking megadoses, which can cause thrombophlebitis. Vitamin E is fat soluble.

Evaluation

- Patient regains normal vitamin E level.
- Patient and family state understanding of drug therapy.

voriconazole

(vhor-i-KHAN-a-zawl)
Vfend

Pharmacologic class: synthetic triazole
Therapeutic class: antifungal
Pregnancy risk category: D

Indications and dosages

▶ **Invasive aspergillosis; serious infections caused by *Fusarium* species and *Scedosporium apiospermum* in patients intolerant of or refractory to other therapy.** *Adults:* Initially, 6 mg/kg I.V. q 12 hours for two doses; then 4 mg/kg I.V. q 12 hours for maintenance. Switch to P.O. form as tolerated, using the following maintenance dosages:
Adults weighing 40 kg (88 lb) or more: Maintenance dosage, 200 mg P.O. q 12 hours. May increase to 300 mg P.O. q 12 hours, if needed.
Adults weighing less than 40 kg: Maintenance dosage, 100 mg P.O. q 12 hours. May increase to 150 mg P.O. q 12 hours, if needed.

▶ **Candidemia in nonneutropenic patients; candida infections of the kidney, abdomen, bladder wall, wounds, and skin (disseminated).** *Adults:* Initially, 6 mg/kg I.V. q 12 hours for two doses; then 4 mg/kg I.V. q 12 hours for maintenance. If patient unable to tolerate maintenance dose, decrease to 3 mg/kg. Switch to P.O. form as tolerated, using the maintenance dosages shown here.
Adults weighing 40 kg (88 lb) or more: 200 mg P.O. q 12 hours. May increase to 300 mg P.O. q 12 hours, if needed.

Adults weighing less than 40 kg: 100 mg P.O. q 12 hours. May increase to 150 mg P.O. q 12 hours, if needed.

▶ **Esophageal candidiasis.** *Adults weighing 40 kg or more:* 200 mg P.O. q 12 hours. Treat for a minimum of 14 days and for at least 7 days following resolution of symptoms.

Adults weighing less than 40 kg: 100 mg P.O. q 12 hours. Treat for a minimum of 14 days and for at least 7 days following resolution of symptoms.

Adjust-a-dose: In patients with mild to moderate hepatic cirrhosis, decrease the maintenance dosage by one-half.

I.V. administration

- Reconstitute powder with 19 ml of sterile water for injection to obtain a volume of 20 ml of clear concentrate containing 10 mg/ml of drug. If a vacuum doesn't pull the diluent into the vial, discard the vial. Shake vial until all the powder is dissolved.
- Further dilute the solution to a concentration of 5 mg/ml or less. Follow the manufacturer's instructions for diluting.
- Infuse over 1 to 2 hours, at a concentration of 5 mg/ml or less and a maximum of 3 mg/kg hourly.
- Infusion reactions, including flushing, fever, sweating, tachycardia, chest tightness, dyspnea, faintness, nausea, pruritus, and rash, may occur as soon as infusion starts. If reaction occurs, notify prescriber. Infusion may need to be stopped.
- Monitor creatinine level in patient with moderate to severe renal dysfunction (creatinine clearance less than 50 ml/minute). If creatinine level increases, consider changing to P.O. form.
- Store unreconstituted vials at controlled room temperature (59° to 86° F [15° to 30° C]). Use reconstituted solution immediately.

⊗ **Incompatibilities**

Blood products, electrolyte supplements, 4.2% sodium bicarbonate infusion.

Contraindications and cautions

- Contraindicated in patients hypersensitive to the drug or any of its components and in those with rare hereditary problems of galactose intolerance, Lapp lactase deficiency, or glucose-galactose malabsorption. Also contraindicated in patients taking rifampin, carbamazepine, long-acting barbiturates, sirolimus, rifabutin, ergot alkaloids, pimozide, quinidine, efavirenz, or ritonavir.
- Use cautiously in patients hypersensitive to other azoles. Use I.V. form cautiously in patients with creatinine clearance less than 50 ml/minute.

Lifespan: In pregnant women, don't use; drug can harm fetus. In breast-feeding women, use cautiously; it's unknown whether drug appears in breast milk. In children younger than age 12, safety and effectiveness haven't been established.

Adverse reactions

CNS: dizziness, hallucinations, headache, fever.
CV: hypertension, hypotension, peripheral edema, ***prolonged QT interval,*** tachycardia, vasodilation.
EENT: *abnormal vision,* chromatopsia, dry mouth, photophobia.
GI: abdominal pain, diarrhea, nausea, vomiting.
GU: ***acute renal failure.***
Hepatic: cholestatic jaundice.
Metabolic: hypokalemia, hypomagnesemia.
Skin: pruritus, rash.
Other: chills.

Interactions

Drug-drug. *Benzodiazepines, calcium channel blockers, lovastatin, omeprazole, sulfonylureas, vinca alkaloids:* May increase levels of these drugs. Adjust dosages of these drugs, and monitor patient for adverse effects.

Carbamazepine, long-acting barbiturates, rifabutin, rifampin: May decrease voriconazole level. Avoid use together.

Coumarin anticoagulants, warfarin: May significantly increase PT. Monitor PT or other appropriate anticoagulant test results.

Cyclosporine, tacrolimus: May increase levels of these drugs. Reduce their dosages, and monitor levels. Adjust doses and monitor levels of these drugs when voriconazole is stopped.

Efavirenz: May significantly decrease voriconazole level and significantly increase efavirenz level. Avoid use together.

Ergot alkaloids (such as ergotamine), sirolimus: May increase levels of these drugs. Avoid use together.

HIV protease inhibitors (amprenavir, nelfinavir, saquinavir), nonnucleoside reverse transcrip-

V

tase inhibitors (delavirdine): May increase levels of both drugs. Monitor patient for adverse effects.
Oral contraceptives containing ethinyl estradiol and norethindrone: May increase levels and adverse effects of these drugs. Monitor patient closely.
Phenytoin: May decrease voriconazole level and increase phenytoin level. Increase voriconazole maintenance dose, and monitor phenytoin level.
Pimozide, quinidine: May increase levels of these drugs, possibly leading to QT prolongation and torsades de pointes. Avoid use together.
Ritonavir: May significantly decrease voriconazole level. Avoid use together.
Drug-lifestyle. *Sun exposure:* May cause photosensitivity reaction. Tell patient to avoid excessive or unprotected sun exposure.

Effects on lab test results

- May increase AST, ALT, bilirubin, alkaline phosphatase, and creatinine levels. May decrease potassium, magnesium, and hemoglobin levels and hematocrit.
- May decrease platelet, WBC, and RBC counts.

Pharmacokinetics

Absorption: Oral bioavailability is about 96%.
Distribution: Extensive. 58% protein-bound.
Metabolism: By CYP2C19, CYP2C9, and CYP3A4.
Excretion: Via hepatic metabolism, with less than 2% unchanged in urine. *Half-life:* Depends on dose.

Route	Onset	Peak	Duration
P.O., I.V.	Immediate	1–2 hr	12 hr

Action

Chemical effect: Inhibits an essential step in fungal ergosterol biosynthesis.
Therapeutic effect: Kills susceptible fungi.

Available forms

Injection: 200 mg
Powder for oral suspension: 45 g (40 mg/ml after reconstitution)
Tablets: 50 mg, 200 mg

NURSING PROCESS

Assessment

- Assess patient's condition before starting therapy and regularly thereafter to monitor drug's effectiveness.
- Monitor liver function test results throughout therapy. Monitor patient who develops abnormal liver function test results for more severe hepatic dysfunction.
- Monitor renal function during treatment.
- If treatment lasts more than 28 days, monitor visual acuity, visual fields, and color perception.
- Assess patient's and family's knowledge of drug therapy.

Nursing diagnoses

- Risk for infection related to presence of fungus
- Risk for injury related to adverse CNS effects of drug
- Deficient knowledge related to drug therapy

Planning and implementation

- Use oral form in patient with moderate to severe renal impairment unless benefits of I.V. use outweigh risks.
- Reconstitute powder for oral suspension with 46 ml of water. Shake the bottle vigorously for about 1 minute. Remove cap, push bottle adaptor into neck of the bottle, and replace cap. The reconstituted suspension should be shaken for about 10 seconds before each use. Administer using the supplied oral dispenser.
- The reconstituted oral suspension should not be mixed with any other medication or flavoring agent and should not be further diluted. Reconstituted suspension can be stored at a controlled room temperature (59° to 86° F [15 to 30° C]) for 14 days.
- If patient develops signs and symptoms of liver disease that may be caused by therapy, stop drug.

Patient teaching

- Tell patient to take oral drug at least 1 hour before or 1 hour after a meal.
- Advise patient to avoid driving or operating machinery while taking drug, especially at night, because vision changes, including blurring and photophobia, may occur.
- Tell patient to avoid strong, direct sunlight during therapy.

• Tell woman of childbearing potential to use effective contraception during treatment.

Evaluation
• Infection is successfully treated.
• Patient sustains no injury.
• Patient and family state understanding of drug therapy.

warfarin sodium
(WAR-feh-rin SOH-dee-um)
Coumadin, Jantoven, Warfilone ♦

Pharmacologic class: coumarin derivative
Therapeutic class: anticoagulant
Pregnancy risk category: X

Indications and dosages

▶ **Pulmonary embolism related to deep vein thrombosis, MI, rheumatic heart disease with heart valve damage, prosthetic heart valves, chronic atrial fibrillation.** *Adults:* Initially, 2 to 5 mg P.O. or I.V daily for 2 to 4 days. Use PT and INR determinations to establish optimum dose. Usual maintenance dosage, 2 to 10 mg daily.

I.V. administration

• Reconstitute by adding 2.7 ml of sterile water for injection to vial of 5 mg of warfarin. Resulting solution contains 2 mg/ml.
• Inject dose slowly over 1 to 2 minutes.
⊗ **Incompatibilities**
None reported.

Contraindications and cautions

• Contraindicated in patients with bleeding or hemorrhagic tendencies, GI ulcerations, severe hepatic or renal disease, severe uncontrolled hypertension, subacute bacterial endocarditis, polycythemia vera, or vitamin K deficiency. Also contraindicated in patients who have had recent eye, brain, or spinal cord surgery.
• Use cautiously in patients with diverticulitis, colitis, mild or moderate hypertension, mild or moderate hepatic or renal disease, drainage tubes in any orifice, or regional or lumbar block anesthesia. Also use cautiously if patient has any condition that increases the risk of hemorrhage.
Lifespan: In pregnant women, drug is contraindicated. In breast-feeding women, use cautiously; it's unknown if the drug appears in breast milk. Infants, especially neonates, may be more susceptible to anticoagulants because of vitamin K deficiency. In elderly patients, use a lower dose because they have an increased risk of bleeding.

Adverse reactions

CNS: *fever,* headache.
GI: anorexia, cramps, *diarrhea,* melena, mouth ulcerations, nausea, sore mouth, vomiting.
GU: excessive menstrual bleeding, hematuria.
Hematologic: ***hemorrhage.***
Hepatic: ***hepatitis,*** jaundice.
Skin: alopecia, dermatitis, gangrene, necrosis, *rash,* urticaria.

Interactions

Drug-drug. *Acetaminophen:* May increase bleeding with more than 2 weeks of acetaminophen therapy at dosages of more than 2 g/day. Monitor patient carefully.
Allopurinol, amiodarone, anabolic steroids, cephalosporins, chloramphenicol, cimetidine, clofibrate, danazol, diazoxide, diflunisal, disulfiram, erythromycin, ethacrynic acid, fluoroquinolones, glucagon, heparin, influenza virus vaccine, isoniazid, lovastatin, meclofenamate, methimazole, methylthiouracil, metronidazole, miconazole, nalidixic acid, neomycin (oral), pentoxifylline, propafenone, propoxyphene, quinidine, sulfonamides, tamoxifen, tetracyclines, thiazides, thrombolytics, thyroid drugs, tricyclic antidepressants, vitamin E: May increase PT. Monitor patient for bleeding. Reduce anticoagulant dosage.
Anticonvulsants: May increase levels of phenytoin and phenobarbital. Monitor patient for toxicity.
Barbiturates, carbamazepine, corticosteroids, corticotropin, hormonal contraceptives containing estrogen, mercaptopurine, methaqualone, nafcillin, rifampin, spironolactone, sucralfate, trazodone: May decrease PT with reduced anticoagulant effect. Monitor patient carefully.

Chloral hydrate, glutethimide, propylthiouracil, sulfinpyrazone: May increase or decrease PT. Avoid use, if possible. Monitor patient carefully.
Cholestyramine: May decrease response when given too close together. Give 6 hours after oral anticoagulants.
NSAIDs, salicylates: May increase PT and ulcerogenic effects. Don't use together.
Sulfonylureas (oral antidiabetics): May increase hypoglycemic response. Monitor glucose level.
Drug-herb. *Angelica:* May significantly prolong PT when used together. Discourage use together.
Arnica, ginkgo biloba, ginseng, motherwort, pau d'arco, red clover: May increase risk of bleeding. Discourage use together.
Drug-food. *Foods or enteral products containing vitamin K:* May impair anticoagulation. Tell patient to maintain consistent daily intake of leafy green vegetables.
Drug-lifestyle. *Alcohol use:* May increase anticoagulant effects. Discourage alcohol intake; however, one or two drinks daily are unlikely to affect warfarin response.

Effects on lab test results

- May increase ALT and AST levels.
- May increase INR, PT, and PTT.

Pharmacokinetics

Absorption: Rapid and complete.
Distribution: Extensively protein-bound; especially to albumin.
Metabolism: In liver.
Excretion: Metabolites reabsorbed from bile and excreted in urine. *Half-life:* 1 to 3 days.

Route	Onset	Peak	Duration
P.O.	½–3 days	Unknown	2–5 days
I.V.	Unknown	Unknown	2–5 days

Action

Chemical effect: Inhibits vitamin K–dependent activation of clotting factors II, VII, IX, and X, formed in liver.
Therapeutic effect: Reduces ability of blood to clot.

Available forms

Powder for injection: 5 mg
Tablets: 1 mg, 2 mg, 2.5 mg, 3 mg, 4 mg, 5 mg, 6 mg, 7.5 mg, 10 mg

NURSING PROCESS

Assessment

- Assess patient's condition before starting therapy and regularly thereafter to monitor drug's effectiveness.
- Draw blood to establish baseline coagulation parameters before starting therapy.

ALERT: INR determinations are essential for proper control. Clinicians typically try to maintain INR at two to three times normal; risk of bleeding is high when INR exceeds six times normal.

- Be alert for adverse reactions and drug interactions. An elderly patient or a patient with renal or hepatic failure is especially sensitive to warfarin effect.
- Regularly inspect patient for bleeding gums, bruises on arms or legs, petechiae, nosebleed, melena, tarry stools, hematuria, and hematemesis.
- Observe the breast-fed infant of a mother taking the drug for unexpected bleeding.
- Assess patient's and family's knowledge of drug therapy.

Nursing diagnoses

- Risk for injury related to potential for blood clot formation from underlying condition
- Ineffective protection related to increased risk of bleeding
- Deficient knowledge related to drug therapy

Planning and implementation

- Give drug at same time each day.
- I.V. form may be obtained from manufacturer for rare patient who can't have oral therapy. Follow guidelines carefully to prepare and give the drug.
- Because onset of action is delayed, heparin sodium is commonly given during first few days of treatment. When heparin is given simultaneously, blood for PT shouldn't be drawn within 5 hours of intermittent I.V. heparin administration. Blood for PT may be drawn at any time during continuous heparin infusion.

ALERT: If patient has a fever and rash, notify the prescriber immediately and don't give the dose; these symptoms may signal severe adverse reactions.

- The drug's anticoagulant effect can be neutralized by vitamin K injections.

• Drug is best oral anticoagulant for patient taking antacids or phenytoin.

Patient teaching

• Stress importance of compliance with prescribed dosage and follow-up appointments. Patient should wear or carry medical identification that indicates his increased risk of bleeding.
• Instruct patient and family to watch for signs of bleeding and to immediately notify the prescriber if they occur.
• Warn patient to avoid OTC products containing aspirin, other salicylates, or drugs that may interact with warfarin.
• Tell patient to notify prescriber if menses are heavier than usual; dosage adjustment may be needed.
• Tell patient to use an electric razor when shaving, to avoid scratching skin, and to use soft toothbrush.
• Instruct patient to read food labels. Food and enteral feedings that contain vitamin K may impair anticoagulation.
• Tell patient to daily eat a consistent amount of leafy green vegetables that contain vitamin K. Eating varying amounts may alter anticoagulant effects.

☑ Evaluation

• Patient doesn't develop blood clots.
• Patient recounts appropriate bleeding precautions.
• Patient and family state understanding of drug therapy.

Z

zafirlukast

(zay-FEER-loo-kast)
Accolate

Pharmacologic class: synthetic, selective peptide leukotriene receptor antagonist
Therapeutic class: anti-inflammatory, bronchodilator
Pregnancy risk category: B

Indications and dosages

▶ **Prevention and long-term treatment of chronic asthma.** *Adults and children age 12 and older:* 20 mg P.O. b.i.d. taken 1 hour before or 2 hours after meals.
Children ages 5 to 11: Give 10 mg P.O. b.i.d. taken 1 hour before or 2 hours after meals.
▶ **Prevention of seasonal allergic rhinitis ‡.** *Adults:* 20 to 40 mg P.O. as a single dose before exposure to allergen.

Contraindications and cautions

• Contraindicated in patients hypersensitive to the drug or any of its components.
• Use cautiously in patients with hepatic impairment.

Lifespan: In pregnant women, drug should be used only if clearly needed. In breast-feeding women, drug shouldn't be given because it appears in breast milk. In children younger than age 5, safety and effectiveness haven't been established. In elderly patients, use cautiously.

Adverse reactions

CNS: asthenia, dizziness, fever, *headache,* pain.
GI: abdominal pain, diarrhea, dyspepsia, nausea, vomiting.
Musculoskeletal: back pain, myalgia.
Other: accidental injury, infection.

Interactions

Drug-drug. *Aspirin:* May increase zafirlukast level. Monitor patient.
Erythromycin, theophylline: May decrease zafirlukast level. Monitor patient.
Warfarin: May increase PT. Monitor PT and INR levels, and adjust dosage of anticoagulant.
Drug-food. *Any food:* May reduce rate and extent of drug absorption. Give drug 1 hour before or 2 hours after meals.

Effects on lab test results

• May increase liver enzyme levels.

Pharmacokinetics

Absorption: Rapid.
Distribution: Unknown.
Metabolism: Extensive.
Excretion: Mainly in feces; 10% in urine. *Half-life:* 10 hours.

Route	Onset	Peak	Duration
P.O.	Unknown	3 hr	Unknown

Z

Action

Chemical effect: Selectively competes for leukotriene receptor sites. Blocks inflammatory action and inhibits bronchoconstriction.
Therapeutic effect: Improves breathing.

Available forms

Tablets: 10 mg, 20 mg

NURSING PROCESS

Assessment

- Assess patient's and family's understanding of drug therapy.

Nursing diagnoses

- Impaired gas exchange related to bronchospasm
- Deficient knowledge related to drug therapy

Planning and implementation

ALERT: Don't use drug for reversing bronchospasm in acute asthma attack.
ALERT: Reducing dose may rarely cause eosinophilia, vasculitic rash, worsening pulmonary symptoms, cardiac complications, or neuropathy, such as Churg-Strauss syndrome.

Patient teaching

- Tell patient to keep taking drug even if symptoms disappear.
- Advise patient to continue taking other antiasthmatics.
- Instruct patient to take drug 1 hour before or 2 hours after meals.

Evaluation

- Patient has improved gas exchange.
- Patient and family state understanding of drug therapy.

zaleplon
(ZAL-eh-plon)
Sonata

Pharmacologic class: pyrazolopyrimidine
Therapeutic class: hypnotic
Pregnancy risk category: C
Controlled substance schedule: IV

Indications and dosages

▶ **Short-term treatment of insomnia.** *Adults:* 10 mg P.O. at bedtime; may increase dose to 20 mg if needed. Low-weight adults may respond to 5-mg dose.
Elderly and debilitated patients: Initially, 5 mg P.O. at bedtime; doses over 10 mg aren't recommended.
Adjust-a-dose: For patients with mild to moderate hepatic impairment and those taking cimetidine, give 5 mg P.O. daily.

Contraindications and cautions

- Don't use in patients with severe hepatic impairment.
- Use cautiously in debilitated patients, in those with compromised respiratory function, and in those with signs and symptoms of depression.

Lifespan: In pregnant and breast-feeding women, drug isn't recommended. In children, safety and effectiveness haven't been established. In elderly patients, use cautiously.

Adverse reactions

CNS: amnesia, anxiety, asthenia, complex sleep disorders, depersonalization, depression, difficulty concentrating, dizziness, fever, hallucinations, *headache,* hypertonia, hypesthesia, malaise, migraine, nervousness, paresthesia, somnolence, tremor, vertigo.
CV: chest pain, peripheral edema.
EENT: abnormal vision, conjunctivitis, ear pain, epistaxis, eye pain, hyperacusis, parosmia.
GI: abdominal pain, anorexia, colitis, constipation, dry mouth, dyspepsia, nausea.
GU: dysmenorrhea.
Musculoskeletal: arthritis, back pain, myalgia.
Respiratory: bronchitis.
Skin: photosensitivity reactions, pruritus, rash.
Other: ***anaphylaxis, angioedema.***

Interactions

Drug-drug. *Cimetidine:* May cause pharmacokinetic interaction. For patient taking cimetidine, use an initial zaleplon dose of 5 mg.
CNS depressants (imipramine, thioridazine): May produce additive CNS effects. Use cautiously together.
CYP3A4 inducers (carbamazepine, phenobarbital, phenytoin, rifampin, others): May reduce zaleplon effectiveness. Consider a different hypnotic.

Drug-food. *High-fat foods, heavy meals:* May prolong absorption, delaying peak zaleplon level by about 2 hours; sleep onset may be delayed. Separate drug from meals.
Drug-lifestyle. *Alcohol use:* May increase CNS effects. Discourage use together.

Effects on lab test results

None reported.

Pharmacokinetics

Absorption: Rapid and almost complete. Level peaks within 1 hour. Taking drug after a high-fat or heavy meal delays peak level by about 2 hours.
Distribution: Substantially into extravascular tissues. About 60% protein-bound.
Metabolism: Extensive, mainly by aldehyde oxidase and, to a lesser extent, CYP3A4 to inactive metabolites. Less than 1% of dose is excreted unchanged in urine.
Excretion: Rapid. *Half-life:* 1 hour.

Route	Onset	Peak	Duration
P.O.	1 hr	1 hr	3–4 hr

Action

Chemical effect: Has a chemical structure unrelated to benzodiazepines but interacts with the GABA and benzodiazepine receptor complex in the CNS. Modulation of this complex is hypothesized to be responsible for sedative, anxiolytic, muscle relaxant, and anticonvulsant effects of benzodiazepines.
Therapeutic effect: Promotes sleep.

Available forms

Capsules: 5 mg, 10 mg

NURSING PROCESS

Assessment

- Carefully assess patient because sleep disturbances may be a symptom of an underlying physical or psychiatric disorder.
- Closely monitor elderly or debilitated patient, or patient with compromised respiratory function because of illness.
- Monitor patient for drug abuse and dependence.
- Assess patient's and family's knowledge of drug therapy.

Nursing diagnoses

- Insomnia related to underlying disorder
- Risk for injury related to drug-induced adverse CNS reactions
- Deficient knowledge related to drug therapy

Planning and implementation

- Don't give drug with or after a high-fat or heavy meal.
- Drug works rapidly; give right before bedtime or after patient has been unable to sleep.
- Adverse reactions are usually dose-related. Give lowest effective dose.
- Limit hypnotic use to 7 to 10 days. If hypnotics will be taken for more than 3 weeks, prescriber should reevaluate patient.
- To reduce the risk of drug abuse and dependence, drug shouldn't be given as more than a 1-month supply.

Patient teaching

- Advise patient that drug works rapidly and should be taken immediately before bedtime or after trying unsuccessfully to sleep.
- Advise patient to take drug only if he can sleep undisturbed for at least 4 hours.
- Warn patient that drowsiness, dizziness, lightheadedness, and difficulty with coordination occur most often within 1 hour after taking drug.
- Warn patient about possibility of complex sleep disorders.
- Advise patient to avoid performing activities that require mental alertness until the drug's CNS effects are known.
- Advise patient not to drink alcohol while taking drug and to notify prescriber before taking any prescription or OTC drugs.
- Tell patient not to take drug after a high-fat or heavy meal.
- Advise patient to report any continued sleep problems despite use of drug.
- Tell patient that dependence can occur; drug is recommended for short-term use only.
- Warn patient not to abruptly stop drug because withdrawal symptoms, including discomfort, stomach and muscle cramps, vomiting, sweating, shakiness, and seizures, may occur.
- Tell patient that insomnia may recur for a few nights after stopping drug, but should resolve on its own.
- Advise patient that zaleplon may cause changes in behavior and thinking, including outgoing or aggressive behavior, loss of personal identity, confusion, strange behavior, perform-

ing complex activities while sleeping, agitation, hallucinations, worsening of depression, or suicidal thoughts. Tell patient to notify prescriber immediately if any of these problems occur.

Evaluation

- Patient states that drug effectively promotes sleep.
- Patient sustains no injury from drug-induced adverse CNS reactions.
- Patient and family state understanding of drug therapy.

zanamivir

(zah-NAM-ah-veer)

Relenza

Pharmacologic class: neuraminidase inhibitor
Therapeutic class: antiviral
Pregnancy risk category: C

Indications and dosages

▶ **Uncomplicated acute illness caused by influenza A and B virus in patients who have been symptomatic for no more than 2 days.** *Adults and children age 7 and older:* 2 oral inhalations (one 5-mg blister per inhalation for a total dose of 10 mg) b.i.d. using the Diskhaler inhalation device for 5 days. Give two doses on the first day of treatment with at least 2 hours between doses. Subsequent doses should be about 12 hours apart (in the morning and evening) at about the same time each day.

▶ **To prevent influenza in a household setting.** *Adults and children age 5 and older:* 2 oral inhalations (one 5-mg blister per inhalation for total dose of 10 mg) once daily for 10 days.

▶ **To prevent influenza in a community setting.** *Adults and adolescents:* 2 oral inhalations (one 5-mg blister per inhalation for total dose of 10 mg) once daily for 28 days.

Contraindications and cautions

- Contraindicated in patients hypersensitive to the drug or any of its components. Drug is not recommended for patients with underlying airway disease (such as asthma and COPD).

Lifespan: In pregnant women, use only if benefits outweigh risks. In breast-feeding women, use cautiously; it's unknown if the drug appears in breast milk. In children younger than age 5, safety and effectiveness haven't been established.

Adverse reactions

CNS: dizziness, headache,
EENT: ear, nose, and throat infections; nasal signs and symptoms; sinusitis.
GI: diarrhea, nausea, vomiting.
Hematologic: lymphopenia, ***neutropenia.***
Respiratory: bronchitis, ***bronchospasm,*** cough.

Interactions

None reported.

Effects on lab test results

- May increase ALT, AST, and CK levels.
- May decrease lymphocyte and neutrophil counts.

Pharmacokinetics

Absorption: About 4% to 17%, with peak level occurring 1 to 2 hours following a 10-mg dose.
Distribution: Less than 10% protein-bound.
Metabolism: Not metabolized.
Excretion: In urine, unchanged, within 24 hours. Unabsorbed drug in feces. *Half-life:* 2½ to 5¼ hours.

Route	Onset	Peak	Duration
Inhalation	Unknown	1–2 hr	Unknown

Action

Chemical effect: Probably inhibits the enzyme neuraminidase on the surface of the influenza virus, possibly altering virus particle aggregation and release. When neuraminidase is inhibited, the virus can't escape from its host cell to attack others, thereby inhibiting the process of viral proliferation.
Therapeutic effect: Lessens the symptoms of influenza.

Available forms

Powder for inhalation: 5 mg per blister

NURSING PROCESS

Assessment

- Obtain accurate patient medical history before starting therapy.
- Lymphopenia, neutropenia, and a rise in liver enzyme and CK levels may occur during treatment. Monitor patient appropriately.

• Monitor patient for bronchospasm and decline in lung function. If they occur, stop giving the drug.
• Assess patient's and family's knowledge of drug therapy.

Nursing diagnoses
• Risk for infection related to influenza virus
• Imbalanced nutrition: less than body requirements related to drug's adverse GI effects
• Deficient knowledge related to drug therapy

Planning and implementation
ALERT: Serious cases of bronchospasm, including death, have been reported during treatment. Stop drug in any patient who develops bronchospasm or a decline in respiratory function.
• Have patient exhale fully before inserting the mouthpiece. Then, keeping the Diskhaler level, have patient close his lips around the mouthpiece, and have him breathe in steadily and deeply. Instruct patient to hold his breath for a few seconds after inhaling to help keep the drug in his lungs.
• There is no information suggesting drug is effective when started more than 48 hours after symptoms appear.

Patient teaching
• Teach patient how to properly use the drug with the Diskhaler inhalation device, and tell him to carefully read the instructions.
• Advise patient to keep the Diskhaler level when loading and inhaling drug. Tell patient to check inside the mouthpiece of the Diskhaler before each use to make sure it's free of foreign objects.
• Instruct patient with respiratory disease who has an impending scheduled dose of inhaled bronchodilator to take it before taking zanamivir. Tell patient with asthma to have a fast-acting bronchodilator available in case of wheezing during therapy.
• Tell patient to finish the entire 5-day course even if he feels better and symptoms improve before the fifth day.
• Inform patient that zanamivir hasn't been shown to reduce the risk of transmitting influenza virus to others.

Evaluation
• Patient recovers from influenza.
• Patient has no adverse GI effects.
• Patient and family state understanding of drug therapy.

zidovudine (azidothymidine, AZT)
(zigh-DOH-vyoo-deen)
Apo-Zidovudine ♦, Novo-AZT ♦, Retrovir

Pharmacologic class: thymidine analogue
Therapeutic class: antiretroviral
Pregnancy risk category: C

Indications and dosages
▶ **HIV infection.** *Adults:* 600 mg P.O. daily in divided doses given with other antiretrovirals. Or, for patients who can't take the oral form, 1 mg/kg I.V. over 1 hour, q 4 hours around the clock until oral therapy can be used.
Children ages 6 weeks to 12 years: 160 mg/m² P.O. q 8 hours. Maximum, 200 mg q 8 hours. Give with other antiretrovirals.
Adjust-a-dose: Patients with end-stage renal disease (creatinine clearance less than 15 ml/minute) maintained on dialysis should receive 1 mg/kg I.V. q 6 to 8 hours.
▶ **To prevent maternal-fetal HIV transmission.** *Pregnant women past 14 weeks' gestation:* 100 mg P.O. five times daily until the start of labor. Then, 2 mg/kg I.V. over 1 hour followed by a continuous I.V. infusion of 1 mg/kg/hour until the umbilical cord is clamped.
Neonates: 2 mg/kg P.O. q 6 hours starting within 12 hours after birth and continuing until age 6 weeks. Or, give 1.5 mg/kg via I.V. infusion over 30 minutes q 6 hours.
Adjust-a-dose: For patients on hemodialysis or peritoneal dialysis, give 100 mg P.O. q 6 to 8 hours. For patients with mild to moderate hepatic dysfunction or liver cirrhosis, reduce daily dose.
▶ **Prophylaxis after occupational or nonoccupational exposure to HIV‡.** *Adults:* 600 mg P.O. daily in two or three divided doses for 4 weeks given with other antiretrovirals. Prophylaxis should begin as soon as possible after exposure, preferably within hours.

I.V. administration
• Dilute drug before use. Remove calculated dose from vial; add to D_5W to yield no more than 4 mg/ml.

Z

• Adding solution to biological or colloidal fluids (such as blood products and protein solutions) isn't recommended.
• Infuse drug over 1 hour at constant rate; give q 4 hours around the clock. Avoid rapid infusion or bolus injection.
• Solution is physically and chemically stable for 24 hours at room temperature and for 48 hours if refrigerated at 36° to 46° F (2° to 8° C). Store undiluted vials at 59° to 77° F (15° to 25° C) and protect them from light.

⊗ **Incompatibilities**
Biological or colloidal solutions, such as blood products or protein-containing solutions; meropenem.

Contraindications and cautions

• Contraindicated in patients hypersensitive to the drug or any of its components.
• Use cautiously and with close monitoring in patients with advanced symptomatic HIV infection and in those with severe bone marrow depression. Also use cautiously in patients with hepatomegaly, hepatitis, or other known risk factors for hepatic disease.
Lifespan: In breast-feeding women, drug shouldn't be used. In elderly patients, use cautiously.

Adverse reactions

CNS: asthenia, dizziness, fever, headache, insomnia, malaise, paresthesia, ***seizures***, somnolence.
GI: abdominal pain, anorexia, constipation, diarrhea, dyspepsia, nausea, taste perversion, vomiting.
Hematologic: ***agranulocytosis, bone marrow suppression, thrombocytopenia.***
Metabolic: ***lactic acidosis.***
Musculoskeletal: myalgia.
Skin: diaphoresis, *rash*.

Interactions

Drug-drug. *Atovaquone, fluconazole, methadone, probenecid, valproic acid:* May increase zidovudine level. Adjust dosage if needed.
Doxorubicin, ribavirin, stavudine: May antagonize zidovudine. Avoid use together.
Ganciclovir, interferon alfa, other bone marrow suppressants or cytotoxic drugs: May increase hematologic toxicity of zidovudine. Use cautiously as with other reverse transcriptase inhibitors.
Nelfinavir, rifampin, ritonavir: May decrease zidovudine bioavailability. Dosage adjustment isn't needed.
Phenytoin: May alter phenytoin level and decrease zidovudine clearance by 30%. Monitor patient closely.

Effects on lab test results

• May increase ALT, AST, alkaline phosphatase, and LDH levels. May decrease hemoglobin level and hematocrit.
• May decrease granulocyte and platelet counts.

Pharmacokinetics

Absorption: Rapid.
Distribution: Good CSF penetration. About 36% protein-bound.
Metabolism: Rapid, to inactive compound.
Excretion: In urine. *Half-life:* 1 hour.

Route	Onset	Peak	Duration
P.O.	Unknown	30–90 min	Unknown
I.V.	Immediate	30–90 min	Unknown

Action

Chemical effect: Prevents replication of HIV by inhibiting the enzyme reverse transcriptase.
Therapeutic effect: Reduces symptoms of HIV infection.

Available forms

Capsules: 100 mg
Injection: 10 mg/ml
Syrup: 50 mg/5 ml
Tablets: 300 mg

NURSING PROCESS

Assessment

• Assess patient's condition before starting therapy and regularly thereafter to monitor drug's effectiveness.
• Monitor CBC with differential and platelet counts q 2 weeks to detect anemia or agranulocytosis.
• Be alert for adverse reactions and drug interactions.
• Assess patient's and family's knowledge of drug therapy.

Nursing diagnoses

• Risk for infection related to presence of HIV

• Ineffective protection related to drug-induced adverse hematologic reactions
• Deficient knowledge related to drug therapy

Planning and implementation

• Drug temporarily decreases illness and risk of death in certain patients with AIDS or AIDS-related complex.
• Optimum duration of treatment and optimum dosage for effectiveness with minimum toxicity aren't yet known.
ALERT: Notify prescriber of abnormal hematologic study results. Significant anemia (hemoglobin level of less than 7.5 g/dl or reduction of more than 25% of baseline) or significant neutropenia (granulocyte count of less than 750/mm^3 or reduction of more than 50% from baseline) may warrant interrupting therapy until marrow begins to recover.

Patient teaching

• Advise patient that blood transfusions may be needed during treatment. Drug often causes low RBC count.
• Stress importance of compliance with every-4-hours dose. Suggest ways to avoid missing doses, perhaps by using an alarm clock.
• Warn patient not to take other drugs for AIDS (especially street drugs) unless approved by prescriber. Some supposed AIDS cures may interfere with drug's effectiveness.
• Advise pregnant HIV-infected women that drug therapy only reduces risk of HIV transmission to neonates. Long-term risks to infants are unknown.
• Advise patient considering drug as prophylaxis against HIV after exposure (such as after needle-stick injury) that its safety and effectiveness haven't been proven.

Evaluation

• Patient has reduced severity and frequency of symptoms linked to HIV infection.
• Patient doesn't develop complications from therapy.
• Patient and family state understanding of drug therapy.

ziprasidone

(zi-PRAY-si-done)
Geodon

Pharmacologic class: atypical antipsychotic
Therapeutic class: psychotropic
Pregnancy risk category: C

Indications and dosages

▶ **Symptomatic schizophrenia.** *Adults:* Initially, 20 mg P.O. b.i.d. with food. Dosages are highly individualized. Dosage adjustments should occur no sooner than q 2 days, but to allow for lowest possible doses, the interval should be several weeks. Effective dosage range is usually 20 to 80 mg b.i.d. Maximum recommended dosage is 100 mg b.i.d.
▶ **Rapid control of acute agitation in schizophrenic patients.** *Adults:* 10 to 20 mg I.M. as a single dose. Doses of 10 mg may be given q 2 hours; doses of 20 mg may be given q 4 hours. Maximum cumulative dose is 40 mg daily.
▶ **Acute bipolar mania, including manic and mixed episodes, with or without psychotic features.** *Adults:* 40 mg P.O. b.i.d. on day 1. Increase to 60 or 80 mg P.O. b.i.d. on day 2 with subsequent adjustments based on patient response within the range of 40 to 80 mg b.i.d. Give with food.

Contraindications and cautions

• Contraindicated in patients hypersensitive to the drug or any of its components. Also contraindicated in patients taking drugs that prolong QT interval and in those who have a QTc interval longer than 500 msec. Contraindicated in patients with a history of QT-interval prolongation, congenital QT-interval syndrome, recent MI, and uncompensated heart failure.
• Use cautiously in patients with acute diarrhea and in patients with a history of bradycardia, hypokalemia, seizures, aspiration pneumonia, or hypomagnesemia.
• Give I.M. ziprasidone with caution to patients with impaired renal function.
Lifespan: In pregnant women, use only if benefits outweigh risks. Breast-feeding women should stop breast-feeding or shouldn't use the drug. In children, safety and effectiveness haven't been established. In elderly patients,

Z

safety and effectiveness of I.M. use haven't been established.

Adverse reactions

P.O. use
CNS: dystonia.
CV: tachycardia.
EENT: abnormal vision.
Musculoskeletal: myalgia.
Respiratory: cough.
Skin: rash.
I.M. use
CNS: speech disorders.
CV: vasodilation.
GU: priapism.
Musculoskeletal: back pain.
Skin: sweating.
Other: flulike syndrome, tooth disorder.
Both routes
CNS: agitation, akathisia, anxiety, asthenia, cogwheel rigidity, dizziness, extrapyramidal symptoms, *headache,* hypertonia, insomnia, ***neuroleptic malignant syndrome,*** paresthesia, personality disorder, psychosis, *somnolence,* ***suicide attempt.***
CV: ***bradycardia,*** hypertension, orthostatic hypotension.
EENT: rhinitis.
GI: abdominal pain, anorexia, constipation, diarrhea, dry mouth, dyspepsia, *nausea,* ***rectal hemorrhage,*** vomiting.
GU: dysmenorrhea.
Metabolic: hyperglycemia.
Skin: furunculosis, injection site pain.

Interactions

Drug-drug. *Antihypertensives:* May enhance hypotensive effects. Monitor blood pressure.
Carbamazepine: May decrease ziprasidone level. Higher ziprasidone doses may be needed to achieve desired effect.
Drugs that increase dopamine level, such as levodopa and dopamine agonists: May have antagonistic effect on ziprasidone. Use together cautiously.
Drugs that lower potassium and magnesium levels, such as diuretics: May increase risk of arrhythmias. If giving together, monitor potassium and magnesium levels.
Drugs that prolong QT interval, including arsenic trioxide, chlorpromazine, dofetilide, dolasetron mesylate, droperidol, halofantrine, levomethadyl acetate, mefloquine, mesoridazine, moxifloxacin, pentamidine, pimozide, probucol, quinidine, sotalol, sparfloxacin, tacrolimus, thioridazine, or other class IA and III antiarrhythmics: May increase risk of arrhythmias when used together. Don't give together.
Itraconazole, ketoconazole: May increase ziprasidone level. Lower doses of ziprasidone may be needed to achieve desired effect.

Effects on lab test results

• May increase glucose level.

Pharmacokinetics

Absorption: Doubled when taken with food, which is recommended. Level peaks in about 6 to 8 hours.
Distribution: Extensively protein-bound.
Metabolism: Hepatic metabolism; no active metabolites. Less than one-third of drug is metabolized through cytochrome P-450 system, mainly via CYP3A4 and partly via CYP1A2.
Excretion: Unknown. *Half-life:* 2¼ to 7 hours.

Route	Onset	Peak	Duration
P.O.	1–3 days	6–8 hr	12 hr
I.M.	Unknown	1 hr	Unknown

Action

Chemical effect: May work by antagonizing dopamine and serotonin, the neurotransmitters usually targeted for treatment of positive and negative symptoms of schizophrenia. Blocking these neurotransmitters allows symptomatic improvement with minimal adverse effects in the extrapyramidal system.
Therapeutic effect: Relieves psychotic signs and symptoms of schizophrenia.

Available forms

Capsules: 20 mg, 40 mg, 60 mg, 80 mg
Injection: 20-mg/ml single-dose vials (after reconstitution)

NURSING PROCESS

Assessment

• Assess patient's condition before starting therapy and regularly thereafter to monitor drug's effectiveness.
• Assess and monitor patient who experiences dizziness, palpitations, or syncope.
• Drug may prolong QT interval. Other antipsychotics should be considered in patient with a

history of QT-interval prolongation, acute MI, congenital QT-interval syndrome, and other conditions that place the patient at risk for life-threatening arrhythmias. Don't give other drugs that prolong the QT interval with ziprasidone.
• Patient taking antipsychotics is at risk for developing neuroleptic malignant syndrome or tardive dyskinesia.
• Electrolyte disturbances, such as hypokalemia or hypomagnesemia, increase the risk of arrhythmias. Before starting therapy, monitor potassium and magnesium levels and correct imbalances.
• Assess patient's and family's knowledge of drug therapy.

Nursing diagnoses

• Disturbed thought processes related to underlying condition
• Risk for falls related to adverse CNS effects of drug
• Deficient knowledge related to ziprasidone therapy

Planning and implementation

• Don't adjust dosage sooner than q 2 days. Longer intervals may be needed because symptoms may take 4 to 6 weeks to respond.
• Monitor patient for prolonged QT interval during therapy. Further monitor patient with symptoms of arrhythmias. If QTc interval is greater than 500 msec, stop drug.
ALERT: Hyperglycemia may occur in patient taking drug. Regularly monitor patient with diabetes. Patient with risk factors for diabetes should undergo fasting blood glucose testing at baseline and periodically during therapy. Monitor every patient for symptoms of hyperglycemia including polydipsia, polyuria, polyphagia, and weakness; if symptoms develop, perform fasting blood glucose testing. Hyperglycemia may be reversible when antipsychotic is stopped.
• Immediately treat patient with symptoms of neuroleptic malignant syndrome, which can be life-threatening.
• Monitor patient for tardive dyskinesia.
• If long-term ziprasidone therapy is needed, switch to P.O. route as soon as possible. Effect of I.M. administration for more than 3 consecutive days isn't known.
• Don't give drug I.M. to schizophrenic patient already taking ziprasidone P.O.
• Give oral drug with food, which increases the effect.
• For I.M. use, add 1.2 ml of sterile water for injection to vial and shake vigorously until entire drug is dissolved.
• Don't mix I.M. injection with any other product besides sterile water for injection.
• Inspect for particulate matter and discoloration before administration, whenever solution and container permit.
• Store dry form at room temperature. Store reconstituted form for up to 24 hours at room temperature or up to 7 days refrigerated (36° to 46° F [2° to 8° C]). Protect from light.

Patient teaching

• Tell patient to take drug with food.
• Tell patient to immediately report to prescriber symptoms of dizziness, fainting, irregular heartbeat, or relevant cardiac problems.
• Advise patient to report to prescriber any recent episodes of diarrhea.
• Advise patient to report to prescriber abnormal movements.
• Tell patient to report to prescriber sudden fever, muscle rigidity, or change in mental status.

Evaluation

• Patient has reduced psychotic symptoms with drug therapy.
• Patient doesn't fall.
• Patient and family state understanding of drug therapy.

zoledronic acid

(zoe-LEH-druh-nick ASS-id)
Zometa

Pharmacologic class: bisphosphonate
Therapeutic class: antihypercalcemic
Pregnancy risk category: D

Indications and dosages

▶ **Hypercalcemia related to malignancy.** *Adults:* 4 mg by I.V. infusion over at least 15 minutes. If albumin-corrected calcium level doesn't return to normal, consider retreatment with 4 mg. Allow at least 7 days to pass before retreatment to allow a full response to the initial dose.

Z

▶ **Multiple myeloma and bone metastases of solid tumors (given with standard antineoplastic therapy).** *Adults:* 4 mg infused over at least 15 minutes q 3 to 4 weeks. Duration of treatment in studies was 15 months for prostate cancer, 12 months for breast cancer and multiple myeloma, and 9 months for other solid tumors. Prostate cancer should have progressed after treatment with at least one hormonal therapy.

Adjust-a-dose: For patients with creatinine clearance of 50 to 60 ml/minute, give 3.5 mg. If clearance is 40 to 49 ml/minute, give 3.3 mg. If clearance is 30 to 39 ml/minute, give 3 mg.

For patients with normal baseline creatinine level but an increase of 0.5 mg/dl during therapy, and in those with abnormal baseline creatinine level who have an increase of 1 mg/dl, withhold drug. Resume treatment only when creatinine level has returned to within 10% of baseline value.

I.V. administration

- Reconstitute by adding 5 ml of sterile water to each vial. Powder must be completely dissolved.
- Withdraw 5 ml for 4 mg of drug and mix in 100 ml of normal saline solution or D_5W.
- To withdraw the appropriate dose for a patient with creatinine clearance 60 ml/minute or less: withdraw 4.4 ml for the 3.5 mg dose, 4.1 ml for the 3.3 mg dose, and 3.8 ml for the 3 mg dose.
- Inspect solution for particulate matter and discoloration before giving it.
- The drug must be given as an I.V. infusion over at least 15 minutes. Give drug as a single I.V. solution in a line separate from all other drugs.
- If not used immediately after reconstitution, solution must be refrigerated and given within 24 hours.

⊗ **Incompatibilities**

Other I.V. drugs; solutions that contain calcium, such as lactated Ringer's solution.

Contraindications and cautions

- Contraindicated in patients with clinically significant hypersensitivity to drug, other bisphosphonates, or ingredients in formulation.
- Not recommended in patients with hypercalcemia of malignancy with creatinine greater than 4.5 mg/dl. Not recommended in patients with bone metastases with creatinine greater than 3 mg/dl.
- Use cautiously in patients with aspirin-sensitive asthma because other bisphosphonates may cause bronchoconstriction in these patients.

Lifespan: In pregnant women, don't use. Women of childbearing age should avoid becoming pregnant. In breast-feeding women, use cautiously; it's unknown if the drug appears in breast milk. In children, safety and effectiveness haven't been established. In elderly patients, monitor renal function.

Adverse reactions

Hypercalcemia

CNS: agitation, anxiety, confusion, *depression, dizziness,* fever, *headache, insomnia,* somnolence.
CV: hypotension.
GI: abdominal pain, anorexia, constipation, diarrhea, dysphagia, nausea, vomiting.
GU: candidiasis, ***renal failure,*** UTI.
Hematologic: anemia, ***granulocytopenia, pancytopenia, thrombocytopenia.***
Metabolic: dehydration.
Musculoskeletal: arthralgia, osteonecrosis of the jaw, *skeletal pain.*
Respiratory: *cough, dyspnea,* pleural effusion.
Other: infection, **PROGRESSION OF CANCER.**

Bone metastases

CNS: *anxiety, depression, dizziness,* fatigue, fever, *headache, hypoesthesia, insomnia, paresthesia,* weakness.
CV: hypotension, leg edema.
GI: *abdominal pain, anorexia, constipation, diarrhea, increased appetite, nausea, vomiting.*
GU: ***renal failure,*** *UTI.*
Hematologic: anemia, ***neutropenia.***
Metabolic: dehydration, weight loss.
Musculoskeletal: *arthralgia, back pain, myalgia,* osteonecrosis of the jaw, *skeletal pain.*
Respiratory: *cough, dyspnea.*
Skin: alopecia, dermatitis.
Other: infection, **PROGRESSION OF CANCER,** rigors.

Interactions

Drug-drug. *Aminoglycosides, loop diuretics:* May have additive effects to lower calcium level. Give together cautiously, and monitor calcium level.

Thalidomide: May increase risk of renal dysfunction in multiple myeloma patients. Use together cautiously.

Effects on lab test results

- May increase creatinine level. May decrease calcium, phosphorus, magnesium, potassium, and hemoglobin levels and hematocrit.
- May decrease RBC, WBC, and platelet counts.

Pharmacokinetics

Absorption: Given I.V.
Distribution: About 22% protein-bound. Postinfusion decline of level is consistent with a triphasic process: Low level observed up to 28 days after a dose.
Metabolism: Doesn't inhibit cytochrome P-450 enzymes or undergo biotransformation in vivo.
Excretion: Mainly via kidneys. *Half-life:* Alpha is about 15 minutes; beta is 1¾ hours for early distribution. *Terminal half-life:* About 7 days.

Route	Onset	Peak	Duration
I.V.	Unknown	Unknown	7–28 days

Action

Chemical effect: Inhibits bone resorption, probably by inhibiting osteoclast activity and osteoclastic resorption of mineralized bone and cartilage, decreasing calcium release induced by the stimulatory factors produced by tumors.
Therapeutic effect: Lowers calcium level in malignant disease.

Available forms

Injection: 4 mg zoledronic acid, 220 mg mannitol, and 24 mg sodium citrate

NURSING PROCESS

Assessment

- Assess patient's condition before starting therapy and regularly thereafter to monitor drug's effectiveness.
- Assess kidney function before and during therapy because drug is excreted mainly via the kidneys. The risk of adverse reactions may be greater in a patient with renal impairment. If patient has renal impairment, give drug only if benefits outweigh risks, and at a lower dose.
- Measure creatinine level before each dose.
- Make sure patient is adequately hydrated before giving drug; urine output should be about 2 L daily.
- Assess patient's dental health before starting therapy. Make sure patient has had a dental exam with appropriate preventive dentistry before being treated with bisphosphonates, especially patients with cancer, those receiving chemotherapy or corticosteroids, and those with poor oral hygiene.
- Assess patient's and family's knowledge of drug therapy.

Nursing diagnoses

- Ineffective protection related to adverse hematologic effects
- Ineffective health maintenance related to underlying condition
- Deficient knowledge related to drug therapy

Planning and implementation

ALERT: A significant decline in renal function could progress to renal failure; single doses shouldn't exceed 4 mg, and infusion should last at least 15 minutes.

ALERT: After giving drug, carefully monitor renal function and calcium, phosphate, magnesium, and creatinine levels.

- Other bisphosphonates have been linked to bronchoconstriction in patients with asthma and aspirin sensitivity.
- Give patient an oral calcium supplement of 500 mg and a multiple vitamin containing 400 international units of vitamin D daily.

Patient teaching

- Review use and administration of drug with patient and family.
- Instruct patient to report adverse effects promptly.
- Explain importance of periodic laboratory tests to monitor therapy and renal function.
- Advise patient to notify prescriber if she is pregnant.

Evaluation

- Patient has no adverse hematologic reactions.
- Patient shows improvement in condition.
- Patient and family state understanding of drug therapy.

zolmitriptan

(zohl-muh-TRIP-tan)
Zomig, Zomig-ZMT

Pharmacologic class: selective 5-hydroxytryptamine (5-HT_1) receptor agonist
Therapeutic class: antimigraine drug
Pregnancy risk category: C

Indications and dosages

▶ **Acute migraine headache.** *Adults:* Initially, 2.5 mg or less P.O. increased to 5 mg per dose, if needed. If headache returns after initial dose, second dose may be given after 2 hours. Maximum dose is 10 mg in 24-hour period. Or, give 2.5 mg P.O. of orally disintegrating tablets; don't break tablets in half. Or, 5 mg (one nasal spray) into one nostril. If headache returns after initial dose, a second dose may be given after 2 hours. Maximum dose is 10 mg in 24-hour period.

Adjust-a-dose: For patients with liver disease, use doses lower than 2.5 mg. Also, don't use orally disintegrating tablets; they shouldn't be split. Avoid use of nasal spray because doses lower than 5 mg can't be given.

Contraindications and cautions

- Contraindicated in patients hypersensitive to the drug or any of its components, in those with uncontrolled hypertension, and in those with symptoms or findings consistent with ischemic heart disease (angina pectoris, history of MI or documented silent ischemia), coronary artery vasospasm (including Prinzmetal variant angina), or other significant heart disease.
- Avoid use within 24 hours of other 5-HT_1 agonists or drugs containing ergot, or within 2 weeks of stopping MAO inhibitor therapy. Also avoid use in patients with hemiplegic or basilar migraine.
- Use cautiously in patients with liver disease and in patients who may be at risk for coronary artery disease, such as postmenopausal women, men older than age 40, or patients with hypertension, hypercholesterolemia, obesity, diabetes, smoking, or family history of coronary artery disease.

Lifespan: In pregnant women, use cautiously. In breast-feeding women, use cautiously; it's unknown if the drug appears in breast milk. In children, safety and effectiveness haven't been established.

Adverse reactions

CNS: asthenia, *dizziness,* hypesthesia, pain, paresthesia, somnolence, vertigo.
CV: ***coronary artery vasospasm; MI;*** pain, tightness, pressure, or heaviness in chest; palpitations; ***transient myocardial ischemia; ventricular fibrillation; ventricular tachycardia.***
EENT: pain, tightness, or pressure in the neck, throat, or jaw.
GI: dry mouth, dyspepsia, dysphagia, nausea.
Musculoskeletal: myalgia, myasthenia.
Skin: sweating.
Other: warm or cold sensations.

Interactions

Drug-drug. *Cimetidine:* May double zolmitriptan half-life. Monitor patient closely.
Ergot-containing drugs, serotonin$_{1B/1D}$ agonists: May cause additive effects. Avoid use within 24 hours of almotriptan.
Hormonal contraceptives: May increase zolmitriptan level. Monitor patient closely.
MAO inhibitors: May increase zolmitriptan level. Avoid using drug within 2 weeks of stopping MAO inhibitor therapy.
SSRIs: May cause additive serotonin effects, resulting in weakness, hyperreflexia, or incoordination. If given together, monitor patient closely.

Effects on lab test results

- May increase glucose level.

Pharmacokinetics

Absorption: Well absorbed following P.O. use; absolute bioavailability of 40%.
Distribution: 25% protein-bound.
Metabolism: Converted to active N-desmethyl metabolite.
Excretion: About 65% of dose is recovered in urine (8% unchanged) and 30% in feces. *Half-life:* 3 hours.

Route	Onset	Peak	Duration
P.O.	Unknown	2 hr	3 hr
P.O. orally disintegrating	Unknown	2 hr	Unknown
Nasal spray	5 min	3 hr	Unknown

Action

Chemical effect: Selective serotonin receptor agonist causes constriction of cranial blood vessels and inhibits proinflammatory neuropeptide release.

Therapeutic effect: Relieves migraine headache pain.

Available forms

Nasal spray: 5 mg
Tablets: 2.5 mg, 5 mg
Tablets (orally disintegrating): 2.5 mg, 5 mg

NURSING PROCESS

Assessment

- Assess patient's history of migraine headaches before starting therapy and regularly thereafter to monitor drug's effectiveness.
- Assess patient for history of coronary artery disease, hypertension, arrhythmias, or presence of risk factors for coronary artery disease.
- Monitor liver function test results before starting drug therapy, and report abnormalities.
- Use drug only when a clear diagnosis of migraine has been established.
- Assess patient's and family's knowledge of drug therapy.

Nursing diagnoses

- Acute pain related to presence of migraine headache
- Ineffective cardiopulmonary tissue perfusion related to drug-induced adverse cardiac events
- Deficient knowledge related to drug therapy

Planning and implementation

- Use a lower dose in a patient with moderate to severe hepatic impairment; don't give orally disintegrating tablets because they can't be split.
- Don't give drug to prevent migraine headaches or to treat hemiplegic migraines, basilar migraines, or cluster headaches.

ALERT: Don't give drug within 24 hours of ergot-containing drugs or within 2 weeks of MAO inhibitor.

Patient teaching

- Tell patient that drug is intended to relieve the symptoms of migraines, not to prevent them.
- Advise patient to take drug as prescribed. Caution against taking a second dose unless instructed by prescriber. Tell patient that if a second dose is indicated and permitted, he should take it at least 2 hours after initial dose.
- Advise patient to immediately report pain or tightness in chest or throat, heart throbbing, rash, skin lumps, or swelling of face, lips, or eyelids.
- Inform the patient that safety of treating an average of more than 3 headaches in 30 days with the tablets, or an average of more than 4 headaches in 30 days with the nasal spray hasn't been established.
- Tell woman not to take drug if she's planning or suspects a pregnancy.
- Instruct patient to remove the orally disintegrating tablet from the blister pack just before use and to let it dissolve on the tongue.
- Advise patient not to break the orally disintegrating tablets in half.

Evaluation

- Patient has relief from migraine headache.
- Patient has no pain or tightness in the chest or throat, arrhythmias, increases in blood pressure, or MI.
- Patient and family state understanding of drug therapy.

zolpidem tartrate

(ZOHL-peh-dim TAR-trayt)
Ambien, Ambien CR

Pharmacologic class: imidazopyridine
Therapeutic class: hypnotic
Pregnancy risk category: C
Controlled substance schedule: IV

Indications and dosages

▶ Short-term management of insomnia.
Adults: 10 mg P.O. (immediate release) or 12.5 mg P.O. (extended release) immediately before bedtime.

Adjust-a-dose: *Elderly patients:* 5 mg P.O. (immediate release) or 6.25 mg (extended release) immediately before bedtime. Maximum daily dose is 10 mg (immediate release) or 6.25 mg (extended release).
Debilitated patients and those with hepatic insufficiency: 5 mg P.O. immediately before bedtime. Maximum daily dose is 10 mg. If using the extended-release tablet, maximum daily dose is 6.25 mg.

Z

Contraindications and cautions

• Use cautiously in patients with conditions that could affect metabolism or hemodynamic responses and in those with compromised respiratory status, because hypnotics may depress respiratory drive. Also use cautiously in patients with depression or history of alcohol or drug abuse.

Lifespan: In pregnant women, use only if benefits outweigh fetal risks. In breast-feeding women, drug isn't recommended. In children, safety and effectiveness haven't been established.

Adverse reactions

CNS: abnormal dreams, amnesia, daytime drowsiness, depression, dizziness, hangover effect, *headache,* lethargy, lightheadedness, complex sleep disorders.
CV: palpitations.
EENT: pharyngitis, sinusitis.
GI: abdominal pain, constipation, diarrhea, dry mouth, dyspepsia, nausea, vomiting.
Musculoskeletal: arthralgia, back or chest pain, myalgia.
Skin: rash.
Other: ***anaphylaxis, angioedema,*** flulike syndrome, hypersensitivity reactions.

Interactions

Drug-drug. *CNS depressants:* May increase CNS depression. Use together cautiously.
Drug-food. *Any food:* May decrease rate and extent of absorption. Tell patient to take drug on an empty stomach.
Drug-lifestyle. *Alcohol use:* May cause excessive CNS depression. Discourage use together.

Effects on lab test results

None reported.

Pharmacokinetics

Absorption: Rapid. Food delays drug absorption.
Distribution: About 92.5% protein-bound.
Metabolism: In liver.
Excretion: Mainly in urine. *Half-life:* 2½ hours.

Route	Onset	Peak	Duration
P.O.	Rapid	30 min–2 hr	Unknown

Action

Chemical effect: Interacts with one of three identified GABA and benzodiazepine receptor complexes but isn't a benzodiazepine. Exhibits hypnotic activity but has no muscle relaxant or anticonvulsant properties.
Therapeutic effect: Promotes sleep.

Available forms

Tablets: 5 mg, 10 mg
Tablets (extended-release): 6.25 mg, 12.5 mg

NURSING PROCESS

Assessment

• Assess patient's condition before starting therapy and regularly thereafter to monitor drug's effectiveness.
• Be alert for adverse reactions and drug interactions.
• Assess patient's and family's knowledge of drug therapy.

Nursing diagnoses

• Insomnia related to underlying disorder
• Risk for injury related to drug-induced adverse CNS reactions
• Deficient knowledge related to drug therapy

Planning and implementation

• Drug has a rapid onset of action; give when patient is ready to sleep.
• Use hypnotics only for short-term management of insomnia, usually 7 to 10 days. Persistent insomnia may indicate primary psychiatric or medical disorder.
• Because most adverse reactions are dose-related, use smallest effective dose in all patients, especially elderly or debilitated patients.
• Give drug at least 1 hour before meals or 2 hours after meals.
ALERT: Don't confuse Ambien with Amen.

Patient teaching

• Tell patient to take drug immediately before going to bed.
• For faster onset, instruct patient not to take drug with or immediately after a meal. Food decreases drug's absorption.
• Warn patient about possible complex sleep disorders.
ALERT: Tell patient not to crush, chew, or divide the extended-release tablets.

• Warn patient about performing activities that require mental alertness or physical coordination. For inpatient, supervise walking and raise bed rails, particularly for geriatric patient.

Evaluation

• Patient states that drug effectively promotes sleep.
• Patient sustains no injury from adverse CNS reactions.
• Patient and family state understanding of drug therapy.

zoster vaccine, live
(ZOSS-tur vack-SEEN)
Zostavax

Pharmacologic class: vaccine, live attenuated
Therapeutic class: vaccine
Pregnancy risk category: C

Indications and dosages

▶ **Prevention of herpes zoster (shingles).** *Adults age 60 and older:* One reconstituted vial subcutaneously as a single dose.

Contraindications and cautions

• Contraindicated in patients with a history of anaphylactic or anaphylactoid reactions to gelatin, neomycin, or any component of the vaccine; patients with primary or acquired immunodeficiency; patients taking immunosuppressive therapy or corticosteroids; patients with active, untreated tuberculosis; and pregnant women.

Lifespan: In pregnant patients, avoid use during and for 3 months after pregnancy. In breast-feeding patients, it isn't known if vaccine appears in breast milk; use cautiously. In children, Zostavax shouldn't be used; it can't be substituted for Varivax.

Adverse reactions

CNS: asthenia, fever, headache.
EENT: rhinitis.
GI: diarrhea.
Musculoskeletal: polymyalgia rheumatica.
Respiratory: ***asthma exacerbation,*** respiratory disorder, respiratory infection.
Skin: hematoma, *injection site reactions (redness, pain, tenderness, swelling),* pruritus, skin disorder, warmth.
Other: flulike syndrome.

Interactions

Drug-drug. *Immunosuppressants, including corticosteroids.* May decrease immune response. Use together is contraindicated.

Effects on lab test results

None reported.

Pharmacokinetics

Absorption: Unknown.
Distribution: Unknown.
Metabolism: Unknown.
Excretion: Unknown.

Route	Onset	Peak	Duration
SubQ	6 wk	Unknown	4 yr

Action

Chemical effect: Stimulates active immunity to varicella-zoster virus.
Therapeutic effect: Protects against herpes zoster.

Available forms

Injection: Lyophilized vaccine in a single-dose vial with supplied diluent

NURSING PROCESS

Assessment

• Ask if patient has ever had a reaction to a vaccine. Keep epinephrine 1:1000 available for immediate use to treat anaphylaxis.
• Monitor patient for hypersensitivity reaction.
• Assess patient's and family's knowledge of drug therapy.

Nursing diagnoses

• Health-seeking behavior to protect against herpes zoster
• Deficient knowledge related to drug therapy

Planning and implementation

ALERT: Drug is given only by subcutaneous injection; don't give by I.V. route.
• Defer vaccination if patient has acute illness or a fever higher than 101.3° F (38.5° C).

Z

• Inject diluent into the vial of lyophilized vaccine and gently agitate to mix thoroughly.
• Inject the total volume subcutaneously, immediately after reconstitution, into outer aspect of upper arm.
• If reconstituted vaccine isn't used within 30 minutes, discard it.
• Store frozen at 5° F (–15° C) or colder until ready to use.

Patient teaching

• Explain to patient the benefits and risks of the vaccine.
• Inform patient that injection site reactions are common and may include redness, pain, swelling, itching, and bruising.

☑ Evaluation

• Patient gains immunity against herpes zoster.
• Patient and family state understanding of drug therapy.

Herbal Medicines

aloe

Reported uses

• Externally as a topical gel for minor burns, sunburn, cuts, frostbite, skin irritation, and other wounds and abrasions
• Amenorrhea, asthma, colds, seizures, bleeding, and ulcers. Preparations also used to treat acne, AIDS, arthritis, blindness, bursitis, cancer, colitis, depression, diabetes, glaucoma, hemorrhoids, multiple sclerosis, peptic ulcers, and varicose veins

Cautions

• External preparations shouldn't be used by people hypersensitive to herb or those with a history of allergic reactions to plants in the Liliaceae family (such as garlic, onions, and tulips).
• Aloe shouldn't be taken orally by people with cardiac or kidney disease (because of risk of hypokalemia and disturbance of cardiac rhythm), by those with intestinal obstruction, and by those with Crohn disease or ulcerative colitis.
Lifespan: Pregnant women, breast-feeding women, and children shouldn't use.

Adverse reactions

CV: arrhythmias.
GI: damage to intestinal mucosa, harmless brown discoloration of intestinal mucous membranes, painful intestinal spasms, ***severe hemorrhagic diarrhea.***
GU: kidney damage, red discoloration of urine, reflex stimulation of uterine musculature causing miscarriage or premature birth.
Metabolic: fluid and electrolyte loss, hypokalemia.
Musculoskeletal: accelerated bone deterioration, muscle weakness.
Skin: contact dermatitis, delayed healing of deep wounds.

Interactions

Herb-drug. *Antiarrhythmics, digoxin:* Oral form may lead to toxic reaction. Monitor patient closely.
Corticosteroids, diuretics: Increases potassium loss. Monitor patient for signs of hypokalemia.
Disulfiram: Tincture contains alcohol and could precipitate a disulfiram reaction. Discourage use together.
Herb-herb. *Licorice:* Increases risk of potassium deficiency. Discourage use together.

angelica

Reported uses

• Gynecologic disorders, postmenopausal symptoms, menstrual discomfort, anemia, and mild peptic discomfort, such as GI spasms, flatulence, bloating, colic, and loss of appetite; to strengthen the heart; to improve circulation in the limbs; and to relieve osteoporosis, hay fever, cough, asthma, bronchitis, acne, and eczema

Cautions

• People with diabetes should use caution because various species of this plant contain polysaccharides that may disrupt glucose control.
Lifespan: Pregnant or breast-feeding women shouldn't use angelica because it may have stimulant effects on the uterus.

Adverse reactions

CV: hypotension.
Skin: photodermatitis, phototoxicity.

Interactions

Herb-drug. *Antacids, H_2-receptor antagonists, proton pump inhibitors, sucralfate:* Herb may increase acid production in the stomach and may interfere with absorption of these drugs. Discourage use together.
Anticoagulants: Excessive amounts of herb may potentiate anticoagulant effects. Monitor patient for bleeding.
Herb-lifestyle. *Sun exposure:* Photosensitivity reaction may occur. Advise a person taking angelica to avoid unprotected or prolonged exposure to sunlight.

*Liquid may contain alcohol.

bilberry

Reported uses

• Visual and circulatory problems, glaucoma, cataracts, diabetic retinopathy, macular degeneration, varicose veins, and hemorrhoids
• To improve night vision

Cautions

• Urge caution in those taking anticoagulants. Herb may be unsuitable for those with a bleeding disorder.
Lifespan: Pregnant and breast-feeding women should avoid herb.

Adverse reactions

Other: toxic reaction.

Interactions

Herb-drug. *Anticoagulants, antiplatelets:* Inhibits platelet aggregation, possibly increasing the risk of bleeding. Monitor patient.
Disulfiram: May cause disulfiram reaction if herbal preparation contains alcohol. Advise patient to avoid use together.

capsicum

Reported uses

• Bowel disorders, chronic laryngitis, and peripheral vascular disease
• Counterirritant and external analgesic
• Topical preparation FDA-approved for temporary relief of pain from rheumatoid arthritis, osteoarthritis, postherpetic neuralgia (shingles), and diabetic neuropathy.
• FDA-tested for psoriasis, intractable pruritus, vitiligo, phantom limb pain, mastectomy pain, Guillain-Barré syndrome, neurogenic bladder, vulvar vestibulitis, apocrine chromhidrosis, and reflex sympathetic dystrophy
• In personal defense sprays and for refractory pruritus and pruritus caused by renal failure

Cautions

• People hypersensitive to herb or chili pepper products should avoid capsicum. Those with irritable bowel syndrome should avoid it because capsicum has irritant and peristaltic effects.
• Those with asthma who use capsicum may experience more bronchospasms.
Lifespan: Pregnant women should avoid capsicum because of possible uterine stimulant effects.

Adverse reactions

EENT: blepharospasm, extreme burning pain, lacrimation, conjunctival edema, hyperemia, burning pain in nose, sneezing, serous discharge.
GI: oral burning, diarrhea, gingival irritation, bleeding gums.
Respiratory: ***bronchospasm,*** cough, retrosternal discomfort.
Skin: transient skin irritation, itching, stinging, erythema without vesicular eruption, contact dermatitis.

Interactions

Herb-drug. *ACE inhibitors:* Increases risk of cough when applied topically. Monitor patient closely.
Anticoagulants: May alter anticoagulant effects. Monitor PT and INR closely; tell patient to avoid use together.
Antiplatelets, heparin and low–molecular-weight heparin, warfarin: Increases risk of bleeding. Advise patient to avoid use together. If used together, monitor patient for bleeding.
Aspirin, salicylic acid compounds: Reduces bioavailability of these drugs. Discourage use together.
MAO inhibitors: Herb increases catecholamine secretion and increases risk of hypertensive crisis. Discourage use together.
Theophylline: Herb increases theophylline absorption. Discourage use together.
Herb-herb. *Feverfew, garlic, ginger, ginkgo, ginseng:* Increases anticoagulant effects of capsicum, and increases risk of bleeding. Discourage use together. Anyone who uses them together should be monitored closely for bleeding.

cat's claw

Reported uses

- GI problems, including inflammatory bowel disease (Crohn disease or ulcerative colitis) diverticulitis, gastritis, dysentery, ulcerations and hemorrhoids, and to enhance immunity
- Systemic inflammatory diseases such as arthritis and rheumatism
- By cancer patients for its antimutagenic effects
- With zidovudine to stimulate the immune system by patients with HIV infection
- As a contraceptive

Cautions

- Those who have had transplant surgery, and those who have an autoimmune disease, multiple sclerosis, or tuberculosis should avoid use. Anyone who has a coagulation disorder or takes an anticoagulant also should avoid use.
- People with a history of peptic ulcer disease or gallstones should use caution when taking this herb because it stimulates stomach acid secretion.

Lifespan: Women who are pregnant or breast-feeding shouldn't use this herb.

Adverse reactions

CV: hypotension.

Interactions

Herb-drug. *Antihypertensives:* May potentiate hypotensive effects. Discourage use together.
Immunosuppressants: May counteract therapeutic effects because herb has immunostimulant properties. Discourage use together.
Herb-food. *Food:* May enhance absorption of herb.

chamomile

Reported uses

- Sedation or relaxation (main use)
- Stomach disorders, such as GI spasms and other GI inflammatory conditions
- Insomnia
- Menstrual disorders, migraine, epidermolysis bullosa, eczema, eye irritation, throat discomfort, and hemorrhoids
- As a topical bacteriostat and mouthwash

Cautions

- Probably an abortifacient, and some of its components may have teratogenic effects.
- Urge caution in those hypersensitive to components of volatile oils and in those at risk for contact dermatitis.
- Safety in people with liver or kidney disorders hasn't been established, and they should avoid use.

Lifespan: Discourage use by pregnant or breast-feeding women. Herb shouldn't be given to babies or children younger than age 2.

Adverse reactions

EENT: conjunctivitis, eyelid angioedema.
GI: nausea, vomiting.
Skin: contact dermatitis, eczema.
Other: ***anaphylaxis.***

Interactions

Herb-drug. *Anticoagulants:* May potentiate effects. Discourage use together.
Other drugs: Potential for decreased absorption of drugs because of antispasmodic activity of herb in the GI tract. Discourage use together.

echinacea

Reported uses

- As a wound-healing agent for abscesses, burns, eczema, varicose ulcers of the leg, and other skin wounds
- As a nonspecific immunostimulant for the supportive treatment of upper respiratory tract infections, the common cold, and UTIs

Cautions

- Shouldn't be used by anyone with severe illness, such as HIV infection, collagen disease, leukosis, multiple sclerosis, tuberculosis, or autoimmune disease.

Lifespan: Discourage use by pregnant or breast-feeding women because effects of herb are unknown.

*Liquid may contain alcohol.

Adverse reactions

CNS: fever.
GI: nausea, minor GI symptoms, unpleasant taste, vomiting.
GU: diuresis.
Other: allergic reaction in patients allergic to plants belonging to the daisy family, tachyphylaxis.

Interactions

Herb-drug. *Disulfiram, metronidazole:* Herbal products that contain alcohol may cause a disulfiram reaction. Discourage use together.
Immunosuppressants such as cyclosporine: Decreases effectiveness of these drugs. Discourage use together.
Herb-lifestyle. *Alcohol use:* Echinacea preparations containing alcohol may enhance CNS depression. Discourage use together.

eucalyptus

Reported uses

- Internally and externally as an expectorant and for infections and fevers
- Topically to treat sore muscles and rheumatism

Cautions

- People who have had an allergic reaction to eucalyptus or its vapors should avoid use.
- Those who have liver disease or intestinal tract inflammation shouldn't use.
- Essential oil preparations shouldn't be applied to an infant's or child's face because of risk of severe bronchial spasm.

Lifespan: Pregnant and breast-feeding women shouldn't use.

Adverse reactions

CNS: delirium, dizziness, ***seizures.***
EENT: miosis.
GI: epigastric burning, nausea, vomiting.
Musculoskeletal: muscular weakness.
Respiratory: ***asthma-like attacks.***

Interactions

Herb-drug. *Antidiabetics:* Enhances effects. Discourage use together.
Other drugs: Eucalyptus oil induces detoxication enzyme systems in the liver and may affect any drug metabolized in liver. Watch for intended drug effects and toxic reactions.
Herb-herb. Other herbs that cause hypoglycemia (basil, glucomannan, Queen Anne's lace): Decreases glucose level. Advise caution.

evening primrose

Reported uses

- Infusion for sedative and astringent properties
- Asthmatic coughs, GI disorders, whooping cough, psoriasis, multiple sclerosis, asthma, Raynaud disease, and Sjögren syndrome
- Poultices made from oil to speed wound healing
- Pruritic symptoms of atopic dermatitis and eczema, breast pain and tenderness from premenstrual syndrome, benign breast disease, and diabetic neuropathy
- In rheumatoid arthritis, to improve symptoms and reduce the need for pain medication; also used to lower serum cholesterol, improve hypertension, and decrease platelet aggregation
- To calm hyperactive children
- To reduce mammary tumors from baseline size

Cautions

- Urge caution or discourage use in people with schizophrenia and in those taking antiseizure drugs.

Lifespan: In pregnant women, discourage use; effects are unknown.

Adverse reactions

CNS: headache, temporal lobe epilepsy.
CV: thrombosis.
GI: nausea.
Skin: rash.
Other: *immunosuppression,* inflammation.

Interactions

Herb-drug. *Phenothiazines:* May increase risk of seizures. Discourage use together.

fennel

Reported uses

- To increase milk secretion, promote menses, facilitate birth, and increase libido
- As an expectorant to manage cough and bronchitis
- Mild spastic disorders of the GI tract, feelings of fullness, and flatulence
- Upper respiratory tract infections in children (syrup)

Cautions

- Should be used cautiously by people allergic to other members of the Umbelliferae family, such as celery, carrots, or mugwort.
- Discourage use in those with a history of seizures.

Lifespan: In pregnant women, discourage use.

Adverse reactions

CNS: *seizures,* hallucinations.
GI: nausea, vomiting.
Respiratory: *pulmonary edema.*
Skin: contact dermatitis, photodermatitis.
Other: allergic reaction.

Interactions

Herb-drug. *Anticonvulsants, drugs that lower the seizure threshold:* Increases risk of seizure. Monitor patient very closely.
Herb-lifestyle. *Sun exposure:* Increases risk of photosensitivity reactions. Person taking fennel should wear protective clothing and sunscreen and should limit exposure to direct sunlight.

feverfew

Reported uses

- As an antipyretic
- Psoriasis, toothache, insect bites, rheumatism, asthma, stomachache, and menstrual problems
- Migraine prophylaxis

Cautions

- Shouldn't be taken internally by anyone allergic to members of the daisy, or Asteraceae, family—including yarrow, southernwood, wormwood, chamomile, marigold, goldenrod, coltsfoot, and dandelion—or anyone who has had previous reaction to herb.
- Those taking anticoagulants such as warfarin and heparin should use herb cautiously.

Lifespan: Pregnant women shouldn't use because of herb's potential abortifacient properties. Breast-feeding women shouldn't use. Children shouldn't use.

Adverse reactions

CNS: dizziness.
CV: tachycardia.
GI: GI upset, mouth ulcerations.
Skin: contact dermatitis.

Interactions

Herb-drug. *Anticoagulants, antiplatelet drugs including aspirin and thrombolytics:* Herb inhibits prostaglandin synthesis and platelet aggregation. Monitor patient for increased bleeding.

flax

Reported uses

- Constipation, functional disorders of the colon resulting from laxative abuse, irritable bowel syndrome, and diverticulitis
- As a supplement to decrease the risk of hypercholesterolemia and atherosclerosis
- As a poultice for areas of local inflammation

Cautions

- People with an ileus or esophageal stricture, and those experiencing an acute inflammatory illness of the GI tract, should avoid use.

Lifespan: Pregnant and breast-feeding women, and women planning to become pregnant, shouldn't use.

Adverse reactions

GI: diarrhea, flatulence, nausea.

Interactions

Herb-drug. *Laxatives, stool softeners:* Possible increase in laxative actions of herb. Discourage use together.

*Liquid may contain alcohol.

Oral drugs: Because of herb's fibrous content and binding potential, drug absorption may be altered or prevented. Advise patient to avoid taking herb within 2 hours of a drug.

garlic

Reported uses

- To decrease total cholesterol level, decrease triglyceride level, and increase HDL level
- To help prevent atherosclerosis because of its effect on blood pressure and platelet aggregation
- To decrease the risk of cancer, especially cancer of the GI tract; of stroke; and of MI
- Cough, colds, fevers, and sore throats
- Asthma, diabetes, inflammation, heavy metal poisoning, constipation, and athlete's foot
- As an antimicrobial and to reduce symptoms in patients with AIDS

Cautions

- Shouldn't be used by anyone sensitive to garlic or other members of the Liliaceae family or by those with GI disorders, such as peptic ulcer or reflux disease.

Lifespan: Herb shouldn't be used by pregnant women because it has oxytocic effects.

Adverse reactions

CNS: dizziness.
GI: halitosis; irritation of mouth, esophagus, and stomach; nausea; vomiting.
Hematologic: decreased hemoglobin production and lysis of RBCs (with long-term use or excessive amounts).
Skin: contact dermatitis, diaphoresis.
Other: allergic reaction, ***anaphylaxis,*** garlic odor.

Interactions

Herb-drug. *Anticoagulants, NSAIDs, prostacyclin:* May increase bleeding time. Discourage use together.
Antidiabetics: Glucose level may be decreased further. Advise caution if using together, and tell patient to monitor glucose level closely.
Drugs metabolized by the enzyme CYP2E1 (such as acetaminophen): Decreases metabolism of these drugs. Monitor patient for therapeutic effects and toxic reaction.
Herb-herb. *Herbs with anticoagulant effects:* Increases bleeding time. Discourage use together.
Herbs with antihyperglycemic effects: Glucose level may be further decreased. Advise caution and close monitoring of glucose level.

ginger

Reported uses

- As an antiemetic, GI protectant, anti-inflammatory for arthritis treatment, CV stimulant, antitumor agent, antioxidant, and as therapy for microbial and parasitic infestations
- Seasickness, morning or motion sickness, and postoperative nausea and vomiting, and to provide relief from pain and swelling caused by rheumatoid arthritis, osteoarthritis, or muscular discomfort

Cautions

- People with gallstones or with an allergy to herb should avoid use.
- Those with bleeding disorders should avoid using large amounts of herb.
- Anyone taking a CNS depressant or an antiarrhythmic should use ginger cautiously.

Lifespan: Pregnant women should avoid using large amounts of herb.

Adverse reactions

CNS: CNS depression.
CV: ***arrhythmias,*** increased bleeding time.
GI: heartburn.

Interactions

Herb-drug. *Anticoagulants and other drugs that can increase bleeding time:* May further increase bleeding time. Discourage use together.
Herb-herb. *Herbs that may increase bleeding time:* May further increase bleeding time. Discourage use together.

Bold italic type indicates that reaction may be life-threatening.

ginkgo

Reported uses

- Primarily to manage cerebral insufficiency, dementia, and circulatory disorders such as intermittent claudication
- Headaches, asthma, colitis, impotence, depression, altitude sickness, tinnitus, cochlear deafness, vertigo, premenstrual syndrome, macular degeneration, diabetic retinopathy, and allergies
- As an adjunctive treatment for pancreatic cancer and schizophrenia
- In addition to physical therapy for Fontaine stage IIIB peripheral arterial disease to decrease pain during ambulation with a minimum of 6 weeks of treatment

Cautions

- People with a history of an allergic reaction to ginkgo or any of its components and those with increased risk of intracranial hemorrhage (hypertension, diabetes) should avoid use.
- Anyone taking an antiplatelet or an anticoagulant should avoid use because of the increased risk of bleeding.
- Herb should be avoided before surgery.

Lifespan: Pregnant women shouldn't use.

Adverse reactions

CNS: headache, ***seizures,*** subarachnoid hemorrhage.
GI: diarrhea, flatulence, nausea, vomiting.
Skin: contact hypersensitivity reaction, dermatitis.

Interactions

Herb-drug. *Anticoagulants, antiplatelets, high-dose vitamin E:* May increase the risk of bleeding. Discourage use together.
MAO inhibitors: Theoretically, herb can potentiate the activity of these drugs. Advise patient to stop taking herb.
SSRIs: Herb extracts may reverse the sexual dysfunction caused by these drugs. Urge patient to consult prescriber before using together.
Warfarin: Possibly increases INR when taken together. Monitor INR.
Herb-herb. *Garlic and other herbs that increase bleeding time:* Potentiates anticoagulant effects. Advise caution.

ginseng

Reported uses

- To minimize or reduce the activity of the thymus gland
- As a sedative, demulcent (soothes irritated or inflamed internal tissues or organs), aphrodisiac, antidepressant, sleep aid, and diuretic
- To improve stamina, concentration, healing, stress resistance, vigilance, and work efficiency and to improve well-being in elderly people with debilitated or degenerative conditions
- To decrease fasting glucose and hemoglobin A1c levels and for hyperlipidemia, hepatic dysfunction, and impaired cognitive function

Cautions

- Should be used cautiously by anyone with CV disease, hypertension, hypotension, or diabetes, and by those receiving steroid therapy.

Lifespan: In pregnant or breast-feeding women, discourage use; effects are unknown.

Adverse reactions

CNS: headache, insomnia, nervousness.
CV: chest pain, hypertension, palpitations.
EENT: epistaxis.
GI: diarrhea, nausea, vomiting.
GU: impotence, vaginal bleeding.
Skin: pruritus, skin eruptions (with ginseng abuse).
Other: breast pain.

Interactions

Herb-drug. *Anticoagulants, antiplatelet drugs:* May decrease the effects of these drugs. Monitor PT and INR.
Antidiabetics, insulin: Increases hypoglycemic effects. Monitor glucose level.
Drugs metabolized by CYP3A4: Herb may inhibit this enzyme system. Monitor patient for clinical effects and toxicity.
Phenelzine, other MAO inhibitors: May cause headache, irritability, visual hallucinations, and other interactions. Discourage use together.
Warfarin: Herb may decrease drug effect. Discourage using herb.

*Liquid may contain alcohol.

goldenseal

Reported uses

- GI disorders, gastritis, peptic ulceration, anorexia, postpartum hemorrhage, dysmenorrhea, eczema, pruritus, tuberculosis, cancer, mouth ulcerations, otorrhea, tinnitus, and conjunctivitis
- As a wound antiseptic, diuretic, laxative, and anti-inflammatory agent
- To shorten the duration of acute *Vibrio cholera* diarrhea and diarrhea caused by some species of *Giardia, Salmonella, Shigella,* and some *Enterobacteriaceae*
- To improve biliary secretion and function in hepatic cirrhosis

Cautions

- People with hypertension, heart failure, or arrhythmias, or severe renal or hepatic disease should avoid use.

Lifespan: Pregnant or breast-feeding women shouldn't use. Infants shouldn't use.

Adverse reactions

CNS: delirium, hallucinations, paralysis, paresthesia, reduced mental alertness, sedation.
CV: *asystole, heart block,* hypertension, hypotension.
GI: diarrhea, GI cramping, mouth ulcerations, nausea, vomiting.
Hematologic: ***leukopenia,*** megaloblastic anemia from decreased vitamin B absorption.
Respiratory: ***respiratory depression.***
Skin: contact dermatitis.

Interactions

Herb-drug. *Anticoagulants:* May reduce anticoagulant effect. Discourage use together.
Antidiabetics, insulin: Increases hypoglycemic effects. Discourage use together; advise patient to monitor glucose level closely.
Antihypertensives: May reduce or enhance hypotensive effect. Discourage use together.
Beta blockers, calcium channel blockers, digoxin: May interfere with or enhance cardiac effects. Discourage use together.
Cephalosporins, disulfiram, metronidazole: May cause disulfiram-like reaction when taken with liquid herbal preparations. Discourage use together.
CNS depressants, such as benzodiazepines: May enhance sedative effects. Discourage use together.
Herb-lifestyle. *Alcohol use:* May enhance sedative effects. Discourage use together.

grapeseed, pinebark

Reported uses

- As an antioxidant for circulatory disorders (hypoxia from atherosclerosis, inflammation, and cardiac or cerebral infarction)
- Pain, limb heaviness, and swelling from peripheral circulatory disorders and to treat inflammatory conditions, varicose veins, and cancer

Cautions

- People with liver dysfunction should use cautiously.

Lifespan: No considerations reported.

Adverse reactions

Hepatic: ***hepatotoxicity.***

Interactions

None reported.

kava

Reported uses

- Nervous anxiety, stress, and restlessness
- Orally as a sedative, to promote wound healing, and for headaches, seizure disorders, the common cold, respiratory tract infection, tuberculosis, and rheumatism
- Urogenital infections, including chronic cystitis, venereal disease, uterine inflammation, menstrual problems, and vaginal prolapse
- As an aphrodisiac
- As juice, for skin diseases, including leprosy
- As a poultice, for intestinal problems, otitis, and abscesses

Cautions

- People hypersensitive to herb or any of its components should avoid it. Depressed people should avoid herb because of possible sedative activity; those with endogenous depression should avoid it because of increased risk of suicide.

• People with renal disease, thrombocytopenia, or neutropenia should use cautiously.

Lifespan: Pregnant women shouldn't use this herb because of possible loss of uterine tone. Breast-feeding women shouldn't use. Children shouldn't use.

Adverse reactions

CNS: mild euphoric changes characterized by feelings of happiness, fluent and lively speech, and increased sensitivity to sounds; morning fatigue, sedation, ***suicidal thoughts.***
EENT: disorders of oculomotor equilibrium, pupil dilation, visual accommodation disorders.
GI: mild GI disturbances, mouth numbness.
Hepatic: ***liver toxicity.***
Metabolic: increased HDL cholesterol; reduced levels of albumin, bilirubin, total protein, and urea.
Respiratory: pulmonary hypertension.
Skin: scaly rash.

Interactions

Herb-drug. *Antiplatelet drugs, type B MAO inhibitors:* Possible additive effects. Monitor patient closely.
Barbiturates, benzodiazepines: Kava lactones potentiate the effects of CNS depressants, leading to toxicity. Discourage use together.
Levodopa: Possible reduced effectiveness of levodopa therapy in patients with Parkinson disease, apparently because of dopamine antagonism. Advise patient to use cautiously.
Herb-herb. *Calamus, calendula, California poppy, capsicum, catnip, celery, couch grass, elecampane, German chamomile, goldenseal, gotu kola, hops, Jamaican dogwood, lemon balm, sage, sassafras, shepherd's purse, Siberian ginseng, skullcap, stinging nettle, St. John's wort, valerian, wild lettuce, yerba maté:* Additive sedative effects may occur. Advise great caution.
Herb-lifestyle. *Alcohol use:* Increases risk of CNS depression and liver damage. Discourage use together.

milk thistle

Reported uses

• Dyspepsia, liver damage from chemicals, Amanita mushroom poisoning, support in inflammatory liver disease and cirrhosis, loss of appetite, and gallbladder and spleen disorders
• As a liver protectant

Cautions

• Herb shouldn't be used by people hypersensitive to it or to plants in the Asteraceae family. Use in decompensated cirrhosis isn't recommended.

Lifespan: Pregnant and breast-feeding women shouldn't use.

Adverse reactions

GI: diarrhea, nausea, vomiting.

Interactions

Herb-drug. *Aspirin:* May improve aspirin metabolism in people with liver cirrhosis. Advise person to consult prescriber before use.
Cisplatin: May prevent kidney damage by cisplatin. Advise patient to consult prescriber before use.
Disulfiram: Herbal products that contain alcohol may cause a disulfiram-like reaction. Discourage use together.
Hepatotoxic drugs: May prevent liver damage from butyrophenones, phenothiazines, phenytoin, acetaminophen, and halothane. Advise patient to consult prescriber before use.
Tacrine: Silymarin reduces adverse cholinergic effects when given together. Advise patient to consult prescriber before use.

nettle

Reported uses

• Allergic rhinitis, osteoarthritis, rheumatoid arthritis, kidney stones, asthma, and BPH
• As a diuretic, an expectorant, a general health tonic, a blood builder and purifier, a pain reliever and anti-inflammatory, and a lung tonic for ex-smokers

*Liquid may contain alcohol.

- Eczema, hives, bursitis, tendinitis, laryngitis, sciatica, and premenstrual syndrome
- Possibly hay fever and irrigation of the urinary tract

Cautions

Lifespan: Herb shouldn't be used by women who are pregnant or breast-feeding because of its diuretic and uterine stimulation properties. Children shouldn't use.

Adverse reactions

CV: edema.
GI: gastric irritation, gingivostomatitis.
GU: decreased urine formation, increased diuresis in patients with arthritic conditions and those with myocardial or chronic venous insufficiency, ***oliguria.***
Skin: burning sensation, topical irritation.

Interactions

Herb-drug. *Disulfiram:* Possible disulfiram reaction if taken with liquid extract or tincture. Discourage use together.
Herb-lifestyle. *Alcohol use:* Possible additive effect from liquid extract and tincture. Discourage alcohol use.

passion flower

Reported uses

- As a sedative, a hypnotic, and an antispasmodic for treating muscle spasms
- As an analgesic for menstrual cramping, pain, or migraines
- For neuralgia, generalized seizures, hysteria, nervous agitation, and insomnia
- Crushed leaves and flowers topically for cuts and bruises

Cautions

- Excessive amounts may cause sedation and may potentiate MAO inhibitor therapy.
- Those with liver disease or a history of alcoholism should avoid products that contain alcohol.

Lifespan: Women who are pregnant or breast-feeding shouldn't use.

Adverse reactions

CNS: agitation, confusion, drowsiness, flushing, headache, psychosis.
CV: hypotension, ***shock,*** tachycardia, ***ventricular arrhythmias.***
GI: nausea, vomiting.
Respiratory: *asthma.*
Other: allergic reaction.

Interactions

Herb-drug. *Disulfiram, metronidazole:* Herbal products that contain alcohol may cause a disulfiram-like reaction. Discourage use together.
Hexobarbital: Increases sleeping time; other barbiturate effects may be potentiated. Monitor patient's level of consciousness carefully.
MAO inhibitors: Actions can be potentiated by herb. Discourage use together.

St. John's wort

Reported uses

- Depression, bronchial inflammation, burns, cancer, enuresis, gastritis, hemorrhoids, hypothyroidism, insect bites and stings, insomnia, kidney disorders, and scabies, and as a wound-healing agent
- HIV infection
- Topically for phototherapy of skin diseases, including psoriasis, cutaneous T-cell lymphoma, warts, and Kaposi sarcoma

Cautions

- Transplant patients maintained on cyclosporine therapy should avoid this herb because of the risk of organ rejection.

Lifespan: Pregnant women and both men and women planning pregnancy shouldn't use this herb because of mutagenic risk to sperm cells and oocytes and adverse effects on reproductive cells.

Adverse reactions

CNS: fatigue, headache, neuropathy, restlessness.
GI: abdominal pain, constipation, diarrhea, digestive complaints, dry mouth, fullness sensation, nausea.

Skin: photosensitivity reactions, pruritus.
Other: delayed hypersensitivity.

Interactions

Herb-drug. *Amitriptyline, chemotherapeutics, cyclosporine, digoxin, drugs metabolized by the cytochrome P-450 enzyme system, hormonal contraceptives, protease inhibitors, theophylline, warfarin:* Decreases effectiveness of these drugs. May require adjustment of drug dosage. Monitor patient closely; discourage use together.
Barbiturates: Decreases sedative effects. Monitor patient closely.
Indinavir: Substantially reduces drug level, causing loss of therapeutic effects. Discourage use together.
MAO inhibitors, including phenelzine and tranylcypromine: May increase effects and cause toxicity and hypertensive crisis. Discourage use together.
Opioids: Increases sedative effects. Discourage use together.
Reserpine: Antagonizes effects of reserpine. Discourage use together.
SSRIs, such as citalopram, fluoxetine, paroxetine, sertraline: Increases risk of serotonin syndrome. Discourage use together.
Herb-herb. *Herbs with sedative effects, such as calamus, calendula, California poppy, capsicum, catnip, celery, couch grass, elecampane, German chamomile, goldenseal, gotu kola, Jamaican dogwood, kava, lemon balm, sage, sassafras, shepherd's purse, Siberian ginseng, skullcap, stinging nettle, valerian, wild carrot, wild lettuce:* May enhance effects of herbs. Discourage use together.
Herb-food. *Tyramine-containing foods such as beer, cheese, dried meats, fava beans, liver, wine, and yeast:* May cause hypertensive crisis when used together. Advise person to separate food from herb.
Herb-lifestyle. *Alcohol use:* May increase sedative effects. Discourage use together.
Sun exposure: Increases risk of photosensitivity reaction. Advise person to avoid unprotected or prolonged exposure to sunlight.

saw palmetto

Reported uses

- As a mild diuretic
- GU problems such as BPH and to increase sperm production, breast size, and sexual vigor

Cautions

- Those with breast cancer or hormone-dependent illnesses other than BPH should avoid this herb.

Lifespan: Women of childbearing potential and women who are pregnant or breast-feeding shouldn't use this herb.

Adverse reactions

CNS: headache.
CV: hypertension.
GI: abdominal pain, constipation, diarrhea, nausea.
GU: dysuria, impotence, urine retention.
Musculoskeletal: back pain.
Other: decreased libido.

Interactions

Herb-drug. *Adrenergics, hormones, hormone-like drugs:* May cause estrogen, androgen, and alpha-blocking effects. Drug dosages may need adjustment if patient takes this herb. Monitor patient closely.

valerian

Reported uses

- Menstrual cramps, restlessness and sleep disorders from nervous conditions, and other symptoms of psychological stress, such as anxiety, nervous headaches, and gastric spasms
- Topically as a bath additive for restlessness and sleep disorders

Cautions

- People with hepatic impairment shouldn't use this herb because of the risk of hepatotoxicity.
- People with acute or major skin injuries, fever, infectious diseases, cardiac insufficiency, or hypertonia shouldn't bathe with valerian products.

*Liquid may contain alcohol.

Lifespan: Women who are pregnant or breast-feeding shouldn't use this herb; its effects are unknown.

Adverse reactions

CNS: excitability, headache, insomnia.
CV: cardiac disturbance.
EENT: blurred vision.
GI: nausea.
Other: hypersensitivity reaction.

Interactions

Herb-drug. *Barbiturates, benzodiazepines:* May have additive effects. Monitor patient closely.
CNS depressants: May have additive effects. Discourage use together.
Disulfiram: Disulfiram reaction may occur if herbal extract or tincture contains alcohol. Discourage use together.
Herb-herb. *Herbs with sedative effects, such as catnip, hops, kava, passion flower, skullcap:* May increase sedative effects. Advise caution.
Herb-lifestyle. *Alcohol use:* May increase sedative effects. Discourage using together.

Appendices and Index

Glossary

Absorption: progress of a drug from the time it's administered, through the time it passes to the tissues, until it becomes available for use by the body.

Agranulocytosis: an abnormal blood condition characterized by a severe reduction in the number of granulocytes, basophils, eosinophils, and neutrophils that results in high fever, exhaustion, and bleeding ulcers of the throat, mucous membranes, and GI tract; an acute disease that may be an adverse reaction to drug or radiation therapy.

Allergic reaction: a local or general reaction after exposure to an allergen to which the patient has already been exposed and sensitized; may range from localized dermatitis to anaphylaxis.

Alopecia: absence or loss of hair.

Angioedema: a potentially life-threatening condition characterized by sudden swelling of tissue in the face, neck, lips, tongue, throat, hands, feet, genitals, or intestine.

Aplastic anemia: a deficiency of all of the formed elements of the blood related to bone marrow failure; caused by neoplastic bone marrow disease or by destruction of the bone marrow by exposure to toxic chemicals, radiation, or certain drugs; also known as *pancytopenia.*

Arthralgia: any pain that affects a joint.

Azotemia: a toxic condition caused by renal insufficiency and subsequent retention of urea in the blood; also called *uremia.*

Cushing syndrome: a metabolic disorder caused by increased production of adrenocorticotropic hormone from a tumor of the adrenal cortex or of the anterior lobe of the pituitary gland, or by excessive intake of glucocorticoids; characterized by central obesity, "moon face," glucose intolerance, growth suppression in children, and weakening of the muscles.

Disseminated intravascular coagulation (DIC): a life-threatening coagulopathy resulting from overstimulation of the body's clotting and anticlotting processes in response to disease, septicemia, neoplasms, obstetric emergencies, severe trauma, prolonged surgery, and hemorrhage.

Distribution: the process by which the drug is delivered to the tissues and fluids of the body.

Duration of action: length of time the drug produces its therapeutic effect.

Eosinophilia: an increase in the number of eosinophils in the blood accompanying many inflammatory conditions; substantial increases are considered a reflection of an allergic response.

Erythema: redness of the skin caused by dilation and congestion of the superficial capillaries, often a sign of inflammation or infection.

Excretion: the elimination of drugs from the body.

Gray baby syndrome: a life-threatening condition that can occur in newborns (especially premature one) who are given chloramphenicol for a bacterial infection such as meningitis; symptoms, usually appearing 2 to 9 days after therapy has begun, include vomiting, loose green stools, refusal to suck, hypotension, cyanosis, low body temperature, and CV collapse; the baby becomes limp and has a gray coloring.

Half-life: the time it takes for half of the drug to be eliminated by the body.

Hemolytic anemia: a disorder characterized by the premature destruction of RBCs; anemia may be minimal or absent, reflecting the ability of the bone marrow to increase production of RBCs.

Hepatitis: inflammation of the liver, usually from a viral infection but sometimes from toxic agents.

Hirsutism: excessive growth of dark, coarse body hair in a characteristically male pattern.

Hypercalcemia: greater-than-normal amounts of calcium in the blood; signs and symptoms include confusion, anorexia, abdominal pain, muscle pain, and weakness.

Hyperglycemia: greater-than-normal amounts of glucose in the blood; signs and symptoms include excessive hunger, thirst, frequent urination, fatigue, weight loss, blurred vision, and poor wound healing.

Hyperkalemia: greater-than-normal amounts of potassium in the blood; signs and symptoms include nausea, fatigue, weakness, and palpitations or irregular pulse.

Hypermagnesemia: greater-than-normal amounts of magnesium in the blood; toxic levels may cause cardiac arrhythmias and may depress deep tendon reflexes and respiration.

Hypernatremia: greater-than-normal amounts of sodium in the blood; signs and symptoms include confusion, seizures, coma, dysrhythmic muscle twitching, lethargy, tachycardia, and irritability.

Hyperplasia: an increase in the number of cells.

Hypersensitivity reaction: an abnormal and undesirable reaction in response to a foreign agent; classified by the mechanism involved and the time it takes to occur and assigned a rating of 1 through 4 (Types I, II, III, IV).

Hypocalcemia: less-than-normal amounts of calcium in the blood; signs and symptoms of severe hypocalcemia include cardiac arrhythmias and muscle cramping and twitching as well as numbness and tingling of the hands, feet, lips, and tongue.

Hypoglycemia: less-than-normal amounts of glucose in the blood; signs and symptoms include weakness, drowsiness, confusion, hunger, dizziness, pallor, irritability, tremor, sweating, headache, a cold and clammy feeling, rapid heart beat, and if left untreated, delirium, coma, and death.

Hypokalemia: less-than-normal amounts of potassium in the blood; signs and symptoms include palpitations, muscle weakness or cramping, paresthesias, frequent urination, delirium, depression, and GI complaints such as constipation, nausea, vomiting, and abdominal cramping.

Hypomagnesemia: less-than-normal amounts of magnesium in the blood; signs and symptoms include nausea, vomiting, muscle weakness, tremors, tetany, and lethargy.

Hyponatremia: less-than-normal amounts of sodium in the blood; signs and symptoms may range from mild anorexia, headache, or muscle cramps to obtundation, coma, or seizures.

Leukocytosis: an abnormal increase in the number of circulating WBCs; types are basophilia, eosinophilia, and neutrophilia.

Leukopenia: an abnormal decrease in the number of WBCs to fewer than 5,000/mm^3.

Metabolism: the body's ability to change a drug from its dosage form to a more water-soluble form that can then be excreted.

Myalgia: diffuse muscle pain, usually occurring with malaise.

Nephrotic syndrome: an abnormal kidney condition characterized by marked proteinuria, hypoalbuminemia, and edema.

Neuroleptic malignant syndrome: the rarest and most serious of the neuroleptic-induced movement disorders, a neurologic emergency in most cases; signs and symptoms include fever, rigidity, tremor, drowsiness, and confusion progressing to stupor and coma, seizures, and cardiac arrhythmias.

Neutropenia: an abnormal decrease in the number of circulating neutrophils in the blood.

Onset of action: time interval that starts when the drug is administered and ends when the therapeutic effect begins.

Pancytopenia: a deficiency of all of the formed elements of the blood related to bone marrow failure caused by neoplastic bone marrow disease or by destruction of the bone marrow after exposure to toxic chemicals, radiation, or certain drugs; also known as *aplastic anemia.*

Peak concentration: reached when the absorption rate of a drug equals the elimination rate.

Pharmacodynamics: the study of drug action in the body at the tissue site; includes uptake, movement, binding, and interactions.

Pharmacokinetics: the study of the action of drugs within the body, including the routes and mechanisms of absorption and excretion, the rate at which a drug's action begins, the duration of effect, the biotransformation of the substance in the body, and the effects and routes of metabolite excretion.

Pseudomembranous colitis: a complication of antibiotic therapy that causes severe local tissue inflammation of the colon; signs and symptoms include watery diarrhea, abdominal pain or cramping, and low-grade fever.

Pseudotumor cerebri: benign intracranial hypertension, most common in women ages 20 to 50, caused by increased pressure within the brain; symptoms include headache, dizziness, nausea, vomiting, and ringing or rushing sound in the ears.

Pruritus: itching.

Psoriasis: a common skin disorder characterized by the eruption of red, silvery-scaled maculopapules, predominantly on the elbows, knees, scalp, and trunk.

Reye syndrome: an encephalopathy that affects children; linked to the use of aspirin and other salicylate-containing drug, as well as other causes; the syndrome may follow an upper respiratory infection or chicken pox; its onset is rapid, usually starting with irritable, combative behavior and vomiting, progressing to semiconsciousness, seizures, coma, and possibly death.

Serotonin syndrome: a typically mild, yet potentially serious drug-related condition most often reported in patients taking two or more drugs that increase CNS serotonin levels; the most common combinations involve MAO inhibitors, SSRIs, and tricyclic antidepressants; signs and symptoms include confusion, agitation, restlessness, rapid heart rate, muscle rigidity or twitching, tremors, and nausea.

Serum sickness: an immune complex disease appearing 1 or 2 weeks after infection of a foreign serum or serum protein, with local and systemic reactions, such as urticaria, fever, general lymphadenopathy, edema, arthritis, and occasionally albuminuria or severe nephritis.

Syncope: a brief loss of consciousness caused by oxygen deficiency to the brain, often preceded by a feeling of dizziness; have the patient lie down or place his head between his knees to prevent it.

Thrombocytopenia: an abnormal decrease in the number of platelets in the blood, predisposing the patient to bleeding disorders.

Thrombocytopenic purpura: a bleeding disorder characterized by a marked decrease in the number of platelets, causing multiple bruises, petechiae, and hemorrhage into the tissues.

Tinnitus: sound in one or both ears, such as buzzing, ringing, or whistling, occurring without external stimuli; it may be from an ear infection, the use of certain drugs, a blocked auditory tube or canal, or head trauma.

Urticaria: an itchy skin condition characterized by pale wheals with well-defined red edges; this may be the result of an allergic response to insect bites, food, or drugs.

Preventing miscommunication

Although abbreviations can save time, they also raise the risk of misinterpretation, which can lead to potentially disastrous consequences, especially when dealing with drug administration. To help reduce the risk of being misunderstood, always take the time to write legibly and to spell out anything that could be misread. This caution extends to how you write numbers as well as drug names and other drug-related instructions.

Dosages

For instance, when writing a drug dosage, never add a zero after a decimal point and never fail to add a zero before a decimal point. If you write 1.0 mg instead of the correct 1 mg, the dosage easily could be misread as 10 mg. Likewise, if you write .5 mg instead of the correct 0.5 mg, the dosage could be misread as 5 mg.

Drug names

Be careful with drug names as well. For instance, If you write $MgSO_4$ as shorthand for magnesium sulfate, you could be misread as meaning morphine sulfate. The opposite is also true; if you write MS or $MS0_4$, meaning morphine sulfate, you could be misread as meaning magnesium sulfate. Instead, make sure to clearly write out all drug names, particularly those that could be easily confused or could be dangerous if confused.

Common dangerous abbreviations

Finally, try to avoid these common—and dangerous—abbreviations.

Abbreviation	Intended use	Potential misreading	Preferred use
BT	bedtime	May be read as "bid" or twice daily	Spell out "bedtime."
cc	cubic centimeters	May be read as "u" or units	Use milliliters, abbreviated as mL or ml.
D/C	discharge or discontinue	May lead to premature discontinuation of drug therapy or premature discharge	Spell out discharge or discontinue.
hs	bedtime	May be read as "half-strength"	Spell out bedtime.
HS	half-strength	May be read as "bedtime"	Spell out half-strength.
IJ	injection	May be read as "IV"	Spell out "injection."
IN	intranasal	May be read as "IM" or "IV"	Spell out "intranasal" or use "NAS."
IU	international unit	May be read as "IV" or "10"	Spell out "international unit."
µg	microgram	May be read as "mg"	Use "mcg."
o.d. or O.D.	once daily	May be read as "right eye"	Spell out "once daily."

Abbreviation	Intended use	Potential misreading	Preferred use
per os	by mouth	May be read as "left eye"	Use "PO" or spell out "orally."
q.d. or QD	daily	May be read as "qid"	Spell out "daily."
q1d	once daily	May be read as "qid"	Spell out "once daily."
qhs	every bedtime	May be read as "qhr" (every hour)	Spell out "nightly."
qn	every night	May be read as "qh" (every hour)	Spell out "nightly" or "at bedtime."
q.o.d. or QOD	every other day	May be read as "q.d." (daily) or "q.i.d." (four times daily)	Spell out "every other day."
SC, SQ	subcutaneous	May be read as "SL" (sublingual) or "5 every"	Spell out "subcutaneous" or use "subcut" or "SubQ."
U or u	unit	May be read as "0" (100 instead of 10U)	Spell out "unit."
x7d	for 7 days	May be read as "for seven doses"	Spell out "for 7 days."
°	hour	May be read as a zero	Spell out "hour" or use "hr."

Pregnancy risk categories

The FDA has assigned a pregnancy risk category to each drug based on available clinical and preclinical information. The five categories (A, B, C, D, X) reflect a drug's potential to cause birth defects. Although drugs should ideally be avoided during pregnancy, sometimes they're needed; this rating system permits rapid assessment of the risk-benefit ratio. Drugs in category A are generally considered safe to use in pregnancy; drugs in category X are generally contraindicated.

- A: Adequate studies in pregnant women haven't shown a risk to fetus.
- B: Animal studies haven't shown a risk to fetus, but controlled studies haven't been conducted in pregnant women; or animal studies have shown an adverse effect on fetus, but adequate studies in pregnant women haven't shown a risk to fetus.
- C: Animal studies have shown an adverse effect on fetus, but adequate studies haven't been conducted in pregnant women. The benefits from use in pregnant women may be acceptable despite risks.
- D: The drug may cause risk to fetus, but the potential benefits of use in pregnant women may be acceptable despite the risks (such as in a life-threatening situation or a serious disease for which safer drugs can't be used or are ineffective).
- X: Studies in animals or humans show fetal abnormalities, or adverse-reaction reports indicate evidence of fetal risk. The risks involved clearly outweigh potential benefits.
- NR: Not rated.

Controlled substance schedules

Drugs regulated under the jurisdiction of the Controlled Substances Act of 1970 are divided into the following groups or schedules:

- Schedule I (C-I): High abuse potential and no accepted medical use. Examples include heroin, cocaine, and LSD.
- Schedule II (C-II): High abuse potential with severe dependence liability. Examples include opioids, amphetamines, and some barbiturates.
- Schedule III (C-III): Less abuse potential than schedule II drugs and moderate dependence liability. Examples include nonbarbiturate sedatives, nonamphetamine stimulants, anabolic steroids, dronabinol, and limited amounts of certain opioids.
- Schedule IV (C-IV): Less abuse potential than schedule III drugs and limited dependence liability. Examples include some sedatives, anxiolytics, and non-opioid analgesics.
- Schedule V (C-V): Limited abuse potential. This category includes mainly small amounts of opioids, such as codeine, used as antitussives or antidiarrheals. Under federal law, limited quantities of certain C-V drugs may be purchased without a prescription directly from a pharmacist if allowed under specific state laws. The purchaser must be at least age 18 and must furnish suitable identification. All such transactions must be recorded by the dispensing pharmacist.

Combination drug products

Accuretic

Generic components
Tablets
10 mg quinapril and 12.5 mg hydrochlorothiazide
20 mg quinapril and 12.5 mg hydrochlorothiazide
20 mg quinapril and 25 mg hydrochlorothiazide

Dosages
Adults: 1 tablet P.O. per day in the morning. Adjust drug using the individual products; then switch to appropriate dosage of the combination product.

Activella
femHRT

Generic components
Tablets
2.5 mcg ethinyl estradiol and 0.5 mg norethindrone acetate (femHRT)
5 mcg ethinyl estradiol and 1 mg norethindrone acetate (femHRT)
1 mg ethinyl estradiol and 0.5 mg norethindrone acetate (Activella)

Dosages
Signs and symptoms of menopause and prevention of osteoporosis
Women with intact uterus: 1 tablet P.O. daily.

ACTOPlus MET

Generic components
Tablets
15 mg pioglitazone hydrochloride and 500 mg metformin hydrochloride
15 mg pioglitazone hydrochloride and 850 mg metformin hydrochloride

Dosages
Adults: For patients inadequately controlled on metformin alone or for patients who initially responded to pioglitazone alone but now require additional glycemic control, start with either the 15 mg/500 mg or 15 mg/850 mg combination P.O. once daily or b.i.d.; adjust dosage based on therapeutic response.

Adderall
Adderall XL
Controlled Substance Schedule (CSS) II

Generic components
Tablets
5 mg: 1.25 mg dextroamphetamine sulfate, 1.25 mg dextroamphetamine saccharate, and 1.25 mg amphetamine aspartate, 1.25 mg amphetamine sulfate
7.5 mg: 1.875 mg dextroamphetamine sulfate, 1.875 mg dextroamphetamine saccharate, 1.875 mg amphetamine aspartate, and 1.875 mg amphetamine sulfate
10 mg: 2.5 mg dextroamphetamine sulfate, 2.5 mg dextroamphetamine saccharate, 2.5 mg amphetamine aspartate, and 2.5 mg amphetamine sulfate
12.5 mg: 3.125 mg dextroamphetamine sulfate, 3.125 mg dextroamphetamine saccharate, 3.125 mg amphetamine aspartate, and 3.125 mg amphetamine sulfate
15 mg: 3.75 mg dextroamphetamine sulfate, 3.75 mg dextroamphetamine saccharate, 3.75 mg amphetamine aspartate, and 3.75 mg amphetamine sulfate
20 mg: 5 mg dextroamphetamine sulfate, 5 mg dextroamphetamine saccharate, 5 mg amphetamine aspartate, and 5 mg amphetamine sulfate
30 mg: 7.5 mg dextroamphetamine sulfate, 7.5 mg dextroamphetamine saccharate, 7.5 mg amphetamine aspartate, and 7.5 mg amphetamine sulfate
Capsules (extended-release)
5 mg: 1.25 mg dextroamphetamine sulfate, 1.25 mg dextroamphetamine saccharate, 1.25 mg amphetamine aspartate, and 1.25 mg amphetamine sulfate
10 mg: 2.5 mg dextroamphetamine sulfate, 2.5 mg dextroamphetamine saccharate, 2.5 mg amphetamine aspartate, and 2.5 mg amphetamine sulfate
15 mg: 3.75 mg dextroamphetamine sulfate, 3.75 mg dextroamphetamine saccharate,

3.75 mg amphetamine aspartate, and 3.75 mg amphetamine sulfate
20 mg: 5 mg dextroamphetamine sulfate, 5 mg dextroamphetamine saccharate, 5 mg amphetamine aspartate, and 5 mg amphetamine sulfate
25 mg: 6.25 mg dextroamphetamine sulfate, 6.25 mg dextroamphetamine saccharate, 6.25 mg amphetamine aspartate, and 6.25 mg amphetamine sulfate
30 mg: 7.5 mg dextroamphetamine sulfate, 7.5 mg dextroamphetamine saccharate, 7.5 mg amphetamine aspartate, and 7.5 mg amphetamine sulfate

Dosages
Narcolepsy
Adults and children age 12 and older: Initially, 10 mg immediate-release tablet daily. Increase by 10 mg weekly to maximum dose of 60 mg in two or three divided doses q 4 to 6 hours.
Children ages 6 to 12: Initially, 5 mg immediate-release tablet P.O. daily. Increase by 5 mg at weekly intervals to maximum of 60 mg in divided doses.
Attention deficit hyperactivity disorder
Adults: 20 mg extended-release capsules P.O. daily.
Adolescents ages 13 to 17: Initially, 10 mg extended-release capsule P.O. daily. Increase after 1 week to 20 mg daily if needed.
Children age 6 and older: Initially, 5 mg immediate-release tablet P.O. daily or b.i.d. Increase by 5 mg at weekly intervals until expected response. Dosage should rarely exceed 40 mg.
Children ages 6 to 12: Initially, 10 mg extended-release capsule P.O. daily in a.m. Increase by 5 to 10 mg in weekly intervals to a maximum dose of 30 mg.
Children ages 3 to 5: Initially 2.5 mg immediate-release tablet P.O. daily. Increase by 2.5 mg at weekly intervals until optimal response. Divide total daily amount into two or three doses and give 4 to 6 hours apart.

Advicor

Generic components
Tablets
20 mg lovastatin and 500 mg niacin
20 mg lovastatin and 1,000 mg niacin

Dosages
Adults: 1 tablet daily P.O. at night.

Aggrenox

Generic components
Capsules
25 mg aspirin and 200 mg dipyridamole

Dosages
Adults: To decrease risk of stroke, 1 capsule P.O. b.i.d. in the morning and evening. Swallow capsule whole; may be taken with or without food.

Aldactazide

Generic components
Tablets
25 mg spironolactone and 25 mg hydrochlorothiazide
50 mg spironolactone and 50 mg hydrochlorothiazide

Dosages
Adults: One to eight 25 mg spironolactone and 25 mg hydrochlorothiazide tablets daily. Or, one to four 50 mg spironolactone and 50 mg hydrochlorothiazide tablets daily.

Aldoclor

Generic components
Tablets
250 mg methyldopa and 150 mg chlorothiazide
250 mg methyldopa and 250 mg chlorothiazide

Dosages
Adults: 1 tablet P.O. per day taken in the morning. Adjust dosage using the individual products; then switch to the combination product when patient's adjustment schedule is stable.

Aldoril
Aldoril D

Generic components
Tablets
250 mg methyldopa and 15 mg hydrochlorothiazide
250 mg methyldopa and 25 mg hydrochlorothiazide
500 mg methyldopa and 30 mg hydrochlorothiazide
500 mg methyldopa and 50 mg hydrochlorothiazide

Dosages
Adults: 1 tablet P.O. daily, in the morning. Adjust dosage using the individual products; then switch to the combination product when patient's adjustment schedule is stable.

Alor 5/500
Azdone
Damason-P
Lortab ASA
Panasal 5/500
CSS III

Generic components
Tablets
500 mg aspirin and 5 mg hydrocodone bitartrate

Dosages
Moderate to moderately severe pain
Adults: 1 or 2 tablets q 4 hours. Maximum dosage, 8 tablets in 24 hours.

Anexsia 5/325
Norco 5/325
CSS III

Generic components
Tablets
325 mg acetaminophen and 5 mg hydrocodone bitartrate

Dosages
Moderate to moderately severe pain
Adults: 1 to 2 tablets q 4 to 6 hours. Maximum dosage, 12 tablets in 24 hours.

Anexsia 5/500
Co-Gesic
Lorcet HD
Lortab 5/500
Panacet 5/500
Vicodin
CSS III

Generic components
Tablets
500 mg acetaminophen and 5 mg hydrocodone bitartrate

Dosages
Moderate to moderately severe pain
Adults: 1 to 2 tablets q 4 to 6 hours. Maximum dosage, 8 tablets in 24 hours.

Anexsia 7.5/325
Norco 7.5/325
CSS III

Generic components
Tablets
325 mg acetaminophen and 7.5 mg hydrocodone bitartrate

Dosages
Moderate to moderately severe pain
Adults: 1 to 2 tablets q 4 to 6 hours. Maximum dosage, 12 tablets in 24 hours.

Anexsia 7.5/650
Lorcet Plus
CSS III

Generic components
Tablets
650 mg acetaminophen and 7.5 mg hydrocodone bitartrate

Dosages
Arthralgia, bone pain, dental pain, headache, migraine, moderate pain
Adults: 1 to 2 tablets q 4 hours. Maximum dosage, 6 tablets in 24 hours.

Anexsia 10/660
Vicodin HP
CSS III

Generic components
Tablets
660 mg acetaminophen and 10 mg hydrocodone bitartrate

Dosages
Arthralgia, bone pain, dental pain, headache, migraine, moderate pain
Adults: 1 tablet q 4 to 6 hours. Maximum dosage, 6 tablets in 24 hours.

Atacand HCT

Generic components
Tablets
16 mg candesartan and 12.5 mg hydrochlorothiazide
32 mg candesartan and 12.5 mg hydrochlorothiazide

Dosages
Adults: 1 tablet P.O. daily in the morning. Adjust dosage using the individual products; then switch to appropriate dosage.

Atripla

Generic components
Tablets
600 mg efavirenz, 200 mg emtricitabine, and 300 mg tenofovir disoproxil fumarate

Dosages
Adults: 1 tablet P.O. once daily on an empty stomach. Taking at bedtime may lessen nervous system symptoms.

Avalide

Generic components
Tablets
150 mg irbesartan and 12.5 mg hydrochlorothiazide
300 mg irbesartan and 12.5 mg hydrochlorothiazide
300 mg irbesartan and 25 mg hydrochlorothiazide

Dosages
Adults: 1 tablet P.O. daily. Adjust dosage with individual products; then switch to combination product when patient's condition is stabilized. Maximum daily dose, 300 mg irbesartan and 25 mg hydrochlorothiazide.

Avandamet

Generic components
Tablets
2 mg rosiglitazone hydrochloride and 500 mg metformin hydrochloride
4 mg rosiglitazone hydrochloride and 500 mg metformin hydrochloride

Dosages
Adults: For drug-naive patients, as initial therapy, give 2 mg/500 mg combination P.O. once daily. For second-line treatment, give 4 mg/500 mg combination P.O. once daily or 2 mg/500 mg combination P.O. b.i.d. Adjust dosages based on therapeutic response.

Benicar HCT

Generic components
Tablets
20 mg olmesartan and 12.5 mg hydrochlorothiazide
40 mg olmesartan and 12.5 mg hydrochlorothiazide
40 mg olmesartan and 25 mg hydrochlorothiazide

Dosages
Adults: 1 tablet P.O. per day in the morning. Adjust dosage using the individual products; then switch to the combination product when patient's adjustment schedule is stable.

BiDil

Generic components
Tablets
20 mg isosorbide dinitrate and 37.5 mg hydralazine

Dosages
Adults: 1 to 2 tablets P.O. t.i.d.

Caduet

Generic components
Tablets
5 mg amlodipine and 10 mg atorvastatin
5 mg amlodipine and 20 mg atorvastatin
5 mg amlodipine and 40 mg atorvastatin
5 mg amlodipine and 80 mg atorvastatin

Dosages
Adults: 5 to 10 mg with 10 to 80 mg atorvastatin P.O. once daily. Determine most effective dosage for each component, and then select most appropriate combination.

Capital with Codeine
Tylenol with Codeine Elixir
CSS V

Generic components
Elixir
120 mg acetaminophen and 12 mg codeine phosphate/5 ml

Dosages
Mild to moderate pain
Adults: 15 ml q 4 hours.

Capozide

Generic components
Tablets
25 mg captopril and 15 mg hydrochlorothiazide
50 mg captopril and 15 mg hydrochlorothiazide
25 mg captopril and 25 mg hydrochlorothiazide
50 mg captopril and 25 mg hydrochlorothiazide

Dosages
Adults: 1 to 2 tablets P.O. daily, in the morning. Adjust dosage using the individual products; then switch to the combination product when patient's adjustment schedule is stable.

Clorpres
Combipres

Generic components
Tablets
15 mg chlorthalidone and 0.1 mg clonidine hydrochloride
15 mg chlorthalidone and 0.2 mg clonidine hydrochloride
15 mg chlorthalidone and 0.3 mg clonidine hydrochloride

Dosages
Adults: 1 to 2 tablets per day P.O. in the morning. Adjust dosage using the individual products; then switch to the combination product when patient's adjustment schedule is stable.

CombiPatch

Generic components
Transdermal patch
0.05 mg/day estradiol and 0.14 mg/day norethindrone
0.05 mg/day estradiol and 0.25 mg/day norethindrone

Dosages
To relieve menopause symptoms
Women: Change patch twice a week.

Combivent

Generic components
Metered-dose inhaler
18 mcg ipratropium bromide and 90 mcg albuterol

Dosages
Bronchospasm with COPD in patients who require more than a single bronchodilator
Adults: Two inhalations q.i.d. Not for use during acute attack. Use caution with known sensitivity to atropine, soy, or peanuts.

Combivir

Generic components
Tablets
150 mg lamivudine and 300 mg zidovudine

Dosages
Adults and children 12 and older who weigh more than 50 kg (110 lb): 1 tablet P.O. b.i.d.

Corzide

Generic components
Tablets
40 mg nadolol and 5 mg bendroflumethiazide
80 mg nadolol and 5 mg bendroflumethiazide

Dosages
Adults: 1 tablet P.O. per day in the morning. Adjust dosage using the individual products; then switch to the combination product when patient's adjustment schedule is stable.

Darvocet-A500
CSS IV

Generic components
Tablets
500 mg acetaminophen and 100 mg propoxyphene napsylate

Dosages
Mild to moderate pain
Adults: 1 tablet q 4 hours. Maximum dosage, 8 tablets in 24 hours.

Darvocet-N50
CSS IV

Generic components
Tablets
325 mg acetaminophen and 50 mg propoxyphene napsylate

Dosages
Mild to moderate pain
Adults: 2 tablets q 4 hours. Maximum dosage, 12 tablets in 24 hours.

Darvocet-N100
CSS IV

Generic components
Tablets
650 mg acetaminophen and 100 mg propoxyphene napsylate

Dosages
Mild to moderate pain
Adults: 1 tablet q 4 hours. Maximum dosage, 6 tablets in 24 hours.

Diovan HCT

Generic components
Tablets
80 mg valsartan and 12.5 mg hydrochlorothiazide
160 mg valsartan and 12.5 mg hydrochlorothiazide
160 mg valsartan and 25 mg hydrochlorothiazide

Dosages
Adults: 1 tablet per day P.O. Not for initial therapy; start using each component first.

Duetact

Generic components
Tablets
30 mg pioglitazone and 2 mg glimepiride
30 mg pioglitazone and 4 mg glimepiride

Dosages
Adults: For patients currently on glimepiride alone, start with either 30 mg/2 mg or 30 mg/4 mg combination P.O. once daily; adjust dosage based on therapeutic response.
Adults: For patients currently on pioglitazone alone, start with 30 mg/2 mg combination P.O. once daily; adjust dosage based on therapeutic response.

Dyazide

Generic components
Capsules
37.5 mg triamterene and 25 mg hydrochlorothiazide

Dosages
Adults: 1 to 2 capsules daily.

Empirin with Codeine No. 3
CSS III

Generic components
Tablets
325 mg aspirin and 30 mg codeine phosphate

Dosages
Fever and mild to moderate pain
Adults: 1 to 2 tablets q 4 hours. Maximum dosage, 12 tablets in 24 hours.

Empirin with Codeine No. 4
CSS III

Generic components
Tablets
325 mg aspirin and 60 mg codeine phosphate

Dosages
Fever and mild to moderate pain
Adults: 1 tablet q 4 hours. Maximum dosage, 6 tablets in 24 hours.

Endocet 5/325
Percocet 5/325
Roxicet
CSS II

Generic components
Tablets
325 mg acetaminophen and 5 mg oxycodone hydrochloride

Dosages
Moderate to moderately severe pain
Adults: 1 tablet q 6 hours. Maximum dosage, 12 tablets in 24 hours.

Endocet 7.5/325
Percocet 7.5/325
CSS II

Generic components
Tablets
325 mg acetaminophen and 7.5 mg oxycodone hydrochloride

Dosages
Moderate to moderately severe pain
Adults: 1 tablet q 6 hours. Maximum dosage, 8 tablets in 24 hours.

Endocet 7.5/500
Percocet 7.5/500
CSS II

Generic components
Tablets
500 mg acetaminophen and 7.5 mg oxycodone hydrochloride

Dosages
Moderate to moderately severe pain
Adults: 1 to 2 tablets q 4 to 6 hours. Maximum dosage, 8 tablets in 24 hours.

Endocet 10/325
Percocet 10/325
CSS II

Generic components
Tablets
325 mg acetaminophen and 10 mg oxycodone hydrochloride

Dosages
Moderate to moderately severe pain
Adults: 1 tablet q 6 hours. Maximum dosage, 6 tablets in 24 hours.

Endodan
Percodan
CSS II

Generic components
Tablets
325 mg aspirin, 4.5 mg oxycodone hydrochloride, and 0.38 mg oxycodone terephthalate

Dosages
Moderate to moderately severe pain
Adults: 1 tablet q 6 hours. Maximum dosage, 12 tablets in 24 hours.

Epzicom

Generic components
Tablets
600 mg abacavir with 300 mg lamivudine

Dosages
Adults: 1 tablet daily, taken without regard to food and with other antiretrovirals.

Eryzole
Pediazole

Generic components
Granules for oral suspension
Erythromycin ethylsuccinate (equivalent of 200 mg erythromycin activity) and 600 mg sulfisoxazole per 5 ml when reconstituted according to manufacturer's directions

Dosages
Acute otitis media
Children: 50 mg/kg/day erythromycin and 150 mg/kg/day sulfisoxazole in divided doses q.i.d. for 10 days. Give without regard to meals. Refrigerate after reconstitution; use within 14 days.

Fiorinal with Codeine
Fioricet with Codeine
CSS III

Generic components
Capsules
325 mg acetaminophen, 50 mg butalbital, 40 mg caffeine, and 30 mg codeine phosphate

Dosages
Headache, mild to moderate pain
Adults: 1 to 2 capsules q 4 hours. Maximum dosage, 6 capsules in 24 hours.

Hyzaar

Generic components
Tablets
50 mg losartan and 12.5 mg hydrochlorothiazide
100 mg losartan and 25 mg hydrochlorothiazide

Dosages
Adults: 1 tablet per day P.O. in the morning. Not for initial therapy; start using each component and if desired effects are obtained, Hyzaar may be used.

Inderide

Generic components
Tablets
40 mg propranolol hydrochloride and 25 mg hydrochlorothiazide
80 mg propranolol hydrochloride and 25 mg hydrochlorothiazide

Dosages
Adults: 1 tablet P.O. b.i.d. Adjust dosage using the individual products; then switch to the combination product when patient's adjustment schedule is stable. Maximum total daily dose shouldn't exceed 160 mg propranolol and 50 mg hydrochlorothiazide.

Lexxel

Generic components

Extended-release tablets

5 mg enalapril maleate and 2.5 mg felodipine
5 mg enalapril maleate and 5 mg felodipine

Dosages

Adults: 1 tablet per day P.O. Adjust dosage using the individual products; then switch to the combination product when patient's adjustment schedule is stable. Make sure that patient swallows tablet whole. Don't cut, crush, or allow him to chew.

Limbitrol

Limbitrol DS

Generic components

Tablets

5 mg chlordiazepoxide and 12.5 mg amitriptyline
10 mg chlordiazepoxide and 25 mg amitriptyline

Dosages

Adults: 10 mg chlordiazepoxide with 25 mg amitriptyline 3 to 4 times per day up to 6 times daily. For patients who don't tolerate the higher doses, 5 mg chlordiazepoxide with 12.5 mg amitriptyline 3 to 4 times per day. Reduce dosage after initial response.

Lopressor HCT

Generic components

Tablets

50 mg metoprolol and 25 mg hydrochlorothiazide
100 mg metoprolol and 25 mg hydrochlorothiazide
100 mg metoprolol and 50 mg hydrochlorothiazide

Dosages

Adults: 1 tablet P.O. per day. Adjust dosage using the individual products; then switch to the combination product when patient's adjustment schedule is stable.

Lorcet 10/650

CSS III

Generic components

Tablets

650 mg acetaminophen and 10 mg hydrocodone bitartrate

Dosages

Moderate to moderately severe pain

Adults: 1 tablet q 4 to 6 hours. Maximum dosage, 6 tablets in 24 hours.

Lortab 2.5/500

CSS III

Generic components

Tablets

500 mg acetaminophen and 2.5 mg hydrocodone bitartrate

Dosages

Moderate to moderately severe pain

Adults: 1 to 2 tablets q 4 to 6 hours. Maximum dosage, 8 tablets in 24 hours.

Lortab 7.5/500

CSS III

Generic components

Tablets

500 mg acetaminophen and 7.5 mg hydrocodone bitartrate

Dosages

Moderate to moderately severe pain

Adults: 1 tablet q 4 to 6 hours. Maximum dosage, 8 tablets in 24 hours.

Lortab 10/500

CSS III

Generic components

Tablets

500 mg acetaminophen and 10 mg hydrocodone bitartrate

Dosages
Moderate to moderately severe pain
Adults: 1 tablet q 4 to 6 hours. Maximum dosage, 6 tablets in 24 hours.

Lortab Elixir
CSS III

Generic components
Elixir
167 mg acetaminophen and 2.5 mg/5 ml hydrocodone bitartrate

Dosages
Moderately severe pain
Adults: 15 ml q 4 to 6 hours. Maximum dosage, 90 ml/day.

Lotensin HCT

Generic components
Tablets
5 mg benazepril and 6.25 mg hydrochlorothiazide
10 mg benazepril and 12.5 mg hydrochlorothiazide
20 mg benazepril and 12.5 mg hydrochlorothiazide
20 mg benazepril and 25 mg hydrochlorothiazide

Dosages
Adults: 1 tablet per day P.O. in the morning. Adjust dosage using the individual products; then switch to the combination product when patient's adjustment schedule is stable.

Lotrel

Generic components
Capsules
2.5 mg amlodipine and 10 mg benazepril
5 mg amlodipine and 10 mg benazepril
5 mg amlodipine and 20 mg benazepril
10 mg amlodipine and 20 mg benazepril

Dosages
Adults: 1 tablet P.O. daily in the morning. Monitor patient for hypertension and adverse effects closely over first 2 weeks and regularly thereafter.

Maxzide

Generic components
Tablets
75 mg triamterene and 50 mg hydrochlorothiazide

Dosages
Adults: 1 tablet daily.

Micardis HCT

Generic components
Tablets
40 mg telmisartan and 12.5 mg hydrochlorothiazide
80 mg telmisartan and 12.5 mg hydrochlorothiazide
80 mg telmisartan and 25 mg hydrochlorothiazide

Dosages
Adults: 1 tablet P.O. per day; may be adjusted up to 160 mg telmisartan and 25 mg hydrochlorothiazide, based on patient's response.

Minizide

Generic components
Tablets
1 mg prazosin and 0.5 mg polythiazide
2 mg prazosin and 0.5 mg polythiazide
5 mg prazosin and 0.5 mg polythiazide

Dosages
Adults: 1 capsule P.O. b.i.d. or t.i.d. Adjust drug using the individual products; then switch to appropriate dosage of the combination product.

Moduretic

Generic components
Tablets
5 mg amiloride and 50 mg hydrochlorothiazide

Dosages
Adults: 1 to 2 tablets per day with meals.

Monopril-HCT

Generic components
Tablets
10 mg fosinopril and 12.5 mg hydrochlorothiazide
20 mg fosinopril and 12.5 mg hydrochlorothiazide

Dosages
Adults: 1 tablet P.O. per day in the morning. Adjust dosage using the individual products, then switch to appropriate dosage of the combination product.

Norco 325/10
CSS III

Generic components
Tablets
325 mg acetaminophen and 10 mg hydrocodone bitartrate

Dosages
Moderate to moderately severe pain
Adults: 1 tablet q 4 to 6 hours. Maximum dosage, 6 tablets in 24 hours.

Percocet 2.5/325
CSS II

Generic components
Tablets
325 mg acetaminophen and 2.5 mg oxycodone hydrochloride

Dosages
Moderate to moderately severe pain
Adults: 1 to 2 tablets q 4 to 6 hours. Maximum dosage, 12 tablets in 24 hours.

Percocet 10/650
CSS II

Generic components
Tablets
650 mg acetaminophen and 10 mg oxycodone hydrochloride

Dosages
Moderate to moderately severe pain
Adults: 1 tablet q 4 hours. Maximum dosage, 6 tablets in 24 hours.

Prefest

Generic components
Tablets
1 mg estradiol and 0.09 mg norgestimate

Dosages
Moderate to severe symptoms of menopause; to prevent osteoporosis
Women with intact uterus: 1 tablet/day P.O. (3 days of pink tablets: estradiol alone; followed by 3 days of white tablets: estradiol and norgestimate combination; continue cycle uninterrupted).

Premphase

Generic components
Tablets
0.625 mg conjugated estrogens; 0.625 mg conjugated estrogens with 5 mg medroxyprogesterone

Dosages
Moderate to severe symptoms of menopause and prevention of osteoporosis
Women with intact uterus: 1 tablet per day P.O. Use estrogen alone on days 1 to 14 and estrogen-medroxyprogesterone tablet on days 15 to 28.

Prempro

Generic components
Tablets
0.3 mg conjugated estrogen and 1.5 mg medroxyprogesterone
0.45 mg conjugated estrogen and 1.5 mg medroxyprogesterone
0.625 mg estrogen and 2.5 mg medroxyprogesterone
0.625 mg conjugated estrogen and 5 mg medroxyprogesterone

Dosages

To relieve symptoms of menopause; to prevent osteoporosis

Women with intact uterus: 1 tablet per day P.O.

Prinzide

Zestoretic

Generic components

Tablets

10 mg lisinopril and 12.5 mg hydrochlorothiazide
20 mg lisinopril and 12.5 mg hydrochlorothiazide
20 mg lisinopril and 25 mg hydrochlorothiazide

Dosages

Adults: 1 tablet per day P.O. taken in the morning. Adjust dosage using the individual products; then switch to the combination product when patient's adjustment schedule is stable.

Roxicet 5/500

Roxilox

Tylox

CSS II

Generic components

Tablets

500 mg acetaminophen and 5 mg oxycodone hydrochloride

Dosages

Moderate to moderately severe pain

Adults: 1 tablet q 6 hours.

Roxicet Oral Solution

CSS II

Generic components

Solution

325 mg acetaminophen and 5 mg/5 ml oxycodone hydrochloride

Dosages

Moderate to moderately severe pain

Adults: 5 ml q 6 hours. Maximum dosage, 60 ml in 24 hours.

Symbicort

Generic components

Inhalation aerosol

80 mcg budesonide and 4.5 mcg formoterol fumarate dihydrate
160 mcg budesonide and 4.5 mcg formoterol fumarate dihydrate

Dosages

Adults and children age 12 and older: 2 inhalations b.i.d. (morning and evening) select dosage based on asthma severity and other drugs being taken. Maximum daily dosage, 640 mcg budesonide/18 mcg formoterol.

Symbyax

Generic components

Capsules

6 mg olanzapine and 25 mg fluoxetine
6 mg olanzapine and 50 mg fluoxetine
12 mg olanzapine and 25 mg fluoxetine
12 mg olanzapine and 50 mg fluoxetine

Dosages

Adults: 1 capsule daily in the evening. Begin with 6 mg/25 mg capsule and adjust according to efficacy and tolerability.

Talacen

CSS IV

Generic components

Tablets

650 mg acetaminophen and 25 mg pentazocine hydrochloride

Dosages

Mild to moderate pain

Adults: 1 tablet q 4 hours. Maximum dosage, 6 tablets in 24 hours.

Talwin Compound
CSS IV

Generic components
Tablets
325 mg aspirin and 12.5 mg pentazocine hydrochloride

Dosages
Moderate pain
Adults: 2 tablets q 6 to 8 hours. Maximum dosage, 8 tablets in 24 hours.

Talwin NX
CSS IV

Generic components
Tablets
0.5 mg naloxone and 50 mg pentazocine hydrochloride

Dosages
Moderate to severe pain
Adults: 1 to 2 tablets q 3 to 4 hours. Maximum dosage, 12 tablets daily.

Tarka

Generic components
Tablets
1 mg trandolapril and 240 mg verapamil
2 mg trandolapril and 180 mg verapamil
2 mg trandolapril and 240 mg verapamil
4 mg trandolapril and 240 mg verapamil

Dosages
Adults: 1 tablet P.O. per day, taken with food. Adjust dosage using the individual products; then switch to the combination product when patient's adjustment schedule is stable. Make sure that patient swallows tablet whole. Don't cut, crush, or allow him to chew.

Teczem

Generic components
Extended-release tablets
5 mg enalapril maleate and 180 mg diltiazem hydrochloride

Dosages
Adults: 1 to 2 tablets per day P.O. in the morning. Adjust dosage using the individual products; then switch to the combination product when patient's adjustment schedule is stable. Make sure that patient swallows tablet whole. Don't cut, crush, or allow him to chew.

Tenoretic

Generic components
Tablets
50 mg atenolol and 25 mg chlorthalidone
100 mg atenolol and 25 mg chlorthalidone

Dosages
Adults: 1 tablet P.O. daily in the morning. Adjust dosage using the individual products; then switch to appropriate dosage.

Teveten HCT

Generic components
Tablets
600 mg eprosartan and 12.5 mg hydrochlorothiazide
600 mg eprosartan and 25 mg hydrochlorothiazide

Dosages
Adults: 1 tablet P.O. each day. Establish dosage with each component alone before using the combination product; if blood pressure isn't controlled on 600 mg/25 mg tablet, 300 mg eprosartan may be added each evening.

Trizivir

Generic components
Tablets
300 mg abacavir sulfate, 300 mg zidovudine, and 150 mg lamivudine

Dosages
Adults and adolescents who weigh more than 40 kg (88 lb): 1 tablet P.O. b.i.d. Carefully monitor patient for hypersensitivity reactions.

Truvada

Generic components
Tablets
200 mg emtricitabine with 300 mg tenofovir

Dosages
Adults and adolescents weighing more than 40 kg (88 lb): 1 tablet daily, taken without regard to food and with other antiretrovirals.

Tylenol with Codeine No. 2
CSS III

Generic components
Tablets
300 mg acetaminophen and 15 mg codeine phosphate

Dosages
Fever, mild to moderate pain
Adults: 1 to 2 tablets q 4 hours. Maximum dosage, 12 tablets in 24 hours.

Tylenol with Codeine No. 3
CSS III

Generic components
Tablets
300 mg acetaminophen and 30 mg codeine phosphate

Dosages
Fever, mild to moderate pain
Adults: 1 to 2 tablets q 4 hours. Maximum dosage, 12 tablets in 24 hours.

Tylenol with Codeine No. 4
CSS III

Generic components
Tablets
300 mg acetaminophen and 60 mg codeine phosphate

Dosages
Fever, mild to moderate pain
Adults: 1 tablet q 4 hours. Maximum dosage, 12 tablets in 24 hours.

Tylox 5/500
CSS II

Generic components
Tablets
500 mg acetaminophen and 5 mg oxycodone hydrochloride

Dosages
Moderate to moderately severe pain
Adults: 1 capsule q 6 hours. Maximum dosage, 8 capsules in 24 hours.

Uniretic

Generic components
Tablets
7.5 mg moexipril and 12.5 mg hydrochlorothiazide
15 mg moexipril and 25 mg hydrochlorothiazide

Dosages
Adults: 0.5 to 2 tablets per day. Not for initial therapy. Adjust dose to maintain appropriate blood pressure.

Vaseretic

Generic components
Tablets
5 mg enalapril maleate and 12.5 mg hydrochlorothiazide
10 mg enalapril maleate and 25 mg hydrochlorothiazide

Dosages
Adults: 1 to 2 tablets per day P.O. in the morning. Adjust dosage using the individual products; then switch to the combination product when patient's adjustment schedule is stable. Make sure that patient swallows tablet whole. Don't cut, crush, or allow him to chew.

Vicodin ES

CSS III

Generic components

Tablets

750 mg acetaminophen and 7.5 mg hydrocodone bitartrate

Dosages

Moderate to moderately severe pain

Adults: 1 tablet q 4 to 6 hours. Maximum dosage, 5 tablets in 24 hours.

Vytorin

Generic components

Tablets

10 mg ezetimibe with 10, 20, 40, or 80 mg simvastatin

Dosages

Adults: 1 tablet daily, taken in the evening with a cholesterol-lowering diet and exercise. Dosage of simvastatin in the combination may be adjusted based on patient response. If given with a bile sequestrant, must be given at least 2 hours before or 4 hours after the bile sequestrant.

Wygesic

CSS IV

Generic components

Tablets

650 mg acetaminophen and 65 mg propoxyphene napsylate

Dosages

Mild to moderate pain

Adults: 1 tablet q 4 hours. Maximum dosage, 6 tablets in 24 hours.

Ziac

Generic components

Tablets

2.5 mg bisoprolol and 6.25 mg hydrochlorothiazide

5 mg bisoprolol and 6.25 mg hydrochlorothiazide

10 mg bisoprolol and 6.25 mg hydrochlorothiazide

Dosages

Adults: 1 tablet daily P.O. in morning. Initial dose is 2.5/6.25 mg tablet P.O. daily. Adjust dosage within 1 week; optimum antihypertensive effect may require 2 to 3 weeks.

Zydone 5/400

CSS III

Generic components

Tablets

400 mg acetaminophen and 5 mg hydrocodone bitartrate

Dosages

Moderate to moderately severe pain

Adults: 1 to 2 tablets q 4 to 6 hours. Maximum dosage, 8 tablets in 24 hours.

Zydone 7.5/400

CSS III

Generic components

Tablets

400 mg acetaminophen and 7.5 mg hydrocodone bitartrate

Dosages

Moderate to moderately severe pain

Adults: 1 tablet q 4 to 6 hours. Maximum dosage, 6 tablets in 24 hours.

Zydone 10/400

CSS III

Generic components

Tablets

400 mg acetaminophen and 10 mg hydrocodone bitartrate

Dosages

Moderate to moderately severe pain

Adults: 1 tablet q 4 to 6 hours. Maximum dosage, 6 tablets in 24 hours.

Toxic drug–drug interactions

Interaction	Drugs	Interacting drugs
Decreased corticosteroid effects	*corticosteroids* (betamethasone, cortisone, dexamethasone, fludrocortisone, hydrocortisone, methylprednisolone, prednisolone, prednisone, triamcinolone)	*rifamycins* (rifabutin, rifampin, rifapentine)
Digoxin toxicity and arrhythmias	*digoxin* (Lanoxin)	*tetracyclines* (demeclocycline, doxycycline, minocycline, tetracycline) *thiazide diuretics* (chlorothiazide, hydrochlorothiazide, indapamide, methyclothiazide, metolazone, polythiazide, trichlormethiazide) verapamil (Calan)
Hearing loss	*aminoglycosides* (amikacin, gentamicin, kanamycin, netilmicin, streptomycin, tobramycin)	*loop diuretics* (bumetanide, ethacrynic acid, furosemide, torsemide)
Increased bleeding	*warfarin* (Coumadin)	*alteplase* (Activase, tPA) *androgens* [17-alkyl] (danazol, fluoxymesterone, methyltestosterone, oxandrolone) *cimetidine* (Tagamet) *fibric acids* (clofibrate, fenofibrate, gemfibrozil) *cranberry juice* *salicylates* (aspirin, methylsalicylate)
		amiodarone (Cordarone, Pacerone) *azole antifungals* (fluconazole, itraconazole, ketoconazole, miconazole, voriconazole) *macrolide antibiotics* (azithromycin, clarithromycin, erythromycin) *metronidazole* (Flagyl) *quinine derivatives* (quinidine, quinine) *quinolones* (ciprofloxacin, levofloxacin, moxifloxacin, norfloxacin, ofloxacin) *sulfinpyrazone* (Anturane) *sulfonamides* (sulfasalazine, sulfisoxazole trimethoprim-sulfamethoxazole) *thyroid hormones* (levothyroxine, liothyronine, liotrix, thyroid) *vitamin E*
Increased potassium level	*potassium-sparing diuretics* (amiloride, spironolactone, triamterene)	*angiotensin-converting enzyme (ACE) inhibitors* (benazepril, captopril, enalapril, fosinopril, lisinopril, moexipril, perindopril, quinapril, ramipril, trandolapril) *angiotensin II receptor antagonists* (candesartan, eprosartan, irbesartan, losartan, olmesartan, telmisartan, valsartan) *potassium preparations* (potassium acetate, potassium phosphate, potassium bicarbonate, potassium chloride, potassium citrate, potassium gluconate, potassium iodine, potassium phosphate)

Nursing considerations
• Avoid use together, if possible. • Effects may persist for 2 to 3 weeks after stopping therapy.
• Use together cautiously. • Monitor serum digoxin levels. The therapeutic range for digoxin is 0.8 to 2 nanograms/ml. • Effects of tetracyclines on digoxin may persist for several months after the antibiotic is stopped. • Monitor serum potassium and magnesium levels if patient is taking both thiazide diuretics and digoxin. • Monitor patient for evidence of digoxin toxicity, including arrhythmias (such as bradycardia, atrioventricular [AV] block, ventricular ectopy), lethargy, drowsiness, confusion, hallucinations, headache, syncope, vision disturbance, nausea, anorexia, vomiting, or diarrhea.
• Use together cautiously. • Patients with renal insufficiency are at greater risk. • Irreversible hearing loss is more likely with this combination than when either drug is used alone.
• Avoid use together, if possible. • If drugs must be used together, monitor coagulation values carefully; the dosage requirements for warfarin will be decreased. • Suggest taking a different histamine$_2$ antagonist. • Aspirin doses of 500 mg or more daily cause a greater risk.
• Use together cautiously. • Monitor prothrombin time and international normalized ratio closely when starting or stopping any of these drugs. • Bleeding effects may persist after interacting drug is stopped. • Typically, the warfarin dose needs to be reduced. • Vitamin E doses of less than 400 mg daily may not have this effect.
• Use together cautiously. • High-risk patients include those with renal impairment, type 2 diabetes, decreased renal perfusion, and those who are elderly. • Don't use potassium preparations and potassium-sparing diuretics unless the patient has severe hypokalemia that isn't responding to either drug class alone. • Monitor the patient's potassium level; also monitor patient for palpitations, chest pain, nausea and vomiting, paresthesias, and muscle weakness.

(continued)

Interaction	Drugs	Interacting drugs
Increased risk of pregnancy, breakthrough bleeding	*barbiturates* (amobarbital, butabarbital, pentobarbital, phenobarbital, primidone, secobarbital)	*hormonal contraceptives* (Ortho-Evra, Yasmin-28)
Life-threatening hypertension	*clonidine* (Catapres)	*beta blockers* (acebutolol, atenolol, betaxolol, carteolol, esmolol, metoprolol, nadolol, penbutolol, pindolol, propranolol, timolol)
		tricyclic antidepressants (amitriptyline, amoxapine, clomipramine, desipramine, doxepin, imipramine, nortriptyline, protriptyline, trimipramine)
	monoamine oxidase (MAO) inhibitors (isocarboxazid, phenelzine, tranylcypromine)	*anorexiants* (amphetamine, benzphetamine, dextroamphetamine, methamphetamine, phentermine)
		methylphenidate (dexmethylphenidate, Concerta)
Methotrexate toxicity	*methotrexate* (Rheumatrex, Trexall)	*nonsteroidal anti-inflammatory drugs (NSAIDs)* (diclofenac, etodolac, fenoprofen, flurbiprofen, ibuprofen, indomethacin, ketoprofen, ketorolac, meclofenamate, nabumetone, naproxen, oxaprozin, piroxicam, sulindac, tolmetin) *penicillins* (amoxicillin, ampicillin, carbenicillin, cloxacillin, dicloxacillin, oxacillin, penicillin G, penicillin V, piperacillin, ticarcillin)
Reduced penicillin effectiveness	*penicillins* (amoxicillin, ampicillin, carbenicillin, cloxacillin, dicloxacillin, nafcillin, oxacillin, Penicillin G, Penicillin V, piperacillin, ticarcillin)	*tetracyclines* (demeclocycline, doxycycline, minocycline, tetracycline)
Rhabdomyolysis and myopathy	*HMG-CoA reductase inhibitors* (atorvastatin, fluvastatin, lovastatin, pravastatin, rosuvastatin, simvastatin)	*cyclosporine* (Neoral) *gemfibrozil* (Lopid) *protease inhibitors* (amprenavir, atazanavir, indinavir, lopinavir with ritonavir, nelfinavir, ritonavir, saquinavir)
		macrolide antibiotics (azithromycin, clarithromycin, erythromycin)
Serious cardiac events	*quinidine*	*verapamil* (Calan)
Serotonin syndrome	*selective serotonin reuptake inhibitors (SSRIs)* (fluoxetine, paroxetine, sertraline)	*risperidone* (Risperdal)

Nursing considerations
• Use together cautiously. • Suggest use of an alternative barrier form of contraception during therapy with both drugs.
• Use together cautiously. • Monitor blood pressure closely when starting and stopping clonidine and beta blockers simultaneously; stop the beta blocker first.
• Use together is contraindicated.
• Avoid using these drugs together, if possible. • Several deaths have occurred as a result of hypertensive crisis leading to cerebral hemorrhage. • Monitor patient for hypertension, hyperpyrexia, and seizures. • Hypertensive reaction may occur for several weeks after stopping an MAO inhibitor.
• Use together is contraindicated.
• Use together cautiously. • Monitor patient for mouth sores, hematemesis, diarrhea with melena, nausea and weakness, and bone marrow suppression. • Methotrexate toxicity is less likely to occur with weekly low-dose methotrexate regimens for rheumatoid arthritis and other inflammatory diseases. • Longer leucovorin rescue should be considered when giving NSAIDs and methotrexate at antineoplastic doses. • Obtain methotrexate levels twice weekly for the first 2 weeks of concurrent penicillin and methotrexate therapy.
• Avoid use together, if possible.
• Use of nelfinavir with simvastatin is contraindicated. • Avoid use together, if possible. • Monitor patient taking an HMG-CoA reductase inhibitor and gemfibrozil for signs of acute renal failure, including decreased urine output, elevated blood urea nitrogen and creatinine levels, edema, dyspnea, tachycardia, distended neck veins, nausea, vomiting, weakness, fatigue, confusion, and agitation. • Monitor patient for fatigue, muscle aches and weakness, joint pain, unintentional weight gain, seizures, dramatically increased serum creatine kinase level, and dark, red, or cola-colored urine.
• Use together cautiously. • Monitor patient for rhabdomyolysis, especially 5 to 21 days after starting the macrolide antibiotic.
• Use together only when there are no other alternatives. • Monitor patient for hypotension, bradycardia, ventricular tachycardia, and AV block. • Tell patient to report diaphoresis, dizziness, or blurred vision as well as palpitations, shortness of breath, dizziness or fainting, and chest pain. • Complications of this interaction may be noticed after as little as 1 day or as long as 5 months of combined therapy.
• Monitor patient carefully if an SSRI is started or stopped or if dosage is changed during risperidone therapy. Risperidone levels may increase. • Assess patient for central nervous system (CNS) irritability, increased muscle tone, muscle twitching or jerking, and changes in level of consciousness (LOC). • Although average doses of fluoxetine and paroxetine may cause this interaction, higher doses of sertraline (greater than 100 mg daily) are needed.

(continued)

Interaction	Drugs	Interacting drugs
Serotonin syndrome *(continued)*	*SSRIs* (citalopram, fluoxetine, fluvoxamine, nefazodone, paroxetine, sertraline, venlafaxine)	*selective 5-HT$_1$ receptor agonists* (almotriptan, eletriptan, frovatriptan, naratriptan, rizatriptan, sumatriptan, zolmitriptan)
	serotonin reuptake inhibitors (citalopram, escitalopram, fluoxetine, fluvoxamine, nefazodone, paroxetine, sertraline, venlafaxine)	*MAO inhibitors* (isocarboxazid, phenelzine, selegiline, tranylcypromine)
		sibutramine (Meridia) *sympathomimetics* (amphetamine, dextroamphetamine, methamphetamine, phentermine)
Severe arrhythmias	*dofetilide* (Tikosyn)	*thiazide diuretics* (chlorothiazide, hydrochlorothiazide, indapamide, methyclothiazide, metolazone, polythiazide, trichlormethiazide) *verapamil* (Calan)
	pimozide (Orap)	*SSRIs* (citalopram, sertraline)
	quinolones (gatifloxacin, levofloxacin, moxifloxacin)	*antiarrhythmics* (amiodarone, bretylium, disopyramide, procainamide, quinidine, sotalol) *erythromycin* (E-mycin, Eryc) *phenothiazines* (chlorpromazine, fluphenazine, mesoridazine, perphenazine, prochlorperazine, promethazine, thioridazine) *tricyclic antidepressants* (amitriptyline, amoxapine, clomipramine, desipramine, doxepin, imipramine, nortriptyline, trimipramine)
		ziprasidone (Geodon)
	thioridazine (Mellaril)	*fluoxetine* (Prozac)
Severe hypotension	*nitrates* (amyl nitrite, isosorbide dinitrate, isosorbide mononitrate, nitroglycerin)	*sildenafil* (Viagra) *tadalafil* (Cialis) *vardenafil* (Levitra)
	protease inhibitors (amprenavir, indinavir, nelfinavir, ritonavir, saquinavir)	*sildenafil* (Viagra) *tadalafil* (Cialis) *vardenafil* (Levitra)
Severe muscular depression	*cholinesterase inhibitors* (ambenonium, edrophonium, neostigmine, pyridostigmine)	*Corticosteroids* (betamethasone, corticotrophin, cortisone, cosyntropin, dexamethasone, fludrocortisone, hydrocortisone, methylprednisolone, prednisolone, prednisone, triamcinolone)

Nursing considerations

- Avoid combining these drugs if possible.
- If concurrent use can't be avoided, start with the lowest dosages possible, and observe the patient closely.
- Stop the selective 5-HT_1 receptor agonist at the first sign of interaction. Begin an antiserotonergic drug such as cyproheptadine (Periactin).
- Some patients may note increased frequency of migraine and reduced effectiveness of antimigraine drugs if a serotonin reuptake inhibitor is begun.
- Monitor patient for evidence of serotonin syndrome, including CNS irritability, motor weakness, shivering, muscle twitching, and altered LOC.

- Don't use these drugs together.
- Allow 1 week after stopping nefazodone or venlafaxine before giving an MAO inhibitor.
- Allow 2 weeks after stopping citalopram, escitalopram, fluvoxamine, paroxetine, or sertraline before giving an MAO inhibitor.
- Allow 5 weeks after stopping fluoxetine before giving an MAO inhibitor.
- Allow 2 weeks after stopping an MAO inhibitor before giving any serotonin reuptake inhibitor.
- Serotonin syndrome effects include CNS irritability, motor weakness, shivering, myoclonus, and altered LOC.
- The selective MAO type-B inhibitor selegiline has been given with fluoxetine, paroxetine, or sertraline to patients with Parkinson disease without negative effects.

- Don't use these drugs together, if possible.
- If this combination must be used, carefully monitor the patent for adverse effects, which require immediate medical attention.
- Monitor the patient closely for increased CNS effects, such as anxiety, jitteriness, agitation and restlessness, plus dizziness, nausea, vomiting, motor weakness, shivering, myoclonus, and altered LOC.

- Use together is contraindicated.
- In the event of inadvertent use together, monitor electrocardiogram for excessive prolongation of the QTc interval or the development of ventricular arrhythmias.
- Use of a thiazide diuretic increases potassium excretion.
- Monitor renal function and QTc interval every 3 months during dofetilide and verapamil therapy.

- Use together is contraindicated.
- Life-threatening risk is from prolongation of the QTc interval.

- Use of class IA or III antiarrhythmics, erythromycin, phenothiazines, or tricyclic antidepressants with levofloxacin should be avoided.
- Gatifloxacin and moxifloxacin may be used with caution and increased monitoring with phenothiazines and tricyclic antidepressants but should be avoided with antiarrhythmics and erythromycin.

- Use together is contraindicated.

- Use together is contraindicated.
- Risk increases proportional to increased dose of thioridazine.

- Use together is contraindicated.
- Before giving a nitrate, find out if a patient with chest pain has taken a drug for erectile dysfunction during the previous 24 to 48 hours.

- Use together is contraindicated.
- Tell patient to take sildenafil exactly as prescribed. Dosage may be reduced to 25 mg and an interval of at least 48 hours between drugs may be needed.

- If given together in a patient with myasthenia gravis, watch for severe muscle deterioration unresponsive to cholinesterase inhibitor therapy.
- Be prepared to provide respiratory support and mechanical ventilation, as needed.
- Corticosteroid therapy may have long-term benefits in patients with myasthenia gravis.

Dialyzable drugs

The amount of a drug removed by dialysis differs among patients and depends on several factors, including the patient's condition, the drug's properties, length of dialysis and dialysate used, rate of blood flow or dwell time, and purpose of dialysis. This table indicates the effect of conventional hemodialysis on selected drugs.

Drug	Level reduced by hemodialysis?
acebutolol	Yes
acetaminophen	Yes (may not influence toxicity)
acetazolamide	No
acetylcysteine	Yes
acyclovir	Yes
albuterol	No
allopurinol	Yes
alprazolam	No
amantadine	No
amikacin	Yes
amiodarone	No
amitriptyline	No
amlodipine	No
amoxicillin	Yes
amoxicillin and clavulanate potassium	Yes
amphotericin B	No
ampicillin	Yes
ampicillin and sulbactam sodium	Yes
aprepitant	No
arsenic trioxide	No
ascorbic acid	Yes
aspirin	Yes
atenolol	Yes
atorvastatin	No
atropine	No
auranofin	No
azathioprine	Yes
aztreonam	Yes

Drug	Level reduced by hemodialysis?
bivalirudin	Yes
bumetanide	No
bupropion	No
buspirone	No
busulfan	Yes
captopril	Yes
carbamazepine	No
carbenicillin	Yes
carboplatin	Yes
carisoprodol	Yes
carmustine	No
carvedilol	No
cefaclor	Yes
cefadroxil	Yes
cefazolin	Yes
cefepime	Yes
cefoperazone	Yes
cefotaxime	Yes
ceforanide	Yes
cefoxitin	Yes
cefpirome	Yes
cefpodoxime	Yes
ceftazidime	Yes
ceftibuten	Yes
ceftizoxime	Yes
ceftriaxone	No
cefuroxime	Yes
cephalexin	Yes
cephalothin	Yes
cephradine	Yes

Drug	Level reduced by hemodialysis
chloral hydrate	Yes
chlorambucil	No
chloramphenicol	Yes (very small amount)
chlordiazepoxide	No
chloroquine	No
chlorpheniramine	Yes
chlorpromazine	No
chlorthalidone	No
cilastatin	Yes
cilazapril	Yes
cimetidine	Yes
ciprofloxacin	Yes (only by 10%)
cisplatin	No
clavulanic acid	Yes
clindamycin	No
clofibrate	No
clonazepam	No
clonidine	No
clorazepate	No
cloxacillin	No
codeine	No
colchicine	No
cortisone	No
co-trimoxazole	Yes
cyclophosphamide	Yes
deferoxime	Yes
desloratadine	No
dexamethasone	No
diazepam	No
diazoxide	Yes
diclofenac	No
dicloxacillin	No
didanosine	Yes
digoxin	No
digoxine immune Fab	No
diltiazem	No

Drug	Level reduced by hemodialysis
diphenhydramine	No
dipyridamole	No
disopyramide	No
dopamine	No
doxazosin	No
doxepin	No
doxorubicin	No
doxycycline	No
drotrecogin alfa	Unknown
emtricitabine	Yes
enalapril	Yes
enoxaparin	No
epoetin alfa	No
erythromycin	Yes (only by 20%)
ethacrynic acid	No
ethambutol	Yes (only by 20%)
ethosuximide	Yes
famciclovir	Yes
famotidine	No
fenoprofen	No
filgrastim	No
flecainide	No
fluconazole	Yes
flucytosine	Yes
fluorouracil	No
fluoxetine	No
flurazepam	No
foscarnet	Yes
fosinopril	No
furosemide	No
gabapentin	Yes
ganciclovir	Yes
gemcitabine	Yes
gemfibrozil	No
gemifloxacin	Yes
gentamicin	Yes

Drug	Level reduced by hemodialysis
glipizide	No
gluthemide	No
glyburide	No
guanfacine	No
haloperidol	No
heparin	No
hydralazine	No
hydrochlorothiazide	No
hydroxyzine	No
ibuprofen	No
ifosfamide	Yes
imipramine	No
indapamide	No
indomethacin	No
insulin	No
irbesartan	No
iron dextran	No
isoniazid	No
isosorbide	Yes
isradipine	No
kanamycin	Yes
ketoconazole	No
labetalol	No
lamivudine	No
lansoprazole	No
levofloxacin	No
lidocaine	No
linezolid	Yes
lisinopril	Yes
lithium	Yes
lomefloxacin	No
lomustine	No
loracarbef	Yes
loratadine	No
lorazepam	No
mannitol	Yes

Drug	Level reduced by hemodialysis
mechlorethamine	No
mefenamic acid	No
meperidine	No
meprobamate	Yes
mercaptopurine	Yes
meropenem	Yes
mesalamine	Yes
metformin	Yes
methadone	No
methicillin	No
methotrexate	Yes
methyldopa	Yes
methylprednisolone	Yes
metoclopramide	No
metolazone	No
metoprolol	Yes
metronidazole	Yes
mexiletine	Yes
miconazole	No
midazolam	No
minocycline	No
minoxidil	Yes
misoprostol	No
morphine	No
nabumetone	No
nadolol	Yes
nafcillin	No
nalmefene	No
naltrexone	No
naproxen	No
nelfinavir	No
nicardipine	No
nifedipine	No
nimodipine	No
nitazoxanide	No
nitrofurantoin	Yes

Drug	Level reduced by hemodialysis
nitroglycerin	No
nitroprusside	Yes
nizatidine	No
norfloxacin	No
nortriptyline	No
octreotide	Yes
ofloxacin	Yes
olanzapine	No
omeprazole	No
oxacillin	No
oxazepam	No
paclitaxel	No
paroxetine	No
penicillin	Yes
pentamidine	No
pentazocine	Yes
pentobarbital	No
perindopril	Yes
phenobarbital	Yes
phenylbutazone	No
phenytoin	No
piperacillin	Yes
piroxicam	No
prazosin	No
prednisone	No
pregabalin	Yes
primidone	Yes
procainamide	Yes
promethazine	No
proprofol	Unknown
propoxyphene	No
propranolol	No
protriptyline	No
pseudoephedrine	No
pyrazinamide	Yes
pyridoxine	Yes

Drug	Level reduced by hemodialysis
quinapril	No
quinidine	No
quinine	No
ramipril	No
ranitidine	Yes
rifampin	No
ritodrine	Yes
rituximab	No
rosiglitazone	No
salsalate	Yes
sertraline	No
sotalol	Yes
stavudine	Yes
streptomycin	Yes
sucralfate	No
sulbactam	Yes
sulfamethoxazole	Yes
sulfisoxazole	Yes
sulindac	No
tazobactam	Yes
temazepam	No
theophylline	Yes
ticarcillin	Yes
ticarcillin and clavulanate	Yes
timolol	No
tirofiban	Yes
tobramycin	Yes
tocainide	Yes
tolbutamide	No
topiramate	Yes
topotecan	Yes
torsemide	No
tramadol	No
trandolapril	Yes
trazodone	No
triazolam	No

Drug	Level reduced by hemodialysis
trimethoprim	Yes
valacyclovir	Yes
valganciclovir	Yes
valproic acid	No
valsartan	No
vancomycin	Yes
venlafaxine	No
verapamil	No
vigabatrin	Yes
warfarin	No
zolpidem	No
zonisamide	Yes

Herb–drug interactions

Herb	Drug	Possible effects
aloe (dried juice from leaf [latex])	antiarrhythmics, digoxin	May lead to hypokalemia, which may potentiate digoxin and antiarrhythmics.
	thiazide diuretics, other potassium-wasting drugs, such as corticosteroids	May cause additive effect of potassium wasting.
	oral drugs	May decrease drug absorption because of more rapid GI transit time.
	stimulant laxatives	May increase risk of potassium loss.
bilberry	anticoagulants, antiplatelets	Decreases platelet aggregation.
	hypoglycemics, insulin	May increase insulin level, causing hypoglycemia; additive effect with antidiabetics.
capsicum	ACE inhibitors	May cause cough.
	anticoagulants, antiplatelets	Decreases platelet aggregation and increases fibrinolytic activity, prolonging bleeding time.
	antihypertensives	May interfere with antihypertensives by increasing catecholamine secretion.
	aspirin, NSAIDs	Stimulates GI secretions to help protect against NSAID-induced GI irritation.
	CNS depressants, such as barbiturates, benzodiazepines, opioids	Increases sedative effect.
	cocaine	May increase effects of drug and risk of adverse reactions, including death. Use together includes exposure to capsicum in pepper spray.
	H_2 blockers, proton-pump inhibitors	Decreases effects of the increased catecholamine secretion by herb.
	hepatically metabolized drugs	May increase hepatic metabolism of drugs by increasing G6PD and adipose lipase activity.
	MAO inhibitors	May decrease efficacy because of increased acid secretion by capsicum.
	theophylline	Increases absorption of theophylline, possibly leading to higher drug level or toxicity.
chamomile	anticoagulants	Warfarin constituents in herb may enhance drug therapy and prolong bleeding time.
	drugs requiring GI absorption	May delay drug absorption.

(continued)

Herb	Drug	Possible effects
chamomile *(continued)*	drugs with sedative properties, such as benzodiazepines	May cause additive effects and adverse reactions.
	iron	Tannic acid content in herb may reduce iron absorption.
echinacea	hepatotoxic drugs	Hepatotoxicity may increase with drugs known to elevate liver enzyme levels.
	immunosuppressants	Herb may counteract drugs.
	warfarin	Increases bleeding time without increased INR.
evening primrose oil	anticonvulsants	Lowers seizure threshold.
	antiplatelets, anticoagulants	Increases risk of bleeding and bruising.
feverfew	anticoagulants, antiplatelets	May decrease platelet aggregation and increase fibrinolytic activity.
	methysergide	May potentiate drug.
garlic	anticoagulants, antiplatelets	Enhances platelet inhibition, leading to increased anticoagulation.
	antihyperlipidemics	May have additive lipid-lowering properties.
	antihypertensives	May cause additive hypotension.
	cyclosporine	May decrease efficacy of drug. May induce metabolism and decrease drug level to subtherapeutic; may cause rejection.
	hormonal contraceptives	May decrease efficacy of drugs.
	insulin, other drugs causing hypoglycemia	May increase insulin level, causing hypoglycemia, an additive effect with these drugs.
	nonnucleotide reverse transcriptase inhibitors (NNRTIs)	May affect metabolism of these drugs.
	saquinavir	Decreases drug level, causing therapeutic failure and increased viral resistance.
ginger	anticoagulants, antiplatelets	Inhibits platelet aggregation by antagonizing thromboxane synthetase and enhancing prostacyclin, leading to prolonged bleeding time.
	antidiabetics	May interfere with diabetes therapy because of hypoglycemic effects.
	antihypertensives	May antagonize drug effects.
	barbiturates	May enhance drug effects.

Herb	Drug	Possible effects
ginger *(continued)*	calcium channel blockers	May increase calcium uptake by myocardium, leading to altered drug effects.
	chemotherapy	May reduce nausea caused by chemotherapy.
	H_2 blockers, proton-pump inhibitors	May decrease efficacy because of increased acid secretion by herb.
ginkgo	anticoagulants, antiplatelets	May enhance platelet inhibition, leading to increased anti-coagulation.
	anticonvulsants	May decrease effectiveness of drugs.
	drugs known to lower seizure threshold	May further reduce seizure threshold.
	insulin	Ginkgo leaf extract can alter insulin secretion and metabolism, affecting glucose level.
	thiazide diuretics	Ginkgo leaf may increase blood pressure.
ginseng	alcohol	Increases alcohol clearance, possibly by increasing activity of alcohol dehydrogenase.
	anabolic steroids, hormones	May potentiate effects of drugs. Estrogenic effects of herb may cause vaginal bleeding and breast nodules.
	antibiotics	Herb may enhance effects of some antibiotics.
	anticoagulants, antiplatelets	Decreases platelet adhesiveness.
	antidiabetics	May enhance glucose-lowering effects.
	antipsychotics	Because of CNS stimulant activity, avoid use with these drugs.
	digoxin	May falsely elevate drug level.
	furosemide	May decrease diuretic effect with this drug.
	immunosuppressants	May interfere with drug therapy.
	MAO inhibitors	Potentiates action of MAO inhibitors. May cause insomnia, headache, tremors, and hypomania.
	stimulants	May potentiate drug effects.
	warfarin	Causes antagonism of warfarin, resulting in a decreased INR.

(continued)

Herb	Drug	Possible effects
goldenseal	antihypertensives	Large amounts of herb may interfere with blood pressure control.
	CNS depressants, such as barbiturates, benzodiazepines, opioids	Increases sedative effect.
	diuretics	Causes additive drug effect.
	general anesthetics	May potentiate hypotensive action of drugs.
	heparin	May counteract anticoagulant effect of drug.
	H_2 blockers, proton-pump inhibitors	May decrease efficacy because of increased acid secretion by herb.
grapeseed	warfarin	Increases effects and INR because of tocopherol content of herb.
green tea	acetaminophen, aspirin	May increase efficacy of these drugs by as much as 40%.
	adenosine	May inhibit hemodynamic effects of drug.
	albuterol, isoproterenol, metaproterenol, terbutaline	May increase the cardiac inotropic effect of these drugs.
	clozapine	May cause acute worsening of psychotic symptoms.
	disulfiram	Increases risk of adverse effects of caffeine; decreases clearance and increases half-life of caffeine.
	ephedrine	Increases risk of agitation, tremors, and insomnia.
	hormonal contraceptives	Decreases clearance by 40% to 65%. Increases effects and adverse effects.
	lithium	Abrupt caffeine withdrawal increases drug level; may cause lithium tremor.
	MAO inhibitors	Large amounts of herb may precipitate hypertensive crisis.
	mexiletine	Decreases caffeine elimination by 50%. Increases effects and adverse effects.
	verapamil	Increases caffeine level by 25%; increases effects and adverse effects.
	warfarin	Causes antagonism resulting from vitamin content of herb.
hawthorn berry	cardiovascular drugs	May potentiate or interfere with conventional therapies used for congestive heart failure, hypertension, angina, and arrhythmias.
	CNS depressants	Causes additive effects.

Herb	Drug	Possible effects
hawthorn berry *(continued)*	coronary vasodilators	Causes additive vasodilator effects when used with theophylline, caffeine, papaverine, sodium nitrate, adenosine, and epinephrine.
	digoxin	Causes additive positive inotropic effect, with potential for drug toxicity.
kava	alcohol	Potentiates depressant effect of alcohol and other CNS depressants.
	benzodiazepines	Use with these drugs may result in comalike states.
	CNS depressants or stimulants	May hinder therapy with CNS stimulants.
	hepatotoxic drugs	May increase risk of liver damage.
	levodopa	Decreases efficacy because of dopamine antagonism by herb.
licorice	antihypertensives	Decreases effect of drug therapy. Large amounts of herb cause sodium and water retention and hypertension.
	aspirin	May provide protection against aspirin-induced damage to GI mucosa.
	corticosteroids	Causes additive and enhanced effects of drugs.
	digoxin	Herb causes hypokalemia, which predisposes to drug toxicity.
	hormonal contraceptives	Increases fluid retention and potential for increased blood pressure resulting from fluid overload.
	hormones	Interferes with estrogen or antiestrogen therapy.
	insulin	Causes hypokalemia and sodium retention.
	spironolactone	Decreases effects of drug.
ma huang (ephedra)	amitriptyline	May decrease hypertensive effects of herb.
	antidiabetics	IDecreases drug effect because of hyperglycemia caused by herb.
	caffeine	ncreases risk of stimulatory adverse effects of ephedra and caffeine and risk of hypertension, myocardial infarction, stroke, and death.
	caffeine, CNS stimulants, theophylline	Causes additive CNS stimulation.
	dexamethasone	Increases clearance and decreases efficacy of drug.
	digoxin	Increases risk of arrhythmias.

(continued)

Herb	Drug	Possible effects
ma huang (ephedra) *(continued)*	MAO inhibitors	Potentiates drugs.
	oxytocin	May cause hypertension.
	theophylline	May increase risk of stimulatory adverse effects.
melatonin	CNS depressants, such as barbiturates, benzodiazepines, opioids	Increases sedative effect.
	fluoxetine	Improves sleep in some patients with major depressive disorder.
	fluvoxamine	May significantly increase melatonin level; may decrease melatonin metabolism.
	immunosuppressants	May stimulate immune function and interfere with drug therapy.
	isoniazid	May enhance effects of drug against some *Mycobacterium* species.
	nifedipine	May decrease efficacy of drug; increases heart rate.
	verapamil	Increases melatonin excretion.
milk thistle	drugs causing diarrhea	Increases bile secretion and often causes loose stools. May increase effect of other drugs commonly causing diarrhea.
	hepatotoxic drugs, such as acetaminophen, butyrophenones, ethanol, phenothiazines, phenytoin	May have liver membrane-stabilization and antioxidant effects, leading to protection from liver damage.
	indinavir	May decrease trough level of drug, reducing virologic response.
nettle	anticonvulsants	May increase sedative adverse effects; may increase risk of seizure.
	anxiolytics, hypnotics, opioids	May increase sedative adverse effects.
	iron	Tannic acid content of herb may reduce iron absorption.
	warfarin	Antagonism resulting from vitamin K content of aerial parts of herb.
passion flower	CNS depressants, such as barbiturates, benzodiazepines, opioids	Increases sedative effect.
St. John's wort	5-hydroxytriptamine$_1$ (5-HT$_1$) agonists (triptans)	Increases risk of serotonin syndrome.
	alcohol, opioids	Enhances the sedative effect of these drugs.
	anesthetics	May prolong effect of drugs.

Herb	Drug	Possible effects
St. John's wort *(continued)*	barbiturates	Decreases drug-induced sleep time.
	cyclosporine	Decreases drug level below therapeutic levels, threatening transplanted organ rejection.
	digoxin	May reduce drug level, which decreases therapeutic effects.
	human immunodeficiency virus (HIV) protease inhibitors, indinavir, NNRTIs	Induces cytochrome P-450 metabolic pathway, which may decrease therapeutic effects of drugs using this pathway for metabolism. Avoid use together because of the potential for subtherapeutic antiretroviral level and insufficient virologic response that could lead to resistance or class cross-resistance.
	hormonal contraceptives	Increases breakthrough bleeding; decreases level and efficacy of drugs.
	irinotecan	Decreases drug level by 50%.
	iron	Tannic acid content of herb may reduce iron absorption.
	MAO inhibitors, nefazodone, SSRIs, trazodone	Causes additive effects with MAO inhibitors, SSRIs, and other antidepressants, potentially leading to serotonin syndrome, especially when combined with SSRIs.
	photosensitizing drugs	Increases photosensitivity.
	reserpine	Antagonizes effects of drug.
	sympathomimetic amines, such as pseudoephedrine	Causes additive effects.
	theophylline	May decrease drug level, making the drug less effective.
	warfarin	May alter INR. Reduces efficacy of anticoagulant, requiring increased dosage of drug.
valerian	alcohol	May be risk of increased sedation.
	CNS depressants, sedative hypnotics	Enhances effects of these drugs.
	iron	Tannic acid content of herb may reduce iron absorption.

Dietary teaching for drug therapy

This table contains important dietary information that should be included when teaching patients about drug therapy.

Foods and dietary concerns	Representative foods
Calcium-rich foods (needed by children, patients with hypocalcemia, and post-menopausal women)	Bok choy Broccoli Calcium-fortified beverages, cereals, and breads Canned salmon Canned sardines Clams Cheese Collard greens Creamed soup Kale Milk Molasses Oysters Sardines Soy beans and other soy-based products Spinach Tofu Turnip greens Yogurt
High-sodium foods (should be avoided with CHF, fluid overload, and hyperten-sion)	Beer Butter Buttermilk Canned seafood Canned soup Canned spaghetti Cookies Cured meat Fast food Pickles Prepackaged dinners Pretzels Salad dressings Sauces Sauerkraut Snack foods, such as potato chips, crackers, and cheese puffs Tomato ketchup
Iron-rich foods (helpful for maintaining RBCs)	Beets Cereals Dried beans and peas Dried fruit Enriched grains Leafy green vegetables Organ meats, such as liver, heart, kidney

Foods and dietary concerns	Representative foods
Low-sodium foods (patients with CHF, fluid overload, and hypertension should include in diet)	Egg yolks Fresh fruit Fresh vegetables Grits Honey Jam and jelly Lean meat Lima beans Macaroons Potatoes Poultry Pumpkin Red kidney beans Sherbet Unsalted nuts
Potassium-rich foods (should be eaten when taking potassium-wasting diuretics)	Avocados Bananas Broccoli Cantaloupe Dried fruit Grapefruit Lima beans Nuts Navy beans Oranges Peaches Potatoes Prunes Rhubarb Spinach Sunflower seeds Tomatoes
Purine-rich foods (should be avoided with gout)	Anchovies Kidneys Lentils Liver Sardines Sweetbreads
Tyramine-rich foods (should be avoided when taking MAO inhibitors and some antihypertensives)	Aged cheese Avocados Bananas Beer Bologna Caffeinated beverages Chocolate Liver Pepperoni Pickled fish Red wine (Chianti) Ripe fruit Salami

(continued)

Foods and dietary concerns	Representative foods
Tyramine-rich foods *(continued)*	Smoked fish Yeast Yogurt
Urine acidifiers (helpful for excretion of some drugs)	Cheese Cranberries Eggs Fish Grains Plums Poultry Prunes Red meat
Urine alkalinizers (helpful for excretion of some drugs)	Apples Berries Citrus fruit Milk Vegetables
Vitamin K-rich foods (should be avoided or strictly limited when taking anticoagulants)	Collard greens Kale Mustard greens Parsley (raw) Spinach Swiss chard Turnip greens

Table of equivalents and conversions

Metric system equivalents

Metric weight

1 kilogram (kg or Kg)	=	1,000 grams (g or gm)
1 gram	=	1,000 milligrams (mg)
1 milligram	=	1,000 micrograms (mcg)
0.6 g	=	600 mg
0.3 g	=	300 mg
0.1 g	=	100 mg
0.06 g	=	60 mg
0.03 g	=	30 mg
0.015 g	=	15 mg
0.001 g	=	1 mg

Metric volume

1 liter (l or L)	=	1,000 milliliters (ml)*
1 milliliter	=	1,000 microliters (mcl)

Household		Metric
1 teaspoon (tsp)	=	5 ml
1 tablespoon (T or tbs)	=	15 ml
2 tablespoons	=	30 ml
8 ounces	=	240 ml
1 pint (pt)	=	473 ml
1 quart (qt)	=	946 ml
1 gallon (gal)	=	3,785 ml

Weight conversions

1 oz = 30 g

1 lb = 453.6 g

2.2 lb = 1 kg

Temperature conversions

Centigrade degrees	Fahrenheit degrees	Centigrade degrees	Fahrenheit degrees	Centigrade degrees	Fahrenheit degrees
41.1	106.0	38.1	100.6	35.1	95.2
41.0	105.8	38.0	100.4	35.0	95.0
40.9	105.6	37.9	100.2	34.9	94.8
40.8	105.4	37.8	100.0	34.8	94.6
40.7	105.2	37.7	99.8	34.7	94.4
40.6	105.0	37.6	99.6	34.6	94.2
40.4	104.8	37.4	99.4	34.4	94.0
40.3	104.6	37.3	99.2	34.3	93.8
40.2	104.4	37.2	99.0	34.2	93.6
40.1	104.2	37.1	98.8	34.1	93.4
40.0	104.0	37.0	98.6	34.0	93.2
39.9	103.8	36.9	98.4	33.9	93.0
39.8	103.6	36.8	98.2	33.8	92.8
39.7	103.4	36.7	98.0	33.7	92.6
39.6	103.2	36.5	97.8	33.6	92.4
39.4	103.0	36.4	97.6	33.4	92.2
39.3	102.8	36.3	97.4	33.3	92.0
39.2	102.6	36.2	97.2	33.2	91.8
39.1	102.4	36.1	97.0	33.1	91.6
39.0	102.2	36.0	96.8	33.0	91.4
38.9	102.0	35.9	96.6	32.9	91.2
38.8	101.8	35.8	96.4	32.8	91.0
38.7	101.6	35.7	96.2	32.7	90.8
38.6	101.4	35.6	96.0	32.6	90.6
38.4	101.2	35.4	95.8	32.4	90.4
38.3	101.0	35.3	95.6	32.3	90.2
38.2	100.8	35.2	95.4	32.2	90.0

*1 ml = 1 cubic centimeter (cc); however, ml is the preferred measurement term.

Adverse reactions misinterpreted as age-related changes

In elderly patients, adverse drug reactions can easily be misinterpreted as the typical signs and symptoms of aging. The table below, which shows possible adverse reactions for common drug classifications, can help you avoid such misinterpretations.

Drug Classifications	Adverse Reactions							
	Agitation	Anxiety	Arrhythmias	Ataxia	Changes in appetite	Confusion	Constipation	Depression
ACE inhibitors						●	●	●
Alpha$_1$ adrenergic blockers		●					●	●
Antianginals	●	●	●			●		
Antiarrhythmics			●				●	
Anticholinergics	●	●				●	●	●
Anticonvulsants	●		●	●	●	●	●	●
Antidepressants, tricyclic	●	●	●	●	●	●	●	
Antidiabetics, oral								
Antihistamines					●	●	●	
Antilipemics							●	
Antiparkinsonians	●	●		●	●	●	●	●
Antipsychotics	●	●	●	●	●	●	●	●
Barbiturates	●	●	●			●		
Benzodiazepines	●			●		●	●	●
Beta blockers		●	●					●
Calcium channel blockers		●	●				●	
Corticosteroids	●					●		●
Diuretics						●		
NSAIDs		●				●	●	●
Opioids	●	●				●	●	●
Skeletal muscle relaxants	●	●		●		●		●
Thyroid hormones			●		●			

Difficulty breathing	Disorientation	Dizziness	Drowsiness	Edema	Fatigue	Hypotension	Insomnia	Memory loss	Muscle weakness	Restlessness	Sexual dysfunction	Tremors	Urinary dysfunction	Visual changes
		●			●	●	●				●			●
		●		●	●	●	●				●		●	●
		●		●	●						●		●	●
●		●		●	●									
	●	●	●		●	●		●		●			●	●
					●	●	●					●	●	●
●	●	●			●	●	●			●	●		●	●
		●			●									
	●	●	●		●							●	●	●
					●		●				●		●	●
	●	●	●		●	●	●		●			●	●	●
		●			●	●	●			●	●		●	●
●	●		●		●	●				●			●	●
●	●	●			●		●		●			●	●	●
●		●			●	●		●			●	●	●	●
●		●		●	●	●	●		●		●		●	●
				●	●	●			●				●	
					●	●			●				●	
		●	●		●		●		●					●
●	●	●	●		●	●	●	●		●	●		●	●
					●	●	●						●	
							●					●		

Drugs that shouldn't be crushed

Slow-release, enteric-coated, encapsulated-bead, wax-matrix, sublingual, and buccal drug forms are made to release their active ingredients over a certain period of time or at preset points after administration. Crushing these drug forms can dramatically affect their absorption rate and increase the risk of adverse reactions.

Other reasons not to crush some drug forms include taste, tissue irritation, and unusual formulation—for example, a capsule within a capsule, a liquid within a capsule, or a multiple-compressed tablet. Some drugs shouldn't be crushed because they're teratogenic. Avoid crushing the following brand-name drugs, for the reasons noted beside them.

Accutane (irritant)

Aciphex (delayed release)

Actifed 12-Hour (sustained release)

Adalat CC (sustained release)

Advicor (extended release)

Aggrenox (extended release)

Allegra D (extended release)

Allerest 12 Hour (sustained release)

Altocor (extended release)

Ambien CR (extended release)

Amnesteem (irritant)

Ansaid (taste)

Aricept ODT (orally disintegrating)

Arthrotec (delayed release)

Asacol (delayed release)

Aspirin (enteric coated)

Atrohist LA (long acting)

Augmentin XR (extended release)

Avinza (extended release)

Avodart (irritant)

Azulfidine EN-tabs (enteric coated)

Biaxin XL (extended release)

Biohist LA (long acting)

Bisacodyl (enteric coated)

Bontril Slow-Release (slow release)

Bromfed (slow release)

Bromfed-PD (slow release)

Bronkodyl SR (slow release)

Calan SR (sustained release)

Carbatrol (extended release)

Cardizem CD, LA (slow release)

Cartia XT (extended release)

Ceclor CD (slow release)

Ceftin (strong, persistent taste)

Cellcept (teratogenic)

Chloral Hydrate (liquid within a capsule, taste)

Chlor-Trimeton Allergy 8-hour and 12-hour (slow release)

Choledyl SA (slow release)

Cipro XR (extended release)

Citalopram HBr (orally disintegrating)

Claritin-D 12-hour (slow release)

Claritin-D 24-hour (slow release)

Cleocin (taste)

Colace (liquid within a capsule)

Colazal (granules within capsules must reach colon intact)

Colestid (protective coating)

Compazine Spansules (slow release)

Concerta (extended release)

Contac 12 Hour, Maximum Strength 12 Hour (slow release)

Cotazym-S (enteric coated)

Covera-HS (extended release)

Creon (enteric coated)

Cytovene (irritant)

Cytoxan (toxic)

Dallergy, Dallergy-Jr (slow release)

Deconamine SR (slow release)

Depakene (slow release, mucous membrane irritant)

Depakote (enteric coated)

Depakote ER (extended release)

Dexedrine Spansule (slow release)

Diamox Sequels (slow release)

Dilacor XR (extended release)

Dilatrate-SR (slow release)

Dilt XR (extended release)

Diltia XT (extended release)

Dimetane Extentabs (extended release)

Dimetapp Extentabs (slow release)

Ditropan XL (slow release)

Dolobid (irritant)

Donnatel Extentabs (extended release)

Doxidan Liquigels (liquid within capsule)

Drisdol (liquid filled)

Dristan (protective coating)

Drixoral (slow release)

Dulcolax (enteric coated)

Dynabac (slow release)

DynaCirc CR (slow release)

Easprin (enteric coated)

Ecotrin (enteric coated)

Ecotrin Maximum Strength (enteric coated)

E.E.S. 400 Filmtab (enteric coated)

Effexor XR (extended release)

Emend (hard gelatin capsule)

E-Mycin (enteric coated)

Entex LA (slow release)

Entex PSE (slow release)

Equanil (extended release)

Ergostat (sublingual)

Eryc (enteric coated)

Ery-Tab (enteric coated)

Erythrocin Stearate (enteric coated)

Erythromycin Base (enteric coated)

Eskalith CR (slow release)

Extendryl JR, SR (slow release)

Feldene (mucous membrane irritant)

Feosol (enteric coated)

Feratab (enteric coated)

Fergon (slow release)

Fero-Folic 500 (slow release)

Fero-Grad-500 (slow release)

Ferro-Sequel (slow release)

Feverall Children's Capsules, Sprinkle (taste)

Flomax (slow release)

Focalin XR (extended release)

Fumatinic (slow release)

Geocillin (taste)

Glucophage XR (extended release)

Glucotrol XL (slow release)

Glumetza (extended release)

Guaifed (slow release)

Guaifed-PD (slow release)

Guaifenex LA (slow release)

Guaifenex PPA (slow release)

Guaifenex PSE (slow release)

Guaimax-D (slow release)

Hydergine LC (sublingual)

Hytakerol (liquid filled)

Iberet (slow release)

ICAPS Plus (slow release)

ICAPS Time Release (slow release)

Ilotycin (enteric coated)

Imdur (slow release)

Inderal LA (slow release)

Indocin SR (slow release)

InnoPran XL (extended release)

Ionamin (slow release)

Isoptin SR (sustained release)

Isordil Sublingual (sublingual)

Isordil Tembids (slow release)

Isosorbide Dinitrate Sublingual (sublingual)

Kadian (extended release)

Kaletra (extended release)

Kaon-Cl (slow release)

K-Dur (slow release)

Klor-Con (slow release)

Klotrix (slow release)

K-Tab (slow release)

Levbid (slow release)

Levsinex Timecaps (slow release)

Lithobid (slow release)

Macrobid (slow release)

Mestinon Timespans (slow release)

Metadate CD, ER (extended release)

Methylin ER (extended release)

Micro-K Extencaps (slow release)

Modane (enteric coated)

Motrin (taste)

MS Contin (slow release)

Mucinex (extended release)

Naprelan (slow release)

Nexium (sustained release)

Niaspan (extended release)

Nicotinic acid (slow release)

Nifedical XL (extended release)

Nitroglyn (slow release)

Nitrostat (sublingual)

Noctec (liquid within capsule)

Norflex (slow release)

Norpace CR (slow release)

Oramorph SR (slow release)

Orapred ODT (orally disintegrating)

Oruvail (extended release)

OxyContin (slow release)

Pancrease (enteric coated)

Pancrease MT (enteric coated)

Paxil CR (controlled-release)

PCE (slow release)

Pentasa (controlled release)

Phazyme (slow release)

Phazyme 95 (slow release)

Phenytek (extended release)

Plendil (slow release)

Prelu-2 (slow release)

Prevacid, Prevacid SoluTab (delayed release)

Prilosec (slow release)

Prilosec OTC (delayed-release)

Pro-Banthine (taste)

Procanbid (slow release)

Procardia XL (slow release)

Propecia (adverse effects when handled by pregnant women)

Proscar (adverse effects when handled by pregnant women)

Protonix (delayed release)

Proventil Repetabs (slow release)

Prozac Weekly (slow release)

Quibron-T/SR (slow release)

Quinaglute Duratabs (extended release)

Quinidex Extentabs (slow release)

Respaire SR (slow release)

Respbid (extended release)

Risperdal (orally disintegrating)

Risperdal M-Tab (delayed-release)

Ritalin-LA, -SR (slow release)

Rondec-TR (slow release)

Roxanol SR (sustained release)

Sinemet CR (slow release)

Slo-bid Gyrocaps (slow release)
Slo-Niacin (slow release)
Slo-Phyllin GG, Gyrocaps (slow release)
Slow FE (slow release)
Slow-K (slow release)
Slow-Mag (slow release)
Sorbitrate (sublingual)
Sotret (irritant)
Sudafed 12 Hour (slow release)
Sular (extended release)
Surfac Liquigels (liquid within capsule)
Taztia XT (extended release)
Tegretol-XR (extended release)
Ten-K (slow release)
Tenuate Dospan (slow release)
Tessalon Perles (slow release)
Theochron (slow release)
Theoclear LA (slow release)
Theo-24 (slow release)
TheoDur (extended release)
Thorazine Spansules (slow release)
Tiazac (sustained release)
Topamax (taste)
Toprol XL (extended release)
Trental (slow release)
Tylenol Extended Relief (slow release)
Uniphyl (slow release)
Uroxatral (extended release)
Vantin (taste)
Verelan, Verelan PM (slow release)
Volmax (slow release)
Voltaren (enteric coated)
Voltaren-XR (extended release)
Wellbutrin SR (sustained release)
Xanax XR (extended release)
Zerit XR (extended release)
Zomig-ZMT (delayed-release)
ZORprin (slow release)
Zyban (slow release)
Zyrtec-D 12 hour (extended release)

Normal laboratory test values

Normal values may differ from laboratory to laboratory. Standard international units are abbreviated SI.

Hematology

Bleeding time
Template: 3–6 min (SI, 3–6 m)
Ivy: 3–6 min (SI, 3–6 m)
Duke: 1–3 min (SI, 1–3 m)

Fibrinogen, plasma
200–400 mg/dl (SI, 2–4 g/L)

Hematocrit
Men: 42%–52% (SI, 0.42–0.52)
Women: 36%–48% (SI, 0.36–0.48)

Hemoglobin, total
Men: 14–17.4 g/dl (SI, 140–174 g/L)
Women: 12–16 g/dl (SI, 120–160 g/L)

Partial thromboplastin time, activated
21–35 sec (SI, 21–35 sec)

Platelet aggregation
3–5 min (SI, 3–5 min)

Platelet count
140,000–400,000/mm^3 (SI, 140–400 × 10^9/L)

Prothrombin time
10–14 sec (SI, 10–14 sec); INR for patients not receiving warfarin, 1.12–1.46; INR for patients receiving warfarin, 2–3 (SI, 2–3) (those with prosthetic heart valve, 2.5–3.5 [SI, 2.5–3.5])

Red blood cell count
Men: 4.5–5.5 million/mm^3 (SI, 4.5–5.5 × 10^{12}/L) venous blood
Women: 4–5 million/mm^3 (SI, 4–5 × 10^{12}/L) venous blood

Red blood cell indices
Mean corpuscular volume: 82–98 femtoliters
Mean corpuscular hemoglobin: 26–34 picograms/cell
Mean corpuscular hemoglobin concentration: 31–37 g/dl

Reticulocyte count
0.5%–1.5% (SI, 0.005–0.025) of total RBC count

White blood cell count
4,500–10,500 cells/mm^3

White blood cell differential, blood
Neutrophils: 54%–75% (SI, 0.54–0.75)
Lymphocytes: 25%–40% (SI, 0.25–0.4)
Monocytes: 2%–8% (SI, 0.02–0.08)
Eosinophils: up to 4% (SI, up to 0.04)
Basophils: up to 1% (SI, up to 0.01)

Blood chemistry

Alanine aminotransferase
Adults: 10–35 units/L (SI, 0.17–0.6 μkat/L)
Newborns: 13–45 units/L (SI, 0.22–0.77 μkat/L)

Amylase, serum
Adults ≥ age 18: 30–175 units/L (SI, 0.5–2.83 μkat/L)

Arterial blood gases
pH: 7.35–7.45 (SI, 7.35–7.45)
$Paco_2$: 35–45 mm Hg (SI, 4.7–5.3 kPa)
Pao_2: 80–100 mm Hg (SI, 10.6–13.3 kPa)
HCO_3^-: 22–26 mEq/L (SI, 22–25 mmol/L)
Sao_2: 94%–100% (SI, 0.94–1.00)

Aspartate aminotransferase
Men: 14–20 units/L (SI, 0.23–0.33 μkat/L)
Women: 7–34 units/L (SI, 0.12–0.58 μkat/L)

Bilirubin, serum
Adults, total: 0.2–1 mg/dl (SI, 3.5–17 μmol/L)
Neonates, total: 1–10 mg/dl (SI, 17–170 μmol/L)
Neonates, unconjugated indirect: 0–10 mg/dl (SI, 0–170 μmol/L)

Blood urea nitrogen
8–20 mg/dl (SI, 2.9–7.5 mmol/L)

Calcium, serum
Adults: 8.2–10.2 mg/dl (SI, 2.05–2.54 mmol/L)
Children: 8.6–11.2 mg/dl (SI, 2.15–2.79 mmol/L)

Carbon dioxide, total blood
22–26 mEq/L (SI, 22–26 mmol/L)

Cholesterol, total serum
Men: < 205 mg/dl (SI, < 5.30 mmol/L) (desirable)
Women: < 190 mg/dl (SI, < 4.90 mmol/L) (desirable)

Creatine kinase, isoenzymes
CK–BB: none
CK–MB: 0–7%
CK–MM: 96–100%

Creatinine, serum
Adults: 0.6–1.3 mg/dl (SI, 53–115 μmol/L)

Glucose, plasma, fasting
70–110 mg/dl (SI, 3.9–6.1 mmol/L)

Glucose, plasma, 2-hour postprandial
< 145 mg/dl (SI, < 8 mmol/L)

Lactate dehydrogenase
Total: 71–207 units/L in adults (SI, 1.2–3.52 μkat/L)
LD1: 14%–26% (SI, 0.14–0.26)
LD2: 29%–39% (SI, 0.29–0.39)
LD3: 20%–26% (SI, 0.20–0.26)
LD4: 8%–16% (SI, 0.08–0.16)
LD5: 6%–16% (SI, 0.06–0.16)

Lipase
< 160 units/L (SI, < 2.72 μkat/L)

Magnesium, serum
1.8–2.6 mg/dl (SI, 0.74–1.07 mmol/L)

Phosphates, serum
2.7–4.5 mg/dl (SI, 0.87–1.45 mmol/L)

Potassium, serum
3.8–5 mEq/L (SI, 3.5–5 mmol/L)

Protein, serum
Total: 6.3–8.3 g/dl (SI, 64–83 g/L)
Albumin fraction: 3.5–5 g/dl (SI, 35–50 g/L)

Sodium, serum
135–145 mEq/L (SI, 135–145 mmol/L)

Triglycerides, serum
Men > age 20: 40–180 mg/dl (SI, 0.11–2.01 mmol/L)
Women > age 20: 10–190 mg/dl (SI, 0.11–2.21 mmol/L)

Uric acid, serum
Men: 3.4–7 mg/dl (SI, 202–416 μmol/L)
Women: 2.3–6 mg/dl (SI, 143–357 μmol/L)

English-to-Spanish drug phrase translator

Medication history

Do you take any medications?	**¿Toma usted medicamentos?**
– Prescription?	– ¿Bajo receta?
– Over-the-counter?	– ¿De venta libre?
– Other?	– ¿Otro?
Which prescription medications do you take routinely?	**¿Qué medicamentos bajo receta toma como rutina?**
Which over-the-counter medications do you take routinely?	**¿Qué medicamentos de venta libre toma como rutina?**
– How often do you take them?	– ¿Con qué frecuencia los toma?
– Once daily?	– ¿Una vez al día?
– Twice daily?	– ¿Dos veces al día?
– Three times daily?	– ¿Tres veces al día?
– Four times daily?	– ¿Cuátro veces al día?
– More often?	– ¿Con más frecuencia?
Why do you take these medications?	**¿Por qué toma estos medicamentos?**
What is the dosage for each medication?	**¿Cuál es la dosis para cada medicamento?**
Are you allergic to any medications?	**¿Es usted alérgico(a) a algún medicamento?**

Medication teaching

Purpose of the medication

This medication will:	**Este medicamento:**
– elevate your blood pressure.	– elevará su presión sanguínea.
– improve circulation to your ____.	– mejorará la circulación a su ____.
– lower your blood pressure.	– reducirá su presión sanguínea.
– lower your blood sugar.	– reducirá el nivel de azúcar en su sangre.
– make your heart rhythm more even.	– hará que su ritmo cardiaco sea más uniforme.
– raise your blood sugar.	– elevará el nivel de azúcar en su sangre.
– reduce or prevent the formation of blood clots.	– reducirá o evitará la formación de coágulos.
– remove fluid from your body.	– eliminará el liquido de su cuerpo.
– remove fluid from your feet, ankles, or legs.	– eliminará el liquido de sus pies, tobillos o piernas.
– remove fluid from your lungs so that they work better.	– eliminará el liquido de sus pulmones para que funcionen mejor.
– remove fluid from your pancreas so that it works better.	– eliminará el liquido de su páncreas para que funcione mejor.
– kill the bacteria in your ____.	– matará las bacterias en su _____.
– slow down your heart rate.	– hará más lento su ritmo cardiaco.
– soften your bowel movements.	– ablandará sus evacuaciones intestinales.
– speed up your heart rate.	– acelerará su ritmo cardiaco.
– help your body to use insulin more efficiently.	– ayudará a su cuerpo a usar la insulina de manera más eficaz.

This medication will help you to:	**Este medicamento le ayudará a:**
– breathe better.	– respirar mejor.
– fight infections.	– combatir infecciones.
– relax.	– relajarse.
– sleep.	– dormir.
– think more clearly.	– pensar con mayor claridad.
This medication will relieve or reduce:	**Este medicamento le aliviará o reducirá:**
– the acid production in your stomach.	– la producción de ácido en su estómago.
– anxiety.	– la ansiedad.
– bladder spasms.	– los espasmos en la vejiga.
– burning in your stomach or chest.	– el ardor en su estómago o pecho.
– burning when you urinate.	– el ardor al orinar.
– diarrhea.	– la diarrea.
– muscle cramps.	– los calambres musculares.
– nausea.	– las nauseas.
– pain in your _____.	– el dolor en su _____.

Medication administration

I would like to give you:	**Quisiera darle:**
– an injection.	– una inyección.
– an I.V. medication.	– un medicamento por vía intravenosa.
– a liquid medication.	– un medicamento en forma líquida.
– a medicated cream or powder.	– un medicamento en pomada o polvo.
– a medication through your epidural catheter.	– un medicamento a través de su catéter epidural.
– a medication through your rectum.	– un medicamento por vía rectal.
– a medication through your _____ tube.	– un medicamento a través de su tubo de _____.
– a medication under your tongue.	– un medicamento debajo de la lengua.
– some pill(s).	– algunas píldoras.
– a suppository.	– un supositorio.
This is how you take this medication.	**Así se toma este medicamento.**
If you can't swallow this pill, I can get it in another form.	**Si usted no logra tragar esta píldora, puede obtenerla en otra forma.**
If you can't swallow a pill, you can crush it and mix it in soft food.	**Si usted no logra tragar una píldora, puede molerla y mezclarla con alimentos blandos.**
I need to mix this medication in juice or water.	**Necesito mezclar este medicamento en jugo o agua.**
I need to give you this injection in your:	**Necesito ponerle esta inyección en:**
– abdomen.	– el abdomen.
– buttocks.	– las nalgas.
– hip.	– la cadera.
– outer arm.	– la parte externa el brazo.
– thigh.	– el muslo.

Some medications are coated with a special substance to protect your stomach from getting upset.

Algunos medicamentos están revestidos con una sustancia especial para protegerlo(a) contra malestar estomacal.

Do not chew:
- enteric-coated pills.
- long-acting pills.
- capsules.
- sublingual medication.

No masque:
- píldoras con recubrimiento entérico.
- píldoras de efecto prolongado.
- cápsulas.
- medicamentos sublinguales.

Ask your doctor or pharmacist whether you can:
- mix your medication with food or fluids.
- take your medication with or without food.

Pregunte a su médico o farmacéutico si usted puede:
- mezclar su medicamento con alimentos o líquidos.
- tomar su medicamento con o sin alimentos.

You need to take your medication:
- after meals.
- before meals.
- on an empty stomach.
- with meals or food.

Usted debe tomar su medicamento:
- después de las comidas.
- antes de las comidas.
- con el estómago vacío.
- con comidas o alimentos.

Skipping doses

If you skip or miss a dose:
- Take it as soon as you remember it.
- Wait until the next dose.
- Call the doctor if you are not sure.
- Do not take an extra dose.

Si usted se salta u omite una dosis:
- Tómela apenas se acuerde.
- Espere hasta la próxima dosis.
- Llame a su médico si no está seguro(a).
- No tome una dosis adicional.

Adverse effects

Some common adverse effects of _____ are:
- constipation
- diarrhea
- difficulty sleeping
- dry mouth
- fatigue
- headache
- itching
- light-headedness
- nausea
- poor appetite
- rash
- upset stomach
- weight loss or gain
- frequent urination.

Algunos afectos adversos comunes de _____ son:
- constipación
- diarrea
- dificultad para dormir
- boca seca
- fatiga
- dolor de cabeza
- picazón (comezón)
- mareos
- náuseas
- disminución del apetito
- erupción
- malestar estomacal
- aumento o pérdida de peso
- orinar con frecuencia.

These adverse effects:
- will go away after your body gets used to the medication.
- may persist as long as you take the medication.

Estos efectos adversos:
- desaparecerán cuanao su cuerpo se acostumbre al medicamento.
- podrán persistir mientras usted tome el medicamento.

If you have an adverse reaction to your medication, call your doctor right away.

Si usted tiene una reacción adversa a su medicamento, llame a su médico de inmediato.

Other concerns

Tell your doctor if you are pregnant or breast-feeding.

Dígale a su médico si usted está embarazada o amamantando.

While you are taking this medication, ask your doctor if:
- you can safely take other over-the-counter medications.
- you can drink alcoholic beverages.
- your medications interact with each other.

Mientras tome este medicamento, pregúntele a su médico si:
- usted puede tomar otros medicamentos de venta libre sin peligro.
- usted puede tomar bebidas alcohólicas.
- sus medicamentos tienen interacción entre si.

Storing medication

You should keep your medication:
- in a cool, dry place.
- in the refrigerator.
- at room temperature.
- out of direct sunlight.
- away from heat.
- away from children.

Usted debe guardar sus medicamentos:
- en un lugar fresco y seco.
- en el refrigerador.
- al temperatura ambiente.
- fuera de la luz directa del sol.
- lejos del calor.
- lejos del alcance de los niños.

Subcutaneous injection

To give yourself an injection, follow these steps:
- Draw up the medication.
- Replace the cap carefully.
- Decide where you are going to give the injection.
- Clean the skin area with alcohol.
- Gently pinch up a little skin over the area.
- Using a dartlike motion, stab the needle into your skin.
- Gently pull back on the plunger to see if there is any blood in the syringe.
- Steadily push the medication into your skin.
- Pull the needle out.
- Apply gentle pressure with the alcohol wipe.
- Dispose of the needle in a proper receptacle.

Para ponerse una inyección, haga lo siguiente:
- Extraiga el medicamento.
- Vuelva a colocar la tapa con cuidado.
- Decida dónde colocará la inyección.
- Limpie el área de la piel con alcohol.
- Suavemente, pellizque un poco de la piel sobre el área.
- Con un movimiento como si estuviera arrojando un dardo, penetre la piel con la aguja.
- Tire suavemente del émbolo para ver si hay sangre en la jeringa.
- Coloque el medicamento en la piel de manera uniforme.
- Retire la aguja.
- Aplique presión suave con un paño con alcohol.
- Deseche la aguja en un recipiente apropiado.

Insulin preparation and administration

The doctor has ordered insulin for you.

El médico le ha recetado insulina.

To draw up insulin, follow these steps:
- Wipe the rubber top of the insulin bottle with alcohol.

Para extraer la insulina, siga los siguientes pasos:
- Limpie la tapa de goma del frasco de insulina con alcohol.

- Remove the needle cap.
- Pull out the plunger until the end of the plunger in the barrel aligns with the number of units of insulin that you need.
- Push the needle through the rubber top of the insulin bottle.
- Inject the air into the bottle.
- Without removing the needle from the bottle, turn it upside down.
- Withdraw the plunger until the end of the plunger aligns with the number of units you need.
- Gently pull the needle out of the bottle.

- Retire la tapa de la aguja.
- Tire del émbolo hasta que la extremidad del émbolo en la barril esté al nivel de la cantidad de unidades de insulina que usted necesita.
- Empuje la aguja a través de la tapa de goma del frasco de insulina.
- Inyecte el aire dentro del frasco.
- Sin retirar la aguja del frasco, gírelo boca abajo.
- Retire el émbolo hasta que la extremidad del émbolo esté al nivel de la cantidad de unidades que necesita.
- Suavamente, retire la aguja del frasco.

To mix insulin, follow these steps:

- Wipe the rubber tops of the insulin bottles with alcohol.
- Gently roll the cloudy insulin between your palms.
- Remove the needle cap.
- Pull out the plunger until the end of the plunger in the barrel aligns with the number of units of NPH or Lente insulin that you need.
- Push the needle through the rubber top of the cloudy insulin bottle.
- Inject the air into the bottle.
- Remove the needle.
- Pull out the plunger until the end of the plunger in the barrel aligns with the number of units of clear regular insulin that you need.
- Push the needle through the rubber top of the clear insulin bottle.
- Inject the air into the bottle.
- Without removing the needle, turn the bottle upside down.
- Withdraw the plunger until it aligns with the number of units of clear regular insulin that you need.
- Gently pull the needle out of the bottle.
- Push the needle into the cloudy (NPH or Lente) insulin without injecting it into the bottle.
- Withdraw the plunger until you reach your total dosage of insulin in units (regular combined with NPH or Lente).
- We will practice again.

Para mezclar la insulina siga los siguientes pasos:

- Limpie las tapas de goma de los frascos de insulina con alcohol.
- Suavemente, gire el frasco de insulina turbia entre las palmas de la mano.
- Retire la tapa de la aguja.
- Tire del émbolo hasta que la extremidad del émbolo en el barril esté alineado con la cantidad de unidades de NPH o Lente que usted necesita.
- Empuje la aguja a través de la tapa de goma del frasco de insulina clara.
- Inyecte el aire en el frasco.
- Sin retirar la aguja, gire el frasco boca abajo.
- Tire del émbolo hasta que este al nivel de la cantidad de unidades de insulina común clara que usted necesita.
- Empuje la aguja a través de la tapa de goma del frasco de insulina clara.
- Inyecte el aire en el frasco.
- Sin retirar la aguja, gire el frasco boca abajo.
- Tire del émbolo hasta que al nive de la cantidad de unidades de insulina común clara que usted necesita.
- Suavemente, retire la aguja del frasco.
- Empuje la aguja hacia dentro de la insulina turbia (NPH o Lente) sin inyectarla en el frasco.
- Tire del émbolo hasta llegar ala dosis total de insulina en unidades (común combinada con NPH o Lente).
- Practicaremos nuevamente.

Home care phrases

Wash your hands before touching medications.	**Lávese las manos antes de tocar medicamentos.**
Check the medication bottle for name, dose, and frequency (how often it's supposed to be taken).	**Verifique el nombre, dosis y frecuencia (cada cuanto lo debe tomar) en al frasco del medicamento.**
Check the expiration date on all medications.	**Verifique la fecha de vencimiento de todos los medicamentos.**
Store medications according to pharmacy instructions.	**Almacene los medicamentos de acuerdo con las instrucciones de la farmacia.**
Under adequate lighting, read medication labels carefully before taking doses.	**Con luz adequada, lea las etiquetas de los medicamentos con mucho cuidado antes de tomar las dosis.**
Don't crush medication without first asking the doctor or pharmacist.	**No machaque el medicamento sin preguntar al médico o al farmaceútico.**
Contact your doctor if a new or unexpected symptom or another problem appears.	**Contacte a su médico si aparece u síntoma nuevo o imprevisto u otro problema.**
Don't stop taking medication unless instructed by your doctor.	**No deje de tomar el medicamento sin indicación médica.**
Discard outdated medications.	**Deseche los medicamentos vencidos.**
Never take someone else's medications.	**Nunca tome los medicamentos de otra persona.**
Keep a record of your current medications.	**Mantenga un registro de sus medicamentos actuales.**

General drug therapy phrases

Drug classes

Analgesic	**Analgésico**
Anesthetic	**Anestético**
Antacid	**Antiácido**
Antianginal agent	**Agente antianginal**
Antianxiety agent	**Agente ansiolítico**
Antiarrhythmic agent	**Agente antiarrítmico**
Antibiotic	**Antibiótico**
Anticancer agent	**Agente anticarcinógeno**
Anticoagulant	**Anticoagulante**
Anticonvulsant	**Anticonvulsivante**
Antidepressant	**Antidepresivo**
Antidiarrheal	**Antidiarreico**
Antifungal agent	**Agente antifúngico**
Antigout agent	**Agente antigota**

Antihistamine	Antihistamínico
Antihyperlipemic agent	Agente hiperlipémico
Antihypertensive agent	Agente antihipertenso
Anti-inflammatory agent	Agente antiinflamatorio
Antimalarial agent	Agente antimalárico
Antiparkinsonian agent	Agente antiparkinsoniano
Antipsychotic agent	Agente antipsicótico
Antipyretic	Antipirético
Antiseptic	Antiséptico
Antispasmodic	Antiespasmódico
Antithyroid agent	Agente antitiroideo
Antituberculosis agent	Agente antituberculoso
Antitussive agent	Agente antitusígeno
Antiviral agent	Agente antiviral
Appetite stimulant	Estimulante para el apetito
Appetite suppressant	Supresor de apetito
Bronchodilator	Broncodilatador
Decongestant	Descongestivo
Digestant	Digestivo (agente que estimula la digestión)
Diuretic	Diurético
Emetic	Emético
Fertility agent	Agente para la fertilidad
Hypnotic	Hipnótico
Insulin	Insulina
Laxative	Laxante
Muscle relaxant	Relajante de músculos
Oral contraceptive	Anticonceptivo oral
Oral hypoglycemic agent	Agente hipoglucémico oral
Sedative	Sedante
Steroid	Esteroide
Thyroid hormone	Hormona de la glándula tiroides
Vaccine	Vacuna
Vasodilator	Vasodilatador
Vitamin	Vitamina

Preparations

Capsule	Cápsula
Cream	Pomada
Drops	Gotas
Elixir	Elixir
Inhaler	Inhalador

Injection	**Inyección**
Lotion	**Loción**
Lozenge	**Pastilla**
Powder	**Polvo**
Spray	**Atomizador**
Suppository	**Supositorio**
Suspension	**Suspensión**
Syrup	**Jarabe**
Tablet	**Tableta**

Frequency

Once daily	**Una vez al día**
Twice daily	**Dos veces al día**
Three times daily	**Tres veces al día**
Four times daily	**Cuatro veces al día**
In the morning	**Por la mañana**
With meals	**Con las comidas**
Before meals	**Antes de las comidas**
After meals	**Después de las comidas**
Before bedtime	**Antes de acostarse**
When you have_____	**Cuando Ud. tome_____**
Only when you need it	**Sólo cuando lo necesite**
Every four hours	**Cada cuatro horas**
Every six hours	**Cada seis horas**
Every eight hours	**Cada ocho horas**

Acknowledgments

We would like to thank the following companies for granting us permission to include their drugs in the full-color photoguide.

Abbott Laboratories
Depakote®
Hytrin®
Kaletra®

AstraZeneca LP
Arimidex®
Crestor®
Prilosec®
Tenormin®
Toprol-XL®

Aventis Pharmaceuticals
DiaBeta®
Lasix®

Bayer Pharmaceuticals Corporation
Cipro®
Levitra®
Ranexa®

Biovail Pharmaceuticals, Inc.
Cardizem®
Cardizem CD®
Cardizem LA®
Vasotec®

Bristol-Myers Squibb Company
Capoten®
Coumadin®
Monopril®
Pravachol®

Elan Pharmaceuticals, Inc.
Frova®

Forest Pharmaceuticals, Inc.
Campral®
Celexa®
Lexapro®

GlaxoSmithKline
Reproduced with permission of GlaxoSmithKline.
Avandia®
Lanoxin®
Wellbutrin SR®

Janssen Pharmaceutica, Inc.
Risperdal®
Risperdal® M-Tab™

King Pharmaceuticals, Inc.
Levoxyl®

Eli Lilly and Company
Copyright Eli Lilly and Company. Used with permission 2007.
Cymbalta®
Prozac®
Strattera®

Mallinckrodt, Inc.
Pamelor®

Merck & Co., Inc.
Used with permission of Merck & Co., Inc.
Cozaar®
Fosamax®
Januvia®
Mevacor®
Pepcid®
Prinivil®
Singulair®
Zocor®

Merck/Schering-Plough
Used with permission of Merck/Schering-Plough.
Zetia™

Merck Santé
An associate of Merck KGaA, Darmstadt, Germany
Glucophage®
Glucophage XR®

Novartis Pharmaceuticals, Inc.
Enablex®
Ritalin®

Onyx Pharmaceuticals
Nexavar®

Ortho-McNeil Pharmaceutical
Levaquin®

Otsuka Pharmaceutical Company, Ltd.
Abilify®

Pfizer, Inc.
Used with pemission from Pfizer Inc.
Accupril®
Calan®
Cardura®
Celebrex®
Chantix®
Diflucan®
Dilantin® Kapseals®
Glucotrol®
Glucotrol XL®
Lipitor®
Micronase
Neurontin®
Norvasc®
Procardia XL®
Sutent®
Viagra®
Zithromax®
Zoloft®

Pharmacia Corporation, a Pfizer, Inc. corporation
Registered trademarks of Pharmacia Corporation, a Pfizer Inc. corporation. All rights reserved. Courtesy of Pfizer Inc.
Provera®
Xanax®

Procter & Gamble Pharmaceuticals, Inc.
Actonel®

Purdue Pharma L.P.
OxyContin®

Roche Laboratories, Inc.
Valium®

Sanofi-Synthelabo, Inc.
Ambien®

Schering Corporation and Key Pharmaceuticals, Inc.
Clarinex®
K-Dur®

Sepracor, Inc.
Lunesta®

Sucampo Pharmaceuticals, Inc.
Amitiza®

Teva Neuroscience, Inc.
Azilect®

Tap Pharmaceuticals, Inc.
Prevacid®

Warner Chilcott Laboratories, Inc.
Duricef®
Eryc®
Estrace®

Wyeth Pharmaceuticals
The appearance of these tablets and capsules is a trademark of Wyeth Pharmaceuticals, Philadelphia, Pa.
Effexor XR®

Index

♦ Canada ◇ Australia

t refers to a table; **boldface** refers to the drug's monograph; ***boldface italic*** refers to a full-color photograph.

t refers to a table; **boldface** refers to the drug's monograph; ***boldface italic*** refers to a full-color photograph.

B

♦ Canada ◇ Australia

t refers to a table; **boldface** refers to the drug's monograph; ***boldface italic*** refers to a full-color photograph.

t refers to a table; **boldface** refers to the drug's monograph; ***boldface italic*** refers to a full-color photograph.

♦ Canada ◇ Australia

t refers to a table; **boldface** refers to the drug's monograph; ***boldface italic*** refers to a full-color photograph.

♦ Canada ◇ Australia

E

◆ Canada ◇ Australia

F

t refers to a table; **boldface** refers to the drug's monograph; ***boldface italic*** refers to a full-color photograph.

t refers to a table; **boldface** refers to the drug's monograph; ***boldface italic*** refers to a full-color photograph.

I

t refers to a table; **boldface** refers to the drug's monograph; ***boldface italic*** refers to a full-color photograph.

t refers to a table; **boldface** refers to the drug's monograph; ***boldface italic*** refers to a full-color photograph.

M

t refers to a table; **boldface** refers to the drug's monograph; ***boldface italic*** refers to a full-color photograph.

♦ Canada ◇ Australia

t refers to a table; **boldface** refers to the drug's monograph; ***boldface italic*** refers to a full-color photograph.

♦ Canada ◇ Australia

t refers to a table; **boldface** refers to the drug's monograph; ***boldface italic*** refers to a full-color photograph.

t refers to a table; **boldface** refers to the drug's monograph; ***boldface italic*** refers to a full-color photograph.

♦ Canada ◊ Australia

Q

t refers to a table; **boldface** refers to the drug's monograph; ***boldface italic*** refers to a full-color photograph.

S

t refers to a table; **boldface** refers to the drug's monograph; ***boldface italic*** refers to a full-color photograph.

♦ Canada ◊ Australia

T

t refers to a table; **boldface** refers to the drug's monograph; ***boldface italic*** refers to a full-color photograph.

U

W

X